AHA Guide® to the Health Care Field

2018 Edition

AHA Members $270
Nonmembers $405
AHA Item Number 010018
Telephone ORDERS 1–800–AHA–2626

ISSN 0094–8969
ISBN–13: 978–0–87258–979–7

Contents

C

Indexes

Acknowledgements

The AHA Guide® to the Health Care Field is published annually by Health Forum LLC, an affiliate of the American Hospital Association. Contributions are made by Information Systems and Technology, Member Relations, Office of the President, Office of the Secretary, Printing Services Group, AHA Resource Center and the following participants:

Grant Denten	Peter Kralovec
Matthew Diener	Mary Krzywicki
Dianna Doyle	Andrea Liebig
DeAnn Ellis	Denise Loggins
Joan Finn	Rob Merrell
Deanna Frazier	Bethany Parnell
Robyn Gray	Kathy Poole
Tan Harris	Jennifer Sikora
Stella Hines	Susan Sheffey
Clisby Jackson	Elaine Singh
Danny Jackson	Jill Syftestad
Kimberly Jackson	Marty Weitzel

Health Forum LLC acknowledges the cooperation given by many professional groups and government agencies in the health care field, particularly the following: American College of Surgeons; American Medical Association; Council of Teaching Hospitals of the Association of American Medical Colleges; The Joint Commission; DNV Healthcare Inc.; Center for Improvement in Healthcare Quality; Commission on Accreditation of Rehabilitation Facilities; American Osteopathic Association, Centers for Medicare & Medicaid Services; and various offices within the U.S. Department of Health and Human Services.

Advisements

The data published here should be used with the following advisements: The data is based on replies to an annual survey that seeks a variety of information, not all of which is published in this book. The information gathered by the survey includes specific services, but not all of each hospital's services. Therefore, the data does not reflect an exhaustive list of all services offered by all hospitals. For information on the availability of additional data and products, please contact Health Forum LLC at 800/821–2039, or visit our web site.

Health Forum LLC does not assume responsibility for the accuracy of information voluntarily reported by the individual institutions surveyed. **The purpose of this publication is to provide basic data reflecting the delivery of health care in the United States and associated areas, and is not to serve as an official and all inclusive list of services offered by individual hospitals. The information reflected is based on data collected as of September 12, 2017.**

An Introduction to AHA Guide

Welcome, and thank you for purchasing the 2018 edition of *AHA Guide®*. This section is designed to aid you in using the book. While the primary focus of *AHA Guide* is on hospitals, it also contains information on other areas of the health care field, divided across its two major sections:

A. Hospitals

B. Health care systems, networks, and alliances

The information contained within this publication was compiled using AHA membership, and the AHA Annual Survey of Hospitals. *AHA Guide* is the leading hospital directory and represents hospitals with or without AHA membership.

Additional information contained in the front of AHA Guide includes:

- A section by section table of contents
- Recognition of the source of data in the *Acknowledgements and Advisements* section
- Information on AHA's history as well as a listing of our awards in *AHA Offices, Officers, Historical Data, and Awards*

Open the front cover and *AHA Guide* begins with the *2018 AHA Guide Code Chart*. This two page section (front and back) explains how to find and understand the most important elements of each hospital's listing.

The *Code Chart* is a very useful tool to have when reading. It allows new users to become familiar with the data, and it aids returning users in understanding the new design and layout of *AHA Guide*. At the top of the chart, there is a sample listing. If you have used this publication before, you will notice the new columnar listing of all hospital entries by city. The city and county names are highlighted in gray, and all hospitals within the city follow. After the hospital name, you will find the address, telephone number, approval, facility and service codes, and health care systems to which the hospital belongs. Following this are the chief administrators and classifications for the hospital.

Utilization data for the hospital is found in the box at the bottom of each hospital's entry in *AHA Guide*.

The chart further demonstrates how to understand these important elements:

1. **Approval codes** refer to certifications held by a hospital; they represent information supplied by various national approving and reporting bodies. For example, code A–3 indicates accreditation under one of the programs of the Accreditation Council for Graduate Medical Education, evidence that the hospital has been approved for participation in residency training.
2. **Physician codes** represent the different types of arrangements the hospital participates in with its physicians. In this section, code P-1 signifies a closed physician-hospital organization.
3. **Health Care System names** reference specific health care system headquarters to which the hospital belongs. The presence of a system name indicates that the hospital is a member. If no names are listed, the hospital does not belong to a system.
4. **Titles of Chief Administrators** including the Chief Executive Officer and, when available, other C-Suite officers such as the Chief Financial Officer, Chief Information Officer, Chief Medical Officer, Chief Operating Officer, Chief Human Resources Officer, and Chief Nursing Officer.
5. **Classification** refers to two items in *AHA Guide*. **Control** classification indicates the organization that operates the hospital, and **Service** classification refers to the type of service the hospital offers. Previously, this section utilized numerical codes corresponding with a literal value, but the new

2018 AHA Guide Code Chart

Sample Hospital Listing:

1. = Approval Codes
2. = Physician Codes
3. = Health Care System Name
4. = Titles of Chief Administrators
5. = Control and Service Classifications
6. = Utilization Data
7. = Facility Codes

Hospital, Medicare Provider Number, Address, Telephone, Approval, Facility, and Physician Codes, Health Care System

★ American Hospital Association (AHA) membership
☐ The Joint Commission accreditation
○ Healthcare Facilities Accreditation Program
○ DNV Healthcare Inc. accreditation
◊ Center for Improvement in Healthcare Quality Accreditation
△ Commission on Accreditation of Rehabilitation Facilities (CARF) accreditation

① Approval Codes
Reported by the approving bodies specified, as of the dates noted

1 Accreditation under the hospital program of The Joint Commission (February 2017).
2 Cancer program approved by American College of Surgeons (January 2017).
3 Participating site recognized for one or more Accreditation Council for Graduate Medical Education accredited programs (April 2017).
5 Medical school affiliation, reported to the American Medical Association (March 2017).
7 Accreditation by Commission on Accreditation of Rehabilitation Facilities (January 2017).

8 Member of Council of Teaching Hospitals of the Association of American Medical Colleges (March 2017).
10 Certified for participation in the Health Insurance for the Aged (Medicare) Program by the Centers for Medicare and Medicaid Services (January 2017).
11 Healthcare Facilities Accreditation Program (April 2017).
12 Internship approved by American Osteopathic Association (March 2016).

13 Residency or fellowship approved by American Osteopathic Association (March 2017).
18 Critical Access Hospitals (March 2017).
19 Rural Referral Center (March 2017).
20 Sole Community Provider (March 2017).
21 Accreditation by DNV Healthcare Inc. (March 2017).
22 Accreditation by Center for Improvement in Healthcare Quality (January 2017)

Nonreporting indicates that the 2016 Annual Survey questionnaire for the hospital was not received prior to publication.

② Physician Codes
Actually available within, and reported by the institution; for definitions, see page A12.

(Alphabetical/Numerical Order)
1 Closed physician-hospital organization (PHO)
2 Equity model
3 Foundation
4 Group practice without walls
5 Independent practice association (IPA)
6 Integrated salary model
7 Management service organization (MSO)
8 Open physician-hospital organization (PHO)

③ Healthcare System Name
The inclusion of the letter "S" (1) indicates that the hospital belongs to a health care system and (2) identifies the specific system to which the hospital belongs.

④ Titles of Chief Administrators

⑤ Control and Service Classification
For a list of control and service classifications, see page A13.

Control–The type of organization that is responsible for establishing policy for overall operation of the hospital.

Service–The type of service the hospital provides to the majority of admissions.

⑥ Utilization Data
Definitions are based on the American Hospital Association's Hospital Administration Terminology. In completing the survey, hospitals were requested to report data for a full year, in accord with their fiscal year, ending in 2015.

Beds–Number of beds regularly maintained (set up and staffed for use) for inpatients as of the close of the reporting period. Excludes newborn bassinets.

Admissions–Number of patients accepted for inpatient service during a 12-month period; does not include newborn.

Census–Average number of inpatients receiving care each day during the 12-month reporting period; does not include newborn.

Outpatient Visits–A visit by a patient who is not lodged in the hospital while receiving medical, dental, or other services. Each appearance of an outpatient in each unit constitutes one visit regardless of the number of diagnostic and/or therapeutic treatments that a patient receives.

Births–Number of infants born in the hospital and accepted for service in a newborn infant bassinet during a 12-month period; excludes stillbirths.

Expense–Expense for a 12-month period; both total expense and payroll components are shown. Payroll expenses include all salaries and wages.

Personnel: Represents personnel situations as they existed at the end of the reporting period; includes full-time equivalents of part-time personnel. Full-time equivalents were calculated on the basis that two part-time persons equal one full-time person.

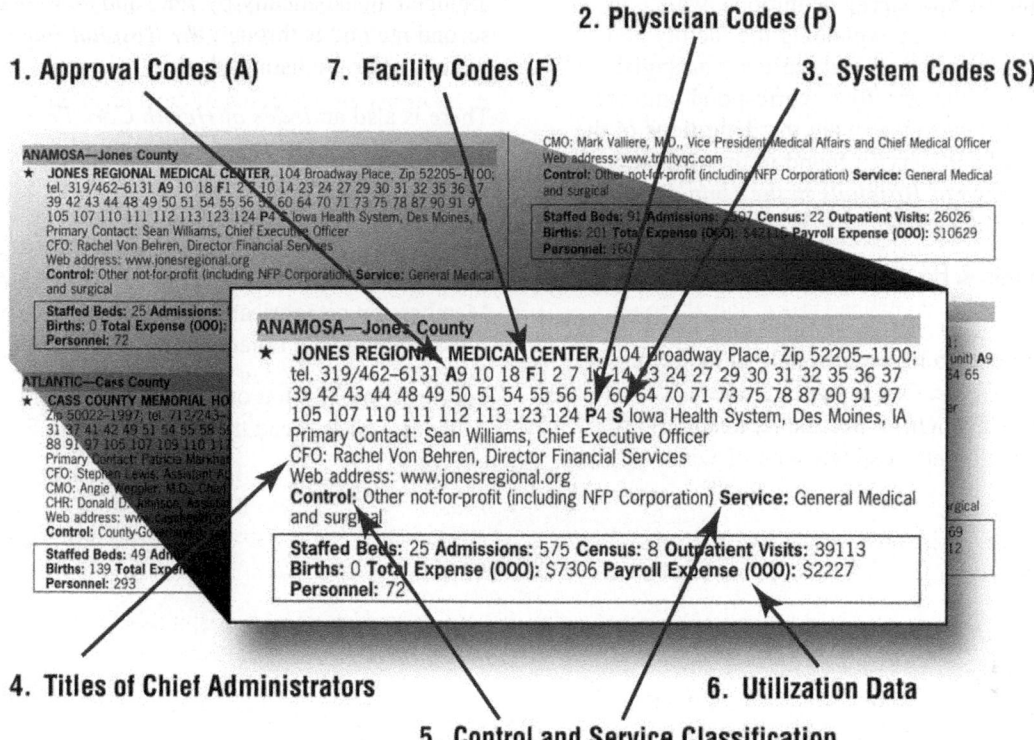

1. Approval Codes (A) **7. Facility Codes (F)** **2. Physician Codes (P)** **3. System Codes (S)**

ANAMOSA—Jones County

★ **JONES REGIONAL MEDICAL CENTER**, 104 Broadway Place, Zip 52205–1100; tel. 319/462–6131 **A9** 10 18 **F1** 2 7 10 14 23 24 27 29 30 31 32 35 36 37 39 42 43 44 48 49 50 51 54 55 56 57 60 64 70 71 73 75 78 87 90 91 97 105 107 110 111 112 113 123 124 **P4 S** Iowa Health System, Des Moines, IA
Primary Contact: Sean Williams, Chief Executive Officer
CFO: Rachel Von Behren, Director Financial Services
Web address: www.jonesregional.org
Control: Other not-for-profit (including NFP Corporation) **Service:** General Medical and surgical

Staffed Beds: 25 **Admissions:** 575 **Census:** 8 **Outpatient Visits:** 39113 **Births:** 0 **Total Expense (000):** $7306 **Payroll Expense (000):** $2227 **Personnel:** 72

4. Titles of Chief Administrators **6. Utilization Data**

5. Control and Service Classification

---

design of *AHA Guide* bypasses the codes and instead displays the literal classifications for control and service.

- **Control:** In this section, organizations are divided among nonfederal government hospitals, nongovernment not-for-profit hospitals, investor owned for-profit hospitals, and federal government hospitals.
- **Service:** This section displays the primary type of service that a hospital offers. The most common value is general hospital. Among the other services listed in this section are specialties such as psychiatric hospitals or children's hospitals.

6. **Utilization Data** contains the statistics related to the day-to-day and cumulative operation of the hospital. The information included in this section consists of:

- **Beds:** Number of beds regularly maintained.
- **Admissions:** Amount of patients accepted for inpatient services over a 12-month period.
- **Census:** Average number of patients receiving care each day.
- **Outpatient Visits:** Amount of visits by patients not lodged in the hospital while receiving care.

- **Births:** Number of infants born in the hospital and accepted for service in a newborn infant bassinet.
- **Expense:** Includes all expenses (including payroll) that the hospital had over the 12- month period.
- **Personnel:** Represents personnel situations as they existed at the end of the reporting period. In this area, full time equivalency is calculated on the basis that two part-time persons equal one full-time person.

7. **Facility codes** provide a description of the specific services offered by a hospital. Code F-14, for instance, indicates that the hospital contains a Blood Donor Center.

How To Use This Book

Section A begins with the *AHA Guide Hospital Listing Requirements*. This explains the requisite accreditations or characteristics a hospital must meet to be included in *AHA Guide*.

After this there is *An Explanation of the Hospital Listings*. These two pages review the information included in the Code Chart and are a vital resource in identifying the information, symbols, and codes for each hospital's listing.

Next up are the *Annual Survey* definitions, which go into even greater detail in explaining the facility and physician codes. Please note that these are arranged alphabetically and numerically to correspond with the code chart. Also included here are the definitions of the terms for Control and Service found in the Classification section. The listings of *Hospitals in the United States, by State* follow the definitions.

Finding Hospitals & Health Care Professionals in Section A

There are two ways to locate hospitals in the print version of *AHA Guide*. One is by the hospital's geographic classification. In Section A, hospitals are arranged alphabetically by state and then by city. The second method is through the *Hospital Index* that appears directly after the listings.

There is also an *Index of Health Care Professionals* which begins after the first index that lists key people from hospitals and health systems.

AHA Membership Organizations

Section A ends with a description of the AHA Membership categories along with a listing of various AHA Membership organizations.

For more information on Systems, Networks, and Alliances, please read the introduction to Section B.

AHA Offices, Officers, and Historical Data

Chicago: 155 N. Wacker Drive, Chicago, IL 60606; tel. 312/422–3000

Washington: 800 10th Street, N.W., Two CityCenter, Suite 400, Washington, DC 20001; tel. 202/638–1100

Chairman of the Board of Trustees: Nancy Howell Agee, Carilion Clinic, 1906 Belleview Avenue, Roanoke, VA 24014
Chairman–Elect of the Board of Trustees: Brian Gragnolati, Atlantic Health System, 475 South Street, PO Box 1905, Morristown, NJ 07962
Immediate Past Chairman of the Board of Trustees: Eugene A. Woods, Carolinas Healthcare System, PO Box 32861, Charlotte, NC 32861

President & CEO: Richard J. Pollack , 800 10th Street, NW, Two CityCenter, Suite 400, Washington, DC 20001
Senior Vice President and Secretary: Gail Lovinger Goldblatt, 155 N. Wacker Drive, Chicago, IL 60606
Senior Vice President, Association Services and Chief Financial Officer: Christina Fisher, 155 N. Wacker Drive, Chicago, IL 60606

Executive Vice President and Chief Operating Officer: Maryjane Wurth, 155 N. Wacker Drive, Chicago, IL 60606

Past Presidents/Chairs†

1899	★James S. Knowles	1939	★G. Harvey Agnew, M.D.	1979	W. Daniel Barker
1900	★James S. Knowles	1940	★Fred G. Carter, M.D.	1980	★Sister Irene Kraus
1901	★Charles S. Howell	1941	★B. W. Black, M.D.	1981	★Bernard J. Lachner
1902	★J. T. Duryea	1942	★Basil C. MacLean, M.D.	1982	★Stanley R. Nelson
1903	★John Fehrenbatch	1943	★James A. Hamilton	1983	★Elbert E. Gilbertson
1904	★Daniel D. Test	1944	★Frank J. Walter	1984	Thomas R. Matherlee
1905	★George H. M. Rowe, M.D.	1945	★Donald C. Smelzer, M.D.	1985	★Jack A. Skarupa
1906	★George P. Ludlam	1946	★Peter D. Ward, M.D.	1986	Scott S. Parker
1907	★Renwick R. Ross, M.D.	1947	★John H. Hayes	1987	Donald C. Wegmiller
1908	★Sigismund S. Goldwater, M.D.	1948	★Graham L. Davis	1988	★Eugene W. Arnett
1909	★John M. Peters, M.D.	1949	★Joseph G. Norby	1989	Edward J. Connors
1910	★H. B. Howard, M.D.	1950	★John N. Hatfield	1990	David A. Reed
1911	★W. L. Babcock, M.D.	1951	★Charles F. Wilinsky, M.D.	1991	C. Thomas Smith
1912	★Henry M. Hurd, M.D.	1952	★Anthony J. J. Rourke, M.D.	1992	D. Kirk Oglesby, Jr.
1913	★F. A. Washburn, M.D.	1953	★Edwin L. Crosby, M.D.	1993	Larry L. Mathis
1914	★Thomas Howell, M.D.	1954	★Ritz E. Heerman	1994	Carolyn C. Roberts
1915	★William O. Mann, M.D.	1955	★Frank R. Bradley	1995	Gail L. Warden
1916	★Winford H. Smith, M.D.	1956	★Ray E. Brown	1996	Gordon M. Sprenger
1917	★Robert J. Wilson, M.D.	1957	★Albert W. Snoke, M.D.	1997	Reginald M. Ballantyne III
1918	★A. B. Ancker, M.D.	1958	★Tol Terrell	1998	John G. King
1919	★A. R. Warner, M.D.	1959	★Ray Amberg	1999	Fred L. Brown
1920	★Joseph B. Howland, M.D.	1960	★Russell A. Nelson, M.D.	2000	★Carolyn Boone Lewis
1921	★Louis B. Baldwin, M.D.	1961	★Frank S. Groner	2001	Gary A. Mecklenburg
1922	★George O'Hanlon, M.D.	1962	★Jack Masur, M.D.	2002	Sr. Mary Roch Rocklage, RSM
1923	★Asa S. Bacon	1963	★T. Stewart Hamilton, M.D.	2003	Dennis R. Barry
1924	★Malcolm T. MacEachern, M.D.	1964	★Stanley A. Ferguson	2004	David L. Bernd
1925	★E. S. Gilmore	1965	★Clarence E. Wonnacott	2005	George F. Lynn
1926	★Arthur C. Bachmeyer, M.D.	1966	★Philip D. Bonnet, M.D.	January–April 2006	Richard J. Umbdenstock
1927	★R. G. Brodrick, M.D.	1967	★George E. Cartmill	April–December 2006	George F. Lynn
1928	★Joseph C. Doane, M.D.	1968	★David B. Wilson, M.D.	2007	Kevin E. Lofton
1929	★Louis H. Burlingham, M.D.	1969	★George William Graham, M.D.	2008	William D. Petasnick
1930	★Christopher G. Parnall, M.D.	1970	★Mark Berke	2009	Thomas M. Priselac
1931	★Lewis A. Sexton, M.D.	1971	★Jack A. L. Hahn	2010	Richard P. de Filippi
1932	★Paul H. Fesler	1972	★Stephen M. Morris	2011	John W. Bluford
1933	★George F. Stephens, M.D.	1973	★John W. Kauffman	2012	Teri G. Fontenot
1934	★Nathaniel W. Faxon, M.D.	1974	★Horace M. Cardwell	2013	Benjamin K. Chu, MD
1935	★Robert Jolly	1975	Wade Mountz	2014	James H. Hinton
1936	★Robin C. Buerki, M.D.	1976	★H. Robert Cathcart	2015	Jonathan B. Perlin, MD, PhD
1937	★Claude W. Munger, M.D.	1977	★John M. Stagl	2016	Jim Skogsbergh
1938	★Robert E. Neff	1978	★Samuel J. Tibbitts	2017	Eugene A. Woods

Chief Executive Officers

1917–18	★William H. Walsh, M.D.	1954–72	★Edwin L. Crosby, M.D.	1991–2007	★Richard J. Davidson
1919–24	★Andrew Robert Warner, M.D.	1972	★Madison B. Brown, M.D. (acting)	2007–2015	Richard J. Umbdenstock
1925–27	★William H. Walsh, M.D.	1972–86	★J. Alexander McMahon	2015	Richard J. Pollack (current)
1928–42	★Bert W. Caldwell, M.D.	1986–91	Carol M. McCarthy, Ph.D., J.D.		
1943–54	★George Bugbee	1991	★Jack W. Owen (acting)		

★Deceased

Distinguished Service Award

The award recognizes significant lifetime contributions and service to health care institutions and associations.

1934	Matthew O. Foley	1966	Frank S. Groner		Jack W. Owen
1939	Malcolm T. MacEachern, M.D.	1967	Rev. John J. Flanagan, S.J.	1994	George Adams
1940	Sigismund S. Goldwater, M.D.	1968	Stanley W. Martin	1995	Scott S. Parker
1941	Frederic A. Washburn, M.D.	1969	T. Stewart Hamilton, M.D.	1996	John A. Russell
1942	Winford H. Smith, M.D.	1970	Charles Patteson Cardwell, Jr.	1997	D. Kirk Oglesby, Jr.
1943	Arthur C. Bachmeyer, M.D.	1971	Mark Berke	1998	Henry B. Betts, M.D.
1944	Rt. Rev. Msgr. Maurice F. Griffin, LL.D.	1972	Stanley A. Ferguson	1999	Mitchell T. Rabkin, M.D.
1945	Asa S. Bacon	1973	Jack A. L. Hahn	2000	Gail L. Warden
1946	George F. Stephens, M.D.	1974	George William Graham, M.D.	2001	Gordon M. Sprenger
1947	Robin C. Buerki, M.D.	1975	George E. Cartmill	2002	Carolyn Boone Lewis
1948	James A. Hamilton	1976	D. O. McClusky, Jr.	2003	C. Thomas Smith
1949	Claude W. Munger, M.D.	1977	Boone Powell	2004	Michael C. Waters
1950	Nathaniel W. Faxon, M.D.	1978	Richard J. Stull	2005	John G. King
1951	Bert W. Caldwell, M.D.	1979	Horace M. Cardwell	2006	Gary A. Mecklenburg
1952	Fred G. Carter, M.D.	1980	Donald W. Cordes		Sr. Mary Roch Rocklage, RSM
1953	Basil C. MacLean, M.D.	1981	Sister Mary Brigh Cassidy	2007	Richard J. Davidson
1954	George Bugbee	1982	R. Zach Thomas, Jr.	2008	Fred L. Brown
1955	Joseph G. Norby	1983	H. Robert Cathcart	2009	George F. Lynn
1956	Charles F. Wilinsky, M.D.	1984	Matthew F. McNulty, Jr., Sc.D.	2010	James J. Mongan, M.D.
1957	John H. Hayes	1985	J. Alexander McMahon	2011	Thomas C. Royer, M.D.
1958	John N. Hatfield	1986	Sister Irene Kraus	2012	Karen Davis, Ph.D.
1959	Edwin L. Crosby, M.D.	1987	W. Daniel Barker	2013	Thomas C. Dolan, Ph.D., FACHE
1960	Oliver G. Pratt	1988	Elbert E. Gilbertson	2014	Thomas M. Priselac
1961	E. M. Bluestone, M.D.	1989	Donald G. Shropshire	2015	Richard P. de Filippi
1962	Mother Loretto Bernard, S.C., R.N.	1990	John W. Colloton	2016	William Petasnick
1963	Ray E. Brown	1991	Carol M. McCarthy, Ph.D., J.D.	2017	Richard J. Umbdenstock
1964	Russell A. Nelson, M.D.	1992	David H. Hitt		
1965	Albert W. Snoke, M.D.	1993	Edward J. Connors		

†On June 3, 1972, the House of Delegates changed the title of the chief elected officer to chairman of the Board of Trustees, and the title of president was conferred on the chief executive officer of the Association.

Award of Honor

Awarded to individuals, organizations, or groups to recognize an exemplary contribution to the health and well being of the people through leadership on a major health policy or social initiative.

1966	Senator Lister Hill		Habitat for Humanity International	2008	Regina M. Benjamin, MD, MBA Alfred G. Stubblefield
1967	Emory W. Morris, D.D.S.	1998	John E. Curley, Jr.	2009	The Center to Advance Palliative Care Paul B.
1971	Special Committee on Provision of Health Services		National Civic League		Hofmann, Dr.PH
	(staff also)	1999	Joseph Cardinal Bernardin, Literacy Volunteers of	2010	Jack Bovender
1982	Walter J. McNerney		America	2011	Cary Medical Center, Caribou, ME
1989	Ruth M. Rothstein	2000	Institute for Safe Medication Practices	2012	Ronald McDonald House Charities
1990	Joyce C. Clifford, R.N.	2001	Dennis R. Barry		The Schwartz Center for Compassionate Healthcare
1991	Haynes Rice	2002	Donald M. Berwick, M.D.	2013	George C. Halvorson
1992	Donald W. Dunn	2003	Steven A. Schroeder, M.D.		Reach Out and Read
	Ira M. Lane, Jr.		Dan S. Wilford	2014	Rhonda Anderson, RN
1993	Elliott C. Roberts, Sr.	2004	Ron J. Anderson, M.D.		Ohio Hospital Association
	William A. Spencer, M.D.		Johnson & Johnson	2015	Spencer C. Johnson
1994	Robert A. Derzon	2005	Sr. Mary Jean Ryan		Robert Wood Johnson Foundation
1995	Russell G. Mawby, Ph.D. John K. Springer	2006	Jordan J. Cohen, M.D.	2016	Henry J. Kaiser Family Foundation
1996	Stephen J. Hegarty		James W. Varnum	2017	Joel T. Allison
	Mothers Against Drunk Driving (MADD)	2007	Edward A. Eckenhoff		Doug Leonard
1997	Paul B. Batalden, M.D.		Stanley F. Hupfeld		

Justin Ford Kimball Innovators Award

Recognition to individuals or organizations that have made outstanding, innovative contributions to health care financing and/or delivery that improves access or coordination of care.

1958	E. A. van Steenwyk	1974	William H. Ford, Ph.D.	1995	E. George Middleton, Jr.
1959	George A. Newbury	1975	Earl H. Kammer		Glenn R. Mitchell
1960	C. Rufus Rorem, Ph.D.	1976	J. Ed McConnell	1997	Harvey Pettry
1961	James E. Stuart	1978	Edwin R. Werner		D. David Sniff
1962	Frank Van Dyk	1979	Robert M. Cunningham, Jr.	1998	Montana Health Research and Education Foundation
1963	William S. McNary	1981	Maurice J. Norby	1999	Kenneth W. Kizer, M.D.
1964	Frank S. Groner	1982	Robert E. Rinehimer	2002	David M. Lawrence, M.D.
1965	J. Douglas Colman	1983	John B. Morgan, Jr.	2003	Lowell C. Kruse
1967	Walter J. McNemey	1984	Joseph F. Duplinsky	2006	Spencer Foreman, M.D.
1968	John W. Paynter	1985	David W. Stewart	2009	On Lok
1970	Edwin L. Crosby, M.D.	1988	Ernest W. Saward, M.D.	2012	Thomas S. Nesbitt, M.D.
1971	H. Charles Abbott	1990	James A. Vohs	2015	Glenn D. Steele, Jr., MD
1972	John R. Mannix	1993	John C. Lewin, M.D.	2016	Dan Wolterman
1973	Herman M. Somers	1994	Donald A. Brennan	2017	James N. Weinstein, DO

Board of Trustees Award

Individuals or groups who have made substantial and noteworthy contributions to the work of the American Hospital Association.

1959	Joseph V. Friel	1982	John Bigelow	2002	Victor L. Campbell
	John H. Hayes		Robert W. O'Leary		Joseph A. Parker
1960	Duncan D. Sutphen, Jr.		Jack W. Owen	2003	J. Richard Gaintner, M.D.
1963	Eleanor C. Lambertsen, R.N., Ed.D.	1984	Howard J. Berman		Donald A. Wilson
1964	John R. Mannix		O. Ray Hurst	2004	Richard L. Clarke
1965	Albert G. Hahn		James R. Neely		Thelma Traut
	Maurice J. Norby	1985	James E. Ferguson	2005	Merrill Gappmayer
1966	Madison B. Brown, M.D.		Cleveland Rodgers		Leo Greenawalt
	Kenneth Williamson	1986	Rex N. Olsen	2006	Robert L. Harman
1967	Alanson W. Wilcox	1987	Michael Lesparre		Kenneth G. Stella
1968	E. Dwight Barnett, M.D.	1988	Barbara A. Donaho, R.N.	2007	Deborah Freund, Ph.D.
1969	Vane M. Hoge, M.D.	1989	Walter H. MacDonald		Michael D. Stephens
	Joseph H. McNinch, M.D.		Donald R. Newkirk	2008	James R. Castle
1972	David F. Drake, Ph.D.	1990	William T. Robinson	2009	Richard M. Knapp, Ph.D.
	Paul W. Earle	1992	Jack C. Bills	2010	Fred Hessler
	Michael Lesparre		Anne Hall Davis		John G. O'Brien
	Andrew Pattullo	1993	Theodore C. Eickhoff, M.D.	2011	Carolyn F. Scanlan
1973	Tilden Cummings		Stephen W. Gamble		Charlotte S. Yeh, MD
	Edmond J. Lanigan		Yoshi Honkawa	2012	Larry S. Gage
1974	James E. Hague	1994	Roger M. Busfield, Jr., Ph.D.		Larry McAndrews
	Sister Marybelle	1995	Stephen E. Dorn	2013	Jeffrey D. Selberg
1975	Helen T. Yast		William L. Yates	2014	Russell D. Harrington, Jr.
1976	Boynton P. Livingston	1996	Leigh E. Morris		Daniel Sisto
	James Ludlam		John Quigley	2015	Todd C. Linden
	Helen McGuire	1998	John D. Leech		R. Timothy Rice
1979	Newton J. Jacobson	1999	Sister Carol Keehan	2016	Sandra Bennett Bruce
	Edward W. Weimer		C. Edward McCauley		Michael G. Rock, M.D.
1980	Robert B. Hunter, M.D.		Stephen Rogness	2017	Kris A. Doody, RN
	Samuel J. Tibbitts	2000	Dennis May		Daniel L. Gross, RN
1981	Vernon A. Knutson	2001	Spencer C. Johnson		
	John E. Sullivan		Michael M. Mitchel		

Citation for Meritorious Service

1968	F. R. Knautz		Gordon McLachlan	1983	David M. Kinzer
	Sister Conrad Mary, R.N.	1977	Theodore Cooper, M.D.	1984	Donald L. Custis, M.D.
1971	Hospital Council of Southern California	1979	Norman D. Burkett	1985	John A. D. Cooper, M.D.
1972	College of Misericordia, Dallas, PA		John L. Quigley		Imperial Council of the Ancient Arabic Order of the
1973	Madison B. Brown, M.D.		William M. Whelan		Nobles of the Mystic Shrine for North America
	Samuel J. Tibbitts	1980	Sister Grace Marie Hiltz	1986	Howard F. Cook
1975	Kenneth B. Babcock, M.D.		Leo J. Gehrig, M.D.	1987	David H. Hitt
	Sister Mary Maurita Sengelaube	1981	Richard Davi		Lucile Packard
1976	Chaiker Abbis		Pearl S. Fryar		
	Susan Jenkins	1982	Jorge Brull Nater		

This citation is no longer awarded

AHA NOVA Awards

This award honors effective, collaborative programs focused on improving community health status.

1994

Health Partners of Philadelphi (PA): Albert Einstein Medical Center, Episcopal Hospital, Frankford Hospital, Medical College of Pennsylvania Hospital, St. Christopher's Hospital for Children, Temple University Hospital

Decker Family Development Center: Children's Hospital Medical Center of Akron (OH)
Denver (CO) School–Based Clinics: The Children's Hospital

Basic Health Plan: Dominican Network; Mount Carmel Hospital, Colville, WA; St. Joseph's Hospital, Chewelah, WA; and Holy Family Hospital, Spokane, WA
HealthLink: Lakes Region General Hospital, Laconia, NH

1995

Bladen Community Care Network: Bladen County Hospital, Elizabethtown, NC
Building a Healthier Community: Community– Kimball Health Care System, Toms River, NJ '

Injury Prevention Program: Harlem Hospital Center, New York City, NY
The Community Ministries & Outreach Program: Reaching Out to Our Vickery/Meadow Neighborhood: Presbyterian Healthcare System, Dallas, TX

"CHOICES": Shriners Hospitals for Crippled Children, Tampa, FL

1996

Lincoln and Sunnyslope: John C. Lincoln Hospital and Health Center, Sunnyslope, AZ
Growing into Life Task Force: Aiken (SC) Regional Medical Centers

People Caring for People: Beatrice (NE) Community Hospital and Health Center
Injury Prevention Center of the Greater Dayton (OH) Area: The Children's Medical Center, Good Samaritan Hospital and Health Center, Grandview Hospital, Kettering Memorial

Hospital, Miami Valley Hospital, and St. Elizabeth Medical Center
Family Road: Hutzel Hospital, Detroit, MI

1997

Health Promotion Schools of Excellence Program: Alliant Health System and Kosair Children's Hospital, Louisville, KY
Health, Outreach, Prevention, and Education (HOPE): Health First Holmes Regional Medical Center, Melbourne, FL

Healthy Community Initiative: Roper Care Alliance, Charleston, SC
Obstetrical Care and Prenatal Counseling Program: St. Alexius Medical Center, Bismarck, ND

HIV/AIDS Neighborhood Service Program: Yale–New Haven Hospital, New Haven, CT

1998

Partners for a Healthier Community: Evergreen Community Health Care, Group Health Cooperative of Puget Sound, Overlake Hospital Medical Center, Providence Health System/Medalia HealthCare, Seattle, WA
Glenwood–Lyndale Community Clinic: Hennepin County Medical Center, Minneapolis, MN

Greater Dallas (TX) Injury Prevention Center: Parkland Health & Hospital System, Children's Medical Center of Dallas, Baylor Health Care System, Methodist Hospitals of Dallas, and Presbyterian Healthcare System
Network of Trust: Phoebe Putney Memorial Hospital, Albany, GA

The Lauderdale Court: A Community Partnership:St. Joseph Hospital and Health Centers, Memphis, TN

1999

Making a Case for Community Health: Middletown (OH) Regional Hospital
The Family Resource Center: Mount Carmel Medical Center, Pittsburgh, KS

The Health Neighborhood Project: St. Patrick Hospital, Missoula, MT
Kids for Health: Washington Regional Medical Center, Fayetteville, AR

Children's Village: Yakima Memorial Hospital, Yakima, WA

2000

Community Healthcare Network: Columbus (GA) Regional Healthcare System
Pasadena County Asthma Project: Huntington Memorial Hospital, Pasadena, CA

Ashe County Health Council "Health Carolinias Task Force": Ashe Memorial Hospital, Jefferson, NC
Caritas–Connection Project: St. Mary's Hospital, Passaic, NJ

Correctional Health Care Program: Baystate Health System, Springfield, MA

2001

J.C. Lewis Health Center: Memorial Health and St. Joseph's Candler Health System, Savannah, GA
Project C.A.R.E.: Mercy Medical Center, Canton, OH

TeenHealthFX.com: Atlantic Health System, Florham Park, NJ
Vista ElderCARE: Vista Health, Waukegan, IL

Western Village Enterprise School: INTEGRIS Health, Oklahoma City, OK

2002

Chester Community Connections: Crozer– Keystone Health System, Springfield, PA
The Hope Street Family Center: California Hospital Medical Center, Los Angeles, CA

Mobile Health Outreach Ministry: St. Vincent's Health System, Jacksonville, FL
Operation Access: Kaiser Foundation Hospitals, Oakland; Sutter Health, Sacramento; San Francisco General Hospital,

San Francisco; St. Rose Hospital, Hayward; and Santa Rosa Memorial Hospital, Santa Rosa, CA
Wilmington Health Access for Teens: New Hanover Health Network, Wilmington, NC

2003

C.O.A.C.H. for Kids: Cedars–Sinai Medical Center, Los Angeles, CA
Community Action Network: Trinity Regional Medical Center, Fort Dodge, IA

Hearts N' Health: Glendale Adventist Medical Center, Glendale, CA
Saint Joseph Health Center: Saint Joseph Regional Medical Center, South Bend, IN

St. Mary Medical Center Bensalem Ministries: St. Mary Medical Center, Langhorne, PA

2004

Better Beginnings: Brockton Hospital, Brockton, MA
Buffalo County Community Health Partners: Good Samaritan Health Systems, Kearney, NE

Quad City Health Initiative: Genesis Health System, Davenport, IA and Trinity Regional Health System, Rock Island, IL
Quality of Life in the Truckee Meadows: Washoe Health System, Reno, NV

Solano Coalition for Better Health, Inc.: NorthBay Healthcare Group, Fairfield, CA; Sutter Solano Medical Center, Vallejo, CA; and Kaiser Permanente, Martinez, CA

2005

Children's Health Connection: McKay-Dee Hospital Center, Ogden, UT
Palmetto Health's Vision Health Initiative: Palmetto Health, Columbia, SC

Project Dulce, Whittier Institute for Diabetes: Scripps Health, San Diego, CA
Toledo/Lucas County CareNet: Mercy Health Partners, ProMedica Health System, and Medical University of Ohio, all of Toledo, OH and St. Luke's Hospital, Maumee, O

Volunteer Health Advisor (VHA) Program: Cambridge Health Alliance, Cambridge, MA

2006

Healthy Learners, Columbia, SC: Allendale County Hospital, Fairfax, SC; McLeod Medical Center–Dillon, Dillon, SC; Sisters of Charity Providence Hospitals, Columbia, SC; and Self Regional Healthcare, Greenwood, SC

Primary Care Access Network (PCAN): Health Central, Ocoee, FL; Florida Hospital, Winter Park, FL; and Orlando Regional Healthcare, Orlando, FL **ProHealth Care Community Health Outreach Initiative:** ProHealth Care, Waukesha, WI

St. Joseph Mobile Health Services: Saint Joseph HealthCare Inc., Lexington, KY
Yonkers Childhood Health Initiative: St. John's Riverside, Yonkers, NY

2007
Medical-Legal Partnership for Children: Boston Medical Center, Boston, MA
NOW (Nutritional Options for Wellness) Program: Spectrum Health, Grand Rapids, MI
Richland Care: Palmetto Health, Columbia, SC

Trauma Nurses Talk Tough: Legacy Health System, Portland, OR
UMass Memorial Medical Center Healthy Youth Development Initiative: UMass Memorial Health Care, Worcester, MA

Youth Health Partnership-Patee Market Youth Dental Clinic: Heartland Health, St. Joseph, MO

2008
Partnership for Community Health: California Pacific Medical Center, San Francisco, CA
Every Child Succeeds: Cincinnati Children's Hospital Medical Center, Cincinnati, OH

Memorial Hermann Health Centers for Schools: Memorial Hermann, Houston, TX
Nutrition Center of Maine: Saint Mary's Health System, Lewiston, ME

ENERGIZE! **Pediatric Diabetes Intervention Program:** WakeMed Health & Hospitals, Raleigh, NC

2009
Lighten Up 4 Life: Mission Health System, Asheville, NC
Project BRIEF: Jacobi Medical Center and North Central Bronx Hospital, Bronx, NY

Really Awesome Health (RAH) and Wholesome Routines: Duke Raleigh Hospital, Raleigh, NC

Student Success Jobs Program: Brigham and Women's Hospital, Boston, MA
Taos First Steps Program: Holy Cross Hospital, Taos, NM

2010
Community-Based Alternatives to the Emergency Room: Lee Memorial Health System, Fort Meyers, FL
Health-e-Access Telemedicine: University of Rochester Medical Center, Rochester, NY

Healthy Futures: Munson Healthcare System, Traverse City, MI
Healthy San Francisco: San Francisco General Hospital, University of California Medical Center, Chinese Hospital, California Pacific Medical Center, Saint Francis Memorial

Hospital, St. Mary's Medical Center, and Kaiser Permanente, San Francisco, CA
Pediatric Asthma Program: Sinai Health System, Chicago, IL

2011
Emergency Department Consistent Care Program: Providence St. Peter Hospital, Olympia, WA
Integrated Community Nursing Program at Parkview Health: Parkview Health, Fort Wayne, IN

Milwaukee Health Care Partnership: Aurora Health Care, Children's Hospital & Health System, Inc., Columbia St. Mary's, and Froedtert Health, all of Milwaukee, WI, and Wheaton Franciscan Healthcare, Glendale, WI

The Diabetes Collaborative: Northwestern Memorial Hospital, Chicago, IL
Rochester Youth Violence Partnership: University of Rochester Medical Center and Rochester General Health System, Rochester, NY

2012
The Beth Embraces Wellness: An Integrated Approach to Prevention in the Community: Newark Beth Israel Medical Center and Children's Hospital of New Jersey, Newark, NJ

CARE Network: St. Joseph Health Queen of the Valley Medical Center, Napa, CA
Fitness in the City: Boston Children's Hospital, Boston, MA
Puff City: Henry Ford Health System, Detroit, MI

Rural Health Initiative: Shawano Medical Center of ThedaCare, Shawano, WI

2013
Bangor Beacon Community: EMHS, Brewer, ME and St. Joseph Healthcare, Bangor, ME
Chippewa Health Improvement Partnership (CHIP): St. Joseph's Hospital, Chippewa Falls, WI

Core Health Program of Healthier Communities: Spectrum Health, Grand Rapids, MI
Free Preventive Screenings Program: Good Samaritan Hospital, Vincennes, IN

Hope Clinic and Pharmacy: Ephraim McDowell Health, Danville, KY

2014
FirstReach: FirstHealth of the Carolinas, Pinehurst, NC
Children's Hospital Center for Pediatric Medicine Asthma Action Team: Greenville Health System, Greenville, SC

Let's Go!: The Barbara Bush Children's Hospital at Maine Medical Center, Portland, ME
Hearts Beat Back: The Heart of New Ulm (HONU) Project: New Ulm Medical Center, part of Allina Health, New Ulm, MN

Finney County Community Health Coalition: St. Catherine Hospital, Garden City, KS

2015
Activate Whittier: PIH Health, Whittier, Calif. And Kaiser Permanente Downey Medical Center, Downey, CA
Bithlo Transformation Effort: Florida Hospital, Orlando, FL

Blood Pressure Advocate Program: University of Rochester Medical Center, Rochester, NY
Community Health: Healthy Eating: Presbyterian Healthcare Services, Albuquerque, NM

Mayor's Healthy City Initiative (Healthy BR): Baton Rouge General Medical Center, Ochsner Medical Center-Baton Rouge, Our Lady of the Lake Regional Medical Center and Woman's Hospital, Baton Rouge, LA

2016
Baylor Scott & White Health's Diabetes Health and Wellness Institute at the Juanita J. Craft Recreation Center: Baylor Scott & White Health, Dallas, TX

Building a Healthy Community Initiative, East Ocean View: Bon Secours Hampton Roads Health System, Norfolk, VA
Memorial Hermann Mobile Dental Program: Memorial Hermann Health System, Houston, TX

Spectrum Health Healthier Communities – Strong Beginnings: Spectrum Health, Grand Rapids, MI
Get Healthy, Live Well: Tanner Health System, Carrollton, GA

2017
Morrison County Community-Based Care Coordination: CHI St. Gabriel's Health, Little Falls, MN
The Health and Wellness Alliance Asthma Collaboration: Children's Health, Dallas, TX

Healthy Youth Transitions: Memorial Healthcare System, Hollywood, FL
Pediatric Care-A-Van: Norwegian American Hospital, Chicago, IL

Palmetto Health Dental Health Initiative: Palmetto Health, Columbia, SC

The Carolyn Boone Lewis Living the Vision Award

Organizations and individuals living AHA's vision of a society of healthy communities where all individuals reach their highest potential for health.

1998	Memorial Healthcare System, Hollywood, FL Baptist Health System, Montgomery, AL	2004	Jamaica Hospital Medical Center, Jamaica, NY
1999	Robert A. DeVries, Battle Creek, MI Memorial Health System, South Bend, IN	2005	Fairbanks Memorial Hospital, Fairbanks, AK Boston Medical Center, Boston, MA
2000	Rockingham Memorial Hospital, Harrisonburg, VA	2010	Lehigh Valley Health Network, Allentown, PA
2001	Salina Regional Health Center, Salina, KS	2011	Alaska Native Tribal Health Consortium, Anchorage, AK
2002	Health Improvement Collaborative of Greater Cincinnati, Cincinnati, OH	2013	St. Joseph's Hospital Health Center, Syracuse, NY Cheshire Medical Center/Dartmouth–Hitchcock Keene, Keene, NH
2003	Franklin Memorial Hospital, Farmington, ME		

2014 — TPR Collaborative, MD
2016 — Saint Elizabeth's Medical Center, Wabasha, MN

Circle of Life Award

This award celebrates innovation in palliative and end-of-life care.

2000

Improving Care through the End of Life, Franciscan Health System, Gig Harbor, WA

The Hospice of The Florida Suncoast, Largo, FL

Louisiana State Penitentiary Hospice Program, Angola, LA

2001

Department of Pain Medicine and Palliative Care, Beth Israel Medical Center, New York, NY

Palliative CareCenter & Hospice of the North Shore, Evanston , IL

St. Joseph's Manor, Trumbull, CT

2002

Children's Program of San Diego Hospice and Children's Hospital and Health Center of San Diego, San Diego, CA Hospice of the Bluegrass, Lexington, KY

Project Safe Conduct, Hospice of the Western Reserve and Ireland Cancer Center, Cleveland, OH

Special Circle of Life Award Population–based Palliative Care Research Network (PoPCRN), Denver, CO

2003

Hospice & Palliative CareCenter, Winston–Salem, NC

Providence Health System, Portland, OR

University of California Davis Health System, Sacramento, CA

2004

Hope Hospice and Palliative Care, Fort Myers, FL St. Mary's Healthcare System for Children, Bayside, NY

University of Texas M.D. Anderson Cancer Center Palliative Care, Houston, TX

2005

High Point Regional Health System, High Point, NC

Palliative and End-of-life Care Program, Hoag Memorial Hospital Presbyterian, Newport Beach, CA

Thomas Palliative Care Unit, VCU Massey Cancer Center, Richmond, VA

2006

Continuum Hospice Care, New York, NY

Mercy Supportive Care, St. Joseph Mercy Oakland, Pontiac, MI

Transitions and Life Choices, Fairview Health Services, Minneapolis, MN

2007

UCSF Palliative Care Program, San Francisco, CA Covenant Hospice, Pensacola, FL

Woodwell: A Program of Presbyterian SeniorCare and Family Hospice and Palliative Care, Oakmont, PA

2008

Children's Hospitals and Clinics of Minnesota, Pain and Palliative Care Program, Minneapolis, MN

Haven Hospice, Gainesville, FL

The Pediatric Advanced Care Team, The Children's Hospital of Philadelphia, Philadelphia, PA

2009

Four Seasons, Flat Rock, NC

Oregon Health and Science University Palliative Medicine & Comfort Care Program, Portland, OR

Wishard Health Services Palliative Care Program, Indianapolis, IN

2010

Department of Veteran Affairs, VA New York/New Jersey Healthcare Network, Brooklyn, NY

Kansas City Hospice & Palliative Care, Kansas City, MO Snohomish Palliative Partnership, Everett, WA

2011

The Center for Hospice & Palliative Care, Cheektowaga, NY

Gilchrist Hospice Care, Hunt Valley, MD

St. John Providence Health System, Detroit, MI

2012

Haslinger Family Pediatric Palliative Care Center, Akron Children's Hospital, Akron, OH

Calvary Hospital, Bronx, NY Sharp HealthCare, San Diego, CA

2013

The Denver Hospice and Optio Health Services, Denver, CO

Hertzberg Palliative Care Institute at the Mount Sinai Medical Center, New York, NY

UnityPoint Health, Iowa and Illinois

2014

OACIS/Palliative Medicine, Lehigh Valley Health Network, Allentown, PA

Supportive & Palliative Care, Baylor Health Care System, Dallas, TX

Yakima Valley Memorial Hospital, Yakima, WA

2015

Care Dimensions, Danvers, MA

2016

Bon Secours Palliative Medicine, Richmond, VA

Cambia Palliative Care Center of Excellence at UW Medicine, Seattle, WA

Susquehanna Health Hospice and Palliative Care, Williamsport, PA

2017

Bluegrass Care Navigators, formerly Hospice of the Bluegrass, Lexington, KY

Providence TrinityCare Hospice, Providence Little Company of Mary Medical Center Torrance and Providence Institute for Human Caring, Torrance, CA

The American Hospital Association Quest for Quality Prize*

Honoring Leadership and Innovation in Patient Care Quality, Safety, and Commitment

2002

Missouri Baptist Medical Center, St. Louis, MO

Finalist: Fairview Hospital, Greater, Barrington, MA

Finalist: Minnesota Children's Hospital and Clinics, Minneapolis, MN

(*This award was sponsored from 2001-2016 by McKesson. RL Solutions is the current sponsor.)

2003
Abington Memorial Hospital, Abington, PA | **Finalist:** Beaumont Hospitals, Royal Oak, MI | **Finalist:** University of Wisconsin Hospital and Clinics, Madison, WI

2004
Sentara Norfolk General Hospital, Norfolk, VA | **Finalist:** The Johns Hopkins Hospital, Baltimore, MD | **Finalist:** Mary Lanning Memorial Hospital, Hastings, NE

2005
North Mississippi Medical Center, Tupelo, MS | **Finalist:** El Camino Hospital, Mountain View, CA | **Finalist:** NewYork-Presbyterian Hospital, New York, NY

2006
Cincinnati Children's Hospital Medical Center, Cincinnati, OH

2007
Columbus Regional Hospital, Columbus, IN | **Finalist:** Cedars-Sinai Medical Center, Los Angeles, CA | **Finalist:** INTEGRIS Baptist Medical Center, Oklahoma City, OK

2008
Munson Medical Center, Traverse City, MI | **Finalist:** University of Michigan Hospitals & Health Centers, Ann Arbor, MI

2009
Bronson Methodist Hospital, Kalamazoo, MI | **Finalist:** Beth Israel Deaconess Medical Center, Boston, MA

2010
McLeod Regional Medical Center, Florence, SC | **Finalist:** Henry Ford Hospital, Detroit, MI

2011
Memorial Regional Hospital, Hollywood, FL | **Finalist:** AtlantiCare Regional Medical Center, Atlantic City, NJ | **Finalist:** Northwestern Memorial Hospital, Chicago, IL

2012
University Hospitals Case Medical Center, Cleveland, OH | **Finalist:** Lincoln Medical and Mental Health Center, Bronx, NY | **Finalist:** University of North Carolina Hospitals, Chapel Hill, NC and Life Choices, Fairview Health Services, Minneapolis, MN

2013
Beth Israel Deaconess Medical Center, Boston, MA | **Finalist:** Franklin Woods Community Hospital, Johnson City, TN

2014
VCU Medical Center, Richmond, VA | **Finalist:** Carolinas Medical Center-Northeast, Concord, NC

2015
Children's Hospital Colorado in Aurora, CO | **Finalist:** Duke University Hospital, Durham, NC

2016
Memorial Medical Center, Springfield, IL | **Finalist:** Memorial Hermann Greater Heights, Houston, TX

Foster G. McGaw Prize

Honors health delivery organizations that have demonstrated exceptional commitment to community service.

1986	Lutheran Medical Center, Brooklyn, NY	1995	Our Lady of Lourdes Medical Center, Camden, NJ	2006	Memorial Healthcare System, Hollywood, FL
1987	Copley Hospital, Morrisville, VT Mount Sinai Hospital, Hartford, CT	1996	St. Mary's Hospital, Rochester, NY	2007	Harborview Medical Center, Seattle, WA
		1997	Bladen County Hospital Rural Health Network, Elizabethtown, NC	2008	St. Mary's Health System, Lewiston, ME
1988	MetroHealth System, Cleveland, OH			2009	Heartland Health, St. Joseph, MO
1989	Greater Southeast Healthcare System, Washington, DC	1998	Allina Health System, Minneapolis, MN	2010	Allegiance Health, Jackson, MI
1990	Mount Zion Medical Center of The University of California-San Francisco, San Francisco, CA	1999	LAC+USC Healthcare Network, Los Angeles, CA	2011	Mt. Ascutney Hospital and Health Center, Windsor, VT
		2000	Kaweah Delta Health Care District, Visalia, CA	2012	St. Joseph's/Candler Health System, Savannah, GA
1991	Franklin Regional Hospital, Franklin, NH	2001	Memorial Hospital of South Bend, South Bend, IN	2013	Crozer–Keystone Health System, Delaware County, PA
1992	Mount Sinai Hospital Medical Center of Chicago, Chicago, IL	2002	John C. Lincoln Health Network, Phoenix, AZ	2014	Palmetto Health, Columbia, SC
		2003	Phoebe Putney Memorial Hospital, Albany, GA	2015	Massachusetts General Hospital, Boston
1993	The Cambridge Hospital, Cambridge, MA	2004	Henry Ford Health System, Detroit, MI	2016	Spectrum Health, Grand Rapids, MI
1994	Parkland Memorial Hospital, Dallas, TX	2005	Venice Family Clinic, Venice, CA		

Dick Davidson Quality Milestone Award for Allied Association Leadership

The award recognizes state, regional or metropolitan hospital association leadership in improving health care quality.

2011	Michigan Health & Hospital Association South Carolina Hospital Association	2013	Florida Hospital Association Tennessee Hospital Association	2015	Minnesota Hospital Association
2012	Iowa Hospital Association Washington State Hospital Association	2014	Connecticut Hospital Association Wisconsin Hospital Association	2016	Maryland Hospital Association
				2017	California's Hospital Quality Institute

AHA Equity of Care Award

The award is presented to hospitals or care systems that are noteworthy leaders and examples to the field in the area of equitable care.

2014	Massachusetts General Hospital, Boston, MA
2015	Henry Ford Health System, Detroit, MI Robert Wood Johnson University Hospital, New Brunswick, NJ
2016	Cleveland Clinic, Cleveland, OH
2017	Kaiser Permanente, Oakland, CA

An institution is considered a hospital by the American Hospital Association if it is licensed as general or specialty hospital by the appropriate state agency, and accredited as a hospital by one of the following organizations: The Joint Commission; Healthcare Facilities Accreditation Program (HFAP); DNV Healthcare accreditation; Center for Improvement in Healthcare Quality accreditation; or Medicare certified as a provider of acute service under Title 18 of the Social Security Act.

Types of Hospitals

Hospitals are listed as one of four types of hospitals: general, special, rehabilitation and chronic disease, or psychiatric. The following definitions of function by type of hospital and special requirements are:

General

The primary function of the institution is to provide patient services, diagnostic and therapeutic, for a variety of medical conditions. A general hospital also shall provide:

- diagnostic x–ray services with facilities and staff for a variety of procedures
- clinical laboratory service with facilities and staff for a variety of procedures and with anatomical pathology services regularly and conveniently available
- operating room service with facilities and staff.

Special

The primary function of the institution is to provide diagnostic and treatment services for patients who have specified medical conditions, both surgical and nonsurgical. A special hospital also shall provide:

- such diagnostic and treatment services as may be determined by the Executive Committee of the Board of Trustees of the American Hospital Association to be appropriate for the specified medical conditions for which medical services are provided shall be maintained in the institution with suitable facilities and staff. If such conditions do not normally require diagnostic x–ray service, laboratory service, or operating room service, and if any such services are therefore not maintained in the institution, there shall be written arrangements to make them available to patients requiring them.
- clinical laboratory services capable of providing tissue diagnosis when offering pregancy termination services.

Rehabilitation and Chronic Disease

The primary function of the institution is to provide diagnostic and treatment services to handicapped or disabled individuals requiring restorative and adjustive services. A rehabilitation and chronic disease hospital also shall provide:

- arrangements for diagnostic x–ray services, as required, on a regular and conveniently available basis
- arrangements for clinical laboratory service, as required on a regular and conveniently available basis
- arrangements for operating room service, as required, on a regular and conveniently available basis
- a physical therapy service with suitable facilities and staff in the institution

- an occupational therapy service with suitable facilities and staff in the institution
- arrangements for psychological and social work services on a regular and conveniently available basis
- arrangements for educational and vocational services on a regular and conveniently available basis
- written arrangements with a general hospital for the transfer of patients who require medical, obstetrical, or surgical services not available in the institution.

Psychiatric

The primary function of the institution is to provide diagnostic and treatment services for patients who have psychiatric–related illnesses. A psychiatric hospital also shall provide:

- arrangements for clinical laboratory service, as required, on a regular and conveniently available basis
- arrangements for diagnostic x–ray services, as required on a regular and conveniently available basis
- psychiatric, psychological, and social work service with facilities and staff in the institution
- arrangements for electroencephalograph services, as required, on a regular and conveniently available basis
- written arrangements with a general hospital for the transfer of patients who require medical, obstetrical, or surgical services not available in the institution

The American Hospital Association may, at the sole discretion of the Executive Committee of the Board of Trustees, grant, deny, or withdraw the listing of an institution.

---

* Physician–Term used to describe an individual with an M.D. or D.O. degree who is fully licensed to practice medicine in all its phases.
‡ The completed records in general shall contain at least the following: the patient's identifying data and consent forms, medical history, record of physical examination, physicians' progress notes, operative notes, nurses' notes, routine x–ray and laboratory reports, doctors' orders, and final diagnosis.

Explanation of Hospital Listings

Sample Hospital Listing:

ANYTOWN, Universal County

⊞ **ANYTOWN HOSPITAL & CLINICS (777777)**, (Formerly Anytown Area
Community Hospital and Clinic), 100 South Main Street, Zip 12345–6789;
tel. 123/456–7890 **A**9 10] ①
F10 12 23 24 29 30 31 37 39 49 51 55 57 64 65 66 68 70 71 72 77
78 83 87 88 91 96 97 106 107 110 111 113 124 **P**1 2 3 **S** Universal ⑦
County Health System ② ③
Primary Contact: Ann M. Generic, Chief Executive Officer
COO: Ann M. Generic
CFO: Michael M. Generic ④
CMO: Peterl Van Generic, President Medical Staff
CHR: Jerry Generic, Human Resources Director
CNO: Danielle Generic, R.N., Chief Nursing Officer
Web address: www.website.org
Control: Other not–for–profit (including NFP Corporation) **Service:** General ⑤
Medical and Surgical

Staffed Beds: 25 **Admissions:** 892 **Census:** 9 **Outpatient Visits:** 44014
Births: 51 **Total Expense ($000):** 19210 **Payroll Expense ($000):** 5864   ⑥
Personnel: 182

ANYTOWN, Universal County

⊞ **ANYTOWN HOSPITAL & CLINICS (777777)**, (Formerly Anytown Area
Community Hospital and Clinic), 100 South Main Street, Zip 12345–6789;
tel. 123/456–7890 **A**9 10

① = Approval Codes
② = Physician Codes
③ = Health Care System Name
④ = Titles of Chief Administrators
⑤ = Control and Service Classifications
⑥ = Utilization Data
⑦ = Facility Codes

Hospital, Medicare Provider Number, Address, Telephone, Approval, Facility, and Physician Codes, Health Care System

★ American Hospital Association (AHA) membership   ○ Healthcare Facilities Accreditation Program   ⇑ Center for Improvement in Healthcare Quality Accreditation
□ The Joint Commission accreditation   ◇ DNV Healthcare Inc. accreditation   △ Commission on Accreditation of Rehabilitation Facilities (CARF) accreditation

---

① Approval Codes

Reported by the approving bodies specified, as of the dates noted.

1 Accreditation under the hospital program of The Joint Commission (February 2017).
2 Cancer program approved by American College of Surgeons (January 2017).
3 Participating site recognized for one or more Accreditation Council for Graduate Medical Education accredited programs (April 2017).
5 Medical school affiliation, reported to the American Medical Association (March 2017).
7 Accreditation by Commission on Accreditation of Rehabilitation Facilities (January 2017).

8 Member of Council of Teaching Hospitals of the Association of American Medical Colleges (March 2017).
10 Certified for participation in the Health Insurance for the Aged (Medicare) Program by the Centers for Medicare and Medicaid Services (January 2017).
11 Healthcare Facilities Accreditation Program (April 2017).
12 Internship approved by American Osteopathic Association (March 2016).

13 Residency or fellowship approved by American Osteopathic Association (March 2017).
18 Critical Access Hospitals (March 2017).
19 Rural Referral Center (March 2017).
20 Sole Community Provider (March 2017).
21 Accreditation by DNV Healthcare Inc. (March 2017).
22 Accreditation by Center for Improvement in Healthcare Quality (January 2017)

Nonreporting indicates that the 2016 Annual Survey questionnaire for the hospital was not received prior to publication.

---

② Physician Codes

Actually available within, and reported by the institution; for definitions, see page A12.

(Alphabetical/Numerical Order)

1 Closed physician–hospital organization (PHO)
2 Equity model
3 Foundation

4 Group practice without walls
5 Independent practice association (IPA)
6 Integrated salary model

7 Management service organization (MSO)
8 Open physician–hospital organization (PHO)

---

③ Healthcare System Name

The inclusion of the letter "S" (1) indicates that the hospital belongs to a health care system and (2) identifies the specific system to which the hospital belongs.

---

④ Titles of Chief Administrators

⑤ Control and Service Classification

For a list of control and service classifications, see page A13.

Control–The type of organization that is responsible for establishing policy for overall operation of the hospital.

Service–The type of service the hospital provides to the majority of admissions.

---

⑥ Utilization Data

Definitions are based on the American Hospital Association's Hospital Administration Terminology. In completing the survey, hospitals were requested to report data for a full year, in accord with their fiscal year, ending in 2015.

Beds–Number of beds regularly maintained (set up and staffed for use) for inpatients as of the close of the reporting period. Excludes newborn bassinets.

Admissions–Number of patients accepted for inpatient service during a 12–month period; does not include newborn.

Census–Average number of inpatients receiving care each day during the 12–month reporting period; does not include newborn.

Outpatient Visits–A visit by a patient who is not lodged in the hospital while receiving medical, dental, or other services. Each appearance of an outpatient in each unit constitutes one visit regardless of the number of diagnostic and/or therapeutic treatments that a patient receives.

Births–Number of infants born in the hospital and accepted for service in a newborn infant bassinet during a 12–month period; excludes stillbirths.

Expense: Expense for a 12–month period; both total expense and payroll components are shown. Payroll expenses include all salaries and wages.

Personnel: Represents personnel situations as they existed at the end of the reporting period; includes full-time equivalents of part–time personnel. Full-time equivalents were calculated on the basis that two part–time persons equal one full–time person.

Sample Hospital Listing:

ANYTOWN, Universal County

✠ **ANYTOWN HOSPITAL & CLINICS (777777)**, (Formerly Anytown Area
Community Hospital and Clinic), 100 South Main Street, Zip 12345–6789;
tel. 123/456–7890 <u>A9 10</u>] ①
<u>F</u>10 12 23 24 29 30 31 37 39 49 51 55 57 64 65 66 68 70 71 72 77] ⑦
78 83 87 88 91 96 97 106 107 110 111 113 124 **P**1 2 3 **S** Universal
County Health System ② ③
Primary Contact: Ann M. Generic, Chief Executive Officer
COO: Ann M. Generic
CFO: Michael M. Generic ④
CMO: Peterl Van Generic, President Medical Staff
CHR: Jerry Generic, Human Resources Director
CNO: Danielle Generic, R.N., Chief Nursing Officer
Web address: www.website.org
Control: Other not–for–profit (including NFP Corporation) **Service:** General] ⑤
Medical and Surgical

Staffed Beds: 25 **Admissions:** 892 **Census:** 9 **Outpatient Visits:** 44014
Births: 51 **Total Expense ($000):** 19210 **Payroll Expense ($000):** 5864
Personnel: 182

ANYTOWN, Universal County

✠ **ANYTOWN HOSPITAL & CLINICS (777777)**, (Formerly Anytown Area
Community Hospital and Clinic), 100 South Main Street, Zip 12345–6789;
tel. 123/456–7890 **A**9 10

① = **Approval Codes**
② = **Physician Codes**
③ = **Health Care System Name**
④ = **Titles of Chief Administrators**
⑤ = **Control and Service Classifications**
⑥ = **Utilization Data**
⑦ = **Facility Codes**

⑥

Hospital, Medicare Provider Number, Address, Telephone, Approval, Facility, and Physician Codes, Health Care System

★ American Hospital Association (AHA) membership ○ Healthcare Facilities Accreditation Program ⇑ Center for Improvement in Healthcare Quality Accreditation
□ The Joint Commission accreditation ◇ DNV Healthcare Inc. accreditation △ Commission on Accreditation of Rehabilitation Facilities (CARF) accreditation

---

⑦ **Facility Codes**

Provided directly by the hospital; for definitions, see page A6.

(Numerical Order)

1 Acute long-term care
2 Adult day care program
3 Airborne infection isolation room
4 Alcoholism-drug abuse or dependency inpatient services
5 Alcoholism-drug abuse or dependency outpatient services
6 Alzheimer center
7 Ambulance services
8 Ambulatory surgery center
9 Arthritis treatment center
10 Assisted living
11 Auxiliary
12 Bariatric/weight control services
13 Birthing room-LDR room-LDRP room
14 Blood donor center
15 Breast cancer screening/mammograms
16 Burn care services
17 Cardiac intensive care
18 Adult cardiology services
19 Pediatric cardiology services
20 Adult diagnostic catheterization
21 Pediatric diagnostic catheterization
22 Adult interventional cardiac catheterization
23 Pediatric interventional cardiac catheterization
24 Adult cardiac surgery
25 Pediatric cardiac surgery
26 Adult cardiac electrophysiology
27 Pediatric cardiac electrophysiology
28 Cardiac rehabilitation
29 Case management
30 Chaplaincy/pastoral care services
31 Chemotherapy
32 Children's wellness program
33 Chiropractic services
34 Community health education
35 Community outreach
36 Complementary and alternative medicine services
37 Computer assisted orthopedic surgery (CAOS)
38 Crisis prevention
39 Dental services
40 Emergency department
41 Pediatric emergency department
42 Satellite emergency department
43 Trauma center (certified)
44 Enabling services
45 Optical colonoscopy
46 Endoscopic ultrasound
47 Ablation of Barrett's esophagus
48 Esophageal impedance study
49 Endoscopic retrograde cholangiopancrea-tography (ERCP)
50 Enrollment assistance services

51 Extracorporeal shock wave lithotripter (ESWL)
52 Fertility clinic
53 Fitness center
54 Freestanding outpatient care center
55 Genetic testing/counseling
56 Geriatric services
57 Health fair
58 Health research
59 Health screenings
60 Hemodialysis
61 HIV–AIDS services
62 Home health services
63 Hospice program
64 Hospital–based outpatient care center services
65 Immunization program
66 Indigent care clinic
67 Intermediate nursing care
68 Linguistic/translation services
69 Meals on wheels
70 Medical surgical intensive care services
71 Mobile health services
72 Neonatal intensive care
73 Neonatal intermediate care
74 Neurological services
75 Nutrition programs
76 Obstetrics
77 Occupational health services
78 Oncology services
79 Orthopedic services
80 Other special care
81 Outpatient surgery
82 Pain management program
83 Inpatient palliative care unit
84 Palliative care program
85 Patient controlled analgesia (PCA)
86 Patient education center
87 Patient representative services
88 Pediatric intensive care services
89 Pediatric medical–surgical care
90 Physical rehabilitation inpatient services
91 Assistive technology center
92 Electrodiagnostic services
93 Physical rehabilitation outpatient services
94 Prosthetic and orthotic services
95 Robot-assisted walking therapy
96 Simulated rehabilitation environment
97 Primary care department
98 Psychiatric care
99 Psychiatric child–adolescent services
100 Psychiatric consultation–liaison services
101 Psychiatric education services
102 Psychiatric emergency services
103 Psychiatric geriatric services

104 Psychiatric outpatient services
105 Psychiatric partial hospitalization services
106 Psychiatric residential treatment
107 CT scanner
108 Diagnostic radioisotope facility
109 Electron beam computed tomography (EBCT)
110 Full–field digital mammography (FFDM)
111 Magnetic resonance imaging (MRI)
112 Intraoperative magnetic resonance imaging
113 Magnetoencephalography (MEG)
114 Multi–slice spiral computed tomography (MSCT) (<64 slice CT)
115 Multi–slice spiral computed tomography (64 + slice CT)
116 Positron emission tomography (PET)
117 Positron emission tomography/CT (PET/CT)
118 Single photon emission computerized tomography (SPECT)
119 Ultrasound
120 Image–guided radiation therapy (IGRT)
121 Intensity–modulated radiation therapy (IMRT)
122 Proton beam therapy
123 Shaped beam radiation therapy
124 Stereotactic radiosurgery
125 Retirement housing
126 Robotic surgery
127 Rural health clinic
128 Skilled nursing care
129 Sleep center
130 Social work services
131 Sports medicine
132 Support groups
133 Swing bed services
134 Teen outreach services
135 Tobacco treatment/cessation program
136 Bone marrow transplant services
137 Heart transplant
138 Kidney transplant
139 Liver transplant
140 Lung transplant
141 Tissue transplant
142 Other transplant
143 Transportation to health services
144 Urgent care center
145 Virtual colonoscopy
146 Volunteer services department
147 Women's health center/services
148 Wound management services
149 Violence prevention programs for the workplace
150 Violence prevention programs for the community

Annual Survey

Each year, an annual survey of hospitals is conducted by the American Hospital Association through its Health Forum affiliate.

The facilities and services found below are provided by the hospital. For data products reflecting the services provided by a hospital through its health care system, or network or through a formal arrangement with another provider contact Health Forum at 800/821–2039, or visit www.healthforum.com.

The AHA Guide to the Health Care Field does not include all data collected from the 2015 Annual Survey. Requests for purchasing other Annual Survey data should be directed to Health Forum LLC, an affiliate of the American Hospital Association, 155 N. Wacker Drive, Chicago, IL 60606, 800/821–2039.

Definitions of Facility Codes

1. **Acute long–term care.** Provides specialized acute hospital care to medically complex patients who are critically ill, have multisystem complications and/or failure, and require hospitalization averaging 25 days, in a facility offering specialized treatment programs and therapeutic intervention on a 24–hour/7 day a week basis.

2. **Adult day care program.** Program providing supervision, medical and psychological care, and social activities for older adults who live at home or in another family setting, but cannot be alone or prefer to be with others during the day. May include intake assessment, health monitoring, occupational therapy, personal care, noon meal, and transportation services.

3. **Airborne infection isolation room.** A single–occupancy room for patient care where environmental factors are controlled in an effort to minimize the transmission of those infectious agents, usually spread person to person by droplet nuclei associated with coughing and inhalation. Such rooms typically have specific ventilation requirements for controlled ventilation, air pressure and filtration.

4. **Alcoholism–drug abuse or dependency inpatient unit.** Provides diagnosis and therapeutic services to patients with alcoholism or other drug dependencies. Includes care for inpatient/residential treatment for patients whose course of treatment involves more intensive care than provided in an outpatient setting or where patient requires supervised withdrawal.

5. **Alcoholism–drug abuse or dependency outpatient unit.** Organized hospital services that provide medical care and/or rehabilitative treatment services to outpatients for whom the primary diagnosis is alcoholism or other chemical dependency.

6. **Alzheimer center.** Facility that offers care to persons with Alzheimer's disease and their families through an integrated program of clinical services, research, and education.

7. **Ambulance services.** Provision of ambulance services to the ill and injured who require medical attention on a scheduled or unscheduled basis.

8. **Ambulatory surgery center.** Facility that provides care to patients requiring surgery who are admitted and discharged on the same day. Ambulatory surgery centers are distinct from same day surgical units within the hospital outpatient departments for purposes of Medicare payments.

9. **Arthritis treatment center.** Specifically equipped and staffed center for the diagnosis and treatment of arthritis and other joint disorders.

10. **Assisted living.** A special combination of housing, supportive services, personalized assistance and health care designed to respond to the individual needs of those who need help in activities of daily living and instrumental activities of daily living. Supportive services are available, 24 hours a day, to meet scheduled and unscheduled needs, in a way that promotes maximum independence and dignity for each resident and encourages the involvement of a resident's family, neighbor and friends.

11. **Auxiliary.** A volunteer community organization formed to assist the hospital in carrying out its purpose and to serve as a link between the institution and the community.

12. **Bariatric/weight control services.** Bariatrics is the medical practice of weight reduction.

13. **Birthing room–LDR room–LDRP room.** A single room–type of maternity care with a more homelike setting for families than the traditional three–room unit (labor/delivery/recovery) with a separate postpartum area. A birthing room combines labor and delivery in one room. An LDR room accommodates three stages in the birthing process—labor, delivery, and recovery. An LDRP room accommodates all four stages of the birth process—labor, delivery, recovery and postpartum.

14. **Blood donor center.** A facility that performs, or is responsible for the collection, processing, testing or distribution of blood and components.

15. **Breast cancer screening/mammograms.** Mammography screening–the use of breast x–ray to detect unsuspected breast cancer in asymptomatic women. Diagnostic mammography–the x–ray imaging of breast tissue in symptomatic women who are considered to have a substantial likelihood of having breast cancer already.

16. **Burn care services.** Provides care to severely burned patients. Severely burned patients are those with any of the following: 1. Second–degree burns of more than 25% total body surface area for adults or 20% total body surface area for children; 2. Third–degree burns of more than 10% total body surface area; 3. Any severe burns of the hands, face, eyes, ears or feet or; 4. All inhalation injuries, electrical burns, complicated burn injuries involving fractures and other major traumas, and all other poor risk factors.

17. **Cardiac intensive care.** Provides patient care of a more specialized nature than the usual medical and surgical care, on the basis of

physicians' orders and approved nursing care plans. The unit is staffed with specially trained nursing personnel and contains monitoring and specialized support or treatment equipment for patients who, because of heart seizure, one-heart surgery, or other life-threatening conditions, require intensified, comprehensive observation and care. May include myocardial infarction, pulmonary care, and heart transplant units.

18. **Adult cardiology services.** An organized clinical service offering diagnostic and interventional procedures to manage the full range of adult heart conditions.

19. **Pediatric cardiology services.**

20. **Adult diagnostic catheterization.** (also called coronary angiography or coronary arteriography) is used to assist in diagnosing complex heart conditions. Cardiac angiography involves the insertion of a tiny catheter up into the artery in the groin then carefully threading the catheter up into the aorta where the coronary arteries originate. Once the catheter is in place, a dye is injected which allows the cardiologist to see the size, shape and distribution of the coronary arteries. These images are used to diagnose heart disease and to determine, among other things, whether or not surgery is indicated.

21. **Pediatric diagnostic catheterization.** (also called coronary angiography or coronary arteriography) is used to assist in diagnosing complex heart conditions. Cardiac angiography involves the insertion of a tiny catheter up into the artery in the groin then carefully threading the catheter up into the aorta where the coronary arteries originate. Once the catheter is in place, a dye is injected which allows the cardiologist to see the size, shape and distribution of the coronary arteries. These images are used to diagnose heart disease and to determine, among other things, whether or not surgery is indicated.

22. **Adult interventional cardiac catheterization.** Nonsurgical procedure that utilizes the same basic principles as diagnostic catheterization and then uses advanced the techniques to improve the heart's function. It can be less invasive alternative to heart surgery.

23. **Pediatric diagnostic catheterization.** Nonsurgical procedure that utilizes the same basic principles as diagnostic cathereterization and then uses advanced the techniques to improve the heart's function. It can be less invasive alternative to heart surgery.

24. **Adult cardiac surgery.** Includes minimally invasive procedures that include surgery done with only a small incision or no incision at all, such as through a laparoscope or an endoscope and more invasive major surgical procedures that include open chest and open heart surgery.

25. **Pediatric cardiac surgery.** Includes minimally invasive procedures that include surgery done with only a small incision or no incision at all, such as through a laparoscope or an endoscope and more invasive major surgical procedures that include open chest and open heart surgery defibrillator implantation and follow- up.

26. **Adult cardiac electrophysiology.** Evaluation and management of patients with complex rhythm or conduction abnormalities, including diagnostic testing, treatment of arrhythmias by catheter ablation or drug therapy, and pacemaker/ defibrillator implantation and follow- up.

27. **Pediatric cardiac electrophysiology.**

28. **Cardiac rehabilitation.** A medically supervised program to help heart patients recover quickly and improve their overall physical and mental functioning. The goal is to reduce risk of another cardiac event or to keep an already present heart condition from getting worse. Cardiac rehabilitation programs include: counseling to patients, an exercise program, helping patients modify risk factors such as smoking and high blood pressure, providing vocational guidance to enable the patient to return to work, supplying information on physical limitations and lending emotional support.

29. **Case management.** A system of assessment, treatment planning, referral and follow–up that ensures the provision of comprehensive and continuous services and the coordination of payment and reimbursement for care.

30. **Chaplaincy/pastoral care services.** A service ministering religious activities and providing pastoral counseling to patients, their families, and staff of a health care organization.

31. **Chemotherapy.** An organized program for the treatment of cancer by the use of drugs or chemicals.

32. **Children's wellness program.** A program that encourages improved health status and a healthful lifestyle of children through health education, exercise, nutrition and health promotion.

33. **Chiropractic services.** An organized clinical service including spinal manipulation or adjustment and related diagnostic and therapeutic services.

34. **Community health education.** Education that provides health information to individuals and populations as well as support for personal, family and community health decisions with the objective of improving health status.

35. **Community outreach.** A program that systematically interacts with the community to identify those in need of services, alerting persons and their families to the availability of services, locating needed services, and enabling persons to enter the service delivery system.

36. **Complementary and alternative medicine services.** Organized hospital services or formal arrangements to providers that provide care or treatment not based solely on traditional western allopathic medical teachings as instructed in most U.S. medical schools. Includes any of the following; acupuncture, chiropractic, homeopathy, osteopathy, diet and lifestyle changes, herbal medicine, massage therapy, etc.

37. **Computer assisted orthopedic surgery (CAOS).** Orthopedic surgery using computer technology, enabling three–dimensional graphic models to visualize a patient's anatomy.

38. **Crisis prevention.** Services provided in order to promote physical and mental well being and the early identification of disease and ill health prior to the onset and recognition of symptoms so as to permit early treatment.

39. **Dental services.** An organized dental service, not necessarily involving special facilities, that provides dental or oral services to inpatients or outpatients.

40. **Emergency department.** Hospital facilities for the provision of unscheduled outpatient services to patients whose conditions require immediate care. Must be staffed 24 hours a day.

41. **Pediatric emergency department.** Hospital facilities for the provision of unscheduled outpatient services to patients whose conditions require immediate care.

42. **Satellite emergency department.** A facility owned and operated by the hospital but physically separate from the hospital for the provision of unscheduled outpatient services to patients whose conditions require.

43. **Trauma center (certified).** A facility certified to provide emergency and specialized intensive care to critically ill and injured patients.

44. **Enabling services.** A program that is designed to help the patient access health care services by offering any of the following linguistic services, transportation services, and/or referrals to local social services agencies.

45. **Optical colonoscopy.** An examination of the interior of the colon using a long, flexible, lighted tube with a small built-in camera.

46. **Endoscopic ultrasound.** Specially designed endoscope that incorporates an ultrasound transducer used to obtain detailed images of organs in the chest and abdomen. The endoscope can be passed through the mouth or the anus. When combined with needle biopsy the procedure can assist in diagnosis and staging of cancer.

47. **Ablation of Barrett's esophagus.** Premalignant condition that can lead to adenocarcinoma of the esophagus. The non surgical ablation of the premalignant tissue in Barrett's esophagus by the application of thermal energy or light through an endoscope passed from the mouth into the esophagus.

48. **Esophageal impedance study.** A test in which a catheter is placed through the nose into the esophagus to measure whether gas or liquids are passing from the stomach into the esophagus and causing symptoms.

49. **Endoscopic retrograde cholangiopancreatography (ERCP).** A procedure in which a catheter is introduced through an endoscope into the bile ducts and pancreatic ducts. Injection of contrast materials permits detailed x-ray of these structures. The procedure is used diagnostically as well as therapeutically to relieve obstruction or remove stones

50. **Enrollment assistance services.** A program that provides enrollment assistance for patients who are potentially eligible for public health insurance programs such as Medicaid, State Children's Health Insurance, or local/state indigent care programs. The specific services offered could include explanation of benefits, assist applicants in completing the application and locating all relevant documents, conduct eligibilty interviews, and/or forward applications and documentation to state/local social service or health agency.

51. **Extracorporeal shock wave lithotripter (ESWL).** A medical device used for treating stones in the kidney or urethra. The device disintegrates kidney stones noninvasively through the transmission of acoustic shock waves directed at the stones.

52. **Fertility clinic.** A specialized program set in an infertility center that provides counseling and education as well as advanced reproductive techniques such as: injectable therapy, reproductive surgeries, treatment for endometriosis, male factor infertility, tubal reversals, in vitro fertilization (IVF), donor eggs, and other such services to help patients achieve successful pregnancies.

53. **Fitness center.** Provides exercise, testing, or evaluation programs and fitness activities to the community and hospital employees.

54. **Freestanding outpatient care center.** A facility owned and operated by the hospital, but physically separate from the hospital, that provides various medical treatments on an outpatient basis only. In addition to treating minor illnesses or injuries, the center will stabilize seriously ill or injured patients before transporting them to a hospital. Laboratory and radiology services are usually available.

55. **Genetic testing/counseling.** A service equipped with adequate laboratory facilities and directed by a qualified physician to advise parents and prospective parents on potential problems in cases of genetic defects. A genetic test is the analysis of human DNA, RNA, chromosomes, proteins, and certain metabolites in order to detect heritable disease- related genotypes, mutations, phenotypes, or karyotypes for clinical purposes. Genetic tests can have diverse purposes, including the diagnosis of genetic diseases in newborns, children, and adults; the identification of future health risks; the prediction of drug responses; and the assessment of risks to future children.

56. **Geriatric services.** The branch of medicine dealing with the physiology of aging and the diagnosis and treatment of disease affecting the aged. Services could include: Adult day care program; Alzheimer's diagnostic–assessment services; Comprehensive geriatric assessment; Emergency response system; Geriatric acute care unit; and/or Geriatric clinics.

57. **Health fair.** Community health education events that focus on the prevention of disease and promotion of health through such activities as audiovisual exhibits and free diagnostic services.

58. **Health research.** Organized hospital research program in any of the following areas: basic research, clinical research, community health research, and/or research on innovative health care delivery.

59. **Health screenings.** A preliminary procedure, such as a test or examination to detect the most characteristic sign or signs of a disorder that may require further investigation.

60. **Hemodialysis.** Provision of equipment and personnel for the treatment of renal insufficiency on an inpatient or outpatient basis.

61. **HIV–AIDS services.** Services may include one or more of the following: HIV–AIDS unit (special unit or team designated and equipped specifically for diagnosis, treatment, continuing care planning, and counseling services for HIV–AIDS patients and their families.) General inpatient care for HIV–AIDS (inpatient diagnosis and treatment for human immunodeficiency virus and acquired immunodeficiency syndrome patients, but dedicated unit is not available.) Specialized outpatient program for HIV–AIDS (special outpatient program providing diagnostic, treatment, continuing care planning, and counseling for HIV–AIDS patients and their families.)

62. **Home health services.** Service providing nursing, therapy, and health–related homemaker or social services in the patient's home.

63. **Hospice program.** A program providing palliative care, chiefly medical relief of pain and supportive services, addressing the emotional, social, financial, and legal needs of terminally ill patients and their families. Care can be provided in a variety of settings, both inpatient and at home.

64. **Hospital–based outpatient care center services.** Organized hospital health care services offered by appointment on an ambulatory basis. Services may include outpatient surgery, examination, diagnosis, and treatment of a variety of medical conditions on a nonemergency basis, and laboratory and other diagnostic testing as ordered by staff or outside physician referral.

65. **Immunization program.** Program that plans, coordinates and conducts immunization services in the community.

66. **Indigent care clinic.** Health care services for uninsured and underinsured persons where care is free of charge or charged on a sliding scale. This would include "free clinics" staffed by volunteer practitioners, but could also be staffed by employees with sponsoring health care organizations subsidizing the cost of service.

67. **Intermediate nursing care.** Provides health–related services (skilled nursing care and social services) to residents with a variety of physical conditions or functional disabilities. These residents do not require the care provided by a hospital or skilled nursing facility, but do need supervision and support services.

68. **Linguistic/translation services.** Services provided by the hospital designed to make health care more accessible to non–English speaking patients and their physicians.

69. **Meals on wheels.** A hospital sponsored program which delivers meals to people, usually the elderly, who are unable to prepare their own meals. Low cost, nutritional meals are delivered to individuals' homes on a regular basis.

70. **Medical surgical intensive care services.** Provides patient care of a more intensive nature than the usual medical and surgical care, on the basis of physicians' orders and approved nursing care plans. These units are staffed with specially trained nursing personnel and contain monitoring and specialized support equipment of patients who, because of shock, trauma, or other life–threatening conditions, require intensified, comprehensive observation and care. Includes mixed intensive care units.

71. **Mobile health services.** Vans and other vehicles used to deliver primary care services.

72. **Neonatal intensive care.** A unit that must be separate from the newborn nursery providing intensive care to all sick infants including those with the very lowest birth weights (less that 1500 grams). NICU has potential for providing mechanical ventilation, neonatal surgery, and special care for the sickest infants born in the hospital or transferred from another institution. A full–time neonatologist serves   as director of the NICU.

73. **Neonatal intermediate care.** A unit that must be separate from the normal newborn nursery and that provides intermediate and/or recovery care and some specialized services, including immediate resuscitation, intravenous therapy, and capacity for prolonged oxygen therapy and monitoring.

74. **Neurological services.** Services provided by the hospital dealing with the operative and nonoperative management of disorders of the central, peripheral, and autonomic nervous system.

75. **Nutrition programs.** Those services within a health care facility which are designed to provide inexpensive, nutritionally sound meals to patients.

76. **Obstetrics.** Levels should be designated: (1) unit provides services for uncomplicated maternity and newborn cases; (2) unit provides services for uncomplicated cases, the majority of complicated problems, and special neonatal services; and (3) unit provides services for all serious illnesses and abnormalities and is supervised by a full–time maternal/fetal specialist.

77. **Occupational health services.** Includes services designed to protect the safety of employees from hazards in the work environment.

78. **Oncology services.** Inpatient and outpatient services for patients with cancer, including comprehensive care, support and guidance in addition to patient education and preventiion, chemotherapy, counseling, and other treatment methods.

79. **Orthopedic services.** Services provided for the prevention or correction of injuries or disorders of the skeletal system and associated muscles, joints, and ligaments.

80. **Other special care.** Provides care to patients requiring care more intensive than that provided in the acute area, yet not sufficiently intensive to require admission to an intensive care unit. Patients admitted to the area are usually transferred here from an intensive care unit once their condition has improved. These units are sometimes referred to as definitive observation, step–down, or progressive care units.

81. **Outpatient surgery.** Scheduled surgical services provided to patients who do not remain in the hospital overnight. The surgery may be performed in operating suites also used for inpatient surgery, specially designated surgical suites for outpatient surgery, or procedure rooms within an outpatient care facility.

82. **Pain management program.** A hospital wide formalized program that includes staff education for the management of chronic and acute pain based on guidelines and protocols like those developed by the agency for Health Care Policy Research, etc.

83. **Inpatient palliative care unit.** An inpatient palliative care ward is a physically discreet, inpatient nursing unit where the focus is palliative care. The patient care focus is on symptom relief for complex patients who may be continuing to undergo primary treatment. Care is delivered by palliative medicine specialists.

84. **Palliative care program.** An organized program providing specialized medical care, drugs or therapies for the management of acute or chronic pain and/or the control of symptoms adminstered by specially trained physicians and other clinicians; and supportive care services, such as counseling on advanced directives, spiritual care, and social services, to patients with advanced disease and their families.

85. **Patient controlled analgesia (PCA).** Patient Controlled Analgesia

(PCA) is intravenously administered pain medicine under the patient's control. The patient has a button on the end of a cord than can be pushed at will, whenever more pain medicine is desired. This button will only deliver more pain medicine at pre-determined intervals, as programmed by the doctor's order.

86. **Patient education center.** Written goals and objectives for the patient and/or family related to therapeutic regimens, medical procedures, and self care.

87. **Patient representative services.** Organized hospital services providing personnel through whom patients and staff can seek solutions to institutional problems affecting the delivery of high–quality care and services.

88. **Pediatric intensive care services.** Provides care to pediatric patients that is of a more intensive nature than that usually provided to pediatric patients. The unit is staffed with specially trained personnel and contains monitoring and specialized support equipment for treatment of patients who, because of shock, trauma, or other life–threatening conditions, require intensified, comprehensive observation and care.

89. **Pediatric medical–surgical care.** Provides acute care to pediatric settings) or in a traditional setting (gymnasium) using motor learning principles.

90. **Physical rehabilitation inpatient services.** Provides care encompassing a comprehensive array of restoration services for the disabled and all support services necessary to help patients attain their maximum functional capacity.

91. **Assistive technology center.** A program providing access to specialized hardware and software with adaptations allowing individuals greater independence with mobility, dexterity, or increased communication options.

92. **Electrodiagnostic services.** Diagnostic testing services for nerve and muscle function including services such as nerve conduction studies and needle electromyography.

93. **Physical rehabilitation outpatient services.** Outpatient program providing medical, health–related, therapy, social, and/or vocational services to help disabled persons attain or retain their maximum functional capacity.

94. **Prosthetic and orthotic services.** Services providing comprehensive prosthetic and orthotic evaluation, fitting, and training.

95. **Robot-assisted walking therapy.** A form of physical therapy that uses a courts, public health nurses, welfare agencies, clergy and so forth. The purpose is to expand the mental health knowledge and competence of personnel not working in the mental health field and to promote good mental health through improved understanding, attitudes, and behavioral patterns.

96. **Simulated rehabilitation environment.** Rehabilitation focused on retraining functional skills in a contextually appropriate environment (simulated home and community settings) or in a traditional setting (gymnasium) using motor learning principles.

97. **Primary care department.** A unit or clinic within the hospital that provides primary care services (e.g. general pediatric care, general internal medicine, family practice and gynecology) through hospital–salaried medical and or nursing staff, focusing on evaluating and diagnosing medical problems and providing medical treatment on an outpatient basis.

98. **Psychiatric care.** Provides acute or long–term care to emotionally disturbed patients, including patients admitted for diagnosis and those admitted for treatment of psychiatric problems, on the basis of physicians' orders and approved nursing care plans. Long–term care may include intervention, and assistance to persons suffering acute emotional or mental distress.

99. **Psychiatric child–adolescent services.** Provides care to emotionally disturbed children and adolescents, including those admitted for diagnosis and those admitted for treatment.

100. **Psychiatric consultation–liaison services.** Provides organized psychiatric consultation/liaison services to nonpsychiatric hospital staff and/or department on psychological aspects of medical care that may be generic or specific to individual patients.

101. **Psychiatric education services.** Provides psychiatric educational services to community agencies and workers such as schools, police, courts, public health nurses, welfare agencies, clergy and so forth. The purpose is to expand the mental health knowledge and competence of personnel not working in the mental health field and to promote good mental health through improved understanding, attitudes, and behavioral patterns.

102. **Psychiatric emergency services.** Services or facilities available on a 24–hour basis to provide immediate unscheduled outpatient care, diagnosis, evaluation, crisis intervention, and assistance to persons suffering acute emotional or mental distress.

103. **Psychiatric geriatric services.** Provides care to emotionally disturbed elderly patients, including those admitted for diagnosis and those admitted for treatment.

104. **Psychiatric outpatient services.** Provides medical care, including diagnosis and treatment of psychiatric outpatients.

105. **Psychiatric partial hospitalization services.** Organized hospital services of intensive day/evening outpatient services of three hours or more duration, distinguished from other outpatient visits of one hour.

106. **Psychiatric residential treatment.**

107. **CT scanner.** Computed tomographic scanner for head and whole body scans.

108. **Diagnostic radioisotope facility.** The use of radioactive isotopes (Radiopharmaceutical) as tracers or indicators to detect an abnormal condition or disease.

109. **Electron beam computed tomography (EBCT).** A high tech computed tomography scan used to detect coronary artery disease by measuring coronary calcifications. This imaging procedure uses electron beams which are magnetically steered to produce a visual of the coronary artery and the images are produced faster than conventional CT scans.

110. **Full–field digital mammography (FFDM).** Combines the x–ray generators and tubes used in analog screen–film mammography (SFM) with a detector plate that converts the x–rays into a digital signal.

111. **Magnetic resonance imaging (MRI).** The use of a uniform magnetic field and radio frequencies to study tissue and structure of the body. This procedure enables the visualization of biochemical activity of the cell in vivo without the use of ionizing radiation, radioisotopic substances, or high–frequency sound.

112. **Intraoperative magnetic resonance imaging.** An integrated surgery system which provides an MRI system in an operating room. The system allows for immediate evaluation of the degree to tumor resection while the patient is undergoing a surgical resection. Intraoperative MRI exists when a MRI (low–field or high–field) is placed in the operating theater and is used during surgical resection without moving the patient from the operating room to the diagnostic imaging suite.

113. **Magnetoencephalography (MEG).** A noninvasive neurophysiological measurement tool used to study magnetic fields generated by neuronal activity of the brain. MEG provides direct information about the dynamics of evoked and spontaneous neural activity and the location of their sources in the brain. The primary uses of MEG include assisting surgeons in localizing the source of epilepsy, sensory mapping and the study of brain function. When it is combined with structural imaging, it is known as magnetic source imaging (MSI).

114. **Multi–slice spiral computed tomography (MSCT) (<64 slice CT).** A specialized computed tomography cycles per second to visualize internal body structures.

115. **Multi–slice spiral computed tomography (64 + slice CT).** Involves the acquisition of volumetric tomographic x–ray absorption data expressed in Hounsfield units using multiple rows of detectors. 64+ systems reconstruct the equivalent of 64 or greater slices to cover the imaged volume.

116. **Positron emission tomography (PET).** A nuclear medicine imaging technology which uses radioactive (positron emitting) isotopes created in a cyclotron or generator and computers to produce composite pictures of the brain and heart at work. PET scanning produces sectional images depicting metabolic activity or blood flow rather than anatomy.

117. **Positron emission tomography/ CT (PET/CT).** Provides metabolic functional information for the monitoring of chemotherapy, radiotherapy and surgical planning.

118. **Single photon emission computerized tomography (SPECT).** A nuclear medicine imaging technology that combines existing technology of gamma camera imaging with computed tomographic imaging technology to provide a more precise and clear image.

119. **Ultrasound.** The use of acoustic waves above the range of 20,000 cycles per second to visualize internal body structures.

120. **Image–guided radiation therapy (IGRT).** Automated system for image– guided radiation therapy that enables clinicians to obtain high–resolution x– ray images to pinpoint tumor sites, adjust patient positioning when necessary, and complete a treatment, all within the standard treatment time slot, allowing for more effective cancer treatments.

121. **Intensity–modulated radiation Therapy (IMRT).** A type of three–dimensional radiation therapy, which improves the targeting of treatment delivery in a way that is likely to decrease damage to normal tissues and allows varying intensities diagnosis of genetic diseases in newborns, children, and adults; the identification of future health risks; arrange for acute and long term care through affiliated institutions.

122. **Proton beam therapy.** A form of radiation therapy which administers proton beams. While producing the same biologic effects as x–ray beams, the energy distribution of protons differs from conventional x–ray beams in that they can be more precisely focused in tissue volumes in a three–dimensional pattern resulting in less surrounding tissue damage than conventional radiation therapy permitting administration of higher doses.

123. **Shaped beam radiation therapy.** A precise, non–invasive treatment that involves targeting beams of radiation that mirror the exact size and shape of a tumor at a specific area of a tumor to shrink or destroy cancerous cells. This procedure delivers a therapeutic dose of radiation that conforms precisely to the shape of the tumor, thus minimizing the risk to nearby tissues.

124. **Stereotactic radiosurgery.** Stereotactic radiosurgery (SRS) is a radiotherapy modality that delivers a high dosage of radiation to a discrete treatment area in as few as one treatment session. Includes gamma knife, cyberknife, etc.

125. **Retirement housing.** A facility which provides social activities to senior citizens, usually retired persons, who do not require health care but some short–term skilled nursing care may be provided. A retirement center may furnish housing and may also have acute hospital and long–term care facilities, or it may arrange for acute and long term care through affiliated institutions.

126. **Robotic surgery.** The use of mechanical guidance devices to remotely manipulate surgical instrumentation.

127. **Rural health clinic.** A clinic located in a rural, medically under-served area in the United States that has a separate reimbursement structure from the standard medical office under the Medicare and Medicaid programs.

128. **Skilled nursing care.** Provides non–acute medical and skilled nursing care services, therapy, and social services under the supervision of a licensed registered nurse on a 24–hour basis.

129. **Sleep center.** Specially equipped and staffed center for the diagnosis and treatment of sleep disorders.

130. **Social work services.** Services may include one or more of the following: Organized social work services (services that are properly directed and sufficiently staffed by qualified individuals who provide assistance and counseling to patients and their families in dealing with social, emotional, and environmental problems associated with illness or disability, often in the context of financial or discharge planning coordination.) Outpatient social work services (social work services provided in ambulatory care areas.) Emergency department social work services (social work services provided to emergency department patients by social workers dedicated to the emergency department or on call.)

131. **Sports medicine.** Provision of diagnostic screening and assessment and clinical and rehabilitation services for the prevention and treatment of sports–related injuries.

132. Support groups. A hospital sponsored program which allows a group of individuals with the same or similar problems who meet periodically to share experiences, problems, and solutions, in order to support each other.

133. Swing bed services. A hospital bed that can be used to provide either acute or long–term care depending on community or patients needs. To be eligible a hospital must have a Medicare provider agreement in place, have fewer than 100 beds, be located in a rural area, not have a 24 hour nursing service waiver in effect, have not been terminated from the program in the prior two years, and meet various service conditions.

134. Teen outreach services. A program focusing on the teenager which encourages an improved health status and a healthful lifestyle including physical, emotional, mental, social, spiritual and economic health through education, exercise, nutrition and health promotion.

135. Tobacco treatment/cessation program. Organized hospital services with the purpose of ending tobacco–use habits of patients addicted to tobacco/nicotine.

136.–142. Transplant services. The branch of medicine that transfers an organ or tissue from one person to another or from one body part to another to replace a diseased structure or to restore function or to change appearance. Services could include: Bone marrow transplant program (136. Bone marrow); heart (137. Heart transplant), kidney (138. Kidney transplant), liver (139. Liver transplant) lung (140. Lung transplant), tissue (141. Tissue transplant). Please include heart/lung or other multi- transplant surgeries inn other (142. Other Transplant).

143. Transportation to health services. A long–term care support service designed to assist the mobility of the elderly. Some programs offer improved financial access by offering reduced rates and barrier–free buses or vans with ramps and lifts to assist the elderly or handicapped; others offer subsidies for public transport systems or operate mini–bus services

144. Urgent care center. A facility that provides care and treatment for problems that are not life–threatening but require attention over the short term. These units function like emergency rooms but are separate from hospitals with which they may have backup affiliation arrangements.

145. Virtual colonoscopy. Noninvasive screening procedure used to visualize, analyze and detect cancerous or potentially cancerous polyps in the colon.

146. Volunteer services department. An organized hospital department responsible for coordinating the services of volunteers working within the institution.

147. Women's center. An area set aside for coordinated education and treatment services specifically for and promoted by women as provided by this special unit. Services may or may not include obstetrics but include a range of services other than OB.

148. Wound management services. Services for patients with chronic wounds and non–healing wounds often resulting from diabetes, poor circulation, improper seating and immunocompromising conditions. The goals are to progress chronic wounds through stages of healing, reduce and eliminate infections, increase physical function to minimize complications from current wounds and prevent future chronic wounds. Wound management services are provided on an inpatient or outpatient basis, depending on the intensity of service needed.

149. Violence prevention programs for the workplace. A violence prevention program with goals and objectives for preventing workplace violence against staff and patients.

150. Violence prevention programs for the community. An organized program that attempts to make a positive impact on the type(s) of violence a community is experiencing. For example, it can assist victims of violent crimes, e.g., rape, or incidents, e.g., bullying, to hospital or to community services to prevent further victimization or retaliation. A program that targets the underlying circumstances that contribute to violence such as poor housing, insufficient job training, and/or substance abuse through means such as direct involvement and support, education, mentoring, anger management, crisis intervention and training programs would also qualify.

Definitions of Physician Codes

1. Closed physician–hospital organization (PHO). A PHO that restricts physician membership to those practitioners who meet criteria for cost effectiveness and/or high quality.

2. Equity model. Allows established practitioners to become shareholders in a professional corporation in exchange for tangible and intangible assets of their existing practices.

3. Foundation. A corporation, organized either as a hospital affiliate or subsidiary, which purchases both the tangible and intangible assets of one or more medical group practices. Physicians remain in a separate corporate entity but sign a professional services agreement with the foundation.

4. Group practice without walls. Hospital sponsors the formation of, or provides capital to physicians to establish, a 'quasi' group to share administrative expenses while remaining independent practitioners.

5. Independent practice association (IPA). A legal entity that hold managed care contracts. The IPA then contracts with physicians, usually in solo practice, to provide care either on a fee–for–services or capitated basis. The purpose of an IPA is to assist solo physicians in obtaining managed care contracts.

6. Integrated salary model. Physicians are salaried by the hospital or another entity of a health system to provide medical services for primary care and specialty care.

7. Management services organization (MSO). A corporation, owned by the hospital or a physician/ hospital joint venture, that provides management services to one or more medical group practices. The MSO purchases the tangible assets of the practices and leases them back as part of a full–service management agreement, under which the MSO employs all non–physician staff and provides all supplies/administrative systems for a fee.

8. Open physician–hospital organization (PHO). A joint venture between the hospital and all members of the medical staff who wish to participate. The PHO can act as a unified agent in managed care contracting, own a managed care plan, own and operate ambulatory care centers or ancillary services projects, or provide administrative services to physician members.

Control and Service Classifications

Control

Government, nonfederal
State
County
City
City–county
Hospital district or authority

Nongovernment not-for-profit
Church operated
Other

Investor–owned (for–profit)
Individual
Partnership
Corporation

Government, federal
Air
Force
Army
Navy

Public Health Service other than 47
Veterans Affairs

Osteopathic
Church operated Other not–for–profit
Other
Individual for–profit
Partnership for–profit
Corporation for–profit

Service

General medical and surgical
Hospital unit of an institution (prison hospital, college infirmary, etc.)
Hospital unit within a facility for persons with intellectual disabilities
Surgical
Psychiatric
Tuberculosis and other respiratory diseases
Cancer
Heart
Obstetrics and gynecology

Eye, ear, nose, and throat
Rehabilitation
Orthopedic
Chronic disease
Other specialty
Children's general
Children's hospital unit of an institution
Children's psychiatric
Children's tuberculosis and other respiratory diseases
Children's eye, ear, nose, and throat

Children's rehabilitation
Children's orthopedic
Children's chronic disease
Children's other specialty
Intellectual disabilities
Long–Term Acute Care
Alcoholism and other chemical dependency
Children's Long–Term Acute Care
Children's Cancer
Children's Heart

ALABAMA

ALABASTER—Shelby County

☐ **NOLAND HOSPITAL SHELBY (012013)**, 1000 First Street North, 3rd Floor, Zip 35007–8703; tel. 205/620–8641, **A**1 10 **F**1 3 17 18 26 28 29 30 60 61 67 70 75 77 79 80 84 90 91 92 103 107 111 115 119 128 130 148 **S** Noland Health Services, Inc., Birmingham, AL
Primary Contact: Laura S. Wills, Administrator
Web address: www.nolandhospitals.com
Control: Other not–for–profit (including NFP Corporation) **Service:** Acute long–term care hospital

> **Staffed Beds:** 52 **Admissions:** 129 **Census:** 11 **Outpatient Visits:** 0 **Births:** 0

⊞ **SHELBY BAPTIST MEDICAL CENTER (010016)**, 1000 First Street North, Zip 35007–8703; tel. 205/620–8100, **A**1 3 10 **F**3 8 11 12 13 15 17 18 20 22 24 26 28 29 30 31 34 35 40 43 45 47 48 49 50 57 59 64 70 72 74 75 76 77 79 81 82 84 85 87 93 98 103 107 108 110 111 114 115 118 119 124 126 127 129 130 131 135 146 147 148 149 **S** TENET Healthcare Corporation, Dallas, TX
Primary Contact: Mike Rickman, Chief Executive Officer
CFO: Jennifer Pittman, Chief Financial Officer
CMO: Mark Scofield M.D., Chief Medical Officer
CIO: Mike Nighman, Facility Coordinator Information Systems
CHR: Cindy Nicholson, Director Human Resources
CNO: Ed Price, Chief Nurse Officer
Web address: www.brookwoodbaptisthealth.com
Control: Corporation, Investor–owned (for–profit) **Service:** General medical and surgical

> **Staffed Beds:** 231 **Admissions:** 12384 **Census:** 176 **Outpatient Visits:** 111267 **Births:** 1117 **Total Expense ($000):** 153014 **Payroll Expense ($000):** 50924 **Personnel:** 952

ALEXANDER CITY—Tallapoosa County

☐ **RUSSELL MEDICAL CENTER (010065)**, 3316 Highway 280, Zip 35010–3369, Mailing Address: P.O.Box 939, 35011–0939; tel. 256/329–7100, **A**1 3 10 19 **F**3 11 13 15 18 20 22 28 29 30 31 34 35 40 43 45 50 51 53 57 58 59 60 64 67 68 74 75 76 77 78 79 80 81 82 85 87 89 93 107 108 110 111 115 116 119 121 123 126 129 131 132 143 146 148 149
Primary Contact: Lother E. Peace III, President and Chief Executive Officer
CFO: J. Matthew Fisher, Chief Financial Officer
CMO: Michele Goldhagen M.D., Chief of Staff
CIO: Tommy Spraggins, Director Information Services
CHR: Mary Shockley, Director Human Resources
Web address: www.russellmedcenter.com
Control: Other not–for–profit (including NFP Corporation) **Service:** General medical and surgical

> **Staffed Beds:** 69 **Admissions:** 3058 **Census:** 28 **Outpatient Visits:** 95843 **Births:** 415 **Total Expense ($000):** 76869 **Payroll Expense ($000):** 25110 **Personnel:** 542

ANDALUSIA—Covington County

⊞ **ANDALUSIA HEALTH (010036)**, 849 South Three Notch Street, Zip 36420–5325, Mailing Address: P.O.Box 760, 36420–1214; tel. 334/222–8466, **A**1 10 **F**3 8 11 13 15 29 30 34 35 40 43 45 46 51 57 59 60 64 65 68 69 74 75 76 77 79 80 81 82 85 87 89 93 107 108 110 111 114 116 117 119 129 131 133 135 146 147 148 **S** LifePoint Health, Brentwood, TN
Primary Contact: John C. Yanes, Chief Executive Officer
COO: Melissa Davis, Chief Operating Officer
CFO: Shirley M Smith, Chief Financial Officer
CIO: Matthew Perry, Director Information Systems
CHR: Brian Woods, Human Resources Director
CNO: Melissa Davis, Chief Clinical Officer
Web address: www.andalusiahealth.com
Control: Corporation, Investor–owned (for–profit) **Service:** General medical and surgical

> **Staffed Beds:** 88 **Admissions:** 2964 **Census:** 27 **Births:** 412

ANNISTON—Calhoun County

☐ **NOLAND HOSPITAL ANNISTON (012011)**, 400 East 10th Street, 4th Fl, Zip 36207–4716; tel. 256/741–6141, **A**1 10 **F**1 3 29 148 **S** Noland Health Services, Inc., Birmingham, AL
Primary Contact: Trina Woods, Administrator
Web address: www.nolandhealth.com
Control: Other not–for–profit (including NFP Corporation) **Service:** Acute long–term care hospital

> **Staffed Beds:** 38 **Admissions:** 303 **Census:** 21 **Outpatient Visits:** 0 **Births:** 0

⊞ **RMC ANNISTON (010078)**, 400 East Tenth Street, Zip 36207–4716, Mailing Address: P.O.Box 2208, 36202–2208; tel. 256/235–5121, (Nonreporting) **A**1 2 10 **F**12 15 18 19 20 22 24 26 29 30 31 34 35 40 43 45 47 48 49 50 51 56 57 59 60 64 65 68 69 70 71 74 75 77 78 79 81 82 85 86 87 93 97 107 108 111 114 119 129 130 131 132 135 141 146 148 **S** Regional Medical Center, Anniston, AL
Primary Contact: Louis A. Bass, Chief Executive Officer
CMO: David Zinn M.D., Vice President Medical Affairs
CIO: Pete Furlow, Director Information Technology Services
CHR: Michael S Simms Sr., Vice President Human Resources
CNO: Elaine Davis, Chief Nursing Officer and Vice President Patient Services
Web address: www.rmccares.org
Control: Hospital district or authority, Government, Nonfederal **Service:** General medical and surgical

> **Staffed Beds:** 271

⊞ **RMC–STRINGFELLOW MEMORIAL HOSPITAL (010038)**, 301 East 18th Street, Zip 36207–3952; tel. 256/235–8900, **A**1 10 **F**3 10 11 15 29 30 34 35 40 45 49 50 53 57 59 62 63 64 68 70 75 77 79 81 85 87 91 93 96 100 107 108 114 119 128 129 130 135 145 146 148 **S** Regional Medical Center, Anniston, AL
Primary Contact: Joe Weaver, Chief Executive Officer
CIO: Peggy Henderson, Director Health Information
CHR: Tamatha Johnson, Director Human Resources
Web address: www.stringfellowmemorial.com
Control: Corporation, Investor–owned (for–profit) **Service:** General medical and surgical

> **Staffed Beds:** 88 **Admissions:** 3303 **Census:** 30 **Births:** 0

ASHLAND—Clay County

CLAY COUNTY HOSPITAL (010073), 83825 Highway 9, Zip 36251–7981, Mailing Address: P.O.Box 1270, 36251–1270; tel. 256/354–2131, (Total facility includes 83 beds in nursing home–type unit) **A**10 **F**3 7 8 11 13 15 28 29 34 35 40 43 46 48 50 51 53 54 56 57 58 59 64 68 70 73 75 76 77 79 81 82 85 86 87 89 93 98 107 108 109 110 111 114 115 118 119 129 130 131 132 143 144 146 147 148 149
Primary Contact: Joel W. Tate, FACHE, Chief Executive Officer
CFO: Kerry W Tomlin, Associate Administrator
CMO: David Hensleigh, Director Medical Staff
CIO: Patrick Smith, Director Information Technology
CHR: Linda T Smith, Director Human Resources
CNO: Charles Griffin, Director of Nursing
Web address: www.claycountyhospital.com
Control: Church operated, Nongovernment, not–for–profit **Service:** General medical and surgical

> **Staffed Beds:** 129 **Admissions:** 1306 **Census:** 85 **Births:** 0

Hospital, Medicare Provider Number, Address, Telephone, Approval, Facility, and Physician Codes, Health Care System

★ American Hospital Association (AHA) membership
☐ The Joint Commission accreditation
○ Healthcare Facilities Accreditation Program
◇ DNV Healthcare Inc. accreditation
⇑ Center for Improvement in Healthcare Quality Accreditation
△ Commission on Accreditation of Rehabilitation Facilities (CARF) accreditation

---

ATHENS—Limestone County

☐ **ATHENS–LIMESTONE HOSPITAL (010079)**, 700 West Market Street,
Zip 35611–2457, Mailing Address: P.O.Box 999, 35612–0999; tel. 256/233–
9292, **A**1 5 10 **S** Huntsville Hospital Health System, Huntsville, AL
Primary Contact: David Pryor, President
COO: Randy Comer, Chief Operating Officer
CFO: Randy Comer, Chief Financial Officer
CMO: Jon Bignault M.D., Chief of Staff
CIO: Kim Hoback, Supervisor Information Systems
CHR: Rachel Frey, Director Human Resources
CNO: Jan Lenz, Chief Nursing Officer
Web address: www.athenslimestonehospital.com
Control: Hospital district or authority, Government, Nonfederal **Service**: General
medical and surgical

> **Staffed Beds: 71 Admissions: 4076 Census: 40 Outpatient Visits:** 131317
> **Births: 513 Total Expense ($000):** 77936 **Payroll Expense ($000):** 34714
> **Personnel:** 746

ATMORE—Escambia County

ATMORE COMMUNITY HOSPITAL (010169), 401 Medical Park Drive,
Zip 36502–3091; tel. 251/368–2500, **A**10 **F**3 11 15 29 30 40 62 64 70 77
81 85 91 93 97 107 110 115 119 127 128 133 144 146 **S** Infirmary Health
System, Mobile, AL
Primary Contact: Douglas Tanner, President
CFO: Keith Strickling, Chief Financial Officer
CHR: Linda Lowrey, Human Resources Officer
CNO: Ashley Chunn, Director of Nursing
Web address: www.ebaptisthealthcare.org/AtmoreCommunityHospital/
Control: County, Government, Nonfederal **Service**: General medical and surgical

> **Staffed Beds: 33 Admissions: 1408 Census: 14 Births: 0 Personnel:** 195

BAY MINETTE—Baldwin County

NORTH BALDWIN INFIRMARY (010129), 1815 Hand Avenue, Zip 36507–
4110, Mailing Address: P.O.Box 1409, 36507–1409; tel. 251/937–5521, **A**10
F13 15 29 30 31 40 53 59 70 76 79 81 93 98 100 101 102 103 104 107 108
111 119 130 146 **S** Infirmary Health System, Mobile, AL
Primary Contact: Benjamin K. Hansert, Administrator
CFO: J Patrick Murphy, Chief Financial Officer
Web address: www.mobileinfirmary.org
Control: Other not–for–profit (including NFP Corporation) **Service**: General
medical and surgical

> **Staffed Beds: 50 Admissions: 1979 Census: 25 Births:** 222

BESSEMER—Jefferson County

☐ **MEDICAL WEST (010114)**, 995 Ninth Avenue SW, Zip 35022–4527; tel.
205/481–7000, **A**1 3 10 **F**3 11 13 15 18 20 29 30 31 34 40 42 43 45 49 50
53 54 57 59 60 64 68 70 74 75 76 77 78 79 80 81 82 85 86 90 92 93 94 96
98 100 101 102 103 104 107 108 110 111 114 115 118 119 129 130 132
143 146 147 148 149 **P**6 **S** UAB Health System, Birmingham, AL
Primary Contact: Brian Keith. Pennington, President and Chief Executive Officer
COO: Sean Tinney FACHE, Chief Operating Officer
CFO: Brandon H Slocum, Senior Vice President and Chief Financial Officer
CMO: Conrad De Los Santos, President Medical Staff
CIO: Bob Duckworth, Director Information Systems
CHR: Gannon Davis, Director Human Resources
CNO: Pamela Spencer Autrey R.N., Ph.D., MSN, Chief Nursing Officer
Web address: www.medicalwesthospital.org
Control: Hospital district or authority, Government, Nonfederal **Service**: General
medical and surgical

> **Staffed Beds: 231 Admissions: 7183 Census: 114 Outpatient Visits:**
> 225914 **Births: 406 Total Expense ($000):** 116315 **Payroll Expense
> ($000):** 48968 **Personnel:** 1108

BIRMINGHAM—Jefferson County

⊞ **BIRMINGHAM VETERANS AFFAIRS MEDICAL CENTER**, 700 South 19th Street,
Zip 35233–1927; tel. 205/933–8101, (Nonreporting) **A**1 2 3 5 8 **S** Department of
Veterans Affairs, Washington, DC
Primary Contact: Thomas C. Smith III, FACHE, Director
COO: Phyllis J. Smith, Associate Director
CFO: Mary S Mitchell, Chief Resource Management Services
CMO: William F Harper M.D., Chief of Staff
CIO: Antonia Mohamed, Acting Chief Information Officer
CHR: Jacqueline Caron, Chief Human Resources
CNO: Cynthia Cleveland Ph.D., R.N., Associate Director for Patient Care Services
and Nurse Executive
Web address: www.birmingham.va.gov/
Control: Veterans Affairs, Government, federal **Service**: General medical and surgical

> **Staffed Beds:** 151

⊞ **BROOKWOOD BAPTIST MEDICAL CENTER (010139)**, 2010 Brookwood
Medical Center Drive, Zip 35209–6875; tel. 205/877–1000, **A**1 2 3 5 10 **F**3 11
12 13 15 18 20 22 24 26 29 30 31 34 35 38 40 42 43 45 46 47 48 49 50 56
57 58 59 64 74 75 78 79 81 82 85 86 87 100 101 102 103 104 105 107 108
109 110 111 114 115 116 117 118 119 120 121 123 124 126 129 130 132
135 145 146 147 148 **S** TENET Healthcare Corporation, Dallas, TX
Primary Contact: Keith Parrott, FACHE, Interim President and Chief Executive
Officer
COO: Kathy Healy–Collier, Chief Operating Officer
CFO: Brandon Willams, Chief Financial Officer
CMO: Vish Sachdev, Chief Medical Officer
CIO: Manuel Price, Director Information Systems
CHR: Ronnelle Stewart, SPHR, SHRM–SCP, Chief Human Resources Officer
CNO: Marye Elliott, Chief Nursing Officer
Web address: www.brookwoodbaptisthealth.com/
Control: Corporation, Investor–owned (for–profit) **Service**: General medical and
surgical

> **Staffed Beds: 607 Admissions: 24277 Census: 378 Outpatient Visits:**
> 110219 **Births: 3955 Total Expense ($000):** 350117 **Payroll Expense
> ($000):** 114154

⊞ **CHILDREN'S OF ALABAMA (013300)**, 1600 Seventh Avenue South, Zip 35233–
1785; tel. 205/638–9100, **A**1 3 5 10 **F**3 7 8 9 11 12 16 17 19 20 21 22 23 25
27 29 30 31 32 34 35 38 39 40 41 43 46 48 50 54 55 57 58 59 60 61 64 65
68 72 74 75 77 78 79 80 81 82 84 85 86 87 88 89 91 92 93 94 96 97 98 99
100 101 102 104 107 108 109 111 114 115 116 117 118 119 126 129 130
131 132 134 135 136 137 138 139 142 143 146 148 149
Primary Contact: Wm. Michael. Warren Jr, President and Chief Executive Officer
COO: Tom Shufflebarger, Chief Operating Officer
CFO: Dawn Walton, Chief Financial Officer
CMO: Crayton A Fargason M.D., Medical Director
CIO: Robert Sarnecki, Interim Chief Information Officer
CHR: Douglas B Dean, Chief Human Resources Officer
CNO: Deb Wesley MSN, Chief Nursing Officer
Web address: www.childrensal.org
Control: Other not–for–profit (including NFP Corporation) **Service**: Children's
general medical and surgical

> **Staffed Beds: 345 Admissions: 15777 Census: 252 Outpatient Visits:**
> 676484 **Total Expense ($000):** 666325 **Payroll Expense ($000):** 251984
> **Personnel:** 4089

⊞ **GRANDVIEW MEDICAL CENTER (010104)**, 3690 Grandview Parkway,
Zip 35243–3326; tel. 205/971–1000, **A**1 2 3 5 10 13 **F**3 11 12 13 15 17 18 20
22 24 26 28 29 30 31 34 35 40 43 45 46 47 48 49 50 51 54 57 58 59 64 70
72 74 75 76 77 78 79 81 82 84 85 90 93 96 98 99 100 101 102 103 107 108
110 111 115 119 126 129 130 131 132 135 146 147 148 149 **S** Community
Health Systems, Inc., Franklin, TN
Primary Contact: Drew Mason, President and Chief Executive Officer
COO: Drew Mason, Chief Operating Officer
CFO: Julie Soekoro, Chief Financial Officer
CMO: Rebecca Byrd, President Medical Staff
CIO: Tim Townes, Director Information Systems
CHR: Jeri Wink, Director Human Resources
CNO: James Epperson, Interim Chief Nursing Officer
Web address: www.grandviewhealth.com
Control: Corporation, Investor–owned (for–profit) **Service**: General medical and surgical

> **Staffed Beds: 379 Admissions: 16328 Census: 244 Outpatient Visits:**
> 247926 **Births: 956 Total Expense ($000):** 326118 **Payroll Expense
> ($000):** 107164 **Personnel:** 1941

⊞ **HEALTHSOUTH LAKESHORE REHABILITATION HOSPITAL (013025)**, 3800
Ridgeway Drive, Zip 35209–5599; tel. 205/868–2000, **A**1 10 **F**3 29 75 77 86 87
90 91 93 95 96 130 132 135 148 **S** HEALTHSOUTH Corporation, Birmingham, AL
Primary Contact: Vickie Demers, Chief Executive Officer
CFO: Kimberly Thrasher, Controller
CMO: Michael Rosemore M.D., Medical Director
CHR: Julie Smith, Director Human Resources
CNO: April Cobb, Chief Nursing Officer
Web address: www.healthsouthlakeshorerehab.com
Control: Corporation, Investor–owned (for–profit) **Service**: Rehabilitation

> **Staffed Beds: 100 Admissions: 2725 Census: 89 Outpatient Visits:** 10726
> **Births: 0 Total Expense ($000):** 33394 **Payroll Expense ($000):** 17420
> **Personnel:** 342

☐ **HILL CREST BEHAVIORAL HEALTH SERVICES (014000)**, 6869 Fifth Avenue
South, Zip 35212–1866; tel. 205/833–9000, **A**1 10 **F**98 99 100 101 102 104
106 **S** Universal Health Services, Inc., King of Prussia, PA
Primary Contact: Steve McCabe, Chief Executive Officer
CFO: Mark Teske, Chief Financial Officer
Web address: www.hillcrestbhs.com
Control: Corporation, Investor–owned (for–profit) **Service**: Psychiatric

> **Staffed Beds: 80 Admissions: 1033 Census: 70 Outpatient Visits: 0 Births:** 0

Many Facility Codes have changed. Please refer to the AHA Guide Code Chart. © 2017 AHA Guide

☐ **NOLAND HOSPITAL BIRMINGHAM (012009)**, 50 Medical Park East Drive, 8th Floor, Zip 35235; tel. 205/808–5100, **A**1 10 **F**1 29 130 148 **S** Noland Health Services, Inc., Birmingham, AL
Primary Contact: Laura S. Wills, Administrator
COO: Sharon Engle, Director Clinical Services
CMO: Mark Middlebrooks M.D., Medical Director
CHR: Ashley Clark, Coordinator Human Resources
CNO: Rachel Chapman, Nurse Manager
Web address: www.nolandhealth.com
Control: Other not–for–profit (including NFP Corporation) **Service**: Acute long–term care hospital

Staffed Beds: 45 Admissions: 322 Census: 27 Outpatient Visits: 0 Births: 0

✠ **PRINCETON BAPTIST MEDICAL CENTER (010103)**, 701 Princeton Avenue SW, Zip 35211–1303; tel. 205/783–3000, **A**1 2 3 5 10 **F**3 11 12 13 15 17 18 20 22 24 26 28 29 30 31 34 35 40 43 45 46 47 48 49 50 55 56 57 58 59 64 67 70 72 74 75 76 78 79 81 82 83 84 85 87 91 92 93 94 98 103 107 108 110 111 114 115 117 118 119 120 121 123 124 126 129 130 131 132 146 147 148 149 **S** TENET Healthcare Corporation, Dallas, TX
Primary Contact: Betsy Postlethwait, President
COO: Sarah Nunnelly, Chief Operating Officer
CFO: Beverly Haymon, Chief Financial Officer
CMO: Alan Craig M.D., Physician Advisor
CNO: Paula Davenport, Chief Nursing Officer
Web address: www.bhsala.com
Control: Partnership, Investor–owned (for–profit) **Service**: General medical and surgical

Staffed Beds: 311 Admissions: 14180 Census: 223 Outpatient Visits: 108269 Births: 325 Total Expense ($000): 227047 Payroll Expense ($000): 79140 Personnel: 1345

✠ **SELECT SPECIALTY HOSPITAL–BIRMINGHAM (012008)**, 2010 Brookwood Medical Center Drive, 3rd Floor, Zip 35209–6804; tel. 205/599–4600, **A**1 10 **F**1 60 77 82 84 103 105 111 115 116 117 118 119 148 **S** Select Medical Corporation, Mechanicsburg, PA
Primary Contact: Andrea White, Chief Executive Officer
CMO: Allan Goldstein M.D., Medical Director and Chief of Staff
Web address: www.selectspecialtyhospitals.com/company/locations/birmingham.aspx
Control: Corporation, Investor–owned (for–profit) **Service**: Acute long–term care hospital

Staffed Beds: 38 Admissions: 312 Census: 32 Outpatient Visits: 0 Births: 0

✠ **ST. VINCENT'S BIRMINGHAM (010056)**, 810 St Vincent's Drive, Zip 35205–1695, Mailing Address: P.O.Box 12407, 35202–2407; tel. 205/939–7000, **A**1 2 3 5 10 **F**3 11 13 15 17 18 20 22 24 26 28 29 30 31 34 35 37 40 43 45 53 57 58 59 60 62 68 70 72 74 77 78 79 81 82 84 85 86 87 91 93 94 107 110 111 114 119 120 121 123 124 126 131 132 135 146 147 149 **S** Ascension Healthcare, Saint Louis, MO
Primary Contact: Evan Ray, FACHE, Chief Executive Officer
COO: Andy Davis, Chief Operating Officer
CFO: Wilma Newton, Executive Vice President and Chief Financial Officer
CMO: Gregory L James D.O., Chief Medical Officer
CIO: Timothy Stettheimer, Vice President and Chief Information Officer
CHR: Michelle Galipeau, Director Human Resources
Web address: www.stvhs.com
Control: Other not–for–profit (including NFP Corporation) **Service**: General medical and surgical

Staffed Beds: 409 Admissions: 20139 Census: 262 Outpatient Visits: 187209 Births: 3580 Total Expense ($000): 389275 Payroll Expense ($000): 104306 Personnel: 1891

✠ **ST. VINCENT'S EAST (010011)**, 50 Medical Park East Drive, Zip 35235–9987; tel. 205/838–3000, **A**1 2 3 5 10 **F**3 11 12 13 15 17 18 20 22 24 26 28 29 30 31 35 40 43 44 45 46 47 49 50 51 53 57 59 70 72 74 76 77 78 79 81 85 86 87 90 93 98 100 102 103 107 108 111 114 118 119 120 121 123 124 129 130 132 135 146 147 149 **S** Ascension Healthcare, Saint Louis, MO
Primary Contact: Andrew Gnann, Vice President Operations
COO: Andrew Gnann, Vice President Operations
CFO: Jan DiCesare, Vice President Financial Operations
CMO: Frank Malensek M.D., Chief Medical Officer
CIO: Beverly Golightly, Director Information Technology
CHR: Carol Maietta, Vice President Human Resources and Chief Learning Officer
CNO: Amy Shelton, Chief Nursing Officer
Web address: www.stvhs.com
Control: Other not–for–profit (including NFP Corporation) **Service**: General medical and surgical

Staffed Beds: 362 Admissions: 16118 Census: 252 Outpatient Visits: 129271 Births: 947 Total Expense ($000): 219361 Payroll Expense ($000): 70958 Personnel: 1138

UAB HIGHLANDS See University of Alabama Hospital

✠ **UNIVERSITY OF ALABAMA HOSPITAL (010033)**, 619 19th Street South, Zip 35249–1900; tel. 205/934–4011, (Includes UAB HIGHLANDS, 1201 11th Avenue South, Birmingham, Alabama, Zip 35205–5299, tel. 205/930–7000; Anthony Patterson, Chief Operating Officer) **A**1 2 3 5 8 10 **F**1 3 4 5 7 8 9 11 12 13 15 16 17 18 20 22 24 26 27 28 29 30 31 33 34 35 37 38 39 40 43 44 45 46 47 48 49 50 52 53 54 55 56 57 58 59 60 61 62 64 65 66 67 68 70 71 72 73 74 75 76 77 78 79 80 81 82 83 84 85 86 87 88 89 90 91 92 93 94 95 96 97 98 99 100 101 102 103 104 107 108 110 111 113 114 115 116 117 118 119 120 121 123 124 126 128 129 130 131 132 135 136 137 138 139 140 141 142 143 144 145 146 147 148 149 **P**3 **S** UAB Health System, Birmingham, AL
Primary Contact: Anthony Patterson, FACHE, Senior Vice President Inpatient Services
CFO: Mary Beth Briscoe, Chief Financial Officer
CMO: Loring Rue M.D., Senior Vice President, Quality Patient Safety and Clinical Effectiveness
CIO: Joan Hicks, Chief Information Officer
CHR: Alesia Jones, Chief Human Resources Officer
CNO: Terri Lyn Poe, Interim Chief Nursing Officer
Web address: www.uabmedicine.org
Control: State, Government, Nonfederal **Service**: General medical and surgical

Staffed Beds: 1191 Admissions: 49569 Census: 971 Outpatient Visits: 698529 Births: 4378 Total Expense ($000): 1467499 Payroll Expense ($000): 543905 Personnel: 9122

VETERANS AFFAIRS MEDICAL CENTER See Birmingham Veterans Affairs Medical Center

BOAZ—Marshall County

☐ **MARSHALL MEDICAL CENTER SOUTH (010005)**, U S Highway 431 North, Zip 35957–0999, Mailing Address: P.O.Box 758, 35957–0758; tel. 256/593–8310, **A**1 10 19 **F**3 7 8 9 11 12 13 15 18 20 22 26 28 29 31 32 34 35 37 40 43 45 46 50 51 53 54 57 59 64 68 70 74 75 76 78 79 81 84 85 86 87 89 92 93 100 107 108 110 111 114 115 117 119 121 123 129 130 131 132 135 141 146 147 148 149 **P**6 **S** Marshall Health System, Guntersville, AL
Primary Contact: John D. Anderson, FACHE, Administrator
CFO: Kathy Nelson, Chief Financial Officer
Web address: www.mmcenters.com//index.php/facilities/marshall_south
Control: Hospital district or authority, Government, Nonfederal **Service**: General medical and surgical

Staffed Beds: 114 Admissions: 4606 Census: 52 Outpatient Visits: 298072 Births: 614 Total Expense ($000): 95519 Payroll Expense ($000): 32605 Personnel: 630

BREWTON—Escambia County

☐ **D. W. MCMILLAN MEMORIAL HOSPITAL (010099)**, 1301 Belleville Avenue, Zip 36426–1306, Mailing Address: P.O.Box 908, 36427–0908; tel. 251/867–8061, **A**1 10 **F**3 7 11 13 15 29 30 31 34 35 40 45 57 59 62 64 70 75 76 78 79 81 85 86 93 100 107 108 111 114 119 127 129 130 131 132 133 135 143 146 149 **P**6
Primary Contact: Christopher B. Griffin, Chief Executive Officer
CFO: Rick Owens, Chief Financial Officer
CIO: Ian Vickery, Director Information Technology
CHR: Autherine Davis, Director Human Resources
CNO: Bob Ellis, Director of Nursing
Web address: www.dwmmh.org
Control: Hospital district or authority, Government, Nonfederal **Service**: General medical and surgical

Staffed Beds: 49 Admissions: 1767 Census: 16 Outpatient Visits: 48948 Births: 255 Total Expense ($000): 27223 Payroll Expense ($000): 9875 Personnel: 229

BUTLER—Choctaw County

CHOCTAW GENERAL HOSPITAL (011304), 401 Vanity Fair Avenue, Zip 36904–3032; tel. 205/459–9100, **A**10 18 **F**3 13 29 30 34 35 40 41 80 87 88 89 90 91 93 103 104 107 119 128 133 146 148 **S** Rush Health Systems, Meridian, MS
Primary Contact: J W. Cowan, Administrator
Web address: www.choctawgeneral.com/cgh/
Control: Other not–for–profit (including NFP Corporation) **Service**: General medical and surgical

Staffed Beds: 25 Admissions: 198 Census: 6 Births: 0

Hospital, Medicare Provider Number, Address, Telephone, Approval, Facility, and Physician Codes, Health Care System

★ American Hospital Association (AHA) membership ○ Healthcare Facilities Accreditation Program ⇑ Center for Improvement in Healthcare Quality Accreditation
☐ The Joint Commission accreditation ◇ DNV Healthcare Inc. accreditation △ Commission on Accreditation of Rehabilitation Facilities (CARF) accreditation

Hospitals, U.S. / ALABAMA

CARROLLTON—Pickens County

PICKENS COUNTY MEDICAL CENTER (010109), 241 Robert K Wilson Drive, Zip 35447, Mailing Address: P.O.Box 478, 35447–0478; tel. 205/367–8111, (Nonreporting) **A**10 20
CFO: Janice Winters, Controller
CMO: William R Brooke M.D., President Medical Staff
CHR: Dottie D Wilson, Director Human Resources
Web address: www.dchsystem.com
Control: County, Government, Nonfederal **Service**: General medical and surgical

Staffed Beds: 52

CENTRE—Cherokee County

✠ **CHEROKEE MEDICAL CENTER (010022)**, 400 Northwood Drive, Zip 35960–1023; tel. 256/927–5531, **A**1 10 **F**3 5 8 11 15 29 30 34 35 40 43 45 48 50 51 57 59 62 63 64 70 74 75 77 79 81 85 87 92 93 107 108 110 114 119 127 130 131 132 133 146 **P**6
Primary Contact: Terry Long, Chief Executive Officer
CFO: Zac Allen CPA, Chief Financial Officer
CHR: Marlene Benefield, Director Human Resources
Web address: www.cherokeemedicalcenter.com
Control: Corporation, Investor–owned (for–profit) **Service**: General medical and surgical

Staffed Beds: 45 Admissions: 836 Census: 12 Outpatient Visits: 21154 Births: 0 Total Expense ($000): 15579 Payroll Expense ($000): 5085 Personnel: 140

CENTREVILLE—Bibb County

BIBB MEDICAL CENTER (010058), 208 Pierson Avenue, Zip 35042–2918; tel. 205/926–4881, (Total facility includes 131 beds in nursing home–type unit) **A**3 10 13 **F**3 11 13 15 29 31 34 35 40 45 50 53 56 57 59 64 66 75 76 77 80 81 86 87 93 97 107 114 119 125 127 128 130 133 143 144 146 148 149 150 **P**6
Primary Contact: Joseph Marchant, Administrator
CFO: Heather Desmond, Chief Financial Officer
CMO: John Meigs M.D., Jr, Chief of Staff
CHR: Karen Daniel, Director Human Resources
Web address: www.bibbmedicalcenter.com
Control: Hospital district or authority, Government, Nonfederal **Service**: General medical and surgical

Staffed Beds: 180 Admissions: 644 Census: 124 Outpatient Visits: 48161 Births: 79 Total Expense ($000): 18299 Payroll Expense ($000): 8584 Personnel: 228

CHATOM—Washington County

★ **WASHINGTON COUNTY HOSPITAL (011300)**, 14600 St Stephens Avenue, Zip 36518–9998, Mailing Address: P.O.Box 1299, 36518–1299; tel. 251/847–2223, **A**10 18 **F**29 34 40 57 59 64 107 114 119 128 133 148
Primary Contact: Teresa G. Grimes, Chief Executive Officer
CFO: Alyson Overstreet, Chief Financial Officer
CMO: Steve Donald M.D., Chief of Staff
CIO: Brady Wright, Information Technology Network Administrator
CHR: Linda Randolph, Director Personnel Services
CNO: Michelle Alford R.N., MSN, Director of Nursing
Web address: www.wchnh.org
Control: County, Government, Nonfederal **Service**: General medical and surgical

Staffed Beds: 20 Admissions: 257 Census: 7 Births: 0

CLANTON—Chilton County

★ **ST. VINCENT'S CHILTON HOSPITAL**, 2030 Lay Dam Road, Zip 35045; tel. 205/258–4400, (Nonreporting) **S** Ascension Healthcare, Saint Louis, MO
Primary Contact: Suzannah Campbell, Administrator
Web address: www.stvhs.com/chilton/
Control: Church operated, Nongovernment, not–for–profit
Service: General medical and surgical

Staffed Beds: 30

CULLMAN—Cullman County

☐ **CULLMAN REGIONAL MEDICAL CENTER (010035)**, 1912 Alabama Highway 157, Zip 35055, Mailing Address: P.O.Box 1108, 35056–1108; tel. 256/737–2000, **A**1 10 **F**3 7 11 12 13 15 18 20 22 26 28 29 30 34 35 37 40 43 45 46 49 50 51 53 57 59 62 63 70 71 74 75 76 79 81 82 83 84 85 86 87 89 93 97 107 108 110 111 114 118 119 125 127 128 130 131 132 133 134 135 146 147 148 149
Primary Contact: James Clements, Chief Executive Officer
CFO: Nesha Donaldson, Chief Financial Officer
CMO: Bill Smith M.D., Chief of Staff
CIO: Nancy Zavatchen, Director Information Technology
CHR: Toni Geddings, Director Human Resources
CNO: Cheryl Bailey R.N., Chief Nursing Officer Vice President Patient Care Services
Web address: www.crmchospital.com
Control: Other not–for–profit (including NFP Corporation) **Service**: General medical and surgical

Staffed Beds: 115 Admissions: 7498 Census: 78 Outpatient Visits: 96883 Births: 639 Total Expense ($000): 100545 Payroll Expense ($000): 38429 Personnel: 896

DADEVILLE—Tallapoosa County

LAKE MARTIN COMMUNITY HOSPITAL (010052), 201 Mariarden Road, Zip 36853–6251, Mailing Address: P.O.Box 629, 36853–0629; tel. 256/825–7821, **A**10 **F**11 29 40 45 50 59 62 63 64 65 68 81 82 107 111 119 127
Primary Contact: Michael D. Bruce, Chief Executive Officer
CHR: Karen Treadwell, Director Human Resources
Web address: www.lakemartincommunityhospital.com
Control: Partnership, Investor–owned (for–profit) **Service**: General medical and surgical

Staffed Beds: 25 Admissions: 569 Census: 6 Births: 0

DAPHNE—Baldwin County

✠ **EASTPOINTE HOSPITAL (014017)**, 7400 Roper Lane, Zip 36526–5274; tel. 251/378–6500, **A**1 10 **F**29 98 130 143 **S** AltaPointe Health Systems, Mobile, AL
Primary Contact: Philip L. Cusa, Hospital Director
CFO: Kevin Markham, Chief Financial Officer
CMO: Sandra K Parker M.D., Chief Medical Officer
CIO: Steve Dolan, Chief Information Officer
CHR: Alicia Donoghue, Director Human Resources
Web address: www.altapointe.org/eastpointe.php
Control: Other not–for–profit (including NFP Corporation) **Service**: Psychiatric

Staffed Beds: 66 Admissions: 1389 Census: 40 Outpatient Visits: 0 Births: 0 Total Expense ($000): 11100 Payroll Expense ($000): 6887 Personnel: 153

DECATUR—Morgan County

☐ **DECATUR MORGAN HOSPITAL (010085)**, 1201 Seventh Street SE, Zip 35601–3303, Mailing Address: P.O.Box 2239, 35609–2239; tel. 256/341–2000, (Includes DECATUR MORGAN HOSPITAL PARKWAY CAMPUS, 1874 Beltline Road SW, Decatur, Alabama, Zip 35601–5509, PO Box 2239, 35609–2239, tel. 256/350–2211; DECATUR MORGAN HOSPITAL–WEST, 2205 Beltline Road SW, Decatur, Alabama, Zip 35601–3687, PO Box 2240, 35609–2240, tel. 256/306–4000) **A**1 5 10 **F**3 6 11 13 15 18 20 28 29 30 31 34 35 38 40 41 43 45 49 50 51 53 55 56 57 59 60 61 65 68 70 73 74 75 76 77 78 79 81 85 86 87 89 91 92 93 97 98 99 100 101 102 103 104 105 107 108 110 111 113 114 119 120 121 123 126 129 130 131 132 134 135 145 146 147 148 **S** Huntsville Hospital Health System, Huntsville, AL
Primary Contact: Nathaniel Richardson Jr, President
CFO: Kim Shrewsbury, Vice President and Chief Financial Officer
CMO: Allen J Schmidt M.D., President, Medical Staff
CIO: Mark Megehee, Vice President and Chief Information Officer
CNO: Anita Walden, Vice President and Chief Nursing Officer
Web address: www.decaturgeneral.org
Control: Hospital district or authority, Government, Nonfederal **Service**: General medical and surgical

Staffed Beds: 110 Admissions: 6309 Census: 91

PARKWAY MEDICAL CENTER See Decatur Morgan Hospital Parkway Campus, Decatur

DEMOPOLIS—Marengo County

BRYAN W. WHITFIELD MEMORIAL HOSPITAL (010112), 105 U S Highway 80 East, Zip 36732–3616, Mailing Address: P.O.Box 890, 36732–0890; tel. 334/289–4000, **A**3 10 20 **F**2 3 7 11 12 13 15 29 30 34 35 40 50 53 57 58 59 62 64 68 70 75 76 78 79 81 85 86 93 97 107 108 111 119 120 130 131 133 134 146 148
Primary Contact: Arthur D. Evans, Chief Executive Officer and Administrator
COO: Dereck Morrison, Assistant Administrator
CFO: Doug A. Brooker, Chief Financial Officer
CMO: John G. Kahler M.D., Radiologist
CHR: Marsha Pugh, Director Human Resources
CNO: Marcia Pugh M.D., Chief Nursing Officer
Web address: www.bwwmh.com
Control: Hospital district or authority, Government, Nonfederal **Service**: General medical and surgical

Staffed Beds: 47 Admissions: 1999 Census: 29

DOTHAN—Houston County

✠ **FLOWERS HOSPITAL (010055)**, 4370 West Main Street, Zip 36305–4000, Mailing Address: P.O.Box 6907, 36302–6907; tel. 334/793–5000, **A**1 2 3 10 19 **F**3 4 12 13 15 16 17 18 19 20 22 24 26 28 29 30 31 34 35 40 43 46 48 49 50 51 56 57 59 60 61 64 67 68 70 74 75 76 77 78 79 81 82 85 86 87 89 90 92 93 97 98 100 107 108 110 111 114 115 116 117 118 119 126 128 129 130 131 132 134 135 146 147 148 **S** Community Health Systems, Inc., Franklin, TN
Primary Contact: Heath Phillips, Chief Executive Officer
COO: Thomas Roddy, Chief Operating Officer
CFO: Talana Bell, Chief Financial Officer
CIO: Matthew Garrett, Director Information Systems
CHR: Jennifer Odom, Interim Director Human Resources
CNO: Dan L Cumbie, Chief Nursing Officer
Web address: www.flowershospital.com
Control: Corporation, Investor–owned (for–profit) **Service**: General medical and surgical

Staffed Beds: 141 Admissions: 11382 Census: 136 Outpatient Visits: 198212 Births: 1275 Total Expense ($000): 179352 Payroll Expense ($000): 53551 Personnel: 1097

✠ **HEALTHSOUTH REHABILITATION HOSPITAL (013030)**, 1736 East Main Street, Zip 36301–3040, Mailing Address: P.O.Box 6708, 36302–6708; tel. 334/712–6333, **A**1 10 **F**28 29 34 35 56 57 59 64 74 75 77 79 90 91 93 95 96 130 132 **S** HEALTHSOUTH Corporation, Birmingham, AL
Primary Contact: Margaret A. Futch, Chief Executive Officer
CFO: Heath Watson, Controller
CHR: Lydia Christion, Director Human Resources
Web address: www.healthsouthdothan.com
Control: Corporation, Investor–owned (for–profit) **Service:** Rehabilitation

Staffed Beds: 51 **Admissions:** 1449 **Census:** 50 **Births:** 0

☐ **LAUREL OAKS BEHAVIORAL HEALTH CENTER (014013)**, 700 East Cottonwood Road, Zip 36301–3644; tel. 334/794–7373, **A**1 10 **F**29 98 99 106 130 **S** Universal Health Services, Inc., King of Prussia, PA
Primary Contact: Derek Johnson, Chief Executive Officer
CMO: Nelson Handol M.D., Medical Director
CHR: Lorrie Evans, Director Human Resources
Web address: www.laureloaksbhc.com
Control: Corporation, Investor–owned (for–profit) **Service:** Children's hospital psychiatric

Staffed Beds: 38 **Admissions:** 984 **Census:** 37 **Outpatient Visits:** 0 **Births:** 0

☐ **NOLAND HOSPITAL DOTHAN (012010)**, 1108 Ross Clark Circle, 4th Floor, Zip 36301–3022; tel. 334/699–4300, **A**1 10 **F**1 29 130 148 **S** Noland Health Services, Inc., Birmingham, AL
Primary Contact: Kaye Burk, Administrator
Web address: www.nolandhealth.com
Control: Other not–for–profit (including NFP Corporation) **Service:** Acute long–term care hospital

Staffed Beds: 38 **Admissions:** 334 **Census:** 24 **Outpatient Visits:** 0 **Births:** 0

✠ ⇑ **SOUTHEAST ALABAMA MEDICAL CENTER (010001)**, 1108 Ross Clark Circle, Zip 36301–3024, Mailing Address: P.O.Box 6987, 36302–6987; tel. 334/793–8111, **A**1 2 10 13 21 **F**3 8 12 13 15 18 20 22 24 26 28 29 30 31 32 34 35 37 40 43 44 45 49 50 51 53 54 56 57 59 60 62 63 64 68 70 71 72 74 75 76 77 78 79 80 81 82 84 85 86 87 89 92 93 94 98 100 101 102 103 104 105 107 108 110 111 114 115 116 117 118 119 120 121 123 124 126 127 129 130 132 135 146 147 148
Primary Contact: Richard O. Sutton, FACHE, Chief Executive Officer
COO: Charles C Brannen, Senior Vice President and Chief Operating Officer
CFO: Derek Miller, Senior Vice President and Chief Financial Officer
CMO: Charles Harkness D.O., Vice President Medical Affairs
CIO: Eric Allen Daffron, Division Director, Information Systems
CHR: Tony Welch, Vice President Human Resources
CNO: Diane Buntyn MSN, R.N., Vice President Patient Care Services
Web address: www.samc.org
Control: Hospital district or authority, Government, Nonfederal **Service:** General medical and surgical

Staffed Beds: 387 **Admissions:** 19615 **Census:** 255 **Outpatient Visits:** 122144 **Births:** 1526 **Total Expense ($000):** 333571 **Payroll Expense ($000):** 150916 **Personnel:** 2543

✠ **MEDICAL CENTER ENTERPRISE (010049)**, 400 North Edwards Street, Zip 36330–2510; tel. 334/347–0584, **A**1 10 **F**3 13 15 29 34 40 45 57 59 70 76 79 81 85 93 107 110 111 114 118 119 129 130 131 146 149 **S** Community Health Systems, Inc., Franklin, TN
Primary Contact: Suzanne Woods, Chief Executive Officer
CFO: Greg McGilvray, Chief Financial Officer
CMO: Rick Harrelson M.D., President Medical Staff
CIO: Stephen Smothers, Director Information Systems
CHR: Toni Kaminski, Director Human Resources
CNO: Bobby Phillips, Chief Nursing Officer
Web address: www.mcehospital.com
Control: Corporation, Investor–owned (for–profit) **Service:** General medical and surgical

Staffed Beds: 70 **Admissions:** 3426 **Census:** 23 **Outpatient Visits:** 37122 **Births:** 981

MEDICAL CENTER BARBOUR (010069), 820 West Washington Street, Zip 36027–1899; tel. 334/688–7000, **A**10 20 **F**3 11 15 29 30 34 35 40 45 46 50 57 59 64 68 70 81 97 98 103 107 108 119 127 130 133 135 146 149
Primary Contact: Ralph H. Clark Jr, FACHE, Chief Executive Officer
CFO: Debbie Norton, Chief Financial Officer
CHR: Cindy Griffin, Director Human Resources
CNO: Steven Skeen R.N., Chief Clinical Officer
Web address: www.medctrbarbour.org
Control: Hospital district or authority, Government, Nonfederal **Service:** General medical and surgical

Staffed Beds: 47 **Admissions:** 1297 **Census:** 18 **Outpatient Visits:** 41436 **Births:** 0 **Total Expense ($000):** 16021 **Payroll Expense ($000):** 6938 **Personnel:** 179

★ **GREENE COUNTY HEALTH SYSTEM (010051)**, 509 Wilson Avenue, Zip 35462–1099; tel. 205/372–3388, (Total facility includes 72 beds in nursing home–type unit) **A**10 **F**11 15 29 40 54 59 62 64 65 90 93 97 107 110 119 127 128 130 133 143 146
Primary Contact: Elmore Patterson, Chief Executive Officer
Web address: www.gcheutaw.com
Control: County, Government, Nonfederal **Service:** General medical and surgical

Staffed Beds: 92 **Admissions:** 291 **Census:** 51 **Births:** 0

EVERGREEN MEDICAL CENTER (010148), 101 Crestview Avenue, Zip 36401–3333, Mailing Address: P.O.Box 706, 36401–0706; tel. 251/578–2480, **A**10 **F**3 29 30 34 40 49 50 53 57 59 62 81 87 89 93 97 98 107 111 114 119 127 130 135 **S** Gilliard Health Services, Montgomery, AL
Primary Contact: Tom McLendon, Administrator
CFO: Sharon Jones, Chief Financial Officer
CMO: William Farmer M.D., Chief of Staff
CHR: Tracey Rhodes, Coordinator Human Resources
CNO: Angie Hendrix, Director of Nursing
Web address: www.evergreenmedical.org
Control: Partnership, Investor–owned (for–profit) **Service:** General medical and surgical

Staffed Beds: 39 **Admissions:** 1555 **Census:** 13 **Outpatient Visits:** 19345 **Births:** 0

☐ **THOMAS HOSPITAL (010100)**, 750 Morphy Avenue, Zip 36532–1812, Mailing Address: P.O.Box 929, 36533–0929; tel. 251/928–2375, **A**1 10 19 **F**3 4 5 8 11 13 14 15 18 20 22 24 26 28 29 30 32 33 34 35 39 40 41 43 45 46 48 49 50 51 53 54 57 58 59 60 61 62 64 65 68 70 73 74 75 76 77 78 79 81 82 85 86 87 89 92 93 97 100 101 104 105 107 108 110 111 113 114 115 117 119 129 130 131 132 134 135 144 146 147 **S** Infirmary Health System, Mobile, AL
Primary Contact: Ormand P. Thompson, President
COO: Douglas Garner, Vice President
CMO: Michael McBrearty M.D., Vice President Medical Affairs
CNO: Julie Rowell R.N., Chief Nursing Officer
Web address: www.thomashospital.com
Control: Other not–for–profit (including NFP Corporation) **Service:** General medical and surgical

Staffed Beds: 136 **Admissions:** 9057 **Census:** 102 **Births:** 1258

☐ **FAYETTE MEDICAL CENTER (010045)**, 1653 Temple Avenue North, Zip 35555–1314, Mailing Address: P O Drawer 710, 35555–0710; tel. 205/932–5966, (Total facility includes 122 beds in nursing home–type unit) **A**1 10 **F**3 11 15 28 29 30 34 35 40 43 50 57 59 64 68 70 74 75 77 78 79 81 93 107 110 111 114 119 124 128 130 132 133 **S** DCH Health System, Tuscaloosa, AL
Primary Contact: Donald J. Jones, FACHE, Administrator
CFO: Jeff Huff, Assistant Administrator Finance
CHR: Felicia Solomon–Owens, Director Human Resources
Web address: www.dchsystem.com
Control: Hospital district or authority, Government, Nonfederal **Service:** General medical and surgical

Staffed Beds: 167 **Admissions:** 960 **Census:** 128 **Outpatient Visits:** 47589 **Births:** 0 **Total Expense ($000):** 39967 **Payroll Expense ($000):** 11625 **Personnel:** 275

Hospital, Medicare Provider Number, Address, Telephone, Approval, Facility, and Physician Codes, Health Care System

★ American Hospital Association (AHA) membership ☐ The Joint Commission accreditation ○ Healthcare Facilities Accreditation Program ◇ DNV Healthcare Inc. accreditation ⇑ Center for Improvement in Healthcare Quality Accreditation △ Commission on Accreditation of Rehabilitation Facilities (CARF) accreditation

FLORENCE—Lauderdale County

☐ **ELIZA COFFEE MEMORIAL HOSPITAL (010006)**, 205 Marengo Street, Zip 35630–6033, Mailing Address: P.O.Box 818, 35631–0818; tel. 256/768–9191, **A**1 10 **F**3 13 15 17 18 20 22 24 26 28 29 31 40 43 45 49 50 51 55 57 59 60 64 68 70 74 75 76 77 78 79 80 81 84 85 87 89 90 92 93 103 107 108 114 115 116 117 118 119 129 130 145 146 148 **S** RCCH HealthCare Partners, Brentwood, TN
Primary Contact: Russell Pigg, Chief Executive Officer
COO: Mike Howard, Chief Operating Officer
CFO: Steve E. Hobbs, Chief Financial Officer
CMO: Oliver Matthews M.D., Chief Medical Officer
CIO: Raul Velez, Information Technology Director
CHR: Cheryl Lee, Human Resources Director
CNO: Gilbert Glenn Humbert Jr, Interim Chief Nursing Officer
Web address: www.chgroup.org
Control: Hospital district or authority, Government, Nonfederal
Service: General medical and surgical

Staffed Beds: 278 Admissions: 15555 Census: 170 Births: 1233

FOLEY—Baldwin County

⊞ **SOUTH BALDWIN REGIONAL MEDICAL CENTER (010083)**, 1613 North McKenzie Street, Zip 36535–2299; tel. 251/949–3400, **A**1 10 19 **F**2 12 13 15 18 20 28 29 30 31 34 35 38 40 43 45 49 50 51 54 57 59 60 62 64 65 68 70 75 76 77 79 81 82 85 86 87 93 107 108 110 111 114 116 117 118 119 130 131 132 133 134 135 144 146 147 148 **S** Community Health Systems, Inc., Franklin, TN
Primary Contact: Keith Newton, Chief Executive Officer
CFO: Brad Hardcastle, Chief Financial Officer
CMO: Lee Eslava, Chief Medical Officer
CHR: Pam Brunson, Director Human Resources
CNO: Margaret Roley, Chief Nursing Officer
Web address: www.southbaldwinrmc.com
Control: Corporation, Investor–owned (for–profit) **Service**: General medical and surgical

Staffed Beds: 112 Admissions: 6506 Census: 69 Births: 610

FORT PAYNE—Dekalb County

⊞ **DEKALB REGIONAL MEDICAL CENTER (010012)**, 200 Medical Center Drive, Zip 35968–3458, Mailing Address: P.O.Box 680778, 35968–1608; tel. 256/845–3150, **A**1 10 20 **F**3 8 12 13 15 18 20 22 26 28 29 35 40 43 45 46 53 56 57 59 70 74 75 76 79 81 82 87 98 103 107 108 110 111 114 119 129 146 147 **S** Quorum Health, Brentwood, TN
Primary Contact: Patrick Trammell, Chief Executive Officer
CFO: Chris Benson, Chief Financial Officer
CMO: Anthony Sims M.D., Chief of Staff
CIO: Joseph Helms, Director Information Systems
CHR: Diane McMichen, Director Human Resources
CNO: Marquita Bailey, Chief Nursing Officer
Web address: www.dekalbregional.com
Control: Corporation, Investor–owned (for–profit)
Service: General medical and surgical

Staffed Beds: 115 Admissions: 3320 Census: 42 Births: 691

GADSDEN—Etowah County

⊞ **GADSDEN REGIONAL MEDICAL CENTER (010040)**, 1007 Goodyear Avenue, Zip 35903–1195; tel. 256/494–4000, **A**1 2 10 **F**3 11 13 15 18 20 22 24 29 30 31 34 35 40 43 45 50 56 57 59 60 64 68 70 74 76 77 78 79 80 81 89 93 98 99 102 103 105 107 108 111 112 113 114 115 119 121 124 126 129 130 131 146 147 148 **S** Community Health Systems, Inc., Franklin, TN
Primary Contact: Corey Ewing, Chief Executive Officer
COO: Josh Hester, Chief Operating Officer
CFO: Michael Cotton, Chief Financial Officer
CMO: Arthur Boykin M.D., Chief of Staff
CIO: Glenn Phillips, Director Information Systems
CHR: Gale H Sanders, Director
CNO: Martha Seahorn, Chief Nursing Officer
Web address: www.gadsdenregional.com
Control: Corporation, Investor–owned (for–profit)
Service: General medical and surgical

Staffed Beds: 274 Admissions: 14443 Census: 195 Births: 1078

⊞ **HEALTHSOUTH REHABILITATION OF GADSDEN (013032)**, 801 Goodyear Avenue, Zip 35903–1133; tel. 256/439–5000, **A**1 10 **F**28 30 90 91 94 95 96 148 **S** HEALTHSOUTH Corporation, Birmingham, AL
Primary Contact: Kayla Feazell, Chief Executive Officer
COO: Kayla Feazell, Chief Executive Officer
CFO: Lori Norman, Chief Financial Officer
CMO: Vladimir Slutsker, Medical Director
CIO: Lori Norman, Chief Financial Officer
CHR: Rhonda Young, Human Resource Director
CNO: Barry Eads, Chief Nursing Officer
Web address: www.healthsouthgadsden.com
Control: Corporation, Investor–owned (for–profit) **Service**: Rehabilitation

Staffed Beds: 44 Admissions: 1132 Census: 40 Births: 0

☐ **MOUNTAIN VIEW HOSPITAL (014006)**, 3001 Scenic Highway, Zip 35904–3047, Mailing Address: P.O.Box 8406, 35902–8406; tel. 256/546–9265, (Nonreporting) **A**1 10
Primary Contact: G Michael. Shehi, M.D., Chief Executive Officer
COO: Sara Romano R.N., Vice President
CFO: Mary Jensen, Controller
CMO: G Michael Shehi M.D., Medical Director
CHR: Dave Jensen, Director Human Resources, Performance Improvement and Risk Management
Web address: www.mtnviewhospital.com
Control: Corporation, Investor–owned (for–profit) **Service**: Psychiatric

Staffed Beds: 68

⊞ **RIVERVIEW REGIONAL MEDICAL CENTER (010046)**, 600 South Third Street, Zip 35901–5399; tel. 256/543–5200, **A**1 10 **F**5 8 12 15 17 18 20 22 24 26 29 30 34 37 40 41 45 46 47 48 49 50 51 56 57 59 60 68 69 70 74 75 77 79 81 85 87 91 92 93 94 97 98 103 107 108 109 110 111 114 115 118 119 120 126 129 130 146 148 149 **S** Prime Healthcare, Ontario, CA
Primary Contact: Ruben Garza, Interim Chief Executive Officer
CIO: Jay Terrell, Manager Management Information Systems
CHR: Leslie Morton, Manager Human Resources
CNO: Tammy Harlow, Chief Nurse Executive
Web address: www.riverviewregional.com
Control: Corporation, Investor–owned (for–profit) **Service**: General medical and surgical

Staffed Beds: 280 Admissions: 7580 Census: 87 Outpatient Visits: 70355 Births: 0 Total Expense ($000): 100428 Payroll Expense ($000): 32282

GENEVA—Geneva County

★ **WIREGRASS MEDICAL CENTER (010062)**, 1200 West Maple Avenue, Zip 36340–1694; tel. 334/684–3655, (Total facility includes 96 beds in nursing home–type unit) **A**10 **F**3 15 29 30 34 35 40 41 45 50 56 57 59 64 68 70 79 81 83 84 85 86 87 98 99 101 102 105 107 108 114 119 128 130 132 146
Primary Contact: Jeffrey M. Brannon, Chief Executive Officer
CHR: Tim Tidwell, Human Resources Director
CNO: Ashley Tanner, Director of Nursing
Web address: www.alaweb.com/~tgarske
Control: Hospital district or authority, Government, Nonfederal **Service**: General medical and surgical

Staffed Beds: 165 Admissions: 1598 Census: 140 Births: 0

GEORGIANA—Butler County

GEORGIANA HOSPITAL (010047), 515 Miranda Street, Zip 36033–4519, Mailing Address: P.O.Box 548, 36033–0548; tel. 334/376–2205, **A**10 **F**40 62 64 107 119 130
Primary Contact: Harry Cole Jr, Administrator
Web address: www.georgianahospital.com/
Control: Partnership, Investor–owned (for–profit) **Service**: General medical and surgical

Staffed Beds: 22 Admissions: 493 Census: 4 Births: 0

GREENSBORO—Hale County

HALE COUNTY HOSPITAL (010095), 508 Green Street, Zip 36744–2316; tel. 334/624–3024, (Nonreporting) **A**10
Primary Contact: Shay Fondren, Administrator
Web address: www.halecountyhospital.com
Control: Hospital district or authority, Government, Nonfederal **Service**: General medical and surgical

Staffed Beds: 20

GREENVILLE—Butler County

⊞ **L. V. STABLER MEMORIAL HOSPITAL (010150)**, 29 L V Stabler Drive, Zip 36037–3800; tel. 334/382–2671, **A**1 5 10 **F**3 15 17 29 35 40 56 57 62 64 81 93 98 103 107 111 119 133 146 147 **S** Quorum Health, Brentwood, TN
Primary Contact: Donald R. Rentfro, Chief Executive Officer
CMO: Norman F McGowin M.D., III, Chief of Staff
CIO: Doug Burkett, Manager Information Technology
CHR: Robert Foster, Director Human Resources
CNO: Kimberli Weaver, Chief Nursing Officer
Web address: www.lvstabler.com
Control: Corporation, Investor–owned (for–profit) **Service**: General medical and surgical

Staffed Beds: 61 Admissions: 1060 Census: 15 Births: 0

Many Facility Codes have changed. Please refer to the AHA Guide Code Chart.

© 2017 AHA Guide

GROVE HILL—Clarke County

★ **GROVE HILL MEMORIAL HOSPITAL (010091)**, 295 South Jackson Street, Zip 36451–3231, Mailing Address: P.O.Box 935, 36451–0935; tel. 251/275–3191, **A**10 **F**3 11 13 15 28 29 30 32 34 35 40 43 56 57 59 64 66 75 76 81 86 87 89 97 98 101 103 104 107 114 119 127 129 132 135 146
Primary Contact: Emily Steadham, Administrator
CFO: Elaine Averett, Chief Financial Officer
CMO: Eniola Fagbongbe M.D., Chief Medical Staff
CIO: Aaron Harrell, Director
CHR: Aubrey Sheffield, Administrative Assistant Human Resources and Public Relations
CNO: Karen Coleman, Director of Nursing
Web address: www.grovehillmemorial.org
Control: City, Government, Nonfederal **Service:** General medical and surgical

Staffed Beds: 34 **Admissions:** 1103 **Census:** 12 **Births:** 207

GUNTERSVILLE—Marshall County

MARSHALL MEDICAL CENTER NORTH (010010), 8000 Alabama Highway 69, Zip 35976; tel. 256/753–8000, **A**5 10 **F**3 11 12 13 15 26 28 29 32 34 35 37 38 40 43 45 49 50 51 53 54 57 59 64 68 70 74 75 76 79 81 82 85 86 87 89 92 93 99 100 102 103 104 107 108 110 111 114 115 119 130 131 132 135 141 146 147 149 **P**6 **S** Marshall Health System, Guntersville, AL
Primary Contact: Cheryl M. Hays, FACHE, Administrator and Chief Operating Officer
COO: Cheryl M Hays FACHE, Administrator and Chief Operating Officer
CFO: Kathy Nelson, Chief Financial Officer
CMO: Don Jones M.D., Chief Medical Officer
CIO: Kim Bunch, Director Information Technology
CHR: Sabrina Weaver, Director of Human Resources
CNO: Kathy Woodruff R.N., MSN, Chief Nursing Officer
Web address: www.mmcenters.com
Control: Hospital district or authority, Government, Nonfederal **Service:** General medical and surgical

Staffed Beds: 90 **Admissions:** 3975 **Census:** 52 **Outpatient Visits:** 172012 **Births:** 435 **Total Expense ($000):** 58895 **Payroll Expense ($000):** 22578 **Personnel:** 342

HALEYVILLE—Winston County

☐ **LAKELAND COMMUNITY HOSPITAL (010125)**, Highway 195 East, Zip 35565–9536, Mailing Address: P.O.Box 780, 35565–0780; tel. 205/486–5213, **A**1 10 **F**3 15 29 30 34 40 43 62 70 77 81 93 98 103 107 110 115 119 130 131 133 146 **S** Curae Health, Clinton, TN
Primary Contact: Cynthia Nichols, R.N., MSN, Chief Executive Officer
CFO: Penny Westmoreland, Chief Financial Officer
Web address: www.lakelandcommunityhospital.com/
Control: Corporation, Investor–owned (for–profit) **Service:** General medical and surgical

Staffed Beds: 59 **Admissions:** 1542 **Census:** 21 **Births:** 0

HAMILTON—Marion County

⊞ **NORTH MISSISSIPPI MEDICAL CENTER–HAMILTON (010044)**, 1256 Military Street South, Zip 35570–5003; tel. 205/921–6200, **A**1 10 **F**40 53 57 59 77 81 93 107 111 119 133 **S** North Mississippi Health Services, Inc., Tupelo, MS
Primary Contact: Robert Trimm, Administrator
CMO: Jarred Sartain M.D., President Medical Staff
CHR: Anne Lawler, Director Human Resources
CNO: Jennifer Cagle, Director of Nursing
Web address: www.nmhs.net
Control: Other not–for–profit (including NFP Corporation) **Service:** General medical and surgical

Staffed Beds: 15 **Admissions:** 670 **Census:** 11 **Births:** 0

HUNTSVILLE—Madison County

BEHAVIORAL HEALTHCARE CENTER AT HUNTSVILLE (014018), 5315 Millennium Drive NW, Zip 35806–2458; tel. 256/964–6700, **A**10 **F**6 29 34 35 38 56 59 65 75 77 86 87 98 101 103 130 135 148 **S** Tennessee Health Management, Parsons, TN
Primary Contact: Bradley Moss, Administrator
Web address: www.thmgt.com/locations/behavioral–healthcare–center–at–huntsville
Control: Corporation, Investor–owned (for–profit) **Service:** Hospital unit within a facility for persons with intellectual disabilities

Staffed Beds: 20 **Admissions:** 260 **Census:** 11 **Outpatient Visits:** 0 **Births:** 0 **Total Expense ($000):** 2899 **Personnel:** 42

⊞ **CRESTWOOD MEDICAL CENTER (010131)**, One Hospital Drive, Zip 35801–3403; tel. 256/429–4000, **A**1 5 10 **F**3 5 11 12 13 15 17 18 20 22 26 28 29 30 31 34 35 40 43 45 47 49 50 51 54 56 57 59 60 64 65 68 70 72 74 75 76 77 78 79 81 85 86 87 89 93 97 98 99 100 101 102 103 104 105 107 108 110 111 114 115 119 126 129 130 131 132 135 146 147 148 149 **S** Community Health Systems, Inc., Franklin, TN
Primary Contact: Pamela Hudson, M.D., Chief Executive Officer
COO: Bobby Ginn, Chief Operating Officer
CFO: Sherry J Jones, Chief Financial Officer
CHR: Elyria Sinclair, Director Human Resources
CNO: Martha Delaney Walls R.N., MSN, Chief Nursing Officer
Web address: www.crestwoodmedcenter.com
Control: Corporation, Investor–owned (for–profit)
Service: General medical and surgical

Staffed Beds: 177 **Admissions:** 11023 **Census:** 118 **Outpatient Visits:** 117526 **Births:** 862 **Total Expense ($000):** 171807

⊞ **HEALTHSOUTH REHABILITATION HOSPITAL OF NORTH ALABAMA (013029)**, 107 Governors Drive SW, Zip 35801–4326; tel. 256/535–2300, **A**1 10 **F**3 29 30 90 93 95 130 **S** HEALTHSOUTH Corporation, Birmingham, AL
Primary Contact: Douglas H. Beverly, Chief Executive Officer
Web address: www.healthsouthhuntsville.com
Control: Corporation, Investor–owned (for–profit) **Service:** Rehabilitation

Staffed Beds: 70 **Admissions:** 1845 **Census:** 66 **Births:** 0

☐ **HUNTSVILLE HOSPITAL (010039)**, 101 Sivley Road SW, Zip 35801–4470; tel. 256/265–1000, (Includes HUNTSVILLE HOSPITAL FOR WOMEN AND CHILDREN, 911 Big Cove Road SE, Huntsville, Alabama, Zip 35801–3784, tel. 256/265–1000; MADISON HOSPITAL, 8375 Highway 72 West, Madison, Alabama, Zip 35758–9573, tel. 256/265–2012; Mary Lynne Wright, President) **A**1 2 3 5 10 **F**5 7 8 12 13 14 15 17 18 19 20 21 22 24 25 26 28 29 30 31 35 37 38 40 41 43 46 49 50 51 53 54 56 57 59 60 63 64 68 70 71 72 73 76 78 79 80 81 82 84 85 86 87 88 89 93 96 98 99 100 101 102 103 104 105 107 108 109 110 111 114 115 116 117 118 119 126 129 130 131 142 145 146 147 148 **S** Huntsville Hospital Health System, Huntsville, AL
Primary Contact: David S. Spillers, Chief Executive Officer
COO: Jeff Samz, Chief Operating Officer
CFO: Kelli Powers, Chief Financial Officer
CMO: Robert Chappell M.D., Chief Medical Officer and Chief Quality Officer
CIO: Rick Corn, Chief Information Officer
CHR: Andrea P Rosler, Vice President Human Resources
CNO: Karol Jones, Chief Nursing Officer
Web address: www.huntsvillehospital.org
Control: Hospital district or authority, Government, Nonfederal **Service:** General medical and surgical

Staffed Beds: 914 **Admissions:** 46843 **Census:** 629 **Outpatient Visits:** 807154 **Births:** 5196 **Total Expense ($000):** 839879 **Payroll Expense ($000):** 328663 **Personnel:** 7145

JACKSON—Clarke County

JACKSON MEDICAL CENTER (010128), 220 Hospital Drive, Zip 36545–2459, Mailing Address: P.O.Box 428, 36545–0428; tel. 251/246–9021, **A**10 **F**3 11 15 29 34 40 45 57 59 62 76 81 85 89 107 108 111 115 119 133 134 144 **S** Gilliard Health Services, Montgomery, AL
Primary Contact: Jennifer M. Ryland, R.N., Chief Executive Officer
COO: Jennifer M Ryland R.N., Chief Administrative Officer
CHR: Kathy Jones, Director Human Resources
Web address: www.jacksonmedicalcenter.org
Control: Partnership, Investor–owned (for–profit) **Service:** General medical and surgical

Staffed Beds: 26 **Admissions:** 898 **Census:** 11 **Births:** 0

JACKSONVILLE—Calhoun County

☐ **RMC JACKSONVILLE (010146)**, 1701 Pelham Road South, Zip 36265–3399, Mailing Address: P.O.Box 999, 36265–0999; tel. 256/435–4970, **A**1 10 **F**3 4 29 30 34 35 40 48 50 56 57 59 64 65 68 69 79 81 82 85 93 98 103 107 108 111 114 119 135 146 **S** Regional Medical Center, Anniston, AL
Primary Contact: Joe Weaver, Chief Executive Officer
COO: Carlos Farmer R.N., Director Clinical Operations
CFO: Robbin Curlee, Controller
CMO: Rey Gavino M.D., Chief of Staff
CIO: Richard Maust, Chief Information Officer
CHR: Doug Scott, Director Human Resources
CNO: Jean Ann McMurrey R.N., MSN, Chief Nursing Officer
Web address: www.jmchealth.com
Control: Hospital district or authority, Government, Nonfederal **Service:** General medical and surgical

Staffed Beds: 65 **Admissions:** 1061 **Census:** 18 **Outpatient Visits:** 17245 **Births:** 0 **Total Expense ($000):** 17028 **Payroll Expense ($000):** 7627 **Personnel:** 176

Hospital, Medicare Provider Number, Address, Telephone, Approval, Facility, and Physician Codes, Health Care System

★ American Hospital Association (AHA) membership
☐ The Joint Commission accreditation
○ Healthcare Facilities Accreditation Program
◇ DNV Healthcare Inc. accreditation
⇑ Center for Improvement in Healthcare Quality Accreditation
△ Commission on Accreditation of Rehabilitation Facilities (CARF) accreditation

Hospitals, U.S. / ALABAMA

JASPER—Walker County

✠ **WALKER BAPTIST MEDICAL CENTER (010089)**, 3400 Highway 78 East, Zip 35501–8907, Mailing Address: P.O.Box 3547, 35502–3547; tel. 205/387–4000, **A**1 10 20 **F**4 8 11 13 15 18 20 24 29 30 31 34 38 39 40 45 46 48 50 51 56 57 59 60 65 66 68 70 74 75 76 77 78 79 81 82 84 86 87 89 91 92 93 97 98 100 101 102 103 104 107 110 111 114 115 116 119 124 126 127 130 131 132 146 147 148 **S** TENET Healthcare Corporation, Dallas, TX
Primary Contact: Robert A. Phillips, Chief Executive Officer
CFO: Amanda Dyle, Chief Financial Officer
CIO: Kenny Horton, Director Information Systems
CHR: Pat Morrow, Director Human Resources
CNO: Robbie Hindman, Vice President Patient Care Services and Chief Nursing Officer
Web address: www.bhsala.com
Control: Corporation, Investor–owned (for–profit) **Service:** General medical and surgical

Staffed Beds: 158 Admissions: 7451 Census: 96 Outpatient Visits: 80550 Births: 772 Total Expense ($000): 87966 Payroll Expense ($000): 25224 Personnel: 615

LUVERNE—Crenshaw County

☐ **BEACON CHILDREN'S HOSPITAL (014015)**, 150 Hospital Drive, Zip 36049; tel. 334/335–5040, (Nonreporting) **A**1 10
Primary Contact: Bradley Eisemann, Administrator
Web address: www.beaconchildrenshospital.com
Control: Other not–for–profit (including NFP Corporation) **Service:** Children's hospital psychiatric

Staffed Beds: 24

CRENSHAW COMMUNITY HOSPITAL (010008), 101 Hospital Circle, Zip 36049–7344; tel. 334/335–3374, **A**10 **F**3 4 11 13 15 29 38 40 53 60 64 76 79 81 98 100 101 102 103 107 119 143 144 148
Primary Contact: Lee Anne Montgomery, R.N., Administrator
COO: Victoria Lawrenson, Chief Operating Officer
CMO: Charles Tompkins M.D., Chief of Staff
CHR: Patricia Jarry, Manager Human Resources
Control: Partnership, Investor–owned (for–profit) **Service:** General medical and surgical

Staffed Beds: 65 Admissions: 1127 Census: 19 Births: 0

MADISON—Madison County

BRADFORD HEALTH SERVICES AT HUNTSVILLE, 1600 Browns Ferry Road, Zip 35758–9601, Mailing Address: P.O.Box 1488, 35758–0176; tel. 256/461–7272, (Nonreporting) **S** Bradford Health Services, Birmingham, AL
Primary Contact: Bob Hinds, Executive Director
Web address: www.bradfordhealth.com
Control: Corporation, Investor–owned (for–profit) **Service:** Alcoholism and other chemical dependency

Staffed Beds: 84

MOBILE—Mobile County

★ **BAYPOINTE BEHAVIORAL HEALTH (014014)**, 5800 Southland Drive, Zip 36693–3313; tel. 251/661–0153, **A**3 10 **F**38 98 99 100 101 102 130 132 **S** AltaPointe Health Systems, Mobile, AL
Primary Contact: Jarett Crum, Hospital Director
Web address: www.altapointe.org
Control: Other not–for–profit (including NFP Corporation) **Service:** Children's hospital psychiatric

Staffed Beds: 60 Admissions: 999 Census: 26 Outpatient Visits: 0 Births: 0 Total Expense ($000): 6698 Payroll Expense ($000): 4287 Personnel: 168

☐ **INFIRMARY LONG TERM ACUTE CARE HOSPITAL (012006)**, 5 Mobile Infirmary Circle, Zip 36607–3513, Mailing Address: P.O.Box 2226, 36652–2226; tel. 251/660–5239, (Nonreporting) **A**1 10 **S** Infirmary Health System, Mobile, AL
Primary Contact: Susanne Marmande, Administrator
Web address: www.theinfirmary.com/
Control: Other not–for–profit (including NFP Corporation) **Service:** Acute long–term care hospital

Staffed Beds: 36

☐ △ **MOBILE INFIRMARY MEDICAL CENTER (010113)**, 5 Mobile Infirmary Drive North, Zip 36607–3513, Mailing Address: P.O.Box 2144, 36652–2144; tel. 251/435–2400, (Includes ROTARY REHABILITATION HOSPITAL, 5 Mobile Infirmary Circle, Mobile, Alabama, Zip 36607, P O Box 2144, 36652, tel. 251/435–3400) **A**1 3 5 7 10 **F**1 3 8 11 12 13 15 17 18 20 22 24 26 28 29 30 34 35 40 41 43 45 46 47 48 49 50 51 52 53 54 56 57 59 60 64 68 70 74 75 76 77 78 79 80 81 82 85 86 87 89 90 91 92 93 96 98 102 103 107 108 110 111 114 115 118 119 120 121 124 126 129 130 131 132 145 146 147 148 **S** Infirmary Health System, Mobile, AL
Primary Contact: Jennifer Eslinger, President
CFO: Joe Denton, Executive Vice President and Chief Financial Officer
CMO: John Dixon, Chief Medical Officer
CIO: Eddy Stephens, Vice President Information Technology
CHR: Sheila Young, Vice President Human Resources
Web address: www.infirmaryhealth.org
Control: Other not–for–profit (including NFP Corporation) **Service:** General medical and surgical

Staffed Beds: 554 Admissions: 27322 Census: 434 Births: 1145

✠ **PROVIDENCE HOSPITAL (010090)**, 6801 Airport Boulevard, Zip 36608–3785, Mailing Address: P.O.Box 850429, 36685–0429; tel. 251/633–1000, **A**1 2 3 5 10 **F**3 11 13 15 17 18 20 22 24 26 28 29 30 31 34 35 40 44 45 49 50 51 53 54 55 57 58 59 60 61 64 65 68 70 73 74 75 76 77 78 79 80 81 82 83 84 85 86 87 89 92 93 96 102 107 108 110 111 114 115 117 119 120 121 124 126 129 130 131 132 135 142 146 148 149 **P**5 6 **S** Ascension Healthcare, Saint Louis, MO
Primary Contact: Todd S. Kennedy, President and Chief Executive Officer
CFO: C Susan Cornejo, Senior Vice President Finance and Chief Financial Officer
CMO: William M Lightfoot M.D., Vice President Medical Services
CIO: Kathy Ross, Chief Information Officer
CHR: Christopher Cockrell, Executive Director Human Resources
CNO: Peter Lindquist, Vice President and Chief Nursing Officer
Web address: www.providencehospital.org
Control: Church operated, Nongovernment, not–for–profit **Service:** General medical and surgical

Staffed Beds: 302 Admissions: 15380 Census: 211 Outpatient Visits: 95006 Births: 1690 Total Expense ($000): 223690 Payroll Expense ($000): 77926 Personnel: 1443

ROTARY REHABILITATION HOSPITAL See Mobile Infirmary Medical Center, Mobile

☐ **SPRINGHILL MEMORIAL HOSPITAL (010144)**, 3719 Dauphin Street, Zip 36608–1798, Mailing Address: P.O.Box 8246, 36689–0246; tel. 251/344–9630, **A**1 10 **F**11 13 15 17 18 20 22 24 26 28 29 30 31 34 40 46 47 49 50 51 57 60 70 74 75 76 77 78 79 81 82 85 86 87 88 89 90 93 107 110 111 115 118 119 126 127 129 130 132 146 147 148 149
Primary Contact: Jeffery M. St Clair, President and Chief Executive Officer
COO: Rene Areaux, Vice President and Chief Operating Officer
CFO: Jan Grigsby, Vice President and Chief Financial Officer
CMO: Liston Jones M.D., Medical Director
CIO: Mark Kilborn, Director Information Systems
CHR: Daniela Batchelor, Director Human Resources
CNO: Paul Read R.N., MSN, Vice President and Chief Nursing Officer
Web address: www.springhillmedicalcenter.com
Control: Corporation, Investor–owned (for–profit) **Service:** General medical and surgical

Staffed Beds: 207 Admissions: 10673 Census: 157 Outpatient Visits: 173125 Births: 862 Total Expense ($000): 160703 Payroll Expense ($000): 49356 Personnel: 1130

✠ **UNIVERSITY OF SOUTH ALABAMA CHILDREN'S AND WOMEN'S HOSPITAL (013301)** (Childrens and Womens), 1700 Center Street, Zip 36604–3301; tel. 251/415–1000, **A**1 3 5 10 **F**7 11 13 15 21 27 29 31 40 48 49 52 55 58 59 64 72 73 74 75 76 77 78 79 81 85 86 87 88 89 93 107 111 114 126 130 146 147 **S** University of South Alabama Hospitals, Mobile, AL
Primary Contact: Chris Jett, Administrator
CFO: Traci Jones, Chief Financial Officer
CIO: Mark Lauteren, Chief Information Officer
CHR: Janice Rehm, Manager Human Resources
CNO: Scotty Roberson, Assistant Administrator and Chief Nursing Officer
Web address: www.usahealthsystem.com/usacwh
Control: State, Government, Nonfederal **Service:** Other specialty treatment

Staffed Beds: 180 Admissions: 8839 Census: 163 Outpatient Visits: 65936 Births: 2605 Total Expense ($000): 128551 Payroll Expense ($000): 56967 Personnel: 1078

Many Facility Codes have changed. Please refer to the AHA Guide Code Chart. © 2017 AHA Guide

☒ **UNIVERSITY OF SOUTH ALABAMA MEDICAL CENTER (010087)**, 2451
Fillingim Street, Zip 36617–2293; tel. 251/471-7000, **A**1 2 3 5 8 10 **F**3 11
12 16 17 18 20 22 24 26 29 31 34 40 43 46 47 48 49 57 58 59 60 61 63
64 70 74 78 79 80 81 85 87 107 108 111 114 115 119 130 145 146 148 **S**
University of South Alabama Hospitals, Mobile, AL
Primary Contact: Sam Dean, Administrator
CFO: Traci Jones, Chief Financial Officer
CIO: Mark Lauteren, Chief Information Officer
CHR: Anita Shirah, Director Human Resources
CNO: Lisa Mestas, Associate Administrator and System Chief Nursing Officer
Web address: www.usahealthsystem.com/usamc
Control: State, Government, Nonfederal **Service:** General medical and surgical

> **Staffed Beds:** 142 **Admissions:** 6942 **Census:** 118 **Outpatient Visits:**
> 68331 **Births:** 0 **Total Expense ($000):** 189880 **Payroll Expense ($000):**
> 87209 **Personnel:** 1532

MONROEVILLE—Monroe County

☐ **MONROE COUNTY HOSPITAL (010120)**, 2016 South Alabama Avenue,
Zip 36460–3044, Mailing Address: P.O.Box 886, 36461–0886; tel. 251/575-
3111, **A**1 10 20 **F**11 13 15 29 31 34 40 57 62 70 76 78 79 107 111 129 147
Primary Contact: Wes Nall, Interim Chief Executive Officer
CFO: Wes Nall, Chief Financial Officer
CMO: David Stallworth M.D., Chief of Staff
CIO: Jody Falkenberry, Director Information Systems
CHR: Tara Nowling, Director Human Resources
CNO: Barbara Harned R.N., MSN, Chief Nursing Officer
Web address: www.mchcare.com
Control: Hospital district or authority, Government, Nonfederal **Service:** General
medical and surgical

> **Staffed Beds:** 44 **Admissions:** 1132 **Census:** 9 **Births:** 196

MONTGOMERY—Montgomery County

☐ **BAPTIST MEDICAL CENTER EAST (010149)**, 400 Taylor Road, Zip 36117–
3512, Mailing Address: P.O.Box 241267, 36124–1267; tel. 334/277-8330, **A**1
3 10 **F**3 11 12 13 15 29 30 34 35 40 44 45 47 49 50 56 57 63 64 68 70 72
73 75 76 77 79 81 82 85 86 89 90 93 94 107 108 111 114 115 119 126 129
130 132 135 146 147 **S** Baptist Health, Montgomery, AL
Primary Contact: Jeff G. Rains, Chief Executive Officer
CFO: Katrina Belt, Chief Financial Officer
CHR: Kay R Bennett, Vice President Human Resources
CNO: Kathy Gaston, Chief Nursing Officer
Web address: www.baptistfirst.org
Control: Hospital district or authority, Government, Nonfederal **Service:** General
medical and surgical

> **Staffed Beds:** 164 **Admissions:** 10094 **Census:** 126 **Outpatient Visits:**
> 105617 **Births:** 3607 **Total Expense ($000):** 103648 **Payroll Expense
> ($000):** 44970 **Personnel:** 876

☐ **BAPTIST MEDICAL CENTER SOUTH (010023)**, 2105 East South Boulevard,
Zip 36116–2409, Mailing Address: Box 11010, 36111–0010; tel. 334/288-
2100, **A**1 3 5 10 **F**3 5 11 12 13 15 17 18 20 22 24 26 28 29 30 31 34 35 40
43 44 45 46 47 49 50 56 57 58 59 60 61 63 64 68 70 72 74 75 76 78 79 81
82 84 85 86 87 89 90 93 94 98 100 101 102 103 104 105 107 108 110 111
114 115 116 117 118 119 126 129 130 131 132 135 146 147 148 **S** Baptist
Health, Montgomery, AL
Primary Contact: J Peter. Selman, FACHE, Chief Executive Officer
CFO: Melissa Johnson, Chief Financial Officer
CMO: Donovan Kendrick M.D., Chief Medical Officer
CIO: Steve Miller, Director Information Systems
CHR: Kay R Bennett, System Director Human Resources
CNO: Karen McCaa R.N., Vice President Patient Care Services and Chief Nursing
Officer
Web address: www.baptistfirst.org
Control: Hospital district or authority, Government, Nonfederal **Service:** General
medical and surgical

> **Staffed Beds:** 389 **Admissions:** 18316 **Census:** 268 **Outpatient Visits:**
> 235927 **Births:** 707 **Total Expense ($000):** 378896 **Payroll Expense
> ($000):** 106365 **Personnel:** 1956

☒ **CENTRAL ALABAMA VETERANS HEALTH CARE SYSTEM**, 215 Perry Hill Road,
Zip 36109–3798; tel. 334/272-4670, (Nonreporting) (Includes MONTGOMERY
DIVISION, 215 Perry Hill Road, Montgomery, Alabama, Zip 36109–3798, tel.
334/272-4670; TUSKEGEE DIVISION, 2400 Hospital Road, Tuskegee, Alabama,
Zip 36083–5001, tel. 334/727-0550) **A**1 3 **S** Department of Veterans Affairs,
Washington, DC
Primary Contact: Linda Lake. Boyle, R.N., MSN, Director
CFO: Debra Nicholson, Manager Finance
CMO: Cliff Robinson M.D., Chief of Staff
CIO: Rhoda Tyson, Chief Information Officer
CHR: Janice Hardy, Chief Human Resource Management Service
Web address: www.centralalabama.va.gov/
Control: Veterans Affairs, Government, federal **Service:** General medical and
surgical

> **Staffed Beds:** 245

☒ **HEALTHSOUTH REHABILITATION HOSPITAL OF MONTGOMERY (013028)**,
4465 Narrow Lane Road, Zip 36116–2900; tel. 334/284-7700, **A**1 10 **F**3 9 28
29 34 35 54 56 57 59 64 74 75 77 86 90 93 95 130 131 132 143 146 148 **P**5
S HEALTHSOUTH Corporation, Birmingham, AL
Primary Contact: Randy Thompson, Chief Executive Officer
CFO: Heath Watson, Controller
CMO: Jeffrey Eng M.D., Medical Director
CIO: Anidra Billingslea, Health Insurance Management
CHR: Kim McDaniel, Director Human Resources
CNO: Kim Headley R.N., Chief Nursing Officer
Web address: www.healthsouthmontgomery.com
Control: Corporation, Investor–owned (for–profit) **Service:** Rehabilitation

> **Staffed Beds:** 70 **Admissions:** 1774 **Census:** 59 **Outpatient Visits:** 4242
> **Births:** 0 **Total Expense ($000):** 18860 **Payroll Expense ($000):** 11142
> **Personnel:** 194

☒ **JACKSON HOSPITAL AND CLINIC (010024)**, 1725 Pine Street, Zip 36106–
1117; tel. 334/293-8000, **A**1 3 10 **F**13 15 17 18 20 22 24 26 29 30 31 34 40
45 46 49 57 59 64 68 70 74 76 77 78 79 81 82 84 85 86 87 89 107 108 110
111 115 117 118 119 126 130 131 135 144 146 147 **P**6
Primary Contact: Joe B. Riley, FACHE, President and Chief Executive Officer
COO: Michael James, Chief Operations Officer
CFO: Paul Peiffer, Chief Financial Officer and Vice President
CHR: Gilbert Darrington, Director Human Resources
CNO: Sharon A Goodison R.N., MS, Chief Nursing Officer
Web address: www.jackson.org
Control: Other not–for–profit (including NFP Corporation) **Service:** General
medical and surgical

> **Staffed Beds:** 230 **Admissions:** 13657 **Census:** 193 **Outpatient Visits:**
> 131678 **Births:** 1200 **Total Expense ($000):** 205566 **Payroll Expense
> ($000):** 86083 **Personnel:** 1300

LONG TERM CARE HOSPITAL See Noland Hospital Montgomery

MONTGOMERY DIVISION See Central Alabama Veterans Health Care System

☐ **NOLAND HOSPITAL MONTGOMERY (012007)**, 1725 Pine Street, 5 North,
Zip 36106–1109; tel. 334/240-0532, **A**1 10 **F**1 29 130 148 **S** Noland Health
Services, Inc., Birmingham, AL
Primary Contact: Dale Jones, Administrator
Web address: www.nolandhealth.com
Control: Other not–for–profit (including NFP Corporation) **Service:** Acute long–
term care hospital

> **Staffed Beds:** 65 **Admissions:** 264 **Census:** 19 **Outpatient Visits:** 0
> **Births:** 0

MOULTON—Lawrence County

☐ **LAWRENCE MEDICAL CENTER (010059)**, 202 Hospital Street, Zip 35650–
1218, Mailing Address: P.O.Box 39, 35650–0039; tel. 256/974-2200, **A**1 10 **F**3
15 28 29 30 34 35 40 45 46 47 50 54 56 57 59 62 64 65 66 68 70 75 81 85
86 87 93 97 107 108 111 114 118 119 127 130 132 135 146 147 **S** Huntsville
Hospital Health System, Huntsville, AL
Primary Contact: Dean A. Griffin, Chief Executive Officer
CFO: Jim Crawford, Chief Financial Officer
CIO: Jeremy Duncan, Director Information Systems
CHR: Diane K Secor, Director Human Resources
Web address: www.lawrencemedicalcenter.com
Control: County, Government, Nonfederal **Service:** General medical and surgical

> **Staffed Beds:** 43 **Admissions:** 636 **Census:** 8 **Births:** 0

Hospital, Medicare Provider Number, Address, Telephone, Approval, Facility, and Physician Codes, Health Care System

★ American Hospital Association (AHA) membership ○ Healthcare Facilities Accreditation Program ⇑ Center for Improvement in Healthcare Quality Accreditation
☐ The Joint Commission accreditation ◇ DNV Healthcare Inc. accreditation △ Commission on Accreditation of Rehabilitation Facilities (CARF) accreditation

MUSCLE SHOALS—Colbert County

☐ **SHOALS HOSPITAL (010157)**, 201 Avalon Avenue, Zip 35661–2805, Mailing Address: P.O.Box 3359, 35662–3359; tel. 256/386–1600, **A**1 10 **F**3 15 29 30 39 40 51 57 64 68 70 75 77 78 79 81 85 87 93 97 100 108 111 115 119 124 146 **S** RCCH HealthCare Partners, Brentwood, TN
Primary Contact: Kidada Hawkins, Chief Executive Officer
CFO: Steve E. Hobbs, Chief Financial Officer
CMO: Terry true M.D., Chief of Staff
CIO: William Johnson, Director Information Systems
CHR: Nancy Bowling, Director Human Resources
Web address: www.shoalshospital.com
Control: Hospital district or authority, Government, Nonfederal
Service: General medical and surgical

> **Staffed Beds:** 137 **Admissions:** 3104 **Census:** 58 **Births:** 0

ONEONTA—Blount County

☒ **ST. VINCENT'S BLOUNT (010050)**, 150 Gilbreath, Zip 35121–2827, Mailing Address: P.O.Box 1000, 35121–0013; tel. 205/274–3000, **A**1 10 18 **F**3 11 15 18 29 30 35 40 45 46 50 57 59 60 64 70 81 85 87 93 97 107 108 110 111 119 127 133 135 146 149 **S** Ascension Healthcare, Saint Louis, MO
Primary Contact: Greg Brown, Administrator
CFO: Jennifer Kingry, Chief Financial Officer
CMO: David R Wilson M.D., Chief of Staff
CIO: John Laliberte, Chief Information Officer
CHR: Kristin L. Costanzo, Direct–In–Market Lead Human Relations Partner
CNO: Kira Schnittker, Director of Nursing
Web address: www.stvhs.com
Control: Other not–for–profit (including NFP Corporation)
Service: General medical and surgical

> **Staffed Beds:** 25 **Admissions:** 1057 **Census:** 15 **Outpatient Visits:** 37454 **Births:** 0 **Total Expense ($000):** 20841 **Payroll Expense ($000):** 7032 **Personnel:** 118

OPELIKA—Lee County

☒ **EAST ALABAMA MEDICAL CENTER (010029)**, 2000 Pepperell Parkway, Zip 36801–5452; tel. 334/749–3411, (Includes EAST ALABAMA MEDICAL CENTER–LANIER, 4800 48th Street, Valley, Alabama, Zip 36854–3666, tel. 334/756–9180; Greg Nichols, Chief Executive Officer) (Total facility includes 129 beds in nursing home–type unit) **A**1 2 3 10 13 19 **F**3 7 10 11 13 15 17 18 20 22 24 26 28 29 30 31 32 34 40 43 45 50 51 53 54 56 57 59 60 61 64 65 66 67 68 70 74 75 76 77 78 79 81 82 83 84 85 86 87 89 92 93 97 98 99 100 101 102 104 107 108 110 111 114 115 116 117 118 119 120 121 124 125 126 128 129 130 131 132 143 144 146 147 148
Primary Contact: Terry W. Andrus, President
COO: Laura D Grill R.N., Executive Vice President and Administrator
CFO: Sam Price, Executive Vice President Finance/Chief Financial Officer
CMO: William Golden M.D., Chief Medical Officer
CIO: Sarah Gray, Vice President Information Services
CHR: Susan Johnston, Vice President Human Resources
CNO: Jane Fullum, Vice President Patient Care Services
Web address: www.eamc.org
Control: Hospital district or authority, Government, Nonfederal
Service: General medical and surgical

> **Staffed Beds:** 475 **Admissions:** 15214 **Census:** 312 **Births:** 1842

OPP—Covington County

MIZELL MEMORIAL HOSPITAL (010007), 702 Main Street, Zip 36467–1626, Mailing Address: P.O.Box 1010, 36467–1010; tel. 334/493–3541, **A**10 **F**11 29 30 35 40 53 79 81 103 107 110 111 114
Primary Contact: Jana Wyatt, Chief Executive Officer
CFO: Amy Bess, Chief Financial Officer
CIO: Elizabeth Cook, Chief Information Officer
CHR: Dianne Morrison, Director Human Resources
CNO: Steven Skeen R.N., Chief Nursing Officer
Web address: www.mizellmh.com
Control: Other not–for–profit (including NFP Corporation)
Service: General medical and surgical

> **Staffed Beds:** 59 **Admissions:** 1445 **Census:** 22 **Births:** 0 **Personnel:** 197

OZARK—Dale County

DALE MEDICAL CENTER (010021), 126 Hospital Avenue, Zip 36360–2080; tel. 334/774–2601, **A**10 **F**8 11 13 15 17 29 40 51 53 54 57 59 62 63 70 75 76 77 81 85 86 89 93 98 103 107 108 111 118 119 144 147
Primary Contact: Vernon Johnson, Administrator
CFO: Brad Hull, Chief Financial Officer
CMO: Steve Brandt M.D., Chief of Staff
CHR: Sheila Dunn, Assistant Administrator Human Resources
Web address: www.dalemedical.org
Control: Corporation, Investor–owned (for–profit) **Service:** General medical and surgical

> **Staffed Beds:** 69 **Admissions:** 1779 **Census:** 31 **Births:** 0 **Outpatient Visits:** 47508 **Total Expense ($000):** 30955 **Payroll Expense ($000):** 14538 **Personnel:** 337

PELL CITY—St. Clair County

☒ **ST. VINCENT'S ST. CLAIR (010130)**, 7063 Veterans Parkway, Zip 35125–1499; tel. 205/814–2105, **A**1 10 **F**3 11 15 29 30 35 40 43 45 46 50 59 60 64 68 70 79 81 82 85 87 93 107 108 110 111 119 130 135 146 148 149 **S** Ascension Healthcare, Saint Louis, MO
Primary Contact: Lisa Nichols, R.N., Administrator
CFO: Jason Lynn, Director Finance
Web address: www.stvhs.com
Control: Other not–for–profit (including NFP Corporation) **Service:** General medical and surgical

> **Staffed Beds:** 40 **Admissions:** 1841 **Census:** 18 **Outpatient Visits:** 50092 **Births:** 0 **Total Expense ($000):** 26900 **Payroll Expense ($000):** 9361 **Personnel:** 159

PHENIX CITY—Russell County

☐ **JACK HUGHSTON MEMORIAL HOSPITAL (010168)**, 4401 Riverchase Drive, Zip 36867–7483; tel. 334/732–3000, **A**1 3 10 13 **F**3 29 40 70 79 81 89 107 111 115 119 131
Primary Contact: Mark A. Baker, Chief Executive Officer
COO: Rachel H. Crenshaw, Chief Operating Officer
CFO: Angela Shelton, Chief Financial Officer
CMO: James F. Zumstein M.D., Chief of Medicine
CHR: Lana Thomas–Folds, System Director Human Resources
CNO: Sylvia Thomas, Chief Nursing Officer
Web address: www.hughston.com
Control: Corporation, Investor–owned (for–profit) **Service:** General medical and surgical

> **Staffed Beds:** 35 **Admissions:** 2522 **Census:** 19 **Outpatient Visits:** 21585 **Births:** 0 **Total Expense ($000):** 44647 **Payroll Expense ($000):** 13282 **Personnel:** 283

☒ **REGIONAL REHABILITATION HOSPITAL (013033)**, 3715 Highway 280/431 North, Zip 36867; tel. 334/732–2200, **A**1 10 **F**3 29 30 90 93 95 132 **S** HEALTHSOUTH Corporation, Birmingham, AL
Primary Contact: Michael Bartell, Chief Executive Officer
CFO: Bobby Edmondson, Controller
CMO: Nitin Desei M.D., Medical Director
CIO: Jacki Cuevas, Director Health Information Services
CHR: Cindy Glynn, Director Human Resources
CNO: Wendy Lee, Chief Nursing Officer
Web address: www.regionalrehabhospital.com
Control: Partnership, Investor–owned (for–profit) **Service:** Rehabilitation

> **Staffed Beds:** 48 **Admissions:** 1284 **Census:** 45 **Births:** 0

PRATTVILLE—Autauga County

☐ **PRATTVILLE BAPTIST HOSPITAL (010108)**, 124 South Memorial Drive, Zip 36067–3619, Mailing Address: P.O.Box 681630, 36068–1638; tel. 334/365–0651, **A**1 3 10 **F**3 11 12 15 18 29 30 34 35 40 44 45 50 56 57 59 60 63 64 68 70 74 75 81 82 84 85 86 87 93 107 111 114 119 129 132 146 **S** Baptist Health, Montgomery, AL
Primary Contact: Eric Morgan, Chief Executive Officer
CFO: LaDonna McDaniel, Financial Manager
CIO: B Blaine Brown, Vice President and General Counsel
CHR: Kymberli Skipper, Manager Human Resources
Web address: www.baptistfirst.org/facilities/prattville–baptist–hospital/default.aspx
Control: Hospital district or authority, Government, Nonfederal **Service:** General medical and surgical

> **Staffed Beds:** 50 **Admissions:** 3200 **Census:** 35 **Outpatient Visits:** 81215 **Births:** 0 **Total Expense ($000):** 38355 **Payroll Expense ($000):** 15301 **Personnel:** 317

RED BAY—Franklin County

★ **RED BAY HOSPITAL (011302)**, 211 Hospital Road, Zip 35582–3858, Mailing Address: P.O.Box 490, 35582–0490; tel. 256/356–9532, **A**10 18 **F**7 11 15 29 34 35 40 43 50 53 54 56 57 59 64 65 68 75 77 81 82 85 86 90 91 92 93 94 97 107 110 114 119 127 130 131 132 133 135 146 147 148 **S** Huntsville Hospital Health System, Huntsville, AL
Primary Contact: Sherry Jolley, Director of Operations and Nursing
CFO: Penny Westmoreland, Chief Financial Officer
CMO: Kristy Crandell M.D., Medical Staff President
CHR: Amy Leigh Bishop, Director Human Resources
CNO: Margaret Thorn, Interim Director of Nursing
Web address: www.redbayhospital.com
Control: Hospital district or authority, Government, Nonfederal **Service:** General medical and surgical

> **Staffed Beds:** 25 **Admissions:** 373 **Census:** 8 **Outpatient Visits:** 6515 **Births:** 0 **Total Expense ($000):** 9286 **Payroll Expense ($000):** 4148 **Personnel:** 100

RUSSELLVILLE—Franklin County

☐ **RUSSELLVILLE HOSPITAL (010158)**, 15155 Highway 43, Zip 35653–1975,
Mailing Address: P.O.Box 1089, 35653–1089; tel. 256/332–1611, **A**1 10 **F**3 8
13 14 15 20 29 34 37 40 45 47 48 50 56 57 59 62 68 70 76 77 79 81 82 85
87 93 107 108 110 111 115 119 130 133 146 **S** Curae Health, Clinton, TN
Primary Contact: Christine R. Stewart, FACHE, Chief Executive Officer
CFO: Penny Westmoreland, Chief Financial Officer
CHR: Stephen Proctor, Director of Human Resources/Risk
CNO: Belinda Johnson R.N., Chief Nursing Officer/Chief Clinical Officer
Web address: www.russellvillehospital.com
Control: Partnership, Investor–owned (for–profit) **Service:** General medical and
surgical

Staffed Beds: 92 **Admissions:** 1970 **Census:** 19 **Births:** 0	

SCOTTSBORO—Jackson County

☐ **HIGHLANDS MEDICAL CENTER (010061)**, 380 Woods Cove Road, Zip 35768–
2428, Mailing Address: P.O.Box 1050, 35768–1050; tel. 256/259–4444, **A**1 5
10 20 **F**11 13 70 76 77 89 108 111 119 130 146
Primary Contact: Lonnie Albin, M.D., Interim Chief Executive Officer
CFO: Dan Newell, Chief Financial Officer
CIO: Doug Newby, Chief Information Officer
CHR: Susanna S Sivley, Chief Personnel Officer
Web address: www.highlandsmedcenter.com
Control: Hospital district or authority, Government, Nonfederal **Service:** General
medical and surgical

Staffed Beds: 92 **Admissions:** 3393 **Census:** 33 **Births:** 363	

SELMA—Dallas County

✚ **VAUGHAN REGIONAL MEDICAL CENTER (010118)**, 1015 Medical Center
Parkway, Zip 36701–6352; tel. 334/418–4100, **A**1 3 5 10 **F**8 11 13 15 17 20
29 30 34 40 45 51 53 60 68 70 74 76 79 81 85 89 93 107 108 110 111 114
115 118 119 120 127 129 130 131 146 **S** LifePoint Health, Brentwood, TN
Primary Contact: J. David. McCormack, Chief Executive Officer
CFO: Tyler Adkins, Chief Financial Officer
CMO: Walid Freij M.D., Chief of Staff
CIO: Matthew McHugh, Director Information Services
CHR: Dionne Williams, Director Human Resources
CNO: Patricia Hannon, Chief Nursing Officer
Web address: www.vaughanregional.com
Control: Corporation, Investor–owned (for–profit) **Service:** General medical and surgical

Staffed Beds: 149 **Admissions:** 5472 **Census:** 48 **Outpatient Visits:** 39310 **Births:** 1102 **Total Expense ($000):** 54027 **Payroll Expense ($000):** 21497	

SHEFFIELD—Colbert County

☐ **HELEN KELLER HOSPITAL (010019)**, 1300 South Montgomery Avenue,
Zip 35660–6334, Mailing Address: P.O.Box 610, 35660–0610; tel. 256/386–
4196, **A**1 10 **F**3 7 8 11 13 15 18 20 21 28 29 30 31 34 35 40 45 47 49 50 51
53 57 59 60 64 65 68 70 74 75 76 77 78 79 80 81 82 83 84 85 86 87 89 91
92 93 94 107 108 110 111 114 115 117 118 119 126 129 130 131 132 135
145 146 147 148 149 **S** Huntsville Hospital Health System, Huntsville, AL
Primary Contact: Paul Storey, FACHE, President and Chief Executive Officer
CFO: Morris S Strickland, Chief Financial Officer
CHR: Pam Bryant, Director Human Resources
Web address: www.helenkeller.com
Control: Hospital district or authority, Government, Nonfederal **Service:** General
medical and surgical

Staffed Beds: 145 **Admissions:** 6604 **Census:** 67 **Outpatient Visits:** 54856 **Births:** 806 **Total Expense ($000):** 96203 **Payroll Expense ($000):** 39343 **Personnel:** 823	

SYLACAUGA—Talladega County

☐ **COOSA VALLEY MEDICAL CENTER (010164)**, 315 West Hickory Street,
Zip 35150–2996; tel. 256/401–4000, **A**1 10 **F**13 14 15 17 18 20 22 28 29 30
31 32 34 35 38 40 45 52 53 56 57 60 64 74 75 76 77 78 81 82 86 98 100
101 102 104 107 108 110 111 114 117 119 128 130 135 147 148
Primary Contact: Glenn C. Sisk, President
CFO: Janice Brown, Chief Financial Officer
CIO: Sandra Murchison, Director Medical Records
CHR: Christy Knowles, Chief Human Resources Officer
Web address: www.cvhealth.net
Control: Hospital district or authority, Government, Nonfederal **Service:** General
medical and surgical

Staffed Beds: 101 **Admissions:** 3337 **Census:** 35 **Outpatient Visits:** 68475 **Births:** 473	

TALLADEGA—Talladega County

✚ **CITIZENS BAPTIST MEDICAL CENTER (010101)**, 604 Stone Avenue,
Zip 35160–2217, Mailing Address: P.O.Box 978, 35161–0978; tel. 256/362–
8111, **A**1 10 19 **F**3 4 5 11 13 15 29 30 34 35 40 49 50 53 57 59 60 62 63 64
65 67 70 74 75 76 79 81 82 86 87 93 98 103 107 108 110 111 112 114 118
119 129 131 132 135 146 **S** TENET Healthcare Corporation, Dallas, TX
Primary Contact: Douglas Brewer, Chief Executive Officer
CFO: Zach Abercrombie, Chief Financial Officer
CHR: Sandra Willis, Director of Human Resources
CNO: Ann McEntire MSN, R.N., Chief Nursing Officer
Web address: www.brookwoodbaptisthealth.org
Control: Corporation, Investor–owned (for–profit) **Service:** General medical and
surgical

Staffed Beds: 72 **Admissions:** 2669 **Census:** 32 **Outpatient Visits:** 57766 **Births:** 212 **Total Expense ($000):** 32879 **Payroll Expense ($000):** 13836 **Personnel:** 286	

TALLASSEE—Elmore County

☐ **COMMUNITY HOSPITAL (010034)**, 805 Friendship Road, Zip 36078–1234; tel.
334/283–6541, **A**10 **F**18 21 28 29 35 40 62 63 64 70 81 82 86 87 98 100
101 102 103 104 107 119 146
Primary Contact: Jennie R. Rhinehart, Administrator and Chief Executive Officer
Web address: www.chal.org
Control: Other not–for–profit (including NFP Corporation) **Service:** General
medical and surgical

Staffed Beds: 47 **Admissions:** 1359 **Census:** 24 **Births:** 0	

TROY—Pike County

☐ **TROY REGIONAL MEDICAL CENTER (010126)**, 1330 Highway 231 South,
Zip 36081–3058; tel. 334/670–5000, **A**1 10 **F**4 29 30 40 45 50 57 68 70 79
81 85 93 107 108 110 114 119 129 133 135 146
Primary Contact: Ronald Dean, Chief Executive Officer
CFO: Janet Smith, Chief Financial Officer
CMO: Paul Dulaney M.D., Chief of Staff
CIO: Michael Moore, Director Information Systems
CHR: Beth Nissen, Director Human Resources
CNO: Amy Minor, Chief Nursing Officer
Web address: www.troymedicalcenter.com
Control: Hospital district or authority, Government, Nonfederal **Service:** General
medical and surgical

Staffed Beds: 43 **Admissions:** 1653 **Census:** 18 **Outpatient Visits:** 46547 **Births:** 0 **Total Expense ($000):** 30493 **Payroll Expense ($000):** 15414 **Personnel:** 250	

TUSCALOOSA—Tuscaloosa County

☐ **BRYCE HOSPITAL (014007)**, 200 University Boulevard, Zip 35401–1294; tel.
205/507–8299, (Nonreporting) **A**1 3 5 10
Primary Contact: Shelia Penn, Facility Director
CFO: Wendell Summerville, Chief Financial Officer
CMO: Cynthia Moore Sledge M.D., Medical Director
CIO: Ronene Howell, Director Health Information Management
CHR: Jim Elliott, Director Human Resources
Web address: www.mh.alabama.gov/
Control: State, Government, Nonfederal **Service:** Psychiatric

Staffed Beds: 820	

☐ **DCH REGIONAL MEDICAL CENTER (010092)**, 809 University Boulevard East,
Zip 35401–2029; tel. 205/759–7111, (Includes NORTHPORT MEDICAL CENTER,
2700 Hospital Drive, Northport, Alabama, Zip 35476–3360, tel. 205/333–4500;
Luke Standeffer, Administrator) **A**1 2 3 5 10 20 **F**3 11 12 13 15 17 18 20 22 24
26 28 29 30 31 35 38 40 43 48 49 50 51 57 59 60 61 62 64 66 68 70 72 74
75 76 77 78 79 81 82 86 87 88 89 90 93 94 98 100 101 102 103 104 105
106 107 108 110 111 114 115 116 117 118 119 121 126 129 130 131 132 **S**
DCH Health System, Tuscaloosa, AL
Primary Contact: William H. Cassels, Administrator
CFO: Nina Dusang, Vice President Finance and Chief Financial Officer
CMO: Kenneth Aldridge M.D., Vice President Medical Affairs
CIO: Kim Ligon, Director Information Services
CHR: Peggy Sease, Vice President Human Resources
CNO: Lorraine Yehlen R.N., Vice President Patient Care Services
Web address: www.dchsystem.com
Control: Hospital district or authority, Government, Nonfederal **Service:** General
medical and surgical

Staffed Beds: 876 **Admissions:** 41447 **Census:** 617	

Hospital, Medicare Provider Number, Address, Telephone, Approval, Facility, and Physician Codes, Health Care System

★ American Hospital Association (AHA) membership   ○ Healthcare Facilities Accreditation Program   ⇑ Center for Improvement in Healthcare Quality Accreditation
☐ The Joint Commission accreditation   ◇ DNV Healthcare Inc. accreditation   △ Commission on Accreditation of Rehabilitation Facilities (CARF) accreditation

☐ **MARY S HARPER GERIATRIC PSYCHIATRY CENTER (014012)**, 200 University Boulevard, Zip 35401–1250; tel. 205/759–0900, (Nonreporting) **A**1 10
Primary Contact: Beverly White, MS, Facility Director
CFO: Sarah Mitchell, Director Finance
CMO: Robin Barton Lariscy M.D., Medical Director
CIO: Sarah Mitchell, Director Finance
CHR: Jim Elliott, Director Human Resources
Web address: www.mh.alabama.gov
Control: Corporation, Investor–owned (for–profit) **Service:** Psychiatric

Staffed Beds: 96

☐ **NOLAND HOSPITAL TUSCALOOSA (012012)**, 809 University Blvd E, 4th Fl, Zip 35401–2029; tel. 205/759–7241, **A**1 10 **F**1 29 130 148 **S** Noland Health Services, Inc., Birmingham, AL
Primary Contact: Jack Gibson, Administrator
Web address: www.nolandhealth.com
Control: Other not–for–profit (including NFP Corporation) **Service:** Acute long–term care hospital

Staffed Beds: 32 **Admissions:** 325 **Census:** 22 **Outpatient Visits:** 0 **Births:** 0

☐ **TAYLOR HARDIN SECURE MEDICAL FACILITY (014011)**, 1301 Jack Warner Parkway, Zip 35404–1060; tel. 205/556–7060, (Nonreporting) **A**1 10
Primary Contact: Barbara Jackson, Ed.D., Acting Facility Director
Web address: www.mh.alabama.gov/
Control: Corporation, Investor–owned (for–profit) **Service:** Psychiatric

Staffed Beds: 114

☒ **TUSCALOOSA VETERANS AFFAIRS MEDICAL CENTER**, 3701 Loop Road East, Zip 35404–5015; tel. 205/554–2000, (Nonreporting) **A**1 5 **S** Department of Veterans Affairs, Washington, DC
Primary Contact: John F. Merkle, Medical Center Director
COO: Gary D Trende FACHE, Associate Director
CFO: Angelia Stevenson, Manager Finance
CMO: Carlos E. Berry M.D., Acting Chief of Staff
Web address: www.tuscaloosa.va.gov
Control: Veterans Affairs, Government, federal **Service:** Psychiatric

Staffed Beds: 366

TUSKEGEE—Macon County

TUSKEGEE DIVISION See CENTRAL ALABAMA VETERANS HEALTH CARE SYSTEM, Montgomery

UNION SPRINGS—Bullock County

BULLOCK COUNTY HOSPITAL (010110), 102 West Conecuh Avenue, Zip 36089–1303; tel. 334/738–2140, **A**10 20 **F**3 15 29 30 32 35 40 50 57 62 64 77 93 98 101 102 103 107 119 130
Primary Contact: Jacques Jarry, Administrator
COO: Victoria Lawrenson, Chief Operating Officer
CMO: Maria Bernardo M.D., Chief of Staff
Web address: www.unionspringsalabama.com/
Control: Corporation, Investor–owned (for–profit) **Service:** General medical and surgical

Staffed Beds: 54 **Admissions:** 1377 **Census:** 25 **Births:** 0

WARRIOR—Jefferson County

BRADFORD HEALTH SERVICES AT WARRIOR LODGE, 1189 Allbritt Road, Zip 35180, Mailing Address: P.O.Box 129, 35180–0129; tel. 205/647–1945, (Nonreporting) **S** Bradford Health Services, Birmingham, AL
Primary Contact: Roy M. Ramsey, Executive Director
Web address: www.bradfordhealth.com
Control: Corporation, Investor–owned (for–profit) **Service:** Alcoholism and other chemical dependency

Staffed Beds: 100

WEDOWEE—Randolph County

WEDOWEE HOSPITAL (010032), 209 North Main Street, Zip 36278–7428, Mailing Address: P.O.Box 307, 36278–0307; tel. 256/357–2111, **A**10 **F**3 40 81 107 111 114 119 129 130 132 133
Primary Contact: Jerry Morris, Administrator
Web address: www.wedoweehospital.org/
Control: Church operated, Nongovernment, not–for–profit **Service:** General medical and surgical

Staffed Beds: 26 **Admissions:** 347 **Census:** 4 **Births:** 0

WETUMPKA—Elmore County

ELMORE COMMUNITY HOSPITAL (010097), 500 Hospital Drive, Zip 36092–1625, Mailing Address: P.O.Box 130, 36092–0003; tel. 334/567–4311, **A**10 **F**3 4 11 29 40 45 57 59 62 70 81 82 97 107 111 114 119 143 144
Primary Contact: Michael Ritzhs, Administrator
CFO: Mike Bruce, Chief Financial Officer
CHR: Cindy Futral, Director Human Resources
Web address: www.elmorehospital.com/
Control: Partnership, Investor–owned (for–profit) **Service:** General medical and surgical

Staffed Beds: 49 **Admissions:** 748 **Census:** 9 **Births:** 0

WINFIELD—Marion County

☐ **NORTHWEST MEDICAL CENTER (010086)**, 1530 U S Highway 43, Zip 35594–5056; tel. 205/487–7000, **A**1 10 **F**3 8 15 18 29 34 35 40 50 53 56 57 59 64 68 70 79 81 85 90 98 103 107 108 110 111 114 119 127 130 132 133 135 **S** Curae Health, Clinton, TN
Primary Contact: Michael D. Windham, Chief Executive Officer
CFO: Glenda Reyes, Chief Financial Officer
CMO: David Corbett M.D., Chief of Staff
Web address: www.northwestmedcenter.com
Control: Corporation, Investor–owned (for–profit) **Service:** General medical and surgical

Staffed Beds: 66 **Admissions:** 1482 **Census:** 22 **Births:** 0

YORK—Sumter County

HILL HOSPITAL OF SUMTER COUNTY (010138), 751 Derby Drive, Zip 36925–2121; tel. 205/392–5263, **A**10 **F**4 5 29 34 35 40 57 59 62 66 128 133
Primary Contact: Loretta Wilson, Administrator
CFO: Joyce Wedgeworth, Financial Clerk
CMO: Gary Walton M.D., Chief Medical Officer
CNO: Cynthia Brown, Director of Nursing
Control: Hospital district or authority, Government, Nonfederal **Service:** General medical and surgical

Staffed Beds: 33 **Admissions:** 401 **Census:** 7 **Outpatient Visits:** 5968 **Births:** 0

Many Facility Codes have changed. Please refer to the AHA Guide Code Chart.

© 2017 AHA Guide

ALASKA

ANCHORAGE—Anchorage County

☒ **ALASKA NATIVE MEDICAL CENTER (020026)**, 4315 Diplomacy Drive, Zip 99508–5926; tel. 907/563–2662, **A**1 3 5 10 **F**1 3 8 11 13 15 16 18 20 22 29 30 31 32 34 35 38 39 40 41 43 44 45 46 47 48 49 50 51 54 55 56 57 58 59 61 63 64 65 66 67 68 70 72 73 74 75 76 77 78 79 81 82 84 85 86 87 88 89 90 92 93 94 99 100 101 102 107 110 111 114 115 119 127 135 141 142 143 144 146 147 148 149 **P**6
Primary Contact: Roald Helgesen, Chief Executive Officer
CMO: Paul Franke M.D., Chief Medical Officer
CHR: Sonya Conant, Senior Director Human Resources
Web address: www.dhss.alaska.gov/dbh/Pages/api/default.aspx
Control: Other not–for–profit (including NFP Corporation) **Service**: General medical and surgical

Staffed Beds: 172 **Admissions:** 7464 **Census:** 122 **Outpatient Visits:** 390363 **Births:** 1646 **Total Expense ($000):** 367932 **Payroll Expense ($000):** 143315 **Personnel:** 1747

☐ **ALASKA PSYCHIATRIC INSTITUTE (024002)**, 3700 Piper Street, Zip 99508–4677; tel. 907/269–7100, **A**1 10 **F**98 99 100 101 102 103 130 132 135
COO: Gavin H Carmichael FACHE, Chief Operating Officer
CFO: Gavin H Carmichael FACHE, Chief Operating Officer
CIO: Stephen Schneider, Manager Information Services
CHR: Katie E. Gratrix, Administrative Assistant III
CNO: Sharon Bergstedt, Director of Nursing
Web address: www.hss.state.ak.us/dbh/API/
Control: State, Government, Nonfederal **Service**: Psychiatric

Staffed Beds: 80 **Admissions:** 1519 **Census:** 71 **Outpatient Visits:** 0 **Births:** 0 **Total Expense ($000):** 33500

☒ **ALASKA REGIONAL HOSPITAL (020017)**, 2801 Debarr Road, Zip 99508–2997, Mailing Address: P.O.Box 143889, 99514–3889; tel. 907/264–1754, (Nonreporting) **A**1 2 10 **S** HCA Healthcare, Nashville, TN
Primary Contact: Julie Taylor, FACHE, Chief Executive Officer
COO: Victor Rosenbaum, Chief Operating Officer
CFO: Lynn Kennington, Chief Financial Officer
CMO: David Cadogan, Chief Medical Officer
CIO: Gene Kaplanis, Director Information Technology
CHR: Tammy Kaminski, Director Human Resources
CNO: Linda Doughty, Chief Nursing Officer
Web address: www.alaskaregional.com
Control: Corporation, Investor–owned (for–profit) **Service**: General medical and surgical

Staffed Beds: 132

☒ **NORTH STAR BEHAVIORAL HEALTH SYSTEM (024001)**, 2530 DeBarr Circle, Zip 99508–2948; tel. 907/258–7575, (Includes NORTH STAR BEHAVIORAL HEALTH, 1650 South Bragaw, Anchorage, Alaska, Zip 99508–3467, tel. 907/258–7575) **A**1 3 5 10 **F**98 99 106 130 **S** Universal Health Services, Inc., King of Prussia, PA
Primary Contact: Andrew Mayo, Ph.D., Chief Executive Officer and Managing Director
CFO: Alan Barnes, Chief Financial Officer
CMO: Ruth Dukoff M.D., Medical Director
CIO: Brian O'Connell, Director Information Services
CHR: Sabrina Ben, Director Human Resources
CNO: Brandy Proctor, Director of Nursing
Web address: www.northstarbehavioral.com
Control: Corporation, Investor–owned (for–profit) **Service**: Children's hospital psychiatric

Staffed Beds: 200 **Admissions:** 1079 **Census:** 144 **Outpatient Visits:** 0 **Births:** 0 **Total Expense ($000):** 28713 **Payroll Expense ($000):** 16779 **Personnel:** 274

☒ **PROVIDENCE ALASKA MEDICAL CENTER (020001)**, 3200 Providence Drive, Zip 99508–4615, Mailing Address: P.O.Box 196604, 99519–6604; tel. 907/562–2211, (Includes CHILDREN'S HOSPITAL AT PROVIDENCE, 3200 Providence Drive, Anchorage, Alaska, Zip 99508, tel. 907/212–3130) **A**1 2 3 5 10 13 **F**3 8 11 12 13 17 18 19 20 21 22 24 25 26 28 29 30 31 34 35 38 39 40 41 43 45 46 47 49 50 53 55 56 57 58 59 60 62 63 65 67 68 70 72 74 75 77 78 79 81 82 83 84 85 86 87 88 90 92 93 94 97 98 99 100 101 102 104 105 106 107 108 111 115 118 119 120 121 123 124 126 130 131 132 146 148 149 **S** Providence St. Joseph Health, Renton, WA
Primary Contact: Richard Mandsager, M.D., Executive Officer
CFO: Anthony Dorsch, Chief Financial Officer
CMO: Roy Davis M.D., Chief Medical Officer
CIO: Stephanie Morton, Chief Information Officer
CHR: Scott Jungwirth, Chief Human Resources Officer
Web address: www.alaska.providence.org/locations/p/pamc
Control: Church operated, Nongovernment, not–for–profit **Service**: General medical and surgical

Staffed Beds: 401 **Admissions:** 15964 **Census:** 286 **Outpatient Visits:** 358603 **Births:** 2839 **Total Expense ($000):** 438775 **Payroll Expense ($000):** 213854 **Personnel:** 2584

☒ **ST. ELIAS SPECIALTY HOSPITAL (022001)**, 4800 Cordova Street, Zip 99503–7218; tel. 907/561–3333, **A**1 10 **F**1 3 18 28 29 30 60 65 68 75 77 86 107 114 119 129 **P**4
Primary Contact: Sharon H. Kurz, Ph.D., Chief Executive Officer
CFO: Andrew Fitch, Chief Financial Officer
Web address: www.st–eliashospital.com
Control: Partnership, Investor–owned (for–profit) **Service**: Acute long–term care hospital

Staffed Beds: 59 **Admissions:** 295 **Census:** 35 **Outpatient Visits:** 0 **Births:** 0 **Total Expense ($000):** 37653 **Payroll Expense ($000):** 14511 **Personnel:** 212

BARROW—North Slope County

☒ **SAMUEL SIMMONDS MEMORIAL HOSPITAL (021312)**, 7000 Uulu Street, Zip 99723, Mailing Address: P.O.Box 29, 99723–0029; tel. 907/852–4611, (Nonreporting) **A**1 10 18
Primary Contact: Richard Hall, Chief Executive Officer
CMO: Devon Allen M.D., Chief of Medical Staff
Web address: www.arcticslope.org
Control: Other not–for–profit (including NFP Corporation) **Service**: General medical and surgical

Staffed Beds: 14

BETHEL—Bethel County

☒ **YUKON–KUSKOKWIM DELTA REGIONAL HOSPITAL (020018)**, 700 Chief Eddie Hoffman Highway, Zip 99559–3000, Mailing Address: P.O.Box 528, 99559–0528; tel. 907/543–6300, **A**1 3 5 10 **F**3 5 13 15 29 34 35 38 39 40 45 50 53 54 57 58 59 64 65 66 68 71 75 81 82 84 85 87 91 93 97 99 100 101 102 103 104 105 106 107 110 127 130 134 135 144 147 148 **P**6
Primary Contact: Dan Winkelman, President and Chief Executive Officer
CFO: Vanetta Van Cleave, Chief Financial Officer
CIO: William Pearch, Chief Information Officer
Web address: www.ykhc.org
Control: Other not–for–profit (including NFP Corporation) **Service**: General medical and surgical

Staffed Beds: 37 **Admissions:** 1613 **Census:** 18 **Outpatient Visits:** 205049 **Births:** 402

CORDOVA—Valdez—Cordova County

★ **CORDOVA COMMUNITY MEDICAL CENTER (021307)**, 602 Chase Avenue, Zip 99574, Mailing Address: P.O.Box 160, 99574–0160; tel. 907/424–8000, (Nonreporting) **A**10 18
Primary Contact: Scot Mitchell, FACHE, Chief Executive Officer and Administrator
CFO: Lee W Bennett, Interim Chief Financial Officer
CMO: Sam Blackadar M.D., Medical Director
CHR: Kim Wilson, Human Resources Coordinator
CNO: Mary Rios R.N., Interim Director of Nursing
Web address: www.cdvcmc.com
Control: City, Government, Nonfederal **Service**: General medical and surgical

Staffed Beds: 23

Hospital, Medicare Provider Number, Address, Telephone, Approval, Facility, and Physician Codes, Health Care System

★ American Hospital Association (AHA) membership
☐ The Joint Commission accreditation
○ Healthcare Facilities Accreditation Program
◇ DNV Healthcare Inc. accreditation
⇑ Center for Improvement in Healthcare Quality Accreditation
△ Commission on Accreditation of Rehabilitation Facilities (CARF) accreditation

AK

DILLINGHAM—Dillingham County

⊞ **BRISTOL BAY AREA HEALTH CORPORATION (021309)**, 6000 Kanakanak Road, Zip 99576, Mailing Address: P.O.Box 130, 99576–0130; tel. 907/842–5201, **A**1 3 10 18 **F**3 29 32 34 35 39 40 41 42 43 45 46 47 48 49 50 57 58 59 61 62 64 65 66 68 75 87 89 90 93 100 107 110 119 120 127 130 133 135
Primary Contact: Robert J. Clark, President and Chief Executive Officer
COO: Lucrecia Scotford, Executive Vice President and Chief Operations Officer
CFO: David Morgan, Vice President and Chief Financial Officer
CMO: Arnold Loera M.D., Clinical Director
CIO: Bill Wilcox, Chief Information Technology Officer
CHR: John Davis, Chief Human Resources Officer
CNO: Starla Fox, Director of Nursing
Web address: www.bbahc.org
Control: PHS, Indian Service, Government, federal **Service:** General medical and surgical

Staffed Beds: 16 Admissions: 387 Census: 3 Outpatient Visits: 13859 Births: 48 Total Expense ($000): 59766 Payroll Expense ($000): 23835 Personnel: 304

ELMENDORF AFB—Anchorage County

⊞ **U.S. AIR FORCE REGIONAL HOSPITAL**, 5955 Zeamer Avenue, Zip 99506–3702; tel. 907/580–3006, (Nonreporting) **A**1 **S** Department of the Air Force, Washington, DC
Primary Contact: Major Mark Lamey, Commander
COO: ColonelRebecca Seese, Chief Operating Officer
CFO: MajorFelicia Burks, Chief Financial Officer
CMO: ColonelMarriner Oldham M.D., Chief Medical Officer
CIO: MajorPhillip Oliphant, Chief Information Officer
CHR: Mark Clark, Human Resources Liaison
Web address: www.elmendorf.af.mil/
Control: Air Force, Government, federal **Service:** General medical and surgical

Staffed Beds: 64

FAIRBANKS—Fairbanks North Star County

⊞ **FAIRBANKS MEMORIAL HOSPITAL (020012)**, 1650 Cowles Street, Zip 99701–5998; tel. 907/452–8181, (Total facility includes 82 beds in nursing home–type unit) **A**1 2 3 5 10 **F**3 13 15 18 20 22 28 29 30 34 35 40 45 46 48 50 51 57 59 60 62 63 64 67 70 72 74 75 76 77 78 79 81 82 84 85 86 87 89 93 96 98 100 101 102 103 107 108 110 111 114 115 119 120 121 126 128 129 130 132 135 144 146 148
Primary Contact: Gregory Johnson, D.D.S., Chief Executive Officer
CFO: Steve Leslie, Chief Financial Officer
CIO: Carl J Kegley, System Director Information Technology
CHR: Nicole Welch, Chief Human Resources Officer
CNO: Karen Justin-Tanner R.N., Chief Nursing Officer
Web address: www.foundationhealth.org/fmh
Control: Other not–for–profit (including NFP Corporation) **Service:** General medical and surgical

Staffed Beds: 216 Admissions: 4625 Census: 126 Outpatient Visits: 335306 Births: 1172 Total Expense ($000): 254438 Payroll Expense ($000): 89544 Personnel: 1460

FORT WAINWRIGHT—Fairbanks North Star County

⊞ **BASSETT ARMY COMMUNITY HOSPITAL**, 1060 Gaffney Road, Box 7400, Zip 99703–5001, Mailing Address: 1060 Gaffney Road, Box 7440, 99703–5001; tel. 907/361–4000, (Nonreporting) **A**1 **S** Department of the Army, Office of the Surgeon General, Falls Church, VA
Primary Contact: Timothy Bergeron, Deputy Commander, Administration
CMO: ColonelLeo Bennett M.D., Deputy Commander Clinical Services
CHR: Terri Morefield, Deputy Chief Human Resources Division
Web address: www.alaska.amedd.army.mil
Control: Army, Government, federal **Service:** General medical and surgical

Staffed Beds: 24

HOMER—Kenai Peninsula County

★ **SOUTH PENINSULA HOSPITAL (021313)**, 4300 Bartlett Street, Zip 99603–7000; tel. 907/235–8101, (Total facility includes 28 beds in nursing home–type unit) **A**10 18 **F**3 13 15 18 29 30 31 34 35 36 40 45 50 56 57 59 62 64 65 67 68 70 74 75 76 77 78 79 81 82 85 87 91 92 93 94 97 100 107 110 111 115 119 128 129 130 133 147 148 149 **P**6 8
Primary Contact: Robert F. Letson, FACHE, Chief Executive Officer
CMO: Sarah Spencer M.D., Chief of Staff
CIO: Jim Bartilson, Manager Information Systems
CNO: Shara Sutherlin R.N., Director Patient Care Services
Web address: www.sphosp.org
Control: Hospital district or authority, Government, Nonfederal **Service:** General medical and surgical

Staffed Beds: 50 Admissions: 945 Census: 37 Outpatient Visits: 55135 Births: 146 Total Expense ($000): 64578 Payroll Expense ($000): 28405 Personnel: 347

JUNEAU—Juneau County

⊞ **BARTLETT REGIONAL HOSPITAL (020008)**, 3260 Hospital Drive, Zip 99801–7808; tel. 907/796–8900, **A**1 5 10 20 **F**3 4 5 13 15 28 29 31 34 40 43 45 50 51 57 59 64 70 75 76 77 81 82 85 86 91 93 98 99 100 101 102 104 105 107 108 110 111 114 115 119 120 129 130 132 135 148 **P**6
Primary Contact: Charles E. Bill, Chief Executive Officer
CFO: Alan Ulrich, Chief Financial Officer
CMO: Sharon Fisher M.D., Chief of Staff
CIO: Martha Palicka, Director Information Systems
CHR: Dallas Hargrave, Human Resources Director
CNO: William Gardner, Chief Clinical Officer
Web address: www.bartletthospital.org
Control: City, Government, Nonfederal **Service:** General medical and surgical

Staffed Beds: 73 Admissions: 2496 Census: 25 Outpatient Visits: 47477 Births: 342 Total Expense ($000): 96543 Payroll Expense ($000): 39130 Personnel: 484

KETCHIKAN—Ketchikan Gateway County

★ ⇑ **PEACEHEALTH KETCHIKAN MEDICAL CENTER (021311)**, 3100 Tongass Avenue, Zip 99901–5746; tel. 907/225–5171, (Total facility includes 25 beds in nursing home–type unit) **A**5 10 18 21 **F**11 13 15 18 19 29 30 31 40 43 45 46 50 62 63 65 70 74 75 76 77 78 79 81 82 84 87 93 94 97 102 104 107 108 109 110 111 115 119 128 129 130 131 132 146 147 148 149 150 **P**6 **S** PeaceHealth, Vancouver, WA
Primary Contact: Edward E. Freysinger, Chief Administrative Officer
CFO: Ken Tonjes, Chief Financial Officer
CMO: Peter Rice M.D., Medical Director
CIO: Tim Walker, Manager Information Services
CHR: Lanetta Lundberg, Vice President Culture and People
Web address: www.peacehealth.org
Control: Church operated, Nongovernment, not–for–profit **Service:** General medical and surgical

Staffed Beds: 50 Admissions: 1138 Census: 29 Births: 207

KODIAK—Kodiak Island County

⊞ **PROVIDENCE KODIAK ISLAND MEDICAL CENTER (021306)**, 1915 East Rezanof Drive, Zip 99615–6602; tel. 907/486–3281, (Nonreporting) **A**1 10 18 **S** Providence St. Joseph Health, Renton, WA
Primary Contact: Barbara Bigelow, Administrator
COO: Brenda Zawacki, Chief Operating Manager
CFO: Timothy Hocum, Chief Financial Officer
CMO: Steve Smith M.D., Chief of Staff
CIO: David Johnson, Manager Information Services
CNO: LeeAnn Horn, Chief Nurse Executive
Web address: www.providence.org
Control: Other not–for–profit (including NFP Corporation) **Service:** General medical and surgical

Staffed Beds: 25

KOTZEBUE—Northwest Arctic County

☐ **MANIILAQ HEALTH CENTER (021310)**, 436 5th Avenue, Zip 99752–0043, Mailing Address: P.O.Box 43, 99752–0043; tel. 907/442–7344, (Nonreporting) **A**1 10 18
Primary Contact: Paul Hansen, Administrator
COO: Timothy Schuerch, President and Chief Executive Officer
CFO: Lucy Nelson, Director Finance, Vice President
CMO: Patricia Clancy M.D., Director Medical Services
CIO: Eugene Smith, Chief Information Officer
CHR: Gerty Gallahom, Director Human Resources
CNO: CommanderDonna K Biagioni R.N., MSN, Director of Nursing
Web address: www.maniilaq.org
Control: Other not–for–profit (including NFP Corporation) **Service:** General medical and surgical

Staffed Beds: 17

NOME—Nome County

⊞ **NORTON SOUND REGIONAL HOSPITAL (021308)**, Bering Straits, Zip 99762, Mailing Address: P.O.Box 966, 99762–0966; tel. 907/443–3311, (Nonreporting) **A**1 10 18
Primary Contact: Angela Gorn, Vice President
COO: Roy Agloinga, Chief Administrative Officer
CMO: David Head M.D., Chief Medical Staff
CIO: Dan Bailey, Director Information Systems
CHR: Tiffany Martinson, Director Human Resources
Web address: www.nortonsoundhealth.org
Control: Other not–for–profit (including NFP Corporation) **Service:** General medical and surgical

Staffed Beds: 36

Many Facility Codes have changed. Please refer to the AHA Guide Code Chart.
© 2017 AHA Guide

PALMER—Matanuska—Susitna County

☒ **MAT-SU REGIONAL MEDICAL CENTER (020006)**, 2500 South Woodworth Loop, Zip 99645–8984, Mailing Address: P.O.Box 1687, 99645–1687; tel. 907/861–6000, (Nonreporting) **A**1 3 10 20 **S** Community Health Systems, Inc., Franklin, TN
Primary Contact: David Wallace, Chief Executive Officer
CMO: Christopher Sahlstrom M.D., Chief of Staff
CIO: Bryan Meurer, Director Information Systems
CHR: Cathy Babuscio, Director Human Resources
CNO: Emily Stevens, Chief Nursing Officer
Web address: www.matsuregional.com
Control: Partnership, Investor–owned (for–profit) **Service**: General medical and surgical

Staffed Beds: 74

PETERSBURG—Petersburg County

★ **PETERSBURG MEDICAL CENTER (021304)**, 103 Fram Street, Zip 99833, Mailing Address: Box 589, 99833–0589; tel. 907/772–4291, (Total facility includes 15 beds in nursing home–type unit) **A**10 18 **F**15 31 34 40 45 56 57 59 62 64 67 77 79 81 84 85 93 97 107 110 114 119 133 146 148 149 **P**6
Primary Contact: Elizabeth Woodyard, R.N., MSN, Chief Executive Officer
CFO: Doran Hammett, Chief Financial Officer
CHR: Cynthia Newman, Manager Human Resources
CNO: Jennifer Bryner, Director Nursing
Web address: www.pmcak.org
Control: City–county, Government, Nonfederal **Service**: General medical and surgical

Staffed Beds: 27 **Admissions**: 112 **Census**: 18 **Outpatient Visits**: 10238 **Births**: 0 **Total Expense ($000)**: 15616 **Payroll Expense ($000)**: 8412 **Personnel**: 93

SEWARD—Kenai Peninsula County

★ **PROVIDENCE SEWARD MEDICAL CENTER (021302)**, 417 First Avenue, Zip 99664, Mailing Address: P.O.Box 365, 99664–0365; tel. 907/224–5205, (Nonreporting) **A**10 18 **S** Providence St. Joseph Health, Renton, WA
Primary Contact: Joseph Fong, Administrator
Web address: www.providence.org
Control: Church operated, Nongovernment, not–for–profit **Service**: General medical and surgical

Staffed Beds: 46

SITKA—Sitka County

☒ **SEARHC MT. EDGECUMBE HOSPITAL (020027)**, 222 Tongass Drive, Zip 99835–9416; tel. 907/966–2411, **A**1 5 10 18 **F**3 5 13 15 29 30 32 39 40 43 44 45 48 50 64 68 70 75 76 77 79 81 82 85 87 93 97 107 110 111 115 119 130 131 133 134 135 143 147 148
Primary Contact: Charles Clement, Chief Executive Officer
COO: Daniel P Neumeister, Senior Vice President and Chief Operating Officer
CFO: Barbara Searls, Chief Financial Officer
CMO: David Vastola, Medical Director
CIO: Bob Cita, Chief Information Officer
CHR: Peggy Bernhardt–Kadlec, Chief Human Resources Officer
CNO: Patricia L Giampa, Chief Nursing Officer
Web address: www.searhc.org
Control: Other not–for–profit (including NFP Corporation) **Service**: General medical and surgical

Staffed Beds: 25 **Admissions**: 588 **Census**: 9 **Outpatient Visits**: 110618 **Births**: 57 **Total Expense ($000)**: 116659 **Payroll Expense ($000)**: 60656 **Personnel**: 660

★ **SITKA COMMUNITY HOSPITAL (021303)**, 209 Moller Avenue, Zip 99835–7142; tel. 907/747–3241, (Total facility includes 15 beds in nursing home–type unit) **A**10 18 **F**3 11 13 15 28 29 31 32 33 34 35 40 43 44 45 50 53 56 59 62 64 65 76 77 81 82 85 87 89 90 93 94 96 97 102 107 110 114 119 128 130 131 133 135 148 149
Primary Contact: Rob Allen, Chief Executive Officer
CFO: Lee W Bennett, Chief Financial Officer
CHR: Shannon Callahan, Director Human Resources
Web address: www.sitkahospital.org
Control: City, Government, Nonfederal **Service**: Acute long–term care hospital

Staffed Beds: 27 **Admissions**: 198 **Census**: 13 **Outpatient Visits**: 2434 **Births**: 25 **Total Expense ($000)**: 26420 **Payroll Expense ($000)**: 11327 **Personnel**: 145

SOLDOTNA—Kenai Peninsula County

☒ **CENTRAL PENINSULA HOSPITAL (020024)**, 250 Hospital Place, Zip 99669–6999; tel. 907/714–4404, (Total facility includes 58 beds in nursing home–type unit) **A**1 3 10 20 **F**3 4 5 11 13 15 28 29 30 31 34 35 36 38 40 45 46 47 48 49 51 57 59 65 68 70 74 75 76 77 78 79 81 82 84 85 86 87 93 97 107 108 110 111 115 119 128 129 130 131 132 133 134 135 145 146 147 148 149
Primary Contact: Richard Davis, Chief Executive Officer
COO: Matt Dammeyer Ph.D., Chief Operating Officer
CMO: Gregg Motonaga M.D., Chief of Staff
CIO: Bryan Downs, Director Information Systems
CHR: John Dodd, Vice President Human Resources
Web address: www.cpgh.org
Control: Other not–for–profit (including NFP Corporation) **Service**: General medical and surgical

Staffed Beds: 117 **Admissions**: 2724 **Census**: 81 **Outpatient Visits**: 132199 **Births**: 462 **Total Expense ($000)**: 136499 **Payroll Expense ($000)**: 59587 **Personnel**: 718

VALDEZ—Valdez—Cordova County

★ **PROVIDENCE VALDEZ MEDICAL CENTER (021301)**, 911 Meals Avenue, Zip 99686–0550, Mailing Address: P.O.Box 550, 99686–0550; tel. 907/835–2249, (Nonreporting) **A**10 18 **S** Providence St. Joseph Health, Renton, WA
Primary Contact: Jeremy O'Neil, Administrator
CMO: John Cullen M.D., Chief of Staff and Medical Director Long Term Care
CHR: Maureen Radotich, Director Human Resources
Web address: www.providence.org/alaska
Control: City, Government, Nonfederal **Service**: General medical and surgical

Staffed Beds: 21

WRANGELL—Wrangell County

★ **WRANGELL MEDICAL CENTER (021305)**, First Avenue & Bennett Street, Zip 99929, Mailing Address: P.O.Box 1081, 99929–1081; tel. 907/874–7000, (Nonreporting) **A**10 18
Primary Contact: Robert A. Rang, R.N., Chief Executive Officer
CIO: Cathy Gross, Director Health Information Management Systems
CNO: Sherri Austin MSN, R.N., Chief Nursing Officer
Web address: www.wrangellmedicalcenter.org/
Control: City, Government, Nonfederal **Service**: General medical and surgical

Staffed Beds: 22

Hospital, Medicare Provider Number, Address, Telephone, Approval, Facility, and Physician Codes, Health Care System

★ American Hospital Association (AHA) membership   ○ Healthcare Facilities Accreditation Program   ⇑ Center for Improvement in Healthcare Quality Accreditation
□ The Joint Commission accreditation   ◇ DNV Healthcare Inc. accreditation   △ Commission on Accreditation of Rehabilitation Facilities (CARF) accreditation

ARIZONA

AZ

APACHE JUNCTION—Pinal County

⊠ **BANNER GOLDFIELD MEDICAL CENTER (030134)**, 2050 West Southern Avenue, Zip 85120–7305; tel. 480/733–3300, **A**1 10 **F**3 11 29 34 40 49 50 68 77 79 81 85 87 107 119 130 146 **S** Banner Health, Phoenix, AZ
Primary Contact: Sharon Lind, MSN, FACHE, Chief Executive Officer
CFO: Tracy French, Chief Financial Officer
CMO: Jason Brown M.D., Chief Medical Officer
CHR: Rebecca McLaughlin, Chief Human Resource Officer
CNO: Terresa Ann Paulus, Chief Nursing Officer
Web address: www.bannerhealth.com/Locations/Arizona/
Banner+Goldfield+Medical+Center/_Welcome+to+Banner+Goldfield.htm
Control: Other not–for–profit (including NFP Corporation) **Service:** General medical and surgical

Staffed Beds: 20 **Admissions:** 664 **Census:** 5 **Total Expense ($000):** 20884 **Payroll Expense ($000):** 8021 **Personnel:** 111

BENSON—Cochise County

★ **BENSON HOSPITAL (031301)**, 450 South Ocotillo Street, Zip 85602–6403, Mailing Address: P.O.Box 2290, 85602–2290; tel. 520/586–2261, **A**10 18 **F**3 11 29 30 34 40 43 50 54 57 59 64 75 77 80 86 87 93 107 111 114 119 132 133 146 148
Primary Contact: Richard Polheber, Chief Executive Officer
COO: Teresa Vincifora, Chief Operating Officer
CFO: Ken Goranson, Chief Financial Officer
CMO: Barbara Hartley, Chief Medical Officer
CIO: Rob Roberts, Director Information Technology
CHR: Ashley Dickey, Director Human Resources
Web address: www.bensonhospital.org
Control: Other not–for–profit (including NFP Corporation) **Service:** General medical and surgical

Staffed Beds: 22 **Admissions:** 384 **Census:** 5 **Outpatient Visits:** 15088 **Births:** 0 **Total Expense ($000):** 13919 **Payroll Expense ($000):** 7190 **Personnel:** 135

BISBEE—Cochise County

★ **COPPER QUEEN COMMUNITY HOSPITAL (031312)**, 101 Cole Avenue, Zip 85603–1399; tel. 520/432–5383, (Nonreporting) **A**10 18
Primary Contact: James J. Dickson, Administrator and Chief Executive Officer
COO: Daniel Roe M.D., Chief Operating Officer
CFO: James Ehasz, Chief Financial Officer
CMO: Daniel Roe M.D., Chief Medical Officer
CIO: David Chmura, Chief Information Officer
CHR: Virginia Martinez, Director Human Resources
CNO: Sadie Maestas, Interim Chief Nursing Officer
Web address: www.cqch.org
Control: Other not–for–profit (including NFP Corporation) **Service:** General medical and surgical

Staffed Beds: 14

BULLHEAD CITY—Mohave County

⊠ **WESTERN ARIZONA REGIONAL MEDICAL CENTER (030101)**, 2735 Silver Creek Road, Zip 86442–8303; tel. 928/763–2273, (Nonreporting) **A**1 10 19 **S** Community Health Systems, Inc., Franklin, TN
Primary Contact: Thomas A. Salerno, Chief Executive Officer
CFO: Kenneth Pannell, Chief Financial Officer
CNO: Tara Barth, Chief Nursing Officer
Web address: www.warmc.com
Control: Corporation, Investor–owned (for–profit) **Service:** General medical and surgical

Staffed Beds: 139

CASA GRANDE—Pinal County

⊠ **BANNER CASA GRANDE MEDICAL CENTER (030016)**, 1800 East Florence Boulevard, Zip 85122–5399; tel. 520/381–6300, **A**1 10 **F**3 13 15 18 20 22 29 30 31 34 36 39 40 44 45 49 50 53 57 59 61 64 68 70 72 74 75 76 77 78 79 81 85 86 87 92 93 100 107 108 110 111 114 115 118 119 126 129 130 132 135 144 145 146 147 148 149 **S** Banner Health, Phoenix, AZ
Primary Contact: Rona Curphy, President and Chief Executive Officer
CFO: Robert Bender, Chief Financial Officer
CMO: Devin Minior M.D., Chief Medical Officer
CHR: Carol D'Souza, Chief Human Resources Officer
CNO: Dan Lingle, Chief Nursing Officer
Web address: www.bannerhealth.com/Locations/Arizona/Banner+Casa+Grande+Medical+Center/_Banner+Casa+Grande+Medical+Center.htm
Control: Other not–for–profit (including NFP Corporation) **Service:** General medical and surgical

Staffed Beds: 135 **Admissions:** 5299 **Census:** 59 **Births:** 709 **Total Expense ($000):** 116816 **Payroll Expense ($000):** 44422 **Personnel:** 698

CHANDLER—Maricopa County

☐ **ARIZONA ORTHOPEDIC SURGICAL HOSPITAL (030112)**, 2905 West Warner Road, Suite 1, Zip 85224–1674; tel. 480/603–9000, **A**1 10 **F**8 29 64 79 81 85 111 **S** United Surgical Partners International, Addison, TX
Primary Contact: Patricia K. Alice, Chief Executive Officer
CFO: Shalen Young, Chief Financial Officer
CMO: Randall Hardison M.D., Chief Medical Officer
CIO: John Langenfeld, Medical Records Coordinator
CNO: Caroline Herpfer, Chief Nursing Officer
Web address: www.azosh.com
Control: Corporation, Investor–owned (for–profit) **Service:** Orthopedic

Staffed Beds: 24 **Admissions:** 980 **Census:** 6 **Births:** 0

⊠ **CHANDLER REGIONAL MEDICAL CENTER (030036)**, 1955 West Frye Road, Zip 85224–6282; tel. 480/728–3000, **A**1 3 10 **F**3 8 11 13 15 17 18 20 22 24 26 28 29 30 31 32 34 35 37 40 41 42 43 44 45 46 47 48 49 50 51 54 57 58 59 60 64 65 66 68 70 71 72 73 74 75 76 77 78 79 81 82 83 84 85 86 87 93 96 107 108 110 111 114 115 119 126 130 131 132 135 143 144 146 147 148 P6 **S** Dignity Health, San Francisco, CA
Primary Contact: Jane E. Hanson, R.N., Interim Chief Executive Officer
COO: Jane E Hanson R.N., Chief Operating Officer
CFO: Mark Kem, Vice President Finance and Chief Financial Officer
CMO: Terry J Happel M.D., Vice President and Chief Medical Officer
CHR: Renea Brunke, Vice President Human Resources
CNO: Peg Smith, Vice President and Chief Nursing Officer
Web address: www.chandlerregional.com
Control: Other not–for–profit (including NFP Corporation) **Service:** General medical and surgical

Staffed Beds: 338 **Admissions:** 24535 **Census:** 282 **Outpatient Visits:** 195283 **Births:** 3983 **Total Expense ($000):** 463000 **Payroll Expense ($000):** 167689 **Personnel:** 2828

OASIS BEHAVIORAL HEALTH – CHANDLER (034029), 2190 North Grace Boulevard, Zip 85225–3416; tel. 480/917–9301, (Nonreporting) **S** Acadia Healthcare Company, Inc., Franklin, TN
Primary Contact: James Gallagher, Chief Executive Officer
CFO: Dino Quarante CPA, Chief Financial Officer
CHR: Barbara Mitchell, Director Human Resources
CNO: Charissa Davis, Chief Nursing Officer and Director of Nursing
Web address: www.obhhospital.com/about/location
Control: Corporation, Investor–owned (for–profit) **Service:** Psychiatric

Staffed Beds: 47

CHINLE—Apache County

⊠ **CHINLE COMPREHENSIVE HEALTH CARE FACILITY (030084)**, Highway 191, Zip 86503, Mailing Address: P O Drawer PH, 86503–8000; tel. 928/674–7001, (Nonreporting) **A**1 10 **S** U. S. Indian Health Service, Rockville, MD
Primary Contact: Ron Tso, Chief Executive Officer
CFO: Philene Tyler, Chief Finance Officer
CMO: Eric Ritchie M.D., Clinical Director
CIO: Perry Francis, Supervisory Information Technology Specialist
CHR: Lorraine Begaye, Supervisory Human Resource Specialist
Web address: www.ihs.gov
Control: PHS, Indian Service, Government, federal **Service:** General medical and surgical

Staffed Beds: 60

COTTONWOOD—Yavapai County

★ ⇑ **VERDE VALLEY MEDICAL CENTER (030007)**, 269 South Candy Lane, Zip 86326–4170; tel. 928/639–6000, **A**10 13 20 21 **F**3 8 11 13 15 18 19 20 22 28 29 30 31 32 34 35 36 40 42 44 45 46 47 48 49 50 53 54 57 58 59 60 64 68 70 75 76 77 78 79 81 82 85 86 87 89 91 92 93 94 96 97 98 99 100 101 102 103 107 108 110 111 114 115 118 119 120 121 123 124 129 130 131 132 135 143 145 146 147 148 149 **S** Northern Arizona Healthcare, Flagstaff, AZ
Primary Contact: Barbara Firminger, Chief Administrative Officer
CFO: Jeffrey Treasure, Chief Financial Officer, Northern Arizona Healthcare
CMO: Amy Gottschalk M.D., Chief Medical Officer, Verde Valley Medical Center; Vice President Quality, Northern Arizona Healthcare
CIO: Marilynn Black, Chief Information Officer, Northern Arizona Healthcare
CHR: Ronald Haase, Chief Human Resources Officer, Northern Arizona Healthcare
CNO: Lori A Stevens MSN, R.N., Interim Chief Nursing Officer
Web address: www.nahealth.com
Control: Other not–for–profit (including NFP Corporation) **Service:** General medical and surgical

Staffed Beds: 110 **Admissions:** 4100 **Census:** 50 **Outpatient Visits:** 115489 **Births:** 544 **Total Expense ($000):** 122143

Many Facility Codes have changed. Please refer to the AHA Guide Code Chart.

FLAGSTAFF—Coconino County

★ ⇑ **FLAGSTAFF MEDICAL CENTER (030023)**, 1200 North Beaver Street, Zip 86001–3118; tel. 928/779–3366, (Nonreporting) **A**3 5 10 21 **S** Northern Arizona Healthcare, Flagstaff, AZ
Primary Contact: Florence (Flo). Spyrow, Chief Administrative Officer
CFO: Jeffrey Treasure, Chief Financial Officer, Northern Arizona Healthcare
CMO: Richard Neff M.D., Interim Chief Medical Officer
CIO: Marilynn Black, Chief Information Officer, Northern Arizona Healthcare
CHR: Ronald Haase, Chief Human Resources Officer, Northern Arizona Healthcare
CNO: Katy Wilkens, Chief Nursing Officer and Vice President, Northern Arizona Healthcare
Web address: www.nahealth.com
Control: Other not–for–profit (including NFP Corporation) **Service**: General medical and surgical

Staffed Beds: 267

☐ **GUIDANCE CENTER (034023)**, 2187 North Vickey Street, Zip 86004–6121; tel. 928/527–1899, (Nonreporting) **A**1 10
CFO: Steve Finch, Chief Financial Officer
CMO: Chris Linskey M.D., Acting Chief Medical Officer
CIO: John Crockett, Chief Information Officer
Web address: www.tgcaz.org
Control: Other not–for–profit (including NFP Corporation) **Service**: Psychiatric

Staffed Beds: 10

FLORENCE—Pinal County

⇑ **FLORENCE HOSPITAL AT ANTHEM (030132)**, 4545 North Hunt Highway, Zip 85132–6937; tel. 520/868–3333, (Nonreporting) **A**10 21
Primary Contact: Bryan J. Hargis, FACHE, Chief Executive Officer
CFO: Dennis E Rutherford CPA, Chief Financial Officer
CNO: Marla Meggers, Chief Nursing Officer and Chief Operating Officer
Web address: www.fhanthem.com
Control: Partnership, Investor–owned (for–profit) **Service**: General medical and surgical

Staffed Beds: 36

FORT DEFIANCE—Apache County

★ **TSEHOOTSOOI MEDICAL CENTER (030071)**, Highway 12 & Bonito Drive, Zip 86504, Mailing Address: P.O.Box 649, 86504–0649; tel. 928/729–8000, (Nonreporting) **A**3 10
Primary Contact: Sandi Aretino, M.D., Chief Executive Officer
COO: Valonia Hardy, Chief Healthy Living Officer
CFO: Rachel Sorrell, Chief Financial Officer
CMO: Michael Tutt M.D., Chief Medical Officer
CIO: Virgil Chavez, Director Information Technology
CHR: Vivian Santistevan, Chief Human Resources
CNO: Tori Davidson R.N., Chief Nursing Officer
Web address: www.fdihb.org
Control: Public Health Service, Public, Federal **Service**: General medical and surgical

Staffed Beds: 39

FORT MOHAVE—Mohave County

⊞ **VALLEY VIEW MEDICAL CENTER (030117)**, 5330 South Highway 95, Zip 86426–9225; tel. 928/788–2273, (Nonreporting) **A**1 10 **S** LifePoint Health, Brentwood, TN
Primary Contact: Feliciano Jiron, Chief Executive Officer
CFO: Emma Canlas, Chief Financial Officer
CIO: Monique Murphy–Mijares, Chief Information Officer
CHR: Bonnie Guerrero, Director Human Resources
CNO: Lesa Lock, Chief Nursing Officer
Web address: www.valleyviewmedicalcenter.net
Control: Corporation, Investor–owned (for–profit) **Service**: General medical and surgical

Staffed Beds: 90

GANADO—Apache County

⊞ **SAGE MEMORIAL HOSPITAL (031309)**, Highway 264, Zip 86505, Mailing Address: P.O.Box 457, 86505–0457; tel. 928/755–4500, (Nonreporting) **A**1 10 18
Primary Contact: Christi J. El–Meligi, R.N., Chief Executive Officer
COO: Netrisha Dalgai, Director of Operations
CFO: Michael Katigbak, Chief Financial Officer
CMO: Jeremy Wray D.O., Medical Director
CIO: Michael Katigbak, Director Computer Services
CHR: Gary Pahe, Manager Human Resources
CNO: Ernasha McIntosh, Interim Director of Nursing
Web address: www.sagememorial.com
Control: Other not–for–profit (including NFP Corporation) **Service**: General medical and surgical

Staffed Beds: 25

GILBERT—Maricopa County

⊞ **BANNER GATEWAY MEDICAL CENTER (030122)**, 1900 North Higley Road, Zip 85234–1604; tel. 480/543–2000, **A**1 3 10 **F**3 8 12 13 15 29 30 31 34 35 36 40 45 46 47 48 49 50 54 55 57 58 59 60 64 68 70 72 75 76 77 78 79 80 81 82 83 84 85 86 87 92 97 100 107 108 109 110 111 114 115 116 117 118 119 120 121 123 124 126 130 131 132 133 135 136 145 146 147 148 **S** Banner Health, Phoenix, AZ
Primary Contact: Lamont M. Yoder, R.N., MSN, FACHE, Chief Executive Officer
COO: James R Powell, Associate Administrator
CFO: Thomas M Matenaer, Chief Financial Officer
CMO: Nikunj Doshi D.O., Chief Medical Officer
CHR: Michele Mustacchia, Chief Human Resources Officer
CNO: Debra Adornetto–Garcia MSN, R.N., Chief Nursing Officer
Web address: www.bannerhealth.com/Locations/Arizona/Banner+Gateway+Medical+Center/
Control: Other not–for–profit (including NFP Corporation) **Service**: General medical and surgical

Staffed Beds: 177 **Admissions**: 12034 **Census**: 122 **Births**: 3766 **Total Expense ($000)**: 302243 **Payroll Expense ($000)**: 90348

GILBERT HOSPITAL (030120), 5656 South Power Road, Zip 85295–8487; tel. 480/984–2000, (Nonreporting) **A**10
Primary Contact: Bryan J. Hargis, FACHE, Chief Executive Officer
CFO: Dennis E Rutherford CPA, Chief Financial Officer
CMO: Timothy Johns M.D., Chief Medical Officer
CIO: Michelle Cianfrani, Director Information Technology
CNO: Marla Meggers R.N., MSN, Chief Nursing Officer
Web address: www.gilberter.com
Control: Corporation, Investor–owned (for–profit) **Service**: General medical and surgical

Staffed Beds: 19

⊞ **MERCY GILBERT MEDICAL CENTER (030119)**, 3555 South Val Vista Road, Zip 85297–7323; tel. 480/728–8000, **A**1 10 **F**3 8 11 13 15 18 20 22 26 28 29 30 31 32 34 35 37 38 40 41 42 44 45 46 47 49 50 51 57 58 59 60 64 65 66 68 70 73 74 75 76 77 78 79 81 82 83 84 85 86 87 96 100 101 102 103 107 108 110 111 114 115 119 126 129 130 131 132 135 144 145 146 147 148 **P**6 **S** Dignity Health, San Francisco, CA
Primary Contact: Jane E. Hanson, R.N., Interim President and Chief Executive Officer
COO: Jane E Hanson R.N., Chief Operating Officer
CFO: Chuck Sowers, Vice President Finance and Chief Financial Officer
CMO: Phil Fracica M.D., Vice President and Chief Medical Officer
CIO: Larissa Spraker, Vice President Business Development and Chief Strategy Officer
CHR: Anita Harger, Director Human Resources
Web address: www.mercygilbert.org
Control: Other not–for–profit (including NFP Corporation) **Service**: General medical and surgical

Staffed Beds: 198 **Admissions**: 15242 **Census**: 149 **Outpatient Visits**: 87757 **Births**: 3450 **Total Expense ($000)**: 255528 **Payroll Expense ($000)**: 89905 **Personnel**: 1419

AZ

Hospital, Medicare Provider Number, Address, Telephone, Approval, Facility, and Physician Codes, Health Care System

★ American Hospital Association (AHA) membership   ○ Healthcare Facilities Accreditation Program   ⇑ Center for Improvement in Healthcare Quality Accreditation
☐ The Joint Commission accreditation   ◇ DNV Healthcare Inc. accreditation   △ Commission on Accreditation of Rehabilitation Facilities (CARF) accreditation

© 2017 AHA Guide   *Many Facility Codes have changed. Please refer to the AHA Guide Code Chart.*   Hospitals **A29**

GLENDALE—Maricopa County

☒ **ABRAZO ARROWHEAD CAMPUS (030094)**, 18701 North 67th Avenue, Zip 85308-7100; tel. 623/561-1000, (Nonreporting) (Includes ARIZONA HEART HOSPITAL, 1930 East Thomas Road, Phoenix, Arizona, Zip 85016, tel. 602/532-1000) **A**1 3 10 **S** TENET Healthcare Corporation, Dallas, TX
Primary Contact: Frank L. Molinaro, Chief Executive Officer
CMO: Patrick Smith M.D., Chief Medical Officer
CHR: Sharon M Chadwick, Director Human Resources
Web address: www.arrowheadhospital.com
Control: Corporation, Investor-owned (for-profit) **Service**: General medical and surgical

Staffed Beds: 234

☐ **AURORA BEHAVIORAL HEALTH SYSTEM WEST (034024)**, 6015 West Peoria Avenue, Zip 85302-1213; tel. 623/344-4400, (Nonreporting) **A**1 10 **S** Signature Healthcare Services, Corona, CA
Primary Contact: Bruce Waldo, Chief Executive Officer
CFO: Rebekah Francis JD, Chief Financial Officer
CHR: Vicki Thomsen, Director Human Resources
CNO: Lori Milus R.N., MSN, Director of Nursing
Web address: www.aurorabehavioral.com
Control: Corporation, Investor-owned (for-profit) **Service**: Psychiatric

Staffed Beds: 90

☒ **BANNER THUNDERBIRD MEDICAL CENTER (030089)**, 5555 West Thunderbird Road, Zip 85306-4696; tel. 602/865-5555, (Includes BANNER BEHAVIORAL HEALTH CENTER-THUNDERBIRD CAMPUS, 5555 West Thunderbird Road, Glendale, Arizona, Zip 85306, tel. 602/588-5555) **A**1 3 10 **F**3 5 13 15 18 19 20 22 24 26 28 29 30 31 34 35 36 37 38 39 40 41 44 45 46 49 50 51 60 61 64 68 70 72 74 75 76 77 78 79 81 84 85 86 87 88 89 91 92 93 96 98 100 101 102 104 105 107 108 110 111 114 115 116 117 118 119 120 121 123 124 126 129 130 132 135 145 146 147 148 149 **S** Banner Health, Phoenix, AZ
Primary Contact: Debra J. Krmpotic, R.N., Chief Executive Officer
CFO: Richard Miller, Administrator Finance
CMO: Kathryn Perkins M.D., Chief Medical Officer
CHR: Laura Witt, Administrator Human Resources
Web address: www.bannerhealth.com/Locations/Arizona/Banner+Thunderbird+Medical+Center/
Control: Other not-for-profit (including NFP Corporation) **Service**: General medical and surgical

Staffed Beds: 428 **Admissions:** 25742 **Census:** 344 **Births:** 5530 **Total Expense ($000):** 442465 **Payroll Expense ($000):** 160637 **Personnel:** 2803

☒ **HEALTHSOUTH VALLEY OF THE SUN REHABILITATION HOSPITAL (033032)**, 13460 North 67th Avenue, Zip 85304-1042; tel. 623/878-8800, (Nonreporting) **A**1 10 **S** HEALTHSOUTH Corporation, Birmingham, AL
Primary Contact: Beth Bacher, Chief Executive Officer
CFO: Kathryn Haney, Controller
CMO: Michael Kravetz M.D., Medical Director
CHR: Danette Garcia, Director Human Resources
CNO: Stephanie Palmer, Chief Nursing Officer
Web address: www.healthsouthvalleyofthesun.com
Control: Corporation, Investor-owned (for-profit) **Service**: Rehabilitation

Staffed Beds: 75

GLOBE—Gila County

COBRE VALLEY COMMUNITY HOSPITAL See COBRE VALLEY REGIONAL MEDICAL CENTER

★ **COBRE VALLEY REGIONAL MEDICAL CENTER (031314)**, 5880 South Hospital Drive, Zip 85501-9454; tel. 928/425-3261, (Nonreporting) **A**10 18 **S** HealthTech Management Services, Brentwood, TN
Primary Contact: Neal Jensen, Chief Executive Officer
CFO: Frank Napier, Interim Chief Financial Officer
CIO: Sharon Bennett, Manager Management Information Systems
CHR: Rita Murphy, Director Human Resources
Web address: www.cvrmc.org
Control: Other not-for-profit (including NFP Corporation) **Service**: General medical and surgical

Staffed Beds: 25

GOODYEAR—Maricopa County

☒ **ABRAZO WEST CAMPUS (030110)**, 13677 West McDowell Road, Zip 85395-2635; tel. 623/882-1500, (Nonreporting) **A**1 10 **S** TENET Healthcare Corporation, Dallas, TX
Primary Contact: Stan Holm, Chief Executive Officer
COO: Jeffrey Dossett, Chief Operating Officer
CFO: Asja DiMuria, Chief Financial Officer
CNO: Scott David Morey, Chief Nursing Officer
Web address: www.abrazohealth.com
Control: Corporation, Investor-owned (for-profit) **Service**: General medical and surgical

Staffed Beds: 106

☒ **WESTERN REGIONAL MEDICAL CENTER (030127)**, 14200 West Celebrate Life way, Zip 85338-3005; tel. 623/207-3000, **A**1 2 10 **F**3 15 29 30 31 33 34 36 46 47 49 55 57 64 68 70 75 77 78 79 81 82 83 84 85 86 87 93 96 100 104 107 108 110 111 114 115 116 117 118 119 120 121 123 124 126 130 132 135 144 146 148 **P**6 **S** Cancer Treatment Centers of America, Schaumburg, IL
Primary Contact: Matthew McGuire, President and Chief Executive Officer
Web address: www.cancercenter.com/western-hospital.cfm
Control: Corporation, Investor-owned (for-profit) **Service**: Cancer

Staffed Beds: 24 **Admissions:** 560 **Census:** 7 **Outpatient Visits:** 26266 **Births:** 0 **Personnel:** 529

GREEN VALLEY—Cochise County

⇑ **GREEN VALLEY HOSPITAL (030137)**, 4455 South I-19 Frontage Road, Zip 85614; tel. 520/393-4700, (Nonreporting) **A**21
Primary Contact: John E. Matuska, Chief Executive Officer
CFO: Sara Ghali, Chief Financial Officer
CNO: Mona R. Smith, Chief Nursing Officer
Web address: www.greenvalleyhospital.com
Control: Corporation, Investor-owned (for-profit) **Service**: General medical and surgical

Staffed Beds: 98

KEAMS CANYON—Navajo County

☒ **HOPI HEALTH CARE CENTER (031305)**, Highway 264 Mile Marker 388, Zip 86042, Mailing Address: P.O.Box 4000, Polacca, 86042-4000; tel. 928/737-6000, (Nonreporting) **A**1 3 10 18 **S** U. S. Indian Health Service, Rockville, MD
Primary Contact: Mose Herne, Chief Executive Officer
COO: Leonard H Lopez, Chief Operating Officer
CFO: Dorothy Sulu, Budget Analyst
CMO: Darren Vicenti M.D., Clinical Director
CHR: Trudy Begay, Human Resources Specialist
Web address: www.ihs.gov/index.asp
Control: PHS, Indian Service, Government, federal **Service**: General medical and surgical

Staffed Beds: 15

KINGMAN—Mohave County

★ ⇑ **KINGMAN REGIONAL MEDICAL CENTER (030055)**, 3269 Stockton Hill Road, Zip 86409-3691; tel. 928/757-2101, **A**10 13 21 **F**11 13 15 17 18 20 22 24 28 29 30 31 32 33 34 35 36 40 43 45 46 47 48 53 57 59 60 62 63 64 65 68 69 70 75 76 77 78 79 81 82 83 84 85 86 87 89 90 92 93 96 97 100 107 108 110 111 114 115 117 118 119 121 129 130 131 132 143 144 145 146 147 148 **P**6 7
Primary Contact: Brian Turney, Chief Executive Officer
COO: Ryan Kennedy, Chief Operating Officer
CFO: Timothy D Blanchard, Chief Financial Officer
CMO: Thomas Gaughan M.D., Chief Medical Officer
CIO: Cheryl Martin, Chief Information Officer
CHR: Anita Harger, Chief Human Resource Officer
CNO: Kimberly Miyauchi R.N., Chief Nursing Officer
Web address: www.azkrmc.com
Control: Hospital district or authority, Government, Nonfederal **Service**: General medical and surgical

Staffed Beds: 200 **Admissions:** 8573 **Census:** 145 **Births:** 637 **Total Expense ($000):** 269570 **Payroll Expense ($000):** 113928 **Personnel:** 1703

LAKE HAVASU CITY—Mohave County

⊞ **HAVASU REGIONAL MEDICAL CENTER (030069)**, 101 Civic Center Lane,
Zip 86403–5683; tel. 928/855–8185, (Nonreporting) **A**1 10 **S** LifePoint Health,
Brentwood, TN
Primary Contact: Michael N. Patterson, Chief Executive Officer
COO: Wes Taylor, Chief Operating Officer
CFO: Christina DiMambro, Chief Financial Officer
CMO: Michael Rosen M.D., Chief Medical Officer
CIO: Linda Toy, Director Information Systems
Web address: www.havasuregional.com
Control: Corporation, Investor–owned (for–profit) **Service**: General medical and
surgical

Staffed Beds: 162

LAKESIDE—Navajo County

CCC AT PINEVIEW HOSPITAL (034027), 1920 West Commerce Drive,
Zip 85929; tel. 928/368–4110, (Nonreporting) **A**10
Primary Contact: Rosemary Anderson, Administrator
Web address: www.ccc–az.org
Control: Other not–for–profit (including NFP Corporation) **Service**: Psychiatric

Staffed Beds: 16

LAVEEN—Maricopa County

☐ **DIGNITY HEALTH ARIZONA GENERAL HOSPITAL (030136)**, 7171 South 51st
Avenue, Zip 85339–2923; tel. 602/246–3400, (Nonreporting) **A**1
Primary Contact: Robert C. Honeycutt, Chief Executive Officer
CFO: Anthony Cirocco, Chief Financial Officer
CMO: Fred Johnson M.D., Chief Medical Officer
CNO: Victoria Nugent, Chief Nursing Officer
Web address: www.dignityhealth.org/arizonageneral/
Control: Other not–for–profit (including NFP Corporation) **Service**: Acute long–
term care hospital

Staffed Beds: 16

MESA—Maricopa County

☐ **ARIZONA SPINE AND JOINT HOSPITAL (030107)**, 4620 East Baseline Road,
Zip 85206–4624; tel. 480/832–4770, (Nonreporting) **A**1 10 **S** National Surgical
Healthcare, Chicago, IL
Primary Contact: Todd Greene, Chief Executive Officer
CHR: Diane Hearne, Director Human Resources
CNO: Stacy Hayes R.N., Chief Nursing Officer
Web address: www.azspineandjoint.com
Control: Corporation, Investor–owned (for–profit) **Service**: Orthopedic

Staffed Beds: 23

⊞ **BANNER BAYWOOD MEDICAL CENTER (030088)**, 6644 East Baywood
Avenue, Zip 85206–1797; tel. 480/321–2000, **A**1 10 **F**3 13 15 18 29 30 31 34
35 36 37 40 41 43 44 45 46 47 48 49 50 51 56 57 58 59 60 61 63 64 68 70
74 75 76 77 78 79 80 81 82 84 85 86 87 90 91 92 94 96 100 102 103 107
108 110 111 113 114 115 116 118 119 126 129 130 132 135 141 146 147
148 **S** Banner Health, Phoenix, AZ
Primary Contact: Lamont M. Yoder, R.N., MSN, FACHE, Chief Executive Officer
CFO: Derek Lythgoe, Chief Financial Officer
CMO: Michael P O'Connor M.D., Chief Medical Officer
CIO: Lori Matthews, Vice President Information Technology System
CHR: Tiffany Werner, Senior Human Resource Business Partner
CNO: Kelley Kieffer, Chief Nursing Officer
Web address: www.bannerhealth.com/locations/Arizona/
banner+baywood+medical+center
Control: Other not–for–profit (including NFP Corporation) **Service**: General
medical and surgical

**Staffed Beds: 388 Admissions: 16470 Census: 216 Births: 795 Total
Expense ($000): 253235 Payroll Expense ($000): 96476 Personnel: 1733**

BANNER CHILDREN'S HOSPITAL See CARDON CHILDREN'S MEDICAL CENTER

⊞ **BANNER DESERT MEDICAL CENTER (030065)**, 1400 South Dobson
Road, Zip 85202–4707; tel. 480/412–3000, (Includes CARDON CHILDREN'S
MEDICAL CENTER, 1400 South Dobson Road, Mesa, Arizona, Zip 85202–4707,
tel. 480/412–3000; Justin Bradshaw, Chief Executive Officer; SAMARITAN
BEHAVIORAL HEALTH CENTER–DESERT SAMARITAN MEDICAL CENTER, 2225 West
Southern Avenue, Mesa, Arizona, Zip 85202, tel. 602/464–4000) **A**1 3 5 10 **F**3
11 13 17 18 19 20 21 22 23 24 25 26 27 28 29 30 31 32 34 35 36 37 38 40
41 43 45 46 47 48 49 50 51 57 58 59 60 61 64 68 70 71 72 73 74 75 76 77
78 79 81 82 84 85 87 88 89 92 93 96 97 102 107 108 111 114 115 118 119
120 121 123 124 126 129 130 132 134 135 146 147 148 **S** Banner Health,
Phoenix, AZ
Primary Contact: Laura Robertson, R.N., Chief Executive Officer
COO: Cristal Mackay, Chief Operating Officer
CFO: Scott Leckey, Chief Financial Officer
CMO: Tanya Kne M.D., Chief Medical Officer
CIO: Stacey Hinkle, Director Information Technology
CHR: Kevin McVeigh, Chief Human Resources Officer
Web address: www.bannerhealth.com/Locations/Arizona/
Banner+Desert+Medical+Center
Control: Other not–for–profit (including NFP Corporation) **Service**: General
medical and surgical

**Staffed Beds: 595 Admissions: 31597 Census: 400 Births: 4268 Total
Expense ($000): 581575 Payroll Expense ($000): 202877 Personnel: 3491**

⊞ **BANNER HEART HOSPITAL (030105)**, 6750 East Baywood Avenue,
Zip 85206–1749; tel. 480/854–5000, **A**1 10 **F**3 17 18 20 22 24 26 28 29 30
34 35 36 44 45 46 50 56 57 58 59 60 61 64 68 74 75 77 81 82 84 85 86
87 92 94 100 103 113 119 126 130 132 135 146 147 148 **S** Banner Health,
Phoenix, AZ
Primary Contact: Lamont M. Yoder, R.N., MSN, FACHE, Chief Executive Officer
CFO: Derek Lythgoe, Chief Financial Officer
CMO: Paul Hurst M.D., Chief Medical Officer
CIO: Lori Matthews, Vice President, Information Technology System
CHR: Tiffany Werner, Senior Human Resource Business Partner
CNO: Kelley Kieffer, Chief Nursing Officer
Web address: www.bannerhealth.com/Locations/Arizona/Banner+Heart+Hospital/
Control: Other not–for–profit (including NFP Corporation) **Service**: Heart

**Staffed Beds: 111 Admissions: 4552 Census: 55 Births: 0 Total Expense
($000): 111151 Payroll Expense ($000): 28438 Personnel: 456**

CARDON CHILDREN'S MEDICAL CENTER See BANNER DESERT MEDICAL
CENTER

HACIENDA CHILDREN'S HOSPITAL (033303), 610 West Jerome Avenue,
Zip 85210; tel. 480/579–2400, (Nonreporting)
Primary Contact: William Timmons, President and Chief Executive Officer
Web address: www.haciendahealthcare.org/careproviders/hacienda–childrens–
hospital/
Control: Other not–for–profit (including NFP Corporation) **Service**: Children's
general medical and surgical

Staffed Beds: 24

⊞ **HEALTHSOUTH EAST VALLEY REHABILITATION HOSPITAL (033037)**, 5652
East Baseline Road, Zip 85206–4713; tel. 480/567–0350, (Nonreporting) **A**1 10
S HEALTHSOUTH Corporation, Birmingham, AL
Primary Contact: Jerry Gray, Interim Chief Executive Officer
CMO: Martin Yee M.D., Medical Director
CHR: Nancy Pickler, Director of Human Resources
CNO: Hope Dunn, Chief Nursing Officer
Web address: www.healthsoutheastvalley.com
Control: Corporation, Investor–owned (for–profit) **Service**: Rehabilitation

Staffed Beds: 60

★ ⇑ **MOUNTAIN VISTA MEDICAL CENTER (030121)**, 1301 South Crismon
Road, Zip 85209–3767; tel. 480/358–6100, (Nonreporting) **A**10 13 21 **S** IASIS
Healthcare, Franklin, TN
Primary Contact: Jacob Golich, Chief Executive Officer
CFO: Marty Bakos, Chief Financial Officer
CNO: Elizabeth Kearney R.N., Chief Nursing Officer
Web address: www.mvmedicalcenter.com
Control: Corporation, Investor–owned (for–profit) **Service**: General medical and
surgical

Staffed Beds: 172

Hospital, Medicare Provider Number, Address, Telephone, Approval, Facility, and Physician Codes, Health Care System

★ American Hospital Association (AHA) membership   ○ Healthcare Facilities Accreditation Program   ⇑ Center for Improvement in Healthcare Quality Accreditation
☐ The Joint Commission accreditation   ◇ DNV Healthcare Inc. accreditation   △ Commission on Accreditation of Rehabilitation Facilities (CARF) accreditation

© 2017 AHA Guide   *Many Facility Codes have changed. Please refer to the AHA Guide Code Chart.*   Hospitals **A31**

AZ

AZ

PROMISE HOSPITAL OF PHOENIX (032006), 433 East 6th Street, Zip 85203–7104; tel. 480/427–3000, (Nonreporting) **A**10 **S** Promise Healthcare, Boca Raton, FL
Primary Contact: Scott Floden, Chief Executive Officer
COO: Wendy Larson, Chief Clinical Officer
CFO: Theo Clark, Director Financial Services
CMO: Syed Shahryar M.D., Medical Director
CHR: Christie Brea, Manager Human Resources
Web address: www.promise–phoenix.com
Control: Corporation, Investor–owned (for–profit) **Service**: Acute long–term care hospital

Staffed Beds: 40

SAMARITAN BEHAVIORAL HEALTH CENTER–DESERT SAMARITAN MEDICAL CENTER See BANNER DESERT MEDICAL CENTER

NOGALES—Santa Cruz County

CARONDELET HOLY CROSS HOSPITAL (031313), 1171 West Target Range Road, Zip 85621–2415; tel. 520/285–3000, **A**1 3 10 18 **F**3 13 29 30 31 32 34 35 40 50 51 56 57 59 64 65 68 70 75 76 77 79 81 85 86 87 89 93 107 111 119 130 132 133 134 135 146 149 **S** TENET Healthcare Corporation, Dallas, TX
Primary Contact: Debbie Knapheide, MSN, Site Administrator, Chief Nursing Officer and Chief Operating Officer
COO: Debbie Knapheide MSN, Site Administrator, Chief Nursing Officer and Chief Operating Officer
CFO: Alan Strauss, Chief Financial Officer
CMO: Roy Farrell M.D., Chief Medical Officer
CNO: Debbie Knapheide MSN, Site Administrator, Chief Nursing Officer and Chief Operating Officer
Web address: www.carondelet.org
Control: Corporation, Investor–owned (for–profit) **Service**: General medical and surgical

Staffed Beds: 25 **Admissions:** 1085 **Census:** 6 **Outpatient Visits:** 48834 **Births:** 695 **Total Expense ($000):** 23396 **Payroll Expense ($000):** 11525 **Personnel:** 150

ORO VALLEY—Pima County

ORO VALLEY HOSPITAL (030114), 1551 East Tangerine Road, Zip 85755–6213; tel. 520/901–3500, (Nonreporting) **A**1 10 **S** Community Health Systems, Inc., Franklin, TN
Primary Contact: Jae Dale, Chief Executive Officer
CFO: Maurene Polashek, Chief Financial Officer
CNO: Julie Hunt R.N., MS, Chief Nursing Officer
Web address: www.orovalleyhospital.com
Control: Corporation, Investor–owned (for–profit) **Service**: General medical and surgical

Staffed Beds: 144

PAGE—Coconino County

PAGE HOSPITAL (031304), 501 North Navajo Drive, Zip 86040, Mailing Address: P.O.Box 1447, 86040–1447; tel. 928/645–2424, **A**1 10 18 **F**3 13 15 29 31 32 34 35 36 40 41 43 45 46 47 50 57 59 64 68 70 71 74 75 76 77 85 93 94 107 108 110 111 114 115 119 131 133 146 148 **S** Banner Health, Phoenix, AZ
Primary Contact: Brian Kellar, Chief Executive Officer
CFO: Darcy Robertson, Chief Financial Officer
CMO: Thomas Wood M.D., Chief Medical Officer
CIO: Paul Caldwell, Facility Coordinator Information Technology Customer Relations
CHR: Ed Franklin, Chief Human Resources Officer
CNO: Susan Eubanks, Chief Nursing Officer
Web address: www.bannerhealth.com/Locations/Arizona/Page+Hospital
Control: Other not–for–profit (including NFP Corporation) **Service**: General medical and surgical

Staffed Beds: 25 **Admissions:** 427 **Census:** 3 **Births:** 159 **Total Expense ($000):** 14250 **Payroll Expense ($000):** 7004 **Personnel:** 100

PARKER—La Paz County

LA PAZ REGIONAL HOSPITAL (031317), 1200 West Mohave Road, Zip 85344–6349; tel. 928/669–9201, (Nonreporting) **A**10 18
Primary Contact: Kevin Brown, Chief Executive Officer
CFO: Carl J. Flanagan, Chief Financial Officer
CMO: Jack Dunn M.D., Chief of Staff
CHR: Regina M Martinez, Director Human Resources
CNO: Maria Martinez, Chief Nursing Officer
Web address: www.lapazhospital.org
Control: Other not–for–profit (including NFP Corporation) **Service**: General medical and surgical

Staffed Beds: 25

U.S. PUBLIC HEALTH SERVICE INDIAN HOSPITAL (031307), 12033 Agency Road, Zip 85344–7718; tel. 928/669–2137, (Nonreporting) **A**1 10 18 **S** U. S. Indian Health Service, Rockville, MD
Primary Contact: Elizabeth Helsel, Chief Executive Officer
CFO: Robin Tahbo, Financial Management Officer
CMO: Laurence Norick M.D., Clinical Director
CIO: JayLynn Saavedra, Chief Information Officer
Web address: www.ihs.gov
Control: PHS, Indian Service, Government, federal **Service**: General medical and surgical

Staffed Beds: 20

PAYSON—Gila County

BANNER PAYSON MEDICAL CENTER (030033), 807 South Ponderosa Street, Zip 85541–5599; tel. 928/474–3222, **A**1 10 20 **F**3 11 13 15 18 26 27 29 30 31 34 35 40 45 46 48 50 57 59 62 64 66 70 74 75 76 77 79 81 85 89 90 93 97 107 108 109 110 111 114 119 127 130 131 145 146 149 **S** Banner Health, Phoenix, AZ
Primary Contact: Lance Porter, Chief Executive Officer
CFO: Peter Finelli, Chief Financial Officer
CMO: John Vandruff M.D., Chief of Staff
CIO: Nick Vandermeer, Director Information Systems
CHR: Shawn M. Thomas, Director Human Resources
CNO: Hart Hintze, Chief Nursing Officer
Web address: www.paysonhospital.com
Control: Corporation, Investor–owned (for–profit) **Service**: General medical and surgical

Staffed Beds: 44 **Admissions:** 1535 **Census:** 12 **Outpatient Visits:** 32613 **Births:** 148 **Total Expense ($000):** 45034 **Payroll Expense ($000):** 14259 **Personnel:** 250

PEORIA—Maricopa County

CURAHEALTH PHOENIX See CURAHEALTH PHOENIX, Phoenix

PERIDOT—Gila County

SAN CARLOS APACHE HEALTHCARE CORPORATION (030077), 103 Medicine Way Road, Zip 85542; tel. 928/475–1400, (Nonreporting) **A**1 10 **S** U. S. Indian Health Service, Rockville, MD
Primary Contact: Victoria D. Began, R.N., MS, President and Chief Executive Officer
CFO: Vivie Hosteenez, Chief Financial Officer
CMO: Douglas Brinkerhoff M.D., Clinical Director
CIO: Nimmy Mathews, Acting Director Quality Management
CHR: Shirley M Boni, Administrative Officer
Web address: www.ihs.gov
Control: PHS, Indian Service, Government, federal **Service**: General medical and surgical

Staffed Beds: 8

PHOENIX—Maricopa County

ABRAZO CENTRAL CAMPUS (030030), 2000 West Bethany Home Road, Zip 85015–2443; tel. 602/249–0212, (Nonreporting) **A**1 3 5 10 **S** TENET Healthcare Corporation, Dallas, TX
Primary Contact: Frank L. Molinaro, Chief Executive Officer
COO: Jayleen Casano Ph.D., FACHE, Chief Operations and Nursing Officer
CFO: Paul Hymel, Chief Financial Officer
CHR: Dana George, Chief Human Resources Officer
Web address: www.abrazohealth.com
Control: Corporation, Investor–owned (for–profit) **Service**: General medical and surgical

Staffed Beds: 215

ABRAZO MARYVALE CAMPUS (030001), 5102 West Campbell Avenue, Zip 85031–1799; tel. 623/848–5000, **A**1 10 **F**3 13 18 20 22 26 29 34 35 40 45 49 59 68 70 74 75 81 85 86 107 108 111 119 130 146 147 **S** TENET Healthcare Corporation, Dallas, TX
Primary Contact: Stan Holm, Chief Executive Officer
CFO: Julie Hastings–Smith, Associate Chief Financial Officer
CHR: Angela Giese, Chief Human Resource Officer
CNO: Scott David Morey, Chief Nursing Officer
Web address: www.maryvalehospital.com
Control: Corporation, Investor–owned (for–profit) **Service**: General medical and surgical

Staffed Beds: 78 **Admissions:** 3274 **Census:** 38 **Outpatient Visits:** 45962 **Births:** 0 **Total Expense ($000):** 43018 **Payroll Expense ($000):** 20782 **Personnel:** 356

Many Facility Codes have changed. Please refer to the AHA Guide Code Chart. © 2017 AHA Guide

AZ

⊞ **ABRAZO SCOTTSDALE CAMPUS (030083)**, 3929 East Bell Road, Zip 85032–2196; tel. 602/923–5000, (Nonreporting) **A**1 10 **S** TENET Healthcare Corporation, Dallas, TX
Primary Contact: Frank L. Molinaro, M.D., Chief Executive Officer
CFO: Jeffrey Zyla, Chief Financial Officer
CMO: David Tupponce M.D., Chief Medical Officer
CHR: Kendrick Russell, Chief Human Resources Officer
CNO: Vicki Lynn Huber R.N., MSN, Chief Nursing Officer
Web address: www.abrazoscottsdale.com
Control: Corporation, Investor–owned (for–profit) **Service:** General medical and surgical

Staffed Beds: 142

☐ **ARIZONA STATE HOSPITAL (034021)**, 2500 East Van Buren Street, Zip 85008–6079; tel. 602/244–1331, (Nonreporting) **A**1 3 10
Primary Contact: Aaron Bowen, Chief Executive Officer
COO: Donna Noriega, Chief Operating Officer
CFO: Donna Noriega, Chief Operating Officer
CMO: Steve Dingle M.D., Chief Medical Officer
CIO: Bruce Randolph, Chief Information Technology
CHR: Jeanine Decker, Manager Human Resources
Web address: www.hs.state.az.us
Control: State, Government, Nonfederal **Service:** Psychiatric

Staffed Beds: 299

⊞ △ **BANNER – UNIVERSITY MEDICAL CENTER PHOENIX (039802)**, 1111 East McDowell Road, Zip 85006–2666, Mailing Address: P.O.Box 2989, 85062–2989; tel. 602/239–2000, **A**1 3 5 7 8 10 **F**1 3 8 9 11 12 13 14 15 16 17 18 19 20 22 24 26 28 29 30 31 34 35 36 37 38 39 40 43 44 45 46 47 48 49 50 51 53 54 55 56 57 58 59 60 64 65 66 68 70 72 74 75 76 77 78 79 80 81 82 83 84 85 86 87 90 91 92 93 94 96 97 98 100 101 102 103 104 107 108 110 111 114 115 116 117 118 119 120 121 123 124 126 129 130 131 132 135 138 139 141 142 143 145 146 147 148 149 150 **S** Banner Health, Phoenix, AZ
Primary Contact: Steve Narang, M.D., Chief Executive Officer
CFO: Kathy Kotin, Chief Financial Officer
CMO: Paul Stander M.D., Chief Medical Officer
CIO: Michael S Warden, Senior Vice President Information Technology
CHR: Michael Fleming, Chief People Officer
Web address: www.bannerhealth.com/Locations/Arizona/Banner+Good+Samaritan+Medical+Center
Control: Other not–for–profit (including NFP Corporation) **Service:** General medical and surgical

Staffed Beds: 685 **Admissions:** 30925 **Census:** 480 **Outpatient Visits:** 113746 **Births:** 5707 **Total Expense ($000):** 727864 **Payroll Expense ($000):** 234418 **Personnel:** 3937

⊞ **BANNER ESTRELLA MEDICAL CENTER (030115)**, 9201 West Thomas Road, Zip 85037–3332; tel. 623/327–4000, **A**1 3 10 **F**3 5 11 12 13 18 20 22 24 28 29 30 31 34 35 36 37 38 40 41 43 44 45 46 49 50 51 57 58 59 60 61 64 68 73 74 75 76 77 78 79 81 82 85 86 87 96 102 107 108 111 114 115 119 126 130 131 132 135 144 145 146 147 148 149 **S** Banner Health, Phoenix, AZ
Primary Contact: Courtney Ophaug, FACHE, Chief Executive Officer
COO: Gary Foster R.N., Associate Administrator
CFO: Dean Shepardson, Chief Financial Officer
CHR: Wendy Labadie, Chief Human Resource Officer
CNO: Sheri Dahlstrom R.N., Chief Nursing Officer
Web address: www.bannerhealth.com/Locations/Arizona/Banner+Estrella+Medical+Center/
Control: Other not–for–profit (including NFP Corporation) **Service:** General medical and surgical

Staffed Beds: 269 **Admissions:** 15837 **Census:** 172 **Births:** 4553 **Total Expense ($000):** 250424 **Payroll Expense ($000):** 92438 **Personnel:** 1496

⊞ **CURAHEALTH PHOENIX (032000)**, 40 East Indianola Avenue, Zip 85012–2059; tel. 602/280–7000, (Nonreporting) (Includes CURAHEALTH PHOENIX, 13216 North Plaza Del Rio Boulevard, Peoria, Arizona, Zip 85381–4907, tel. 623/974–5463; Karen Shammas, Chief Executive Officer) **A**1 10 **S** Curahealth Hospitals, Garland, TX
Primary Contact: Karen Cawley, Chief Executive Officer
Web address: www.curahealth.com
Control: Corporation, Investor–owned (for–profit) **Service:** Acute long–term care hospital

Staffed Beds: 58

HAVEN SENIOR HORIZONS (034020), 1201 South 7th Avenue, Suite 200, Zip 85007–4076; tel. 623/236–2000, **A**10 **F**56 68 98 100 101 102 103 **P**5 **S** Haven Behavioral Healthcare, Nashville, TN
Primary Contact: Kathy Shaw, Chief Executive Officer
CHR: Erin McEldowney, Manager Human Resources
CNO: Char Ralstin, Director of Nursing
Web address: www.havenbehavioral.com
Control: Corporation, Investor–owned (for–profit) **Service:** Psychiatric

Staffed Beds: 45 **Admissions:** 980 **Census:** 36 **Outpatient Visits:** 0 **Births:** 0 **Personnel:** 92

★ ⇑ **HONORHEALTH DEER VALLEY MEDICAL CENTER (030092)**, 19829 North 27th Avenue, Zip 85027–4002; tel. 623/879–6100, (Nonreporting) **A**10 21 **S** HonorHealth, Scottsdale, AZ
Primary Contact: David Price, Chief Executive Officer
CMO: Mary Ann Turley D.O., Medical Director
CHR: Frank L Cummins, Vice President Human Resources
Web address: www.jcl.com
Control: Other not–for–profit (including NFP Corporation) **Service:** General medical and surgical

Staffed Beds: 204

★ ⇑ **HONORHEALTH JOHN C. LINCOLN MEDICAL CENTER (030014)**, 250 East Dunlap Avenue, Zip 85020–2825; tel. 602/943–2381, (Nonreporting) **A**3 10 13 21 **S** HonorHealth, Scottsdale, AZ
Primary Contact: Margaret Elizabeth. Griffin, Chief Executive Officer
CMO: Christopher Shearer M.D., Chief Medical Officer
CNO: Jelden Arcilla R.N., Vice President and Chief Nursing Officer
Web address: www.jcl.com
Control: Other not–for–profit (including NFP Corporation) **Service:** General medical and surgical

Staffed Beds: 262

LOS NINOS HOSPITAL (033301), 2303 East Thomas Road, Zip 85016–7827; tel. 602/954–7311, (Nonreporting) **A**10
Primary Contact: William Timmons, Chief Executive Officer
Web address: www.losninoshospital.com
Control: Other not–for–profit (including NFP Corporation) **Service:** Children's other specialty

Staffed Beds: 15

★ ⇑ **MARICOPA INTEGRATED HEALTH SYSTEM (030022)**, 2601 East Roosevelt Street, Zip 85008–4956; tel. 602/344–5011, (Nonreporting) (Includes ARIZONA CHILDREN'S CENTER, 2601 East Roosevelt Street, Phoenix, Arizona, Zip 85008–4973, tel. 602/344–5051) **A**3 5 8 10 21
Primary Contact: Stephen A. Purves, FACHE, President and Chief Executive Officer
COO: Kris Gaw, Executive Vice President and Chief Operating Officer
CFO: Kathleen Benaquista, Executive Vice President and Chief Financial Officer
CMO: John Hitt M.D., Executive Vice President and Chief Medical Officer
CIO: Kelly Summers, Chief Information Officer
CHR: Marshall Jones, Senior Vice President Human Resources
CNO: Sherry Stotler R.N., MSN, Chief Nursing Officer
Web address: www.mihs.org
Control: County, Government, Nonfederal **Service:** General medical and surgical

Staffed Beds: 522

⊞ **MAYO CLINIC HOSPITAL (039801)**, 5777 East Mayo Boulevard, Zip 85054–4502; tel. 480/342–2000, **A**1 2 3 5 8 10 **F**3 6 8 9 11 12 14 15 17 18 20 22 24 26 28 29 30 31 34 35 36 37 39 40 44 45 46 47 48 49 50 51 54 55 56 57 58 59 60 61 64 65 68 70 74 75 77 78 79 80 81 82 84 85 86 87 90 92 93 96 97 100 103 104 107 108 110 111 112 114 115 116 117 118 119 120 121 122 123 124 126 129 130 131 132 135 136 137 138 139 141 142 145 146 147 148 149 **P**6 **S** Mayo Clinic, Rochester, MN
Primary Contact: Wyatt Decker, Chief Executive Officer, Mayo Clinic in Arizona
CFO: Jeffrey R Froisland, Chief Financial Officer
CMO: Alyssa B Chapital M.D., Medical Director, Mayo Clinic Hospital
CIO: Paul Lenko, Section Head Information Technology
CHR: Nichelle A Baker, Chair Human Resources
CNO: Teresa Connolly R.N., Chief Nursing Officer
Web address: www.mayoclinic.org/arizona/
Control: Other not–for–profit (including NFP Corporation) **Service:** General medical and surgical

Staffed Beds: 268 **Admissions:** 14765 **Census:** 198 **Outpatient Visits:** 67643 **Births:** 0 **Personnel:** 3157

AZ

☐ **OASIS HOSPITAL (030131)**, 750 North 40th Street, Zip 85008–6486; tel. 602/797–7700, (Nonreporting) **A**1 3 10
Primary Contact: Tim Bogardus, Chief Executive Officer
Web address: www.oasishospital.com
Control: Partnership, Investor–owned (for–profit) **Service**: Orthopedic

Staffed Beds: 64

✠ **PHOENIX CHILDREN'S HOSPITAL (039804)**, 1919 East Thomas Road, Zip 85016–7710; tel. 602/933–1000, (Nonreporting) **A**1 3 5 10
Primary Contact: Robert L. Meyer, President and Chief Executive Officer
COO: Betsy Kuzas, Executive Vice President and Chief Operating Officer
CFO: Douglas Myers, Executive Vice President and Chief Financial Officer
CMO: H. Stacy Nicholson M.D., M.P.H., Physician in Chief
CIO: David Higginson, Executive Vice President and Chief Administrative Officer
CHR: Lisa Phelps, Senior Vice President, Human Resources
CNO: Julie Bowman, Senior Vice President, Patient Care and Chief Nursing Officer
Web address: www.phoenixchildrens.com
Control: Other not–for–profit (including NFP Corporation) **Service**: Children's general medical and surgical

Staffed Beds: 331

✠ **PHOENIX VETERANS AFFAIRS HEALTH CARE SYSTEM**, 650 East Indian School Road, Zip 85012–1892; tel. 602/277–5551, (Nonreporting) **A**1 3 5 **S** Department of Veterans Affairs, Washington, DC
Primary Contact: RimaAnn O. Nelson, R.N., Director
CFO: Christine Hollingsworth, Chief Financial Officer
CMO: Maureen McCarthy M.D., Chief of Staff
Web address: www.phoenix.va.gov/
Control: Veterans Affairs, Government, federal **Service**: General medical and surgical

Staffed Beds: 197

★ **QUAIL RUN BEHAVIORAL HEALTH (034031)**, 2545 West Quail Avenue, Zip 85027–2418; tel. 602/455–5700, (Nonreporting)
Primary Contact: David Carnahan, Chief Executive Officer
Web address: www.quailrunbehavioral.com/
Control: Other not–for–profit (including NFP Corporation) **Service**: Psychiatric

Staffed Beds: 102

✠ **SELECT SPECIALTY HOSPITAL–PHOENIX (032001)**, 350 West Thomas Road, 3rd Floor Main, Zip 85013–4409; tel. 602/406–6802, **A**1 10 **F**1 29 75 77 87 148 **S** Select Medical Corporation, Mechanicsburg, PA
Primary Contact: Sharon Anthony, Chief Executive Officer
Web address: www.phoenix.selectspecialtyhospitals.com/
Control: Corporation, Investor–owned (for–profit) **Service**: Acute long–term care hospital

Staffed Beds: 48 Admissions: 509 Census: 38 Outpatient Visits: 0 Births: 0 Total Expense ($000): 24120 Payroll Expense ($000): 10153

✠ **SELECT SPECIALTY HOSPITAL–PHOENIX DOWNTOWN (032005)**, 1012 East Wiletta Street, 4th Floor, Zip 85006; tel. 602/239–6134, (Nonreporting) **A**1 **S** Select Medical Corporation, Mechanicsburg, PA
Primary Contact: Sharon Anthony, Market Administrator
Web address: www.selectmedicalcorp.com
Control: Corporation, Investor–owned (for–profit) **Service**: Acute long–term care hospital

Staffed Beds: 33

✠ △ **ST. JOSEPH'S HOSPITAL AND MEDICAL CENTER (039803)**, 350 West Thomas Road, Zip 85013–4496, Mailing Address: P.O.Box 2071, 85001–2071; tel. 602/406–3000, (Includes CHILDREN'S HEALTH CENTER, 350 West Thomas Road, Phoenix, Arizona, Zip 85013–4409, tel. 602/344–5051; ST. JOSEPH'S WESTGATE MEDICAL CENTER, 7300 North 99th Avenue, Glendale, Arizona, Zip 85307–3003, tel. 602/406–0000) **A**1 2 3 5 7 8 10 **F**2 3 6 10 11 12 13 15 17 18 20 22 24 26 29 30 31 32 34 35 36 38 39 40 42 43 44 45 46 47 48 49 50 51 53 55 56 57 58 59 60 61 64 66 68 70 71 72 74 75 76 77 78 79 80 81 82 84 85 86 87 90 91 92 93 95 96 97 100 102 104 107 108 110 111 112 114 115 117 118 119 120 121 123 124 126 127 130 131 132 134 135 138 139 140 141 145 146 147 148 149 150 **P**6 **S** Dignity Health, San Francisco, CA
Primary Contact: Patty White, R.N., MS, President
CFO: Matthew Cox, Chief Financial Officer
CMO: Edward Donahue M.D., Chief Medical Officer
CHR: Maureen Sterbach, Vice President Human Resources
CNO: Julie Ward MSN, R.N., Chief Nursing Officer
Web address: www.stjosephs–phx.org
Control: Other not–for–profit (including NFP Corporation) **Service**: General medical and surgical

Staffed Beds: 573 Admissions: 30807 Census: 438 Outpatient Visits: 627883 Births: 4839 Total Expense ($000): 1094697 Payroll Expense ($000): 427133 Personnel: 4869

☐ **ST. LUKE'S BEHAVIORAL HEALTH CENTER (034013)**, 1800 East Van Buren, Zip 85006–3742; tel. 602/251–8546, (Nonreporting) **A**1 10 **S** IASIS Healthcare, Franklin, TN
Primary Contact: Gregory L. Jahn, R.N., Chief Executive Officer
CFO: Ruby Majhail, Chief Financial Officer
CMO: Mario Tafur M.D., Chief of Staff
CIO: Chris Ulrey, Director Management Information Systems
CHR: Amy M Howell, Director Human Resources
Web address: www.iasishealthcare.com
Control: Corporation, Investor–owned (for–profit) **Service**: Psychiatric

Staffed Beds: 85

★ ⇑ **ST. LUKE'S MEDICAL CENTER (030037)**, 1800 East Van Buren Street, Zip 85006–3742; tel. 602/251–8100, (Includes TEMPE ST. LUKE'S HOSPITAL, 1500 South Mill Avenue, Tempe, Arizona, Zip 85281–6699, tel. 480/784–5510; James Flinn, Chief Executive Officer) **A**3 10 21 **F**3 11 12 13 18 20 22 24 26 28 29 30 34 35 37 40 45 46 47 49 50 51 56 57 58 59 60 61 64 68 70 71 74 75 76 79 81 82 85 87 90 91 92 93 94 98 100 102 103 107 108 111 115 119 126 129 130 131 132 146 147 148 149 **S** IASIS Healthcare, Franklin, TN
Primary Contact: James Flinn, JD, FACHE, Chief Executive Officer
CFO: Ken Walsh, Chief Financial Officer
CHR: Trinise Thompson, Director Human Resources
Web address: www.stlukesmedcenter.com
Control: Corporation, Investor–owned (for–profit) **Service**: General medical and surgical

Staffed Beds: 283 Admissions: 8610 Census: 112 Outpatient Visits: 74331 Births: 427 Total Expense ($000): 182367 Payroll Expense ($000): 51692 Personnel: 896

☐ **THE CORE INSTITUTE SPECIALTY HOSPITAL (030108)**, 6501 North 19th Avenue, Zip 85015–1646; tel. 602/795–6020, (Nonreporting) **A**1 10
Primary Contact: Kurt Loveless, Chief Executive Officer
CFO: Barbara Chacon, Chief Financial Officer
CMO: Christopher A. Yeung M.D., Chief of Staff
CHR: Sherrie A Wagner, Manager Human Resources
CNO: Deborah Roberts R.N., Chief Nursing Officer
Web address: www.thecoreinstitutehospital.com/
Control: Corporation, Investor–owned (for–profit) **Service**: Surgical

Staffed Beds: 33

✠ **U.S. PUBLIC HEALTH SERVICE PHOENIX INDIAN MEDICAL CENTER (030078)**, 4212 North 16th Street, Zip 85016–5389; tel. 602/263–1200, (Nonreporting) **A**1 3 5 10 **S** U. S. Indian Health Service, Rockville, MD
Primary Contact: Rear Admiral Michael Weakhee, Chief Executive Officer
CFO: Geraldine Harney, Chief Financial Officer
CMO: Dave Civic M.D., Associate Director Clinical Services
CIO: Vina Montour, Director Information Technology
CHR: Betty Weston, Chief Human Resources Officer
Web address: www.ihs.gov
Control: PHS, Indian Service, Government, federal **Service**: General medical and surgical

Staffed Beds: 127

☐ **VALLEY HOSPITAL PHOENIX (034026)**, 3550 East Pinchot Avenue, Zip 85018–7434; tel. 602/957–4000, (Nonreporting) **A**1 10 **S** Universal Health Services, Inc., King of Prussia, PA
Primary Contact: Michelle David, Chief Executive Officer
Web address: www.valleyhospital–phoenix.com
Control: Corporation, Investor–owned (for–profit) **Service**: Psychiatric

Staffed Beds: 122

PRESCOTT—Yavapai County

✠ **NORTHERN ARIZONA VETERANS AFFAIRS HEALTH CARE SYSTEM**, 500 Highway 89 North, Zip 86313–5000; tel. 928/445–4860, (Nonreporting) **A**1 **S** Department of Veterans Affairs, Washington, DC
Primary Contact: Malcolm Keith. Piatt, M.D., Interim Director
COO: James Belmont, Associate Director
CFO: Ame Callahan, Acting Manager Resource Management Service
CMO: A Panneer Selvam M.D., Chief of Staff
CIO: Scott McCrimmon, Manager Information Technology
CHR: Jane Lewerke, Manager Human Resources
Web address: www.prescott.va.gov/
Control: Veterans Affairs, Government, federal **Service**: General medical and surgical

Staffed Beds: 147

Many Facility Codes have changed. Please refer to the AHA Guide Code Chart. © 2017 AHA Guide

★ **YAVAPAI REGIONAL MEDICAL CENTER (030012)**, 1003 Willow Creek Road,
Zip 86301–1668; tel. 928/445–2700, **A**10 **F**3 11 15 17 18 20 22 24 26 28 29
30 31 32 34 35 40 45 46 50 53 54 57 59 60 64 68 70 71 74 75 77 78 79 81
82 84 85 86 87 91 93 107 108 111 114 118 119 130 131 132 135 146 148 **P**6
Primary Contact: John Amos, President and Chief Executive Officer
COO: Larry P Burns Jr, Chief Operating Officer
CFO: Lee Livin, Chief Financial Officer
CMO: Joseph Goldberger M.D., Chief Medical Officer
CHR: Mark Timm, Executive Director Human Resources
CNO: Diane Drexler R.N., Chief Nursing Officer
Web address: www.yrmc.org
Control: Other not–for–profit (including NFP Corporation) **Service:** General
medical and surgical

Staffed Beds: 134 **Admissions:** 6910 **Census:** 66 **Outpatient Visits:**
103449 **Births:** 0 **Total Expense ($000):** 193470 **Payroll Expense ($000):**
62676 **Personnel:** 890

PRESCOTT VALLEY—Yavapai County

☐ **MOUNTAIN VALLEY REGIONAL REHABILITATION HOSPITAL (033036)**, 3700
North Windsong Drive, Zip 86314–1253; tel. 928/759–8800, (Nonreporting) **A**1
10 **S** Ernest Health, Inc., Albuquerque, NM
Primary Contact: Judy Baum, Chief Executive Officer
CFO: Mark A. Roth, Chief Financial Officer
CMO: Alan S. Berman M.D., Medical Director
CHR: Troy Eagar, Director Human Resources
CNO: Leah Walters R.N., Director of Nursing
Web address: www.mvrrh.ernesthealth.com
Control: Corporation, Investor–owned (for–profit) **Service:** Rehabilitation

Staffed Beds: 16

WINDHAVEN PSYCHIATRIC HOSPITAL (034025), 3347 North Windsong Drive,
Zip 86314–2283, Mailing Address: 3343 North Windsong Drive, 86314–1213;
tel. 928/445–5211, (Nonreporting) **A**10
Primary Contact: Larry D. Green Jr, Chief Executive Officer
COO: Pamela Pierce, Deputy Chief Executive Officer
CFO: Doug Oliver, Chief Financial Officer
CMO: Shane Russell–Jenkins M.D., Medical Director
CIO: Laura Norman, Chief Development and Information Officer
CHR: Pamela Pierce, Deputy Chief Executive Officer
CNO: Esther Grear, Director Hospital Social Work and Assistant Hospital
Administrator
Web address: www.wygc.org
Control: Other not–for–profit (including NFP Corporation) **Service:** Psychiatric

Staffed Beds: 16

★ **YAVAPAI REGIONAL MEDICAL CENTER – EAST (030118)**, 7700 East
Florentine Road, Zip 86314–2245; tel. 928/445–2700, **A**10 **F**3 11 13 15 29 30
31 40 68 70 72 75 76 77 78 81 84 85 86 87 89 93 107 108 111 114 116 117
118 119 130 146 147 148
Primary Contact: John Amos, Chief Executive Officer
CFO: Lee Livin, Chief Financial Officer
CMO: Joseph Goldberger M.D., Chief Medical Officer
CHR: Mark Timm, Executive Director Human Resources
CNO: Diane Drexler R.N., Chief Nursing Officer
Web address: www.yrmc.org
Control: Other not–for–profit (including NFP Corporation) **Service:** General
medical and surgical

Staffed Beds: 72 **Admissions:** 4218 **Census:** 31 **Outpatient Visits:** 85174
Births: 1035 **Total Expense ($000):** 55243 **Payroll Expense ($000):** 26688
Personnel: 398

SACATON—Pinal County

☐ **HUHUKAM MEMORIAL HOSPITAL (031308)**, 483 West Seed Farm Road,
Zip 85147, Mailing Address: P.O.Box 38, 85147–0001; tel. 602/528–1200,
(Nonreporting) **A**1 3 10 18
Primary Contact: Lorrie Henderson, Ph.D., Chief Executive Officer
COO: Pamela Thompson, Chief Operations Officer
CMO: Noel Habib M.D., Chief Medical Officer
CHR: Michael Freeman, Director Human Resources
Web address: www.grhc.org
Control: Other not–for–profit (including NFP Corporation) **Service:** General
medical and surgical

Staffed Beds: 12

SAFFORD—Graham County

★ **MT. GRAHAM REGIONAL MEDICAL CENTER (030068)**, 1600 South 20th
Avenue, Zip 85546–4097; tel. 928/348–4000, **A**3 10 20 **F**3 11 13 15 18 29 30
31 34 35 40 43 45 46 47 48 49 50 57 59 63 64 66 70 75 77 78 79 81 84 85
97 107 108 110 111 114 119 127 129 130 132 133 135 146 147 148 **P**6
Primary Contact: Mark E. Marchetti, President and Chief Executive Officer
CFO: Keith Bryce, Vice President Finance and Chief Financial Officer
CIO: Anthon Ellsworth, Director Information Technology
CHR: Irvan Wick"" Lewis, Vice President Human Resources
CNO: Lori Burress, Vice President Patient Services and Chief Nursing Officer
Web address: www.mtgraham.org
Control: Hospital district or authority, Government, Nonfederal **Service:** General
medical and surgical

Staffed Beds: 49 **Admissions:** 1340 **Census:** 13 **Outpatient Visits:** 69673
Births: 617 **Total Expense ($000):** 55660 **Payroll Expense ($000):** 24189
Personnel: 376

SAN TAN VALLEY—Pinal County

⊞ **BANNER IRONWOOD MEDICAL CENTER (030130)**, 37000 North Gantzel
Road, Zip 85140–7303; tel. 480/394–4000, **A**1 10 **F**3 11 13 29 34 40 43
49 50 51 65 68 70 73 76 77 79 85 87 107 111 115 119 130 146 **S** Banner
Health, Phoenix, AZ
Primary Contact: Sharon Lind, MSN, FACHE, Chief Executive Officer
CFO: Tracy French, Chief Financial Officer
CMO: Darren West M.D., Interim Chief Medical Officer
CHR: Janine Polito, Chief Human Resources Officer
CNO: Terresa Ann Paulus, Chief Nursing Officer
Web address: www.bannerhealth.com/Locations/Arizona/Banner+Ironwood/
Control: Other not–for–profit (including NFP Corporation) **Service:** General
medical and surgical

Staffed Beds: 53 **Admissions:** 2574 **Census:** 22 **Births:** 921 **Total Expense
($000):** 64383 **Payroll Expense ($000):** 20450 **Personnel:** 373

SCOTTSDALE—Maricopa County

⊞ **BANNER BEHAVIORAL HEALTH HOSPITAL – SCOTTSDALE (034004)**, 7575
East Earll Drive, Zip 85251–6915; tel. 480/941–7500, **A**1 3 10 **F**5 29 30 34
35 38 44 50 54 57 68 75 86 87 98 99 101 102 104 130 132 134 135 146 **S**
Banner Health, Phoenix, AZ
Primary Contact: Brian Beutin, MS, Chief Executive Officer
CFO: Michael A. Cimino Jr, Chief Financial Officer
CMO: Gagandeep Singh M.D., Chief Medical Officer Behavioral Health
CHR: Zsaber Gere, Chief Human Resource Officer
CNO: Cherri Anderson, Chief Nursing Officer
Web address: www.bannerhealth.com/Locations/Arizona/
Banner+Behavioral+Health
Control: Other not–for–profit (including NFP Corporation) **Service:** Psychiatric

Staffed Beds: 60 **Admissions:** 2981 **Census:** 57 **Births:** 0 **Total Expense
($000):** 31285 **Payroll Expense ($000):** 14871 **Personnel:** 311

⊞ **HEALTHSOUTH SCOTTSDALE REHABILITATION HOSPITAL (033025)**, 9630
East Shea Boulevard, Zip 85260–6267; tel. 480/551–5400, (Nonreporting) **A**1 10
S HEALTHSOUTH Corporation, Birmingham, AL
Primary Contact: Kenneth Bell, Chief Executive Officer
CFO: Lisa Barrick, Controller
CMO: Keith W Cunningham M.D., Medical Director
CHR: Mary Beth Giczi, Director Human Resources
CNO: Diane M Caruso MSN, Chief Nursing Officer
Web address: www.healthsouthscottsdale.com
Control: Corporation, Investor–owned (for–profit) **Service:** Rehabilitation

Staffed Beds: 60

⊞ **HONORHEALTH REHABILITATION HOSPITAL (033038)**, 8850 East Pima
Center Parkway, Zip 85258–4619; tel. 480/800–3900, (Nonreporting) **A**1 10 **S**
Select Medical Corporation, Mechanicsburg, PA
Primary Contact: Scott R. Keen, Chief Executive Officer
Web address: www.scottsdale–rehab.com/
Control: Partnership, Investor–owned (for–profit) **Service:** Rehabilitation

Staffed Beds: 50

Hospital, Medicare Provider Number, Address, Telephone, Approval, Facility, and Physician Codes, Health Care System

★ American Hospital Association (AHA) membership   ○ Healthcare Facilities Accreditation Program   ⇑ Center for Improvement in Healthcare Quality Accreditation
☐ The Joint Commission accreditation   ◇ DNV Healthcare Inc. accreditation   △ Commission on Accreditation of Rehabilitation Facilities (CARF) accreditation

AZ

★ ⇑ **HONORHEALTH SCOTTSDALE OSBORN MEDICAL CENTER (030038)**, 7400 East Osborn Road, Zip 85251–6403; tel. 480/882–4000, (Nonreporting) **A**2 3 5 8 10 21 **S** HonorHealth, Scottsdale, AZ
Primary Contact: Kimberly Post, Senior Vice President and Chief Executive Officer
CMO: James Burke M.D., Senior Vice President and Chief Medical Officer
CIO: James R Cramer, Vice President and Chief Information Officer
Web address: www.shc.org
Control: Other not–for–profit (including NFP Corporation) **Service**: General medical and surgical

Staffed Beds: 347

★ ⇑ **HONORHEALTH SCOTTSDALE SHEA MEDICAL CENTER (030087)**, 9003 East Shea Boulevard, Zip 85260–6771; tel. 480/323–3000, (Nonreporting) **A**2 3 5 10 21 **S** HonorHealth, Scottsdale, AZ
Primary Contact: Gary E. Baker, Senior Vice President and Chief Executive Officer
CMO: James Burke M.D., Senior Vice President and Chief Medical Officer
CIO: James R Cramer, Vice President and Chief Information Officer
Web address: www.shc.org
Control: Other not–for–profit (including NFP Corporation) **Service**: General medical and surgical

Staffed Beds: 409

★ ⇑ **HONORHEALTH SCOTTSDALE THOMPSON PEAK MEDICAL CENTER (030123)**, 7400 East Thompson Peak Parkway, Zip 85255–4109; tel. 480/324–7000, **A**3 10 21 **F**3 5 20 22 24 26 29 30 31 34 35 37 40 45 46 49 50 51 57 58 59 70 77 78 79 81 82 107 110 111 112 119 126 130 131 132 133 134 135 143 144 145 146 147 148 149 150 **S** HonorHealth, Scottsdale, AZ
Primary Contact: David Price, Chief Executive Officer
COO: Bruce Pearson, Senior Vice President and Chief Operating Officer
CFO: Alice H Pope, Chief Financial Officer
CMO: Stephanie Jackson M.D., Vice President and Chief Medical Officer
CIO: Charles Scully, Chief Information Officer
CHR: Wendy Crawford, Chief Human Resource Officer
CNO: Kimberly Post, Senior Vice President and Chief Clinical Officer
Web address: www.shc.org
Control: Other not–for–profit (including NFP Corporation) **Service**: General medical and surgical

Staffed Beds: 92 **Admissions:** 6115 **Census:** 55 **Outpatient Visits:** 29961 **Births:** 0 **Total Expense ($000):** 108835 **Payroll Expense ($000):** 40018 **Personnel:** 516

⇑ **SCOTTSDALE LIBERTY HOSPITAL**, 17500 North Perimeter Drive, Zip 85255–7808; tel. 480/586–2300, (Nonreporting) **A**21 **S** Nobilis Health Corporation, Houston, TX
Primary Contact: Steven M. Siwek, M.D., President and Chief Executive Officer
COO: Michael Adams, Chief Operating Officer
CFO: Douglas B Kell, Chief Financial Officer
CMO: Natalie Shand M.D., Vice President Integrative Medicine and Chief Medical Officer
CIO: Milad Najjar, Information Technology
CHR: Samantha Mendez, Human Resources
CNO: Jani Manseau, Vice President Operations and Chief Nursing Officer
Web address: www.freedompainhospital.com
Control: Corporation, Investor–owned (for–profit) **Service**: Other specialty treatment

Staffed Beds: 12

SELLS—Pima County

⊞ **U.S. PUBLIC HEALTH SERVICE INDIAN HOSPITAL–SELLS (030074)**, Highway 86 & Topawa Road, Zip 85634, Mailing Address: P.O.Box 548, 85634–0548; tel. 520/383–7251, (Nonreporting) **A**1 10 **S** U. S. Indian Health Service, Rockville, MD
Primary Contact: Angela Fallon, Acting Chief Executive Officer
COO: Diane Shanley, Deputy Service Unit Director
CFO: Vivian Draper, Chief Financial Officer
CMO: Peter Ziegler M.D., Acting Chief Medical Officer
CIO: Karen Wade, Chief Information Officer
CNO: Donna Hobbs, Nurse Executive
Web address: www.ihs.gov
Control: PHS, Indian Service, Government, federal **Service**: General medical and surgical

Staffed Beds: 12

SHOW LOW—Navajo County

★ **SUMMIT HEALTHCARE REGIONAL MEDICAL CENTER (030062)**, 2200 East Show Low Lake Road, Zip 85901–7800; tel. 928/537–4375, **A**3 10 20 **F**11 13 15 18 20 22 28 29 30 31 32 34 35 36 38 40 41 43 45 46 47 53 54 57 59 62 64 65 68 70 71 73 75 76 77 78 79 81 82 84 91 92 93 97 107 108 110 111 114 115 118 119 121 127 129 130 131 132 135 146 147 148 149 **P**4 6
Primary Contact: Ronald L. McArthur, Chief Executive Officer
COO: Doug Gilchrist, Chief Operating Officer
CFO: David Rothenberger, Chief Financial Officer
CMO: Alan Neil DeWitt, Chief Medical Officer
CIO: Aaron Young, Chief Information Officer
CHR: Connie Kakavas, Chief Human Resources Officer
CNO: Cynthia Ebert–Loomis R.N., Chief Nursing Officer
Web address: www.summithealthcare.net
Control: Other not–for–profit (including NFP Corporation) **Service**: General medical and surgical

Staffed Beds: 89 **Admissions:** 4448 **Census:** 35 **Outpatient Visits:** 64817 **Births:** 964 **Total Expense ($000):** 159754 **Payroll Expense ($000):** 65561

SIERRA VISTA—Cochise County

☐ **CANYON VISTA MEDICAL CENTER (030043)**, 5700 East Highway 90, Zip 85635–9110; tel. 520/263–2000, **A**1 10 13 20 **F**3 13 15 18 20 22 24 26 28 29 30 31 34 35 40 43 44 45 51 57 59 60 61 63 64 70 72 74 75 76 77 79 80 81 85 93 94 96 98 100 103 107 108 109 111 114 115 118 119 120 122 123 130 131 145 146 147 148 **P**6 **S** RCCH HealthCare Partners, Brentwood, TN
Primary Contact: Randy Anderson, Chief Executive Officer
COO: Ashley L. Johnson, Chief Operations Officer
CIO: Jorge Moreno, Director Information Technology Operations
CHR: Traci Meyer, Director Human Resources
Web address: www.canyonvistamedicalcenter.com/
Control: Corporation, Investor–owned (for–profit) **Service**: General medical and surgical

Staffed Beds: 100 **Admissions:** 5633 **Census:** 56 **Outpatient Visits:** 106274 **Births:** 1033 **Total Expense ($000):** 102228 **Payroll Expense ($000):** 35559 **Personnel:** 602

SPRINGERVILLE—Apache County

WHITE MOUNTAIN REGIONAL MEDICAL CENTER (031315), 118 South Mountain Avenue, Zip 85938–5104; tel. 928/333–4368, (Nonreporting) **A**10 18
Primary Contact: Gregory J. Was, CPA, Chief Executive Officer
CFO: James Hamblin, Chief Financial Officer
CMO: Scott Hamblin M.D., President Medical Staff
Web address: www.wmrmc.com
Control: Other not–for–profit (including NFP Corporation) **Service**: General medical and surgical

Staffed Beds: 20

SUN CITY—Maricopa County

⊞ **BANNER BOSWELL MEDICAL CENTER (030061)**, 10401 West Thunderbird Blvd, Zip 85351–3004, Mailing Address: P.O.Box 1690, 85372–1690; tel. 623/832–4000, (Total facility includes 78 beds in nursing home–type unit) **A**1 2 3 10 **F**3 11 15 17 18 20 22 24 26 28 29 30 31 34 35 36 37 40 41 44 45 46 49 50 51 53 56 57 58 59 60 61 63 64 65 69 70 74 75 78 79 81 84 85 86 87 90 91 92 93 94 96 100 107 108 110 111 114 115 117 119 120 121 124 126 128 130 131 132 135 141 143 145 146 147 148 **S** Banner Health, Phoenix, AZ
Primary Contact: Debbie Flores, Interim Chief Executive Officer
CFO: Jeremy Williams, Chief Financial Officer
CMO: Kathryn Perkins M.D., Chief Medical Officer
CHR: Brenda Dietrich, Chief Human Resources Officer
Web address: www.bannerhealth.com/locations/sun-city/banner-boswell-medical-center
Control: Other not–for–profit (including NFP Corporation) **Service**: General medical and surgical

Staffed Beds: 437 **Admissions:** 14730 **Census:** 234 **Births:** 0 **Total Expense ($000):** 298676 **Payroll Expense ($000):** 106819 **Personnel:** 1864

Many Facility Codes have changed. Please refer to the AHA Guide Code Chart. © 2017 AHA Guide

AZ

SUN CITY WEST—Maricopa County

☒ **BANNER DEL E. WEBB MEDICAL CENTER (030093)**, 14502 West Meeker Boulevard, Zip 85375–5299; tel. 623/524–4000, **A1** 3 10 **F3** 4 5 9 13 15 18 20 22 28 29 30 31 34 35 36 37 39 40 41 43 44 45 46 47 48 49 50 51 56 57 58 59 60 61 64 65 68 70 74 75 76 77 78 79 80 81 82 84 85 86 87 90 91 92 93 94 96 98 100 102 103 104 105 107 108 110 111 114 115 118 119 126 130 131 132 135 145 146 147 148 **S** Banner Health, Phoenix, AZ
Primary Contact: Debbie Flores, Chief Executive Officer
COO: Nathan Shinagawa, Chief Operating Officer
CFO: Dan Stimpson, Chief Financial Officer
CMO: Scott Anderson, Chief Medical Officer
CHR: Carole Smith, Senior Human Resource Business Partner
CNO: Nancy Adamson, Chief Nursing Officer
Web address: www.bannerhealth.com/Locations/Arizona/Banner+Del+Webb+Medical+Center/
Control: Other not–for–profit (including NFP Corporation) **Service:** General medical and surgical

Staffed Beds: 365 **Admissions:** 16112 **Census:** 213 **Births:** 1791 **Total Expense ($000):** 263043 **Payroll Expense ($000):** 94386 **Personnel:** 1711

SURPRISE—Maricopa County

COBALT REHABILITATION HOSPITAL (033039), 13060 West Bell Road, Zip 85378–1200; tel. 623/499–9100, (Data for 347 days) **F28** 29 54 65 75 77 90 91 95 96 100 145 **P5**
Primary Contact: Sharon Noe, Chief Executive Officer
Web address: www.colbaltrehab.com
Control: Corporation, Investor–owned (for–profit) **Service:** Rehabilitation

Staffed Beds: 40 **Admissions:** 461 **Census:** 17 **Outpatient Visits:** 2334 **Births:** 0 **Total Expense ($000):** 12225 **Payroll Expense ($000):** 4526 **Personnel:** 95

TEMPE—Maricopa County

☐ **AURORA BEHAVIORAL HEALTH SYSTEM EAST (034028)**, 6350 South Maple Street, Zip 85283–2857; tel. 480/345–5400, (Nonreporting) **A1** 10 **S** Signature Healthcare Services, Corona, CA
Primary Contact: Bruce Waldo, Chief Executive Officer
CFO: Rebekah Francis JD, Chief Financial Officer
CMO: Jason Friday M.D., Medical Director
CHR: Vicki Thomsen, Director Human Resources
Web address: www.auroraarizona.com
Control: Partnership, Investor–owned (for–profit) **Service:** Psychiatric

Staffed Beds: 70

TUBA CITY—Coconino County

☒ **TUBA CITY REGIONAL HEALTH CARE CORPORATION (030073)**, 167 Main Street, Zip 86045–0611, Mailing Address: P.O.Box 600, 86045–0600; tel. 928/283–2501, (Nonreporting) **A1** 3 5 10
Primary Contact: Lynette Bonar, FACHE, R.N., Chief Executive Officer
CFO: Christine Keyonnie CPA, Chief Financial Officer
CMO: Holly Van Dyk M.D., Interim Chief Medical Officer
CIO: Shawn Davis, Chief Information Officer
CHR: George Hunter, Interim Chief Human Resources Officer
CNO: Alvina Rosales R.N., Chief Nursing Officer
Web address: www.tchealth.org
Control: Other not–for–profit (including NFP Corporation) **Service:** General medical and surgical

Staffed Beds: 53

TUCSON—Pima County

☒ **BANNER – UNIVERSITY MEDICAL CENTER SOUTH (030111)**, 2800 East Ajo Way, Zip 85713–6289; tel. 520/874–2000, **A1** 3 5 10 **F3** 11 18 20 22 29 30 34 35 38 40 43 45 47 48 49 50 51 54 56 57 58 59 60 61 64 65 67 68 70 71 74 75 77 79 81 82 84 85 86 87 93 97 98 99 100 101 102 103 104 107 108 111 114 115 119 130 131 135 146 148 149 **S** Banner Health, Phoenix, AZ
Primary Contact: Thomas C. Dickson, Chief Executive Officer
COO: Sarah Frost, Administrator and Chief Operating Officer
CFO: Jeff Buehrle, Chief Financial Officer
CMO: David Sheinbein, Chief Medical Officer
CIO: Ryan K Smith, Senior Vice President Information Technology
CHR: Jennifer L Sherwood, Division, Human Resource Business Partner
CNO: Cathy Townsend, Chief Nursing Officer
Web address: www.bannerhealth.com
Control: Other not–for–profit (including NFP Corporation) **Service:** General medical and surgical

Staffed Beds: 167 **Admissions:** 7365 **Census:** 105 **Births:** 0 **Total Expense ($000):** 153230 **Payroll Expense ($000):** 51161 **Personnel:** 894

☒ **BANNER – UNIVERSITY MEDICAL CENTER TUCSON (039800)**, 1501 North Campbell Avenue, Zip 85724–5128; tel. 520/694–0111, (Includes DIAMOND CHILDREN'S HOSPITAL, 1501 North Campbell Avenue, Tucson, Arizona, Zip 85724–0001, tel. 520/694–0111) **A1** 2 3 5 8 10 **F3** 11 12 13 15 16 18 19 20 21 22 23 24 25 26 27 28 29 30 31 34 35 40 41 43 45 46 47 49 50 51 53 54 55 56 57 58 59 60 61 64 65 67 68 70 71 72 74 75 76 77 78 79 80 81 82 84 85 86 87 88 89 92 93 97 100 104 107 108 110 111 114 115 116 117 118 119 120 121 123 124 126 129 130 131 132 135 136 137 138 139 140 141 145 146 147 148 149 **S** Banner Health, Phoenix, AZ
Primary Contact: Thomas C. Dickson, Chief Executive Officer
COO: Sarah Frost, Chief Operating Officer and Administrator, University of Arizona Medical Center – South Campus
CFO: Misty Hansen, Chief Financial Officer
CMO: Andreas Theodorou, Chief Medical Officer
CIO: Dan Critchley, Chief Information Officer
CHR: John Marques, Vice President Human Resources
Web address: www.uahealth.com
Control: Other not–for–profit (including NFP Corporation) **Service:** General medical and surgical

Staffed Beds: 421 **Admissions:** 22006 **Census:** 349 **Births:** 1715 **Total Expense ($000):** 723792 **Payroll Expense ($000):** 201066 **Personnel:** 3375

☒ **CARONDELET ST. JOSEPH'S HOSPITAL (030011)**, 350 North Wilmot Road, Zip 85711–2678; tel. 520/873–3000, **A1** 5 10 **F3** 5 12 13 18 20 22 28 29 30 31 34 35 38 40 44 45 46 47 49 50 57 59 60 61 64 68 69 70 72 74 75 76 77 78 79 81 82 83 84 85 86 87 90 92 93 98 100 101 102 103 104 105 107 108 114 115 118 119 126 129 130 132 135 145 146 147 148 **S** TENET Healthcare Corporation, Dallas, TX
Primary Contact: Mark A. Benz, President and Chief Executive Officer
CFO: Alan Strauss, Chief Financial Officer
CMO: Donald Denmark M.D., Chief Medical Officer
CIO: Sally Zambrello, Chief Information Officer
CHR: Igor Shegolev, Vice President Human Resources
CNO: Robin Conklin R.N., Chief Nursing Officer
Web address: www.carondelet.org
Control: Corporation, Investor–owned (for–profit) **Service:** General medical and surgical

Staffed Beds: 486 **Admissions:** 15459 **Census:** 191 **Outpatient Visits:** 90742 **Births:** 2382 **Total Expense ($000):** 230781 **Payroll Expense ($000):** 82752 **Personnel:** 1267

☒ **CARONDELET ST. MARY'S HOSPITAL (030010)**, 1601 West St Mary's Road, Zip 85745–2682; tel. 520/872–3000, **A1** 5 10 **F3** 15 17 18 20 22 24 26 28 29 30 31 34 38 40 44 45 46 47 49 50 51 53 56 57 58 59 60 61 63 64 68 70 74 77 78 79 81 82 84 85 87 90 92 93 96 98 100 101 102 103 107 108 110 111 114 115 118 119 129 130 131 132 146 148 149 **S** TENET Healthcare Corporation, Dallas, TX
Primary Contact: Amy Beiter, M.D., President and Chief Executive Officer
CMO: Donald Denmark M.D., Chief Medical Officer
Web address: www.carondelet.org
Control: Corporation, Investor–owned (for–profit) **Service:** General medical and surgical

Staffed Beds: 300 **Admissions:** 11299 **Census:** 170 **Outpatient Visits:** 118162 **Births:** 0 **Total Expense ($000):** 198683 **Payroll Expense ($000):** 79262 **Personnel:** 1170

☐ **CHG HOSPITAL TUCSON, LLC (032004)**, 7220 East Rosewood Drive, Zip 85710–1350; tel. 520/546–4595, (Nonreporting) **A1** 10 **S** Cornerstone Healthcare Group, Dallas, TX
Primary Contact: Vanessa Acevedo, Interim Chief Executive Officer
CFO: Kurt Schultz, Group Chief Financial Officer
CMO: Haroon Haque M.D., Medical Director
CIO: Adam Davis, Director Information Technology
CHR: Deborah Darcy, Human Resources
CNO: Jose' Sanchez, Chief Nursing Officer
Web address: www.chghospitals.com
Control: Corporation, Investor–owned (for–profit) **Service:** Acute long–term care hospital

Staffed Beds: 34

☒ **CURAHEALTH TUCSON (032002)**, 355 North Wilmot Road, Zip 85711–2601; tel. 520/584–4500, (Nonreporting) **A1** 10 **S** Curahealth Hospitals, Garland, TX
Primary Contact: Camie Overton, Chief Executive Officer
CMO: Sunil Natrajan M.D., Medical Director
CNO: Globert Empedrad, Chief Clinical Officer
Web address: www.curahealth.com
Control: Corporation, Investor–owned (for–profit) **Service:** Acute long–term care hospital

Staffed Beds: 51

Hospital, Medicare Provider Number, Address, Telephone, Approval, Facility, and Physician Codes, Health Care System

★ American Hospital Association (AHA) membership   ○ Healthcare Facilities Accreditation Program   ⇑ Center for Improvement in Healthcare Quality Accreditation
☐ The Joint Commission accreditation   ◇ DNV Healthcare Inc. accreditation   △ Commission on Accreditation of Rehabilitation Facilities (CARF) accreditation

AZ

✠ **HEALTHSOUTH REHABILITATION HOSPITAL OF SOUTHERN ARIZONA (033029)**, 1921 West Hospital Drive, Zip 85704–7806; tel. 520/742–2800, (Nonreporting) **A**1 10 **S** HEALTHSOUTH Corporation, Birmingham, AL
Primary Contact: Timothy T. Poore, Chief Executive Officer
CFO: Kaleigh Hotchkiss, Controller
CMO: Susan R. Bulen M.D., Medical Director
CHR: Neil Cullen, Director Human Resources
CNO: Virginia Ragonese–Green, Chief Nursing Officer
Web address: www.healthsouthsouthernarizona.com
Control: Corporation, Investor–owned (for–profit) **Service:** Rehabilitation

Staffed Beds: 60

✠ **HEALTHSOUTH REHABILITATION INSTITUTE OF TUCSON (033028)**, 2650 North Wyatt Drive, Zip 85712–6108; tel. 520/325–1300, **A**1 3 5 10 **F**29 34 35 62 90 93 96 130 132 **S** HEALTHSOUTH Corporation, Birmingham, AL
Primary Contact: Jeffrey Christensen, Chief Executive Officer
CFO: Mary Donovan, Controller
CMO: Jon Larson M.D., Medical Director
CHR: Dawn Mosier, Director Human Resources
Web address: www.rehabinstituteoftucson.com
Control: Corporation, Investor–owned (for–profit) **Service:** Rehabilitation

Staffed Beds: 80 **Admissions:** 1443 **Census:** 51 **Outpatient Visits:** 0 **Births:** 0 **Total Expense ($000):** 19099 **Payroll Expense ($000):** 10448 **Personnel:** 173

✠ **NORTHWEST MEDICAL CENTER (030085)**, 6200 North La Cholla Boulevard, Zip 85741–3599; tel. 520/742–9000, (Nonreporting) **A**1 5 10 **S** Community Health Systems, Inc., Franklin, TN
Primary Contact: Kevin Stockton, Chief Executive Officer
CFO: Ronald Patrick, Chief Financial Officer
CIO: David Bullock, Director Information Services
CNO: Kay Stubbs, Chief Nursing Officer
Web address: www.northwestmedicalcenter.com
Control: Corporation, Investor–owned (for–profit) **Service:** General medical and surgical

Staffed Beds: 270

PALO VERDE BEHAVIORAL HEALTH (034030), 2695 North Craycroft Road, Zip 85712–2244; tel. 520/322–2888, (Nonreporting) **A**3 5 10 **S** Universal Health Services, Inc., King of Prussia, PA
Primary Contact: Melissa Eckstein, Chief Executive Officer
CFO: Richard N England, Chief Financial Officer
CHR: Michelle Carrasco, Director Human Resources
Web address: www.paloverdebh.com/
Control: Other not–for–profit (including NFP Corporation) **Service:** Psychiatric

Staffed Beds: 48

☐ **SONORA BEHAVIORAL HEALTH HOSPITAL (034022)**, 6050 North Corona Road, #3, Zip 85704–1096; tel. 520/469–8700, **A**1 10 **F**4 5 29 50 98 99 100 102 103 104 105 130 132 **S** Acadia Healthcare Company, Inc., Franklin, TN
Primary Contact: Edeli Kinsala, Chief Executive Officer
CMO: Steven Bupp M.D., Medical Director
CHR: Ciria Soto, Director Human Resources
CNO: Angel Payne, Clinical Director, Director of Nursing
Control: Corporation, Investor–owned (for–profit) **Service:** Psychiatric

Staffed Beds: 92 **Admissions:** 2875 **Census:** 60 **Births:** 0 **Total Expense ($000):** 17176 **Payroll Expense ($000):** 10292 **Personnel:** 150

✠ △ **SOUTHERN ARIZONA VETERANS AFFAIRS HEALTH CARE SYSTEM**, 3601 South 6th Avenue, Zip 85723–0002; tel. 520/792–1450, **A**1 3 5 7 8 **F**3 4 5 15 18 20 22 24 26 28 29 30 31 33 34 35 36 38 39 40 44 45 46 49 52 53 54 56 57 58 59 60 61 63 64 65 66 70 71 74 75 77 78 79 80 81 82 83 84 85 86 87 90 91 92 93 94 96 97 98 100 101 102 103 104 105 106 107 108 111 114 116 117 118 119 127 128 129 130 132 135 143 146 147 148 149 150 **P**6 **S** Department of Veterans Affairs, Washington, DC
Primary Contact: Jennifer S. Gutowski, FACHE, Acting Director
CFO: Larry Korn, Manager Finance
CMO: Jayendra H Shah M.D., Chief Medical Officer
CIO: John Walston, Chief Information Officer
CHR: Patrice Craig, Manager Human Resources
Web address: www.tucson.va.gov
Control: Veterans Affairs, Government, federal **Service:** General medical and surgical

Staffed Beds: 323 **Admissions:** 1251 **Census:** 208 **Births:** 0 **Personnel:** 2482

TMC FOR CHILDREN See TMC HEALTHCARE

★ **TMC HEALTHCARE (030006)**, 5301 East Grant Road, Zip 85712–2874; tel. 520/324–5461, (Includes TMC FOR CHILDREN, 5301 East Grant Road, Tucson, Arizona, Zip 85712–2805, tel. 520/327–5461; Judy F. Rich, President and Chief Executive Officer) **A**3 5 10 **F**3 8 11 12 13 15 17 18 19 20 22 24 26 28 29 30 31 32 34 35 37 40 41 45 46 47 48 49 50 51 53 56 57 58 59 60 63 64 65 66 68 69 72 74 75 76 77 78 79 81 82 84 85 87 88 89 98 100 102 103 104 107 110 111 114 115 118 119 124 126 129 130 132 135 146 147 148 149 **P**6
Primary Contact: Judy F. Rich, MSN, R.N., President and Chief Executive Officer
COO: Karen Mlawsky, Senior Vice President and Chief Operations Officer
CFO: Stephen Bush, Chief Financial Officer
CMO: Rick Anderson M.D., Senior Vice President and Chief Medical Officer
CIO: Frank Marini, Senior Vice President and Chief Information Officer
CHR: Alex Horvath, Vice President and Chief Human Resources Officer
CNO: Mimi Coomler R.N., Vice President and Chief Nursing Officer
Web address: www.tmcaz.com
Control: Other not–for–profit (including NFP Corporation) **Service:** General medical and surgical

Staffed Beds: 586 **Admissions:** 32767 **Census:** 375 **Outpatient Visits:** 161285 **Births:** 5304 **Total Expense ($000):** 488561 **Payroll Expense ($000):** 191983 **Personnel:** 3448

TUCSON—Pinal County

☐ **SIERRA TUCSON**, 39580 South Lago Del Oro Parkway, Zip 85739–1091; tel. 520/624–4000, (Nonreporting) **A**1 3 **S** CRC Health Group, Inc., Cupertino, CA
Primary Contact: Stephen P. Fahey, Executive Director
COO: Stephen P Fahey, Executive Director
CFO: Amy Fritton, Controller
CMO: Jerome Lerner M.D., Medical Director
CHR: Betty Dickens, Director Human Resources
CNO: Sue Menzie R.N., Director Patient Care
Web address: www.sierratucson.com
Control: Corporation, Investor–owned (for–profit) **Service:** Alcoholism and other chemical dependency

Staffed Beds: 139

WHITERIVER—Navajo County

☐ **U. S. PUBLIC HEALTH SERVICE INDIAN HOSPITAL–WHITERIVER (030113)**, 200 West Hospital Drive, Zip 85941–0860, Mailing Address: State Route 73, Box 860, 85941–0860; tel. 928/338–4911, **A**1 3 10 **F**3 8 13 29 31 32 34 35 36 38 39 40 44 45 46 50 53 54 56 57 59 61 64 65 66 68 75 76 78 79 81 82 84 85 86 87 89 91 93 94 97 100 101 104 107 115 119 130 131 132 135 146 147 148 149 **S** U. S. Indian Health Service, Rockville, MD
Primary Contact: Michelle Martinez, Chief Executive Officer
COO: Brian Campbell, Director Professional Services
CFO: Desdemona Leslie, Finance Officer
CMO: John Umhau M.D., Clinical Officer
CIO: Russell Barker, Information Officer
CHR: Lena Fasthorse, Supervisor Human Resource
CNO: Jana Towne, Nurse Executive
Web address: www.ihs.gov
Control: PHS, Indian Service, Government, federal **Service:** General medical and surgical

Staffed Beds: 35 **Admissions:** 830 **Census:** 10 **Outpatient Visits:** 218817 **Births:** 46 **Personnel:** 430

WICKENBURG—Maricopa County

★ **WICKENBURG COMMUNITY HOSPITAL (031300)**, 520 Rose Lane, Zip 85390–1447; tel. 928/684–5421, (Nonreporting) **A**10 18
Primary Contact: James Tavary, Chief Executive Officer
CMO: Todd Kravetz, Chief of Staff
CIO: Michael McKay, Chief Information Officer
CHR: Kate Pina, Director Human Resources
CNO: Linda Brockwell, Chief Nursing Officer
Web address: www.wickhosp.com
Control: Other not–for–profit (including NFP Corporation) **Service:** General medical and surgical

Staffed Beds: 19

WILLCOX—Cochise County

★ **NORTHERN COCHISE COMMUNITY HOSPITAL (031302)**, 901 West Rex Allen Drive, Zip 85643–1009; tel. 520/384–3541, **A**10 18 **F**11 29 34 35 40 41 43 57 59 64 65 75 77 87 90 93 107 110 111 115 119 127 128 133 146 149
Primary Contact: Roland Knox, Chief Executive Officer
CFO: Kim Aguirre, Director Finance
CMO: Hisham Hamam M.D., Chief of Staff
CIO: Dennis Drury, Director Information Technology
CNO: Pam Noland, Director of Nursing
Web address: www.ncch.com
Control: Hospital district or authority, Government, Nonfederal **Service:** General medical and surgical

Staffed Beds: 24 **Admissions:** 484 **Census:** 13 **Births:** 0 **Total Expense ($000):** 16463 **Payroll Expense ($000):** 7132 **Personnel:** 133

AZ

LITTLE COLORADO MEDICAL CENTER (031311), 1501 Williamson Avenue, Zip 86047–2797; tel. 928/289–4691, **A**10 18 **F**29 34 40 50 65 79 81 107 127 130 133
Primary Contact: John J. Dempsey, Chief Executive Officer
CFO: Gina Reffner, Chief Financial Officer
CMO: Perry Mitchell M.D., Chief of Staff
CIO: Jacob Garcia, Chief Information Officer
CHR: Nina L Ferguson, Director Human Resources
Web address: www.lcmcwmh.com
Control: Other not–for–profit (including NFP Corporation) **Service**: General medical and surgical

Staffed Beds: 25 **Admissions**: 1209 **Census**: 10 **Births**: 211 **Total Expense ($000)**: 28129 **Payroll Expense ($000)**: 12445 **Personnel**: 210

★ ○ **YUMA REGIONAL MEDICAL CENTER (030013)**, 2400 South Avenue 'A', Zip 85364–7170; tel. 928/344–2000, **A**3 5 10 11 **F**3 12 13 15 18 20 22 24 26 28 29 30 31 32 34 35 39 40 41 45 46 47 48 49 50 54 57 58 59 64 68 70 72 74 75 76 77 78 79 81 82 83 84 85 86 87 89 97 104 107 108 109 111 114 115 116 117 118 119 120 121 122 123 124 126 130 132 141 146 147 148 149 **P**6
Primary Contact: Robert Trenschel, D.O., FACHE, M.P.H., President and Chief Executive Officer
CFO: David Willie, Chief Financial Officer
CMO: Bharat Magu M.D., Chief Medical Officer
CIO: Fred Peet, Chief Information Officer
CHR: Marshall Jones, Vice President Human Resources
CNO: Deb Aders MS, R.N., Interim Chief Nursing Officer
Web address: www.yumaregional.org
Control: Other not–for–profit (including NFP Corporation) **Service**: General medical and surgical

Staffed Beds: 406 **Admissions**: 17935 **Census**: 203 **Outpatient Visits**: 265370 **Births**: 3344 **Total Expense ($000)**: 394575 **Payroll Expense ($000)**: 150930 **Personnel**: 2065

⊞ **YUMA REHABILITATION HOSPITAL (033034)**, 901 West 24th Street, Zip 85364–6384; tel. 928/726–5000, (Nonreporting) **A**1 10 **S** HEALTHSOUTH Corporation, Birmingham, AL
Primary Contact: Ian Hodge, Chief Executive Officer
CMO: Bapu Aluri M.D., Chief Medical Officer
CHR: Linda Woen, Director Human Resources
CNO: Kristin Parra, Chief Nursing Officer
Web address: www.yumarehabhospital.com
Control: Corporation, Investor–owned (for–profit) **Service**: Rehabilitation

Staffed Beds: 41

Hospital, Medicare Provider Number, Address, Telephone, Approval, Facility, and Physician Codes, Health Care System
★ American Hospital Association (AHA) membership   ○ Healthcare Facilities Accreditation Program   ⇑ Center for Improvement in Healthcare Quality Accreditation
□ The Joint Commission accreditation   ◇ DNV Healthcare Inc. accreditation   △ Commission on Accreditation of Rehabilitation Facilities (CARF) accreditation

© 2017 AHA Guide   *Many Facility Codes have changed. Please refer to the AHA Guide Code Chart.*   Hospitals **A39**

ARKANSAS

AR

ARKADELPHIA—Clark County

☒ **BAPTIST HEALTH MEDICAL CENTER–ARKADELPHIA (041321)**, 3050 Twin Rivers Drive, Zip 71923–4299; tel. 870/245–2622, **A**1 10 18 **F**3 11 13 15 29 30 34 35 40 41 45 46 50 57 59 64 65 68 69 70 75 76 79 81 85 87 93 96 97 102 107 110 111 114 119 127 129 130 131 133 135 146 **S** Baptist Health, Little Rock, AR
Primary Contact: Tony Hardage, Assistant Vice President and Administrator
CFO: Robert C Roberts, Vice President and Chief Financial Officer
CMO: Eddie Phillips M.D., Chief Medical Officer
CIO: David House, Vice President and Chief Information Officer
CHR: Anthony Kendall, Vice President Human Resources
Web address: www.baptist-health.com/locations/accesspoint.aspx?accessPointID=187
Control: Other not–for–profit (including NFP Corporation) **Service:** General medical and surgical

Staffed Beds: 25 **Admissions:** 1378 **Census:** 14 **Outpatient Visits:** 34254
Births: 493 **Total Expense ($000):** 23559 **Payroll Expense ($000):** 9917
Personnel: 217

ASHDOWN—Little River County

★ **LITTLE RIVER MEMORIAL HOSPITAL (041320)**, 451 West Locke Street, Zip 71822–3325; tel. 870/898–5011, (Nonreporting) **A**10 18
Primary Contact: James Dowell, Administrator and Chief Executive Officer
CFO: Jackie Rainey, Chief Financial Officer
CIO: Mitchell Jones, Director Information Technology
CHR: Vicki Keener, Administrative Assistant and Director Human Resources
CNO: Cynthia Metzger, Chief Nursing and Operations Officer
Web address: www.little-river-memorial-hospital.placestars.com/
Control: County, Government, Nonfederal **Service:** General medical and surgical

Staffed Beds: 25

BARLING—Sebastian County

☐ **VALLEY BEHAVIORAL HEALTH SYSTEM (044006)**, 10301 Mayo Drive, Zip 72923–1660; tel. 479/494–5700, (Nonreporting) **A**1 10 **S** Acadia Healthcare Company, Inc., Franklin, TN
Primary Contact: Angel Piper, Chief Executive Officer
CFO: Paul D Ervin, Chief Financial Officer
CMO: Richard Livingston M.D., Medical Director
CHR: Patricia J Moore, Director Human Resource
CNO: Landon Horton, Director of Nursing
Web address: www.valleybehavioral.com
Control: Corporation, Investor–owned (for–profit) **Service:** Psychiatric

Staffed Beds: 75

BATESVILLE—Independence County

★ **WHITE RIVER MEDICAL CENTER (040119)**, 1710 Harrison Street, Zip 72501–7303, Mailing Address: P.O.Box 2197, 72503–2197; tel. 870/262–1200, (Total facility includes 11 beds in nursing home–type unit) **A**10 **F**3 8 11 12 13 15 17 20 22 28 29 30 31 34 35 38 40 42 43 44 45 48 50 51 56 57 59 60 64 68 70 74 75 76 77 78 79 81 82 84 85 86 87 90 92 93 98 100 101 103 104 107 108 110 111 114 115 119 121 126 127 128 129 130 131 132 135 144 146 147 148 **P**6 **S** White River Health System, Batesville, AR
Primary Contact: Gary Bebow, FACHE, Administrator and Chief Executive Officer
CFO: Phillip Hacker, Chief Financial Officer
CMO: Doug Bernard M.D., Chief Medical Officer
CIO: Gary Paxson, Chief Information Officer
CHR: Gary McDonald, Chief Facilities and Personnel Officer
CNO: Terri Bunch MSN, R.N., Chief Nursing Officer
Web address: www.whiteriverhealthsystem.com
Control: Other not–for–profit (including NFP Corporation) **Service:** General medical and surgical

Staffed Beds: 210 **Admissions:** 7927 **Census:** 99 **Outpatient Visits:** 355945
Births: 655 **Total Expense ($000):** 182097 **Payroll Expense ($000):** 77449
Personnel: 1298

BENTON—Saline County

☐ **RIVENDELL BEHAVIORAL HEALTH SERVICES OF ARKANSAS (044007)**, 100 Rivendell Drive, Zip 72019–9100; tel. 501/316–1255, **A**1 10 **F**29 38 59 75 87 98 99 100 101 102 103 104 105 130 132 **P**5 **S** Universal Health Services, Inc., King of Prussia, PA
Primary Contact: Jay Shehi, Chief Executive Officer
CFO: Mike Rainbolt, Chief Financial Officer
Web address: www.rivendellofarkansas.com
Control: Corporation, Investor–owned (for–profit) **Service:** Psychiatric

Staffed Beds: 80 **Admissions:** 2824 **Census:** 63 **Outpatient Visits:** 1362
Births: 0 **Total Expense ($000):** 12387 **Payroll Expense ($000):** 6541
Personnel: 102

★ **SALINE MEMORIAL HOSPITAL (040084)**, 1 Medical Park Drive, Zip 72015–3354; tel. 501/776–6000, **A**10 **F**3 7 11 12 13 15 17 18 20 22 29 30 34 35 39 40 41 43 50 57 59 62 63 64 70 74 75 76 77 79 81 85 87 89 90 93 98 107 108 110 111 114 115 118 119 129 130 131 132 135 146 148 **P**8
Primary Contact: Bob Trautman, Chief Executive Officer
COO: Carla Robertson, Chief Operating Officer and Chief Financial Officer
CFO: Carla Robertson, Chief Operating Officer and Chief Financial Officer
CIO: Andy Dick, Director Information Services
CHR: Carol Matthews, Director Human Resources
CNO: Debbie Burrow R.N., Chief Nursing Officer
Web address: www.salinememorial.org
Control: Other not–for–profit (including NFP Corporation) **Service:** General medical and surgical

Staffed Beds: 120 **Admissions:** 5820 **Census:** 75 **Outpatient Visits:** 66568
Births: 570 **Total Expense ($000):** 95654 **Payroll Expense ($000):** 43138
Personnel: 639

BERRYVILLE—Carroll County

☒ **MERCY HOSPITAL BERRYVILLE (041329)**, 214 Carter Street, Zip 72616–4303; tel. 870/423–3355, **A**1 10 18 **F**3 11 15 28 29 30 31 34 35 40 41 45 46 48 50 57 59 61 64 75 78 81 82 85 86 87 93 96 107 108 110 111 114 119 129 130 131 132 133 146 148 **S** Mercy, Chesterfield, MO
Primary Contact: Douglas M. Stroemel, Administrator
CFO: Sherry Clouse Day, Vice President Finance
CHR: Taya James, Director
CNO: Michele Gann, Vice President Patient Services
Web address: www.mercy.net/berryvillear
Control: Church operated, Nongovernment, not–for–profit **Service:** General medical and surgical

Staffed Beds: 25 **Admissions:** 496 **Census:** 5 **Outpatient Visits:** 28833
Births: 0 **Total Expense ($000):** 16343 **Payroll Expense ($000):** 8108
Personnel: 121

BLYTHEVILLE—Mississippi County

☒ **GREAT RIVER MEDICAL CENTER (040069)**, 1520 North Division Street, Zip 72315–1448, Mailing Address: P.O.Box 108, 72316–0108; tel. 870/838–7300, **A**1 10 **F**13 15 28 29 34 43 45 46 53 57 59 64 68 70 75 76 79 81 82 89 93 97 107 108 111 114 119 120 135 147 148 **P**7 **S** QHR, Brentwood, TN
Primary Contact: Chris Lee. Raymer, R.N., MSN, Chief Executive Officer
COO: Paul Pieffer, Chief Operating Officer
CFO: Randy Nichols, Chief Financial Officer
CIO: Tammy Bratcher, Director System Information Technology
CHR: Cheri Blurton, Director Human Resources, HIPAA Privacy Officer
CNO: Felicia Pierce R.N., Chief Nursing Officer
Web address: www.mchsys.org
Control: County, Government, Nonfederal **Service:** General medical and surgical

Staffed Beds: 73 **Admissions:** 1773 **Census:** 12 **Outpatient Visits:** 33102
Births: 350 **Total Expense ($000):** 22738 **Payroll Expense ($000):** 9470
Personnel: 264

Many Facility Codes have changed. Please refer to the AHA Guide Code Chart. © 2017 AHA Guide

BOONEVILLE—Logan County

★ **MERCY HOSPITAL BOONEVILLE (041318)**, 880 West Main Street, Zip 72927–3443; tel. 479/675–2800, **A**10 18 **F**3 11 35 40 43 45 57 59 62 64 65 68 81 85 107 119 127 133 148 149 **P**8 **S** Mercy, Chesterfield, MO
Primary Contact: Teresa Williams, R.N., Regional Administrator
CFO: J. Stuart Lisko, Regional Director Operations, Critical Access Hospital Operations
CMO: Michael Miranda, Chief of Staff
CHR: Doris Whitaker, Vice President and Manager
CNO: Candace Bollinger, Director of Nursing
Web address: www.mercy.net
Control: Church operated, Nongovernment, not–for–profit **Service:** General medical and surgical

> **Staffed Beds:** 25 **Admissions:** 229 **Census:** 3 **Outpatient Visits:** 16858 **Births:** 0 **Total Expense ($000):** 13686 **Payroll Expense ($000):** 5032 **Personnel:** 75

CALICO ROCK—Logan County

COMMUNITY MEDICAL CENTER OF IZARD COUNTY (041306), 61 Grasse Street, Zip 72519, Mailing Address: P.O.Box 438, 72519–0438; tel. 870/297–3726, **A**10 18 **F**3 29 30 34 40 43 45 57 81 93 107 111 119 127 128 129 133 146
Primary Contact: Kim Skidmore, Chief Executive Officer
COO: Cathy Franks RN, Chief Operating Officer
CMO: Bethany Knight M.D., Chief of Staff
CIO: Quentin Wildhagen, Systems Administrator
CHR: Crystal R Moody, Director Human Resources
CNO: Dana Hicks, Director of Nursing
Web address: www.cmcofic.org
Control: Other not–for–profit (including NFP Corporation) **Service:** General medical and surgical

> **Staffed Beds:** 25 **Admissions:** 457 **Census:** 5 **Outpatient Visits:** 3025 **Births:** 0 **Total Expense ($000):** 6169 **Payroll Expense ($000):** 2605 **Personnel:** 69

CAMDEN—Ouachita County

★ **OUACHITA COUNTY MEDICAL CENTER (040050)**, 638 California Avenue SW, Zip 71701–4699, Mailing Address: P.O.Box 797, 71711–0797; tel. 870/836–1000, **A**10 20 **F**4 5 7 8 11 13 15 29 31 34 40 41 43 46 48 49 50 57 59 62 63 64 68 69 70 75 77 78 79 81 85 87 92 93 97 100 102 107 108 110 111 114 115 119 127 129 130 132 133 135 145 146 148
Primary Contact: Peggy L. Abbott, President and Chief Executive Officer
CFO: Robert Anders, Chief Financial Officer
CIO: Kenny Frachiseur, Chief Information Officer
CHR: Mary Bridges, Director Human Resources
CNO: Diane Isaacs, Director of Nursing
Web address: www.ouachitamedcenter.com
Control: Other not–for–profit (including NFP Corporation) **Service:** General medical and surgical

> **Staffed Beds:** 65 **Admissions:** 1604 **Census:** 16 **Outpatient Visits:** 47591 **Births:** 214 **Total Expense ($000):** 33561 **Payroll Expense ($000):** 14129 **Personnel:** 393

OUACHITA MEDICAL CENTER See Ouachita County Medical Center

CLARKSVILLE—Johnson County

★ **JOHNSON REGIONAL MEDICAL CENTER (040002)**, 1100 East Poplar Street, Zip 72830–4419, Mailing Address: P.O.Box 738, 72830–0738; tel. 479/754–5454, **A**10 **F**3 7 11 13 15 29 34 35 40 45 50 51 57 62 64 68 70 75 76 77 79 81 85 90 91 93 96 98 103 104 107 108 110 111 115 119 129 130 132 133 135 147 148
Primary Contact: Michael A. Dorsey, FACHE, Chief Executive Officer
CFO: Joe Jeans CPA, Chief Financial Officer
CIO: Scott Cook, Chief Information Officer
CHR: Betty Collier, Chief Human Resources Officer
CNO: Nancy Hill R.N., Chief Nursing Officer
Web address: www.jrmc.com
Control: Other not–for–profit (including NFP Corporation) **Service:** General medical and surgical

> **Staffed Beds:** 90 **Admissions:** 2337 **Census:** 32 **Outpatient Visits:** 43942 **Births:** 350 **Total Expense ($000):** 42536 **Payroll Expense ($000):** 18930 **Personnel:** 336

CLINTON—Van Buren County

OZARK HEALTH MEDICAL CENTER (041313), Highway 65 South, Zip 72031–9045, Mailing Address: P.O.Box 206, 72031–0206; tel. 501/745–7000, (Total facility includes 118 beds in nursing home–type unit) **A**10 18 **F**11 15 28 29 34 35 40 43 45 57 59 62 64 65 75 79 81 93 107 110 111 114 119 128 132 133 146
Primary Contact: David Deaton, Chief Executive Officer
CFO: Mike Deaton, Chief Financial Officer
CMO: Steve Schoettle M.D., Chief Medical Staff
CHR: Sally Cassell, Manager Human Resources
CNO: Edna Prosser, Chief Nursing Officer
Web address: www.ozarkhealthinc.com
Control: Other not–for–profit (including NFP Corporation) **Service:** General medical and surgical

> **Staffed Beds:** 143 **Admissions:** 752 **Census:** 93 **Outpatient Visits:** 29126 **Births:** 1 **Total Expense ($000):** 19880 **Payroll Expense ($000):** 9248 **Personnel:** 294

CONWAY—Faulkner County

★ **BAPTIST HEALTH MEDICAL CENTER – CONWAY**, 1555 Exchange Avenue, Zip 72032–7824; tel. 501/585–2000, (Data for 107 days) **F**3 12 15 18 20 22 29 30 31 35 40 45 46 51 59 68 70 79 81 85 87 107 108 110 111 115 118 119 130 133 141 146 148 **S** Baptist Health, Little Rock, AR
Primary contact: Tim Bowen, Administrator
CNO: Stephana Loyd, Vice President, Chief Nursing Officer
Web address: www.baptist–health.com/location/baptist–health–medical–center–conway–conway
Control: Other not–for–profit (including NFP Corporation) **Service:** General medical and surgical

> **Staffed Beds:** 28 **Admissions:** 407 **Census:** 11 **Outpatient Visits:** 7435 **Births:** 0 **Total Expense ($000):** 29849 **Payroll Expense ($000):** 8700 **Personnel:** 193

✠ **CONWAY REGIONAL MEDICAL CENTER (040029)**, 2302 College Avenue, Zip 72034–6297; tel. 501/329–3831, **A**1 10 **F**3 8 11 13 15 17 18 20 22 24 28 29 30 31 35 40 43 45 49 50 51 53 56 57 59 60 62 64 70 74 75 77 78 79 81 84 85 87 93 103 107 108 110 111 115 117 119 120 127 130 131 132 146 147 148 **P**8
Primary Contact: Matthew Troup, Chief Executive Officer
COO: Alan Finley, Chief Operating Officer
CFO: Steven P Rose, Chief Financial Officer
CMO: James France M.D., Chief of Staff
CHR: Richard Tyler, Corporate Director Human Resources
CNO: Jacquelyn Wilkerson R.N., Chief Nursing Officer
Web address: www.conwayregional.org
Control: Other not–for–profit (including NFP Corporation) **Service:** General medical and surgical

> **Staffed Beds:** 154 **Admissions:** 8088 **Census:** 87 **Outpatient Visits:** 111539 **Births:** 1758 **Total Expense ($000):** 154865 **Payroll Expense ($000):** 53748 **Personnel:** 1024

CONWAY REGIONAL REHABILITATION HOSPITAL (043033), 2210 Robinson Avenue, Zip 72034–4943; tel. 501/932–3500, **A**10 **F**3 29 90 91 96 130 132 143 **P**8
Primary Contact: Alicia Kunert, MS, Executive Director
COO: Christy Scroggin, Chief Operating Officer
CMO: Roy Denton M.D., Chief Medical Officer
CNO: Darrallyn Webb R.N., Chief Nursing Officer
Web address: www.conwayregional.org
Control: Partnership, Investor–owned (for–profit) **Service:** Rehabilitation

> **Staffed Beds:** 26 **Admissions:** 452 **Census:** 15 **Outpatient Visits:** 0 **Births:** 0 **Personnel:** 48

AR

Hospital, Medicare Provider Number, Address, Telephone, Approval, Facility, and Physician Codes, Health Care System

★ American Hospital Association (AHA) membership ○ Healthcare Facilities Accreditation Program ⇧ Center for Improvement in Healthcare Quality Accreditation
□ The Joint Commission accreditation ◇ DNV Healthcare Inc. accreditation △ Commission on Accreditation of Rehabilitation Facilities (CARF) accreditation

© 2017 AHA Guide   *Many Facility Codes have changed. Please refer to the AHA Guide Code Chart.*   Hospitals **A41**

CROSSETT—Ashley County

★ **ASHLEY COUNTY MEDICAL CENTER (041323)**, 1015 Unity Road, Zip 71635–9443, Mailing Address: P.O.Box 400, 71635–0400; tel. 870/364–4111, **A**10 18 **F**3 11 13 15 18 29 30 31 34 35 40 45 50 53 56 57 59 62 64 68 70 75 76 77 78 79 81 85 93 98 100 103 104 105 107 108 110 111 115 119 127 129 130 132 133 148
Primary Contact: Phillip K. Gilmore, FACHE, Chief Executive Officer
CFO: Bill Couch, Chief Financial Officer
CMO: Brad Walsh M.D., Chief of Staff
CIO: Dan Austin, Manager Data Processing
CHR: Shirley White, Director Human Resources
CNO: Emily Bendinelli, Director of Nurses
Web address: www.acmconline.org
Control: Other not–for–profit (including NFP Corporation) **Service:** General medical and surgical

Staffed Beds: 33 **Admissions:** 1138 **Census:** 15 **Outpatient Visits:** 98408 **Births:** 135 **Total Expense ($000):** 28681 **Payroll Expense ($000):** 13532 **Personnel:** 249

DANVILLE—Yell County

★ **CHAMBERS MEMORIAL HOSPITAL (040011)**, 719 Detroit Avenue, Zip 72833–9607, Mailing Address: P.O.Box 639, 72833–0639; tel. 479/495–2241, **A**10 20 **F**3 11 15 29 34 35 40 43 45 57 59 62 75 77 81 87 93 96 97 107 110 114 119 128 130 133 **P**6
Primary Contact: Mike McCoy, Chief Executive Officer
CMO: Thomas Tinnesz M.D., Chief Medical Officer
CIO: Ken Masters, Director Information Technology
CNO: Joeann Bowerman, Director of Nursing
Web address: www.chambershospital.com
Control: Other not–for–profit (including NFP Corporation) **Service:** General medical and surgical

Staffed Beds: 41 **Admissions:** 1991 **Census:** 16 **Outpatient Visits:** 37815 **Births:** 0 **Total Expense ($000):** 18923 **Payroll Expense ($000):** 8995 **Personnel:** 217

DARDANELLE—Yell County

RIVER VALLEY MEDICAL CENTER (041302), 200 North Third Street, Zip 72834–3802, Mailing Address: P.O.Box 578, 72834–0578; tel. 479/229–4677, **A**10 18 **F**3 40 45 56 57 59 64 65 68 75 81 93 98 103 107 128 129 133 148 **S** Allegiance Health Management, Shreveport, LA
Primary Contact: Peter Savoy III, Administrator
CMO: William P Scott M.D., Chief of Staff
CHR: Kathy Hastin, Administrative Assistant Human Resources
Control: Corporation, Investor–owned (for–profit) **Service:** General medical and surgical

Staffed Beds: 35 **Admissions:** 878 **Census:** 4 **Outpatient Visits:** 4896 **Births:** 0

DE QUEEN—Sevier County

DE QUEEN MEDICAL CENTER (041319), 1306 Collin Raye Drive, Zip 71832–2502; tel. 870/584–4111, **A**10 18 **F**3 11 29 30 34 35 40 57 59 62 64 65 68 75 77 87 89 90 91 93 94 96 97 107 108 109 114 119 133 146 148
Primary Contact: Jeremy Icenhower, Administrator and Chief Executive Officer
CFO: Vicky Kelly, Chief Financial Officer
CMO: Jason Lofton M.D., Medical Director
CIO: David Harris, Director Information Systems
CHR: Ramona Driver, Director Human Resources
CNO: Kristy Richardson, Director of Nursing
Web address: www.dequeenhospital.com
Control: Corporation, Investor–owned (for–profit) **Service:** General medical and surgical

Staffed Beds: 35 **Admissions:** 616 **Census:** 11 **Outpatient Visits:** 64274 **Births:** 2 **Personnel:** 161

DEWITT—Arkansas County

★ **DEWITT HOSPITAL (041314)**, 1641 South Whitehead Drive, Zip 72042–9481, Mailing Address: P.O.Box 32, 72042–0032; tel. 870/946–3571, **A**10 18 **F**3 7 11 29 30 34 35 40 57 59 64 87 97 107 111 119 127 129 132 133 143 145 149 **P**6
Primary Contact: Philip S. Hanna, Chief Executive Officer
CFO: Brandon Cotten, Chief Financial Officer
CMO: Stan Burleson M.D., Chief Medical Staff
CIO: Brian Brooks, Information Manager
CHR: Alisa Brown, Administrative Assistant
CNO: Jerrilyn Horton R.N., Chief Nursing Officer
Web address: www.dhnh.org
Control: Other not–for–profit (including NFP Corporation) **Service:** General medical and surgical

Staffed Beds: 25 **Admissions:** 744 **Census:** 5 **Births:** 0

DUMAS—Desha County

DELTA MEMORIAL HOSPITAL (041326), 811 South Highway 65, Zip 71639–3006, Mailing Address: P.O.Box 887, 71639–0887; tel. 870/382–4303, (Nonreporting) **A**10 18
Primary Contact: Ashley Anthony, R.N., Chief Executive Officer
CMO: Thomas Lewellen D.O., Chief of Staff
CIO: Chris McTigrit, Manager Information Technology
CHR: Doris Fortenberry, Coordinator Human Resources
CNO: Dana Miles, Chief Nursing Officer and Chief Clinical Officer
Web address: www.deltamem.org
Control: Other not–for–profit (including NFP Corporation) **Service:** General medical and surgical

Staffed Beds: 25

EL DORADO—Union County

✉ **MEDICAL CENTER OF SOUTH ARKANSAS (040088)**, 700 West Grove Street, Zip 71730–4416; tel. 870/863–2000, **A**1 10 **F**3 11 13 15 17 18 20 22 24 28 29 31 34 40 43 45 46 50 56 57 59 64 65 70 73 75 76 78 79 80 81 85 89 90 93 96 107 108 110 111 115 118 119 130 146 147 149 **P**7 8 **S** Community Health Systems, Inc., Franklin, TN
Primary Contact: Robert Rupp, Chief Executive Officer
CFO: Dale Maddox, Chief Financial Officer
CMO: Misty Kneeland, Chief Medical Staff
CIO: Rob Robison, Director Information Technology
CHR: LaKeitha Davis, Director Human Resources
CNO: Kathy Degenstein Gartman, Chief Nursing Officer
Web address: www.themedcenter.net
Control: Corporation, Investor–owned (for–profit) **Service:** General medical and surgical

Staffed Beds: 121 **Admissions:** 3760 **Census:** 38 **Outpatient Visits:** 54079 **Births:** 615 **Total Expense ($000):** 59454 **Payroll Expense ($000):** 22642 **Personnel:** 437

EUREKA SPRINGS—Carroll County

EUREKA SPRINGS HOSPITAL (041304), 24 Norris Street, Zip 72632–3541; tel. 479/253–7400, **A**10 18 **F**3 29 30 34 40 41 43 45 57 64 77 81 84 85 89 93 104 107 130 131 133 146 148 **S** Allegiance Health Management, Shreveport, LA
Primary Contact: Peter Savoy III, Chief Executive Officer
CFO: Taylor Smith, Chief Financial Officer
CMO: John House M.D., Chief of Staff
CIO: Drew Wood, Director Information Technology
CHR: Jodi Smith, Administrative Assistant Human Resources
CNO: Vicki Andert, Chief Nursing Officer
Web address: www.eurekaspringshospital.com
Control: Corporation, Investor–owned (for–profit) **Service:** General medical and surgical

Staffed Beds: 15 **Admissions:** 239 **Census:** 5 **Outpatient Visits:** 6223 **Births:** 0 **Total Expense ($000):** 7461 **Payroll Expense ($000):** 2898 **Personnel:** 80

FAYETTEVILLE—Washington County

✉ **HEALTHSOUTH REHABILITATION HOSPITAL (043032)**, 153 East Monte Painter Drive, Zip 72703–4002; tel. 479/444–2200, **A**1 10 **F**3 29 34 42 57 59 75 77 79 90 91 92 94 95 96 149 **P**8 **S** HEALTHSOUTH Corporation, Birmingham, AL
Primary Contact: Jack C. Mitchell, FACHE, Chief Executive Officer
CMO: Marty Hurlbut M.D., Medical Director
CHR: Missy Cole, Director Human Resources
CNO: Miriam Irvin, CNO
Web address: www.healthsouthfayetteville.com
Control: Corporation, Investor–owned (for–profit) **Service:** Rehabilitation

Staffed Beds: 80 **Admissions:** 1632 **Census:** 55 **Outpatient Visits:** 0 **Births:** 0 **Total Expense ($000):** 17421 **Payroll Expense ($000):** 9817 **Personnel:** 202

★ ○ **PHYSICIANS' SPECIALTY HOSPITAL (040152)**, 3873 North Parkview Drive, Zip 72703–6286; tel. 479/571–7070, (Data for 275 days)**A**3 10 11 **F**3 12 29 40 45 50 59 68 79 81 82 85 107 111 114 119 131 135 **P**2 **S** Community Health Systems, Inc., Franklin, TN
Primary Contact: Sharif Omar, Chief Executive Officer
CFO: Joshua Harmond, Assistant Chief Financial Officer
CNO: Tim Kimball, Chief Nursing Officer
Web address: www.pshfay.com
Control: Partnership, Investor–owned (for–profit) **Service:** Surgical

Staffed Beds: 20 **Admissions:** 980 **Census:** 5 **Outpatient Visits:** 11350 **Births:** 0 **Total Expense ($000):** 23809 **Payroll Expense ($000):** 5492 **Personnel:** 143

Many Facility Codes have changed. Please refer to the AHA Guide Code Chart.

☒ **SPRINGWOODS BEHAVIORAL HEALTH HOSPITAL (044019)**, 1955 West Truckers Drive, Zip 72704–5637; tel. 479/973–6000, **A**1 10 **F**5 34 38 56 57 98 99 100 101 103 104 105 106 130 132 134 **P**6 **S** Universal Health Services, Inc., King of Prussia, PA
Primary Contact: Fred Richmond, Chief Executive Officer
Web address: www.springwoodsbehavioral.com
Control: Corporation, Investor–owned (for–profit) **Service**: Psychiatric

> **Staffed Beds:** 80 **Admissions:** 2066 **Census:** 44 **Outpatient Visits:** 1675 **Births:** 0 **Total Expense ($000):** 14603 **Payroll Expense ($000):** 5906 **Personnel:** 134

☐ **VANTAGE POINT OF NORTHWEST ARKANSAS (044004)**, 4253 North Crossover Road, Zip 72703–4596; tel. 479/521–5731, **A**1 10 **F**29 56 87 98 99 100 101 102 103 104 105 106 130 132 **P**6 **S** Acadia Healthcare Company, Inc., Franklin, TN
Primary Contact: Connie Borengasser, Chief Executive Officer
CFO: Ben Winbery, Chief Financial Officer
CMO: Norman Snyder M.D., Medical Director
CIO: Margaret Brown, Director Medical Records
CHR: Kathy Vickers, Director Human Resources
CNO: Suzette Branscum, Director of Nursing
Web address: www.vantagepointnwa.com
Control: Corporation, Investor–owned (for–profit) **Service**: Psychiatric

> **Staffed Beds:** 114 **Admissions:** 2426 **Census:** 100 **Outpatient Visits:** 137698 **Births:** 0 **Total Expense ($000):** 27654 **Payroll Expense ($000):** 16566 **Personnel:** 346

☒ **VETERANS HEALTH CARE SYSTEM OF THE OZARKS**, 1100 North College Avenue, Zip 72703–1944; tel. 479/443–4301, (Nonreporting) **A**1 2 3 **S** Department of Veterans Affairs, Washington, DC
Primary Contact: Bryan C. Matthews, Director
COO: Doris B Cassidy, Associate Director
CMO: Bonnie Baker M.D., Chief Medical Services
CIO: Michael Gracie, Chief Information Officer
CHR: Kathryn L Barker, Chief Human Resources Management
Web address: www.fayettevillear.va.gov
Control: Veterans Affairs, Government, federal **Service**: General medical and surgical

> **Staffed Beds:** 72

☒ **WASHINGTON REGIONAL MEDICAL CENTER (040004)**, 3215 North Hills Boulevard, Zip 72703–4424; tel. 479/463–1000, **A**1 3 10 **F**3 9 11 13 14 15 17 18 20 22 24 26 28 29 30 31 34 35 39 40 41 43 45 46 47 48 49 50 53 54 56 57 58 59 60 61 62 63 64 65 68 70 71 72 74 75 76 77 78 79 80 81 83 84 85 86 87 89 93 99 100 102 107 108 111 115 119 126 129 130 131 132 135 144 145 146 147 148 149 **P**6 8
Primary Contact: J. Larry. Shackelford, President and Chief Executive Officer
CFO: Dan Eckels, Chief Financial Officer
CMO: David Ratcliff M.D., Chief Medical Affairs
CIO: Becky Magee, Chief Information Officer
CHR: Laurie Morrow, Executive Director Human Resources
CNO: Meredith Green, Chief Nursing Officer
Web address: www.wregional.com
Control: Other not–for–profit (including NFP Corporation) **Service**: General medical and surgical

> **Staffed Beds:** 365 **Admissions:** 15000 **Census:** 166 **Outpatient Visits:** 168161 **Births:** 1512 **Total Expense ($000):** 238546 **Payroll Expense ($000):** 88265 **Personnel:** 2394

FORDYCE—Dallas County

★ **DALLAS COUNTY MEDICAL CENTER (041317)**, 201 Clifton Street, Zip 71742–3099; tel. 870/352–6300, (Nonreporting) **A**10 18
Primary Contact: Kenneth Sanders, Chief Executive Officer
CFO: Billie Launius, Director Business Finance
CMO: Michael Payne M.D., Chief of Staff
CHR: Audrey Allen, Coordinator Benefits
CNO: Hollie Raney, Director of Nursing
Web address: www.dallascountymedicalcenter.com
Control: County, Government, Nonfederal **Service**: General medical and surgical

> **Staffed Beds:** 22

FORREST CITY—St. Francis County

☒ **FORREST CITY MEDICAL CENTER (040019)**, 1601 Newcastle Road, Zip 72335–2218; tel. 870/261–0000, **A**1 10 20 **F**3 13 15 29 30 34 40 43 45 56 57 68 70 78 81 85 87 91 92 93 98 100 102 103 107 108 109 110 111 112 114 115 119 129 130 133 135 145 146 147 148 **P**6 **S** Quorum Health, Brentwood, TN
Primary Contact: Kevin Decker, Chief Executive Officer
CFO: Misty Gates, Chief Financial Officer
CMO: James DeRossitt M.D., Chief of Staff
CIO: David Shaw, Director Information Technology
CHR: Sherry McLaughlin, Director Human Resources
CNO: Leslie Harris, Chief Nursing Officer
Web address: www.forrestcitymedicalcenter.com
Control: Corporation, Investor–owned (for–profit) **Service**: General medical and surgical

> **Staffed Beds:** 55 **Admissions:** 2200 **Census:** 21 **Outpatient Visits:** 36806 **Births:** 901 **Total Expense ($000):** 22154 **Payroll Expense ($000):** 9737 **Personnel:** 224

FORT SMITH—Sebastian County

☒ **CHRISTUS DUBUIS HOSPITAL OF FORT SMITH (042008)**, 7301 Rogers Avenue, 4th Floor, Zip 72903–4100; tel. 479/314–4900, **A**1 10 **F**1 3 29 30 68 75 77 82 84 85 91 130 148 **S** CHRISTUS Health, Irving, TX
Primary Contact: Keith Rogers, Administrator
CFO: Paul Veillon CPA, Chief Financial Officer
Web address: www.christusdubuis.org/fortsmith
Control: Church operated, Nongovernment, not–for–profit **Service**: Acute long–term care hospital

> **Staffed Beds:** 25 **Admissions:** 208 **Census:** 16 **Outpatient Visits:** 0 **Births:** 0 **Total Expense ($000):** 7053 **Payroll Expense ($000):** 2767 **Personnel:** 52

☒ **HEALTHSOUTH REHABILITATION HOSPITAL OF FORT SMITH (043028)**, 1401 South 'J' Street, Zip 72901–5155; tel. 479/785–3300, **A**1 10 **F**28 29 34 35 77 90 91 94 95 96 130 131 132 149 **S** HEALTHSOUTH Corporation, Birmingham, AL
Primary Contact: Dawn Watts, Chief Executive Officer
CFO: Brenda Forbes, Controller
CMO: Cygnet Schroeder D.O., Medical Director
CIO: Donna England, Director Medical Records
CHR: S Janette Daniels, Director Human Resources
CNO: Jacqueline Floyd, Chief Nursing Officer
Web address: www.healthsouthfortsmith.com
Control: Corporation, Investor–owned (for–profit) **Service**: Rehabilitation

> **Staffed Beds:** 60 **Admissions:** 1474 **Census:** 46 **Outpatient Visits:** 0 **Births:** 0 **Total Expense ($000):** 15422 **Payroll Expense ($000):** 8742 **Personnel:** 201

☒ **MERCY HOSPITAL FORT SMITH (040062)**, 7301 Rogers Avenue, Zip 72903–4189, Mailing Address: P.O.Box 17000, 72917–7000; tel. 479/314–6000, (Includes MERCY ORTHOPEDIC HOSPITAL FORT SMITH, 3601 South 79th Street, Fort Smith, Arkansas, Zip 72903–6255, tel. 479/709–8500; Ryan Gehrig, President) **A**1 2 10 13 **F**3 12 13 15 17 18 20 22 24 26 28 29 30 31 32 34 35 36 38 40 43 44 45 49 50 53 56 57 58 59 60 61 62 63 64 65 68 70 71 72 73 74 75 76 77 78 79 81 82 83 84 85 86 87 89 90 92 93 95 96 102 107 108 110 111 114 115 116 117 119 120 121 123 124 126 129 130 134 135 143 146 147 148 149 **P**8 **S** Mercy, Chesterfield, MO
Primary Contact: Ryan Gehrig, President
COO: Julianne Stec, Chief Operating Officer
CFO: Greta Wilcher, Senior Vice President and Chief Financial Officer
CMO: David Hunton M.D., Chief Medical Officer
CHR: Bryan Brown, Executive Director
CNO: Marianne Rataj R.N., MS, Chief Nursing Officer
Web address: www.mercy.net/fortsmithar
Control: Church operated, Nongovernment, not–for–profit **Service**: General medical and surgical

> **Staffed Beds:** 370 **Admissions:** 15773 **Census:** 196 **Outpatient Visits:** 195428 **Births:** 2251 **Total Expense ($000):** 284416 **Payroll Expense ($000):** 99602 **Personnel:** 1644

☒ **SELECT SPECIALTY HOSPITAL–FORT SMITH (042006)**, 1001 Towson Avenue, 6 Central, Zip 72901–4921; tel. 479/441–3960, **A**1 10 **F**1 3 29 34 45 46 57 74 75 78 79 94 148 **S** Select Medical Corporation, Mechanicsburg, PA
Primary Contact: Cindy McLain, Chief Executive Officer
Web address: www.selectspecialtyhospitals.com/company/locations/fortsmith.aspx
Control: Corporation, Investor–owned (for–profit) **Service**: Acute long–term care hospital

> **Staffed Beds:** 34 **Admissions:** 372 **Census:** 26 **Outpatient Visits:** 0 **Births:** 0 **Total Expense ($000):** 13139 **Payroll Expense ($000):** 5192 **Personnel:** 75

Hospital, Medicare Provider Number, Address, Telephone, Approval, Facility, and Physician Codes, Health Care System

★ American Hospital Association (AHA) membership   ○ Healthcare Facilities Accreditation Program   ⇑ Center for Improvement in Healthcare Quality Accreditation
☐ The Joint Commission accreditation   ◇ DNV Healthcare Inc. accreditation   △ Commission on Accreditation of Rehabilitation Facilities (CARF) accreditation

AR

✉ **SPARKS REGIONAL MEDICAL CENTER (040055)**, 100 Towson Avenue, Zip 72901–2632, Mailing Address: P.O.Box 2406, 72917–7006; tel. 479/441–4000, **A**1 3 10 **F**3 8 12 13 14 15 17 18 20 21 22 24 26 28 29 30 31 34 35 40 45 46 47 48 49 50 51 53 54 56 58 59 60 62 64 67 70 72 74 75 76 77 78 79 81 82 85 86 87 89 93 97 98 103 107 108 109 110 111 112 113 114 115 117 119 120 121 122 124 126 127 129 130 144 146 147 148 **P**8 **S** Community Health Systems, Inc., Franklin, TN
Primary Contact: Daniel E. McKay, Chief Executive Officer
COO: Jeremy Drinkwitz, Chief Operating Officer
CFO: Brandon Bullard, Chief Financial Officer
CMO: Katherine Irish–Clardy M.D., Chief Medical Officer
CIO: Tom Sallis, Director Information Systems
CHR: Robert Freeman, Director Human Resources
CNO: Stephanie Whitaker, Chief Nursing Officer
Web address: www.sparks.org
Control: Corporation, Investor–owned (for–profit) **Service:** General medical and surgical

Staffed Beds: 303 **Admissions:** 16226 **Census:** 213 **Outpatient Visits:** 202557 **Births:** 1169 **Total Expense ($000):** 242849 **Payroll Expense ($000):** 69532 **Personnel:** 1374

GRAVETTE—Benton County

OZARKS COMMUNITY HOSPITAL (041331), 1101 Jackson Street Sw, Zip 72736–9121; tel. 479/787–5291, **A**10 18 **F**3 29 34 40 44 45 50 56 57 59 64 65 75 77 79 81 82 85 87 89 93 96 97 100 104 107 111 115 119 127 128 129 130 131 133 143 148 **P**6
Primary Contact: Paul Taylor, Administrator
Web address: www.ochonline.com/
Control: Corporation, Investor–owned (for–profit) **Service:** General medical and surgical

Staffed Beds: 25 **Admissions:** 599 **Census:** 19 **Outpatient Visits:** 46945 **Births:** 0 **Total Expense ($000):** 32493 **Payroll Expense ($000):** 14078 **Personnel:** 265

HARRISON—Boone County

★ **NORTH ARKANSAS REGIONAL MEDICAL CENTER (040017)**, 620 North Main Street, Zip 72601–2911; tel. 870/414–4000, **A**10 **F**3 7 8 11 13 15 17 18 28 29 30 31 32 34 35 39 40 41 43 45 48 50 53 56 57 59 62 63 64 65 68 70 73 75 76 77 78 79 81 82 85 86 87 89 93 97 98 102 103 104 107 108 110 111 114 115 118 119 120 121 123 127 129 130 131 132 135 144 146 147 148 149 **P**8
Primary Contact: Vincent Leist, President and Chief Executive Officer
CFO: Deana Thomas, Vice President Finance and Chief Financial Officer
CMO: John Leslie M.D., Chief Medical Officer
CIO: William J Bogle, Director Information Systems
CNO: Sammie Cribbs, Vice President Clinical Services and Chief Nursing Officer
Web address: www.narmc.com
Control: Other not–for–profit (including NFP Corporation) **Service:** General medical and surgical

Staffed Beds: 127 **Admissions:** 3342 **Census:** 25 **Outpatient Visits:** 195109 **Births:** 736 **Total Expense ($000):** 80529 **Payroll Expense ($000):** 34618 **Personnel:** 724

HEBER SPRINGS—Cleburne County

✉ **BAPTIST HEALTH MEDICAL CENTER–HEBER SPRINGS (041312)**, 1800 Bypass Road, Zip 72543–9135; tel. 501/887–3000, **A**1 10 18 **F**3 8 11 14 15 18 28 29 30 31 34 35 36 40 43 45 48 50 51 57 59 64 68 74 75 77 78 79 81 82 85 93 102 107 110 111 115 116 117 119 127 129 131 132 133 134 135 143 146 148 149 **S** Baptist Health, Little Rock, AR
Primary Contact: Edward L. Lacy, FACHE, Vice President and Administrator
Web address: www.baptist–health.com/maps–directions/bhmc–heber–springs
Control: Other not–for–profit (including NFP Corporation) **Service:** General medical and surgical

Staffed Beds: 25 **Admissions:** 894 **Census:** 10 **Outpatient Visits:** 30566 **Births:** 0 **Total Expense ($000):** 20561 **Payroll Expense ($000):** 7026 **Personnel:** 156

HELENA—Phillips County

✉ **HELENA REGIONAL MEDICAL CENTER (040085)**, 1801 Martin Luther King Drive, Zip 72342, Mailing Address: P.O.Box 788, 72342–0788; tel. 870/338–5800, **A**1 10 20 **F**3 11 13 15 28 29 34 40 43 50 59 62 70 74 76 79 81 82 86 87 89 91 93 97 107 108 111 113 114 119 130 132 133 135 145 146 147 148 **S** Quorum Health, Brentwood, TN
Primary Contact: Leah Osbahr, M.P.H., Chief Executive Officer
CFO: Amy Rice, Chief Financial Officer
CIO: Christopher Hunt, Director, Information Technologies, FISO
CHR: Juril Fonzie, Director Human Resources
CNO: Judith LeAnn Gerlach, Chief Nursing Officer
Web address: www.helenarmc.com
Control: Corporation, Investor–owned (for–profit) **Service:** General medical and surgical

Staffed Beds: 105 **Admissions:** 1578 **Census:** 12 **Outpatient Visits:** 28785 **Births:** 210 **Total Expense ($000):** 22726 **Payroll Expense ($000):** 7538 **Personnel:** 147

HOPE—Hempstead County

⇑ **WADLEY REGIONAL MEDICAL CENTER AT HOPE (040153)**, 2001 South Main Street, Zip 71801–8194; tel. 870/722–3800, **A**10 21 **F**3 11 15 18 29 34 35 40 50 56 57 59 64 70 86 93 98 103 107 110 111 114 119 127 130 **S** IASIS Healthcare, Franklin, TN
Primary Contact: Thomas D. Gilbert, FACHE, Chief Executive Officer
CFO: Bonny Sorensen, Chief Financial Officer
CIO: Matt Kesterson, Director Information Services
CHR: Debby Butler, Director Human Resources
CNO: Shelly Strayhorn R.N., Chief Nursing Officer
Web address: www.wadleyhealthathope.com
Control: Corporation, Investor–owned (for–profit) **Service:** General medical and surgical

Staffed Beds: 79 **Admissions:** 1054 **Census:** 15 **Outpatient Visits:** 27118 **Births:** 0 **Total Expense ($000):** 13123 **Payroll Expense ($000):** 5921 **Personnel:** 127

HOT SPRINGS—Garland County

✉ **CHI ST. VINCENT HOT SPRINGS (040026)**, 300 Werner Street, Zip 71913–6406; tel. 501/622–1000, **A**1 2 10 19 **F**3 11 12 13 15 17 18 20 22 24 26 28 29 30 31 34 35 37 38 40 43 45 47 49 50 56 57 59 62 64 65 66 68 69 70 71 74 75 76 77 78 79 81 82 85 86 87 89 92 93 98 103 107 108 110 111 112 114 115 116 117 118 119 120 121 123 124 129 130 132 135 146 147 148 149 150 **P**6 **S** Catholic Health Initiatives, Englewood, CO
Primary Contact: Anthony Houston, FACHE, President
CFO: Tadd M Richert, Chief Financial Officer
CMO: Thomas H. Cummins M.D., Chief Medical Officer
CIO: Tracy Kirby, Assistant Vice President Business Relationship Management
CHR: Aaron Austin, Market Vice President Human Resources
CNO: Bryan Williams R.N., Vice President Patient Care Services
Web address: www.chistvincent.com/Hospitals/st-vincent-hot-springs
Control: Church operated, Nongovernment, not–for–profit **Service:** General medical and surgical

Staffed Beds: 262 **Admissions:** 12557 **Census:** 164 **Outpatient Visits:** 166805 **Births:** 936 **Total Expense ($000):** 187733 **Payroll Expense ($000):** 62465 **Personnel:** 1105

☐ △ **NATIONAL PARK MEDICAL CENTER (040078)**, 1910 Malvern Avenue, Zip 71901–7799; tel. 501/321–1000, **A**1 7 10 19 **F**3 11 12 13 15 17 18 20 22 24 28 29 30 31 34 35 40 45 46 47 49 56 57 59 64 70 73 74 75 76 78 79 81 85 87 89 90 92 93 98 103 107 110 111 119 124 130 131 132 146 148 **P**1 **S** RCCH HealthCare Partners, Brentwood, TN
Primary Contact: Jerry D. Mabry, FACHE, Chief Executive Officer
COO: Brian Bell, Associate Administrator and Chief Operating Officer
CFO: Robbie Pettey, Chief Financial Officer
CMO: Robert Breving M.D., Chief of Staff
CIO: Brian Coffman, Director Information System
CHR: Tina Albright, Director Human Resources
CNO: Patsy Sue Crumpton R.N., Chief Nursing Officer
Web address: www.nationalparkmedical.com
Control: Corporation, Investor–owned (for–profit) **Service:** General medical and surgical

Staffed Beds: 208 **Admissions:** 6020 **Census:** 88 **Outpatient Visits:** 51714 **Births:** 472 **Total Expense ($000):** 79351 **Payroll Expense ($000):** 27101 **Personnel:** 592

HOT SPRINGS NATIONAL PARK—Garland County

✉ **CHRISTUS DUBUIS HOSPITAL OF HOT SPRINGS (042004)**, 300 Werner Street, 3rd Floor East, Zip 71913–6406; tel. 501/609–4300, **A**1 10 **F**1 3 29 30 45 68 77 79 85 87 118 130 135 148 **S** CHRISTUS Health, Irving, TX
Primary Contact: Keith Rogers, Administrator
CFO: Paul Veillon CPA, Chief Financial Officer
CIO: David Cook, Manager Information Systems
Web address: www.christusdubuis.org/hotsprings
Control: Church operated, Nongovernment, not–for–profit **Service:** Acute long–term care hospital

Staffed Beds: 26 **Admissions:** 135 **Census:** 11 **Outpatient Visits:** 0 **Births:** 0 **Total Expense ($000):** 5509 **Payroll Expense ($000):** 2131 **Personnel:** 46

★ **LEVI HOSPITAL (040132)**, 300 Prospect Avenue, Zip 71901–4097; tel. 501/624–1281, **A**10 **F**40 57 59 64 93 98 102 103 104 107 130 131 132
Primary Contact: Patrick G. McCabe Jr, FACHE, President and Chief Executive Officer
CFO: Stuart Lisko, Vice President, Chief Financial Officer and Compliance Officer
CMO: P Ross Bandy M.D., Chief Medical Officer and Chief of Staff
CIO: Stuart Lisko, Vice President, Chief Financial Officer and Compliance Officer
CHR: Susan Kramer, Director of Human Resources
CNO: Steven Boyd R.N., Nurse Executive
Web address: www.levihospital.com
Control: Other not–for–profit (including NFP Corporation) **Service:** Psychiatric

Staffed Beds: 50 **Admissions:** 1409 **Census:** 17 **Outpatient Visits:** 16042 **Births:** 0 **Total Expense ($000):** 7937 **Payroll Expense ($000):** 4345 **Personnel:** 99

Many Facility Codes have changed. Please refer to the AHA Guide Code Chart. © 2017 AHA Guide

JACKSONVILLE—Pulaski County

NORTH METRO MEDICAL CENTER (040074), 1400 West Braden Street, Zip 72076–3788; tel. 501/985–7000, (Nonreporting) **A**10 **S** Allegiance Health Management, Shreveport, LA
Primary Contact: Bill Bledsoe, Administrator
CFO: Lynn Muller, Chief Financial Officer
CMO: Ann Layton M.D., Chief of Staff
CHR: Jane Rockwell, Director Support Services
Web address: www.northmetromed.com
Control: Other not–for–profit (including NFP Corporation) **Service**: General medical and surgical

Staffed Beds: 73

JONESBORO—Craighead County

✖ **HEALTHSOUTH REHABILITATION HOSPITAL OF JONESBORO (043029)**, 1201 Fleming Avenue, Zip 72401–4311, Mailing Address: P.O.Box 1680, 72403–1680; tel. 870/932–0440, **A**1 10 **F**3 90 93 95 96 132 148 **P**5 **S** HEALTHSOUTH Corporation, Birmingham, AL
Primary Contact: Donna Harris, Chief Executive Officer
CFO: Allan Jones, Controller
CMO: Virendar Verma M.D., Medical Director
CHR: Tammy Barley, Director, Human Resources
CNO: Becky Kimble R.N., Chief Nursing Officer
Web address: www.healthsouthjonesboro.com
Control: Corporation, Investor–owned (for–profit) **Service**: Rehabilitation

Staffed Beds: 67 **Admissions:** 1604 **Census:** 52 **Outpatient Visits:** 7630
Births: 0 **Total Expense ($000):** 16009 **Payroll Expense ($000):** 9622
Personnel: 258

✖ **NEA BAPTIST MEMORIAL HOSPITAL (040118)**, 4800 East Johnson Avenue, Zip 72401–8413; tel. 870/936–1000, **A**1 3 10 13 **F**3 11 12 13 15 17 18 20 22 24 26 28 29 30 31 34 39 40 43 45 46 48 49 57 58 59 60 74 75 76 77 78 79 81 82 84 85 86 87 90 93 96 107 108 110 111 115 118 119 120 121 123 124 126 130 132 135 146 148 **P**8 **S** Baptist Memorial Health Care Corporation, Memphis, TN
Primary Contact: Brad Parsons, FACHE, Administrator and Chief Executive Officer
CFO: Kyle Sanders, Chief Financial Officer
CMO: Stephen Woodruff M.D., Chief Medical Officer
CIO: Terry Crider, Information Technology Site Manager
CHR: James Keller, Director Human Resources
CNO: Paula Grimes R.N., MSN, Chief Nursing Officer
Web address: www.neabaptist.com
Control: Other not–for–profit (including NFP Corporation) **Service**: General medical and surgical

Staffed Beds: 216 **Admissions:** 11009 **Census:** 133 **Outpatient Visits:** 96144 **Births:** 935 **Total Expense ($000):** 169778 **Payroll Expense ($000):** 50918 **Personnel:** 942

✖ **ST. BERNARDS MEDICAL CENTER (040020)**, 225 East Jackson Avenue, Zip 72401–3119; tel. 870/207–4100, **A**1 2 3 10 13 19 **F**3 5 11 12 13 15 17 18 19 20 22 24 26 27 28 29 30 31 32 34 35 38 39 40 43 45 46 49 50 51 53 54 56 57 59 60 62 63 64 68 70 71 72 74 75 76 77 78 79 81 82 83 84 85 86 87 89 92 93 98 100 101 102 103 104 105 107 108 109 110 111 114 115 116 117 118 119 120 121 123 126 129 130 131 132 135 141 145 146 147 148 149
Primary Contact: Chris B. Barber, FACHE, President and Chief Executive Officer
COO: Michael K Givens FACHE, Administrator
CFO: Harry Hutchison, Vice President Fiscal Services
CMO: Kasey Holder M.D., Vice President Medical Affairs
CIO: Josh Melton, Chief Information Officer
CHR: Lori J. Smith, Vice President Human Resources
CNO: Susan Greenwood R.N., Vice President and Chief Nursing Officer
Web address: www.stbernards.info
Control: Church operated, Nongovernment, not–for–profit **Service**: General medical and surgical

Staffed Beds: 386 **Admissions:** 17926 **Census:** 219 **Outpatient Visits:** 271987 **Births:** 1302 **Total Expense ($000):** 293331

LAKE VILLAGE—Chicot County

★ **CHICOT MEMORIAL MEDICAL CENTER (041328)**, 2729 Highway 65 and 82 South, Zip 71653; tel. 870/265–5351, **A**10 18 **F**3 7 11 15 29 34 35 40 43 49 53 57 59 62 64 75 76 77 80 81 82 85 87 93 107 111 114 119 128 129 130 132 133 146 147 148 **P**6
Primary Contact: David Mantz, Chief Executive Officer
CFO: Vicki Allen, Chief Financial Officer
CMO: Michael Bradley Mayfield M.D., Chief of Staff
CIO: David Andrews, Manager Information Systems
CNO: Eric Selby R.N., Chief Nursing Officer
Web address: www.chicotmemorial.com
Control: Other not–for–profit (including NFP Corporation) **Service**: General medical and surgical

Staffed Beds: 25 **Admissions:** 1025 **Census:** 11 **Outpatient Visits:** 20503
Births: 85 **Total Expense ($000):** 17764 **Payroll Expense ($000):** 7758
Personnel: 170

SOUTHEAST REHABILITATION HOSPITAL (043034), 2729–A Highway 65 and 82 South, Zip 71653; tel. 870/265–4333, (Nonreporting) **A**10
Primary Contact: Stacy Noble, Administrator
CNO: Michael Vaughn, Director of Nursing
Web address: www.southeastrehab.com
Control: Partnership, Investor–owned (for–profit) **Service**: Rehabilitation

Staffed Beds: 15

LITTLE ROCK—Pulaski County

ALLEGIANCE SPECIALTY HOSPITAL OF LITTLE ROCK See Cornerstone Hospital of Little Rock

✖ **ARKANSAS CHILDREN'S HOSPITAL (043300)**, 1 Children's Way, Zip 72202–3500; tel. 501/364–1100, **A**1 3 5 8 10 **F**3 7 11 12 16 17 19 21 23 25 27 28 29 30 31 32 34 35 38 39 40 41 43 45 46 48 50 53 55 57 58 59 60 64 68 71 72 74 75 77 78 79 80 81 82 84 85 86 87 88 89 90 91 93 94 97 102 107 108 111 115 118 119 126 129 130 131 132 135 136 137 138 143 146 149 150 **P**8
Primary Contact: Marcella Doderer, FACHE, President and Chief Executive Officer
COO: Chanda Cashen Chacon, Executive Vice President and Chief Operating Officer
CFO: Gena Wingfield, Senior Vice President and Chief Financial Officer
CMO: Robert Williams M.D., Chief Medical Officer
CIO: Jonathan Goldberg, Senior Vice President and Chief Information Officer
CHR: Andree Trosclair, Vice President Human Resources
CNO: Lee Anne Eddy, Senior Vice President and Chief Nursing Officer
Web address: www.archildrens.org
Control: Other not–for–profit (including NFP Corporation) **Service**: Children's general medical and surgical

Staffed Beds: 334 **Admissions:** 14867 **Census:** 221 **Outpatient Visits:** 357914 **Births:** 0 **Total Expense ($000):** 499128 **Payroll Expense ($000):** 210652 **Personnel:** 3441

✖ **ARKANSAS HEART HOSPITAL (040134)**, 1701 South Shackleford Road, Zip 72211–4335; tel. 501/219–7000, **A**1 3 5 10 **F**3 11 12 17 18 20 22 24 26 28 29 30 34 35 40 45 46 54 57 58 59 64 70 71 74 75 81 85 86 87 102 107 111 114 119 127 129 130 132 148 149
Primary Contact: Bruce Murphy, M.D., President and Chief Executive Officer
CHR: Brent Davis, Human Resources Team Leader
Web address: www.arheart.com
Control: Partnership, Investor–owned (for–profit) **Service**: Heart

Staffed Beds: 112 **Admissions:** 5517 **Census:** 53 **Outpatient Visits:** 25945
Births: 0 **Total Expense ($000):** 169194 **Payroll Expense ($000):** 46065
Personnel: 983

☐ **ARKANSAS STATE HOSPITAL (044011)**, 305 South Palm Street, Zip 72205–5432; tel. 501/686–9000, (Nonreporting) **A**1 3 5 10
Primary Contact: Steven Domon, M.D., Interim Chief Executive Officer
CFO: Gary W Hollis, Comptroller
CMO: Steven Domon M.D., Medical Director
CIO: Tina Grissom, Chief Information Technology Officer
CHR: Donna Sadler, Director Human Resources
CNO: James Scoggins, Director of Nursing
Web address: www.state.ar.us/dhs/dmhs
Control: State, Government, Nonfederal **Service**: Psychiatric

Staffed Beds: 222

Hospital, Medicare Provider Number, Address, Telephone, Approval, Facility, and Physician Codes, Health Care System

★ American Hospital Association (AHA) membership   ○ Healthcare Facilities Accreditation Program   ⇧ Center for Improvement in Healthcare Quality Accreditation
☐ The Joint Commission accreditation   ◇ DNV Healthcare Inc. accreditation   △ Commission on Accreditation of Rehabilitation Facilities (CARF) accreditation

AR

★ **BAPTIST HEALTH EXTENDED CARE HOSPITAL (042012)**, 9601 Baptist Health Drive, Zip 72205–7202; tel. 501/202–1070, **A**10 **F**1 3 29 31 77 87 130 148 **S** Baptist Health, Little Rock, AR
Primary Contact: Lee Gentry, FACHE, Vice President and Administrator
CFO: Robert C Roberts, Vice President
CMO: Gail McCracken M.D., Medical Director
CIO: David House, Vice President
CHR: Anthony Kendall, Vice President Human Resources
CNO: Diane Smith, Chief Nursing Officer
Web address: www.baptist-health.com/maps–directions/bh_extended_care/default.aspx
Control: Other not–for–profit (including NFP Corporation) **Service**: Acute long–term care hospital

Staffed Beds: 55 **Admissions:** 339 **Census:** 29 **Outpatient Visits:** 0 **Births:** 0 **Total Expense ($000):** 15288 **Payroll Expense ($000):** 6374 **Personnel:** 109	

⊞ △ **BAPTIST HEALTH MEDICAL CENTER–LITTLE ROCK (040114)**, 9601 Baptist Health Drive, Zip 72205–7299; tel. 501/202–2000, **A**1 3 5 7 10 **F**3 4 5 7 8 11 12 13 15 17 18 20 22 24 26 28 29 30 31 32 34 35 36 37 38 40 43 44 45 49 50 54 56 57 58 59 60 61 62 64 65 67 68 70 72 73 74 75 76 77 78 79 81 82 84 85 86 87 89 93 98 99 100 101 102 103 104 107 108 110 111 114 118 119 126 128 129 130 131 132 134 135 137 138 143 144 146 147 148 **S** Baptist Health, Little Rock, AR
Primary Contact: Greg Crain, FACHE, Vice President and Administrator
CFO: Robert C Roberts, Senior Vice President Financial Services
CMO: Anthony Bennett M.D., Chief Clinical Affairs
CIO: David House, Vice President and Chief Information Officer
CHR: Anthony Kendall, Vice President Human Resources
CNO: Jill Massiet R.N., Vice President Patient Care
Web address: www.baptist-health.org/maps–directions/bhmc–lr
Control: Other not–for–profit (including NFP Corporation) **Service**: General medical and surgical

Staffed Beds: 682 **Admissions:** 29457 **Census:** 437 **Outpatient Visits:** 142206 **Births:** 2705 **Total Expense ($000):** 489342 **Payroll Expense ($000):** 152331 **Personnel:** 2769	

⊞ △ **BAPTIST HEALTH REHABILITATION INSTITUTE (043026)**, 9601 Interstate 630, Exit 7, Zip 72205–7202; tel. 501/202–7000, **A**1 3 5 7 10 **F**29 30 34 35 50 53 64 75 86 87 90 91 93 95 96 130 132 143 **S** Baptist Health, Little Rock, AR
Primary Contact: Mike Perkins, Vice President and Administrator
CFO: Robert C Roberts, Senior Vice President
CIO: David House, Vice President and Chief Information Officer
CHR: Anthony Kendall, Vice President Human Resources
Web address: www.baptist-health.com/locations/accesspoint.aspx?accessPointID=202
Control: Other not–for–profit (including NFP Corporation) **Service**: Rehabilitation

Staffed Beds: 120 **Admissions:** 1394 **Census:** 46 **Outpatient Visits:** 80754 **Births:** 0 **Total Expense ($000):** 29710 **Payroll Expense ($000):** 13843 **Personnel:** 208	

⊞ △ **CENTRAL ARKANSAS VETERANS HEALTHCARE SYSTEM**, 4300 West Seventh Street, Zip 72205–5446; tel. 501/257–1000, (Nonreporting) (Includes NORTH LITTLE ROCK DIVISION, 2200 Fort Roots Drive, North Little Rock, Arkansas, Zip 72114–1706; tel. 501/661–1202) **A**1 2 3 5 7 8 **S** Department of Veterans Affairs, Washington, DC
Primary Contact: Margie A. Scott, M.D., Director
CFO: ColonelNate Todd, Chief Financial Officer
CIO: Jim Hall, Acting Chief Information Officer
CHR: Richard Nelson, Chief of Human Resources Management Services
Web address: www.littlerock.va.gov/
Control: Veterans Affairs, Government, federal **Service**: General medical and surgical

Staffed Beds: 551	

⊞ **CHI ST. VINCENT INFIRMARY MEDICAL CENTER (040007)**, Two St Vincent Circle, Zip 72205–5499; tel. 501/552–3000, **A**1 3 5 10 **F**3 11 13 17 18 20 22 24 26 28 29 30 31 34 35 37 40 43 44 45 46 48 49 50 51 53 54 56 57 58 59 60 61 64 68 70 72 74 75 76 77 78 79 80 81 82 84 85 86 87 91 92 93 96 97 98 100 101 102 107 108 109 110 111 112 114 115 116 117 118 119 124 126 129 130 132 135 143 146 147 148 149 150 **P**6 7 **S** Catholic Health Initiatives, Englewood, CO
Primary Contact: Polly J. Davenport, FACHE, R.N., President
CFO: Tadd M Richert, Chief Financial Officer
CMO: Thomas H. Cummins M.D., Chief Medical Officer
CIO: Tracy Kirby, Assistant Vice President Business Relationship Management
CHR: Aaron Austin, Market Vice President Human Resources
CNO: Kathy E. Neely R.N., Interim Vice President Patient Care Services
Web address: www.chistvincent.com/
Control: Church operated, Nongovernment, not–for–profit **Service**: General medical and surgical

Staffed Beds: 423 **Admissions:** 20648 **Census:** 303 **Outpatient Visits:** 170429 **Births:** 912 **Total Expense ($000):** 401561 **Payroll Expense ($000):** 147799 **Personnel:** 1871	

CORNERSTONE HOSPITAL OF LITTLE ROCK (042010), 2 Saint Vincent Circle, 6th Floor, Zip 72205–5423; tel. 501/265–0600, (Nonreporting) **A**10 **S** Cornerstone Healthcare Group, Dallas, TX
Primary Contact: James H. Rogers, FACHE, Chief Executive Officer
CNO: Joy Miller, Chief Nursing Officer
Web address: www.chghospitals.com/littlerock/
Control: Corporation, Investor–owned (for–profit) **Service**: Acute long–term care hospital

Staffed Beds: 40	

☐ **PINNACLE POINTE HOSPITAL (044013)**, 11501 Financial Center Parkway, Zip 72211–3715; tel. 501/223–3322, **A**1 10 **F**5 29 34 35 38 50 64 75 77 87 98 99 101 102 105 106 130 134 143 149 **S** Universal Health Services, Inc., King of Prussia, PA
Primary Contact: Shane Frazier, Chief Executive Officer
CFO: Gina Dailey, Chief Financial Officer
CMO: Ben Nimmo M.D., Medical Director
CIO: James L Howe, Director Human Resources
CHR: James L Howe, Director Human Resources
CNO: Bobby Alexander R.N., Chief Nursing Officer
Web address: www.pinnaclepointehospital.com
Control: Corporation, Investor–owned (for–profit) **Service**: Children's hospital psychiatric

Staffed Beds: 124 **Admissions:** 3071 **Census:** 110 **Outpatient Visits:** 0 **Births:** 0 **Total Expense ($000):** 18385 **Payroll Expense ($000):** 11024 **Personnel:** 238	

⊞ **UAMS MEDICAL CENTER (040016)**, 4301 West Markham Street, Zip 72205–7101; tel. 501/686–7000, **A**1 3 5 8 10 **F**3 11 12 13 15 17 18 20 22 24 26 29 30 31 34 40 43 44 45 46 47 48 49 50 52 53 54 55 56 57 58 59 60 61 64 68 70 72 73 74 75 76 77 78 79 80 81 82 84 85 86 87 91 92 93 94 96 97 98 99 100 101 102 103 104 107 108 110 111 114 115 116 117 118 119 120 121 123 124 126 129 130 131 132 136 138 139 141 142 145 146 147 148 **P**6
Primary Contact: Richard Turnage, M.D., Chief Executive Officer
COO: Timothy Hill, Chief Operating Officer
CFO: William Bowes, Chief Financial Officer
CMO: Nicholas P Lang M.D., Chief Medical Officer
CIO: David L. Miller, Chief Information Officer
CHR: Jeff Risinger, Director Human Resources
CNO: Mary Helen Forrest R.N., Chief Nursing Officer
Web address: www.uams.edu/medcenter
Control: State, Government, Nonfederal **Service**: General medical and surgical

Staffed Beds: 510 **Admissions:** 24898 **Census:** 426 **Outpatient Visits:** 545338 **Births:** 3660 **Total Expense ($000):** 714666 **Payroll Expense ($000):** 225737 **Personnel:** 4926	

MAGNOLIA—Columbia County

★ **MAGNOLIA REGIONAL MEDICAL CENTER (040067)**, 101 Hospital Drive, Zip 71753–2415, Mailing Address: P.O.Box 629, 71754–0629; tel. 870/235–3000, **A**3 10 20 **F**3 11 13 15 29 31 34 35 40 43 45 50 59 62 64 70 76 81 87 93 107 108 110 111 115 119 129 130 132 133 146 147 148 149
Primary Contact: Rex Jones, Chief Executive Officer
CFO: Roxane Stewart, Chief Financial Officer
CMO: James W Chambliss, Chief of Staff
CHR: Shawnee Cooper, Director Human Resources
CNO: Joycelyn Watkins R.N., Chief Nursing Officer
Web address: www.magnoliarmc.org
Control: City, Government, Nonfederal **Service**: General medical and surgical

Staffed Beds: 49 **Admissions:** 1353 **Census:** 12 **Outpatient Visits:** 170120 **Total Expense ($000):** 25013 **Payroll Expense ($000):** 11472 **Personnel:** 181	

MALVERN—Hot Spring County

★ **BAPTIST HEALTH MEDICAL CENTER–HOT SPRING COUNTY (040076)**, 1001 Schneider Drive, Zip 72104–4811; tel. 501/332–1000, **A**10 **F**3 11 15 17 29 30 34 35 40 43 45 57 59 64 70 75 81 93 98 102 107 110 111 115 119 129 130 132 146 **S** Baptist Health, Little Rock, AR
Primary Contact: Sheila Williams, Vice President and Administrator
CMO: Allen Gerber M.D., Chief of Staff
CHR: Kelli Hopkins, Director Human Resources
CNO: Dee Schall R.N., Chief Nursing Officer
Web address: www.baptist-health.org
Control: Other not–for–profit (including NFP Corporation) **Service**: General medical and surgical

Staffed Beds: 72 **Admissions:** 2278 **Census:** 25 **Outpatient Visits:** 23007 **Births:** 0 **Total Expense ($000):** 20828 **Payroll Expense ($000):** 8840 **Personnel:** 194	

MAUMELLE—Pulaski County

☐ **METHODIST BEHAVIORAL HOSPITAL OF ARKANSAS (044017)**, 1601 Murphy Drive, Zip 72113–6187; tel. 501/803–3388, **A**1 10 **F**98 99 104 106
Primary Contact: Andy Altom, Chief Executive Officer
Web address: www.umch.org
Control: Other not–for–profit (including NFP Corporation) **Service**: Children's hospital psychiatric

Staffed Beds: 60 **Admissions**: 1736 **Census**: 56 **Outpatient Visits**: 99350 **Births**: 0 **Total Expense ($000)**: 18598 **Payroll Expense ($000)**: 8223 **Personnel**: 120

MCGEHEE—Desha County

★ **MCGEHEE–DESHA COUNTY HOSPITAL (041308)**, 900 South Third, Zip 71654–2562, Mailing Address: P.O.Box 351, 71654–0351; tel. 870/222–5600, **A**10 18 **F**3 11 29 40 57 59 62 64 68 107 114 119 132 133 135 146 148
Primary Contact: John E. Heard, Chief Executive Officer
CFO: Teresa Morgan, Chief Financial Officer
CMO: James Young M.D., Chief of Staff
CIO: Shaun Perry, Chief Information Officer
CNO: Sarah Calvert, Chief Nursing Officer
Control: Other not–for–profit (including NFP Corporation) **Service**: General medical and surgical

Staffed Beds: 25 **Admissions**: 210 **Census**: 2 **Outpatient Visits**: 27574 **Births**: 0 **Total Expense ($000)**: 11506 **Payroll Expense ($000)**: 5542 **Personnel**: 126

MENA—Polk County

★ **MENA REGIONAL HEALTH SYSTEM (040015)**, 311 North Morrow Street, Zip 71953–2516; tel. 479/394–6100, (Nonreporting) **A**10 20
Primary Contact: Jay Quebedeaux, Chief Executive Officer
CFO: Mark Henke, Chief Financial Officer
CMO: Richard Lochala, Chief of Staff
CIO: Nicholas Dunn, Director Information Systems
CHR: Chandler Cox, Director Human Resources
CNO: Teresa Wise R.N., Chief Nursing Officer
Web address: www.menaregional.com
Control: City, Government, Nonfederal **Service**: General medical and surgical

Staffed Beds: 65

MONTICELLO—Drew County

★ **DREW MEMORIAL HEALTH SYSTEM (040051)**, 778 Scogin Drive, Zip 71655–5729; tel. 870/367–2411, **A**10 20 **F**3 11 13 15 29 31 34 35 40 43 45 50 57 59 62 64 68 70 75 76 77 78 81 82 86 87 91 93 94 96 100 103 107 110 111 115 119 128 129 130 132 133 147 148
Primary Contact: Scott G. Barrilleaux, FACHE, Chief Executive Officer
COO: Wade Smith, Chief Operating Officer
CFO: Melodie Colwell, Chief Financial Officer
CMO: Julia Nichoson M.D., Chief Medical Officer
CIO: Rusty Bryant, Director Information Technology
CHR: Seth Givens, Chief Human Resource Officer
CNO: Jonathan Schell, Chief Nursing Officer
Web address: www.drewmemorial.org
Control: Other not–for–profit (including NFP Corporation) **Service**: General medical and surgical

Staffed Beds: 49 **Admissions**: 2429 **Census**: 23 **Outpatient Visits**: 50309 **Births**: 417 **Total Expense ($000)**: 32440 **Payroll Expense ($000)**: 13744 **Personnel**: 303

MORRILTON—Conway County

★ **CHI ST. VINCENT MORRILTON (041324)**, 4 Hospital Drive, Zip 72110–4510; tel. 501/977–2300, **A**10 18 **F**3 11 15 28 29 30 34 35 40 44 45 50 57 59 62 64 77 79 80 81 85 87 93 97 107 110 111 119 127 130 133 145 146 149 150 **P**1 **S** Catholic Health Initiatives, Englewood, CO
Primary Contact: Leslie Arnold, Chief Executive Officer and Administrator
CFO: Tadd M Richert, Chief Financial Officer
CMO: Thomas H. Cummins M.D., Chief Medical Officer
CIO: Tracy Kirby, Assistant Vice President Business Relationship Management
CHR: Aaron Austin, Market Vice President Human Resources
CNO: Kathy E. Neely R.N., Interim Vice President Patient Care Services
Web address: www.chistvincent.com/Hospitals/st-vincent-morrilton
Control: Church operated, Nongovernment, not–for–profit **Service**: General medical and surgical

Staffed Beds: 25 **Admissions**: 714 **Census**: 7 **Outpatient Visits**: 36054 **Births**: 0 **Total Expense ($000)**: 19541 **Payroll Expense ($000)**: 8446 **Personnel**: 118

ST. ANTHONY'S MEDICAL CENTER See Chi St. Vincent Morrilton

MOUNTAIN HOME—Baxter County

★ **BAXTER REGIONAL MEDICAL CENTER (040027)**, 624 Hospital Drive, Zip 72653–2955; tel. 870/508–1000, **A**10 **F**7 11 13 15 17 18 20 22 24 28 29 30 31 36 40 41 43 45 46 47 49 53 56 57 59 62 63 64 70 71 76 77 78 79 81 82 85 86 87 89 90 93 98 103 104 107 108 111 114 115 116 117 119 124 126 127 129 130 132 135 146 147 148 149 **P**6 8
Primary Contact: Ron Peterson, FACHE, President and Chief Executive Officer
COO: Rudy Darling, Chief Operating Officer
CFO: Ivan Holleman, Chief Financial Officer
CHR: Karen Adams, Vice President Human Resources
Web address: www.baxterregional.org
Control: Other not–for–profit (including NFP Corporation) **Service**: General medical and surgical

Staffed Beds: 209 **Admissions**: 8567 **Census**: 99 **Outpatient Visits**: 148688 **Births**: 702 **Total Expense ($000)**: 179535 **Payroll Expense ($000)**: 73469 **Personnel**: 1455

MOUNTAIN VIEW—Stone County

★ **STONE COUNTY MEDICAL CENTER (041310)**, 2106 East Main Street, Zip 72560–6439, Mailing Address: P.O.Box 510, 72560–0510; tel. 870/269–4361, **A**10 18 **F**3 11 15 29 34 40 43 45 57 59 64 79 81 93 107 110 111 114 119 128 133 146 147 148 **S** White River Health System, Batesville, AR
Primary Contact: Kevin Spears, Chief Executive Officer
CFO: Phillip Hacker, Chief Financial Officer
CIO: Gary Paxson, Associate Administrator Information Systems
CHR: Gary McDonald, Associate Administrator Human Resources
CNO: Diana Shelden, Chief Nursing Officer
Web address: www.whiterivehealthsystem.com/doctors/facilities/stone–county–medical–center
Control: Other not–for–profit (including NFP Corporation) **Service**: General medical and surgical

Staffed Beds: 25 **Admissions**: 732 **Census**: 7 **Outpatient Visits**: 26686 **Births**: 3 **Total Expense ($000)**: 14663 **Payroll Expense ($000)**: 5891 **Personnel**: 113

NASHVILLE—Howard County

★ **HOWARD MEMORIAL HOSPITAL (041311)**, 130 Medical Circle, Zip 71852–8606; tel. 870/845–4400, **A**10 18 **F**3 11 15 28 29 30 34 35 40 43 45 50 53 57 64 65 70 77 81 85 87 93 102 103 107 108 110 115 119 133 146 **P**6
Primary Contact: Debra J. Wright, R.N., Chief Executive Officer
CFO: William J Craig CPA, Chief Financial Officer
CMO: John Hearnsberger M.D., Chief of Staff
CHR: Gayla Lacefield, Director Human Resources
CNO: Alesha Danielle Collins MSN, R.N., Chief Nursing Officer
Web address: www.howardmemorial.com
Control: Other not–for–profit (including NFP Corporation) **Service**: General medical and surgical

Staffed Beds: 20 **Admissions**: 564 **Census**: 6 **Outpatient Visits**: 34188 **Births**: 0 **Total Expense ($000)**: 18925 **Payroll Expense ($000)**: 8043 **Personnel**: 161

NORTH LITTLE ROCK—Pulaski County

☐ **ARKANSAS SURGICAL HOSPITAL (040147)**, 5201 North Shore Drive, Zip 72118–5312; tel. 501/748–8000, **A**1 10 **F**3 29 35 40 64 74 75 79 81 82 85 86 87 107 111 114 119 126 130 131 146 148 149
Primary Contact: Carrie Helm, Chief Executive Officer
CFO: Charles Powell, Chief Financial Officer
CMO: Kenneth A Martin M.D., Chief of Staff
CIO: Scott Davis, Manager Information Technology
CNO: Judy Jones, Chief Clinical Officer
Web address: www.ArkSurgicalHospital.com
Control: Corporation, Investor–owned (for–profit) **Service**: General medical and surgical

Staffed Beds: 49 **Admissions**: 3468 **Census**: 18 **Outpatient Visits**: 16553 **Births**: 0 **Total Expense ($000)**: 53034 **Payroll Expense ($000)**: 13287 **Personnel**: 226

Hospital, Medicare Provider Number, Address, Telephone, Approval, Facility, and Physician Codes, Health Care System

★ American Hospital Association (AHA) membership
☐ The Joint Commission accreditation
○ Healthcare Facilities Accreditation Program
◇ DNV Healthcare Inc. accreditation
⇑ Center for Improvement in Healthcare Quality Accreditation
△ Commission on Accreditation of Rehabilitation Facilities (CARF) accreditation

AR

☒ △ **BAPTIST HEALTH MEDICAL CENTER – NORTH LITTLE ROCK (040036)**, 3333 Springhill Drive, Zip 72117–2922; tel. 501/202-3000, **A**1 7 10 **F**3 8 11 13 15 17 18 20 22 24 26 28 29 30 31 38 40 43 45 46 47 48 49 50 53 54 56 59 60 64 65 70 72 74 75 76 77 78 79 81 85 86 87 89 90 93 94 107 108 110 111 114 115 118 119 124 126 129 130 135 144 146 147 148 **S** Baptist Health, Little Rock, AR
Primary Contact: Steven B. Webb, FACHE, Vice President and Administrator
COO: Doug Weeks, Executive Vice President and Chief Operations Officer
CFO: Robert C Roberts, Senior Vice President Financial Services
CMO: Eddie Phillips M.D., Chief Medical Affairs
CIO: David House, Vice President and Chief Information Officer
CHR: Cathy C Dickinson, Vice President Human Resources
CNO: Kelley Hamby, Vice President Patient Care
Web address: www.baptist–health.com/location/baptist–health–medical–center–north–little–rock–north–little–rock
Control: Other not–for–profit (including NFP Corporation) **Service**: General medical and surgical

Staffed Beds: 225 **Admissions**: 10927 **Census**: 128 **Outpatient Visits**: 104725 **Births**: 1332 **Total Expense ($000)**: 172374 **Payroll Expense ($000)**: 57501 **Personnel**: 1002

NORTH LITTLE ROCK DIVISION See Central Arkansas Veterans Healthcare System, Little Rock

☐ **THE BRIDGEWAY (044005)**, 21 Bridgeway Road, Zip 72113–9516; tel. 501/771-1500, **A**1 10 **F**4 5 34 56 98 99 101 102 103 104 105 106 149 **P**5 6 **S** Universal Health Services, Inc., King of Prussia, PA
Primary Contact: Jason Miller, M.P.H., Chief Executive Officer
CFO: Fred Woods, Chief Financial Officer
CMO: Philip L Mizell M.D., Medical Director
CHR: Neely Robison, Director Human Resources
CNO: Sherrie James R.N., Director of Nursing
Web address: www.thebridgeway.com
Control: Corporation, Investor–owned (for–profit) **Service**: Psychiatric

Staffed Beds: 127 **Admissions**: 4629 **Census**: 94 **Outpatient Visits**: 30765 **Births**: 0 **Total Expense ($000)**: 23323 **Payroll Expense ($000)**: 9847 **Personnel**: 196

OSCEOLA—Mississippi County

☒ **SOUTH MISSISSIPPI COUNTY REGIONAL MEDICAL CENTER (041316)**, 611 West Lee Avenue, Zip 72370–3001, Mailing Address: P.O.Box 108, Blytheville, 72316–0108; tel. 870/563-7000, **A**1 10 **F**29 40 57 59 68 75 81 93 107 114 130 133 146 **S** QHR, Brentwood, TN
Primary Contact: Chris Lee. Raymer, R.N., MSN, Chief Executive Officer
COO: Paul Pieffer, Chief Operating Officer
CFO: Randy Nichols, Chief Financial Officer
CMO: Pratapji Thakor M.D., Chief of Staff
CIO: Tammy Bratcher, Director Information Technology
CHR: Cheri Blurton, Director Human Resources
CNO: Felicia Pierce R.N., Chief Nursing Officer
Web address: www.mchsys.org
Control: County, Government, Nonfederal **Service**: General medical and surgical

Staffed Beds: 25 **Admissions**: 526 **Census**: 5 **Outpatient Visits**: 13245 **Births**: 0 **Total Expense ($000)**: 9646 **Payroll Expense ($000)**: 3810 **Personnel**: 63

OZARK—Franklin County

★ **MERCY HOSPITAL OZARK (041303)**, 801 West River Street, Zip 72949–3023; tel. 479/667-4138, **A**10 18 **F**3 35 40 43 45 57 59 64 65 68 81 85 107 119 129 133 148 149 **P**6 8 **S** Mercy, Chesterfield, MO
Primary Contact: Teresa Williams, R.N., Administrator and Director of Nursing
COO: Brent Hubbard, Chief Operating Officer
CMO: John Lachowsky M.D., Chief Medical Officer
CIO: Tiana Bolduc, Chief Information Officer
Web address: www.mercy.net/northwestarar/practice/mercy–hospital–ozark
Control: Church operated, Nongovernment, not–for–profit **Service**: General medical and surgical

Staffed Beds: 25 **Admissions**: 243 **Census**: 3 **Outpatient Visits**: 13363 **Births**: 0 **Total Expense ($000)**: 10514 **Payroll Expense ($000)**: 3840 **Personnel**: 54

PARAGOULD—Greene County

☒ △ **ARKANSAS METHODIST MEDICAL CENTER (040039)**, 900 West Kingshighway, Zip 72450–5942, Mailing Address: P.O.Box 339, 72451–0339; tel. 870/239-7000, **A**1 7 10 13 19 **F**3 7 10 11 13 15 18 20 22 28 29 32 34 35 39 40 43 45 49 50 51 53 54 57 59 62 64 68 70 75 76 78 79 81 85 86 87 89 90 93 97 107 108 110 111 114 115 119 125 129 130 131 132 133 135 146 147 148 **P**6 8
Primary Contact: Barry L. Davis, FACHE, President and Chief Executive Officer
CFO: Brad Bloemer, Vice President Finance and Chief Financial Officer
CMO: Aaron Thompson M.D., Chief of Staff
CIO: Dan Austin, Director Information Technology
CHR: Kevin Thielemier, Director Human Resources
CNO: Lana R Williams, Chief Nursing Officer
Web address: www.arkansasmethodist.org
Control: Other not–for–profit (including NFP Corporation) **Service**: General medical and surgical

Staffed Beds: 125 **Admissions**: 4165 **Census**: 51 **Outpatient Visits**: 129612 **Births**: 594 **Total Expense ($000)**: 60679 **Payroll Expense ($000)**: 27335 **Personnel**: 627

PARIS—Logan County

★ **MERCY HOSPITAL PARIS (041300)**, 500 East Academy, Zip 72855–4040; tel. 479/963-6101, **A**10 18 **F**3 35 40 43 45 57 59 64 65 68 81 85 107 119 127 129 133 148 149 **P**6 8 **S** Mercy, Chesterfield, MO
Primary Contact: Sharon D. Sorey, R.N., Administrator
COO: Brent Hubbard, Chief Operating Officer
Web address: www.mercy.net/fortsmithar
Control: Church operated, Nongovernment, not–for–profit **Service**: General medical and surgical

Staffed Beds: 16 **Admissions**: 90 **Census**: 1 **Outpatient Visits**: 13626 **Births**: 0 **Total Expense ($000)**: 9315 **Payroll Expense ($000)**: 3864 **Personnel**: 54

PIGGOTT—Clay County

★ **PIGGOTT COMMUNITY HOSPITAL (041330)**, 1206 Gordon Duckworth Drive, Zip 72454–1911; tel. 870/598-3881, **A**10 18 **F**3 7 8 11 29 30 34 35 40 43 45 46 50 57 59 62 64 65 71 77 81 86 87 93 107 111 114 119 127 129 130 132 133 135 143 146 148 **P**6
Primary Contact: James L. Magee, Executive Director
CFO: Linda Ort, Chief Financial Officer
Web address: www.piggottcommunityhospital.com
Control: City, Government, Nonfederal **Service**: General medical and surgical

Staffed Beds: 25 **Admissions**: 831 **Census**: 12 **Outpatient Visits**: 20349 **Births**: 0 **Total Expense ($000)**: 15985 **Payroll Expense ($000)**: 8252 **Personnel**: 201

PINE BLUFF—Jefferson County

★ △ **JEFFERSON REGIONAL MEDICAL CENTER (040071)**, 1600 West 40th Avenue, Zip 71603–6301; tel. 870/541-7100, **A**3 7 10 20 **F**3 8 11 13 15 17 18 20 22 28 29 30 31 34 35 40 43 45 46 48 49 50 51 53 54 56 57 59 60 61 64 65 70 72 73 74 75 76 77 78 79 81 85 86 87 89 90 96 97 98 100 101 102 103 107 108 110 111 114 115 116 117 118 119 124 128 130 131 132 135 143 144 145 146 147 148 149 **P**6 7
Primary Contact: Brian N. Thomas, President
CFO: Bryan G Jackson, Vice President and Chief Financial Officer
CMO: Reid Pierce M.D., Chief Medical Officer
CIO: Patrick Neece, Chief Information Officer
CHR: M Daryl Scott, Assistant Vice President
CNO: Louise Hickman R.N., Vice President of Patient Care Services
Web address: www.jrmc.org
Control: Other not–for–profit (including NFP Corporation) **Service**: General medical and surgical

Staffed Beds: 333 **Admissions**: 8988 **Census**: 140 **Outpatient Visits**: 190052 **Births**: 727 **Total Expense ($000)**: 167717 **Payroll Expense ($000)**: 70015 **Personnel**: 1336

POCAHONTAS—Randolph County

FIVE RIVERS MEDICAL CENTER (040047), 2801 Medical Center Drive, Zip 72455–9436; tel. 870/892-6000, **A**10 20 **F**3 11 29 40 43 45 50 57 59 62 68 70 79 81 85 93 98 103 107 111 115 119 127 129 130 131 133 146
Primary Contact: Luther J. Lewis, FACHE, Chief Executive Officer
CFO: Joey Radcliff, Chief Financial Officer
CHR: Anita Dickson, Director Human Resources
CNO: Paula Lewis, Interim Chief Nursing Officer
Web address: www.fiveriversmc.com
Control: Other not–for–profit (including NFP Corporation) **Service**: General medical and surgical

Staffed Beds: 36 **Admissions**: 688 **Census**: 13 **Outpatient Visits**: 21662 **Births**: 0 **Total Expense ($000)**: 16576 **Payroll Expense ($000)**: 8016 **Personnel**: 176

Many Facility Codes have changed. Please refer to the AHA Guide Code Chart. © 2017 AHA Guide

ROGERS—Benton County

☒ **MERCY HOSPITAL ROGERS (040010)**, 2710 Rife Medical Lane, Zip 72758–1452; tel. 479/338–8000, **A**1 3 10 **F**3 11 12 13 15 17 18 20 22 24 26 28 29 30 34 35 40 42 43 45 46 48 49 54 57 59 62 64 68 70 71 72 74 75 76 77 79 81 82 84 85 86 89 93 104 107 108 110 111 114 115 118 119 129 130 131 135 146 147 148 **S** Mercy, Chesterfield, MO
Primary Contact: Eric Pianalto, President
COO: Brenda Chase, Chief Operating Officer
CFO: Benny Stover, Vice President Finance
CMO: Chris Johnson M.D., Chief of Staff
CHR: Rick Barclay, Vice President Support Services
Web address: www.mercyhealthnwa.smhs.com
Control: Church operated, Nongovernment, not–for–profit **Service:** General medical and surgical

Staffed Beds: 191 **Admissions:** 12503 **Census:** 116 **Outpatient Visits:** 267359 **Births:** 1684 **Total Expense ($000):** 194942 **Payroll Expense ($000):** 69971 **Personnel:** 1098

RUSSELLVILLE—Pope County

☐ **SAINT MARY'S REGIONAL MEDICAL CENTER (040041)**, 1808 West Main Street, Zip 72801–2724; tel. 479/968–2841, (Nonreporting) **A**1 10 19 **S** RCCH HealthCare Partners, Brentwood, TN
Primary Contact: James Davidson, Chief Executive Officer
COO: Scott Bailey, Chief Operating Officer
CFO: Wendell VanEs, Chief Financial Officer
CMO: Vickie Henderson M.D., Chief Medical Officer
CHR: Connie Gragg, Director Human Resources
CNO: Carol Gore MSN, R.N., Chief Nursing Officer
Web address: www.saintmarysregional.com
Control: Corporation, Investor–owned (for–profit) **Service:** General medical and surgical

Staffed Beds: 151

SALEM—Fulton County

FULTON COUNTY HOSPITAL (041322), 679 North Main Street, Zip 72576–9451, Mailing Address: P.O.Box 517, 72576–0517; tel. 870/895–2691, **A**10 18 **F**3 7 11 28 29 30 34 40 43 45 57 59 75 107 114 119 133 146 148
Primary Contact: Charles Willett, Administrator and Chief Executive Officer
Web address: www.fultoncountyhospital.org
Control: County, Government, Nonfederal **Service:** General medical and surgical

Staffed Beds: 25 **Admissions:** 743 **Census:** 9 **Outpatient Visits:** 12317 **Births:** 0 **Total Expense ($000):** 10378 **Payroll Expense ($000):** 4422 **Personnel:** 153

SEARCY—White County

ADVANCED CARE HOSPITAL OF WHITE COUNTY (042011), 1200 South Main Street, Zip 72143–7321; tel. 501/278–3155, **A**10 **F**1 3 29 68 **P**5
Primary Contact: Terri L. Parsons, Administrator
CMO: Miguel Aguinaga M.D., FACS, Medical Director
CNO: Mistie Vannatter, Chief Nursing Officer
Web address: www.advancedcarehospital.com
Control: Other not–for–profit (including NFP Corporation) **Service:** Acute long–term care hospital

Staffed Beds: 27 **Admissions:** 204 **Census:** 15 **Outpatient Visits:** 0 **Births:** 0 **Total Expense ($000):** 7131 **Payroll Expense ($000):** 3077 **Personnel:** 81

★ **UNITY HEALTH WHITE COUNTY MEDICAL CENTER (040014)**, 3214 East Race Avenue, Zip 72143–4810; tel. 501/268–6121, (Includes UNITY HEALTH HARRIS MEDICAL CENTER, 1205 McLain Street, Newport, Arkansas, Zip 72112–3533, tel. 870/523–8911; Darren Caldwell, Vice President and Administrator; UNITY HEALTH SPECIALTY CARE, 1200 South Main Street, Searcy, Arkansas, Zip 72143–7397, tel. 501/278–3100; Raymond W Montgomery II, Chief Executive Officer) **A**10 13 20 **F**1 3 11 12 13 15 17 18 20 22 24 28 29 30 31 34 35 38 39 40 43 45 51 54 57 59 61 62 63 64 65 68 70 74 75 76 77 78 79 81 84 85 86 87 89 90 93 98 99 100 102 103 105 107 108 111 114 115 119 126 129 130 131 132 134 135 144 145 146 147 148 **P**2 6
Primary Contact: Raymond W. Montgomery II, FACHE, President and Chief Executive Officer
CFO: Stuart Hill, Vice President and Treasurer
CMO: John Henderson M.D., Chief Medical Officer
CIO: Phil Miller, Chief Information Officer
CHR: Pamela G Williams, Director Human Resources
CNO: Peggy Turner, Assistant Vice President and Director of Nursing
Web address: www.unity–health.org
Control: Other not–for–profit (including NFP Corporation) **Service:** General medical and surgical

Staffed Beds: 373 **Admissions:** 13052 **Census:** 157 **Outpatient Visits:** 116850 **Births:** 1473 **Total Expense ($000):** 224647 **Payroll Expense ($000):** 105259 **Personnel:** 1876

SHERWOOD—Pulaski County

★ **CHI ST. VINCENT MEDICAL CENTER–NORTH (040137)**, 2215 Wildwood Avenue, Zip 72120–5089; tel. 501/552–7100, **A**10 **F**3 11 15 18 20 22 26 29 30 35 40 44 45 50 64 68 70 74 79 81 85 87 107 110 111 115 118 119 129 130 146 149 150 **P**6 **S** Catholic Health Initiatives, Englewood, CO
Primary Contact: Polly J. Davenport, FACHE, R.N., Senior Vice President, Chief Operating Officer, President CHI St. Vincent Infirmary Medical Center a
CFO: Tadd M Richert, Senior Vice President and Chief Financial Officer
CMO: Thomas H. Cummins M.D., Senior Vice President and Chief Medical Officer
Web address: www.stvincenthealth.com
Control: Church operated, Nongovernment, not–for–profit **Service:** General medical and surgical

Staffed Beds: 69 **Admissions:** 1655 **Census:** 16 **Outpatient Visits:** 34955 **Births:** 0 **Total Expense ($000):** 26841 **Payroll Expense ($000):** 10811 **Personnel:** 173

☒ **ST. VINCENT REHABILITATION HOSPITAL (043031)**, 2201 Wildwood Avenue, Zip 72120–5074; tel. 501/834–1800, **A**1 10 **F**3 29 50 60 68 87 90 91 96 98 130 132 135 143 146 148 **S** HEALTHSOUTH Corporation, Birmingham, AL
Primary Contact: Lisa Watson, Chief Executive Officer
CFO: Stacy Shilling, Controller
CMO: Kevin J. Collins M.D., Medical Director
CNO: Shannon Moreno–Cook, Chief Nursing Officer
Web address: www.stvincenthealth.com/svrehabhospital/index.html
Control: Corporation, Investor–owned (for–profit) **Service:** Rehabilitation

Staffed Beds: 80 **Admissions:** 1754 **Census:** 57 **Outpatient Visits:** 0 **Births:** 0 **Total Expense ($000):** 22331 **Payroll Expense ($000):** 13489 **Personnel:** 189

SILOAM SPRINGS—Benton County

☒ **SILOAM SPRINGS REGIONAL HOSPITAL (040001)**, 603 North Progress Avenue, Zip 72761–4352; tel. 479/215–3000, **A**1 10 **F**3 11 13 15 28 29 30 34 40 43 45 50 57 59 64 68 70 75 76 77 79 81 85 91 93 107 108 110 111 115 118 119 129 130 144 146 147 **P**6 **S** Community Health Systems, Inc., Franklin, TN
Primary Contact: Patrick Kerrwood, Chief Executive Officer
CFO: Todd Williams, Chief Financial Officer
CMO: Ashish Mathur M.D., Chief of Staff
CHR: Cindy Ruffing, Director Human Resources
CNO: Maria Wleklinski, Chief Nursing Officer
Web address: www.ssrh.net
Control: Corporation, Investor–owned (for–profit) **Service:** General medical and surgical

Staffed Beds: 44 **Admissions:** 1525 **Census:** 10 **Outpatient Visits:** 48768 **Births:** 607 **Total Expense ($000):** 30486 **Payroll Expense ($000):** 12814 **Personnel:** 212

SPRINGDALE—Washington County

☒ **NORTHWEST MEDICAL CENTER – SPRINGDALE (040022)**, 609 West Maple Avenue, Zip 72764–5394, Mailing Address: P.O.Box 47, 72765–0047; tel. 479/751–5711, (Includes NORTHWEST MEDICAL CENTER – BENTONVILLE, 3000 Medical Center Parkway, Bentonville, Arkansas, Zip 72712, tel. 479/553–1000; Sharif Omar, Chief Executive Officer; WILLOW CREEK WOMEN'S HOSPITAL, 4301 Greathouse Springs Road, Johnson, Arkansas, Zip 72741–0544, P O Box 544, 72741–0544, tel. 479/684–3000; Sharif Omar, Chief Executive Officer) **A**1 3 10 **F**3 8 11 12 13 15 17 18 20 22 24 26 28 29 30 37 40 43 45 46 47 48 49 50 51 56 60 61 70 72 74 76 77 79 81 82 85 86 87 90 91 92 93 96 98 102 107 108 110 111 114 115 118 119 124 129 130 131 135 146 147 148 **P**5 8 **S** Community Health Systems, Inc., Franklin, TN
Primary Contact: Sharif Omar, Chief Executive Officer
COO: Tom Sledge, Chief Operating Officer
CMO: James Tanner M.D., Chief Medical Officer
CIO: Mark Bokon, Chief Information Officer
CHR: Les S Abercrombie III, Vice President Human Resouces
CNO: Karen Y Labonte, Chief Nursing Officer
Web address: www.northwesthealth.com
Control: Corporation, Investor–owned (for–profit) **Service:** General medical and surgical

Staffed Beds: 295 **Admissions:** 15625 **Census:** 155 **Outpatient Visits:** 154963 **Births:** 3578 **Total Expense ($000):** 213505 **Payroll Expense ($000):** 73898 **Personnel:** 1518

Hospital, Medicare Provider Number, Address, Telephone, Approval, Facility, and Physician Codes, Health Care System

★ American Hospital Association (AHA) membership
☐ The Joint Commission accreditation
○ Healthcare Facilities Accreditation Program
◇ DNV Healthcare Inc. accreditation
⇑ Center for Improvement in Healthcare Quality Accreditation
△ Commission on Accreditation of Rehabilitation Facilities (CARF) accreditation

AR

✠ **REGENCY HOSPITAL OF NORTHWEST ARKANSAS – SPRINGDALE (042009)**, 609 West Maple Avenue, 6th Fl, Zip 72764; tel. 479/757–2600, **A**1 10 **F**1 3 29 84 130 148 **S** Select Medical Corporation, Mechanicsburg, PA
Primary Contact: Jerry Alexander, Chief Executive Officer
COO: Ruth Jones, Chief Clinical Officer
CMO: Gary Templeton M.D., Medical Director
CHR: Melissa Ross–Cole, Director Human Resources
Web address: www.regencyhospital.com
Control: Corporation, Investor–owned (for–profit) **Service**: Acute long–term care hospital

Staffed Beds: 25 **Admissions**: 265 **Census**: 18 **Outpatient Visits**: 0 **Births**: 0 **Total Expense ($000)**: 9709 **Payroll Expense ($000)**: 4343 **Personnel**: 69

STUTTGART—Arkansas County

★ **BAPTIST HEALTH MEDICAL CENTER–STUTTGART (040072)**, 1703 North Buerkle Road, Zip 72160–1905, Mailing Address: P.O.Box 1905, 72160–1905; tel. 870/673–3511, **A**10 **F**3 11 13 15 18 29 30 34 35 39 40 43 45 53 56 57 59 64 68 75 76 78 79 81 85 87 93 97 98 103 107 110 111 114 119 127 129 130 132 133 135 146 148 **S** Baptist Health, Little Rock, AR
Primary Contact: Kevin L. Storey, Vice President and Administrator
CMO: Seth M. Kleinbeck M.D., Chief of Staff
CIO: Warren Horton, Information Technologist
CNO: Susan Williams R.N., Chief Nursing Officer
Web address: www.baptist–health.com/location/baptist–health–medical–center–stuttgart–stuttgart
Control: Church operated, Nongovernment, not–for–profit **Service**: General medical and surgical

Staffed Beds: 49 **Admissions**: 1337 **Census**: 15 **Outpatient Visits**: 23863 **Births**: 217 **Total Expense ($000)**: 28381 **Payroll Expense ($000)**: 10053 **Personnel**: 219

TEXARKANA—Miller County

☐ **RIVERVIEW BEHAVIORAL HEALTH (044020)**, 701 Arkansas Boulevard, Zip 71854–2105; tel. 870/772–5028, **A**1 10 **F**29 32 34 35 36 38 50 57 65 68 71 75 98 99 100 101 102 103 104 106 130 132 134 135 143 149 **P**6 **S** Acadia Healthcare Company, Inc., Franklin, TN
Primary Contact: Angie Crawford, R.N., Chief Executive Officer
CFO: Kimberly Hibschman, Chief Financial Officer
CIO: Jim Cruson, Chief Information Officer
CHR: Roberta Bachman, Director Human Resources
CNO: Carrie Gray, Director of Nursing
Web address: www.riverviewbehavioralhealth.com
Control: Public Health Service, Public, Federal **Service**: Psychiatric

Staffed Beds: 62 **Admissions**: 1412 **Census**: 40 **Outpatient Visits**: 0 **Births**: 0 **Total Expense ($000)**: 13155 **Payroll Expense ($000)**: 8170

VAN BUREN—Crawford County

✠ **SPARKS MEDICAL CENTER – VAN BUREN (040018)**, East Main and South 20th Streets, Zip 72956–5715, Mailing Address: P.O.Box 409, 72957–0409; tel. 479/474–3401, **A**1 10 **F**12 29 40 43 68 79 81 82 107 108 111 116 117 **S** Community Health Systems, Inc., Franklin, TN
Primary Contact: Daniel E. McKay, Chief Executive Officer
CHR: James Ford, Director Human Resources
Web address: www.sparkshealth.com/locations/sparks–medical–center–van–buren
Control: Corporation, Investor–owned (for–profit) **Service**: General medical and surgical

Staffed Beds: 30 **Admissions**: 727 **Census**: 5 **Outpatient Visits**: 32241 **Births**: 0 **Total Expense ($000)**: 17699 **Payroll Expense ($000)**: 5799 **Personnel**: 107

WALDRON—Scott County

★ **MERCY HOSPITAL WALDRON (041305)**, 1341 West 6th Street, Zip 72958–7642; tel. 479/637–4135, **A**10 18 **F**3 35 40 43 45 57 59 64 65 68 81 85 107 119 127 129 133 148 149 **P**8 **S** Mercy, Chesterfield, MO
Primary Contact: Teresa Williams, R.N., Regional Administrator
COO: Brent Hubbard, Chief Operating Officer
CFO: Greta Wilcher, Senior Vice President and Chief Financial Officer
CMO: Nathan Bennett M.D., Chief Medical Officer
CNO: Nick Hunt, Interim Director of Nursing
Web address: www.stedwardmercy.com
Control: Church operated, Nongovernment, not–for–profit **Service**: General medical and surgical

Staffed Beds: 24 **Admissions**: 202 **Census**: 3 **Outpatient Visits**: 14944 **Births**: 0 **Total Expense ($000)**: 10934 **Payroll Expense ($000)**: 4121 **Personnel**: 61

WALNUT RIDGE—Lawrence County

✠ **LAWRENCE MEMORIAL HOSPITAL (041309)**, 1309 West Main, Zip 72476–1430, Mailing Address: P.O.Box 839, 72476–0839; tel. 870/886–1200, (Total facility includes 179 beds in nursing home–type unit) **A**1 10 18 **F**3 4 11 15 28 29 32 34 35 40 45 46 47 57 59 84 85 97 107 111 114 119 127 128 129 130 133 135 146
Primary Contact: Gary R. Sparks, Interim President
COO: Junior Briner, Chief Operating Officer
CFO: Vanessa Wagner, Chief Financial Officer
CMO: Kevin M. Diamond M.D., Chief Medical Officer
CIO: Josh Wise, Director Information Technology
CHR: Brigett Montgomery, Director Human Resource
CNO: Rosalind C Casillas, Chief Nursing Officer
Web address: www.lawrencehealth.net
Control: County, Government, Nonfederal **Service**: General medical and surgical

Staffed Beds: 204 **Admissions**: 1151 **Census**: 167 **Outpatient Visits**: 28269 **Births**: 0 **Total Expense ($000)**: 23379 **Payroll Expense ($000)**: 11363 **Personnel**: 284

WARREN—Bradley County

★ **BRADLEY COUNTY MEDICAL CENTER (041327)**, 404 South Bradley Street, Zip 71671–3493; tel. 870/226–3731, **A**10 18 **F**11 13 15 29 30 34 35 40 45 49 50 56 57 59 62 68 81 87 98 103 104 107 108 110 111 115 118 119 129 130 132 133 146 147 **P**6
Primary Contact: Steve Henson, Chief Executive Officer
CFO: Brandon Gorman, Chief Financial Officer
CMO: Joe H Wharton M.D., Chief of Staff
CHR: Brooke Hatch, Director Human Resource
CNO: Sarah Tucker, Chief Nursing Officer
Web address: www.bradleycountymedicalcenter.com
Control: Other not–for–profit (including NFP Corporation) **Service**: General medical and surgical

Staffed Beds: 33 **Admissions**: 1016 **Census**: 13 **Outpatient Visits**: 79630 **Births**: 105 **Total Expense ($000)**: 20394 **Payroll Expense ($000)**: 8634 **Personnel**: 244

WYNNE—Cross County

✠ **CROSSRIDGE COMMUNITY HOSPITAL (041307)**, 310 South Falls Boulevard, Zip 72396–3013, Mailing Address: P.O.Box 590, 72396–0590; tel. 870/238–3300, **A**1 10 18 **F**3 11 15 28 34 35 40 50 57 59 62 64 68 69 77 81 93 107 110 111 114 119 130 133 146
Primary Contact: Gary R. Sparks, Administrator
COO: Bryan Mattes, Associate Administrator
CFO: Janice Morris, Accountant
CIO: Gail Copeland, Director Management Information Systems
CHR: Bertha Ragle, Director Personnel
CNO: Amelia Davis, Director of Nursing
Web address: www.stbernards.info
Control: Church operated, Nongovernment, not–for–profit **Service**: General medical and surgical

Staffed Beds: 15 **Admissions**: 743 **Census**: 9 **Outpatient Visits**: 20820 **Births**: 0 **Total Expense ($000)**: 15117 **Payroll Expense ($000)**: 6239 **Personnel**: 138

Many Facility Codes have changed. Please refer to the AHA Guide Code Chart. © 2017 AHA Guide

CALIFORNIA

ALAMEDA—Alameda County

★ **ALAMEDA HOSPITAL (050211)**, 2070 Clinton Avenue, Zip 94501–4397; tel. 510/522–3700, (Total facility includes 181 beds in nursing home–type unit) **A**10 **F**3 11 15 17 18 29 31 34 35 36 39 40 43 46 50 57 58 59 70 77 78 79 81 82 85 93 97 107 108 110 114 118 119 128 130 131 132 146 147 148 **S** Alameda Health System, San Leandro, CA
Primary Contact: James E. T. Jackson, M.P.H., Chief Administrative Officer
CFO: Robert C Anderson, Interim Chief Financial Officer
CMO: Aika Sharma M.D., President Medical Staff
CIO: Robert Lundy–Paine, Director Information Systems
CHR: Phyllis Weiss, Director Human Resources
Web address: www.alamedahospital.org
Control: Hospital district or authority, Government, Nonfederal **Service:** General medical and surgical

Staffed Beds: 227 **Admissions:** 2590 **Census:** 201 **Outpatient Visits:** 31569 **Births:** 0 **Total Expense ($000):** 98138 **Payroll Expense ($000):** 43739 **Personnel:** 509

ALHAMBRA—Los Angeles County

☐ **ALHAMBRA HOSPITAL MEDICAL CENTER (050281)**, 100 South Raymond Avenue, Zip 91801–3199, Mailing Address: P.O.Box 510, 91802–2510; tel. 626/570–1606, (Nonreporting) **A**1 10 **S** AHMC & Healthcare, Inc., Alhambra, CA
Primary Contact: Iris Lai, Chief Executive Officer
CFO: Linda Marsh, Vice President Financial Services and Chief Financial Officer
CMO: Stephen Chen M.D., Chief Medicare
CIO: Johnson Legaspi, Director Information Systems
CHR: Elizabeth Sabandit, Director Human Resources
CNO: Eleanor Martinez, Chief Nursing Officer
Web address: www.alhambrahospital.com
Control: Partnership, Investor–owned (for–profit) **Service:** General medical and surgical

Staffed Beds: 144

ALTURAS—Modoc County

MODOC MEDICAL CENTER (051330), 228 West McDowell Avenue, Zip 96101–3934; tel. 530/233–5131, (Nonreporting) **A**10 18
Primary Contact: Kevin Kramer, Chief Executive Officer
CMO: Ed Richert M.D., Chief of Staff
CHR: Diane Hagelthorn, Human Resources Generalist
Web address: www.modocmedicalcenter.org
Control: County, Government, Nonfederal **Service:** General medical and surgical

Staffed Beds: 87

ANAHEIM—Orange County

☐ **AHMC ANAHEIM REGIONAL MEDICAL CENTER (050226)**, 1111 West La Palma Avenue, Zip 92801–2881; tel. 714/774–1450, (Nonreporting) **A**1 10 **S** AHMC & Healthcare, Inc., Alhambra, CA
Primary Contact: Richard Castro, Chief Executive Officer
COO: Deborah G Webber, Chief Operating Officer
CFO: Michael Chung, Chief Financial Officer
CMO: Amitabh Prakash M.D., Chief Medical Officer
CIO: Jeff DesRoches, Manager Information Systems
CHR: Kathy Doi, Executive Director Human Resources
CNO: Phyllis Snyder, Chief Nursing Officer
Web address: www.anaheimregionalmc.com
Control: Other not–for–profit (including NFP Corporation) **Service:** General medical and surgical

Staffed Beds: 223

☐ **ANAHEIM GLOBAL MEDICAL CENTER (050744)**, 1025 South Anaheim Boulevard, Zip 92805–5806; tel. 714/533–6220, (Nonreporting) **A**1 10 **S** KPC Healthcare, Inc., Santa Ana, CA
Primary Contact: Scott Rifkin, Chief Executive Officer
CFO: John Collins, Chief Financial Officer
CMO: Beena Shah M.D., Chief of Staff and Chief Medical Officer
CNO: Bonita Wells Veal, Chief Nursing Officer
Web address: www.westernmedanaheim.com
Control: Corporation, Investor–owned (for–profit) **Service:** General medical and surgical

Staffed Beds: 188

ANAHEIM MEDICAL CENTER See Kaiser Permanente Orange County Anaheim Medical Center, Anaheim

⊞ **KAISER PERMANENTE ORANGE COUNTY ANAHEIM MEDICAL CENTER (050609)**, 3440 East La Palma Avenue, Zip 92806–2020; tel. 714/644–2000, (Includes ORANGE COUNTY IRVINE MEDICAL CENTER, 6640 Alton Parkway, Irvine, California, Zip 92618, tel. 949/932–5000; Mark E Costa, Executive Director) **A**1 3 5 10 **F**3 13 14 15 18 19 20 29 30 31 35 37 40 44 45 46 47 48 49 50 59 61 62 63 64 65 68 70 72 74 75 76 78 79 80 81 82 84 85 87 89 92 93 100 107 108 111 114 115 119 130 135 143 146 148 149 **S** Kaiser Foundation Hospitals, Oakland, CA
Primary Contact: Mark E. Costa, Executive Director
COO: Margie Harrier MSN, R.N., Medical Center Chief Operations Officer
CFO: Marcus Hoffman, Area Chief Financial Officer
CMO: Nancy Gin M.D., Area Associate Medical Director
CIO: James Brady, Area Information Officer
CHR: Jocelyn A. Herrera, Director Human Resources
CNO: Martha Dispoto R.N., I, Chief Nurse Executive, Anaheim Medical Center
Web address: www.kp.org
Control: Other not–for–profit (including NFP Corporation) **Service:** General medical and surgical

Staffed Beds: 436 **Admissions:** 34934 **Census:** 319 **Births:** 6382

⊞ **WEST ANAHEIM MEDICAL CENTER (050426)**, 3033 West Orange Avenue, Zip 92804–3183; tel. 714/827–3000, **A**1 10 13 **F**3 11 15 17 18 20 22 24 29 40 45 49 70 79 81 85 98 103 105 107 108 111 114 119 128 130 146 148 149 **S** Prime Healthcare, Ontario, CA
Primary Contact: Virgis Narbutas, Chief Executive Officer
CFO: Kora Guoyavatin, Chief Financial Officer
CMO: Hassan Alkhouli M.D., Chief Medical Officer
CIO: Vic Mahan, Director Information Technology
CHR: Stephanie Sioson, Director Human Resources
Web address: www.westanaheimmedctr.com
Control: Partnership, Investor–owned (for–profit) **Service:** General medical and surgical

Staffed Beds: 219 **Admissions:** 5907 **Census:** 101 **Outpatient Visits:** 40280 **Births:** 0 **Personnel:** 635

ANTIOCH—Contra Costa County

⊞ **KAISER PERMANENTE ANTIOCH MEDICAL CENTER (050760)**, 4501 Sand Creek Road, Zip 94531–8687; tel. 925/813–6500, (Nonreporting) **A**1 2 5 10 **S** Kaiser Foundation Hospitals, Oakland, CA
Primary Contact: Colleen McKeown, Senior Vice President and Area Manager
CFO: Kerry Easthope, Area Finance Officer
CMO: Dale Poppert M.D., Chief of Staff
CIO: Mical Cayton, Area Information Officer
CHR: Davida Lindsay–Bell, Area Human Resources Leader
CNO: Janet Jule, Chief Nurse Executive
Web address: www.health.kaiserpermanente.org/wps/portal/facility/100382
Control: Other not–for–profit (including NFP Corporation) **Service:** General medical and surgical

Staffed Beds: 150

⊞ **SUTTER DELTA MEDICAL CENTER (050523)**, 3901 Lone Tree Way, Zip 94509–6253; tel. 925/779–7200, **A**1 10 **F**3 8 11 13 15 18 20 22 26 29 30 31 34 35 40 41 45 47 49 50 51 60 64 65 66 68 70 72 74 75 76 77 78 79 81 82 83 84 85 86 93 96 107 108 110 111 114 115 119 127 130 132 146 147 148 149 **P**3 5 **S** Sutter Health, Sacramento, CA
Primary Contact: Dori Stevens, Chief Executive Officer
CFO: Julie Peterson, Chief Financial Officer
CMO: Anupam Mapara M.D., Chief of Staff
CIO: Kathy Frederickson, Information Systems Site Lead
CHR: Noemi Whitehead, Administrative Director Human Resources
CNO: James Christopher Reedy, Chief Nursing Officer
Web address: www.sutterdelta.org
Control: Other not–for–profit (including NFP Corporation) **Service:** General medical and surgical

Staffed Beds: 132 **Admissions:** 7200 **Census:** 82 **Outpatient Visits:** 85007 **Births:** 882 **Total Expense ($000):** 196240 **Payroll Expense ($000):** 66646 **Personnel:** 770

Hospital, Medicare Provider Number, Address, Telephone, Approval, Facility, and Physician Codes, Health Care System

★ American Hospital Association (AHA) membership
☐ The Joint Commission accreditation
○ Healthcare Facilities Accreditation Program
◇ DNV Healthcare Inc. accreditation
⇑ Center for Improvement in Healthcare Quality Accreditation
△ Commission on Accreditation of Rehabilitation Facilities (CARF) accreditation

CA

APPLE VALLEY—San Bernardino County

✠ **ST. MARY MEDICAL CENTER (050300)**, 18300 Highway 18, Zip 92307–2206, Mailing Address: P.O.Box 7025, 92307–0725; tel. 760/242–2311, **A**1 10 **F**8 11 13 15 18 20 22 24 26 28 29 30 34 35 40 45 46 50 57 59 60 64 65 68 70 71 72 75 76 77 78 79 81 82 84 85 86 87 89 93 107 108 111 115 119 126 127 130 132 135 143 146 147 148 149 **P**5 **S** Providence St. Joseph Health, Renton, WA
Primary Contact: Alan H. Garrett, President and Chief Executive Officer
CFO: Tracey Fernandez, Chief Financial Officer
CMO: Riad Z. Abdelkarim M.D., Vice President and Chief Medical Officer
CIO: Doug Kleine, IT Director
CHR: Amanda Lens, Director, Human Resources
CNO: Marilyn Drone R.N., MSN, Vice President, CNO
Web address: www.stmaryapplevalley.com/
Control: Church operated, Nongovernment, not–for–profit **Service**: General medical and surgical

Staffed Beds: 212 **Admissions**: 14740 **Census**: 172 **Outpatient Visits**: 150381 **Births**: 2432 **Total Expense ($000)**: 288493 **Payroll Expense ($000)**: 99725 **Personnel**: 1463

ARCADIA—Los Angeles County

✠ **METHODIST HOSPITAL OF SOUTHERN CALIFORNIA (050238)**, 300 West Huntington Drive, Zip 91007–3473, Mailing Address: P.O.Box 60016, 91066–6016; tel. 626/898–8000, **A**1 2 3 10 **F**3 12 13 14 15 17 18 20 22 24 26 28 29 30 31 34 35 37 38 40 45 46 48 49 50 51 55 56 57 58 59 60 64 65 68 70 72 73 74 75 76 77 78 79 81 82 84 85 86 87 90 92 94 96 107 108 111 114 115 119 130 132 135 146 147 148
Primary Contact: Dan F. Ausman, President and Chief Executive Officer
COO: Steven A. Sisto, Senior Vice President and Chief Operating Officer
CFO: William E. Grigg, Senior Vice President and Chief Financial Officer
CHR: Gwen Chambers, Executive Director Human Resources
CNO: Roberta A McCaffrey R.N., Vice President and Chief Nursing Officer
Web address: www.methodisthospital.org
Control: Other not–for–profit (including NFP Corporation) **Service**: General medical and surgical

Staffed Beds: 260 **Admissions**: 16142 **Census**: 197 **Outpatient Visits**: 80363 **Births**: 1703 **Total Expense ($000)**: 255390 **Payroll Expense ($000)**: 123060 **Personnel**: 1258

ARCATA—Humboldt County

○ **MAD RIVER COMMUNITY HOSPITAL (050028)**, 3800 Janes Road, Zip 95521–4788, Mailing Address: P.O.Box 1115, 95518–1115; tel. 707/822–3621, (Nonreporting) **A**10 11
Primary Contact: Douglas A. Shaw, Chief Executive Officer
CFO: Michael Young, Chief Financial Officer
CMO: Bonnie MacEvoy, Chief of Staff
CIO: Jedd Rudd, Director of Ancillary Services and Safety
CNO: Sara Isaacson, Chief Nursing Officer
Web address: www.madriverhospital.com
Control: Corporation, Investor–owned (for–profit) **Service**: General medical and surgical

Staffed Beds: 42

ATASCADERO—San Luis Obispo County

☐ **ATASCADERO STATE HOSPITAL**, 10333 El Camino Real, Zip 93422–5808, Mailing Address: P.O.Box 7001, 93423–7001; tel. 805/468–2000, (Nonreporting) **A**1
Primary Contact: Bob Hushing–Kline, Hospital Administrator
COO: David Landrum, Chief Police Services
CFO: Janie Pagnini, Administrator Accounting
CMO: David Fennell M.D., Acting Medical Director
CIO: James Grover, Manager Data Processing
CHR: Elizabeth Andres, Director Human Resources
CNO: Liz Souza, Coordinator Nursing Services
Web address: www.dmh.ca.gov/statehospitals/atascadero
Control: State, Government, Nonfederal **Service**: Psychiatric

Staffed Beds: 1275

AUBURN—Placer County

✠ **SUTTER AUBURN FAITH HOSPITAL (050498)**, 11815 Education Street, Zip 95602–2410; tel. 530/888–4500, **A**1 2 10 **F**3 5 8 11 12 15 17 18 20 28 29 30 31 34 35 37 39 40 44 45 47 49 50 57 58 59 62 63 64 68 70 74 75 78 79 81 85 86 87 90 92 93 107 108 110 111 114 119 130 132 135 145 146 147 148 **P**3 5 **S** Sutter Health, Sacramento, CA
Primary Contact: Mitchell J. Hanna, Chief Executive Officer
CFO: Gary Hubschman, Administrative Director Finance
CMO: John Mesic M.D., Chief Medical Officer
CIO: Tom Ream, Regional Chief Information Officer
CHR: Yvette Martinez, Director Human Resources
CNO: Gina Temple, Chief Nurse Executive
Web address: www.sutterhealth.org
Control: Other not–for–profit (including NFP Corporation) **Service**: General medical and surgical

Staffed Beds: 72 **Admissions**: 3678 **Census**: 33 **Outpatient Visits**: 69215 **Births**: 0 **Total Expense ($000)**: 135076 **Payroll Expense ($000)**: 41766 **Personnel**: 417

AVALON—Los Angeles County

★ **CATALINA ISLAND MEDICAL CENTER (051307)**, 100 Falls Canyon Road, Zip 90704, Mailing Address: P.O.Box 1563, 90704–1563; tel. 310/510–0700, **A**10 18 **F**3 11 28 34 36 40 50 57 64 65 75 93 96 107 113 119 127 128 130 134 146
Primary Contact: Jason Paret, Chief Executive Officer
CFO: John Lovrich, Chief Financial Officer
CMO: Laura Ulibarri M.D., Chief of Staff
CIO: Jami Fuller, Manager Information Technology
CHR: Krista Steuter, Director Human Resources
CNO: Lorrie Mortensen, Chief Nursing Officer
Web address: www.catalinaislandmedicalcenter.org
Control: Other not–for–profit (including NFP Corporation) **Service**: General medical and surgical

Staffed Beds: 12 **Admissions**: 10 **Census**: 7 **Births**: 0 **Total Expense ($000)**: 10953 **Payroll Expense ($000)**: 3400 **Personnel**: 61

BAKERSFIELD—Kern County

☐ **BAKERSFIELD HEART HOSPITAL (050724)**, 3001 Sillect Avenue, Zip 93308–6337; tel. 661/316–6000, **A**1 10 **F**3 18 20 22 24 26 28 29 34 40 45 46 47 50 57 59 68 70 79 81 85 107 111 119 130 141 147 148
Primary Contact: Michelle Oxford, Chief Operating Officer, Acting Chief Executive Officer
COO: Michelle Oxford, Chief Operating Officer, Acting Chief Executive Officer
CFO: Vickie Scharr, Chief Financial Officer
CMO: Brijesh Bhambi M.D., Chief Medical Officer
CIO: Peter Mayer, Director Information Systems
CHR: Linda Hansen, Director Human Resources
Web address: www.bakersfieldhearthospital.com
Control: Partnership, Investor–owned (for–profit) **Service**: General medical and surgical

Staffed Beds: 47 **Admissions**: 3386 **Census**: 38 **Births**: 0 **Total Expense ($000)**: 74215 **Payroll Expense ($000)**: 29868

✠ **BAKERSFIELD MEMORIAL HOSPITAL (050036)**, 420 34th Street, Zip 93301–2237; tel. 661/327–1792, **A**1 3 5 10 13 **F**3 11 13 15 17 18 20 22 24 26 28 29 30 31 37 40 45 50 58 60 68 70 72 74 75 76 77 78 79 81 84 85 86 88 89 93 107 108 109 111 114 115 119 120 124 126 130 146 147 148 149 **S** Dignity Health, San Francisco, CA
Primary Contact: Jon Van Boening, President and Chief Executive Officer
COO: Bruce Peters, Vice President and Chief Operating Officer
CFO: Jesica Hanson, Vice President and Chief Financial Officer
CMO: Rodney Mark Root D.O., Vice President Medical Affairs
CHR: Sheri Comaianni, Vice President Human Resources
Web address: www.bakersfieldmemorial.org
Control: Other not–for–profit (including NFP Corporation) **Service**: General medical and surgical

Staffed Beds: 398 **Admissions**: 15387 **Census**: 169 **Outpatient Visits**: 150385 **Births**: 3109 **Total Expense ($000)**: 392092 **Payroll Expense ($000)**: 138218 **Personnel**: 1410

☐ **GOOD SAMARITAN HOSPITAL–NORTH (050257)**, 901 Olive Drive, Zip 93308–4144, Mailing Address: P.O.Box 85002, 93380–5002; tel. 661/215–7500, **A**1 10 **F**29 35 45 60 64 70 74 75 81 85 98 100 101 103 107 115 117 119 130 135 148 **P**8
Primary Contact: Ganesh Acharya, Chief Executive Officer
COO: Anand Manohara, Chief Operating Officer
CFO: Rogelio Monzon, Chief Financial Officer
CMO: Gurmant Singh, Chief Medical Officer
CHR: Anand Manohara, Chief Operating Officer
CNO: Toby Davis, Chief Nursing Officer
Web address: www.goodsamhospital.com
Control: Partnership, Investor–owned (for–profit) **Service**: General medical and surgical

Staffed Beds: 64 **Admissions**: 1909 **Census**: 21 **Outpatient Visits**: 3656 **Births**: 0 **Total Expense ($000)**: 50788 **Payroll Expense ($000)**: 9659 **Personnel**: 294

✠ **HEALTHSOUTH BAKERSFIELD REHABILITATION HOSPITAL (053031)**, 5001 Commerce Drive, Zip 93309–0689; tel. 661/323–5500, **A**1 10 **F**3 28 29 35 59 77 82 90 91 92 95 96 100 148 149 **S** HEALTHSOUTH Corporation, Birmingham, AL
Primary Contact: Martha Samora, R.N., FACHE, Chief Executive Officer
CFO: Robert Mosesian, Controller
CMO: Chris Yoon M.D., Medical Director
CHR: Lori Brackett, Director Human Resources
CNO: Kathleen Szura R.N., Chief Nursing Officer
Web address: www.healthsouthbakersfield.com
Control: Corporation, Investor–owned (for–profit) **Service**: Rehabilitation

Staffed Beds: 70 **Admissions**: 1871 **Census**: 62 **Outpatient Visits**: 0 **Births**: 0 **Total Expense ($000)**: 28306 **Payroll Expense ($000)**: 13854 **Personnel**: 261

□ **KERN MEDICAL CENTER (050315)**, 1700 Mount Vernon Avenue, Zip 93306–4018; tel. 661/326–2000, (Nonreporting) **A**1 2 3 5 10
Primary Contact: Russell V. Judd, Chief Executive Officer
COO: Jared Leavitt, Chief Operating Officer
CFO: Andrew Cantu, Chief Financial Officer
CMO: Glenn Goldis, Chief Medical Officer
CHR: Lisa K. Hockersmith, Vice President Human Resources
CNO: Toni Smith, Chief Nursing Officer
Web address: www.kernmedical.com
Control: County, Government, Nonfederal **Service:** General medical and surgical

Staffed Beds: 188

⊞ **MERCY HOSPITALS OF BAKERSFIELD (050295)**, 2215 Truxtun Avenue, Zip 93301–3698, Mailing Address: P.O.Box 119, 93302–0119; tel. 661/632–5000, (Nonreporting) (Includes MERCY SOUTHWEST HOSPITAL, 400 Old River Road, Bakersfield, California, Zip 93311, tel. 661/663–6000) **A**1 2 3 10 **S** Dignity Health, San Francisco, CA
Primary Contact: Bruce Peters, Chief Executive Officer
CFO: Rodney Winegarner, Chief Financial Officer
CIO: Jeff Vague, Regional Manager Information Systems
CHR: Jay King, Vice President Human Resources
Web address: www.mercybakersfield.org
Control: Church operated, Nongovernment, not–for–profit **Service:** General medical and surgical

Staffed Beds: 222

⊞ **SAN JOAQUIN COMMUNITY HOSPITAL (050455)**, 2615 Chester Avenue, Zip 93301–2014, Mailing Address: P.O.Box 2615, 93303–2615; tel. 661/395–3000, **A**1 10 **F**3 8 11 12 13 15 16 18 20 22 24 26 28 29 30 31 34 35 36 40 45 46 47 48 49 50 51 54 55 56 57 59 64 65 68 70 71 72 74 75 76 77 78 79 81 82 84 85 86 87 89 91 107 108 110 111 114 115 116 117 118 119 120 121 123 124 126 130 132 135 146 147 148 149 **S** Adventist Health, Roseville, CA
Primary Contact: Sharlet Briggs, Ph.D., Market Chief Executive Officer and President
COO: Sharlet Briggs Ph.D., Chief Operating Officer
CFO: Brent Soper, Chief Financial Officer
CHR: Marlene Kreidler, Executive Director Human Resources
Web address: www.sanjoaquinhospital.org
Control: Church operated, Nongovernment, not–for–profit **Service:** General medical and surgical

Staffed Beds: 254 Admissions: 18127 Census: 186 Outpatient Visits: 175244 Births: 3260 Total Expense ($000): 374724 Payroll Expense ($000): 125022 Personnel: 1917

BALDWIN PARK—Los Angeles County

BALDWIN PARK MEDICAL CENTER See Kaiser Permanente Baldwin Park Medical Center

⊞ **KAISER PERMANENTE BALDWIN PARK MEDICAL CENTER (050723)**, 1011 Baldwin Park Boulevard, Zip 91706–5806; tel. 626/851–1011, **A**1 3 10 **F**3 8 13 15 18 29 30 31 34 35 40 41 49 56 57 58 59 60 61 62 63 64 65 68 70 72 74 75 76 77 78 79 81 82 84 85 86 87 93 94 107 111 119 130 146 147 148 149 **S** Kaiser Foundation Hospitals, Oakland, CA
Primary Contact: Margaret H. Pierce, Executive Director
COO: Payman Roshan, Chief Operating Officer
CFO: Rebecca Wheeler, Director Finance
CMO: John Bigley M.D., Medical Director
CIO: Linda C Salazar, Information Technology Leader
CNO: Michelle Nowicki R.N., MSN, Chief Nurse Executive
Web address: www.kp.org
Control: Other not–for–profit (including NFP Corporation) **Service:** General medical and surgical

Staffed Beds: 257 Admissions: 12392 Census: 108 Outpatient Visits: 359198 Births: 2972

⊞ **KINDRED HOSPITAL–BALDWIN PARK (052045)**, 14148 Francisquito Avenue, Zip 91706–6120; tel. 626/388–2700, **A**1 10 **F**1 3 29 45 60 68 77 84 87 107 111 119 130 148 **S** Kindred Healthcare, Louisville, KY
Primary Contact: Fiona Basa–Reyes, Chief Executive Officer
COO: Dina Garrow, Chief Nursing Officer and Chief Operating Officer
CFO: Christine Saltonstall, Chief Financial Officer
CMO: Anil Gupta M.D., Chief of Staff
CHR: Antoinette Bibal, Director Human Resources
CNO: Dina Garrow, Chief Nursing Officer and Chief Operating Officer
Web address: www.khbaldwinpark.com
Control: Corporation, Investor–owned (for–profit) **Service:** Acute long–term care hospital

Staffed Beds: 91 Admissions: 979 Census: 72 Outpatient Visits: 0 Births: 0 Total Expense ($000): 38368 Payroll Expense ($000): 18423 Personnel: 276

VISTA SPECIALTY HOSPITAL OF SAN GABRIEL VALLEY See Kindred Hospital–Baldwin Park

BANNING—Riverside County

⊞ **SAN GORGONIO MEMORIAL HOSPITAL (050054)**, 600 North Highland Springs Avenue, Zip 92220–3046; tel. 951/845–1121, **A**1 10 22 **F**3 8 11 13 15 18 28 29 30 34 35 40 45 49 50 56 57 68 70 76 79 81 82 85 87 104 107 108 110 115 119 130 146 147 148 149
Primary Contact: Steven Barron, Interim Chief Executive Officer
CFO: David Recupero, Chief Financial Officer
CMO: Richard Sheldon M.D., Vice President Medical Affairs
CIO: Dan Howard, Director, Information Services
CHR: Annah Karam, Director Human Resources
CNO: Pat Brown R.N., Chief Nursing Officer
Web address: www.sgmh.org
Control: Hospital district or authority, Government, Nonfederal **Service:** General medical and surgical

Staffed Beds: 79 Admissions: 3798 Census: 44 Outpatient Visits: 52217 Births: 397 Total Expense ($000): 84117 Payroll Expense ($000): 34153 Personnel: 597

BARSTOW—San Bernardino County

⊞ **BARSTOW COMMUNITY HOSPITAL (050298)**, 820 East Mountain View Street, Zip 92311–3004; tel. 760/256–1761, (Nonreporting) **A**1 10 20 **S** Quorum Health, Brentwood, TN
Primary Contact: Matthew H. Blevins, Chief Executive Officer
CFO: Carrie Howell, Chief Financial Officer
CIO: Scott Bullock, Director Information Systems
CNO: Donna M Smith, Chief Nursing Officer
Web address: www.barstowhospital.com
Control: Corporation, Investor–owned (for–profit) **Service:** General medical and surgical

Staffed Beds: 30

BERKELEY—Alameda County

⊞ **ALTA BATES SUMMIT MEDICAL CENTER (050305)**, 2450 Ashby Avenue, Zip 94705–2067; tel. 510/204–4444, (Includes ALTA BATES MEDICAL CENTER–HERRICK CAMPUS, 2001 Dwight Way, Berkeley, California, Zip 94704, tel. 510/204–4444) **A**1 3 5 10 **F**3 5 8 11 12 13 15 17 18 20 22 26 28 29 30 31 34 35 36 37 40 45 46 47 49 51 55 56 57 58 59 60 61 64 68 70 72 74 75 76 77 78 79 81 82 84 85 86 87 90 93 98 99 100 103 104 105 107 108 110 111 114 116 117 118 119 120 121 123 124 130 132 135 136 141 146 147 148 149 **P**3 5 **S** Sutter Health, Sacramento, CA
Primary Contact: Charles Prosper, Chief Executive Officer
CFO: Robert Petrina, Chief Financial Officer
CMO: John Gentile M.D., Vice President Medical Affairs
Web address: www.altabatessummit.org/
Control: Other not–for–profit (including NFP Corporation) **Service:** General medical and surgical

Staffed Beds: 441 Admissions: 16952 Census: 183 Outpatient Visits: 175911 Births: 5863 Total Expense ($000): 686043 Payroll Expense ($000): 176081 Personnel: 1264

CA

BIG BEAR LAKE—San Bernardino County

★ **BEAR VALLEY COMMUNITY HOSPITAL (051335)**, 41870 Garstin Drive, Zip 92315, Mailing Address: P.O.Box 1649, 92315-1649; tel. 909/866-6501, (Total facility includes 21 beds in nursing home–type unit) **A**10 18 **F**3 15 29 34 35 40 50 57 59 81 85 90 93 97 104 107 110 114 119 127 128 133 146 149 150 **S** QHR, Brentwood, TN
Primary Contact: John P. Friel, Chief Executive Officer
COO: Wade Sturgeon, Chief Operating Officer and Chief Financial Officer
CFO: Garth Hamblin, Chief Financial Officer
CMO: Michael Norman M.D., Chief Medical Staff
CHR: Kathy Norris, Director Human Resources
CNO: Mary Norman R.N., Risk and Compliance Officer
Web address: www.bvchd.com
Control: Hospital district or authority, Government, Nonfederal **Service:** General medical and surgical

Staffed Beds: 30 **Admissions:** 163 **Census:** 17 **Outpatient Visits:** 31393 **Births:** 0 **Total Expense ($000):** 20861 **Payroll Expense ($000):** 8754 **Personnel:** 155	

BISHOP—Inyo County

⊞ **NORTHERN INYO HOSPITAL (051324)**, 150 Pioneer Lane, Zip 93514-2599; tel. 760/873-5811, (Nonreporting) **A**1 10 18
Primary Contact: Kevin Flanigan, M.D., Chief Executive Officer
COO: Kelli Huntsinger, Chief Operating Officer
CMO: Thomas Boo M.D., Chief of Staff
CIO: Adam Taylor, Manager Information Technology
CHR: Georgan L. Stottlemyre, Chief Human Relations Officer
CNO: Tracy Aspel, Chief Nursing Officer
Web address: www.nih.org
Control: Hospital district or authority, Government, Nonfederal **Service:** General medical and surgical

Staffed Beds: 25	

BLYTHE—Riverside County

⇑ **PALO VERDE HOSPITAL (050423)**, 250 North First Street, Zip 92225-1702; tel. 760/922-4115, **A**10 20 21 **F**29 34 35 40 50 59 70 76 81 107 119 127 149
Primary Contact: Sandra J. Anaya, R.N., Chief Executive Officer
CFO: Christa Ronde, Assistant Chief Financial Officer
CMO: Hossain Sahlolbei M.D., Chief of Staff
CIO: Jerome Learson, Manager Information Technology and Chief Security Officer
CHR: Myrna Davis, Manager Human Resources
CNO: Nena Foreman, Chief Nursing Officer
Web address: www.paloverdehospital.org
Control: Hospital district or authority, Government, Nonfederal **Service:** General medical and surgical

Staffed Beds: 32 **Admissions:** 844 **Census:** 8 **Outpatient Visits:** 20206 **Births:** 142 **Total Expense ($000):** 23560 **Payroll Expense ($000):** 9806 **Personnel:** 125	

BRAWLEY—Imperial County

★ ⇑ **PIONEERS MEMORIAL HEALTHCARE DISTRICT (050342)**, 207 West Legion Road, Zip 92227-7780; tel. 760/351-3333, (Nonreporting) **A**3 10 21
Primary Contact: Lawrence E. Lewis, Chief Executive Officer
COO: Stephen J Campbell, Chief Operating Officer
CFO: Roger Armstrong, Interim Chief Financial Officer
CMO: Kestutis V Kuraitis M.D., Chief of Staff
CIO: Kathleen S. McKernan, Director Information Systems
CHR: Julie Cunningham, Associate Administrator and Chief Human Resources Officer
CNO: Robyn Atadero R.N., Chief Nursing Officer
Web address: www.pmhd.org
Control: Hospital district or authority, Government, Nonfederal **Service:** General medical and surgical

Staffed Beds: 107	

BREA—Orange County

⊞ **KINDRED HOSPITAL–BREA (052039)**, 875 North Brea Boulevard, Zip 92821-2699; tel. 714/529-6842, (Nonreporting) **A**1 10 **S** Kindred Healthcare, Louisville, KY
Primary Contact: Diane Zeoli, Chief Executive Officer
COO: Denise Jenkins, Chief Clinical Officer
CFO: John Browne, Assistant Administrator Finance
CMO: Jyotika Wali M.D., Chief of Staff
Web address: www.kindredhospitalbrea.com/
Control: Corporation, Investor–owned (for–profit) **Service:** Acute long–term care hospital

Staffed Beds: 48	

BURBANK—Los Angeles County

⊞ △ **PROVIDENCE SAINT JOSEPH MEDICAL CENTER (050235)**, 501 South Buena Vista Street, Zip 91505-4866; tel. 818/843-5111, **A**1 2 3 7 10 **F**3 11 12 13 15 17 18 20 22 24 26 29 31 34 35 36 39 40 41 45 46 47 48 49 50 51 53 55 56 57 58 59 62 63 64 65 70 72 74 75 76 77 78 79 81 82 83 84 85 86 87 90 92 93 97 100 101 107 108 110 111 114 115 116 117 119 120 121 122 123 124 126 130 131 132 143 145 146 147 148 149 **P**2 3 5 **S** Providence St. Joseph Health, Renton, WA
Primary Contact: Kelly Linden, Chief Executive Officer
CFO: Glenn Bales, Chief Financial Officer
CMO: Nick Testa M.D., Chief Medical Officer
CIO: Anne Marie Brody, Director Information Systems Customer Service
CHR: LaDonna Najieb, Service Area Director Human Resources
CNO: Elizabeth Hart R.N., MSN, Chief Nursing Officer
Web address: www.providence.org
Control: Church operated, Nongovernment, not–for–profit **Service:** General medical and surgical

Staffed Beds: 383 **Admissions:** 16853 **Census:** 200 **Outpatient Visits:** 284688 **Births:** 2466 **Total Expense ($000):** 336189 **Payroll Expense ($000):** 157336 **Personnel:** 2076	

BURLINGAME—San Mateo County

⊞ **MILLS–PENINSULA HEALTH SERVICES (050007)**, 1501 Trousdale Drive, Zip 94010-3282; tel. 650/696-5400, (Includes MILLS HEALTH CENTER, 100 South San Mateo Drive, San Mateo, California, Zip 94401, tel. 650/696-4400; Janet Wagner, R.N., Chief Executive Officer; MILLS–PENINSULA MEDICAL CENTER, 1501 Trousdale Drive, Burlingame, California, Zip 94010-3205, tel. 650/696-5400; Janet Wagner, R.N., Chief Executive Officer) **A**1 10 **F**2 3 4 5 6 11 12 13 15 17 18 20 22 24 26 28 29 30 31 34 35 36 37 40 41 44 45 46 47 48 49 50 51 53 54 55 56 57 58 59 61 64 65 68 69 73 74 75 76 77 78 79 81 84 85 87 90 93 98 99 100 102 103 104 105 107 108 110 111 115 116 117 118 119 120 121 123 124 126 130 132 135 146 147 148 149 **P**3 5 **S** Sutter Health, Sacramento, CA
Primary Contact: Janet Wagner, R.N., Chief Executive Officer
COO: Dolores S. Gomez R.N., Chief Operating Officer
CFO: Catherine Messman, Chief Financial Officer
CMO: Ranjit Hundal M.D., Chief Medical Executive
CIO: Michael Reandeau, Chief Information Officer
CHR: Claudia Christensen, Director, Human Resources
CNO: Vicki White R.N., MS, Chief Nurse Executive
Web address: www.mills–peninsula.org
Control: Other not–for–profit (including NFP Corporation) **Service:** General medical and surgical

Staffed Beds: 266 **Admissions:** 13216 **Census:** 160 **Outpatient Visits:** 346462 **Births:** 2070 **Total Expense ($000):** 538761 **Payroll Expense ($000):** 150690 **Personnel:** 1535	

CAMARILLO—Ventura County

★ **ST. JOHN'S PLEASANT VALLEY HOSPITAL (050616)**, 2309 Antonio Avenue, Zip 93010-1414; tel. 805/389-5800, (Nonreporting) **A**10 **S** Dignity Health, San Francisco, CA
Primary Contact: Darren W. Lee, President and Chief Executive Officer
COO: Richard Montmeny, Vice President Professional Services, On–Site Administrator
CFO: Donald P Bernard, Chief Financial Officer
CMO: Sahin Yanik M.D., Vice President Medical Associate
CIO: Jeff Perry, Director Information Technology
CHR: Ed Gonzales, Vice President Human Resources
CNO: Dana Littlepage, Interim Chief Nursing Officer
Web address: www.dignityhealth.org/pleasantvalley
Control: Other not–for–profit (including NFP Corporation) **Service:** General medical and surgical

Staffed Beds: 127	

CAMP PENDLETON—San Diego County

⊞ **NAVAL HOSPITAL CAMP PENDLETON**, 200 Mercy Circle, Zip 92055-5191, Mailing Address: P.O.Box 555191, 92055-5191; tel. 760/725-1304, (Nonreporting) **A**1 3 5 **S** Bureau of Medicine and Surgery, Department of the Navy, Falls Church, VA
Primary Contact: Captain Lisa Mulligan, Commanding Officer
CFO: CommanderGordon Blighton, Director Resource Management
CIO: Gabe Vallido, Chief Information Officer
CHR: LieutenantJet Ramos, Head Staff Administration
Web address: www.cpen.med.navy.mil/
Control: Navy, Government, federal **Service:** General medical and surgical

Staffed Beds: 72	

Many Facility Codes have changed. Please refer to the AHA Guide Code Chart.
© 2017 AHA Guide

CANOGA PARK—Los Angeles County, See Los Angeles

CARMICHAEL—Sacramento County

⊞ **MERCY SAN JUAN MEDICAL CENTER (050516)**, 6501 Coyle Avenue, Zip 95608–0306; tel. 916/537–5000, **A**1 2 3 5 10 **F**3 8 11 12 13 15 17 18 20 22 24 26 28 29 30 31 34 35 37 40 43 45 46 47 48 49 50 51 57 58 62 63 64 70 72 74 75 76 77 78 79 81 82 83 84 85 87 89 92 93 100 107 108 111 115 118 119 126 129 130 132 135 146 148 **P**3 **S** Dignity Health, San Francisco, CA
Primary Contact: Brian K. Ivie, President
COO: Paul R Luehrs, Chief Operating Officer
CFO: Robert Pascuzzi, Chief Financial Officer
CMO: Mark Owens M.D., Vice President Medical Affairs
CHR: Donna Utley, Vice President Human Resources
Web address: www.mercysanjuan.org
Control: Church operated, Nongovernment, not–for–profit **Service:** General medical and surgical

Staffed Beds: 340 **Admissions:** 21081 **Census:** 284 **Outpatient Visits:** 100042 **Births:** 2082 **Personnel:** 2020

CASTRO VALLEY—Alameda County

⊞ **EDEN MEDICAL CENTER (050488)**, 20103 Lake Chabot Road, Zip 94546–5305; tel. 510/537–1234, **A**1 2 3 10 **F**3 5 11 13 15 18 29 30 31 34 35 38 40 43 46 47 49 50 51 53 54 56 57 58 59 60 65 68 70 73 74 75 76 77 78 79 81 84 85 87 93 100 101 102 107 108 110 111 115 117 118 119 120 121 123 130 132 135 144 146 147 148 **P**3 5 **S** Sutter Health, Sacramento, CA
Primary Contact: Theresa Glubka, R.N., Chief Executive Officer
Web address: www.edenmedcenter.org
Control: Other not–for–profit (including NFP Corporation) **Service:** General medical and surgical

Staffed Beds: 130 **Admissions:** 8217 **Census:** 106 **Outpatient Visits:** 94352 **Births:** 1012 **Total Expense ($000):** 341561 **Payroll Expense ($000):** 110383 **Personnel:** 1042

CEDARVILLE—Modoc County

SURPRISE VALLEY HEALTH CARE DISTRICT (051308), 741 North Main Street, Zip 96104, Mailing Address: P.O.Box 246, 96104–0246; tel. 530/279–6111, (Nonreporting) **A**10 18
Primary Contact: Richard Cornwell, Chief Executive Officer
CFO: Renae Sweet, Chief Financial Officer
CMO: Chuck Colas M.D., Medical Director
CHR: William Bostic, Administrative Assistant Human Resources
Web address: www.svhospital.org/
Control: Hospital district or authority, Government, Nonfederal **Service:** General medical and surgical

Staffed Beds: 4

CERRITOS—Los Angeles County

☐ **COLLEGE HOSPITAL CERRITOS (054055)**, 10802 College Place, Zip 90703–1579; tel. 562/924–9581, (Nonreporting) **A**1 10 **S** College Health Enterprises, Santa Fe Springs, CA
Primary Contact: Stephen Witt, President and Chief Executive Officer
CFO: Roderick Bell, Chief Financial Officer
CHR: Holly Risha, Administrative Director Human Resources
Web address: www.collegehospitals.com
Control: Corporation, Investor–owned (for–profit) **Service:** Psychiatric

Staffed Beds: 157

CHESTER—Plumas County

SENECA HEALTHCARE DISTRICT (051327), 130 Brentwood Drive, Zip 96020–0737, Mailing Address: P.O.Box 737, 96020–0737; tel. 530/258–2151, (Nonreporting) **A**5 10 18
Primary Contact: Linda S. Wagner, R.N., MSN, FACHE, Chief Executive Officer
CFO: Carlene Slusher, Director Finance
CMO: Dana Ware M.D., Chief of Staff
CIO: Elizabeth Steffen, Director Information Technology
CHR: Marie Stuersel, Director Human Resources
CNO: Teresa L Whitfield MS, R.N., Chief Nursing Officer
Web address: www.senecahospital.org
Control: Hospital district or authority, Government, Nonfederal **Service:** General medical and surgical

Staffed Beds: 26

CHICO—Butte County

⊞ **ENLOE MEDICAL CENTER (050039)**, 1531 Esplanade, Zip 95926–3386; tel. 530/332–7300, (Includes ENLOE MEDICAL CENTER–COHASSET, 560 Cohasset Road, Chico, California, Zip 95926, tel. 530/332–7300) **A**1 10 **F**3 7 8 11 12 13 17 18 19 20 22 24 26 28 29 30 31 34 35 36 38 39 40 43 44 45 46 49 50 51 54 57 59 61 62 63 64 65 68 69 70 73 74 75 76 77 78 79 81 84 85 87 89 90 91 92 93 94 96 98 99 100 101 102 103 107 108 109 111 114 115 116 117 118 119 120 121 123 124 130 132 143 144 146 147 148 149
Primary Contact: Michael C. Wiltermood, President and Chief Executive Officer
CMO: Forrest Olson M.D., Chief Medical Officer
CHR: Carol Linscheid, Vice President Human Resources
Web address: www.enloe.org
Control: Other not–for–profit (including NFP Corporation) **Service:** General medical and surgical

Staffed Beds: 298 **Admissions:** 16159 **Census:** 207 **Outpatient Visits:** 16493 **Births:** 1560 **Total Expense ($000):** 522320 **Payroll Expense ($000):** 179911 **Personnel:** 2515

CHINO—San Bernardino County

☐ **CANYON RIDGE HOSPITAL (054111)**, 5353 'G' Street, Zip 91710–5250; tel. 909/590–3700, (Nonreporting) **A**1 3 10 **S** Universal Health Services, Inc., King of Prussia, PA
Primary Contact: Burt Harris, Acting Chief Executive Officer
CFO: Burt Harris, Chief Financial Officer
CMO: Mir Ali–Khan M.D., Medical Director
CIO: Maria Patterson, Manager Health Information Management
CHR: Ericca Lopez, Director Human Resources
Web address: www.canyonridgehospital.com
Control: Corporation, Investor–owned (for–profit) **Service:** Psychiatric

Staffed Beds: 106

★ ○ **CHINO VALLEY MEDICAL CENTER (050586)**, 5451 Walnut Avenue, Zip 91710–2672; tel. 909/464–8600, (Nonreporting) **A**10 11 12 13 **S** Prime Healthcare, Ontario, CA
Primary Contact: James M. Lally, D.O., President and Chief Medical Officer
CIO: Vic Mahan, Chief Information Officer
Web address: www.cvmc.com
Control: Corporation, Investor–owned (for–profit) **Service:** General medical and surgical

Staffed Beds: 126

CHULA VISTA—San Diego County

SCRIPPS MERCY HOSPITAL CHULA VISTA See Scripps Mercy Hospital, San Diego

⊞ **SHARP CHULA VISTA MEDICAL CENTER (050222)**, 751 Medical Center Court, Zip 91911–6699, Mailing Address: P.O.Box 1297, 91912–1297; tel. 619/502–5800, (Total facility includes 100 beds in nursing home–type unit) **A**1 2 10 **F**8 11 12 13 15 17 18 20 22 24 26 28 29 30 31 34 35 40 46 47 49 51 53 54 57 59 60 63 64 65 70 72 75 76 77 78 79 81 82 84 85 86 87 93 107 108 114 115 119 120 121 123 124 126 128 130 132 143 146 147 148 **P**5 **S** Sharp HealthCare, San Diego, CA
Primary Contact: Pablo Velez, Chief Executive Officer
CMO: Lynn Welling M.D., Chief Medical Officer
CHR: Zoe Gardner, Manager Human Resources
Web address: www.sharp.com
Control: Other not–for–profit (including NFP Corporation) **Service:** General medical and surgical

Staffed Beds: 343 **Admissions:** 15693 **Census:** 275 **Outpatient Visits:** 177086 **Births:** 2788 **Total Expense ($000):** 364671 **Payroll Expense ($000):** 146802 **Personnel:** 1718

CA

CA

CLEARLAKE—Lake County

⊞ **ST. HELENA HOSPITAL CLEAR LAKE (051317)**, 15630 18th Avenue, Zip 95422–9336, Mailing Address: P.O.Box 6710, 95422; tel. 707/994–6486, (Nonreporting) **A**1 10 18 **S** Adventist Health, Roseville, CA
Primary Contact: David Santos, President and Chief Executive Officer
COO: David Santos, President Chief Executive Officer
CFO: Carlton Jacobson, Vice President of Finance
CMO: Marc Shapiro M.D., Chief Medical Officer
CIO: Cambria Wheeler, Communications and Marketing
CHR: Audrey Barrall, Director Human Resources
CNO: Colleen Assavapisitkul, Chief Nursing Officer
Web address: www.adventisthealth.org
Control: Church operated, Nongovernment, not–for–profit **Service**: General medical and surgical

Staffed Beds: 25

CLOVIS—Fresno County

CLOVIS COMMUNITY MEDICAL CENTER (050492), 2755 Herndon Avenue, Zip 93611–6801; tel. 559/324–4000, (Nonreporting) **A**10 **S** Community Medical Centers, Fresno, CA
Primary Contact: Craig Castro, Chief Executive Officer
CFO: Tracy Kiritani, Vice President and Chief Financial Officer
CIO: George Vasquez, Chief Technology Officer
CHR: Ginny Burdick, Senior Vice President and Chief Human Resources Officer
Web address: www.communitymedical.org
Control: Other not–for–profit (including NFP Corporation) **Service**: General medical and surgical

Staffed Beds: 109

COALINGA—Fresno County

COALINGA REGIONAL MEDICAL CENTER (050397), 1191 Phelps Avenue, Zip 93210–9636; tel. 559/935–6400, (Nonreporting) **A**10 20
Primary Contact: Sharon A. Spurgeon, Chief Executive Officer
CFO: Sandra Earls, Chief Financial Officer
CMO: Kenneth Smith M.D., Emergency Medicine Medical Director
CIO: Chris Burrage, Manager Information Technology
CHR: Connie Pierce, Manager Human Resources
CNO: Rita Sypitkowski, Director of Patient Services
Web address: www.coalingamedicalcenter.com
Control: Hospital district or authority, Government, Nonfederal **Service**: General medical and surgical

Staffed Beds: 123

COLTON—San Bernardino County

★ ○ **ARROWHEAD REGIONAL MEDICAL CENTER (050245)**, 400 North Pepper Avenue, Zip 92324–1819; tel. 909/580–1000, **A**3 5 10 11 12 13 **F**3 8 13 15 16 18 20 22 28 29 30 31 32 34 35 36 39 40 43 45 47 49 50 51 52 54 55 56 57 60 64 66 68 70 71 72 74 75 76 77 78 79 81 82 84 85 86 87 89 91 92 93 97 98 100 101 102 107 108 110 111 114 115 116 118 119 120 121 130 132 135 146 147 148 149 150 **P**5
Primary Contact: William L. Gilbert, Hospital Director
CFO: Frank Arambula, Chief Financial Officer
CMO: Richard Pitts D.O., Ph.D., Medical Director
CIO: Felix Ekpo, Manager, Information Systems
CHR: Kevin Saunders, Human Resources Officer III
CNO: Michelle Sayre R.N., Chief Nursing Officer
Web address: www.arrowheadmedcenter.org
Control: County, Government, Nonfederal **Service**: General medical and surgical

Staffed Beds: 436 Admissions: 22270 Census: 314 Outpatient Visits: 386001 Births: 3300 Total Expense ($000): 564886 Payroll Expense ($000): 186956 Personnel: 2990

CONCORD—Contra Costa County

⊞ **JOHN MUIR BEHAVIORAL HEALTH CENTER (054131)**, 2740 Grant Street, Zip 94520–2265; tel. 925/674–4100, (Nonreporting) **A**1 10 **S** John Muir Health, Walnut Creek, CA
Primary Contact: Cindy Bolter, Chief Nursing and Operations Officer
COO: Arman Danielyan M.D., Chief of Staff
CFO: Christian Pass, Senior Vice President and Chief Financial Officer
CMO: O B Towery M.D., Chief of Staff
CIO: Jim Wesley, Senior Vice President and Chief Information Officer
CHR: Lisa Foust, Senior Vice President Human Resources
CNO: Cindy Bolter, Chief Nursing and Operations Officer
Web address: www.johnmuirhealth.com
Control: Other not–for–profit (including NFP Corporation) **Service**: Psychiatric

Staffed Beds: 73

⊞ **JOHN MUIR MEDICAL CENTER, CONCORD (050496)**, 2540 East Street, Zip 94520–1906; tel. 925/682–8200, **A**1 2 10 **F**3 12 15 17 18 20 22 24 26 28 29 30 31 34 37 39 40 41 44 45 46 47 48 49 50 55 56 57 58 59 61 64 68 70 74 75 77 78 79 80 81 82 83 84 85 86 87 93 100 102 107 108 110 115 118 119 120 121 123 126 130 132 141 145 146 148 149 **P**3 5 7 **S** John Muir Health, Walnut Creek, CA
Primary Contact: Michael S. Thomas, President and Chief Administrative Officer
COO: Michael S Thomas, President and Chief Administrative Officer
CFO: Christian Pass, Interim Chief Financial Officer
CMO: John Merson M.D., Chief of Staff
CIO: Jon Russell, Senior Vice President and Chief Information Officer
CHR: Lisa Foust, Senior Vice President Human Resources
CNO: Donna Brackley R.N., MSN, Senior Vice President Patient Care Services
Web address: www.johnmuirhealth.com
Control: Other not–for–profit (including NFP Corporation) **Service**: General medical and surgical

Staffed Beds: 195 Admissions: 10657 Census: 139 Outpatient Visits: 179761 Births: 0 Total Expense ($000): 453638 Payroll Expense ($000): 169715 Personnel: 1194

CORONA—Riverside County

☐ **CORONA REGIONAL MEDICAL CENTER (050329)**, 800 South Main Street, Zip 92882–3400; tel. 951/737–4343, (Includes CORONA REGIONAL MEDICAL CENTER–REHABILITATION, 730 Magnolia Avenue, Corona, California, Zip 92879, tel. 951/736–7200) **A**1 10 **F**1 3 4 13 15 16 17 18 20 22 26 29 30 34 35 38 40 41 42 45 46 49 50 51 57 62 63 67 70 72 73 74 75 76 79 80 81 84 85 87 88 89 90 97 98 101 102 104 105 107 110 111 115 119 128 130 135 143 146 148 **S** Universal Health Services, Inc., King of Prussia, PA
Primary Contact: Mark H. Uffer, Chief Executive Officer
COO: Mitchell Winnik, Chief Operating Officer
CFO: Kanner Tillman, Chief Financial Officer
CMO: Alaa Y Afifi M.D., Chief of Staff
CIO: De'Niro Pankey, Director Information Systems
CHR: Dale Cole, Director, Human Resources
CNO: Kim Colonnelli, Chief Nursing Officer
Web address: www.coronaregional.com
Control: Corporation, Investor–owned (for–profit) **Service**: General medical and surgical

Staffed Beds: 238 Admissions: 8394 Census: 140 Outpatient Visits: 67157 Births: 904 Total Expense ($000): 132561 Payroll Expense ($000): 67419 Personnel: 937

CORONADO—San Diego County

⊞ **SHARP CORONADO HOSPITAL AND HEALTHCARE CENTER (050234)**, 250 Prospect Place, Zip 92118–1999; tel. 619/522–3600, (Total facility includes 122 beds in nursing home–type unit) **A**1 10 **F**3 8 11 15 29 30 34 35 36 37 40 41 45 46 47 49 53 57 58 59 60 64 65 68 70 74 75 77 79 81 82 84 85 86 87 91 93 107 111 114 119 126 128 130 132 135 146 148 149 **S** Sharp HealthCare, San Diego, CA
Primary Contact: Susan Stone, R.N., Ph.D., Senior Vice President and Chief Executive Officer
CFO: Victoria Day, Chief Financial Officer and Vice President of Ancillary Services
CHR: Rachel Davis, Director
CNO: Christopher Walker, Chief Nursing Officer
Web address: www.sharp.com
Control: Other not–for–profit (including NFP Corporation) **Service**: General medical and surgical

Staffed Beds: 181 Admissions: 2125 Census: 119 Outpatient Visits: 89637 Births: 0 Total Expense ($000): 92069 Payroll Expense ($000): 37946 Personnel: 422

COSTA MESA—Orange County

☐ **COLLEGE HOSPITAL COSTA MESA (050543)**, 301 Victoria Street, Zip 92627–7131; tel. 949/642–2734, (Nonreporting) **A**1 10 **S** College Health Enterprises, Santa Fe Springs, CA
Primary Contact: Susan L. Taylor, JD, Chief Executive Officer
CFO: Dale Bracy, Chief Financial Officer
CMO: Michael Schwartz M.D., Chief of Staff
CIO: Eladio Aldana, Manager Information Systems
CHR: Sharon DuBruyne, Director Human Resources
Web address: www.collegehospitals.com/cosHome
Control: Corporation, Investor–owned (for–profit) **Service**: Psychiatric

Staffed Beds: 122

FAIRVIEW DEVELOPMENTAL CENTER (050548), 2501 Harbor Boulevard, Zip 92626; tel. 714/957–5000, **A**10
Primary Contact: Cheryl Bright, Executive Director
Web address: www.dds.ca.gov/fairview/index.cfm
Control: State, Government, Nonfederal **Service**: Intellectual disabilities

Staffed Beds: 237

Many Facility Codes have changed. Please refer to the AHA Guide Code Chart. © 2017 AHA Guide

COVINA—Los Angeles County

☐ **AURORA CHARTER OAK HOSPITAL (054069)**, 1161 East Covina Boulevard, Zip 91724–1599; tel. 626/966–1632, **A**1 10 **F**4 5 29 35 87 98 101 102 104 105 130 135 **S** Signature Healthcare Services, Corona, CA
Primary Contact: Todd A. Smith, Chief Executive Officer
COO: Sheila Cordova, Director Clinical Services and Chief Operating Officer
CMO: Adib Bitar M.D., Medical Director
CHR: Christine de la Paz, Director Human Resources
CNO: Sheila Cordova, Chief Operating Officer and Chief Nursing Officer
Web address: www.charteroakhospital.com
Control: Corporation, Investor–owned (for–profit) **Service**: Psychiatric

> **Staffed Beds:** 146 **Admissions:** 7293 **Census:** 129 **Outpatient Visits:** 15492 **Births:** 0

★ **CITRUS VALLEY MEDICAL CENTER–INTER COMMUNITY CAMPUS (050382)**, 210 West San Bernadino Road, Zip 91723–1515, Mailing Address: P.O.Box 6108, 91722–5108; tel. 626/331–7331, (Includes CITRUS VALLEY MEDICAL CENTER–INTER–COMMUNITY CAMPUS, 210 West San Bernardino Road, Covina, California, Zip 91723–1515, P O Box 6108, 91722–5108, tel. 626/331–7331; Robert H Curry, President and Chief Executive Officer; CITRUS VALLEY MEDICAL CENTER–QUEEN OF THE VALLEY CAMPUS, 1115 South Sunset Avenue, West Covina, California, Zip 91790–3940, P O Box 1980, 91793–1980, tel. 626/962–4011; Robert H Curry, President and Chief Executive Officer) **A**10 **F**3 7 8 11 13 15 17 18 20 22 24 25 26 27 28 29 30 31 32 34 35 40 41 44 45 46 47 49 50 51 55 56 57 59 64 65 69 70 71 72 74 75 76 77 78 79 80 81 82 83 84 85 86 87 89 90 92 93 96 98 102 103 105 107 108 110 111 114 115 118 119 120 121 124 126 128 129 130 131 132 135 143 146 147 148 149 150 **P**5 **S** Citrus Valley Health Partners, Covina, CA
Primary Contact: Robert H. Curry, President and Chief Executive Officer
CFO: Roger Sharma, Executive Vice President/Chief Financial Officer
CIO: Daniel J Nash, Chief Information Officer
CHR: Ryan Burke Esq, Vice President, Human Resources
CNO: Melissa Howard, Chief Nurse Executive, ICH & FPH
Web address: www.cvhp.org
Control: Other not–for–profit (including NFP Corporation) **Service**: General medical and surgical

> **Staffed Beds:** 332 **Admissions:** 24480 **Census:** 291 **Outpatient Visits:** 181565 **Births:** 4251 **Total Expense ($000):** 414041 **Payroll Expense ($000):** 139691 **Personnel:** 1818

CRESCENT CITY—Del Norte County

✠ **SUTTER COAST HOSPITAL (050417)**, 800 East Washington Boulevard, Zip 95531–8359; tel. 707/464–8511, **A**1 10 20 **F**3 8 11 13 15 18 24 29 30 34 35 40 43 44 45 46 47 48 50 51 54 57 59 62 64 65 68 70 75 76 77 79 81 85 87 89 90 93 97 107 108 110 111 114 118 119 127 130 132 144 146 147 148 149 **P**3 **S** Sutter Health, Sacramento, CA
Primary Contact: Mitchell J. Hanna, Chief Executive Officer
CNO: Rose Corcoran R.N., Chief Nursing Executive
Web address: www.sutterhealth.org
Control: Other not–for–profit (including NFP Corporation) **Service**: General medical and surgical

> **Staffed Beds:** 49 **Admissions:** 2075 **Census:** 22 **Outpatient Visits:** 91719 **Births:** 293 **Total Expense ($000):** 76149 **Payroll Expense ($000):** 22236 **Personnel:** 343

CULVER CITY—Los Angeles County

SOUTHERN CALIFORNIA HOSPITAL AT CULVER CITY (050752), 3828 Delmas Terrace, Zip 90232–6806; tel. 310/836–7000, (Nonreporting) **S** Prospect Medical Holdings, Los Angeles, CA
Primary Contact: Gerald B. Clute, Chief Executive Officer
CFO: Vincent Rubin, Chief Financial Officer
CMO: Martha Sonnenberg M.D., Chief of Staff
CIO: Carrie Bonar, Chief Information Officer
CHR: Betty J Harris, Director Human Resources
Web address: www.sch–culvercity.com
Control: Corporation, Investor–owned (for–profit) **Service**: General medical and surgical

> **Staffed Beds:** 239

DALY CITY—San Mateo County

✠ **SETON MEDICAL CENTER (050289)**, 1900 Sullivan Avenue, Zip 94015–2229; tel. 650/992–4000, (Total facility includes 116 beds in nursing home–type unit) **A**1 2 3 10 **F**8 13 15 18 20 22 24 26 29 30 31 34 35 37 39 40 41 42 44 45 46 48 49 50 51 56 57 58 59 60 64 66 68 74 75 77 78 79 81 82 85 87 92 93 96 102 103 107 108 110 111 114 116 117 118 119 120 121 123 124 126 130 132 135 141 143 146 147 148 149 **P**3 5 **S** Verity Health System, Los Angeles, CA
Primary Contact: John Ferrelli, Chief Executive Officer
COO: Stephanie Mearns, Vice President Patient Care Services and Chief Nurse Executive
CFO: Richard Wood, Chief Financial Officer
CMO: Timothy Ranney M.D., Chief Medical Officer
CHR: Patricia White, Vice President Human Resources
CNO: Mark Brown, BSN, MSN, Chief Nursing Officer
Web address: www.setonmedicalcenter.org
Control: Other not–for–profit (including NFP Corporation) **Service**: General medical and surgical

> **Staffed Beds:** 410 **Admissions:** 5472 **Census:** 220 **Outpatient Visits:** 143212 **Births:** 0 **Total Expense ($000):** 278096 **Personnel:** 935

DAVIS—Yolo County

✠ **SUTTER DAVIS HOSPITAL (050537)**, 2000 Sutter Place, Zip 95616–6201, Mailing Address: P.O.Box 1617, 95617–1617; tel. 530/756–6440, **A**1 3 5 10 **F**3 5 8 11 13 15 18 28 29 30 31 40 45 57 65 70 75 76 78 79 83 85 86 87 92 107 108 111 119 124 130 131 141 142 146 147 149 **P**3 5 **S** Sutter Health, Sacramento, CA
Primary Contact: Jennifer Maher, Chief Executive Officer
CFO: Patti Pilgrim, Chief Financial Officer
CMO: Deven Merchant M.D., Chief Medical Executive
CHR: Don Hartman, Director Human Resources
CNO: Myrna Chang, Chief Nursing Executive
Web address: www.sutterhealth.org
Control: Other not–for–profit (including NFP Corporation) **Service**: General medical and surgical

> **Staffed Beds:** 48 **Admissions:** 3708 **Census:** 27 **Outpatient Visits:** 47247 **Births:** 1146 **Total Expense ($000):** 103118 **Payroll Expense ($000):** 32792 **Personnel:** 386

DELANO—Kern County

○ **DELANO REGIONAL MEDICAL CENTER (050608)**, 1401 Garces Highway, Zip 93215–3690, Mailing Address: P.O.Box 460, 93216–0460; tel. 661/725–4800, (Nonreporting) **A**10 11
Primary Contact: Bahram Ghaffari, President
CFO: Bahram Ghaffari, President
CIO: Sandy Bakich, Director Information Management
CHR: Del Garbanzos, Director Human Resources
CNO: Amy Scroggs, Chief Nursing Officer
Web address: www.drmc.com
Control: Other not–for–profit (including NFP Corporation) **Service**: General medical and surgical

> **Staffed Beds:** 100

DOWNEY—Los Angeles County

✠ **KAISER PERMANENTE DOWNEY MEDICAL CENTER (050139)**, 9333 Imperial Highway, Zip 90242–2812; tel. 562/657–9000, **A**1 3 10 **F**3 8 13 15 18 19 29 30 31 35 38 40 45 46 49 50 58 60 64 65 68 70 72 74 75 76 78 79 81 82 83 84 85 87 88 89 92 100 107 110 111 114 115 119 126 130 132 146 148 **S** Kaiser Foundation Hospitals, Oakland, CA
Primary Contact: James Branchick, R.N., MS, Senior Vice President and Area Manager
CNO: Patricia J Clausen R.N., Chief Nurse Executive
Web address: www.kaiserpermanente.org
Control: Other not–for–profit (including NFP Corporation) **Service**: General medical and surgical

> **Staffed Beds:** 352 **Admissions:** 27402 **Census:** 255 **Outpatient Visits:** 196865 **Births:** 4157 **Personnel:** 3738

CA

Hospital, Medicare Provider Number, Address, Telephone, Approval, Facility, and Physician Codes, Health Care System

★ American Hospital Association (AHA) membership   ○ Healthcare Facilities Accreditation Program   ⇑ Center for Improvement in Healthcare Quality Accreditation
☐ The Joint Commission accreditation   ◇ DNV Healthcare Inc. accreditation   △ Commission on Accreditation of Rehabilitation Facilities (CARF) accreditation

CA

★ ⇑ **PIH HEALTH HOSPITAL – DOWNEY (050393)**, 11500 Brookshire Avenue, Zip 90241–4917; tel. 562/904–5000, **A**10 12 13 21 **F**3 8 11 13 15 18 20 22 24 29 30 40 41 45 49 50 56 60 69 70 72 74 75 76 77 79 81 85 91 93 107 108 110 111 115 118 119 130 146 148 149 **P**3 5 **S** PIH Health, Whittier, CA
Primary Contact: James R. West, President and Chief Executive Officer
COO: Ramona Pratt, Chief Operating Officer
CFO: Greg Williams, Chief Financial Officer
CIO: Jason Fischer, Chief Information Officer
CHR: Sherri Hollingsworth, Chief Human Resources Officer
CNO: Judy Pugach, Chief Nursing Officer
Web address: www.PIHHealth.org
Control: Other not–for–profit (including NFP Corporation) **Service:** General medical and surgical

Staffed Beds: 181 **Admissions:** 7887 **Census:** 78 **Outpatient Visits:** 91544 **Births:** 1049 **Total Expense ($000):** 151623 **Payroll Expense ($000):** 67164 **Personnel:** 982

☐ △ **RANCHO LOS AMIGOS NATIONAL REHABILITATION CENTER (050717)**, 7601 East Imperial Highway, Zip 90242–3496; tel. 562/401–7111, (Nonreporting) **A**1 3 5 7 10 **S** Los Angeles County–Department of Health Services, Los Angeles, CA
Primary Contact: Jorge Orozco, Chief Executive Officer
COO: Benjamin Ovando, Chief Operations Officer
CFO: Robin Bayus, Chief Financial Officer
CMO: Mindy Aisen M.D., Chief Medical Officer
CIO: Francis Tang, Chief Information Officer
CHR: Elizabeth Jacobi, Associate Director Human Resources
CNO: Aries Limbaga R.N., Chief Nursing Officer
Web address: www.rancho.org
Control: County, Government, Nonfederal **Service:** Rehabilitation

Staffed Beds: 207

DUARTE—Los Angeles County

⊞ **CITY OF HOPE'S HELFORD CLINICAL RESEARCH HOSPITAL (050146)**, 1500 East Duarte Road, Zip 91010–3012; tel. 626/256–4673, **A**1 2 3 5 8 10 **F**3 8 11 14 15 18 29 30 31 34 35 36 38 44 45 46 47 49 50 55 56 57 58 59 61 63 64 68 70 74 75 77 78 79 80 81 82 84 85 86 87 88 89 91 92 93 96 99 100 101 102 103 104 107 108 110 111 115 117 118 119 120 121 123 124 126 130 132 134 135 136 141 142 144 145 146 147 148 149 **P**3
Primary Contact: Robert Stone, President and Chief Executive Officer
COO: Marty Sargeant, Chief Operating Officer
CMO: William D. Boswell M.D., Jr, Chief Medical Officer
CHR: Stephanie Neuvirth, Chief Human Resource and Diversity Officer
Web address: www.cityofhope.org
Control: Other not–for–profit (including NFP Corporation) **Service:** Cancer

Staffed Beds: 217 **Admissions:** 6402 **Census:** 185 **Outpatient Visits:** 232573 **Births:** 0 **Total Expense ($000):** 928849 **Payroll Expense ($000):** 285579 **Personnel:** 3332

EL CENTRO—Imperial County

⊞ **EL CENTRO REGIONAL MEDICAL CENTER (050045)**, 1415 Ross Avenue, Zip 92243–4398; tel. 760/339–7100, **A**1 10 **F**3 11 13 15 18 26 29 30 31 34 40 43 45 46 47 48 49 50 51 54 57 59 60 64 66 70 74 75 78 79 81 82 85 86 87 93 97 107 108 110 111 114 115 116 117 119 126 127 130 131 145 146 147 148
Primary Contact: Adolphe Edward, Chief Executive Officer
COO: Tomas Virgen R.N., MSN, Chief Operating Officer
CFO: Kathleen Farmer, Assistant Administrator Finance and Chief Financial Officer
CIO: John Gaede, Director Information Systems
CHR: Bill Moore, Chief Human Resources
Web address: www.ecrmc.org
Control: City, Government, Nonfederal **Service:** General medical and surgical

Staffed Beds: 161 **Admissions:** 5900 **Census:** 58 **Births:** 1596 **Total Expense ($000):** 122252 **Payroll Expense ($000):** 46838

ELDRIDGE—Sonoma County

SONOMA DEVELOPMENTAL CENTER (050547), 15000 Arnold Drive, Zip 95431–8900, Mailing Address: P.O.Box 1493, 95431–1493; tel. 707/938–6000, (Nonreporting) **A**10
Primary Contact: Aleana Carreon, Executive Director
COO: Karen Clark, Director Administrative Services
CMO: Carol Castillo, Medical Director
CHR: Brenda Dukes, Director Human Resources
Web address: www.dds.ca.gov/sonoma
Control: State, Government, Nonfederal **Service:** Intellectual disabilities

Staffed Beds: 546

ENCINITAS—San Diego County

⊞ △ **SCRIPPS MEMORIAL HOSPITAL–ENCINITAS (050503)**, 354 Santa Fe Drive, Zip 92024–5182, Mailing Address: P.O.Box 230817, 92023–0817; tel. 760/633–6501, **A**1 7 10 **F**3 8 11 13 14 15 18 20 22 26 29 30 31 34 35 40 44 49 54 57 58 59 64 65 68 70 74 75 76 77 78 79 81 82 84 85 86 87 90 91 92 93 95 96 107 108 111 114 115 118 119 130 132 141 146 148 **P**3 5 **S** Scripps Health, San Diego, CA
Primary Contact: Carl J. Etter, Chief Executive and Senior Vice President
COO: Jan Zachry R.N., Vice President and Chief Nurse and Operations Executive
CFO: Sharon Creal, Vice President Financial Operations
CHR: Steve Rust, Director, Human Resources
CNO: Jan Zachry R.N., Vice President, Chief Nursing and Operations Executive
Web address: www.scripps.org
Control: Other not–for–profit (including NFP Corporation) **Service:** General medical and surgical

Staffed Beds: 194 **Admissions:** 11621 **Census:** 133 **Outpatient Visits:** 82223 **Births:** 2035 **Total Expense ($000):** 258888 **Payroll Expense ($000):** 98115 **Personnel:** 1243

ENCINO—Los Angeles County, See Los Angeles

ESCONDIDO—San Diego County

⊞ △ **PALOMAR MEDICAL CENTER (050115)**, 2185 West Citracado Parkway, Zip 92029–4159; tel. 760/739–3000, **A**1 3 5 7 10 **F**3 12 13 15 17 18 20 22 24 26 28 29 30 31 40 43 45 46 50 51 62 64 68 70 74 75 76 77 78 79 81 82 84 85 87 90 93 96 98 100 102 103 104 105 107 108 111 112 114 115 119 120 121 123 124 126 129 130 146 147 148 149 **P**3 **S** Palomar Health, Escondido, CA
Primary Contact: Mariellena Sudak, R.N., MSN, Vice President and Chief Nursing Officer
CMO: Duane Buringrud M.D., Chief Medical and Quality Officer
CIO: Prudence August, Chief Information Officer
CHR: Brenda C Turner, Chief Human Resources Officer
CNO: Mariellena Sudak R.N., MSN, Vice President and Chief Nursing Officer
Web address: www.palomarhealth.org
Control: Hospital district or authority, Government, Nonfederal **Service:** General medical and surgical

Staffed Beds: 309 **Admissions:** 24667 **Census:** 270 **Outpatient Visits:** 196356 **Births:** 3105 **Total Expense ($000):** 524734 **Payroll Expense ($000):** 192056 **Personnel:** 1535

EUREKA—Humboldt County

HUMBOLDT COUNTY MENTAL HEALTH (054124), 720 Wood Street, Zip 95501–4413; tel. 707/268–2900, (Nonreporting) **A**10
Primary Contact: Jet L. DeKruse, Administrator
CMO: Harpreet Duggal M.D., Medical Director, Department of Health and Human Services
CNO: Sherry Gallagher, Director Nursing, Department of Health and Human Services
Web address: www.co.humboldt.ca.us/hhs/mhb/
Control: County, Government, Nonfederal **Service:** Psychiatric

Staffed Beds: 16

⊞ **ST. JOSEPH HOSPITAL (050006)**, 2700 Dolbeer Street, Zip 95501–4799; tel. 707/445–8121, (Includes GENERAL HOSPITAL, 2200 Harrison Avenue, Eureka, California, Zip 95501–3299, tel. 707/445–5111) **A**1 2 10 19 **F**3 8 11 12 13 15 17 18 20 22 24 26 28 29 30 31 35 39 40 43 45 46 47 48 49 53 54 62 63 64 68 70 72 74 75 76 78 79 81 82 84 85 86 87 90 93 96 107 108 110 111 114 115 118 119 120 123 124 129 130 131 146 148 **P**5 **S** Providence St. Joseph Health, Renton, WA
Primary Contact: David O'Brien, M.D., President
CFO: Michel Riccioni, Chief Financial Officer
CMO: Mathew Miller M.D., Vice President and Chief Medical Officer
CIO: Wendy Thorpe, Area Director Information Systems
CHR: Linda Cook, Vice President Human Resources
CNO: Carol Reeder R.N., Chief Nursing Officer
Web address: www.stjosepheureka.org
Control: Church operated, Nongovernment, not–for–profit **Service:** General medical and surgical

Staffed Beds: 153 **Admissions:** 6591 **Census:** 88 **Outpatient Visits:** 175064 **Births:** 425 **Total Expense ($000):** 171995 **Payroll Expense ($000):** 63465 **Personnel:** 975

Many Facility Codes have changed. Please refer to the AHA Guide Code Chart. © 2017 AHA Guide

CA

FAIRFIELD—Solano County

⊞ **NORTHBAY MEDICAL CENTER (050367)**, 1200 B. Gale Wilson Boulevard, Zip 94533–3587; tel. 707/646–5000, (Includes NORTHBAY VACAVALLEY HOSPITAL, 1000 Nut Tree Road, Vacaville, California, Zip 95687–4100, tel. 707/624–7000; B. Konard Jones, Chief Executive Officer) **A**1 2 5 10 **F**2 3 6 8 11 13 17 18 19 20 22 24 26 28 29 30 31 43 44 46 49 50 51 54 56 59 62 63 64 65 70 72 73 74 75 76 77 78 79 80 81 82 84 85 87 89 92 93 94 96 97 100 104 107 114 115 118 119 121 130 131 132 146 147 148 **P**3
Primary Contact: B. Konard. Jones, Chief Executive Officer
CFO: Arthur E DeNio, Vice President and Chief Financial Officer
CIO: Christopher Timbers, Vice President and Chief Information Officer
CHR: Ken McCollum, Vice President, Human Resources
CNO: Traci A Duncan, Vice President, Chief Nursing Officer
Web address: www.northbay.org
Control: Other not–for–profit (including NFP Corporation) **Service:** General medical and surgical

Staffed Beds: 180 **Admissions:** 9084 **Census:** 122 **Outpatient Visits:** 369746 **Births:** 1320 **Total Expense ($000):** 532103 **Payroll Expense ($000):** 235351 **Personnel:** 1521		

FALL RIVER MILLS—Shasta County

★ **MAYERS MEMORIAL HOSPITAL DISTRICT (051305)**, 43563 Highway 299 East, Zip 96028–0459, Mailing Address: P.O.Box 459, 96028–0459; tel. 530/336–5511, (Total facility includes 87 beds in nursing home–type unit) **A**10 18 **F**3 6 7 11 13 18 28 34 40 41 45 50 53 56 57 59 63 64 65 75 79 81 85 86 89 93 107 114 119 128 130 132 133 135 146 148 149
Primary Contact: Louis James. Ward, Interim Chief Executive Officer
COO: Louis James Ward, Chief Operating Officer
CFO: Travis Lakey, Chief Financial Officer
CMO: Thomas Watson M.D., Chief of Staff
CIO: Chris Broadway, Manager Information Technology
CHR: Julie Thompson, Manager Personnel and Payroll
CNO: Sherry Wilson R.N., Chief Nursing Officer
Web address: www.mayersmemorial.com
Control: Hospital district or authority, Government, Nonfederal **Service:** General medical and surgical

Staffed Beds: 97 **Admissions:** 413 **Census:** 81 **Outpatient Visits:** 16211 **Births:** 0		

FOLSOM—Sacramento County

⊞ **MERCY HOSPITAL OF FOLSOM (050414)**, 1650 Creekside Drive, Zip 95630–3400; tel. 916/983–7400, **A**1 5 10 **F**3 8 11 12 13 29 30 34 35 36 37 39 40 49 57 59 60 64 66 68 70 74 75 77 79 81 82 84 85 86 93 107 108 114 115 118 119 130 132 146 147 148 **P**3 4 5 **S** Dignity Health, San Francisco, CA
Primary Contact: Edmundo Castaneda, President
COO: Randall Castillo, Vice President, Operations
CFO: Robin Rogness, Vice President and Chief Financial Officer
CHR: Anthony Robinson, Manager, Human Resources
CNO: Josh Freilich, Vice President and Chief Nurse Executive
Web address: www.mercyfolsom.org
Control: Church operated, Nongovernment, not–for–profit **Service:** General medical and surgical

Staffed Beds: 106 **Admissions:** 6785 **Census:** 65 **Outpatient Visits:** 56654 **Births:** 835 **Total Expense ($000):** 185004 **Payroll Expense ($000):** 70600 **Personnel:** 602		

⊞ **VIBRA HOSPITAL OF SACRAMENTO (052033)**, 330 Montrose Drive, Zip 95630–2720; tel. 916/351–9151, **A**1 10 **F**1 3 45 49 68 70 75 77 84 85 91 119 130 148 149 **S** Vibra Healthcare, Mechanicsburg, PA
Primary Contact: Kimberly Horton, R.N., MSN, Chief Executive Officer
CFO: Todd Scott, Chief Financial Officer
CMO: S. Kwon Lee M.D., Chief of Staff
CHR: Glenda Franco, Director, Human Resources
Web address: www.vhsacramento.com
Control: Individual, Investor–owned (for–profit) **Service:** Acute long–term care hospital

Staffed Beds: 58 **Admissions:** 388 **Census:** 43 **Outpatient Visits:** 0 **Births:** 0 **Total Expense ($000):** 30861 **Payroll Expense ($000):** 13086 **Personnel:** 192		

FONTANA—San Bernardino County

⊞ **KAISER PERMANENTE FONTANA MEDICAL CENTER (050140)**, 9961 Sierra Avenue, Zip 92335–6794; tel. 909/427–5000, (Includes KAISER PERMANENTE ONTARIO MEDICAL CENTER, 2295 South Vineyard Avenue, Ontario, California, Zip 91761–7925, tel. 909/724–5000; Greg Christian, Executive Director) **A**1 3 5 10 **F**3 8 11 13 15 17 18 20 22 24 26 29 30 31 35 40 41 44 45 46 48 49 50 51 57 58 59 60 62 63 64 65 68 70 72 73 74 75 76 77 78 79 81 82 84 85 86 87 88 89 100 102 107 108 110 111 114 115 117 118 119 126 130 135 141 145 146 148 149 **S** Kaiser Foundation Hospitals, Oakland, CA
Primary Contact: Greg Christian, Executive Director
CFO: Donald P Bernard, Chief Financial Officer
CMO: David Quam M.D., Area Medical Director
CIO: David Young M.D., Area Information Officer
CHR: Kimberly Labiaga, Human Resources Leader
CNO: Toni Andersen R.N., Chief Nurse Executive
Web address: www.kaiserpermanente.org
Control: Other not–for–profit (including NFP Corporation) **Service:** General medical and surgical

Staffed Beds: 490 **Admissions:** 30482 **Census:** 349 **Outpatient Visits:** 177802 **Births:** 6738 **Personnel:** 4744		

FORT BRAGG—Mendocino County

⊞ **MENDOCINO COAST DISTRICT HOSPITAL (051325)**, 700 River Drive, Zip 95437–5495; tel. 707/961–1234, **A**1 10 18 **F**7 8 11 13 15 18 29 30 31 34 36 40 57 59 62 63 70 75 76 77 78 79 81 85 86 87 93 94 96 97 107 108 110 111 114 115 119 127 130 132 133 148 149
Primary Contact: Bob S. Edwards Jr, FACHE, Chief Executive Officer
CFO: Wayne Allen, Chief Financial Officer
CMO: John Kermen D.O., Chief Medical Staff
CIO: Jeff Edwards, Manager Information Services
CHR: Ellen L Hardin, Chief Human Resources Officer
CNO: Bonnie Kittner R.N., Chief Nursing Officer
Web address: www.mcdh.org
Control: Hospital district or authority, Government, Nonfederal **Service:** General medical and surgical

Staffed Beds: 25 **Admissions:** 1066 **Census:** 12 **Outpatient Visits:** 56502 **Births:** 99 **Total Expense ($000):** 52495 **Payroll Expense ($000):** 15839 **Personnel:** 320		

FORT IRWIN—San Bernardino County

⊞ **WEED ARMY COMMUNITY HOSPITAL**, Inner Loop Road and 4th Street, Building 166, Zip 92310–5065, Mailing Address: P.O.Box 105109, 92310–5109; tel. 760/380–3108, (Nonreporting) **A**1 **S** Department of the Army, Office of the Surgeon General, Falls Church, VA
Primary Contact: Colonel Martin Doperak, Commander
CIO: Michael Haenelt, Chief Information Management
Web address: www.irwin.amedd.army.mil
Control: Army, Government, federal **Service:** General medical and surgical

Staffed Beds: 27		

FORTUNA—Humboldt County

★ **REDWOOD MEMORIAL HOSPITAL (051318)**, 3300 Renner Drive, Zip 95540–3198; tel. 707/725–3361, **A**10 18 **F**3 11 13 15 17 18 29 30 34 35 39 40 45 50 53 56 57 59 63 64 68 70 75 76 77 79 81 82 84 85 86 93 107 110 114 119 130 131 132 133 146 **S** Providence St. Joseph Health, Renton, WA
Primary Contact: David O'Brien, M.D., President
COO: Joseph J Rogers, Vice President and Chief Operating Officer
CHR: Bob Sampson, Vice President Human Resources
Web address: www.redwoodmemorial.org/
Control: Church operated, Nongovernment, not–for–profit **Service:** General medical and surgical

Staffed Beds: 25 **Admissions:** 1382 **Census:** 14 **Outpatient Visits:** 44443 **Births:** 394 **Total Expense ($000):** 33630 **Payroll Expense ($000):** 19620 **Personnel:** 164		

Hospital, Medicare Provider Number, Address, Telephone, Approval, Facility, and Physician Codes, Health Care System

★ American Hospital Association (AHA) membership
□ The Joint Commission accreditation
○ Healthcare Facilities Accreditation Program
◇ DNV Healthcare Inc. accreditation
⇑ Center for Improvement in Healthcare Quality Accreditation
△ Commission on Accreditation of Rehabilitation Facilities (CARF) accreditation

---

CA

FOUNTAIN VALLEY—Orange County

FOUNTAIN VALLEY REGIONAL HOSPITAL AND MEDICAL CENTER (050570), 17100 Euclid Street, Zip 92708-4043; tel. 714/966-7200, **A**1 2 5 10 **F**3 12 13 18 19 20 22 24 26 28 29 30 31 34 35 40 41 45 47 48 49 50 55 57 58 59 64 65 70 72 74 75 76 77 78 79 81 82 84 85 87 88 89 107 108 111 114 115 119 126 130 132 146 147 148 149 **P**1 3 5 **S** TENET Healthcare Corporation, Dallas, TX
Primary Contact: Kenneth D. McFarland, Chief Executive Officer
COO: Edward Littlejohn, Chief Operating Officer
CFO: Ken Jordan, Chief Financial Officer
CMO: Daniel Hilton M.D., Chief of Staff
CIO: Freddie Sanchez, Director Information Systems
CHR: Tim Howard, Chief Human Resources Officer
CNO: Barbara Vargas, Interim Chief Nursing Officer
Web address: www.fountainvalleyhospital.com
Control: Corporation, Investor-owned (for-profit) **Service:** General medical and surgical

Staffed Beds: 342 **Admissions:** 18465 **Census:** 233 **Outpatient Visits:** 71633 **Births:** 3526 **Personnel:** 1317

ORANGE COAST MEMORIAL MEDICAL CENTER (050678), 9920 Talbert Avenue, Zip 92708-5115; tel. 714/378-7000, **A**1 2 10 **F**3 8 11 12 13 15 18 20 22 24 26 28 29 30 31 34 35 38 40 44 45 46 47 48 49 50 51 53 55 56 57 58 59 64 65 68 70 72 74 75 76 77 78 79 81 82 84 85 86 87 93 107 108 110 111 114 115 116 117 118 119 124 126 130 131 132 135 143 145 146 147 149 **S** MemorialCare, Fountain Valley, CA
Primary Contact: Marcia Manker, Chief Executive Officer
COO: Emily Randle, Vice President Operations
CFO: Steve McNamara, Chief Financial Officer
CIO: Scott Raymond, Director Information Systems
CHR: Michelle Gutierrez, Executive Director Human Resources
CNO: Dale Vital, Chief Nursing Officer
Web address: www.memorialcare.org
Control: Other not-for-profit (including NFP Corporation) **Service:** General medical and surgical

Staffed Beds: 218 **Admissions:** 11236 **Census:** 114 **Outpatient Visits:** 84786 **Births:** 1571 **Total Expense ($000):** 280159 **Payroll Expense ($000):** 77506 **Personnel:** 1143

FREMONT—Alameda County

FREMONT HOSPITAL (054110), 39001 Sundale Drive, Zip 94538-2005; tel. 510/796-1100, **A**1 10 **F**3 5 29 30 38 98 99 100 101 102 103 104 105 130 132 135 143 **S** Universal Health Services, Inc., King of Prussia, PA
Primary Contact: Marlon Rollins, Ph.D., Chief Executive Officer
CMO: Vikas Duvvuri M.D., Medical Director
CHR: Tom Piz, Director Human Resources
Web address: www.fremonthospital.com
Control: Corporation, Investor-owned (for-profit) **Service:** Psychiatric

Staffed Beds: 148 **Admissions:** 5744 **Census:** 113 **Outpatient Visits:** 9600 **Births:** 0 **Total Expense ($000):** 29804 **Payroll Expense ($000):** 18764 **Personnel:** 293

KAISER PERMANENTE FREMONT MEDICAL CENTER (050512), 39400 Paseo Padre Parkway, Zip 94538-2310; tel. 510/248-3000, (Nonreporting) **A**1 10 **S** Kaiser Foundation Hospitals, Oakland, CA
Primary Contact: Victoria O'Gorman, Administrator
Web address: www.kp.org
Control: Other not-for-profit (including NFP Corporation) **Service:** General medical and surgical

Staffed Beds: 106

WASHINGTON HOSPITAL HEALTHCARE SYSTEM (050195), 2000 Mowry Avenue, Zip 94538-1746; tel. 510/797-1111, (Nonreporting) **A**1 2 10
Primary Contact: Nancy D. Farber, Chief Executive Officer
COO: Edward J Fayen, Associate Administrator Operations and Support
CFO: Chris Henry, Associate Administrator and Chief Financial Officer
CMO: Albert Brooks M.D., Chief Medical Staff Services
CIO: Robert Thorwald, Chief Information Officer
CHR: Bryant Welch, Chief Human Resources
CNO: Stephanie Williams R.N., Chief Nursing Officer
Web address: www.whhs.com
Control: Hospital district or authority, Government, Nonfederal **Service:** General medical and surgical

Staffed Beds: 269

FRENCH CAMP—San Joaquin County

SAN JOAQUIN GENERAL HOSPITAL (050167), 500 West Hospital Road, Zip 95231-9693, Mailing Address: P.O.Box 1020, Stockton, 95201-3120; tel. 209/468-6000, (Nonreporting) **A**1 3 5 10
Primary Contact: David K. Culberson, Chief Executive Officer
CFO: Ron Kreutner, Chief Financial Officer
CMO: Sheela Kapre M.D., Chief Medical Officer
CIO: Don Johnston, Chief Information Officer
CHR: Lisa M Lopez, Director Human Resources
CNO: Erlinda Bolor R.N., Chief Nursing Officer
Web address: www.sjgeneral.org/
Control: County, Government, Nonfederal **Service:** General medical and surgical

Staffed Beds: 110

FRESNO—Fresno County

COMMUNITY BEHAVIORAL HEALTH CENTER, 7171 North Cedar Avenue, Zip 93720-3311; tel. 559/449-8000, (Nonreporting) **S** Community Medical Centers, Fresno, CA
Primary Contact: Craig Wagoner, Chief Executive Officer
CFO: Stephen Walter, Senior Vice President and Chief Financial Officer
CMO: Tom Utecht M.D., Senior Vice President and Chief Quality Officer
CIO: George Vasquez, Vice President Information Services
CHR: Ginny Burdick, Vice President Human Resources
CNO: Karen L Buckley R.N., Chief Nursing Officer
Web address: www.communitymedical.org
Control: Corporation, Investor-owned (for-profit) **Service:** Psychiatric

Staffed Beds: 61

COMMUNITY REGIONAL MEDICAL CENTER (050060), 2823 Fresno Street, Zip 93721-1324, Mailing Address: P.O.Box 1232, 93715-1232; tel. 559/459-6000, (Total facility includes 106 beds in nursing home-type unit) **A**1 2 3 5 8 10 **F**1 3 13 15 16 17 18 19 20 22 24 26 27 28 29 30 31 34 35 38 39 40 41 43 44 46 50 53 54 55 56 57 58 59 60 61 62 63 64 65 66 68 70 72 74 75 76 77 78 79 81 82 83 84 86 87 88 89 90 91 92 93 94 95 96 97 98 99 100 101 102 103 105 107 109 110 111 112 113 114 115 116 117 118 119 120 121 124 126 130 131 132 135 141 143 144 145 146 147 148 149 **P**5 **S** Community Medical Centers, Fresno, CA
Primary Contact: Craig Wagoner, Chief Executive Officer
COO: Patrick W Rafferty, Executive Vice President and Chief Operating Officer
CFO: Stephen Walter, Senior Vice President and Chief Financial Officer
CMO: Tom Utecht M.D., Chief Medical and Quality Officer
CIO: Craig Castro, Chief Information Officer
CHR: Ginny Burdick, Vice President Human Resources
Web address: www.communitymedical.org
Control: Other not-for-profit (including NFP Corporation) **Service:** General medical and surgical

Staffed Beds: 852 **Admissions:** 42019 **Census:** 717 **Outpatient Visits:** 348009 **Births:** 5365

FRESNO HEART AND SURGICAL HOSPITAL (050732), 15 East Audubon Drive, Zip 93720-1542; tel. 559/433-8000, (Nonreporting) **A**1 3 10 **S** Community Medical Centers, Fresno, CA
Primary Contact: Ben Armfield, Associate Administrator
CFO: Ben Armfield, Chief Financial Officer
CMO: Tom Utecht M.D., Corporate Chief Quality Officer
CIO: George Vasquez, Corporate Chief Information Officer
CHR: Julie Adair, Interim Corporate Chief Human Resources Officer
CNO: Heather Rodriguez, Chief Nursing Officer
Web address: www.fresnoheartandsurgical.org
Control: Corporation, Investor-owned (for-profit) **Service:** Heart

Staffed Beds: 60

FRESNO MEDICAL CENTER See Kaiser Permanente Fresno Medical Center

FRESNO SURGICAL HOSPITAL (050708), 6125 North Fresno Street, Zip 93710-5207; tel. 559/431-8000, (Nonreporting) **A**1 10
Primary Contact: Kristine Kassahn, Chief Executive Officer
CFO: Bruce Cecil, Chief Financial Officer
CMO: Bruce Witmer M.D., Medical Director
CHR: Laura Patillo, Manager Human Resources
Web address: www.fresnosurgicalhospital.com
Control: Partnership, Investor-owned (for-profit) **Service:** Surgical

Staffed Beds: 16

Many Facility Codes have changed. Please refer to the AHA Guide Code Chart. © 2017 AHA Guide

⊞ **KAISER PERMANENTE FRESNO MEDICAL CENTER (050710)**, 7300 North Fresno Street, Zip 93720–2942; tel. 559/448–4500, (Nonreporting) **A**1 3 5 10 **S** Kaiser Foundation Hospitals, Oakland, CA
Primary Contact: Debbie Hemker, Senior Vice President and Area Manager
CFO: Richard Alves, Chief Financial Officer
CMO: Varouj Altebarmakian M.D., Physician in Chief
CIO: David Bonnar, Chief Information Officer
CNO: Karen S Strauman R.N., M.P.H., Chief Nurse Executive
Web address: www.kaiserpermanente.org
Control: Other not–for–profit (including NFP Corporation) **Service**: General medical and surgical

Staffed Beds: 169

⊞ **SAINT AGNES MEDICAL CENTER (050093)**, 1303 East Herndon Avenue, Zip 93720–3397; tel. 559/450–3000, **A**1 2 3 10 **F**3 8 11 13 15 17 18 20 22 24 26 28 29 30 31 34 35 37 40 44 45 46 47 49 50 51 55 56 57 58 59 61 64 66 70 74 75 76 77 78 79 81 82 84 85 86 87 91 92 93 94 95 96 97 102 107 108 110 111 112 113 114 115 116 117 118 119 120 121 123 124 126 130 132 135 146 147 148 149 **P**1 5 **S** Trinity Health, Livonia, MI
Primary Contact: Nancy Hollingsworth, R.N., MSN, President and Chief Executive Officer
COO: Mark T Bateman, Interim Chief Operating Officer
CFO: Phil Robinson, Chief Financial Officer
CMO: Stephen Soldo M.D., Chief Medical Officer
CIO: Irfan Ali, Director Information Services
CHR: Stacy Vaillancourt, Vice President Marketing, Communications, Advocacy and Human Resources
Web address: www.samc.com
Control: Church operated, Nongovernment, not–for–profit **Service**: General medical and surgical

Staffed Beds: 436 Admissions: 21011 Census: 253 Outpatient Visits: 220484 Births: 2985 Total Expense ($000): 461211 Payroll Expense ($000): 158601 Personnel: 1868

⊞ △ **SAN JOAQUIN VALLEY REHABILITATION HOSPITAL (053032)**, 7173 North Sharon Avenue, Zip 93720–3329; tel. 559/436–3600, (Nonreporting) **A**1 7 10 **S** Vibra Healthcare, Mechanicsburg, PA
Primary Contact: Mary Jo Jacobson, Chief Executive Officer
CFO: Margaret Casarez, Chief Financial Officer
CMO: Michael Azevedo M.D., Medical Director
CIO: Christi Rolff, Director Business Development
CHR: Jennifer Morrow, Director Human Resources
Web address: www.sanjoaquinrehab.com
Control: Corporation, Investor–owned (for–profit) **Service**: Rehabilitation

Staffed Beds: 62

⊞ **VETERANS AFFAIRS CENTRAL CALIFORNIA HEALTH CARE SYSTEM**, 2615 East Clinton Avenue, Zip 93703–2223; tel. 559/225–6100, (Nonreporting) **A**1 3 5 **S** Department of Veterans Affairs, Washington, DC
Primary Contact: Stephen R. Bauman, Medical Center Director
CMO: Wessel H. Meyer M.D., Chief of Staff
CHR: Sandra Stein, Chief Human Resources Management
Web address: www.fresno.va.gov/
Control: Veterans Affairs, Government, federal **Service**: General medical and surgical

Staffed Beds: 117

FULLERTON—Orange County

⊞ △ **ST. JUDE MEDICAL CENTER (050168)**, 101 East Valencia Mesa Drive, Zip 92835–3875; tel. 714/992–3000, **A**1 2 3 5 7 10 **F**2 3 8 9 11 12 13 15 18 20 22 24 26 28 29 30 31 32 34 35 36 39 40 43 44 45 46 47 48 49 50 51 53 54 55 56 57 58 59 60 61 62 63 64 65 66 68 70 71 72 74 75 76 77 78 79 81 82 83 84 85 86 87 90 91 92 93 95 96 97 100 107 108 109 110 111 112 114 115 116 117 118 119 120 121 123 124 126 129 130 131 132 134 135 143 145 146 147 148 149 **P**3 5 **S** Providence St. Joseph Health, Renton, WA
Primary Contact: Brian Helleland, Chief Executive Officer
CFO: Ed Salvador, Chief Financial Officer
CMO: Eugene P. Kim M.D., Chief Medical Officer
CIO: Ryan Olsen, Vice President of Operations
CHR: Mark Jablonski, Vice President Mission Integration
CNO: Linda Jenkins R.N., Vice President Patient Care Services
Web address: www.stjudemedicalcenter.org
Control: Church operated, Nongovernment, not–for–profit **Service**: General medical and surgical

Staffed Beds: 320 Admissions: 14926 Census: 196 Outpatient Visits: 478195 Births: 2377 Total Expense ($000): 514451 Payroll Expense ($000): 160173 Personnel: 2153

GARBERVILLE—Humboldt County

★ **JEROLD PHELPS COMMUNITY HOSPITAL (051309)**, 733 Cedar Street, Zip 95542–3292; tel. 707/923–3921, (Total facility includes 8 beds in nursing home–type unit) **A**10 18 **F**34 35 40 50 65 77 82 91 97 110 119 127 128 133 **P**5
Primary Contact: Matthew Rees, Administrator
COO: Kent Scown, Director Operations and Information Services
CFO: Harry Jasper, Chief Financial Officer
CMO: Marcin Matuszkiewicz M.D., Chief of Staff and Medical Director
CIO: Kent Scown, Director Operations and Information Services
CHR: Dee Way, Director Human Resources
CNO: Sarah Beach, Director of Nursing
Web address: www.shchd.org
Control: Hospital district or authority, Government, Nonfederal **Service**: General medical and surgical

Staffed Beds: 17 Admissions: 45 Census: 8 Outpatient Visits: 7814 Births: 0 Total Expense ($000): 9314 Payroll Expense ($000): 3477 Personnel: 68

GARDEN GROVE—Orange County

⊞ **GARDEN GROVE HOSPITAL AND MEDICAL CENTER (050230)**, 12601 Garden Grove Boulevard, Zip 92843–1959; tel. 714/537–5160, (Nonreporting) **A**1 10 **S** Prime Healthcare, Ontario, CA
Primary Contact: Richard M. Rowe, PharmD, Chief Executive Officer
CFO: Kora Guoyavatin, Chief Financial Officer
CMO: Hassan Alkhouli M.D., Chief Medical Officer
CIO: Vic Mahan, Director Information Systems
CHR: Stephanie Sioson, Director Human Resources
CNO: Wanda Ruben R.N., Chief Nursing Officer
Web address: www.gardengrovehospital.com
Control: Corporation, Investor–owned (for–profit) **Service**: General medical and surgical

Staffed Beds: 167

GARDENA—Los Angeles County

⊞ **KINDRED HOSPITAL SOUTH BAY (052050)**, 1246 West 155th Street, Zip 90247–4062; tel. 310/323–5330, (Nonreporting) **A**1 10 **S** Kindred Healthcare, Louisville, KY
Primary Contact: Isaac Lin, Chief Executive Officer
CHR: Michelle Parra, Director Human Resources
Web address: www.khsouthbay.com/
Control: Corporation, Investor–owned (for–profit) **Service**: Acute long–term care hospital

Staffed Beds: 84

⊞ **MEMORIAL HOSPITAL OF GARDENA (050468)**, 1145 West Redondo Beach Boulevard, Zip 90247–3528; tel. 310/532–4200, (Nonreporting) **A**1 10 **S** Avanti Hospitals, El Segundo, CA
Primary Contact: Kathy Wojno, R.N., MSN, Administrator
CFO: Daniel R Heckathorne, Chief Financial Officer
CMO: Nosratian Farshao M.D., Chief Medical Staff
CHR: Matthew Kempiak, Director Human Resources and Administrative Services
CNO: Glenda Luce, Chief Nursing Officer
Web address: www.mhglax.com/
Control: Corporation, Investor–owned (for–profit) **Service**: General medical and surgical

Staffed Beds: 172

VISTA HOSPITAL OF SOUTH BAY See Kindred Hospital South Bay

GILROY—Santa Clara County

⊞ **SAINT LOUISE REGIONAL HOSPITAL (050688)**, 9400 No Name Uno, Zip 95020–3528; tel. 408/848–2000, **A**1 10 **F**3 11 13 15 17 29 30 31 34 35 37 40 41 45 46 47 54 54 57 59 60 64 68 69 70 75 76 78 79 81 82 85 107 108 111 114 118 130 132 135 143 144 146 148 **S** Verity Health System, Los Angeles, CA
Primary Contact: Jordan Herget, President and Chief Executive Officer
COO: Carol Furgurson, Chief Operating Officer
CFO: Nicole Thomson, Chief Financial Officer
CIO: Dick Hutsell, Vice President Information Technology Services
CHR: Lin Velasquez, Vice President Human Resources
CNO: Marilyn Gerrior R.N., MSN, Chief Nursing Executive
Web address: www.verity.org
Control: Church operated, Nongovernment, not–for–profit **Service**: General medical and surgical

Staffed Beds: 93 Admissions: 2621 Census: 26 Outpatient Visits: 44059 Births: 329 Total Expense ($000): 93389 Payroll Expense ($000): 37205

CA

Hospital, Medicare Provider Number, Address, Telephone, Approval, Facility, and Physician Codes, Health Care System

★ American Hospital Association (AHA) membership
□ The Joint Commission accreditation
○ Healthcare Facilities Accreditation Program
◇ DNV Healthcare Inc. accreditation
⇑ Center for Improvement in Healthcare Quality Accreditation
△ Commission on Accreditation of Rehabilitation Facilities (CARF) accreditation

---

CA

GLENDALE—Los Angeles County

⊞ **ADVENTIST HEALTH GLENDALE (050058)**, 1420 South Central Avenue, Zip 91204–2594; tel. 818/502–1900, **A**1 10 **F**3 12 13 15 17 18 20 22 24 26 28 29 30 31 34 35 37 40 41 45 46 47 48 49 50 53 56 57 58 59 64 68 70 72 74 75 76 78 79 81 82 84 85 90 91 92 93 98 99 102 107 108 110 111 114 115 119 120 128 130 131 132 146 147 148 149 **S** Dignity Health, San Francisco, CA
Primary Contact: Julie Sprengel, Interim President
CFO: Rebecca Cheng, Chief Financial Officer
CIO: Brian Gregor, Manager Information Technology Operations
CHR: Nga Nguyen, Manager Human Resources and Organizational Development
CNO: Jason Black, Vice President and Chief Nurse Executive
Web address: www.glendalememorial.com
Control: Other not–for–profit (including NFP Corporation) **Service**: General medical and surgical

Staffed Beds: 334 Admissions: 10058 **Census:** 145 **Outpatient Visits:** 101711 **Births:** 1815 **Total Expense ($000):** 254620 **Payroll Expense ($000):** 87559 **Personnel:** 971

⊞ ⇑ **ADVENTIST HEALTH GLENDALE (050239)**, 8700 Beverly Blvd, NT–3138, Zip 90048, Mailing Address: 1509 Wilson Terrace, Glendale, 91206–4098; tel. 818/409–8000, **A**1 2 3 5 10 21 **F**3 4 5 8 12 13 15 17 18 20 22 24 26 28 29 30 31 32 34 35 36 37 39 40 44 45 46 47 48 49 51 53 54 56 57 58 59 63 64 65 68 70 71 72 74 75 76 77 78 79 81 82 83 84 85 86 87 89 90 91 92 93 96 98 101 102 103 104 105 106 107 108 109 110 111 114 115 118 119 120 121 124 126 128 129 130 131 132 135 145 146 147 148 149 **P**3 **S** Adventist Health, Roseville, CA
Primary Contact: Kevin A. Roberts, FACHE, President and Chief Executive Officer
COO: Warren Tetz, Senior Vice President and Chief Operating Officer
CFO: Kelly Turner, Senior Vice President Finance and Chief Financial Officer
CMO: Arby Nahapetian M.D., Vice President Medical Affairs and Quality
CIO: Sharon Correa, Vice President and Chief Information Officer
CNO: Judy Blair, Senior Vice President Clinical Services and Chief Nursing Officer
Web address: www.glendaleadventist.com
Control: Church operated, Nongovernment, not–for–profit **Service**: General medical and surgical

Staffed Beds: 462 Admissions: 21118 **Census:** 284 **Outpatient Visits:** 292945 **Births:** 2413 **Total Expense ($000):** 460529 **Payroll Expense ($000):** 157118 **Personnel:** 2458

★ ⇑ **USC VERDUGO HILLS HOSPITAL (050124)**, 1812 Verdugo Boulevard, Zip 91208–1409; tel. 818/790–7100, **A**10 21 **F**3 11 12 13 14 15 17 18 28 29 30 31 34 35 37 38 40 41 44 45 49 50 51 53 56 57 58 59 60 64 65 68 70 74 75 76 77 78 79 81 83 84 85 86 87 91 93 94 96 98 100 101 102 103 104 107 108 110 111 114 119 124 126 128 130 131 132 135 145 146 147 148 149 **P**8 **S** Keck Medicine of USC, Los Angeles, CA
Primary Contact: Keith Hobbs, Chief Executive Officer
COO: Kenny Pawlek, Chief Operating Officer
CFO: Robert Allen, Chief Financial Officer
CMO: Stephanie Hall M.D., Chief Medical Officer
CHR: Eva Herberger, Administrator Human Resources
CNO: Theresa Murphy, Chief Nursing Officer
Web address: www.uscvhh.org
Control: Other not–for–profit (including NFP Corporation) **Service**: General medical and surgical

Staffed Beds: 132 Admissions: 6098 **Census:** 84 **Outpatient Visits:** 36370 **Births:** 429 **Total Expense ($000):** 99958 **Payroll Expense ($000):** 46057 **Personnel:** 596

GLENDORA—Los Angeles County

⊞ **FOOTHILL PRESBYTERIAN HOSPITAL (050597)**, 250 South Grand Avenue, Zip 91741–4218; tel. 626/963–8411, **A**1 10 **F**3 7 11 13 15 17 18 29 30 31 34 35 40 41 44 45 49 50 51 60 64 68 70 74 75 76 77 78 79 81 85 86 87 107 108 114 119 130 131 143 146 **S** Citrus Valley Health Partners, Covina, CA
Primary Contact: Robert H. Curry, President and Chief Executive Officer
COO: Elvia Foulke, Executive Vice President and Chief Operating Officer
CMO: John DiMare M.D., Medical Director
CIO: David McCobb, Chief Information Officer
Web address: www.cvhp.org/Our_Facilities/Foothill_Presbyterian.aspx
Control: Other not–for–profit (including NFP Corporation) **Service**: Obstetrics and gynecology

Staffed Beds: 72 Admissions: 5694 **Census:** 55 **Outpatient Visits:** 59128 **Births:** 1075 **Total Expense ($000):** 88877 **Payroll Expense ($000):** 35261 **Personnel:** 439

★ ○ **GLENDORA COMMUNITY HOSPITAL (050205)**, 150 West Route 66, Zip 91740–6207; tel. 626/852–5000, (Nonreporting) **A**10 11 **S** Prime Healthcare, Ontario, CA
Primary Contact: Sofia Abrina, R.N., Chief Executive Officer
CFO: Robert Bonner, Chief Financial Officer
CMO: Oliver Solomon M.D., Chief Medical Officer
CIO: Jeffrey Cox, Chief Information Officer
CHR: Diana Cancel, Director Human Resources
CNO: Mary Ann Bennett, Chief Nursing Officer
Web address: www.evhmc.com
Control: Other not–for–profit (including NFP Corporation) **Service**: General medical and surgical

Staffed Beds: 128

GRANADA HILLS—Los Angeles County, See Los Angeles

GRASS VALLEY—Nevada County

⊞ **SIERRA NEVADA MEMORIAL HOSPITAL (050150)**, 155 Glasson Way, Zip 95945–5723, Mailing Address: P.O.Box 1029, 95945–1029; tel. 530/274–6000, (Nonreporting) **A**1 2 10 19 **S** Dignity Health, San Francisco, CA
Primary Contact: Katherine A. Medeiros, President and Chief Executive Officer
CFO: Carolyn Canady, Chief Financial Officer
CMO: Brian Evans M.D., Chief of Medicine
CHR: Terri Labriola, Human Resources Officer
CNO: Jill McWilliams, Chief Nursing Officer
Web address: www.snmh.org
Control: Other not–for–profit (including NFP Corporation) **Service**: General medical and surgical

Staffed Beds: 121

GREENBRAE—Marin County

⊞ **MARIN GENERAL HOSPITAL (050360)**, 250 Bon Air Road, Zip 94904–1784, Mailing Address: P.O.Box 8010, San Rafael, 94912–8010; tel. 415/925–7000, **A**1 2 10 **F**3 8 13 15 18 20 22 24 26 28 29 30 31 34 35 36 37 40 43 45 47 49 57 58 59 60 68 70 72 74 75 76 77 78 79 81 84 85 86 87 89 93 98 100 104 105 107 108 110 111 114 115 116 117 118 119 120 121 123 124 126 130 132 141 146 148 149 **P**3 4 5
Primary Contact: Lee Domanico, Chief Executive Officer
CFO: David W Cox, Chief Financial Officer
CMO: Jeffrey M. Rosenburg M.D., Chief Medical Officer
CIO: Mark Zielazinski, Chief Information and Technology Integration Officer
CHR: Linda Lang, Chief Human Resources Officer
Web address: www.maringeneral.org
Control: Other not–for–profit (including NFP Corporation) **Service**: General medical and surgical

Staffed Beds: 176 Admissions: 9162 **Census:** 114 **Outpatient Visits:** 198606 **Births:** 1331 **Total Expense ($000):** 364451 **Payroll Expense ($000):** 156737 **Personnel:** 1349

GRIDLEY—Butte County

★ ⇑ **ORCHARD HOSPITAL (051311)**, 240 Spruce Street, Zip 95948–2216, Mailing Address: P.O.Box 97, 95948–0097; tel. 530/846–5671, (Nonreporting) **A**10 18 21
Primary Contact: Steve Stark, Chief Executive Officer
COO: Tracy Atkins, Chief Operating and Nursing Officer
CFO: Kristina Sanke, Chief Financial Officer
CMO: Henry Starkes M.D., Medical Director
CIO: John Helvey, Chief Information Officer
CNO: Tracy Atkins, Chief Operating and Nursing Officer
Web address: www.orchardhospital.com
Control: Other not–for–profit (including NFP Corporation) **Service**: General medical and surgical

Staffed Beds: 45

HANFORD—Kings County

⊞ **ADVENTIST MEDICAL CENTER – HANFORD (050121)**, 115 Mall Drive, Zip 93230–3513; tel. 559/582–9000, (Nonreporting) (Includes ADVENTIST MEDICAL CENTER–SELMA, 1141 Rose Avenue, Selma, California, Zip 93662–3241, tel. 559/891–1000; Richard L Rawson, President and Chief Executive Officer) **A**1 3 5 10 **S** Adventist Health, Roseville, CA
Primary Contact: Wayne Ferch, President and Chief Executive Officer
CIO: Michael Aubry, Director Information Systems
Web address: www.adventisthealthcv.com/hospital_newhanfordhospital.aspx
Control: Church operated, Nongovernment, not–for–profit **Service**: General medical and surgical

Staffed Beds: 199

CA

☒ **CENTRAL VALLEY GENERAL HOSPITAL (050196)**, 1025 North Douty Street,
Zip 93230–3722, Mailing Address: P.O.Box 480, 93232–2113; tel. 559/583–
2100, (Nonreporting) **A**1 3 10 **S** Adventist Health, Roseville, CA
Primary Contact: Wayne Ferch, President and Chief Executive Officer
Web address: www.hanfordhealth.com
Control: Corporation, Investor–owned (for–profit) **Service:** General medical and
surgical

Staffed Beds: 49

HARBOR CITY—Los Angeles County, See Los Angeles

HAYWARD—Alameda County

☐ **ST. ROSE HOSPITAL (050002)**, 27200 Calaroga Avenue, Zip 94545–4383;
tel. 510/264–4000, (Nonreporting) **A**1 10 **S** Alecto Healthcare, Irvine, CA
Primary Contact: Aman Dhuper, President and Chief Executive Officer
CFO: Michael Taylor, Vice President Financial Services and Chief Financial Officer
CMO: Charles S Feldstein M.D., Vice President Medical Affairs
CHR: John Davini, Vice President
Web address: www.srhca.org
Control: Church operated, Nongovernment, not–for–profit **Service:** General
medical and surgical

Staffed Beds: 150

HEALDSBURG—Sonoma County

☐ **HEALDSBURG DISTRICT HOSPITAL (051321)**, 1375 University Avenue,
Zip 95448–3382; tel. 707/431–6500, **A**1 10 18 **F**15 29 30 34 35 40 45 46 48
51 54 56 57 64 65 68 70 75 77 79 81 85 93 97 104 107 111 115 119 128
130 132 133 146 147 148 149
Primary Contact: Nancy Schmid, Chief Executive Officer
COO: Regina Novello R.N., Chief Operating Officer
CFO: John S Parigi II, Interim Chief Financial Officer
CMO: Judy Widger M.D., Chief of Staff
CIO: Steven Hansen, Director Information Technology
CHR: Kristina Holloway, Chief Human Resources Officer
CNO: Susan G Spoelma MSN, R.N., Chief Nursing Officer
Web address: www.nschd.org
Control: Hospital district or authority, Government, Nonfederal **Service:** General
medical and surgical

Staffed Beds: 38 Admissions: 787 Census: 15 Outpatient Visits: 47034 Births: 0 Total Expense ($000): 39383 Payroll Expense ($000): 17892 Personnel: 219

HEMET—Riverside County

☐ **HEMET VALLEY MEDICAL CENTER (050390)**, 1117 East Devonshire Avenue,
Zip 92543–3083; tel. 951/652–2811, **A**1 10 12 13 **F**3 4 13 15 17 18 20 22 26
29 30 31 34 35 39 40 45 46 49 50 51 56 57 60 64 68 70 74 75 76 77 78 79
80 81 82 85 87 92 93 97 99 100 107 108 111 114 119 121 128 130 132 146 148
149 **S** Physicians for Healthy Hospitals, Hemet, CA
Primary Contact: Dan C. McLaughlin, Chief Hospital Executive Officer
CFO: John R Collins, Chief Financial Officer
CHR: Michele Bird, Chief Human Resources Officer
CNO: Kathryn McLaughlin, Chief Nursing Officer
Web address: www.physiciansforhealthyhospitals.com
Control: Corporation, Investor–owned (for–profit) **Service:** General medical and
surgical

Staffed Beds: 238 Admissions: 10121 Census: 119 Births: 1058 Total Expense ($000): 137732 Payroll Expense ($000): 49753

HOLLISTER—San Benito County

☒ **HAZEL HAWKINS MEMORIAL HOSPITAL (050296)**, 911 Sunset Drive,
Zip 95023–5695; tel. 831/637–5711, (Includes WILLIAM AND INEZ MABIE
SKILLED NURSING FACILITY, 911 Sunset Drive, Hollister, California, Zip 95023,
tel. 408/637–5711) (Total facility includes 119 beds in nursing home–type unit) **A**1
10 **F**3 8 11 13 15 29 30 34 35 39 40 45 49 50 51 57 59 62 64 65 66 68 70
74 75 76 77 79 81 82 84 85 86 87 91 93 97 107 110 111 112 115 119 127
128 129 130 131 132 146 147 148 149 **P**5
Primary Contact: Ken Underwood, Chief Executive Officer
CFO: Mark Robinson, Associate Administrator and Chief Financial Officer
CIO: Julio Gil, Manager Information Services
CHR: Ysidro Gallardo, Associate Administrator Human Resources
Web address: www.hazelhawkins.com
Control: Hospital district or authority, Government, Nonfederal **Service:** General
medical and surgical

Staffed Beds: 181 Admissions: 2394 Census: 122 Outpatient Visits: 171785 Births: 489 Total Expense ($000): 96540 Payroll Expense ($000): 41147

HOLLYWOOD—Los Angeles County, See Los Angeles

HUNTINGTON BEACH—Orange County

☒ **HUNTINGTON BEACH HOSPITAL (050526)**, 17772 Beach Boulevard, Zip 92647–
6896; tel. 714/843–5000, (Nonreporting) **A**1 10 **S** Prime Healthcare, Ontario, CA
Primary Contact: Richard M. Rowe, PharmD, Chief Executive Officer
CFO: Alan H Smith, Chief Financial Officer
CMO: Hassan Alkhouli M.D., Medical Director
CIO: Adam Morquecho, Director Information Technology
CHR: Stephanie Sioson, Director Human Resources
Web address: www.hbhospital.com
Control: Other not–for–profit (including NFP Corporation) **Service:** General
medical and surgical

Staffed Beds: 131

HUNTINGTON PARK—Los Angeles County

COMMUNITY AND MISSION HOSPITALS OF HUNTINGTON PARK See
Community Hospital of Huntington Park

○ **COMMUNITY HOSPITAL OF HUNTINGTON PARK (050091)**, 2623 East Slauson
Avenue, Zip 90255–2926; tel. 323/583–1931, **A**10 11 **F**3 29 40 41 45 49 50 65
70 75 77 79 81 85 107 119 130 135 148 **S** Avanti Hospitals, El Segundo, CA
Primary Contact: Araceli Lonergan, Chief Executive Officer
CFO: Cheryl Tong, Corporate Chief Financial Officer
CMO: Jose Rivas M.D., Chief of Staff
CIO: Jason Cervantes, Corporate Chief Information Officer
CHR: Paul Celuch, Corporate Human Resources Director
CNO: Lisa Jacobson, Director of Nursing
Web address: www.chhplax.com
Control: Corporation, Investor–owned (for–profit) **Service:** General medical and
surgical

Staffed Beds: 81 Admissions: 3270 Census: 38 Outpatient Visits: 45352 Births: 0 Total Expense ($000): 52513 Payroll Expense ($000): 20740 Personnel: 298

INDIO—Riverside County

☒ **JOHN F. KENNEDY MEMORIAL HOSPITAL (050534)**, 47111 Monroe Street,
Zip 92201–6799; tel. 760/347–6191, **A**1 10 **F**3 8 18 20 29 30 34 35 37 40 46
47 48 49 50 54 56 57 59 68 70 74 76 78 79 81 85 87 89 90 97 107 108 111
118 119 126 130 146 148 **S** TENET Healthcare Corporation, Dallas, TX
Primary Contact: Gary Honts, Chief Executive Officer
COO: Philip Fitzgerald, Chief Operating Officer
CFO: Lorna Curtis, Chief Financial Officer
CMO: Charles Anderson M.D., Market Chief Medical Officer
CHR: Raymond Konieczek, Chief Human Resources Officer
CNO: Pat Swaller, Interim Chief Nursing Officer
Web address: www.jfkmemorialhosp.com
Control: Corporation, Investor–owned (for–profit) **Service:** General medical and
surgical

Staffed Beds: 145 Admissions: 6917 Census: 53 Outpatient Visits: 50476 Births: 2204 Total Expense ($000): 114422 Payroll Expense ($000): 53306 Personnel: 626

INGLEWOOD—Los Angeles County

☒ **CENTINELA HOSPITAL MEDICAL CENTER (050739)**, 555 East Hardy Street,
Zip 90301–4011, Mailing Address: P.O.Box 720, 90312–6720; tel. 310/673–
4660, (Nonreporting) **A**1 10 **S** Prime Healthcare, Ontario, CA
Primary Contact: Linda Bradley, Chief Executive Officer
CFO: Paul Sennett, Chief Financial Officer
CMO: Paryus Patel M.D., Chief Medical Officer
CIO: Martin Cordova, Director Information Services
CHR: George Akopyan, Director Human Resources
CNO: Mohammad Abdelnaser, Chief Nursing Officer
Web address: www.centinelamed.com
Control: Corporation, Investor–owned (for–profit) **Service:** General medical and
surgical

Staffed Beds: 369

IRVINE—Orange County

⇑ **HOAG ORTHOPEDIC INSTITUTE (050769)**, 16250 Sand Canyon Avenue,
Zip 92618–3714; tel. 949/517–3149, **A**3 21 **F**3 8 29 65 68 77 79 81 85 130
131 134 146 149
Primary Contact: Carlos Prietto, President and Chief Executive Officer
Web address: www.hoag.org/Locations/Pages/HoagHospOrthoInstitute.aspx
Control: Partnership, Investor–owned (for–profit) **Service:** Orthopedic

Staffed Beds: 70 Admissions: 5619 Census: 29 Outpatient Visits: 902 Births: 0 Personnel: 253

ORANGE COUNTY IRVINE MEDICAL CENTER See Kaiser Permanente Orange County Anaheim Medical Center, Anaheim

JACKSON—Amador County

☒ **SUTTER AMADOR HOSPITAL (050014)**, 200 Mission Boulevard, Zip 95642–2564; tel. 209/223–7500, **A**1 5 10 20 **F**29 34 35 40 46 47 49 54 59 64 65 70 75 76 77 78 79 81 84 85 87 93 102 107 108 110 111 115 119 129 130 132 146 148 **P**3 5 **S** Sutter Health, Sacramento, CA
Primary Contact: Anne Platt, Chief Executive Officer
CFO: Brett Moore CPA, Assistant Administrator Finance
CMO: Ron Hood M.D., Chief of Staff
CIO: Joy Bailey, Director Information Technology
CHR: Beverly Revels, Director Human Resources
CNO: Nikki Allen, Patient Care Executive
Web address: www.sutteramador.org
Control: Other not–for–profit (including NFP Corporation) **Service**: General medical and surgical

Staffed Beds: 52 **Admissions**: 2400 **Census**: 24 **Outpatient Visits**: 49324 **Births**: 295 **Total Expense ($000)**: 74865 **Payroll Expense ($000)**: 25591 **Personnel**: 303

KENTFIELD—Marin County

☒ **KENTFIELD REHABILITATION AND SPECIALTY HOSPITAL (052043)**, 1125 Sir Francis Drake Boulevard, Zip 94904–1455; tel. 415/456–9680, (Nonreporting) **A**1 10 **S** Vibra Healthcare, Mechanicsburg, PA
Primary Contact: Lauren Suarez, Chief Executive Officer
CFO: Stephanie Lawrence, Chief Financial Officer
CMO: Curtis Roebken M.D., Chief Medical Staff
CHR: Julene English, Director Human Resources
Web address: www.kentfieldrehab.com
Control: Corporation, Investor–owned (for–profit) **Service**: Acute long–term care hospital

Staffed Beds: 48

KING CITY—Monterey County

☐ **MEE MEMORIAL HOSPITAL (050189)**, 300 Canal Street, Zip 93930–3431; tel. 831/385–6000, (Nonreporting) **A**1 10 20
Primary Contact: Susan M. Childers, CPA, Chief Executive Officer
CFO: Gary L Wangsmo, Chief Financial Officer
CMO: Schindelheim Roy M.D., Chief of Staff
CIO: Mike McNamara, Chief Information Officer
CHR: Karen Wong, Chief Human Resources Officer
Web address: www.meememorial.com
Control: Other not–for–profit (including NFP Corporation) **Service**: General medical and surgical

Staffed Beds: 119

LA JOLLA—San Diego County

☒ **SCRIPPS GREEN HOSPITAL (050424)**, 10666 North Torrey Pines Road, Zip 92037–1093; tel. 858/455–9100, **A**1 5 8 10 **F**3 8 11 12 14 15 17 18 20 22 24 26 28 29 30 31 34 35 36 37 44 45 46 47 49 50 51 54 57 58 59 61 64 68 70 74 75 77 78 79 80 81 82 84 85 86 87 93 107 108 110 111 114 115 118 119 120 121 123 124 126 130 131 132 136 138 139 141 142 146 148 **P**3 **S** Scripps Health, San Diego, CA
Primary Contact: Robin Brown, Chief Executive, Senior Vice President
CFO: Richard Rothberger, Corporate Executive Vice President and Chief Financial Officer
CMO: James LaBelle M.D., Chief Medical Officer
CIO: Andy Crowder, Chief Information Officer and Corporate Senior Vice President
CHR: Victor Buzachero, Corporate Senior Vice President for Innovation, Human Resources and Performance Management
Web address: www.scrippshealth.org
Control: Other not–for–profit (including NFP Corporation) **Service**: General medical and surgical

Staffed Beds: 173 **Admissions**: 9214 **Census**: 94 **Outpatient Visits**: 84921 **Births**: 0 **Total Expense ($000)**: 314113 **Payroll Expense ($000)**: 95862 **Personnel**: 1138

☒ **SCRIPPS MEMORIAL HOSPITAL–LA JOLLA (050324)**, 9888 Genesee Avenue, Zip 92037–1200, Mailing Address: P.O.Box 28, 92038–0028; tel. 858/626–4123, **A**1 3 5 10 **F**3 8 11 12 13 14 15 17 18 20 22 24 26 28 29 30 31 34 35 40 43 44 45 46 48 49 51 53 54 55 57 58 59 64 65 68 70 74 75 76 77 78 79 81 82 84 85 86 87 91 92 93 94 100 101 102 107 108 110 111 114 115 117 118 119 124 126 130 132 141 145 146 147 148 **P**3 5 **S** Scripps Health, San Diego, CA
Primary Contact: Gary G. Fybel, FACHE, Chief Executive, Senior Vice President
COO: Cindy Steckel Ph.D., R.N., Vice President Chief Nurse and Operations Executive
CFO: Alan Mandal, Vice President Financial Operations
CMO: James LaBelle M.D., Chief Medical Officer
CHR: Shelly Blazakis, Director Human Resources Services
CNO: Cindy Steckel Ph.D., R.N., Vice President Chief Nurse and Operations Executive
Web address: www.scripps.org/locations/hospitals__scripps–memorial–hospital–la–jolla
Control: Other not–for–profit (including NFP Corporation) **Service**: General medical and surgical

Staffed Beds: 277 **Admissions**: 16789 **Census**: 206 **Outpatient Visits**: 98608 **Births**: 3530 **Total Expense ($000)**: 517614 **Payroll Expense ($000)**: 174147 **Personnel**: 2333

LA MESA—San Diego County

☐ **ALVARADO PARKWAY INSTITUTE BEHAVIORAL HEALTH SYSTEM (054075)**, 7050 Parkway Drive, Zip 91942–1535; tel. 619/465–4411, **A**1 10 **F**1 4 5 16 17 29 30 34 35 38 50 59 67 68 70 72 73 75 80 87 88 89 90 98 100 101 103 104 105 128 130 132 135 149
Primary Contact: Patrick C. Ziemer, Chief Executive Officer
CFO: Chad Engbrecht, Chief Financial Officer
CMO: R. Bradley Sanders D.O., Executive Medical Director
CNO: Bonnie Asada, Chief Nursing Officer
Web address: www.apibhs.com
Control: Corporation, Investor–owned (for–profit) **Service**: Psychiatric

Staffed Beds: 66 **Admissions**: 2357 **Census**: 61 **Outpatient Visits**: 129680 **Births**: 0 **Total Expense ($000)**: 25789 **Payroll Expense ($000)**: 13712 **Personnel**: 244

☒ **SHARP GROSSMONT HOSPITAL (050026)**, 5555 Grossmont Center Drive, Zip 91942–3019, Mailing Address: 10992 San Diego Mission Road, Ste 2400, San Diego, 92108; tel. 619/740–6000, (Total facility includes 30 beds in nursing home–type unit) **A**1 2 3 10 **F**3 8 11 13 15 17 18 20 22 24 26 28 29 30 31 34 35 38 39 40 44 45 46 47 48 49 50 51 54 55 56 57 58 59 61 62 63 64 65 66 68 70 72 73 74 75 77 78 79 80 81 82 83 84 85 86 87 90 91 92 93 94 96 98 100 101 102 103 104 105 107 108 109 110 111 114 115 116 117 118 119 120 121 123 124 126 128 129 130 132 135 141 143 145 146 147 148 149 **S** Sharp HealthCare, San Diego, CA
Primary Contact: Scott Evans, PharmD, FACHE, Senior Vice President and Chief Executive Officer
COO: Maryann Cone, Chief Operating Officer
CFO: Kari Cornicelli, Chief Financial Officer
CMO: Michael Murphy M.D., JD, Chief Medical Officer
CIO: Kenneth Lawonn, Senior Vice President and Chief Information Officer
CHR: George Holtz, Director Human Resources
Web address: www.sharp.com
Control: Other not–for–profit (including NFP Corporation) **Service**: General medical and surgical

Staffed Beds: 509 **Admissions**: 27491 **Census**: 357 **Outpatient Visits**: 355896 **Births**: 3299 **Total Expense ($000)**: 670008 **Payroll Expense ($000)**: 267368 **Personnel**: 3070

LA MIRADA—Los Angeles County

☒ **KINDRED HOSPITAL–LA MIRADA (052038)**, 14900 East Imperial Highway, Zip 90638–2172; tel. 562/944–1900, (Nonreporting) (Includes KINDRED HOSPITAL SAN GABRIEL VALLEY, 845 North Lark Ellen Avenue, West Covina, California, Zip 91791–1069, tel. 626/339–5451; Julie Myers, Chief Executive Officer; KINDRED HOSPITAL SANTA ANA, 1901 North College Avenue, Santa Ana, California, Zip 92706–2334, tel. 714/564–7800) **A**1 10 **S** Kindred Healthcare, Louisville, KY
Primary Contact: David Kowalski, Chief Executive Officer
CFO: Rishab Punjabi, Chief Financial Officer
CMO: Prakash Chandra Patel M.D., Chief of Staff
CHR: Susan Bergquist, Human Resources Generalist
CNO: Esperanza Sanchez, Chief Clinical Officer
Web address: www.kindredlamirada.com/
Control: Corporation, Investor–owned (for–profit) **Service**: Acute long–term care hospital

Staffed Beds: 216

Many Facility Codes have changed. Please refer to the AHA Guide Code Chart.
© 2017 AHA Guide

LA PALMA—Orange County

✠ **LA PALMA INTERCOMMUNITY HOSPITAL (050580)**, 7901 Walker Street, Zip 90623–1764; tel. 714/670–7400, **A1** 10 **F3** 8 13 15 17 18 20 22 29 35 40 41 45 49 56 59 64 70 76 77 79 81 85 98 101 102 103 107 108 111 114 119 130 146 147 148 149 **S** Prime Healthcare, Ontario, CA
Primary Contact: Virgis Narbutas, Chief Executive Officer
CFO: Alan H Smith, Chief Financial Officer
CMO: Sami Shoukair M.D., Chief Medical Officer
CIO: Vic Mahan, Director Information Technology
CHR: Stephanie Sioson, Director Human Resources
CNO: Hilda Manzo–Luna, Chief Nursing Officer
Web address: www.lapalmaintercommunityhospital.com
Control: Other not–for–profit (including NFP Corporation) **Service**: General medical and surgical

Staffed Beds: 140 **Admissions**: 3392 **Census**: 48 **Outpatient Visits**: 22922
Births: 287 **Personnel**: 278

LAGUNA HILLS—Orange County

✠ **SADDLEBACK MEMORIAL MEDICAL CENTER (050603)**, 24451 Health Center Drive, Zip 92653–3689; tel. 949/837–4500, **A1** 10 **F3** 11 13 14 15 18 20 22 24 26 28 29 30 31 34 35 36 38 40 44 45 46 47 48 49 50 51 53 54 55 56 57 58 59 62 63 64 65 68 70 72 74 75 76 77 78 79 81 82 84 85 86 87 93 94 100 107 108 110 111 115 116 117 118 119 120 121 123 124 126 130 132 135 141 142 143 145 146 147 148 149 **S** MemorialCare, Fountain Valley, CA
Primary Contact: Marcia Manker, Chief Executive Officer
COO: Cheryl Jacob, Chief Operating Officer
CFO: Adolfo Chanez, Vice President Finance and Chief Financial Officer
CMO: Ernest Hayward M.D., Chief of Staff
CIO: J Scott Joslyn, Senior Vice President and Chief Information Officer
CHR: Kayce H Hudson, Executive Director Human Resources
CNO: Kathy Dawson R.N., MSN, Chief Nursing Officer
Web address: www.memorialcare.org
Control: Other not–for–profit (including NFP Corporation) **Service**: General medical and surgical

Staffed Beds: 313 **Admissions**: 14258 **Census**: 146 **Outpatient Visits**: 222138
Births: 2789 **Total Expense ($000)**: 329722 **Payroll Expense ($000)**: 106342
Personnel: 1303

LAKE ARROWHEAD—San Bernardino County

✠ **SAN BERNARDINO MOUNTAINS COMMUNITY HOSPITAL DISTRICT (051312)**, 29101 Hospital Road, Zip 92352–9706, Mailing Address: P.O.Box 70, 92352–0070; tel. 909/336–3651, (Nonreporting) **A1** 10 18
Primary Contact: Charles Harrison, Chief Executive Officer
COO: Terry Pena, Chief Operating Officer and Chief Nursing Officer
CFO: Yvonne Waggener, Chief Financial Officer
CMO: Walter M. Maier, Chief of Staff
CIO: Patrick Miller, Technology Coordinator
CHR: Julie Atwood, Director Human Resources
CNO: Terry Pena, Chief Operating Officer and Chief Nursing Officer
Web address: www.mchcares.com
Control: Hospital district or authority, Government, Nonfederal **Service**: General medical and surgical

Staffed Beds: 37

LAKE ISABELLA—Kern County

KERN VALLEY HEALTHCARE DISTRICT (051314), 6412 Laurel Avenue, Zip 93240–9529, Mailing Address: P.O.Box 1628, 93240–1628; tel. 760/379–2681, (Nonreporting) **A**10 18
Primary Contact: Timothy McGlew, Chief Executive Officer
CFO: Chester Beedle, Chief Financial Officer
CMO: Gary A Finstad M.D., Chief of Staff
CIO: Paul Quinn, Information Systems Manager
CHR: Debra Hoffman, Manager Human Resources
CNO: Mark Gordon, Chief Nursing Officer
Web address: www.kvhd.org
Control: Hospital district or authority, Government, Nonfederal **Service**: General medical and surgical

Staffed Beds: 99

LAKEPORT—Lake County

✠ **SUTTER LAKESIDE HOSPITAL (051329)**, 5176 Hill Road East, Zip 95453–6300; tel. 707/262–5000, **A1** 10 18 **F3** 5 8 11 13 15 18 29 30 34 35 36 40 43 45 46 51 53 54 56 57 59 61 64 65 66 68 70 74 75 76 79 81 82 85 86 87 91 93 96 97 107 110 111 114 115 118 119 127 130 131 133 135 146 147 148 149 **P3** 5 **S** Sutter Health, Sacramento, CA
Primary Contact: Dan Peterson, Chief Administrative Officer
CFO: Linnea Humble, Director of Finance
CMO: Diane Pege M.D., Vice President Medical Affairs
CIO: Jack Buell, Director Information Services
CHR: Brenda DeRamus, Manager Human Resources
CNO: Teresa Campbell R.N., Chief Nursing Executive
Web address: www.sutterlakeside.org
Control: Other not–for–profit (including NFP Corporation) **Service**: General medical and surgical

Staffed Beds: 25 **Admissions**: 1712 **Census**: 17 **Outpatient Visits**: 60320
Births: 307 **Total Expense ($000)**: 77540 **Payroll Expense ($000)**: 25433
Personnel: 305

LAKEWOOD—Los Angeles County

✠ **LAKEWOOD REGIONAL MEDICAL CENTER (050581)**, 3700 East South Street, Zip 90712–1498, Mailing Address: P.O.Box 6070, 90712; tel. 562/531–2550, **A1** 10 **F3** 11 15 17 18 20 22 24 26 29 30 34 35 38 40 45 49 50 51 57 59 64 68 70 74 75 77 79 81 85 87 93 107 108 109 111 115 118 119 120 126 130 132 143 146 148 149 **S** TENET Healthcare Corporation, Dallas, TX
Primary Contact: John A. Grah, FACHE, Chief Executive Officer
COO: Robert Shappley, Chief Operating Officer
CFO: Eric Delgado, Chief Financial Officer
CMO: Ronald L Kaufman M.D., FACHE, Chief Medical Officer
CIO: Pat Pierce, Director Information Systems
CHR: Mary Okuhara, Chief Human Resource Officer
CNO: Terri Newton, Chief Nursing Officer
Web address: www.lakewoodregional.com
Control: Corporation, Investor–owned (for–profit) **Service**: General medical and surgical

Staffed Beds: 153 **Admissions**: 8271 **Census**: 109 **Outpatient Visits**: 64574 **Births**: 0 **Total Expense ($000)**: 160713 **Payroll Expense ($000)**: 76921 **Personnel**: 805

LANCASTER—Los Angeles County

✠ **ANTELOPE VALLEY HOSPITAL (050056)**, 1600 West Avenue 'J', Zip 93534–2894; tel. 661/949–5000, (Nonreporting) **A1** 2 3 5 10
Primary Contact: Michael L. Wall, FACHE, President and Chief Executive Officer
COO: Ronald T Bingham, Chief Operating Officer
CFO: Colette Menzel Ph.D., Chief Financial Officer
CMO: Radha Krishnan M.D., Chief Medical Officer
CIO: Dale Lepper, Chief Information Officer
CHR: George Leisher Jr, Chief Human Resources Officer
CNO: Jack J Burke MS, R.N., Chief Operating Officer and Chief Nursing Officer
Web address: www.avhospital.org
Control: Hospital district or authority, Government, Nonfederal **Service**: General medical and surgical

Staffed Beds: 368

LEMOORE—Kings County

★ **NAVAL HOSPITAL LEMOORE**, 937 Franklin Avenue, Zip 93246–0001; tel. 559/998–4481, (Nonreporting) **S** Bureau of Medicine and Surgery, Department of the Navy, Falls Church, VA
Primary Contact: Captain Mary A. Mahony, Commanding Officer
CFO: Thomas M Brui, Director Resource Management
CMO: Scott Cota M.D., Director Medical Services
CIO: Victor Dela Torre, Command Legal Officer
CHR: Billy Newman, Department Head
Web address: www.med.navy.mil/sites/nhlem/Pages/index.aspx
Control: Navy, Government, federal **Service**: General medical and surgical

Staffed Beds: 16

LIVERMORE—Alameda County

VALLEY MEMORIAL See Stanford Health Care – Valleycare, Pleasanton

VETERANS AFFAIRS PALO ALTO HEALTH CARE SYSTEM, LIVERMORE DIVISION See Va Palo Alto Health Care System, Palo Alto

---

Hospital, Medicare Provider Number, Address, Telephone, Approval, Facility, and Physician Codes, Health Care System

★ American Hospital Association (AHA) membership   ○ Healthcare Facilities Accreditation Program   ⇑ Center for Improvement in Healthcare Quality Accreditation
☐ The Joint Commission accreditation   ◇ DNV Healthcare Inc. accreditation   △ Commission on Accreditation of Rehabilitation Facilities (CARF) accreditation

LODI—San Joaquin County

✠ **LODI MEMORIAL HOSPITAL (050336)**, 975 South Fairmont Avenue, Zip 95240–5118, Mailing Address: P.O.Box 3004, 95241–1908; tel. 209/334–3411, (Nonreporting) (Includes LODI MEMORIAL HOSPITAL WEST, 800 South Lower Sacramento Road, Lodi, California, Zip 95242, tel. 209/333–0211) **A**1 3 10 **S** Adventist Health, Roseville, CA
Primary Contact: Daniel Wolcott, President and Chief Executive Officer
CFO: Terry Deak, Chief Financial Officer
CHR: Mark T Wallace, Director Human Resources
CNO: Debbie Moreno R.N., Chief Nursing Officer
Web address: www.lodihealth.org
Control: Other not–for–profit (including NFP Corporation) **Service**: General medical and surgical

Staffed Beds: 190

LOMA LINDA—San Bernardino County

LOMA LINDA UNIVERSITY CHILDREN'S HOSPITAL (050778), 11234 Anderson Street, Zip 92354–2804; tel. 909/558–8000, **A**5 **F**3 11 13 19 21 23 25 27 29 31 34 39 44 50 54 55 57 58 59 60 61 64 65 66 68 71 72 74 75 76 77 78 79 80 81 82 84 85 86 87 88 89 97 119 130 132 134 135 136 137 138 141 146 147 **P**3 **S** Loma Linda University Adventist Health Sciences Center, Loma Linda, CA
Primary Contact: Kerry Heinrich, JD, Chief Executive Officer
Web address: www.llu.edu/lluch
Control: Other not–for–profit (including NFP Corporation) **Service**: Children's general medical and surgical

Staffed Beds: 337 **Admissions**: 13134 **Census**: 231 **Outpatient Visits**: 96268 **Births**: 2874 **Total Expense ($000)**: 387388 **Payroll Expense ($000)**: 157951 **Personnel**: 1286

LOMA LINDA UNIVERSITY HEART & SURGICAL HOSPITAL See Loma Linda University Medical Center

✠ △ **LOMA LINDA UNIVERSITY MEDICAL CENTER (050327)**, 11234 Anderson Street, Zip 92354–2804, Mailing Address: P.O.Box 2000, 92354–0200; tel. 909/558–4000, (Includes LOMA LINDA UNIVERSITY EAST CAMPUS HOSPITAL, 25333 Barton Road, Loma Linda, California, Zip 92354–3053, tel. 909/558–6000; LOMA LINDA UNIVERSITY HEART & SURGICAL HOSPITAL, 26780 Barton Road, Loma Linda, California, Zip 92354, tel. 909/583–2900) **A**1 2 3 5 7 8 10 **F**2 3 8 11 12 15 17 18 20 22 24 26 28 29 30 31 34 35 37 40 41 43 44 45 46 47 48 49 50 54 57 58 59 60 62 63 64 65 68 70 74 75 77 78 79 81 82 84 85 86 87 90 91 92 93 94 96 107 108 110 111 114 115 117 118 119 120 121 122 123 124 126 129 130 132 137 138 139 141 142 143 144 146 147 148 **P**3 **S** Loma Linda University Adventist Health Sciences Center, Loma Linda, CA
Primary Contact: Kerry Heinrich, JD, Chief Executive Officer
COO: Trevor Wright, Chief Operating Officer
CFO: Steve Mohr, Senior Vice President Finance and Chief Financial Officer
CMO: H Roger Hadley M.D., Vice President, Medical Affairs
CIO: Mark Zirkelbach, Chief Information Officer
CNO: Judith Storfjell Ph.D., R.N., Senior Vice President and Chief Nursing Officer
Web address: www.llumc.edu
Control: Other not–for–profit (including NFP Corporation) **Service**: General medical and surgical

Staffed Beds: 538 **Admissions**: 21580 **Census**: 351 **Outpatient Visits**: 637432 **Births**: 0 **Total Expense ($000)**: 999616 **Payroll Expense ($000)**: 327611 **Personnel**: 4450

✠ △ **VETERANS AFFAIRS LOMA LINDA HEALTHCARE SYSTEM**, 11201 Benton Street, Zip 92357–1000; tel. 909/825–7084, (Nonreporting) **A**1 2 3 5 7 8 **S** Department of Veterans Affairs, Washington, DC
Primary Contact: Barbara Fallen, FACHE, Director
COO: Shane Elliott, Associate Director Administration
CFO: Eric C Sorenson, Chief Financial Officer
CMO: Dwight Evans M.D., Chief of Staff
CIO: Doug Wirthgen, Facility Chief Information Officer
CHR: Eugene Wylie, Chief Human Resources Officer
CNO: Anne Gillespie R.N., Associate Director Patient Care and Nursing Services
Web address: www.lomalinda.va.gov
Control: Veterans Affairs, Government, federal **Service**: General medical and surgical

Staffed Beds: 268

LOMPOC—Santa Barbara County

★ **LOMPOC VALLEY MEDICAL CENTER (050110)**, 1515 East Ocean Avenue, Zip 93436–7092, Mailing Address: P.O.Box 1058, 93438–1058; tel. 805/737–3300, (Nonreporting) **A**10 22
Primary Contact: James J. Raggio, Chief Executive Officer
COO: Naishadh Buch, Chief Operating Officer
CFO: Robert M Baden, Chief Financial Officer
CMO: Randall Michel M.D., Chief of Staff
CIO: Jim White, Chief Information Officer
CHR: Edwin R Braxton, Director Human Resources
CNO: Jayne Scalise R.N., Chief Nursing Executive
Web address: www.lompocvmc.com
Control: Hospital district or authority, Government, Nonfederal **Service**: General medical and surgical

Staffed Beds: 170

LONE PINE—Inyo County

SOUTHERN INYO HEALTHCARE DISTRICT (051302), 501 East Locust Street, Zip 93545–1009, Mailing Address: P.O.Box 1009, 93545–1009; tel. 760/876–5501, (Nonreporting) **A**10 18
Primary Contact: Alan Germany, Chief Executive Officer and Chief Restructuring Officer
CFO: Marise Andrade, Controller
CIO: Phyllis Gregory, Registered Health Information Administrator
CHR: Nancy Erickson, Human Resource Director
CNO: Colleen Wilson, Chief Nursing Officer
Web address: www.sihd.org
Control: Hospital district or authority, Government, Nonfederal **Service**: General medical and surgical

Staffed Beds: 4

LONG BEACH—Los Angeles County

⇑ **COLLEGE MEDICAL CENTER (050776)**, 2776 Pacific Avenue, Zip 90806–2613; tel. 562/595–1911, (Nonreporting) **A**10 12 13 21
Primary Contact: Joseph Avelino, Chief Executive Officer
COO: Jennifer Ensminger, Chief Operating Officer
CFO: Jim Canedo, Chief Financial Officer
CMO: Luke Watson M.D., Chief of Staff
CIO: Rohan Corea, Director Healthcare Information Technology
CHR: Ann Mattia Schiller, Vice President Human Resources
Web address: www.collegemedicalcenter.com/
Control: Other not–for–profit (including NFP Corporation) **Service**: General medical and surgical

Staffed Beds: 184

□ **COMMUNITY HOSPITAL LONG BEACH (050727)**, 1720 Termino Avenue, Zip 90804–2104; tel. 562/498–1000, **A**1 5 10 **F**3 4 5 8 11 12 18 26 28 29 30 31 34 35 38 40 45 46 49 50 53 54 56 57 59 64 65 68 70 71 75 77 79 81 82 85 86 87 93 98 100 101 102 103 104 105 107 108 111 115 119 130 132 135 146 148 149 150 **S** MemorialCare, Fountain Valley, CA
Primary Contact: John Bishop, Chief Executive Officer
CFO: Yair Katz, Chief Financial Officer
CMO: S Gainer Pillsbury M.D., Associate Chief Medical Officer
CIO: Richele Steele, Vice President, Marketing and Public Relations
CHR: Marcie Atchison, Vice President Human Resources
CNO: Sheryl Howland R.N., Executive Director, Patient Care Services
Web address: www.memorialcare.org
Control: Other not–for–profit (including NFP Corporation) **Service**: General medical and surgical

Staffed Beds: 158 **Admissions**: 5584 **Census**: 65 **Outpatient Visits**: 33354 **Births**: 0 **Total Expense ($000)**: 69679 **Payroll Expense ($000)**: 28933 **Personnel**: 513

✠ △ **LONG BEACH MEMORIAL MEDICAL CENTER (050485)**, 2801 Atlantic Avenue, Zip 90806–1701, Mailing Address: P.O.Box 1428, 90801–1428; tel. 562/933–2000, **A**1 2 3 5 7 8 10 **F**3 8 9 11 12 14 15 17 18 20 22 24 26 28 29 30 31 34 35 36 37 38 39 40 43 44 45 47 48 49 50 52 53 55 56 57 58 59 61 63 64 65 68 70 74 75 77 78 79 81 82 84 85 86 87 90 93 96 97 107 108 110 111 114 115 116 117 118 119 120 121 123 124 126 128 129 130 131 132 135 141 142 143 144 146 147 148 149 150 **S** MemorialCare, Fountain Valley, CA
Primary Contact: John Bishop, Chief Executive Officer
COO: Ikenna Mmeje, Chief Operating Officer
CFO: Yair Katz, Chief Financial Officer
CMO: Susan Melvin D.O., Chief Medical Officer
CIO: Danny Asaoka, Executive Director Information Systems
CHR: Marcie Atchison, Vice President Human Resources
CNO: Judith A Fix R.N., MSN, Senior Vice President and Chief Nursing Officer
Web address: www.memorialcare.org/LongBeach
Control: Other not–for–profit (including NFP Corporation) **Service**: General medical and surgical

Staffed Beds: 458 **Admissions**: 20401 **Census**: 284 **Outpatient Visits**: 200538 **Births**: 0 **Total Expense ($000)**: 586972 **Payroll Expense ($000)**: 191091 **Personnel**: 3343

□ **MILLER CHILDREN'S & WOMEN'S HOSPITAL LONG BEACH (053309)**, 2801 Atlantic Avenue, Zip 90806–1701; tel. 562/933–5437, **A**1 2 3 5 10 **F**3 11 12 13 14 15 19 21 23 25 27 29 30 31 32 34 35 36 37 38 40 41 43 44 45 47 48 49 50 52 53 54 55 57 58 59 61 64 65 66 68 72 74 75 76 77 78 79 81 82 84 85 86 87 88 89 93 96 97 99 100 101 102 104 107 108 111 114 115 116 117 118 119 120 121 123 124 126 129 130 132 134 135 141 142 143 144 146 147 148 149 **S** MemorialCare, Fountain Valley, CA
Primary Contact: John Bishop, Chief Executive Officer
COO: Tamra Kaplan PharmD, Chief Operating Officer
CFO: Yair Katz, Chief Financial Officer
CIO: Danny Asaoka, Executive Director Information Systems
CHR: Marcie Atchison, Vice President Human Resources
Web address: www.memorialcare.org
Control: Other not–for–profit (including NFP Corporation) **Service**: Children's general medical and surgical

Staffed Beds: 371 **Admissions:** 15599 **Census:** 197 **Outpatient Visits:** 107572 **Births:** 6031 **Total Expense ($000):** 408546 **Payroll Expense ($000):** 137305 **Personnel:** 1315

⊞ **ST. MARY MEDICAL CENTER (050191)**, 1050 Linden Avenue, Zip 90813–3321, Mailing Address: P.O.Box 887, 90801–0887; tel. 562/491–9000, **A**1 3 5 10 **F**3 8 12 13 15 18 19 20 22 24 26 28 29 30 31 32 34 35 38 39 40 41 43 45 46 47 48 49 50 54 55 56 57 59 60 61 64 65 66 68 70 71 72 74 75 76 77 78 79 80 81 82 84 85 86 87 89 90 92 93 96 97 100 104 107 108 110 111 114 115 118 119 120 121 122 123 130 143 145 146 147 148 **P**5 **S** Dignity Health, San Francisco, CA
Primary Contact: Paul M. Czajka, Interim Chief Executive Officer
COO: Paul M Czajka, Vice President Chief Operating Officer
CFO: Leon Choiniere, Vice President, Chief Financial Officer
CIO: David Ung, Site Director
CHR: Denise Livingston, Director Human Resources
CNO: Jodi Hein R.N., Vice President Chief Nurse Executive
Web address: www.stmarymedicalcenter.org
Control: Other not–for–profit (including NFP Corporation) **Service**: General medical and surgical

Staffed Beds: 302 **Admissions:** 11153 **Census:** 149 **Outpatient Visits:** 128235 **Births:** 2314 **Total Expense ($000):** 306229 **Payroll Expense ($000):** 118175 **Personnel:** 1111

⊞ △ **VA LONG BEACH HEALTHCARE SYSTEM**, 5901 East 7th Street, Zip 90822–5201; tel. 562/826–8000, (Nonreporting) **A**1 2 3 5 7 8 **S** Department of Veterans Affairs, Washington, DC
Primary Contact: Tracye B. Davis, Acting Director
COO: Anthony DeFrancesco, Associate Director
CFO: Michael J Rupert, Chief Financial Officer
CMO: Sandor Szabo M.D., Ph.D., M.P.H., Chief of Staff
CIO: Rodney Sagmit, Chief Information Management
CHR: Mary E McCartan, Manager Human Resources
Web address: www.longbeach.va.gov/
Control: Veterans Affairs, Government, federal **Service**: General medical and surgical

Staffed Beds: 356

LOS ALAMITOS—Orange County

⊞ **LOS ALAMITOS MEDICAL CENTER (050551)**, 3751 Katella Avenue, Zip 90720–3164; tel. 562/598–1311, (Nonreporting) **A**1 10 13 **S** TENET Healthcare Corporation, Dallas, TX
Primary Contact: Kent G. Clayton, Chief Executive Officer
COO: Clay Farell, Chief Operation Officer
CFO: Dave Vickers, Chief Financial Officer
CMO: Nirav Patel M.D., Chief of Staff
CIO: Sally Andrada, Chief Information Officer
CHR: Lisa Oremus, Interim Chief Human Resource Officer
CNO: Judy Chabot, Chief Nursing Officer
Web address: www.losalamitosmedctr.com
Control: Corporation, Investor–owned (for–profit) **Service**: General medical and surgical

Staffed Beds: 167

LOS ANGELES—Los Angeles County

(Mailing Addresses – Canoga Park, Encino, Granada Hills, Harbor City, Hollywood, Mission Hills, North Hollywood, Northridge, Panorama City, San Pedro, Sepulveda, Sherman Oaks, Sun Valley, Sylmar, Tarzana, Van Nuys, West Hills, West Los Angeles, Woodland Hills)

⊞ **BARLOW RESPIRATORY HOSPITAL (052031)**, 2000 Stadium Way, Zip 90026–2696; tel. 213/250–4200, **A**1 10 **F**1 3 14 29 30 35 45 46 64 68 84 93 103 130 132 148
Primary Contact: Amit Mohan, President and Chief Executive Officer
CFO: Edward Engesser, Chief Financial Officer and Chief Information Officer
CMO: David Nelson M.D., Medical Director
CIO: Edward Engesser, Chief Financial Officer and Chief Information Officer
CHR: Rashawn Woods, Vice President Human Resources
CNO: Gladys D'Souza, Chief Nursing Officer
Web address: www.barlow2000.org
Control: Other not–for–profit (including NFP Corporation) **Service**: Acute long–term care hospital

Staffed Beds: 105 **Admissions:** 862 **Census:** 66 **Outpatient Visits:** 0 **Births:** 0 **Total Expense ($000):** 52078 **Payroll Expense ($000):** 26012 **Personnel:** 340

⊞ **CALIFORNIA HOSPITAL MEDICAL CENTER (050149)**, 1401 South Grand Avenue, Zip 90015–3010; tel. 213/748–2411, (Total facility includes 31 beds in nursing home–type unit) **A**1 3 5 10 **F**75 78 79 81 82 84 87 102 107 108 110 111 114 118 119 120 121 130 132 135 143 146 147 **S** Dignity Health, San Francisco, CA
Primary Contact: Margaret R. Peterson, Ph.D., R.N., President
CFO: Rebecca Cheng, Chief Financial Officer
CMO: Joseph Nussbaum M.D., Chief of Staff
CIO: David Ung, Director, Information Technology
CHR: Kristin Anderson, Director, Human Resources
CNO: Valarie Fleming MSN, Chief Nursing Executive
Web address: www.chmcla.org
Control: Other not–for–profit (including NFP Corporation) **Service**: General medical and surgical

Staffed Beds: 318 **Admissions:** 18264 **Census:** 232 **Outpatient Visits:** 101599 **Births:** 3676 **Total Expense ($000):** 419254 **Payroll Expense ($000):** 155293 **Personnel:** 1488

★ **CALIFORNIA REHABILITATION INSTITUTE**, 2070 Century Park East, Zip 90067–1907; tel. 424/363–1000, (Nonreporting) **S** Select Medical Corporation, Mechanicsburg, PA
Primary Contact: John Behzad, Chief Executive Officer
Web address: www.californiarehabinstitute.com/
Control: Corporation, Investor–owned (for–profit) **Service**: Rehabilitation

Staffed Beds: 138

⊞ △ **CEDARS–SINAI MEDICAL CENTER (050625)**, 8700 Beverly Boulevard, Zip 90048–1865, Mailing Address: Box 48750, 90048–0750; tel. 310/423–5000, **A**1 2 3 5 7 8 10 **F**3 5 6 8 9 11 12 13 14 15 17 18 19 20 21 22 23 24 25 26 27 28 29 30 31 32 33 34 35 36 37 38 39 40 43 44 45 46 47 48 49 50 51 52 53 54 55 56 57 58 59 60 61 64 65 66 68 69 70 71 72 74 75 76 77 78 79 81 82 83 84 85 86 87 88 89 90 91 92 93 96 97 100 102 107 108 109 110 111 112 113 114 115 116 117 118 119 120 121 122 123 124 126 130 131 132 133 134 135 136 137 138 139 140 141 142 144 145 146 147 148 149 150 **P**3 5 6 **S** Cedars–Sinai, West Hollywood, CA
Primary Contact: Thomas M. Priselac, President and Chief Executive Officer
COO: Mark R Gavens, Executive Vice President Health System Hospital Operations and Chief Operating Officer of Cedars–Sinai Medical Center
CFO: Edward M Prunchunas, Executive Vice President and Chief Financial Officer
CMO: Michael L Langberg M.D., Senior Vice President Medical Affairs and Chief Medical Officer
CIO: Darren Dworkin, Senior Vice President Enterprise Information Systems and Chief Information Officer
CHR: Jeanne Flores, Consultant to the President
CNO: Linda Burnes Bolton R.N., Vice President and Chief Nursing Officer
Web address: www.cedars–sinai.edu
Control: Other not–for–profit (including NFP Corporation) **Service**: General medical and surgical

Staffed Beds: 885 **Admissions:** 49437 **Census:** 696 **Outpatient Visits:** 841291 **Births:** 6740 **Total Expense ($000):** 2879764 **Payroll Expense ($000):** 1060306 **Personnel:** 12623

CA

Hospital, Medicare Provider Number, Address, Telephone, Approval, Facility, and Physician Codes, Health Care System

★ American Hospital Association (AHA) membership	○ Healthcare Facilities Accreditation Program	⇑ Center for Improvement in Healthcare Quality Accreditation
□ The Joint Commission accreditation	◇ DNV Healthcare Inc. accreditation	△ Commission on Accreditation of Rehabilitation Facilities (CARF) accreditation

✠ **CHILDREN'S HOSPITAL LOS ANGELES (053302)**, 4650 West Sunset Boulevard, Zip 90027–6062, Mailing Address: 4650 West Sunset Boulevard, MS #1, 90027–6062; tel. 323/660–2450, **A**1 3 5 8 10 **F**3 5 14 17 19 21 23 25 27 29 30 31 32 34 35 36 38 39 40 41 43 44 45 46 49 50 51 54 55 57 58 59 60 61 64 68 71 72 74 75 77 78 79 80 81 82 84 85 86 87 88 89 90 92 93 95 96 99 100 104 107 108 111 114 115 116 117 118 119 120 121 122 123 124 126 129 130 131 132 134 135 136 137 138 139 141 142 146 148 149 150
Primary Contact: Paul S. Viviano, President and Chief Executive Officer
CFO: Lannie Tonnu, Senior Vice President and Chief Financial Officer
CMO: Brent Polk M.D., Chair Department of Pediatrics and Vice President Academic Affairs
CIO: TJ Malseed, Vice President and Chief Information Officer
CHR: Myra Gregorian, Vice President and Chief Human Resources Officer
CNO: Mary Dee Hacker R.N., Vice President, Patient Care Services and Chief Nursing Officer
Web address: www.chla.org
Control: Other not–for–profit (including NFP Corporation) **Service**: Children's general medical and surgical

Staffed Beds: 357 **Admissions:** 16289 **Census:** 290 **Outpatient Visits:** 392073 **Births:** 0 **Total Expense ($000):** 1028741 **Payroll Expense ($000):** 393789 **Personnel:** 5203

☐ **EAST LOS ANGELES DOCTORS HOSPITAL (050641)**, 4060 Whittier Boulevard, Zip 90023–2526; tel. 323/268–5514, **A**1 10 **F**1 3 7 8 13 17 29 30 35 40 41 76 77 79 80 81 84 85 87 89 91 107 114 119 130 143 148 **S** Avanti Hospitals, El Segundo, CA
Primary Contact: Gerald Clute, Chief Executive Officer
CFO: Steven Blake, Corporate Chief Financial Officer
CMO: Janine King M.D., Chief of Staff
CIO: Jason Cervantes, Chief Information Officer
CHR: Paul Celuch, Chief Human Resource Officer
CNO: Kimberly Frazier R.N., Chief Nursing Officer
Web address: www.avantihospitals.com
Control: Partnership, Investor–owned (for–profit) **Service**: General medical and surgical

Staffed Beds: 127 **Admissions:** 4244 **Census:** 80 **Outpatient Visits:** 18998 **Births:** 502 **Total Expense ($000):** 64053 **Payroll Expense ($000):** 24184 **Personnel:** 351

✠ **ENCINO HOSPITAL MEDICAL CENTER (050158)**, 16237 Ventura Boulevard, Zip 91436–2272; tel. 818/995–5000, (Total facility includes 25 beds in nursing home–type unit) **A**1 10 **F**4 17 29 35 38 40 51 57 70 79 81 98 103 107 118 119 128 130 146 149 **S** Prime Healthcare, Ontario, CA
Primary Contact: Bockhi Park, Chief Executive Officer
CFO: Kanner Tillman, Chief Financial Officer
CMO: Muhammad Anwar M.D., Chief Medical Officer
CIO: Edward Barrera, Director Communications
CHR: Barbara Back, Manager Human Resources
CNO: Vilma L Dinham R.N., Chief Nursing Officer
Web address: www.encinomed.com
Control: Other not–for–profit (including NFP Corporation) **Service**: General medical and surgical

Staffed Beds: 78 **Admissions:** 3942 **Census:** 75 **Outpatient Visits:** 12400 **Births:** 0 **Total Expense ($000):** 53782 **Payroll Expense ($000):** 21123 **Personnel:** 281

○ **GATEWAYS HOSPITAL AND MENTAL HEALTH CENTER (054028)**, 1891 Effie Street, Zip 90026–1793; tel. 323/644–2000, (Nonreporting) **A**10 11
Primary Contact: Philip Wong, PsyD, Chief Executive Officer
COO: Philip Wong PsyD, Chief Operating Officer
CMO: Imani Walker M.D., Medical Director
CIO: Rozelle DeVera, Director of Information Systems
CHR: Vahan Demlakian, Director of Human Resources
Web address: www.gatewayshospital.org
Control: Other not–for–profit (including NFP Corporation) **Service**: Psychiatric

Staffed Beds: 55

☐ ⇑ **GOOD SAMARITAN HOSPITAL (050471)**, 1225 Wilshire Boulevard, Zip 90017–2395; tel. 213/977–2121, **A**1 2 3 5 10 21 **F**3 7 8 11 13 14 15 17 18 20 22 24 26 28 29 30 31 34 35 37 40 43 45 46 47 48 49 50 51 53 57 58 59 60 64 65 68 70 72 74 75 76 77 78 79 81 85 86 87 93 107 108 110 111 114 115 117 118 119 120 121 123 124 126 129 130 132 143 145 146 148 149 **P**5
Primary Contact: Andrew B. Leeka, President and Chief Executive Officer
CFO: Alan Ino, Chief Financial Officer
CMO: Margaret Bates, Chief of Staff
CIO: Dean Campbell, Vice President Information Services and Chief Information Officer
CHR: Lexie Schuster, Vice President Human Resources
CNO: Margaret Pfeiffer R.N., MSN, Vice President Patient Care Services
Web address: www.goodsam.org
Control: Other not–for–profit (including NFP Corporation) **Service**: General medical and surgical

Staffed Beds: 374 **Admissions:** 11962 **Census:** 158 **Outpatient Visits:** 74439 **Births:** 3201 **Total Expense ($000):** 314635 **Payroll Expense ($000):** 106221 **Personnel:** 1298

✠ **HOLLYWOOD PRESBYTERIAN MEDICAL CENTER (050063)**, 1300 North Vermont Avenue, Zip 90027–6306; tel. 213/413–3000, **A**1 3 5 10 **F**3 8 13 15 17 18 20 22 24 26 29 30 31 34 40 41 45 46 49 50 51 56 57 59 60 61 64 68 70 72 74 75 76 77 78 79 80 81 85 87 89 90 92 96 97 107 108 110 111 115 119 130 146 147 148 149 **P**3 5
Primary Contact: Gerald B. Clute, Chief Executive Officer
CIO: Steve Giles, Chief Information Officer
CHR: George Leisher Jr, Vice President Human Resources
CNO: Julieta M. Padilla, Chief Nursing Officer
Web address: www.hollywoodpresbyterian.com
Control: Partnership, Investor–owned (for–profit) **Service**: General medical and surgical

Staffed Beds: 434 **Admissions:** 12960 **Census:** 242 **Outpatient Visits:** 52983 **Births:** 3597 **Total Expense ($000):** 258662 **Payroll Expense ($000):** 112122 **Personnel:** 1093

KAISER FOUNDATION MENTAL HEALTH CENTER See Kaiser Permanente Los Angeles Medical Center

✠ **KAISER PERMANENTE LOS ANGELES MEDICAL CENTER (050138)**, 4867 Sunset Boulevard, Zip 90027–5961; tel. 323/783–4011, (Includes KAISER FOUNDATION MENTAL HEALTH CENTER, 765 West College Street, Los Angeles, California, Zip 90012, tel. 213/580–7200) **A**1 3 5 8 10 **F**3 5 8 13 15 17 18 19 20 21 22 23 24 26 28 29 30 31 35 36 38 40 41 44 45 46 47 49 50 51 54 55 56 57 58 59 60 61 62 63 64 65 66 68 70 72 73 74 75 76 77 78 79 80 81 82 83 84 85 86 87 88 89 92 93 94 97 98 99 100 101 102 103 104 105 106 107 108 109 110 111 113 114 115 118 119 120 121 122 123 124 126 129 130 131 132 135 144 146 147 148 149 150 **P**6 **S** Kaiser Foundation Hospitals, Oakland, CA
Primary Contact: William N. Grice, Executive Director
COO: Derek Berz, Chief Operating Officer
CFO: Brad Malsed, Area Chief Financial Officer
CMO: Michael Tome M.D., Medical Director
CIO: David Strickland, Area Information Officer
CHR: Paul J Martin, Director Human Resources
Web address: www.kaiserpermanente.org
Control: Other not–for–profit (including NFP Corporation) **Service**: General medical and surgical

Staffed Beds: 528 **Admissions:** 26976 **Census:** 371 **Outpatient Visits:** 2681112 **Births:** 2738 **Personnel:** 6031

✠ **KAISER PERMANENTE PANORAMA CITY MEDICAL CENTER (050137)**, 13652 Cantara Street, Zip 91402–5497; tel. 818/375–2000, (Nonreporting) **A**1 3 5 10 **S** Kaiser Foundation Hospitals, Oakland, CA
Primary Contact: Payman Roshan, Senior Vice President and Area Manager
COO: Murtaza Sanwari, Chief Operating Officer
CFO: Karla Valle, Area Chief Financial Officer
CMO: James Lau M.D., Area Medical Director
CIO: Earle Johnson, Area Information Officer
CHR: Carole L Erken, Human Resources Leader
CNO: Celeste Farugia R.N., MSN, Chief Nurse Executive
Web address: www.kaiserpermanente.org
Control: Other not–for–profit (including NFP Corporation) **Service**: General medical and surgical

Staffed Beds: 194

✠ **KAISER PERMANENTE SOUTH BAY MEDICAL CENTER (050411)**, 25825 Vermont Avenue, Zip 90710–3599; tel. 310/325–5111, **A**1 3 10 **F**3 12 13 15 16 17 29 30 31 34 35 40 44 45 46 47 48 49 50 51 54 55 56 57 58 59 60 61 64 65 68 70 72 73 74 75 76 77 78 79 81 82 84 85 86 87 88 89 97 107 108 110 111 114 115 116 117 118 119 130 132 135 146 147 148 149 **P**6 **S** Kaiser Foundation Hospitals, Oakland, CA
Primary Contact: Lesley A. Wille, Executive Director
Web address: www.kaiserpermanente.org
Control: Other not–for–profit (including NFP Corporation) **Service**: General medical and surgical

Staffed Beds: 170 **Admissions:** 10979 **Census:** 107 **Outpatient Visits:** 75164 **Births:** 2290 **Personnel:** 2277

✠ **KAISER PERMANENTE WEST LOS ANGELES MEDICAL CENTER (050561)**, 6041 Cadillac Avenue, Zip 90034–1700; tel. 323/857–2201, **A**1 3 5 10 **F**3 9 12 13 15 29 30 31 32 34 35 37 40 45 46 47 48 49 50 55 56 57 59 60 61 64 65 68 70 72 73 74 75 76 77 78 79 80 81 82 83 84 85 86 87 97 100 101 103 104 105 107 108 110 111 114 115 116 117 119 126 130 131 132 135 144 146 147 148 149 **P**6 **S** Kaiser Foundation Hospitals, Oakland, CA
Primary Contact: Georgina R. Garcia, R.N., Executive Director
CFO: Alice H Issai, Business Strategy and Finance Leader
CMO: Fred Alexander M.D., Medical Director
CIO: Gregory M Sincock, Information Technology Leader
Web address: www.kaiserpermanente.org
Control: Other not–for–profit (including NFP Corporation) **Service:** General medical and surgical

> **Staffed Beds:** 126 **Admissions:** 16768 **Census:** 149 **Outpatient Visits:** 83294 **Births:** 1884 **Total Expense ($000):** 1309377 **Payroll Expense ($000):** 114227 **Personnel:** 1402

✠ **KAISER PERMANENTE WOODLAND HILLS MEDICAL CENTER (050677)**, 5601 DeSoto Avenue, Zip 91367–6798; tel. 818/719–2000, **A**1 3 5 10 **F**3 13 15 29 30 31 34 40 41 45 46 48 49 50 51 55 56 57 60 61 64 65 68 70 73 74 75 76 77 78 79 80 81 82 84 85 86 87 89 92 93 100 102 103 107 108 110 111 114 115 117 119 124 130 132 141 146 147 148 149 150 **P**6 **S** Kaiser Foundation Hospitals, Oakland, CA
Primary Contact: Dennis C. Benton, Senior Vice President and Area Manager
COO: Richard Trogman FACHE, Chief Operating Officer
CFO: Marilou Cheung, Assistant Administrator Finance
CMO: Gregory Kelman M.D., Area Medical Director
CIO: Earle Johnson, Area Information Officer
CHR: Cathy Cousineau, Director Human Resources
CNO: Nancy Tankel R.N., Chief Nurse Executive
Web address: www.kaiserpermanente.org
Control: Other not–for–profit (including NFP Corporation) **Service:** General medical and surgical

> **Staffed Beds:** 130 **Admissions:** 9388 **Census:** 101 **Outpatient Visits:** 87364 **Births:** 1568 **Personnel:** 1508

✠ **KECK HOSPITAL OF USC (050696)**, 1500 San Pablo Street, Zip 90033–5313; tel. 323/442–8500, **A**1 3 5 8 10 **F**3 6 8 9 11 12 15 17 18 20 22 24 26 29 30 31 34 35 36 37 38 39 43 44 45 46 47 48 49 50 51 52 53 54 56 57 58 59 60 61 64 65 68 70 71 74 75 77 78 79 81 82 84 85 86 87 90 92 93 94 95 96 97 100 101 103 104 107 108 109 110 111 112 113 114 115 116 117 118 119 120 121 123 124 126 129 130 131 132 135 137 138 139 140 141 142 143 145 146 147 148 149 150 **P**6 **S** Keck Medicine of USC, Los Angeles, CA
Primary Contact: Rodney B. Hanners, Chief Executive Officer
COO: Alice H Issai, Chief Operating Officer
CFO: Robert Allen, Chief Financial Officer
CMO: Stephanie Hall M.D., Chief Medical Officer
CHR: Matthew McElrath, Chief Human Resources Officer
CNO: Annette Sy, Chief Nursing Officer
Web address: www.keckhospitalofusc.org
Control: Other not–for–profit (including NFP Corporation) **Service:** General medical and surgical

> **Staffed Beds:** 401 **Admissions:** 12097 **Census:** 234 **Outpatient Visits:** 318527 **Births:** 0 **Total Expense ($000):** 899088 **Payroll Expense ($000):** 298603 **Personnel:** 2956

KEDREN COMMUNITY MENTAL HEALTH CENTER (054083), 4211 South Avalon Boulevard, Zip 90011–5699; tel. 323/233–0425, (Nonreporting) **A**10
Primary Contact: John H. Griffith, Ph.D., President & Chief Executive Officer
COO: Madeline Valencerina, Chief Operating Officer
CFO: Rizwan A. Uraizee, Chief Financial Officer
CMO: Frank L. Williams, Executive Vice President/ Medical Director
CNO: Essie Adams, Director of Nursing
Web address: www.kedrenmentalhealth.com
Control: Other not–for–profit (including NFP Corporation) **Service:** Psychiatric

> **Staffed Beds:** 72

✠ **KINDRED HOSPITAL–LOS ANGELES (052032)**, 5525 West Slauson Avenue, Zip 90056–1067; tel. 310/642–0325, (Nonreporting) **A**1 10 **S** Kindred Healthcare, Louisville, KY
Primary Contact: Phillip R. Wolfe, Chief Executive Officer
CFO: Charles Natcher, Chief Financial Officer
Web address: www.kindredhospitalla.com/
Control: Corporation, Investor–owned (for–profit) **Service:** Acute long–term care hospital

> **Staffed Beds:** 81

☐ **LAC–OLIVE VIEW–UCLA MEDICAL CENTER (050040)**, 14445 Olive View Drive, Zip 91342–1438; tel. 818/364–1555, **A**1 3 5 10 **F**3 13 15 18 19 20 22 26 29 30 31 40 41 45 46 48 49 50 51 58 59 60 61 62 63 64 65 66 68 70 72 74 76 78 79 81 83 84 85 87 89 93 94 97 98 100 102 103 104 105 107 108 110 111 114 115 116 117 118 130 143 144 146 147 148 149 **S** Los Angeles County–Department of Health Services, Los Angeles, CA
Primary Contact: Carolyn F. Rhee, Chief Executive Officer
COO: Niloo Shahi, Chief Operating Officer
CFO: Anthony Gray, Chief Financial Officer
CMO: Shannon Thyne, Chief Medical Officer
CIO: Susan Aintablian, Chief Information Officer
CHR: Thomas Beggane, Manager Human Resources
CNO: Dellone Pascascio, Chief Nursing Officer
Web address: www.ladhs.org
Control: County, Government, Nonfederal **Service:** General medical and surgical

> **Staffed Beds:** 198 **Admissions:** 10735 **Census:** 175 **Outpatient Visits:** 248957 **Births:** 635 **Total Expense ($000):** 490889 **Payroll Expense ($000):** 202695 **Personnel:** 2520

☐ **LAC+USC MEDICAL CENTER (050373)**, 2051 Marengo Street, Zip 90033–1352; tel. 323/409–1000, (Nonreporting) (Includes GENERAL HOSPITAL, 1200 North State Street, Los Angeles, California, Zip 90033, tel. 213/580–7200; WOMEN'S AND CHILDREN'S HOSPITAL, 1240 North Mission Road, Los Angeles, California, Zip 90033, tel. 213/580–7200) **A**1 2 3 5 10 **S** Los Angeles County–Department of Health Services, Los Angeles, CA
Primary Contact: Dan A. Castillo, FACHE, Chief Executive Officer
COO: Henry Ornelas, Chief Operating Officer
CFO: Mark Corbet, Interim Chief Financial Officer
CMO: Brad Spellberg M.D., Chief Medical Officer
CIO: Oscar Autelli, Chief Information Officer
CHR: Elizabeth Jacobi, Human Resources Director
CNO: Isabel Milan R.N., Chief Nursing Officer
Web address: www.lacusc.org
Control: County, Government, Nonfederal **Service:** General medical and surgical

> **Staffed Beds:** 664

☐ **LOS ANGELES COMMUNITY HOSPITAL AT LOS ANGELES (050663)**, 4081 East Olympic Boulevard, Zip 90023–3330; tel. 323/267–0477, (Nonreporting) (Includes LOS ANGELES COMMUNITY HOSPITAL OF NORWALK, 13222 Bloomfield Avenue, Norwalk, California, Zip 90650, tel. 562/863–4763) **A**1 10 **S** Prospect Medical Holdings, Los Angeles, CA
Primary Contact: Omar Ramirez, Chief Executive Officer
CFO: Johnnette Chong, Chief Financial Officer
Web address: www.altacorp.com/altacorp/our–hospitals/lach–menu.html
Control: Corporation, Investor–owned (for–profit) **Service:** General medical and surgical

> **Staffed Beds:** 180

LOS ANGELES COUNTY CENTRAL JAIL HOSPITAL, 441 Bauchet Street, Zip 90012–2906; tel. 213/473–6100, (Nonreporting)
Primary Contact: Tom Flaherty, Assistant Administrator
Control: County, Government, Nonfederal **Service:** Hospital unit of an institution (prison hospital, college infirmary, etc.)

> **Staffed Beds:** 190

LOS ANGELES MEDICAL CENTER See Kaiser Permanente Los Angeles Medical Center

MARTIN LUTHER KING, JR. COMMUNITY HOSPITAL (050779), 1680 East 120th Street, Zip 90059–3026; tel. 424/338–8000 **F**3 13 18 28 29 30 31 34 35 40 45 51 56 57 59 60 68 70 74 76 78 79 81 84 85 86 87 91 100 107 111 119 120 130 146 148 149
Primary Contact: Elaine Batchlor, M.D., M.P.H., Chief Executive Officer
COO: Myrna Allen R.N., MS, Chief Operating and Nursing Officer
CMO: John Fisher M.D., Chief Medical Officer
CIO: Sajid Ahmed, Chief Information and Innovation Officer
CHR: Susan M Burrows, Vice President Human Resources
CNO: Myrna Allen R.N., MS, Chief Operating and Nursing Officer
Web address: www.mlkcommunityhospital.org/
Control: Other not–for–profit (including NFP Corporation) **Service:** General medical and surgical

> **Staffed Beds:** 131 **Admissions:** 7540 **Census:** 83 **Outpatient Visits:** 78233 **Births:** 572 **Total Expense ($000):** 192853 **Payroll Expense ($000):** 40075

Hospital, Medicare Provider Number, Address, Telephone, Approval, Facility, and Physician Codes, Health Care System

★ American Hospital Association (AHA) membership ☐ The Joint Commission accreditation ○ Healthcare Facilities Accreditation Program ◇ DNV Healthcare Inc. accreditation ⇑ Center for Improvement in Healthcare Quality Accreditation △ Commission on Accreditation of Rehabilitation Facilities (CARF) accreditation

☐ **MIRACLE MILE MEDICAL CENTER (050751)**, 6000 San Vicente Boulevard, Zip 90036–4404; tel. 323/930–1040, (Nonreporting) **A**1 10
Primary Contact: Gil Tepper, M.D., Chief Executive Officer
COO: Liz Cheever, Administrator
CFO: Bert Roberts, Controller
CMO: Gil Tepper M.D., Chief of Staff
CIO: Jonathan Lindell, Director Information Technology
CHR: Liz Cheever, Administrator
CNO: Melody Bradley, Chief Nursing Officer
Web address: www.miraclemilemedicalcenter.com
Control: Individual, Investor–owned (for–profit) **Service**: General medical and surgical

Staffed Beds: 17

☐ **MISSION COMMUNITY HOSPITAL (050704)**, 14850 Roscoe Boulevard, Zip 91402–4677; tel. 818/787–2222, (Nonreporting) **A**1 5 10
Primary Contact: James Theiring, Chief Executive Officer
CMO: Glenn Marshak M.D., Chief of Staff
CIO: Eric Rivers, Chief Information Officer
CHR: Carolyn Fish, Director Human Resources
CNO: Gwendolyn Dianne Wagner R.N., MSN, Chief Nursing Officer
Web address: www.mchonline.org
Control: Other not–for–profit (including NFP Corporation) **Service**: General medical and surgical

Staffed Beds: 145

MOTION PICTURE AND TELEVISION FUND HOSPITAL AND RESIDENTIAL SERVICES (050552), 23388 Mulholland Drive, Zip 91364–2792; tel. 818/876–1888, (Nonreporting) **A**10
Primary Contact: Bob Beitcher, Chief Executive Officer
COO: David Asplund, Chief Operating Officer
CFO: Frank Guarrera, Executive Vice President and Chief Financial Officer
CHR: Nancy Rubin, Vice President Human Resources
Web address: www.mptvfund.org
Control: Other not–for–profit (including NFP Corporation) **Service**: General medical and surgical

Staffed Beds: 20

⊞ △ **NORTHRIDGE HOSPITAL MEDICAL CENTER (050116)**, 18300 Roscoe Boulevard, Zip 91328–4167; tel. 818/885–8500, **A**1 2 3 5 7 10 **F**1 2 3 5 8 11 13 14 15 17 18 20 22 24 26 28 29 30 31 34 35 38 40 41 43 48 49 56 57 58 59 60 61 64 68 70 72 73 74 75 76 77 78 79 81 82 84 85 86 87 88 89 90 93 97 98 99 100 101 102 103 104 105 107 108 110 111 114 117 118 119 121 124 126 129 130 132 134 146 147 148 **S** Dignity Health, San Francisco, CA
Primary Contact: Saliba Salo, President
CFO: Michael Taylor, Vice President Finance
CHR: Susan Paulsen, Director Human Resources
CNO: Mary Jane Jones R.N., MSN, Vice President Nursing Operations
Web address: www.northridgehospital.org
Control: Other not–for–profit (including NFP Corporation) **Service**: General medical and surgical

Staffed Beds: 371 **Admissions**: 13966 **Census**: 170 **Outpatient Visits**: 67317 **Births**: 1022 **Total Expense ($000)**: 387883 **Payroll Expense ($000)**: 138563 **Personnel**: 1583

⇪ **OLYMPIA MEDICAL CENTER (050742)**, 5900 West Olympic Boulevard, Zip 90036–4671; tel. 310/657–5900, (Nonreporting) **A**3 10 21 **S** Alecto Healthcare, Irvine, CA
Primary Contact: Matthew Williams, R.N., Chief Executive Officer
CFO: Matthew Williams R.N., Chief Financial Officer
CMO: Panch Jeyakumar M.D., Chief of Staff
CIO: Jason Williams, Director Information Systems
CHR: Joseph Ambrosini, Director Human Resources
CNO: Sylvia A Ventura R.N., MS, Chief Nursing Officer
Web address: www.olympiamc.com
Control: Partnership, Investor–owned (for–profit) **Service**: General medical and surgical

Staffed Beds: 204

☐ **PACIFIC ALLIANCE MEDICAL CENTER (050018)**, 531 West College Street, Zip 90012–2385; tel. 213/624–8411, (Nonreporting) **A**1 10
Primary Contact: John R. Edwards, Administrator and Chief Executive Officer
CFO: Allan Shubin, Chief Financial Officer
CIO: John D Brown, Director Information Systems
Web address: www.pamc.net
Control: Partnership, Investor–owned (for–profit) **Service**: General medical and surgical

Staffed Beds: 138

☐ **PACIFICA HOSPITAL OF THE VALLEY (050378)**, 9449 San Fernando Road, Zip 91352–1489; tel. 818/767–3310, (Nonreporting) **A**1 10 **S** Southwest Healthcare System, Scottsdale, AZ
Primary Contact: Ayman Mousa, R.N., Ph.D., Chief Executive Officer
COO: Daniel Santos, Director Ancillary Services
CFO: Eileen Fisler, Chief Financial Officer
CMO: Joseph Eipe M.D., Chief Medical Officer
CIO: Mubashir Hashmi, Chief Information Officer
CHR: Patti Alonzo, Manager Human Resources
CNO: Janet B. Latto, Chief Nursing Officer and Disaster Officer
Web address: www.pacificahospital.com
Control: Corporation, Investor–owned (for–profit) **Service**: General medical and surgical

Staffed Beds: 231

PANORAMA CITY MEDICAL CENTER See Kaiser Permanente Panorama City Medical Center

☐ **PROMISE HOSPITAL OF EAST LOS ANGELES (052046)**, 443 South Soto Street, Zip 90033–4398; tel. 323/261–1181, (Includes PROMISE HOSPITAL OF EAST LOS ANGELES, SUBURBAN MEDICAL CENTER CAMPUS, 16453 South Colorado Avenue, Paramount, California, Zip 90723–5000, tel. 562/531–3110; Michael D Kerr, Chief Executive Officer) **A**1 10 **F**3 29 30 31 35 36 56 57 59 60 61 63 65 68 70 74 75 77 78 79 81 82 84 85 86 87 91 92 100 101 103 107 108 119 143 148 149 **S** Promise Healthcare, Boca Raton, FL
Primary Contact: Michael D. Kerr, Chief Executive Officer
Web address: www.promiseeastla.com
Control: Corporation, Investor–owned (for–profit) **Service**: Acute long–term care hospital

Staffed Beds: 213 **Admissions**: 7034 **Census**: 148 **Outpatient Visits**: 1140 **Births**: 0 **Total Expense ($000)**: 84893 **Payroll Expense ($000)**: 44672 **Personnel**: 667

⊞ △ **PROVIDENCE HOLY CROSS MEDICAL CENTER (050278)**, 15031 Rinaldi Street, Zip 91345–1207; tel. 818/365–8051, (Total facility includes 48 beds in nursing home–type unit) **A**1 2 7 10 **F**3 8 11 13 15 17 18 20 22 24 26 28 29 30 31 34 35 36 40 41 43 44 45 46 49 50 54 55 56 57 58 59 60 61 64 65 68 70 71 72 74 75 77 78 79 81 82 83 84 85 87 90 93 94 97 107 108 110 111 114 115 116 117 119 120 121 123 124 126 128 130 131 132 133 143 146 147 148 149 150 **S** Providence St. Joseph Health, Renton, WA
Primary Contact: Bernard Klein, M.D., Chief Executive
CFO: Paul Steinke, Chief Financial Officer
CMO: Bob Raggi M.D., Chief Medical Officer
CHR: Pam Stahl, Regional Chief Human Resources Officer
CNO: Ann Dechairo–Marino R.N., Ph.D., Chief Nursing Officer
Web address: www.california.providence.org/holy–cross/Pages/default.aspx
Control: Church operated, Nongovernment, not–for–profit **Service**: General medical and surgical

Staffed Beds: 377 **Admissions**: 18390 **Census**: 252 **Outpatient Visits**: 132132 **Births**: 3567 **Total Expense ($000)**: 342114 **Payroll Expense ($000)**: 160554 **Personnel**: 2045

⊞ △ **PROVIDENCE LITTLE COMPANY OF MARY MEDICAL CENTER SAN PEDRO (050078)**, 1300 West Seventh Street, Zip 90732–3505; tel. 310/832–3311, (Total facility includes 125 beds in nursing home–type unit) **A**1 7 10 **F**2 3 4 5 11 13 14 15 18 29 30 32 34 35 40 44 45 49 50 51 56 57 59 60 65 66 68 70 71 74 75 76 77 78 79 81 82 84 85 86 87 90 92 93 94 95 96 98 100 101 102 103 104 107 108 110 111 119 120 123 128 130 131 132 135 145 146 147 149 150 **P**5 **S** Providence St. Joseph Health, Renton, WA
Primary Contact: Mary E. Kingston, FACHE, R.N., Chief Executive Officer
COO: Garry M. Olney, Chief Operating Officer
CFO: Elizabeth Zuanich, Chief Financial Officer
CMO: Richard Glimp M.D., Chief Medical Officer
CIO: Kim Brant–Lucich, Director, Information Systems
CHR: Melissa Baker, Director, Human Resources
Web address: www.california.providence.org/san–pedro
Control: Church operated, Nongovernment, not–for–profit **Service**: General medical and surgical

Staffed Beds: 318 **Admissions**: 6587 **Census**: 200 **Outpatient Visits**: 52978 **Births**: 571 **Total Expense ($000)**: 129057 **Payroll Expense ($000)**: 74352 **Personnel**: 1038

CA

⊞ **PROVIDENCE TARZANA MEDICAL CENTER (050761)**, 18321 Clark Street, Zip 91356–3521; tel. 818/881–0800, **A**1 10 **F**3 7 13 15 17 18 19 20 22 24 26 27 28 29 30 31 34 35 40 41 45 46 49 50 56 57 59 61 63 64 65 70 72 74 75 76 77 78 79 81 82 83 84 85 86 87 88 89 91 92 93 107 108 110 111 114 115 119 126 130 131 132 143 145 146 147 148 **P**2 3 5 **S** Providence St. Joseph Health, Renton, WA
Primary Contact: Dale Surowitz, Chief Executive
COO: Phyllis Bushart R.N., Chief Operating Officer
CMO: Howard Z Davis M.D., Chief Medical Officer
CIO: Alex Nury, Chief Information Officer
CHR: Beverly Murray, Director of Human Resources
CNO: Deborah Carver, Chief Nursing Officer
Web address: www.providence.org/tarzana
Control: Church operated, Nongovernment, not–for–profit **Service:** General medical and surgical

Staffed Beds: 249 Admissions: 13520 Census: 143 Outpatient Visits: 70459 Births: 2499 Total Expense ($000): 223821 Payroll Expense ($000): 105457 Personnel: 1087

⊞ **RONALD REAGAN UCLA MEDICAL CENTER (050262)**, 757 Westwood Plaza, Zip 90095–8358; tel. 310/825–9111, (Includes MATTEL CHILDREN'S HOSPITAL, 757 Westwood Plaza, Los Angeles, California, Zip 90095, tel. 310/825–9111) **A**1 3 5 8 10 **F**3 6 7 8 9 11 12 13 14 15 17 18 19 20 21 22 23 24 25 26 27 28 29 30 31 32 34 35 36 39 40 41 43 44 45 46 47 48 49 50 51 52 54 55 56 57 58 59 61 62 64 65 66 68 70 71 72 74 75 76 77 78 79 81 82 84 85 86 87 88 89 90 92 93 94 96 97 102 107 108 110 111 112 113 114 115 116 117 118 119 120 121 123 124 126 129 130 131 132 135 136 137 138 139 140 141 142 143 145 146 147 148 149 **P**6 **S** University of California Systemwide Administration, Oakland, CA
Primary Contact: Johnese Spisso, Chief Executive Officer
COO: J. Shannon O'Kelley, Chief Operating Officer
CFO: Paul Staton, Chief Financial Officer
CMO: Robert Cherry M.D., Chief Medical and Quality Officer
CIO: Michael Pfeffer M.D., Chief Information Officer
CHR: Susi Takeuchi, Chief Human Resources and Organization Development Officer
CNO: Karen A Grimley, Chief Nursing Executive
Web address: www.uclahealth.org
Control: State, Government, Nonfederal **Service:** General medical and surgical

Staffed Beds: 456 Admissions: 23414 Census: 459 Outpatient Visits: 592788 Births: 1905 Total Expense ($000): 1763450 Payroll Expense ($000): 679300 Personnel: 7722

⊞ **SHERMAN OAKS HOSPITAL (050755)**, 4929 Van Nuys Boulevard, Zip 91403–1777; tel. 818/981–7111, (Nonreporting) **A**1 5 10 **S** Prime Healthcare, Ontario, CA
Primary Contact: Bockhi Park, Chief Executive Officer
CFO: Daniel Leon, Chief Financial Officer
CMO: Michael Malamed M.D., Chief of Staff
Web address: www.shermanoakshospital.com
Control: Other not–for–profit (including NFP Corporation) **Service:** General medical and surgical

Staffed Beds: 91

☐ **SILVER LAKE MEDICAL CENTER (050763)**, 1711 West Temple Street, Zip 90026–5421; tel. 213/989–6100, (Includes SILVER LAKE MEDICAL CENTER–INGLESIDE HOSPITAL, 7500 East Hellman Avenue, Rosemead, California, Zip 91770, tel. 626/288–1160) **A**1 10 **F**3 29 34 35 38 44 45 46 49 51 56 57 59 60 64 65 68 70 74 75 79 81 85 86 87 91 93 96 98 100 101 102 103 104 105 107 108 114 119 120 126 130 131 135 143 144 148 149 **S** Success Healthcare, Boca Raton, FL
Primary Contact: Brent A. Cope, Chief Executive Officer
CFO: John Cowles, Chief Financial Officer
CMO: Louis Acosta M.D., Chief of Staff
CIO: Scott Musack, Chief Information Officer
CHR: Sylvia Cloud, Director Human Resources
Web address: www.silverlakemc.com
Control: Partnership, Investor–owned (for–profit) **Service:** General medical and surgical

Staffed Beds: 175 Admissions: 7034 Census: 148 Outpatient Visits: 13823 Births: 0 Total Expense ($000): 70692 Payroll Expense ($000): 35673 Personnel: 697

☐ **SOUTHERN CALIFORNIA HOSPITAL AT HOLLYWOOD (050135)**, 6245 De Longpre Avenue, Zip 90028–9001; tel. 323/462–2271, (Nonreporting) (Includes SOUTHERN CALIFORNIA HOSPITAL AT VAN NUYS, 14433 Emelita Street, Van Nuys, California, Zip 91401, tel. 818/787–1511) **A**1 10 **S** Prospect Medical Holdings, Los Angeles, CA
Primary Contact: Bruce P. Grimshaw, FACHE, Chief Executive Officer
Web address: www.hollywoodcommunityhospital.org/
Control: Corporation, Investor–owned (for–profit) **Service:** General medical and surgical

Staffed Beds: 45

SOUTHERN CALIFORNIA HOSPITAL AT VAN NUYS See Southern California Hospital at Hollywood, Los Angeles

⊞ **ST. VINCENT MEDICAL CENTER (050502)**, 2131 West Third Street, Zip 90057–2901, Mailing Address: P.O.Box 57992, 90057–0992; tel. 213/484–7111, (Total facility includes 27 beds in nursing home–type unit) **A**1 3 10 **F**3 15 18 20 22 24 26 29 30 31 34 35 36 40 45 47 49 50 54 57 58 59 60 63 64 65 68 71 74 75 77 78 79 81 82 85 87 91 93 96 107 108 110 111 116 118 119 120 121 130 136 138 142 143 146 148 149 **S** Verity Health System, Los Angeles, CA
Primary Contact: Frank J. Cracolici, President and Chief Executive Officer
CFO: Michael Garko, Chief Financial Officer
CMO: Brian Itagaki M.D., Chief of Staff
CIO: Dan Robbins, Information Technology and Account Executive
CHR: Gail Watts, Director
CNO: Judy McCurdy R.N., Vice President and Chief Nursing Officer
Web address: www.stvincentmedicalcenter.com
Control: Other not–for–profit (including NFP Corporation) **Service:** General medical and surgical

Staffed Beds: 271 Admissions: 10046 Census: 156 Outpatient Visits: 82449 Births: 0 Personnel: 1264

⊞ **STEWART & LYNDA RESNICK NEUROPSYCHIATRIC HOSPITAL AT UCLA (054009)**, 150 UCLA Medical Plaza, Zip 90095–8353; tel. 310/825–9989, **A**1 3 5 10 **F**3 5 6 29 30 35 40 42 43 55 56 64 68 77 86 87 98 99 100 101 102 103 104 105 130 132 134 147 149 **P**1 **S** University of California Systemwide Administration, Oakland, CA
Primary Contact: Peter Whybrow, M.D., Chief Executive Officer
COO: Ruth Irwin, Associate Director Clinical Operations
CFO: Ronald Anthony Davis, Chief Financial Officer – UCLA Hospital System
CMO: Thomas Strouse M.D., Medical Director and Professor of Clinical Psych
CIO: Michael Pfeffer M.D., Chief Medical Informatics Officer, UCLA Health
CHR: Monica Rodriquez, Director of Human Resources
CNO: Patricia Matos, Chief Nursing Officer
Web address: www.semel.ucla.edu/resnick
Control: State, Government, Nonfederal **Service:** Psychiatric

Staffed Beds: 74 Admissions: 1774 Census: 70 Outpatient Visits: 21160 Births: 0 Total Expense ($000): 64322 Payroll Expense ($000): 35494 Personnel: 332

⊞ **USC NORRIS COMPREHENSIVE CANCER CENTER (050660)**, 1441 Eastlake Avenue, Zip 90089–0112; tel. 323/865–3000, **A**1 2 3 5 8 10 **F**3 8 9 11 15 29 30 31 34 35 36 38 39 44 45 46 47 48 49 50 51 52 53 54 55 56 57 58 59 60 61 63 64 65 66 68 70 74 75 77 78 81 82 84 85 86 87 91 92 93 94 97 100 101 104 107 108 110 111 114 115 118 119 120 121 123 124 130 132 134 135 136 143 145 146 147 148 149 150 **P**6 **S** Keck Medicine of USC, Los Angeles, CA
Primary Contact: Rodney B. Hanners, Chief Executive Officer
COO: Tarek Salaway, Chief Operating Officer
CFO: Robert Allen, Chief Financial Officer
CMO: Stephanie Hall M.D., Medical Director
CHR: Matthew McElrath, Chief Human Resources Officer
CNO: Annette Sy, Chief Nursing Officer
Web address: www.uscnorriscancerhospital.org
Control: Other not–for–profit (including NFP Corporation) **Service:** Cancer

Staffed Beds: 60 Admissions: 1550 Census: 32 Outpatient Visits: 113998 Births: 0 Total Expense ($000): 176393 Payroll Expense ($000): 49875 Personnel: 424

USC UNIVERSITY HOSPITAL See Keck Hospital of USC

CA

CA

☒ △ **VA GREATER LOS ANGELES HEALTHCARE SYSTEM**, 11301 Wilshire Boulevard, Zip 90073–1003; tel. 310/478–3711, (Total facility includes 187 beds in nursing home–type unit) **A**1 5 7 8 **F**2 3 5 7 8 9 11 14 15 18 20 22 24 26 28 29 30 31 33 34 35 36 37 38 39 40 44 45 46 47 48 49 50 51 53 54 55 56 57 58 59 60 61 62 63 64 65 66 67 68 69 70 71 74 75 77 78 79 80 81 82 83 84 85 86 87 90 91 92 93 94 96 97 98 100 101 102 103 104 107 108 109 110 111 112 114 116 117 118 119 120 121 122 123 124 126 127 128 129 130 131 132 133 135 143 145 146 147 148 149 150 **P**6 **S** Department of Veterans Affairs, Washington, DC
Primary Contact: Ann R. Brown, M.D., Director
COO: Susan Shyshka, Associate Director
CFO: Joseph Schmitt, Chief Financial Officer
CIO: Eugene Archey, Chief Information Technology
CHR: Brenda Cabunoc, Chief Human Resources
CNO: James Doelling, Chief Nurse Executive
Web address: www.losangeles.va.gov/
Control: Veterans Affairs, Government, federal **Service**: General medical and surgical

Staffed Beds: 708 **Admissions**: 8776 **Census**: 673 **Outpatient Visits**: 1474909 **Births**: 0 **Total Expense ($000)**: 826497 **Payroll Expense ($000)**: 456000

★ ⇑ **VALLEY PRESBYTERIAN HOSPITAL (050126)**, 15107 Vanowen Street, Zip 91405–4597; tel. 818/782–6600, (Nonreporting) **A**5 10 21
Primary Contact: Gustavo A. Valdespino, President and Chief Executive Officer
COO: Lori Cardle, Senior Vice President, Chief Operating Officer
CFO: Janice Klostermeier, Senior Vice President and Chief Financial Officer
CIO: Jeff Allport, Vice President, Chief Information Officer
CHR: Deborah Gac, Vice President Human Resources
CNO: Lori Burnell R.N., Ph.D., Senior Vice President and Chief Nursing Officer
Web address: www.valleypres.org
Control: Other not–for–profit (including NFP Corporation) **Service**: General medical and surgical

Staffed Beds: 350

☒ **WEST HILLS HOSPITAL AND MEDICAL CENTER (050481)**, 7300 Medical Center Drive, Zip 91307–1900; tel. 818/676–4000, (Nonreporting) **A**1 10 **S** HCA Healthcare, Nashville, TN
Primary Contact: Douglas Long, President and Chief Executive Officer
COO: John Neidenbach, Vice President and Chief Operating Officer
CFO: David Cantrell CPA, Vice President and Chief Financial Officer
CHR: Diana Steel, Vice President Human Resources
CNO: Stephanie Mearns R.N., Vice President and Chief Nursing Officer
Web address: www.westhillshospital.com
Control: Corporation, Investor–owned (for–profit) **Service**: General medical and surgical

Staffed Beds: 225

WEST LOS ANGELES MEDICAL CENTER See Kaiser Permanente West Los Angeles Medical Center

☒ **WHITE MEMORIAL MEDICAL CENTER (050103)**, 1720 Cesar Chavez Avenue, Zip 90033–2414; tel. 323/268–5000, (Total facility includes 27 beds in nursing home–type unit) **A**1 2 3 5 8 10 **F**3 11 13 15 17 18 19 20 22 24 26 27 28 29 30 31 34 35 40 41 45 46 47 48 49 50 51 53 57 58 59 64 68 70 72 74 75 76 78 79 81 82 84 85 86 87 88 89 90 91 92 93 96 98 99 102 103 107 108 109 110 111 114 115 116 117 118 119 120 121 123 128 130 131 132 146 147 148 149 **S** Adventist Health, Roseville, CA
Primary Contact: John Raffoul, Chief Executive Officer
CIO: Ralf Weissenberger, Director Information Systems
CHR: Natasha Milatovich, Association Vice President Human Resources
CNO: Patricia Stone R.N., MSN, Senior Vice President Operations and Chief Nursing Officer
Web address: www.whitememorial.com
Control: Church operated, Nongovernment, not–for–profit **Service**: General medical and surgical

Staffed Beds: 353 **Admissions**: 19701 **Census**: 239 **Outpatient Visits**: 69072 **Births**: 3834 **Total Expense ($000)**: 417694 **Payroll Expense ($000)**: 131712 **Personnel**: 1713

WOODLAND HILLS MEDICAL CENTER See Kaiser Permanente Woodland Hills Medical Center

LOS BANOS—Merced County

☒ **MEMORIAL HOSPITAL LOS BANOS (050528)**, 520 West 'I' Street, Zip 93635–3498; tel. 209/826–0591, **A**1 10 20 **F**3 8 11 13 15 18 29 30 34 35 40 44 45 46 49 50 54 57 59 60 64 65 68 70 74 75 76 81 82 85 86 87 107 110 111 115 119 127 130 132 135 146 149 **S** Sutter Health, Sacramento, CA
Primary Contact: Doug Archer, Administrator
CFO: Timothy J Noakes, Chief Financial Officer
CHR: Shawn Garcia, Manager Human Resources
CNO: Kristie Marion, Chief Nurse Executive
Web address: www.memoriallosbanos.org/
Control: Other not–for–profit (including NFP Corporation) **Service**: General medical and surgical

Staffed Beds: 44 **Admissions**: 1638 **Census**: 11 **Outpatient Visits**: 64804 **Births**: 683 **Total Expense ($000)**: 52290 **Payroll Expense ($000)**: 16741 **Personnel**: 234

LYNWOOD—Los Angeles County

☒ **ST. FRANCIS MEDICAL CENTER (050104)**, 3630 East Imperial Highway, Zip 90262–2636; tel. 310/900–8900, (Nonreporting) **A**1 10 **S** Verity Health System, Los Angeles, CA
Primary Contact: Gerald T. Kozai, PharmD, President and Chief Executive Officer
COO: Jeffrey Stout MSN, R.N., Chief Operating Officer
CFO: Anil Jain, Chief Financial Officer
CMO: Rahul Dhawan M.D., Chief Medical Officer
CIO: Judi Binderman, Chief Information Technology Officer and Chief Medical Informatics Officer
CHR: Laura Kato, Vice President Human Resources
CNO: Derek Scott Drake, Chief Nursing Officer
Web address: www.dochs.org
Control: Church operated, Nongovernment, not–for–profit **Service**: General medical and surgical

Staffed Beds: 323

MADERA—Madera County

○ **MADERA COMMUNITY HOSPITAL (050568)**, 1250 East Almond Avenue, Zip 93637–5696, Mailing Address: P.O.Box 1328, 93639–1328; tel. 559/675–5501, (Nonreporting) **A**10 11 19
Primary Contact: Evan J. Rayner, Chief Executive Officer
COO: Karen Paolmelli, Chief Operating Officer
CFO: Mark Foote, Chief Financial Officer
CIO: Jerry Kovalski, Director Information Systems
CHR: Christine M Watts–Johnson, Assistant Vice President
CNO: Meri Combs R.N., Vice President and Chief Nursing Officer
Web address: www.maderahospital.org
Control: Other not–for–profit (including NFP Corporation) **Service**: General medical and surgical

Staffed Beds: 106

☒ △ **VALLEY CHILDREN'S HEALTHCARE (053300)**, 9300 Valley Children's Place, Zip 93636–8761; tel. 559/353–3000, **A**1 3 5 7 8 10 **F**3 8 9 11 19 21 23 25 27 28 29 30 31 32 34 35 38 40 41 43 44 46 48 49 50 54 55 57 58 59 60 61 62 64 65 68 72 73 74 75 77 78 79 81 82 84 85 86 87 88 89 90 93 94 97 107 108 111 114 115 119 127 129 130 131 132 134 143 146 147 148 149 **P**3
Primary Contact: Todd A. Suntrapak, President and Chief Executive Officer
CFO: Michele Waldron, Senior Vice President and Chief Financial Officer
CMO: David Christensen M.D., Senior Vice President and Chief Medical Officer
CIO: Kevin Shimamoto, Vice President and Chief Informational Officer
CHR: Nat Ponticello, Vice President Human Resources
CNO: Beverly P. Hayden–Pugh R.N., Senior Vice President and Chief Nursing Officer
Web address: www.valleychildrens.org
Control: Other not–for–profit (including NFP Corporation) **Service**: Children's general medical and surgical

Staffed Beds: 358 **Admissions**: 12966 **Census**: 205 **Outpatient Visits**: 343931 **Births**: 0 **Total Expense ($000)**: 526548 **Payroll Expense ($000)**: 191215 **Personnel**: 2341

MAMMOTH LAKES—Mono County

⇑ **MAMMOTH HOSPITAL (051303)**, 85 Sierra Park Road, Zip 93546–2073, Mailing Address: P.O.Box 660, 93546–0660; tel. 760/934–3311, **A**10 18 21 **F**3 11 13 15 29 31 34 35 39 40 45 46 50 53 57 59 64 65 68 70 74 75 76 77 78 79 81 82 85 93 94 97 107 110 111 114 119 127 131 132 146 147 149
Primary Contact: Gary Myers, Chief Executive Officer
CFO: Melanie Van Winkle, Chief Financial Officer
CMO: Yuri Parisky M.D., Chief of Staff
CIO: Mark Lind, Chief Information Officer
CHR: Sarah Vigilante, Manager Human Resources
CNO: Kathleen Alo, Chief Nursing Officer
Web address: www.mammothhospital.com
Control: Hospital district or authority, Government, Nonfederal **Service**: General medical and surgical

Staffed Beds: 17 **Admissions**: 692 **Census**: 4 **Outpatient Visits**: 126712 **Births**: 103 **Total Expense ($000)**: 57247 **Payroll Expense ($000)**: 19746 **Personnel**: 330

Many Facility Codes have changed. Please refer to the AHA Guide Code Chart. © 2017 AHA Guide

MANTECA—San Joaquin County

☒ **DOCTORS HOSPITAL OF MANTECA (050118)**, 1205 East North Street, Zip 95336–4900; tel. 209/823–3111, **A**1 10 **F**3 11 12 13 15 29 31 34 35 40 45 49 50 51 64 75 76 78 79 81 85 102 107 108 110 111 115 116 117 118 119 130 132 146 147 148 149 **S** TENET Healthcare Corporation, Dallas, TX
Primary Contact: Carmen Silva, R.N., Interim Chief Executive Officer
COO: Warren Kirk, Chief Operating Officer
CFO: Michael Szymanski, Chief Financial Officer
CHR: Traci Holzer, Chief Human Resources Officer
CNO: Antonio M. Garcia, Chief Nursing Officer
Web address: www.doctorsmanteca.com
Control: Corporation, Investor–owned (for–profit) **Service:** General medical and surgical

Staffed Beds: 56 **Admissions:** 3873 **Census:** 40 **Outpatient Visits:** 68844 **Births:** 652 **Total Expense ($000):** 87355 **Payroll Expense ($000):** 40232 **Personnel:** 436

☒ **KAISER PERMANENTE MANTECA MEDICAL CENTER (050748)**, 1777 West Yosemite Avenue, Zip 95337–5187; tel. 209/825–3700, (Nonreporting) (Includes MODESTO MEDICAL CENTER, 4601 Dale Road, Modesto, California, Zip 95356–9718, tel. 209/735–5000; Corwin N Harper, Administrator) **A**1 10 **S** Kaiser Foundation Hospitals, Oakland, CA
Primary Contact: Corwin N. Harper, Senior Vice President and Area Manager
COO: Corwin N Harper, Senior Vice President and Area Manager
CFO: Debra L Brown, Area Financial Officer
CMO: Moses D Elam M.D., Physician–in–Chief
CIO: Tom J Osteen, Director Area Technology
CHR: Pat McKeldin, Human Resource Business Partner
Web address: www.kaiserpermanente.org
Control: Other not–for–profit (including NFP Corporation) **Service:** General medical and surgical

Staffed Beds: 239

MARINA DEL REY—Los Angeles County

☒ **MARINA DEL REY HOSPITAL (050740)**, 4650 Lincoln Boulevard, Zip 90292–6306; tel. 310/823–8911, (Nonreporting) **A**1 10 **S** Cedars–Sinai, West Hollywood, CA
Primary Contact: Paulette Heitmeyer, Administrator and Chief Operating Officer
COO: Phyllis Buchart, Chief Operating Officer
CFO: Stephen A Hargett, Senior Vice President and Chief Financial Officer
Web address: www.marinahospital.com
Control: Corporation, Investor–owned (for–profit) **Service:** General medical and surgical

Staffed Beds: 145

MARIPOSA—Mariposa County

★ **JOHN C. FREMONT HEALTHCARE DISTRICT (051304)**, 5189 Hospital Road, Zip 95338–9524, Mailing Address: P.O.Box 216, 95338–0216; tel. 209/966–3631, **A**10 18 **F**15 29 30 34 40 45 50 57 59 61 62 63 74 78 91 99 104 107 111 114 119 127 128 130 133 146
Primary Contact: Alan MacPhee, Chief Executive Officer
CFO: Matthew Matthiessen, Chief Financial Officer
CMO: Kenneth P Smith, Chief of Staff
CIO: Phil Blas, Chief Information Officer
CHR: Martha Robichaux, Chief Human Resources Officer
CNO: Theresa Loya R.N., Chief Nursing Officer
Web address: www.jcf-hospital.com
Control: Hospital district or authority, Government, Nonfederal **Service:** General medical and surgical

Staffed Beds: 33 **Admissions:** 270 **Census:** 4 **Outpatient Visits:** 43573 **Births:** 0

MARTINEZ—Contra Costa County

☒ **CONTRA COSTA REGIONAL MEDICAL CENTER (050276)**, 2500 Alhambra Avenue, Zip 94553–3156; tel. 925/370–5000, **A**1 2 3 10 **F**3 11 13 15 18 30 31 35 36 39 40 45 49 50 54 56 59 61 62 64 65 66 68 70 71 72 73 74 75 76 77 78 79 81 82 84 85 86 87 93 97 98 100 102 103 104 107 108 111 115 119 130 132 143 146 147 148 **P**6
Primary Contact: Anna M. Roth, R.N., MS, M.P.H., Chief Executive Officer
COO: Timothy Thompson–Cook, Chief Operating Officer
CFO: Patrick Godley, Chief Financial Officer
CMO: David Goldstein M.D., Chief Medical Officer
CNO: Jaspreet Benepal, Chief Nursing Officer
Web address: www.cchealth.org/medical_center/
Control: County, Government, Nonfederal **Service:** General medical and surgical

Staffed Beds: 124 **Admissions:** 8573 **Census:** 122 **Outpatient Visits:** 493960 **Births:** 2164 **Total Expense ($000):** 519727 **Payroll Expense ($000):** 181094 **Personnel:** 2015

KAISER FOUNDATION HOSPITAL See Kaiser Permanente Walnut Creek Medical Center, Walnut Creek

MARYSVILLE—Yuba County

★ **RIDEOUT MEMORIAL HOSPITAL (050133)**, 726 Fourth Street, Zip 95901–5600; tel. 530/749–4300, (Includes FREMONT MEDICAL CENTER, 970 Plumas Street, Yuba City, California, Zip 95991–4087, tel. 530/751–4000) **A**2 10 20 **F**3 8 13 15 17 18 20 22 24 28 29 30 31 40 41 43 45 49 54 59 64 68 70 72 74 76 77 78 79 81 82 85 89 91 93 96 97 107 108 110 111 114 115 116 117 118 119 120 121 123 124 130 147 148 149 **P**3
Primary Contact: Gino Patrizio, Chief Executive Officer
COO: Cyndy Gordon, Chief Operating Officer
CIO: Tarun Ghosh, Chief Information Officer
CHR: Tresha Moreland MS, Vice President Human Resources
Web address: www.frhg.org
Control: Other not–for–profit (including NFP Corporation) **Service:** General medical and surgical

Staffed Beds: 219 **Admissions:** 10830 **Census:** 142 **Outpatient Visits:** 258880 **Births:** 2062 **Total Expense ($000):** 380409 **Payroll Expense ($000):** 124698 **Personnel:** 1600

MENLO PARK—San Mateo County

☒ **MENLO PARK SURGICAL HOSPITAL (050754)**, 570 Willow Road, Zip 94025–2617; tel. 650/324–8500, **A**1 10 **F**18 29 35 64 68 78 79 81 82 85 **P**3 5 **S** Sutter Health, Sacramento, CA
Primary Contact: Jeanette Engle–Ramirez, Chief Executive Officer
CMO: Andrew Gutow M.D., Medical Director
CNO: Marjorie Eckford, Chief Nursing Officer
Web address: www.pamf.org/mpsh
Control: Other not–for–profit (including NFP Corporation) **Service:** General medical and surgical

Staffed Beds: 16 **Admissions:** 204 **Census:** 1 **Outpatient Visits:** 2808 **Births:** 0 **Total Expense ($000):** 13768 **Payroll Expense ($000):** 4013 **Personnel:** 42

MERCED—Merced County

☒ **MERCY MEDICAL CENTER MERCED (050444)**, 333 Mercy Avenue, Zip 95340–8319; tel. 209/564–5000, (Includes MERCY MEDICAL CENTER MERCED–DOMINICAN CAMPUS, 2740 'M' Street, Merced, California, Zip 95340–2880, tel. 209/384–6444; Charles Kassis, President) **A**1 3 5 10 19 **F**3 8 13 15 18 20 26 28 29 30 32 34 35 40 41 45 46 49 50 54 57 59 62 64 65 66 68 69 70 71 74 76 77 78 79 81 83 84 85 86 87 88 90 92 93 96 97 107 108 110 111 115 119 120 127 130 132 146 148 149 **P**3 **S** Dignity Health, San Francisco, CA
Primary Contact: Charles Kassis, President
CFO: Michael Strasser, Vice President and Chief Financial Officer
CMO: Robert Streeter M.D., Vice President Medical Affairs
CIO: Daniel Andresen, Chief information Officer
CHR: Julie Rocha, Vice President Human Resources
CNO: Greg Rouleau, Vice President Nursing
Web address: www.mercymercedcares.org
Control: Other not–for–profit (including NFP Corporation) **Service:** General medical and surgical

Staffed Beds: 186 **Admissions:** 11025 **Census:** 126 **Outpatient Visits:** 179697 **Births:** 2715 **Total Expense ($000):** 283399 **Payroll Expense ($000):** 103229 **Personnel:** 1220

MISSION HILLS—Los Angeles County, See Los Angeles

MISSION VIEJO—Orange County

☐ **CHOC CHILDREN'S AT MISSION HOSPITAL (053306)**, 27700 Medical Center Road, Zip 92691–6426; tel. 949/364–1400, **A**1 5 10 **F**3 11 29 36 72 74 79 81 85 88 89 129
Primary Contact: Kimberly C. Cripe, President and Chief Executive Officer
COO: Matthew S Gerlach, Chief Operating Officer
CFO: Kerri Ruppert Schiller, Senior Vice President and Chief Financial Officer
CMO: Maria Minon M.D., Vice President Medical Affairs and Chief Medical Officer
CIO: Mark Headland, Chief Information Officer
CHR: Mamoon Syed, Vice President Human Resources
Web address: www.choc.org
Control: Other not–for–profit (including NFP Corporation) **Service:** Children's general medical and surgical

Staffed Beds: 54 **Admissions:** 2146 **Census:** 22 **Outpatient Visits:** 23172 **Births:** 0 **Total Expense ($000):** 53412 **Payroll Expense ($000):** 9536 **Personnel:** 112

CA

Hospital, Medicare Provider Number, Address, Telephone, Approval, Facility, and Physician Codes, Health Care System

★ American Hospital Association (AHA) membership
☐ The Joint Commission accreditation
○ Healthcare Facilities Accreditation Program
◇ DNV Healthcare Inc. accreditation
⇑ Center for Improvement in Healthcare Quality Accreditation
△ Commission on Accreditation of Rehabilitation Facilities (CARF) accreditation

CA

☒ △ **MISSION HOSPITAL (050567)**, 27700 Medical Center Road, Zip 92691–6474; tel. 949/364–1400, (Includes MISSION HOSPITAL LAGUNA BEACH, 31872 Coast Highway, Laguna Beach, California, Zip 92651–6775, tel. 949/499–1311; Richard Afable, M.D., M.P.H., Interim President and Chief Executive Officer) **A1** 2 7 10 **F3** 4 5 11 13 14 15 17 18 20 22 24 26 28 29 30 31 34 35 36 37 40 41 43 44 45 46 47 49 50 53 54 57 58 59 61 64 65 68 70 74 75 76 77 78 79 80 81 82 84 85 86 87 90 93 98 100 101 102 103 104 105 107 108 110 111 112 114 115 116 117 118 119 120 121 123 126 129 130 131 132 134 135 141 143 146 147 148 149 **P**3 5 **S** Providence St. Joseph Health, Renton, WA
Primary Contact: Tarek Salaway, Chief Executive
COO: Tarek Salaway, Chief Operating Officer
CFO: Eileen Haubl, Senior Vice President and Chief Financial Officer
CMO: Linda Sieglen M.D., Chief Medical Officer
CIO: Bill Russell, Senior Chief Information Officer
CHR: Terri Covert, Vice President Human Resources
Web address: www.mission4health.com
Control: Church operated, Nongovernment, not–for–profit **Service**: General medical and surgical

Staffed Beds: 249 **Admissions**: 19485 **Census**: 226 **Outpatient Visits**: 204838 **Births**: 2574 **Total Expense ($000)**: 534648 **Payroll Expense ($000)**: 158787 **Personnel**: 1922

MODESTO—Stanislaus County

★ ⇑ **CENTRAL VALLEY SPECIALTY HOSPITAL (052055)**, 730 17th Street, Zip 95354–1209; tel. 209/248–7700, (Nonreporting) **A**21
Primary Contact: Gia Smith, Chief Executive Officer
Web address: www.centralvalleyspecialty.org/CVSH/
Control: Partnership, Investor–owned (for–profit) **Service**: Acute long–term care hospital

Staffed Beds: 36

☒ **DOCTORS MEDICAL CENTER OF MODESTO (050464)**, 1441 Florida Avenue, Zip 95350–4418, Mailing Address: P.O.Box 4138, 95352–4138; tel. 209/578–1211, **A**1 2 3 10 **F3** 13 17 18 20 22 24 26 28 29 31 34 35 40 41 43 45 46 48 49 50 51 55 57 59 60 65 70 72 74 75 76 77 78 79 80 81 85 89 98 102 103 107 108 109 110 111 112 113 114 115 116 117 118 119 126 130 132 146 147 149 **S** TENET Healthcare Corporation, Dallas, TX
Primary Contact: Warren J. Kirk, Chief Executive Officer
CFO: Greg Berry, Chief Financial Officer
CMO: Edward Stanford M.D., Chief Medical officer
CIO: Debbie Fuller, Director Health Information Systems and Chief Information Officer
CHR: Michele Bava, Director Human Resources
CNO: Cheryl Harless, Chief Nursing Officer
Web address: www.dmc–modesto.com
Control: Corporation, Investor–owned (for–profit) **Service**: General medical and surgical

Staffed Beds: 455 **Admissions**: 25753 **Census**: 352 **Outpatient Visits**: 158000 **Births**: 3754 **Total Expense ($000)**: 490233 **Payroll Expense ($000)**: 224506 **Personnel**: 2231

HEALTHSOUTH REHABILITATION HOSPITAL OF MODESTO, 1303 Mable Avenue, Zip 95355; tel. 209/857–3400, (Nonreporting)
Primary Contact: Kay E. Peck, Ph.D., Chief Executive Officer
CFO: Seth Rogers, Controller
CMO: Greg A. Vigna M.D., Medical Director
CHR: Tina Reed, Director of Human Resources
CNO: Mark Dinardo, Chief Nursing Officer
Web address: www.healthsouthmodesto.com/
Control: Corporation, Investor–owned (for–profit) **Service**: Rehabilitation

Staffed Beds: 50

☒ **MEMORIAL MEDICAL CENTER (050557)**, 1700 Coffee Road, Zip 95355–2869, Mailing Address: P.O.Box 942, 95353–0942; tel. 209/526–4500, (Includes MEMORIAL MEDICAL CENTER, 1700 Coffee Road, Modesto, California, Zip 95355, Box 942, 95353, tel. 209/526–4500) **A**1 2 10 **F3** 5 8 11 12 13 15 18 20 22 24 26 28 29 30 31 34 35 36 40 43 44 45 46 47 48 49 50 51 57 58 59 60 64 68 70 72 74 75 76 77 78 79 81 82 84 85 86 87 89 107 108 111 114 115 119 120 121 123 124 126 130 132 146 147 148 **P**3 5 **S** Sutter Health, Sacramento, CA
Primary Contact: Daryn J. Kumar, Chief Executive Officer
COO: Steve Mitchell, Chief Operating Officer
CFO: Eric Dalton, Chief Financial Officer
CIO: Patrick Anderson, Chief Information Officer
CHR: Paula Rafala, Director, Human Resources
CNO: Sandra Proctor R.N., MS, Chief Nurse Executive
Web address: www.memorialmedicalcenter.org
Control: Other not–for–profit (including NFP Corporation) **Service**: General medical and surgical

Staffed Beds: 222 **Admissions**: 17143 **Census**: 216 **Outpatient Visits**: 122242 **Births**: 1853 **Total Expense ($000)**: 541130 **Payroll Expense ($000)**: 159811 **Personnel**: 1915

MODESTO MEDICAL CENTER See Kaiser Permanente Manteca Medical Center, Manteca

★ **STANISLAUS SURGICAL HOSPITAL (050726)**, 1421 Oakdale Road, Zip 95355–3356; tel. 209/572–2700, **A**5 10 **F3** 15 45 46 47 51 74 79 81 82 93 107 111 116 117 119 147 148 **S** Sutter Health, Sacramento, CA
Primary Contact: Douglas V. Johnson, Chief Executive Officer
CFO: Richard Hart, Chief Financial Officer
CMO: Wesley Kinzie M.D., Chief of Staff
CIO: Richard Hart, Chief Financial Officer
CHR: Tyson Hubbard, Director Human Resources
CNO: Susan Gonzalez, Director of Clinical Services
Web address: www.stanislaussurgical.com
Control: Corporation, Investor–owned (for–profit) **Service**: Surgical

Staffed Beds: 23 **Admissions**: 506 **Census**: 3 **Outpatient Visits**: 7919 **Births**: 0 **Total Expense ($000)**: 30657 **Payroll Expense ($000)**: 11431 **Personnel**: 230

MONROVIA—Los Angeles County

○ **MONROVIA MEMORIAL HOSPITAL (052054)**, 323 South Heliotrope Avenue, Zip 91016–2914; tel. 626/408–9800, (Nonreporting) **A**10 11
Primary Contact: Ron Kupferstein, Chief Executive Officer
Web address: www.monroviamemorial.com
Control: Partnership, Investor–owned (for–profit) **Service**: Acute long–term care hospital

Staffed Beds: 49

MONTCLAIR—San Bernardino County

☒ **MONTCLAIR HOSPITAL MEDICAL CENTER (050758)**, 5000 San Bernardino Street, Zip 91763–2326; tel. 909/625–5411, (Nonreporting) **A**1 10 **S** Prime Healthcare, Ontario, CA
Primary Contact: Sofia Abrina, R.N., Administrator
CFO: Robert Bonner, Chief Financial Officer
CMO: Joseph Hourany, Chief Medical Officer
CNO: Gail Aviado, Chief Nursing Officer
Web address: www.montclair–hospital.com
Control: Other not–for–profit (including NFP Corporation) **Service**: General medical and surgical

Staffed Beds: 102

MONTEBELLO—Los Angeles County

⇑ **BEVERLY HOSPITAL (050350)**, 309 West Beverly Boulevard, Zip 90640–4308; tel. 323/726–1222, (Nonreporting) **A**10 21
Primary Contact: Alice Cheng, President and Chief Executive Officer
CFO: Larry Pugh, Vice President and Chief Financial Officer
CIO: Mark Turner, Director Information Systems
CHR: John Barnes, Administrative Director Human Resources
CNO: Kathy Wojno R.N., MSN, Vice President Nursing Services and Chief Nursing Officer
Web address: www.beverly.org
Control: Other not–for–profit (including NFP Corporation) **Service**: General medical and surgical

Staffed Beds: 102

MONTEREY—Monterey County

☒ **COMMUNITY HOSPITAL OF THE MONTEREY PENINSULA (050145)**, 23625 Holman Highway, Zip 93940–5902, Mailing Address: Box 'HH', 93942–6032; tel. 831/624–5311, (Total facility includes 28 beds in nursing home–type unit) **A**1 2 10 **F3** 5 11 12 13 15 17 18 20 22 24 26 28 29 30 31 32 34 35 37 40 44 45 46 47 48 49 50 51 53 54 57 58 59 60 61 62 63 64 68 70 73 74 75 76 77 78 79 81 82 83 84 85 86 87 89 90 91 92 93 94 96 98 99 100 101 102 103 104 105 107 110 111 114 115 116 117 118 119 120 121 123 124 128 129 130 132 134 135 145 146 148 149 150
Primary Contact: Steven J. Packer, M.D., President and Chief Executive Officer
CFO: Laura Zehm, Vice President and Chief Financial Officer
CMO: Anthony D Chavis M.D., Vice President Enterprise Medical Officer, Community Hospital Foundation
Web address: www.chomp.org
Control: Other not–for–profit (including NFP Corporation) **Service**: General medical and surgical

Staffed Beds: 248 **Admissions**: 11554 **Census**: 156 **Outpatient Visits**: 330956 **Births**: 1168 **Total Expense ($000)**: 471986 **Payroll Expense ($000)**: 172369 **Personnel**: 1755

MONTEREY PARK—Los Angeles County

☐ **GARFIELD MEDICAL CENTER (050737)**, 525 North Garfield Avenue,
Zip 91754–1205; tel. 626/573–2222, (Nonreporting) **A**1 10 **S** AHMC &
Healthcare, Inc., Alhambra, CA
Primary Contact: Patrick A. Petre, Chief Executive Officer
COO: Herbert Villafuerte, Chief Operating Officer/Chief Nursing Officer
CFO: Steve Maekawa, Chief Financial Officer
CMO: Thomas Lam, Chief Medical Officer
CIO: Allan Carpenter, Chief Information Officer
CHR: Rebecca R Ricartti, Interim Director Human Resources
CNO: Herbert Villafuerte, Chief Operating Officer and Chief Nursing Officer
Web address: www.garfieldmedicalcenter.com
Control: Partnership, Investor–owned (for–profit) **Service:** General medical and
surgical

Staffed Beds: 210

☐ **MONTEREY PARK HOSPITAL (050736)**, 900 South Atlantic Boulevard,
Zip 91754–4780; tel. 626/570–9000, **A**1 10 **F**3 15 29 34 35 40 49 50 57
59 60 70 75 81 86 87 107 113 114 119 130 142 143 146 149 **S** AHMC &
Healthcare, Inc., Alhambra, CA
Primary Contact: Philip A. Cohen, Chief Executive Officer
COO: Ericka Smith, Chief Operating Officer
CFO: Daniel Song, Chief Financial Officer
CMO: Ruben Ramirez M.D., Chief of Staff
CIO: Angelica Ching, Director Information Systems
CHR: Gretchen Lindeman, Director of Human Resources
CNO: Shirley Tang R.N., Chief Nursing Officer
Web address: www.montereyparkhosp.com
Control: Partnership, Investor–owned (for–profit) **Service:** General medical and
surgical

Staffed Beds: 101 **Admissions:** 5794 **Census:** 56 **Outpatient Visits:** 28169
Births: 1585 **Total Expense ($000):** 92154 **Payroll Expense ($000):** 26509
Personnel: 348

MORENO VALLEY—Riverside County

⊞ **KAISER PERMANENTE MORENO VALLEY MEDICAL CENTER (050765)**,
27300 Iris Avenue, Zip 92555–4800; tel. 951/243–0811, **A**1 10 **F**3 13 17 29
30 35 40 44 45 46 49 50 59 60 64 65 68 70 75 76 77 79 81 82 84 85 87 97
100 102 107 108 109 111 115 119 130 135 146 148 149 **S** Kaiser Foundation
Hospitals, Oakland, CA
Primary Contact: Vita M. Willett, Senior Vice President
COO: Corey A Seale, Chief Operating Officer
Control: Other not–for–profit (including NFP Corporation) **Service:** General
medical and surgical

Staffed Beds: 75 **Admissions:** 4137 **Census:** 33 **Outpatient Visits:** 46205
Births: 1337 **Personnel:** 271

⊞ **RIVERSIDE UNIVERSITY HEALTH SYSTEM–MEDICAL CENTER (050292)**,
26520 Cactus Avenue, Zip 92555–3911; tel. 951/486–4000, (Nonreporting) **A**1
3 5 10 12 13
Primary Contact: Zareh Sarrafian, Chief Executive Officer
COO: Jennifer Cruikshank R.N., Chief Operating Officer
CFO: Christopher Hans, Chief Financial Officer
CMO: Arnold Tabuenca M.D., Medical Director
CNO: Judi Nightingale R.N., Dr.PH, Chief Nursing Officer
Web address: www.rcrmc.org
Control: County, Government, Nonfederal **Service:** General medical and surgical

Staffed Beds: 439

MOUNT SHASTA—Siskiyou County

⊞ **MERCY MEDICAL CENTER MOUNT SHASTA (051319)**, 914 Pine Street,
Zip 96067–2143; tel. 530/926–6111, **A**1 10 18 **F**3 11 13 15 29 30 35 40 43
50 53 56 57 59 62 63 64 68 70 75 76 77 79 81 82 84 89 93 107 108 110
111 114 118 119 121 127 130 131 132 133 143 146 148 149 **S** Dignity
Health, San Francisco, CA
Primary Contact: Kenneth E S. Platou, President
CFO: Kimberly Miranda, Chief Financial Officer
CMO: Todd Guthrie, Chief of Staff
CHR: Michelle Michl, Director Human Resources
CNO: Lisa Hubbard, Vice President and Chief Nursing Executive
Web address: www.mercymtshasta.org
Control: Other not–for–profit (including NFP Corporation) **Service:** General
medical and surgical

Staffed Beds: 33 **Admissions:** 1003 **Census:** 8 **Outpatient Visits:** 62685
Births: 156 **Total Expense ($000):** 55164 **Payroll Expense ($000):** 20060
Personnel: 220

MOUNTAIN VIEW—Santa Clara County

⊞ **EL CAMINO HOSPITAL (050308)**, 2500 Grant Road, Zip 94040–4302, Mailing
Address: P.O.Box 7025, 94039–7025; tel. 650/940–7000, (Includes EL CAMINO
HOSPITAL LOS GATOS, 815 Pollard Road, Los Gatos, California, Zip 95032–1438,
tel. 408/378–6131) **A**1 2 3 10 **F**3 4 5 11 12 13 15 17 18 20 22 24 26 28 29
30 31 34 35 40 45 49 50 51 54 55 56 57 58 59 60 64 65 70 72 74 75 76
77 78 79 81 82 84 85 86 87 89 90 93 98 101 102 103 104 105 107 108 110
111 114 115 116 117 118 119 120 121 123 124 126 129 130 132 135 143
146 147
Primary Contact: Dan Woods, Chief Executive Officer
COO: Mike Zdeblick, Chief Operating Officer
CFO: Iftikhar Hussain, Chief Financial Officer
CMO: Eric Pifer M.D., Chief Medical Officer
CIO: Greg Walton, Chief Information Officer
CHR: Kathryn M Fisk, Chief Human Resources Officer
CNO: Cheryl Reinking R.N., MS, Chief Nursing Officer
Web address: www.elcaminohospital.org
Control: Hospital district or authority, Government, Nonfederal **Service:** General
medical and surgical

Staffed Beds: 420 **Admissions:** 19171 **Census:** 242 **Outpatient Visits:**
139937 **Births:** 4709 **Total Expense ($000):** 743044 **Payroll Expense
($000):** 334140 **Personnel:** 2275

MURRIETA—Riverside County

☐ **LOMA LINDA UNIVERSITY MEDICAL CENTER–MURRIETA (050770)**, 28062
Baxter Road, Zip 92563–1401; tel. 951/290–4000, **A**1 10 **F**3 8 11 13 15 18
20 22 24 26 28 29 30 31 34 35 37 40 41 44 45 46 47 48 49 50 54 57 58 59
60 64 65 68 70 74 75 76 77 78 79 81 82 85 86 87 90 91 92 93 96 107 108
110 111 114 115 117 118 119 120 121 123 124 126 129 130 143 146 147
148 149 150 **S** Loma Linda University Adventist Health Sciences Center, Loma
Linda, CA
Primary Contact: Greg Henderson, Interim Administrator
COO: Richard M Tibbits, Vice President and Chief Operating Officer
CFO: James Uli, Chief Financial Officer
CMO: Jeff Conner M.D., Chief Medical Staff
Web address: www.llumcmurrieta.org
Control: Other not–for–profit (including NFP Corporation) **Service:** General
medical and surgical

Staffed Beds: 106 **Admissions:** 8204 **Census:** 79 **Outpatient Visits:** 71556
Births: 952 **Total Expense ($000):** 190259 **Payroll Expense ($000):** 53194
Personnel: 738

⊞ **RANCHO SPRINGS MEDICAL CENTER (050701)**, 25500 Medical Center
Drive, Zip 92562–5965; tel. 951/696–6000, (Includes INLAND VALLEY MEDICAL
CENTER, 36485 Inland Valley Drive, Wildomar, California, Zip 92595–9700,
tel. 951/677–1111; Bradley D Neet, FACHE, Chief Executive Officer; RANCHO
SPRINGS MEDICAL CENTER, 25500 Medical Center Drive, Murrieta, California,
Zip 92562–5965, tel. 951/696–6000) **A**1 10 **F**3 8 11 12 13 15 29 30 34 35 37
40 43 45 48 49 50 51 57 59 67 68 70 72 76 77 79 81 84 85 87 93 96 107
108 110 111 114 115 118 119 126 130 132 146 147 149 **S** Universal Health
Services, Inc., King of Prussia, PA
Primary Contact: Bradley D. Neet, FACHE, Chief Executive Officer
COO: Jared Giles, Chief Operating Officer
CFO: Jon Zilkow, Chief Financial Officer
CMO: Reza Vaezazizi M.D., Chief of Staff
CIO: Jeffrey Upcraft, Director Information Services
CHR: Della G Stange, Director Human Resources
CNO: Kristen Johnson, Chief Nursing Officer
Web address: www.swhealthcaresystem.com/
Control: Corporation, Investor–owned (for–profit) **Service:** General medical and
surgical

Staffed Beds: 240 **Admissions:** 15868 **Census:** 160 **Outpatient Visits:**
110252 **Births:** 3569 **Total Expense ($000):** 234250 **Payroll Expense
($000):** 101424 **Personnel:** 1481

CA

Hospital, Medicare Provider Number, Address, Telephone, Approval, Facility, and Physician Codes, Health Care System

★ American Hospital Association (AHA) membership
☐ The Joint Commission accreditation
○ Healthcare Facilities Accreditation Program
◇ DNV Healthcare Inc. accreditation
⇑ Center for Improvement in Healthcare Quality Accreditation
△ Commission on Accreditation of Rehabilitation Facilities (CARF) accreditation

CA

NAPA—Napa County

☐ **NAPA STATE HOSPITAL (054122)**, 2100 Napa–Vallejo Highway, Zip 94558–6293; tel. 707/253–5000, **A**1 3 5 10 **F**30 39 53 56 59 61 67 68 77 86 98 103 128 130 132 135 146 149 **P**6
Primary Contact: Dolly Matteucci, Executive Director
COO: Dolly Matteucci, Executive Director
Web address: www.dmh.ca.gov
Control: State, Government, Nonfederal **Service**: Psychiatric

Staffed Beds: 1284 **Admissions**: 784 **Census**: 1192 **Outpatient Visits**: 0
Births: 0 **Total Expense ($000)**: 300945 **Payroll Expense ($000)**: 185012
Personnel: 2116

⊞ **QUEEN OF THE VALLEY MEDICAL CENTER (050009)**, 1000 Trancas Street, Zip 94558–2906, Mailing Address: P.O.Box 2340, 94558–0688; tel. 707/252–4411, **A**1 2 10 **F**3 13 15 17 18 20 22 24 26 29 30 31 34 35 37 39 40 41 43 44 45 46 47 48 49 50 51 53 54 57 59 64 68 70 71 72 74 75 76 77 78 79 81 82 84 85 86 87 90 91 92 93 96 107 108 110 111 114 115 116 117 118 119 120 121 123 124 126 130 132 135 146 **P**3 **S** Providence St. Joseph Health, Renton, WA
Primary Contact: Larry Coomes, Chief Executive Officer
COO: Vincent Morgese M.D., Executive Vice President, Chief Operating Officer and Chief Medical Officer
CFO: Michel Riccioni, Vice President and Chief Financial Officer, Northern California Region
CMO: Vincent Morgese M.D., Executive Vice President, Chief Operating Officer and Chief Medical Officer
CHR: Robert A Eisen, Vice President Human Resources, Northern California Region
Web address: www.thequeen.org
Control: Other not–for–profit (including NFP Corporation) **Service**: General medical and surgical

Staffed Beds: 120 **Admissions**: 6969 **Census**: 83 **Outpatient Visits**: 133549 **Births**: 740 **Total Expense ($000)**: 252017 **Payroll Expense ($000)**: 73995 **Personnel**: 915

NATIONAL CITY—San Diego County

⊞ △ **PARADISE VALLEY HOSPITAL (050024)**, 2400 East Fourth Street, Zip 91950–2099; tel. 619/470–4321, (Nonreporting) (Includes BAYVIEW BEHAVIORAL HEALTH CAMPUS, 330 Moss Street, Chula Vista, California, Zip 91911–2005, tel. 619/470–4321; Neerav Jadeja, Administrator) **A**1 3 7 10 **S** Prime Healthcare, Ontario, CA
Primary Contact: Neerav Jadeja, Administrator
CFO: Becky Levy, Chief Financial Officer
CMO: Rosemarie Lim M.D., Chief Medical Officer
CIO: Allan Tojino, Director, Information Systems
CHR: Lorraine Villegas, Manager Human Resources
CNO: Gemma Rama–Banaag R.N., MSN, Chief Nursing Officer
Web address: www.paradisevalleyhospital.org
Control: Corporation, Investor–owned (for–profit) **Service**: General medical and surgical

Staffed Beds: 291

NEEDLES—San Bernardino County

★ **COLORADO RIVER MEDICAL CENTER (051323)**, 1401 Bailey Avenue, Zip 92363–3198; tel. 760/326–7100, **A**10 18 **F**29 34 40 45 46 47 48 49 50 53 57 59 66 68 81 87 107 111 114 119 143 145 146 148 149
Primary Contact: Steve Kelley. Lopez, Chief Executive Officer
COO: Knaya Tabora, Chief Operating Officer and Chief Nursing Officer
CFO: Steve Kelley Lopez, Chief Financial Officer
CMO: Robert Strecker M.D., Chief of Staff
CIO: Ron Chieffo, Chief Information Officer
CHR: Pam Barrett, Human Resources Director
CNO: Knaya Tabora, Chief Operating Officer and Chief Nursing Officer
Web address: www.crmccares.com
Control: Other not–for–profit (including NFP Corporation) **Service**: General medical and surgical

Staffed Beds: 25 **Admissions**: 485 **Census**: 4 **Outpatient Visits**: 6128 **Births**: 0 **Total Expense ($000)**: 9190 **Payroll Expense ($000)**: 4137 **Personnel**: 82

NEWPORT BEACH—Orange County

★ ⇑ **HOAG MEMORIAL HOSPITAL PRESBYTERIAN (050224)**, One Hoag Drive, Zip 92663–4120, Mailing Address: P.O.Box 6100, 92658–6100; tel. 949/764–4624, (Includes HOAG HOSPITAL IRVINE, 16200 Sand Canyon Avenue, Irvine, California, Zip 92618–3714, tel. 949/764–8240) **A**3 5 10 21 **F**3 4 5 8 11 13 14 15 17 18 20 22 24 26 28 29 30 31 34 35 36 37 40 44 45 46 47 48 49 50 51 52 53 54 55 57 58 59 64 68 70 72 74 75 76 77 78 79 81 82 84 85 86 87 92 93 94 96 97 100 102 103 107 108 110 111 113 114 115 116 117 118 119 120 121 123 124 126 129 130 131 132 135 144 145 146 147 148 149 150 **P**3 **S** Providence St. Joseph Health, Renton, WA
Primary Contact: Robert Braithwaite, President and Chief Executive Officer
COO: Michael Ricks, Chief Operating Officer
CFO: Andrew Guarni, Chief Financial Officer
CIO: Patrick Anderson, Chief Information Officer and Senior Vice President
CHR: Jan L Blue, Vice President Human Resources
CNO: Richard A Martin MSN, R.N., Senior Vice President and Chief Nursing Officer
Web address: www.hoaghospital.org
Control: Other not–for–profit (including NFP Corporation) **Service**: General medical and surgical

Staffed Beds: 470 **Admissions**: 28705 **Census**: 307 **Outpatient Visits**: 409573 **Births**: 6362 **Total Expense ($000)**: 860710 **Payroll Expense ($000)**: 313836 **Personnel**: 4610

NEWPORT BAY HOSPITAL (054135), 1501 East 16th Street, Zip 92663–5924; tel. 949/650–9750, **A**10 **F**3 29 35 56 98 100 101 103 130 132 135 148
Primary Contact: James E. Parkhurst, President and Chief Executive Officer
COO: Garry Hardwick R.N., Chief Operating Officer
CFO: Rocky Gentner, Chief Financial Officer
CMO: Jason Kellogg M.D., Chief of Staff
CIO: Nina Swenson, Director Business Services
CHR: Phyllis Parkhurst, Vice President Support Services
CNO: Diana Hakenson, Director of Patient Care Services
Web address: www.newportbayhospital.com
Control: Corporation, Investor–owned (for–profit) **Service**: Psychiatric

Staffed Beds: 34 **Admissions**: 912 **Census**: 32 **Outpatient Visits**: 0 **Births**: 0

NORTH HOLLYWOOD—Los Angeles County, See Los Angeles

NORTHRIDGE—Los Angeles County, See Los Angeles

NORWALK—Los Angeles County

COAST PLAZA DOCTORS HOSPITAL See Coast Plaza Hospital

☐ **COAST PLAZA HOSPITAL (050771)**, 13100 Studebaker Road, Zip 90650–2500; tel. 562/868–3751, (Nonreporting) **A**1 10 **S** Avanti Hospitals, El Segundo, CA
Primary Contact: Gregory Padilla, Administrator
CFO: Mihi Lee, Chief Financial Officer
CMO: Galal S Gough M.D., Chief of Staff
CIO: Linda K Roman, Administrator
Web address: www.avantihospitals.com/coast–plaza–hospital
Control: Corporation, Investor–owned (for–profit) **Service**: General medical and surgical

Staffed Beds: 123

LOS ANGELES COMMUNITY HOSPITAL OF NORWALK See Los Angeles Community Hospital at Los Angeles, Los Angeles

☐ **METROPOLITAN STATE HOSPITAL (054133)**, 11401 Bloomfield Avenue, Zip 90650–2015; tel. 562/863–7011, (Nonreporting) **A**1 10
Primary Contact: Michael Barsom, M.D., Executive Director
CFO: Maybelle Manlagnit, Senior Accounting Officer
CIO: Paul Mello, Manager Data Processing
CHR: Jorge Banuedos, Director Human Resources
Web address: www.dmh.ca.gov
Control: State, Government, Nonfederal **Service**: Psychiatric

Staffed Beds: 657

NOVATO—Marin County

⊞ **NOVATO COMMUNITY HOSPITAL (050131)**, 180 Rowland Way, Zip 94945–5009, Mailing Address: P.O.Box 1108, 94948–1108; tel. 415/209–1300, **A**1 10 **F**3 15 18 29 30 34 36 40 45 50 51 54 56 59 60 64 68 70 75 77 79 81 84 85 87 93 107 108 111 115 119 130 131 132 143 144 146 148 **P**3 5 **S** Sutter Health, Sacramento, CA
Primary Contact: Brian Alexander, Chief Administrative Officer
CMO: Barbara Nylund M.D., Chief of Staff
CIO: Kathryn Graham, Director Communications and Community Relations
CHR: Diana G Johnson, Acting Chief Human Resources Officer
Web address: www.novatocommunity.sutterhealth.org
Control: Other not–for–profit (including NFP Corporation) **Service**: General medical and surgical

Staffed Beds: 40 **Admissions**: 1758 **Census**: 17 **Outpatient Visits**: 93295 **Births**: 0 **Total Expense ($000)**: 77637 **Payroll Expense ($000)**: 23982 **Personnel**: 197

Many Facility Codes have changed. Please refer to the AHA Guide Code Chart.
© 2017 AHA Guide

OAKDALE—Stanislaus County

✠ **OAK VALLEY HOSPITAL DISTRICT (050067)**, 350 South Oak Avenue,
Zip 95361–3581; tel. 209/847–3011, (Nonreporting) **A**1 10
Primary Contact: John McCormick, President and Chief Executive Officer
CMO: Albert Gelders M.D., Chief of Staff
CIO: Sherry Peral, Manager Information Systems
CHR: Brian Beck,PHR,MHROD, Vice President Human Resources
CNO: Joann L. Saporito R.N., Vice President Nursing Services
Web address: www.oakvalleycares.org
Control: Hospital district or authority, Government, Nonfederal **Service**: General
medical and surgical

Staffed Beds: 150

OAKLAND—Alameda County

✠ △ **ALTA BATES SUMMIT MEDICAL CENTER – SUMMIT CAMPUS (050043)**,
350 Hawthorne Avenue, Zip 94609–3100; tel. 510/655–4000, **A**1 2 5 7 10 **F**3 4
5 8 11 12 15 17 18 20 22 24 26 29 30 31 34 35 36 40 45 46 47 49 51 56 57
58 59 60 61 64 68 70 74 75 77 78 79 81 82 84 85 86 87 90 97 107 108 111
114 115 116 117 118 119 120 121 123 124 126 130 132 135 146 148 149
P3 5 **S** Sutter Health, Sacramento, CA
Primary Contact: Charles Prosper, Chief Executive Officer
CMO: John Gentile M.D., Vice President Medical Affairs
CHR: Mark Beiting, Vice President Human Resources
Web address: www.altabatessummit.com
Control: Other not–for–profit (including NFP Corporation) **Service**: General
medical and surgical

Staffed Beds: 333 Admissions: 13633 Census: 254 Outpatient Visits:
128600 Births: 0 Total Expense ($000): 508731 Payroll Expense ($000):
149243 Personnel: 1511

✠ **HIGHLAND HOSPITAL (050320)**, 1411 East 31st Street, Zip 94602–1018;
tel. 510/437–4800, (Includes FAIRMONT HOSPITAL, 15400 Foothill Boulevard,
San Leandro, California, Zip 94578–1009, tel. 510/895–4200; Richard Espinoza,
Chief Administrative Officer; JOHN GEORGE PSYCHIATRIC HOSPITAL, 2060
Fairmont Drive, San Leandro, California, Zip 94578–1001, tel. 510/346–1300;
Guy C Qvistgaard, Chief Executive Officer) (Total facility includes 109 beds in
nursing home–type unit) **A**1 3 5 10 **F**3 5 11 13 15 18 20 22 28 29 30 31 32 34
35 36 38 39 40 43 44 45 46 49 50 54 56 57 58 59 60 61 64 65 69 70 71
73 74 75 76 77 78 79 81 82 84 85 86 87 90 92 93 94 96 97 98 100 101 102
104 105 107 111 112 114 115 119 128 130 132 134 135 142 143 144 146
147 148 **P**6 **S** Alameda Health System, San Leandro, CA
Primary Contact: Delvecchio Finley, Chief Executive Officer
CFO: Marion Schales, Chief Financial Officer
CMO: Sang–ick Chang M.D., M.P.H., Chief Medical Officer
CHR: Jeanette L Louden Corbett, Chief Human Resources Officer
Web address: www.alamedahealthsystem.org
Control: Hospital district or authority, Government, Nonfederal **Service**: General
medical and surgical

Staffed Beds: 374 Admissions: 14911 Census: 320 Outpatient Visits:
388880 Births: 1144 Total Expense ($000): 725136 Payroll Expense
($000): 321789 Personnel: 2841

✠ **KAISER PERMANENTE OAKLAND MEDICAL CENTER (050075)**, 3600
Broadway, Zip 94611–5693; tel. 510/752–1000, (Nonreporting) (Includes KAISER
PERMANENTE RICHMOND MEDICAL CENTER, 901 Nevin Avenue, Richmond,
California, Zip 94801–2555, tel. 510/307–1500) **A**1 2 3 5 8 10 **S** Kaiser
Foundation Hospitals, Oakland, CA
Primary Contact: Mark Fratzke, R.N., Senior Vice President and Area Manager
CFO: Dennis Morris, Area Finance Officer
CMO: John Loftus M.D., Chief of Staff
CIO: Johnny Law, Area Information Officer
CHR: Rick Mead, Human Resources Leader
CNO: Charlene Boyer, Chief Nursing Officer
Web address: www.kaiserpermanente.org
Control: Other not–for–profit (including NFP Corporation) **Service**: General
medical and surgical

Staffed Beds: 267

OAKLAND MEDICAL CENTER See Kaiser Permanente Oakland Medical Center

☐ **TELECARE HERITAGE PSYCHIATRIC HEALTH CENTER (054146)**, 2633 East
27th Street, Zip 94601–1912; tel. 510/535–5115, (Nonreporting) **A**1 10
Primary Contact: Anne L. Bakar, President and Chief Executive Officer
Web address: www.tbhcare.com/
Control: Partnership, Investor–owned (for–profit) **Service**: Psychiatric

Staffed Beds: 26

✠ **USCF BENIOFF CHILDREN'S HOSPITAL OAKLAND (053301)**, 747 52nd
Street, Zip 94609–1859; tel. 510/428–3000, **A**1 3 5 10 **F**3 19 21 23 25 29 30
32 34 35 38 40 41 43 44 45 46 50 54 55 57 58 59 61 65 66 68 72 74 75 77
78 79 81 84 86 87 88 90 93 97 99 100 101 102 104 107 111 119 129 130
131 132 134 136 143 146 149
Primary Contact: Bertram Lubin, M.D., President and Chief Executive Officer
CIO: Don Livsey, Vice President and Chief Information Officer
Web address: www.childrenshospitaloakland.org
Control: Other not–for–profit (including NFP Corporation) **Service**: Children's
general medical and surgical

Staffed Beds: 190 Admissions: 9322 Census: 125 Outpatient Visits:
269402 Births: 0 Total Expense ($000): 551590 Payroll Expense ($000):
239841 Personnel: 1957

OCEANSIDE—San Diego County

✠ **TRI–CITY MEDICAL CENTER (050128)**, 4002 Vista Way, Zip 92056–4593;
tel. 760/724–8411, (Nonreporting) **A**1 2 3 5 10
Primary Contact: Steve Dietlin, Chief Executive Officer
COO: Casey Fatch, Chief Operating Officer
CMO: Scott Worman, Chief of Staff
CIO: Kim Cook, Interim Clinical Applications Services Manager
CHR: Esther Beverly, Vice President Human Resources
CNO: Sharon A Schultz MSN, R.N., M.P.H., Chief Nurse Executive and Vice
President
Web address: www.tricitymed.org
Control: Hospital district or authority, Government, Nonfederal **Service**: General
medical and surgical

Staffed Beds: 330

OJAI—Ventura County

⇑ **OJAI VALLEY COMMUNITY HOSPITAL (051334)**, 1306 Maricopa Highway,
Zip 93023–3163; tel. 805/646–1401, (Nonreporting) **A**18 21 **S** Community
Memorial Health System, Ventura, CA
Primary Contact: Haady Lashkari, Chief Administrative Officer
CFO: David Glyer, Vice President Finance
CIO: Mark Turner, Manager Information Technology
CHR: Deborah Gallagher, Manager Human Resources
Web address: www.ojaihospital.org
Control: Other not–for–profit (including NFP Corporation) **Service**: General
medical and surgical

Staffed Beds: 96

ONTARIO—San Bernardino County

✠ **KINDRED HOSPITAL–ONTARIO (052037)**, 550 North Monterey Avenue,
Zip 91764–3399; tel. 909/391–0333, (Nonreporting) **A**1 10 **S** Kindred
Healthcare, Louisville, KY
Primary Contact: Vincent Trac, Chief Executive Officer
CFO: Omar Oregel, Controller
CMO: Marc Lynch D.O., Chief of Staff
CHR: Laurel Scharber, Administrative Assistant and Coordinator Human Resources
CNO: Holly Ramos R.N., Chief Clinical Officer
Web address: www.khontario.com/
Control: Corporation, Investor–owned (for–profit) **Service**: Acute long–term care
hospital

Staffed Beds: 91

ORANGE—Orange County

☐ **CHAPMAN GLOBAL MEDICAL CENTER (050745)**, 2601 East Chapman
Avenue, Zip 92869–3296; tel. 714/633–0011, (Nonreporting) **A**1 10 **S** KPC
Healthcare, Inc., Santa Ana, CA
Primary Contact: Ronald J. Galonsky Jr, Chief Executive Officer
COO: Ada Yeh, Chief Operating Officer and Chief Nursing Officer
CFO: John Collins, Corporate Chief Financial Officer
CMO: Gary Bennett M.D., Chief of Medical Staff
CIO: Sri Yarramsetti, Chief Information Officer
CHR: JoAnne Suehs, Manager Human Resources
CNO: Ada Yeh, Chief Operating Officer and Chief Nursing Officer
Web address: www.Chapman–GMC.com
Control: Corporation, Investor–owned (for–profit) **Service**: General medical and
surgical

Staffed Beds: 100

☐ **CHILDREN'S HOSPITAL OF ORANGE COUNTY (053304)**, 1201 West La
Veta Avenue, Zip 92868–4203, Mailing Address: PO Box 5700, 92863–5700;
tel. 714/997–3000, **A**1 3 5 10 **F**3 14 17 19 21 23 25 27 29 30 31 32 34 35 40
41 43 50 55 57 58 59 60 61 64 65 66 68 71 72 74 75 77 78 79 81 82 84 85
86 87 88 89 91 92 93 97 99 100 101 104 107 111 113 114 115 116 117 118
119 120 121 123 126 129 130 131 132 134 136 146 149 **P**3 8
Primary Contact: Kimberly C. Cripe, President and Chief Executive Officer
COO: Matthew S Gerlach, Chief Operating Officer
CFO: Kerri Ruppert Schiller, Senior Vice President and Chief Financial Officer
CMO: Maria Minon M.D., Vice President Medical Affairs and Chief Medical Officer
CIO: John Henderson, Vice President and Chief Information Officer
CHR: Mamoon Syed, Vice President Human Resources
CNO: Melanie Patterson R.N., Vice President Patient Care Services and Chief
Nursing Officer
Web address: www.choc.org
Control: Other not–for–profit (including NFP Corporation) **Service**: Children's
general medical and surgical

Staffed Beds: 279 Admissions: 11995 Census: 180 Outpatient Visits:
391960 **Births:** 0 **Total Expense ($000):** 613308 **Payroll Expense ($000):**
182815 **Personnel:** 2527

⇑ **HEALTHBRIDGE CHILDREN'S HOSPITAL (053308)**, 393 South Tustin Street,
Zip 92866–2501; tel. 714/289–2400, **A**10 21 **F**3 29 64 65 75 77 90 93 128
130 132 146 148 149 150 **S** Nexus Health Systems, Houston, TX
Primary Contact: Alex Villarruz, Chief Executive Officer
CIO: Roberta Consolver, Chief Information Officer
Web address: www.HealthBridgeOrange.com
Control: Partnership, Investor–owned (for–profit) **Service**: Children's rehabilitation

Staffed Beds: 27 Admissions: 121 Census: 24 Outpatient Visits: 3000
Births: 0

⊠ **ST. JOSEPH HOSPITAL (050069)**, 1100 West Stewart Drive, Zip 92868–3849,
Mailing Address: P.O.Box 5600, 92863–5600; tel. 714/633–5600, **A**1 2 3 5 10
F3 5 8 12 13 15 17 18 19 20 22 24 26 28 29 30 31 34 35 37 40 41 42 45 46
47 49 50 51 53 54 55 57 58 59 60 64 65 68 69 70 74 75 76 77 78 79 80 81
82 84 85 86 87 91 92 93 98 100 101 102 104 105 107 108 109 110 111 113
114 115 116 117 118 119 120 121 123 124 126 129 130 131 132 135 138
141 146 147 148 149 **P**3 5 **S** Providence St. Joseph Health, Renton, WA
Primary Contact: Steven C. Moreau, President and Chief Executive Officer
COO: Jeremy Zoch, Executive Vice President and Chief Operating Officer
CFO: Kristi Liberatore, Vice President and Chief Financial Officer
CMO: Scott Rusk M.D., Chief Medical Officer
CIO: Jeremy Zoch, Executive Vice President and Chief Operating Officer
CHR: Mary P Leahy, Vice President Human Resources
CNO: Katie Skelton MSN, R.N., Vice President Nursing and Chief Nursing Officer
Web address: www.sjo.org
Control: Other not–for–profit (including NFP Corporation) **Service**: General
medical and surgical

Staffed Beds: 379 Admissions: 20818 Census: 216 Outpatient Visits:
329211 **Births:** 4818 **Total Expense ($000):** 599693 **Payroll Expense
($000):** 178626 **Personnel:** 2438

⊠ **UC IRVINE MEDICAL CENTER (050348)**, 101 The City Drive South, Zip 92868–
3298; tel. 714/456–6011, **A**1 2 3 5 8 10 **F**3 6 8 9 11 12 13 14 15 16 17 18 19
20 22 24 26 28 29 30 31 32 34 35 36 37 38 39 40 41 43 44 45 46 47 48 49
50 51 53 54 55 56 57 58 59 60 61 63 64 65 66 67 68 70 71 72 73 74 75 76
77 78 79 80 81 82 84 85 86 87 88 89 90 91 92 93 96 97 98 99 100 101 102
103 104 105 107 108 110 111 114 115 116 117 118 119 120 121 123 124
126 130 131 132 134 135 138 141 142 144 145 146 147 148 149 150 **P**4 5
S University of California Systemwide Administration, Oakland, CA
Primary Contact: Howard Federoff, M.D., Vice Chancellor, Health Affairs & Chief
Executive Officer, UC Irvine Health
COO: Richard J. Gannotta, Chief Operating Officer
CFO: Ajay Sial, Chief Financial Officer, UC Irvine Health
CMO: William Wilson M.D., Chief Medical Officer
CIO: Charles H Podesta, Chief Information Officer
CHR: Ramona Agrela, Associate Chancellor & Chief Human Resources Executive
CNO: Sonia Lane, Interim Chief Nursing Officer
Web address: www.ucirvinehealth.org
Control: State, Government, Nonfederal **Service**: General medical and surgical

Staffed Beds: 411 Admissions: 20777 Census: 338 Outpatient Visits:
751629 **Births:** 1660 **Total Expense ($000):** 1015596 **Payroll Expense
($000):** 380160 **Personnel:** 4405

OROVILLE—Butte County

★ **OROVILLE HOSPITAL (050030)**, 2767 Olive Highway, Zip 95966–6118;
tel. 530/533–8500, **A**10 **F**3 5 11 13 15 18 19 26 27 28 29 30 31 32 33 34 35
36 38 39 40 41 44 45 46 47 48 49 50 51 52 54 56 57 59 60 61 62 63 64 65
66 68 70 74 75 76 77 78 79 81 82 83 84 85 86 87 91 93 94 96 97 107 108
110 111 114 115 116 117 118 119 120 121 123 124 126 127 129 130 131
132 134 135 144 145 146 147 148 149
Primary Contact: Robert J. Wentz, President and Chief Executive Officer
COO: Scott Chapple, Chief Operating Officer
CFO: Ashok Khanchandani, Chief Financial Officer
CMO: Mathew N. Fine M.D., Chief Medical Officer
CIO: Denise LeFevre, Chief Information Officer
CHR: Scott Chapple, Chief Operating Officer
CNO: Carol Speer–Smith R.N., Chief Nursing Officer
Web address: www.orovillehospital.com
Control: Other not–for–profit (including NFP Corporation) **Service**: General
medical and surgical

Staffed Beds: 133 Admissions: 12396 Census: 114 Outpatient Visits: 426538
Births: 456 **Total Expense ($000):** 244607 **Payroll Expense ($000):** 94842
Personnel: 1086

OXNARD—Ventura County

⊠ **ST. JOHN'S REGIONAL MEDICAL CENTER (050082)**, 1600 North Rose
Avenue, Zip 93030–3723; tel. 805/988–2500, (Nonreporting) **A**1 2 10 **S** Dignity
Health, San Francisco, CA
Primary Contact: Darren W. Lee, President and Chief Executive Officer
CFO: Donald P Bernard, Chief Financial Officer
CMO: Sahin Yanik M.D., Vice President Medical Administration
CIO: Jeff Perry, Director Information Technology
CHR: Ed Gonzales, Vice President Human Resources
Web address: www.stjohnshealth.org
Control: Other not–for–profit (including NFP Corporation) **Service**: General
medical and surgical

Staffed Beds: 139

PALM SPRINGS—Riverside County

⊠ ⇑ **DESERT REGIONAL MEDICAL CENTER (050243)**, 1150 North Indian
Canyon Drive, Zip 92262–4872; tel. 760/323–6511, (Total facility includes 30
beds in nursing home–type unit) **A**1 2 3 10 13 21 **F**3 12 13 15 17 18 20 22 24
26 28 29 30 31 34 35 40 43 45 46 47 48 49 50 51 52 53 54 55 56 57 58 59
60 61 62 64 65 68 70 72 74 75 77 78 79 81 82 85 86 87 89 90 92 93 94 100
102 107 108 109 110 111 114 115 116 117 119 120 124 126 128 130 131
132 144 146 147 148 **S** TENET Healthcare Corporation, Dallas, TX
Primary Contact: Michele Finney, Chief Executive Officer
CFO: Judi Stimson, Chief Financial Officer
CMO: Charles Anderson M.D., Chief Medical Officer
CIO: Robert Klingseis, Director Information Systems
CHR: Frederick K. Owusu, Chief Human Resources Officer
CNO: Kristin Schmidt R.N., FACHE, Chief Nursing Officer
Web address: www.desertregional.com
Control: Individual, Investor–owned (for–profit) **Service**: General medical and
surgical

Staffed Beds: 382 Admissions: 20184 Census: 265 Outpatient Visits:
164406 **Births:** 3155 **Total Expense ($000):** 420997 **Payroll Expense
($000):** 204316 **Personnel:** 2041

PALMDALE—Los Angeles County

☐ **PALMDALE REGIONAL MEDICAL CENTER (050204)**, 38600 Medical Center
Drive, Zip 93551–4483; tel. 661/382–5000, (Nonreporting) **A**1 10 **S** Universal
Health Services, Inc., King of Prussia, PA
Primary Contact: Richard Allen, Chief Executive Officer
CFO: Kurt Broten, Chief Financial Officer
CIO: Roy Singleton, Director Computer Information Systems
CHR: Karen Hickling, Director Human Resources
Web address: www.palmdaleregional.com
Control: Corporation, Investor–owned (for–profit) **Service**: General medical and
surgical

Staffed Beds: 157

PALMDALE REGIONAL MEDICAL CENTER (Nonreporting) **A**1 10
CFO: Kurt Broten, Chief Financial Officer
CIO: Roy Singleton, Director Computer Information Systems
CHR: Karen Hickling, Director Human Resources
Web address: www.palmdaleregional.com

CA

PALO ALTO—Santa Clara County

⊞ **LUCILE SALTER PACKARD CHILDREN'S HOSPITAL STANFORD (053305)**, 725 Welch Road, Zip 94304–1614; tel. 650/497–8000, **A**1 3 5 10 **F**3 7 8 11 12 13 17 19 25 27 28 29 30 31 32 34 35 36 38 39 44 45 46 47 48 49 50 52 54 55 57 58 59 60 61 63 64 65 66 68 71 72 73 74 75 76 77 78 79 80 81 82 84 85 86 87 88 89 91 92 93 96 97 99 100 101 104 107 111 115 119 124 126 129 130 131 132 134 136 137 138 139 140 141 142 144 145 146 148 149 **P**3
Primary Contact: Christopher G. Dawes, President and Chief Executive Officer
COO: Anne McCune, Chief Operating Officer
CMO: Kenneth Cox M.D., Chief Medical Officer
CIO: James McCaughey, Chief Strategy Officer
CHR: Greg Souza, Vice President Human Resources
CNO: Susan Costello, Chief Nursing Officer
Web address: www.stanfordchildrens.org
Control: Other not–for–profit (including NFP Corporation) **Service**: Children's general medical and surgical

> **Staffed Beds:** 249 **Admissions:** 13472 **Census:** 227 **Outpatient Visits:** 123416 **Births:** 4585 **Total Expense ($000):** 1065234 **Payroll Expense ($000):** 360702 **Personnel:** 3306

⊞ **STANFORD HEALTH CARE (050441)**, 300 Pasteur Drive, Suite H3200, Zip 94304–2203; tel. 650/723–4000, **A**1 3 5 8 10 **F**3 5 6 7 8 9 11 12 14 15 17 18 20 21 22 23 24 26 27 28 29 30 31 33 34 35 36 37 38 39 40 41 43 44 45 46 47 48 49 50 51 54 55 56 57 58 59 60 61 63 64 65 66 68 70 74 75 77 78 79 80 81 82 84 85 86 87 92 93 95 96 97 98 100 101 102 103 104 107 108 110 111 114 115 117 118 119 120 121 123 124 126 129 130 131 132 136 137 138 139 140 141 142 144 145 146 147 148 149 150 **P**6 **S** Stanford Health Care, Palo Alto, CA
Primary Contact: David Entwistle, President and Chief Executive Officer
COO: Quinn McKenna, Chief Operating Officer
CFO: Daniel Morrissette, Chief Financial Officer
CMO: Norman Rizk M.D., Chief Medical Officer
CIO: Pravene Nath, Chief Information Officer
CHR: Kety Duron, Vice President Human Resources
CNO: Nancy Lee R.N., MSN, Vice President Patient Care Services and Chief Nursing Officer
Web address: www.stanfordhealthcare.org
Control: Other not–for–profit (including NFP Corporation) **Service**: General medical and surgical

> **Staffed Beds:** 491 **Admissions:** 26093 **Census:** 422 **Outpatient Visits:** 1553362 **Births:** 0 **Total Expense ($000):** 3478536 **Payroll Expense ($000):** 1069372 **Personnel:** 12004

⊞ △ **VA PALO ALTO HEALTH CARE SYSTEM**, 3801 Miranda Avenue, Zip 94304–1207; tel. 650/493–5000, (Nonreporting) (Includes PALO ALTO DIVISION, 3801 Miranda Avenue, Palo Alto, California, Zip 94304–1207, tel. 650/493–5000; VETERANS AFFAIRS PALO ALTO HEALTH CARE SYSTEM, LIVERMORE DIVISION, 4951 Arroyo Road, Livermore, California, Zip 94550, tel. 510/447–2560) **A**1 2 3 5 7 **S** Department of Veterans Affairs, Washington, DC
Primary Contact: Thomas J. Fitzgerald III, Interim Director
CFO: Mel Niese, Chief Fiscal Service
CMO: Lawrence Leung M.D., Chief of Staff
CIO: Doug Wirthgen, Chief Information Officer
CHR: Lori Peery, Chief Human Resource Management Services
Web address: www.paloalto.va.gov/
Control: Veterans Affairs, Government, federal **Service**: General medical and surgical

> **Staffed Beds:** 808

PANORAMA CITY—Los Angeles County, See Los Angeles

PARADISE—Butte County

⊞ **FEATHER RIVER HOSPITAL (050225)**, 5974 Pentz Road, Zip 95969–5593; tel. 530/877–9361, (Nonreporting) **A**1 2 10 **S** Adventist Health, Roseville, CA
Primary Contact: Monty E. Knittel, Chief Executive Officer
CFO: Dan Gordon, Chief Financial Officer
CMO: Anthony Nasr M.D., Chief Medical Staff
CIO: Dan Gordon, Chief Financial Officer
CHR: Denton Gruzensky, Director Human Resources
Web address: www.frhosp.org
Control: Church operated, Nongovernment, not–for–profit **Service**: General medical and surgical

> **Staffed Beds:** 54

PASADENA—Los Angeles County

⊞ **HUNTINGTON MEMORIAL HOSPITAL (050438)**, 100 West California Boulevard, Zip 91105–3097, Mailing Address: P.O.Box 7013, 91109–7013; tel. 626/397–5000, **A**1 2 3 5 10 **F**1 3 4 5 8 11 12 13 14 15 16 17 18 20 22 24 26 28 29 30 31 34 35 37 40 41 43 44 45 46 47 48 49 50 51 53 56 58 59 60 61 63 64 65 66 67 68 70 72 73 74 75 76 77 78 79 80 81 82 84 86 87 88 89 90 92 93 97 98 100 101 102 103 104 105 106 107 108 111 114 115 118 119 120 121 123 126 128 129 130 132 146 147 148 149 **P**3 5 7
Primary Contact: Lori Morgan, M.D., President and Chief Executive Officer
CFO: James S Noble, Chief Financial Officer
CMO: Paula Verrette M.D., Senior Vice President Quality and Physician Services and Chief Medical Officer
CIO: Debbie Tafoya, Vice President and Chief Information Officer
CHR: Debbie Ortega, Chief Human Resource Officer and Vice President Administrative Services
CNO: Gloria Sanchez–Rico, Chief Nursing Officer and Vice President
Web address: www.huntingtonhospital.com
Control: Other not–for–profit (including NFP Corporation) **Service**: General medical and surgical

> **Staffed Beds:** 619 **Admissions:** 29342 **Census:** 356 **Outpatient Visits:** 136777 **Births:** 3337 **Total Expense ($000):** 691291 **Payroll Expense ($000):** 265183 **Personnel:** 3472

☐ **LAS ENCINAS HOSPITAL (054078)**, 2900 East Del Mar Boulevard, Zip 91107–4399; tel. 626/795–9901, (Nonreporting) **A**1 10 **S** Signature Healthcare Services, Corona, CA
Primary Contact: Thomas J. Mahle, Chief Executive Officer
CMO: Daniel Suzuki M.D., Medical Director
CIO: Eric Kim, Chief Information Officer
CHR: Veronica Herrera, Director Human Resources
Web address: www.lasencinashospital.com
Control: Corporation, Investor–owned (for–profit) **Service**: Psychiatric

> **Staffed Beds:** 138

PATTON—San Bernardino County

☐ **PATTON STATE HOSPITAL**, 3102 East Highland Avenue, Zip 92369–7813; tel. 909/425–7000, **A**1 3 **F**3 29 30 39 53 57 58 59 61 65 74 75 77 86 87 98 100 101 103 130 132 135 143 146 149 **P**1
Primary Contact: Harry Oreol, Acting Chief Executive Officer
CFO: Kathleen Gamble, Fiscal Officer
CMO: George Christison M.D., Medical Director
CIO: Cindy Barrett, Administrative Assistant
CHR: Nancy Varela, Director Human Resources
Web address: www.dmh.cahwnet.gov/statehospitals/patton
Control: State, Government, Nonfederal **Service**: Psychiatric

> **Staffed Beds:** 1527 **Admissions:** 1395 **Census:** 1519 **Outpatient Visits:** 0 **Births:** 0 **Total Expense ($000):** 328721 **Payroll Expense ($000):** 206215 **Personnel:** 2346

PERRIS—Riverside County

★ ○ **KINDRED HOSPITAL RIVERSIDE (052052)**, 2224 Medical Center Drive, Zip 92571–2638; tel. 951/436–3535, (Nonreporting) **A**10 11 **S** Kindred Healthcare, Louisville, KY
Primary Contact: William Mitchell, Chief Executive Officer and Administrator
COO: Guay Khim Fugate, Chief Operations Officer
CFO: John Browne, Senior Chief Financial Officer
CHR: Tom Wright, Director Human Resources
Web address: www.khriverside.com
Control: Corporation, Investor–owned (for–profit) **Service**: Acute long–term care hospital

> **Staffed Beds:** 40

PETALUMA—Sonoma County

⊞ **PETALUMA VALLEY HOSPITAL (050136)**, 400 North McDowell Boulevard, Zip 94954–2366; tel. 707/778–1111, **A**1 10 **F**3 11 13 15 29 30 31 35 40 44 45 46 49 50 51 57 60 63 64 68 70 74 75 76 77 78 79 81 84 85 87 91 92 93 100 107 108 110 111 115 119 130 146 148 149 150 **S** Providence St. Joseph Health, Renton, WA
Primary Contact: Todd Salnas, President
CFO: Michel Riccioni, Chief Financial Officer
CIO: Patrick Wylie, Director Information Systems
Web address: www.stjosephhealth.org/About–Us/Facilities/Petaluma–Valley–Hospital.aspx
Control: Other not–for–profit (including NFP Corporation) **Service**: General medical and surgical

> **Staffed Beds:** 51 **Admissions:** 2449 **Census:** 27 **Outpatient Visits:** 62828 **Births:** 456 **Total Expense ($000):** 91306 **Payroll Expense ($000):** 30777 **Personnel:** 324

CA

Hospital, Medicare Provider Number, Address, Telephone, Approval, Facility, and Physician Codes, Health Care System

★ American Hospital Association (AHA) membership   ○ Healthcare Facilities Accreditation Program   ⇑ Center for Improvement in Healthcare Quality Accreditation
☐ The Joint Commission accreditation   ◇ DNV Healthcare Inc. accreditation   △ Commission on Accreditation of Rehabilitation Facilities (CARF) accreditation

CA

PLACENTIA—Orange County

☒ **PLACENTIA–LINDA HOSPITAL (050589)**, 1301 North Rose Drive, Zip 92870–3899; tel. 714/993–2000, (Nonreporting) **A**1 10 **S** TENET Healthcare Corporation, Dallas, TX
Primary Contact: Christina E. Oh, Chief Executive Officer
COO: Dwayne Richardson, Chief Operating Officer
CFO: Brittany Whitaker, Chief Financial Officer
CIO: Eleanor Laneaux, Director Information Systems
CHR: Diane McCluskey, Chief Human Resources Officer
CNO: Nancy Lee, Chief Nursing Officer
Web address: www.placentialinda.com
Control: Corporation, Investor–owned (for–profit) **Service**: General medical and surgical

Staffed Beds: 114

PLACERVILLE—El Dorado County

☒ **MARSHALL MEDICAL CENTER (050254)**, 1100 Marshall Way, Zip 95667–5722; tel. 530/622–1441, (Total facility includes 14 beds in nursing home–type unit) **A**1 2 10 **F**3 8 11 13 15 18 20 22 28 29 31 34 35 40 41 43 46 49 50 51 56 57 59 62 65 66 70 74 75 77 78 79 81 84 85 86 87 93 107 108 110 111 115 116 117 119 126 127 128 129 130 135 143 146 147 148 149 150 **P**3
Primary Contact: James Whipple, Chief Executive Officer
COO: Shannon Truesdell, Chief Operating Officer
CFO: Laurie Eldridge, Chief Financial Officer
CMO: Rajiv Pathak, Chief of Staff
CIO: Mike Jones, Executive Director
CHR: Scott M Comer, Vice President Human Resources
CNO: Kathy Blair Krejci, Chief Nursing Officer
Web address: www.marshallmedical.org
Control: Other not–for–profit (including NFP Corporation) **Service**: General medical and surgical

Staffed Beds: 113 **Admissions:** 5528 **Census:** 69 **Outpatient Visits:** 438492 **Births:** 490 **Total Expense ($000):** 223108 **Payroll Expense ($000):** 83903 **Personnel:** 1048

PLEASANTON—Alameda County

☒ **STANFORD HEALTH CARE – VALLEYCARE (050283)**, 5555 West Las Positas Boulevard, Zip 94588–4000; tel. 925/847–3000, (Includes VALLEY MEMORIAL, 1111 East Stanley Boulevard, Livermore, California, Zip 94550–4115, tel. 925/447–7000) (Total facility includes 22 beds in nursing home–type unit) **A**1 2 10 **F**3 8 10 11 12 13 15 17 18 20 22 24 26 28 29 30 31 34 35 39 40 41 45 47 49 50 53 56 57 59 60 69 70 72 74 75 76 77 78 79 81 83 85 89 93 98 103 107 111 116 119 126 128 129 130 131 132 144 146 147 **S** Stanford Health Care, Palo Alto, CA
Primary Contact: Scott Gregerson, President and Chief Executive Officer
COO: Tracey Lewis–Taylor, Chief Operating Officer
CMO: Dat Nguyen M.D., Chief of Staff
CIO: Bob Woods, Chief Information Officer
CHR: Chris Faber, Human Resources Analyst
Web address: www.valleycare.com
Control: Other not–for–profit (including NFP Corporation) **Service**: General medical and surgical

Staffed Beds: 207 **Admissions:** 8027 **Census:** 110 **Outpatient Visits:** 194459 **Births:** 1355 **Total Expense ($000):** 274078 **Payroll Expense ($000):** 114117 **Personnel:** 1168

POMONA—Los Angeles County

☒ △ **CASA COLINA HOSPITAL AND HEALTH SYSTEMS (053027)**, 255 East Bonita Avenue, Zip 91767–1923, Mailing Address: P.O.Box 6001, 91769–6001; tel. 909/596–7733, **A**1 7 10 13 **F**2 3 18 28 29 30 34 35 37 44 45 46 48 49 53 54 56 58 59 64 65 68 70 74 75 79 81 85 86 87 90 91 92 93 95 96 97 104 107 108 110 111 115 119 126 130 131 132 134 145 146 147 148
Primary Contact: Felice L. Loverso, Ph.D., President and Chief Executive Officer
CFO: David Morony, Chief Financial Officer
CMO: Christopher Chalian M.D., Medical Director
CIO: Ross Lesins, Chief Information Officer
CHR: Karen Du Pont, Chief Human Resource Officer
CNO: Kathryn Johnson, Chief Nursing Officer
Web address: www.casacolina.org
Control: Other not–for–profit (including NFP Corporation) **Service**: Rehabilitation

Staffed Beds: 99 **Admissions:** 2602 **Census:** 73 **Outpatient Visits:** 97701 **Births:** 0 **Total Expense ($000):** 77640 **Payroll Expense ($000):** 35890 **Personnel:** 493

☒ **POMONA VALLEY HOSPITAL MEDICAL CENTER (050231)**, 1798 North Garey Avenue, Zip 91767–2918; tel. 909/865–9500, **A**1 2 3 5 10 **F**3 11 13 15 17 18 20 22 24 26 28 29 30 31 34 35 40 41 45 46 47 49 50 51 53 54 55 57 58 59 60 61 63 64 68 69 70 72 74 75 76 77 78 79 81 84 85 89 92 93 107 108 110 111 114 115 116 117 118 119 120 121 123 124 126 129 130 131 132 135 144 145 146 147 148 149 **P**5 7
Primary Contact: Richard E. Yochum, FACHE, President and Chief Executive Officer
CFO: Michael Nelson, Executive Vice President and Chief Financial Officer
CMO: Kenneth Nakamoto M.D., Vice President Medical Affairs
CIO: Kent Hoyos, Chief Information Officer
CHR: Ray Inge, Vice President Human Resources
CNO: Darlene Scafiddi R.N., MSN, Vice President Nursing and Patient Care Services
Web address: www.pvhmc.org
Control: Other not–for–profit (including NFP Corporation) **Service**: General medical and surgical

Staffed Beds: 399 **Admissions:** 22312 **Census:** 247 **Outpatient Visits:** 543219 **Births:** 7111 **Total Expense ($000):** 486331 **Payroll Expense ($000):** 240562 **Personnel:** 2616

PORTERVILLE—Tulare County

PORTERVILLE DEVELOPMENTAL CENTER (050546), 26501 Avenue 140, Zip 93257–9109, Mailing Address: P.O.Box 2000, 93258–2000; tel. 559/782–2222, (Nonreporting) **A**10
Primary Contact: Theresa Billeci, Executive Director
COO: Betty Davis, Director Administrative Services
CFO: Karen Warren, Fiscal Officer
CMO: Joseph Mendoza M.D., Medical Director
CIO: Vincent Chandler, Director Information Services
CHR: Shawna Gregg, Director Human Resources
CNO: Tom Shelton, Coordinator of Nursing Services
Web address: www.pdc.dds.ca.gov
Control: State, Government, Nonfederal **Service**: Intellectual disabilities

Staffed Beds: 484

☐ **SIERRA VIEW MEDICAL CENTER (050261)**, 465 West Putnam Avenue, Zip 93257–3320; tel. 559/784–1110, (Total facility includes 35 beds in nursing home–type unit) **A**1 10 **F**3 13 15 29 30 31 34 35 40 42 45 49 54 57 59 60 65 68 70 72 75 76 78 79 81 85 87 89 93 107 108 110 111 114 115 119 120 121 123 130 132 135 146 147 148 149
Primary Contact: Donna J. Hefner, R.N., President and Chief Executive Officer
CFO: John Chivers, Senior Vice President Finance
CIO: Traci Follett, Director Clinical Infomatics
CHR: Sharon Brown, Vice President Human Resources
Web address: www.sierra–view.com
Control: Hospital district or authority, Government, Nonfederal **Service**: General medical and surgical

Staffed Beds: 158 **Admissions:** 5695 **Census:** 95 **Outpatient Visits:** 171123 **Births:** 1542 **Total Expense ($000):** 136487 **Payroll Expense ($000):** 48616 **Personnel:** 795

PORTOLA—Plumas County

EASTERN PLUMAS HEALTH CARE (051300), 500 First Avenue, Zip 96122–9406; tel. 530/832–6500, (Total facility includes 66 beds in nursing home–type unit) **A**10 18 **F**3 7 39 40 45 50 57 59 65 66 68 79 81 82 87 90 91 97 104 107 114 119 120 127 128 133 135 144 145 146 148 **P**5
Primary Contact: Thomas P. Hayes, Chief Executive Officer
CFO: Jeri Nelson, Chief Financial Officer
CMO: Eric Bugna M.D., Chief of Staff
CHR: Cathy Conant, Chief Human Resources and Personnel
Web address: www.ephc.org
Control: Hospital district or authority, Government, Nonfederal **Service**: General medical and surgical

Staffed Beds: 75 **Admissions:** 247 **Census:** 51 **Outpatient Visits:** 33212 **Births:** 0 **Total Expense ($000):** 23166 **Payroll Expense ($000):** 10339 **Personnel:** 235

POWAY—San Diego County

☒ **POMERADO HOSPITAL (050636)**, 15615 Pomerado Road, Zip 92064–2460; tel. 858/613–4000, (Total facility includes 125 beds in nursing home–type unit) **A**1 10 **F**3 11 12 13 15 29 30 34 35 36 38 44 45 46 47 49 50 51 54 55 56 57 58 59 64 65 67 68 70 72 74 75 76 77 79 81 82 84 85 87 91 94 97 98 100 101 102 103 107 108 110 111 119 120 128 130 132 143 144 146 147 148 149 **P**3 **S** Palomar Health, Escondido, CA
Primary Contact: Cheryl Olson, Vice President
CIO: Steven Tanaka, Chief Information Officer
CHR: Brenda C Turner, Chief Human Resources Officer
Web address: www.pph.org
Control: Hospital district or authority, Government, Nonfederal **Service**: General medical and surgical

Staffed Beds: 201 **Admissions:** 6629 **Census:** 183 **Outpatient Visits:** 89227 **Births:** 1254 **Total Expense ($000):** 161788 **Payroll Expense ($000):** 63765

Many Facility Codes have changed. Please refer to the AHA Guide Code Chart. © 2017 AHA Guide

QUINCY—Plumas County

☐ **PLUMAS DISTRICT HOSPITAL (051326)**, 1065 Bucks Lake Road, Zip 95971–9599; tel. 530/283–2121, (Nonreporting) **A**1 5 10 18
Primary Contact: Jeffrey Kepple, M.D., Chief Executive Officer
CMO: Vincent Frantz M.D., Chief of Staff
CIO: Brenda Compton, Manager Information Technology
CHR: Denise Harding, Director Human Resources
Web address: www.pdh.org
Control: Hospital district or authority, Government, Nonfederal **Service**: General medical and surgical

Staffed Beds: 25

RANCHO CUCAMONGA—San Bernardino County

☒ **KINDRED HOSPITAL RANCHO (052049)**, 10841 White Oak Avenue, Zip 91730–3811; tel. 909/581–6400, (Nonreporting) **A**1 10 **S** Kindred Healthcare, Louisville, KY
Primary Contact: Victor Carrasco, Chief Executive Officer
COO: Jody Knox, Chief Operating Officer
Web address: www.khrancho.com
Control: Corporation, Investor–owned (for–profit) **Service**: Acute long–term care hospital

Staffed Beds: 55

RANCHO MIRAGE—Riverside County

☒ △ **EISENHOWER MEDICAL CENTER (050573)**, 39000 Bob Hope Drive, Zip 92270–3221; tel. 760/340–3911, **A**1 2 3 7 10 **F**2 3 9 11 12 15 17 18 20 22 24 26 28 29 30 31 34 35 37 40 41 45 47 49 50 53 54 56 57 58 59 60 61 64 65 68 70 74 75 77 78 79 81 82 84 85 86 87 89 90 93 96 97 100 101 102 104 105 107 108 109 110 111 112 114 115 118 119 120 121 123 124 126 129 130 131 132 135 144 145 146 147 148 149 **P**3
Primary Contact: G Aubrey. Serfling, President and Chief Executive Officer
COO: Martin Massiello, Executive Vice President and Chief Operating Officer
CFO: Ken Wheat, Senior Vice President and Chief Financial Officer
CMO: Alan Williamson M.D., Chief Medical Officer
CIO: David Perez, Vice President and Chief Information Officer
CHR: Liz Guignier, Vice President Human Resources
CNO: Ann R Mostofi MSN, R.N., Vice President Patient Care and Chief Nursing Officer
Web address: www.emc.org
Control: Other not–for–profit (including NFP Corporation) **Service**: General medical and surgical

Staffed Beds: 410 **Admissions**: 19504 **Census**: 217 **Outpatient Visits**: 857414 **Births**: 0 **Total Expense ($000)**: 662089 **Payroll Expense ($000)**: 234516 **Personnel**: 3152

RED BLUFF—Tehama County

☒ **ST. ELIZABETH COMMUNITY HOSPITAL (050042)**, 2550 Sister Mary Columba Drive, Zip 96080–4397; tel. 530/529–8000, (Nonreporting) **A**1 10 20 **S** Dignity Health, San Francisco, CA
Primary Contact: G. Todd. Smith, President
CFO: Kim Miranda, Chief Financial Officer
CMO: James DeSoto M.D., Vice President Medical Affairs
CIO: Henry Niessink, Senior Manager Information Technology Systems
CHR: Denise Little, Director Human Resources
Web address: www.mercy.org
Control: Church operated, Nongovernment, not–for–profit **Service**: General medical and surgical

Staffed Beds: 65

REDDING—Shasta County

☒ **MERCY MEDICAL CENTER REDDING (050280)**, 2175 Rosaline Avenue, Zip 96001–2549, Mailing Address: P.O.Box 496009, 96049–6009; tel. 530/225–6000, (Nonreporting) **A**1 2 3 5 10 **S** Dignity Health, San Francisco, CA
Primary Contact: James DeSoto, M.D., Interim President
COO: Patrick Varga, Chief Operating Officer
CFO: Kimberly Miranda, Regional Vice President Finance and Chief Financial Officer
CMO: James DeSoto M.D., Vice President Medical Affairs
CIO: Henry Niessink, Regional Director Information Technology Services
CNO: Kimberly Shaw, Vice President Patient Care and Chief Nursing Executive
Web address: www.mercy.org
Control: Church operated, Nongovernment, not–for–profit **Service**: General medical and surgical

Staffed Beds: 267

NORTHERN CALIFORNIA REHABILITATION HOSPITAL See Vibra Hospital of Northern California

PATIENTS' HOSPITAL OF REDDING (050697), 2900 Eureka Way, Zip 96001–0220; tel. 530/225–8700, (Nonreporting) **A**10
Primary Contact: Shari Lejsek, Administrator
CFO: Kim Needles, Manager Business Office
CMO: James Tate M.D., Chief of Staff
CIO: Kim Cameron, Manager Health Information Services
CHR: Brenda Meline, Manager Human Resources
CNO: Diane Rieke, Director Patient Care Services
Web address: www.patientshospital.com
Control: Individual, Investor–owned (for–profit) **Service**: Surgical

Staffed Beds: 10

☒ **SHASTA REGIONAL MEDICAL CENTER (050764)**, 1100 Butte Street, Zip 96001–0853, Mailing Address: P.O.Box 496072, 96049–6072; tel. 530/244–5400, **A**1 5 10 **F**11 17 18 20 22 24 28 29 30 37 40 43 45 46 49 59 74 75 79 81 84 87 98 103 107 108 111 114 115 119 126 130 135 146 147 148 149 **S** Prime Healthcare, Ontario, CA
Primary Contact: Richard Fletcher, PharmD, Chief Executive Officer
COO: Becky Levy, Chief Operating Officer
CFO: Becky Levy, Chief Financial Officer
CMO: Marcia McCampbell M.D., Chief Medical Officer
CIO: Tony VanBoekel, Director Information Systems
CHR: Andrew Torge, Director Human Resources
CNO: Leslie Woodson R.N., MSN, Chief Nursing Officer
Web address: www.shastaregional.com
Control: Corporation, Investor–owned (for–profit) **Service**: General medical and surgical

Staffed Beds: 100 **Admissions**: 7353 **Census**: 91 **Outpatient Visits**: 67349 **Births**: 0 **Total Expense ($000)**: 148089 **Payroll Expense ($000)**: 46787 **Personnel**: 724

☒ **VIBRA HOSPITAL OF NORTHERN CALIFORNIA (052047)**, 2801 Eureka Way, Zip 96001–0222; tel. 530/246–9000, (Total facility includes 32 beds in nursing home–type unit) **A**1 10 **F**1 3 29 45 64 77 119 128 130 148 **S** Vibra Healthcare, Mechanicsburg, PA
Primary Contact: Chris Jones, Chief Executive Officer
COO: Lisa Stevens, Chief Clinical Officer and Chief Operating Officer
CFO: Rebecca Andrews, Chief Financial Officer
CMO: Nanda Kumar M.D., Chief of Staff
CIO: Mark Cardenas, Director Plant Operations
CHR: Wendy Tempest, Director Human Resources
Web address: www.norcalrehab.com
Control: Corporation, Investor–owned (for–profit) **Service**: Acute long–term care hospital

Staffed Beds: 88 **Admissions**: 1114 **Census**: 75 **Outpatient Visits**: 3676 **Births**: 0

REDLANDS—San Bernardino County

☒ **LOMA LINDA UNIVERSITY BEHAVIORAL MEDICINE CENTER (054093)**, 1710 Barton Road, Zip 92373–5304; tel. 909/558–9200, **A**1 5 10 **F**4 5 29 30 34 38 44 50 57 87 98 99 100 101 103 104 105 130 132 134 135 **S** Loma Linda University Adventist Health Sciences Center, Loma Linda, CA
Primary Contact: Edward Field, Administrator
COO: Ruthita J Fike, Chief Executive Officer
CFO: Steve Mohr, Senior Vice President Finance and Chief Financial Officer
CMO: William Murdoch M.D., Medical Director
CIO: Mark Zirkelback, Chief Information Officer
CHR: Mark Hubbard, Vice President Risk Management
CNO: Norie Lee Reyes Bencito Aca–ac R.N., MS, Director of Nursing
Web address: www.llu.edu
Control: Church operated, Nongovernment, not–for–profit **Service**: Psychiatric

Staffed Beds: 89 **Admissions**: 4575 **Census**: 73 **Outpatient Visits**: 38561 **Births**: 0 **Total Expense ($000)**: 37217 **Payroll Expense ($000)**: 17728 **Personnel**: 306

CA

Hospital, Medicare Provider Number, Address, Telephone, Approval, Facility, and Physician Codes, Health Care System

★ American Hospital Association (AHA) membership ○ Healthcare Facilities Accreditation Program ⇑ Center for Improvement in Healthcare Quality Accreditation
☐ The Joint Commission accreditation ◇ DNV Healthcare Inc. accreditation △ Commission on Accreditation of Rehabilitation Facilities (CARF) accreditation

CA

⊞ **REDLANDS COMMUNITY HOSPITAL (050272)**, 350 Terracina Boulevard, Zip 92373–0742, Mailing Address: P.O.Box 3391, 92373–0742; tel. 909/335–5500, (Total facility includes 16 beds in nursing home–type unit) **A**1 3 10 **F**3 11 13 15 18 20 28 29 30 31 34 35 40 45 46 47 49 54 57 59 62 63 64 65 66 68 69 70 72 74 75 76 77 78 79 81 82 84 85 87 93 96 97 98 102 104 105 107 108 110 111 114 115 116 117 119 121 126 128 130 132 143 146 147 148 **P**5
Primary Contact: James R. Holmes, President and Chief Executive Officer
CFO: Michelle Mok, Chief Financial Officer
CHR: Lisa Guzman, Human Resource Vice President
CNO: Lauren Spilsbury R.N., MSN, Vice President for Patient Care Services
Web address: www.redlandshospital.org
Control: Other not–for–profit (including NFP Corporation) **Service:** General medical and surgical

> **Staffed Beds:** 197 **Admissions:** 11268 **Census:** 116 **Outpatient Visits:** 162708 **Births:** 2509 **Total Expense ($000):** 291759 **Payroll Expense ($000):** 93719 **Personnel:** 1327

REDWOOD CITY—San Mateo County

⊞ **KAISER PERMANENTE REDWOOD CITY MEDICAL CENTER (050541)**, 1100 Veterans Boulevard, Zip 94063–2087; tel. 650/299–2000, (Nonreporting) **A**1 3 5 10 **S** Kaiser Foundation Hospitals, Oakland, CA
Primary Contact: Michelle Gaskill–Hames, R.N., Senior Vice President & Area Manager
COO: Sheila Gilson R.N., Chief Operating Officer
CFO: Doug Reynolds, Area Finance Officer
CMO: William Firtch M.D., Physician In Chief
CHR: Kimberly A Seitz, Area Human Resources Leader
CNO: Jodi B. Galli R.N., Chief Nursing Officer
Web address: www.kaiserpermanente.org
Control: Other not–for–profit (including NFP Corporation) **Service:** General medical and surgical

> **Staffed Beds:** 213

⊞ **SEQUOIA HOSPITAL (050197)**, 170 Alameda De Las Pulgas, Zip 94062–2799; tel. 650/369–5811, **A**1 10 **F**11 12 13 15 18 20 22 24 26 28 29 30 31 32 34 35 37 40 45 46 49 50 53 57 59 60 64 68 70 74 75 76 77 78 79 81 84 86 87 92 93 94 107 108 110 111 114 115 118 119 120 121 123 126 130 132 135 146 147 148 149 **P**3 5 **S** Dignity Health, San Francisco, CA
Primary Contact: Bill Graham, President
CFO: Kim Osborn, Chief Financial Officer
CMO: Anita Chandrasena M.D., Vice President Medical Affairs
CIO: Ian Vallely, Information Technology Site Leader
CHR: Linde Cheema, Vice President Human Resources
CNO: Sherie Ambrose, Chief Nurse Executive
Web address: www.sequoiahospital.org
Control: Other not–for–profit (including NFP Corporation) **Service:** General medical and surgical

> **Staffed Beds:** 129 **Admissions:** 5290 **Census:** 54 **Outpatient Visits:** 87986 **Births:** 1432 **Total Expense ($000):** 276111 **Payroll Expense ($000):** 89472 **Personnel:** 784

REEDLEY—Fresno County

⊞ **ADVENTIST MEDICAL CENTER–REEDLEY (050192)**, 372 West Cypress Avenue, Zip 93654–2199; tel. 559/638–8155, (Nonreporting) **A**1 3 10 **S** Adventist Health, Roseville, CA
Primary Contact: Wayne Ferch, President and Chief Executive Officer
CFO: Teresa Jacques, Interim Chief Financial Officer
CMO: Todd Spencer M.D., Chief Medical Staff
CIO: Valerie Alvarez, Executive Assistant
CHR: Ramona Alvarado, Interim Manager Human Resources
Web address: www.skdh.org
Control: Hospital district or authority, Government, Nonfederal **Service:** General medical and surgical

> **Staffed Beds:** 49

RESEDA—Los Angeles County

☐ **JOYCE EISENBERG–KEEFER MEDICAL CENTER (054147)**, 7150 Tampa Avenue, Zip 91335–3700; tel. 818/774–3000, (Total facility includes 239 beds in nursing home–type unit) **A**1 10 **F**29 30 34 35 39 50 53 56 62 63 65 68 74 75 77 82 84 90 98 103 128 130 132 143 146 148 149
Primary Contact: Molly Forrest, President and Chief Executive Officer
CNO: Haya Berci, Executive Director of Nursing
Web address: www.jha.org
Control: Other not–for–profit (including NFP Corporation) **Service:** Psychiatric

> **Staffed Beds:** 249 **Admissions:** 487 **Census:** 244 **Outpatient Visits:** 0 **Births:** 0 **Total Expense ($000):** 43362 **Payroll Expense ($000):** 17464 **Personnel:** 408

RICHMOND—Contra Costa County

KAISER PERMANENTE RICHMOND MEDICAL CENTER See Kaiser Permanente Oakland Medical Center, Oakland

RIDGECREST—Kern County

★ ⇑ **RIDGECREST REGIONAL HOSPITAL (051333)**, 1081 North China Lake Boulevard, Zip 93555–3130; tel. 760/446–3551, (Nonreporting) **A**10 18 21
Primary Contact: James A. Suver, FACHE, Chief Executive Officer
CFO: Lois Johnson, Administrator Fiscal Services
CMO: Victoria Schauf M.D., Chief of Staff
CIO: Randy Ferguson, Chief Information Officer
CHR: Dave Shary, Administrator Human Resources
Web address: www.rrh.org
Control: Other not–for–profit (including NFP Corporation) **Service:** General medical and surgical

> **Staffed Beds:** 150

RIVERSIDE—Riverside County

⊞ **KAISER PERMANENTE RIVERSIDE MEDICAL CENTER (050686)**, 10800 Magnolia Avenue, Zip 92505–3000; tel. 951/353–2000, **A**1 3 5 10 **F**3 13 15 17 28 29 30 31 34 35 40 44 45 46 48 49 50 51 59 60 62 63 64 65 68 70 72 74 75 76 77 78 79 81 82 84 85 86 87 89 92 93 97 100 102 107 108 109 110 111 114 115 116 117 118 119 130 144 146 147 148 149 150 **S** Kaiser Foundation Hospitals, Oakland, CA
Primary Contact: Vita M. Willett, Executive Director
COO: Robin D. Mackenroth, Chief Operating Officer
CFO: JiJi Abraham, Chief Financial Officer
CMO: Frank M. Flowers M.D., Area Medical Director
CIO: Alfred T Velasquez, Area Information Officer
CHR: Michelle Skipper, Director Human Resources
CNO: Rosemary M Butler R.N., MSN, Chief Nurse Executive
Web address: www.kaiserpermanente.org
Control: Other not–for–profit (including NFP Corporation) **Service:** General medical and surgical

> **Staffed Beds:** 226 **Admissions:** 10755 **Census:** 119 **Outpatient Visits:** 57877 **Births:** 3287 **Personnel:** 1158

☐ **PACIFIC GROVE HOSPITAL (054130)**, 5900 Brockton Avenue, Zip 92506–1862; tel. 951/275–8400, (Nonreporting) **A**1 10 **S** Acadia Healthcare Company, Inc., Franklin, TN
Primary Contact: Nichol Sheffield, Chief Executive Officer
Web address: www.pacificgrovehospital.com
Control: Corporation, Investor–owned (for–profit) **Service:** Psychiatric

> **Staffed Beds:** 68

☐ **PARKVIEW COMMUNITY HOSPITAL MEDICAL CENTER (050102)**, 3865 Jackson Street, Zip 92503–3998; tel. 951/688–2211, **A**1 10 **F**1 3 4 8 11 12 13 15 16 17 18 29 34 35 40 45 46 49 50 56 57 59 60 62 65 67 68 70 72 73 74 75 76 77 79 80 81 84 85 86 87 88 89 90 98 100 107 110 111 114 115 119 128 130 132 135 143 145 146 147 148 149
Primary Contact: Steven Popkin, Chief Executive Officer
COO: Robert Brown, Chief Operating Officer
CFO: Patti Lepe, Chief Financial Officer
CMO: Dong Kim M.D., Chief of Staff
CIO: John Ciccarelli, Director Information Technology
CNO: Thomas Santos R.N., Chief Nursing Officer
Web address: www.pchmc.org
Control: Other not–for–profit (including NFP Corporation) **Service:** General medical and surgical

> **Staffed Beds:** 193 **Admissions:** 9151 **Census:** 106 **Outpatient Visits:** 73744 **Births:** 2226 **Total Expense ($000):** 146456 **Payroll Expense ($000):** 61282 **Personnel:** 996

RIVERSIDE CENTER FOR BEHAVIORAL MEDICINE See Pacific Grove Hospital

⊞ **RIVERSIDE COMMUNITY HOSPITAL (050022)**, 4445 Magnolia Avenue, Zip 92501–4199; tel. 951/788–3000, (Nonreporting) **A**1 2 5 10 **S** HCA Healthcare, Nashville, TN
Primary Contact: Patrick D. Brilliant, President and Chief Executive Officer
COO: Daniel Bowers, Chief Operating Officer
CFO: Todd LaCaze, Chief Financial Officer
CMO: David Tito M.D., President Medical Staff
CIO: Cae Swanger, Chief Information Officer
CHR: Tammy Kaminski, Vice President Human Relations
CNO: Annette June Greenwood, Chief Nursing Officer
Web address: www.riversidecommunityhospital.com
Control: Corporation, Investor–owned (for–profit) **Service:** General medical and surgical

> **Staffed Beds:** 373

Many Facility Codes have changed. Please refer to the AHA Guide Code Chart. © 2017 AHA Guide

RIVERSIDE MEDICAL CENTER See Kaiser Permanente Riverside Medical Center

ROSEMEAD—Los Angeles County

☐ **BHC ALHAMBRA HOSPITAL (054032)**, 4619 North Rosemead Boulevard, Zip 91770–1478, Mailing Address: P.O.Box 369, 91770–0369; tel. 626/286–1191, (Nonreporting) **A**1 10 **S** Universal Health Services, Inc., King of Prussia, PA
Primary Contact: Peggy Minnick, R.N., Chief Executive Officer
CFO: Michelle Jackson, Chief Financial Officer
CMO: Wakelin McNeel M.D., Medical Director
CIO: Debbie Irvin, Director Health Information Management
CHR: Venus Taylor, Director Human Resources
Web address: www.bhcalhambra.com
Control: Corporation, Investor–owned (for–profit) **Service:** Psychiatric

Staffed Beds: 97

ROSEVILLE—Placer County

✠ **KAISER PERMANENTE ROSEVILLE MEDICAL CENTER (050772)**, 1600 Eureka Road, Zip 95661–3027; tel. 916/784–4000, (Nonreporting) **A**1 2 5 10 **S** Kaiser Foundation Hospitals, Oakland, CA
Primary Contact: Jeffrey A. Collins, M.D., Senior Vice President and Area Manager
Web address: www.kp.org
Control: Other not–for–profit (including NFP Corporation) **Service:** General medical and surgical

Staffed Beds: 340

✠ **SUTTER ROSEVILLE MEDICAL CENTER (050309)**, One Medical Plaza Drive, Zip 95661–3037; tel. 916/781–1000, **A**1 2 5 10 **F**3 5 8 12 13 15 18 20 22 28 29 30 31 34 35 40 43 45 46 50 55 56 58 59 60 63 64 65 68 70 72 74 75 76 78 79 81 82 84 85 89 90 93 94 96 97 100 107 108 109 111 114 116 119 126 130 131 132 141 146 147 148 **P**3 5 **S** Sutter Health, Sacramento, CA
Primary Contact: Patrick R. Brady, Chief Executive Officer
COO: Dionne Miller, Chief Operating Officer
CFO: Gary Hubschman, Administrative Director Finance
CMO: Stuart Bostrom M.D., Director Medical Affairs
CIO: Nancy Turner, Director Communications
CHR: Lynda Dasaro, Director Human Resources
CNO: Barbara J Nelson Ph.D., R.N., Chief Nursing Executive
Web address: www.sutterroseville.org
Control: Other not–for–profit (including NFP Corporation) **Service:** General medical and surgical

Staffed Beds: 328 Admissions: 20260 Census: 256 Outpatient Visits: 159267 Births: 2572 Total Expense ($000): 513963 Payroll Expense ($000): 165409 Personnel: 1647

SACRAMENTO—Sacramento County

☐ **HERITAGE OAKS HOSPITAL (054104)**, 4250 Auburn Boulevard, Zip 95841–4164; tel. 916/489–3336, (Nonreporting) **A**1 3 5 10 **S** Universal Health Services, Inc., King of Prussia, PA
Primary Contact: Shawn Silva, Chief Executive Officer
CFO: Art Wong, Chief Financial Officer
CMO: Joseph Sison M.D., Medical Director
CHR: Lisa Myers, Director Human Resources
Web address: www.heritageoakshospital.com
Control: Corporation, Investor–owned (for–profit) **Service:** Psychiatric

Staffed Beds: 120

✠ **KAISER PERMANENTE SACRAMENTO MEDICAL CENTER (050425)**, 2025 Morse Avenue, Zip 95825–2100; tel. 916/973–5000, **A**1 2 3 5 10 **F**3 8 15 17 18 20 29 30 34 35 40 41 44 45 46 48 49 50 51 56 57 60 64 65 68 70 74 75 77 78 79 81 82 84 85 102 107 108 111 114 115 119 120 129 130 146 148 **S** Kaiser Foundation Hospitals, Oakland, CA
Primary Contact: Sandy Sharon, Senior Vice President and Area Manager
CFO: Jim Eldridge, Area Financial Officer
CMO: Chris Palkowski M.D., Physician in Chief
CIO: Philip Fasano, Chief Information Officer
CHR: Gay Westfall, Senior Vice President Human Resources
Web address: www.kp.org
Control: Other not–for–profit (including NFP Corporation) **Service:** General medical and surgical

Staffed Beds: 144 Admissions: 11005 Census: 124 Births: 0

✠ **KAISER PERMANENTE SOUTH SACRAMENTO MEDICAL CENTER (050674)**, 6600 Bruceville Road, Zip 95823–4691; tel. 916/688–2430, **A**1 3 5 10 **F**3 8 12 13 15 20 22 29 30 31 34 35 40 43 44 45 49 50 58 59 61 62 63 64 65 68 70 73 74 75 76 77 78 79 81 82 84 85 86 87 89 93 96 97 100 104 107 108 109 110 111 114 115 119 126 129 130 131 135 144 146 147 148 149 150 **S** Kaiser Foundation Hospitals, Oakland, CA
Primary Contact: Patricia M. Rodriguez, Senior Vice President and Area Manager
CFO: Kevin L Smith, Area Finance Officer
CIO: Michelle Odell, Director of Public Affairs
CHR: James Kevin Peterson, Human Resources Leader
CNO: Terri Owensby R.N., Chief Nursing Executive
Web address: www.kp.org
Control: Other not–for–profit (including NFP Corporation) **Service:** General medical and surgical

Staffed Beds: 181 Admissions: 13736 Census: 133 Outpatient Visits: 130278 Personnel: 1522

✠ △ **MERCY GENERAL HOSPITAL (050017)**, 4001 'J' Street, Zip 95819–3600; tel. 916/453–4545, **A**1 2 3 5 7 10 **F**3 8 11 13 15 17 18 20 22 24 26 28 29 30 31 34 35 36 37 38 39 40 44 45 46 47 48 49 50 51 53 56 57 58 59 63 64 66 68 70 74 75 76 77 78 79 81 82 84 85 86 87 90 91 93 94 96 99 100 107 108 109 111 114 115 119 124 126 130 131 132 135 143 145 146 149 **P**3 5 **S** Dignity Health, San Francisco, CA
Primary Contact: Edmundo Castaneda, President
COO: Patricia Monczewski, Chief Operating Officer
CFO: Ronald Kroll, Chief Financial Officer
CMO: Robert Wiebe M.D., M.P.H., Chief Medical Officer
CHR: Cyndi Kirch, Vice President Human Resources
Web address: www.mercygeneral.org
Control: Other not–for–profit (including NFP Corporation) **Service:** General medical and surgical

Staffed Beds: 254 Admissions: 14691 Census: 183 Outpatient Visits: 101878 Births: 977 Total Expense ($000): 550535 Payroll Expense ($000): 187721 Personnel: 1652

✠ **METHODIST HOSPITAL OF SACRAMENTO (050590)**, 7500 Hospital Drive, Zip 95823–5477; tel. 916/423–3000, (Total facility includes 171 beds in nursing home–type unit) **A**1 3 5 10 **F**3 8 11 12 17 29 30 34 35 37 40 41 47 49 50 56 57 58 60 61 64 68 70 72 74 75 77 79 81 84 85 86 87 93 96 97 102 107 108 111 115 119 128 130 131 132 146 147 148 149 **P**5 **S** Dignity Health, San Francisco, CA
Primary Contact: Brian K. Ivie, President and Chief Executive Officer
COO: Anita J Kennedy, Vice President Operations
CFO: Bonnie Jenkins, Chief Financial Officer
CMO: Amir Sweha M.D., Vice President Medical Administration
CHR: Cyndi Kirch, Vice President Human Resources
CNO: Martina Evans–Harrison R.N., MSN, Chief Nurse Executive
Web address: www.methodistsacramento.org
Control: Other not–for–profit (including NFP Corporation) **Service:** General medical and surgical

Staffed Beds: 329 Admissions: 11315 Census: 260 Outpatient Visits: 93003 Births: 1947 Total Expense ($000): 298078 Payroll Expense ($000): 121893 Personnel: 904

☐ **SHRINERS HOSPITALS FOR CHILDREN–NORTHERN CALIFORNIA (053311)**, 2425 Stockton Boulevard, Zip 95817–2215; tel. 916/453–2000, (Nonreporting) **A**1 3 5 10 **S** Shriners Hospitals for Children, Tampa, FL
Primary Contact: Margaret Bryan, Administrator
COO: Margaret Bryan, Administrator
CFO: William Dalby, Director Fiscal Services
CIO: John Bevel, Manager Information Systems
CHR: Deborah Rubens, Director Human Resources
Web address: www.shrinershospitalsforchildren.org/Hospitals/Locations/NorthernCalifornia.aspx
Control: Other not–for–profit (including NFP Corporation) **Service:** Children's general medical and surgical

Staffed Beds: 70

Hospital, Medicare Provider Number, Address, Telephone, Approval, Facility, and Physician Codes, Health Care System

★ American Hospital Association (AHA) membership ○ Healthcare Facilities Accreditation Program ⇑ Center for Improvement in Healthcare Quality Accreditation
☐ The Joint Commission accreditation ◇ DNV Healthcare Inc. accreditation △ Commission on Accreditation of Rehabilitation Facilities (CARF) accreditation

CA

☐ **SIERRA VISTA HOSPITAL (054087)**, 8001 Bruceville Road, Zip 95823–2329; tel. 916/288–0300, **A**1 10 **F**4 5 29 35 38 50 64 98 99 101 102 104 105 130 149 **S** Universal Health Services, Inc., King of Prussia, PA
Primary Contact: Mike Zauner, Chief Executive Officer
COO: Ixel Morell, Chief Operating Officer
CFO: Nicole Samuel, Chief Financial Officer
CMO: Alok Banga M.D., Medical Director
CNO: Gwen Hubbard, Chief Nursing Officer
Web address: www.sierravistahospital.com
Control: Corporation, Investor–owned (for–profit) **Service**: Psychiatric

Staffed Beds: 171 **Admissions**: 4936 **Census**: 122 **Outpatient Visits**: 0 **Births**: 0

SOUTH SACRAMENTO MEDICAL CENTER See Kaiser Permanente South Sacramento Medical Center

☒ **SUTTER CENTER FOR PSYCHIATRY (054096)**, 7700 Folsom Boulevard, Zip 95826–2608; tel. 916/386–3000, **A**1 10 **F**29 30 34 35 44 68 98 99 100 101 104 105 130 132 133 134 143 **S** Sutter Health, Sacramento, CA
Primary Contact: John W. Boyd, PsyD, Chief Executive Officer
CFO: Pamela Ansley, Director Finance
CMO: Cindy Thygeson M.D., Director Medical Affairs
CHR: Kristin Daniels, Manager Human Resources
Web address: www.sutterpsychiatry.org
Control: Other not–for–profit (including NFP Corporation) **Service**: Psychiatric

Staffed Beds: 71 **Admissions**: 2943 **Census**: 57 **Outpatient Visits**: 12912 **Births**: 0 **Total Expense ($000)**: 29814 **Payroll Expense ($000)**: 14335 **Personnel**: 218

☒ **SUTTER MEDICAL CENTER, SACRAMENTO (050108)**, 2801 'L' Street, Zip 95816–5680; tel. 916/454–3333, (Includes SUTTER CHILDREN'S CENTER, 5151 F Street, Sacramento, California, Zip 95819–3223, tel. 800/478–8837; SUTTER GENERAL HOSPITAL, 2801 'L' Street, Sacramento, California, Zip 95816, tel. 916/454–2222) **A**1 2 3 5 10 **F**3 11 12 15 17 18 19 20 21 22 23 24 25 26 27 28 29 30 31 34 35 36 37 39 40 41 45 46 48 49 55 56 58 59 61 63 64 68 70 72 74 75 76 77 78 79 81 84 85 86 87 88 89 93 102 107 108 111 114 115 119 124 126 129 130 132 134 136 137 146 147 148 **P**3 5 **S** Sutter Health, Sacramento, CA
Primary Contact: David Cheney, Chief Executive Officer
COO: Faraaz Yousuf, Chief Operating Officer
CFO: Richard SooHoo, Chief Financial Officer
CMO: Muhammed Afzal M.D., Chief of Staff
CIO: Jim Mills, Regional Director Information Technology
CHR: Colleen Peschel, Director Human Resources
CNO: Marchelle M McGriff, Chief Nursing Executive
Web address: www.sutterhealth.org
Control: Other not–for–profit (including NFP Corporation) **Service**: General medical and surgical

Staffed Beds: 523 **Admissions**: 29296 **Census**: 367 **Outpatient Visits**: 207537 **Births**: 5879 **Total Expense ($000)**: 1037650 **Payroll Expense ($000)**: 292654 **Personnel**: 3006

☒ **UNIVERSITY OF CALIFORNIA, DAVIS MEDICAL CENTER (050599)**, 2315 Stockton Boulevard, Zip 95817–2282; tel. 916/734–2011, (Includes UNIVERSITY OF CALIFORNIA DAVIS CHILDREN'S HOSPITAL, 2315 Stockton Boulevard, Sacramento, California, Zip 95817–2201, tel. 800/282–3284; Ann Madden Rice, Chief Executive Officer) **A**1 2 3 5 8 10 **F**3 6 8 9 11 12 13 15 16 17 18 19 20 21 22 23 24 25 26 27 28 29 30 31 32 34 35 36 37 38 39 40 41 43 44 45 46 47 48 49 50 51 53 54 55 56 57 58 59 60 61 62 63 64 65 66 68 70 72 73 74 75 76 77 78 79 81 82 83 84 85 86 87 88 89 90 91 92 93 94 95 96 97 99 100 101 102 103 104 107 108 110 111 114 115 116 117 118 119 120 121 123 124 126 129 130 131 132 134 135 136 138 141 142 145 146 147 148 149 150 **P**6 **S** University of California Systemwide Administration, Oakland, CA
Primary Contact: Ann Madden. Rice, Chief Executive Officer
COO: Brad Simmons, Chief Operating Officer
CFO: Timothy Maurice, Chief Financial Officer
CMO: J. Douglas Kirk M.D., Chief Medical Officer
CIO: John Cook, Interim Chief Information Officer
CHR: Stephen Chilcott, Associate Director Human Resources
CNO: Toby Marsh MSN, R.N., Interim Chief Patient Care Services Officer
Web address: www.ucdmc.ucdavis.edu
Control: Other not–for–profit (including NFP Corporation) **Service**: General medical and surgical

Staffed Beds: 601 **Admissions**: 33176 **Census**: 504 **Outpatient Visits**: 1275214 **Births**: 1784 **Total Expense ($000)**: 1892006 **Payroll Expense ($000)**: 783261 **Personnel**: 8158

SAINT HELENA—Napa County

☒ **ADVENTIST HEALTH ST. HELENA (050013)**, 10 Woodland Road, Zip 94574–9554; tel. 707/963–3611, **A**1 10 **F**3 4 5 8 15 17 18 20 22 24 26 28 29 30 31 34 35 36 37 40 45 47 50 51 53 57 58 59 60 62 64 65 70 74 75 76 77 78 79 81 82 84 85 86 87 92 97 98 99 100 101 102 103 104 105 107 108 110 111 115 117 119 120 121 126 130 131 135 146 147 148 **P**3 **S** Adventist Health, Roseville, CA
Primary Contact: Steven Herber, M.D., FACS, President and Chief Executive Officer
COO: Hal Chilton, Senior Vice President and Chief Operating Officer
CMO: Steven Herber M.D., FACS, President and Chief Executive Officer
CIO: Mark Heringer, Interim Director Information Systems
CHR: Sylvia Seals–Barnes II, Director Human Resources
CNO: Nia Lendaris, Regional Vice President Patient Care
Web address: www.sthelenahospital.org
Control: Church operated, Nongovernment, not–for–profit **Service**: General medical and surgical

Staffed Beds: 116 **Admissions**: 5872 **Census**: 76 **Outpatient Visits**: 91382 **Births**: 214 **Total Expense ($000)**: 237364 **Payroll Expense ($000)**: 59907 **Personnel**: 838

SALINAS—Monterey County

☒ **NATIVIDAD MEDICAL CENTER (050248)**, 1441 Constitution Boulevard, Zip 93906–3100, Mailing Address: P.O.Box 81611, 93912–1611; tel. 831/647–7611, **A**1 3 5 10 **F**3 11 12 13 15 18 19 26 29 30 31 34 35 37 39 40 43 44 45 46 47 48 49 50 51 57 59 61 64 65 68 70 72 74 75 76 78 79 81 82 84 85 86 87 89 90 91 92 93 96 97 98 100 102 107 108 110 111 114 115 118 119 124 130 131 132 135 143 146 147 148 149 150 **P**6
Primary Contact: Gary Gray, D.O., Chief Executive Officer
CMO: Craig Walls M.D., Ph.D., Chief Medical Officer
CIO: Ari Entin, Chief Information Officer
CHR: Lawanda Janine Bouyea, Director Human Resources
Web address: www.natividad.com
Control: County, Government, Nonfederal **Service**: General medical and surgical

Staffed Beds: 157 **Admissions**: 8690 **Census**: 105 **Outpatient Visits**: 164803 **Births**: 2499 **Total Expense ($000)**: 237415 **Payroll Expense ($000)**: 91998 **Personnel**: 1007

☒ **SALINAS VALLEY MEMORIAL HEALTHCARE SYSTEM (050334)**, 450 East Romie Lane, Zip 93901–4098; tel. 831/757–4333, **A**1 2 10 **F**3 13 15 17 18 19 20 22 24 26 28 29 30 31 34 35 37 40 45 46 49 50 57 58 59 64 66 68 70 72 74 75 76 77 78 79 81 84 85 87 89 107 108 110 111 115 118 119 126 127 129 130 132 146 147 148 149
Primary Contact: Pete Delgado, President and Chief Executive Officer
COO: Henry Ornelas, Chief Operating Officer
CFO: Augustine Lopez, Chief Financial Officer
CMO: Allen Radner M.D., Chief Medical Officer
CIO: Audrey Parks, Senior Administrative Director Information Technology
CHR: Michelle Childs, Senior Administrative Director Human Resources
CNO: Christie Gonder, Chief Nursing Officer
Web address: www.svmh.com
Control: Hospital district or authority, Government, Nonfederal **Service**: General medical and surgical

Staffed Beds: 230 **Admissions**: 10653 **Census**: 127 **Outpatient Visits**: 110544 **Births**: 1802 **Total Expense ($000)**: 387493 **Payroll Expense ($000)**: 203620 **Personnel**: 1386

SAN ANDREAS—Calaveras County

☒ **MARK TWAIN MEDICAL CENTER (051332)**, 768 Mountain Ranch Road, Zip 95249–9998; tel. 209/754–3521, **A**1 10 18 **F**1 3 4 11 15 16 17 18 28 29 30 31 34 35 40 45 50 57 59 65 67 68 70 72 73 75 77 78 79 80 81 82 83 84 85 87 88 89 90 91 93 96 98 100 104 107 110 111 115 116 117 119 127 128 130 145 146 147 148 149 **P**6 **S** Dignity Health, San Francisco, CA
Primary Contact: Robert Diehl, President
CFO: Jacob Lewis, Chief Financial Officer
CHR: Nancy Vargas, Director Human Resources
Web address: www.marktwainhospital.com
Control: Other not–for–profit (including NFP Corporation) **Service**: General medical and surgical

Staffed Beds: 25 **Admissions**: 1033 **Census**: 10 **Outpatient Visits**: 80504 **Births**: 0 **Total Expense ($000)**: 68845 **Payroll Expense ($000)**: 26520 **Personnel**: 282

CA

SAN BERNARDINO—San Bernardino County

☒ △ **BALLARD REHABILITATION HOSPITAL (053037)**, 1760 West 16th Street, Zip 92411–1160; tel. 909/473–1200, **A**1 7 10 **F**29 34 35 50 64 79 90 93 96 130 132 135 148 149 **S** Vibra Healthcare, Mechanicsburg, PA
Primary Contact: Mary Miles. Hunt, Chief Executive Officer
CFO: Jonathan Silver, Chief Financial Officer
CMO: Van Chen M.D., Medical Director
CNO: Chris Bauman, Director of Nursing
Web address: www.ballardrehab.com
Control: Corporation, Investor–owned (for–profit) **Service:** Rehabilitation

Staffed Beds: 60 **Admissions:** 1061 **Census:** 40 **Outpatient Visits:** 10782 **Births:** 0 **Total Expense ($000):** 20295 **Payroll Expense ($000):** 11951 **Personnel:** 211

☒ **COMMUNITY HOSPITAL OF SAN BERNARDINO (050089)**, 1805 Medical Center Drive, Zip 92411–1214; tel. 909/887–6333, (Nonreporting) **A**1 10 **S** Dignity Health, San Francisco, CA
Primary Contact: June Collison, President
COO: Victoria Selby MHA, BSN,, Vice President, Ancillary and Support Services
CFO: Dave Evans, Chief Financial Officer
CIO: James Borrenpohl, Market Site Director
CHR: Deena Marano, Human Resources Director
CNO: Roz Nolan, Interim Chief Nursing Officer
Web address: www.dignityhealth.org/san-bernardino
Control: Other not–for–profit (including NFP Corporation) **Service:** General medical and surgical

Staffed Beds: 379

☒ **ST. BERNARDINE MEDICAL CENTER (050129)**, 2101 North Waterman Avenue, Zip 92404–4855; tel. 909/883–8711, **A**1 3 10 **F**3 8 11 12 15 17 18 20 22 24 26 28 29 30 31 34 35 40 45 46 47 49 50 54 58 60 64 65 68 70 72 74 75 76 77 78 79 81 84 85 86 87 92 93 100 102 107 108 110 111 114 115 119 120 121 126 130 131 132 134 143 144 146 147 148 149 **P**3 8 **S** Dignity Health, San Francisco, CA
Primary Contact: Douglas V. Kleam, President
CMO: Betty Daniels M.D., Chief of Staff
CIO: James Croker, Director Information Systems
CHR: Dee Webb, Vice President Human Resources
Web address: www.stbernardinemedicalcenter.com
Control: Other not–for–profit (including NFP Corporation) **Service:** General medical and surgical

Staffed Beds: 342 **Admissions:** 13991 **Census:** 186 **Outpatient Visits:** 167564 **Births:** 1611 **Total Expense ($000):** 405953 **Payroll Expense ($000):** 149772 **Personnel:** 1173

SAN DIEGO—San Diego County

☒ **ALVARADO HOSPITAL MEDICAL CENTER (050757)**, 6655 Alvarado Road, Zip 92120–5208; tel. 619/287–3270, **A**1 3 10 **F**3 11 12 14 17 18 20 22 24 26 29 30 34 37 39 40 43 44 45 46 47 48 49 50 51 53 57 59 60 61 64 65 68 70 74 75 77 79 81 85 86 87 91 93 94 96 100 126 130 132 146 148 149 **S** Prime Healthcare, Ontario, CA
Primary Contact: Robin Gomez, R.N., MSN, Administrator
CMO: Larry Emdur D.O., Chief Medical Officer
CIO: Wayne Bartlett, Director Information Systems
CHR: Sara Turner, Director Human Resources
CNO: Peggy Jezsu, Chief Nursing Officer
Web address: www.alvaradohospital.com
Control: Corporation, Investor–owned (for–profit) **Service:** General medical and surgical

Staffed Beds: 137 **Admissions:** 5659 **Census:** 75 **Outpatient Visits:** 46434 **Births:** 0 **Total Expense ($000):** 144535 **Payroll Expense ($000):** 49960 **Personnel:** 631

☐ **AURORA BEHAVIORAL HEALTHCARE SAN DIEGO (054095)**, 11878 Avenue of Industry, Zip 92128–3490; tel. 858/487–3200, (Nonreporting) **A**1 10 **S** Signature Healthcare Services, Corona, CA
Primary Contact: Alain Azcona, Chief Executive Officer
COO: Barbara Kennison, Director Clinical Services
CFO: Gene Fantano, Chief Financial Officer
CMO: Thomas Flanagan M.D., Medical Director
CIO: Alain Azcona, Director Business Development
CHR: Susan Haas, Director Human Resources
Web address: www.sandiego.aurorabehavioral.com/
Control: Corporation, Investor–owned (for–profit) **Service:** Psychiatric

Staffed Beds: 80

☒ **KAISER PERMANENTE SAN DIEGO MEDICAL CENTER (050515)**, 4647 Zion Avenue, Zip 92120–2507; tel. 619/528–5000, (Includes KAISER PERMANENTE SAN DIEGO MEDICAL CENTER, 9455 Clairemont Mesa Boulevard, San Diego, California, Zip 92123–1297, tel. 800/282–3284; Jane Finley, Senior Vice President and Area Manager) **A**1 3 5 10 **F**3 13 15 29 30 31 40 41 45 46 47 48 49 50 51 55 56 58 59 60 61 62 63 64 68 70 72 74 75 76 77 78 79 81 82 84 85 86 87 89 91 92 93 94 96 97 100 102 103 104 107 110 111 115 117 118 119 130 131 146 148 149 **S** Kaiser Foundation Hospitals, Oakland, CA
Primary Contact: Jane Finley, Senior Vice President & Area Manager
COO: Sam Totah, Chief Operating Officer
CFO: Lynette Seid, Area Chief Financial Officer
CMO: Paul E Bernstein M.D., Area Medical Director
CIO: Laura Sullivant, Area Chief Information Officer
CHR: Jocelyn A. Herrera, Human Resources Director
CNO: Anne Marie Watkins, Chief Nurse Executive
Web address: www.kaiserpermanente.org
Control: Other not–for–profit (including NFP Corporation) **Service:** General medical and surgical

Staffed Beds: 414 **Admissions:** 31320 **Census:** 310 **Outpatient Visits:** 133415 **Births:** 4556 **Personnel:** 2813

☒ **KINDRED HOSPITAL–SAN DIEGO (052036)**, 1940 El Cajon Boulevard, Zip 92104–1096; tel. 619/543–4500, (Nonreporting) **A**1 10 **S** Kindred Healthcare, Louisville, KY
Primary Contact: Natalie Germuska, R.N., MSN, Market Chief Executive Officer
CMO: Davies Wong M.D., Medical Director
CHR: Jody Dewen Moore, District Director Human Resources
CNO: Maureen Bodine, Chief Clinical Officer
Web address: www.kindredsandiego.com
Control: Corporation, Investor–owned (for–profit) **Service:** Acute long–term care hospital

Staffed Beds: 70

☒ **NAVAL MEDICAL CENTER SAN DIEGO**, 34800 Bob Wilson Drive, Zip 92134–5000; tel. 619/532–6400, (Nonreporting) **A**1 2 3 5 **S** Bureau of Medicine and Surgery, Department of the Navy, Falls Church, VA
Primary Contact: Captain Joel A. Roos, Commanding Officer
CFO: CommanderThomas J. Piner, Director for Resources Management
CIO: Lieutenant CommanderRyan Jarmer, Chief Information Officer
Web address: www.med.navy.mil/sites/nmcsd/Pages/default.aspx
Control: Navy, Government, federal **Service:** General medical and surgical

Staffed Beds: 285

☐ **PROMISE HOSPITAL OF SAN DIEGO (052051)**, 5550 University Avenue, Zip 92105–2307; tel. 619/582–3800, (Nonreporting) **A**1 10 **S** Promise Healthcare, Boca Raton, FL
Primary Contact: Timothy L. Clark, Interim Chief Executive Officer
CFO: Kevin Ohler, Director of Finance
CMO: Larry Emdur D.O., Chief of Staff
CIO: Jim Wilson, Vice President Information Technology
CHR: Kathleen Greene, Director Human Resources
CNO: Kevin Wood, Interim Chief Clinical Officer
Web address: www.promisesandiego.com
Control: Corporation, Investor–owned (for–profit) **Service:** Acute long–term care hospital

Staffed Beds: 100

☐ **RADY CHILDREN'S HOSPITAL – SAN DIEGO (053303)**, 3020 Childrens Way, Zip 92123–4223; tel. 858/576–1700, (Total facility includes 43 beds in nursing home–type unit) **A**1 3 5 10 **F**1 3 4 7 9 10 11 12 16 17 19 20 21 22 23 24 25 26 27 28 29 30 31 32 34 35 36 38 39 40 41 43 45 46 47 48 50 54 55 57 58 59 60 61 62 63 64 65 66 67 68 70 71 72 73 74 75 77 78 79 80 81 82 83 84 85 86 87 88 89 90 91 92 93 94 98 99 100 101 102 104 105 106 107 108 111 114 115 118 119 122 124 128 129 130 131 132 133 134 135 136 137 138 139 141 143 144 145 146 148 149 150 **P**3 5
Primary Contact: Donald Kearns, M.D., President and Chief Executive Officer
COO: Meg Norton, Executive Vice President and Chief Administrative Officer
CFO: Roger Roux, Chief Financial Officer
CMO: Irvin A Kaufman M.D., Chief Medical Officer
CIO: Albert Oriol, Vice President Information Management and Chief Information Officer
CHR: Mamoon Syed, Vice President Human Resources
CNO: Mary Fagan MSN, R.N., Chief Nursing Officer
Web address: www.rchsd.org
Control: Other not–for–profit (including NFP Corporation) **Service:** Children's general medical and surgical

Staffed Beds: 432 **Admissions:** 19234 **Census:** 296 **Outpatient Visits:** 507731 **Births:** 0 **Total Expense ($000):** 1042875 **Payroll Expense ($000):** 325956 **Personnel:** 4258

RADY CHILDREN'S HOSPITAL AND HEALTH CENTER See Rady Children's Hospital – San Diego

☐ **SAN DIEGO COUNTY PSYCHIATRIC HOSPITAL (054114)**, 3853 Rosecrans Street, Zip 92110–3115, Mailing Address: P.O.Box 85524, 92186–5524; tel. 619/692–8211, (Nonreporting) **A**1 10
Primary Contact: Izabela Karmach, R.N., Administrator
COO: Izabela Karmach R.N., Administrator
CFO: Raul J Loyo–Rodriguez, Administrative Analyst III
CMO: Michael Krelstein M.D., Medical Director
CIO: Linda Cannon, Chief Medical Records Services
CHR: Francisco Puentes, Human Resource Officer
Web address: www.sdcounty.ca.gov
Control: County, Government, Nonfederal **Service**: Psychiatric

Staffed Beds: 357

SAN DIEGO MEDICAL CENTER See Kaiser Permanente San Diego Medical Center

⊞ **SCRIPPS MERCY HOSPITAL (050077)**, 4077 Fifth Avenue, Zip 92103–2105; tel. 619/294–8111, (Includes SCRIPPS MERCY HOSPITAL CHULA VISTA, 435 'H' Street, Chula Vista, California, Zip 91912–6617, P O Box 1537, 91910–1537, tel. 619/691–7000) **A**1 2 3 5 10 **F**3 8 11 12 13 14 15 17 18 20 22 24 26 28 29 30 31 32 34 35 39 40 43 44 45 46 49 50 51 54 56 57 58 59 61 64 65 66 68 70 73 74 75 76 77 78 79 81 82 84 85 86 87 92 93 97 98 100 101 102 103 104 105 107 108 110 111 114 115 119 126 130 132 134 135 141 146 147 148 **P**3 5 **S** Scripps Health, San Diego, CA
Primary Contact: Thomas A. Gammiere, Chief Executive, Senior Vice President
CFO: Edward Turk, Vice President Finance
CMO: Davis Cracroft M.D., Senior Director Medical Affairs
CIO: Drexel DeFord, Chief Information Officer
Web address: www.scrippshealth.org
Control: Other not–for–profit (including NFP Corporation) **Service**: General medical and surgical

Staffed Beds: 392 **Admissions:** 31174 **Census:** 393 **Outpatient Visits:** 179618 **Births:** 3665 **Total Expense ($000):** 692919 **Payroll Expense ($000):** 263254 **Personnel:** 3138

⊞ **SHARP MEMORIAL HOSPITAL (050100)**, 7901 Frost Street, Zip 92123–2701; tel. 858/939–3400, **A**1 2 3 10 **F**3 8 11 12 15 17 18 20 22 24 26 28 29 30 31 33 34 35 36 40 43 44 45 46 49 50 56 57 58 59 60 62 64 65 68 70 74 75 77 78 79 80 81 82 84 85 86 87 90 92 93 107 108 109 110 114 115 117 118 119 120 121 123 124 126 129 130 131 132 135 137 138 142 143 145 146 148 149 150 **P**5 **S** Sharp HealthCare, San Diego, CA
Primary Contact: Tim Smith, Senior Vice President and Chief Executive Officer
COO: Janie Kramer, Chief Operating Officer
CFO: Kari Cornicelli, Chief Financial Officer
CMO: Geoffrey Stiles M.D., Chief Medical Officer
CIO: Kenneth Lawonn, Senior Vice President and Chief Information Officer
CHR: Connie Duquette, Director Human Resources
CNO: Pamela Wells R.N., MSN, Chief Nursing Officer
Web address: www.sharp.com
Control: Other not–for–profit (including NFP Corporation) **Service**: General medical and surgical

Staffed Beds: 437 **Admissions:** 19551 **Census:** 272 **Outpatient Visits:** 448946 **Births:** 0 **Total Expense ($000):** 710434 **Payroll Expense ($000):** 265891 **Personnel:** 3565

⊞ **SHARP MESA VISTA HOSPITAL (054145)**, 7850 Vista Hill Avenue, Zip 92123–2717; tel. 858/278–4110, (Includes SHARP MCDONALD CENTER, 7989 Linda Vista Road, San Diego, California, Zip 92111–5106, tel. 858/637–6920; Trisha Khaleghi, Chief Executive Officer) **A**1 10 **F**4 5 11 29 30 31 34 35 37 40 49 56 57 58 59 64 68 87 98 99 100 101 102 103 104 105 106 130 132 135 143 146 149 150 **P**5 **S** Sharp HealthCare, San Diego, CA
Primary Contact: Trisha Khaleghi, Senior Vice President and Chief Executive Officer
CFO: Kari Cornicelli, Chief Financial Officer
CMO: Michael Plopper M.D., Chief Medical Officer
CIO: Kenneth Lawonn, Senior Vice President Information Systems
CHR: Carlisle Lewis III, Senior Vice President Legal and Human Resources
CNO: Cheryl Odell R.N., Chief Nursing Officer
Web address: www.sharp.com
Control: Other not–for–profit (including NFP Corporation) **Service**: Psychiatric

Staffed Beds: 172 **Admissions:** 5720 **Census:** 137 **Outpatient Visits:** 87576 **Births:** 0 **Total Expense ($000):** 79332 **Payroll Expense ($000):** 43979 **Personnel:** 568

⊞ **UC SAN DIEGO HEALTH (050025)**, 200 West Arbor Drive, Zip 92103–9000; tel. 619/543–6222, (Includes THORNTON HOSPITAL, 9300 Campus Point Drive, La Jolla, California, Zip 92037–1300, tel. 858/657–7000; UC SAN DIEGO SHILEY EYE INSTITUTE, 9415 Campus Point Drive, Room 2411 Dept Of, Department of Ophthalmology, Mail Code 0946, La Jolla, California, Zip 92093–0946, 9415 Campus Point Drive, 92093–0946, tel. 858/534–6290; Karen Anisko Ryan, Director Business Development and Communications) **A**1 2 3 5 8 10 **F**3 6 9 11 12 13 15 16 17 18 20 22 24 26 29 30 31 34 36 37 40 43 44 45 46 47 48 49 50 51 54 55 56 57 58 59 60 61 64 65 66 68 70 72 73 74 75 76 77 78 79 80 81 82 84 85 86 87 91 92 93 97 98 99 100 101 102 103 104 107 108 109 110 111 113 114 115 117 118 119 120 121 123 124 126 129 130 131 132 136 137 138 139 140 141 142 145 146 147 148 149 **P**8 **S** University of California Systemwide Administration, Oakland, CA
Primary Contact: Patty Maysent, Interim Chief Executive Officer
COO: Margarita Baggett MSN, R.N., Interim Chief Operating Officer
CFO: Lori Donaldson, Chief Financial Officer
CMO: Angela Scioscia M.D., Chief Medical Officer
CIO: Ed Babakanian, Chief Information Officer
CHR: William J Murin, Chief Human Resources Officer
CNO: Margarita Baggett MSN, R.N., Chief Nursing Officer
Web address: www.health.ucsd.edu
Control: State, Government, Nonfederal **Service**: General medical and surgical

Staffed Beds: 542 **Admissions:** 28713 **Census:** 476 **Outpatient Visits:** 802697 **Births:** 2560 **Total Expense ($000):** 1449185 **Payroll Expense ($000):** 501341 **Personnel:** 6119

UNIVERSITY OF CALIFORNIA SAN DIEGO MEDICAL CENTER See UC San Diego Health

⊞ △ **VA SAN DIEGO HEALTHCARE SYSTEM**, 3350 LaJolla Village Drive, Zip 92161–0002; tel. 858/552–8585, (Total facility includes 30 beds in nursing home–type unit) **A**1 3 5 7 8 **F**1 3 4 5 12 15 16 17 18 20 22 24 26 29 30 34 35 36 37 38 39 40 44 45 46 47 48 49 50 54 55 56 57 58 59 60 61 63 64 65 67 68 70 71 72 73 74 75 76 77 79 80 81 82 83 84 85 86 87 88 89 90 91 92 93 94 95 96 97 98 100 101 102 103 104 105 106 107 110 111 114 115 116 117 118 119 126 128 129 130 132 135 143 144 145 146 147 148 149 **S** Department of Veterans Affairs, Washington, DC
Primary Contact: Robert M. Smith, M.D., Director
COO: Cynthia Abair, Associate Director
CFO: Ronald Larson, Chief Financial Officer
CIO: Ruey Keller, Acting Chief Information Officer
CHR: Stephanie Wright, Director Human Resources Management
Web address: www.sandiego.va.gov
Control: Veterans Affairs, Government, federal **Service**: General medical and surgical

Staffed Beds: 248 **Admissions:** 6743 **Census:** 160 **Outpatient Visits:** 946224 **Births:** 0 **Personnel:** 3299

⊞ **VIBRA HOSPITAL OF SAN DIEGO (052044)**, 555 Washington Street, Zip 92103–2294; tel. 619/260–8300, **A**1 10 **F**1 3 29 64 70 91 148 **P**5 **S** Vibra Healthcare, Mechanicsburg, PA
Primary Contact: Yameeka Jones, Chief Executive Officer
CFO: Mike Gonzales, Chief Financial Officer
CMO: John Fox M.D., Medical Director
CHR: Tania Khalique, Director Human Resources
Web address: www.vhsandiego.com/
Control: Partnership, Investor–owned (for–profit) **Service**: Acute long–term care hospital

Staffed Beds: 80 **Admissions:** 915 **Census:** 66 **Outpatient Visits:** 2582 **Births:** 0

SAN DIMAS—Los Angeles County

⊞ **SAN DIMAS COMMUNITY HOSPITAL (050588)**, 1350 West Covina Boulevard, Zip 91773–3219; tel. 909/599–6811, **A**1 10 **F**3 13 15 29 30 40 45 46 49 50 56 70 74 76 79 81 85 107 108 110 115 119 126 130 146 148 149 **S** Prime Healthcare, Ontario, CA
Primary Contact: Kurt Weinmeister, Chief Executive Officer
CFO: Robert Bonner, Chief Financial Officer
CMO: Rajnish Jandial M.D., Chief Medical Officer
CIO: Jeffrey Cox, Director Information Technology
CHR: Elena Mayo, Manager, Human Resources
CNO: Holly Nagatoshi R.N., Chief Nursing Officer
Web address: www.sandimashospital.com/
Control: Corporation, Investor–owned (for–profit) **Service**: General medical and surgical

Staffed Beds: 101 **Admissions:** 3800 **Census:** 37 **Outpatient Visits:** 23255 **Births:** 585 **Total Expense ($000):** 55790 **Payroll Expense ($000):** 20640 **Personnel:** 354

SAN FRANCISCO—San Francisco County

⊠ △ **CALIFORNIA PACIFIC MEDICAL CENTER (050047)**, 2333 Buchanan Street, Zip 94115–1925, Mailing Address: P.O.Box 7999, 94120–7999; tel. 415/600–6000, (Total facility includes 38 beds in nursing home–type unit) **A**1 2 3 5 7 8 10 **F**2 3 5 6 7 8 12 13 15 18 19 20 22 24 26 28 29 30 31 32 34 35 36 37 38 39 40 41 45 46 47 48 49 50 51 52 55 56 57 58 59 60 61 63 64 65 68 70 72 74 75 76 77 78 79 81 82 83 84 85 86 87 88 89 90 91 92 93 96 97 98 99 100 101 102 104 107 108 110 111 114 115 116 117 118 119 120 121 123 124 126 128 130 132 133 135 137 138 139 141 142 143 144 145 146 147 148 **P**3 5 **S** Sutter Health, Sacramento, CA
Primary Contact: Warren S. Browner, M.D., M.P.H., Chief Executive Officer
COO: Hamila Kownacki, Chief Operating Officer
CFO: Henry Yu, Vice President Finance and Chief Financial Officer
CMO: Vernon Giang M.D., Chief Medical Executive
CIO: Ann Barr, Chief Information Officer – Bay Area
CHR: Edward Battista, Vice President Human Resources
CNO: Diana M. Karner R.N., MSN, Chief Nursing Officer
Web address: www.cpmc.org
Control: Other not-for-profit (including NFP Corporation) **Service**: General medical and surgical

Staffed Beds: 642 **Admissions**: 25137 **Census**: 407 **Outpatient Visits**: 514371 **Births**: 4558 **Total Expense ($000)**: 1150290 **Payroll Expense ($000)**: 372681 **Personnel**: 3650

★ **CALIFORNIA PACIFIC MEDICAL CENTER–DAVIES CAMPUS (050008)**, Castro and Duboce Streets, Zip 94114; tel. 415/600–6000, (Nonreporting) **A**3 5 **S** Sutter Health, Sacramento, CA
Primary Contact: Mary Lanier, Vice President, Post Acute Services and Site Administrator
Web address: www.cpmc.org
Control: Other not-for-profit (including NFP Corporation) **Service**: General medical and surgical

Staffed Beds: 154

⊠ **CALIFORNIA PACIFIC MEDICAL CENTER–ST. LUKE'S CAMPUS (050055)**, 3555 Cesar Chavez Street, Zip 94110–4403; tel. 415/600–6000, (Total facility includes 79 beds in nursing home–type unit) **A**1 3 5 10 **F**3 5 8 13 15 18 29 30 34 35 40 50 55 63 64 66 67 68 70 72 75 76 77 78 79 81 82 84 85 87 89 93 97 100 107 108 110 111 114 118 119 128 130 143 146 147 148 **S** Sutter Health, Sacramento, CA
Primary Contact: Warren S. Browner, M.D., M.P.H., Chief Executive Officer
COO: Hamila Kownacki, Chief Operating Officer
CFO: Henry Yu, Vice President Finance and Chief Financial Officer
CMO: Vernon Giang M.D., Chief Medical Executive
CIO: Ann Barr, Chief Information Officer – Bay Area
CHR: Edward Battista, Vice President Human Resources
CNO: Diana M. Karner R.N., MSN, Chief Nursing Executive
Web address: www.stlukes–sf.org
Control: Other not-for-profit (including NFP Corporation) **Service**: General medical and surgical

Staffed Beds: 175 **Admissions**: 4304 **Census**: 105 **Outpatient Visits**: 76413 **Births**: 882 **Total Expense ($000)**: 167907 **Payroll Expense ($000)**: 54608 **Personnel**: 564

⊠ **CHINESE HOSPITAL (050407)**, 845 Jackson Street, Zip 94133–4899; tel. 415/982–2400, **A**1 10 **F**3 11 15 18 29 30 31 34 35 36 40 45 47 49 50 57 59 64 65 70 75 77 78 79 81 86 87 97 107 110 115 118 119 130 132 135 145 146 147
Primary Contact: Brenda Yee, R.N., MSN, Chief Executive Officer
COO: Jian Q Zhang MSN, Chief Operating Officer
CFO: Scott Goodin, Interim Chief Financial Officer
CMO: William Chung M.D., Chief of Staff
CIO: Keith Minard, Chief Information Officer
CHR: Lydia Mahr–Chan, Director of Human Resources
CNO: Peggy Cmiel R.N., Chief Nursing Officer
Web address: www.chinesehospital–sf.org
Control: Other not-for-profit (including NFP Corporation) **Service**: General medical and surgical

Staffed Beds: 28 **Admissions**: 1390 **Census**: 17 **Outpatient Visits**: 73891 **Births**: 0 **Total Expense ($000)**: 131347 **Payroll Expense ($000)**: 34900 **Personnel**: 300

JEWISH HOME OF SAN FRANCISCO (054089), 302 Silver Avenue, Zip 94112–1510; tel. 415/334–2500, (Nonreporting) **A**10
Primary Contact: Daniel R. Ruth, President and Chief Executive Officer
COO: Kevin Ward, Chief Operating Officer
CFO: Victor E Meinke, Chief Financial Officer
CNO: Edwin Cabigao, Chief Nursing Officer
Web address: www.jhsf.org
Control: Other not-for-profit (including NFP Corporation) **Service**: Psychiatric

Staffed Beds: 374

⊠ **KAISER PERMANENTE SAN FRANCISCO MEDICAL CENTER (050076)**, 2425 Geary Boulevard, Zip 94115–3358; tel. 415/833–2000, (Nonreporting) **A**1 2 3 5 10 **S** Kaiser Foundation Hospitals, Oakland, CA
Primary Contact: Ronald Groepper, Senior Vice President and Area Manager
COO: Helen Archer–Duste, Chief Operating Officer
CFO: Alex Khoo, Interim Area Finance Officer
CMO: Robert Mithun M.D., Physician in Chief
CIO: Peti Arunamata, Interim Area Director Information Technology
CHR: Diane J Easterwood, Human Resources Business Partner
Web address: www.kaiserpermanente.org
Control: Other not-for-profit (including NFP Corporation) **Service**: General medical and surgical

Staffed Beds: 215

★ **LAGUNA HONDA HOSPITAL AND REHABILITATION CENTER (050668)** (General Acute Care Hospital with Distinct part SNF), 375 Laguna Honda Boulevard, Zip 94116–1499; tel. 415/759–2300, (Total facility includes 769 beds in nursing home–type unit) **A**10 **F**3 29 30 38 53 56 61 63 64 65 68 74 75 77 82 83 84 90 92 93 94 96 100 103 104 127 128 130 132 135 146 148
Primary Contact: Mivic Hirose, Executive Administrator
COO: Michael R Llewellyn, Chief Operating Officer
CFO: Tess Navarro, Chief Financial Officer
CMO: Colleen Riley M.D., Medical Director
CIO: Pat Skala, Chief Information Officer
CHR: Willie Ramirez, Manager Labor Relations
Web address: www.lagunahonda.org/
Control: City–county, Government, Nonfederal **Service**: Other specialty treatment

Staffed Beds: 780 **Admissions**: 916 **Census**: 738 **Outpatient Visits**: 50000 **Births**: 0 **Total Expense ($000)**: 242788 **Payroll Expense ($000)**: 130558 **Personnel**: 1612

⊠ △ **SAINT FRANCIS MEMORIAL HOSPITAL (050152)**, 900 Hyde Street, Zip 94109–4899, Mailing Address: P.O.Box 7726, 94120–7726; tel. 415/353–6000, (Nonreporting) **A**1 2 3 7 10 **S** Dignity Health, San Francisco, CA
Primary Contact: David G. Klein, M.D., President
CFO: Alan Fox, Chief Financial Officer
CHR: Richard Mead, Senior Director Human Resources
Web address: www.saintfrancismemorial.org
Control: Other not-for-profit (including NFP Corporation) **Service**: General medical and surgical

Staffed Beds: 239

SAN FRANCISCO MEDICAL CENTER See Kaiser Permanente San Francisco Medical Center

⊠ **SAN FRANCISCO VA MEDICAL CENTER**, 4150 Clement Street, Zip 94121–1545; tel. 415/221–4810, (Total facility includes 108 beds in nursing home–type unit) **A**1 3 5 **F**3 5 6 8 10 11 12 15 18 20 22 24 26 28 29 30 31 34 35 36 37 38 39 40 44 45 46 47 49 50 51 54 56 57 58 59 60 61 62 63 64 65 66 68 74 75 77 78 79 81 82 83 84 85 86 87 91 92 93 94 97 98 100 101 102 103 104 106 107 108 111 112 113 114 115 116 117 118 119 120 121 122 123 124 126 127 128 129 130 132 135 143 144 145 146 147 148 149 150 **S** Department of Veterans Affairs, Washington, DC
Primary Contact: Bonnie S. Graham, Director
CFO: Brian Kelly, Acting Chief Fiscal Service
CMO: C. Diana Nicoll M.D., Ph.D., Chief of Staff
CIO: Ryan Chun, Information Resources Management
CHR: Jerry Mills, Chief Human Resources Management Services
CNO: Shirley Pikula MSN, Associate Director Patient Center Care
Web address: www.sanfrancisco.va.gov/
Control: Veterans Affairs, Government, federal **Service**: General medical and surgical

Staffed Beds: 241 **Admissions**: 13183 **Census**: 181 **Outpatient Visits**: 37291 **Births**: 0 **Total Expense ($000)**: 594960 **Payroll Expense ($000)**: 256181 **Personnel**: 2769

Hospital, Medicare Provider Number, Address, Telephone, Approval, Facility, and Physician Codes, Health Care System

★ American Hospital Association (AHA) membership ◯ Healthcare Facilities Accreditation Program ⇑ Center for Improvement in Healthcare Quality Accreditation
□ The Joint Commission accreditation ◇ DNV Healthcare Inc. accreditation △ Commission on Accreditation of Rehabilitation Facilities (CARF) accreditation

CA

⊞ △ **ST. MARY'S MEDICAL CENTER (050457)**, 450 Stanyan Street, Zip 94117–1079; tel. 415/668–1000, (Nonreporting) **A**1 2 3 5 7 10 **S** Dignity Health, San Francisco, CA
Primary Contact: Pamela Lindemoen, President
COO: Deborah Kolhede, Vice President and Chief Operating Officer
CFO: Eric Brettner, Vice President and Chief Financial Officer
CMO: Francis Charlton M.D., Jr, Chief Medical Staff
CHR: Barbara Morrissett, Vice President Human Resources
CNO: Barbara Eusebio R.N., JD, Vice President, Chief Nurse Executive
Web address: www.stmarysmedicalcenter.com
Control: Other not–for–profit (including NFP Corporation) **Service**: General medical and surgical

Staffed Beds: 232

⊞ **UCSF MEDICAL CENTER (050454)**, 500 Parnassus Avenue, Zip 94143–0296, Mailing Address: 500 Parnassus Avenue, Box 0296, 94143–0296; tel. 415/476–1000, (Includes UCSF BENIOFF CHILDREN'S HOSPITAL, 500 Parnassus Avenue, San Francisco, California, Zip 94143–2203, 505 Parnassus Avenue, 94143–2203, tel. 888/689–8273; Michael Anderson, M.D., President; UCSF MEDICAL CENTER MISSION BAY, 1975 4th Street, San Francisco, California, Zip 94158–2351, tel. 415/353–3000) **A**1 2 3 5 8 10 **F**3 6 7 8 9 11 12 13 14 15 17 18 19 20 21 23 24 25 26 27 29 30 31 33 34 35 36 37 38 39 40 41 43 44 45 46 47 48 49 50 51 52 53 54 55 56 57 58 59 60 61 63 64 65 66 68 70 72 73 74 75 76 77 78 79 81 82 83 84 85 86 87 88 89 91 92 93 94 96 97 99 100 101 102 103 104 105 107 108 110 111 112 113 114 115 116 117 118 119 121 123 124 126 127 128 129 130 131 132 134 135 136 137 138 139 140 141 142 144 145 146 147 148 149 150 **S** University of California Systemwide Administration, Oakland, CA
Primary Contact: Mark R. Laret, Chief Executive Officer
COO: Ken M Jones, Chief Operating Officer
CFO: Barrie Strickland, Chief Financial Officer
CMO: Josh Adler M.D., Chief Medical Officer
CIO: Joe Bergfort, Chief Information Officer
CHR: David Odato, Chief Administrative and Chief Human Resources Officer
CNO: Sheila Antrum R.N., President
Web address: www.ucsfhealth.org
Control: Other not–for–profit (including NFP Corporation) **Service**: General medical and surgical

Staffed Beds: 782 **Admissions:** 33472 **Census:** 590 **Outpatient Visits:** 1122040 **Births:** 2980 **Total Expense ($000):** 3149743 **Payroll Expense ($000):** 1135237 **Personnel:** 9628

VETERANS AFFAIRS MEDICAL CENTER See San Francisco Va Medical Center

⊞ **ZUCKERBERG SAN FRANCISCO GENERAL HOSPITAL AND TRAUMA CENTER (050228)**, 1001 Potrero Avenue, Zip 94110–3594; tel. 415/206–8000, (Nonreporting) **A**1 2 3 5 8 10
Primary Contact: Susan P. Ehrlich, M.D., Chief Executive Officer
COO: Tosan O. Boyo, Chief Operating Officer
CFO: Valerie Inouye, Chief Financial Officer
CMO: Todd May M.D., Chief Medical Officer
CIO: Winona Windolovich, Associate Chief Information Officer
CHR: Karen Hill, Departmental Personnel Officer
CNO: Terry Dentoni, Chief Nursing Officer
Web address: www.zuckerbergsanfranciscogeneral.org/
Control: City–county, Government, Nonfederal **Service**: General medical and surgical

Staffed Beds: 441

SAN GABRIEL—San Francisco County

☐ **SAN GABRIEL VALLEY MEDICAL CENTER (050132)**, 438 West Las Tunas Drive, Zip 91776–1216, Mailing Address: P.O.Box 1507, 91778–1507; tel. 626/289–5454, (Nonreporting) **A**1 10 **S** AHMC & Healthcare, Inc., Alhambra, CA
Primary Contact: Karen Price–Gharzeddine, R.N., MS, Chief Executive Officer
CFO: Andrew Grim, Chief Financial Officer
CIO: Bernie Sauer, Director Information Technology
CHR: Victor Voisard, Director Human Resources
CNO: Gail Freeman, Chief Nursing Officer
Web address: www.sgvmc.org
Control: Partnership, Investor–owned (for–profit) **Service**: General medical and surgical

Staffed Beds: 273

SAN JOSE—Santa Clara County

⊞ **GOOD SAMARITAN HOSPITAL (050380)**, 2425 Samaritan Drive, Zip 95124–3997, Mailing Address: P.O.Box 240002, 95154–2402; tel. 408/559–2011, (Nonreporting) **A**1 2 3 10 **S** HCA Healthcare, Nashville, TN
Primary Contact: Joseph DeSchryver, Chief Executive Officer
COO: Jordan Herget, Chief Operating Officer
CFO: Lana Arad, Chief Financial Officer
CMO: Bruce Wilbur M.D., Chief Medical Officer
CIO: Darrell O'Dell, Director Information Services
CHR: Edward Battista, Vice President Human Resources
CNO: Darina Kavanagh R.N., MSN, Chief Nursing Officer
Web address: www.goodsamsanjose.com
Control: Corporation, Investor–owned (for–profit) **Service**: General medical and surgical

Staffed Beds: 332

⊞ **KAISER PERMANENTE SAN JOSE MEDICAL CENTER (050604)**, 250 Hospital Parkway, Zip 95119–1199; tel. 408/972–7000, **A**1 2 5 10 **F**1 3 4 8 13 16 17 18 20 22 29 30 31 35 40 46 49 51 56 67 68 70 72 73 74 76 78 79 80 81 82 84 85 87 88 89 90 98 104 107 108 110 111 114 115 119 128 130 141 146 148 149 **S** Kaiser Foundation Hospitals, Oakland, CA
Primary Contact: Irene Chavez, Senior Vice President and Area Manager
COO: Irene Chavez, Senior Vice President and Area Manager
CFO: Stephen L Kalsman, Area Finance Officer
CMO: Raj Bhandari M.D., Physician–in–Chief
CIO: Greg Tuck, Area Information Officer
CHR: Susan Franzella, Human Resource Business Partner
CNO: Theresa R Nero R.N., MS, Chief Nursing Officer
Web address: www.kaiserpermanente.org
Control: Other not–for–profit (including NFP Corporation) **Service**: General medical and surgical

Staffed Beds: 222 **Admissions:** 10238 **Census:** 99 **Outpatient Visits:** 206308 **Births:** 2406 **Personnel:** 1183

⊞ **O'CONNOR HOSPITAL (050153)**, 2105 Forest Avenue, Zip 95128–1471; tel. 408/947–2500, **A**1 2 3 5 10 **F**1 3 4 8 11 13 15 16 17 18 19 20 22 24 26 28 29 30 31 34 35 37 40 44 46 48 49 50 53 54 57 59 60 64 66 67 68 70 72 73 74 75 76 77 78 79 80 81 84 85 86 87 88 89 90 93 97 98 100 107 108 110 111 114 116 117 118 119 121 123 128 130 131 132 135 146 147 148 149 **S** Verity Health System, Los Angeles, CA
Primary Contact: Jordan Herget, President and Chief Executive Officer
CIO: Richard Hutsell, Vice President and Chief Information Officer, Daughters of Charity Health System
CHR: Julie Hatcher, Vice President Human Resources
CNO: Dawn Marie Goeringer, Chief Clinical Care Officer
Web address: www.oconnorhospital.org
Control: Other not–for–profit (including NFP Corporation) **Service**: General medical and surgical

Staffed Beds: 202 **Admissions:** 9587 **Census:** 121 **Outpatient Visits:** 137855 **Births:** 2271 **Total Expense ($000):** 304969 **Payroll Expense ($000):** 122900

⊞ **REGIONAL MEDICAL CENTER OF SAN JOSE (050125)**, 225 North Jackson Avenue, Zip 95116–1603; tel. 408/259–5000, (Nonreporting) **A**1 2 10 **S** HCA Healthcare, Nashville, TN
Primary Contact: Michael T. Johnson, FACHE, President and Chief Executive Officer
COO: Brian J Knecht, Chief Operating Officer
CFO: Fred Ashworth, Chief Financial Officer
CMO: William Scott M.D., Vice President Medical Affairs
CIO: Shirley Joyal, Director Information Systems
CHR: Nancy Clark, Vice President Human Resources
Web address: www.regionalmedicalsanjose.com
Control: Partnership, Investor–owned (for–profit) **Service**: General medical and surgical

Staffed Beds: 193

SAN JOSE BEHAVORIAL HEALTH, 455 Silicon Valley Boulevard, Zip 95138–1858; tel. 888/210–2484, (Data for 275 days) **F**29 34 35 38 57 68 75 86 87 98 99 100 101 103 130 149 **S** Acadia Healthcare Company, Inc., Franklin, TN
Primary Contact: Rob Marsh, Chief Executive Officer
Web address: www.sanjosebh.com
Control: Corporation, Investor–owned (for–profit) **Service**: Psychiatric

Staffed Beds: 80 **Admissions:** 291 **Census:** 10 **Outpatient Visits:** 0 **Births:** 0 **Personnel:** 157

SAN JOSE MEDICAL CENTER See Kaiser Permanente San Jose Medical Center

Many Facility Codes have changed. Please refer to the AHA Guide Code Chart. © 2017 AHA Guide

☐ △ **SANTA CLARA VALLEY MEDICAL CENTER (050038)**, 751 South Bascom Avenue, Zip 95128–2699; tel. 408/885–5000, **A**1 3 5 7 10 **F**3 5 9 11 12 15 16 17 18 19 20 22 24 26 28 29 30 31 32 34 35 36 39 40 41 43 44 45 46 49 50 51 54 55 56 58 59 60 61 64 65 66 68 70 71 72 74 75 76 77 78 79 80 81 82 84 85 86 87 88 89 90 91 92 93 95 96 97 98 99 100 101 102 103 104 107 108 110 111 114 115 117 118 119 120 121 123 124 129 130 131 132 134 135 142 144 146 147 148 149 **P**6
Primary Contact: Paul E. Lorenz, Chief Executive Officer
COO: Benita McLarin, Chief Operating Officer
CMO: Jeffrey Arnold M.D., Chief Medical Officer
CIO: Lee Herrmann, Chief Healthcare Technology Officer
CHR: David Manson, Manager Human Resources
CNO: Trudy Johnson R.N., RN, Chief Nursing Officer
Web address: www.scvmed.org
Control: County, Government, Nonfederal **Service:** General medical and surgical

Staffed Beds: 481 **Admissions:** 25082 **Census:** 355 **Outpatient Visits:** 819564 **Births:** 3483 **Total Expense ($000):** 1487531 **Payroll Expense ($000):** 590303 **Personnel:** 5468

SAN LEANDRO—Alameda County

FAIRMONT HOSPITAL See Highland Hospital, Rochester, Oakland

✠ **KAISER PERMANENTE SAN LEANDRO MEDICAL CENTER (050777)**, 2500 Merced Street, Zip 94577–4201; tel. 510/454–1000, (Nonreporting) **A**1 10 **S** Kaiser Foundation Hospitals, Oakland, CA
Primary Contact: Thomas S. Hanenburg, Senior Vice President and Area Manager
Web address: www.kaiserpermanente.org
Control: Other not–for–profit (including NFP Corporation) **Service:** General medical and surgical

Staffed Beds: 264

✠ **KINDRED HOSPITAL–SAN FRANCISCO BAY AREA (052034)**, 2800 Benedict Drive, Zip 94577–6840; tel. 510/357–8300, (Nonreporting) **A**1 10 **S** Kindred Healthcare, Louisville, KY
Primary Contact: Jacob M. McCarty, Chief Executive Officer
CFO: Ziba Aflak, Chief Financial Officer
CHR: Erin Greene, Coordinator Human Resources
CNO: Emily Gard, Chief Clinical Officer
Web address: www.kindredhospitalsfba.com
Control: Corporation, Investor–owned (for–profit) **Service:** Acute long–term care hospital

Staffed Beds: 99

☐ **SAN LEANDRO HOSPITAL (050773)**, 13855 East 14th Street, Zip 94578–2600; tel. 510/357–6500, **A**1 10 **F**3 15 18 29 30 31 34 35 40 43 44 45 50 51 57 59 60 68 70 77 79 81 87 107 108 110 111 114 119 130 146 **S** Alameda Health System, San Leandro, CA
Primary Contact: James E T. Jackson, M.P.H., Chief Administrative Officer
Web address: www.sanleandrohospital.org
Control: Hospital district or authority, Government, Nonfederal **Service:** General medical and surgical

Staffed Beds: 45 **Admissions:** 3077 **Census:** 35 **Outpatient Visits:** 36648 **Births:** 0 **Total Expense ($000):** 73852 **Payroll Expense ($000):** 39205 **Personnel:** 341

☐ **WILLOW ROCK CENTER (054149)**, 2050 Fairmont Drive, Zip 94578–1001; tel. 510/895–5502, (Nonreporting) **A**1 10
Primary Contact: Anne L. Bakar, President and Chief Executive Officer
Web address: www.tbhcare.com
Control: County, Government, Nonfederal **Service:** Psychiatric

Staffed Beds: 16

SAN LUIS OBISPO—San Luis Obispo County

CALIFORNIA MENS COLONY CORRECTIONAL TREATMENT CENTER, Highway 1, Zip 93409–8101, Mailing Address: P.O.Box 8101, 93403–8101; tel. 805/547–7913, (Nonreporting)
Primary Contact: Martha Wallace, Administrator
CFO: William Cook, Associate Warden Business Service
CIO: Terry Knight, Public Information Officer and Administrative Assistant
Web address: www.yaca.ca.gov/visitors/fac_prison_cmc.html
Control: State, Government, Nonfederal **Service:** Hospital unit of an institution (prison hospital, college infirmary, etc.)

Staffed Beds: 39

✠ **FRENCH HOSPITAL MEDICAL CENTER (050232)**, 1911 Johnson Avenue, Zip 93401–4197; tel. 805/543–5353, **A**1 2 10 **F**8 11 15 18 20 22 24 26 28 29 30 32 34 35 40 46 50 51 53 54 57 59 64 68 70 75 76 77 78 79 81 84 85 86 87 89 97 100 102 107 108 110 111 114 115 117 119 130 132 134 146 147 148 149 **S** Dignity Health, San Francisco, CA
Primary Contact: Alan Iftiniuk, Chief Executive Officer
COO: Julia Fogelson R.N., Chief Operating Officer and Chief Nursing Executive
CFO: Sue Andersen, Chief Financial Officer
CMO: Chris Voge, Chief of Staff
CIO: Cyndi Lang, Director Information Services
CHR: Barry Nateman, Manager Human Resources
CNO: Julia Fogelson R.N., Chief Operating Officer and Chief Nursing Executive
Web address: www.frenchmedicalcenter.org
Control: Other not–for–profit (including NFP Corporation) **Service:** General medical and surgical

Staffed Beds: 72 **Admissions:** 4194 **Census:** 42 **Outpatient Visits:** 120513 **Births:** 502 **Total Expense ($000):** 140686 **Payroll Expense ($000):** 46198 **Personnel:** 445

✠ **SIERRA VISTA REGIONAL MEDICAL CENTER (050506)**, 1010 Murray Avenue, Zip 93405–1806, Mailing Address: P.O.Box 1367, 93405; tel. 805/546–7600, **A**1 2 10 19 **F**3 13 15 17 18 20 29 30 31 34 40 43 45 46 49 50 57 59 64 65 70 72 73 74 75 76 77 78 79 80 81 84 85 86 89 107 108 110 111 114 115 119 126 130 131 132 145 146 147 148 149 **S** TENET Healthcare Corporation, Dallas, TX
Primary Contact: Timothy P. Menton, Interim Chief Executive Officer
COO: Michael Bell, Chief Operating Officer
CFO: Rollie Pirkl, Chief Financial Officer
CIO: Robert Leonard, Director Information Services
CHR: Kristin Flynn, Chief Human Resources Officer
CNO: Nicki E Edwards Ph.D., R.N., Interim Chief Nursing Officer
Web address: www.sierravistaregional.com
Control: Corporation, Investor–owned (for–profit) **Service:** General medical and surgical

Staffed Beds: 164 **Admissions:** 5486 **Census:** 64 **Outpatient Visits:** 42194 **Births:** 1325 **Total Expense ($000):** 125909 **Payroll Expense ($000):** 56203 **Personnel:** 586

SAN MATEO—San Mateo County

MILLS HEALTH CENTER See Mills–Peninsula Health Services, Burlingame

☐ **SAN MATEO MEDICAL CENTER (050113)**, 222 West 39th Avenue, Zip 94403–4398; tel. 650/573–2222, (Nonreporting) **A**1 3 5 10
Primary Contact: Chester Kunnappilly, M.D., Interim Chief Executive Officer
COO: John Thomas, Chief Operating Officer
CFO: David S McGrew, Chief Financial Officer
CMO: Susan Fernyak M.D., Interim Chief Medical Officer & Chief Quality Officer
CIO: Michael Aratow M.D., Chief Information Officer
CHR: Angela Gonzales, Manager Human Resources
CNO: Joan G Spicer R.N., Chief Nursing Officer
Web address: www.sanmateomedicalcenter.org
Control: County, Government, Nonfederal **Service:** General medical and surgical

Staffed Beds: 90

SAN PEDRO—Los Angeles County, See Los Angeles

SAN RAFAEL—Marin County

✠ **KAISER PERMANENTE SAN RAFAEL MEDICAL CENTER (050510)**, 99 Montecillo Road, Zip 94903–3397; tel. 415/444–2000, (Nonreporting) **A**1 5 10 **S** Kaiser Foundation Hospitals, Oakland, CA
Primary Contact: Judy Coffey, R.N., Senior Vice President and Area Manager
CFO: John Groesbeck, Area Finance Officer
CMO: Gary Mizono M.D., Physician–in–Chief
CIO: Stanley Dobrawa, Area Technology Director
CNO: Dennis Kneeppel R.N., Chief Nurse Executive and Chief Operating Officer
Web address: www.kaiserpermanente.org
Control: Other not–for–profit (including NFP Corporation) **Service:** General medical and surgical

Staffed Beds: 116

CA

Hospital, Medicare Provider Number, Address, Telephone, Approval, Facility, and Physician Codes, Health Care System

★ American Hospital Association (AHA) membership
☐ The Joint Commission accreditation
◯ Healthcare Facilities Accreditation Program
◇ DNV Healthcare Inc. accreditation
⇧ Center for Improvement in Healthcare Quality Accreditation
△ Commission on Accreditation of Rehabilitation Facilities (CARF) accreditation

SAN RAMON—Contra Costa County

☒ **SAN RAMON REGIONAL MEDICAL CENTER (050689)**, 6001 Norris Canyon Road, Zip 94583–5400; tel. 925/275–9200, **A**1 10 **F**3 8 11 13 15 18 20 22 24 26 28 29 30 31 34 35 37 40 45 46 47 48 49 53 57 59 64 70 72 75 76 77 78 79 81 85 86 87 93 107 108 110 118 119 126 130 131 132 146 147 148 149 **P**3 5 **S** TENET Healthcare Corporation, Dallas, TX
Primary Contact: Gary Sloan, Chief Executive Officer
CFO: Beenu Chadha, Chief Financial Officer
CMO: Raymond Cheung M.D., Chief of Staff
CIO: Anthony Abbate, Director of Information Services
CHR: Dennis Mills, Chief Human Resources Officer
CNO: Lani Dickinson, Interim Chief Nursing Officer
Web address: www.sanramonmedctr.com
Control: Partnership, Investor–owned (for–profit) **Service**: General medical and surgical

> **Staffed Beds**: 123 **Admissions**: 5097 **Census**: 53 **Outpatient Visits**: 71662 **Births**: 772 **Total Expense ($000)**: 148237 **Payroll Expense ($000)**: 70511 **Personnel**: 485

SANTA ANA—Orange County

☐ **ORANGE COUNTY GLOBAL MEDICAL CENTER, INC. (050746)**, 1001 North Tustin Avenue, Zip 92705–3577; tel. 714/953–3500, (Nonreporting) **A**1 3 5 10 **S** KPC Healthcare, Inc., Santa Ana, CA
Primary Contact: Suzanne Richards, Chief Executive Officer
COO: Ann Abe, Administrator and Chief Operating Officer
CFO: John Collins, Chief Financial Officer
CMO: Steven Bui M.D., Chief of Staff
CIO: Charles Flack, Interim Chief Information Officer
CHR: Terry Bohn, Director, Human Resources
CNO: Sandra Moreno, Chief Nursing Officer
Web address: www.orangecounty-gmc.com
Control: Corporation, Investor–owned (for–profit) **Service**: General medical and surgical

> **Staffed Beds**: 282

☐ **SOUTH COAST GLOBAL MEDICAL CENTER (050747)**, 2701 South Bristol Street, Zip 92704–6278; tel. 714/754–5454, (Nonreporting) **A**1 10 **S** KPC Healthcare, Inc., Santa Ana, CA
Primary Contact: Ronald J. Galonsky Jr, Chief Executive Officer
CFO: John Collins, Chief Financial Officer
CHR: Cynthia Garren–Oster, Human Resource Manager
Web address: www.SouthCoast–GMC.com
Control: Corporation, Investor–owned (for–profit) **Service**: General medical and surgical

> **Staffed Beds**: 178

SANTA BARBARA—Santa Barbara County

COTTAGE REHABILITATION HOSPITAL See Santa Barbara Cottage Hospital

☒ **GOLETA VALLEY COTTAGE HOSPITAL (050357)**, 351 South Patterson Avenue, Zip 93111–2496, Mailing Address: Box 6306, 93160–6306; tel. 805/967–3411, **A**1 10 **F**8 11 12 15 29 40 65 68 70 79 81 107 110 114 119 124 130 148 149 **S** Cottage Health, Santa Barbara, CA
Primary Contact: Ronald C. Werft, President and Chief Executive Officer
COO: Steven A Fellows, Executive Vice President and Chief Operating Officer
CFO: Joan Bricher, Senior Vice President Finance and Chief Financial Officer
CMO: Edmund Wroblewski M.D., Vice President Medical Affairs and Chief Medical Officer
CIO: Alberto Kywi, Chief Information Officer
CHR: Patrice Ryan, Vice President Human Resources
Web address: www.sbch.org
Control: Other not–for–profit (including NFP Corporation) **Service**: General medical and surgical

> **Staffed Beds**: 28 **Admissions**: 1641 **Census**: 11 **Outpatient Visits**: 48055 **Births**: 0 **Total Expense ($000)**: 73870 **Payroll Expense ($000)**: 26355 **Personnel**: 279

☒ △ **SANTA BARBARA COTTAGE HOSPITAL (050396)**, 400 West Pueblo Street, Zip 93105–4390, Mailing Address: P.O.Box 689, 93102–0689; tel. 805/682–7111, (Includes COTTAGE CHILDREN'S HOSPITAL, 400 West Pueblo Street, Santa Barbara, California, Zip 93105–4353, tel. 877/247–3260; COTTAGE REHABILITATION HOSPITAL, 2415 De la Vina Street, Santa Barbara, California, Zip 93105–3819, tel. 805/687–7444; Melinda Staveley, President and Chief Executive Officer) **A**1 2 3 5 7 10 **F**3 4 5 8 11 12 13 15 17 18 20 22 24 26 28 29 30 31 34 35 40 42 43 46 50 53 54 57 58 59 60 64 65 68 70 72 74 75 76 78 79 81 84 86 88 89 90 91 92 93 96 98 100 102 103 104 106 107 110 111 114 115 117 119 126 130 132 135 146 148 149 **S** Cottage Health, Santa Barbara, CA
Primary Contact: Ronald C. Werft, President and Chief Executive Officer
COO: Steven A Fellows, Executive Vice President and Chief Operating Officer
CFO: Joan Bricher, Senior Vice President Finance and Chief Financial Officer
CMO: Edmund Wroblewski M.D., Vice President Medical Affairs and Chief Medical Officer
CIO: Alberto Kywi, Chief Information Officer
CHR: Patrice Ryan, Vice President Human Resources
CNO: Herb J Geary, Vice President Patient Care Services and Chief Nursing Officer
Web address: www.cottagehealthsystem.org
Control: Other not–for–profit (including NFP Corporation) **Service**: General medical and surgical

> **Staffed Beds**: 351 **Admissions**: 17625 **Census**: 233 **Outpatient Visits**: 128348 **Births**: 2295 **Total Expense ($000)**: 639030 **Payroll Expense ($000)**: 224176 **Personnel**: 2423

SANTA BARBARA COUNTY PSYCHIATRIC HEALTH FACILITY (054125), 315 Camino Del Remedio, Zip 93110–1332; tel. 805/681–5244, (Nonreporting) **A**10
Primary Contact: Ole Behrendtsen, M.D., Interim Director
CFO: Michael C. Evans, Chief Executive Officer and Deputy Director of Finance and Administration
CMO: Ole Behrendtsen M.D., Medical Director
CIO: Dana Fahey, Manager Management Information Systems
CHR: Elena Molelus, Manager Human Resources
Web address: www.countyofsb.org
Control: County, Government, Nonfederal **Service**: Psychiatric

> **Staffed Beds**: 16

SANTA CLARA—Santa Clara County

☒ **KAISER PERMANENTE SANTA CLARA MEDICAL CENTER (050071)**, 700 Lawrence Expressway, Zip 95051–5173; tel. 408/851–1000, **A**1 2 3 5 10 **F**3 5 8 11 12 13 15 17 18 19 20 21 22 23 24 26 28 29 31 32 34 35 36 38 40 41 44 45 48 49 50 51 52 53 54 55 56 57 58 59 60 61 62 63 64 65 68 70 71 72 74 75 76 77 78 79 81 82 83 84 85 86 87 88 89 91 92 93 94 96 97 99 100 101 104 107 108 109 110 111 114 115 116 117 118 119 120 121 123 124 126 129 130 131 132 134 135 144 146 147 148 149 150 **S** Kaiser Foundation Hospitals, Oakland, CA
Primary Contact: Christopher L. Boyd, Senior Vice President and Area Manager
CFO: Tim O'Connor, Area Finance Officer
CMO: Susan Smarr M.D., Physician–in–Chief
CIO: Scott May, Area Director Technology
CHR: Robert Hyde, Human Resources Business Partner
CNO: Lori Armstrong R.N., MSN, Chief Nursing Officer
Web address: www.kaiserpermanente.org
Control: Other not–for–profit (including NFP Corporation) **Service**: General medical and surgical

> **Staffed Beds**: 327 **Admissions**: 19210 **Census**: 216 **Births**: 4299

SANTA CRUZ—Santa Cruz County

☒ **DOMINICAN HOSPITAL (050242)**, 1555 Soquel Drive, Zip 95065–1794; tel. 831/462–7700, (Nonreporting) **A**1 2 10 **S** Dignity Health, San Francisco, CA
Primary Contact: Nanette Mickiewicz, M.D., President
COO: Chris Wernke, Chief Operating Officer
CFO: Rick Harron, Chief Financial Officer
CMO: Freddie Weinstein M.D., Chief Medical Officer
CIO: Lee Vanderpool, Vice President
CHR: Vicki Miranda, Vice President Human Resources
Web address: www.dominicanhospital.org
Control: Church operated, Nongovernment, not–for–profit **Service**: General medical and surgical

> **Staffed Beds**: 223

Many Facility Codes have changed. Please refer to the AHA Guide Code Chart. © 2017 AHA Guide

SUTTER MATERNITY AND SURGERY CENTER OF SANTA CRUZ (050714) (Maternity and General Surgery), 2900 Chanticleer Avenue, Zip 95065–1816; tel. 831/477–2200, **A**1 10 **F**3 13 29 34 45 51 57 68 76 77 79 81 85 119 126 132 135 146 **P**3 5 **S** Sutter Health, Sacramento, CA
Primary Contact: Stephen Gray, Chief Administrative Officer
CFO: Bonnie Liang, Divisional Finance Officer
CMO: Joseph Fabry D.O., Chief of Staff
CIO: Ann Barr, Chief Information Officer, Sutter Health Bay Area
CHR: Maynard Jenkins, Regional Vice President Human Resources
CNO: Sherri Stout–Torres R.N., Chief Nursing Executive
Web address: www.suttersantacruz.org
Control: Other not–for–profit (including NFP Corporation) **Service**: Other specialty treatment

Staffed Beds: 30 **Admissions**: 1541 **Census**: 11 **Outpatient Visits**: 12781 **Births**: 1101 **Total Expense ($000)**: 66924 **Payroll Expense ($000)**: 20928 **Personnel**: 200

SANTA MARIA—Santa Barbara County

MARIAN REGIONAL MEDICAL CENTER (050107), 1400 East Church Street, Zip 93454–5906; tel. 805/739–3000, (Nonreporting) (Includes ARROYO GRANDE COMMUNITY HOSPITAL, 345 South Halcyon Road, Arroyo Grande, California, Zip 93420–3896, tel. 805/489–4261; Kenneth Dalebout, Site Administrator) **A**1 2 3 10 13 **S** Dignity Health, San Francisco, CA
Primary Contact: Charles J. Cova, Senior Vice President, Operations
COO: Mark Allen, Chief Operating Officer
CFO: Sue Andersen, Vice President and Service Area and Chief Financial Officer
CMO: Chuck Merrill M.D., Vice President Medical Affairs
CIO: Patricia Haase, Director Information Technology and Communications
CHR: Ed Gonzales, Vice President Human Resources
CNO: Candice Monge R.N., Chief Nurse Executive Officer
Web address: www.marianmedicalcenter.org
Control: Church operated, Nongovernment, not–for–profit **Service**: General medical and surgical

Staffed Beds: 286

SANTA MONICA—Los Angeles County

PROVIDENCE SAINT JOHN'S HEALTH CENTER (050290), 2121 Santa Monica Boulevard, Zip 90404–2091; tel. 310/829–5511, **A**1 2 10 **F**3 8 14 15 18 20 22 24 26 29 30 31 34 35 37 40 42 43 45 46 47 48 49 50 55 58 59 60 64 70 72 74 76 78 79 81 84 85 93 99 107 108 110 111 118 119 120 121 123 124 126 130 131 132 146 147 **P**2 3 5 **S** Providence St. Joseph Health, Renton, WA
Primary Contact: Marcel C. Loh, FACHE, Chief Executive Officer
COO: David A Tam M.D., FACHE, Chief Operating Officer
CFO: James Uli, Chief Financial Officer
CMO: Donald Larsen M.D., Chief Medical Officer
CIO: Martha Ponce, Director Information Technologies and Telecommunications
CHR: Laura Morton Rowe, Director of Human Resources
CNO: Dawna Hendel R.N., Chief Nursing Officer and Vice President Patient Care Services
Web address: www.providence.org/saintjohns
Control: Church operated, Nongovernment, not–for–profit **Service**: General medical and surgical

Staffed Beds: 228 **Admissions**: 12370 **Census**: 148 **Outpatient Visits**: 180607 **Births**: 1770 **Total Expense ($000)**: 295319 **Payroll Expense ($000)**: 131951 **Personnel**: 1558

UCLA MEDICAL CENTER–SANTA MONICA (050112), 1250 16th Street, Zip 90404–1249; tel. 310/319–4000, **A**1 3 5 10 **F**3 8 9 11 12 13 15 18 20 22 24 26 29 30 31 34 35 37 39 40 41 45 46 47 48 49 50 51 52 54 55 56 57 58 59 62 64 65 68 70 72 74 75 76 78 79 81 82 83 84 85 86 87 89 93 96 97 102 107 108 110 111 114 115 116 117 118 119 130 131 143 145 146 147 149 **P**6 **S** University of California Systemwide Administration, Oakland, CA
Primary Contact: Paul Watkins, JD, Chief Administrative Officer
COO: Posie Carpenter R.N., MSN, Chief Administrative Officer
CFO: Paul Staton, Chief Financial Officer
CMO: James Atkinson M.D., Medical Director
CIO: Virginia McFerran, Chief Information Officer
CHR: Mark Speare, Senior Associate Director Patient Relations and Human Resources
Web address: www.healthcare.ucla.edu
Control: State, Government, Nonfederal **Service**: General medical and surgical

Staffed Beds: 265 **Admissions**: 16075 **Census**: 215 **Outpatient Visits**: 192411 **Births**: 1447 **Total Expense ($000)**: 512280 **Payroll Expense ($000)**: 184320 **Personnel**: 1871

SANTA ROSA—Sonoma County

AURORA SANTA ROSA HOSPITAL (054151), 1287 Fulton Road, Zip 95401–4923; tel. 707/800–7700, (Nonreporting)
Primary Contact: Kay E. Seim, Chief Executive Officer
Web address: www.aurorasantarosa.com
Control: Corporation, Investor–owned (for–profit) **Service**: Rehabilitation

Staffed Beds: 95

KAISER PERMANENTE SANTA ROSA MEDICAL CENTER (050690), 401 Bicentennial Way, Zip 95403–2192; tel. 707/571–4000, (Nonreporting) **A**1 3 5 10 **S** Kaiser Foundation Hospitals, Oakland, CA
Primary Contact: Judy Coffey, R.N., Senior Vice President and Area Manager
COO: Vicky Locey R.N., MSN, Chief Operating and Chief Nursing Officer
CFO: John Groesbeck, Area Finance Officer
CMO: Kirk Pappas M.D., Physician–in–Chief
CIO: Stanley Dobrawa, Area Technology Director
CNO: Vicky Locey R.N., MSN, Chief Operating and Chief Nursing Officer
Web address: www.kaiserpermanente.org
Control: Other not–for–profit (including NFP Corporation) **Service**: General medical and surgical

Staffed Beds: 117

SANTA ROSA MEMORIAL HOSPITAL (050174), 1165 Montgomery Drive, Zip 95405–4897, Mailing Address: P.O.Box 522, 95402–0522; tel. 707/546–3210, **A**1 2 10 **F**2 3 8 11 13 15 18 20 22 24 26 29 30 31 32 34 35 40 42 43 45 46 47 49 50 54 58 59 62 63 64 65 66 68 70 71 72 74 75 76 77 78 79 81 82 83 84 85 87 89 90 91 93 94 100 104 107 108 110 111 114 115 116 117 118 119 120 121 123 129 130 132 143 144 146 148 149 150 **S** Providence St. Joseph Health, Renton, WA
Primary Contact: Todd Salnas, President
CFO: Michel Riccioni, Chief Financial Officer
CMO: Richard Carvolth M.D., Chief Medical Officer
CIO: Benjamin Richard, Regional Information Technology Director
CHR: John Omel, Regional Vice President, Human Resources
CNO: Vicki White, Chief Nursing Officer
Web address: www.stjosephhealth.org
Control: Other not–for–profit (including NFP Corporation) **Service**: General medical and surgical

Staffed Beds: 278 **Admissions**: 11881 **Census**: 176 **Outpatient Visits**: 273315 **Births**: 677 **Total Expense ($000)**: 449366 **Payroll Expense ($000)**: 129964 **Personnel**: 1505

SUTTER SANTA ROSA REGIONAL HOSPITAL (050291), 30 Mark West Springs Road, Zip 95403; tel. 707/576–4000, (Includes WARRACK CAMPUS, 2449 Summerfield Road, Santa Rosa, California, Zip 95405–7815, tel. 707/576–4200) **A**1 3 5 10 **F**3 11 12 13 18 20 22 24 26 29 30 31 34 35 36 40 45 49 50 51 56 59 60 61 64 65 68 70 72 75 76 77 78 79 81 84 85 87 107 108 111 119 126 130 146 148 **P**3 5 **S** Sutter Health, Sacramento, CA
Primary Contact: Mike Purvis, Chief Administrative Officer
CMO: William Carroll M.D., Chief Medical Executive
Web address: www.sutterhealth.org
Control: Other not–for–profit (including NFP Corporation) **Service**: General medical and surgical

Staffed Beds: 84 **Admissions**: 6406 **Census**: 74 **Outpatient Visits**: 58701 **Births**: 1752 **Total Expense ($000)**: 243643 **Payroll Expense ($000)**: 72741 **Personnel**: 536

SEBASTOPOL—Sonoma County

SONOMA WEST MEDICAL CENTER (050385), 501 Petaluma Avenue, Zip 95472–4215; (Nonreporting) **A**10 21
Primary Contact: John Peleuses, Interim Chief Executive Officer
CFO: Robert Heinemeier, Interim Chief Financial Officer
Web address: www.sonomawesthealth.org/
Control: Hospital district or authority, Government, Nonfederal **Service**: General medical and surgical

Staffed Beds: 25

SEPULVEDA—Los Angeles County, See Los Angeles

SHERMAN OAKS—Los Angeles County, See Los Angeles

SIMI VALLEY—Ventura County

⊞ **SIMI VALLEY HOSPITAL (050236)**, 2975 North Sycamore Drive, Zip 93065–1277; tel. 805/955–6000, **A**1 2 10 **F**3 8 11 13 15 18 20 22 24 26 29 30 31 32 34 35 36 40 41 44 45 46 49 50 51 54 56 57 58 59 62 63 64 65 68 70 72 74 75 76 77 78 79 81 82 84 85 86 87 93 96 97 100 101 102 103 107 108 110 111 114 115 118 119 130 131 132 134 141 146 147 148 149 150 **P**3 4 **S** Adventist Health, Roseville, CA
Primary Contact: Jennifer Swenson, President and Chief Executive Officer
COO: Caroline Esparza, Sr. VP, COO & CNO
CFO: Brian Anderson, Chief Financial Officer
CMO: John Dingilian M.D., Chief Medical Officer
CIO: Bridget Nakamura, Director Information Systems
CHR: Susan Crabtree, Director Human Resources
CNO: Caroline Esparza, Senior Vice President, Chief Operating Officer and Chief Nurse Officer
Web address: www.simivalleyhospital.com
Control: Church operated, Nongovernment, not–for–profit **Service:** General medical and surgical

Staffed Beds: 144 **Admissions:** 7113 **Census:** 78 **Outpatient Visits:** 85451 **Births:** 549 **Total Expense ($000):** 144611 **Payroll Expense ($000):** 55946 **Personnel:** 763	

SOLVANG—Santa Barbara County

⊞ **SANTA YNEZ VALLEY COTTAGE HOSPITAL (051331)**, 2050 Viborg Road, Zip 93463–2295; tel. 805/688–6431, **A**1 10 18 **F**15 28 40 57 68 81 85 107 111 114 119 143 146 149 **S** Cottage Health, Santa Barbara, CA
Primary Contact: Ronald C. Werft, President and Chief Executive Officer
COO: Steven A Fellows, Executive Vice President and Chief Operating Officer
CFO: Brett Tande, Chief Financial Officer
CMO: Edmund Wroblewski M.D., Vice President Medical Affairs and Chief Medical Officer
CHR: Patrice Ryan, Vice President Human Resources
CNO: Herb J Geary, Chief Nursing Officer
Web address: www.cottagehealthsystem.org
Control: Other not–for–profit (including NFP Corporation) **Service:** General medical and surgical

Staffed Beds: 11 **Admissions:** 259 **Census:** 2 **Outpatient Visits:** 19532 **Births:** 0 **Total Expense ($000):** 16104 **Payroll Expense ($000):** 7445 **Personnel:** 64	

SONOMA—Sonoma County

SONOMA VALLEY HOSPITAL (050090), 347 Andrieux Street, Zip 95476–6811, Mailing Address: P.O.Box 600, 95476–0600; tel. 707/935–5000, (Total facility includes 27 beds in nursing home–type unit) **A**10 22 **F**3 12 13 15 29 34 35 40 44 45 49 50 57 59 62 63 68 70 75 76 77 79 81 82 84 85 93 107 111 117 119 128 130 146 147 148
Primary Contact: Kelly Mather, Chief Executive Officer
CFO: Jeanette Tarver, Director of Finance
CMO: Robert Cohen M.D., Chief Medical Officer
CIO: Fe Sendaydiego, Director Information Systems
CHR: Paula M Davis, Chief Human Resources Officer
CNO: Leslie Lovejoy R.N., Ph.D., Chief Nursing and Quality Officer
Web address: www.svh.com
Control: Hospital district or authority, Government, Nonfederal **Service:** General medical and surgical

Staffed Beds: 65 **Admissions:** 1544 **Census:** 32 **Outpatient Visits:** 67164 **Births:** 156 **Total Expense ($000):** 62399 **Payroll Expense ($000):** 29826 **Personnel:** 345	

SONORA—Tuolumne County

⊞ **ADVENTIST HEALTH SONORA (050335)**, 1000 Greenley Road, Zip 95370–4819; tel. 209/536–5000, (Total facility includes 68 beds in nursing home–type unit) **A**1 10 **F**3 8 11 13 15 17 18 20 28 29 30 31 34 35 37 39 40 45 49 53 54 56 57 59 62 63 64 70 71 75 76 77 78 79 81 84 85 86 87 93 94 96 97 104 107 108 110 111 114 115 117 118 119 120 121 123 127 128 129 130 131 132 133 135 143 144 145 146 148 **P**6 **S** Adventist Health, Roseville, CA
Primary Contact: Andrew Jahn, President and Chief Executive Officer
CFO: Greg McCulloch CPA, Vice President of Finance and Chief Financial Officer
CMO: Ed Clinite D.O., Chief of Staff
CIO: Manty Drews, Chief Information Officer
CNO: Julie Kline, Senior Vice President Patient Services
Web address: www.sonoramedicalcenter.org/
Control: Church operated, Nongovernment, not–for–profit **Service:** General medical and surgical

Staffed Beds: 152 **Admissions:** 4697 **Census:** 120 **Outpatient Visits:** 360182 **Births:** 547 **Total Expense ($000):** 233445 **Payroll Expense ($000):** 80355 **Personnel:** 1184	

SOUTH EL MONTE—Los Angeles County

☐ **GREATER EL MONTE COMMUNITY HOSPITAL (050738)**, 1701 Santa Anita Avenue, Zip 91733–3411; tel. 626/579–7777, **A**1 10 **F**3 13 14 17 18 29 34 35 40 41 45 49 50 57 59 64 68 70 75 76 77 78 79 81 82 85 87 89 92 93 107 108 119 128 130 146 **S** AHMC & Healthcare, Inc., Alhambra, CA
Primary Contact: Stanley Toy Jr, M.D., Chief Executive Officer
COO: Jose Ortega, Chief Operating Officer
CFO: Michael Chung, Chief Financial Officer
CMO: Dilip Patel M.D., Chief of Staff
CIO: Jay Geldhof, Director Information Systems
CHR: Jason Jaquez, Director Human Resources
CNO: Evelyn Calubaquib, Chief Nursing Officer
Web address: www.greaterelmonte.com
Control: Hospital district or authority, Government, Nonfederal **Service:** General medical and surgical

Staffed Beds: 117 **Admissions:** 3519 **Census:** 53 **Outpatient Visits:** 19341 **Births:** 359 **Total Expense ($000):** 67311 **Payroll Expense ($000):** 21681 **Personnel:** 291	

SOUTH LAKE TAHOE—El Dorado County

⊞ **BARTON MEMORIAL HOSPITAL (050352)**, 2170 South Avenue, Zip 96150–7026, Mailing Address: P.O.Box 9578, 96158–9578; tel. 530/541–3420, (Total facility includes 48 beds in nursing home–type unit) **A**1 5 10 20 **F**3 8 11 13 15 18 29 30 32 34 35 38 40 43 45 46 47 48 50 54 57 59 62 63 64 65 66 68 70 75 76 77 79 81 82 83 84 85 86 87 89 90 92 93 94 96 97 99 100 104 107 109 110 111 112 113 114 115 116 117 118 119 121 122 123 124 126 127 128 129 130 131 132 135 143 144 146 147 148 149
Primary Contact: Clint Purvance, M.D., President and Chief Executive Officer
CFO: Richard P Derby, Vice President Finance
CMO: Rhonda Sneeringer M.D., Chief Medical Officer
CIO: Jason Roberts, Director of Information Services
CNO: Susan Fairley, Chief Nursing Officer
Web address: www.bartonhealth.org
Control: Other not–for–profit (including NFP Corporation) **Service:** General medical and surgical

Staffed Beds: 111 **Admissions:** 2138 **Census:** 63 **Outpatient Visits:** 181917 **Births:** 365 **Total Expense ($000):** 103700 **Payroll Expense ($000):** 48930 **Personnel:** 837	

SOUTH SAN FRANCISCO—San Mateo County

⊞ **KAISER PERMANENTE SOUTH SAN FRANCISCO (050070)**, 1200 El Camino Real, Zip 94080–3208; tel. 650/742–2000, (Nonreporting) **A**1 3 5 10 **S** Kaiser Foundation Hospitals, Oakland, CA
Primary Contact: Ronald Groepper, Senior Vice President and Area Manager
CMO: Michelle Caughey M.D., Physician In Chief
CIO: Angel Shew, Director Area Technology
CHR: Sharon Barncord, Human Resource Business Partner
Web address: www.kaiserpermanente.org
Control: Other not–for–profit (including NFP Corporation) **Service:** General medical and surgical

Staffed Beds: 120	

STOCKTON—San Joaquin County

☐ **DAMERON HOSPITAL (050122)**, 525 West Acacia Street, Zip 95203–2484; tel. 209/944–5550, (Nonreporting) **A**1 10
Primary Contact: Lorraine P. Auerbach, FACHE, President and Chief Executive Officer
COO: Michael Glasberg, Senior Vice President, Chief Operating Officer
CFO: Elizabeth R Propp, Vice President Finance and Chief Financial Officer
CMO: Bradley Reinke M.D., Vice President Medical Affairs and Chief Medical Officer
CIO: David Kerrins, Vice President Information Services and Chief Information Officer
CHR: Tresha Moreland MS, Regional Vice President Human Resources
CNO: Denise J. Hair, Vice President of Nursing Services and Chief Nursing Officer
Web address: www.dameronhospital.org
Control: Other not–for–profit (including NFP Corporation) **Service:** General medical and surgical

Staffed Beds: 202	

⊞ **ST. JOSEPH'S BEHAVIORAL HEALTH CENTER (054123)**, 2510 North California Street, Zip 95204–5568; tel. 209/461–2000, **A**1 10 **F**5 29 38 68 98 100 101 103 104 105 130 132 143 146 **S** Dignity Health, San Francisco, CA
Primary Contact: Paul Rains, R.N., MSN, President
CFO: Doreen Hartmann, Chief Financial Officer
CMO: David Robinson D.O., Medical Director
CHR: Nancy Vargas, Chief Human Resources
CNO: Benny Lee Lucas Jr, Chief Nursing Executive
Web address: www.stjosephscanhelp.org
Control: Church operated, Nongovernment, not–for–profit **Service:** Psychiatric

Staffed Beds: 35 **Admissions:** 1915 **Census:** 33 **Outpatient Visits:** 11421 **Births:** 0 **Total Expense ($000):** 17820 **Payroll Expense ($000):** 9811 **Personnel:** 113	

☒ **ST. JOSEPH'S MEDICAL CENTER (050084)**, 1800 North California Street, Zip 95204–6019, Mailing Address: P.O.Box 213008, 95213–9008; tel. 209/943–2000, (Nonreporting) **A**1 2 3 10 **S** Dignity Health, San Francisco, CA
Primary Contact: Donald J. Wiley, President and Chief Executive Officer
COO: Michaell Rose, Chief Operating Officer
CFO: Nikki Ochoa, Interim Chief Financial Officer
CIO: Randall Gamino, Director Perot Site
CHR: Nancy Vargas, Vice President Human Resources
Web address: www.stjosephsCARES.org
Control: Church operated, Nongovernment, not–for–profit **Service:** General medical and surgical

Staffed Beds: 273

SUN CITY—Riverside County

☐ **MENIFEE VALLEY MEDICAL CENTER (050684)**, 28400 McCall Boulevard, Zip 92585–9537; tel. 951/679–8888, **A**1 10 **F**1 3 15 17 18 20 26 29 30 31 34 40 45 46 47 49 50 51 56 57 70 78 79 81 85 93 97 107 114 119 130 135 146 149 **S** Physicians for Healthy Hospitals, Hemet, CA
Primary Contact: Dan C. McLaughlin, Chief Executive Officer
CHR: Michele Bird, Chief Human Resources Officer
Web address: www.valleyhealthsystem.com
Control: Corporation, Investor–owned (for–profit) **Service:** General medical and surgical

Staffed Beds: 84 Admissions: 2723 Census: 30 Outpatient Visits: 21848 Births: 0 Total Expense ($000): 42105 Payroll Expense ($000): 15306

SUN VALLEY—Los Angeles County, See Los Angeles

SUSANVILLE—Lassen County

☒ **BANNER LASSEN MEDICAL CENTER (051320)**, 1800 Spring Ridge Drive, Zip 96130–6100; tel. 530/252–2000, **A**1 10 18 **F**3 13 15 29 30 31 34 38 39 40 45 59 76 79 81 85 87 93 107 110 111 114 119 129 130 146 148 149 **S** Banner Health, Phoenix, AZ
Primary Contact: Catherine S. Harshbarger, R.N., Chief Executive Officer
CFO: Jon R McMillan, Chief Financial Officer
CMO: Hal Meadows M.D., Chief Medical Officer
CIO: Randy Moore, Chief Information Officer
CHR: Ruth Smith, Chief Human Resource Officer
CNO: Sandy Goldstein R.N., Chief Nursing Officer
Web address: www.bannerhealth.com/locations/susanville/banner–lassen–medical–center
Control: Other not–for–profit (including NFP Corporation) **Service:** General medical and surgical

Staffed Beds: 25 Admissions: 1007 Census: 9 Outpatient Visits: 32805 Births: 248 Total Expense ($000): 31354 Payroll Expense ($000): 13590 Personnel: 191

SYLMAR—Los Angeles County, See Los Angeles

TARZANA—Los Angeles County, See Los Angeles

TEHACHAPI—Kern County

★ ⇑ **ADVENTIST HEALTH MEDICAL CENTER – TEHACHAPI VALLEY (051301)**, 115 West 'E' Street, Zip 93561–1607, Mailing Address: P.O.Box 1900, 93581–1900; tel. 661/823–3000, (Nonreporting) **A**10 18 21 **S** Adventist Health, Roseville, CA
Primary Contact: Eugene Suksi, Chief Executive Officer
CFO: Chester Beedle, Interim Chief Financial Officer
CMO: Susan Cribbs D.O., Chief of Staff
CIO: Dusty Colvard, Manager Information Technology
CHR: Susan Nelson–Jones, Director Human Resources
CNO: Juliana Kay Kirby R.N., MSN, Chief Nursing Officer
Web address: www.tvhd.org
Control: Hospital district or authority, Government, Nonfederal **Service:** General medical and surgical

Staffed Beds: 24

TEMECULA—Riverside County

☒ **TEMECULA VALLEY HOSPITAL (050775)**, 31700 Temecula Parkway, Zip 92592–5896; tel. 951/331–2216, (Nonreporting) **A**1 10 **S** Universal Health Services, Inc., King of Prussia, PA
Primary Contact: Darlene Wetton, R.N., Chief Executive Officer
Web address: www.temeculavalleyhospital.com
Control: Corporation, Investor–owned (for–profit) **Service:** General medical and surgical

Staffed Beds: 140

TEMPLETON—San Luis Obispo County

☒ **TWIN CITIES COMMUNITY HOSPITAL (050633)**, 1100 Las Tablas Road, Zip 93465–9796; tel. 805/434–3500, **A**1 10 **F**3 8 13 29 30 34 39 40 45 46 47 48 49 50 51 55 56 57 59 60 64 67 68 70 74 75 76 77 79 81 84 85 87 107 108 111 115 119 130 146 148 149 **S** TENET Healthcare Corporation, Dallas, TX
Primary Contact: Mark P. Lisa, FACHE, Chief Executive Officer
COO: Mike Lane, Chief Operating Officer
CFO: Paul Posmoga, Chief Financial Officer
CHR: Keith Stanhill, Chief Human Resources Officer
CNO: Joan Fonda, Chief Nursing Officer
Web address: www.twincitieshospital.com
Control: Corporation, Investor–owned (for–profit) **Service:** General medical and surgical

Staffed Beds: 89 Admissions: 4304 Census: 41 Outpatient Visits: 48220 Births: 622

THOUSAND OAKS—Ventura County

☒ ⇑ **LOS ROBLES HOSPITAL AND MEDICAL CENTER (050549)**, 215 West Janss Road, Zip 91360–1899; tel. 805/497–2727, (Nonreporting) (Includes THOUSAND OAKS SURGICAL HOSPITAL, 401 Rolling Oaks Drive, Thousand Oaks, California, Zip 91361–1050, tel. 805/497–2727; Natalie Mussi, President and Chief Executive Officer) **A**1 2 10 21 **S** HCA Healthcare, Nashville, TN
Primary Contact: Natalie Mussi, President and Chief Executive Officer
CMO: Hannah Grossman M.D., Chief Medical Officer
CIO: Alex Bryer, Director Information Management
CHR: John Bibby, Vice President Human Resources
CNO: Cynthia J Johnson R.N., Chief Nursing Officer
Web address: www.losrobleshospital.com
Control: Corporation, Investor–owned (for–profit) **Service:** General medical and surgical

Staffed Beds: 367

TORRANCE—Los Angeles County

☐ **DEL AMO HOSPITAL (054053)**, 23700 Camino Del Sol, Zip 90505–5000; tel. 310/530–1151, (Nonreporting) **A**1 10 **S** Universal Health Services, Inc., King of Prussia, PA
Primary Contact: Steven Oppenheimer, Chief Executive Officer
Web address: www.delamohospital.com
Control: Corporation, Investor–owned (for–profit) **Service:** Psychiatric

Staffed Beds: 70

☐ **HARBOR–UCLA MEDICAL CENTER (050376)**, 1000 West Carson Street, Zip 90502–2059; tel. 310/222–2345, **A**1 2 3 5 8 10 **F**3 11 12 13 14 15 17 18 19 20 22 24 25 26 29 30 31 32 34 35 39 40 41 42 43 44 45 46 47 48 49 50 52 55 56 57 59 60 61 62 64 65 66 68 70 72 74 76 77 78 79 81 82 83 84 85 87 88 89 93 97 98 99 100 101 102 107 108 110 114 115 116 118 119 120 129 130 131 132 134 135 138 141 146 147 148 149 150 **P**3 **S** Los Angeles County–Department of Health Services, Los Angeles, CA
Primary Contact: Kimberly McKenzie, R.N., MSN, Interim Chief Executive Officer
COO: Kimberly McKenzie R.N., MSN, Chief Nursing Officer and Chief Operations Officer
CFO: Jody Nakasuji, Chief Financial Officer
CMO: Timothy Van Natta M.D., Chief Medical Officer
CIO: Sandy Mungovan, Chief Information Officer
CHR: Karyl Smith, Director Human Resources
CNO: Kimberly McKenzie R.N., MSN, Chief Nursing Officer and Chief Operations Officer
Web address: www.harbor–ucla.org
Control: County, Government, Nonfederal **Service:** General medical and surgical

Staffed Beds: 373 Admissions: 18598 Census: 303 Outpatient Visits: 303265 Births: 858

CA

Hospital, Medicare Provider Number, Address, Telephone, Approval, Facility, and Physician Codes, Health Care System

★ American Hospital Association (AHA) membership
☐ The Joint Commission accreditation
○ Healthcare Facilities Accreditation Program
◇ DNV Healthcare Inc. accreditation
⇑ Center for Improvement in Healthcare Quality Accreditation
△ Commission on Accreditation of Rehabilitation Facilities (CARF) accreditation

✠ **PROVIDENCE LITTLE COMPANY OF MARY MEDICAL CENTER – TORRANCE (050353)**, 4101 Torrance Boulevard, Zip 90503–4664; tel. 310/540–7676, (Total facility includes 77 beds in nursing home–type unit) **A**1 2 10 **F**3 8 11 13 14 15 18 19 20 22 24 26 29 30 31 34 35 37 40 41 44 45 46 49 50 51 55 57 59 60 62 64 68 70 72 74 75 76 77 78 79 81 82 84 85 86 87 89 91 92 93 94 100 107 108 110 111 114 115 116 117 118 119 120 121 123 126 128 130 131 132 143 145 146 147 148 149 150 **P**5 **S** Providence St. Joseph Health, Renton, WA
Primary Contact: Mary E. Kingston, FACHE, R.N., Chief Executive Officer, South Bay Community
COO: Garry M. Olney, Chief Operating Officer
CFO: Elizabeth Zuanich, Chief Financial Officer
CMO: Richard Glimp M.D., Chief Medical Officer
CIO: Andrea Flores, Director, Information Systems
CHR: Melissa Baker, Director, Human Resources
CNO: Michael Jongsma R.N., Chief Nursing Officer
Web address: www.providence.org
Control: Church operated, Nongovernment, not–for–profit **Service:** General medical and surgical

Staffed Beds: 381 Admissions: 20692 Census: 250 Outpatient Visits: 306226 Births: 2636 Total Expense ($000): 325049 Payroll Expense ($000): 162026 Personnel: 2064

✠ **TORRANCE MEMORIAL MEDICAL CENTER (050351)**, 3330 Lomita Boulevard, Zip 90505–5073; tel. 310/325–9110, **A**1 2 10 **F**3 5 8 11 12 13 14 15 16 17 18 19 20 22 24 26 28 29 30 31 32 34 35 36 37 39 40 41 44 45 46 47 48 49 50 51 55 57 58 59 60 61 62 63 64 68 70 72 74 75 76 77 78 79 81 82 83 84 85 86 87 89 91 92 93 96 107 108 109 110 111 114 115 116 117 118 119 120 121 123 124 126 128 129 130 132 134 135 141 143 145 146 147 148 149 **P**2 3 5 7
Primary Contact: Craig Leach, President and Chief Executive Officer
CFO: Bill Larson, Vice President Finance and Chief Financial Officer
CMO: John McNamara M.D., Senior Vice President, Chief Medical Officer
CIO: Bernadette Reid, Vice President, Information Technology and Chief Information Officer
CHR: Linda Dobie R.N., JD, Vice President, Legal Affairs
CNO: Margaret Berwald R.N., MSN, Senior Vice President Patient Services
Web address: www.torrancememorial.org
Control: Other not–for–profit (including NFP Corporation) **Service:** General medical and surgical

Staffed Beds: 412 Admissions: 25980 Census: 302 Outpatient Visits: 419471 Births: 3039 Total Expense ($000): 613065 Payroll Expense ($000): 229523 Personnel: 3075

TRACY—San Joaquin County

✠ **SUTTER TRACY COMMUNITY HOSPITAL (050313)**, 1420 North Tracy Boulevard, Zip 95376–3497; tel. 209/835–1500, **A**1 10 **F**3 11 13 15 18 29 30 31 34 35 39 40 44 45 46 49 50 54 57 59 60 64 65 68 70 74 75 76 77 78 79 81 82 84 85 86 87 93 107 108 110 111 115 119 124 130 132 135 146 148 149 **P**3 5 **S** Sutter Health, Sacramento, CA
Primary Contact: David M. Thompson, Chief Executive Officer
CFO: Eric Dalton, Chief Financial Officer
CIO: Catherine M Larsen, Director Marketing
CHR: Melanie Wallace, Manager Human Resources
Web address: www.suttertracy.org
Control: Other not–for–profit (including NFP Corporation) **Service:** General medical and surgical

Staffed Beds: 77 Admissions: 3931 Census: 34 Outpatient Visits: 94009 Births: 676 Total Expense ($000): 110553 Payroll Expense ($000): 39468 Personnel: 478

TRAVIS AFB—Solano County

✠ **DAVID GRANT USAF MEDICAL CENTER**, 101 Bodin Circle, Zip 94535–1809; tel. 707/423–7300, (Nonreporting) **A**1 3 5 **S** Department of the Air Force, Washington, DC
Primary Contact: Lieutenant Michael Higgins, Commander
CFO: MajorJonathan Richards, Chief Financial Officer
CMO: ColonelChris Scharenbrock M.D., Chief Medical Staff
Web address: www.travis.af.mil/units/dgmc/index.asp
Control: Air Force, Government, federal **Service:** General medical and surgical

Staffed Beds: 116

TRUCKEE—Nevada County

★ **TAHOE FOREST HOSPITAL DISTRICT (051328)**, 10121 Pine Avenue, Zip 96161–4856, Mailing Address: P.O.Box 759, 96160–0759; tel. 530/587–6011, (Total facility includes 36 beds in nursing home–type unit) **A**2 3 5 10 18 **F**8 11 13 28 29 30 31 34 40 45 49 53 57 58 59 62 63 64 65 66 74 75 77 78 79 81 82 84 85 86 87 93 97 107 108 110 111 115 116 117 119 121 122 123 130 131 132 133 135 146 147 148 149 **P**3 7 **S** Tahoe Forest Health System, Truckee, CA
Primary Contact: Harry Weis, Chief Executive Officer
COO: Judy Newland R.N., Chief Operating Officer
CFO: Crystal Betts, Chief Financial Officer
CMO: Jeff Dodd M.D., Chief of Staff
CIO: Jake Dorst, Chief Information Officer
CHR: Jayne O'Flanagan, Chief Human Resources Officer
CNO: Judy Newland R.N., Chief Nursing Officer
Web address: www.tfhd.com
Control: Hospital district or authority, Government, Nonfederal **Service:** General medical and surgical

Staffed Beds: 62 Admissions: 1632 Census: 48 Outpatient Visits: 59449 Births: 341 Total Expense ($000): 127863 Payroll Expense ($000): 41098 Personnel: 568

TULARE—Tulare County

⇑ **TULARE REGIONAL MEDICAL CENTER (050359)**, 869 North Cherry Street, Zip 93274–2287; tel. 559/688–0821, **A**10 21 **F**1 3 4 11 13 15 16 17 20 26 29 34 35 40 45 46 47 48 49 50 53 56 57 59 60 62 64 65 66 67 68 70 71 72 73 74 75 76 79 80 81 85 86 88 89 90 93 97 98 107 108 110 111 114 119 127 128 129 130 131 132 135 146 147 148 149 150
Primary Contact: Alan Germany, Interim Chief Executive Officer
COO: Alan Germany, Chief Operating Officer
CFO: Michael Bernstein, Chief Financial Officer
CMO: Pradeep Kamboj M.D., Chief Medical Staff
CIO: Jim Peelgren, Chief Information Officer
CHR: John Barbadian, Vice President Human Resources
CNO: Patricia Mathewson, Chief Nursing Officer
Web address: www.tulareregional.org
Control: Hospital district or authority, Government, Nonfederal **Service:** General medical and surgical

Staffed Beds: 103 Admissions: 3366 Census: 41 Outpatient Visits: 98060 Births: 750 Total Expense ($000): 74744 Payroll Expense ($000): 28911 Personnel: 339

TURLOCK—Stanislaus County

✠ **EMANUEL MEDICAL CENTER (050179)**, 825 Delbon Avenue, Zip 95382–2016, Mailing Address: P.O.Box 819005, 95382; tel. 209/667–4200, **A**1 10 **F**3 8 11 15 18 20 22 24 26 29 30 31 34 40 47 48 49 54 59 60 64 68 70 73 75 76 77 78 79 81 89 93 97 107 108 110 111 114 115 118 119 120 121 123 130 132 146 147 148 149 **S** TENET Healthcare Corporation, Dallas, TX
Primary Contact: Susan C. Micheletti, Chief Executive Officer
CFO: David Neapolitan, Chief Financial Officer
CIO: Beth Walker, Chief Information Officer
CHR: Terry Gray, Vice President Human Resources
CNO: Constance Fairchilds R.N., Vice President Patient Care Services
Web address: www.emanuelmed.org
Control: Corporation, Investor–owned (for–profit) **Service:** General medical and surgical

Staffed Beds: 209 Admissions: 8647 Census: 98 Outpatient Visits: 123642 Births: 1395 Total Expense ($000): 171668 Payroll Expense ($000): 77029 Personnel: 998

TUSTIN—Orange County

○ **FOOTHILL REGIONAL MEDICAL CENTER (052053)**, 14662 Newport Avenue, Zip 92780–6064; tel. 714/838–9600, (Nonreporting) **A**10 11
Primary Contact: Barbara Schneider, R.N., Chief Executive Officer
COO: Kara Bourne R.N., MSN, Chief Nursing Officer and Chief Operating Officer
CIO: Darla Kennedy, Chief Information Officer
CHR: Aprille Major, Director Human Resources
Web address: www.hfcis.cdph.ca.gov/longtermcare/Facility.aspx?fac=060000013
Control: Corporation, Investor–owned (for–profit) **Service:** Acute long–term care hospital

Staffed Beds: 42

✠ **HEALTHSOUTH TUSTIN REHABILITATION HOSPITAL (053034)**, 14851 Yorba Street, Zip 92780–2925; tel. 714/832–9200, (Nonreporting) **A**1 10 **S** HEALTHSOUTH Corporation, Birmingham, AL
Primary Contact: Diana C. Hanyak, Chief Executive Officer
CFO: Paula Redmond, Controller
CMO: Rodric Bell M.D., Medical Director
CHR: JoAnn Roiz, Director Human Resources
Web address: www.tustinrehab.com
Control: Corporation, Investor–owned (for–profit) **Service:** Rehabilitation

Staffed Beds: 48

CA

TWENTYNINE PALMS—San Bernardino County

✠ **ROBERT E. BUSH NAVAL HOSPITAL**, 1145 Sturgis Road, Zip 92278, Mailing Address: Box 788250, MCAGCC, 92278–8250; tel. 760/830–2190, (Nonreporting) **A**1 3 **S** Bureau of Medicine and Surgery, Department of the Navy, Falls Church, VA
Primary Contact: Captain Jay C. Sourbeer, Commanding Officer
CHR: Virginia Ward, Human Resources Officer
CNO: CaptainSandra Mason MSN, R.N., Director Nursing Services and Senior Nurse Executive
Web address: www.med.navy.mil/sites/nhtp/Pages/default.aspx
Control: Navy, Government, federal **Service**: General medical and surgical

Staffed Beds: 29

UKIAH—Mendocino County

✠ **UKIAH VALLEY MEDICAL CENTER (050301)**, 275 Hospital Drive, Zip 95482–4531; tel. 707/462–3111, **A**1 5 10 **F**3 8 11 12 13 15 18 29 30 31 32 34 35 36 38 40 44 45 46 48 49 50 51 54 57 59 60 64 65 68 70 72 75 76 77 78 79 81 82 84 85 86 87 93 94 97 107 108 110 111 114 115 116 117 118 119 127 130 131 132 135 144 146 147 148 **P**3 **S** Adventist Health, Roseville, CA
Primary Contact: Gwen Matthews, R.N., MSN, Chief Executive Officer
CIO: David Eastman, Site Director
CHR: Rebecca Ryan, Interim Director Human Resources and Employee Health
Web address: www.adventisthealth.org
Control: Church operated, Nongovernment, not–for–profit **Service**: General medical and surgical

Staffed Beds: 50 Admissions: 3471 Census: 32 Outpatient Visits: 130069 Births: 801 Total Expense ($000): 147004 Payroll Expense ($000): 46438 Personnel: 696

UPLAND—San Bernardino County

✠ **SAN ANTONIO REGIONAL HOSPITAL (050099)**, 999 San Bernardino Road, Zip 91786–4920, Mailing Address: Box 5001, 91785–5001; tel. 909/985–2811, **A**1 2 10 **F**3 8 11 13 15 17 18 20 22 24 26 28 29 31 35 38 40 45 46 49 50 54 57 59 60 61 64 65 69 70 72 74 75 76 77 78 79 80 81 82 83 84 85 86 87 89 91 92 93 94 107 108 110 111 114 115 118 119 121 123 124 130 132 146 147 148
Primary Contact: Harris F. Koenig, President and Chief Executive Officer
CFO: Wah Chung Hsu, Senior Vice President Finance
CMO: Carlos Vigil M.D., President Medical Staff
CIO: Kamel Pandya, Director Information Services
CHR: Laura Kato, Vice President of Human Resources
CNO: Gudrun Moll R.N., MSN, Chief Nursing Officer
Web address: www.sarh.org
Control: Other not–for–profit (including NFP Corporation) **Service**: General medical and surgical

Staffed Beds: 271 Admissions: 15910 Census: 158 Outpatient Visits: 227695 Births: 2139 Total Expense ($000): 318973 Payroll Expense ($000): 131305 Personnel: 1863

VACAVILLE—Solano County

CALIFORNIA MEDICAL FACILITY, 1600 California Drive, Zip 95687; tel. 707/448–6841, (Nonreporting)
Primary Contact: David Horch, Chief Executive
CMO: Raymond Andreasen M.D., Chief Medical Officer–Inpatient
Web address: www.cya.ca.gov/visitors/fac_prison_cmf.html
Control: State, Government, Nonfederal **Service**: Hospital unit of an institution (prison hospital, college infirmary, etc.)

Staffed Beds: 215

✠ **KAISER PERMANENTE VACAVILLE MEDICAL CENTER (050767)**, 1 Quality Drive, Zip 95688–9494; tel. 707/624–4000, (Nonreporting) **A**1 2 3 10 **S** Kaiser Foundation Hospitals, Oakland, CA
Primary Contact: Norair Jemjemian, Senior Vice President and Area Manager
Web address: www.kp.org
Control: Other not–for–profit (including NFP Corporation) **Service**: General medical and surgical

Staffed Beds: 140

NORTHBAY VACAVALLEY HOSPITAL See Northbay Medical Center, Fairfield

VALENCIA—Los Angeles County

✠ **HENRY MAYO NEWHALL HOSPITAL (050624)**, 23845 McBean Parkway, Zip 91355–2083; tel. 661/200–2000, **A**1 2 10 **F**3 8 11 13 15 17 18 20 22 24 26 28 29 30 31 34 35 38 40 41 43 45 49 50 55 57 59 60 64 70 72 74 76 77 78 79 81 82 84 85 86 87 90 93 98 100 102 107 108 110 115 119 130 132 135 146 147 148 **P**7
Primary Contact: Roger E. Seaver, President and Chief Executive Officer
COO: John V Schleif, Senior Vice President and Chief Operating Officer
CFO: Anna Brewer, Interim Chief Financial Officer
CMO: Richard Frankenstein M.D., Vice President and Chief Medical Officer
CIO: Ray Moss, Vice President and Chief Information Officer
CHR: Mark Puleo, Vice President and Chief Human Resources Officer
CNO: Jennifer Castaldo R.N., Vice President, Patient Care and Chief Nursing Officer
Web address: www.henrymayo.com
Control: Other not–for–profit (including NFP Corporation) **Service**: General medical and surgical

Staffed Beds: 238 Admissions: 12131 Census: 158 Outpatient Visits: 110268 Births: 1332 Total Expense ($000): 305650 Payroll Expense ($000): 99738 Personnel: 1447

VALLEJO—Solano County

✠ **ADVENTIST HEALTH ST. HELENA (054074)**, 525 Oregon Street, Zip 94590–3201; tel. 707/648–2200, **A**1 10 **F**29 30 50 64 65 68 98 99 104 105 130 146 **P**3 **S** Adventist Health, Roseville, CA
Primary Contact: Steven Herber, M.D., FACS, President and Chief Executive Officer
CFO: Edward A McDonald, Chief Financial Officer
Web address: www.sthelenahospitals.org/location/center–for–behavioral–health
Control: Other not–for–profit (including NFP Corporation) **Service**: Psychiatric

Staffed Beds: 58 Admissions: 2443 Census: 57 Outpatient Visits: 17349 Births: 0 Total Expense ($000): 24431 Payroll Expense ($000): 13036 Personnel: 122

✠ △ **KAISER PERMANENTE VALLEJO MEDICAL CENTER (050073)**, 975 Sereno Drive, Zip 94589–2441; tel. 707/651–1000, (Nonreporting) **A**1 2 3 5 7 10 **S** Kaiser Foundation Hospitals, Oakland, CA
Primary Contact: Corwin N. Harper, Senior Vice President and Area Manager
COO: Karen Grisnak R.N., Chief Operating Officer and Assistant Administrator Quality Services
CFO: Joseph D'Angina, Area Finance Officer
CMO: Steven Stricker M.D., Physician in Chief
CIO: Gale Austin–Moore, Director Area Technology
CHR: Sherri Stegge, Director Human Resources
Web address: www.kaiserpermanente.org
Control: Other not–for–profit (including NFP Corporation) **Service**: General medical and surgical

Staffed Beds: 248

✠ **SUTTER SOLANO MEDICAL CENTER (050101)**, 300 Hospital Drive, Zip 94589–2574, Mailing Address: P.O.Box 3189, 94590–0669; tel. 707/554–4444, **A**1 2 10 **F**3 8 11 13 15 18 29 30 31 34 35 40 41 45 46 49 50 51 55 57 58 59 64 68 70 74 75 76 77 78 79 81 84 85 86 87 89 100 107 108 110 111 114 118 119 120 121 123 124 130 132 146 **P**3 5 **S** Sutter Health, Sacramento, CA
Primary Contact: Abhishek Dosi, Chief Executive Officer
CHR: Jean Willhite, Director Human Resources
Web address: www.suttersolano.org
Control: Other not–for–profit (including NFP Corporation) **Service**: General medical and surgical

Staffed Beds: 108 Admissions: 4250 Census: 49 Outpatient Visits: 62889 Births: 516 Total Expense ($000): 149675 Payroll Expense ($000): 49666 Personnel: 489

VAN NUYS—Los Angeles County, See Los Angeles

VENTURA—Ventura County

★ ⇧ **COMMUNITY MEMORIAL HOSPITAL (050394)**, 147 North Brent Street, Zip 93003–2809; tel. 805/652–5011, (Includes COMMUNITY MEMORIAL HOSPITAL, 147 North Brent Street, Ventura, California, Zip 93003–2854, tel. 805/652–5011) (Total facility includes 66 beds in nursing home–type unit) **A**2 3 5 10 13 21 **F**3 8 11 12 13 15 17 18 19 20 22 24 26 28 29 30 31 32 34 35 40 45 46 47 48 49 53 54 57 59 64 65 66 68 70 71 72 74 75 77 78 79 81 82 83 84 85 86 89 91 93 97 104 107 108 110 111 114 115 118 119 126 127 128 130 131 132 141 144 145 146 147 148 **P**4 5 7 **S** Community Memorial Health System, Ventura, CA
Primary Contact: Gary Wilde, President and Chief Executive Officer
COO: Adam Thunell, Chief Operating Officer and Vice President Operations
CFO: David Glyer, Vice President Finance
CMO: Stanley Frochtzwajg M.D., Chief Medical Officer
CIO: Ron Sandifer, Chief Information Officer
CHR: Diany Klein, Vice President Human Resources
Web address: www.cmhshealth.org
Control: Other not–for–profit (including NFP Corporation) **Service**: General medical and surgical

Staffed Beds: 284 Admissions: 12957 Census: 210 Outpatient Visits: 489312 Births: 2780 Total Expense ($000): 365566 Payroll Expense ($000): 130271 Personnel: 1924

Hospital, Medicare Provider Number, Address, Telephone, Approval, Facility, and Physician Codes, Health Care System

★ American Hospital Association (AHA) membership
□ The Joint Commission accreditation
○ Healthcare Facilities Accreditation Program
◇ DNV Healthcare Inc. accreditation
⇧ Center for Improvement in Healthcare Quality Accreditation
△ Commission on Accreditation of Rehabilitation Facilities (CARF) accreditation

⊞ **VENTURA COUNTY MEDICAL CENTER (050159)**, 3291 Loma Vista Road, Zip 93003–3099; tel. 805/652–6000, (Nonreporting) **A**1 3 10
Primary Contact: Kim S. Milstien, Chief Executive Officer
CMO: Bryan Wong M.D., Medical Director
CIO: Terry Theobald, Chief Information Officer
CHR: Tim Rhyne, Personnel Officer
CNO: Susan Scott, Chief Nurse Executive
Web address: www.vchca.org
Control: County, Government, Nonfederal **Service**: General medical and surgical

Staffed Beds: 160

☐ **VISTA DEL MAR HOSPITAL (054077)**, 801 Seneca Street, Zip 93001–1411; tel. 805/653–6434, (Nonreporting) **A**1 10 **S** Signature Healthcare Services, Corona, CA
Primary Contact: Mayla Krebsbach, Chief Executive Officer
CFO: Kurt Broten, Chief Financial Officer
CMO: Steve Ruths M.D., Chief Medical Officer
Web address: www.vistadelmarhospital.com
Control: Corporation, Investor–owned (for–profit) **Service**: Psychiatric

Staffed Beds: 87

VICTORVILLE—San Bernardino County

★ ○ **DESERT VALLEY HOSPITAL (050709)**, 16850 Bear Valley Road, Zip 92395–5795; tel. 760/241–8000, (Nonreporting) **A**10 11 **S** Prime Healthcare, Ontario, CA
Primary Contact: Fred Hunter, R.N., Chief Executive Officer
COO: Luis Leon, Chief Operating Officer
CFO: Martin Mansukhani, Chief Financial Officer
CIO: Sreekant Gotti, Director Information Systems
Web address: www.dvmc.com
Control: Corporation, Investor–owned (for–profit) **Service**: General medical and surgical

Staffed Beds: 110

☐ **VICTOR VALLEY GLOBAL MEDICAL CENTER (050517)**, 15248 Eleventh Street, Zip 92395–3704; tel. 760/245–8691, (Nonreporting) **A**1 10
Primary Contact: Suzanne Richards, R.N., M.P.H., FACHE, Chief Executive Officer
COO: Doreen Dann R.N., Chief Operating Officer
CIO: Joe Archer, Chief Information Officer
CHR: Cesar Lugo, Director Human Resources
Web address: www.vvgmc.com
Control: Other not–for–profit (including NFP Corporation) **Service**: General medical and surgical

Staffed Beds: 101

VISALIA—Tulare County

⊞ △ **KAWEAH DELTA MEDICAL CENTER (050057)**, 400 West Mineral King Boulevard, Zip 93291–6263; tel. 559/624–2000, (Includes SOUTH CAMPUS, 1633 South Court Street, Visalia, California, Zip 93277, tel. 559/624–6090) **A**1 5 7 10 **F**3 13 15 17 18 20 22 24 26 28 29 30 31 34 35 40 41 43 45 49 50 51 53 54 56 57 59 60 62 63 64 65 68 70 73 74 75 76 77 78 79 81 82 84 85 86 87 89 90 93 97 98 99 100 101 102 103 104 107 108 110 111 114 116 117 118 119 123 124 126 127 128 129 130 131 132 134 135 144 146 147 148 149 **P**3 5 7
Primary Contact: Garay Herbst, Chief Executive Officer
COO: Thomas J Rayner, Senior Vice President and Chief Operating Officer
CFO: Gary Herbst, Senior Vice President and Chief Financial Officer
CMO: Edward Hirsch M.D., Vice President Chief Medical and Quality Officer
CIO: Doug Leeper, Chief Information Officer
CHR: Dianne E Cox, Vice President of Human Resources
CNO: Regina Sawyer, Vice President Chief Nursing Officer
Web address: www.kaweahdelta.org
Control: Hospital district or authority, Government, Nonfederal **Service**: General medical and surgical

Staffed Beds: 437 Admissions: 25484 Census: 400 Outpatient Visits: 679356 Births: 4425 Total Expense ($000): 581120 Payroll Expense ($000): 232697 Personnel: 3866

WALNUT CREEK—Contra Costa County

⊞ △ **JOHN MUIR MEDICAL CENTER, WALNUT CREEK (050180)**, 1601 Ygnacio Valley Road, Zip 94598–3194; tel. 925/939–3000, **A**1 2 7 10 **F**3 11 13 15 17 18 19 20 22 24 26 28 29 30 31 32 34 35 37 39 40 41 43 44 45 46 47 48 49 50 54 55 56 57 58 59 62 64 65 68 70 72 74 75 76 77 78 79 80 81 82 83 84 85 86 87 88 89 90 91 93 95 96 100 102 108 110 118 119 120 121 123 124 126 130 131 132 141 145 146 147 148 149 150 **P**3 5 7 **S** John Muir Health, Walnut Creek, CA
Primary Contact: Jane Willemsen, President and Chief Administrative Officer
COO: Raymond Nassief, Senior Vice President, Hospital Operations and Support Services
CFO: Christian Pass, Senior Vice President & Chief Financial Officer
CMO: Irving Pike M.D., Senior Vice President and Chief Medical Officer
CIO: Jon Russell, Senior Vice President & Chief Information Officer
CHR: Lisa Foust, Senior Vice President, Human Resources
CNO: Michelle Anne Lopes MSN, R.N., Senior Vice President, Patient Care Services & Chief Nursing Officer
Web address: www.johnmuirhealth.com/
Control: Other not–for–profit (including NFP Corporation) **Service**: General medical and surgical

wStaffed Beds: 425 Admissions: 19461 Census: 267 Outpatient Visits: 316787 Births: 2792 Total Expense ($000): 799830 Payroll Expense ($000): 282446 Personnel: 2263

⊞ **KAISER PERMANENTE WALNUT CREEK MEDICAL CENTER (050072)**, 1425 South Main Street, Zip 94596–5300; tel. 925/295–4000, (Nonreporting) (Includes KAISER FOUNDATION HOSPITAL, 200 Muir Road, Martinez, California, Zip 94553–4696, tel. 510/372–1000) **A**1 2 3 5 10 **S** Kaiser Foundation Hospitals, Oakland, CA
Primary Contact: Colleen McKeown, Senior Vice President and Area Manager
CFO: Yakesun Wing, Business Strategy and Finance Leader
Web address: www.kaiserpermanente.org
Control: Other not–for–profit (including NFP Corporation) **Service**: General medical and surgical

Staffed Beds: 233

WATSONVILLE—Santa Cruz County

⊞ **WATSONVILLE COMMUNITY HOSPITAL (050194)**, 75 Nielson Street, Zip 95076–2468; tel. 831/724–4741, **A**1 10 **F**3 11 13 15 18 20 29 34 35 40 45 49 50 51 57 60 64 68 70 72 74 76 77 79 81 87 89 93 97 107 111 115 119 126 130 146 148 149 **S** Quorum Health, Brentwood, TN
Primary Contact: Audra Earle, FACHE, Chief Executive Officer
CFO: Rachel Jones, Chief Financial Officer
CIO: Sergio Nell, Director Information Systems
CNO: Donna Salvi, Chief Nursing Officer
Web address: www.watsonvillehospital.com
Control: Corporation, Investor–owned (for–profit) **Service**: General medical and surgical

Staffed Beds: 106 Admissions: 3690 Census: 41 Outpatient Visits: 74580 Births: 945 Total Expense ($000): 110721 Payroll Expense ($000): 47664 Personnel: 605

WEAVERVILLE—Trinity County

TRINITY HOSPITAL (051315), 60 Easter Avenue, Zip 96093, Mailing Address: P.O.Box 1229, 96093–1229; tel. 530/623–5541, (Nonreporting) **A**10 18
Primary Contact: Aaron Rogers, Chief Executive Officer
CFO: Kathy Walker, Chief Financial Officer
CMO: Donald Krouse M.D., Chief of Staff
CIO: Jake Odom, Chief Information Officer
CHR: Heidi Corrigan, Manager Human Resources
CNO: Judy Nordlund R.N., Chief Nursing Officer
Web address: www.mcmedical.org
Control: Hospital district or authority, Government, Nonfederal **Service**: General medical and surgical

Staffed Beds: 47

WEST COVINA—Los Angeles County

☐ **WEST COVINA MEDICAL CENTER (050096)**, 725 South Orange Avenue, Zip 91790–2614; tel. 626/338–8481, **A**1 10 **F**29 79 81 104 105 108 128 130 148
Primary Contact: Gerald H. Wallman, Administrator
CFO: Kami Horvat, Chief Financial Officer
CMO: Erich Pollak M.D., Chief of Staff
CHR: Lourdes Meza, Coordinator Human Resources
CNO: Guadalupe Ojeda R.N., Chief Nursing Officer
Control: Corporation, Investor–owned (for–profit) **Service**: General medical and surgical

Staffed Beds: 46 Admissions: 602 Census: 33 Outpatient Visits: 7360 Births: 0 Total Expense ($000): 13855 Payroll Expense ($000): 7066

WEST HILLS—Los Angeles County, See Los Angeles

WEST LOS ANGELES—Los Angeles County, See Los Angeles

WESTMINSTER—Orange County

⊞ **KINDRED HOSPITAL–WESTMINSTER (052035)**, 200 Hospital Circle, Zip 92683–3910; tel. 714/893–4541, (Nonreporting) **A**1 10 **S** Kindred Healthcare, Louisville, KY
Primary Contact: Julie Myers, Chief Executive Officer
CFO: Dale Wagner, Chief Financial Officer
Web address: www.khwestminster.com/
Control: Corporation, Investor–owned (for–profit) **Service**: Acute long–term care hospital

Staffed Beds: 109

WHITTIER—Los Angeles County

☒ **PIH HEALTH HOSPITAL–WHITTIER (050169)**, 12401 Washington Boulevard, Zip 90602–1099; tel. 562/698–0811, (Total facility includes 35 beds in nursing home–type unit) **A**1 2 3 5 10 **F**3 11 12 13 15 18 20 22 24 26 28 29 30 31 34 35 36 37 40 41 44 45 46 49 50 51 54 55 56 57 58 59 60 61 62 63 64 65 66 68 69 70 72 74 75 76 77 78 79 81 84 85 86 87 89 90 92 93 96 107 108 110 111 114 115 116 117 118 119 120 121 123 124 128 130 131 132 135 143 145 146 147 148 149 **P**3 5 **S** PIH Health, Whittier, CA
Primary Contact: James R. West, President and Chief Executive Officer
COO: Reanna Thompson R.N., Chief Operating Officer and Chief Nursing Officer
CFO: Greg Williams, Chief Financial Officer
CMO: Rosalio J Lopez M.D., Senior Vice President and Chief Medical Officer
CIO: Jason Fischer, Chief Information Officer
CHR: Sherri Hollingsworth, Chief Human Resources Officer
CNO: Reanna Thompson R.N., Chief Operating Officer and Chief Nursing Officer
Web address: www.PIHHealth.org
Control: Other not–for–profit (including NFP Corporation) **Service:** General medical and surgical

Staffed Beds: 245 **Admissions:** 18078 **Census:** 212 **Outpatient Visits:** 285767 **Births:** 2715 **Total Expense ($000):** 525604 **Payroll Expense ($000):** 188931 **Personnel:** 2852

☐ **WHITTIER HOSPITAL MEDICAL CENTER (050735)**, 9080 Colima Road, Zip 90605–1600; tel. 562/945–3561, (Nonreporting) **A**1 10 **S** AHMC & Healthcare, Inc., Alhambra, CA
Primary Contact: Richard Castro, Chief Executive Officer
COO: Mary Anne Monje, Chief Financial Officer and Chief Operating Officer
CFO: Mary Anne Monje, Chief Financial Officer and Chief Operating Officer
CIO: Jay Geldhof, Director Information Systems
CHR: Martha Salcedo, Interim Director Human Resources
CNO: Sarkis Vartanian, Chief Nursing Officer
Web address: www.whittierhospital.com
Control: Corporation, Investor–owned (for–profit) **Service:** General medical and surgical

Staffed Beds: 81

WILLITS—Mendocino County

☒ **FRANK R. HOWARD MEMORIAL HOSPITAL (051310)**, One Marcela Drive, Zip 95490–4298; tel. 707/459–6801, **A**1 10 18 **F**11 15 29 30 34 35 40 57 59 68 70 75 79 81 93 97 107 110 111 115 119 127 131 132 133 135 146 147 148 **S** Adventist Health, Roseville, CA
Primary Contact: Jason Wells, President and Chief Executive Officer
CFO: Judson Howe, Chief Financial Officer
CMO: Kimberly Faucher M.D., Chief Medical Officer
CIO: Cecilia Winiger, Community Outreach and Communication Manager
CHR: Darcy De Leon, Executive Director, Human Resources
CNO: Karen M Scott, Vice President Patient Care
Web address: www.howardhospital.com
Control: Church operated, Nongovernment, not–for–profit **Service:** General medical and surgical

Staffed Beds: 25 **Admissions:** 1509 **Census:** 17 **Outpatient Visits:** 38128 **Births:** 0 **Total Expense ($000):** 61290 **Payroll Expense ($000):** 22003 **Personnel:** 224

WILLOWS—Glenn County

GLENN MEDICAL CENTER (051306), 1133 West Sycamore Street, Zip 95988–2745; tel. 530/934–1800, (Nonreporting) **A**10 18
Primary Contact: Barbara Rydgren, Administrator
CFO: John Lovrich, Chief Financial Officer
CHR: Deborah McMillan, Director Human Resources
Web address: www.glennmed.org
Control: Other not–for–profit (including NFP Corporation) **Service:** General medical and surgical

Staffed Beds: 15

WOODLAND—Yolo County

☒ **WOODLAND HEALTHCARE (050127)**, 1325 Cottonwood Street, Zip 95695–5199; tel. 530/662–3961, **A**1 5 10 **F**2 3 8 11 13 18 20 26 28 29 30 31 34 35 40 45 46 47 49 50 51 56 57 58 59 60 61 62 64 68 70 72 74 75 76 78 79 81 82 84 85 86 87 89 98 100 102 107 108 111 115 119 129 130 132 146 147 148 149 **P**3 **S** Dignity Health, San Francisco, CA
Primary Contact: H Kevin. Vaziri, President
CMO: Sarada Mylavarapu M.D., Chief Medical Officer
Web address: www.woodlandhealthcare.org
Control: Other not–for–profit (including NFP Corporation) **Service:** General medical and surgical

Staffed Beds: 108 **Admissions:** 4391 **Census:** 56 **Outpatient Visits:** 56024 **Births:** 652 **Total Expense ($000):** 174142 **Payroll Expense ($000):** 61288 **Personnel:** 602

WOODLAND HILLS—Los Angeles County, See Los Angeles

YREKA—Siskiyou County

☐ **FAIRCHILD MEDICAL CENTER (051316)**, 444 Bruce Street, Zip 96097–3450; tel. 530/842–4121, (Nonreporting) **A**1 10 18
Primary Contact: Jonathon Andrus, Chief Executive Officer
CFO: Kelly Martin, Chief Financial Officer
CMO: David Della Lana M.D., Chief of Staff
CIO: Joan Munson, Manager Information Systems
CHR: Joann Sarmento, Manager Human Resources
CNO: Kathy Shelvock R.N., Assistant Administrator Patient Care Services
Web address: www.fairchildmed.org
Control: Other not–for–profit (including NFP Corporation) **Service:** General medical and surgical

Staffed Beds: 25

YUBA CITY—Sutter County

FREMONT MEDICAL CENTER See Rideout Memorial Hospital, Marysville

☐ **SUTTER SURGICAL HOSPITAL – NORTH VALLEY (050766)**, 455 Plumas Boulevard, Zip 95991–5074; tel. 530/749–5700, **A**1 10 **F**3 26 29 30 34 46 57 64 68 74 79 81 85 86 111 146 **S** Sutter Health, Sacramento, CA
Primary Contact: Shawndra Simpson, Interim Chief Executive Officer
CHR: Michelle Guina, Manager Human Resources
CNO: David Cooke, Chief Nursing Officer
Web address: www.sshnv.org
Control: Corporation, Investor–owned (for–profit) **Service:** Surgical

Staffed Beds: 14 **Admissions:** 483 **Census:** 3 **Outpatient Visits:** 5510 **Births:** 0 **Total Expense ($000):** 25045 **Payroll Expense ($000):** 6055 **Personnel:** 78

YUCCA VALLEY—San Bernardino County

☒ **HI-DESERT MEDICAL CENTER (050279)**, 6530 La Contenta, Suite 100, Zip 92284, Mailing Address: 6601 White Feather Road, Joshua Tree, 92252–6607; tel. 760/366–3711, (Total facility includes 120 beds in nursing home–type unit) **A**1 10 20 **F**3 8 13 15 18 29 30 34 35 40 45 50 54 62 63 64 68 70 75 76 77 79 81 82 85 87 92 93 104 107 108 110 111 115 119 128 130 135 146 148 149 **S** TENET Healthcare Corporation, Dallas, TX
Primary Contact: Karen Faulis, Chief Executive Officer
CMO: Sumit Mahajan M.D., Chief Medical Staff
CIO: Robin Schmelling, Chief Information Officer
CHR: Barbara Staresinic, Director Human Resources
Web address: www.hdmc.org
Control: Corporation, Investor–owned (for–profit) **Service:** General medical and surgical

Staffed Beds: 179 **Admissions:** 2739 **Census:** 139 **Outpatient Visits:** 57607 **Births:** 432 **Total Expense ($000):** 65575 **Payroll Expense ($000):** 29134 **Personnel:** 476

CA

COLORADO

CO

ALAMOSA—Alamosa County

★ **SAN LUIS VALLEY HEALTH (060008)**, 106 Blanca Avenue, Zip 81101–2393; tel. 719/589–2511, **A**3 10 20 **F**3 7 11 13 15 18 28 29 30 31 33 40 43 45 53 70 74 75 77 78 79 81 85 93 107 108 110 111 115 119 129 130 131 133 146 147 148 **P**6 **S** San Luis Valley Health, Alamosa, CO
Primary Contact: Konnie Martin, Chief Executive Officer
COO: Patti Thompson, Chief Operating Officer
CFO: Shane Mortensen, Chief Financial Officer
CMO: Gregory McAuliffe M.D., Chief Medical Officer
CIO: Chuck Laufle, Director of Information Services
CHR: Mandy Lee Crockett, Director Human Resources
Web address: www.sanluisvalleyhealth.org
Control: Other not–for–profit (including NFP Corporation) **Service:** General medical and surgical

Staffed Beds: 44 **Admissions:** 2049 **Census:** 18 **Outpatient Visits:** 113493 **Births:** 469 **Total Expense ($000):** 77388 **Payroll Expense ($000):** 36715 **Personnel:** 587

ASPEN—Pitkin County

✠ **ASPEN VALLEY HOSPITAL (061324)**, 0401 Castle Creek Road, Zip 81611–1159; tel. 970/925–1120, **A**1 10 18 **F**3 7 8 10 11 13 15 18 28 29 31 34 35 36 37 40 43 50 53 54 57 59 64 68 70 75 76 77 78 79 81 82 85 86 87 89 91 93 107 108 110 111 115 118 119 126 129 130 131 132 133 135 144 146 147 148 149
Primary Contact: David Ressler, Chief Executive Officer
CFO: Ginette Sebenaler, Associate Chief Financial Officer
CMO: J Christopher Beck D.O., President Medical Staff
CIO: Ginny Dyche, Director Community Relations
CHR: Alicia Miller, Director Human Resources
CNO: Elaine Gerson, Chief Clinical Officer and General Counsel
Web address: www.avhaspen.org
Control: Hospital district or authority, Government, Nonfederal **Service:** General medical and surgical

Staffed Beds: 25 **Admissions:** 995 **Census:** 8 **Outpatient Visits:** 35032 **Births:** 243 **Total Expense ($000):** 86554 **Payroll Expense ($000):** 36948 **Personnel:** 414

AURORA—Adams County

✠ **CHILDREN'S HOSPITAL COLORADO (063301)**, 13123 East 16th Avenue, Zip 80045–7106; tel. 720/777–1234, (Includes CHILDREN'S HOSPITAL OF COLORADO AT MEMORIAL, 1400 East Boulder Street, Colorado Springs, Colorado, Zip 80909–5533; tel. 719/365–5000) **A**1 3 5 10 **F**3 11 12 13 14 17 19 21 23 25 27 28 29 30 31 32 34 35 36 38 39 40 41 42 43 44 45 46 48 49 50 53 54 55 58 59 60 61 64 65 66 68 71 72 74 75 76 77 78 79 80 81 82 84 85 86 87 88 89 91 92 93 95 96 97 98 99 100 101 102 104 105 106 107 108 111 114 115 116 117 119 126 129 130 131 132 134 136 137 138 139 141 144 146 147 148
Primary Contact: Jena Hausmann, President and Chief Executive Officer
COO: David Biggerstaff, Chief Operating Officer
CFO: Jeff Harrington, Chief Financial Officer
CMO: Joan Bothner M.D., Chief Medical Officer
CIO: Mary Anne Leach, Vice President and Chief Information Officer
CHR: Nita Mosby Henry, Senior Vice President Human Resources and Chief Inclusion Officer
CNO: Andrea Ferretti, Interim Chief Nursing Officer, Vice President and Associate Chief Nursing Officer Network of Care
Web address: www.thechildrenshospital.org
Control: Other not–for–profit (including NFP Corporation) **Service:** Children's general medical and surgical

Staffed Beds: 486 **Admissions:** 15062 **Census:** 266

✠ **SPALDING REHABILITATION HOSPITAL (063027)**, 900 Potomac Steet, Zip 80011–6716; tel. 303/367–1166, (Nonreporting) **A**1 10 **S** HCA Healthcare, Nashville, TN
Primary Contact: Daniel Miller, FACHE, President and Chief Executive Officer
COO: Debbie Petersen R.N., Chief Operating Officer and Chief Nursing Officer
CFO: Joyce Webber, Chief Financial Officer
CHR: Donna Greeley, Director Human Resources
CNO: Debbie Petersen R.N., Chief Operating Officer and Chief Nursing Officer
Web address: www.spaldingrehab.com
Control: Partnership, Investor–owned (for–profit) **Service:** Rehabilitation

Staffed Beds: 40

✠ **UNIVERSITY OF COLORADO HOSPITAL (060024)**, 12401 East 17th Avenue, MS F417, Zip 80045–2545; tel. 720/848–0000, **A**1 2 3 5 8 10 **F**3 4 5 6 8 9 11 12 13 15 16 17 18 20 22 24 26 28 29 30 31 33 34 35 36 37 38 40 43 44 45 46 47 48 49 50 52 53 54 55 56 57 58 59 60 61 64 65 68 70 71 72 74 75 76 77 78 79 80 81 82 83 84 85 86 87 90 91 92 93 94 96 97 98 100 101 102 103 104 107 108 109 110 111 112 113 114 115 117 118 119 120 121 123 124 126 130 131 132 134 135 136 137 138 139 140 141 142 146 147 148 149 150 **S** University of Colorado Health, Fort Collins, CO
Primary Contact: William Cook, President and Chief Executive Officer
COO: Thomas Gronow, Chief Operating Officer
CFO: Barbara Carveth, Chief Financial Officer
CMO: Jean Kutner M.D., Chief Medical Officer
CIO: Steve Hess, Vice President Information Services and Chief Information Officer
CNO: Carolyn Lucey Sanders, Senior Vice President Patient Services and Chief Nursing Officer
Web address: www.uchealth.org
Control: Hospital district or authority, Government, Nonfederal **Service:** General medical and surgical

Staffed Beds: 661 **Admissions:** 29870 **Census:** 491 **Outpatient Visits:** 1102847 **Births:** 3166 **Total Expense ($000):** 1266347 **Payroll Expense ($000):** 432196 **Personnel:** 5553

AURORA—Arapahoe County

✠ **KINDRED HOSPITAL–AURORA (062013)**, 700 Potomac Street 2nd Floor, Zip 80011–6844; tel. 720/857–8333, (Nonreporting) **A**1 10 **S** Kindred Healthcare, Louisville, KY
Primary Contact: Jeanette Williams, Chief Executive Officer
CMO: Eric Yaeger M.D., Chief Medical Officer
CHR: Becky Small, Chief Human Resources Officer
CNO: Paul Green, Chief Clinical Officer
Web address: www.khaurora.com/
Control: Corporation, Investor–owned (for–profit) **Service:** Acute long–term care hospital

Staffed Beds: 37

✠ **MEDICAL CENTER OF AURORA (060100)**, 1501 South Potomac Street, Zip 80012–5411; tel. 303/695–2600, (Includes MEDICAL CENTER OF AURORA NORTH, 700 Potomac Street, Aurora, Colorado, Zip 80011–6792, tel. 303/363–7200; MEDICAL CENTER OF AURORA, 700 Potomac Street, Aurora, Colorado, Zip 80011, tel. 303/360–3030; Daniel Miller, FACHE, President and Chief Executive Officer; SOUTH CAMPUS, 1501 South Potomac, Aurora, Colorado, Zip 80012, tel. 303/695–2600) **A**1 2 3 10 **F**3 11 13 15 17 18 20 22 24 26 28 29 30 31 34 35 37 38 39 40 41 42 43 45 46 47 48 49 53 54 56 57 58 59 63 64 65 68 70 72 74 75 76 77 78 79 81 82 84 85 86 87 89 92 93 94 97 98 99 100 101 102 103 104 105 107 108 110 111 114 115 116 117 118 119 126 129 130 132 134 135 146 147 148 **P**6 8 **S** HCA Healthcare, Nashville, TN
Primary Contact: Daniel Miller, FACHE, President and Chief Executive Officer
COO: Mark S Deno, Chief Operating Officer
CFO: Bryce DeHaven, Chief Financial Officer
CMO: Dianne McCallister M.D., Chief Medical Officer
Web address: www.auroramed.com
Control: Corporation, Investor–owned (for–profit) **Service:** General medical and surgical

Staffed Beds: 341 **Admissions:** 15289 **Census:** 214 **Outpatient Visits:** 144338 **Births:** 1275 **Personnel:** 1115

BOULDER—Boulder County

✠ △ **BOULDER COMMUNITY HEALTH (060027)**, 4747 Arapahoe Ave, Zip 80303–1133, Mailing Address: P.O.Box 9019, 80301–9019; tel. 303/415–7000, (Includes BOULDER COMMUNITY FOOTHILLS HOSPITAL, 4747 Arapahoe Avenue, Boulder, Colorado, Zip 80303–1133, P O Box 9047, 80301–9047, tel. 720/854–7000; Robert Vissers, M.D., President and Chief Executive Officer) **A**1 2 3 5 7 10 **F**3 5 8 13 15 18 20 22 24 26 28 29 30 31 34 35 36 37 40 43 45 46 49 50 53 54 59 60 61 62 64 65 68 70 72 74 75 76 77 78 79 81 82 84 85 87 90 93 96 97 98 100 101 102 104 105 107 109 111 112 114 115 119 126 130 132 144 146 147 148 149 **P**4 5 6
Primary Contact: Robert Vissers, M.D., President and Chief Executive Officer
CFO: Bill Munson, Vice President and Chief Financial Officer
CMO: Paul Lewis M.D., Chief Medical Officer, Vice President
CNO: Jacqueline M Attlesey–Pries MS, R.N., Chief Nursing Officer, Vice President
Web address: www.bch.org
Control: Other not–for–profit (including NFP Corporation) **Service:** General medical and surgical

Staffed Beds: 178 **Admissions:** 8309 **Census:** 94 **Outpatient Visits:** 399263 **Births:** 891 **Total Expense ($000):** 330874 **Payroll Expense ($000):** 144409 **Personnel:** 1520

Many Facility Codes have changed. Please refer to the AHA Guide Code Chart. © 2017 AHA Guide

BRIGHTON—Adams County

✠ **PLATTE VALLEY MEDICAL CENTER (060004)**, 1600 Prairie Center Parkway, Zip 80601–4006; tel. 303/498–1600, **A**1 5 10 **F**3 7 13 15 18 20 22 26 28 29 30 31 34 35 40 43 45 49 57 68 70 72 74 75 76 77 78 79 81 85 87 90 92 93 107 108 110 111 115 119 130 132 135 146 147 148 **S** SCL Health, Broomfield, CO
Primary Contact: John R. Hicks, President and Chief Executive Officer
COO: Kurt G Gensert FACHE, R.N., Vice President Operations
CFO: Harold Dupper, Chief Financial Officer
CMO: Kirk Quackenbush M.D., Chief of Staff
CIO: Timothy Brannigan, Director Information Services
CHR: Jackie J. Dunkin, Director Human Resources
Web address: www.pvmc.org
Control: Other not–for–profit (including NFP Corporation) **Service**: General medical and surgical

Staffed Beds: 70 **Admissions**: 3239 **Census**: 27 **Outpatient Visits**: 72296 **Births**: 903 **Total Expense ($000)**: 107198 **Payroll Expense ($000)**: 35690 **Personnel**: 551

BROOMFIELD—Denver County

UCHEALTH BROOMFIELD HOSPITAL, 11820 Destination Drive, Zip 80021; tel. 303/460–6000, (Nonreporting) **S** University of Colorado Health, Fort Collins, CO
Primary Contact: Derek Rushing, Chief Executive Officer
Web address: www.uchealth.org/pages/OHAM/OrgUnitDetails.aspx?
Control: Other not–for–profit (including NFP Corporation) **Service**: General medical and surgical

Staffed Beds: 22

BRUSH—Morgan County

★ **EAST MORGAN COUNTY HOSPITAL (061303)**, 2400 West Edison Street, Zip 80723–1640; tel. 970/842–6200, **A**10 18 **F**3 13 15 28 29 30 32 34 35 36 40 43 45 50 53 57 59 64 65 68 74 75 77 79 81 85 86 87 93 96 97 107 108 110 115 119 127 130 131 132 133 135 141 146 147 148 **S** Banner Health, Phoenix, AZ
Primary Contact: Linda Thorpe, Chief Executive Officer
CFO: Edith Pemberton, Chief Financial Officer
CHR: Cynthia Wentworth, Chief Human Resource Officer
CNO: Linda Lyn Roan, Chief Nursing Officer
Web address: www.emchbrush.com
Control: Other not–for–profit (including NFP Corporation) **Service**: General medical and surgical

Staffed Beds: 19 **Admissions**: 462 **Census**: 4 **Outpatient Visits**: 25292 **Births**: 56

BURLINGTON—Kit Carson County

★ **KIT CARSON COUNTY HEALTH SERVICE DISTRICT (061313)**, 286 16th Street, Zip 80807–1697; tel. 719/346–5311, (Nonreporting) **A**10 18
Primary Contact: Corey J. Fedie, Chief Operating Officer
COO: Corey J Fedie, Chief Operating Officer
CMO: Bong Pham, Chief Medical Officer
CIO: Paul Velasco, IT Manager
CHR: Robin Konecne, Manager Human Resources
CNO: Kandi Kuper, Chief Nursing Officer
Web address: www.kcchsd.org
Control: Hospital district or authority, Government, Nonfederal **Service**: General medical and surgical

Staffed Beds: 19

CANON CITY—Fremont County

✠ **ST. THOMAS MORE HOSPITAL (060016)**, 1338 Phay Avenue, Zip 81212–2302; tel. 719/285–2000, **A**1 10 20 **F**3 8 11 12 13 15 29 30 34 35 40 43 51 53 57 59 64 66 69 70 75 77 79 81 82 85 86 87 93 97 107 108 110 111 119 127 129 131 132 133 135 146 147 148 **S** Catholic Health Initiatives, Englewood, CO
Primary Contact: Sheri Trahern, CPA, FACHE, Chief Executive Officer
COO: Dennis Bruens, Vice President Operations
CFO: Gwenyth Howard, Vice President Finance
CMO: Kern Low M.D., Chief Medical Officer
CIO: Jillian Maes, Director Marketing and Public Relations
CHR: Janet Reedy, Manager Human Resources
CNO: James Woodard, Chief Nursing Officer
Web address: www.stmhospital.org
Control: Church operated, Nongovernment, not–for–profit **Service**: General medical and surgical

Staffed Beds: 25 **Admissions**: 1767 **Census**: 16 **Outpatient Visits**: 43200 **Births**: 232 **Total Expense ($000)**: 45478 **Payroll Expense ($000)**: 18173 **Personnel**: 390

CASTLE ROCK—Douglas County

✠ **CASTLE ROCK ADVENTIST HOSPITAL (060125)**, 2350 Meadows Boulevard, Zip 80109–8405; tel. 720/455–5000, **A**1 10 **F**3 11 13 15 18 20 22 29 30 32 34 35 37 38 40 43 45 48 49 50 57 59 60 62 64 65 67 68 70 72 74 75 76 77 79 81 85 86 87 89 91 93 102 107 108 110 111 114 115 118 119 129 130 131 135 146 147 148 **P**6 **S** Adventist Health System Sunbelt Health Care Corporation, Altamonte Springs, FL
Primary Contact: Todd Folkenberg, Chief Executive Officer
CFO: Jeremy Pittman, Chief Financial Officer
Web address: www.castlerockhospital.org
Control: Church operated, Nongovernment, not–for–profit **Service**: General medical and surgical

Staffed Beds: 53 **Admissions**: 2606 **Census**: 22 **Outpatient Visits**: 29510 **Births**: 717 **Total Expense ($000)**: 71249 **Payroll Expense ($000)**: 26132 **Personnel**: 500

CHEYENNE WELLS—Cheyenne County

★ **KEEFE MEMORIAL HOSPITAL (060043)**, 602 North 6th Street West, Zip 80810, Mailing Address: P.O.Box 578, 80810–0578; tel. 719/767–5661, **A**10 20 **F**3 15 29 34 35 36 40 41 43 57 59 64 68 89 90 93 97 102 107 110 114 119 127 128 133 147 148 149 **P**6
Primary Contact: Stella Worley, Interim Chief Executive Officer
CFO: Stella Worley, Director of Finance
CMO: Christine Connolly M.D., Chief of Staff
CIO: Jeanne Moffat, Manager Information Technology
CHR: Carrie Rico, Chief Human Resource Officer
CNO: Jesse Smith, Director of Nursing
Web address: www.keefememorial.com
Control: Other not–for–profit (including NFP Corporation) **Service**: General medical and surgical

Staffed Beds: 11 **Admissions**: 61 **Census**: 1 **Outpatient Visits**: 4197 **Births**: 0 **Total Expense ($000)**: 6411 **Payroll Expense ($000)**: 2867 **Personnel**: 55

COLORADO SPRINGS—El Paso County

☐ **CEDAR SPRINGS HOSPITAL (064009)**, 2135 Southgate Road, Zip 80906–2693; tel. 719/633–4114, (Nonreporting) **A**1 10 **S** Universal Health Services, Inc., King of Prussia, PA
Primary Contact: Christopher D. Burke, Ph.D., Chief Executive Officer
CFO: Cynthia D Deboer, Chief Financial Officer
CMO: Larry Shores M.D., Executive Medical Director
CHR: Jessica McCoy, Director Human Resources
CNO: Jodi Mattson, Director of Nursing
Web address: www.cedarspringsbhs.com
Control: Corporation, Investor–owned (for–profit) **Service**: Psychiatric

Staffed Beds: 110

✠ **HEALTHSOUTH REHABILITATION HOSPITAL OF COLORADO SPRINGS (063030)**, 325 Parkside Drive, Zip 80910–3134; tel. 719/630–8000, (Nonreporting) **A**1 10 **S** HEALTHSOUTH Corporation, Birmingham, AL
Primary Contact: Stephen Schaefer, Chief Executive Officer
CFO: Stephanie Davis, Controller
CHR: Diana Crepeau, Director Human Resources
CNO: Cindy Nordell, Chief Nursing Officer
Web address: www.healthsouthcoloradosprings.com
Control: Corporation, Investor–owned (for–profit) **Service**: Rehabilitation

Staffed Beds: 56

☐ **PEAK VIEW BEHAVIORAL HEALTH (064026)**, 7353 Sisters Grove, Zip 80923–2615; tel. 719/444–8484, **A**1 10 13 **F**29 35 38 54 56 98 99 100 101 102 103 104 105 106 **S** Strategic Behavioral Health, LLC, Memphis, TN
Primary Contact: Dan Zarecky, Chief Executive Officer
Web address: www.strategicbh.com/peakview.html
Control: Corporation, Investor–owned (for–profit) **Service**: Psychiatric

Staffed Beds: 112 **Admissions**: 4795 **Census**: 76 **Outpatient Visits**: 1141 **Births**: 0 **Total Expense ($000)**: 14149 **Payroll Expense ($000)**: 9120 **Personnel**: 301

CO

Hospital, Medicare Provider Number, Address, Telephone, Approval, Facility, and Physician Codes, Health Care System

★ American Hospital Association (AHA) membership
☐ The Joint Commission accreditation
○ Healthcare Facilities Accreditation Program
◇ DNV Healthcare Inc. accreditation
⇑ Center for Improvement in Healthcare Quality Accreditation
△ Commission on Accreditation of Rehabilitation Facilities (CARF) accreditation

⊞ △ **PENROSE–ST. FRANCIS HEALTH SERVICES (060031)**, 2222 North Nevada Avenue, Zip 80907–6799; tel. 719/776–5000, (Includes PENROSE HOSPITAL, 2222 North Nevada Avenue, Colorado Springs, Colorado, Zip 80907, tel. 719/776–5000; Margaret D Sabin, Chief Executive Officer; ST. FRANCIS MEDICAL CENTER, 6001 East Woodmen Road, Colorado Springs, Colorado, Zip 80923–2601, tel. 719/776–5000; Margaret D Sabin, Chief Executive Officer) **A**1 2 3 7 10 **F**3 5 11 12 13 14 15 17 18 20 22 24 26 28 29 30 31 34 35 36 37 38 39 40 41 43 44 45 46 47 48 49 50 52 53 54 55 56 57 58 59 61 62 64 65 68 70 71 72 74 75 76 77 78 79 81 82 84 85 86 87 89 90 91 93 94 96 97 99 100 101 102 103 107 108 110 114 115 118 119 120 121 123 124 126 127 129 130 131 132 135 144 146 147 148 149 **P**5 **S** Catholic Health Initiatives, Englewood, CO
Primary Contact: Margaret D. Sabin, President and Chief Executive Officer
COO: Lonnie Cramer, Chief Operating Officer
CFO: Danny Reeves, Chief Financial Officer
CMO: David Dull M.D., Chief Medical Officer
CHR: James Humphrey, Vice President Talent Resources and Human Resources for South Side Operating Group
CNO: Cynthia Latney, Chief Nursing Officer
Web address: www.penrosestfrancis.org
Control: Church operated, Nongovernment, not–for–profit **Service**: General medical and surgical

Staffed Beds: 444 **Admissions**: 23102 **Census**: 252 **Outpatient Visits**: 187692 **Births**: 3221 **Total Expense ($000)**: 475093 **Payroll Expense ($000)**: 152463

UCHEALTH GRANDVIEW HOSPITAL, 5623 Pulpit Peak View, Zip 80918; tel. 719/272–3600, (Nonreporting) **S** University of Colorado Health, Fort Collins, CO
Primary Contact: Derek Rushing, Chief Executive Officer
Web address: www.uchealth.org/Pages/OHAM/OrgUnitDetails.aspx?OrganizationalUnitId=514
Control: Other not–for–profit (including NFP Corporation) **Service**: General medical and surgical

Staffed Beds: 22

⊞ **UCHEALTH MEMORIAL (060022)**, 1400 East Boulder Street, Zip 80909–5599; tel. 719/365–5000, (Includes UCHEALTH MEMORIAL HOSPITAL NORTH, 4050 Briargate Parkway, Colorado Springs, Colorado, Zip 80909, 1400 East Boulder Street, 80909, tel. 719/365–5000; Joel P. Yuhas, FACHE, President and Chief Executive Officer) **A**1 2 3 10 **F**3 8 11 13 15 17 18 19 20 21 22 23 24 26 27 28 29 30 31 34 35 36 40 41 43 44 45 46 48 49 54 55 57 58 59 64 68 70 72 74 76 77 78 79 81 82 84 85 86 87 88 89 90 92 93 96 97 107 108 109 110 111 114 115 116 117 118 119 120 121 123 124 126 129 130 132 135 141 144 146 148 **P**6 8 **S** University of Colorado Health, Fort Collins, CO
Primary Contact: Joel P. Yuhas, FACHE, President and Chief Executive Officer
COO: Cherie Gorby, Chief Operations Officer
CFO: Dan Rieber, Chief Financial Officer
CMO: Jose Melendez M.D., Chief Medical Officer
CHR: Jeffrey Johnson, Vice President
CNO: Kay J Miller R.N., MSN, Chief Nursing Officer
Web address: www.uchealth.org/southerncolorado
Control: Other not–for–profit (including NFP Corporation) **Service**: General medical and surgical

Staffed Beds: 557 **Admissions**: 23725 **Census**: 235 **Outpatient Visits**: 698382

CORTEZ—Montezuma County

★ ⋔ **SOUTHWEST HEALTH SYSTEM (061327)**, 1311 North Mildred Road, Zip 81321–2299; tel. 970/565–6666, (Nonreporting) **A**10 18 21
Primary Contact: W Kent. Rogers, Chief Executive Officer
CFO: Angela Kobel, Chief Financial Officer
CIO: Angela Kobel, Chief Information Officer
CHR: Travis Parker, Director Human Resources
CNO: Karen Pasquin MSN, R.N., Chief Nursing Officer
Web address: www.swhealth.org
Control: Other not–for–profit (including NFP Corporation) **Service**: General medical and surgical

Staffed Beds: 25

CRAIG—Moffat County

⊞ ⋔ **MEMORIAL REGIONAL HEALTH (061314)**, 750 Hospital Loop, Zip 81625–8750; tel. 970/824–9411, **A**1 10 18 21 **F**3 7 11 13 15 18 29 31 32 34 35 40 43 45 49 50 51 57 59 68 70 75 76 77 78 79 81 85 86 87 91 93 97 102 107 108 110 111 112 114 119 129 130 131 132 133 135 146 147 148
Primary Contact: Andrew J. Daniels, Chief Executive Officer
COO: Jennifer Riley, Vice President Operations
CFO: Denise Arola, Chief Financial Officer
CMO: Scott Ellis D.O., Chief Medical Officer
CIO: Bryan Curtis, Chief Information Officer
CNO: Amy Peck R.N., Chief Nursing Officer
Web address: www.thememorialhospital.com
Control: County, Government, Nonfederal **Service**: General medical and surgical

Staffed Beds: 25 **Admissions**: 1078 **Census**: 9

DEL NORTE—Rio Grande County

★ **RIO GRANDE HOSPITAL (061301)**, 310 County Road 14, Zip 81132–8719; tel. 719/657–2510, **A**10 18 **F**34 40 43 57 65 81 93 107 111 115 119 127 129 133 **P**6
Primary Contact: Arlene Harms, Chief Executive Officer
CFO: Greg Porter, Chief Financial Officer
CMO: Heidi E Helgeson M.D., Chief Medical Officer
CIO: Denise Fietek, Information Technology
CHR: Paula Warner–Pacheco, Chief Human Resources
CNO: Candice Allen, Director of Nursing
Web address: www.rio–grande–hospital.org/
Control: Other not–for–profit (including NFP Corporation) **Service**: General medical and surgical

Staffed Beds: 17 **Admissions**: 434 **Census**: 6 **Outpatient Visits**: 44608 **Births**: 0

DELTA—Delta County

★ ⋔ **DELTA COUNTY MEMORIAL HOSPITAL (060071)**, 1501 East 3rd Street, Zip 81416–2815, Mailing Address: P.O.Box 10100, 81416–0008; tel. 970/874–7681, **A**10 21 **F**3 8 9 13 15 28 29 30 31 34 40 43 45 50 57 59 62 70 75 76 77 78 79 81 85 87 90 93 107 108 110 111 115 119 129 135 141 144 146 147 148 **P**5 8
Primary Contact: Jason Cleckler, Chief Executive Officer
CFO: Bev Carlson, Chief Financial Officer
CMO: John P Knutson M.D., Chief Medical Staff
CIO: Mitch Van Scoyk, Manager Information Systems
CHR: Larry Vincent, Director Human Resources
Web address: www.deltahospital.org
Control: Hospital district or authority, Government, Nonfederal **Service**: General medical and surgical

Staffed Beds: 49 **Admissions**: 1561 **Census**: 13 **Outpatient Visits**: 110306

DENVER—Denver, Adams and Arapaho Coun County

⊞ **COLORADO ACUTE LONG TERM HOSPITAL (062012)**, 1690 North Meade Street, Zip 80204–1552; tel. 303/264–6900, (Nonreporting) **A**1 10 **S** LifeCare Management Services, Plano, TX
Primary Contact: Craig Bailey, MS, Chief Executive Officer and Administrator
Web address: www.lifecare–hospitals.com/hospital/colorado
Control: Corporation, Investor–owned (for–profit) **Service**: Acute long–term care hospital

Staffed Beds: 63

☐ **COLORADO MENTAL HEALTH INSTITUTE AT FORT LOGAN (064003)**, 3520 West Oxford Avenue, Zip 80236–3197; tel. 303/866–7066, (Nonreporting) **A**1 3 5 10
Primary Contact: Nancy Kehiayan, Acting Director
CFO: Sabina Genesio, Finance Officer for Institutes
CMO: Bruce Leonard M.D., Medical Director and Chief of Psychiatry
CNO: Nancy Kehiayan, Director of Nursing
Web address: www.cdhs.state.co.us/cmhifl
Control: State, Government, Nonfederal **Service**: Psychiatric

Staffed Beds: 297

⊞ **DENVER HEALTH (060011)**, 777 Bannock Street, Zip 80204–4507, Mailing Address: 777 Bannock Street, MC0278, 80204–4507; tel. 303/436–6000, **A**1 3 5 10 **F**3 5 7 8 11 12 13 15 18 19 20 22 26 28 29 30 31 32 34 35 36 37 38 39 40 41 42 43 44 45 46 49 50 52 53 54 55 56 57 58 59 60 61 64 65 66 68 70 71 72 74 75 76 77 78 79 80 81 82 84 85 86 87 88 89 90 92 93 94 96 97 98 99 100 101 102 103 104 105 107 108 110 111 114 115 118 119 127 129 130 131 132 134 135 143 144 146 147 148 149 **P**6
Primary Contact: Robin D. Wittenstein, Ed.D., Chief Executive Officer
COO: Tim Harlin M.D., Chief Operations Officer
CFO: Peg Burnette, Chief Financial Officer
CMO: Connie Price M.D., Chief Medical Officer
CIO: Jeff Pelot, Interim Chief Information Officer
CHR: Tim Hansen, Interim Chief Human Resource Officer
CNO: Kathy Boyle R.N., Ph.D., Chief Nursing Officer
Web address: www.denverhealth.org
Control: Hospital district or authority, Government, Nonfederal **Service**: General medical and surgical

Staffed Beds: 441 **Admissions**: 19768 **Census**: 298 **Outpatient Visits**: 872010 **Births**: 3474 **Total Expense ($000)**: 1018734 **Payroll Expense ($000)**: 478586 **Personnel**: 6511

Many Facility Codes have changed. Please refer to the AHA Guide Code Chart.   © 2017 AHA Guide

★ **KINDRED HOSPITAL DENVER SOUTH (062015)**, 2525 South Downing Street, 3 South, Zip 80210–5817; tel. 303/715-7373, (Nonreporting) **S** Kindred Healthcare, Louisville, KY
Primary Contact: Marc Lemon, Chief Executive Officer
Web address: www.kindreddenversouth.com/
Control: Corporation, Investor–owned (for–profit) **Service:** Acute long–term care hospital

Staffed Beds: 28

✠ **KINDRED HOSPITAL–DENVER (062009)**, 1920 High Street, Zip 80218–1213; tel. 303/320–5871, **A**1 10 **F**1 119 130 148 **S** Kindred Healthcare, Louisville, KY
Primary Contact: Janelle Kircher, R.N., MSN, Chief Executive Officer
CFO: Tim Stecker, Chief Financial Officer
CMO: Eric Yaeger M.D., Medical Director
Web address: www.kh–denver.com
Control: Corporation, Investor–owned (for–profit) **Service:** Acute long–term care hospital

Staffed Beds: 68 Admissions: 324 Census: 34

✠ **NATIONAL JEWISH HEALTH (060107)**, 1400 Jackson Street, Zip 80206–2762; tel. 303/388–4461, **A**1 3 5 10 **F**1 3 9 11 12 17 18 20 28 29 30 31 32 34 35 36 44 45 46 48 50 53 54 55 57 58 59 61 62 64 65 66 68 70 74 75 77 78 84 86 87 89 90 93 96 97 98 99 100 101 104 107 108 111 114 115 116 117 118 119 127 129 130 132 134 135 143 145 146 147 **P**6
Primary Contact: Michael Salem, M.D., President and Chief Executive Officer
COO: Ron Berge, Executive Vice President and Chief Operating Officer
CFO: Christine Forkner, Executive Vice President and Chief Financial Officer
CMO: Gary Cott M.D., Executive Vice President Medical and Clinical Services
CIO: Lots Pook, Chief Information Officer
CHR: Sarah Taylor, Chief Human Resources
CNO: Jeff Downing R.N., MS, Chief Nursing Officer
Web address: www.njhealth.org
Control: Other not–for–profit (including NFP Corporation) **Service:** Tuberculosis and other respiratory diseases

Staffed Beds: 76 Admissions: 37 Census: 1 Outpatient Visits: 113717 Births: 0 Total Expense ($000): 242027 Payroll Expense ($000): 120266 Personnel: 1595

✠ **PORTER ADVENTIST HOSPITAL (069864)**, 2525 South Downing Street, Zip 80210–5876; tel. 303/778–1955, **A**1 2 10 **F**3 4 5 6 8 11 15 17 18 20 22 24 26 28 29 30 31 34 35 36 37 38 39 40 43 44 45 46 47 48 49 50 53 54 55 56 57 58 59 60 63 64 65 68 70 74 75 77 78 79 81 82 83 84 85 86 87 90 91 92 93 94 96 97 98 100 101 102 103 104 105 106 107 108 109 110 111 112 114 115 116 117 118 119 120 121 122 123 124 125 126 129 130 131 132 135 138 139 141 142 146 147 148 **P**6 **S** Adventist Health System Sunbelt Health Care Corporation, Altamonte Springs, FL
Primary Contact: Morre Dean, Chief Executive Officer
COO: David Dookeeram, Chief Operating Officer
CFO: Andrew Gaasch, Chief Financial Officer
CHR: Oz Muller, Director Human Resources
Web address: www.porterhospital.org/poh/home/
Control: Church operated, Nongovernment, not–for–profit **Service:** General medical and surgical

Staffed Beds: 250 Admissions: 10026 Census: 131 Outpatient Visits: 65753 Births: 0 Total Expense ($000): 262646 Payroll Expense ($000): 90097 Personnel: 1720

✠ **PRESBYTERIAN–ST. LUKE'S MEDICAL CENTER (069865)**, 1719 East 19th Avenue, Zip 80218–1281; tel. 303/839–6000, (Includes ROCKY MOUNTAIN HOSPITAL FOR CHILDREN, 1719 East 19th Avenue, Denver, Colorado, Zip 80218–1235, tel. 720/754–1000; Maureen Tarrant, President and Chief Executive Officer) **A**1 2 3 5 10 **F**3 8 11 12 13 14 15 18 19 20 21 22 23 24 25 26 27 28 29 30 31 34 35 36 37 40 41 44 45 46 47 48 49 50 53 54 55 56 58 59 60 61 64 65 66 68 70 72 73 74 75 76 77 78 79 80 81 82 84 85 86 87 88 89 91 92 93 94 95 96 97 102 107 108 111 114 115 116 117 118 119 120 121 123 126 129 130 131 132 134 136 138 139 146 147 148 **P**2 4 6 **S** HCA Healthcare, Nashville, TN
Primary Contact: Maureen Tarrant, President and Chief Executive Officer
CFO: Shari Collier, Chief Financial Officer
CMO: Stephen Cobb M.D., Chief Medical Officer
CIO: Jason Brakenhoff, Director Information Services
CHR: Keri Moore, Vice President Human Resources and Support Services
CNO: Amanda Veit R.N., Chief Nursing Officer
Web address: www.pslmc.com
Control: Corporation, Investor–owned (for–profit) **Service:** General medical and surgical

Staffed Beds: 399 Admissions: 11147 Census: 218 Outpatient Visits: 59087 Births: 1486 Personnel: 1570

✠ **ROSE MEDICAL CENTER (060032)**, 4567 East Ninth Avenue, Zip 80220–3941; tel. 303/320–2121, **A**1 2 3 5 10 **F**3 8 9 11 12 13 15 18 20 22 24 26 28 29 30 31 34 35 40 42 44 45 46 49 50 52 53 54 55 58 59 60 61 64 68 70 72 74 75 76 77 78 79 81 82 84 85 86 87 91 92 93 94 97 100 101 102 107 108 110 111 112 113 114 115 116 118 119 120 121 122 123 126 129 130 131 132 135 146 147 148 149 **P**3 6 8 **S** HCA Healthcare, Nashville, TN
Primary Contact: Kenneth H. Feiler, President and Chief Executive Officer
COO: Ryan Tobin, Chief Operating Officer
CFO: Jac Connelly, Chief Financial Officer
CMO: Andrew Ziller M.D., Chief Medical Officer
CIO: Dave Trevathan, Director Information Systems
CHR: Clarence McDavid, Vice President Human Resources
CNO: Lynne Wagner R.N., Chief Nursing Officer
Web address: www.rosebabies.com
Control: Corporation, Investor–owned (for–profit) **Service:** General medical and surgical

Staffed Beds: 280 Admissions: 11024 Census: 108 Outpatient Visits: 113766 Births: 3374

✠ **SAINT JOSEPH HOSPITAL (060028)**, 1375 East 19th Avenue, Zip 80218–1126; tel. 303/837–7111, **A**1 2 3 5 10 **F**3 8 11 12 13 15 18 20 22 24 26 28 29 30 31 34 35 37 40 43 45 46 49 50 55 58 60 63 64 66 68 70 71 72 74 75 76 77 78 79 81 82 84 85 87 93 107 108 110 111 115 116 117 119 120 121 123 124 126 130 145 146 147 149 **P**6 7 **S** SCL Health, Broomfield, CO
Primary Contact: Jameson Smith, President
COO: Barbara A. Jahn, Chief Operating Officer
CFO: Alice W. Rigdon, Vice President Finance
CMO: Shawn Dufford M.D., Vice President Medical Affairs and Chief Medical Officer
CHR: William R Gould, Vice President Human Resources
CNO: Mary Shepler R.N., Vice President and Chief Nursing Officer
Web address: www.saintjosephdenver.org/
Control: Other not–for–profit (including NFP Corporation) **Service:** General medical and surgical

Staffed Beds: 374 Admissions: 19547 Census: 248 Outpatient Visits: 146318 Births: 4597 Total Expense ($000): 491884 Payroll Expense ($000): 152751 Personnel: 2090

✠ **VETERANS AFFAIRS EASTERN COLORADO HEALTH CARE SYSTEM**, 1055 Clermont Street, Zip 80220–3877; tel. 303/399–8020, (Nonreporting) **A**1 3 5 **S** Department of Veterans Affairs, Washington, DC
Primary Contact: Sallie Houser–Hanfelder, FACHE, Director
CFO: Eliott R Vanderstek, Chief Fiscal Service
CMO: Ellen Mangione M.D., Chief of Staff
CIO: Don Huckaby, Chief Information Management Service
CHR: Lorene Connel, Chief Human Resources Management Service
Web address: www.denver.va.gov/
Control: Veterans Affairs, Government, federal **Service:** General medical and surgical

Staffed Beds: 271

DURANGO—La Plata County

✠ **ANIMAS SURGICAL HOSPITAL (060117)**, 575 Rivergate Lane, Zip 81301–7487; tel. 970/247–3537, (Nonreporting) **A**10
Primary Contact: Brett Gosney, Chief Executive Officer
Web address: www.animassurgical.com/
Control: Corporation, Investor–owned (for–profit) **Service:** Surgical

Staffed Beds: 12

✠ **MERCY REGIONAL MEDICAL CENTER (060013)**, 1010 Three Springs Boulevard, Zip 81301–8296; tel. 970/247–4311, **A**1 2 10 20 **F**11 13 15 17 18 20 22 24 26 27 28 29 30 31 35 36 40 42 43 45 49 50 59 60 61 66 70 72 73 76 78 79 81 84 85 87 89 94 96 97 107 111 115 119 126 127 129 130 131 132 133 135 146 147 148 149 150 **P**6 **S** Catholic Health Initiatives, Englewood, CO
Primary Contact: William McConnell, Ph.D., President and Chief Executive Officer
CFO: Jane Strobel, Vice President and Chief Financial Officer
CMO: William Plauth M.D., Vice President Operations and Chief Medical Officer
CIO: Neil Stock, Director Technology and Facilities
CHR: Cathy Roberts, Vice President Mission Integration and Human Resources
CNO: Nancy Hoyt R.N., Vice President Operations/Clinical and Chief Nursing Officer
Web address: www.mercydurango.org
Control: Church operated, Nongovernment, not–for–profit **Service:** General medical and surgical

Staffed Beds: 82 Admissions: 4365 Census: 39 Outpatient Visits: 134526 Births: 949 Total Expense ($000): 131418 Payroll Expense ($000): 43366 Personnel: 1007

CO

Hospital, Medicare Provider Number, Address, Telephone, Approval, Facility, and Physician Codes, Health Care System

★ American Hospital Association (AHA) membership   ○ Healthcare Facilities Accreditation Program   ⇑ Center for Improvement in Healthcare Quality Accreditation
□ The Joint Commission accreditation   ◇ DNV Healthcare Inc. accreditation   △ Commission on Accreditation of Rehabilitation Facilities (CARF) accreditation

CO

EADS—Kiowa County

★ **WEISBROD MEMORIAL COUNTY HOSPITAL (061300)**, 1208 Luther Street, Zip 81036, Mailing Address: P.O.Box 817, 81036–0817; tel. 719/438–5401, **A**10 18 **F**2 7 29 30 34 40 57 59 64 75 82 84 87 93 96 97 127 133 135 143 148
Primary Contact: Charlene Korrell, Interim Chief Executive Officer
CFO: Shannon Dixon, Manager Business Office
CMO: Jeff Waggoner M.D., Chief of Staff
CHR: Shannon Dixon, Manager Business Office
CNO: Wendy McDowell R.N., Director of Nursing
Web address: www.kchd.org
Control: Hospital district or authority, Government, Nonfederal **Service**: General medical and surgical

Staffed Beds: 25 Admissions: 48 Census: 1 Outpatient Visits: 2373 Births: 0 Total Expense ($000): 5923 Payroll Expense ($000): 2873 Personnel: 37

ENGLEWOOD—Arapahoe County

✠ **CRAIG HOSPITAL (062011)**, 3425 South Clarkson Street, Zip 80113–2899; tel. 303/789–8000, **A**1 3 5 10 **F**29 30 34 35 36 44 50 53 58 64 68 74 75 77 81 86 87 90 91 93 95 96 97 100 104 130 132 146 148 149
Primary Contact: Michael L. Fordyce, President and Chief Executive Officer
CFO: Julie Keegan, Vice President Finance
CMO: Thomas E Balazy M.D., Medical Director
CIO: Chris Watkins, Director of Information Technology
CHR: Stacy L Abel, Director Human Resources
CNO: Diane Reinhard R.N., Vice President of Patient Care Services
Web address: www.craighospital.org
Control: Other not–for–profit (including NFP Corporation) **Service**: Rehabilitation

Staffed Beds: 93 Admissions: 486 Census: 79 Outpatient Visits: 14178 Births: 0 Total Expense ($000): 92094 Payroll Expense ($000): 44211 Personnel: 731

DENVER SPRINGS, 8835 American Way, Zip 80112–7056; tel. 720/643–4300, (Nonreporting)
Primary Contact: David Morris, Chief Executive Officer
Web address: www.denversprings.com/
Control: Other not–for–profit (including NFP Corporation) **Service**: General medical and surgical

Staffed Beds: 25

✠ **SWEDISH MEDICAL CENTER (060034)**, 501 East Hampden Avenue, Zip 80113–2702; tel. 303/788–5000, **A**1 2 3 10 13 **F**3 7 8 11 12 13 15 16 18 19 20 22 24 26 28 29 30 31 32 34 35 36 37 38 39 40 41 42 43 44 45 46 47 48 49 50 51 53 54 55 56 57 58 59 60 64 65 66 68 70 72 74 75 76 77 78 79 81 82 83 84 85 86 87 88 89 90 91 92 93 96 97 99 100 101 102 107 108 109 110 111 114 115 116 117 118 119 120 121 122 123 124 126 129 130 131 132 135 143 145 146 147 148 149 150 **P**6 8 **S** HCA Healthcare, Nashville, TN
Primary Contact: Richard A. Hammett, President and Chief Executive Officer
CFO: Kathy Ashenfelter, Chief Financial Officer
CMO: Paul Hancock M.D., Chief Medical Officer
CIO: Jeff Schnoor, Director Information Systems
CHR: Lisa Morris, Vice President Human Resources
CNO: Shari Chavez, Chief Nursing Officer
Web address: www.swedishhospital.com
Control: Partnership, Investor–owned (for–profit) **Service**: General medical and surgical

Staffed Beds: 427 Admissions: 19476 Census: 260 Outpatient Visits: 157740 Births: 1910 Total Expense ($000): 365153 Payroll Expense ($000): 129572 Personnel: 1529

ESTES PARK—Larimer County

★ **ESTES PARK MEDICAL CENTER (061312)**, 555 Prospect Avenue, Zip 80517–6312, Mailing Address: P.O.Box 2740, 80517–2740; tel. 970/586–2317, (Total facility includes 52 beds in nursing home–type unit) **A**10 18 **F**3 7 8 13 29 30 31 34 35 40 43 56 57 62 63 64 75 76 77 78 79 81 85 91 93 107 114 119 128 129 130 132 133 143 145 146 147 148 149
Primary Contact: Larry E. Leaming, Ph.D., FACHE, Chief Executive Officer
CFO: Tim Cashman, Chief Financial Officer
CMO: Paul Fonken M.D., Chief of Staff
CIO: Gary Hall, Vice President of Information Technology
CHR: Randy Brigham, Chief Human Resource Officer
CNO: Cynthia Standlee R.N., Chief Nursing Officer
Web address: www.epmedcenter.com
Control: Hospital district or authority, Government, Nonfederal **Service**: General medical and surgical

Staffed Beds: 79 Admissions: 408 Census: 40 Outpatient Visits: 42916 Births: 98 Total Expense ($000): 41575 Payroll Expense ($000): 18884 Personnel: 287

FORT CARSON—El Paso County

✠ **EVANS U. S. ARMY COMMUNITY HOSPITAL**, 1650 Cochrane Circle, Building 7500, Zip 80913–4613; tel. 719/526–7200, **A**1 3 **F**3 5 7 8 11 12 13 15 18 28 29 30 31 32 33 34 35 36 37 38 39 40 46 47 48 49 50 51 53 54 55 56 57 58 59 61 64 65 74 75 77 79 81 82 85 86 87 91 92 93 94 96 97 98 99 100 101 102 103 104 105 106 107 108 109 110 111 112 113 114 115 118 119 126 129 130 131 132 134 135 143 144 145 146 147 148 149 150 **P**1 **S** Department of the Army, Office of the Surgeon General, Falls Church, VA
Primary Contact: Colonel Patrick M. Garman, Commander
CFO: MajorBradley Robinson, Chief Financial Officer
CHR: Lieutenant ColonelLory Gurr, Chief Human Resources Division
Web address: www.evans.amedd.army.mil
Control: Army, Government, federal **Service**: General medical and surgical

Staffed Beds: 68 Admissions: 6512 Census: 42 Outpatient Visits: 877856 Births: 1793 Total Expense ($000): 225462 Payroll Expense ($000): 105319 Personnel: 2085

FORT COLLINS—Larimer County

★ **BANNER FORT COLLINS MEDICAL CENTER (060126)**, 4700 Lady Moon Drive, Zip 80528–4426; tel. 970/821–4000 **F**3 13 18 29 30 34 35 36 38 40 44 45 50 57 59 60 68 70 74 76 77 79 81 84 85 87 89 107 108 111 114 115 119 130 135 146 149 **S** Banner Health, Phoenix, AZ
Primary Contact: Margo Karsten, Ph.D., MSN, Chief Executive Officer
COO: Marilyn Fain R.N., MSN, Chief Operating Officer
CFO: Lori Sehrt, Associate Chief Financial Officer Northern Colorado
CMO: Bert Honea M.D., Associate Chief Medical Officer Northern Colorado
CHR: Kelly Hurt, Chief Human Resources Officer Northern Colorado and Western Region
CNO: Roberta Bean R.N., Associate Chief Nursing Officer
Web address: www.bannerhealth.com/Locations/Colorado/Banner+Fort+Collins+Medical+Center
Control: Other not–for–profit (including NFP Corporation) **Service**: General medical and surgical

Staffed Beds: 22 Admissions: 818 Census: 6 Outpatient Visits: 13919 Births: 202 Total Expense ($000): 44332 Payroll Expense ($000): 11510

✠ **POUDRE VALLEY HOSPITAL (060010)**, 1024 South Lemay Avenue, Zip 80524–3998, Mailing Address: 2315 East Harmony Road, Suite 200, 80528; tel. 970/495–7000, (Includes MOUNTAIN CREST HOSPITAL, 4601 Corbett Drive, Fort Collins, Colorado, Zip 80525, tel. 970/270–4800) **A**1 2 3 5 10 19 **F**3 5 7 11 12 13 14 15 18 20 22 28 29 30 31 32 34 35 38 39 40 42 43 44 45 46 47 48 49 50 53 54 55 57 58 59 60 61 64 65 66 68 69 70 72 73 74 75 76 77 78 79 80 81 82 83 84 85 86 87 89 92 93 98 99 100 101 102 103 104 105 106 107 108 110 111 114 115 118 119 120 121 123 124 126 129 130 131 132 134 135 143 146 147 148 149 150 **S** University of Colorado Health, Fort Collins, CO
Primary Contact: Kevin L. Unger, Ph.D., FACHE, President and Chief Executive Officer
COO: Yvonne Rockwood, Chief Operating Officer
CFO: Stephanie Doughty, Chief Financial Officer
CMO: Thomas Downes M.D., Chief Medical Officer
CIO: Fernando Pedroza, Vice President Information Technology
CNO: Donna D Poduska MS, R.N., Chief Nursing Officer
Web address: www.uchealth.org
Control: Other not–for–profit (including NFP Corporation) **Service**: General medical and surgical

Staffed Beds: 275 Admissions: 14840 Census: 146 Outpatient Visits: 307265 Births: 2190 Total Expense ($000): 423986 Payroll Expense ($000): 157145 Personnel: 1794

FORT MORGAN—Morgan County

✠ **COLORADO PLAINS MEDICAL CENTER (060044)**, 1000 Lincoln Street, Zip 80701–3298; tel. 970/867–3391, **A**1 3 10 20 **F**3 11 13 15 29 31 34 35 40 43 44 45 46 48 50 51 53 56 57 59 64 65 70 75 76 77 79 81 85 86 87 89 93 94 97 98 100 101 103 104 107 108 110 111 115 119 129 130 133 146 147 148 **P**6 **S** LifePoint Health, Brentwood, TN
Primary Contact: Gene L. O'Hara, Chief Executive Officer
CFO: Christina Patton, Chief Financial Officer
CHR: Janet Brinkman, Director Human Resources
CNO: Sonya Bass MS, Chief Nursing Officer
Web address: www.coloradoplainsmedicalcenter.com
Control: Corporation, Investor–owned (for–profit) **Service**: General medical and surgical

Staffed Beds: 50 Admissions: 1345 Census: 18 Outpatient Visits: 46258 Births: 348 Total Expense ($000): 34295 Payroll Expense ($000): 13632 Personnel: 250

Many Facility Codes have changed. Please refer to the AHA Guide Code Chart.   © 2017 AHA Guide

FRISCO—Summit County

⊞ **ST. ANTHONY SUMMIT MEDICAL CENTER (060118)**, 340 Peak One Drive, Zip 80443, Mailing Address: P.O. Box 738, 80443–0738; tel. 970/668–3300, **A**1 10 **F**3 34 40 42 43 45 57 59 68 70 75 76 77 79 81 82 84 85 97 107 110 111 119 129 130 132 144 146 147 **S** Catholic Health Initiatives, Englewood, CO
Primary Contact: Paul J. Chodkowski, President and Chief Executive Officer
CMO: Marshall Denkinger M.D., Chief Medical Officer
CNO: Trixie VanderSchaaff, Chief Nursing Officer
Web address: www.summitmedicalcenter.org
Control: Church operated, Nongovernment, not–for–profit **Service:** General medical and surgical

Staffed Beds: 34 **Admissions:** 1200 **Census:** 9 **Outpatient Visits:** 22249 **Births:** 353 **Total Expense ($000):** 45909 **Payroll Expense ($000):** 16659 **Personnel:** 339

FRUITA—Mesa County

★ **COLORADO CANYONS HOSPITAL AND MEDICAL CENTER (061302)**, 300 West Ottley Avenue, Zip 81521–2118, Mailing Address: P.O. Box 130, 81521–0130; tel. 970/858–9871, (Total facility includes 70 beds in nursing home–type unit) **A**10 18 **F**3 6 9 10 15 29 30 34 35 36 40 41 43 45 49 50 54 56 57 59 64 65 68 74 75 79 81 82 85 86 87 90 91 93 107 110 111 115 119 128 130 132 133 135 143 146 147 148 149 **P**6
Primary Contact: Mark J. Francis, President and Chief Executive Officer
CFO: Mark J Francis, President and Chief Executive Officer
CMO: Christopher Wibblesman M.D., Chief of Staff
CIO: Derrick Diddle, Chief Information Officer
CHR: Kelly Murphy, Vice President Human Resources
CNO: Lori Henderson, Chief Nursing Officer, Vice President Clinical
Web address: www.fhw.org
Control: Other not–for–profit (including NFP Corporation) **Service:** General medical and surgical

Staffed Beds: 86 **Admissions:** 582 **Census:** 73 **Outpatient Visits:** 46276 **Births:** 0 **Total Expense ($000):** 39135 **Payroll Expense ($000):** 14794 **Personnel:** 324

GLENWOOD SPRINGS—Garfield County

⊞ **VALLEY VIEW HOSPITAL (060075)**, 1906 Blake Avenue, Zip 81601–4259; tel. 970/945–6535, **A**1 2 10 20 **F**3 4 11 13 14 15 18 20 22 26 28 29 30 31 32 34 35 36 43 45 46 49 50 51 54 57 58 59 64 68 69 70 74 75 76 77 78 79 81 82 85 86 87 92 93 94 97 100 104 107 108 110 111 114 115 116 117 119 120 121 123 124 126 129 130 131 132 135 145 146 147 148 **P**6
Primary Contact: Gary L. Brewer, Chief Executive Officer
CFO: Charles Crevling, Chief Financial Officer
CMO: David Brooks M.D., Chief Medical Officer
CHR: Daniel Biggs, Director Human Resources
CNO: Sandra Hurley MS, R.N., Chief Nursing Officer
Web address: www.vvh.org
Control: Other not–for–profit (including NFP Corporation) **Service:** General medical and surgical

Staffed Beds: 49 **Admissions:** 2807 **Census:** 33 **Outpatient Visits:** 91300 **Births:** 796 **Total Expense ($000):** 216689 **Payroll Expense ($000):** 86969 **Personnel:** 909

GRAND JUNCTION—Mesa County

⊞ **COMMUNITY HOSPITAL (060054)**, 2351 G Road, Zip 81505; tel. 970/242–0920, (Nonreporting) **A**1 10 **S** QHR, Brentwood, TN
Primary Contact: Chris Thomas, FACHE, President and Chief Executive Officer
CMO: Donald Nicolay M.D., Chief Medical Officer
CIO: Bart Butzine, Director Information Technology
CNO: Kristin Gundt, Chief Nursing Officer
Web address: www.yourcommunityhospital.com
Control: Other not–for–profit (including NFP Corporation) **Service:** General medical and surgical

Staffed Beds: 42

⊞ **GRAND JUNCTION VETERANS HEALTH CARE SYSTEM**, 2121 North Avenue, Zip 81501–6428; tel. 970/242–0731, (Nonreporting) **A**1 **S** Department of Veterans Affairs, Washington, DC
Primary Contact: Michael T. Kilmer, Director
COO: Patricia A Hitt, Associate Director
CFO: Laquita Gruver, Fiscal Officer
CMO: William R Berryman M.D., Chief of Staff
CIO: Craig Frerichs, Chief Information Technology Service
CHR: William Chester, Manager Human Resources
Web address: www.grandjunction.va.gov/
Control: Veterans Affairs, Government, federal **Service:** General medical and surgical

Staffed Beds: 23

⊞ **ST. MARY'S HOSPITAL AND MEDICAL CENTER (060023)**, 2635 North 7th Street, Zip 81501–8209, Mailing Address: P.O. Box 1628, 81502–1628; tel. 970/298–2273, **A**1 2 3 10 **F**3 7 12 13 14 15 17 18 20 22 24 26 28 29 30 31 34 35 37 40 43 45 46 48 49 50 51 54 55 57 58 59 60 61 64 65 67 68 69 70 72 74 75 76 77 78 79 81 82 84 85 86 87 89 90 91 92 93 96 97 100 102 107 108 109 110 111 113 114 115 116 117 119 120 121 122 123 124 126 129 130 131 132 135 143 145 146 147 148 149 **P**6 **S** SCL Health, Broomfield, CO
Primary Contact: Brian Davidson, M.D., President and Chief Medical Officer
COO: Reza Kaleel, Executive Vice President and Chief Operating Officer
CFO: Terri Chinn, Vice President Finance
CIO: John Bullard, Director Information Technology
CHR: Judy White House, Vice President Human Resources
CNO: Shelley Peterson R.N., Vice President Patient Services and Chief Nursing Officer
Web address: www.stmarygj.com
Control: Church operated, Nongovernment, not–for–profit **Service:** General medical and surgical

Staffed Beds: 311 **Admissions:** 13103 **Census:** 179 **Outpatient Visits:** 191801 **Births:** 1725 **Total Expense ($000):** 385686 **Payroll Expense ($000):** 113627 **Personnel:** 1935

VETERANS AFFAIRS MEDICAL CENTER See Grand Junction Veterans Health Care System

WEST SPRINGS HOSPITAL (064023), 515 28 3/4 Road, Zip 81501–5016; tel. 970/263–4918, (Nonreporting) **A**10
Primary Contact: Sharon Raggio, President and Chief Executive Officer
COO: Brandi Kroese, Director Operations
CFO: John Rattle, Chief Financial Officer
CMO: Jules Rosen M.D., Chief Medical Officer
CIO: Charles Andrews, Director Information Technology
CHR: Karen Birmingham, Director Human Resources
CNO: Deborah Sharpe R.N., Director of Nursing
Web address: www.WestSpringsHospital.org
Control: Other not–for–profit (including NFP Corporation) **Service:** Psychiatric

Staffed Beds: 32

GREELEY—Weld County

⊞ **NORTH COLORADO MEDICAL CENTER (060001)**, 1801 16th Street, Zip 80631–5154; tel. 970/352–4121, **A**1 2 3 10 **F**3 7 11 13 14 15 16 18 20 22 24 26 28 29 30 31 34 35 36 38 40 42 43 44 46 49 50 51 53 54 55 57 58 59 60 61 64 65 68 70 73 74 75 76 77 78 79 80 81 82 84 85 86 87 89 93 96 100 102 107 108 110 111 114 115 116 117 118 119 120 121 123 126 129 130 131 132 133 135 141 143 146 148 **S** Banner Health, Phoenix, AZ
Primary Contact: Margo Karsten, Ph.D., MSN, Chief Executive Officer
COO: Wendy Sparks, Chief Operating Officer
CFO: Mary McCabe, Chief Financial Officer
CHR: Jeannie Gallagher, Chief Human Resource Officer
CNO: Tiffany Erin Hettinger, Associate Chief Nursing Officer
Web address: www.ncmcgreeley.com
Control: Other not–for–profit (including NFP Corporation) **Service:** General medical and surgical

Staffed Beds: 236 **Admissions:** 10292 **Census:** 113 **Births:** 1714 **Total Expense ($000):** 343142 **Payroll Expense ($000):** 101368 **Personnel:** 2294

GUNNISON—Gunnison County

⊞ **GUNNISON VALLEY HOSPITAL (061320)**, 711 North Taylor Street, Zip 81230–2296; tel. 970/641–1456, **A**1 10 18 **F**3 7 11 13 15 29 30 31 32 34 35 40 43 44 45 56 57 59 64 68 76 77 78 85 87 93 97 107 110 111 114 119 129 132 133 135 146 147 148
Primary Contact: Robert J. Santilli, Chief Executive Officer
CFO: James P Barbuat, Chief Financial Officer
CIO: Trevor Smith, Chief Management Information Services
CHR: Christina Lovelace, Director Human Resources
CNO: Lisa Loughran, Chief Nursing Officer
Web address: www.gvh–colorado.org
Control: County, Government, Nonfederal **Service:** General medical and surgical

Staffed Beds: 24 **Admissions:** 564 **Census:** 4

CO

Hospital, Medicare Provider Number, Address, Telephone, Approval, Facility, and Physician Codes, Health Care System
★ American Hospital Association (AHA) membership ○ Healthcare Facilities Accreditation Program ⇑ Center for Improvement in Healthcare Quality Accreditation
□ The Joint Commission accreditation ◇ DNV Healthcare Inc. accreditation △ Commission on Accreditation of Rehabilitation Facilities (CARF) accreditation

HAXTUN—Phillips County

★ **HAXTUN HOSPITAL DISTRICT (061304)**, 235 West Fletcher Street, Zip 80731–2737; tel. 970/774–6123, **A**10 18 **F**7 40 54 59 64 65 75 77 87 93 97 107 114 119 129 133 146
Primary Contact: Larry E. Schrage, FACHE, Chief Executive Officer
CFO: Rick Lee Nader, Chief Financial Officer
CMO: Colby Jolley D.O., Acting Chief of Staff
CIO: Andrea Evers, Director Information Technology
CNO: Gail Phelps R.N., Chief Nursing Officer
Web address: www.haxtunhealth.org
Control: Hospital district or authority, Government, Nonfederal **Service**: General medical and surgical

Staffed Beds: 25 **Admissions**: 107 **Census**: 21 **Outpatient Visits**: 28931 **Births**: 0

HOLYOKE—Phillips County

★ **MELISSA MEMORIAL HOSPITAL (061305)**, 1001 East Johnson Street, Zip 80734–1854; tel. 970/854–2241, **A**10 18 **F**3 7 8 15 18 28 29 34 40 41 43 53 57 64 66 68 82 87 90 93 97 107 108 109 110 112 114 115 116 119 127 128 133 144 146 147 148 150 **P**3
Primary Contact: Trampas Hutches, Chief Executive Officer
CFO: Jason McCormick, Interim Chief Financial Officer
CMO: Dennis Jelden M.D., Chief of Staff
CIO: David Bickford, Chief Information Officer
CHR: Sharon Greenman, Director Human Resources
CNO: Pat Notter R.N., Chief Nursing Officer and Director Quality
Web address: www.melissamemorial.org
Control: Hospital district or authority, Government, Nonfederal **Service**: General medical and surgical

Staffed Beds: 13 **Admissions**: 122 **Census**: 2 **Births**: 0 **Total Expense ($000)**: 12621 **Payroll Expense ($000)**: 5031 **Personnel**: 98

HUGO—Lincoln County

★ **LINCOLN COMMUNITY HOSPITAL AND NURSING HOME (061306)**, 111 6th Street, Zip 80821–0248, Mailing Address: P.O.Box 248, 80821–0248; tel. 719/743–2421, (Total facility includes 35 beds in nursing home–type unit) **A**10 18 **F**7 10 15 28 34 40 43 45 59 62 63 64 79 81 82 93 97 99 100 101 102 103 104 107 110 111 114 119 128 130 133 143 **P**6
Primary Contact: Kevin M. Stansbury, Chief Executive Officer
CMO: Mark Olson M.D., Chief of Staff
CIO: Michael Gaskins, Director Information Technology
CHR: Susan Petersen, Human Resources
CNO: Dan Walker, Chief Nursing Officer
Web address: www.lincolncommunityhospital.com
Control: County, Government, Nonfederal **Service**: General medical and surgical

Staffed Beds: 50 **Admissions**: 197 **Census**: 27 **Outpatient Visits**: 30598 **Births**: 0 **Total Expense ($000)**: 11327 **Personnel**: 174

JOHNSTOWN—Larimer County

☐ **NORTHERN COLORADO LONG TERM ACUTE HOSPITAL (062017)**, 4401 Union Street, Zip 80534; tel. 970/619–3663, (Nonreporting) **A**1 10 **S** Ernest Health, Inc., Albuquerque, NM
Primary Contact: Lamar McBride, Chief Executive Officer
Web address: www.ncltah.ernesthealth.com/
Control: Partnership, Investor–owned (for–profit) **Service**: Acute long–term care hospital

Staffed Beds: 40

⊞ **NORTHERN COLORADO REHABILITATION HOSPITAL (063033)**, 4401 Union Street, Zip 80534–2800; tel. 970/619–3400, (Nonreporting) **A**1 10 **S** Ernest Health, Inc., Albuquerque, NM
Primary Contact: Elizabeth Bullard, Chief Executive Officer
CFO: Bonnie Cushman, Chief Financial Officer
CMO: Revelyn Arrogante M.D., Medical Director
CHR: Amy Lauridsen, Director Human Resources
CNO: Mark Smith, Director Nursing Operations
Web address: www.ncrh.ernesthealth.com
Control: Corporation, Investor–owned (for–profit) **Service**: Rehabilitation

Staffed Beds: 40

JULESBURG—Sedgwick County

SEDGWICK COUNTY HEALTH CENTER (061310), 900 Cedar Street, Zip 80737–1199; tel. 970/474–3323, (Total facility includes 52 beds in nursing home–type unit) **A**10 18 **F**3 10 13 15 32 40 43 45 53 56 57 59 64 65 66 67 68 76 77 81 89 107 110 111 114 119 127 128 133 145 148 **P**6
Primary Contact: David Garnas, Chief Executive Officer
COO: David Garnas, Chief Executive Officer
CFO: Karla Dunker, Director Finance
CMO: Donald Regier M.D., Chief Medical Officer
CHR: Sonja Bell, Coordinator Human Resources
Control: County, Government, Nonfederal **Service**: General medical and surgical

Staffed Beds: 67 **Admissions**: 156 **Census**: 43 **Outpatient Visits**: 14345 **Births**: 25 **Total Expense ($000)**: 9721 **Payroll Expense ($000)**: 4918 **Personnel**: 82

KREMMLING—Grand County

★ **MIDDLE PARK MEDICAL CENTER–KREMMLING (061318)**, 214 South Fourth Street, Zip 80459, Mailing Address: P.O.Box 399, 80459–0399; tel. 970/724–3442, (Includes MIDDLE PARK MEDICAL CENTER – GRANBY, 1000 Granby Park South, Granby, Colorado, Zip 80446, P.O. Box 399, Kremmling, 80446, tel. 970/270–4800; Robert Flake, Chief Executive Officer) **A**10 18 **F**3 8 11 14 15 18 26 28 29 30 32 34 35 36 40 44 45 46 50 54 59 64 65 66 68 75 77 79 81 87 93 97 100 107 110 111 115 119 127 128 130 131 133 144 146 147 148 **P**6
Primary Contact: Robert Flake, Chief Executive Officer
CFO: Robert Flake, Chief Financial Officer
CMO: Thomas C. Coburn M.D., Chief Medical Officer
CHR: Jason Bryan, Director Human Resources
CNO: Debra Plemmons, Chief Nursing Officer
Web address: www.mpmc.org
Control: Hospital district or authority, Government, Nonfederal **Service**: General medical and surgical

Staffed Beds: 10 **Admissions**: 154 **Census**: 1

LA JARA—Conejos County

★ **SAN LUIS VALLEY HEALTH CONEJOS COUNTY HOSPITAL (061308)**, 19021 U S Highway 285, Zip 81140–0639, Mailing Address: P.O.Box 639, 81140–0639; tel. 719/274–5121, **A**10 18 **F**3 29 40 43 54 56 59 64 70 76 87 89 93 97 107 114 119 127 128 133 **S** San Luis Valley Health, Alamosa, CO
Primary Contact: Kelly Gallegos, Administrator
CFO: Shane Mortensen, Chief Financial Officer
CMO: Gregory McAuliffe M.D., Chief Medical Officer
CIO: Kathy Rogers, Vice President Marketing
CHR: Mandy Lee Crockett, Director Human Resources
CNO: Tandra Dunn, Director of Nursing
Web address: www.sanluisvalleyhealth.org/locations/conejos–county–hospital
Control: Other not–for–profit (including NFP Corporation) **Service**: General medical and surgical

Staffed Beds: 17 **Admissions**: 124 **Census**: 2

LA JUNTA—Otero County

⊞ **ARKANSAS VALLEY REGIONAL MEDICAL CENTER (060036)**, 1100 Carson Avenue, Zip 81050–2799; tel. 719/383–6000, (Nonreporting) **A**1 10 20 **S** QHR, Brentwood, TN
Primary Contact: Lynn Crowell, Chief Executive Officer
CMO: Kent E. Gay M.D., Chief of Medical Staff
CIO: Heidi Gearhart, Director Information Systems
CHR: Kelsey B. Brundage, Director Human Resources
CNO: Carrie Cutrell, Chief Nursing Officer
Web address: www.avrmc.org
Control: Other not–for–profit (including NFP Corporation) **Service**: General medical and surgical

Staffed Beds: 163

LAFAYETTE—Boulder County

⊞ **GOOD SAMARITAN MEDICAL CENTER (060116)**, 200 Exempla Circle, Zip 80026–3370; tel. 303/689–4000, **A**1 2 10 **F**3 11 12 13 15 18 20 22 26 28 29 30 31 35 36 40 41 42 43 45 46 49 51 60 64 68 70 72 74 75 76 77 78 79 80 81 84 85 86 87 91 92 93 100 102 107 108 110 111 114 115 119 120 121 126 130 132 135 145 146 147 148 149 150 **P**6 **S** SCL Health, Broomfield, CO
Primary Contact: Jennifer Alderfer, President
COO: Beth Forsyth, Chief Operating Officer
CFO: John Higgins, Vice President and Chief Financial Officer
CMO: Todd Mydler M.D., Vice President and Chief Medical Officer
CHR: Amy Pacey, Vice President Human Resources
CNO: Susan Kerschen MS, R.N., Vice President and Chief Nursing Officer
Web address: www.goodsamaritancolorado.org/
Control: Other not–for–profit (including NFP Corporation) **Service**: General medical and surgical

Staffed Beds: 207 **Admissions**: 13282 **Census**: 142 **Outpatient Visits**: 101244 **Births**: 2211 **Total Expense ($000)**: 266780 **Payroll Expense ($000)**: 85596 **Personnel**: 1209

LAKEWOOD—Jefferson County

✠ **ORTHOCOLORADO HOSPITAL (060124)**, 11650 West 2nd Place, Zip 80228–1527; tel. 720/321–5000, (Nonreporting) **A**1 10 **S** Catholic Health Initiatives, Englewood, CO
Primary Contact: Jude Torchia, Chief Executive Officer
Web address: www.orthocolorado.org
Control: Partnership, Investor–owned (for–profit) **Service**: Orthopedic

| Staffed Beds: 48 |

✠ **ST. ANTHONY HOSPITAL (060015)**, 11600 West Second Place, Zip 80228–1527; tel. 720/321–0000, **A**1 2 3 5 10 13 **F**3 7 11 12 15 17 18 20 22 24 26 28 29 30 31 34 35 36 40 43 45 46 47 48 49 50 53 56 57 59 64 65 68 70 74 75 77 78 79 81 82 84 85 87 90 91 92 93 96 97 102 107 108 111 114 115 116 117 118 119 120 121 123 124 126 129 130 132 133 134 135 146 147 148 **S** Catholic Health Initiatives, Englewood, CO
Primary Contact: Edward H. Sim, Chief Executive Officer
CMO: Brian Erling, Group Chief Medical Officer
CIO: Dana Moore, Senior Vice President Information Services
CHR: Michelle Fornier–Johnson, Group Vice President Human Resources
CNO: Linda Goodwin, Group Chief Nursing Officer
Web address: www.stanthonyhosp.org
Control: Church operated, Nongovernment, not–for–profit **Service**: General medical and surgical

| Staffed Beds: 217 Admissions: 11757 Census: 174 Outpatient Visits: 90684 Births: 0 Total Expense ($000): 324122 Payroll Expense ($000): 108102 Personnel: 2023 |

LAMAR—Prowers County

★ **PROWERS MEDICAL CENTER (061323)**, 401 Kendall Drive, Zip 81052–3993; tel. 719/336–4343, **A**3 10 18 **F**3 11 13 15 18 20 28 29 31 34 35 40 44 45 50 56 57 59 62 64 65 66 68 76 77 78 81 85 86 93 96 97 107 111 119 127 130 131 132 133 146 147 148 **P**6 **S** QHR, Brentwood, TN
Primary Contact: Craig Loveless, Chief Executive Officer
COO: Karen Bryant, Chief Support Services Officer
CFO: Audrey Kane, Interim Chief Financial Officer
CMO: Barry Portner M.D., Chief of Staff
CIO: Jason Spano, Director of Information Technology
CHR: Karen Bryant, Chief Support Services Officer
Web address: www.prowersmedical.com
Control: Hospital district or authority, Government, Nonfederal **Service**: General medical and surgical

| Staffed Beds: 25 Admissions: 1039 Census: 9 Outpatient Visits: 30984 Births: 177 Total Expense ($000): 24756 Payroll Expense ($000): 10908 Personnel: 198 |

LEADVILLE—Lake County

★ **ST. VINCENT GENERAL HOSPITAL DISTRICT (061319)**, 822 West 4th Street, Zip 80461–3897; tel. 719/486–0230, (Nonreporting) **A**10 18
Primary Contact: Gary Campbell, Chief Executive Officer
CMO: Gary Petry M.D., Chief of Staff
CHR: Cheryl Snider, Director Human Resources
CNO: Von Kilpatrick, Chief Nursing Officer
Web address: www.svghd.org
Control: Hospital district or authority, Government, Nonfederal **Service**: General medical and surgical

| Staffed Beds: 25 |

LITTLETON—Jefferson County

FEDERAL CORRECTIONAL INSTITUTE HOSPITAL, 9595 West Quincy Street, Zip 80123–1159; tel. 303/985–1566, (Nonreporting)
Primary Contact: Mike Hudson, Administrator
Control: Department of Justice, Government, federal **Service**: Hospital unit of an institution (prison hospital, college infirmary, etc.)

| Staffed Beds: 6 |

LITTLETON—Arapahoe County

✠ **HEALTHSOUTH REHABILITATION HOSPITAL OF LITTLETON (063034)**, 1001 West Mineral Avenue, Zip 80120–4507; tel. 303/334–1100, (Nonreporting) **A**1 10 **S** HEALTHSOUTH Corporation, Birmingham, AL
Primary Contact: David H. Shefte, Chief Executive Officer
CFO: Liz Freudenberg, Chief Financial Officer
CMO: Jill Castro M.D., Medical Director
CHR: Sarah Thomas, Director of Human Resources
Web address: www.healthsouthdenver.com
Control: Corporation, Investor–owned (for–profit) **Service**: Rehabilitation

| Staffed Beds: 28 |

✠ **LITTLETON ADVENTIST HOSPITAL (060113)**, 7700 South Broadway Street, Zip 80122–2628; tel. 303/730–8900, **A**1 2 5 10 **F**3 11 13 15 17 18 20 22 26 29 30 31 34 35 36 37 39 40 41 43 44 45 46 47 48 49 50 53 54 55 57 59 64 68 70 72 74 75 76 77 78 81 82 83 84 85 86 87 89 90 92 93 97 107 108 110 111 114 115 116 117 118 119 120 121 126 130 131 132 135 146 147 148 **P**6 **S** Adventist Health System Sunbelt Health Care Corporation, Altamonte Springs, FL
Primary Contact: Brett Spenst, Chief Executive Officer
COO: Geoff Lawton, Vice President Operations
CFO: Cheryl Curry, Chief Financial Officer
CMO: Lawrence Wood M.D., Chief Medical Officer
CHR: Rita K Arthur, Director Human Resources
CNO: Rhonda Ward R.N., MSN, Chief Nursing Officer
Web address: www.centura.org
Control: Church operated, Nongovernment, not–for–profit **Service**: General medical and surgical

| Staffed Beds: 201 Admissions: 9265 Census: 112 Outpatient Visits: 58249 Births: 1672 Total Expense ($000): 193254 Payroll Expense ($000): 72007 Personnel: 1292 |

LITTLETON—Douglas County

☐ **HIGHLANDS BEHAVIORAL HEALTH SYSTEM (064024)**, 8565 South Poplar Way, Zip 80130–3602; tel. 720/348–2800, (Nonreporting) **A**1 10 **S** Universal Health Services, Inc., King of Prussia, PA
Primary Contact: Lisa Strub, Interim Chief Executive Officer
Web address: www.highlandsbhs.com
Control: Corporation, Investor–owned (for–profit) **Service**: Psychiatric

| Staffed Beds: 86 |

LONE TREE—Douglas County

✠ **SKY RIDGE MEDICAL CENTER (060112)**, 10101 Ridge Gate Parkway, Zip 80124–5522; tel. 720/225–1000, **A**1 2 3 5 10 12 13 **F**3 8 12 13 15 17 18 19 20 22 28 29 30 31 34 35 36 37 40 41 42 43 45 46 47 48 49 54 58 59 64 70 72 73 74 75 76 77 78 79 81 82 84 85 86 87 89 93 97 107 108 111 114 115 119 120 121 123 126 129 130 131 132 135 146 147 148 149 **S** HCA Healthcare, Nashville, TN
Primary Contact: Susan Hicks, Chief Executive Officer
CFO: Craig Sammons, Chief Financial Officer
CMO: David Markenson M.D., Chief Medical Officer
CIO: Evan Tice, Director Information Technology and Systems
CHR: Jim Ritchey, Director Human Resources
CNO: Marian Savitsky R.N., Chief Nursing Officer
Web address: www.skyridgemedcenter.com
Control: Corporation, Investor–owned (for–profit) **Service**: General medical and surgical

| Staffed Beds: 275 Admissions: 16043 Census: 144 Outpatient Visits: 98279 Births: 3483 Personnel: 1035 |

LONGMONT—Boulder County

✠ **LONGMONT UNITED HOSPITAL (060003)**, 1950 West Mountain View Avenue, Zip 80501–3162, Mailing Address: P.O.Box 1659, 80502–1659; tel. 303/651–5111, (Total facility includes 15 beds in nursing home–type unit) **A**1 2 10 **F**2 3 11 13 15 18 20 22 28 29 30 31 34 35 36 37 40 43 44 45 47 48 49 50 53 54 56 57 59 61 64 68 70 73 74 75 76 77 78 79 81 82 84 85 86 87 89 92 93 107 108 110 111 114 115 118 119 121 123 126 128 129 130 131 132 135 146 148 149 150 **P**6 **S** Catholic Health Initiatives, Englewood, CO
Primary Contact: Mitchell C. Carson, President and Chief Executive Officer
CFO: Daniel Frank, Chief Financial Officer
CMO: Wyatt Hall M.D., Chief Medical Officer
CHR: Warren Laughlin, Vice President Human Resources
CNO: Nancy Driscoll, Chief Nursing Officer
Web address: www.luhcares.org
Control: Other not–for–profit (including NFP Corporation) **Service**: General medical and surgical

| Staffed Beds: 146 Admissions: 6942 Census: 78 Outpatient Visits: 131806 Births: 1009 Total Expense ($000): 172511 Payroll Expense ($000): 66677 Personnel: 1004 |

CO

LOUISVILLE—Boulder County

✠ **AVISTA ADVENTIST HOSPITAL (060103)**, 100 Health Park Drive, Zip 80027–9583; tel. 303/673–1000, **A**1 10 **F**3 8 11 13 15 17 18 20 22 28 29 30 31 34 40 42 43 44 45 47 48 49 50 56 59 60 62 63 64 68 70 72 74 75 76 77 79 81 82 84 85 86 87 93 107 108 111 114 115 119 129 130 131 132 135 146 147 **P**6 **S** Adventist Health System Sunbelt Health Care Corporation, Altamonte Springs, FL
Primary Contact: Brent Davis, Interim Chief Executive Officer
CMO: David Ehrenberger M.D., Chief Medical Officer
CHR: Becky Ortega, Manager Human Resources
CNO: Lavah Boyers Lowe, Chief Nursing Officer
Web address: www.avistahospital.org
Control: Church operated, Nongovernment, not–for–profit **Service:** General medical and surgical

Staffed Beds: 114 **Admissions:** 4225 **Census:** 37 **Outpatient Visits:** 46841 **Births:** 2062 **Total Expense ($000):** 90674 **Payroll Expense ($000):** 35269 **Personnel:** 632

☐ **CENTENNIAL PEAKS HOSPITAL (064007)**, 2255 South 88th Street, Zip 80027–9716; tel. 303/673–9990, (Nonreporting) **A**1 10 **S** Universal Health Services, Inc., King of Prussia, PA
Primary Contact: Elicia Bunch, Chief Executive Officer
COO: Lisa Strub, Chief Operating Officer
CFO: Tim Ryan, Chief Financial Officer
CMO: Konoy Mandal M.D., Medical Director
CHR: Suzanne Martinez, Director Human Resources
CNO: Donia L Andersen, Director of Nursing
Web address: www.centennialpeaks.com
Control: Other not–for–profit (including NFP Corporation) **Service:** Psychiatric

Staffed Beds: 72

LOVELAND—Larimer County

✠ **MCKEE MEDICAL CENTER (060030)**, 2000 Boise Avenue, Zip 80538–4281; tel. 970/669–4640, **A**1 2 10 **F**2 3 8 11 13 14 15 18 20 22 26 28 29 30 31 34 35 36 40 43 44 45 49 50 54 56 59 60 62 64 65 68 70 74 75 76 77 78 79 81 84 85 87 89 92 93 97 107 108 110 111 114 115 119 120 121 122 123 124 126 129 130 135 144 146 147 148 **S** Banner Health, Phoenix, AZ
Primary Contact: Margo Karsten, Ph.D., MSN, Chief Executive Officer
COO: Julie Klein, Chief Operating Officer
CFO: Lori Sehrt, Chief Financial Officer
CMO: Bert Honea M.D., Medical Director
CIO: Steve Rains, Director Information Services
CHR: Jeannie Gallagher, jeanie.gallagher@bannerhealth.com
CNO: Kelly Sturler, Chief Nursing Officer
Web address: www.mckeeloveland.com
Control: Other not–for–profit (including NFP Corporation) **Service:** General medical and surgical

Staffed Beds: 96 **Admissions:** 3400 **Census:** 28 **Births:** 780 **Total Expense ($000):** 119994 **Payroll Expense ($000):** 36701 **Personnel:** 579

✠ **MEDICAL CENTER OF THE ROCKIES (060119)**, 2500 Rocky Mountain Avenue, Zip 80538–9004; tel. 970/624–2500, **A**1 3 5 10 **F**3 8 11 13 14 15 17 18 20 22 24 26 28 29 30 31 32 34 35 38 39 40 42 43 44 45 47 49 50 54 55 57 58 59 60 61 64 65 68 70 74 75 76 77 78 79 80 81 82 83 84 85 86 87 89 90 91 92 93 96 100 107 108 110 111 114 115 118 119 126 129 130 131 132 134 135 143 146 147 148 149 150 **S** University of Colorado Health, Fort Collins, CO
Primary Contact: Kevin L. Unger, Ph.D., FACHE, President and Chief Executive Officer
CFO: Stephanie Doughty, Chief Financial Officer
CMO: William Neff M.D., Chief Medical Officer
CIO: Steve Hess, Vice President & Chief Information Officer
Web address: www.medctrrockies.org
Control: Other not–for–profit (including NFP Corporation) **Service:** General medical and surgical

Staffed Beds: 187 **Admissions:** 10869 **Census:** 124 **Outpatient Visits:** 80371 **Births:** 1279 **Total Expense ($000):** 349273 **Payroll Expense ($000):** 103001 **Personnel:** 1060

MEEKER—Rio Blanco County

★ **PIONEERS MEDICAL CENTER (061325)**, 100 Pioneers Medical Center Drive, Zip 81641–3181; tel. 970/878–5047, (Nonreporting) **A**10 18 **S** QHR, Brentwood, TN
Primary Contact: Kenneth Harman, Chief Executive Officer
COO: Karen Iacuone, Chief Nursing Officer and Chief Operating Officer
CFO: James W Worrell, Chief Financial Officer
CMO: Christopher Williams M.D., Chief of Staff
CIO: Curtis Cooper, Manager Information Systems
CHR: Twyla Jensen, Director Human Resources
CNO: Karen Iacuone, Chief Nursing Officer
Web address: www.pioneershospital.org
Control: Hospital district or authority, Government, Nonfederal **Service:** General medical and surgical

Staffed Beds: 40

MONTROSE—Montrose County

✠ **MONTROSE MEMORIAL HOSPITAL (060006)**, 800 South Third Street, Zip 81401–4212; tel. 970/249–2211, **A**1 10 20 **F**3 13 15 18 20 22 24 28 29 30 31 34 35 38 40 43 45 46 47 48 50 51 54 56 57 59 68 70 74 75 76 77 78 79 81 82 84 85 89 90 92 93 94 96 97 107 108 109 110 111 112 115 118 119 126 129 130 132 135 143 146 147 148 **P**1 5 **S** QHR, Brentwood, TN
Primary Contact: Cindy Bradley, Interim CEO
COO: Mary E Snyder, Chief Operations Officer
CFO: Stephan A Wilson, Chief Financial Officer
CMO: Richard Shannon M.D., Chief of Staff
CIO: Carlos Lovera, Director Information Systems
CHR: Kathy McKie, Director Human Resources
Web address: www.montrosehospital.com
Control: Other not–for–profit (including NFP Corporation) **Service:** General medical and surgical

Staffed Beds: 60 **Admissions:** 2721 **Census:** 29 **Outpatient Visits:** 112576 **Births:** 400 **Total Expense ($000):** 100314 **Payroll Expense ($000):** 37320 **Personnel:** 610

NORTHGLENN—Adams County

SCL HEALTH COMMUNITY HOSPITAL – NORTHGLENN, 11900 Grant Street, Zip 80233; tel. 720/573–5095, (Nonreporting) **S** SCL Health, Broomfield, CO
Primary Contact: Sean Stricker, Chief Executive Officer
Web address: www.sclhealthsystem.org
Control: Church operated, Nongovernment, not–for–profit **Service:** General medical and surgical

Staffed Beds: 8

PAGOSA SPRINGS—Archuleta County

PAGOSA SPRINGS MEDICAL CENTER (061328), 95 South Pagosa Boulevard, Zip 81147–8329; tel. 970/731–3700, (Nonreporting) **A**10 18
Primary Contact: Bradley Cochennet, Chief Executive Officer
Control: Other not–for–profit (including NFP Corporation) **Service:** General medical and surgical

Staffed Beds: 11

PARKER—Douglas County

✠ **PARKER ADVENTIST HOSPITAL (060114)**, 9395 Crown Crest Boulevard, Zip 80138–8573; tel. 303/269–4000, **A**1 2 10 **F**3 11 12 13 15 20 22 29 30 31 34 35 36 37 38 40 42 43 45 46 49 50 54 55 57 59 64 70 72 73 74 75 76 77 78 79 81 82 83 84 85 87 93 96 97 107 110 111 114 115 116 117 119 120 123 126 129 130 131 132 146 147 148 **P**6 **S** Adventist Health System Sunbelt Health Care Corporation, Altamonte Springs, FL
Primary Contact: Sam D. Huenergardt, Chief Executive Officer
CFO: Andrew Gaasch, Chief Financial Officer
Web address: www.parkerhospital.org
Control: Church operated, Nongovernment, not–for–profit **Service:** General medical and surgical

Staffed Beds: 167 **Admissions:** 7823 **Census:** 83 **Outpatient Visits:** 68981 **Births:** 1566 **Total Expense ($000):** 182223 **Payroll Expense ($000):** 65047 **Personnel:** 1216

PUEBLO—Pueblo County

☐ **COLORADO MENTAL HEALTH INSTITUTE AT PUEBLO (064001)**, 1600 West 24th Street, Zip 81003–1499; tel. 719/546–4000, (Nonreporting) **A**1 3 5 10
Primary Contact: Ron Hale, Superintendent
CFO: Jim Duff, Chief Financial Officer
CMO: Al Singleton M.D., Chief Psychiatry and Chief Medical Staff
CIO: Eunice Wolther, Public Information Officer
CHR: Mary Young, Director Human Resources
Web address: www.cdhs.state.co.us/cmhip
Control: State, Government, Nonfederal **Service:** Psychiatric

Staffed Beds: 514

✠ △ **PARKVIEW MEDICAL CENTER (060020)**, 400 West 16th Street, Zip 81003–2781; tel. 719/584–4000, (Total facility includes 20 beds in nursing home–type unit) **A**1 3 7 10 13 **F**2 3 4 5 8 11 13 15 18 20 22 24 26 28 29 30 31 34 35 37 38 40 42 43 45 46 49 50 51 53 54 56 57 58 59 62 64 70 72 74 75 76 78 79 81 82 84 85 86 87 89 90 92 93 94 95 96 97 98 99 100 101 102 103 104 105 107 108 111 114 115 116 119 126 128 129 130 131 132 135 141 146 147 148 **P**6 8
Primary Contact: Michael T. Baxter, President and Chief Executive Officer
CFO: Leslie Barnes, Chief Financial Officer
CMO: Steve Nafziger M.D., Vice President Medical Affairs
CIO: Steve Shirley, Chief Information Officer
CHR: Darrin Smith, Vice President Human Resources
CNO: Linda Flores R.N., MSN, Vice President Nursing Services
Web address: www.parkviewmc.com
Control: Other not–for–profit (including NFP Corporation) **Service:** General medical and surgical

Staffed Beds: 370 **Admissions:** 15716 **Census:** 247 **Outpatient Visits:** 228205 **Births:** 1523 **Total Expense ($000):** 312364 **Payroll Expense ($000):** 122543 **Personnel:** 2584

Many Facility Codes have changed. Please refer to the AHA Guide Code Chart. © 2017 AHA Guide

✠ **ST. MARY–CORWIN MEDICAL CENTER (060012)**, 1008 Minnequa Avenue, Zip 81004–3798; tel. 719/557–4000, **A**1 2 3 10 13 **F**3 13 15 18 20 22 26 28 29 30 31 34 35 40 43 45 47 48 49 50 51 53 55 57 58 59 64 68 70 72 73 75 76 78 79 81 82 84 85 86 87 89 90 107 108 110 111 114 115 117 119 120 121 123 124 126 129 130 131 132 135 146 147 148 149 **P**6 **S** Catholic Health Initiatives, Englewood, CO
Primary Contact: Brian Moore, President and Chief Executive Officer
COO: Michael Cafasso, Vice President Operations
CFO: Vanessa Kochevar, Chief Financial Officer
CMO: Robert Underwood M.D., MS, Chief Medical Officer
CHR: Timea Kennedy, Director Human Resources
CNO: Constance Schmidt FACHE, R.N., Vice President Patient Care Services and Chief Nursing Officer
Web address: www.stmarycorwin.org
Control: Church operated, Nongovernment, not–for–profit **Service**: General medical and surgical

Staffed Beds: 125 **Admissions**: 6060 **Census**: 72 **Outpatient Visits**: 91912 **Births**: 537 **Total Expense ($000)**: 152145 **Payroll Expense ($000)**: 54529 **Personnel**: 799

RANGELY—Rio Blanco County

★ **RANGELY DISTRICT HOSPITAL (061307)**, 225 Eagle Crest Drive, Zip 81648–2104; tel. 970/675–5011, **A**10 18 **F**1 3 7 10 15 29 32 34 35 40 43 45 50 54 57 59 62 64 65 67 68 90 91 93 97 107 110 115 116 127 128 129 131 133 144 148 149
Primary Contact: Nick Goshe, Chief Executive Officer
COO: Bernard Rice, Chief Compliance Officer
CFO: Jim Dillon, Chief Financial Officer
CMO: Abigail R. Urish M.D., Chief of Staff
CHR: Cynthia S. Stults, Executive Assistant and Human Resources Director
CNO: Sharma Vaughn Esq, Chief Nursing Officer
Web address: www.rangelyhospital.com
Control: Hospital district or authority, Government, Nonfederal **Service**: Acute long–term care hospital

Staffed Beds: 25 **Admissions**: 37 **Census**: 12 **Outpatient Visits**: 3997 **Births**: 0 **Total Expense ($000)**: 19535 **Payroll Expense ($000)**: 8355 **Personnel**: 113

RIFLE—Garfield County

★ **GRAND RIVER HOSPITAL DISTRICT (061317)**, 501 Airport Road, Zip 81650–8510, Mailing Address: P.O.Box 912, 81650–0912; tel. 970/625–1510, (Total facility includes 57 beds in nursing home–type unit) **A**10 18 **F**3 11 12 15 29 34 35 39 40 41 43 45 50 55 57 59 64 68 69 75 77 79 81 85 87 93 96 97 107 108 110 111 115 119 127 128 129 130 131 132 133 144 146 147 148 149 **P**6
Primary Contact: James Coombs, Chief Executive Officer
COO: Bill Noel, Chief Operating Officer
CFO: Cris Bolin, Chief Financial Officer
CMO: Kevin Coleman M.D., Chief Medical Officer
CIO: Diana Murray, Director Information Systems
CHR: Dawn Hodges, Director Human Resources
CNO: Stacy Pemberton, Chief Nursing Officer
Web address: www.grhd.org
Control: Hospital district or authority, Government, Nonfederal **Service**: General medical and surgical

Staffed Beds: 69 **Admissions**: 583 **Census**: 51 **Outpatient Visits**: 215396 **Births**: 0 **Total Expense ($000)**: 71618 **Payroll Expense ($000)**: 35891 **Personnel**: 512

SALIDA—Chaffee County

★ **HEART OF THE ROCKIES REGIONAL MEDICAL CENTER (061322)**, 1000 Rush Drive, Zip 81201–9627, Mailing Address: P.O.Box 429, 81201–0429; tel. 719/530–2200, **A**10 18 **F**3 5 11 13 15 28 29 31 34 35 40 43 45 50 54 57 64 68 70 74 75 76 77 78 79 81 82 85 91 93 97 107 110 111 115 119 127 129 130 131 132 133 135 146 147 148
Primary Contact: Robert A. Morasko, Chief Executive Officer
CFO: Lesley Fagerberg, Vice President Fiscal Services
CMO: Daniel Wardrop M.D., Medical Director
CIO: Andy Waldbart, Department Manager
CHR: Barbara Lutz, Vice President Human Resources
CNO: Linda Johnson R.N., Vice President, Patient Services Risk Management and Chief Nursing Officer
Web address: www.hrrmc.com
Control: Hospital district or authority, Government, Nonfederal **Service**: General medical and surgical

Staffed Beds: 25 **Admissions**: 1059 **Census**: 10 **Outpatient Visits**: 77608 **Births**: 121 **Total Expense ($000)**: 55216 **Payroll Expense ($000)**: 24195 **Personnel**: 389

SPRINGFIELD—Baca County

★ **SOUTHEAST COLORADO HOSPITAL DISTRICT (061311)**, 373 East Tenth Avenue, Zip 81073–1699; tel. 719/523–4501, (Total facility includes 56 beds in nursing home–type unit) **A**10 18 **F**3 6 7 11 29 34 35 40 45 50 54 56 57 62 63 66 68 77 81 91 93 97 107 119 127 133 147 148 **P**6
Primary Contact: David Engel, Chief Executive Officer and Administrator
CFO: Dorothy Burke, Chief Financial Officer
CMO: Andrea Wismann M.D., Chief of Staff
CIO: Chris Westphal, Chief Information Technology Officer
CHR: Sherrilyn Turner, Director Human Resources
CNO: Cecelia Deen Esq, Chief Nursing Officer
Web address: www.sechosp.org
Control: Hospital district or authority, Government, Nonfederal **Service**: General medical and surgical

Staffed Beds: 79 **Admissions**: 242 **Census**: 52 **Outpatient Visits**: 38009 **Births**: 0 **Total Expense ($000)**: 14640 **Payroll Expense ($000)**: 7342 **Personnel**: 188

STEAMBOAT SPRINGS—Routt County

✠ **YAMPA VALLEY MEDICAL CENTER (060049)**, 1024 Central Park Drive, Zip 80487–8813; tel. 970/879–1322, **A**1 2 10 20 **F**3 13 15 18 28 29 30 31 34 35 36 40 43 45 46 48 49 50 51 57 64 68 70 73 75 76 77 78 79 81 82 84 85 86 87 93 97 107 110 111 115 119 126 129 130 131 132 133 135 143 146 147 149
Primary Contact: Frank May, Chief Executive Officer
CFO: Bryan Roach, Chief Financial Officer
CMO: Lisa Kettering, Chief Medical Officer
CIO: Mark Clark, Chief Information Officer
CHR: Soniya Fidler MS, Chief Human Resources and Compliance Officer
CNO: Marie Timlin R.N., Chief Nursing Officer
Web address: www.yvmc.org
Control: Other not–for–profit (including NFP Corporation) **Service**: General medical and surgical

Staffed Beds: 39 **Admissions**: 1496 **Census**: 11 **Outpatient Visits**: 72288 **Births**: 301 **Total Expense ($000)**: 96746 **Payroll Expense ($000)**: 31841 **Personnel**: 417

STERLING—Logan County

✠ **STERLING REGIONAL MEDCENTER (060076)**, 615 Fairhurst Street, Zip 80751–4523; tel. 970/522–0122, **A**1 3 10 20 **F**3 11 13 15 18 28 29 30 31 34 35 40 43 45 57 59 64 70 76 77 78 79 81 85 87 91 93 96 107 108 111 115 119 120 121 127 129 130 131 147 148 **S** Banner Health, Phoenix, AZ
Primary Contact: Hoyt Skabelund, Chief Executive Officer
CFO: Tiffany Weber, Chief Financial Officer
CMO: Jeff Bacon D.O., Chief Medical Officer
CNO: Wade Alan Tyrrell RN, Chief Nursing Officer
Web address: www.bannerhealth.com/Locations/Colorado/Sterling+Regional+MedCenter
Control: Other not–for–profit (including NFP Corporation) **Service**: General medical and surgical

Staffed Beds: 25 **Admissions**: 1085 **Census**: 8 **Births**: 245 **Total Expense ($000)**: 42746 **Payroll Expense ($000)**: 15871 **Personnel**: 239

THORNTON—Adams County

✠ **NORTH SUBURBAN MEDICAL CENTER (060065)**, 9191 Grant Street, Zip 80229–4341; tel. 303/451–7800, **A**1 3 10 **F**3 8 11 12 13 15 20 22 29 30 31 34 35 40 41 42 43 45 48 50 51 54 59 64 70 72 74 75 76 77 78 79 80 81 82 85 87 89 107 108 110 111 114 115 119 126 129 130 132 135 146 147 148 149 **S** HCA Healthcare, Nashville, TN
Primary Contact: Jennifer Alderfer, President and Chief Executive Officer
CIO: Marty Hoesch, Director Information Systems
CHR: Dena Schmaedecke, Vice President Human Resources
CNO: Linnet Jung, Chief Nursing Officer
Web address: www.northsuburban.com
Control: Corporation, Investor–owned (for–profit) **Service**: General medical and surgical

Staffed Beds: 139 **Admissions**: 7704 **Census**: 77 **Outpatient Visits**: 73411 **Births**: 1082 **Personnel**: 656

✠ **VIBRA HOSPITAL OF DENVER (062014)**, 8451 Pearl Street, Zip 80229–4804; tel. 303/288–3000, (Nonreporting) **A**1 10 **S** Vibra Healthcare, Mechanicsburg, PA
Primary Contact: Linda Tautz, Chief Executive Officer
CMO: John Buckley M.D., President Medical Staff
CHR: Lorna Fulton, Director Human Resources
Web address: www.vhdenver.com
Control: Corporation, Investor–owned (for–profit) **Service**: Acute long–term care hospital

Staffed Beds: 71

CO

Hospital, Medicare Provider Number, Address, Telephone, Approval, Facility, and Physician Codes, Health Care System

★ American Hospital Association (AHA) membership
□ The Joint Commission accreditation
○ Healthcare Facilities Accreditation Program
◇ DNV Healthcare Inc. accreditation
⇑ Center for Improvement in Healthcare Quality Accreditation
△ Commission on Accreditation of Rehabilitation Facilities (CARF) accreditation

TRINIDAD—Las Animas County

★ **MT. SAN RAFAEL HOSPITAL (061321)**, 410 Benedicta Avenue, Zip 81082–2093; tel. 719/846–9213, **A**10 18 **F**3 11 15 28 34 35 40 45 46 50 65 75 81 82 85 89 93 94 96 97 107 111 114 119 127 129 133 146 147 148
Primary Contact: John Tucker, Chief Executive Officer
CFO: David W Rollins, Chief Financial Officer
CIO: Michael Archuleta, Chief Information Technology Officer
CHR: Tammy Rogers, Director Human Resources
CNO: Mandy Shaiffer, Chief Nursing Officer
Web address: www.msrhc.org
Control: Other not–for–profit (including NFP Corporation) **Service:** General medical and surgical

Staffed Beds: 18 **Admissions:** 636 **Census:** 9 **Outpatient Visits:** 37114

VAIL—Eagle County

⊞ **VAIL VALLEY HEALTH HOSPITAL (060096)**, 181 West Meadow Drive, Zip 81657–5242, Mailing Address: P.O.Box 40000, 81658–7520; tel. 970/476–2451, **A**1 3 10 20 **F**3 11 13 15 18 28 29 31 34 35 36 37 40 42 43 50 51 54 57 59 64 68 70 72 75 76 77 78 79 81 82 85 86 87 93 107 108 110 111 115 116 117 119 120 121 123 129 130 131 135 141 142 143 144 146 147 148 149 150 **P**6
Primary Contact: Doris Kirchner, President and Chief Executive Officer
CFO: Ted Sirotta, Chief Financial Officer
CMO: Barry Hammaker M.D., Chief Medical Officer and Chief Clinical Officer
CIO: Brian Foster, Chief Information Officer
CHR: Rick Smith, Senior Vice President Human Resources and Chief Administrative Officer
CNO: Sheila Sherman, Vice President Patient Care Services
Web address: www.vvmc.com
Control: Other not–for–profit (including NFP Corporation) **Service:** General medical and surgical

Staffed Beds: 58 **Admissions:** 1786 **Census:** 11 **Outpatient Visits:** 133284 **Births:** 485 **Total Expense ($000):** 150453 **Payroll Expense ($000):** 52909 **Personnel:** 794

WALSENBURG—Huerfano County

★ **SPANISH PEAKS REGIONAL HEALTH CENTER (061316)**, 23500 U S Highway 160, Zip 81089–9524; tel. 719/738–5100, (Total facility includes 120 beds in nursing home–type unit) **A**10 18 **F**7 15 18 26 27 28 29 32 34 35 40 43 45 50 57 59 64 67 69 81 82 85 93 97 107 110 115 119 127 133 134 135 146 147
Primary Contact: Kay L. Whitley, President and Chief Executive Officer
CFO: Lionel J. Montoya, Chief Financial Officer
CMO: Michael A. Moll M.D., Chief Medical Officer and Chief of Staff
CHR: Tony Marostica, Chief Compliance and Human Resource Officer
CNO: Mary Cope R.N., Chief Clinical Officer
Web address: www.sprhc.org
Control: Hospital district or authority, Government, Nonfederal **Service:** General medical and surgical

Staffed Beds: 140 **Admissions:** 175 **Census:** 95 **Outpatient Visits:** 31820 **Total Expense ($000):** 28037 **Payroll Expense ($000):** 15251 **Personnel:** 200

WESTMINSTER—Adams County

⊞ **ST. ANTHONY NORTH HEALTH CAMPUS (060104)**, 14300 Orchard Parkway, Zip 80023–9206; tel. 720/627–0000, **A**1 2 3 10 **F**3 11 13 15 18 20 22 26 28 29 30 31 34 35 36 40 42 43 45 46 49 54 55 57 59 60 63 64 65 68 70 72 74 75 76 77 78 79 81 82 84 85 87 91 92 93 97 102 107 108 110 111 114 115 119 130 131 132 146 147 148 149 150 **S** Catholic Health Initiatives, Englewood, CO
Primary Contact: Kevin Jenkins, President and Chief Executive Officer
CFO: Alison Mizer, Chief Financial Officer
CIO: Dana Moore, Senior Vice President Information Services
CHR: Robert Archibold, Director, Human Resources
CNO: Carol A Butler R.N., MSN, VP Patient Care Services & Operations
Web address: www.stanthonynorth.org
Control: Church operated, Nongovernment, not–for–profit **Service:** General medical and surgical

Staffed Beds: 105 **Admissions:** 5770 **Census:** 53 **Outpatient Visits:** 43303 **Births:** 1253 **Total Expense ($000):** 132741 **Payroll Expense ($000):** 46435 **Personnel:** 963

WHEAT RIDGE—Jefferson County

⊞ **LUTHERAN MEDICAL CENTER (060009)**, 8300 West 38th Avenue, Zip 80033–6005; tel. 303/425–4500, (Includes EXEMPLA WEST PINES, 3400 Lutheran Parkway, Wheat Ridge, Colorado, Zip 80033, tel. 303/467–4000) (Total facility includes 118 beds in nursing home–type unit) **A**1 2 3 10 **F**3 4 5 10 11 13 15 18 20 22 24 26 28 29 30 31 33 35 36 40 43 45 47 48 49 50 55 56 58 59 60 61 63 64 67 68 70 71 72 74 75 76 77 78 79 81 83 84 85 86 87 94 98 100 101 102 103 104 105 107 108 110 111 114 115 119 120 121 123 124 125 126 128 129 130 132 146 147 148 **P**6 **S** SCL Health, Broomfield, CO
Primary Contact: Grant Wicklund, President and Chief Executive Officer
CFO: Karen Scremin, Vice President Finance
CMO: Christina Johnson M.D., Vice President and Chief Clinical and Quality Officer
CHR: Scott Day, Vice President Human Resources
CNO: Geraldine Towndrow R.N., Senior Vice President Nursing
Web address: www.sclhealth.org/locations/lutheran–medical–center/
Control: Other not–for–profit (including NFP Corporation) **Service:** General medical and surgical

Staffed Beds: 518 **Admissions:** 15983 **Census:** 310 **Outpatient Visits:** 253620 **Births:** 2606 **Total Expense ($000):** 339664 **Payroll Expense ($000):** 122861 **Personnel:** 1555

WOODLAND PARK—Teller County

⇑ **PIKES PEAK REGIONAL HOSPITAL (061326)**, 16420 West Highway 24, Zip 80863; tel. 719/687–9999, **A**10 18 21 **F**3 15 29 30 34 40 41 43 45 50 57 59 64 65 68 75 77 79 80 81 85 87 93 97 107 110 111 114 119 129 131 133 146 148 **S** IASIS Healthcare, Franklin, TN
Primary Contact: Kimberly Monjesky, Chief Executive Officer
CFO: Robin Ruff, Chief Financial Officer
CMO: Richard Malyszek M.D., Chief of Staff
CHR: Arianne Randolph, Director Human Resources
CNO: Marsha Sensat R.N., Chief Nursing Officer
Web address: www.pprmc.org
Control: Corporation, Investor–owned (for–profit) **Service:** General medical and surgical

Staffed Beds: 15 **Admissions:** 533 **Census:** 6

WRAY—Yuma County

★ **WRAY COMMUNITY DISTRICT HOSPITAL (061309)**, 1017 West 7th Street, Zip 80758–1420; tel. 970/332–4811, (Nonreporting) **A**3 10 18
Primary Contact: Jennie Sullivan, Chief Executive Officer
CMO: Monte Uyemura, Chief Medical Officer
Web address: www.wraycommunitydistricthospital.com/
Control: Hospital district or authority, Government, Nonfederal **Service:** General medical and surgical

Staffed Beds: 15

YUMA—Yuma County

★ **YUMA DISTRICT HOSPITAL (061315)**, 1000 West 8th Avenue, Zip 80759–2641; tel. 970/848–5405, **A**10 18 **F**3 11 13 15 28 29 30 31 34 35 36 40 43 44 50 53 57 59 62 64 65 68 74 75 76 77 78 79 81 82 87 93 97 99 101 102 103 104 107 111 115 119 127 130 133 148 **P**6
Primary Contact: Beth Saxton, R.N., Chief Executive Officer
CFO: Rick Korf, Chief Financial Officer
CMO: John Wolz M.D., Chief Medical Staff
CIO: Jason Hawley, Manager Information Services
CHR: Gini Adams, Director Employee and Public Relations
Web address: www.yumahospital.org
Control: Hospital district or authority, Government, Nonfederal **Service:** General medical and surgical

Staffed Beds: 12 **Admissions:** 244 **Census:** 2 **Outpatient Visits:** 43846

Many Facility Codes have changed. Please refer to the AHA Guide Code Chart. © 2017 AHA Guide

CONNECTICUT

BETHLEHEM—Litchfield County

WELLSPRING FOUNDATION, 21 Arch Bridge Road, Zip 06751–1612, Mailing Address: P.O.Box 370, 06751–0370; tel. 203/266–7235, (Nonreporting)
Primary Contact: Dan Murray, PsyD, Chief Executive Officer
Web address: www.wellspring.org
Control: Other not–for–profit (including NFP Corporation) **Service**: Psychiatric

Staffed Beds: 36

BRANFORD—New Haven County

☐ **THE CONNECTICUT HOSPICE (070038)**, 100 Double Beach Road, Zip 06405–4909; tel. 203/315–7500, (Nonreporting) **A**1 5 10
Primary Contact: Rosemary Johnson. Hurzeler, President and Chief Executive Officer
Web address: www.hospice.com
Control: Other not–for–profit (including NFP Corporation) **Service**: Other specialty treatment

Staffed Beds: 52

BRIDGEPORT—Fairfield County

⊞ **BRIDGEPORT HOSPITAL (070010)**, 267 Grant Street, Zip 06610–2805, Mailing Address: P.O.Box 5000, 06610–0120; tel. 203/384–3000, **A**1 2 3 5 8 10 **F**3 5 6 8 11 12 13 14 15 16 18 20 22 24 26 28 29 30 31 32 34 35 36 37 38 39 40 41 43 44 45 46 47 48 49 50 51 52 54 55 56 57 58 59 61 64 65 66 68 70 74 75 76 78 79 80 81 82 84 85 86 87 93 96 97 98 99 100 101 102 103 104 105 107 108 110 111 114 115 116 117 118 119 120 121 122 124 126 129 130 131 132 134 144 145 146 147 148 149 **P**3 5 **S** Yale New Haven Health, New Haven, CT
Primary Contact: William M. Jennings, President and Chief Executive Officer
CFO: Patrick McCabe, Senior Vice President Finance and Chief Financial Officer
CMO: Michael Ivy M.D., Senior Vice President for Medical Affairs and Chief Medical Officer
CIO: Daniel Barchi, Senior Vice President, Technical Services and Chief Information Officer
CHR: Melissa Turner, Senior Vice President Human Resources
CNO: MaryEllen Kosturko R.N., Senior Vice President Patient Care Operations and Chief Nursing Officer
Web address: www.bridgeporthospital.org
Control: Other not–for–profit (including NFP Corporation) **Service**: General medical and surgical

Staffed Beds: 358 **Admissions**: 18629 **Census**: 267 **Outpatient Visits**: 307419 **Births**: 2435 **Total Expense ($000)**: 470194 **Payroll Expense ($000)**: 158655 **Personnel**: 2543

☐ **SOUTHWEST CONNECTICUT MENTAL HEALTH SYSTEM (074012)**, 1635 Central Avenue, Zip 06610–2717; tel. 203/551–7400, (Nonreporting) **A**1 10 **S** Connecticut Department of Mental Health and Addiction Services, Hartford, CT
Primary Contact: Alicia Feller, Chief Executive Officer
COO: Cindy Perjon, Associate Director
CFO: Linda Woznikaitis, Chief Financial Officer
CMO: Sandra Gomez–Luna, Medical Director
CIO: Bernetta Witcher–Boateng Ph.D., Director Quality Improvement Services and Compliance
CHR: Nancy Derman, Director Human Resources
Web address: www.ct.gov/dmhas/cwp/view.asp?a=2946&q=378936
Control: State, Government, Nonfederal **Service**: Psychiatric

Staffed Beds: 62

⊞ **ST. VINCENT'S MEDICAL CENTER (070028)**, 2800 Main Street, Zip 06606–4292; tel. 203/576–6000, (Includes ST. VINCENT'S BEHAVIORAL HEALTH, 47 Long Lots Road, Westport, Connecticut, Zip 06880–3800, tel. 203/221–8813; Margaret Hardy, R.N., MS, Vice President) **A**1 2 3 5 10 **F**3 4 5 8 11 12 13 15 17 18 20 22 24 26 28 29 30 31 34 35 36 38 40 43 44 45 46 47 48 49 50 51 54 55 56 57 58 59 61 63 64 65 66 68 70 71 72 73 74 75 76 77 78 79 80 81 82 84 85 86 87 90 93 96 97 98 99 100 101 102 103 104 105 106 107 108 110 111 114 115 116 117 118 119 120 121 122 123 124 126 130 132 134 135 143 144 145 146 147 148 149 150 **P**4 8 **S** Ascension Healthcare, Saint Louis, MO
Primary Contact: Vicki R. Briggs, President and Chief Executive Officer
CFO: Stephen Franko, Senior Vice President and Chief Financial Officer
CMO: Dan Gottschall, Senior Vice President and Chief Clinical Officer
CIO: Rick McCarthy, Chief Information Officer
CNO: Dale G Danowski R.N., Senior Vice President, Chief Nursing Officer
Web address: www.stvincents.org
Control: Other not–for–profit (including NFP Corporation) **Service**: General medical and surgical

Staffed Beds: 373 **Admissions**: 16151 **Census**: 263 **Outpatient Visits**: 241925 **Births**: 980 **Total Expense ($000)**: 493573 **Payroll Expense ($000)**: 200666 **Personnel**: 2528

BRISTOL—Hartford County

⊞ **BRISTOL HOSPITAL (070029)**, Brewster Road, Zip 6011, Mailing Address: P.O.Box 977, 06011–0977; tel. 860/585–3000, (Nonreporting) **A**1 2 5 10
Primary Contact: Kurt A. Barwis, FACHE, President and Chief Executive Officer
COO: Marc D Edelman, Vice President Operations
CFO: Peter Freytag, Senior Vice President Finance and Chief Financial Officer
CMO: Leonard Banco M.D., Senior Vice President and Chief Medical Officer
CIO: David Rackliffe, Assistant Vice President Information Services
CHR: Jeanine Reckdenwald, Vice President Human Resources and Support Services
Web address: www.bristolhospital.org
Control: Other not–for–profit (including NFP Corporation) **Service**: General medical and surgical

Staffed Beds: 134

DANBURY—Fairfield County

⊞ **DANBURY HOSPITAL (070033)**, 24 Hospital Avenue, Zip 06810–6099; tel. 203/739–7000, (Includes NEW MILFORD HOSPITAL, 21 Elm Street, New Milford, Connecticut, Zip 06776–2993, tel. 860/355–2611; John M Murphy, M.D., President and Chief Executive Officer, Western Connecticut Health Network) **A**1 2 3 5 8 10 **F**1 3 4 5 8 9 12 13 14 15 16 17 18 20 22 24 26 28 29 30 31 32 34 35 36 37 38 39 40 43 44 45 46 47 49 50 51 54 55 56 57 58 59 61 64 65 66 67 68 70 72 73 74 75 76 77 78 79 80 81 82 83 84 85 86 87 88 89 90 93 96 97 98 100 101 102 103 104 105 107 108 110 111 115 117 119 120 121 123 124 126 128 129 130 131 132 134 135 144 145 146 147 148 149 **P**8 **S** Western Connecticut Health Network, Danbury, CT
Primary Contact: John M. Murphy, M.D., President and Chief Executive Officer, Western Connecticut Health Network
COO: Sharon Adams, Chief Operating Officer
CFO: Steven Rosenberg, Chief Financial Officer
CMO: Patricia Tietjen M.D., Vice President, Medical Affairs
CIO: Kathleen DeMatteo, Chief Information Officer
CHR: Cathy Frierson, Chief Human Resource Officer
CNO: Sharon Adams, Chief Nursing Officer
Web address: www.danburyhospital.org
Control: Other not–for–profit (including NFP Corporation) **Service**: General medical and surgical

Staffed Beds: 412 **Admissions**: 19143 **Census**: 250 **Outpatient Visits**: 439293 **Births**: 2068 **Total Expense ($000)**: 645611 **Payroll Expense ($000)**: 221223 **Personnel**: 2818

DERBY—New Haven County

✚ **GRIFFIN HOSPITAL (070031)**, 130 Division Street, Zip 06418–1326; tel. 203/735–7421, **A**1 2 3 5 10 **F**3 5 8 12 13 15 18 28 29 30 34 35 36 38 40 45 49 50 51 53 56 57 58 59 64 65 66 68 70 71 74 75 76 77 78 79 81 82 84 85 86 87 92 93 94 96 97 98 99 100 101 102 103 104 105 107 108 110 111 115 116 118 119 120 121 123 129 130 132 134 135 144 146 147 148 149 **P**8
Primary Contact: Patrick Charmel, President and Chief Executive Officer
CMO: Kenneth V Schwartz M.D., Medical Director
CIO: George Tomas, Director Information Services
CHR: Steve Mordecai, Director Human Resources
CNO: Barbara J Stumpo R.N., Vice President Patient Care Services
Web address: www.griffinhealth.org
Control: Other not–for–profit (including NFP Corporation) **Service**: General medical and surgical

Staffed Beds: 111 **Admissions**: 7000 **Census**: 83 **Outpatient Visits**: 189800 **Births**: 599 **Total Expense ($000)**: 150278 **Payroll Expense ($000)**: 62117 **Personnel**: 1006

FARMINGTON—Hartford County

✚ **UCONN, JOHN DEMPSEY HOSPITAL (070036)**, 263 Farmington Avenue, Zip 06032–1941; tel. 860/679–2000, **A**1 2 3 5 8 10 12 13 19 **F**3 5 6 7 8 11 12 13 15 18 20 22 24 26 29 30 31 34 35 36 37 38 39 40 44 45 46 47 48 49 50 51 52 54 55 56 57 58 59 60 61 63 64 65 66 68 70 74 75 76 77 78 79 81 82 83 84 85 86 87 91 92 93 94 97 98 99 100 101 102 103 104 105 107 108 110 111 114 115 117 118 119 120 121 123 124 126 127 129 130 131 132 134 135 143 144 145 146 147 148 149 **P**6
Primary Contact: Andrew Agwunobi, M.D., Interim Chief Executive Officer
COO: Kevin Larsen, Associate Vice President, Business and Ancillary Services
CFO: Jeffrey Geoghegan, Chief Financial Officer
CMO: Richard Simon M.D., Chief of Staff
CIO: Jonathan Carroll, Chief Information Officer
CHR: Carolle Andrews, Vice President, Interim Human Resources Officer
CNO: Ann Marie Capo R.N., Chief Nursing Officer
Web address: www.uchc.edu
Control: State, Government, Nonfederal **Service**: General medical and surgical

Staffed Beds: 176 **Admissions**: 8521 **Census**: 98 **Outpatient Visits**: 304163 **Births**: 547 **Total Expense ($000)**: 374183 **Payroll Expense ($000)**: 116973 **Personnel**: 1362

GREENWICH—Fairfield County

✚ **GREENWICH HOSPITAL (070018)**, 5 Perryridge Road, Zip 06830–4697; tel. 203/863–3000, **A**1 2 3 5 8 10 **F**3 5 8 11 12 13 14 15 18 20 22 26 28 29 30 31 32 34 35 36 37 38 39 40 44 45 46 47 48 49 50 51 52 53 54 55 56 57 58 59 61 63 64 65 66 68 70 72 74 75 76 78 79 80 81 82 84 85 86 87 89 93 96 97 99 100 101 102 103 104 107 108 110 111 114 115 116 117 118 119 120 121 123 124 126 129 130 131 132 134 135 146 147 148 149 **P**2 3 5 **S** Yale New Haven Health, New Haven, CT
Primary Contact: Norman G. Roth, President
COO: Norman G. Roth, Interim Chief Operating Officer
CFO: Eugene Colucci, Vice President Finance
CMO: A Michael Marino M.D., Senior Vice President Medical Administration
Web address: www.greenhosp.org
Control: Other not–for–profit (including NFP Corporation) **Service**: General medical and surgical

Staffed Beds: 174 **Admissions**: 10558 **Census**: 132 **Outpatient Visits**: 280267 **Births**: 2812 **Total Expense ($000)**: 342553 **Payroll Expense ($000)**: 117804 **Personnel**: 1746

HARTFORD—Hartford County

✚ **CONNECTICUT CHILDREN'S MEDICAL CENTER (073300)**, 282 Washington Street, Zip 06106–3322; tel. 860/545–9000, **A**1 3 5 10 **F**3 7 8 11 12 19 21 23 27 29 30 31 32 34 35 36 39 40 41 43 48 49 50 51 54 55 57 58 59 60 61 63 64 65 68 72 74 75 78 79 81 82 84 85 86 87 88 89 90 91 92 93 97 98 107 111 114 115 119 126 129 130 131 132 134 146 149 150
Primary Contact: Gil Peri, President and Chief Operations Officer
CFO: Gerald J Boisvert, Vice President and Chief Financial Officer
CMO: Paul Dworkin M.D., Physician–in–Chief
CIO: Kelly R Styles, Vice President and Chief Information Officer
CHR: Elizabeth Rudden, Vice President Human Resources
Web address: www.ccmckids.org
Control: Other not–for–profit (including NFP Corporation) **Service**: Children's general medical and surgical

Staffed Beds: 186 **Admissions**: 6331 **Census**: 122 **Outpatient Visits**: 186286 **Births**: 0 **Total Expense ($000)**: 302747 **Payroll Expense ($000)**: 125996 **Personnel**: 2213

✚ **HARTFORD HOSPITAL (070025)**, 80 Seymour Street, Zip 06102–8000, Mailing Address: P.O.Box 5037, 06102–5037; tel. 860/545–5000, (Includes INSTITUTE OF LIVING, 400 Washington Street, Hartford, Connecticut, Zip 06106–3392, tel. 860/545–7000) (Total facility includes 104 beds in nursing home–type unit) **A**1 2 3 5 10 19 **F**2 3 5 6 7 8 9 10 11 12 13 15 17 18 20 22 24 26 28 29 30 31 34 35 36 37 38 39 40 43 44 45 46 47 48 49 50 51 52 53 54 55 56 57 58 59 60 61 63 64 65 66 68 70 71 74 75 76 77 78 79 80 81 82 83 84 85 86 87 91 92 93 94 96 97 98 99 100 101 102 103 104 105 106 107 108 110 111 112 114 115 116 117 118 119 120 121 123 124 125 126 128 129 130 131 132 134 135 137 138 139 141 143 145 146 147 148 149 150 **P**6 **S** Hartford HealthCare, Hartford, CT
Primary Contact: Stuart Markowitz, M.D., President
CMO: Stuart Markowitz M.D., Chief Medical Officer
CIO: Stephan O'Neill, Vice President Information Services
CHR: Richard McAloon, Vice President Human Resources
Web address: www.harthosp.org
Control: Other not–for–profit (including NFP Corporation) **Service**: General medical and surgical

Staffed Beds: 862 **Admissions**: 39183 **Census**: 713 **Outpatient Visits**: 481925 **Births**: 3864 **Total Expense ($000)**: 1082920 **Payroll Expense ($000)**: 414372 **Personnel**: 5836

✚ **MOUNT SINAI REHABILITATION HOSPITAL (073025)**, 490 Blue Hills Avenue, Zip 06112–1513; tel. 860/714–3500, **A**1 10 **F**29 30 34 54 58 59 64 68 74 75 82 90 91 92 93 94 95 96 130 131 132 **S** Trinity Health, Livonia, MI
Primary Contact: Robert J. Krug, M.D., Chief Executive Officer
CFO: David Bittner, Chief Financial Officer
Web address: www.stfranciscare.org
Control: Other not–for–profit (including NFP Corporation) **Service**: Rehabilitation

Staffed Beds: 30 **Admissions**: 749 **Census**: 26 **Outpatient Visits**: 42458 **Births**: 0 **Total Expense ($000)**: 37109 **Payroll Expense ($000)**: 14672 **Personnel**: 211

✚ **SAINT FRANCIS HOSPITAL AND MEDICAL CENTER (070002)**, 114 Woodland Street, Zip 06105–1208; tel. 860/714–4000, **A**1 2 3 5 8 10 19 **F**3 8 11 12 13 15 17 18 20 22 24 26 28 29 30 31 34 35 36 38 39 40 43 45 46 47 48 49 50 53 54 55 56 57 58 59 61 64 65 66 68 70 72 74 75 76 77 78 79 81 82 84 85 87 91 92 93 94 95 96 97 98 99 100 101 102 103 104 107 108 110 111 115 117 118 119 120 121 123 124 126 129 130 131 132 135 146 147 148 150 **P**8 **S** Trinity Health, Livonia, MI
Primary Contact: John F. Rodis, M.D., President
CFO: Jennifer S. Schneider, Vice President of Finance
CMO: Michael Grey M.D., Interim Chief Medical Officer
CIO: Linda L. Shanley, Vice President, Chief Information Officer
CHR: Dennis W. Sparks, Vice President of Human Resources
CNO: Denise Peterson R.N., FACHE, Vice President, Professional Nursing Practice & Quality, Chief Nursing Officer
Web address: www.saintfranciscare.com
Control: Church operated, Nongovernment, not–for–profit **Service**: General medical and surgical

Staffed Beds: 567 **Admissions**: 29992 **Census**: 376 **Outpatient Visits**: 266231 **Births**: 2761 **Total Expense ($000)**: 762023 **Payroll Expense ($000)**: 258412 **Personnel**: 4791

MANCHESTER—Hartford County

☐ **MANCHESTER MEMORIAL HOSPITAL (070027)**, 71 Haynes Street, Zip 06040–4188; tel. 860/646–1222, (Nonreporting) **A**1 2 5 10 12 13 **S** Prospect Medical Holdings, Los Angeles, CA
Primary Contact: Peter J. Karl, President and Chief Executive Officer
CFO: Michael D. Veillette, Senior Vice President and Chief Financial Officer
CMO: Joel R Reich M.D., Senior Vice President Medical Affairs
CIO: Richard Daigle, Chief Information Officer
CHR: Natalie Cook, Administrative Director of Human Resources
CNO: Mary Powers R.N., MSN, Senior Vice President and Chief Nursing Officer
Web address: www.echn.org
Control: Other not–for–profit (including NFP Corporation) **Service**: General medical and surgical

Staffed Beds: 156

MANSFIELD CENTER—Tolland County

✚ **NATCHAUG HOSPITAL (074008)**, 189 Storrs Road, Zip 06250–1683; tel. 860/456–1311, **A**1 10 **F**5 98 99 100 103 104 105 106 **S** Hartford HealthCare, Hartford, CT
Primary Contact: Patricia Rehmer, MSN, FACHE, President
COO: David Klein Ph.D., Vice President Operations, Behavioral Health Network
CFO: Paul V Maloney, Vice President Finance, Behavioral Health Network
CMO: Deborah Weidner, Medical Director
CIO: Mark Olson, Interim Chief Information Officer, Behavioral Health Network
CHR: Janet Keown, Vice President Human Resources, Behavioral Health Network
CNO: Justin Sleeper, Vice President Clinical Operations, Behavioral Health Network
Web address: www.natchaug.org
Control: Other not–for–profit (including NFP Corporation) **Service**: Psychiatric

Staffed Beds: 57 **Admissions**: 1970 **Census**: 52 **Births**: 0

MERIDEN—New Haven County

☒ **MIDSTATE MEDICAL CENTER (070017)**, 435 Lewis Avenue, Zip 06451–2101; tel. 203/694–8200, **A**1 2 10 **F**3 11 12 13 15 18 28 29 30 31 34 35 36 38 39 40 44 45 46 47 48 49 50 51 53 54 56 57 59 61 63 64 68 70 74 75 76 78 79 81 82 84 85 86 87 97 102 107 108 110 111 114 115 117 118 119 120 121 123 124 126 129 130 131 132 144 145 146 147 148 149 **P6 S** Hartford HealthCare, Hartford, CT
Primary Contact: Lucille A. Janatka, President
CMO: Kenneth R Kurz M.D., Chief of Staff
CIO: Jennifer Comerford, Manager Information Services
CHR: Ken Cesca, Vice President Human Resources
Web address: www.midstatemedical.org
Control: Other not–for–profit (including NFP Corporation) **Service**: General medical and surgical

Staffed Beds: 80 Admissions: 7660 Census: 88 Outpatient Visits: 147689 Births: 832 Total Expense ($000): 209817 Payroll Expense ($000): 63514 Personnel: 835

MIDDLETOWN—Middlesex County

☐ **ALBERT J. SOLNIT PSYCHIATRIC CENTER – SOUTH CAMPUS**, 915 River Road, Zip 06457–3921, Mailing Address: P.O.Box 2792, 06457–9292; tel. 860/704–4000, (Nonreporting) **A**1 3 5
Primary Contact: Michelle Sarofin, Superintendent
CFO: Connie Tessarzik, Business Manager
CMO: Lesley Siegel M.D., Medical Director
CIO: Andrew J A Kass M.D., Assistant Superintendent
Web address: www.ct.gov/
Control: State, Government, Nonfederal **Service**: Children's hospital psychiatric

Staffed Beds: 75

☐ **CONNECTICUT VALLEY HOSPITAL (074003)**, Eastern Drive, Zip 06457–3947; tel. 860/262–5000, (Includes WHITING FORENSIC DIVISION OF CONNECTICUT VALLEY HOSPITAL, O'Brien Drive, Middletown, Connecticut, Zip 6457, Box 70, 06457–3942, tel. 860/262–5000) **A**1 3 5 10 **F**3 4 29 30 34 36 39 50 53 56 57 58 59 60 61 65 68 74 75 77 82 84 86 87 90 91 94 97 98 99 100 101 102 103 106 119 130 132 135 146 148 149 **S** Connecticut Department of Mental Health and Addiction Services, Hartford, CT
Primary Contact: Helene M. Vartelas, MSN, Chief Executive Officer
COO: John D'Eramo, Chief Operating Officer
CFO: Cindy Butterfield, Director, Fiscal and Administrative Services
CMO: Thomas Pisano M.D., Chief Professional Services
CIO: Kathryn Connelly, Manager Information Technology
CHR: Cheryl Thompson, Facility Director Human Resources
CNO: Jerilynn Lamb–Pagone, Nurse Executive
Web address: www.ct.gov/dmhas/cwp/view.asp?a=3519&q=416778
Control: State, Government, Nonfederal **Service**: Psychiatric

Staffed Beds: 596 Admissions: 3528 Census: 565 Outpatient Visits: 0 Births: 0 Total Expense ($000): 169781 Payroll Expense ($000): 145246

☒ **MIDDLESEX HOSPITAL (070020)**, 28 Crescent Street, Zip 06457–3650; tel. 860/358–6000, **A**1 2 3 5 10 **F**3 5 7 8 12 13 15 18 20 22 24 28 29 30 31 32 34 35 36 38 40 42 45 46 47 49 50 51 54 55 57 58 59 60 62 63 64 65 68 70 74 75 76 77 78 79 81 83 84 85 86 87 89 92 93 94 97 98 99 100 101 102 103 104 105 107 108 110 111 114 115 116 117 118 120 121 123 124 126 129 130 131 132 134 135 143 144 145 146 147 148 149 **P6**
Primary Contact: Vincent G. Capece Jr, President and Chief Executive Officer
CFO: Susan Martin, Vice President Finance
CMO: Arthur V McDowell M.D., III, Vice President Clinical Affairs
CIO: Evan Jackson, Vice President Information Technology
CHR: Gregory Nokes, Vice President Human Resources
CNO: Jacquelyn Calamari MSN, MS, Chief Nursing Officer and Vice President, Patient Care Services
Web address: www.middlesexhospital.org
Control: Other not–for–profit (including NFP Corporation) **Service**: General medical and surgical

Staffed Beds: 222 Admissions: 12218 Census: 142 Outpatient Visits: 590377 Births: 1100 Total Expense ($000): 366705 Payroll Expense ($000): 174263 Personnel: 1823

WHITING FORENSIC DIVISION OF CONNECTICUT VALLEY HOSPITAL See Connecticut Valley Hospital

MILFORD—New Haven County

☒ **MILFORD HOSPITAL (070019)**, 300 Seaside Avenue, Zip 06460–4603; tel. 203/876–4000, **A**1 10 **F**3 8 11 15 29 32 34 35 37 38 40 45 46 49 50 54 57 58 59 63 64 68 70 74 75 76 78 79 81 82 85 87 89 102 107 108 111 114 118 119 126 130 132 135 144 146 149
Primary Contact: Joseph Pelaccia, President and Chief Executive Officer
COO: Lloyd Friedman M.D., Vice President Medical Affairs and Chief Operating Officer
CFO: Laura Smith, Vice President Finance and Chief Financial Officer
CMO: Lloyd Friedman M.D., Vice President Medical Affairs and Chief Operating Officer
CIO: Brian Evans, Chief Information Officer
CHR: Jeffrey Komornik, Director Human Resources
CNO: Joan DeMaio, Vice President Nursing
Web address: www.milfordhospital.org
Control: Other not–for–profit (including NFP Corporation) **Service**: General medical and surgical

Staffed Beds: 31 Admissions: 2880 Census: 30 Outpatient Visits: 46678 Births: 0 Total Expense ($000): 67299 Payroll Expense ($000): 33710 Personnel: 497

NEW BRITAIN—Hartford County

☒ △ **HOSPITAL FOR SPECIAL CARE (072004)**, 2150 Corbin Avenue, Zip 06053–2298; tel. 860/223–2761, **A**1 3 5 7 10 **F**1 3 11 29 30 35 39 53 56 64 77 80 89 90 91 92 93 96 119 130 131 132 135 146 148 149
Primary Contact: Lynn Ricci, President and Chief Executive Officer
CFO: Laurie A Whelan, Senior Vice President Finance and Chief Financial Officer
CMO: Paul Scalise M.D., Chief Pulmonary Medicine and Internal Medicine
CIO: Stan Jankowski, Vice President and Chief Information Officer
CHR: Judi Trczinski, Vice President and Chief Human Resources Officer
Web address: www.hfsc.org
Control: Other not–for–profit (including NFP Corporation) **Service**: Acute long–term care hospital

Staffed Beds: 228 Admissions: 628 Census: 201 Outpatient Visits: 32288 Total Expense ($000): 95308 Payroll Expense ($000): 55529

☒ **THE HOSPITAL OF CENTRAL CONNECTICUT (070035)**, 100 Grand Street, Zip 06052–2017, Mailing Address: P.O.Box 100, 06052–2017; tel. 860/224–5011, (Includes BRADLEY MEMORIAL, 81 Meriden Avenue, Southington, Connecticut, Zip 06489–3297, tel. 860/276–5000; NEW BRITAIN GENERAL, 100 Grand Street, New Britain, Connecticut, Zip 06052–2017, P O Box 100, 06050–0100, tel. 860/224–5011) **A**1 2 3 5 10 **F**3 11 12 13 15 18 20 22 28 29 30 31 34 35 38 40 44 45 49 50 51 53 54 57 58 59 60 61 64 65 66 68 70 72 74 75 76 77 78 79 81 84 85 86 87 89 93 97 98 99 100 101 102 103 104 105 107 108 110 111 114 115 117 118 119 120 121 123 124 126 129 130 132 135 144 146 147 148 149 **P6 S** Hartford HealthCare, Hartford, CT
Primary Contact: Lucille A. Janatka, President, Hartford HealthCare Central Region
CFO: Brian Rogoz, Vice President Finance and Treasurer
CIO: Frank Pinto, Chief Information Officer
CHR: Elizabeth A Lynch, Vice President Human Resources
Web address: www.thocc.org
Control: Other not–for–profit (including NFP Corporation) **Service**: General medical and surgical

Staffed Beds: 170 Admissions: 12745 Census: 168 Outpatient Visits: 372585 Births: 1535 Total Expense ($000): 366064 Payroll Expense ($000): 137134 Personnel: 1490

NEW CANAAN—Fairfield County

☐ **SILVER HILL HOSPITAL (074014)**, 208 Valley Road, Zip 06840–3899; tel. 203/966–3561, **A**1 10 **F**5 82 98 99 104 146
Primary Contact: John Santopietro, M.D., President and Chief Executive Officer
COO: Elizabeth Moore, Chief Operating Officer
CFO: Ruurd Leegstra, Chief Financial Officer
CMO: Sigurd H Ackerman M.D., President and Chief Executive Officer
CIO: Maria Klinga, Director Management Information Systems
CHR: Rich Juliana, Director Human Resources
Web address: www.silverhillhospital.org
Control: Other not–for–profit (including NFP Corporation) **Service**: Psychiatric

Staffed Beds: 121 Admissions: 1276 Census: 32 Outpatient Visits: 0 Births: 0

CT

Hospital, Medicare Provider Number, Address, Telephone, Approval, Facility, and Physician Codes, Health Care System

★ American Hospital Association (AHA) membership
☐ The Joint Commission accreditation
○ Healthcare Facilities Accreditation Program
◇ DNV Healthcare Inc. accreditation
⇑ Center for Improvement in Healthcare Quality Accreditation
△ Commission on Accreditation of Rehabilitation Facilities (CARF) accreditation

Hospitals, U.S. / CONNECTICUT

NEW HAVEN—New Haven County

☐ **CONNECTICUT MENTAL HEALTH CENTER (074011)**, 34 Park Street, Zip 06519–1109, Mailing Address: P.O.Box 1842, 06508–1842; tel. 203/974–7144, **A**1 3 5 10 **F**5 28 35 38 98 100 101 102 103 104 105 **S** Connecticut Department of Mental Health and Addiction Services, Hartford, CT
Primary Contact: Michael Sernyak, M.D., Director
COO: Robert Cole, Chief Operating Officer
CFO: Robert Cole, Chief Operating Officer
CMO: Jeanne Steines D.O., Medical Director
CIO: Paul Moore, Chief Information Officer
CHR: Carolyn Wallace, Director Human Resources
Web address: www.ct.gov/dmhas/cwp/view.asp?a=2906&q=334596
Control: State, Government, Nonfederal **Service**: Psychiatric

Staffed Beds: 32 **Admissions:** 193 **Census:** 26 **Outpatient Visits:** 67172 **Births:** 0

HOSPITAL OF SAINT RAPHAEL See Yale–New Haven Hospital–Saint Raphael Campus

☒ **YALE–NEW HAVEN HOSPITAL (070022)**, 20 York Street, Zip 06510–3202; tel. 203/688–4242, (Includes YALE–NEW HAVEN CHILDREN'S HOSPITAL, 1 Park Street, New Haven, Connecticut, Zip 06504–8901, tel. 203/688–4242; Cynthia Sparer, Senior Vice President and Executive Director Women's & Children; YALE–NEW HAVEN HOSPITAL–SAINT RAPHAEL CAMPUS, 1450 Chapel Street, New Haven, Connecticut, Zip 06511–4405, tel. 203/789–3000; Richard D'Aquila, President; YALE–NEW HAVEN PSYCHIATRIC HOSPITAL, 184 Liberty Street, New Haven, Connecticut, Zip 06519–1625, tel. 203/688–9704; Mark Sevilla, Executive Director) **A**1 2 3 5 8 10 **F**3 5 6 8 9 10 11 12 13 14 15 17 18 19 20 21 22 23 24 25 26 27 28 29 30 31 32 34 35 36 37 38 39 40 41 42 43 44 45 46 47 48 49 50 51 52 53 54 55 56 57 58 59 61 64 65 66 68 70 72 73 74 75 76 78 79 80 81 82 84 85 86 87 88 89 90 91 92 93 94 96 97 98 99 100 101 102 103 104 105 107 108 109 110 111 112 114 115 116 117 118 119 120 121 123 124 126 129 130 131 132 134 135 136 137 138 139 141 142 143 144 145 146 147 148 149 150 **P**2 3 5 6 **S** Yale New Haven Health, New Haven, CT
Primary Contact: Marna P. Borgstrom, Chief Executive Officer
CFO: Vincent Tammaro, Chief Financial Officer
CMO: Thomas Balcezak M.D., Senior Vice President Medical Affairs and Chief Medical Officer
CIO: Lisa Stump, Interim Chief Information Officer
CHR: Kevin A Myatt, Senior Vice President Human Resources
CNO: Patricia Sue Fitzsimons R.N., Ph.D., Senior Vice President Patient Services
Web address: www.ynhh.org
Control: Other not–for–profit (including NFP Corporation) **Service**: General medical and surgical

Staffed Beds: 1394 **Admissions:** 73880 **Census:** 1118 **Outpatient Visits:** 1336011 **Births:** 5610 **Total Expense ($000):** 2580344 **Payroll Expense ($000):** 839059 **Personnel:** 11713

NEW LONDON—New London County

☒ △ **LAWRENCE + MEMORIAL HOSPITAL (070007)**, 365 Montauk Avenue, Zip 06320–4769; tel. 860/442–0711, **A**1 2 3 7 10 **F**3 8 11 13 14 15 17 18 20 22 26 28 29 30 31 34 35 38 39 40 41 42 44 46 49 50 51 54 55 57 59 60 61 63 64 65 68 70 72 74 75 76 77 78 79 81 82 84 85 86 87 89 90 91 92 93 96 98 99 100 102 104 107 108 110 111 114 115 116 117 118 119 120 121 123 124 126 129 130 131 132 135 141 146 147 148 149 **P**3 **S** Yale New Haven Health, New London, CT
Primary Contact: Patrick Green, FACHE, President and Chief Executive Officer
CFO: Seth Van Essendelft, Vice President and Chief Financial Officer
CMO: Oliver Mayorga M.D., Chief Medical Officer
CIO: Kimberly Kalajainen, Vice President Operations and Chief Information Officer
CHR: Donna Epps, Vice President and Chief Human Resources Officer
CNO: Lauren Williams MS, Vice President of Professional Services and Chief Nursing Officer
Web address: www.lmhospital.org
Control: Other not–for–profit (including NFP Corporation) **Service**: General medical and surgical

Staffed Beds: 251 **Admissions:** 13472 **Census:** 145 **Outpatient Visits:** 346900 **Births:** 1456 **Total Expense ($000):** 344831 **Payroll Expense ($000):** 142839 **Personnel:** 1478

NORWALK—Fairfield County

☒ **NORWALK HOSPITAL (070034)**, 34 Maple Street, Zip 06850–3894; tel. 203/852–2000, **A**1 2 3 5 8 10 **F**3 5 7 8 11 12 13 15 17 18 20 22 26 28 29 30 31 34 35 36 39 40 43 44 45 46 47 48 49 50 51 53 54 55 57 58 59 64 66 68 70 72 74 75 76 77 78 79 80 81 82 84 85 87 89 93 96 98 100 101 103 104 105 107 108 110 111 114 115 117 118 119 120 121 123 124 126 129 130 131 132 135 145 146 148 149 **P**8 **S** Western Connecticut Health Network, Danbury, CT
Primary Contact: Michael Daglio, President
CFO: Michael Kruzick, Acting Chief Financial Officer
CMO: Michael Marks M.D., Chief of Staff
CHR: Anthony Aceto, Vice President Human Resources
Web address: www.norwalkhospital.org
Control: Other not–for–profit (including NFP Corporation) **Service**: General medical and surgical

Staffed Beds: 152 **Admissions:** 11459 **Census:** 140 **Outpatient Visits:** 260067 **Births:** 1289 **Total Expense ($000):** 382147 **Payroll Expense ($000):** 139213 **Personnel:** 1373

NORWICH—New London County

☒ **THE WILLIAM W. BACKUS HOSPITAL (070024)**, 326 Washington Street, Zip 06360–2740; tel. 860/889–8331, **A**1 2 3 5 10 **F**3 9 11 12 13 15 18 20 26 28 29 30 31 34 35 36 40 42 43 45 46 49 50 51 54 57 58 59 61 63 64 65 70 71 74 75 76 78 79 81 82 84 85 86 87 89 92 93 97 98 100 101 102 103 104 105 107 108 110 111 114 115 116 117 118 119 120 121 126 130 132 134 135 144 145 146 147 148 149 **P**6 **S** Hartford HealthCare, Hartford, CT
Primary Contact: Bimal Patel, President, Hartford HealthCare East Region
COO: Carolyn Trantalis R.N., MSN, Regional Vice President, Clinical Services and Operations
CFO: Anthony Mastroianni, Regional Vice President Finance
CMO: Robert Sidman M.D., Regional Vice President, Medical Affairs
CIO: Angie Mathieu, System Director Information Technology and Regional Chief Information Officer
CHR: Karen James, Regional Director, Human Resources
CNO: Carolyn Trantalis R.N., MSN, Regional Vice President, Clinical Services and Operations
Web address: www.backushospital.org
Control: Other not–for–profit (including NFP Corporation) **Service**: General medical and surgical

Staffed Beds: 184 **Admissions:** 9621 **Census:** 121 **Outpatient Visits:** 514269 **Births:** 973 **Total Expense ($000):** 269289 **Payroll Expense ($000):** 107460 **Personnel:** 1273

PUTNAM—Windham County

☐ **DAY KIMBALL HOSPITAL (070003)**, 320 Pomfret Street, Zip 06260–1836; tel. 860/928–6541, **A**1 2 5 10 **F**3 8 13 15 17 18 28 29 30 31 34 35 36 38 40 45 50 54 56 58 59 62 63 64 65 68 70 75 76 77 78 79 81 82 85 87 89 93 98 99 100 102 103 104 107 108 109 110 115 118 119 129 130 132 135 145 146 147 148 149 **P**3
Primary Contact: Anne Diamond, President and Chief Executive Officer
CFO: Paul Beaudoin, Chief Financial Officer
CMO: John Graham M.D., Vice President Medical Affairs
CIO: Odile Romanick, Chief information Officer
CHR: Jeffrey T. Corrigan, Interim Director Human Resources
CNO: John O'Keefe, Chief Nursing Officer
Web address: www.daykimball.org
Control: Other not–for–profit (including NFP Corporation) **Service**: General medical and surgical

Staffed Beds: 65 **Admissions:** 3611 **Census:** 41 **Outpatient Visits:** 664567 **Births:** 499 **Total Expense ($000):** 108420 **Payroll Expense ($000):** 43805 **Personnel:** 1238

ROCKY HILL—Hartford County

CONNECTICUT VETERANS HOME AND HOSPITAL (072006), 287 West Street, Zip 06067–3501; tel. 860/616–3606, (Nonreporting) **A**10
Primary Contact: Seam Connolly, Commissioner
CFO: Michael Clark, Fiscal Administrative Manager
CMO: Vamseedhar Alla M.D., Director Medical Staff
CIO: Sheri DeVaux, Information Technology Manager
CHR: Noreen Sinclair, Human Resources Administrator
CNO: Jeff Lord, Director of Nursing
Web address: www.ct.gov/ctva
Control: State, Government, Nonfederal **Service**: Acute long–term care hospital

Staffed Beds: 125

SHARON—Litchfield County

☐ **SHARON HOSPITAL (070004)**, 50 Hospital Hill Road, Zip 06069–2096, Mailing Address: P.O.Box 789, 06069–0789; tel. 860/364–4000, (Nonreporting) **A**1 10 20 **S** Health Quest Systems, Inc., LaGrangeville, NY
Primary Contact: Peter Cordeau, Chief Executive Officer
CMO: Michael Parker M.D., Chief of Staff
CHR: Kathleen Berlinghoff, Director Human Resources
Web address: www.sharonhospital.com
Control: Corporation, Investor–owned (for–profit) **Service**: General medical and surgical

Staffed Beds: 78

SOMERS—Tolland County

CONNECTICUT DEPARTMENT OF CORRECTION'S HOSPITAL, 100 Bilton Road, Zip 06071–1059, Mailing Address: P.O.Box 100, 06071–0100; tel. 860/749–8391, (Nonreporting) **A**5
Primary Contact: Edward A. Blanchette, M.D., Director
Control: State, Government, Nonfederal **Service**: Hospital unit of an institution (prison hospital, college infirmary, etc.)

Staffed Beds: 29

SOUTHINGTON—Hartford County

BRADLEY MEMORIAL See The Hospital Of Central Connecticut, New Britain

STAFFORD SPRINGS—Tolland County

⊞ **JOHNSON MEMORIAL MEDICAL CENTER (070008)**, 201 Chestnut Hill Road, Zip 06076–4005; tel. 860/684–4251, **A**1 2 10 **F**3 5 8 11 13 15 18 28 29 30 31 34 35 38 40 41 50 54 56 57 59 60 61 63 64 68 70 74 75 76 77 78 79 81 82 84 86 87 89 93 98 101 102 103 104 105 107 108 109 110 111 114 115 118 119 129 130 131 132 135 146 147 148 149 **P**5 **S** Trinity Health, Livonia, MI
Primary Contact: Stuart E. Rosenberg, President
CFO: John Grish, Chief Financial Officer
CMO: Ian Tucker M.D., Vice President Medical Affairs
CHR: Donna M Megliola, Assistant Vice President
CNO: Patricia Jagoe, Assistant Vice President Patient Care
Web address: www.jmmc.com
Control: Other not–for–profit (including NFP Corporation) **Service**: General medical and surgical

Staffed Beds: 78 **Admissions**: 2942 **Census**: 42 **Outpatient Visits**: 68977 **Births**: 195 **Total Expense ($000)**: 66931 **Payroll Expense ($000)**: 25748 **Personnel**: 455

STAMFORD—Fairfield County

⊞ **STAMFORD HOSPITAL (070006)**, One Hospital Plaza, Zip 6902, Mailing Address: P.O.Box 9317, 06904–9317; tel. 203/276–1000, **A**1 2 3 5 10 **F**3 8 12 13 15 18 19 20 22 24 26 28 29 30 31 32 34 35 36 37 38 40 41 43 44 45 46 47 48 49 50 52 53 54 55 56 57 58 59 60 61 64 66 68 70 72 74 75 76 77 78 79 81 82 84 85 86 87 89 90 91 92 93 95 96 97 98 100 101 102 103 104 107 108 110 111 114 115 116 117 118 119 120 121 123 124 126 129 130 131 132 135 144 145 146 147 148 149 150 **P**6
Primary Contact: Brian G. Grissler, President and Chief Executive Officer
COO: Kathleen A Silard R.N., MS, FACHE, Executive Vice President Operations and Chief Operating Officer
CFO: Kevin Gage, Chief Financial Officer
CMO: Sharon Kiely M.D., Senior Vice President Medical Affairs and Chief Medical Officer
CIO: Steven Sakovits, Vice President Information Systems and Chief Information Officer
CHR: Elaine Guglielmo, Vice President Human Resources and Organizational Development
CNO: Ellen M Komar R.N., Vice President Patient Care Services and Chief Nursing Officer
Web address: www.stamhealth.org
Control: Other not–for–profit (including NFP Corporation) **Service**: General medical and surgical

Staffed Beds: 305 **Admissions**: 12735 **Census**: 179 **Outpatient Visits**: 475586 **Births**: 2170 **Total Expense ($000)**: 473412 **Payroll Expense ($000)**: 193035 **Personnel**: 2383

TORRINGTON—Litchfield County

☐ **THE CHARLOTTE HUNGERFORD HOSPITAL (070011)**, 540 Litchfield Street, Zip 06790–6679, Mailing Address: P.O.Box 988, 06790–0988; tel. 860/496–6666, **A**1 2 10 **F**3 5 8 11 13 15 18 28 29 30 31 34 35 38 40 41 42 44 45 47 48 49 50 51 54 59 60 64 70 74 75 76 77 78 79 81 82 84 85 87 89 93 97 98 99 100 102 104 105 106 107 110 111 115 117 119 120 121 123 129 130 131 132 144 146 148 **P**6
Primary Contact: Daniel J. McIntyre, President and Chief Executive Officer
CFO: Susan Schapp, Vice President Finance and Treasurer
CMO: Mark Prete M.D., Vice President Medical Affairs
CHR: R James Elliott, Vice President Human Resources
Web address: www.charlottehungerford.org
Control: Other not–for–profit (including NFP Corporation) **Service**: General medical and surgical

Staffed Beds: 72 **Admissions**: 5160 **Census**: 61 **Outpatient Visits**: 312583 **Births**: 397 **Total Expense ($000)**: 123502 **Payroll Expense ($000)**: 55898 **Personnel**: 499

VERNON—Tolland County

☐ **ROCKVILLE GENERAL HOSPITAL (070012)**, 31 Union Street, Zip 06066–3160; tel. 860/872–0501, (Nonreporting) **A**1 5 10 **S** Prospect Medical Holdings, Los Angeles, CA
Primary Contact: Peter J. Karl, President and Chief Executive Officer
CFO: Michael D. Veillette, Senior Vice President and Chief Financial Officer
CMO: Joel R Reich M.D., Senior Vice President Medical Affairs
CIO: Richard Daigle, Chief Information Officer
CHR: Natalie Cook, Administrative Director, Human Resources
CNO: Mary Powers R.N., MSN, Senior Vice President and Chief Nursing Officer
Web address: www.echn.org
Control: Other not–for–profit (including NFP Corporation) **Service**: General medical and surgical

Staffed Beds: 47

WALLINGFORD—New Haven County

☐ △ **GAYLORD HOSPITAL (072003)**, 50 Gaylord Farm Road, Zip 06492–7048, Mailing Address: P.O.Box 400, 06492–7048; tel. 203/284–2800, **A**1 5 7 10 **F**1 29 30 31 34 35 50 53 54 59 60 64 74 75 82 84 85 86 87 91 93 94 95 96 104 107 114 119 130 131 132 135 146 148 149 **P**5
Primary Contact: George M. Kyriacou, President and Chief Executive Officer
CFO: Art Tedesco, Interim Chief Financial Officer
CMO: Stephen Holland M.D., Vice President Chief Medical Officer and Medical Director
CIO: Gerry Maroney, Chief Information Officer and Security Officer
CHR: Wally G Harper, Vice President Human Resources
CNO: Virginia Staubach R.N., Chief Nursing Officer and Senior Director of Nursing Services
Web address: www.gaylord.org
Control: Other not–for–profit (including NFP Corporation) **Service**: Acute long–term care hospital

Staffed Beds: 122 **Admissions**: 1392 **Census**: 107 **Outpatient Visits**: 69738 **Births**: 0 **Total Expense ($000)**: 72605 **Payroll Expense ($000)**: 40112 **Personnel**: 482

★ **MASONICARE HEALTH CENTER (070039)**, 22 Masonic Avenue, Zip 06492–3048, Mailing Address: P.O.Box 70, 06492–7001; tel. 203/679–5900, (Nonreporting) **A**3 5 10
Primary Contact: Jon–Paul Venoit, President and Chief Executive Officer
COO: Jon–Paul Venoit, Chief Operating Officer
CFO: Raymond Scott Thelen, Vice President and Chief Financial Officer
CMO: Ronald Schwartz M.D., Medical Director
CIO: Michael Nichols, Chief Information Officer
CHR: Edward Dooling, Vice President, Human Resources
CNO: Patti Russell, Vice President Nursing
Web address: www.masonicare.org
Control: Other not–for–profit (including NFP Corporation) **Service**: Other specialty treatment

Staffed Beds: 65

CT

WATERBURY—New Haven County

✠ **SAINT MARY'S HOSPITAL (070016)**, 56 Franklin Street, Zip 06706–1281;
tel. 203/709–6000, **A**1 2 3 5 10 **F**3 5 8 11 12 13 15 17 18 20 22 24 26 28 29
30 31 34 35 36 37 40 41 43 45 46 48 49 50 54 56 59 64 70 72 73 74 75 76
77 78 79 80 81 82 85 87 92 93 98 100 102 104 105 107 108 110 111 115
119 120 126 129 130 132 135 144 146 147 149 **P**6 **S** Trinity Health, Livonia, MI
Primary Contact: Chad W. Wable, President and Chief Executive Officer
COO: Charles Flinn, Vice President, Chief Operating Officer
CFO: Ralph W Becker, Vice President, Chief Financial Officer
CMO: Steven E. Schneider M.D., Chief Medical Officer
CIO: Michael Novak, Vice President, Operations and Chief Information Officer
CHR: M Clark Kearney, Vice President Human Resources
CNO: Elizabeth Bozzuto R.N., Chief Nursing Officer and Vice President
Web address: www.stmh.org
Control: Church operated, Nongovernment, not–for–profit **Service:** General
medical and surgical

Staffed Beds: 156 **Admissions:** 10599 **Census:** 119 **Outpatient Visits:**
287272 **Births:** 1024 **Total Expense ($000):** 252715 **Payroll Expense
($000):** 92109 **Personnel:** 1704

✠ **WATERBURY HOSPITAL (070005)**, 64 Robbins Street, Zip 06708–2600;
tel. 203/573–6000, (Nonreporting) **A**1 2 3 5 10 **S** Prospect Medical Holdings, Los
Angeles, CA
Primary Contact: Peter J. Adamo, President and Chief Executive Officer
CFO: Colleen M Scott, Vice President Finance
CMO: David Puzzuto M.D., Vice President Medical Affairs and Chief Medical Officer
CIO: Michael J Cemeno, Chief Information Officer
CHR: Diane Woolley, Vice President Human Resources
CNO: Sandra Ladarola, Chief Nursing Officer
Web address: www.waterburyhospital.org
Control: Other not–for–profit (including NFP Corporation) **Service:** General
medical and surgical

Staffed Beds: 176

WEST HARTFORD—Hartford County

★ **HEBREW CENTER FOR HEALTH REHABILITATION (070040)**, 1 Abrahms
Boulevard, Zip 06117–1525; tel. 860/523–3800, (Nonreporting) **A**10
Primary Contact: Gary Jones, Interim President and Chief Executive Officer
COO: Marcia H Hickey, Senior Vice President Operations
CFO: David Houle, Executive Vice President and Chief Financial Officer
CMO: Ava Pannullo M.D., Vice President Medical Services and Physician in Chief
CHR: Sam Vogt, Manager Human Resources
Web address: www.hebrewhealthcare.org
Control: Other not–for–profit (including NFP Corporation) **Service:** Other specialty
treatment

Staffed Beds: 322

WEST HAVEN—New Haven County

✠ **VETERANS AFFAIRS CONNECTICUT HEALTHCARE SYSTEM**, 950 Campbell
Avenue, Zip 06516–2770; tel. 203/932–5711, (Nonreporting) (Includes WEST
HAVEN DIVISION, 950 Campbell Avenue, West Haven, Connecticut, Zip 06516–
2700, tel. 203/932–5711) **A**1 2 3 5 8 **S** Department of Veterans Affairs,
Washington, DC
Primary Contact: Gerald F. Culliton, Medical Center Director
CFO: Joseph LaMadeleine, Chief Financial Officer
CMO: Michael Ebert M.D., Chief of Staff
CIO: Joseph Erdos M.D., Chief Information Officer
CHR: Mark Bain, Chief Human Resources
Web address: www.connecticut.va.gov
Control: Veterans Affairs, Government, federal **Service:** General medical and
surgical

Staffed Beds: 197

WESTPORT—Fairfield County

ST. VINCENT'S BEHAVIORAL HEALTH See St. Vincent's Medical Center,
Bridgeport

WILLIMANTIC—Windham County

WINDHAM COMMUNITY MEMORIAL HOSPITAL See Windham Hospital

✠ **WINDHAM HOSPITAL (070021)**, 112 Mansfield Avenue, Zip 06226–2040;
tel. 860/456–9116, **A**1 2 5 10 **F**3 8 11 12 13 15 18 28 29 30 31 32 34 35 36
40 45 48 50 51 53 54 56 57 59 60 61 64 65 66 68 75 76 77 78 79 80 81 82
85 86 87 90 93 94 100 102 107 108 110 111 115 116 117 118 119 129 130
131 132 134 135 144 146 147 148 149 **P**6 **S** Hartford HealthCare, Hartford, CT
Primary Contact: Bimal Patel, President, Hartford Healthcare East Region
COO: Carolyn Trantalis R.N., MSN, Chief Operating Officer, East Region
CFO: Daniel E Lohr, Regional Vice President Finance
CMO: Nadia Nashid M.D., Chief of Staff
CHR: Theresa L Buss, Regional Vice President Human Resources
Web address: www.windhamhospital.org
Control: Other not–for–profit (including NFP Corporation) **Service:** General
medical and surgical

Staffed Beds: 56 **Admissions:** 2063 **Census:** 23 **Outpatient Visits:** 128820
Births: 146 **Total Expense ($000):** 81552 **Payroll Expense ($000):** 31799
Personnel: 405

Many Facility Codes have changed. Please refer to the AHA Guide Code Chart. © 2017 AHA Guide

DELAWARE

DOVER—Kent County

BAYHEALTH MEDICAL CENTER (080004), 640 South State Street, Zip 19901–3530; tel. 302/674–4700, (Includes BAYHEALTH MEDICAL CENTER AT KENT GENERAL, 640 South State Street, Dover, Delaware, Zip 19901–3597, tel. 203/932–5711; BAYHEALTH MEDICAL CENTER, MILFORD MEMORIAL HOSPITAL, 21 West Clarke Avenue, Milford, Delaware, Zip 19963–1840, P O Box 199, 19963–0199, tel. 302/430–5738; Michael Ashton, Administrator) **A**1 2 3 5 10 **F**3 8 11 12 13 15 17 18 20 22 24 26 28 29 30 31 32 34 35 38 40 41 42 43 44 45 47 48 49 50 51 53 54 55 57 58 59 60 61 62 64 67 68 70 72 73 74 75 76 77 78 79 81 82 84 85 86 87 88 89 90 93 94 98 99 100 101 102 103 104 107 108 110 111 114 115 117 118 119 120 121 123 124 126 129 130 131 132 134 135 144 146 147 148
Primary Contact: Terry Murphy, President and Chief Executive Officer
COO: Deborah Watson, Senior Vice President and Chief Operating Officer
CFO: Mike Tretina, Senior Vice President and Chief Financial Officer
CMO: Gary M Siegelman M.D., MSC, Senior Vice President and Chief Medical Officer
CIO: Richard Mohnk, Vice President Corporate Services
CHR: Shana Ross, Vice President Human Resources
CNO: Bonnie I Perratto MSN, R.N., FACHE, Senior Vice President, Chief Nurse Executive
Web address: www.bayhealth.org
Control: Other not–for–profit (including NFP Corporation) **Service:** General medical and surgical

Staffed Beds: 351 **Admissions:** 17555 **Census:** 249 **Outpatient Visits:** 626205 **Births:** 2342 **Total Expense ($000):** 548909 **Payroll Expense ($000):** 244663 **Personnel:** 3236

DOVER BEHAVIORAL HEALTH SYSTEM (084004), 725 Horsepond Road, Zip 19901–7232; tel. 302/741–0140 **A**1 10 **F**98 99 102 104 105 135 **P**6 **S** Universal Health Services, Inc., King of Prussia, PA
Primary Contact: Jean–Charles Constant, Administrator
Web address: www.doverbehavioral.com
Control: Corporation, Investor–owned (for–profit) **Service:** Psychiatric

Staffed Beds: 80 **Admissions:** 3223 **Census:** 78 **Outpatient Visits:** 0 **Births:** 0

LEWES—Sussex County

BEEBE HEALTHCARE (080007), 424 Savannah Road, Zip 19958–1462; tel. 302/645–3300 **A**1 2 3 10 19 **F**2 3 8 11 12 13 15 17 18 20 22 24 26 28 29 30 31 32 34 35 36 38 40 43 45 46 49 50 51 53 54 55 56 57 58 59 60 61 62 64 65 68 70 74 75 76 77 78 79 80 81 84 85 87 89 93 97 100 107 108 110 111 114 115 116 117 118 119 120 121 123 124 130 131 132 134 143 146 147 148 149 **P**4
Primary Contact: Jeffrey M. Fried, FACHE, President and Chief Executive Officer
CFO: Paul Pernice, Vice President Finance
CMO: Jeffrey Hawtof M.D., Vice President Medical Operations and Informatics
CIO: Michael Maksymow, Vice President Information Systems
CHR: Catherine Halen, Vice President Human Resources
CNO: Steve Rhone R.N., MS, Vice President Patient Care Services
Web address: www.beebemed.org
Control: Other not–for–profit (including NFP Corporation) **Service:** General medical and surgical

Staffed Beds: 155 **Admissions:** 10257 **Census:** 120 **Outpatient Visits:** 395381 **Births:** 915 **Total Expense ($000):** 349398 **Payroll Expense ($000):** 117053 **Personnel:** 2147

MIDDLETOWN—New Castle County

HEALTHSOUTH REHABILITATION HOSPITAL OF MIDDLETOWN (083026), 250 East Hampden Road, Zip 19709–5303; tel. 302/464–3400, (Nonreporting) **S** HEALTHSOUTH Corporation, Birmingham, AL
Primary Contact: Mathew Gooch, Chief Executive Officer
CFO: Lisa Trimble, Controller
CMO: Ashish Khandelwal M.D., Medical Director
CHR: Anitra Robinson, Human Resources Director
CNO: Rebecca Boney R.N., Chief Nursing Officer
Web address: www.healthsouthmiddletown.com
Control: Corporation, Investor–owned (for–profit) **Service:** Rehabilitation

Staffed Beds: 34

MILFORD—Sussex County

BAYHEALTH MEDICAL CENTER, MILFORD MEMORIAL HOSPITAL See Bayhealth Medical Center

NEW CASTLE—New Castle County

DELAWARE PSYCHIATRIC CENTER (084001), 1901 North Dupont Highway, Zip 19720–1199; tel. 302/255–2700 **A**1 3 5 10 **F**30 34 39 59 65 68 75 86 87 98 100 101 103 106 130 132 135 143 149 **P**1
Primary Contact: Norman Vetter, Chief Executive Officer, Division of Substance Abuse and Mental Health
CIO: James Nau, Manager Computer and Applications Support
Web address: www.dhss.delaware.gov
Control: State, Government, Nonfederal **Service:** Psychiatric

Staffed Beds: 168 **Admissions:** 413 **Census:** 104 **Outpatient Visits:** 0 **Births:** 0 **Total Expense ($000):** 39042 **Payroll Expense ($000):** 18515 **Personnel:** 384

MEADOW WOOD BEHAVIORAL HEALTH SYSTEM (084003), 575 South Dupont Highway, Zip 19720–4606; tel. 302/328–3330, (Nonreporting) **A**1 10 **S** Acadia Healthcare Company, Inc., Franklin, TN
Primary Contact: Bill A. Mason, Chief Executive Officer
CFO: Maria Valdenegro, Chief Financial Officer
Web address: www.meadowwoodhospital.com
Control: Corporation, Investor–owned (for–profit) **Service:** Psychiatric

Staffed Beds: 53

NEWARK—New Castle County

CHRISTIANA CARE HEALTH SYSTEM (080001), 4755 Ogletown–Stanton Road, Zip 19718–0002, Mailing Address: P.O.Box 6001, 19718; tel. 302/733–1000 **A**1 2 3 5 8 10 12 13 **F**2 3 5 6 7 8 11 12 13 15 17 18 20 22 24 26 28 29 30 31 32 34 35 36 37 38 39 40 41 42 43 44 45 46 47 48 49 50 53 54 55 56 57 58 59 60 61 62 64 65 66 68 70 72 74 75 76 77 78 79 80 81 82 84 85 86 87 89 90 92 93 94 96 97 98 100 101 102 103 104 107 108 110 111 114 115 116 117 118 119 120 121 123 124 126 129 130 131 132 134 135 136 138 143 144 145 146 147 148 149 150 **P**6 **S** Christiana Care Health System, Wilmington, DE
Primary Contact: Janice E. Nevin, M.D., M.P.H., Chief Executive Officer
CFO: Thomas L Corrigan, Senior Vice President Finance, Managed Care and Chief Financial Officer
CMO: Kenneth L Silverstein M.D., Chief Clinical Officer
CIO: Randall Gaboriault, Chief Information Officer
CHR: Christopher Cowan, Senior Vice President and Chief Human Resources Officer
CNO: Ric Cuming, Chief Nurse Executive
Web address: www.christianacare.org
Control: Other not–for–profit (including NFP Corporation) **Service:** General medical and surgical

Staffed Beds: 1065 **Admissions:** 53259 **Census:** 776 **Outpatient Visits:** 612958 **Births:** 6545 **Total Expense ($000):** 1630664 **Payroll Expense ($000):** 777880 **Personnel:** 9932

ROCKFORD CENTER (084002), 100 Rockford Drive, Zip 19713–2121; tel. 302/996–5480 **A**1 3 10 **F**5 98 99 102 103 104 105 **P**6 **S** Universal Health Services, Inc., King of Prussia, PA
Primary Contact: John F. McKenna, Chief Executive Officer and Managing Director
CFO: Kumar Purohit, Chief Financial Officer
CMO: Saurabh Gupta, Chief Medical Officer
CHR: Jessi Stewart, Director Human Resources
CNO: Michelle Singletary–Twyman, Chief Nursing Officer
Web address: www.rockfordcenter.com
Control: Corporation, Investor–owned (for–profit) **Service:** Psychiatric

Staffed Beds: 128 **Admissions:** 4717 **Census:** 126 **Outpatient Visits:** 16269 **Births:** 0 **Total Expense ($000):** 28332 **Payroll Expense ($000):** 15261 **Personnel:** 253

DE

Hospital, Medicare Provider Number, Address, Telephone, Approval, Facility, and Physician Codes, Health Care System

★ American Hospital Association (AHA) membership
☐ The Joint Commission accreditation
○ Healthcare Facilities Accreditation Program
◇ DNV Healthcare Inc. accreditation
⇑ Center for Improvement in Healthcare Quality Accreditation
△ Commission on Accreditation of Rehabilitation Facilities (CARF) accreditation

SEAFORD—Sussex County

✠ **NANTICOKE MEMORIAL HOSPITAL (080006)**, 801 Middleford Road,
Zip 19973–3636; tel. 302/629–6611 **A**1 2 10 19 **F**3 12 13 15 18 20 22 28 29
30 31 32 34 35 37 40 43 45 50 51 54 57 59 60 64 65 68 70 74 75 76 77 78
79 81 84 85 86 87 89 93 107 108 111 114 115 117 119 120 121 123 129
130 132 135 144 146 147 148 149
Primary Contact: Steven A Rose, R.N., President and Chief Executive Officer
COO: Penny Short R.N., Chief Operating Officer
CFO: Denise Jester, Chief Financial Officer
CMO: Robert Ferber M.D., Chief Clinical Innovation Officer
CIO: Charles Palmer, Director Information Technology
CNO: Lori L Lee, Assistant Vice President Nursing
Web address: www.nanticoke.org
Control: Other not–for–profit (including NFP Corporation) **Service**: General
medical and surgical

Staffed Beds: 99 **Admissions**: 5315 **Census**: 52 **Outpatient Visits**: 145009
Births: 911 **Total Expense ($000)**: 128157 **Payroll Expense ($000)**: 42943
Personnel: 831

WILMINGTON—New Castle County

✠ △ **ALFRED I. DUPONT HOSPITAL FOR CHILDREN (083300)**, 1600
Rockland Road, Zip 19803–3616, Mailing Address: Box 269, 19899–0269;
tel. 302/651–4000 **A**1 2 3 5 7 10 **F**3 8 11 12 17 18 19 20 21 22 23 24 25 26
27 29 30 31 32 34 35 36 37 39 40 41 43 44 45 47 48 53 54 55 56 57 58
59 60 61 64 65 68 72 73 74 75 77 78 79 80 81 82 84 85 86 87 88 89 90
91 92 93 94 96 97 99 100 101 102 104 107 111 115 116 118 119 126 127
129 130 131 132 134 136 137 138 139 143 144 146 148 149 **S** Nemours,
Jacksonville, FL
Primary Contact: Roy Proujansky, M.D., Chief Executive Officer
COO: Paul D Kempinski, Chief Operating Officer
CFO: William N Britton, Associate Administrator Finance
CMO: Brent R King, Chief Medical Officer and Chief Physician
Web address: www.nemours.org
Control: Other not–for–profit (including NFP Corporation) **Service**: Children's
general medical and surgical

Staffed Beds: 200 **Admissions**: 9724 **Census**: 139 **Outpatient Visits**:
214742 **Births**: 0 **Total Expense ($000)**: 413347 **Payroll Expense ($000)**:
144237 **Personnel**: 2509

✠ **SELECT SPECIALTY HOSPITAL—WILMINGTON (082000)**, 701 North Clayton
Street, 5th Floor, Zip 19805–3948; tel. 302/421–4545 **A**1 10 **F**1 18 29 74 79
130 148 **S** Select Medical Corporation, Mechanicsburg, PA
Primary Contact: Donna Gares, R.N., FACHE, MSN, Chief Executive Officer
CFO: David Huffman, Vice President and Controller
CMO: Hummayun Ismail M.D., Medical Director
CHR: Barbara A Foster, Regional Human Resources Director
Web address: www.wilmington.selectspecialtyhospitals.com
Control: Corporation, Investor–owned (for–profit) **Service**: Acute long–term care
hospital

Staffed Beds: 35 **Admissions**: 337 **Census**: 29 **Outpatient Visits**: 0 **Births**: 0
Total Expense ($000): 17005 **Payroll Expense ($000)**: 7517 **Personnel**: 115

✠ **ST. FRANCIS HOSPITAL (080003)**, Seventh and Clayton Streets, Zip 19805—
0500, Mailing Address: P.O.Box 2500, 19805–0500; tel. 302/421–4100 **A**1 2 3
5 10 **F**3 7 8 11 12 13 14 15 16 17 18 20 22 24 26 28 29 30 31 32 34 35 37
38 40 41 43 44 45 46 47 48 49 50 51 54 55 56 57 58 59 60 61 62 64 65 66
68 70 71 73 74 75 76 77 78 79 81 82 84 86 87 90 93 96 97 99 100 101 102
103 104 107 108 109 110 111 112 113 114 115 116 117 118 119 126 127
129 130 131 132 135 143 144 146 147 148 149 **S** Trinity Health, Livonia, MI
Primary Contact: David A. Ricci, Interim President and Chief Executive Officer
CIO: Paul W Rowe, Director Information Technology
CHR: Charlene J Wilson, Vice President Human Resources
Web address: www.stfrancishealthcare.org
Control: Other not–for–profit (including NFP Corporation) **Service**: General
medical and surgical

Staffed Beds: 154 **Admissions**: 4269 **Census**: 53 **Outpatient Visits**:
185954 **Births**: 717 **Total Expense ($000)**: 159330 **Payroll Expense
($000)**: 67251 **Personnel**: 883

✠ **WILMINGTON VETERANS AFFAIRS MEDICAL CENTER**, 1601 Kirkwood
Highway, Zip 19805—4989; tel. 302/994–2511, (Nonreporting) **A**1 3 5 8 **S**
Department of Veterans Affairs, Washington, DC
Primary Contact: Robert W. Callahan Jr, Interim Director
CFO: Mary Ann Kozel, Chief Fiscal
CMO: Enrique Guttin M.D., FACS, Chief of Staff
CIO: Scott Vlars, Chief Information Technology Services
CHR: Louis McCloskey, Chief Human Resources
Web address: www.va.gov/wilmington
Control: Veterans Affairs, Government, federal **Service**: General medical and
surgical

Staffed Beds: 60

DISTRICT OF COLUMBIA

WASHINGTON—District Of Columbia County

☐ **BRIDGEPOINT HOSPITAL CAPITOL HILL (092002)**, 700 Constitution Avenue NE, Zip 20002–6058; tel. 202/546–5700, (Nonreporting) **A**1 10 **S** BridgePoint Healthcare, Portsmouth, NH
Primary Contact: James Linhares, Chief Executive Officer
COO: Delores Clair Oliver, Chief Clinical Officer and Chief Operating Officer
CFO: Michael Grubb, Chief Financial Officer
CMO: Gerald Moawad, Chief Medical Officer
CHR: Karen Brown, Senior Director of Human Resources
CNO: Delores Clair Oliver, Chief Clinical Officer and Chief Operating Officer
Web address: www.bridgepointhealthcare.com/
Control: Corporation, Investor–owned (for–profit) **Service**: Acute long–term care hospital

Staffed Beds: 177

☐ **BRIDGEPOINT HOSPITAL NATIONAL HARBOR (092003)**, 4601 Martin Luther King Jr Avenue, SW, Zip 20032–1131; tel. 202/574–5700, (Nonreporting) **A**1 10 **S** BridgePoint Healthcare, Portsmouth, NH
Primary Contact: Kevin Chavez, Chief Executive Officer
CFO: Michael Grubb, Chief Financial Officer
CMO: Khosrow Davachi, Chief Medical Officer
CHR: Antoninette Saldivar, Vice President, Human Resources
CNO: Diane White, Chief Clinical Officer and Chief Nursing Officer
Web address: www.bridgepointhealthcare.com/
Control: Corporation, Investor–owned (for–profit) **Service**: Acute long–term care hospital

Staffed Beds: 82

✚ **CHILDREN'S NATIONAL HEALTH SYSTEM (093300)**, 111 Michigan Avenue NW, Zip 20010–2916; tel. 202/476–5000 **A**1 3 5 8 10 **F**1 3 4 5 7 8 11 12 14 16 17 18 19 21 23 25 27 29 30 31 32 34 35 36 38 39 40 41 42 43 44 45 46 48 49 50 51 54 55 57 58 59 60 61 64 65 66 67 68 70 71 72 73 74 75 77 78 79 80 81 82 83 84 85 86 87 88 89 90 91 92 93 94 96 97 98 99 100 102 104 107 111 112 115 116 117 118 119 126 128 129 130 131 132 134 136 137 138 141 142 146 148 **P**6
Primary Contact: Kurt Newman, M.D., President and Chief Executive Officer
COO: Kathleen Gorman MSN, R.N., Executive Vice President Patient Care Services and Chief Operating Officer
CMO: Mark L Batshaw M.D., Physician–in–Chief, Executive Vice President and Chief Academic Officer
CIO: Brian Jacobs M.D., Vice President Chief Information Officer and Chief Medical Information Officer
CHR: Darryl Varnado, Executive Vice President and Chief People Officer
CNO: Linda Talley MS, R.N., Vice President and Chief Nursing Officer
Web address: www.childrensnational.org
Control: Other not–for–profit (including NFP Corporation) **Service**: Children's general medical and surgical

Staffed Beds: 313 Admissions: 15141 Census: 258 Outpatient Visits: 513844 **Births:** 0 **Total Expense ($000):** 761308 **Payroll Expense ($000):** 353484 **Personnel:** 5516

✚ △ **GEORGE WASHINGTON UNIVERSITY HOSPITAL (090001)**, 900 23rd Street NW, Zip 20037–2342; tel. 202/715–4000 **A**1 2 3 5 7 8 10 **F**3 8 12 13 15 17 18 20 22 24 26 29 31 34 35 40 43 45 46 47 48 49 50 51 54 55 56 57 58 59 64 70 72 74 76 78 79 80 81 82 85 86 87 90 91 92 93 94 96 98 107 108 110 111 114 115 116 117 118 119 120 121 123 126 129 130 131 132 135 136 138 141 146 149 150 **P**6 **S** Universal Health Services, Inc., King of Prussia, PA
Primary Contact: Kimberly Russo, Chief Executive Officer
COO: Kimberly Russo, Chief Operating Officer
CFO: Richard Davis, Chief Financial Officer
CMO: Gary Little M.D., Medical Director
CIO: Louis Duhe, Senior Director Information Technology
CHR: Erin Fagan, Manager Human Resources
Web address: www.gwhospital.com
Control: Partnership, Investor–owned (for–profit) **Service**: General medical and surgical

Staffed Beds: 385 Admissions: 19937 Census: 290 Outpatient Visits: 193035 **Births:** 3395 **Total Expense ($000):** 444015 **Payroll Expense ($000):** 166662 **Personnel:** 2083

GEORGETOWN UNIVERSITY HOSPITAL See Medstar Georgetown University Hospital

✚ **HOWARD UNIVERSITY HOSPITAL (090003)**, 2041 Georgia Avenue NW, Zip 20060—0002; tel. 202/865–6100 **A**1 2 3 5 8 10 **F**3 8 12 13 15 17 18 24 26 28 29 30 31 32 34 35 36 38 39 40 41 43 44 45 46 50 54 55 56 57 58 59 60 61 64 65 66 68 70 71 72 74 75 76 77 78 79 81 82 85 86 87 93 97 98 99 100 101 102 103 104 107 108 110 111 114 115 118 119 123 124 129 130 132 146 147 148
Primary Contact: James A. Diegel, FACHE, Chief Executive Officer
COO: James A. Diegel FACHE, Chief Executive Officer
CFO: Ed Gyimah, Chief Financial Officer
CMO: Shelly McDonald–Pinkett, Chief Medical Officer
CIO: Becky Quammen, Chief Information Officer
CHR: Jeronica Goodwin, Senior Director Human Resources
CNO: Shirley Evers–Manly, Chief Nursing Officer
Web address: www.huhealthcare.com
Control: Other not–for–profit (including NFP Corporation) **Service**: General medical and surgical

Staffed Beds: 241 Admissions: 8676 Census: 99 Outpatient Visits: 119349 **Births:** 964 **Total Expense ($000):** 266040 **Payroll Expense ($000):** 102437

✚ **MEDSTAR GEORGETOWN UNIVERSITY HOSPITAL (090004)**, 3800 Reservoir Road NW, Zip 20007—2197; tel. 202/444–2000 **A**1 2 3 5 8 10 **F**3 4 9 11 13 15 17 18 20 26 29 30 31 32 34 35 36 37 40 41 44 45 46 47 48 49 50 51 54 55 56 57 58 59 60 61 63 64 65 66 67 68 70 71 72 73 74 75 76 77 78 79 80 81 82 84 85 86 87 88 89 90 92 93 94 97 98 99 100 102 103 104 105 107 108 109 110 111 114 115 116 117 118 119 120 121 123 124 126 128 129 130 131 132 134 136 138 139 141 142 145 146 147 148 149 **P**6 **S** MedStar Health, Columbia, MD
Primary Contact: Michael Sachtleben, President
CFO: Paul Warda, Chief Financial Officer
CMO: Lisa Boyle M.D., Vice President Medical Affairs and Medical Director
CIO: John Rasmussen, Vice President for Information Technology
CHR: Mary Jo Schweickhardt, Vice President Human Resources
CNO: Eileen Brennan Ferrell MS, R.N., Vice President and Chief Nursing Officer
Web address: www.georgetownuniversityhospital.org
Control: Other not–for–profit (including NFP Corporation) **Service**: General medical and surgical

Staffed Beds: 409 Admissions: 15823 Census: 317 Outpatient Visits: 669957 **Births:** 1020 **Total Expense ($000):** 972105 **Payroll Expense ($000):** 435216 **Personnel:** 4698

✚ △ **MEDSTAR NATIONAL REHABILITATION HOSPITAL (093025)**, 102 Irving Street NW, Zip 20010—2949; tel. 202/877–1000 **A**1 3 5 7 10 **F**9 11 28 29 30 35 36 44 53 54 56 58 59 60 64 68 74 75 77 78 79 82 86 87 89 90 91 92 93 94 95 96 119 129 130 131 132 146 148 149 **P**6 **S** MedStar Health, Columbia, MD
Primary Contact: John D. Rockwood, President
CFO: Michael Boemmel, Vice President and Chief Financial Officer
CMO: Michael R Yochelson M.D., Vice President and Medical Director
CHR: Pamela Ashby, Vice President Human Resources
CNO: Rosemary C Welch R.N., Vice President and Chief Nursing Officer
Web address: www.medstarnrh.org
Control: Other not–for–profit (including NFP Corporation) **Service**: Rehabilitation

Staffed Beds: 137 Admissions: 2163 Census: 101 Outpatient Visits: 374503 **Births:** 0 **Total Expense ($000):** 127202 **Payroll Expense ($000):** 70571 **Personnel:** 1323

DC

Hospital, Medicare Provider Number, Address, Telephone, Approval, Facility, and Physician Codes, Health Care System

★ American Hospital Association (AHA) membership ○ Healthcare Facilities Accreditation Program ⇑ Center for Improvement in Healthcare Quality Accreditation
☐ The Joint Commission accreditation ◇ DNV Healthcare Inc. accreditation △ Commission on Accreditation of Rehabilitation Facilities (CARF) accreditation

✠ **MEDSTAR WASHINGTON HOSPITAL CENTER (090011)**, 110 Irving Street NW, Zip 20010—3017; tel. 202/877–7000 **A**1 2 3 5 8 10 **F**3 5 12 13 15 16 17 18 20 22 24 26 28 29 30 31 34 35 36 37 38 39 40 43 44 45 46 47 48 49 50 51 54 55 56 57 58 59 60 61 62 63 64 65 66 68 70 72 73 74 75 76 77 78 79 80 81 82 84 85 86 87 97 98 100 101 102 103 104 105 107 108 109 110 111 114 115 116 117 118 119 120 121 124 126 130 131 132 134 135 137 144 146 147 148 149 **P**1 6 **S** MedStar Health, Columbia, MD
Primary Contact: John Sullivan, President
COO: Robert Ross, Chief Operating Officer
CFO: William Gayne, Chief Financial Officer
CMO: Gregory J Argyros M.D., Senior Vice President, Medical Affairs & Chief Medical Officer
CIO: Joe Brothman, Assistant Vice President, Information Systems
CHR: James P Hill, Senior Vice President Administrative Services
CNO: Susan E. Eckert R.N., MSN, Senior Vice President and Chief Nursing Officer
Web address: www.whcenter.org
Control: Other not–for–profit (including NFP Corporation) **Service**: General medical and surgical

> **Staffed Beds**: 745 **Admissions**: 33252 **Census**: 604 **Outpatient Visits**: 390047 **Births**: 3564 **Total Expense ($000)**: 1164937 **Payroll Expense ($000)**: 520943 **Personnel**: 5465

NATIONAL REHABILITATION HOSPITAL See Medstar National Rehabilitation Hospital

✠ **PROVIDENCE HOSPITAL (090006)**, 1150 Varnum Street NE, Zip 20017—2104; tel. 202/269–7000, (Total facility includes 252 beds in nursing home–type unit) **A**1 3 5 10 **F**1 4 5 12 13 15 17 20 22 26 29 30 31 32 34 35 40 44 45 46 47 48 49 50 53 54 56 57 59 61 64 65 67 68 70 72 74 75 76 78 79 81 84 85 86 87 90 93 94 97 98 100 104 107 110 111 114 115 116 119 124 128 129 130 131 132 135 143 144 146 147 149 **S** Ascension Healthcare, Saint Louis, MO
Primary Contact: Darcy Burthay, MSN, R.N., President and Chief Executive Officer
CFO: Rick Talento, Senior Vice President and Chief Financial Officer
CMO: Raymond L. Cox M.D., Chief Medical Officer
CIO: Alan Wyman, Chief Information Officer
CHR: Matt Lasecki, Interim Vice President Human Resources
CNO: Thedosia Munford, Senior Vice President and Chief Nursing Officer
Web address: www.provhosp.org
Control: Other not–for–profit (including NFP Corporation) **Service**: General medical and surgical

> **Staffed Beds**: 448 **Admissions**: 11399 **Census**: 381 **Outpatient Visits**: 114283 **Births**: 2145 **Total Expense ($000)**: 218885 **Payroll Expense ($000)**: 93844 **Personnel**: 1363

☐ **PSYCHIATRIC INSTITUTE OF WASHINGTON (094004)**, 4228 Wisconsin Avenue NW, Zip 20016—2138; tel. 202/885–5600 **A**1 5 10 **F**5 54 98 99 101 104 105 106 **P**5
Primary Contact: Daniel J. Body, Chief Executive Officer
COO: Carol Desjeunes, Vice President and Chief Operating Officer
CFO: Aarti Subramanian, Vice President and Chief Financial Officer
CMO: Howard Hoffman M.D., Medical Director
CIO: Ray Santina, Director Information Systems
CHR: Dawn Hatterer–Hoag, Director Human Resources
Web address: www.psychinstitute.com
Control: Corporation, Investor–owned (for–profit) **Service**: Psychiatric

> **Staffed Beds**: 124 **Admissions**: 3732 **Census**: 74 **Outpatient Visits**: 1765 **Births**: 0 **Total Expense ($000)**: 35319 **Payroll Expense ($000)**: 13429 **Personnel**: 210

★ **SAINT ELIZABETHS HOSPITAL (094001)**, 1100 Alabama Avenue SE, Zip 20032—4540; tel. 202/299–5000 **A**3 5 10 **F**29 30 39 56 59 65 74 75 86 91 98 103 130 135 146 148
Primary Contact: Mark J. Chastang, M.P.H., Chief Executive Officer
COO: K. Singh Taneja, Chief Operating Officer
CFO: James V. Jackson, Budget Director
CMO: Hannah Ong, Director, Medical Affairs
CIO: Brady Birdsong, Chief Information Officer
CHR: Frankie Wheeler, Director, Human Resources
CNO: Clotilde Vidoni–Clark Ph.D., R.N., Chief Nursing Executive
Web address: www.dbh.dc.gov/
Control: State, Government, Nonfederal **Service**: Psychiatric

> **Staffed Beds**: 292 **Admissions**: 411 **Census**: 270 **Outpatient Visits**: 0 **Births**: 0 **Personnel**: 753

✠ **SIBLEY MEMORIAL HOSPITAL (090005)**, 5255 Loughboro Road NW, Zip 20016—2633; tel. 202/537–4000, (Total facility includes 36 beds in nursing home–type unit) **A**1 2 3 5 10 **F**3 6 8 10 12 13 15 20 29 30 31 34 35 36 37 38 44 45 46 47 48 49 50 53 54 55 57 58 59 64 68 70 73 74 75 76 77 78 79 81 82 84 85 86 87 91 92 93 96 97 98 107 108 109 110 111 112 113 114 115 116 117 118 119 120 121 123 126 128 130 132 135 146 147 148 **P**6 **S** Johns Hopkins Health System, Baltimore, MD
Primary Contact: Richard O. Davis, Ph.D., President
COO: Sanjay K Saha, Chief Operating Officer
CFO: Marty Basso, Chief Financial Officer
CMO: M. Therese McDonnell M.D., Interim Vice President Patient Safety, Quality and Medical Affairs
CIO: Christopher T Timbers, Chief Information Officer
CHR: Queenie C Plater, Vice President Human Resources for JHM Community Division
CNO: Lynn Meuer, Interim Chief Nursing Officer
Web address: www.sibley.org
Control: Other not–for–profit (including NFP Corporation) **Service**: General medical and surgical

> **Staffed Beds**: 158 **Admissions**: 11354 **Census**: 150 **Outpatient Visits**: 115816 **Births**: 3306 **Total Expense ($000)**: 301213 **Payroll Expense ($000)**: 123719 **Personnel**: 1343

✠ **THE HSC PEDIATRIC CENTER**, 1731 Bunker Hill Road NE, Zip 20017—3096; tel. 202/832–4400 **A**1 3 **F**3 12 29 31 32 34 35 39 50 54 58 64 65 68 71 75 80 83 84 86 90 91 93 94 96 130 132 143 146 148 **P**6
Primary Contact: Nathaniel Beers, M.D., President and Chief Executive Officer
COO: Debbie C Holson R.N., MSN, Chief Operating Officer
CFO: Ray Vicks, Senior Vice President, Finance and Chief Financial Officer
CMO: Andrew Metinko M.D., Chief Medical Officer
CIO: Khalil Bouharoun, Chief Information Officer
CHR: Lynne Hostetter, Vice President Human Resources
Web address: www.hscpediatriccenter.org/
Control: Other not–for–profit (including NFP Corporation) **Service**: Children's chronic disease

> **Staffed Beds**: 118 **Admissions**: 199 **Census**: 22 **Outpatient Visits**: 12179 **Births**: 0 **Total Expense ($000)**: 31715 **Payroll Expense ($000)**: 14387 **Personnel**: 223

✠ **UNITED MEDICAL CENTER (090008)**, 1310 Southern Avenue SE, Zip 20032—4623; tel. 202/574–6000, (Nonreporting) **A**1 10
Primary Contact: Luis A. Hernandez, Chief Executive Officer
CFO: Lilian Chukwuma, Chief Financial Officer
CMO: Julian R Craig, Chief Medical Officer
CIO: Alan Johnson, Interim Chief Information Officer
CHR: Eric M. Johnson, Director
CNO: Maribel Torres, Chief Nursing Officer
Web address: www.united–medicalcenter.com
Control: State, Government, Nonfederal **Service**: General medical and surgical

> **Staffed Beds**: 354

VETERANS AFFAIRS MEDICAL CENTER See Washington DC Veterans Affairs Medical Center

✠ △ **WASHINGTON DC VETERANS AFFAIRS MEDICAL CENTER**, 50 Irving Street NW, Zip 20422—0002; tel. 202/745–8000, (Nonreporting) **A**1 2 3 5 7 **S** Department of Veterans Affairs, Washington, DC
Primary Contact: Charles Faselis, M.D., Acting Medical Center Director
CFO: Frank Filosa, Fiscal Manager
CIO: Amanda Graves, Chief Information Systems
Web address: www.washingtondc.va.gov/
Control: Veterans Affairs, Government, federal **Service**: General medical and surgical

> **Staffed Beds**: 291

WASHINGTON HOSPITAL CENTER See Medstar Washington Hospital Center

DC

FLORIDA

ALTAMONTE SPRINGS—Seminole County

FLORIDA HOSPITAL–ALTAMONTE See Florida Hospital, Pensacola

⊞ **HEALTHSOUTH REHABILITATION HOSPITAL OF ALTAMONTE SPRINGS (103045)**, 831 South State Road 434, Zip 32714–3502; tel. 407/587–8600 **A**1 **F**29 75 86 90 91 95 96 148 149 **S** HEALTHSOUTH Corporation, Birmingham, AL
Primary Contact: Lori Bedard, Interim Chief Executive Officer
Web address: www.healthsouthaltamontesprings.com
Control: State, Government, Nonfederal **Service:** Rehabilitation

Staffed Beds: 50 Admissions: 1043 **Census:** 41 **Outpatient Visits:** 0 **Births:** 0 **Total Expense ($000):** 15636 **Payroll Expense ($000):** 7934	

APALACHICOLA—Franklin County

GEORGE E. WEEMS MEMORIAL HOSPITAL (101305), 135 Avenue G, Zip 32320–1613, Mailing Address: P.O.Box 580, 32329–0580; tel. 850/653–8853 **A**10 18 **F**3 7 30 34 35 40 54 59 64 66 107 128 133 146 **P**6
Primary Contact: Mike Cooper, Chief Executive Officer
CHR: Ginny Griner, Director Human Resources
Web address: www.weemsmemorial.com
Control: County, Government, Nonfederal **Service:** General medical and surgical

Staffed Beds: 15 Admissions: 176 **Census:** 2 **Outpatient Visits:** 11781 **Births:** 0 **Total Expense ($000):** 8392 **Payroll Expense ($000):** 4056	

APOPKA—Orange County

FLORIDA HOSPITAL–APOPKA See Florida Hospital, Sebring

ARCADIA—Desoto County

☐ **DESOTO MEMORIAL HOSPITAL (100175)**, 900 North Robert Avenue, Zip 34266–8712, Mailing Address: P.O.Box 2180, 34265–2180; tel. 863/494–3535 **A**1 10 20 **F**13 15 18 28 29 31 34 35 40 45 46 54 55 57 62 64 65 68 70 74 75 76 77 78 79 81 82 85 87 93 104 105 107 110 111 114 119 120 130 135 146 148 149
Primary Contact: Vincent A. Sica, President and Chief Executive Officer
CFO: Dan Hogan, Chief Financial Officer
CMO: Steven Mishkind M.D., Chief of Staff
CIO: Kristen Spahr, Director of Marketing
CHR: Lois Hilton, Director Human Resources
CNO: Joseph La Cava, Chief Nursing Officer and Director Of Anesthesia
Web address: www.dmh.org
Control: Hospital district or authority, Government, Nonfederal **Service:** General medical and surgical

Staffed Beds: 49 Admissions: 1145 **Census:** 8 **Outpatient Visits:** 79500 **Births:** 323 **Total Expense ($000):** 32426 **Payroll Expense ($000):** 12852 **Personnel:** 224	

ATLANTIS—Palm Beach County

⊞ **JFK MEDICAL CENTER (100080)**, 5301 South Congress Avenue, Zip 33462–1197; tel. 561/965–7300, (Nonreporting) **A**1 2 3 5 10 **S** HCA Healthcare, Nashville, TN
Primary Contact: Gina Melby, Chief Executive Officer
CFO: Jim Leamon, Chief Financial Officer
CIO: Jane Stewart, Director Information Services
CHR: Trudy Bromley, Vice President Human Resources
Web address: www.jfkmc.com
Control: Corporation, Investor–owned (for–profit) **Service:** General medical and surgical

Staffed Beds: 424	

AVENTURA—Miami—Dade County

⊞ **AVENTURA HOSPITAL AND MEDICAL CENTER (100131)**, 20900 Biscayne Boulevard, Zip 33180–1407; tel. 305/682–7000, (Nonreporting) **A**1 2 3 10 **S** HCA Healthcare, Nashville, TN
Primary Contact: Alisa Bert, Interim Chief Executive Officer
COO: Luanne Ansaldo, Chief Operating Officer
CFO: Alisa Bert, Chief Financial Officer
CMO: Martin Grossman, Chief of Staff
CHR: Rosemarie Amberson, Vice President Human Resources
CNO: Jesse Gabuat, Interim Chief Nursing Officer
Web address: www.aventurahospital.com
Control: Corporation, Investor–owned (for–profit) **Service:** General medical and surgical

Staffed Beds: 359	

BARTOW—Polk County

⊞ **BARTOW REGIONAL MEDICAL CENTER (100121)**, 2200 Osprey Boulevard, Zip 33830–3308; tel. 863/533–8111 **A**1 10 **F**3 11 12 15 18 20 22 26 29 30 31 34 35 40 45 46 49 50 51 57 58 59 60 64 68 70 74 75 77 78 79 81 82 84 85 86 87 92 93 94 97 99 100 101 104 107 108 110 111 114 115 118 119 123 124 126 129 130 131 132 135 145 146 147 148 150 **P**6 **S** Trinity Health, Livonia, MI
Primary Contact: Philip Minden, Chief Executive Officer
CFO: Michael Boscia, Chief Financial Officer
CMO: Stuart Patterson M.D., Chief of Staff
CIO: Vilakon Champavannarath, Director Information Systems
CHR: Marie Horton, Director Associate Relations
Web address: www.bartowregional.com
Control: Other not–for–profit (including NFP Corporation) **Service:** General medical and surgical

Staffed Beds: 72 Admissions: 2961 **Census:** 32 **Outpatient Visits:** 36427 **Births:** 0 **Total Expense ($000):** 48285 **Payroll Expense ($000):** 18629 **Personnel:** 325	

BAY PINES—Pinellas County

⊞ △ **BAY PINES VETERANS AFFAIRS HEALTHCARE SYSTEM**, 10000 Bay Pines Boulevard, Zip 33744–8200, Mailing Address: P.O.Box 5005, 33744–5005; tel. 727/398–6661 **A**1 2 3 5 7 **F**3 4 5 8 12 15 18 20 22 26 28 29 30 31 33 35 36 38 39 40 45 46 47 49 51 53 54 56 57 58 59 60 61 62 63 64 65 66 68 70 74 75 76 77 78 79 81 82 83 84 85 86 87 90 91 93 94 97 98 100 101 102 103 104 105 106 107 108 110 111 114 115 116 117 118 119 120 121 123 128 129 130 131 132 135 143 144 146 147 148 149 **P**6 **S** Department of Veterans Affairs, Washington, DC
Primary Contact: Suzanne M. Klinker, Director
COO: Kris Brown, Associate Director
CFO: Jeanine Ergle, Chief Financial Officer
CMO: George F Van Buskirk M.D., Chief of Staff
CIO: John Williams, Chief Information Officer
CHR: Paula Buchele, Chief Human Resources
Web address: www.baypines.va.gov/
Control: Veterans Affairs, Government, federal **Service:** General medical and surgical

Staffed Beds: 396 Admissions: 9855 **Census:** 323 **Outpatient Visits:** 1468395 **Births:** 0 **Total Expense ($000):** 756583 **Payroll Expense ($000):** 335472 **Personnel:** 3958	

BELLE GLADE—Palm Beach County

GLADES GENERAL HOSPITAL See Lakeside Medical Center

⊞ **LAKESIDE MEDICAL CENTER (100130)**, 39200 Hooker Highway, Zip 33430–5368; tel. 561/996–6571 **A**1 10 13 **F**3 11 13 15 29 34 35 36 40 45 50 56 57 60 64 68 70 76 80 81 85 87 89 91 92 107 108 109 110 111 114 119 130 146 147 149
Primary Contact: Richard Roche, Administrator
COO: Darcy Davis, Chief Financial Officer
CFO: Darcy Davis, Chief Financial Officer
CMO: Ron Wiewora M.D., Chief Medical Officer
Web address: www.lakesidemedical.org
Control: Hospital district or authority, Government, Nonfederal **Service:** General medical and surgical

Staffed Beds: 70 Admissions: 1858 **Census:** 48 **Births:** 434 **Total Expense ($000):** 44466 **Payroll Expense ($000):** 17217	

FL

BLOUNTSTOWN—Calhoun County

CALHOUN–LIBERTY HOSPITAL (101304), 20370 NE Burns Avenue, Zip 32424–1045, Mailing Address: P.O.Box 419, 32424–0419; tel. 850/674–5411 **A**10 18 **F**3 7 29 34 40 50 54 57 59 93 97 107 114 119 127 128 133 **P**6 **S** Alliant Management Services, Louisville, KY
Primary Contact: Charles E. Durant Jr, FACHE, Chief Executive Officer
CFO: Nathan Ebersole, Controller
CIO: Michael Flowers, Director Information Management
CHR: Lynn Pitts, Director Human Resources
CNO: Debra Summers, Chief Nursing Officer
Web address: www.calhounlibertyhospital.com
Control: Other not–for–profit (including NFP Corporation) **Service**: General medical and surgical

Staffed Beds: 25 Admissions: 401 Census: 11 Births: 0 Total Expense ($000): 10997 Payroll Expense ($000): 5588

BOCA RATON—Palm Beach County

BOCA RATON COMMUNITY HOSPITAL See Boca Raton Regional Hospital

☐ **BOCA RATON REGIONAL HOSPITAL (100168)**, 800 Meadows Road, Zip 33486–2368; tel. 561/955–7100 **A**1 2 3 5 10 **F**3 6 8 11 12 13 15 17 18 20 22 24 26 28 29 30 31 34 35 36 37 40 44 45 46 47 48 49 50 51 53 54 55 56 57 58 59 60 61 62 64 68 70 71 73 74 75 76 77 78 79 81 82 84 85 86 87 91 92 93 94 96 97 100 102 103 107 108 109 110 111 112 114 115 116 117 118 119 120 121 123 124 126 130 131 132 135 144 145 146 147 148 149 **P**6
Primary Contact: Jerry J. Fedele, President and Chief Executive Officer
COO: Karen Poole, Chief Operating Officer
CFO: Dawn Jauersack, Vice President and Chief Financial Officer
CMO: Charles Posternack M.D., Vice President
CIO: Robin Hildwein, Chief Information Officer
CHR: Mindy Raymond, Vice President Human Resources
CNO: Melissa Durbin R.N., Chief Nursing Officer
Web address: www.brrh.com
Control: Other not–for–profit (including NFP Corporation) **Service**: General medical and surgical

Staffed Beds: 396 Admissions: 18728 Census: 235 Outpatient Visits: 290434 Births: 2416 Total Expense ($000): 459053 Payroll Expense ($000): 184534 Personnel: 2333

☒ **WEST BOCA MEDICAL CENTER (100268)**, 21644 State Road 7, Zip 33428–1899; tel. 561/488–8000 **A**1 5 10 **F**8 13 15 18 19 29 31 35 39 40 41 42 45 49 54 57 59 64 70 72 74 76 78 79 80 81 85 86 87 88 89 91 92 93 107 108 109 110 111 114 115 117 118 119 126 129 130 131 146 147 148 **P**4 5 **S** TENET Healthcare Corporation, Dallas, TX
Primary Contact: Mitchell S. Feldman, Chief Executive Officer
COO: Ryan Lee, Chief Operating Officer
CFO: Brook Thomas, Chief Financial Officer
CMO: Jack L Harari M.D., Chief Medical Officer
CIO: Lauren Spagna, Marketing Director
CHR: Stephanie Sherman, Chief Human Resources Officer
CNO: Ruth Schwarzkopf R.N., Chief Nursing Officer
Web address: www.westbocamedctr.com
Control: Corporation, Investor–owned (for–profit) **Service**: General medical and surgical

Staffed Beds: 195 Admissions: 10911 Census: 95 Births: 2147 Total Expense ($000): 144573 Payroll Expense ($000): 49985

BONIFAY—Holmes County

☐ **DOCTORS MEMORIAL HOSPITAL (101307)**, 2600 Hospital Drive, Zip 32425–4264, Mailing Address: P.O.Box 188, 32425–0188; tel. 850/547–8000 **A**1 10 18 **F**3 11 15 29 30 40 45 50 57 59 64 70 77 81 90 93 107 110 114 119 131 133 146 148
Primary Contact: Joann Baker, Administrator
CFO: Celia F Ward, Controller and Chief Financial Officer
CMO: Leisa Bailey M.D., Chief of Staff
CIO: Rohan Anderson, Chief Information Officer
CHR: Christy Booth, Chief Human Resources Officer
CNO: Karla Rockwell, Director of Nursing
Web address: www.doctorsmemorial.org
Control: Hospital district or authority, Government, Nonfederal **Service**: General medical and surgical

Staffed Beds: 20 Admissions: 588 Census: 6 Births: 0

BOYNTON BEACH—Palm Beach County

☐ **BETHESDA HOSPITAL EAST (100002)**, 2815 South Seacrest Boulevard, Zip 33435–7995; tel. 561/737–7733, (Includes BETHESDA HOSPITAL WEST, 9655 West Boynton Beach Boulevard, Boynton Beach, Florida, Zip 33472–4421, tel. 561/336–7000; Roger L Kirk, President and Chief Executive Officer) **A**1 3 5 10 **F**3 8 11 12 13 17 18 20 22 24 26 27 30 31 32 37 40 41 45 46 49 50 51 56 58 60 61 64 68 70 72 74 75 76 77 78 79 81 86 87 88 89 90 91 92 93 94 96 107 108 109 110 111 112 113 114 115 116 117 118 119 124 126 129 131 143 145 146 147 148 **P**6
Primary Contact: Roger L. Kirk, President and Chief Executive Officer
COO: Ela C Lena, Administrator and Vice President Operations
CFO: Joanne Aquilina, Vice President Finance and Chief Financial Officer
CMO: Albert Biehl M.D., Vice President Medical Affairs
CIO: Leslie Albright, Vice President Information Systems
CHR: Regina Bellucy, Vice President Human Resources
CNO: Ela C Lena, Interim System Chief Nursing Officer
Web address: www.bethesdaweb.com
Control: Other not–for–profit (including NFP Corporation) **Service**: General medical and surgical

Staffed Beds: 481 Admissions: 21591 Census: 293 Outpatient Visits: 261447 Births: 3070 Total Expense ($000): 321240 Payroll Expense ($000): 113681 Personnel: 2068

BRADENTON—Manatee County

☒ △ **BLAKE MEDICAL CENTER (100213)**, 2020 59th Street West, Zip 34209–4669; tel. 941/792–6611 **A**1 2 7 10 **F**3 11 15 16 17 18 20 22 24 26 28 29 30 31 34 35 40 43 45 48 49 50 53 57 58 59 64 68 70 74 75 77 78 79 80 81 85 87 90 91 92 93 94 96 100 107 108 110 111 114 115 118 119 126 129 130 131 132 144 146 147 148 **S** HCA Healthcare, Nashville, TN
Primary Contact: Daniel J. Friedrich III, Chief Executive Officer
CMO: Kirk Cianciolo D.O., Chief Medical Officer
CIO: Shannon Piatkowski, Director Information Technology
CHR: Veronica Lequeux, Vice President Human Resources
Web address: www.blakemedicalcenter.com
Control: Corporation, Investor–owned (for–profit) **Service**: General medical and surgical

Staffed Beds: 383 Admissions: 15438 Census: 206 Births: 0 Total Expense ($000): 214454 Payroll Expense ($000): 69835

CENTERSTONE HOSPITAL (104040) (Substance Abuse Mental Health and Addictions), 2020 26th Avenue East, Zip 34208–7753, Mailing Address: P.O.Box 9478, 34206–9478; tel. 941/782–4600 **A**10 13 **F**4 29 61 98 99 101 102 103 132 135
Primary Contact: Melissa Larkin–Skinner, Chief Executive Officer
CFO: Sean Gingras CPA, Chief Financial Officer
CMO: Ranjay Halder M.D., Chief Medical Director
CIO: Heidi L Blair, Vice President Administration
CHR: Colleen O'Connor, Director Human Resources
Web address: www.manateeglens.org
Control: Other not–for–profit (including NFP Corporation) **Service**: Other specialty treatment

Staffed Beds: 62 Admissions: 3174 Census: 54 Outpatient Visits: 0 Births: 0 Total Expense ($000): 10079 Payroll Expense ($000): 4449 Personnel: 85

☐ **LAKEWOOD RANCH MEDICAL CENTER (100299)**, 8330 Lakewood Ranch Boulevard, Zip 34202–5174; tel. 941/782–2100 (Nonreporting) **A**1 10 **S** Universal Health Services, Inc., King of Prussia, PA
Primary Contact: Andrew Guz, Chief Executive Officer
COO: Linda S Widra FACHE, Ph.D., R.N., Chief Operating Officer
CFO: Gerald Christine, Chief Financial Officer
CHR: Trish Morales, Director Human Resources
Web address: www.lakewoodranchmedicalcenter.com
Control: Corporation, Investor–owned (for–profit) **Service**: General medical and surgical

Staffed Beds: 120

☐ **MANATEE MEMORIAL HOSPITAL (100035)**, 206 Second Street East, Zip 34208–1000; tel. 941/746–5111, (Nonreporting) **A**1 2 5 10 12 13 **S** Universal Health Services, Inc., King of Prussia, PA
Primary Contact: Kevin DiLallo, Chief Executive Officer
CFO: Mark A Tierney, Chief Financial Officer
CMO: Linda Christmann M.D., Chief of Staff
CIO: Troy Beaubien, Director Information Services
CHR: Sheree Threewits, Director Human Resources
CNO: Darlette Tice, Chief Nursing Officer
COO: Camie Patterson, Chief Operating Officer
Web address: www.manateememorial.com
Control: Partnership, Investor–owned (for–profit) **Service**: General medical and surgical

Staffed Beds: 319

FL

Many Facility Codes have changed. Please refer to the AHA Guide Code Chart.
© 2017 AHA Guide

☐ **SUNCOAST BEHAVIORAL HEALTH CENTER (104078)**, 4480 51st Street West, Zip 34210–2855; tel. 941/251–5000 **A**1 **F**4 29 34 50 64 98 99 100 101 102 103 105 149 **S** Universal Health Services, Inc., King of Prussia, PA
Primary Contact: Brandy Hamilton, Chief Executive Officer
CFO: Linda Weymouth, Chief Financial Officer
CMO: Randolph Hemsath M.D., Medical Director
CNO: Janey Sweeney, Chief Nursing Officer
Web address: www.suncoastbhc.com
Control: Corporation, Investor–owned (for–profit) **Service**: Psychiatric

Staffed Beds: 60 Admissions: 1991 Census: 28 Outpatient Visits: 0 Births: 0 Total Expense ($000): 6981 Payroll Expense ($000): 3827

BRANDON—Hillsborough County

☒ **BRANDON REGIONAL HOSPITAL (100243)**, 119 Oakfield Drive, Zip 33511–5779; tel. 813/681–5551, (Nonreporting) **A**1 5 10 **S** HCA Healthcare, Nashville, TN
Primary Contact: Bland Eng, Chief Executive Officer
CFO: Michael T Terrell, Chief Financial Officer
CMO: Joseph C. Corcoran, Chief Medical Officer
CIO: Aaron Fountain, Chief Information Officer
CHR: Doug Goodman, Vice President Human Resources
Web address: www.brandonhospital.com
Control: Corporation, Investor–owned (for–profit) **Service**: General medical and surgical

Staffed Beds: 407

BROOKSVILLE—Hernando County

☒ **BAYFRONT HEALTH BROOKSVILLE (100071)**, 17240 Cortez Boulevard, Zip 34601–8921, Mailing Address: P.O.Box 37, 34605–0037; tel. 352/796–5111, (Nonreporting) (Includes BAYFRONT HEALTH SPRING HILL, 10461 Quality Drive, Spring Hill, Florida, Zip 34609–9634, tel. 352/688–8200; Patrick Maloney, Market Chief Executive Officer) **A**1 10 **S** Community Health Systems, Inc., Franklin, TN
Primary Contact: Kenneth R. Wicker, Chief Executive Officer
COO: Scott Hartsell, Chief Operating Officer
CFO: Matthew Seagroves, Chief Financial Officer
CMO: Mohammad A Joud M.D., Chief of Staff
CIO: Lee Burch, Director Management Information Systems
CHR: Claudia L Jack, Director Associate Relations
Web address: www.brooksvilleregionalhospital.org
Control: Corporation, Investor–owned (for–profit) **Service**: General medical and surgical

Staffed Beds: 120

☒ **HEALTHSOUTH REHABILITATION HOSPITAL OF SPRING HILL (103042)**, 12440 Cortez Boulevard, Zip 34613–2628; tel. 352/592–4250 **A**1 10 **F**3 29 62 64 77 90 93 148 **S** HEALTHSOUTH Corporation, Birmingham, AL
Primary Contact: Jeffrey Alexander, Chief Executive Officer
CFO: Kimberly Lunt, Controller
CMO: Mira Zelin D.O., Medical Director
CIO: Myra Merillo, Supervisor Health Information Management
CHR: Mary Salamanca, Director Human Resources
Web address: www.healthsouthspringhill.com
Control: Corporation, Investor–owned (for–profit) **Service**: Rehabilitation

Staffed Beds: 80 Admissions: 1706 Census: 65 Outpatient Visits: 3142 Births: 0 Total Expense ($000): 21999 Payroll Expense ($000): 11996 Personnel: 226

☒ **OAK HILL HOSPITAL (100264)**, 11375 Cortez Boulevard, Zip 34613–5409; tel. 352/596–6632 **A**1 2 3 10 **F**3 11 15 18 20 22 24 26 29 30 31 34 35 40 41 45 46 48 49 50 51 56 57 59 61 64 70 74 75 77 78 79 81 85 87 89 93 107 108 110 111 114 115 118 119 126 130 131 132 146 147 148 **P**6 **S** HCA Healthcare, Nashville, TN
Primary Contact: Mickey Smith, Chief Executive Officer
CFO: Matt Romero, Chief Financial Officer
CMO: Ed Nast M.D., Chief Medical Officer
CHR: Charles Snider, Vice President Human Resources
CNO: Leanne Salazar, Chief Nursing Officer
Web address: www.oakhillhospital.com
Control: Corporation, Investor–owned (for–profit) **Service**: General medical and surgical

Staffed Beds: 280 Admissions: 15717 Census: 186 Births: 0 Total Expense ($000): 175937 Payroll Expense ($000): 62066

☐ **SPRINGBROOK HOSPITAL (104057)**, 7007 Grove Road, Zip 34609–8610; tel. 352/596–4306 **A**1 10 **F**4 5 98 103 105 149
Primary Contact: Stephen Reider, R.N., Administrator
Web address: www.springbrookhospital.org/
Control: Corporation, Investor–owned (for–profit) **Service**: Psychiatric

Staffed Beds: 66 Admissions: 2638 Census: 65 Outpatient Visits: 0 Births: 0

CAPE CORAL—Lee County

★ ⇑ **CAPE CORAL HOSPITAL (100244)**, 636 Del Prado Boulevard, Zip 33990–2695; tel. 239/424–2000 **A**2 10 21 **F**3 11 13 14 18 20 28 29 30 34 35 40 45 46 48 50 51 53 56 57 59 60 65 66 68 70 74 75 76 77 79 81 82 84 85 86 87 93 94 97 107 108 111 114 119 129 130 132 135 146 147 148 **S** Lee Health, Fort Myers, FL
Primary Contact: Lawrence Antonucci, M.D., Chief Executive Officer
CFO: Ben Spence, Chief Financial Officer
CMO: Mark Greenberg M.D., Chief Medical Officer
CIO: Mike Smith, Chief Information Officer
CHR: Jon C Cecil, Chief Human Resource Officer
CNO: Lisa Sgarlata MSN, Chief Patient Care Officer
Web address: www.leememorial.org
Control: Hospital district or authority, Government, Nonfederal **Service**: General medical and surgical

Staffed Beds: 291 Admissions: 15925 Census: 180 Outpatient Visits: 242504 Births: 1336 Personnel: 1336

CELEBRATION—Osceola County

FLORIDA HOSPITAL CELEBRATION HEALTH See Florida Hospital, Orlando

CHATTAHOOCHEE—Gadsden County

FLORIDA STATE HOSPITAL (104000), U S Highway 90 East, Zip 32324–1000, Mailing Address: P.O.Box 1000, 32324–1000; tel. 850/663–7536, (Nonreporting) **A**10
Primary Contact: Marguerite J. Morgan, Administrator
CFO: Denise Smith, Director Financial Services
Web address: www.dcf.state.fl.us/institutions/fsh
Control: State, Government, Nonfederal **Service**: Psychiatric

Staffed Beds: 987

CHIPLEY—Washington County

☐ **NORTHWEST FLORIDA COMMUNITY HOSPITAL (101308)**, 1360 Brickyard Road, Zip 32428–6303, Mailing Address: P.O.Box 889, 32428–0889; tel. 850/638–1610, (Total facility includes 34 beds in nursing home–type unit) **A**1 10 18 **F**11 15 29 30 34 35 40 45 56 57 59 62 65 68 81 82 85 93 97 104 107 108 110 111 115 119 127 128 130 131 132 133 144 146 148 149 **S** Alliant Management Services, Louisville, KY
Primary Contact: Michael A. Kozar, Chief Executive Officer
COO: Janet Kinney, Chief Operating Officer
CFO: Marcey Black, Chief Financial Officer
CHR: Shelia Schiefelbein, Coordinator Human Resources
CNO: Joan Beard, Chief Nursing Officer
Web address: www.nfch.org
Control: Corporation, Investor–owned (for–profit) **Service**: General medical and surgical

Staffed Beds: 59 Admissions: 1479 Census: 46 Births: 0 Total Expense ($000): 25043 Payroll Expense ($000): 10320

CLEARWATER—Pinellas County

☒ **MORTON PLANT HOSPITAL (100127)**, 300 Pinellas Street, Zip 33756–3804, Mailing Address: P.O.Box 210, 33757–0210; tel. 727/462–7000, (Total facility includes 120 beds in nursing home–type unit) **A**1 2 3 5 10 **F**3 6 11 13 15 17 18 20 22 24 26 28 29 30 31 34 35 36 37 38 40 42 44 45 46 47 48 49 50 51 53 54 55 56 57 58 59 60 61 62 64 65 66 68 70 72 74 75 76 77 78 79 80 81 82 84 85 86 87 92 93 98 100 101 102 107 108 109 110 111 114 115 116 117 118 119 120 121 123 124 126 128 129 130 131 132 135 143 145 146 147 148 149 **S** Morton Plant Mease Health Care, Clearwater, FL
Primary Contact: N. Kristopher. Hoce, President
CFO: Carl Tremonti, Chief Financial Officer
CMO: Jeff Jensen D.O., Vice President, Medical Affairs
CIO: Timothy Thompson, Senior Vice President and Chief Information Officer
CHR: Angel Brown, Director Human Resources
CNO: Thomas Doria, Vice President Patient Services – West
Web address: www.mortonplant.com
Control: Other not–for–profit (including NFP Corporation) **Service**: General medical and surgical

Staffed Beds: 605 Admissions: 25836 Census: 317 Outpatient Visits: 372331 Births: 2209 Total Expense ($000): 458005 Payroll Expense ($000): 144084 Personnel: 2991

FL

★ American Hospital Association (AHA) membership ☐ The Joint Commission accreditation ○ Healthcare Facilities Accreditation Program ◇ DNV Healthcare Inc. accreditation ⇑ Center for Improvement in Healthcare Quality Accreditation △ Commission on Accreditation of Rehabilitation Facilities (CARF) accreditation

☐ **WINDMOOR HEALTHCARE OF CLEARWATER (104017)**, 11300 U S 19 North, Zip 33764; tel. 727/541–2646, (Nonreporting) **A**1 10 **S** Universal Health Services, Inc., King of Prussia, PA
Primary Contact: Wendy Merson, Chief Executive Officer
Web address: www.windmoor.com
Control: Corporation, Investor–owned (for–profit) **Service**: Psychiatric

Staffed Beds: 100

CLERMONT—Lake County

☐ **SOUTH LAKE HOSPITAL (100051)**, 1900 Don Wickham Drive, Zip 34711–1979; tel. 352/394–4071, (Total facility includes 30 beds in nursing home–type unit) **A**1 10 **F**3 8 11 13 15 18 20 22 26 28 29 30 31 32 34 35 37 40 45 46 47 48 49 50 51 53 54 57 59 60 62 64 65 66 68 70 74 75 76 77 78 79 81 82 85 86 87 89 92 93 107 108 110 111 114 115 116 117 119 120 121 124 126 127 128 130 131 132 135 146 147 148 149 **P**6 **S** Orlando Health, Orlando, FL
Primary Contact: John Moore, President
COO: Paul Johns, Chief Operating Officer
CFO: Lance Sewell, Chief Financial Officer
CHR: Joy L. Sylvester, Director, Human Resources and Education
CNO: Bonnie Onofre, Chief Nursing Officer
Web address: www.southlakehospital.com
Control: Hospital district or authority, Government, Nonfederal **Service**: General medical and surgical

Staffed Beds: 170 **Admissions:** 9272 **Census:** 122 **Outpatient Visits:** 117755 **Births:** 684 **Total Expense ($000):** 174165 **Payroll Expense ($000):** 66939 **Personnel:** 1347

CLEWISTON—Hendry County

⊞ **HENDRY REGIONAL MEDICAL CENTER (101309)**, 524 West Sagamore Avenue, Zip 33440–3514; tel. 863/902–3000 **A**1 10 18 **F**3 11 15 29 34 35 40 45 50 57 59 64 65 68 70 75 77 79 81 82 85 91 93 97 107 110 111 114 119 127 133 135 146 **P**6 **S** QHR, Brentwood, TN
Primary Contact: R D Williams, Chief Executive Officer
CFO: John Beltz, Chief Financial Officer
CMO: Karim Kaki M.D., Chief Medical Director
CIO: Leon Hoover, Director Information Systems
CHR: Lisa Miller, Director Human Resources
CNO: Sandra E Viall MSN, Chief Nursing Officer
Web address: www.hendryregional.org
Control: Hospital district or authority, Government, Nonfederal **Service**: General medical and surgical

Staffed Beds: 25 **Admissions:** 646 **Census:** 5 **Outpatient Visits:** 34022 **Births:** 0 **Total Expense ($000):** 28951 **Payroll Expense ($000):** 12921 **Personnel:** 239

COCOA BEACH—Brevard County

⊞ **HEALTH FIRST CAPE CANAVERAL HOSPITAL (100177)**, 701 West Cocoa Beach Causeway, Zip 32931–5595, Mailing Address: P.O.Box 320069, 32932–0069; tel. 321/799–7111 **A**1 10 **F**3 11 13 15 18 20 24 29 30 31 34 40 41 43 45 46 47 49 50 59 60 62 64 68 70 74 75 76 77 78 79 81 85 86 87 102 107 108 109 110 111 114 115 116 117 118 119 129 130 132 141 147 148 149 **S** Health First, Inc., Rockledge, FL
Primary Contact: Aaron Robinson, Chief Executive Officer, Health First Community Hospitals
COO: Deborah Angerami, Chief Operating Officer, Health First Community Hospitals
CFO: Joseph G Felkner, Senior Vice President Finance and Chief Financial Officer
CMO: Lee Scheinbart M.D., Vice President Medical Affairs, Health First Community Hospitals
CIO: Alex Popowycz, Senior Vice President and Chief Information Officer
CHR: Paula Just, Vice President Human Resources
CNO: Connie Bradley R.N., MSN, FACHE, Chief Nursing Officer
Web address: www.health–first.org
Control: Other not–for–profit (including NFP Corporation) **Service**: General medical and surgical

Staffed Beds: 125 **Admissions:** 7109 **Census:** 79 **Outpatient Visits:** 115462 **Births:** 719 **Total Expense ($000):** 123123 **Payroll Expense ($000):** 56031 **Personnel:** 518

CORAL GABLES—Miami—Dade County

⊞ **BAPTIST HEALTH SOUTH FLORIDA, DOCTORS HOSPITAL (100296)**, 5000 University Drive, Zip 33146–2094; tel. 786/308–3000 **A**1 3 5 10 **F**3 11 18 29 30 31 34 35 37 40 45 47 49 53 57 58 59 60 63 64 68 70 74 75 77 78 79 81 82 84 85 86 87 93 94 100 102 107 108 111 114 115 119 124 126 130 131 132 143 146 148 149 150 **S** Baptist Health South Florida, Coral Gables, FL
Primary Contact: Nelson Lazo, Chief Executive Officer
CFO: Maria J Yanez, Chief Financial Officer
Web address: www.baptisthealth.net
Control: Other not–for–profit (including NFP Corporation) **Service**: General medical and surgical

Staffed Beds: 126 **Admissions:** 6261 **Census:** 83 **Outpatient Visits:** 64070 **Births:** 0 **Total Expense ($000):** 183626 **Payroll Expense ($000):** 57731 **Personnel:** 787

⊞ **CORAL GABLES HOSPITAL (100183)**, 3100 Douglas Road, Zip 33134–6914; tel. 305/445–8461, (Nonreporting) **A**1 10 **S** TENET Healthcare Corporation, Dallas, TX
Primary Contact: Cristina Jimenez, Chief Executive Officer
COO: Madison Workman, Chief Operating Officer
CFO: Henry Capote, Interim Chief Financial Officer
CMO: Pedro Friarte, Director of Physician Services
CIO: Mercy Hermosa, Director of Information System
CHR: Ana Paguaga, Director of Human Resources
Web address: www.coralgableshospital.com
Control: Corporation, Investor–owned (for–profit) **Service**: General medical and surgical

Staffed Beds: 256

CORAL SPRINGS—Broward County

⊞ **BROWARD HEALTH CORAL SPRINGS (100276)**, 3000 Coral Hills Drive, Zip 33065–4108; tel. 954/344–3000 **A**1 10 **F**3 11 12 13 15 20 29 31 34 35 40 41 48 51 55 57 58 59 61 63 64 66 68 70 72 74 75 76 77 78 79 80 81 82 84 85 86 87 88 89 93 96 107 108 111 114 115 118 119 126 129 130 131 132 143 146 147 148 **P**6 **S** Broward Health, Fort Lauderdale, FL
Primary Contact: Drew Grossman, Chief Executive Officer
COO: Michael Leopold, Chief Operating Officer
CFO: Onel Rodriguez, Chief Financial Officer
CMO: Kutty Chandran M.D., Regional Medical Officer
CHR: Eileen O'Brien, Regional Director Human Resources
CNO: Kimberley Graham R.N., Chief Nursing Officer
Web address: www.browardhealth.org
Control: Hospital district or authority, Government, Nonfederal **Service**: General medical and surgical

Staffed Beds: 196 **Admissions:** 12228 **Census:** 122 **Outpatient Visits:** 139921 **Births:** 2267 **Total Expense ($000):** 155294 **Payroll Expense ($000):** 62245 **Personnel:** 930

CRESTVIEW—Okaloosa County

⊞ **NORTH OKALOOSA MEDICAL CENTER (100122)**, 151 Redstone Avenue SE, Zip 32539–6026; tel. 850/689–8100 **A**1 10 **F**3 8 11 13 15 18 20 22 28 29 30 34 35 40 47 49 50 54 59 64 70 75 79 81 85 86 87 107 108 109 110 111 114 115 116 117 118 119 126 127 129 130 131 146 147 148 149 150 **S** Community Health Systems, Inc., Franklin, TN
Primary Contact: Ronnie Daves, Chief Executive Officer
CFO: Jim Andrews, Chief Financial Officer
CMO: Michael Foley M.D., Chief Medical Officer
CIO: Jenny Zeitler, Network Administrator
CHR: Melody M Miller–Collette, Director Human Resources
CNO: Nina Perez R.N., MSN, Chief Nursing Officer
Web address: www.northokaloosa.com
Control: Corporation, Investor–owned (for–profit) **Service**: General medical and surgical

Staffed Beds: 110 **Admissions:** 4974 **Census:** 49 **Outpatient Visits:** 115981 **Births:** 486 **Total Expense ($000):** 70713 **Payroll Expense ($000):** 25608 **Personnel:** 506

CRYSTAL RIVER—Citrus County

⊞ **SEVEN RIVERS REGIONAL MEDICAL CENTER (100249)**, 6201 North Suncoast Boulevard, Zip 34428–6712; tel. 352/795–6560, (Nonreporting) **A**1 10 19 **S** Community Health Systems, Inc., Franklin, TN
Primary Contact: Austin Brown, Chief Executive Officer
CFO: Vickie Magurean, Chief Financial Officer
CHR: Joann Mramor, Director Human Resources
CNO: Cynthia Heitzman R.N., Chief Nursing Officer
Web address: www.srrmc.com
Control: Corporation, Investor–owned (for–profit) **Service**: General medical and surgical

Staffed Beds: 128

CUTLER BAY—Miami—Dade County

HEALTHSOUTH REHABILITATION HOSPITAL See Healthsouth Rehabilitation Hospital Of Miami

★ **HEALTHSOUTH REHABILITATION HOSPITAL OF MIAMI (103038)**, 20601 Old Cutler Road, Zip 33189–2400; tel. 305/251–3800 **A**10 **F**3 28 29 77 86 89 90 91 95 96 130 132 135 148 **P**5 **S** HEALTHSOUTH Corporation, Birmingham, AL
Primary Contact: Enrique A. Vicens–Rivera Jr, JD, Chief Executive Officer
CFO: Reyna Hernandez, Chief Financial Officer
CIO: Miguel Cruz, Medical Staff Credentialing Coordinator
CHR: Susan Riley, Director Human Resources
CNO: Ellen Romanowski, Chief Nursing Officer
Web address: www.healthsouthmiami.com
Control: Corporation, Investor–owned (for–profit) **Service**: Rehabilitation

Staffed Beds: 60 **Admissions:** 1400 **Census:** 45 **Outpatient Visits:** 0 **Births:** 0 **Total Expense ($000):** 15067 **Payroll Expense ($000):** 8348

Many Facility Codes have changed. Please refer to the AHA Guide Code Chart. © 2017 AHA Guide

FL

DELRAY BEACH—Palm Beach County

✠ △ **DELRAY MEDICAL CENTER (100258)**, 5352 Linton Boulevard, Zip 33484–6580; tel. 561/498–4440, (Includes FAIR OAKS PAVILION, 5440 Linton Boulevard, Delray Beach, Florida, Zip 33484–6578, tel. 561/495–1000; PINECREST REHABILITATION HOSPITAL, 5360 Linton Boulevard, Delray Beach, Florida, Zip 33484–6538, tel. 561/495–0400) **A**1 3 5 7 10 **F**3 4 11 12 15 17 18 20 22 24 26 28 29 30 31 34 35 37 38 40 42 43 45 46 49 50 51 56 57 58 59 60 64 65 70 74 75 77 78 79 80 81 82 83 84 85 87 90 91 93 94 96 97 98 100 101 102 103 104 107 108 111 114 115 118 119 126 129 130 132 133 135 143 144 146 147 148 **S** TENET Healthcare Corporation, Dallas, TX
Primary Contact: Mark Bryan, Chief Executive Officer
CMO: Anthony Dardano M.D., Chief Medical Officer
CIO: Robens Rosena, Director Information Systems
CHR: Shannon Wills, Director Human Resources
Web address: www.delraymedicalctr.com
Control: Corporation, Investor–owned (for–profit) **Service:** General medical and surgical

Staffed Beds: 439 **Admissions:** 18889 **Census:** 291 **Outpatient Visits:** 87075 **Births:** 0 **Personnel:** 1449

DUNEDIN—Pinellas County

☐ **BAYCARE ALLIANT HOSPITAL (102021)**, 601 Main Street, Zip 34698–5848; tel. 727/736–9991 **A**1 10 **F**1 3 28 29 34 36 57 130 148
Primary Contact: Jacqueline Arocho, Administrator
CFO: John Proni CPA, Manager Finance and Operations
CMO: Leonard Dunn M.D., Chief Medical Officer
CHR: Darlene Shelton, Coordinator Team Resources
Web address: www.baycare.org
Control: Other not–for–profit (including NFP Corporation) **Service:** Acute long–term care hospital

Staffed Beds: 36 **Admissions:** 395 **Census:** 29 **Outpatient Visits:** 0 **Births:** 0 **Total Expense ($000):** 18189 **Payroll Expense ($000):** 6600 **Personnel:** 97

✠ **MEASE DUNEDIN HOSPITAL (100043)**, 601 Main Street, Zip 34698–5891; tel. 727/733–1111 **A**1 10 **F**3 12 15 18 26 29 30 31 34 35 37 38 40 44 45 49 56 57 59 60 62 64 68 70 74 75 78 79 81 84 85 86 87 97 98 99 100 102 103 107 108 110 111 114 118 119 130 132 135 143 145 146 149 **S** Trinity Health, Livonia, MI
Primary Contact: Lou Galdieri, R.N., President
COO: Kelly Cullen R.N., Director of Operations
CFO: Carl Tremonti, Chief Financial Officer
CMO: Tony Schuster M.D., Vice President of Physician Services
CIO: Tim Thompson, Senior Vice President, Information Services and Chief Information Officer
CHR: Kyle J Barr, Senior Vice President, Chief Team Resources Officer
CNO: Thomas Doria, Vice President, Patient Services and Chief Nursing Officer
Web address: www.mpmhealth.com
Control: Other not–for–profit (including NFP Corporation) **Service:** General medical and surgical

Staffed Beds: 120 **Admissions:** 7128 **Census:** 89 **Outpatient Visits:** 37119 **Births:** 0 **Total Expense ($000):** 85903 **Payroll Expense ($000):** 35998 **Personnel:** 597

EGLIN AFB—Okaloosa County

✠ **U.S. AIR FORCE REGIONAL HOSPITAL**, 307 Boatner Road, Suite 114, Zip 32542–1282; tel. 850/883–8221, (Nonreporting) **A**1 3 5 **S** Department of the Air Force, Washington, DC
Primary Contact: Colonel Pamela Smith, Commander
Web address: www.eglin.af.mil
Control: Air Force, Government, federal **Service:** General medical and surgical

Staffed Beds: 57

ENGLEWOOD—Sarasota County

✠ **ENGLEWOOD COMMUNITY HOSPITAL (100267)**, 700 Medical Boulevard, Zip 34223–3978; tel. 941/475–6571, (Nonreporting) **A**1 10 **S** HCA Healthcare, Nashville, TN
Primary Contact: Valerie L. Powell–Stafford, Chief Executive Officer
COO: Alex Chang, Chief Operating Officer
CMO: Eric Pressman D.O., Chair Department of Medicine
CNO: Kathleen Pace MSN, R.N., Chief Nursing Officer
Web address: www.englewoodcommunityhospital.com
Control: Corporation, Investor–owned (for–profit) **Service:** General medical and surgical

Staffed Beds: 100

FERNANDINA BEACH—Nassau County

✠ **BAPTIST MEDICAL CENTER NASSAU (100140)**, 1250 South 18th Street, Zip 32034–3098; tel. 904/321–3500 **A**1 10 **F**3 11 13 15 18 26 29 30 34 35 40 45 49 64 70 74 76 79 81 82 85 91 92 93 102 107 108 110 111 114 115 119 124 129 132 146 148 149 **S** Baptist Health, Jacksonville, FL
Primary Contact: Ed Hubel, President
COO: Patricia K Hausauer, Director Finance
CFO: Patricia K Hausauer, Director Finance
CHR: Jodi Atkins, Human Resources Specialist
Web address: www.baptistjax.com/locations/baptist–medical–center–nassau
Control: Other not–for–profit (including NFP Corporation) **Service:** General medical and surgical

Staffed Beds: 52 **Admissions:** 3830 **Census:** 37 **Outpatient Visits:** 83760 **Births:** 659 **Total Expense ($000):** 60770 **Payroll Expense ($000):** 20008 **Personnel:** 352

FORT LAUDERDALE—Broward County

☐ **ATLANTIC SHORES HOSPITAL (104065)**, 4545 North Federal Highway, Zip 33308–5274; tel. 954/771–2711, (Nonreporting) **A**1 10 **S** Universal Health Services, Inc., King of Prussia, PA
Primary Contact: Manuel R. Llano, Chief Executive Officer
CFO: Michel Duchaussee, Chief Financial Officer
CMO: Sherrie Bieniek M.D., Medical Director
CHR: Carlos A Gato, Director of Human Resources
Web address: www.atlanticshoreshospital.com
Control: Corporation, Investor–owned (for–profit) **Service:** Psychiatric

Staffed Beds: 72

✠ **BROWARD HEALTH IMPERIAL POINT (100200)**, 6401 North Federal Highway, Zip 33308–1495; tel. 954/776–8500 **A**1 10 **F**3 11 12 15 20 29 34 35 40 45 51 53 55 57 58 59 61 63 64 68 70 74 75 77 78 79 80 81 82 84 85 86 87 93 98 100 102 104 105 107 108 110 111 114 115 118 119 126 129 130 131 132 143 146 147 148 **S** Broward Health, Fort Lauderdale, FL
Primary Contact: Alice Taylor, R.N., MSN, Chief Executive Officer
COO: William Thomas Kester, Chief Nursing/Operating Officer
CFO: Susan Newton, Chief Financial Officer
CHR: Carl McDonald, Regional Director Human Resources
CNO: William Thomas Kester, Chief Nursing and Operating Officer
Web address: www.browardhealth.org
Control: Hospital district or authority, Government, Nonfederal **Service:** General medical and surgical

Staffed Beds: 180 **Admissions:** 8049 **Census:** 108 **Outpatient Visits:** 91872 **Births:** 0 **Total Expense ($000):** 121084 **Payroll Expense ($000):** 45013 **Personnel:** 727

✠ **BROWARD HEALTH MEDICAL CENTER (100039)**, 1600 South Andrews Avenue, Zip 33316–2510; tel. 954/355–4400, (Includes CHRIS EVERT CHILDRENS HOSPITAL, 1600 South Andrews Avenue, Fort Lauderdale, Florida, Zip 33316–2510, tel. 954/355–4400; Calvin E Glidewell Jr, Chief Executive Officer) **A**1 2 3 5 10 12 13 **F**3 11 13 15 17 18 20 22 24 26 28 29 30 31 34 35 40 41 43 45 48 49 50 51 53 57 59 60 61 62 63 64 65 66 68 70 71 72 73 74 75 76 77 78 79 80 81 82 83 84 85 87 88 89 93 94 98 100 102 105 107 108 110 111 114 115 116 117 119 120 121 126 129 130 139 146 147 149 **S** Broward Health, Fort Lauderdale, FL
Primary Contact: Mark Sprada, R.N., Interim Chief Executive Officer
COO: Natassia Orr, Chief Operating Officer
CFO: Alexander Fernandez, Chief Financial Officer
CMO: Louis Yogel M.D., Chief of Staff
CIO: Doris Crain, Vice President Information Services
CHR: Dionne Wong, Vice President and Chief Human Resources Officer
CNO: Robyn Farrington, Chief Nursing Officer
Web address: www.browardhealth.org
Control: Hospital district or authority, Government, Nonfederal **Service:** General medical and surgical

Staffed Beds: 656 **Admissions:** 26839 **Census:** 427 **Outpatient Visits:** 240024 **Births:** 3571 **Total Expense ($000):** 498424 **Payroll Expense ($000):** 184769 **Personnel:** 2889

FLORIDA MEDICAL CENTER See Florida Medical Center – A Campus of North Shore

☐ **FORT LAUDERDALE HOSPITAL (104026)**, 1601 East Las Olas Boulevard, Zip 33301–2393; tel. 954/463–4321, (Nonreporting) **A**1 10 **S** Universal Health Services, Inc., King of Prussia, PA
Primary Contact: Manuel R. Llano, Chief Executive Officer
CFO: Varonica Oehl, Chief Financial Officer
CMO: Sherrie Bieniek M.D., Medical Director
CHR: Carlos A Gato, Director of Human Resources
CNO: Maria Spingos, Director of Nursing
Web address: www.fortlauderdalehospital.org
Control: Corporation, Investor–owned (for–profit) **Service:** Psychiatric

Staffed Beds: 100

FL

⊞ **HOLY CROSS HOSPITAL (100073)**, 4725 North Federal Highway, Zip 33308–4668, Mailing Address: P.O.Box 23460, 33307–3460; tel. 954/771–8000 **A**1 2 3 5 10 **F**3 8 11 12 13 15 17 18 20 22 24 26 28 29 30 31 34 35 36 37 40 44 45 46 47 48 49 50 51 53 54 55 56 57 58 59 61 62 64 65 66 67 70 72 74 75 76 77 78 79 80 81 82 84 85 87 90 91 92 93 95 96 97 100 107 108 110 111 114 115 116 117 118 119 120 121 123 124 126 130 131 132 134 143 144 145 146 147 149 **P**6 **S** Trinity Health, Livonia, MI
Primary Contact: Patrick Taylor, M.D., President and Chief Executive Officer
COO: Luisa Gutman, Senior Vice President and Chief Operating Officer
CFO: Linda Wilford CPA, Senior Vice President and Chief Financial Officer
CMO: Kenneth Homer M.D., Chief Medical Officer
CIO: Jeff Smith, Chief Information Officer
CNO: Taren Ruggiero R.N., MSN, Vice President and Chief Nursing Officer
Web address: www.holy–cross.com
Control: Other not–for–profit (including NFP Corporation) **Service**: General medical and surgical

Staffed Beds: 367 **Admissions**: 16349 **Census**: 213 **Outpatient Visits**: 170506 **Births**: 816 **Total Expense ($000)**: 333438 **Payroll Expense ($000)**: 111177 **Personnel**: 2544

IMPERIAL POINT MEDICAL CENTER See Broward Health Imperial Point

⊞ **KINDRED HOSPITAL SOUTH FLORIDA–FORT LAUDERDALE (102010)**, 1516 East Las Olas Boulevard, Zip 33301–2399; tel. 954/764–8900, (Nonreporting) (Includes KINDRED HOSPITAL SOUTH FLORIDA–CORAL GABLES, 5190 SW Eighth Street, Coral Gables, Florida, Zip 33134–2495, tel. 305/445–1364; Brian Soares, Chief Executive Officer; KINDRED HOSPITAL SOUTH FLORIDA–HOLLYWOOD, 1859 Van Buren Street, Hollywood, Florida, Zip 33020–5127, tel. 954/920–9000; Craig A Hoover, Administrator) **A**1 10 **S** Kindred Healthcare, Louisville, KY
Primary Contact: Michael S. Roffelsen, Chief Executive Officer
CFO: Dean Card, Chief Financial Officer
Web address: www.khfortlauderdale.com/
Control: Corporation, Investor–owned (for–profit) **Service**: Acute long–term care hospital

Staffed Beds: 123

FORT MYERS—Lee County

CHILDREN'S HOSPITAL OF SOUTHWEST FLORIDA See Lee Memorial Hospital

★ ⇧ **GULF COAST MEDICAL CENTER (100220)**, 13681 Doctor's Way, Zip 33912–4300; tel. 239/343–1000 **A**10 21 **F**3 11 13 17 18 20 22 24 26 28 29 30 40 45 46 49 60 64 70 74 76 77 79 80 81 84 85 86 87 91 93 102 107 108 111 115 118 119 130 138 146 **S** Lee Health, Fort Myers, FL
Primary Contact: Lawrence Antonucci, M.D., President and Chief Executive Officer
CFO: Ben Spence, Chief Financial Officer
CMO: Mark Greenberg M.D., Medical Director
CIO: Mike Smith, Chief Information Officer
CHR: Jon C Cecil, Chief Human Resource Officer
CNO: Lisa Sgarlata MSN, Chief Patient Care Officer
Web address: www.leememorial.org
Control: Hospital district or authority, Government, Nonfederal **Service**: General medical and surgical

Staffed Beds: 356 **Admissions**: 21913 **Census**: 266 **Outpatient Visits**: 77927 **Births**: 1560 **Personnel**: 1853

★ △ ⇧ **LEE MEMORIAL HOSPITAL (100012)**, 2776 Cleveland Avenue, Zip 33901–5855, Mailing Address: P.O.Box 2218, 33902–2218; tel. 239/343–2000, (Includes CHILDREN'S HOSPITAL OF SOUTHWEST FLORIDA, 9981 South HealthPark Drive, Fort Myers, Florida, Zip 33908, tel. 239/433–7799; James R Nathan, Chief Executive Officer; HEALTHPARK MEDICAL CENTER, 9981 South HealthPark Drive, Fort Myers, Florida, Zip 33908, tel. 239/433–7799; James R Nathan, Chief Executive Officer; THE REHABILITATION HOSPITAL, 2776 Cleveland Avenue, Fort Myers, Florida, Zip 33901, tel. 239/343–3900; James R Nathan, Chief Executive Officer) **A**2 3 7 10 21 **F**3 11 13 14 15 17 18 19 20 21 22 24 26 28 29 30 31 32 34 35 38 40 41 43 45 48 50 51 53 54 56 57 58 59 61 62 64 65 68 70 72 73 74 75 76 77 78 79 81 82 84 85 86 87 88 89 90 93 94 97 98 100 102 103 104 105 106 107 108 110 111 113 114 115 116 117 119 126 129 130 131 132 134 135 146 147 148 **S** Lee Health, Fort Myers, FL
Primary Contact: James R. Nathan, President and Chief Executive Officer
COO: Lawrence Antonucci M.D., Chief Operating Officer
CFO: Ben Spence, Chief Financial Officer
CMO: Alex Daneshmand D.O., Chief Patient Safety Officer
CIO: Mike Smith, Chief Information Officer
CHR: Jon C Cecil, Chief Human Resource Officer
CNO: Donna Giannuzzi R.N., Chief Nursing Officer
Web address: www.leememorial.org
Control: Hospital district or authority, Government, Nonfederal **Service**: General medical and surgical

Staffed Beds: 779 **Admissions**: 38504 **Census**: 494 **Outpatient Visits**: 172346 **Births**: 3291 **Personnel**: 3559

☐ **PARK ROYAL HOSPITAL (104074)**, 9241 Park Royal Drive, Zip 33908–9204; tel. 239/985–2700 (Nonreporting) **A**1 10 **S** Acadia Healthcare Company, Inc., Franklin, TN
Primary Contact: Michael Ham, Chief Executive Officer
CFO: Amy Ciampa, Chief Financial Officer
CHR: Robert Raynor, Human Resources Director
Web address: www.ParkRoyalHospital.com
Control: Corporation, Investor–owned (for–profit) **Service**: Psychiatric

Staffed Beds: 103

PROMISE HOSPITAL OF FORT MYERS (102029), 3050 Champion Ring Road, Zip 33905–5599; tel. 239/313–2900 (Nonreporting) **S** Promise Healthcare, Boca Raton, FL
Primary Contact: Patrick G. Ryan, Chief Executive Officer
Web address: www.promisefortmyers.com
Control: Corporation, Investor–owned (for–profit) **Service**: Acute long–term care hospital

Staffed Beds: 60

FORT PIERCE—St. Lucie County

⊞ △ **LAWNWOOD REGIONAL MEDICAL CENTER & HEART INSTITUTE (100246)**, 1700 South 23rd Street, Zip 34950–4803; tel. 772/461–4000, (Nonreporting) (Includes LAWNWOOD PAVILION, 1860 North Lawnwood Circle, Fort Pierce, Florida, Zip 34950, P O Box 1540, 34954–1540, tel. 361/466–1500) **A**1 7 10 **S** HCA Healthcare, Nashville, TN
Primary Contact: Robert M. Krieger, Chief Executive Officer
CFO: Robert Dunwoody, Chief Financial Officer
CIO: Eric Castle, Director Information Services
CHR: Pam Burchell, Director Human Resources
Web address: www.lawnwoodmed.com
Control: Corporation, Investor–owned (for–profit) **Service**: General medical and surgical

Staffed Beds: 331

FORT WALTON BEACH—Okaloosa County

⊞ **FORT WALTON BEACH MEDICAL CENTER (100223)**, 1000 Mar–Walt Drive, Zip 32547–6795; tel. 850/862–1111, (Nonreporting) **A**1 2 3 10 **S** HCA Healthcare, Nashville, TN
Primary Contact: Mitchell P. Mongell, FACHE, Chief Executive Officer
CFO: Jeffrey Steve Moore, Chief Financial Officer
CMO: ColonelTama Van Decar M.D., Chief Medical Officer
CIO: Amy Caldeira, Director Information Technology and Systems
CHR: Julia Truman, Vice President Human Resources
CNO: Holly McGucken R.N., Chief Nursing Officer
Web address: www.fwbmc.com
Control: Corporation, Investor–owned (for–profit) **Service**: General medical and surgical

Staffed Beds: 257

GAINESVILLE—Alachua County

⊞ **NORTH FLORIDA REGIONAL MEDICAL CENTER (100204)**, 6500 Newberry Road, Zip 32605–4392, Mailing Address: P.O.Box 147006, 32614–7006; tel. 352/333–4000 **A**1 2 3 10 **F**3 12 13 15 17 18 20 22 24 26 28 29 30 31 34 35 37 40 42 45 46 48 49 50 51 56 57 59 60 64 70 72 74 75 76 77 78 79 80 81 85 86 87 98 107 108 109 110 111 113 114 115 116 117 118 119 120 121 123 124 126 129 130 132 135 145 146 147 148 149 **S** HCA Healthcare, Nashville, TN
Primary Contact: Brian Cook, FACHE, President and Chief Executive Officer
CFO: Jay St Pierre, Chief Financial Officer
CMO: Ann Weber M.D., Chief Medical Officer
CIO: Eric Strand, Director Information Services
CHR: Jane Fuller, Vice President Human Resources
CNO: Natalie Ransom, Chief Nursing Officer
Web address: www.nfrmc.com
Control: Corporation, Investor–owned (for–profit) **Service**: General medical and surgical

Staffed Beds: 432 **Admissions**: 26525 **Census**: 290 **Births**: 3363 **Total Expense ($000)**: 339281 **Payroll Expense ($000)**: 94647

FL

Hospital, Medicare Provider Number, Address, Telephone, Approval, Facility, and Physician Codes, Health Care System

★ American Hospital Association (AHA) membership   ○ Healthcare Facilities Accreditation Program   ⇧ Center for Improvement in Healthcare Quality Accreditation
☐ The Joint Commission accreditation   ◇ DNV Healthcare Inc. accreditation   △ Commission on Accreditation of Rehabilitation Facilities (CARF) accreditation

© 2017 AHA Guide   *Many Facility Codes have changed. Please refer to the AHA Guide Code Chart.*   Hospitals **A125**

⊞ **NORTH FLORIDA/SOUTH GEORGIA VETERAN'S HEALTH SYSTEM**, 1601 SW Archer Road, Zip 32608–1135; tel. 352/376–1611, (Includes GAINESVILLE VETERANS AFFAIRS MEDICAL CENTER, 1601 SW Archer Road, Gainesville, Florida, Zip 32608–1197, tel. 352/376–1611; LAKE CITY VETERANS AFFAIRS MEDICAL CENTER, 619 South Marion Avenue, Lake City, Florida, Zip 32025–5898, tel. 386/755–3016) (Total facility includes 250 beds in nursing home–type unit) **A**1 3 5 **F**3 5 8 9 10 11 12 15 17 18 20 22 24 26 28 29 30 31 34 35 36 38 39 40 44 45 46 47 48 49 51 54 55 56 57 58 59 60 61 62 63 64 65 66 68 70 74 75 77 78 79 81 82 83 84 85 86 87 91 92 93 94 97 98 100 101 102 103 104 105 106 107 108 109 110 111 114 115 116 117 118 119 127 128 129 130 131 132 133 135 136 141 143 144 145 146 147 148 149 **P**6 **S** Department of Veterans Affairs, Washington, DC
Primary Contact: Thomas Wisnieski, FACHE, Director
COO: Thomas Sutton, Associate Director
CFO: Jim Taylor, Chief Business Office
CMO: Brad Bender M.D., Chief of Staff
CIO: Deborah Michel–Ogborn, Chief Information Resource Management
CHR: Michelle Manderino, Chief Human Resources
Web address: www.northflorida.va.gov
Control: Veterans Affairs, Government, federal **Service:** General medical and surgical

Staffed Beds: 623 **Admissions:** 12391 **Census:** 381 **Outpatient Visits:** 1423213 **Births:** 0 **Personnel:** 5460

⊞ **SELECT SPECIALTY HOSPITAL–GAINESVILLE (102022)**, 2708 SW Archer Road, Zip 32608–1316; tel. 352/337–3240, (Nonreporting) **A**1 10 **S** Select Medical Corporation, Mechanicsburg, PA
Primary Contact: Ronnie Wagley, Market Chief Executive Officer
Web address: www.gainesville.selectspecialtyhospitals.com/
Control: Corporation, Investor–owned (for–profit) **Service:** Acute long–term care hospital

Staffed Beds: 44

⊞ △ **UF HEALTH SHANDS HOSPITAL (100113)**, 1600 SW Archer Road, Zip 32610–3003, Mailing Address: PO Box 100326, 32610–0326; tel. 352/265–0111, (Includes UF HEALTH SHANDS CANCER HOSPITAL, 1515 SW Archer Road, Gainesville, Florida, Zip 32608–1134, PO Box 100014, 32610–0014, tel. 352/265–0111; Edward Jimenez, Chief Executive Officer; UF HEALTH SHANDS CHILDREN'S HOSPITAL, 1600 SW Archer Road, Gainesville, Florida, Zip 32610–3003, PO Box 100326, 32610–0326, tel. 352/265–0111; Edward Jimenez, Chief Executive Officer; UF HEALTH SHANDS PSYCHIATRIC HOSPITAL, 4101 NW 89th Boulevard, Gainesville, Florida, Zip 32606, tel. 352/265–5481; Edward Jimenez, Chief Executive Officer; UF HEALTH SHANDS REHAB HOSPITAL, 4101 NW 89th Boulevard, Gainesville, Florida, Zip 32606–3813, tel. 352/265–5499; Edward Jimenez, Chief Executive Officer) **A**1 2 3 5 7 8 10 **F**2 3 4 5 6 7 9 11 12 13 15 16 17 18 19 20 21 22 23 24 25 26 27 28 29 30 31 32 34 35 36 37 38 39 40 41 42 43 44 45 46 47 48 49 50 51 52 53 54 55 56 57 58 59 60 61 62 63 64 65 66 68 69 70 72 73 74 75 76 77 78 79 80 81 82 84 85 86 87 88 89 90 91 92 93 94 96 97 98 99 100 101 102 103 104 105 107 108 109 110 111 114 115 116 117 118 119 120 121 123 124 126 129 130 131 132 134 135 136 137 138 139 140 141 142 143 144 145 146 147 148 149 150 **P**6 **S** UF Health Shands, Gainesville, FL
Primary Contact: Edward Jimenez, Chief Executive Officer
CFO: James J. Kelly Jr, Senior Vice President and Chief Financial Officer
CMO: Parker Gibbs M.D., Chief Medical Officer
CIO: Kari Cassel, Senior Vice President and Chief Information Officer
CHR: Janet L. Christie, Senior Vice President Human Resources
CNO: Irene Alexaitis R.N., Vice President of Nursing and Patient Services and Chief Nursing Officer
Web address: www.ufhealth.org/
Control: Other not–for–profit (including NFP Corporation) **Service:** General medical and surgical

Staffed Beds: 966 **Admissions:** 47176 **Census:** 812 **Outpatient Visits:** 1021669 **Births:** 2680 **Total Expense ($000):** 1217232 **Payroll Expense ($000):** 443371 **Personnel:** 7991

UF HEALTH SHANDS REHAB HOSPITAL See UF Health Shands Hospital

CAMPBELLTON GRACEVILLE HOSPITAL (101302), 5429 College Drive, Zip 32440–1897; tel. 850/263–4431 **A**10 18 **F**40 67 75 93 107 119 127 128 133 146 149 150
Primary Contact: George Perez, Chief Executive Officer
CFO: Dena Cooper, Chief Financial Officer
CMO: Steve Davis M.D., Chief Medical Officer
CHR: Judy Austin, Director Human Resources
Web address: www.c–ghospital.com
Control: Hospital district or authority, Government, Nonfederal **Service:** General medical and surgical

Staffed Beds: 25 **Admissions:** 90 **Census:** 3 **Births:** 0

⊞ **KINDRED HOSPITAL NORTH FLORIDA (102015)**, 801 Oak Street, Zip 32043–4317; tel. 904/284–9230 **A**1 10 **F**1 3 29 62 85 91 107 119 148 **P**5 **S** Kindred Healthcare, Louisville, KY
Primary Contact: Patrick McVey, Chief Executive Officer
CFO: Rickie Simmons, Controller
CMO: Uriel Nazario M.D., Chief of Medical Staff
CIO: Rick Chapman, Chief Information Officer
CNO: Ashley McRae, Chief Clinical Officer
Web address: www.khnorthflorida.com
Control: Corporation, Investor–owned (for–profit) **Service:** Acute long–term care hospital

Staffed Beds: 80 **Admissions:** 709 **Census:** 56 **Outpatient Visits:** 8 **Births:** 0 **Total Expense ($000):** 30874 **Payroll Expense ($000):** 11529 **Personnel:** 219

⊞ **GULF BREEZE HOSPITAL (100266)**, 1110 Gulf Breeze Parkway, Zip 32561–4884; tel. 850/934–2000 **A**1 3 10 **F**3 8 11 15 20 26 29 30 31 40 44 45 46 50 54 57 59 64 68 70 74 75 78 79 81 82 84 85 86 91 93 106 107 110 111 114 119 120 121 123 129 130 131 132 143 146 147 148 **S** Baptist Health Care Corporation, Pensacola, FL
Primary Contact: Scott Raynes, President
CFO: Kerry Vermillion, Senior Vice President Finance and Chief Financial Officer
Web address: www.ebaptisthealthcare.org/GulfBreezeHospital/
Control: Other not–for–profit (including NFP Corporation) **Service:** General medical and surgical

Staffed Beds: 61 **Admissions:** 4090 **Census:** 40 **Outpatient Visits:** 126399 **Births:** 0 **Total Expense ($000):** 95426 **Payroll Expense ($000):** 25546 **Personnel:** 492

⊞ **HIALEAH HOSPITAL (100053)**, 651 East 25th Street, Zip 33013–3878; tel. 305/693–6100 **A**1 10 **F**3 12 13 15 18 24 29 31 34 40 41 49 56 57 59 60 61 63 68 70 72 74 76 77 79 81 82 85 93 98 102 107 111 115 119 126 129 130 132 147 148 149 **S** TENET Healthcare Corporation, Dallas, TX
Primary Contact: Ben A. Rodriguez, Chief Executive Officer
CFO: Gary Nymoen, Chief Financial Officer
CMO: Orlando Garcia M.D., Chief Medical Officer
CHR: Yamila Herrera, Director Human Resources
CNO: Lourdes Camps R.N., Chief Nursing Officer
Web address: www.hialeahhosp.com
Control: Corporation, Investor–owned (for–profit) **Service:** General medical and surgical

Staffed Beds: 191 **Admissions:** 13509 **Census:** 137 **Births:** 1552 **Total Expense ($000):** 131025 **Payroll Expense ($000):** 50082

☐ **PALM SPRINGS GENERAL HOSPITAL (100050)**, 1475 West 49th Street, Zip 33012–3275, Mailing Address: P.O.Box 2804, 33012–2804; tel. 305/558–2500, (Data for 335 days)**A**1 10 12 **F**3 8 18 29 31 34 35 40 41 45 46 47 49 50 51 53 56 57 60 61 62 64 65 68 70 74 75 77 78 79 81 82 91 92 93 102 103 107 108 109 114 115 117 119 124 126 130 135 148 **P**8
Primary Contact: Nicholas T. Smith, Chief Executive Officer
CFO: Tony Milian, Chief Financial Officer
CHR: Lourdes Anton, Director Human Resources
Web address: www.psghosp.com
Control: Individual, Investor–owned (for–profit) **Service:** General medical and surgical

Staffed Beds: 130 **Admissions:** 5579 **Census:** 80 **Outpatient Visits:** 18799 **Births:** 0 **Total Expense ($000):** 53601 **Payroll Expense ($000):** 25304 **Personnel:** 734

⊞ **PALMETTO GENERAL HOSPITAL (100187)**, 2001 West 68th Street, Zip 33016–1898; tel. 305/823–5000, (Nonreporting) **A**1 5 10 12 13 **S** TENET Healthcare Corporation, Dallas, TX
Primary Contact: Ana J. Mederos, Chief Executive Officer
COO: Georgina Diaz, Chief Operating Officer
CFO: Oscar Vicente, Chief Financial Officer
CMO: Eloy Roman M.D., Chief of Staff
CHR: Ana Gonzalez–Fajardo, Human Resources Director
CNO: Barbara Vazquez, Chief Nursing Officer
Web address: www.palmettogeneral.com
Control: Corporation, Investor–owned (for–profit) **Service:** General medical and surgical

Staffed Beds: 360

HIALEAH—Dade County

SOUTHERN WINDS HOSPITAL See Westchester General Hospital, Miami

HOLLYWOOD—Broward County

☐ **LARKIN BEHAVIORAL HEALTH SERVICES (104015)**, 1201 North 37th Avenue, Zip 33021–5498; tel. 954/962–1355 **A1 F**98 100 101 103 105 106
Primary Contact: Iris Berges, Chief Executive Officer
COO: Christopher Gabel, Chief Operating Officer
CFO: Rocky Davidson, Chief Financial Officer
CHR: Len Alpert, Director Human Resources
Web address: www.hollywoodpavilion.com
Control: State, Government, Nonfederal **Service**: Psychiatric

Staffed Beds: 50 **Admissions:** 582 **Census:** 23 **Outpatient Visits:** 0 **Births:** 0 **Total Expense ($000):** 4601 **Payroll Expense ($000):** 2126

⊞ △ **MEMORIAL REGIONAL HOSPITAL (100038)**, 3501 Johnson Street, Zip 33021–5421; tel. 954/987–2000, (Includes JOE DIMAGGIO CHILDREN'S HOSPITAL, 1005 Joe DiMaggio Drive, Hollywood, Florida, Zip 33021–5426, tel. 954/987–2000; Chantal Leconte, FACHE, Chief Executive Officer; MEMORIAL REGIONAL HOSPITAL SOUTH, 3600 Washington Street, Hollywood, Florida, Zip 33021–8216, tel. 954/966–4500; Douglas Zaren, FACHE, Administrator and CEO) **A**1 2 3 5 7 8 10 **F**3 5 11 12 13 15 17 18 19 20 21 22 23 24 25 26 27 28 29 30 31 32 34 37 38 39 40 41 43 44 45 46 47 49 50 51 53 54 55 56 57 58 59 60 61 64 65 66 67 68 70 71 72 73 74 75 76 77 78 79 81 82 84 85 87 88 89 90 91 93 95 96 97 98 99 100 101 102 103 104 107 108 110 111 114 115 119 120 121 123 126 129 130 131 132 134 135 137 145 146 147 148 149 150 **P**1 6 **S** Memorial Healthcare System, Hollywood, FL
Primary Contact: Zeff Ross, FACHE, Executive Vice President and Chief Executive Officer
CFO: Walter Bussell, Chief Financial Officer
CMO: Donald Kim M.D., Chief Medical Officer
CIO: Forest Blanton, Administrator Process Engineering
CHR: Margie Vargas, Chief Human Resources Officer
Web address: www.mhs.net
Control: Hospital district or authority, Government, Nonfederal **Service**: General medical and surgical

Staffed Beds: 1057 **Admissions:** 37085 **Census:** 636 **Outpatient Visits:** 441978 **Births:** 5143 **Total Expense ($000):** 902446 **Payroll Expense ($000):** 368316 **Personnel:** 5221

☐ **SOUTH FLORIDA STATE HOSPITAL (104001)**, 800 East Cypress Drive, Zip 33025–4543; tel. 954/392–3000, (Nonreporting) **A1** 10
Primary Contact: Lee Packer, Administrator
Web address: www.geocarellc.com/Locations/SouthFloridaStateHospital
Control: State, Government, Nonfederal **Service**: Psychiatric

Staffed Beds: 355

HOMESTEAD—Miami—Dade County

⊞ **BAPTIST HEALTH SOUTH FLORIDA, HOMESTEAD HOSPITAL (100125)**, 975 Baptist Way, Zip 33033–7600; tel. 786/243–8000 **A1** 10 **F**3 11 13 15 18 29 30 31 34 35 40 41 45 47 49 50 51 53 57 58 59 60 61 63 64 68 70 74 75 76 78 79 81 82 84 85 86 87 89 93 102 107 108 110 111 114 115 119 129 130 131 132 134 135 145 146 147 148 149 150 **S** Baptist Health South Florida, Coral Gables, FL
Primary Contact: William M. Duquette, Chief Executive Officer
COO: Kenneth R Spell, Vice President Operations
CFO: David Abercrombie, Controller
CMO: George R. Tershakovec M.D., President Medical Staff
CIO: Mimi Taylor, Corporate Vice President Information Technology
CHR: Adriene McCoy MS, Corporate Vice President
CNO: Nancy Gail Gordon R.N., MSN, Chief Nursing Officer and Vice President of Nursing
Web address: www.baptisthealth.net
Control: Other not–for–profit (including NFP Corporation) **Service**: General medical and surgical

Staffed Beds: 142 **Admissions:** 11003 **Census:** 100 **Outpatient Visits:** 121759 **Births:** 1611 **Total Expense ($000):** 215812 **Payroll Expense ($000):** 76081 **Personnel:** 1023

HUDSON—Pasco County

⊞ **REGIONAL MEDICAL CENTER BAYONET POINT (100256)**, 14000 Fivay Road, Zip 34667–7199; tel. 727/869–5400 **A1** 2 10 13 **F**3 17 18 20 22 24 26 28 29 30 31 34 35 40 41 43 45 46 48 49 50 51 56 57 58 59 60 64 70 74 75 77 78 79 81 84 85 86 87 91 94 100 107 108 109 111 114 115 118 119 129 130 132 135 141 143 146 148 **S** HCA Healthcare, Nashville, TN
Primary Contact: Shayne George, Chief Executive Officer
COO: Joe Rudisill, Chief Operating Officer
CFO: Thomas Lawhorne, Chief Financial Officer
CMO: Joseph Pino M.D., Chief Medical Officer
CIO: Mike Wilms, Director Information Systems
CHR: Geoffrey A Washburn, Vice President
CNO: Tanya Simpson, Chief Nursing Officer
Web address: www.rmchealth.com
Control: Corporation, Investor–owned (for–profit) **Service**: General medical and surgical

Staffed Beds: 290 **Admissions:** 15004 **Census:** 194 **Outpatient Visits:** 71302 **Births:** 0 **Total Expense ($000):** 179977 **Payroll Expense ($000):** 59896 **Personnel:** 1064

INVERNESS—Citrus County

⊞ **CITRUS MEMORIAL HEALTH SYSTEM (100023)**, 502 West Highland Boulevard, Zip 34452–4754; tel. 352/726–1551 **A1** 10 19 **F**17 18 20 22 24 28 29 30 31 34 35 40 45 46 49 57 59 64 65 70 75 76 78 79 81 82 84 85 86 87 93 94 102 105 107 108 111 114 115 119 124 132 135 146 147 148 149 **S** HCA Healthcare, Nashville, TN
Primary Contact: Ralph A. Aleman, President and Chief Executive Officer
CFO: Mark Williams, Chief Financial Officer
CMO: C. Toumbis M.D., Chief of Staff
CIO: Nick Brooks, Director of Information Systems
CHR: Lee Glotzback, Director Human Resources
CNO: Linda M McCarthy R.N., VP/ Chief Nursing Officer
Web address: www.citrusmh.com
Control: Corporation, Investor–owned (for–profit) **Service**: General medical and surgical

Staffed Beds: 204 **Admissions:** 10264 **Census:** 117 **Births:** 465 **Total Expense ($000):** 136021 **Payroll Expense ($000):** 40447

JACKSONVILLE—Duval County

⊞ **BAPTIST MEDICAL CENTER JACKSONVILLE (100088)**, 800 Prudential Drive, Zip 32207–8202; tel. 904/202–2000, (Includes BAPTIST MEDICAL CENTER SOUTH, 14550 St Augustine Road, Jacksonville, Florida, Zip 32258–2160, tel. 904/821–6000; Nicole B. Thomas, President; WOLFSON CHILDREN'S HOSPITAL, 800 Prudential Drive, Jacksonville, Florida, Zip 32207, tel. 904/202–8000; Michael D Aubin, President) **A1** 2 3 5 10 **F**3 5 6 8 11 12 13 15 17 18 19 20 21 22 23 24 25 26 27 28 29 30 31 32 34 35 36 37 38 39 40 41 42 45 46 47 48 49 50 51 53 54 55 56 57 58 59 60 61 62 64 68 70 72 73 74 75 76 77 78 79 80 81 82 83 85 86 87 88 89 92 93 94 98 99 100 101 102 103 104 105 107 108 109 110 111 112 113 114 115 116 117 118 119 120 121 123 124 126 129 130 132 134 135 136 145 146 147 148 149 **P**6 **S** Baptist Health, Jacksonville, FL
Primary Contact: Michael A. Mayo, FACHE, President
COO: John F Wilbanks FACHE, Chief Operating Officer
CFO: Scott Wooten, Senior Vice President and Chief Financial Officer
CMO: Keith L Stein M.D., Senior Vice President Medical Affairs and Chief Medical Officer
CIO: Roland Garcia, Senior Vice President and Chief Information Officer
CHR: M. Beth Mehaffey, SHRM–SCP, Senior Vice President Human Resources
Web address: www.e–baptisthealth.com
Control: Other not–for–profit (including NFP Corporation) **Service**: General medical and surgical

Staffed Beds: 927 **Admissions:** 52365 **Census:** 699 **Outpatient Visits:** 509708 **Births:** 4655 **Total Expense ($000):** 1011668 **Payroll Expense ($000):** 294319 **Personnel:** 5762

FL

Hospital, Medicare Provider Number, Address, Telephone, Approval, Facility, and Physician Codes, Health Care System

★ American Hospital Association (AHA) membership   ◯ Healthcare Facilities Accreditation Program   ⇑ Center for Improvement in Healthcare Quality Accreditation
☐ The Joint Commission accreditation   ◇ DNV Healthcare Inc. accreditation   △ Commission on Accreditation of Rehabilitation Facilities (CARF) accreditation

☒ △ **BROOKS REHABILITATION HOSPITAL (103039)**, 3599 University Boulevard South, Zip 32216–4252; tel. 904/345–7600 **A**1 3 7 10 **F**10 29 30 54 62 64 90 91 93 95 96 130 132 146 149
Primary Contact: Douglas M. Baer, Chief Executive Officer
COO: Michael Spigel, Executive Vice President & Chief Operating Officer
CMO: Trevor Paris M.D., Medical Director
CIO: Karen Green, Chief Information Officer
CHR: Karen Gallagher, Vice President Human Resources and Learning
CNO: Joanne Hoertz, Vice President of Nursing
Web address: www.brookshealth.org
Control: Other not–for–profit (including NFP Corporation) **Service**: Rehabilitation

Staffed Beds: 144 **Admissions**: 2941 **Census**: 132 **Outpatient Visits**: 290501 **Births**: 0 **Personnel**: 434

★ **MAYO CLINIC JACKSONVILLE (100151)**, 4500 San Pablo Road South, Zip 32224–1865; tel. 904/953–2000 **A**2 3 5 8 10 **F**3 6 8 9 11 12 14 15 17 18 20 22 24 26 28 29 30 31 34 35 36 37 39 40 44 45 46 47 48 49 50 51 54 55 56 57 58 59 60 61 64 65 68 70 74 75 77 78 79 80 81 82 84 85 86 87 92 93 96 97 100 103 104 105 107 108 110 111 112 114 115 116 117 118 119 120 121 123 124 126 129 130 131 132 135 136 137 138 139 140 141 142 145 146 148 149 **P**6 **S** Mayo Clinic, Rochester, MN
Primary Contact: Gianrico Farrugia, M.D., Vice President and Chief Executive Officer
CFO: Kevin Lockett, Interim Chief Financial Officer
CMO: Nancy Dawson M.D., Medical Director
CIO: John Crooks, Chair Information Services
CHR: Daniel Tomlinson, Chair Human Resources
CNO: Ryannon Frederick, Chief Nursing Officer
Web address: www.mayoclinic.org/jacksonville/
Control: Other not–for–profit (including NFP Corporation) **Service**: General medical and surgical

Staffed Beds: 259 **Admissions**: 12495 **Census**: 173 **Outpatient Visits**: 48576 **Births**: 0 **Personnel**: 2643

☒ **MEMORIAL HOSPITAL JACKSONVILLE (100179)**, 3625 University Blvd South, Zip 32216–4207, Mailing Address: P.O.Box 16325, 32245–6325; tel. 904/702–6111 **A**1 2 3 10 **F**3 4 11 12 13 15 17 18 20 22 24 26 28 29 30 32 34 35 38 40 41 42 43 45 47 48 49 51 53 54 55 56 57 58 59 64 65 70 72 74 75 76 77 78 79 81 82 84 87 88 89 97 98 100 101 102 103 104 105 107 108 110 111 114 115 116 117 118 119 124 126 130 146 147 148 149 **S** HCA Healthcare, Nashville, TN
Primary Contact: Bradley S. Talbert, FACHE, President and Chief Executive Officer
COO: Bobby McCullough, Chief Operating Officer
CFO: Andy Miller, Chief Financial Officer
CMO: Aaron West M.D., Chief Medical Officer
CIO: Lance Penton, Director, Information Services
CHR: Stuart Thompson, Vice President Human Resources
CNO: Suzanne Woods, Senior Vice President of Nursing
Web address: www.memorialhospitaljax.com
Control: Corporation, Investor–owned (for–profit) **Service**: General medical and surgical

Staffed Beds: 410 **Admissions**: 22439 **Census**: 282 **Outpatient Visits**: 155979 **Births**: 1446 **Total Expense ($000)**: 301115 **Payroll Expense ($000)**: 99869

☒ **NAVAL HOSPITAL JACKSONVILLE**, 2080 Child Street, Zip 32214–5000; tel. 904/542–7300, (Nonreporting) **A**1 3 5 **S** Bureau of Medicine and Surgery, Department of the Navy, Falls Church, VA
Primary Contact: Commander Darryl Green, Director Administration
CFO: Lieutenant CommanderMichael Gregonis, Comptroller
CMO: CaptainChristopher Quarles M.D., Director Medical Services
CIO: Mike Haytaian, Head Director Information Resources Management
CHR: CaptainRuby Tennyson, Director Administration
Web address: www.med.navy.mil/SITES/NAVALHOSPITALJAX/Pages/default.aspx
Control: Navy, Government, federal **Service**: General medical and surgical

Staffed Beds: 64

☐ **RIVER POINT BEHAVIORAL HEALTH (104016)**, 6300 Beach Boulevard, Zip 32216–2782; tel. 904/724–9202, (Nonreporting) **A**1 10 **S** Universal Health Services, Inc., King of Prussia, PA
Primary Contact: Kevin McGee, Chief Executive Officer
CFO: Jenni Stackhouse, Chief Financial Officer
CIO: Bill Willis, Director Information Technology
CHR: Cathy Calhoun, Director Human Resources
Web address: www.riverpointbehavioral.com
Control: Corporation, Investor–owned (for–profit) **Service**: Psychiatric

Staffed Beds: 92

☒ **SPECIALTY HOSPITAL JACKSONVILLE (102012)**, 4901 Richard Street, Zip 32207–7328; tel. 904/737–3120 **A**1 10 **F**1 18 29 60 75 85 119 130 148 **S** HCA Healthcare, Nashville, TN
Primary Contact: Barbara McCarthy, Chief Executive Officer
CFO: Joshua Szostek, Chief Financial Officer
CMO: Wendell H Williams M.D., Jr, Medical Director
CIO: Patrick Adesso, Director Information Technology and Systems
CHR: Lisa Ayala R.N., Director Human Resources
Web address: www.specialtyhospitaljax.com
Control: Corporation, Investor–owned (for–profit) **Service**: Acute long–term care hospital

Staffed Beds: 62 **Admissions**: 431 **Census**: 31 **Outpatient Visits**: 0 **Births**: 0 **Total Expense ($000)**: 27405 **Payroll Expense ($000)**: 10840

☒ **ST. VINCENT'S MEDICAL CENTER RIVERSIDE (100040)**, 1 Shircliff Way, Zip 32204–4748, Mailing Address: P.O.Box 2982, 32203–2982; tel. 904/308–7300 **A**1 2 3 10 13 **F**3 12 13 15 17 18 20 22 24 26 28 29 30 31 34 40 44 45 46 47 48 49 53 55 57 58 61 64 65 70 72 74 76 78 79 81 85 86 87 91 93 107 108 110 111 114 115 118 119 120 121 123 124 126 130 131 132 146 147 149 **S** Ascension Healthcare, Saint Louis, MO
Primary Contact: Thomas J. VanOsdol, Chief Executive Officer
CFO: Pamela Hess, Chief Financial Officer
CMO: Kenneth Rothfield M.D., System Vice President and Chief Medical Officer
CIO: Ann Carey, Vice President and Chief Information Officer
CHR: Michelle Adamolekun, Chief Human Resource Officer
CNO: Lorraine Keith, Chief Nursing Officer
Web address: www.jaxhealth.com
Control: Church operated, Nongovernment, not–for–profit **Service**: General medical and surgical

Staffed Beds: 482 **Admissions**: 24956 **Census**: 322 **Outpatient Visits**: 114852 **Births**: 1776 **Total Expense ($000)**: 414399 **Payroll Expense ($000)**: 130308 **Personnel**: 2321

☒ **ST. VINCENT'S MEDICAL CENTER SOUTHSIDE (100307)**, 4201 Belfort Road, Zip 32216–1431; tel. 904/296–3700 **A**1 5 10 **F**3 12 13 15 18 20 22 26 29 30 31 34 40 44 47 49 57 60 61 64 65 70 72 74 76 78 79 81 85 86 87 93 96 107 108 110 111 114 115 119 126 128 130 131 132 146 147 149 **S** Ascension Healthcare, Saint Louis, MO
Primary Contact: Thomas J. VanOsdol, Chief Executive Officer
CFO: Pamela Hess, Chief Financial Officer
CIO: Ann Carey, Chief Information Officer
CHR: Kaye W Lunsford, System Director Human Resources
CNO: Lorraine Keith, Chief Nursing Officer
Web address: www.jaxhealth.com
Control: Church operated, Nongovernment, not–for–profit **Service**: General medical and surgical

Staffed Beds: 288 **Admissions**: 11827 **Census**: 133 **Outpatient Visits**: 44424 **Births**: 1658 **Total Expense ($000)**: 166762 **Payroll Expense ($000)**: 47624 **Personnel**: 801

☒ **UF HEALTH JACKSONVILLE (100001)**, 655 West Eighth Street, Zip 32209–6595; tel. 904/244–0411, (Total facility includes 56 beds in nursing home–type unit) **A**1 3 5 8 10 **F**3 5 8 11 12 13 15 17 18 20 22 24 26 28 29 30 31 32 34 35 36 37 38 39 40 41 42 43 44 45 46 47 50 51 52 53 54 55 56 57 58 59 60 62 64 65 66 68 70 71 72 74 75 76 77 78 79 81 82 84 85 86 87 88 92 93 94 96 97 98 99 100 101 102 103 104 105 107 108 109 110 111 114 115 116 117 118 119 120 121 123 124 126 128 129 130 131 132 134 135 141 145 146 147 148 149 150 **S** UF Health Shands, Gainesville, FL
Primary Contact: Russell Armistead, Chief Executive Officer
COO: Greg Miller, Senior Vice President Operations
CFO: William Ryan, Vice President and Chief Financial Officer
CMO: David Vukich M.D., Senior Vice President, Chief Medical Officer and Chief Quality Officer
CIO: Kari Cassel, Senior Vice President and Chief Information Officer
CHR: Lesli Ward, Vice President Human Resources
CNO: Patrice I. Jones R.N., MSN, Vice President and Chief Nursing Officer
Web address: www.ufhealthjax.org/
Control: Other not–for–profit (including NFP Corporation) **Service**: General medical and surgical

Staffed Beds: 589 **Admissions**: 26869 **Census**: 451 **Outpatient Visits**: 535524 **Births**: 3068 **Total Expense ($000)**: 667552 **Payroll Expense ($000)**: 227249 **Personnel**: 4153

☐ **WEKIVA SPRINGS (104069)**, 3947 Salisbury Road, Zip 32216–6115; tel. 904/296–3533 (Nonreporting) **A**1 10 **S** Universal Health Services, Inc., King of Prussia, PA
Primary Contact: Sheila Carr, Chief Executive Officer
Web address: www.wekivacenter.com
Control: Other not–for–profit (including NFP Corporation) **Service**: Psychiatric

Staffed Beds: 60

FL

JACKSONVILLE BEACH—Duval County

☒ **BAPTIST MEDICAL CENTER BEACHES (100117)**, 1350 13th Avenue South, Zip 32250–3205; tel. 904/627–2900 **A**1 10 **F**3 8 11 13 15 18 20 28 29 30 31 36 40 43 45 49 50 53 54 57 59 61 64 74 75 76 77 78 79 80 81 82 85 86 93 107 108 110 111 114 115 118 119 126 129 130 146 147 148 **S** Baptist Health, Jacksonville, FL
Primary Contact: Joseph M. Mitrick, FACHE, President
COO: John F Wilbanks FACHE, Chief Operating Officer
CFO: Scott Wooten, Senior Vice President and Chief Financial Officer
CMO: Keith L Stein M.D., Chief Medical Officer
CIO: Roland Garcia, Senior Vice President and Chief Information Officer
CHR: Dana Voiselle, Director Human Resources and Community Relations
Web address: www.community.e–baptisthealth.com/bmc/beaches/index.html
Control: Other not–for–profit (including NFP Corporation) **Service**: General medical and surgical

Staffed Beds: 135 **Admissions**: 7779 **Census**: 79 **Outpatient Visits**: 82166 **Births**: 1052 **Total Expense ($000)**: 112751 **Payroll Expense ($000)**: 36628 **Personnel**: 646

JAY—Santa Rosa County

★ **JAY HOSPITAL (100048)**, 14114 South Alabama Street, Zip 32565–1219; tel. 850/675–8000 **A**10 **F**3 11 15 18 29 30 34 35 40 45 48 50 57 59 64 75 77 81 82 85 93 107 110 114 119 127 130 133 **S** Baptist Health Care Corporation, Pensacola, FL
Primary Contact: Michael T. Hutchins, Administrator
CFO: Keith Strickling, Chief Accountant
CMO: C David Smith M.D., Chief Medical Officer
CHR: Heather Suggs, Manager Human Resources
CNO: Patsy Jackson, Director of Nursing
Web address: www.bhcpns.org/jayhospital/
Control: Other not–for–profit (including NFP Corporation) **Service**: General medical and surgical

Staffed Beds: 21 **Admissions**: 639 **Census**: 8 **Outpatient Visits**: 19085 **Births**: 0 **Total Expense ($000)**: 12274 **Payroll Expense ($000)**: 5500 **Personnel**: 109

JUPITER—Palm Beach County

☒ **JUPITER MEDICAL CENTER (100253)**, 1210 South Old Dixie Highway, Zip 33458–7299; tel. 561/263–2234 **A**1 2 10 **F**3 8 11 12 13 15 18 19 20 22 28 29 30 31 34 35 36 37 40 41 44 45 46 47 48 49 50 53 54 55 57 58 59 64 65 66 70 71 74 75 76 77 78 79 80 81 82 84 85 86 87 89 93 107 108 109 110 111 114 115 116 117 118 119 120 121 123 126 129 130 132 135 143 144 145 146 147 148 **P**8
Primary Contact: Steven Seeley, Interim President and Chief Operating Officer
COO: Steven Seeley, Vice President, Chief Operating Officer, Chief Nursing Officer
CFO: Dale E Hocking, Chief Financial Officer
CIO: Tom Crawford, Chief Information Officer
CHR: Peter Gloggner, Chief Human Resources Officer
CNO: Steven Seeley, Vice President, Chief Operating Officer, Chief Nursing Officer
Web address: www.jupitermed.com
Control: Other not–for–profit (including NFP Corporation) **Service**: General medical and surgical

Staffed Beds: 207 **Admissions**: 10715 **Census**: 123 **Outpatient Visits**: 151053 **Births**: 1329 **Total Expense ($000)**: 200414 **Payroll Expense ($000)**: 71789 **Personnel**: 1259

KEY WEST—Monroe County

☒ **LOWER KEYS MEDICAL CENTER (100150)**, 5900 College Road, Zip 33040–4396, Mailing Address: P.O.Box 9107, 33041–9107; tel. 305/294–5531, (Nonreporting) (Includes DE POO HOSPITAL, 1200 Kennedy Drive, Key West, Florida, Zip 33041, tel. 305/294–4692) **A**1 10 **S** Community Health Systems, Inc., Franklin, TN
Primary Contact: David Clay, Chief Executive Officer
COO: Meylan Love–Watler, Chief Operating Officer
CFO: Dale Guffey, Chief Financial Officer
CMO: Jerome Covington M.D., Chief Medical Officer
CIO: Les Jackson, Manager Information Systems
CHR: Donald Canalejo, Director Human Resources
Web address: www.lkmc.com
Control: Corporation, Investor–owned (for–profit) **Service**: General medical and surgical

Staffed Beds: 90

KISSIMMEE—Osceola County

FLORIDA HOSPITAL KISSIMMEE See Florida Hospital, Orlando

☒ **OSCEOLA REGIONAL MEDICAL CENTER (100110)**, 700 West Oak Street, Zip 34741–4996; tel. 407/846–2266 **A**1 2 3 5 8 10 13 **F**3 8 11 13 15 17 18 20 22 24 26 28 29 30 31 34 35 37 38 40 41 42 43 45 46 47 48 49 50 57 58 59 60 68 70 73 74 76 77 78 79 80 81 85 87 88 89 91 92 93 98 100 101 102 104 105 107 108 110 111 114 115 119 126 130 131 132 145 146 147 148 149 **S** HCA Healthcare, Nashville, TN
Primary Contact: Davide M. Carbone, FACHE, Chief Executive Officer
CFO: Carrie Biggar, Chief Financial Officer
CMO: Stephens Stoops M.D., Chief Medical Officer
CHR: Sylvia Lollis, Director Human Resources
Web address: www.osceolaregional.com
Control: Corporation, Investor–owned (for–profit) **Service**: General medical and surgical

Staffed Beds: 332 **Admissions**: 24000 **Census**: 273 **Births**: 2000

☒ **POINCIANA MEDICAL CENTER (100320)**, 325 Cypress Parkway, Zip 34758; tel. 407/530–2000, (Nonreporting) **A**1 10 **S** HCA Healthcare, Nashville, TN
Primary Contact: Christopher Cosby, Chief Executive Officer
CFO: Tom Eisel, Chief Financial Officer
CNO: Sharon Dillard, Chief Nursing Officer
Web address: www.poincianamedicalcenter.com
Control: Corporation, Investor–owned (for–profit) **Service**: General medical and surgical

Staffed Beds: 24

LAKE BUTLER—Union County

LAKE BUTLER HOSPITAL HAND SURGERY CENTER (101303), 850 East Main Street, Zip 32054–1353, Mailing Address: P.O.Box 748, 32054–0748; tel. 386/496–2323 **A**10 18 **F**29 35 40 77 92 93 94 95 96 97 99 119 127 130 133
Primary Contact: Pamela B. Howard, R.N., Chief Executive Officer, Administrator and Risk Manager
COO: Jennifer Thomas, Chief Operating Officer and Director of Public Relations
CFO: Paula Webb, Chief Financial Officer and Compliance Officer
CMO: Cynthia Larimer M.D., Chief of Staff
CIO: Diane Cason, Chief Information Officer, Controller and Director Human Resources
CNO: Mandy Dicks, Director of Nursing
Web address: www.lakebutlerhospital.com
Control: Corporation, Investor–owned (for–profit) **Service**: General medical and surgical

Staffed Beds: 25 **Admissions**: 21 **Census**: 1 **Births**: 0

RECEPTION AND MEDICAL CENTER, State Road 231 South, Zip 32054, Mailing Address: P.O.Box 628, 32054–0628; tel. 386/496–6000, (Nonreporting)
Primary Contact: Maxine Streeter, Administrator
Web address: www.dc.state.fl.us
Control: State, Government, Nonfederal **Service**: Hospital unit of an institution (prison hospital, college infirmary, etc.)

Staffed Beds: 120

LAKE CITY—Columbia County

☒ **LAKE CITY MEDICAL CENTER (100156)**, 340 NW Commerce Drive, Zip 32055–4709; tel. 386/719–9000, (Nonreporting) **A**1 10 **S** HCA Healthcare, Nashville, TN
Primary Contact: Mark Miller, FACHE, Chief Executive Officer
COO: Jennifer B Adams, Chief Operating Officer and Chief Financial Officer
CFO: Jennifer B Adams, Chief Operating Officer and Chief Financial Officer
CMO: Miguel Tepedino M.D., Chief Medicine
CIO: Taylor Dickerson, Chief Information Officer
CHR: Steve Gordon, Director Human Resources
Web address: www.lakecitymedical.com
Control: Corporation, Investor–owned (for–profit) **Service**: General medical and surgical

Staffed Beds: 67

FL

Hospital, Medicare Provider Number, Address, Telephone, Approval, Facility, and Physician Codes, Health Care System

★ American Hospital Association (AHA) membership
☐ The Joint Commission accreditation
○ Healthcare Facilities Accreditation Program
◇ DNV Healthcare Inc. accreditation
⇑ Center for Improvement in Healthcare Quality Accreditation
△ Commission on Accreditation of Rehabilitation Facilities (CARF) accreditation

© 2017 AHA Guide   *Many Facility Codes have changed. Please refer to the AHA Guide Code Chart.*   Hospitals **A129**

✠ **SHANDS LAKE SHORE REGIONAL MEDICAL CENTER (100102)**, 368 NE Franklin Street, Zip 32055–3047; tel. 386/292–8000, (Nonreporting) **A**1 3 10 **S** Community Health Systems, Inc., Franklin, TN
Primary Contact: Rhonda Kay. Sherrod, R.N., MSN, Administrator
COO: Francis A Pommett Jr, Chief Operating Officer
CFO: Steve Davis, Chief Financial Officer
CMO: Mohammad Faisal, President Medical Staff
CHR: Angie Altman, Director Human Resources
CNO: Gary Goelz R.N., Chief Nursing Officer
Web address: www.shandslakeshore.com
Control: Partnership, Investor–owned (for–profit) **Service:** General medical and surgical

Staffed Beds: 85

VETERANS AFFAIRS MEDICAL CENTER See Lake City Veterans Affairs Medical Center

LAKE WALES—Polk County

✠ **LAKE WALES MEDICAL CENTER (100099)**, 410 South 11th Street, Zip 33853–4256; tel. 863/676–1433 **A**1 10 **F**3 11 15 18 20 29 30 34 35 40 45 46 49 50 56 57 59 64 70 74 75 79 81 82 85 86 87 89 91 92 93 94 96 98 103 107 108 110 111 114 115 119 124 129 131 132 146 147 148 149 **S** Community Health Systems, Inc., Franklin, TN
Primary Contact: Rebecca Brewer, FACHE, Chief Executive Officer
CFO: Danny Warren, Chief Financial Officer
CMO: Sunil Nihalani M.D., Chief Medical Staff
CIO: Erwin Jaropillo, Director Information Systems
CHR: Renee Latterner, Director Human Resources
CNO: Jennifer Huston, Chief Nursing Officer
Web address: www.lakewalesmedicalcenter.com
Control: Corporation, Investor–owned (for–profit) **Service:** General medical and surgical

Staffed Beds: 131 Admissions: 4296 Census: 54 Births: 0

LAKE WORTH—Palm Beach County

✠ **SELECT SPECIALTY HOSPITAL–PALM BEACH (102023)**, 3060 Melaleuca Lane, Zip 33461–5174; tel. 561/357–7200, (Nonreporting) **A**1 10 **S** Select Medical Corporation, Mechanicsburg, PA
Primary Contact: Larry Melby, Chief Executive Officer
Web address: www.selectspecialtyhospitals.com/company/locations/palmbeach.aspx
Control: Corporation, Investor–owned (for–profit) **Service:** Acute long–term care hospital

Staffed Beds: 60

LAKELAND—Polk County

✠ **LAKELAND REGIONAL HEALTH (100157)**, 1324 Lakeland Hills Blvd, Zip 33805–4543, Mailing Address: P.O.Box 95448, 33804–5448; tel. 863/687–1100 **A**1 2 3 5 10 **F**3 11 13 18 20 22 24 26 28 29 30 31 34 37 38 40 41 43 44 45 46 47 49 51 55 56 57 58 59 60 61 64 65 66 70 71 72 74 75 76 77 78 79 80 81 82 83 84 85 86 87 88 89 90 93 95 96 98 99 100 101 102 103 104 107 108 109 110 111 114 115 118 119 120 121 123 124 126 130 131 132 135 143 144 146 147 148 **P**6
Primary Contact: Timothy Regan, M.D., President and Chief Medical Officer
COO: Sarah Bhagat, Chief Operating Officer and Vice President of Organizational Effectiveness
CFO: Evan Jones, Executive Vice President and Chief Financial Officer
CMO: Timothy Regan M.D., President and Chief Medical Officer
CIO: Elizabeth Kerns, Senior Vice President and Chief Information Officer
CHR: Scott Dimmick, Senior Vice President and Chief Human Resources Officer
CNO: Janet Fansler R.N., Executive Vice President and Chief Nurse Executive
Web address: www.mylrh.org
Control: Other not–for–profit (including NFP Corporation) **Service:** General medical and surgical

Staffed Beds: 810 Admissions: 40570 Census: 514 Outpatient Visits: 273799 Births: 2994 Total Expense ($000): 617755 Payroll Expense ($000): 241901 Personnel: 4200

LAND O'LAKES—Pasco County

✠ **FLORIDA HOSPITAL AT CONNERTON LONG TERM ACUTE CARE (102026)**, 9441 Health Center Drive, Zip 34637–5837; tel. 813/903–3701 **A**1 10 **F**1 3 29 30 31 34 91 107 119 146 148 **S** Adventist Health System Sunbelt Health Care Corporation, Altamonte Springs, FL
Primary Contact: Brian Adams, President and Chief Executive Officer
COO: Debora Martoccio R.N., Chief Operating Officer
CMO: Sharad Patel M.D., Medical Director
CNO: Rafael Padilla R.N., Chief Nursing Officer
Web address: www.elevatinghealthcare.org
Control: Church operated, Nongovernment, not–for–profit **Service:** Acute long–term care hospital

Staffed Beds: 50 Admissions: 658 Census: 48 Outpatient Visits: 0 Births: 0 Total Expense ($000): 27147 Payroll Expense ($000): 11425 Personnel: 180

LARGO—Pinellas County

✠ **HEALTHSOUTH REHABILITATION HOSPITAL (103037)**, 901 North Clearwater–Largo Road, Zip 33770–4126; tel. 727/586–2999, (Nonreporting) **A**1 10 **S** HEALTHSOUTH Corporation, Birmingham, AL
Primary Contact: Tripp Smith, Chief Executive Officer
CFO: Judith Johnson, Controller
CMO: Richard A Liles M.D., Medical Director
CHR: Jackie Chalk, Director Human Resources
CNO: Pattie Brenner R.N., Chief Nursing Officer
Web address: www.healthsouthlargo.com
Control: Corporation, Investor–owned (for–profit) **Service:** Rehabilitation

Staffed Beds: 70

✠ △ **LARGO MEDICAL CENTER (100248)**, 201 14th Street SW, Zip 33770–3133; tel. 727/588–5200, (Nonreporting) (Includes LARGO MEDICAL CENTER – INDIAN ROCKS, 2025 Indian Rocks Road, Largo, Florida, Zip 33774–1096, P O Box 2025, 33779–2025, tel. 727/581–9474) **A**1 2 5 7 10 12 13 **S** HCA Healthcare, Nashville, TN
Primary Contact: Anthony M Degina, President and Chief Executive Officer
CFO: Robert E Billings, Chief Financial Officer
CMO: David Weiland M.D., Chief Medical Officer
CIO: David Saly, Director, Information Services
CNO: Brenda Simpson R.N., Chief Nursing Officer
Web address: www.largomedical.com
Control: Corporation, Investor–owned (for–profit) **Service:** General medical and surgical

Staffed Beds: 243

LAUDERDALE LAKES—Broward County

☐ △ **ST. ANTHONY'S REHABILITATION HOSPITAL (103027)**, 3485 NW 30th Street, Zip 33311–1890; tel. 954/739–6233 **A**1 7 10 **F**28 29 30 34 35 60 64 68 74 75 79 86 90 91 93 94 96 130 131 132 148 149 **S** Catholic Health Services, Lauderdale Lakes, FL
Primary Contact: Joseph M. Catania, Chief Executive Officer
COO: James Ball, Chief Operating Officer, Executive
CFO: David D'Amico
CMO: Mark Reiner, Chief Medical Office, Executive
CIO: Dario Achury, Director of Information Management
CHR: Barbara Griffith, Vice President Human Resources
Web address: www.catholichealthservices.org
Control: Church operated, Nongovernment, not–for–profit **Service:** Rehabilitation

Staffed Beds: 26 Admissions: 475 Census: 17 Outpatient Visits: 2544 Births: 0 Total Expense ($000): 7765 Payroll Expense ($000): 3569 Personnel: 80

LEESBURG—Lake County

✠ **LEESBURG REGIONAL MEDICAL CENTER (100084)**, 600 East Dixie Avenue, Zip 34748–5999; tel. 352/323–5762 **A**1 2 10 **F**3 8 11 13 15 17 18 20 22 24 26 28 29 30 31 34 35 40 45 47 48 49 53 54 57 59 64 68 70 74 75 77 78 79 81 82 84 85 87 90 93 96 107 108 110 111 114 115 119 130 132 135 144 146 147 149 **P**6 7 8 **S** Central Florida Health, Leesburg, FL
Primary Contact: Donald G. Henderson, FACHE, President and Chief Executive Officer
COO: Saad Ehtisham R.N., FACHE, Vice President and Chief Operating Officer
CFO: Diane P Harden, Chief Financial Officer
CIO: David Steele, Vice President Information Technology
CHR: Amie Richason, Vice President Human Resources
CNO: Joshua Fleming, Vice President Chief Clinical Officer
Web address: www.cfhalliance.org
Control: Other not–for–profit (including NFP Corporation) **Service:** General medical and surgical

Staffed Beds: 330 Admissions: 15169 Census: 224 Outpatient Visits: 85397 Births: 1399 Total Expense ($000): 218834 Payroll Expense ($000): 85631 Personnel: 1423

FL

LIFESTREAM BEHAVIORAL CENTER (104018), 2020 Tally Road, Zip 34748–3426, Mailing Address: P.O.Box 491000, 34749–1000; tel. 352/315–7500 (Nonreporting) **A**10
Primary Contact: Jonathan M. Cherry, President and Chief Executive Officer
COO: David Braughton, Chief Operating Officer
CFO: Carol Dozier, Chief Financial Officer
CMO: T. J. Valente M.D., Medical Director
CIO: Chad Heim, Management Information System Director
CHR: Ben Hargrove, Human Resources Director
Web address: www.lsbc.net
Control: Other not–for–profit (including NFP Corporation) **Service:** Psychiatric

Staffed Beds: 46

LEHIGH ACRES—Lee County

✠ **LEHIGH REGIONAL MEDICAL CENTER (100107)**, 1500 Lee Boulevard, Zip 33936–4835; tel. 239/369–2101, (Nonreporting) **A**1 10 **S** Prime Healthcare, Ontario, CA
Primary Contact: Gary C. Bell, LFACHE, Chief Executive Officer
CFO: Osman Gruhonjic, Chief Financial Officer
CMO: Joe Lemmons D.O., Chief of Staff
CIO: Jeff Hampton, Director Information Systems
CHR: Mary Gray, Director Human Resources
CNO: Julie G Banker R.N., MSN, Chief Nursing Officer
Web address: www.lehighregional.com
Control: Corporation, Investor–owned (for–profit) **Service:** General medical and surgical

Staffed Beds: 88

LIVE OAK—Suwannee County

✠ **SHANDS LIVE OAK REGIONAL MEDICAL CENTER (101301)**, 1100 SW 11th Street, Zip 32064–3608; tel. 386/362–0800 **A**1 10 18 **F**15 18 29 34 35 40 41 45 50 54 56 57 59 64 68 75 81 91 92 93 97 102 107 108 110 111 119 127 135 146 147 **S** Community Health Systems, Inc., Franklin, TN
Primary Contact: Rhonda Kay. Sherrod, R.N., MSN, Interim Chief Executive Officer
CFO: Jennifer Grafton, Chief Financial Officer
CMO: Andrew C. Bass M.D., Medical Director
CIO: Justin Marlowe, Information Technology Director
CHR: Dana Abbott, Market Human Resources Director
CNO: Donna Ragan R.N., Chief Nursing Officer
Web address: www.shandsliveoak.com/
Control: Corporation, Investor–owned (for–profit) **Service:** General medical and surgical

Staffed Beds: 25 **Admissions:** 1124 **Census:** 10 **Births:** 0

LOXAHATCHEE—Palm Beach County

✠ **PALMS WEST HOSPITAL (100269)**, 13001 Southern Boulevard, Zip 33470–9203; tel. 561/798–3300 **A**1 10 **F**3 8 13 15 18 19 20 22 29 30 31 34 35 39 40 41 45 46 49 50 51 56 57 58 60 61 64 68 70 74 75 76 77 78 79 80 81 82 84 85 86 87 88 89 93 107 108 110 111 114 115 119 124 126 130 131 141 146 147 148 149 **S** HCA Healthcare, Nashville, TN
Primary Contact: Eric Goldman, Chief Executive Officer
COO: Lorna Kernivan, Chief Operating Officer
CFO: Steven Burroughs, Chief Financial Officer
CIO: Martha Stinson, Director of Information Technology
CHR: Marcy Mills–Mathews, Director Human Resources
CNO: Silvia Stradi, Chief Nursing Officer
Web address: www.palmswesthospital.com
Control: Corporation, Investor–owned (for–profit) **Service:** General medical and surgical

Staffed Beds: 204 **Admissions:** 13989 **Census:** 152 **Births:** 1509 **Total Expense ($000):** 153667 **Payroll Expense ($000):** 51642

MACCLENNY—Baker County

ED FRASER MEMORIAL HOSPITAL AND BAKER COMMUNITY HEALTH CENTER (100134), 159 North Third Street, Zip 32063–2103, Mailing Address: P.O.Box 484, 32063–0484; tel. 904/259–3151, (Nonreporting) **A**10 20
Primary Contact: Dennis R. Markos, Chief Executive Officer
CFO: W. Steve Dudley CPA, Chief Financial Officer
CMO: Mark Hardin M.D., Medical Director
CIO: Ernie Waller, Director Information Technology
CHR: Stacey Conner, Director Personnel
CNO: Valerie Markos, Chief Nursing Officer
Web address: www.bcmedsvcs.com
Control: Other not–for–profit (including NFP Corporation) **Service:** General medical and surgical

Staffed Beds: 68

MADISON—Madison County

MADISON COUNTY MEMORIAL HOSPITAL (101311), 224 NW Crane Avenue, Zip 32340–2561; tel. 850/973–2271 **A**10 18 **F**3 11 15 29 30 34 35 40 41 42 57 59 63 64 68 74 75 77 81 91 92 93 96 107 110 114 119 148
Primary Contact: Tammy Stevens, Chief Executive Officer
CFO: Patrick Halfhill, Chief Financial Officer
CMO: Brett Perkins M.D., Chief Medical Staff
CIO: Patrick Stiff, Coordinator Information Technology
CHR: Cindi Burnett, Chief Human Resources Officer
Web address: www.mcmh.us/
Control: Hospital district or authority, Government, Nonfederal **Service:** General medical and surgical

Staffed Beds: 25 **Admissions:** 526 **Census:** 13 **Outpatient Visits:** 17962 **Births:** 0 **Total Expense ($000):** 9509 **Payroll Expense ($000):** 4151 **Personnel:** 131

MARATHON—Monroe County

✠ **FISHERMEN'S HOSPITAL (101312)**, 3301 Overseas Highway, Zip 33050–2329; tel. 305/743–5533 **A**1 10 18 **F**3 11 15 17 18 29 34 35 40 45 46 50 51 57 59 64 68 70 75 77 79 81 82 85 91 93 97 107 108 110 111 114 119 124 130 133 141 146 149 **P**8 **S** Baptist Health South Florida, Coral Gables, FL
Primary Contact: Rick Freeburg, Chief Executive Officer
COO: Lynn Mauck R.N., Chief Operating Officer and Chief Nursing Officer
CFO: H D Cannington, Interim Chief Financial Officer
CMO: Harlan Pettit M.D., Chief of Medical Staff
CIO: Patrick Stitt, Director of Information Systems
CHR: Chris Fletcher, Director of Human Resources
CNO: Lynn Mauck R.N., Chief Operating Officer and Chief Nursing Officer
Web address: www.fishermenshospital.org
Control: Other not–for–profit (including NFP Corporation) **Service:** General medical and surgical

Staffed Beds: 25 **Admissions:** 463 **Census:** 4 **Outpatient Visits:** 11037 **Births:** 0 **Personnel:** 150

MARGATE—Broward County

✠ **NORTHWEST MEDICAL CENTER (100189)**, 2801 North State Road 7, Zip 33063–5727; tel. 954/974–0400 **A**1 3 10 **F**3 8 11 12 13 15 17 18 22 24 26 29 31 34 35 40 41 44 45 46 47 49 50 53 56 57 59 60 61 63 64 65 68 70 73 74 75 76 77 78 79 80 81 82 83 85 86 87 89 93 107 108 110 111 114 115 117 118 119 126 129 130 131 132 135 146 147 148 149 **S** HCA Healthcare, Nashville, TN
Primary Contact: Erica Gulrich, Chief Executive Officer
CFO: Ananda Rampat, Chief Financial Officer
CMO: Jose Martinez M.D., Chief Medical Officer
CIO: David Irizarri, Director Information Technology
CHR: Lynda Bryan, Vice President Human Resources
CNO: Sandra Emeott R.N., Chief Nursing Officer
Web address: www.northwestmed.com
Control: Corporation, Investor–owned (for–profit) **Service:** General medical and surgical

Staffed Beds: 228 **Admissions:** 16027 **Census:** 161 **Births:** 1967 **Total Expense ($000):** 184025 **Payroll Expense ($000):** 58042

MARIANNA—Jackson County

✠ **JACKSON HOSPITAL (100142)**, 4250 Hospital Drive, Zip 32446–1917, Mailing Address: P.O.Box 1608, 32447–5608; tel. 850/526–2200 **A**1 10 20 **F**1 3 4 11 13 15 17 29 30 31 34 35 40 45 49 50 53 54 57 59 70 72 73 75 76 78 81 85 86 87 88 89 90 97 98 107 108 110 111 114 119 120 127 128 130 132 133 135 146 147 148 149 **S** QHR, Brentwood, TN
Primary Contact: James Platt, Chief Executive Officer
CFO: Kevin Rovito, Chief Financial Officer
CMO: Steven Walter Spence M.D., Chief Medical Officer
CIO: Jamie Hussey, Chief Information Officer
CHR: Brooke G Donaldson, Assistant Administrator Human Resources
CNO: Robbin K Pumphrey, Chief Nursing Officer
Web address: www.jacksonhosp.com
Control: Hospital district or authority, Government, Nonfederal **Service:** General medical and surgical

Staffed Beds: 68 **Admissions:** 2816 **Census:** 36 **Outpatient Visits:** 37898 **Births:** 426 **Total Expense ($000):** 49131 **Payroll Expense ($000):** 22905 **Personnel:** 481

FL

Hospital, Medicare Provider Number, Address, Telephone, Approval, Facility, and Physician Codes, Health Care System

★ American Hospital Association (AHA) membership ○ Healthcare Facilities Accreditation Program ⇑ Center for Improvement in Healthcare Quality Accreditation
□ The Joint Commission accreditation ◇ DNV Healthcare Inc. accreditation △ Commission on Accreditation of Rehabilitation Facilities (CARF) accreditation

MELBOURNE—Brevard County

☐ **CIRCLES OF CARE (104024)**, 400 East Sheridan Road, Zip 32901–3184; tel. 321/722–5200, (Nonreporting) **A**1 5 10
Primary Contact: David L. Feldman, President and Chief Executive Officer
CFO: David L Feldman, Executive Vice President and Treasurer
CMO: Jose Alvarez M.D., Chief Medical Staff
CHR: Linda Brannon, Vice President Human Resources
Web address: www.circlesofcare.org
Control: Other not–for–profit (including NFP Corporation) **Service**: Psychiatric

Staffed Beds: 134

DEVEREUX HOSPITAL AND CHILDREN'S CENTER OF FLORIDA, 8000 Devereux Drive, Zip 32940–7907; tel. 321/242–9100, (Nonreporting) **S** Devereux, Villanova, PA
Primary Contact: Steven Murphy, Executive Director
COO: Eva Horner, Assistant Executive Director Operations
CFO: Kelly Messer, Director of Finance
CMO: Manal Durgin, Network Medical Director
CIO: Diana Deitrick, Director Information Services
CHR: Tim Dillion, Vice President of Human Resources
Web address: www.devereux.org
Control: Other not–for–profit (including NFP Corporation) **Service**: Children's hospital psychiatric

Staffed Beds: 100

✠ **HEALTH FIRST HOLMES REGIONAL MEDICAL CENTER (100019)**, 1350 South Hickory Street, Zip 32901–3224; tel. 321/434–7000 **A**1 5 10 **F**3 11 13 17 18 20 22 24 26 28 29 30 31 34 40 41 43 45 46 47 48 49 50 59 60 64 68 70 72 73 74 75 76 77 78 79 81 84 85 86 87 89 100 102 107 108 111 114 115 118 119 126 130 132 141 146 147 148 149 **S** Health First, Inc., Rockledge, FL
Primary Contact: Brett A. Esrock, FACHE, Chief Executive Officer
CFO: Joseph G Felkner, Executive Vice President, Finance and Chief Financial Officer
CMO: Mark Rosenbloom, Vice President of Medical Affairs
CIO: Dustin Leek, Vice President of Enterprise Technical Services
CHR: Paula Just, Chief Human Resources Officer
CNO: Barbara Seymour, Vice President of Nursing
Web address: www.health–first.org
Control: Other not–for–profit (including NFP Corporation) **Service**: General medical and surgical

Staffed Beds: 514 Admissions: 28311 Census: 359 Outpatient Visits: 226050 Births: 3145 Total Expense ($000): 452556 Payroll Expense ($000): 168375 Personnel: 2128

☐ **HEALTH FIRST VIERA HOSPITAL (100315)**, 8745 North Wickham Road, Zip 32940–5997; tel. 321/434–9164 **A**1 5 10 **F**3 12 15 18 20 29 30 31 40 41 45 46 47 48 49 50 59 60 63 64 68 70 74 75 77 78 79 80 81 85 86 87 93 107 108 109 110 111 115 117 118 119 126 129 130 132 141 146 148 149 **S** Health First, Inc., Rockledge, FL
Primary Contact: Aaron Robinson, Chief Executive Officer, Health First Community Hospitals
COO: Deborah Angerami, Chief Operating Officer
CFO: Joseph G Felkner, Chief Financial Officer
CMO: Scott Gettings M.D., Senior Vice President and Chief Medical Officer
CIO: Alex Popowycz, Chief Information Officer
CHR: Paula Just, Chief Human Resources Officer
CNO: Connie Bradley R.N., MSN, FACHE, Senior Vice President and Chief Nursing Officer
Web address: www.vierahospital.org
Control: Other not–for–profit (including NFP Corporation) **Service**: General medical and surgical

Staffed Beds: 84 Admissions: 4514 Census: 47 Outpatient Visits: 63367 Births: 0 Total Expense ($000): 88294 Payroll Expense ($000): 29694 Personnel: 387

✠ **HEALTHSOUTH SEA PINES REHABILITATION HOSPITAL (103034)**, 101 East Florida Avenue, Zip 32901–8301; tel. 321/984–4600, (Nonreporting) **A**1 10 **S** HEALTHSOUTH Corporation, Birmingham, AL
Primary Contact: Denise B. McGrath, Chief Executive Officer
CFO: Dana Edwards, Chief Financial Officer
CMO: Juan Lebron M.D., Medical Director
CHR: James L Henry, Director Human Resources
CNO: Lisa Truman, Chief Nursing Officer
Web address: www.healthsouthseapines.com
Control: Corporation, Investor–owned (for–profit) **Service**: Rehabilitation

Staffed Beds: 90

✠ **KINDRED HOSPITAL MELBOURNE (102027)**, 765 West Nasa Boulevard, Zip 32901–1815; tel. 321/733–5725 **A**1 10 **F**1 3 29 70 107 114 148 **S** Kindred Healthcare, Louisville, KY
Primary Contact: Pamela R. Reed, Chief Executive Officer
Web address: www.khmelbourne.com
Control: Corporation, Investor–owned (for–profit) **Service**: Acute long–term care hospital

Staffed Beds: 60 Admissions: 459 Census: 35 Outpatient Visits: 0 Births: 0 Total Expense ($000): 26034 Payroll Expense ($000): 7793

✠ **WUESTHOFF MEDICAL CENTER – MELBOURNE (100291)**, 250 North Wickham Road, Zip 32935–8625; tel. 321/752–1200 **A**1 10 **F**3 12 15 18 20 22 26 29 30 34 39 40 45 49 51 56 70 74 79 81 85 93 107 108 110 111 115 119 126 130 131 146 148 149 **S** Steward Health Care System, LLC, Boston, MA
Primary Contact: Ron Gicca, Chief Executive Officer
CFO: Steve Bender, Chief Financial Officer
Web address: www.wuesthoff.com/locations/wuesthoff–medical–center–melbourne
Control: Corporation, Investor–owned (for–profit) **Service**: General medical and surgical

Staffed Beds: 119 Admissions: 3273 Census: 39 Outpatient Visits: 34450 Births: 0 Total Expense ($000): 67166 Payroll Expense ($000): 19295 Personnel: 404

MIAMI—Miami—Dade County

✠ △ **BAPTIST HEALTH SOUTH FLORIDA, BAPTIST HOSPITAL OF MIAMI (100008)**, 8900 North Kendall Drive, Zip 33176–2197; tel. 786/596–1960, (Includes BAPTIST CHILDREN'S HOSPITAL, 8900 North Kendall Drive, Miami, Florida, Zip 33176–2118, tel. 786/596–1960) **A**1 2 3 5 7 10 **F**3 8 11 13 15 17 18 19 20 22 24 26 28 29 30 31 32 34 35 40 41 45 46 47 49 50 51 53 54 55 56 57 58 59 60 61 62 63 64 66 68 70 72 73 74 75 76 77 78 79 81 82 84 85 86 87 88 89 90 91 92 93 96 100 102 107 108 109 110 111 112 114 115 116 117 118 119 120 121 123 124 126 129 130 132 135 144 145 146 147 148 149 150 **S** Baptist Health South Florida, Coral Gables, FL
Primary Contact: Albert Boulenger, Chief Executive Officer
COO: Randall Lee, Vice President and Chief Operating Officer
CFO: Ralph E Lawson, Executive Vice President and Chief Financial Officer
CMO: Mark J Hauser M.D., Chief Medical Officer
CIO: Mimi Taylor, Corporate Vice President Information Technology
Web address: www.baptisthealth.net
Control: Other not–for–profit (including NFP Corporation) **Service**: General medical and surgical

Staffed Beds: 720 Admissions: 32186 Census: 505 Outpatient Visits: 400326 Births: 4182 Total Expense ($000): 841403 Payroll Expense ($000): 281843 Personnel: 4202

✠ **BAPTIST HEALTH SOUTH FLORIDA, SOUTH MIAMI HOSPITAL (100154)**, 6200 SW 73rd Street, Zip 33143–4679; tel. 786/662–4000 **A**1 2 3 10 **F**3 5 11 12 13 15 16 17 18 20 22 24 26 28 29 30 31 34 35 36 40 46 48 49 50 51 52 53 54 57 58 59 60 61 64 68 70 72 74 75 76 77 78 79 81 82 84 85 86 87 93 107 108 110 111 114 115 116 117 118 119 120 121 123 124 126 129 130 132 135 144 146 147 148 149 150 **S** Baptist Health South Florida, Coral Gables, FL
Primary Contact: Lincoln S. Mendez, Chief Executive Officer
COO: Jeanette Stone, Vice President Operations
CFO: Erik Long, Controller
CMO: Jeremy Tabak M.D., President Medical Staff
CIO: Mimi Taylor, Vice President Information Technology
CHR: Diana Montenegro, Director Human Resources
CNO: Kathy Sparger R.N., MSN, Chief Nursing Officer
Web address: www.baptisthealth.net
Control: Other not–for–profit (including NFP Corporation) **Service**: General medical and surgical

Staffed Beds: 336 Admissions: 15597 Census: 214 Outpatient Visits: 276584 Births: 4143 Total Expense ($000): 495372 Payroll Expense ($000): 152955 Personnel: 1934

✠ **BAPTIST HEALTH SOUTH FLORIDA, WEST KENDALL BAPTIST HOSPITAL (100314)**, 9555 SW 162nd Avenue, Zip 33196–6408; tel. 786/467–2000 **A**1 3 10 **F**3 11 13 18 19 29 30 34 35 40 41 45 49 50 51 53 57 58 59 60 63 64 68 70 74 75 76 78 79 81 82 84 85 86 87 93 100 102 107 108 109 111 114 115 119 126 130 131 132 135 146 147 148 149 150 **S** Baptist Health South Florida, Coral Gables, FL
Primary Contact: Javier Hernandez–Lichtl, Chief Executive Officer
CFO: Odalys Remigio, Assistant Vice President, Finance
CMO: Juan–Carlos Verdeja M.D., President of Medical Staff
CHR: Hilde Zamora de Aguero, Human Resources Site Director
CNO: Denise H. Harris R.N., MSN, Chief Nursing Officer
Web address: www.baptisthealth.net/en/facilities/West–Kendall–Baptist–Hospital/Pages/default.aspx
Control: Other not–for–profit (including NFP Corporation) **Service**: General medical and surgical

Staffed Beds: 133 Admissions: 8700 Census: 94 Outpatient Visits: 87546 Births: 989 Total Expense ($000): 200763 Payroll Expense ($000): 66950 Personnel: 993

BASCOM PALMER EYE INSTITUTE–ANNE BATES LEACH EYE HOSPITAL (100240), 900 NW 17th Street, Zip 33136–1199, Mailing Address: Box 016880, 33101–6880; tel. 305/326–6000 **A**1 3 5 10 **F**31 40 44 50 57 58 59 64 66 68 71 78 79 81 85 87 93 94 107 111 115 129 130 141 149 **P**6 **S** University of Miami Health System, Miami, FL
Primary Contact: Michael B. Gittelman, Administrator
COO: Charles Pappas M.D., Chief Operating Officer
CFO: Harry Rohrer, Chief Financial Officer
CMO: Eduardo Alfonso M.D., Chairman Ophthalmology
Web address: www.bascompalmer.org
Control: Other not–for–profit (including NFP Corporation) **Service**: Eye, ear, nose and throat

Staffed Beds: 56 **Admissions**: 56 **Census**: 1 **Outpatient Visits**: 250107
Births: 0 **Personnel**: 598

JACKSON BEHAVIORAL HEALTH HOSPITAL See Jackson Health System

JACKSON HEALTH SYSTEM (100022), 1611 NW 12th Avenue, Zip 33136–1005; tel. 305/585–1111, (Includes HOLTZ CHILDREN'S HOSPITAL, 1611 NW 12th Avenue, Miami, Florida, Zip 33136–1005, tel. 305/585–5437; Don S Steigman, Chief Executive Officer; JACKSON BEHAVIORAL HEALTH HOSPITAL, 1695 NW Ninth Avenue, Miami, Florida, Zip 33136–1409, tel. 305/324–4357; Nicolette B Tessler, Chief Executive Officer of Behavioral Health Hospital; JACKSON MEMORIAL HOSPITAL, 1611 NW 12th Avenue, Miami, Florida, Zip 33136, tel. 305/585–1111; David Zambrana, R.N., Chief Executive Officer; JACKSON NORTH MEDICAL CENTER, 160 NW 170th Street, North Miami Beach, Florida, Zip 33169–5576, tel. 305/651–1100; JACKSON SOUTH COMMUNITY HOSPITAL, 9333 SW 152nd Street, Miami, Florida, Zip 33157–1780, tel. 305/251–2500; Georgina Diaz, Chief Executive Officer) (Total facility includes 342 beds in nursing home–type unit) **A**1 3 5 7 8 10 **F**1 3 4 5 8 11 12 13 15 16 17 18 19 20 21 22 23 24 25 26 27 28 29 30 31 34 35 38 39 40 41 43 44 45 49 50 54 55 56 57 58 59 60 61 63 64 65 66 67 68 70 71 72 73 74 75 76 77 78 79 80 81 82 83 84 85 86 87 88 89 90 93 94 96 97 98 99 100 101 102 103 104 106 107 108 109 110 111 114 115 116 117 118 119 120 121 123 124 126 128 129 130 131 132 135 136 137 138 139 140 141 142 146 147 148 149 **P**6
Primary Contact: Carlos A. Migoya, President and Chief Executive Officer
COO: Don S Steigman, Chief Operating Officer
CFO: Mark T Knight, Executive Vice President and Chief Financial Officer
CMO: Peter G Paige, Chief Medical Officer
CIO: Michael A Garcia, Vice President and Chief Information Officer
CHR: Julie Staub, Chief Human Resources Officer
Web address: www.jacksonhealth.org
Control: County, Government, Nonfederal **Service**: General medical and surgical

Staffed Beds: 2013 **Admissions**: 65157 **Census**: 1520 **Outpatient Visits**: 553613 **Births**: 6803 **Total Expense ($000)**: 1768219 **Payroll Expense ($000)**: 834998 **Personnel**: 10543

JACKSON SOUTH COMMUNITY HOSPITAL See Jackson Health System

KENDALL REGIONAL MEDICAL CENTER (100209), 11750 Bird Road, Zip 33175–3530; tel. 305/223–3000, (Nonreporting) **A**1 3 10 **S** HCA Healthcare, Nashville, TN
Primary Contact: Brandon Haushalter, Chief Executive Officer
COO: Randy Gross, Chief Operating Officer
CFO: Scott Herndon, Chief Financial Officer
CMO: Bradley Shumaker, Chief Medical Officer
CIO: Matt Hernandez, Director of Information Technology and System
CHR: Knicole S White, Director Human Resources
CNO: Wendy Stuart, Chief Nursing Officer
Web address: www.kendallmed.com
Control: Partnership, Investor–owned (for–profit) **Service**: General medical and surgical

Staffed Beds: 300

MIAMI JEWISH HOME AND HOSPITAL FOR AGED (100277), 5200 NE Second Avenue, Zip 33137–2706; tel. 305/751–8626, (Nonreporting) **A**1 3 5 10
Primary Contact: Jeffrey P. Freimark, Chief Executive Officer
CFO: Lisa Jo Desmarteau, Chief Financial Officer
CMO: Brian Kiedrowski M.D., Chief Medical Director
CHR: Larry McDonald, Director Human Resources
Web address: www.mjhha.org
Control: Other not–for–profit (including NFP Corporation) **Service**: General medical and surgical

Staffed Beds: 32

MIAMI VETERANS AFFAIRS HEALTHCARE SYSTEM, 1201 NW 16th Street, Zip 33125–1624; tel. 305/575–7000, (Nonreporting) **A**1 3 5 7 **S** Department of Veterans Affairs, Washington, DC
Primary Contact: Paul M. Russo, FACHE, Director
COO: Lance Davis PharmD, Associate Director
CFO: Albert Tucker, Chief Financial Officer
CMO: Vincent DeGennaro M.D., Chief of Staff
CIO: Anthony Brooks, Chief Information Officer
CHR: Loyman Marin, Chief Human Resources
CNO: Marcia C Lysaght R.N., MSN, Associate Director Patient Care Services
Web address: www.miami.va.gov/
Control: Veterans Affairs, Government, federal **Service**: General medical and surgical

Staffed Beds: 401

NICKLAUS CHILDREN'S HOSPITAL (103301), 3100 SW 62nd Avenue, Zip 33155–3009; tel. 305/666–6511 **A**2 3 5 8 10 12 13 21 **F**1 3 4 7 8 9 16 17 18 19 20 21 22 23 24 25 26 27 29 30 31 32 34 35 36 37 38 39 40 41 43 44 45 46 47 48 49 50 51 53 54 55 57 58 59 60 61 64 65 66 67 68 70 71 72 73 74 75 77 78 79 80 81 82 84 85 86 87 88 89 90 92 93 94 97 98 99 100 101 102 104 105 107 108 109 111 112 114 115 116 117 118 119 126 128 129 130 131 132 134 135 136 142 143 144 145 146 148 **P**6
Primary Contact: M Narendra. Kini, M.D., President and Chief Executive Officer
COO: Martha McGill, Executive Vice President and Chief Operating Officer
CFO: Timothy L Birkenstock, Chief Financial Officer
CMO: Deise Granado–Villar M.D., Chief Medical Officer and Senior Vice President Medical Affairs
CIO: Edward Martinez, Chief Information Officer
CHR: Michael S Kushner, Senior Vice President and Chief Talent Officer
CNO: Jacqueline Gonzalez, Senior Vice President and Chief Nursing Officer
Web address: www.mch.com
Control: Other not–for–profit (including NFP Corporation) **Service**: Children's general medical and surgical

Staffed Beds: 272 **Admissions**: 10544 **Census**: 178 **Outpatient Visits**: 526260
Births: 0 **Total Expense ($000)**: 549138 **Payroll Expense ($000)**: 208242
Personnel: 3851

NORTH SHORE MEDICAL CENTER (100029), 1100 NW 95th Street, Zip 33150–2098; tel. 305/835–6000, (Nonreporting) (Includes FLORIDA MEDICAL CENTER – A CAMPUS OF NORTH SHORE, 5000 West Oakland Park Boulevard, Fort Lauderdale, Florida, Zip 33313–1585, tel. 954/735–6000; Trey Abshier, Chief Executive Officer) **A**1 10 **S** TENET Healthcare Corporation, Dallas, TX
Primary Contact: Manuel Linares, Chief Executive Officer
COO: Shana Crittenden, Chief Operating Officer
CFO: Howard Brown, Chief Financial Officer
CMO: Marcia Bierman M.D., Chief of Staff
CIO: Luis Estrada, Director Multifacility Information Systems
CHR: Carmen Gomez, Director Human Resources
Web address: www.northshoremedical.com
Control: Corporation, Investor–owned (for–profit) **Service**: General medical and surgical

Staffed Beds: 816

PROMISE HOSPITAL OF MIAMI (100326), 14001 NW 82nd Avenue, Zip 33158; tel. 786/609–9200 (Nonreporting) **S** Promise Healthcare, Boca Raton, FL
Primary Contact: Charles Doten, Chief Executive Officer
Web address: www.promise–miami.com
Control: Corporation, Investor–owned (for–profit) **Service**: Acute long–term care hospital

Staffed Beds: 60

SELECT SPECIALTY HOSPITAL–MIAMI (102001), 955 NW 3rd Street, Zip 33128–1274; tel. 305/416–5700, (Nonreporting) **A**1 10 **S** Select Medical Corporation, Mechanicsburg, PA
Primary Contact: Dionisio Bencomo, Chief Executive Officer
Web address: www.selectspecialtyhospitals.com/company/locations/miami.aspx
Control: Corporation, Investor–owned (for–profit) **Service**: Acute long–term care hospital

Staffed Beds: 47

FL

Hospital, Medicare Provider Number, Address, Telephone, Approval, Facility, and Physician Codes, Health Care System

★ American Hospital Association (AHA) membership ○ Healthcare Facilities Accreditation Program ⇑ Center for Improvement in Healthcare Quality Accreditation
☐ The Joint Commission accreditation ◇ DNV Healthcare Inc. accreditation △ Commission on Accreditation of Rehabilitation Facilities (CARF) accreditation

☐ **SISTER EMMANUEL HOSPITAL (102016)**, 3663 South Miami Avenue, Zip 33133–4253; tel. 305/285–2939 **A**1 10 **F**1 3 29 30 31 60 75 77 78 79 82 92 93 148
Primary Contact: Miguel Vasquez, Chief Executive Officer
CFO: Miguel Vasquez, Chief Financial Officer
CMO: Hugo Gonzalez M.D., Chief Medical Officer
CIO: Macarena Restrepo, Manager Business Office
CHR: Kathy Mainieri, Human Resource Specialist
Web address: www.sisteremmanuelhospital.org/
Control: Corporation, Investor–owned (for–profit) **Service**: Acute long–term care hospital

Staffed Beds: 29 **Admissions**: 263 **Census**: 23 **Outpatient Visits**: 0 **Births**: 0
Total Expense ($000): 11819 **Payroll Expense ($000)**: 4663

⇑ **THE MIAMI MEDICAL CENTER (100328)**, 5959 NW Seventh Street, Zip 33126–3198; tel. 305/267–8662, (Nonreporting) **A**10 21
Primary Contact: Jeffrey Mason, Chief Executive Officer
CFO: Alex A Mendez, Chief Financial Officer
Web address: www.miamimedicalcenter.com
Control: Corporation, Investor–owned (for–profit) **Service**: General medical and surgical

Staffed Beds: 69

⊞ **UNIVERSITY OF MIAMI HOSPITAL (100009)**, 1400 NW 12th Avenue, Zip 33136–1003; tel. 305/325–5511 **A**1 2 3 5 10 **F**3 12 15 17 18 20 22 24 26 29 30 31 34 35 38 39 40 43 44 45 46 47 48 49 50 51 54 57 58 59 63 64 68 70 71 74 75 77 78 79 80 81 82 84 85 86 87 90 91 92 93 96 97 98 100 101 102 103 104 105 107 108 110 111 114 115 118 119 126 130 131 135 141 146 148 149 **S** University of Miami Health System, Miami, FL
Primary Contact: Michael B. Gittelman, Interim Chief Executive Officer
CFO: Harry Rohrer, Chief Financial Officer
CMO: Francisco Kerdel M.D., President Medical Staff
CIO: Craig Scott, Interim Director Management Information Systems
CHR: Errol Douglas, Director Human Resources
Web address: www.umiamihospital.com
Control: Other not–for–profit (including NFP Corporation) **Service**: General medical and surgical

Staffed Beds: 464 **Admissions**: 22003 **Census**: 344 **Outpatient Visits**: 165114 **Births**: 0 **Total Expense ($000)**: 445043 **Payroll Expense ($000)**: 136932 **Personnel**: 2091

⊞ **UNIVERSITY OF MIAMI HOSPITAL AND CLINICS (100079)**, 1475 NW 12th Avenue, Zip 33136–1002; tel. 305/243–4000 **A**1 2 3 5 10 **F**3 11 12 15 18 19 29 30 31 32 34 35 36 38 44 45 46 47 48 49 50 52 54 55 57 58 59 61 63 64 65 68 70 74 75 77 78 79 80 81 82 84 85 86 87 91 92 93 97 99 100 101 103 104 107 108 110 111 114 115 117 118 119 120 121 123 124 126 130 132 135 136 141 145 146 147 148 149 **S** University of Miami Health System, Miami, FL
Primary Contact: Richard R. Ballard, Chief Executive Officer and Administrator
CFO: Harry Rohrer, Chief Financial Officer
CMO: W Jarrad Goodwin M.D., Director
Web address: www.uhealthsystem.com
Control: Other not–for–profit (including NFP Corporation) **Service**: Cancer

Staffed Beds: 40 **Admissions**: 1244 **Census**: 32 **Outpatient Visits**: 393425 **Births**: 0 **Total Expense ($000)**: 455320 **Payroll Expense ($000)**: 82827 **Personnel**: 1146

VETERANS AFFAIRS MEDICAL CENTER See Miami Veterans Affairs Healthcare System

⊞ △ **WEST GABLES REHABILITATION HOSPITAL (103036)**, 2525 SW 75th Avenue, Zip 33155–2800; tel. 305/262–6800 **A**1 7 10 **F**7 29 34 74 75 79 87 90 91 93 96 130 131 148 149 **S** Select Medical Corporation, Mechanicsburg, PA
Primary Contact: Walter Concepcion, Chief Executive Officer
CFO: Sara Reohr, Regional Controller
CMO: Jose L Vargas M.D., Medical Director
CHR: Barbara Etchason, HR Manager
CNO: Constance Hughes, Director of Nursing
Web address: www.westgablesrehabhospital.com/
Control: Corporation, Investor–owned (for–profit) **Service**: Rehabilitation

Staffed Beds: 60 **Admissions**: 1393 **Census**: 49 **Outpatient Visits**: 11102 **Births**: 0 **Total Expense ($000)**: 19766 **Payroll Expense ($000)**: 11441 **Personnel**: 188

○ **WESTCHESTER GENERAL HOSPITAL (100284)**, 2500 SW 75th Avenue, Zip 33155–2805; tel. 305/264–5252, (Includes SOUTHERN WINDS HOSPITAL, 4225 West 20th Street, Hialeah, Florida, Zip 33012–5835, tel. 305/558–9700) **A**10 11 12 13 **F**3 15 18 29 31 40 45 49 56 65 70 74 75 77 78 79 81 85 87 98 99 100 102 103 107 108 110 114 115 119 130
Primary Contact: Rudy Garcia, Chief Executive Officer
CFO: Joel Snook, Chief Financial Officer
CMO: Rogelio Zaldivar M.D., Medical Director
CHR: Jennifer Ricardo, Director of Human Resources
Web address: www.westchesterhospital.com
Control: Corporation, Investor–owned (for–profit) **Service**: General medical and surgical

Staffed Beds: 125 **Admissions**: 4766 **Census**: 82 **Outpatient Visits**: 28659 **Births**: 0 **Total Expense ($000)**: 59569 **Payroll Expense ($000)**: 28563 **Personnel**: 522

MIAMI BEACH—Dade County

MIAMI HEART CAMPUS AT MOUNT SINAI MEDICAL CENTER See Mount Sinai Medical Center

☐ △ **MOUNT SINAI MEDICAL CENTER (100034)**, 4300 Alton Road, Zip 33140–2948; tel. 305/674–2121, (Includes MIAMI HEART CAMPUS AT MOUNT SINAI MEDICAL CENTER, 4701 North Meridian Avenue, Miami Beach, Florida, Zip 33140–2910, tel. 305/672–1111) **A**1 2 3 5 7 8 10 13 **F**1 3 4 6 8 9 12 13 14 15 16 17 18 19 20 22 24 26 28 29 30 31 34 35 36 37 38 39 40 41 42 44 45 46 47 48 49 50 51 53 54 55 56 57 58 59 60 61 62 63 64 65 66 67 68 70 71 72 73 74 75 76 77 78 79 80 81 82 83 84 85 86 87 88 89 90 91 92 93 96 97 98 100 101 102 103 104 107 108 110 111 114 115 118 119 120 121 123 124 126 128 129 130 131 132 135 141 143 145 146 147 148 149 **P**6
Primary Contact: Steven D. Sonenreich, President and Chief Executive Officer
COO: Angel Pallin, Senior Vice President of Operations
CFO: Alex A Mendez, Executive Vice President of Operations and Chief Financial Officer
CMO: Robert Goldszer M.D., Senior Vice President and Chief Medical Officer
CIO: Tom Gillette, Senior Vice President and Chief Information Officer
CHR: Georgia McLean, Director Human Resources
CNO: Karen W Moyer R.N., Senior Vice President and Chief Nursing Officer
Web address: www.msmc.com
Control: Other not–for–profit (including NFP Corporation) **Service**: General medical and surgical

Staffed Beds: 608 **Admissions**: 22312 **Census**: 359 **Outpatient Visits**: 200740 **Births**: 2678 **Total Expense ($000)**: 522833 **Payroll Expense ($000)**: 247712 **Personnel**: 3913

MIDDLEBURG—Clay County

⊞ **ST. VINCENT'S MEDICAL CENTER CLAY COUNTY (100321)**, 1670 St. Vincent's Way, Zip 32068–8427, Mailing Address: 1670 St. Vincents Way, 32068–8447; tel. 904/602–1000 **A**1 10 **F**3 15 18 20 29 30 34 40 44 49 57 61 64 65 70 74 79 81 84 85 86 87 93 107 108 110 111 114 115 118 119 124 130 131 132 146 147 149 **S** Ascension Healthcare, Saint Louis, MO
Primary Contact: James Machado, President
Web address: www.jaxhealth.com/
Control: Church operated, Nongovernment, not–for–profit **Service**: General medical and surgical

Staffed Beds: 64 **Admissions**: 5830 **Census**: 56 **Outpatient Visits**: 42875 **Births**: 0 **Total Expense ($000)**: 70848 **Payroll Expense ($000)**: 24917 **Personnel**: 485

MILTON—Santa Rosa County

⊞ **SANTA ROSA MEDICAL CENTER (100124)**, 6002 Berryhill Road, Zip 32570–5062; tel. 850/626–7762 **A**1 10 **F**3 11 13 15 18 20 29 30 34 35 40 45 49 54 57 59 64 65 74 75 76 77 79 81 85 87 97 107 108 111 115 119 126 129 130 132 135 144 146 147 148 149 **S** Community Health Systems, Inc., Franklin, TN
Primary Contact: Doug Sills, Chief Executive Officer
CFO: Jared Whipkey, Chief Financial Officer
CIO: Rick Payne, Director Information Systems
CHR: Christopher Foreman, Director Human Resources
CNO: Trish Davis, Chief Nursing Officer
Web address: www.santarosamedicalcenter.org
Control: Corporation, Investor–owned (for–profit) **Service**: General medical and surgical

Staffed Beds: 68 **Admissions**: 3511 **Census**: 33 **Births**: 360

WEST FLORIDA COMMUNITY CARE CENTER (104027), 5500 Stewart Street, Zip 32570–4304; tel. 850/983–5500 (Nonreporting) **A**10
Primary Contact: Joshua Willis, Chief Executive Officer
Web address: www.elakeviewcenter.org/MentalHealth/Adult/Inpatient–WFCCC.aspx
Control: Other not–for–profit (including NFP Corporation) **Service**: Psychiatric

Staffed Beds: 80

FL

MIRAMAR—Broward County

☒ **MEMORIAL HOSPITAL MIRAMAR (100285)**, 1901 SW 172nd Avenue, Zip 33029–5592; tel. 954/538–5000 **A**1 10 **F**3 13 15 29 30 35 40 41 45 49 50 55 57 59 61 64 68 70 72 74 75 76 78 79 81 82 84 85 87 91 93 107 108 110 111 114 115 119 126 130 131 132 135 145 146 147 **S** Memorial Healthcare System, Hollywood, FL
Primary Contact: Grisel Fernandez–Bravo, R.N., Administrator and Chief Executive Officer
CFO: Judy Sada, Chief Financial Officer
CMO: Stanley Marks M.D., FACS, Chief Medical Officer
CIO: Forest Blanton, Senior VP and Chief Information Officer
CHR: Ray Kendrick, Chief Human Resources Officer
CNO: Denise Reynolds, Chief Nursing Officer
Web address: www.mhs.net
Control: Hospital district or authority, Government, Nonfederal **Service:** General medical and surgical

Staffed Beds: 178 **Admissions:** 9010 **Census:** 87 **Outpatient Visits:** 135521 **Births:** 3459 **Total Expense ($000):** 146506 **Payroll Expense ($000):** 71093 **Personnel:** 876

MIRAMAR BEACH—Walton County

☒ **SACRED HEART HOSPITAL ON THE EMERALD COAST (100292)**, 7800 Highway 98 West, Zip 32550; tel. 850/278–3000 **A**1 10 **F**3 11 15 18 20 22 26 28 29 30 31 34 35 36 37 39 40 44 49 50 51 53 58 59 60 64 68 70 74 75 76 77 78 79 81 82 84 85 86 87 93 96 107 108 110 111 114 115 116 117 118 119 121 123 124 130 132 146 147 148 **S** Ascension Healthcare, Saint Louis, MO
Primary Contact: Roger L. Hall, President
CMO: Gary M. Pablo M.D., Chief Medical Officer
Web address: www.sacredheartemerald.org
Control: Other not–for–profit (including NFP Corporation) **Service:** General medical and surgical

Staffed Beds: 58 **Admissions:** 5207 **Census:** 40 **Births:** 1200 **Total Expense ($000):** 91525 **Payroll Expense ($000):** 2997

NAPLES—Collier County

LANDMARK HOSPITAL OF SOUTHWEST FLORIDA, 1285 Creekside Boulevard East, Zip 34108; tel. 239/529–1800 (Nonreporting) **A**22 **S** Landmark Hospitals, Cape Girardeau, MO
Primary Contact: Jimmy Dascani, Chief Executive Officer
Web address: www.landmarkhospitals.com/naples.aspx
Control: Partnership, Investor–owned (for–profit) **Service:** Acute long–term care hospital

Staffed Beds: 50

☒ △ **NCH DOWNTOWN NAPLES HOSPITAL (100018)**, 350 Seventh Street North, Zip 34102–5754, Mailing Address: P.O.Box 413029, 34101–3029; tel. 239/624–4000, (Includes NCH NORTH NAPLES HOSPITAL, 11190 Health Park Blvd, Naples, Florida, Zip 34110–5729, 11190 Health Park Boulevard, 34110–5729, tel. 239/552–7000) **A**1 2 7 10 **F**3 11 13 14 17 18 20 22 24 26 28 29 30 31 34 35 37 40 41 42 44 45 47 48 49 50 53 56 57 59 64 68 70 72 74 75 76 77 78 79 81 84 85 86 87 88 89 90 91 92 93 95 96 98 100 102 103 107 108 110 111 114 115 116 117 119 126 130 135 146 147 148 149 **P**6
Primary Contact: Allen S. Weiss, M.D., President and Chief Executive Officer
COO: Phillip C Dutcher, Chief Operating Officer
CFO: Mike Stephens, Chief Financial Officer
CMO: Doug Ardion M.D., Chief Medical Officer
CHR: John McGirl, Chief Human Resources Officer
CNO: Michele Thoman R.N., Chief Nursing Officer
Web address: www.nchmd.org
Control: Other not–for–profit (including NFP Corporation) **Service:** General medical and surgical

Staffed Beds: 713 **Admissions:** 29374 **Census:** 373 **Outpatient Visits:** 327616 **Births:** 3644 **Total Expense ($000):** 430427 **Payroll Expense ($000):** 174374 **Personnel:** 2804

☒ **PHYSICIANS REGIONAL – PINE RIDGE (100286)**, 6101 Pine Ridge Road, Zip 34119–3900; tel. 239/348–4000, (Nonreporting) (Includes PHYSICIANS REGIONAL, 8300 Collier Boulevard, Naples, Florida, Zip 34114, tel. 239/354–6000; C Scott Campbell, Market Chief Executive Officer) **A**1 10 **S** Community Health Systems, Inc., Franklin, TN
Primary Contact: Scott Lowe, Interim Market Chief Executive Officer
COO: Susan Takacs, Market Chief Operating Officer
CFO: Ken Warriner, Market Chief Financial Officer
CHR: Jill Gaffoli, Director Human Resources
Web address: www.physiciansregional.com
Control: Corporation, Investor–owned (for–profit) **Service:** General medical and surgical

Staffed Beds: 201

☐ **THE WILLOUGH AT NAPLES (104063)**, 9001 Tamiami Trail East, Zip 34113–3304; tel. 239/775–4500, (Nonreporting) **A**1 10
Primary Contact: James E. O'Shea, Administrator
CFO: Steve Baldwin, Vice President Finance
Web address: www.thewilloughatnaples.com/
Control: Corporation, Investor–owned (for–profit) **Service:** Psychiatric

Staffed Beds: 80

NEW PORT RICHEY—Pasco County

☒ △ **MORTON PLANT NORTH BAY HOSPITAL (100063)**, 6600 Madison Street, Zip 34652–1900; tel. 727/842–8468 **A**1 7 10 **F**3 11 18 20 22 28 29 30 31 34 35 40 44 45 47 49 50 57 58 59 64 68 70 74 75 78 79 81 84 85 86 87 90 91 93 96 98 99 100 102 107 108 111 114 115 118 119 129 130 132 135 143 146 147 149 **S** Morton Plant Mease Health Care, Clearwater, FL
Primary Contact: Sarah Naumowich, Interim President
CFO: Carl Tremonti, Chief Financial Officer
CMO: Jeff Jensen D.O., Vice President, Medical Affairs
CIO: Timothy Thompson, Senior Vice President and Chief Information Officer
CHR: Kyle J Barr, Senior Vice President, Chief Team Resources Officer
CNO: Thomas Doria, Vice President and Patient Services – West
Web address: www.mpmhealth.com
Control: Other not–for–profit (including NFP Corporation) **Service:** General medical and surgical

Staffed Beds: 222 **Admissions:** 12635 **Census:** 169 **Outpatient Visits:** 42065 **Births:** 0 **Total Expense ($000):** 127427 **Payroll Expense ($000):** 52674 **Personnel:** 889

NEW SMYRNA BEACH—Volusia County

☒ **FLORIDA HOSPITAL NEW SMYRNA (100014)**, 401 Palmetto Street, Zip 32168–7399; tel. 386/424–5000, (Data for 275 days) **A**1 10 **F**3 11 15 18 20 22 28 29 30 33 34 40 45 46 49 50 57 59 60 66 68 70 74 78 79 81 84 93 107 108 110 111 114 115 119 120 121 135 148 **S** Adventist Health System Sunbelt Health Care Corporation, Altamonte Springs, FL
Primary Contact: Kenneth R. Mattison, Chief Executive Officer
COO: Steven W Harrell FACHE, Chief Operating Officer
CFO: Al W Allred, Chief Financial Officer
CMO: Eric Lo M.D., Chief Medical Staff
CIO: Calvin Patrick II, Director Information Services
CHR: Nancy K Evolga, Director Human Resources
CNO: Linda G Breum R.N., MSN, Chief Nursing Officer
Web address: www.floridahospital.com/new-smyrna
Control: Church operated, Nongovernment, not–for–profit **Service:** General medical and surgical

Staffed Beds: 95 **Admissions:** 3616 **Census:** 55 **Outpatient Visits:** 73774 **Births:** 0 **Total Expense ($000):** 71958 **Payroll Expense ($000):** 25933

NICEVILLE—Okaloosa County

☒ **TWIN CITIES HOSPITAL (100054)**, 2190 Highway 85 North, Zip 32578–1045; tel. 850/678–4131 **A**1 10 **F**3 29 34 35 45 50 59 70 75 79 81 82 85 93 107 108 110 111 115 119 124 147 149 **S** HCA Healthcare, Nashville, TN
Primary Contact: David Whalen, Chief Executive Officer
CFO: Mark Day, Chief Financial Officer
CHR: Cyndi Ronca, Director Human Resources
Web address: www.tchealthcare.com
Control: Corporation, Investor–owned (for–profit) **Service:** General medical and surgical

Staffed Beds: 65 **Admissions:** 1897 **Census:** 17 **Births:** 0 **Total Expense ($000):** 39372 **Payroll Expense ($000):** 10903

FL

NORTH MIAMI—Miami—Dade County

☐ △ **ST. CATHERINE'S REHABILITATION HOSPITAL (103026)**, 1050 NE 125th Street, Zip 33161–5881; tel. 305/357–1735, (Nonreporting) **A**1 7 10 **S** Catholic Health Services, Lauderdale Lakes, FL
Primary Contact: Jaime Gonzalez, Administrator
COO: Jim Ball, Chief Operating Officer
CFO: Mary Jo Frick, Director Finance
CMO: Miriam Feliz M.D., Medical Director
Web address: www.catholichealthservices.org
Control: Other not–for–profit (including NFP Corporation) **Service:** Rehabilitation

Staffed Beds: 60

NORTH MIAMI BEACH—Miami—Dade County

JACKSON NORTH MEDICAL CENTER See Jackson Health System

OCALA—Marion County

✚ **HEALTHSOUTH REHABILITATION HOSPITAL OF OCALA (103043)**, 2275 SW 22nd Lane, Zip 34471–7710; tel. 352/282–4000 **A**1 10 **F**29 64 75 90 93 96 100 148 **S** HEALTHSOUTH Corporation, Birmingham, AL
Primary Contact: Karthik Muthu, Chief Executive Officer
CFO: Sammy King, Controller
CMO: Amy Clunn M.D., Medical Director
CHR: Tracy Sapp, Director Human Resources
CNO: Wendy Milam, Chief Nursing Officer
Web address: www.healthsouthocala.com
Control: Corporation, Investor–owned (for–profit) **Service:** Rehabilitation

Staffed Beds: 60 **Admissions:** 1443 **Census:** 52 **Outpatient Visits:** 248 **Births:** 0

✚ **KINDRED HOSPITAL OCALA (102019)**, 1500 SW 1st Avenue, Zip 34471–6504; tel. 352/369–0513, (Nonreporting) **A**1 10 **S** Kindred Healthcare, Louisville, KY
Primary Contact: Merlene Bhoorasingh, Administrator
CFO: Dean Cocchi, Chief Financial Officer
Web address: www.kindredocala.com/
Control: Corporation, Investor–owned (for–profit) **Service:** Acute long–term care hospital

Staffed Beds: 31

✚ **MUNROE REGIONAL MEDICAL CENTER (100062)**, 1500 SW 1st Avenue, Zip 34471–6504, Mailing Address: P.O.Box 6000, 34478–6000; tel. 352/351–7200 **A**1 3 5 10 **F**3 12 13 17 18 20 22 24 26 28 29 30 34 35 37 38 40 41 42 45 49 50 51 53 57 59 60 64 65 67 68 70 74 75 76 77 79 81 84 85 86 87 89 91 92 93 96 100 107 108 111 114 115 118 119 126 130 132 146 147 148 **P**6 **S** Community Health Systems, Inc., Franklin, TN
Primary Contact: Philoron A. Wright II, FACHE, Interim Chief Executive Officer
COO: Philoron A. Wright FACHE, II, Chief Operating Officer
CFO: Eric LaChance, Chief Financial Officer
CMO: Lon McPherson M.D., Senior Vice President Medical Affairs and Chief Quality Officer
CIO: Carl Candullo, Chief Information Officer
CNO: Pamela W Michell R.N., Vice President, Chief Nursing Officer
Web address: www.munroeregional.com
Control: Corporation, Investor–owned (for–profit) **Service:** General medical and surgical

Staffed Beds: 300 **Admissions:** 20374 **Census:** 258 **Outpatient Visits:** 110433 **Births:** 2488 **Total Expense ($000):** 266433 **Payroll Expense ($000):** 91957 **Personnel:** 3051

✚ **OCALA REGIONAL MEDICAL CENTER (100212)**, 1431 SW First Avenue, Zip 34471–6500, Mailing Address: P.O.Box 2200, 34478–2200; tel. 352/401–1000, (Nonreporting) (Includes WEST MARION COMMUNITY HOSPITAL, 4600 SW 46th Court, Ocala, Florida, Zip 34474, tel. 352/291–3000) **A**1 2 3 10 13 **S** HCA Healthcare, Nashville, TN
Primary Contact: Chad Christianson, Chief Executive Officer
CMO: Art Osberg M.D., Chief Medical Officer
CIO: Brandon Holbert, Director, Information Services
CHR: Wayne Nielsen, Director Human Resources
Web address: www.ocalaregional.com
Control: Corporation, Investor–owned (for–profit) **Service:** General medical and surgical

Staffed Beds: 270

THE CENTERS (104068), 5664 SW 60th Avenue, Zip 34474–5677; tel. 352/291–5500 (Nonreporting) **A**10
Primary Contact: Timothy Cowart, Chief Executive Officer
Web address: www.thecenters.us
Control: Other not–for–profit (including NFP Corporation) **Service:** Psychiatric

Staffed Beds: 61

THE VINES (104071), 3130 SW 27th Avenue, Zip 34471–4306; tel. 352/671–3130 **A**10 **F**4 5 98 99 101 102 103 104 105 106 147 **S** Universal Health Services, Inc., King of Prussia, PA
Primary Contact: Stephen Quintyne, Chief Executive Officer
Web address: www.thevineshospital.com
Control: Corporation, Investor–owned (for–profit) **Service:** Psychiatric

Staffed Beds: 98 **Admissions:** 2968 **Census:** 50 **Outpatient Visits:** 2030 **Births:** 0

OCOEE—Orange County

✚ **HEALTH CENTRAL HOSPITAL (100030)**, 10000 West Colonial Drive, Zip 34761–3499; tel. 407/296–1000, (Total facility includes 228 beds in nursing home–type unit) **A**1 10 **F**3 8 11 12 15 17 18 20 22 26 28 29 30 34 35 37 40 42 45 49 50 51 57 59 60 74 76 79 80 81 82 85 86 87 93 97 107 108 110 111 115 118 119 128 130 132 144 146 148 149 **P**6 **S** Orlando Health, Orlando, FL
Primary Contact: Mark A. Marsh, President
COO: Rick Smith, Chief Operating Officer
CFO: Michael E Mueller, Chief Financial Officer
CMO: James Barton Rodier M.D., Chief Quality Officer
CIO: John T Sills, Chief Information Officer
CHR: Nancy Dinon, Vice President Human Resources
CNO: Christina Marie McGuirk R.N., Chief Nursing Officer
Web address: www.healthcentral.org
Control: Other not–for–profit (including NFP Corporation) **Service:** General medical and surgical

Staffed Beds: 429 **Admissions:** 11120 **Census:** 336 **Outpatient Visits:** 110893 **Births:** 752 **Total Expense ($000):** 196357 **Payroll Expense ($000):** 87513 **Personnel:** 1231

OKEECHOBEE—Okeechobee County

✚ **RAULERSON HOSPITAL (100252)**, 1796 Highway 441 North, Zip 34972–1918, Mailing Address: P.O.Box 1307, 34973–1307; tel. 863/763–2151, (Nonreporting) **A**1 10 20 **S** HCA Healthcare, Nashville, TN
Primary Contact: Brian Melear, Chief Executive Officer
CFO: Terry L Brown, Chief Financial Officer
CMO: Arif Shakoor, Chief of Staff
CIO: Tim Hearing, Associate Information Technology Director
CHR: Cynthia Jackson, Vice President Human Resources
CNO: Adam Kless, Chief Nursing Officer
Web address: www.raulersonhospital.com
Control: Corporation, Investor–owned (for–profit) **Service:** General medical and surgical

Staffed Beds: 100

ORANGE CITY—Volusia County

✚ **FLORIDA HOSPITAL FISH MEMORIAL (100072)**, 1055 Saxon Boulevard, Zip 32763–8468; tel. 386/917–5000 **A**1 10 **F**1 3 4 11 15 16 17 20 28 29 30 31 34 35 37 40 45 48 49 50 54 59 64 67 70 72 73 74 75 76 77 78 79 80 81 82 85 87 88 89 90 91 92 93 98 100 104 107 108 110 111 114 115 116 117 118 119 120 121 128 129 130 132 135 144 146 147 148 149 **P**8 **S** Adventist Health System Sunbelt Health Care Corporation, Altamonte Springs, FL
Primary Contact: Robert Deininger, Chief Executive Officer
COO: Danielle Johnson, Chief Operating Officer
CFO: Eric Osterly, Chief Financial Officer
CMO: Leighton Smith M.D., Chief Medical Officer
CHR: Jannina Garcia, Director of Human Resources
CNO: Jennifer Shull R.N., Chief Nursing Officer
Web address: www.fhfishmemorial.org
Control: Church operated, Nongovernment, not–for–profit **Service:** General medical and surgical

Staffed Beds: 175 **Admissions:** 9671 **Census:** 121 **Births:** 0 **Total Expense ($000):** 142990 **Payroll Expense ($000):** 57143

ORANGE PARK—Clay County

✚ **ORANGE PARK MEDICAL CENTER (100226)**, 2001 Kingsley Avenue, Zip 32073–5156; tel. 904/639–8500 **A**1 2 3 10 **F**3 8 11 15 17 18 20 22 24 26 28 29 30 31 34 35 40 45 46 48 49 50 60 67 68 70 72 74 76 77 79 81 84 85 87 93 94 97 98 100 101 102 103 104 107 108 110 111 114 115 118 119 126 131 132 135 146 147 148 149 **S** HCA Healthcare, Nashville, TN
Primary Contact: Chad Patrick, President and Chief Executive Officer
COO: J. Christopher Mosley, Chief Operating Officer
CFO: Heath King, Chief Financial Officer
CMO: Lawrence Coots M.D., Chief Medical Officer
CHR: Chris Marlin, Director Human Resources
CNO: Kathy Hester, Chief Nursing Officer
Web address: www.opmedical.com
Control: Corporation, Investor–owned (for–profit) **Service:** General medical and surgical

Staffed Beds: 317 **Admissions:** 19257 **Census:** 225 **Births:** 2383 **Total Expense ($000):** 245825 **Payroll Expense ($000):** 76741

FL

Many Facility Codes have changed. Please refer to the AHA Guide Code Chart. © 2017 AHA Guide

ORLANDO—Orange County

ARNOLD PALMER CHILDREN'S HOSPITAL See Orlando Regional Medical Center

ASPIRE HEALTH PARTNERS (104067), 1800 Mercy Drive, Zip 32808–5646; tel. 407/875–3700 **A**10 **F**5 29 35 38 61 66 98 99 102 104 106 130 132 134 143 146
Primary Contact: Jerry Kassab, President and Chief Executive Officer
Web address: www.lakesidecares.org
Control: Other not–for–profit (including NFP Corporation) **Service:** Psychiatric

Staffed Beds: 64 **Admissions:** 1728 **Census:** 51 **Outpatient Visits:** 28800 **Births:** 0

☐ **CENTRAL FLORIDA BEHAVIORAL HOSPITAL (104072)**, 6601 Central Florida Parkway, Zip 32821–8064; tel. 407/370–0111 (Nonreporting) **A**1 5 10 **S** Universal Health Services, Inc., King of Prussia, PA
Primary Contact: Vickie Lewis, Chief Executive Officer
CFO: Marsha Burick, Chief Financial Officer
Web address: www.centralfloridabehavioral.com
Control: Other not–for–profit (including NFP Corporation) **Service:** Psychiatric

Staffed Beds: 126

★ △ ⇑ **FLORIDA HOSPITAL (100007)**, 601 East Rollins Street, Zip 32803–1248; tel. 407/303–6611, (Includes FLORIDA HOSPITAL CELEBRATION HEALTH, 400 Celebration Place, Celebration, Florida, Zip 34747, tel. 407/303–4000; Monica Reed, M.D., Administrator; FLORIDA HOSPITAL EAST ORLANDO, 7727 Lake Underhill Drive, Orlando, Florida, Zip 32822, tel. 407/277–8110; FLORIDA HOSPITAL FOR CHILDREN–WALT DISNEY PAVILION, 601 East Rollins Street, Orlando, Florida, Zip 32803–1248, tel. 407/303–9732; Lars D Houmann, President; FLORIDA HOSPITAL KISSIMMEE, 2450 North Orange Blossom Trai, Kissimmee, Florida, Zip 34741, tel. 407/846–4343; William Haupt, Administrator; FLORIDA HOSPITAL–ALTAMONTE, 601 East Altamonte Drive, Altamonte Springs, Florida, Zip 32701, tel. 407/830–4321; David Ottati, Regional Chief Executive Officer; FLORIDA HOSPITAL–APOPKA, 201 North Park Avenue, Apopka, Florida, Zip 32703, tel. 407/889–2566; Verbelee Neilsen Swanson, Administrator; WINTER PARK MEMORIAL HOSPITAL, 200 North Lakemont Avenue, Winter Park, Florida, Zip 32792–3273, tel. 407/646–7000; Ken Bradley, Administrator) **A**2 3 5 7 8 10 21 **F**3 6 7 9 11 12 13 15 17 18 19 20 21 22 23 24 25 26 27 28 29 30 31 32 34 35 36 37 38 39 40 41 42 44 45 46 47 48 49 50 51 53 54 56 57 58 59 60 61 62 64 65 66 68 70 71 72 73 74 75 76 77 78 79 80 81 82 84 85 86 87 88 89 90 92 93 94 96 97 98 100 101 102 103 107 108 109 110 111 112 113 114 115 116 117 118 119 120 121 123 124 126 129 130 131 132 134 135 136 137 138 139 140 141 142 145 146 147 148 149 **P**1 5 6 **S** Adventist Health System Sunbelt Health Care Corporation, Altamonte Springs, FL
Primary Contact: Daryl Tol, President and Chief Executive Officer
COO: Brian Paradis, Chief Operating Officer
CFO: Eddie Soler, Chief Financial Officer
CMO: David Moorhead M.D., Chief Medical Officer
CHR: Sheryl Dodds, Chief Clinical Officer
Web address: www.floridahospital.com/orlando
Control: Other not–for–profit (including NFP Corporation) **Service:** General medical and surgical

Staffed Beds: 2829 **Admissions:** 151183 **Census:** 1949 **Outpatient Visits:** 1193717 **Births:** 11632 **Total Expense ($000):** 3081221 **Payroll Expense ($000):** 1138703 **Personnel:** 18487

✠ **NEMOURS CHILDREN'S HOSPITAL (103304)**, 13535 Nemours Parkway, Zip 32827–7402; tel. 407/567–4000 **A**1 5 10 **F**7 8 17 18 19 21 23 25 27 29 30 31 34 35 39 40 41 45 53 55 61 68 72 73 74 75 77 78 79 81 82 85 88 89 90 91 92 93 97 107 111 115 116 118 119 129 130 131 144 146 148 149 **S** Nemours, Jacksonville, FL
Primary Contact: Dana Bledsoe, MS, R.N., Chief Executive Officer
CMO: Lane Donnelly M.D., Chief Medical Officer
Web address: www.nemours.org
Control: Other not–for–profit (including NFP Corporation) **Service:** Children's general medical and surgical

Staffed Beds: 80 **Admissions:** 2733 **Census:** 39 **Outpatient Visits:** 79755 **Births:** 0 **Total Expense ($000):** 170343 **Payroll Expense ($000):** 50415 **Personnel:** 776

✠ △ **ORLANDO REGIONAL MEDICAL CENTER (100006)**, 52 West Underwood Street, Zip 32806; tel. 407/841–5111, (Includes ARNOLD PALMER CHILDREN'S HOSPITAL, 92 West Miller Street, Orlando, Florida, Zip 32806, tel. 407/649–6960; Kathy Swanson, President; ORLANDO REGIONAL SOUTH SEMINOLE HOSPITAL, 555 West State Road 434, Longwood, Florida, Zip 32750–4999, tel. 407/767–1200; Karen Frenier, President; WINNIE PALMER HOSPITAL FOR WOMEN AND BABIES, 83 West Miller Street, Orlando, Florida, Zip 32806, tel. 321/843–2201; Kathy Swanson, President) **A**1 2 3 5 7 10 **F**3 4 7 8 11 12 13 15 16 17 18 19 20 21 22 23 24 25 26 27 28 29 30 31 34 35 36 37 40 41 43 44 45 46 47 48 49 50 51 53 54 55 57 58 59 60 61 62 64 68 70 71 72 73 74 75 76 77 78 79 80 81 82 84 85 86 87 88 89 90 91 92 93 94 96 97 98 99 100 101 102 103 104 107 108 110 111 114 115 116 117 118 119 120 121 122 123 124 126 129 130 131 132 134 135 143 146 147 148 149 **P**6 **S** Orlando Health, Orlando, FL
Primary Contact: Mark A. Jones, President
COO: Carlos Carrasco, Chief Operating Officer
CFO: Bernadette Spong, Chief Financial Officer
CMO: Aurelio Duran, Chief of Staff
CIO: Rick Schooler, Vice President and Chief Information Officer
CHR: Greg Thompson, Corporate Director, Human Resources
CNO: Jayne Willis, Vice President Nursing and Chief Nursing Officer
Web address: www.orlandohealth.com/facilities/orlando–regional–medical–center
Control: Other not–for–profit (including NFP Corporation) **Service:** General medical and surgical

Staffed Beds: 1181 **Admissions:** 76488 **Census:** 1054 **Outpatient Visits:** 886321 **Births:** 14602 **Total Expense ($000):** 1686375 **Payroll Expense ($000):** 664707 **Personnel:** 12489

ORLANDO VA MEDICAL CENTER, 13800 Veterans Way, Zip 32827–7403; tel. 407/631–1000 (Nonreporting) **S** Department of Veterans Affairs, Washington, DC
Primary Contact: Timothy Liezert, Medical Center Director
Web address: www.orlando.va.gov
Control: Veterans Affairs, Government, federal **Service:** General medical and surgical

Staffed Beds: 134

✠ **SELECT SPECIALTY HOSPITAL–ORLANDO (102003)**, 2250 Bedford Road, Zip 32803–1443; tel. 407/303–7869, (Nonreporting) (Includes SELECT SPECIALTY HOSPITAL–ORLANDO SOUTH, 5579 South Orange Avenue, Orlando, Florida, Zip 32809–3493, tel. 407/241–4800) **A**1 10 **S** Select Medical Corporation, Mechanicsburg, PA
Primary Contact: Theodore Mena, Chief Executive Officer
Web address: www.selectspecialtyhospitals.com/company/locations/orlando.aspx
Control: Corporation, Investor–owned (for–profit) **Service:** Acute long–term care hospital

Staffed Beds: 75

WINNIE PALMER HOSPITAL FOR WOMEN AND BABIES See Orlando Regional Medical Center

OVIEDO—Seminole County

★ **OVIEDO MEDICAL CENTER**, 8300 Red Bug Lake Road, Zip 32765–6801; tel. 407/890–2273 (Nonreporting) **S** HCA Healthcare, Nashville, TN
Primary Contact: Kenneth C. Donahey, Chief Executive Officer
Web address: www.oviedomedicalcenter.com
Control: Other not–for–profit (including NFP Corporation) **Service:** General medical and surgical

Staffed Beds: 64

OXFORD—Sumter County

PROMISE HOSPITAL OF FLORIDA AT THE VILLAGES (102028), 5050 County Road, Zip 34484; tel. 352/689–6400 **A**10 **F**1 29 75 77 82 84 90 98 107 119 **P**5 **S** Promise Healthcare, Boca Raton, FL
Primary Contact: Hoyt Ross, Chief Executive Officer
CNO: Janice M McCoy MS, R.N., Chief Clinical Officer
Web address: www.promise–villages.com
Control: Corporation, Investor–owned (for–profit) **Service:** Acute long–term care hospital

Staffed Beds: 40 **Admissions:** 489 **Census:** 33 **Births:** 0

FL

Hospital, Medicare Provider Number, Address, Telephone, Approval, Facility, and Physician Codes, Health Care System

★ American Hospital Association (AHA) membership ○ Healthcare Facilities Accreditation Program ⇑ Center for Improvement in Healthcare Quality Accreditation
☐ The Joint Commission accreditation ◇ DNV Healthcare Inc. accreditation △ Commission on Accreditation of Rehabilitation Facilities (CARF) accreditation

PALATKA—Putnam County

☒ **PUTNAM COMMUNITY MEDICAL CENTER (100232)**, 611 Zeagler Drive,
Zip 32177–3810; tel. 386/328–5711 **A**1 10 **F**3 11 13 15 18 20 22 29 30 34 35
40 45 49 50 51 54 57 59 60 64 68 70 74 75 76 77 79 81 85 87 93 107 108
110 111 114 115 119 129 130 133 135 146 147 148 149 **S** HCA Healthcare,
Nashville, TN
Primary Contact: J. Christopher. Mosley, Chief Executive Officer
CFO: Stewart Whitmore, Chief Financial Officer
CIO: Yvette A Jones, Health Information Management Director
CHR: John Schneider, Human Resources Director
CNO: Kari Bolin, Chief Nursing Officer
Web address: www.pcmcfl.com
Control: Corporation, Investor–owned (for–profit) **Service**: General medical and
surgical

Staffed Beds: 99 **Admissions:** 5191 **Census:** 55 **Births:** 289 **Total Expense
($000):** 67435 **Payroll Expense ($000):** 22809

PALM BAY—Brevard County

☐ **HEALTH FIRST PALM BAY HOSPITAL (100316)**, 1425 Malabar Road NE,
Zip 32907–2506; tel. 321/434–8000 **A**1 5 10 **F**3 11 20 29 30 34 35 40 45 50
59 60 61 64 68 70 74 75 77 79 81 84 85 86 98 102 103 104 105 107 108
110 111 114 115 119 130 146 148 149 **S** Health First, Inc., Rockledge, FL
Primary Contact: Aaron Robinson, Chief Executive Officer, Health First Community
Hospitals
COO: Deborah Angerami, Chief Operating Officer, Health First Community Hospitals
CFO: Joseph G Felkner, Executive Vice President and Chief Financial Officer
CMO: Lee Scheinbart M.D., Vice President Medical Affairs, Health First Community
Hospitals
CIO: Alex Popowycz, Senior Vice President and Chief Information Officer
CHR: Paula Just, Chief Human Resources Officer
CNO: Connie Bradley R.N., MSN, FACHE, Chief Nursing Officer
Web address: www.health–first.org/hospitals_services/pbch/index.cfm
Control: Other not–for–profit (including NFP Corporation) **Service**: General
medical and surgical

Staffed Beds: 133 **Admissions:** 5869 **Census:** 70 **Outpatient Visits:** 86496
Births: 0 **Total Expense ($000):** 88386 **Payroll Expense ($000):** 38234
Personnel: 502

PALM BEACH GARDENS—Palm Beach County

☒ **PALM BEACH GARDENS MEDICAL CENTER (100176)**, 3360 Burns Road,
Zip 33410–4323; tel. 561/622–1411, (Nonreporting) **A**1 10 **S** TENET Healthcare
Corporation, Dallas, TX
Primary Contact: Dianne Goldenberg, Chief Executive Officer
COO: Teresa C. Urquhart, Chief Operating Officer
CFO: Judi Stimson, Chief Financial Officer
CIO: James Vega, Director Information Systems
CHR: Kevin Caracciolo, Chief Human Resources Officer
Web address: www.pbgmc.com
Control: Corporation, Investor–owned (for–profit) **Service**: General medical and
surgical

Staffed Beds: 199

PALM COAST—Flagler County

☒ **FLORIDA HOSPITAL–FLAGLER (100118)**, 60 Memorial Medical Parkway,
Zip 32164–5980; tel. 386/586–2000 **A**1 2 10 **F**3 8 11 15 18 20 21 28 29 30
31 34 35 40 45 46 47 49 50 51 54 57 59 60 62 63 64 68 70 74 75 77 78 79
81 83 84 85 86 87 92 93 97 107 108 109 110 111 114 115 116 117 119 120
121 123 124 126 130 131 132 135 146 147 148 **P**6 **S** Adventist Health System
Sunbelt Health Care Corporation, Altamonte Springs, FL
Primary Contact: Ronald Jimenez, M.D., Chief Executive Officer
COO: JoAnne King, Chief Operating Officer
CFO: Cory Domayer, Chief Financial Officer
CMO: Ron Thomas M.D., Chief Medical Officer
CHR: Joshua I Champion, Director
CNO: Robert Davis, Chief Nursing Officer
Web address: www.floridahospitalflagler.com/
Control: Church operated, Nongovernment, not–for–profit **Service**: General
medical and surgical

Staffed Beds: 99 **Admissions:** 7810 **Census:** 91 **Births:** 0 **Total Expense
($000):** 158871 **Payroll Expense ($000):** 66651

PANAMA CITY—Bay County

☒ **BAY MEDICAL CENTER SACRED HEART HEALTH SYSTEM (100026)**,
615 North Bonita Avenue, Zip 32401–3600, Mailing Address: P.O.Box 59515,
32412–0515; tel. 850/769–1511 **A**1 2 10 **F**3 11 13 14 15 17 18 20 22 24 26
28 29 30 31 34 35 40 43 45 47 49 50 53 54 57 58 59 60 61 64 65 68 70 74
75 76 77 78 79 81 85 87 89 93 107 108 109 110 111 114 115 119 126 129
130 131 132 144 146 149 **S** Ardent Health Services, Nashville, TN
Primary Contact: Stephen Grubbs, Chief Executive Officer
COO: Randy Currin, Chief Operating Officer
CHR: Donna Baird, Vice President Corporate Services
CNO: Jan Thornton, Chief Nursing Officer
Web address: www.baymedical.org
Control: Corporation, Investor–owned (for–profit) **Service**: General medical and
surgical

Staffed Beds: 286 **Admissions:** 14135 **Census:** 213 **Outpatient Visits:**
128322 **Births:** 484 **Total Expense ($000):** 214902 **Payroll Expense
($000):** 67952 **Personnel:** 1471

☐ **EMERALD COAST BEHAVIORAL HOSPITAL (104073)**, 1940 Harrison Avenue,
Zip 32405–4542; tel. 850/763–0017 (Nonreporting) **A**1 10 **S** Universal Health
Services, Inc., King of Prussia, PA
Primary Contact: Tim Bedford, Chief Executive Officer
CFO: Michael J Zenone, Chief Financial Officer
CMO: Roy Deal, Chief Medical Officer
CNO: Michael B Barbour, Chief Nursing Officer
Web address: www.emeraldcoastbehavioral.com
Control: Corporation, Investor–owned (for–profit) **Service**: Psychiatric

Staffed Beds: 86

☒ **GULF COAST MEDICAL CENTER (100242)**, 449 West 23rd Street, Zip 32405–
4593, Mailing Address: P.O.Box 15309, 32406–5309; tel. 850/769–8341 **A**1 2
10 **F**3 8 12 13 15 20 22 26 29 30 31 34 35 37 39 40 41 46 47 48 49 51 54
56 57 59 60 64 68 70 72 74 75 76 77 78 79 80 81 85 86 87 89 93 107 108
109 111 114 116 117 118 119 126 130 131 132 135 144 146 147 148 149 **S**
HCA Healthcare, Nashville, TN
Primary Contact: Brad Griffin, Chief Executive Officer
COO: Holly Jackson, Chief Operating Officer
CFO: Laurie Haynes, Chief Financial Officer
CHR: Tracy McGlon, Director Human Resources
CNO: Mary Reval R.N., MSN, Chief Nursing Officer
Web address: www.egulfcoastmedical.com
Control: Corporation, Investor–owned (for–profit) **Service**: General medical and
surgical

Staffed Beds: 176 **Admissions:** 11938 **Census:** 123 **Births:** 2428 **Total
Expense ($000):** 163093 **Payroll Expense ($000):** 47708

☒ **HEALTHSOUTH EMERALD COAST REHABILITATION HOSPITAL (103040)**,
1847 Florida Avenue, Zip 32405–4640; tel. 850/914–8600 **A**1 10 **F**3 28 29
34 57 59 68 75 77 85 86 87 90 91 95 96 130 131 132 148 **S** HEALTHSOUTH
Corporation, Birmingham, AL
Primary Contact: Tony N. Bennett, Chief Executive Officer
CFO: Bradley Tilghman, Controller
CMO: Michael Hennigan M.D., Medical Director
CHR: Traci Powell, Director Human Resources
CNO: Sharon Hamilton, Chief Nursing Officer
Web address: www.healthsouthpanamacity.com
Control: Corporation, Investor–owned (for–profit) **Service**: Rehabilitation

Staffed Beds: 75 **Admissions:** 1631 **Census:** 56 **Outpatient Visits:** 0
Births: 0 **Total Expense ($000):** 20615 **Payroll Expense ($000):** 10719
Personnel: 213

☒ **SELECT SPECIALTY HOSPITAL–PANAMA CITY (102017)**, 615 North Bonita
Avenue, 3rd Floor, Zip 32401–3623; tel. 850/767–3180 **A**1 10 **F**1 3 29 148 **S**
Select Medical Corporation, Mechanicsburg, PA
Primary Contact: Randal S. Hamilton, Chief Executive Officer
CMO: Amir Manzoor M.D., Medical Director
Web address: www.selectspecialtyhospitals.com/company/locations/panamacity.
aspx
Control: Corporation, Investor–owned (for–profit) **Service**: Acute long–term care
hospital

Staffed Beds: 30 **Admissions:** 371 **Census:** 29 **Outpatient Visits:** 0 **Births:**
0 **Total Expense ($000):** 14310 **Payroll Expense ($000):** 6117

FL

PEMBROKE PINES—Broward County

⊞ **MEMORIAL HOSPITAL PEMBROKE (100230)**, 7800 Sheridan Street, Zip 33024–2536; tel. 954/883–8482 **A**1 10 **F**3 12 17 29 30 34 40 42 44 45 46 47 48 49 50 51 59 64 65 66 70 74 75 79 81 82 85 86 87 107 108 111 114 115 119 126 130 132 144 146 148 **S** Memorial Healthcare System, Hollywood, FL
Primary Contact: Mark Doyle, Administrator and Chief Executive Officer
CFO: Joseph Stuczynski, Assistant Administrator Finance and Support
CMO: Stanley Marks M.D., FACS, Chief Medical Officer
CIO: Forest Blanton, Chief Information Officer
CNO: Judy Frum R.N., Chief Nursing Officer
Web address: www.memorialpembroke.com/
Control: Hospital district or authority, Government, Nonfederal **Service**: General medical and surgical

Staffed Beds: 157 **Admissions**: 6849 **Census**: 81 **Outpatient Visits**: 66219 **Births**: 0 **Total Expense ($000)**: 139789 **Payroll Expense ($000)**: 57841 **Personnel**: 813

⊞ **MEMORIAL HOSPITAL WEST (100281)**, 703 North Flamingo Road, Zip 33028–1014; tel. 954/436–5000 **A**1 2 10 **F**3 12 13 15 17 18 20 22 26 28 29 30 31 34 35 36 40 41 45 46 47 49 53 55 56 57 58 60 61 68 70 72 74 75 76 78 79 81 82 84 85 87 91 93 107 108 110 111 114 115 119 120 121 123 124 126 130 131 132 136 145 146 147 **S** Memorial Healthcare System, Hollywood, FL
Primary Contact: Leah A. Carpenter, Administrator and Chief Executive Officer
CFO: Walter Bussell, Chief Financial Officer
CMO: Eric Freling M.D., Director Medical Staff Affairs
CIO: Forest Blanton, Chief Information Officer
CHR: Maria Naranjo, Director Human Resources
Web address: www.mhs.net
Control: Hospital district or authority, Government, Nonfederal **Service**: General medical and surgical

Staffed Beds: 384 **Admissions**: 21149 **Census**: 274 **Outpatient Visits**: 287044 **Births**: 3924 **Total Expense ($000)**: 401676 **Payroll Expense ($000)**: 158928 **Personnel**: 2046

PENSACOLA—Escambia County

⊞ **BAPTIST HOSPITAL (100093)**, 1000 West Moreno, Zip 32501–2316, Mailing Address: P.O.Box 17500, 32522–7500; tel. 850/434–4011 **A**1 2 3 10 **F**3 8 11 12 13 15 17 18 20 22 24 26 28 29 30 31 34 35 37 40 43 45 46 47 48 49 50 51 53 54 55 56 57 58 59 60 61 63 64 67 70 71 74 75 76 77 78 79 80 81 82 84 85 86 87 91 92 93 97 98 99 100 101 102 103 104 107 108 110 111 114 115 116 117 118 119 120 121 123 124 126 130 131 132 135 146 147 148 **S** Baptist Health Care Corporation, Pensacola, FL
Primary Contact: Scott Raynes, President
CFO: Sharon Nobles, Interim Chief Financial Officer
CMO: Mike Oleksyk M.D., Vice President and Chief Medical Officer
CIO: Steven Sarros, Vice President and Chief Information Officer
CHR: Darlene Stone, Vice President Human Resources
CNO: Cynde Gamache R.N., Vice President and Chief Nursing Officer
Web address: www.ebaptisthealthcare.org
Control: Other not–for–profit (including NFP Corporation) **Service**: General medical and surgical

Staffed Beds: 337 **Admissions**: 18887 **Census**: 240 **Outpatient Visits**: 250247 **Births**: 991 **Total Expense ($000)**: 286612 **Payroll Expense ($000)**: 94126 **Personnel**: 1686

⊞ **NAVAL HOSPITAL PENSACOLA**, 6000 West Highway 98, Zip 32512–0003; tel. 850/505–6601, (Nonreporting) **A**1 3 5 **S** Bureau of Medicine and Surgery, Department of the Navy, Falls Church, VA
Primary Contact: Commander Devin Morrison, Director Administration
COO: CommanderDevin Morrison, Director for Administration
CMO: CommanderCarolyn Rice M.D., Director Medical Services
CIO: Lieutenant CommanderWilliam Berg, Chief Information Officer
CHR: CommanderDevin Morrison, Director for Administration
CNO: CaptainAmy Tarbay, Director Nursing Services
Web address: www.med.navy.mil/sites/pcola/Pages/default.aspx
Control: Navy, Government, federal **Service**: General medical and surgical

Staffed Beds: 28

⊞ **SACRED HEART HOSPITAL PENSACOLA (100025)**, 5151 North Ninth Avenue, Zip 32504–8795, Mailing Address: P.O.Box 2700, 32513–2700; tel. 850/416–7000 **A**1 2 3 5 10 13 **F**3 8 11 12 13 15 17 18 19 20 21 22 24 26 28 29 30 31 34 35 40 41 43 45 46 47 48 49 50 54 55 57 58 59 60 61 65 70 71 72 73 74 75 76 77 78 79 81 82 84 85 87 88 89 90 92 93 96 97 107 108 110 111 112 114 116 117 119 120 124 126 130 131 132 135 145 146 147 148 149 **S** Ascension Healthcare, Saint Louis, MO
Primary Contact: Henry Stovall, President
COO: Terri Smith, Chief Operating Officer
CFO: C Susan Cornejo, Chief Financial Officer
CMO: Peter Jennings M.D., Chief Medical Officer
CIO: Donna Roach, Chief Information Officer
CHR: Michelle Adamolekun, Vice President Human Resource Market Lead Florida/Alabama Ministry Market
CNO: Terrie Fontenot, Chief Nursing Officer
Web address: www.sacred–heart.org
Control: Other not–for–profit (including NFP Corporation) **Service**: General medical and surgical

Staffed Beds: 440 **Admissions**: 24954 **Census**: 336 **Outpatient Visits**: 321967 **Births**: 3691 **Total Expense ($000)**: 423476 **Payroll Expense ($000)**: 123895

⊞ **SELECT SPECIALTY HOSPITAL–PENSACOLA (102024)**, 7000 Cobble Creek Drive, Zip 32504–8638; tel. 850/473–4800, (Nonreporting) **A**1 10 **S** Select Medical Corporation, Mechanicsburg, PA
Primary Contact: David Goodson, Chief Executive Officer
CMO: John Bray M.D., Medical Director
Web address: www.selectspecialtyhospitals.com/company/locations/pensacola.aspx
Control: Corporation, Investor–owned (for–profit) **Service**: Acute long–term care hospital

Staffed Beds: 75

⊞ △ **WEST FLORIDA HOSPITAL (100231)**, 8383 North Davis Highway, Zip 32514–6088; tel. 850/494–4000, (Nonreporting) (Includes THE PAVILION, 8383 North Davis Highway, Pensacola, Florida, Zip 32523, P O Box 18900, 32523, tel. 904/494–5000; WEST FLORIDA REHABILITATION INSTITUTE, 8383 North Davis Highway, Pensacola, Florida, Zip 32514, P O Box 18900, 32523, tel. 850/494–6000) **A**1 2 7 10 **S** HCA Healthcare, Nashville, TN
Primary Contact: Carlton Ulmer, President and Chief Executive Officer
COO: Jessica O'Neal, Chief Operating Officer
CFO: Randy Butler, Chief Financial Officer
CMO: Terry Stallings M.D., Chief Medical Officer
CIO: Jeff Amerson, Director Information System
CHR: Wanda Salley, Vice President Human Resources
CNO: Karen White–Trevino, Chief Nursing Officer
Web address: www.westfloridahospital.com
Control: Corporation, Investor–owned (for–profit) **Service**: General medical and surgical

Staffed Beds: 339

WEST FLORIDA REHABILITATION INSTITUTE See West Florida Hospital

PERRY—Taylor County

DOCTOR'S MEMORIAL HOSPITAL (100106), 333 North Byron Butler Parkway, Zip 32347–2300; tel. 850/584–0800 **A**10 20 **F**3 7 11 15 29 30 34 35 40 45 50 57 59 62 70 81 85 89 90 93 107 110 111 114 119 127 129 132 133 146
Primary Contact: Thomas J. Stone, FACHE, Chief Executive Officer
CMO: Ron Emerick M.D., Chief of Staff
CHR: Sarah Brus, Director Human Resources
CNO: Mary Lescher, Chief Clinical Officer
Web address: www.doctorsmemorial.com
Control: Other not–for–profit (including NFP Corporation) **Service**: General medical and surgical

Staffed Beds: 24 **Admissions**: 842 **Census**: 7 **Births**: 2 **Total Expense ($000)**: 25408 **Payroll Expense ($000)**: 11506

FL

Hospital, Medicare Provider Number, Address, Telephone, Approval, Facility, and Physician Codes, Health Care System

★ American Hospital Association (AHA) membership
□ The Joint Commission accreditation
○ Healthcare Facilities Accreditation Program
◇ DNV Healthcare Inc. accreditation
⇑ Center for Improvement in Healthcare Quality Accreditation
△ Commission on Accreditation of Rehabilitation Facilities (CARF) accreditation

© 2017 AHA Guide   *Many Facility Codes have changed. Please refer to the AHA Guide Code Chart.*   Hospitals **A139**

PLANT CITY—Hillsborough County

SOUTH FLORIDA BAPTIST HOSPITAL (100132), 301 North Alexander Street, Zip 33563–4303; tel. 813/757–1200 **A**1 10 **F**3 11 12 13 15 18 20 22 28 29 30 31 34 35 37 40 41 44 45 47 48 49 50 51 57 59 60 64 68 70 71 74 75 76 77 78 79 81 85 87 89 93 107 108 110 111 114 115 118 119 124 126 130 131 132 135 145 146 147 148 **S** Trinity Health, Livonia, MI
Primary Contact: Karen Kerr, R.N., President
COO: Beth Tancredo, Director Operations
CFO: Carl Tremonti, Chief Financial Officer
CMO: Mark Vaaler M.D., Chief Medical Officer
CIO: Tim Thompson, Senior Vice President, Chief Information Officer
CHR: Pat Lipton, Director Team Resources
CNO: Teresa Colletti, Director Patient Services
Web address: www.baycare.org/sfbh
Control: Other not-for-profit (including NFP Corporation) **Service:** General medical and surgical

Staffed Beds: 124 **Admissions:** 7451 **Census:** 76 **Outpatient Visits:** 57956 **Births:** 520 **Total Expense ($000):** 108159 **Payroll Expense ($000):** 40923 **Personnel:** 708

PLANTATION—Broward County

PLANTATION GENERAL HOSPITAL (100167), 401 NW 42nd Avenue, Zip 33317–2882; tel. 954/587–5010, (Nonreporting) (Includes MERCY HOSPITAL – A CAMPUS OF PLANTATION GENERAL HOSPITAL, 3663 South Miami Avenue, Miami, Florida, Zip 33133–4237, tel. 305/854–4400; Barbara Simmons, R.N., Chief Executive Officer) **A**1 2 3 10 **S** HCA Healthcare, Nashville, TN
Primary Contact: Madeline Nava, Chief Executive Officer
COO: Patrick Rohan, Chief Operating Officer
CFO: Irfan Mirza, Chief Financial Officer
CIO: Mia McGlynn, Director Management Information Systems
CHR: Jennifer Allen, Vice President Human Resources
Web address: www.plantationgeneral.com/
Control: Corporation, Investor-owned (for-profit) **Service:** General medical and surgical

Staffed Beds: 264

WESTSIDE REGIONAL MEDICAL CENTER (100228), 8201 West Broward Boulevard, Zip 33324–2701; tel. 954/473–6600 **A**1 10 **F**3 8 11 15 17 18 20 22 24 26 29 30 31 34 35 40 44 45 48 49 50 57 59 60 68 70 74 75 77 78 79 80 81 82 85 86 87 93 107 108 110 111 114 115 117 119 126 129 130 131 132 145 146 148 **S** HCA Healthcare, Nashville, TN
Primary Contact: Barbara Simmons, R.N., Chief Executive Officer
COO: Shana Sappington-Crittenden, Chief Operating Officer
CFO: Kevin Corcoran, Chief Financial Officer
CMO: Brian Weinstein M.D., Chief of Staff
CIO: Andres Blanco, Director Management Information Systems
CHR: Maria Rivera, Director Human Resources
Web address: www.westsideregional.com
Control: Corporation, Investor-owned (for-profit) **Service:** General medical and surgical

Staffed Beds: 224 **Admissions:** 14338 **Census:** 178 **Births:** 0 **Total Expense ($000):** 183015 **Payroll Expense ($000):** 54342

PORT CHARLOTTE—Charlotte County

BAYFRONT HEALTH PORT CHARLOTTE (100077), 2500 Harbor Boulevard, Zip 33952–5000; tel. 941/766–4122 **A**1 5 10 **F**12 13 15 17 18 20 22 24 26 29 30 34 40 45 46 48 49 50 54 64 70 72 74 75 76 77 79 81 85 89 93 107 111 114 115 119 126 132 135 146 147 148 **S** Community Health Systems, Inc., Franklin, TN
Primary Contact: Timothy J. Cerullo, Chief Executive Officer
COO: Brian Cruddas, Chief Operating Officer
CFO: Jeffrey Mullis, Interim Chief Financial Officer
CMO: Thomas Noone M.D., Chief Medical Officer
CHR: Karen Gardiner, Human Resources Director
CNO: Debra Clark, Chief Nursing Officer
Web address: www.bayfrontcharlotte.com
Control: Corporation, Investor-owned (for-profit) **Service:** General medical and surgical

Staffed Beds: 254 **Admissions:** 10195 **Census:** 137 **Outpatient Visits:** 50998 **Births:** 983 **Total Expense ($000):** 128511 **Payroll Expense ($000):** 44084 **Personnel:** 860

△ **FAWCETT MEMORIAL HOSPITAL (100236)**, 21298 Olean Boulevard, Zip 33952–6765; tel. 941/629–1181 **A**1 2 7 10 **F**3 8 15 18 20 22 26 29 30 31 34 35 40 45 46 47 48 49 51 57 59 64 70 74 75 77 78 79 81 85 86 87 90 91 93 96 107 108 110 111 114 119 131 132 146 147 148 **S** HCA Healthcare, Nashville, TN
Primary Contact: William Hawley, President and Chief Executive Officer
COO: Sally Seymour, Chief Operating Officer
CFO: Phillip Baker, Vice President and Chief Financial Officer
CMO: Mark Callman M.D., Chief Medical Officer
CHR: Linda Bryan, Vice President Human Resources
CNO: Marcy Frisina, Chief Nursing Officer
Web address: www.fawcetthospital.com
Control: Corporation, Investor-owned (for-profit) **Service:** General medical and surgical

Staffed Beds: 237 **Admissions:** 11954 **Census:** 171 **Births:** 0 **Total Expense ($000):** 159154 **Payroll Expense ($000):** 51109

PORT ST. JOE—Gulf County

SACRED HEART HOSPITAL ON THE GULF (100313), 3801 East Highway 98, Zip 32456–5318; tel. 850/229–5600 **A**1 10 **F**1 3 4 11 15 16 17 29 30 31 34 35 40 44 45 48 50 54 57 59 64 67 68 70 72 73 79 80 81 85 88 89 90 93 98 107 110 111 114 119 128 130 131 133 146 147 **P**7 **S** Ascension Healthcare, Saint Louis, MO
Primary Contact: Roger L. Hall, President
CNO: Katherine L Chastain R.N., Chief Nursing Officer
Web address: www.sacred-heart.org/gulf/
Control: Other not-for-profit (including NFP Corporation) **Service:** General medical and surgical

Staffed Beds: 19 **Admissions:** 463 **Census:** 4 **Births:** 0 **Total Expense ($000):** 20352 **Payroll Expense ($000):** 6646

PORT ST. LUCIE—St. Lucie County

☐ **PORT ST. LUCIE HOSPITAL (104070)**, 2550 SE Walton Road, Zip 34952–7168; tel. 772/335–0400 **A**1 10 **F**4 5 98 102 103 105 106 130
Primary Contact: Mercy Estevez, Administrator
Web address: www.portstluciehospitalinc.com
Control: Corporation, Investor-owned (for-profit) **Service:** Psychiatric

Staffed Beds: 75 **Admissions:** 1572 **Census:** 66 **Outpatient Visits:** 0 **Births:** 0 **Personnel:** 187

ST. LUCIE MEDICAL CENTER (100260), 1800 SE Tiffany Avenue, Zip 34952–7521; tel. 772/335–4000, (Nonreporting) **A**1 10 13 **S** HCA Healthcare, Nashville, TN
Primary Contact: Jay Finnegan, Chief Executive Officer
COO: Calvin Thomas IV, Chief Operating Officer
CFO: Kevin Keeling, Chief Financial Officer
Web address: www.stluciemed.com
Control: Corporation, Investor-owned (for-profit) **Service:** General medical and surgical

Staffed Beds: 194

PUNTA GORDA—Charlotte County

BAYFRONT HEALTH PUNTA GORDA (100047), 809 East Marion Avenue, Zip 33950–3819, Mailing Address: P.O.Box 51–1328, 33951–1328; tel. 941/639–3131 **A**1 10 **F**3 15 18 28 29 30 31 34 35 36 38 39 40 44 45 50 53 54 56 59 60 64 68 70 74 75 77 78 79 81 85 86 87 93 94 96 98 100 101 102 103 104 107 108 110 111 115 118 119 130 131 132 135 146 148 149 **S** Community Health Systems, Inc., Franklin, TN
Primary Contact: Andrew Emery, Chief Executive Officer
Web address: www.bayfrontcharlotte.com
Control: Corporation, Investor-owned (for-profit) **Service:** General medical and surgical

Staffed Beds: 190 **Admissions:** 5034 **Census:** 90 **Outpatient Visits:** 66889 **Births:** 0 **Total Expense ($000):** 63903 **Payroll Expense ($000):** 30104

RIVIERA BEACH—Palm Beach County

KINDRED HOSPITAL THE PALM BEACHES (102025), 5555 West Blue Heron Boulevard, Zip 33418–7813; tel. 561/840–0754 **A**1 10 **F**1 3 18 29 30 45 48 70 74 75 77 79 82 84 85 91 97 100 107 148 **S** Kindred Healthcare, Louisville, KY
Primary Contact: Elayne Lopreato, Chief Executive Officer
CFO: Dean Card, Chief Financial Officer
CNO: Elayne Lopreato, Chief Clinical Officer
Web address: www.khthepalmbeaches.com/
Control: Corporation, Investor-owned (for-profit) **Service:** Acute long-term care hospital

Staffed Beds: 70 **Admissions:** 617 **Census:** 52 **Outpatient Visits:** 0 **Births:** 0 **Total Expense ($000):** 23023 **Payroll Expense ($000):** 10452 **Personnel:** 139

FL

Many Facility Codes have changed. Please refer to the AHA Guide Code Chart. © 2017 AHA Guide

ROCKLEDGE—Brevard County

☒ **WUESTHOFF MEDICAL CENTER – ROCKLEDGE (100092)**, 110 Longwood Avenue, Zip 32955–2887, Mailing Address: P.O.Box 565002, Mail Stop 1, 32956–5002; tel. 321/636–2211 **A**1 2 10 **F**3 15 17 18 19 20 22 24 26 28 29 30 31 35 40 46 49 50 51 59 60 64 68 70 72 74 75 76 78 79 80 81 82 84 85 89 93 98 102 107 111 114 115 117 119 126 130 131 132 135 146 147 148 149 **S** Steward Health Care System, LLC, Boston, MA
Primary Contact: Andy Romine, Chief Executive Officer
CFO: Richard Haun, Chief Financial Officer
CMO: Vinay Mehindru M.D., Medical Director
CIO: David Barnhart, Director Information Systems
CHR: Marchita H Marino, Vice President Human Resources
Web address: www.wuesthoff.org
Control: Corporation, Investor–owned (for–profit) **Service**: General medical and surgical

Staffed Beds: 298 **Admissions:** 10871 **Census:** 144 **Births:** 490 **Total Expense ($000):** 138362 **Payroll Expense ($000):** 49539

SAFETY HARBOR—Pinellas County

☒ **MEASE COUNTRYSIDE HOSPITAL (100265)**, 3231 McMullen Booth Road, Zip 34695–6607; tel. 727/725–6111 **A**1 2 10 **F**3 8 13 15 17 18 20 22 26 28 29 30 31 32 34 35 37 38 40 41 44 46 49 50 51 55 56 57 59 60 62 64 68 70 72 74 75 76 77 78 79 81 84 85 86 87 89 92 93 107 108 109 111 114 115 116 117 118 119 126 129 130 131 132 135 143 145 146 147 148 149 **S** Trinity Health, Livonia, MI
Primary Contact: Lou Galdieri, R.N., President
COO: Kelly Cullen R.N., Director of Operations
CFO: Carl Tremonti, Chief Financial Officer
CMO: Tony Schuster M.D., Vice President of Physician Services
CIO: Tim Thompson, Senior Vice President, Informant Services and Chief Information Officer
CHR: Kyle Barr, Senior Vice President, Chief Team Resources Officer
CNO: Thomas Doria, Vice President, Patient Services and Chief Nursing Officer
Web address: www.mpmhealth.com
Control: Other not–for–profit (including NFP Corporation) **Service**: General medical and surgical

Staffed Beds: 311 **Admissions:** 18076 **Census:** 210 **Outpatient Visits:** 123289 **Births:** 2283 **Total Expense ($000):** 260695 **Payroll Expense ($000):** 94758 **Personnel:** 1663

SAINT AUGUSTINE—St. Johns County

☐ **FLAGLER HOSPITAL (100090)**, 400 Health Park Boulevard, Zip 32086–5784; tel. 904/819–5155 **A**1 2 5 10 20 **F**3 5 8 11 12 13 14 15 18 20 22 24 28 29 30 31 34 35 38 40 45 49 56 57 58 59 60 65 70 72 73 74 75 76 78 79 81 82 85 86 87 89 93 98 100 101 102 104 105 106 107 108 110 111 114 115 119 120 126 129 130 131 132 135 146 **P**8
Primary Contact: Jason P. Barrett, Chief Executive Officer
CFO: Lynda I Kirker, Chief Financial Officer
CMO: Douglas Dew M.D., President Medical Staff
CIO: Bill Rieger, Chief Information Officer
CHR: Jeff Hurley, Vice President Human Resources
Web address: www.flaglerhospital.org
Control: Other not–for–profit (including NFP Corporation) **Service**: General medical and surgical

Staffed Beds: 350 **Admissions:** 13987 **Census:** 173 **Outpatient Visits:** 166549 **Births:** 1623 **Total Expense ($000):** 238289 **Payroll Expense ($000):** 84995 **Personnel:** 1637

SAINT CLOUD—Osceola County

☒ **ST. CLOUD REGIONAL MEDICAL CENTER (100302)**, 2906 17th Street, Zip 34769–6099; tel. 407/892–2135 **A**1 10 **F**3 15 18 29 30 34 35 40 45 46 49 51 57 59 70 74 75 77 78 79 81 82 85 86 87 91 93 94 96 97 107 108 110 111 115 119 146 **S** Community Health Systems, Inc., Franklin, TN
Primary Contact: Brent Burish, Chief Executive Officer
COO: Andrea Thomas, Chief Operating Officer
CFO: Carl Caley, Chief Financial Officer
CIO: James Devlin, Director Information Systems
CHR: Jennifer Harmon, Director of Human Resources
CNO: Perry Horne, Chief Nursing Officer
Web address: www.stcloudregional.com
Control: Corporation, Investor–owned (for–profit) **Service**: General medical and surgical

Staffed Beds: 84 **Admissions:** 3764 **Census:** 43 **Births:** 0

SAINT PETERSBURG—Pinellas County

☒ **BAYFRONT HEALTH ST. PETERSBURG (100032)**, 701 Sixth Street South, Zip 33701–4891; tel. 727/823–1234, (Nonreporting) **A**1 3 5 10 **S** Community Health Systems, Inc., Franklin, TN
Primary Contact: John R. McLain, President and Chief Executive Officer
COO: Lavah Lowe, Executive Vice President and Chief Operating Officer
CFO: Eric Smith, Chief Financial Officer
CIO: Kevin Murphy, Director, Information Technology Services
CHR: Jim Reames, Director Human Resources
CNO: Karen Long R.N., FACHE, Vice President Nursing
Web address: www.bayfrontstpete.com
Control: Corporation, Investor–owned (for–profit) **Service**: General medical and surgical

Staffed Beds: 382

☒ **JOHNS HOPKINS ALL CHILDREN'S HOSPITAL (103300)**, 501 6th Avenue South, Zip 33701–4634; tel. 727/898–7451 **A**1 3 5 8 10 **F**3 11 12 17 18 19 20 21 22 23 24 25 26 27 29 30 31 32 34 35 36 37 39 40 41 43 44 45 46 47 48 49 50 54 55 57 58 59 60 61 62 64 65 68 72 73 74 75 77 78 79 81 82 84 85 86 87 88 89 90 92 93 96 97 99 100 107 111 114 115 116 118 119 126 129 130 131 132 134 135 136 137 141 142 143 144 146 147 148 **S** Johns Hopkins Health System, Baltimore, MD
Primary Contact: Jonathan M. Ellen, M.D., President
CFO: Nancy Templin, Vice President Finance and Chief Financial Officer
CMO: Michael Epstein M.D., Senior Vice President Medical Affairs
CIO: John McLendon, Vice President and Chief Information Officer
CHR: Jay Kuhns, Vice President Human Resources
Web address: www.allkids.org
Control: Other not–for–profit (including NFP Corporation) **Service**: Children's general medical and surgical

Staffed Beds: 259 **Admissions:** 6887 **Census:** 161 **Outpatient Visits:** 366882 **Births:** 0 **Total Expense ($000):** 398481 **Payroll Expense ($000):** 150396 **Personnel:** 2777

☒ ⇑ **NORTHSIDE HOSPITAL (100238)**, 6000 49th Street North, Zip 33709–2145; tel. 727/521–4411 **A**1 10 12 13 21 **F**3 11 17 18 20 22 24 26 28 29 30 34 40 45 49 50 51 53 56 57 58 59 63 65 68 70 74 75 77 79 81 85 87 92 93 100 107 108 111 114 115 119 126 135 146 148 **S** HCA Healthcare, Nashville, TN
Primary Contact: Dia Nichols, Chief Executive Officer
COO: Jayme Chancellor, Chief Operating Officer
CFO: Peggy Gatliff, Chief Financial Officer
CMO: Ira Siegman M.D., Chief Medical Officer
CIO: Kirk Hendrick, Director Information Systems
CHR: Maggie Miklos, Director Human Resources
CNO: Wendy Lincoln, Chief Nursing Officer
Web address: www.northsidehospital.com
Control: Corporation, Investor–owned (for–profit) **Service**: General medical and surgical

Staffed Beds: 217 **Admissions:** 10317 **Census:** 145 **Births:** 0 **Total Expense ($000):** 167524 **Payroll Expense ($000):** 53232

☒ **PALMS OF PASADENA HOSPITAL (100126)**, 1501 Pasadena Avenue South, Zip 33707–3798; tel. 727/381–1000 **A**1 10 **F**3 12 15 29 30 34 35 37 39 40 41 45 46 47 48 49 50 54 56 57 59 60 63 64 65 66 67 68 70 74 75 77 79 81 82 84 85 86 87 90 107 108 110 111 114 115 118 119 130 132 135 146 148 149 **S** HCA Healthcare, Nashville, TN
Primary Contact: Sharon Hayes, Chief Executive Officer
CFO: James B. Gilbert, Chief Financial Officer
CMO: George Hutter M.D., Chief of Staff
CIO: Danny Waters, Director, Information Services
CHR: Karen Casteel, Director Human Resources
CNO: Brandy Hershberger, Chief Nursing Officer
Web address: www.palmspasadena.com
Control: Corporation, Investor–owned (for–profit) **Service**: General medical and surgical

Staffed Beds: 187 **Admissions:** 5477 **Census:** 90 **Births:** 0 **Total Expense ($000):** 98953 **Payroll Expense ($000):** 30029

FL

Hospital, Medicare Provider Number, Address, Telephone, Approval, Facility, and Physician Codes, Health Care System

★ American Hospital Association (AHA) membership ○ Healthcare Facilities Accreditation Program ⇑ Center for Improvement in Healthcare Quality Accreditation
☐ The Joint Commission accreditation ◇ DNV Healthcare Inc. accreditation △ Commission on Accreditation of Rehabilitation Facilities (CARF) accreditation

✠ **ST. ANTHONY'S HOSPITAL (100067)**, 1200 Seventh Avenue North, Zip 33705–1388, Mailing Address: P.O.Box 12588, 33733–2588; tel. 727/825–1100 **A**1 2 5 10 **F**3 11 12 15 17 18 20 22 26 28 29 30 31 34 35 40 44 45 46 49 51 57 59 60 64 68 70 74 75 77 78 79 81 84 85 87 93 98 100 102 103 107 108 110 111 114 115 117 118 119 121 123 124 126 129 130 131 132 135 146 148 149 **S** Trinity Health, Livonia, MI
Primary Contact: M. Scott Smith, President
CFO: Carl Tremonti, Chief Financial Officer
CMO: James McClintic M.D., Vice President Medical Affairs
CIO: Tim Thompson, Senior Vice President and Chief Informatics Officer
CHR: Kristen A Betts, Director Team Resources
CNO: Thomas Doria, Vice President and Patient Services West
Web address: www.stanthonys.com/
Control: Other not–for–profit (including NFP Corporation) **Service:** General medical and surgical

Staffed Beds: 393 **Admissions:** 20118 **Census:** 262 **Outpatient Visits:** 103353 **Births:** 0 **Total Expense ($000):** 283445 **Payroll Expense ($000):** 107918 **Personnel:** 1966

✠ **ST. PETERSBURG GENERAL HOSPITAL (100180)**, 6500 38th Avenue North, Zip 33710–1629; tel. 727/384–1414, (Nonreporting) **A**1 2 10 12 13 **S** HCA Healthcare, Nashville, TN
Primary Contact: Janice Balzano, President and Chief Executive Officer
COO: Stephanie McNulty, Chief Operating Officer
CFO: Shawn Gregory, Chief Financial Officer
CMO: George Hutter M.D., Chief Medical Officer
CHR: Jennifer B Robinson, Vice President Human Resources
CNO: JoAnne Cattell, Chief Nursing Officer
Web address: www.stpetegeneral.com
Control: Corporation, Investor–owned (for–profit) **Service:** General medical and surgical

Staffed Beds: 219

SANFORD—Seminole County

✠ △ **CENTRAL FLORIDA REGIONAL HOSPITAL (100161)**, 1401 West Seminole Boulevard, Zip 32771–6764; tel. 407/321–4500, (Nonreporting) **A**1 7 10 **S** HCA Healthcare, Nashville, TN
Primary Contact: Wendy H. Brandon, Chief Executive Officer
COO: Glenn Carney, Chief Operating Officer
CFO: Richard Read, Chief Financial Officer
CIO: Jerry Ballard, Director Information Systems
CHR: Linda V Smith, Vice President Human Resources
CNO: Maria Calloway R.N., MSN, Chief Nursing Officer
Web address: www.centralfloridaregional.com
Control: Corporation, Investor–owned (for–profit) **Service:** General medical and surgical

Staffed Beds: 226

SARASOTA—Sarasota County

✠ **COMPLEX CARE HOSPITAL AT RIDGELAKE (102018)**, 6150 Edgelake Drive, Zip 34240–8803; tel. 941/342–3000 **A**1 10 **F**1 3 60 85 107 114 130 **S** LifeCare Management Services, Plano, TX
Primary Contact: Robert E. Mallicoat, Chief Executive Officer
CFO: Leah Drabant, Director of Finance
CMO: Craig Harcup M.D., Hospital Medical Director
CHR: Jennifer Sparks, Human Resources Generalist
CNO: Timothy Mitchell R.N., Chief Nursing Officer
Web address: www.lifecare–hospitals.com/hospital.php?id=23
Control: Corporation, Investor–owned (for–profit) **Service:** Acute long–term care hospital

Staffed Beds: 40 **Admissions:** 476 **Census:** 35 **Outpatient Visits:** 0 **Births:** 0 **Total Expense ($000):** 24145 **Payroll Expense ($000):** 8751

✠ **DOCTORS HOSPITAL OF SARASOTA (100166)**, 5731 Bee Ridge Road, Zip 34233–5056; tel. 941/342–1100, (Nonreporting) **A**1 10 **S** HCA Healthcare, Nashville, TN
Primary Contact: Robert C. Meade, Chief Executive Officer
COO: Wyatt Chocklett, Chief Operating Officer
CFO: Charles Schwaner III, Chief Financial Officer
CMO: Thomas Trinchetto M.D., Chief Medical Officer
CHR: Theresa Levering, Director Human Resources
CNO: Kathy Mitchell R.N., Chief Nursing Officer
Web address: www.doctorsofsarasota.com
Control: Corporation, Investor–owned (for–profit) **Service:** General medical and surgical

Staffed Beds: 168

✠ △ **HEALTHSOUTH REHABILITATION HOSPITAL OF SARASOTA (103031)**, 6400 Edgelake Drive, Zip 34240–8813; tel. 941/921–8600 **A**1 7 10 **F**28 29 30 62 63 90 95 96 143 **S** HEALTHSOUTH Corporation, Birmingham, AL
Primary Contact: Marcus Braz, Chief Executive Officer
CFO: Barbara Bierut, Chief Financial Officer
CMO: Alexander De Jesus M.D., Medical Director
CHR: Brenda Benner, Director Human Resources
Web address: www.healthsouthsarasota.com
Control: Corporation, Investor–owned (for–profit) **Service:** Rehabilitation

Staffed Beds: 96 **Admissions:** 2283 **Census:** 82 **Outpatient Visits:** 0 **Births:** 0 **Total Expense ($000):** 24275 **Payroll Expense ($000):** 13753 **Personnel:** 271

HEALTHSOUTH RIDGELAKE HOSPITAL See Complex Care Hospital At Ridgelake

□ △ ⇑ **SARASOTA MEMORIAL HEALTH CARE SYSTEM (100087)**, 1700 South Tamiami Trail, Zip 34239–3555; tel. 941/917–9000 **A**1 2 3 5 7 8 10 21 **F**3 6 7 8 11 12 13 15 17 18 19 20 22 24 26 28 29 30 31 32 34 35 36 37 38 39 40 42 43 44 45 46 47 48 49 50 51 53 54 55 56 57 58 59 60 61 62 64 66 68 70 72 73 74 75 76 77 78 79 80 81 82 84 85 86 87 89 90 91 92 93 95 96 97 98 99 100 101 102 103 107 108 110 111 114 115 118 119 124 126 129 130 131 132 134 135 143 144 145 146 147 148 149 150 **P**5
Primary Contact: David Verinder, President and Chief Executive Officer
COO: David Verinder, President and Chief Executive Officer
CFO: Bill Woeltjen, Chief Financial Officer
CMO: Steve Taylor M.D., Chief Medical Officer
CIO: Denis Baker, Chief Information Officer
CHR: Laurie Bennett, Director Human Resources
CNO: Connie Andersen R.N., MS, Chief Nursing Officer
Web address: www.smh.com
Control: Hospital district or authority, Government, Nonfederal **Service:** General medical and surgical

Staffed Beds: 701 **Admissions:** 31946 **Census:** 423 **Outpatient Visits:** 561948 **Births:** 3477 **Total Expense ($000):** 606527 **Payroll Expense ($000):** 234173 **Personnel:** 4481

SEBASTIAN—Indian River County

✠ **SEBASTIAN RIVER MEDICAL CENTER (100217)**, 13695 North U S Hwy 1, Zip 32958–3230, Mailing Address: Box 780838, 32978–0838; tel. 772/589–3186, (Total facility includes 33 beds in nursing home–type unit) **A**1 10 **F**3 11 12 15 18 20 22 28 29 30 31 34 40 45 47 48 49 50 51 54 60 63 68 70 74 75 77 78 79 81 82 83 84 85 87 89 93 94 107 108 109 111 114 115 116 117 119 126 128 129 130 132 135 145 146 148 **P**8 **S** Steward Health Care System, LLC, Boston, MA
Primary Contact: Kelly Enriquez, Chief Executive Officer
CFO: John McEachern, Controller
CMO: Ralph Geiger M.D., Chief of Staff
CHR: Kam Storey, Director Human Resources
Web address: www.sebastianrivermedical.com
Control: Corporation, Investor–owned (for–profit) **Service:** General medical and surgical

Staffed Beds: 154 **Admissions:** 5124 **Census:** 64 **Births:** 0 **Total Expense ($000):** 83873 **Payroll Expense ($000):** 27469

SEBRING—Highlands County

✠ **FLORIDA HOSPITAL HEARTLAND MEDICAL CENTER (100109)**, 4200 Sun'n Lake Boulevard, Zip 33872–1986, Mailing Address: P.O.Box 9400, 33871–9400; tel. 863/314–4466, (Includes FLORIDA HOSPITAL LAKE PLACID, 1210 US 27 North, Lake Placid, Florida, Zip 33852–7948, tel. 863/465–3777; Eric Stevens, Chief Executive Officer) **A**1 10 19 **F**11 13 15 18 20 22 24 26 28 29 30 34 35 37 40 44 45 49 50 51 53 54 57 59 60 62 64 70 75 76 78 79 81 86 87 89 97 98 100 101 103 104 107 108 110 111 114 115 116 117 118 119 126 127 129 130 132 135 146 147 148 149 **P**6 **S** Adventist Health System Sunbelt Health Care Corporation, Altamonte Springs, FL
Primary Contact: Randy Surber, Chief Executive Officer
CFO: Rosalie Oliver, Chief Financial Officer
CMO: Jorge F Gonzalez M.D., Chief Medical Officer
CHR: Anthony Stahl, Vice President
CNO: Gloria N Santos R.N., MS, Chief Nursing Officer
Web address: www.floridahospital.com/heartland/our–location
Control: Church operated, Nongovernment, not–for–profit **Service:** General medical and surgical

Staffed Beds: 197 **Admissions:** 10810 **Census:** 141 **Outpatient Visits:** 143945 **Births:** 818 **Total Expense ($000):** 194420 **Payroll Expense ($000):** 84078 **Personnel:** 1371

Many Facility Codes have changed. Please refer to the AHA Guide Code Chart. © 2017 AHA Guide

FL

✠ **HIGHLANDS REGIONAL MEDICAL CENTER (100049)**, 3600 South Highlands Avenue, Zip 33870–5495, Mailing Address: Drawer 2066, 33871–2066; tel. 863/385–6101 **A**1 10 19 **F**3 11 12 13 15 18 20 22 29 34 40 45 49 50 51 57 59 64 70 76 79 81 85 87 93 97 107 108 110 114 119 124 129 135 146 **S** Community Health Systems, Inc., Franklin, TN
Primary Contact: John D. Montois, Interim Chief Executive Officer
CFO: Paul Damron, Chief Financial Officer
CIO: Nate Johnson, Chief Information Officer
CHR: Brenda Dane, Director, Human Resources
CNO: Adam Kless, Chief Nursing Officer
Web address: www.highlandsregional.com
Control: Corporation, Investor–owned (for–profit) **Service:** General medical and surgical

Staffed Beds: 80 **Admissions:** 3468 **Census:** 35 **Births:** 430 **Total Expense ($000):** 64679 **Payroll Expense ($000):** 16695

SOUTH MIAMI—Miami—Dade County

☐ **LARKIN COMMUNITY HOSPITAL (100181)**, 7031 SW 62nd Avenue, Zip 33143–4781; tel. 305/284–7500 **A**1 3 10 12 13 **F**3 5 7 8 10 15 26 29 31 34 35 38 40 44 45 46 49 54 56 57 58 59 60 62 64 65 68 70 71 74 75 77 78 79 81 82 84 85 87 91 92 93 96 97 98 99 100 101 102 103 104 105 107 108 110 111 114 117 118 119 124 126 129 130 131 132 135 143 144 146 148 149 150
Primary Contact: Sandra Sosa–Guerrero, Chief Executive Officer
COO: George J Michel, Chief Operating Officer
CFO: Edgar Castillo, Chief Financial Officer
CMO: Mario Almeida–Suarez M.D., Chief of Staff
CIO: Orlando Suarez, Director Information Technology
CHR: Carolina Pena, Assistant Director Administrator
CNO: Mercedes Perez, Vice President Nursing
Web address: www.larkinhospital.com
Control: Individual, Investor–owned (for–profit) **Service:** General medical and surgical

Staffed Beds: 146 **Admissions:** 5628 **Census:** 82 **Outpatient Visits:** 23010 **Births:** 0 **Total Expense ($000):** 105987 **Payroll Expense ($000):** 46568 **Personnel:** 1268

STARKE—Bradford County

SHANDS STARKE See Shands Starke Regional Medical Center

✠ **SHANDS STARKE REGIONAL MEDICAL CENTER (101310)**, 922 East Call Street, Zip 32091–3699; tel. 904/368–2300 **A**1 3 10 12 13 **F**3 11 15 29 30 34 35 40 44 45 50 57 59 64 68 74 75 77 81 85 93 97 107 111 114 119 127 129 131 132 135 **P**6 **S** Community Health Systems, Inc., Franklin, TN
Primary Contact: Charles D. Nasem, FACHE, Chief Executive Officer
CFO: Wendy Martin, Chief Financial Officer
Web address: www.shandsstarke.com
Control: Partnership, Investor–owned (for–profit) **Service:** General medical and surgical

Staffed Beds: 49 **Admissions:** 1392 **Census:** 14 **Births:** 0

STUART—Martin County

✠ **HEALTHSOUTH REHABILITATION HOSPITAL AT MARTIN HEALTH (103044)**, 5850 SE Community Drive, Zip 34997–6420; tel. 772/324–3500 (Nonreporting) **A**1 10 **S** HEALTHSOUTH Corporation, Birmingham, AL
Primary Contact: Ivette Miranda, Chief Executive Officer
CFO: Dawn Salas, Controller
CMO: Stephen L Chastain M.D., Chief Medical Officer
CHR: Donna Holder–Hooper, Chief Human Resource Officer
CNO: Charmaine Blanchard, Chief Nursing Officer
Web address: www.healthsouthmartin.com
Control: Corporation, Investor–owned (for–profit) **Service:** Rehabilitation

Staffed Beds: 54

✠ **MARTIN HEALTH SYSTEM (100044)**, 200 SE Hospital Avenue, Zip 34994–2346, Mailing Address: P.O.Box 9010, 34995–9010; tel. 772/287–5200, (Includes MARTIN MEMORIAL HOSPITAL SOUTH, 2100 SE Salerno Road, Stuart, Florida, Zip 34997, tel. 772/223–2300; Mark E Robitaille, FACHE, President and Chief Executive Officer; TRADITION MEDICAL CENTER, 10000 SW Innovation Way, Port St Lucie, Florida, Zip 34987–2111, tel. 772/345–8100; Mark E Robitaille, FACHE, President and Chief Executive Officer) **A**1 2 10 **F**3 8 11 12 13 15 17 18 20 22 24 26 28 29 30 31 35 36 37 40 42 45 46 47 49 50 51 53 55 60 64 68 70 72 74 75 77 78 79 81 82 85 86 87 91 93 94 95 107 108 110 111 114 115 116 117 118 119 120 121 123 124 126 129 130 132 143 144 146 149 **P**6
Primary Contact: Robert L. Lord, JD, President and Chief Executive Officer
CFO: Chuck Cleaver, Vice President and Chief Financial Officer
CMO: Fernando Petry M.D., Vice President and Chief Medical Officer
CIO: Edmund Collins, Chief Information Officer
CHR: Angie L Metcalf, Vice President and Chief Human Resource Officer
CNO: Mary Elizabeth Flippo R.N., MSN, Vice President and Chief Nursing Officer
Web address: www.martinhealth.org
Control: Other not–for–profit (including NFP Corporation) **Service:** General medical and surgical

Staffed Beds: 335 **Admissions:** 24621 **Census:** 297 **Outpatient Visits:** 136911 **Births:** 2452 **Total Expense ($000):** 441446 **Payroll Expense ($000):** 187587 **Personnel:** 3831

SUN CITY CENTER—Hillsborough County

✠ **SOUTH BAY HOSPITAL (100259)**, 4016 Sun City Center Blvd, Zip 33573–5298; tel. 813/634–3301 **A**1 10 **F**3 15 18 29 30 31 34 35 37 40 45 49 50 57 59 64 68 70 74 75 77 78 79 81 82 85 86 87 93 107 108 110 111 114 118 119 132 146 148 149 **S** HCA Healthcare, Nashville, TN
Primary Contact: Sharon L. Roush, Chief Executive Officer
COO: Daniel Bender, Chief Operating Officer
CFO: Phillip Sensing, Chief Financial Officer
CIO: Eric Young, Director Information Technology and Systems
CHR: Stacie Novosel, Vice President, Human Resources
CNO: Sherry Collins, Chief Nursing Officer
Web address: www.southbayhospital.com/
Control: Corporation, Investor–owned (for–profit) **Service:** General medical and surgical

Staffed Beds: 138 **Admissions:** 6485 **Census:** 74 **Outpatient Visits:** 31127 **Births:** 0

SUNRISE—Broward County

✠ **HEALTHSOUTH SUNRISE REHABILITATION HOSPITAL (103028)**, 4399 North Nob Hill Road, Zip 33351–5899; tel. 954/749–0300 **A**1 3 10 **F**3 18 29 34 35 56 57 59 62 82 90 91 93 95 96 130 132 148 **S** HEALTHSOUTH Corporation, Birmingham, AL
Primary Contact: Michael S. Roffelsen, Chief Executive Officer
CFO: Ruth Goodstein, Controller
CMO: Scott Tannenbaum M.D., Medical Director
CIO: Angela Manning, Director Health Information Services
CHR: Barbara Dunkiel, Director Human Resources
CNO: Omaira D. Riano, Chief Nursing Officer
Web address: www.healthsouthsunrise.com
Control: Corporation, Investor–owned (for–profit) **Service:** Rehabilitation

Staffed Beds: 126 **Admissions:** 2502 **Census:** 89 **Outpatient Visits:** 22862 **Births:** 0 **Total Expense ($000):** 34816 **Payroll Expense ($000):** 18854 **Personnel:** 351

TALLAHASSEE—Leon County

✠ **CAPITAL REGIONAL MEDICAL CENTER (100254)**, 2626 Capital Medical Boulevard, Zip 32308–4499; tel. 850/325–5000, (Nonreporting) **A**1 2 10 **S** HCA Healthcare, Nashville, TN
Primary Contact: Mark Robinson, FACHE, President and Chief Executive Officer
CMO: Steve West M.D., Chief Medical Officer
CIO: Robert A Steed, Director Information Systems
CHR: Louise Truitt, Vice President Human Resources
Web address: www.capitalregionalmedicalcenter.com
Control: Individual, Investor–owned (for–profit) **Service:** General medical and surgical

Staffed Beds: 198

FL

EASTSIDE PSYCHIATRIC HOSPITAL (104059), 2634 Capital Circle NE, Zip 32308–4106; tel. 850/523–3333 (Nonreporting) **A**10
Primary Contact: Jay A. Reeve, Ph.D., President and Chief Executive Officer
COO: Sue Conger, Chief Operating Officer
CFO: Virginia Kelly, Chief Financial Officer
CMO: Ludmila de Faria M.D., Chief Medical Officer
CIO: Thad Moorer, Chief Information Officer
CHR: Candy Landry, Chief Human Resource Officer
CNO: Judy Goreau R.N., Director of Nursing
Web address: www.apalacheecenter.org
Control: Other not–for–profit (including NFP Corporation) **Service:** Psychiatric

Staffed Beds: 24

HEALTHSOUTH REHABILITATION HOSPITAL OF TALLAHASSEE (103033), 1675 Riggins Road, Zip 32308–5315; tel. 850/656–4800, (Nonreporting) **A**1 10 **S** HEALTHSOUTH Corporation, Birmingham, AL
Primary Contact: K. Dale. Neely, FACHE, Chief Executive Officer
CFO: Jennifer Spooner, Controller
CMO: Robert Rowland M.D., Medical Director
CIO: Michael Spangler, Health Information Management Services Supervisor
CHR: Carol Bugayong, Human Resources Director
CNO: Elizabeth Squires R.N., Chief Nursing Officer
Web address: www.healthsouthtallahassee.com
Control: Corporation, Investor–owned (for–profit) **Service:** Rehabilitation

Staffed Beds: 76

SELECT SPECIALTY HOSPITAL–TALLAHASSEE (102020), 1554 Surgeons Drive, Zip 32308–4631; tel. 850/219–6950, (Nonreporting) **A**1 10 **S** Select Medical Corporation, Mechanicsburg, PA
Primary Contact: Lora Davis, FACHE, Chief Executive Officer
Web address: www.tallahassee.selectspecialtyhospitals.com/
Control: Corporation, Investor–owned (for–profit) **Service:** Acute long–term care hospital

Staffed Beds: 29

TALLAHASSEE MEMORIAL HEALTHCARE (100135), 1300 Miccosukee Road, Zip 32308–5054; tel. 850/431–1155, (Total facility includes 42 beds in nursing home–type unit) **A**1 2 3 5 10 **F**1 2 3 5 6 8 11 12 15 17 18 19 20 22 24 26 28 29 30 31 34 35 37 40 42 43 46 47 48 49 50 51 53 54 55 56 57 58 59 60 61 62 64 65 68 70 72 73 74 75 76 77 78 79 80 81 82 84 85 86 87 88 89 91 93 96 97 98 99 100 102 103 104 107 108 110 113 114 115 117 118 119 120 121 123 124 126 127 128 129 130 131 132 135 143 144 146 147 148 149 **P**6
Primary Contact: Jay W. Faherty, Chief Executive Officer
COO: Jason H Moore, Vice President and Chief Operating Officer
CFO: William A Giudice, Vice President and Chief Financial Officer
CMO: Dean Watson M.D., Chief Medical Officer
CIO: Don Lindsey, Vice President and Chief Information Officer
CHR: Steven W Adriaanse, Vice President and Chief Human Resources Officer
Web address: www.tmh.org
Control: Other not–for–profit (including NFP Corporation) **Service:** General medical and surgical

Staffed Beds: 495 Admissions: 28484 Census: 385 Outpatient Visits: 796177 Births: 3764 Total Expense ($000): 613735 Payroll Expense ($000): 252412 Personnel: 3800

UNIVERSITY HOSPITAL AND MEDICAL CENTER (100224), 7201 North University Drive, Zip 33321–2996; tel. 954/721–2200, (Nonreporting) (Includes UNIVERSITY PAVILION, 7425 North University Drive, Tamarac, Florida, Zip 33328, tel. 305/722–9933) **A**1 10 **S** HCA Healthcare, Nashville, TN
Primary Contact: Dana C. Oaks, Chief Executive Officer
CFO: Aurelio Gonzalez, Chief Financial Officer
CMO: Ran Abrahamy M.D., Chief of Staff
CIO: Tom Scharff, Director Information Services
Web address: www.uhmchealth.com
Control: Corporation, Investor–owned (for–profit) **Service:** General medical and surgical

Staffed Beds: 317

FLORIDA HOSPITAL CARROLLWOOD (100069), 7171 North Dale Mabry Highway, Zip 33614–2665; tel. 813/932–2222 **A**1 3 10 **F**3 8 11 15 18 20 22 26 29 30 34 40 44 45 48 49 50 54 56 57 58 59 60 64 65 68 70 74 75 77 78 79 80 81 82 85 86 87 92 93 107 110 111 114 119 126 129 130 131 132 143 145 146 148 **S** Adventist Health System Sunbelt Health Care Corporation, Altamonte Springs, FL
Primary Contact: Joe Johnson, FACHE, Chief Executive Officer
COO: Mary C Whillock R.N., MS, Associate Nursing Officer and Chief Operating Officer
CFO: Chris Sauder, Vice President and Chief Financial Officer
Web address: www.elevatinghealthcare.org/locations/carrollwood
Control: Church operated, Nongovernment, not–for–profit **Service:** General medical and surgical

Staffed Beds: 96 Admissions: 5148 Census: 52 Outpatient Visits: 45224 Births: 0 Total Expense ($000): 117973 Payroll Expense ($000): 35037 Personnel: 503

△ **FLORIDA HOSPITAL TAMPA (100173)**, 3100 East Fletcher Avenue, Zip 33613–4688; tel. 813/971–6000 **A**1 3 5 7 10 **F**1 3 4 12 13 15 16 17 18 19 20 21 22 24 25 26 27 28 29 30 31 34 35 37 40 41 44 45 46 47 48 49 50 54 57 58 59 60 64 65 67 70 72 73 74 75 76 77 78 79 80 81 82 84 85 86 87 88 89 90 91 92 93 96 98 107 108 109 110 111 112 114 115 116 117 118 119 120 121 123 124 126 128 129 130 132 135 143 144 146 147 148 149 **P**6 7 **S** Adventist Health System Sunbelt Health Care Corporation, Altamonte Springs, FL
Primary Contact: Brian Adams, President and CEO
COO: Dick Tibbits, Vice President and Chief Operating Officer
CFO: Dima Didenko, Chief Financial Officer
CMO: Brad Bjornstad M.D., Vice President and Chief Medical Officer
CHR: Dick Tibbits, Vice President and Chief Operating Officer
CNO: Joy B Solomita R.N., Ph.D., MSN, M.P.H., Vice President and Chief Nursing Officer
Web address: www.floridahospital.com/tampa
Control: Other not–for–profit (including NFP Corporation) **Service:** General medical and surgical

Staffed Beds: 482 Admissions: 23178 Census: 342 Outpatient Visits: 138809 Births: 1733 Total Expense ($000): 459953 Payroll Expense ($000): 155317 Personnel: 2484

H. LEE MOFFITT CANCER CENTER AND RESEARCH INSTITUTE (100271), 12902 Magnolia Drive, Zip 33612–9497; tel. 813/745–4673 **A**1 2 3 5 10 **F**3 8 15 26 29 30 31 34 35 36 37 45 46 47 49 50 54 56 57 58 59 64 68 70 71 74 75 77 78 79 81 82 84 85 86 87 91 92 93 96 97 100 101 103 104 107 108 110 111 114 115 117 118 119 120 121 123 124 126 130 132 135 136 144 145 146 147 148 149 **P**6
Primary Contact: Alan F. List, President and Chief Executive Officer
COO: John A Kolosky, Executive Vice President and Chief Operating Officer
CFO: Yvette Tremonti, Chief Financial Officer
CMO: Bob Keenan, Chief Medical Officer
CIO: Jennifer Greenman, Vice President Chief Information Officer
CHR: Mariana Bugallo–Muros, Vice President Chief Human Resources Officer
CNO: Jane Fusilero, Vice President Chief Nursing Officer
Web address: www.moffitt.org
Control: Other not–for–profit (including NFP Corporation) **Service:** Cancer

Staffed Beds: 206 Admissions: 9384 Census: 164 Outpatient Visits: 351421 Births: 0 Total Expense ($000): 992869 Payroll Expense ($000): 402052 Personnel: 5208

△ **JAMES A. HALEY VETERANS' HOSPITAL–TAMPA**, 13000 Bruce B Downs Boulevard, Zip 33612–4745; tel. 813/972–2000, (Total facility includes 64 beds in nursing home–type unit) **A**1 3 5 7 8 **F**3 5 9 12 15 17 18 20 22 24 26 28 29 30 31 33 34 35 36 38 39 40 45 46 47 48 49 50 51 53 54 55 56 57 58 59 60 61 62 63 64 65 70 71 74 75 77 78 79 80 81 82 83 84 85 86 87 90 91 92 93 94 95 96 97 98 100 101 102 103 104 105 106 107 108 109 110 111 113 114 115 116 117 118 119 120 121 123 127 128 129 130 131 132 135 143 144 146 147 148 149 **P**1 **S** Department of Veterans Affairs, Washington, DC
Primary Contact: Joe Battle, Director
COO: David Van Meter, Deputy Director
CFO: Robert Konkel, Manager Finance
CMO: Edward Cutolo M.D., Jr, Chief of Staff
CIO: Jose Seymour, Chief Information Resource Management
CHR: Andrew Sutton, Chief, Human Resources Management Service
CNO: Laureen Doloresco R.N., Associate Director for Patient Care and Nursing Services
Web address: www.tampa.va.gov/
Control: Veterans Affairs, Government, federal **Service:** General medical and surgical

Staffed Beds: 499 Admissions: 11795 Census: 370 Births: 0 Total Expense ($000): 533303 Payroll Expense ($000): 400113 Personnel: 5171

FL

✚ **KINDRED HOSPITAL BAY AREA–TAMPA (102009)**, 4555 South Manhattan Avenue, Zip 33611–2397; tel. 813/839–6341, (Includes KINDRED HOSPITAL–BAY AREA ST. PETERSBURG, 3030 Sixth Street South, Saint Petersburg, Florida, Zip 33705–3720, tel. 727/894–8719; Debra Plummer, Chief Executive Officer) **A**1 10 **F**1 3 18 28 29 30 34 56 57 59 68 74 75 82 84 85 87 100 119 **S** Kindred Healthcare, Louisville, KY
Primary Contact: Suthanthira M. Ratnasamy, R.N., FACHE, Chief Executive Officer
CFO: Frank Billy, Chief Financial Officer
CHR: Deborah Basria, Human Resources Payroll Administrator
Web address: www.khtampa.com/
Control: Hospital district or authority, Government, Nonfederal **Service**: Acute long–term care hospital

Staffed Beds: 73 **Admissions:** 584 **Census:** 65 **Outpatient Visits:** 0 **Births:** 0 **Total Expense ($000):** 28089 **Payroll Expense ($000):** 11113

✚ **KINDRED HOSPITAL CENTRAL TAMPA (102013)**, 4801 North Howard Avenue, Zip 33603–1411; tel. 813/874–7575, (Nonreporting) **A**1 10 **S** Kindred Healthcare, Louisville, KY
Primary Contact: Ralph Selner, Chief Executive Officer
CFO: John Miner, Chief Financial Officer
Web address: www.kindredcentraltampa.com/
Control: Corporation, Investor–owned (for–profit) **Service**: Acute long–term care hospital

Staffed Beds: 102

✚ **MEMORIAL HOSPITAL OF TAMPA (100206)**, 2901 Swann Avenue, Zip 33609–4057; tel. 813/873–6400, (Nonreporting) **A**1 5 10 **S** HCA Healthcare, Nashville, TN
Primary Contact: Sonia I. Wellman, Chief Executive Officer
CFO: Shelley V Kolseth, Chief Financial Officer
CIO: John Riton, Director Information Services
Web address: www.memorialhospitaltampa.com
Control: Corporation, Investor–owned (for–profit) **Service**: General medical and surgical

Staffed Beds: 139

☐ **SHRINERS HOSPITALS FOR CHILDREN–TAMPA (103303)**, 12502 USF Pine Drive, Zip 33612–9499; tel. 813/972–2250 **A**1 3 5 10 **F**3 29 34 35 50 57 64 68 74 77 79 81 85 89 90 91 93 94 95 107 131 146 149 **S** Shriners Hospitals for Children, Tampa, FL
Primary Contact: Fleury Yelvington, Administrator
CFO: Ruth Gregos, Director Finance
CMO: Maureen Maciel M.D., Chief of Staff
CHR: Amy Schenker, Human Resources Director
Web address: www.shrinershospitalsforchildren.org/Hospitals/Locations/Tampa.aspx
Control: Other not–for–profit (including NFP Corporation) **Service**: Children's orthopedic

Staffed Beds: 60 **Admissions:** 202 **Census:** 1 **Outpatient Visits:** 11615 **Births:** 0 **Total Expense ($000):** 22837 **Payroll Expense ($000):** 11159 **Personnel:** 169

✚ **ST. JOSEPH'S HOSPITAL (100075)**, 3001 West Martin Luther King Jr. Boulevard, Zip 33607–6387, Mailing Address: P.O.Box 4227, 33677–4227; tel. 813/870–4000, (Includes ST. JOSEPH'S CHILDREN'S HOSPITAL, 3001 Dr Martin Luther King Jr Boulevard, Tampa, Florida, Zip 33607, tel. 813/554–8500; Kate Reed, President; ST. JOSEPH'S HOSPITAL – NORTH, 4211 Van Dyke Road, Lutz, Florida, Zip 33558–8005, tel. 813/443–7000; Paula McGinnis, Chief Executive Officer; ST. JOSEPH'S HOSPITAL BEHAVIORAL HEALTH CENTER, 4918 North Habana Avenue, Tampa, Florida, Zip 33614–6815, tel. 813/870–4300; ST. JOSEPH'S HOSPITAL–SOUTH, 6901 Simmons Loop, Riverview, Florida, Zip 33578–9498, tel. 813/302–8000; Scott Smith, President; ST. JOSEPH'S WOMEN'S HOSPITAL, 3030 West Dr Martin L King Boulevard, Tampa, Florida, Zip 33607–6394, tel. 813/872–2950; Kate Reed, President) **A**1 2 3 5 10 **F**1 3 4 7 11 12 13 15 17 18 19 20 21 22 23 24 25 26 27 28 29 30 31 32 34 35 36 37 39 40 41 43 44 45 46 48 49 51 55 57 58 59 60 64 67 68 70 71 72 73 74 75 76 78 79 80 81 82 84 85 86 87 88 89 90 92 93 94 98 99 100 101 102 107 108 110 111 112 114 115 118 119 120 121 123 126 127 128 129 130 131 132 135 145 146 147 148 149 150 **S** Trinity Health, Livonia, MI
Primary Contact: Kimberly Guy, President
CFO: Cathy Yoder, Chief Financial Officer
CMO: Mark Vaaler M.D., Vice President Medical Staff Affairs
CIO: Lindsey Jarrell, Vice President Information Services
CHR: Pat Lipton, Director Team Resources
Web address: www.sjbhealth.org
Control: Other not–for–profit (including NFP Corporation) **Service**: General medical and surgical

Staffed Beds: 1030 **Admissions:** 58788 **Census:** 729 **Outpatient Visits:** 548891 **Births:** 8604 **Total Expense ($000):** 970910 **Payroll Expense ($000):** 353939 **Personnel:** 4605

✚ **TAMPA COMMUNITY HOSPITAL (100255)**, 6001 Webb Road, Zip 33615–3291; tel. 813/888–7060 **A**1 5 10 **F**3 4 5 15 18 20 29 40 45 46 47 48 49 70 74 79 81 82 85 92 93 98 102 103 107 110 111 114 115 118 119 126 128 130 146 148 **P**4 5 **S** HCA Healthcare, Nashville, TN
Primary Contact: Jacob Fisher, Chief Executive Officer
COO: Paulina Tam, Vice President of Operations
CIO: Albert Lacy, Associate Director of Information Technology
CHR: Stephanie Kunkel, Vice President of Human Resources
CNO: Susan Laber R.N., Chief Nursing Officer
Web address: www.tampacommunityhospital.com/
Control: Corporation, Investor–owned (for–profit) **Service**: General medical and surgical

Staffed Beds: 201 **Admissions:** 4715 **Census:** 60 **Births:** 0 **Total Expense ($000):** 61861 **Payroll Expense ($000):** 21376

✚ △ **TAMPA GENERAL HOSPITAL (100128)**, 1 Tampa General Circle, Zip 33606–3571, Mailing Address: P.O.Box 1289, 33601–1289; tel. 813/844–7000, (Includes TAMPA GENERAL HOSPITAL CHILDREN'S MEDICAL CENTER, 1 Tampa General Circle, Tampa, Florida, Zip 33606–3571, tel. 813/844–7000) **A**1 3 5 7 8 10 **F**3 7 11 12 13 15 16 17 18 19 20 22 24 26 28 29 30 31 32 34 35 36 37 38 39 40 41 43 44 45 46 47 48 49 50 52 53 54 55 56 57 58 59 60 61 62 63 64 66 68 70 72 73 74 75 76 77 78 79 81 82 83 84 85 86 87 88 89 90 91 92 93 94 96 97 99 100 101 102 103 107 108 109 110 111 112 114 115 119 120 121 123 124 126 129 130 132 134 135 137 138 139 140 141 142 143 145 146 147 148 149 **P**6
Primary Contact: John D. Couris, Chief Executive Officer
COO: Deana Nelson FACHE, R.N., Executive Vice President and Chief Operating Officer
CFO: Judith M. Ploszek, Chief Financial Officer
CMO: Sally Houston M.D., Executive Vice President and Chief Medical Officer
CIO: Scott Arnold, Senior Vice President Information Systems
CHR: Chris Roederer, Senior Vice President Human Resources
CNO: Janet Davis R.N., MS, Senior Vice President and Chief Nursing Officer
Web address: www.tgh.org
Control: Other not–for–profit (including NFP Corporation) **Service**: General medical and surgical

Staffed Beds: 1011 **Admissions:** 46613 **Census:** 787 **Outpatient Visits:** 429681 **Births:** 6097 **Total Expense ($000):** 1168940 **Payroll Expense ($000):** 438959 **Personnel:** 7529

TARPON SPRINGS—Pinellas County

✚ **FLORIDA HOSPITAL NORTH PINELLAS (100055)**, 1395 South Pinellas Avenue, Zip 34689–3790; tel. 727/942–5000 **A**1 5 10 **F**3 11 13 15 17 18 20 22 26 28 29 30 31 34 35 40 45 46 48 49 50 57 59 64 70 71 75 76 78 79 81 93 94 96 97 107 108 110 111 125 128 129 130 131 132 146 147 148 **S** Adventist Health System Sunbelt Health Care Corporation, Altamonte Springs, FL
Primary Contact: Tricia Williams, President and Chief Executive Officer
CFO: Steven Miller, Chief Financial Officer
CMO: Brian Williams M.D., Chief of Medical Staff
CIO: Brett Peterson, Director of Information Services
CHR: Vernon Elarbee, Director of Human Resources
CNO: Karen Owensby R.N., Chief Clinical Officer
Web address: www.fhnorthpinellas.com/
Control: Church operated, Nongovernment, not–for–profit **Service**: General medical and surgical

Staffed Beds: 168 **Admissions:** 5502 **Census:** 71 **Births:** 169 **Total Expense ($000):** 102623 **Payroll Expense ($000):** 35571

TAVARES—Lake County

✚ **FLORIDA HOSPITAL WATERMAN (100057)**, 1000 Waterman Way, Zip 32778–5266; tel. 352/253–3333 **A**1 2 10 **F**3 11 13 15 17 18 20 22 24 26 28 29 30 31 32 34 35 36 37 40 45 49 50 53 54 55 56 57 59 62 64 66 70 74 75 76 77 78 79 81 85 86 87 89 91 93 107 108 110 111 114 115 116 117 118 119 120 121 123 124 126 130 132 143 144 146 147 148 149 **P**8 **S** Adventist Health System Sunbelt Health Care Corporation, Altamonte Springs, FL
Primary Contact: Abel Biri, Chief Executive Officer
COO: Anita Young, Chief Operating Officer
CFO: Frances H Crunk, Vice President and Chief Financial Officer
CMO: Vinay Mehindru M.D., Vice President/Chief Medical Officer
CHR: Madge Springer, Director Human Resources
CNO: Patricia R Dolan R.N., MS, Vice President/ Chief Nursing Officer
Web address: www.fhwat.org
Control: Church operated, Nongovernment, not–for–profit **Service**: General medical and surgical

Staffed Beds: 269 **Admissions:** 14175 **Census:** 174 **Outpatient Visits:** 121220 **Births:** 546 **Total Expense ($000):** 214428 **Payroll Expense ($000):** 79114 **Personnel:** 1389

FL

Hospital, Medicare Provider Number, Address, Telephone, Approval, Facility, and Physician Codes, Health Care System

★ American Hospital Association (AHA) membership　　○ Healthcare Facilities Accreditation Program　　⇑ Center for Improvement in Healthcare Quality Accreditation
☐ The Joint Commission accreditation　　◇ DNV Healthcare Inc. accreditation　　△ Commission on Accreditation of Rehabilitation Facilities (CARF) accreditation

FL

TAVERNIER—Monroe County

☒ **BAPTIST HEALTH SOUTH FLORIDA, MARINERS HOSPITAL (101313)**, 91500 Overseas Highway, Zip 33070–2547; tel. 305/434–3000 **A**1 10 18 **F**3 11 15 18 28 29 30 31 34 35 40 45 47 50 53 57 59 68 70 74 75 78 79 81 84 85 93 97 102 107 108 110 111 114 115 119 129 130 131 132 133 145 146 147 148 149 150 **P**8 **S** Baptist Health South Florida, Coral Gables, FL
Primary Contact: Rick Freeburg, Chief Executive Officer
CFO: Erik Long, Controller
CIO: Mimi Taylor, Vice President Information Technology
CHR: John Williamson, Human Resources Site Manager
Web address: www.baptisthealth.net/en/facilities/mariners–hospital/Pages/default.aspx
Control: Other not–for–profit (including NFP Corporation) **Service:** General medical and surgical

Staffed Beds: 25 **Admissions:** 615 **Census:** 6 **Outpatient Visits:** 36727 **Births:** 0 **Total Expense ($000):** 49519 **Payroll Expense ($000):** 15091 **Personnel:** 193

THE VILLAGES—Sumter County

☒ **THE VILLAGES REGIONAL HOSPITAL (100290)**, 1451 El Camino Real, Zip 32159–0041; tel. 352/751–8000 **A**1 2 10 **F**3 8 11 15 18 20 22 24 28 29 30 31 34 35 40 45 51 54 57 59 64 68 70 74 75 77 78 79 81 84 85 87 93 107 108 110 111 114 115 116 119 130 132 135 144 146 149 **P**6 8 **S** Central Florida Health, Leesburg, FL
Primary Contact: Donald G. Henderson, FACHE, President and Chief Executive Officer
COO: Saad Ehtisham R.N., FACHE, Vice President and Chief Operating Officer
CFO: Diane P Harden, Senior Vice President and Chief Financial Officer
CHR: Amie Richason, Vice President Human Resources
CNO: Mary Jane Curry–Pelyak R.N., Vice President and Chief Clinical Officer
Web address: www.cfhalliance.org
Control: Other not–for–profit (including NFP Corporation) **Service:** General medical and surgical

Staffed Beds: 277 **Admissions:** 14502 **Census:** 178 **Outpatient Visits:** 50095 **Births:** 0 **Total Expense ($000):** 163843 **Payroll Expense ($000):** 63556 **Personnel:** 936

THE VILLAGES REGIONAL HOSPITAL See The Villages Regional Hospital

TITUSVILLE—Brevard County

☐ **PARRISH MEDICAL CENTER (100028)**, 951 North Washington Avenue, Zip 32796–2163; tel. 321/268–6111 **A**1 2 10 **F**3 11 13 15 18 20 22 28 29 30 34 35 40 45 47 50 51 53 54 56 57 59 60 62 64 68 69 70 74 75 76 77 78 79 80 81 82 83 84 85 86 87 89 92 93 94 107 108 110 111 116 126 129 130 132 134 135 143 144 146 147 148
Primary Contact: George Mikitarian Jr, FACHE, President and Chief Executive Officer
CFO: Timothy Skeldon, Senior Vice President and Chief Financial Officer
CMO: Lisa Alexanda M.D., Vice President Medical Affairs
CIO: William Moore, Chief Information Officer
Web address: www.parrishmed.com
Control: Hospital district or authority, Government, Nonfederal **Service:** General medical and surgical

Staffed Beds: 210 **Admissions:** 6633 **Census:** 85 **Births:** 602 **Total Expense ($000):** 170989 **Payroll Expense ($000):** 62523

TRINITY—Pasco County

COMMUNITY HOSPITAL See Medical Center Of Trinity

MEDICAL CENTER OF TRINITY A1 2 10 **F**8 11 13 15 18 20 22 26 29 30 31 34 35 38 40 45 46 47 48 49 57 59 60 67 68 70 74 75 76 77 78 79 80 81 82 84 85 86 87 93 94 98 102 103 107 108 110 111 119 126 130 132 135 146 147 148
COO: Kenneth West, Chief Operating Officer
CFO: Michael Wyers, Chief Financial Officer
CMO: Linda Badillo M.D., Chief of Medical Staff
CIO: Kurt Hornung, Director
CHR: Christena Miano, Human Resources Director
CNO: Nancy Maysilles R.N., Chief Nursing Officer
Web address: www.medicalcentertrinity.com

☒ **MEDICAL CENTER OF TRINITY (100191)**, 9330 State Road 54, Zip 34655–1808; tel. 727/834–4900 **A**1 2 10 **F**8 11 13 15 18 20 22 26 29 30 31 34 35 38 40 45 46 47 48 49 57 59 60 67 68 70 74 75 76 77 78 79 80 81 82 84 85 86 87 93 94 98 102 103 107 108 110 111 119 126 130 132 135 146 147 148 **S** HCA Healthcare, Nashville, TN
Primary Contact: Leigh Massengill, Chief Executive Officer
COO: Kenneth West, Chief Operating Officer
CFO: Michael Wyers, Chief Financial Officer
CMO: Linda Badillo M.D., Chief of Medical Staff
CIO: Kurt Hornung, Director
CHR: Christena Miano, Human Resources Director
CNO: Nancy Maysilles R.N., Chief Nursing Officer
Web address: www.medicalcentertrinity.com
Control: Corporation, Investor–owned (for–profit) **Service:** General medical and surgical

Staffed Beds: 276 **Admissions:** 13600 **Census:** 168 **Births:** 1337 **Total Expense ($000):** 215855 **Payroll Expense ($000):** 71663

VENICE—Sarasota County

☒ **VENICE REGIONAL BAYFRONT HEALTH (100070)**, 540 The Rialto, Zip 34285–2900; tel. 941/485–7711 **A**1 10 **F**3 8 11 12 15 17 18 20 22 24 26 28 29 31 34 35 37 40 45 46 47 49 50 51 54 56 57 59 64 70 74 77 78 79 81 82 85 87 93 96 107 108 110 111 114 118 119 126 129 130 146 148 149 **S** Community Health Systems, Inc., Franklin, TN
Primary Contact: Bob Moore, FACHE, Chief Executive Officer
COO: Kristen Gentry, Chief Operating Officer
CFO: Maria Caruso, Chief Financial Officer
CIO: Eloy Rivas, Director of Information Systems
CHR: John Ware, Director of Human Resources
CNO: Walter A Pannone, Chief Nursing Officer
Web address: www.veniceregional.com
Control: Corporation, Investor–owned (for–profit) **Service:** General medical and surgical

Staffed Beds: 221 **Admissions:** 8370 **Census:** 92 **Outpatient Visits:** 100529 **Births:** 0 **Total Expense ($000):** 144742 **Payroll Expense ($000):** 49944 **Personnel:** 834

VERO BEACH—Indian River County

☒ **HEALTHSOUTH TREASURE COAST REHABILITATION HOSPITAL (103032)**, 1600 37th Street, Zip 32960–4863; tel. 772/778–2100, (Nonreporting) **A**1 10 **S** HEALTHSOUTH Corporation, Birmingham, AL
Primary Contact: Michael Kissner, Chief Executive Officer
CFO: Kevin Hardy, Chief Financial Officer
CMO: Jimmy Wayne Lockhart M.D., Medical Director
CHR: Linda Rinehart, Director Human Resources
Web address: www.healthsouthtreasurecoast.com
Control: Corporation, Investor–owned (for–profit) **Service:** Rehabilitation

Staffed Beds: 80

☒ **INDIAN RIVER MEDICAL CENTER (100105)**, 1000 36th Street, Zip 32960–6592; tel. 772/567–4311, (Includes BEHAVIORAL HEALTH CENTER, 1190 37th Street, Vero Beach, Florida, Zip 32960–6507, tel. 772/563–4666; Jeffrey L Susi, President and Chief Executive Officer) **A**1 2 10 **F**3 11 12 13 15 17 18 20 22 24 26 28 29 30 31 34 35 37 40 44 45 46 47 48 49 50 51 57 58 59 60 61 64 70 74 75 76 77 78 79 80 81 82 84 85 87 89 92 93 96 97 98 99 100 101 102 103 104 107 108 110 111 114 115 116 117 118 119 120 121 124 126 129 130 131 132 135 144 146 147 148 **P**6
Primary Contact: Jeffrey L. Susi, President and Chief Executive Officer
CFO: Greg Gardner, Senior Vice President and Chief Financial Officer
CMO: Charles Mackett M.D., Senior Vice President and Chief Medical Officer
CIO: William Neil, Vice President and Chief Information Officer
CNO: Linda Walton R.N., MSN, Chief Nursing Officer
Web address: www.irmc.cc
Control: Other not–for–profit (including NFP Corporation) **Service:** General medical and surgical

Staffed Beds: 220 **Admissions:** 13467 **Census:** 159 **Outpatient Visits:** 127563 **Births:** 988 **Total Expense ($000):** 241113 **Payroll Expense ($000):** 115650 **Personnel:** 1576

WAUCHULA—Hardee County

⊞ **FLORIDA HOSPITAL WAUCHULA (101300)**, 533 West Carlton Street, Zip 33873–3407; tel. 863/773–3101 **A**1 10 18 **F**3 29 30 40 107 110 111 119 127 130 133 149 **P**6 **S** Adventist Health System Sunbelt Health Care Corporation, Altamonte Springs, FL
Primary Contact: Denise Grimsley, R.N., Vice President and Administrator
CFO: Rosalie Oliver, Senior Vice President and Chief Financial Officer
CMO: Jorge F Gonzalez M.D., Vice President and Chief Nursing Officer
CIO: Jeff McDonald, Information Technology Manager
CHR: Michelle F. Myers, Director Human Resources
CNO: Gloria N Santos R.N., MS, Vice President and Chief Nursing Officer
Web address: www.fh.floridahospital.com/heartland/home.aspx
Control: Church operated, Nongovernment, not–for–profit **Service:** General medical and surgical

Staffed Beds: 25 **Admissions:** 732 **Census:** 22 **Outpatient Visits:** 24432 **Births:** 0 **Total Expense ($000):** 23138 **Payroll Expense ($000):** 8799 **Personnel:** 99

WELLINGTON—Palm Beach County

☐ **WELLINGTON REGIONAL MEDICAL CENTER (100275)**, 10101 Forest Hill Boulevard, Zip 33414–6199; tel. 561/798–8500 **A**1 10 12 13 **F**3 7 8 12 13 15 18 20 22 26 29 30 31 34 35 40 49 50 51 53 54 57 58 59 64 68 70 72 73 74 75 76 77 78 79 81 85 86 87 93 107 110 111 114 115 119 121 124 126 130 132 135 146 147 148 **P**2 3 6 **S** Universal Health Services, Inc., King of Prussia, PA
Primary Contact: Robbin Lee, Chief Executive Officer
COO: Pamela S Tahan, Chief Operating Officer
CFO: Tonja Mosley, Chief Financial Officer
CMO: Richard Hays M.D., Chief Medical Officer
CIO: Pierre Bergeron, Information Services Director
CHR: Mary Jo Caracciolo, Human Resource Director
CNO: Asenath Cassel, Chief Nursing Officer
Web address: www.wellingtonregional.com
Control: Individual, Investor–owned (for–profit) **Service:** General medical and surgical

Staffed Beds: 233 **Admissions:** 18273 **Census:** 151 **Outpatient Visits:** 84569 **Births:** 2377 **Personnel:** 790

WESLEY CHAPEL—Pasco County

★ ⇑ **FLORIDA HOSPITAL WESLEY CHAPEL (100319)**, 2600 Bruce B Downs Boulevard, Zip 33544–9207; tel. 813/929–5000 **A**5 10 21 **F**3 11 13 15 18 20 22 26 29 30 34 35 40 45 46 47 49 51 53 57 59 64 70 74 75 76 77 79 81 85 87 93 107 108 109 110 111 115 117 119 120 126 130 132 145 146 149 **S** Adventist Health System Sunbelt Health Care Corporation, Altamonte Springs, FL
Primary Contact: Denyse Bales–Chubb, President and Chief Executive Officer
Web address: www.floridahospital.com/wesley–chapel
Control: Other not–for–profit (including NFP Corporation) **Service:** General medical and surgical

Staffed Beds: 121 **Admissions:** 6479 **Census:** 63 **Outpatient Visits:** 58796 **Births:** 436 **Total Expense ($000):** 135532 **Payroll Expense ($000):** 44556 **Personnel:** 866

☐ **NORTH TAMPA BEHAVIORAL HEALTH (104075)**, 29910 State Road 56, Zip 33543–8800; tel. 813/922–3300 **A**1 10 **F**4 5 98 100 101 102 103 104 105 106 143 **P**4 **S** Acadia Healthcare Company, Inc., Franklin, TN
Primary Contact: Tracy Rogers, Chief Executive Officer
Web address: www.northtampabehavioralhealth.com
Control: Corporation, Investor–owned (for–profit) **Service:** Psychiatric

Staffed Beds: 78 **Admissions:** 3152 **Census:** 74 **Births:** 0

WEST PALM BEACH—Palm Beach County

⊞ **GOOD SAMARITAN MEDICAL CENTER (100287)**, 1309 North Flagler Drive, Zip 33401–3499; tel. 561/655–5511, (Nonreporting) **A**1 2 5 10 **S** TENET Healthcare Corporation, Dallas, TX
Primary Contact: Mark Nosacka, Chief Executive Officer
CFO: Cynthia McCauley, Chief Financial Officer
CIO: Candace Helms, Director Information Services
Web address: www.goodsamaritanmc.com
Control: Corporation, Investor–owned (for–profit) **Service:** General medical and surgical

Staffed Beds: 174

☐ **JEROME GOLDEN CENTER FOR BEHAVIORAL HEALTH, INC. (104008)**, 1041 45th Street, Zip 33407–2494; tel. 561/383–8000, (Nonreporting) **A**1 10
Primary Contact: Linda De Piano, Ph.D., Chief Executive Officer
CFO: America Cordoves, Controller
CMO: Suresh Rajpara M.D., Chief Medical Officer
CIO: Iris Garcia, Director, Information Services
CHR: Nadine Wilson, Manager, Human Resources
CNO: Holly Horvath, Director of Nursing
Web address: www.goldenctr.org
Control: Other not–for–profit (including NFP Corporation) **Service:** Psychiatric

Staffed Beds: 44

⊞ **JFK MEDICAL CENTER NORTH CAMPUS (100234)**, 2201 45th Street, Zip 33407–2047; tel. 561/842–6141 **A**1 10 **F**3 29 34 35 40 45 49 57 59 60 70 79 81 82 93 98 99 101 102 103 104 105 107 110 111 119 146 148 149 **S** HCA Healthcare, Nashville, TN
Primary Contact: Patricia Burns, Chief Executive Officer
COO: Patrick Chapman, Assistant Vice President Operations
CMO: Paul Seltzer M.D., Chief of Staff
CIO: Kenneth Vasquez, Associate Director
CHR: Donna Boyle, Director
CNO: Geraldine DeStefano R.N., MS, Chief Nursing Officer
Web address: www.westpalmhospital.com
Control: Corporation, Investor–owned (for–profit) **Service:** General medical and surgical

Staffed Beds: 245 **Admissions:** 9735 **Census:** 119 **Births:** 0

⊞ △ **ST. MARY'S MEDICAL CENTER (100288)**, 901 45th Street, Zip 33407–2495; tel. 561/844–6300, (Includes PALM BEACH CHILDREN'S HOSPITAL, 901 45th Street, West Palm Beach, Florida, Zip 33407, tel. 561/844–6300) **A**1 7 10 **F**3 6 8 11 12 13 15 17 18 19 20 21 22 23 24 25 29 30 31 34 35 38 39 40 41 43 44 45 47 48 49 50 51 56 57 58 59 60 64 65 68 70 72 73 74 75 76 77 78 79 81 85 86 87 88 89 90 92 93 94 96 98 100 101 102 103 107 108 110 111 114 115 119 120 121 123 130 131 132 134 135 146 147 148 **S** TENET Healthcare Corporation, Dallas, TX
Primary Contact: Gabrielle Finley–Hazle, Chief Executive Officer
COO: Joey Bulfin R.N., Interim Chief Executive Officer
CFO: Tom Schlemmer, Chief Financial Officer
CMO: Jeffrey Davis D.O., Chief Medical Officer
CIO: Rich Avato, Director
CHR: Thomas J Piszczatoski, Chief Human Resource Officer
CNO: Donna Small R.N., Chief Nursing Officer
Web address: www.stmarysmc.com
Control: Corporation, Investor–owned (for–profit) **Service:** General medical and surgical

Staffed Beds: 464 **Admissions:** 18135 **Census:** 250 **Births:** 3294 **Total Expense ($000):** 279972 **Payroll Expense ($000):** 103859

VETERANS AFFAIRS MEDICAL CENTER See West Palm Beach Veterans Affairs Medical Center

⊞ **WEST PALM BEACH VETERANS AFFAIRS MEDICAL CENTER**, 7305 North Military Trail, Zip 33410–6400; tel. 561/422–8262, (Nonreporting) **A**1 3 5 **S** Department of Veterans Affairs, Washington, DC
Primary Contact: Donna Katen–Bahensky, Director
CFO: Lori Hancock, Chief Business Officer
CMO: Deepak Mandi M.D., Chief of Staff
CIO: Karen Gabaldon, Chief Management Information Systems
CHR: David Green, Chief Human Resources
Web address: www.westpalmbeach.va.gov/
Control: Veterans Affairs, Government, federal **Service:** General medical and surgical

Staffed Beds: 300

FL

Hospital, Medicare Provider Number, Address, Telephone, Approval, Facility, and Physician Codes, Health Care System

★ American Hospital Association (AHA) membership   ○ Healthcare Facilities Accreditation Program   ⇑ Center for Improvement in Healthcare Quality Accreditation
☐ The Joint Commission accreditation   ◇ DNV Healthcare Inc. accreditation   △ Commission on Accreditation of Rehabilitation Facilities (CARF) accreditation

© 2017 AHA Guide   *Many Facility Codes have changed. Please refer to the AHA Guide Code Chart.*   Hospitals **A147**

WESTON—Broward County

✠ **CLEVELAND CLINIC FLORIDA (100289)**, 2950 Cleveland Clinic Boulevard,
Zip 33331–3602; tel. 954/659–5000 **A**1 2 3 5 10 **F**3 7 8 9 11 12 15 17 18 20
22 24 26 28 29 30 31 34 35 36 37 39 40 41 44 45 46 47 48 49 50 51 54 55
56 57 58 59 60 61 63 64 65 68 70 71 74 75 77 78 79 80 81 82 84 85 86 87
91 92 93 96 97 100 107 108 109 110 111 114 115 116 117 119 120 121
123 124 126 129 130 131 132 135 137 138 139 141 145 146 147 148 149
P6 **S** Cleveland Clinic Health System, Cleveland, OH
Primary Contact: Wael Barsoum, M.D., President
CFO: Keith Nilsson, Chief Financial Officer
CMO: Raul Rosenthal M.D., Interim Chief of Staff
CIO: John Santangelo, Director Information Technology
CHR: Jackie Puntel, Senior Director Human Resources
CNO: Kerry Major R.N., MSN, Chief Nursing Officer
Web address: www.clevelandclinic.org/florida
Control: Other not–for–profit (including NFP Corporation) **Service**: General
medical and surgical

Staffed Beds: 155 **Admissions:** 10551 **Census:** 123 **Outpatient Visits:**
54872 **Births:** 0 **Total Expense ($000):** 239844 **Payroll Expense ($000):**
86313 **Personnel:** 2418

WILLISTON—Levy County

NATURE COAST REGIONAL HOSPITAL See Regional General Hospital

REGIONAL GENERAL HOSPITAL (100322), 125 SW Seventh Street,
Zip 32696–2403; tel. 352/528–2801, (Nonreporting) **A**10
Primary Contact: Edith Mears, Chief Executive Officer
CFO: Barbara Miller, Manager Business Office
CMO: Jeremie Young M.D., Chief of Staff
CHR: Karla Dass, Director Human Resources
Web address: www.regionalgeneral.com/
Control: Partnership, Investor–owned (for–profit) **Service**: General medical and
surgical

Staffed Beds: 20

WINTER HAVEN—Polk County

✠ △ **WINTER HAVEN HOSPITAL (100052)**, 200 Avenue F NE, Zip 33881–
4193; tel. 863/293–1121 **A**1 7 10 **F**3 8 11 13 14 15 17 18 20 22 24 26 28 29
30 31 34 40 45 47 49 57 58 59 60 64 68 70 72 73 74 75 76 77 78 79 81 82
84 85 86 87 89 90 93 94 98 100 101 102 104 107 108 110 111 114 115 118
119 120 121 123 126 130 132 135 144 146 147 148 **P**6 7 **S** Trinity Health,
Livonia, MI
Primary Contact: Stephen A. Nierman, President
COO: Jacques Vasconcellos, Director, Operations
CFO: Tina Solomon, Executive Director Finance
CMO: Khurram Kamran M.D., Vice President, Physician Services
CIO: Cal Cole, Director Information Systems
CHR: Rosemary Myers, Manager, Team Resources
CNO: Carol Koeppel–Olsen, Vice President, Patient Care Services
Web address: www.winterhavenhospital.org
Control: Other not–for–profit (including NFP Corporation) **Service**: General
medical and surgical

Staffed Beds: 361 **Admissions:** 18657 **Census:** 235 **Outpatient Visits:**
119007 **Births:** 1562 **Total Expense ($000):** 274593 **Payroll Expense
($000):** 112139 **Personnel:** 2052

WINTER PARK—Orange County

WINTER PARK MEMORIAL HOSPITAL See Florida Hospital, Orlando

ZEPHYRHILLS—Pasco County

✠ **FLORIDA HOSPITAL ZEPHYRHILLS (100046)**, 7050 Gall Boulevard,
Zip 33541–1399; tel. 813/788–0411 **A**1 5 10 **F**3 12 13 14 15 17 18 20 22
24 26 28 29 30 31 32 34 35 37 40 44 45 46 47 48 49 51 53 54 56 57 59 60
62 63 64 68 70 74 76 77 79 81 82 83 86 87 91 92 93 97 107 108 110 111
114 115 116 119 124 126 129 130 132 133 135 146 147 148 149 150 **P**6 **S**
Adventist Health System Sunbelt Health Care Corporation, Altamonte Springs, FL
Primary Contact: Amanda Maggard, Chief Executive Officer
COO: Donald E Welch, Chief Operating Officer
CFO: Bill Heinrich, Chief Financial Officer
CMO: Hugar McNamee D.O., Chief Medical Officer
CIO: Kelley Sasser, Director Information Systems
CHR: Laura Asaftei, Administrative Director
CNO: Gwen Alonso, Chief Nursing Officer
Web address: www.fhzeph.org
Control: Church operated, Nongovernment, not–for–profit **Service**: General
medical and surgical

Staffed Beds: 149 **Admissions:** 8260 **Census:** 90 **Outpatient Visits:** 60070
Births: 533 **Total Expense ($000):** 136582 **Payroll Expense ($000):** 52156
Personnel: 888

FL

Many Facility Codes have changed. Please refer to the AHA Guide Code Chart. © 2017 AHA Guide

GEORGIA

ADEL—Cook County

✠ **COOK MEDICAL CENTER–A CAMPUS OF TIFT REGIONAL MEDICAL CENTER (110101)**, 706 North Parrish Avenue, Zip 31620–1511; tel. 229/896–8000, (Total facility includes 95 beds in nursing home–type unit) **A**1 10 **F**11 15 29 30 34 35 40 45 46 47 56 57 59 63 64 65 68 75 77 81 84 85 86 87 93 97 98 101 103 104 107 108 110 111 114 118 119 127 129 130 133 135 146 147 148 149 **P**6 **S** Tift Regional Health System, Tifton, GA
Primary Contact: Michael L. Purvis, Chief Executive Officer
COO: Kim Wills, Chief Operating Officer
CIO: Barry Medley, Director Information Systems
CHR: Shirley Padgett, Director Human Resources
Web address: www.cookmedicalcenter.com
Control: Hospital district or authority, Government, Nonfederal **Service:** General medical and surgical

Staffed Beds: 155 **Admissions:** 695 **Census:** 99 **Outpatient Visits:** 18593 **Births:** 0 **Total Expense ($000):** 19788 **Payroll Expense ($000):** 8740 **Personnel:** 181

ALBANY—Dougherty County

★ ⇑ **PHOEBE PUTNEY MEMORIAL HOSPITAL (110007)**, 417 West Third Avenue, Zip 31701–1943, Mailing Address: P.O.Box 3770, 31706–3770; tel. 229/312–4100, (Includes PHOEBE NORTH, 2000 Palmyra Road, Albany, Georgia, Zip 31701–1528, P O Box 1908, 31702–1908, tel. 229/434–2000) **A**2 3 5 10 **F**3 5 7 11 12 13 15 17 18 20 22 24 26 28 29 30 31 34 35 40 44 45 46 49 50 51 53 54 56 57 59 60 62 63 64 68 70 72 73 74 75 76 77 78 79 81 82 83 84 85 86 87 89 90 91 92 93 94 96 97 98 100 101 102 103 104 105 107 108 110 111 114 115 116 117 118 119 120 121 123 124 126 127 129 130 131 132 134 135 136 144 145 146 147 148 149 **P**1 7 **S** Phoebe Putney Health System, Albany, GA
Primary Contact: Joel Wernick, President and Chief Executive Officer
COO: Joe Austin, Executive Vice President and Chief Operating Officer
CFO: Brian Church, Senior Vice President and Chief Financial Officer
CMO: Steven Kitchen M.D., Chief Medical Officer
CIO: Jesse Diaz, Chief Information Officer
CHR: David J Baranski, Vice President Human Resources
CNO: Laura Shearer R.N., MSN, Senior Vice President and Chief Nursing Officer
Web address: www.phoebeputney.com
Control: Other not–for–profit (including NFP Corporation) **Service:** General medical and surgical

Staffed Beds: 524 **Admissions:** 19727 **Census:** 297 **Outpatient Visits:** 1140975 **Births:** 2341 **Total Expense ($000):** 526296 **Payroll Expense ($000):** 148217 **Personnel:** 2662

ALMA—Bacon County

✠ **BACON COUNTY HOSPITAL AND HEALTH SYSTEM (111327)**, 302 South Wayne Street, Zip 31510–2922, Mailing Address: P O Drawer 1987, 31510–0987; tel. 912/632–8961, (Nonreporting) **A**1 10 18
Primary Contact: Cindy R. Turner, Chief Executive Officer
COO: Cindy R Turner, Chief Executive Officer
CFO: Kyle Kimmel, Chief Financial Officer
CMO: Lou Ellen Hutcheson M.D., Chief of Staff
CIO: Neil O'Steen, Director Information Technology
CHR: Kerry Hancock, Director Human Resources
CNO: Deanna Hoff R.N., Director of Nursing
Web address: www.baconcountyhospital.com
Control: Other not–for–profit (including NFP Corporation) **Service:** General medical and surgical

Staffed Beds: 113

AMERICUS—Sumter County

★ ⇑ **PHOEBE SUMTER MEDICAL CENTER (110044)**, 126 Highway 280 West, Zip 31719; tel. 229/924–6011, (Nonreporting) **A**10 21 **S** Phoebe Putney Health System, Albany, GA
Primary Contact: Brandi Lunneborg, Chief Executive Officer
CHR: Cassandra Haynes Aldridge, Chief Human Resources Officer
CNO: Susan Bruns, Chief Nursing Officer
Web address: www.phoebesumter.org
Control: Other not–for–profit (including NFP Corporation) **Service:** General medical and surgical

Staffed Beds: 45

ATHENS—Clarke County

☐ **LANDMARK HOSPITAL OF ATHENS (112017)**, 775 Sunset Drive, Zip 30606–2211; tel. 706/425–1500 **A**1 10 22 **F**1 3 29 45 130 148 **S** Landmark Hospitals, Cape Girardeau, MO
Primary Contact: Vivian Goff, R.N., Chief Executive Officer
Web address: www.landmarkhospitals.com
Control: Individual, Investor–owned (for–profit) **Service:** Acute long–term care hospital

Staffed Beds: 42 **Admissions:** 426 **Census:** 32 **Outpatient Visits:** 0 **Births:** 0 **Personnel:** 112

✠ **PIEDMONT ATHENS REGIONAL MEDICAL CENTER (110074)**, 1199 Prince Avenue, Zip 30606–2797; tel. 706/475–7000 **A**1 2 3 10 **F**3 8 13 15 17 18 20 22 24 26 28 29 30 31 32 34 35 36 40 43 45 46 47 48 49 50 51 54 55 56 57 58 59 60 61 62 64 66 68 70 71 72 73 74 76 77 78 79 80 81 83 84 85 86 87 89 91 92 93 94 96 100 102 107 108 110 111 114 115 116 117 118 119 120 121 123 124 126 129 130 131 132 135 144 145 146 147 148 **S** Piedmont Healthcare, Atlanta, GA
Primary Contact: Charles A. Peck, M.D., Interim President and Chief Executive Officer
CFO: Wendy J. Cook, Senior Vice President and Chief Financial Officer
CMO: James L Moore M.D., Senior Vice President and Chief Medical Officer
CIO: Mike Koehler, Interim Chief Information Officer
CHR: Robert D. Finch, Vice President Human Resources
CNO: Lori Giles, Interim Chief Nursing Officer
Web address: www.armc.org
Control: Other not–for–profit (including NFP Corporation) **Service:** General medical and surgical

Staffed Beds: 343 **Admissions:** 19386 **Census:** 238 **Outpatient Visits:** 302283 **Births:** 2339 **Total Expense ($000):** 401044 **Payroll Expense ($000):** 156959 **Personnel:** 2679

✠ △ **ST. MARY'S HEALTH CARE SYSTEM (110006)**, 1230 Baxter Street, Zip 30606–3791; tel. 706/389–3000 **A**1 3 7 10 **F**3 11 12 13 15 18 20 22 26 28 29 30 31 34 35 40 41 45 46 48 49 50 53 54 57 58 59 61 62 63 64 68 70 72 74 75 76 77 79 80 81 83 84 85 87 89 90 93 97 107 110 111 114 115 118 119 126 129 130 131 132 135 141 145 146 147 148 149 **S** Trinity Health, Livonia, MI
Primary Contact: Donald McKenna, President and Chief Executive Officer
CFO: Marty Hutson, Chief Financial Officer
CMO: Bruce Middendorf M.D., Chief Medical Officer
CIO: Kerry Vaughn, Chief Information Officer
CHR: Jeff English, Vice President Human Resources
Web address: www.stmarysathens.com
Control: Church operated, Nongovernment, not–for–profit **Service:** General medical and surgical

Staffed Beds: 183 **Admissions:** 9831 **Census:** 128 **Outpatient Visits:** 207072 **Births:** 1627 **Total Expense ($000):** 185093 **Payroll Expense ($000):** 68818 **Personnel:** 1279

ATLANTA—Fulton and De Kalb County

☐ **ANCHOR HOSPITAL (114032)**, 5454 Yorktowne Drive, Zip 30349–5317; tel. 770/991–6044, (Nonreporting) **A**1 10 **S** Universal Health Services, Inc., King of Prussia, PA
Primary Contact: Randall G. Hines, Ph.D., Chief Executive Officer
CFO: John Kim, Chief Financial Officer
CMO: Athena Sotus–Nawar M.D., Medical Director
CIO: Michael Delpleache, Specialist Information Technology
CHR: Rhian Sharp, Director Human Resources
CNO: Kim Butts, System Nurse Executive
Web address: www.anchorhospital.com
Control: Corporation, Investor–owned (for–profit) **Service:** Alcoholism and other chemical dependency

Staffed Beds: 122

Hospital, Medicare Provider Number, Address, Telephone, Approval, Facility, and Physician Codes, Health Care System

★ American Hospital Association (AHA) membership ○ Healthcare Facilities Accreditation Program ⇑ Center for Improvement in Healthcare Quality Accreditation
☐ The Joint Commission accreditation ◇ DNV Healthcare Inc. accreditation △ Commission on Accreditation of Rehabilitation Facilities (CARF) accreditation

GA

□ △ **CHILDREN'S HEALTHCARE OF ATLANTA (113301)**, 1600 Tullie Circle, NE, Zip 30329–2303; tel. 404/785–7000, (Nonreporting) (Includes CHILDREN'S HEALTHCARE OF ATLANTA AT EGLESTON, 1600 Tullie Circle, Atlanta, Georgia, Zip 30329, tel. 404/325–6000; CHILDREN'S HEALTHCARE OF ATLANTA AT HUGHES SPALDING, 35 Jesse Hill Jr Drive, SE, Atlanta, Georgia, Zip 30303–3032, tel. 404/785–9500; CHILDREN'S HEALTHCARE OF ATLANTA AT SCOTTISH RITE, 1001 Johnson Ferry Road NE, Atlanta, Georgia, Zip 30342–1600, tel. 404/256–5252) **A**1 3 5 7 8 10
Primary Contact: Donna W. Hyland, President and Chief Executive Officer
COO: Carolyn Kenny, Executive Vice President Clinical Care
CFO: Ruth Fowler, Senior Vice President and Chief Financial Officer
CMO: Daniel Salinas M.D., Senior Vice President and Chief Medical Officer
CIO: Allana Cummings, Chief Information Officer
CHR: Linda Matzigkeit, Senior Vice President Human Resources
Web address: www.choa.org
Control: Other not–for–profit (including NFP Corporation) **Service**: Children's general medical and surgical

Staffed Beds: 496

⊞ **EMORY REHABILITATION HOSPITAL (113031)**, 1441 Clifton Road NE, Zip 30322–1004; tel. 404/712–5512 **A**1 10 **F**11 29 30 34 35 36 50 56 58 64 68 74 75 77 79 82 85 86 87 90 93 94 95 96 130 131 132 135 146 148 149 **P**6 **S** Emory Healthcare, Atlanta, GA
Primary Contact: Michael Eric. Garrard, FACHE, Chief Executive Officer
CMO: S. Byron Milton M.D., Medical Director
CHR: Janine Diaz, Human Resources Manager
CNO: Deborah Almauhy R.N., Chief Nursing Officer
Web address: www.emoryhealthcare.org/rehabilitation
Control: Corporation, Investor–owned (for–profit) **Service**: Rehabilitation

Staffed Beds: 46 Admissions: 1013 Census: 38 Outpatient Visits: 20318 Births: 0 Total Expense ($000): 21966 Payroll Expense ($000): 12363 Personnel: 181

⊞ **EMORY SAINT JOSEPH'S HOSPITAL OF ATLANTA (110082)**, 5665 Peachtree Dunwoody Road NE, Zip 30342–1701; tel. 678/843–7001 **A**1 2 3 10 **F**3 12 15 17 18 20 22 24 26 28 29 30 31 34 35 37 40 44 45 46 47 50 51 53 54 55 57 58 59 60 64 68 70 71 74 75 77 78 79 81 82 84 85 86 87 100 102 107 108 110 111 115 117 118 119 120 121 123 124 126 130 132 135 145 146 147 148 149 **P**6 **S** Emory Healthcare, Atlanta, GA
Primary Contact: Heather Dexter, Chief Executive Officer
CFO: Kevin Brenan, Chief Financial Officer
CMO: Paul Scheinberg M.D., Chief of Staff
CIO: Dedra Cantrell, Chief Information Officer
CHR: Audra Farish, Vice President Human Resources
Web address: www.emoryhealthcare.org/locations/hospitals/emory–saint–josephs–hospital/
Control: Other not–for–profit (including NFP Corporation) **Service**: General medical and surgical

Staffed Beds: 272 Admissions: 14484 Census: 187 Outpatient Visits: 120545 Births: 1 Total Expense ($000): 321529 Payroll Expense ($000): 102037 Personnel: 1527

⊞ **EMORY UNIVERSITY HOSPITAL (110010)**, 1364 Clifton Road NE, Zip 30322; tel. 404/712–2000, (Includes EMORY UNIVERSITY ORTHOPAEDIC AND SPINE HOSPITAL, 1455 Montreal Road, Tucker, Georgia, Zip 30084, tel. 404/251–3600; June Conner, R.N., Chief Operating Officer; EMORY WESLEY WOODS GERIATRIC HOSPITAL, 1821 Clifton Road NE, Atlanta, Georgia, Zip 30329–4021, tel. 404/728–6200; Jennifer Schuck, Associate Administrator) **A**1 2 3 5 8 10 **F**3 11 12 15 17 18 20 22 24 26 28 29 30 31 34 35 36 38 39 40 44 45 46 47 48 49 50 55 56 57 58 59 60 61 63 64 68 70 74 75 77 78 79 80 81 82 84 85 86 87 93 98 100 101 102 103 104 105 107 108 110 111 114 115 116 117 118 119 120 121 123 124 126 129 130 131 132 135 136 137 138 139 140 141 142 145 146 147 148 149 **P**6 **S** Emory Healthcare, Atlanta, GA
Primary Contact: Bryce D. Gartland, M.D., Chief Executive Officer
CFO: Carla Chandler, Vice President and Chief Financial Officer
CMO: Chad W.M. Ritenour M.D., Chief Medical Officer
CIO: Sheila M Sanders, Chief Information Officer
CHR: Mary Beth Allen, Vice President Human Resources
CNO: Nancye R. Feistritzer, Chief Nursing Officer
Web address: www.emoryhealthcare.org
Control: Other not–for–profit (including NFP Corporation) **Service**: General medical and surgical

Staffed Beds: 558 Admissions: 26564 Census: 466 Outpatient Visits: 166748 Births: 0 Total Expense ($000): 787812 Payroll Expense ($000): 241610 Personnel: 3591

⊞ **EMORY UNIVERSITY HOSPITAL MIDTOWN (110078)**, 550 Peachtree Street NE, Zip 30308–2247; tel. 404/686–4411 **A**1 2 3 5 8 10 **F**3 11 12 13 15 17 18 20 22 24 26 28 29 30 31 34 35 36 38 40 44 45 46 47 48 49 50 51 52 55 57 58 59 60 61 64 68 70 72 73 74 75 76 77 78 79 81 82 84 85 86 87 92 93 107 108 110 111 114 115 116 117 118 121 123 124 126 130 131 132 135 141 146 147 148 149 **P**6 **S** Emory Healthcare, Atlanta, GA
Primary Contact: Daniel Owens, Chief Executive Officer
CMO: James P Steinberg M.D., Chief Medical Officer
CIO: Dedra Cantrell, Chief Information Officer
CHR: Dallis Howard–Crow, Chief Human Resources Officer
Web address: www.emoryhealthcare.org
Control: Other not–for–profit (including NFP Corporation) **Service**: General medical and surgical

Staffed Beds: 459 Admissions: 22749 Census: 360 Outpatient Visits: 240468 Births: 4431 Total Expense ($000): 697837 Payroll Expense ($000): 194066 Personnel: 2581

⊞ **GRADY MEMORIAL HOSPITAL (110079)**, 80 Jesse Hill Jr Drive SE, Zip 30303–3031, Mailing Address: P.O.Box 26189, 31329–0386; tel. 404/616–1000, (Total facility includes 265 beds in nursing home–type unit) **A**1 2 3 5 8 10 **F**2 3 5 7 8 13 15 16 18 20 22 24 26 29 30 31 34 35 38 39 40 43 45 46 47 49 50 51 52 53 54 55 56 57 58 59 60 61 62 63 64 65 66 68 70 72 73 74 75 76 77 78 79 80 81 82 84 85 86 87 93 94 97 98 100 101 102 103 104 105 107 108 109 110 111 112 113 114 115 116 117 118 119 120 121 128 129 130 132 134 135 143 144 146 147 148
Primary Contact: John M. Haupert, FACHE, Chief Executive Officer
COO: Christopher R Mosley FACHE, Chief Operating Officer
CFO: Mark Meyer, Chief Financial Officer
CMO: Curtis Lewis M.D., Chief of Staff
CIO: Ben McKeeby, Senior Vice President and Chief Information Officer
CHR: Larry A. Callahan, Senior Vice President Human Resources
CNO: Rhonda A Scott Ph.D., R.N., Chief Nursing Officer and Executive Vice President
Web address: www.gradyhealthsystem.org
Control: Other not–for–profit (including NFP Corporation) **Service**: General medical and surgical

Staffed Beds: 993 Admissions: 30949 Census: 767 Outpatient Visits: 671483 Births: 3098 Total Expense ($000): 969995 Payroll Expense ($000): 354726 Personnel: 5031

⊞ **NORTHSIDE HOSPITAL (110161)**, 1000 Johnson Ferry Road NE, Zip 30342–1611; tel. 404/851–8000 **A**1 2 3 10 **F**3 5 8 11 12 13 15 17 18 20 22 26 28 29 30 31 34 35 37 40 44 45 46 47 48 49 50 51 53 54 55 57 58 59 60 64 68 70 71 72 73 74 75 76 77 78 79 80 81 82 84 85 86 87 93 100 104 105 107 108 110 111 114 115 117 118 119 120 121 123 124 126 129 130 132 135 136 144 145 146 147 148 **S** Northside Healthcare System, Atlanta, GA
Primary Contact: Robert Quattrocchi, President and Chief Executive Officer
CFO: Debbie Mitcham, Chief Financial Officer
CIO: Tina Wakim, Vice President Information
Web address: www.northside.com
Control: Other not–for–profit (including NFP Corporation) **Service**: General medical and surgical

Staffed Beds: 601 Admissions: 35452 Census: 390 Outpatient Visits: 1550018 Births: 16254 Total Expense ($000): 1787613 Payroll Expense ($000): 554963 Personnel: 8516

□ **PEACHFORD BEHAVIORAL HEALTH SYSTEM (114010)**, 2151 Peachford Road, Zip 30338–6599; tel. 770/455–3200, (Nonreporting) **A**1 10 **S** Universal Health Services, Inc., King of Prussia, PA
Primary Contact: Matthew Crouch, Chief Executive Officer and Managing Director
COO: Sharon Stackhouse, Assistant Administrator and Director Risk Management
CFO: April Hughes, Chief Financial Officer
CMO: Asaf Aleem M.D., Medical Director
CHR: Clay Boyles, Director Human Resources
Web address: www.peachfordhospital.com
Control: Corporation, Investor–owned (for–profit) **Service**: Psychiatric

Staffed Beds: 246

⇧ **PIEDMONT HOSPITAL (110083)**, 1968 Peachtree Road NW, Zip 30309–1281; tel. 404/605–5000 **A**2 3 5 10 21 **F**3 8 11 12 13 15 17 18 20 22 24 26 28 29 30 31 34 35 40 44 45 46 47 48 49 50 51 53 54 55 56 57 58 59 60 61 64 65 68 70 72 73 74 75 76 77 78 79 81 82 84 85 86 87 92 93 107 108 110 111 114 115 116 117 118 119 120 121 123 124 126 129 130 131 132 135 137 138 139 141 142 145 146 147 148 **P**1 6 **S** Piedmont Healthcare, Atlanta, GA
Primary Contact: Patrick M. Battey, M.D., Chief Executive Officer
COO: Ed Lovern, Chief Operating Officer
CFO: Sheryl Klink, Chief Financial Officer
CMO: Mark Cohen M.D., Chief Medical Officer
CHR: Greg Prokopchak, Senior Director Human Resources
CNO: Kelly Hulsey, Chief Nursing Officer
Web address: www.piedmonthospital.org
Control: Other not–for–profit (including NFP Corporation) **Service**: General medical and surgical

Staffed Beds: 510 Admissions: 27489 Census: 399 Outpatient Visits: 338696 Births: 3297 Personnel: 3284

GA

Many Facility Codes have changed. Please refer to the AHA Guide Code Chart.
© 2017 AHA Guide

SAINT JOSEPH'S HOSPITAL OF ATLANTA See Emory Saint Joseph's Hospital of Atlanta

☒ **SELECT SPECIALTY HOSPITAL – NORTHEAST ATLANTA (112005)**, 1821 Clifton Road NE, 2nd Floor, Zip 30329–4021; tel. 404/728–6200 (Nonreporting) **A**1 10 **S** Select Medical Corporation, Mechanicsburg, PA
Primary Contact: Jeffrey R. Fenn, Chief Executive Officer
CFO: Theodore Saunders, Assistant Controller
CMO: Jeffrey Mikell M.D., Chief Medical Officer
CIO: Vicky Goziah, Software Administrator
CNO: Annette Branan, Chief Nursing Officer and Vice President Patient Care Services
Web address: www.selectspecialtyhospitals.com/
Control: Corporation, Investor–owned (for–profit) **Service:** Acute long–term care hospital

Staffed Beds: 18

☒ **SELECT SPECIALTY HOSPITAL MIDTOWN ATLANTA (112004)**, 705 Juniper Street NE, Zip 30308–1307; tel. 404/873–2871, (Nonreporting) **A**1 10 **S** Select Medical Corporation, Mechanicsburg, PA
Primary Contact: Jeffrey R. Fenn, Chief Executive Officer
CFO: Michael Nelson, Chief Financial Officer
CMO: David N. DeRuyter M.D., President Medical Staff
CHR: Armetria Gibson, Human Resources Generalist
CNO: Annette Harrilson, Chief Clinical Officer
Web address: www.selectspecialtyhospitals.com/
Control: Partnership, Investor–owned (for–profit) **Service:** Acute long–term care hospital

Staffed Beds: 72

☒ **SELECT SPECIALTY HOSPITAL–ATLANTA (112009)**, 550 Peachtree Street NE, Zip 30308–2247; tel. 404/815–0348, (Nonreporting) **A**1 10 **S** Select Medical Corporation, Mechanicsburg, PA
Primary Contact: Michelle Tenhengel–deVille, Chief Executive Officer
Web address: www.selectspecialtyhospitals.com/company/locations/atlanta.aspx
Control: Corporation, Investor–owned (for–profit) **Service:** Acute long–term care hospital

Staffed Beds: 30

☐ △ **SHEPHERD CENTER (112003)**, 2020 Peachtree Road NW, Zip 30309–1465; tel. 404/352–2020 **A**1 3 5 7 10 **F**3 29 30 34 35 53 58 59 64 65 70 74 75 77 82 90 91 93 94 111 119 130 131 132 143 146 148 **P**6
Primary Contact: Sarah Morrison, President and Chief Executive Officer
CFO: Stephen B Holleman, Chief Financial Officer
CMO: Donald P Leslie M.D., Medical Director
CIO: Brian Barnette, Chief Information Officer
CHR: Lorie Hutcheson, Vice President of Human Resources
CNO: Tamara King R.N., MSN, Chief Nurse Executive
Web address: www.shepherd.org
Control: Other not–for–profit (including NFP Corporation) **Service:** Rehabilitation

Staffed Beds: 127 Admissions: 927 Census: 123 Outpatient Visits: 67834 Births: 0 Total Expense ($000): 193035 Payroll Expense ($000): 91049 Personnel: 1120

☒ **WELLSTAR ATLANTA MEDICAL CENTER (110115)**, 303 Parkway Drive NE, Zip 30312–1212; tel. 404/265–4000, (Includes ATLANTA MEDICAL CENTER – SOUTH CAMPUS, 1170 Cleveland Avenue, Atlanta, Georgia, Zip 30344–3665, tel. 404/466–1170; Daniel Jackson, Chief Administrative Officer) **A**1 2 3 5 8 10 **F**11 12 13 15 17 18 20 22 24 26 28 29 30 31 34 35 36 37 38 40 43 44 45 46 50 53 54 56 57 59 60 61 64 65 66 70 72 73 74 75 76 77 78 79 81 84 85 86 87 90 93 96 97 98 100 101 102 103 104 107 108 111 114 118 119 126 129 130 132 134 144 146 147 148 149 150 **S** WellStar Health System, Marietta, GA
Primary Contact: Kimberly Ryan, President
COO: Greg Brickner, Vice President and Director, Business Development
CFO: Sandra Albrecht, Interim Chief Financial Officer
CMO: Albert Barrocas M.D., Chief Medical Officer
CIO: Maryland McCarty, Director Information Systems
CHR: Stacey J Hancock, Vice President, Human Resources
CNO: Paula Yvonne Butts, Chief Nursing Officer
Web address: www.atlantamedcenter.com
Control: Other not–for–profit (including NFP Corporation) **Service:** General medical and surgical

Staffed Beds: 490 Admissions: 19932 Census: 310 Outpatient Visits: 188579 Births: 2324 Personnel: 1785

WESLEY WOODS GERIATRIC HOSPITAL OF EMORY UNIVERSITY See Emory Wesley Woods Geriatric Hospital

WESLEY WOODS LONG TERM CARE HOSPITAL See Select Specialty Hospital – Northeast Atlanta

AUGUSTA—Richmond County

☒ **AUGUSTA UNIVERSITY MEDICAL CENTER (110034)**, 1120 15th Street, Zip 30912–0004; tel. 706/721–0211, (Nonreporting) (Includes CHILDREN'S HOSPITAL OF GEORGIA, 1446 Harper Street, Augusta, Georgia, Zip 30912–0012, tel. 706/721–5437; Peter Buckley, M.D., Interim Chief Executive Officer) **A**1 2 3 5 8 10 13
Primary Contact: Lee Ann Liska, Chief Executive Officer
COO: Shawn Vincent, Interim Chief Operating Officer
CFO: Greg Damron, Vice President Finance and Chief Financial Officer
CMO: Kevin Dellsperger M.D., Chief Medical Officer
CIO: Charles Enicks, Chief Information Officer
CHR: Susan Norton, Vice President Human Resources
CNO: Laura E Brower R.N., MSN, Chief Nursing Officer
Web address: www.grhealth.org
Control: Other not–for–profit (including NFP Corporation) **Service:** General medical and surgical

Staffed Beds: 408

☒ △ **CHARLIE NORWOOD VETERANS AFFAIRS MEDICAL CENTER**, 1 Freedom Way, Zip 30904–6285; tel. 706/733–0188, (Nonreporting) **A**1 2 3 5 7 8 **S** Department of Veterans Affairs, Washington, DC
Primary Contact: Maria R. Andrews, MS, Director
COO: John D Stenger, Acting Associate Director
CFO: Earline Corder, Chief Fiscal
CIO: Sandy Williford, Chief Health Information Management and Revenue Administration
CHR: Roger W Buterbaugh, Chief Human Resources Officer
CNO: Michelle Cox–Henley R.N., MSN, Associate Director for Patient and Nursing Services
Web address: www.augusta.va.gov/
Control: Veterans Affairs, Government, federal **Service:** General medical and surgical

Staffed Beds: 338

☒ **DOCTORS HOSPITAL (110177)**, 3651 Wheeler Road, Zip 30909–6426; tel. 706/651–3232, (Nonreporting) **A**1 2 3 5 10 **S** HCA Healthcare, Nashville, TN
Primary Contact: Douglas Welch, Chief Executive Officer
CIO: Dona Hornung, Director Information and Technology Services
Web address: www.doctors–hospital.net
Control: Corporation, Investor–owned (for–profit) **Service:** General medical and surgical

Staffed Beds: 307

☐ **EAST CENTRAL REGIONAL HOSPITAL (114029)**, 3405 Mike Padgett Highway, Zip 30906–3897; tel. 706/790–2011, (Includes EAST CENTRAL REGIONAL HOSPITAL, 100 Myrtle Boulevard, Gracewood, Georgia, Zip 30812–1299, tel. 706/790–2011) **A**1 3 5 10 **F**29 34 38 39 59 65 67 75 77 98 101 102 128 130 132 135 **P**6
Primary Contact: Paul Brock, Administrator
CFO: Candace Walker, Chief Financial Officer
Web address: www.dbhdd.ga.gov
Control: State, Government, Nonfederal **Service:** Psychiatric

Staffed Beds: 411 Admissions: 687 Census: 339 Outpatient Visits: 0 Births: 0 Total Expense ($000): 88982 Payroll Expense ($000): 32204 Personnel: 1068

☒ **HEALTHSOUTH WALTON REHABILITATION HOSPITAL (113030)**, 1355 Independence Drive, Zip 30901–1037; tel. 706/724–7746 **A**1 3 5 10 **F**29 62 63 90 96 **S** HEALTHSOUTH Corporation, Birmingham, AL
Primary Contact: Eric Crossan, Chief Executive Officer
CMO: Pamela Salazar M.D., Chief of Staff
CIO: Ann Keller, Supervisor Health Information Management
CHR: Volante Henderson, Director Human Resources
CNO: Lynn Beaulieu R.N., Chief Nursing Officer
Web address: www.healthsouthwalton.com/
Control: Corporation, Investor–owned (for–profit) **Service:** Rehabilitation

Staffed Beds: 50 Admissions: 1196 Census: 40 Outpatient Visits: 0 Births: 0 Personnel: 129

MEDICAL COLLEGE OF GEORGIA HEALTH See Augusta University Medical Center

GA

Hospital, Medicare Provider Number, Address, Telephone, Approval, Facility, and Physician Codes, Health Care System
★ American Hospital Association (AHA) membership ○ Healthcare Facilities Accreditation Program ⇑ Center for Improvement in Healthcare Quality Accreditation ☐ The Joint Commission accreditation ◇ DNV Healthcare Inc. accreditation △ Commission on Accreditation of Rehabilitation Facilities (CARF) accreditation

✉ **SELECT SPECIALTY HOSPITAL–AUGUSTA (112013)**, 1537 Walton Way, Zip 30904–3764; tel. 706/731–1200, (Nonreporting) **A**1 10 **S** Select Medical Corporation, Mechanicsburg, PA
Primary Contact: Racheal Z. Fischer, Chief Executive Officer
CHR: Terrie Richardson, Coordinator Human Resources
CNO: Kim Pippin, Chief Nursing Officer
Web address: www.augusta.selectspecialtyhospitals.com
Control: Corporation, Investor–owned (for–profit) **Service**: Acute long–term care hospital

Staffed Beds: 80

✉ **UNIVERSITY HOSPITAL (110028)**, 1350 Walton Way, Zip 30901–2629; tel. 706/722–9011 **A**1 2 3 5 10 **F**3 12 13 15 17 18 20 22 24 26 28 29 30 31 34 35 37 38 40 41 44 48 49 50 54 55 56 57 59 60 62 64 68 70 71 72 73 74 75 76 77 78 79 80 81 82 83 84 85 86 87 89 93 96 100 107 108 110 111 114 115 116 117 118 119 126 129 130 132 134 135 146 147 148 149 150 **P**8 **S** University Health Care System, Augusta, GA
Primary Contact: James R. Davis, Chief Executive Officer
COO: Marilyn A Bowcutt R.N., MSN, President and Chief Operating Officer
CFO: David Belkoski, Senior Vice President and Chief Financial Officer
CMO: William L Farr M.D., Chief Medical Officer
CIO: Shirley Gabriel, Vice President and Chief Information Officer
CHR: Laurie Ott, Vice President Human Resources and President University Health Care Foundation
CNO: Lynda Watts R.N., Vice President Patient Care Services
Web address: www.universityhealth.org
Control: Other not–for–profit (including NFP Corporation) **Service**: General medical and surgical

Staffed Beds: 521 Admissions: 24033 Census: 323 Outpatient Visits: 535844 Births: 3208 Total Expense ($000): 440138 Payroll Expense ($000): 157939 Personnel: 2453

✉ **UNIVERSITY HOSPITAL SUMMERVILLE (110039)**, 2260 Wrightsboro Road, Zip 30904–4726; tel. 706/481–7000, (Nonreporting) **A**1 3 10 **S** University Health Care System, Augusta, GA
Primary Contact: James R. Davis, Chief Executive Officer
CFO: Rodney Sisk, Chief Financial Officer
CMO: C. Judson Pickett, Chief of Staff
CIO: Charlotte Choate, Director Information Systems
CHR: Diana Maxson, Director Human Resources
Web address: www.trinityofaugusta.com
Control: Corporation, Investor–owned (for–profit) **Service**: General medical and surgical

Staffed Beds: 105

VETERANS AFFAIRS MEDICAL CENTER See Charlie Norwood Veterans Affairs Medical Center

WALTON REHABILITATION HOSPITAL See Healthsouth Walton Rehabilitation Hospital

AUSTELL—Cobb County

✉ △ **WELLSTAR COBB HOSPITAL (110143)**, 3950 Austell Road, Zip 30106–1121; tel. 470/732–4000 **A**1 2 3 7 10 **F**3 4 11 13 15 16 17 18 20 22 26 28 29 30 31 37 38 40 41 44 45 48 49 50 51 53 54 55 58 59 60 61 64 65 66 68 70 72 73 74 75 76 77 78 79 81 82 84 85 86 87 90 93 94 96 97 98 100 101 102 104 105 106 107 108 110 111 114 115 118 119 120 121 123 124 126 130 132 135 141 146 147 148 **P**5 6 **S** WellStar Health System, Marietta, GA
Primary Contact: Amy Frey. Carrier, President
COO: Callie Andrews, Chief Operating Officer and Facility Compliance Officer
CFO: Darold Etheridge, Vice President and Chief Financial Officer
CMO: Thomas McNamara D.O., Vice President Medical Affairs
CIO: Jonathan B Morris M.D., Senior Vice President and Chief Information Officer
CHR: Danyale Ziglor, Assistant Vice President Human Resources
CNO: Kay Kennedy, Chief Nurse Executive
Web address: www.wellstar.org
Control: Other not–for–profit (including NFP Corporation) **Service**: General medical and surgical

Staffed Beds: 387 Admissions: 20936 Census: 258 Outpatient Visits: 218501 Births: 3488 Personnel: 1931

BAINBRIDGE—Decatur County

⇑ **MEMORIAL HOSPITAL AND MANOR (110132)**, 1500 East Shotwell Street, Zip 39819–4256; tel. 229/246–3500, (Nonreporting) **A**10 21
Primary Contact: William J. Walker Jr, Chief Executive Officer
COO: Lee Harris, Assistant Administrator Support Services
CFO: Karen Faircloth, Chief Financial Officer
CMO: Shawn Surratt M.D., Chief of Staff
CIO: Nelda Moore, Director Data Processing
CHR: Angel Sykes, Director Human Resources
CNO: Cynthia Vickers R.N., Assistant Administrator for Nursing Services
Web address: www.mh–m.org
Control: Hospital district or authority, Government, Nonfederal **Service**: General medical and surgical

Staffed Beds: 80

BAXLEY—Appling County

⇑ **APPLING HEALTHCARE SYSTEM (110071)**, 163 East Tollison Street, Zip 31513–0120; tel. 912/367–9841, (Nonreporting) **A**10 20 21
Primary Contact: Raymond J. Leadbetter Jr, Interim Chief Executive Officer
COO: Judy M Long R.N., MS, Chief Nursing Officer and Chief Operating Officer
CFO: Raymond J. Leadbetter Jr, Revenue Cycle Consultant
CMO: Garland Martin M.D., Chief of Staff
CIO: Gary Gower, Chief Information Officer
CHR: Carla McLendon, Director Human Resources
CNO: Judy M Long R.N., MS, Chief Nursing Officer and Chief Operating Officer
Web address: www.appling–hospital.org
Control: County, Government, Nonfederal **Service**: General medical and surgical

Staffed Beds: 150

BLAIRSVILLE—Union County

★ ⇑ **UNION GENERAL HOSPITAL (110051)**, 35 Hospital Road, Zip 30512–3139; tel. 706/745–2111, (Total facility includes 150 beds in nursing home–type unit) **A**10 20 21 **F**7 11 13 15 18 28 29 30 34 35 40 45 49 51 53 56 57 59 64 65 66 70 75 76 79 81 85 86 87 93 96 97 100 103 104 107 108 110 111 115 119 127 129 130 132 133 135 143 146 147 148 **P**1 **S** Union General Hospital, Inc., Blairsville, GA
Primary Contact: Lewis Kelley, Interim Chief Executive Officer
COO: Lewis Kelley, Chief Operating Officer
CFO: Stephanie L Fletcher CPA, Chief Financial Officer
CMO: Andre Schaeffer M.D., Chief of Staff
CIO: Mike Johnston, Director Facilities Operations
CHR: Kathy Hood, Administrative Assistant Human Resources
CNO: Julia Barnett, Chief Nursing Officer
Web address: www.uniongeneralhospital.com
Control: Other not–for–profit (including NFP Corporation) **Service**: General medical and surgical

Staffed Beds: 195 Admissions: 2429 Census: 160 Outpatient Visits: 62900 Births: 409 Total Expense ($000): 57365 Payroll Expense ($000): 24135 Personnel: 659

BLAKELY—Early County

★ ⇑ **PIONEER COMMUNITY HOSPITAL OF EARLY (111314)**, 11740 Columbia Street, Zip 39823–2574; tel. 229/723–4241, (Nonreporting) **A**10 18 21 **S** Pioneer Health Services, Magee, MS
Primary Contact: Ginger Cushing, Chief Executive Officer
Web address: www.pchearly.com
Control: Corporation, Investor–owned (for–profit) **Service**: General medical and surgical

Staffed Beds: 151

BLUE RIDGE—Fannin County

✉ **FANNIN REGIONAL HOSPITAL (110189)**, 2855 Old Highway 5, Zip 30513–6248; tel. 706/632–3711, (Nonreporting) **A**1 10 **S** Quorum Health, Brentwood, TN
Primary Contact: David S. Sanders, Chief Executive Officer
CFO: Phillip Fouts, Chief Financial Officer
CIO: Timothy Snider, Manager Information Systems
CHR: Terrasina Ensley, Director Human Resources
CNO: Jason L. Jones R.N., Chief Nursing Officer
Web address: www.fanninregionalhospital.com
Control: Corporation, Investor–owned (for–profit) **Service**: General medical and surgical

Staffed Beds: 50

GA

BRASELTON—Hall County

NORTHEAST GEORGIA MEDICAL CENTER BRASELTON, 1400 River Place, Zip 30517–5600; tel. 770/219–9000 (Nonreporting) **S** Northeast Georgia Health System, Gainesville, GA
Primary Contact: Carol H. Burrell, Chief Executive Officer
Web address: www.nghs.com/locations/braselton
Control: Other not–for–profit (including NFP Corporation) **Service:** General medical and surgical

Staffed Beds: 100

BREMEN—Haralson County

✠ **TANNER HIGGINS GENERAL HOSPITAL (111320)**, 200 Allen Memorial Drive, Zip 30110–2012; tel. 770/824–2000 **A1** 10 18 **F3** 11 15 29 31 38 40 45 48 50 51 59 60 68 81 97 107 110 111 114 119 127 130 133 146 **P1** 6 **S** Tanner Health System, Carrollton, GA
Primary Contact: Bonnie Boles, M.D., Administrator
COO: James D Griffith, Chief Operating Officer
CFO: Carol Crews, Chief Financial Officer
CMO: Bill Waters M.D., Chief Medical Officer
CIO: Terri Lee, Chief Information Office
CHR: Shari W Gainey, Human Resource Director
CNO: B. J. Brock, Nursing Director
Web address: www.tanner.org/Main/HigginsGeneralHospitalBremen.aspx
Control: Other not–for–profit (including NFP Corporation) **Service:** General medical and surgical

Staffed Beds: 23 **Admissions:** 724 **Census:** 15 **Outpatient Visits:** 89035 **Births:** 0 **Total Expense ($000):** 26662 **Payroll Expense ($000):** 14149 **Personnel:** 230

BRUNSWICK—Glynn County

✠ **SOUTHEAST GEORGIA HEALTH SYSTEM BRUNSWICK CAMPUS (110025)**, 2415 Parkwood Drive, Zip 31520–4722, Mailing Address: P.O.Box 1518, 31521–1518; tel. 912/466–7000, (Total facility includes 278 beds in nursing home–type unit) **A1** 2 10 **F3** 6 8 11 12 13 15 17 18 20 22 26 28 29 30 31 34 35 37 40 44 45 46 47 48 49 50 51 54 57 59 64 66 68 70 71 74 75 76 77 78 79 81 84 85 86 87 89 91 93 94 96 100 107 108 110 111 114 115 117 119 120 121 124 126 129 131 132 135 144 146 147 148 149 **P5 S** Southeast Georgia Health System, Brunswick, GA
Primary Contact: Michael D. Scherneck, President and Chief Executive Officer
CFO: Janice Dunn, Vice President and Chief Financial Officer
CMO: Robert Bernasek M.D., Vice President and Chief Medical Officer
CIO: Charles Bumgardner
CNO: Judith Henson, Vice President Patient Care Services
Web address: www.sghs.org
Control: Other not–for–profit (including NFP Corporation) **Service:** General medical and surgical

Staffed Beds: 532 **Admissions:** 11714 **Census:** 383 **Outpatient Visits:** 237496 **Births:** 1302 **Total Expense ($000):** 321773 **Payroll Expense ($000):** 144063 **Personnel:** 1313

BRYON—Peach County

★ ⇑ **MEDICAL CENTER OF PEACH COUNTY, NAVICENT HEALTH (111310)**, 1960 Highway 247 Connector, Zip 31008; tel. 478/654–2000, (Nonreporting) **A**10 18 21 **S** Navicent Health, Macon, GA
Primary Contact: Darren Pearce, Administrator and Chief Executive Officer
CFO: Lisa Urbistondo, Chief Financial Officer
CMO: Crystal Brown M.D., Medical Director
CNO: Brenda Goodman, Chief Nursing Officer
Web address: www.navicenthealth.org
Control: Hospital district or authority, Government, Nonfederal **Service:** General medical and surgical

Staffed Beds: 25

CAIRO—Grady County

✠ **GRADY GENERAL HOSPITAL (110121)**, 1155 Fifth Street SE, Zip 39828–3142, Mailing Address: P.O.Box 360, 39828–0360; tel. 229/377–1150, (Nonreporting) **A1** 10 **S** Archbold Medical Center, Thomasville, GA
Primary Contact: Crystal Ramm, Administrator
COO: Jim Carter, Chief Operating Officer
CFO: Skip Hightower, Chief Financial Officer
CIO: Tracy Gray, Chief Information Officer
CHR: Michelle Pledger, Coordinator Human Resources
CNO: Tammy Harlow, Director of Nursing
Web address: www.archbold.org
Control: Hospital district or authority, Government, Nonfederal **Service:** General medical and surgical

Staffed Beds: 48

CALHOUN—Gordon County

✠ ○ **GORDON HOSPITAL (110023)**, 1035 Red Bud Road, Zip 30701–2082, Mailing Address: P.O.Box 12938, 30703–7013; tel. 706/629–2895 **A1** 2 10 11 19 **F3** 7 11 13 15 18 20 29 30 31 34 35 37 40 46 57 59 62 64 70 75 76 77 78 79 81 82 85 86 87 93 107 108 111 115 119 120 121 123 129 130 135 144 146 147 148 **P1** 6 **S** Adventist Health System Sunbelt Health Care Corporation, Altamonte Springs, FL
Primary Contact: Pete M. Weber, President and Chief Executive Officer
COO: Brandon M Nudd, Chief Operating Officer
CFO: Cory Reeves, Chief Financial Officer
CMO: Will Theus M.D., Chief of Staff
CHR: Jeni Hasselbrack, Director Human Resources
CNO: Amy Jordan, Chief Nursing Officer/Vice President of Nursing
Web address: www.gordonhospital.com
Control: Church operated, Nongovernment, not–for–profit **Service:** General medical and surgical

Staffed Beds: 82 **Admissions:** 4051 **Census:** 43 **Outpatient Visits:** 259855 **Births:** 605 **Total Expense ($000):** 126950 **Payroll Expense ($000):** 54094 **Personnel:** 979

CAMILLA—Mitchell County

✠ **MITCHELL COUNTY HOSPITAL (111331)**, 90 East Stephens Street, Zip 31730–1836, Mailing Address: P.O.Box 639, 31730–0639; tel. 229/336–5284, (Total facility includes 156 beds in nursing home–type unit) **A1** 10 18 **F3** 11 15 18 29 34 35 40 50 57 59 68 75 87 93 97 107 110 111 114 119 127 130 133 146 **P6 S** Archbold Medical Center, Thomasville, GA
Primary Contact: James Womack, Administrator
COO: LaDon Toole, Vice President Network Operations
CFO: Skip Hightower, Senior Vice President and Chief Financial Officer
CIO: Tracy Gray, Chief Information Officer
CHR: Vickie County–Teemer, Coordinator Human Resources
CNO: Carla Beasley, Director of Nursing
Web address: www.archbold.org
Control: Hospital district or authority, Government, Nonfederal **Service:** General medical and surgical

Staffed Beds: 181 **Admissions:** 455 **Census:** 162 **Outpatient Visits:** 16172 **Births:** 0

CANTON—Cherokee County

✠ **NORTHSIDE HOSPITAL–CHEROKEE (110008)**, 201 Hospital Road, Zip 30114–2408, Mailing Address: P.O.Box 906, 30169–0906; tel. 770/720–5100 **A1** 10 **F3** 8 11 12 13 15 18 20 22 26 28 29 30 31 34 35 40 44 45 49 50 54 55 57 59 60 64 68 70 73 74 75 76 78 79 81 82 85 86 87 93 107 108 110 111 114 119 120 121 123 126 129 130 131 132 144 145 146 147 148 **S** Northside Healthcare System, Atlanta, GA
Primary Contact: William M. Hayes, Chief Executive Officer
COO: Mike Patterson, Director of Operations
CFO: Brian Jennette, Chief Financial Officer
CMO: Alexander Kessler M.D., Chief of Staff
CIO: Bill Dunford, Manager
CHR: Roslyn Roberts, Manager
Web address: www.northside.com
Control: Other not–for–profit (including NFP Corporation) **Service:** General medical and surgical

Staffed Beds: 88 **Admissions:** 6317 **Census:** 72 **Outpatient Visits:** 296548 **Births:** 1185 **Total Expense ($000):** 220790 **Payroll Expense ($000):** 95295 **Personnel:** 1499

CARROLLTON—Carroll County

✠ **TANNER MEDICAL CENTER–CARROLLTON (110011)**, 705 Dixie Street, Zip 30117–3818; tel. 770/836–9666 **A1** 2 10 **F3** 11 13 15 18 20 22 26 28 29 30 31 34 35 40 45 47 49 56 57 58 59 62 63 64 68 70 71 73 74 75 76 78 79 81 82 84 85 87 89 90 107 108 110 111 115 116 117 118 119 120 121 123 124 126 129 130 132 143 146 147 148 149 **P1** 6 **S** Tanner Health System, Carrollton, GA
Primary Contact: James D. Griffith, Chief Operating Officer
COO: James D Griffith, Chief Operating Officer
CHR: Vivian C Barr, Director Human Resources
Web address: www.tanner.org
Control: Other not–for–profit (including NFP Corporation) **Service:** General medical and surgical

Staffed Beds: 162 **Admissions:** 8682 **Census:** 98 **Outpatient Visits:** 254857 **Births:** 1383 **Total Expense ($000):** 273154 **Payroll Expense ($000):** 104367 **Personnel:** 1683

GA

CARTERSVILLE—Bartow County

✠ **CARTERSVILLE MEDICAL CENTER (110030)**, 960 Joe Frank Harris Parkway, Zip 30120–2129; tel. 770/382–1530, (Nonreporting) **A**1 2 10 **S** HCA Healthcare, Nashville, TN
Primary Contact: Keith Sandlin, Chief Executive Officer
COO: Lori Rakes, Chief Operating Officer
CNO: Jan Tidwell, Chief Nursing Officer
Web address: www.cartersvillemedical.com
Control: Corporation, Investor–owned (for–profit) **Service:** General medical and surgical

Staffed Beds: 80

CEDARTOWN—Polk County

✠ **POLK MEDICAL CENTER (111330)**, 2360 Rockmart Highway, Zip 30125–6029; tel. 770/748–2500 **A**1 10 18 **F**3 15 28 29 30 34 35 40 50 56 57 59 64 68 75 77 81 93 103 107 108 110 114 119 129 130 132 133 135 143 146 147 148 149
Primary Contact: Matt Gorman, Administrator
CFO: Rick Sheerin, Chief Financial Officer
CHR: Jeanna Smith, Administrative Assistant and Human Resources Officer
Web address: www.polkhospital.org
Control: Hospital district or authority, Government, Nonfederal **Service:** General medical and surgical

Staffed Beds: 25 **Admissions:** 572 **Census:** 19 **Outpatient Visits:** 36437
Births: 0 **Total Expense ($000):** 22178 **Payroll Expense ($000):** 8912
Personnel: 146

CHATSWORTH—Murray County

✠ **MURRAY MEDICAL CENTER (110050)**, 707 Old Dalton Ellijay Road, Zip 30705–2060, Mailing Address: P.O.Box 1406, 30705–1406; tel. 706/695–4564 **A**1 10 **F**3 7 15 29 30 34 35 40 57 59 64 79 81 93 107 111 115 119 146 **P**6 8 **S** Adventist Health System Sunbelt Health Care Corporation, Altamonte Springs, FL
Primary Contact: Karen Steely, Administrator
CMO: Blaine Minor M.D., Chief of Staff
CIO: Jose C Rios, Director Information Services
CHR: Brandy Rymer, Coordinator Human Resources
CNO: Susan Shook, Interim Chief Executive officer
Web address: www.murraymedical.org/
Control: Church operated, Nongovernment, not–for–profit **Service:** General medical and surgical

Staffed Beds: 33 **Admissions:** 509 **Census:** 4 **Outpatient Visits:** 27892
Births: 0 **Total Expense ($000):** 17117 **Payroll Expense ($000):** 5696
Personnel: 155

CLAXTON—Evans County

✠ **EVANS MEMORIAL HOSPITAL (110142)**, 200 North River Street, Zip 30417–1659, Mailing Address: P.O.Box 518, 30417–0518; tel. 912/739–2611 **A**1 10 **F**3 15 29 34 40 45 53 57 59 68 75 81 93 97 107 110 111 115 119 127 130 133 135 146
Primary Contact: Nikki NeSmith, Chief Executive Officer and Chief Nursing Officer
CFO: John Wiggins, Chief Financial Officer
CMO: Kyle Parks M.D., Chief of Staff
CIO: Steve Schmidt, Director Information Systems
CHR: Gina Waters, Director Human Resources
CNO: Nikki NeSmith, Chief Nursing Officer
Web address: www.evansmemorialhospital.org/
Control: Hospital district or authority, Government, Nonfederal **Service:** General medical and surgical

Staffed Beds: 10 **Admissions:** 603 **Census:** 5 **Outpatient Visits:** 42880
Births: 0 **Total Expense ($000):** 12645 **Payroll Expense ($000):** 5139
Personnel: 104

CLAYTON—Rabun County

MOUNTAIN LAKES MEDICAL CENTER (111336), 196 Ridgecrest Circle, Zip 30525–4111; tel. 706/782–4233 **A**10 18 **F**3 15 29 35 40 45 50 59 64 75 77 81 82 85 86 87 93 107 114 119 133 135 148 149
Primary Contact: Jeff Dowis, M.D., Interim Chief Executive Officer
CFO: Jimmy Norman, Chief Financial Officer
CHR: Charles Harbaugh, Director Human Resources
Web address: www.mountainlakesmedicalcenter.com
Control: Individual, Investor–owned (for–profit) **Service:** General medical and surgical

Staffed Beds: 25 **Admissions:** 359 **Census:** 3 **Outpatient Visits:** 26550
Births: 1 **Personnel:** 168

COCHRAN—Bleckley County

⇑ **BLECKLEY MEMORIAL HOSPITAL (111302)**, 145 East Peacock Street, Zip 31014–7846, Mailing Address: P.O.Box 536, 31014–0536; tel. 478/934–6211, (Nonreporting) **A**10 18 21
Primary Contact: Courtney Moore, CPA, Chief Executive Officer
Web address: www.bleckleymemorial.com
Control: Hospital district or authority, Government, Nonfederal **Service:** General medical and surgical

Staffed Beds: 25

COLQUITT—Miller County

⇑ **MILLER COUNTY HOSPITAL (111305)**, 209 North Cuthbert Street, Zip 39837–3518, Mailing Address: P.O.Box 7, 39837–0007; tel. 229/758–3305, (Total facility includes 163 beds in nursing home–type unit) **A**10 18 21 **F**15 28 29 32 34 35 40 44 45 50 56 57 59 66 68 75 81 83 84 85 86 87 89 93 97 103 107 110 119 127 128 129 130 133 135 148 149
Primary Contact: Robin Rau, Chief Executive Officer
CFO: Jill Brown, Chief Financial Officer
CMO: William Swofford M.D., Chief of Staff
CIO: Keith Lovering, Information Technician
CHR: Karie Spence, Director Human Resources
CNO: Shawn Whittaker, Chief Nursing Officer
Web address: www.millercountyhospital.com
Control: Hospital district or authority, Government, Nonfederal **Service:** General medical and surgical

Staffed Beds: 188 **Admissions:** 962 **Census:** 175 **Outpatient Visits:** 48732
Births: 0 **Total Expense ($000):** 33860 **Payroll Expense ($000):** 16852
Personnel: 391

COLUMBUS—Muscogee County

BRADLEY CENTER OF ST. FRANCIS See St. Francis Hospital

☐ **COLUMBUS SPECIALTY HOSPITAL (112012)**, 616 19th Street, Zip 31901–1528, Mailing Address: P.O.Box 910, 31902–0910; tel. 706/494–4075 **A**1 10 **F**1 3 29 30 68 85
Primary Contact: William Eckstein, Chief Executive Officer and Chief Financial Officer
CFO: William Eckstein, Chief Executive Officer and Chief Financial Officer
CHR: Myra Whitley, Vice President, Human Resources
Web address: www.columbusspecialtyhospital.net
Control: Other not–for–profit (including NFP Corporation) **Service:** Acute long–term care hospital

Staffed Beds: 33 **Admissions:** 240 **Census:** 18 **Outpatient Visits:** 0 **Births:** 0
Total Expense ($000): 10397 **Payroll Expense ($000):** 3997 **Personnel:** 70

HUGHSTON HOSPITAL See Northside Medical Center

☐ **MIDTOWN MEDICAL CENTER (110064)**, 710 Center Street, Zip 31901–1527, Mailing Address: P.O.Box 951, 31902–0951; tel. 706/571–1000, (Nonreporting) **A**1 2 3 5 10 12 13 **S** Columbus Regional Healthcare System, Columbus, GA
Primary Contact: Ryan Chandler, President and Chief Executive Officer
Web address: www.columbusregional.com
Control: Other not–for–profit (including NFP Corporation) **Service:** General medical and surgical

Staffed Beds: 497

MIDTOWN MEDICAL CENTER WEST, 616 19th Street, Zip 31901–1528, Mailing Address: P.O.Box 2188, 31902–2188; tel. 706/494–4262, (Nonreporting) **S** Columbus Regional Healthcare System, Columbus, GA
Primary Contact: Ryan Chandler, Chief Executive Officer
CMO: Thomas L Theus M.D., Chief of Medicine
CIO: Ryan Sanders, Director Information Services
Web address: www.columbusregional.com
Control: Other not–for–profit (including NFP Corporation) **Service:** General medical and surgical

Staffed Beds: 171

Many Facility Codes have changed. Please refer to the AHA Guide Code Chart. © 2017 AHA Guide

☐ **NORTHSIDE MEDICAL CENTER (110200)**, 100 Frist Court, Zip 31909–3578,
Mailing Address: P.O.Box 7188, 31908–7188; tel. 706/494–2100, (Nonreporting)
A1 3 10 **S** Columbus Regional Healthcare System, Columbus, GA
Primary Contact: Ryan Chandler, Interim Chief Executive Officer
COO: Michelle Breitfelder, Chief Operating Officer
CFO: Roland Thacker, Chief Financial Officer
CMO: Lyle Norwood M.D., Chief of Staff
CIO: Douglas Colburn, Chief Information Officer
CHR: Becky Augustyniak, Director Human Resources
Web address: www.columbusregional.com
Control: Hospital district or authority, Government, Nonfederal **Service**:
Orthopedic

Staffed Beds: 100

✠ **ST. FRANCIS HOSPITAL (110129)**, 2122 Manchester Expressway, Zip 31904–
6878, Mailing Address: P.O.Box 7000, 31908–7000; tel. 706/596–4000,
(Includes BRADLEY CENTER OF ST. FRANCIS, 2000 16th Avenue, Columbus,
Georgia, Zip 31906–0308, tel. 706/320–3700) **A**1 3 10 **F**3 11 13 15 17 18 20
22 24 26 28 29 30 31 34 35 40 45 46 49 50 51 53 54 56 59 60 64 70 74 75
76 77 78 79 81 82 85 86 98 99 100 101 102 103 104 105 106 107 108 110
111 115 119 126 129 130 131 144 145 146 147 148 **P**6 **S** LifePoint Health,
Brentwood, TN
Primary Contact: Danny L. Jones Jr, FACHE, Chief Executive Officer
CFO: Greg Hembree, Senior Vice President and Chief Financial Officer
CMO: Bobbi Farber M.D., Chief Medical Officer
CIO: Jonathon R Jager, Chief Information Officer
CHR: E Rick Lowe FACHE, Operations Support Risk Management and Compliance
CNO: Charlene Falgout, Chief Nursing Officer
Web address: www.mystfrancis.com
Control: Corporation, Investor–owned (for–profit) **Service**: General medical and
surgical

Staffed Beds: 331 **Admissions**: 14387 **Census**: 194 **Outpatient Visits**: 189380 **Births**: 1421 **Total Expense ($000)**: 255419 **Payroll Expense ($000)**: 82743 **Personnel**: 2235

☐ **WEST CENTRAL GEORGIA REGIONAL HOSPITAL (114013)**, 3000 Schatulga
Road, Zip 31907–3117, Mailing Address: P.O.Box 12435, 31917–2435;
tel. 706/568–5000 **A**1 10 **F**39 98 99 106 130 135 149
Primary Contact: John L. Robertson, Administrator
COO: Marcia Capshaw, Chief Operating Officer
CFO: John Frederick, Chief Financial Officer
CMO: David Morton M.D., Clinical Director
CIO: Karen Fisher–Ford, Director of Health Information Management
CHR: Peri Johnson, Human Resources Director
CNO: Nicolise Claassens, Nurse Executive
Web address: www.dbhdd.georgia.gov/west–central–georgia–regional–hospital–
columbus
Control: State, Government, Nonfederal **Service**: Psychiatric

Staffed Beds: 186 **Admissions**: 263 **Census**: 181 **Outpatient Visits**: 0 **Births**: 0 **Personnel**: 566

COMMERCE—Jackson County

✠ **NORTHRIDGE MEDICAL CENTER (110040)**, 70 Medical Center Drive,
Zip 30529–1078; tel. 706/335–1000, (Total facility includes 155 beds in nursing
home–type unit) **A**1 10 **F**3 15 17 18 29 30 34 40 45 53 56 57 59 68 70 79 81
82 85 89 90 98 100 103 107 108 110 111 114 119 128 130 133 **P**6
Primary Contact: Judy Warrner, Chief Operating Officer
CMO: Narasimhulu Neelagaru M.D., Chief of Staff
Web address: www.northridgemc.com
Control: Other not–for–profit (including NFP Corporation) **Service**: General
medical and surgical

Staffed Beds: 221 **Admissions**: 1518 **Census**: 173 **Outpatient Visits**: 31909 **Births**: 0 **Total Expense ($000)**: 31529 **Payroll Expense ($000)**: 12876 **Personnel**: 320

CONYERS—Rockdale County

✠ **ROCKDALE MEDICAL CENTER (110091)**, 1412 Milstead Avenue NE,
Zip 30012–3877; tel. 770/918–3000 **A**1 5 10 **F**3 11 13 15 18 20 22 28 29 30
34 35 36 40 45 46 47 49 57 59 64 70 72 75 76 79 81 82 85 86 87 92 93 107
108 110 111 114 115 118 119 126 130 131 132 135 145 146 147 148 149 **S**
LifePoint Health, Brentwood, TN
Primary Contact: Alan E. George, Chief Executive Officer
COO: Blake Watts, Chief Operating Officer
CFO: Diane Roth, Chief Financial Officer
CMO: Lisa Gillespie M.D., Chief Medical Officer
CIO: Gail Waldo, Director Information Technology
CHR: Marianne Freeman, Vice President Human Resources
CNO: Eleanor Post R.N., Chief Nursing Officer
Web address: www.rockdalemedicalcenter.org
Control: Corporation, Investor–owned (for–profit) **Service**: General medical and
surgical

Staffed Beds: 158 **Admissions**: 8842 **Census**: 108 **Outpatient Visits**: 118998 **Births**: 1701 **Total Expense ($000)**: 130655 **Payroll Expense ($000)**: 52559 **Personnel**: 825

CORDELE—Crisp County

✠ **CRISP REGIONAL HOSPITAL (110104)**, 902 North Seventh Street, Zip 31015–
3234; tel. 229/276–3100, (Total facility includes 243 beds in nursing home–type
unit) **A**1 3 10 20 **F**3 10 11 13 15 29 30 31 34 35 40 43 44 45 48 49 50 51 54
56 57 58 59 60 61 62 63 64 65 68 70 75 76 77 78 79 81 84 85 86 87 89 90
93 96 97 107 108 110 111 114 115 117 118 125 127 128 129 132 133 135
144 146 147 148 149 **P**2 8
Primary Contact: Steven Gautney, Chief Executive Officer
COO: Mary Jim Montgomery R.N., MSN, FACHE, Chief Operating Officer
CFO: Jessica Y Carter, Chief Financial Officer
CMO: David Kavtaradze M.D., Chief of Staff
CHR: George M Laurin, Interim Director Human Resources
CNO: Marsha L. Mulderig R.N., MSN, Chief Nursing Officer
Web address: www.crispregional.org
Control: County, Government, Nonfederal **Service**: General medical and surgical

Staffed Beds: 316 **Admissions**: 2892 **Census**: 177 **Outpatient Visits**: 104143 **Births**: 327 **Personnel**: 514

COVINGTON—Newton County

☐ **PIEDMONT NEWTON HOSPITAL (110018)**, 5126 Hospital Drive, Zip 30014–
2567; tel. 770/786–7053, (Nonreporting) **A**1 10 **S** Piedmont Healthcare, Atlanta, GA
Primary Contact: Eric Bour, M.D., FACS, Chief Executive Officer
CFO: Troy Brooks, Assistant Administrator Fiscal Services
CMO: B. Carter Rogers, Chief of Staff
CIO: Brad Collier, Director
CHR: Greg H Richardson,   Assistant Administrator Human Resources
CNO: Jeremiah Bame R.N., Chief Nursing Officer
Web address: www.newtonmedical.com
Control: Other not–for–profit (including NFP Corporation) **Service**: General
medical and surgical

Staffed Beds: 101

CUMMING—Forsyth County

✠ **NORTHSIDE HOSPITAL–FORSYTH (110005)**, 1200 Northside Forsyth Drive,
Zip 30041–7659; tel. 770/844–3200 **A**1 10 **F**3 8 11 12 13 15 18 20 22 26 28
29 30 31 34 35 37 40 44 45 48 49 50 54 55 57 59 60 64 68 70 71 72 73 74
75 76 78 79 81 82 85 86 87 93 107 108 110 111 114 115 117 119 120 121
123 124 126 129 130 132 135 144 145 146 147 148 **S** Northside Healthcare
System, Atlanta, GA
Primary Contact: Lynn Jackson, Administrator
CFO: Eric Caldwell, Director Finance
Web address: www.northside.com
Control: Other not–for–profit (including NFP Corporation) **Service**: General
medical and surgical

Staffed Beds: 252 **Admissions**: 14251 **Census**: 181 **Outpatient Visits**: 391232 **Births**: 3219 **Total Expense ($000)**: 433008 **Payroll Expense ($000)**: 158136 **Personnel**: 2581

GA

CUTHBERT—Randolph County

★ ⇑ **SOUTHWEST GEORGIA REGIONAL MEDICAL CENTER (111300)**, 361 Randolph Street, Zip 39840–6127; tel. 229/732–2181, (Nonreporting) **A**10 18 21 **S** Phoebe Putney Health System, Albany, GA
Primary Contact: Kim Gilman, Chief Executive Officer and Chief Nursing Officer
CFO: Candace Guarnieri, Chief Financial Officer
CNO: Kim Gilman, Chief Executive Officer and Chief Nursing Officer
Web address: www.phoebeputney.com/
Control: Hospital district or authority, Government, Nonfederal **Service:** General medical and surgical

Staffed Beds: 25

DAHLONEGA—Lumpkin County

☐ **CHESTATEE REGIONAL HOSPITAL (110187)**, 227 Mountain Drive, Zip 30533–1606; tel. 706/864–6136, (Nonreporting) **A**1 10 **S** Sunlink Health Systems, Atlanta, GA
Primary Contact: Aaron Durall, Chief Executive Officer
CFO: Molly Lindquist, Interim Chief Financial Officer
CMO: Richard Wherry M.D., Chief of Staff
CHR: Barbara Patrick, Director Human Resources
CNO: Barbara Arnau R.N., Chief Nursing Officer
Web address: www.chestateeregionalhospital.com
Control: Corporation, Investor–owned (for–profit) **Service:** General medical and surgical

Staffed Beds: 49

DALTON—Whitfield County

⊞ **HAMILTON MEDICAL CENTER (110001)**, 1200 Memorial Drive, Zip 30720–2529, Mailing Address: P.O.Box 1168, 30722–1168; tel. 706/272–6000 **A**1 2 10 19 **F**3 4 5 8 12 13 15 18 20 22 26 28 29 30 31 34 35 40 43 44 45 46 47 48 49 50 51 53 54 57 59 60 62 63 64 68 70 72 73 74 75 76 77 78 79 81 82 84 85 86 87 89 93 96 97 98 100 101 102 103 104 105 107 108 110 111 114 115 116 117 118 119 120 121 123 124 126 129 130 131 132 135 144 146 147 148 149
Primary Contact: Jeffrey D. Myers, President and Chief Executive Officer
COO: Sandra D. McKenzie, Executive Vice President and Chief Operating Officer
CFO: Gary L Howard, Senior Vice President and Chief Financial Officer
CMO: Stephen G. Rohn M.D., Vice President and Chief Medical Officer
CIO: John M Forrester, Director Information Services
CHR: Jason Hopkins, Director, Human Resources
CNO: Cathy Ferguson R.N., MSN, Vice President and Chief Nursing Officer
Web address: www.hamiltonhealth.com
Control: Other not–for–profit (including NFP Corporation) **Service:** General medical and surgical

Staffed Beds: 223 Admissions: 9631 Census: 113 Outpatient Visits: 238988 Births: 1824 Personnel: 1168

DECATUR—Dekalb County

⊞ **ATLANTA VETERANS AFFAIRS MEDICAL CENTER**, 1670 Clairmont Road, Zip 30033–4004; tel. 404/321–6111, (Nonreporting) **A**1 2 3 5 8 **S** Department of Veterans Affairs, Washington, DC
Primary Contact: Annette Walker, Director
CFO: Pamela Watkins, Chief Financial Officer
CMO: David Bower M.D., Chief of Staff
CIO: William Brock, Chief Information Officer
CHR: Zeta Ferguson, Chief Human Resources
CNO: Sandy Leake MSN, R.N., Associate Director, Nursing and Patient Care Services
Web address: www.atlanta.va.gov/
Control: Veterans Affairs, Government, federal **Service:** General medical and surgical

Staffed Beds: 239

☐ **DEKALB MEDICAL AT DOWNTOWN DECATUR (112006)**, 450 North Candler Street, Zip 30030–2671; tel. 404/501–6700, (Nonreporting) **A**1 5 10 **S** DeKalb Regional Health System, Decatur, GA
Primary Contact: Robert E. Wilson Esq, Chief Executive Officer
CMO: David Snyder M.D., Chief of Staff
CHR: Tom Crawford, Vice President Human Resources
Web address: www.dekalbmedicalcenter.org
Control: Other not–for–profit (including NFP Corporation) **Service:** Acute long–term care hospital

Staffed Beds: 44

⊞ **DEKALB MEDICAL AT NORTH DECATUR (110076)**, 2701 North Decatur Road, Zip 30033–5995; tel. 404/501–1000, (Nonreporting) **A**1 2 3 10 **S** DeKalb Regional Health System, Decatur, GA
Primary Contact: Robert E. Wilson Esq, Chief Executive Officer
COO: Jim Forstner, Chief Operating Officer
CFO: Robin Nichols, Interim Chief Financial Officer
CIO: Beth Patino, Chief Information Officer
CHR: LeRoy Walker, Vice President Human Resources
CNO: Susan Breslin R.N., MSN, Vice President Patient Care Services and Chief Nursing Officer
Web address: www.dekalbmedical.org
Control: Other not–for–profit (including NFP Corporation) **Service:** General medical and surgical

Staffed Beds: 417

☐ **GEORGIA REGIONAL HOSPITAL AT ATLANTA (114019)**, 3073 Panthersville Road, Zip 30034–3828; tel. 404/243–2100, (Nonreporting) **A**1 3 5 10
Primary Contact: Susan Trueblood, Chief Executive Officer
COO: Sonny Slate, Chief Operating Officer
CFO: Reginald Jones, Business Manager
CMO: Emile Risby M.D., Clinical Director
CIO: Elfie Early, Manager Data Services
CHR: Lorraine Farr, Manager Human Resources
Web address: www.atlantareg.dhr.state.ga.us
Control: State, Government, Nonfederal **Service:** Psychiatric

Staffed Beds: 319

VETERANS AFFAIRS MEDICAL CENTER See Atlanta Veterans Affairs Medical Center

DEMOREST—Habersham County

★ ⇑ **HABERSHAM MEDICAL CENTER (110041)**, 541 Historic Highway 441, Zip 30535–3118, Mailing Address: P.O.Box 37, 30535–0037; tel. 706/754–2161, (Total facility includes 84 beds in nursing home–type unit) **A**10 21 **F**7 8 13 15 28 29 30 34 35 40 45 46 50 53 57 59 64 68 70 75 76 77 79 81 82 87 91 93 97 102 107 111 114 119 128 129 130 133 143 146
Primary Contact: Jerry R. Wise, Chief Executive Officer
COO: Michael Gay, Chief Operating Officer
CFO: Barbara Duncan, Chief Financial Officer
CMO: Josh Garrett, Chief of Staff
CHR: Ryan Snow, Director Human Resources
Web address: www.habershammedical.com/
Control: Hospital district or authority, Government, Nonfederal **Service:** General medical and surgical

Staffed Beds: 137 Admissions: 2264 Census: 105 Outpatient Visits: 50957 Births: 411 Total Expense ($000): 41954 Payroll Expense ($000): 18276 Personnel: 572

DONALSONVILLE—Seminole County

⇑ **DONALSONVILLE HOSPITAL (110194)**, 102 Hospital Circle, Zip 39845–1199; tel. 229/524–5217, (Total facility includes 75 beds in nursing home–type unit) **A**10 21 **F**13 34 40 45 46 57 59 64 68 76 77 81 87 93 107 111 115 119 128 133 147 148
Primary Contact: Charles H. Orrick, Administrator
CFO: James Moody, Chief Financial Officer
CMO: C O Walker M.D., Chief of Staff
CHR: Jo Adams, Director Human Resources
Control: Other not–for–profit (including NFP Corporation) **Service:** General medical and surgical

Staffed Beds: 140 Admissions: 1054 Census: 69 Outpatient Visits: 24116 Births: 215 Total Expense ($000): 29658 Payroll Expense ($000): 11651 Personnel: 284

DOUGLAS—Coffee County

☐ **COFFEE REGIONAL MEDICAL CENTER (110089)**, 1101 Ocilla Road, Zip 31533–2207, Mailing Address: P.O.Box 1287, 31534–1287; tel. 912/384–1900 **A**1 10 20 **F**3 7 11 13 15 18 20 26 28 29 30 34 35 40 44 45 47 50 51 53 54 56 57 59 60 61 64 65 68 70 74 75 76 79 81 82 85 86 87 89 92 93 97 107 108 110 111 114 115 119 124 127 130 131 132 135 143 146 147 148 149
Primary Contact: Vicki Lewis, R.N., MS, FACHE, President and Chief Executive Officer
CFO: Donald C Lewis Jr, Vice President and Chief Financial Officer
CHR: Laura Bloom, Director Human Resources
Web address: www.coffeeregional.org
Control: Other not–for–profit (including NFP Corporation) **Service:** General medical and surgical

Staffed Beds: 88 Admissions: 4451 Census: 46 Outpatient Visits: 77855 Births: 579 Total Expense ($000): 79945 Payroll Expense ($000): 31040 Personnel: 582

GA

DOUGLASVILLE—Douglas County

★ **WELLSTAR DOUGLAS HOSPITAL (110184)**, 8954 Hospital Drive, Zip 30134–2282; tel. 770/949–1500 **A**2 10 **F**3 11 13 15 18 20 22 28 29 30 31 37 38 40 44 45 48 49 50 51 54 58 59 60 61 64 68 70 74 75 76 77 78 79 81 82 84 85 86 87 93 94 102 107 108 110 111 114 115 117 118 119 129 130 132 135 146 147 148 **P**5 6 **S** WellStar Health System, Marietta, GA
Primary Contact: Craig A. Owens, President
CFO: Bradley Greene, Chief Financial Officer
CMO: Noel Holtz M.D., Chief Medical Officer
CHR: Danyale Ziglor, Assistant Director Human Resources
Web address: www.wellstar.org
Control: Other not–for–profit (including NFP Corporation) **Service:** General medical and surgical

Staffed Beds: 108 **Admissions:** 6818 **Census:** 69 **Outpatient Visits:** 128808 **Births:** 450 **Personnel:** 707

YOUTH VILLAGES INNER HARBOUR CAMPUS, 4685 Dorsett Shoals Road, Zip 30135–4999; tel. 770/942–2391, (Nonreporting)
Primary Contact: Patrick Lawler, Chief Executive Officer
CFO: J Steve Lewis, Director Finance
CIO: Laura Sellers, Director Information Systems
CHR: Sherry Kollmeyer, Vice President Human Resources
Web address: www.innerharbour.org
Control: Other not–for–profit (including NFP Corporation) **Service:** Children's hospital psychiatric

Staffed Beds: 176

DUBLIN—Laurens County

⊞ **CARL VINSON VETERANS AFFAIRS MEDICAL CENTER**, 1826 Veterans Boulevard, Zip 31021–3620; tel. 478/272–1210, (Nonreporting) **A**1 **S** Department of Veterans Affairs, Washington, DC
Primary Contact: Maryalice Morro, MSN, R.N., Director
COO: Gerald M DeWorth, Associate Director
CFO: Angela Stevenson, Chief Financial Officer
CMO: Christopher Blasy M.D., Chief of Staff
CIO: Mark Cowart, Chief Information Officer
CHR: Kurt Oster, Human Resources Officer
CNO: Connie Hampton, Nurse Executive
Web address: www.dublin.va.gov/
Control: Veterans Affairs, Government, federal **Service:** General medical and surgical

Staffed Beds: 178

⊞ **FAIRVIEW PARK HOSPITAL (110125)**, 200 Industrial Boulevard, Zip 31021–2997, Mailing Address: P.O.Box 1408, 31040–1408; tel. 478/275–2000, (Nonreporting) **A**1 10 19 **S** HCA Healthcare, Nashville, TN
Primary Contact: Donald R. Avery, FACHE, President and Chief Executive Officer
COO: Matthew Steven Hasbrouck, Chief Operating Officer
CFO: Ted Short, Chief Financial Officer
CMO: Jeri Miller M.D., President Medical Staff
CIO: Marsha Morris, Manager Information Services
CHR: Jeff Bruton, Director Human Resources
CNO: Donna Trickey R.N., Chief Nursing Officer
Web address: www.fairviewparkhospital.com
Control: Corporation, Investor–owned (for–profit) **Service:** General medical and surgical

Staffed Beds: 168

DULUTH—De Kalb County

GWINNETT MEDICAL CENTER–DULUTH See Gwinnett Hospital System, Lawrenceville

EAST POINT—Fulton County

⊞ **REGENCY HOSPITAL OF SOUTH ATLANTA (112014)**, 1170 Cleveland Avenue, 4th Floor, Zip 30344–3615; tel. 404/466–6250, (Nonreporting) **A**1 3 10 **S** Select Medical Corporation, Mechanicsburg, PA
Primary Contact: Michelle Tenhengel–deVille, Chief Executive Officer
Web address: www.regencyhospital.com
Control: Corporation, Investor–owned (for–profit) **Service:** Acute long–term care hospital

Staffed Beds: 40

EASTMAN—Dodge County

⇑ **DODGE COUNTY HOSPITAL (110092)**, 901 Griffin Avenue, Zip 31023–6720, Mailing Address: PO BOX 4309, 31023–4309; tel. 478/374–4000 **A**10 21 **F**3 11 13 15 29 30 31 40 45 53 57 59 64 69 70 75 76 79 81 85 86 98 101 103 107 108 110 111 114 119 146 147
Primary Contact: Kevin Bierschenk, Chief Executive Officer
CFO: Jan Hamrick, Chief Financial Officer
CIO: Victor Woodard, Manager Information Technology
CHR: Wendy Selph, Director Human Resources
CNO: Sandra M. Campbell R.N., Chief Nursing Officer
Web address: www.dodgecountyhospital.com
Control: Hospital district or authority, Government, Nonfederal **Service:** General medical and surgical

Staffed Beds: 35 **Admissions:** 1348 **Census:** 19 **Outpatient Visits:** 32885 **Births:** 125 **Total Expense ($000):** 19492 **Payroll Expense ($000):** 8973 **Personnel:** 239

EATONTON—Putnam County

☐ **PUTNAM GENERAL HOSPITAL (111313)**, 101 Lake Oconee Parkway, Zip 31024–6054; tel. 706/485–2711 **A**1 10 18 **F**3 11 15 18 28 29 30 35 40 45 47 50 51 57 59 64 67 81 93 107 110 111 114 119 128 129 132 133
Primary Contact: Alan Horton, Administrator
CFO: Judy Ware, Chief Financial Officer
CMO: Omar Akhras M.D., Chief of Staff
CIO: Marcel Lundy, Chief Information Officer
CHR: Jeanine Martinez, Director Human Resources
CNO: Pam Douglas, Chief Nursing Officer
Web address: www.putnamgeneral.com
Control: Hospital district or authority, Government, Nonfederal **Service:** General medical and surgical

Staffed Beds: 25 **Admissions:** 673 **Census:** 9 **Outpatient Visits:** 19826 **Births:** 0 **Total Expense ($000):** 13287 **Payroll Expense ($000):** 4946 **Personnel:** 115

ELBERTON—Elbert County

⊞ **ELBERT MEMORIAL HOSPITAL (110026)**, 4 Medical Drive, Zip 30635–1897; tel. 706/283–3151 **A**1 10 20 **F**3 11 15 29 40 45 50 53 57 59 70 77 79 81 85 87 89 102 107 110 119 128 130 133 146 147 **P**6
Primary Contact: Brandon Clary, Chief Executive Officer
CFO: Kerry A Trapnell, Chief Financial Officer
CIO: Greg Fields, Director Information Technology
CHR: Georgian Walton, Director Human Resources
CNO: Sonya Elrod, Chief Nursing Officer
Web address: www.emhcare.net
Control: Hospital district or authority, Government, Nonfederal **Service:** General medical and surgical

Staffed Beds: 37 **Admissions:** 700 **Census:** 9 **Outpatient Visits:** 19250 **Births:** 1 **Total Expense ($000):** 10940 **Payroll Expense ($000):** 5419 **Personnel:** 132

FAYETTEVILLE—Fayette County

⇑ **PIEDMONT FAYETTE HOSPITAL (110215)**, 1255 Highway 54 West, Zip 30214–4526; tel. 770/719–7000, (Nonreporting) **A**2 3 10 21 **S** Piedmont Healthcare, Atlanta, GA
Primary Contact: Michael Burnett, Chief Executive Officer
COO: Nathan Nipper, Chief Operating Officer
CFO: Scott A. Wolfe, Chief Financial Officer
CMO: Frederick Willms M.D., Chief Medical Officer
CIO: Geoffrey Brown, Chief Information Officer
CHR: Holly Sawyer, Director and Human Resources Business Partner
CNO: Merry Heath, Chief Nursing Officer
Web address: www.piedmont.org
Control: Other not–for–profit (including NFP Corporation) **Service:** General medical and surgical

Staffed Beds: 172

GA

| Hospital, Medicare Provider Number, Address, Telephone, Approval, Facility, and Physician Codes, Health Care System |

★ American Hospital Association (AHA) membership   ○ Healthcare Facilities Accreditation Program   ⇑ Center for Improvement in Healthcare Quality Accreditation
☐ The Joint Commission accreditation   ◇ DNV Healthcare Inc. accreditation   △ Commission on Accreditation of Rehabilitation Facilities (CARF) accreditation

© 2017 AHA Guide   *Many Facility Codes have changed. Please refer to the AHA Guide Code Chart.*   Hospitals **A157**

FITZGERALD—Ben Hill County

⇑ **DORMINY MEDICAL CENTER (110073)**, 200 Perry House Road, Zip 31750–8857, Mailing Address: P.O.Box 1447, 31750–1447; tel. 229/424–7100 **A**10 21 **F**3 11 13 15 29 31 35 39 40 57 59 60 63 70 75 76 77 78 79 81 84 85 87 90 93 107 110 111 114 119 127 129 130 132 133 146 148
Primary Contact: Mel Pyne, Regional Chief Executive Officer
CFO: Paige Wynn, Chief Financial Officer
CMO: Davey Herring M.D., Chief Medical Officer
CIO: Chris Ward, Director Management Information Systems
CHR: Denise Steverson, Director Human Resources
CNO: Staci Mims, Chief Nursing Officer
Web address: www.dorminymedical.org
Control: Hospital district or authority, Government, Nonfederal **Service**: General medical and surgical

Staffed Beds: 58 Admissions: 1009 Census: 10 Outpatient Visits: 30939 Births: 131 Total Expense ($000): 21482 Payroll Expense ($000): 7088 Personnel: 170

FORSYTH—Monroe County

☐ **MONROE COUNTY HOSPITAL (111318)**, 88 Martin Luther King Jr Drive, Zip 31029–1682, Mailing Address: P.O.Box 1068, 31029–1068; tel. 478/994–2521 **A**1 10 18 **F**3 11 15 29 35 40 57 59 68 75 77 81 107 110 111 114 119 132 133 146 148 **P**1 2 3
Primary Contact: Darren Pearce, Interim Chief Executive Officer
CFO: Judy King Ware, Chief Financial Officer
CMO: Jeremy Goodwin M.D., President, Medical Staff
CIO: Donna Hogg, Supervisor Medical Records
CHR: Deborah Flowers, Director Human Resources
CNO: Donna Nash, Director of Nursing
Web address: www.monroehospital.org
Control: Hospital district or authority, Government, Nonfederal **Service**: General medical and surgical

Staffed Beds: 25 Admissions: 417 Census: 6 Outpatient Visits: 13431 Births: 0 Total Expense ($000): 10546 Payroll Expense ($000): 4174 Personnel: 134

FORT BENNING—Muscogee County

⊞ **MARTIN ARMY COMMUNITY HOSPITAL**, 7950 Martin Loop, Zip 31905–5648, Mailing Address: 7950 Martin Loop, B9200, Room 010, 31905–5648; tel. 706/544–2516, (Nonreporting) **A**1 3 5 **S** Department of the Army, Office of the Surgeon General, Falls Church, VA
Primary Contact: Colonel Marie Dominguez, Commander
CHR: MajorBernita Hightower, Chief Human Resources
Web address: www.martin.amedd.army.mil
Control: Army, Government, federal **Service**: General medical and surgical

Staffed Beds: 57

FORT GORDON—Richmond County

⊞ **DWIGHT DAVID EISENHOWER ARMY MEDICAL CENTER**, 300 West Hospital Road, Zip 30905–5741; tel. 706/787–5811, (Nonreporting) **A**1 2 3 5 **S** Department of the Army, Office of the Surgeon General, Falls Church, VA
Primary Contact: Colonel John P. Lamoureux, Commander
CMO: ColonelJames M Baunchalk, Deputy Chief Clinical Services
CIO: MajorJoseph A Ponce, Chief Information Management
CHR: Elizabeth Shelt, Civilian Personnel Officer
Web address: www.ddeamc.amedd.army.mil
Control: Army, Government, federal **Service**: General medical and surgical

Staffed Beds: 107

FORT OGLETHORPE—Catoosa County

⇑ **CORNERSTONE MEDICAL CENTER (110236)**, 100 Gross Crescent Circle, Zip 30742–3669; tel. 706/858–2000, (Nonreporting) **A**10 21
Primary Contact: Jessica Long, Chief Executive Officer
COO: Kevin Hopkins,   Vice President of Operations
CFO: Farrell Hayes, Chief Financial Officer
CMO: John Erdman M.D., Chief of Staff
CIO: Ruth Wright–Whitaker, Director Information Services
CHR: Cathy Hulsey, Manager of Human Resources
CNO: Sandra Siniard, Vice President of Patient Care Services
Web address: www.hutcheson.org
Control: Hospital district or authority, Government, Nonfederal **Service**: General medical and surgical

Staffed Beds: 179

GAINESVILLE—Hall County

★ △ ⇑ **NORTHEAST GEORGIA MEDICAL CENTER (110029)**, 743 Spring Street NE, Zip 30501–3899; tel. 770/219–3553, (Nonreporting) **A**2 7 10 19 21 **S** Northeast Georgia Health System, Gainesville, GA
Primary Contact: Carol H. Burrell, Chief Executive Officer
CFO: Brian D Steines, Chief Financial Officer
CMO: Sam Johnson M.D., Chief Medical Officer
CIO: Chris Paravate, Chief Information Officer
CHR: Deborah Weber, Chief Human Resource Officer
CNO: Brenda Simpson, Chief Nursing Officer
Web address: www.nghs.com
Control: Other not-for-profit (including NFP Corporation) **Service**: General medical and surgical

Staffed Beds: 773

GRACEWOOD—Richmond County

EAST CENTRAL REGIONAL HOSPITAL See East Central Regional Hospital, Augusta

GREENSBORO—Greene County

⊞ **ST. MARY'S GOOD SAMARITAN HOSPITAL (111329)**, 5401 Lake Oconee Parkway, Zip 30642–4232; tel. 706/453–7331 **A**1 10 18 **F**3 11 15 18 26 29 30 34 35 40 45 51 57 59 64 65 68 74 75 77 79 81 85 87 93 107 108 115 119 129 130 133 146 147 **S** Trinity Health, Livonia, MI
Primary Contact: D. Montez. Carter, President
CMO: Dave Ringer M.D., Chief of Staff
CNO: Celia Covington MSN, R.N., Director of Nursing
Web address: www.stmarysgoodsam.org
Control: Church operated, Nongovernment, not-for-profit **Service**: General medical and surgical

Staffed Beds: 25 Admissions: 880 Census: 12 Outpatient Visits: 36026 Births: 0 Total Expense ($000): 20386 Payroll Expense ($000): 7725 Personnel: 168

GRIFFIN—Spalding County

⊞ **WELLSTAR SPALDING REGIONAL HOSPITAL (110031)**, 601 South Eighth Street, Zip 30224–4294, Mailing Address: P O Drawer 'V', 30224–1168; tel. 770/228–2721 **A**1 2 10 **F**3 7 11 13 15 18 20 22 29 30 31 34 35 40 49 50 51 53 54 57 59 64 70 73 74 75 76 77 78 79 81 85 87 89 93 107 108 111 114 115 119 129 130 131 135 143 146 147 148 **S** WellStar Health System, Marietta, GA
Primary Contact: Tamara Ison, Senior Vice President and President
COO: Tamara Ison, Chief Operating Officer
CMO: Philip Osehobo M.D., Chief Medical Officer
CIO: Steve Brown, Director Information Systems
CHR: Amanda Remington, Director Human Resources
CNO: Wadra McCullough, Chief Nursing Officer
Web address: www.spaldingregional.com
Control: Other not-for-profit (including NFP Corporation) **Service**: General medical and surgical

Staffed Beds: 162 Admissions: 8661 Census: 101 Outpatient Visits: 101023 Births: 949 Personnel: 692

HAWKINSVILLE—Pulaski County

⇑ **TAYLOR REGIONAL HOSPITAL (110135)**, Macon Highway, Zip 31036, Mailing Address: P.O.Box 1297, 31036–7297; tel. 478/783–0200, (Nonreporting) **A**3 10 21
Primary Contact: E.R. McDannald, Interim Chief Executive Officer
CFO: Lisa Halliday, Director Accounting Services
CMO: Al Baggett M.D., Interim Chief of Staff
CIO: Dawn Warnock, Director Medical Records
Web address: www.taylorregional.org
Control: Other not-for-profit (including NFP Corporation) **Service**: General medical and surgical

Staffed Beds: 57

HAZLEHURST—Jeff Davis County

☐ **JEFF DAVIS HOSPITAL (111333)**, 163 South Tallahassee Street, Zip 31539–2921, Mailing Address: P.O.Box 1690, 31539–1690; tel. 912/375–7781 **A**1 10 18 **F**29 30 40 57 59 70 80 81 104 107 111 119 133
Primary Contact: Tammy Mims, Chief Executive Officer
CFO: Cathy Cason, Chief Financial Officer
CIO: Brian Fowler, Information Technology Director
CHR: Brenda McEachin, Human Resources Director
CNO: Allen Crawford, Chief Nursing Officer
Web address: www.jeffdavishospital.org
Control: Hospital district or authority, Government, Nonfederal **Service**: General medical and surgical

Staffed Beds: 25 Admissions: 577 Census: 6 Outpatient Visits: 22025 Births: 0

Many Facility Codes have changed. Please refer to the AHA Guide Code Chart. © 2017 AHA Guide

GA

HIAWASSEE—Towns County

CHATUGE REGIONAL HOSPITAL AND NURSING HOME (111324), 110 Main Street, Zip 30546–3408, Mailing Address: P.O.Box 509, 30546–0509; tel. 706/896–2222, (Total facility includes 112 beds in nursing home–type unit) **A**10 18 **F**7 11 13 15 18 28 29 30 34 35 40 45 49 51 53 56 57 59 64 65 66 70 75 79 81 85 86 87 93 96 97 98 100 103 104 107 108 110 111 115 119 127 128 129 130 132 133 135 143 146 147 148 **P**1 **S** Union General Hospital, Inc., Blairsville, GA
Primary Contact: Ryan Snow, Administrator
CFO: Tim Henry, Accountant
CMO: Robert F Stahlkuppe M.D., Chief of Staff
CIO: Walt Stafford, Director Information Technology
CHR: Rita Bradshaw, Director Human Resources
Web address: www.chatugeregionalhospital.org
Control: Hospital district or authority, Government, Nonfederal **Service:** General medical and surgical

Staffed Beds: 150 **Admissions:** 823 **Census:** 118 **Outpatient Visits:** 25817 **Births:** 0 **Total Expense ($000):** 22476 **Payroll Expense ($000):** 10586 **Personnel:** 308

HINESVILLE—Liberty County

☐ **LIBERTY REGIONAL MEDICAL CENTER (111335)**, 462 Elma G Miles Parkway, Zip 31313–4000, Mailing Address: P.O.Box 919, 31310–0919; tel. 912/369–9400, (Nonreporting) **A**1 10 18
Primary Contact: Michael Hester, Chief Executive Officer
Web address: www.libertyregional.org
Control: Hospital district or authority, Government, Nonfederal **Service:** General medical and surgical

Staffed Beds: 25

⊞ **WINN ARMY COMMUNITY HOSPITAL**, 1061 Harmon Avenue, Zip 31314–5641, Mailing Address: 1061 Harmon Avenue, Suite 2311B, 31314–5641; tel. 912/435–6965, (Nonreporting) **A**1 3 5 **S** Department of the Army, Office of the Surgeon General, Falls Church, VA
Primary Contact: Colonel Kirk W. Eggleston, Commanding Officer
CIO: Arthur N Kirshner, Chief Information Management
CHR: MajorYvette McCrea, Chief Human Resources
CNO: ColonelSharon Brown, Deputy Commander Nursing
Web address: www.winn.amedd.army.mil/
Control: Army, Government, federal **Service:** General medical and surgical

Staffed Beds: 37

HIRAM—Paulding County

⊞ **WELLSTAR PAULDING HOSPITAL (110042)**, 2518 Jimmy Lee Smith Parkway, Zip 30141; tel. 470/644–7000, (Total facility includes 182 beds in nursing home–type unit) **A**1 2 10 **F**3 11 15 18 20 28 29 30 31 37 38 40 41 44 45 49 50 53 54 55 59 61 64 68 70 75 77 78 79 80 81 82 85 86 87 93 102 107 108 110 111 114 118 119 120 121 123 124 128 129 130 135 146 148 **P**5 6 **S** WellStar Health System, Marietta, GA
Primary Contact: Mark Haney, President
COO: Lindsay Rehn, Executive Director of Financial Operations
CFO: Lindsay Rehn, Executive Director of Financial Operations
CMO: Guillermo Pierluisi, Vice President of Medical Affairs
CHR: Jessica Bedsole, Director, Human Resources
CNO: Vicky Hogue R.N., Vice President Patient Services and Chief Nursing Officer
Web address: www.wellstar.com
Control: Other not–for–profit (including NFP Corporation) **Service:** General medical and surgical

Staffed Beds: 238 **Admissions:** 5282 **Census:** 219 **Outpatient Visits:** 124620 **Births:** 0 **Personnel:** 738

HOMERVILLE—Clinch County

★ **CLINCH MEMORIAL HOSPITAL (111308)**, 1050 Valdosta Highway, Zip 31634–9701, Mailing Address: P.O.Box 516, 31634–0516; tel. 912/487–5211 **A**10 18 **F**3 7 11 15 34 40 45 57 59 64 77 93 107 114 119 129 130 133 146
Primary Contact: Wallace D. Mincey, Chief Executive Officer
COO: Wallace D Mincey, Chief Executive Officer
CFO: Sandra Hughes, Chief Financial Officer
CMO: Samuel Cobarrubias M.D., Chief of Staff
CIO: Shelly Studebaker, Director Management Information Systems
CHR: Shelly Studebaker, Manager Human Resources
CNO: Kellie Register, Director of Nursing
Web address: www.clinchmemorialhospital.org
Control: County, Government, Nonfederal **Service:** General medical and surgical

Staffed Beds: 25 **Admissions:** 228 **Census:** 2 **Outpatient Visits:** 12631 **Births:** 0 **Total Expense ($000):** 10407 **Payroll Expense ($000):** 3891 **Personnel:** 95

JACKSON—Butts County

★ **WELLSTAR SYLVAN GROVE HOSPITAL (111319)**, 1050 McDonough Road, Zip 30233–1599; tel. 770/775–7861 **A**10 18 **F**15 29 34 35 40 50 57 59 68 77 93 107 119 130 133 **S** WellStar Health System, Marietta, GA
Primary Contact: Tamara Ison, Senior Vice President and President
CFO: Tamara Ison, Chief Financial Officer
CIO: Steve Brown, Chief Information Officer
CHR: Amanda Remington, Director Human Resources
Web address: www.sylvangrovehospital.com
Control: Other not–for–profit (including NFP Corporation) **Service:** General medical and surgical

Staffed Beds: 24 **Admissions:** 382 **Census:** 13 **Outpatient Visits:** 19911 **Births:** 0 **Personnel:** 65

JASPER—Pickens County

⇑ **PIEDMONT MOUNTAINSIDE HOSPITAL (110225)**, 1266 Highway 515 South, Zip 30143–4872; tel. 706/692–2441 **A**10 21 **F**3 13 15 20 28 29 34 35 40 41 45 46 49 53 57 59 64 70 76 77 79 81 85 107 108 110 111 114 115 119 129 130 132 135 148 **S** Piedmont Healthcare, Atlanta, GA
Primary Contact: Denise Ray, Chief Executive Officer
CMO: Moiz Master M.D., Medical Director of Quality
CIO: Geoffrey Brown, Chief Information Officer
CHR: Frank Leist, Human Resources Manager
CNO: Michelle Breitfelder, Chief Nursing Officer
Web address: www.piedmont.org
Control: Other not–for–profit (including NFP Corporation) **Service:** General medical and surgical

Staffed Beds: 52 **Admissions:** 2961 **Census:** 31 **Outpatient Visits:** 70001 **Births:** 361 **Total Expense ($000):** 52716 **Payroll Expense ($000):** 22563 **Personnel:** 368

JESUP—Wayne County

☐ **WAYNE MEMORIAL HOSPITAL (110124)**, 865 South First Street, Zip 31545–0210, Mailing Address: P.O.Box 410, 31598–0410; tel. 912/427–6811, (Nonreporting) **A**1 10 20
Primary Contact: Joseph P. Ierardi, Chief Executive Officer
CFO: Greg Jones, Chief Financial Officer
CMO: Dan Collipp M.D., Chief of Staff
CIO: Deborah Six, Coordinator Data Processing
CHR: John Mclwain, Director Human Resources
Web address: www.wmhweb.com
Control: County, Government, Nonfederal **Service:** General medical and surgical

Staffed Beds: 84

JOHNS CREEK—Fulton County

⊞ **EMORY JOHNS CREEK HOSPITAL (110230)**, 6325 Hospital Parkway, Zip 30097–5775; tel. 678/474–7000 **A**1 2 3 10 **F**3 11 12 13 15 18 20 22 26 29 30 31 34 35 36 40 45 49 50 54 57 58 59 60 64 68 70 72 73 74 75 76 77 78 79 81 82 84 85 86 87 93 100 102 107 108 110 111 115 116 117 119 126 129 130 131 132 141 146 147 148 149 **P**6 **S** Emory Healthcare, Atlanta, GA
Primary Contact: Marilyn Margolis, MSN, Chief Executive Officer
COO: Laurie Hansen, Vice President of Operations
CFO: JoAnn Manning, Chief Financial Officer
CMO: Adedapo Odetoyinbo M.D., Chief Medical Office
CHR: Hannah Henry, Interim Vice President of Human Resources
CNO: Heather Redrick, Chief Nursing Officer
Web address: www.emoryjohnscreek.com
Control: Other not–for–profit (including NFP Corporation) **Service:** General medical and surgical

Staffed Beds: 113 **Admissions:** 6895 **Census:** 77 **Outpatient Visits:** 70067 **Births:** 1328 **Total Expense ($000):** 128205 **Payroll Expense ($000):** 44588 **Personnel:** 632

GA

KENNESAW—Cobb County

DEVEREUX GEORGIA TREATMENT NETWORK, 1291 Stanley Road NW, Zip 30152–4359; tel. 770/427–0147 **F**98 99 106 **S** Devereux, Villanova, PA
Primary Contact: Gwendolyn Skinner, Executive Director
COO: Mary H Esposito, Assistant Executive Director
CFO: Kathy Goggin, Director Administrative Services
CMO: Yolanda Graham M.D., Medical Director
CIO: Sam Maguta, Coordinator Information Systems
CHR: Rudie Delien, Director Human Resources
CNO: Debra Sharpton, Director of Nursing
Web address: www.devereuxga.org
Control: Other not–for–profit (including NFP Corporation) **Service**: Children's hospital psychiatric

Staffed Beds: 100 **Admissions:** 174 **Census:** 73 **Outpatient Visits:** 74 **Births:** 0 **Total Expense ($000):** 18905 **Personnel:** 346

LAGRANGE—Troup County

✠ **WEST GEORGIA HEALTH (110016)**, 1514 Vernon Road, Zip 30240–4131; tel. 706/882–1411, (Total facility includes 260 beds in nursing home–type unit) (Data for 274 days)**A**1 2 10 19 **F**3 11 12 13 15 18 20 22 26 28 29 30 31 34 35 40 44 47 48 49 50 56 57 58 59 62 63 64 66 68 70 73 74 75 76 77 78 79 80 81 82 84 85 86 87 89 92 93 96 107 108 110 111 114 115 119 120 121 123 124 128 129 130 132 135 146 147 148 149 **P**6 **S** WellStar Health System, Marietta, GA
Primary Contact: Gerald N. Fulks, President
COO: Charis L Acree, Vice President and Chief Operating Officer
CFO: Paul R Perrotti CPA, Chief Financial Officer
CIO: Alan Whitehouse, Chief Information Officer
CHR: Tommy Britt, Vice President of Human Resources
CNO: Tracy Gynther R.N., Vice President and Chief Nursing Officer
Web address: www.wghealth.org/
Control: Other not–for–profit (including NFP Corporation) **Service**: General medical and surgical

Staffed Beds: 390 **Admissions:** 5831 **Census:** 310 **Outpatient Visits:** 107524 **Births:** 750 **Personnel:** 1381

LAKELAND—Lanier County

✠ **SOUTH GEORGIA MEDICAL CENTER LANIER CAMPUS (111326)**, 116 West Thigpen Avenue, Zip 31635–1011; tel. 229/482–3110, (Nonreporting) **A**1 10 18
Primary Contact: Richard Huth, Administrator
CFO: Libby Flemming, Controller and Chief Information Officer
CMO: Bruce Herrington M.D., Chief Medical Officer
CIO: Libby Flemming, Controller and Chief Information Officer
CHR: Vicki Dinkins, Director Human Resources
Web address: www.sgmc.org
Control: Other not–for–profit (including NFP Corporation) **Service**: Other specialty treatment

Staffed Beds: 87

LAVONIA—Franklin County

✠ **ST. MARY'S SACRED HEART HOSPITAL (110027)**, 367 Clear Creek Parkway, Zip 30553–4173; tel. 706/356–7800 **A**1 10 **F**3 11 13 15 18 29 30 34 35 40 49 53 57 59 70 74 75 76 79 81 85 87 93 107 108 110 111 115 119 129 130 132 149 **S** Trinity Health, Livonia, MI
Primary Contact: Jeff English, Interim Chief Executive Officer
CIO: Tim Vickery, Chief Information Officer
CHR: Lauren Papka, Chief Administrative Officer
CNO: Evelyn Murphy R.N., Chief Nursing Officer
Web address: www.stmaryssacredheart.org/
Control: Church operated, Nongovernment, not–for–profit **Service**: General medical and surgical

Staffed Beds: 35 **Admissions:** 1599 **Census:** 14 **Outpatient Visits:** 47166 **Births:** 277 **Total Expense ($000):** 27239 **Payroll Expense ($000):** 10910 **Personnel:** 217

LAWRENCEVILLE—Gwinnett County

✠ **GWINNETT HOSPITAL SYSTEM (110087)**, 1000 Medical Center Boulevard, Zip 30046–7694, Mailing Address: P.O.Box 348, 30046–0348; tel. 678/312–1000, (Includes GWINNETT MEDICAL CENTER–DULUTH, 3620 Howell Ferry Road, Duluth, Georgia, Zip 30096, tel. 678/312–6800; GWINNETT MEDICAL CENTER, 1000 Medical Center Boulevard, Lawrenceville, Georgia, Zip 30245, Box 348, 30246, tel. 678/312–1000; Thomas Shepherd, Executive Vice President and Chief Operating Officer) (Total facility includes 89 beds in nursing home–type unit) **A**1 2 3 8 10 13 **F**3 8 11 12 13 15 17 18 20 22 24 26 28 29 30 31 34 35 36 37 38 40 41 43 44 45 46 47 48 49 50 53 54 55 56 58 59 64 67 68 70 71 72 73 74 75 76 77 78 79 81 82 84 85 86 87 90 93 96 97 107 108 110 111 114 115 116 117 118 119 126 128 129 130 131 132 134 135 146 147 148 149 **P**6 8
Primary Contact: Philip R. Wolfe, President and Chief Executive Officer
COO: Thomas Shepherd, Executive Vice President and Chief Operating Officer
CFO: Thomas Y McBride III, Executive Vice President and Chief Financial Officer
CMO: Alan Bier M.D., Executive Vice President and Chief Medical Officer
CIO: Patricia A Lavely FACHE, Senior Vice President and Chief Information Officer
CHR: Stephen Nadeau, Senior Vice President Human Resources
CNO: Carol Danielson R.N., Senior Vice President and Chief Nursing Officer
Web address: www.gwinnettmedicalcenter.org
Control: Other not–for–profit (including NFP Corporation) **Service**: General medical and surgical

Staffed Beds: 569 **Admissions:** 30518 **Census:** 496 **Outpatient Visits:** 430379 **Births:** 5532 **Total Expense ($000):** 683635 **Payroll Expense ($000):** 266857 **Personnel:** 3923

☐ **SUMMITRIDGE HOSPITAL (114004)**, 250 Scenic Highway, Zip 30046–5675; tel. 678/442–5800 **A**1 10 **F**4 5 98 99 102 103 104 105
Primary Contact: Tim E. Merritt, Chief Executive Officer
Web address: www.summitridgehospital.net
Control: Corporation, Investor–owned (for–profit) **Service**: Psychiatric

Staffed Beds: 86 **Admissions:** 3370 **Census:** 70 **Outpatient Visits:** 7754 **Births:** 0 **Total Expense ($000):** 13886 **Payroll Expense ($000):** 7907 **Personnel:** 150

LITHONIA—Dekalb County

☐ **DEKALB MEDICAL AT HILLANDALE (110226)**, 2801 DeKalb Medical Parkway, Zip 30058–4996; tel. 404/501–8700 (Nonreporting) **A**1 10 **S** DeKalb Regional Health System, Decatur, GA
Primary Contact: Vernell Nunn, Chief Medical Officer
CMO: Duane Barclay D.O., Chief Medical Officer
CIO: Mark Trocino, Chief Information Officer
CHR: Tom Crawford, Vice President Human Resources
Web address: www.dekalbmedical.org
Control: Other not–for–profit (including NFP Corporation) **Service**: General medical and surgical

Staffed Beds: 80

LOUISVILLE—Jefferson County

⇑ **JEFFERSON HOSPITAL (110100)**, 1067 Peachtree Street, Zip 30434–1599; tel. 478/625–7000, (Nonreporting) **A**10 20 21
Primary Contact: Lou Semrad, Interim Chief Executive Officer
CMO: James Polhill M.D., Chief Medical Officer
CHR: Catherine Hall, Manager Human Resources
CNO: Ben Doyle R.N., Director of Nursing
Web address: www.jeffersonhosp.com
Control: City–county, Government, Nonfederal **Service**: General medical and surgical

Staffed Beds: 37

MACON—Bibb County

✠ **COLISEUM MEDICAL CENTERS (110164)**, 350 Hospital Drive, Zip 31217–3871; tel. 478/765–7000, (Nonreporting) (Includes COLISEUM CENTER FOR BEHAVIORAL HEALTH, 340 Hospital Drive, Macon, Georgia, Zip 31217–3838, tel. 478/741–1355; Stephen J. Daugherty, Interim Chief Executive Officer) **A**1 2 10 **S** HCA Healthcare, Nashville, TN
Primary Contact: Stephen J. Daugherty, Interim Chief Executive Officer
COO: Todd Dixon R.N., Chief Operating Officer
CFO: Elmer Polite, Chief Financial Officer
CIO: Joan Morstad, Director Information Systems
CHR: Laura Booras, Vice President Human Resources
Web address: www.coliseumhealthsystem.com
Control: Corporation, Investor–owned (for–profit) **Service**: General medical and surgical

Staffed Beds: 227

⊞ **COLISEUM NORTHSIDE HOSPITAL (110201)**, 400 Charter Boulevard, Zip 31210–4853, Mailing Address: P.O.Box 4627, 31208–4627; tel. 478/757–8200, (Nonreporting) **A**1 10 **S** HCA Healthcare, Nashville, TN
Primary Contact: Stephen J. Daugherty, Chief Executive Officer
COO: Todd Dixon R.N., Chief Operating Officer
CFO: Elmer Polite, Chief Financial Officer
CHR: Louise Truitt, Human Resource Director
CNO: Patricia Derrico FACHE, R.N., Chief Nursing Officer
Web address: www.coliseumhealthsystem.com
Control: Corporation, Investor–owned (for–profit) **Service**: General medical and surgical

Staffed Beds: 103

★ ⇧ **MEDICAL CENTER, NAVICENT HEALTH (110107)**, 777 Hemlock Street, Zip 31201–2155; tel. 478/633–1000, (Includes CHILDREN'S HOSPITAL, NAVICENT HEALTH, 888 Pine Street, Macon, Georgia, Zip 31201–2155, tel. 478/633–1000) **A**2 3 5 8 10 21 **F**3 5 7 8 11 12 13 14 15 17 18 20 22 24 26 28 29 30 31 32 34 35 36 39 40 43 44 45 46 47 48 49 50 51 53 54 56 57 58 59 60 61 62 63 64 65 66 68 70 72 73 74 75 76 77 78 79 81 82 83 84 85 86 87 88 89 92 93 94 97 98 99 100 101 102 103 104 105 107 108 110 111 114 115 119 126 130 132 135 143 144 145 146 147 148 149 150 **P**1 **S** Navicent Health, Macon, GA
Primary Contact: Ninfa M. Saunders, Chief Executive Officer
COO: Susan Harris R.N., Chief Operating Officer
CFO: Rhonda S. Perry, Chief Financial Officer
CMO: Christopher Hendry M.D., Chief Medical Officer
CIO: Ed Brown, Chief Information Officer
CHR: Bernard J Price, Chief Human Resources Officer
CNO: Tracey Blalock MSN, R.N., Chief Nurse Executive
Web address: www.navicenthealth.org/
Control: Other not–for–profit (including NFP Corporation) **Service**: General medical and surgical

Staffed Beds: 659 Admissions: 30405 Census: 487 Outpatient Visits: 394083 Births: 2527 Total Expense ($000): 603419 Payroll Expense ($000): 225239 Personnel: 4190

⊞ **REGENCY HOSPITAL OF CENTRAL GEORGIA (112016)**, 535 Coliseum Drive, Zip 31217–0104; tel. 478/803–7300, (Nonreporting) **A**1 10 **S** Select Medical Corporation, Mechanicsburg, PA
Primary Contact: Wayne Boutwell, Chief Executive Officer
Web address: www.regencyhospital.com
Control: Corporation, Investor–owned (for–profit) **Service**: Acute long–term care hospital

Staffed Beds: 60

★ ⇧ **REHABILITATION HOSPITAL, NAVICENT HEALTH (113029)**, 3351 Northside Drive, Zip 31210–2587; tel. 478/201–6500, (Nonreporting) **A**3 10 21 **S** Navicent Health, Macon, GA
Primary Contact: Gina Tipton, Director of Operations
COO: Darren Pearce, Executive Director
CFO: Beverly Owens, Controller
CMO: Allison Scheetz M.D., Medical Director
Web address: www.navicenthealth.org/service–center/rehabilitation–hospital–navicent–health
Control: Other not–for–profit (including NFP Corporation) **Service**: Rehabilitation

Staffed Beds: 58

MADISON—Morgan County

☐ **MORGAN MEMORIAL HOSPITAL (111304)**, 1077 South Main Street, Zip 30650–2073, Mailing Address: P.O.Box 860, 30650–0860; tel. 706/342–1667 **A**1 10 18 **F**29 30 34 35 40 41 43 45 49 57 59 67 77 81 89 90 93 97 107 119 128 133
Primary Contact: Ralph A. Castillo, CPA, Chief Executive Officer
CFO: Kyle Wilkinson, Chief Financial Officer
CMO: Dan Zant M.D., Chief of Staff
CIO: Patrick Cook, Vice President Support Services
CHR: Sarah Phillips, Manager Human Resources
CNO: Beth O'Neill, Chief Nursing Officer
Web address: www.mmh.org
Control: Hospital district or authority, Government, Nonfederal **Service**: General medical and surgical

Staffed Beds: 25 Admissions: 119 Census: 15 Births: 0 Total Expense ($000): 13856 Payroll Expense ($000): 6107

MARIETTA—Cobb County

⊞ △ **WELLSTAR KENNESTONE HOSPITAL (110035)**, 677 Church Street, Zip 30060–1148; tel. 770/793–5000 **A**1 2 3 5 7 10 **F**3 10 11 12 13 15 17 18 20 22 24 26 28 29 30 31 34 36 37 38 40 41 43 44 45 46 47 48 49 50 51 53 54 55 58 59 60 61 64 66 68 70 72 73 74 75 76 77 78 79 80 81 82 84 85 86 87 89 90 93 94 96 97 100 102 107 108 110 111 114 115 117 118 119 120 121 123 124 125 126 129 130 132 141 146 147 148 **P**5 6 **S** WellStar Health System, Marietta, GA
Primary Contact: Dan Woods, President
CFO: Douglas Arvin, Vice President Finance and Chief Financial Officer
CMO: Robert Lubitz M.D., Vice President of Medical Affairs
CIO: Jonathan B Morris M.D., Senior Vice President and Chief Information Officer
CHR: Jimmy Duncan, Vice President Human Resources
CNO: Lynn Meurer MSN, R.N., Interim Chief Nursing Officer
Web address: www.wellstar.org
Control: Other not–for–profit (including NFP Corporation) **Service**: General medical and surgical

Staffed Beds: 657 Admissions: 39703 Census: 513 Outpatient Visits: 443591 Births: 5554 Personnel: 3894

⊞ **WELLSTAR WINDY HILL HOSPITAL (112007)**, 2540 Windy Hill Road, Zip 30067–8632; tel. 770/644–1000 **A**1 2 10 **F**1 3 5 11 15 28 29 30 44 45 50 51 60 61 64 68 75 77 79 81 82 85 86 87 93 100 101 107 108 110 111 114 118 119 129 130 131 135 141 146 147 148 **P**5 6 **S** WellStar Health System, Marietta, GA
Primary Contact: Monte Wilson, President
CFO: Marsha Burke, Senior Vice President and Chief Financial Officer
CMO: Larry Haldeman M.D., Executive Vice President and Chief Medical Officer
CIO: Leigh Cox, Chief Information Officer
Web address: www.wellstar.org
Control: Other not–for–profit (including NFP Corporation) **Service**: Acute long–term care hospital

Staffed Beds: 55 Admissions: 333 Census: 25 Outpatient Visits: 85121 Births: 0 Personnel: 331

METTER—Candler County

☐ **CANDLER COUNTY HOSPITAL (111334)**, 400 Cedar Street, Zip 30439–3338, Mailing Address: P.O.Box 597, 30439–0597; tel. 912/685–5741, (Nonreporting) **A**1 10 18
Primary Contact: Mel Pyne, Chief Executive Officer
COO: David Flanders, Chief Operating Officer
CNO: Christy Blackburn R.N., Chief Nursing Officer
Web address: www.candlercountyhospital.com
Control: Hospital district or authority, Government, Nonfederal **Service**: General medical and surgical

Staffed Beds: 25

MILLEDGEVILLE—Baldwin County

☐ **CENTRAL STATE HOSPITAL**, 620 Broad Street, Zip 31062–0001; tel. 478/445–4128 **A**1 3 **F**30 39 59 75 77 86 87 97 98 100 130 132 149
Primary Contact: Susan Trueblood, Regional Hospital Administrator
COO: Terry McGee, Chief Operations Officer
CMO: Scott VanSant M.D., Chief Medical Officer
CIO: Betsy Bradley, Coordinator Performance Improvement
CHR: Myra Holloway, Director Human Resources Management
Web address: www.centralstatehospital.org
Control: State, Government, Nonfederal **Service**: Psychiatric

Staffed Beds: 184 Admissions: 117 Census: 179 Outpatient Visits: 0 Births: 0 Total Expense ($000): 56981 Payroll Expense ($000): 22300 Personnel: 621

⊞ **OCONEE REGIONAL MEDICAL CENTER (110150)**, 821 North Cobb Street, Zip 31061–2351, Mailing Address: P.O.Box 690, 31059–0690; tel. 478/454–3505, (Total facility includes 15 beds in nursing home–type unit) **A**1 10 19 **F**3 11 13 15 28 29 30 31 34 35 37 40 45 46 49 50 51 53 57 59 60 64 68 70 75 76 78 79 80 81 85 86 87 89 92 93 107 108 110 111 114 116 117 119 120 121 123 128 129 132 135 146 147 **S** Navicent Health, Macon, GA
Primary Contact: Steven Johnson, Interim Chief Executive Officer
CFO: Brenda Qualls, Chief Financial Officer
CNO: Deborah Block, Vice President Nursing and Chief Nursing Officer
Web address: www.oconeeregional.com
Control: Other not–for–profit (including NFP Corporation) **Service**: General medical and surgical

Staffed Beds: 90 Admissions: 2783 Census: 36 Outpatient Visits: 115108 Births: 511 Total Expense ($000): 60663 Payroll Expense ($000): 20223 Personnel: 411

GA

Hospital, Medicare Provider Number, Address, Telephone, Approval, Facility, and Physician Codes, Health Care System

★ American Hospital Association (AHA) membership
☐ The Joint Commission accreditation
○ Healthcare Facilities Accreditation Program
◇ DNV Healthcare Inc. accreditation
⇧ Center for Improvement in Healthcare Quality Accreditation
△ Commission on Accreditation of Rehabilitation Facilities (CARF) accreditation

MILLEN—Jenkins County

OPTIM MEDICAL CENTER – JENKINS (111311), 931 East Winthrope Avenue, Zip 30442–1839; tel. 478/982–4221, (Nonreporting) **A**10 18 **S** National Surgical Healthcare, Chicago, IL
Primary Contact: Robert R. Sellers, Chief Executive Officer
CFO: Cindy Bierschenk, Director of Financial Services
CIO: Christian Rekowski, Information Technology Director
CHR: Natalie Peterson, Director of Human Resources
CNO: S Lagina Evans R.N., Assistant Chief Nursing Officer
Web address: www.optimhealth.com
Control: Hospital district or authority, Government, Nonfederal **Service:** General medical and surgical

Staffed Beds: 25

MONROE—Walton County

☒ **CLEARVIEW REGIONAL MEDICAL CENTER (110046)**, 2151 West Spring Street, Zip 30655–3115, Mailing Address: PO BOX 1346, 30655–1346; tel. 770/267–8461 **A**1 10 **F**3 12 13 29 34 40 43 45 46 47 49 50 59 68 70 75 76 77 79 81 82 85 87 89 93 107 110 111 115 119 135 144 146 147 148 149 **S** Quorum Health, Brentwood, TN
Primary Contact: Michael Johnson, Chief Executive Officer
CFO: Jeffrey Mullis, Interim Chief Financial Officer
CMO: Douglas Miller M.D., Chief of Medical Staff
CIO: Cory Crayton, Director of Information Systems
CHR: Michele Monsrud, Director Human Resources
CNO: Sharon H Queen R.N., Chief Nursing Officer
Web address: www.clearviewregionalmedicalcenter.com/
Control: Corporation, Investor–owned (for–profit) **Service:** General medical and surgical

Staffed Beds: 52 Admissions: 2739 Census: 24 Outpatient Visits: 55803 Births: 392 Total Expense ($000): 46687 Payroll Expense ($000): 16934 Personnel: 305

MONTEZUMA—Macon County

⇑ **FLINT RIVER COMMUNITY HOSPITAL (110190)**, 509 Sumter Street, Zip 31063–1733, Mailing Address: P.O.Box 770, 31063–2502; tel. 478/472–3100, (Nonreporting) **A**10 21
Primary Contact: Michael C. Patterson, Chief Executive Officer
CMO: Quincy Jordan M.D., Chief of Staff
CHR: Vicki Stotts, Coordinator Human Resources
CNO: Lee Hughes R.N., Chief Nursing Officer
Web address: www.flintriverhospital.com/
Control: Corporation, Investor–owned (for–profit) **Service:** General medical and surgical

Staffed Beds: 49

MONTICELLO—Jasper County

JASPER MEMORIAL HOSPITAL (111303), 898 College Street, Zip 31064–1258; tel. 706/468–6411, (Total facility includes 55 beds in nursing home–type unit) **A**10 18 **F**11 18 29 34 40 57 59 65 77 93 97 107 111 119 128 133 146 148 149 **P**6
Primary Contact: Jan Gaston, Administrator
CFO: Stuart Abney, Controller
CHR: Laura Hammonds, Assistant Administrator
CNO: Robin Carey, Director of Nursing
Web address: www.jaspermemorialhospital.org
Control: Other not–for–profit (including NFP Corporation) **Service:** General medical and surgical

Staffed Beds: 67 Admissions: 175 Census: 56 Outpatient Visits: 12844 Births: 0 Total Expense ($000): 9919 Payroll Expense ($000): 4828 Personnel: 128

MOULTRIE—Colquitt County

☒ ○ **COLQUITT REGIONAL MEDICAL CENTER (110105)**, 3131 South Main Street, Zip 31768–6925, Mailing Address: P.O.Box 40, 31776–0040; tel. 229/985–3420 **A**1 10 11 **F**3 7 11 12 13 15 17 20 29 30 31 32 34 35 39 40 45 47 48 49 56 57 59 60 61 62 63 65 68 70 74 75 76 77 78 79 81 82 85 86 87 89 91 93 97 107 108 110 111 115 119 126 127 129 130 131 132 135 143 144 146 147 148
Primary Contact: James L. Matney, President and Chief Executive Officer
COO: Greg K Johnson, Chief Operating Officer
CFO: Shamb Purohit, Chief Financial Officer
CMO: Andy Wills M.D., Medical Director
CIO: Bill Bishop, Chief Information Officer
CHR: Dawn Johns, Director Human Resources
CNO: Dena Zinker MSN, R.N., Vice President Patient Services
Web address: www.colquittregional.com
Control: Hospital district or authority, Government, Nonfederal **Service:** General medical and surgical

Staffed Beds: 99 Admissions: 4622 Census: 55 Outpatient Visits: 136110 Births: 563 Total Expense ($000): 97602 Payroll Expense ($000): 40188 Personnel: 865

TURNING POINT HOSPITAL (110209), 3015 Veterans Parkway South, Zip 31788–6705, Mailing Address: P.O.Box 1177, 31776–1177; tel. 229/985–4815 **A**10 **F**4 5 30 75 87 98 102 130 135 143 **P**6 **S** Universal Health Services, Inc., King of Prussia, PA
Primary Contact: Judy H. Payne, Chief Executive Officer
COO: Stephen Smith, Associate Administrator
CFO: Edwin Bennett, Controller
CMO: Muhammed M Alam, Medical Director
CHR: Jennifer Azar, Director Human Resources
CNO: Faith Connell, Director of Nursing
Web address: www.turningpointcare.com
Control: Corporation, Investor–owned (for–profit) **Service:** Alcoholism and other chemical dependency

Staffed Beds: 59 Admissions: 3680 Census: 55 Outpatient Visits: 32282 Births: 0 Total Expense ($000): 24038 Payroll Expense ($000): 12971 Personnel: 232

NASHVILLE—Berrien County

☒ **SOUTH GEORGIA MEDICAL CENTER BERRIEN CAMPUS (110234)**, 1221 East McPherson Avenue, Zip 31639–2326, Mailing Address: P.O.Box 665, 31639–0665; tel. 229/543–7100, (Nonreporting) **A**1 10
Primary Contact: Richard Huth, Administrator
Web address: www.sgmc.org/
Control: Other not–for–profit (including NFP Corporation) **Service:** General medical and surgical

Staffed Beds: 39

NEWNAN—Coweta County

⇑ **PIEDMONT NEWNAN HOSPITAL (110229)**, 745 Poplar Road, Zip 30265–1618; tel. 770/400–1000 **A**2 10 21 **F**3 11 12 13 15 18 20 26 28 29 30 31 34 35 40 45 46 49 51 53 57 59 60 64 68 70 72 73 74 75 76 77 78 79 81 84 85 86 87 93 107 108 110 111 114 115 116 117 118 119 120 121 123 126 129 130 132 135 146 148 **S** Piedmont Healthcare, Atlanta, GA
Primary Contact: Michael Robertson, Chief Executive Officer
COO: Nathan Nipper, Vice President and Chief Operating Officer
CFO: John Miles, Chief Financial Officer
CMO: Jeffrey R Folk M.D., Vice President Medical Affairs and Chief Medical Officer
CIO: Henry Scott, Executive Director, Technical Services
CHR: Clay Boyles, Executive Director, Human Resources
CNO: Jason Smith, Chief Nursing Officer
Web address: www.piedmont.org/locations/piedmont–newnan/pnh–home
Control: Other not–for–profit (including NFP Corporation) **Service:** General medical and surgical

Staffed Beds: 146 Admissions: 8337 Census: 92 Outpatient Visits: 123070 Births: 1250 Total Expense ($000): 129846 Payroll Expense ($000): 52518 Personnel: 896

☐ **SOUTHEASTERN REGIONAL MEDICAL CENTER (110233)**, 600 Celebrate Life Parkway, Zip 30265–8000; tel. 770/400–6000 **A**1 2 10 **F**3 26 29 30 31 33 34 35 36 38 45 46 47 49 55 57 58 59 64 65 67 70 75 77 78 80 81 82 84 85 86 87 93 104 107 108 109 110 111 114 115 116 117 118 119 120 121 123 124 126 130 132 135 142 146 148 **P**6 **S** Cancer Treatment Centers of America, Schaumburg, IL
Primary Contact: Anne Meisner, MSN, President and Chief Executive Officer
COO: David Kent, Chief Operating Officer
CFO: Scott Walker, Chief Financial Officer
CNO: Gloria V. Barnes MSN, Assistant Vice President Patient Care Services
Web address: www.cancercenter.com/southeastern–hospital.cfm
Control: Corporation, Investor–owned (for–profit) **Service:** Cancer

Staffed Beds: 50 Admissions: 1916 Census: 35 Outpatient Visits: 24429 Births: 0 Personnel: 934

NORCROSS—Gwinnett County

LAKEVIEW BEHAVIORAL HEALTH, 1 Technology Parkway South, Zip 30092–2928; tel. 678/713–2600 (Nonreporting) **S** Acadia Healthcare Company, Inc., Franklin, TN
Primary Contact: Carmen Kramer, Chief Executive Officer
Web address: www.lakeviewbehavioralhealth.com
Control: Corporation, Investor–owned (for–profit) **Service:** Psychiatric

Staffed Beds: 70

OCILLA—Irwin County

⇧ **IRWIN COUNTY HOSPITAL (110130)**, 710 North Irwin Avenue, Zip 31774–5011; tel. 229/468–3800, (Nonreporting) **A**10 21
Primary Contact: Paige Wynn, Administrator
CFO: Tami Gray, Chief Financial Officer
CMO: Ashfaq Saiyed M.D., Medical Director
CHR: Becky Edwards, Manager Human Resources
Web address: www.irwincntyhospital.com
Control: County, Government, Nonfederal **Service:** General medical and surgical

Staffed Beds: 64

PERRY—Houston County

⌧ **PERRY HOSPITAL (110153)**, 1120 Morningside Drive, Zip 31069–2906; tel. 478/987–3600 **A**1 10 **F**3 11 15 18 29 30 34 35 39 40 45 48 50 57 59 61 68 70 75 79 81 82 85 86 87 89 93 100 107 110 111 114 115 119 129 130 131 132 133 134 135 146 149 **S** Houston Healthcare System, Warner Robins, GA
Primary Contact: David Campbell, Administrator
COO: Charles G Briscoe FACHE, Chief Operating Officer
CFO: Sean Whilden, Chief Financial Officer
CMO: Larry D. Stewart Jr, Chief Medical Officer and Vice President, Medical Affairs
CHR: Michael O'Hara, Senior Executive Director
CNO: Melinda D. Hartley R.N., Vice President Patient Care Services
Web address: www.hhc.org
Control: Other not–for–profit (including NFP Corporation) **Service:** General medical and surgical

Staffed Beds: 39 **Admissions:** 1538 **Census:** 20 **Outpatient Visits:** 41356 **Births:** 0 **Total Expense ($000):** 26204 **Payroll Expense ($000):** 10306 **Personnel:** 215

QUITMAN—Brooks County

⌧ **BROOKS COUNTY HOSPITAL (111332)**, 903 North Court Street, Zip 31643–1315, Mailing Address: P.O.Box 5000, 31643–5000; tel. 229/263–4171, (Nonreporting) **A**1 10 18 **S** Archbold Medical Center, Thomasville, GA
Primary Contact: Nancy M. Williams, R.N., Administrator
CFO: Skip Hightower, Chief Financial Officer
CMO: Michael Sopt M.D., Chief of Staff
CHR: Janet Eldridge, Director Human Resources and Personnel
CNO: June Furney R.N., Director of Nursing
Web address: www.archbold.org
Control: Other not–for–profit (including NFP Corporation) **Service:** General medical and surgical

Staffed Beds: 25

REIDSVILLE—Tattnall County

★ **OPTIM MEDICAL CENTER – TATTNALL (111323)**, 247 South Main Street, Zip 30453–4605; tel. 912/557–1000, (Nonreporting) **A**10 18 **S** National Surgical Healthcare, Chicago, IL
Primary Contact: Rob Snipes, Administrator
Web address: www.optimmedicalcenter.com
Control: Corporation, Investor–owned (for–profit) **Service:** Orthopedic

Staffed Beds: 25

RIVERDALE—Clayton County

⌧ **SOUTHERN CRESCENT HOSPITAL FOR SPECIALTY CARE (112015)**, 11 Upper Riverdale Road SW, 6th Floor, Zip 30274–2615; tel. 770/897–7600 **A**1 10 **F**1 29 30 35 44 75 77 82 84 87 148 **S** CHRISTUS Health, Irving, TX
Primary Contact: Fiona Adams, Interim Administrator
Web address: www.christusdubuis.org/SouthernCrescentHospitalforSpecialtyCare
Control: Church operated, Nongovernment, not–for–profit **Service:** Acute long–term care hospital

Staffed Beds: 30 **Admissions:** 206 **Census:** 16 **Outpatient Visits:** 0 **Births:** 0 **Total Expense ($000):** 9041 **Payroll Expense ($000):** 3518 **Personnel:** 71

⌧ **SOUTHERN REGIONAL MEDICAL CENTER (110165)**, 11 Upper Riverdale Road SW, Zip 30274–2615; tel. 770/991–8000, (Nonreporting) **A**1 2 3 5 10 **S** Prime Healthcare, Ontario, CA
Primary Contact: Charlotte W. Dupre, Chief Executive Officer
COO: Therese O Sucher, Senior Vice President Operations
CFO: Richard G Stovall, Senior Vice President Fiscal Services and Chief Financial Officer
CMO: Willie Cochran M.D., Jr, Chief of Staff
CIO: Karen Moore, Vice President Information Technology and Chief Information Officer
CHR: Norma Adams, Director Human Resources
Web address: www.southernregional.org
Control: Other not–for–profit (including NFP Corporation) **Service:** General medical and surgical

Staffed Beds: 331

ROME—Floyd County

⌧ **FLOYD MEDICAL CENTER (110054)**, 304 Turner McCall Boulevard, Zip 30165–5621, Mailing Address: P.O.Box 233, 30162–0233; tel. 706/509–5000 **A**1 2 3 5 10 13 19 **F**3 4 5 6 7 8 9 11 12 13 15 17 18 20 22 26 28 29 30 31 32 34 35 36 37 38 39 40 43 44 45 46 48 49 50 51 53 54 56 57 58 59 61 63 64 65 66 68 70 71 72 74 75 76 77 78 79 81 82 84 85 86 87 88 89 90 93 96 97 98 100 101 102 103 104 107 108 110 111 114 115 118 119 129 130 131 132 134 135 143 144 146 147 148 149
Primary Contact: Kurt Stuenkel, FACHE, President and Chief Executive Officer
COO: Warren Alston Rigas, Executive Vice President and Chief Operating Officer
CFO: Rick Sheerin, Vice President Fiscal Services
CMO: Joseph Biuso M.D., Vice President and Chief of Medical Affairs
CIO: Jeff Buda, Chief Information Officer
CHR: Beth Bradford, Director Human Resources
CNO: Sheila Bennett R.N., Vice President & Chief Nursing Officer
Web address: www.floyd.org
Control: Other not–for–profit (including NFP Corporation) **Service:** General medical and surgical

Staffed Beds: 327 **Admissions:** 14622 **Census:** 202 **Outpatient Visits:** 178026 **Births:** 2354 **Total Expense ($000):** 301939 **Payroll Expense ($000):** 123491 **Personnel:** 2486

⌧ **KINDRED HOSPITAL ROME (112010)**, 304 Turner McCall Boulevard, Zip 30165–5621; tel. 706/378–6800, (Nonreporting) **A**1 10 **S** Kindred Healthcare, Louisville, KY
Primary Contact: Al Diaz, M.D., Chief Executive Officer
CFO: Julia Smith, Chief Financial Officer
CMO: Brij Singh, Medical Staff Director
CHR: Holly Murdock, Human Resources Coordinator
CNO: Jennifer Johnstone, Chief Clinical Officer
Web address: www.kindredrome.com
Control: Corporation, Investor–owned (for–profit) **Service:** Acute long–term care hospital

Staffed Beds: 45

⌧ **REDMOND REGIONAL MEDICAL CENTER (110168)**, 501 Redmond Road, Zip 30165–1415, Mailing Address: P.O.Box 107001, 30164–7001; tel. 706/291–0291, (Nonreporting) **A**1 2 10 19 **S** HCA Healthcare, Nashville, TN
Primary Contact: John Quinlivan, Chief Executive Officer
COO: David Bradley Stockton, Chief Operating Officer
CFO: Kenneth Metteauer, Chief Financial Officer
CMO: Julie Coffman Barnes M.D., Chief Medical Officer
CIO: Brad Treglown, Director Information Systems
CHR: Patsy Adams, Vice President Human Resources
CNO: Stephanie Jones R.N., Chief Nursing Officer
Web address: www.redmondregional.com
Control: Corporation, Investor–owned (for–profit) **Service:** General medical and surgical

Staffed Beds: 230

SPECIALTY HOSPITAL See Kindred Hospital Rome

GA

Hospital, Medicare Provider Number, Address, Telephone, Approval, Facility, and Physician Codes, Health Care System

★ American Hospital Association (AHA) membership
□ The Joint Commission accreditation
○ Healthcare Facilities Accreditation Program
◇ DNV Healthcare Inc. accreditation
⇧ Center for Improvement in Healthcare Quality Accreditation
△ Commission on Accreditation of Rehabilitation Facilities (CARF) accreditation

© 2017 AHA Guide
Many Facility Codes have changed. Please refer to the AHA Guide Code Chart.
Hospitals **A163**

ROSWELL—Fulton County

✉ **WELLSTAR NORTH FULTON HOSPITAL (110198)**, 3000 Hospital Boulevard, Zip 30076–3899; tel. 770/751–2500 **A**1 2 3 10 13 **F**3 13 15 18 20 22 28 29 31 34 35 37 40 43 45 48 49 55 57 59 67 68 70 73 74 75 76 77 78 79 81 82 85 86 87 90 91 92 107 110 111 114 115 118 119 126 130 146 147 148 **S** WellStar Health System, Marietta, GA
Primary Contact: Jon–Paul Croom, President
COO: Lindsey Petrini, Chief Operating Officer
CFO: Felix Sotoizaguirre, Chief Financial Officer
CMO: Karim Godamunne M.D., Chief Medical Officer
CHR: Susan Brown, Chief Human Resources Officer
CNO: Nancy Melcher, Chief Nursing Officer
Web address: www.nfultonhospital.com
Control: Other not–for–profit (including NFP Corporation) **Service:** General medical and surgical

Staffed Beds: 173 **Admissions:** 6916 **Census:** 100 **Outpatient Visits:** 81777 **Births:** 953 **Personnel:** 741

SAINT MARYS—Camden County

✉ **SOUTHEAST GEORGIA HEALTH SYSTEM CAMDEN CAMPUS (110146)**, 2000 Dan Proctor Drive, Zip 31558–3810; tel. 912/576–6200 **A**1 10 20 **F**3 11 13 15 18 29 30 31 34 35 40 45 46 47 48 49 50 57 59 64 68 70 71 75 76 77 78 79 81 85 86 87 93 94 107 108 110 111 114 116 117 119 120 129 130 131 132 146 149 **P**5 **S** Southeast Georgia Health System, Brunswick, GA
Primary Contact: Howard W. Sepp Jr, Vice President and Administrator
CFO: Michael D Scherneck, President and Chief Executive Officer and Chief Financial Officer
CMO: Steve Nickisch, Chief of Staff
CIO: Charles Bumgardner, Director
CHR: Patrick D Ebri Ph.D., FACHE, Vice President Human Resources
Web address: www.sghs.org
Control: City–county, Government, Nonfederal **Service:** General medical and surgical

Staffed Beds: 40 **Admissions:** 1920 **Census:** 17 **Outpatient Visits:** 85757 **Births:** 728 **Total Expense ($000):** 41078 **Payroll Expense ($000):** 14587 **Personnel:** 248

SAINT SIMONS ISLAND—Glynn County

☐ **SAINT SIMONS BY–THE–SEA HOSPITAL (114016)**, 2927 Demere Road, Zip 31522–1620; tel. 912/638–1999, (Nonreporting) **A**1 10 **S** Universal Health Services, Inc., King of Prussia, PA
Primary Contact: Chuck Flavio, Chief Executive Officer
CMO: Kim Masters M.D., Medical Director
CIO: Chisty Mosely, Director Information Management
Web address: www.ssbythesea.com
Control: Corporation, Investor–owned (for–profit) **Service:** Psychiatric

Staffed Beds: 101

SANDERSVILLE—Washington County

☐ **WASHINGTON COUNTY REGIONAL MEDICAL CENTER (110086)**, 610 Sparta Road, Zip 31082–1860, Mailing Address: P.O.Box 636, 31082–0636; tel. 478/240–2000, (Nonreporting) **A**1 10 20
Primary Contact: Robert M. Trimm, Interim Chief Executive Officer
CFO: Cythia Parker, Fiscal Director
CMO: Robert Wright M.D., Chief of Staff
CHR: Gayle Prince, Director Human Resources
CNO: Pamela Stewart, Director of Nursing
Web address: www.wcrmc.com
Control: Hospital district or authority, Government, Nonfederal **Service:** General medical and surgical

Staffed Beds: 116

SAVANNAH—Chatham County

✉ △ **CANDLER HOSPITAL (110024)**, 5353 Reynolds Street, Zip 31405–6015; tel. 912/819–6000, (Total facility includes 11 beds in nursing home–type unit) **A**1 7 10 **F**2 3 11 13 15 18 20 29 30 31 32 34 35 36 38 39 40 44 45 46 47 48 49 50 54 57 58 59 60 61 64 65 68 70 71 73 74 75 76 77 78 80 81 82 84 85 86 87 89 90 91 93 94 96 107 108 110 111 115 117 118 119 120 121 123 124 126 128 129 130 131 132 135 146 147 148 149
Primary Contact: Paul P. Hinchey, President and Chief Executive Officer
CFO: Gregory J Schaack CPA, Vice President and Chief Financial Officer
CMO: James Scott M.D., Vice President Medical Affairs
CIO: George Evans, Vice President and Chief Information Officer
CHR: Don Stubbs, Vice President Human Resources
CNO: Sherry Danello MSN, R.N., Vice President and Chief Nursing Officer
Web address: www.sjchs.org
Control: Church operated, Nongovernment, not–for–profit **Service:** General medical and surgical

Staffed Beds: 285 **Admissions:** 11606 **Census:** 174 **Outpatient Visits:** 262677 **Births:** 2968 **Total Expense ($000):** 274172 **Payroll Expense ($000):** 99815 **Personnel:** 1704

☐ **COASTAL HARBOR TREATMENT CENTER (114008)**, 1150 Cornell Avenue, Zip 31406–2702; tel. 912/354–3911, (Nonreporting) **A**1 10 **S** Universal Health Services, Inc., King of Prussia, PA
Primary Contact: Sally Perry, Chief Executive Officer
COO: Ray Heckerman, Chief Executive Officer and Managing Director
CFO: Brad Lavoie, Chief Financial Officer
CMO: Reemon Bishara M.D., Medical Director
CHR: Kellie Carlson, Director Human Resources
CNO: Jillisa Thornton, Director of Nursing
Web address: www.coastalharbor.com
Control: Corporation, Investor–owned (for–profit) **Service:** Psychiatric

Staffed Beds: 193

GEORGE AND MARIE BACKUS CHILDREN'S HOSPITAL See Memorial Children's Hospital

☐ **GEORGIA REGIONAL HOSPITAL AT SAVANNAH (114028)**, 1915 Eisenhower Drive, Zip 31406–5098; tel. 912/356–2011, (Nonreporting) **A**1 10
Primary Contact: Andy Mannich, Regional Administrator
COO: Thomas F Kurtz Jr, Chief Operating Officer
CFO: Janet Edenfield, Director Financial Services
CMO: Donald Manning M.D., Clinical Director
CHR: Jamekia Powers, Assistant Director Human Resources
Web address: www.dbhdd.georgia.gov/georgia–regional–hospital–savannah
Control: State, Government, Nonfederal **Service:** Psychiatric

Staffed Beds: 105

LANDMARK HOSPITAL OF SAVANNAH (112018), 800 East 68th Street, Zip 31405–4710; tel. 912/298–1000 (Nonreporting) **A**22 **S** Landmark Hospitals, Cape Girardeau, MO
Primary Contact: John Salandi, Chief Executive Officer
Web address: www.landmarkhospitals.com/savannah
Control: Partnership, Investor–owned (for–profit) **Service:** Acute long–term care hospital

Staffed Beds: 50

✉ △ **MEMORIAL HEALTH (110036)**, 4700 Waters Avenue, Zip 31404–6283, Mailing Address: P.O.Box 23089, 31403–3089; tel. 912/350–8000, (Includes MEMORIAL CHILDREN'S HOSPITAL, 4700 Waters Avenue, Savannah, Georgia, Zip 31404–6220, PO Box 23089, 31403–3089, tel. 912/350–7337) **A**1 2 3 5 7 8 10 **F**3 8 11 12 13 14 15 17 18 19 20 22 24 26 28 29 30 31 32 34 35 36 37 39 40 41 43 44 45 46 49 50 53 54 55 56 57 59 60 61 64 65 66 68 70 71 72 73 74 75 76 77 78 79 80 81 82 83 84 85 86 87 88 89 92 93 96 97 98 100 101 102 103 104 107 110 111 115 117 118 119 120 121 122 123 124 126 129 130 131 132 135 143 144 146 147 148 149 **P**6
Primary Contact: Kerry Watson, Interim Chief Executive Officer
COO: Mary Chatman Ph.D., Senior Vice President, Chief Operating Officer and Chief Nursing Officer
CFO: Laura Dow, Chief Financial Officer
CMO: Ramon V Meguiar M.D., Chief Medical Officer
CIO: Kathryn McClellan, Chief Information Officer
CHR: Alisa R Griner, Director, Human Resources
CNO: Mary Chatman Ph.D., Senior Vice President, Chief Operating Officer and Chief Nursing Officer
Web address: www.memorialhealth.com
Control: Other not–for–profit (including NFP Corporation) **Service:** General medical and surgical

Staffed Beds: 508 **Admissions:** 27039 **Census:** 423 **Outpatient Visits:** 244317 **Births:** 2871 **Total Expense ($000):** 497795 **Payroll Expense ($000):** 176025 **Personnel:** 3396

★ **REHABILITATION HOSPITAL OF SAVANNAH**, 6510 Seawright DR, Zip 31406–2752; tel. 800/622–7269 **F**29 65 75 90 **S** HEALTHSOUTH Corporation, Birmingham, AL
Primary Contact: Kathy Kleinsteuber, Chief Executive Officer
Web address: www.rehabilitationhospitalsavannah.com
Control: Corporation, Investor–owned (for–profit) **Service:** Rehabilitation

Staffed Beds: 50 **Admissions:** 1031 **Census:** 35 **Outpatient Visits:** 0 **Births:** 0

✉ **SELECT SPECIALTY HOSPITAL–SAVANNAH (112011)**, 5353 Reynolds Street, 4 South, Zip 31405–6015; tel. 912/819–7972, (Nonreporting) **A**1 10 **S** Select Medical Corporation, Mechanicsburg, PA
Primary Contact: Greg Wuther, Chief Executive Officer
Web address: www.selectspecialtyhospitals.com/company/locations/savannah.aspx
Control: Corporation, Investor–owned (for–profit) **Service:** Acute long–term care hospital

Staffed Beds: 40

ST. JOSEPH'S CANDLER HOSPITAL See Candler Hospital

GA

☐ △ **ST. JOSEPH'S HOSPITAL (110043)**, 11705 Mercy Boulevard, Zip 31419–1791; tel. 912/819–4100, (Total facility includes 11 beds in nursing home–type unit) **A**1 2 7 10 **F**3 11 15 17 18 20 22 24 26 28 29 30 34 35 36 37 38 39 40 41 44 45 49 50 56 57 58 59 60 65 70 74 75 77 79 80 81 82 84 85 86 90 94 96 110 111 114 115 119 126 128 130 131 132 135 146 148 149 150
Primary Contact: Paul P. Hinchey, President and Chief Executive Officer
COO: Kyle McCann, Chief Operating Officer
CFO: Gregory J Schaack CPA, Vice President and Chief Financial Officer
CMO: James Scott M.D., Vice President Medical Affairs
CIO: Nolan Henessee, Vice President and Chief Information Officer
CHR: Steve Pound, Vice President Human Resources
CNO: Sherry Danello MSN, R.N., Vice President and Chief Nursing Officer
Web address: www.sjchs.org
Control: Church operated, Nongovernment, not–for–profit **Service**: General medical and surgical

Staffed Beds: 233 **Admissions**: 11252 **Census**: 169 **Outpatient Visits**: 88764 **Births**: 0 **Total Expense ($000)**: 215001 **Payroll Expense ($000)**: 75984 **Personnel**: 1265

SMYRNA—Cobb County

⊞ **RIDGEVIEW INSTITUTE (114012)**, 3995 South Cobb Drive SE, Zip 30080–6397; tel. 770/434–4567 **A**1 5 10 **F**4 5 29 35 38 75 87 98 99 100 101 103 104 105 130 132 147 **P**8
Primary Contact: Frank Sartor, President and Chief Executive Officer
CFO: Ruth Jenkins, Chief Financial Officer
CMO: Thomas Bradford Johns M.D., Medical Director
CIO: Lynn Leger, Director Information Systems
CHR: Betty Sonderman, Manager Human Resources
Web address: www.ridgeviewinstitute.com
Control: Other not–for–profit (including NFP Corporation) **Service**: Psychiatric

Staffed Beds: 110 **Admissions**: 5192 **Census**: 83 **Outpatient Visits**: 41092 **Births**: 0 **Total Expense ($000)**: 32447 **Payroll Expense ($000)**: 18471 **Personnel**: 344

SNELLVILLE—Gwinnett County

⊞ **EASTSIDE MEDICAL CENTER (110192)**, 1700 Medical Way, Zip 30078–2195; tel. 770/979–0200, (Nonreporting) **A**1 2 10 **S** HCA Healthcare, Nashville, TN
Primary Contact: Trent Lind, Chief Executive Officer
COO: Callie Andrews, Chief Operating Officer
CMO: Michael O'Neill M.D., Chief Medical Officer
CIO: Pattie Page, Director Marketing and Public Relations
Web address: www.eastsidemedical.com
Control: Corporation, Investor–owned (for–profit) **Service**: General medical and surgical

Staffed Beds: 294

SPRINGFIELD—Effingham County

⊞ **EFFINGHAM HOSPITAL (111306)**, 459 Highway 119 South, Zip 31329–3021, Mailing Address: P.O.Box 386, 31329–0386; tel. 912/754–6451, (Total facility includes 105 beds in nursing home–type unit) **A**1 10 18 **F**3 6 11 15 18 26 27 29 32 34 35 40 43 45 49 50 54 56 57 59 61 64 74 77 79 81 85 86 97 107 110 111 114 119 127 128 130 133 134 135 146 147 148 **P**6
Primary Contact: Francine Baker–Witt, R.N., Interim Chief Executive Officer
CFO: Matthew Moore, Director of Financial Reporting
CMO: Claude Sanks, Chief Medical Staff
CIO: Mary Pizzino, Chief Information Officer
CHR: Marie Murphy, Director Human Resources
CNO: Betsy Smith, Chief Nursing Officer
Web address: www.effinghamhospital.org
Control: Hospital district or authority, Government, Nonfederal **Service**: General medical and surgical

Staffed Beds: 130 **Admissions**: 898 **Census**: 106 **Outpatient Visits**: 44142 **Births**: 0 **Total Expense ($000)**: 42376 **Payroll Expense ($000)**: 18280 **Personnel**: 317

STATESBORO—Bulloch County

⊞ **EAST GEORGIA REGIONAL MEDICAL CENTER (110075)**, 1499 Fair Road, Zip 30458–1683, Mailing Address: P.O.Box 1048, 30459–1048; tel. 912/486–1000, (Nonreporting) **A**1 10 19 **S** Community Health Systems, Inc., Franklin, TN
Primary Contact: Paul Theriot, Chief Executive Officer
COO: Erin Smith, Chief Operating Officer
CFO: Christine Markowitz, Chief Financial Officer
CMO: Mark McCracken M.D., Chief of Staff
CIO: Brian Girardeau, Director Information System
CHR: Michael Black, Director Human Resources
CNO: Marie Burdette, Chief Nursing Officer
Web address: www.eastgeorgiaregional.com
Control: Corporation, Investor–owned (for–profit) **Service**: General medical and surgical

Staffed Beds: 149

WILLINGWAY HOSPITAL, 311 Jones Mill Road, Zip 30458–4765; tel. 912/764–6236, (Nonreporting) **A**3
Primary Contact: Cherie Tolley, Chief Executive Officer
CMO: Robert W Mooney M.D., Medical Director
Web address: www.willingway.com
Control: Corporation, Investor–owned (for–profit) **Service**: Alcoholism and other chemical dependency

Staffed Beds: 40

STOCKBRIDGE—Henry County

⇑ **PIEDMONT HENRY HOSPITAL (110191)**, 1133 Eagle's Landing Parkway, Zip 30281–5099; tel. 678/604–1000 **A**2 10 21 **F**3 8 11 13 15 18 20 22 26 29 30 31 34 35 37 40 45 49 54 57 59 61 64 70 72 73 74 75 76 77 78 79 81 82 84 85 86 87 93 100 107 108 110 111 114 115 118 119 120 121 124 130 132 135 144 146 147 148 **S** Piedmont Healthcare, Atlanta, GA
Primary Contact: Deborah Armstrong, Chief Executive Officer
COO: James Atkins PharmD, Chief Operating Officer
CFO: Wesley James, Chief Financial Officer
CMO: Lily Henson M.D., Chief Medical Officer
CHR: Jana Warren, Human Resources Business Partner
CNO: Paula Yvonne Butts, Chief Nursing Officer
Web address: www.piedmont.org
Control: Other not–for–profit (including NFP Corporation) **Service**: General medical and surgical

Staffed Beds: 214 **Admissions**: 13020 **Census**: 167 **Outpatient Visits**: 144196 **Births**: 2186 **Total Expense ($000)**: 186898 **Payroll Expense ($000)**: 75027 **Personnel**: 1235

SWAINSBORO—Emanuel County

⇑ **EMANUEL MEDICAL CENTER (110109)**, 117 Kite Road, Zip 30401–3231, Mailing Address: P.O.Box 879, 30401–0879; tel. 478/289–1100, (Nonreporting) **A**10 20 21
Primary Contact: Mel Pyne, Chief Executive Officer
CFO: Rhonda Durden, Chief Financial Officer
CMO: Cedric Porter M.D., President Medical Staff
CIO: Damien Scott, Chief Information Officer
CHR: Ellen Boyd, Director Human Resources
Web address: www.emanuelmedical.org
Control: Hospital district or authority, Government, Nonfederal **Service**: General medical and surgical

Staffed Beds: 91

SYLVANIA—Screven County

★ **OPTIM MEDICAL CENTER – SCREVEN (111312)**, 215 Mims Road, Zip 30467–2097; tel. 912/564–7426, (Nonreporting) **A**10 18 **S** National Surgical Healthcare, Chicago, IL
Primary Contact: Robert R. Sellers, Chief Executive Officer
CFO: Cindy Bierschenk, Director Financial Services
CIO: Christian Rekowski, Information Technology Director
CHR: Natalie Peterson, Human Resources Director
CNO: S Lagina Evans R.N., Assistant Chief Nursing Officer
Web address: www.optimhealth.com
Control: County, Government, Nonfederal **Service**: General medical and surgical

Staffed Beds: 25

SYLVESTER—Worth County

★ ⇑ **PHOEBE WORTH MEDICAL CENTER (111328)**, 807 South Isabella Street, Zip 31791–7554, Mailing Address: P.O.Box 545, 31791–0545; tel. 229/776–6961, (Nonreporting) **A**10 18 21 **S** Phoebe Putney Health System, Albany, GA
Primary Contact: Kim Gilman, Chief Executive Officer
CFO: Candace Guarnieri, Chief Financial Officer
CMO: Natu M Patel M.D., Chief of Staff
CHR: Mandy Gordon, Human Resource Coordinator
CNO: Kim Gilman, Chief Nursing Officer
Web address: www.phoebeputney.com
Control: Other not–for–profit (including NFP Corporation) **Service**: General medical and surgical

Staffed Beds: 16

GA

Hospital, Medicare Provider Number, Address, Telephone, Approval, Facility, and Physician Codes, Health Care System

★ American Hospital Association (AHA) membership
☐ The Joint Commission accreditation
○ Healthcare Facilities Accreditation Program
◇ DNV Healthcare Inc. accreditation
⇑ Center for Improvement in Healthcare Quality Accreditation
△ Commission on Accreditation of Rehabilitation Facilities (CARF) accreditation

THOMASTON—Upson County

★ ⇧ **UPSON REGIONAL MEDICAL CENTER (110002)**, 801 West Gordon Street, Zip 30286–3426, Mailing Address: P.O.Box 1059, 30286–0027; tel. 706/647–8111 **A**10 21 **F**3 11 13 15 28 29 30 31 34 35 36 40 45 46 49 50 57 59 61 64 70 76 78 79 80 81 82 85 86 87 89 107 108 111 114 115 118 119 124 130 131 132 135 148 **P**6 **S** HealthTech Management Services, Brentwood, TN
Primary Contact: Tripp Penn, Chief Executive Officer
CFO: John Williams, Chief Financial Officer
CIO: Douglas Thompson, Chief Information Officer
CHR: Rich Williams, Director Human Resources
CNO: Marilyn Ray MSN, Chief Nursing Officer
Web address: www.urmc.org
Control: Other not–for–profit (including NFP Corporation) **Service**: General medical and surgical

Staffed Beds: 77 **Admissions**: 2888 **Census**: 31 **Outpatient Visits**: 77287 **Births**: 365 **Total Expense ($000)**: 63756 **Payroll Expense ($000)**: 24223 **Personnel**: 592

THOMASVILLE—Thomas County

⊞ **JOHN D. ARCHBOLD MEMORIAL HOSPITAL (110038)**, 915 Gordon Avenue, Zip 31792–6614, Mailing Address: P.O.Box 1018, 31799–1018; tel. 229/228–2000, (Total facility includes 64 beds in nursing home–type unit) **A**1 2 10 19 **F**3 4 5 8 11 12 13 15 18 19 20 22 26 28 29 30 31 32 34 35 36 38 40 43 45 46 47 48 49 50 51 54 56 57 58 59 60 61 62 63 64 65 66 68 70 74 75 76 77 78 79 81 85 86 87 89 90 91 92 93 96 97 98 100 101 102 103 104 107 108 110 111 114 115 116 117 119 120 121 123 124 126 128 129 130 132 135 143 144 146 147 148 149 **P**6 **S** Archbold Medical Center, Thomasville, GA
Primary Contact: J Perry. Mustian, President and Chief Executive Officer
CFO: Skip Hightower, Senior Vice President and Chief Financial Officer
CIO: Tracy Gray, Senior Vice President Information Services
CHR: Zachariah P Wheeler, Senior Vice President Human Resources
CNO: Amy Griffin, Vice President Patient Care Services
Web address: www.archbold.org
Control: Other not–for–profit (including NFP Corporation) **Service**: General medical and surgical

Staffed Beds: 328 **Admissions**: 10226 **Census**: 220 **Outpatient Visits**: 311242 **Births**: 767 **Total Expense ($000)**: 239275 **Payroll Expense ($000)**: 76396 **Personnel**: 1484

THOMSON—McDuffie County

⊞ **UNIVERSITY HOSPITAL MCDUFFIE (110111)**, 2460 Washington Road, NE, Zip 30824; tel. 706/595–1411 **A**1 10 **F**3 11 15 29 30 40 45 50 59 64 68 79 81 85 87 107 110 114 119 129 130 132 133 146 148 149 **S** University Health Care System, Augusta, GA
Primary Contact: Bob Kepshire, R.N., MS, Administrator and Chief Nursing Officer
CFO: Dave Belkoski, Chief Financial Officer
CNO: Bob Kepshire R.N., MS, Administrator and Chief Nursing Officer
Web address: www.universityhealth.org/mcduffie
Control: Other not–for–profit (including NFP Corporation) **Service**: General medical and surgical

Staffed Beds: 25 **Admissions**: 581 **Census**: 9 **Outpatient Visits**: 32830 **Births**: 1 **Total Expense ($000)**: 18745 **Payroll Expense ($000)**: 7082 **Personnel**: 118

TIFTON—Tift County

⊞ **TIFT REGIONAL MEDICAL CENTER (110095)**, 901 East 18th Street, Zip 31794–3648, Mailing Address: Drawer 747, 31793–0747; tel. 229/382–7120 **A**1 2 10 19 **F**3 8 9 11 12 13 15 18 20 22 26 28 29 30 31 33 34 35 40 45 47 49 50 54 57 59 60 63 64 68 70 74 75 76 77 78 79 81 82 84 85 86 87 89 92 93 97 100 104 107 108 110 111 114 115 118 119 120 121 123 126 129 130 131 132 135 143 144 146 147 148 149 **P**6 **S** Tift Regional Health System, Tifton, GA
Primary Contact: William T. Richardson, President and Chief Executive Officer
COO: Christopher Dorman, Senior Vice President/Chief Operating Officer
CFO: Dennis L Crum, Senior Vice President and Chief Financial Officer
CMO: William Guest M.D., Senior Vice President and Chief Medical Officer
CIO: Guy McAllister, Vice President and Chief Information Officer
CHR: Lori S Folsom, Assistant Vice President Human Resources
CNO: Carol Smith, Vice President Patient Care and Chief Nursing Officer
Web address: www.tiftregional.com
Control: Hospital district or authority, Government, Nonfederal **Service**: General medical and surgical

Staffed Beds: 181 **Admissions**: 9225 **Census**: 106 **Outpatient Visits**: 191787 **Births**: 1211 **Total Expense ($000)**: 316468 **Payroll Expense ($000)**: 136281 **Personnel**: 1711

TOCCOA—Stephens County

⊞ **STEPHENS COUNTY HOSPITAL (110032)**, 163 Hospital Drive, Zip 30577–6820; tel. 706/282–4200, (Total facility includes 92 beds in nursing home–type unit) **A**1 10 **F**3 7 11 13 15 28 30 34 35 40 45 51 57 59 60 64 65 68 70 75 76 77 79 81 85 86 89 93 107 108 110 111 115 119 125 129 130 146 148 149
Primary Contact: Lynne Anderson, Chief Executive Officer
CFO: Jeff Laird, Controller
CHR: Diane Hardeman, Director Personnel
CNO: Faye M Taylor R.N., Director of Nursing
Web address: www.stephenscountyhospital.com
Control: Hospital district or authority, Government, Nonfederal **Service**: General medical and surgical

Staffed Beds: 188 **Admissions**: 1945 **Census**: 119 **Outpatient Visits**: 35027 **Births**: 288 **Total Expense ($000)**: 47694 **Payroll Expense ($000)**: 22064 **Personnel**: 479

VALDOSTA—Lowndes County

☐ **GREENLEAF CENTER (114036)**, 2209 Pineview Drive, Zip 31602–7316; tel. 229/247–4357 **A**1 10 **F**5 38 98 99 100 101 103 104 105 130 132 134 143 **P**5 6 **S** Acadia Healthcare Company, Inc., Franklin, TN
Primary Contact: Stephen Register, Chief Executive Officer
Web address: www.greenleafcounseling.net
Control: Corporation, Investor–owned (for–profit) **Service**: Psychiatric

Staffed Beds: 73 **Admissions**: 2753 **Census**: 66 **Outpatient Visits**: 8631 **Births**: 0 **Total Expense ($000)**: 13516 **Payroll Expense ($000)**: 6698 **Personnel**: 151

⊞ **SOUTH GEORGIA MEDICAL CENTER (110122)**, 2501 North Patterson Street, Zip 31602–1735, Mailing Address: P.O.Box 1727, 31603–1727; tel. 229/333–1000, (Nonreporting) (Includes SMITH NORTHVIEW HOSPITAL, 4280 North Valdosta Road, Valdosta, Georgia, Zip 31602, P O Box 10010, 31604, tel. 229/671–2000; Leonard Carter, Campus Administrator) **A**1 2 10 19
Primary Contact: C. Ross. Berry, Chief Executive Officer
COO: Andrew Flemer, Chief Operating Officer
CFO: Raymond A. Snead FACHE, Interim Chief Financial Officer
CMO: Kimberly Megow M.D., Chief Medical Officer
CIO: Bob Foster, Chief Information Officer
CHR: Johnny Percy Ball III, Assistant Administrator Human Resources
CNO: Denida A. Cox, Chief Nursing Officer
Web address: www.sgmc.org
Control: Other not–for–profit (including NFP Corporation) **Service**: General medical and surgical

Staffed Beds: 302

VIDALIA—Toombs County

⊞ **MEADOWS REGIONAL MEDICAL CENTER (110128)**, One Meadows Parkway, Zip 30474–8759, Mailing Address: P.O.Box 1048, 30475–1048; tel. 912/535–5555 **A**1 10 20 **F**11 13 15 18 20 22 29 30 31 34 35 37 40 43 45 46 47 50 51 53 54 57 59 60 64 68 70 74 75 76 77 78 79 81 85 86 87 93 97 107 108 110 111 115 118 119 120 121 123 124 127 129 130 131 132 146 147 148 **P**6
Primary Contact: Alan Kent, Chief Executive Officer
COO: Shirley Hoskins, Chief Operating Officer
CFO: John Cornell, Vice President Finance
CIO: Charles Bondurant, Chief Information Officer
Web address: www.meadowsregional.org
Control: Other not–for–profit (including NFP Corporation) **Service**: General medical and surgical

Staffed Beds: 57 **Admissions**: 4412 **Census**: 43 **Outpatient Visits**: 84915 **Births**: 873 **Total Expense ($000)**: 108488 **Payroll Expense ($000)**: 38821 **Personnel**: 585

VILLA RICA—Carroll County

⊞ **TANNER MEDICAL CENTER–VILLA RICA (110015)**, 601 Dallas Highway, Zip 30180–1202; tel. 770/456–3000 **A**1 10 **F**3 5 11 13 15 18 20 22 29 30 31 34 38 40 49 50 59 64 68 70 74 76 78 79 81 85 91 98 99 100 101 102 103 104 105 107 108 110 111 115 118 119 129 135 147 149 **P**1 6 **S** Tanner Health System, Carrollton, GA
Primary Contact: Bonnie Boles, M.D., Administrator
COO: Jerry Morris, Chief Operating Officer
CFO: Carol Crews, Senior Vice President and Chief Financial Officer
CMO: William Waters M.D., IV, Executive Vice President
CIO: Terri Lee
CHR: Shari W Gainey, Chief Human Resource Officer
CNO: Deborah Matthews, Senior Vice President
Web address: www.tanner.org
Control: Other not–for–profit (including NFP Corporation) **Service**: General medical and surgical

Staffed Beds: 118 **Admissions**: 6125 **Census**: 88 **Outpatient Visits**: 121758 **Births**: 495 **Total Expense ($000)**: 74922 **Payroll Expense ($000)**: 34333 **Personnel**: 578

GA

WARM SPRINGS—Meriwether County

☐ **ROOSEVELT WARM SPRINGS REHABILITATION AND SPECIALTY HOSPITALS – LTAC (112000)**, 6135 Roosevelt Highway, Zip 31830–2757, Mailing Address: P.O.Box 280, 31830–2757; tel. 706/655–5291 **A**1 10 **F**1 29 30 34 35 57 60 74 75 77 84 86 87 90 91 100 101 119 148 **P**4
Primary Contact: David L. Mork Jr, Chief Executive Officer
CFO: Susan Wilder, Director Financial Services
CMO: Carlos Parrado M.D., Sr., Chief Medical Officer
CHR: Laura Stokes, Director Human Resources
CNO: Cathy Harbin, Chief Nursing Officer
Web address: www.augustahealth.org/roosevelt–warm–springs/rwsh
Control: Other not–for–profit (including NFP Corporation) **Service:** Acute long–term care hospital

Staffed Beds: 20 **Admissions:** 170 **Census:** 12 **Outpatient Visits:** 0 **Births:** 0 **Total Expense ($000):** 6459 **Payroll Expense ($000):** 3714

☒ **ROOSEVELT WARM SPRINGS REHABILITATION HOSPITAL – REHAB (113028)**, 6135 Roosevelt Highway, Zip 31830–2757, Mailing Address: P.O.Box 280, 31830–0280; tel. 706/655–5515 **A**1 10 **F**29 30 60 74 77 82 85 87 90 119 148
Primary Contact: David L. Mork Jr, Chief Executive Officer
CFO: Susan Wilder, Director Financial Services
CMO: Ara Chitchyan M.D., Medical Director
CIO: Christen Carter, Director Public Relations
CHR: Laura Stokes, Director Human Resources
CNO: Cathy Harbin, Chief Nursing Officer
Web address: www.augustahealth.org/roosevelt–warm–springs/rwsh
Control: Other not–for–profit (including NFP Corporation) **Service:** Rehabilitation

Staffed Beds: 22 **Admissions:** 376 **Census:** 16 **Outpatient Visits:** 0 **Births:** 0 **Total Expense ($000):** 10352 **Payroll Expense ($000):** 4326

☒ **WARM SPRINGS MEDICAL CENTER (111316)**, 5995 Spring Street, Zip 31830–2149, Mailing Address: P.O.Box 8, 31830–0008; tel. 706/655–3331, (Total facility includes 79 beds in nursing home–type unit) **A**1 10 18 **F**3 15 29 30 34 35 40 41 45 46 47 48 57 59 60 64 65 68 75 81 93 107 110 114 119 128 130 133 135 143 146 148 149
Primary Contact: Karen Daniel, Chief Executive Officer
CFO: Patrick Flynn, Chief Financial Officer
CMO: Alan Thompson M.D., President Medical Staff
CIO: Milo Varnadoe, Director Information Systems
CHR: Theresa Passarelli, Human Resources Generalist
CNO: Lynda Ligon, Chief Nursing Officer
Web address: www.warmspringsmc.org
Control: Partnership, Investor–owned (for–profit) **Service:** General medical and surgical

Staffed Beds: 104 **Admissions:** 381 **Census:** 75 **Outpatient Visits:** 9424 **Births:** 1 **Total Expense ($000):** 13570 **Payroll Expense ($000):** 6132 **Personnel:** 141

WARNER ROBINS—Houston County

☒ **HOUSTON MEDICAL CENTER (110069)**, 1601 Watson Boulevard, Zip 31093–3431, Mailing Address: P.O.Box 2886, 31099–2886; tel. 478/922–4281 **A**1 10 13 **F**3 11 13 15 18 20 22 26 28 29 30 31 34 35 38 39 40 45 46 48 49 50 51 54 57 59 60 61 64 68 70 73 74 75 76 78 79 81 82 85 86 87 89 91 92 93 98 100 102 103 107 108 110 111 114 115 117 118 119 129 130 131 132 134 135 144 146 147 148 149 150 **P**6 **S** Houston Healthcare System, Warner Robins, GA
Primary Contact: Cary Martin, Chief Executive Officer
COO: Charles G Briscoe FACHE, Chief Operating Officer
CFO: Sean Whilden, Chief Financial Officer
CIO: George Curtis, Chief Information Officer
CHR: Michael O'Hara, Senior Executive Director Human Resources
Web address: www.hhc.org
Control: Other not–for–profit (including NFP Corporation) **Service:** General medical and surgical

Staffed Beds: 237 **Admissions:** 13681 **Census:** 168 **Outpatient Visits:** 233557 **Births:** 1922 **Total Expense ($000):** 209887 **Payroll Expense ($000):** 87476 **Personnel:** 1994

WASHINGTON—Wilkes County

☐ **WILLS MEMORIAL HOSPITAL (111325)**, 120 Gordon Street, Zip 30673–1602, Mailing Address: P.O.Box 370, 30673–0370; tel. 706/678–2151, (Nonreporting) **A**1 10 18
Primary Contact: Tracie Haughey, Chief Executive Officer and Chief Financial Officer
CFO: Tracie Haughey, Chief Executive Officer and Chief Financial Officer
CMO: Robert J. Williams M.D., Chief Medical Staff
CIO: David Harper, Chief Information Officer
CHR: Tom Urban, Director Human Resources
CNO: Angie Vickery, Director of Nursing
Web address: www.willsmemorialhospital.com
Control: Hospital district or authority, Government, Nonfederal **Service:** General medical and surgical

Staffed Beds: 25

WAYCROSS—Ware County

☒ **MEMORIAL SATILLA HEALTH (110003)**, 1900 Tebeau Street, Zip 31501–6357, Mailing Address: P.O.Box 139, 31502–0139; tel. 912/283–3030, (Nonreporting) **A**1 2 3 5 10 **S** HCA Healthcare, Nashville, TN
Primary Contact: Bobby McCullough, Interim Chief Executive Officer
COO: Mark Roberts, Chief Operating Officer
CFO: Patrick Sloan, Chief Financial Officer
CIO: Barry Rudd, Chief Information Officer
CHR: Brigitte Churchill, Director of Human Resources
CNO: Holli Sweat, Associate Administrator and Chief Nursing Officer
Web address: www.memorialsatillahealth.com/
Control: Other not–for–profit (including NFP Corporation) **Service:** General medical and surgical

Staffed Beds: 199

WAYNESBORO—Burke County

☐ **BURKE MEDICAL CENTER (110113)**, 351 Liberty Street, Zip 30830–9686; tel. 706/554–4435, (Nonreporting) **A**1 10
Primary Contact: Thomas K. Steiner, Interim Chief Executive Officer
CFO: Karen ONeal, Chief Financial Officer
CHR: Kim Anthony, Director Human Resources
CNO: Debra Burch, Chief Nursing Officer
Web address: www.burkemedical.net
Control: Hospital district or authority, Government, Nonfederal **Service:** General medical and surgical

Staffed Beds: 40

WINDER—Barrow County

☒ **NORTHEAST GEORGIA MEDICAL CENTER BARROW (110045)**, 316 North Broad Street, Zip 30680–2150, Mailing Address: P.O.Box 688, 30680–0688; tel. 770/867–3400 **A**1 10 **F**3 11 15 29 34 35 40 45 50 51 57 59 60 68 70 74 75 77 79 81 82 85 93 97 107 108 110 111 114 118 119 124 130 131 132 135 143 146 147 148 **P**6 **S** Northeast Georgia Health System, Gainesville, GA
Primary Contact: Chad Hatfield, Chief Executive Officer
CMO: Jon Horn M.D., Chief of Staff
CIO: Cory Crayton, Director Information Systems
CHR: Carlotta Newman, Director Human Resources
CNO: Gene Street, Chief Nursing Officer
Web address: www.barrowregional.com
Control: Corporation, Investor–owned (for–profit) **Service:** General medical and surgical

Staffed Beds: 56 **Admissions:** 1387 **Census:** 12 **Outpatient Visits:** 29538 **Births:** 0 **Personnel:** 206

GA

HAWAII

AIEA—Honolulu County

⊞ **PALI MOMI MEDICAL CENTER (120026)**, 98–1079 Moanalua Road, Zip 96701–4713; tel. 808/486–6000 **A**1 2 5 10 **F**3 12 15 18 20 22 26 29 31 32 34 35 40 43 44 45 46 49 50 54 57 59 63 64 65 70 74 75 77 78 79 80 81 84 85 86 87 92 107 108 110 111 114 115 118 119 126 130 132 135 146 147 148 149 **P8 S** Hawaii Pacific Health, Honolulu, HI
Primary Contact: Art Gladstone, R.N., Chief Executive Officer
CFO: David Okabe, Executive Vice President, Chief Financial Officer and Treasurer
CMO: James Kakuda M.D., Chief of Staff
CIO: Steve Robertson, Senior Vice President
CHR: Gail Lerch R.N., Vice President Human Resources
CNO: Brigitte McKale MSN, FACHE, Vice President and Chief Nurse Executive
Web address: www.palimomi.org
Control: Other not–for–profit (including NFP Corporation) **Service**: General medical and surgical

Staffed Beds: 118 **Admissions:** 5893 **Census:** 88 **Outpatient Visits:** 205993 **Births:** 0 **Total Expense ($000):** 203937 **Payroll Expense ($000):** 74782 **Personnel:** 956

EWA BEACH—Honolulu County

⊞ **KAHI MOHALA BEHAVIORAL HEALTH (124001)**, 91–2301 Old Fort Weaver Road, Zip 96706–3602; tel. 808/671–8511 **A**1 3 10 **F**29 30 35 44 68 98 99 100 101 103 104 105 106 127 130 132 133 143 **S** Sutter Health, Sacramento, CA
Primary Contact: Leonard Licina, Chief Executive Officer
CFO: Quin Ogawa, Chief Financial Officer
CMO: Steven Chaplin M.D., Medical Director
CHR: Christina Enoka, Director Human Resources and Risk Management
CNO: Charles St. Louis, Director of Patient Care Services
Web address: www.kahimohala.org
Control: Other not–for–profit (including NFP Corporation) **Service**: Psychiatric

Staffed Beds: 76 **Admissions:** 428 **Census:** 72 **Outpatient Visits:** 2732 **Births:** 0 **Total Expense ($000):** 23100 **Payroll Expense ($000):** 10053 **Personnel:** 167

HILO—Hawaii County

⊞ **HILO MEDICAL CENTER (120005)**, 1190 Waianuenue Avenue, Zip 96720–2089; tel. 808/932–3000, (Nonreporting) **A**1 3 5 10 20 **S** Hawaii Health Systems Corporation, Honolulu, HI
Primary Contact: Dan Brinkman, R.N., Chief Executive Officer
COO: Dan Brinkman R.N., Chief Operating Officer
CFO: Janiece McNichols, Regional Chief Financial Officer
CMO: Ted Peskin M.D., Acute Care Medical Director
CIO: Money Atwal, Chief Information Officer
CHR: Holly Ka'akimaka, Director Human Resources
CNO: Arthur Sampaga, Assistant Director Nursing
Web address: www.hilomedicalcenter.org/
Control: State, Government, Nonfederal **Service**: General medical and surgical

Staffed Beds: 276

HONOKAA—Hawaii County

★ **HALE HO'OLA HAMAKUA (121307)**, 45–547 Plumeria Street, Zip 96727–6902; tel. 808/932–4100, (Total facility includes 66 beds in nursing home–type unit) **A**5 10 18 **F**3 40 41 42 56 67 68 77 80 91 93 103 128 130 143 146 148 **S** Hawaii Health Systems Corporation, Honolulu, HI
Primary Contact: Kerry Pitcher, Administrator
CFO: Janiece McNichols, Regional Chief Financial Officer
CMO: Bruce Graves M.D., Chief of Staff
CNO: Gayle Green, Director of Nursing
Web address: www.halehoolahamakua.org
Control: State, Government, Nonfederal **Service**: General medical and surgical

Staffed Beds: 77 **Admissions:** 211 **Census:** 63 **Outpatient Visits:** 3689 **Births:** 0

HONOLULU—Honolulu County

⊞ **KAISER PERMANENTE MEDICAL CENTER (120011)**, 3288 Moanalua Road, Zip 96819–1469; tel. 808/432–0000, (Total facility includes 28 beds in nursing home–type unit) **A**1 2 3 5 10 **F**3 12 13 15 17 18 19 20 21 22 24 26 29 30 31 32 34 35 36 38 40 41 45 46 47 48 49 50 51 54 55 56 57 58 59 60 61 62 64 65 68 70 72 74 75 76 77 78 79 80 81 82 83 84 85 86 87 88 89 92 93 94 97 99 100 101 104 107 108 110 111 115 119 128 129 130 131 134 135 146 148 **P1 S** Kaiser Foundation Hospitals, Oakland, CA
Primary Contact: Ray Hahn, Hospital Administrator
CFO: Thomas Risse, Chief Financial Officer and Vice President Business Services
CMO: Keith Ogasawara M.D., Associate Medical Director and Professional Chief of Staff
CIO: Donna Scannell, Vice President Information Technology
CHR: Jean Melnikoff, Vice President Human Resources
CNO: Kecia Kelly R.N., Chief Nurse Executive
Web address: www.kaiserpermanente.org
Control: Other not–for–profit (including NFP Corporation) **Service**: General medical and surgical

Staffed Beds: 212 **Admissions:** 11393 **Census:** 177 **Outpatient Visits:** 66022 **Births:** 1559 **Personnel:** 1570

☐ **KAPIOLANI MEDICAL CENTER FOR WOMEN & CHILDREN (123300)** (Women & Children), 1319 Punahou Street, Zip 96826–1001; tel. 808/983–6000 **A**1 2 3 5 10 **F**3 13 15 19 25 29 31 32 34 35 36 38 40 41 43 44 45 50 52 53 54 55 57 58 59 64 65 68 70 72 73 74 75 76 77 78 79 81 84 85 86 87 88 89 91 92 93 94 99 100 102 107 108 110 111 114 115 119 126 130 131 132 134 135 136 146 147 148 149 **S** Hawaii Pacific Health, Honolulu, HI
Primary Contact: Martha Smith, Chief Executive Officer
CFO: David Okabe, Senior Vice President, Chief Financial Officer and Treasurer
CIO: Steve Robertson, Vice President
CHR: Gail Lerch R.N., Vice President
Web address: www.kapiolani.org
Control: Other not–for–profit (including NFP Corporation) **Service**: Other specialty treatment

Staffed Beds: 180 **Admissions:** 11130 **Census:** 178 **Outpatient Visits:** 197124 **Births:** 6359 **Total Expense ($000):** 306522 **Payroll Expense ($000):** 123997 **Personnel:** 1417

⊞ **KUAKINI MEDICAL CENTER (120007)**, 347 North Kuakini Street, Zip 96817–2381; tel. 808/536–2236 **A**1 2 3 5 10 **F**3 15 17 18 20 22 24 26 28 29 31 34 35 40 45 46 49 57 58 59 60 68 70 74 75 77 78 79 80 81 82 85 86 87 107 108 110 111 114 115 117 118 119 121 129 130 131 132 135 145 146 147 148 149 **P1**
Primary Contact: Gary K. Kajiwara, President and Chief Executive Officer
CFO: Quin Ogawa, Vice President Finance and Chief Financial Officer
CMO: Nobuyuki Miki M.D., Vice President Medical Services and Chief Medical Officer
CIO: Gary K Kajiwara, President and Chief Executive Officer
CHR: Ann N. Choy, Manager Human Resources and Payroll
CNO: Virginia Walker, Vice President Nursing Services and Chief Nursing Officer
Web address: www.kuakini.org
Control: Other not–for–profit (including NFP Corporation) **Service**: General medical and surgical

Staffed Beds: 84 **Admissions:** 4291 **Census:** 74 **Outpatient Visits:** 55181 **Births:** 0 **Total Expense ($000):** 139293 **Payroll Expense ($000):** 60128 **Personnel:** 805

★ **LEAHI HOSPITAL (122001)** (TB and LTC), 3675 Kilauea Avenue, Zip 96816–2398; tel. 808/733–8000, (Total facility includes 117 beds in nursing home–type unit) **A**10 **F**2 3 77 128 130 146 148 149 **S** Hawaii Health Systems Corporation, Honolulu, HI
Primary Contact: Reid Kondo, Interim Administrator
CFO: Edward Chu, Chief Financial Officer
CMO: Albert Yazawa M.D., Regional Medical Director
CHR: Russel Higa JD, Regional Director Human Resources
CNO: Amy Vasunaga, Chief Nurse Executive
Web address: www.hhsc.org
Control: State, Government, Nonfederal **Service**: Other specialty treatment

Staffed Beds: 126 **Admissions:** 108 **Census:** 117 **Outpatient Visits:** 6767 **Births:** 0 **Total Expense ($000):** 20938 **Payroll Expense ($000):** 11603 **Personnel:** 213

HI

Many Facility Codes have changed. Please refer to the AHA Guide Code Chart. © 2017 AHA Guide

☒ **REHABILITATION HOSPITAL OF THE PACIFIC (123025)**, 226 North Kuakini Street, Zip 96817–2488; tel. 808/531–3511 **A**1 10 **F**3 11 28 29 34 36 44 54 58 64 68 74 75 77 79 90 91 93 94 95 96 130 131 132 135 143 146 147 148
Primary Contact: Timothy J. Roe, M.D., President and Chief Executive Officer
CFO: Wendy Manuel, Vice President and Chief Financial Officer
CMO: Jason Chang M.D., Chief Medical Director
CIO: Scott Morimoto, Director Clinical Informatics
CHR: Faye Miyamoto, Assistant Vice President Human Resources
CNO: Brenda Hiromoto, Director of Nursing
Web address: www.rehabhospital.org
Control: Other not–for–profit (including NFP Corporation) **Service**: Rehabilitation

Staffed Beds: 68 **Admissions**: 1855 **Census**: 62 **Outpatient Visits**: 53115 **Births**: 0 **Total Expense ($000)**: 45947 **Payroll Expense ($000)**: 23592 **Personnel**: 341

☐ **SHRINERS HOSPITALS FOR CHILDREN–HONOLULU (123301)**, 1310 Punahou Street, Zip 96826–1099; tel. 808/941–4466, (Nonreporting) **A**1 3 5 10 **S** Shriners Hospitals for Children, Tampa, FL
Primary Contact: John R. White, Administrator
CFO: Patricia Miyasawa CPA, Director Fiscal Service
CMO: Craig Ono M.D., Chief of Staff
CIO: Gregory A Wolf, Director Information Systems
CHR: Derek Ito, Director Human Resources
CNO: Andrea Kubota R.N., MSN, Director Patient Care Services and Nurse Executive
Web address: www.shrinershospitalsforchildren.org/Hospitals/Locations/Honolulu. aspx
Control: Other not–for–profit (including NFP Corporation) **Service**: Children's orthopedic

Staffed Beds: 16

☐ **STRAUB MEDICAL CENTER (120022)**, 888 South King Street, Zip 96813–3097; tel. 808/522–4000 **A**1 2 3 5 10 **F**3 9 15 16 18 20 21 22 23 24 26 27 28 29 31 34 35 40 44 45 47 48 49 50 54 56 57 59 63 64 65 68 70 71 74 75 77 78 79 80 81 84 85 86 87 92 93 97 100 104 107 108 110 111 115 119 129 130 131 132 135 144 145 146 147 148 149 **P**6 8 **S** Hawaii Pacific Health, Honolulu, HI
Primary Contact: Art Gladstone, R.N., Chief Executive Officer
COO: Maureen Flannery, Vice President Clinic Operations
CFO: David Okabe, Executive Vice President, Chief Financial Officer and Treasurer
CMO: Randy Yates M.D., Chief Medical Officer
CIO: Steve Robertson, Executive Vice President and Chief Information Officer
CHR: Gail Lerch R.N., Executive Vice President Human Resources
CNO: Patricia Boeckmann R.N., Chief Operating Officer and Chief Nursing Officer
Web address: www.straubhealth.org
Control: Other not–for–profit (including NFP Corporation) **Service**: General medical and surgical

Staffed Beds: 120 **Admissions**: 6982 **Census**: 113 **Outpatient Visits**: 886307 **Births**: 0 **Total Expense ($000)**: 439531 **Payroll Expense ($000)**: 197770 **Personnel**: 1834

☒ **THE QUEEN'S MEDICAL CENTER (120001)**, 1301 Punchbowl Street, Zip 96813–2499; tel. 808/691–5100, (Includes QUEEN'S MEDICAL CENTER – WEST OAHU, 91–2141 Fort Weaver Road, Ewa Beach, Hawaii, Zip 96706–1993, tel. 808/691–3000; Susan Murray, FACHE, Chief Operating Officer) (Total facility includes 28 beds in nursing home–type unit) **A**1 2 3 5 10 **F**3 5 11 12 13 15 17 18 20 22 24 28 29 31 34 35 37 38 39 40 43 44 45 46 47 48 49 50 51 55 56 57 58 59 60 61 62 63 64 66 68 70 74 75 76 77 78 79 81 82 84 85 86 87 93 96 97 98 99 100 101 102 103 104 105 107 108 110 111 115 117 118 119 120 121 124 126 128 129 130 131 132 135 138 139 143 146 147 148 **S** Queen's Health Systems, Honolulu, HI
Primary Contact: Arthur A. Ushijima, FACHE, President
COO: Jason Chang, Executive Vice President and Chief Operating Officer
CFO: Michel Riccioni, Chief Financial Officer
CMO: Whitney Limm M.D., Executive Vice President and Chief Physician Executive
CIO: Brian Yoshii, Vice President Information Technology and Chief Information Officer
CHR: Nona Tamanaha, Vice President Human Resources
CNO: Madeline Harris R.N., Vice President and Chief Nursing Officer
Web address: www.queensmedicalcenter.org
Control: Other not–for–profit (including NFP Corporation) **Service**: General medical and surgical

Staffed Beds: 527 **Admissions**: 29657 **Census**: 515 **Outpatient Visits**: 477073 **Births**: 1917 **Total Expense ($000)**: 1034709 **Payroll Expense ($000)**: 400108 **Personnel**: 4484

☒ **TRIPLER ARMY MEDICAL CENTER**, 1 Jarret White Road, Zip 96859–5001; tel. 808/433–6661 **A**1 2 3 5 **F**3 7 8 12 13 14 15 18 19 20 21 22 23 24 25 26 27 29 30 31 32 33 34 39 40 41 43 44 45 46 47 48 50 51 52 53 54 55 56 57 58 59 60 64 65 67 68 70 72 74 75 76 77 78 79 81 82 85 86 87 88 89 91 92 93 94 96 97 98 99 100 101 102 103 104 105 106 107 108 110 111 115 116 117 118 119 120 121 123 124 126 127 129 130 131 132 133 134 135 143 144 145 146 147 148 149 **S** Department of the Army, Office of the Surgeon General, Falls Church, VA
Primary Contact: Colonel Andrew M. Barr, Commanding Officer
COO: MajorElias B. Lozano, Executive Officer
CFO: Lieutenant ColonelChristopher A. Wodarz, Chief, Resource Management Division
CMO: CaptainAndrew L. Findlay, Deputy Commander Clinical Services
CIO: Lieutenant ColonelDonna E Beed, Chief Information Management Division
CHR: ColonelJames N. Davidson, Troop Commander
CNO: ColonelJennifer L. Bedick, Deputy Commander Nursing
Web address: www.tamc.amedd.army.mil
Control: Army, Government, federal **Service**: General medical and surgical

Staffed Beds: 194 **Admissions**: 12609 **Census**: 120 **Outpatient Visits**: 1119369 **Births**: 2458 **Total Expense ($000)**: 698226 **Payroll Expense ($000)**: 367771

★ **VETERANS AFFAIRS PACIFIC ISLANDS HEALTH CARE SYSTEM**, 459 Patterson Road, Zip 96819–1522; tel. 808/433–0600 (Nonreporting) **S** Department of Veterans Affairs, Washington, DC
Primary Contact: Jennifer S. Gutowski, FACHE, Director
Web address: www.hawaii.va.gov/
Control: Veterans Affairs, Government, federal **Service**: General medical and surgical

Staffed Beds: 80

KAHUKU—Honolulu County

★ **KAHUKU MEDICAL CENTER (121304)**, 56–117 Pualalea Street, Zip 96731–2052; tel. 808/293–9221, (Total facility includes 6 beds in nursing home–type unit) **A**10 18 **F**3 29 34 35 40 41 59 64 69 75 82 86 87 91 97 107 108 114 119 128 130 133 135 146 148 149 **P**6
Primary Contact: Stephany Nihipali. Vaioleti, President and Chief Executive Officer
CFO: Francis Daquioag, Controller
CMO: P Douglas Nielson M.D., Chief of Staff
Web address: www.kahuku.hhsc.org/
Control: Other not–for–profit (including NFP Corporation) **Service**: General medical and surgical

Staffed Beds: 21 **Admissions**: 172 **Census**: 17 **Outpatient Visits**: 11657 **Births**: 0 **Total Expense ($000)**: 14800 **Payroll Expense ($000)**: 5971 **Personnel**: 158

KAILUA—Honolulu County

☒ **CASTLE MEDICAL CENTER (120006)**, 640 Ulukahiki Street, Zip 96734–4454; tel. 808/263–5500 **A**1 3 10 **F**3 8 12 13 15 18 20 22 24 26 29 30 31 32 34 35 37 40 45 46 49 50 51 54 56 57 59 64 68 69 70 74 75 76 78 79 81 84 85 86 91 92 93 97 98 102 107 108 110 111 114 119 120 126 127 130 135 146 147 149 **P**6 8 **S** Adventist Health, Roseville, CA
Primary Contact: Kathryn A. Raethel, R.N., M.P.H., President and Chief Executive Officer
COO: Travis Clegg, Vice President, Operations
CFO: Jeff Nye, Chief Financial Officer
CMO: Alan Cheung M.D., Vice President Medical Affairs
CHR: Todd Reese, Director Human Resources
CNO: Laura R. Westphal, Vice President Patient Care Services
Web address: www.castlemed.org
Control: Church operated, Nongovernment, not–for–profit **Service**: General medical and surgical

Staffed Beds: 160 **Admissions**: 7276 **Census**: 88 **Outpatient Visits**: 113470 **Births**: 1108 **Total Expense ($000)**: 153982 **Payroll Expense ($000)**: 59930 **Personnel**: 833

KAMUELA—Hawaii County

☒ **NORTH HAWAII COMMUNITY HOSPITAL (120028)**, 67–1125 Mamalahoa Highway, Zip 96743–8496; tel. 808/885–4444 **A**1 10 20 **F**3 8 13 15 18 26 29 30 31 34 35 36 40 41 43 45 46 49 50 53 54 57 59 62 64 68 70 75 76 77 78 79 81 85 86 93 97 107 108 110 111 115 119 130 131 146 147 148 **P**6 **S** Queen's Health Systems, Honolulu, HI
Primary Contact: Cynthia Kamikawa, R.N., MSN, President
CFO: Michel Riccioni, Chief Financial Officer
CMO: Gary Goldberg M.D., Chief Medical Officer
CHR: Nona Tamanaha, Vice President, Human Resources
CNO: Miquel Noelani Simms R.N., Chief Nursing Officer
Web address: www.nhch.com
Control: Other not–for–profit (including NFP Corporation) **Service**: General medical and surgical

Staffed Beds: 35 **Admissions**: 1707 **Census**: 15 **Outpatient Visits**: 36465 **Births**: 478 **Total Expense ($000)**: 67825 **Payroll Expense ($000)**: 26452 **Personnel**: 414

HI

Hospital, Medicare Provider Number, Address, Telephone, Approval, Facility, and Physician Codes, Health Care System

★ American Hospital Association (AHA) membership
☐ The Joint Commission accreditation
○ Healthcare Facilities Accreditation Program
◇ DNV Healthcare Inc. accreditation
⇑ Center for Improvement in Healthcare Quality Accreditation
△ Commission on Accreditation of Rehabilitation Facilities (CARF) accreditation

KANEOHE—Honolulu County

☐ **HAWAII STATE HOSPITAL**, 45–710 Keaahala Road, Zip 96744–3597; tel. 808/247–2191, (Nonreporting) **A**1 3 5
Primary Contact: William J. May, Administrator
COO: Anthony Fraiola, Associate Administrator Administrative and Support Services
CFO: Stephen Teeter, Business Manager
CMO: James Westphal M.D., AMHD Medical Director
CIO: John Jansen, Management Information Specialist
CHR: Karen Hara, Personnel Management Specialist
CNO: Lani Tsuneishi, Nursing Services Manager
Web address: www.hawaii.gov/health/
Control: State, Government, Nonfederal **Service**: Psychiatric

Staffed Beds: 178

KAPAA—Kauai County

★ **SAMUEL MAHELONA MEMORIAL HOSPITAL (121306)**, 4800 Kawaihau Road, Zip 96746–1971; tel. 808/822–4961, (Nonreporting) **A**10 18 **S** Hawaii Health Systems Corporation, Honolulu, HI
Primary Contact: Peter Klune, Chief Executive Officer
CFO: Michael Perel, Regional Chief Financial Officer
CMO: Gerald Tomory M.D., Regional Medical Director
CIO: Sandra McMaster, Regional Chief Information Officer
CHR: Lani Aranio, Regional Director Human Resources
Web address: www.smmh.hhsc.org
Control: State, Government, Nonfederal **Service**: General medical and surgical

Staffed Beds: 80

KAUNAKAKAI—Maui County

✠ **MOLOKAI GENERAL HOSPITAL (121303)**, 280 Home Olu Place, Zip 96748–0408, Mailing Address: P.O.Box 408, 96748–0408; tel. 808/553–5331 **A**1 10 18 **F**3 15 29 34 35 40 41 44 50 57 59 63 64 65 66 68 69 75 76 77 78 82 84 87 93 97 107 110 115 119 127 130 132 133 134 135 147 148 149 **P**6 **S** Queen's Health Systems, Honolulu, HI
Primary Contact: Janice Kalanihuia, President
CFO: Zessica L Apiki, Accountant
CMO: William Thomas M.D., Jr, Medical Director Clinical and Internal Affairs
CIO: Sampson Wescoatt, Manager Information Technology
CHR: Alicia Teves, Coordinator Human Resources
Web address: www.queens.org
Control: Other not–for–profit (including NFP Corporation) **Service**: General medical and surgical

Staffed Beds: 15 **Admissions**: 122 **Census**: 2 **Outpatient Visits**: 36708
Births: 24 **Personnel**: 69

KEALAKEKUA—Hawaii County

✠ **KONA COMMUNITY HOSPITAL (120019)**, 79–1019 Haukapila Street, Zip 96750–7920; tel. 808/322–9311 **A**1 10 20 **F**3 8 11 12 13 29 30 31 34 35 40 43 44 47 50 68 70 77 78 79 81 84 98 107 108 109 111 115 119 120 121 123 130 132 **S** Hawaii Health Systems Corporation, Honolulu, HI
Primary Contact: Jay E. Kreuzer, FACHE, Chief Executive Officer
CFO: Dean Herzog, Chief Financial Officer
CMO: Richard McDowell M.D., Medical Director
CHR: Kathryn Salomon, Director Human Resources
CNO: Patricia Kalua, Chief Nurse Executive
Web address: www.kch.hhsc.org
Control: State, Government, Nonfederal **Service**: General medical and surgical

Staffed Beds: 94 **Admissions**: 3532 **Census**: 46 **Outpatient Visits**: 50066
Births: 560 **Total Expense ($000)**: 84355 **Payroll Expense ($000)**: 30852
Personnel: 392

KOHALA—Hawaii County

★ **KOHALA HOSPITAL (121302)**, 54–383 Hospital Road, Zip 96755, Mailing Address: P.O.Box 10, Kapaau, 96755–0010; tel. 808/889–6211, (Nonreporting) **A**10 18 **S** Hawaii Health Systems Corporation, Honolulu, HI
Primary Contact: Eugene Amar Jr, Administrator
CMO: Silvia Sonnenschein M.D., Chief of Staff
Web address: www.koh.hhsc.org
Control: State, Government, Nonfederal **Service**: General medical and surgical

Staffed Beds: 28

KULA—Maui County

★ **KULA HOSPITAL (121308)**, 100 Keokea Place, Zip 96790–7450; tel. 808/878–1221, (Nonreporting) **A**10 18 **S** Kaiser Foundation Hospitals, Oakland, CA
Primary Contact: Paul Harper–O'Connor, Interim Regional Administrator
CFO: Nerissa Garrity, Chief Financial Officer
CMO: Nicole Apoliona M.D., Medical Director
Web address: www.mauihealthsystem.org/kula–hospital/
Control: Other not–for–profit (including NFP Corporation) **Service**: General medical and surgical

Staffed Beds: 6

LANAI CITY—Maui County

★ **LANAI COMMUNITY HOSPITAL (121305)**, 628 Seventh Street, Zip 96763–0650, Mailing Address: P.O.Box 630650, 96763–0650; tel. 808/565–8450, (Nonreporting) **A**10 18 **S** Kaiser Foundation Hospitals, Oakland, CA
Primary Contact: Paul Harper–O'Connor, Interim Administrator
Web address: www.mauihealthsystem.org/lanai–hospital/
Control: Other not–for–profit (including NFP Corporation) **Service**: General medical and surgical

Staffed Beds: 24

LIHUE—Kauai County

☐ **WILCOX MEDICAL CENTER (120014)**, 3–3420 Kuhio Highway, Zip 96766–1099; tel. 808/245–1100 **A**1 2 10 20 **F**3 13 15 18 28 29 31 32 34 35 37 39 40 41 43 44 45 49 50 55 57 59 63 64 65 70 74 75 76 77 78 79 81 82 84 85 86 87 89 93 107 108 110 111 114 115 119 130 132 133 135 146 147 148 149 **P**8 **S** Hawaii Pacific Health, Honolulu, HI
Primary Contact: Jen Chahanovich, President and Chief Executive Officer
CFO: David Okabe, Executive Vice President, Chief Financial Officer and Treasurer
CMO: Craig Netzer M.D., President Medical Staff
CIO: Steve Robertson, Executive Vice President Revenue Cycle Management and Chief Information Officer
CNO: Mary Ann England, Chief Nurse Executive
Web address: www.wilcoxhealth.org
Control: Other not–for–profit (including NFP Corporation) **Service**: General medical and surgical

Staffed Beds: 65 **Admissions**: 3734 **Census**: 43 **Outpatient Visits**: 95296
Births: 541 **Total Expense ($000)**: 106839 **Payroll Expense ($000)**: 35703
Personnel: 457

PAHALA—Hawaii County

★ **KAU HOSPITAL (121301)**, 1 Kamani Street, Zip 96777, Mailing Address: P.O.Box 40, 96777–0040; tel. 808/932–4200, (Nonreporting) **A**10 18 **S** Hawaii Health Systems Corporation, Honolulu, HI
Primary Contact: Merilyn Harris, Administrator
CFO: Janiece McNichols, Regional Chief Financial Officer
CMO: Clifford Field M.D., Medical Director
Web address: www.hhsc.org
Control: State, Government, Nonfederal **Service**: General medical and surgical

Staffed Beds: 21

WAHIAWA—Honolulu County

✠ **WAHIAWA GENERAL HOSPITAL (120004)**, 128 Lehua Street, Zip 96786–2036; tel. 808/621–8411, (Nonreporting) **A**1 3 5 10
Primary Contact: Brian Cunningham, Chief Executive Officer
CMO: Manuel Abundo M.D., Chief of Staff
CIO: Jason Fujinaka, Manager Information System
CHR: Liflor Barrera, Manager Human Resources
CNO: Tammy Kohrer, Director of Nursing–Acute
Web address: www.wahiawageneral.org
Control: Other not–for–profit (including NFP Corporation) **Service**: General medical and surgical

Staffed Beds: 160

WAILUKU—Maui County

✠ **MAUI MEMORIAL MEDICAL CENTER (120002)**, 221 Mahalani Street, Zip 96793–2581; tel. 808/244–9056, (Nonreporting) **A**1 10 20 **S** Kaiser Foundation Hospitals, Oakland, CA
Primary Contact: Michael Rembis M.D., Chief Executive Officer
CIO: Dana Mendoza, Chief Information Officer
Web address: www.mauihealthsystem.org/maui–memorial/
Control: Other not–for–profit (including NFP Corporation) **Service**: General medical and surgical

Staffed Beds: 213

WAIMEA—Kauai County

✠ **KAUAI VETERANS MEMORIAL HOSPITAL (121300)**, 4643 Waimea Canyon Road, Zip 96796, Mailing Address: P.O.Box 337, 96796–0337; tel. 808/338–9431, (Nonreporting) **A**1 10 18 **S** Hawaii Health Systems Corporation, Honolulu, HI
Primary Contact: Peter Klune, Chief Executive Officer
CFO: Michael Perel, Regional Chief Financial Officer
CMO: Gerald Tomory M.D., Regional Medical Director
CIO: Sandra McMaster, Regional Chief Information Officer
CHR: Solette Perry, Regional Director Human Resources
Web address: www.kvmh.hhsc.org
Control: State, Government, Nonfederal **Service**: General medical and surgical

Staffed Beds: 45

HI

Many Facility Codes have changed. Please refer to the AHA Guide Code Chart. © 2017 AHA Guide

IDAHO

AMERICAN FALLS—Power County

★ **POWER COUNTY HOSPITAL DISTRICT (131304)**, 510 Roosevelt Street, Zip 83211–1362, Mailing Address: P.O.Box 420, 83211–0420; tel. 208/226–3200, (Nonreporting) **A**10 18
Primary Contact: Dallas Clinger, Administrator
COO: Rock Roy, Professional Services Director
CFO: Jeremy Claunch, Chief Financial Officer
CMO: Spencer Garrett Seibold M.D., Chief of Medical Staff
CIO: Mindy Earl, Health Information Manager
CHR: Kendra Sweat, Director Human Resources
CNO: June Mortenson R.N., Director of Nursing
Web address: www.pchd.net
Control: Hospital district or authority, Government, Nonfederal **Service**: General medical and surgical

Staffed Beds: 10

ARCO—Butte County

LOST RIVERS MEDICAL CENTER (131324), 551 Highland Drive, Zip 83213–9771, Mailing Address: P.O.Box 145, 83213–0145; tel. 208/527–8206, (Nonreporting) **A**10 18
Primary Contact: Brad Huerta, Chief Executive Officer and Administrator
CFO: Jon Smith, Chief Financial Officer
CMO: Jeffrey Haskell M.D., Chief Medical Staff
CHR: Tina Akins, Director Human Resources
CNO: Geri Cammack R.N., Director of Nursing
Web address: www.lostriversmedical.com
Control: Hospital district or authority, Government, Nonfederal **Service**: General medical and surgical

Staffed Beds: 43

BLACKFOOT—Bingham County

⊞ **BINGHAM MEMORIAL HOSPITAL (131325)**, 98 Poplar Street, Zip 83221–1799; tel. 208/785–4100, (Total facility includes 60 beds in nursing–type unit) **A**1 5 10 18 **F**3 12 13 15 18 20 22 26 29 34 35 36 37 40 44 45 46 47 50 51 52 55 56 57 58 59 64 66 68 70 76 77 79 81 82 85 86 87 92 93 97 107 108 109 110 111 115 119 127 128 129 130 131 132 133 134 135 144 146 147 148 **P**6
Primary Contact: D. Jeffery. Daniels, Chief Executive Officer
COO: Jake Erickson, Chief Operating Officer
CFO: John Fullmer, Chief Financial Officer
CIO: Robert Weis, Director Information Systems
CHR: Tara Preston, Director Human Resources
CNO: Carolyn Hansen, Chief Nursing Officer
Web address: www.binghammemorial.org
Control: Other not–for–profit (including NFP Corporation) **Service**: General medical and surgical

Staffed Beds: 85 Admissions: 2056 Census: 58 Outpatient Visits: 158075 Births: 322 Total Expense ($000): 101812 Payroll Expense ($000): 43024 Personnel: 634

MOUNTAIN RIVER BIRTHING AND SURGERY CENTER (130067), 350 North Meridian Street, Zip 83221–1625; tel. 208/782–0300 **A**10 **F**8 68 79 81 87
Primary Contact: D. Jeffery. Daniels, Chief Executive Officer
COO: Dan Cochran, Chief Operating Officer
CIO: Robert Weis, Director Information Technology
CHR: Tara Preston, Director Human Resources
CNO: Nathan Buck R.N., Nursing Manager
Web address: www.binghmemorial.org
Control: Partnership, Investor–owned (for–profit) **Service**: Surgical

Staffed Beds: 8 Admissions: 61 Census: 1 Outpatient Visits: 6874 Births: 0 Total Expense ($000): 4562 Payroll Expense ($000): 734

□ **STATE HOSPITAL SOUTH (134010)**, 700 East Alice Street, Zip 83221–4925, Mailing Address: P.O.Box 400, 83221–0400; tel. 208/785–1200, (Nonreporting) **A**1 10
Primary Contact: James Price, Hospital Administrator
COO: Greg Horton, Director Support Services
CFO: Angela Loosli, Assistant Administrator, Operations
CMO: Kelly Palmer D.O., Medical Director
CIO: Julie Sutton, Director Performance Improvement
CHR: Sheryl Donnelly, Human Resources Specialist
CNO: Randy Walker, Director Nursing Services
Web address: www.healthandwelfare.idaho.gov
Control: State, Government, Nonfederal **Service**: Psychiatric

Staffed Beds: 77

BOISE—Ada County

BOISE BEHAVIORAL HEALTH HOSPITAL See Safe Haven Hospital Of Treasure Valley

⊞ **BOISE VETERANS AFFAIRS MEDICAL CENTER**, 500 West Fort Street, Zip 83702–4598; tel. 208/422–1000, (Total facility includes 28 beds in nursing home–type unit) **A**1 3 5 **F**1 2 3 4 5 8 9 10 12 29 30 31 34 35 38 39 40 43 45 46 47 50 53 54 56 57 58 59 60 61 62 63 64 65 66 67 68 70 71 74 75 77 78 79 81 82 83 84 85 86 87 90 91 92 93 94 96 97 98 100 101 102 103 104 105 106 107 108 111 112 119 120 121 122 123 124 127 128 129 130 132 133 135 143 144 145 146 147 148 149 150 **S** Department of Veterans Affairs, Washington, DC
Primary Contact: David P. Wood, FACHE, Director
CFO: Ron Blanton, Chief Fiscal Services
CMO: Paul Lambert M.D., Chief of Staff
CHR: Randy Turner, Chief Human Resource Management Services
Web address: www.boise.va.gov/
Control: Veterans Affairs, Government, federal **Service**: General medical and surgical

Staffed Beds: 100 Admissions: 2928 Census: 66 Outpatient Visits: 370154 Births: 0 Total Expense ($000): 241025 Payroll Expense ($000): 142000 Personnel: 1226

IDAHO ELKS REHABILITATION HOSPITAL See St. Luke's Rehabilitation Hospital

□ **INTERMOUNTAIN HOSPITAL (134002)**, 303 North Allumbaugh Street, Zip 83704–9208; tel. 208/377–8400, (Nonreporting) **A**1 10 **S** Universal Health Services, Inc., King of Prussia, PA
Primary Contact: Jeffrey F. Morrell, Chief Executive Officer
CFO: JeDonne Hines, Chief Financial Officer
CMO: Charles Novak M.D., Chief Medical Officer
CHR: Nancy Nelson, Director Human Resources
CNO: Jennifer Beaulieu, Director of Nursing
Web address: www.intermountainhospital.com
Control: Corporation, Investor–owned (for–profit) **Service**: Psychiatric

Staffed Beds: 140

SAFE HAVEN HOSPITAL OF TREASURE VALLEY (134009), 8050 Northview Street, Zip 83704–7126; tel. 208/327–0504 (Nonreporting) **A**10 **S** Safe Haven Health Care, Pocatello, ID
Primary Contact: Scott Proctor, Chief Executive Officer
CMO: David Kent M.D., Chief Medical Officer
CIO: Debra Alexander, Chief Information Officer
CHR: Kathy Cady, Coordinator Human Resources, Accounts Payable and Payroll
Web address: www.boisepsychhospital.com
Control: Corporation, Investor–owned (for–profit) **Service**: Psychiatric

Staffed Beds: 22

ID

✠ △ **SAINT ALPHONSUS REGIONAL MEDICAL CENTER (130007)**, 1055 N Curtis Rd, Zip 83706–1309, Mailing Address: 1055 North Curtis Road, 83706–1309; tel. 208/367-2121 **A**1 2 3 5 7 10 **F**3 5 7 8 9 11 12 13 14 15 17 18 20 22 24 26 28 29 30 31 32 33 34 35 36 37 38 39 40 42 43 44 45 48 49 50 52 53 54 55 56 57 58 59 61 64 65 68 70 71 72 74 75 76 77 78 79 81 82 83 84 85 86 87 89 90 91 93 94 96 97 98 99 100 101 102 104 107 108 109 110 111 114 115 116 117 118 119 120 121 123 124 126 127 128 129 130 131 132 135 144 146 147 148 149 **P**6 8 **S** Trinity Health, Livonia, MI
Primary Contact: Odette Bolano, R.N., President
CFO: Kenneth Fry, Chief Financial Officer
CMO: Steve Brown M.D., Chief Quality Officer
CIO: Dwight Pond, TIS Boise
CHR: Teresa Sargent, Vice President Human Resources
CNO: Sherry Parks R.N., MS, Chief Nursing Officer
Web address: www.saintalphonsus.org
Control: Church operated, Nongovernment, not–for–profit **Service**: General medical and surgical

Staffed Beds: 399 Admissions: 17356 Census: 238 Outpatient Visits: 1060964 Births: 1434 Total Expense ($000): 581003 Payroll Expense ($000): 237017 Personnel: 3609

✠ **SOUTHWEST IDAHO ADVANCED CARE HOSPITAL (132003)**, 6651 West Franklin Road, Zip 83709–0914; tel. 208/685-2400 **A**1 10 **F**1 3 75 91 96 119 148 **S** Ernest Health, Inc., Albuquerque, NM
Primary Contact: David Tupper, Chief Executive Officer
COO: Bridgette Hunter, Chief Operating Officer
CFO: Connie Johnson, Chief Financial Officer
Web address: www.siach.ernesthealth.com/
Control: Corporation, Investor–owned (for–profit) **Service**: Acute long–term care hospital

Staffed Beds: 22 Admissions: 344 Census: 24 Total Expense ($000): 13252

✠ **ST. LUKE'S REGIONAL MEDICAL CENTER (130006)**, 190 East Bannock Street, Zip 83712–6241; tel. 208/381-2222, (Includes ST. LUKE'S CHILDREN'S HOSPITAL, 190 East Bannock Street, Boise, Idaho, Zip 83712–6241, tel. 208/381-2222; ST. LUKE'S MERIDIAN MEDICAL CENTER, 520 South Eagle Road, Meridian, Idaho, Zip 83642, 520 S Eagle RD, 83642–6351, tel. 208/706-5000) **A**1 2 3 10 **F**7 8 11 12 13 15 17 18 19 20 21 22 23 24 25 26 27 28 29 30 31 32 34 35 36 37 40 41 42 46 47 48 49 53 54 56 57 58 59 60 61 62 63 64 68 69 70 71 72 74 75 76 77 78 79 81 82 84 86 87 88 89 90 93 107 108 110 111 114 115 116 117 118 119 120 121 124 126 127 129 130 131 132 134 135 136 144 146 147 **P**6 8 **S** St. Luke's Health System, Boise, ID
Primary Contact: David M. McFadyen, Administrator
CFO: Jeff Taylor, Vice President Finance
CMO: Jim Souza, Chief Medical Officer
CIO: Marc Chasin M.D., Chief Information Officer
CHR: Phillip Johnson, Vice President, Chief Human Resources Officer
CNO: Cynthia Gearhard, Chief Nursing Officer
Web address: www.stlukesonline.org/boise
Control: Other not–for–profit (including NFP Corporation) **Service**: General medical and surgical

Staffed Beds: 604 Admissions: 31014 Census: 358 Outpatient Visits: 1566133 Births: 5550 Total Expense ($000): 1433753 Payroll Expense ($000): 688953 Personnel: 9624

★ △ **ST. LUKE'S REHABILITATION HOSPITAL (133025)**, 600 North Robbins Road, Zip 83702–4565, Mailing Address: P.O.Box 1100, 83701–1100; tel. 208/489-4444, (Nonreporting) **A**5 7 10 **S** St. Luke's Health System, Boise, ID
Primary Contact: Nolan Hoffer, Senior Director
COO: Melissa Honsinger, Chief Operating Officer
CFO: Doug Lewis, Chief Financial Officer
CMO: Lee Kornfield M.D., Medical Director
CIO: Scott Pyrah, Director Information Systems
CHR: Jim Atkins, Director Employee Services
Web address: www.idahoelksrehab.org
Control: Other not–for–profit (including NFP Corporation) **Service**: Rehabilitation

Staffed Beds: 31

☐ **TREASURE VALLEY HOSPITAL (130063)**, 8800 West Emerald Street, Zip 83704–8205; tel. 208/373-5000, (Nonreporting) **A**1 3 10
Primary Contact: Nick Genna, Administrator
CMO: Jeffrey Hessing M.D., Medical Director
CHR: Kathleen Phelps, Director Human Resources
Web address: www.treasurevalleyhospital.com
Control: Corporation, Investor–owned (for–profit) **Service**: General medical and surgical

Staffed Beds: 9

VETERANS AFFAIRS MEDICAL CENTER See Boise Veterans Affairs Medical Center

ID

★ ⇧ **BOUNDARY COMMUNITY HOSPITAL (131301)**, 6640 Kaniksu Street, Zip 83805–7532; tel. 208/267-3141, (Total facility includes 28 beds in nursing home–type unit) **A**10 18 21 **F**3 11 15 28 29 34 35 40 41 50 57 59 64 75 77 79 81 85 90 93 97 107 110 111 115 119 127 128 130 132 133 143 149
Primary Contact: Craig A. Johnson, Chief Executive Officer
CFO: Holly McDonald, Controller
CMO: Chuck Newhouse M.D., Chief of Staff
CHR: Ann Coughlin, Director Human Resources
CNO: Tari Yourzek, Chief Nursing Officer
Web address: www.boundarycommunityhospital.org
Control: County, Government, Nonfederal **Service**: General medical and surgical

Staffed Beds: 48 Admissions: 132 Census: 28 Outpatient Visits: 22337 Births: 0 Total Expense ($000): 13254 Payroll Expense ($000): 7557 Personnel: 170

✠ **CASSIA REGIONAL MEDICAL CENTER (131326)**, 1501 Hiland Avenue, Zip 83318–2688; tel. 208/678-4444 **A**1 10 18 **F**3 7 8 11 13 15 18 28 29 30 31 34 35 38 40 41 50 57 59 64 68 70 74 75 76 77 78 79 81 82 85 86 93 97 107 108 110 111 114 119 129 130 131 132 146 147 148 149 **P**6 **S** Intermountain Healthcare, Inc., Salt Lake City, UT
Primary Contact: Ben Smalley, Administrator
CFO: Mark Christensen, Director, Finance
CMO: Bernard Boehmer M.D., Medical Director
CIO: Carie Call, Computer Support
CHR: Keri Perrigot, Manager Human Resources
CNO: Michele Pond–Bell R.N., Nurse Administrator
Web address: www.cassiaregional.org
Control: Other not–for–profit (including NFP Corporation) **Service**: General medical and surgical

Staffed Beds: 25 Admissions: 1479 Census: 10 Outpatient Visits: 108711 Births: 588 Total Expense ($000): 50247 Payroll Expense ($000): 20188 Personnel: 335

✠ **WEST VALLEY MEDICAL CENTER (130014)**, 1717 Arlington, Zip 83605–4802; tel. 208/459-4641 **A**1 3 5 10 **F**3 8 11 12 13 15 18 20 26 28 29 30 34 35 40 41 44 45 50 51 57 59 60 64 68 69 70 75 76 77 79 81 82 85 87 89 91 92 93 98 100 101 102 103 105 107 108 110 111 114 115 127 129 130 131 132 135 146 147 148 **S** HCA Healthcare, Nashville, TN
Primary Contact: Elizabeth Hunsicker, Chief Executive Officer
COO: Jennifer Opsut, Interim Chief Operating Officer
CFO: Kate Fowler, Chief Financial Officer
CMO: Richard Augustus M.D., Chief Medical Officer
CIO: Jason Martinez, Director Information Technology
CHR: Senta Cornelius, Director Human Resources
CNO: Edith E Irving R.N., MS, FACHE, Chief Nursing Officer
Web address: www.westvalleymedctr.com
Control: Corporation, Investor–owned (for–profit) **Service**: General medical and surgical

Staffed Beds: 86 Admissions: 4611 Census: 47

CASCADE MEDICAL CENTER (131308), 402 Lake Cascade Pkwy, Zip 83611–7702, Mailing Address: P.O.Box 1330, 83611–1330; tel. 208/382-4242, (Nonreporting) **A**10 18
Primary Contact: Charles Johnston, Chief Executive Officer
CFO: Penny Lancaster, Controller
CMO: Mikael Bedell M.D., Medical Director
CNO: Teri Coombs R.N., Director Nursing Services
Web address: www.cascademedicalcenter.net
Control: Hospital district or authority, Government, Nonfederal **Service**: General medical and surgical

Staffed Beds: 8

Many Facility Codes have changed. Please refer to the AHA Guide Code Chart. © 2017 AHA Guide

COEUR D'ALENE—Kootenai County

★ ⇑ **KOOTENAI HEALTH (130049)**, 2003 Kootenai Health Way, Zip 83814–2677; tel. 208/625–4000, (Includes KOOTENAI BEHAVIORAL HEALTH, 2301 North Ironwood Place, Coeur D'Alene, Idaho, Zip 83814–2650, tel. 208/625–4800) **A**2 3 5 10 19 21 **F**2 3 4 5 9 11 15 18 20 22 24 26 28 29 30 31 32 34 35 37 40 41 43 44 45 46 47 48 49 50 51 53 54 56 57 58 59 60 63 64 65 68 70 71 72 74 75 76 78 79 81 82 83 84 85 86 87 89 91 93 95 96 97 98 99 100 101 102 103 104 107 108 110 111 114 115 116 117 119 121 124 126 127 129 130 131 132 135 143 145 146 148 149 **P**6
Primary Contact: Jon Ness, Chief Executive Officer
COO: Jeremy Evans, Vice President Operations
CFO: Kimberly Webb, Chief Financial Officer
CMO: Walter Fairfax M.D., Chief Medical Officer
CHR: Daniel Klocko, Vice President Human Resources
CNO: Joan M. Simon R.N., FACHE, Chief Nursing Officer
Web address: www.kh.org
Control: Hospital district or authority, Government, Nonfederal **Service:** General medical and surgical

Staffed Beds: 292 **Admissions:** 13722 **Census:** 182 **Outpatient Visits:** 309319 **Births:** 1704 **Total Expense ($000):** 447146 **Payroll Expense ($000):** 205398 **Personnel:** 2576

COTTONWOOD—Idaho County

★ **ST. MARY'S HOSPITAL (131321)**, 701 Lewiston Street, Zip 83522–9750, Mailing Address: P.O.Box 137, 83522–0137; tel. 208/962–3251, (Nonreporting) **A**5 10 18 **S** Essentia Health, Duluth, MN
Primary Contact: Lenne Bonner, President
CFO: Jyl Ruland, Chief Financial Officer
CHR: Debbie Schumacher, Chief Human Resource Officer
Web address: www.smh–cvhc.org/getpage.php?name=index
Control: Other not–for–profit (including NFP Corporation) **Service:** General medical and surgical

Staffed Beds: 28

DRIGGS—Teton County

★ **TETON VALLEY HEALTH CARE (131313)**, 120 East Howard Street, Zip 83422–5112; tel. 208/354–2383 **A**10 18 **F**7 15 30 31 34 40 41 45 57 59 64 65 68 74 79 81 82 85 87 89 90 93 97 107 110 111 114 119 127 128 131 133 135 146 148
Primary Contact: Keith Gnagey, Chief Executive Officer
CFO: Wesley D White, Chief Financial Officer
CMO: Nathan Levanger M.D., Chief of Staff
CHR: Dory Harris, Director Human Resource
CNO: Angela Booker, Director of Nursing Services
Web address: www.tvhcare.org
Control: Other not–for–profit (including NFP Corporation) **Service:** General medical and surgical

Staffed Beds: 13 **Admissions:** 148 **Census:** 2 **Births:** 1 **Total Expense ($000):** 16119 **Personnel:** 101

EMMETT—Gem County

⇑ **VALOR HEALTH (131318)**, 1202 East Locust Street, Zip 83617–2715; tel. 208/365–3561 **A**10 18 21 **F**11 13 29 31 34 35 40 45 48 50 57 59 75 76 78 81 83 85 89 97 107 111 115 119 127 129 133 135 144 146 148
Primary Contact: Brad Turpen, FACHE, Interim Chief Executive Officer
CHR: Susan Vahlberg, Director Employee and Community Relations
Web address: www.wkmh.org
Control: County, Government, Nonfederal **Service:** General medical and surgical

Staffed Beds: 12 **Admissions:** 218 **Census:** 2 **Births:** 64 **Total Expense ($000):** 17752

GOODING—Gooding County

★ **NORTH CANYON MEDICAL CENTER (131302)**, 267 North Canyon Drive, Zip 83330–5500; tel. 208/934–4433 **A**10 18 **F**3 5 11 15 29 33 34 35 40 41 44 45 47 49 50 53 56 57 59 63 64 68 71 75 81 84 87 90 93 97 107 110 111 114 119 127 130 131 133 135 143 148 **S** St. Luke's Health System, Boise, ID
Primary Contact: Tim Powers, Chief Executive Officer
COO: J'Dee Adams, Chief Operating Officer
CFO: Sara DeMoe, Chief Financial Officer
CMO: Jennifer Olsen M.D., Chief of Staff
CIO: Margie McLeod, Director Information Technology
CHR: Sara Otto, Chief Compliance Officer
CNO: Lisa Mangum, Chief Nursing Officer
Web address: www.ncm–c.org
Control: Hospital district or authority, Government, Nonfederal **Service:** General medical and surgical

Staffed Beds: 18 **Admissions:** 522 **Census:** 6 **Outpatient Visits:** 28542 **Births:** 0 **Total Expense ($000):** 23565 **Payroll Expense ($000):** 8617 **Personnel:** 175

GRANGEVILLE—Idaho County

★ **SYRINGA HOSPITAL AND CLINICS (131315)**, 607 West Main Street, Zip 83530–1396; tel. 208/983–1700 **A**10 18 **F**7 13 29 30 50 59 76 81 89 93 107 119 127 130 133
Primary Contact: Betty A. Watson, Interim Chief Executive Officer
CFO: Betty A Watson, Chief Financial Officer
CMO: Daniel Griffis M.D., Chief Medical Officer
CIO: Darla Whitley, Manager Health Information Technology
CHR: Katy Eimers, Human Resources Officer
CNO: Cindy Daly R.N., Director of Nursing
Web address: www.syringahospital.org
Control: Hospital district or authority, Government, Nonfederal **Service:** General medical and surgical

Staffed Beds: 14 **Admissions:** 489 **Census:** 5 **Outpatient Visits:** 16520 **Births:** 39 **Total Expense ($000):** 14449 **Payroll Expense ($000):** 7549 **Personnel:** 130

IDAHO FALLS—Bonneville County

⊞ **EASTERN IDAHO REGIONAL MEDICAL CENTER (130018)**, 3100 Channing Way, Zip 83404–7533, Mailing Address: P.O.Box 2077, 83403–2077; tel. 208/529–6111, (Nonreporting) **A**1 10 19 **S** HCA Healthcare, Nashville, TN
Primary Contact: Douglas Crabtree, Chief Executive Officer
COO: Sandee Moore, Chief Operating Officer
CFO: Judd Taylor, Chief Financial Officer
CMO: R. Lee Biggs M.D., Chief Medical Officer
CHR: Wendy Andersen, Director Human Resources
CNO: Ann Marie Kjosa R.N., MSN, Chief Nursing Officer
Web address: www.eirmc.com
Control: Corporation, Investor–owned (for–profit) **Service:** General medical and surgical

Staffed Beds: 293

MOUNTAIN VIEW HOSPITAL (130065), 2325 Coronado Street, Zip 83404–7407; tel. 208/557–2700 (Nonreporting) **A**5 10
Primary Contact: James Adamson, Chief Executive Officer
COO: Peter Fabrick, Vice President Clinical Operations
CHR: Eilene Horne, Manager Human Resources
Web address: www.mountainviewhospital.org
Control: Corporation, Investor–owned (for–profit) **Service:** General medical and surgical

Staffed Beds: 22

JEROME—Jerome County

★ **ST. LUKE'S JEROME (131310)**, 709 North Lincoln Street, Zip 83338–1851, Mailing Address: 709 North Lincoln Avenue, 83338–1851; tel. 208/814–9500 **A**3 10 18 **F**7 13 15 29 30 32 34 39 40 56 57 59 64 65 68 76 77 79 81 86 87 97 107 111 119 127 133 146 147 **P**6 **S** St. Luke's Health System, Boise, ID
Primary Contact: Curtis Maier, Administrator
CMO: Elizabeth Sugden M.D., Chief Medical Officer
CHR: Mark Stevens, Director Human Resources
CNO: Jill Howell, Chief Nursing Officer
Web address: www.stlukesonline.org/jerome/
Control: Other not–for–profit (including NFP Corporation) **Service:** General medical and surgical

Staffed Beds: 25 **Admissions:** 460 **Census:** 7 **Outpatient Visits:** 41249 **Births:** 186 **Total Expense ($000):** 18045 **Payroll Expense ($000):** 10599 **Personnel:** 175

KELLOGG—Shoshone County

⇑ **SHOSHONE MEDICAL CENTER (131314)**, 25 Jacobs Gulch, Zip 83837–2023; tel. 208/784–1221, (Nonreporting) **A**10 18 21
Primary Contact: Jerry Brantz, Chief Executive Officer and Chief Financial Officer
CMO: David Lawhorn M.D., Chief Medical Officer
CIO: John Wohlman, Manager Information Systems
CHR: Dana Hemphill, Manager Human Resources
CNO: Karen Mann R.N., Chief Nursing Officer
Web address: www.shoshonehealth.com
Control: Hospital district or authority, Government, Nonfederal **Service:** General medical and surgical

Staffed Beds: 25

ID

Hospital, Medicare Provider Number, Address, Telephone, Approval, Facility, and Physician Codes, Health Care System

★ American Hospital Association (AHA) membership   ○ Healthcare Facilities Accreditation Program   ⇑ Center for Improvement in Healthcare Quality Accreditation
□ The Joint Commission accreditation   ◇ DNV Healthcare Inc. accreditation   △ Commission on Accreditation of Rehabilitation Facilities (CARF) accreditation

KETCHUM—Blaine County

✠ **ST. LUKE'S WOOD RIVER MEDICAL CENTER (131323)**, 100 Hospital Drive, Zip 83340, Mailing Address: P.O.Box 100, 83340–0100; tel. 208/727–8800 **A**1 5 10 18 **F**3 7 11 13 15 29 30 31 32 34 35 36 37 39 40 43 45 50 54 56 57 59 62 64 65 68 74 75 76 77 79 81 82 85 86 87 91 93 97 99 101 103 104 107 108 110 111 114 115 119 126 130 131 132 133 134 135 143 146 147 148 **P**6 8 **S** St. Luke's Health System, Boise, ID
Primary Contact: Cody Langbehn, Administrator
CNO: Suzanne Miller R.N., MSN, Senior Director Patient Care Services and Nursing
Web address: www.slrmc.org
Control: Other not–for–profit (including NFP Corporation) **Service:** General medical and surgical

> **Staffed Beds:** 25 **Admissions:** 992 **Census:** 7 **Outpatient Visits:** 94164 **Births:** 196 **Total Expense ($000):** 62657 **Payroll Expense ($000):** 30058 **Personnel:** 358

LEWISTON—Nez Perce County

✠ **ST. JOSEPH REGIONAL MEDICAL CENTER (130003)**, 415 Sixth Street, Zip 83501–2431; tel. 208/743–2511 **A**1 2 10 **F**8 11 15 18 20 22 26 29 30 31 34 35 40 41 43 44 45 46 47 48 49 50 54 57 59 60 63 64 68 69 70 71 74 75 76 77 78 79 80 81 83 84 86 87 89 91 93 97 98 101 102 104 107 108 109 110 111 114 115 116 117 118 121 123 124 129 130 132 135 146 148 **P**6 **S** RCCH HealthCare Partners, Brentwood, TN
Primary Contact: Blain Claypool, Interim Chief Executive Officer
CFO: Thomas Safley, Chief Financial Officer
CMO: Michael T Rooney M.D., Chief of Staff
CHR: Susan Dokken, Chief Human Resources
CNO: Joan Agee, Vice President Patient Care Services
Web address: www.sjrmc.org
Control: Church operated, Nongovernment, not–for–profit **Service:** General medical and surgical

> **Staffed Beds:** 123 **Admissions:** 4981 **Census:** 46 **Outpatient Visits:** 132932 **Births:** 772 **Total Expense ($000):** 151159 **Payroll Expense ($000):** 61684 **Personnel:** 796

MALAD CITY—Oneida County

NELL J. REDFIELD MEMORIAL HOSPITAL (131303), 150 North 200 West, Zip 83252–1239, Mailing Address: Box 126, 83252–0126; tel. 208/766–2231, (Nonreporting) **A**10 18
Primary Contact: John Williams, Administrator and Chief Executive Officer
CFO: Cindy Howard, Director Financial Services
CHR: Kathy Hubbard, Manager Human Resources
Web address: www.oneidahospital.com
Control: County, Government, Nonfederal **Service:** General medical and surgical

> **Staffed Beds:** 11

MCCALL—Valley County

★ **ST. LUKE'S MCCALL (131312)**, 1000 State Street, Zip 83638–3704; tel. 208/634–2221 **A**5 10 18 **F**3 8 9 11 15 30 32 34 35 36 38 40 45 46 50 57 59 64 66 68 79 81 85 86 87 93 97 107 115 119 130 132 133 134 135 146 149 **P**6 8 **S** St. Luke's Health System, Boise, ID
Primary Contact: Sean McCallister, Administrator
CFO: Matt Groenig, Vice President Finance
Web address: www.stlukesonline.org/communities–and–locations/facilities/hospitals–and–medical–centers/st–lukes–mccall–medical–center
Control: Other not–for–profit (including NFP Corporation) **Service:** General medical and surgical

> **Staffed Beds:** 15 **Admissions:** 564 **Census:** 4 **Outpatient Visits:** 54003 **Births:** 94 **Total Expense ($000):** 31015 **Payroll Expense ($000):** 16997 **Personnel:** 225

MERIDIAN—Ada County

ST. LUKE'S MERIDIAN MEDICAL CENTER See St. Luke's Regional Medical Center, Boise

✠ **VIBRA HOSPITAL OF BOISE (132002)**, 2131 South Bonito Way, Zip 83642–1659; tel. 877/801–2244, (Nonreporting) **A**1 3 10 **S** Vibra Healthcare, Mechanicsburg, PA
Primary Contact: Cynthia Newsom, Chief Executive Officer
Web address: www.vhboise.com
Control: Corporation, Investor–owned (for–profit) **Service:** Acute long–term care hospital

> **Staffed Beds:** 60

MONTPELIER—Bear Lake County

★ **BEAR LAKE MEMORIAL HOSPITAL (131316)**, 164 South Fifth Street, Zip 83254–1597; tel. 208/847–1630, (Total facility includes 36 beds in nursing home–type unit) **A**10 18 **F**1 2 3 10 11 12 13 15 18 28 29 32 34 35 40 45 50 53 54 57 59 60 62 64 65 68 70 76 77 79 81 82 85 86 87 90 93 97 102 105 107 110 115 119 127 128 129 130 131 133 135 143 146 147 148
Primary Contact: Dennis Carlson, Chief Executive Officer
Web address: www.blmhospital.com
Control: County, Government, Nonfederal **Service:** General medical and surgical

> **Staffed Beds:** 57 **Admissions:** 381 **Census:** 35 **Outpatient Visits:** 80273 **Births:** 72 **Total Expense ($000):** 22933 **Payroll Expense ($000):** 10583 **Personnel:** 180

MOSCOW—Latah County

✠ **GRITMAN MEDICAL CENTER (131327)**, 700 South Main Street, Zip 83843–3056; tel. 208/882–4511 **A**1 10 18 **F**3 8 11 13 15 19 28 29 34 35 36 37 40 45 46 49 51 53 54 56 57 59 64 65 70 75 76 77 79 81 82 85 86 87 89 91 93 96 97 107 108 110 111 115 119 124 127 129 130 131 132 133 135 143 146 147 148 149 **S** QHR, Brentwood, TN
Primary Contact: Kara Besst, President and Chief Executive Officer
CMO: Michael Patmas M.D., Chief Medical Officer
CIO: Kane Francetich, Chief Information Officer
CHR: Dennis Cockrell, Director Human Resources
Web address: www.gritman.org
Control: Other not–for–profit (including NFP Corporation) **Service:** General medical and surgical

> **Staffed Beds:** 25 **Admissions:** 1278 **Census:** 10 **Outpatient Visits:** 72071 **Births:** 306 **Total Expense ($000):** 54044 **Payroll Expense ($000):** 24913 **Personnel:** 390

MOUNTAIN HOME—Elmore County

✠ **ST. LUKE'S ELMORE (131311)**, 895 North Sixth East Street, Zip 83647–2207, Mailing Address: P.O.Box 1270, 83647–1270; tel. 208/587–8401, (Total facility includes 38 beds in nursing home–type unit) **A**1 10 18 **F**3 7 11 13 29 30 34 35 40 45 57 64 75 77 81 107 111 114 119 127 128 129 130 133 146 149 **P**6 **S** St. Luke's Health System, Boise, ID
Primary Contact: Michael Blauer, Administrator
COO: Cody Mangum, Director Operations
CFO: Tricia Senger, Chief Financial Officer
CNO: Lisa Sanford, Chief Nursing Officer
Web address: www.stlukesonline.org/elmore/
Control: Other not–for–profit (including NFP Corporation) **Service:** General medical and surgical

> **Staffed Beds:** 63 **Admissions:** 798 **Census:** 28 **Outpatient Visits:** 46379 **Births:** 137 **Total Expense ($000):** 26990 **Payroll Expense ($000):** 13691 **Personnel:** 234

NAMPA—Canyon County

MERCY MEDICAL CENTER See Saint Alphonsus Medical Center – Nampa

✠ **SAINT ALPHONSUS MEDICAL CENTER – NAMPA (130013)**, 4300 East Flamingo Avenue, Zip 83686–6008; tel. 208/201–5000 **A**1 10 **F**3 11 12 13 14 15 18 20 22 28 29 30 31 32 34 35 37 39 40 41 42 43 44 45 50 54 57 59 64 65 67 68 69 70 71 72 75 76 77 78 79 80 81 82 85 86 87 89 92 107 108 110 111 114 115 118 119 126 129 130 132 133 134 135 141 143 145 146 147 148 149 **S** Trinity Health, Livonia, MI
Primary Contact: Karl Keeler, President
COO: Phil Harrop, Executive Director Operations
CFO: Lannie Checketts, Chief Financial Officer
CMO: Dustan Hughes M.D., Vice President Medical Affairs
CIO: Daniel Wright, Director Information Technology
CHR: Stefanie Thiel, Senior Human Resources Business Partner
CNO: Clint L Child R.N., Chief Nursing Officer
Web address: www.saintalphonsus.org/nampa
Control: Church operated, Nongovernment, not–for–profit **Service:** General medical and surgical

> **Staffed Beds:** 131 **Admissions:** 5845 **Census:** 53 **Outpatient Visits:** 118850 **Births:** 1194 **Total Expense ($000):** 104662 **Payroll Expense ($000):** 35999 **Personnel:** 602

ID

OROFINO—Clearwater County

★ **CLEARWATER VALLEY HOSPITAL AND CLINICS (131320)**, 301 Cedar, Zip 83544–9029; tel. 208/476–4555, (Nonreporting) **A**10 18 **S** Essentia Health, Duluth, MN
Primary Contact: Lenne Bonner, President
CFO: Jyl Ruland, Chief Financial Officer
CMO: Kelly McGrath, Chief Medical Officer
CHR: Debbie Schumacher, Chief Human Resource Officer
Web address: www.smh–cvhc.org
Control: Other not–for–profit (including NFP Corporation) **Service:** General medical and surgical

Staffed Beds: 23

STATE HOSPITAL NORTH, 300 Hospital Drive, Zip 83544–9034; tel. 208/476–4511, (Nonreporting)
Primary Contact: Todd Hurt, Administrator
CMO: Karla Eisele M.D., Clinical Director
CIO: James Sarbacher, Chief Information Officer
CHR: Heather Vandenbark, Human Resources Specialist
Web address: www.healthandwelfare.idaho.gov
Control: State, Government, Nonfederal **Service:** Psychiatric

Staffed Beds: 60

POCATELLO—Bannock County

✉ **PORTNEUF MEDICAL CENTER (130028)**, 777 Hospital Way, Zip 83201–5175; tel. 208/239–1000 **A**1 3 5 10 20 **F**3 11 12 13 15 17 18 19 20 22 24 26 28 29 31 34 35 39 40 43 44 45 46 47 48 49 50 56 57 58 59 61 64 65 68 70 71 72 74 75 76 77 78 79 80 81 82 85 86 87 88 89 90 93 96 97 98 100 101 102 103 104 107 108 109 110 111 114 115 118 119 120 121 123 124 126 127 129 130 132 143 146 147 149 **P**2 **S** Ardent Health Services, Nashville, TN
Primary Contact: Daniel Ordyna, Chief Executive Officer
COO: Don Wadle, Vice President Clinical and Support Services
CFO: John Abreu, Vice President and Chief Financial Officer
CHR: Don Wadle, Interim Director Human Resources
CNO: Natalie R Smith R.N., MSN, Vice President Patient Care Services and Chief Nursing Officer
Web address: www.portmed.org
Control: Corporation, Investor–owned (for–profit) **Service:** General medical and surgical

Staffed Beds: 175 Admissions: 8746 Census: 94 Outpatient Visits: 268325 Births: 1388 Total Expense ($000): 212215 Payroll Expense ($000): 73727 Personnel: 1006

SAFE HAVEN HOSPITAL OF POCATELLO (134011), 1200 Hospital Way, Zip 83201–2708; tel. 208/232–2570 (Nonreporting) **A**10 **S** Safe Haven Health Care, Pocatello, ID
Primary Contact: Karen Neilson, Administrator
Web address: www.safehavenhealthcare.org/safehaven_hospital/index.html
Control: Individual, Investor–owned (for–profit) **Service:** Rehabilitation

Staffed Beds: 87

POST FALLS—Kootenai County

☐ **NORTHERN IDAHO ADVANCED CARE HOSPITAL (132001)**, 600 North Cecil Road, Zip 83854–6200; tel. 208/262–2800 (Nonreporting) **A**1 10 **S** Ernest Health, Inc., Albuquerque, NM
Primary Contact: Una Alderman, Chief Executive Officer
Web address: www.niach.ernesthealth.com
Control: Corporation, Investor–owned (for–profit) **Service:** Acute long–term care hospital

Staffed Beds: 40

☐ **NORTHWEST SPECIALTY HOSPITAL (130066)**, 1593 East Polston Avenue, Zip 83854–5326; tel. 208/262–2300 **A**1 10 **F**3 29 34 35 45 47 48 49 54 59 64 65 75 77 79 81 82 87 107 111 119 129 144 **P**8 **S** National Surgical Healthcare, Chicago, IL
Primary Contact: Rick Rasmussen, Chief Executive Officer
CIO: Craig McIntosh, Chief Information Officer
CHR: Gina Schneider, Director Human Resources
CNO: Christi Nance R.N., MSN, Chief Nursing Officer
Web address: www.northwestspecialtyhospital.com
Control: Corporation, Investor–owned (for–profit) **Service:** Surgical

Staffed Beds: 34 Admissions: 25 Census: 5 Outpatient Visits: 15200 Births: 0

△ **REHABILITATION HOSPITAL OF THE NORTHWEST (133027)**, 3372 East Jenalan Avenue, Zip 83854–7787; tel. 208/262–8700 (Nonreporting) **A**7 **S** Ernest Health, Inc., Albuquerque, NM
Primary Contact: Darby Brockette, Chief Executive Officer
Web address: www.ernesthealth.com
Control: Investor–owned (for–profit) **Service:** Rehabilitation

Staffed Beds: 25

PRESTON—Franklin County

FRANKLIN COUNTY MEDICAL CENTER (131322), 44 North First East Street, Zip 83263–1399; tel. 208/852–0137 **A**10 18 **F**2 3 11 13 31 40 45 57 62 63 68 75 77 79 81 82 84 85 91 93 96 107 114 119 130 131 133 146
Primary Contact: Richard Westerberg, Interim Chief Executive Officer
CFO: Paul Smart CPA, Chief Financial Officer
CHR: Courtney Dursteler, Chief Human Resources Officer
CNO: Patrica Bowles R.N., Chief Nursing Officer
Web address: www.fcmc.org
Control: County, Government, Nonfederal **Service:** General medical and surgical

Staffed Beds: 20 Admissions: 663 Census: 7

REXBURG—Madison County

★ ⇑ **MADISON MEMORIAL HOSPITAL (130025)**, 450 East Main Street, Zip 83440–2048, Mailing Address: P.O.Box 310, 83440–0310; tel. 208/359–6900 **A**10 21 **F**3 11 13 28 29 31 34 35 39 40 41 45 54 57 59 60 65 66 68 70 72 75 76 77 78 79 81 82 85 86 87 89 91 93 96 107 108 111 115 118 119 130 131 146 147 148 149 **P**8
Primary Contact: Rachel Ann. Gonzales, Chief Executive Officer
COO: Audrey Fletcher, Chief Operating Officer
CFO: Troy Christensen, Chief Financial Officer
CMO: Clay Prince M.D., Chief Medical Officer
Web address: www.madisonmemorial.org
Control: County, Government, Nonfederal **Service:** General medical and surgical

Staffed Beds: 69 Admissions: 2492 Census: 20 Outpatient Visits: 24969 Births: 1284 Total Expense ($000): 59144 Payroll Expense ($000): 22989 Personnel: 434

RUPERT—Minidoka County

★ **MINIDOKA MEMORIAL HOSPITAL (131319)**, 1224 Eighth Street, Zip 83350–1599; tel. 208/436–0481, (Total facility includes 43 beds in nursing home–type unit) **A**10 18 **F**3 7 8 11 15 29 30 34 35 37 40 45 50 56 57 59 62 63 64 65 68 70 75 77 79 81 83 84 85 86 87 97 107 108 111 114 119 127 128 130 131 132 133 134 143 146 147 148 149 **P**1 3 5
Primary Contact: Tom Murphy, Chief Executive Officer
CFO: Jason Gibbons, Chief Financial Officer
CMO: Brian Muir, Chief of Staff
CIO: Nick Martin, Chief Information Officer
CHR: Eric Gochnour, Director Human Resources
CNO: Erinn Neilson, Chief Nursing Officer
Web address: www.minidokamemorial.com
Control: County, Government, Nonfederal **Service:** General medical and surgical

Staffed Beds: 72 Admissions: 431 Census: 45 Outpatient Visits: 20011 Births: 0 Total Expense ($000): 19791 Payroll Expense ($000): 10960 Personnel: 199

MINIDOKA MEMORIAL HOSPITAL AND EXTENDED CARE FACILITY See Minidoka Memorial Hospital

SAINT MARIES—Benewah County

⇑ **BENEWAH COMMUNITY HOSPITAL (131317)**, 229 South Seventh Street, Zip 83861–1803; tel. 208/245–5551 **A**10 18 21 **F**13 15 29 31 34 35 40 56 57 59 64 76 79 81 89 90 93 96 97 107 110 111 114 119 127 129 130 131 133 135 146 147 **P**6
Primary Contact: Anthony Koroush, Chief Executive Officer
CFO: Lori Minier, Chief Financial Officer
CMO: William Wheeler M.D., Chief of Staff
CIO: Joseph Getchius, Director Information Technology
CHR: Marlana Martin, Director Human Resources
CNO: Rhonda Smith, Chief Nursing Officer
Web address: www.bchmed.org
Control: County, Government, Nonfederal **Service:** General medical and surgical

Staffed Beds: 19 Admissions: 376 Census: 4 Outpatient Visits: 16439 Births: 39 Total Expense ($000): 20512 Payroll Expense ($000): 8164

ID

Hospital, Medicare Provider Number, Address, Telephone, Approval, Facility, and Physician Codes, Health Care System

★ American Hospital Association (AHA) membership
☐ The Joint Commission accreditation
○ Healthcare Facilities Accreditation Program
◇ DNV Healthcare Inc. accreditation
⇑ Center for Improvement in Healthcare Quality Accreditation
△ Commission on Accreditation of Rehabilitation Facilities (CARF) accreditation

SALMON—Lemhi County

★ **STEELE MEMORIAL MEDICAL CENTER (131305)**, 203 South Daisy Street,
Zip 83467–4709; tel. 208/756–5600 **A**10 18 **F**3 11 13 15 18 28 29 31 34 35
40 45 55 57 59 64 65 66 68 75 76 77 78 79 81 82 85 86 87 90 93 97 104 107
110 111 115 119 127 131 132 133 135 146 148 **P**6 **S** QHR, Brentwood, TN
Primary Contact: Jeanine Gentry, Chief Executive Officer
COO: Abner King, Chief Operating Officer
CFO: Jim Peterson, Chief Financial Officer
CMO: Richard Natelson M.D., Chief of Staff
CHR: Libby Brittain, Director Human Resources
CNO: Stephanie Orr, Chief Nursing Officer
Web address: www.steelemh.org
Control: County, Government, Nonfederal **Service**: General medical and surgical

Staffed Beds: 18 **Admissions**: 392 **Census**: 3 **Births**: 48 **Total Expense
($000)**: 22531

SANDPOINT—Bonner County

★ ⇑ **BONNER GENERAL HOSPITAL (131328)**, 520 North Third Avenue,
Zip 83864–1507; tel. 208/263–1441 **A**10 18 21 **F**3 11 13 15 17 22 26 28 29
30 34 35 40 45 46 47 48 54 57 59 62 63 64 68 75 76 77 79 81 85 86 87 93
102 107 108 110 111 114 118 119 130 131 132 144 146 148
Primary Contact: Sheryl Rickard, Chief Executive Officer
CFO: John Hennessy, Chief Financial Officer
CIO: Jeremy Welser, Director Information Systems
CHR: Brad Waterbury, Director Human Resources
CNO: Misty Robertson R.N., Chief Nursing Officer
Web address: www.bonnergeneral.org
Control: Other not–for–profit (including NFP Corporation) **Service**: General
medical and surgical

Staffed Beds: 25 **Admissions**: 1920 **Census**: 14 **Outpatient Visits**: 74534
Births: 344 **Total Expense ($000)**: 51734 **Payroll Expense ($000)**: 22336
Personnel: 346

SODA SPRINGS—Caribou County

★ **CARIBOU MEMORIAL HOSPITAL AND LIVING CENTER (131309)**, 300 South
Third West, Zip 83276–1598; tel. 208/547–3341, (Nonreporting) **A**10 18
Primary Contact: Jon Smith, Chief Executive Officer
CMO: John K Franson M.D., Chief Medical Staff
CIO: Johnathan Inskeep, Chief Information Officer
CHR: Michael D Peck, Assistant Administrator
CNO: Brenda Bergholm MSN, R.N., Chief Nursing Officer
Web address: www.cmhlc.org/
Control: County, Government, Nonfederal **Service**: General medical and surgical

Staffed Beds: 55

TWIN FALLS—Twin Falls County

⊞ △ **ST. LUKE'S MAGIC VALLEY MEDICAL CENTER (130002)**, 801 Pole
Line Road West, Zip 83301–5810, Mailing Address: P.O.Box 409, 83303–0409;
tel. 208/814–1000 **A**1 2 3 7 10 **F**3 5 7 8 11 13 15 18 20 22 29 30 31 35 40
57 62 63 68 70 72 76 77 78 79 81 85 87 89 90 93 96 98 104 106 107 110
111 114 119 130 146 **P**6 8 **S** St. Luke's Health System, Boise, ID
Primary Contact: Michael A. Fenello, Administrator and West Region Chief
Executive Officer
CFO: Joshua Custer, Director Finance
CIO: Melissa Capps, Site Leader Information Technology
CHR: Mark Stevens, Senior Director Human Resources
CNO: Amy Bearden R.N., MSN, Vice President Patient Care Services and Chief
Nursing Officer
Web address: www.stlukesonline.org
Control: Other not–for–profit (including NFP Corporation) **Service**: General
medical and surgical

Staffed Beds: 224 **Admissions**: 10415 **Census**: 111 **Outpatient Visits**:
544434 **Births**: 1832 **Total Expense ($000)**: 353227 **Payroll Expense
($000)**: 121761 **Personnel**: 2114

WEISER—Washington County

★ ⇑ **WEISER MEMORIAL HOSPITAL (131307)**, 645 East Fifth Street,
Zip 83672–2202; tel. 208/549–0370 **A**10 18 21 **F**3 11 13 32 34 35 40 43 45
46 57 59 65 68 76 79 81 89 97 107 114 119 127 129 130 131 133 135 144
146 147 148 149 **S** St. Luke's Health System, Boise, ID
Primary Contact: Steven D. Hale, FACHE, Chief Executive Officer
CFO: Mark Christensen, Chief Financial Officer
CMO: Lore Wooton M.D., Chief of Medical Staff
CHR: Terri Kautz, Manager Human Resources
Web address: www.weisermemorialhospital.org
Control: Hospital district or authority, Government, Nonfederal **Service**: General
medical and surgical

Staffed Beds: 18 **Admissions**: 320 **Census**: 2 **Outpatient Visits**: 4878
Births: 59 **Total Expense ($000)**: 16024 **Payroll Expense ($000)**: 5867
Personnel: 115

ILLINOIS

ALEDO—Mercer County

★ **GENESIS MEDICAL CENTER–ALEDO (141304)**, 409 NW Ninth Avenue,
Zip 61231–1296; tel. 309/582–9100 **A**10 18 **F**3 5 11 15 28 29 34 40 45 50
56 57 59 64 67 75 81 82 87 89 93 94 97 107 108 115 119 127 128 130 131
133 144 146 149 **P**6 **S** Genesis Health System, Davenport, IA
Primary Contact: Ted Rogalski, Administrator
CFO: Mark G Rogers, Chief Financial Officer
CMO: Julio Santiago M.D., Chief of Staff
CIO: Robert Frieden, Vice President Information Systems
CHR: Megan Clark, Coordinator Human Resources
CNO: Heidi Hess, Chief Nursing Officer
Web address: www.genesishealth.com
Control: Other not–for–profit (including NFP Corporation) **Service**: General
medical and surgical

**Staffed Beds: 22 Admissions: 239 Census: 4 Outpatient Visits: 17450
Births: 0 Total Expense ($000): 14795 Payroll Expense ($000): 5403
Personnel: 96**

ALTON—Madison County

⊞ **ALTON MEMORIAL HOSPITAL (140002)**, One Memorial Drive, Zip 62002–
6722; tel. 618/463–7311, (Total facility includes 54 beds in nursing home–type
unit) **A**1 10 **F**3 6 7 11 13 15 18 20 22 29 30 31 34 35 36 38 39 40 45 46 49
50 56 57 59 64 69 70 74 75 76 77 78 79 81 82 85 86 87 89 92 93 96 98 103
104 107 108 110 111 114 115 116 117 118 119 120 121 123 128 129 130
131 132 146 148 149 **S** BJC HealthCare, Saint Louis, MO
Primary Contact: David A. Braasch, President
COO: Brad Goacher, Vice President Administration
CFO: Susan Koesterer, Vice President, Finance
CMO: Sebastian Rueckert M.D., Vice President and Chief Medical Officer
CIO: Jerry Fox Jr, Chief Information Officer
CHR: Bryan Hartwick, Vice President Human Resources
CNO: Debra Turpin R.N., MSN, Vice President Patient Care Services and Chief
Nursing Officer
Web address: www.altonmemorialhospital.org
Control: Other not–for–profit (including NFP Corporation) **Service**: General
medical and surgical

**Staffed Beds: 227 Admissions: 8078 Census: 134 Outpatient Visits: 158403
Births: 732 Total Expense ($000): 139348 Payroll Expense ($000): 52439
Personnel: 758**

☐ **ALTON MENTAL HEALTH CENTER (144016)**, 4500 College Avenue,
Zip 62002–5099; tel. 618/474–3800, (Nonreporting) **A**1 10 **S** Division of Mental
Health, Department of Human Services, Springfield, IL
Primary Contact: Brian E. Thomas, Administrator
CFO: Susan Shobe, Director Administration and Support Services
CMO: Claudia Kachigion M.D., Medical Director
Control: State, Government, Nonfederal **Service**: Psychiatric

Staffed Beds: 165

⊞ **OSF SAINT ANTHONY'S HEALTH CENTER (140052)**, 1 Saint Anthony's Way,
Zip 62002–4579, Mailing Address: PO Box 340, 62002–0340; tel. 618/465–
2571, (Includes OSF SAINT CLARE'S HOSPITAL, 915 East Fifth Street, Alton,
Illinois, Zip 62002–6434, tel. 618/463–5151) (Total facility includes 30 beds in
nursing home–type unit) **A**1 2 10 **F**2 3 5 10 11 13 15 18 20 22 29 30 31 34 35
37 38 39 40 41 44 45 47 48 49 50 51 53 56 57 58 59 60 61 64 65 68 69 70
74 75 76 77 78 79 81 82 84 85 86 87 89 90 91 92 93 95 96 99 100 101 102
103 104 107 108 110 111 114 115 116 117 118 119 120 121 123 125 128
129 130 131 132 134 135 146 147 148 149 **P**6 **S** OSF Healthcare System,
Peoria, IL
Primary Contact: Ajay Pathak, President
COO: SisterM Anselma, Chief Operating Officer
CFO: Matthew Hanley, Chief Financial Officer
CMO: James Piephoff, Chief Medical Officer
CIO: Georgia Henke, Operational Account Manager
CHR: Robyn Grissom, Director Employee Relations
CNO: Denise Boettger, Vice President Nursing and Chief Nursing Officer
Web address: www.osfsaintanthonys.org
Control: Church operated, Nongovernment, not–for–profit **Service**: General
medical and surgical

**Staffed Beds: 203 Admissions: 3592 Census: 50 Outpatient Visits: 81252
Births: 342 Total Expense ($000): 84932 Payroll Expense ($000): 26223
Personnel: 369**

ANNA—Union County

☐ **CHOATE MENTAL HEALTH CENTER (144038)**, 1000 North Main Street,
Zip 62906–1699; tel. 618/833–5161 **A**1 10 **F**34 39 59 65 75 86 98 101 102
103 130 143 149 **S** Division of Mental Health, Department of Human Services,
Springfield, IL
Primary Contact: Elaine Ray, Administrator
COO: Elaine Ray, Administrator
CMO: John Larcas M.D., Acting Medical Director
CIO: Cindy Flamm, Manager Quality
CHR: Tammy Tellor, Acting Director Human Resources
Control: State, Government, Nonfederal **Service**: Psychiatric

**Staffed Beds: 79 Admissions: 105 Census: 44 Outpatient Visits: 0 Births:
0 Total Expense ($000): 43378 Payroll Expense ($000): 35123**

⊞ **UNION COUNTY HOSPITAL (141342)**, 517 North Main Street, Zip 62906–1696;
tel. 618/833–4511, (Nonreporting) **A**1 10 18 **S** Quorum Health, Brentwood, TN
Primary Contact: James R. Farris, FACHE, Chief Executive Officer
CFO: Terry Paligo, Chief Financial Officer
CMO: Christine Lucas, Chief of Staff
CIO: John Hegger, Director Information Systems
CHR: Tammy Davis, Director Human Resources
CNO: Tammy H. Wheaton, Interim Chief Nursing Officer
Web address: www.unioncountyhospital.com
Control: Corporation, Investor–owned (for–profit) **Service**: General medical and
surgical

Staffed Beds: 47

ARLINGTON HEIGHTS—Cook County

⊞ **NORTHWEST COMMUNITY HOSPITAL (140252)**, 800 West Central Road,
Zip 60005–2392; tel. 847/618–1000 **A**1 2 5 10 **F**3 5 8 13 15 18 20 22 24 26
28 29 30 31 32 33 34 35 37 38 39 40 41 43 44 45 46 47 49 50 53 54 55 56
57 59 61 62 63 64 65 68 70 71 72 73 74 75 76 77 78 79 81 82 84 85 86 87
89 90 91 92 93 94 96 98 99 100 101 102 103 104 105 106 107 108 110 111
114 115 116 117 118 119 120 121 123 124 126 129 130 131 132 135 144
145 146 147 148 149 **P**8
Primary Contact: Stephen Scogna, President and Chief Executive Officer
COO: Michael Hartke, Executive Vice President, Chief Operating Officer
CFO: Marsha Liu, Executive Vice President and Chief Financial Officer
CIO: Glen Malan, Vice President Information Technology and Chief Information
Officer
CHR: Ann M Patrick, Vice President Human Resources
CNO: Kimberly Nagy R.N., MS, Executive Vice President, Patient Services and
Chief Nursing Officer
Web address: www.nch.org
Control: Other not–for–profit (including NFP Corporation) **Service**: General
medical and surgical

**Staffed Beds: 395 Admissions: 20304 Census: 244 Outpatient Visits:
396216 Births: 2676 Total Expense ($000): 456766 Payroll Expense
($000): 183664 Personnel: 3132**

AURORA—Du Page and Kane Counties County

⊞ **PRESENCE MERCY MEDICAL CENTER (140174)**, 1325 North Highland
Avenue, Zip 60506–1449; tel. 630/859–2222 **A**1 2 10 **F**3 5 12 13 15 18 20
22 24 26 28 29 30 31 34 35 36 38 40 43 45 46 49 56 57 59 61 65 68 70 75
76 77 78 79 81 82 85 86 87 89 93 97 98 99 100 101 102 103 104 105 107
111 114 115 119 125 126 130 132 135 144 146 147 **P**5 **S** Presence Health,
Chicago, IL
Primary Contact: Michael L. Brown, Regional President and Chief Executive Officer
COO: Roxann E Barber, Regional Ambulatory Care and Ancillary Services Officer
CFO: Kevin Larkin, Regional Chief Financial Officer
CMO: Anil Gopinath FACHE, M.D., Regional Chief Medical Officer
CHR: Michael O'Rourke, Regional Human Resource Officer
CNO: Grace McBride, Regional Chief Nursing Officer
Web address: www.presencehealth.org/mercy/
Control: Church operated, Nongovernment, not–for–profit **Service**: General
medical and surgical

**Staffed Beds: 242 Admissions: 8145 Census: 102 Outpatient Visits:
210258 Births: 208 Total Expense ($000): 181370 Payroll Expense
($000): 48594 Personnel: 927**

IL

Hospital, Medicare Provider Number, Address, Telephone, Approval, Facility, and Physician Codes, Health Care System

★ American Hospital Association (AHA) membership   ○ Healthcare Facilities Accreditation Program   ⇑ Center for Improvement in Healthcare Quality Accreditation
☐ The Joint Commission accreditation   ◇ DNV Healthcare Inc. accreditation   △ Commission on Accreditation of Rehabilitation Facilities (CARF) accreditation

PROVENA MERCY MEDICAL CENTER See Presence Mercy Medical Center

✠ △ **RUSH–COPLEY MEDICAL CENTER (140029)**, 2000 Ogden Avenue, Zip 60504–7222; tel. 630/978–6200 **A**1 2 3 5 7 10 **F**3 7 8 13 15 17 18 19 20 22 24 26 28 29 30 31 32 34 35 36 38 39 40 42 43 44 45 46 47 49 50 51 52 53 54 55 56 57 58 59 60 61 64 65 66 68 70 72 73 74 75 76 77 78 79 81 82 84 85 86 87 89 90 92 93 94 96 97 107 108 110 111 114 115 117 118 119 120 121 123 124 126 130 131 132 134 135 143 144 145 146 147 148 149 **P**6 **S** Rush University Medical Center, Chicago, IL
Primary Contact: Barry C. Finn, President and Chief Executive Officer
COO: John A Diederich, Senior Vice President Operations and Chief Operating Officer
CFO: Brenda VanWyhe, Senior Vice President Finance and Chief Financial Officer
CMO: Steve B Lowenthal M.D., M.P.H., FACS, Senior Vice President Medical Affairs and Chief Medical Officer
CIO: Dennis DeMasie, Vice President Information Systems and Chief Information Officer
CNO: Mary Shilkaitis, Vice President Patient Care and Chief Nursing Officer
Web address: www.rushcopley.com
Control: Other not–for–profit (including NFP Corporation) **Service**: General medical and surgical

Staffed Beds: 210 **Admissions**: 12412 **Census**: 144 **Outpatient Visits**: 226669 **Births**: 3296 **Total Expense ($000)**: 284122 **Payroll Expense ($000)**: 119730 **Personnel**: 1757

BARRINGTON—Lake County

★ ⇑ **ADVOCATE GOOD SHEPHERD HOSPITAL (140291)**, 450 West Highway 22, Zip 60010–1919; tel. 847/381–0123 **A**2 10 21 **F**3 11 12 13 15 17 18 19 20 22 24 26 28 29 30 31 34 35 36 37 40 43 45 46 47 48 49 54 57 59 63 64 65 68 70 74 75 76 77 78 79 81 82 84 87 89 91 92 93 94 97 100 107 108 110 111 114 115 116 117 118 119 120 121 123 124 126 129 130 131 132 135 144 146 **P**8 **S** Advocate Health Care, Downers Grove, IL
Primary Contact: Karen A. Lambert, President
COO: Michael Ploszek, Vice President Physician Strategy and Clinical Operations
CFO: George Teufel, Vice President Finance
CMO: Barry Rosen M.D., Vice President Medical Management
CIO: Chuck Malik, Director Information Systems
CHR: Jason Spigner, Vice President Human Resources
CNO: Marianne D Araujo R.N., Ph.D., FACHE, Vice President Nursing and Chief Nurse Executive
Web address: www.advocatehealth.com/gshp/
Control: Church operated, Nongovernment, not–for–profit **Service**: General medical and surgical

Staffed Beds: 176 **Admissions**: 9812 **Census**: 109 **Outpatient Visits**: 252646 **Births**: 1306 **Total Expense ($000)**: 238966 **Payroll Expense ($000)**: 73620 **Personnel**: 1193

BELLEVILLE—St. Clair County

✠ △ **HSHS ST. ELIZABETH'S HOSPITAL (140187)**, 211 South Third Street, Zip 62220–1998; tel. 618/234–2120 **A**1 3 5 7 10 **F**3 11 13 15 18 20 22 24 26 28 29 30 31 34 35 40 45 46 49 50 51 54 64 65 68 70 74 75 76 77 78 79 81 82 87 90 91 93 107 108 111 115 119 124 126 129 130 144 146 147 148 **S** HSHS Hospital Sisters Health System, Springfield, IL
Primary Contact: Peggy A. Sebastian, MSN, R.N., President and Chief Executive Officer
CFO: David Nosacka, Chief Financial Officer
CMO: Shelly Harkins M.D., Chief Medical Officer
CIO: Leslee Martin, Manager Information Technology
CHR: Jason T Snow, Director People Services
Web address: www.steliz.org
Control: Church operated, Nongovernment, not–for–profit **Service**: General medical and surgical

Staffed Beds: 224 **Admissions**: 8556 **Census**: 92 **Outpatient Visits**: 201750 **Births**: 1031 **Total Expense ($000)**: 184827 **Payroll Expense ($000)**: 55014 **Personnel**: 1032

★ ○ **MEMORIAL HOSPITAL (140185)**, 4500 Memorial Drive, Zip 62226–5399; tel. 618/233–7750, (Total facility includes 68 beds in nursing home–type unit) **A**3 10 11 **F**3 11 13 15 18 20 22 24 26 28 29 30 31 34 40 45 46 47 48 49 53 54 57 59 60 62 64 70 74 76 77 79 81 82 84 85 87 92 93 94 107 108 110 111 114 115 118 119 126 128 129 130 131 132 145 146 147 148 **P**8 **S** BJC HealthCare, Saint Louis, MO
Primary Contact: Mark J. Turner, President and Chief Executive Officer
COO: Michael T McManus, Chief Operating Officer
CFO: Amy Thomas, Vice President Finance
CMO: William Casperson M.D., Vice President Medical Affairs
CIO: Jennifer Meinkoth, Chief Information Officer
CHR: John C Ziegler FACHE, Vice President Human Resources
CNO: Nancy R Weston R.N., MSN, Vice President Nursing Services
Web address: www.memhosp.com
Control: Other not–for–profit (including NFP Corporation) **Service**: General medical and surgical

Staffed Beds: 227 **Admissions**: 15564 **Census**: 227 **Outpatient Visits**: 323226 **Births**: 804 **Total Expense ($000)**: 241320 **Payroll Expense ($000)**: 100119 **Personnel**: 1835

BENTON—Franklin County

★ **FRANKLIN HOSPITAL DISTRICT (141321)**, 201 Bailey Lane, Zip 62812–1969; tel. 618/439–3161 **A**10 18 **F**11 15 29 30 34 35 40 45 56 57 59 66 75 77 81 93 97 107 114 119 127 132 133 **P**6
Primary Contact: James Johnson, Chief Executive Officer
COO: Derek Johnson Sr., Chief Operating Officer
CFO: James Johnson, Chief Financial officer
CMO: Tim Morthland, Chief of Staff
CIO: David Williams, Director Information Technology
CHR: Nancy Seibert, Director Human Resources
CNO: Terri Hermann R.N., Chief Nursing Officer
Web address: www.franklinhospital.net
Control: Hospital district or authority, Government, Nonfederal **Service**: General medical and surgical

Staffed Beds: 16 **Admissions**: 528 **Census**: 3 **Outpatient Visits**: 25579 **Births**: 0 **Total Expense ($000)**: 19502 **Payroll Expense ($000)**: 9091 **Personnel**: 183

BERWYN—Cook County

✠ **MACNEAL HOSPITAL (140054)**, 3249 South Oak Park Avenue, Zip 60402–0715; tel. 708/783–9100 **A**1 2 3 5 8 10 13 **F**3 5 12 13 15 18 19 20 22 24 26 28 29 30 31 34 35 37 38 40 41 43 44 45 46 47 48 49 50 54 56 57 58 59 62 64 65 68 70 74 75 76 77 78 79 81 82 85 86 87 89 90 91 93 96 97 98 99 100 101 102 103 104 105 107 108 110 111 113 114 115 117 118 119 126 128 130 131 132 143 144 146 147 148 149 150 **P**5 6 **S** TENET Healthcare Corporation, Dallas, TX
Primary Contact: Mary Elizabeth. Cleary, Chief Executive Officer
COO: Sharon Oxendale, Chief Operating Officer
CMO: Charles Bareis M.D., Medical Director
CIO: Tom Haslett, Interim Chief Information Officer
CHR: Richard Dodsworth, Chief Human Resource Officer
Web address: www.macneal.com
Control: Corporation, Investor–owned (for–profit) **Service**: General medical and surgical

Staffed Beds: 359 **Admissions**: 14254 **Census**: 186 **Outpatient Visits**: 231611 **Births**: 1509

BLOOMINGTON—Mclean County

✠ **OSF ST. JOSEPH MEDICAL CENTER (140162)**, 2200 East Washington Street, Zip 61701–4323; tel. 309/662–3311, (Total facility includes 12 beds in nursing home–type unit) **A**1 2 10 **F**3 11 12 13 15 18 20 22 24 26 28 30 31 34 35 37 40 43 45 49 50 51 53 54 57 59 60 61 64 65 68 70 74 75 76 77 78 79 81 82 84 85 86 87 89 92 93 96 97 107 108 110 111 114 115 118 119 127 128 129 131 132 135 144 146 147 148 149 150 **P**6 **S** OSF Healthcare System, Peoria, IL
Primary Contact: Chad Boore, President
CFO: John R Zell, Chief Financial Officer
CMO: Paul E Pedersen M.D., Vice President and Chief Medical Officer
CHR: Sue A. Herriott R.N., Executive Director Support Services
CNO: Deborah S Smith R.N., MS, Vice President, Chief Nursing Officer
Web address: www.osfstjoseph.org
Control: Church operated, Nongovernment, not–for–profit **Service**: General medical and surgical

Staffed Beds: 149 **Admissions**: 6585 **Census**: 69 **Outpatient Visits**: 165334 **Births**: 811 **Total Expense ($000)**: 137155 **Payroll Expense ($000)**: 44630 **Personnel**: 818

BLUE ISLAND—Cook County

✠ **METROSOUTH MEDICAL CENTER (140118)**, 12935 South Gregory Street, Zip 60406–2470; tel. 708/597–2000, (Nonreporting) **A**1 10 **S** Quorum Health, Brentwood, TN
Primary Contact: John D. Baird, Chief Executive Officer
CHR: Alanna Barker, Director Human Resources
CNO: Kathleen Hartman, Chief Nursing Officer
Web address: www.metrosouthmedicalcenter.com
Control: Corporation, Investor–owned (for–profit) **Service**: General medical and surgical

Staffed Beds: 285

Many Facility Codes have changed. Please refer to the AHA Guide Code Chart.
© 2017 AHA Guide

IL

BOLINGBROOK—Will County

⊞ **AMITA HEALTH ADVENTIST MEDICAL CENTER BOLINGBROOK (140304)**, 500 Remington Boulevard, Zip 60440–4906; tel. 630/312–5000 **A**1 10 **F**3 6 7 12 13 15 18 20 22 28 29 30 31 32 34 35 37 40 43 44 45 46 49 50 54 56 57 58 59 62 63 64 68 70 73 74 75 76 78 79 81 82 84 85 86 87 92 93 98 100 101 102 103 107 108 110 111 114 115 119 124 129 130 131 132 135 141 143 145 146 147 149 **S** Adventist Health System Sunbelt Health Care Corporation, Altamonte Springs, FL
Primary Contact: Bruce Christian, President and Chief Executive Officer
COO: Richard Roehr, Chief Operating Officer
CFO: Rebecca Mathis, Chief Financial Officer
CMO: Richard Carroll M.D., Chief Medical officer
CIO: John McLendon, Senior Vice President and Chief Information Officer
CHR: Katie Baio, Human Resource Director
CNO: Obed Cruz, Vice President and Chief Nursing Officer
Web address: www.keepingyouwell.com/abh/
Control: Church operated, Nongovernment, not–for–profit **Service:** General medical and surgical

Staffed Beds: 144 **Admissions:** 6026 **Census:** 62 **Outpatient Visits:** 99366 **Births:** 1010 **Total Expense ($000):** 126051 **Payroll Expense ($000):** 36111 **Personnel:** 409

BREESE—Clinton County

⊞ **HSHS ST. JOSEPH'S HOSPITAL (140145)**, 9515 Holy Cross Lane, Zip 62230–3618, Mailing Address: PO Box 99, 62230–0099; tel. 618/526–4511 **A**1 10 **F**3 11 13 15 28 29 30 31 32 34 35 38 40 43 45 50 53 54 57 59 64 68 70 76 78 79 81 85 87 89 91 93 94 96 97 104 107 108 110 111 115 118 119 127 129 130 131 132 135 146 147 149 **P**6 **S** HSHS Hospital Sisters Health System, Springfield, IL
Primary Contact: Amy Ballance, Interim Chief Executive Officer
CFO: John Jeffries, Director Finance
CNO: Helen Essenpreis MSN, R.N., Chief Nursing Officer
Web address: www.stjoebreese.com
Control: Church operated, Nongovernment, not–for–profit **Service:** General medical and surgical

Staffed Beds: 65 **Admissions:** 1229 **Census:** 9 **Outpatient Visits:** 96735 **Births:** 558 **Total Expense ($000):** 50508 **Payroll Expense ($000):** 18218 **Personnel:** 339

CANTON—Fulton County

⊞ **GRAHAM HOSPITAL ASSOCIATION (140001)**, 210 West Walnut Street, Zip 61520–2497; tel. 309/647–5240, (Total facility includes 38 beds in nursing home–type unit) **A**1 3 10 20 **F**3 11 13 15 26 28 29 30 40 45 54 57 59 62 63 64 65 67 70 75 76 79 81 82 85 87 89 91 97 107 108 110 111 114 115 119 124 127 128 129 130 131 132 135 143 144 145 146 **P**3
Primary Contact: Robert G. Senneff, FACHE, President and Chief Executive Officer
CFO: Eric Franz, Vice President, Finance and Chief Financial Officer
CIO: Jim Schreiner, Chief Information Officer
CHR: Canise A McComb, Director Human Resources
CNO: Teresa L McConkey MSN, R.N., Vice President of Nursing and Chief Nursing Officer
Web address: www.grahamhealthsystem.org
Control: Other not–for–profit (including NFP Corporation) **Service:** General medical and surgical

Staffed Beds: 79 **Admissions:** 2331 **Census:** 47 **Outpatient Visits:** 205129 **Births:** 300 **Total Expense ($000):** 78242 **Payroll Expense ($000):** 29302 **Personnel:** 626

CARBONDALE—Jackson County

⊞ **MEMORIAL HOSPITAL OF CARBONDALE (140164)**, 405 West Jackson Street, Zip 62901–1467, Mailing Address: P.O.Box 10000, 62902–9000; tel. 618/549–0721 **A**1 2 3 5 10 13 19 **F**3 11 13 18 20 22 24 26 28 29 30 31 34 35 40 45 46 48 49 54 56 57 59 64 68 70 72 74 75 76 77 78 79 81 82 83 84 85 86 87 89 107 108 111 114 115 119 120 121 126 130 131 132 135 145 146 147 **P**1 **S** Southern Illinois Healthcare, Carbondale, IL
Primary Contact: Bart Millstead, Administrator
CFO: Michael Kasser, Vice President Chief Financial Officer and Treasurer
CMO: Marci Moore–Connelly M.D., Vice President Chief Medical Officer
CIO: David Holland, Vice President Chief Innovation Officer
CHR: Pamela S Henderson, Vice President Human Resources
CNO: Julie Firman R.N., FACHE, Vice President and Chief Nursing Officer
Web address: www.sih.net
Control: Other not–for–profit (including NFP Corporation) **Service:** General medical and surgical

Staffed Beds: 167 **Admissions:** 10759 **Census:** 97 **Outpatient Visits:** 120460 **Births:** 2111 **Total Expense ($000):** 261986 **Payroll Expense ($000):** 63411 **Personnel:** 1214

CARLINVILLE—Macoupin County

★ **CARLINVILLE AREA HOSPITAL (141347)**, 20733 North Broad Street, Zip 62626–1499; tel. 217/854–3141 **A**10 18 **F**11 15 28 29 34 35 40 45 64 77 79 81 91 93 107 110 115 127 129 133 148 149 **P**6 **S** HealthTech Management Services, Brentwood, TN
Primary Contact: Kenneth G. Reid, President and Chief Executive Officer
CFO: Mike Brown, Chief Financial Officer
CMO: Therese Polo, Medical Staff President
CIO: Jerod Cottingham, Director Information Systems
CHR: Tracy Koster, Director Human Resources
CNO: Sara McPeak, Chief Nursing Officer
Web address: www.cahcare.com
Control: Other not–for–profit (including NFP Corporation) **Service:** General medical and surgical

Staffed Beds: 25 **Admissions:** 709 **Census:** 10 **Outpatient Visits:** 22487 **Births:** 0 **Total Expense ($000):** 22836 **Payroll Expense ($000):** 8354 **Personnel:** 172

CARROLLTON—Greene County

THOMAS H. BOYD MEMORIAL HOSPITAL (141300), 800 School Street, Zip 62016–1498; tel. 217/942–6946, (Nonreporting) **A**10 18
Primary Contact: Deborah Campbell, Administrator
CHR: Lisa Eldridge, Human Resources Officer
Control: Other not–for–profit (including NFP Corporation) **Service:** General medical and surgical

Staffed Beds: 65

CARTHAGE—Hancock County

☐ **MEMORIAL HOSPITAL (141305)**, 1454 North County Road 2050, Zip 62321–3551, Mailing Address: P.O.Box 160, 62321–0160; tel. 217/357–8500 **A**1 10 18 **F**3 11 13 15 28 29 30 31 34 35 36 40 45 56 57 59 64 75 76 80 81 82 85 87 103 104 107 108 110 115 119 125 127 129 130 132 133 144 146
Primary Contact: Ada Bair, Chief Executive Officer
COO: Florine Dixon, Chief Operating Officer
CFO: Teresa Smith, Chief Financial Officer
CIO: Syndi Horn, Director Information Systems
CHR: Dan Smith, Director Human Resources
Web address: www.mhtlc.org
Control: Other not–for–profit (including NFP Corporation) **Service:** General medical and surgical

Staffed Beds: 18 **Admissions:** 541 **Census:** 5 **Outpatient Visits:** 52507 **Births:** 118 **Total Expense ($000):** 24854 **Payroll Expense ($000):** 10153 **Personnel:** 186

CENTRALIA—Marion County

⊞ **SSM HEALTH ST. MARY'S HOSPITAL CENTRALIA (140034)**, 400 North Pleasant Avenue, Zip 62801–3056; tel. 618/436–8000 **A**1 2 10 **F**3 5 11 12 13 15 18 20 26 28 29 30 31 32 34 35 37 38 40 44 45 46 50 54 56 57 59 60 61 64 68 70 73 74 75 76 77 78 79 80 81 82 84 85 86 87 89 90 91 92 93 94 98 99 100 101 102 103 104 105 107 108 110 111 114 118 119 120 121 129 130 131 132 135 144 146 147 148 149 **P**6 8 **S** SSM Health, Saint Louis, MO
Primary Contact: John R. Sigsbury, President
COO: Mark A Clark, Vice President Operations
CFO: Deland Evischi, Chief Financial Officer
CMO: Rajendra Shroff M.D., Administrative Medical Director
CIO: Steve Murphy, Director Information Systems
CHR: Brenda Alexander, System Vice President, Human Resources
CNO: Sherry Dunlay R.N., MSN, Vice President Patient Care Services and Chief Nursing Officer
Web address: www.ssmhealthillinois.com
Control: Church operated, Nongovernment, not–for–profit **Service:** General medical and surgical

Staffed Beds: 124 **Admissions:** 5152 **Census:** 51 **Outpatient Visits:** 203178 **Births:** 313 **Total Expense ($000):** 94068 **Payroll Expense ($000):** 32372 **Personnel:** 848

IL

CENTREVILLE—St. Clair County

☐ **TOUCHETTE REGIONAL HOSPITAL (140077)**, 5900 Bond Avenue, Zip 62207–2326; tel. 618/332–3060 **A**1 10 **F**3 11 13 15 18 29 39 40 45 47 50 54 55 62 64 68 70 73 75 76 79 81 85 87 92 98 99 101 102 103 104 105 107 108 110 114 119 125 130 135 143 146 148 149
Primary Contact: Larry W. McCulley, President and Chief Executive Officer
COO: Tom Mikkelson M.D., Interim Chief Operating Officer
CFO: John Majchrzak, Chief Financial Officer
CMO: Tom Mikkelson M.D., Vice President Medical Affairs
Web address: www.touchette.org
Control: Other not–for–profit (including NFP Corporation) **Service**: General medical and surgical

Staffed Beds: 121 **Admissions**: 2656 **Census**: 27 **Outpatient Visits**: 57489 **Births**: 210 **Total Expense ($000)**: 58579 **Payroll Expense ($000)**: 25999 **Personnel**: 475

CHAMPAIGN—Champaign County

☐ **THE PAVILION (144029)**, 809 West Church Street, Zip 61820–3399; tel. 217/373–1700, (Nonreporting) **A**1 10 **S** Universal Health Services, Inc., King of Prussia, PA
Primary Contact: Joseph Sheehy, Chief Executive Officer and Managing Director
CFO: Edith Frasca, Controller and Chief Financial Officer
Web address: www.pavilionhospital.com
Control: Corporation, Investor–owned (for–profit) **Service**: Psychiatric

Staffed Beds: 46

CHESTER—Randolph County

☐ **CHESTER MENTAL HEALTH CENTER**, Chester Road, Zip 62233–0031, Mailing Address: Box 31, 62233–0031; tel. 618/826–4571, (Nonreporting) **A**1 **S** Division of Mental Health, Department of Human Services, Springfield, IL
Primary Contact: Leah Hammel, Acting Administrator
CFO: Sarah Imhoff, Business Administrator
CMO: Maitra Rupa M.D., Acting Medical Director
CIO: Anthony Young, Information Services Specialist
CHR: Kim Holsapple, Human Resource Specialist
CNO: Jennifer Klingeman, Director of Nursing
Control: State, Government, Nonfederal **Service**: Psychiatric

Staffed Beds: 245

☐ **MEMORIAL HOSPITAL (141338)**, 1900 State Street, Zip 62233–1116, Mailing Address: P.O.Box 609, 62233–0609; tel. 618/826–4581, (Nonreporting) **A**1 10 18
Primary Contact: Brett Bollmann, Administrator
CFO: Gail Miesner, Chief Financial Officer
CMO: Alan Liefer M.D., President Medical Staff
CIO: Becky Bunselmeyer, Director Information Services
CHR: May Rose, Director Human Resources
Web address: www.mhchester.com
Control: Hospital district or authority, Government, Nonfederal **Service**: General medical and surgical

Staffed Beds: 25

CHICAGO—Cook County

ADVOCATE BETHANY HOSPITAL See RML Specialty Hospital

★ ⇑ **ADVOCATE ILLINOIS MASONIC MEDICAL CENTER (140182)**, 836 West Wellington Avenue, Zip 60657–5147; tel. 773/975–1600 **A**2 3 5 8 10 13 21 **F**3 12 13 15 17 18 20 22 24 26 28 29 30 31 32 34 35 37 38 40 43 44 45 46 47 48 49 50 53 54 55 56 57 58 59 60 61 64 66 68 70 71 72 73 74 75 76 77 78 79 81 82 84 85 86 87 89 90 92 93 96 97 98 99 100 101 102 103 104 107 110 111 115 117 118 119 120 123 124 126 129 130 131 132 134 141 143 146 147 148 149 **P**8 **S** Advocate Health Care, Downers Grove, IL
Primary Contact: Susan Nordstrom. Lopez, President
CFO: Jack Gilbert, Vice President Finance and Facilities
CMO: Clifton Clarke, Vice President Medical Management
CIO: Chuck Malik, Director Information Systems
CHR: Katie Bata, Vice President Human Resources
CNO: Donna King R.N., FACHE, Vice President Clinical Operations and Chief Nursing Executive
Web address: www.advocatehealth.com/masonic
Control: Other not–for–profit (including NFP Corporation) **Service**: General medical and surgical

Staffed Beds: 336 **Admissions**: 14668 **Census**: 183 **Outpatient Visits**: 182119 **Births**: 2209 **Total Expense ($000)**: 361124 **Payroll Expense ($000)**: 140043 **Personnel**: 2266

★ ⇑ **ADVOCATE TRINITY HOSPITAL (140048)**, 2320 East 93rd Street, Zip 60617–3909; tel. 773/967–2000 **A**10 21 **F**1 3 4 13 15 16 17 18 20 22 24 26 28 29 30 31 34 35 40 45 49 50 55 56 57 58 59 60 61 64 65 67 68 70 72 73 74 75 76 77 78 79 80 81 82 87 88 89 90 92 93 98 107 110 111 114 115 119 126 128 130 132 135 146 148 **P**8 **S** Advocate Health Care, Downers Grove, IL
Primary Contact: Terika Richardson, M.P.H., President
COO: Dan Doherty, Vice President, Operations
CFO: Maureen Morrison, Vice President, Finance
CMO: James Keller M.D., Vice President, Medical Management
CIO: Bonita Brown–Roberts, Director Information Systems
CHR: Kristin Landini, Vice President, Human Resources
CNO: Jacquelyn Whitten MSN, R.N., Chief Nurse Executive and Vice President, Nursing
Web address: www.advocatehealth.com/trin/
Control: Other not–for–profit (including NFP Corporation) **Service**: General medical and surgical

Staffed Beds: 186 **Admissions**: 8645 **Census**: 97 **Outpatient Visits**: 74260 **Births**: 960 **Total Expense ($000)**: 150918 **Payroll Expense ($000)**: 54142 **Personnel**: 845

⊠ **ANN & ROBERT H. LURIE CHILDREN'S HOSPITAL OF CHICAGO (143300)**, 225 East Chicago Avenue, Zip 60611–2991; tel. 312/227–4000 **A**1 3 5 8 10 **F**3 8 9 11 12 17 18 19 21 23 24 25 27 29 30 31 32 34 35 36 37 38 39 40 41 43 44 45 46 48 49 50 51 52 54 55 57 58 59 60 61 63 64 65 68 72 74 75 78 79 81 82 84 85 86 87 88 89 91 92 93 94 96 97 98 99 100 101 102 104 105 107 108 111 115 116 117 118 119 124 126 129 130 131 132 134 136 137 138 139 141 142 144 146 148 149 150
Primary Contact: Patrick M. Magoon, President and Chief Executive Officer
COO: Michelle Stephenson R.N., Executive Vice President & Chief Operations Officer
CFO: Ron Blaustein, Chief Financial Officer
CMO: Michael Kelleher, Chief Medical Officer
CIO: Lisa Dykstra, Senior Vice President and Chief Information Officer
CHR: Joani Duncan, Chief Human Resource Officer
CNO: Brian M Stahulak R.N., Chief Nursing Officer
Web address: www.luriechildrens.org
Control: Other not–for–profit (including NFP Corporation) **Service**: Children's general medical and surgical

Staffed Beds: 288 **Admissions**: 12428 **Census**: 213 **Outpatient Visits**: 593350 **Births**: 0 **Total Expense ($000)**: 694757 **Payroll Expense ($000)**: 288834 **Personnel**: 5284

BERNARD MITCHELL HOSPITAL See University Of Chicago Medical Center

☐ **CHICAGO LAKESHORE HOSPITAL (144005)**, 4840 North Marine Drive, Zip 60640–4296; tel. 773/878–9700, (Nonreporting) **A**1 3 5 10 **S** Signature Healthcare Services, Corona, CA
Primary Contact: Patrick Moallemian, Chief Executive Officer
CFO: Carol Peart, Chief Financial Officer
CMO: Peter Nierman M.D., Chief Medical Officer
CHR: Michelle Culpepper, Director Human Resources
Web address: www.chicagolakeshorehospital.com
Control: Corporation, Investor–owned (for–profit) **Service**: Psychiatric

Staffed Beds: 115

CHICAGO LYING–IN (CLI) See University Of Chicago Medical Center

☐ **CHICAGO–READ MENTAL HEALTH CENTER (144010)**, 4200 North Oak Park Avenue, Zip 60634–1457; tel. 773/794–4000, (Nonreporting) **A**1 10 **S** Division of Mental Health, Department of Human Services, Springfield, IL
Primary Contact: Richard Carmik, Facility Director and Hospital Administrator
Control: State, Government, Nonfederal **Service**: Psychiatric

Staffed Beds: 200

CHILDREN'S MEMORIAL HOSPITAL See Ann & Robert H. Lurie Children's Hospital of Chicago

COMER CHILDREN'S HOSPITAL See University Of Chicago Medical Center

☐ **COMMUNITY FIRST MEDICAL CENTER (140251)**, 5645 West Addison Street, Zip 60634–4403; tel. 773/282–7000, (Nonreporting) **A**1 3 10
Primary Contact: Dennis FitzMaurice, Interim Chief Executive Officer
COO: Dennis FitzMaurice, Vice President, Professional Services
CFO: Richard Franco, Chief Financial Officer
CMO: David Bordo M.D., Vice President and Chief Medical Officer
CIO: George Chessum, Senior Vice President and Chief Information Officer
CHR: Ivy McKinley, Regional Human Resources Officer
Web address: www.cfmedicalcenter.com
Control: Church operated, Nongovernment, not–for–profit **Service**: General medical and surgical

Staffed Beds: 279

Many Facility Codes have changed. Please refer to the AHA Guide Code Chart.
© 2017 AHA Guide

IL

☐ **GARFIELD PARK HOSPITAL (144039)**, 520 North Ridgeway Avenue, Zip 60624–1232; tel. 773/265–3700 **A**1 10 **S** Universal Health Services, Inc., King of Prussia, PA
Primary Contact: Len Kirby, Chief Executive Officer
CMO: Tina Mahera M.D., Chief Medical Officer
CHR: Janice Clark, Manager Human Resources
Web address: www.garfieldparkhospital.com
Control: Corporation, Investor–owned (for–profit) **Service**: Children's hospital psychiatric

Staffed Beds: 88

☐ **HARTGROVE HOSPITAL (144026)**, 5730 West Roosevelt Road, Zip 60644–1580; tel. 773/413–1700, (Nonreporting) **A**1 10 **S** Universal Health Services, Inc., King of Prussia, PA
Primary Contact: Steven Airhart, Chief Executive Officer
CFO: Srbo Nikolic, Chief Financial Officer
CMO: Johnny Williamson M.D., Chief Medical Officer
CHR: Anthony Rivera, Director Human Resources
CNO: Jody Bhambra, Chief Nursing Officer
Web address: www.hartgrovehospital.com
Control: Corporation, Investor–owned (for–profit) **Service**: Psychiatric

Staffed Beds: 128

★ ○ **HOLY CROSS HOSPITAL (140133)**, 2701 West 68th Street, Zip 60629–1882; tel. 773/884–9000, (Nonreporting) **A**10 11 **S** Sinai Health System, Chicago, IL
Primary Contact: Lori Pacura, MSN, R.N., President
COO: Donnica Austin, Vice President, Operations
CFO: Charles Weis, Executive Vice President and Chief Financial Officer
CMO: James Richardson, Chief Medical Officer
CIO: Ben Patel, Chief Information Officer
CHR: Ann Hatches, Director, Human Resources
CNO: Deborah Davisson MSN, Chief Nursing Officer and Vice President, Patient Care Services
Web address: www.holycrosshospital.org
Control: Corporation, Investor–owned (for–profit) **Service**: General medical and surgical

Staffed Beds: 213

☐ **JACKSON PARK HOSPITAL AND MEDICAL CENTER (140177)**, 7531 Stony Island Avenue, Zip 60649–3993; tel. 773/947–7500, (Nonreporting) **A**1 3 10
Primary Contact: William Dorsey, M.D., Board Chairman and Chief Executive Officer
COO: Randall Smith, Executive Vice President
CFO: Nelson Vasquez, Vice President Finance
CMO: Bangalore Murthy M.D., Director Medical Staff
CIO: Thomas Pankow, Chief Information Officer
CHR: Tracey Jones, Director Human Resources
Web address: www.jacksonparkhospital.org
Control: Other not–for–profit (including NFP Corporation) **Service**: General medical and surgical

Staffed Beds: 118

⊞ △ **JESSE BROWN VETERANS AFFAIRS MEDICAL CENTER**, 820 South Damen, Zip 60612–3776; tel. 312/569–8387 **A**1 3 5 7 **F**2 3 5 8 10 11 12 14 15 17 18 20 22 24 26 28 29 30 31 34 35 38 39 40 44 45 46 47 48 50 53 54 56 57 58 59 60 61 62 63 64 65 68 70 71 74 75 77 78 79 80 81 82 84 85 86 87 93 94 97 98 100 101 102 104 105 106 107 111 119 126 127 129 130 132 133 135 143 144 146 147 148 149 150 **S** Department of Veterans Affairs, Washington, DC
Primary Contact: Marc Magill, Director
COO: Michelle Blakely, Associate Director
CFO: Kalpana Mehta, Chief Fiscal Services
CMO: Wendy W Brown M.D., M.P.H., Chief of Staff
CIO: Howard Loewenstein, Chief Information Resource Management Services
CHR: Wayne Davis, Manager Human Resources
Web address: www.chicago.va.gov/
Control: Veterans Affairs, Government, federal **Service**: General medical and surgical

Staffed Beds: 207 Admissions: 8452 Census: 171 Outpatient Visits: 926154 Births: 0 Total Expense ($000): 459754 Payroll Expense ($000): 222565

⊞ **JOHN H. STROGER JR. HOSPITAL OF COOK COUNTY (140124)**, 1969 West Ogden Avenue, Zip 60612–3714; tel. 312/864–6000 **A**1 2 3 5 8 10 13 **F**3 5 11 13 15 16 17 18 19 20 22 24 29 30 31 34 35 36 38 39 40 41 43 44 45 46 47 48 49 50 51 52 54 55 56 57 58 59 60 61 64 65 68 70 72 74 75 76 77 78 79 81 82 84 85 86 87 88 89 91 92 93 94 97 99 100 101 102 103 104 107 108 110 111 114 115 118 119 121 123 129 130 132 134 135 146 147 148 149 **P**6 **S** Cook County Health and Hospitals System, Chicago, IL
Primary Contact: John Jay. Shannon, M.D., Chief Executive Officer
CFO: John R Morales, Chief Financial Officer
CMO: Claudia Fegan M.D., Chief Medical Officer
CIO: Bala Hota, Interim Chief Information Officer
CHR: Paris I Partee, Associate Administrator and Director Human Resources
CNO: Antoinette Williams, Chief Nursing Officer
Web address: www.cookcountyhealth.net
Control: County, Government, Nonfederal **Service**: General medical and surgical

Staffed Beds: 450 Admissions: 21085 Census: 266 Outpatient Visits: 947864 Births: 887 Total Expense ($000): 988389 Payroll Expense ($000): 469397 Personnel: 5438

JOHNSTON R. BOWMAN HEALTH CENTER See Rush University Medical Center

KINDRED CHICAGO LAKESHORE See Kindred Chicago–Central Hospital

⊞ **KINDRED CHICAGO–CENTRAL HOSPITAL (142009)**, 4058 West Melrose Street, Zip 60641–4797; tel. 773/736–7000, (Nonreporting) (Includes KINDRED CHICAGO LAKESHORE, 6130 North Sheridan Road, Chicago, Illinois, Zip 60660, tel. 773/381–1222; Diane Otteman, Chief Executive Officer; KINDRED HOSPITAL CHICAGO NORTH, 2544 West Montrose Avenue, Chicago, Illinois, Zip 60618–1589, tel. 773/267–2622; Larry Foster, R.N., MSN, Chief Executive Officer) **A**1 10 **S** Kindred Healthcare, Louisville, KY
Primary Contact: , R.N., MSN
COO: Joanne Garcia, Chief Operating Officer
CFO: Mary Treacy Shiff, Chief Financial Officer
Web address: www.khchicagocentral.com
Control: Corporation, Investor–owned (for–profit) **Service**: Acute long–term care hospital

Staffed Beds: 187

KINDRED HOSPITAL CHICAGO NORTH See Kindred Chicago–Central Hospital

⊞ **LA RABIDA CHILDREN'S HOSPITAL (143301)**, 6501 South Promontory Drive, Zip 60649–1003; tel. 773/363–6700 **A**1 3 5 10 **F**3 12 19 28 29 32 34 35 38 40 41 50 57 59 64 65 74 75 77 79 82 84 85 86 87 89 91 93 94 96 97 99 100 101 104 107 119 130 132 134 143 144 146 148 149 **P**6
Primary Contact: Brenda J. Wolf, President and Chief Executive Officer
CFO: Mark Renfree, Chief Financial Officer
CMO: David Soglin, Chief Medical Officer
CIO: Sheelah Cabrera, Chief Information Officer
CHR: Frances Lefkow, Director Human Resources
CNO: Aden Henry R.N., Vice President, Patient Care
Web address: www.larabida.org
Control: Other not–for–profit (including NFP Corporation) **Service**: Children's chronic disease

Staffed Beds: 30 Admissions: 432 Census: 22 Outpatient Visits: 28008 Births: 0 Total Expense ($000): 52154 Payroll Expense ($000): 25371 Personnel: 430

☐ **LORETTO HOSPITAL (140083)**, 645 South Central Avenue, Zip 60644–5059; tel. 773/626–4300, (Nonreporting) **A**1 10
Primary Contact: Sonia Mehta, M.D., Chief Executive Officer and Chief Medical Officer
CFO: John Valles, Senior Vice President and Chief Financial Officer
CMO: Sonia Mehta M.D., Chief Executive Officer and Chief Medical Officer
CIO: Suresh Krishnan, Vice President and Chief Information Officer
CHR: Amy Coleman, Director Human Resources
CNO: James M Renneker MSN, R.N., FACHE, Vice President and Chief Nursing Officer
Web address: www.lorettohospital.org
Control: Other not–for–profit (including NFP Corporation) **Service**: General medical and surgical

Staffed Beds: 147

IL

✠ **LOUIS A. WEISS MEMORIAL HOSPITAL (140082)**, 4646 North Marine Drive, Zip 60640–5759; tel. 773/878–8700 **A**1 2 3 5 10 **F**3 8 9 15 18 20 22 24 26 28 29 30 31 34 35 36 40 44 45 49 52 56 57 58 59 61 64 65 66 68 70 74 75 77 78 79 81 82 85 86 87 90 91 92 93 96 97 98 100 101 102 103 107 108 109 110 111 114 115 119 121 126 129 130 131 132 135 141 143 146 147 148 149 150 **P**5 6 8 **S** TENET Healthcare Corporation, Dallas, TX
Primary Contact: Charles Orlando, Interim Chief Executive Officer
CFO: Jeffrey L Meigs, Chief Financial Officer
CIO: Thomas Crawford, Chicago Market Chief Information Officer
CHR: Keoni Nader, Director Human Resources
Web address: www.weisshospital.com
Control: Corporation, Investor–owned (for–profit) **Service**: General medical and surgical

Staffed Beds: 153 **Admissions:** 5767 **Census:** 90 **Outpatient Visits:** 68295 **Births:** 0

★ ○ **MERCY HOSPITAL AND MEDICAL CENTER (140158)**, 2525 South Michigan Avenue, Zip 60616–2333; tel. 312/567–2000 **A**2 3 5 10 11 **F**3 5 12 13 15 17 18 20 22 24 26 28 29 30 31 32 33 34 35 36 40 44 45 46 49 50 51 53 54 55 56 57 58 59 61 64 65 66 70 74 76 77 78 79 81 82 84 85 86 87 89 90 91 92 93 96 97 98 99 100 101 102 103 104 105 107 108 110 111 114 115 117 118 119 120 121 123 124 126 129 130 131 132 133 134 135 143 144 145 146 147 148 149 150 **P**1 5 **S** Trinity Health, Livonia, MI
Primary Contact: Carol L. Schneider, President and Chief Executive Officer
COO: Richard Cerceo, Executive Vice President and Chief Operating Officer
CFO: Eric Krueger, Chief Financial Officer
CMO: Michael McDonnell M.D., Chief Medical Officer
CIO: John Romeo, Chief Information Officer
CHR: Nancy L Hill–Davis, Vice President Human Resources
CNO: Carla Campbell R.N., Chief Nurse Officer
Web address: www.mercy–chicago.org
Control: Other not–for–profit (including NFP Corporation) **Service**: General medical and surgical

Staffed Beds: 189 **Admissions:** 14454 **Census:** 170 **Outpatient Visits:** 414631 **Births:** 2408 **Personnel:** 1454

○ **METHODIST HOSPITAL OF CHICAGO (140197)**, 5025 North Paulina Street, Zip 60640–2772; tel. 773/271–9040, (Nonreporting) **A**10 11
Primary Contact: Joseph Chandy, Administrator
CFO: Jim Gregory, Controller
Web address: www.bethanymethodist.org
Control: Other not–for–profit (including NFP Corporation) **Service**: General medical and surgical

Staffed Beds: 189

✠ **MOUNT SINAI HOSPITAL (140018)**, 1500 South Fairfield Avenue, Zip 60608–1729; tel. 773/542–2000, (Includes SINAI CHILDREN'S HOSPITAL, California Avenue at 15th Street, Chicago, Illinois, Zip 60608, tel. 773/542–2000; Karen Teitelbaum, President and Chief Executive Officer) **A**1 2 3 5 8 10 **F**3 5 11 12 13 15 17 18 19 20 22 24 25 26 28 29 30 31 32 34 35 38 40 43 44 45 49 50 55 56 57 58 59 60 61 64 65 66 68 70 72 74 75 76 78 79 81 82 84 85 86 87 88 89 97 98 99 100 101 102 103 104 107 108 110 111 114 115 118 119 121 123 130 132 134 135 143 144 146 147 148 149 150 **P**8 **S** Sinai Health System, Chicago, IL
Primary Contact: Loren Chandler, President
CFO: Charles Weis, Chief Financial Officer
CMO: Mark Multach M.D., Chief Medical Officer
CIO: Ben Patel, Chief Information Officer
CHR: Ann Hatches, Interim Director Human Resources
CNO: Michele A Mazurek, Interim Vice President Patient Care Services and Chief Nursing Officer
Web address: www.sinai.org
Control: Other not–for–profit (including NFP Corporation) **Service**: General medical and surgical

Staffed Beds: 288 **Admissions:** 14024 **Census:** 179 **Outpatient Visits:** 217369 **Births:** 2172 **Total Expense ($000):** 256858 **Payroll Expense ($000):** 112837 **Personnel:** 1549

✠ **NORTHWESTERN MEMORIAL HOSPITAL (140281)**, 251 East Huron Street, Zip 60611–2908; tel. 312/926–2000, (Includes PRENTICE WOMEN'S HOSPITAL, 250 East Superior Street, Chicago, Illinois, Zip 60611, tel. 312/926–2000; STONE INSTITUTE OF PSYCHIATRY, 251 East Huron Street, Chicago, Illinois, Zip 60611, tel. 312/926–2000) **A**1 2 3 5 8 10 **F**3 4 5 6 8 9 11 12 13 14 15 17 18 20 22 24 26 28 29 30 31 33 34 35 36 37 38 39 40 43 44 45 46 47 48 49 50 51 52 54 55 56 57 58 59 60 61 63 64 65 66 68 70 72 73 74 75 76 77 78 79 80 81 82 83 84 85 86 87 92 93 96 97 98 100 101 102 103 104 107 108 110 111 114 115 116 117 118 119 120 121 123 124 126 129 130 131 132 135 136 137 138 139 140 141 142 144 146 147 148 149 150 **P**6 **S** Northwestern Memorial HealthCare, Chicago, IL
Primary Contact: Dean M. Harrison, Chief Executive Officer
CFO: Francis D Fraher, Vice President and Chief Financial Officer, Northwestern Memorial Hospital
CMO: Gary Noskin, Senior Vice President and Chief Medical Officer, Northwestern Memorial Hospital
CIO: Carl Christensen, Senior Vice President and Chief Information Officer, Northwestern Memorial HealthCare
CHR: Dean Manheimer, Senior Vice President Human Resources, Northwestern Memorial Healthcare
CNO: Kristin Ramsey R.N., Senior Vice President and Chief Nursing Executive, Northwestern Memorial Hospital
Web address: www.nm.org
Control: Other not–for–profit (including NFP Corporation) **Service**: General medical and surgical

Staffed Beds: 882 **Admissions:** 44805 **Census:** 653 **Outpatient Visits:** 1696296 **Births:** 11694 **Total Expense ($000):** 2153948 **Payroll Expense ($000):** 792595 **Personnel:** 9739

✠ **NORWEGIAN AMERICAN HOSPITAL (140206)**, 1044 North Francisco Avenue, Zip 60622–2743; tel. 773/292–8200, (Nonreporting) **A**1 3 5 10
Primary Contact: Jose R. Sanchez, President and Chief Executive Officer
COO: Justin Bynum, Chief Operating Officer
CFO: Gary M Krugel, Chief Financial Officer
CMO: James Kolka D.O., Chief Medical Officer
CIO: Stephen DePooter, Chief Information Officer
CHR: Neil Teatsorth, Vice President Human Resources
CNO: Deborah Jones, Interim Chief Nursing Officer
Web address: www.nahospital.org
Control: Other not–for–profit (including NFP Corporation) **Service**: General medical and surgical

Staffed Beds: 195

OUR LADY OF THE RESURRECTION MEDICAL CENTER See Community First Medical Center

PRENTICE WOMEN'S HOSPITAL See Northwestern Memorial Hospital

✠ △ **PRESENCE RESURRECTION MEDICAL CENTER (140117)**, 7435 West Talcott Avenue, Zip 60631–3746; tel. 773/774–8000 **A**1 2 3 5 7 10 13 **F**3 11 13 15 17 18 19 20 22 24 26 27 28 29 30 31 34 35 37 38 39 40 41 45 46 47 49 50 53 57 58 59 60 62 64 66 68 70 73 74 75 76 78 79 81 82 83 84 85 86 87 89 90 91 93 96 97 100 107 108 110 111 114 115 117 118 119 120 121 123 124 126 130 131 132 133 135 146 147 148 **S** Presence Health, Chicago, IL
Primary Contact: Robert Dahl, President and Chief Executive Officer
CFO: Colleen Koppenhaver, Interim Chief Financial Officer
CMO: David Bordo M.D., Chief Medical Officer
CHR: Ivy McKinley, Regional Lead Human Resources
CNO: Pam Bell, Vice President Patient Care Services and Chief Nursing Officer
Web address: www.presencehealth.org
Control: Church operated, Nongovernment, not–for–profit **Service**: General medical and surgical

Staffed Beds: 333 **Admissions:** 12480 **Census:** 184 **Outpatient Visits:** 191282 **Births:** 1071 **Total Expense ($000):** 264570 **Payroll Expense ($000):** 93835 **Personnel:** 1376

✠ **PRESENCE SAINT JOSEPH HOSPITAL (140224)**, 2900 North Lake Shore Drive, Zip 60657–6274; tel. 773/665–3000 **A**1 2 3 5 10 **F**3 5 8 11 12 13 15 18 19 20 22 24 25 26 28 29 30 31 32 33 34 35 36 38 39 40 41 45 46 47 48 49 50 53 54 55 56 57 58 59 60 61 63 64 65 66 68 70 72 74 75 76 77 78 79 81 82 84 85 86 87 89 90 92 93 96 97 98 100 101 102 103 104 107 108 110 111 114 115 117 118 119 120 121 122 123 124 126 128 129 130 131 132 135 143 145 146 147 148 **P**8 **S** Presence Health, Chicago, IL
Primary Contact: James L. Robinson III, PsyD, President
CFO: Stanley Kazmierczak, Controller
CMO: M Todd Grendon M.D., President Medical Staff
CIO: George Chessum, Senior Vice President Information Systems and Chief Information Officer
CHR: Denise Brown, Vice President Human Resources
Web address: www.reshealth.org
Control: Church operated, Nongovernment, not–for–profit **Service**: General medical and surgical

Staffed Beds: 361 **Admissions:** 11919 **Census:** 173 **Outpatient Visits:** 107809 **Births:** 1332 **Total Expense ($000):** 225789 **Payroll Expense ($000):** 77049 **Personnel:** 1156

IL

☒ **PRESENCE SAINTS MARY & ELIZABETH MEDICAL CENTER (140180)**, 2233 West Division Street, Zip 60622–3086; tel. 312/770–2000, (Includes PRESENCE SAINTS MARY & ELIZABETH MEDICAL CENTER, CLAREMONT AVENUE, 1431 North Claremont Avenue, Chicago, Illinois, Zip 60622–1791, tel. 773/278–2000; Martin H Judd, Regional President and Chief Executive Officer) (Total facility includes 28 beds in nursing home–type unit) **A** 1 2 3 5 10 **F** 3 4 13 15 18 19 20 22 24 26 28 29 30 31 32 34 35 36 38 40 45 47 49 50 52 57 58 59 60 64 65 66 68 70 74 75 76 77 78 79 81 82 84 85 86 87 89 90 91 92 93 94 96 98 99 100 101 102 103 107 108 110 111 114 115 116 117 119 120 121 123 126 128 129 130 132 135 143 146 147 148 149 150 **P** 8 **S** Presence Health, Chicago, IL
Primary Contact: Martin H. Judd, Regional President and Chief Executive Officer
CFO: Bob Cech, Regional Finance Officer
CMO: Laura Concannon M.D., Regional Chief Medical Officer
CIO: David Lundal, System Vice President, Information Systems and Chief Information Officer
CHR: Melanie Saenz, Regional Human Resources Officer
CNO: Suzanne Lambert R.N., Regional Chief Nursing Officer and Support Services
Web address: www.presencehealth.org/presence–saints–mary–and–elizabeth–medical–center–chicago
Control: Church operated, Nongovernment, not–for–profit **Service:** General medical and surgical

Staffed Beds: 492 **Admissions:** 18624 **Census:** 287 **Outpatient Visits:** 204844 **Births:** 1412 **Total Expense ($000):** 289639 **Payroll Expense ($000):** 97427 **Personnel:** 1538

☒ **PROVIDENT HOSPITAL OF COOK COUNTY (140300)**, 500 East 51st Street, Zip 60615–2494; tel. 312/572–2000 **A** 1 3 5 10 **F** 3 8 15 18 29 30 34 35 40 45 50 53 57 59 61 64 66 68 70 78 81 85 87 92 94 104 107 119 130 132 135 143 146 147 149 **S** Cook County Health and Hospitals System, Chicago, IL
Primary Contact: John Jay. Shannon, M.D., Chief Executive Officer
CFO: Barbara Patterson, Chief Financial Officer
CMO: Aaron Hamb M.D., Chief Medical Officer
CIO: Donna Hart, Chief Information Officer
Web address: www.ccbhs.org/pages/ProvidentHospitalofCookCounty.htm
Control: County, Government, Nonfederal **Service:** General medical and surgical

Staffed Beds: 25 **Admissions:** 710 **Census:** 8 **Outpatient Visits:** 31302 **Births:** 0 **Total Expense ($000):** 59778 **Payroll Expense ($000):** 35705 **Personnel:** 372

RESURRECTION MEDICAL CENTER See Presence Resurrection Medical Center

★ **RML SPECIALTY HOSPITAL (142012)**, 3435 West Van Buren Street, Zip 60624–3312; tel. 773/826–6300 **F** 1 3 18 29 30 31 45 53 58 74 85 107 114 119 130 146 148 149 **P** 6
Primary Contact: James R. Prister, President and Chief Executive Officer
COO: Ken Pawola, Chief Operating Officer
CFO: Tom Pater, Vice President Finance and Chief Financial Officer
CMO: Patrick Fahey M.D., Chief Medical Director
CIO: Vincent S Vitali, Chief Information Officer
CHR: John Landstrom, Vice President Human Resources and Operations
CNO: Marti Edwards MSN, R.N., Chief Nursing Officer
Web address: www.rmlspecialtyhospital.org
Control: Other not–for–profit (including NFP Corporation) **Service:** Acute long–term care hospital

Staffed Beds: 69 **Admissions:** 626 **Census:** 55 **Outpatient Visits:** 0 **Births:** 0 **Total Expense ($000):** 33062 **Payroll Expense ($000):** 16922 **Personnel:** 305

○ **ROSELAND COMMUNITY HOSPITAL (140068)**, 45 West 111th Street, Zip 60628–4294; tel. 773/995–3000, (Nonreporting) **A** 10 11
Primary Contact: Timothy Egan, President and Chief Executive Officer
CMO: Rogelio Cave M.D., Medical Director
CIO: William Spence, Director
CNO: Winifred Lewis R.N., Chief Nursing Officer
Web address: www.roselandhospital.org
Control: Other not–for–profit (including NFP Corporation) **Service:** General medical and surgical

Staffed Beds: 115

☒ △ **RUSH UNIVERSITY MEDICAL CENTER (140119)**, 1653 West Congress Parkway, Zip 60612–3833; tel. 312/942–5000, (Includes JOHNSTON R. BOWMAN HEALTH CENTER, 700 South Paulina, Chicago, Illinois, Zip 60612, tel. 312/942–7000; RUSH CHILDREN'S HOSPITAL, 1653 Wes Congress Parkway, Chicago, Illinois, Zip 60612–3833, tel. 888/352–7874) **A** 1 2 3 5 7 8 10 **F** 2 3 6 8 9 11 12 13 14 15 17 18 19 20 21 22 23 24 25 26 27 28 29 30 31 32 34 35 36 37 38 39 40 41 43 44 45 46 47 48 49 50 51 52 53 54 55 56 57 58 59 60 61 62 63 64 65 66 68 70 72 73 74 75 76 77 78 79 81 82 83 84 85 86 87 88 89 90 91 92 93 94 95 96 97 98 99 100 101 102 103 104 105 107 110 111 114 115 117 118 119 120 121 123 124 125 126 129 130 131 132 134 135 136 137 138 139 141 142 145 146 147 148 149 **P** 8 **S** Rush University Medical Center, Chicago, IL
Primary Contact: Larry J. Goodman, M.D., Chief Executive Officer
COO: Michael J Dandorph, President and Chief Operating Officer
CFO: John P Mordach, Senior Vice President and Chief Financial Officer
CMO: David A Ansell M.D., Senior Vice President Clinical Affairs and Chief Medical Officer
CIO: Lac Tran, Senior Vice President Information Services
CHR: Mary Ellen Schopp, Senior Vice President Human Resources
CNO: Angelique Richard R.N., Ph.D., Vice President Clinical Nursing, Chief Nursing Officer and Associate Dean for Practice, College of Nursing
Web address: www.rush.edu
Control: Other not–for–profit (including NFP Corporation) **Service:** General medical and surgical

Staffed Beds: 673 **Admissions:** 31962 **Census:** 495 **Outpatient Visits:** 611514 **Births:** 2338 **Total Expense ($000):** 1118406 **Payroll Expense ($000):** 313313 **Personnel:** 8794

☒ **SAINT ANTHONY HOSPITAL (140095)**, 2875 West 19th Street, Zip 60623–3596; tel. 773/484–1000 **A** 1 3 10 **F** 3 13 15 18 19 29 30 31 32 34 35 40 41 44 49 50 51 53 54 57 59 60 64 65 68 70 74 75 76 77 78 79 81 82 85 86 87 89 93 96 97 98 100 101 102 104 107 108 110 111 114 118 119 130 131 132 143 144 146 147 148 149 **P** 8
Primary Contact: Guy A. Medaglia, President and Chief Executive Officer
CFO: Justin Bynum, Chief Financial Officer
CIO: Mark Jennings, Chief Information Officer
CHR: Malinda Yvonne Carter, Vice President Human Resources
Web address: www.sahchicago.org
Control: Church operated, Nongovernment, not–for–profit **Service:** General medical and surgical

Staffed Beds: 151 **Admissions:** 5586 **Census:** 82 **Outpatient Visits:** 126087 **Births:** 1276 **Total Expense ($000):** 114182 **Payroll Expense ($000):** 57746 **Personnel:** 835

SAINT JOSEPH HOSPITAL See Presence Saint Joseph Hospital

SAINTS MARY & ELIZABETH MEDICAL CENTER See Presence Saints Mary & Elizabeth Medical Center

☒ **SCHWAB REHABILITATION HOSPITAL (143025)**, 1401 South California Avenue, Zip 60608–1858; tel. 773/522–2010 **A** 1 3 5 10 **F** 9 29 30 34 35 44 50 57 58 59 64 66 68 77 86 87 90 91 92 93 96 128 131 143 **P** 8 **S** Sinai Health System, Chicago, IL
Primary Contact: Karen Teitelbaum, Chief Executive Officer
CFO: Charles Weis, Chief Financial Officer
CMO: Michelle Gittler M.D., Medical Director
CNO: Mary A Gollinger MS, R.N., Director of Nursing
Web address: www.schwabrehab.org
Control: Other not–for–profit (including NFP Corporation) **Service:** Rehabilitation

Staffed Beds: 83 **Admissions:** 1605 **Census:** 57 **Outpatient Visits:** 9906 **Births:** 0 **Total Expense ($000):** 35530 **Payroll Expense ($000):** 20687 **Personnel:** 248

☒ **SHIRLEY RYAN ABILITYLAB (143026)**, 345 East Erie Street, Zip 60611–2654, Mailing Address: 355 East Erie Street, 60611–2654; tel. 312/238–1000, (Nonreporting) **A** 1 5 8 10
Primary Contact: Joanne C. Smith, M.D., President and Chief Executive Officer
COO: Peggy Kirk, Senior Vice President Clinical Operations
CFO: Ed Case, Executive Vice President and Chief Financial Officer
CMO: James Sliwa M.D., Chief Medical Officer
CIO: Tim McKula, Vice President Information Systems and Chief Information Officer
CHR: Lois Huggins, Chief Human Resources Officer and Senior Vice President Human Resources
CNO: Karen M Colby MS, Chief Nursing Officer
Web address: www.ric.org
Control: Other not–for–profit (including NFP Corporation) **Service:** Rehabilitation

Staffed Beds: 182

IL

Hospital, Medicare Provider Number, Address, Telephone, Approval, Facility, and Physician Codes, Health Care System

★ American Hospital Association (AHA) membership
□ The Joint Commission accreditation
○ Healthcare Facilities Accreditation Program
◇ DNV Healthcare Inc. accreditation
⇑ Center for Improvement in Healthcare Quality Accreditation
△ Commission on Accreditation of Rehabilitation Facilities (CARF) accreditation

☐ **SHRINERS HOSPITALS FOR CHILDREN–CHICAGO (143302)**, 2211 North Oak Park Avenue, Zip 60707–3392; tel. 773/622–5400, (Nonreporting) **A**1 3 5 10 **S** Shriners Hospitals for Children, Tampa, FL
Primary Contact: Mark L. Niederpruem, FACHE, Administrator
CFO: Philip Magid, Director Fiscal Services
CMO: Jeffrey D. Ackman M.D., Chief of Staff
CHR: James E Pawlowicz, Director Human Resources
CNO: Terry Wheat R.N., M.P.H., Director of Patient Care Services
Web address: www.shrinershospitalsforchildren.org/Hospitals/Locations/Chicago.aspx
Control: Other not–for–profit (including NFP Corporation) **Service:** Children's orthopedic

Staffed Beds: 36

○ **SOUTH SHORE HOSPITAL (140181)**, 8012 South Crandon Avenue, Zip 60617–1124; tel. 773/768–0810 **A**10 11 **F**4 5 11 15 18 29 31 34 35 40 45 46 50 54 56 57 59 60 61 64 65 68 70 74 75 77 78 79 81 82 87 91 92 93 98 101 102 103 106 107 110 115 119 129 130 143 146 148
Primary Contact: Timothy Caveney, President
CFO: Scott Spencer, Chief Financial Officer
CMO: James Bob Achebe M.D., President Medical Staff
CIO: Jim Ritchie, Director Management Information Systems
CHR: Roger Rak, Director Human Resources
CNO: Laura Gonzalez, Interim Chief Nurse Executive
Web address: www.southshorehospital.com
Control: Other not–for–profit (including NFP Corporation) **Service:** General medical and surgical

Staffed Beds: 136 **Admissions:** 3335 **Census:** 65 **Outpatient Visits:** 24520 **Births:** 0 **Total Expense ($000):** 47419 **Payroll Expense ($000):** 21549 **Personnel:** 469

☐ **ST. BERNARD HOSPITAL AND HEALTH CARE CENTER (140103)**, 326 West 64th Street, Zip 60621–3146; tel. 773/962–3900, (Nonreporting) **A**1 10
Primary Contact: Charles Holland, President and Chief Executive Officer
COO: Roland Abellera, Vice President and Chief Operating Officer
CFO: James P Porter, Chief Financial Officer
CNO: Evelyn Jones R.N., Vice President Nursing Services
Web address: www.stbernardhospital.com
Control: Church operated, Nongovernment, not–for–profit **Service:** General medical and surgical

Staffed Beds: 100

★ ○ **SWEDISH COVENANT HOSPITAL (140114)**, 5145 North California Avenue, Zip 60625–3661; tel. 773/878–8200 **A**2 3 5 10 11 13 **F**3 8 13 15 18 19 20 22 24 26 28 29 30 31 32 33 34 35 36 38 40 45 46 47 49 50 53 56 57 58 59 60 62 64 68 70 74 75 76 78 79 81 82 83 84 85 86 87 89 90 92 93 96 97 98 100 101 102 103 107 110 111 114 115 116 117 118 119 121 123 124 126 128 129 130 131 132 134 135 143 146 147 148 **P**1 5 7
Primary Contact: Anthony Guaccio, President and Chief Executive Officer
CFO: Thomas J Garvey, Senior Vice President Operations and Chief Financial Officer
CMO: Derek J Kelly M.D., Vice President Transformation and Chief Medical Information Officer
CIO: Karen Sheehan, Vice President and Chief Information Officer
CNO: Mary Shehan R.N., MSN, Senior Vice President and Chief Nursing Officer
Web address: www.schosp.org
Control: Church operated, Nongovernment, not–for–profit **Service:** General medical and surgical

Staffed Beds: 267 **Admissions:** 12797 **Census:** 174 **Outpatient Visits:** 285358 **Births:** 2074 **Total Expense ($000):** 253967 **Payroll Expense ($000):** 99824 **Personnel:** 1741

○ **THOREK MEMORIAL HOSPITAL (140115)**, 850 West Irving Park Road, Zip 60613–3077; tel. 773/525–6780, (Nonreporting) **A**3 10 11
Primary Contact: Edward Budd, President and Chief Executive Officer
COO: Peter N Kamberos, Chief Operating Officer
CMO: Ilona Carlos M.D., President Medical Staff
CIO: Tony Vavarutsos, Director Information Systems
CHR: Brett Wakefield, Director Human Resources
CNO: Mary McCahill, Chief Nursing Officer
Web address: www.thorek.org
Control: Other not–for–profit (including NFP Corporation) **Service:** General medical and surgical

Staffed Beds: 134

✉ **UNIVERSITY OF CHICAGO MEDICAL CENTER (140088)**, 5841 South Maryland Avenue, Zip 60637–1447; tel. 773/702–1000, (Includes BERNARD MITCHELL HOSPITAL, 5815 South Maryland Avenue, Chicago, Illinois, Zip 60637, 5841 S. Maryland Ave., 60637, tel. 773/702–1000; Sharon L O'Keefe, President, University of Chicago Medical Center; CHICAGO LYING–IN (CLI), 5815 South Maryland Avenue, Chicago, Illinois, Zip 60637, 5841 South Maryland Avenue, 60637, tel. 773/702–1000; Sharon L O'Keefe, President, University of Chicago Medical Center; COMER CHILDREN'S HOSPITAL, 5721 South Maryland Avenue, Chicago, Illinois, Zip 60637, 5841 South Maryland Avenue, 60637, tel. 773/702–1000; Sharon L O'Keefe, President, University of Chicago Medical Center) **A**1 2 3 5 8 10 **F**3 5 6 9 11 12 13 14 15 16 17 18 19 20 21 22 23 24 25 26 27 28 29 30 31 32 34 35 36 37 38 40 41 43 44 45 46 47 48 49 50 51 52 53 54 55 56 57 58 59 60 61 63 64 65 68 70 71 72 73 74 75 76 77 78 79 80 81 82 83 84 85 86 87 88 89 92 93 97 99 100 101 102 103 104 107 108 109 110 111 112 114 115 116 117 118 119 120 121 123 124 126 129 130 131 132 134 135 136 137 138 139 140 141 142 143 144 145 146 147 148 149 150 **P**1 **S** University of Chicago Medicine, Chicago, IL
Primary Contact: Sharon L. O'Keefe, President
COO: Jason Keeler, Executive Vice President and Chief Operating Officer
CFO: James Watson, Chief Financial Officer
CMO: Stephen Weber M.D., Chief Medical Officer
CIO: Eric Yablonka, Vice President and Chief Information Officer
CHR: Bob Hanley, Chief Human Resources Officer
CNO: Debra Albert MSN, R.N., Senior Vice President Patient Care and Chief Nursing Officer
Web address: www.uchospitals.edu
Control: Other not–for–profit (including NFP Corporation) **Service:** General medical and surgical

Staffed Beds: 664 **Admissions:** 29809 **Census:** 515 **Outpatient Visits:** 761029 **Births:** 2069 **Total Expense ($000):** 1510195 **Payroll Expense ($000):** 555323 **Personnel:** 8522

✉ △ **UNIVERSITY OF ILLINOIS HOSPITAL & HEALTH SCIENCES SYSTEM (140150)**, 1740 West Taylor Street, Zip 60612–7232; tel. 312/996–7000 **A**1 2 3 5 7 8 10 **F**3 12 13 15 17 18 19 20 21 22 23 24 25 26 27 28 29 30 31 32 34 35 37 38 39 40 41 45 46 47 48 49 50 52 54 55 56 57 58 59 60 61 64 65 66 68 70 72 73 74 75 76 77 78 79 81 82 84 85 86 87 88 89 90 91 92 93 96 97 98 99 100 101 102 103 104 107 108 110 111 114 115 116 117 118 119 120 121 123 124 126 129 130 131 132 134 135 136 138 139 141 142 144 145 146 147 148 150 **P**4
Primary Contact: Avijit Ghosh, M.D., Chief Executive Officer
COO: David Loffing, Chief Operating Officer
CFO: Michael B Zenn, Chief Financial Officer
CMO: Bernard Pygon M.D., Chief Medical Officer
CIO: Audrius Polikaitis, Chief Information Officer
CHR: Mary Jo Smith, Chief Human Resources Officer
CNO: Dale E Beatty MSN, R.N., Chief Nursing Officer
Web address: www.hospital.uillinois.edu/
Control: State, Government, Nonfederal **Service:** General medical and surgical

Staffed Beds: 396 **Admissions:** 19030 **Census:** 319 **Outpatient Visits:** 601209 **Births:** 2378 **Total Expense ($000):** 920701 **Payroll Expense ($000):** 299646 **Personnel:** 3674

CHICAGO HEIGHTS—Cook County

ST. JAMES HOSPITAL AND HEALTH CENTERS – CHICAGO HEIGHTS CAMPUS See Franciscan Health Olympia Fields, Olympia Fields

CLINTON—De Witt County

WARNER HOSPITAL AND HEALTH SERVICES (141303), 422 West White Street, Zip 61727–2272; tel. 217/935–9571, (Nonreporting) **A**10 18
Primary Contact: Paul Skowron, Chief Executive Officer
CFO: Donna Wisner, Chief Financial Officer
CMO: Brit Williams M.D., President Medical Staff
CIO: Larry Schleicher, Manager Information Services
CHR: Sarah Gerke, Manager Human Resources
CNO: Heidi Cook, Chief Nursing Officer
Web address: www.djwhospital.org
Control: City, Government, Nonfederal **Service:** General medical and surgical

Staffed Beds: 25

IL

DANVILLE—Vermilion County

☒ **PRESENCE UNITED SAMARITANS MEDICAL CENTER (140093)**, 812 North Logan, Zip 61832–3788; tel. 217/443–5000 **A**1 2 5 10 19 **F**3 8 13 15 18 20 29 30 31 34 35 40 57 59 64 68 70 74 75 76 78 79 81 82 85 87 89 102 107 108 110 111 114 115 118 119 120 121 124 126 129 130 132 134 146 147 148 **S** Presence Health, Chicago, IL
Primary Contact: Jared Rogers, M.D., President and Chief Executive Officer
COO: Jennifer Cord R.N., Vice President Operations
CFO: Deb Schimerowski, Chief Financial Officer
CMO: Vincent Kucich FACHE, FACS, M.D., Chief Medical Officer
CIO: Paula Keele, Manager Information Systems
CHR: Michael Zimmerman, Human Resource Officer
CNO: Molly Nicholson MS, R.N., Vice President of Patient Care/Chief Nurse Executive
Web address: www.presencehealth.org/usmc
Control: Church operated, Nongovernment, not–for–profit **Service:** General medical and surgical

Staffed Beds: 117 **Admissions:** 5052 **Census:** 45 **Outpatient Visits:** 189575 **Births:** 645 **Total Expense ($000):** 93129 **Payroll Expense ($000):** 29938 **Personnel:** 534

☒ **VETERANS AFFAIRS ILLIANA HEALTH CARE SYSTEM**, 1900 East Main Street, Zip 61832–5198; tel. 217/554–3000, (Nonreporting) **A**1 3 5 **S** Department of Veterans Affairs, Washington, DC
Primary Contact: Diana Carranza, Interim Director
COO: Diana Carranza, Associate Director
CFO: Becky Tissier, Chief Fiscal Service
CMO: Khiem Tran M.D., Acting Chief of Staff
CIO: Frank D. Jackson III, Facility Chief Information Officer
CHR: Connie Ohl, Acting Chief Human Resources
Web address: www.danville.va.gov/
Control: Veterans Affairs, Government, federal **Service:** General medical and surgical

Staffed Beds: 221

DECATUR—Macon County

☒ △ **DECATUR MEMORIAL HOSPITAL (140135)**, 2300 North Edward Street, Zip 62526–4192; tel. 217/876–8121 **A**1 2 3 5 7 10 19 **F**3 8 11 12 13 15 17 18 19 20 22 24 26 28 29 30 31 34 35 37 40 43 45 46 47 48 49 51 53 54 56 57 58 59 60 61 62 63 65 69 70 71 73 74 75 76 77 78 79 81 82 84 85 86 87 89 91 92 93 94 96 97 98 100 102 103 104 107 108 110 111 112 114 115 116 117 118 119 120 121 123 124 126 129 130 131 132 133 135 141 143 144 145 146 147 148 149
Primary Contact: Timothy D. Stone Jr, President and Chief Executive Officer
COO: John Ridley, Executive Vice President & Chief Operating Officer
CFO: Deborah L Bragg, Senior Vice President, Finance
CMO: David Baumberger M.D., Chief Medical Officer
CHR: Kevin Horath, Vice President Human Resources
CNO: Linda L Fahey R.N., Chief Nurse Executive
Web address: www.dmhcares.com
Control: Other not–for–profit (including NFP Corporation) **Service:** General medical and surgical

Staffed Beds: 202 **Admissions:** 8389 **Census:** 94 **Outpatient Visits:** 263541 **Births:** 813 **Total Expense ($000):** 283634 **Payroll Expense ($000):** 119892 **Personnel:** 1918

☒ △ **HSHS ST. MARY'S HOSPITAL (140166)**, 1800 East Lake Shore Drive, Zip 62521–3883; tel. 217/464–2966, (Total facility includes 14 beds in nursing home–type unit) **A**1 3 7 10 **F**2 3 5 11 13 15 18 20 22 28 29 30 31 34 35 40 44 45 50 54 56 57 59 64 66 70 74 75 76 77 78 79 81 82 85 86 87 89 90 92 93 96 98 99 100 101 102 103 104 105 107 108 110 111 114 115 117 119 120 121 123 124 126 128 129 130 131 132 141 142 146 148 149 150 **P**7 **S** HSHS Hospital Sisters Health System, Springfield, IL
Primary Contact: Joan M. Coffman, FACHE, President and Chief Executive Officer
CMO: Phil Barnell, Chief Medical Officer
CHR: Denise Smith, Director People Services
CNO: Michelle Oliver, Chief Nursing Officer
Web address: www.stmarysdecatur.com
Control: Church operated, Nongovernment, not–for–profit **Service:** General medical and surgical

Staffed Beds: 244 **Admissions:** 7697 **Census:** 102 **Outpatient Visits:** 176429 **Births:** 635 **Total Expense ($000):** 140837 **Payroll Expense ($000):** 43043 **Personnel:** 738

DEKALB—DeKalb County

☒ **NORTHWESTERN MEDICINE KISHWAUKEE HOSPITAL (140286)**, 1 Kish Hospital Drive, Zip 60115–9602, Mailing Address: P.O.Box 707, 60115–0707; tel. 815/756–1521 **A**1 2 10 **F**3 5 8 11 13 15 18 20 22 24 26 28 29 30 31 32 34 35 36 38 40 43 45 46 48 49 51 57 58 59 60 64 65 66 68 70 71 73 74 75 76 77 78 79 80 81 82 85 86 87 89 93 94 96 97 98 99 100 101 102 103 104 107 108 110 111 114 115 117 118 119 127 129 130 131 132 133 135 145 146 147 148 149 150 **P**6 8 **S** Northwestern Memorial HealthCare, Chicago, IL
Primary Contact: Jay Anderson, President
COO: Brad Copple, President
CFO: Loren Foelske, Vice President Finance
CMO: Michael Kulisz D.O., Chief Medical Officer
CHR: Michele McClelland, Vice President Human Resources
CNO: Pamela Duffy, Vice President Operations and Chief Nursing Officer
Web address: www.nm.org
Control: Other not–for–profit (including NFP Corporation) **Service:** General medical and surgical

Staffed Beds: 98 **Admissions:** 5188 **Census:** 55 **Outpatient Visits:** 465803 **Births:** 820 **Total Expense ($000):** 191691 **Payroll Expense ($000):** 65590 **Personnel:** 954

DES PLAINES—Cook County

HOLY FAMILY MEDICAL CENTER See Presence Holy Family Medical Center

☒ **PRESENCE HOLY FAMILY MEDICAL CENTER (142011)**, 100 North River Road, Zip 60016–1255; tel. 847/297–1800 **A**1 10 **F**1 3 5 15 18 29 30 34 35 45 46 50 53 57 59 60 63 64 65 66 81 82 84 85 87 91 92 93 107 110 111 118 119 124 129 130 132 135 141 143 146 147 148 149 150 **S** Presence Health, Chicago, IL
Primary Contact: Yolande Wilson–Stubbs, President
CFO: Gene Yakovenko, Director of Finance
CMO: David Bordo M.D., Chief Medical Officer
CIO: David Lundal, Senior Vice President Information Systems and Chief Information Officer
CHR: Ivy McKinley, Director Human Resources
Web address: www.presencehealth.org
Control: Church operated, Nongovernment, not–for–profit **Service:** Acute long–term care hospital

Staffed Beds: 128 **Admissions:** 1442 **Census:** 85 **Outpatient Visits:** 27073 **Births:** 0 **Total Expense ($000):** 72699 **Payroll Expense ($000):** 29489 **Personnel:** 463

DIXON—Lee County

★ **KATHERINE SHAW BETHEA HOSPITAL (140012)**, 403 East First Street, Zip 61021–3187; tel. 815/288–5531 **A**3 5 10 **F**3 11 13 15 18 20 22 28 29 30 34 35 38 39 40 44 45 46 47 50 54 56 57 59 61 62 64 65 69 70 74 75 76 79 81 82 84 85 86 87 89 91 92 93 94 96 97 98 100 101 102 103 104 107 108 110 111 115 118 119 127 129 130 131 132 135 145 146 147 148 149 150 **P**6
Primary Contact: David L. Schreiner, FACHE, President and Chief Executive Officer
COO: Julie D Mann, Vice President and Chief Administrative Officer
CFO: Anthony Evers, Chief Financial Officer
CMO: A. Timothy Appenheimer M.D., Vice President and Chief Medical Officer
CHR: Christy Pierce, Director of Human Resources
CNO: Linda Clemen R.N., MS, Vice President and Chief Nursing Officer
Web address: www.ksbhospital.com
Control: Other not–for–profit (including NFP Corporation) **Service:** General medical and surgical

Staffed Beds: 64 **Admissions:** 2744 **Census:** 28 **Outpatient Visits:** 194261 **Births:** 349 **Total Expense ($000):** 123914 **Payroll Expense ($000):** 57585 **Personnel:** 771

IL

Hospital, Medicare Provider Number, Address, Telephone, Approval, Facility, and Physician Codes, Health Care System

★ American Hospital Association (AHA) membership
☐ The Joint Commission accreditation
○ Healthcare Facilities Accreditation Program
◇ DNV Healthcare Inc. accreditation
⇑ Center for Improvement in Healthcare Quality Accreditation
△ Commission on Accreditation of Rehabilitation Facilities (CARF) accreditation

DOWNERS GROVE—Dupage County

★ ⇑ **ADVOCATE GOOD SAMARITAN HOSPITAL (140288)**, 3815 Highland Avenue, Zip 60515–1590; tel. 630/275–5900 **A**2 5 10 21 **F**3 5 11 12 13 15 17 18 20 22 24 26 28 29 30 31 32 34 35 36 37 38 40 41 43 44 45 46 47 49 50 53 54 55 56 57 59 60 63 64 68 70 72 74 75 76 78 79 81 82 84 85 86 87 93 98 100 101 102 103 104 105 107 108 109 110 111 114 115 118 119 120 121 123 124 126 129 130 131 132 135 144 145 146 147 148 149 **P**8 **S** Advocate Health Care, Downers Grove, IL
Primary Contact: David Fox, President
COO: Sandi Churchill, Vice President Business Development and Operations, Professional Services
CFO: Mary Treacy–Shiff, Vice President Finance
CMO: Charles Derus M.D., Vice President Medical Management
CHR: Elizabeth Calby, Vice President Human Resources
CNO: Susan K Okuno–Jones, Vice President Patient Care Services and Chief Nursing Executive
Web address: www.advocatehealth.com/gsam
Control: Church operated, Nongovernment, not–for–profit **Service:** General medical and surgical

Staffed Beds: 275 **Admissions:** 15013 **Census:** 181 **Outpatient Visits:** 135698 **Births:** 1810 **Total Expense ($000):** 337193 **Payroll Expense ($000):** 119477 **Personnel:** 1840

DU QUOIN—Perry County

☒ **MARSHALL BROWNING HOSPITAL (141331)**, 900 North Washington Street, Zip 62832–1233, Mailing Address: P.O.Box 192, 62832–0192; tel. 618/542–2146 **A**1 10 18 **F**3 11 15 28 29 34 35 40 57 59 81 93 97 104 107 114 119 125 127 129 133 144
Primary Contact: Dan Eaves, Chief Executive Officer
CFO: Brice Harsy, Chief Financial Officer
CIO: Brian Schandl, Chief Information Officer
CHR: Sarah J. Dickey, Director Human Resources
CNO: Laurie Kellerman MSN, Chief Clinical Officer
Web address: www.marshallbrowninghospital.com
Control: Other not–for–profit (including NFP Corporation) **Service:** General medical and surgical

Staffed Beds: 25 **Admissions:** 613 **Census:** 8 **Outpatient Visits:** 38389 **Births:** 0 **Total Expense ($000):** 22184 **Payroll Expense ($000):** 8740 **Personnel:** 178

EFFINGHAM—Effingham County

☒ **HSHS ST. ANTHONY'S MEMORIAL HOSPITAL (140032)**, 503 North Maple Street, Zip 62401–2099; tel. 217/342–2121 **A**1 2 3 5 10 19 **F**3 11 13 15 18 20 28 29 30 31 32 34 35 37 40 45 50 57 59 62 63 64 68 70 75 76 79 81 82 84 85 87 89 93 107 108 110 111 114 115 117 118 119 126 129 130 131 132 144 146 147 **S** HSHS Hospital Sisters Health System, Springfield, IL
Primary Contact: Theresa Rutherford, R.N., MS, FACHE, President and Chief Executive Officer
CFO: Dave Storm, Director Business Support
CNO: Kelly Sage, Chief Nursing Officer
Web address: www.stanthonyshospital.org
Control: Church operated, Nongovernment, not–for–profit **Service:** General medical and surgical

Staffed Beds: 123 **Admissions:** 5150 **Census:** 45 **Outpatient Visits:** 328253 **Births:** 721 **Total Expense ($000):** 118450 **Payroll Expense ($000):** 40131 **Personnel:** 696

ELDORADO—Saline County

★ **FERRELL HOSPITAL (141324)**, 1201 Pine Street, Zip 62930–1634; tel. 618/273–3361 **A**10 18 **F**3 11 15 28 29 30 34 45 57 59 65 68 77 81 85 87 89 101 103 104 107 110 114 119 127 133 146
Primary Contact: Alisa Coleman, Chief Executive Officer
CFO: Joseph Hohenberger, Chief Financial Officer
CIO: Brent Volkert, Director Information Technology
CHR: Caleigh Bruce, Vice President Human Resources
CNO: Rachael Prather, Chief Nursing Officer
Web address: www.ferrellhosp.org
Control: Other not–for–profit (including NFP Corporation) **Service:** General medical and surgical

Staffed Beds: 25 **Admissions:** 704 **Census:** 7 **Outpatient Visits:** 40655 **Births:** 1 **Total Expense ($000):** 16634 **Payroll Expense ($000):** 7564 **Personnel:** 184

ELGIN—Kane County

★ ⇑ **ADVOCATE SHERMAN HOSPITAL (140030)**, 1425 North Randall Road, Zip 60123–2300; tel. 847/742–9800 **A**2 10 21 **F**3 11 13 15 18 20 22 24 26 28 29 30 31 34 35 38 40 43 45 46 47 48 49 50 54 57 59 64 65 68 70 71 73 74 75 76 77 78 79 81 82 85 87 89 92 93 100 102 107 108 110 111 114 115 118 119 120 121 123 130 132 135 144 146 147 148 149 **P**6 8 **S** Advocate Health Care, Downers Grove, IL
Primary Contact: Linda Deering, MSN, R.N., President
CMO: Bruce Hyman M.D., Vice President Clinical Performance
CHR: Melissa O'Neill, Vice President Human Resources
CNO: Cheri Goll MSN, R.N., Chief Nursing Executive
Web address: www.advocatehealth.com/sherman
Control: Other not–for–profit (including NFP Corporation) **Service:** General medical and surgical

Staffed Beds: 255 **Admissions:** 14560 **Census:** 160 **Outpatient Visits:** 307960 **Births:** 2574 **Total Expense ($000):** 282027 **Payroll Expense ($000):** 98152 **Personnel:** 1417

☐ **ELGIN MENTAL HEALTH CENTER (144037)**, 750 South State Street, Zip 60123–7692; tel. 847/742–1040 **A**1 3 5 10 **F**29 30 38 39 50 59 65 68 87 98 101 102 103 130 132 143 **S** Division of Mental Health, Department of Human Services, Springfield, IL
Primary Contact: Meredith Kiss, Administrator
CFO: Tajudeen Ibrahim, Interim Business Administrator
CMO: Malini Patel M.D., Medical Director
CIO: Kelly Callahan, Public Information Officer
CHR: Darek Williams, Director Human Resources
Web address: www.dhs.state.il.us
Control: State, Government, Nonfederal **Service:** Psychiatric

Staffed Beds: 383 **Admissions:** 940 **Census:** 383 **Outpatient Visits:** 0 **Births:** 0 **Total Expense ($000):** 68000 **Payroll Expense ($000):** 37000 **Personnel:** 681

☒ △ **PRESENCE SAINT JOSEPH HOSPITAL (140217)**, 77 North Airlite Street, Zip 60123–4912; tel. 847/695–3200 **A**1 2 7 10 **F**5 11 15 17 18 20 22 24 26 28 29 30 31 34 35 36 37 38 40 44 49 50 53 54 56 57 58 59 60 61 62 63 64 65 68 69 70 74 75 77 78 79 81 82 84 85 86 87 90 93 94 96 97 98 99 100 101 102 103 104 105 107 108 111 114 115 117 119 120 121 123 124 130 132 134 135 143 145 146 147 148 **P**5 **S** Presence Health, Chicago, IL
Primary Contact: Michael L. Brown, Regional President and Chief Executive Officer
CFO: Kevin Larkin, Regional Chief Financial Officer
CIO: Trevor O'Malley, Site Manager
CHR: Michael O'Rourke, Regional Human Resources Lead
Web address: www.provena.org
Control: Other not–for–profit (including NFP Corporation) **Service:** General medical and surgical

Staffed Beds: 184 **Admissions:** 6966 **Census:** 108 **Outpatient Visits:** 160052 **Births:** 0 **Total Expense ($000):** 139741 **Payroll Expense ($000):** 39341 **Personnel:** 723

PROVENA SAINT JOSEPH HOSPITAL See Presence Saint Joseph Hospital

⇑ **SHERMAN HOSPITAL** See Advocate Sherman Hospital

ELK GROVE VILLAGE—Cook County

☒ **AMITA HEALTH ELK GROVE VILLAGE (140258)**, 800 Biesterfield Road, Zip 60007–3397; tel. 847/437–5500, (Includes AMITA HEALTH REHABILITATION HOSPITAL, 935 Beisner Road, Elk Grove Village, Illinois, Zip 60007, tel. 847/640–5600; John Dunkin, Executive Director) **A**1 2 3 5 10 **F**3 12 13 15 17 18 19 20 22 24 26 28 29 30 31 34 35 36 37 39 40 41 43 44 45 46 47 48 49 50 54 55 57 59 62 63 64 70 73 74 75 76 78 79 81 82 84 85 86 87 89 90 91 92 93 95 96 103 107 108 110 111 114 115 116 117 119 120 121 124 126 129 130 132 135 143 145 146 147 148 149 **P**5 6 **S** Ascension Healthcare, Saint Louis, MO
Primary Contact: John P. Werrbach, President and Chief Executive Officer
COO: Laurence Dry, Chief Operating Officer, Acute Care Hospitals Northern Region
CFO: Henry Zeisel, Chief Financial Officer, Northern Region
CIO: Sherrie Russell, Senior Vice President & Chief Information Officer
CHR: Donald Russell, Senior Vice President and Chief Human Resources Officer
CNO: Chris Budzinsky, Vice President, Nursing and Chief Nursing Officer
Web address: www.AMITAHealth.org
Control: Church operated, Nongovernment, not–for–profit **Service:** General medical and surgical

Staffed Beds: 381 **Admissions:** 18190 **Census:** 274 **Outpatient Visits:** 423053 **Births:** 1931 **Total Expense ($000):** 415062 **Payroll Expense ($000):** 141791 **Personnel:** 2064

IL

Many Facility Codes have changed. Please refer to the AHA Guide Code Chart. © 2017 AHA Guide

ELMHURST—Dupage County

✠ **ELMHURST HOSPITAL (140200)**, 155 East Brush Hill Road, Zip 60126–5658; tel. 331/221–1000 **A**1 2 5 10 **F**3 5 7 12 13 15 18 19 20 22 24 26 28 29 30 31 32 34 35 36 37 38 39 40 41 43 44 45 46 47 48 49 50 54 55 57 58 59 61 63 64 65 68 70 73 74 75 76 77 78 79 81 82 84 85 86 87 89 91 92 93 96 97 99 100 101 102 103 104 107 108 109 110 111 114 115 117 119 120 121 123 124 126 129 130 131 132 135 144 146 147 148 149 **P**3 6 8 **S** Edward–Elmhurst Healthcare, Naperville, IL
Primary Contact: Pamela L. Dunley, MS, R.N., Chief Executive Officer
CMO: Daniel Sullivan D.O., Chief Medical Officer, Vice President Medical Administration
CHR: Robert Blazek, System Director, Human Resources Business Partners
CNO: Jean Lydon MS, R.N., System Vice President Operations, Chief Nursing Officer
Web address: www.eehealth.org
Control: Other not–for–profit (including NFP Corporation) **Service:** General medical and surgical

> **Staffed Beds:** 267 **Admissions:** 16008 **Census:** 173 **Outpatient Visits:** 464489 **Births:** 1895 **Total Expense ($000):** 393921 **Payroll Expense ($000):** 125908 **Personnel:** 1802

EUREKA—Woodford County

★ ⇧ **ADVOCATE EUREKA HOSPITAL (141309)**, 101 South Major Street, Zip 61530–1246; tel. 309/467–2371 **A**10 18 21 **F**3 15 18 28 29 30 31 34 35 39 40 44 45 50 56 57 59 64 65 66 67 68 74 75 77 78 79 81 82 85 86 87 89 90 93 107 108 110 111 114 119 128 129 130 132 133 144 146 149 **P**8 **S** Advocate Health Care, Downers Grove, IL
Primary Contact: Colleen Kannaday, FACHE, President
CFO: Aron Klein, Vice President of Finance
CMO: Steven K Jones M.D., Medical Director
CIO: David Harper, Director, Site Information Systems
CHR: Antonio Coletta, Vice President Human Resources
CNO: Nancy Allen R.N., MS, Director, Patient Services and Chief Nursing Executive
Web address: www.advocatehealth.com/eureka/
Control: Church operated, Nongovernment, not–for–profit **Service:** General medical and surgical

> **Staffed Beds:** 18 **Admissions:** 235 **Census:** 3 **Outpatient Visits:** 31596 **Births:** 0 **Total Expense ($000):** 15469 **Payroll Expense ($000):** 5849 **Personnel:** 97

⇧ **EUREKA COMMUNITY HOSPITAL** See Advocate Eureka Hospital

EVANSTON—Cook County

✠ **NORTHSHORE UNIVERSITY HEALTH SYSTEM (140010)**, 2650 Ridge Avenue, Zip 60201–1613; tel. 847/570–2000, (Includes NORTHSHORE EVANSTON HOSPITAL, 2650 Ridge Avenue, Evanston, Illinois, Zip 60201–1797, tel. 847/570–2000; Douglas M Silverstein, President; NORTHSHORE GLENBROOK HOSPITAL, 2100 Pfingsten Road, Glenview, Illinois, Zip 60025, tel. 847/657–5800; NORTHSHORE HIGHLAND PARK HOSPITAL, 718 Glenview Avenue, Highland Park, Illinois, Zip 60035–2497, tel. 847/432–8000; NORTHSHORE SKOKIE HOSPITAL, 9600 Gross Point Road, Skokie, Illinois, Zip 60076–1257, tel. 847/677–9600; Kristen Murtos, FACHE, President) **A**1 2 3 5 8 10 **F**3 5 8 9 11 12 13 14 15 18 19 20 22 24 26 28 29 30 31 32 34 35 36 37 38 39 40 43 44 45 46 47 48 49 50 54 55 56 57 58 59 60 61 62 63 64 65 66 68 70 72 74 75 76 77 78 79 81 82 84 85 86 87 88 89 90 92 93 96 97 98 99 100 101 102 103 104 105 107 108 110 111 114 115 116 117 118 119 120 121 123 124 126 129 130 131 132 134 135 136 144 145 146 147 148 149 **P**5
Primary Contact: Douglas M. Silverstein, President
COO: J. P. Gallagher, Chief Operating Officer
CFO: Gary Weiss, Chief Financial Officer
CIO: Steven Smith, Chief Information Officer
CHR: Bill Luehrs, Chief Human Resources Officer
CNO: Nancy Semerdjian R.N., Chief Nursing Officer
Web address: www.northshore.org
Control: Other not–for–profit (including NFP Corporation) **Service:** General medical and surgical

> **Staffed Beds:** 672 **Admissions:** 38399 **Census:** 461 **Outpatient Visits:** 2092653 **Births:** 4921 **Total Expense ($000):** 1284830 **Payroll Expense ($000):** 487682 **Personnel:** 6122

✠ **PRESENCE SAINT FRANCIS HOSPITAL (140080)**, 355 Ridge Avenue, Zip 60202–3399; tel. 847/316–4000 **A**1 2 3 5 10 **F**3 11 12 13 15 18 20 22 24 26 28 29 30 31 34 35 38 40 41 43 44 45 47 48 49 56 57 58 59 60 61 64 68 70 72 74 75 76 77 78 79 81 82 84 85 86 87 92 93 97 100 107 108 110 111 114 115 118 119 120 121 123 125 126 129 130 131 132 146 147 148 **P**8 **S** Presence Health, Chicago, IL
Primary Contact: Kenneth Jones, President
CMO: David DiLoreto M.D., Executive Vice President and Chief Medical Officer
CIO: George Chessum, Vice President Information Systems
CHR: Paul Skiem, Senior Vice President Human Resources
Web address: www.reshealth.org
Control: Church operated, Nongovernment, not–for–profit **Service:** General medical and surgical

> **Staffed Beds:** 215 **Admissions:** 7782 **Census:** 87 **Outpatient Visits:** 114623 **Births:** 681 **Total Expense ($000):** 174545 **Payroll Expense ($000):** 54395 **Personnel:** 832

SAINT FRANCIS HOSPITAL See Presence Saint Francis Hospital

EVERGREEN PARK—Cook County

☐ **LITTLE COMPANY OF MARY HOSPITAL AND HEALTH CARE CENTERS (140179)**, 2800 West 95th Street, Zip 60805–2795; tel. 708/422–6200 **A**1 2 10 **F**3 5 11 12 13 15 17 18 20 22 26 29 30 31 34 35 36 38 40 41 45 46 47 49 50 54 56 57 59 60 62 63 64 65 71 73 74 75 76 77 78 79 81 82 83 84 85 86 87 89 92 93 94 98 100 101 102 103 104 105 107 108 110 111 114 115 119 120 121 124 126 129 130 131 132 133 135 144 146 147 148 149 150 **P**6 7 8 **S** American Province of Little Company of Mary Sisters, Evergreen Park, IL
Primary Contact: Dennis A. Reilly, President and Chief Executive Officer
COO: Mary Freyer, Chief Operating Officer
CFO: Randy Ruther, Vice President Finance and Chief Financial Officer
CMO: Kent A W Armbruster M.D., Vice President Medical Affairs
CIO: Darryl Mazzuca, Director Management Information Systems
CHR: Colleen Rohan, Director Human Resources
CNO: Lisa DiMarco R.N., FACHE, Vice President Patient Care Service and Chief Nursing Officer
Web address: www.lcmh.org
Control: Other not–for–profit (including NFP Corporation) **Service:** General medical and surgical

> **Staffed Beds:** 241 **Admissions:** 12515 **Census:** 150 **Outpatient Visits:** 202306 **Births:** 1102 **Total Expense ($000):** 197101 **Payroll Expense ($000):** 89584 **Personnel:** 1724

FAIRFIELD—Wayne County

✠ **FAIRFIELD MEMORIAL HOSPITAL (141311)**, 303 NW 11th Street, Zip 62837–1203; tel. 618/842–2611, (Total facility includes 30 beds in nursing home–type unit) **A**1 10 18 **F**3 11 15 18 28 31 34 35 38 40 41 45 46 50 56 57 59 62 64 70 75 77 81 85 86 87 93 97 99 103 104 107 108 110 115 119 127 128 130 132 135 144 146 148 149 **P**6
Primary Contact: Katherine Bunting, Chief Executive Officer
COO: Dana Shantel Taylor, Director Organizational Development
CFO: Melody Morgan, Chief Financial Officer
CMO: Wesley Thompson M.D., President Medical Staff
CIO: Brad August, Director Information Systems
CHR: Robert Musoiu, Director Human Resources
CNO: Ann Ignas R.N., MSN, Chief Nurse Executive
Web address: www.fairfieldmemorial.org
Control: Other not–for–profit (including NFP Corporation) **Service:** General medical and surgical

> **Staffed Beds:** 55 **Admissions:** 723 **Census:** 27 **Outpatient Visits:** 105324 **Births:** 0 **Total Expense ($000):** 28888 **Payroll Expense ($000):** 13573 **Personnel:** 279

FLORA—Clay County

✠ **CLAY COUNTY HOSPITAL (141351)**, 911 Stacy Burk Drive, Zip 62839–3241, Mailing Address: P.O.Box 280, 62839–0280; tel. 618/662–2131, (Nonreporting) **A**1 10 18 **S** SSM Health, Saint Louis, MO
Primary Contact: Chris Hunt, President
COO: Jamie Veach, Chief Operating Officer
CFO: Mike Hobbs, Chief Financial Officer
CMO: Colleen Murphy M.D., Chief of Staff
CIO: Phil Bute, Manager Information Technology
CHR: Chelsea Musgrave, Director of Human Resources
Web address: www.claycountyhospital.org
Control: County, Government, Nonfederal **Service:** General medical and surgical

> **Staffed Beds:** 22

Hospital, Medicare Provider Number, Address, Telephone, Approval, Facility, and Physician Codes, Health Care System

★ American Hospital Association (AHA) membership   ○ Healthcare Facilities Accreditation Program   ⇧ Center for Improvement in Healthcare Quality Accreditation
☐ The Joint Commission accreditation   ◇ DNV Healthcare Inc. accreditation   △ Commission on Accreditation of Rehabilitation Facilities (CARF) accreditation

IL

FOREST PARK—Cook County

☐ **RIVEREDGE HOSPITAL (144009)**, 8311 West Roosevelt Road, Zip 60130–2500; tel. 708/771–7000, (Nonreporting) **A**1 10 **S** Universal Health Services, Inc., King of Prussia, PA
Primary Contact: Carey Carlock, Chief Executive Officer
CFO: Michael E Nelson, Chief Financial Officer
CMO: Lucyna M. Puszkarska M.D., Medical Director
CIO: Kyle Heinze, Coordinator Information Technology
CHR: Joseph Baw, Director Human Resources
Web address: www.riveredgehospital.com
Control: Corporation, Investor–owned (for–profit) **Service**: Psychiatric

Staffed Beds: 224

FREEPORT—Stephenson County

★ **FHN MEMORIAL HOSPITAL (140160)**, 1045 West Stephenson Street, Zip 61032–4899; tel. 815/599–6000 **A**10 **F**3 11 13 14 15 18 20 22 28 29 30 31 32 34 38 40 46 47 48 49 50 51 53 57 59 61 63 64 65 68 69 74 75 76 77 78 79 81 82 84 85 86 87 93 97 99 100 101 102 103 104 107 108 109 110 111 114 119 129 130 131 132 135 146 149 **P**6 8
Primary Contact: Mark Gridley, FACHE, President and Chief Executive Officer
CFO: Michael Clark, Executive Vice President and Chief Financial Officer
CMO: Robert D Geller M.D., Vice President Medical Affairs
CIO: Mike Willams, Chief Information Officer
CHR: Leonard M Carter, Chief Human Resources Officer
CNO: Kathryn J Martinez, Chief Nursing Officer
Web address: www.fhn.org
Control: Other not–for–profit (including NFP Corporation) **Service**: General medical and surgical

Staffed Beds: 100 **Admissions**: 3830 **Census**: 36 **Outpatient Visits**: 107951 **Births**: 322 **Total Expense ($000)**: 104986 **Payroll Expense ($000)**: 31695 **Personnel**: 446

GALENA—Jo Daviess County

★ **MIDWEST MEDICAL CENTER (141302)**, One Medical Center Drive, Zip 61036–1697; tel. 815/777–1340, (Nonreporting) **A**10 18
Primary Contact: Tracy Bauer, Chief Executive Officer
COO: Steve Busch, Chief Operating Officer
CMO: Grant Westenfelder M.D., Chief Medical Officer
CHR: Melissa Conley, Director Human Resources
Web address: www.midwestmedicalcenter.org
Control: Corporation, Investor–owned (for–profit) **Service**: General medical and surgical

Staffed Beds: 25

GALESBURG—Knox County

✠ **GALESBURG COTTAGE HOSPITAL (140040)**, 695 North Kellogg Street, Zip 61401–2885; tel. 309/343–8131, (Nonreporting) **A**1 10 19 **S** Quorum Health, Brentwood, TN
Primary Contact: James Flynn, Chief Executive Officer
CFO: Millie Smith, Interim Chief Financial Officer
CMO: Parthasarathy Srinivasan M.D., President Medical Staff
CIO: Richard Tran, Director Information Technology
CHR: Anita Sells, Director Human Resources
CNO: Pam Davis, Chief Nursing Officer
Web address: www.cottagehospital.com
Control: Other not–for–profit (including NFP Corporation) **Service**: General medical and surgical

Staffed Beds: 119

✠ **OSF ST. MARY MEDICAL CENTER (140064)**, 3333 North Seminary Street, Zip 61401–1299; tel. 309/344–3161 **A**1 10 **F**3 11 13 15 18 26 28 29 30 31 34 35 40 43 44 45 46 49 50 51 53 56 57 59 63 64 65 70 75 76 77 78 79 81 82 84 85 86 87 89 93 96 107 108 110 111 115 118 119 129 130 131 132 135 145 146 147 149 **P**6 **S** OSF Healthcare System, Peoria, IL
Primary Contact: Roxanna Crosser, President
COO: Don Shadensack, Vice President Clinical Services
CFO: Curt Lipe, Vice President, Chief Financial Officer
CMO: Mark Meeker D.O., Medical Staff President
CIO: Becky Lynch, Manager Business Entity Management and Information Systems
CHR: Jenny Jacobs, Director Human Resources
CNO: Alice Snyder, Vice President, Chief Nursing Officer
Web address: www.osfstmary.org
Control: Church operated, Nongovernment, not–for–profit **Service**: General medical and surgical

Staffed Beds: 81 **Admissions**: 3046 **Census**: 32 **Outpatient Visits**: 103231 **Births**: 349 **Total Expense ($000)**: 70538 **Payroll Expense ($000)**: 26010 **Personnel**: 427

GENESEO—Henry County

★ ⇧ **HAMMOND–HENRY HOSPITAL (141319)**, 600 North College Avenue, Zip 61254–1099; tel. 309/944–6431, (Total facility includes 38 beds in nursing home–type unit) **A**10 18 21 **F**3 8 11 13 15 28 29 34 35 40 44 45 49 50 57 59 62 70 75 76 81 87 88 89 93 107 111 114 119 128 129 130 131 132 133 144 146 **P**2 **S** HealthTech Management Services, Brentwood, TN
Primary Contact: Michael Lieb, Interim Chief Executive Officer
CFO: Jodie Criswell, Vice President Fiscal Services
CIO: Heather Henry, Manager Information Systems
CHR: Hazel Butter, Manager Human Resources
CNO: Laura Domino R.N., Vice President Patient Care Services
Web address: www.hammondhenry.com
Control: Hospital district or authority, Government, Nonfederal **Service**: General medical and surgical

Staffed Beds: 61 **Admissions**: 1419 **Census**: 44 **Outpatient Visits**: 105682 **Births**: 252 **Total Expense ($000)**: 40173 **Payroll Expense ($000)**: 13484 **Personnel**: 255

GENEVA—Kane County

✠ **NORTHWESTERN MEDICINE DELNOR HOSPITAL (140211)**, 300 Randall Road, Zip 60134–4200; tel. 630/208–3000 **A**1 2 10 **F**3 8 10 12 13 15 18 20 22 26 28 29 30 31 33 34 35 36 39 40 43 44 45 46 47 48 49 50 51 53 55 57 59 60 64 65 68 70 73 74 75 76 77 78 79 81 82 84 85 86 87 89 93 94 96 97 100 101 102 104 105 107 108 110 111 114 115 116 117 118 119 120 121 123 125 126 129 130 131 132 135 146 147 148 149 **P**6 7 **S** Northwestern Memorial HealthCare, Chicago, IL
Primary Contact: Maureen A. Bryant, FACHE, President
CFO: John Orsini, Executive Vice President and Chief Financial Officer
CMO: Mark Daniels M.D., Vice President Physician Enterprise
CIO: Daniel F Kinsella, Executive Vice President Information Technology
CHR: Michael Wukitsch, Vice President Human Resources
Web address: www.nm.org
Control: Other not–for–profit (including NFP Corporation) **Service**: General medical and surgical

Staffed Beds: 149 **Admissions**: 7834 **Census**: 78 **Outpatient Visits**: 388214 **Births**: 1417 **Total Expense ($000)**: 307920 **Payroll Expense ($000)**: 107257 **Personnel**: 1727

GIBSON CITY—Ford County

✠ **GIBSON AREA HOSPITAL AND HEALTH SERVICES (141317)**, 1120 North Melvin Street, Zip 60936–1477, Mailing Address: P.O.Box 429, 60936–0429; tel. 217/784–4251, (Total facility includes 42 beds in nursing home–type unit) **A**1 5 10 18 **F**3 7 11 13 15 18 28 29 31 34 35 40 43 44 45 49 50 51 53 55 56 57 59 63 64 65 67 68 69 70 75 76 77 79 81 82 85 87 93 99 100 101 103 104 107 108 110 111 115 119 127 128 129 131 132 133 143 146 147 148 **P**6 7 8 **S** Alliant Management Services, Louisville, KY
Primary Contact: Robert C. Schmitt II, Chief Executive Officer
COO: Robin Rose R.N., Chief Operating Officer
CFO: Matthew Ertel, Chief Financial Officer
CMO: Mark Spangler M.D., Chief Medical Officer
CIO: Julie Bowen, Executive Director of Information Technology
CHR: Ty Royal, Executive Director of Support Services and Human Resources
CNO: Cynthia Philipchuck R.N., Executive Director of Nursing
Web address: www.gibsonhospital.org
Control: Other not–for–profit (including NFP Corporation) **Service**: General medical and surgical

Staffed Beds: 67 **Admissions**: 953 **Census**: 45 **Outpatient Visits**: 139511 **Births**: 212 **Total Expense ($000)**: 85743 **Payroll Expense ($000)**: 41782 **Personnel**: 682

GLENDALE HEIGHTS—DuPage County

✠ **AMITA HEALTH ADVENTIST MEDICAL CENTER GLENOAKS (140292)**, 701 Winthrop Avenue, Zip 60139–1403; tel. 630/545–8000 **A**1 10 **F**3 11 13 15 18 20 22 26 29 30 31 34 35 38 40 41 43 44 45 49 50 57 58 59 64 70 73 74 75 76 78 79 81 82 85 86 87 89 92 96 97 98 100 101 102 103 107 108 110 111 114 115 118 119 130 131 132 146 147 148 **P**6 8 **S** Adventist Health System Sunbelt Health Care Corporation, Altamonte Springs, FL
Primary Contact: Bruce C. Christian, President and Chief Executive Officer
COO: Richard Roehr, Vice President and Chief Operating Officer
CFO: Chase Aalborg, Vice President and Chief Financial Officer
CMO: Richard Carroll M.D., Vice President and Chief Medical Officer
CIO: Sherrie Russell, AMITA Health Senior Vice President and Chief Information Officer
CHR: Donald Russell, AMITA Health Senior Vice President and Chief Human Resources Officer
CNO: Suzette Mahneke, Associate Vice President of Nursing
Web address: www.AMITAHealth.org
Control: Church operated, Nongovernment, not–for–profit **Service**: General medical and surgical

Staffed Beds: 120 **Admissions**: 5509 **Census**: 79 **Outpatient Visits**: 40170 **Births**: 375 **Total Expense ($000)**: 87021 **Payroll Expense ($000)**: 32058 **Personnel**: 494

Many Facility Codes have changed. Please refer to the AHA Guide Code Chart. © 2017 AHA Guide

GLENVIEW—Cook County

NORTHSHORE GLENBROOK HOSPITAL See Northshore University Health System, Evanston

GRANITE CITY—Madison County

☒ **GATEWAY REGIONAL MEDICAL CENTER (140125)**, 2100 Madison Avenue, Zip 62040–4799; tel. 618/798–3000 **A**1 10 **F**3 8 11 13 15 17 18 20 22 24 26 28 29 31 34 35 40 45 49 50 51 54 59 64 70 74 75 76 77 78 79 81 82 85 87 90 91 92 93 94 97 98 99 100 101 102 103 104 107 108 110 111 114 115 119 126 128 129 130 132 135 144 146 147 148 149 **S** Quorum Health, Brentwood, TN
Primary Contact: M Edward. Cunningham, Chief Executive Officer
CFO: Ronald Leazer, Chief Financial Officer
CMO: Mike Adams M.D., Chief Medical Officer
CIO: Dennis Kampwerth, Director Management Information Systems
CHR: Reva S Weems, Director Human Resources
CNO: Sam R White, Chief Nursing Officer
Web address: www.gatewayregional.net
Control: Corporation, Investor–owned (for–profit) **Service**: General medical and surgical

Staffed Beds: 172 **Admissions**: 7506 **Census**: 108 **Outpatient Visits**: 92633 **Births**: 290 **Total Expense ($000)**: 94608 **Payroll Expense ($000)**: 35318 **Personnel**: 695

GREENVILLE—Bond County

★ ○ **HSHS HOLY FAMILY HOSPITAL IN GREENVILLE (140137)**, 200 Healthcare Drive, Zip 62246–1154; tel. 618/664–1230, (Data for 182 days)**A**10 11 **F**3 11 13 15 18 30 31 34 40 41 45 49 50 56 57 59 76 78 79 81 85 89 93 94 97 98 103 104 107 110 111 115 119 125 127 129 130 133 135 **P**6 **S** HSHS Hospital Sisters Health System, Springfield, IL
Primary Contact: Brian Nall, President and Chief Operating Officer
CHR: Vicki Kloeckner, Director Human Resources
CNO: Tammy Lett R.N., Chief Nursing Officer
Web address: www.greenvilleregionalhospital.com
Control: Other not–for–profit (including NFP Corporation) **Service**: General medical and surgical

Staffed Beds: 42 **Admissions**: 682 **Census**: 14 **Outpatient Visits**: 17162 **Births**: 111 **Total Expense ($000)**: 15822 **Payroll Expense ($000)**: 6102 **Personnel**: 228

HARRISBURG—Saline County

☒ **HARRISBURG MEDICAL CENTER (140210)**, 100 Dr Warren Tuttle Drive, Zip 62946–2718, Mailing Address: P.O.Box 428, 62946–0428; tel. 618/253–7671 **A**1 10 20 **F**3 8 11 15 28 29 30 31 34 40 45 50 56 57 59 61 62 64 75 77 78 79 81 82 85 87 91 93 94 97 98 100 101 102 103 104 107 108 110 114 118 119 127 129 130 131 133 146
Primary Contact: Rodney Smith, President and Chief Executive Officer
COO: Danny Lampley, Chief Operating Officer
CFO: June Hayes, Chief Financial Officer
CIO: Rick Pyle, Director Information Systems
CHR: Dorene L Ewell, Director Human Resources and Education
CNO: Cindy Ford R.N., Chief Nursing Officer
Web address: www.harrisburgmc.com
Control: Other not–for–profit (including NFP Corporation) **Service**: General medical and surgical

Staffed Beds: 76 **Admissions**: 3046 **Census**: 39 **Outpatient Visits**: 82126 **Births**: 0 **Total Expense ($000)**: 65213 **Payroll Expense ($000)**: 24933 **Personnel**: 453

HARVARD—Mchenry County

☒ **MERCYHEALTH HOSPITAL AND MEDICAL CENTER – HARVARD (141335)**, 901 Grant Street, Zip 60033–1898, Mailing Address: P.O.Box 850, 60033–0850; tel. 815/943–5431, (Total facility includes 32 beds in nursing home–type unit) **A**1 10 18 **F**3 11 15 28 29 30 35 40 45 46 57 59 62 63 64 69 70 75 77 79 81 82 85 87 93 96 107 108 110 119 128 129 130 132 143 146 **P**6 **S** Mercy Health System, Janesville, WI
Primary Contact: Javon R. Bea, Chief Executive Officer
COO: Jennifer Hallatt, Chief Operating Officer
CFO: Shannon Dunphy–Alexander, Director
CMO: Douglas Bryan, President, Medical Staff
CHR: Heather Niles, Director Human Resources Operations
CNO: Caryn Lynn Oleston MSN, R.N., FACHE, Chief Nursing Officer
Web address: www.mercyhealthsystem.org
Control: Other not–for–profit (including NFP Corporation) **Service**: General medical and surgical

Staffed Beds: 50 **Admissions**: 527 **Census**: 29 **Outpatient Visits**: 67293 **Births**: 2 **Total Expense ($000)**: 22862 **Payroll Expense ($000)**: 8664 **Personnel**: 105

HARVEY—Cook County

★ △ ⇑ **INGALLS MEMORIAL HOSPITAL (140191)**, One Ingalls Drive, Zip 60426–3591; tel. 708/333–2300 **A**2 3 5 7 10 21 **F**3 8 11 12 13 15 18 20 22 24 26 28 29 30 31 34 35 36 37 40 42 43 45 46 47 49 50 51 54 56 57 58 59 60 62 63 64 68 70 74 75 76 77 78 79 81 82 84 85 86 87 89 90 92 93 96 97 98 99 101 102 103 104 105 107 108 110 111 113 114 115 116 117 118 119 120 121 123 124 126 129 130 131 132 135 143 144 146 147 148 **P**8 **S** University of Chicago Medicine, Chicago, IL
Primary Contact: Kurt E. Johnson, President and Chief Executive Officer
COO: Michael L Hicks, Senior Vice President and Chief Operating Officer
CFO: Andrew Stefo, Senior Vice President Finance and Chief Financial Officer
CHR: Aletha Ross, Vice President Human Resources
CNO: Kathleen A Mikos R.N., Vice President and Chief Nursing Officer
Web address: www.ingallshealthsystem.org
Control: Other not–for–profit (including NFP Corporation) **Service**: General medical and surgical

Staffed Beds: 352 **Admissions**: 13185 **Census**: 177 **Outpatient Visits**: 365599 **Births**: 922 **Total Expense ($000)**: 297328 **Payroll Expense ($000)**: 96249 **Personnel**: 1469

HAVANA—Mason County

☒ **MASON DISTRICT HOSPITAL (141313)**, 615 North Promenade Street, Zip 62644–1243, Mailing Address: P.O.Box 530, 62644–0530; tel. 309/543–4431 **A**1 10 18 **F**3 7 8 11 15 28 29 30 34 35 40 45 49 50 53 54 56 57 59 62 64 65 68 75 77 79 81 93 97 102 103 107 108 110 114 118 119 127 129 130 131 132 133 143 146 **P**6
Primary Contact: Douglas D. Kosier, Chief Executive Officer
CMO: Tad A. Yetter M.D., President Medical Staff
CIO: Aaron Coots, Information Technology Director
CHR: Anne Davis, Director Human Resources
CNO: Rhonda Hine R.N., Interim Chief Nursing Executive
Web address: www.masondistricthospital.org
Control: Hospital district or authority, Government, Nonfederal **Service**: General medical and surgical

Staffed Beds: 20 **Admissions**: 291 **Census**: 3 **Outpatient Visits**: 24264 **Births**: 0 **Total Expense ($000)**: 23526 **Payroll Expense ($000)**: 11253 **Personnel**: 263

HAZEL CREST—Cook County

★ ⇑ **ADVOCATE SOUTH SUBURBAN HOSPITAL (140250)**, 17800 South Kedzie Avenue, Zip 60429–0989; tel. 708/799–8000, (Total facility includes 39 beds in nursing home–type unit) **A**2 10 21 **F**3 11 13 15 18 20 22 24 26 28 29 30 31 34 35 36 40 45 46 47 49 50 51 53 55 57 59 60 63 64 68 70 75 76 78 79 81 82 85 87 89 92 93 100 107 108 110 111 114 115 118 119 126 128 130 132 145 146 147 148 149 **P**8 **S** Advocate Health Care, Downers Grove, IL
Primary Contact: Richard Heim, President
COO: Karen Clark MS, R.N., Vice President Operations
CFO: Brian Kelly, Vice President Finance
CMO: Richard Multack D.O., Vice President Medical Management
CIO: Beth Turek, Site Manager Information Systems
CHR: Kristin Landini, Vice President Human Resources
CNO: Sharon A Otten, Vice President Nursing
Web address: www.advocatehealth.com/ssub/
Control: Church operated, Nongovernment, not–for–profit **Service**: General medical and surgical

Staffed Beds: 258 **Admissions**: 10923 **Census**: 140 **Outpatient Visits**: 145600 **Births**: 1095 **Total Expense ($000)**: 212354 **Payroll Expense ($000)**: 74188 **Personnel**: 916

HERRIN—Williamson County

☐ **HERRIN HOSPITAL (140011)**, 201 South 14th Street, Zip 62948–3631; tel. 618/942–2171 **A**1 5 10 **F**3 11 12 18 28 29 30 34 35 40 45 47 49 50 51 54 56 57 59 60 61 64 68 70 74 75 78 79 81 82 84 85 86 87 90 92 93 100 107 108 111 114 115 119 130 131 132 135 143 146 148 **P**1 **S** Southern Illinois Healthcare, Carbondale, IL
Primary Contact: Terence Farrell, Vice President and Administrator
CFO: Michael Kasser, Chief Financial Officer
CMO: Michelle Jenkins M.D., President Medical Staff
CIO: David Holland, Chief Information Officer
CHR: Teresa A Lovellette, Manager Human Resources
Web address: www.sih.net
Control: Other not–for–profit (including NFP Corporation) **Service**: General medical and surgical

Staffed Beds: 114 **Admissions**: 6583 **Census**: 75 **Outpatient Visits**: 155005 **Births**: 0 **Total Expense ($000)**: 139640 **Payroll Expense ($000)**: 41948 **Personnel**: 876

IL

Hospital, Medicare Provider Number, Address, Telephone, Approval, Facility, and Physician Codes, Health Care System

★ American Hospital Association (AHA) membership   ○ Healthcare Facilities Accreditation Program   ⇑ Center for Improvement in Healthcare Quality Accreditation
☐ The Joint Commission accreditation   ◇ DNV Healthcare Inc. accreditation   △ Commission on Accreditation of Rehabilitation Facilities (CARF) accreditation

---

HIGHLAND—Madison County

☒ **HSHS ST. JOSEPH'S HOSPITAL (141336)**, 12866 Troxler Avenue, Zip 62249–1698; tel. 618/651–2600 **A**1 10 18 **F**3 8 11 15 26 27 28 29 30 34 35 40 41 44 45 47 49 51 53 57 59 64 70 75 79 81 84 86 87 93 97 107 108 110 111 114 119 124 126 129 130 131 132 133 135 143 146 147 **S** HSHS Hospital Sisters Health System, Springfield, IL
Primary Contact: John A. Ludwig, R.N., President and Chief Operating Officer
CFO: David Nosacka, Southern Illinois Division Chief Financial Officer
CHR: Christie Silvey, Director People Services
CNO: Teresa Cornelius R.N., Interim Chief Nursing Officer
Web address: www.stjosephshighland.com
Control: Church operated, Nongovernment, not–for–profit **Service**: General medical and surgical

Staffed Beds: 25 **Admissions:** 1399 **Census:** 15 **Outpatient Visits:** 58694 **Births:** 0 **Total Expense ($000):** 38708 **Payroll Expense ($000):** 11912 **Personnel:** 226		

HIGHLAND PARK—Lake County

NORTHSHORE HIGHLAND PARK HOSPITAL See Northshore University Health System, Evanston

HILLSBORO—Montgomery County

☒ **HILLSBORO AREA HOSPITAL (141332)**, 1200 East Tremont Street, Zip 62049–1900; tel. 217/532–6111 **A**1 10 18 **F**2 3 10 15 28 29 30 34 35 40 56 57 59 64 65 75 77 79 81 85 86 87 89 92 93 94 97 107 110 111 115 125 129 130 131 133 135 146 148 **S** HealthTech Management Services, Brentwood, TN
Primary Contact: Rex H. Brown, President and Chief Executive Officer
CFO: Terri L Carroll, Vice President Financial Services
CHR: Sharon Clark, Director Human Resources
Web address: www.hillsborohealth.org
Control: Other not–for–profit (including NFP Corporation) **Service**: General medical and surgical

Staffed Beds: 25 **Admissions:** 432 **Census:** 6 **Outpatient Visits:** 21833 **Births:** 0 **Total Expense ($000):** 19476 **Payroll Expense ($000):** 7032 **Personnel:** 184		

HINES—Cook County

☒ △ **EDWARD HINES, JR. VETERANS AFFAIRS HOSPITAL**, 5000 South Fifth Avenue, Zip 60141–3030, Mailing Address: P.O.Box 5000, 60141–5000; tel. 708/202–8387, (Nonreporting) **A**1 2 3 5 7 **S** Department of Veterans Affairs, Washington, DC
Primary Contact: Steven E. Braverman, M.D., Director
CFO: Yolanda Martinez, Chief Fiscal Services
CMO: Jack Bulmash M.D., Chief of Staff
CIO: Robert Tanjuakio, Chief Information Resources Management
CNO: Marianne Locke R.N., MSN, Associate Director Patient Care Services
Web address: www.hines.va.gov/
Control: Veterans Affairs, Government, federal **Service**: General medical and surgical

Staffed Beds: 485		

☐ **JOHN J. MADDEN MENTAL HEALTH CENTER (144028)**, 1200 South First Avenue, Zip 60141–0800; tel. 708/338–7202, (Nonreporting) **A**1 3 5 10 **S** Division of Mental Health, Department of Human Services, Springfield, IL
Primary Contact: Edith Newman, Interim Administrator
CFO: Janice Evans, Chief Financial Officer
Control: State, Government, Nonfederal **Service**: Psychiatric

Staffed Beds: 125		

VETERANS AFFAIRS EDWARD HINES, JR. HOSPITAL See Edward Hines, Jr. Veterans Affairs Hospital

HINSDALE—DuPage County

☒ **AMITA HEALTH ADVENTIST MEDICAL CENTER – HINSDALE (140122)**, 120 North Oak Street, Zip 60521–3890; tel. 630/856–6001 **A**1 2 3 5 10 13 **F**3 13 15 18 20 22 24 26 28 29 30 31 32 34 35 37 38 39 40 41 43 44 45 47 49 50 54 55 56 57 58 59 60 62 63 64 66 68 70 72 73 74 75 76 78 79 81 82 84 85 86 87 88 89 92 93 97 98 99 100 101 102 107 108 110 111 114 115 117 119 120 121 124 126 129 130 131 132 135 141 143 146 147 149 **S** Adventist Health System Sunbelt Health Care Corporation, Altamonte Springs, FL
Primary Contact: Michael Goebel, FACHE, Vice President and Chief Executive Officer
CFO: Rebecca Mathis, Vice President and Chief Financial Officer
CMO: Bonny Chen M.D., Vice President and Chief Medical Officer
CHR: Trish Leurck, Human Resources Director
CNO: Mary S Murphy MSN, Vice President and Chief Nursing Officer
Web address: www.AMITAhealth.org
Control: Church operated, Nongovernment, not–for–profit **Service**: General medical and surgical

Staffed Beds: 275 **Admissions:** 11646 **Census:** 132 **Outpatient Visits:** 249854 **Births:** 2497 **Total Expense ($000):** 298847 **Payroll Expense ($000):** 85114 **Personnel:** 1110		

☒ **RML SPECIALTY HOSPITAL (142010)**, 5601 South County Line Road, Zip 60521–4875; tel. 630/286–4000 **A**1 3 5 10 **F**1 3 18 29 30 31 45 53 58 74 85 107 114 119 130 146 148 149 **P**6
Primary Contact: James R. Prister, President and Chief Executive Officer
COO: Ken Pawola, Chief Operating Officer
CFO: Tom Pater, Chief Financial Officer
CMO: Patrick Fahey M.D., Chief Medical Officer
CIO: Vincent S Vitali, Chief Information Officer
CHR: John Landstrom, Director Human Resources
CNO: Marti Edwards MSN, R.N., Chief Nursing Officer
Web address: www.rmlspecialtyhospital.org
Control: Other not–for–profit (including NFP Corporation) **Service**: Acute long–term care hospital

Staffed Beds: 95 **Admissions:** 874 **Census:** 90 **Outpatient Visits:** 0 **Births:** 0 **Total Expense ($000):** 54117 **Payroll Expense ($000):** 28665 **Personnel:** 426		

HOFFMAN ESTATES—Cook County

☒ **ALEXIAN BROTHERS BEHAVIORAL HEALTH HOSPITAL (144031)**, 1650 Moon Lake Boulevard, Zip 60169–1010; tel. 847/882–1600 **A**1 5 10 **F**4 5 29 30 34 35 38 50 56 57 68 75 98 99 100 101 102 103 104 105 130 132 134 146 **S** Ascension Healthcare, Saint Louis, MO
Primary Contact: Clayton Ciha, President and Chief Executive Officer
COO: Christopher Novak, Chief Operating Officer
CFO: David Jones, Chief Financial Officer
CMO: Gregory Teas M.D., Chief Medical Officer
CIO: Sherrie Russell, Vice President and Chief Information Officer
CNO: Christine Quinlan MS, R.N., Chief Nursing Officer
Web address: www.abbhh.org
Control: Other not–for–profit (including NFP Corporation) **Service**: Psychiatric

Staffed Beds: 141 **Admissions:** 5671 **Census:** 129 **Outpatient Visits:** 178991 **Births:** 0 **Total Expense ($000):** 76014 **Payroll Expense ($000):** 39116 **Personnel:** 583		

☒ **AMITA HEALTH HOFFMAN ESTATES (140290)**, 1555 Barrington Road, Zip 60169–1019; tel. 847/843–2000, (Includes AMITA HEALTH WOMEN & CHILDREN'S HOSPITAL, 1555 Barrington Road, Hoffman Estates, Illinois, Zip 60169–1019, tel. 847/843–2000; Kevin Rath, Vice President and Executive Director) **A**1 2 3 5 10 **F**3 8 12 13 15 18 19 20 22 26 29 30 31 32 34 35 37 39 40 41 43 44 45 46 47 48 49 50 54 55 57 59 63 64 70 72 73 74 75 76 77 78 79 81 82 84 85 86 87 88 89 93 107 108 110 111 114 115 119 120 121 124 126 130 132 145 146 147 148 149 **P**5 6 **S** Ascension Healthcare, Saint Louis, MO
Primary Contact: Leonard Wilk, President and Chief Executive Officer
COO: Laurence Dry, Chief Operating Officer, Acute Care Hospitals Northern Region
CFO: Henry Zeisel, Chief Financial Officer, Northern Region
CIO: Sherrie Russell, Senior Vice President and Chief Information Officer
CHR: Donald Russell, Senior Vice President and Chief Human Resources Officer
CNO: Chris Budzinsky, Vice President Nursing and Chief Nursing Officer Alexian Brothers Acute Care Ministries
Web address: www.AMITAHealth.org
Control: Church operated, Nongovernment, not–for–profit **Service**: General medical and surgical

Staffed Beds: 286 **Admissions:** 17521 **Census:** 208 **Outpatient Visits:** 238213 **Births:** 3780 **Total Expense ($000):** 303973 **Payroll Expense ($000):** 98578 **Personnel:** 1346		

HOOPESTON—Vermilion County

★ ⇑ **CARLE HOOPESTON REGIONAL HEALTH CENTER (141316)**, 701 East Orange Street, Zip 60942–1801; tel. 217/283–5531, (Nonreporting) **A**3 10 18 21 **S** Carle Foundation, Urbana, IL
Primary Contact: Harry Brockus, Chief Executive Officer
CHR: Melodee Bowers, Director Human Resources
Web address: www.carle.org
Control: Other not–for–profit (including NFP Corporation) **Service**: General medical and surgical

Staffed Beds: 13		

HOPEDALE—Tazewell County

HOPEDALE MEDICAL COMPLEX (141330), 107 Tremont Street, Zip 61747–7525; tel. 309/449–3321, (Total facility includes 52 beds in nursing home–type unit) **A**10 18 **F**10 18 28 29 30 32 34 35 40 45 49 53 56 57 59 64 65 67 70 78 79 81 83 97 107 110 111 115 119 125 128 129 130 131 133 145 146 147 149
Primary Contact: Alfred N. Rossi, M.D., Chief Executive Officer
COO: Mark F Rossi, Chief Operating Officer and General Counsel
CHR: Andrea Halley, Director Human Resources
CNO: Timothy Sondag, Senior Nursing Officer
Web address: www.hopedalemc.com
Control: Other not–for–profit (including NFP Corporation) **Service**: General medical and surgical

Staffed Beds: 77 **Admissions:** 471 **Census:** 56 **Outpatient Visits:** 79970 **Births:** 0 **Total Expense ($000):** 23824 **Payroll Expense ($000):** 9676 **Personnel:** 89		

Many Facility Codes have changed. Please refer to the AHA Guide Code Chart. © 2017 AHA Guide

IL

JACKSONVILLE—Morgan County

☒ **PASSAVANT AREA HOSPITAL (140058)**, 1600 West Walnut Street, Zip 62650–1136; tel. 217/245–9541, (Total facility includes 15 beds in nursing home–type unit) **A**1 14 15 28 29 30 31 34 35 40 41 45 50 51 57 58 59 64 68 70 75 76 78 79 81 82 85 86 87 89 93 97 98 104 107 108 110 111 115 118 119 121 124 127 128 129 130 131 141 146 147 148 **S** Memorial Health System, Springfield, IL
Primary Contact: Harry M. Schmidt, President and Chief Executive Officer
CFO: David Bolen, Vice President and Chief Financial Officer
CMO: Charles Sheaff M.D., President Medical Staff
CIO: Janie Cook, Director Information Systems
CHR: Jim Bormann, Director Human Resources
CNO: Karen Daum R.N., MS, Vice President and Chief Nursing Officer
Web address: www.passavanthospital.com
Control: Church operated, Nongovernment, not–for–profit **Service:** General medical and surgical

Staffed Beds: 118 **Admissions:** 3528 **Census:** 41 **Outpatient Visits:** 98750 **Births:** 377 **Total Expense ($000):** 89214 **Payroll Expense ($000):** 37059 **Personnel:** 710

JERSEYVILLE—Jersey County

☒ **JERSEY COMMUNITY HOSPITAL (140059)**, 400 Maple Summit Road, Zip 62052–2028, Mailing Address: P.O.Box 426, 62052–0426; tel. 618/498–6402 **A**1 10 **F**3 7 11 15 18 28 29 31 32 34 35 36 38 40 41 46 51 53 57 59 64 70 79 81 85 87 94 97 107 111 114 115 117 118 119 127 129 130 131 132 133 146 147 148 **P**6
Primary Contact: Jonathan O. Wade, Chief Executive Officer
CFO: Beth King, Chief Financial Officer
CMO: Michael McNear M.D., Chief Medical Officer
CIO: Shane Winters, Chief Information Officer
CHR: Sharon K Sanford, Director Human Resources
CNO: Julie Smith R.N., MSN, Director of Nursing
Web address: www.jch.org
Control: Hospital district or authority, Government, Nonfederal **Service:** General medical and surgical

Staffed Beds: 46 **Admissions:** 946 **Census:** 8 **Outpatient Visits:** 153600 **Births:** 0 **Total Expense ($000):** 38820 **Payroll Expense ($000):** 18158 **Personnel:** 375

JOLIET—Will County

☒ △ **PRESENCE SAINT JOSEPH MEDICAL CENTER (140007)**, 333 North Madison Street, Zip 60435–8200; tel. 815/725–7133 **A**1 2 7 10 **F**3 5 8 11 12 13 15 17 18 20 22 24 26 28 29 30 31 32 34 35 36 37 38 39 40 41 43 44 45 46 49 50 53 54 56 57 58 59 60 61 64 65 68 70 71 72 74 75 76 78 79 80 81 82 84 85 86 87 88 89 90 91 92 93 96 97 98 99 100 101 102 103 105 107 108 110 111 114 115 118 119 120 121 123 124 126 129 130 131 132 134 135 143 144 145 146 147 149 150 **P**8 **S** Presence Health, Chicago, IL
Primary Contact: Robert J. Erickson, President
CFO: Deb Schimerowski, Regional Finance Officer
CMO: Gary Lipinski M.D., Regional Chief Medical Officer
CIO: Russell Soliman, System Manager Client Services and Management Information Services
CHR: Andre' Harrison, Regional Human Resource Officer
Web address: www.presencehealth.org/stjoes
Control: Church operated, Nongovernment, not–for–profit **Service:** General medical and surgical

Staffed Beds: 461 **Admissions:** 21949 **Census:** 278 **Outpatient Visits:** 486974 **Births:** 1089 **Total Expense ($000):** 391588 **Payroll Expense ($000):** 122914 **Personnel:** 1921

PROVENA SAINT JOSEPH MEDICAL CENTER See Presence Saint Joseph Medical Center

KANKAKEE—Kankakee County

☒ **PRESENCE ST. MARY'S HOSPITAL (140155)**, 500 West Court Street, Zip 60901–3661; tel. 815/937–2400 **A**1 2 10 **F**3 5 11 12 13 15 18 20 22 26 28 29 30 31 32 34 35 36 38 39 40 43 45 48 49 50 54 56 59 60 61 63 64 65 68 70 74 75 76 78 79 81 82 83 84 85 86 87 89 92 93 97 98 99 100 101 102 103 104 105 106 107 108 110 111 114 115 116 119 129 130 131 132 135 143 146 147 148 **S** Presence Health, Chicago, IL
Primary Contact: Chris Shride, President
CFO: Deb Schimerowski, Regional Chief Financial Officer
CMO: Gary Lipinski M.D., Regional Chief Medical Officer
CIO: Russell Soliman, Director Information Services
CHR: Andre' Harrison, Regional Chief Human Resources Officer
Web address: www.presencehealth.org/presence–st–marys–hospital–kankakee
Control: Church operated, Nongovernment, not–for–profit **Service:** General medical and surgical

Staffed Beds: 156 **Admissions:** 5511 **Census:** 61 **Outpatient Visits:** 180994 **Births:** 402 **Total Expense ($000):** 118316 **Payroll Expense ($000):** 34539 **Personnel:** 635

PROVENA ST. MARY'S HOSPITAL See Presence St. Mary's Hospital

★ △ ⇑ **RIVERSIDE MEDICAL CENTER (140186)**, 350 North Wall Street, Zip 60901–2901; tel. 815/933–1671 **A**2 5 7 10 13 21 **F**3 4 5 6 7 8 9 12 13 15 17 18 19 20 22 24 26 28 29 30 31 32 34 35 36 38 39 40 41 43 44 45 46 47 49 50 51 54 55 56 57 58 59 61 62 64 65 66 68 70 71 74 75 76 77 78 79 81 82 84 85 86 87 89 90 92 93 96 97 98 99 100 101 102 103 104 105 106 107 108 110 111 114 115 118 119 120 121 123 124 126 127 129 130 131 132 134 135 141 143 144 145 146 147 148 149 150 **P**1
Primary Contact: Phillip M. Kambic, President and Chief Executive Officer
CFO: Bill Douglas, Senior Vice President and Chief Financial Officer
CMO: Keith A Moss, Vice President & Chief Medical Informatics Officers
CIO: Kyle Hansen, Corporate Director Information Systems
CHR: Becky Kay Hinrichs, Vice President Human Resources
CNO: Michael Mutterer, Senior Vice President and Chief Nursing Officer
Web address: www.riversidehealthcare.org
Control: Other not–for–profit (including NFP Corporation) **Service:** General medical and surgical

Staffed Beds: 318 **Admissions:** 11214 **Census:** 156 **Outpatient Visits:** 496016 **Births:** 1046 **Total Expense ($000):** 295046 **Payroll Expense ($000):** 130442 **Personnel:** 2118

KEWANEE—Henry County

★ **OSF SAINT LUKE MEDICAL CENTER (141325)**, 1051 West South Street, Zip 61443–8354, Mailing Address: P.O.Box 747, 61443–0747; tel. 309/852–7500 **A**10 18 **F**3 11 15 29 30 32 34 35 36 38 40 45 50 57 59 64 65 66 70 75 77 78 81 82 85 86 87 92 93 96 97 108 110 111 115 119 127 129 130 131 132 133 135 146 147 148 149 **P**6 **S** OSF Healthcare System, Peoria, IL
Primary Contact: Lynn Fulton, President
CFO: John Bowser, Vice President, Chief Financial Officer
CHR: Renee A Salisbury, Director Human Resources
CNO: Jacqueline D. Kernan, Vice President, Chief Nursing Officer
Web address: www.osfsaintluke.org
Control: Other not–for–profit (including NFP Corporation) **Service:** General medical and surgical

Staffed Beds: 25 **Admissions:** 423 **Census:** 4 **Outpatient Visits:** 38791 **Births:** 3 **Total Expense ($000):** 27216 **Payroll Expense ($000):** 10665 **Personnel:** 141

LA GRANGE—Cook County

☒ **AMITA HEALTH ADVENTIST MEDICAL CENTER LAGRANGE (140065)**, 5101 South Willow Spring Road, Zip 60525–2600; tel. 708/245–9000 **A**1 2 3 5 10 13 **F**3 13 15 18 20 22 24 29 30 31 32 34 35 37 40 41 43 44 49 50 54 56 57 58 59 61 62 63 64 66 68 70 73 74 75 76 78 79 81 82 84 85 86 87 90 91 93 96 97 100 101 102 107 108 110 111 114 115 119 124 126 129 130 131 141 143 146 147 148 149 **S** Adventist Health System Sunbelt Health Care Corporation, Altamonte Springs, FL
Primary Contact: Michael Murrill, MBA, President and Chief Executive Officer
CFO: Rebecca Mathis, Chief Financial Officer
CIO: Thomas Schoenig, Chief Information Officer
CHR: Garry Giertuga, Site Manager Human Resources
CNO: Mary S Murphy MSN, Regional Chief Nursing Officer
Web address: www.keepingyouwell.com
Control: Church operated, Nongovernment, not–for–profit **Service:** General medical and surgical

Staffed Beds: 200 **Admissions:** 8117 **Census:** 102 **Outpatient Visits:** 103517 **Births:** 383 **Total Expense ($000):** 166718 **Payroll Expense ($000):** 51771 **Personnel:** 636

IL

Hospital, Medicare Provider Number, Address, Telephone, Approval, Facility, and Physician Codes, Health Care System

★ American Hospital Association (AHA) membership
☐ The Joint Commission accreditation
○ Healthcare Facilities Accreditation Program
◇ DNV Healthcare Inc. accreditation
⇑ Center for Improvement in Healthcare Quality Accreditation
△ Commission on Accreditation of Rehabilitation Facilities (CARF) accreditation

LAKE FOREST—Lake County

LAKE FOREST HOSPITAL See Northwestern Medicine Lake Forest Hospital

✉ **NORTHWESTERN MEDICINE LAKE FOREST HOSPITAL (140130)**, 660 North Westmoreland Road, Zip 60045–1696; tel. 847/234–5600, (Total facility includes 62 beds in nursing home–type unit) **A**1 2 3 5 10 **F**2 3 8 9 11 13 15 18 20 22 26 28 29 30 31 32 34 35 36 38 40 42 43 44 45 46 48 49 50 51 52 53 54 55 56 57 58 59 60 62 64 65 66 67 68 70 73 74 75 76 77 78 79 81 82 84 85 86 87 89 92 93 96 97 100 104 107 108 110 111 114 115 116 117 119 120 121 123 126 128 129 130 131 132 135 144 146 147 148 149 150 **P**6 **S** Northwestern Memorial HealthCare, Chicago, IL
Primary Contact: Thomas J. McAfee, President, North Market
CFO: Matthew J Flynn, Senior Vice President and Chief Financial Officer
CMO: Michael G Ankin M.D., Vice President Medical Affairs & Chief Medical Officer
CNO: Denise Mageski MSN, R.N., Chief Nurse Executive
Web address: www.nm.org
Control: Other not–for–profit (including NFP Corporation) **Service**: General medical and surgical

Staffed Beds: 197 **Admissions:** 7417 **Census:** 86 **Outpatient Visits:** 477550 **Births:** 1427 **Total Expense ($000):** 321673 **Payroll Expense ($000):** 147898 **Personnel:** 1850

LAWRENCEVILLE—Lawrence County

LAWRENCE COUNTY MEMORIAL HOSPITAL (141344), 2200 West State Street, Zip 62439–1852; tel. 618/943–1000 **A**10 18 **F**3 11 15 28 29 30 35 40 75 77 81 93 107 110 111 114 127 130 133 **S** QHR, Brentwood, TN
Primary Contact: Doug Florkowski, Chief Executive Officer
CFO: Larry Spore, Chief Financial Officer
CIO: Gary Theriac, Director Information Technology
CHR: Kim Alldredge, Director Human Resources
CNO: Rita Garvey, Chief Nursing Officer
Web address: www.lcmhosp.org
Control: Other not–for–profit (including NFP Corporation) **Service**: General medical and surgical

Staffed Beds: 25 **Admissions:** 654 **Census:** 7 **Outpatient Visits:** 51014 **Births:** 0 **Total Expense ($000):** 15916 **Payroll Expense ($000):** 6649 **Personnel:** 149

LIBERTYVILLE—Lake County

★ ⇧ **ADVOCATE CONDELL MEDICAL CENTER (140202)**, 801 South Milwaukee Avenue, Zip 60048–3199; tel. 847/362–2900 **A**2 10 21 **F**1 2 3 4 11 12 13 15 16 17 18 19 20 22 24 26 28 29 30 31 32 34 35 36 37 39 40 41 43 44 45 46 47 48 49 50 51 53 54 55 56 57 59 60 64 65 67 68 70 72 73 74 75 76 77 78 79 80 81 82 85 86 87 88 89 90 92 93 94 96 98 107 108 110 111 114 115 117 118 119 120 121 123 124 126 128 130 132 135 144 145 146 147 148 **P**8 **S** Advocate Health Care, Downers Grove, IL
Primary Contact: Karen A. Lambert, President
CFO: David A Cartwright, Vice President Finance and Support Services
CMO: Debra Susie–Lattner M.D., Vice President Medical Management
CIO: Harold Kromer, Director Site Information Systems
CHR: Amy Antani Logue Ph.D., Vice President Human Resources
CNO: Mary Hillard R.N., MSN, Vice President Patient Care Services and Clinical Operations, Chief Nursing Executive
Web address: www.advocatehealth.com/condell/
Control: Other not–for–profit (including NFP Corporation) **Service**: General medical and surgical

Staffed Beds: 283 **Admissions:** 16817 **Census:** 184 **Outpatient Visits:** 232855 **Births:** 2186 **Total Expense ($000):** 297118 **Payroll Expense ($000):** 99599 **Personnel:** 1473

LINCOLN—Logan County

✉ **ABRAHAM LINCOLN MEMORIAL HOSPITAL (141322)**, 200 Stahlhut Drive, Zip 62656–5066; tel. 217/732–2161 **A**1 10 18 **F**13 15 28 29 30 34 35 40 57 59 64 75 76 77 79 81 82 87 93 107 108 110 111 119 129 130 131 132 133 144 146 **P**5 **S** Memorial Health System, Springfield, IL
Primary Contact: Dolan Dalpoas, President and Chief Executive Officer
CFO: Andrew Costic, Regional Chief Financial Officer
CMO: Amir J. Wahab M.D., Medical Staff President
CIO: Keenan Leesman, Director Information Systems
CHR: Michelle Long, Human Resources Business Partner
CNO: Roxanne Harling, Chief Nursing Officer
Web address: www.almh.org
Control: Other not–for–profit (including NFP Corporation) **Service**: General medical and surgical

Staffed Beds: 25 **Admissions:** 915 **Census:** 10 **Outpatient Visits:** 49040 **Births:** 220 **Total Expense ($000):** 40370 **Payroll Expense ($000):** 15126 **Personnel:** 258

LITCHFIELD—Montgomery County

✉ **HSHS ST. FRANCIS HOSPITAL (141350)**, 1215 Franciscan Drive, Zip 62056–1799, Mailing Address: P.O.Box 1215, 62056–0999; tel. 217/324–2191 **A**1 10 18 **F**3 8 11 13 15 18 28 29 30 31 34 35 40 44 45 46 50 56 57 59 64 68 70 74 75 76 77 78 79 81 82 85 86 87 92 93 107 111 114 118 119 129 131 132 133 134 135 146 147 149 **S** HSHS Hospital Sisters Health System, Springfield, IL
Primary Contact: Aaron Puchbauer, Interim Chief Executive Officer
CFO: Marisa Murray CPA, Director Finance
CNO: John Peipert R.N., Chief Nursing Officer
Web address: www.stfrancis–litchfield.org
Control: Church operated, Nongovernment, not–for–profit **Service**: General medical and surgical

Staffed Beds: 25 **Admissions:** 1367 **Census:** 12 **Outpatient Visits:** 67269 **Births:** 245 **Total Expense ($000):** 40683 **Payroll Expense ($000):** 11275 **Personnel:** 217

MACOMB—Mcdonough County

✉ **MCDONOUGH DISTRICT HOSPITAL (140089)**, 525 East Grant Street, Zip 61455–3318; tel. 309/833–4101 **A**1 10 20 **F**2 3 5 7 11 13 15 28 29 31 34 35 38 40 45 47 48 50 51 54 56 57 59 62 63 64 68 70 75 76 77 78 79 81 82 84 85 86 91 93 94 96 97 98 99 100 101 102 103 104 107 108 110 115 119 124 127 129 130 131 132 133 135 146 147 148 **P**8
Primary Contact: Kenneth Boyd Jr, President and Chief Executive Officer
CFO: Linda Dace, Vice President Finance
CMO: Edwin Card, President Medical Staff
CIO: Harlan T Baker, Department Leader Information Systems
CHR: Sue Dexter, Administrative Department Leader Human Resources
CNO: Wanda Foster R.N., MS, FACHE, MSN, Vice President Nursing
Web address: www.mdh.org
Control: Hospital district or authority, Government, Nonfederal **Service**: General medical and surgical

Staffed Beds: 60 **Admissions:** 1552 **Census:** 16 **Outpatient Visits:** 215960 **Births:** 298 **Total Expense ($000):** 77001 **Payroll Expense ($000):** 36132 **Personnel:** 524

MARION—Williamson County

✉ **HEARTLAND REGIONAL MEDICAL CENTER (140184)**, 3333 West DeYoung, Zip 62959–5884; tel. 618/998–7000, (Nonreporting) **A**1 10 **S** Quorum Health, Brentwood, TN
Primary Contact: Melisa Adkins, Chief Executive Officer
COO: Kolbe Sheridan, Chief Operating Officer
CFO: Jeff Thomas, Chief Financial Officer
CHR: Sam Hood, Director Human Resources
Web address: www.heartlandregional.com
Control: Corporation, Investor–owned (for–profit) **Service**: General medical and surgical

Staffed Beds: 92

✉ **MARION VETERANS AFFAIRS MEDICAL CENTER**, 2401 West Main Street, Zip 62959–1188; tel. 618/997–5311 **A**1 3 5 **F**3 4 5 8 11 12 18 20 22 29 30 31 34 35 36 38 39 40 44 45 50 53 54 56 57 58 62 63 64 65 68 70 75 77 78 79 81 82 83 84 86 87 91 92 93 94 96 97 100 101 102 103 104 106 107 108 111 112 114 115 116 117 119 127 128 130 132 135 143 146 147 148 149 **S** Department of Veterans Affairs, Washington, DC
Primary Contact: Jo–Ann M. Ginsberg, R.N., MSN, Director
COO: Frank Kehus, Associate Director for Operations
CFO: Connie McDonald, Chief Financial Officer
CMO: Michael Ladwig M.D., Chief of Staff
CIO: Adam Powell, Program Manager
CHR: Tim Hartwell, Chief Human Resources
CNO: Rose Burke, Associate Director Patient Care Services
Web address: www.marion.va.gov
Control: Veterans Affairs, Government, federal **Service**: General medical and surgical

Staffed Beds: 54 **Admissions:** 4039 **Census:** 118 **Outpatient Visits:** 431437 **Births:** 0 **Personnel:** 1500

MARYVILLE—Madison County

✉ △ **ANDERSON HOSPITAL (140289)**, 6800 State Route 162, Zip 62062–8500; tel. 618/288–5711 **A**1 7 10 **F**3 11 13 15 18 20 22 28 29 30 31 34 35 40 49 50 54 57 59 62 64 70 74 75 76 78 79 81 85 90 93 107 110 111 115 118 119 126 129 130 132 144 146 147 148
Primary Contact: Keith Allen. Page, President and Chief Executive Officer
CFO: Michael Marshall, Vice President Finance and Chief Financial Officer
CMO: Charles A. Lane, Chief Medical Officer
CIO: Michael Ward, Director Information Services
CHR: Robin Steinmann, Administrative Director Human Resources
CNO: Lisa Klaustermeier R.N., MSN, Chief Nursing Officer
Web address: www.andersonhospital.org
Control: Other not–for–profit (including NFP Corporation) **Service**: General medical and surgical

Staffed Beds: 154 **Admissions:** 7415 **Census:** 80 **Outpatient Visits:** 167493 **Births:** 1598 **Total Expense ($000):** 125524 **Payroll Expense ($000):** 51604 **Personnel:** 948

IL

MATTOON—Coles County

⊞ **SARAH BUSH LINCOLN HEALTH CENTER (140189)**, 1000 Health Center Drive, Zip 61938–9253; tel. 217/258–2525 **A1** 10 20 **F3** 11 12 13 15 18 20 22 28 29 30 31 32 34 35 36 38 39 40 44 45 49 50 53 54 56 57 59 61 62 63 64 65 66 68 69 70 71 74 75 76 77 78 79 81 82 84 85 86 87 89 93 97 98 99 100 101 102 103 104 105 107 110 111 115 117 119 120 121 123 127 129 130 131 132 134 135 144 145 146 147 148 **P6**
Primary Contact: Jerry Esker, President and Chief Executive Officer
COO: Dennis Pluard, Vice President Finance and Operations
CFO: Dennis Pluard, Vice President Finance and Operations
CMO: James Hildebrandt D.O., Vice President Medical Affairs
CIO: Maggie Ratliff, Vice President Information Systems
CHR: Eric Benson, Vice President Human Resources & Wellness
CNO: Lisa J. Hernandez R.N., Vice President, Patient Care Continuum and Chief Nursing Officer
Web address: www.sarahbush.org
Control: Other not–for–profit (including NFP Corporation) **Service**: General medical and surgical

> **Staffed Beds:** 118 **Admissions:** 7209 **Census:** 70 **Outpatient Visits:** 523574 **Births:** 788 **Total Expense ($000):** 268918 **Payroll Expense ($000):** 132656 **Personnel:** 2035

MAYWOOD—Cook County

⊞ **LOYOLA UNIVERSITY MEDICAL CENTER (140276)**, 2160 South First Avenue, Zip 60153–3328; tel. 708/216–9000, (Includes RONALD MCDONALD CHILDREN'S HOSPITAL, 2160 South 1St Avenue, Maywood, Illinois, Zip 60153–3328, tel. 888/584–7888) **A1** 2 3 5 8 10 **F3** 6 7 8 9 11 12 13 14 15 16 17 18 19 20 21 22 23 24 25 26 27 28 29 30 31 32 33 34 35 36 37 38 39 40 41 43 44 45 46 47 48 49 50 51 54 55 56 57 58 59 60 61 64 65 66 68 70 71 72 73 74 75 76 77 78 79 80 81 82 84 85 86 87 88 89 90 91 92 93 94 96 97 99 100 101 102 103 104 107 108 110 111 114 115 116 117 118 119 120 121 123 124 126 129 130 131 132 134 135 136 137 138 139 140 141 142 143 144 145 146 147 148 149 150 **P5** 6 **S** Trinity Health, Livonia, MI
Primary Contact: Chad Whelan, M.D., President
CFO: Jay Sial, Chief Financial Officer
CMO: Joshua Lee M.D., Chief Medical Officer
CIO: Arthur J Krumrey, Chief Information Officer
CHR: Vicky Piper, Vice President Human Resources
Web address: www.loyolamedicine.org/Medical_Services/index.cfm
Control: Other not–for–profit (including NFP Corporation) **Service**: General medical and surgical

> **Staffed Beds:** 517 **Admissions:** 23018 **Census:** 376 **Outpatient Visits:** 1667448 **Births:** 1270 **Personnel:** 6762

MCHENRY—Mchenry County

⊞ **CENTEGRA HOSPITAL – MCHENRY (140116)**, 4201 Medical Center Drive, Zip 60050–8409; tel. 815/344–5000, (Includes CENTEGRA HOSPITAL–HUNTLEY, 10400 Haligus Road, Huntley, Illinois, Zip 60142, tel. 224/654–0000; Michael S Eesley, Chief Executive Officer) **A1** 2 3 5 10 **F3** 4 11 12 13 15 18 20 22 24 26 28 29 30 31 34 35 37 38 39 40 41 43 44 45 49 50 51 54 55 57 58 59 62 64 68 69 70 74 75 76 78 79 81 82 85 86 87 90 92 93 96 100 101 102 107 108 110 111 114 115 117 118 119 120 121 123 124 126 129 130 131 132 143 144 146 147 148 **P6** 8 **S** Centegra Health System, Crystal Lake, IL
Primary Contact: Michael S. Eesley, Chief Executive Officer
COO: Jason Sciarro, President and Chief Operating Officer
CFO: David Tomlinson, Executive Vice President Chief Financial Officer and Chief Information Officer
CMO: Irfan Hafiz, Vice President Medical Affairs
CIO: David Tomlinson, Executive Vice President Chief Financial Officer and Chief Information Officer
CHR: Bernadette S Szczepanski, Senior Vice President, Human Resources
Web address: www.centegra.org
Control: Other not–for–profit (including NFP Corporation) **Service**: General medical and surgical

> **Staffed Beds:** 166 **Admissions:** 9851 **Census:** 116 **Outpatient Visits:** 286234 **Births:** 1586 **Total Expense ($000):** 286507 **Payroll Expense ($000):** 102312 **Personnel:** 1341

MCLEANSBORO—Hamilton County

HAMILTON MEMORIAL HOSPITAL DISTRICT (141326), 611 South Marshall Avenue, Zip 62859–1213, Mailing Address: P.O.Box 429, Mc Leansboro, 62859–0429; tel. 618/643–2361 **A10** 18 **F3** 11 15 28 29 40 43 57 81 93 107 108 114 119 127 129 130 133 148
Primary Contact: Gregory F. Sims, Chief Executive Officer
CFO: Kent Mitchell, Chief Financial Officer
CIO: David Cutsinger, Chief Information Officer
CHR: Sheila Thompson, Director Human Resources
CNO: Patty Blazier, Chief Nursing Officer
Web address: www.hmhospital.org
Control: Hospital district or authority, Government, Nonfederal **Service**: General medical and surgical

> **Staffed Beds:** 25 **Admissions:** 604 **Census:** 5 **Outpatient Visits:** 44797 **Births:** 0 **Total Expense ($000):** 16234 **Payroll Expense ($000):** 6925 **Personnel:** 121

MELROSE PARK—Cook County

⊞ **GOTTLIEB MEMORIAL HOSPITAL (140008)**, 701 West North Avenue, Zip 60160–1612; tel. 708/681–3200 **A1** 3 5 10 **F2** 3 11 12 13 15 18 20 22 24 26 28 29 30 31 34 35 36 39 40 43 44 45 47 49 50 53 54 56 57 59 60 64 65 68 70 74 75 76 77 78 79 81 85 86 87 89 92 93 96 97 98 103 107 108 110 111 114 116 117 118 119 126 128 129 130 131 132 143 144 145 146 147 148 149 150 **P8** 8 **S** Trinity Health, Livonia, MI
Primary Contact: Lori Price, President
CFO: Ellyn Chin, Vice President Finance
CMO: Gerald Luger M.D., President Medical Staff
CIO: Maurita Adler, Director Information Services
CHR: Brett Wakefield, Vice President Human Resources
Web address: www.gottliebhospital.org
Control: Other not–for–profit (including NFP Corporation) **Service**: General medical and surgical

> **Staffed Beds:** 205 **Admissions:** 7448 **Census:** 107 **Outpatient Visits:** 85968 **Births:** 732 **Personnel:** 911

⊞ **WESTLAKE HOSPITAL (140240)**, 1225 Lake Street, Zip 60160–4000; tel. 708/681–3000, (Nonreporting) **A1** 3 5 10 **S** TENET Healthcare Corporation, Dallas, TX
Primary Contact: Michael Ditoro, Interim Chief Executive Officer
COO: Michael Ditoro, Chief Operating Officer
CFO: Jennifer Lamont, Chief Financial Officer
CMO: Robert Chase M.D., Chief Medical Officer
CHR: Nancy Gunnell, Chief Human Resource Officer
CNO: Ruth Matthei R.N., MS, Chief Nursing Officer
Web address: www.westlakehosp.com
Control: Corporation, Investor–owned (for–profit) **Service**: General medical and surgical

> **Staffed Beds:** 181

MENDOTA—Lasalle County

★ **OSF SAINT PAUL MEDICAL CENTER (141310)**, 1401 East 12th Street, Zip 61342–9216; tel. 815/539–7461 **A10** 18 **F3** 11 15 28 29 30 31 34 40 49 57 59 64 69 70 77 78 79 81 82 85 93 107 110 111 115 127 129 130 133 146 **S** OSF Healthcare System, Peoria, IL
Primary Contact: Jennifer Junis, MSN, R.N., President
CFO: Dawn Trompeter, Vice President Finance I–80 Region and Chief Financial Officer
CMO: Leonardo Lopez, President Medical Staff
CHR: Kimberly Kennedy, Manager Human Resources
CNO: Heather Bomstad MSN, R.N., Vice President Patient Care Services and Chief Nursing Officer
Web address: www.osfhealthcare.org/saint-paul
Control: Other not–for–profit (including NFP Corporation) **Service**: General medical and surgical

> **Staffed Beds:** 25 **Admissions:** 579 **Census:** 6 **Outpatient Visits:** 44003 **Births:** 0 **Total Expense ($000):** 34131 **Payroll Expense ($000):** 12758 **Personnel:** 164

IL

Hospital, Medicare Provider Number, Address, Telephone, Approval, Facility, and Physician Codes, Health Care System

★ American Hospital Association (AHA) membership
□ The Joint Commission accreditation
○ Healthcare Facilities Accreditation Program
◇ DNV Healthcare Inc. accreditation
⇑ Center for Improvement in Healthcare Quality Accreditation
△ Commission on Accreditation of Rehabilitation Facilities (CARF) accreditation

---

METROPOLIS—Massac County

★ **MASSAC MEMORIAL HOSPITAL (141323)**, 28 Chick Street, Zip 62960–2467, Mailing Address: P.O.Box 850, 62960–0850; tel. 618/524–2176 **A**10 18 **F**7 11 15 18 28 29 30 34 40 45 46 47 48 49 50 59 64 66 68 75 81 82 93 97 104 107 108 110 111 115 119 127 128 129 133 143 148 **P**6
Primary Contact: Rick Goins, Chief Executive Officer
CFO: Randy Rushing, Chief Financial Officer
CHR: Johnna Douglas, Human Resources Manager
Web address: www.massachealth.org
Control: Hospital district or authority, Government, Nonfederal **Service**: General medical and surgical

Staffed Beds: 25 **Admissions**: 678 **Census**: 8 **Outpatient Visits**: 62620 **Births**: 0 **Total Expense ($000)**: 21921 **Personnel**: 198	

MOLINE—Rock Island County

UNITYPOINT HEALTH – TRINITY MOLINE See Unitypoint Health – Trinity Rock Island, Rock Island

MONMOUTH—Warren County

★ **OSF HOLY FAMILY MEDICAL CENTER (141318)**, 1000 West Harlem Avenue, Zip 61462–1007; tel. 309/734–3141 **A**10 18 **F**11 15 28 29 30 34 40 45 46 50 57 59 64 65 68 75 77 81 85 87 93 97 107 110 115 118 119 127 129 130 132 133 135 143 145 146 **P**6 **S** OSF Healthcare System, Peoria, IL
Primary Contact: Patricia A. Luker, President
CFO: Theresa Springer, Chief Financial Officer
CMO: Frank Lasala M.D., President Medical Staff
CIO: Lew McCann, Director Management Information Systems
CHR: Jenny Jacobs, Director Human Resources
CNO: Shelley Wiborg MS, R.N., Director of Nursing
Web address: www.osfholyfamily.org
Control: Church operated, Nongovernment, not–for–profit **Service**: General medical and surgical

Staffed Beds: 23 **Admissions**: 373 **Census**: 5 **Outpatient Visits**: 70656 **Births**: 0 **Total Expense ($000)**: 27538 **Payroll Expense ($000)**: 6886 **Personnel**: 102	

MONTICELLO—Piatt County

✠ **KIRBY MEDICAL CENTER (141301)**, 1000 Medical Center Drive, Zip 61856–2116; tel. 217/762–2115, (Nonreporting) **A**1 5 10 18
Primary Contact: Steven D. Tenhouse, FACHE, Chief Executive Officer
COO: Mark Fred R.N., Chief Operating Officer
CFO: Alexander Nazarian CPA, Chief Financial Officer
CMO: Narain Mandhan M.D., Chief Medical Officer
CIO: Alexander Nazarian CPA, Director Information Technology
CHR: Andrew Buffenbarger, Chief Compliance Officer
CNO: Jennifer Moss MS, R.N., Chief Clinical Officer
Web address: www.kirbyhealth.org
Control: Other not–for–profit (including NFP Corporation) **Service**: General medical and surgical

Staffed Beds: 16	

MORRIS—Grundy County

★ ○ **MORRIS HOSPITAL & HEALTHCARE CENTERS (140101)**, 150 West High Street, Zip 60450–1497; tel. 815/942–2932 **A**2 10 11 **F**3 11 13 15 18 19 20 22 26 28 29 34 35 40 43 45 47 49 50 54 57 59 64 66 69 70 75 76 77 78 79 81 82 85 86 87 89 93 97 102 107 108 110 111 114 115 118 119 120 121 123 130 132 135 143 144 146 149 **P**6
Primary Contact: Mark B. Steadham, President and Chief Executive Officer
CFO: Dean M Marketti, Vice President Finance
CIO: Dean M Marketti, Chief Information Officer
CHR: Erin Murphy–Frobish, Vice President Human Resources
CNO: Kimberly A. Landers MS, R.N., Vice President Patient Care Services
Web address: www.morrishospital.org
Control: Other not–for–profit (including NFP Corporation) **Service**: General medical and surgical

Staffed Beds: 89 **Admissions**: 4233 **Census**: 42 **Outpatient Visits**: 332572 **Births**: 511 **Total Expense ($000)**: 149402 **Payroll Expense ($000)**: 68219 **Personnel**: 829	

MORRISON—Whiteside County

★ **MORRISON COMMUNITY HOSPITAL (141329)**, 303 North Jackson Street, Zip 61270–3042; tel. 815/772–4003, (Nonreporting) **A**10 18
Primary Contact: Pam Pfister, Chief Executive Officer
COO: Pam Pfister, Chief Executive Officer
CFO: Cami Megli, Controller
CMO: Duncan Dinkha M.D., Chief of Staff
CIO: Pam Pfister, Chief Executive Officer
CHR: Amber L Temple, Director Human Resources
Web address: www.morrisonhospital.com
Control: Hospital district or authority, Government, Nonfederal **Service**: General medical and surgical

Staffed Beds: 63	

MOUNT CARMEL—Wabash County

✠ **WABASH GENERAL HOSPITAL (141327)**, 1418 College Drive, Zip 62863–2638; tel. 618/262–8621, (Nonreporting) **A**1 10 18 **S** Alliant Management Services, Louisville, KY
Primary Contact: Jay Purvis, President and Chief Executive Officer
COO: Karissa Turner, Vice President Operations
CFO: Steve McGill, Vice President Finance and Chief Financial Officer
CMO: Justin Miller M.D., Chief of Staff
CIO: Bobby Gage, Director Information Technology
CHR: Bridget Shepard, Vice President Human Resources
CNO: Tamara Gould R.N., Vice President Clinical Services and Chief Nursing Officer
Web address: www.wabashgeneral.com
Control: County, Government, Nonfederal **Service**: General medical and surgical

Staffed Beds: 25	

MOUNT VERNON—Jefferson County

✠ **CROSSROADS COMMUNITY HOSPITAL (140294)**, 8 Doctors Park Road, Zip 62864–6224; tel. 618/244–5500 **A**1 10 **F**3 11 12 15 18 29 30 40 45 47 50 57 59 70 75 79 81 85 87 97 107 110 111 115 119 126 127 129 132 146 **S** Quorum Health, Brentwood, TN
Primary Contact: Finny Mathew, Chief Executive Officer
CIO: Bryan Delaney, Director Information Technology
CHR: Jessica Connaway, Director Human Resources
CNO: Stephanie Maines, Chief Nursing Officer
Web address: www.crossroadshospital.com
Control: Corporation, Investor–owned (for–profit) **Service**: General medical and surgical

Staffed Beds: 31 **Admissions**: 866 **Census**: 7 **Outpatient Visits**: 45696 **Births**: 0 **Total Expense ($000)**: 35388 **Payroll Expense ($000)**: 9633 **Personnel**: 179	

✠ **GOOD SAMARITAN REGIONAL HEALTH CENTER (140046)**, 1 Good Samaritan Way, Zip 62864–2402; tel. 618/242–4600 **A**1 2 10 19 **F**3 4 11 13 15 18 20 22 24 26 28 29 30 31 34 35 38 40 44 45 46 50 51 54 56 57 59 61 64 68 70 73 74 75 76 77 78 79 80 81 82 84 85 86 87 89 90 93 94 107 108 110 111 114 115 119 126 130 131 132 135 144 145 146 147 148 149 **P**6 8 **S** SSM Health, Saint Louis, MO
Primary Contact: Michael D. Warren, President
COO: Mark A Clark, Vice President Operations
CFO: Deland Evischi, Regional Chief Financial Officer, Southern Illinois
CMO: Daniel Hoffman M.D., Administrative Medical Director
CIO: Steve Murphy, FM–East Region IS
CHR: Thomas W Blythe, System Vice President Human Resources
CNO: Chris Adams, Vice President Patient Care Services
Web address: www.smgsi.com
Control: Church operated, Nongovernment, not–for–profit **Service**: General medical and surgical

Staffed Beds: 134 **Admissions**: 7981 **Census**: 84 **Outpatient Visits**: 221490 **Births**: 1141 **Total Expense ($000)**: 163466 **Payroll Expense ($000)**: 53864 **Personnel**: 1281	

MURPHYSBORO—Jackson County

★ **ST. JOSEPH MEMORIAL HOSPITAL (141334)**, 2 South Hospital Drive, Zip 62966–3333; tel. 618/684–3156 **A**10 18 **F**3 11 18 28 29 30 31 34 35 40 45 56 57 59 64 74 75 77 78 79 81 85 86 87 93 107 114 119 129 130 132 133 135 146 148 **P**1 **S** Southern Illinois Healthcare, Carbondale, IL
Primary Contact: Susan Odle, Administrator
CMO: Emily Hanson M.D., President, Medical Staff
CIO: David Holland, Vice President Information Services
CHR: Kelly Stevens, Manager Human Resources
CNO: Julie Firman R.N., FACHE, Chief Nursing Officer
Web address: www.sih.net
Control: Other not–for–profit (including NFP Corporation) **Service**: General medical and surgical

Staffed Beds: 25 **Admissions**: 683 **Census**: 12 **Outpatient Visits**: 76429 **Births**: 0 **Total Expense ($000)**: 52713 **Payroll Expense ($000)**: 12829 **Personnel**: 235	

IL

Many Facility Codes have changed. Please refer to the AHA Guide Code Chart. © 2017 AHA Guide

NAPERVILLE—Dupage County

☒ **EDWARD HOSPITAL (140231)**, 801 South Washington Street, Zip 60540-7499; tel. 630/527-3000 **A**1 2 10 **F**3 5 7 12 13 15 17 18 19 20 22 24 26 28 29 30 31 32 34 35 37 38 39 40 41 42 43 44 45 46 47 48 49 50 53 54 55 57 58 59 61 63 64 65 68 70 72 73 74 75 76 77 78 79 81 82 84 85 86 87 88 89 91 92 93 96 97 99 100 101 102 107 108 110 111 114 115 117 118 119 120 121 123 124 126 129 130 131 132 135 144 146 147 148 149 **P**6 8 **S** Edward–Elmhurst Healthcare, Naperville, IL
Primary Contact: Bill Kottmann, President and Chief Executive Officer
CMO: Sanjeeb Khatua M.D., Chief Medical Officer and Vice President
CHR: Chris Devereux, Human Resources Director, Business Partner
CNO: Lynn Cochran R.N., System Vice President Operations,Chief Nursing Officer
Web address: www.eehealth.org
Control: Other not-for-profit (including NFP Corporation) **Service:** General medical and surgical

Staffed Beds: 350 **Admissions:** 22151 **Census:** 243 **Outpatient Visits:** 632046 **Births:** 3194 **Total Expense ($000):** 581044 **Payroll Expense ($000):** 190120 **Personnel:** 2597

☒ **LINDEN OAKS HOSPITAL (144035)**, 852 South West Street, Zip 60540-6400; tel. 630/305-5500 **A**1 3 5 10 **F**4 5 29 34 35 38 56 57 59 64 68 75 87 98 99 100 101 103 104 105 130 132 134 149 **P**6 8 **S** Edward–Elmhurst Healthcare, Naperville, IL
Primary Contact: Gina Sharp, FACHE, President and Chief Executive Officer
CFO: Kristen Refness, Director, Financial Operations
CMO: Barry Rabin M.D., Regional Medical Director
CIO: David Pickering, System Director, Applications
CHR: Lisa Dixon, Business Partner and Human Resource Director
CNO: Trish Fairbanks R.N., Associate Vice President and Chief Nursing Officer
Web address: www.eehealth.org/services/behavioral–health
Control: Other not-for-profit (including NFP Corporation) **Service:** Psychiatric

Staffed Beds: 108 **Admissions:** 4381 **Census:** 87 **Outpatient Visits:** 61798 **Births:** 0 **Total Expense ($000):** 44842 **Payroll Expense ($000):** 25773 **Personnel:** 434

NASHVILLE—Washington County

☒ **WASHINGTON COUNTY HOSPITAL (141308)**, 705 South Grand Avenue, Zip 62263-1534; tel. 618/327-8236, (Total facility includes 28 beds in nursing home–type unit) **A**1 10 18 **F**8 11 15 28 29 31 34 40 49 50 57 59 64 65 78 81 85 93 104 107 114 119 127 133 145 146 148 **P**6
Primary Contact: Nancy M. Newby, R.N., Ph.D., FACHE, President and Chief Executive Officer
CFO: Elaine Matzenbacher, Chief Financial Officer
CMO: Alfonso Urdaneta M.D., President Medical Staff
CIO: Kim Larkin, Chief Information Officer
CHR: David Davenport, Director Human Resources
Web address: www.washingtoncountyhospital.org
Control: Hospital district or authority, Government, Nonfederal **Service:** General medical and surgical

Staffed Beds: 50 **Admissions:** 206 **Census:** 30 **Outpatient Visits:** 32908 **Births:** 0 **Total Expense ($000):** 14549 **Payroll Expense ($000):** 6749 **Personnel:** 141

NEW LENOX—Will County

☒ △ **SILVER CROSS HOSPITAL (140213)**, 1900 Silver Cross Boulevard, Zip 60451-9509; tel. 815/300-1100 **A**1 2 7 10 **F**3 5 11 13 15 18 20 22 26 27 28 29 30 32 35 37 38 40 42 43 44 46 47 48 49 50 54 56 57 62 63 64 68 70 71 75 76 81 84 85 86 87 89 90 91 92 96 97 98 100 101 102 104 105 107 108 110 111 114 115 116 117 119 126 129 130 132 135 144 145 146 147 148 149 **P**5 8
Primary Contact: Paul Pawlak, President and Chief Executive Officer
COO: Mary Bakken, Executive Vice President and Chief Operating Officer
CFO: John Krepps, Senior Vice President Finance
CMO: Christopher Udovich M.D., Chief of Staff
CIO: Kevin Lane, Vice President Information Systems
CHR: Mark Jepson, Vice President
CNO: Peggy Gricus R.N., Vice President, Patient Care Services and Chief Nursing Officer
Web address: www.silvercross.org
Control: Other not-for-profit (including NFP Corporation) **Service:** General medical and surgical

Staffed Beds: 296 **Admissions:** 21153 **Census:** 223 **Outpatient Visits:** 252872 **Births:** 3024 **Total Expense ($000):** 345312 **Payroll Expense ($000):** 119267 **Personnel:** 1739

SILVER CROSS HOSPITAL (Nonreporting) **A**1 2 7 10 **F**3 5 11 13 15 18 20 22 26 27 28 29 30 32 35 37 38 40 42 43 44 46 47 48 49 50 54 56 57 62 63 64 68 70 71 75 76 81 84 85 86 87 89 90 91 92 96 97 98 100 101 102 104 105 107 108 110 111 114 115 116 117 119 126 129 130 132 135 144 145 146 147 148 149 **P**5 8
Primary Contact: , R.N.
COO: Mary Bakken, Executive Vice President and Chief Operating Officer
CFO: John Krepps, Senior Vice President Finance
CMO: Christopher Udovich M.D., Chief of Staff
CIO: Kevin Lane, Vice President Information Systems
CHR: Mark Jepson, Vice President
CNO: Peggy Gricus R.N., Vice President, Patient Care Services and Chief Nursing Officer
Web address: www.silvercross.org

NORMAL—Mclean County

★ ⇑ **ADVOCATE BROMENN MEDICAL CENTER (140127)**, 1304 Franklin Avenue, Zip 61761-3558, Mailing Address: P.O.Box 2850, Bloomington, 61702-2850; tel. 309/454-1400, (Includes ADVOCATE BROMENN REGIONAL MEDICAL CENTER, 1304 Franklin Avenue, Normal, Illinois, Zip 61761-3558, PO Box 2850, Bloomington, 61702-2850, tel. 309/454-1400; Colleen Kannaday, FACHE, President) **A**2 5 10 13 21 **F**2 3 4 11 12 13 15 18 20 22 24 26 28 29 30 31 32 34 35 37 38 39 40 43 44 45 49 50 51 54 55 57 59 64 65 66 68 70 74 75 76 77 78 79 81 82 84 85 86 87 89 90 93 96 97 98 100 101 102 103 107 108 110 111 114 115 118 119 126 129 130 131 132 135 141 146 147 148 149 **P**8 **S** Advocate Health Care, Downers Grove, IL
Primary Contact: Colleen Kannaday, FACHE, President
CFO: Aron Klein, Vice President Finance
CMO: James Nevin M.D., Vice President Medical Management
CHR: Antonio Coletta, Vice President Human Resources
CNO: Laurie Round MS, R.N., Chief Nurse Executive
Web address: www.advocatehealth.com
Control: Church operated, Nongovernment, not-for-profit **Service:** General medical and surgical

Staffed Beds: 198 **Admissions:** 8802 **Census:** 93 **Outpatient Visits:** 125180 **Births:** 1611 **Total Expense ($000):** 169094 **Payroll Expense ($000):** 56796 **Personnel:** 1082

⇑ **ADVOCATE BROMENN REGIONAL MEDICAL CENTER** See Advocate Bromenn Medical Center

NORTH CHICAGO—Lake County

☒ **CAPTAIN JAMES A. LOVELL FEDERAL HEALTH CARE CENTER**, 3001 Green Bay Road, Zip 60064-3049; tel. 847/688-1900, (Total facility includes 121 beds in nursing home–type unit) **A**1 3 5 8 **F**3 4 5 8 14 15 17 18 29 30 31 32 34 35 36 38 39 40 44 45 46 48 49 50 53 54 56 57 58 59 61 62 63 64 65 68 70 74 75 77 78 79 81 83 84 86 87 90 91 92 94 96 97 98 99 100 101 102 103 104 105 106 107 108 110 111 115 118 119 128 129 130 131 132 135 143 146 147 148 149 **P**6 **S** Department of Veterans Affairs, Washington, DC
Primary Contact: Stephen R. Holt, M.D., Director
CFO: Barbara Meadows, Chief Financial Manager
CMO: Tariq Hassan M.D., Associate Director of Patient Care
CIO: Jonathan Friedman, Public Affairs Officer
CHR: Amy Sanders, Chief Human Resources
CNO: Sarah Fouse, Associate Director of Patient Services
Web address: www.lovell.fhcc.va.gov
Control: Veterans Affairs, Government, federal **Service:** General medical and surgical

Staffed Beds: 314 **Admissions:** 4785 **Census:** 45 **Outpatient Visits:** 657438 **Births:** 0 **Personnel:** 1748

NORTHLAKE—Cook County

☒ **KINDRED HOSPITAL CHICAGO–NORTHLAKE (142008)**, 365 East North Avenue, Zip 60164-2628; tel. 708/345-8100, (Nonreporting) **A**1 10 **S** Kindred Healthcare, Louisville, KY
Primary Contact: Beverly Foster, Chief Executive Officer
COO: Sandra Buckhoy, Chief Clinical Officer
CFO: Jay Schweikart, Chief Financial Officer
CMO: Maher Najjar M.D., Medical Director
Web address: www.kindrednorthlake.com/
Control: Corporation, Investor–owned (for-profit) **Service:** Acute long–term care hospital

Staffed Beds: 94

IL

OAK LAWN—Cook County

★ △ ⇑ **ADVOCATE CHRIST MEDICAL CENTER (140208)**, 4440 West 95th Street, Zip 60453–2699; tel. 708/684–8000, (Includes ADVOCATE HOPE CHILDREN'S HOSPITAL, 4440 West 95th Street, Oak Lawn, Illinois, Zip 60453–2600, tel. 708/684–8000) **A**2 3 5 7 8 10 13 21 **F**3 5 8 11 13 15 17 18 19 20 21 22 23 24 25 26 27 28 29 30 31 32 34 35 37 38 39 40 41 43 44 45 46 47 48 49 50 52 54 55 56 57 58 59 60 61 62 63 64 65 66 68 70 71 72 74 75 77 78 79 81 82 84 85 86 87 88 90 92 93 96 97 98 99 100 101 102 103 104 105 107 108 109 110 111 114 115 116 117 118 119 120 121 123 124 126 129 130 131 132 134 135 137 138 140 143 145 146 147 148 149 **P**8 **S** Advocate Health Care, Downers Grove, IL
Primary Contact: Kenneth W. Lukhard, President
COO: Michael Wilkins, Chief Operating Officer
CFO: Robert Pekofske, Vice President Finance
CMO: Robert Stein M.D., Vice President Medical Management
CIO: Brian Banbury, Director Site Information Systems
Web address: www.advocatehealth.com/christ
Control: Other not–for–profit (including NFP Corporation) **Service**: General medical and surgical

Staffed Beds: 761 **Admissions**: 42409 **Census**: 632 **Outpatient Visits**: 353954 **Births**: 4248 **Total Expense ($000)**: 1056166 **Payroll Expense ($000)**: 353132 **Personnel**: 4963

OAK PARK—Cook County

✠ **RUSH OAK PARK HOSPITAL (140063)**, 520 South Maple Avenue, Zip 60304–1097; tel. 708/383–9300, (Total facility includes 18 beds in nursing home–type unit) **A**1 3 5 10 **F**3 11 15 18 20 22 29 30 34 35 40 45 47 49 50 56 57 58 59 64 70 74 75 77 79 81 82 85 87 90 91 92 93 94 96 107 108 110 111 114 115 119 128 130 141 145 146 148 149 **P**1 8 **S** Rush University Medical Center, Chicago, IL
Primary Contact: Bruce M. Elegant, FACHE, President and Chief Executive Officer
COO: Robert S Spadoni, Vice President of Hospital Operations
CFO: Elvy Yap, Director of Finance
CMO: Michael R. Silver M.D., Vice President Medical Affairs
CIO: Michael R. Silver M.D., Chief Information Officer
CHR: Arlene Cruz, Director
CNO: Karen M Mayer R.N., FACHE, Senior Vice President Patient Care Services
Web address: www.roph.org
Control: Other not–for–profit (including NFP Corporation) **Service**: General medical and surgical

Staffed Beds: 96 **Admissions**: 4665 **Census**: 64 **Outpatient Visits**: 123073 **Births**: 0 **Total Expense ($000)**: 116403 **Payroll Expense ($000)**: 54132 **Personnel**: 781

✠ **WEST SUBURBAN MEDICAL CENTER (140049)**, 3 Erie Court, Zip 60302–2599; tel. 708/383–6200, (Nonreporting) **A**1 2 3 5 10 13 **S** TENET Healthcare Corporation, Dallas, TX
Primary Contact: Joseph Ottolino, Interim Chief Executive Officer
COO: Joseph Ottolino, Chief Operating Officer
CFO: Jennifer Lamont, Chief Financial Officer
CMO: Robert Chase M.D., Physician Advisor
CHR: Nancy Gunnell, Chief Human Resource Officer
CNO: Roslyn J Lennon R.N., MS, Chief Nursing Officer
Web address: www.westsuburbanmc.com/Home.aspx
Control: Corporation, Investor–owned (for–profit) **Service**: General medical and surgical

Staffed Beds: 172

OLNEY—Richland County

★ ○ **CARLE RICHLAND MEMORIAL HOSPITAL (140147)**, 800 East Locust Street, Zip 62450–2553; tel. 618/395–2131, (Total facility includes 34 beds in nursing home–type unit) **A**10 11 **F**3 7 11 13 15 28 29 31 34 35 40 45 57 59 61 62 63 64 68 69 70 75 76 78 79 81 85 87 89 93 97 98 100 102 103 107 108 110 111 115 119 127 128 129 130 131 132 133 135 143 146 147 **P**6 **S** Carle Foundation, Urbana, IL
Primary Contact: David B. Allen, Chief Executive Officer
CFO: Mike Stoverink, Chief Financial Officer
CMO: Robert Nash M.D., Chief of Staff
CIO: Tim Gillespie, Manager Information Systems
CHR: Jill Van Hyning, Director Human Resources
CNO: Gina Thomas, Chief Nursing Officer & Director of Patient Care Services
Web address: www.richlandmemorial.com
Control: Other not–for–profit (including NFP Corporation) **Service**: General medical and surgical

Staffed Beds: 90 **Admissions**: 2083 **Census**: 27 **Outpatient Visits**: 61140 **Births**: 305 **Total Expense ($000)**: 51136 **Payroll Expense ($000)**: 23788 **Personnel**: 510

OLYMPIA FIELDS—Cook County

★ ○ **FRANCISCAN HEALTH OLYMPIA FIELDS (140172)**, 20201 South Crawford Avenue, Zip 60461–1010; tel. 708/747–4000, (Nonreporting) (Includes FRANCISCAN HEALTH OLYMPIA FIELDS, 20201 Crawford Avenue, Olympia Fields, Illinois, Zip 60461–1010, tel. 708/747–4000; ST. JAMES HOSPITAL AND HEALTH CENTERS – CHICAGO HEIGHTS CAMPUS, 1423 Chicago Road, Chicago Heights, Illinois, Zip 60411–3483, tel. 708/756–1000; Allan M Spooner, President and Chief Executive Officer) **A**3 10 11 12 13 **S** Franciscan Health, Mishawaka, IN
Primary Contact: Allan M. Spooner, President and Chief Executive Officer
CIO: Stephen Maes, Director Information Systems
Web address: www.franciscanalliance.org/hospitals/olympiafields/pages/default.aspx
Control: Church operated, Nongovernment, not–for–profit **Service**: General medical and surgical

Staffed Beds: 329

ST. JAMES HOSPITAL AND HEALTH CENTERS See Franciscan Health Olympia Fields

OTTAWA—Lasalle County

✠ **OSF SAINT ELIZABETH MEDICAL CENTER (140110)**, 1100 East Norris Drive, Zip 61350–1687; tel. 815/433–3100 **A**1 10 19 **F**3 11 13 15 18 28 29 30 34 35 40 42 45 48 49 53 56 57 59 68 70 75 76 77 79 81 82 84 85 86 87 93 94 98 99 100 101 102 103 104 105 107 108 110 111 115 116 117 118 119 120 121 129 130 131 132 135 143 144 146 148 149 **S** OSF Healthcare System, Peoria, IL
Primary Contact: Kenneth Beutke, President
CFO: Dawn Trompeter, Chief Financial Officer
CMO: Brian S Rosborough M.D., Chief Medical Officer
CHR: Robert L Gibson, Director Employee Relations
CNO: Maeanne Stevens R.N., Chief Nursing Officer
Web address: www.osfsaintelizabeth.org
Control: Church operated, Nongovernment, not–for–profit **Service**: General medical and surgical

Staffed Beds: 87 **Admissions**: 4052 **Census**: 39 **Outpatient Visits**: 133257 **Births**: 435 **Total Expense ($000)**: 88738 **Payroll Expense ($000)**: 32153 **Personnel**: 442

PALOS HEIGHTS—Cook County

☐ **PALOS HEALTH (140062)**, 12251 South 80th Avenue, Zip 60463–0930; tel. 708/923–4000, (Nonreporting) **A**1 2 10
Primary Contact: Terrence Moisan, M.D., Chief Executive Officer
CFO: Hugh Rose, Vice President Fiscal Management
CIO: Peggy Carroll, Chief Information Officer
CHR: Mary Denisienko, Vice President Human Resources
Web address: www.paloshealth.com/
Control: Other not–for–profit (including NFP Corporation) **Service**: General medical and surgical

Staffed Beds: 362

PANA—Christian County

★ **PANA COMMUNITY HOSPITAL (141341)**, 101 East Ninth Street, Zip 62557–1785; tel. 217/562–2131 **A**10 18 **F**3 11 15 29 30 31 34 35 40 46 49 50 53 55 57 62 63 69 75 77 78 79 81 87 90 91 93 107 115 124 127 130 131 132 133 143 146 148 149 **P**6
Primary Contact: Trina Casner, President and Chief Executive Officer
CFO: James Moon, Chief Financial Officer
CMO: Alan Frigy M.D., President Medical Staff
CIO: Dianne Bailey, Chief Information Officer
CHR: Luann A Funk, Administrative Assistant and Manager Human Resources
CNO: Vickie Coen, Chief Clinical Officer and Nurse Executive
Web address: www.panahospital.com
Control: Other not–for–profit (including NFP Corporation) **Service**: General medical and surgical

Staffed Beds: 22 **Admissions**: 325 **Census**: 3 **Outpatient Visits**: 51229 **Births**: 0 **Total Expense ($000)**: 22219 **Payroll Expense ($000)**: 10191 **Personnel**: 181

IL

PARIS—Edgar County

⊞ **PARIS COMMUNITY HOSPITAL (141320)**, 721 East Court Street, Zip 61944–2460; tel. 217/465–4141 **A**1 10 18 **F**3 12 15 28 29 30 31 34 35 40 45 47 50 57 59 64 65 69 74 75 77 78 79 81 82 85 86 87 93 107 108 110 111 115 119 127 129 130 131 132 133 144 146 148 **P**6 **S** Alliant Management Services, Louisville, KY
Primary Contact: Oliver Smith, President and Chief Executive Officer
CFO: Martin D. Adams CPA, Vice President Finance and Chief Financial Officer
CIO: Ed Weeks, Manager Information Services
CHR: Cathy Thompson, Manager Human Resources
CNO: Susan Livvix R.N., MSN, Vice President Nursing Services
Web address: www.pariscommunityhospital.com
Control: Other not–for–profit (including NFP Corporation) **Service:** General medical and surgical

Staffed Beds: 25 **Admissions:** 613 **Census:** 6 **Outpatient Visits:** 126837 **Births:** 0 **Total Expense ($000):** 46203 **Payroll Expense ($000):** 22940 **Personnel:** 301

PARK RIDGE—Cook County

★ △ ⇑ **ADVOCATE LUTHERAN GENERAL HOSPITAL (140223)**, 1775 Dempster Street, Zip 60068–1174; tel. 847/723–2210 **A**2 3 5 7 8 10 13 21 **F**2 3 5 6 8 9 11 12 13 15 17 18 19 20 22 23 24 25 26 27 28 29 30 31 32 34 35 37 38 39 40 41 43 44 45 46 47 48 49 50 53 55 56 57 58 59 60 61 63 64 65 66 68 69 70 72 74 75 76 78 79 80 81 82 84 85 86 87 88 89 90 92 93 94 97 98 99 100 101 102 103 104 105 106 107 108 110 111 112 114 115 116 117 118 119 120 121 123 124 126 129 130 131 132 134 135 136 143 146 147 148 149 150 **P**6 8 **S** Advocate Health Care, Downers Grove, IL
Primary Contact: Dominica Tallarico, President
COO: Allyson Wyler, Vice President, Operations
CFO: Beth Hickey, Vice President, Finance
CMO: Leo Kelly, Vice President Medical Management
CIO: Mark Beitzel, Director Information Systems
CHR: Katie Bata, Vice President Human Resources
CNO: Jane Denten MSN, R.N., Chief Nurse Executive
Web address: www.advocatehealth.com/luth/
Control: Other not–for–profit (including NFP Corporation) **Service:** General medical and surgical

Staffed Beds: 625 **Admissions:** 28322 **Census:** 423 **Outpatient Visits:** 332588 **Births:** 4178 **Total Expense ($000):** 673672 **Payroll Expense ($000):** 243007 **Personnel:** 3500

PEKIN—Tazewell County

⊞ **PEKIN HOSPITAL (140120)**, 600 South 13th Street, Zip 61554–4936; tel. 309/347–1151, (Nonreporting) **A**1 5 10 **S** UnityPoint Health, West Des Moines, IA
Primary Contact: Bob J. Haley, Chief Executive Officer
CFO: Steve Hall, Chief Financial Officer
CMO: Kathryn Kramer M.D., President Medical Staff
CHR: Anne Dierker, Vice President Hospital Services
Web address: www.pekinhospital.org
Control: Other not–for–profit (including NFP Corporation) **Service:** General medical and surgical

Staffed Beds: 107

PEORIA—Peoria County

GREATER PEORIA SPECIALTY HOSPITAL See Kindred Hospital Peoria

⊞ **KINDRED HOSPITAL PEORIA (142013)**, 500 West Romeo B Garrett Avenue, Zip 61605–2301; tel. 309/680–1500, (Nonreporting) **A**1 10 **S** Kindred Healthcare, Louisville, KY
Primary Contact: Christopher Curry, Chief Executive Officer
CMO: Michael Peil M.D., Chief Medical Director
Web address: www.khpeoria.com/
Control: Corporation, Investor–owned (for–profit) **Service:** Acute long–term care hospital

Staffed Beds: 50

METHODIST MEDICAL CENTER OF ILLINOIS See Unitypoint Health – Peoria

⊞ △ **OSF SAINT FRANCIS MEDICAL CENTER (140067)**, 530 NE Glen Oak Avenue, Zip 61637–0001; tel. 309/655–2000, (Includes CHILDREN'S HOSPITAL OF ILLINOIS, 530 NE Glen Oak Avenue, Peoria, Illinois, Zip 61637–0001, tel. 309/655–7171; Kelly Nierstedt, President) **A**1 2 3 5 7 8 10 **F**3 8 9 11 12 13 15 17 18 19 20 21 22 23 24 25 26 27 28 29 30 31 32 34 35 37 38 39 40 41 43 44 45 46 47 48 49 50 51 52 54 56 57 58 59 60 64 65 66 67 69 70 71 72 73 74 75 76 77 78 79 80 81 82 83 84 85 86 87 88 89 90 91 92 93 94 96 97 99 100 102 104 105 107 108 110 111 112 114 115 116 117 118 119 120 121 123 124 126 127 129 130 132 134 138 145 146 147 148 **P**6 **S** OSF Healthcare System, Peoria, IL
Primary Contact: Michael A. Cruz, M.D., President
COO: Robert G Anderson Jr, Executive Vice President and Chief Operating Officer
CFO: Ken Harbaugh, Vice President and Chief Financial Officer
CMO: Robert T. Sparrow M.D., Vice President, Chief Medical Officer
CHR: Jacki L. Fugitt, Director Employee Relations
CNO: Jennifer Hopwood, Vice President, Chief Nursing Officer
Web address: www.osfsaintfrancis.org
Control: Church operated, Nongovernment, not–for–profit **Service:** General medical and surgical

Staffed Beds: 609 **Admissions:** 31761 **Census:** 480 **Outpatient Visits:** 682060 **Births:** 2698 **Total Expense ($000):** 893618 **Payroll Expense ($000):** 301781 **Personnel:** 4412

⊞ **UNITYPOINT HEALTH – PEORIA (140209)**, 221 NE Glen Oak Avenue, Zip 61636–4310; tel. 309/672–5522 **A**1 2 3 5 10 13 **F**3 8 9 11 12 13 15 17 18 20 22 24 26 29 30 31 32 34 35 36 38 40 43 44 45 46 47 48 49 50 53 54 56 57 58 59 60 62 63 64 68 70 74 75 76 77 78 79 81 82 84 85 86 87 89 90 92 93 96 98 99 100 101 102 103 104 105 107 108 110 111 114 115 116 117 118 119 120 121 126 127 129 130 131 132 134 135 136 143 144 145 146 147 148 149 150 **P**8 **S** UnityPoint Health, West Des Moines, IA
Primary Contact: Deborah R. Simon, R.N., President and Chief Executive Officer
COO: Keith Knepp M.D., Executive Vice President and Chief Operating Officer
CFO: Robert Quin, Vice President Finance and Chief Financial Officer
CMO: Gary Knepp D.O., Chief Medical Officer and Chief Quality Officer
CHR: Joy Ledbetter, Vice President, Chief Human Resources Officer
CNO: Jeanine R Spain R.N., MS, Vice President Hospital Operations and Chief Nursing Officer
Web address: www.unitypoint.org/peoria
Control: Other not–for–profit (including NFP Corporation) **Service:** General medical and surgical

Staffed Beds: 277 **Admissions:** 13831 **Census:** 181 **Outpatient Visits:** 588586 **Births:** 1857 **Total Expense ($000):** 388912 **Payroll Expense ($000):** 178516 **Personnel:** 2361

☐ **UNITYPOINT HEALTH – PROCTOR (140013)**, 5409 North Knoxville Avenue, Zip 61614–5069; tel. 309/691–1000, (Total facility includes 20 beds in nursing home–type unit) **A**1 3 5 10 **F**3 4 5 11 15 18 20 22 24 28 29 30 34 40 44 45 49 51 53 54 57 59 60 64 70 74 75 79 81 85 86 87 93 98 103 104 105 107 108 110 111 115 118 119 128 129 130 132 135 145 146 148 149 150 **S** UnityPoint Health, West Des Moines, IA
Primary Contact: Deborah R. Simon, R.N., President and Chief Executive Officer
CFO: Roger Armstrong, Vice President Finance and Chief Financial Officer
CHR: Linda K Buck, Vice President Human Resources
Web address: www.proctor.org
Control: Other not–for–profit (including NFP Corporation) **Service:** General medical and surgical

Staffed Beds: 121 **Admissions:** 3927 **Census:** 64 **Outpatient Visits:** 59798 **Births:** 0 **Total Expense ($000):** 89858 **Payroll Expense ($000):** 28687 **Personnel:** 562

PERU—Lasalle County

★ **ILLINOIS VALLEY COMMUNITY HOSPITAL (140234)**, 925 West Street, Zip 61354–2757; tel. 815/223–3300 **A**10 **F**2 3 11 13 15 18 28 29 30 31 34 35 38 40 45 46 47 48 49 50 51 54 57 59 63 64 65 66 68 69 70 74 75 76 77 79 81 82 85 87 93 96 97 104 107 110 111 114 118 119 127 129 130 131 132 133 135 143 144 146 147 148 149 **P**8
Primary Contact: Tommy Hobbs, Chief Executive Officer
COO: Bobby Smith, Vice President Physician Services and Quality
CFO: Stephen Davis, Chief Financial Officer
CMO: Mark Fernandez M.D., Chief of Staff and President Medical Staff
CIO: Nancy McDonnell, Manager Information Systems
CHR: Mary Beth Herron, Director of Human Resources
CNO: Wilma Hart–Flynn MSN, Ph.D., R.N., Vice President Patient Care Services and Chief Nursing Officer
Web address: www.ivch.org
Control: Other not–for–profit (including NFP Corporation) **Service:** General medical and surgical

Staffed Beds: 49 **Admissions:** 2467 **Census:** 20 **Outpatient Visits:** 192064 **Births:** 434 **Total Expense ($000):** 82643 **Payroll Expense ($000):** 31051 **Personnel:** 501

IL

Hospital, Medicare Provider Number, Address, Telephone, Approval, Facility, and Physician Codes, Health Care System

★ American Hospital Association (AHA) membership   ○ Healthcare Facilities Accreditation Program   ⇑ Center for Improvement in Healthcare Quality Accreditation
☐ The Joint Commission accreditation   ◇ DNV Healthcare Inc. accreditation   △ Commission on Accreditation of Rehabilitation Facilities (CARF) accreditation

PINCKNEYVILLE—Perry County

★ **PINCKNEYVILLE COMMUNITY HOSPITAL (141307)**, 5383 State Route 154, Zip 62274–1099, Mailing Address: PO Box 437, 62274–1099; tel. 618/357–2187 **A**10 18 **F**3 15 28 29 31 34 40 43 45 50 53 56 57 65 78 81 85 93 107 108 110 119 127 130 132 133 **P**6
Primary Contact: Randall W. Dauby, CPA, Chief Executive Officer
CFO: Kara Jo Carson, Chief Financial Officer
CIO: Jeff Roberts, Director Information Technology
CHR: Christie Gajewski, Director Human Resources
CNO: Eva Hopp, Chief Nurse Executive
Web address: www.pvillehosp.org/
Control: Hospital district or authority, Government, Nonfederal **Service:** General medical and surgical

Staffed Beds: 17 **Admissions:** 486 **Census:** 7 **Outpatient Visits:** 44912
Births: 0 **Total Expense ($000):** 23290 **Payroll Expense ($000):** 9810
Personnel: 179

PITTSFIELD—Pike County

⊞ **ILLINI COMMUNITY HOSPITAL (141315)**, 640 West Washington Street, Zip 62363–1350; tel. 217/285–2113 **A**1 10 18 **F**3 15 18 19 28 29 30 31 34 40 46 50 53 59 64 65 68 70 75 78 81 82 85 87 89 93 97 98 100 101 103 104 107 110 115 119 127 129 130 131 133 146 149 **P**6
Primary Contact: Kathy Hull, President and Chief Executive Officer
CFO: Tim Moore, Vice President Finance
CMO: Bashar Alzein M.D., President Medical Staff
CHR: Becky Myers, Human Resources Specialist
CNO: Holly A Jones, Administrative Director Nursing Services
Web address: www.illinihospital.org
Control: Other not–for–profit (including NFP Corporation) **Service:** General medical and surgical

Staffed Beds: 25 **Admissions:** 458 **Census:** 6 **Outpatient Visits:** 7437
Births: 4 **Total Expense ($000):** 24009 **Payroll Expense ($000):** 9054
Personnel: 196

PONTIAC—Livingston County

⊞ **OSF SAINT JAMES – JOHN W. ALBRECHT MEDICAL CENTER (140161)**, 2500 West Reynolds, Zip 61764–9774; tel. 815/842–2828 **A**1 10 20 **F**3 8 11 13 15 18 28 29 30 32 34 35 40 45 50 51 56 57 59 64 68 70 75 76 77 81 82 84 85 86 87 89 90 91 93 96 107 110 111 115 117 118 119 128 129 130 131 132 133 135 144 146 147 **S** OSF Healthcare System, Peoria, IL
Primary Contact: Bradley V. Solberg, FACHE, President
CFO: Paula Corrigan, Vice President and Chief Financial Officer
CMO: John M. Rinker, Chief Medical Officer
CNO: Elizabeth Davidson R.N., MSN, Vice President, Patient Care Services
Web address: www.osfsaintjames.org
Control: Church operated, Nongovernment, not–for–profit **Service:** General medical and surgical

Staffed Beds: 42 **Admissions:** 1744 **Census:** 16 **Outpatient Visits:** 75139
Births: 193 **Total Expense ($000):** 51399 **Payroll Expense ($000):** 16702
Personnel: 253

PRINCETON—Bureau County

PERRY MEMORIAL HOSPITAL (141337), 530 Park Avenue East, Zip 61356–2598; tel. 815/875–2811 **A**10 18 **F**3 15 18 28 29 30 31 32 34 35 40 45 48 49 56 57 59 64 65 70 75 77 78 79 81 82 85 86 87 89 90 93 97 100 103 107 108 110 111 115 116 118 119 127 128 129 130 131 132 133 144 145 146 148 149
Primary Contact: Annette Schnabel, FACHE, President and Chief Executive Officer
COO: Chris J. Williams FACHE, Vice President Operations
CFO: Mike DeFoe, Chief Financial Officer
CMO: T Doran M.D., Chief of Staff
CIO: Karen Behrens, Director Technology Services
CHR: James Lewandowski, Vice President Human Resources
Web address: www.perry–memorial.org
Control: City, Government, Nonfederal **Service:** General medical and surgical

Staffed Beds: 25 **Admissions:** 906 **Census:** 7 **Outpatient Visits:** 81126
Births: 0 **Total Expense ($000):** 41655 **Payroll Expense ($000):** 17720
Personnel: 293

QUINCY—Adams County

⊞ △ **BLESSING HOSPITAL (140015)**, Broadway at 11th Street, Zip 62305–7005, Mailing Address: P.O.Box 7005, 62305–7005; tel. 217/223–1200, (Includes BLESSING HOSPITAL, Broadway & 14th Street, Quincy, Illinois, Zip 62301, P O Box 7005, 62305–7005, tel. 217/223–1200) (Total facility includes 20 beds in nursing home–type unit) **A**1 2 3 5 7 10 13 **F**3 5 8 11 12 13 15 17 18 20 22 24 26 28 29 30 31 32 34 35 40 43 44 48 49 50 53 56 57 58 59 60 61 62 63 64 66 68 70 73 74 75 76 77 78 79 81 82 84 85 86 87 89 90 94 96 98 99 100 101 102 103 104 107 108 110 111 114 115 118 119 120 121 123 124 126 127 128 129 130 131 132 135 144 146 147 148 149 **P**8
Primary Contact: Maureen A. Kahn, R.N., President and Chief Executive Officer
COO: Tim Moore, Chief Accounting Officer and Vice President Ancillary Services and Finance
CFO: Patrick M Gerveler, Vice President Finance and Chief Financial Officer
CMO: George Liesmann M.D., Chief Medical Officer
CNO: Jill K Mason MS, R.N., Chief Nursing Officer
Web address: www.blessinghospital.org
Control: Other not–for–profit (including NFP Corporation) **Service:** General medical and surgical

Staffed Beds: 306 **Admissions:** 14716 **Census:** 176 **Outpatient Visits:** 330545 **Births:** 1168 **Total Expense ($000):** 321332 **Payroll Expense ($000):** 107952 **Personnel:** 2162

RED BUD—Randolph County

⊞ **RED BUD REGIONAL HOSPITAL (141348)**, 325 Spring Street, Zip 62278–1105; tel. 618/282–3831, (Total facility includes 115 beds in nursing home–type unit) **A**1 10 18 **F**1 3 15 18 29 34 35 40 45 50 56 57 59 64 65 75 81 87 93 97 103 104 107 108 110 111 115 119 127 129 130 132 133 135 146 148 **S** Quorum Health, Brentwood, TN
Primary Contact: Shane Watson, Chief Executive Officer
CFO: Benjamin Wells, Chief Financial Officer
CMO: Stephanie Skelly, President Medical Staff
CIO: Nick Behnken, Supervisor Information Technology
CHR: Lori Brooks, Director Human Resources
CNO: Linda Harbison, Chief Nursing Officer
Web address: www.redbudregional.com
Control: Corporation, Investor–owned (for–profit) **Service:** General medical and surgical

Staffed Beds: 140 **Admissions:** 1058 **Census:** 96 **Births:** 0

ROBINSON—Crawford County

★ **CRAWFORD MEMORIAL HOSPITAL (141343)**, 1000 North Allen Street, Zip 62454–1167; tel. 618/544–3131, (Total facility includes 38 beds in nursing home–type unit) **A**10 18 **F**3 11 12 13 15 28 30 31 40 46 53 59 62 64 76 77 78 79 80 81 82 85 93 107 108 111 119 127 128 129 130 132 133 146 147 **S** QHR, Brentwood, TN
Primary Contact: Lucinda A. Bradley, Interim Chief Executive Officer
CFO: Richard Carlson, Chief Financial Officer
CMO: Gary Tennison M.D., Chief of Staff
CIO: Tim Richard, IT Coordinator
CHR: Kristi Zane, Chief Human Resources Officer
CNO: Tammy Fralicker MS, R.N., Chief Nursing Officer
Web address: www.crawfordmh.net
Control: Hospital district or authority, Government, Nonfederal **Service:** General medical and surgical

Staffed Beds: 63 **Admissions:** 931 **Census:** 30 **Outpatient Visits:** 54435
Births: 208 **Total Expense ($000):** 46422 **Payroll Expense ($000):** 21289
Personnel: 364

ROCHELLE—Ogle County

⊞ **ROCHELLE COMMUNITY HOSPITAL (141312)**, 900 North Second Street, Zip 61068–1764; tel. 815/562–2181 **A**1 10 18 **F**3 15 29 30 31 34 35 40 41 45 50 53 57 59 64 68 70 74 75 77 78 81 82 85 86 87 93 97 107 110 115 130 132 133 135 144 146 **P**6
Primary Contact: Mark Batty, Chief Executive Officer
CFO: Lori Gutierrez, Chief Financial Officer
CMO: Jason Popp, Chief of Medical Staff
CIO: Scott Stewart, Manager Information Services
CHR: Laura Cirone, Manager Human Resources
CNO: Julie Norem MSN, Chief Nursing Officer
Web address: www.rcha.net
Control: Other not–for–profit (including NFP Corporation) **Service:** General medical and surgical

Staffed Beds: 16 **Admissions:** 505 **Census:** 4 **Outpatient Visits:** 45177
Births: 0 **Total Expense ($000):** 28660 **Payroll Expense ($000):** 10987
Personnel: 224

IL

Many Facility Codes have changed. Please refer to the AHA Guide Code Chart. © 2017 AHA Guide

ROCK ISLAND—Rock Island County

☒ △ **UNITYPOINT HEALTH – TRINITY ROCK ISLAND (140280)**, 2701 17th Street, Zip 61201–5393; tel. 309/779–5000, (Includes UNITYPOINT HEALTH – TRINITY MOLINE, 500 John Deere Road, Moline, Illinois, Zip 61265, tel. 309/779–5000) (Total facility includes 29 beds in nursing home–type unit) **A**1 7 10 **F**3 5 11 12 13 15 18 20 22 24 26 28 29 30 31 34 35 37 38 40 43 44 45 46 47 48 49 50 57 58 59 64 70 74 76 78 79 81 82 85 86 87 89 90 93 96 98 99 102 103 104 105 107 108 110 114 115 118 119 120 121 123 126 128 129 130 132 146 147 148 149 150 **P**8 **S** UnityPoint Health, West Des Moines, IA
Primary Contact: Richard A. Seidler, FACHE, President and Chief Executive Officer
CFO: Katie A Marchik, Interim Chief Financial Officer
CMO: Paul McLoone M.D., Chief Medical Officer
CHR: Cara Fuller, Vice President Human Resources
CNO: Ginger L Renkiewicz, Chief Clinical Officer, Chief Nursing Executive, and Chief Quality Officer
Web address: www.trinityqc.com
Control: Other not–for–profit (including NFP Corporation) **Service:** General medical and surgical

Staffed Beds: 343 **Admissions:** 14752 **Census:** 182 **Outpatient Visits:** 304980 **Births:** 1438 **Total Expense ($000):** 333014 **Payroll Expense ($000):** 106031 **Personnel:** 1878

ROCKFORD—Winnebago County

☒ **MERCYHEALTH HOSPITAL – ROCKTON AVENUE (140239)**, 2400 North Rockton Avenue, Zip 61103–3655; tel. 815/971–5000 **A**1 2 3 5 10 **F**3 11 12 13 18 19 20 22 24 26 27 28 29 30 31 32 34 35 39 40 41 43 44 45 46 47 48 49 50 51 53 54 55 56 57 59 63 64 65 68 70 71 72 74 75 76 77 78 79 81 82 83 84 85 86 87 88 89 91 93 97 98 100 101 102 103 107 108 111 114 115 118 119 121 122 123 126 129 130 131 132 135 145 146 147 148 149 **P**6 **S** Mercy Health System, Janesville, WI
Primary Contact: Javon R. Bea, President and Chief Executive Officer
COO: Sue Ripsch, Senior Vice President & Chief Operating Officer
CFO: John Cook, Senior Vice President & Chief Financial Officer
CMO: John T Dorsey M.D., Vice President Physician Services and Chief Medical Officer
CIO: Ruth Yarbrough, Vice President
CHR: Heidi Elsbree, Vice President People and Culture
Web address: www.rhsnet.org
Control: Other not–for–profit (including NFP Corporation) **Service:** General medical and surgical

Staffed Beds: 288 **Admissions:** 12675 **Census:** 177 **Outpatient Visits:** 322895 **Births:** 1487 **Total Expense ($000):** 325134 **Payroll Expense ($000):** 114962 **Personnel:** 2078

☒ **OSF SAINT ANTHONY MEDICAL CENTER (140233)**, 5666 East State Street, Zip 61108–2425; tel. 815/226–2000 **A**1 2 3 5 10 **F**3 11 12 13 15 16 17 18 19 20 22 24 26 28 29 30 31 32 34 35 36 37 38 39 40 41 43 44 45 46 49 50 51 53 55 56 57 58 59 63 64 66 70 73 74 75 76 77 78 79 81 82 84 85 86 87 89 92 93 107 108 110 111 114 115 116 117 118 119 120 121 123 124 126 129 130 131 132 135 145 146 147 148 149 150 **P**6 **S** OSF Healthcare System, Peoria, IL
Primary Contact: Paula A. Carynski, MS, R.N., President
COO: James Girardy M.D., Vice President, Chief Surgical Officer
CFO: David Stenerson, Vice President and Chief Financial Officer
CMO: Harneet Bath M.D., Vice President, Chief Medicine Officer
CIO: Kathy Peterson, Director Information Services
CHR: Karen C Brown, Vice President Chief Operating Officer
Web address: www.osfhealth.com
Control: Church operated, Nongovernment, not–for–profit **Service:** General medical and surgical

Staffed Beds: 235 **Admissions:** 11735 **Census:** 138 **Outpatient Visits:** 230185 **Births:** 575 **Total Expense ($000):** 325371 **Payroll Expense ($000):** 107367 **Personnel:** 1386

☒ **SWEDISHAMERICAN – A DIVISION OF UW HEALTH (140228)**, 1401 East State Street, Zip 61104–2315; tel. 815/968–4400 **A**1 2 3 5 10 **F**3 13 15 17 18 20 22 24 26 28 29 30 31 34 35 36 37 38 39 40 43 44 45 46 49 50 57 58 59 60 61 63 64 65 68 70 73 74 75 76 77 78 79 81 82 84 85 86 87 89 92 93 98 99 100 101 102 103 104 105 107 108 110 111 114 115 118 119 126 129 130 132 135 146 147 148 149 **P**6
Primary Contact: Michael Born, M.D., President and Chief Executive Officer
COO: Don Daniels, Executive Vice President and Chief Operating Officer
CFO: Patti DeWane, Vice President Finance and Treasurer
CIO: Sheryl Johnson, Chief Information Officer
CNO: Ann M Gantzer Ph.D., R.N., Vice President Patient Services and Chief Nursing Officer
Web address: www.swedishamerican.org
Control: Other not–for–profit (including NFP Corporation) **Service:** General medical and surgical

Staffed Beds: 286 **Admissions:** 15354 **Census:** 179 **Outpatient Visits:** 263526 **Births:** 2542 **Total Expense ($000):** 326410 **Payroll Expense ($000):** 122644 **Personnel:** 1928

☒ **VAN MATRE HEALTHSOUTH REHABILITATION HOSPITAL (143028)**, 950 South Mulford Road, Zip 61108–4274; tel. 815/381–8500 **A**1 10 **F**28 29 34 57 64 68 74 75 82 86 90 91 93 95 96 130 131 132 148 **P**5 **S** HEALTHSOUTH Corporation, Birmingham, AL
Primary Contact: Ken Bowman, Chief Executive Officer
CFO: Tim Anderson, Controller
CMO: Ricardo Knight, Interim Medical Director
CIO: Angela Bergman, Director of Quality, Risk and Health Information Management
CHR: Dorothy Richardson, Director Human Resources
CNO: Nancy Miller R.N., Chief Nursing Officer
Web address: www.healthsouth.com
Control: Partnership, Investor–owned (for–profit) **Service:** Rehabilitation

Staffed Beds: 61 **Admissions:** 1533 **Census:** 53 **Outpatient Visits:** 7969 **Births:** 0 **Total Expense ($000):** 24825 **Payroll Expense ($000):** 10381 **Personnel:** 194

ROSICLARE—Hardin County

★ **HARDIN COUNTY GENERAL HOSPITAL (141328)**, 6 Ferrell Road, Zip 62982, Mailing Address: P.O.Box 2467, 62982–2467; tel. 618/285–6634 **A**10 18 **F**11 14 15 29 34 40 45 48 50 56 57 59 64 65 66 75 77 90 93 97 103 107 114 119 127 129 130 133
Primary Contact: Roby D. Williams, Administrator
CFO: Janie Parker, Chief Financial Officer
CMO: Marcos N Sunga M.D., Chief of Staff
CIO: Brian Casteel, Information Technology Technician
CHR: Joyce Shelby, Manager Human Resources
CNO: Courtney Spivey, Chief Nursing Officer
Web address: www.ilhcgh.org
Control: Other not–for–profit (including NFP Corporation) **Service:** General medical and surgical

Staffed Beds: 25 **Admissions:** 451 **Census:** 4 **Outpatient Visits:** 16340 **Total Expense ($000):** 10870 **Payroll Expense ($000):** 5956 **Personnel:** 128

RUSHVILLE—Schuyler County

★ **SARAH D. CULBERTSON MEMORIAL HOSPITAL (141333)**, 238 South Congress Street, Zip 62681–1472; tel. 217/322–4321 **A**10 18 **F**15 28 29 31 34 40 56 57 59 65 69 75 77 81 85 93 96 97 103 104 107 110 114 119 125 127 129 130 132 133 135 146 148 149 **P**6
Primary Contact: Lynn E. Stambaugh, R.N., Chief Executive Officer
CFO: Alan Palo, Chief Financial Officer
CMO: Marguerite Taillefer M.D., Acting President Medical Staff
CIO: Dan Wise, Manager Information Technology
CNO: Lisa M Downs R.N., Chief Nursing Officer
Web address: www.cmhospital.com
Control: Hospital district or authority, Government, Nonfederal **Service:** General medical and surgical

Staffed Beds: 22 **Admissions:** 177 **Census:** 2 **Outpatient Visits:** 47448 **Births:** 0 **Total Expense ($000):** 22718 **Payroll Expense ($000):** 7946 **Personnel:** 158

SALEM—Marion County

★ **SALEM TOWNSHIP HOSPITAL (141345)**, 1201 Ricker Drive, Zip 62881–4263; tel. 618/548–3194, (Nonreporting) **A**10 18
Primary Contact: John E. Kessler, President and Chief Executive Officer
CFO: Teresa Stroud, Chief Financial Officer
CMO: Seth Hahs, Chief of Staff
CIO: Steve Turner, Director Information Technology
CHR: Diane Boswell, Director Human Resources and Marketing
Web address: www.sthcares.org
Control: City–county, Government, Nonfederal **Service:** General medical and surgical

Staffed Beds: 22

IL

Hospital, Medicare Provider Number, Address, Telephone, Approval, Facility, and Physician Codes, Health Care System

★ American Hospital Association (AHA) membership ☐ The Joint Commission accreditation ○ Healthcare Facilities Accreditation Program ◇ DNV Healthcare Inc. accreditation ⇑ Center for Improvement in Healthcare Quality Accreditation △ Commission on Accreditation of Rehabilitation Facilities (CARF) accreditation

© 2017 AHA Guide   *Many Facility Codes have changed. Please refer to the AHA Guide Code Chart.*   Hospitals **A199**

SANDWICH—Dekalb County

✠ **NORTHWESTERN MEDICINE VALLEY WEST HOSPITAL (141340)**, 1302 North Main Street, Zip 60548–2587; tel. 815/786–8484 **A**1 10 18 **F**3 11 13 15 18 28 29 30 31 32 34 35 36 38 40 45 46 49 50 51 57 58 59 64 70 71 73 75 76 77 78 79 81 82 85 87 89 93 102 104 107 110 115 119 129 130 131 132 135 146 147 149 150 **S** Northwestern Memorial HealthCare, Chicago, IL
Primary Contact: Jay Anderson, President
COO: Brad Copple, Vice President Operations
CFO: Loren Foelske, Vice President Finance
CMO: Michael Kulisz D.O., Chief Medical Officer
CIO: Heath Bell, Vice President, Chief Information Officer
CHR: Michele McClelland, Vice President Human Resources
CNO: Pamela Duffy, Vice President Operations and Chief Nursing Officer
Web address: www.nm.org
Control: Other not–for–profit (including NFP Corporation) **Service:** General medical and surgical

Staffed Beds: 25 **Admissions:** 837 **Census:** 6 **Outpatient Visits:** 42650
Births: 158 **Total Expense ($000):** 39222 **Payroll Expense ($000):** 11479
Personnel: 174

SHELBYVILLE—Shelby County

★ ⇑ **SHELBY MEMORIAL HOSPITAL (140019)**, 200 South Cedar Street, Zip 62565–1838; tel. 217/774–3961 **A**10 20 21 **F**3 15 28 29 34 35 40 45 57 59 62 64 77 81 93 97 107 108 110 118 119 127 129 131 132 133 146 **P**5
Primary Contact: Marilyn Sears, President and Chief Executive Officer
CFO: Marilyn Sears, Chief Financial Officer
CMO: David Oligschlaeger, Medical Staff President
CIO: Ian Kuhlman, Manager Information Technology
CHR: Amy Koehler, Director Human Resources
CNO: Michelle Oliver, Chief Nursing Executive
Web address: www.mysmh.org
Control: Other not–for–profit (including NFP Corporation) **Service:** General medical and surgical

Staffed Beds: 30 **Admissions:** 549 **Census:** 5 **Outpatient Visits:** 24711
Births: 0 **Total Expense ($000):** 16616 **Payroll Expense ($000):** 7027
Personnel: 169

SHILOH—St. Clair County

★ ○ **MEMORIAL HOSPITAL EAST**, 1404 Cross Street, Zip 62269–2988; tel. 618/607–1000, (Data for 263 days)**A**11 **F**3 11 13 18 20 22 29 30 31 40 45 49 60 64 70 74 76 78 79 81 82 84 85 87 107 108 111 115 119 130 146 148 **S** BJC HealthCare, Saint Louis, MO
Primary Contact: Mark J. Turner, President and Chief Executive Officer
Web address: www.memhospeast.com
Control: Other not–for–profit (including NFP Corporation) **Service:** General medical and surgical

Staffed Beds: 68 **Admissions:** 2893 **Census:** 35 **Outpatient Visits:** 35709
Births: 753 **Total Expense ($000):** 64767 **Payroll Expense ($000):** 22488
Personnel: 433

SILVIS—Rock Island County

✠ **GENESIS MEDICAL CENTER, SILVIS (140275)**, 801 Illini Drive, Zip 61282–1893; tel. 309/281–4000 **A**1 10 **F**3 7 11 13 15 18 20 22 26 28 29 30 31 34 35 40 43 45 46 47 50 51 53 59 60 62 64 65 68 70 75 76 77 79 81 84 85 87 89 107 108 110 111 114 119 129 130 132 135 146 147 149 **S** Genesis Health System, Davenport, IA
Primary Contact: Theresa Summers–Main, R.N., Interim President
CFO: Mark G Rogers, Interim Vice President Finance and Chief Financial Officer
CMO: Peter Metcalf M.D., President Medical Staff
CIO: Robert Frieden, Vice President Information Systems
CHR: Heidi Kahly–McMahon, Vice President Human Resources
Web address: www.genesishealth.com
Control: Other not–for–profit (including NFP Corporation) **Service:** General medical and surgical

Staffed Beds: 135 **Admissions:** 3809 **Census:** 31 **Outpatient Visits:** 109461 **Births:** 336 **Total Expense ($000):** 78032 **Payroll Expense ($000):** 23158 **Personnel:** 413

SPARTA—Randolph County

SPARTA COMMUNITY HOSPITAL (141349), 818 East Broadway Street, Zip 62286–1820, Mailing Address: P.O.Box 297, 62286–0297; tel. 618/443–2177 **A**10 18 **F**3 11 15 28 29 34 35 40 41 45 53 57 59 62 64 65 75 77 81 89 93 97 107 110 111 115 119 127 130 132 133 143 146 147 **P**5
Primary Contact: Joann Emge, Chief Executive Officer
CFO: Paul Mueller, Chief Financial Officer
CMO: Mark Pruess M.D., Chief Medical Staff
CIO: Susan Gutjahr, Reimbursement Specialist
CHR: Darla Shawgo, Director Human Resources
CNO: Lori Clinton, Chief Nursing Officer
Web address: www.spartahospital.com
Control: Hospital district or authority, Government, Nonfederal **Service:** General medical and surgical

Staffed Beds: 25 **Admissions:** 678 **Census:** 3 **Outpatient Visits:** 90047
Births: 0 **Total Expense ($000):** 31693 **Payroll Expense ($000):** 13043
Personnel: 256

SPRING VALLEY—Bureau County

ST. MARGARET'S HOSPITAL (140143), 600 East First Street, Zip 61362–1512; tel. 815/664–5311 **A**10 **F**3 11 13 15 28 29 30 31 32 34 35 38 40 44 45 46 47 49 53 57 58 59 63 70 74 75 76 77 79 81 82 84 85 87 90 93 96 107 108 110 111 115 116 119 129 130 131 132 133 135 143 144 146 147 148 149 **P**6 8 **S** Sisters of Mary of the Presentation Health System, Fargo, ND
Primary Contact: Tim Muntz, President and Chief Executive Officer
CFO: Kim D Santman, Vice President Finance
CIO: John Sabotta, Director Information Systems
CHR: Lisa R Blackburn, Director Human Resources
CNO: Mary Vega R.N., MSN, Vice President Nursing
Web address: www.aboutsmh.org
Control: Church operated, Nongovernment, not–for–profit **Service:** General medical and surgical

Staffed Beds: 54 **Admissions:** 1768 **Census:** 16 **Outpatient Visits:** 279316
Births: 333 **Total Expense ($000):** 78478 **Payroll Expense ($000):** 33683
Personnel: 528

SPRINGFIELD—Sangamon County

☐ **ANDREW MCFARLAND MENTAL HEALTH CENTER (144021)**, 901 East Southwind Road, Zip 62703–5125; tel. 217/786–6994, (Nonreporting) **A**1 5 10 **S** Division of Mental Health, Department of Human Services, Springfield, IL
Primary Contact: Karen Schweighart, R.N., MS, Administrator
CFO: Jeff Frey, Business Administrator
CMO: Kasturi Kripakaran M.D., Medical Director
CIO: Josh Kates, Information Technology Analyst
CNO: Frances Collins, Director of Nursing
Control: State, Government, Nonfederal **Service:** Psychiatric

Staffed Beds: 118

KINDRED HOSPITAL SPRINGFIELD See Vibra Hospital Of Springfield

☐ **LINCOLN PRAIRIE BEHAVIORAL HEALTH CENTER**, 5230 South Sixth Street, Zip 62703–5128; tel. 217/585–1180 **A**1 3 5 **F**29 35 98 99 100 101 104 105 **S** Universal Health Services, Inc., King of Prussia, PA
Primary Contact: Mark Littrell, Chief Executive Officer
CFO: Chris Statz, Chief Financial Officer
CMO: Pamela Campbell M.D., Medical Director
CNO: Renae Hale, Chief Nursing Officer
Web address: www.lincolnprairiebhc.com/
Control: Corporation, Investor–owned (for–profit) **Service:** Children's hospital psychiatric

Staffed Beds: 97 **Admissions:** 1932 **Census:** 71 **Births:** 0

✠ △ **MEMORIAL MEDICAL CENTER (140148)**, 701 North First Street, Zip 62781–0001; tel. 217/788–3000 **A**1 2 3 5 7 8 10 **F**3 8 11 12 13 14 15 16 17 18 20 22 24 26 28 29 30 31 32 34 35 36 37 40 43 44 45 46 47 48 49 50 51 54 57 58 59 60 61 63 64 68 69 70 74 75 76 77 78 79 81 82 84 85 86 87 89 90 92 93 96 97 98 100 101 102 103 104 105 107 108 110 111 114 115 116 117 118 119 120 121 124 126 129 130 131 132 134 135 138 141 142 145 146 147 148 149 **S** Memorial Health System, Springfield, IL
Primary Contact: Edgar J. Curtis, FACHE, President and Chief Executive Officer
COO: Charles D Callahan Ph.D., Executive Vice President and Chief Operating Officer
CFO: Robert W Kay, Senior Vice President and Chief Financial Officer
CMO: Rajesh G Govindaiah M.D., Chief Medical Officer
CIO: David B Graham M.D., Senior Vice President and Chief Information Officer
CHR: Robert F Scott, Vice President and Chief Human Resources Officer
CNO: Marsha A Prater Ph.D., R.N., Senior Vice President and Chief Nursing Officer
Web address: www.memorialmedical.com
Control: Other not–for–profit (including NFP Corporation) **Service:** General medical and surgical

Staffed Beds: 470 **Admissions:** 25779 **Census:** 337 **Outpatient Visits:** 525362 **Births:** 1535 **Total Expense ($000):** 678838 **Payroll Expense ($000):** 208024 **Personnel:** 3577

IL

✠ **ST. JOHN'S HOSPITAL (140053)**, 800 East Carpenter Street, Zip 62769–0002; tel. 217/544–6464, (Includes ST. JOHN'S CHILDREN'S HOSPITAL, 800 East Carpenter Street, Springfield, Illinois, Zip 62769, tel. 217/544–6464) (Total facility includes 37 beds in nursing home–type unit) **A**1 2 3 5 10 **F**3 8 11 13 15 17 18 19 20 22 24 26 28 29 30 31 32 34 35 36 37 39 40 41 43 44 45 46 47 48 49 50 51 53 54 56 57 58 59 60 61 62 63 64 68 70 72 74 75 76 77 78 79 81 82 83 84 85 86 87 88 89 92 93 94 96 98 102 103 105 107 108 110 111 114 115 116 117 118 119 120 121 122 123 124 126 128 129 130 131 132 135 145 146 147 148 149 150 **S** HSHS Hospital Sisters Health System, Springfield, IL
Primary Contact: Charles Lucore, M.D., President and Chief Executive Officer
COO: David R Olejniczak, Chief Operating Officer
CFO: Patty Allen, St. John's Vice President Finance
CIO: Ryan Leach, Chief Information Officer
CHR: Becky Puclik, Division Chief People Officer
CNO: Sherri Greenwood, Chief Nursing Officer
Web address: www.st-johns.org
Control: Other not–for–profit (including NFP Corporation) **Service:** General medical and surgical

Staffed Beds: 432 Admissions: 18630 Census: 278 Outpatient Visits: 246840 Births: 1956 Total Expense ($000): 483839 Payroll Expense ($000): 141648 Personnel: 2556

✠ **VIBRA HOSPITAL OF SPRINGFIELD (142014)**, 701 North Walnut Street, Zip 62702–4931; tel. 217/528–1217, (Nonreporting) **A**1 3 10 **S** Vibra Healthcare, Mechanicsburg, PA
Primary Contact: Charles Nordyke, Chief Executive Officer
CHR: Cynthia J. Dodge, Director Human Resources
CNO: Cathy Harding, Chief Clinical Officer
Web address: www.vhspringfield.com
Control: Corporation, Investor–owned (for–profit) **Service:** Acute long–term care hospital

Staffed Beds: 30

STAUNTON—Macoupin County

COMMUNITY HOSPITAL OF STAUNTON (141306), 400 Caldwell Street, Zip 62088–1499; tel. 618/635–2200 **A**10 18 **F**3 11 15 28 29 31 40 45 54 56 64 78 79 81 85 97 107 110 115 129 130 132 133 146 149 **P**5
Primary Contact: Susie Campbell, Chief Executive Officer
CFO: Brian Engelke, Chief Financial Officer
CMO: Joshua Poos M.D., President Medical Staff
CIO: Cheryl Horner, Supervisor Data Processing
CHR: Marilyn Herbeck, Coordinator Human Resources
CNO: Roberta Brown, Chief Nursing Officer
Web address: www.stauntonhospital.org
Control: Other not–for–profit (including NFP Corporation) **Service:** General medical and surgical

Staffed Beds: 25 Admissions: 298 Census: 3 Outpatient Visits: 23455 Births: 0 Total Expense ($000): 16054 Payroll Expense ($000): 5812 Personnel: 117

STERLING—Whiteside County

✠ **CGH MEDICAL CENTER (140043)**, 100 East LeFevre Road, Zip 61081–1279; tel. 815/625–0400 **A**1 10 **F**3 7 8 13 15 18 20 22 28 29 30 31 34 35 40 45 47 49 50 51 57 59 62 64 68 70 74 76 78 79 81 82 85 86 87 89 93 97 105 107 108 110 111 112 115 116 117 118 119 124 129 130 132 133 135 144 145 146 147 148 **P**6
Primary Contact: Paul Steinke, D.O., President and Chief Executive Officer
COO: Cynthia L Zander, Vice President and Chief Operating Officer
CFO: Ben Schaab, VP Fiscal Services/ Chief Financial Officer
CMO: Keith Martin M.D., Vice President and Medical Director
CIO: Randy Davis, Vice President and Chief Information Officer
CHR: Shane Brown, Vice President and Chief Human Resources Officer
CNO: Kristie A Geil, VP, Chief Nursing Officer
Web address: www.cghmc.com
Control: City, Government, Nonfederal **Service:** General medical and surgical

Staffed Beds: 99 Admissions: 4400 Census: 39 Outpatient Visits: 377187 Births: 525 Total Expense ($000): 202562 Payroll Expense ($000): 89993 Personnel: 914

STREAMWOOD—Cook County

☐ **STREAMWOOD BEHAVIORAL HEALTH CENTER (144034)**, 1400 East Irving Park Road, Zip 60107–3203; tel. 630/837–9000, (Nonreporting) **A**1 10 **S** Universal Health Services, Inc., King of Prussia, PA
Primary Contact: Ron Weglarz, Chief Executive Officer and Managing Director
CFO: Patricia Ellison, Chief Financial Officer
CMO: Joseph McNally M.D., Medical Director
CHR: Joseph Rinke, Director Human Resources
CNO: Olieth Lightbourne, Chief Nursing Officer
Web address: www.streamwoodhospital.com
Control: Corporation, Investor–owned (for–profit) **Service:** Children's hospital psychiatric

Staffed Beds: 178

SYCAMORE—Dekalb County

✠ **KINDRED HOSPITAL–SYCAMORE (142006)**, 225 Edward Street, Zip 60178–2137; tel. 815/895–2144, (Nonreporting) **A**1 10 **S** Kindred Healthcare, Louisville, KY
Primary Contact: Jim Cohick, Chief Executive Officer
CFO: Jay Schweikart, Chief Financial Officer
CMO: Thomas Liske M.D., Chief Medical Officer
CHR: Eileen Strachan, Coordinator Human Resources
Web address: www.kindredhospitalsyc.com/
Control: Corporation, Investor–owned (for–profit) **Service:** Acute long–term care hospital

Staffed Beds: 69

TAYLORVILLE—Christian County

✠ **TAYLORVILLE MEMORIAL HOSPITAL (141339)**, 201 East Pleasant Street, Zip 62568–1597; tel. 217/824–3331 **A**1 3 5 10 18 **F**8 15 28 29 30 34 35 40 45 46 50 57 59 64 75 77 79 81 87 89 93 103 107 108 110 111 115 119 129 130 131 132 133 144 146 **P**5 **S** Memorial Health System, Springfield, IL
Primary Contact: Kimberly L. Bourne, Chief Executive Officer
CFO: Andrew Costic, Regional Chief Financial Officer
CHR: Michelle Long, Regional Human Resource Manager
CNO: Tracy Seaton, Director of Nursing
Web address: www.taylorvillememorial.org
Control: Other not–for–profit (including NFP Corporation) **Service:** General medical and surgical

Staffed Beds: 25 Admissions: 937 Census: 9 Outpatient Visits: 37097 Births: 0 Total Expense ($000): 36729 Payroll Expense ($000): 14500 Personnel: 276

URBANA—Champaign County

★ △ ⇑ **CARLE FOUNDATION HOSPITAL (140091)**, 611 West Park Street, Zip 61801–2595; tel. 217/383–3311 **A**2 3 5 7 10 13 21 **F**3 5 7 8 11 12 13 15 17 18 20 22 24 26 28 29 30 31 32 34 35 40 43 44 45 46 47 48 49 50 51 53 56 57 58 59 60 61 62 63 64 65 68 70 72 73 74 75 76 78 79 80 81 84 85 86 87 89 90 91 93 94 96 107 108 110 111 114 115 116 117 119 126 129 130 131 132 135 145 146 148 149 **S** Carle Foundation, Urbana, IL
Primary Contact: James C. Leonard, M.D., President and Chief Executive Officer
COO: John Snyder, Executive Vice President and System Chief Operating Officer
CFO: Dennis Hesch, Executive Vice President Finance, System Chief Financial Officer
CMO: Matthew Gibb M.D., Executive Vice President and System Chief Medical Officer
CIO: Rick Rinehart, Vice President, Chief Information Officer
CHR: L J Fallon JD, Executive Vice President, Chief Legal and Human Resources Officer
CNO: Pamela Bigler MSN, R.N., Senior Vice President, Chief Nursing Officer
Web address: www.carle.org
Control: Other not–for–profit (including NFP Corporation) **Service:** General medical and surgical

Staffed Beds: 412 Admissions: 23655 Census: 310 Outpatient Visits: 1195627 Births: 2727 Total Expense ($000): 581743 Payroll Expense ($000): 161369 Personnel: 2917

Hospital, Medicare Provider Number, Address, Telephone, Approval, Facility, and Physician Codes, Health Care System

★ American Hospital Association (AHA) membership   ○ Healthcare Facilities Accreditation Program   ⇑ Center for Improvement in Healthcare Quality Accreditation
☐ The Joint Commission accreditation   ◇ DNV Healthcare Inc. accreditation   △ Commission on Accreditation of Rehabilitation Facilities (CARF) accreditation

© 2017 AHA Guide   *Many Facility Codes have changed. Please refer to the AHA Guide Code Chart.*   Hospitals **A201**

✠ △ **PRESENCE COVENANT MEDICAL CENTER (140113)**, 1400 West Park Street, Zip 61801–2396; tel. 217/337–2000 **A**1 3 5 7 10 **F**3 13 15 18 20 22 24 26 28 29 30 31 34 35 40 49 57 59 68 70 72 74 75 76 78 79 81 82 85 87 89 90 97 98 100 101 102 103 107 108 110 111 114 115 119 126 130 132 146 147 148 **S** Presence Health, Chicago, IL
Primary Contact: Jared Rogers, M.D., President and Chief Executive Officer
COO: Jennifer Cord R.N., Chief Ambulatory, Ancillary, and Mission Officer
CFO: Deb Schimerowski, Vice President Finance and Chief Financial Officer
CMO: Vincent Kucich FACHE, FACS, M.D., Chief Medical Officer
CIO: Paula Keele, Manager Information Systems
CHR: Michael Zimmerman, Human Resource Officer
CNO: Molly Nicholson MS, R.N., Chief Nurse Executive
Web address: www.presencehealth.org/covenant
Control: Church operated, Nongovernment, not–for–profit **Service**: General medical and surgical

Staffed Beds: 181 Admissions: 7038 Census: 79 Outpatient Visits: 237172 Births: 709 Total Expense ($000): 128765 Payroll Expense ($000): 37625 Personnel: 695

VANDALIA—Fayette County

✠ **FAYETTE COUNTY HOSPITAL (141346)**, 650 West Taylor Street, Zip 62471–1296; tel. 618/283–1231, (Total facility includes 85 beds in nursing home–type unit) **A**1 10 18 **F**3 7 11 15 28 29 30 34 40 45 49 57 59 77 80 81 86 93 107 110 111 112 114 116 117 119 127 128 130 132 133 144 145 146 **P**5 **S** Alliant Management Services, Louisville, KY
Primary Contact: Gregory D. Starnes, Chief Executive Officer
CFO: David H Wiesman, Interim Chief Financial Officer
CMO: Glenn Skow M.D., Chief of Staff
CIO: Lisa Tessman, Manager Information Technology
CHR: Susan Crawford, Manager Human Resources
CNO: Marci Barth, Chief Nursing Officer
Web address: www.fayettecountyhospital.org
Control: Corporation, Investor–owned (for–profit) **Service**: General medical and surgical

Staffed Beds: 110 Admissions: 526 Census: 53 Outpatient Visits: 50813 Births: 0 Total Expense ($000): 29184 Payroll Expense ($000): 11174 Personnel: 261

WATSEKA—Iroquois County

☐ **IROQUOIS MEMORIAL HOSPITAL AND RESIDENT HOME (140167)**, 200 Fairman Avenue, Zip 60970–1644; tel. 815/432–5841, (Nonreporting) **A**1 3 10 20
Primary Contact: Tim Smith, Chief Executive Officer
CMO: Philip Zumwalt M.D., Chief of Staff
CHR: Jamie Neumann, Director Human Resources
CNO: Leslie Cottrell R.N., MSN, Nurse Lead
Web address: www.iroquoismemorial.com
Control: Other not–for–profit (including NFP Corporation) **Service**: General medical and surgical

Staffed Beds: 68

WAUKEGAN—Lake County

✠ **VISTA MEDICAL CENTER EAST (140084)**, 1324 North Sheridan Road, Zip 60085–2161; tel. 847/360–3000 **A**1 2 3 5 10 **F**3 12 13 15 18 20 22 24 26 28 29 30 31 34 35 38 39 40 41 42 43 44 45 46 47 48 49 50 57 59 68 70 74 76 78 79 81 82 84 85 87 89 93 100 102 107 108 110 111 114 115 119 126 129 130 132 146 147 148 **S** Quorum Health, Brentwood, TN
Primary Contact: Norman F. Stephens, Interim Chief Executive Officer
COO: Kim Needham, Assistant Chief Executive Officer
CFO: Kerry Hill, Chief Financial Officer
CMO: Daniel Liesen M.D., Chief Medical Officer
CHR: Michael R Isaacs, Vice President Human Resources
CNO: Trisha E Musich R.N., Chief Nursing Officer
Web address: www.vistahealth.com
Control: Corporation, Investor–owned (for–profit) **Service**: General medical and surgical

Staffed Beds: 190 Admissions: 10797 Census: 116 Outpatient Visits: 137467 Births: 1088 Total Expense ($000): 163362 Payroll Expense ($000): 53329 Personnel: 828

✠ △ **VISTA MEDICAL CENTER WEST (140033)**, 2615 Washington Street, Zip 60085–4988; tel. 847/249–3900 **A**1 7 10 **F**29 30 34 35 38 40 42 43 56 57 59 64 68 77 87 90 96 98 99 101 102 103 104 105 107 119 130 132 135 **S** Quorum Health, Brentwood, TN
Primary Contact: Norman F. Stephens, Interim Chief Executive Officer
COO: Kim Needham, Assistant Chief Executive Officer
CFO: Kerry Hill, Chief Financial Officer
CMO: Daniel Liesen M.D., Chief Medical Officer
CHR: Michael R Isaacs, Vice President Human Resources
CNO: Trisha E Musich R.N., Chief Nursing Officer
Web address: www.vistahealth.com
Control: Corporation, Investor–owned (for–profit) **Service**: Psychiatric

Staffed Beds: 67 Admissions: 1566 Census: 32 Outpatient Visits: 11511 Births: 0 Total Expense ($000): 16190 Payroll Expense ($000): 7370 Personnel: 96

WHEATON—Du Page County

✠ △ **MARIANJOY REHABILITATION HOSPITAL (143027)**, 26 West 171 Roosevelt Road, Zip 60187–0795, Mailing Address: P.O.Box 795, 60187–0795; tel. 630/909–8000, (Total facility includes 27 beds in nursing home–type unit) **A**1 3 7 10 **F**11 28 29 30 34 35 36 44 50 53 54 57 58 64 68 75 77 79 82 86 87 90 91 92 93 94 95 96 99 103 104 128 130 131 132 143 146 148 149 **P**6 **S** Northwestern Memorial HealthCare, Chicago, IL
Primary Contact: Kathleen C. Yosko, President
COO: John Brady, Vice President Physician Services and Organizational Planning
CFO: Michael Hedderman, Senior Vice President Finance and Chief Financial Officer
CMO: Jeffrey Oken, Vice President of Medical Affairs
CIO: Robert Sinickas, Director Information Services
CHR: Teresa Chapman, Vice President Human Resources
CNO: Kathleen C Yosko, President
Web address: www.marianjoy.org
Control: Other not–for–profit (including NFP Corporation) **Service**: Rehabilitation

Staffed Beds: 127 Admissions: 3102 Census: 116 Outpatient Visits: 55571 Births: 0 Total Expense ($000): 92107 Payroll Expense ($000): 53584 Personnel: 801

WINFIELD—DuPage County

✠ **NORTHWESTERN MEDICINE CENTRAL DUPAGE HOSPITAL (140242)**, 25 North Winfield Road, Zip 60190; tel. 630/933–1600, (Includes BEHAVIORAL HEALTH CENTER, 27 West 350 High Lake Road, Winfield, Illinois, Zip 60190, tel. 630/653–4000) **A**1 2 3 5 10 **F**3 4 5 8 9 11 12 13 15 17 19 20 22 24 26 28 29 30 31 32 34 35 36 37 38 39 40 41 42 43 44 45 46 47 48 49 50 54 55 57 58 59 60 64 65 68 70 72 73 74 75 76 77 78 79 81 82 84 85 86 87 88 89 91 92 93 94 96 97 98 99 100 101 102 103 104 105 107 108 110 111 112 114 115 116 117 118 119 120 121 122 123 124 126 129 130 131 132 135 144 145 146 147 148 149 **P**6 **S** Northwestern Memorial HealthCare, Chicago, IL
Primary Contact: Brian J. Lemon, President
CFO: John Orsini, Executive Vice President and Chief Financial Officer
CMO: Kevin Most D.O., Vice President Medical Affairs
CIO: Daniel F Kinsella, Vice President and Chief Information Officer
CHR: Michael Wukitsch, Vice President Human Resources
Web address: www.nm.org
Control: Other not–for–profit (including NFP Corporation) **Service**: General medical and surgical

Staffed Beds: 422 Admissions: 21054 Census: 256 Outpatient Visits: 1416549 Births: 3191 Total Expense ($000): 878192 Payroll Expense ($000): 329739 Personnel: 5249

WOODSTOCK—Mchenry County

★ **CENTEGRA HOSPITAL – WOODSTOCK (140176)**, 3701 Doty Road, Zip 60098–7509, Mailing Address: P.O.Box 1990, 60098–1990; tel. 815/338–2500 **A**10 **F**3 4 5 11 12 15 18 28 29 30 31 34 35 37 38 39 40 41 44 45 47 49 50 51 54 57 58 59 64 68 69 70 74 75 78 79 81 82 85 86 87 92 93 98 100 101 102 103 104 105 107 108 110 111 114 118 119 126 130 131 132 143 146 147 148 **P**6 8 **S** Centegra Health System, Crystal Lake, IL
Primary Contact: Michael S. Eesley, Chief Executive Officer
COO: Jason Sciarro, President and Chief Operating Officer
CFO: David Tomlinson, Executive Vice President Chief Financial Officer and Chief Information Officer
CMO: Irfan Hafiz, Vice President Medical Affairs
CIO: David Tomlinson, Senior Vice President, Chief Information Officer
CHR: Bernadette S Szczepanski, Senior Vice President Human Resources
Web address: www.centegra.org
Control: Other not–for–profit (including NFP Corporation) **Service**: General medical and surgical

Staffed Beds: 104 Admissions: 5126 Census: 61 Outpatient Visits: 69831 Births: 0 Total Expense ($000): 119311 Payroll Expense ($000): 47527 Personnel: 576

ZION—Lake County

✠ **MIDWESTERN REGIONAL MEDICAL CENTER (140100)**, 2520 Elisha Avenue, Zip 60099–2587; tel. 847/872–4561 **A**1 2 3 10 **F**3 7 8 15 18 26 28 29 30 31 33 34 36 37 38 40 44 45 46 48 49 50 54 55 57 58 59 60 61 64 65 68 74 75 77 78 79 81 82 85 86 87 92 93 94 95 97 100 101 102 104 107 108 110 111 115 117 118 119 120 121 123 124 126 129 130 132 133 135 136 143 144 146 147 148 **P**6 **S** Cancer Treatment Centers of America, Schaumburg, IL
Primary Contact: Scott Jones, President and Chief Executive Officer
COO: Pete Govorchin, Senior Vice President Operations
CFO: Cecilia Taylor, Chief Financial Officer
CMO: Bradford Tan M.D., Chief Medical Officer
CHR: Amy VanStrien, Director Talent Operations
CNO: Jacklynn Lesniak R.N., MS, Vice President Patient Care Services and Chief Nursing Officer
Web address: www.cancercenter.com
Control: Corporation, Investor–owned (for–profit) **Service**: Cancer

Staffed Beds: 72 Admissions: 2089 Census: 31 Outpatient Visits: 43077 Births: 0 Personnel: 1375

IL

INDIANA

ANDERSON—Madison County

✠ **COMMUNITY HOSPITAL OF ANDERSON & MADISON COUNTY (150113)**, 1515 North Madison Avenue, Zip 46011–3453; tel. 765/298–4242 **A**1 2 10 **F**3 6 10 11 13 15 18 20 22 28 29 30 31 32 34 35 40 44 46 49 50 51 54 55 56 57 58 59 60 61 64 68 70 74 75 76 77 78 79 81 82 85 86 87 89 93 107 108 109 110 111 114 115 119 120 121 122 123 126 129 130 132 135 143 144 146 147 148 149 **P**6 **S** Community Health Network, Indianapolis, IN
Primary Contact: Beth S. Tharp, R.N., President and Chief Executive Officer
CFO: John B. Harris, Vice President Finance and Chief Financial Officer
CHR: Michael Harpe, Vice President Human Resources
CNO: Carol Whitesel MSN, R.N., Vice President Patient Care Services and Chief Nursing Officer
Web address: www.communityanderson.com
Control: Other not–for–profit (including NFP Corporation) **Service**: General medical and surgical

Staffed Beds: 140 **Admissions**: 6201 **Census**: 64 **Outpatient Visits**: 206706 **Births**: 860 **Total Expense ($000)**: 143944 **Payroll Expense ($000)**: 60202 **Personnel**: 1123

✠ **ST. VINCENT ANDERSON REGIONAL HOSPITAL (150088)**, 2015 Jackson Street, Zip 46016–4339; tel. 765/649–2511 **A**1 2 10 **F**3 4 5 8 11 13 14 15 18 20 22 28 29 30 31 32 34 35 36 38 39 40 43 44 45 46 49 50 51 54 55 56 57 58 59 60 61 64 65 66 68 70 74 75 76 77 78 79 81 82 84 85 86 87 89 90 92 93 94 96 98 99 100 101 102 103 104 105 106 107 108 110 111 114 115 116 117 118 119 120 121 123 124 129 130 132 134 135 145 146 147 148 149 **P**6 **S** Ascension Healthcare, Saint Louis, MO
Primary Contact: Mike Schroyer, FACHE, MSN, R.N., President
COO: Nick Theohares, Executive Director, Operations
CFO: Laura L Adams, Vice President, Finance
CIO: Robert Pope, Information Technology Director and Ministry Liaison
CHR: Ross Brodhead, Executive Director, Human Resources
CNO: Nancy Pitcock, Vice President Nursing and Chief Nursing Officer
Web address: www.stvincent.org/andersonregional
Control: Church operated, Nongovernment, not–for–profit **Service**: General medical and surgical

Staffed Beds: 141 **Admissions**: 6288 **Census**: 95 **Outpatient Visits**: 184000 **Births**: 389 **Total Expense ($000)**: 186376 **Payroll Expense ($000)**: 59039 **Personnel**: 784

ANGOLA—Steuben County

★ **CAMERON MEMORIAL COMMUNITY HOSPITAL (151315)**, 416 East Maumee Street, Zip 46703–2015; tel. 260/665–2141 **A**10 18 **F**3 11 13 15 18 28 29 30 34 35 40 44 45 50 53 57 59 62 63 65 68 75 76 77 79 81 85 86 87 90 93 97 103 104 107 108 110 111 114 115 117 119 125 127 129 130 131 132 133 144 146 149 **P**6
Primary Contact: Connie McCahill, R.N., President and Chief Executive Officer
CFO: Douglas Bomba, Chief Financial Officer
CMO: Jon Alley D.O., President Medical Staff
CIO: Kris Keen, Chief Information Officer
CHR: Nancy Covell, Director Human Resources
CNO: Sharon Springer, Chief Nursing Officer
Web address: www.cameronmch.com
Control: Other not–for–profit (including NFP Corporation) **Service**: General medical and surgical

Staffed Beds: 25 **Admissions**: 1241 **Census**: 9 **Outpatient Visits**: 113038 **Births**: 202 **Total Expense ($000)**: 56370 **Payroll Expense ($000)**: 19166 **Personnel**: 381

AUBURN—Dekalb County

★ **DEKALB HEALTH (150045)**, 1316 East Seventh Street, Zip 46706–2515, Mailing Address: P.O.Box 542, 46706–0542; tel. 260/925–4600 **A**10 **F**3 7 11 13 15 28 29 32 34 35 36 40 45 53 56 57 59 62 63 64 70 73 75 76 77 79 81 82 84 85 86 87 89 93 97 107 108 110 111 114 115 119 129 130 132 135 144 146 147 148 149 **P**4 6
Primary Contact: Craig Polkow, Chief Executive Officer
CMO: Emilio Vazquez M.D., Chief Medical Officer
CIO: Ed Hobbs, Director Information Services
CNO: Donna S Wisemore R.N., Vice President and Chief Nursing Officer
Web address: www.dekalbhealth.com
Control: Other not–for–profit (including NFP Corporation) **Service**: General medical and surgical

Staffed Beds: 56 **Admissions**: 2176 **Census**: 18 **Outpatient Visits**: 107681 **Births**: 442 **Total Expense ($000)**: 66220 **Payroll Expense ($000)**: 27340 **Personnel**: 462

NORTHEASTERN CENTER (154050), 1850 Wesley Road, Zip 46706–3653; tel. 260/927–0726 **A**10 **F**98 103 133
Primary Contact: Jerry Hollister, Chief Executive Officer
Web address: www.necmh.org
Control: Other not–for–profit (including NFP Corporation) **Service**: Psychiatric

Staffed Beds: 16 **Admissions**: 609 **Census**: 11 **Outpatient Visits**: 0 **Births**: 0 **Total Expense ($000)**: 2810 **Payroll Expense ($000)**: 1239 **Personnel**: 27

AVON—Hendricks County

CLARIAN WEST MEDICAL CENTER See Indiana University Health West Hospital

✠ **INDIANA UNIVERSITY HEALTH WEST HOSPITAL (150158)**, 1111 North Ronald Reagan Parkway, Zip 46123–7085; tel. 317/217–3000 **A**1 2 3 5 10 **F**3 13 15 18 22 26 28 29 30 34 35 40 45 47 48 49 50 51 57 59 64 70 73 74 75 76 77 78 79 81 82 85 86 87 89 93 100 107 110 111 113 114 115 119 120 121 129 130 132 135 146 147 148 **S** Indiana University Health, Indianapolis, IN
Primary Contact: Doug Puckett, President
CMO: Andrew Nigh M.D., Chief of Staff
CHR: Tamarah Brownlee, Vice President, Human Resources
CNO: Lisa Sparks R.N., Chief Nursing Officer and Vice President Patient Care Services
Web address: www.iuhealth.org
Control: Other not–for–profit (including NFP Corporation) **Service**: General medical and surgical

Staffed Beds: 127 **Admissions**: 6689 **Census**: 79 **Outpatient Visits**: 240983 **Births**: 935 **Total Expense ($000)**: 141995 **Payroll Expense ($000)**: 44246 **Personnel**: 710

BATESVILLE—Ripley County

✠ **MARGARET MARY HEALTH (151329)**, 321 Mitchell Avenue, Zip 47006–8909, Mailing Address: P.O.Box 226, 47006–0226; tel. 812/934–6624 **A**1 2 10 18 **F**3 13 15 28 30 31 34 35 36 40 45 46 50 54 56 59 62 63 64 65 70 75 76 77 78 81 85 86 87 93 107 108 110 111 114 115 118 119 121 123 129 130 131 132 135 144 146 148 **P**1
Primary Contact: Timothy L. Putnam, FACHE, President and Chief Executive Officer
CFO: Brian Daeger, Vice President Financial Services
CMO: Charles McGovern, Chief of Staff
CIO: Trisha Prickel, Director Information Systems
CHR: Kimberly Inscho, Vice President Community Relations and Human Resources
CNO: Elizabeth Leising, Chief Nursing Officer and Vice President, Outpatient Services
Web address: www.mmhealth.org
Control: Other not–for–profit (including NFP Corporation) **Service**: General medical and surgical

Staffed Beds: 25 **Admissions**: 1695 **Census**: 12 **Outpatient Visits**: 167232 **Births**: 467 **Total Expense ($000)**: 87283 **Payroll Expense ($000)**: 38232 **Personnel**: 528

IN

Hospital, Medicare Provider Number, Address, Telephone, Approval, Facility, and Physician Codes, Health Care System

★ American Hospital Association (AHA) membership
□ The Joint Commission accreditation
○ Healthcare Facilities Accreditation Program
◇ DNV Healthcare Inc. accreditation
⇧ Center for Improvement in Healthcare Quality Accreditation
△ Commission on Accreditation of Rehabilitation Facilities (CARF) accreditation

BEDFORD—Lawrence County

BEDFORD REGIONAL MEDICAL CENTER See Indiana University Health Bedford Hospital

DUNN MEMORIAL HOSPITAL See St. Vincent Dunn Hospital

✠ **INDIANA UNIVERSITY HEALTH BEDFORD HOSPITAL (151328)**, 2900 West 16th Street, Zip 47421–3583; tel. 812/275–1200 **A**1 2 10 18 **F**3 7 11 15 18 28 29 30 31 34 35 36 38 40 41 44 45 46 49 50 53 57 59 64 65 68 70 74 75 77 78 79 81 85 86 87 91 92 93 94 97 102 107 108 110 111 115 118 119 129 130 131 132 133 134 135 146 149 **P**6 **S** Indiana University Health, Indianapolis, IN
Primary Contact: Bradford W. Dykes, President and Chief Executive Officer
CFO: Mike Craig, Vice President, Chief Financial Officer
CMO: Joanne F Smart M.D., Director Medical Affairs
CHR: Bruce Wade, Vice President Human Resources
CNO: Brenda Davis, Vice President Patient Services
Web address: www.iuhealth.org
Control: Other not–for–profit (including NFP Corporation) **Service**: General medical and surgical

Staffed Beds: 25 Admissions: 980 **Census:** 11 **Outpatient Visits:** 80065 **Births:** 0 **Total Expense ($000):** 44416 **Payroll Expense ($000):** 14602 **Personnel:** 210

✠ **ST. VINCENT DUNN HOSPITAL (151335)**, 1600 23rd Street, Zip 47421–4704; tel. 812/275–3331, (Nonreporting) **A**1 10 18 **S** Ascension Healthcare, Saint Louis, MO
Primary Contact: Matt Balla, Chief Executive Officer
CFO: Crystal Plano, Controller
CMO: Deborah W Craton M.D., Chief Medical Officer
CIO: Chad Damon, Contractor
CHR: Darci Medlock, Manager Human Resources
CNO: Michelle Dotts–McCool, Chief Nursing Officer
Web address: www.stvincent.org/St-Vincent–Dunn/Default.aspx
Control: Other not–for–profit (including NFP Corporation) **Service**: General medical and surgical

Staffed Beds: 25

BLOOMFIELD—Lawrence County

✠ **MONROE HOSPITAL (150164)**, 5811 East Slick Rock lane, Zip 47424, Mailing Address: 4011 South Monroe Medical Park Boulevard, Bloomington, 47403–8000; tel. 812/825–1111 **A**1 10 **F**3 15 18 20 29 34 35 40 41 45 46 47 48 49 50 56 57 59 64 65 68 70 75 79 80 81 85 86 87 91 97 107 108 109 110 111 114 115 119 126 127 130 134 135 144 148 149 **S** Prime Healthcare, Ontario, CA
Primary Contact: Nancy Bakewell, Administrator
CFO: Hilary Dolbee, Chief Financial Officer
CMO: Armandeep Singh, Chief Medical Officer
CHR: Pamela S Hoffman, Director of Human Resources
CNO: Brenda Cook, Chief Nursing Officer
Web address: www.monroehospital.com
Control: Corporation, Investor–owned (for–profit) **Service**: General medical and surgical

Staffed Beds: 32 Admissions: 1496 **Census:** 14 **Outpatient Visits:** 28616 **Births:** 0 **Total Expense ($000):** 28452 **Payroll Expense ($000):** 10559 **Personnel:** 290

BLOOMINGTON—Monroe County

BLOOMINGTON HOSPITAL See Indiana University Health Bloomington Hospital

☐ **BLOOMINGTON MEADOWS HOSPITAL (154041)**, 3600 North Prow Road, Zip 47404–1616; tel. 812/331–8000 **A**1 10 **F**4 98 99 101 102 104 105 106 **S** Universal Health Services, Inc., King of Prussia, PA
Primary Contact: Jean Scallon, Chief Executive Officer
CFO: Becky T Nyberg, Chief Financial Officer
CMO: David Gilliam M.D., Medical Director
CHR: Amanda Shettlesworth, Director Human Resources
CNO: Penny Caswell, Director of Nursing
Web address: www.bloomingtonmeadows.com
Control: Corporation, Investor–owned (for–profit) **Service**: Psychiatric

Staffed Beds: 67 Admissions: 1528 **Census:** 52 **Outpatient Visits:** 5006 **Births:** 0 **Total Expense ($000):** 10927 **Payroll Expense ($000):** 6933 **Personnel:** 160

✠ △ **INDIANA UNIVERSITY HEALTH BLOOMINGTON HOSPITAL (150051)**, 601 West Second Street, Zip 47403–2317, Mailing Address: P.O.Box 1149, 47402–1149; tel. 812/336–6821 **A**1 2 7 10 19 **F**3 7 8 11 12 13 18 19 20 22 24 26 28 29 30 31 32 34 35 38 40 45 46 47 48 49 50 53 54 55 57 59 61 62 63 64 65 69 70 74 75 76 77 78 79 81 82 84 85 86 87 89 90 91 92 93 94 97 98 100 101 102 103 104 107 108 111 114 115 119 120 121 124 126 129 130 131 132 135 143 144 146 147 148 149 **P**6 **S** Indiana University Health, Indianapolis, IN
Primary Contact: Matthew D. Bailey, FACHE, President
COO: Brian T Shockney FACHE, Chief Operating Officer
CFO: Mike Craig, Chief Financial Officer
CMO: Ken Marshall M.D., Chief Medical Officer
CIO: Mark W McMath, Chief Information Officer
CHR: Steven D Deckard, Vice President Human Resources
Web address: www.iuhealth.org
Control: Other not–for–profit (including NFP Corporation) **Service**: General medical and surgical

Staffed Beds: 273 Admissions: 11572 **Census:** 146 **Outpatient Visits:** 163965 **Births:** 2001 **Total Expense ($000):** 325911 **Payroll Expense ($000):** 103941 **Personnel:** 1760

BLUFFTON—Wells County

✠ **BLUFFTON REGIONAL MEDICAL CENTER (150075)**, 303 South Main Street, Zip 46714–2503; tel. 260/824–3210, (Total facility includes 13 beds in nursing home–type unit) **A**1 10 19 **F**3 13 15 18 28 29 30 34 35 40 41 45 49 50 57 59 64 70 74 75 79 81 85 86 87 91 93 94 96 97 107 108 110 111 114 119 128 129 130 132 135 146 147 148 149 150 **S** Community Health Systems, Inc., Franklin, TN
Primary Contact: Brent Parsons, Chief Executive Officer
COO: Julie Thompson, Chief Operating Officer and Chief Nursing Officer
CFO: Larry W DeBolt, Chief Financial Officer
CMO: Harish Ardeshna, Chief Medical Officer
CNO: Julie Thompson, Chief Operating Officer and Chief Nursing Officer
Web address: www.blufftonregional.com
Control: Corporation, Investor–owned (for–profit) **Service**: General medical and surgical

Staffed Beds: 54 Admissions: 1904 **Census:** 14 **Outpatient Visits:** 43076 **Births:** 212 **Total Expense ($000):** 33475 **Payroll Expense ($000):** 11985 **Personnel:** 212

BOONVILLE—Warrick County

✠ **ST. VINCENT WARRICK HOSPITAL (151325)**, 1116 Millis Avenue, Zip 47601–2204; tel. 812/897–4800 **A**1 10 18 **F**3 6 11 15 28 29 30 40 45 50 53 56 57 59 64 67 68 79 81 85 87 89 93 98 103 107 111 114 118 119 128 130 133 135 146 149 **S** Ascension Healthcare, Saint Louis, MO
Primary Contact: Kathy J. Hall, Administrator
CFO: Crystal Heaton, Director of Finance
CNO: Karen Waters, Chief Nursing Officer
Web address: www.stmarys.org/warrick
Control: Other not–for–profit (including NFP Corporation) **Service**: General medical and surgical

Staffed Beds: 35 Admissions: 652 **Census:** 19 **Outpatient Visits:** 21626 **Births:** 0 **Total Expense ($000):** 15484 **Payroll Expense ($000):** 5445 **Personnel:** 115

BRAZIL—Clay County

✠ **ST. VINCENT CLAY HOSPITAL (151309)**, 1206 East National Avenue, Zip 47834–2797, Mailing Address: P.O.Box 489, 47834–0489; tel. 812/442–2500 **A**1 10 18 **F**3 12 15 18 29 30 34 35 40 45 50 57 59 65 68 75 77 79 81 82 85 86 87 107 108 110 111 115 119 128 130 132 133 135 146 148 **S** Ascension Healthcare, Saint Louis, MO
Primary Contact: Jerry Laue, Administrator
CFO: Wayne Knight, Director Finance
CMO: Craig Johnson D.O., Medical Director
CHR: Danielle Abrams, Manager Human Resources, Marketing and Executive Assistant
CNO: Sandra Haggart, Chief Nursing Officer
Web address: www.stvincent.org
Control: Church operated, Nongovernment, not–for–profit **Service**: General medical and surgical

Staffed Beds: 25 Admissions: 468 **Census:** 5 **Outpatient Visits:** 35819 **Births:** 0 **Total Expense ($000):** 17241 **Payroll Expense ($000):** 5490 **Personnel:** 77

BREMEN—Marshall County

★ **COMMUNITY HOSPITAL OF BREMEN (151300)**, 1020 High Road, Zip 46506–1093, Mailing Address: P.O.Box 8, 46506–0008; tel. 574/546–2211 **A**10 18 **F**3 11 13 15 29 34 35 40 45 50 57 59 64 69 75 76 77 79 81 82 85 93 107 110 111 115 119 129 130 132 133 135 146 149 **P**6
Primary Contact: David Bailey, FACHE, Chief Executive Officer
CFO: Amy Lashbrook, Chief Financial Officer
CMO: Jason Marker M.D., Chief Medical Officer
CIO: Linda Barrett, Vice President of Information Services
CHR: Patricia Board, Vice President Human Resources
CNO: Sue Bettcher R.N., Vice President of Nursing Services
Web address: www.bremenhospital.com
Control: Other not–for–profit (including NFP Corporation) **Service**: General medical and surgical

Staffed Beds: 24 **Admissions:** 329 **Census:** 2 **Outpatient Visits:** 55530 **Births:** 111 **Total Expense ($000):** 19868 **Payroll Expense ($000):** 8367 **Personnel:** 136

DOCTORS NEUROPSYCHIATRIC HOSPITAL AND RESEARCH INSTITUTE (154058), 417 South Whitlock Street, Zip 46506–1626; tel. 574/546–0330 (Nonreporting) **A**10 **S** NeuroPsychiatric Hospitals, Mishawaka, IN
Primary Contact: Christy Gilbert, Interim Chief Executive Officer
Control: Investor–owned (for–profit) **Service**: Psychiatric

Staffed Beds: 20

CARMEL—Hamilton County

CLARIAN NORTH MEDICAL CENTER See Indiana University Health North Hospital

○ **FRANCISCAN ST. FRANCIS HEALTH–CARMEL (150182)**, 12188B North Meridian Street, Zip 46032–4840; tel. 317/705–4500 (Nonreporting) **A**10 11 **S** Franciscan Health, Mishawaka, IN
Primary Contact: Stephen J. Wheatley, Director of Operations
CFO: Keith A. Lauter, Chief Financial Officer
CMO: Christopher Doehring M.D., Vice President of Medical Affairs
CIO: Rebecca Merkel, Privacy Officer
CHR: Corey Baute, Vice President of Human Resource
CNO: Susan McRoberts R.N., MSN, Chief Nursing Officer
Web address: www.franciscanalliance.org/hospitals/carmel/Pages/default.aspx
Control: Other not–for–profit (including NFP Corporation) **Service**: General medical and surgical

Staffed Beds: 6

✉ **INDIANA UNIVERSITY HEALTH NORTH HOSPITAL (150161)**, 11700 North Meridian Avenue, Zip 46032–4656; tel. 317/688–2000 **A**1 3 5 10 **F**3 13 15 18 19 20 22 25 29 30 31 34 35 36 37 40 45 47 49 55 57 60 64 68 70 72 74 75 76 78 79 81 85 87 88 89 91 92 93 107 108 110 111 115 119 124 130 132 135 146 147 148 **S** Indiana University Health, Indianapolis, IN
Primary Contact: Jonathan R. Goble, FACHE, President and Chief Executive Officer
COO: Randall C Yust, Chief Operating Officer and Chief Financial Officer
CFO: Randall C Yust, Chief Operating Officer and Chief Financial Officer
CMO: Paul Calkins M.D., Chief Medical Officer
CIO: Steve Bodenham, Senior Manager Clinical Engineering
CHR: Steven E Kile, Vice President Human Resources
CNO: Ruth Ann A. Kain MSN, R.N., Chief Nursing Officer and Vice President Patient Care Services
Web address: www.iuhealth.org/north
Control: Other not–for–profit (including NFP Corporation) **Service**: General medical and surgical

Staffed Beds: 149 **Admissions:** 7049 **Census:** 83 **Outpatient Visits:** 214839 **Births:** 2533 **Total Expense ($000):** 187215 **Payroll Expense ($000):** 55402 **Personnel:** 859

✉ **ST. VINCENT CARMEL HOSPITAL (150157)**, 13500 North Meridian Street, Zip 46032–1456; tel. 317/582–7000 **A**1 10 **F**3 12 13 15 29 30 34 35 36 37 40 44 45 49 50 54 57 58 59 61 64 68 69 70 72 75 76 78 79 80 81 85 87 92 96 107 108 110 111 119 126 130 132 135 146 147 148 149 **S** Ascension Healthcare, Saint Louis, MO
Primary Contact: Michael D. Chittenden, President
COO: Daniel LaReau, Executive Director Operations and Information
CFO: Robert A. Bates, Executive Director Finance and Chief Financial Officer
CMO: Steven L. Priddy M.D., Vice President Physician Affairs and Chief Medical Officer
CIO: Daniel LaReau, Executive Director Operations and Information
CHR: Charles Jeffras, Executive Director Human Resources
CNO: Gwynn Perlich, Vice President of Patient Services and Chief Nursing Officer
Web address: www.stvincent.org
Control: Church operated, Nongovernment, not–for–profit **Service**: General medical and surgical

Staffed Beds: 121 **Admissions:** 5136 **Census:** 48 **Outpatient Visits:** 119371 **Births:** 1587 **Total Expense ($000):** 119375 **Payroll Expense ($000):** 42830

CLARKSVILLE—Clark County

○ **KENTUCKIANA MEDICAL CENTER (150176)**, 4601 Medical Plaza Way, Zip 47129–9204; tel. 812/284–6100 (Nonreporting) **A**10 11
Primary Contact: Paul Newsom, Chief Operating Officer
Web address: www.kentuckianamedcen.com/
Control: Corporation, Investor–owned (for–profit) **Service**: General medical and surgical

Staffed Beds: 40

CLINTON—Vermillion County

UNION HOSPITAL CLINTON (151326), 801 South Main Street, Zip 47842–2261; tel. 765/832–1234 **A**10 18 **F**3 11 15 18 29 30 34 35 40 45 50 57 59 64 65 68 70 75 81 85 86 87 91 93 97 107 108 110 115 119 130 132 133 146 **P**6
Primary Contact: Terri L. Hill, Vice President and Administrator
CFO: Wayne Hutson, Chief Financial Officer
CIO: Jack Hill, Vice President and Chief Operating Officer
CNO: Rhonda E. Smith R.N., MSN, Chief Nursing Officer
Web address: www.myunionhospital.org/unionhospital/union–hospital–clinton
Control: Other not–for–profit (including NFP Corporation) **Service**: General medical and surgical

Staffed Beds: 21 **Admissions:** 866 **Census:** 6 **Outpatient Visits:** 47553 **Births:** 0 **Total Expense ($000):** 21096 **Payroll Expense ($000):** 8080 **Personnel:** 118

COLUMBIA CITY—Whitley County

✉ **PARKVIEW WHITLEY HOSPITAL (150101)**, 1260 East State Road 205, Zip 46725–9492; tel. 260/248–9000 **A**1 10 **F**3 5 7 8 13 15 28 29 30 34 35 38 40 42 45 50 54 57 59 64 70 75 76 79 81 82 85 89 91 93 96 102 107 108 110 111 115 119 129 132 135 143 146 148 **S** Parkview Health, Fort Wayne, IN
Primary Contact: Scott F. Gabriel, President
COO: Scott F Gabriel, President
CFO: Lisa Peppler, Financial Manager
CMO: Jeffrey Brookes M.D., Medical Director
CHR: Dianne P Potter, Manager Human Resources
CNO: Bridget Dolohanty–Johnson MSN, R.N., Vice President Patient Care Services
Web address: www.parkview.com
Control: Other not–for–profit (including NFP Corporation) **Service**: General medical and surgical

Staffed Beds: 30 **Admissions:** 1621 **Census:** 11 **Outpatient Visits:** 60202 **Births:** 456 **Total Expense ($000):** 56953 **Payroll Expense ($000):** 16477 **Personnel:** 257

COLUMBUS—Bartholomew County

★ ○ **COLUMBUS REGIONAL HOSPITAL (150112)**, 2400 East 17th Street, Zip 47201–5360; tel. 812/379–4441 **A**2 10 11 19 **F**3 7 11 12 13 15 18 20 22 24 26 28 29 30 31 34 35 38 39 40 45 47 49 50 51 53 58 59 68 70 73 74 75 76 77 78 79 81 85 86 87 89 90 93 98 100 101 102 103 107 108 110 111 114 115 117 118 119 120 121 123 124 126 129 130 131 132 135 146 147 148 149 **P**6 8
Primary Contact: Jim Bickel, Chief Executive Officer
CFO: Marlene Weatherwax, Vice President and Chief Financial Officer
CMO: Thomas Sonderman M.D., Vice President and Chief Medical Officer
CIO: Steve Baker, Vice President and Chief Technology and Information Officer
CHR: John R Loya, Vice President Human Resources and Organizational Development
CNO: Holly Cheek, Vice President and Chief Nursing Officer
Web address: www.crh.org
Control: County, Government, Nonfederal **Service**: General medical and surgical

Staffed Beds: 198 **Admissions:** 8961 **Census:** 92 **Outpatient Visits:** 244844 **Births:** 1269 **Total Expense ($000):** 238022 **Payroll Expense ($000):** 76194 **Personnel:** 1535

IN

Hospital, Medicare Provider Number, Address, Telephone, Approval, Facility, and Physician Codes, Health Care System

★ American Hospital Association (AHA) membership ○ Healthcare Facilities Accreditation Program ⇑ Center for Improvement in Healthcare Quality Accreditation
□ The Joint Commission accreditation ◇ DNV Healthcare Inc. accreditation △ Commission on Accreditation of Rehabilitation Facilities (CARF) accreditation

CONNERSVILLE—Fayette County

○ **FAYETTE REGIONAL HEALTH SYSTEM (150064)**, 1941 Virginia Avenue, Zip 47331–2833; tel. 765/825–5131, (Nonreporting) **A**10 11
Primary Contact: Randall White, Chief Executive Officer
CFO: Debra Michalek, Chief Financial Officer
CMO: Mike Rowe M.D., Chief of Staff
CIO: Andy Merida, Director Management Information Systems
CHR: Rhonda McPherson, Vice President Human Resources
CNO: Beth A Wampler R.N., Chief Nursing Officer
Web address: www.fayetteregional.org
Control: Other not–for–profit (including NFP Corporation) **Service**: General medical and surgical

Staffed Beds: 75

CORYDON—Harrison County

★ **HARRISON COUNTY HOSPITAL (151331)**, 1141 Hospital Drive N W, Zip 47112–1774; tel. 812/738–4251, (Nonreporting) **A**10 18
Primary Contact: Steven L. Taylor, Chief Executive Officer
CFO: Jeff Davis, Chief Financial Officer
CIO: Chuck Wiley, Manager Information Systems
CHR: Loren Haverstock, Manager Human Resources
CNO: Ruth Donahue R.N., Chief Nursing Officer
Web address: www.hchin.org
Control: County, Government, Nonfederal **Service**: General medical and surgical

Staffed Beds: 25

CRAWFORDSVILLE—Montgomery County

○ **FRANCISCAN ST. ELIZABETH HEALTH – CRAWFORDSVILLE (150022)**, 1710 Lafayette Road, Zip 47933–1099; tel. 765/362–2800 **A**10 11 **F**3 11 15 18 19 28 29 30 31 35 40 45 50 54 57 64 69 70 75 77 78 79 81 82 85 87 93 98 102 103 104 107 108 110 111 114 115 118 119 120 121 126 129 130 132 135 145 146 148 **S** Franciscan Health, Mishawaka, IN
Primary Contact: Terrence Klein, Ph.D., Vice President and Chief Operating Officer
COO: Terrence Klein Ph.D., Vice President and Chief Operating Officer
CFO: Keith A. Lauter, Vice President Finance
Web address: www.stclaremedical.org
Control: Church operated, Nongovernment, not–for–profit **Service**: General medical and surgical

Staffed Beds: 42 Admissions: 1269 Census: 14 Outpatient Visits: 48380 Births: 0 Total Expense ($000): 45607 Payroll Expense ($000): 10266 Personnel: 160

ST. CLARE MEDICAL CENTER See Franciscan St. Elizabeth Health – Crawfordsville

CROWN POINT—Lake County

○ **FRANCISCAN ST. ANTHONY HEALTH – CROWN POINT (150126)**, 1201 South Main Street, Zip 46307–8483; tel. 219/738–2100, (Nonreporting) **A**2 10 11 **S** Franciscan Health, Mishawaka, IN
Primary Contact: Barbara M. Anderson, President and Chief Executive Officer
CFO: Marc Golan, Chief Financial Officer
CMO: Daniel McCormick M.D., Vice President Medical Staff Affairs
CIO: Tim Loosemore, Director
CNO: Carol E Schuster R.N., Chief Nursing Officer and Vice President Patient Care Services
Web address: www.franciscanalliance.org
Control: Church operated, Nongovernment, not–for–profit **Service**: General medical and surgical

Staffed Beds: 254

○ **PINNACLE HOSPITAL (150166)**, 9301 Connecticut Drive, Zip 46307–7486; tel. 219/756–2100 (Nonreporting) **A**10 11
Primary Contact: Haroon Naz, Chief Executive Officer
Web address: www.pinnaclehealthcare.net
Control: Partnership, Investor–owned (for–profit) **Service**: General medical and surgical

Staffed Beds: 18

ST. ANTHONY MEDICAL CENTER See Franciscan St. Anthony Health – Crown Point

⊞ **VIBRA HOSPITAL OF NORTHWESTERN INDIANA (152028)**, 9509 Georgia Street, Zip 46307–6518; tel. 219/472–2200 **A**1 10 **F**1 3 29 56 75 77 85 86 87 130 148 **S** Vibra Healthcare, Mechanicsburg, PA
Primary Contact: Charles Nordyke, Chief Executive Officer
CFO: Douglas Morris, Chief Financial Officer
CMO: Raja Devanathan M.D., Chief Medical Officer
CNO: Robert Beard, Chief Clinical Officer
Web address: www.vhnwindiana.com/
Control: Corporation, Investor–owned (for–profit) **Service**: Acute long–term care hospital

Staffed Beds: 40 Admissions: 528 Census: 34 Outpatient Visits: 0 Births: 0 Total Expense ($000): 17965 Payroll Expense ($000): 7727

DANVILLE—Hendricks County

★ ○ **HENDRICKS REGIONAL HEALTH (150005)**, 1000 East Main Street, Zip 46122–1948, Mailing Address: P.O.Box 409, 46122–0409; tel. 317/745–4451 **A**2 3 5 10 11 **F**3 8 9 11 13 15 17 18 20 22 26 28 29 30 31 32 34 35 38 40 41 43 44 45 47 48 50 53 54 55 56 57 58 59 60 61 64 65 66 69 70 71 73 74 75 76 77 78 79 81 82 83 84 85 86 87 89 90 92 93 94 96 97 107 108 109 110 111 114 115 118 119 120 121 123 127 128 129 130 131 132 133 135 144 146 147 148 150 **P**6
Primary Contact: Kevin Speer, Chief Executive Officer
CFO: John Komenda, Chief Financial Officer
CMO: John Sparzo M.D., Vice President Medical Affairs
CIO: Lowell Nicodemus, Director Information Systems
CHR: Gary Lenard, Director Human Resources
Web address: www.hendrickshospital.org
Control: County, Government, Nonfederal **Service**: General medical and surgical

Staffed Beds: 127 Admissions: 5658 Census: 50 Outpatient Visits: 346734 Births: 1321 Total Expense ($000): 248372 Payroll Expense ($000): 101896 Personnel: 1353

DECATUR—Adams County

★ **ADAMS MEMORIAL HOSPITAL (151330)**, 1100 Mercer Avenue, Zip 46733–2303, Mailing Address: P.O.Box 151, 46733–0151; tel. 260/724–2145, (Total facility includes 204 beds in nursing home–type unit) **A**10 18 **F**3 5 7 10 13 15 29 30 34 35 38 40 50 53 57 59 64 65 66 67 68 70 74 75 77 79 81 82 85 86 87 92 93 96 97 98 100 101 102 103 104 107 108 110 111 115 119 125 128 129 130 131 132 133 135 143 144 145 146 147 148 **P**6
Primary Contact: JoEllen Eidam, FACHE, Chief Executive Officer
CFO: Dane Wheeler, Chief Financial Officer
CMO: Scott Smith M.D., Chief Medical Officer
CIO: Nick Nelson, Director Support Services
CHR: Alison Kukelhan, Manager Human Resources
CNO: Theresa Bradtmiller MSN, R.N., Chief Nursing Officer
Web address: www.adamshospital.com
Control: County, Government, Nonfederal **Service**: General medical and surgical

Staffed Beds: 239 Admissions: 1826 Census: 176 Outpatient Visits: 128515 Births: 198 Total Expense ($000): 73569 Payroll Expense ($000): 27013 Personnel: 603

DYER—Lake County

☐ ○ **FRANCISCAN HEALTH DYER (150090)**, 24 Joliet Street, Zip 46311–1799; tel. 219/865–2141 (Nonreporting) **A**1 5 10 11 **S** Franciscan Health, Mishawaka, IN
Primary Contact: Patrick J. Maloney, Chief Executive Officer
Control: Church operated, Nongovernment, not–for–profit **Service**: General medical and surgical

Staffed Beds: 341

SAINT MARGARET MERCY HEALTHCARE CENTERS–SOUTH CAMPUS See Franciscan Health Dyer

EAST CHICAGO—Lake County

⊞ **REGENCY HOSPITAL OF NORTHWEST INDIANA (152024)**, 4321 Fir Street, 4th Floor, Zip 46312–3049; tel. 219/392–7799, (Nonreporting) (Includes REGENCY HOSPITAL OF PORTER COUNTY, 3630 Willow Creek Road, Portage, Indiana, Zip 46368, tel. 219/364–3800) **A**1 10 **S** Select Medical Corporation, Mechanicsburg, PA
Primary Contact: Eleyce Winn, Chief Executive Officer
Web address: www.regencyhospital.com/company/locations/indiana–northwest–indiana.aspx
Control: Corporation, Investor–owned (for–profit) **Service**: Acute long–term care hospital

Staffed Beds: 61

☐ △ **ST. CATHERINE HOSPITAL (150008)**, 4321 Fir Street, Zip 46312–3097; tel. 219/392–1700 **A**1 7 10 **F**1 3 5 11 13 15 17 18 20 22 24 26 28 29 30 31 34 35 40 46 49 54 57 58 59 60 61 62 64 68 74 75 76 77 78 79 80 81 82 85 86 87 89 92 98 99 100 101 102 103 104 107 108 110 111 112 115 119 129 130 132 135 146 147 148 149 **P**5 8 **S** Community Healthcare System, Hammond, IN
Primary Contact: Leo Correa, Chief Executive Officer and Administrator
COO: Craig Bolda, Chief Operating Officer
CMO: John Griep M.D., Chief Medical Director
CIO: Gary Weiner, Chief Information Officer
CNO: Paula C Swenson R.N., Vice President and Chief Nursing Officer
Web address: www.stcatherinehospital.org
Control: Other not–for–profit (including NFP Corporation) **Service**: General medical and surgical

Staffed Beds: 220 Admissions: 7546 Census: 114 Outpatient Visits: 150348 Births: 548 Total Expense ($000): 200575 Payroll Expense ($000): 56082 Personnel: 833

Many Facility Codes have changed. Please refer to the AHA Guide Code Chart.

© 2017 AHA Guide

ELKHART—Elkhart County

★ ○ △ **ELKHART GENERAL HOSPITAL (150018)**, 600 East Boulevard, Zip 46514–2499, Mailing Address: P.O.Box 1329, 46515–1329; tel. 574/294–2621 **A**2 7 10 11 **F**3 12 13 15 17 18 20 22 24 26 28 29 30 31 34 35 40 45 46 48 49 50 57 59 64 68 69 70 72 74 75 76 77 78 79 81 82 84 85 86 87 89 90 91 92 93 98 99 100 102 104 107 108 110 111 114 115 118 119 120 121 123 129 130 131 132 134 135 146 147 148 **P**8 **S** Beacon Health System, South Bend, IN
Primary Contact: Carl W. Risk II, President
CFO: Jeff Costello, Chief Financial Officer
CMO: William Buckley M.D., Chief of Staff
CIO: Steve Huffman, Chief Information Officer
CHR: Steven M Eller, Vice President Human Resources
CNO: Karra Heggen R.N., Vice President Nursing
Web address: www.egh.org
Control: Other not–for–profit (including NFP Corporation) **Service**: General medical and surgical

Staffed Beds: 265 **Admissions**: 10887 **Census**: 121 **Outpatient Visits**: 306687 **Births**: 1481 **Total Expense ($000)**: 253975 **Payroll Expense ($000)**: 78875 **Personnel**: 1414

ELWOOD—Madison County

✠ **ST. VINCENT MERCY HOSPITAL (151308)**, 1331 South 'A' Street, Zip 46036–1942; tel. 765/552–4600 **A**1 2 10 18 **F**3 11 15 28 29 30 31 34 35 40 44 45 50 53 57 59 64 68 74 75 78 79 81 82 85 86 87 89 93 107 108 110 111 114 119 129 130 132 133 135 146 148 149 150 **S** Ascension Healthcare, Saint Louis, MO
Primary Contact: Francis G. Albarano, Administrator
CFO: John Arthur, Chief Financial Officer
CMO: Gary Brazel M.D., Chief Medical Officer
CHR: Ross Brodhead, Manager Human Resources
CNO: Ann C Yates R.N., MSN, Director Patient Care and Clinical Services
Web address: www.stvincent.org
Control: Church operated, Nongovernment, not–for–profit **Service**: General medical and surgical

Staffed Beds: 15 **Admissions**: 420 **Census**: 4 **Outpatient Visits**: 33874 **Births**: 0 **Total Expense ($000)**: 22277 **Payroll Expense ($000)**: 7463 **Personnel**: 136

EVANSVILLE—Vanderburgh County

★ ○ **DEACONESS HOSPITAL (150082)**, 600 Mary Street, Zip 47710–1658; tel. 812/450–5000, (Includes DEACONESS CROSS POINTE CENTER, 7200 East Indiana Street, Evansville, Indiana, Zip 47715, tel. 812/476–7200; Cheryl Rietman, Chief Administrative Officer) **A**2 3 10 11 **F**3 5 9 11 12 15 17 18 19 20 22 24 26 29 30 31 32 34 35 36 38 39 40 43 44 45 46 47 48 49 50 51 53 54 56 57 58 59 60 61 65 66 68 70 71 74 75 77 78 79 81 82 84 85 86 87 88 89 92 93 94 96 97 98 99 100 101 102 104 105 107 108 110 111 114 115 116 117 118 119 120 121 123 124 126 129 130 132 134 135 143 144 145 146 148 149 150 **P**6 8 **S** Deaconess Health System, Evansville, IN
Primary Contact: Shawn W. McCoy, Chief Executive Officer
CFO: Cheryl A Wathen, Interim Chief Financial Officer
CHR: Larry Pile, Director Human Resources
Web address: www.deaconess.com
Control: Other not–for–profit (including NFP Corporation) **Service**: General medical and surgical

Staffed Beds: 516 **Admissions**: 27185 **Census**: 351 **Outpatient Visits**: 628499 **Births**: 0 **Total Expense ($000)**: 661176 **Payroll Expense ($000)**: 238502 **Personnel**: 3620

EVANSVILLE PSYCHIATRIC CHILDREN CENTER (15J200), 3300 East Morgan Avenue, Zip 47715–2232; tel. 812/477–6436 **A**10 **F**98 99 146 149
Primary Contact: Lottie Cook, Superintendent
COO: Melinda Kendle, Manager Business Office
CMO: Shannon Jones M.D., Medical Director and Attending Psychiatrist
CIO: David Wirtz, Supervisor Information Technology
CHR: Jennifer Sontz, Director Human Resources
CNO: Elizabeth Angermeier, Director of Nursing
Web address: www.ih.gov
Control: State, Government, Nonfederal **Service**: Children's hospital psychiatric

Staffed Beds: 24 **Admissions**: 23 **Census**: 10 **Outpatient Visits**: 0 **Births**: 0 **Total Expense ($000)**: 3614 **Payroll Expense ($000)**: 2081 **Personnel**: 57

□ **EVANSVILLE STATE HOSPITAL (154056)**, 3400 Lincoln Avenue, Zip 47714–0146; tel. 812/469–6800 **A**1 10 **F**30 98 130 132 135 146
Primary Contact: Cathe Fulcher, Superintendent
CFO: Melinda Kendle, Director Fiscal Management
CMO: Melba Briones M.D., Medical Director
CIO: David Wirtz, Senior LAN Administrator
CHR: Jennifer Sontz, Director Human Resources
Control: State, Government, Nonfederal **Service**: Psychiatric

Staffed Beds: 168 **Admissions**: 77 **Census**: 150 **Outpatient Visits**: 0 **Births**: 0 **Total Expense ($000)**: 34933 **Payroll Expense ($000)**: 12413 **Personnel**: 299

✠ **HEALTHSOUTH DEACONESS REHABILITATION HOSPITAL (153025)**, 4100 Covert Avenue, Zip 47714–5567, Mailing Address: P.O.Box 5349, 47716–5349; tel. 812/476–9983 **A**1 10 **F**28 29 57 64 68 75 87 90 91 93 94 95 96 130 132 143 148 149 **S** HEALTHSOUTH Corporation, Birmingham, AL
Primary Contact: Blake Bunner, Chief Executive Officer
CFO: Rhonda Ramsey, Controller
CMO: Ashok Dhingra M.D., Executive Medical Director
CHR: Darlene Moog, Director Human Resources
CNO: Trish Draeger, Chief Nursing Officer
Web address: www.healthsouthdeaconess.com
Control: Corporation, Investor–owned (for–profit) **Service**: Rehabilitation

Staffed Beds: 103 **Admissions**: 2217 **Census**: 78 **Outpatient Visits**: 7036 **Births**: 0 **Total Expense ($000)**: 26215 **Payroll Expense ($000)**: 13032 **Personnel**: 282

✠ **SELECT SPECIALTY HOSPITAL–EVANSVILLE (152014)**, 400 SE 4th Street, Zip 47713–1206; tel. 812/421–2500, (Nonreporting) **A**1 10 **S** Select Medical Corporation, Mechanicsburg, PA
Primary Contact: Scott A. Butler, Chief Executive Officer
Web address: www.selectspecialtyhospitals.com/company/locations/evansville.aspx
Control: Corporation, Investor–owned (for–profit) **Service**: Acute long–term care hospital

Staffed Beds: 60

✠ △ **ST. VINCENT MEDICAL CENTER OF EVANSVILLE (150100)**, 3700 Washington Avenue, Zip 47714–0541; tel. 812/485–4000, (Nonreporting) **A**1 2 7 10 **S** Ascension Healthcare, Saint Louis, MO
Primary Contact: Daniel A. Parod, Interim President
COO: Daniel A Parod, Chief Operating Officer
CFO: John Zabrowski, Chief Financial Officer
CMO: Vernon Maas M.D., Vice President, Medical Affairs
CIO: Jose Diaz, Director Information Systems
CHR: Marty Mattingly, Chief Human Resources Officer
CNO: Darcy Ellison R.N., MSN, Senior Vice President, Chief Nursing Officer and Inpatient Flow
Web address: www.stmarys.org
Control: Church operated, Nongovernment, not–for–profit **Service**: General medical and surgical

Staffed Beds: 436

FISHERS—Hamilton County

✠ **ST. VINCENT FISHERS HOSPITAL (150181)**, 13861 Olio Road, Zip 46037–3487; tel. 317/415–9000 **A**1 10 **F**3 13 15 29 30 34 35 39 40 45 46 49 50 53 57 59 60 64 75 76 77 79 81 82 87 91 93 97 107 110 111 114 119 129 130 131 132 146 147 148 **S** Ascension Healthcare, Saint Louis, MO
Primary Contact: Gary Fammartino, Administrator
CMO: Craig Wilson, Chief Medical Officer
Web address: www.stvincent.org
Control: Church operated, Nongovernment, not–for–profit **Service**: General medical and surgical

Staffed Beds: 46 **Admissions**: 1531 **Census**: 8 **Outpatient Visits**: 63584 **Births**: 428 **Total Expense ($000)**: 43954 **Payroll Expense ($000)**: 15133 **Personnel**: 167

IN

FORT WAYNE—Allen County

✠ **DUPONT HOSPITAL (150150)**, 2520 East Dupont Road, Zip 46825–1675; tel. 260/416–3000 **A**1 10 **F**3 8 13 15 18 29 30 34 35 39 40 45 50 56 57 58 59 60 64 65 68 70 72 73 74 75 76 77 78 79 81 82 83 84 85 86 87 89 107 110 111 114 115 118 119 126 129 130 131 132 135 141 146 147 148 **S** Community Health Systems, Inc., Franklin, TN
Primary Contact: Lisa Dolan, Interim Chief Executive Officer
COO: Darrick Hoopingarner, Chief Operating Officer
CFO: Brian Schneider, Chief Financial Officer
CIO: Janis Gray, Chief Information Officer
CNO: Kimberly Fulkerson, Chief Nursing Officer
Web address: www.thedupontdifference.com
Control: Partnership, Investor–owned (for–profit) **Service**: General medical and surgical

Staffed Beds: 131 Admissions: 5129 Census: 52 Outpatient Visits: 102724 Births: 2540 Total Expense ($000): 95903 Payroll Expense ($000): 32338 Personnel: 534

✠ **LUTHERAN HOSPITAL OF INDIANA (150017)**, 7950 West Jefferson Boulevard, Zip 46804–4140; tel. 260/435–7001 **A**1 2 3 5 10 **F**2 3 5 7 8 11 12 13 14 15 17 18 19 20 21 22 23 24 25 26 27 28 29 30 31 32 33 34 35 36 37 38 39 40 41 42 43 44 45 46 47 48 49 50 51 52 54 55 56 57 58 59 60 61 62 63 64 65 66 68 70 72 74 75 76 77 78 79 80 81 82 83 84 85 86 87 88 89 91 92 93 94 96 97 99 100 101 102 103 104 105 106 107 108 109 110 111 112 113 114 115 116 117 118 119 120 121 122 123 124 126 127 129 130 131 132 133 134 135 136 137 138 141 142 144 145 146 **S** Community Health Systems, Inc., Franklin, TN
Primary Contact: Michael Poore, Interim Chief Executive Officer
CFO: Cully Chapman, Chief Financial Officer
CIO: Keith A. Neuman, Chief Information Officer
CHR: Maria Kurtz, Director Human Resources
CNO: Angela Logan, Chief Nursing Officer
Web address: www.lutheranhospital.com
Control: Corporation, Investor–owned (for–profit) **Service**: General medical and surgical

Staffed Beds: 396 Admissions: 18852 Census: 265 Outpatient Visits: 456740 Births: 951 Total Expense ($000): 368208 Payroll Expense ($000): 112577 Personnel: 2363

✠ **ORTHOPAEDIC HOSPITAL OF LUTHERAN HEALTH NETWORK (150168)**, 7952 West Jefferson Boulevard, Zip 46804–4140; tel. 260/435–2999 **A**1 10 **F**29 30 34 35 37 64 77 79 80 81 82 90 93 94 96 111 131 **P**8 **S** Community Health Systems, Inc., Franklin, TN
Primary Contact: Lorie Ailor, Chief Executive Officer
CFO: Amy Hochstetler, Chief Financial Officer
CMO: Kevin Rahn, President Medical Staff
CIO: Keith A. Neuman, Chief Information Officer
CHR: Maria Kurtz, Director Human Resources
CNO: Marci Hamilton, Chief Nursing Officer
Web address: www.theorthohospital.com
Control: Corporation, Investor–owned (for–profit) **Service**: Orthopedic

Staffed Beds: 44 Admissions: 2836 Census: 17 Outpatient Visits: 52162 Births: 0 Total Expense ($000): 56445 Payroll Expense ($000): 13449 Personnel: 218

✠ **PARKVIEW ORTHO HOSPITAL (150167)**, 11130 Parkview Circle Drive, Zip 46845–1735; tel. 260/672–5000 **A**1 10 **F**3 8 29 30 34 45 50 58 65 68 79 81 82 84 85 86 87 90 91 93 94 96 107 111 119 131 135 141 149 **S** Parkview Health, Fort Wayne, IN
Primary Contact: Julie Fleck, Chief Operating Officer
Web address: www.parkview.com
Control: Corporation, Investor–owned (for–profit) **Service**: Orthopedic

Staffed Beds: 37 Admissions: 2688 Census: 15 Outpatient Visits: 8179 Births: 0 Total Expense ($000): 67627 Payroll Expense ($000): 13929 Personnel: 331

✠ **PARKVIEW REGIONAL MEDICAL CENTER (150021)**, 11109 Parkview Plaza Drive, Zip 46845–1701; tel. 260/266–1000, (Includes PARKVIEW HOSPITAL RANDALLIA, 2200 Randallia Drive, Fort Wayne, Indiana, Zip 46805–4699, tel. 260/373–4000; Marlon Wardlow, Chief Operating Officer; PARKVIEW NORTH HOSPITAL, 11115 Parkview Plaza Drive, Fort Wayne, Indiana, Zip 46845, tel. 260/672–4000) (Total facility includes 31 beds in nursing home–type unit) **A**1 2 10 **F**3 5 7 11 12 13 14 15 17 18 20 22 24 26 28 29 30 31 32 34 35 39 40 41 43 44 45 46 47 48 49 50 51 53 54 55 56 57 58 59 60 61 62 63 64 65 67 68 70 72 74 75 76 78 79 80 81 82 83 84 85 86 89 90 91 92 93 96 98 99 100 101 102 103 104 105 107 108 109 111 114 115 118 119 120 121 123 124 126 128 129 130 131 132 135 141 146 147 148 149 **S** Parkview Health, Fort Wayne, IN
Primary Contact: Ben Miles, President
CNO: Judy Boerger MSN, Chief Nursing Executive
Web address: www.parkview.com
Control: Other not–for–profit (including NFP Corporation) **Service**: General medical and surgical

Staffed Beds: 690 Admissions: 36039 Census: 503 Outpatient Visits: 531208 Births: 3225 Total Expense ($000): 804765 Payroll Expense ($000): 231833 Personnel: 3843

✠ △ **REHABILITATION HOSPITAL OF FORT WAYNE (153030)**, 7970 West Jefferson Boulevard, Zip 46804–4140; tel. 260/435–6100 **A**1 7 10 **F**29 30 60 68 69 90 94 96 130 132 146 148 **P**5 **S** Community Health Systems, Inc., Franklin, TN
Primary Contact: Shelley Boxell, R.N., Chief Nursing Officer and Interim Chief Operating Officer
COO: Shelley Boxell R.N., Interim Chief Operating Officer
CFO: Edward Romero, Chief Financial Officer
CMO: Preeti Dembla, Chief Medical Officer and Medical Director
CIO: Janis Gray, Chief Information Officer
CHR: Deborah Giardina, Director Human Resources and Medical Staff Services
CNO: Shelley Boxell R.N., Chief Nursing Officer
Web address: www.rehabhospital.com
Control: Corporation, Investor–owned (for–profit) **Service**: Rehabilitation

Staffed Beds: 36 Admissions: 665 Census: 19 Outpatient Visits: 71 Births: 0 Total Expense ($000): 10256 Payroll Expense ($000): 5690 Personnel: 86

✠ **ST. JOSEPH HOSPITAL (150047)**, 700 Broadway, Zip 46802–1493; tel. 260/425–3000, (Total facility includes 20 beds in nursing home–type unit) **A**1 3 5 10 13 **F**3 4 5 13 15 16 17 18 20 22 24 34 35 38 40 45 46 47 49 50 51 53 54 55 56 57 58 59 64 65 68 69 70 72 74 76 77 79 80 81 85 87 92 93 96 98 100 101 102 103 104 105 107 108 110 111 114 115 118 119 126 128 130 132 142 146 147 148 149 **P**6 **S** Community Health Systems, Inc., Franklin, TN
Primary Contact: Vince Green, Interim Chief Administrative Officer
COO: Vince Green, Chief Operating Officer
CFO: Pamela Hess, Chief Financial Officer
CHR: Steve Heggen, Administrative Director Human Resources
Web address: www.stjoehospital.com
Control: Corporation, Investor–owned (for–profit) **Service**: General medical and surgical

Staffed Beds: 182 Admissions: 5589 Census: 92 Outpatient Visits: 97702 Births: 316 Total Expense ($000): 88500 Payroll Expense ($000): 31075 Personnel: 529

✠ **VETERANS AFFAIRS NORTHERN INDIANA HEALTH CARE SYSTEM**, 2121 Lake Avenue, Zip 46805–5100; tel. 260/426–5431, (Nonreporting) (Includes VETERANS AFFAIRS NORTHERN INDIANA HEALTH CARE SYSTEM–MARION CAMPUS, 1700 East 38th Street, Marion, Indiana, Zip 46953–4589, tel. 765/674–3321) **A**1 **S** Department of Veterans Affairs, Washington, DC
Primary Contact: Mark Murdock, FACHE, Director
COO: Helen Rhodes R.N., Associate Director Operations
CFO: Jay H Vandermark, Chief Financial Officer
CMO: Ajay Dhawan M.D., Chief of Staff
CIO: David Troyer, Chief Information Officer
CHR: Brian Flynn, Chief Human Resources Officer
Web address: www.northernindiana.va.gov/
Control: Veterans Affairs, Government, federal **Service**: General medical and surgical

Staffed Beds: 26

✠ **VIBRA HOSPITAL OF FORT WAYNE (152027)**, 2200 Randallia Drive, Zip 46805–4638; tel. 260/399–2900 **A**1 10 **F**1 3 29 75 85 148 149 **S** Vibra Healthcare, Mechanicsburg, PA
Primary Contact: Ryan Cassedy, Chief Executive Officer
Web address: www.vhfortwayne.com
Control: Corporation, Investor–owned (for–profit) **Service**: Acute long–term care hospital

Staffed Beds: 24 Admissions: 336 Census: 21 Outpatient Visits: 0 Births: 0 Total Expense ($000): 10736 Payroll Expense ($000): 4450 Personnel: 61

FRANKFORT—Clinton County

✠ **INDIANA UNIVERSITY HEALTH FRANKFORT (151316)**, 1300 South Jackson Street, Zip 46041–3313; tel. 765/656–3000 **A**1 10 18 **F**3 11 13 15 28 29 30 34 35 40 45 50 57 59 64 65 68 75 76 77 79 81 82 85 86 89 90 93 97 107 111 114 119 130 132 133 135 144 146 **S** Ascension Healthcare, Saint Louis, MO
Primary Contact: Kelly Braverman, President
CFO: Wayne Knight, Chief Financial Officer
CMO: Stephen Tharp M.D., Medical Director
CHR: Krista Wright, Director Human Resources
Web address: www.stvincent.org
Control: Church operated, Nongovernment, not–for–profit **Service**: General medical and surgical

Staffed Beds: 25 Admissions: 589 Census: 6 Outpatient Visits: 32003 Births: 111 Total Expense ($000): 20062 Payroll Expense ($000): 6907 Personnel: 66

IN

FRANKLIN—Johnson County

★ ○ **JOHNSON MEMORIAL HOSPITAL (150001)**, 1125 West Jefferson Street, Zip 46131–2140, Mailing Address: P.O.Box 549, 46131–0549; tel. 317/736–3300 **A**5 10 11 **F**12 13 15 18 20 22 28 29 30 31 34 35 36 40 44 45 49 50 54 57 59 62 64 68 70 74 75 76 77 78 79 81 82 85 87 90 93 97 107 108 110 111 113 114 118 119 129 130 131 132 134 135 144 146 147 148 **P**8
Primary Contact: Larry Heydon, President and Chief Executive Officer
COO: Steve Wohlford, Chief Operating Officer
CFO: Tim Balasia, Chief Financial Officer
CMO: David Dunkle, Vice President Medical Affairs
CIO: Scott Krodel, Vice President Information Systems
CHR: Judy Ware, Director Human Resources
CNO: Anita M. Keller R.N., MSN, Chief Nursing Officer
Web address: www.johnsonmemorial.org
Control: County, Government, Nonfederal **Service**: General medical and surgical

Staffed Beds: 102 **Admissions**: 2157 **Census**: 23 **Outpatient Visits**: 135890 **Births**: 403 **Total Expense ($000)**: 80001 **Payroll Expense ($000)**: 38293 **Personnel**: 705

GARY—Lake County

★ ○ △ **METHODIST HOSPITALS (150002)**, 600 Grant Street, Zip 46402–6099; tel. 219/886–4000, (Includes SOUTHLAKE CAMPUS, 8701 Broadway, Merrillville, Indiana, Zip 46410, tel. 219/738–5500) **A**2 3 5 7 10 11 **F**3 8 11 12 13 15 18 20 22 24 26 28 29 30 31 32 34 35 37 40 43 45 47 48 49 50 51 54 55 57 59 62 64 67 70 72 73 74 75 76 77 78 79 81 82 85 86 87 89 90 91 93 96 98 99 100 101 102 103 107 108 110 111 114 115 118 119 120 121 123 124 126 130 132 133 135 146 147 148 **P**6
Primary Contact: Raymond Grady, FACHE, President and Chief Executive Officer
CFO: Matthew Doyle, Chief Financial Officer
CIO: Timothy Diamond, Chief Information Officer
CHR: Alex Horvath, Vice President Human Resources
CNO: Shelly Major, Chief Nursing Officer
Web address: www.methodisthospitals.org
Control: Other not–for–profit (including NFP Corporation) **Service**: General medical and surgical

Staffed Beds: 504 **Admissions**: 16604 **Census**: 275 **Outpatient Visits**: 313123 **Births**: 1327 **Total Expense ($000)**: 339523 **Payroll Expense ($000)**: 148179 **Personnel**: 2110

GOSHEN—Elkhart County

GOSHEN GENERAL HOSPITAL See Goshen Hospital

☒ **GOSHEN HOSPITAL (150026)**, 200 High Park Avenue, Zip 46526–4899, Mailing Address: P.O.Box 139, 46527–0139; tel. 574/533–2141 **A**1 2 10 **F**3 8 11 12 13 15 17 18 20 22 24 26 28 29 30 31 34 35 36 40 45 46 47 49 50 53 54 57 58 59 60 62 63 64 68 70 71 74 75 76 77 78 79 80 81 82 83 84 85 86 87 89 91 92 93 107 109 110 111 112 114 115 116 117 118 119 120 121 122 123 124 126 130 131 132 135 136 141 142 144 146 147 **P**4 8
Primary Contact: Randal Christophel, President and Chief Executive Officer
COO: Robert T Myers, Chief Operating Officer
CMO: Randall Cammenga M.D., Vice President Medical Affairs
CHR: Alan Weldy, Vice President Human Resources, Compliance and Legal Services
Web address: www.goshenhealth.com/Home
Control: Other not–for–profit (including NFP Corporation) **Service**: General medical and surgical

Staffed Beds: 123 **Admissions**: 5410 **Census**: 56 **Outpatient Visits**: 168619 **Births**: 1287 **Total Expense ($000)**: 218244 **Payroll Expense ($000)**: 69851 **Personnel**: 1435

OAKLAWN PSYCHIATRIC CENTER (154031), 330 Lakeview Drive, Zip 46528–9365, Mailing Address: P.O.Box 809, 46527–0809; tel. 574/533–1234, (Nonreporting) **A**10
Primary Contact: Laurie N. Nafziger, President and Chief Executive Officer
CFO: Joseph Barkman, Vice President Financial Services
CMO: Daniel Kinsey M.D., Medical Director
CIO: Jennifer Glick, Manager Clinical Informatics
CHR: Jill Seifer, Vice President Human Resources
CNO: Elaine G Miller, Director of Nursing
Web address: www.oaklawn.org
Control: Other not–for–profit (including NFP Corporation) **Service**: Psychiatric

Staffed Beds: 16

GREENCASTLE—Putnam County

PUTNAM COUNTY HOSPITAL (151333), 1542 Bloomington Street, Zip 46135–2297; tel. 765/653–5121, (Nonreporting) **A**2 10 18
Primary Contact: Dennis Weatherford, Chief Executive Officer
CFO: Kevin Fowler, Director Finance
Web address: www.pchosp.org/
Control: County, Government, Nonfederal **Service**: General medical and surgical

Staffed Beds: 25

GREENFIELD—Hancock County

★ ○ **HANCOCK REGIONAL HOSPITAL (150037)**, 801 North State Street, Zip 46140–1270, Mailing Address: P.O.Box 827, 46140–0827; tel. 317/462–5544 **A**10 11 **F**3 11 12 13 15 18 20 22 28 29 30 31 32 34 35 38 40 44 45 46 47 48 49 50 53 54 56 57 59 63 64 70 75 76 78 79 81 82 84 85 86 87 89 92 93 96 98 103 107 108 110 111 114 115 119 120 121 123 127 129 130 132 134 135 146 147 148 **P**8
Primary Contact: Steven V. Long, FACHE, President and Chief Executive Officer
COO: Robert Lawrence Matt, Vice President and Chief Operating Officer
CFO: Rick Edwards, Vice President and Chief Financial Officer
CMO: Michael Fletcher M.D., Vice President and Chief Medical Officer
CIO: Jon Miller, Director Accounting and Information Services
CHR: Laura L Nichols, Director Human Resources
Web address: www.hancockregional.org
Control: County, Government, Nonfederal **Service**: General medical and surgical

Staffed Beds: 68 **Admissions**: 3173 **Census**: 34 **Outpatient Visits**: 154191 **Births**: 365 **Total Expense ($000)**: 106896 **Payroll Expense ($000)**: 40563 **Personnel**: 704

GREENSBURG—Decatur County

★ ⇧ **DECATUR COUNTY MEMORIAL HOSPITAL (151332)**, 720 North Lincoln Street, Zip 47240–1398; tel. 812/663–4331, (Total facility includes 370 beds in nursing home–type unit) **A**2 10 18 21 **F**3 7 11 13 15 18 28 29 31 34 35 40 45 50 54 57 59 62 64 65 68 74 75 76 77 78 79 80 81 85 87 89 92 93 96 97 103 104 107 108 110 111 115 118 119 128 129 130 131 132 133 135 143 144 146 147 148 **P**6
Primary Contact: Rex McKinney, President and Chief Executive Officer
COO: Eric Stokes, Vice President of Operations
CFO: Jerry Marks, Vice President Finance
CMO: Jennifer Fletcher, Chief of Staff
CHR: Amy Lynn Wickens, Executive Director Human Resources
CNO: Kathy Stephens, Vice President of Patient Care
Web address: www.dcmh.net
Control: County, Government, Nonfederal **Service**: General medical and surgical

Staffed Beds: 395 **Admissions**: 1560 **Census**: 246 **Outpatient Visits**: 146000 **Births**: 245 **Total Expense ($000)**: 55376 **Payroll Expense ($000)**: 25099 **Personnel**: 571

GREENWOOD—Johnson County

☒ **KINDRED HOSPITAL INDIANAPOLIS SOUTH (152008)**, 607 Greenwood Springs Drive, Zip 46143–6377; tel. 317/888–8155, (Nonreporting) **A**1 10 **S** Kindred Healthcare, Louisville, KY
Primary Contact: Matthew Keppler, Market Chief Executive Officer
CFO: William Brenner, Chief Financial Officer
CMO: Steven Samuels M.D., Medical Director
CNO: Jennifer Stallings, Chief Clinical Officer
Web address: www.khindysouth.com/
Control: Corporation, Investor–owned (for–profit) **Service**: Acute long–term care hospital

Staffed Beds: 60

☐ **VALLE VISTA HOSPITAL (154024)**, 898 East Main Street, Zip 46143–1400; tel. 317/887–1348, (Nonreporting) **A**1 10 **S** Universal Health Services, Inc., King of Prussia, PA
Primary Contact: Sherri R. Jewett, Chief Executive Officer
CFO: Tim Sides, Chief Financial Officer
CMO: Jennifer Comer M.D., Medical Director
CIO: Karen Hayden, Director Health Information Services, Performance Improvement and Risk Management
CHR: Ismael Santos, Director Human Resources
Web address: www.vallevistahospital.com
Control: Corporation, Investor–owned (for–profit) **Service**: Psychiatric

Staffed Beds: 102

IN

Hospital, Medicare Provider Number, Address, Telephone, Approval, Facility, and Physician Codes, Health Care System

★ American Hospital Association (AHA) membership   ○ Healthcare Facilities Accreditation Program   ⇧ Center for Improvement in Healthcare Quality Accreditation
☐ The Joint Commission accreditation   ◇ DNV Healthcare Inc. accreditation   △ Commission on Accreditation of Rehabilitation Facilities (CARF) accreditation

HAMMOND—Lake County

★ ○ △ **FRANCISCAN HEALTH HAMMOND (150004)**, 5454 Hohman Avenue, Zip 46320–1999; tel. 219/932–2300, (Nonreporting) (Includes SAINT MARGARET MERCY HEALTHCARE CENTERS–NORTH CAMPUS, 5454 Hohman Avenue, Hammond, Indiana, Zip 46320, tel. 219/932–2300) **A**2 7 10 11 **S** Franciscan Health, Mishawaka, IN
Primary Contact: Patrick J. Maloney, Chief Executive Officer
CFO: Marc Golan, Chief Financial Officer
Web address: www.franciscanhealth.org/healthcare–facilities/franciscan–health–hammond–18
Control: Church operated, Nongovernment, not–for–profit **Service**: General medical and surgical

Staffed Beds: 500

✠ **KINDRED HOSPITAL NORTHWEST INDIANA (152012)**, 5454 Hohman Avenue, 5th Floor, Zip 46320–1931; tel. 219/937–9900, (Nonreporting) **A**1 10 **S** Kindred Healthcare, Louisville, KY
Primary Contact: Frank A. Solare, Chief Executive Officer
Web address: www.khnwindiana.com
Control: Corporation, Investor–owned (for–profit) **Service**: Acute long–term care hospital

Staffed Beds: 70

SAINT MARGARET MERCY HEALTHCARE CENTERS See Franciscan Health Hammond

TRIUMPH HOSPITAL NORTHWEST INDIANA See Kindred Hospital Northwest Indiana

HARTFORD CITY—Blackford County

BLACKFORD COMMUNITY HOSPITAL See Indiana University Health Blackford Hospital

✠ **INDIANA UNIVERSITY HEALTH BLACKFORD HOSPITAL (151302)**, 410 Pilgrim Boulevard, Zip 47348–1897; tel. 765/348–0300 **A**1 10 18 **F**3 11 15 28 29 34 35 40 44 45 57 59 64 75 81 85 87 93 107 110 115 119 130 132 133 **S** Indiana University Health, Indianapolis, IN
Primary Contact: Steven J. West, Chief Executive Officer
CFO: Judy Coleman, Chief Financial Officer, Indiana University Health Ball Memorial Hospital
CIO: Steven J West, Chief Executive Officer
CHR: Steven J West, Chief Executive Officer
CNO: Rodney Stevens R.N., East Central Region Director of Nursing Practice
Web address: www.iuhealth.org/blackford
Control: Other not–for–profit (including NFP Corporation) **Service**: General medical and surgical

Staffed Beds: 15 **Admissions:** 441 **Census:** 6 **Outpatient Visits:** 33567 **Births:** 0 **Total Expense ($000):** 15518 **Payroll Expense ($000):** 6625 **Personnel:** 88

HOBART—Lake County

☐ △ **ST. MARY MEDICAL CENTER (150034)**, 1500 South Lake Park Avenue, Zip 46342–6699; tel. 219/942–0551 **A**1 2 7 10 **F**3 8 11 12 13 15 18 20 22 24 26 28 29 30 31 34 35 36 38 39 40 45 47 49 50 54 57 58 59 62 64 65 70 74 75 76 77 78 79 80 81 82 85 86 87 89 90 92 93 96 107 108 110 111 114 115 119 120 121 123 126 129 130 131 132 135 144 146 147 148 **P**8 **S** Community Healthcare System, Hammond, IN
Primary Contact: Janice L. Ryba, JD, Chief Executive Officer
CFO: Mary Sudicky, Chief Financial Officer
CIO: Gary Weiner, Vice President Information Technology and Chief Information Officer
CHR: Tony Ferracane, Vice President Human Resources
CNO: Tammie R. Jones R.N., Chief Nursing Officer
Web address: www.comhs.org
Control: Other not–for–profit (including NFP Corporation) **Service**: General medical and surgical

Staffed Beds: 200 **Admissions:** 11448 **Census:** 160 **Outpatient Visits:** 218202 **Births:** 626 **Total Expense ($000):** 235197 **Payroll Expense ($000):** 67332 **Personnel:** 1008

HUNTINGTON—Huntington County

✠ **PARKVIEW HUNTINGTON HOSPITAL (150091)**, 2001 Stults Road, Zip 46750–1291; tel. 260/355–3000 **A**1 10 **F**3 7 8 13 15 28 29 30 31 32 34 35 36 38 39 40 44 45 46 50 53 56 57 59 64 68 69 70 75 76 77 78 79 81 85 86 87 93 96 97 107 108 111 119 129 130 131 132 134 135 146 148 **S** Parkview Health, Fort Wayne, IN
Primary Contact: Juli Johnson, MSN, R.N., President
CMO: Jeffrey Brooks M.D., Chief Medical Officer
CIO: Ron Double, Chief Information Officer
CHR: Dena M Jacquay, Chief Human Resource Officer
CNO: Doug R Selig MSN, R.N., Vice President of Patient Services
Web address: www.parkview.com
Control: Other not–for–profit (including NFP Corporation) **Service**: General medical and surgical

Staffed Beds: 36 **Admissions:** 1676 **Census:** 13 **Outpatient Visits:** 45211 **Births:** 368 **Total Expense ($000):** 45126 **Payroll Expense ($000):** 14179 **Personnel:** 245

INDIANAPOLIS—Marion County

CLARIAN HEALTH PARTNERS See Indiana University Health University Hospital

✠ **COMMUNITY HOSPITAL EAST (150074)**, 1500 North Ritter Avenue, Zip 46219–3095; tel. 317/355–1411, (Includes COMMUNITY HEART AND VASCULAR HOSPITAL, 8075 North Shadeland Avenue, Indianapolis, Indiana, Zip 46250–2693, tel. 317/621–8000; Kathleen R Krusie, FACHE, President) **A**1 2 3 5 10 **F**3 11 13 17 18 20 22 26 28 29 30 31 34 35 38 40 43 44 45 46 47 48 49 50 51 53 56 57 59 70 74 75 76 77 78 79 80 81 85 87 92 96 98 107 111 114 115 118 119 120 121 123 124 126 129 130 132 146 147 148 149 **S** Community Health Network, Indianapolis, IN
Primary Contact: Scott L. Teffeteller, President
Web address: www.ecommunity.com/east/
Control: Other not–for–profit (including NFP Corporation) **Service**: General medical and surgical

Staffed Beds: 335 **Admissions:** 16241 **Census:** 196 **Outpatient Visits:** 494731 **Births:** 933 **Total Expense ($000):** 749802 **Payroll Expense ($000):** 161433 **Personnel:** 1488

✠ **COMMUNITY HOSPITAL NORTH (150169)**, 7150 Clearvista Drive, Zip 46256–1695, Mailing Address: 7250 Clearvista Drive, Suite 200, 46256–1695; tel. 317/355–2469 **A**1 3 10 **F**3 11 13 29 30 31 34 35 40 41 43 45 46 47 48 49 50 52 56 57 59 65 70 72 74 75 76 77 78 79 80 81 85 87 88 89 96 107 111 114 119 126 129 130 132 145 146 147 148 **S** Community Health Network, Indianapolis, IN
Primary Contact: Kathleen R. Krusie, FACHE, President
CFO: Amy Campbell, Chief Financial Officer
CMO: Wesley Wong M.D., Acting Vice President Medical and Academic Affairs
CIO: Ron Thieme Ph.D., Chief Knowledge and Information Officer
CHR: Steve Pearcy, Director Human Resources
Web address: www.ecommunity.com/north
Control: Other not–for–profit (including NFP Corporation) **Service**: General medical and surgical

Staffed Beds: 336 **Admissions:** 16528 **Census:** 208 **Outpatient Visits:** 229811 **Births:** 3711 **Total Expense ($000):** 409146 **Payroll Expense ($000):** 212175 **Personnel:** 1429

✠ **COMMUNITY HOSPITAL SOUTH (150128)**, 1402 East County Line Road South, Zip 46227–0963; tel. 317/887–7000 **A**1 3 10 **F**3 11 12 13 15 18 20 22 28 29 30 31 35 37 40 45 46 47 48 49 54 60 64 69 70 73 74 75 76 77 78 79 81 82 84 85 86 89 107 108 110 111 114 115 119 126 129 130 131 135 145 146 147 148 **P**8 **S** Community Health Network, Indianapolis, IN
Primary Contact: David Kiley, M.D., Interim President
CFO: Leslie Yoder, Executive Director, Finance
CMO: Randy Lee M.D., Senior Vice President Medical Affairs
CHR: Edie Garriott, Director Human Resources
CNO: Anita Capps R.N., Chief Nursing Executive
Web address: www.ecommunity.com
Control: Other not–for–profit (including NFP Corporation) **Service**: General medical and surgical

Staffed Beds: 158 **Admissions:** 9545 **Census:** 95 **Outpatient Visits:** 129522 **Births:** 1679 **Total Expense ($000):** 207553 **Payroll Expense ($000):** 56170 **Personnel:** 846

IN

Many Facility Codes have changed. Please refer to the AHA Guide Code Chart.
© 2017 AHA Guide

□ **ESKENAZI HEALTH (150024)**, 720 Eskenazi Avenue, Zip 46202–5166; tel. 317/880–0000 **A**1 3 5 8 10 **F**3 5 7 10 13 14 15 16 18 20 22 28 29 30 31 32 34 35 36 38 39 40 43 44 47 48 49 50 53 54 55 56 57 59 61 62 64 65 66 68 70 71 72 74 75 76 77 78 79 81 82 83 84 85 86 87 93 97 98 99 100 101 102 103 104 105 106 107 110 111 115 119 130 132 134 135 143 144 145 146 147 148 150
Primary Contact: Lisa E. Harris, M.D., Chief Executive Officer
COO: Parveen Chand, Chief Operating Officer
CFO: Kathi Johnson, Chief Financial Officer
CMO: David W Crabb M.D., Chief Medical Officer
CIO: David Shaw, Vice President Information Systems
CHR: Christia Hicks, Vice President Human Resources
CNO: Lee Ann Blue MSN, R.N., Chief Nursing Officer and Executive Vice President Patient Care Services
Web address: www.eskenazihealth.edu
Control: County, Government, Nonfederal **Service**: General medical and surgical

Staffed Beds: 259 **Admissions**: 15924 **Census**: 214 **Outpatient Visits**: 908924 **Births**: 2316 **Total Expense ($000)**: 658767 **Payroll Expense ($000)**: 236736 **Personnel**: 4085

□ **FAIRBANKS (150179)**, 8102 Clearvista Parkway, Zip 46256–4698; tel. 317/849–8222 **A**1 3 10 **F**4 5 29 30 35 36 75 87 100 105 135 **P**6
Primary Contact: Barb Elliott, Interim President and Chief Executive Officer
CFO: Barb Elliott, Chief Financial Officer
CMO: Dennis Rhyne M.D., Acting Medical Director
CIO: Randy Walls, Manager Information Services
CHR: Sharon Baker, Director Support Services
CNO: Jennifer M Horstman R.N., Chief Nursing Officer and Chief Information Officer
Web address: www.fairbankscd.org
Control: Other not–for–profit (including NFP Corporation) **Service**: Alcoholism and other chemical dependency

Staffed Beds: 86 **Admissions**: 3990 **Census**: 56 **Outpatient Visits**: 23205 **Births**: 0 **Total Expense ($000)**: 24034 **Payroll Expense ($000)**: 12172 **Personnel**: 294

○ △ **FRANCISCAN ST. FRANCIS HEALTH – INDIANAPOLIS (150162)**, 8111 South Emerson Avenue, Zip 46237–8601; tel. 317/528–5000, (Nonreporting) **A**2 3 5 7 10 11 **S** Franciscan Health, Mishawaka, IN
Primary Contact: James Callaghan III, M.D., President and Chief Executive Officer
CFO: Keith A. Lauter, Regional Chief Financial Officer
CMO: Christopher Doehring M.D., Vice President Medical Affairs
CIO: Barbara Coulter, Director Information Systems
CHR: Corey Baute, Vice President Human Resources
CNO: Susan McRoberts R.N., MSN, Vice President and Chief Nursing Officer
Web address: www.stfrancishospitals.org
Control: Church operated, Nongovernment, not–for–profit **Service**: General medical and surgical

Staffed Beds: 485

○ **INDIANA ORTHOPAEDIC HOSPITAL (150160)**, 8400 Northwest Boulevard, Zip 46278–1381; tel. 317/956–1000 **A**3 10 11 **F**3 29 30 34 35 37 57 64 68 75 77 79 81 82 83 84 86 87 92 93 107 111 114 115 119 131 135
Primary Contact: Stacie Vance, Chief Nursing Officer and Chief Operations Officer
COO: Stacie Vance, Chief Nursing Officer and
CFO: Anthony Gioia, Chief Financial Officer
CMO: Joseph Randolph M.D., Chairman Medical Executive Committee
CIO: Paul Frey, Director Information Technology Applications
CHR: Kristy Hensley, Director Human Resources
CNO: Stacie Vance, Chief Nursing Officer and Vice President Operations
Web address: www.orthoindy.com
Control: Partnership, Investor–owned (for–profit) **Service**: Orthopedic

Staffed Beds: 38 **Admissions**: 3103 **Census**: 17 **Births**: 0

INDIANA UNIVERSITY HEALTH METHODIST HOSPITAL See Indiana University Health University Hospital

⊠ **INDIANA UNIVERSITY HEALTH UNIVERSITY HOSPITAL (150056)**, 550 University Boulevard, Zip 46202–5149, Mailing Address: P.O.Box 1367, 46206–1367; tel. 317/944–5000, (Includes INDIANA UNIVERSITY HEALTH METHODIST HOSPITAL, 1701 North Senate Boulevard, Indianapolis, Indiana, Zip 46202, 1701 North Senate Bouleverd, 46202, tel. 317/962–2000; Ryan Nagy, M.D., Interim President and Chief Medical Officer; INDIANA UNIVERSITY HEALTH SAXONY HOSPITAL, 13000 East 136th Street, Fishers, Indiana, Zip 46037–9478, tel. 317/678–2000; Jonathan R Goble, FACHE, Chief Executive Officer; INDIANA UNIVERSITY HOSPITAL, 550 North University Boulevard, Indianapolis, Indiana, Zip 46202–5262, tel. 317/274–5000; RILEY HOSPITAL FOR CHILDREN AT INDIANA UNIVERSITY HEALTH, 702 Barnhill Drive, Indianapolis, Indiana, Zip 46202–5225, 705 Riley Hospital Dr, 46202, tel. 317/274–5000) **A**1 2 3 5 8 10 **F**5 6 7 8 9 11 12 13 15 16 17 18 19 20 21 22 23 24 25 26 27 28 29 30 31 32 33 34 35 36 37 38 39 40 41 43 44 45 46 47 48 49 50 51 52 53 54 55 56 57 58 59 60 61 62 63 64 65 68 69 70 71 72 73 74 75 76 77 78 79 80 81 82 83 84 85 86 87 88 89 91 92 93 94 96 97 98 99 100 101 102 103 104 105 106 107 108 109 110 111 112 113 114 115 116 117 118 119 120 121 122 123 124 126 129 130 131 132 134 135 136 137 138 139 140 141 144 145 146 147 148 **S** Indiana University Health, Indianapolis, IN
Primary Contact: Ryan Nagy, M.D., Interim President and Chief Medical Officer
Web address: www.iuhealth.org
Control: Other not–for–profit (including NFP Corporation) **Service**: General medical and surgical

Staffed Beds: 1253 **Admissions**: 46362 **Census**: 905 **Outpatient Visits**: 1278235 **Births**: 3250 **Total Expense ($000)**: 2817300 **Payroll Expense ($000)**: 942369 **Personnel**: 14063

INDIANA UNIVERSITY HOSPITAL See Indiana University Health University Hospital

⊠ **KINDRED HOSPITAL INDIANAPOLIS NORTH (152013)**, 8060 Knue Road, Zip 46250–1976; tel. 317/813–8900, (Nonreporting) **A**1 10 **S** Kindred Healthcare, Louisville, KY
Primary Contact: Nakia Tremble, Chief Executive Officer
CHR: Kelly Becker, Administrative Coordinator Human Resources
Web address: www.kindredindynorth.com/
Control: Corporation, Investor–owned (for–profit) **Service**: Acute long–term care hospital

Staffed Beds: 45

⊠ **KINDRED HOSPITAL–INDIANAPOLIS (152007)**, 1700 West 10th Street, Zip 46222–3802; tel. 317/636–4400, (Nonreporting) **A**1 10 **S** Kindred Healthcare, Louisville, KY
Primary Contact: Bryan Chatterton, Chief Executive Officer
COO: Angela Lynne Rotert, Chief Clinical Officer
CFO: William Brenner, Chief Financial Officer
CHR: Joe Housh, District Director Human Resources
Web address: www.kindredhospitalindy.com/
Control: Corporation, Investor–owned (for–profit) **Service**: Acute long–term care hospital

Staffed Beds: 59

□ **LARUE D. CARTER MEMORIAL HOSPITAL (154008)**, 2601 Cold Spring Road, Zip 46222–2273; tel. 317/941–4000, (Nonreporting) **A**1 5 10
Primary Contact: Robert Clover, Interim Superintendent
CFO: Michael Logar, Assistant Superintendent
CMO: Beth Pfau M.D., Chief Medical Officer
CIO: Denton Gross, Director Information Services
CHR: Rebecca Dutton, Director Human Resources
CNO: Todd Rittman, Director of Nursing
Control: State, Government, Nonfederal **Service**: Psychiatric

Staffed Beds: 148

METHODIST HOSPITAL See Indiana University Health Methodist Hospital

NEUROPSYCHIATRIC HOSPITAL OF INDIANAPOLIS (154063), 6720 Parkdale Place, Zip 46254–4668; tel. 317/744–9200 (Nonreporting) **S** NeuroPsychiatric Hospitals, Mishawaka, IN
Primary Contact: Corey Simmons, Chief Executive Officer
Web address: www.neuropsychrichospitals.net
Control: Investor–owned (for–profit) **Service**: Psychiatric

Staffed Beds: 50

IN

Hospital, Medicare Provider Number, Address, Telephone, Approval, Facility, and Physician Codes, Health Care System

★ American Hospital Association (AHA) membership   ○ Healthcare Facilities Accreditation Program   ⇑ Center for Improvement in Healthcare Quality Accreditation
□ The Joint Commission accreditation   ◇ DNV Healthcare Inc. accreditation   △ Commission on Accreditation of Rehabilitation Facilities (CARF) accreditation

☐ **OPTIONS BEHAVIORAL HEALTH SYSTEM (154057)**, 5602 Caito Drive, Zip 46226–1346; tel. 317/544–4340 (Nonreporting) **A**1 10 **S** Acadia Healthcare Company, Inc., Franklin, TN
Primary Contact: Chris Rupert, Chief Executive Officer
Web address: www.optionsbehavioralhealthsystem.com/
Control: Corporation, Investor–owned (for–profit) **Service:** Psychiatric

Staffed Beds: 84

☐ △ **REHABILITATION HOSPITAL OF INDIANA (153028)**, 4141 Shore Drive, Zip 46254–2607; tel. 317/329–2000 **A**1 3 5 7 10 **F**28 29 30 33 54 58 64 75 79 86 87 90 91 92 93 96 130 131 132 146 148 **P**5 **S** Indiana University Health, Indianapolis, IN
Primary Contact: Daniel B. Woloszyn, Chief Executive Officer
COO: Monte Spence, Chief Operating Officer
CFO: Marjorie Basey, Chief Financial Officer
CMO: Flora Hammond M.D., Chief Medical Affairs
CIO: Gary Skinner, Director Information Technology
CHR: Joni Brown, Director Human Resources
CNO: Debra Cordes, Chief Nursing Officer
Web address: www.rhin.com
Control: Other not–for–profit (including NFP Corporation) **Service:** Rehabilitation

Staffed Beds: 83 Admissions: 1312 Census: 54 Outpatient Visits: 22799 Births: 0 Total Expense ($000): 39571 Payroll Expense ($000): 19874 Personnel: 360

☒ △ **RICHARD L. ROUDEBUSH VETERANS AFFAIRS MEDICAL CENTER**, 1481 West Tenth Street, Zip 46202–2884; tel. 317/554–0000 **A**1 2 3 5 7 8 **F**3 5 18 20 22 24 26 28 29 30 31 33 34 35 36 38 39 40 44 45 46 47 49 50 53 54 56 57 58 59 60 61 62 63 64 65 66 67 70 71 74 75 77 78 79 80 81 82 83 84 85 86 87 90 91 92 93 94 96 97 98 100 101 102 103 104 105 106 107 108 111 115 117 118 119 120 121 123 124 126 127 130 132 135 143 144 146 147 148 149 **S** Department of Veterans Affairs, Washington, DC
Primary Contact: Brian Hancock, M.D., Director
COO: Ginny L Creasman, Associate Director
CFO: Colin Lennon, Chief Financial Officer
CMO: Chowdry Bashir M.D., Chief of Staff
CIO: Steve Stoner, Chief Information Officer
CHR: Chari Weddle, Chief Human Resource Management Service
CNO: Patricia Mathis, Associate Director Patient Care Service
Web address: www.indianapolis.va.gov
Control: Veterans Affairs, Government, federal **Service:** General medical and surgical

Staffed Beds: 209 Admissions: 7778 Census: 140 Outpatient Visits: 770353 Births: 0 Total Expense ($000): 563613 Payroll Expense ($000): 223310 Personnel: 2805

RILEY HOSPITAL FOR CHILDREN See Riley Hospital For Children At Indiana University Health

RILEY HOSPITAL FOR CHILDREN AT INDIANA UNIVERSITY HEALTH See Indiana University Health University Hospital

ST. FRANCIS HOSPITAL AND HEALTH CENTERS – SOUTH CAMPUS See Franciscan St. Francis Health – Indianapolis

☒ **ST. VINCENT HEART CENTER (150153)**, 10580 North Meridian Street, Zip 46290–1028; tel. 317/583–5000 **A**1 10 **F**3 18 20 22 24 26 28 29 30 34 35 40 43 45 46 58 59 75 81 85 86 87 107 111 115 119 129 130 135 148 149 **P**2 **S** Ascension Healthcare, Saint Louis, MO
Primary Contact: Blake A. Dye, President
CFO: Becky Jacobson, Vice President Finance
CMO: William Storer M.D., Medical Director
CIO: Roger Strange, Chief Information Officer
Web address: www.bestheartcare.com/
Control: Partnership, Investor–owned (for–profit) **Service:** Heart

Staffed Beds: 80 Admissions: 4437 Census: 54 Outpatient Visits: 11420 Births: 0 Total Expense ($000): 109469 Payroll Expense ($000): 29725 Personnel: 347

☒ **ST. VINCENT INDIANAPOLIS HOSPITAL (150084)**, 2001 West 86th Street, Zip 46260–1991, Mailing Address: P.O.Box 40970, 46240–0970; tel. 317/338–2345, (Includes PEYTON MANNING CHILDREN'S HOSPITAL AT ST. VINCENT, 2001 West 86th Street, Indianapolis, Indiana, Zip 46260, P O Box 40970, 46240–0970, tel. 317/415–8111; Hossain Marandi, M.D., FACHE, President and Chief Executive Officer; PEYTON MANNING CHILDREN'S HOSPITAL, 1707 West 86th Street, Indianapolis, Indiana, Zip 46240, P O Box 40407, 46240, tel. 317/415–5500; Hossain Marandi, M.D., FACHE, President and Chief Executive Officer; ST. VINCENT STRESS CENTER, 8401 Harcourt Road, Indianapolis, Indiana, Zip 46260, P O Box 80160, 46280, tel. 317/338–4600; Sheila Mishler, Chief Executive Officer; ST. VINCENT WOMEN'S HOSPITAL, 8111 Township Line Road, Indianapolis, Indiana, Zip 46260–8043, tel. 317/415–8111; Anne Coleman, Administrator) **A**1 2 3 5 8 10 **F**3 4 5 7 8 9 11 13 15 17 18 19 20 21 22 23 24 25 26 27 28 29 30 31 32 34 35 36 37 38 39 40 41 43 44 45 46 47 48 49 50 51 53 54 55 56 57 58 59 61 62 63 64 65 66 68 70 71 72 73 74 75 76 77 78 79 81 82 83 84 85 86 87 88 89 90 91 92 93 94 95 96 97 98 99 100 101 102 103 104 105 106 107 108 109 110 111 114 115 117 118 119 120 121 124 126 129 130 131 132 134 135 137 138 141 142 143 144 146 147 148 149 **P**6 **S** Ascension Healthcare, Saint Louis, MO
Primary Contact: Joel Feldman, Regional President
COO: Erica Wehrmeister, Chief Operating Officer
CFO: Terry Metzger, Vice President, Finance
CMO: Richard Freeman, Chief Medical Officer
CIO: Randy Cox, Chief Information Officer
CHR: Audra Pratt, Chief Human Resource Officer
CNO: Mary Myers R.N., MSN, Chief Nursing Officer
Web address: www.stvincent.org
Control: Church operated, Nongovernment, not–for–profit **Service:** General medical and surgical

Staffed Beds: 832 Admissions: 32920 Census: 552 Outpatient Visits: 731234 Births: 3047 Total Expense ($000): 1025478 Payroll Expense ($000): 355664 Personnel: 4289

☒ **ST. VINCENT SETON SPECIALTY HOSPITAL (152020)**, 8050 Township Line Road, Zip 46260–2478; tel. 317/415–8500 **A**1 10 **F**1 3 29 30 31 35 44 68 75 85 107 114 119 130 132 148 **S** Ascension Healthcare, Saint Louis, MO
Primary Contact: Joel Feldman, Regional President
COO: Troy T Reiff, Corporate Director Operations
CFO: David M Girten, Corporate Director Financial Services
CMO: Ronald Reisman M.D., Chief Medical Director
CHR: Terry A Wignall, Director Human Resources
Web address: www.stvincent.org/
Control: Church operated, Nongovernment, not–for–profit **Service:** Acute long–term care hospital

Staffed Beds: 74 Admissions: 544 Census: 58 Outpatient Visits: 0 Births: 0 Total Expense ($000): 36790 Payroll Expense ($000): 17648 Personnel: 211

JASPER—Dubois County

☒ **MEMORIAL HOSPITAL AND HEALTH CARE CENTER (150115)**, 800 West Ninth Street, Zip 47546–2516; tel. 812/996–2345, (Total facility includes 20 beds in nursing home–type unit) **A**1 2 10 19 **F**3 5 7 8 11 12 13 15 18 20 22 24 26 28 29 30 31 34 35 36 40 41 42 45 46 47 48 49 51 54 56 57 59 62 64 66 68 70 74 75 76 77 78 79 81 82 84 85 86 87 89 90 93 97 98 100 101 102 103 104 105 107 108 110 111 112 113 114 115 116 117 118 119 120 121 127 128 129 130 131 132 135 144 146 147 148 149 **P**6 **S** American Province of Little Company of Mary Sisters, Evergreen Park, IL
Primary Contact: E Kyle. Bennett, President and Chief Executive Officer
CFO: Randall Russell, Vice President and Chief Financial Officer
CMO: Stan Tretter M.D., Chief Medical Officer
CIO: Gary Light, Vice President and Chief Information Officer
CHR: Richard Pea, Director Human Resources
CNO: Tonya Heim R.N., MSN, Vice President Patient Services and Chief Nursing Officer
Web address: www.mhhcc.org
Control: Church operated, Nongovernment, not–for–profit **Service:** General medical and surgical

Staffed Beds: 143 Admissions: 5648 Census: 67 Outpatient Visits: 253856 Births: 936 Total Expense ($000): 207226 Payroll Expense ($000): 94768 Personnel: 1325

JEFFERSONVILLE—Clark County

✠ **CLARK MEMORIAL HOSPITAL (150009)**, 1220 Missouri Avenue, Zip 47130–3743, Mailing Address: P.O.Box 69, 47131–0600; tel. 812/282–6631 **A**1 2 3 5 10 **F**3 5 8 11 12 15 17 18 20 22 26 28 29 30 31 34 35 38 40 45 46 49 50 54 56 57 59 64 65 70 74 75 76 77 78 79 81 82 85 86 87 92 97 98 100 101 102 103 104 105 107 108 110 111 114 115 119 124 129 130 132 135 144 145 146 147 148 149 **P**6 **S** LifePoint Health, Brentwood, TN
Primary Contact: Martin Padgett, President and Chief Executive Officer
CFO: Kirk Strack, Vice President and Chief Financial Officer
CMO: William Templeton M.D., III, Medical Director
CIO: Larry Reverman, Director Information Systems
CHR: Scott Hicks, Vice President
CNO: Kathy Neuner R.N., Chief Nursing Officer
Web address: www.clarkmemorial.org
Control: Corporation, Investor–owned (for–profit) **Service**: General medical and surgical

Staffed Beds: 178 **Admissions:** 10087 **Census:** 108 **Outpatient Visits:** 111826 **Births:** 1330 **Total Expense ($000):** 174111 **Payroll Expense ($000):** 71241 **Personnel:** 1320		

☐ **WELLSTONE REGIONAL HOSPITAL (154051)**, 2700 Vissing Park Road, Zip 47130–5989; tel. 812/284–8000 **A**1 10 **F**4 5 33 38 50 56 64 98 99 100 101 103 104 105 130 132 135 143 149 **P**5 **S** Universal Health Services, Inc., King of Prussia, PA
Primary Contact: Greg Stewart, Chief Executive Officer
CFO: Gracia Winsett, Chief Financial Officer
CMO: Asad Ismail M.D., Medical Director
CIO: Billy Leftwitch, Director, Information Technology
CHR: Tiffany Smith, Director Human Resources
CNO: Anthony Aemmer, Director of Nursing
Web address: www.wellstonehospital.com
Control: Corporation, Investor–owned (for–profit) **Service**: Psychiatric

Staffed Beds: 100 **Admissions:** 3425 **Census:** 76 **Outpatient Visits:** 8858 **Births:** 0 **Total Expense ($000):** 14697 **Payroll Expense ($000):** 9189 **Personnel:** 178		

KENDALLVILLE—Noble County

✠ **PARKVIEW NOBLE HOSPITAL (150146)**, 401 Sawyer Road, Zip 46755–2568; tel. 260/347–8700 **A**1 10 **F**3 7 13 15 28 29 34 35 40 45 46 47 50 54 57 59 64 70 74 75 76 79 81 82 85 87 93 97 107 108 110 111 114 118 119 129 130 132 135 143 145 146 **P**6 **S** Parkview Health, Fort Wayne, IN
Primary Contact: Gary W. Adkins, President
COO: Gary W Adkins, Chief Executive Officer
CFO: Kem Prince, Manager of Finance
CMO: Gerald Warrener M.D., Chief Medical Officer
CIO: Ron Double, Chief Information Officer
CHR: Bruce Buttermore, Manager Human Resources
CNO: Catherine Byrd, Vice President Patient Services
Web address: www.parkview.com
Control: Other not–for–profit (including NFP Corporation) **Service**: General medical and surgical

Staffed Beds: 31 **Admissions:** 1804 **Census:** 15 **Outpatient Visits:** 60188 **Births:** 243 **Total Expense ($000):** 48243 **Payroll Expense ($000):** 14712 **Personnel:** 235		

KNOX—Starke County

✠ **STARKE HOSPITAL (150102)**, 102 East Culver Road, Zip 46534–2216, Mailing Address: P.O.Box 339, 46534–0339; tel. 574/772–6231 **A**1 10 **F**3 15 18 29 30 32 34 35 38 40 45 46 49 50 53 57 59 65 68 74 75 77 79 81 85 87 93 94 107 108 110 111 114 115 116 117 119 130 132 135 146 147 148 **S** Community Health Systems, Inc., Franklin, TN
Primary Contact: Jeff Vice, Interim Chief Executive Officer
CFO: Drew Keesbury, Chief Financial Officer
CMO: A N Damodaran M.D., President Medical Staff
CIO: Ashley Norem, Chief Information Systems
CHR: Doug Jesch, Director Human Resources
CNO: Anetra Jones R.N., M.P.H., Chief Nursing Officer
Web address: www.iuhealth.org/starke/
Control: Other not–for–profit (including NFP Corporation) **Service**: General medical and surgical

Staffed Beds: 15 **Admissions:** 365 **Census:** 3 **Outpatient Visits:** 31538 **Births:** 0 **Total Expense ($000):** 15736 **Payroll Expense ($000):** 5293		

STARKE MEMORIAL HOSPITAL See Starke Hospital

KOKOMO—Howard County

✠ **COMMUNITY HOWARD REGIONAL HEALTH (150007)**, 3500 South Lafountain Street, Zip 46902–3803, Mailing Address: P.O.Box 9011, 46904–9011; tel. 765/453–0702 **A**1 2 10 **F**3 5 7 11 13 15 17 18 20 22 26 28 29 30 31 32 34 35 38 40 41 45 47 48 49 53 54 55 57 58 59 61 63 64 65 67 70 71 72 74 75 76 77 78 79 80 81 84 85 86 87 89 92 93 94 96 97 98 99 100 101 102 103 104 105 106 107 108 109 110 111 114 115 117 119 120 121 128 129 130 131 132 134 135 145 146 147 148 149 **S** Community Health Network, Indianapolis, IN
Primary Contact: Joseph Hooper, President and Chief Executive Officer
COO: Theodore Brown, Chief Operating Officer
CFO: Theodore Brown, Vice President Financial Services
CIO: Kevin Purvis, Chief Information Officer
CHR: Michael L Williams FACHE, Vice President Human Resources
CNO: Melodi Greene R.N., MS, Chief Nursing Officer
Web address: www.howardregional.org
Control: Other not–for–profit (including NFP Corporation) **Service**: General medical and surgical

Staffed Beds: 159 **Admissions:** 4606 **Census:** 41 **Outpatient Visits:** 166092 **Births:** 423 **Total Expense ($000):** 124501 **Payroll Expense ($000):** 38032 **Personnel:** 672		

✠ **COMMUNITY HOWARD SPECIALTY HOSPITAL (153039)**, 829 North Dixon Road, Zip 46901–7709; tel. 765/452–6700 **A**1 10 **F**28 29 30 34 57 77 90 93 129 131 132 **S** Community Health Network, Indianapolis, IN
Primary Contact: Clayton L. Clement, Interim Administrator
CFO: Julie Pena, Director Finance
CMO: Brad Vossberg M.D., Chief Rehabilitation
CNO: Claudia Jean Lowry R.N., Director of Nursing
Web address: www.communityhoward.org
Control: Partnership, Investor–owned (for–profit) **Service**: Rehabilitation

Staffed Beds: 30 **Admissions:** 457 **Census:** 15 **Outpatient Visits:** 33141 **Births:** 0 **Total Expense ($000):** 12199 **Payroll Expense ($000):** 5875 **Personnel:** 123		

HOWARD REGIONAL HEALTH SYSTEM See Community Howard Regional Health

HOWARD REGIONAL HEALTH SYSTEM WEST CAMPUS SPECIALTY HOSPITAL See Community Howard Specialty Hospital

✠ **ST. VINCENT KOKOMO (150010)**, 1907 West Sycamore Street, Zip 46901–4197; tel. 765/452–5611 **A**1 10 **F**3 4 5 7 8 13 15 18 20 28 29 30 31 34 35 36 40 44 45 49 50 51 53 55 57 59 64 66 68 69 70 73 74 75 76 77 78 79 81 82 85 86 87 89 90 93 96 98 99 100 101 102 103 104 105 107 108 110 111 115 119 120 121 123 129 130 131 132 135 143 145 146 147 148 149 **S** Ascension Healthcare, Saint Louis, MO
Primary Contact: Margaret M. Johnson, President, St. Vincent Northwest Region
CFO: Dennis Ressler, Chief Financial Officer
CMO: David L Williams M.D., Chief Medical Officer
CIO: Jeffrey Scott, Chief Information Officer
CHR: Cindy Babb, Executive Director Human Resources and Organizational Effectiveness
CNO: Kathleen K Peoples R.N., MS, Vice President of Nursing
Web address: www.stvincent.org/stjoseph
Control: Church operated, Nongovernment, not–for–profit **Service**: General medical and surgical

Staffed Beds: 129 **Admissions:** 5041 **Census:** 65 **Outpatient Visits:** 188626 **Births:** 798 **Total Expense ($000):** 126246 **Payroll Expense ($000):** 40294 **Personnel:** 653		

IN

Hospital, Medicare Provider Number, Address, Telephone, Approval, Facility, and Physician Codes, Health Care System

★ American Hospital Association (AHA) membership   ○ Healthcare Facilities Accreditation Program   ⇑ Center for Improvement in Healthcare Quality Accreditation
☐ The Joint Commission accreditation   ◇ DNV Healthcare Inc. accreditation   △ Commission on Accreditation of Rehabilitation Facilities (CARF) accreditation

LA PORTE—Laporte County

☒ **LA PORTE HOSPITAL (150006)**, 1007 Lincolnway, Zip 46350–3201, Mailing Address: P.O.Box 250, 46352–0250; tel. 219/326–1234, (Data for 274 days)**A**1 2 10 19 **F**1 3 4 8 11 13 15 16 17 18 19 20 22 24 26 28 29 30 31 32 34 35 36 39 40 45 46 47 48 49 50 51 53 54 56 57 59 60 62 63 64 65 66 67 68 70 71 72 73 74 75 76 77 78 79 81 85 86 87 88 89 91 92 93 94 96 97 98 107 108 110 111 115 118 119 126 128 129 130 131 132 135 144 145 146 147 148 149 **S** Community Health Systems, Inc., Franklin, TN
Primary Contact: Ashley Dickinson, Chief Executive Officer
CFO: Drew Keesbury, Chief Financial Officer
CNO: Anetra Jones R.N., M.P.H., Chief Nursing Officer
Web address: www.iuhealth.org
Control: Corporation, Investor–owned (for–profit) **Service:** General medical and surgical

Staffed Beds: 129 **Admissions:** 3855 **Census:** 56 **Outpatient Visits:** 104096 **Births:** 621 **Total Expense ($000):** 121694 **Payroll Expense ($000):** 43086 **Personnel:** 1250

LA PORTE REGIONAL HEALTH SYSTEM See La Porte Hospital

LAFAYETTE—Tippecanoe County

CLARIAN ARNETT HOSPITAL See Indiana University Health Arnett Hospital

○ **FRANCISCAN HEALTH LAFAYETTE EAST (150109)**, 1701 South Creasy Lane, Zip 47905–4972; tel. 765/502–4000, (Includes FRANCISCAN HEALTH LAFAYETTE CENTRAL, 1501 Hartford Street, Lafayette, Indiana, Zip 47904–2134, tel. 765/423–6011; Terrance E Wilson, President and Chief Executive Officer) **A**2 5 10 11 **F**3 11 13 15 17 18 19 20 22 24 26 28 29 30 31 34 35 37 40 43 45 49 50 51 54 55 57 60 62 63 64 68 69 70 72 75 76 77 78 79 81 82 84 85 87 89 90 93 94 96 97 98 102 107 110 111 114 115 118 119 120 121 126 129 130 132 135 145 146 147 148 **S** Franciscan Health, Mishawaka, IN
Primary Contact: Terrance E. Wilson, President and Chief Executive Officer
Web address: www.ste.org
Control: Church operated, Nongovernment, not–for–profit **Service:** General medical and surgical

Staffed Beds: 187 **Admissions:** 10764 **Census:** 126 **Outpatient Visits:** 373242 **Births:** 2095 **Total Expense ($000):** 303122 **Payroll Expense ($000):** 89570 **Personnel:** 1103

★ ○ **INDIANA UNIVERSITY HEALTH ARNETT HOSPITAL (150173)**, 5165 McCarty Lane, Zip 47905–8764, Mailing Address: P.O.Box 5545, 47903–5545; tel. 765/448–8000 **A**2 3 5 10 11 **F**3 11 12 13 15 17 18 20 22 24 26 28 29 30 31 34 35 40 43 45 46 49 50 51 54 57 59 61 64 65 68 69 70 72 74 75 76 77 78 79 81 82 85 87 89 93 97 99 100 104 107 108 110 111 114 115 116 117 118 119 120 121 126 129 130 131 132 135 144 146 147 148 **P**6 **S** Indiana University Health, Indianapolis, IN
Primary Contact: Donald Clayton, M.D., President
CFO: Cara Breidster, Chief Financial Officer
CMO: Jeffrey P Brown M.D., Chief Medical Officer
CIO: Rusty McGill, System Director Information Technology
CHR: Koreen H Kyhnell, Vice President Human Resources
Web address: www.iuhealth.org
Control: Other not–for–profit (including NFP Corporation) **Service:** General medical and surgical

Staffed Beds: 191 **Admissions:** 8615 **Census:** 104 **Outpatient Visits:** 103328 **Births:** 1606 **Total Expense ($000):** 381628 **Payroll Expense ($000):** 161536 **Personnel:** 1744

☒ **LAFAYETTE REGIONAL REHABILITATION HOSPITAL (153042)**, 950 Park East Boulevard, Zip 47905–0792; tel. 765/447–4040 **A**1 10 **F**3 28 29 35 60 64 75 90 93 94 132 143 148 **P**5 **S** Ernest Health, Inc., Albuquerque, NM
Primary Contact: Michelle Russell, Chief Executive Officer
Web address: www.lrrh.ernesthealth.com
Control: Corporation, Investor–owned (for–profit) **Service:** Rehabilitation

Staffed Beds: 40 **Admissions:** 620 **Census:** 22 **Outpatient Visits:** 2998 **Births:** 0 **Total Expense ($000):** 11790 **Payroll Expense ($000):** 5442 **Personnel:** 198

ST. ELIZABETH CENTRAL See Franciscan Health Lafayette Central

☐ **SYCAMORE SPRINGS HOSPITAL (154059)**, 833 Park East Boulevard, Zip 47905–0785; tel. 765/743–4400 **A**1 10 **F**4 5 40 98 102 103 104 105 **P**5 6
Primary Contact: Zoe Frantz, Chief Executive Officer
CFO: Michael Huth, Chief Financial Officer
CMO: Nizar El Khalili M.D., Medical Director
CHR: Pam Sichts, Director Human Resources
CNO: Brooke Lavignette, Director of Nursing
Web address: www.sycamorespringshealth.com
Control: Corporation, Investor–owned (for–profit) **Service:** Psychiatric

Staffed Beds: 48 **Admissions:** 1787 **Census:** 41 **Outpatient Visits:** 9177 **Births:** 0 **Total Expense ($000):** 11747 **Payroll Expense ($000):** 6264 **Personnel:** 115

LAGRANGE—Lagrange County

☒ **PARKVIEW LAGRANGE HOSPITAL (151323)**, 207 North Townline Road, Zip 46761–1325; tel. 260/463–9000 **A**1 10 18 **F**3 7 13 15 17 26 29 30 34 35 40 45 50 51 57 59 63 64 70 75 76 79 81 82 83 84 85 86 87 89 90 93 96 107 108 109 110 111 114 118 119 128 129 130 132 133 143 146 148 **S** Parkview Health, Fort Wayne, IN
Primary Contact: Jordi K. Disler, President
CFO: Vickie Stanski, Financial Manager
CMO: Jeffrey Brookes M.D., Chief Medical Officer
CIO: Ron Double, Chief Information Technology Officer
CHR: Bruce Buttermore, Director Human Resources
CNO: Jared Beasley R.N., Vice President Patient Care
Web address: www.parkview.com
Control: Other not–for–profit (including NFP Corporation) **Service:** General medical and surgical

Staffed Beds: 25 **Admissions:** 943 **Census:** 8 **Outpatient Visits:** 26339 **Births:** 238 **Total Expense ($000):** 31298 **Payroll Expense ($000):** 9777 **Personnel:** 153

LAWRENCEBURG—Dearborn County

COMMUNITY MENTAL HEALTH CENTER (154011), 285 Bielby Road, Zip 47025–1055; tel. 812/537–1302 **A**10 **F**98 100 101 102 104
Primary Contact: Tom Talbot, Chief Executive Officer
CFO: Georgii Zhirkin, Chief Financial Officer
CMO: Hasan Bakhtier M.D., Medical Director
CIO: John McKinley, Director, Information Technology
CHR: Kelly Stewart, Director of Human Resources
Web address: www.cmhcinc.org
Control: Other not–for–profit (including NFP Corporation) **Service:** Psychiatric

Staffed Beds: 16 **Admissions:** 419 **Census:** 7 **Outpatient Visits:** 0 **Births:** 0 **Total Expense ($000):** 2512 **Payroll Expense ($000):** 1419 **Personnel:** 26

★ ○ **DEARBORN COUNTY HOSPITAL (150086)**, 600 Wilson Creek Road, Zip 47025–2751; tel. 812/537–1010 **A**10 11 **F**3 4 11 13 15 20 28 30 34 35 37 40 43 44 45 46 47 49 50 57 59 62 63 64 70 75 76 77 79 81 84 85 86 87 92 93 107 108 110 111 115 116 117 118 119 129 130 131 132 146 148 **P**7
Primary Contact: Michael W. Schwebler, President and Chief Executive Officer
CFO: David Parlato, Vice President, Finance
CMO: Nancy A. Kennedy M.D., Chief Medical Officer
CNO: Angela Scudder MSN, R.N., Vice President Patient Care Services
Web address: www.dch.org
Control: County, Government, Nonfederal **Service:** General medical and surgical

Staffed Beds: 88 **Admissions:** 4147 **Census:** 38 **Outpatient Visits:** 148025 **Births:** 384 **Total Expense ($000):** 78396 **Payroll Expense ($000):** 34833 **Personnel:** 660

LEBANON—Boone County

☒ **WITHAM HEALTH SERVICES (150104)**, 2605 North Lebanon Street, Zip 46052–1476, Mailing Address: P.O.Box 1200, 46052–3005; tel. 765/485–8000 **A**1 10 **F**3 7 13 15 18 20 28 29 30 34 40 42 45 54 56 57 59 64 65 68 69 70 75 76 77 79 81 82 83 85 86 87 93 94 97 98 99 103 107 108 110 111 114 115 118 119 128 129 130 132 135 141 142 143 144 146 147 148 **P**1
Primary Contact: Raymond V. Ingham, Ph.D., President and Chief Executive Officer
COO: Diane Feder R.N., FACHE, Senior Vice President and Chief Operating Officer
CFO: George Pogas CPA, Senior Vice President and Chief Financial Officer
CMO: Anthony Steele M.D., Chief Medical Officer
CIO: George Pogas CPA, Senior Vice President and Chief Financial Officer
CHR: Gary A Deater, Vice President Administration, Human Resources and Risk Management
CNO: Diane Feder R.N., FACHE, Senior Vice President and Chief Operating Officer
Web address: www.witham.org
Control: County, Government, Nonfederal **Service:** General medical and surgical

Staffed Beds: 70 **Admissions:** 2778 **Census:** 39 **Outpatient Visits:** 136150 **Births:** 476 **Total Expense ($000):** 119675 **Payroll Expense ($000):** 51543 **Personnel:** 673

LINTON—Greene County

✠ **GREENE COUNTY GENERAL HOSPITAL (151317)**, 1185 North 1000 West, Zip 47441–5282; tel. 812/847–2281 **A**1 10 18 **F**1 3 6 11 13 15 18 19 26 27 29 30 31 34 35 40 41 45 50 55 57 58 59 62 64 65 66 67 68 70 75 76 77 78 79 81 85 86 87 90 91 93 107 108 110 114 119 125 127 128 130 133 135 146 147 148 149 **P**6
Primary Contact: Brenda Reetz, FACHE, Chief Executive Officer
CFO: April Settles, Chief Financial Officer
CMO: Frederick R. Ridge, Chief of Staff
CIO: Steve Phillips, Information Officer
CHR: Jean Prather, Director of Human Resources
CNO: Lea Ann Camp R.N., Chief Nursing Officer
Web address: www.greenecountyhospital.com
Control: County, Government, Nonfederal **Service:** General medical and surgical

Staffed Beds: 25 **Admissions:** 709 **Census:** 6 **Outpatient Visits:** 649345 **Births:** 70 **Total Expense ($000):** 27176 **Payroll Expense ($000):** 11783 **Personnel:** 257

LOGANSPORT—Cass County

FOUR COUNTY COUNSELING CENTER (154035), 1015 Michigan Avenue, Zip 46947–1526; tel. 574/722–5151 (Nonreporting) **A**10
Primary Contact: C.J. Davis, Chief Executive Officer/ Executive Director
COO: Carrie Cadwell M.D., Chief Clinical Officer
CFO: Jason Cadwell, Chief Financial Officer
CMO: John Yarling M.D., Medical Director
CIO: Becky Mulis, Director of Health Information Management Systems
CHR: Steve Curry, Regional Director Human Resources
CNO: Donna Henry, Vice President of Nursing Services
Web address: www.fourcounty.org
Control: Other not–for–profit (including NFP Corporation) **Service:** Psychiatric

Staffed Beds: 15

★ ○ **LOGANSPORT MEMORIAL HOSPITAL (150072)**, 1101 Michigan Avenue, Zip 46947–1528, Mailing Address: P.O.Box 7013, 46947–7013; tel. 574/753–7541 **A**10 11 20 **F**3 11 13 15 28 29 32 34 35 36 40 44 45 48 49 50 51 57 59 64 65 68 69 70 75 76 77 78 79 81 85 86 87 93 97 107 108 110 111 114 119 124 129 130 132 135 146 147 149 **P**6
Primary Contact: Perry Gay, President and Chief Executive Officer
CFO: Sherri Gehlhausen, Assistant Chief Financial Officer
CIO: Beth Jump, Chief Information Officer
CHR: Lynda J Shrock, Vice President Human Resources
CNO: Tara McVay, Chief Nursing Officer
Web address: www.logansportmemorial.org
Control: County, Government, Nonfederal **Service:** General medical and surgical

Staffed Beds: 83 **Admissions:** 1730 **Census:** 14 **Outpatient Visits:** 109905 **Births:** 498 **Total Expense ($000):** 70187 **Payroll Expense ($000):** 31318 **Personnel:** 550

☐ **LOGANSPORT STATE HOSPITAL**, 1098 South State Road 25, Zip 46947–6723; tel. 574/737–3633, (Nonreporting) **A**1
Primary Contact: Robert Clover, Superintendent and Chief Executive Officer
CFO: Misty Moss, Director Business Administration
CMO: Danny Meadows M.D., Medical Director
CIO: Joe McIntosh, Director Management Information Systems
CHR: Dianne Renner, Director Human Resources
Web address: www.lshonline.org
Control: State, Government, Nonfederal **Service:** Psychiatric

Staffed Beds: 170

MADISON—Jefferson County

★ ○ **KING'S DAUGHTERS' HEALTH (150069)**, 1373 East State Road 62, Zip 47250–3357, Mailing Address: P.O.Box 447, 47250–0447; tel. 812/801–0800 **A**2 10 11 **F**3 7 8 13 15 18 20 22 28 29 30 31 32 34 35 40 42 45 48 50 55 56 57 59 62 63 64 65 68 70 74 75 76 77 78 79 81 82 84 85 86 87 89 91 93 94 97 107 108 110 111 115 119 120 121 123 129 130 131 132 134 135 144 145 146 147 148 149 150 **P**6
Primary Contact: Carol Dozier, President and Chief Executive Officer
CFO: Steve Meacham, Vice President Finance
CIO: Linda Darnell, Director Management Information Systems
CHR: Susan Poling, Director Human Resources
CNO: Lisa Morgan R.N., Vice President Patient Services
Web address: www.kdhhs.org
Control: Other not–for–profit (including NFP Corporation) **Service:** General medical and surgical

Staffed Beds: 77 **Admissions:** 3250 **Census:** 33 **Outpatient Visits:** 204120 **Births:** 500 **Total Expense ($000):** 120583 **Payroll Expense ($000):** 51490 **Personnel:** 747

☐ **MADISON STATE HOSPITAL (154019)**, 711 Green Road, Zip 47250–2199; tel. 812/265–2611, (Nonreporting) **A**1 10
Primary Contact: Peggy Stephens, M.D., Superintendent and Medical Director
COO: Peggy Stephens M.D., Superintendent and Medical Director
CFO: Carolyn Copeland, Business Administrator
CMO: Peggy Stephens M.D., Superintendent and Medical Director
CIO: Ric Martin, Information Specialist
Web address: www.in.gov/fssa/msh
Control: State, Government, Nonfederal **Service:** Psychiatric

Staffed Beds: 150

MARION—Grant County

☐ **GRANT–BLACKFORD MENTAL HEALTH CENTER (154021)**, 505 North Wabash Avenue, Zip 46952–2608; tel. 765/662–3971 (Nonreporting) **A**1 10
Primary Contact: Paul Kuczora, Chief Executive Officer
Web address: www.cornerstone.org/
Control: Other not–for–profit (including NFP Corporation) **Service:** Psychiatric

Staffed Beds: 16

★ ○ **MARION GENERAL HOSPITAL (150011)**, 441 North Wabash Avenue, Zip 46952–2690; tel. 765/660–6000 **A**2 10 11 **F**3 7 8 11 13 15 18 20 22 26 28 29 30 31 34 35 40 41 44 45 47 50 54 57 58 59 64 68 70 74 76 77 78 79 81 82 85 86 87 89 90 91 92 93 96 97 107 108 110 111 112 114 115 116 117 118 119 129 130 132 135 145 146 147 148 149 **P**6
Primary Contact: Stephanie Hilton–Siebert, MSN, President and Chief Executive Officer
CFO: Jeff Wakefield CPA, Chief Financial Officer
CMO: Edward L. Keppler M.D., Chief Medical Officer
CIO: Emmanuel Ndow, Chief Information Officer
CHR: Karen Jones, Administrative Director Human Resources
CNO: Cynthia Futrell MSN, R.N., Chief Nursing Officer
Web address: www.mgh.net
Control: Other not–for–profit (including NFP Corporation) **Service:** General medical and surgical

Staffed Beds: 115 **Admissions:** 5522 **Census:** 58 **Outpatient Visits:** 240140 **Births:** 628 **Total Expense ($000):** 163278 **Payroll Expense ($000):** 45875 **Personnel:** 1001

VETERANS AFFAIRS NORTHERN INDIANA HEALTH CARE SYSTEM–MARION CAMPUS See Veterans Affairs Northern Indiana Health Care System, Fort Wayne

MERRILLVILLE—Lake County

REGIONAL MENTAL HEALTH CENTER (154020), 8555 Taft Street, Zip 46410–6123; tel. 219/769–4005 (Nonreporting) **A**10
Primary Contact: Robert D. Krumwied, President and Chief Executive Officer
Web address: www.regionalmentalhealth.org/
Control: Corporation, Investor–owned (for–profit) **Service:** Psychiatric

Staffed Beds: 16

SOUTHLAKE CAMPUS See Methodist Hospitals, Gary

MICHIGAN CITY—Laporte County

○ **FRANCISCAN ST. ANTHONY HEALTH – MICHIGAN CITY (150015)**, 301 West Homer Street, Zip 46360–4358; tel. 219/879–8511, (Nonreporting) **A**2 10 11 19 **S** Franciscan Health, Mishawaka, IN
Primary Contact: Dean Mazzoni, President and Chief Executive Officer
CFO: Marc Golan, Regional Chief Financial Officer
CIO: Tim Loosemore, Regional Director Information Systems
CHR: John Barrett, Regional Director Human Resources
CNO: Trish Weber R.N., FACHE, Vice President Operations and Chief Nursing Officer
Web address: www.franciscanalliance.org
Control: Church operated, Nongovernment, not–for–profit **Service:** General medical and surgical

Staffed Beds: 171

SAINT ANTHONY MEMORIAL See Franciscan St. Anthony Health – Michigan City

IN

MISHAWAKA—St. Joseph County

✠ **KINDRED HOSPITAL OF NORTHERN INDIANA (152018)**, 215 West Fourth Street, Suite 200, Zip 46544–1917; tel. 574/252–2000, (Nonreporting) **A**1 10 **S** Kindred Healthcare, Louisville, KY
Primary Contact: Lori Skora, Chief Executive Officer
CFO: Christy Henrich, Controller
CMO: Matthew F. Koscielski M.D., Medical Director
CNO: Jennifer Pierce, Chief Clinical Officer
Web address: www.khnorthernindiana.com/
Control: Corporation, Investor–owned (for–profit) **Service**: Acute long–term care hospital

Staffed Beds: 32

✠ **MISHAWAKA MEDICAL CENTER (150012)**, 5215 Holy Cross Parkway, Zip 46545–1469; tel. 574/335–5000 **A**1 2 3 5 10 **F**3 11 13 15 17 18 19 20 21 22 23 24 26 28 29 30 31 34 35 36 37 39 40 41 45 46 47 48 49 50 52 54 55 57 58 59 61 63 64 65 66 68 70 71 72 74 75 76 77 78 79 80 81 82 83 84 85 86 87 89 90 91 92 93 96 97 107 108 110 114 115 117 118 119 120 121 124 126 130 131 132 135 146 147 148 149 **S** Trinity Health, Livonia, MI
Primary Contact: Chad Towner, Chief Executive Officer
COO: Christopher J Karam, Chief Operating Officer
CFO: Kevin J Higdon, Chief Financial Officer
CMO: Stephen Anderson M.D., Chief Medical Officer
CIO: Gary L Miller, Senior Director Information Systems
CHR: Kurt A Meyer, Chief Human Resource Officer
CNO: Kenneth C Hall R.N., Chief Nursing Officer
Web address: www.sjmed.com
Control: Other not–for–profit (including NFP Corporation) **Service**: General medical and surgical

Staffed Beds: 294 **Admissions:** 14987 **Census:** 184 **Outpatient Visits:** 208516 **Births:** 1780 **Total Expense ($000):** 292175 **Payroll Expense ($000):** 84328 **Personnel:** 1533

☐ **RIVERCREST SPECIALTY HOSPITAL (154061)**, 1625 East Jefferson Boulevard, Zip 46545–7103; tel. 574/255–1400 **A**1 10 **F**3 6 29 30 35 38 56 75 77 98 101 103 132 135 148 149 **S** NeuroPsychiatric Hospitals, Mishawaka, IN
Primary Contact: Christy Gilbert, Chief Executive Officer
Web address: www.physicianshospitalsystem.net/
Control: Corporation, Investor–owned (for–profit) **Service**: Psychiatric

Staffed Beds: 30 **Admissions:** 585 **Census:** 28 **Outpatient Visits:** 0 **Births:** 0 **Total Expense ($000):** 5977 **Payroll Expense ($000):** 3454 **Personnel:** 66

TRIUMPH OUR LADY OF PEACE HOSPITAL See Kindred Hospital Of Northern Indiana

○ **UNITY MEDICAL & SURGICAL HOSPITAL (150177)**, 4455 Edison Lakes Parkway, Zip 46545–1442; tel. 574/968–0867 (Nonreporting) **A**10 11
Primary Contact: John M. Day, Chief Executive Officer
COO: Donald Allen, Chief Operating Officer
CFO: Matthew M Sherwood, Chief Financial Officer
CMO: Viraj Patel M.D., Chief Medical Officer
CIO: Richard Leighton, Financial Application Analyst
CHR: Emyle Kruyer–Collins, Chief Human Resources Officer
CNO: Sylvia K Coffing R.N., MSN, Chief Nursing and Compliance Officer
Web address: www.umsh.net
Control: Partnership, Investor–owned (for–profit) **Service**: Surgical

Staffed Beds: 15

MONTICELLO—White County

★ **INDIANA UNIVERSITY HEALTH WHITE MEMORIAL HOSPITAL (151312)**, 720 South Sixth Street, Zip 47960–8182; tel. 574/583–7111 **A**10 18 **F**3 11 15 29 30 31 34 35 40 45 50 57 59 64 69 70 75 77 78 79 81 85 91 93 107 108 110 111 114 119 129 133 135 146 147 149 150 **S** Indiana University Health, Indianapolis, IN
Primary Contact: Mary Minier, President
CMO: Adel Khdour M.D., Chief Medical Officer
CIO: Michelle Baker, Director Information Systems
CHR: JoEllyn Brockmeyer, Director Human Resources
CNO: Robin C Smith, Chief Nursing Officer
Web address: www.iuhealth.org/white–memorial
Control: Other not–for–profit (including NFP Corporation) **Service**: General medical and surgical

Staffed Beds: 25 **Admissions:** 549 **Census:** 5 **Outpatient Visits:** 38556 **Births:** 0 **Total Expense ($000):** 23656 **Payroll Expense ($000):** 7564 **Personnel:** 133

MOORESVILLE—Morgan County

○ **FRANCISCAN ST. FRANCIS HEALTH – MOORESVILLE (150057)**, 1201 Hadley Road, Zip 46158–1789; tel. 317/831–1160, (Nonreporting) **A**3 5 10 11 **S** Franciscan Health, Mishawaka, IN
Primary Contact: Peter J. Murphy, Senior Vice President and Chief Operating Officer
CIO: Barbara Coulter, Director Information Systems
CHR: John Ross, Vice President
Web address: www.franciscanalliance.org/hospitals/mooresville/Pages/default.aspx
Control: Church operated, Nongovernment, not–for–profit **Service**: General medical and surgical

Staffed Beds: 115

ST. FRANCIS HOSPITAL–MOORESVILLE See Franciscan St. Francis Health – Mooresville

MUNCIE—Delaware County

○ **AMG SPECIALTY HOSPITAL – MUNCIE (152025)**, 2401 West University Avenue, 8th Floor, Zip 47303–3428; tel. 765/751–5253 (Nonreporting) **A**10 11
Primary Contact: James Whitacre, Chief Executive Officer
CNO: Lisa G. Hayes, Chief Clinical Officer
Web address: www.amgmuncie.com/
Control: Corporation, Investor–owned (for–profit) **Service**: Acute long–term care hospital

Staffed Beds: 32

BALL MEMORIAL HOSPITAL See Indiana University Health Ball Memorial Hospital

✠ △ **INDIANA UNIVERSITY HEALTH BALL MEMORIAL HOSPITAL (150089)**, 2401 University Avenue, Zip 47303–3499; tel. 765/747–3111 **A**1 2 3 5 7 10 19 **F**11 12 13 15 17 18 20 22 24 26 27 28 29 30 31 32 34 35 39 40 41 43 45 49 50 51 53 54 56 57 58 59 60 64 65 66 69 70 72 74 75 76 77 78 79 80 81 82 83 84 85 86 87 89 90 91 92 93 94 96 97 99 100 102 107 110 111 114 115 116 117 118 119 120 121 123 124 126 129 130 132 146 147 148 **S** Indiana University Health, Indianapolis, IN
Primary Contact: Michael E. Haley, President
COO: Jeffrey C Bird M.D., Chief Operating Officer and Chief Medical Officer
CFO: Lori Luther CPA, Chief Financial Officer
CMO: Jeffrey C Bird M.D., Chief Operating Officer and Chief Medical Officer
CHR: Ann M. McGuire, Regional Vice President Human Resources
CNO: Carla C. Cox, Chief Nursing Officer
Web address: www.iuhealth.org
Control: Other not–for–profit (including NFP Corporation) **Service**: General medical and surgical

Staffed Beds: 339 **Admissions:** 15770 **Census:** 227 **Outpatient Visits:** 302321 **Births:** 1454 **Total Expense ($000):** 340833 **Payroll Expense ($000):** 103930 **Personnel:** 1804

MERIDIAN HEALTH SERVICES (154053), 240 North Tillotson Avenue, Zip 47304; tel. 765/747–3281 (Nonreporting) **A**10
Primary Contact: Hank A. Milius, Chief Executive Officer
CMO: Sarfraz Khan, Medical Director
Web address: www.meridianhs.org
Control: Other not–for–profit (including NFP Corporation) **Service**: Psychiatric

Staffed Beds: 20

RENAISSANCE SPECIALTY HOSPITAL OF CENTRAL INDIANA See AMG Specialty Hospital – Muncie

MUNSTER—Lake County

☐ **COMMUNITY HOSPITAL (150125)**, 901 Macarthur Boulevard, Zip 46321–2959; tel. 219/836–1600 **A**1 2 10 **F**8 11 12 13 15 17 18 20 22 24 26 28 29 30 31 34 35 36 38 39 40 45 46 47 49 50 53 54 55 57 58 59 62 64 70 72 73 74 75 77 78 79 80 81 82 85 86 87 90 92 93 96 107 108 110 111 114 115 116 119 120 121 123 124 126 129 130 131 132 135 144 146 147 148 **S** Community Healthcare System, Hammond, IN
Primary Contact: Luis F. Molina, Chief Executive Officer and Administrator
CFO: Daniel R. O'Brien, Vice President and Chief Financial Officer
CMO: David Robinson, President Medical and Dental Staff
CIO: Gary Weiner, Vice President Information Technology, Chief Information Officer
CHR: Debbie Brandt, Director Human Resources
CNO: Ronda McKay R.N., Vice President Patient Care Services, Chief Nursing Officer
Web address: www.comhs.org
Control: Other not–for–profit (including NFP Corporation) **Service**: General medical and surgical

Staffed Beds: 491 **Admissions:** 18645 **Census:** 301 **Outpatient Visits:** 380350 **Births:** 1981 **Total Expense ($000):** 458380 **Payroll Expense ($000):** 161184 **Personnel:** 2551

IN

○ **FRANCISCAN HEALTHCARE – MUNSTER (150165)**, 701 Superior Avenue, Zip 46321–4037; tel. 219/924–1300, (Nonreporting) **A**10 11 **S** Franciscan Health, Mishawaka, IN
Primary Contact: Patrick J. Maloney, Chief Executive Officer
CFO: Harold E Collins JD, Chief Financial Officer
CMO: Vijay D Gupta M.D., President and Chief Executive Officer
CIO: Steven Krause, Manager Information Technology
Web address: www.franciscanphysicianshospital.org
Control: Partnership, Investor–owned (for–profit) **Service**: General medical and surgical

Staffed Beds: 32

NEW ALBANY—Floyd County

★ ○ **BAPTIST HEALTH FLOYD (150044)**, 1850 State Street, Zip 47150–4997; tel. 812/949–5500 **A**2 3 5 10 11 **F**3 8 11 12 13 15 17 18 20 22 24 26 28 29 30 31 34 35 40 43 45 49 50 56 57 58 59 62 64 70 74 75 77 78 79 80 81 82 84 85 86 87 92 93 100 107 108 109 110 111 114 115 116 117 118 119 120 121 123 129 130 131 132 135 144 146 147 148 149 **S** Baptist Health, Louisville, KY
Primary Contact: Daniel J. Eichenberger, M.D., President and Chief Executive Officer
COO: Mark Truman, Vice President of Operations
CFO: Ted Miller, Chief Financial Officer
CIO: Brian Cox, Director Information Systems
CHR: Sue Christopher, Vice President, Human Resources
CNO: Kelly McMinoway R.N., Vice President, Nursing
Web address: www.floydmemorial.com
Control: Other not–for–profit (including NFP Corporation) **Service**: General medical and surgical

Staffed Beds: 246 Admissions: 12087 Census: 146 Outpatient Visits: 725187 Births: 1232 Total Expense ($000): 363584 Payroll Expense ($000): 149293 Personnel: 2065

□ **PHYSICIANS' MEDICAL CENTER (150172)**, 4023 Reas Lane, Zip 47150–2228; tel. 812/206–7660 **A**1 10 **F**3 12 29 45 51 77 81 82 85 89 94 107 111 144
Primary Contact: Dennis Medley, Chief Executive Officer and Administrator
COO: Rob Jones, Director of Nursing and Operations
CFO: Dennis Medley, Chief Executive Officer
CMO: Perry Cassady M.D., Medical Director
CIO: Rob Jones, Director of Nursing and Operations
CHR: Mary Arntz, Manager Business Office and Executive Assistant
CNO: Rob Jones, Director of Nursing and Operations
Web address: www.pmcindiana.com
Control: Partnership, Investor–owned (for–profit) **Service**: General medical and surgical

Staffed Beds: 12 Admissions: 1145 Census: 4 Outpatient Visits: 21139 Births: 0 Total Expense ($000): 51695 Payroll Expense ($000): 6956 Personnel: 222

⊠ △ **SOUTHERN INDIANA REHABILITATION HOSPITAL (153037)**, 3104 Blackiston Boulevard, Zip 47150–9579; tel. 812/941–8300, (Total facility includes 26 beds in nursing home–type unit) **A**1 7 10 **F**3 28 29 34 35 50 57 59 74 75 77 79 86 87 90 91 128 130 132 135 143 146 **P**5 **S** Catholic Health Initiatives, Englewood, CO
Primary Contact: William Boso, Executive Director, Administrator
CFO: Robert Steltenpohl, Vice President
CMO: John C Shaw M.D., Medical Director
CHR: Lisa Burris, Director Human Resources
CNO: Suzann Byers, Director of Nursing
Web address: www.sirh.org
Control: Other not–for–profit (including NFP Corporation) **Service**: Rehabilitation

Staffed Beds: 60 Admissions: 1167 Census: 42 Outpatient Visits: 98737 Births: 0 Total Expense ($000): 18984 Payroll Expense ($000): 10159 Personnel: 185

NEW CASTLE—Henry County

★ ○ **HENRY COUNTY HOSPITAL (150030)**, 1000 North 16th Street, Zip 47362–4319, Mailing Address: P.O.Box 490, 47362–0490; tel. 765/521–0890, (Nonreporting) **A**10 11
Primary Contact: Paul Janssen, President and Chief Executive Officer
COO: Brian K Ring, Chief Operating Officer
CFO: Darin Brown, Vice President Finance
CMO: Wylie McGlothlin M.D., Chief Medical Officer
CIO: Mike Spencer, Chief Information Officer
CHR: Deanna Malott, Director Human Resources
CNO: Leslie Cowan R.N., Chief Nursing Officer
Web address: www.hcmhcares.org
Control: County, Government, Nonfederal **Service**: General medical and surgical

Staffed Beds: 90

NEWBURGH—Warrick County

□ **BRENTWOOD MEADOWS (154055)**, 4455 Roslin Road, Zip 47630; tel. 812/858–7200 **A**1 10 **F**5 98 102 104 105
Primary Contact: Jessica Black, Chief Executive Officer
Web address: www.brentwoodmeadows.com
Control: Corporation, Investor–owned (for–profit) **Service**: Psychiatric

Staffed Beds: 48 Admissions: 1797 Census: 38 Outpatient Visits: 0 Births: 0 Total Expense ($000): 10186 Payroll Expense ($000): 5062 Personnel: 108

★ ○ **THE HEART HOSPITAL AT DEACONESS GATEWAY (150175)**, 4007 Gateway Boulevard, Zip 47630–8947; tel. 812/842–4784 **A**10 11 **F**3 17 18 20 22 24 26 28 29 30 34 35 57 58 59 60 62 63 64 68 81 83 84 85 86 87 107 108 109 111 114 115 116 117 118 119 130 132 149 **S** Deaconess Health System, Evansville, IN
Primary Contact: Rebecca Malotte, Executive Director and Chief Nursing Officer
COO: Rebecca Malotte, Executive Director and Chief Nursing Officer
CFO: Tracy Hoefling, Chief Financial Officer
CMO: Lee Wagmeister M.D., President Medical Staff
CIO: Lisa Hobgood, Chief Information Officer
CHR: Sarah Bryan, Manager Human Resources
CNO: Rebecca Malotte, Executive Director and Chief Nursing Officer
Web address: www.deaconess.com/
Control: Partnership, Investor–owned (for–profit) **Service**: Heart

Staffed Beds: 24 Admissions: 1590 Census: 17 Outpatient Visits: 18446 Births: 0 Total Expense ($000): 42968 Payroll Expense ($000): 8464 Personnel: 151

★ ○ **THE WOMEN'S HOSPITAL (150149)**, 4199 Gateway Boulevard, Zip 47630–8940; tel. 812/842–4200 **A**3 10 11 **F**3 13 15 29 30 34 35 36 40 50 53 55 57 59 63 64 65 72 75 76 77 81 84 85 86 87 93 110 119 126 130 132 134 135 147 **P**6 **S** Deaconess Health System, Evansville, IN
Primary Contact: Christina M. Ryan, R.N., Chief Executive Officer
CFO: Tina Cady, Controller
CIO: Jenny Skelton, System Integration Manager
CHR: Jerri Sue Traylor, Director Human Resources
CNO: Christina M Ryan R.N., Chief Executive Officer and Chief Nursing Officer
Web address: www.deaconess.com
Control: Partnership, Investor–owned (for–profit) **Service**: Obstetrics and gynecology

Staffed Beds: 74 Admissions: 3833 Census: 55 Outpatient Visits: 37518 Births: 3123 Total Expense ($000): 79979 Payroll Expense ($000): 34268 Personnel: 547

NOBLESVILLE—Hamilton County

○ △ **RIVERVIEW HEALTH (150059)**, 395 Westfield Road, Zip 46060–1425, Mailing Address: P.O.Box 220, 46061–0220; tel. 317/773–0760 **A**2 7 10 11 **F**3 8 11 13 15 17 18 20 22 24 26 28 29 30 31 34 35 37 40 45 46 49 50 53 54 56 57 59 60 62 63 64 65 70 73 74 75 76 77 78 79 81 82 85 86 87 89 90 91 93 94 97 107 108 110 111 114 115 116 118 119 120 121 123 128 129 130 131 132 135 144 146 147 148 149
Primary Contact: Seth Warren, President and Chief Executive Officer
COO: Lawrence Christman, Chief Financial Officer and Chief Operating Officer
CFO: Brenda Baker, Chief Financial Officer
CMO: Eric Marcotte M.D., Chief Medical Officer
CIO: Brant Bucciarelli, Chief Information Officer
CHR: Ann Kuzee, Executive Director Human Resources
CNO: Joyce Wood, Vice President Organizational Improvement and Chief Nursing Officer
Web address: www.riverview.org
Control: County, Government, Nonfederal **Service**: General medical and surgical

Staffed Beds: 156 Admissions: 4722 Census: 71 Outpatient Visits: 464180 Births: 656 Total Expense ($000): 185216 Payroll Expense ($000): 69691 Personnel: 1151

IN

NORTH VERNON—Jennings County

⊞ **ST. VINCENT JENNINGS HOSPITAL (151303)**, 301 Henry Street, Zip 47265–1097; tel. 812/352–4200 **A**1 10 18 **F**3 18 29 30 34 35 40 45 46 50 57 59 62 64 65 68 75 77 79 81 85 93 97 103 107 111 115 119 128 130 133 135 144 146 148 **S** Ascension Healthcare, Saint Louis, MO
Primary Contact: Jessica Kietzman, R.N., Interim Administrator
CFO: Joseph Kubala, Chief Financial Officer
CMO: Jennifer Stanley M.D., Chief Medical Officer
CHR: Kathryn Johnson, Manager Human Resources, Marketing and Public Relations
CNO: Jessica Kietzman R.N., Chief Nursing Officer
Web address: www.stvincent.org
Control: Other not–for–profit (including NFP Corporation) **Service:** General medical and surgical

Staffed Beds: 17 **Admissions:** 332 **Census:** 3 **Outpatient Visits:** 33531 **Births:** 0 **Total Expense ($000):** 15778 **Payroll Expense ($000):** 4824	

PAOLI—Orange County

BLOOMINGTON HOSPITAL OF ORANGE COUNTY See Indiana University Health Paoli Hospital

⊞ **INDIANA UNIVERSITY HEALTH PAOLI HOSPITAL (151306)**, 642 West Hospital Road, Zip 47454–9672, Mailing Address: P.O.Box 499, 47454–0499; tel. 812/723–2811 **A**1 10 18 **F**3 13 15 29 30 35 40 45 50 57 59 64 76 77 81 84 85 89 93 107 110 111 114 119 129 132 133 135 146 148 149 150 **S** Indiana University Health, Indianapolis, IN
Primary Contact: Larry Bailey, Chief Executive Officer
COO: Sonya M. Zeller R.N., Vice President, Chief Operating Officer and Chief Nursing Officer
CMO: Vincent John Waldron M.D., President Medical Staff
CNO: Sonya M. Zeller R.N., Vice President, Chief Operating Officer and Chief Nursing Officer
Web address: www.iuhealth.org/paoli
Control: Other not–for–profit (including NFP Corporation) **Service:** General medical and surgical

Staffed Beds: 25 **Admissions:** 212 **Census:** 2 **Outpatient Visits:** 27655 **Births:** 120 **Total Expense ($000):** 20802 **Payroll Expense ($000):** 7282 **Personnel:** 123	

PERU—Miami County

⊞ **DUKES MEMORIAL HOSPITAL (151318)**, 275 West 12th Street, Zip 46970–1638; tel. 765/472–8000 **A**1 10 18 **F**3 7 8 13 15 17 18 28 29 34 35 40 41 50 51 57 59 64 68 69 70 75 76 77 79 81 85 87 89 90 93 97 107 108 110 111 115 118 119 129 130 132 133 135 144 146 147 **P**6 **S** Community Health Systems, Inc., Franklin, TN
Primary Contact: Debra Close, Chief Executive Officer
CFO: Adam Cumbo, Chief Financial Officer
CMO: Neil Stalker M.D., Chief of Staff
Web address: www.dukesmemorialhosp.com
Control: Corporation, Investor–owned (for–profit) **Service:** General medical and surgical

Staffed Beds: 25 **Admissions:** 1120 **Census:** 10 **Outpatient Visits:** 41176 **Births:** 149 **Total Expense ($000):** 37920 **Payroll Expense ($000):** 16934 **Personnel:** 238	

PLYMOUTH—Marshall County

☐ **MICHIANA BEHAVIORAL HEALTH CENTER (154047)**, 1800 North Oak Drive, Zip 46563–3492; tel. 574/936–3784, (Nonreporting) **A**1 10 **S** Universal Health Services, Inc., King of Prussia, PA
Primary Contact: Michael Perry, Chief Executive Officer
CFO: Jeff Calvin, Chief Financial Officer
CMO: Robert Raster M.D., Medical Director
CIO: Leslie McLaughlin, Director of Business Development
CHR: Becky Nowicki, Director Human Resources
CNO: Brandi Richard, Chief Nursing Officer
Web address: www.michianabhc.com
Control: Corporation, Investor–owned (for–profit) **Service:** Psychiatric

Staffed Beds: 75	

⊞ **PLYMOUTH MEDICAL CENTER (150076)**, 1915 Lake Avenue, Zip 46563–9366, Mailing Address: P.O.Box 670, 46563–0670; tel. 574/948–4000 **A**1 10 **F**3 8 13 15 18 20 29 30 31 34 35 40 45 46 50 51 54 57 59 64 65 66 68 70 74 75 76 78 79 81 84 85 86 87 89 91 92 93 97 107 108 110 114 115 118 119 120 121 123 124 129 132 135 146 148 149 **S** Trinity Health, Livonia, MI
Primary Contact: Loretta Schmidt, President
COO: Tamara Awald, Chief Nursing Officer and Chief Operating Officer
CFO: Janice Dunn, Chief Financial Officer
CMO: Stephen Anderson M.D., Chief Medical Officer
CIO: Gary L Miller, Regional Director Information Systems
CHR: Kurt A Meyer, Chief Human Resources Officer
CNO: Tamara Awald, Chief Nursing Officer and Chief Operating Officer
Web address: www.sjmed.com
Control: Other not–for–profit (including NFP Corporation) **Service:** General medical and surgical

Staffed Beds: 48 **Admissions:** 1954 **Census:** 15 **Outpatient Visits:** 88185 **Births:** 234 **Total Expense ($000):** 47173 **Payroll Expense ($000):** 15717 **Personnel:** 317	

PORTLAND—Jay County

⊞ **JAY COUNTY HOSPITAL (151320)**, 500 West Votaw Street, Zip 47371–1322; tel. 260/726–7131 **A**1 10 18 **F**3 8 11 13 15 28 29 30 32 34 35 40 45 50 57 59 68 70 75 76 77 81 85 86 87 103 107 108 110 111 114 119 129 130 132 133 135 146 148 149 **P**6 **S** Indiana University Health, Indianapolis, IN
Primary Contact: David W. Hyatt, Chief Executive Officer
CFO: Don Michael, Vice President, Chief Financial Officer
CIO: Jeff Horn, Vice President, Information and Support Services
CHR: Jerry Bozell, Vice President, Human Resources
CNO: Lisa Craiger, Vice President, Chief Nursing Officer
Web address: www.jaycountyhospital.com
Control: County, Government, Nonfederal **Service:** General medical and surgical

Staffed Beds: 35 **Admissions:** 1046 **Census:** 13 **Outpatient Visits:** 105174 **Births:** 65 **Total Expense ($000):** 41030 **Payroll Expense ($000):** 17261 **Personnel:** 311	

PRINCETON—Gibson County

⊞ **GIBSON GENERAL HOSPITAL (151319)**, 1808 Sherman Drive, Zip 47670–1043; tel. 812/385–3401, (Total facility includes 45 beds in nursing home–type unit) **A**1 10 18 **F**3 5 11 15 28 29 30 31 34 35 38 40 45 49 50 54 56 57 58 59 62 64 68 70 75 77 79 81 82 89 93 97 99 100 101 102 103 104 107 110 111 115 119 128 129 130 131 132 133 146 148 **P**6 **S** Deaconess Health System, Evansville, IN
Primary Contact: Emmett C. Schuster, President and Chief Executive Officer
CFO: James R Childers, Vice President and Chief Financial Officer
CMO: Krishna Murthy M.D., Chief of Medical Staff
CIO: James R Childers, Vice President and Chief Financial Officer
CHR: D Deann Hunt, Director Human Resources
CNO: Lori Phillips, Vice President and Chief Nursing Officer
Web address: www.gibsongeneral.com
Control: Other not–for–profit (including NFP Corporation) **Service:** General medical and surgical

Staffed Beds: 70 **Admissions:** 461 **Census:** 47 **Outpatient Visits:** 32004 **Births:** 0 **Total Expense ($000):** 24720 **Payroll Expense ($000):** 10626 **Personnel:** 264	

RENSSELAER—Jasper County

FRANCISCAN HEALTH RENSSELAER (151324), 1104 East Grace Street, Zip 47978–3296; tel. 219/866–5141, (Total facility includes 21 beds in nursing home–type unit) **A**10 18 **F**1 3 11 15 29 30 31 35 40 43 49 50 51 54 57 62 63 64 67 69 70 75 77 78 79 81 85 91 93 94 107 108 110 111 115 118 119 127 128 129 130 132 133 135 145 148 **S** Franciscan Health, Mishawaka, IN
Primary Contact: Timothy M. Schreeg, President and Chief Executive Officer
CFO: Jeffrey D Webb CPA, Chief Financial Officer
CIO: Kirby Reed, Director Information Systems
CHR: Deana Brown, Director Administrative Services
CNO: Stacie Klingler R.N., Vice President of Patient Services
Web address: www.jchh.com
Control: Church operated, Nongovernment, not–for–profit **Service:** General medical and surgical

Staffed Beds: 46 **Admissions:** 714 **Census:** 21 **Outpatient Visits:** 85959 **Births:** 0 **Total Expense ($000):** 38906 **Payroll Expense ($000):** 13469 **Personnel:** 194	

IN

RICHMOND—Wayne County

★ ○ **REID HEALTH (150048)**, 1100 Reid Parkway, Zip 47374–1157; tel. 765/983–3000 **A**2 10 11 13 **F**3 8 11 13 15 18 20 22 24 26 28 29 30 31 32 34 35 37 40 43 44 45 47 49 50 51 54 55 56 57 58 59 61 63 64 68 69 70 74 75 77 78 79 81 82 84 85 86 87 90 91 92 93 95 96 97 98 100 101 102 103 104 107 108 110 111 114 115 116 117 118 119 120 121 123 124 126 127 129 130 131 132 135 144 146 147 148 149 150 **P**6 7 8
Primary Contact: Craig C. Kinyon, President
CFO: Christopher D. Knight, Vice President Finance and Chief Financial Officer
CMO: Thomas Huth M.D., Vice President Medical Affairs
CIO: Tim Love, Director Information Services
CHR: Scott C Rauch, Vice President Human Resources
CNO: Misti Foust–Cofield R.N., Vice President and Chief Nursing Officer
Web address: www.reidhealth.org
Control: Other not–for–profit (including NFP Corporation) **Service:** General medical and surgical

Staffed Beds: 221 **Admissions:** 11940 **Census:** 137 **Outpatient Visits:** 379127 **Births:** 679 **Total Expense ($000):** 413923 **Payroll Expense ($000):** 173307 **Personnel:** 2275

□ **RICHMOND STATE HOSPITAL (154018)**, 498 NW 18th Street, Zip 47374–2851; tel. 765/966–0511 **A**1 10 **F**56 98 103 106 130 135 146 **P**1
Primary Contact: Terry Suttle, Superintendent
CFO: Dave Shelford, Assistant Superintendent
CMO: Donald Graber M.D., Medical Director
CIO: Robert Boatman, Director Information Technology
CHR: Sarah Witt, Director Human Resources
Web address: www.richmondstatehospital.org
Control: State, Government, Nonfederal **Service:** Psychiatric

Staffed Beds: 180 **Admissions:** 131 **Census:** 169 **Outpatient Visits:** 0 **Births:** 0 **Total Expense ($000):** 30722 **Payroll Expense ($000):** 15745 **Personnel:** 342

ROCHESTER—Fulton County

★ **WOODLAWN HOSPITAL (151313)**, 1400 East Ninth Street, Zip 46975–8937; tel. 574/223–3141 **A**10 18 **F**3 11 13 15 29 30 31 34 40 46 56 57 59 63 65 68 69 75 76 77 78 79 80 81 82 83 90 91 92 93 94 97 107 108 111 115 116 119 129 130 132 133 135 143 146 147 148 **P**6
Primary Contact: John L. Alley, Chief Executive Officer
CFO: Dave Cholger, Chief Financial Officer
CHR: Debra J Lemasters, Director Human Resources
Web address: www.woodlawnhospital.com
Control: County, Government, Nonfederal **Service:** General medical and surgical

Staffed Beds: 25 **Admissions:** 1020 **Census:** 10 **Outpatient Visits:** 51837 **Births:** 183 **Total Expense ($000):** 52314 **Payroll Expense ($000):** 24714 **Personnel:** 368

RUSHVILLE—Rush County

★ **RUSH MEMORIAL HOSPITAL (151304)**, 1300 North Main Street, Zip 46173–1198, Mailing Address: P.O.Box 608, 46173–0608; tel. 765/932–4111 **A**10 18 **F**3 7 11 15 18 24 28 29 31 35 36 40 46 50 51 52 57 59 63 64 65 74 75 77 78 79 81 85 93 97 107 111 114 117 120 121 122 129 130 131 132 133 135 146 147 148 **P**6
Primary Contact: Bradley Smith, President and Chief Executive Officer
COO: Debbie Jones–Browning, Vice President Operations and Physician Services and Chief Operating Officer
CFO: Karen Meyer, Vice President Finance and Chief Financial Officer
CMO: Daniel Stahl D.O., Chief of Staff
CIO: Jim Boyer, Vice President Information Technology and Chief Information Officer
CHR: Dennis Fogle, Vice President of Human Resources
CNO: Gretchen Smith, Vice President Nursing and Compliance and Risk
Web address: www.rushmemorial.com
Control: County, Government, Nonfederal **Service:** General medical and surgical

Staffed Beds: 25 **Admissions:** 638 **Census:** 5 **Outpatient Visits:** 33903 **Births:** 0 **Total Expense ($000):** 26540 **Payroll Expense ($000):** 13293 **Personnel:** 245

SALEM—Washington County

⊠ **ST. VINCENT SALEM HOSPITAL (151314)**, 911 North Shelby Street, Zip 47167–1694; tel. 812/883–5881 **A**1 10 18 **F**3 11 15 28 29 30 32 34 40 45 47 49 57 59 75 77 79 81 82 85 93 107 111 114 119 124 129 130 131 132 133 144 148 **P**6 **S** Ascension Healthcare, Saint Louis, MO
Primary Contact: Dana M. Muntz, Chief Executive Officer
CFO: Joseph Kubala, Director Financial and Support Services
CMO: S E Kemker M.D., President Medical Staff
CIO: Jeremy Long, Manager Information Systems
CHR: Val Potter, Director Human Resources
Web address: www.stvincent.org/St-Vincent-Salem/Default.aspx
Control: Other not-for-profit (including NFP Corporation) **Service:** General medical and surgical

Staffed Beds: 25 **Admissions:** 155 **Census:** 2 **Outpatient Visits:** 32220 **Births:** 0 **Total Expense ($000):** 16595 **Payroll Expense ($000):** 6167 **Personnel:** 75

SCOTTSBURG—Scott County

⊠ **SCOTT MEMORIAL HOSPITAL (151334)**, 1415 North Gardner Street, Zip 47170, Mailing Address: Box 430, 47170–0430; tel. 812/752–3456, (Nonreporting) **A**1 10 18 **S** LifePoint Health, Brentwood, TN
Primary Contact: Michael Everett, Chief Executive Officer
CFO: Angela Doan, Chief Financial Officer
CNO: Dawn Mays, Chief Nursing Officer
Web address: www.scottmemorial.com
Control: County, Government, Nonfederal **Service:** General medical and surgical

Staffed Beds: 25

SEYMOUR—Jackson County

⊠ **SCHNECK MEDICAL CENTER (150065)**, 411 West Tipton Street, Zip 47274–2363, Mailing Address: P.O.Box 2349, 47274–5000; tel. 812/522–2349 **A**1 2 10 **F**3 12 13 15 18 28 29 30 31 34 35 36 40 45 56 57 59 62 63 64 65 68 70 74 75 76 77 78 79 81 82 84 85 87 89 93 96 104 107 110 111 114 115 119 120 121 123 124 126 129 130 131 132 133 135 144 146 147 148 **P**8
Primary Contact: Warren Forgey, CPA, FACHE, President and Chief Executive Officer
CFO: Deborah Ridlen CPA, Vice President Fiscal Services and Chief Financial Officer
CMO: Douglas Towriss, Vice President and Chief Medical Officer
CIO: Craig Rice, Director Information
CHR: Kathy Covert MSN, Vice President Human Resources
CNO: Amy Pettit R.N., Vice President Nursing Services and Chief Nursing Officer
Web address: www.schneckmed.org
Control: County, Government, Nonfederal **Service:** General medical and surgical

Staffed Beds: 93 **Admissions:** 2850 **Census:** 30 **Outpatient Visits:** 220051 **Births:** 760 **Total Expense ($000):** 123015 **Payroll Expense ($000):** 54970 **Personnel:** 863

SHELBYVILLE—Shelby County

★ ○ **MAJOR HOSPITAL (150097)**, 150 West Washington Street, Zip 46176–1236, Mailing Address: 2451 Intelliplex Drive, 46176; tel. 317/392–3211 **A**2 10 11 **F**3 12 13 15 28 29 30 31 34 35 40 47 50 57 59 62 63 64 68 70 73 74 75 76 77 78 79 80 81 82 84 85 89 93 97 107 108 110 111 114 118 119 120 121 123 129 130 131 132 135 144 146 147 148 **P**6
Primary Contact: John M. Horner, President and Chief Executive Officer
CFO: Ralph Mercuri, Vice President and Chief Financial Officer
CMO: Douglas S Carter M.D., Vice President and Chief Medical Officer
CIO: Carol Huesman, Chief Information Officer
CHR: Nicki Sparling, Manager Human Resources
CNO: Valerie L Miller MSN, R.N., Director of Nursing
Web address: www.majorhospital.org
Control: City-county, Government, Nonfederal **Service:** General medical and surgical

Staffed Beds: 72 **Admissions:** 2840 **Census:** 28 **Outpatient Visits:** 165619 **Births:** 353 **Total Expense ($000):** 99359 **Payroll Expense ($000):** 43817 **Personnel:** 729

IN

Hospital, Medicare Provider Number, Address, Telephone, Approval, Facility, and Physician Codes, Health Care System

★ American Hospital Association (AHA) membership   ○ Healthcare Facilities Accreditation Program   ⇑ Center for Improvement in Healthcare Quality Accreditation
□ The Joint Commission accreditation   ◇ DNV Healthcare Inc. accreditation   △ Commission on Accreditation of Rehabilitation Facilities (CARF) accreditation

SOUTH BEND—St. Joseph County

☒ △ **MEMORIAL HOSPITAL OF SOUTH BEND (150058)**, 615 North Michigan Street, Zip 46601-1033; tel. 574/647-1000, (Includes MEMORIAL CHILDREN'S HOSPITAL, 615 North Michigan Street, South Bend, Indiana, Zip 46601, tel. 574/647-1000) **A**1 2 3 7 10 **F**3 7 8 11 12 13 15 17 18 19 20 22 24 26 28 29 30 31 35 36 38 40 43 46 49 50 53 55 56 58 59 60 61 64 65 67 68 70 72 73 74 75 76 77 78 79 81 82 84 85 86 87 88 89 90 91 92 93 96 98 99 102 103 107 108 110 114 115 116 117 118 119 120 121 123 124 126 129 130 131 132 135 146 147 148 150 **P**8 **S** Beacon Health System, South Bend, IN
Primary Contact: Philip A. Newbold, Chief Executive Officer, Beacon Health System
COO: Kreg Gruber, Chief Operating Officer
CFO: Jeff Costello, Chief Financial Officer
CMO: Cheryl Wibbens M.D., Vice President Medical Staff Affairs
CIO: Mark Warlick, Chief Information Officer
CHR: Steven M Eller, Chief Human Resources Officer, Beacon Health System
Web address: www.qualityoflife.org
Control: Other not-for-profit (including NFP Corporation) **Service**: General medical and surgical

Staffed Beds: 445 **Admissions:** 19667 **Census:** 282 **Outpatient Visits:** 195960 **Births:** 2404 **Total Expense ($000):** 415544 **Payroll Expense ($000):** 143776 **Personnel:** 2554

SULLIVAN—Sullivan County

★ **SULLIVAN COUNTY COMMUNITY HOSPITAL (151327)**, 2200 North Section Street, Zip 47882-7523, Mailing Address: P.O.Box 10, 47882-0010; tel. 812/268-4311 **A**10 18 **F**3 8 13 15 28 29 32 34 35 40 44 45 47 48 50 53 56 57 59 61 62 65 69 70 75 76 77 78 79 81 86 87 93 97 107 110 111 114 127 129 130 131 133 146 147 148 **P**7 **S** QHR, Brentwood, TN
Primary Contact: Michelle Sly-Franklin, Chief Executive Officer
CFO: Scott Andritsch, Chief Financial Officer
CMO: Divyesh Purohit M.D., Chief of Staff
CIO: Hap Beckes, Director Information Systems
CHR: Denise Hart, Director Human Resources
CNO: Lori Resler R.N., Chief Nurse
Web address: www.schosp.com
Control: County, Government, Nonfederal **Service**: General medical and surgical

Staffed Beds: 25 **Admissions:** 763 **Census:** 6 **Outpatient Visits:** 74000 **Births:** 112 **Total Expense ($000):** 32833 **Payroll Expense ($000):** 16271 **Personnel:** 202

TELL CITY—Perry County

★ **PERRY COUNTY MEMORIAL HOSPITAL (151322)**, 8885 State Road 237, Zip 47586-2750; tel. 812/547-7011 **A**10 18 **F**3 7 13 15 18 28 29 30 31 34 35 40 45 50 56 57 59 62 64 65 68 70 74 75 76 77 78 79 81 85 107 111 115 119 127 129 130 132 133 135 146 148 **S** Alliant Management Services, Louisville, KY
Primary Contact: Brian J. Herwig, Chief Executive Officer
CMO: Juan Cornejo M.D., Chief of Staff
CIO: Mark Miller, Director Information Systems
CHR: Sheila Gaynor, Director Human Resources
CNO: Michele Howard, Vice President Nursing Services
Web address: www.pchospital.org
Control: County, Government, Nonfederal **Service**: General medical and surgical

Staffed Beds: 25 **Admissions:** 842 **Census:** 9 **Outpatient Visits:** 83019 **Births:** 75 **Total Expense ($000):** 32986 **Payroll Expense ($000):** 9914 **Personnel:** 273

TERRE HAUTE—Vigo County

HAMILTON CENTER (154009), 620 Eighth Avenue, Zip 47804-2744; tel. 812/231-8323 **A**10 **F**5 35 87 98 99 100 101 102 103 104 106
Primary Contact: Melvin Burks, Chief Executive Officer
COO: Robb Johnson, Director Operations
CFO: Renee Utley, Chief Financial Officer
CMO: Ahsan Mahmood M.D., Chief Medical Officer
CIO: Hans Eilbracht, Chief Information Officer
CHR: Margie Anshutz, Chief Development Officer
CNO: Rose Christy, Executive Director of Medical Services
Web address: www.hamiltoncenter.org
Control: State, Government, Nonfederal **Service**: Psychiatric

Staffed Beds: 16 **Admissions:** 600 **Census:** 15 **Outpatient Visits:** 226026 **Births:** 0 **Total Expense ($000):** 34900 **Payroll Expense ($000):** 19493 **Personnel:** 441

☐ **HARSHA BEHAVIORAL CENTER (154054)**, 1420 East Crossing Boulevard, Zip 47802-5316; tel. 866/644-8880, (Nonreporting) **A**1 10
Primary Contact: Roopam Harshawat, Chief Executive Officer
COO: Holly Near, Chief Administrative Officer
CFO: Holly Near, Chief Administrative Officer
CMO: Paras Harshawat M.D., Medical Director
CHR: Karen Hunt, Executive Director
CNO: Cindy Dowers, Chief Nursing Officer
Web address: www.harshacenter.com
Control: Corporation, Investor-owned (for-profit) **Service**: Psychiatric

Staffed Beds: 36

☒ **TERRE HAUTE REGIONAL HOSPITAL (150046)**, 3901 South Seventh Street, Zip 47802-5709; tel. 812/232-0021, (Nonreporting) **A**1 2 10 **S** HCA Healthcare, Nashville, TN
Primary Contact: Nathan Vooys, Chief Executive Officer
COO: Andrea Gwyn, Chief Operating Officer
CIO: Mike Kuckewich, Director Information Systems
CNO: Angela Ellis R.N., Chief Nursing Officer
Web address: www.regionalhospital.com
Control: Corporation, Investor-owned (for-profit) **Service**: General medical and surgical

Staffed Beds: 208

★ ○ **UNION HOSPITAL (150023)**, 1606 North Seventh Street, Zip 47804-2780; tel. 812/238-7000 **A**2 3 10 11 19 **F**3 8 13 15 18 20 22 24 26 28 29 30 31 34 35 36 40 43 45 46 47 48 49 50 51 53 54 57 59 64 68 70 72 73 74 75 76 77 78 79 81 85 86 87 89 90 91 92 93 94 95 96 97 100 107 108 110 111 112 114 115 116 117 118 119 120 121 123 124 126 127 130 131 132 135 144 146 147 **P**6
Primary Contact: Steve M. Holman, Chief Executive Officer
CFO: Wayne Hutson, Executive Vice President and Chief Financial Officer
CMO: John Bolinger M.D., Vice President Medical Affairs
CIO: Kym Pfrank, Senior Vice President and Chief Operating Officer
CHR: Sally Zuel, Vice President Human Resources
CNO: Rhonda E. Smith R.N., MSN, Vice President Patient Care Services and Chief Nursing Officer
Web address: www.uhhg.org
Control: Other not-for-profit (including NFP Corporation) **Service**: General medical and surgical

Staffed Beds: 218 **Admissions:** 15092 **Census:** 177 **Outpatient Visits:** 411758 **Births:** 1942 **Total Expense ($000):** 414422 **Payroll Expense ($000):** 109285 **Personnel:** 1722

TIPTON—Tipton County

☒ **INDIANA UNIVERSITY HEALTH TIPTON HOSPITAL (151311)**, 1000 South Main Street, Zip 46072-9799; tel. 765/675-8500 **A**1 10 18 **F**3 11 15 18 28 29 30 31 34 35 39 40 45 46 47 48 53 57 59 70 74 75 77 78 79 81 82 85 86 87 93 107 108 110 111 115 119 129 131 132 133 135 146 147 148 **S** Indiana University Health, Indianapolis, IN
Primary Contact: Michael Harlowe, President and Chief Executive Officer
CFO: Randall C Yust, Chief Financial Officer NCR
CMO: Gaurau Arora M.D., Chief Medical Officer
CHR: Shelly E Huff, Manager Human Resources
CNO: Jo Ellen Scott R.N., MS, Senior Vice President of Patient Care Services and Chief Nursing Officer
Web address: www.iuhealth.org
Control: Other not-for-profit (including NFP Corporation) **Service**: General medical and surgical

Staffed Beds: 25 **Admissions:** 905 **Census:** 9 **Outpatient Visits:** 52388 **Births:** 0 **Total Expense ($000):** 33341 **Payroll Expense ($000):** 10456 **Personnel:** 173

TIPTON HOSPITAL See Indiana University Health Tipton Hospital

VALPARAISO—Porter County

☒ **PORTER REGIONAL HOSPITAL (150035)**, 85 East U. S. Highway 6, Zip 46383-8947; tel. 219/983-8300, (Nonreporting) **A**1 5 10 **S** Community Health Systems, Inc., Franklin, TN
Primary Contact: Stephen Lunn, Chief Executive Officer
CFO: Douglas Browning, Chief Financial Officer
CMO: Ramireddy K Tummuru M.D., Chief Medical Officer
CIO: Robert Richardson, Information Technology Administrator
CHR: Angie Hampton, Director Human Resources
Web address: www.porterhealth.com
Control: Corporation, Investor-owned (for-profit) **Service**: General medical and surgical

Staffed Beds: 276

IN

Many Facility Codes have changed. Please refer to the AHA Guide Code Chart.
© 2017 AHA Guide

PORTER–STARKE SERVICES (154052), 601 Wall Street, Zip 46383–2512; tel. 219/531–3500 **A**10 **F**5 29 34 35 39 44 54 57 59 65 66 97 98 99 101 103 104 130 135 147 **P**6
Primary Contact: Rocco Schiralli, President/Chief Executive Officer
CFO: Mary Idstein, Chief Financial Officer
CMO: Anand Popli, Medical Director
Web address: www.porterstarke.org
Control: Other not–for–profit (including NFP Corporation) **Service:** Psychiatric

Staffed Beds: 16 **Admissions:** 671 **Census:** 8 **Outpatient Visits:** 121233 **Births:** 0 **Total Expense ($000):** 18308 **Payroll Expense ($000):** 10470 **Personnel:** 251

VINCENNES—Knox County

△ **GOOD SAMARITAN HOSPITAL (150042)**, 520 South Seventh Street, Zip 47591–1038; tel. 812/882–5220 **A**1 2 7 10 19 **F**3 4 5 8 13 15 18 20 22 28 29 30 31 34 35 36 38 40 41 43 44 45 46 47 48 49 50 51 53 56 57 58 59 60 63 64 65 66 67 70 74 75 76 77 78 79 80 81 82 84 85 86 87 89 90 93 94 96 97 98 100 101 102 103 104 106 107 110 111 115 118 119 120 121 123 127 129 131 132 134 135 144 145 146 147 148 149 150 **P**6
Primary Contact: Robert D. McLin, President and Chief Executive Officer
COO: Adam Thacker, Chief Operating Officer
CFO: Thomas M Cook, Chief Financial Officer
CMO: Charles C Hedde M.D., Chief Medical Officer
CIO: Daniel Scott, Director of Information Systems
CHR: Dean Wagoner, Director Human Resources
CNO: Karen S. Haak R.N., MSN, Chief Nursing Officer
Web address: www.gshvin.org/goodsamaritan
Control: County, Government, Nonfederal **Service:** General medical and surgical

Staffed Beds: 191 **Admissions:** 6844 **Census:** 90 **Outpatient Visits:** 508164 **Births:** 499 **Total Expense ($000):** 322858 **Payroll Expense ($000):** 137631 **Personnel:** 1664

WABASH—Wabash County

PARKVIEW WABASH COUNTY HOSPITAL (151310), 710 North East Street, Zip 46992–1924; tel. 260/563–3131 **A**1 10 18 **F**3 15 28 29 30 31 34 35 40 44 45 46 47 50 56 57 59 62 63 68 69 70 75 77 78 79 81 85 93 107 108 110 111 119 129 130 131 132 133 135 146 148 **S** Parkview Health, Fort Wayne, IN
Primary Contact: Marilyn J. Custer–Mitchell, President
CMO: Jeff Miller M.D., Chief of Staff
CIO: David Brinson, Director Information Technology
CHR: Kimberly R Shininger, Manger, Human Resources
CNO: Cathy Allyson Wolfe, Chief Nursing Officer
Web address: www.wchospital.com
Control: Other not–for–profit (including NFP Corporation) **Service:** General medical and surgical

Staffed Beds: 25 **Admissions:** 685 **Census:** 5 **Outpatient Visits:** 29268 **Births:** 0 **Total Expense ($000):** 40986 **Payroll Expense ($000):** 9703 **Personnel:** 155

WARSAW—Kosciusko County

KOSCIUSKO COMMUNITY HOSPITAL (150133), 2101 East Dubois Drive, Zip 46580–3288; tel. 574/267–3200 **A**1 10 19 **F**3 7 8 12 13 15 28 29 30 31 32 34 35 40 44 49 50 51 53 57 58 59 64 65 68 70 74 75 76 77 78 79 81 85 86 89 90 93 107 108 110 111 114 115 116 118 119 120 121 129 130 131 132 144 146 147 148 **P**6 **S** Community Health Systems, Inc., Franklin, TN
Primary Contact: Kirk M. Ray, Chief Executive Officer
CFO: Douglas J BeMent, Chief Financial Officer
CMO: Patrick Silveus M.D., Medical Director
CIO: Tammy Lukens, Director Information
CHR: Joe Jarboe, Director Human Resources
CNO: Kim Finch, Chief Nursing Officer
Web address: www.kch.com
Control: Corporation, Investor–owned (for–profit) **Service:** General medical and surgical

Staffed Beds: 72 **Admissions:** 3372 **Census:** 29 **Outpatient Visits:** 107951 **Births:** 468 **Total Expense ($000):** 68937 **Payroll Expense ($000):** 22157 **Personnel:** 517

★ **OTIS R. BOWEN CENTER FOR HUMAN SERVICES (154014)**, 2621 East Jefferson Street, Zip 46580–3880; tel. 574/267–7169 **A**10 **F**5 29 34 38 54 98 99 100 101 102 103 104 106 135 149 150 **P**1
Primary Contact: Kurt Carlson, Chief Executive Officer
Web address: www.bowencenter.org
Control: Other not–for–profit (including NFP Corporation) **Service:** Psychiatric

Staffed Beds: 16 **Admissions:** 1312 **Census:** 8 **Outpatient Visits:** 530809 **Births:** 0 **Total Expense ($000):** 48048 **Payroll Expense ($000):** 29805 **Personnel:** 982

WASHINGTON—Daviess County

△ **DAVIESS COMMUNITY HOSPITAL (150061)**, 1314 East Walnut Street, Zip 47501–2860, Mailing Address: P.O.Box 760, 47501–0760; tel. 812/254–2760, (Nonreporting) **A**1 7 10 **S** Ascension Healthcare, Saint Louis, MO
Primary Contact: Tracy Conroy, Chief Executive Officer
CFO: Amanda Rodewald, Interim Chief Financial Officer
CMO: Michael Baker D.O., Chief of Staff
CIO: Richard Meinhart, Manager Information Systems
CHR: Marilyn Richard, Director Human Resources
Web address: www.dchosp.org
Control: County, Government, Nonfederal **Service:** General medical and surgical

Staffed Beds: 48

WEST LAFAYETTE—Tippecanoe County

★ **RIVER BEND HOSPITAL (154005)**, 2900 North River Road, Zip 47906–3744; tel. 765/464–0400, (Nonreporting) **A**10
Primary Contact: Stephanie Long, President and Chief Executive Officer
COO: Tom Gillian, Chief Operating Officer
CFO: Jeff Nagy, Chief Financial Officer
CMO: Richard Rahdert M.D., Medical Director
CIO: Craig Anderson, Director Management Information Systems
CHR: Jan Shaw, Director Personnel
CNO: Megan Gibson, Nurse Manager
Web address: www.nchsi.com/riverbendhospital.cfm
Control: Other not–for–profit (including NFP Corporation) **Service:** Psychiatric

Staffed Beds: 16

WABASH VALLEY HOSPITAL See River Bend Hospital

WILLIAMSPORT—Warren County

ST. VINCENT WILLIAMSPORT HOSPITAL (151307), 412 North Monroe Street, Zip 47993–1049; tel. 765/762–4000 **A**1 10 18 **F**3 7 15 29 30 34 35 40 45 50 57 59 64 75 77 79 81 85 86 87 93 97 107 110 111 114 119 127 131 132 133 135 143 146 149 **P**6 **S** Ascension Healthcare, Saint Louis, MO
Primary Contact: Jane Craigin, Chief Executive Officer
CFO: Janet Merritt, Chief Financial Officer
Web address: www.stvincent.org
Control: Other not–for–profit (including NFP Corporation) **Service:** General medical and surgical

Staffed Beds: 16 **Admissions:** 652 **Census:** 7 **Outpatient Visits:** 74495 **Births:** 0 **Total Expense ($000):** 19411 **Payroll Expense ($000):** 8601 **Personnel:** 127

WINAMAC—Pulaski County

★ **PULASKI MEMORIAL HOSPITAL (151305)**, 616 East 13th Street, Zip 46996–1117, Mailing Address: P.O.Box 279, 46996–0279; tel. 574/946–2100 **A**10 18 **F**3 11 13 15 18 28 29 30 31 34 35 40 43 45 50 53 56 57 59 62 63 64 65 68 73 75 76 77 78 79 81 82 85 86 87 89 90 91 93 96 97 103 107 110 114 119 127 128 130 131 132 133 135 146 148 149 **P**6
Primary Contact: Thomas Barry, Chief Executive Officer
CFO: Gregg Malott, Chief Financial Officer
CMO: Rex Allman M.D., President Medical Staff
CIO: Jeff Boer, Director Information Technology
CHR: Mark Fenn, Director Human Resources
CNO: Linda Webb R.N., Chief Nursing Executive
Web address: www.pmhnet.com
Control: County, Government, Nonfederal **Service:** General medical and surgical

Staffed Beds: 25 **Admissions:** 690 **Census:** 9 **Outpatient Visits:** 30724 **Births:** 88 **Total Expense ($000):** 30591 **Payroll Expense ($000):** 14772 **Personnel:** 265

WINCHESTER—Randolph County

ST. VINCENT RANDOLPH HOSPITAL (151301), 473 Greenville Avenue, Zip 47394–9436; tel. 765/584–0004 **A**1 10 18 **F**3 11 13 15 28 29 30 31 34 35 40 44 45 50 57 59 64 65 68 75 76 77 79 81 85 86 87 89 93 107 110 111 114 119 129 130 131 132 133 135 146 147 148 149 150 **S** Ascension Healthcare, Saint Louis, MO
Primary Contact: Francis G. Albarano, Administrator
CFO: John Arthur, Chief Financial Officer
CMO: Gary Brazel M.D., Chief Medical Officer
CHR: Richard Ross Brodhead, Director Human Resources
CNO: Carla Fouse, Chief Nursing Officer
Web address: www.stvincent.org
Control: Other not–for–profit (including NFP Corporation) **Service:** General medical and surgical

Staffed Beds: 16 **Admissions:** 560 **Census:** 5 **Outpatient Visits:** 44832 **Births:** 221 **Total Expense ($000):** 21450 **Payroll Expense ($000):** 7613 **Personnel:** 158

IN

Hospital, Medicare Provider Number, Address, Telephone, Approval, Facility, and Physician Codes, Health Care System

★ American Hospital Association (AHA) membership
□ The Joint Commission accreditation
○ Healthcare Facilities Accreditation Program
◇ DNV Healthcare Inc. accreditation
⇑ Center for Improvement in Healthcare Quality Accreditation
△ Commission on Accreditation of Rehabilitation Facilities (CARF) accreditation

IOWA

ALBIA—Monroe County

★ **MONROE COUNTY HOSPITAL AND CLINICS (161342)**, 6580 165th Street, Zip 52531–8793; tel. 641/932–2134 **A**10 18 **F**1 4 7 11 15 16 17 28 29 31 34 40 43 50 57 59 67 70 72 73 80 81 88 89 90 93 98 107 110 114 119 127 128 130 132 133 **P**6
Primary Contact: Veronica Fuhs, Chief Executive Officer
Web address: www.mchalbia.com
Control: County, Government, Nonfederal **Service:** General medical and surgical

Staffed Beds: 25 **Admissions:** 428 **Census:** 6 **Outpatient Visits:** 46572
Births: 0 **Total Expense ($000):** 19058 **Payroll Expense ($000):** 8513
Personnel: 137

ALGONA—Kossuth County

★ **KOSSUTH REGIONAL HEALTH CENTER (161353)**, 1515 South Phillips Street, Zip 50511–3649; tel. 515/295–2451 **A**10 18 **F**11 13 15 17 28 29 30 31 32 34 35 36 40 41 43 50 56 57 59 62 63 64 65 67 68 70 75 76 77 78 81 82 84 86 87 89 92 93 97 107 114 119 127 128 130 131 132 133 135 146 147 148 149 **P**8 **S** Trinity Health, Livonia, MI
Primary Contact: Scott A. Curtis, Administrator and Chief Executive Officer
CFO: Jason Feucht, Chief Financial Officer
CMO: Michael Lampe M.D., Chief of Staff
CIO: Nancy Erickson, Administrator Information Systems
CHR: Paula Seely, Manager Human Resources
CNO: Darlene M Elbert R.N., MS, Assistant Administrator and Chief Nursing Officer
Web address: www.krhc.com
Control: County, Government, Nonfederal **Service:** General medical and surgical

Staffed Beds: 23 **Admissions:** 816 **Census:** 10 **Outpatient Visits:** 30044
Births: 125 **Total Expense ($000):** 33933 **Payroll Expense ($000):** 11690
Personnel: 212

AMES—Story County

⌧ △ ⇑ **MARY GREELEY MEDICAL CENTER (160030)**, 1111 Duff Avenue, Zip 50010–5745; tel. 515/239–2011 **A**1 2 7 10 19 21 **F**3 7 8 11 12 13 15 17 18 20 22 26 28 29 30 31 34 35 36 37 38 40 43 44 45 46 47 49 50 53 55 57 58 59 61 62 63 64 65 68 69 70 72 74 75 76 77 78 79 81 82 84 85 86 89 90 92 93 96 98 99 100 101 102 103 104 107 108 110 111 114 115 118 119 120 121 123 124 126 129 130 131 132 135 145 146 148 149
Primary Contact: Brian Dieter, President and Chief Executive Officer
CFO: Gary Botine, Vice President, Chief Financial Officer
CIO: Scott Carlson, Director
CHR: Betsy V Schoeller, Director Human Resources and Education
Web address: www.mgmc.org
Control: City, Government, Nonfederal **Service:** General medical and surgical

Staffed Beds: 171 **Admissions:** 7867 **Census:** 98 **Outpatient Visits:** 169016 **Births:** 1098 **Total Expense ($000):** 174170 **Payroll Expense ($000):** 63869 **Personnel:** 1062

ANAMOSA—Jones County

★ **UNITYPOINT HEALTH – JONES REGIONAL MEDICAL CENTER (161306)**, 1795 Highway 64 East, Zip 52205–2112; tel. 319/462–6131 **A**10 18 **F**3 7 11 12 15 28 29 30 31 34 35 38 40 43 45 50 56 57 59 64 65 68 71 75 77 81 82 84 85 87 91 93 96 97 99 100 101 102 103 104 107 110 114 118 119 126 129 130 132 133 135 145 146 148 149 150 **P**6 **S** UnityPoint Health, West Des Moines, IA
Primary Contact: Eric Briesemeister, Chief Executive Officer
CFO: Rachel Von Behren, Director Financial Services
CMO: Victor Salas M.D., President Medical Staff
CHR: Donna Condry, Director Human Resources
Web address: www.jonesregional.org
Control: Other not–for–profit (including NFP Corporation) **Service:** General medical and surgical

Staffed Beds: 22 **Admissions:** 432 **Census:** 6 **Outpatient Visits:** 85187
Births: 0 **Total Expense ($000):** 22129 **Payroll Expense ($000):** 7313
Personnel: 170

ATLANTIC—Cass County

★ **CASS COUNTY MEMORIAL HOSPITAL (161376)**, 1501 East Tenth Street, Zip 50022–1997; tel. 712/243–3250 **A**10 18 **F**3 13 15 28 29 31 34 35 40 45 50 57 59 64 65 70 75 76 77 78 79 81 82 85 93 97 98 99 101 102 103 104 107 108 111 115 119 124 127 129 130 132 133 135 146 147 148 **P**6 8
Primary Contact: Brett Altman, Chief Executive Officer
COO: Alison Bruckner, Chief Operating Officer
CFO: Abbey Stangl, Chief Financial Officer
CMO: Todd Bean, Chief Medical Officer
CIO: Jeff Osegard, Chief Information Officer
CHR: Denise Coder, Chief Human Resource Officer
Web address: www.casshealth.org
Control: County, Government, Nonfederal **Service:** General medical and surgical

Staffed Beds: 29 **Admissions:** 1059 **Census:** 11 **Outpatient Visits:** 100138
Births: 144 **Total Expense ($000):** 44556 **Payroll Expense ($000):** 16240
Personnel: 320

AUDUBON—Audubon County

AUDUBON COUNTY MEMORIAL HOSPITAL (161330), 515 Pacific Street, Zip 50025–1056; tel. 712/563–2611 **A**10 18 **F**3 11 15 28 31 40 43 45 53 59 64 67 78 79 81 85 93 110 119 127 128 133 135
Primary Contact: Suzanne Cooner, R.N., MSN, Chief Executive Officer
CFO: Melinda Alt, Chief Financial Officer
CMO: James Cunnigham D.O., Chief of Staff
CIO: Mike Card, Chief Information Officer
CNO: Holly Kjergaard, Chief Nursing Officer
Web address: www.acmhhosp.org
Control: County, Government, Nonfederal **Service:** General medical and surgical

Staffed Beds: 25 **Admissions:** 156 **Census:** 2 **Outpatient Visits:** 15464
Births: 0 **Total Expense ($000):** 12469 **Payroll Expense ($000):** 5178
Personnel: 100

BELMOND—Wright County

★ ⇑ **IOWA SPECIALTY HOSPITAL–BELMOND (161301)**, 403 1st Street SE, Zip 50421–1201; tel. 641/444–3223 **A**10 18 21 **F**3 7 11 12 15 28 29 32 34 35 40 43 45 46 50 56 57 59 62 63 64 65 67 68 75 77 79 81 82 85 87 89 92 93 96 97 100 101 102 104 107 110 119 127 128 129 130 131 132 133 135 146 148 149 150 **P**6 **S** Iowa Specialty Hospitals, Clarion, IA
Primary Contact: Amy McDaniel, Chief Executive Officer
CFO: Greg Polzin, Chief Financial Officer
CMO: Charles B Brindle M.D., Chief Medical Staff
CHR: Holly Martin, Director Human Resource
CNO: Lisa Weatherwax R.N., Chief Nursing Officer
Web address: www.iowaspecialtyhospital.com
Control: City, Government, Nonfederal **Service:** General medical and surgical

Staffed Beds: 22 **Admissions:** 561 **Census:** 5 **Outpatient Visits:** 33240
Births: 0 **Total Expense ($000):** 24706 **Payroll Expense ($000):** 5459
Personnel: 140

BETTENDORF—Scott County

⌧ **UNITYPOINT HEALTH – TRINITY BETTENDORF (160104)**, 4500 Utica Ridge Road, Zip 52722–1626; tel. 563/742–5000 **A**1 10 13 **F**3 11 13 15 18 20 22 24 26 29 30 34 35 37 40 44 45 46 48 50 57 59 64 70 73 74 75 76 79 81 82 85 86 87 89 93 96 97 102 104 107 108 110 114 119 130 132 135 146 147 148 149 150 **P**8 **S** UnityPoint Health, West Des Moines, IA
Primary Contact: Richard A. Seidler, FACHE, President and Chief Executive Officer
COO: Jay Willsher, Chief Operating Officer
CFO: Greg Pagliuzza, Chief Financial Officer
CMO: Paul McLoone M.D., Chief Medical Officer
CHR: Cara Fuller, Vice President Human Resources
CNO: Jean B Doerge MS, R.N., Chief Nursing Executive
Web address: www.trinityqc.com
Control: Other not–for–profit (including NFP Corporation) **Service:** General medical and surgical

Staffed Beds: 76 **Admissions:** 4425 **Census:** 36 **Outpatient Visits:** 63547
Births: 938 **Total Expense ($000):** 77715 **Payroll Expense ($000):** 24296
Personnel: 418

IA

Many Facility Codes have changed. Please refer to the AHA Guide Code Chart. © 2017 AHA Guide

BLOOMFIELD—Davis County

★ **DAVIS COUNTY HOSPITAL (161327)**, 509 North Madison Street, Zip 52537–1271; tel. 641/664–2145 **A**10 18 **F**3 7 11 15 28 29 34 35 40 44 45 50 57 59 63 64 65 69 75 79 81 84 85 86 87 97 107 110 111 115 119 132 133 135 146 **P**6
Primary Contact: Kirby Johnson, Chief Executive Officer
CFO: Kendra Warning, Chief Financial Officer
CMO: Robert Floyd D.O., Chief Medical Staff
CIO: Lynn Sims, Director Information Technology
CHR: Pam Young, Director Human Resources
CNO: Susan Kay Pankey, Chief Nursing Officer
Web address: www.daviscountyhospital.org
Control: County, Government, Nonfederal **Service**: General medical and surgical

> **Staffed Beds**: 13 **Admissions**: 340 **Census**: 4 **Outpatient Visits**: 31744 **Births**: 0 **Total Expense ($000)**: 22547 **Payroll Expense ($000)**: 7977 **Personnel**: 155

BOONE—Boone County

★ **BOONE COUNTY HOSPITAL (161372)**, 1015 Union Street, Zip 50036–4821; tel. 515/432–3140 **A**10 18 **F**2 3 7 11 13 15 28 29 30 31 34 35 40 43 45 50 56 57 59 62 64 65 69 70 75 76 77 78 79 81 82 85 86 87 89 91 93 97 107 110 111 114 119 131 132 133 134 145 146 147 148 **P**6 **S** QHR, Brentwood, TN
Primary Contact: Joseph S. Smith, Chief Executive Officer
CFO: Joseph Devin, Chief Financial Officer
CMO: Tammara Chance D.O., Chief of Staff
CIO: Matthew Sabus, Director Information Systems
CHR: Kim Schwartz, Assistant Administrator of Human Resources and Outpatient Services
Web address: www.boonehospital.com
Control: County, Government, Nonfederal **Service**: General medical and surgical

> **Staffed Beds**: 25 **Admissions**: 1319 **Census**: 14 **Outpatient Visits**: 78742 **Births**: 137 **Total Expense ($000)**: 42465 **Payroll Expense ($000)**: 17583 **Personnel**: 333

BRITT—Hancock County

★ **HANCOCK COUNTY HEALTH SYSTEM (161307)**, 532 First Street NW, Zip 50423–1227; tel. 641/843–5000 **A**10 18 **F**3 15 28 29 34 35 36 40 43 45 46 50 53 56 57 59 62 64 65 75 77 81 82 85 93 97 99 100 103 104 107 110 114 119 129 130 131 132 133 135 146 148 **P**1 **S** Trinity Health, Livonia, MI
Primary Contact: Jeffry Stampohar, Chief Executive Officer
CFO: Julie Damm, Chief Financial Officer
CMO: Catherine Butler M.D., Chief Medical Staff
CIO: Julie Damm, Chief Financial Officer
CHR: Denise Jakoubeck, Director Human Resources
CNO: Laura Zwiefel, Chief Nursing Officer and Assistant Administration
Web address: www.trusthchs.com/hancock–county–health–system
Control: County, Government, Nonfederal **Service**: General medical and surgical

> **Staffed Beds**: 25 **Admissions**: 503 **Census**: 7 **Outpatient Visits**: 22031 **Births**: 0 **Total Expense ($000)**: 23126 **Payroll Expense ($000)**: 7727 **Personnel**: 176

CARROLL—Carroll County

★ **ST. ANTHONY REGIONAL HOSPITAL (160005)**, 311 South Clark Street, Zip 51401–3038, Mailing Address: P.O.Box 628, 51401–0628; tel. 712/792–3581, (Total facility includes 79 beds in nursing home–type unit) **A**10 20 **F**6 11 13 15 28 29 30 31 34 35 37 38 39 40 43 44 45 46 50 51 56 57 59 60 61 62 63 64 65 67 68 69 70 74 75 76 77 78 79 81 82 84 85 86 87 89 93 97 98 99 100 101 102 103 104 107 108 110 111 115 118 119 125 126 127 129 130 131 132 133 134 135 145 146 147 148 **P**6
Primary Contact: Edward H. Smith, President and Chief Executive Officer
CFO: John Munson, Vice President and Chief Financial Officer
CMO: Kyle Ulveling M.D., Chief of Staff
CIO: Chad Lawson, Chief Information Officer
CHR: Anna Fitzpatrick, Director Human Resources
CNO: Karen Timm R.N., MSN, Vice President Patient Services
Web address: www.stanthonyhospital.org
Control: Church operated, Nongovernment, not–for–profit **Service**: General medical and surgical

> **Staffed Beds**: 155 **Admissions**: 2219 **Census**: 105 **Outpatient Visits**: 119823 **Births**: 359 **Total Expense ($000)**: 72697 **Payroll Expense ($000)**: 29521 **Personnel**: 567

CEDAR FALLS—Black Hawk County

⊞ **SARTORI MEMORIAL HOSPITAL (160040)**, 515 College Street, Zip 50613–2500; tel. 319/268–3000 **A**1 10 **F**3 7 8 11 12 15 29 30 35 40 43 44 46 53 57 59 64 68 70 75 77 79 81 91 93 97 98 103 107 110 111 119 130 131 132 146 **P**1 6 **S** Trinity Health, Livonia, MI
Primary Contact: MaryJo Kavalier, Administrator
CFO: Michele Panicucci, Senior Vice President and Chief Financial Officer
CMO: James Lehman M.D., Vice President Medical Affairs
CNO: Kelly Richards MSN, Senior Vice President and Chief Nursing Officer
Web address: www.wheatoniowa.org
Control: Church operated, Nongovernment, not–for–profit **Service**: General medical and surgical

> **Staffed Beds**: 50 **Admissions**: 1331 **Census**: 19 **Outpatient Visits**: 42436 **Births**: 0 **Total Expense ($000)**: 35113 **Payroll Expense ($000)**: 11184 **Personnel**: 191

CEDAR RAPIDS—Linn County

☐ **CONTINUING CARE HOSPITAL AT ST. LUKE'S (162002)**, 1026 'A' Avenue NE, 6th Floor, Zip 52402–5036; tel. 319/369–8142 **A**1 10 **F**1 3 29 30 75 84 85 87 148 **S** CHRISTUS Health, Irving, TX
Primary Contact: Elly Steffen, Administrator
CNO: Mary Beth Keuter, Director Patient Care
Web address: www.christusdubuis.org/ContinuingCareHospitalatStLukes
Control: Other not–for–profit (including NFP Corporation) **Service**: Acute long–term care hospital

> **Staffed Beds**: 16 **Admissions**: 281 **Census**: 11 **Outpatient Visits**: 0 **Births**: 0 **Total Expense ($000)**: 7245 **Payroll Expense ($000)**: 2255 **Personnel**: 51

⊞ **MERCY MEDICAL CENTER, CEDAR RAPIDS, IOWA (160079)**, 701 Tenth Street SE, Zip 52403–1292; tel. 319/398–6011, (Total facility includes 76 beds in nursing home–type unit) **A**1 2 3 5 10 **F**3 4 5 11 12 13 15 18 20 22 26 28 29 30 31 32 34 35 36 38 40 43 45 48 49 50 51 54 55 56 57 58 59 60 61 62 63 64 65 67 68 70 71 72 74 75 76 77 78 79 81 82 84 85 86 87 88 89 90 91 92 93 98 99 100 101 102 103 104 107 108 109 110 114 115 116 117 118 119 120 121 123 124 126 128 130 131 132 135 145 146 147 148 149 **P**2 8
Primary Contact: Timothy L. Charles, President and Chief Executive Officer
CFO: Nathan Van Genderen, Executive Vice President and Chief Financial Officer
CMO: Tim Quinn M.D., Executive Vice President and Chief of Clinical Operations and President Mercy Care Management
CIO: Jeff Cash, Senior Vice President and Chief Information Officer
CHR: Doug Jontz, Senior Vice President Human Resources
CNO: Mary Brobst R.N., MSN, Senior Vice President Patient Care Services and Chief Nursing Officer
Web address: www.mercycare.org
Control: Church operated, Nongovernment, not–for–profit **Service**: General medical and surgical

> **Staffed Beds**: 302 **Admissions**: 10571 **Census**: 182 **Outpatient Visits**: 331075 **Births**: 809 **Total Expense ($000)**: 306040 **Payroll Expense ($000)**: 113156 **Personnel**: 1949

ST. LUKE'S HOSPITAL See Unitypoint Health – St. Luke's Hospital

⊞ △ **UNITYPOINT HEALTH – ST. LUKE'S HOSPITAL (160045)**, 1026 'A' Avenue NE, Zip 52402–3026, Mailing Address: P.O.Box 3026, 52406–3026; tel. 319/369–7211 **A**1 2 3 5 7 10 **F**3 5 8 11 12 13 15 17 18 19 20 22 24 26 28 29 30 31 32 34 35 36 37 39 40 43 45 46 49 50 54 55 56 57 59 60 61 62 63 64 65 66 70 72 74 75 76 77 78 79 81 82 84 85 86 87 88 89 90 91 92 93 95 96 98 99 100 101 103 104 105 107 110 115 117 118 119 120 121 123 124 126 130 131 132 134 135 145 146 147 148 149 **P**6 **S** UnityPoint Health, West Des Moines, IA
Primary Contact: Theodore E. Townsend, FACHE, President and Chief Executive Officer
COO: Michelle Niermann, Senior Vice President and Chief Operating Officer
CFO: Milton E Aunan CPA, II, Senior Vice President and Chief Financial Officer
CMO: Dustin Arnold D.O., Chief Medical Officer
CHR: Susan L Slattery, Director Human Resources
CNO: Mary Ann Osborn R.N., Senior Vice President and Chief Care Coordinator Officer
Web address: www.unitypoint.org
Control: Other not–for–profit (including NFP Corporation) **Service**: General medical and surgical

> **Staffed Beds**: 347 **Admissions**: 15225 **Census**: 203 **Outpatient Visits**: 495639 **Births**: 2424 **Total Expense ($000)**: 313659 **Payroll Expense ($000)**: 120757 **Personnel**: 2183

IA

Hospital, Medicare Provider Number, Address, Telephone, Approval, Facility, and Physician Codes, Health Care System

★ American Hospital Association (AHA) membership
☐ The Joint Commission accreditation
○ Healthcare Facilities Accreditation Program
◇ DNV Healthcare Inc. accreditation
⇑ Center for Improvement in Healthcare Quality Accreditation
△ Commission on Accreditation of Rehabilitation Facilities (CARF) accreditation

© 2017 AHA Guide *Many Facility Codes have changed. Please refer to the AHA Guide Code Chart.* Hospitals **A223**

CENTERVILLE—Appanoose County

★ **MERCY MEDICAL CENTER–CENTERVILLE (161377)**, 1 St Joseph's Drive, Zip 52544–8055; tel. 641/437–4111, (Total facility includes 20 beds in nursing home–type unit) **A**10 18 **F**1 3 4 8 11 13 15 16 17 28 29 30 31 34 40 45 46 50 54 57 59 64 67 70 72 73 75 76 77 78 80 81 85 86 87 88 89 90 93 97 98 107 110 111 113 115 117 119 127 128 129 130 132 133 135 **P**6 **S** Catholic Health Initiatives, Englewood, CO
Primary Contact: Clinton J. Christianson, FACHE, President
CHR: Tonya Clawson, Manager Human Resources
CNO: Sherri L Doggett, Vice President Patient Services
Web address: www.mercycenterville.org
Control: Church operated, Nongovernment, not–for–profit **Service**: General medical and surgical

Staffed Beds: 45 **Admissions**: 726 **Census**: 26 **Outpatient Visits**: 84332 **Births**: 70 **Total Expense ($000)**: 25960 **Payroll Expense ($000)**: 10886 **Personnel**: 189

CHARITON—Lucas County

★ **LUCAS COUNTY HEALTH CENTER (161341)**, 1200 North Seventh Street, Zip 50049–1258; tel. 641/774–3000 **A**10 18 **F**3 5 7 11 13 15 16 17 28 29 30 31 34 38 40 43 44 45 47 50 64 66 68 70 75 76 81 85 87 89 90 93 97 104 107 115 119 127 128 130 132 133 143 145 146 148 **S** UnityPoint Health, West Des Moines, IA
Primary Contact: Brian Sims, Chief Executive Officer
CMO: David Marcowitz M.D., Chief of Staff
CIO: Terri Black, Network Manager
CHR: Lana Kuball, Director Administrative Services
CNO: JoBeth Lawless, Chief Nursing Officer, Nursing Services and Director Emergency Management Services
Web address: www.lchcia.com
Control: County, Government, Nonfederal **Service**: General medical and surgical

Staffed Beds: 25 **Admissions**: 366 **Census**: 4 **Outpatient Visits**: 19080 **Births**: 66 **Total Expense ($000)**: 19911 **Payroll Expense ($000)**: 8977 **Personnel**: 192

CHARLES CITY—Floyd County

FLOYD COUNTY MEDICAL CENTER (161347), 800 Eleventh Street, Zip 50616–6830 **A**10 18 **F**11 13 15 28 29 34 35 40 45 57 59 64 75 79 81 86 91 93 97 107 115 119 127 130 132 133 146 148 149 **S** Mayo Clinic, Rochester, MN
Primary Contact: Bill D. Faust, Administrator
CFO: Ron Timpe, Chief Financial Officer
CHR: Don Nosbisch, Director Human Resources
CNO: Viva Boerschel, Director of Nursing
Web address: www.fcmc.us.com/
Control: County, Government, Nonfederal **Service**: General medical and surgical

Staffed Beds: 25 **Admissions**: 689 **Census**: 10 **Outpatient Visits**: 57909 **Births**: 95 **Total Expense ($000)**: 23882 **Payroll Expense ($000)**: 8939 **Personnel**: 178

CHEROKEE—Cherokee County

★ **CHEROKEE REGIONAL MEDICAL CENTER (161362)**, 300 Sioux Valley Drive, Zip 51012–1205; tel. 712/225–5101 **A**10 18 **F**7 11 13 15 17 28 29 34 35 40 43 45 53 56 57 59 62 63 64 65 67 68 69 75 76 77 78 81 84 86 87 89 93 96 97 107 111 114 119 125 127 128 129 130 131 132 133 135 146 147 148 **P**6
Primary Contact: Matthew Johnson, Chief Executive Officer and President
CFO: Joan Bierman, Vice President Finance
CIO: Kevin Naslund, Manager Information Technology
CHR: Theresa Conley, Manager Human Resources
CNO: Christy Syndergaard, Vice President Nursing
Web address: www.cherokeermc.org
Control: Other not–for–profit (including NFP Corporation) **Service**: General medical and surgical

Staffed Beds: 25 **Admissions**: 902 **Census**: 9 **Outpatient Visits**: 44297 **Births**: 121 **Total Expense ($000)**: 21911 **Payroll Expense ($000)**: 9155 **Personnel**: 171

☐ **MENTAL HEALTH INSTITUTE (164002)**, 1251 West Cedar Loop, Zip 51012–1599; tel. 712/225–2594 **A**1 10 **F**98 99 101 102 130 149 **P**6
Primary Contact: Chris Tosteberg, Superintendent
CFO: Tony Morris, Business Manager
CHR: Mary Ann Hanson, Director Personnel
Web address: www.dhs.state.ia.us
Control: State, Government, Nonfederal **Service**: Psychiatric

Staffed Beds: 36 **Admissions**: 475 **Census**: 33 **Outpatient Visits**: 59 **Births**: 0 **Total Expense ($000)**: 16231 **Payroll Expense ($000)**: 9231 **Personnel**: 169

CLARINDA—Page County

★ **CLARINDA REGIONAL HEALTH CENTER (161352)**, 220 Essie Davison Drive, Zip 51632–2915, Mailing Address: P.O.Box 217, 51632–0217; tel. 712/542–2176 **A**10 18 **F**3 7 11 15 28 29 31 34 36 40 42 43 50 57 59 64 65 69 75 79 81 85 86 87 93 97 110 111 114 118 119 127 128 129 130 133 135 143 146 148 150 **P**3 6 **S** Bryan Health, Lincoln, NE
Primary Contact: Christopher R. Stipe, FACHE, Chief Executive Officer
COO: Elaine Otte, Chief Operating Officer
CMO: Autumn Morales, Chief Medical Staff Officer
CIO: Richard Morgan–Fine, IT Director
CHR: Melissa Walter, Director Human Resources
CNO: Sherrie L Laubenthal R.N., Chief Nursing Officer
Web address: www.clarindahealth.com
Control: City, Government, Nonfederal **Service**: General medical and surgical

Staffed Beds: 25 **Admissions**: 486 **Census**: 4 **Outpatient Visits**: 64444 **Births**: 0 **Total Expense ($000)**: 29473 **Payroll Expense ($000)**: 12014 **Personnel**: 239

CLARION—Wright County

★ ⇑ **IOWA SPECIALTY HOSPITAL–CLARION (161302)**, 1316 South Main Street, Zip 50525–2019; tel. 515/532–2811 **A**10 18 21 **F**11 13 15 28 29 31 32 34 35 40 43 45 46 50 56 57 59 63 64 65 68 69 75 76 77 79 81 82 85 86 87 92 93 97 107 110 111 114 119 125 127 129 131 132 133 134 135 146 147 148 149 **P**6 **S** Iowa Specialty Hospitals, Clarion, IA
Primary Contact: Steven J. Simonin, President and Chief Executive Officer
COO: Kirk Rier, Chief Operating Officer
CFO: Greg Polzin, Chief Financial Officer
CMO: Dennis Colby M.D., Chief of Staff
CHR: Holly Martin, Human Resources Leader
CNO: Abby Young, Chief Nursing Officer
Web address: www.iowaspecialtyhospital.com
Control: City, Government, Nonfederal **Service**: General medical and surgical

Staffed Beds: 25 **Admissions**: 1171 **Census**: 8 **Outpatient Visits**: 104014 **Births**: 298 **Total Expense ($000)**: 49385 **Payroll Expense ($000)**: 18887 **Personnel**: 336

CLINTON—Clinton County

⊞ **MERCY MEDICAL CENTER–CLINTON (160080)**, 1410 North Fourth Street, Zip 52732–2940; tel. 563/244–5555, (Includes MERCY SERVICES FOR AGING, 600 14th Avenue North, Clinton, Iowa, Zip 52732, tel. 563/244–3888) (Total facility includes 183 beds in nursing home–type unit) **A**1 10 **F**3 11 13 15 18 20 22 28 29 30 31 34 35 36 38 40 44 45 47 49 50 53 56 57 59 60 61 62 63 64 68 70 74 75 76 77 78 79 80 81 82 84 85 87 89 93 98 99 100 101 102 103 107 108 110 111 115 118 119 121 123 128 129 130 132 146 148 **S** Trinity Health, Livonia, MI
Primary Contact: Sean J. Williams, President and Chief Executive Officer
CFO: Paul Mangin, Vice President Finance
CHR: Shane Buer, Vice President, Human Resources
CNO: Amy Berentes R.N., MSN, Vice President Patient Care Services
Web address: www.mercyclinton.com
Control: Church operated, Nongovernment, not–for–profit **Service**: General medical and surgical

Staffed Beds: 290 **Admissions**: 5319 **Census**: 186 **Outpatient Visits**: 76499 **Births**: 430 **Total Expense ($000)**: 96138 **Payroll Expense ($000)**: 39006 **Personnel**: 767

CORALVILLE—Johnson County

IOWA MEDICAL AND CLASSIFICATION CENTER, 2700 Coral Ridge Avenue, Zip 52241–4708, Mailing Address: 2700 Coral Rigde Avenue, 52241; tel. 319/626–2391 **F**29 38 39 59 75 98 101 102 103 105 130 132 143
Primary Contact: James McKinney, Warden
Web address: www.oakdaleprison.com/
Control: State, Government, Nonfederal **Service**: Psychiatric

Staffed Beds: 20 **Admissions**: 30 **Census**: 7 **Outpatient Visits**: 0 **Births**: 0 **Personnel**: 26

CORNING—Adams County

★ **CHI HEALTH MERCY CORNING (161304)**, 603 Rosary Drive, Zip 50841–1683; tel. 641/322–3121 **A**10 18 **F**3 11 15 17 28 30 31 34 40 43 46 50 53 56 57 59 64 67 70 74 75 77 78 79 81 85 89 90 97 107 110 115 119 127 128 129 130 132 133 135 146 147 148 149 **P**6 **S** Catholic Health Initiatives, Englewood, CO
Primary Contact: Lisa Wolfe, President
CMO: Maen Haddadin M.D., President Medical Staff
CIO: Kenneth Lawonn, Senior Vice President and Chief Information Officer
CHR: Sandra Lammers, Coordinator Human Resources and Finance
Web address: www.alegent.com
Control: Church operated, Nongovernment, not–for–profit **Service**: General medical and surgical

Staffed Beds: 22 **Admissions**: 190 **Census**: 2 **Outpatient Visits**: 75166 **Births**: 0 **Total Expense ($000)**: 18493 **Payroll Expense ($000)**: 6597 **Personnel**: 84

IA

Many Facility Codes have changed. Please refer to the AHA Guide Code Chart. © 2017 AHA Guide

CORYDON—Wayne County

★ **WAYNE COUNTY HOSPITAL (161358)**, 417 South East Street, Zip 50060–1860, Mailing Address: P.O.Box 305, 50060–0305; tel. 641/872–2260 **A**10 18 **F**7 13 15 28 29 31 34 35 40 43 51 56 57 59 60 64 69 70 75 76 77 78 79 81 85 87 89 91 92 93 97 107 110 114 119 127 130 131 133 148 149 **P**6
Primary Contact: Daren Relph, Chief Executive Officer
COO: Michael Thomas, Associate Administrator
CFO: Diane Hook, Chief Financial Officer
CMO: Joel Baker D.O., Chief Medical Officer
CIO: Laurie Ehrich, Chief Communications Officer
CHR: Dave Carlyle, Director Human Resources
CNO: Sheila Mattly, Chief Nursing Officer
Web address: www.waynecountyhospital.org
Control: County, Government, Nonfederal **Service**: General medical and surgical

Staffed Beds: 25 **Admissions:** 499 **Census:** 5 **Outpatient Visits:** 28349 **Births:** 150 **Total Expense ($000):** 24317 **Payroll Expense ($000):** 11383 **Personnel:** 207	

COUNCIL BLUFFS—Pottawattamie County

⊞ **CHI HEALTH MERCY COUNCIL BLUFFS (160028)**, 800 Mercy Drive, Zip 51503–3128, Mailing Address: P.O.Box 1C, 51502–3001; tel. 712/328–5000 **A**1 2 5 10 **F**3 11 12 13 15 18 20 22 26 28 29 31 34 35 40 41 43 47 48 49 50 57 59 68 70 73 74 76 77 78 79 81 82 84 85 87 89 91 93 98 99 100 101 102 104 105 106 107 108 110 111 114 115 119 129 130 132 146 147 **P**8 **S** Catholic Health Initiatives, Englewood, CO
Primary Contact: Marie E. Knedler, R.N., FACHE, President
CFO: Jeanette Wojtalewicz, Chief Financial Officer
CMO: Joseph Hoagbin M.D., Chief Quality Officer
CIO: Thomas Haley, Information Technology Services Site Director
CHR: Nancy Wallace, Senior Vice President Human Resources
CNO: Brenda Bergman–Evans, Interim Chief Nursing Officer
Web address: www.chihealth.com/chi–health–mercy–council–bluffs
Control: Church operated, Nongovernment, not–for–profit **Service**: General medical and surgical

Staffed Beds: 163 **Admissions:** 7152 **Census:** 71 **Outpatient Visits:** 79233 **Births:** 516 **Total Expense ($000):** 90359 **Payroll Expense ($000):** 32030 **Personnel:** 499	

JENNIE EDMUNDSON HOSPITAL See Methodist Jennie Edmundson Hospital

⊞ **METHODIST JENNIE EDMUNDSON HOSPITAL (160047)**, 933 East Pierce Street, Zip 51503–4652, Mailing Address: P.O.Box 2C, 51502–3002; tel. 712/396–6000 **A**1 2 5 10 **F**3 11 13 15 18 20 22 26 28 29 30 31 34 35 39 40 43 44 45 47 49 50 57 58 59 61 64 68 70 74 75 76 78 79 81 82 85 86 87 89 92 93 98 100 101 102 103 107 108 110 111 115 118 119 120 121 123 124 129 130 131 132 135 143 145 146 147 148 149 **S** Nebraska Methodist Health System, Inc., Omaha, NE
Primary Contact: Steven P. Baumert, President and Chief Executive Officer
CFO: Jeffrey Francis, Vice President Finance and Chief Financial Officer
CMO: Scott Bomgaars M.D., Vice President Medical Affairs
CIO: Steven Zuber, Vice President
CHR: Holly Huerter, Vice President Human Resources
CNO: Peggy Helget R.N., MSN, Vice President Patient Services and Chief Nursing Officer
Web address: www.bestcare.org
Control: Other not–for–profit (including NFP Corporation) **Service**: General medical and surgical

Staffed Beds: 114 **Admissions:** 5562 **Census:** 60 **Outpatient Visits:** 62327 **Births:** 454 **Total Expense ($000):** 97849 **Payroll Expense ($000):** 37675 **Personnel:** 508	

CRESCO—Howard County

★ **REGIONAL HEALTH SERVICES OF HOWARD COUNTY (161328)**, 235 Eighth Avenue West, Zip 52136–1098; tel. 563/547–2101 **A**10 18 **F**3 7 11 13 15 28 29 30 34 35 36 40 43 45 50 54 56 57 59 62 63 64 65 68 75 76 81 82 87 89 96 103 104 107 110 115 127 128 130 132 133 146 147 **P**8 **S** Trinity Health, Livonia, MI
Primary Contact: Robin M. Schluter, Chief Executive Officer
CFO: Greg Burkel, Chief Financial Officer
CMO: Paul Jensen M.D., Chief of Staff
CIO: Greg Burkel, Chief Financial Officer
CHR: Jennalee Pedretti, Vice President Operations
CNO: Carol Kerian–Masters RN, BSN, Chief Nursing Officer
Web address: www.rhshc.com
Control: County, Government, Nonfederal **Service**: General medical and surgical

Staffed Beds: 19 **Admissions:** 244 **Census:** 3 **Outpatient Visits:** 19784 **Births:** 42 **Total Expense ($000):** 20487 **Payroll Expense ($000):** 7157 **Personnel:** 138	

CRESTON—Union County

★ ⇑ **GREATER REGIONAL MEDICAL CENTER (161365)**, 1700 West Townline Street Suite 3, Zip 50801–1099; tel. 641/782–7091 **A**10 18 21 **F**3 7 11 13 15 28 29 31 34 35 40 43 45 50 56 57 59 64 65 66 70 75 76 77 78 79 81 85 86 93 96 97 103 104 107 108 109 110 111 115 119 120 121 122 123 124 125 127 129 131 132 133 146 147 148 149 **P**6 **S** UnityPoint Health, West Des Moines, IA
Primary Contact: Monte Neitzel, Chief Executive Officer
CFO: Matt McCutchan, Chief Financial Officer
CMO: Steve Reeves M.D., Chief Medical Staff
CIO: Karla Alford, Chief Information Officer
CHR: Amy Rieck, Human Resources Officer
CNO: Amanda Mohr, Chief Nursing Officer
Web address: www.greaterregional.org
Control: County, Government, Nonfederal **Service**: General medical and surgical

Staffed Beds: 25 **Admissions:** 762 **Census:** 6 **Outpatient Visits:** 84713 **Births:** 153 **Total Expense ($000):** 46341 **Payroll Expense ($000):** 20088 **Personnel:** 316	

DAVENPORT—Scott County

⊞ △ **GENESIS MEDICAL CENTER–DAVENPORT–WEST CENTRAL PARK (160033)**, 1227 East Rusholme Street, Zip 52803–2498; tel. 563/421–1000, (Includes GENESIS MEDICAL CENTER–EAST CAMPUS, 1227 East Rusholme Street, Davenport, Iowa, Zip 52803, tel. 563/421–1000; GENESIS MEDICAL CENTER–WEST CAMPUS, 1401 West Central Park, Davenport, Iowa, Zip 52804–1769, tel. 563/421–1000) **A**1 2 3 5 7 10 **F**3 7 11 12 13 15 17 18 20 22 24 26 28 29 30 31 34 35 37 38 40 43 44 46 49 50 53 54 57 58 59 63 64 68 70 72 74 75 77 78 79 81 82 84 85 86 87 90 91 92 93 94 96 97 98 100 102 103 107 111 114 115 116 118 119 120 121 123 124 126 129 130 131 132 135 146 147 148 **P**6 **S** Genesis Health System, Davenport, IA
Primary Contact: Jordan Voigt, Administrator
CFO: Mark G Rogers, Interim Vice President Finance and Chief Financial Officer
CMO: Frank Claudy M.D., Vice President Medical Staff Affairs
CIO: Robert Frieden, Vice President Information Systems
CHR: Heidi Kahly–McMahon, Interim Vice President Human Resources
Web address: www.genesishealth.com
Control: Other not–for–profit (including NFP Corporation) **Service**: General medical and surgical

Staffed Beds: 368 **Admissions:** 16433 **Census:** 187 **Outpatient Visits:** 215841 **Births:** 2134 **Total Expense ($000):** 328125 **Payroll Expense ($000):** 90127 **Personnel:** 1419	

⊞ **SELECT SPECIALTY HOSPITAL–QUAD CITIES (162001)**, 1111 West Kimberly Road, Zip 52806–5711; tel. 563/468–2000 **A**1 10 **F**1 3 29 45 75 85 119 130 148 **S** Select Medical Corporation, Mechanicsburg, PA
Primary Contact: Connie K. Siffring, Chief Executive Officer
Web address: www.selectmedicalcorp.com
Control: Corporation, Investor–owned (for–profit) **Service**: Acute long–term care hospital

Staffed Beds: 50 **Admissions:** 312 **Census:** 22 **Outpatient Visits:** 0 **Births:** 0 **Total Expense ($000):** 14634 **Payroll Expense ($000):** 5920 **Personnel:** 106	

DE WITT—Clinton County

⊞ **GENESIS MEDICAL CENTER, DEWITT (161313)**, 1118 11th Street, Zip 52742–1296; tel. 563/659–4200, (Total facility includes 75 beds in nursing home–type unit) **A**1 10 18 **F**3 7 8 11 15 28 29 30 34 35 38 40 43 44 45 49 50 57 59 64 68 69 74 75 77 78 79 81 82 84 85 86 87 93 97 102 107 108 110 115 119 129 130 131 132 133 135 146 148 149 **P**6 **S** Genesis Health System, Davenport, IA
Primary Contact: Curt Coleman, FACHE, Chief Executive Officer
CMO: Steven Fowler M.D., President Medical Staff
CHR: Kristin Nicholson, Coordinator Human Resources
CNO: Wanda Haack MSN, R.N., Chief Nursing Officer
Web address: www.genesishealth.com
Control: Other not–for–profit (including NFP Corporation) **Service**: General medical and surgical

Staffed Beds: 86 **Admissions:** 322 **Census:** 72 **Outpatient Visits:** 20378 **Births:** 0 **Total Expense ($000):** 19310 **Payroll Expense ($000):** 7189 **Personnel:** 80	

IA

Hospital, Medicare Provider Number, Address, Telephone, Approval, Facility, and Physician Codes, Health Care System		
★ American Hospital Association (AHA) membership	○ Healthcare Facilities Accreditation Program	⇑ Center for Improvement in Healthcare Quality Accreditation
□ The Joint Commission accreditation	◇ DNV Healthcare Inc. accreditation	△ Commission on Accreditation of Rehabilitation Facilities (CARF) accreditation

DECORAH—Winneshiek County

✠ **WINNESHIEK MEDICAL CENTER (161371)**, 901 Montgomery Street, Zip 52101–2325; tel. 563/382–2911 **A1** 10 18 **F3** 7 8 11 13 15 28 29 31 34 35 38 40 43 45 50 56 57 59 61 62 63 64 65 68 69 75 76 77 78 79 81 82 86 87 93 94 97 102 104 107 110 111 115 119 128 129 130 131 132 133 135 144 146 147 148 149 **S** Mayo Clinic, Rochester, MN
Primary Contact: Lisa Radtke, Chief Administrative Officer
COO: David Rooney, Administrator Operations
CFO: Lynn Luloff, Chief Financial Officer
CMO: Robert Flinchbaugh D.O., Chief Medical Officer
CHR: Laurie Bulman, Director Human Resources
CNO: Susan Heitman, Chief Nursing Officer
Web address: www.winmedical.org
Control: County, Government, Nonfederal **Service:** General medical and surgical

Staffed Beds: 25 **Admissions:** 1056 **Census:** 10 **Outpatient Visits:** 72077 **Births:** 255 **Total Expense ($000):** 54051 **Payroll Expense ($000):** 19612 **Personnel:** 384

DENISON—Crawford County

★ **CRAWFORD COUNTY MEMORIAL HOSPITAL (161369)**, 100 Medical Parkway, Zip 51442–2299; tel. 712/265–2500 **A**10 18 **F3** 7 8 11 13 15 17 28 29 31 34 35 40 45 50 54 56 57 59 64 65 67 68 70 75 76 77 78 79 81 82 85 87 89 93 97 99 101 107 110 111 115 119 127 128 133 135 143 148 **P6**
Primary Contact: Bill Bruce, FACHE, Chief Executive Officer
CFO: Rachel Melby, Vice President, Chief Financial Officer
CIO: Angie Anderson, Director Information Technology
CHR: Brad L. Bonner, Executive Director, Human Resources and General Counsel
CNO: Erin Muck, Vice President, Clinical Nursing
Web address: www.ccmhia.com
Control: County, Government, Nonfederal **Service:** General medical and surgical

Staffed Beds: 25 **Admissions:** 635 **Census:** 5 **Outpatient Visits:** 42468 **Births:** 159 **Total Expense ($000):** 32812 **Payroll Expense ($000):** 14263 **Personnel:** 259

DES MOINES—Polk County

✠ **BROADLAWNS MEDICAL CENTER (160101)**, 1801 Hickman Road, Zip 50314–1597; tel. 515/282–2200 **A**1 3 5 10 **F3** 5 11 13 15 18 29 30 31 32 34 35 38 39 40 43 44 45 48 50 52 53 56 57 58 59 64 65 66 68 70 74 75 76 77 78 79 81 82 85 86 87 92 93 94 97 98 99 100 101 102 103 104 105 106 107 111 114 119 129 130 131 132 135 144 146 147 148 **P6**
Primary Contact: Jody J. Jenner, President and Chief Executive Officer
CFO: Karlis Vilums, Chief Financial Officer
CMO: Vincent Mandracchia DPM, Chief Medical Officer
CHR: Julie Kilgore, Vice President, Human Resources
CNO: Susan N. Kirstein R.N., MSN, Chief Nursing Officer
Web address: www.broadlawns.org
Control: County, Government, Nonfederal **Service:** General medical and surgical

Staffed Beds: 113 **Admissions:** 2869 **Census:** 52 **Outpatient Visits:** 240473 **Births:** 343 **Total Expense ($000):** 141509 **Payroll Expense ($000):** 66817 **Personnel:** 899

DES MOINES DIVISION See Veterans Affairs Central Iowa Health Care System

⇑ **IOWA LUTHERAN HOSPITAL** See Unitypoint Health–Iowa Lutheran Hospital

✠ △ **MERCY MEDICAL CENTER–DES MOINES (160083)**, 1111 6th Avenue, Zip 50314–2611; tel. 515/247–3121, (Includes MERCY MEDICAL CENTER – WEST LAKES, 1755 59th Place, West Des Moines, Iowa, Zip 50266–7737, tel. 515/358–8000; Robert P Ritz, President) **A**1 2 3 7 10 13 **F3** 4 5 6 7 8 9 11 13 15 16 17 18 19 20 21 22 23 24 25 26 27 28 29 30 31 32 34 35 36 38 39 40 41 43 44 46 48 49 50 53 54 55 56 57 58 59 60 61 62 63 64 65 66 68 70 71 72 73 74 75 76 77 78 79 81 82 84 85 86 87 88 89 90 91 92 93 94 96 97 98 99 100 101 102 103 104 105 106 107 108 109 110 111 114 115 116 117 118 119 120 121 123 124 126 130 131 132 133 134 135 138 141 142 143 144 145 146 147 148 149 150 **P6 S** Catholic Health Initiatives, Englewood, CO
Primary Contact: Robert P. Ritz, President
COO: Michael Wegner, Senior Vice President and Chief Operating Officer
CFO: Randy Rubin, Senior Vice President and Chief Financial Officer
CMO: Tommy Ibrahim M.D., Chief Physician Officer
CIO: James Strother, Site Director Information Technology Systems
CHR: Kevin Elsberry, Senior Vice President Human Resources
CNO: Mary J. Brown MSN, R.N., Vice President and Chief Nursing Officer
Web address: www.mercydesmoines.org
Control: Church operated, Nongovernment, not–for–profit **Service:** General medical and surgical

Staffed Beds: 613 **Admissions:** 33120 **Census:** 455 **Outpatient Visits:** 262330 **Births:** 4511 **Total Expense ($000):** 664439 **Payroll Expense ($000):** 256432 **Personnel:** 4182

✠ **SELECT SPECIALTY HOSPITAL–DES MOINES (162003)**, 1111 6th Avenue, 4th Floor Main, Zip 50314–2610; tel. 515/247–4400 **A**1 10 **F1** 29 75 148 **S** Select Medical Corporation, Mechanicsburg, PA
Primary Contact: Glen Griesheim, Chief Executive Officer
Web address: www.selectspecialtyhospitals.com
Control: Corporation, Investor–owned (for–profit) **Service:** Acute long–term care hospital

Staffed Beds: 30 **Admissions:** 268 **Census:** 19 **Outpatient Visits:** 0 **Births:** 0 **Total Expense ($000):** 11485 **Payroll Expense ($000):** 4879 **Personnel:** 86

★ △ ⇑ **UNITYPOINT HEALTH – IOWA METHODIST MEDICAL CENTER (160082)**, 1200 Pleasant Street, Zip 50309–1406; tel. 515/241–6212, (Includes POWELL CONVALESCENT CENTER, 1200 Pleasant, Des Moines, Iowa, Zip 50309, tel. 515/241–6212; UNITY POINT HEALTH – JOHN STODDARD CANCER CENTER, 1221 Pleasant Street, Des Moines, Iowa, Zip 50309–1423, tel. 515/241–6212; UNITYPOINT HEALTH – BLANK CHILDREN'S HOSPITAL, 1200 Pleasant Street, Des Moines, Iowa, Zip 50309–1406, tel. 515/241–5437; David A Stark, FACHE, President; UNITYPOINT HEALTH – METHODIST WEST HOSPITAL, 1660 60th Street, West Des Moines, Iowa, Zip 50266–7700, tel. 515/343–1000; YOUNKER MEMORIAL REHABILITATION CENTER, 1200 Pleasant Road, Des Moines, Iowa, Zip 50308, tel. 515/241–6212) **A**2 5 7 8 10 21 **F3** 7 8 11 12 13 17 18 20 22 24 26 28 29 30 31 32 34 35 39 40 41 43 44 45 46 47 49 50 53 54 55 56 57 58 59 60 61 64 65 68 70 71 72 74 75 76 77 78 79 81 82 84 85 86 87 88 89 90 91 92 93 95 96 97 100 107 108 111 114 115 116 117 118 119 120 121 123 124 126 129 130 131 132 134 135 138 146 147 148 149 **P6 S** UnityPoint Health, West Des Moines, IA
Primary Contact: Eric T. Crowell, President and Chief Executive Officer
COO: David A Stark FACHE, Executive Vice President and Chief Operating Officer
CFO: Joe Corfits, Senior Vice President, Chief Financial Officer
CMO: Mark Purtle M.D., Vice President Medical Affairs
CHR: Joyce McDanel, Vice President Human Resources and Education
CNO: Debra Moyer R.N., Chief Nursing Executive and Vice President Nursing Services
Web address: www.unitypoint.org
Control: Other not–for–profit (including NFP Corporation) **Service:** General medical and surgical

Staffed Beds: 518 **Admissions:** 26056 **Census:** 245 **Outpatient Visits:** 289898 **Births:** 4624 **Total Expense ($000):** 584972 **Payroll Expense ($000):** 248693 **Personnel:** 4027

★ ⇑ **UNITYPOINT HEALTH–IOWA LUTHERAN HOSPITAL (160024)**, 700 East University Avenue, Zip 50316–2392; tel. 515/263–5612, (Total facility includes 16 beds in nursing home–type unit) **A**3 5 10 21 **F3** 4 5 8 11 13 15 17 18 20 22 26 28 29 30 34 35 38 39 40 43 44 45 49 50 51 53 56 57 58 59 60 61 64 65 68 70 71 74 75 76 79 81 82 84 85 86 87 91 92 93 95 96 97 98 99 100 101 102 103 104 105 107 108 110 111 114 115 118 119 128 130 132 134 135 146 147 148 149 **P6 S** UnityPoint Health, West Des Moines, IA
Primary Contact: Eric T. Crowell, President and Chief Executive Officer
COO: Eric L Lothe FACHE, Senior Vice President and Chief Operating Officer
CFO: Joe Corfits, Chief Financial Officer
CMO: Mark Purtle M.D., Vice President Medical Affairs
CHR: Joyce McDanel, Vice President Human Resources and Education
CNO: Debra Moyer R.N., Chief Nurse Executive
Web address: www.unitypoint.org
Control: Other not–for–profit (including NFP Corporation) **Service:** General medical and surgical

Staffed Beds: 205 **Admissions:** 7711 **Census:** 119 **Outpatient Visits:** 61110 **Births:** 395 **Total Expense ($000):** 131365 **Payroll Expense ($000):** 56023 **Personnel:** 855

✠ △ **VETERANS AFFAIRS CENTRAL IOWA HEALTH CARE SYSTEM**, 3600 30th Street, Zip 50310–5753; tel. 515/699–5999, (Includes DES MOINES DIVISION, 3600 30th Street, Des Moines, Iowa, Zip 50310–5774, tel. 515/699–5999; KNOXVILLE DIVISION, 1515 West Pleasant, Knoxville, Iowa, Zip 50138–3399, tel. 515/842–3101) (Total facility includes 85 beds in nursing home–type unit) **A**1 3 5 7 **F2** 3 4 5 8 11 12 15 18 20 22 24 28 29 30 31 33 34 35 36 37 38 44 45 46 50 53 54 55 56 57 59 61 62 63 64 65 66 70 71 74 75 77 78 79 80 81 82 83 84 85 86 87 93 94 96 97 98 100 101 102 103 104 105 106 107 108 110 111 115 117 118 119 127 128 129 130 132 135 143 146 147 148 149 **S** Department of Veterans Affairs, Washington, DC
Primary Contact: Gail L. Graham, Director
CMO: Fredrick Bahls M.D., Chief of Staff
CIO: James Danuser, Chief Information Officer
CHR: Sabrina Owen, Human Resources Officer
Web address: www.centraliowa.va.gov/
Control: Veterans Affairs, Government, federal **Service:** General medical and surgical

Staffed Beds: 200 **Admissions:** 3068 **Census:** 148 **Outpatient Visits:** 383483 **Births:** 0 **Total Expense ($000):** 280678 **Payroll Expense ($000):** 145594 **Personnel:** 1582

IA

DUBUQUE—Dubuque County

FINLEY HOSPITAL See Unitypoint Health – Finley Hospital

✉ △ **MERCY MEDICAL CENTER–DUBUQUE (160069)**, 250 Mercy Drive, Zip 52001–7360; tel. 563/589–8000, (Total facility includes 40 beds in nursing home–type unit) **A**1 7 10 **F**3 4 5 8 11 13 15 18 20 22 24 26 28 29 30 31 32 34 35 36 38 39 40 43 44 49 50 51 53 56 57 58 59 61 62 64 65 67 70 72 74 75 76 77 78 79 80 81 84 85 86 87 89 90 91 93 97 98 99 100 101 102 103 104 107 108 110 111 114 115 117 118 119 126 128 129 130 131 132 134 135 144 146 147 148 149 150 **P**8 **S** Trinity Health, Livonia, MI
Primary Contact: Kay Takes, R.N., President
CFO: Robert Shafer, Vice President Finance
CIO: Joe Billmeyer, Director, Information Services
CHR: Kathryn Roberts, Director Human Resources
CNO: Robert Wethal R.N., Vice President and Chief Nursing Officer
Web address: www.mercydubuque.com
Control: Church operated, Nongovernment, not–for–profit **Service:** General medical and surgical

Staffed Beds: 235 **Admissions:** 9105 **Census:** 143 **Outpatient Visits:** 45682 **Births:** 850 **Total Expense ($000):** 156587 **Payroll Expense ($000):** 48179 **Personnel:** 1060

✉ △ **UNITYPOINT HEALTH – FINLEY HOSPITAL (160117)**, 350 North Grandview Avenue, Zip 52001–6392; tel. 563/582–1881 **A**1 7 10 **F**3 11 12 13 15 18 20 22 26 28 29 30 31 34 35 39 40 43 44 45 46 48 49 50 56 57 59 60 61 62 64 65 70 72 74 75 76 77 78 79 81 82 84 85 86 87 90 91 93 96 97 98 99 103 107 108 110 111 115 117 118 119 120 121 123 124 126 129 130 131 132 135 144 146 147 148 149 **P**1 5 **S** UnityPoint Health, West Des Moines, IA
Primary Contact: David R. Brandon, President and Chief Executive Officer
COO: Tim Ahlers, Chief Operating Officer
CFO: Dan Carpenter, Chief Financial Officer
CMO: Bryan Pechous M.D., Vice President Medical Affairs
CIO: Tim Loeffelholz, Account Executive Information Technology
CHR: Karla Waldbillig, Director Human Resources
CNO: Mary Peters, Chief Nursing Officer
Web address: www.unitypoint.org
Control: Other not–for–profit (including NFP Corporation) **Service:** General medical and surgical

Staffed Beds: 109 **Admissions:** 4472 **Census:** 53 **Outpatient Visits:** 98443 **Births:** 670 **Total Expense ($000):** 122635 **Payroll Expense ($000):** 53346 **Personnel:** 882

DYERSVILLE—Dubuque County

★ **MERCY MEDICAL CENTER–DYERSVILLE (161378)**, 1111 Third Street SW, Zip 52040–1725; tel. 563/875–7101 **A**10 18 **F**11 15 34 35 36 39 40 44 50 56 57 59 64 65 75 79 81 85 86 93 119 130 131 132 133 134 135 146 147 149 **P**8 **S** Trinity Health, Livonia, MI
Primary Contact: Kay Takes, R.N., President
CFO: Robert Shafer, Vice President Finance
Web address: www.mercydubuque.com/mercy–dyersville
Control: Church operated, Nongovernment, not–for–profit **Service:** General medical and surgical

Staffed Beds: 20 **Admissions:** 97 **Census:** 3 **Outpatient Visits:** 3801 **Births:** 0 **Total Expense ($000):** 5171 **Payroll Expense ($000):** 2491 **Personnel:** 52

ELKADER—Clayton County

★ **CENTRAL COMMUNITY HOSPITAL (161319)**, 901 Davidson Street NW, Zip 52043–9015; tel. 563/245–7000 **A**10 18 **F**7 11 15 28 34 35 40 43 50 57 59 64 67 68 75 81 85 87 91 93 107 110 114 128 133 146 **S** Trinity Health, Livonia, MI
Primary Contact: Brooke Kensinger, Chief Executive Officer
CFO: Patricia Borel, Chief Financial Officer
CIO: Jonathan Holliday, Manager Information Technology
CHR: Angie Gerndt, Human Resources Manager
CNO: Natalie Shea, Chief Nursing Officer
Web address: www.centralcommunityhospital.com
Control: Other not–for–profit (including NFP Corporation) **Service:** General medical and surgical

Staffed Beds: 15 **Admissions:** 160 **Census:** 1 **Outpatient Visits:** 7020 **Births:** 0 **Total Expense ($000):** 6870 **Payroll Expense ($000):** 2242 **Personnel:** 83

EMMETSBURG—Palo Alto County

★ **PALO ALTO COUNTY HEALTH SYSTEM (161357)**, 3201 First Street, Zip 50536–2516; tel. 712/852–5500, (Total facility includes 22 beds in nursing home–type unit) **A**10 18 **F**3 7 11 13 15 28 29 30 34 35 40 43 45 46 50 57 59 61 62 63 64 65 67 69 71 75 76 77 81 82 85 87 93 107 110 115 119 125 127 130 132 133 135 143 146 **S** Trinity Health, Livonia, MI
Primary Contact: Charles P. Kelch, Interim Chief Executive Officer
CFO: Renay Hauswirth, Chief Financial Officer
CMO: Paul Matthews M.D., President of Medical Staff
CIO: Randy Beaver, Chief Information Officer
CHR: Amy Knoup, Director Human Resources
CNO: Sara Travis, Chief Nursing Officer and Assistant Administrator
Web address: www.pachs.com
Control: County, Government, Nonfederal **Service:** General medical and surgical

Staffed Beds: 47 **Admissions:** 388 **Census:** 26 **Outpatient Visits:** 21158 **Births:** 97 **Total Expense ($000):** 25651 **Payroll Expense ($000):** 9863 **Personnel:** 191

ESTHERVILLE—Emmet County

★ **AVERA HOLY FAMILY HOSPITAL (161351)**, 826 North Eighth Street, Zip 51334–1598; tel. 712/362–2631 **A**10 18 **F**3 11 13 15 28 29 30 31 34 35 40 45 57 59 64 68 69 70 75 76 77 78 79 81 85 87 93 97 107 110 111 114 119 130 131 132 133 146 **P**4 **S** Avera Health, Sioux Falls, SD
Primary Contact: Dale Hustedt, Chief Executive Officer
CFO: Shannon Adams, Chief Financial Officer
CMO: Keith Probst M.D., Chief of Staff
CHR: Janette Jensen, Manager Human Resources
CNO: Cathi Rae Scharnberg R.N., M.P.H., Vice President Patient Services
Web address: www.avera–holyfamily.org
Control: Church operated, Nongovernment, not–for–profit **Service:** General medical and surgical

Staffed Beds: 25 **Admissions:** 693 **Census:** 6 **Outpatient Visits:** 68121 **Births:** 78 **Total Expense ($000):** 23959 **Payroll Expense ($000):** 10028 **Personnel:** 174

FAIRFIELD—Jefferson County

★ **JEFFERSON COUNTY HEALTH CENTER (161364)**, 2000 S Main, Zip 52556–9572, Mailing Address: P.O.Box 588, 52556–0010; tel. 641/472–4111 **A**10 18 **F**11 15 28 30 31 34 35 36 40 43 45 50 57 59 67 68 70 75 77 78 79 81 85 89 93 96 102 107 110 111 112 114 115 119 127 128 129 132 133 135 143 144 146 148 **P**5
Primary Contact: Bryan Hunger, Chief Executive Officer
CFO: Larry Peach, Chief Financial Officer
CHR: Nanette Everly, Manager Human Resources and Administrative Assistant
Web address: www.jeffersoncountyhealthcenter.org
Control: County, Government, Nonfederal **Service:** General medical and surgical

Staffed Beds: 25 **Admissions:** 806 **Census:** 12 **Outpatient Visits:** 69670 **Births:** 0 **Total Expense ($000):** 41410 **Payroll Expense ($000):** 14037 **Personnel:** 277

FORT DODGE—Webster County

★ ⇑ **UNITYPOINT HEALTH – TRINITY REGIONAL MEDICAL CENTER (160016)**, 802 Kenyon Road, Zip 50501–5795; tel. 515/573–3101 **A**2 10 21 **F**3 7 8 11 13 15 18 20 22 26 28 29 30 31 32 34 35 36 38 40 43 44 45 46 47 48 49 50 53 57 59 64 68 70 74 75 77 78 79 81 82 84 85 86 87 92 93 102 107 108 110 111 115 118 119 120 121 123 129 130 131 132 135 145 146 148 149 150 **P**6 **S** UnityPoint Health, West Des Moines, IA
Primary Contact: Mike Dewerff, President and Chief Executive Officer
COO: Troy Martens, Chief Operating Officer
CFO: Brent Feickert, Chief Financial Officer
CHR: Ted W Vaughn, Director Human Resources
CNO: Debra Shriver R.N., MSN, Chief Nurse Executive
Web address: www.trmc.org
Control: Other not–for–profit (including NFP Corporation) **Service:** General medical and surgical

Staffed Beds: 107 **Admissions:** 3460 **Census:** 34 **Outpatient Visits:** 97817 **Births:** 493 **Total Expense ($000):** 99810 **Payroll Expense ($000):** 47879 **Personnel:** 668

IA

Hospital, Medicare Provider Number, Address, Telephone, Approval, Facility, and Physician Codes, Health Care System

★ American Hospital Association (AHA) membership ○ Healthcare Facilities Accreditation Program ⇑ Center for Improvement in Healthcare Quality Accreditation
□ The Joint Commission accreditation ◇ DNV Healthcare Inc. accreditation △ Commission on Accreditation of Rehabilitation Facilities (CARF) accreditation

FORT MADISON—Lee County

✠ **FORT MADISON COMMUNITY HOSPITAL (160122)**, 5445 Avenue 'O', Zip 52627–9611, Mailing Address: P.O.Box 174, 52627–0174; tel. 319/372–6530 **A**1 10 **F**3 11 13 15 28 29 31 34 40 43 45 50 51 53 57 59 62 64 67 68 70 74 75 76 77 78 79 81 85 86 87 90 91 93 94 96 97 99 100 101 102 103 104 107 108 110 111 115 117 118 119 128 129 130 131 132 133 143 144 146 147 148 149 **P**6 **S** QHR, Brentwood, TN
Primary Contact: Jeremy Alexander, Interim Chief Executive Officer
CFO: Bradley J Kokjohn, Chief Financial Officer
CMO: David Wenger–Keller M.D., Chief of Staff
CIO: Shane Tapper, Director Management Information Systems
CHR: Vicki Kokjohn, Director Employee Relations
CNO: Shelby Dickens, Director, Patient Care Services
Web address: www.fmchosp.com
Control: Other not–for–profit (including NFP Corporation) **Service**: General medical and surgical

Staffed Beds: 50 Admissions: 1392 Census: 13 Outpatient Visits: 101991 Births: 403 Total Expense ($000): 57998 Payroll Expense ($000): 27911 Personnel: 464

GREENFIELD—Adair County

★ **ADAIR COUNTY HEALTH SYSTEM (161310)**, 609 SE Kent Street, Zip 50849–9454; tel. 641/743–2123 **A**10 18 **F**3 7 8 11 15 18 28 34 35 40 43 45 50 57 59 62 64 65 69 75 81 97 107 108 110 114 119 127 128 133 135 149 **P**6
Primary Contact: Marcia Hendricks, R.N., FACHE, Interim Chief Executive Officer
CMO: Cassie Rasmussen M.D., Chief Medical Officer
CIO: Thom Richards, Chief Information Technology
CHR: Angie Frankl, Director Human Resources
CNO: Cindy K Peeler R.N., Chief Nursing Officer
Web address: www.adaircountyhealthsystem.org
Control: County, Government, Nonfederal **Service**: General medical and surgical

Staffed Beds: 17 Admissions: 92 Census: 1 Outpatient Visits: 10584 Births: 0 Total Expense ($000): 13447 Payroll Expense ($000): 4527 Personnel: 130

GRINNELL—Poweshiek County

★ **GRINNELL REGIONAL MEDICAL CENTER (160147)**, 210 Fourth Avenue, Zip 50112–1898; tel. 641/236–7511 **A**10 **F**3 11 12 13 15 28 29 30 31 32 34 35 36 38 40 43 44 45 46 47 50 53 54 56 57 59 61 62 63 64 65 66 70 75 76 77 78 81 84 85 86 87 89 93 94 95 96 97 99 100 101 102 103 104 107 108 110 111 115 118 119 126 127 130 131 132 133 134 135 144 146 147 148 149 150 **P**6 7
Primary Contact: Todd C. Linden, President and Chief Executive Officer
CFO: Kyle M Wilcox, Vice President Finance
CIO: David L Ness, Vice President Operations
CHR: Debra S. Nowachek, Director Human Resources
CNO: Doris Rindels, Vice President Operations
Web address: www.grmc.us
Control: Other not–for–profit (including NFP Corporation) **Service**: General medical and surgical

Staffed Beds: 49 Admissions: 1311 Census: 12 Outpatient Visits: 41360 Births: 145 Total Expense ($000): 46756 Payroll Expense ($000): 19597 Personnel: 337

GRUNDY CENTER—Grundy County

★ **GRUNDY COUNTY MEMORIAL HOSPITAL (161303)**, 201 East 'J' Avenue, Zip 50638–2096; tel. 319/824–5421, (Total facility includes 55 beds in nursing home–type unit) **A**10 18 **F**15 28 29 34 35 40 43 57 59 63 64 67 68 75 78 79 81 82 86 87 93 107 110 111 114 119 128 129 130 131 132 133 135 146 148 **S** UnityPoint Health, West Des Moines, IA
Primary Contact: Jennifer Havens, Chief Executive Officer and Director of Nursing Operations
COO: Ryan Bingman, Director Operations
CFO: Lisa Zinkula, Chief Financial Officer
CMO: Douglas Cooper M.D., Chief Medical Officer
CIO: Scott Lufkin, Director Information Technology
CHR: Aaron Wedo, Manager, Human Resources
Web address: www.grundycountyhospital.com
Control: County, Government, Nonfederal **Service**: General medical and surgical

Staffed Beds: 80 Admissions: 305 Census: 56 Outpatient Visits: 40064 Births: 0 Total Expense ($000): 20143 Payroll Expense ($000): 8392 Personnel: 144

GUTHRIE CENTER—Guthrie County

★ **GUTHRIE COUNTY HOSPITAL (161314)**, 710 North 12th Street, Zip 50115–1544; tel. 641/332–2201 **A**10 18 **F**11 15 18 28 29 31 34 35 40 43 45 53 56 57 59 64 69 75 79 81 85 93 107 110 114 119 128 130 132 133 143 148 **S** UnityPoint Health, West Des Moines, IA
Primary Contact: Patrick Peters, Chief Executive Officer
CFO: Melinda Alt, Chief Financial Officer
CMO: Steven Bascom M.D., Chief Medical Officer
CIO: Jeff Cobb, Information Technologist
CHR: Kimberly Myers, Director Human Resources
CNO: Gregory Opseth, Chief Nursing Officer
Web address: www.guthriecountyhospital.org
Control: County, Government, Nonfederal **Service**: General medical and surgical

Staffed Beds: 17 Admissions: 358 Census: 3 Outpatient Visits: 45120 Births: 0 Total Expense ($000): 14926 Payroll Expense ($000): 6586 Personnel: 102

GUTTENBERG—Clayton County

✠ **GUTTENBERG MUNICIPAL HOSPITAL (161312)**, 200 Main Street, Zip 52052–9108, Mailing Address: P.O.Box 550, 52052–0550; tel. 563/252–1121 **A**1 10 18 **F**3 7 11 13 15 28 34 35 40 45 50 57 59 64 68 76 81 93 97 102 107 110 111 115 119 126 127 128 130 132 133 **P**5 6 **S** UnityPoint Health, West Des Moines, IA
Primary Contact: Kimberley A. Gau, FACHE, Chief Executive Officer
CMO: Andrew Smith M.D., Chief of Staff
CIO: Scott R Pauls, Director Information Technology– HealthNet Connect
CHR: Linda Aulwes, Human Resources Coordinator
CNO: Kimberley A Gau FACHE, Interim Chief Nursing Officer
Web address: www.guttenberghospital.org
Control: City, Government, Nonfederal **Service**: General medical and surgical

Staffed Beds: 20 Admissions: 322 Census: 2 Outpatient Visits: 25139 Births: 36 Total Expense ($000): 14706 Payroll Expense ($000): 6414 Personnel: 132

HAMBURG—Fremont County

GEORGE C GRAPE COMMUNITY HOSPITAL (161324), 2959 US Highway 275, Zip 51640–5067; tel. 712/382–1515, (Total facility includes 6 beds in nursing home–type unit) **A**10 18 **F**11 15 18 28 31 34 35 40 43 45 50 53 57 59 62 64 65 68 75 77 78 79 81 82 85 91 93 107 114 119 128 129 130 131 133 135 148
Primary Contact: Michael O'Neal, Administrator and Chief Executive Officer
CFO: Hilary Christiansen, Chief Financial Officer
CMO: Kelli Woltemath D.O., Chief Medical Staff
CIO: Craig Wells, Chief Information Officer
CHR: Jackie Wertz, Director Human Resources
CNO: Gloria Mattice R.N., Director Patient Care
Web address: www.grapehospital.com
Control: Other not–for–profit (including NFP Corporation) **Service**: General medical and surgical

Staffed Beds: 25 Admissions: 223 Census: 5 Outpatient Visits: 18193 Births: 0 Total Expense ($000): 9951 Payroll Expense ($000): 4170 Personnel: 88

HAMPTON—Franklin County

★ **FRANKLIN GENERAL HOSPITAL (161308)**, 1720 Central Avenue East, Suite A, Zip 50441–1867; tel. 641/456–5000, (Total facility includes 52 beds in nursing home–type unit) **A**10 18 **F**7 10 11 15 28 30 34 40 43 57 59 63 64 65 67 68 75 77 79 81 82 85 86 89 90 93 103 107 111 115 119 127 128 129 130 131 132 133 135 146 147 148 **S** Trinity Health, Livonia, MI
Primary Contact: Kim Price, Chief Executive Officer
CFO: Bonnie Lettow, Chief Financial Officer
CHR: Victoria Kruse, Manager Human Resources
CNO: Ronda Reimer R.N., Chief Nursing Officer and Assistant Administrator
Web address: www.franklingeneral.com
Control: County, Government, Nonfederal **Service**: General medical and surgical

Staffed Beds: 77 Admissions: 290 Census: 53 Outpatient Visits: 21095 Births: 0 Total Expense ($000): 19052 Payroll Expense ($000): 5965 Personnel: 133

Many Facility Codes have changed. Please refer to the AHA Guide Code Chart. © 2017 AHA Guide

HARLAN—Shelby County

★ **MYRTUE MEDICAL CENTER (161374)**, 1213 Garfield Avenue, Zip 51537–2057; tel. 712/755–5161 **A**10 18 **F**3 11 13 15 28 29 31 32 34 35 38 40 43 45 46 50 53 56 57 59 62 63 64 65 68 75 76 77 78 81 85 87 92 93 97 99 101 102 103 104 107 110 114 119 127 129 130 131 132 133 135 146 148 **P**6 8
Primary Contact: Barry Jacobsen, CPA, Chief Executive Officer
CFO: Kristy Hansen CPA, Chief Financial Officer
CMO: David Erlbacher M.D., Chief of Staff
CIO: David Sirek, Chief Information Officer
CHR: Donna Christensen–Mores JD, Director Human Resources
CNO: Karen Buman, Chief Nursing Executive
Web address: www.myrtuemedical.org
Control: County, Government, Nonfederal **Service:** General medical and surgical

> **Staffed Beds: 25 Admissions: 979 Census: 11 Outpatient Visits: 99861**
> **Births: 80 Total Expense ($000): 37264 Payroll Expense ($000): 14709**
> **Personnel: 315**

HAWARDEN—Sioux County

★ **HAWARDEN REGIONAL HEALTHCARE (161311)**, 1111 11th Street, Zip 51023–1999; tel. 712/551–3100 **A**10 18 **F**11 15 28 29 31 34 35 40 43 53 59 64 68 69 75 77 81 89 90 92 93 107 108 114 127 128 131 132 133 135 148 **P**3 **S** Trinity Health, Livonia, MI
Primary Contact: Jayson Pullman, Chief Executive Officer
CFO: Jessica Hughes, Director Finance
CMO: Dale Nystrom M.D., Chief Medical Officer, Physician
CHR: Maggie Hofer, Human Resources Representative
Web address: www.hawardenregionalhealthcare.com/
Control: City, Government, Nonfederal **Service:** General medical and surgical

> **Staffed Beds: 18 Admissions: 128 Census: 2 Outpatient Visits: 17020**
> **Births: 0 Total Expense ($000): 8293 Payroll Expense ($000): 3236**
> **Personnel: 68**

HUMBOLDT—Humboldt County

★ **HUMBOLDT COUNTY MEMORIAL HOSPITAL (161334)**, 1000 North 15th Street, Zip 50548–1008; tel. 515/332–4200, (Total facility includes 28 beds in nursing home–type unit) **A**10 18 **F**7 8 10 11 12 14 15 28 29 31 34 35 40 41 43 45 47 50 51 59 62 63 65 68 69 75 77 78 79 81 82 84 85 87 93 102 104 107 110 111 114 119 125 127 128 129 130 133 134 135 **S** UnityPoint Health, West Des Moines, IA
Primary Contact: Michelle Sleiter, Chief Executive Officer
CFO: Betty Etherington, Chief Financial Officer
CHR: Mary Moritz, Administrator Human Resources
Web address: www.humboldthospital.org
Control: County, Government, Nonfederal **Service:** General medical and surgical

> **Staffed Beds: 49 Admissions: 413 Census: 32 Outpatient Visits: 79148**
> **Births: 0 Total Expense ($000): 16661 Payroll Expense ($000): 6621**
> **Personnel: 152**

IDA GROVE—Ida County

★ **HORN MEMORIAL HOSPITAL (161354)**, 701 East Second Street, Zip 51445–1699; tel. 712/364–3311 **A**10 18 **F**11 15 28 29 34 40 45 50 57 59 62 63 64 65 66 68 75 77 79 81 82 85 89 93 97 107 108 110 111 115 119 127 128 129 130 131 132 133 135 146 147 148 **P**6
Primary Contact: Marcia Fehring, Chief Financial Officer and Interim Chief Executive Officer
CFO: Marcia Fehring, Chief Financial Officer
CIO: Robbie Todd, Director Information Technology
CHR: Lorraine Davis, Vice President Human Resources
CNO: Jo Hayes, Chief Nursing Officer
Web address: www.hornmemorialhospital.org
Control: Other not–for–profit (including NFP Corporation) **Service:** General medical and surgical

> **Staffed Beds: 16 Admissions: 407 Census: 6 Outpatient Visits: 47301**
> **Births: 0 Total Expense ($000): 18595 Payroll Expense ($000): 8536**
> **Personnel: 159**

INDEPENDENCE—Buchanan County

★ **BUCHANAN COUNTY HEALTH CENTER (161335)**, 1600 First Street East, Zip 50644–3155; tel. 319/332–0999, (Total facility includes 39 beds in nursing home–type unit) **A**10 18 **F**3 11 15 28 29 32 34 35 40 43 45 50 53 56 57 59 64 65 67 75 77 79 81 82 86 87 91 93 97 107 110 111 114 119 125 129 130 131 132 133 135 146 148 **P**6
Primary Contact: Steve Robert. Slessor, Chief Executive Officer
CFO: Ben Stevens, Chief Financial Officer
CNO: Rachel Goldenstein R.N., Chief Nursing Officer
Web address: www.bchealth.info
Control: County, Government, Nonfederal **Service:** General medical and surgical

> **Staffed Beds: 58 Admissions: 310 Census: 37 Outpatient Visits: 43818**
> **Births: 0 Total Expense ($000): 22894 Payroll Expense ($000): 9919**
> **Personnel: 176**

☐ **MENTAL HEALTH INSTITUTE (164003)**, 2277 Iowa Avenue, Zip 50644–9106; tel. 319/334–2583 **A**1 10 **F**59 65 75 98 99 101 102 130 135 143 146 149 **P**6
Primary Contact: Bhasker J. Dave, M.D., Superintendent
CFO: Kevin Jimmerson, Business Manager
CMO: Bhasker J Dave M.D., Superintendent
Web address: www.dhs.state.ia.us
Control: State, Government, Nonfederal **Service:** Psychiatric

> **Staffed Beds: 60 Admissions: 160 Census: 51 Outpatient Visits: 26**
> **Births: 0 Total Expense ($000): 21936 Payroll Expense ($000): 12555**
> **Personnel: 204**

IOWA CITY—Johnson County

▣ **IOWA CITY VETERANS AFFAIRS HEALTH CARE SYSTEM**, 601 Highway 6 West, Zip 52246–2208; tel. 319/338–0581 **A**1 3 5 8 **F**3 5 8 11 12 17 18 20 22 24 29 30 31 33 34 35 36 38 39 40 43 44 45 46 47 50 51 53 54 56 57 58 59 60 61 62 64 65 70 71 74 75 78 79 81 82 83 84 85 86 87 91 92 93 94 97 98 100 101 102 103 104 106 107 108 110 111 114 115 116 117 118 119 129 130 135 138 142 143 146 147 148 149 **P**6 **S** Department of Veterans Affairs, Washington, DC
Primary Contact: Judith Johnson–Mekota, Director
COO: Kevin Kosek, Associate Director Operations
CFO: Jennifer Ruppert, Chief Financial Officer
CMO: Richard A Charlat, Chief of Staff
CIO: Dwight Schuessler, Chief Information Officer
CHR: Dan Helle, Human Resources Officer
CNO: Dawn Oxley R.N., Associate Director Patient Care Services and Nurse Executive
Web address: www.iowacity.va.gov/
Control: Veterans Affairs, Government, federal **Service:** General medical and surgical

> **Staffed Beds: 74 Admissions: 3553 Census: 53 Outpatient Visits: 522769**
> **Births: 0 Total Expense ($000): 355265 Payroll Expense ($000): 135412**
> **Personnel: 1935**

▣ **MERCY IOWA CITY (160029)**, 500 East Market Street, Zip 52245–2689; tel. 319/339–0300, (Total facility includes 16 beds in nursing home–type unit) **A**1 2 10 **F**3 5 8 11 12 13 15 18 20 22 24 26 28 29 30 31 34 35 38 40 41 43 44 45 47 48 50 51 54 56 57 58 59 62 63 64 65 70 72 73 74 75 76 77 78 79 81 85 86 87 89 97 98 100 101 102 103 104 105 107 108 110 111 114 115 116 117 119 126 127 129 130 132 135 144 145 146 148 **P**8
Primary Contact: Shane Cerone, Interim President and Chief Executive Officer
CFO: Doug Davenport, Interim Chief Financial Officer
CMO: Martin Izakovic M.D., Vice President Medical Staff Affairs and Chief Medical Officer
CIO: David Fishbaugher, Chief Medical Information
CHR: Dena M Brockhouse, Director Human Resources
CNO: Cindy L Penney R.N., Vice President Nursing
Web address: www.mercyiowacity.org
Control: Church operated, Nongovernment, not–for–profit **Service:** General medical and surgical

> **Staffed Beds: 234 Admissions: 6937 Census: 68 Outpatient Visits: 346167 Births: 1231 Total Expense ($000): 152031 Payroll Expense ($000): 61854 Personnel: 900**

UNIVERSITY HOSPITAL SCHOOL See Center For Disabilities And Development

IA

✠ **UNIVERSITY OF IOWA HOSPITALS AND CLINICS (160058)**, 200 Hawkins Drive, Zip 52242–1009; tel. 319/356–1616, (Includes CENTER FOR DISABILITIES AND DEVELOPMENT, 200 Hawkins Drive, Iowa City, Iowa, Zip 52242, tel. 319/356–1347; CHEMICAL DEPENDENCY CENTER, 200 Hawkins Drive, Iowa City, Iowa, Zip 52242–1007, tel. 319/384–8765; STATE PSYCHIATRIC HOSPITAL, 200 Hawkins Drive, Iowa City, Iowa, Zip 52242, tel. 319/356–4658; UNIVERSITY OF IOWA CHILDREN'S HOSPITAL, 200 Hawkins Drive, Iowa City, Iowa, Zip 52242–1009, tel. 888/573–5437) **A**1 2 3 5 8 10 **F**3 5 6 7 8 9 11 12 13 14 15 16 17 18 19 20 21 22 23 24 25 26 27 28 29 30 31 32 33 34 35 36 37 38 39 40 41 43 44 45 46 47 48 49 50 51 52 53 54 55 56 57 58 59 60 61 62 63 64 65 66 68 70 72 73 74 75 76 77 78 79 80 81 82 83 84 85 86 87 88 89 90 91 92 93 94 96 97 98 99 100 101 102 103 104 105 107 108 109 110 111 114 115 116 117 118 119 120 121 123 124 126 127 129 130 131 132 135 136 137 138 139 140 141 142 143 145 146 147 148 **P**1 7
Primary Contact: Kenneth P. Kates, Chief Executive Officer
COO: Scott Turner, Co–Chief Operating Officer
CFO: Kenneth Fisher, Associate Vice President Finance and Chief Financial Officer
CMO: Theresa Brennan M.D., Chief Medical Officer
CIO: Lee Carmen, Associate Vice President Health Care Information Systems
CHR: Jana Wessels, Associate Vice President Human Resources
Web address: www.uihealthcare.org
Control: State, Government, Nonfederal **Service**: General medical and surgical

Staffed Beds: 724 **Admissions:** 33117 **Census:** 598 **Outpatient Visits:** 1374628 **Births:** 2254 **Total Expense ($000):** 1361563 **Payroll Expense ($000):** 470060 **Personnel:** 8292

IOWA FALLS—Hardin County

★ **HANSEN FAMILY HOSPITAL (161380)**, 920 South Oak, Zip 50126–9506; tel. 641/648–4631 **A**10 18 **F**3 11 13 15 28 29 30 34 40 41 43 45 50 53 57 59 64 65 75 76 77 81 82 85 86 87 89 93 97 100 104 107 110 115 119 133 135 147 **P**6 **S** Trinity Health, Livonia, MI
Primary Contact: Katie Ricks, Interim Chief Executive Officer
CFO: Mike White, Chief Financial Officer
CMO: George Pfaltzgraff, Chief Medical Officer
CHR: Cheri Geitz, Director Human Resources
CNO: Katie Rieks, Chief Nursing Officer
Web address: www.hansenfamilyhospital.com
Control: City, Government, Nonfederal **Service**: General medical and surgical

Staffed Beds: 21 **Admissions:** 589 **Census:** 8 **Outpatient Visits:** 34835 **Births:** 101 **Total Expense ($000):** 24523 **Payroll Expense ($000):** 10450 **Personnel:** 229

JEFFERSON—Greene County

★ **GREENE COUNTY MEDICAL CENTER (161325)**, 1000 West Lincolnway, Zip 50129–1645; tel. 515/386–2114, (Total facility includes 60 beds in nursing home–type unit) **A**10 18 **F**3 11 13 15 28 29 31 34 35 36 40 46 56 57 59 63 64 65 67 68 75 76 77 79 81 82 85 93 107 110 114 119 125 128 130 131 132 133 147 149 150 **S** UnityPoint Health, West Des Moines, IA
Primary Contact: Carl P. Behne, Chief Executive Officer
CFO: Mark A VanderLinden, Chief Financial Officer
CMO: Jon Van Der Veer D.O., Vice President Medical Affairs
CIO: Roger Overby, Executive Director Information Systems
CHR: Cathy Krieger, Human Resources Director
CNO: Katie Heldt, Chief Nursing Officer
Web address: www.gcmchealth.com
Control: County, Government, Nonfederal **Service**: General medical and surgical

Staffed Beds: 85 **Admissions:** 441 **Census:** 43 **Outpatient Visits:** 31541 **Births:** 34 **Total Expense ($000):** 26438 **Payroll Expense ($000):** 10195 **Personnel:** 215

KEOKUK—Lee County

✠ **UNITYPOINT HEALTH–KEOKUK (160008)**, 1600 Morgan Street, Zip 52632–3456; tel. 319/524–7150 **A**1 10 **F**3 11 15 28 29 34 35 40 43 45 46 57 59 62 64 68 70 77 79 81 85 86 87 93 96 107 108 111 114 115 118 119 129 130 131 132 133 146 148 149 **P**6 **S** UnityPoint Health, West Des Moines, IA
Primary Contact: Donza T. Worden, M.D., Chief Clinical Officer
CMO: Neville Crenshaw D.O., Chief of Staff
CIO: Linda Atterberg, Chief Information Officer
CHR: Lora Taylor, Director Human Resources and Compliance Officer
CNO: Vickie White, Director of Nursing
Web address: www.keokukhealthsystems.org
Control: Other not–for–profit (including NFP Corporation) **Service**: General medical and surgical

Staffed Beds: 42 **Admissions:** 970 **Census:** 8 **Outpatient Visits:** 31214 **Births:** 0 **Total Expense ($000):** 20345 **Payroll Expense ($000):** 8492 **Personnel:** 229

KEOSAUQUA—Van Buren County

★ **VAN BUREN COUNTY HOSPITAL (161337)**, 304 Franklin Street, Zip 52565–1164; tel. 319/293–3171 **A**10 18 **F**3 7 10 11 13 15 28 29 32 34 35 40 43 45 46 50 56 57 59 64 65 70 75 76 77 81 85 86 87 89 93 97 102 107 110 111 115 119 125 127 128 130 132 133 135 146 147 148 **P**6
Primary Contact: Ray Brownsworth, Chief Executive Officer
CFO: Kara McEntee, Chief Financial Officer
CIO: Chris McEntee, Network Specialist
CNO: Rhonda Fellows R.N., Chief Nursing Officer
Web address: www.vbch.org
Control: County, Government, Nonfederal **Service**: General medical and surgical

Staffed Beds: 25 **Admissions:** 398 **Census:** 4 **Outpatient Visits:** 16352 **Births:** 53 **Total Expense ($000):** 15463 **Payroll Expense ($000):** 7493 **Personnel:** 164

KNOXVILLE—Marion County

KNOXVILLE DIVISION See Veterans Affairs Central Iowa Health Care System, Des Moines

★ **KNOXVILLE HOSPITAL & CLINICS (161355)**, 1002 South Lincoln Street, Zip 50138–3155; tel. 641/842–2151 **A**10 18 **F**3 8 11 15 28 29 34 35 40 43 45 47 48 49 50 54 57 59 64 65 75 77 79 81 85 86 93 97 102 107 108 110 111 114 118 119 129 130 131 132 133 135 146 147 148 **P**6 **S** Catholic Health Initiatives, Englewood, CO
Primary Contact: Kevin Kincaid, Chief Executive Officer
CFO: Maggie Hamilton–Beyer, Chief Financial Officer
CMO: Brent Hoehns M.D., Chief of Medical Staff
CIO: Thom Richards, Director Information Technology
CNO: MaryJane Applegate, Chief Clinical Officer
Web address: www.knoxvillehospital.org
Control: Other not–for–profit (including NFP Corporation) **Service**: General medical and surgical

Staffed Beds: 25 **Admissions:** 1044 **Census:** 9 **Outpatient Visits:** 64581 **Births:** 0 **Total Expense ($000):** 28770 **Payroll Expense ($000):** 11770 **Personnel:** 266

LAKE CITY—Calhoun County

★ **STEWART MEMORIAL COMMUNITY HOSPITAL (161350)**, 1301 West Main, Zip 51449–1585; tel. 712/464–3171 **A**10 18 **F**11 12 13 15 28 29 30 31 34 40 43 45 50 59 62 63 64 65 69 70 75 76 77 78 81 82 86 93 94 107 110 114 119 127 130 133 135 147 **P**5 6 **S** UnityPoint Health, West Des Moines, IA
Primary Contact: Cynthia L. Carstens, R.N., President and Chief Executive Officer
CFO: Jim Henkenius, Chief Financial Officer
CHR: Bill Albright, Director Human Resources
Web address: www.stewartmemorial.org
Control: Other not–for–profit (including NFP Corporation) **Service**: General medical and surgical

Staffed Beds: 25 **Admissions:** 468 **Census:** 5 **Outpatient Visits:** 44759 **Births:** 91 **Total Expense ($000):** 33196 **Payroll Expense ($000):** 14309 **Personnel:** 236

LE MARS—Plymouth County

★ **FLOYD VALLEY HEALTHCARE (161368)**, 714 Lincoln Street NE, Zip 51031–3314; tel. 712/546–7871 **A**10 18 **F**3 10 11 13 15 28 29 31 32 34 40 43 45 50 53 57 59 62 64 65 67 68 76 78 79 80 81 85 86 87 89 107 110 111 114 119 128 130 132 133 135 146 148 **S** Avera Health, Sioux Falls, SD
Primary Contact: Michael T. Donlin, FACHE, Administrator
CFO: Daryl Friedenbach, Director Fiscal Services
CMO: Mark Stelzer M.D., President Medical Staff
CIO: Jason Uhl, Chief Information Officer
CHR: Mary Helen Gibson, Director Human Resources
CNO: Loretta Myers MS, R.N., Director, Patient Care
Web address: www.floydvalley.org
Control: City, Government, Nonfederal **Service**: General medical and surgical

Staffed Beds: 25 **Admissions:** 693 **Census:** 7 **Outpatient Visits:** 51433 **Births:** 97 **Total Expense ($000):** 34830 **Payroll Expense ($000):** 12367 **Personnel:** 264

LEON—Decatur County

★ **DECATUR COUNTY HOSPITAL (161340)**, 1405 NW Church Street, Zip 50144–1299; tel. 641/446–4871 **A**10 18 **F**3 7 11 15 28 29 31 34 40 41 45 50 57 59 64 68 71 75 78 79 81 82 85 93 107 111 114 119 130 133 146 148 149
Primary Contact: Greg Boattenhamer, Chief Executive Officer
CFO: Tara Spidle, Chief Financial Officer
CMO: Ed Wehling, Chief Medical Staff
CHR: Jo Beth Smith, Vice President Human Resources
Web address: www.decaturcountyhospital.org
Control: County, Government, Nonfederal **Service**: General medical and surgical

Staffed Beds: 11 **Admissions:** 232 **Census:** 3 **Outpatient Visits:** 10840 **Births:** 0 **Total Expense ($000):** 12700 **Payroll Expense ($000):** 4477 **Personnel:** 94

IA

Many Facility Codes have changed. Please refer to the AHA Guide Code Chart. © 2017 AHA Guide

MANCHESTER—Delaware County

★ **REGIONAL MEDICAL CENTER (161343)**, 709 West Main Street, Zip 52057–1526, Mailing Address: P.O.Box 359, 52057–0359; tel. 563/927–3232 **A**10 18 **F**3 7 11 13 15 17 28 29 34 35 36 40 43 44 50 53 57 59 61 62 63 64 65 66 68 70 75 76 77 79 81 82 85 86 89 93 94 97 99 104 107 110 111 114 119 126 127 128 129 130 131 132 146 148 **P**6
Primary Contact: Charlie A. Button, Chief Executive Officer
CFO: Danette Kramer, Chief Financial Officer
CIO: Amy Mensen, Chief Administrative Officer
CHR: Amy Mensen, Chief Administrative Officer
CNO: Heather Ries MSN, R.N., Chief Nursing Officer
Web address: www.regmedctr.org
Control: County, Government, Nonfederal **Service:** General medical and surgical

Staffed Beds: 25 **Admissions:** 892 **Census:** 8 **Outpatient Visits:** 169913 **Births:** 180 **Total Expense ($000):** 47640 **Payroll Expense ($000):** 22812 **Personnel:** 378

MANNING—Carroll County

★ **MANNING REGIONAL HEALTHCARE CENTER (161332)**, 1550 6th Street, Zip 51455–1093; tel. 712/655–2072, (Total facility includes 56 beds in nursing home–type unit) **A**10 18 **F**3 4 5 11 13 15 31 34 35 38 40 43 45 50 56 57 59 64 68 75 76 81 85 89 92 93 97 107 110 114 119 128 130 132 133 **P**6
Primary Contact: John O'Brien, Chief Executive Officer
CFO: Amy McLaughlin CPA, Chief Financial Officer
CMO: Douglas McLaws D.O., Chief Medical Officer
CIO: Kim C Jahn, Chief Plant Operations and Chief Information Officer
CHR: Shelli Lorenzen, Chief Human Resources Officer
CNO: Linn Block R.N., Chief Nursing Officer
Web address: www.mrhcia.com
Control: Other not–for–profit (including NFP Corporation) **Service:** General medical and surgical

Staffed Beds: 73 **Admissions:** 247 **Census:** 48 **Outpatient Visits:** 8580 **Births:** 17 **Total Expense ($000):** 16729 **Payroll Expense ($000):** 6650 **Personnel:** 186

MAQUOKETA—Jackson County

✠ **JACKSON COUNTY REGIONAL HEALTH CENTER (161329)**, 700 West Grove Street, Zip 52060–2163; tel. 563/652–2474 **A**1 10 18 **F**3 7 11 15 28 34 40 43 45 50 53 64 75 81 82 85 87 93 107 110 114 119 128 129 133 146 148 **S** Genesis Health System, Davenport, IA
Primary Contact: Curt Coleman, FACHE, Administrator
CFO: Donna Roeder, Chief Financial Officer
CHR: Shannon Langenberg, Director Human Resources
Web address: www.jcrhc.org
Control: County, Government, Nonfederal **Service:** General medical and surgical

Staffed Beds: 25 **Admissions:** 186 **Census:** 3 **Outpatient Visits:** 17962 **Births:** 0 **Total Expense ($000):** 14126 **Payroll Expense ($000):** 5114 **Personnel:** 118

MARENGO—Iowa County

★ **COMPASS MEMORIAL HEALTHCARE (161317)**, 300 West May Street, Zip 52301–1261; tel. 319/642–5543 **A**10 18 **F**3 15 28 29 31 34 35 38 40 43 45 50 59 64 65 69 75 77 78 79 81 82 85 87 93 96 97 107 110 111 115 119 127 129 130 131 133 135 145 146 149 **P**6 **S** UnityPoint Health, West Des Moines, IA
Primary Contact: Barry Goettsch, FACHE, Chief Executive Officer
COO: Mikaela Gehring, Chief Operating Officer
CFO: Matthew Murphy, Chief Financial Officer
CHR: Lesa Waddell, Director Human Resources
CNO: Teresa Sauerbrei, Chief Nursing Officer
Web address: www.compassmemorial.org
Control: City, Government, Nonfederal **Service:** General medical and surgical

Staffed Beds: 25 **Admissions:** 346 **Census:** 7 **Outpatient Visits:** 15325 **Births:** 0 **Total Expense ($000):** 18616 **Payroll Expense ($000):** 8595 **Personnel:** 131

MARSHALLTOWN—Marshall County

★ **UNITYPOINT HEALTH – MARSHALLTOWN (160001)**, 3 South Fourth Avenue, Zip 50158–2998; tel. 641/754–5151 **A**10 **F**3 7 11 13 15 18 20 22 28 30 34 39 40 43 44 45 50 53 54 56 57 59 62 64 65 68 69 70 75 76 79 81 82 85 86 87 89 97 107 108 110 111 114 115 119 127 129 130 132 133 143 144 146 147 149 **P**6 **S** UnityPoint Health, West Des Moines, IA
Primary Contact: Dustin Wright, President and Chief Executive Officer
CMO: Russell Adams M.D., Chief Medical Officer
CHR: Jill Petermeier, Senior Executive Human Resources
Web address: www.marshalltown.unitypoint.org
Control: Other not–for–profit (including NFP Corporation) **Service:** General medical and surgical

Staffed Beds: 40 **Admissions:** 2079 **Census:** 18 **Outpatient Visits:** 189391 **Births:** 478 **Total Expense ($000):** 79664 **Payroll Expense ($000):** 25785 **Personnel:** 422

MASON CITY—Cerro Gordo County

✠ **MERCY MEDICAL CENTER–NORTH IOWA (160064)**, 1000 Fourth Street SW, Zip 50401–2800; tel. 641/428–7000 **A**1 2 3 5 10 13 **F**3 11 12 13 15 18 20 22 24 26 28 29 30 31 34 35 37 39 40 42 43 44 45 46 47 48 49 50 54 55 56 57 58 59 60 61 62 63 64 65 68 70 71 72 74 75 76 77 78 79 81 82 84 85 86 87 89 90 91 93 96 97 98 99 100 101 102 103 104 105 107 108 110 111 113 115 117 118 119 120 121 123 124 125 126 128 129 130 131 132 135 144 145 146 147 148 149 **P**1 6 **S** Trinity Health, Livonia, MI
Primary Contact: Daniel Varnum, President and Chief Executive Officer
COO: Diane Fischels, Senior Vice President and Chief Operating Officer
CFO: Danette Zook, Chief Financial Officer
CMO: Paul Manternach M.D., Senior Vice President Physician Integration
CIO: Terry Chartier, Director, Information Systems
CHR: Jackie Luecht, Chief Human Resources Officer
CNO: Kim Chamberlin, Vice President Patient Services and Chief Nursing Officer
Web address: www.mercynorthiowa.com
Control: Church operated, Nongovernment, not–for–profit **Service:** General medical and surgical

Staffed Beds: 205 **Admissions:** 11444 **Census:** 126 **Outpatient Visits:** 452838 **Births:** 875 **Total Expense ($000):** 347726 **Payroll Expense ($000):** 137320 **Personnel:** 2118

MISSOURI VALLEY—Harrison County

★ **CHI HEALTH MISSOURI VALLEY (161309)**, 631 North Eighth Street, Zip 51555–1102; tel. 712/642–2784 **A**10 18 **F**3 28 34 40 44 45 47 50 54 57 58 59 60 61 75 81 82 83 84 86 87 93 94 97 99 100 101 107 110 114 119 127 129 133 135 144 146 **P**8 **S** Catholic Health Initiatives, Englewood, CO
Primary Contact: Robert A. Valentine, President
CMO: Daniel Richter M.D., Chief of Staff
CIO: Ravae Smallwood, IS Coordinator
CHR: Heidi Winters, Business Partner Human Resources
CNO: Darcy Behrendt R.N., Vice President, Patient Care Services
Web address: www.chihealth.com/chi–health–missouri–valley
Control: Other not–for–profit (including NFP Corporation) **Service:** General medical and surgical

Staffed Beds: 16 **Admissions:** 563 **Census:** 5 **Outpatient Visits:** 23120 **Births:** 0 **Total Expense ($000):** 27816 **Payroll Expense ($000):** 9854 **Personnel:** 86

MOUNT AYR—Ringgold County

RINGGOLD COUNTY HOSPITAL (161373), 504 North Cleveland Street, Zip 50854–2201; tel. 641/464–3226 **A**10 18 **F**3 7 15 28 29 31 34 35 38 40 43 50 56 57 59 64 65 81 93 97 107 111 115 119 127 133 148 **P**6
Primary Contact: Gordon W. Winkler, Administrator and Chief Executive Officer
CFO: Teresa Roberts, Chief Financial Officer
CIO: Beth Kosman, Director Health Information Management
CHR: Mitzi Hymbaugh, Chief Personnel
Web address: www.rchmtayr.org
Control: Hospital district or authority, Government, Nonfederal **Service:** General medical and surgical

Staffed Beds: 16 **Admissions:** 298 **Census:** 3 **Outpatient Visits:** 33092 **Total Expense ($000):** 19370 **Payroll Expense ($000):** 7364 **Personnel:** 134

IA

Hospital, Medicare Provider Number, Address, Telephone, Approval, Facility, and Physician Codes, Health Care System

★ American Hospital Association (AHA) membership ○ Healthcare Facilities Accreditation Program ⇧ Center for Improvement in Healthcare Quality Accreditation
☐ The Joint Commission accreditation ◇ DNV Healthcare Inc. accreditation △ Commission on Accreditation of Rehabilitation Facilities (CARF) accreditation

© 2017 AHA Guide *Many Facility Codes have changed. Please refer to the AHA Guide Code Chart.* Hospitals **A231**

MOUNT PLEASANT—Henry County

★ **HENRY COUNTY HEALTH CENTER (161356)**, 407 South White Street, Zip 52641–2263; tel. 319/385–3141, (Total facility includes 49 beds in nursing home–type unit) **A**10 18 **F**3 7 11 13 15 28 29 31 32 34 35 40 41 43 44 45 50 53 57 59 64 65 67 68 70 75 76 77 78 79 81 82 85 86 87 89 93 96 97 102 107 108 110 111 115 118 119 128 129 130 131 132 133 135 143 146 147 **P**6
Primary Contact: Robb Gardner, Chief Executive Officer
CFO: David Muhs, Chief Financial Officer
CMO: Joel Ryon M.D., Chief of Staff
CHR: Lynn Humphreys, Director Human Resources
CNO: Jodi Geerts, Chief Nursing Officer
Web address: www.hchc.org
Control: County, Government, Nonfederal **Service**: General medical and surgical

Staffed Beds: 74 **Admissions:** 689 **Census:** 52 **Outpatient Visits:** 50345
Births: 138 **Total Expense ($000):** 35220 **Payroll Expense ($000):** 13579
Personnel: 241

MUSCATINE—Muscatine County

✠ **UNITYPOINT HEALTH – TRINITY MUSCATINE (160013)**, 1518 Mulberry Avenue, Zip 52761–3499; tel. 563/264–9100 **A**1 10 20 **F**3 5 11 13 15 18 28 29 31 34 38 40 43 45 50 55 56 57 59 61 64 65 68 69 70 75 76 77 81 85 87 97 102 107 108 110 111 114 119 124 129 130 131 132 134 135 147 148 149 **S** UnityPoint Health, West Des Moines, IA
Primary Contact: Angela Johnson, Executive Director
CFO: Katie A Marchik, Vice President, Consolidated Services, UnityPoint Health and Interim Chief Financial Officer, Trinity Regional Health Sy
CMO: Manasi Nadkarni M.D., Vice President Medical Affairs
CIO: Sean Liddell, Manager Regional Service Information Technology
CHR: Karla Blaser, Director Human Resources
CNO: Pam Askew R.N., Vice President Patient Care Services
Web address: www.unitypoint.org/quadcities/trinity–muscatine.aspx
Control: Other not–for–profit (including NFP Corporation) **Service**: General medical and surgical

Staffed Beds: 45 **Admissions:** 1322 **Census:** 11 **Outpatient Visits:** 87814
Births: 299 **Total Expense ($000):** 46171 **Payroll Expense ($000):** 15797
Personnel: 277

NEVADA—Story County

★ **STORY COUNTY MEDICAL CENTER (161333)**, 640 South 19th Street, Zip 50201–2902; tel. 515/382–2111, (Total facility includes 65 beds in nursing home–type unit) **A**10 18 **F**3 7 11 28 29 32 34 35 36 40 43 50 53 57 59 64 65 68 75 81 85 87 97 107 114 119 127 130 133 146 148 **P**6 **S** UnityPoint Health, West Des Moines, IA
Primary Contact: Nate Thompson, Chief Executive Officer
CFO: Jane Ramthun, Chief Financial Officer
CMO: Arthur Check M.D., Chief Medical Officer
CHR: Jessica Lingo, Human Resource Generalist
CNO: Beth Rehbein, Chief Nursing and Quality Officer
Web address: www.storymedical.org
Control: County, Government, Nonfederal **Service**: General medical and surgical

Staffed Beds: 77 **Admissions:** 425 **Census:** 67 **Outpatient Visits:** 28306
Births: 0 **Total Expense ($000):** 24696 **Payroll Expense ($000):** 10868
Personnel: 167

NEW HAMPTON—Chickasaw County

★ **MERCY MEDICAL CENTER–NEW HAMPTON (161331)**, 308 North Maple Avenue, Zip 50659–1142; tel. 641/394–4121 **A**10 18 **F**3 11 13 15 28 29 34 35 40 43 45 48 56 57 59 64 65 68 74 75 76 77 79 81 85 93 97 107 110 119 131 133 146 149 **P**1 **S** Trinity Health, Livonia, MI
Primary Contact: Aaron Flugum, Chief Executive Officer
CFO: Jennifer Rapenske, Manager Financial Services
CMO: Jack Kline M.D., Chief of Staff
CIO: Terry Chartier, Director, Information Systems
CHR: Jackie Luecht, Director, Human Resources
CNO: Cheryl Kay Haggerty, Chief Nursing Officer, Assistant Chief Executive Officer
Web address: www.mercynewhampton.com
Control: Church operated, Nongovernment, not–for–profit **Service**: General medical and surgical

Staffed Beds: 18 **Admissions:** 299 **Census:** 3 **Outpatient Visits:** 30191
Births: 42 **Total Expense ($000):** 17461 **Payroll Expense ($000):** 6412
Personnel: 116

NEWTON—Jasper County

★ **SKIFF MEDICAL CENTER (160032)**, 204 North Fourth Avenue East, Zip 50208–3100, Mailing Address: P.O.Box 1006, 50208–1006; tel. 641/792–1273 **A**10 **F**3 11 13 15 17 28 29 30 31 34 35 40 43 44 45 50 57 59 63 64 70 75 76 77 78 79 81 82 85 89 90 93 96 102 107 108 110 111 115 119 128 130 131 132 133 135 145 146 148 149 **S** Catholic Health Initiatives, Englewood, CO
Primary Contact: Laurie A. Conner, FACHE, Interim Chief Executive Officer
COO: Sonja Ranck MSN, R.N., Chief Operating Officer and Chief Nursing Officer
CIO: Amber Wentz, Director of Clinical Information Systems & Clinical Informatics
CHR: Teresa Wermager, Human Resources Business Partner
CNO: Sonja Ranck MSN, R.N., Chief Operating Officer and Chief Nursing Officer
Web address: www.skiffmed.com
Control: Other not–for–profit (including NFP Corporation) **Service**: General medical and surgical

Staffed Beds: 48 **Admissions:** 1256 **Census:** 12 **Outpatient Visits:** 73898
Births: 166 **Total Expense ($000):** 32102 **Payroll Expense ($000):** 12708
Personnel: 216

OELWEIN—Fayette County

★ **MERCY HOSPITAL OF FRANCISCAN SISTERS (161338)**, 201 Eighth Avenue SE, Zip 50662–2447; tel. 319/283–6000, (Total facility includes 39 beds in nursing home–type unit) **A**10 18 **F**7 11 15 29 30 34 35 40 57 59 69 75 79 81 93 97 107 110 111 119 127 128 130 132 133 146 147 **P**1 **S** Trinity Health, Livonia, MI
Primary Contact: Terri Derflinger, Site Administrator
CFO: Michele Panicucci, Senior Vice President and Chief Financial Officer
CMO: James Lehman M.D., Vice President Medical Affairs
CNO: Kelly Richards MSN, Senior Vice President and Chief Nursing Officer
Web address: www.wheatoniowa.org
Control: Church operated, Nongovernment, not–for–profit **Service**: General medical and surgical

Staffed Beds: 64 **Admissions:** 276 **Census:** 33 **Outpatient Visits:** 24587
Births: 0 **Total Expense ($000):** 13441 **Payroll Expense ($000):** 5495
Personnel: 120

ONAWA—Monona County

★ **BURGESS HEALTH CENTER (161359)**, 1600 Diamond Street, Zip 51040–1548; tel. 712/423–2311 **A**10 18 **F**3 7 11 13 15 28 29 31 32 34 35 40 45 47 50 53 56 57 59 62 63 64 65 67 68 70 75 76 77 78 79 81 82 85 93 97 99 100 101 103 104 107 111 114 119 127 128 130 132 133 135 146 148 149 **P**6
Primary Contact: Francis G. Tramp, President
CFO: Shawn Gosch, Chief Financial Officer
CMO: John Garred M.D., Sr., Chief Medical Officer
CIO: Grady Warner, Director of Information Technology
CHR: Erin Brekke, Director Human Resources
CNO: Patty Sandmann, Senior Director of Nursing
Web address: www.burgesshc.org
Control: Other not–for–profit (including NFP Corporation) **Service**: General medical and surgical

Staffed Beds: 25 **Admissions:** 781 **Census:** 8 **Outpatient Visits:** 69753
Births: 50 **Total Expense ($000):** 29748 **Payroll Expense ($000):** 12806
Personnel: 288

ORANGE CITY—Sioux County

★ **ORANGE CITY AREA HEALTH SYSTEM (161360)**, 1000 Lincoln Circle SE, Zip 51041–1862; tel. 712/737–4984, (Total facility includes 83 beds in nursing home–type unit) **A**10 18 **F**7 10 11 13 15 18 28 29 31 34 35 40 45 50 53 56 57 59 60 62 63 64 67 68 69 70 75 76 77 78 79 81 82 85 86 87 89 93 97 99 100 101 102 103 104 107 110 111 114 117 119 120 125 127 130 131 132 133 146 147 148 **P**6 **S** Sanford Health, Sioux Falls, SD
Primary Contact: Martin W. Guthmiller, Chief Executive Officer
COO: Daniel P McCarty, Chief Operating Officer
CFO: Dina Baas, Director Financial Services
CMO: Alan Laird M.D., Chief Medical Officer
CHR: Jason Jauron, Director Human Resources
Web address: www.ochealthsystem.org
Control: City, Government, Nonfederal **Service**: General medical and surgical

Staffed Beds: 108 **Admissions:** 974 **Census:** 93 **Outpatient Visits:** 78334
Births: 257 **Total Expense ($000):** 45559 **Payroll Expense ($000):** 18605
Personnel: 411

IA

Many Facility Codes have changed. Please refer to the AHA Guide Code Chart. © 2017 AHA Guide

OSAGE—Mitchell County

★ **MITCHELL COUNTY REGIONAL HEALTH CENTER (161323)**, 616 North Eighth Street, Zip 50461–1498; tel. 641/732–6000 **A**10 18 **F**7 8 11 15 18 28 29 34 35 40 45 50 56 57 59 63 64 65 75 81 85 87 93 103 107 110 114 119 127 130 132 133 144 146 **P**8 **S** Trinity Health, Livonia, MI
Primary Contact: Shelly Russell, Chief Executive Officer
CFO: Gregory Burkel, Chief Financial Officer
CMO: Jeff Nasstrom D.O., Chief of Staff
CHR: Jodie Anderson, Director Human Resources
CNO: Shelly Russell, Chief Nursing Officer
Web address: www.mitchellcohospital–clinics.com
Control: County, Government, Nonfederal **Service**: General medical and surgical

Staffed Beds: 25 **Admissions**: 327 **Census**: 4 **Outpatient Visits**: 59629
Births: 0 **Total Expense ($000)**: 21392 **Payroll Expense ($000)**: 7546
Personnel: 158

OSCEOLA—Clarke County

★ **CLARKE COUNTY HOSPITAL (161348)**, 800 South Fillmore Street, Zip 50213–1619; tel. 641/342–2184 **A**10 18 **F**7 11 15 18 28 29 31 34 35 40 45 50 57 59 64 67 68 75 77 78 79 81 89 90 93 94 96 107 111 115 116 117 118 119 128 129 130 131 132 133 135 148 **S** UnityPoint Health, West Des Moines, IA
Primary Contact: Brian G. Evans, FACHE, Chief Executive Officer
CFO: Michael Thilges, Chief Financial Officer
CMO: George Fotiadis M.D., Chief of Staff
CIO: Dennis Blazek, Chief Information Officer
CHR: Kate Emanuel, Director Human Resources
Web address: www.clarkehosp.org
Control: County, Government, Nonfederal **Service**: General medical and surgical

Staffed Beds: 25 **Admissions**: 290 **Census**: 10 **Outpatient Visits**: 21271
Births: 0 **Total Expense ($000)**: 19224 **Payroll Expense ($000)**: 6671
Personnel: 142

OSKALOOSA—Mahaska County

✠ **MAHASKA HEALTH PARTNERSHIP (161379)**, 1229 'C' Avenue East, Zip 52577–4298; tel. 641/672–3100 **A**1 10 18 **F**3 5 7 8 11 13 15 28 29 30 31 32 34 35 36 38 40 43 45 46 47 50 54 56 57 59 61 62 63 64 65 66 68 69 70 75 76 77 78 79 81 84 85 87 93 94 97 98 99 100 101 102 103 104 107 110 111 114 119 126 129 130 132 133 135 146 148 149 150 **P**6
Primary Contact: Jay Christensen, FACHE, Chief Executive Officer
COO: Erin Baldwin M.P.H., Chief Operating Officer
CMO: Matt Whitis, Chief Medical Officer
CHR: Jacky Bresnahan, Director Human Resources
Web address: www.mahaskahealth.com
Control: County, Government, Nonfederal **Service**: General medical and surgical

Staffed Beds: 33 **Admissions**: 1550 **Census**: 22 **Outpatient Visits**: 151381
Births: 250 **Total Expense ($000)**: 55776 **Payroll Expense ($000)**: 29416
Personnel: 391

OTTUMWA—Wapello County

□ △ **OTTUMWA REGIONAL HEALTH CENTER (160089)**, 1001 Pennsylvania Avenue, Zip 52501–2186; tel. 641/684–2300 **A**1 7 10 **F**3 7 11 13 15 18 20 22 28 29 30 34 35 40 41 43 45 46 47 48 50 51 53 54 56 57 59 60 62 64 73 74 75 76 77 79 80 81 82 85 87 89 90 93 98 102 103 107 108 110 111 114 115 116 117 118 119 120 121 123 126 129 130 131 132 135 146 147 148 **P**6 **S** RCCH HealthCare Partners, Brentwood, TN
Primary Contact: Philip J. Noel III, Chief Executive Officer
COO: Jason Hotchkiss CPA, Chief Financial Officer / Chief Operating Officer
CFO: Jason Hotchkiss CPA, Chief Financial Officer
CMO: Sandro Younadam M.D., Chief Medical Officer
CIO: Scott Garrett, Director of IS
CHR: Lidia Bryant, Director Human Resources
CNO: Lori Bailey R.N., Vice President and Chief Nursing Officer
Web address: www.ottumwaregionalhealth.com
Control: Corporation, Investor–owned (for–profit) **Service**: General medical and surgical

Staffed Beds: 101 **Admissions**: 3142 **Census**: 40 **Outpatient Visits**: 136139 **Births**: 481 **Total Expense ($000)**: 72651 **Payroll Expense ($000)**: 21934 **Personnel**: 483

PELLA—Marion County

✠ **PELLA REGIONAL HEALTH CENTER (161367)**, 404 Jefferson Street, Zip 50219–1257; tel. 641/628–3150, (Total facility includes 15 beds in nursing home–type unit) **A**1 10 18 **F**3 11 13 15 18 28 29 30 31 32 34 35 40 43 45 50 51 53 57 59 62 63 64 65 66 70 74 75 76 77 78 79 81 82 84 85 86 87 91 93 94 97 102 107 108 110 111 115 119 126 127 128 129 130 131 132 133 146 147 148 149 **P**6
Primary Contact: Robert D. Kroese, FACHE, Chief Executive Officer
COO: Robert D Kroese FACHE, Chief Executive Officer
CFO: Bruce Heifner, Chief Financial Officer
CIO: Tait Smock, Manager Information Systems
CHR: Teri Lickteig, Director Human Resources
CNO: Yvonne M O'Brien–Evans MS, R.N., Chief of Nursing
Web address: www.pellahealth.org
Control: Other not–for–profit (including NFP Corporation) **Service**: General medical and surgical

Staffed Beds: 40 **Admissions**: 1497 **Census**: 16 **Outpatient Visits**: 140260
Births: 536 **Total Expense ($000)**: 53372 **Payroll Expense ($000)**: 20337
Personnel: 605

PERRY—Dallas County

★ **DALLAS COUNTY HOSPITAL (161322)**, 610 10th Street, Zip 50220–2221; tel. 515/465–3547 **A**10 18 **F**15 18 28 29 31 34 35 39 40 41 43 45 47 50 57 59 68 75 77 78 79 81 82 85 89 93 107 110 114 119 128 130 132 133 135 146 148
Primary Contact: Angela Mortoza, Chief Executive Officer
CFO: Randy Loomis, Chief Financial Officer
CMO: Steven Sohn M.D., President Medical Staff
CHR: Sherry Smith, Manager Human Resources
CNO: Tonya Summerson, Chief Clinical Officer
Web address: www.dallascohospital.org
Control: County, Government, Nonfederal **Service**: General medical and surgical

Staffed Beds: 15 **Admissions**: 221 **Census**: 2 **Outpatient Visits**: 22662
Births: 0 **Total Expense ($000)**: 13316 **Payroll Expense ($000)**: 4513
Personnel: 87

POCAHONTAS—Pocahontas County

★ **POCAHONTAS COMMUNITY HOSPITAL (161305)**, 606 NW Seventh Street, Zip 50574–1099; tel. 712/335–3501 **A**10 18 **F**7 11 15 17 28 29 31 35 40 43 45 59 62 63 64 67 70 75 77 78 79 81 84 85 89 90 93 107 110 115 119 128 130 132 133 135 146 148 **P**6 **S** UnityPoint Health, West Des Moines, IA
Primary Contact: James D. Roetman, President and Chief Executive Officer
CFO: Lynn Raveling, Chief Financial Officer
CNO: Susie Aden, Director of IP Services
Web address: www.pocahontashospital.org
Control: City, Government, Nonfederal **Service**: General medical and surgical

Staffed Beds: 20 **Admissions**: 178 **Census**: 2 **Outpatient Visits**: 21742
Births: 0 **Total Expense ($000)**: 10232 **Payroll Expense ($000)**: 3743
Personnel: 85

PRIMGHAR—O'brien County

★ **BAUM HARMON MERCY HOSPITAL (161300)**, 255 North Welch Avenue, Zip 51245–7765, Mailing Address: P.O.Box 528, 51245–0528; tel. 712/957–2300 **A**10 18 **F**11 15 28 29 34 35 40 45 53 59 64 67 75 77 81 89 110 119 127 128 132 133 **P**6 **S** Trinity Health, Livonia, MI
Primary Contact: Angie Shilling, Chief Executive Officer
CFO: Sue E McCauley, Director Finance
CMO: Shailesh Desai M.D., Chief of Staff
Web address: www.baumharmon.org
Control: Church operated, Nongovernment, not–for–profit **Service**: General medical and surgical

Staffed Beds: 11 **Admissions**: 115 **Census**: 1 **Outpatient Visits**: 20630
Births: 0 **Total Expense ($000)**: 7881 **Payroll Expense ($000)**: 4153
Personnel: 64

Hospital, Medicare Provider Number, Address, Telephone, Approval, Facility, and Physician Codes, Health Care System

★ American Hospital Association (AHA) membership   ○ Healthcare Facilities Accreditation Program   ⇧ Center for Improvement in Healthcare Quality Accreditation
□ The Joint Commission accreditation   ◇ DNV Healthcare Inc. accreditation   △ Commission on Accreditation of Rehabilitation Facilities (CARF) accreditation

RED OAK—Montgomery County

★ **MONTGOMERY COUNTY MEMORIAL HOSPITAL (161363)**, 2301 Eastern Avenue, Zip 51566–1300, Mailing Address: P.O.Box 498, 51566–0498; tel. 712/623–7000 **A**10 18 **F**3 11 12 13 15 28 29 31 34 35 40 44 45 50 53 57 59 62 63 64 68 69 70 71 75 76 77 78 79 81 82 85 86 87 93 107 110 111 114 118 119 128 129 130 133 135 146 147 148
Primary Contact: David E. Abercrombie, Chief Executive Officer
CFO: Rick J Leinen, Chief Financial Officer
CMO: Warren Hayes, Chief of Staff
CIO: Ron Kloewer, Chief Information Officer
CHR: Shayla Jennings, Human Resources Director
CNO: Diane McGrew, Chief Nurse Executive
Web address: www.mcmh.org
Control: County, Government, Nonfederal **Service**: General medical and surgical

Staffed Beds: 25 **Admissions:** 886 **Census:** 11 **Outpatient Visits:** 46336
Births: 62 **Total Expense ($000):** 35396 **Payroll Expense ($000):** 15988
Personnel: 280

ROCK RAPIDS—Lyon County

SANFORD MERRILL MEDICAL CENTER See Sanford Rock Rapids Medical Center

★ **SANFORD ROCK RAPIDS MEDICAL CENTER (161321)**, 801 South Greene Street, Zip 51246–1998; tel. 712/472–2591 **A**10 18 **F**11 28 31 34 40 45 53 57 59 65 66 75 77 81 87 89 97 107 114 119 127 130 131 133 146 149 **P**6 **S** Sanford Health, Sioux Falls, SD
Primary Contact: Tammy Loosbrock, Chief Executive Officer
CFO: Stanley Knobloch, Director Fiscal Services
CMO: Beta Hamon, Chief Medical Officer
CHR: Holly Anderson, Supervisor Human Resources
CNO: Jack Johnson R.N., Director of Nursing
Web address: www.sanfordrockrapids.org
Control: Other not–for–profit (including NFP Corporation) **Service**: General medical and surgical

Staffed Beds: 14 **Admissions:** 284 **Census:** 3 **Outpatient Visits:** 20441
Births: 0 **Total Expense ($000):** 8590 **Payroll Expense ($000):** 3798
Personnel: 75

ROCK VALLEY—Sioux County

★ **HEGG MEMORIAL HEALTH CENTER AVERA (161336)**, 1202 21st Avenue, Zip 51247–1497; tel. 712/476–8000, (Total facility includes 60 beds in nursing home–type unit) **A**10 18 **F**3 11 13 15 17 28 29 31 34 35 36 40 41 43 45 50 53 57 59 62 64 65 67 68 70 73 75 76 77 78 79 81 82 84 85 89 93 97 107 110 115 119 128 130 131 132 133 135 144 147 148 **S** Avera Health, Sioux Falls, SD
Primary Contact: Glenn Zevenbergen, Chief Executive Officer
CFO: Kari Timmer, Chief Financial Officer
CMO: Kevin Post D.O., Chief Medical Officer
CHR: Tammy Faber, Director Human Resources
CNO: Linda VerSteeg, Director of Nursing
Web address: www.hegghc.org
Control: Other not–for–profit (including NFP Corporation) **Service**: General medical and surgical

Staffed Beds: 85 **Admissions:** 338 **Census:** 63 **Outpatient Visits:** 36184
Births: 93 **Total Expense ($000):** 18342 **Payroll Expense ($000):** 9622
Personnel: 203

SAC CITY—Sac County

★ **LORING HOSPITAL (161370)**, 211 Highland Avenue, Zip 50583–2424; tel. 712/662–7105 **A**10 18 **F**3 11 15 28 29 30 31 34 35 40 43 45 50 57 59 64 68 75 77 78 79 81 84 86 87 93 107 110 115 119 125 129 130 132 133 146 148 **S** UnityPoint Health, West Des Moines, IA
Primary Contact: Brian Martin, Chief Executive Officer
CFO: Angie Fischer, Chief Financial Officer
CMO: Les Marczewski M.D., Chief Medical Officer
CIO: Leah Snyder, Director Health Information Services
CHR: Becky Pontious, Human Resources/Accounting
Web address: www.loringhospital.org
Control: Other not–for–profit (including NFP Corporation) **Service**: General medical and surgical

Staffed Beds: 25 **Admissions:** 391 **Census:** 4 **Outpatient Visits:** 20049
Births: 0 **Total Expense ($000):** 11977 **Payroll Expense ($000):** 3968
Personnel: 111

SHELDON—O'brien County

★ **SANFORD SHELDON MEDICAL CENTER (161381)**, 118 North Seventh Avenue, Zip 51201–1235, Mailing Address: P.O.Box 250, 51201–0250; tel. 712/324–5041, (Total facility includes 70 beds in nursing home–type unit) **A**10 18 **F**3 11 13 15 28 29 31 32 34 35 38 40 43 45 50 53 57 59 62 63 64 65 67 68 74 75 76 77 78 79 81 82 84 86 87 91 93 96 97 99 100 101 102 103 104 107 108 110 111 114 119 127 129 130 131 132 133 135 146 148 149 150 **P**6 **S** Sanford Health, Sioux Falls, SD
Primary Contact: Richard E. Nordahl, Chief Executive Officer
CFO: Richard E Nordahl, Chief Financial Officer
CMO: Scott Lichty M.D., Physician
CIO: Jason Brown, Director Information Systems
CHR: Dianne Wolthulzen, Director Human Resources
CNO: Joni DeKok, Chief Nursing Officer
Web address: www.sanfordsheldon.org
Control: Other not–for–profit (including NFP Corporation) **Service**: General medical and surgical

Staffed Beds: 95 **Admissions:** 926 **Census:** 68 **Outpatient Visits:** 109270
Births: 117 **Total Expense ($000):** 28780 **Payroll Expense ($000):** 12806
Personnel: 250

SHENANDOAH—Page County

★ **SHENANDOAH MEDICAL CENTER (161366)**, 300 Pershing Avenue, Zip 51601–2355; tel. 712/246–1230, (Total facility includes 50 beds in nursing home–type unit) **A**10 18 **F**3 13 15 18 28 29 31 34 36 38 40 41 43 45 50 53 56 57 59 62 63 64 65 67 68 69 70 74 75 76 77 78 79 81 83 84 85 87 91 93 104 107 108 110 111 115 117 118 119 127 129 130 131 132 133 135 144 146 147 148 149 **P**6
Primary Contact: Karen S. Cole, MS, FACHE, Chief Executive Officer
CFO: Matt Sells CPA, Chief Financial Officer
CMO: Scott King M.D., Chief Medical Officer
CIO: Chuck Dougherty, Chief Information Officer
CHR: Keli Royal, Chief Human Resources Officer
CNO: Alicia Sells, Interim Chief Nursing Officer
Web address: www.smchospital.com/
Control: Other not–for–profit (including NFP Corporation) **Service**: General medical and surgical

Staffed Beds: 75 **Admissions:** 639 **Census:** 50 **Outpatient Visits:** 157457
Births: 116 **Total Expense ($000):** 43738 **Payroll Expense ($000):** 22194
Personnel: 280

SIBLEY—Page County

★ **OSCEOLA COMMUNITY HOSPITAL (161345)**, 600 Ninth Avenue North, Zip 51249–1012, Mailing Address: P.O.Box 258, 51249–0258; tel. 712/754–2574 **A**10 18 **F**3 8 9 10 11 12 13 15 17 18 26 28 29 31 32 34 35 36 40 43 45 46 53 56 57 59 61 62 64 65 67 68 70 75 76 77 78 79 81 82 84 85 86 87 89 107 108 110 114 119 125 128 129 130 131 132 133 135 143 144 145 146 147 148 149 **P**5 **S** Avera Health, Sioux Falls, SD
Primary Contact: Ben Davis, Interim Chief Executive Officer
CFO: Jerri Palsrok, Manager Business Office
CMO: Gregory J Kosters D.O., Chief Medical Officer
CIO: Sherry McElroy, Director Health Information Management
Web address: www.osceolacommunityhospital.org
Control: Other not–for–profit (including NFP Corporation) **Service**: General medical and surgical

Staffed Beds: 25 **Admissions:** 282 **Census:** 5 **Outpatient Visits:** 22630
Births: 21 **Total Expense ($000):** 14054 **Payroll Expense ($000):** 4112
Personnel: 89

SIGOURNEY—Keokuk County

KEOKUK COUNTY HEALTH CENTER (161315), 23019 Highway 149, Zip 52591–8341; tel. 641/622–2720 **A**10 18 **F**1 2 3 7 11 12 15 28 29 30 34 35 38 40 43 44 45 46 50 56 57 59 63 64 65 67 75 77 82 84 86 87 90 91 93 97 107 110 127 128 130 131 132 133 135 146 147 148 **P**5 6
Primary Contact: Matthew Ives, Administrator and Chief Financial Officer
CFO: Matthew Ives, Interim Chief Executive Officer and Chief Financial Officer
Web address: www.kchc.net
Control: County, Government, Nonfederal **Service**: General medical and surgical

Staffed Beds: 14 **Admissions:** 166 **Census:** 6 **Outpatient Visits:** 22042
Births: 0 **Total Expense ($000):** 9880 **Payroll Expense ($000):** 5035
Personnel: 94

IA

Many Facility Codes have changed. Please refer to the AHA Guide Code Chart. © 2017 AHA Guide

SIOUX CENTER—Sioux County

★ **SIOUX CENTER HEALTH (161346)**, 1101 9th Street SE, Zip 51250; tel. 712/722–8107, (Total facility includes 69 beds in nursing home–type unit) **A**10 18 **F**3 8 10 13 15 17 18 28 29 30 31 34 35 40 41 43 45 50 56 57 59 62 63 64 65 67 68 74 75 76 77 78 79 81 82 84 85 86 87 89 93 96 97 107 110 111 114 119 125 128 130 131 132 133 144 146 147 148 **P**6 **S** Avera Health, Sioux Falls, SD
Primary Contact: Kayleen R. Lee, Chief Executive Officer
CFO: Jackson Schuiteman, Chief Financial Officer
CHR: Theresa Tucker, Human Resources Officer
Web address: www.siouxcenterhealth.org
Control: Other not–for–profit (including NFP Corporation) **Service:** General medical and surgical

Staffed Beds: 88 **Admissions:** 617 **Census:** 71 **Outpatient Visits:** 48633 **Births:** 172 **Total Expense ($000):** 38152 **Payroll Expense ($000):** 15855 **Personnel:** 346

SIOUX CITY—Woodbury County

⊞ **MERCY MEDICAL CENTER–SIOUX CITY (160153)**, 801 Fifth Street, Zip 51101–1326, Mailing Address: P.O.Box 3168, 51102–3168; tel. 712/279–2010 **A**1 2 3 5 10 **F**3 5 8 11 12 13 15 17 18 20 22 24 26 28 29 30 31 32 34 35 36 37 38 40 43 44 45 49 50 52 55 56 57 59 64 65 68 70 71 74 75 76 77 78 79 81 82 84 85 87 89 90 91 93 96 97 98 100 102 107 108 110 111 114 115 118 119 124 126 127 129 130 132 134 135 144 146 147 148 149 150 **P**6 8 **S** Trinity Health, Livonia, MI
Primary Contact: James G. Fitzpatrick, FACHE, Chief Executive Officer
CFO: Hugh DePaulis, Interim Vice President and Chief Financial Officer
CMO: Jerome Pierson, Chief Medical Officer
CIO: Steve Larson M.D., Director Information Systems
CHR: Julie Anfinson, Director Human Resources
CNO: Tracy Larson MS, Vice President Patient Care Services and Chief Nursing Officer
Web address: www.mercysiouxcity.com
Control: Church operated, Nongovernment, not–for–profit **Service:** General medical and surgical

Staffed Beds: 186 **Admissions:** 9128 **Census:** 122 **Outpatient Visits:** 218535 **Births:** 260 **Total Expense ($000):** 194581 **Payroll Expense ($000):** 79439 **Personnel:** 1254

★ ⇑ **UNITYPOINT HEALTH – ST. LUKES'S SIOUX CITY (160146)**, 2720 Stone Park Boulevard, Zip 51104–3734; tel. 712/279–3500 **A**3 5 10 21 **F**3 11 13 15 17 18 20 22 26 28 29 30 31 34 35 39 40 43 45 49 50 51 54 56 57 58 59 60 64 68 70 72 73 74 75 76 77 78 79 81 82 83 85 86 88 89 90 91 92 93 96 97 98 102 104 107 108 111 114 118 119 126 129 130 131 132 135 142 143 144 145 146 147 149 **P**6 **S** UnityPoint Health, West Des Moines, IA
Primary Contact: Lynn Wold, President and Chief Executive Officer
COO: Lynn Wold, Chief Operation Officer
CFO: James Gobell, Chief Financial Officer
CIO: James Gobell, Chief Financial Officer
CHR: Tammy Hartnett, Employee Relations Manager
CNO: Priscilla Stokes MS, R.N., Vice President Patient Care and Hospital Operations
Web address: www.stlukes.org
Control: Other not–for–profit (including NFP Corporation) **Service:** General medical and surgical

Staffed Beds: 156 **Admissions:** 9103 **Census:** 104 **Outpatient Visits:** 94861 **Births:** 2051 **Total Expense ($000):** 167461 **Payroll Expense ($000):** 65268 **Personnel:** 1092

SPENCER—Clay County

★ **SPENCER HOSPITAL (160112)**, 1200 First Avenue East, Suite 1, Zip 51301–4342; tel. 712/264–6111 **A**10 **F**3 7 8 11 13 15 28 29 30 31 34 35 39 40 43 45 50 53 57 59 60 62 63 64 65 69 70 75 76 77 78 79 81 82 85 86 87 93 96 98 107 108 109 110 111 115 118 119 120 121 123 126 127 129 130 131 132 133 135 146 147 148 149
Primary Contact: William J. Bumgarner, President
CFO: Stacy E Mol CPA, Director Finance
CMO: Sonia Sather M.D., President Medical Staff
CIO: Brenda Marie Tiefenthaler R.N., MSN, Vice President Patient Care and Informatics
CHR: Stephen Deutsch, Vice President Operations and Support
CNO: Brenda Marie Tiefenthaler R.N., MSN, Vice President Patient Care and Informatics
Web address: www.spencerhospital.org
Control: City, Government, Nonfederal **Service:** General medical and surgical

Staffed Beds: 69 **Admissions:** 2502 **Census:** 28 **Outpatient Visits:** 123499 **Births:** 270 **Total Expense ($000):** 79908 **Payroll Expense ($000):** 22910 **Personnel:** 428

SPIRIT LAKE—Dickinson County

★ **LAKES REGIONAL HEALTHCARE (160124)**, 2301 Highway 71 South, Zip 51360–0159, Mailing Address: P.O.Box AB, 51360–0159; tel. 712/336–1230 **A**10 **F**3 7 11 13 15 28 29 30 31 34 35 37 40 41 45 50 57 59 62 63 64 65 69 70 75 76 77 78 79 81 85 89 91 93 97 107 111 114 119 126 128 129 130 132 133 143 146 148 149 **P**6 **S** Avera Health, Sioux Falls, SD
Primary Contact: Jason Harrington, FACHE, President and Chief Executive Officer
CFO: Steve Alger, Senior Vice President and Chief Financial Officer
CMO: Brett J Olson M.D., Medical Chief of Staff
CIO: Derek Larson, Information Technology Network
CHR: Sonja Hamm, Vice President Human and Foundation Resources
CNO: Connie Lange R.N., Vice President Quality, Inpatient and Community Services
Web address: www.lakeshealth.org
Control: County, Government, Nonfederal **Service:** General medical and surgical

Staffed Beds: 30 **Admissions:** 747 **Census:** 8 **Outpatient Visits:** 97187 **Births:** 139 **Total Expense ($000):** 37384 **Payroll Expense ($000):** 11441 **Personnel:** 211

STORM LAKE—Buena Vista County

⊞ **BUENA VISTA REGIONAL MEDICAL CENTER (161375)**, 1525 West Fifth Street, Zip 50588–3027, Mailing Address: P.O.Box 309, 50588–0309; tel. 712/732–4030 **A**1 10 18 **F**3 7 8 11 13 15 18 28 29 30 31 34 40 43 45 53 55 56 57 59 63 64 68 70 74 75 76 77 78 79 81 82 84 85 86 87 93 96 98 103 107 108 110 111 115 117 118 119 128 129 130 131 132 133 135 146 147 148 **S** UnityPoint Health, West Des Moines, IA
Primary Contact: Steven Colerick, Chief Executive Officer
CFO: Krista Ketcham, Chief Financial Officer
CMO: David Crippin, Chief Medical Officer
CIO: Brian Granville, Director Information Technology
CHR: Carrie Turnquist, Director Human Resources
CNO: Dawn M Bach MS, Chief Clinical Officer
Web address: www.bvrmc.org
Control: County, Government, Nonfederal **Service:** General medical and surgical

Staffed Beds: 35 **Admissions:** 1191 **Census:** 15 **Outpatient Visits:** 71080 **Births:** 336 **Total Expense ($000):** 43899 **Payroll Expense ($000):** 17822 **Personnel:** 328

SUMNER—Bremer County

★ **COMMUNITY MEMORIAL HOSPITAL (161320)**, 909 West First Street, Zip 50674–1203, Mailing Address: P.O.Box 148, 50674–0148; tel. 563/578–3275 **A**10 18 **F**3 11 15 28 29 34 40 45 57 59 64 81 82 85 86 97 107 114 119 127 128 129 131 133 135 148 149 **P**5 6 **S** UnityPoint Health, West Des Moines, IA
Primary Contact: Steve Robert. Slessor, Interim Chief Executive Officer
CFO: Dawn Everding, Chief Financial Officer
CMO: Jeff Roske D.O., Chief Medical Staff
CHR: Robin Elliott, Personnel Officer
CNO: Lynne Niemann, Director Nurses and Patient Care
Web address: www.cmhsumner.org
Control: Other not–for–profit (including NFP Corporation) **Service:** General medical and surgical

Staffed Beds: 16 **Admissions:** 131 **Census:** 3 **Outpatient Visits:** 31984 **Births:** 0 **Total Expense ($000):** 13081 **Payroll Expense ($000):** 4928 **Personnel:** 93

VINTON—Benton County

★ **VIRGINIA GAY HOSPITAL (161349)**, 502 North 9th Avenue, Zip 52349–2299; tel. 319/472–6200, (Total facility includes 40 beds in nursing home–type unit) **A**10 18 **F**3 15 28 29 34 40 43 45 53 57 59 62 63 64 75 77 81 85 86 87 96 97 107 111 114 119 125 127 129 130 131 132 133 143 146 **P**6
Primary Contact: Michael J. Riege, Chief Executive Officer
CFO: Barry Dietsch, Chief Financial Officer
CMO: Brian Meeker D.O., President Medical Staff
CIO: Sherri Isbell, Chief Information Officer
CHR: Kim Frank, Chief Human Resources Officer
CNO: Tina M Eden, Director of Nursing
Web address: www.myvgh.org
Control: Other not–for–profit (including NFP Corporation) **Service:** General medical and surgical

Staffed Beds: 65 **Admissions:** 406 **Census:** 40 **Outpatient Visits:** 91000 **Births:** 0 **Total Expense ($000):** 24451 **Payroll Expense ($000):** 12221 **Personnel:** 231

IA

WASHINGTON—Washington County

★ **WASHINGTON COUNTY HOSPITAL AND CLINICS (161344)**, 400 East Polk Street, Zip 52353–1237, Mailing Address: P.O.Box 909, 52353–0909; tel. 319/653–5481, (Total facility includes 43 beds in nursing home–type unit) **A**10 18 **F**3 13 15 18 28 29 34 36 40 43 45 50 57 59 64 67 68 74 75 76 77 81 85 86 93 96 97 107 110 111 114 119 127 130 132 133 146 147 148 **P**6
Primary Contact: Dennis Hunger, Chief Executive Officer
CFO: Steve Sanders, Chief Financial Officer
CMO: Matt Prihoda M.D., Chief of Staff
CIO: Makyla Maize, Director Information Services
CHR: Tracy Ousey, Director Human Resources
CNO: Andrea Leyden RN, Chief Nursing Officer
Web address: www.wchc.org
Control: County, Government, Nonfederal **Service**: General medical and surgical

Staffed Beds: 68 **Admissions**: 989 **Census**: 48 **Outpatient Visits**: 87631 **Births**: 124 **Total Expense ($000)**: 36387 **Payroll Expense ($000)**: 15915 **Personnel**: 279

WATERLOO—Black Hawk County

ALLEN MEMORIAL HOSPITAL See Unitypoint Health – Waterloo

✣ △ **COVENANT MEDICAL CENTER (160067)**, 3421 West Ninth Street, Zip 50702–5401; tel. 319/272–8000, (Includes KIMBALL–RIDGE CENTER, 2101 Kimball Avenue, Waterloo, Iowa, Zip 50702, tel. 319/272–8000; Jack Dusenbery, President and Chief Executive Officer) **A**1 2 3 5 7 10 **F**3 4 5 7 11 13 15 18 19 20 22 26 28 29 30 31 33 34 35 40 43 44 46 49 50 51 53 57 58 59 60 61 62 64 68 70 71 72 74 75 76 77 78 79 81 82 89 90 93 97 98 99 100 104 105 107 108 110 111 114 115 116 118 119 120 126 127 129 130 131 132 143 144 146 147 148 **P**1 6 **S** Trinity Health, Livonia, MI
Primary Contact: Jack Dusenbery, President and Chief Executive Officer
CFO: Michele Panicucci, Senior Vice President and Chief Financial Officer
CMO: James Lehman M.D., Vice President Medical Affairs
CIO: Marge Ray, Director Information Systems
CHR: Suzanne M Burt, Director Human Resources
CNO: Kelly Richards MSN, Senior Vice President and Chief Nursing Officer
Web address: www.wheatoniowa.org
Control: Church operated, Nongovernment, not–for–profit **Service**: General medical and surgical

Staffed Beds: 229 **Admissions**: 7813 **Census**: 95 **Outpatient Visits**: 651813 **Births**: 1406 **Total Expense ($000)**: 293532 **Payroll Expense ($000)**: 132070 **Personnel**: 1937

✣ △ **UNITYPOINT HEALTH – WATERLOO (160110)**, 1825 Logan Avenue, Zip 50703–1916; tel. 319/235–3941 **A**1 3 5 7 10 **F**3 8 11 13 15 18 20 22 24 26 28 29 30 31 34 35 37 40 43 45 46 48 49 50 51 54 56 57 59 63 64 66 68 70 72 74 75 76 77 78 79 81 82 84 85 86 87 88 90 91 92 93 96 97 98 99 100 101 102 103 104 107 108 110 111 114 115 118 119 126 127 129 130 132 135 146 147 148 149 **P**6 **S** UnityPoint Health, West Des Moines, IA
Primary Contact: Pamela K. Delagardelle, President and Chief Executive Officer
COO: Jennifer Friedly, Chief Operating Officer and Vice President
CFO: Dan Carpenter, Chief Financial Officer
CMO: Timothy Horrigan M.D., Chief Quality Officer
CIO: Daniel Norman, Regional Service Manager
CHR: Steven Sesterhenn, Vice President
CNO: Mary Hagen R.N., MSN, VP and Chief Nursing Officer
Web address: www.unitypoint.org/waterloo
Control: Other not–for–profit (including NFP Corporation) **Service**: General medical and surgical

Staffed Beds: 201 **Admissions**: 8940 **Census**: 93 **Outpatient Visits**: 278592 **Births**: 992 **Total Expense ($000)**: 253465 **Payroll Expense ($000)**: 90649 **Personnel**: 1414

WAUKON—Allamakee County

★ **VETERANS MEMORIAL HOSPITAL (161318)**, 40 First Street SE, Zip 52172–2099; tel. 563/568–3411 **A**10 18 **F**7 11 13 15 28 34 35 40 45 46 57 59 62 64 65 75 76 77 79 81 93 107 110 111 119 131 132 133 134 144 146
Primary Contact: Michael D. Myers, R.N., Chief Executive Officer
CFO: Scott Knode, Chief Financial Officer
CHR: Erin Berns, Director Human Resources
Web address: www.vmhospital.com
Control: City, Government, Nonfederal **Service**: General medical and surgical

Staffed Beds: 25 **Admissions**: 594 **Census**: 7 **Outpatient Visits**: 44613 **Births**: 139 **Total Expense ($000)**: 17137 **Payroll Expense ($000)**: 8106 **Personnel**: 157

WAVERLY—Bremer County

✣ **WAVERLY HEALTH CENTER (161339)**, 312 Ninth Street SW, Zip 50677–2999; tel. 319/352–4120 **A**1 10 18 **F**3 7 8 11 13 15 18 26 28 29 34 35 36 40 43 45 50 57 59 63 64 75 76 77 81 85 86 97 104 107 110 111 114 119 127 130 132 133 134 135 144 146 147 **P**6
Primary Contact: James Atty, Chief Executive Officer
CFO: Lisa Bennett, Chief Financial Officer
CMO: John Zehr M.D., Chief Medical Officer
CIO: Jerry Tiedt, Director Information Systems
CHR: Angie Tye, Director Human Resources
CNO: Joanne Nathem MSN, R.N., Chief Clinical and Nursing Officer
Web address: www.waverlyhealthcenter.org
Control: City, Government, Nonfederal **Service**: General medical and surgical

Staffed Beds: 25 **Admissions**: 853 **Census**: 8 **Outpatient Visits**: 118082 **Births**: 267 **Total Expense ($000)**: 52887 **Payroll Expense ($000)**: 25153 **Personnel**: 337

WEBSTER CITY—Hamilton County

HAMILTON HOSPITAL See Van Diest Medical Center

★ **VAN DIEST MEDICAL CENTER (161361)**, 2350 Hospital Drive, Zip 50595–6600, Mailing Address: P.O.Box 430, 50595–0430; tel. 515/832–9400 **A**10 18 **F**3 7 8 11 13 15 28 29 31 34 35 36 38 40 43 45 50 56 59 64 68 75 78 79 81 82 85 86 87 93 97 100 101 102 103 104 107 110 111 115 117 119 128 129 130 132 133 143 146 147 148 149 **P**6
Primary Contact: Michael Trachta, Interim Chief Executive Officer
CFO: Alice Heinrichs CPA, Chief Financial Officer
CMO: Nicole Ehn M.D., Chief of Staff
CIO: Erick Schrier, Supervisor Information Technology
CHR: Jodie Harker, Director Human Resources
CNO: Janet Naset–Payne MS, R.N., Chief Nursing Officer
Web address: www.vandiestmc.org
Control: County, Government, Nonfederal **Service**: General medical and surgical

Staffed Beds: 25 **Admissions**: 1037 **Census**: 11 **Outpatient Visits**: 21201 **Births**: 128 **Total Expense ($000)**: 25700 **Payroll Expense ($000)**: 9887 **Personnel**: 187

WEST BURLINGTON—Des Moines County

✣ △ **GREAT RIVER MEDICAL CENTER (160057)**, 1221 South Gear Avenue, Zip 52655–1681; tel. 319/768–1000, (Total facility includes 160 beds in nursing home–type unit) **A**1 7 10 19 **F**3 4 5 7 11 13 15 18 20 22 28 29 30 31 32 34 35 36 38 40 43 45 48 50 53 57 59 60 62 63 64 67 68 69 70 73 75 76 77 78 79 81 82 84 85 86 87 89 90 91 92 93 96 98 99 100 101 102 103 104 105 107 108 110 111 114 115 116 117 118 119 120 121 123 128 129 130 131 132 143 146 147 148 **P**6
Primary Contact: Mark D. Richardson, President and Chief Executive Officer
CFO: Todd J Sladky, Chief Financial Officer
CMO: John Phillips, Chief of Staff
CIO: Gary Davis, Director Information Systems
CHR: James M Kammerer, Vice President Support Services
CNO: Teresa Colgan, VP of Nursing
Web address: www.greatrivermedical.org
Control: Other not–for–profit (including NFP Corporation) **Service**: General medical and surgical

Staffed Beds: 314 **Admissions**: 6413 **Census**: 214 **Outpatient Visits**: 287000 **Births**: 580 **Total Expense ($000)**: 170751 **Payroll Expense ($000)**: 67210 **Personnel**: 1149

WEST UNION—Fayette County

★ **GUNDERSEN PALMER LUTHERAN HOSPITAL AND CLINICS (161316)**, 112 Jefferson Street, Zip 52175–1022; tel. 563/422–3811 **A**10 18 **F**3 8 11 13 15 28 29 30 31 34 35 40 43 45 50 56 57 59 62 63 64 65 68 70 76 77 78 79 81 82 85 86 93 96 107 110 111 114 119 127 128 129 130 131 132 133 135 144 146 148 **P**1
Primary Contact: Tanya Tysland, Chief Executive Officer
CFO: Joni Gisleson, Director Finance
CMO: Chaudri Rasool D.O., Chief of Staff
CIO: Kurt Chicken, Director Support Services
CHR: Cheryl Meyer, Director Human Resources
CNO: Kathy Begalske, Chief Nursing Officer
Web address: www.palmerlutheran.org
Control: Other not–for–profit (including NFP Corporation) **Service**: General medical and surgical

Staffed Beds: 25 **Admissions**: 315 **Census**: 5 **Outpatient Visits**: 71152 **Births**: 89 **Total Expense ($000)**: 24201 **Payroll Expense ($000)**: 8103 **Personnel**: 188

IA

Many Facility Codes have changed. Please refer to the AHA Guide Code Chart. © 2017 AHA Guide

WINTERSET—Madison County

★ **MADISON COUNTY HEALTH CARE SYSTEM (161326)**, 300 West Hutchings Street, Zip 50273–2109; tel. 515/462–2373 **A**10 18 **F**3 15 18 28 31 35 37 40 43 45 57 59 64 78 79 81 89 93 97 107 110 114 119 127 128 129 130 131 133 135 146 149 **P**6 **S** Catholic Health Initiatives, Englewood, CO
Primary Contact: Marcia Hendricks, R.N., FACHE, Chief Executive Officer
CFO: Rebekah Mitchell, Chief Financial Officer
CMO: Sherri Broadbent D.O., Chief of Staff
CIO: Dan VandenBosch, Chief Information Officer
CHR: Jennifer Hannon, Director Human Resources
CNO: Kim Hulbert R.N., Chief Clinical Officer
Web address: www.madisonhealth.com
Control: County, Government, Nonfederal **Service**: General medical and surgical

Staffed Beds: 25 **Admissions:** 343 **Census:** 4 **Outpatient Visits:** 59756
Births: 0 **Total Expense ($000):** 20311 **Payroll Expense ($000):** 7516
Personnel: 143

IA

KANSAS

ABILENE—Dickinson County

★ **MEMORIAL HEALTH SYSTEM (171381)**, 511 NE Tenth Street, Zip 67410–2153; tel. 785/263–2100, (Total facility includes 74 beds in nursing home–type unit) **A**10 18 **F**2 3 11 13 15 18 28 29 31 34 36 40 45 53 57 59 62 63 64 68 69 75 76 77 78 79 81 82 85 87 89 93 98 103 104 107 108 110 111 115 119 127 128 129 130 131 132 133 143 146 148 **P**6
Primary Contact: Harold Courtois, Chief Executive Officer
CFO: Elgin Glanzer, Chief Financial Officer
CMO: W L Short M.D., Chief Medical Officer
CIO: Blaine Cappel, Director Information Systems
CNO: Brenda L. Moffitt, Chief Nursing Officer
Web address: www.mhsks.org
Control: Hospital district or authority, Government, Nonfederal **Service:** General medical and surgical

> **Staffed Beds:** 109 **Admissions:** 772 **Census:** 78 **Outpatient Visits:** 26251 **Births:** 39 **Total Expense ($000):** 32361 **Payroll Expense ($000):** 14782 **Personnel:** 331

ANDOVER—Butler County

KANSAS MEDICAL CENTER (170197), 1124 West 21st Street, Zip 67002–5500; tel. 316/300–4000 **A**10 **F**3 17 18 20 22 24 28 29 30 40 49 51 60 64 68 70 75 77 79 81 82 85 87 93 102 107 108 111 115 119 126 130 131 146 148
Primary Contact: Badr Idbeis, M.D., Chief Executive Officer
COO: Daryl W Thornton, Chief Operating Officer
CFO: Steven N Hadley, Chief Financial Officer
CMO: G. Whitney Reader M.D., Chief Medical Officer
CIO: Mike Buffington, Manager Information Technology
CHR: Norm Nevins, Manager Human Resources
CNO: Janet Kaiser R.N., Chief Nursing Officer
Web address: www.ksmedcenter.com/
Control: Corporation, Investor–owned (for–profit) **Service:** General medical and surgical

> **Staffed Beds:** 58 **Admissions:** 2662 **Census:** 27 **Outpatient Visits:** 11298 **Births:** 0 **Personnel:** 210

ANTHONY—Harper County

★ **ANTHONY MEDICAL CENTER (171346)**, 1101 East Spring Street, Zip 67003–2122; tel. 620/842–5111 **A**10 18 **F**15 40 48 53 57 64 67 81 93 97 107 110 119 127 128 133 148 **P**6
Primary Contact: Lori Allen, Chief Financial Officer and Interim Chief Executive Officer
CFO: Lori Allen, Chief Financial Officer
CMO: Sidney Stranathan D.O., Chief of Staff
CIO: Jim Harbert, Chief Technology Officer
CHR: Kim Barwick, Vice President Human Resources
Web address: www.amcks.org
Control: Hospital district or authority, Government, Nonfederal **Service:** General medical and surgical

> **Staffed Beds:** 25 **Admissions:** 176 **Census:** 7 **Outpatient Visits:** 20356 **Births:** 0 **Total Expense ($000):** 8859 **Payroll Expense ($000):** 4243 **Personnel:** 83

ARKANSAS CITY—Cowley County

★ **SOUTH CENTRAL KANSAS MEDICAL CENTER (170150)**, 6401 Patterson Parkway, Zip 67005–5701, Mailing Address: P.O.Box 1107, 67005–1107; tel. 620/442–2500 **A**10 20 **F**3 11 12 13 15 29 30 34 35 39 40 45 50 52 57 59 64 68 70 75 76 77 79 81 82 85 87 91 93 97 107 108 110 111 115 119 127 129 130 132 133 135 146 147 148 149
Primary Contact: Virgil Watson, Chief Executive Officer
CFO: Holly Beaty, Chief Financial Officer
CMO: Kamran Shahzada M.D., Chief Medical Staff
CHR: Clayton Pappan, Director Human Resources and Marketing
CNO: Patricia Davis, Chief Nursing Officer
Web address: www.sckrmc.org
Control: City, Government, Nonfederal **Service:** General medical and surgical

> **Staffed Beds:** 37 **Admissions:** 898 **Census:** 8 **Outpatient Visits:** 24785 **Births:** 128 **Total Expense ($000):** 18504 **Payroll Expense ($000):** 6805 **Personnel:** 150

ASHLAND—Clark County

★ **ASHLAND HEALTH CENTER (171304)**, 709 Oak Street, Zip 67831–0188, Mailing Address: P.O.Box 188, 67831–0188; tel. 620/635–2241 **A**10 18 **F**2 30 34 40 53 59 62 64 67 68 85 87 93 107 127 128 133 143 **P**6 **S** Great Plains Health Alliance, Inc., Wichita, KS
Primary Contact: Michael Mages, Chief Executive Officer
CFO: Debbie Filson, Chief Financial Officer
CMO: Daniel Shuman D.O., Chief Medical Officer
CIO: Alan Romans, Director Information Technology
CHR: Debbie Filson, Chief Financial Officer
CNO: Patty Young R.N., Chief Nursing Officer
Web address: www.ashlandhc.org
Control: Hospital district or authority, Government, Nonfederal **Service:** General medical and surgical

> **Staffed Beds:** 25 **Admissions:** 107 **Census:** 18 **Outpatient Visits:** 0 **Births:** 0 **Total Expense ($000):** 5812 **Payroll Expense ($000):** 2976 **Personnel:** 87

ATCHISON—Atchison County

★ **ATCHISON HOSPITAL (171382)**, 800 Raven Hill Drive, Zip 66002–9204; tel. 913/367–2131 **A**10 18 **F**3 11 13 15 28 29 30 31 34 35 39 40 45 49 50 57 59 62 63 64 65 68 70 75 76 77 79 81 82 85 87 89 92 93 97 107 108 110 111 114 118 119 127 129 130 131 132 133 135 146 147 148 149 **P**6
Primary Contact: John L. Jacobson, Chief Executive Officer
COO: Sandra Leggett, Chief Operating Officer
CFO: Gary R Foll, Chief Financial Officer
CMO: McGarrett Groth, Chief of Staff
CIO: Terry Davis, Manager Information Systems
CHR: Jill Wenger, Director Human Resources
Web address: www.atchisonhospital.org
Control: Other not–for–profit (including NFP Corporation) **Service:** General medical and surgical

> **Staffed Beds:** 25 **Admissions:** 981 **Census:** 11 **Outpatient Visits:** 78567 **Births:** 149 **Total Expense ($000):** 38248 **Payroll Expense ($000):** 17685 **Personnel:** 275

ATWOOD—Rawlins County

★ **RAWLINS COUNTY HEALTH CENTER (171307)**, 707 Grant Street, Zip 67730–1526, Mailing Address: P.O.Box 47, 67730–0047; tel. 785/626–3211 **A**10 18 **F**3 28 29 30 34 40 41 45 59 64 65 66 75 81 83 85 87 89 93 97 107 114 125 127 128 130 131 132 133 135 147 148 **P**6 **S** Great Plains Health Alliance, Inc., Wichita, KS
Primary Contact: Sharon K. Cox, FACHE, Chief Executive Officer
COO: Ryan Marvin, Support Services Director
CFO: Heather Prideaux, Chief Financial Officer
CMO: Brewster Kellogg D.O., Chief Medical Officer
CIO: Destiny Schroeder, Information Systems Director
CHR: Tara Bowles, Employee Relations Director
CNO: Amber Withington R.N., Chief Nursing Officer
Web address: www.rchc.us
Control: County, Government, Nonfederal **Service:** General medical and surgical

> **Staffed Beds:** 24 **Admissions:** 224 **Census:** 4 **Outpatient Visits:** 16782 **Births:** 0 **Total Expense ($000):** 8270 **Payroll Expense ($000):** 2948 **Personnel:** 58

BELLEVILLE—Republic County

★ **REPUBLIC COUNTY HOSPITAL (171361)**, 2420 'G' Street, Zip 66935–2400; tel. 785/527–2254 **A**10 18 **F**3 13 15 28 29 30 31 35 39 40 45 56 57 64 67 68 75 76 77 78 79 81 85 86 87 89 93 107 108 114 119 128 130 131 133 **S** Great Plains Health Alliance, Inc., Wichita, KS
Primary Contact: David–Paul Cavazos, Chief Executive Officer
CFO: Barry Bottger, Chief Financial Officer
Web address: www.rphospital.org
Control: Other not–for–profit (including NFP Corporation) **Service:** General medical and surgical

> **Staffed Beds:** 63 **Admissions:** 747 **Census:** 40 **Outpatient Visits:** 14389 **Births:** 47 **Total Expense ($000):** 14145 **Payroll Expense ($000):** 6630 **Personnel:** 145

KS

Many Facility Codes have changed. Please refer to the AHA Guide Code Chart.   © 2017 AHA Guide

BELOIT—Mitchell County

★ **MITCHELL COUNTY HOSPITAL HEALTH SYSTEMS (171375)**, 400 West Eighth, Zip 67420–1605, Mailing Address: P.O.Box 399, 67420–0399; tel. 785/738–2266, (Total facility includes 40 beds in nursing home–type unit) **A**10 18 **F**3 11 13 15 28 29 31 34 40 43 45 48 50 56 59 62 63 64 68 69 74 76 77 81 82 84 86 87 93 98 103 106 107 111 114 119 128 129 130 132 133 148 149
Primary Contact: Jeremy Armstrong, FACHE, Chief Executive Officer
CFO: Eldon Koepke, Chief Financial Officer
CIO: Nate Richards, Director Information Technology
CHR: Phyllis Oetting, Director Human Resources
CNO: Jan Kemmerer, Director of Nursing
Web address: www.mchks.com
Control: County, Government, Nonfederal **Service:** General medical and surgical

Staffed Beds: 75 **Admissions:** 1399 **Census:** 60 **Outpatient Visits:** 17118 **Births:** 104 **Total Expense ($000):** 25285 **Payroll Expense ($000):** 11474 **Personnel:** 266

BURLINGTON—Coffey County

★ **COFFEY COUNTY HOSPITAL (170094)**, 801 North 4th Street, Zip 66839–2602; tel. 620/364–2121, (Total facility includes 42 beds in nursing home–type unit) **A**10 20 **F**3 7 10 11 13 15 17 29 30 31 34 40 45 50 57 59 62 64 65 67 68 70 75 76 77 78 79 81 82 85 87 93 107 110 111 114 119 125 127 128 130 133 146 149 **P**6
Primary Contact: Leonard Hernandez, Chief Executive Officer
CFO: Jim Van Hoet, Chief Financial Officer
CMO: John Shell M.D., Chief Medical Officer
CIO: Adam Haag, Manager Information Technology
CHR: Theresa Thoele, Director Human Resources
CNO: Melissa Hall, Chief Nursing Officer
Web address: www.coffeyhealth.org
Control: County, Government, Nonfederal **Service:** General medical and surgical

Staffed Beds: 78 **Admissions:** 502 **Census:** 32 **Outpatient Visits:** 23766 **Births:** 98 **Total Expense ($000):** 24297 **Payroll Expense ($000):** 13544 **Personnel:** 159

CALDWELL—Sumner County

★ **SUMNER COUNTY HOSPITAL DISTRICT ONE (171329)**, 601 South Osage Street, Zip 67022–1654; tel. 620/845–6492 **A**10 18 **F**7 40 50 57 59 64 67 75 81 90 93 107 111 114 119 133 146 **P**5
Primary Contact: Thomas Henton, Chief Executive Officer
CFO: Jennifer Marcrum, Chief Financial Officer
CMO: Jim Blunk D.O., Chief Medical Officer
CIO: Trey Watson, Network Administrator
Web address: www.schd1.com
Control: Hospital district or authority, Government, Nonfederal **Service:** General medical and surgical

Staffed Beds: 16 **Admissions:** 93 **Census:** 2 **Outpatient Visits:** 3633 **Births:** 0 **Total Expense ($000):** 4656 **Payroll Expense ($000):** 1865 **Personnel:** 38

CHANUTE—Neosho County

★ ⇑ **NEOSHO MEMORIAL REGIONAL MEDICAL CENTER (171380)**, 629 South Plummer, Zip 66720–1928, Mailing Address: P.O.Box 426, 66720–0426; tel. 620/431–4000 **A**10 18 21 **F**3 7 11 13 15 28 29 30 34 40 43 47 48 50 52 53 57 62 63 64 76 77 79 81 82 85 89 93 107 108 110 111 114 119 126 127 128 129 130 133 143 146 147 149 **P**8 **S** QHR, Brentwood, TN
Primary Contact: Dennis Franks, FACHE, Chief Executive Officer
COO: Wendy Brazil, Chief Operating Officer
CFO: Nancy Woodyard, Chief Financial Officer
CMO: Charles Van Houden M.D., Chief Medical Officer
CIO: Gretchen Keller, Director Health Information
CHR: R C Rowan, Director Human Resources
CNO: Jennifer Newton R.N., Chief Nursing Officer
Web address: www.nmrmc.com
Control: County, Government, Nonfederal **Service:** General medical and surgical

Staffed Beds: 25 **Admissions:** 1689 **Census:** 18 **Outpatient Visits:** 52066 **Births:** 376 **Total Expense ($000):** 51705 **Payroll Expense ($000):** 21682 **Personnel:** 377

CLAY CENTER—Clay County

★ **CLAY COUNTY MEDICAL CENTER (171371)**, 617 Liberty Street, Zip 67432–1564, Mailing Address: P.O.Box 512, 67432–0512; tel. 785/632–2144 **A**10 18 **F**13 15 18 19 28 29 30 31 40 45 50 53 55 59 63 64 68 70 74 75 76 77 78 79 81 82 84 85 86 87 93 96 107 108 111 114 119 127 130 132 133 148 149
Primary Contact: Austin M. Gillard, Chief Executive Officer
CFO: James Garbarino, Chief Financial Officer
CIO: Chris Wolf, Director Information Technology
CHR: Cindy Rush, Director Human Resources
CNO: Sara Beikman, Director of Nursing
Web address: www.ccmcks.org
Control: County, Government, Nonfederal **Service:** General medical and surgical

Staffed Beds: 25 **Admissions:** 677 **Census:** 10 **Outpatient Visits:** 63932 **Births:** 57 **Total Expense ($000):** 19312 **Payroll Expense ($000):** 8927 **Personnel:** 213

COFFEYVILLE—Montgomery County

⊞ **COFFEYVILLE REGIONAL MEDICAL CENTER (170145)**, 1400 West Fourth, Zip 67337–3306; tel. 620/251–1200, (Total facility includes 20 beds in nursing home–type unit) **A**1 10 **F**3 7 11 13 15 28 29 30 31 34 40 45 46 47 50 57 59 62 64 70 75 76 77 78 79 81 82 85 93 97 107 108 110 111 112 114 117 119 120 121 123 128 130 131 132 135 145 146 147 **P**8
Primary Contact: Mark Woodring, Chief Executive Officer
CFO: Dean Ohmart, Chief Financial Officer
CIO: Kris Penco, Director Information Systems
CHR: Becky McCune, Director Human Resources, Community Relations and Education
CNO: Lori Rexwinkle, Chief Nursing Officer
Web address: www.crmcinc.com
Control: Other not-for-profit (including NFP Corporation) **Service:** General medical and surgical

Staffed Beds: 69 **Admissions:** 1738 **Census:** 14 **Outpatient Visits:** 50217 **Births:** 307 **Total Expense ($000):** 46483 **Payroll Expense ($000):** 19260

COLBY—Thomas County

★ **CITIZENS MEDICAL CENTER (171362)**, 100 East College Drive, Zip 67701–3799; tel. 785/462–7511, (Total facility includes 57 beds in nursing home–type unit) **A**10 18 **F**3 11 13 15 28 30 31 34 35 40 43 50 64 67 68 74 76 77 78 79 81 85 86 87 93 97 107 108 110 111 114 119 127 130 133 146 148 **P**6
Primary Contact: Greg Unruh, Chief Executive Officer
CFO: Darcy Howard, Chief Financial Officer
CMO: Kelly Gabel, Chief of Staff
CIO: Jacee Dobbs, Chief Information Officer
CHR: Margaret Kummer, Chief Human Resource Officer
CNO: Jenny Niblock, Chief Clinical Officer
Web address: www.cmciks.com
Control: Other not-for-profit (including NFP Corporation) **Service:** General medical and surgical

Staffed Beds: 82 **Admissions:** 710 **Census:** 59 **Outpatient Visits:** 11938 **Births:** 169 **Total Expense ($000):** 33930 **Payroll Expense ($000):** 17152 **Personnel:** 143

COLDWATER—Comanche County

★ **COMANCHE COUNTY HOSPITAL (171312)**, 202 South Frisco Street, Zip 67029–9101, Mailing Address: HC 65, Box 8A, 67029–9500; tel. 620/582–2144 **A**10 18 **F**3 11 30 31 40 43 53 59 61 68 75 78 93 102 107 128 133 **P**6 **S** Great Plains Health Alliance, Inc., Wichita, KS
Primary Contact: Nancy Zimmerman, R.N., Administrator
CFO: Lisa Brooks, Chief Financial Officer
CMO: Daniel Schowengerdt M.D., Chief of Staff
CIO: LaNell Wagnon, Director Medical Records
CHR: Lisa Brooks, Chief Financial Officer
CNO: Sandra Dobrinski, Director of Nursing
Web address: www.gpha.com
Control: County, Government, Nonfederal **Service:** General medical and surgical

Staffed Beds: 12 **Admissions:** 113 **Census:** 2 **Outpatient Visits:** 11669 **Births:** 0 **Total Expense ($000):** 5201 **Payroll Expense ($000):** 2556 **Personnel:** 51

COLUMBUS—Cherokee County

★ **MERCY HOSPITAL COLUMBUS (171308)**, 220 North Pennsylvania Avenue,
Zip 66725–1110; tel. 620/429–2545 **A**10 18 **F**11 15 40 45 59 77 93 119 133
P8 **S** Mercy, Chesterfield, MO
Primary Contact: Angie Saporito, Administrator
Web address: www.mercy.net/newsroom–mercy–maude–norton–hospital–quick–
facts
Control: Church operated, Nongovernment, not–for–profit **Service**: General
medical and surgical

> **Staffed Beds**: 18 **Admissions**: 76 **Census**: 1 **Outpatient Visits**: 9612 **Births**: 0
> **Total Expense ($000)**: 4749 **Payroll Expense ($000)**: 2490 **Personnel**: 46

CONCORDIA—Cloud County

★ **CLOUD COUNTY HEALTH CENTER (171349)**, 1100 Highland Drive, Zip 66901–
3923; tel. 785/243–1234 **A**10 18 **F**3 11 15 28 31 34 35 40 41 45 56 57 59 64
65 70 74 75 77 79 81 82 85 86 87 93 96 97 102 107 108 114 118 119 127
130 133 135 146 148 **P**6 **S** Salina Regional Health Center, Salina, KS
Primary Contact: Cherri Waites, Chief Executive Officer
CFO: Pamela Blochlinger, Acting Vice President Finance
CMO: Justin Poore D.O., Chief Medical Staff
CIO: Jenny Bergstrom, Project Manager Information Technology
CHR: Dawn Thoman, Vice President Human Resources
CNO: Michelle Metro, Vice President Nursing
Web address: www.cchc.org
Control: Other not–for–profit (including NFP Corporation) **Service**: General
medical and surgical

> **Staffed Beds**: 25 **Admissions**: 365 **Census**: 5 **Outpatient Visits**: 36636
> **Births**: 0 **Total Expense ($000)**: 13661 **Payroll Expense ($000)**: 7498
> **Personnel**: 141

COUNCIL GROVE—Morris County

★ **MORRIS COUNTY HOSPITAL (171379)**, 600 North Washington Street,
Zip 66846–1422; tel. 620/767–6811 **A**10 18 **F**7 11 13 15 18 28 31 35 40 45
59 64 65 70 76 77 81 87 93 94 96 107 110 111 130 132 133 146 148 149 **P**5
Primary Contact: Rita K. Buurman, Interim Chief Executive Officer
CFO: Ron Christenson, Chief Financial Officer
CMO: Lora Siegle M.D., Chief Medical Officer
CIO: Bill Lauer, Chief Information Officer
CHR: Don Zimmerman, Director Human Resources
CNO: Stephanne Wolf, Chief Nursing Officer
Web address: www.mrcohosp.com
Control: County, Government, Nonfederal **Service**: General medical and surgical

> **Staffed Beds**: 25 **Admissions**: 300 **Census**: 4 **Outpatient Visits**: 12434
> **Births**: 19 **Total Expense ($000)**: 9614 **Payroll Expense ($000)**: 3319
> **Personnel**: 87

DIGHTON—Lane County

★ **LANE COUNTY HOSPITAL (171303)**, 235 West Vine, Zip 67839–0969, Mailing
Address: P.O.Box 969, 67839–0969; tel. 620/397–5321 **A**10 18 **F**30 40 56 77
93 97 127 128 131 133 **P**6 **S** Great Plains Health Alliance, Inc., Wichita, KS
Primary Contact: Donna McGowan, Administrator
CFO: Marcia Gabel, Chief Financial Officer
CMO: Paul Chinburg M.D., Medical Director
CHR: Dina Casey, Human Resources Officer
CNO: Jennifer Whipple, Director Nursing
Web address: www.lanecountyhospital.com/
Control: County, Government, Nonfederal **Service**: General medical and surgical

> **Staffed Beds**: 25 **Admissions**: 77 **Census**: 14 **Outpatient Visits**: 8689
> **Births**: 0 **Total Expense ($000)**: 5387 **Payroll Expense ($000)**: 2143
> **Personnel**: 49

DODGE CITY—Ford County

✠ **WESTERN PLAINS MEDICAL COMPLEX (170175)**, 3001 Avenue 'A',
Zip 67801–6508, Mailing Address: P.O.Box 1478, 67801–1478; tel. 620/225–
8400 **A**1 3 5 10 20 **F**1 3 4 8 11 15 17 18 20 22 28 29 30 34 35 40
50 57 60 64 67 70 72 73 74 75 76 77 79 80 81 85 88 89 90 93 98 107 108
110 111 115 119 128 130 131 132 133 146 149 150 **P**5 **S** LifePoint Health,
Brentwood, TN
Primary Contact: Kerry Tirman, JD, FACHE, Chief Executive Officer
CFO: Michael Gordian, Chief Financial Officer
CMO: Merrill Conant M.D., Chief of Staff
CIO: Shawna Culver, Director Information Systems
CHR: Corry Israel, Director Human Resources
CNO: Edna Dunn, Chief Nursing Officer
Web address: www.westernplainsmc.com
Control: Corporation, Investor–owned (for–profit) **Service**: General medical and
surgical

> **Staffed Beds**: 45 **Admissions**: 2040 **Census**: 15 **Outpatient Visits**: 26778
> **Births**: 693

EL DORADO—Butler County

✠ **SUSAN B. ALLEN MEMORIAL HOSPITAL (170017)**, 720 West Central Avenue,
Zip 67042–2112; tel. 316/321–3300 **A**1 10 **F**3 11 13 15 28 30 40 45 59 60 62
69 70 76 79 81 85 92 93 96 97 107 108 110 111 115 119 120 121 123 130
133 144 146 148
Primary Contact: James B. Kirkbride, President and Chief Executive Officer
COO: Mark Rooker, Chief Operations and Information Officer
CFO: Gene Kaberline, Chief Financial Officer
CMO: Paige Dodson M.D., M.P.H., Chief Medical Officer
CIO: Mark Rooker, Chief Operations and Information Officer
CHR: D. Gay Kimble, Chief Human Resource Officer
CNO: Cecilia B Goebel R.N., Chief Nursing Officer
Web address: www.sbamh.com
Control: Other not–for–profit (including NFP Corporation) **Service**: General
medical and surgical

> **Staffed Beds**: 52 **Admissions**: 1405 **Census**: 12 **Outpatient Visits**: 91392
> **Births**: 283 **Total Expense ($000)**: 49488 **Payroll Expense ($000)**: 20156
> **Personnel**: 373

ELKHART—Morton County

★ **MORTON COUNTY HEALTH SYSTEM (170166)**, 445 Hilltop Street, Zip 67950–
0937, Mailing Address: P.O.Box 937, 67950–0937; tel. 620/697–2141 **A**10 20
F3 28 29 34 40 54 56 57 59 64 70 81 83 86 87 93 94 96 97 107 114 119
127 130 131 132 133 135 143 148 149 **P**6
Primary Contact: Richard Q. Bergling, Chief Executive Officer
CHR: Sonja May, Director Human Resources
Web address: www.mchswecare.com
Control: County, Government, Nonfederal **Service**: General medical and surgical

> **Staffed Beds**: 28 **Admissions**: 209 **Census**: 2 **Outpatient Visits**: 7606
> **Births**: 0 **Total Expense ($000)**: 8638 **Payroll Expense ($000)**: 3996
> **Personnel**: 89

ELLINWOOD—Barton County

★ **ELLINWOOD DISTRICT HOSPITAL (171301)**, 605 North Main Street,
Zip 67526–1440; tel. 620/564–2548 **A**10 18 **F**11 40 64 65 93 107 127 128
133 **P**6 **S** Great Plains Health Alliance, Inc., Wichita, KS
Primary Contact: Kile Magner, Administrator
CFO: Summer Zink, Chief Financial Officer
CMO: Charlie Joslin M.D., Chief of Staff
CIO: Becky L Burns, Manager Health Information Management
CHR: Chris Robl, Human Resources
CNO: Jill Ritchie, Director of Nursing
Web address: www.ellinwooddistricthospital.org
Control: Other not–for–profit (including NFP Corporation) **Service**: General
medical and surgical

> **Staffed Beds**: 25 **Admissions**: 176 **Census**: 6 **Outpatient Visits**: 12474
> **Births**: 0 **Total Expense ($000)**: 6369 **Payroll Expense ($000)**: 3182
> **Personnel**: 75

ELLSWORTH—Ellsworth County

★ **ELLSWORTH COUNTY MEDICAL CENTER (171327)**, 1604 Aylward Street,
Zip 67439–0087, Mailing Address: P.O.Box 87, 67439–0087; tel. 785/472–3111
A10 18 **F**3 11 28 29 34 35 40 45 47 53 57 59 64 67 75 77 85 86 87 93 97
107 115 119 127 128 130 133 146 **P**6
Primary Contact: Roger A. Masse, FACHE, Chief Executive Officer
CFO: Preston Sauers, Chief Financial Officer
CIO: Lynette Dick, Director of Support Services
CHR: Christa N Bohnen, Director Human Resources
CNO: Amanda Thrasher, Director Nursing
Web address: www.ewmed.com
Control: County, Government, Nonfederal **Service**: General medical and surgical

> **Staffed Beds**: 20 **Admissions**: 638 **Census**: 6 **Outpatient Visits**: 15855
> **Births**: 0 **Total Expense ($000)**: 16115 **Payroll Expense ($000)**: 7868
> **Personnel**: 137

EMPORIA—Lyon County

★ **NEWMAN REGIONAL HEALTH (171384)**, 1201 West 12th Avenue, Zip 66801–
2597; tel. 620/343–6800 **A**10 18 **F**3 11 13 15 17 18 20 22 26 28 29 31 39 40
41 45 51 53 59 61 63 64 65 68 70 76 77 78 79 81 82 84 85 86 87 89 90 93
96 102 107 108 111 114 118 119 129 130 131 132 133 135 144 146 147
148 149 **P**6
Primary Contact: Robert N. Wright, Chief Executive Officer
CFO: Holly French, Chief Financial Officer
CMO: James Geitz M.D., Chief of Staff
CHR: Kathy Orear, Director Human Resources
CNO: Julia Pyle R.N., Chief Nursing Officer
Web address: www.newmanrh.org
Control: County, Government, Nonfederal **Service**: General medical and surgical

> **Staffed Beds**: 32 **Admissions**: 2204 **Census**: 21 **Outpatient Visits**: 96831
> **Births**: 439 **Total Expense ($000)**: 65114 **Payroll Expense ($000)**: 27325
> **Personnel**: 507

EUREKA—Greenwood County

GREENWOOD COUNTY HOSPITAL (171339), 100 West 16th Street,
Zip 67045–1064; tel. 620/583–7451 **A**10 18 **F**3 40 43 53 57 62 81 93 96 107
119 127 128 133 135 146 **P**6
Primary Contact: Sandra Dickerson, Chief Executive Officer
CFO: Marian Drake, Chief Financial Officer
CIO: Jason Clark, Director Quality Improvement, Risk Management and Information
System
CHR: Janel M Palmer, Director Human Resources
CNO: Tracy Harrod, Director of Nursing
Web address: www.gwch.org
Control: County, Government, Nonfederal **Service**: General medical and surgical

> **Staffed Beds: 25 Admissions: 464 Census: 7 Outpatient Visits: 0 Births: 0
> Personnel: 117**

FORT SCOTT—Bourbon County

⊞ **MERCY HOSPITAL FORT SCOTT (170058)**, 401 Woodland Hills Boulevard,
Zip 66701–8797; tel. 620/223–2200 **A**1 10 **F**3 7 11 13 15 28 29 30 34 35
40 53 57 59 62 63 65 70 75 76 77 79 81 82 84 85 93 97 107 108 110 111
114 118 119 127 129 130 131 132 133 143 144 145 146 148 149 150 **P**6 **S**
Mercy, Chesterfield, MO
Primary Contact: Reta K. Baker, President
CFO: Shelly Hunter, Chief Financial Officer
CMO: Robert R Nichols M.D., Vice President Medical Affairs
CIO: Lori Sturgill, Vice President Business Partnership
CHR: Timothy Murphy, Vice President Human Resources
CNO: Patrick Callanan, Vice President Patient Care Services
Web address: www.mercykansas.com
Control: Church operated, Nongovernment, not–for–profit **Service**: General
medical and surgical

> **Staffed Beds: 46 Admissions: 1409 Census: 12 Outpatient Visits: 107083
> Births: 300 Total Expense ($000): 30394 Payroll Expense ($000): 13707
> Personnel: 323**

FREDONIA—Wilson County

★ **FREDONIA REGIONAL HOSPITAL (171374)**, 1527 Madison Street, Zip 66736–
1751, Mailing Address: P.O.Box 579, 66736–0579; tel. 620/378–2121 **A**10 18
F3 7 11 15 30 40 81 82 85 93 98 103 107 110 114 119 128 133 **S** Great
Plains Health Alliance, Inc., Wichita, KS
Primary Contact: John Hart, Chief Executive Officer
CFO: Tracy Row, Manager Business Office
CMO: Jennifer McKenney M.D., Chief Medical Officer
CIO: Tyler Row, Director Information Technology
CHR: Debbie Marr, Administrative Assistant and Director Human Resources
CNO: Ryan Duft R.N., Chief Nursing Officer
Web address: www.fredoniaregionalhospital.org
Control: City, Government, Nonfederal **Service**: General medical and surgical

> **Staffed Beds: 34 Admissions: 589 Census: 13 Outpatient Visits: 24715
> Births: 0 Total Expense ($000): 15666 Payroll Expense ($000): 5107
> Personnel: 145**

GALENA—Cherokee County

⇑ **PREMIER SURGICAL INSTITUTE (170203)**, 1619 West 7th Street, Zip 66739;
tel. 620/783–1732 (Nonreporting) **A**10 21
Primary Contact: Travis W. Roderick, Chief Executive Officer
Web address: www.premiersurgicalinstitute.com/
Control: City, Government, Nonfederal **Service**: General medical and surgical

> **Staffed Beds: 25**

GARDEN CITY—Finney County

⊞ **ST. CATHERINE HOSPITAL (170023)**, 401 East Spruce Street, Zip 67846–
5679; tel. 620/272–2561 **A**1 10 20 **F**3 8 13 15 18 20 22 29 30 31 34 35 40
45 49 51 57 59 60 63 64 65 68 69 70 73 74 75 77 78 79 81 82 83 84 85 86
87 90 91 92 93 94 96 97 98 99 100 101 102 103 107 108 109 110 111 112
113 114 115 116 117 118 119 120 121 122 123 124 127 129 130 131 132
135 144 146 147 148 **P**5 6 **S** Catholic Health Initiatives, Englewood, CO
Primary Contact: Scott J. Taylor, President and Chief Executive Officer
CFO: Amanda Vaughan, Chief Financial Officer
CMO: Matthew C Byrnes M.D., Chief Medical Officer
CIO: Lance Kellenbarger, Site Director Information Systems
CHR: Kathy E Morrison, Executive Director Human Resources
CNO: Margaret Elizabeth Prewitt, Vice President Patient Services and Chief Nursing
Officer
Web address: www.StCatherineHosp.org
Control: Church operated, Nongovernment, not–for–profit **Service**: General
medical and surgical

> **Staffed Beds: 104 Admissions: 4161 Census: 47 Outpatient Visits:
> 163853 Births: 785 Total Expense ($000): 100914 Payroll Expense
> ($000): 37896 Personnel: 455**

GARDNER—Johnson County

★ △ **MEADOWBROOK REHABILITATION HOSPITAL (173033)**, 427 West Main
Street, Zip 66030–1183; tel. 913/856–8747, (Nonreporting) **A**7 10
Primary Contact: Angela Hullinger, Chief Executive Officer
CFO: Kelly Taul, Business Manager
CMO: David Edalati M.D., Medical Director
CHR: Carrie Moore, Director Human Resources
CNO: Lisa Perez R.N., Director Nursing
Web address: www.meadowbrookrehab.com
Control: Partnership, Investor–owned (for–profit) **Service**: Rehabilitation

> **Staffed Beds: 96**

GARNETT—Anderson County

★ **ANDERSON COUNTY HOSPITAL (171316)**, 421 South Maple, Zip 66032–
1334, Mailing Address: P.O.Box 309, 66032–0309; tel. 785/448–3131, (Total
facility includes 36 beds in nursing home–type unit) **A**10 18 **F**3 7 8 11 15 29 30
34 35 40 41 43 45 56 57 59 64 65 67 75 79 81 87 91 93 97 104 107 108
110 114 127 130 133 **P**6 **S** Saint Luke's Health System, Kansas City, MO
Primary Contact: Rick McKain, Chief Executive Officer
CFO: Vicki L Mills, Chief Financial Officer
CMO: Mackenzie Peterson M.D., Chief of Staff
CHR: Karen Gillespie, Director Human Resources
CNO: Margo L Williams R.N., Chief Nursing Officer
Web address: www.saint–lukes.org
Control: Other not–for–profit (including NFP Corporation) **Service**: General
medical and surgical

> **Staffed Beds: 48 Admissions: 212 Census: 36 Outpatient Visits: 48564
> Births: 0 Total Expense ($000): 24094 Payroll Expense ($000): 9337
> Personnel: 200**

GIRARD—Crawford County

★ **GIRARD MEDICAL CENTER (171376)**, 302 North Hospital Drive, Zip 66743–
2000; tel. 620/724–8291 **A**10 18 **F**3 6 8 11 12 15 29 34 35 40 43 44 45 47
50 51 53 56 57 59 62 64 65 68 75 77 79 81 87 93 97 98 101 103 104 107
114 119 127 130 131 132 133 144 146 148 149 **P**6
Primary Contact: Michael E. Payne, Administrator
CFO: Holly Koch, Chief Financial Officer
CIO: Jeff Barnes, Director Information Technology
CHR: Gregory Sullivan, Manager Human Resources
CNO: Joyce Geier, Director Nursing
Web address: www.girardmedicalcenter.com
Control: Hospital district or authority, Government, Nonfederal **Service**: General
medical and surgical

> **Staffed Beds: 35 Admissions: 582 Census: 12 Outpatient Visits: 20345
> Births: 0 Total Expense ($000): 19807 Payroll Expense ($000): 9620
> Personnel: 185**

GOODLAND—Sherman County

★ **GOODLAND REGIONAL MEDICAL CENTER (171370)**, 220 West Second
Street, Zip 67735–1602; tel. 785/890–3625 **A**10 18 **F**11 13 15 28 29 31 34 40
57 59 60 62 64 65 69 75 76 77 78 79 81 82 87 93 96 97 107 110 114 119
127 129 130 132 133 135 148 **P**6
Primary Contact: Chris Smolik, Chief Executive Officer
CFO: Donald Lee Wade, Chief Financial Officer
CIO: Christopher Biel, Chief Information Officer
CHR: Linda Taylor, Chief Human Resources Officer
Web address: www.goodlandregional.com
Control: County, Government, Nonfederal **Service**: General medical and surgical

> **Staffed Beds: 25 Admissions: 463 Census: 5 Outpatient Visits: 41843
> Births: 69**

GREAT BEND—Barton County

GREAT BEND REGIONAL HOSPITAL (170191), 514 Cleveland Street,
Zip 67530–3562; tel. 620/792–8833 **A**10 20 22 **F**3 7 8 13 15 29 30 34 40 43
45 50 57 59 64 65 68 70 75 76 79 81 82 89 107 110 111 114 119 127 130
133 135 144 146 147
Primary Contact: Kerry Noble, Chief Executive Officer
COO: Adina Gregory, Chief Operating Officer
CFO: Timothy Latimer, Chief Financial Officer
CMO: Randall Hildebrand M.D., Chief Medical Officer
CHR: Brenda Kaiser, Director Human Resources
CNO: Adina Gregory, Chief Nursing Officer
Web address: www.gbregional.com
Control: Partnership, Investor–owned (for–profit) **Service**: General medical and
surgical

> **Staffed Beds: 33 Admissions: 1499 Census: 12 Outpatient Visits: 48912
> Births: 337 Total Expense ($000): 38537 Payroll Expense ($000): 15133
> Personnel: 328**

Hospital, Medicare Provider Number, Address, Telephone, Approval, Facility, and Physician Codes, Health Care System

★ American Hospital Association (AHA) membership   ○ Healthcare Facilities Accreditation Program   ⇑ Center for Improvement in Healthcare Quality Accreditation
□ The Joint Commission accreditation   ◇ DNV Healthcare Inc. accreditation   △ Commission on Accreditation of Rehabilitation Facilities (CARF) accreditation

KS

GREENSBURG—Kiowa County

★ **KIOWA COUNTY MEMORIAL HOSPITAL (171332)**, 721 West Kansas Avenue, Zip 67054–1633; tel. 620/723–3341 **A**10 18 **F**3 7 11 34 40 50 53 59 64 68 107 114 127 128 133 **P**6 **S** Great Plains Health Alliance, Inc., Wichita, KS
Primary Contact: Mary Sweet, Administrator
CFO: Ron Tucker, Business Office Manager
CMO: Nizar Kibar M.D., Chief Medical Staff
CIO: Jeremy Steven Hoover, Chief Information Officer
CHR: Cathy McFall, Human Resources Manager
CNO: Vanessa Kirk, Director of Nursing
Web address: www.kcmh.net
Control: Other not–for–profit (including NFP Corporation) **Service:** General medical and surgical

Staffed Beds: 15 **Admissions:** 123 **Census:** 5 **Outpatient Visits:** 11505 **Births:** 0 **Total Expense ($000):** 8436 **Payroll Expense ($000):** 3277 **Personnel:** 76

HANOVER—Washington County

★ **HANOVER HOSPITAL (171365)**, 205 South Hanover, Zip 66945–8924, Mailing Address: P.O.Box 38, 66945–0038; tel. 785/337–2214 **A**10 18 **F**2 7 40 53 69 81 133 **P**4
Primary Contact: Brittni Oehmke, Administrator
CFO: Sheryl Adam, Chief Financial Officer
Control: Hospital district or authority, Government, Nonfederal **Service:** General medical and surgical

Staffed Beds: 25 **Admissions:** 137 **Census:** 3 **Outpatient Visits:** 2150 **Births:** 2 **Total Expense ($000):** 4007 **Payroll Expense ($000):** 2178 **Personnel:** 50

HARPER—Harper County

★ **HARPER HOSPITAL DISTRICT FIVE (171366)**, 700 West 13th Street, Zip 67058–1401; tel. 620/896–7324 **A**10 18 **F**3 10 29 34 35 40 43 45 46 50 53 54 57 59 64 65 67 68 75 77 79 81 84 87 90 93 97 107 111 114 119 125 127 128 130 131 133 135 146 147 148 **P**6
Primary Contact: Sandra Owen, Interim Chief Executive Officer
CFO: Sandra Owen, Director Fiscal and Accounting
CMO: Ralph Imlay M.D., Chief of Staff
CIO: Cindi Beadman, Director Medical Records
CHR: Troy Hickman, Director Human Resources
CNO: Karen Aldis, Director of Nursing
Web address: www.hhd5.com
Control: Hospital district or authority, Government, Nonfederal **Service:** General medical and surgical

Staffed Beds: 25 **Admissions:** 242 **Census:** 11 **Outpatient Visits:** 33016 **Births:** 0 **Total Expense ($000):** 9182 **Payroll Expense ($000):** 4336 **Personnel:** 110

HAYS—Ellis County

★ ⇑ **HAYS MEDICAL CENTER (170013)**, 2220 Canterbury Drive, Zip 67601–2370, Mailing Address: P.O.Box 8100, 67601–8100; tel. 785/623–5000 **A**3 5 10 21 **F**3 11 12 13 15 18 20 22 24 26 28 29 30 31 32 34 35 36 37 38 40 41 43 45 46 53 55 56 57 59 60 63 64 65 66 68 69 70 71 72 73 74 75 76 77 78 79 80 81 82 84 85 86 87 89 92 93 96 97 107 108 110 111 115 118 119 120 121 123 126 127 128 129 130 131 132 135 144 146 147 148 149 **P**6
Primary Contact: John H. Jeter, M.D., President and Chief Executive Officer
COO: Bryce A Young, Chief Operating Officer
CFO: George Harms, Chief Financial Officer
CIO: Scott Rohleder, Chief Information Officer
CHR: Bryce A Young, Chief Operating Officer
CNO: Terry Siek MSN, R.N., Chief Nursing Officer
Web address: www.haysmed.com
Control: Other not–for–profit (including NFP Corporation) **Service:** General medical and surgical

Staffed Beds: 127 **Admissions:** 4988 **Census:** 57 **Outpatient Visits:** 295622 **Births:** 717 **Total Expense ($000):** 182799 **Payroll Expense ($000):** 80987 **Personnel:** 1330

HERINGTON—Dickinson County

HERINGTON MUNICIPAL HOSPITAL (171340), 100 East Helen Street, Zip 67449–1606; tel. 785/258–2207 **A**10 18 **F**3 11 15 28 29 40 45 50 54 57 59 64 68 75 77 81 93 97 107 114 115 119 127 133 144
Primary Contact: Alan Meisinger, Chief Financial Officer
CFO: Alan Meisinger, Chief Financial Officer
CMO: John Mosier D.O., Chief of Staff
CHR: Nicole Will, Human Resources Officer
CNO: Roni Baker, Director of Nursing
Web address: www.heringtonhospital.org
Control: City, Government, Nonfederal **Service:** General medical and surgical

Staffed Beds: 25 **Admissions:** 366 **Census:** 3 **Outpatient Visits:** 11427 **Births:** 0 **Total Expense ($000):** 8972 **Payroll Expense ($000):** 3135 **Personnel:** 64

HIAWATHA—Brown County

★ **HIAWATHA COMMUNITY HOSPITAL (171341)**, 300 Utah Street, Zip 66434–2314; tel. 785/742–2131 **A**10 18 **F**8 11 13 15 28 29 40 45 62 67 69 70 76 81 85 107 111 114 119 127 128 130 133 143 146 149 **P**6
Primary Contact: Jeffrey Shelton, Chief Executive Officer
CFO: Jenny Knudson, Controller
CMO: Steffen Shamburg M.D., Chief of Staff
CIO: Cheryl Wenger, Manager Health Information and Quality Assurance
CHR: Alison Keri, Director Human Resources
CNO: Lisa Thompson MSN, R.N., Director of Nursing
Web address: www.hch–ks.org
Control: Other not–for–profit (including NFP Corporation) **Service:** General medical and surgical

Staffed Beds: 25 **Admissions:** 848 **Census:** 10 **Outpatient Visits:** 35086 **Births:** 70 **Total Expense ($000):** 22841 **Payroll Expense ($000):** 9623 **Personnel:** 224

HILL CITY—Graham County

★ **GRAHAM COUNTY HOSPITAL (171325)**, 304 West Prout Street, Zip 67642–1435; tel. 785/421–2121 **A**10 18 **F**3 11 34 40 50 53 57 59 64 65 67 68 81 82 84 93 107 114 127 128 133 148 149
Primary Contact: Melissa Atkins, CPA, Chief Executive Officer
CHR: Donella Belleau, Director Human Resources
Web address: www.grahamcountyhospital.org
Control: County, Government, Nonfederal **Service:** General medical and surgical

Staffed Beds: 20 **Admissions:** 262 **Census:** 3 **Outpatient Visits:** 948 **Births:** 0 **Total Expense ($000):** 6872 **Payroll Expense ($000):** 3468 **Personnel:** 73

HILLSBORO—Marion County

HILLSBORO COMMUNITY HOSPITAL (171357), 701 South Main Street, Zip 67063–1553; tel. 620/947–3114 **A**10 18 **F**3 11 29 30 34 35 40 45 47 50 57 59 64 65 75 77 79 81 82 85 87 93 97 107 114 127 130 131 133 146 148 **P**5 6 **S** Rural Community Hospitals of America, Kansas City, MO
Primary Contact: Marion Regier, Chief Executive Officer
COO: Johna Magnuson, Director Nursing
CIO: Marsha Setzkorn–Meyer, Director Public Relations and Marketing
CHR: Wendy McCarty, Director Human Resources
Web address: www.hchks.com
Control: Corporation, Investor–owned (for–profit) **Service:** General medical and surgical

Staffed Beds: 10 **Admissions:** 159 **Census:** 1 **Outpatient Visits:** 8054 **Births:** 0

HOISINGTON—Barton County

★ **CLARA BARTON HOSPITAL (171333)**, 250 West Ninth Street, Zip 67544–1706; tel. 620/653–2114 **A**10 18 **F**11 15 28 40 51 56 57 59 64 77 79 81 85 92 93 97 107 114 119 127 128 133 148 **P**6
Primary Contact: James Blackwell, President and Chief Executive Officer
CMO: Nathan Knackstedt D.O., Chief of Staff
CHR: John Moshier, Director Human Resources
CNO: Jane Schepmann, Vice President and Chief Nursing Officer
Web address: www.clarabartonhospital.org
Control: Other not–for–profit (including NFP Corporation) **Service:** General medical and surgical

Staffed Beds: 23 **Admissions:** 556 **Census:** 9 **Outpatient Visits:** 45159 **Births:** 0 **Total Expense ($000):** 20532 **Payroll Expense ($000):** 9729 **Personnel:** 195

HOLTON—Jackson County

★ **HOLTON COMMUNITY HOSPITAL (171319)**, 1110 Columbine Drive, Zip 66436–8824; tel. 785/364–2116 **A**10 18 **F**3 11 13 15 18 28 29 34 40 43 45 50 59 62 63 64 65 74 75 77 79 81 82 87 93 97 107 114 119 127 130 131 132 133 135 146 147 148
Primary Contact: Carrie L. Saia, Chief Executive Officer
CFO: Bart Kenton, Chief Financial Officer
CMO: Joel Hutchsin M.D., Chief Medical Staff
CIO: Holli Peters, Director Health Information Management
CHR: Gretchen Snavely, Director Human Resources
CNO: Mandy Bontrager, Director Nursing
Web address: www.holtonhospital.com
Control: Other not–for–profit (including NFP Corporation) **Service:** General medical and surgical

Staffed Beds: 12 **Admissions:** 350 **Census:** 4 **Outpatient Visits:** 44872 **Births:** 53 **Total Expense ($000):** 14233 **Payroll Expense ($000):** 7161 **Personnel:** 142

Many Facility Codes have changed. Please refer to the AHA Guide Code Chart. © 2017 AHA Guide

KS

HORTON—Brown County

HORTON COMMUNITY HOSPITAL (171320), 240 West 18th Street, Zip 66439–1245; tel. 785/486–2642 **A**10 18 **F**1 4 7 15 16 17 28 29 40 45 46 64 67 70 76 80 81 89 90 98 107 114 119 127 128 133 **P**6 **S** Rural Community Hospitals of America, Kansas City, MO
Primary Contact: James D. Noble, Chief Executive Officer
CFO: Sue Kidd, Chief Financial Officer
CMO: William Buck, Chief of Staff
CHR: Barbara McClain, Human Resources
CNO: Ty Compton, Chief Nursing Officer
Web address: www.horton–hospital.com
Control: Corporation, Investor–owned (for–profit) **Service**: General medical and surgical

Staffed Beds: 25 Admissions: 163 Census: 3 Outpatient Visits: 5481 Births: 0 Total Expense ($000): 5436 Payroll Expense ($000): 2900 Personnel: 58

HOXIE—Sheridan County

SHERIDAN COUNTY HEALTH COMPLEX (171347), 826 18th Street, Zip 67740–0167, Mailing Address: P.O.Box 167, 67740–0167; tel. 785/675–3281, (Total facility includes 35 beds in nursing home–type unit) **A**10 18 **F**10 11 29 30 34 35 40 45 50 53 56 57 59 64 66 67 68 69 75 81 85 86 87 93 107 115 119 130 133 **P**6
Primary Contact: Niceta Farber, Chief Executive Officer
CFO: Michael O'Dell, Chief Financial Officer
CMO: Victor Nemechek M.D., Chief of Staff and Chief Medical Officer
CHR: Shelby Moss, Human Resource Officer
CNO: Hannah Schoendaler, Chief Nursing Officer
Web address: www.sheridancountyhospital.com
Control: County, Government, Nonfederal **Service**: General medical and surgical

Staffed Beds: 53 Admissions: 240 Census: 33 Outpatient Visits: 5752 Births: 0 Total Expense ($000): 10234 Payroll Expense ($000): 4596 Personnel: 123

HUGOTON—Stevens County

★ **STEVENS COUNTY HOSPITAL (171335)**, 1006 South Jackson Street, Zip 67951–2858, Mailing Address: P.O.Box 10, 67951–0010; tel. 620/544–8511, (Total facility includes 83 beds in nursing home–type unit) **A**10 18 **F**3 11 15 28 29 30 40 50 57 59 67 68 81 93 107 111 119 127 128 130 133 135 145 146
Primary Contact: Linda Stalcup, Chief Executive Officer
CMO: Samer Al–hashmi M.D., Chief Medical Staff
Web address: www.stevenscountyhospital.com/
Control: County, Government, Nonfederal **Service**: General medical and surgical

Staffed Beds: 100 Admissions: 263 Census: 400 Outpatient Visits: 11459 Births: 0 Total Expense ($000): 16028 Payroll Expense ($000): 7624 Personnel: 79

HUTCHINSON—Reno County

⊞ △ **HUTCHINSON REGIONAL MEDICAL CENTER (170020)**, 1701 East 23rd Avenue, Zip 67502–1191; tel. 620/665–2000, (Total facility includes 60 beds in nursing home–type unit) **A**1 7 10 **F**3 7 11 13 18 20 22 24 26 28 29 30 31 34 35 40 43 47 48 49 50 51 53 57 60 64 68 70 74 76 77 78 79 81 82 83 85 87 89 90 93 98 102 103 106 107 108 111 114 115 119 120 121 123 126 128 129 130 143 146 148 **P**6
Primary Contact: Ken Johnson, President and Chief Executive Officer
CFO: Cassie Dolen, Vice President Finance and Chief Financial Officer
CMO: Thomas Smith M.D., Vice President Medical Affairs
CIO: Calvin Wright, Chief Information Officer
CHR: Kevin Chiles, Vice President Human Resources
CNO: Julie R. Ward MSN, R.N., Vice President Patient Care Services
Web address: www.hutchregional.com
Control: Other not–for–profit (including NFP Corporation) **Service**: General medical and surgical

Staffed Beds: 206 Admissions: 6050 Census: 123 Outpatient Visits: 112491 Births: 592 Total Expense ($000): 123681 Payroll Expense ($000): 42801 Personnel: 838

SUMMIT SURGICAL (170198), 1818 East 23rd Avenue, Zip 67502–1106; tel. 620/663–4800 **A**10 **F**3 29 45 64 77 79 81 85 91 93 94 **P**2
Primary Contact: Ann Hentzen Page, M.D., Chief Executive Officer
COO: Nancy Corwin, Chief Operating Officer
CMO: Ann Hentzen Page M.D., Medical Director
CNO: Nancy Corwin, Chief Nursing Officer
Web address: www.summitks.com/index_surgical.htm
Control: Corporation, Investor–owned (for–profit) **Service**: Surgical

Staffed Beds: 10 Admissions: 299 Census: 1 Outpatient Visits: 18152 Births: 0 Total Expense ($000): 8284 Payroll Expense ($000): 2427 Personnel: 29

IOLA—Allen County

⊞ **ALLEN COUNTY REGIONAL HOSPITAL (171373)**, 3066 N. Kentucky St, Zip 66749, Mailing Address: P.O.Box 540, 66749–0540; tel. 620/365–1000 **A**1 10 18 **F**3 11 13 15 29 30 31 34 35 40 43 45 56 57 59 62 63 64 75 76 77 78 81 82 84 85 86 89 103 104 107 110 114 119 127 129 130 132 133 146 147 148 149 150
Primary Contact: Marion A. Thompson, FACHE, Chief Executive Officer
CFO: Larry Peterson, Chief Financial Officer
CMO: Brian Wolfe, Chief of Staff
CHR: Paula Sell, Director Human Resources
CNO: Patty McGuffin R.N., Chief Nursing Officer
Web address: www.allencountyhospital.com
Control: County, Government, Nonfederal **Service**: General medical and surgical

Staffed Beds: 25 Admissions: 716 Census: 9 Outpatient Visits: 17705 Births: 83 Total Expense ($000): 22853 Payroll Expense ($000): 6977 Personnel: 148

JETMORE—Hodgeman County

★ **HODGEMAN COUNTY HEALTH CENTER (171369)**, 809 Bramley Street, Zip 67854–9320, Mailing Address: P.O.Box 310, 67854–0310; tel. 620/357–8361, (Total facility includes 25 beds in nursing home–type unit) **A**10 18 **F**3 40 53 67 81 107 114 125 127 130 133 143 **P**4
Primary Contact: Teresa L. Deuel, Chief Executive Officer
Web address: www.hchconline.org
Control: County, Government, Nonfederal **Service**: General medical and surgical

Staffed Beds: 38 Admissions: 251 Census: 29 Outpatient Visits: 36950 Births: 0 Total Expense ($000): 8551 Payroll Expense ($000): 4003 Personnel: 80

JOHNSON—Stanton County

STANTON COUNTY HOSPITAL (171343), 404 North Chestnut Street, Zip 67855–5001, Mailing Address: P.O.Box 779, 67855–0779; tel. 620/492–6250, (Total facility includes 25 beds in nursing home–type unit) **A**10 18 **F**3 11 13 34 35 40 41 45 50 54 56 57 59 64 68 75 76 81 82 86 87 89 93 97 107 114 127 130 131 133 143 **P**6
Primary Contact: Jay Tusten, Chief Executive Officer
CFO: Robert Nahmensen, Chief Financial Officer and Chief Operations Officer
CMO: Bill Troup M.D., Chief of Staff
CIO: Marco Medina, Chief Information Officer
CHR: Camille Davidson, Director Human Resources
CNO: Marianne Mills R.N., Chairperson
Web address: www.stantoncountyhospital.com
Control: County, Government, Nonfederal **Service**: General medical and surgical

Staffed Beds: 40 Admissions: 107 Census: 22 Outpatient Visits: 12564 Births: 20 Total Expense ($000): 9258 Payroll Expense ($000): 4514 Personnel: 99

JUNCTION CITY—Geary County

⊞ **GEARY COMMUNITY HOSPITAL (170074)**, 1102 St Mary's Road, Zip 66441–4196, Mailing Address: P.O.Box 490, 66441–0490; tel. 785/238–4131, (Nonreporting) **A**1 10
Primary Contact: Joseph Stratton, FACHE, Chief Executive Officer
CFO: William Kloppe, Chief Financial Officer
CMO: Jimmy Jenkins M.D., Chief Medical Officer
CIO: Kyle Ibarra, Director Information Systems
CHR: Loren Streit, Director Human Resources
CNO: Dawn M Engel, Chief Nursing Officer
Web address: www.gchks.org
Control: County, Government, Nonfederal **Service**: General medical and surgical

Staffed Beds: 58

⊞ **IRWIN ARMY COMMUNITY HOSPITAL**, 600 Caisson Hill Road, Zip 66442–7037; tel. 785/239–7000, (Nonreporting) **A**1 3 5 **S** Department of the Army, Office of the Surgeon General, Falls Church, VA
Primary Contact: Colonel Risa Ware, Commander
CMO: Lieutenant ColonelMark S Ochoa M.D., Deputy Commander, Clinical Services
CIO: David Dougherty, Chief Information Management Officer
CHR: Hope Brunton, Chief Manpower Branch
Web address: www.iach.amedd.army.mil
Control: Army, Government, federal **Service**: General medical and surgical

Staffed Beds: 44

Hospital, Medicare Provider Number, Address, Telephone, Approval, Facility, and Physician Codes, Health Care System

★ American Hospital Association (AHA) membership
□ The Joint Commission accreditation
○ Healthcare Facilities Accreditation Program
◇ DNV Healthcare Inc. accreditation
⇑ Center for Improvement in Healthcare Quality Accreditation
△ Commission on Accreditation of Rehabilitation Facilities (CARF) accreditation

KS

KANSAS CITY—Wyandotte County

☐ **KVC PRAIRIE RIDGE PSYCHIATRIC HOSPITAL**, 4300 Brenner Drive, Zip 66104–1163; tel. 913/334–0294 **A**1 3 5 **F**32 38 50 98 99 106
Primary Contact: Jason R. Hooper, President and Chief Executive Officer
COO: Ryan Speier, Vice President Administration
CMO: Vishal Adma M.D., Medical Director
Web address: www.kvc.org
Control: Other not–for–profit (including NFP Corporation) **Service:** Children's hospital psychiatric

Staffed Beds: 109 **Admissions:** 3073 **Census:** 88 **Total Expense ($000):** 18849 **Payroll Expense ($000):** 9117 **Personnel:** 199

⊞ **PROVIDENCE MEDICAL CENTER (170146)**, 8929 Parallel Parkway, Zip 66112–1689; tel. 913/596–4000 **A**1 10 **F**3 13 15 17 18 20 22 24 28 29 30 31 34 35 40 41 44 45 49 50 53 56 57 59 64 70 74 75 76 77 78 79 81 82 84 85 87 89 93 97 102 103 107 108 110 111 114 119 120 121 123 124 126 129 130 131 132 135 143 146 147 148 149 **P**6 **S** Prime Healthcare, Ontario, CA
Primary Contact: Karen Orr, Administrator and Chief Nursing Officer
CFO: David Dulny, Chief Financial Officer
CMO: Sabato Sisillo M.D., Chief Medical Officer
CIO: Charles Soeken, Director Information Technology
CHR: Brenda Farwell, Director Human Resources
CNO: Karen Orr, Chief Nursing Officer
Web address: www.providencekc.com
Control: Individual, Investor–owned (for–profit) **Service:** General medical and surgical

Staffed Beds: 170 **Admissions:** 9781 **Census:** 96 **Outpatient Visits:** 196096 **Births:** 573 **Total Expense ($000):** 156034 **Payroll Expense ($000):** 58622 **Personnel:** 953

RAINBOW MENTAL HEALTH FACILITY (174010), 2205 West 36th Avenue, Zip 66103–2107; tel. 913/755–7000 (Nonreporting) **A**5 10
Primary Contact: Jerry A. Rea, Ph.D., Interim Superintendent
CFO: Donna Dean, Chief Financial Officer
CMO: Maria Gustilo M.D., Medical Director
CHR: Marilyn Williamson, Chief Human Resources Officer
Web address: www.srskansas.org/osh/osh–rmhf_main.html
Control: State, Government, Nonfederal **Service:** Psychiatric

Staffed Beds: 36

⊞ **SELECT SPECIALTY HOSPITAL–KANSAS CITY (172005)**, 1731 North 90th Street, Zip 66112–1515; tel. 913/732–5900, (Nonreporting) **A**1 10 **S** Select Medical Corporation, Mechanicsburg, PA
Primary Contact: Kevin J. Thorpe, Chief Executive Officer
Web address: www.selectspecialtyhospitals.com
Control: Corporation, Investor–owned (for–profit) **Service:** Acute long–term care hospital

Staffed Beds: 40

SELECT SPECIALTY HOSPITAL–KANSAS CITY(Nonreporting) **A**1 10
Web address: www.selectspecialtyhospitals.com
⊞ **THE UNIVERSITY OF KANSAS HEALTH SYSTEM (170040)**, 3901 Rainbow Boulevard, Zip 66160–7200; tel. 913/588–5000, (Includes THE UNIVERSITY OF KANSAS HOSPITAL – INDIAN CREEK CAMPUS, 10720 Nall Avenue, Overland Park, Kansas, Zip 66211–1206, tel. 913/754–5000) **A**1 2 3 5 8 10 **F**3 8 9 11 12 13 15 16 17 18 20 21 22 24 25 26 27 28 29 30 31 34 35 36 37 38 39 40 41 43 44 45 46 47 48 49 50 51 52 54 55 56 57 58 59 60 61 63 64 65 68 70 71 72 74 75 76 77 78 79 80 81 82 83 84 85 86 87 88 89 90 92 93 96 97 98 99 100 101 102 103 104 107 108 110 111 114 115 116 117 118 119 120 121 123 124 126 129 130 131 132 135 136 138 139 141 142 144 145 146 147 148 149 **P**6
Primary Contact: Bob Page, Chief Executive Officer
COO: Tammy Peterman R.N., MS, Executive Vice President, Chief Operating Officer and Chief Nursing Officer
CFO: Bill Marting, Senior Vice President and Chief Financial Officer
CMO: Lou Wetzel M.D., Chief of Staff
CIO: Chris Hansen, Senior Vice President Ambulatory Services and Chief Information Officer
CHR: Alisa Ford, Vice President Human Resources
CNO: Tammy Peterman R.N., MS, Executive Vice President, Chief Operating Officer and Chief Nursing Officer
Web address: www.kumed.com
Control: Hospital district or authority, Government, Nonfederal **Service:** General medical and surgical

Staffed Beds: 784 **Admissions:** 36435 **Census:** 557 **Outpatient Visits:** 1026846 **Births:** 1945 **Total Expense ($000):** 1599133 **Payroll Expense ($000):** 653004 **Personnel:** 9894

KINGMAN—Kingman County

★ **KINGMAN COMMUNITY HOSPITAL (171378)**, 750 Avenue D West, Zip 67068–0376; tel. 620/532–3147 **A**10 18 **F**3 11 15 17 18 28 29 31 34 35 40 54 56 57 59 62 64 67 69 70 75 77 78 81 86 87 89 90 93 97 107 114 119 127 128 129 130 132 133 145 146 148 **P**6
Primary Contact: Shannan Flach, Chief Executive Officer
CFO: Kent Hudson, Chief Financial Officer
CIO: Jay Gehring, Director Information Systems
CHR: Nancy Stucky, Director Human Resources and Public Relations
CNO: Nita McFarland, Director of Nursing
Web address: www.kchks.com
Control: Other not–for–profit (including NFP Corporation) **Service:** General medical and surgical

Staffed Beds: 25 **Admissions:** 499 **Census:** 8 **Outpatient Visits:** 21687 **Births:** 0 **Total Expense ($000):** 10826 **Payroll Expense ($000):** 5505 **Personnel:** 119

KINSLEY—Edwards County

★ **EDWARDS COUNTY HOSPITAL AND HEALTHCARE CENTER (171317)**, 620 West Eighth Street, Zip 67547–2329, Mailing Address: P.O.Box 99, 67547–0099; tel. 620/659–3621 **A**10 18 **F**7 11 15 18 19 28 29 30 34 35 40 45 47 53 54 56 57 59 64 65 68 75 77 79 93 97 98 103 107 114 119 127 130 133 146 148
Primary Contact: Jimmie W. Hansel, Ph.D., Chief Executive Officer
CHR: Tammy K Lampe, Director Human Resources
Web address: www.edwardscohospital.com
Control: County, Government, Nonfederal **Service:** General medical and surgical

Staffed Beds: 22 **Admissions:** 361 **Census:** 15 **Outpatient Visits:** 9803 **Births:** 0 **Total Expense ($000):** 9131 **Payroll Expense ($000):** 3342 **Personnel:** 67

KIOWA—Barber County

★ **KIOWA DISTRICT HOSPITAL AND MANOR (171331)**, 810 Drumm Street, Zip 67070–1626, Mailing Address: P.O.Box 184, 67070–0184; tel. 620/825–4131, (Total facility includes 29 beds in nursing home–type unit) **A**10 18 **F**1 2 3 4 12 16 17 34 40 41 45 56 57 59 64 65 67 69 70 72 73 80 81 84 85 87 88 89 90 91 92 93 97 98 107 114 119 127 128 133 148 150 **P**6
Primary Contact: Margaret Grismer, Chief Executive Officer
CFO: Robin Lewis, Chief Financial Officer
CMO: Paul Wilhelm M.D., Chief of Staff
CHR: Tara Girty, Director Human Resources
Web address: www.k–d–h.com
Control: Hospital district or authority, Government, Nonfederal **Service:** General medical and surgical

Staffed Beds: 39 **Admissions:** 212 **Census:** 24 **Outpatient Visits:** 7262 **Births:** 0 **Total Expense ($000):** 5259 **Payroll Expense ($000):** 2266 **Personnel:** 63

LA CROSSE—Rush County

★ **RUSH COUNTY MEMORIAL HOSPITAL (171342)**, 801 Locust Street, Zip 67548–9673, Mailing Address: P.O.Box 520, 67548–0520; tel. 785/222–2545, (Total facility includes 20 beds in nursing home–type unit) **A**10 18 **F**3 40 45 50 53 59 64 77 81 93 97 107 111 114 119 127 133 **P**6
Primary Contact: Brenda Legleiter, R.N., Chief Executive Officer
CFO: Jane Oborny, Chief Financial Officer
CMO: Harley Calvin D.O., Chief Medical Officer
CHR: Charlene Goodman, Director Human Resources
Web address: www.rushcountymemorialhospital.com
Control: County, Government, Nonfederal **Service:** General medical and surgical

Staffed Beds: 36 **Admissions:** 90 **Census:** 20 **Outpatient Visits:** 3973 **Births:** 0 **Total Expense ($000):** 5822 **Payroll Expense ($000):** 2245 **Personnel:** 73

LAKIN—Kearny County

★ **KEARNY COUNTY HOSPITAL (171313)**, 500 Thorpe Street, Zip 67860–9625; tel. 620/355–7111, (Total facility includes 75 beds in nursing home–type unit) **A**10 18 **F**2 3 6 10 13 15 28 29 34 35 40 45 50 56 57 58 59 62 64 67 68 69 75 79 81 85 86 87 93 97 107 114 119 125 127 128 130 131 132 133 143 149 **P**6
Primary Contact: Benjamin Anderson, Chief Executive Officer and Administrator
COO: Shari Campbell, Chief Operating Officer
CFO: Kelly Ann Speckman, Chief Financial Officer
CMO: Arlo Reimer M.D., Chief of Staff
CIO: Lisa Kay–Garcia, Chief Information Officer
CHR: Laci Williams, Director Human Resources
CNO: Susan D Stingley, Chief Nursing Officer
Web address: www.kearnycountyhospital.com
Control: County, Government, Nonfederal **Service:** General medical and surgical

Staffed Beds: 100 **Admissions:** 522 **Census:** 74 **Outpatient Visits:** 40115 **Births:** 218 **Total Expense ($000):** 22399 **Payroll Expense ($000):** 11833 **Personnel:** 255

KS

LARNED—Pawnee County

☐ **LARNED STATE HOSPITAL (174006)**, 1301 Kansas Highway 264, Zip 67550; tel. 620/285-2131 **A**1 10 **F**3 30 50 53 57 68 75 77 86 87 97 98 100 101 102 103 106 130 132 135 143 146 149
Primary Contact: Thomas Kinlen, Superintendent
COO: Steve Spain, Chief Operating Officer
CMO: Sayed Jehan M.D., Interim Medical Director
CIO: Sid Smith, Director Information Resources
CHR: Kerri Barnard, Director Human Resources
CNO: Holly Hertel, Director Nursing
Web address: www.larnedstatehospital.org
Control: State, Government, Nonfederal **Service**: Psychiatric

Staffed Beds: 532 **Admissions**: 1177 **Census**: 532 **Outpatient Visits**: 0 **Births**: 0 **Total Expense ($000)**: 57868 **Payroll Expense ($000)**: 30000 **Personnel**: 591

★ **PAWNEE VALLEY COMMUNITY HOSPITAL (171345)**, 923 Carroll Avenue, Zip 67550-2429; tel. 620/285-3161 **A**10 18 **F**3 11 28 29 30 34 40 43 45 46 57 68 77 81 82 84 85 86 87 91 93 94 102 104 107 111 115 127 129 130 131 132 133 135 147 148 149 **P**6
Primary Contact: Eric Lybarger, Administrator
COO: Bryce A Young, Chief Operating Officer
CFO: George Harms, Chief Financial Officer
CMO: David Sanger M.D., Chief Medical Officer
CHR: Bruce Whittington, Vice President Human Resources
CNO: Paul Henry Carrington, Chief Nursing Officer
Web address: www.pawneevalleyhospital.com
Control: County, Government, Nonfederal **Service**: General medical and surgical

Staffed Beds: 22 **Admissions**: 259 **Census**: 5 **Outpatient Visits**: 14190 **Births**: 0 **Total Expense ($000)**: 12853 **Payroll Expense ($000)**: 6628 **Personnel**: 103

LAWRENCE—Douglas County

✚ **LAWRENCE MEMORIAL HOSPITAL (170137)**, 325 Maine Street, Zip 66044-1360; tel. 785/505-5000, (Total facility includes 14 beds in nursing home-type unit) **A**1 3 5 10 20 **F**3 11 13 15 18 19 20 22 26 28 29 30 31 34 35 38 39 40 43 44 45 49 50 51 54 55 56 57 59 61 64 65 69 70 73 74 75 76 77 78 79 81 82 84 85 86 87 89 90 93 94 96 97 100 102 107 110 111 114 115 118 119 120 124 126 128 129 130 131 132 135 146 147 148 **P**6 8
Primary Contact: Russell W. Johnson, President and Chief Executive Officer
COO: Karen J Shumate R.N., Chief Operating Officer
CFO: Joe Pedley CPA, Vice President and Chief Financial Officer
CIO: Michael Williams, Chief Information Officer
CHR: Carolyn Bowmer
CNO: Traci Hoopingarner R.N., Chief Nursing Officer
Web address: www.lmh.org
Control: City, Government, Nonfederal **Service**: General medical and surgical

Staffed Beds: 145 **Admissions**: 6872 **Census**: 66 **Outpatient Visits**: 185449 **Births**: 1113 **Total Expense ($000)**: 212306 **Payroll Expense ($000)**: 89141 **Personnel**: 1287

LEAVENWORTH—Leavenworth County

✚ **SAINT JOHN HOSPITAL (170009)**, 3500 South Fourth Street, Zip 66048-5043; tel. 913/680-6000 **A**1 10 **F**3 8 15 18 29 30 34 40 44 45 46 50 54 56 57 59 64 68 70 74 75 77 81 84 85 87 93 98 100 103 107 115 119 130 133 146 147 148 149 **P**6 **S** Prime Healthcare, Ontario, CA
Primary Contact: Paula Ellis, Administrator
CFO: David Dulny, Chief Financial Officer
CMO: Sabato Sisillo M.D., Chief Medical Officer
CIO: Charles Soeken, Director Information Technology
CHR: Brenda Farwell, Director Human Resources
CNO: Jodi Fincher, Vice President Patient Care Services
Web address: www.providence-health.org/sjh
Control: Individual, Investor-owned (for-profit) **Service**: General medical and surgical

Staffed Beds: 48 **Admissions**: 1704 **Census**: 25 **Outpatient Visits**: 46681 **Births**: 0 **Total Expense ($000)**: 29768 **Payroll Expense ($000)**: 12072 **Personnel**: 155

✚ **SAINT LUKE'S CUSHING HOSPITAL (170133)**, 711 Marshall Street, Zip 66048-3235; tel. 913/684-1100 **A**1 10 **F**3 11 13 15 28 29 31 34 35 40 44 45 50 57 59 64 65 70 74 75 76 77 79 81 82 84 85 86 87 93 94 100 102 107 108 110 111 115 119 129 130 132 135 146 148 149 **S** Saint Luke's Health System, Kansas City, MO
Primary Contact: Adele Ducharme, MSN, R.N., Chief Executive Officer
CFO: Julie Murphy, Chief Financial Officer
CMO: Nicholas Brockert, President
CHR: Donna Kunz, System Director Human Resources
CNO: Karin Sundblom MSN, R.N., Chief Nursing Officer
Web address: www.saintlukeshealthsystem.org/locations/saint-lukes-cushing-hospital
Control: Other not-for-profit (including NFP Corporation) **Service**: General medical and surgical

Staffed Beds: 25 **Admissions**: 968 **Census**: 7 **Outpatient Visits**: 34957 **Births**: 144 **Total Expense ($000)**: 33058 **Payroll Expense ($000)**: 11349 **Personnel**: 192

VETERANS AFFAIRS EASTERN KANSAS HEALTH CARE SYSTEM-DWIGHT D. EISENHOWER VETERANS AFFAIRS MEDICAL CENTER See Veterans Affairs Eastern Kansas Health Care System, Topeka

LEAWOOD—Johnson County

☐ **DOCTOR'S HOSPITAL (170194)**, 4901 College Boulevard, Zip 66211-1602; tel. 913/529-1801 **A**1 10 **F**39 79 81 82 111 **P**5
Primary Contact: Phil Harness, Chief Executive Officer
Web address: www.dshospital.net
Control: Partnership, Investor-owned (for-profit) **Service**: General medical and surgical

Staffed Beds: 9 **Admissions**: 175 **Census**: 1 **Outpatient Visits**: 11168 **Births**: 0 **Total Expense ($000)**: 17525 **Payroll Expense ($000)**: 2756 **Personnel**: 48

KANSAS CITY ORTHOPAEDIC INSTITUTE (170188), 3651 College Boulevard, Zip 66211-1910; tel. 913/338-4100 **A**3 5 10 **F**29 77 79 81 82 93 111 **P**5
Primary Contact: Charles E. Rhoades, M.D., Chief Executive Officer
CIO: Jim Leveling, Director Information Technology
CHR: Laura Sinclair, Director Human Resources
Web address: www.kcoi.com
Control: Partnership, Investor-owned (for-profit) **Service**: Orthopedic

Staffed Beds: 9 **Admissions**: 830 **Census**: 5 **Outpatient Visits**: 29363 **Births**: 0 **Personnel**: 114

LENEXA—Johnson County

☐ **MINIMALLY INVASIVE SURGERY HOSPITAL (170199)**, 11217 Lakeview Avenue, Zip 66219-1399; tel. 913/322-7401 **A**1 10 **F**3 18 26 31 45 64 68 70 78 81 82 85 86 107 111 115 119 129 **P**6
Primary Contact: Parajeet Sabharrwal, Chief Executive Officer
Web address: www.mishhospital.com
Control: Corporation, Investor-owned (for-profit) **Service**: Surgical

Staffed Beds: 9 **Admissions**: 144 **Census**: 1 **Outpatient Visits**: 3885 **Births**: 0 **Personnel**: 30

LEOTI—Wichita County

★ **WICHITA COUNTY HEALTH CENTER (171306)**, 211 East Earl Street, Zip 67861-9620; tel. 620/375-2233, (Total facility includes 17 beds in nursing home-type unit) **A**10 18 **F**2 3 11 29 34 35 40 41 45 50 56 57 59 64 69 75 77 86 87 93 97 102 107 119 127 130 133 135 146 148 **P**6 **S** Great Plains Health Alliance, Inc., Wichita, KS
Primary Contact: Teresa Clark, Chief Executive Officer and Administrator
CFO: Janice Campas, Chief Financial Officer
CMO: Jeffrey Alpert M.D., Medical Director
CHR: Patti Whalen, Manager Human Resources
Web address: www.wichitacountyhealthcenter.com
Control: County, Government, Nonfederal **Service**: General medical and surgical

Staffed Beds: 42 **Admissions**: 121 **Census**: 29 **Outpatient Visits**: 5377 **Births**: 0 **Total Expense ($000)**: 8152 **Payroll Expense ($000)**: 3558 **Personnel**: 94

LIBERAL—Seward County

☐ **SOUTHWEST MEDICAL CENTER (170068)**, 315 West 15th Street, Zip 67901–2455, Mailing Address: Box 1340, 67905–1340; tel. 620/624–1651, (Total facility includes 18 beds in nursing home–type unit) **A**1 10 **F**1 3 4 11 13 15 16 17 28 29 31 34 40 45 48 49 57 59 67 68 70 72 73 75 76 77 79 80 81 85 87 88 89 90 93 96 98 103 104 107 108 110 111 114 118 119 128 129 130 131 145 148 149
Primary Contact: William Ermann, President and Chief Executive Officer
COO: Robert Whitaker, Vice President of Operations
CFO: Amber Williams, Vice President and Chief Financial Officer
CHR: Lisa L Mathes, Human Resources Director
CNO: Jo L Harrison, Vice President of Patient Care Services
Web address: www.swmedcenter.com
Control: County, Government, Nonfederal **Service**: General medical and surgical

Staffed Beds: 101 Admissions: 2167 Census: 18 Outpatient Visits: 48985 Births: 752 Total Expense ($000): 46693 Payroll Expense ($000): 19768 Personnel: 390

LINCOLN—Lincoln County

LINCOLN COUNTY HOSPITAL (171360), 624 North Second Street, Zip 67455–1738, Mailing Address: P.O.Box 406, 67455–0406; tel. 785/524–4403 **A**10 18 **F**3 11 15 34 40 57 69 107 110 111 112 114 119 127 129 133 **P**6
Primary Contact: Steven L. Granzow, Chief Executive Officer
CFO: Tawnya Seitz, Chief Financial Officer
CNO: Christa Haesemeyer, Chief Nursing Officer
Web address: www.lincolncountyhospital.net
Control: County, Government, Nonfederal **Service**: General medical and surgical

Staffed Beds: 14 Admissions: 104 Census: 1 Outpatient Visits: 5420 Births: 0 Total Expense ($000): 8267 Payroll Expense ($000): 3208 Personnel: 70

LINDSBORG—Mcpherson County

★ **LINDSBORG COMMUNITY HOSPITAL (171358)**, 605 West Lincoln Street, Zip 67456–2328; tel. 785/227–3308 **A**10 18 **F**3 28 29 40 53 57 59 62 64 65 67 81 93 97 107 115 119 128 130 133 144 **P**6 **S** Salina Regional Health Center, Salina, KS
Primary Contact: Larry VanDerWege, Administrator
CFO: Laraine Gengler, Chief Financial Officer
CIO: Jeremy Snapp, Director Information Systems
CHR: Brad Malm, Director Human Resources and Education
CNO: Beth Hedberg R.N., Director Nursing
Web address: www.lindsborghospital.org
Control: Other not–for–profit (including NFP Corporation) **Service**: General medical and surgical

Staffed Beds: 21 Admissions: 263 Census: 4 Outpatient Visits: 21835 Births: 0 Total Expense ($000): 10690 Payroll Expense ($000): 4394 Personnel: 98

LYONS—Rice County

★ **HOSPITAL DISTRICT NO 1 OF RICE COUNTY (171330)**, 619 South Clark Street, Zip 67554–3003, Mailing Address: P.O.Box 828, 67554–0828; tel. 620/257–5173 **A**10 18 **F**1 3 4 13 16 17 28 29 30 34 35 40 43 45 67 70 72 73 75 76 77 80 81 88 89 90 93 98 107 125 127 128 130 132 133 143
Primary Contact: George M. Stover, Chief Executive Officer
CFO: Terry Pound, Chief Financial Officer
CMO: Kristina Darnauer M.D., Chief of Staff
CNO: Judy Hogdson R.N., Chief Nursing Officer
Web address: www.ricecountyhospital.com
Control: Hospital district or authority, Government, Nonfederal **Service**: General medical and surgical

Staffed Beds: 25 Admissions: 385 Census: 13 Outpatient Visits: 14289 Births: 76 Total Expense ($000): 14219 Payroll Expense ($000): 6866 Personnel: 128

MANHATTAN—Riley County

MANHATTAN SURGICAL (170190), 1829 College Avenue, Zip 66502–3381; tel. 785/776–5100 **A**10 **F**45 48 79 81 82 85 131
Primary Contact: Scott Chapman, Administrator
Web address: www.manhattansurgical.com
Control: Partnership, Investor–owned (for–profit) **Service**: Surgical

Staffed Beds: 13 Admissions: 576 Census: 2 Outpatient Visits: 10508 Births: 0 Personnel: 90

★ ○ **VIA CHRISTI HOSPITAL MANHATTAN, INC. (170142)**, 1823 College Avenue, Zip 66502–3346; tel. 785/776–3322 **A**10 11 19 **F**3 7 11 12 13 15 18 22 28 29 30 31 34 35 37 40 41 44 45 49 50 51 60 67 70 76 77 79 81 82 83 84 85 86 87 89 90 92 94 95 96 99 102 104 107 108 109 110 111 115 119 126 129 130 132 133 145 146 147 148 149 **S** Ascension Healthcare, Saint Louis, MO
Primary Contact: Robert C. Copple, FACHE, Senior Administrator
CFO: James Fraser, Administrator Finance
CIO: Andy Gagnon, Manager Information Technology
CHR: Renee Reed, Director Human Resources
CNO: Jennifer Goehring R.N., Assistant Chief Nursing Officer
Web address: www.viachristi.org/manhattan
Control: Other not–for–profit (including NFP Corporation) **Service**: General medical and surgical

Staffed Beds: 96 Admissions: 4524 Census: 41 Outpatient Visits: 97112 Births: 1222 Total Expense ($000): 84539 Payroll Expense ($000): 32477 Personnel: 401

MANKATO—Jewell County

JEWELL COUNTY HOSPITAL (171309), 100 Crestvue Avenue, Zip 66956–2407, Mailing Address: P.O.Box 327, 66956–0327; tel. 785/378–3137 **A**10 18 **F**2 3 29 40 50 64 75 77 87 93 107 127 128 130 133 148 **P**6
Primary Contact: Doyle L. McKimmy, FACHE, Chief Executive Officer
COO: Eric Borden, Chief Operating Officer and Chief Financial Officer
CFO: Eric Borden, Chief Operating Officer and Chief Financial Officer
Web address: www.jewellcountyhospital.com
Control: County, Government, Nonfederal **Service**: General medical and surgical

Staffed Beds: 25 Admissions: 87 Census: 18 Outpatient Visits: 19061 Births: 0 Total Expense ($000): 4900 Payroll Expense ($000): 2400 Personnel: 60

MARION—Marion County

ST. LUKE HOSPITAL AND LIVING CENTER (171356), 535 South Freeborn, Zip 66861–1256; tel. 620/382–2177, (Total facility includes 32 beds in nursing home–type unit) **A**10 18 **F**3 11 15 26 28 29 34 40 43 45 48 50 56 59 62 64 65 67 68 75 81 93 97 107 108 110 114 119 127 128 133 135 143 144 147 **P**6
Primary Contact: Jeremy Ensey, Chief Executive Officer
CFO: Bev Reid, Chief Financial Officer
CMO: Don Hodson M.D., Chief Medical Officer
CIO: Jeff Methvin, Manager Information Technology
CHR: Sharon Zogelman, Director Human Resources
Web address: www.slhmarion.org
Control: Hospital district or authority, Government, Nonfederal **Service**: General medical and surgical

Staffed Beds: 39 Admissions: 172 Census: 28 Outpatient Visits: 31343 Births: 0 Total Expense ($000): 10501 Payroll Expense ($000): 4819 Personnel: 105

MARYSVILLE—Marshall County

★ **COMMUNITY MEMORIAL HEALTHCARE (171363)**, 708 North 18th Street, Zip 66508–1338; tel. 785/562–2311 **A**10 18 **F**3 13 15 28 29 30 34 35 40 43 45 47 50 57 59 62 64 68 69 75 76 77 81 85 87 93 97 107 108 114 119 127 128 129 130 131 132 133 135 146 147 148 **P**6
Primary Contact: Curtis R. Hawkinson, Chief Executive Officer
CFO: Therese Landoll, Interim Chief Financial Officer
CMO: John Haefele M.D., Chief Medical Officer
CIO: Colleen Behrens, Director Information Technology
CHR: Jessie Schneider, Director Human Resources
CNO: Diane Luebcke R.N., Director Nursing
Web address: www.cmhcare.org
Control: Other not–for–profit (including NFP Corporation) **Service**: General medical and surgical

Staffed Beds: 25 Admissions: 754 Census: 10 Outpatient Visits: 27514 Births: 61 Total Expense ($000): 21631 Payroll Expense ($000): 9613 Personnel: 190

MCPHERSON—McPherson County

★ **MCPHERSON HOSPITAL (170105)**, 1000 Hospital Drive, Zip 67460–2326; tel. 620/241–2250 **A**10 **F**3 7 11 13 15 28 29 34 35 40 45 50 53 54 59 64 65 70 75 76 77 81 82 85 86 87 97 107 110 114 119 130 133 144 146 148 **P**6
Primary Contact: Terri Gehring, Interim Chief Executive Officer
COO: Terri Gehring, Vice President Operations
CFO: George Halama, Vice President Finance
CHR: Cathy Dunham, Vice President Human Resources
CNO: Beth Worden, Director Nursing Services
Web address: www.mcphersonhospital.org
Control: Other not–for–profit (including NFP Corporation) **Service**: General medical and surgical

Staffed Beds: 33 Admissions: 853 Census: 8 Outpatient Visits: 63864 Births: 117 Total Expense ($000): 27409 Payroll Expense ($000): 13382 Personnel: 261

MEMORIAL HOSPITAL See Mcpherson Hospital

MEADE—Meade County

★ **MEADE DISTRICT HOSPITAL (171321)**, 510 East Carthage Street, Zip 67864–6401, Mailing Address: P.O.Box 820, 67864–0820; tel. 620/873–2141, (Total facility includes 45 beds in nursing home–type unit) **A**10 18 **F**3 15 28 29 34 35 40 45 53 56 57 59 62 64 79 81 82 85 87 93 107 108 114 119 127 128 130 131 133 143 148 149 **P**6
Primary Contact: Steve Stewart, Administrator
CIO: Matt Bobo, Chief Information Officer
Web address: www.meadehospital.com
Control: Hospital district or authority, Government, Nonfederal **Service:** General medical and surgical

Staffed Beds: 65 **Admissions:** 210 **Census:** 45 **Outpatient Visits:** 15265 **Births:** 0

MEDICINE LODGE—Barber County

★ **MEDICINE LODGE MEMORIAL HOSPITAL (171334)**, 710 North Walnut Street, Zip 67104–1019; tel. 620/886–3771 **A**10 18 **F**3 7 11 40 44 45 56 64 81 93 107 119 127 128 133 148 **P**6 **S** Great Plains Health Alliance, Inc., Wichita, KS
Primary Contact: Kevin A. White, Administrator
CFO: Thomas G Lee, Chief Financial Officer
CHR: Johnnie Davis, Director Human Resources
CNO: Kathryn I. Burns R.N., Director of Nursing
Web address: www.mlmh.net/
Control: Hospital district or authority, Government, Nonfederal **Service:** General medical and surgical

Staffed Beds: 25 **Admissions:** 188 **Census:** 13 **Outpatient Visits:** 21917 **Births:** 0 **Total Expense ($000):** 10298 **Payroll Expense ($000):** 4477 **Personnel:** 86

MINNEAPOLIS—Ottawa County

★ **OTTAWA COUNTY HEALTH CENTER (171328)**, 215 East Eighth, Zip 67467–1902, Mailing Address: P.O.Box 290, 67467–0290; tel. 785/392–2122, (Total facility includes 20 beds in nursing home–type unit) **A**10 18 **F**10 28 35 40 53 56 62 64 67 85 86 93 128 130 133 143 **S** Great Plains Health Alliance, Inc., Wichita, KS
Primary Contact: Jody Parks, Administrator
CFO: Cheryl Lanoue, Chief Financial Officer
CIO: Linda Wright, Director Information
CNO: Marlene Gawith, Director of Nursing
Web address: www.ottawacountyhealthcenter.com
Control: Other not–for–profit (including NFP Corporation) **Service:** General medical and surgical

Staffed Beds: 45 **Admissions:** 224 **Census:** 23 **Outpatient Visits:** 4655 **Births:** 0 **Total Expense ($000):** 6061 **Payroll Expense ($000):** 2742 **Personnel:** 72

MINNEOLA—Ford County

★ **MINNEOLA DISTRICT HOSPITAL (171368)**, 212 Main Street, Zip 67865–8511, Mailing Address: P.O.Box 127, 67865–0127; tel. 620/885–4264, (Total facility includes 36 beds in nursing home–type unit) **A**10 18 **F**13 29 40 45 46 56 57 64 65 67 81 83 93 102 107 127 128 130 133 148 **P**6 **S** Great Plains Health Alliance, Inc., Wichita, KS
Primary Contact: Deborah Bruner, Chief Executive Officer and Administrator
CFO: Marion Zirger, Chief Financial Officer
CMO: Tony Luna M.D., Chief of Staff
CHR: Vena Harris, Director Human Resources
CNO: Amanda Stout, Chief Nursing Officer
Web address: www.minneolahealthcare.com
Control: Hospital district or authority, Government, Nonfederal **Service:** General medical and surgical

Staffed Beds: 54 **Admissions:** 310 **Census:** 37 **Outpatient Visits:** 25530 **Births:** 0 **Total Expense ($000):** 11710 **Payroll Expense ($000):** 5770 **Personnel:** 123

MOUNDRIDGE—Mcpherson County

★ **MERCY HOSPITAL (170075)**, 218 East Pack Street, Zip 67107–8815, Mailing Address: P.O.Box 180, 67107–0180; tel. 620/345–6391 **A**10 **F**13 29 30 40 45 76 81 89 93 128 130 133
Primary Contact: Aaron Herbel, Administrator
CFO: Royce Holdeman, Chief Financial Officer
Web address: www.mercyh.org/
Control: Church operated, Nongovernment, not–for–profit **Service:** General medical and surgical

Staffed Beds: 18 **Admissions:** 233 **Census:** 4 **Outpatient Visits:** 8244 **Births:** 27 **Total Expense ($000):** 3426 **Payroll Expense ($000):** 1623 **Personnel:** 35

NEODESHA—Wilson County

★ **WILSON MEDICAL CENTER (171344)**, 2600 Ottawa Road, Zip 66757–1897, Mailing Address: P.O.Box 360, 66757–0360; tel. 620/325–2611 **A**10 18 **F**3 11 15 29 34 35 40 44 45 50 53 57 59 64 81 82 85 86 93 107 108 110 114 119 127 130 133 148 **S** QHR, Brentwood, TN
Primary Contact: Dennis R. Shelby, Chief Executive Officer
CFO: John Gutschenritter, Chief Financial Officer
CIO: Kevin Myers, Director Information Technology
CHR: Laura L Dean, Director Human Resources
CNO: Temple Monroe, Director Nursing Operations
Web address: www.wilsonmedical.org
Control: County, Government, Nonfederal **Service:** General medical and surgical

Staffed Beds: 15 **Admissions:** 260 **Census:** 5 **Outpatient Visits:** 21976 **Births:** 0 **Total Expense ($000):** 16232 **Payroll Expense ($000):** 6891 **Personnel:** 149

NESS CITY—Ness County

★ **NESS COUNTY HOSPITAL DISTRICT NO 2 (171336)**, 312 Custer Street, Zip 67560–1654; tel. 785/798–2291, (Total facility includes 43 beds in nursing home–type unit) **A**10 18 **F**3 7 15 40 45 59 62 67 93 111 114 119 125 127 133
Primary Contact: Curt Thomas, Administrator
CFO: Debra Frank, Chief Financial Officer
CMO: Mikhail Imseis M.D., Chief of Staff
CIO: Vicki Howe, Health Information Management
CHR: Shelly McDonald, Chief Human Resources Officer
CNO: Cindy Maier R.N., Director of Nursing
Web address: www.nchospital.org
Control: Hospital district or authority, Government, Nonfederal **Service:** General medical and surgical

Staffed Beds: 63 **Admissions:** 168 **Census:** 37 **Outpatient Visits:** 9822 **Births:** 0 **Total Expense ($000):** 9573 **Payroll Expense ($000):** 4279 **Personnel:** 125

NEWTON—Harvey County

★ ○ **NEWTON MEDICAL CENTER (170103)**, 600 Medical Center Drive, Zip 67114–8780, Mailing Address: P.O.Box 308, 67114–0308; tel. 316/283–2700 **A**3 10 11 **F**3 11 13 15 20 22 28 29 30 31 34 35 40 45 51 59 62 64 68 70 73 74 75 76 77 79 81 85 86 90 98 103 107 108 110 111 115 119 126 130 131 132 133 146 147 148 149 **P**6
Primary Contact: Vallerie L. Gleason, President and Chief Executive Officer
COO: Todd Tangeman, Chief Operating Officer
CFO: Todd Kasitz, Vice President Finance
CIO: Mike Cottle, Chief Information Officer
CHR: Angela L Anderson, Director Human Resources
CNO: Heather Renee Porter, Chief Clinical Officer
Web address: www.newtonmedicalcenter.com
Control: Other not–for–profit (including NFP Corporation) **Service:** General medical and surgical

Staffed Beds: 103 **Admissions:** 2744 **Census:** 36 **Outpatient Visits:** 55622 **Births:** 468 **Total Expense ($000):** 72556 **Payroll Expense ($000):** 35472 **Personnel:** 638

□ **PRAIRIE VIEW (174016)**, 1901 East First Street, Zip 67114–5010, Mailing Address: P.O.Box 467, 67114–0467; tel. 316/284–6400, (Nonreporting) **A**1 10
Primary Contact: Jessie Kaye, Chief Executive Officer
CFO: Lisa Ramsey, Chief Financial Officer
CMO: Gary Fast M.D., Medical Director
CIO: Chad Roth, Director Information Services
CHR: Joy Robb, Vice President Human Resources
CNO: Patrick Flaming R.N., Director Inpatient Operations
Web address: www.prairieview.org
Control: Other not–for–profit (including NFP Corporation) **Service:** Psychiatric

Staffed Beds: 38

NORTON—Norton County

★ **NORTON COUNTY HOSPITAL (171348)**, 102 East Holme, Zip 67654–1406, Mailing Address: P.O.Box 250, 67654–0250; tel. 785/877–3351 **A**10 18 **F**3 13 15 18 28 29 30 31 34 35 40 45 50 59 64 65 67 69 77 78 79 81 86 87 93 97 107 110 119 127 128 129 130 131 133 146 148 **P**6
Primary Contact: Gina Frack, Interim Chief Executive Officer
CHR: Shannan Hempler, Director Human Resources
Web address: www.ntcohosp.com
Control: County, Government, Nonfederal **Service:** General medical and surgical

Staffed Beds: 25 **Admissions:** 418 **Census:** 8 **Outpatient Visits:** 54844 **Births:** 66 **Total Expense ($000):** 13943 **Payroll Expense ($000):** 6426 **Personnel:** 127

Hospital, Medicare Provider Number, Address, Telephone, Approval, Facility, and Physician Codes, Health Care System

★ American Hospital Association (AHA) membership
□ The Joint Commission accreditation
○ Healthcare Facilities Accreditation Program
◇ DNV Healthcare Inc. accreditation
⇑ Center for Improvement in Healthcare Quality Accreditation
△ Commission on Accreditation of Rehabilitation Facilities (CARF) accreditation

KS

OAKLEY—Logan County

LOGAN COUNTY HOSPITAL (171326), 211 Cherry Street, Zip 67748–1201; tel. 785/672–3211, (Total facility includes 42 beds in nursing home–type unit) **A**10 18 **F**3 26 27 28 40 45 50 53 64 67 69 81 93 107 119 127 130 133 143 148 **P**6
Primary Contact: Meldon L. Snow, Chief Executive Officer
COO: Aimee Zimmerman R.N., Chief Operations Officer
CFO: Bonnie Hagel, Chief Financial Officer
CMO: Celeste Rains D.O., Chief of Staff
CIO: Russ Kahle, Chief Information Officer
CHR: Steve Allison, Director Human Resources
CNO: Marcia Kruse R.N., Director Nursing
Web address: www.logancountyhospital.org
Control: County, Government, Nonfederal **Service**: General medical and surgical

Staffed Beds: 59 **Admissions**: 267 **Census**: 44 **Outpatient Visits**: 6453
Births: 0

OBERLIN—Decatur County

DECATUR HEALTH SYSTEMS (171352), 810 West Columbia Street, Zip 67749–2450, Mailing Address: P.O.Box 268, 67749–0268; tel. 785/475–2208 **A**10 18 **F**3 15 40 45 50 53 56 59 63 64 69 77 84 85 86 93 97 107 110 114 125 127 128 130 133 148 149 **P**6
Primary Contact: Johnathan Owens, Chief Executive Officer
CFO: Amanda Fortin, Manager Finance
CMO: Elizabeth Sliter M.D., Chairman Medical Staff
CIO: Natasha Weishapl, Manager Business Office and Human Resources
CHR: Natasha Weishapl, Manager Business Office and Human Resources
Web address: www.decaturhealthsystems.org
Control: Other not–for–profit (including NFP Corporation) **Service**: General medical and surgical

Staffed Beds: 24 **Admissions**: 145 **Census**: 4 **Outpatient Visits**: 10579
Births: 0 **Total Expense ($000)**: 6325 **Payroll Expense ($000)**: 3449
Personnel: 76

OLATHE—Johnson County

☐ **OLATHE MEDICAL CENTER (170049)**, 20333 West 151st Street, Zip 66061–5350; tel. 913/791–4200 **A**1 2 5 10 **F**3 11 12 13 15 18 20 22 24 26 28 29 30 31 34 35 39 40 45 46 47 48 49 56 57 58 59 61 62 63 64 65 68 70 74 75 76 77 78 79 81 82 84 85 86 87 89 92 93 107 108 110 111 115 116 117 118 119 121 124 129 130 131 132 135 144 145 146 147 148 149
Primary Contact: Frank H. Devocelle, President and Chief Executive Officer
COO: John Staton, Senior Vice President Operations
CFO: Tierney Lynn Grasser, Senior Vice President and Chief Financial Officer
CMO: James L Wetzel M.D., Senior Vice President, Chief Medical Officer
CIO: Randy Rahman, Vice President and Chief Information Officer
CHR: David Klimek, Vice President Human Resources
CNO: Amy J Meglemre R.N., MSN, Senior Vice President and Chief Nursing Officer
Web address: www.olathehealth.org
Control: Other not–for–profit (including NFP Corporation) **Service**: General medical and surgical

Staffed Beds: 227 **Admissions**: 10824 **Census**: 111 **Outpatient Visits**: 302872 **Births**: 1051 **Total Expense ($000)**: 205614 **Payroll Expense ($000)**: 81509 **Personnel**: 1285

ONAGA—Pottawatomie County

★ **COMMUNITY HEALTHCARE SYSTEM (171354)**, 120 West Eighth Street, Zip 66521–9574; tel. 785/889–4272, (Total facility includes 78 beds in nursing home–type unit) **A**10 18 **F**2 3 5 6 10 11 12 13 15 29 31 32 34 35 36 40 43 45 50 53 56 57 59 62 64 65 67 74 75 77 78 81 82 84 85 86 87 93 97 99 100 101 102 103 104 105 106 107 110 111 114 119 125 127 128 130 131 132 133 134 135 143 144 145 146 147 148 **P**6
Primary Contact: Todd Willert, Chief Executive Officer
COO: Marcia S Walsh M.P.H., Chief Operating Officer
CFO: Monica Holthaus, Chief Financial Officer
CMO: Marcus Weiser D.O., Chief of Staff
CIO: Rod Evans, Chief Information Officer
CHR: Terry D. Bernatis, Director Human Resources
CNO: Rosalind Lewis R.N., MSN, Chief Nursing Officer
Web address: www.chcsks.org
Control: Other not–for–profit (including NFP Corporation) **Service**: General medical and surgical

Staffed Beds: 150 **Admissions**: 1068 **Census**: 75 **Outpatient Visits**: 103606 **Births**: 78 **Total Expense ($000)**: 32158 **Payroll Expense ($000)**: 18354 **Personnel**: 276

OSAWATOMIE—Miami County

☐ **OSAWATOMIE STATE HOSPITAL (174004)**, 500 State Hospital Drive, Zip 66064–1813, Mailing Address: P.O.Box 500, 66064–0500; tel. 913/755–7000 **A**1 10 **F**30 50 86 87 98 101 103 130 135 146 **P**6
Primary Contact: Jerry A. Rea, Ph.D., Superintendent
CMO: Maria Gustilo M.D., Medical Director
CHR: Dezerae Curran, Director Human Resources
Web address: www.srskansas.org/osh/osh–rmhf_info.html
Control: State, Government, Nonfederal **Service**: Psychiatric

Staffed Beds: 146 **Admissions**: 1212 **Census**: 143 **Outpatient Visits**: 0
Births: 0 **Total Expense ($000)**: 60978 **Payroll Expense ($000)**: 16260
Personnel: 391

OSBORNE—Osborne County

★ **OSBORNE COUNTY MEMORIAL HOSPITAL (171364)**, 424 West New Hampshire Street, Zip 67473–2314, Mailing Address: P.O.Box 70, 67473–0070; tel. 785/346–2121 **A**10 18 **F**3 11 13 40 45 64 69 76 81 107 119 127 128 133 **P**6 **S** Great Plains Health Alliance, Inc., Wichita, KS
Primary Contact: Marianna Harris, Administrator
CFO: Linda Murphy, Chief Financial Officer
CMO: Erin Baxa M.D., Chief Medical Officer
CNO: Monica Mullender, Director of Nursing
Web address: www.ocmh.org
Control: County, Government, Nonfederal **Service**: General medical and surgical

Staffed Beds: 25 **Admissions**: 250 **Census**: 5 **Outpatient Visits**: 10728
Births: 10 **Total Expense ($000)**: 6096 **Payroll Expense ($000)**: 2885
Personnel: 56

OSWEGO—Labette County

OSWEGO COMMUNITY HOSPITAL (171302), 800 Barker Drive, Zip 67356–9014; tel. 620/795–2921 **A**10 18 **F**3 9 12 29 32 34 35 40 57 59 64 65 75 77 90 93 107 127 130 132 133 135 147 148 149 **P**6 **S** Rural Community Hospitals of America, Kansas City, MO
Primary Contact: Daniel Hiben, Chief Executive Officer
CFO: Christina Schlatter, Chief Financial Officer
CMO: Gordon Kern M.D., Medical Director
CHR: Christina Schlatter, Chief Financial Officer
Web address: www.oswegocommunityhospital.com
Control: Corporation, Investor–owned (for–profit) **Service**: General medical and surgical

Staffed Beds: 12 **Admissions**: 87 **Census**: 3 **Outpatient Visits**: 13328
Births: 0 **Total Expense ($000)**: 4843 **Payroll Expense ($000)**: 2530
Personnel: 49

OTTAWA—Franklin County

⊞ **RANSOM MEMORIAL HOSPITAL (170014)**, 1301 South Main Street, Zip 66067–3598; tel. 785/229–8200 **A**1 10 **F**3 11 13 15 18 28 29 30 34 35 40 41 43 45 50 53 56 57 59 64 65 68 70 74 75 76 77 78 79 81 82 85 86 87 89 92 93 94 96 97 102 107 108 110 111 114 115 116 118 119 127 129 130 131 132 133 134 135 144 145 146 147 148 149 150 **P**6
Primary Contact: Matthew M. Heyn, Chief Executive Officer
Web address: www.ransom.org
Control: County, Government, Nonfederal **Service**: General medical and surgical

Staffed Beds: 44 **Admissions**: 1192 **Census**: 10 **Outpatient Visits**: 135982
Births: 174 **Total Expense ($000)**: 41651 **Payroll Expense ($000)**: 20319
Personnel: 312

OVERLAND PARK—Johnson County

○ **BLUE VALLEY HOSPITAL (170201)**, 12850 Metcalf Avenue, Zip 66213–2622; tel. 913/220–2866 **A**11 **F**12 33 39 45 46 47 48 49 50 59 79 81 82 92 111 112 119 132
Primary Contact: Douglas C. Palzer, Chief Executive Officer
COO: Craig Storck, Chief Operating Officer
CMO: Lee Nigro M.D., Chief Medical Officer
Web address: www.bluevalleysurgical.com/
Control: Corporation, Investor–owned (for–profit) **Service**: General medical and surgical

Staffed Beds: 7 **Admissions**: 99 **Census**: 1 **Outpatient Visits**: 3300 **Births**: 0
Total Expense ($000): 19399 **Payroll Expense ($000)**: 6890 **Personnel**: 132

KS

Many Facility Codes have changed. Please refer to the AHA Guide Code Chart.   © 2017 AHA Guide

☐ **CHILDREN'S MERCY SOUTH (173300)**, 5808 West 110th Street, Zip 66211–2504; tel. 913/696–8000 **A**1 10 **F**3 9 29 30 32 35 36 40 41 44 48 50 59 62 64 68 75 77 79 81 82 85 87 89 93 94 100 101 104 107 111 115 119 129 130 131 132 134 144 146 148 149 150 **P**6
Primary Contact: Randall L. O'Donnell, Ph.D., President and Chief Executive Officer
CFO: Sandra A J Lawrence, Executive Vice President and Chief Financial Officer
CMO: Charles Roberts M.D., Medical Director
CIO: Jean Ann Breedlove, Chief Information Officer
CHR: Dan Wright, Vice President Human Resources
Web address: www.childrens–mercy.org
Control: Other not–for–profit (including NFP Corporation) **Service**: Children's general medical and surgical

Staffed Beds: 50 **Admissions**: 2209 **Census**: 15 **Outpatient Visits**: 137706
Total Expense ($000): 108647 **Payroll Expense ($000)**: 62359 **Personnel**: 742

HEARTLAND SPINE & SPECIALTY HOSPITAL See The University Of Kansas Hospital – Indian Creek Campus, Kansas City

☒ **MENORAH MEDICAL CENTER (170182)**, 5721 West 119th Street, Zip 66209–3722; tel. 913/498–6000 **A**1 2 3 10 **F**3 12 13 15 18 20 22 24 26 28 29 30 31 34 35 38 40 45 46 47 49 55 57 58 59 60 64 65 68 70 72 74 75 76 77 78 79 81 82 84 85 86 87 90 93 97 102 107 108 110 111 114 115 117 119 121 124 126 129 130 131 132 135 145 146 147 148 149 **S** HCA Healthcare, Nashville, TN
Primary Contact: Charles Laird, Chief Executive Officer
CFO: Deborah Gafford, Chief Financial Officer
CMO: James Cheray M.D., Chief Medical Officer
CIO: Christina McGinnis, Director Information Technology
CHR: Amy Hunt, Director Human Resources
CNO: Kelly Reno R.N., Chief Nursing Officer
Web address: www.menorahmedicalcenter.com
Control: Corporation, Investor–owned (for–profit) **Service**: General medical and surgical

Staffed Beds: 158 **Admissions**: 7833 **Census**: 87 **Outpatient Visits**: 64821
Births: 574 **Total Expense ($000)**: 177435 **Payroll Expense ($000)**: 51010
Personnel: 686

☒ **OVERLAND PARK REGIONAL MEDICAL CENTER (170176)**, 10500 Quivira Road, Zip 66215–2306, Mailing Address: P.O.Box 15959, 66215–5959; tel. 913/541–5000 **A**1 2 5 10 **F**3 8 13 15 18 19 20 22 24 26 28 29 30 31 34 35 37 40 41 42 43 45 49 50 56 57 59 60 61 64 65 67 70 72 73 74 75 76 77 78 79 81 82 83 84 85 86 87 88 90 91 92 93 107 108 110 111 114 115 119 126 129 130 131 135 144 145 146 147 148 149 **S** HCA Healthcare, Nashville, TN
Primary Contact: Kevin J. Hicks, President and CEO
COO: Jim Beatty, Chief Operating Officer
CFO: Steven R Cleary, Chief Financial Officer
CMO: George D. Stamos M.D., Chief Medical Officer
CHR: Connie Miller, Vice President Human Resources
CNO: Teresa L Collins R.N., Chief Nursing Officer
Web address: www.oprmc.com
Control: Corporation, Investor–owned (for–profit) **Service**: General medical and surgical

Staffed Beds: 275 **Admissions**: 11351 **Census**: 146 **Outpatient Visits**: 91095 **Births**: 3192 **Total Expense ($000)**: 180378 **Payroll Expense ($000)**: 67224 **Personnel**: 792

☐ **PROMISE HOSPITAL OF OVERLAND PARK (172004)**, 6509 West 103rd Street, Zip 66212–1728; tel. 913/649–3701, (Nonreporting) **A**1 10 **S** Promise Healthcare, Boca Raton, FL
Primary Contact: Karen Leverich, Chief Executive Officer
CFO: William Scott, Chief Financial Officer
CHR: Darren Enochs, Director Human Resources
Web address: www.promise–overlandpark.com
Control: Corporation, Investor–owned (for–profit) **Service**: Acute long–term care hospital

Staffed Beds: 104

REHABILITATION HOSPITAL OF OVERLAND PARK (173032), 5100 Indian Creek Parkway, Zip 66207–4115; tel. 913/544–1957 **S** Post Acute Medical, LLC, Enola, PA
Primary Contact: Portlyn Brogger, Divisional President
Web address: www.warmsprings.org
Control: Corporation, Investor–owned (for–profit) **Service**: Rehabilitation

Staffed Beds: 45

☒ **SAINT LUKE'S SOUTH HOSPITAL (170185)**, 12300 Metcalf Avenue, Zip 66213–1324; tel. 913/317–7000 **A**1 10 **F**3 12 13 15 18 20 22 26 28 29 30 31 34 35 38 39 40 44 45 47 49 54 57 58 59 60 64 70 73 74 75 76 77 78 79 80 81 82 85 86 87 90 92 93 94 96 100 102 107 108 110 111 114 115 117 118 119 126 129 130 131 132 141 146 147 148 149 **S** Saint Luke's Health System, Kansas City, MO
Primary Contact: Bobby Olm–Shipman, Chief Executive Officer
CFO: Shelby Frigon, Chief Financial Officer
CMO: Lisa Heath M.D., President Medical Staff
CIO: Deborah Gash, Chief Information Officer
CHR: Donna Kunz, System Director Human Resources
CNO: Julia Woods R.N., MSN, Vice President and Chief Nursing Officer
Web address: www.saintlukeshealthsystem.org/south
Control: Church operated, Nongovernment, not–for–profit **Service**: General medical and surgical

Staffed Beds: 107 **Admissions**: 5575 **Census**: 55 **Outpatient Visits**: 89042
Births: 623 **Total Expense ($000)**: 121763 **Payroll Expense ($000)**: 32322
Personnel: 499

PAOLA—Miami County

☐ **MIAMI COUNTY MEDICAL CENTER (170109)**, 2100 Baptiste Drive, Zip 66071–1314, Mailing Address: P.O.Box 365, 66071–0365; tel. 913/294–2327 **A**1 5 10 **F**3 11 15 18 34 40 43 57 59 61 64 68 75 77 78 79 81 82 85 87 89 90 93 107 108 110 111 114 119 127 130 131 135 146 148
Primary Contact: Paul W. Luce, R.N., MSN, Vice President Operations
CFO: Cheryl Sharp, Chief Financial Office
CMO: Christopher Eckland M.D., Chief Medical Officer
CIO: Randy Rahman, Chief Information Officer
CHR: David Klimek, Chief Human Resources Officer
CNO: Aubree Slayman, Director Patient Services
Web address: www.olathehealth.org
Control: Other not–for–profit (including NFP Corporation) **Service**: General medical and surgical

Staffed Beds: 18 **Admissions**: 503 **Census**: 3 **Outpatient Visits**: 30248
Births: 0 **Personnel**: 115

PARSONS—Labette County

★ ○ **LABETTE HEALTH (170120)**, 1902 South U S Highway 59, Zip 67357–7404; tel. 620/421–4880 **A**10 11 **F**3 11 13 15 29 30 34 40 43 50 53 59 62 70 74 75 76 77 79 81 86 90 93 97 107 108 110 111 114 119 126 127 129 130 143 144 146 147 148 149 **P**6
Primary Contact: Brian A. Williams, Chief Executive Officer
CFO: Thomas Macaronas, Chief Financial Officer
CHR: Christina Sykes, Director Human Resources
Web address: www.labettehealth.com
Control: County, Government, Nonfederal **Service**: General medical and surgical

Staffed Beds: 56 **Admissions**: 2053 **Census**: 21 **Outpatient Visits**: 77566
Births: 199 **Total Expense ($000)**: 62689 **Payroll Expense ($000)**: 26255
Personnel: 511

PARSONS STATE HOSPITAL AND TRAINING CENTER, 2601 Gabriel Avenue, Zip 67357–2341, Mailing Address: P.O.Box 738, 67357–0738; tel. 620/421–6550 **F**35 39 67 130 146
Primary Contact: Jerry A. Rea, Ph.D., Superintendent
CFO: John Spare, Accountant
CMO: Rema Menon M.D., Clinical Director
CIO: Ron Malmstrom, Information Research Specialist
CHR: Tim B Posch, Business Manager and Director Personnel
Web address: www.pshtc.org
Control: State, Government, Nonfederal **Service**: Intellectual disabilities

Staffed Beds: 188 **Admissions**: 11 **Census**: 165 **Outpatient Visits**: 0
Births: 0 **Total Expense ($000)**: 27017 **Payroll Expense ($000)**: 15504
Personnel: 470

Hospital, Medicare Provider Number, Address, Telephone, Approval, Facility, and Physician Codes, Health Care System

★ American Hospital Association (AHA) membership
☐ The Joint Commission accreditation
○ Healthcare Facilities Accreditation Program
◇ DNV Healthcare Inc. accreditation
⇧ Center for Improvement in Healthcare Quality Accreditation
△ Commission on Accreditation of Rehabilitation Facilities (CARF) accreditation

KS

© 2017 AHA Guide   *Many Facility Codes have changed. Please refer to the AHA Guide Code Chart.*   Hospitals **A249**

PHILLIPSBURG—Phillips County

★ **PHILLIPS COUNTY HOSPITAL (171353)**, 1150 State Street, Zip 67661–1743, Mailing Address: P.O.Box 607, 67661–0607; tel. 785/543–5226 **A**10 18 **F**3 11 15 28 30 31 40 45 50 59 64 68 75 77 78 81 86 87 91 93 107 114 119 127 128 130 132 133 145 146 148 **P**6 **S** Great Plains Health Alliance, Inc., Wichita, KS
Primary Contact: Rex D. Walk, Interim Chief Executive Officer
CFO: Christi Driggs, Chief Financial Officer
CMO: Ben Stephenson M.D., Chief of Staff
CIO: Steven Seems, Director of Information Technology
CHR: Peggy Fabin, Director Human Resources
CNO: Vickie Gibbs, Director Nursing
Web address: www.phillipshospital.org
Control: Other not–for–profit (including NFP Corporation) **Service**: General medical and surgical

Staffed Beds: 25 **Admissions:** 314 **Census:** 5 **Outpatient Visits:** 24868 **Births:** 0 **Total Expense ($000):** 13420 **Payroll Expense ($000):** 5615 **Personnel:** 107

PITTSBURG—Crawford County

✠ **VIA CHRISTI HOSPITAL PITTSBURG (170006)**, 1 Mt. Carmel Way, Zip 66762–7587; tel. 620/231–6100 **A**1 2 10 **F**3 5 11 12 13 15 18 20 22 26 28 29 30 31 34 35 40 43 45 46 47 48 50 51 53 54 56 57 58 59 62 64 68 69 70 74 75 76 77 78 79 81 82 84 85 86 89 90 93 104 107 108 109 110 111 112 114 115 116 117 118 119 120 121 122 123 126 129 130 131 132 133 135 143 144 145 146 147 148 **P**8 **S** Ascension Healthcare, Saint Louis, MO
Primary Contact: Randall R. Cason, FACHE, Senior Administrator
CFO: Mike Joy, Administrator, Finance
CIO: Missy McDown, Director Information Systems
CHR: Laurie Johnson, Director – Human Resources
CNO: Amy Katherine Renn, Interim Administrator, Patient Care and Nursing
Web address: www.viachristi.org/pittsburg
Control: Church operated, Nongovernment, not–for–profit **Service**: General medical and surgical

Staffed Beds: 89 **Admissions:** 3139 **Census:** 35 **Outpatient Visits:** 101657 **Births:** 538 **Total Expense ($000):** 87536 **Payroll Expense ($000):** 33873 **Personnel:** 454

PLAINVILLE—Rooks County

★ **ROOKS COUNTY HEALTH CENTER (171311)**, 1210 North Washington Street, Zip 67663–1632, Mailing Address: P.O.Box 389, 67663–0389; tel. 785/434–4553 **A**10 18 **F**3 13 15 28 29 31 34 35 40 43 45 47 50 57 59 64 67 76 77 79 81 82 87 93 96 107 110 114 119 125 128 130 131 133 135 143 144 146 147 148 149
Primary Contact: Frank A. Rajewski, Chief Financial Officer and Interim Chief Executive Officer
COO: William D Stahl, Chief Operating Officer
CFO: Frank A Rajewski, Chief Financial Officer
CMO: Lynn Fisher M.D., Chief of Staff
CHR: Cindi Knipp, Director Human Resources
Web address: www.rookscountyhealthcenter.com
Control: Hospital district or authority, Government, Nonfederal **Service**: General medical and surgical

Staffed Beds: 20 **Admissions:** 466 **Census:** 7 **Outpatient Visits:** 25091 **Births:** 51 **Total Expense ($000):** 15415 **Payroll Expense ($000):** 6142 **Personnel:** 131

PRATT—Pratt County

★ **PRATT REGIONAL MEDICAL CENTER (170027)**, 200 Commodore Street, Zip 67124–2903; tel. 620/672–7451, (Total facility includes 45 beds in nursing home–type unit) **A**10 20 **F**3 11 13 15 30 31 34 40 45 49 56 57 59 61 62 64 68 70 75 76 77 79 81 82 85 86 87 89 90 93 107 108 114 118 119 124 127 128 130 131 133 145 146 147 148 **P**6
Primary Contact: Susan M. Page, President and Chief Executive Officer
CFO: Vincent Scot Wilczek, Controller
CIO: Vikki Mader, Director Health Information Services
CHR: Ken Brown, Vice President and Chief Human Resource Officer
CNO: Jack L Kennedy R.N., MS, Vice President and Chief Nursing Officer
Web address: www.prmc.org
Control: Other not–for–profit (including NFP Corporation) **Service**: General medical and surgical

Staffed Beds: 80 **Admissions:** 1469 **Census:** 53 **Outpatient Visits:** 106174 **Births:** 265 **Total Expense ($000):** 52792 **Payroll Expense ($000):** 24282 **Personnel:** 389

QUINTER—Gove County

GOVE COUNTY MEDICAL CENTER (171367), 520 West Fifth Street, Zip 67752–0129, Mailing Address: P.O.Box 129, 67752–0129; tel. 785/754–3341, (Total facility includes 37 beds in nursing home–type unit) **A**10 18 **F**3 11 13 28 29 34 40 45 57 62 67 75 81 86 93 107 114 119 125 129 133 135 143 148
Primary Contact: Coleen Tummons, Chief Executive Officer
CFO: Alan Waites, Chief Financial Officer
CIO: Brad Mullins, Director Information Technology
CHR: Valerie Schneider, Director Human Resources
CNO: Renee Wagoner R.N., Director of Nursing
Web address: www.govecountymedicalcenter.org
Control: County, Government, Nonfederal **Service**: General medical and surgical

Staffed Beds: 58 **Admissions:** 565 **Census:** 35 **Outpatient Visits:** 10638 **Births:** 54 **Total Expense ($000):** 14177 **Payroll Expense ($000):** 5918 **Personnel:** 153

RANSOM—Ness County

★ **GRISELL MEMORIAL HOSPITAL DISTRICT ONE (171300)**, 210 South Vermont Avenue, Zip 67572–9525; tel. 785/731–2231, (Total facility includes 30 beds in nursing home–type unit) **A**10 18 **F**3 40 56 67 69 85 93 97 127 128 133 **P**6 **S** Great Plains Health Alliance, Inc., Wichita, KS
Primary Contact: David Caudill, Administrator
CFO: Jolene Schuster, Chief Financial Officer
CMO: Allen McLain M.D., Chief of Staff
CNO: Joni Pfaff, Chief Nursing Officer
Web address: www.grisellmemorialhospital.org
Control: Hospital district or authority, Government, Nonfederal **Service**: General medical and surgical

Staffed Beds: 42 **Admissions:** 54 **Census:** 24 **Outpatient Visits:** 5898 **Births:** 0 **Total Expense ($000):** 5377 **Payroll Expense ($000):** 2595 **Personnel:** 62

RUSSELL—Russell County

★ **RUSSELL REGIONAL HOSPITAL (171350)**, 200 South Main Street, Zip 67665–2920; tel. 785/483–3131, (Total facility includes 22 beds in nursing home–type unit) **A**10 18 **F**9 11 15 29 34 40 45 46 50 53 57 59 64 65 66 67 69 75 81 85 87 93 97 107 108 109 110 115 119 127 129 130 131 133 135 145 146 147 148 **P**6
Primary Contact: Sharon Collins, Interim Chief Executive Officer
COO: Sharon Collins, Director Human Resources and Chief Operating Officer
CFO: Kevin Kreutzer, Chief Financial Officer
CMO: Tyrel Somers M.D., Chief Medical Officer
CIO: David Schraeder, Director Information Systems
CHR: Sharon Collins, Director Human Resources and Chief Operating Officer
CNO: Deb Strobel R.N., Chief Nursing Officer
Web address: www.russellhospital.org
Control: Other not–for–profit (including NFP Corporation) **Service**: General medical and surgical

Staffed Beds: 47 **Admissions:** 387 **Census:** 27 **Outpatient Visits:** 35661 **Births:** 0 **Total Expense ($000):** 17018 **Payroll Expense ($000):** 8334 **Personnel:** 166

SABETHA—Nemaha County

★ **SABETHA COMMUNITY HOSPITAL (171338)**, 14th and Oregon Streets, Zip 66534–0229, Mailing Address: P.O.Box 229, 66534–0229; tel. 785/284–2121 **A**10 18 **F**3 11 13 15 28 34 35 40 43 45 50 56 57 59 62 63 64 68 75 76 77 78 79 81 82 84 85 86 93 107 110 114 119 128 130 132 133 146 148 **P**6 **S** Great Plains Health Alliance, Inc., Wichita, KS
Primary Contact: Lora Key, Chief Executive Officer
CFO: Lori Lackey, Chief Financial Officer
CMO: James Longabaugh M.D., Chief Medical Staff
CIO: Garrett Colglazier, Director Health Information Management
CHR: Julie K Holthaus, Director Human Resources
CNO: Rhonda Spellmeier R.N., Director of Nursing
Web address: www.sabethahospital.com
Control: Other not–for–profit (including NFP Corporation) **Service**: General medical and surgical

Staffed Beds: 25 **Admissions:** 338 **Census:** 5 **Outpatient Visits:** 38803 **Births:** 47 **Total Expense ($000):** 11896 **Payroll Expense ($000):** 5704 **Personnel:** 107

KS

Many Facility Codes have changed. Please refer to the AHA Guide Code Chart. © 2017 AHA Guide

SAINT FRANCIS—Cheyenne County

★ **CHEYENNE COUNTY HOSPITAL (171310)**, 210 West First Street, Zip 67756–3540, Mailing Address: P.O.Box 547, 67756–0547; tel. 785/332–2104 **A**10 18 **F**3 8 11 13 28 29 31 40 57 59 64 65 66 68 76 77 78 81 85 89 93 97 107 119 127 128 133 148 **P**6 **S** Great Plains Health Alliance, Inc., Wichita, KS
Primary Contact: Kelly Pottorff, Chief Executive Officer
CFO: Heidi Tice, Chief Financial Officer
CMO: Mary Beth Miller M.D., Chief of Staff
CIO: Carol Sloper, Manager Information Technology
CHR: Sara Wilson, Director Human Resources
CNO: Judith Ann Hodgson, Chief Nursing Officer
Web address: www.cheyennecountyhospital.com
Control: Other not–for–profit (including NFP Corporation) **Service:** General medical and surgical

Staffed Beds: 16 **Admissions:** 275 **Census:** 3 **Outpatient Visits:** 24404 **Births:** 26 **Total Expense ($000):** 10569 **Payroll Expense ($000):** 4585 **Personnel:** 88

SALINA—Saline County

★ ○ **SALINA REGIONAL HEALTH CENTER (170012)**, 400 South Santa Fe Avenue, Zip 67401–4198, Mailing Address: P.O.Box 5080, 67402–5080; tel. 785/452–7000, (Includes SALINA REGIONAL HEALTH CENTER– PENN CAMPUS, 139 North Penn Street, Salina, Kansas, Zip 67401, P O Box 5080, 67402–5080, tel. 913/452–7000; SALINA REGIONAL HEALTH CENTER–SANTA FE CAMPUS, 400 South Santa Fe Avenue, Salina, Kansas, Zip 67401, Box 5080, 67402–5080, tel. 913/452–7000) **A**3 5 10 11 20 **F**3 13 15 18 19 20 22 24 28 29 30 31 35 40 43 45 46 47 48 49 51 53 54 55 57 59 63 64 65 68 70 71 72 73 74 76 77 78 79 81 85 86 87 89 90 98 99 100 101 102 103 104 105 107 108 110 111 114 115 116 117 118 119 120 121 122 123 124 126 129 130 143 144 145 146 147 148 149 **P**6 **S** Salina Regional Health Center, Salina, KS
Primary Contact: Michael Terry, President and Chief Executive Officer
COO: Joel Phelps, Chief Operating Officer
CFO: Joe Tallon, Vice President Finance
CIO: Larry Barnes, Vice President Information Technology
CHR: David Moody, Vice President Human Resources
Web address: www.srhc.com
Control: Other not–for–profit (including NFP Corporation) **Service:** General medical and surgical

Staffed Beds: 205 **Admissions:** 9944 **Census:** 114 **Outpatient Visits:** 224094 **Births:** 1116 **Total Expense ($000):** 213763 **Payroll Expense ($000):** 97639 **Personnel:** 1741

SALINA SURGICAL HOSPITAL (170187), 401 South Santa Fe Avenue, Zip 67401–4143, Mailing Address: 401 South Sante Fe Avenue, 67401–4143; tel. 785/827–0610 **A**5 10 **F**29 45 48 49 51 59 74 79 81 85 89 131
Primary Contact: LuAnn Puvogel, R.N., Chief Executive Officer
CFO: Elizabeth Bishop, Business Office Manager
CMO: Michael Johnson M.D., Medical Director
CIO: Earl Akers, Supervisor Information Technology
CHR: Elizabeth Bishop, Business Office Manager
CNO: Jolene Glavin R.N., MSN, Director Nursing
Web address: www.salinasurgical.com/
Control: Partnership, Investor–owned (for–profit) **Service:** Surgical

Staffed Beds: 16 **Admissions:** 784 **Census:** 5 **Outpatient Visits:** 7730 **Births:** 0 **Total Expense ($000):** 18876 **Payroll Expense ($000):** 5840 **Personnel:** 100

SATANTA—Haskell County

★ **SATANTA DISTRICT HOSPITAL AND LONG TERM CARE (171324)**, 401 South Cheyenne Street, Zip 67870–0159, Mailing Address: P.O.Box 159, 67870–0159; tel. 620/649–2761, (Total facility includes 44 beds in nursing home–type unit) **A**10 18 **F**3 11 40 43 45 57 64 67 68 75 81 82 87 93 104 107 119 127 128 130 133 **P**4 **S** Great Plains Health Alliance, Inc., Wichita, KS
Primary Contact: Jeremy Clingenpeel, Administrator
CFO: Libby Anderson, Chief Financial Officer
CMO: Virgilio Taduran M.D., Chief Medical Officer
CIO: Ben Leppke, Chief Information Officer
CHR: Samantha Hett, Manager Human Resources
CNO: Tina Pendergraft, Chief Nursing Officer
Web address: www.satantahospital.org
Control: Hospital district or authority, Government, Nonfederal **Service:** General medical and surgical

Staffed Beds: 57 **Admissions:** 159 **Census:** 38 **Outpatient Visits:** 20538 **Births:** 0 **Total Expense ($000):** 12803 **Payroll Expense ($000):** 5996 **Personnel:** 123

SCOTT CITY—Scott County

★ **SCOTT COUNTY HOSPITAL (171372)**, 201 East Albert Avenue, Zip 67871–1203; tel. 620/872–5811 **A**10 18 **F**3 7 13 15 28 29 30 31 35 40 45 46 50 57 59 64 68 69 75 76 77 81 82 85 93 107 110 111 119 127 128 129 130 133 135 145 148 149 **P**6
Primary Contact: Mark Burnett, President and Chief Executive Officer
COO: Karma Huck, Chief Operating Officer
CFO: Joe S Meyer, Chief Financial Officer
CMO: Elizabeth Hineman M.D., Chief Medical Staff
CHR: Pamela R Wheeler, Director Human Resources
Web address: www.scotthospital.net
Control: Other not–for–profit (including NFP Corporation) **Service:** General medical and surgical

Staffed Beds: 22 **Admissions:** 677 **Census:** 10 **Outpatient Visits:** 26710 **Births:** 49 **Total Expense ($000):** 21854 **Payroll Expense ($000):** 10897 **Personnel:** 223

SEDAN—Chautauqua County

SEDAN CITY HOSPITAL (171318), 300 North Street, Zip 67361–1051, Mailing Address: P.O.Box 'C', 67361–0427; tel. 620/725–3115 **A**10 18 **F**29 34 40 57 64 93 107 119 128 130 133 148
Primary Contact: Michelle Williams, Administrator
CFO: Jennifer Seever, Regional Chief Financial Officer
CMO: James McDermott M.D., Chief of Staff
Control: City, Government, Nonfederal **Service:** General medical and surgical

Staffed Beds: 18 **Admissions:** 244 **Census:** 3 **Outpatient Visits:** 9335 **Births:** 0 **Total Expense ($000):** 4741 **Payroll Expense ($000):** 2180 **Personnel:** 39

SENECA—Nemaha County

★ **NEMAHA VALLEY COMMUNITY HOSPITAL (171315)**, 1600 Community Drive, Zip 66538–9739; tel. 785/336–6181 **A**10 18 **F**11 12 13 15 28 31 40 56 57 59 64 65 75 76 77 78 79 81 84 85 89 93 107 114 119 127 129 130 131 132 133 **P**6
Primary Contact: Kiley Floyd, Chief Executive Officer
CFO: Connie Ingwerson, Chief Financial Officer
CMO: Angela Stueve M.D., Chief Medical Officer
CHR: Lynn E Hartter Jr, Director Human Resources
CNO: Lynda Cross R.N., Director of Nurses
Web address: www.nemvch.org
Control: Other not–for–profit (including NFP Corporation) **Service:** General medical and surgical

Staffed Beds: 24 **Admissions:** 265 **Census:** 3 **Outpatient Visits:** 19303 **Births:** 60 **Total Expense ($000):** 13601 **Payroll Expense ($000):** 7027 **Personnel:** 147

SHAWNEE MISSION—Johnson County

⊠ **MID–AMERICA REHABILITATION HOSPITAL (173026)**, 5701 West 110th Street, Zip 66211–2503, Mailing Address: Overland Park, tel. 913/491–2400 **A**1 10 **F**29 36 56 60 64 87 90 93 132 143 148 **S** HEALTHSOUTH Corporation, Birmingham, AL
Primary Contact: Tiffany Kiehl, Chief Executive Officer
CFO: Richard Lane, Chief Financial Officer
CMO: Cielo Dehning M.D., Medical Director
CHR: Elizabeth Gibson, Director Human Resources
CNO: Amy McKay, Chief Nursing Officer
Web address: www.midamericarehabhospital.com
Control: Corporation, Investor–owned (for–profit) **Service:** Rehabilitation

Staffed Beds: 98 **Admissions:** 1721 **Census:** 59 **Outpatient Visits:** 8949 **Births:** 0 **Total Expense ($000):** 25173 **Payroll Expense ($000):** 12682 **Personnel:** 231

Hospital, Medicare Provider Number, Address, Telephone, Approval, Facility, and Physician Codes, Health Care System

★ American Hospital Association (AHA) membership   ○ Healthcare Facilities Accreditation Program   ⇑ Center for Improvement in Healthcare Quality Accreditation
□ The Joint Commission accreditation   ◇ DNV Healthcare Inc. accreditation   △ Commission on Accreditation of Rehabilitation Facilities (CARF) accreditation

KS

✠ **SHAWNEE MISSION MEDICAL CENTER (170104)**, 9100 West 74th Street, Zip 66204–4004, Mailing Address: Box 2923, 66201–1323; tel. 913/676–2000 **A**1 2 3 5 10 **F**3 4 5 8 11 12 13 15 17 18 20 22 24 26 28 29 30 31 32 34 35 36 40 42 45 46 47 48 49 52 53 54 55 56 57 58 59 60 61 62 64 65 70 72 74 75 76 77 78 79 80 81 82 83 84 85 86 87 89 93 96 97 98 100 101 102 103 104 105 107 108 110 111 114 115 117 118 119 120 121 123 124 126 129 130 131 132 135 144 145 146 147 148 149 **P**6 **S** Adventist Health System Sunbelt Health Care Corporation, Altamonte Springs, FL
Primary Contact: Ken J. Bacon, President and Chief Executive Officer
CFO: Karsten Randolph, Executive Vice President and Chief Financial Officer
CMO: Sherri Martin M.D., President Medical Staff
CIO: Mike Allen, Director Information Services
CHR: Brad Hoffman, Administrative Director Human Resources
CNO: Sheri Hawkins, Chief Nursing Officer
Web address: www.shawneemission.org
Control: Church operated, Nongovernment, not–for–profit **Service**: General medical and surgical

Staffed Beds: 403 Admissions: 22002 Census: 239 Outpatient Visits: 565892 Births: 5076 Total Expense ($000): 403530 Payroll Expense ($000): 164743 Personnel: 2512

SMITH CENTER—Smith County

★ **SMITH COUNTY MEMORIAL HOSPITAL (171377)**, 614 South Main Street, Zip 66967–3001; tel. 785/282–6845, (Total facility includes 28 beds in nursing home–type unit) **A**10 18 **F**13 15 28 29 30 31 34 40 43 45 53 64 65 67 68 69 75 76 81 85 89 91 93 107 110 114 119 127 128 133 **P**6 **S** Great Plains Health Alliance, Inc., Wichita, KS
Primary Contact: Allen Van Driel, FACHE, Administrator
CFO: Julie Williams, Chief Financial Officer
CIO: Tammy Gaston, Chief Information Officer
CHR: Jody Maxwell, Manager Business Office
CNO: Sarah Ragsdale R.N., Chief Nursing Officer
Web address: www.gpha.com
Control: Other not–for–profit (including NFP Corporation) **Service**: General medical and surgical

Staffed Beds: 53 Admissions: 508 Census: 27 Outpatient Visits: 29321 Births: 39 Total Expense ($000): 14270 Payroll Expense ($000): 5884 Personnel: 134

STAFFORD—Stafford County

★ **STAFFORD COUNTY HOSPITAL (171323)**, 502 South Buckeye Street, Zip 67578–2035, Mailing Address: P.O.Box 190, 67578–0190; tel. 620/234–5221, (Nonreporting) **A**10 18
Primary Contact: Todd Taylor, Chief Executive Officer
CFO: MeKinzie Hudson, Chief Financial Officer
Web address: www.staffordcountyhospital.org
Control: County, Government, Nonfederal **Service**: General medical and surgical

Staffed Beds: 25

SYRACUSE—Hamilton County

★ **HAMILTON COUNTY HOSPITAL (171322)**, 700 North Huser Street, Zip 67878–0948, Mailing Address: P.O.Box 948, 67878–0948; tel. 620/384–7461 **A**10 18 **F**40 41 57 59 64 85 86 91 93 94 97 99 100 107 111 114 127 133 148 **P**6
Primary Contact: Robert Whitaker, Chief Executive Officer
CMO: Richard Carter M.D., Chief Medical Director
CIO: Merlin Kuder, Chief Information Officer
CHR: Angela Talbot, Manager Human Resources
CNO: Stacey Perry, Director, Nursing
Web address: www.myhch.org
Control: County, Government, Nonfederal **Service**: General medical and surgical

Staffed Beds: 25 Admissions: 51 Census: 1 Outpatient Visits: 8594 Births: 0 Total Expense ($000): 7069 Payroll Expense ($000): 1920 Personnel: 34

TOPEKA—Shawnee County

KANSAS NEUROLOGICAL INSTITUTE, 3107 West 21st Street, Zip 66604–3298; tel. 785/296–5301, (Nonreporting)
Primary Contact: Brent Widick, Superintendent
CFO: Sara Hoyer, Director Administrative Services
CMO: Mary Gingrich, Director Health Care Services
CIO: Cheryl Fuller, Director Information Resources
CHR: Shawna Mercer, Director Human Resources
Web address: www.kdads.ks.gov/state–hospitals–and–institutions/kansas–neurological–institute
Control: State, Government, Nonfederal **Service**: Intellectual disabilities

Staffed Beds: 150

✠ **KANSAS REHABILITATION HOSPITAL (173025)**, 1504 SW Eighth Avenue, Zip 66606–1632; tel. 785/235–6600 **A**1 10 **F**29 75 86 90 91 95 96 130 132 148 **S** HEALTHSOUTH Corporation, Birmingham, AL
Primary Contact: William J. Overbey, Chief Executive Officer
CMO: Joseph Sankoorikal M.D., Chief Medical Staff
CHR: Dina Cox, Director Human Resources
CNO: Carol Swanger, Chief Nursing Officer
Web address: www.kansasrehabhospital.com
Control: Corporation, Investor–owned (for–profit) **Service**: Rehabilitation

Staffed Beds: 57 Admissions: 1258 Census: 39 Outpatient Visits: 0 Births: 0 Total Expense ($000): 15837 Payroll Expense ($000): 7858 Personnel: 143

✠ **ST. FRANCIS HEALTH (170016)**, 1700 SW 7th Street, Zip 66606–1690; tel. 785/295–8000 **A**1 2 10 **F**3 12 13 15 18 20 22 24 26 28 29 30 31 34 35 36 37 38 40 45 47 48 49 50 51 53 54 56 57 58 59 60 61 62 64 65 66 70 71 73 74 75 76 77 78 79 80 81 82 85 86 87 89 90 92 93 95 96 107 108 110 111 114 115 116 117 118 119 120 121 123 126 130 131 132 135 144 146 147 148 149 **P**6 **S** SCL Health, Broomfield, CO
Primary Contact: David P. Setchel, President
CFO: Debra Cartwright, Chief Financial Officer
CMO: Thomas Hamilton D.O., Chief Medical Officer
CIO: Kevin Mapes, Director Kansas Division System and Technology Service Center
CHR: Steve Saffa, Director Human Resources
Web address: www.stfrancistopeka.org
Control: Church operated, Nongovernment, not–for–profit **Service**: General medical and surgical

Staffed Beds: 259 Admissions: 7537 Census: 92 Outpatient Visits: 238708 Births: 867 Total Expense ($000): 241301 Payroll Expense ($000): 62182 Personnel: 1326

✠ **STORMONT VAIL HEALTH (170086)**, 1500 SW Tenth Avenue, Zip 66604–1353; tel. 785/354–6000 **A**1 2 5 10 **F**3 11 12 13 15 17 18 19 20 22 24 26 28 29 30 31 34 35 37 40 43 44 45 47 49 50 51 55 56 57 58 59 60 61 64 65 68 70 71 72 74 75 76 77 78 79 81 82 84 85 86 87 88 89 91 93 97 98 99 101 102 103 104 105 107 108 110 111 112 114 115 117 119 120 121 123 129 130 131 132 135 143 144 145 146 147 148 149 150 **P**6
Primary Contact: Randall Peterson, President and Chief Executive Officer
COO: Janet Stanek, Senior Vice President and Chief Operating Officer
CFO: Kevin Han, Vice President and Chief Financial Officer
CMO: Rob Kenagy M.D., Senior Vice President and Chief Medical Officer
CIO: Judy Corzine, Administrative Director and Chief Information Officer
CNO: Carol Perry R.N., Vice President and Chief Nursing Officer
Web address: www.stormontvail.org
Control: Other not–for–profit (including NFP Corporation) **Service**: General medical and surgical

Staffed Beds: 394 Admissions: 21625 Census: 274 Outpatient Visits: 139082 Births: 1868 Total Expense ($000): 600785 Payroll Expense ($000): 313064 Personnel: 3797

✠ **VETERANS AFFAIRS EASTERN KANSAS HEALTH CARE SYSTEM**, 2200 South West Gage Boulevard, Zip 66622–0002; tel. 785/350–3111, (Nonreporting) (Includes VETERANS AFFAIRS EASTERN KANSAS HEALTH CARE SYSTEM–COLMERY–O'NEIL VETERANS AFFAIRS MEDICAL CENTER, 2200 South West Gage Boulevard, Topeka, Kansas, Zip 66622–0002, tel. 785/350–3111; VETERANS AFFAIRS EASTERN KANSAS HEALTH CARE SYSTEM–DWIGHT D. EISENHOWER VETERANS AFFAIRS MEDICAL CENTER, 4101 South 4th Street Trafficway, Leavenworth, Kansas, Zip 66048–5055, tel. 913/682–2000) **A**1 3 5 **S** Department of Veterans Affairs, Washington, DC
Primary Contact: Anthony Rudy. Klopfer, FACHE, Director
COO: John Moon, Associate Director
CMO: Rajeev Trehan M.D., M.P.H., Chief of Staff
CIO: Joni Davin, Director Information and Business Management Service Line
Web address: www.topeka.va.gov/
Control: Veterans Affairs, Government, federal **Service**: General medical and surgical

Staffed Beds: 213

VETERANS AFFAIRS EASTERN KANSAS HEALTH CARE SYSTEM–COLMERY–O'NEIL VETERANS AFFAIRS MEDICAL CENTER See Veterans Affairs Eastern Kansas Health Care System

TRIBUNE—Greeley County

★ **GREELEY COUNTY HEALTH SERVICES (171359)**, 506 Third Street, Zip 67879–9684, Mailing Address: P.O.Box 338, 67879–0338; tel. 620/376–4221, (Total facility includes 32 beds in nursing home–type unit) **A**10 18 **F**3 17 28 34 40 45 59 64 65 66 69 81 89 107 127 133 147 **S** QHR, Brentwood, TN
Primary Contact: Burke Kline, Chief Executive Officer
CMO: Wendel Ellis D.O., Chief Medical Staff
CIO: Shanon Schneider, Chief Information Officer
CHR: Katelyn Reynolds, Manager Human Resources
CNO: Janie Schmidt, Director of Nursing
Web address: www.mygchs.com
Control: Other not–for–profit (including NFP Corporation) **Service**: General medical and surgical

Staffed Beds: 50 Admissions: 254 Census: 36 Outpatient Visits: 19277 Births: 0 Total Expense ($000): 10641 Payroll Expense ($000): 5168 Personnel: 120

KS

Many Facility Codes have changed. Please refer to the AHA Guide Code Chart. © 2017 AHA Guide

ULYSSES—Grant County

★ **BOB WILSON MEMORIAL GRANT COUNTY HOSPITAL (170110)**, 415 North Main Street, Zip 67880–2133; tel. 620/356–1266 **A**10 20 **F**3 11 13 15 29 30 34 35 40 45 50 57 59 64 68 75 76 79 81 82 85 86 87 91 93 96 97 107 119 127 130 133 146 148 **P**6 **S** Catholic Health Initiatives, Englewood, CO
Primary Contact: Deanna Mustin, R.N., Administrator
CFO: Robert Jacobi, Chief Financial Officer
CIO: Chris Moffet, Director Information Services
CHR: Tammy Oxford, Director Human Resources
Web address: www.bwmgch.com
Control: Corporation, Investor–owned (for–profit) **Service**: General medical and surgical

Staffed Beds: 26 **Admissions**: 324 **Census**: 5 **Outpatient Visits**: 11114
Births: 19 **Total Expense ($000)**: 11010 **Payroll Expense ($000)**: 5032
Personnel: 91

WAKEENEY—Trego County

★ **TREGO COUNTY–LEMKE MEMORIAL HOSPITAL (171355)**, 320 North 13th Street, Zip 67672–2099; tel. 785/743–2182, (Total facility includes 37 beds in nursing home–type unit) **A**10 18 **F**3 8 10 11 15 28 29 34 40 45 53 57 59 62 64 67 69 71 81 86 89 93 107 110 114 127 128 130 133 143 146 148 **P**6 **S** Great Plains Health Alliance, Inc., Wichita, KS
Primary Contact: David Augustine, Chief Executive Officer
CFO: ReChelle Horinek, Chief Financial Officer
CMO: Gordon Lang M.D., Chief of Staff
CHR: Jeff Bieker, Director Human Resource
CNO: Sandy Purinton, Chief Nursing Officer
Web address: www.tclmh.org
Control: County, Government, Nonfederal **Service**: General medical and surgical

Staffed Beds: 62 **Admissions**: 678 **Census**: 47 **Outpatient Visits**: 35407
Births: 0 **Total Expense ($000)**: 18007 **Payroll Expense ($000)**: 7913
Personnel: 178

WAMEGO—Pottawatomie County

★ **WAMEGO HEALTH CENTER (171337)**, 711 Genn Drive, Zip 66547–1179; tel. 785/456–2295 **A**10 18 **F**3 11 15 28 29 32 34 35 40 45 56 59 64 65 75 77 81 93 97 107 114 119 127 130 131 132 133 143 146 147 148 149 **P**6
Primary Contact: Steve Land, Senior Administrator
COO: Brian Smith, Director of Operations
CFO: Keith Zachariasen, Chief Financial Officer
CMO: Roland Darey M.D., Medical Director
CIO: Wes Janzen, Chief Information Officer
CHR: Renee Reed, Director Human Resources
CNO: Tresha Flanary R.N., Chief Clinical Services Officer
Web address: www.wamegohealthcenter.com
Control: Other not–for–profit (including NFP Corporation) **Service**: General medical and surgical

Staffed Beds: 18 **Admissions**: 187 **Census**: 4 **Outpatient Visits**: 35994
Births: 0 **Total Expense ($000)**: 11359 **Payroll Expense ($000)**: 5857
Personnel: 73

WASHINGTON—Washington County

WASHINGTON COUNTY HOSPITAL (171351), 304 East Third Street, Zip 66968–2033; tel. 785/325–2211 **A**10 18 **F**1 3 11 13 15 28 29 31 34 35 40 41 44 45 64 67 68 69 76 81 83 85 91 93 97 107 110 114 133 148 149 **P**6
Primary Contact: Roxanne Schottel, Chief Executive Officer
CFO: Linda Rettig, Director Financial Services
CNO: Kelly Otott R.N., Chief Nursing Officer
Web address: www.washingtoncountyhospital.net
Control: County, Government, Nonfederal **Service**: General medical and surgical

Staffed Beds: 18 **Admissions**: 133 **Census**: 5 **Outpatient Visits**: 6837
Births: 11 **Total Expense ($000)**: 5697 **Payroll Expense ($000)**: 2298
Personnel: 48

WELLINGTON—Sumner County

★ **SUMNER REGIONAL MEDICAL CENTER (170039)**, 1323 North 'A' Street, Zip 67152–4350; tel. 620/326–7451, (Total facility includes 9 beds in nursing home–type unit) **A**10 **F**10 11 13 15 31 35 40 45 56 59 64 76 77 78 79 81 82 85 98 103 107 108 110 111 119 128 129 130
Primary Contact: Les Dean, President and Chief Executive Officer
CFO: Barry Harding, Interim Chief Executive Officer and Chief Financial Officer
CHR: Allen Keller, Director Human Resources
CNO: Darlene Cooney, Director Nursing
Web address: www.srmcks.org
Control: City, Government, Nonfederal **Service**: General medical and surgical

Staffed Beds: 61 **Admissions**: 570 **Census**: 5 **Outpatient Visits**: 21843
Births: 181 **Total Expense ($000)**: 13880 **Payroll Expense ($000)**: 5445
Personnel: 132

WICHITA—Sedgwick County

☐ **AMG SPECIALTY HOSPITAL–WICHITA (172003)**, 8080 East Pawnee Street, Zip 67207–5475; tel. 316/682–0004, (Nonreporting) **A**1 10 **S** AMG Integrated Healthcare Management, Lafayette, LA
Primary Contact: Robert A. Loepp Jr, FACHE, Chief Executive Officer
CFO: Myra Dick, Manager Business Office
CIO: Michelle Bradley, Director Health Information Management
CHR: Adrienne Burkholder, Director Human Resources
Web address: www.amgwichita.com/
Control: Corporation, Investor–owned (for–profit) **Service**: Acute long–term care hospital

Staffed Beds: 26

KANSAS HEART HOSPITAL (170186), 3601 North Webb Road, Zip 67226–8129; tel. 316/630–5000 **A**10 **F**3 17 18 20 22 24 26 29 64 81 85 86 107 115 119 149
Primary Contact: Thomas L. Ashcom, M.D., Ph.D., Chief Executive Officer
COO: Joyce Heismeyer, Chief Operating Officer
CFO: Steve Smith, Chief Financial Officer
CHR: Teresa E Wolfe, Manager Human Resources
CNO: Susan Bradford, Director Nursing
Web address: www.kansasheart.com
Control: Corporation, Investor–owned (for–profit) **Service**: Heart

Staffed Beds: 54 **Admissions**: 1840 **Census**: 21 **Outpatient Visits**: 9537
Births: 0 **Personnel**: 198

KANSAS SPINE AND SPECIALTY HOSPITAL (170196), 3333 North Webb Road, Zip 67226–8123; tel. 316/462–5000 **A**10 **F**3 29 79 81 82 85 87 107 111 114 126 149
Primary Contact: Thomas M. Schmitt, Chief Executive Officer
CFO: Kevin P Vaughn, Chief Financial Officer
CIO: Michael Knocke, Chief Information Officer
CHR: Jean–Marie Jimeson, Manager Human Resources
CNO: John Coslett R.N., Chief Nursing Officer
Web address: www.ksspine.com
Control: Corporation, Investor–owned (for–profit) **Service**: General medical and surgical

Staffed Beds: 36 **Admissions**: 2177 **Census**: 13 **Outpatient Visits**: 7405
Births: 0 **Personnel**: 131

KANSAS SURGERY AND RECOVERY CENTER (170183), 2770 North Webb Road, Zip 67226–8112; tel. 316/634–0090 **A**10 **F**45 51 64 68 81 85 87 93 107 111 114 119
Primary Contact: Ely Bartal, M.D., Chief Executive Officer
CFO: Ashley Simon, Chief Financial Officer
CMO: Ely Bartal M.D., Chief Executive Officer and Medical Director
CIO: Jonathan Wells, Supervisor Information Technology
CNO: Becky Bailey R.N., Director Nursing
Web address: www.ksrc.org
Control: Partnership, Investor–owned (for–profit) **Service**: Surgical

Staffed Beds: 32 **Admissions**: 1855 **Census**: 11 **Outpatient Visits**: 8229
Births: 0 **Total Expense ($000)**: 27219 **Payroll Expense ($000)**: 6945
Personnel: 135

▣ **ROBERT J. DOLE VETERANS AFFAIRS MEDICAL CENTER**, 5500 East Kellogg, Zip 67218–1607; tel. 316/685–2221, (Nonreporting) **A**1 3 5 **S** Department of Veterans Affairs, Washington, DC
Primary Contact: Rick Ament, Chief Executive Officer
CFO: Ronald Dreher, Finance Officer
CMO: Kent Murray M.D., Chief of Staff
CIO: Sharon Williamson, Chief Information Technology
CHR: Nancy Gerstner, Manager Human Resources
Web address: www.wichita.va.gov
Control: Veterans Affairs, Government, federal **Service**: General medical and surgical

Staffed Beds: 41

▣ **SELECT SPECIALTY HOSPITAL–WICHITA (172007)**, 929 North St Francis Street, Zip 67214–3821; tel. 316/261–8303, (Nonreporting) **A**1 10 **S** Select Medical Corporation, Mechanicsburg, PA
Primary Contact: Peggy Cliffe, Chief Executive Officer
CHR: Renee Schaffer, Coordinator Human Resources
CNO: Lindsey Cahoj, Chief Nursing Officer
Web address: www.selectspecialtyhospitals.com/company/locations/wichita.aspx
Control: Corporation, Investor–owned (for–profit) **Service**: Acute long–term care hospital

Staffed Beds: 48

✠ **VIA CHRISTI HOSPITAL ON ST. FRANCIS (170122)**, 929 North St Francis Street, Zip 67214–3882; tel. 316/268–5000, (Includes GOOD SHEPHERD CAMPUS, 8901 East Orme, Wichita, Kansas, Zip 67207, tel. 316/858–0333; ST. FRANCIS CAMPUS, 929 North St Francis Street, Wichita, Kansas, Zip 67214–3882, tel. 316/268–5000; Sherry Hausmann, President; ST. JOSEPH CAMPUS, 3600 East Harry Street, Wichita, Kansas, Zip 67218–3713, tel. 316/685–1111; Claudio J Ferraro, President) **A**1 2 3 5 10 13 **F**3 5 7 11 12 13 15 16 17 18 19 20 21 22 23 24 26 27 28 29 30 31 32 34 35 38 40 43 44 45 46 48 49 50 51 54 56 57 58 59 60 61 62 64 68 70 72 74 75 76 77 78 79 80 81 82 84 85 86 87 88 89 92 93 97 98 99 100 101 102 103 104 105 107 108 110 111 114 115 117 118 119 120 121 123 124 126 130 131 132 135 136 141 142 143 146 147 148 **P**6 **S** Ascension Healthcare, Saint Louis, MO
Primary Contact: Sherry Hausmann, President
CFO: Jeff Seirer, Interim Chief Financial Officer
CMO: Darrell Youngman D.O., Chief Medical Officer
CIO: Donna Roach, Chief Information Officer
CHR: Judy Espinoza, Chief Human Resources Officer
Web address: www.via-christi.org
Control: Church operated, Nongovernment, not–for–profit **Service**: General medical and surgical

Staffed Beds: 710 **Admissions:** 31289 **Census:** 410 **Outpatient Visits:** 300262 **Births:** 2422 **Total Expense ($000):** 527849 **Payroll Expense ($000):** 180430 **Personnel:** 3268

✠ **VIA CHRISTI HOSPITAL ON ST. TERESA (170200)**, 14800 West St. Teresa, Zip 67235–9602; tel. 316/796–7000 **A**1 10 **F**3 8 18 20 22 29 30 34 35 40 45 50 64 68 70 75 78 79 81 85 87 90 92 93 96 107 108 111 114 118 119 130 146 147 148 **S** Ascension Healthcare, Saint Louis, MO
Primary Contact: Claudio J. Ferraro, Senior Administrator
Web address: www.via-christi.org/st-teresa
Control: Church operated, Nongovernment, not–for–profit **Service**: General medical and surgical

Staffed Beds: 57 **Admissions:** 1670 **Census:** 21 **Outpatient Visits:** 21440 **Births:** 0 **Total Expense ($000):** 35963 **Payroll Expense ($000):** 9233 **Personnel:** 157

VIA CHRISTI REGIONAL MEDICAL CENTER See VIA Christi hospital On St. Francis

✠ **VIA CHRISTI REHABILITATION HOSPITAL (173028)**, 1151 North Rock Road, Zip 67206–1262; tel. 316/634–3400 **A**1 10 **F**11 29 30 34 35 44 50 54 57 59 64 77 86 87 90 92 93 95 96 119 129 130 131 132 143 146 148 **S** Ascension Healthcare, Saint Louis, MO
Primary Contact: Sherry Hausmann, President
CMO: Kevin Rieg M.D., President Medical Staff
CNO: Cindy Hagerty, Assistant Chief Nurse Officer and Administrator of Operations
Web address: www.via-christi.org
Control: Church operated, Nongovernment, not–for–profit **Service**: Rehabilitation

Staffed Beds: 58 **Admissions:** 682 **Census:** 23 **Outpatient Visits:** 104595 **Births:** 0 **Total Expense ($000):** 23159 **Payroll Expense ($000):** 10399 **Personnel:** 198

✠ **WESLEY MEDICAL CENTER (170123)**, 550 North Hillside, Zip 67214–4976; tel. 316/962–2000, (Includes WESLEY CHILDREN'S HOSPITAL, 550 North Hillside Street, Wichita, Kansas, Zip 67214–4910, tel. 316/962–2000; WESLEY WOODLAWN HOSPITAL & ER, 2610 North Woodlawn, Wichita, Kansas, Zip 67220, tel. 316/858–2610; Thomas Owings, Chief Executive Officer) **A**1 2 3 5 10 **F**3 7 11 12 13 15 17 18 19 20 22 24 26 28 29 30 31 32 34 35 37 38 39 40 41 43 44 45 46 47 48 49 50 51 54 55 56 57 58 59 60 64 65 68 70 72 73 74 76 78 79 81 82 85 86 87 88 89 92 93 94 97 100 102 107 108 110 111 114 115 119 120 121 123 124 126 129 130 131 132 134 135 146 147 148 149 **P**6 **S** HCA Healthcare, Nashville, TN
Primary Contact: Bill Voloch, President and Chief Executive Officer
CFO: Bradley Schultz, Chief Financial Officer
CMO: Francie H Ekengren M.D., Chief Medical Officer
CIO: Jeffrey Schauf, Director Information Systems
CHR: Jennifer Krier, Vice President Human Resources
Web address: www.wesleymc.com
Control: Corporation, Investor–owned (for–profit) **Service**: General medical and surgical

Staffed Beds: 573 **Admissions:** 27914 **Census:** 360 **Outpatient Visits:** 252801 **Births:** 6133 **Personnel:** 2551

✠ **WESLEY REHABILITATION HOSPITAL (173027)**, 8338 West 13th Street North, Zip 67212–2984; tel. 316/729–9999 **A**1 10 **F**29 34 35 64 68 90 91 93 95 96 132 148 **S** HEALTHSOUTH Corporation, Birmingham, AL
Primary Contact: James F. Grocholski, FACHE, Chief Executive Officer
CFO: Bob Peck, Chief Financial Officer
CIO: Debbie Patterson, Director Health Information Management
CHR: Betty Shuman, Director Human Resources
CNO: Jessika M Workman, Chief Nursing Officer
Web address: www.wesleyrehabhospital.com
Control: Corporation, Investor–owned (for–profit) **Service**: Rehabilitation

Staffed Beds: 65 **Admissions:** 1075 **Census:** 38 **Outpatient Visits:** 11302 **Births:** 0 **Total Expense ($000):** 18760 **Payroll Expense ($000):** 8387 **Personnel:** 152

WICHITA SPECIALTY HOSPITAL See Amg Specialty Hospital–Wichita

WINCHESTER—Jefferson County

★ **F. W. HUSTON MEDICAL CENTER (171314)**, 408 Delaware Street, Zip 66097–4003; tel. 913/774–4340, (Total facility includes 38 beds in nursing home–type unit) **A**10 18 **F**3 10 40 56 57 64 67 69 75 77 93 97 103 104 107 111 125 128 130 133 143 144 148 **P**6 8
Primary Contact: LaMont Cook, Administrator
CFO: Jason Johnson, Controller
CMO: William Greiner M.D., Chief of Staff
CIO: Jason Johnson, Controller
CHR: Melody Keirns, Manager Human Resources
CNO: Heather R Aranda R.N., MSN, Chief Nursing Officer
Web address: www.jcmhospital.org
Control: Other not–for–profit (including NFP Corporation) **Service**: General medical and surgical

Staffed Beds: 69 **Admissions:** 62 **Census:** 31 **Outpatient Visits:** 8190 **Births:** 0 **Total Expense ($000):** 5719 **Payroll Expense ($000):** 3668 **Personnel:** 71

JEFFERSON COUNTY MEMORIAL HOSPITAL See F. W. Huston Medical Center

WINFIELD—Cowley County

★ **WILLIAM NEWTON HOSPITAL (171383)**, 1300 East Fifth Street, Zip 67156–2407; tel. 620/221–2300 **A**3 5 10 18 **F**3 8 9 10 11 12 13 15 28 29 34 35 40 43 45 56 57 59 62 64 68 69 70 76 77 79 81 84 85 87 89 90 93 96 97 107 108 110 111 114 118 119 127 129 130 133 146 147 148 149
Primary Contact: J Ben. Quinton, Administrator
COO: Shona Salzman, Chief Operating Officer
CFO: Debbie Hockenbury, Assistant Administrator and Chief Financial Officer
CMO: Bryan Dennett M.D., Chief of Staff
CIO: Randy Mayo, Director Information Technology
CHR: Cathy McClurg, Director Human Resources
CNO: Tina Wheeler R.N., MSN, Director Nursing
Web address: www.wnmh.org
Control: Other not–for–profit (including NFP Corporation) **Service**: General medical and surgical

Staffed Beds: 25 **Admissions:** 1077 **Census:** 10 **Outpatient Visits:** 79653 **Births:** 244 **Total Expense ($000):** 34611 **Payroll Expense ($000):** 14605 **Personnel:** 275

Many Facility Codes have changed. Please refer to the AHA Guide Code Chart. © 2017 AHA Guide

KENTUCKY

ALBANY—Clinton County

THE MEDICAL CENTER ALBANY (180106), 723 Burkesville Road, Zip 42602–1654; tel. 606/387–8000, (Nonreporting) **A**10 **S** Commonwealth Health Corporation, Bowling Green, KY
Primary Contact: Laura Belcher, Administrator
CFO: Ronald G. Sowell, Executive Vice President, Chief Financial Officer
CIO: Mark Brookman, Chief Information Officer
CHR: Lynn Williams, Vice President, Human Resources
Web address: www.chc.net/services/hospitals/the_medical_center_at_albany.aspx
Control: Other not–for–profit (including NFP Corporation) **Service:** General medical and surgical

Staffed Beds: 42

ASHLAND—Boyd County

☐ **KING'S DAUGHTERS MEDICAL CENTER (180009)**, 2201 Lexington Avenue, Zip 41101–2874, Mailing Address: P.O.Box 151, 41105–0151; tel. 606/408–4000, (Nonreporting) **A**1 2 10
Primary Contact: Kristie Whitlatch, President
COO: Bob Lucas, Vice President Operations
CFO: Paul L McDowell, Vice President Finance and Chief Financial Officer
CMO: Phil Fioret M.D., Vice President Medical Affairs
CIO: David Oliver, Director Information Systems
CHR: Larry Higgins, Vice President Human Resources
Web address: www.kdmc.com
Control: Other not–for–profit (including NFP Corporation) **Service:** General medical and surgical

Staffed Beds: 465

⊞ **OUR LADY OF BELLEFONTE HOSPITAL (180036)**, St Christopher Drive, Zip 41101, Mailing Address: P.O.Box 789, 41105–0789; tel. 606/833–3333 **A**1 2 10 12 13 **F**3 4 5 8 11 15 18 19 20 22 28 29 30 31 34 35 37 39 40 44 45 49 50 53 54 55 56 57 58 59 62 64 65 66 69 70 71 74 75 77 78 79 81 82 84 85 86 87 89 93 96 97 98 100 101 102 103 104 105 106 107 108 110 111 114 115 118 119 126 129 130 131 132 135 143 144 145 146 147 148 **P**6 8 **S** Bon Secours Health System, Inc., Marriottsville, MD
Primary Contact: Kevin Halter, Chief Executive Officer
CFO: Joe Buchheit, Chief Financial Officer
CMO: Dan Goulson M.D., Chief Medical Officer
CIO: Mike Gomez, Site Manager Medical Information Systems
CHR: Judy Daniels, Vice President Human Resources
Web address: www.olbh.com
Control: Church operated, Nongovernment, not–for–profit **Service:** General medical and surgical

Staffed Beds: 147 **Admissions:** 6082 **Census:** 90 **Outpatient Visits:** 261673 **Births:** 0 **Total Expense ($000):** 154289 **Payroll Expense ($000):** 47489 **Personnel:** 978

BARBOURVILLE—Knox County

☐ **BARBOURVILLE ARH HOSPITAL (181328)**, 80 Hospital Drive, Zip 40906–7363, Mailing Address: P.O.Box 10, 40906–0010; tel. 606/546–4175, (Nonreporting) **A**1 10 18 **S** Pacer Health Corporation, Miami Lakes, FL
Primary Contact: Charles D. Lovell Jr, FACHE, Chief Executive Officer
CFO: Amanda Ellis, Chief Financial Officer
CMO: Kamran Hasni M.D., Chief of Medical Staff
CIO: Evan Davis, Director Technology and Environmental Services
CHR: Janet Wilder, Director Human Resources
CNO: Brenda Graham, Chief Nursing Officer
Web address: www.knoxcohospital.com
Control: Corporation, Investor–owned (for–profit) **Service:** General medical and surgical

Staffed Beds: 25

BARDSTOWN—Nelson County

⊞ **FLAGET MEMORIAL HOSPITAL (180025)**, 4305 New Shepherdsville Road, Zip 40004–9019; tel. 502/350–5000 **A**1 2 3 10 **F**3 11 12 13 15 18 29 30 31 34 35 37 40 45 49 55 59 60 62 63 64 70 76 78 79 81 82 84 85 87 91 93 96 107 111 116 117 119 120 128 129 130 132 144 146 147 148 **P**6 **S** Catholic Health Initiatives, Englewood, CO
Primary Contact: Jennifer Nolan, President and Chief Executive Officer
CFO: Jim Wentz, Chief Financial Officer
CMO: Mickey Anderson M.D., Vice President Medical Affairs
CHR: Tanja Oquendo, Chief Human Resources Officer
CNO: Norma Goss R.N., Chief Nursing Officer
Web address: www.kentuckyonehealth.org/flaget
Control: Other not–for–profit (including NFP Corporation) **Service:** General medical and surgical

Staffed Beds: 42 **Admissions:** 1961 **Census:** 19 **Outpatient Visits:** 71197 **Births:** 249 **Total Expense ($000):** 62357 **Payroll Expense ($000):** 15960 **Personnel:** 265

BENTON—Marshall County

⊞ **MARSHALL COUNTY HOSPITAL (181327)**, 615 Old Symsonia Road, Zip 42025–5042; tel. 270/527–4800 **A**1 10 18 **F**3 11 15 18 19 28 29 30 34 35 40 57 59 62 77 79 81 85 89 90 93 107 108 119 132 133 135 149 **P**6
Primary Contact: David G. Fuqua, Chief Executive Officer
CFO: Janice Kelley, Chief Financial Officer
CMO: Edwin Perez M.D., Chief of Medical Staff
CIO: Dave Cope, Director Information Systems
CHR: Jeannie Lee, Director Human Resources
Web address: www.marshallcountyhospital.org
Control: Hospital district or authority, Government, Nonfederal **Service:** General medical and surgical

Staffed Beds: 25 **Admissions:** 777 **Census:** 7 **Outpatient Visits:** 29071 **Births:** 0 **Total Expense ($000):** 22484 **Payroll Expense ($000):** 8671 **Personnel:** 222

MARSHALL COUNTY HOSPITAL A1 10 18 **F**3 11 15 18 19 28 29 30 34 35 40 57 59 62 77 79 81 85 89 90 93 107 108 119 132 133 135 149 **P**6
CFO: Janice Kelley, Chief Financial Officer
CMO: Edwin Perez M.D., Chief of Medical Staff
CIO: Dave Cope, Director Information Systems
CHR: Jeannie Lee, Director Human Resources
Web address: www.marshallcountyhospital.org

BEREA—Madison County

⊞ **SAINT JOSEPH BEREA (181329)**, 305 Estill Street, Zip 40403–1909; tel. 859/986–3151 **A**1 5 10 18 **F**3 29 40 45 70 77 79 81 82 91 97 107 111 114 119 133 **P**4 **S** Catholic Health Initiatives, Englewood, CO
Primary Contact: Eric Gilliam, President
CFO: Christy Spitser, Vice President Finance
CMO: Joshua Huffman M.D., Chief Medical Staff
CHR: Sandra Turqueza, Human Resources Business Partner
CNO: Leslie Adams, Chief Nursing Executive
Web address: www.kentuckyonehealth.org/berea
Control: Other not–for–profit (including NFP Corporation) **Service:** General medical and surgical

Staffed Beds: 25 **Admissions:** 947 **Census:** 11 **Outpatient Visits:** 54902 **Births:** 0 **Total Expense ($000):** 28710 **Payroll Expense ($000):** 10163 **Personnel:** 156

BOWLING GREEN—Warren County

☐ **COMMONWEALTH REGIONAL SPECIALTY HOSPITAL (182005)**, 250 Park Drive, 6th Floor, Zip 42101–1760, Mailing Address: P.O.Box 90010, 42102–9010; tel. 270/796–6200 **A**1 10 **F**1 3 29 30 34 35 50 57 68 85 87 130 135 143 146 148 **P**6 **S** Commonwealth Health Corporation, Bowling Green, KY
Primary Contact: Christa Atkins, Administrator
CFO: Ronald G. Sowell, Executive Vice President
CMO: Doug Thomson M.D., Chief Medical Officer
CIO: Jean Cherry, Executive Vice President
CHR: Lynn Williams, Vice President
Web address: www.commonwealthregionalspecialtyhospital.org
Control: Other not–for–profit (including NFP Corporation) **Service:** Acute long–term care hospital

Staffed Beds: 28 **Admissions:** 233 **Census:** 16 **Outpatient Visits:** 0 **Births:** 0 **Personnel:** 50

☐ **MEDICAL CENTER AT BOWLING GREEN (180013)**, 250 Park Street, Zip 42101–1795, Mailing Address: P.O.Box 90010, 42102–9010; tel. 270/745–1000 **A**1 2 10 13 19 **F**1 3 7 12 13 15 17 18 20 22 24 26 28 29 30 31 34 35 37 39 40 45 46 48 49 50 51 56 57 59 60 62 64 68 70 73 74 75 76 78 79 81 82 85 86 87 89 91 92 93 98 100 102 103 104 107 108 110 111 114 115 116 117 118 119 120 121 122 123 124 126 129 130 132 135 145 146 147 148 **P**6 **S** Commonwealth Health Corporation, Bowling Green, KY
Primary Contact: Connie Smith, Chief Executive Officer
CFO: Ronald G. Sowell, Executive Vice President
CIO: Mark Brookman, Chief Information Officer
CHR: Lynn Williams, Vice President Human Resources
CNO: Betsy Kullman R.N., MSN, Executive Vice President and Chief Nursing Officer
Web address: www.themedicalcenter.org
Control: Other not–for–profit (including NFP Corporation) **Service**: General medical and surgical

Staffed Beds: 337 **Admissions**: 16078 **Census**: 229 **Outpatient Visits**: 137023 **Births**: 2518 **Personnel**: 1976

☐ **RIVENDELL BEHAVIORAL HEALTH (184017)**, 1035 Porter Pike, Zip 42103–9581; tel. 270/843–1199 (Nonreporting) **A**1 10 **S** Universal Health Services, Inc., King of Prussia, PA
Primary Contact: Matt Ours, Chief Executive Officer and Managing Director
CFO: Tim Gore, Chief Financial Officer
Web address: www.rivendellbehavioral.com
Control: Corporation, Investor–owned (for–profit) **Service**: Psychiatric

Staffed Beds: 125

✠ △ **SOUTHERN KENTUCKY REHABILITATION HOSPITAL (183029)**, 1300 Campbell Lane, Zip 42104–4162; tel. 270/782–6900, (Nonreporting) **A**1 7 10 **S** Vibra Healthcare, Mechanicsburg, PA
Primary Contact: Stuart Locke, Chief Executive Officer
COO: Dana Lewis, Director Clinical Services
CMO: Jim Farrage M.D., Medical Director
CHR: Suzanne Cornett, Director Human Resources
Web address: www.skyrehab.com
Control: Corporation, Investor–owned (for–profit) **Service**: Rehabilitation

Staffed Beds: 60

✠ **TRISTAR GREENVIEW REGIONAL HOSPITAL (180124)**, 1801 Ashley Circle, Zip 42104–3362; tel. 270/793–1000 **A**1 10 19 **F**3 8 11 15 18 20 22 29 30 31 34 35 37 40 45 46 48 49 50 51 57 59 64 65 68 70 74 75 78 79 81 82 85 86 87 107 108 110 111 115 117 119 126 128 130 133 135 145 146 149 **S** HCA Healthcare, Nashville, TN
Primary Contact: Michael Sherrod, Chief Executive Officer
COO: Andrew Bedi, Chief Operating Officer
CMO: Wayne Bush M.D., Chief of Staff
CIO: Cyndi Talley, Director Information Systems
CHR: Judy Fulkerson, Director Human Resources
CNO: Anne Leonard R.N., Chief Nursing Officer
Web address: www.greenviewhospital.com
Control: Corporation, Investor–owned (for–profit) **Service**: General medical and surgical

Staffed Beds: 148 **Admissions**: 4674 **Census**: 50 **Outpatient Visits**: 59172 **Births**: 0 **Total Expense ($000)**: 183444 **Payroll Expense ($000)**: 30574 **Personnel**: 422

BURKESVILLE—Cumberland County

CUMBERLAND COUNTY HOSPITAL (181317), 299 Glasgow Road, Zip 42717–9696, Mailing Address: P.O.Box 280, 42717–0280; tel. 270/864–2511, (Nonreporting) **A**10 18
Primary Contact: Richard Neikirk, Chief Executive Officer
COO: Steve Burns, Chief Operating Officer
CFO: Rick Capps, Chief Financial Officer
CMO: Christian Konsavage M.D., Chief of Staff
CHR: Martha Young, Director Human Resources
CNO: Susan S Flowers MSN, R.N., Chief Nursing Officer
Web address: www.cchospital.org
Control: Other not–for–profit (including NFP Corporation) **Service**: General medical and surgical

Staffed Beds: 25

CADIZ—Trigg County

TRIGG COUNTY HOSPITAL (181304), 254 Main Street, Zip 42211–9153, Mailing Address: P.O.Box 312, 42211–0312; tel. 270/522–3215 **A**10 18 **F**3 7 11 15 29 30 34 40 41 45 54 59 64 68 81 87 97 107 110 111 115 119 127 128 133 145 146
Primary Contact: John Sumner, Chief Executive Officer
CFO: Liz Snodgrass, Chief Financial Officer
CMO: Stuart Harris M.D., Chief of Staff
CHR: Janet James, Director Human Resources
Web address: www.trigghospital.org
Control: Other not–for–profit (including NFP Corporation) **Service**: General medical and surgical

Staffed Beds: 19 **Admissions**: 183 **Census**: 1 **Outpatient Visits**: 6517 **Births**: 0 **Total Expense ($000)**: 17497 **Payroll Expense ($000)**: 6678 **Personnel**: 141

CAMPBELLSVILLE—Taylor County

✠ **TAYLOR REGIONAL HOSPITAL (180087)**, 1700 Old Lebanon Road, Zip 42718–9600; tel. 270/465–3561 **A**1 2 10 **F**2 8 11 13 15 18 20 28 29 30 31 34 35 39 40 43 45 46 48 49 50 51 54 56 57 59 64 68 70 74 75 76 77 78 79 81 85 86 87 93 97 107 108 110 111 115 118 119 127 129 130 131 132 134 135 141 143 146 147 148 149 150 **S** Catholic Health Initiatives, Englewood, CO
Primary Contact: Jane Wheatley, Chief Executive Officer
CFO: Paul Phillips, Chief Financial Officer
CIO: Christopher Michael Gibbs, Director Information Management Systems
CHR: Andrea Settle, Director Human Resources
CNO: Dana M. Garrett R.N., Nursing Services Administrator
Web address: www.trhosp.org
Control: Hospital district or authority, Government, Nonfederal **Service**: General medical and surgical

Staffed Beds: 90 **Admissions**: 2587 **Census**: 28 **Outpatient Visits**: 95944 **Births**: 371 **Total Expense ($000)**: 72634 **Payroll Expense ($000)**: 33184 **Personnel**: 587

CARROLLTON—Carroll County

★ **CARROLL COUNTY MEMORIAL HOSPITAL (181310)**, 309 11th Street, Zip 41008–1400; tel. 502/732–4321, (Nonreporting) **A**10 18 **S** Alliant Management Services, Louisville, KY
Primary Contact: Harry Hays, Chief Executive Officer
CMO: Kathy Short D.O., Family Practice
CHR: Kimberly Adams, Manager Human Resources
CNO: Lisa Penick R.N., Chief Nursing Officer
Web address: www.ccmhosp.com
Control: County, Government, Nonfederal **Service**: General medical and surgical

Staffed Beds: 25

COLUMBIA—Adair County

☐ **T.J. HEALTH COLUMBIA (180149)**, 901 Westlake Drive, Zip 42728–1123, Mailing Address: P.O.Box 1269, 42728–6269; tel. 270/384–4753, (Nonreporting) **A**1 10
Primary Contact: Bud Wethington, Chief Executive Officer
CFO: David R Hayes, Chief Financial Officer
CMO: Charles Giles M.D., President Medical Staff
CHR: Tonya Grant, Director Human Resources
CNO: Gidgett Warren, Director of Nursing
Web address: www.healthiercolumbia.org/
Control: Hospital district or authority, Government, Nonfederal **Service**: General medical and surgical

Staffed Beds: 32

CORBIN—Whitley County

★ ⇧ **BAPTIST HEALTH CORBIN (180080)**, 1 Trillium Way, Zip 40701–8420; tel. 606/528–1212 **A**10 19 21 **F**1 3 4 5 13 15 18 20 22 26 28 29 30 31 32 34 35 36 38 40 45 47 48 49 51 53 54 57 59 64 67 68 70 73 76 78 79 81 84 85 86 87 89 90 93 96 98 99 100 101 102 103 104 105 107 108 110 111 114 115 118 119 126 130 132 133 135 145 146 147 148 **S** Baptist Health, Louisville, KY
Primary Contact: Larry Gray, President
CFO: Pamela K. Jones, Executive Director of Finance
CMO: David Worthy M.D., Vice President and Chief Medical Officer
CIO: Rodney Richardson, Director of Information Technology
CHR: Tim Perry, Executive Director of Human Resources
CNO: Sherrie Mays MSN, R.N., Vice President and Chief Nursing Officer
Web address: www.baptisthealth.com/corbin
Control: Other not–for–profit (including NFP Corporation) **Service**: General medical and surgical

Staffed Beds: 273 **Admissions**: 9807 **Census**: 124 **Outpatient Visits**: 149716 **Births**: 931 **Total Expense ($000)**: 179737 **Payroll Expense ($000)**: 56962 **Personnel**: 929

★ **CONTINUECARE HOSPITAL AT BAPTIST HEALTH CORBIN (182006)**, 1 Trillium Way, Lower Level, Zip 40701–8727; tel. 606/523–5150 **A**10 **F**1 3 29 30 34 57 59 85 148 **S** Community Hospital Corporation, Plano, TX
Primary Contact: Keith Rodgers, Interim Chief Executive Officer
COO: Wilson Weber, Chief Operating Officer
CFO: Lisa Young CPA, Chief Financial Officer
CMO: Steve Morton M.D., Chief Medical Officer
CIO: Brian Doerr, Chief Information Officer
CHR: Amie Marcum, Human Resources Coordinator
CNO: Della Rains, Chief Nursing Officer
Web address: www.continuecare.org
Control: Other not–for–profit (including NFP Corporation) **Service:** Acute long–term care hospital

Staffed Beds: 32 Admissions: 324 Census: 28 Outpatient Visits: 0 Births: 0 Total Expense ($000): 12611 Payroll Expense ($000): 5235 Personnel: 73		

COVINGTON—Kenton County

NORTHKEY COMMUNITY CARE (184006), 502 Farrell Drive, Zip 41011–3799, Mailing Address: P.O.Box 2680, 41012–2680; tel. 859/578–3200, (Nonreporting) **A**10
Primary Contact: Owen Nichols, PsyD, President and Chief Executive Officer
CFO: John Metzger, Controller
Web address: www.northkey.org
Control: Other not–for–profit (including NFP Corporation) **Service:** Children's hospital psychiatric

Staffed Beds: 34

ST. ELIZABETH MEDICAL CENTER–NORTH See St. Elizabeth Covington

CYNTHIANA—Harrison County

⊞ **HARRISON MEMORIAL HOSPITAL (180079)**, 1210 KY Highway 36E, Zip 41031–7498; tel. 859/234–2300 **A**1 10 **F**3 11 13 15 18 20 28 29 30 31 34 35 36 39 40 43 44 45 47 49 50 53 57 59 61 64 68 69 70 74 75 76 77 78 79 81 82 85 86 87 89 93 97 107 108 111 115 118 119 129 130 131 132 133 135 146 147 148
Primary Contact: Sheila Currans, Chief Executive Officer
CFO: David Mellett, Chief Financial Officer
CIO: Martha Sullivan, Chief Information Officer
CHR: Rebecca Jenkins, Director Human Resources Management
CNO: Wendy Reeder R.N., Chief Nursing Officer
Web address: www.harrisonmemhosp.com
Control: Other not–for–profit (including NFP Corporation) **Service:** General medical and surgical

Staffed Beds: 50 Admissions: 1316 Census: 13 Outpatient Visits: 73781 Births: 220 Total Expense ($000): 32964 Payroll Expense ($000): 14157 Personnel: 420		

DANVILLE—Boyle County

☐ **EPHRAIM MCDOWELL REGIONAL MEDICAL CENTER (180048)**, 217 South Third Street, Zip 40422–1823; tel. 859/239–1000 **A**1 3 5 10 19 **F**1 3 4 8 10 11 13 15 16 17 18 20 22 28 29 30 31 32 34 35 40 43 45 46 49 51 53 56 57 59 60 64 65 66 67 70 72 73 74 75 76 77 78 79 80 81 82 84 85 87 88 89 90 93 96 97 98 100 101 102 103 107 108 110 111 114 117 118 124 125 127 128 129 130 132 144 146 147 148 **S** Ephraim McDowell Health, Danville, KY
Primary Contact: Sally M. Davenport, R.N., MS, Chief Executive Officer
COO: Sally M Davenport R.N., MS, Chief Nursing Officer and Chief Operating Officer
CFO: William R Snapp III, Vice President Finance and Chief Financial Officer
CMO: Eric Guerrant M.D., President Medical Staff
CIO: Angela Allen–Johnson, Director Information Services
CHR: Carl Metz, Vice President Human Resources
CNO: Sally M Davenport R.N., MS, Chief Nursing Officer and Chief Operating Officer
Web address: www.emrmc.org
Control: Other not–for–profit (including NFP Corporation) **Service:** General medical and surgical

Staffed Beds: 159 Admissions: 6849 Census: 95 Outpatient Visits: 109204 Births: 593 Total Expense ($000): 146342 Payroll Expense ($000): 48492 Personnel: 997		

EDGEWOOD—Kenton County

⊞ **HEALTHSOUTH NORTHERN KENTUCKY REHABILITATION HOSPITAL (183027)**, 201 Medical Village Drive, Zip 41017–3407; tel. 859/341–2044 **A**1 10 **F**28 29 64 79 82 90 91 93 94 95 96 148 **S** HEALTHSOUTH Corporation, Birmingham, AL
Primary Contact: Richard R. Evens, Chief Executive Officer
CFO: Lisa McGue, Controller
CMO: Neal Moser M.D., Medical Director
CHR: Bridgette Keith, Director Human Resources
CNO: Terri Ballard, Chief Nursing Officer
Web address: www.healthsouthkentucky.com
Control: Corporation, Investor–owned (for–profit) **Service:** Rehabilitation

Staffed Beds: 40 Admissions: 1309 Census: 39 Outpatient Visits: 3725 Births: 0 Personnel: 126		

☐ **ST. ELIZABETH EDGEWOOD (180035)**, 1 Medical Village Drive, Zip 41017–3403; tel. 859/301–2000, (Includes ST. ELIZABETH COVINGTON, 1500 James Simpson Jr. Way, Covington, Kentucky, Zip 41014–1585, tel. 859/655–8800) **A**1 2 3 5 10 **F**3 5 8 13 14 15 17 18 20 22 24 26 28 29 30 31 34 35 36 37 38 39 40 44 45 46 47 48 49 50 53 55 57 58 59 60 61 63 64 65 70 71 72 73 74 75 76 77 78 79 80 81 82 83 84 85 86 87 92 93 97 98 100 101 102 103 104 105 107 108 109 110 111 114 115 117 118 119 120 121 123 124 126 129 130 131 132 135 141 145 146 147 148 149 150 **S** St. Elizabeth Healthcare, Edgewood, KY
Primary Contact: Garren Colvin, Chief Executive Officer
CMO: Karl Schmitt M.D., Chief of Staff
CIO: Alex Rodriguez, Vice President and Chief Information Officer
CHR: Martin Oscadal, Vice President Human Resources
Web address: www.stelizabeth.com
Control: Church operated, Nongovernment, not–for–profit **Service:** General medical and surgical

Staffed Beds: 522 Admissions: 28080 Census: 337 Outpatient Visits: 1128347 Births: 4448 Total Expense ($000): 668691 Payroll Expense ($000): 266821 Personnel: 3335		

ST. ELIZABETH HEALTHCARE–EDGEWOOD See St. Elizabeth Edgewood

ELIZABETHTOWN—Hardin County

⊞ **HARDIN MEMORIAL HOSPITAL (180012)**, 913 North Dixie Avenue, Zip 42701–2503; tel. 270/737–1212, (Total facility includes 15 beds in nursing home–type unit) **A**1 2 5 10 19 **F**3 8 11 12 13 15 17 18 20 22 24 28 29 30 31 32 34 35 37 39 40 44 45 48 49 50 51 52 54 57 58 59 64 68 70 71 72 74 75 76 77 78 79 80 81 82 84 85 86 87 89 93 94 96 98 102 107 108 110 111 114 115 117 118 119 120 121 124 126 128 129 130 131 132 134 135 144 146 147 148 149 **S** Baptist Health, Louisville, KY
Primary Contact: Dennis B. Johnson, President and Chief Executive Officer
COO: Tom Carrico, Vice President of Operations
CFO: Lennis Thompson II, Vice President and Chief Financial Officer
CMO: John Godfrey M.D., Vice President and Chief Executive Officer
CIO: Trey Hyberger, Director Information Technology
CHR: Myra Covault, Associate Vice President of Human Resources
CNO: Sharon Wright R.N., Vice President and Chief Nursing Officer
Web address: www.hmh.net
Control: County, Government, Nonfederal **Service:** General medical and surgical

Staffed Beds: 268 Admissions: 12714 Census: 154 Outpatient Visits: 420221 Births: 1625 Total Expense ($000): 274762 Payroll Expense ($000): 121878 Personnel: 2193		

⊞ **HEALTHSOUTH LAKEVIEW REHABILITATION HOSPITAL (183028)**, 134 Heartland Drive, Zip 42701–2778; tel. 270/769–3100 **A**1 10 **F**90 91 **S** HEALTHSOUTH Corporation, Birmingham, AL
Primary Contact: Lori Jarboe, Chief Executive Officer
CFO: Scott Hart, Controller
CMO: Toni Abang M.D., Medical Director
CHR: Janet Morris, Director Human Resources
Web address: www.healthsouthlakeview.com
Control: Corporation, Investor–owned (for–profit) **Service:** Rehabilitation

Staffed Beds: 40 Admissions: 779 Census: 25 Outpatient Visits: 0 Births: 0 Total Expense ($000): 9705 Payroll Expense ($000): 5556 Personnel: 118		

Hospital, Medicare Provider Number, Address, Telephone, Approval, Facility, and Physician Codes, Health Care System

★ American Hospital Association (AHA) membership
☐ The Joint Commission accreditation
○ Healthcare Facilities Accreditation Program
◇ DNV Healthcare Inc. accreditation
⇑ Center for Improvement in Healthcare Quality Accreditation
△ Commission on Accreditation of Rehabilitation Facilities (CARF) accreditation

FLEMINGSBURG—Fleming County

✠ **FLEMING COUNTY HOSPITAL (180053)**, 55 Foundation Drive, Zip 41041–9815, Mailing Address: P.O.Box 388, 41041–0388; tel. 606/849–5000, (Nonreporting) **A**1 10 **S** LifePoint Health, Brentwood, TN
Primary Contact: Brian Springate, Chief Executive Officer
CFO: Theresa Fite R.N., Chief Financial Officer
CMO: Samuel Gehring M.D., Chief of Staff
CIO: Don Daugherty, Director Information Systems
CHR: Marsha Mitchell, Director Human Resources
CNO: Lynda Skaggs, Chief Nursing Officer
Web address: www.flemingcountyhospital.org
Control: Other not-for-profit (including NFP Corporation) **Service:** General medical and surgical

Staffed Beds: 52

FLORENCE—Boone County

☐ **GATEWAY REHABILITATION HOSPITAL (183030)**, 5940 Merchant Street, Zip 41042–1158; tel. 859/426–2400 (Nonreporting) **A**1 10 **S** Vibra Healthcare, Mechanicsburg, PA
Primary Contact: Frank Schneider, FACHE, Chief Executive Officer
CFO: Margaret Cesarez, Chief Financial Officer
CNO: Jenna Wellbrock, Chief Nursing Officer
Web address: www.gatewayflorence.com/
Control: Corporation, Investor–owned (for-profit) **Service:** Rehabilitation

Staffed Beds: 40

☐ **ST. ELIZABETH FLORENCE (180045)**, 4900 Houston Road, Zip 41042–4824; tel. 859/212–5200, (Total facility includes 16 beds in nursing home–type unit) **A**1 10 **F**3 11 12 15 20 28 29 30 34 35 39 40 42 44 45 47 48 49 50 53 55 56 57 59 60 61 64 65 70 71 74 75 77 78 79 80 81 82 84 85 86 87 92 93 97 98 100 101 102 107 108 110 111 115 118 119 126 128 129 130 132 135 141 145 146 147 148 149 150 **S** St. Elizabeth Healthcare, Edgewood, KY
Primary Contact: Garren Colvin, Chief Executive Officer
COO: Chris Carle, Senior Vice President and Chief Operating Officer
CMO: George Hall M.D., Vice President Medical Affairs
CIO: Alex Rodriguez, Vice President and Chief Information Officer
CHR: Martin Oscadal, Senior Vice President Human Resources
Web address: www.stelizabeth.com
Control: Church operated, Nongovernment, not-for-profit **Service:** General medical and surgical

Staffed Beds: 169 **Admissions:** 11264 **Census:** 121 **Outpatient Visits:** 184228 **Births:** 0 **Total Expense ($000):** 137683 **Payroll Expense ($000):** 59112 **Personnel:** 798

ST. ELIZABETH HEALTHCARE FLORENCE See St. Elizabeth Florence

FORT CAMPBELL—Christian County

✠ **COLONEL FLORENCE A. BLANCHFIELD ARMY COMMUNITY HOSPITAL**, 650 Joel Drive, Zip 42223–5318; tel. 270/798–8040, (Nonreporting) **A**1 3 5 **S** Department of the Army, Office of the Surgeon General, Falls Church, VA
Primary Contact: Colonel Telita Crosland, Commander
CHR: MajorTravis Burchett, Troop Commander Human Resources
Web address: www.campbell.amedd.army.mil/
Control: Army, Government, federal **Service:** General medical and surgical

Staffed Beds: 66

FORT KNOX—Hardin County

✠ **IRELAND ARMY COMMUNITY HOSPITAL**, 289 Ireland Avenue, Zip 40121–5111; tel. 502/624–9333 **A**1 5 **F**3 5 7 11 12 13 15 18 29 30 32 33 34 35 39 40 44 45 50 53 57 59 64 65 68 74 75 76 77 79 81 87 89 91 93 97 99 100 101 104 105 107 108 110 111 115 118 119 130 131 132 135 146 **P**6 **S** Department of the Army, Office of the Surgeon General, Falls Church, VA
Primary Contact: Colonel Robert S. Cornes, Commander
Web address: www.iach.knox.amedd.army.mil/
Control: Army, Government, federal **Service:** General medical and surgical

Staffed Beds: 17 **Admissions:** 505 **Census:** 3 **Outpatient Visits:** 477917 **Births:** 193 **Total Expense ($000):** 115930 **Payroll Expense ($000):** 53000 **Personnel:** 662

FORT THOMAS—Campbell County

CARDINAL HILL SPECIALTY HOSPITAL See Select Specialty Hospital–Northern Kentucky

✠ **SELECT SPECIALTY HOSPITAL–NORTHERN KENTUCKY (182004)**, 85 North Grand Avenue, Zip 41075–1793; tel. 859/572–3880 (Nonreporting) **A**1 10 **S** Select Medical Corporation, Mechanicsburg, PA
Primary Contact: Teresa R. Detano, M.P.H., Chief Executive Officer
Web address: www.selectspecialtyhospitals.com
Control: Corporation, Investor–owned (for-profit) **Service:** Acute long–term care hospital

Staffed Beds: 33

☐ **ST. ELIZABETH FORT THOMAS (180001)**, 85 North Grand Avenue, Zip 41075–1796; tel. 859/572–3100, (Includes ST. ELIZABETH FALMOUTH, 512 South Maple Avenue, Falmouth, Kentucky, Zip 41040–1422, tel. 859/572–3500; Garren Colvin, Chief Executive Officer) (Total facility includes 26 beds in nursing home–type unit) **A**1 2 10 **F**3 4 5 11 15 17 18 20 28 29 30 31 34 35 39 40 42 44 45 47 48 49 50 51 53 55 56 57 58 59 60 61 63 64 65 70 71 74 75 77 78 79 80 81 82 85 86 87 91 92 93 94 97 100 102 107 108 110 111 115 118 119 120 121 123 126 128 129 130 135 141 146 147 149 150 **S** St. Elizabeth Healthcare, Edgewood, KY
Primary Contact: Garren Colvin, Chief Executive Officer
COO: Thomas Saalfeld, Senior Vice President and Chief Operating Officer
CMO: George Hall M.D., Vice President Medical Affairs
CIO: Alex Rodriguez, Vice President and Chief Information Officer
CHR: Martin Oscadal, Senior Vice President Human Resources
Web address: www.stelizabeth.com
Control: Church operated, Nongovernment, not-for-profit **Service:** General medical and surgical

Staffed Beds: 171 **Admissions:** 7942 **Census:** 102 **Outpatient Visits:** 137940 **Births:** 0 **Total Expense ($000):** 117465 **Payroll Expense ($000):** 50431 **Personnel:** 689

ST. ELIZABETH HEALTHCARE FORT THOMAS See St. Elizabeth Fort Thomas

FRANKFORT—Franklin County

✠ **FRANKFORT REGIONAL MEDICAL CENTER (180127)**, 299 King's Daughters Drive, Zip 40601–4186; tel. 502/875–5240 **A**1 2 10 19 **F**3 13 15 18 20 22 28 29 30 31 34 40 43 45 49 50 51 57 60 64 68 70 72 74 75 76 77 78 79 81 82 84 85 87 89 93 98 102 103 105 107 111 119 124 129 130 133 135 145 146 147 148 **S** HCA Healthcare, Nashville, TN
Primary Contact: Chip Peal, Chief Executive Officer
CMO: Willis P McKee M.D., Jr, Chief Medical Officer
CIO: Craig Willard, Director Information Technology and Systems
CHR: Bev Young, Director Human Resources
Web address: www.frankfortregional.com
Control: Corporation, Investor–owned (for-profit) **Service:** General medical and surgical

Staffed Beds: 115 **Admissions:** 5526 **Census:** 70 **Outpatient Visits:** 95259 **Births:** 780 **Total Expense ($000):** 88222 **Payroll Expense ($000):** 30924 **Personnel:** 434

FRANKLIN—Simpson County

✠ **MEDICAL CENTER AT FRANKLIN (181318)**, 1100 Brookhaven Road, Zip 42134–2746; tel. 270/598–4800 **A**1 10 18 **F**3 15 28 29 30 34 35 40 46 57 59 64 68 75 77 81 82 86 87 93 107 108 110 111 114 119 127 130 133 135 146 148 **P**6 **S** Commonwealth Health Corporation, Bowling Green, KY
Primary Contact: Annette Runyon, Vice President and Administrator
CFO: Ronald G. Sowell, Executive Vice President
CIO: Mark Brookman, Vice President and Chief Information Officer
Web address: www.themedicalcenterfranklin.org
Control: Other not-for-profit (including NFP Corporation) **Service:** General medical and surgical

Staffed Beds: 25 **Admissions:** 1128 **Census:** 21 **Outpatient Visits:** 24860 **Births:** 0 **Personnel:** 143

GEORGETOWN—Scott County

✠ **GEORGETOWN COMMUNITY HOSPITAL (180101)**, 1140 Lexington Road, Zip 40324–9362; tel. 502/868–1100 **A**1 5 10 **F**3 11 12 13 15 18 28 29 30 31 34 35 40 45 46 47 48 49 50 57 59 60 64 65 66 70 74 75 76 78 79 81 82 85 87 91 92 93 100 107 108 109 110 111 114 115 116 119 124 126 129 130 131 132 133 144 146 147 149 **S** LifePoint Health, Brentwood, TN
Primary Contact: William Haugh, Administrator
CFO: Patrick C Bolander, Chief Financial Officer
CMO: Brian Allen M.D., President Medical Staff
CHR: Marrianne Slonina, Director Human Resources
Web address: www.georgetowncommunityhospital.com
Control: Corporation, Investor–owned (for-profit) **Service:** General medical and surgical

Staffed Beds: 58 **Admissions:** 1973 **Census:** 16 **Outpatient Visits:** 73582 **Births:** 242 **Total Expense ($000):** 43720 **Payroll Expense ($000):** 16352 **Personnel:** 339

GLASGOW—Barren County

☐ **T. J. SAMSON COMMUNITY HOSPITAL (180017)**, 1301 North Race Street, Zip 42141–3483; tel. 270/651–4444, (Total facility includes 16 beds in nursing home–type unit) **A**1 3 5 10 19 **F**3 11 13 15 18 20 22 24 28 29 30 31 34 40 45 57 59 60 62 63 64 70 71 72 74 75 77 78 79 81 82 84 85 86 87 93 97 107 110 111 112 114 115 119 124 127 128 129 130 131 132 135 144 146 147 148
Primary Contact: Bud Wethington, Chief Executive Officer
COO: Margie Gentry, Controller
CFO: Mei Deng, Chief Financial Officer
CMO: Michael Shadowen M.D., Chief of Staff
CIO: Scott Werkstell, Director Information System
CHR: LaDonna Rogers, Director Human Resources
CNO: Margaret Billingsley R.N., MSN, Chief Nursing Officer
Web address: www.tjsamson.org
Control: Other not–for–profit (including NFP Corporation) **Service:** General medical and surgical

Staffed Beds: 114 **Admissions:** 5380 **Census:** 48 **Outpatient Visits:** 405808 **Births:** 1111 **Total Expense ($000):** 150818 **Payroll Expense ($000):** 64659 **Personnel:** 1150

GREENSBURG—Green County

JANE TODD CRAWFORD HOSPITAL (181325), 202–206 Milby Street, Zip 42743–1100, Mailing Address: P.O.Box 220, 42743–0220; tel. 270/932–4211, (Nonreporting) **A**10 18
Primary Contact: Rex A. Tungate, Chief Executive Officer
CFO: Richard Hendershot, Chief Financial Officer
CMO: Shane DeSimone M.D., Chief of Staff
CHR: Mary Ann Quinn, Administrative Assistant
CNO: Roxie Montgomery, Director of Nursing
Web address: www.janetoddhospital.com
Control: County, Government, Nonfederal **Service:** General medical and surgical

Staffed Beds: 45

GREENVILLE—Muhlenberg County

☐ **OWENSBORO HEALTH MUHLENBERG COMMUNITY HOSPITAL (180004)**, 440 Hopkinsville Street, Zip 42345–1172, Mailing Address: P.O.Box 387, 42345–0378; tel. 270/338–8000, (Nonreporting) **A**1 10 **S** Owensboro Health, Owensboro, KY
Primary Contact: Ed Heath, FACHE, Chief Executive Officer
CMO: Vincent P Genovese M.D., President Medical Staff
CIO: Alan Trail, Director Information Systems
CHR: Lisa R Hope, Director Human Resources
CNO: Kathy Mitchell, Chief Nursing Officer
Web address: www.mchky.org
Control: Other not–for–profit (including NFP Corporation) **Service:** General medical and surgical

Staffed Beds: 105

HARDINSBURG—Breckinridge County

⊞ **BRECKINRIDGE MEMORIAL HOSPITAL (181319)**, 1011 Old Highway 60, Zip 40143–2597; tel. 270/756–7000, (Nonreporting) **A**1 5 10 18 **S** Alliant Management Services, Louisville, KY
Primary Contact: Angela Portman, Chief Executive Officer
CFO: Timothy D Crockett, Chief Financial Officer
CMO: Brian O'Donoghue M.D., Chief Medical Officer
CHR: James Turpin, Human Resources
CNO: Tiffany Kennedy, Chief Nursing Officer
Web address: www.breckinridgehealth.org/
Control: Other not–for–profit (including NFP Corporation) **Service:** General medical and surgical

Staffed Beds: 43

HARLAN—Harlan County

☐ **HARLAN ARH HOSPITAL (180050)**, 81 Ball Park Road, Zip 40831–1792; tel. 606/573–8100 **A**1 10 19 **F**3 11 13 15 18 20 28 29 30 32 34 35 40 43 50 54 57 59 62 64 70 75 76 77 78 79 81 82 85 86 87 89 93 97 98 102 103 107 108 111 115 118 119 127 129 130 132 146 147 148 **P**6 **S** Appalachian Regional Healthcare, Inc., Lexington, KY
Primary Contact: Donald R. Fields, Community Chief Executive Officer
CFO: Brad Burkhart, Assistant Administrator
CHR: Sabra Howard, Manager Human Resources
Web address: www.arh.org
Control: Other not–for–profit (including NFP Corporation) **Service:** General medical and surgical

Staffed Beds: 145 **Admissions:** 5287 **Census:** 55 **Outpatient Visits:** 74190 **Births:** 221 **Total Expense ($000):** 65231 **Payroll Expense ($000):** 16702 **Personnel:** 482

HARRODSBURG—Mercer County

⊞ **JAMES B. HAGGIN MEMORIAL HOSPITAL (181302)**, 464 Linden Avenue, Zip 40330–1862; tel. 859/734–5441, (Nonreporting) **A**1 5 10 18 **S** Alliant Management Services, Louisville, KY
Primary Contact: Victoria L. Reed, R.N., FACHE, Chief Executive Officer
CFO: Tony Patterson, Chief Financial Officer
Web address: www.hagginhosp.org
Control: Other not–for–profit (including NFP Corporation) **Service:** General medical and surgical

Staffed Beds: 25

HARTFORD—Ohio County

⊞ **OHIO COUNTY HOSPITAL (181323)**, 1211 Main Street, Zip 42347–1619; tel. 270/298–7411, (Nonreporting) **A**1 10 18 **S** QHR, Brentwood, TN
Primary Contact: Blaine Pieper, Chief Executive Officer
CFO: John Tichenor, Chief Financial Officer
CMO: Joshua Skibba, Chief Medical Officer
CHR: Sue Wydick, Director Human Resources
CNO: Athena Minor, Chief Nursing Officer
Web address: www.ohiocountyhospital.com
Control: Other not–for–profit (including NFP Corporation) **Service:** General medical and surgical

Staffed Beds: 25

HAZARD—Perry County

☐ **HAZARD ARH REGIONAL MEDICAL CENTER (180029)**, 100 Medical Center Drive, Zip 41701–9421; tel. 606/439–6600 **A**1 2 3 5 10 19 **F**3 11 12 13 15 17 18 20 22 24 26 28 29 30 31 32 34 35 40 43 46 47 48 49 50 54 55 57 59 61 62 64 70 71 73 74 75 76 77 78 79 81 82 85 86 87 89 90 93 97 98 101 102 103 107 108 110 111 115 118 119 120 121 124 127 129 130 132 146 147 148 **P**6 **S** Appalachian Regional Healthcare, Inc., Lexington, KY
Primary Contact: Dan Stone, Senior Community Chief Executive Officer
CMO: J D Miller M.D., Chief Medical Officer
CIO: Jeff Brady, Director Information Systems
CHR: Sheila Cornett, Manager Human Resources
Web address: www.arh.org
Control: Other not–for–profit (including NFP Corporation) **Service:** General medical and surgical

Staffed Beds: 358 **Admissions:** 12526 **Census:** 203 **Outpatient Visits:** 125999 **Births:** 401 **Total Expense ($000):** 168691 **Payroll Expense ($000):** 38909 **Personnel:** 1248

HENDERSON—Henderson County

☐ **METHODIST HOSPITAL (180056)**, 1305 North Elm Street, Zip 42420–2775, Mailing Address: P.O.Box 48, 42419–0048; tel. 270/827–7700 **A**1 2 10 13 **F**3 11 12 13 15 18 20 29 30 31 34 35 36 40 45 46 47 49 50 51 53 54 57 58 59 64 66 68 70 72 74 75 76 77 78 79 81 82 85 86 87 89 92 93 107 108 110 111 114 115 118 119 126 127 129 130 131 132 135 146 147 148 **P**8
Primary Contact: Benny Nolen, President and Chief Executive Officer
CFO: David Massengale, Vice President and Chief Financial Officer
CMO: John Logan M.D., Chief Medical Officer
CIO: Randy McCleese, Chief Information Officer
CHR: Ty Kahle, Vice President Human Resources
Web address: www.methodisthospital.net
Control: Church operated, Nongovernment, not–for–profit **Service:** General medical and surgical

Staffed Beds: 115 **Admissions:** 4015 **Census:** 51 **Outpatient Visits:** 336694 **Births:** 677 **Total Expense ($000):** 111133 **Payroll Expense ($000):** 40572 **Personnel:** 1071

HOPKINSVILLE—Christian County

☐ **CUMBERLAND HALL HOSPITAL (184014)**, 270 Walton Way, Zip 42240–6808; tel. 270/886–1919, (Nonreporting) **A**1 10 **S** Universal Health Services, Inc., King of Prussia, PA
Primary Contact: Jason Staats, Chief Executive Officer
CFO: Mark Wallace, Chief Financial Officer
CMO: Deepak Patel M.D., Medical Director
CIO: Patricia Gray, Director Health Information Management
CHR: Kelly Hagy, Director Human Resources
CNO: Denise Lyons, Chief Nursing Officer
Web address: www.cumberlandhallhospital.com
Control: Corporation, Investor–owned (for–profit) **Service:** Psychiatric

Staffed Beds: 97

Hospital, Medicare Provider Number, Address, Telephone, Approval, Facility, and Physician Codes, Health Care System

★ American Hospital Association (AHA) membership
☐ The Joint Commission accreditation
○ Healthcare Facilities Accreditation Program
◇ DNV Healthcare Inc. accreditation
⇑ Center for Improvement in Healthcare Quality Accreditation
△ Commission on Accreditation of Rehabilitation Facilities (CARF) accreditation

Hospitals, U.S. / KENTUCKY

⊞ **JENNIE STUART MEDICAL CENTER (180051)**, 320 West 18th Street, Zip 42240–1965, Mailing Address: P.O.Box 2400, 42241–2400; tel. 270/887–0100, (Nonreporting) **A**1 3 10 20 **S** QHR, Brentwood, TN
Primary Contact: Eric A. Lee, President and Chief Executive Officer
CMO: Casey Covington M.D., President Elect, Medical Staff
CIO: Jerry Houston, Director Information Systems
CHR: Austin Moss, Vice President Human Resources
Web address: www.jsmc.org
Control: Other not–for–profit (including NFP Corporation) **Service:** General medical and surgical

Staffed Beds: 139

☐ **WESTERN STATE HOSPITAL (184002)**, Russellville Road, Zip 42240–3017, Mailing Address: P.O.Box 2200, 42241–2200; tel. 270/889–6025 **A**1 10 **F**98 102 103 130 149 **P**5
Primary Contact: Roger Westfall, Director
CFO: Jessica Cates, Fiscal Manager
CMO: Nayyar Iqbal M.D., Director Medical Staff
CIO: Valerie Majors, Director Information Services
CHR: James L Hayes, Director Human Resources
CNO: Jill Thomas, Director of Nursing
Web address: www.westernstatehospital.ky.gov
Control: State, Government, Nonfederal **Service:** Psychiatric

Staffed Beds: 205 Admissions: 2050 Census: 121 Outpatient Visits: 0 Births: 0 Total Expense ($000): 17907 Payroll Expense ($000): 10150 Personnel: 587

HORSE CAVE—Hart County

THE MEDICAL CENTER AT CAVERNA (181314), 1501 South Dixie Street, Zip 42749–1477; tel. 270/786–2191 **A**10 18 **F**3 15 29 34 40 50 57 59 64 77 89 91 103 104 107 110 111 114 119 127 128 130 133 149 **S** Commonwealth Health Corporation, Bowling Green, KY
Primary Contact: Alan B. Alexander, FACHE, Vice President and Administrator
CFO: Ronald G. Sowell, Executive Vice President and Chief Financial Officer
CIO: Mark Brookman, Vice President, Chief Information Officer
CHR: Lynn Williams, Vice President, Human Resources
Web address: www.TheMedicalCenterCaverna.org
Control: Other not–for–profit (including NFP Corporation) **Service:** General medical and surgical

Staffed Beds: 25 Admissions: 359 Census: 6 Outpatient Visits: 24421 Births: 0 Total Expense ($000): 12170 Payroll Expense ($000): 4793 Personnel: 127

HYDEN—Leslie County

MARY BRECKINRIDGE ARH HOSPITAL (181316), 130 Kate Ireland Drive, Zip 41749–9071, Mailing Address: P.O.Box 447–A, 41749–0717; tel. 606/672–2901 **A**10 18 **F**2 3 11 15 29 30 32 34 35 40 50 57 59 62 65 68 75 77 81 86 87 93 107 110 115 119 130 132 133 135 146 **P**6 **S** Appalachian Regional Healthcare, Inc., Lexington, KY
Primary Contact: Mallie S. Noble, Administrator
COO: Nathan W Lee, Chief Executive Officer
CFO: Robert Besten, Chief Financial Officer
CMO: Roy Varghese M.D., Chief of Staff
CIO: Frank Baker, Chief Information Officer
CHR: Beulah Couch, Director Human Resources
Web address: www.frontiernursing.org
Control: Other not–for–profit (including NFP Corporation) **Service:** General medical and surgical

Staffed Beds: 25 Admissions: 399 Census: 10 Outpatient Visits: 20907 Births: 0 Total Expense ($000): 11571 Payroll Expense ($000): 4002 Personnel: 116

IRVINE—Estill County

★ **MERCY HEALTH – MARCUM AND WALLACE (181301)**, 60 Mercy Court, Zip 40336–1331; tel. 606/723–2115 **A**10 18 **F**3 15 29 30 34 35 40 43 45 50 56 57 59 64 75 77 81 83 93 107 115 119 127 129 130 131 133 146 147 **S** Mercy Health, Cincinnati, OH
Primary Contact: Susan Starling, President and Chief Executive Officer
CFO: Lori Witt, Site Finance Director
CMO: Maher Kassis M.D., Chief Medical Staff
CHR: Dana Stepp, Human Resources Officer
CNO: Trena Stocker, Chief Nursing Executive
Web address: www.marcumandwallace.org
Control: Church operated, Nongovernment, not–for–profit **Service:** General medical and surgical

Staffed Beds: 25 Admissions: 956 Census: 13 Outpatient Visits: 72389 Births: 0 Total Expense ($000): 20188 Payroll Expense ($000): 8615 Personnel: 159

JACKSON—Breathitt County

⊞ **KENTUCKY RIVER MEDICAL CENTER (180139)**, 540 Jett Drive, Zip 41339–9622; tel. 606/666–6000, (Nonreporting) **A**1 10 20 **S** Quorum Health, Brentwood, TN
Primary Contact: John Ballard, Ph.D., Chief Executive Officer
CFO: Michael Ackley, Chief Financial Officer
CMO: Eunice Johnson M.D., Chief Medical Staff
CIO: Diana Tyra, Director Health Information
CHR: Naomi Mitchell, Director Human Resources
Web address: www.kentuckyrivermc.com
Control: Corporation, Investor–owned (for–profit) **Service:** General medical and surgical

Staffed Beds: 54

LA GRANGE—Oldham County

⊞ **BAPTIST HEALTH LA GRANGE (180138)**, 1025 New Moody Lane, Zip 40031–9154; tel. 502/222–5388, (Total facility includes 24 beds in nursing home–type unit) **A**1 5 10 **F**3 7 11 13 15 18 28 29 30 31 34 35 36 40 43 45 46 49 50 54 56 57 59 64 68 70 74 75 76 77 78 79 81 82 85 86 87 93 97 107 108 110 111 114 119 128 129 130 131 132 133 135 146 147 148 149 **P**6 **S** Baptist Health, Louisville, KY
Primary Contact: Christopher Roty, President
CFO: Jim Morris, Vice President Finance
CMO: Matt McDanald M.D., Chief Medical Officer
CIO: David Bensema, Chief Information Officer
CHR: Kayla Batts, Manager Human Resources
CNO: Nathan Wilson R.N., Vice President and Chief Nursing Officer
Web address: www.baptisthealthlagrange.com
Control: Other not–for–profit (including NFP Corporation) **Service:** General medical and surgical

Staffed Beds: 65 Admissions: 2172 Census: 34 Outpatient Visits: 120784 Births: 507 Total Expense ($000): 81605 Payroll Expense ($000): 25067 Personnel: 431

LEBANON—Marion County

⊞ **SPRING VIEW HOSPITAL (180024)**, 320 Loretto Road, Zip 40033–1300; tel. 270/692–3161, (Nonreporting) **A**1 10 **S** LifePoint Health, Brentwood, TN
Primary Contact: Timothy R. Trottier, Chief Executive Officer
CFO: Denise Thomas, Chief Financial Officer
CIO: Douglas Bland, Manager Information Services
CHR: Ann Dabney, Manager Human Resources
CNO: Linda Hunter, Chief Nursing Officer
Web address: www.springviewhospital.com
Control: Corporation, Investor–owned (for–profit) **Service:** General medical and surgical

Staffed Beds: 60

LEITCHFIELD—Grayson County

☐ **TWIN LAKES REGIONAL MEDICAL CENTER (180070)**, 910 Wallace Avenue, Zip 42754–2414; tel. 270/259–9400, (Nonreporting) **A**1 10 **S** Alliant Management Services, Louisville, KY
Primary Contact: Wayne Meriwether, Chief Executive Officer
COO: Deneace Clemons, Chief Operating Officer
CFO: Scott Arndell, Chief Financial Officer
CIO: Robbie Lindsey, Chief Information Officer
CHR: Kim Rayls, Director Human Resources
CNO: David Logdson, Chief Nursing Officer
Web address: www.tlrmc.com
Control: Other not–for–profit (including NFP Corporation) **Service:** General medical and surgical

Staffed Beds: 75

LEXINGTON—Fayette County

⊞ **BAPTIST HEALTH LEXINGTON (180103)**, 1740 Nicholasville Road, Zip 40503–1499; tel. 859/260–6100 **A**1 2 3 10 **F**3 11 12 13 15 18 20 22 24 26 28 29 30 31 34 35 36 40 44 45 48 49 53 54 55 56 57 58 59 60 64 68 70 72 74 75 76 77 78 79 81 84 85 86 87 92 93 97 107 108 110 111 114 115 117 118 119 120 121 124 126 129 130 131 132 135 144 146 147 148 **S** Baptist Health, Louisville, KY
Primary Contact: William G. Sisson, President
COO: Karen S Hill R.N., FACHE, Chief Operating Officer and Chief Nursing Officer
CFO: John Franke, Chief Financial Officer
CMO: James Borders M.D., Chief Medical Officer
CIO: Lisa Fluty, Director Information Services
CHR: Lynette Walker R.N., Ph.D., Vice President Human Resources
Web address: www.baptisthealthlexington.com
Control: Other not–for–profit (including NFP Corporation) **Service:** General medical and surgical

Staffed Beds: 384 Admissions: 18900 Census: 237 Outpatient Visits: 300772 Births: 3475 Total Expense ($000): 436862 Payroll Expense ($000): 133032 Personnel: 2316

Many Facility Codes have changed. Please refer to the AHA Guide Code Chart. © 2017 AHA Guide

★ △ **CARDINAL HILL REHABILITATION HOSPITAL (183026)**, 2050 Versailles Road, Zip 40504–1405; tel. 859/254–5701, (Total facility includes 74 beds in nursing home–type unit) **A**3 5 7 10 **F**3 28 29 56 58 62 64 87 90 91 93 95 96 128 130 **S** HEALTHSOUTH Corporation, Birmingham, AL
Primary Contact: Brad Kennedy, Interim Chief Executive Officer
CFO: Marty Lautner, Vice President Finance and Chief Financial Officer
CMO: William Lester M.D., Vice President Medical Affairs
CIO: LouAnn Hyder, Director Information Integrity Management
CHR: Barry K Lindeman, Director Human Resources
CNO: Maureen Couture, Chief Nursing Officer and Vice President Nursing
Web address: www.cardinalhillhealthsouth.com
Control: Corporation, Investor–owned (for–profit) **Service:** Rehabilitation

Staffed Beds: 232 Admissions: 2497 Census: 91 Outpatient Visits: 47927
Births: 0 **Total Expense ($000):** 60720 **Payroll Expense ($000):** 30230
Personnel: 530

★ **CONTINUING CARE HOSPITAL (182002)**, 1 Saint Joseph Drive, Zip 40504–3742; tel. 859/967–5744 **A**10 **F**1 3 29 30 **S** Catholic Health Initiatives, Englewood, CO
Primary Contact: Jimmie Settles, Interim President and Chief Executive Officer
CMO: Michael Miedler M.D., Chief Medical Officer
CNO: Regina Masters R.N., MSN, Director of Nursing
Web address: www.kentuckyonehealth.org
Control: Church operated, Nongovernment, not–for–profit **Service:** Acute long–term care hospital

Staffed Beds: 43 Admissions: 447 Census: 36 Outpatient Visits: 0 **Births:** 0
Total Expense ($000): 17354 **Payroll Expense ($000):** 5767 **Personnel:** 78

☐ **EASTERN STATE HOSPITAL (184004)**, 1350 Bull Lea Road, Zip 40511; tel. 859/246–7000 **A**1 3 5 10 **F**29 30 35 56 75 77 87 96 97 98 101 103 130 132 135 143 146 149 150 **P**6
Primary Contact: Carrie Rudzik, Chief Administrative Officer
COO: Susan M Griffith, Chief Operations Officer
CFO: Tambara Nalle, Chief Financial Officer
CMO: Scott A Haas M.D., Chief Medical Officer
CIO: Bud Stone, Director Information Systems
CHR: Jerry Kersey, Director Employee Relations
CNO: Kristan Mowder, Director Administration and Patient Care Services
Web address: www.ukhealthcare.uky.edu/ESH/
Control: State, Government, Nonfederal **Service:** Psychiatric

Staffed Beds: 140 Admissions: 2349 Census: 105 Outpatient Visits: 0
Births: 0 **Total Expense ($000):** 45953 **Payroll Expense ($000):** 23382
Personnel: 378

FEDERAL MEDICAL CENTER, 3301 Leestown Road, Zip 40511–8799; tel. 859/255–6812, (Nonreporting)
Primary Contact: Francisco Quintana, Warden
CFO: Mike Kinsel, Controller
CMO: Michael Growse M.D., Clinical Director
Control: Department of Justice, Government, federal **Service:** Hospital unit of an institution (prison hospital, college infirmary, etc.)

Staffed Beds: 22

⊞ **LEXINGTON VETERANS AFFAIRS MEDICAL CENTER**, 1101 Veterans Drive, Zip 40502–2235; tel. 859/281–4901 **A**1 3 5 **F**3 4 5 8 11 17 18 20 22 26 29 30 31 34 35 36 37 39 40 45 46 47 51 54 56 57 58 59 60 61 62 63 64 65 66 70 74 75 77 78 79 81 82 83 84 85 86 87 90 91 92 93 94 96 97 98 100 101 102 103 104 105 107 108 111 114 115 116 117 118 119 126 127 128 129 130 132 135 143 144 146 147 148 149 150 **P**6 **S** Department of Veterans Affairs, Washington, DC
Primary Contact: Emma Metcalf, MSN, R.N., Director
CFO: Patricia Swisshelm, Acting Chief Fiscal Service
CMO: Patricia Breeden M.D., Chief of Staff
CIO: Jeffrey Sutton, Chief Information Officer
CHR: Laura Faulkner, Chief Human Resource Management Service
CNO: Mary Kelly McCullough, Associate Director Patient Care Services
Web address: www.lexington.va.gov/
Control: Veterans Affairs, Government, federal **Service:** General medical and surgical

Staffed Beds: 45 Admissions: 5261 Census: 45 Outpatient Visits: 507086
Births: 0 **Personnel:** 2141

☐ **RIDGE BEHAVIORAL HEALTH SYSTEM (184009)**, 3050 Rio Dosa Drive, Zip 40509–1540; tel. 859/269–2325, (Nonreporting) **A**1 5 10 **S** Universal Health Services, Inc., King of Prussia, PA
Primary Contact: Nina W. Eisner, Chief Executive Officer and Managing Director
CFO: Richard McDowell, Chief Financial Officer
CMO: Michael Rieser M.D., Medical Director
CNO: Georgia Swank, Chief Nursing Officer
Web address: www.ridgebhs.com
Control: Corporation, Investor–owned (for–profit) **Service:** Psychiatric

Staffed Beds: 110

⊞ **SAINT JOSEPH EAST (180143)**, 150 North Eagle Creek Drive, Zip 40509–1805; tel. 859/967–5000, (Includes WOMEN'S HOSPITAL SAINT JOSEPH EAST, 170 North Eagle Creek Drive, Lexington, Kentucky, Zip 40509–9087, tel. 859/572–3500) **A**1 2 5 10 **F**3 8 12 13 15 18 20 22 24 26 28 29 30 31 40 47 49 50 60 68 70 72 74 75 76 77 78 79 81 82 85 86 93 107 108 111 114 118 119 120 121 122 123 126 129 142 146 147 148 **S** Catholic Health Initiatives, Englewood, CO
Primary Contact: Eric Gilliam, President
COO: Christine Mays R.N., MSN, Chief Operating Officer and Chief Nurse Executive
CFO: Melinda S Evans, Vice President Finance
CIO: Janie Fergus, Director and Chief Information Officer
Web address: www.sjhlex.org
Control: Church operated, Nongovernment, not–for–profit **Service:** General medical and surgical

Staffed Beds: 150 Admissions: 9478 Census: 100 Outpatient Visits: 120903 **Births:** 2866 **Total Expense ($000):** 176638 **Payroll Expense ($000):** 49125 **Personnel:** 725

⊞ **SAINT JOSEPH HOSPITAL (180010)**, One St Joseph Drive, Zip 40504–3754; tel. 859/278–3436 **A**1 2 3 10 **F**3 8 11 12 15 17 18 19 20 22 24 25 26 27 28 29 30 31 34 35 37 40 41 42 45 47 49 50 51 54 55 56 57 58 59 64 65 66 68 70 74 77 78 79 81 82 83 84 85 86 87 91 92 93 94 97 107 110 111 114 115 116 117 118 119 120 121 123 126 127 129 130 132 135 144 146 147 148 **S** Catholic Health Initiatives, Englewood, CO
Primary Contact: Bruce J. Tassin, President
COO: Christine Mays R.N., MSN, Chief Operating Officer and Chief Nurse Executive
CFO: Melinda S Evans, Vice President Finance
CIO: Janie Fergus, Director and Chief Information Officer
Web address: www.sjhlex.org
Control: Church operated, Nongovernment, not–for–profit **Service:** General medical and surgical

Staffed Beds: 307 Admissions: 13387 Census: 194 Outpatient Visits: 98979 **Births:** 0 **Total Expense ($000):** 280466 **Payroll Expense ($000):** 80358 **Personnel:** 1276

⊞ **SELECT SPECIALTY HOSPITAL–LEXINGTON (182003)**, 310 South Limestone Street, 3rd Floor, Zip 40508–3008; tel. 859/226–7096, (Nonreporting) **A**1 10 **S** Select Medical Corporation, Mechanicsburg, PA
Primary Contact: Kim Pennington, Chief Executive Officer
CMO: Fadi Bacha M.D., Chief Medical Officer
CHR: Tina Kirkland–Rose, Coordinator Human Resources
CNO: Katie Meredith, Chief Nursing Officer
Web address: www.lexington.selectspecialtyhospitals.com/
Control: Corporation, Investor–owned (for–profit) **Service:** Acute long–term care hospital

Staffed Beds: 41

☐ **SHRINERS HOSPITALS FOR CHILDREN–LEXINGTON (183300)**, 1900 Richmond Road, Zip 40502–1298; tel. 859/266–2101, (Nonreporting) **A**1 3 5 10 **S** Shriners Hospitals for Children, Tampa, FL
Primary Contact: Tony Lewgood, Administrator
CFO: Robert Montgomery, Chief Financial Officer
CMO: Chester Tylkowski M.D., Chief of Staff
CIO: David Brian, Director Information Services
Web address: www.shrinershospitalsforchildren.org/Hospitals/Locations/Lexington.aspx
Control: Other not–for–profit (including NFP Corporation) **Service:** Children's orthopedic

Staffed Beds: 50

Hospital, Medicare Provider Number, Address, Telephone, Approval, Facility, and Physician Codes, Health Care System

★ American Hospital Association (AHA) membership
☐ The Joint Commission accreditation
○ Healthcare Facilities Accreditation Program
◇ DNV Healthcare Inc. accreditation
⇈ Center for Improvement in Healthcare Quality Accreditation
△ Commission on Accreditation of Rehabilitation Facilities (CARF) accreditation

Hospitals, U.S. / KENTUCKY

✠ **UNIVERSITY OF KENTUCKY ALBERT B. CHANDLER HOSPITAL (180067)**, 800 Rose Street, Zip 40536–0293; tel. 859/323–5000, (Includes KENTUCKY CHILDREN'S HOSPITAL, N–100 – 800 Rose Street, Lexington, Kentucky, Zip 40536–0293, tel. 859/257–1000; UK HEALTHCARE GOOD SAMARITAN HOSPITAL, 310 South Limestone Street, Lexington, Kentucky, Zip 40508–3008, tel. 859/226–7000; Michael Karpf, M.D., Executive Vice President of Health Affairs) **A**1 2 3 5 8 10 12 **F**3 5 6 7 9 11 12 13 15 16 17 18 19 20 21 22 23 24 26 27 28 29 30 31 32 34 35 36 37 38 39 40 41 43 44 45 46 47 48 49 50 52 54 55 56 57 58 59 60 61 64 65 66 68 70 72 73 74 75 76 77 78 79 81 82 84 85 86 87 88 89 91 92 93 94 95 96 97 98 99 100 102 104 105 107 108 110 111 113 114 115 118 119 120 121 123 124 126 129 130 131 132 134 135 136 137 138 139 140 141 142 145 146 147 148 149 150 **P**6
Primary Contact: Michael Karpf, M.D., Executive Vice President of Health Affairs
CHR: Kimberly P Wilson, Director Human Resources
Web address: www.ukhealthcare.uky.edu
Control: State, Government, Nonfederal **Service**: General medical and surgical

Staffed Beds: 864 **Admissions:** 37792 **Census:** 709 **Outpatient Visits:** 1505134 **Births:** 1912 **Total Expense ($000):** 1279638 **Payroll Expense ($000):** 385872 **Personnel:** 7391

UNIVERSITY OF KENTUCKY HOSPITAL See University Of Kentucky Albert B. Chandler Hospital

LIBERTY—Casey County

☐ **CASEY COUNTY HOSPITAL (181309)**, 187 Wolford Avenue, Zip 42539–3278; tel. 606/787–6275 (Nonreporting) **A**1 10 18
Primary Contact: Rex A. Tungate, Chief Executive Officer
CFO: Richard Hendershot, Chief Financial Officer
CMO: Housam Haddad M.D., Chief of Staff
CHR: Mary Ann Quinn, Administrative Assistant
CNO: Sue Antle, Director of Nursing
Web address: www.caseycountyhospital.com
Control: County, Government, Nonfederal **Service**: General medical and surgical

Staffed Beds: 24

LONDON—Laurel County

✠ **SAINT JOSEPH LONDON (180011)**, 1001 Saint Joseph Lane, Zip 40741–8345; tel. 606/330–6000 **A**1 10 19 **F**3 13 15 20 22 26 28 29 30 31 34 35 40 42 45 47 49 50 51 57 59 60 61 64 70 74 75 76 78 79 80 81 82 85 87 89 92 93 97 107 108 110 111 114 115 119 127 129 130 131 135 146 147 149 150 **S** Catholic Health Initiatives, Englewood, CO
Primary Contact: Terrence G. Deis, CPA, FACHE, President
CFO: Christy Spitser, Vice President Finance and Business Development
CMO: Shelley Stanko M.D., Chief Medical Officer
CHR: Sandra Turqueza, Senior Human Resources Business Partner
CNO: Lewis Stephen O'Neal R.N., MSN, Chief Nursing Officer
Web address: www.saintjosephhealthsystem.org
Control: Church operated, Nongovernment, not–for–profit **Service**: General medical and surgical

Staffed Beds: 116 **Admissions:** 5389 **Census:** 56 **Outpatient Visits:** 112266 **Births:** 1027 **Total Expense ($000):** 127689 **Payroll Expense ($000):** 37612 **Personnel:** 556

LOUISA—Lawrence County

✠ **THREE RIVERS MEDICAL CENTER (180128)**, 2485 Highway 644, Zip 41230–9242, Mailing Address: P.O.Box 769, 41230–0769; tel. 606/638–9451, (Nonreporting) **A**1 10 20 **S** Quorum Health, Brentwood, TN
Primary Contact: Greg Kiser, Chief Executive Officer
CFO: Michael Ackley, Chief Financial Officer
CHR: Pat Hart, Director Human Resources
CNO: Cathy Heston, Chief Nursing Officer
Web address: www.threeriversmedicalcenter.com
Control: Corporation, Investor–owned (for–profit) **Service**: General medical and surgical

Staffed Beds: 80

LOUISVILLE—Jefferson County

✠ △ **BAPTIST HEALTH LOUISVILLE (180130)**, 4000 Kresge Way, Zip 40207–4676; tel. 502/897–8100 **A**1 2 3 5 7 10 **F**3 5 8 11 12 13 15 17 18 20 22 24 26 28 29 30 31 34 35 37 38 40 44 45 46 47 48 49 50 51 54 56 57 58 59 60 61 62 64 70 72 74 75 76 78 79 81 82 83 84 85 86 87 90 91 92 93 98 100 101 102 103 104 105 107 108 110 111 114 115 116 117 118 119 120 121 123 124 126 129 130 132 135 146 147 148 149 **S** Baptist Health, Louisville, KY
Primary Contact: David L. Gray, FACHE, President
COO: Clint Kaho, Vice President
CFO: Jim Morris, Vice President Finance
CMO: Kenneth Anderson M.D., Vice President and Chief Medical Officer
CIO: Shari Price, Director Information Services
CHR: Kim Scaglione, Vice President Human Resources
CNO: Karen Newman Ed.D., MSN, R.N., Vice President and Chief Nursing Officer
Web address: www.baptisthealthlouisville.com
Control: Other not–for–profit (including NFP Corporation) **Service**: General medical and surgical

Staffed Beds: 500 **Admissions:** 27025 **Census:** 359 **Outpatient Visits:** 315493 **Births:** 2876 **Total Expense ($000):** 479595 **Payroll Expense ($000):** 165348 **Personnel:** 2680

☐ **CENTRAL STATE HOSPITAL (184015)**, 10510 LaGrange Road, Zip 40223–1228; tel. 502/253–7000, (Nonreporting) **A**1 3 5 10
Primary Contact: Vital Shah, M.D., Chief Executive Officer ad Chief Medical Officer
CFO: Robert Underhill, Director of Business Services
CMO: Vital Shah M.D., Chief Executive Officer and Chief Medical Officer
CIO: Randy Spicer, Information Technology Supervisor
CHR: Sonya Wheatley, Human Resources Manager
CNO: Michelle Napier, Director of Nursing
Control: State, Government, Nonfederal **Service**: Psychiatric

Staffed Beds: 112

★ △ **FRAZIER REHAB INSTITUTE**, 220 Abraham Flexner Way, Zip 40202–1887; tel. 502/582–7400 **A**3 5 7 **F**28 29 30 34 35 42 44 50 54 56 57 58 59 60 64 68 74 75 77 78 79 82 84 85 86 87 90 91 93 95 96 100 130 131 132 146 148 **P**6 **S** Catholic Health Initiatives, Englewood, CO
Primary Contact: Cathy Spalding, Vice President of Operations
CFO: Robert Steltenpohl, Vice President and Chief Financial Officer
CMO: Darryl Kaelin M.D., Medical Director
CHR: Lisa Burris, Manager Human Resources
Web address: www.kentuckyonehealth.org/frazier–rehab–institute
Control: Other not–for–profit (including NFP Corporation) **Service**: Rehabilitation

Staffed Beds: 87 **Admissions:** 1694 **Census:** 67 **Outpatient Visits:** 103076 **Births:** 0 **Total Expense ($000):** 57934 **Payroll Expense ($000):** 25416 **Personnel:** 420

✠ **JEWISH HOSPITAL (180040)**, 200 Abraham Flexner Way, Zip 40202–1886; tel. 502/587–4011 **A**1 2 3 5 10 **F**1 3 8 11 14 15 18 20 22 24 26 28 29 30 31 34 35 36 37 40 42 43 44 45 46 47 48 49 50 53 54 56 57 58 59 60 61 64 67 68 70 74 75 78 79 81 82 84 85 87 92 97 100 107 108 110 111 112 114 115 116 117 118 119 121 123 124 126 130 131 132 135 136 137 138 139 140 141 142 145 146 **P**6 **S** Catholic Health Initiatives, Englewood, CO
Primary Contact: Ron Waldridge II, M.D., President and Chief Medical Officer
CFO: Ronald Farr, Chief Financial Officer
CMO: James P Ketterhagen M.D., Senior Vice President and Chief Medical Officer
CIO: Thomas Wittman, Chief Information Officer
CHR: Julie McGregor, Vice President and Chief People Officer
CNO: Cheryl Fugatte MSN, Vice President and Chief Nursing Officer
Web address: www.jewishhospital.org
Control: Other not–for–profit (including NFP Corporation) **Service**: General medical and surgical

Staffed Beds: 342 **Admissions:** 15907 **Census:** 235 **Outpatient Visits:** 101602 **Births:** 0 **Total Expense ($000):** 394885 **Payroll Expense ($000):** 111495 **Personnel:** 1730

KINDRED HOSPITAL LOUISVILLE AT JEWISH HOSPITAL See Kindred Hospital–Louisville

✠ **KINDRED HOSPITAL–LOUISVILLE (182001)**, 1313 Saint Anthony Place, Zip 40204–1740; tel. 502/587–7001, (Nonreporting) (Includes KINDRED HOSPITAL LOUISVILLE AT JEWISH HOSPITAL, 200 Abraham Flexner Way, 2nd Floor, Louisville, Kentucky, Zip 40202, tel. 502/587–3999; David Johnson, Chief Executive Officer) **A**1 3 5 10 **S** Kindred Healthcare, Louisville, KY
Primary Contact: Jack Nicholson, Chief Executive Officer
Web address: www.kindredlouisville.com
Control: Corporation, Investor–owned (for–profit) **Service**: Acute long–term care hospital

Staffed Beds: 117

Many Facility Codes have changed. Please refer to the AHA Guide Code Chart. © 2017 AHA Guide

★ **NORTON AUDUBON HOSPITAL**, One Audubon Plaza Drive, Zip 40217–1300, Mailing Address: P.O.Box 17550, 40217–0550; tel. 502/636–7111 **A**2 3 5 **F**3 11 15 17 18 20 22 24 26 28 29 30 31 34 35 40 45 46 47 48 49 50 56 57 59 64 68 70 74 75 78 79 81 82 85 86 87 107 108 110 111 114 115 118 119 129 130 131 132 146 147 148 149 150 **S** Norton Healthcare, Louisville, KY
Primary Contact: Jon Cooper, Chief Administrative Officer
CFO: Jonathan Presser, Vice President Finance and Operations
Web address: www.nortonhealthcare.com/NortonAudubonHospital
Control: Other not–for–profit (including NFP Corporation) **Service**: General medical and surgical

Staffed Beds: 292 **Admissions**: 14169 **Census**: 207 **Outpatient Visits**: 153724 **Births**: 0 **Total Expense ($000)**: 236848 **Payroll Expense ($000)**: 84608 **Personnel**: 1412

★ **NORTON BROWNSBORO HOSPITAL**, 4960 Norton Healthcare Boulevard, Zip 40241–2831; tel. 502/446–8000 **A**2 **F**3 15 18 20 22 29 30 31 34 35 36 40 44 45 46 47 48 49 50 56 57 59 64 68 70 74 75 78 79 81 82 85 86 87 91 92 93 107 108 110 111 114 115 119 129 130 131 132 146 148 149 150 **S** Norton Healthcare, Louisville, KY
Primary Contact: Andrew Strausbaugh, Chief Administrative Officer
CFO: Michael Logan, Chief Financial Officer
CMO: Gregory Juhl M.D., Medical Director
CNO: Regina J Hymer, DNP, RN, CENP MSN, R.N., Vice President Patient Care Services and Chief Nursing Officer
Web address: www.nortonhealthcare.com/nortonbrownsborohospital
Control: Other not–for–profit (including NFP Corporation) **Service**: General medical and surgical

Staffed Beds: 127 **Admissions**: 8943 **Census**: 93 **Outpatient Visits**: 100149 **Births**: 0 **Total Expense ($000)**: 161665 **Payroll Expense ($000)**: 52887 **Personnel**: 903

★ **NORTON CHILDREN'S HOSPITAL (189801)**, 231 East Chestnut Street, Zip 40202–1821; tel. 502/629–6000 **A**2 3 5 **F**3 8 11 16 19 21 23 25 27 29 30 31 32 34 35 38 39 40 41 42 43 44 45 50 51 54 57 58 59 64 65 68 72 73 74 75 78 79 81 82 84 85 86 87 88 89 91 92 93 96 98 99 100 101 102 107 108 111 114 115 119 130 131 132 134 136 137 138 146 149 150 **S** Norton Healthcare, Louisville, KY
Primary Contact: Thomas D. Kmetz, Division President
Web address: www.kosairchildrens.com/
Control: Other not–for–profit (including NFP Corporation) **Service**: Children's general medical and surgical

Staffed Beds: 267 **Admissions**: 9800 **Census**: 213 **Outpatient Visits**: 139219 **Births**: 0 **Total Expense ($000)**: 321209 **Payroll Expense ($000)**: 106055 **Personnel**: 1604

NORTON HEALTHCARE PAVILION See Norton Hospital

✠ **NORTON HOSPITAL (180088)**, 200 East Chestnut Street, Zip 40202–1800, Mailing Address: P.O.Box 35070, 40232–5070; tel. 502/629–8000, (Includes NORTON HEALTHCARE PAVILION, 315 East Broadway, Louisville, Kentucky, Zip 40202–1703, tel. 502/629–2000) **A**1 2 3 5 10 **F**3 11 12 13 15 17 18 20 22 24 26 28 29 30 31 34 35 36 38 39 40 44 45 46 49 50 51 53 55 56 57 59 64 68 70 74 75 76 78 79 81 82 85 86 87 91 92 93 95 96 98 100 101 102 107 108 110 111 114 115 116 117 118 119 126 130 132 146 147 148 149 150 **S** Norton Healthcare, Louisville, KY
Primary Contact: Matthew Ayers, Chief Administrative Officer
CFO: Carl Amorose, Vice President Finance
Web address: www.nortonhealthcare.com/nortonhospital
Control: Other not–for–profit (including NFP Corporation) **Service**: General medical and surgical

Staffed Beds: 383 **Admissions**: 18638 **Census**: 273 **Outpatient Visits**: 105853 **Births**: 2676 **Total Expense ($000)**: 347813 **Payroll Expense ($000)**: 113407 **Personnel**: 1743

★ **NORTON WOMEN'S AND CHILDREN'S HOSPITAL**, 4001 Dutchmans Lane, Zip 40207–4799; tel. 502/893–1000 **A**2 3 5 **F**3 11 12 13 15 18 20 29 30 31 34 35 36 40 41 44 45 47 49 50 56 57 59 64 68 70 72 73 74 75 76 78 79 81 82 85 86 87 89 107 108 110 111 114 115 118 119 120 121 123 124 126 129 130 132 133 134 135 146 147 149 150 **S** Norton Healthcare, Louisville, KY
Primary Contact: Charlotte Ipsan, Chief Administrative Officer
CFO: Mark Kircher, Associate Vice President Finance
CMO: Steven Hester M.D., Vice President Medical Affairs
CIO: Joseph DeVenuto, Vice President and Chief Information Officer
Web address: www.nortonhealthcare.com/pages/nwkch.aspx
Control: Other not–for–profit (including NFP Corporation) **Service**: General medical and surgical

Staffed Beds: 355 **Admissions**: 16639 **Census**: 203 **Outpatient Visits**: 138526 **Births**: 5368 **Total Expense ($000)**: 247596 **Payroll Expense ($000)**: 87674 **Personnel**: 1481

★ **OUR LADY OF PEACE**, 2020 Newburg Road, Zip 40205–1879; tel. 502/479–4500 **A**5 **F**5 29 30 34 35 53 59 68 98 99 100 101 104 105 106 130 132 143 **S** Catholic Health Initiatives, Englewood, CO
Primary Contact: Jennifer Nolan, President
COO: Martha S Mather, Chief Operating Officer and Vice President
CFO: Beckie Kistler, Director of Finance
CHR: Jan Ostbloom, Human Resources Consultant
CNO: Brad Lincks R.N., Chief Nursing Officer and Vice President
Web address: www.hopehasaplace.org
Control: Other not–for–profit (including NFP Corporation) **Service**: Psychiatric

Staffed Beds: 211 **Admissions**: 8778 **Census**: 167 **Outpatient Visits**: 33778 **Births**: 0 **Total Expense ($000)**: 50696 **Payroll Expense ($000)**: 27577 **Personnel**: 781

✠ **ROBLEY REX VETERANS AFFAIRS MEDICAL CENTER**, 800 Zorn Avenue, Zip 40206–1499; tel. 502/287–4000, (Nonreporting) **A**1 3 5 **S** Department of Veterans Affairs, Washington, DC
Primary Contact: Martin J. Traxler, Chief Executive Officer
CFO: Barbara Roberts, Chief Financial Officer
CMO: Marylee Rothschild M.D., Chief of Staff
CIO: Augustine Bittner, Chief Information Officer
CHR: Angela Dutton, Human Resources Management Service
Web address: www.louisville.va.gov
Control: Veterans Affairs, Government, federal **Service**: General medical and surgical

Staffed Beds: 116

★ **STS. MARY & ELIZABETH HOSPITAL**, 1850 Bluegrass Avenue, Zip 40215–1199; tel. 502/361–6000 **A**3 5 **F**3 8 11 12 15 18 20 22 29 30 31 34 35 40 42 44 45 47 49 50 53 59 60 64 68 69 70 74 75 78 79 81 82 84 85 86 87 107 108 110 111 114 115 118 119 130 132 135 **P**6 **S** Catholic Health Initiatives, Englewood, CO
Primary Contact: Jennifer Nolan, President
COO: Kenneth Johnson, Vice President
CFO: Elaine Hayes, Controller
CMO: Val Slayton M.D., Vice President Medical Affairs
CHR: Julie McGregor, Director Human Resources
Web address: www.jhsmh.org
Control: Other not–for–profit (including NFP Corporation) **Service**: General medical and surgical

Staffed Beds: 174 **Admissions**: 8185 **Census**: 98 **Outpatient Visits**: 101197 **Births**: 0 **Total Expense ($000)**: 126272 **Payroll Expense ($000)**: 44168 **Personnel**: 672

TEN BROECK DUPONT See The Brook At Dupont

☐ **THE BROOK AT DUPONT (184007)**, 1405 Browns Lane, Zip 40207–4608; tel. 502/896–0495 (Nonreporting) **A**1 10 **S** Universal Health Services, Inc., King of Prussia, PA
Primary Contact: Paul Andrews, Chief Executive Officer
Web address: www.thebrookhospitals.com/
Control: Corporation, Investor–owned (for–profit) **Service**: Psychiatric

Staffed Beds: 88

☐ **THE BROOK HOSPITAL – KMI (184008)**, 8521 Old LaGrange Road, Zip 40242–3800; tel. 502/426–6380, (Nonreporting) **A**1 3 5 10 **S** Universal Health Services, Inc., King of Prussia, PA
Primary Contact: Paul Andrews, Chief Executive Officer
COO: Kim Peabody, Chief Operating Officer
CFO: Dennis Collins, Chief Financial Officer
CMO: Timothy Burke M.D., Medical Director
CIO: Joel Roy, Manager Information Systems
CHR: Christina Taylor, Director Human Resources
Web address: www.thebrookhospitals.com
Control: Corporation, Investor–owned (for–profit) **Service**: Psychiatric

Staffed Beds: 94

Hospital, Medicare Provider Number, Address, Telephone, Approval, Facility, and Physician Codes, Health Care System

★ American Hospital Association (AHA) membership   ○ Healthcare Facilities Accreditation Program   ⇑ Center for Improvement in Healthcare Quality Accreditation
☐ The Joint Commission accreditation   ◇ DNV Healthcare Inc. accreditation   △ Commission on Accreditation of Rehabilitation Facilities (CARF) accreditation

✠ **UNIVERSITY OF LOUISVILLE HOSPITAL (180141)**, 530 South Jackson Street, Zip 40202–3611; tel. 502/562–3000 **A**1 2 3 5 8 10 **F**3 13 15 16 17 18 20 22 24 26 28 29 30 31 34 35 40 43 45 46 47 49 50 51 54 55 57 58 59 60 61 64 65 66 68 70 71 72 73 74 75 76 77 78 79 80 81 82 84 86 91 92 93 94 97 98 100 101 102 103 104 105 106 107 108 109 110 111 112 113 114 115 116 117 118 119 120 121 122 123 124 126 130 132 135 136 146 147 148 **S** Catholic Health Initiatives, Englewood, CO
Primary Contact: Kenneth P. Marshall, President and Chief Executive Officer
CMO: Mark P Pfeifer M.D., Senior Vice President and Chief Medical Officer
CIO: Troy May, Chief Information Officer
CNO: Mary Jane Adams R.N., MSN, Senior Vice President and Chief Nursing Officer
Web address: www.ulh.org
Control: Other not–for–profit (including NFP Corporation) **Service**: General medical and surgical

Staffed Beds: 301 Admissions: 16642 Census: 259 Outpatient Visits:
175583 **Births:** 1702 **Total Expense ($000):** 493380 **Payroll Expense ($000):** 128108 **Personnel:** 1664

VETERANS AFFAIRS MEDICAL CENTER–LOUISVILLE See Robley Rex Veterans Affairs Medical Center

MADISONVILLE—Hopkins County

✠ **BAPTIST HEALTH MADISONVILLE (180093)**, 900 Hospital Drive, Zip 42431–1694; tel. 270/825–5100, (Total facility includes 17 beds in nursing home–type unit) **A**1 2 3 5 10 22 **F**3 8 11 14 18 20 22 24 26 28 29 30 31 34 40 44 49 51 53 55 57 58 59 62 63 68 70 73 76 78 79 81 85 87 88 89 90 93 96 98 100 102 103 107 108 111 114 115 117 118 119 120 121 123 128 129 130 131 132 146 148 149 **P**8 **S** Baptist Health, Louisville, KY
Primary Contact: Robert L. Ramey, President
COO: Kevin Moser, Vice President of Operations
CFO: Kim Ashby, Vice President of Finance
CMO: Travis Sewalls, Chief Medical Officer
CIO: Karla Durham, Director of Information Systems
CHR: Lorie A. Oglesby, Director of Human Resources
CNO: Tiffany Cabibbo, Vice President of Nursing
Web address: www.baptisthealthmadisonville.com
Control: Other not–for–profit (including NFP Corporation) **Service**: General medical and surgical

Staffed Beds: 196 Admissions: 8062 Census: 125 Outpatient Visits:
111357 **Births:** 757 **Total Expense ($000):** 184433 **Payroll Expense ($000):** 65152 **Personnel:** 1200

★ **CONTINUECARE HOSPITAL AT MADISONVILLE**, 900 Hospital Drive, 4th Floor, Zip 42431–1644; tel. 270/825–5450 **F**1 3 28 29 34 50 57 85 87 91 **P**5 **S** Community Hospital Corporation, Plano, TX
Primary Contact: Kathy DeVore, Administrator
Web address: www.continuecare.org/madisonville/
Control: Other not–for–profit (including NFP Corporation) **Service**: Acute long–term care hospital

Staffed Beds: 35 Admissions: 77 Census: 5 Outpatient Visits: 0 Births: 0
Total Expense ($000): 3182 **Payroll Expense ($000):** 1374 **Personnel:** 27

MANCHESTER—Clay County

✠ ○ **MANCHESTER MEMORIAL HOSPITAL (180043)**, 210 Marie Langdon Drive, Zip 40962–6388; tel. 606/598–5104 **A**1 10 11 **F**3 13 15 18 29 30 32 34 35 40 45 50 57 59 62 65 68 70 71 75 76 77 79 81 85 86 87 93 97 107 108 110 111 115 119 127 130 135 143 146 147 149 **S** Adventist Health System Sunbelt Health Care Corporation, Altamonte Springs, FL
Primary Contact: Erika Skula, President and Chief Executive Officer
COO: Chris Self, Chief Operating Officer
CFO: Paul Merklin, Vice President Finance and Chief Financial Officer
CMO: Jeff Newswanger M.D., Chief Medical Officer
CHR: Joe Skula, Director Human Resources
CNO: Michael Stimson, Chief Nursing Officer
Web address: www.manchestermemorial.org
Control: Church operated, Nongovernment, not–for–profit **Service**: General medical and surgical

Staffed Beds: 63 Admissions: 1820 Census: 16 Outpatient Visits: 55447
Births: 178 **Total Expense ($000):** 58792 **Payroll Expense ($000):** 25207 **Personnel:** 469

MARION—Crittenden County

☐ **CRITTENDEN COUNTY HOSPITAL (180095)**, 520 West Gum Street, Zip 42064–1516, Mailing Address: P.O.Box 386, 42064–0386; tel. 270/965–5281, (Nonreporting) **A**1 10 20
Primary Contact: Lea Ann H. Klarner, Chief Executive Officer
COO: Robin Curnel MSN, Chief Operating Officer and Chief Nursing Officer
CFO: Karen Paris, Controller
CMO: Steven Burkhart M.D., Chief Medical Officer
CIO: Reese Baker, Director Information Systems
CHR: Jan Gregory, Chief of Human Resources
CNO: Robin Curnel MSN, Chief Operating Officer and Chief Nursing Officer
Web address: www.crittenden–health.org
Control: Other not–for–profit (including NFP Corporation) **Service**: General medical and surgical

Staffed Beds: 48

MARTIN—Floyd County

✠ **SAINT JOSEPH – MARTIN (181305)**, 11203 Main Street, Zip 41649; tel. 606/285–6400 **A**1 10 18 **F**3 15 18 28 35 40 56 81 104 111 114 119 130 **S** Catholic Health Initiatives, Englewood, CO
Primary Contact: Kathy Stumbo, President
CFO: Robert Brock, Vice President Finance
CMO: John Triplett D.O., President Medical Staff
CIO: Chris Dye, Director Information Systems
Web address: www.saintjosephmartin.org
Control: Other not–for–profit (including NFP Corporation) **Service**: General medical and surgical

Staffed Beds: 25 Admissions: 732 Census: 10 Outpatient Visits: 32453
Births: 0 **Total Expense ($000):** 20404 **Payroll Expense ($000):** 7556
Personnel: 93

MAYFIELD—Graves County

✠ **JACKSON PURCHASE MEDICAL CENTER (180116)**, 1099 Medical Center Circle, Zip 42066–1159; tel. 270/251–4100 **A**1 10 19 **F**3 8 11 12 13 15 18 20 22 28 29 34 37 40 43 45 46 47 48 49 51 57 59 60 64 68 70 74 75 76 77 79 80 81 85 87 89 91 93 97 98 103 107 110 111 114 115 117 119 124 127 129 131 132 133 135 144 146 147 148 **S** LifePoint Health, Brentwood, TN
Primary Contact: David Anderson, Chief Executive Officer
CFO: Vicki Parks, Chief Financial Officer
CMO: Rudy Triana M.D., Chief of Staff
CIO: Randy McDaniel, Information Systems Director
CHR: Tressa B Hargrove, Director Human Resources
CNO: Julia Grove, Chief Nursing Officer
Web address: www.jacksonpurchase.com
Control: Corporation, Investor–owned (for–profit) **Service**: General medical and surgical

Staffed Beds: 227 Admissions: 3911 Census: 43 Outpatient Visits: 71423
Births: 620 **Total Expense ($000):** 64574 **Payroll Expense ($000):** 30296

MAYSVILLE—Mason County

✠ **MEADOWVIEW REGIONAL MEDICAL CENTER (180019)**, 989 Medical Park Drive, Zip 41056–8750; tel. 606/759–5311, (Nonreporting) **A**1 10 **S** LifePoint Health, Brentwood, TN
Primary Contact: Joseph G. Koch, Chief Executive Officer
CFO: Clayton Kolodziejczyk, Chief Financial Officer
CMO: Eric Lohman M.D., Chief of Staff
CHR: Diana Kennedy, Director Human Resources
Web address: www.meadowviewregional.com
Control: Corporation, Investor–owned (for–profit) **Service**: General medical and surgical

Staffed Beds: 101

MCDOWELL—Floyd County

☐ **MCDOWELL ARH HOSPITAL (181331)**, Route 122, Zip 41647, Mailing Address: P.O.Box 247, 41647–0247; tel. 606/377–3400 **A**1 10 18 **F**3 11 15 29 30 34 35 40 50 57 59 62 64 65 70 75 77 81 82 86 87 89 93 97 107 111 115 119 127 130 131 133 146 **P**6 **S** Appalachian Regional Healthcare, Inc., Lexington, KY
Primary Contact: Russell Barker, Community Chief Executive Officer
COO: Russell Barker, Community Chief Executive Officer
CMO: Mary A Hall, Chief Medical Staff
CIO: Jeff Brady, Director Information Systems
CHR: Stephanie Owens, Manager Human Resources
Web address: www.arh.org
Control: Other not–for–profit (including NFP Corporation) **Service**: General medical and surgical

Staffed Beds: 25 Admissions: 539 Census: 6 Outpatient Visits: 26169
Births: 0 **Total Expense ($000):** 14210 **Payroll Expense ($000):** 5390
Personnel: 111

MIDDLESBORO—Bell County

☐ **MIDDLESBORO ARH HOSPITAL (180020)**, 3600 West Cumberland Avenue, Zip 40965–2614, Mailing Address: P.O.Box 340, 40965–0340; tel. 606/242–1100 **A**1 10 **F**3 11 13 15 17 18 20 28 29 30 34 35 39 40 45 46 49 50 57 59 62 64 65 70 75 76 77 79 81 85 86 87 89 93 97 107 108 110 111 114 118 119 127 129 132 133 146 147 148 **P**6 **S** Appalachian Regional Healthcare, Inc., Lexington, KY
Primary Contact: Michael Slusher, Community Chief Executive Officer
CFO: Jeremy Hall, Assistant Administrator and Chief Financial Officer
CMO: Maria Hortillosa M.D., Chief of Staff
CIO: Lisa Dooley, Health Information Officer
CHR: Marina Cawood, Administrative Assistant
CNO: Stacy England, Community Chief Nursing Officer
Web address: www.arh.org/middlesboro
Control: Other not–for–profit (including NFP Corporation) **Service**: General medical and surgical

Staffed Beds: 96 Admissions: 2206 Census: 26 Outpatient Visits: 76259
Births: 262 **Total Expense ($000):** 36161 **Payroll Expense ($000):** 11181
Personnel: 219

MONTICELLO—Wayne County

WAYNE COUNTY HOSPITAL (181321), 166 Hospital Street, Zip 42633–2416;
tel. 606/348–9343 **A**10 18 **F**3 15 29 30 40 47 75 81 107 108 114 119 127
133 135 146 **P**6
Primary Contact: Joseph Murrell, Chief Executive Officer
CFO: Anne Sawyer, Chief Financial Officer
CMO: David Mayer, Chief of Staff
CIO: Angela Burton, Privacy Officer
CHR: Mollie Dick, Coordinator Human Resources
CNO: Lora Elam R.N., Chief Nursing Officer
Web address: www.waynehospital.org
Control: Other not–for–profit (including NFP Corporation) **Service:** General
medical and surgical

Staffed Beds: 25 **Admissions:** 612 **Census:** 10 **Outpatient Visits:** 26251
Births: 0 **Total Expense ($000):** 14054 **Payroll Expense ($000):** 5524
Personnel: 157

MOREHEAD—Rowan County

ST. CLAIRE HEALTHCARE (180018), 222 Medical Circle, Zip 40351–1179;
tel. 606/783–6500, (Total facility includes 10 beds in nursing home–type unit) **A**1
2 3 5 10 13 **F**3 5 11 13 15 18 20 22 28 29 30 31 34 35 38 39 40 45 48 49 50
51 54 56 57 58 59 60 61 62 63 64 65 68 70 74 75 76 77 78 79 81 82 84 85
86 87 89 90 93 97 98 99 100 101 102 103 104 107 108 110 111 115 118
119 128 129 130 132 135 146 147 148 **P**6
Primary Contact: Mark J. Neff, FACHE, President and Chief Executive Officer
CFO: Chris McClurg, Vice President Finance and Chief Financial Officer
CMO: William L Melahn M.D., Vice President Medical Affairs and Chief Medical
Officer
CIO: Randy McCleese, Vice President Information Services and Chief Information
Officer
CHR: Travis A Bailey, Vice President Administration
CNO: Lerae Wilson, Vice President Patient Services and Chief Nursing Officer
Web address: www.st–claire.org
Control: Church operated, Nongovernment, not–for–profit **Service:** General
medical and surgical

Staffed Beds: 133 **Admissions:** 5204 **Census:** 58 **Outpatient Visits:**
183370 **Births:** 400 **Total Expense ($000):** 135617 **Payroll Expense
($000):** 67754 **Personnel:** 1146

MORGANFIELD—Union County

METHODIST HOSPITAL UNION COUNTY (181306), 4604 Highway 60 West,
Zip 42437–9570; tel. 270/389–5000 **A**1 10 18 **F**3 7 11 15 29 30 34 40 45 57
68 75 77 81 85 87 93 107 114 119 130 133 135 146 149
Primary Contact: Lynn R. Steinwachs, Vice President and Administrator
CFO: David Massengale, Chief Financial Officer
CMO: William Clapp M.D., Chief of Medical Staff
CIO: Randy McCleese, Chief Information Officer
CHR: Ty Kahle, Assistant Vice President Human Resources
CNO: Peggy F Creighton R.N., Director of Nursing
Web address: www.methodisthospital.net
Control: Church operated, Nongovernment, not–for–profit **Service:** General
medical and surgical

Staffed Beds: 25 **Admissions:** 664 **Census:** 12 **Outpatient Visits:** 23449
Births: 0 **Total Expense ($000):** 15061 **Payroll Expense ($000):** 6095
Personnel: 138

MOUNT STERLING—Montgomery County

SAINT JOSEPH MOUNT STERLING (180064), 225 Falcon Drive, Zip 40353–
1158, Mailing Address: P.O.Box 7, 40353–0007; tel. 859/497–5000 **A**1 3 5 10
F3 13 15 17 28 29 34 35 40 45 46 57 59 64 68 70 74 75 76 77 78 79 81 86
87 93 97 107 114 119 129 130 132 133 135 146 147 148 **S** Catholic Health
Initiatives, Englewood, CO
Primary Contact: Cinda Fluke, R.N., Interim Site Executive
CFO: Amanda Kinman, Director of Finance
CMO: Jeff McGinnis M.D., President Medical Staff
CIO: Jeff Ryder, Director Information Systems
CHR: Annette Saadat, Human Resources Business Partner
CNO: Cinda Fluke R.N., Chief Nursing Officer
Web address: www.sjhlex.org
Control: Other not–for–profit (including NFP Corporation) **Service:** General
medical and surgical

Staffed Beds: 42 **Admissions:** 1802 **Census:** 20 **Outpatient Visits:** 61223
Births: 226 **Total Expense ($000):** 44914 **Payroll Expense ($000):** 12162
Personnel: 212

MOUNT VERNON—Rockcastle County

**ROCKCASTLE REGIONAL HOSPITAL AND RESPIRATORY CARE CENTER
(180115)**, 145 Newcomb Avenue, Zip 40456–2728, Mailing Address: P.O.Box
1310, 40456–1310; tel. 606/256–2195, (Nonreporting) **A**1 10
Primary Contact: Stephen A. Estes, Chief Executive Officer
CFO: Charles Black Jr, Chief Financial Officer
CMO: Jon A Arvin M.D., Chief Medical Officer
CIO: Maleigha Amyx, Chief Information Officer
CHR: Carmen Poynter, Director Human Resources
CNO: Cynthia Burton R.N., Chief Nursing Officer
Web address: www.rockcastleregional.org
Control: Other not–for–profit (including NFP Corporation) **Service:** General
medical and surgical

Staffed Beds: 105

MURRAY—Calloway County

MURRAY–CALLOWAY COUNTY HOSPITAL (180027), 803 Poplar Street,
Zip 42071–2432; tel. 270/762–1100, (Total facility includes 150 beds in nursing
home–type unit) **A**1 2 10 19 **F**3 7 11 12 13 14 15 18 20 28 29 30 31 34 35 40
45 47 49 50 51 53 57 59 62 63 66 68 70 74 75 76 77 78 79 81 82 84 85 87
90 92 93 94 104 107 108 111 114 115 119 121 127 128 129 130 131 132
135 141 146 147 148 **P**5
Primary Contact: Colonel Jerome Penner, Chief Executive Officer
CFO: Dirk Morgan, Vice President
CIO: Brian Benedict, Director of Information Technology
CHR: John R Wilson, Vice President, Human Resources
CNO: Jeffrey L Eye R.N., Vice President Patient Care Services
Web address: www.murrayhospital.org
Control: City–county, Government, Nonfederal **Service:** General medical and
surgical

Staffed Beds: 247 **Admissions:** 4617 **Census:** 187 **Outpatient Visits:**
85625 **Births:** 659 **Total Expense ($000):** 116137 **Payroll Expense ($000):**
46102 **Personnel:** 981

OWENSBORO—Daviess County

△ **OWENSBORO HEALTH REGIONAL HOSPITAL (180038)**, 1201 Pleasant
Valley Road, Zip 42303; tel. 270/417–2000, (Includes HEALTHPARK, 1006 Ford
Avenue, Owensboro, Kentucky, Zip 42301, P O Box 2839, 42302, tel. 270/688–
5433) (Total facility includes 30 beds in nursing home–type unit) **A**1 2 5 7 10 **F**3 5
11 12 13 15 17 18 20 22 24 26 28 29 30 31 32 34 35 40 43 44 45 46 49 53
54 56 57 58 59 61 62 64 65 66 70 72 74 75 76 77 78 79 81 82 83 84 85 86
87 89 90 91 92 93 97 98 100 101 102 103 104 105 107 108 110 111 114
115 116 117 118 119 120 121 123 124 126 127 128 129 130 131 132 135
144 145 146 147 148 149 **P**6 8 **S** Owensboro Health, Owensboro, KY
Primary Contact: Greg Strahan, Interim Chief Executive Officer
COO: Greg Strahan, Chief Operating Officer
CFO: John Hackbarth CPA, Senior Vice President Finance and Chief Financial
Officer
CMO: Wathen Medley M.D., Chief Medical Officer
CIO: Michael Elley, Chief Information Officer
CHR: Mia Suter, Chief Administration Officer
CNO: Vicki Stogsdill R.N., MSN, Chief Nursing Officer
Web address: www.owensborohealth.org
Control: Other not–for–profit (including NFP Corporation) **Service:** General
medical and surgical

Staffed Beds: 360 **Admissions:** 17994 **Census:** 240 **Outpatient Visits:**
923864 **Births:** 2123 **Total Expense ($000):** 457601 **Payroll Expense
($000):** 157153 **Personnel:** 2608

RIVERVALLEY BEHAVIORAL HEALTH HOSPITAL (184013), 1000 Industrial
Drive, Zip 42301–8715; tel. 270/689–6500 **A**10 **F**29 38 40 41 59 98 99 100
101 102 104 105 130 **P**6
Primary Contact: Gayle DiCesare, President and Chief Executive Officer
COO: Michelle Parks, Administrator
CFO: J Michael Mountain, Chief Financial Officer
CMO: David Harmon D.O., Vice President Medical Services
CIO: Travis Taggart, Director Information Technology
CHR: Cathryn H Gaddis, Director Human Resources
Web address: www.rvbh.com
Control: Other not–for–profit (including NFP Corporation) **Service:** Children's
hospital psychiatric

Staffed Beds: 80 **Admissions:** 847 **Census:** 31 **Outpatient Visits:** 1295
Births: 0 **Total Expense ($000):** 5931 **Payroll Expense ($000):** 2725
Personnel: 93

PADUCAH—Mccracken County

✠ **BAPTIST HEALTH PADUCAH (180104)**, 2501 Kentucky Avenue, Zip 42003–3200; tel. 270/575–2100 **A**1 2 10 19 22 **F**3 11 12 13 15 17 18 20 22 24 26 28 29 30 31 32 34 35 40 45 48 50 51 57 58 59 64 68 70 73 74 75 76 77 78 79 81 82 84 85 86 87 91 92 93 96 107 108 109 110 111 112 113 114 115 116 117 118 119 120 121 124 126 128 129 130 131 132 134 135 144 145 146 147 148 149 **S** Baptist Health, Louisville, KY
Primary Contact: William A. Brown, FACHE, President and CEO
COO: Bonnie W Schrock FACHE, Chief Operating Officer
CFO: Scott Leckey, Vice President Finance
CMO: Bradley W. Housman M.D., Chief Medical Officer
CIO: Jay Orazine, Director Information Services
CHR: Kal Keitel, SPHR, Executive Director Human Resources
CNO: Sharon Freyer R.N., Chief Nursing Officer
Web address: www.baptisthealthpaducah.com
Control: Other not–for–profit (including NFP Corporation) **Service**: General medical and surgical

Staffed Beds: 220 **Admissions**: 12001 **Census**: 156 **Outpatient Visits**: 204967 **Births**: 1405 **Total Expense ($000)**: 267040 **Payroll Expense ($000)**: 81827 **Personnel**: 1378

★ **CONTINUECARE HOSPITAL AT BAPTIST HEALTH PADUCAH (180153)**, 2501 Kentucky Avenue, 5th Floor, Zip 42003–3813; tel. 270/575–2598 **F**1 3 29 34 35 148 **S** Community Hospital Corporation, Plano, TX
Primary Contact: Len McDade, Chief Executive Officer
CNO: Mary Lou Young, Chief Nursing Officer
Web address: www.continuecare.org/paducah//
Control: Other not–for–profit (including NFP Corporation) **Service**: Acute long–term care hospital

Staffed Beds: 37 **Admissions**: 72 **Census**: 4 **Outpatient Visits**: 0 **Births**: 0 **Total Expense ($000)**: 3082 **Payroll Expense ($000)**: 1234 **Personnel**: 63

✠ △ **LOURDES HOSPITAL (180102)**, 1530 Lone Oak Road, Zip 42003–7900, Mailing Address: P.O.Box 7100, 42002–7100; tel. 270/444–2444 **A**1 7 10 19 **F**3 7 8 11 13 15 17 18 20 22 24 26 28 29 30 31 34 35 40 45 46 54 57 59 60 62 63 64 68 70 73 74 75 76 77 78 79 81 82 83 84 85 87 90 93 96 97 98 100 101 102 103 104 105 107 108 110 111 114 115 116 118 119 129 130 131 132 135 141 143 144 146 147 148 149 150 **P**6 **S** Mercy Health, Cincinnati, OH
Primary Contact: Michael Yungmann, President and Chief Executive Officer
CHR: Kim Lindsey, Chief Human Resources Officer
Web address: www.lourdes–pad.org
Control: Church operated, Nongovernment, not–for–profit **Service**: General medical and surgical

Staffed Beds: 281 **Admissions**: 10670 **Census**: 135 **Outpatient Visits**: 493117 **Births**: 434 **Total Expense ($000)**: 245688 **Payroll Expense ($000)**: 95201

PAINTSVILLE—Johnson County

✠ **PAUL B. HALL REGIONAL MEDICAL CENTER (180078)**, 625 James S. Trimble Boulevard, Zip 41240–0000; tel. 606/789–3511 **A**1 10 **F**3 15 17 18 29 30 34 35 40 45 50 51 57 59 60 68 70 74 75 79 81 85 89 91 93 94 96 107 108 110 111 115 119 126 129 132 148 **S** Quorum Health, Brentwood, TN
Primary Contact: Deborah Trimble, R.N., Chief Executive Officer
CFO: Pattie Major, Chief Financial Officer
CMO: F K Belhasen M.D., Medical Director
CHR: Carla J. Stapleton, Director Human Resources
Web address: www.pbhrmc.com
Control: Corporation, Investor–owned (for–profit) **Service**: General medical and surgical

Staffed Beds: 72 **Admissions**: 1790 **Census**: 18 **Outpatient Visits**: 36899 **Births**: 0 **Total Expense ($000)**: 31556 **Payroll Expense ($000)**: 10740

PARIS—Bourbon County

✠ **BOURBON COMMUNITY HOSPITAL (180046)**, 9 Linville Drive, Zip 40361–2196; tel. 859/987–3600 **A**1 10 **F**3 15 28 29 34 35 38 39 40 45 49 50 51 56 57 59 64 68 70 74 75 79 81 86 87 93 98 99 100 101 102 103 107 108 110 111 114 119 129 130 133 146 148 **P**7 **S** LifePoint Health, Brentwood, TN
Primary Contact: Matt Smith, Interim Chief Executive Officer
CFO: Michael Snedegar, Chief Financial Officer
CMO: C. Ray Young M.D., Chief Medical Officer
CIO: Phil Osborne, Director Information Technology
CHR: Roger K Davis, Director Human Resources
Web address: www.bourbonhospital.com
Control: Corporation, Investor–owned (for–profit) **Service**: General medical and surgical

Staffed Beds: 58 **Admissions**: 2652 **Census**: 32 **Outpatient Visits**: 35049 **Births**: 0 **Personnel**: 176

PIKEVILLE—Pike County

☐ **PIKEVILLE MEDICAL CENTER (180044)**, 911 Bypass Road, Zip 41501–1689; tel. 606/218–3500 **A**1 2 10 13 **F**3 11 12 13 15 18 20 22 24 26 28 29 30 31 32 34 35 39 40 43 45 49 50 51 57 59 60 61 62 64 66 68 69 70 72 74 75 76 77 78 79 81 82 84 85 86 87 89 90 93 95 96 97 107 108 110 111 115 116 117 118 119 121 123 124 127 129 130 131 132 135 146 147 148 **P**6
Primary Contact: Walter E. May, President and Chief Executive Officer
COO: Juanita Deskins, Chief Operating Officer
CFO: Michelle Hagy, Chief Financial Officer
CMO: Aaron Crum M.D., Chief Medical Officer
CIO: Tony Damron, Vice President Information Services
CNO: Debra Parsons, Chief Nursing Officer
Web address: www.pikevillehospital.org
Control: Other not–for–profit (including NFP Corporation) **Service**: General medical and surgical

Staffed Beds: 291 **Admissions**: 14705 **Census**: 231 **Outpatient Visits**: 461200 **Births**: 960 **Total Expense ($000)**: 460280 **Payroll Expense ($000)**: 180306 **Personnel**: 3188

PINEVILLE—Bell County

PINEVILLE COMMUNITY HOSPITAL ASSOCIATION (180021), 850 Riverview Avenue, Zip 40977–1452; tel. 606/337–3051, (Nonreporting) **A**10
Primary Contact: Gordon Larson, Administrator
CFO: Colan Kelly, Chief Financial Officer
CMO: Michael Peterson M.D., Chief of Staff
CIO: David Hall, Chief Information Officer
CHR: Josh Collett, Director Human Resources
CNO: Dinah Jarvis, Director of Nursing
Web address: www.pinevillehospital.com
Control: Other not–for–profit (including NFP Corporation) **Service**: General medical and surgical

Staffed Beds: 150

PRESTONSBURG—Floyd County

★ ⇧ **HIGHLANDS REGIONAL MEDICAL CENTER (180005)**, 5000 Kentucky Route 321, Zip 41653–1273, Mailing Address: P.O.Box 668, 41653–0668; tel. 606/886–8511, (Nonreporting) **A**2 5 10 19 21
Primary Contact: Harold C. Warman Jr, FACHE, President and Chief Executive Officer
COO: Chris Hoffman, Chief Operating Officer
CFO: Jack Blackwell, Chief Financial Officer
CIO: Michael Roberts, Chief Information Officer
CHR: Susan Renee' Ellis R.N., MSN, Vice President of Human Resources
CNO: Terresa O. Booher, Vice President of Patient Care Services
Web address: www.hrmc.org
Control: Other not–for–profit (including NFP Corporation) **Service**: General medical and surgical

Staffed Beds: 139

PRINCETON—Caldwell County

✠ **CALDWELL MEDICAL CENTER (181322)**, 100 Medical Center Drive, Zip 42445–2430, Mailing Address: P.O.Box 410, 42445–0410; tel. 270/365–0300 **A**1 10 18 **F**11 15 28 29 34 35 40 57 59 64 68 77 81 85 107 108 111 115 118 119 129 133 135 146 149 **S** QHR, Brentwood, TN
Primary Contact: Kelley J. Rushing, Chief Executive Officer
CFO: Shane Whittington, Chief Financial Officer
CHR: Rhonda Burns, Director Human Resources
CNO: Douglas James, Chief Nursing Officer
Web address: www.caldwellhosp.org
Control: Other not–for–profit (including NFP Corporation) **Service**: General medical and surgical

Staffed Beds: 25 **Admissions**: 493 **Census**: 6 **Outpatient Visits**: 26599 **Births**: 1 **Total Expense ($000)**: 14631 **Payroll Expense ($000)**: 4298 **Personnel**: 106

RADCLIFF—Hardin County

☐ **LINCOLN TRAIL BEHAVIORAL HEALTH SYSTEM (184012)**, 3909 South Wilson Road, Zip 40160–8944, Mailing Address: P.O.Box 369, 40159–0369; tel. 270/351–9444, (Nonreporting) **A**1 10 **S** Universal Health Services, Inc., King of Prussia, PA
Primary Contact: Charles L. Webb Jr, Chief Executive Officer
CFO: Debbie Ditto CPA, Controller
CMO: Muhammad W. Sajid M.D., Medical Director
CHR: Charlotte C Davis, Director Human Resources
Web address: www.lincolnbehavioral.com
Control: Corporation, Investor–owned (for–profit) **Service**: Psychiatric

Staffed Beds: 67

RICHMOND—Madison County

★ ○ **BAPTIST HEALTH RICHMOND (180049)**, 801 Eastern Bypass, Zip 40475–2405, Mailing Address: P.O.Box 1600, 40476–2603; tel. 859/623–3131 **A**10 11 19 **F**3 11 15 18 20 28 29 30 31 34 35 40 49 50 51 54 59 68 70 74 75 76 79 81 85 87 91 92 93 107 108 110 111 114 115 118 119 124 129 130 131 132 135 146 147 148 149 **S** Baptist Health, Louisville, KY
Primary Contact: Todd Jones, President
CMO: Richard Shelton M.D., Chief Medical Officer
CIO: Kelly Bonzo, Director
CHR: Joy M Benedict, Director Human Resources
CNO: Mendy Blair MSN, Vice President and Chief Nursing Officer
Web address: www.baptisthealthrichmond.com
Control: Other not–for–profit (including NFP Corporation) **Service:** General medical and surgical

Staffed Beds: 60 **Admissions:** 3023 **Census:** 32 **Outpatient Visits:** 82648 **Births:** 664 **Total Expense ($000):** 78667 **Payroll Expense ($000):** 25910 **Personnel:** 485

RUSSELL SPRINGS—Russell County

★ **RUSSELL COUNTY HOSPITAL (181330)**, 153 Dowell Road, Zip 42642–4579, Mailing Address: P.O.Box 1610, 42642–1610; tel. 270/866–4141 **A**10 18 **F**3 10 15 28 29 30 34 40 50 57 59 70 81 85 91 93 107 111 118 119 127 129 130 133 135 146 148
Primary Contact: Bill Kindred, Chief Executive Officer
CFO: Janie Landis, Chief Financial Officer
CMO: Jerry Lawson M.D., Chief of Medical Staff
CIO: Monte Monsanto, Chief Information Systems
CHR: Jennifer Goode, Director Human Resources
CNO: Judy Chenoweth, Chief Nursing Officer
Web address: www.russellcohospital.org
Control: Hospital district or authority, Government, Nonfederal **Service:** General medical and surgical

Staffed Beds: 25 **Admissions:** 695 **Census:** 9 **Outpatient Visits:** 41996 **Births:** 0 **Total Expense ($000):** 20316 **Payroll Expense ($000):** 10321 **Personnel:** 280

RUSSELLVILLE—Logan County

⊞ **LOGAN MEMORIAL HOSPITAL (180066)**, 1625 South Nashville Road, Zip 42276–8834, Mailing Address: P.O.Box 10, 42276–0010; tel. 270/726–4011 **A**1 10 **F**3 15 28 29 30 34 40 45 50 51 57 59 64 70 75 79 81 87 93 107 108 110 111 114 119 127 129 130 133 146 **S** LifePoint Health, Brentwood, TN
Primary Contact: James Bills, Chief Executive Officer
CFO: Tim Prestridge, Interim Chief Financial Officer
CIO: Randy Compton, Information Technology and System Director
CHR: Susan Renodin Deaton, Human Resources Director
CNO: Deborah Brown, Chief Nursing Officer
Web address: www.loganmemorial.com
Control: Corporation, Investor–owned (for–profit) **Service:** General medical and surgical

Staffed Beds: 53 **Admissions:** 875 **Census:** 10 **Outpatient Visits:** 25521 **Births:** 0 **Total Expense ($000):** 19985 **Payroll Expense ($000):** 7213 **Personnel:** 188

SALEM—Livingston County

LIVINGSTON HOSPITAL AND HEALTHCARE SERVICES (181320), 131 Hospital Drive, Zip 42078–8043; tel. 270/988–2299, (Nonreporting) **A**10 18
Primary Contact: Kent Giles, Interim Chief Executive Officer
CMO: William Guyette M.D., President Medical Staff
CIO: Shannan Landreth, Information Systems
CHR: Carla Wiggins, Director Human Resources
CNO: Joanna Stone, Chief Nursing Officer
Web address: www.lhhs.org
Control: Other not–for–profit (including NFP Corporation) **Service:** General medical and surgical

Staffed Beds: 25

SCOTTSVILLE—Allen County

MEDICAL CENTER AT SCOTTSVILLE (181324), 456 Burnley Road, Zip 42164–6355; tel. 270/622–2800, (Total facility includes 110 beds in nursing home–type unit) **A**10 18 **F**3 15 28 29 30 34 35 40 56 57 59 64 68 75 79 81 82 85 86 87 93 97 103 104 107 110 111 114 119 127 128 130 132 133 135 143 146 148 **P**6 **S** Commonwealth Health Corporation, Bowling Green, KY
Primary Contact: Eric Hagan, R.N., Executive Vice President and Administrator
CFO: Ronald G. Sowell, Chief Financial Officer
CIO: Mark Brookman, Chief Information Officer
CHR: Lynn Williams, Vice President Human Resources
Web address: www.themedicalcenterscottsville.org/
Control: Other not–for–profit (including NFP Corporation) **Service:** General medical and surgical

Staffed Beds: 135 **Admissions:** 732 **Census:** 125 **Outpatient Visits:** 23583 **Births:** 0 **Personnel:** 258

SHELBYVILLE—Shelby County

⊞ **JEWISH HOSPITAL–SHELBYVILLE (180016)**, 727 Hospital Drive, Zip 40065–1699; tel. 502/647–4000 **A**1 10 **F**3 11 15 18 28 29 34 35 39 40 44 45 46 50 57 59 64 68 75 79 80 81 82 84 85 87 91 93 107 108 110 111 114 119 129 132 146 147 148 **P**6 **S** Catholic Health Initiatives, Englewood, CO
Primary Contact: Annessa Baker, Site Executive and Chief Nursing Officer
CFO: Erika McGimsey, Controller
CMO: Tony Perez M.D., President Medical Staff
CHR: Cindy Stewart Rattray, Director Human Resources
Web address: www.kentuckyonehealth.org/jewish–hospital–shelbyville
Control: Other not–for–profit (including NFP Corporation) **Service:** General medical and surgical

Staffed Beds: 30 **Admissions:** 984 **Census:** 8 **Outpatient Visits:** 36891 **Births:** 0 **Total Expense ($000):** 28588 **Payroll Expense ($000):** 9367 **Personnel:** 122

SOMERSET—Pulaski County

⊞ **LAKE CUMBERLAND REGIONAL HOSPITAL (180132)**, 305 Langdon Street, Zip 42503–2750, Mailing Address: P.O.Box 620, 42502–0620; tel. 606/679–7441, (Total facility includes 12 beds in nursing home–type unit) **A**1 2 10 13 **F**3 8 11 12 13 15 17 18 20 22 24 29 30 31 34 39 40 41 42 45 46 49 50 51 54 56 57 58 59 64 65 68 70 73 74 75 76 77 78 79 81 82 85 86 87 89 90 91 93 96 97 98 100 102 103 107 108 109 110 111 114 115 119 120 127 128 129 130 131 132 135 144 146 147 148 149 **S** LifePoint Health, Brentwood, TN
Primary Contact: Timothy A. Bess, Chief Executive Officer
CFO: Steve Sloan, Chief Financial Officer
CMO: Michael Citak M.D., Chief Medical Officer
CIO: Thomas Gilbert, Director Information Technology Services
CHR: James Hughes, Director Human Resources
CNO: Sheryl Glasscock, Chief Nursing Officer
Web address: www.lakecumberlandhospital.com
Control: Corporation, Investor–owned (for–profit) **Service:** General medical and surgical

Staffed Beds: 295 **Admissions:** 10721 **Census:** 147 **Outpatient Visits:** 106665 **Births:** 1191 **Total Expense ($000):** 154796 **Payroll Expense ($000):** 52946 **Personnel:** 1274

SOUTH WILLIAMSON—Pike County

☐ **TUG VALLEY ARH REGIONAL MEDICAL CENTER (180069)**, 260 Hospital Drive, Zip 41503–4072; tel. 606/237–1710, (Total facility includes 35 beds in nursing home–type unit) **A**1 10 19 **F**3 11 13 15 29 30 34 35 40 43 50 54 57 59 60 62 64 67 70 74 75 76 77 79 81 82 85 86 87 89 93 97 107 108 110 111 115 118 119 127 128 129 130 132 146 147 **P**6 **S** Appalachian Regional Healthcare, Inc., Lexington, KY
Primary Contact: Timothy A. Hatfield, Community Chief Executive Officer
CMO: J D Miller M.D., Vice President Medical Affairs
CIO: Jeff Brady, Chief Information Officer
Web address: www.arh.org/locations/tug_valley/about_us.aspx
Control: Other not–for–profit (including NFP Corporation) **Service:** General medical and surgical

Staffed Beds: 141 **Admissions:** 2711 **Census:** 48 **Outpatient Visits:** 58235 **Births:** 102 **Total Expense ($000):** 42003 **Payroll Expense ($000):** 12642 **Personnel:** 381

Hospital, Medicare Provider Number, Address, Telephone, Approval, Facility, and Physician Codes, Health Care System

★ American Hospital Association (AHA) membership ○ Healthcare Facilities Accreditation Program ⇑ Center for Improvement in Healthcare Quality Accreditation
☐ The Joint Commission accreditation ◇ DNV Healthcare Inc. accreditation △ Commission on Accreditation of Rehabilitation Facilities (CARF) accreditation

STANFORD—Lincoln County

☐ **EPHRAIM MCDOWELL FORT LOGAN HOSPITAL (181315)**, 110 Metker Trail,
Zip 40484–1020; tel. 606/365–4600 **A**1 10 18 **F**3 11 13 15 29 30 34 35 40
43 57 59 64 73 76 81 87 89 107 110 111 119 130 133 135 145 **S** Ephraim
McDowell Health, Danville, KY
Primary Contact: Sally M. Davenport, R.N., MS, President and Chief Executive
Officer
CFO: William R Snapp III, Vice President and Chief Financial Officer
CMO: James Turpin, Chief of Staff
CIO: Gary Neat, Director Information Systems
CHR: Carl Metz, Vice President
CNO: Ina Louise Glass, Administrator
Web address: www.fortloganhospital.org
Control: Other not–for–profit (including NFP Corporation) **Service**: General
medical and surgical

Staffed Beds: 25 **Admissions**: 770 **Census**: 6 **Outpatient Visits**: 20199
Births: 431 **Total Expense ($000)**: 14736 **Payroll Expense ($000)**: 6632
Personnel: 141

TOMPKINSVILLE—Monroe County

⊠ **MONROE COUNTY MEDICAL CENTER (180105)**, 529 Capp Harlan Road,
Zip 42167–1840; tel. 270/487–9231 **A**1 10 **F**2 3 7 15 29 34 40 41 45 50
57 59 68 75 77 85 93 107 110 111 115 119 130 132 133 145 **P**8 **S** QHR,
Brentwood, TN
Primary Contact: Vicky McFall, Chief Executive Officer
CFO: Rickie F Brown, Chief Financial Officer
CIO: Paul McKiddy, Director Information Technology
CHR: Sue Page, Director Human Resources
Web address: www.mcmccares.com
Control: Other not–for–profit (including NFP Corporation) **Service**: General
medical and surgical

Staffed Beds: 49 **Admissions**: 1414 **Census**: 15 **Outpatient Visits**: 225963
Births: 0 **Total Expense ($000)**: 18199 **Payroll Expense ($000)**: 8590

VERSAILLES—Woodford County

★ **BLUEGRASS COMMUNITY HOSPITAL (181308)**, 360 Amsden Avenue,
Zip 40383–1286; tel. 859/873–3111 **A**10 18 **F**29 34 40 45 64 79 81 85 107
108 110 111 119 128 133 146 **P**6 **S** LifePoint Health, Brentwood, TN
Primary Contact: Tommy Haggard, Chief Executive Officer
CFO: Shellie Shouse, Chief Financial Officer
CMO: Michele Welling M.D., Chief of Staff
CHR: Marcia Carter, Director Human Resources
CNO: Kathy Russell R.N., Chief Nursing Officer
Web address: www.bluegrasscommunityhospital.com
Control: Corporation, Investor–owned (for–profit) **Service**: General medical and
surgical

Staffed Beds: 17 **Admissions**: 332 **Census**: 4 **Outpatient Visits**: 21788
Births: 0 **Total Expense ($000)**: 13186 **Payroll Expense ($000)**: 4981
Personnel: 86

WEST LIBERTY—Morgan County

☐ **MORGAN COUNTY ARH HOSPITAL (181307)**, 476 Liberty Road, Zip 41472–
2049, Mailing Address: P O Box 579, 41472–0579; tel. 606/743–3186 **A**1 10
18 **F**11 15 28 29 30 34 35 40 43 54 57 59 62 64 75 82 86 87 93 97 107
114 119 129 130 132 133 146 **P**6 **S** Appalachian Regional Healthcare, Inc.,
Lexington, KY
Primary Contact: Stephen M. Gavalchik, FACHE, Community Chief Executive Officer
COO: Paul V Miles, Chief Operating Officer
CMO: J D Miller M.D., Vice President Medical Affairs
CIO: Jeff Brady, Director Information Systems
CHR: Lisa Redding, Manager Human Resources
Web address: www.arh.org
Control: Other not–for–profit (including NFP Corporation) **Service**: General
medical and surgical

Staffed Beds: 25 **Admissions**: 273 **Census**: 4 **Outpatient Visits**: 25692
Births: 0 **Total Expense ($000)**: 13251 **Payroll Expense ($000)**: 4490
Personnel: 101

WHITESBURG—Letcher County

☐ **WHITESBURG ARH HOSPITAL (180002)**, 240 Hospital Road, Zip 41858–7627;
tel. 606/633–3500 **A**1 10 **F**3 11 13 15 18 20 28 29 30 31 32 34 35 40 43 50
54 57 59 62 64 70 75 76 77 81 82 85 86 87 89 93 97 107 108 110 111 114
118 119 127 129 130 133 146 147 **P**6 **S** Appalachian Regional Healthcare, Inc.,
Lexington, KY
Primary Contact: Dena C. Sparkman, FACHE, Community Chief Executive Officer
COO: Paul V Miles, Vice President Administration
CMO: Ricky M Collins M.D., Chief of Staff
CIO: Brent Styer, Director Information Technology
CHR: Daniel Fitzpatrick, Director Human Resources
Web address: www.arh.org/whitesburg
Control: Other not–for–profit (including NFP Corporation) **Service**: General
medical and surgical

Staffed Beds: 87 **Admissions**: 3908 **Census**: 40 **Outpatient Visits**: 65800
Births: 419 **Total Expense ($000)**: 43720 **Payroll Expense ($000)**: 12983
Personnel: 311

WILLIAMSTOWN—Grant County

ST. ELIZABETH GRANT (181311), 238 Barnes Road, Zip 41097–9482;
tel. 859/824–8240 **A**10 18 **F**3 11 15 18 26 29 30 31 34 35 38 40 44 45 50
53 57 59 63 64 65 74 75 78 79 84 93 97 107 108 110 111 115 119 129 130
131 132 135 141 146 148 149 150 **S** St. Elizabeth Healthcare, Edgewood, KY
Primary Contact: Garren Colvin, Chief Executive Officer
Web address: www.stelizabeth.com
Control: Church operated, Nongovernment, not–for–profit **Service**: General
medical and surgical

Staffed Beds: 16 **Admissions**: 196 **Census**: 1 **Outpatient Visits**: 57564
Births: 0 **Total Expense ($000)**: 17383 **Payroll Expense ($000)**: 7954
Personnel: 103

ST. ELIZABETH MEDICAL CENTER–GRANT COUNTY See St. Elizabeth Grant

WINCHESTER—Clark County

⊠ **CLARK REGIONAL MEDICAL CENTER (180092)**, 175 Hospital Drive,
Zip 40391–9591; tel. 859/745–3500, (Nonreporting) **A**1 5 10 **S** LifePoint Health,
Brentwood, TN
Primary Contact: Robert Parker, Chief Executive Officer and Market President
CFO: Amber Goodpaster, Chief Financial Officer
CMO: Ben McQuaide M.D., Chief of Staff
CHR: Deidre Bradley, Vice President Human Resources
CNO: Barbara Kinder R.N., Chief Clinical Officer
Web address: www.clarkregional.org
Control: Corporation, Investor–owned (for–profit) **Service**: General medical and
surgical

Staffed Beds: 79

LOUISIANA

ABBEVILLE—Vermilion Parish

☒ **ABBEVILLE GENERAL HOSPITAL (190034)**, 118 North Hospital Drive, Zip 70510–4077, Mailing Address: P.O.Box 580, 70511–0580; tel. 337/893–5466 **A**1 10 **F**3 11 13 15 29 30 31 34 40 45 50 54 59 60 64 66 68 70 75 76 79 81 82 85 86 87 89 97 98 103 105 107 108 114 119 127 128 130 133 146 149 **P**6
Primary Contact: Ray A. Landry, Chief Executive Officer
COO: Charles W Guidry, Chief Operating Officer
CFO: Troy Hair, Chief Financial Officer
CMO: Weston Miller M.D., Chief Medical Officer
CIO: Kelly Hair, Director Information Systems and Data Analytics
CNO: Heidi Broussard, Chief Nursing Officer
Web address: www.abbgen.net
Control: Hospital district or authority, Government, Nonfederal **Service**: General medical and surgical

Staffed Beds: 60 **Admissions**: 1823 **Census**: 30 **Outpatient Visits**: 99165 **Births**: 245 **Total Expense ($000)**: 43429 **Payroll Expense ($000)**: 21158 **Personnel**: 418

ALEXANDRIA—Rapides Parish

⇑ **CENTRAL LOUISIANA SURGICAL HOSPITAL (190298)**, 651 North Bolton Avenue, Zip 71301–7449, Mailing Address: P.O.Box 8646, 71306–1646; tel. 318/443–3511 **A**10 21 **F**12 68 74 81 85 86 90 107 111 130 149
Primary Contact: Louise Barker, R.N., Chief Executive Officer
CFO: Michael Fuselier FACHE, CPA, R.N., Chief Financial Officer
CMO: Renick Webb M.D., Chief Medical Director
CHR: Debbie Norman, Director Human Resources
CNO: Carol Wells R.N., MSN, Chief Nursing Officer
Web address: www.clshospital.com
Control: Partnership, Investor–owned (for–profit) **Service**: Surgical

Staffed Beds: 24 **Admissions**: 1268 **Census**: 8 **Outpatient Visits**: 34430 **Births**: 0 **Total Expense ($000)**: 48383 **Payroll Expense ($000)**: 12640 **Personnel**: 212

☒ **CHRISTUS DUBUIS HOSPITAL OF ALEXANDRIA (192012)**, 3330 Masonic Drive, 4th Floor, Zip 71301–3841; tel. 318/448–4938 **A**1 10 **F**1 3 29 77 84 85 148 **S** CHRISTUS Health, Irving, TX
Primary Contact: Beth Parsons, R.N., Administrator
CNO: Kimberly Bennett R.N., Director Patient Care
Web address: www.christusdubuis.org/CHRISTUSDubuisHospitalofAlexandriaLA
Control: Church operated, Nongovernment, not–for–profit **Service**: Acute long–term care hospital

Staffed Beds: 25 **Admissions**: 230 **Census**: 16 **Outpatient Visits**: 0 **Births**: 0 **Total Expense ($000)**: 7616 **Payroll Expense ($000)**: 3171 **Personnel**: 63

☒ **CHRISTUS ST. FRANCES CABRINI HOSPITAL (190019)**, 3330 Masonic Drive, Zip 71301–3899; tel. 318/487–1122 **A**1 2 10 **F**3 11 12 13 15 18 20 22 24 26 28 29 30 31 34 35 40 45 46 49 57 58 59 64 66 70 72 74 75 78 79 81 82 84 85 86 87 90 91 93 98 102 103 104 105 107 108 111 114 115 116 117 118 119 120 121 124 126 129 130 131 132 135 144 146 147 148 149 **P**6 **S** CHRISTUS Health, Irving, TX
Primary Contact: Nancy R. Hellyer, R.N., FACHE, Chief Executive Officer
COO: Lisa R. Lauve R.N., Regional Chief Nursing Executive and Chief Operating Officer
CFO: Gary Karg, Interim Vice President Finance
CHR: Wendy Chandler, Regional Vice President Human Resources
Web address: www.cabrini.org/
Control: Church operated, Nongovernment, not–for–profit **Service**: General medical and surgical

Staffed Beds: 281 **Admissions**: 12001 **Census**: 186 **Outpatient Visits**: 180229 **Births**: 996 **Total Expense ($000)**: 230276 **Payroll Expense ($000)**: 73890 **Personnel**: 1338

☐ **COMPASS BEHAVIORAL CENTER OF ALEXANDRIA (194106)**, 6410 Masonic Drve, Zip 71301–2319; tel. 318/442–3163 **A**1 10 **F**29 34 35 38 64 98 100 101 102 103 104 105 130 133 135 149 150 **P**5 **S** Compass Health, Crowley, LA
Primary Contact: Cheryl Lachney, Administrator
CNO: Cheryl Lachney, Director of Nursing
Web address: www.compasshealthcare.com/site191.php
Control: State, Government, Nonfederal **Service**: Psychiatric

Staffed Beds: 16 **Admissions**: 452 **Census**: 11 **Outpatient Visits**: 0 **Births**: 0

☒ **HEALTHSOUTH REHABILITATION HOSPITAL OF ALEXANDRIA (193031)**, 104 North Third Street, Zip 71301–8581; tel. 318/449–1370, (Nonreporting) **A**1 10 **S** HEALTHSOUTH Corporation, Birmingham, AL
Primary Contact: James W. McClung, Chief Executive Officer
CFO: Linda Wright, Chief Financial Officer
CMO: Vasudeva Dhulipala M.D., Medical Director
CHR: Suzie Wagner, Director Human Resources
Web address: www.healthsouthalexandria.com
Control: Partnership, Investor–owned (for–profit) **Service**: Rehabilitation

Staffed Beds: 47

LONGLEAF HOSPITAL (194022), 44 Versailles Boulevard, Zip 71303–3960; tel. 318/445–5111, (Nonreporting) **A**10 **S** Acadia Healthcare Company, Inc., Franklin, TN
Primary Contact: Monica Tatum, Chief Executive Officer and Administrator
Web address: www.longleafhospital.com/
Control: Corporation, Investor–owned (for–profit) **Service**: Psychiatric

Staffed Beds: 70

☐ **OCEANS BEHAVIORAL HOSPITAL OF ALEXANDRIA (194096)**, 2621 North Bolton Avenue, Zip 71303–4506; tel. 318/448–8473 (Nonreporting) **A**1 10 **S** Oceans Healthcare, Lake Charles, LA
Primary Contact: Nicholas D. Guillory, MSN, Interim Administrator
Web address: www.obha.info/
Control: Corporation, Investor–owned (for–profit) **Service**: Psychiatric

Staffed Beds: 24

☒ **RAPIDES REGIONAL MEDICAL CENTER (190026)**, 211 4th ST, Zip 71301–8421, Mailing Address: 211 Fourth Street, 71301–8421; tel. 318/769–3000 **A**1 2 3 5 10 **F**3 11 13 15 17 18 19 20 22 24 26 28 29 30 31 32 34 35 36 38 40 41 43 44 45 46 47 48 49 50 51 52 54 55 57 59 60 61 64 65 66 68 70 72 74 75 76 77 78 79 81 82 84 85 86 87 88 89 97 107 108 110 111 114 115 118 119 120 121 123 124 126 129 130 131 132 135 144 146 147 148 149 **P**1 **S** HCA Healthcare, Nashville, TN
Primary Contact: Jason E. Cobb, FACHE, Chief Executive Officer
COO: Becky Barnes, Chief Operating Officer
CMO: David Rhodes M.D., Senior Vice President Medical Affairs and Chief Medical Officer
CHR: Stephen W Scull, Vice President Ethics and Compliance officer
CNO: Barbara J Griffin MSN, R.N., Chief Nursing Officer
Web address: www.rapidesregional.com
Control: Partnership, Investor–owned (for–profit) **Service**: General medical and surgical

Staffed Beds: 357 **Admissions**: 15952 **Census**: 239 **Outpatient Visits**: 237422 **Births**: 1927 **Total Expense ($000)**: 231672 **Payroll Expense ($000)**: 83746 **Personnel**: 1391

☐ **RIVERSIDE HOSPITAL OF LOUISIANA (192043)**, 211 Fourth Street, 5th Floor, Zip 71301–8421; tel. 318/767–2900, (Nonreporting) **A**1 10
Primary Contact: Chris G. Voinche, Chief Executive Officer
Web address: www.riversidehospital.net
Control: Corporation, Investor–owned (for–profit) **Service**: Acute long–term care hospital

Staffed Beds: 27

Hospital, Medicare Provider Number, Address, Telephone, Approval, Facility, and Physician Codes, Health Care System

★ American Hospital Association (AHA) membership   ○ Healthcare Facilities Accreditation Program   ⇑ Center for Improvement in Healthcare Quality Accreditation
☐ The Joint Commission accreditation   ◇ DNV Healthcare Inc. accreditation   △ Commission on Accreditation of Rehabilitation Facilities (CARF) accreditation

AMITE—Tangipahoa Parish

★ **HOOD MEMORIAL HOSPITAL (191309)**, 301 West Walnut Street, Zip 70422–2098; tel. 985/748–9485 **A**10 18 **F**3 29 35 40 50 57 59 64 65 75 83 84 86 97 107 108 114 119 127 130 133 135 144 146 **P**6
Primary Contact: Edward Dugar, R.N., Chief Executive Officer
CFO: Mike Estay, Chief Financial Officer
CMO: Richard Bridges M.D., Chief of Staff
CIO: Schley Harvin, Information Technology Technician
CHR: Alicia Chatelain, Director Human Resource
CNO: Fran St. Pierre, Chief Nursing Officer
Web address: www.hoodmemorial.com
Control: Hospital district or authority, Government, Nonfederal **Service:** General medical and surgical

Staffed Beds: 25 **Admissions:** 549 **Census:** 17 **Outpatient Visits:** 25755
Births: 0 **Total Expense ($000):** 15185 **Payroll Expense ($000):** 7082
Personnel: 220

ARCADIA—Bienville Parish

BIENVILLE MEDICAL CENTER (191320), 1175 Pine Street, Suite 200, Zip 71001–3122; tel. 318/263–4700, (Nonreporting) **A**10 18 **S** Allegiance Health Management, Shreveport, LA
Primary Contact: Kirk Lemoine, Chief Executive Officer
Web address: www.bienvillemedicalcenter.net/
Control: Other not–for–profit (including NFP Corporation) **Service:** General medical and surgical

Staffed Beds: 21

BASTROP—Morehouse Parish

☐ **LIBERTY HEALTHCARE SYSTEMS (194083)**, 4673 Eugene Ware Boulevard, Zip 71220–1425; tel. 318/281–2448 **A**1 10 **F**2 98 99 130 **P**6
Primary Contact: Alan Miller, Administrator
COO: Christine Murphy MS, Chief Operating Officer
CFO: Paul Coburn, Chief Financial Officer
CMO: Tommy Dansby, Chief Medical Officer
CHR: Lindsay Cobb, Director Human Resources
CNO: Carla Sams R.N., Director of Nursing
Web address: www.libertybh.com/
Control: Partnership, Investor–owned (for–profit) **Service:** Children's hospital psychiatric

Staffed Beds: 60 **Admissions:** 880 **Census:** 20 **Outpatient Visits:** 15584
Births: 0 **Total Expense ($000):** 5651 **Payroll Expense ($000):** 3115

★ **MOREHOUSE GENERAL HOSPITAL (190116)**, 323 West Walnut Avenue, Zip 71220–4521, Mailing Address: P.O.Box 1060, 71221–1060; tel. 318/283–3600 **A**3 10 **F**11 13 15 29 34 39 40 45 50 64 65 70 76 77 79 81 85 86 89 93 97 102 107 108 110 111 114 118 119 127 133 145 146 147 148 **P**5 6 **S** Community Hospital Corporation, Plano, TX
Primary Contact: Derrick A. Frazier, FACHE, Chief Executive Officer
CFO: Tom Ramsey, Chief Financial Officer
CMO: John Coats M.D., Chief Medical Staff
CIO: B J Vail, Director Information Systems
CHR: Debbie Spann, Director Human Resources
CNO: Melinda Jones R.N., Chief Nursing Officer
Web address: www.mghospital.com
Control: Hospital district or authority, Government, Nonfederal **Service:** General medical and surgical

Staffed Beds: 49 **Admissions:** 1901 **Census:** 16 **Outpatient Visits:** 41367
Births: 405

STERLINGTON REHABILITATION HOSPITAL (193069), 370 W Hickory Ave, Zip 71220–4442, Mailing Address: P.O.Box 627, Sterlington, 71280–0627; tel. 318/665–9950 **A**10 **F**28 34 35 50 54 56 57 59 64 65 66 68 75 86 87 90 91 93 94 95 96 97 100 101 103 104 127 130 132 135 143 147 148 149 **P**6
Primary Contact: Catherine M. Waldrop, Administrator
Web address: www.sterlingtonrehab.com
Control: Corporation, Investor–owned (for–profit) **Service:** Rehabilitation

Staffed Beds: 10 **Admissions:** 284 **Census:** 9 **Outpatient Visits:** 1400
Births: 0 **Total Expense ($000):** 8593 **Payroll Expense ($000):** 4716
Personnel: 95

BATON ROUGE—East Baton Rouge Parish

APOLLO BEHAVIORAL HEALTH HOSPITAL (194105), 7414 Sumrall Drive, Zip 70812–1240; tel. 225/663–2881 (Nonreporting)
Primary Contact: Gopinath Gopalam, Chief Executive Officer
Web address: www.apollo–bhh.com/about–us/
Control: Other not–for–profit (including NFP Corporation) **Service:** Psychiatric

Staffed Beds: 25

☐ **BATON ROUGE BEHAVIORAL HOSPITAL (194107)**, 4040 North Boulevard, Zip 70806–3829; tel. 225/300–8470 (Nonreporting) **A**1 10
Primary Contact: Clay Aguillard, R.N., Administrator
COO: James O'Shea, Chief Operating Officer
CFO: Warren Knight, Chief Financial Officer
CMO: Richard Capiola M.D., Chief Medical Officer
CNO: Francine Mineau, Chief Nursing Officer
Web address: www.batonrougebehavioral.com
Control: Corporation, Investor–owned (for–profit) **Service:** Psychiatric

Staffed Beds: 15

☐ **BATON ROUGE GENERAL MEDICAL CENTER (190065)**, 8585 Picardy Avenue, Zip 70809–3679; tel. 225/763–4000, (Includes BATON ROUGE GENERAL MEDICAL CENTER–BLUEBONNET, 8585 Picardy Avenue, Baton Rouge, Louisiana, Zip 70809–3679, P O Box 84330, 70884–4330, tel. 225/763–4000; Edgardo J Tenreiro, Chief Executive Officer and Chief Operating Officer) **A**1 2 3 5 8 10 **F**3 8 11 12 13 15 16 17 18 19 20 22 24 26 28 29 30 31 34 35 38 40 44 45 46 50 53 56 57 58 59 60 61 64 65 68 70 72 74 75 76 77 78 79 81 82 84 86 87 89 90 91 93 96 97 98 99 101 102 103 104 105 107 108 110 111 114 115 117 118 119 120 121 123 124 126 128 129 130 131 132 135 143 144 146 147 148 **P**4 6
Primary Contact: Edgardo J. Tenreiro, Chief Executive Officer and Chief Operating Officer
COO: Edgardo J Tenreiro, Chief Executive Officer and Chief Operating Officer
CFO: Kendall Johnson, Chief Financial Officer
CIO: Bennett Cheramie, Vice President Information Technology
CHR: Paul Douglas, Vice President Human Resources
CNO: Monica Nijoka, Chief Nursing Officer
Web address: www.brgeneral.org
Control: Other not–for–profit (including NFP Corporation) **Service:** General medical and surgical

Staffed Beds: 365 **Admissions:** 15638 **Census:** 232 **Outpatient Visits:** 137785 **Births:** 799 **Total Expense ($000):** 381191 **Payroll Expense ($000):** 117728 **Personnel:** 2387

☐ **BATON ROUGE REHABILITATION HOSPITAL (193028)**, 8595 United Plaza Boulevard, Zip 70809–2251; tel. 225/927–0567, (Nonreporting) **A**1 10
Primary Contact: Trisha Guidry, Administrator
CFO: Nicholas Hluchy, Business Analyst, Support Services Manager
CMO: Sundararama R Vatsavai M.D., Medical Director
CIO: John Derrick Landreneau, Director of Nursing and Marketing Manager
CHR: Michelle Smith, Coordinator Human Resources
CNO: John Derrick Landreneau, Director of Nursing
Web address: www.brrehab.com
Control: Corporation, Investor–owned (for–profit) **Service:** Rehabilitation

Staffed Beds: 80

BETHESDA REHABILITATION HOSPITAL (193092), 7414 Sumrall Drive, Zip 70812–1240, Mailing Address: 8225 Summa Avenue, Suite B, 70809–3422; tel. 225/767–2034 (Nonreporting) **A**10
Primary Contact: Lionel Murphy, Chief Executive Officer and Administrator
Web address: www.bethesdarh.com/
Control: Corporation, Investor–owned (for–profit) **Service:** Rehabilitation

Staffed Beds: 18

HEALTHSOUTH REHABILITATION HOSPITAL OF BATON ROUGE See Baton Rouge Rehabilitation Hospital

OCEANS BEHAVIORAL HOSPITAL OF BATON ROUGE (194086), 11135 Florida Boulevard, Zip 70815–2013; tel. 225/356–7030 (Nonreporting) **A**10 **S** Oceans Healthcare, Lake Charles, LA
Primary Contact: Valerie Dalton, R.N., Administrator
Web address: www.obhbr.info/
Control: Corporation, Investor–owned (for–profit) **Service:** Psychiatric

Staffed Beds: 20

⊞ **OCHSNER MEDICAL CENTER–BATON ROUGE (190202)**, 17000 Medical Center Drive, Zip 70816–3224; tel. 225/752–2470 **A**1 10 **F**3 11 12 13 15 18 20 22 24 26 29 30 31 34 35 40 42 45 46 47 48 49 51 57 58 59 60 64 68 70 72 74 75 76 77 78 79 81 82 85 86 87 93 97 104 107 108 110 111 114 116 117 119 126 129 130 132 135 144 146 147 148 **P**6 **S** Ochsner Health System, New Orleans, LA
Primary Contact: Eric McMillen, Chief Executive Officer
CFO: Stephanie Bushart, Chief Financial Officer
CMO: F Ralph Dauterive M.D., Vice President Medical Affairs
CHR: Jan Rivers, Director Human Resources
Web address: www.ochsner.org/page.cfm?id=103
Control: Other not–for–profit (including NFP Corporation) **Service:** General medical and surgical

Staffed Beds: 152 **Admissions:** 7113 **Census:** 73 **Outpatient Visits:** 97885
Births: 1475 **Total Expense ($000):** 146635 **Payroll Expense ($000):** 49303 **Personnel:** 623

Many Facility Codes have changed. Please refer to the AHA Guide Code Chart. © 2017 AHA Guide

✠ **OUR LADY OF THE LAKE REGIONAL MEDICAL CENTER (190064)**, 5000 Hennessy Boulevard, Zip 70808–4375; tel. 225/765–6565, (Includes OUR LADY OF THE LAKE CHILDREN'S HOSPITAL, 5000 Hennessy Boulevard, Baton Rouge, Louisiana, Zip 70808–4375, tel. 225/765–8886) (Total facility includes 390 beds in nursing home–type unit) **A**1 2 3 5 8 10 **F**3 4 5 8 10 11 12 14 15 17 18 19 20 21 22 24 26 28 29 30 31 32 34 35 37 38 39 40 41 42 43 45 46 47 48 49 50 51 53 54 55 56 57 58 59 60 61 64 66 68 70 71 74 75 77 78 79 81 84 85 86 87 88 89 90 93 94 96 97 98 99 100 101 102 103 104 105 107 108 110 111 114 115 116 117 118 119 124 125 126 127 129 130 131 132 135 141 142 143 145 146 148 149 **P**6 **S** Franciscan Missionaries of Our Lady Health System, Inc., Baton Rouge, LA
Primary Contact: K Scott. Wester, FACHE, President and Chief Executive Officer
COO: Terrie Sterling R.N., MSN, Chief Operating Officer
CFO: Jeff Limbocker, Chief Financial Officer
CMO: Richard Vath M.D., Vice President Medical Affairs
CIO: Vindell Washington M.D., Vice President Performance Excellence and Technology
CHR: Cora Ford, Vice President Human Resources
CNO: Nicole Telhiard MSN, Chief Nursing Officer
Web address: www.ololrmc.com
Control: Church operated, Nongovernment, not–for–profit **Service:** General medical and surgical

Staffed Beds: 1129 **Admissions:** 36371 **Census:** 799 **Outpatient Visits:** 1461654 **Births:** 0 **Total Expense ($000):** 1113227 **Payroll Expense ($000):** 407390

☐ **PROMISE HOSPITAL BATON ROUGE – MAIN CAMPUS (192045)**, 5130 Mancuso Lane, Zip 70809–3583; tel. 225/490–9600, (Nonreporting) **A**1 **S** Promise Healthcare, Boca Raton, FL
Primary Contact: Kiley P. Cedotal, FACHE, Chief Executive Officer
COO: Michael R Sanders MS, Chief Operating Officer
CFO: Trina Arceneaux, Assistant Chief Financial Officer
CMO: Subhaker Gummadi M.D., Chief Medical Staff
CIO: Charmaine T Mosby, Area Director Health Information Management
CHR: Marilyn Hamilton, Director Human Resources
CNO: Larrie Arceneaux, Chief Clinical Officer
Web address: www.promise–batonrouge.com
Control: Corporation, Investor–owned (for–profit) **Service:** Acute long–term care hospital

Staffed Beds: 54

PROMISE HOSPITAL OF BATON ROUGE – MID–CITY CAMPUS (192004), 3600 Florida Boulevard, 4th Floor, Zip 70806–3842; tel. 225/387–7770 (Nonreporting) **A**10 **S** Promise Healthcare, Boca Raton, FL
Primary Contact: Kiley P. Cedotal, FACHE, Chief Executive Officer
CMO: Subhaker Gummadi M.D., President Medical Staff
Web address: www.promise–batonrougemidcity.com
Control: Corporation, Investor–owned (for–profit) **Service:** Acute long–term care hospital

Staffed Beds: 57

PROMISE HOSPITAL OF BATON ROUGE – OCHSNER CAMPUS (192049), 17000 Medical Center Drive, 3rd Floor, Zip 70816–3246; tel. 225/236–5440 (Nonreporting) **A**10 **S** Promise Healthcare, Boca Raton, FL
Primary Contact: Kiley P. Cedotal, FACHE, Chief Executive Officer
CMO: Venkat Banda M.D., President Medical Staff
CHR: Wendy Cobbs, Director of Human Resources
Web address: www.promise–batonrougeochsner.com
Control: Corporation, Investor–owned (for–profit) **Service:** Acute long–term care hospital

Staffed Beds: 29

SAGE REHABILITATION HOSPITAL (193078), 8000 Summa Avenue, Zip 70809–3423, Mailing Address: P.O.Box 82681, 70884–2681; tel. 225/819–0703, (Total facility includes 15 beds in nursing home–type unit) **A**10 **F**29 54 74 75 77 90 91 93 128 130
Primary Contact: Gayla Bryant, R.N., Interim Administrator and Vice President Rehabilitation Operations
CMO: Christopher Belleau M.D., Medical Director
CHR: Kathy Ringe, Director Human Resources
CNO: Beth Sibley, Director of Nursing
Web address: www.sage–rehab.org
Control: Individual, Investor–owned (for–profit) **Service:** Rehabilitation

Staffed Beds: 42 **Admissions:** 617 **Census:** 27 **Outpatient Visits:** 0 **Births:** 0 **Personnel:** 143

☐ **SEASIDE HEALTH SYSTEM (194103)**, 4363 Convention Street, Zip 70806–3906, Mailing Address: 4363 Convention Stret, 70806–3906; tel. 225/238–3043 (Nonreporting) **A**1 10
Primary Contact: Eric Gintoli, Administrator
Web address: www.seasidehc.com/seaside–health–system–locations/
Control: Partnership, Investor–owned (for–profit) **Service:** Psychiatric

Staffed Beds: 24

SPINE HOSPITAL OF LOUISIANA (FORMALLY THE NEUROMEDICAL CENTER SURGICAL HOSPITAL) (190266), 10105 Park Rowe Circle, Suite 250, Zip 70810–1684; tel. 225/763–9900 (Nonreporting) **A**10
Primary Contact: Robert D. Blair, Chief Executive Officer
CFO: Allison Doherty, Chief Financial Officer
CMO: Greg Fautheree M.D., Medical Director
CIO: Jeremy Deprato, Director Information Technology
CHR: Kimberly Jones, Director Human Resources
CNO: Kim Pettijohn R.N., MSN, Chief Nursing Officer
Web address: www.theneuromedicalcenter.com
Control: Corporation, Investor–owned (for–profit) **Service:** Surgical

Staffed Beds: 23

☐ **SURGICAL SPECIALTY CENTER OF BATON ROUGE (190251)**, 8080 Bluebonnet Boulevard, Zip 70810–7827; tel. 225/408–8080 (Nonreporting) **A**1 10
Primary Contact: Ann Heine, Chief Executive Officer
CNO: Kelli Firmin, Interim Chief Nursing Officer, Pre–Op and PACU Manager
Web address: www.sscbr.com
Control: Corporation, Investor–owned (for–profit) **Service:** Surgical

Staffed Beds: 14

THE NEUROMEDICAL CENTER REHABILITATION HOSPITAL (193090), 10101 Park Rowe Avenue, Suite 500, Zip 70810–1685; tel. 225/906–2999 (Nonreporting) **A**10 **S** AMG Integrated Healthcare Management, Lafayette, LA
Primary Contact: Elizabeth Wilson, Administrator
Web address: www.theneuromedicalcenter.com
Control: Corporation, Investor–owned (for–profit) **Service:** Rehabilitation

Staffed Beds: 23

✠ **WOMAN'S HOSPITAL (190128)**, 100 Woman's Way, Zip 70817–5100, Mailing Address: P.O.Box 95009, 70895–9009; tel. 225/927–1300 **A**1 2 3 5 10 **F**3 11 12 13 15 29 31 32 34 35 36 38 40 45 50 53 54 57 58 59 61 64 65 66 68 70 71 72 74 75 76 77 78 79 81 84 85 86 87 93 102 107 110 111 115 119 126 129 130 131 132 134 135 146 147 148 149 **P**6
Primary Contact: Teri G. Fontenot, FACHE, President and Chief Executive Officer
COO: Stephanie Anderson, Executive Vice President and Chief Operating Officer
CFO: Greg Smith CPA, Chief Financial Officer
CMO: Susan Puyau M.D., Medical Director
CIO: Paul Kirk, Vice President
CHR: Donna L Bodin, Vice President
CNO: Patricia Johnson R.N., Senior Vice President
Web address: www.womans.org
Control: Other not–for–profit (including NFP Corporation) **Service:** Obstetrics and gynecology

Staffed Beds: 216 **Admissions:** 11656 **Census:** 142 **Outpatient Visits:** 144255 **Births:** 8638 **Total Expense ($000):** 261998 **Payroll Expense ($000):** 126409 **Personnel:** 1675

BERNICE—Union Parish

REEVES MEMORIAL MEDICAL CENTER (191326), 409 First Street, Zip 71222–4001, Mailing Address: P.O.Box 697, 71222–0697; tel. 318/285–9066, (Nonreporting) **A**10 18
Primary Contact: David Caston, Chief Executive Officer
COO: Beth Jones, Chief Operating Officer
CFO: Charolette Thompson, Chief Financial Officer
CMO: R Brian Harris M.D., Chief of Staff
CIO: Scott Dickson, Director Information Technology
CHR: Robin Adams, Director Human Resources
CNO: Beth Jones, Director of Nursing
Web address: www.reevesmemorial.com/
Control: Hospital district or authority, Government, Nonfederal **Service:** General medical and surgical

Staffed Beds: 11

TRI–WARD GENERAL HOSPITAL See Reeves Memorial Medical Center

Hospital, Medicare Provider Number, Address, Telephone, Approval, Facility, and Physician Codes, Health Care System

★ American Hospital Association (AHA) membership   ○ Healthcare Facilities Accreditation Program   ⇑ Center for Improvement in Healthcare Quality Accreditation
☐ The Joint Commission accreditation   ◇ DNV Healthcare Inc. accreditation   △ Commission on Accreditation of Rehabilitation Facilities (CARF) accreditation

LA

BOGALUSA—Washington Parish

⊞ **OUR LADY OF THE ANGELS HOSPITAL (190312)**, 433 Plaza Street, Zip 70427–3793; tel. 985/730–6700, (Nonreporting) (Includes BOGALUSA COMMUNITY MEDICAL CENTER, 433 Plaza Street, Bogalusa, Louisiana, Zip 70427–3793, tel. 985/730–6700) **A**1 3 5 10 **S** Franciscan Missionaries of Our Lady Health System, Inc., Baton Rouge, LA
Primary Contact: Rene J. Ragas, Chief Operating Officer
COO: Rene J. Ragas, Chief Operating Officer
CFO: Brooke Cummings, Chief Financial Officer
CMO: Hamid Hussain M.D., Medical Director
CIO: Mike Gilly, Chief Information Officer
CHR: Christi Brown, Director Human Resources
CNO: Mark Kellar R.N., Interim Chief Nursing Officer
Web address: www.oloah.org
Control: Church operated, Nongovernment, not–for–profit **Service:** General medical and surgical

Staffed Beds: 57

BOSSIER CITY—Bossier Parish

☐ **CORNERSTONE HOSPITAL OF BOSSIER CITY (192006)**, 4900 Medical Drive, Zip 71112–4521; tel. 318/747–9500, (Nonreporting) **A**1 10 **S** Cornerstone Healthcare Group, Dallas, TX
Primary Contact: Sheri Burnette, R.N., Chief Executive Officer and Administrator
CMO: James Jackson M.D., Chief of Staff
CNO: Tamara Grimm R.N., Chief Clinical Officer and Chief Nursing Officer
Web address: www.chghospitals.com/
Control: Corporation, Investor–owned (for–profit) **Service:** Acute long–term care hospital

Staffed Beds: 54

⇑ **PATHWAY REHABILITATION HOSPITAL (193094)**, 4900 Medical Drive, Zip 71112–4521; tel. 318/841–5555 (Nonreporting) **A**10 21
Primary Contact: James Manning, Administrator
Web address: www.pathrehab.com
Control: Corporation, Investor–owned (for–profit) **Service:** Rehabilitation

Staffed Beds: 24

RED RIVER BEHAVIORAL CENTER (194079), 2800 Melrose Avenue, Zip 71111–5870; tel. 318/549–2033 **A**10 **F**29 38 56 98 100 101 103 130 135 143
Primary Contact: Susan Kottenbrook, Chief Executive Officer
Web address: www.redriverbc.com
Control: Partnership, Investor–owned (for–profit) **Service:** Psychiatric

Staffed Beds: 20 **Admissions:** 331 **Census:** 16 **Outpatient Visits:** 0 **Births:** 0 **Total Expense ($000):** 3746 **Payroll Expense ($000):** 1857 **Personnel:** 54

WILLIS–KNIGHTON BOSSIER HEALTH CENTER See WK Bossier Health Center

⊞ △ **WK BOSSIER HEALTH CENTER (190236)**, 2400 Hospital Drive, Zip 71111–2385; tel. 318/212–7000 **A**1 2 7 10 **F**3 8 11 12 13 15 18 20 22 28 29 30 34 35 38 40 44 45 46 47 48 49 50 53 54 56 57 59 60 61 64 65 68 70 74 75 76 77 78 79 80 81 82 84 85 86 87 93 96 97 100 101 102 103 107 108 109 110 111 114 115 118 119 126 127 130 131 132 135 144 146 147 148 **P**7 **S** Willis–Knighton Health System, Shreveport, LA
Primary Contact: Clifford M. Broussard, FACHE, Administrator
COO: Charles D Daigle, Chief Operating Officer
CFO: Ramona D Fryer, Chief Financial Officer
CMO: Charles Powers M.D., Administrative Medical Director
CIO: Charles Laster, Director Information Management
CHR: Debbie McCall, Director Human Resources
CNO: Sharon Hudnell R.N., Chief Nursing Officer
Web address: www.wkhs.com/wkb/
Control: Other not–for–profit (including NFP Corporation) **Service:** General medical and surgical

Staffed Beds: 166 **Admissions:** 13278 **Census:** 102 **Outpatient Visits:** 133591 **Births:** 833 **Personnel:** 1042

BREAUX BRIDGE—St. Martin Parish

★ **GENESIS BEHAVIORAL HOSPITAL (194089)**, 606 Latiolais Drive, Zip 70517–4231, Mailing Address: PO BOX 159, 70517–0159; tel. 337/442–6084 **A**10 **F**98 100 101 102 103 104 105 **P**1
Primary Contact: William Arledge, Administrator and Chief Financial Officer
COO: Gretchen Kaltenbach R.N., Chief Operating Officer
CFO: William Alredge, Administrator and Chief Financial Officer
Web address: www.genesisbh.com/
Control: Corporation, Investor–owned (for–profit) **Service:** Psychiatric

Staffed Beds: 18 **Admissions:** 579 **Census:** 15 **Outpatient Visits:** 18500 **Births:** 0

★ **ST. MARTIN HOSPITAL (191302)**, 210 Champagne Boulevard, Zip 70517–3700, Mailing Address: P.O.Box 357, 70517–0357; tel. 337/332–2178 **A**10 18 **F**3 15 18 29 34 35 40 54 57 59 64 68 75 77 87 90 91 93 107 110 111 114 119 128 130 133 146 149 **S** Lafayette General Health, Lafayette, LA
Primary Contact: Karen O. Wyble, R.N., Chief Executive Officer
CFO: Shadelle Huval, Director Finance
CHR: Rena B Mouisset, Director Human Resources and Contract Compliance
Web address: www.stmartinhospital.org
Control: Other not–for–profit (including NFP Corporation) **Service:** General medical and surgical

Staffed Beds: 25 **Admissions:** 396 **Census:** 13 **Outpatient Visits:** 135581 **Births:** 0 **Total Expense ($000):** 17288 **Payroll Expense ($000):** 7366 **Personnel:** 126

BROUSSARD—Lafayette Parish

☐ **OCEANS BEHAVIORAL HOSPITAL OF BROUSSARD (194073)**, 418 Albertson Parkway, Zip 70518–4971; tel. 337/237–6444 (Nonreporting) **A**1 10 **S** Oceans Healthcare, Lake Charles, LA
Primary Contact: Amy Dysart–Credeur, Administrator
Web address: www.obhb.info/
Control: Corporation, Investor–owned (for–profit) **Service:** Psychiatric

Staffed Beds: 38

BUNKIE—Avoyelles Parish

BEACON BEHAVIORAL HOSPITAL (194112), 323 Evergreen Street, Zip 71322–1307; tel. 318/346–3143 (Nonreporting) **S** Beacon Health System, South Bend, IN
Primary Contact: Randall Johnson, Administrator
Web address: www.beaconbh.com
Control: Other not–for–profit (including NFP Corporation) **Service:** Psychiatric

Staffed Beds: 17

BUNKIE GENERAL HOSPITAL (191311), 427 Evergreen Highway, Zip 71322, Mailing Address: P.O. Box 380, 71322–0380; tel. 318/346–6681, (Nonreporting) **A**10 18
Primary Contact: Linda F. Deville, Chief Executive Officer
CFO: Layla Chase, Interim Chief Financial Officer
CMO: Mohit Srivastava M.D., Chief of Staff
CIO: Kiland Jackson, Chief Information Officer
CHR: Tina Louise Juneau, Director Human Resources
CNO: Corey Jeansonne, Chief Nursing Officer
Web address: www.bunkiegeneral.com
Control: Hospital district or authority, Government, Nonfederal **Service:** General medical and surgical

Staffed Beds: 18

CAMERON—Cameron Parish

SOUTH CAMERON MEMORIAL HOSPITAL (190307), 5360 West Creole Highway, Zip 70631–5127; tel. 337/542–4111 **A**10 **F**40 64 98 107
Primary Contact: Leslie Trahan, Chief Executive Officer
Control: State, Government, Nonfederal **Service:** General medical and surgical

Staffed Beds: 30 **Admissions:** 887 **Census:** 19 **Outpatient Visits:** 1380 **Births:** 0

CHALMETTE—Saint Bernard Parish

⊞ **ST. BERNARD PARISH HOSPITAL (190308)**, 8000 West Judge Perez Drive, Zip 70043–1668; tel. 504/826–9500 **A**1 10 **F**3 15 18 20 22 24 29 34 40 41 45 46 53 57 59 70 74 77 79 81 82 90 91 93 107 108 110 111 114 119 130 132 148 149 **P**5
Primary Contact: Kimberly Keene, Interim Chief Executive Officer, Assistant Vice President Clinical Operations
CFO: Joseph Kemka, Chief Financial Officer
CMO: Paul Verrette M.D., Chief Medical Officer
CIO: Zane Looney, Chief Information Officer
CHR: Melody M O'Connell, Director Human Resources
CNO: Janice Kishner, Chief Nursing Officer
Web address: www.sbph.net
Control: Hospital district or authority, Government, Nonfederal **Service:** General medical and surgical

Staffed Beds: 40 **Admissions:** 1989 **Census:** 16 **Outpatient Visits:** 35995 **Births:** 0 **Total Expense ($000):** 40302 **Payroll Expense ($000):** 14128 **Personnel:** 284

Many Facility Codes have changed. Please refer to the AHA Guide Code Chart. © 2017 AHA Guide

CHURCH POINT—Acadia Parish

ACADIA–ST. LANDRY HOSPITAL (191319), 810 South Broadway Street, Zip 70525–4497; tel. 337/684–5435, (Nonreporting) **A**10 18
Primary Contact: Cindy Walters, Chief Executive Officer
CFO: Lucille LeJeune, Assistant Administrator and Chief Financial Officer
CMO: Ty Hargroder M.D., Chief of Staff
Web address: www.aslh.org
Control: Other not–for–profit (including NFP Corporation) **Service:** General medical and surgical

Staffed Beds: 25

COLUMBIA—Caldwell Parish

CALDWELL MEMORIAL HOSPITAL (190190), 411 Main Street, Zip 71418–6704, Mailing Address: P.O.Box 899, 71418–0899; tel. 318/649–6111 **A**10 **F**90 149
Primary Contact: Heather Clark, Chief Executive Officer
COO: Lisa Patrick, Chief Operating Officer
CFO: William H Clark, Chief Financial Officer
Control: Other not–for–profit (including NFP Corporation) **Service:** General medical and surgical

Staffed Beds: 47 **Admissions:** 935 **Census:** 12 **Outpatient Visits:** 0 **Births:** 0

CITIZENS MEDICAL CENTER (190184), 7939 U S Highway 165, Zip 71418–1079, Mailing Address: P.O.Box 1079, 71418–1079; tel. 318/649–6106 (Nonreporting) **A**10
Primary Contact: Steve Barbo, R.N., Administrator
Web address: www.citizensmedcenter.com/
Control: Hospital district or authority, Government, Nonfederal **Service:** General medical and surgical

Staffed Beds: 40

COUSHATTA—Red River Parish

✠ **CHRISTUS COUSHATTA HEALTH CARE CENTER (191312)**, 1635 Marvel Street, Zip 71019–9022, Mailing Address: P.O.Box 589, 71019–0589; tel. 318/932–2000 **A**1 10 18 **F**3 15 29 30 34 35 39 40 41 50 54 56 57 59 64 65 66 68 75 77 78 81 82 91 93 97 103 107 110 115 116 117 119 120 127 130 133 135 147 148 149 **S** CHRISTUS Health, Irving, TX
Primary Contact: Brandon Hillman, Interim Administrator, Director of Hospital Services
CFO: Scott Merryman, Chief Financial Officer
CMO: Jonathan Weisul M.D., Vice President Medical Affairs and Chief Medical Officer
CIO: Bruce Honea, Director Information Services
CHR: Donnette Craig, Director Human Resources
Web address: www.christuscoushatta.org
Control: Church operated, Nongovernment, not–for–profit **Service:** General medical and surgical

Staffed Beds: 25 **Admissions:** 802 **Census:** 9 **Outpatient Visits:** 6766 **Births:** 0 **Total Expense ($000):** 19674 **Personnel:** 141

SPECIALTY REHABILITATION HOSPITAL OF COUSHATTA (193080), 1110 Ringgold Avenue Suite B, Zip 71019–9073; tel. 318/932–1770 (Nonreporting) **A**10
Primary Contact: Craig Ball, Chief Executive Officer
COO: Charlie Ball, Chief Operating Officer
CFO: Connie Ball, Chief Financial Officer
CMO: Jalal Joudeh M.D., Chief Medical Officer
CHR: Denise Logan, Director Human Resources
Web address: www.specialtyhealthcare.com
Control: Individual, Investor–owned (for–profit) **Service:** Rehabilitation

Staffed Beds: 12

COVINGTON—St. Tammany Parish

AMG PHYSICAL REHABILITATION HOSPITAL, 5025 Keystone Boulevard, Suite 200, Zip 70433; tel. 985/888–0301 (Nonreporting) **S** AMG Integrated Healthcare Management, Lafayette, LA
Primary Contact: Jay Ivy, R.N., Chief Executive Officer
Web address: www.amgcovintonprh.com
Control: Partnership, Investor–owned (for–profit) **Service:** Rehabilitation

Staffed Beds: 24

COVINGTON BEHAVIOR HEALTH (194069), 201 Greenbrier Boulevard, Zip 70433–7236; tel. 985/893–2970 **A**10 **F**54 56 64 98 100 101 102 103 104 105 149 **S** Acadia Healthcare Company, Inc., Franklin, TN
Primary Contact: Wes Crawford, Chief Executive Officer
CFO: Terri Logsdon, Chief Financial Officer
CMO: Jason Coe M.D., Medical Director
Web address: www.greenbrierhospital.com/
Control: Corporation, Investor–owned (for–profit) **Service:** Psychiatric

Staffed Beds: 60 **Admissions:** 2000 **Census:** 49 **Outpatient Visits:** 15000 **Births:** 0

⇑ **FAIRWAY MEDICAL SURGICAL HOSPITAL (190267)**, 67252 Industry Lane, Zip 70433–8704; tel. 985/809–9888 (Nonreporting) **A**10 21
Primary Contact: Scott Boudreaux, Chief Executive Officer
CFO: Denise Businelle, Chief Financial Officer
CMO: William Preau M.D., Medical Director
CIO: Skip Federico, Director Information Systems
CHR: Pam Collins, Director Human Resources
Web address: www.fairwaymedical.com
Control: Corporation, Investor–owned (for–profit) **Service:** General medical and surgical

Staffed Beds: 21

NORTHSHORE SPECIALTY HOSPITAL See PAM Specialty Hospital of Covington

✠ **PAM SPECIALTY HOSPITAL OF COVINGTON (192048)**, 20050 Crestwood Boulevard, Zip 70433–5207; tel. 985/875–7525 **A**1 10 **F**1 29 67 75 90 130 143 **S** Post Acute Medical, LLC, Enola, PA
Primary Contact: J Cullen. Meyers, Chief Executive Officer
COO: John Bauer, Chief Operating Officer
CFO: Karick Stober, Chief Financial Officer
CMO: Adam Burick M.D., Chief Medical Officer
CIO: Bryan Munchel, Senior Vice President and Chief Information Officer
CHR: Waynea Finley, Senior Vice President Human Resources
CNO: Marsha Medlin, Senior Vice President of Clinical and Operations
Web address: www.postacutemedical.com
Control: Individual, Investor–owned (for–profit) **Service:** Acute long–term care hospital

Staffed Beds: 58 **Admissions:** 540 **Census:** 30 **Outpatient Visits:** 0 **Births:** 0 **Total Expense ($000):** 15797 **Payroll Expense ($000):** 6451 **Personnel:** 205

✠ **ST. TAMMANY PARISH HOSPITAL (190045)**, 1202 South Tyler Street, Zip 70433–2330; tel. 985/898–4000 **A**1 2 10 **F**3 8 11 12 13 15 17 18 20 22 24 26 28 29 30 31 34 35 37 40 41 44 45 46 48 49 50 54 57 59 62 63 64 65 69 70 72 74 75 76 77 78 79 81 82 84 85 86 87 89 90 92 93 96 97 107 108 109 110 111 114 115 119 124 126 129 130 132 135 146 147 148 **P**6
Primary Contact: Patti M. Ellish, FACHE, President and Chief Executive Officer
COO: Sharon A Toups, Senior Vice President and Chief Operating Officer
CFO: Sandra P Dipietro, Chief Financial Officer
CMO: Robert Capitelli M.D., Senior Vice President and Chief Medical Officer
CIO: Craig Doyle, Director and Chief Information Officer
CHR: Carolyn Adema, Vice President, Human Resources
CNO: Kerry K. Milton R.N., Chief Nursing Officer
Web address: www.stph.org
Control: Hospital district or authority, Government, Nonfederal **Service:** General medical and surgical

Staffed Beds: 218 **Admissions:** 11087 **Census:** 133 **Outpatient Visits:** 340603 **Births:** 1680 **Total Expense ($000):** 276435 **Payroll Expense ($000):** 113011 **Personnel:** 1849

CROWLEY—Acadia Parish

★ **ACADIA GENERAL HOSPITAL (190044)**, 1305 Crowley Rayne Highway, Zip 70526–8202; tel. 337/783–3222, (Nonreporting) **A**10 **S** Lafayette General Health, Lafayette, LA
Primary Contact: Joe J. Mitchell, Chief Executive Officer
CNO: Caroline Marceaux MSN, R.N., Chief Nursing Officer
Web address: www.acadiageneral.com
Control: Other not–for–profit (including NFP Corporation) **Service:** General medical and surgical

Staffed Beds: 140

Hospital, Medicare Provider Number, Address, Telephone, Approval, Facility, and Physician Codes, Health Care System

★ American Hospital Association (AHA) membership
☐ The Joint Commission accreditation
○ Healthcare Facilities Accreditation Program
◇ DNV Healthcare Inc. accreditation
⇑ Center for Improvement in Healthcare Quality Accreditation
△ Commission on Accreditation of Rehabilitation Facilities (CARF) accreditation

LA

CUT OFF—Lafourche Parish

★ ⇑ **LADY OF THE SEA GENERAL HOSPITAL (191325)**, 200 West 134th Place, Zip 70345–4143; tel. 985/632–6401, (Nonreporting) **A**10 18 21
Primary Contact: Karen S. Collins, R.N., Chief Executive Officer
COO: Lloyd Guidry, Chief Operating Officer
CFO: Jacquelyn Richoux, Chief Financial Officer
CMO: William Crenshaw M.D., Chief of Staff
CIO: Bennie Smith, Chief Information Officer
CHR: Bennie Smith, Director Human Resources and Risk Management
CNO: Holly Griffin R.N., Chief Nursing Officer
Web address: www.losgh.org
Control: Hospital district or authority, Government, Nonfederal **Service**: General medical and surgical

Staffed Beds: 25

DE RIDDER—Beauregard Parish

⊞ **BEAUREGARD MEMORIAL HOSPITAL (190050)**, 600 South Pine Street, Zip 70634–4942, Mailing Address: P.O.Box 730, 70634–0730; tel. 337/462–7100 **A**1 10 **F**3 11 13 15 18 20 26 28 29 30 31 34 35 39 40 45 46 50 53 57 64 70 75 76 78 81 85 89 91 93 96 107 108 110 111 114 119 129 130 131 133 144 148 **P**6
Primary Contact: William F. Barrow II, Chief Executive Officer
CFO: Darrell L Kingham CPA, Vice President Finance
CMO: David Jones M.D., Chief Medical Officer
CIO: Meg Jackson, Director Information Technology
CHR: Kelli C Broocks, Director Human Resources, Public Relations and Physician Recruitment
CNO: Anita Thibodeaux, Chief Nursing Officer
Web address: www.beauregard.org
Control: Hospital district or authority, Government, Nonfederal **Service**: General medical and surgical

Staffed Beds: 60 Admissions: 2464 Census: 25 Outpatient Visits: 79681 Births: 461 Total Expense ($000): 37640 Payroll Expense ($000): 18048 Personnel: 363

DELHI—Richland Parish

RICHLAND PARISH HOSPITAL (191323), 407 Cincinnati Street, Zip 71232–3007; tel. 318/878–5171 **A**10 18 **F**3 15 18 28 29 34 35 39 40 50 54 56 57 59 64 65 66 71 75 77 81 91 97 103 104 107 111 114 119 127 129 130 132 133 134 135 143 146 148
Primary Contact: Michael W. Carroll, Administrator
CIO: Barbra Hutchison, Director Medical Records
CHR: Patsy Stout, Director Personnel
Web address: www.delhihospital.com
Control: Hospital district or authority, Government, Nonfederal **Service**: General medical and surgical

Staffed Beds: 25 Admissions: 501 Census: 4 Outpatient Visits: 45812 Births: 0 Total Expense ($000): 17889 Payroll Expense ($000): 11172

DENHAM SPRINGS—Livingston Parish

AMG SPECIALTY HOSPITAL–DENHAM SPRINGS (192008), 8375 Florida Boulevard, Zip 70726–7806; tel. 225/665–2664 (Nonreporting) **A**10 **S** AMG Integrated Healthcare Management, Lafayette, LA
Primary Contact: Karen Crayton, Administrator
CFO: Jessica McGee, Chief Financial Officer
CMO: Durwin Walker M.D., Chief Medical Officer
CHR: Kim Hernandez, Chief Human Resources Officer
CNO: Sharon Faulkner, Chief Nursing Officer
Web address: www.amgdenham.com/
Control: Corporation, Investor–owned (for–profit) **Service**: Acute long–term care hospital

Staffed Beds: 117

DEQUINCY—Calcasieu Parish

☐ **DEQUINCY MEMORIAL HOSPITAL (191307)**, 110 West Fourth Street, Zip 70633–3508, Mailing Address: P.O.Box 1166, 70633–1166; tel. 337/786–1200, (Nonreporting) **A**1 10 18
Primary Contact: John A. Matheson, Interim Chief Executive Officer
CFO: Vicky Kelley, Chief Financial Officer
CMO: Jalal Joudeh M.D., Chief of Staff
Web address: www.dequincymemorial.com/
Control: City, Government, Nonfederal **Service**: General medical and surgical

Staffed Beds: 19

DERIDDER—Beauregard Parish

☐ **OCEANS BEHAVIORAL HOSPITAL OF DE RIDDER (194081)**, 1420 Blankenship Drive, Zip 70634–4604; tel. 337/460–9472 (Nonreporting) **A**1 10 **S** Oceans Healthcare, Lake Charles, LA
Primary Contact: Stuart Archer, Chief Executive Officer
Web address: www.obhd.info/
Control: Corporation, Investor–owned (for–profit) **Service**: Psychiatric

Staffed Beds: 20

DONALDSONVILLE—Ascension Parish

⊞ **PREVOST MEMORIAL HOSPITAL (191308)**, 301 Memorial Drive, Zip 70346–4376; tel. 225/473–7931 **A**1 10 18 **F**3 11 15 29 40 57 59 107 110 114 119 130 133 146 149
Primary Contact: Vincent A. Cataldo, Administrator
CFO: Nobie Landry, Chief Financial Officer
CMO: Glenn Schexnayder M.D., Chief of Staff
CHR: Linda Cataldo, Human Resources Secretary
Web address: www.prevosthospital.net
Control: Hospital district or authority, Government, Nonfederal **Service**: General medical and surgical

Staffed Beds: 25 Admissions: 59 Census: 1 Outpatient Visits: 27050 Births: 0 Personnel: 56

FARMERVILLE—Union Parish

UNION GENERAL HOSPITAL (191301), 901 James Avenue, Zip 71241–2234, Mailing Address: P.O.Box 398, 71241–0398; tel. 318/368–9751 **A**10 18 **F**15 29 32 35 40 45 50 56 81 93 104 107 110 114 119 127 128 133 143 149 **P**6
Primary Contact: Evalyn Ormond, Chief Executive Officer
COO: Dianne Davidson, Chief Operating Officer
CFO: William Adcock, Chief Financial Officer
CHR: Sheri Taylor, Director Human Resources
CNO: Darra Jung, Director of Nursing
Web address: www.uniongen.com
Control: Other not–for–profit (including NFP Corporation) **Service**: General medical and surgical

Staffed Beds: 15 Admissions: 366 Census: 5 Outpatient Visits: 33843 Births: 0 Total Expense ($000): 13346 Payroll Expense ($000): 5056 Personnel: 105

FERRIDAY—Concordia Parish

RIVERLAND MEDICAL CENTER (191318), 1700 EE Wallace Boulevard, Zip 71334–0111, Mailing Address: P.O.Box 111, 71334–0111; tel. 318/757–6551 **A**10 18 **F**3 15 29 34 35 40 45 57 59 68 70 75 77 81 85 86 87 93 104 107 110 119 133 **P**6
Primary Contact: William H. Rucker, Administrator
CFO: Spencer Holder, Chief Financial Officer
CMO: Carrie Bonomo M.D., Chief of Staff
CIO: Nekisha Smith, Director Health Information Systems
CHR: Debra Stephens, Director Personnel
CNO: Shelia James, Director of Nursing
Web address: www.riverlandmedical.com/
Control: Hospital district or authority, Government, Nonfederal **Service**: General medical and surgical

Staffed Beds: 25 Admissions: 962 Census: 13 Outpatient Visits: 18794 Births: 0 Total Expense ($000): 16951 Payroll Expense ($000): 7191 Personnel: 147

FORT POLK—Vernon Parish

⊞ **BAYNE–JONES ARMY COMMUNITY HOSPITAL**, 1585 3rd Street, Zip 71459–5102; tel. 337/531–3928, (Nonreporting) **A**1 **S** Department of the Army, Office of the Surgeon General, Falls Church, VA
Primary Contact: Colonel Marla J. Ferguson, Commanding Officer
COO: Larry R. Patterson, Deputy Commander Administration
CFO: CaptainDustin Mullins, Chief Resource Management
CIO: MajorWilliam Callahan, Chief Information Management Division
CHR: CaptainDustin Mullins, Chief Human Resources
Web address: www.polk.amedd.army.mil
Control: Army, Government, federal **Service**: General medical and surgical

Staffed Beds: 13

FRANKLIN—St. Mary Parish

✠ **FRANKLIN FOUNDATION HOSPITAL (191310)**, 1097 Northwest Boulevard, Zip 70538–3407, Mailing Address: P.O.Box 577, 70538–0577; tel. 337/828–0760 **A**1 10 18 **F**3 11 13 15 18 26 29 34 35 40 45 50 57 59 68 70 74 75 76 77 79 81 85 93 107 110 111 114 119 130 133 135 146 147 148 **P**6 **S** QHR, Brentwood, TN
Primary Contact: Stephanie Guidry, Chief Executive Officer
CFO: Ron Bailey, Chief Financial Officer
CMO: Jesus Chua M.D., Chief of Staff
CIO: John Spradlin, Information Systems Director
CHR: Elmo Vinas, Director Human Resources
CNO: Frank Corcoran R.N., Chief Nursing Officer
Web address: www.franklinfoundation.org
Control: Hospital district or authority, Government, Nonfederal **Service**: General medical and surgical

Staffed Beds: 22 Admissions: 622 Census: 10 Outpatient Visits: 26164 Births: 79 Total Expense ($000): 24867 Payroll Expense ($000): 11635 Personnel: 160

FRANKLINTON—Washington Parish

☐ **RIVERSIDE MEDICAL CENTER (191313)**, 1900 Main Street, Zip 70438–3688; tel. 985/839–4431, (Nonreporting) **A**1 10 18
Primary Contact: Peter Sullivan, Chief Executive Officer
CFO: Michael J Magee, Chief Financial Officer
CMO: Chris Foret M.D., Chief of Staff
CHR: John Seal, Director Human Resources
Web address: www.rmchospital.com
Control: Hospital district or authority, Government, Nonfederal **Service**: General medical and surgical

Staffed Beds: 25

GONZALES—Ascension Parish

SOUTH BATON ROUGE REHABILITATION HOSPITAL See United Medical Rehabilitation Hospital – Gonzales

✠ **ST. ELIZABETH HOSPITAL (190242)**, 1125 West Highway 30, Zip 70737–5004; tel. 225/647–5000 **A**1 10 **F**3 8 11 13 15 18 29 30 34 35 40 43 45 46 47 48 49 51 57 59 64 66 70 74 75 77 79 81 82 84 85 87 92 107 108 110 111 114 115 119 129 130 131 132 146 147 149 **P**6 **S** Franciscan Missionaries of Our Lady Health System, Inc., Baton Rouge, LA
Primary Contact: Robert L. Burgess, President and Chief Executive Officer
COO: Sue Knight CPA, Chief Operating Officer
CFO: Scott Richard, Vice President Finance and Chief Financial Officer
CMO: Chris Trevino M.D., Chief Medical Officer
CIO: Shannon Simpson, Director Information Services
CHR: Melissa Miller, Director Human Resources
CNO: Yvonne Pellerin, Chief Nursing Officer
Web address: www.steh.com
Control: Church operated, Nongovernment, not-for-profit **Service**: General medical and surgical

Staffed Beds: 47 Admissions: 2464 Census: 29 Outpatient Visits: 321934 Births: 0 Total Expense ($000): 120678 Payroll Expense ($000): 44366 Personnel: 754

☐ **ST. JAMES BEHAVIORAL HEALTH HOSPITAL (194088)**, 3136 South Saint Landry Road, Zip 70737–5801; tel. 225/647–7524 (Nonreporting) **A**1 10
Primary Contact: Andrew Hines, Administrator
COO: Wendell Smith, Chief Operating Officer
CFO: Rama Kongara, Chief Financial Officer
CMO: Lance Bullock M.D., Medical Director
CHR: Dessa Frederick, Manager Human Resources
Web address: www.sjbhh.net
Control: Corporation, Investor–owned (for–profit) **Service**: Psychiatric

Staffed Beds: 10

GREENSBURG—St. Helena Parish

ST. HELENA PARISH HOSPITAL (191300), 16874 Highway 43, Zip 70441–4834; tel. 225/222–6111, (Nonreporting) **A**10 18
Primary Contact: Naveed Awan, FACHE, Chief Executive Officer
CFO: Theresa Brinkhaus, Chief Financial Officer
CMO: Anjanette Varnado M.D., Chief Medical Officer
CHR: Lorraine L Ballard, Director Human Resources
Web address: www.sthelenaparishhospital.com
Control: Other not–for–profit (including NFP Corporation) **Service**: General medical and surgical

Staffed Beds: 75

GRETNA—Jefferson Parish

UNITED MEDICAL REHABILITATION HOSPITAL (193074), 3201 Wall Boulevard, Suite B, Zip 70056–7755; tel. 504/433–5551 **A**10 **F**29 90 91 **S** United Medical Rehabilitation Hospitals, Gretna, LA
Primary Contact: Rondel Frank, Administrator
Web address: www.umrhospital.com/
Control: Individual, Investor–owned (for–profit) **Service**: Rehabilitation

Staffed Beds: 21 Admissions: 297 Census: 12 Outpatient Visits: 0 Births: 0

HAMMOND—Tangipahoa Parish

⇑ **CYPRESS POINTE SURGICAL HOSPITAL (190303)**, 42570 South Airport Road, Zip 70403–0946; tel. 985/510–6200 (Nonreporting) **A**10 21
Primary Contact: Glenda Dobson, Chief Executive Officer
COO: Scot Treitler, Chief Operating Officer
CFO: Donna Varnado, Vice President Finance
CNO: Denise Fortenberry, Chief Nursing Officer and Chief Compliance Officer
Web address: www.cpsh.org
Control: Corporation, Investor–owned (for–profit) **Service**: Surgical

Staffed Beds: 24

✠ △ **NORTH OAKS MEDICAL CENTER (190015)**, 15790 Paul Vega, MD, Drive, Zip 70403–1436, Mailing Address: P.O.Box 2668, 70404–2668; tel. 985/345–2700 **A**1 3 7 10 19 **F**3 12 13 15 18 20 22 24 26 28 29 30 31 32 34 40 43 45 49 50 54 56 57 58 59 63 64 68 70 72 73 74 75 76 77 78 79 81 82 84 85 86 87 89 93 94 96 102 107 108 110 111 114 115 118 119 126 129 130 131 132 135 143 144 146 147 148 149 **P**6 **S** North Oaks Health System, Hammond, LA
Primary Contact: Michele K. Sutton, FACHE, President and Chief Executive Officer
COO: Michael Watkins, Chief Operating Officer
CFO: Shirley Hsing, Chief Financial Officer
CMO: Robert Peltier M.D., Chief Medical Officer
CIO: Doug Bankston, Director Technical Services
CHR: Jeff Jarreau, Chief Human Resources Officer
CNO: Shelly Welch, Chief Clinical Officer
Web address: www.northoaks.org
Control: Hospital district or authority, Government, Nonfederal **Service**: General medical and surgical

Staffed Beds: 231 Admissions: 10485 Census: 151 Outpatient Visits: 455321 Births: 1323 Total Expense ($000): 293556 Payroll Expense ($000): 158797 Personnel: 2210

☐ **NORTH OAKS REHABILITATION HOSPITAL (193044)**, 1900 South Morrison Boulevard, Zip 70403–5742; tel. 985/542–7777 **A**1 10 **F**29 56 75 86 87 90 130 132 143 **P**6 **S** North Oaks Health System, Hammond, LA
Primary Contact: Sybil K. Paulson, Administrator
CFO: Shirley Hsing, Senior Vice President, Chief Financial Officer, North Oaks Health System
CMO: Robert Peltier M.D., Senior Vice President, Chief Medical Officer, North Oaks Health System
CIO: Herbert Robinson M.D., Vice President, Chief Medical Information Officer, North Oaks Health System
CHR: Jeff Jarreau, Senior Vice President, Human Resources, North Oaks Health System
CNO: Shelly Welch, Senior Vice President, Patient Services, Chief Nursing Officer, North Oaks Health System
Web address: www.northoaks.org
Control: Hospital district or authority, Government, Nonfederal **Service**: Rehabilitation

Staffed Beds: 27 Admissions: 508 Census: 15 Outpatient Visits: 0 Births: 0 Total Expense ($000): 11965 Payroll Expense ($000): 2408 Personnel: 41

✠ **PAM SPECIALTY HOSPITAL OF HAMMOND (192036)**, 42074 Veterans Avenue, Zip 70403–1408; tel. 985/902–8148 **A**1 10 **F**1 29 75 77 148 149 **S** Post Acute Medical, LLC, Enola, PA
Primary Contact: Nicholas Paul. Mendez, Chief Executive Officer
Web address: www.postacutemedical.com
Control: Partnership, Investor–owned (for–profit) **Service**: Acute long–term care hospital

Staffed Beds: 40 Admissions: 487 Census: 29 Outpatient Visits: 0 Births: 0 Total Expense ($000): 13810 Payroll Expense ($000): 5567 Personnel: 106

Hospital, Medicare Provider Number, Address, Telephone, Approval, Facility, and Physician Codes, Health Care System

★ American Hospital Association (AHA) membership
☐ The Joint Commission accreditation
○ Healthcare Facilities Accreditation Program
◇ DNV Healthcare Inc. accreditation
⇑ Center for Improvement in Healthcare Quality Accreditation
△ Commission on Accreditation of Rehabilitation Facilities (CARF) accreditation

LA

UNITED MEDICAL REHABILITATION HOSPITAL (193079), 15717 Belle Drive, Zip 70403–1439; tel. 985/340–5998, (Includes UNITED MEDICAL REHABILITATION HOSPITAL – GONZALES, 333 East Worthy Road, Gonzales, Louisiana, Zip 70737–4234, tel. 225/450–2231; Bruce Walker, MSN, R.N., Chief Executive Officer) (Nonreporting) **A**10 **S** United Medical Rehabilitation Hospitals, Gretna, LA
Primary Contact: Jonathan Landreth, Administrator
CFO: Warren Swenson, Chief Financial Officer
CMO: Luis Franco M.D., Medical Director
CHR: Mark Gros, Director Human Resources
Web address: www.umrhospital.com
Control: Corporation, Investor–owned (for–profit) **Service**: Rehabilitation

Staffed Beds: 20

HOMER—Claiborne Parish

★ ⇑ **CLAIBORNE MEMORIAL MEDICAL CENTER (190114)**, 620 East College Street, Zip 71040–3202; tel. 318/927–2024 **A**10 21 **F**3 15 29 34 35 38 40 45 50 53 54 55 56 57 62 64 65 70 81 85 86 87 98 100 101 102 103 104 107 108 110 111 114 119 130 132 133 143 146 148
Primary Contact: Antonia M. Goodin, Chief Executive Officer and Chief Financial Officer
CMO: Mark Haynes M.D., Chief of Staff
CIO: Angie Costakis, Chief Information Officer
CHR: William Colvin, Human Resources Officer
CNO: Kristie M. Copeland, Interim Chief Nursing Officer
Web address: www.clairbornemedical.com/
Control: Hospital district or authority, Government, Nonfederal **Service**: General medical and surgical

Staffed Beds: 57 Admissions: 1273 Census: 19 Outpatient Visits: 26118
Births: 0 Total Expense ($000): 31501 Payroll Expense ($000): 6644

HOUMA—Terrebonne Parish

AMG SPECIALTY HOSPITAL–HOUMA (192037), 629 Dunn Street, Zip 70360–4707; tel. 985/274–0001 (Nonreporting) **A**10 **S** AMG Integrated Healthcare Management, Lafayette, LA
Primary Contact: Keith Carruth, Chief Executive Officer
Web address: www.amghouma.com/
Control: Corporation, Investor–owned (for–profit) **Service**: Acute long–term care hospital

Staffed Beds: 40

☐ **COMPASS BEHAVIORAL CENTER OF HOUMA (194109)**, 4701 West Park Avenue, Zip 70364–4426; tel. 985/876–1715 **A**1 10 **F**98 101 102 103 104 105 149 **S** Compass Health, Crowley, LA
Primary Contact: Cheryl Turner, Administrator
Web address: www.compasshealthcare.com/site83.php
Control: Individual, Investor–owned (for–profit) **Service**: Psychiatric

Staffed Beds: 20 Admissions: 281 Census: 15 Outpatient Visits: 0 Births: 0

⊞ **LEONARD J. CHABERT MEDICAL CENTER (190183)**, 1978 Industrial Boulevard, Zip 70363–7094; tel. 985/873–2200 **A**1 3 5 10 **F**3 15 18 20 29 31 32 34 35 38 40 44 45 46 48 49 50 51 58 59 61 64 65 66 68 70 74 75 77 78 79 81 82 84 85 86 87 91 92 93 94 97 98 100 101 102 107 108 110 111 115 119 130 132 146 147 148 **S** Ochsner Health System, New Orleans, LA
Primary Contact: Timothy J. Allen, FACHE, Chief Executive Officer
COO: Kendrick Duet, Chief Operating Officer
CNO: Jana Semere, Chief Nursing Officer
Web address: www.ochsner.org/locations/leonard_j_chabert_medical_center/
Control: State, Government, Nonfederal **Service**: General medical and surgical

Staffed Beds: 72 Admissions: 3653 Census: 46 Outpatient Visits: 178709
Births: 0 Total Expense ($000): 93834 Payroll Expense ($000): 32149
Personnel: 813

PHYSICIANS ALLIANCE HOSPITAL OF HOUMA See AMG Specialty Hospital–Houma

PHYSICIANS MEDICAL CENTER (190241), 218 Corporate Drive, Zip 70360–2768; tel. 985/853–1390 (Nonreporting) **A**10
Primary Contact: Connie Martin, Chief Executive Officer and Administrator
Web address: www.physicianshouma.com/
Control: Partnership, Investor–owned (for–profit) **Service**: Surgical

Staffed Beds: 10

⊞ △ **TERREBONNE GENERAL MEDICAL CENTER (190008)**, 8166 Main Street, Zip 70360–3498; tel. 985/873–4141, (Total facility includes 8 beds in nursing home–type unit) **A**1 2 7 10 **F**8 11 13 14 15 17 18 20 22 24 26 29 30 31 34 35 40 44 49 50 53 55 57 58 59 64 65 68 70 72 74 75 76 77 78 79 81 84 85 86 87 89 90 91 92 93 96 102 107 108 109 110 111 112 115 116 117 118 119 121 123 124 128 130 131 132 134 135 143 146 147 148 149 **P**3 5 6
Primary Contact: Phyllis L. Peoples, President and Chief Executive Officer
COO: Diane Yeates, Chief Operating Officer
CFO: Dean Verret, Vice President Financial Services
CMO: Robert Gamble M.D., Chief of Staff
CIO: Jeff Sardella, Director Information Technology
CHR: Mickie Rousseau, Director Human Resources
CNO: Teresita McNabb R.N., FACHE, Vice President Nursing Services
Web address: www.tgmc.com
Control: Hospital district or authority, Government, Nonfederal **Service**: General medical and surgical

Staffed Beds: 230 Admissions: 9222 Census: 124 Outpatient Visits: 128193 Births: 1940 Total Expense ($000): 185921 Payroll Expense ($000): 71712 Personnel: 1335

INDEPENDENCE—Tangipahoa Parish

☐ **LALLIE KEMP MEDICAL CENTER (191321)**, 52579 Highway 51 South, Zip 70443–2231; tel. 985/878–9421 **A**1 3 5 10 18 **F**3 8 15 18 29 31 34 35 40 45 50 56 57 58 59 60 61 64 65 66 70 75 78 81 97 107 110 114 115 119 130 132 133 146 147 148 149 **P**8
Primary Contact: Rhonda G. Green, Administrator
COO: Lisa G Bruhl, Chief Operating Officer
CFO: Chad Thompson, Chief Financial Officer
CMO: Kathy Willis M.D., Medical Director
CIO: Charles Tate, Director Information Technology
CHR: Diane Farnham, Acting Director Human Resources
Web address: www.lsuhospitals.org/Hospitals/LK/LK.aspx
Control: State, Government, Nonfederal **Service**: General medical and surgical

Staffed Beds: 24 Admissions: 624 Census: 6 Outpatient Visits: 81472
Births: 1 Total Expense ($000): 39145 Payroll Expense ($000): 17009
Personnel: 343

JACKSON—East Feliciana Parish

☐ **EASTERN LOUISIANA MENTAL HEALTH SYSTEM (194008)**, 4502 Highway 951, Zip 70748–5842, Mailing Address: P.O.Box 498, 70748–0498; tel. 225/634–0100, (Nonreporting) **A**1 3 10 **S** Louisiana State Hospitals, Baton Rouge, LA
Primary Contact: Hampton P S. Lea, Acting Chief Executive Officer
CFO: Laura Lott, Administrative Director
CMO: John W Thompson M.D., Chief of Staff
CIO: Deborah Brandon, Director Total Quality Management
CHR: Vikki Riggle, Director Human Resources
CNO: Mary Fontenelle, Executive Nurse Director
Web address: www.new.dhh.louisiana.gov/index.cfm/directory/detail/219
Control: State, Government, Nonfederal **Service**: Psychiatric

Staffed Beds: 473

JACKSON—East Feliciana Parish

VILLA FELICIANA MEDICAL COMPLEX (190199), 5002 Highway 10, Zip 70748–3627, Mailing Address: P.O.Box 438, 70748–0438; tel. 225/634–4017, (Total facility includes 289 beds in nursing home–type unit) **A**10 **F**1 3 29 65 67 85 86 91 94 106 128 130 132 135 143 148 149 **P**8
Primary Contact: Mark Anders, Administrator
CFO: Kim Jelks, Fiscal Officer
CMO: John F Piker M.D., Medical Director
CIO: Michael James, Information Technology Technical Support Specialist 1
CHR: Sandra Delatte, Director Human Resources
CNO: Linda Williams, Director of Nursing
Web address: www.dhh.state.la.us/
Control: State, Government, Nonfederal **Service**: Acute long–term care hospital

Staffed Beds: 299 Admissions: 90 Census: 152 Outpatient Visits: 0 Births: 0
Total Expense ($000): 18362 Payroll Expense ($000): 8394 Personnel: 185

JENA—La Salle Parish

★ **LASALLE GENERAL HOSPITAL (190145)**, 187 Ninth Street, Zip 71342–3901, Mailing Address: P.O.Box 2780, 71342–2780; tel. 318/992–9200 **A**10 **F**7 11 15 18 29 33 40 53 57 59 62 64 71 89 93 107 108 110 111 115 119 127 130 133 149 **P**6
Primary Contact: Lana B. Francis, Chief Executive Officer
CHR: Allyson Fannin, Human Resources Officer
CNO: Carolyn Francis R.N., MSN, Director of Nursing
Web address: www.lasallegeneralhospital.com
Control: Hospital district or authority, Government, Nonfederal **Service**: General medical and surgical

Staffed Beds: 20 Admissions: 495 Census: 5 Outpatient Visits: 55129
Births: 0 Total Expense ($000): 16912 Payroll Expense ($000): 7991
Personnel: 187

Many Facility Codes have changed. Please refer to the AHA Guide Code Chart. © 2017 AHA Guide

JENNINGS—Jefferson Davis Parish

☐ **JENNINGS AMERICAN LEGION HOSPITAL (190053)**, 1634 Elton Road, Zip 70546–3614; tel. 337/616–7000 **A**1 10 **F**3 15 18 20 28 29 40 45 64 70 76 79 81 89 107 108 111 115 119 127 133 146 147 149
Primary Contact: Dana D. Williams, Chief Executive Officer
COO: Keith J Simpson, Chief Operating Officer
CFO: Chris Kohlenberg, Chief Financial Officer
CIO: Gary Courrege, Chief Information Officer
CHR: Ruth Carnes, Manager Human Resources
CNO: Theresa L Woods MSN, R.N., FACHE, Chief Nursing Officer
Web address: www.jalh.com
Control: Other not–for–profit (including NFP Corporation) **Service:** General medical and surgical

Staffed Beds: 49 **Admissions:** 2591 **Census:** 28 **Outpatient Visits:** 35871 **Births:** 346 **Total Expense ($000):** 41113 **Payroll Expense ($000):** 18064 **Personnel:** 409

JENNINGS SENIOR CARE HOSPITAL (194082), 1 Hospital Drive, Suite 201, Zip 70546–3641; tel. 337/824–1558 **A**10 **F**98 103 104 105 130 149
Primary Contact: Kirk Perron, Administrator and Chief Administrative Officer
Web address: www.compasshealthcare.com/site74.php
Control: Individual, Investor–owned (for–profit) **Service:** Psychiatric

Staffed Beds: 16 **Admissions:** 308 **Census:** 12 **Outpatient Visits:** 17318 **Births:** 0 **Personnel:** 27

REHABILITATION HOSPITAL OF JENNINGS (193067), 1 Hospital Drive, Suite 101, Zip 70546–3641; tel. 337/821–5353 **A**10 **F**29 30 34 35 56 57 62 65 68 75 77 87 90 91 130 148 149
Primary Contact: Michael Holland, M.D., Chief Executive Officer
Web address: www.jenningsrehab.com
Control: Partnership, Investor–owned (for–profit) **Service:** Rehabilitation

Staffed Beds: 16 **Admissions:** 232 **Census:** 9 **Outpatient Visits:** 0 **Births:** 0 **Personnel:** 44

JONESBORO—Jackson Parish

★ **JACKSON PARISH HOSPITAL (191317)**, 165 Beech Springs Road, Zip 71251–2059; tel. 318/259–4435, (Nonreporting) **A**10 18
Primary Contact: John Morgan, R.N., Chief Executive Officer
CFO: Cora Bradford, Chief Financial Officer
CMO: W. James (Jamie) Slusher M.D., Chief of Staff
CIO: Monie Phillips III, Director Clinical Informatics
CHR: Phillip Thomas Jr, Director Human Resources
CNO: Christy Wyatt R.N., Interim Chief Nursing Officer
Web address: www.jacksonparishhospital.com
Control: Hospital district or authority, Government, Nonfederal **Service:** General medical and surgical

Staffed Beds: 25

KAPLAN—Vermilion Parish

ABROM KAPLAN MEMORIAL HOSPITAL (191322), 1310 West Seventh Street, Zip 70548–2910; tel. 337/643–8300, (Nonreporting) **A**10 18 **S** Lafayette General Health, Lafayette, LA
Primary Contact: Bryce Quebodeaux, Chief Executive Officer
CFO: Michael G. Johnson CPA, Chief Financial Officer
CMO: Scott Bergeaux M.D., Chief Medical Staff
CIO: Michael Cardiff, Systems Supervisor
CHR: Linda Guidry, Human Resources Generalist
CNO: Sally Roberts R.N., Director of Nursing
Web address: www.lafayettegeneral.com
Control: Hospital district or authority, Government, Nonfederal **Service:** General medical and surgical

Staffed Beds: 35

KENNER—Jefferson Parish

LOUISIANA EXTENDED CARE HOSPITAL OF KENNER See Ochsner Extended Care Hospital Of Kenner

☐ **OCEANS BEHAVIORAL HOSPITAL OF GREATER NEW ORLEANS (194098)**, 716 Village Road, Zip 70065–2751; tel. 504/464–8895 (Nonreporting) **A**1 10 **S** Oceans Healthcare, Lake Charles, LA
Primary Contact: Deborah Spier, Administrator
Web address: www.obhgno.info/
Control: Corporation, Investor–owned (for–profit) **Service:** Psychiatric

Staffed Beds: 30

☐ **OCHSNER EXTENDED CARE HOSPITAL OF KENNER (192015)**, 180 West Esplanade Avenue, 5th Floor, Zip 70065–2467; tel. 504/464–8658 (Nonreporting) **A**1 3 10 **S** LHC Group, Lafayette, LA
Primary Contact: Frederick Nelson, Administrator
Web address: www.lhcgroup.com/
Control: Corporation, Investor–owned (for–profit) **Service:** Acute long–term care hospital

Staffed Beds: 32

✠ **OCHSNER MEDICAL CENTER – KENNER (190274)**, 180 West Esplanade Avenue, Zip 70065–6001; tel. 504/468–8600 **A**1 3 5 10 **F**3 13 15 18 20 22 29 30 31 34 35 37 38 40 41 42 44 45 46 47 49 50 51 53 54 56 57 58 59 60 61 64 65 66 68 70 72 74 75 76 77 78 79 81 82 84 85 86 87 91 93 97 102 107 110 111 114 116 117 119 120 129 130 131 132 135 146 147 148 **S** Ochsner Health System, New Orleans, LA
Primary Contact: Stephen Robinson Jr, FACHE, Chief Executive Officer
COO: Eddy Ramirez, Assistant Vice President Business Development
CFO: Mark Eckert, Vice President Finance
CMO: James Tebbe M.D., Vice President Medical Affairs
CIO: Dere Krummel, Director Information Systems
Web address: www.ochsner.org/locations/ochsner–medical–center–kenner/
Control: Other not–for–profit (including NFP Corporation) **Service:** General medical and surgical

Staffed Beds: 110 **Admissions:** 6182 **Census:** 64 **Outpatient Visits:** 153823 **Births:** 999 **Total Expense ($000):** 131019 **Payroll Expense ($000):** 46154 **Personnel:** 793

☐ **ST. THERESA SPECIALTY HOSPITAL (192030)**, 3601 Loyola Drive, Zip 70065–1797; tel. 504/904–7600 (Nonreporting) **A**1 10
Primary Contact: Sam Liljebert, Chief Executive Officer
CMO: Ricardo Febry M.D., Medical Director
CHR: Nicole Wilson, Manager Human Resources
CNO: Collette Jackson R.N., Director of Clinical Services
Web address: www.stmck.com
Control: Corporation, Investor–owned (for–profit) **Service:** Acute long–term care hospital

Staffed Beds: 73

KENTWOOD—Tangipahoa Parish

OCEANS BEHAVIORAL HOSPITAL OF KENTWOOD (194091), 921 Avenue G, Zip 70444–2636; tel. 985/229–0717 (Nonreporting) **A**10 **S** Oceans Healthcare, Lake Charles, LA
Primary Contact: Sarah Chisholm, R.N., Administrator
Web address: www.obhk.info/
Control: Corporation, Investor–owned (for–profit) **Service:** Psychiatric

Staffed Beds: 18

SOUTHEAST REGIONAL MEDICAL CENTER (192040), 719 Avenue G, Zip 70444–2601; tel. 985/229–9193 (Nonreporting) **A**10
Primary Contact: Lionel Murphy, Chief Executive Officer
Control: Corporation, Investor–owned (for–profit) **Service:** Acute long–term care hospital

Staffed Beds: 14

KINDER—Allen Parish

★ **ALLEN PARISH HOSPITAL (190133)**, 108 Sixth Avenue, Zip 70648–3187, Mailing Address: P.O.Box 1670, 70648–1670; tel. 337/738–2527 **A**10 **F**29 32 34 38 40 50 56 57 59 62 64 65 87 93 98 101 102 107 119 127 130 133 148
Primary Contact: Jackie Reviel, R.N., Chief Executive Officer
COO: Terry Willet, Chief Financial Officer
CMO: Ejiro Ughouwa M.D., Chief of Staff
CIO: Bill Marcantel, Chief Information Systems
CHR: Amand Lambert, Director Human Resources
Web address: www.allenparishhospital.com
Control: Hospital district or authority, Government, Nonfederal **Service:** General medical and surgical

Staffed Beds: 49 **Admissions:** 897 **Census:** 18 **Outpatient Visits:** 10576 **Births:** 0 **Total Expense ($000):** 32471 **Payroll Expense ($000):** 5631

Hospital, Medicare Provider Number, Address, Telephone, Approval, Facility, and Physician Codes, Health Care System

★ American Hospital Association (AHA) membership
☐ The Joint Commission accreditation
○ Healthcare Facilities Accreditation Program
◇ DNV Healthcare Inc. accreditation
⇑ Center for Improvement in Healthcare Quality Accreditation
△ Commission on Accreditation of Rehabilitation Facilities (CARF) accreditation

LA

LACOMBE—St. Tammany Parish

BEACON BEHAVIORAL HEALTHCARE (194080), 64026 Highway 434, Suite 300, Zip 70445–5417; tel. 985/882–0226 (Nonreporting) **A**10
Primary Contact: Jessika Scallion, Administrator
Web address: www.magnoliabh.com/
Control: Corporation, Investor–owned (for–profit) **Service:** Psychiatric

Staffed Beds: 16

LAFAYETTE—Lafayette Parish

ACADIA OPTIMA HOSPITAL (194078), 1131 Rue De Belier, Zip 70506–6532; tel. 337/991–0571 (Nonreporting) **A**3 10 **S** Acadia Healthcare Company, Inc., Franklin, TN
Primary Contact: Glynis R. DeRoche, Administrator
Web address: www.optimaspecialtyhospital.com/
Control: Corporation, Investor–owned (for–profit) **Service:** General medical and surgical

Staffed Beds: 24

ACADIA VERMILION HOSPITAL (194044), 2520 North University Avenue, Zip 70507–5306; tel. 337/234–5614, (Nonreporting) **A**10 **S** Acadia Healthcare Company, Inc., Franklin, TN
Primary Contact: Stephanie Bonin, Chief Executive Officer
CFO: Margot Mokdessi, Interim Chief Financial Officer
CMO: Bob Winston M.D., Medical Director
CHR: Claire Rowland, Director Human Resources
CNO: Amy LaHood R.N., Director of Nursing
Web address: www.acadiavermilion.com
Control: Corporation, Investor–owned (for–profit) **Service:** Psychiatric

Staffed Beds: 54

AMG SPECIALTY HOSPITAL–LAFAYETTE (192029), 310 Youngsville Highway, Zip 70508–4524; tel. 337/839–9880, (Nonreporting) **A**10 **S** AMG Integrated Healthcare Management, Lafayette, LA
Primary Contact: Ben Miller, Chief Executive Officer
CFO: Jessica McGee, Chief Financial Officer
CMO: Maximo LaMarche M.D., Chief Medical Officer
CHR: Heather Lamarche, Manager Human Resources
CNO: Mary Bollich, Director of Nurses
Web address: www.amglafayette.com
Control: Corporation, Investor–owned (for–profit) **Service:** Acute long–term care hospital

Staffed Beds: 58

★ **COMPASS BEHAVIORAL CENTER OF LAFAYETTE (194085)**, 312 Youngsville Highway, Zip 70508; tel. 337/534–4655 (Nonreporting) **S** Compass Health, Crowley, LA
Primary Contact: Aimee Monaghan, Chief Executive Officer
Web address: www.compasshealthcare.com/site184.php
Control: Other not–for–profit (including NFP Corporation) **Service:** Psychiatric

Staffed Beds: 16

✠ **HEART HOSPITAL OF LAFAYETTE (190263)**, 1105 Kaliste Saloom Road, Zip 70508–5705; tel. 337/521–1000 **A**1 10 **F**1 3 4 16 17 18 20 22 24 26 28 29 30 34 35 40 46 50 57 59 64 67 68 70 72 73 74 75 80 81 85 87 88 89 90 98 107 108 115 128 135 **P**5 7 8
Primary Contact: Michelle B. Crain, R.N., MSN, Administrator and Chief Operating Officer
CFO: Rachel Hebert, Chief Financial Officer
CHR: Thomas Duhon, Director Human Resources
Web address: www.hearthospitaloflafayette.com
Control: Partnership, Investor–owned (for–profit) **Service:** Heart

Staffed Beds: 32 **Admissions:** 1497 **Census:** 15 **Outpatient Visits:** 20000 **Births:** 0 **Total Expense ($000):** 37077 **Payroll Expense ($000):** 11332 **Personnel:** 217

KINDRED HOSPITAL LAFAYETTE See Pam Specialty Hospital Of Lafayette

✠ **LAFAYETTE GENERAL MEDICAL CENTER (190002)**, 1214 Coolidge Avenue, Zip 70503–2696, Mailing Address: P.O.Box 52009 OCS, 70505–2009; tel. 337/289–7991, (Includes LAFAYETTE BEHAVIORAL HEALTH, 302 Dulles Drive, Lafayette, Louisiana, Zip 70506–3008, tel. 337/289–8595; Sandra Armand, Director; LAFAYETTE GENERAL SOUTHWEST, 2810 Ambassador Caffery Parkway, Lafayette, Louisiana, Zip 70506–5906, tel. 337/981–2949; Jude Fontenot, Administrator) **A**1 2 3 5 10 **F**3 8 11 12 13 15 18 20 22 24 26 28 29 30 31 34 35 37 40 41 43 45 46 47 48 49 50 53 54 55 56 57 58 59 64 65 70 72 74 75 76 77 78 79 81 82 85 87 89 90 92 93 96 98 107 108 110 111 115 117 118 119 120 121 123 124 126 129 130 132 135 146 147 148 149 **P**8 **S** Lafayette General Health, Lafayette, LA
Primary Contact: Patrick W. Gandy Jr, CPA, Executive Vice President and Chief Executive Officer
COO: Court LeMaistre FACHE, Chief Operating Officer
CFO: Lana Adams, Chief Financial Officer
CMO: Stephen G. Rees M.D., Vice President Medical Affairs
CIO: Michael Dozier, Vice President, Chief Information Officer
CHR: Sheena Bouquet, Vice President
CNO: Rebecca Benoit R.N., Chief Nursing Officer
Web address: www.lafayettegeneral.com
Control: Other not–for–profit (including NFP Corporation) **Service:** General medical and surgical

Staffed Beds: 455 **Admissions:** 22667 **Census:** 311 **Outpatient Visits:** 259066 **Births:** 3034 **Total Expense ($000):** 416541 **Payroll Expense ($000):** 137963 **Personnel:** 2237

LAFAYETTE GENERAL SURGICAL HOSPITAL (190268), 1000 West Pinhook Road, Zip 70503–2460; tel. 337/289–8088 **A**10 **F**3 8 29 68 79 81 89 **P**2 **S** Lafayette General Health, Lafayette, LA
Primary Contact: Kimberly H. Dooley, Administrator
CFO: Sandi Hernandez, Controller
CHR: Sheena Bouquet, Vice President
CNO: Veronica Els, Chief Nursing Officer
Web address: www.lafayettegeneral.com/our_facilities/main_facilities/lafayette_general_surgical_hospital.aspx
Control: Partnership, Investor–owned (for–profit) **Service:** General medical and surgical

Staffed Beds: 10 **Admissions:** 125 **Census:** 1 **Outpatient Visits:** 7500 **Births:** 0

LAFAYETTE PHYSICAL REHABILITATION HOSPITAL (193093), 307 Polly Lane, Zip 70508–4960; tel. 337/314–1111 (Nonreporting) **A**10 **S** AMG Integrated Healthcare Management, Lafayette, LA
Primary Contact: Bruce J. Bartels, Interim Chief Executive Officer
Web address: www.lafayettephysicalrehab.com/
Control: Corporation, Investor–owned (for–profit) **Service:** Rehabilitation

Staffed Beds: 32

☐ **LAFAYETTE SURGICAL SPECIALTY HOSPITAL (190259)**, 1101 Kaliste Saloom Road, Zip 70508–5705; tel. 337/769–4100 (Nonreporting) **A**1 10 **S** National Surgical Healthcare, Chicago, IL
Primary Contact: Buffy Domingue, Chief Executive Officer
CFO: Tiffany Mayeux, Interim Chief Financial Officer and Financial Analyst
CNO: Ruth Guidry, Chief Nursing Officer
Web address: www.lafayettesurgical.com
Control: Corporation, Investor–owned (for–profit) **Service:** Surgical

Staffed Beds: 20

LONG TERM ACUTE CARE OF ACADIANA See AMG Specialty Hospital–Lafayette

LOUISIANA EXTENDED CARE HOSPITAL OF LAFAYETTE (192032), 1214 Coolidge Boulevard, Floors 9 & 10, Zip 70503–2621; tel. 337/289–8180, (Includes EUNICE EXTENDED CARE HOSPITAL, 3879 Highway 190, Eunice, Louisiana, Zip 70535, tel. 337/546–0024; Kevin Frank, Administrator; IBERIA EXTENDED CARE HOSPITAL, 2315 East Main Street, 3rd Floor, New Iberia, Louisiana, Zip 70560–4031, tel. 337/289–8190; Kevin Frank, Administrator) (Nonreporting) **A**10 **S** LHC Group, Lafayette, LA
Primary Contact: Kevin Frank, Administrator
Web address: www.lhcgroup.com
Control: Other not–for–profit (including NFP Corporation) **Service:** Acute long–term care hospital

Staffed Beds: 42

OPTIMA SPECIALTY HOSPITAL See Acadia Optima Hospital

Many Facility Codes have changed. Please refer to the AHA Guide Code Chart. © 2017 AHA Guide

✠ **OUR LADY OF LOURDES REGIONAL MEDICAL CENTER (190102)**, 4801 Ambassador Caffery Parkway, Zip 70508–6917; tel. 337/470–2000 **A**1 2 10 **F**3 9 11 12 15 16 18 20 22 24 26 28 29 30 31 32 34 35 38 39 40 42 43 46 48 49 50 51 53 54 56 57 58 59 60 61 64 65 66 68 70 71 74 75 77 78 79 81 82 84 85 86 87 90 93 94 96 107 108 110 111 114 115 117 118 119 126 127 129 130 132 134 135 143 144 146 147 148 149 150 **P**6 **S** Franciscan Missionaries of Our Lady Health System, Inc., Baton Rouge, LA
Primary Contact: W. Bryan. Lee, Chief Executive Officer
COO: Donna F. Landry, Chief Operating Officer
CMO: Anthony P. Blalock M.D., Chief Medical Officer
CIO: Ryan J Latiolais, Director Information Systems
CHR: Jennifer Lynch Trahan, Assistant Vice President Human Resources
CNO: Terry J Broussard, Interim Chief Nursing Officer
Web address: www.lourdesrmc.com
Control: Church operated, Nongovernment, not–for–profit **Service:** General medical and surgical

Staffed Beds: 186 **Admissions:** 9416 **Census:** 129 **Outpatient Visits:** 166026 **Births:** 0 **Total Expense ($000):** 223092 **Payroll Expense ($000):** 60001 **Personnel:** 1311

✠ **PAM SPECIALTY HOSPITAL OF LAFAYETTE (192033)**, 204 Energy Parkway, Zip 70508–3816; tel. 337/232–1905 **A**1 10 **F**1 3 28 29 30 34 35 50 56 57 59 60 67 74 75 77 85 91 135 143 148 **P**5 **S** Post Acute Medical, LLC, Enola, PA
Primary Contact: Jason Branson, Chief Executive Officer
CMO: Vitalis C Okechukwu M.D., President Medical Staff
CNO: Patricia Tweedel, Chief Nursing Officer
Web address: www.postacutemedical.com
Control: Partnership, Investor–owned (for–profit) **Service:** Acute long–term care hospital

Staffed Beds: 50 **Admissions:** 431 **Census:** 26 **Outpatient Visits:** 0 **Births:** 0 **Total Expense ($000):** 13136 **Payroll Expense ($000):** 6349 **Personnel:** 88

⇑ **PARK PLACE SURGICAL HOSPITAL (190255)**, 4811 Ambassador Caffery Parkway, Zip 70508–6917; tel. 337/237–8119 (Nonreporting) **A**10 21
Primary Contact: Brandon Moore, FACHE, Administrator and Chief Executive Officer
Web address: www.parkplacesurgery.com/
Control: Partnership, Investor–owned (for–profit) **Service:** Surgical

Staffed Beds: 10

☐ **UNIVERSITY HOSPITAL AND CLINICS (190006)**, 2390 West Congress Street, Zip 70506–4298; tel. 337/261–6000, (Nonreporting) **A**1 2 3 5 10 **S** Lafayette General Health, Lafayette, LA
Primary Contact: Katherine D. Hebert, Chief Executive Officer
CMO: James B Falterman M.D., Jr, Medical Director
CNO: Laurence Marie Vincent, Chief Nursing Officer
Web address: www.lafayettegeneral.com
Control: Other not–for–profit (including NFP Corporation) **Service:** General medical and surgical

Staffed Beds: 105

✠ **WOMEN'S AND CHILDREN'S HOSPITAL (190205)**, 4600 Ambassador Caffery Parkway, Zip 70508–6923, Mailing Address: P.O.Box 88030, 70598–8030; tel. 337/521–9100 **A**1 3 5 10 **F**3 13 15 19 29 30 31 35 39 40 41 50 52 55 57 59 65 68 70 72 74 75 76 77 78 79 81 85 86 87 88 89 91 93 107 111 114 115 117 119 126 129 130 132 146 147 148 **S** HCA Healthcare, Nashville, TN
Primary Contact: Kathy J. Bobbs, FACHE, President and Chief Executive Officer
COO: Leona Boullion, Chief Operating Officer
CFO: James Miller, Chief Financial Officer
CMO: Donald Mickal M.D., Chief Medical Officer
CIO: John Trahan, Director Information Systems
CHR: Candice Chopin, Vice President Human Resources
CNO: John Marker, Chief Nursing Officer
Web address: www.womens–childrens.com
Control: Corporation, Investor–owned (for–profit) **Service:** Obstetrics and gynecology

Staffed Beds: 161 **Admissions:** 6043 **Census:** 93 **Outpatient Visits:** 55898 **Births:** 3221 **Total Expense ($000):** 85906 **Payroll Expense ($000):** 33683 **Personnel:** 501

LAKE CHARLES—Calcasieu Parish

CALCASIEU OAKS GERIATRIC PSYCHIATRIC HOSPITAL, 2837 Ernest Street, Zip 70601–8785; tel. 337/439–8111 (Nonreporting) **S** Pacer Health Corporation, Miami Lakes, FL
Primary Contact: Erica Williams, Assistant Chief Executive Officer
Control: Corporation, Investor–owned (for–profit) **Service:** Psychiatric

Staffed Beds: 24

✠ **CHRISTUS LAKE AREA HOSPITAL (190201)**, 4200 Nelson Road, Zip 70605–4118; tel. 337/474–6370, (Nonreporting) **A**1 10 **S** CHRISTUS Health, Irving, TX
Primary Contact: Bryan S. Bateman, Chief Executive Officer
CFO: Dawn Johnson–Hatcher, Chief Financial Officer
CIO: Aaron Cook, Director Information Services
CHR: Lisa Friday, Director Human Resources
CNO: Robbin Odom R.N., MSN, Chief Nursing Officer
Web address: www.Lakeareamc.com
Control: Corporation, Investor–owned (for–profit) **Service:** Other specialty treatment

Staffed Beds: 88

✠ △ **CHRISTUS ST. PATRICK HOSPITAL OF LAKE CHARLES (190027)**, 524 Dr Michael Debakey Drive, Zip 70601–5799, Mailing Address: P.O. Box 3401, 70602–3401; tel. 337/436–2511 **A**1 2 7 10 **F**3 11 15 17 18 20 22 24 26 28 29 30 31 32 34 35 37 38 40 44 45 46 47 48 49 50 56 57 59 61 64 65 70 74 75 78 79 81 84 85 86 87 89 90 93 96 97 98 100 101 102 103 104 105 107 108 110 118 119 120 121 122 123 124 126 130 131 132 134 135 146 147 148 **P**8 **S** CHRISTUS Health, Irving, TX
Primary Contact: Donald H. Lloyd II, Chief Executive Officer
CFO: Scott Merryman, Chief Financial Officer
CMO: Timothy Haman M.D., Vice President Medical Affairs
CHR: Wendy Chandler, Assistant Administrator Human Resources
CNO: Marsha White, Chief Nursing Executive
Web address: www.stpatrickhospital.org
Control: Church operated, Nongovernment, not–for–profit **Service:** General medical and surgical

Staffed Beds: 160 **Admissions:** 7041 **Census:** 105 **Outpatient Visits:** 63899 **Births:** 0 **Total Expense ($000):** 143939 **Payroll Expense ($000):** 40937 **Personnel:** 742

✠ **LAKE CHARLES MEMORIAL HOSPITAL (190060)**, 1701 Oak Park Boulevard, Zip 70601–8911; tel. 337/494–3000, (Includes LAKE CHARLES MEMORIAL HOSPITAL FOR WOMEN, 1900 West Gauthier Road, Lake Charles, Louisiana, Zip 70605–7170, tel. 337/480–7000; Marilyn McSwain, MSN, R.N., Administrator) **A**1 2 3 5 10 **F**3 8 11 13 15 17 18 20 22 24 26 28 29 30 31 34 37 40 45 49 50 53 54 56 57 58 60 62 64 66 70 72 73 74 75 76 77 78 79 81 82 85 86 87 89 90 93 98 99 102 103 107 108 110 111 114 115 119 120 121 123 124 126 127 129 130 131 132 144 146 147 148 149 **P**1 6 7
Primary Contact: Larry M. Graham, FACHE, President and Chief Executive Officer
COO: Anna Leah Cazes, Senior Vice President, Chief Operating Officer
CFO: Charles P Whitson CPA, Senior Vice President Finance
CMO: Manley Jordan M.D., Chief Medical Officer
CIO: Belinda Sommers, Chief Information Officer
CHR: Ginger Consigney, Vice President Human Resources
Web address: www.lcmh.com
Control: Other not–for–profit (including NFP Corporation) **Service:** General medical and surgical

Staffed Beds: 324 **Admissions:** 12734 **Census:** 187 **Outpatient Visits:** 317392 **Births:** 2037 **Total Expense ($000):** 280096 **Payroll Expense ($000):** 92759 **Personnel:** 2404

MEMORIAL SPECIALTY HOSPITAL (192019), 524 Doctor Michael Debakey Drive, 3rd Floor, Zip 70601–5725; tel. 337/480–8990 (Nonreporting) **A**10
Primary Contact: Robert R. Lafleur, Administrator
CNO: Julie LeBlanc, Director of Nursing
Web address: www.lcmh.com/
Control: Other not–for–profit (including NFP Corporation) **Service:** Acute long–term care hospital

Staffed Beds: 29

OCEANS BEHAVIORAL HOSPITAL OF LAKE CHARLES (194090), 302 West Mcneese Street, Zip 70605–5604; tel. 337/474–7581 (Nonreporting) **A**10 **S** Oceans Healthcare, Lake Charles, LA
Primary Contact: William L. Willis, Administrator
Web address: www.obhlc.info/
Control: Corporation, Investor–owned (for–profit) **Service:** Psychiatric

Staffed Beds: 20

LAKE PROVIDENCE—East Carroll Parish

EAST CARROLL PARISH HOSPITAL (190208), 336 North Hood Street, Zip 71254–2140; tel. 318/559–4023, (Nonreporting) **A**10
Primary Contact: LaDonna Englerth, Administrator
Control: Hospital district or authority, Government, Nonfederal **Service:** General medical and surgical

Staffed Beds: 11

Hospital, Medicare Provider Number, Address, Telephone, Approval, Facility, and Physician Codes, Health Care System

★ American Hospital Association (AHA) membership
☐ The Joint Commission accreditation
○ Healthcare Facilities Accreditation Program
◇ DNV Healthcare Inc. accreditation
⇑ Center for Improvement in Healthcare Quality Accreditation
△ Commission on Accreditation of Rehabilitation Facilities (CARF) accreditation

LA

LEESVILLE—Vernon Parish

✠ **BYRD REGIONAL HOSPITAL (190164)**, 1020 West Fertitta Boulevard,
Zip 71446–4645; tel. 337/239–9041, (Nonreporting) **A**1 10 **S** Community Health
Systems, Inc., Franklin, TN
Primary Contact: Roger C. LeDoux, Chief Executive Officer
CFO: Jared Graves, Chief Financial Officer
CMO: Charles Caldwell M.D., Chief of Staff
CHR: Karolyne Christian, Director Human Resources
CNO: Beth Westerchil, Chief Nursing Officer
Web address: www.byrdregional.com
Control: Corporation, Investor–owned (for–profit) **Service**: General medical and
surgical

Staffed Beds: 60

DOCTOR'S HOSPITAL OF DEER CREEK (190297), 815 South 10th Street,
Zip 71446–4611, Mailing Address: P.O.Box 1391, 71496–1391; tel. 337/392–
5088, (Nonreporting) **A**10
Primary Contact: Jeffrey Morrow, Chief Executive Officer
CMO: Gregory D Lord M.D., Medical Director
CIO: Kim Smith, Director Business Office
CHR: Annette Hillman, Director Human Resources
CNO: Brenda Willis, Director of Nursing
Web address: www.dhdc.md
Control: Corporation, Investor–owned (for–profit) **Service**: General medical and
surgical

Staffed Beds: 10

☐ **LEESVILLE REHABILITATION HOSPITAL (193086)**, 900 South 6th Street,
Zip 71446–4723; tel. 337/392–8118 (Nonreporting) **A**1 10
Primary Contact: Jack M. Causey, Chief Executive Officer
CMO: Gregory D Lord M.D., Chief Medical Officer
CHR: Jackie Rubar, Administrative Assistant and Director Human Resources
Web address: www.leesvillerehab.com
Control: Corporation, Investor–owned (for–profit) **Service**: Rehabilitation

Staffed Beds: 16

☐ **TRI PARISH REHABILITATION HOSPITAL (193050)**, 8088 Hawks Road,
Zip 71446–6649; tel. 337/462–8880 (Nonreporting) **A**1 10
Primary Contact: Elizabeth Bennett, Interim Chief Executive Officer
Web address: www.triparishrehab.com
Control: Corporation, Investor–owned (for–profit) **Service**: Rehabilitation

Staffed Beds: 20

LULING—St. Charles Parish

✠ **ST. CHARLES PARISH HOSPITAL (190079)**, 1057 Paul Maillard Road,
Zip 70070–4349, Mailing Address: P.O.Box 87, 70070–0087; tel. 985/785–6242
A1 10 **F**3 7 11 15 18 20 22 28 29 30 34 40 45 50 51 59 60 64 68 70 74 75
77 79 81 82 86 93 96 97 98 102 107 108 110 111 115 119 130 131 135 146
148 **P**6 **S** Ochsner Health System, New Orleans, LA
Primary Contact: Austin Reeder, Chief Executive Officer
COO: Terrell Neal R.N., Chief Operating Officer and Chief Nursing Officer
CFO: Peter Torsch, Chief Financial Officer
CMO: Vadakkipalayam N. Devarajan, Chief Medical Staff
CIO: Angela Boudreaux, Director Information Technology
CHR: Karen Ann Judlin, Director Human Resources
CNO: Terrell Neal R.N., Chief Operating Officer and Chief Nursing Officer
Web address: www.ochsner.org/locations/st–charles–parish–hospital/
Control: Hospital district or authority, Government, Nonfederal **Service**: General
medical and surgical

Staffed Beds: 59 **Admissions:** 1785 **Census:** 30 **Outpatient Visits:** 21629
Births: 0 **Total Expense ($000):** 38299 **Payroll Expense ($000):** 7746
Personnel: 96

LUTCHER—St. James Parish

BEACON BEHAVIORAL HOSPITAL (194102), 2471 Louisiana Avenue,
Zip 70071–5413; tel. 225/258–6103 (Nonreporting)
Primary Contact: Sean Wendell, Chief Executive Officer
Web address: www.beaconbh.com
Control: Other not–for–profit (including NFP Corporation) **Service**: Psychiatric

Staffed Beds: 19

✠ **ST. JAMES PARISH HOSPITAL (191305)**, 1645 Lutcher Avenue, Zip 70071–
5150; tel. 225/869–5512 **A**1 10 18 **F**3 15 29 30 34 35 40 45 50 57 59 64 75
77 80 81 85 107 110 111 114 119 128 129 132 133 135 144 149
Primary Contact: Mary Ellen. Pratt, FACHE, Chief Executive Officer
CFO: Tracy L George, Chief Financial Officer
CIO: Jeremy Martin, Chief Support Services Officer
CHR: Lisa Faucheux, Director Human Resources
CNO: Rhonda Zeringue R.N., Chief Nursing Officer
Web address: www.sjph.org
Control: Hospital district or authority, Government, Nonfederal **Service**: General
medical and surgical

Staffed Beds: 25 **Admissions:** 696 **Census:** 9 **Outpatient Visits:** 32026
Births: 0 **Total Expense ($000):** 27249 **Payroll Expense ($000):** 10441
Personnel: 199

MAMOU—Evangeline Parish

✠ **SAVOY MEDICAL CENTER (190025)**, 801 Poinciana Avenue, Zip 70554–2298;
tel. 337/468–5261, (Nonreporting) **A**1 10 **S** CHRISTUS Health, Irving, TX
Primary Contact: Eugene H. Burge, Chief Executive Officer
COO: Gerald Fuselier, Chief Operating Officer
CMO: Greg Savoy M.D., Chief Medical Officer
CIO: Daniel Lahaye, Manager
CHR: Annette Thibodeaux, Director Human Resources
Web address: www.savoymedical.com/
Control: City, Government, Nonfederal **Service**: General medical and surgical

Staffed Beds: 180

MANDEVILLE—St. Tammany Parish

☐ **NORTHLAKE BEHAVIORAL HEALTH SYSTEM (194007)**, 23515 Highway 190,
Zip 70448–7334; tel. 985/626–6300, (Nonreporting) **A**1 3 5 10
Primary Contact: Marty Dean, Chief Executive Officer
CFO: Melissa S. Clayton CPA, Chief Financial Officer
CMO: Hyon Su Kim M.D., Medical Director
CIO: Archie Carriere, Information Technology Technician
CHR: Nicole Messa–Gill, Manager Human Resources
CNO: Jo Nell King, Director of Nursing
Web address: www.northlakebehavioralhealth.com
Control: State, Government, Nonfederal **Service**: Psychiatric

Staffed Beds: 153

MANSFIELD—De Soto Parish

DE SOTO REGIONAL HEALTH SYSTEM (190118), 207 Jefferson Street,
Zip 71052–2603, Mailing Address: P.O.Box 1636, 71052–1636; tel. 318/872–
4610, (Nonreporting) **A**10 20 **S** Willis–Knighton Health System, Shreveport, LA
Primary Contact: Todd Eppler, FACHE, Chief Executive Officer
CFO: Eric Cripps, Chief Financial Officer
CMO: Denis Kamberov M.D., Chief of Staff
CNO: Shane Goodman, Chief Nursing Officer
Web address: www.desotoregional.com
Control: Other not–for–profit (including NFP Corporation) **Service**: General
medical and surgical

Staffed Beds: 10

MANY—Sabine Parish

SABINE MEDICAL CENTER (190218), 240 Highland Drive, Zip 71449–3718;
tel. 318/256–5691, (Nonreporting) **A**10 20 **S** Allegiance Health Management,
Shreveport, LA
Primary Contact: Calvin Green, Chief Executive Officer
COO: Doug Plummer, Chief Operating Officer
CFO: Frances F Hopkins, Chief Financial Officer
CNO: Karen Ford, Chief Nursing Officer
Web address: www.sabinemedicalcenter.net
Control: Individual, Investor–owned (for–profit) **Service**: General medical and
surgical

Staffed Beds: 44

MARKSVILLE—Avoyelles Parish

☐ **AVOYELLES HOSPITAL (190099)**, 4231 Highway 1192, Zip 71351–4711,
Mailing Address: P.O.Box 249, 71351–0249; tel. 318/253–8611 **A**1 10 **F**3 15 29
34 40 56 57 64 65 70 75 81 85 86 107 110 114 119 133 135 146
Primary Contact: David M. Mitchel, Chief Executive Officer
CFO: Douglas Lahasky, Chief Financial Officer
CMO: Donna Breen M.D., Chief of Staff
CIO: Johnny Bergeron, Manager Information Technology
CHR: Allison Ferguson, Director Human Resources
CNO: Cindy K Juneau, Chief Nursing Officer, Manger Quality and Risk
Web address: www.avoyelleshospital.com
Control: Corporation, Investor–owned (for–profit) **Service**: General medical and
surgical

Staffed Beds: 35 **Admissions:** 1810 **Census:** 10 **Outpatient Visits:** 35783
Births: 0 **Total Expense ($000):** 13113 **Payroll Expense ($000):** 6263
Personnel: 159

MARRERO—Jefferson Parish

LOUISIANA CONTINUING CARE HOSPITAL (192007), 1111 Medical Center Boulevard, Suite S–550, Zip 70072–3151; tel. 504/349–2470, (Nonreporting) **A**10
Primary Contact: Phyllis Mauro, Chief Executive Officer
Control: Corporation, Investor–owned (for–profit) **Service**: Acute long–term care hospital

Staffed Beds: 56

⊞ △ **WEST JEFFERSON MEDICAL CENTER (190039)**, 1101 Medical Center Boulevard, Zip 70072–3191; tel. 504/347–5511 **A**1 2 3 5 7 10 **F**3 6 7 11 12 13 15 17 18 20 22 24 26 28 29 30 31 34 35 37 38 39 40 41 43 45 46 47 49 50 51 53 56 57 59 61 64 65 68 70 72 74 75 76 78 79 81 82 84 85 86 87 90 91 93 96 97 98 100 101 102 104 105 107 108 110 111 114 115 117 118 119 120 121 124 126 127 129 130 132 135 144 146 147 148 149 **P**6 7 **S** LCMC Health, New Orleans, LA
Primary Contact: Nancy R. Cassagne, FACHE, Chief Executive Officer
CFO: Bryan McCauley, Chief Financial Officer
CMO: Robert Chugden M.D., Chief Medical Officer
CHR: Floyd Riedlinger, Director Human Resources
CNO: Monica Bologna R.N., Chief Nursing Officer
Web address: www.wjmc.org
Control: Other not–for–profit (including NFP Corporation) **Service**: General medical and surgical

Staffed Beds: 243 Admissions: 10626 Census: 159 Outpatient Visits: 289698 Births: 1203

METAIRIE—Jefferson Parish

⊞ △ **EAST JEFFERSON GENERAL HOSPITAL (190146)**, 4200 Houma Boulevard, Zip 70006–2996; tel. 504/503–4000, (Includes DOCTORS HOSPITAL OF JEFFERSON, 4320 Houma Boulevard, Metairie, Louisiana, Zip 70006–2973, tel. 504/849–4000) **A**1 2 3 5 7 10 **F**3 7 8 11 13 14 15 17 18 20 22 24 26 28 29 30 31 34 35 36 37 40 44 45 46 47 48 49 50 51 53 54 55 56 57 58 59 60 64 65 68 70 72 73 74 75 77 78 79 81 82 84 85 86 87 90 91 92 93 96 97 98 102 103 107 108 110 111 114 115 117 118 119 120 121 123 124 126 128 129 130 131 132 135 141 142 145 146 147 148 149 **P**6
Primary Contact: Gerald L. Parton, FACHE, Chief Executive Officer
COO: Judy Brown, Executive Vice President and Chief Operating Officer
CFO: Robert Riley, Interim Chief Financial Officer
CMO: Raymond P DeCorte M.D., Chief Medical Officer
CHR: Frank Martinez, Senior Vice President Human Resources
CNO: Ruby Brewer RN, Senior Vice President, Chief Nursing and Quality Officer
Web address: www.ejgh.org
Control: Hospital district or authority, Government, Nonfederal **Service**: General medical and surgical

Staffed Beds: 424 Admissions: 14693 Census: 205 Outpatient Visits: 230480 Births: 1393 Total Expense ($000): 359527 Payroll Expense ($000): 102298 Personnel: 2037

⇑ **OMEGA HOSPITAL (190302)**, 2525 Severn Avenue, Zip 70002–5932; tel. 504/832–4200 (Nonreporting) **A**10 21
Primary Contact: Debbie Schenck, Administrator
Web address: www.omega–institute.com
Control: Individual, Investor–owned (for–profit) **Service**: Surgical

Staffed Beds: 10

MINDEN—Webster Parish

⊞ **MINDEN MEDICAL CENTER (190144)**, 1 Medical Plaza, Zip 71055–3330, Mailing Address: P.O.Box 5003, 71058–5003; tel. 318/377–2321 **A**1 10 19 **F**11 13 15 18 20 22 29 30 34 40 45 46 56 57 59 62 64 70 75 76 77 79 81 82 87 89 90 93 98 103 107 111 115 119 129 130 132 146 147 148 **S** LifePoint Health, Brentwood, TN
Primary Contact: Gregory Pearson, Chief Executive Officer
CFO: Jim Williams, Chief Financial Officer
CMO: G Max Stell M.D., Medical Director
CIO: Mace Morgan, Director Information Systems
CHR: Mary Winget, Director Human Resources
CNO: Donna Carter MSN, R.N., Chief Nursing Officer
Web address: www.mindenmedicalcenter.com
Control: Corporation, Investor–owned (for–profit) **Service**: General medical and surgical

Staffed Beds: 161 Admissions: 3624 Census: 43 Outpatient Visits: 48278 Births: 680 Total Expense ($000): 52686 Payroll Expense ($000): 20595 Personnel: 433

MONROE—Ouachita Parish

BASTROP REHABILITATION HOSPITAL (193058), 4310 South Grand Street, Zip 71202–6322; tel. 318/654–8300 **A**10 **F**80 91 96 105
Primary Contact: William H. Means Jr, Administrator
CMO: Jeffery Combetta M.D., Medical Director
CHR: Rhonda Church, Director Human Resources
Control: Corporation, Investor–owned (for–profit) **Service**: Rehabilitation

Staffed Beds: 12 Admissions: 156 Census: 5 Outpatient Visits: 0 Births: 0 Personnel: 28

E. A. CONWAY MEDICAL CENTER See University Health Conway

⇑ **MONROE SURGICAL HOSPITAL (190245)**, 2408 Broadmoor Boulevard, Zip 71201–2963; tel. 318/410–0002, (Nonreporting) **A**10 21
Primary Contact: Robyn Hemphill, Chief Executive Officer and Chief Nursing Officer
Web address: www.monroesurgical.com
Control: Corporation, Investor–owned (for–profit) **Service**: Surgical

Staffed Beds: 10

★ ⇑ **P & S SURGICAL HOSPITAL (190246)**, 312 Grammont Street Suite 101, Zip 71201–7403; tel. 318/388–4040, (Nonreporting) **A**10 21
Primary Contact: Linda S. Holyfield, R.N., MSN, President and Chief Executive Officer
COO: Terri Hicks, Chief Operating Officer and Chief Financial Officer
CFO: Terri Hicks, Chief Operating Officer and Chief Financial Officer
CMO: Bart Liles M.D., Chief of Staff
CIO: Christy Childers, Director Information Technology
CHR: Cheniere Craig, Director Human Resources
CNO: Debbie W Austin MSN, R.N., Vice President Patient Care Services
Web address: www.pssurgery.com
Control: Partnership, Investor–owned (for–profit) **Service**: Surgical

Staffed Beds: 22

SPECIALTY HOSPITAL (192016), 309 Jackson Street, 7th Floor, Zip 71201–7407, Mailing Address: P.O.Box 1532, 71210–1532; tel. 318/966–7045, (Nonreporting) **A**10 **S** LHC Group, Lafayette, LA
Primary Contact: Cleta Munholland, Administrator
Web address: www.lhcgroup.com
Control: Church operated, Nongovernment, not–for–profit **Service**: Acute long–term care hospital

Staffed Beds: 32

⊞ **ST. FRANCIS MEDICAL CENTER (190125)**, 309 Jackson Street, Zip 71201–7407, Mailing Address: P.O.Box 1901, 71210–1901; tel. 318/966–4000 **A**1 10 **F**3 12 13 15 17 18 19 20 21 22 23 24 25 26 27 28 29 30 31 32 34 35 37 39 40 42 44 45 46 49 50 54 55 56 57 59 64 65 68 69 70 71 72 74 75 76 77 78 79 81 84 85 87 88 89 90 92 93 96 97 107 108 110 111 114 115 118 119 124 126 128 129 130 131 132 135 144 146 147 148 **P**8 **S** Franciscan Missionaries of Our Lady Health System, Inc., Baton Rouge, LA
Primary Contact: Kristin Wolkart, R.N., President and Chief Executive Officer
CFO: Dan A. Macksood, Chief Financial Officer
CNO: Kayla Johnson R.N., Vice President Patient Care Services and Chief Nursing Officer
Web address: www.stfran.com
Control: Church operated, Nongovernment, not–for–profit **Service**: General medical and surgical

Staffed Beds: 365 Admissions: 12357 **Census: 202 Outpatient Visits: 227275 Births: 1741 Total Expense ($000): 262481 Payroll Expense ($000): 98232 Personnel: 1762**

ST. FRANCIS SPECIALTY HOSPITAL See Specialty Hospital

☐ **UNIVERSITY HEALTH CONWAY (190011)**, 4864 Jackson Street, Zip 71202–6497, Mailing Address: P.O.Box 1881, 71210–8005; tel. 318/330–7000 **A**1 3 5 10 **F**3 8 11 13 15 18 20 22 24 26 28 29 30 31 32 34 35 36 38 40 41 45 46 50 54 56 57 59 61 64 65 66 68 70 71 72 73 75 76 77 78 79 81 85 86 87 89 91 93 97 98 100 101 102 103 107 108 110 111 112 114 115 119 124 130 135 143 144 146 147 **P**8 **S** University Health System, Shreveport, LA
Primary Contact: Jonathan Phillips, Interim Administrator
CFO: Dorothy Whittington, Chief Financial Officer
CMO: Richard Cavell M.D., Medical Director
CIO: Todd Walters, Director of UHC Information Technology Services
CHR: Rob Hartmann, Assistant Director Human Resources Management
CNO: Traci S. Jordan MS, R.N., Chief Nursing Officer
Web address: www.uhsystem.com
Control: Other not–for–profit (including NFP Corporation) **Service**: General medical and surgical

Staffed Beds: 108 Admissions: 5087 Census: 70 Personnel: 593

Hospital, Medicare Provider Number, Address, Telephone, Approval, Facility, and Physician Codes, Health Care System

★ American Hospital Association (AHA) membership
☐ The Joint Commission accreditation
○ Healthcare Facilities Accreditation Program
◇ DNV Healthcare Inc. accreditation
⇑ Center for Improvement in Healthcare Quality Accreditation
△ Commission on Accreditation of Rehabilitation Facilities (CARF) accreditation

LA

MORGAN CITY—St. Mary Parish

⊞ **TECHE REGIONAL MEDICAL CENTER (190014)**, 1125 Marguerite Street, Zip 70380–1855, Mailing Address: P.O.Box 2308, 70381–2308; tel. 985/384–2200 **A**1 10 20 **F**3 13 15 18 29 30 34 40 45 50 57 59 70 76 79 81 82 84 85 89 90 93 98 100 101 102 105 107 108 110 111 114 117 118 119 129 130 146 147 **S** LifePoint Health, Brentwood, TN
Primary Contact: Jerry Dooley, Interim Chief Executive Officer
COO: Don Knight, Assistant Administrator and Risk Manager
CFO: Lynn Kliebert, Chief Financial Officer
CMO: Eric Melancon, Chief of Staff
CIO: Cheryl Lipari, Manager Information Systems
CHR: Timothy Hebert, Director Human Resources
Web address: www.techeregional.com
Control: Corporation, Investor–owned (for–profit) **Service:** General medical and surgical

Staffed Beds: 164 **Admissions:** 2835 **Census:** 37 **Outpatient Visits:** 52525 **Births:** 387 **Total Expense ($000):** 43516 **Payroll Expense ($000):** 14773 **Personnel:** 267

NAPOLEONVILLE—Assumption Parish

★ **ASSUMPTION COMMUNITY HOSPITAL (191303)**, 135 Highway 402, Zip 70390–2217; tel. 985/369–3600, (Nonreporting) **A**10 18 **S** Franciscan Missionaries of Our Lady Health System, Inc., Baton Rouge, LA
Primary Contact: Christina Hockaday, FACHE, Chief Executive Officer
CHR: Letonia Pierre, Coordinator Human Resources
CNO: Donna Mullings, Director of Nursing
Web address: www.ololrmc.com
Control: Other not–for–profit (including NFP Corporation) **Service:** General medical and surgical

Staffed Beds: 6

NATCHITOCHES—Natchitoches Parish

LOUISIANA EXTENDED CARE HOSPITAL OF NATCHITOCHES (192035), 501 Keyser Avenue, Zip 71457–6018; tel. 318/354–2044 **A**10 **F**1 3 28 29 34 38 50 57 59 68 74 75 85 86 87 91 97 130 148 **S** LHC Group, Lafayette, LA
Primary Contact: John Rivoire, R.N., MSN, Administrator
Web address: www.lhcgroup.com
Control: Partnership, Investor–owned (for–profit) **Service:** Acute long–term care hospital

Staffed Beds: 21 **Admissions:** 246 **Census:** 17 **Outpatient Visits:** 0 **Births:** 0 **Personnel:** 45

⊞ **NATCHITOCHES REGIONAL MEDICAL CENTER (190007)**, 501 Keyser Avenue, Zip 71457–6036, Mailing Address: P.O.Box 2009, 71457–2009; tel. 318/214–4200 **A**1 10 20 **F**3 5 7 8 10 11 13 15 18 28 29 30 31 32 34 35 36 37 38 39 40 41 42 43 45 46 47 50 51 53 54 56 57 58 59 60 61 65 66 69 70 71 74 75 76 77 78 79 81 82 85 86 87 93 94 97 98 100 101 102 103 104 105 106 107 108 109 110 111 112 114 119 120 121 124 125 126 127 129 130 131 132 133 135 143 144 145 146 147 148 **P**5 7 8 **S** CHRISTUS Health, Irving, TX
Primary Contact: D. Kirk. Soileau, FACHE, Chief Executive Officer
CFO: Brad McCormick, Chief Financial Officer
CMO: Phyllis Mason M.D., Chief Medical Officer
CHR: Ernie Scott, Director Human Resources
CNO: Dawna DeBlieux, Vice President Patient Care Services and Chief Nurse Executive
Web address: www.nrmchospital.org
Control: Hospital district or authority, Government, Nonfederal **Service:** General medical and surgical

Staffed Beds: 91 **Admissions:** 2498 **Census:** 26 **Outpatient Visits:** 59836 **Births:** 595 **Total Expense ($000):** 59649 **Payroll Expense ($000):** 28167 **Personnel:** 673

NEW IBERIA—Iberia Parish

☐ **IBERIA MEDICAL CENTER (190054)**, 2315 East Main Street, Zip 70560–4031, Mailing Address: P.O.Box 13338, 70562–3338; tel. 337/364–0441 **A**1 10 **F**3 11 13 15 18 20 22 28 29 30 31 34 39 40 45 46 47 48 49 50 57 68 70 72 74 75 76 77 78 79 81 85 89 93 97 107 108 110 111 115 119 127 130 135 146 **P**6 **S** HealthTech Management Services, Brentwood, TN
Primary Contact: Parker A. Templeton, FACHE, Chief Executive Officer
COO: Shane P Myers, Chief Operating Officer
CFO: Dionne Viator CPA, FACHE, Chief Financial Officer
CMO: Shawn Baquet, Chief of Staff
CIO: Vance Robinson, Chief Information Officer
CHR: Lori Spann, Director Human Resources
CNO: Josie Fletcher, Interim Chief Nursing Officer
Web address: www.iberiamedicalcenter.com
Control: Hospital district or authority, Government, Nonfederal **Service:** General medical and surgical

Staffed Beds: 97 **Admissions:** 4477 **Census:** 41 **Outpatient Visits:** 111835 **Births:** 263 **Total Expense ($000):** 83680 **Payroll Expense ($000):** 31022 **Personnel:** 624

☐ **IBERIA REHABILITATION HOSPITAL (193096)**, 532 Jefferson Terrace, Zip 70560–4948; tel. 337/364–6923 (Nonreporting) **A**1 10
Primary Contact: Athan Olivier III, R.N., FACHE, Administrator and Chief Executive Officer
Web address: www.iberiarehab.net/
Control: Partnership, Investor–owned (for–profit) **Service:** Rehabilitation

Staffed Beds: 24

NEW ORLEANS—Orleans Parish

☐ **BEACON BEHAVIORAL HOSPITAL – NEW ORLEANS (194084)**, 14500 Hayne Boulevard, Suite 200, Zip 70128–1751; tel. 504/210–0460 (Nonreporting) **A**1 10
Primary Contact: Jessika Scallion, Administrator
Control: Corporation, Investor–owned (for–profit) **Service:** Psychiatric

Staffed Beds: 24

☐ △ **CHILDREN'S HOSPITAL (193300)**, 200 Henry Clay Avenue, Zip 70118–5720; tel. 504/899–9511, (Nonreporting) **A**1 2 3 5 7 10 **S** LCMC Health, New Orleans, LA
Primary Contact: Mary R. Perrin, President and Chief Executive Officer
COO: Justin Olsen, Chief Operating Officer
CFO: Courtney Garrett CPA, Senior Vice President, Chief Financial Officer
CMO: John Heaton M.D., Senior Vice President and Medical Director
CIO: Tanya Townsend, Senior Vice President, Chief Information Officer (part of LCMC)
CHR: Wendy L Willis, Vice President Human Resources
CNO: Diane Michel, Senior Vice President, Chief Nursing Officer
Web address: www.chnola.org
Control: Other not–for–profit (including NFP Corporation) **Service:** Children's general medical and surgical

Staffed Beds: 283

☐ **COMMUNITY CARE HOSPITAL (194056)**, 1421 General Taylor Street, Zip 70115–3717; tel. 504/899–2500 (Nonreporting) **A**1 10
Primary Contact: Paul B. Kavanaugh, President and Chief Executive Officer
Web address: www.communitycarehospital.com
Control: State, Government, Nonfederal **Service:** Psychiatric

Staffed Beds: 36

⊞ **CURAHEALTH NEW ORLEANS (192009)**, 3601 Coliseum Street, Zip 70115–3606; tel. 504/899–1555, (Nonreporting) **A**1 3 10 **S** Curahealth Hospitals, Garland, TX
Primary Contact: Richard Daughdrill, R.N., Chief Executive Officer
CFO: Laurie Champagne, Controller
Web address: www.curahealth.com
Control: Corporation, Investor–owned (for–profit) **Service:** Acute long–term care hospital

Staffed Beds: 80

MEDICAL CENTER OF LOUISIANA AT NEW ORLEANS See University Medical Center

☐ **NEW ORLEANS EAST HOSPITAL (190313)**, 5620 Read Boulevard, Zip 70127–3106, Mailing Address: 5620 Read Blvd, 70127–3106; tel. 504/592–6600 **A**1 **F**3 11 15 18 20 22 26 29 30 34 35 38 40 44 45 50 57 59 63 64 68 70 74 75 77 79 81 82 85 86 87 91 93 107 108 110 111 115 118 119 129 130 131 146 147 149 **P**8 **S** LCMC Health, New Orleans, LA
Primary Contact: Takeisha C. Davis, M.D., M.P.H., President and Chief Executive Officer
COO: Dante Green, Assistant Vice President Operations
CFO: Anthony Saul, Chief Financial Officer
CHR: Brion Stanford, Director Human Resources
CNO: Martha Smith R.N., Chief Nursing Officer
Web address: www.noehospital.org
Control: Hospital district or authority, Government, Nonfederal **Service:** General medical and surgical

Staffed Beds: 34 **Admissions:** 795 **Census:** 7 **Outpatient Visits:** 38573 **Births:** 0

✉ △ **OCHSNER MEDICAL CENTER (190036)**, 1514 Jefferson Highway, Zip 70121–2429; tel. 504/842–3000, (Includes OCHSNER BAPTIST MEDICAL CENTER, 2700 Napoleon Avenue, New Orleans, Louisiana, Zip 70115–6914, tel. 504/899–9311; Dawn Anuszkiewicz, Chief Executive Officer; OCHSNER MEDICAL CENTER – WEST BANK, 2500 Belle Chasse Highway, Gretna, Louisiana, Zip 70056–7127, tel. 504/392–3131; Anthony DiGerolamo, R.N., MSN, Chief Executive Officer; OCHSNER MEDICAL CENTER FOR CHILDREN, 1514 Jefferson Highway, New Orleans, Louisiana, Zip 70121–2429, tel. 504/842–3000) (Total facility includes 38 beds in nursing home–type unit) **A**1 2 3 5 7 8 10 **F**3 4 5 6 7 8 9 11 12 13 14 15 17 18 19 20 21 22 23 24 25 26 27 28 29 30 31 32 34 35 36 37 38 40 41 43 44 45 46 47 48 49 50 51 53 54 55 56 57 58 59 60 61 63 64 65 68 70 71 72 73 74 75 76 77 78 79 80 81 82 84 85 86 87 88 89 90 91 92 93 94 96 97 98 99 100 101 102 103 104 105 107 108 110 111 114 115 116 117 118 119 120 121 123 124 126 128 129 130 131 132 134 135 136 137 138 139 140 141 142 145 146 147 148 **P**6 **S** Ochsner Health System, New Orleans, LA
Primary Contact: Robert K. Wolterman, Chief Executive Officer
CFO: Scott J Posecai, Executive Vice President and Chief Financial Officer
CMO: Patrick J Quinlan M.D., Chief Executive Officer
CIO: Lynn Witherspoon, Vice President and Chief Information Officer
CHR: Joan Mollohan, Vice President Human Resources
Web address: www.ochsner.org
Control: Other not–for–profit (including NFP Corporation) **Service:** General medical and surgical

Staffed Beds: 826 **Admissions:** 41418 **Census:** 639 **Outpatient Visits:** 259926 **Births:** 4194 **Total Expense ($000):** 1287950 **Payroll Expense ($000):** 450533 **Personnel:** 8420

PSYCHIATRIC PAVILION NEW ORLEANS See Beacon Behavioral Hospital – New Orleans

☐ **RIVER OAKS HOSPITAL (194031)**, 1525 River Oaks Road West, Zip 70123–2162; tel. 504/734–1740, (Nonreporting) (Includes RIVER OAKS CHILD AND ADOLESCENT HOSPITAL, 1525 River Oaks Road West, New Orleans, Louisiana, Zip 70123–2162, tel. 504/734–1740) **A**1 3 10 **S** Universal Health Services, Inc., King of Prussia, PA
Primary Contact: Deagan Watson, Chief Executive Officer
CFO: Brandon Frazier, Chief Financial Officer
CMO: Lincoln Paine M.D., Medical Director
CIO: Vincent Chatelain, Director Business Development
CHR: Wanda Hoffmann, Director Human Resources
CNO: Michelle Wells, Director of Nursing
Web address: www.riveroakshospital.com
Control: Corporation, Investor–owned (for–profit) **Service:** Psychiatric

Staffed Beds: 126

SEASIDE BEHAVIORAL CENTER (194100), 4201 Woodland Drive, Zip 70131–7339; tel. 504/393–4223 (Nonreporting) **A**3 10
Primary Contact: Mary L. Matamoros, R.N., Chief Executive Officer
CHR: Sherry May Campbell, Director of Human Resources, Medical Records
CNO: Justin Bernier R.N., Director of Nursing
Web address: www.seasidehc.com
Control: Partnership, Investor–owned (for–profit) **Service:** Psychiatric

Staffed Beds: 24

☐ **ST. CATHERINE MEMORIAL HOSPITAL (192023)**, 14500 Hayne Boulevard, Zip 70128–1751; tel. 504/210–3000 (Nonreporting) **A**1 10
Primary Contact: Lexis Landry Nunez, Chief Executive Officer
Web address: www.stcatherine–hospital.com
Control: Corporation, Investor–owned (for–profit) **Service:** Acute long–term care hospital

Staffed Beds: 21

⇑ **ST. CHARLES SURGICAL HOSPITAL (190300)**, 1717 Saint Charles Avenue, Zip 70130–5223; tel. 504/529–6600, (Nonreporting) **A**10 21
Primary Contact: Cheri Saltaformaggio, Chief Executive Officer
Web address: www.scsh.com
Control: Corporation, Investor–owned (for–profit) **Service:** Surgical

Staffed Beds: 39

✉ △ **TOURO INFIRMARY (190046)**, 1401 Foucher Street, Zip 70115–3593; tel. 504/897–7011, (Includes TOURO REHABILITATION CENTER, 1401 Foucher Street, New Orleans, Louisiana, Zip 70115–3515, tel. 504/897–8560; Susan E. Andrews, Chief Executive Officer) **A**1 2 3 5 7 8 10 **F**3 8 10 11 13 15 18 20 22 24 28 29 30 31 34 35 36 37 39 40 44 45 46 50 53 54 55 57 59 60 61 62 63 64 68 70 72 74 75 76 77 78 79 81 83 84 85 86 87 90 92 93 96 97 107 108 109 110 111 114 115 116 117 118 119 120 121 123 124 125 126 130 131 132 135 143 146 147 148 149 **P**8 **S** LCMC Health, New Orleans, LA
Primary Contact: Susan E. Andrews, Chief Executive Officer
COO: David Elgarico, Chief Operating Officer
CFO: Mark Wack, Senior Vice President and Chief Financial Officer
CMO: Jeffrey Coco M.D., Chief Medical Officer
CIO: Leann Hughes–Mickel, Chief Information Officer
CHR: Cindy Mousa, Director Human Resources
CNO: Danita S Sullivan R.N., Chief Nursing Officer
Web address: www.touro.com
Control: Other not–for–profit (including NFP Corporation) **Service:** General medical and surgical

Staffed Beds: 280 **Admissions:** 11269 **Census:** 187 **Outpatient Visits:** 307228 **Births:** 3426 **Total Expense ($000):** 249972 **Payroll Expense ($000):** 96554

✉ **TULANE MEDICAL CENTER (190176)**, 1415 Tulane Avenue, Zip 70112–2600; tel. 504/988–5263, (Includes LAKEVIEW REGIONAL MEDICAL CENTER, 95 Judge Tanner Boulevard, Covington, Louisiana, Zip 70433–7507, tel. 985/867–3800; Bret G. Kolman, CPA, FACHE, Chief Executive Officer; TULANE–LAKESIDE HOSPITAL, 4700 South I 10 Service Road West, Metairie, Louisiana, Zip 70001–1269, tel. 504/780–4200) **A**1 2 3 5 8 10 **F**3 12 13 15 17 18 20 21 22 23 24 25 26 27 28 29 30 31 32 34 35 40 41 45 46 47 48 49 50 51 52 55 58 60 61 64 65 70 72 74 75 76 77 78 79 80 81 85 87 88 89 90 91 92 93 97 99 100 102 104 107 108 109 110 111 114 115 118 119 120 121 122 123 124 126 129 130 131 132 136 138 139 141 142 146 147 148 **P**4 5 **S** HCA Healthcare, Nashville, TN
Primary Contact: William Lunn, M.D., Chief Executive Officer
CFO: Regina Ramazani, Chief Financial Officer
CMO: John Pigott M.D., Chief Medical Officer
CIO: Sue Rachuig, Director Information Services
CHR: Leah Grau, Director Human Resources
CNO: Jana S Stonestreet R.N., Ph.D., Chief Nursing Officer
Web address: www.tuhc.com
Control: Corporation, Investor–owned (for–profit) **Service:** General medical and surgical

Staffed Beds: 294 **Admissions:** 13645 **Census:** 200 **Outpatient Visits:** 369890 **Births:** 2258 **Total Expense ($000):** 401552 **Payroll Expense ($000):** 113455 **Personnel:** 1412

☐ **UNIVERSITY MEDICAL CENTER (190005)**, 2000 Canal Street, Zip 70112–3018; tel. 504/903–3000 **A**1 2 3 5 8 10 **F**3 11 15 18 20 22 24 26 29 30 31 34 35 39 40 43 45 46 49 50 51 58 61 64 65 66 70 74 78 79 81 85 86 87 93 94 97 98 102 107 108 110 111 114 115 116 117 118 119 123 126 130 135 141 146 147 148 **S** LCMC Health, New Orleans, LA
Primary Contact: William J. Masterton, President and Chief Executive Officer
COO: Lisa Miranda, Vice President Operations
CFO: Christine Williams, Chief Financial Officer
CNO: Denise Danna Esq, Chief Nursing Officer
Web address: www.umcno.org
Control: Other not–for–profit (including NFP Corporation) **Service:** General medical and surgical

Staffed Beds: 272 **Admissions:** 12153 **Census:** 199 **Outpatient Visits:** 330348 **Births:** 0 **Total Expense ($000):** 546482 **Payroll Expense ($000):** 118776 **Personnel:** 1693

NEW ROADS—Pointe Coupee Parish

★ **POINTE COUPEE GENERAL HOSPITAL (191316)**, 2202 False River Drive, Zip 70760–2614; tel. 225/638–6331 **A**10 18 **F**40 45 64 75 77 81 93 107 111 119 129 130 133 146
Primary Contact: Chad E. Olinde, CPA, Administrator and Chief Executive Officer
CFO: John Cazayoux, Chief Financial Officer
CMO: Paul Rachal M.D., Chief Medical Officer
CIO: Anthony Sauro, Chief Information Officer
CHR: Lisa Patterson, Director Human Resources
CNO: Valerie Sparks Jarreau R.N., Chief Nursing Officer
Web address: www.pcgh.org
Control: Hospital district or authority, Government, Nonfederal **Service:** General medical and surgical

Staffed Beds: 25 **Admissions:** 263 **Census:** 5 **Outpatient Visits:** 49641 **Births:** 0 **Total Expense ($000):** 15902 **Payroll Expense ($000):** 7141 **Personnel:** 181

Hospital, Medicare Provider Number, Address, Telephone, Approval, Facility, and Physician Codes, Health Care System

★ American Hospital Association (AHA) membership   ○ Healthcare Facilities Accreditation Program   ⇑ Center for Improvement in Healthcare Quality Accreditation
☐ The Joint Commission accreditation   ◇ DNV Healthcare Inc. accreditation   △ Commission on Accreditation of Rehabilitation Facilities (CARF) accreditation

LA

OAK GROVE—West Carroll Parish

WEST CARROLL MEMORIAL HOSPITAL (190081), 706 Ross Street, Zip 71263–9798; tel. 318/428–3237, (Nonreporting) **A**10
Primary Contact: R Randall. Morris, Administrator
Control: Other not–for–profit (including NFP Corporation) **Service:** General medical and surgical

Staffed Beds: 21

OAKDALE—Allen Parish

☐ **OAKDALE COMMUNITY HOSPITAL (190106)**, 130 North Hospital Drive, Zip 71463–3035, Mailing Address: P.O.Box 629, 71463–0629; tel. 318/335–3700, (Nonreporting) **A**1 10
Primary Contact: Billy Tingle, Chief Executive Officer
CFO: Suzette Fatula, Chief Financial Officer
CMO: Tommy Davis M.D., Chief of Staff
CIO: Sheri Dugas, Director Health Information Management
CHR: Becky Johnson, Director Human Resources
CNO: Kari Broussard, Chief Nursing Officer
Web address: www.oakdalecommunityhospital.com/
Control: Partnership, Investor–owned (for–profit) **Service:** General medical and surgical

Staffed Beds: 27

OLLA—Caldwell Parish

HARDTNER MEDICAL CENTER (191315), 1102 North Pine Road, Zip 71465–4804; tel. 318/495–3131, (Nonreporting) **A**10 18
Primary Contact: Paul G. Mathews, CPA, Administrator
CIO: Sarah Thompson, Director Health Information Management
CNO: Cherry B Salter, Director of Nursing
Web address: www.hardtnermedical.com
Control: Hospital district or authority, Government, Nonfederal **Service:** General medical and surgical

Staffed Beds: 35

OPELOUSAS—St. Landry Parish

☐ **OCEANS BEHAVIORAL HOSPITAL OF OPELOUSAS (194095)**, 1310 Heather Drive, Zip 70570–7714; tel. 337/948–8820 (Nonreporting) **A**1 10 **S** Oceans Healthcare, Lake Charles, LA
Primary Contact: Theresa Fontenot, Executive Director
Web address: www.obho.info/
Control: Corporation, Investor–owned (for–profit) **Service:** Psychiatric

Staffed Beds: 20

✠ **OPELOUSAS GENERAL HEALTH SYSTEM (190017)**, 539 East Prudhomme Street, Zip 70570–6499, Mailing Address: P.O.Box 1389, 70571–1389; tel. 337/948–3011, (Includes OPELOUSAS GENERAL HEALTH SYSTEM–SOUTH CAMPUS, 3983 I–49 South Service Road, Opelousas, Louisiana, Zip 70570–8975, tel. 337/948–2100; Kenneth Cochran, R.N., FACHE, President and Chief Executive Officer) **A**1 2 10 19 **F**3 13 15 28 31 34 37 40 44 45 48 49 50 53 57 60 65 68 77 78 79 81 85 87 91 93 96 97 102 103 104 105 107 108 110 111 112 114 115 116 117 119 121 129 130 131 132 146 147 148 **P**6
Primary Contact: Kenneth Cochran, R.N., FACHE, President and Chief Executive Officer
COO: Bob Hardy, Chief Operating Officer
CFO: James B Juneau, Chief Financial Officer
CMO: Hunt Deblanc M.D., Chief of Staff
CIO: Jared Lormand, Vice President Information Technology
CHR: Suzanne F Kidder, Human Resources Officer
CNO: Kimberly Probus, Chief Nursing Officer
Web address: www.opelousasgeneral.com
Control: Other not–for–profit (including NFP Corporation) **Service:** General medical and surgical

Staffed Beds: 201 Admissions: 7295 Census: 100 Outpatient Visits: 141448 **Births:** 1136 **Total Expense ($000):** 145500 **Payroll Expense ($000):** 44618 **Personnel:** 849

ST. LANDRY EXTENDED CARE HOSPITAL (192034), 3983 1–49 South Service Road, 2nd Floor, Zip 70570; tel. 337/948–2251 (Nonreporting) **A**10 **S** LHC Group, Lafayette, LA
Primary Contact: Biff David, R.N., Administrator
Web address: www.lhcgroup.com
Control: Corporation, Investor–owned (for–profit) **Service:** Acute long–term care hospital

Staffed Beds: 41

PINEVILLE—Rapides Parish

✠ **ALEXANDRIA VETERANS AFFAIRS HEALTH CARE SYSTEM**, 2495 Shreveport Highway, 71 N, Zip 71360–4044, Mailing Address: P.O.Box 69004, Alexandria, 71306–9004; tel. 318/473–0010, (Nonreporting) **A**1 5 **S** Department of Veterans Affairs, Washington, DC
Primary Contact: Peter C. Dancy Jr, Director
CFO: Bianca A. Obey, Chief Financial Officer
CMO: Robert Bernard M.D., Chief of Staff
CIO: Robin McBryde, Chief Information Officer
CHR: Alex Love, Acting Manager Human Resources
CNO: Amy Lesniewski, Associate Director Patient Care Services
Web address: www.alexandria.va.gov/
Control: Veterans Affairs, Government, federal **Service:** General medical and surgical

Staffed Beds: 143

☐ **CENTRAL LOUISIANA STATE HOSPITAL (194025)**, 242 West Shamrock Avenue, Zip 71306–6439, Mailing Address: P.O.Box 5031, 71361–5031; tel. 318/484–6200 **A**1 10 **F**98 100 101 103 105 106 149 **S** Louisiana State Hospitals, Baton Rouge, LA
Primary Contact: Ronald G. Williams, Administrator
COO: Paul Benoit, Associate Administrator
CFO: Tina Darbonne, Chief Financial Officer
CMO: L Lee Tynes M.D., Ph.D., Jr, Medical Director
CIO: William Haynes, Director Information Technology
CHR: Tom Crout MS, Director Human Resources
Web address: www.dhh.louisiana.gov/index.cfm/directory/detail/217
Control: State, Government, Nonfederal **Service:** Psychiatric

Staffed Beds: 120 Admissions: 48 Census: 119 Outpatient Visits: 0 Births: 0

VETERANS AFFAIRS MEDICAL CENTER – ALEXANDRIA See Alexandria Veterans Affairs Health Care System

PLAQUEMINE—Iberville Parish

MMO REHABILITATION AND WELLNESS CENTER (193070), 59213 Riverwest Drive, Zip 70764–6552; tel. 225/687–8100 (Nonreporting) **A**10
Primary Contact: Julene Mcalister, Administrator
Web address: www.mmoinc.com
Control: Other not–for–profit (including NFP Corporation) **Service:** Rehabilitation

Staffed Beds: 8

RACELAND—Lafourche Parish

✠ **OCHSNER ST. ANNE GENERAL HOSPITAL (191324)**, 4608 Highway 1, Zip 70394–2623; tel. 985/537–6841 **A**1 10 18 **F**3 4 5 13 15 17 18 29 30 34 35 40 45 57 59 63 65 70 74 75 76 79 81 85 86 87 89 98 99 100 101 102 103 104 107 108 110 111 114 118 119 127 130 133 135 146 147 **S** Ochsner Health System, New Orleans, LA
Primary Contact: Timothy J. Allen, FACHE, Chief Executive Officer
COO: Fernis LeBlanc, Chief Operating Officer
CFO: Lisa Kirkpatrick, Chief Financial Officer
CNO: Jana Semere, Chief Nursing Officer
Web address: www.ochsner.org/locations/ochsner–st–anne
Control: Other not–for–profit (including NFP Corporation) **Service:** General medical and surgical

Staffed Beds: 35 Admissions: 1681 Census: 18 Outpatient Visits: 80306 Births: 350 Total Expense ($000): 33499 Payroll Expense ($000): 14178 Personnel: 461

RAYNE—Acadia Parish

☐ **OCEANS BEHAVIORAL HOSPITAL OF CROWLEY (194097)**, 2021 Crowley Rayne Highway, Zip 70578–4027; tel. 337/788–0091 (Nonreporting) **A**1 10
Primary Contact: Theresa Fontenot, Administrator
Control: Corporation, Investor–owned (for–profit) **Service:** Psychiatric

Staffed Beds: 18

RAYVILLE—Richland Parish

RICHARDSON MEDICAL CENTER (190151), 254 Highway 3048 Christian Drive, Zip 71269–0388, Mailing Address: P.O.Box 388, 71269–0388; tel. 318/728–4181 **A**10 **F**17 18 20 29 34 40 45 48 50 53 56 57 59 65 70 71 77 81 87 93 97 103 104 107 108 110 111 119 127 129 130 133 146 147 **P**5
Primary Contact: James W. Barrett Jr, Chief Executive Officer
CFO: Mallory Gulley Wells CPA, Chief Financial Officer
CMO: David Thompson M.D., Chief of Staff
CHR: Rita Brown, Director Human Resources
CNO: Earlene Chriceol, Chief Nursing Officer
Web address: www.richardsonmed.org
Control: Hospital district or authority, Government, Nonfederal **Service:** General medical and surgical

Staffed Beds: 37 Admissions: 777 Census: 8 Outpatient Visits: 18471 Births: 0 Total Expense ($000): 18775 Payroll Expense ($000): 8423 Personnel: 155

Many Facility Codes have changed. Please refer to the AHA Guide Code Chart. © 2017 AHA Guide

LA

RUSTON—Lincoln Parish

LIBERTY HEALTHCARE SYSTEMS See Serenity Springs Specialty Hospital

☒ **NORTHERN LOUISIANA MEDICAL CENTER (190086)**, 401 East Vaughn
Avenue, Zip 71270–5950; tel. 318/254–2100, (Nonreporting) (Includes GREEN
CLINIC SURGICAL HOSPITAL, 1118 Farmerville Street, Ruston, Louisiana,
Zip 71270–5914, tel. 318/232–7700; Chad Conner, Administrator) **A**1 10 19 **S**
Community Health Systems, Inc., Franklin, TN
Primary Contact: David Fuller, Interim Chief Executive Officer
CFO: Michael Lockridge, Chief Financial Officer
CMO: Derek McClusky M.D., Chief of Staff
CIO: Heather Nolan, Director Information Services
CHR: Tonya Duggan, Director Human Resources
CNO: Ronnie Ursin R.N., Chief Nursing Officer
Web address: www.northernlouisianamedicalcenter.com
Control: Other not–for–profit (including NFP Corporation) **Service**: General
medical and surgical

Staffed Beds: 104

☒ **RUSTON REGIONAL SPECIALTY HOSPITAL (192022)**, 1401 Ezell Street,
Zip 71270–7218; tel. 318/251–3126, (Nonreporting) **A**1 10
Primary Contact: Mark J. Rice, Administrator
Web address: www.lifecare–hospitals.com/hospital.php?id=19
Control: Corporation, Investor–owned (for–profit) **Service**: Acute long–term care
hospital

Staffed Beds: 55

SERENITY SPRINGS SPECIALTY HOSPITAL (194074), 1495 Frazier Road,
Zip 71270–1632; tel. 318/202–3860 **A**10 **F**98 103 104 130
Primary Contact: Adrian Williams, Chief Executive Officer
Web address: www.serenityhospital.com
Control: Corporation, Investor–owned (for–profit) **Service**: Psychiatric

Staffed Beds: 18 **Admissions**: 664 **Census**: 15 **Outpatient Visits**: 0 **Births**: 0

SAINT FRANCISVILLE—West Feliciana Parish

☒ **WEST FELICIANA PARISH HOSPITAL (191306)**, 5266 Commerce Street,
Zip 70775, Mailing Address: P.O.Box 368, 70775–0368; tel. 225/635–3811 **A**1
10 18 **F**3 7 34 40 57 59 68 77 93 104 107 110 111 114 119 128 129 133
143 148 **P**5
Primary Contact: Lee Chastant, Chief Executive Officer
CFO: Linda Harvey, Chief Financial Officer
CHR: Neta F Leake, Administrative Assistant Human Resources
CNO: Angela Noble, Director of Nursing
Web address: www.wfph.org
Control: Hospital district or authority, Government, Nonfederal **Service**: General
medical and surgical

Staffed Beds: 22 **Admissions**: 60 **Census**: 1 **Outpatient Visits**: 21906
Births: 0 **Total Expense ($000)**: 18094 **Payroll Expense ($000)**: 7243
Personnel: 126

SHREVEPORT—Caddo Parish

☐ **BRENTWOOD HOSPITAL (194020)**, 1006 Highland Avenue, Zip 71101–4103;
tel. 318/678–7500, (Nonreporting) **A**1 3 10 **S** Universal Health Services, Inc.,
King of Prussia, PA
Primary Contact: William Weaver, Chief Executive Officer
COO: Charles Lee, Director Clinical Operations
CFO: Kae Bell, Chief Financial Officer
CMO: ColonelDaniel Feeney M.D., Medical Director
CHR: Talicia Johnson, Director Human Resources
CNO: Ravon Dominique, Chief Nursing Officer
Web address: www.brentwoodbehavioral.com
Control: Corporation, Investor–owned (for–profit) **Service**: Psychiatric

Staffed Beds: 172

☒ **CHRISTUS HEALTH SHREVEPORT–BOSSIER (190041)**, 1453 East Bert Kouns
Industrial Loop, Zip 71105–6800; tel. 318/681–5000, (Includes CHRISTUS
HIGHLAND MEDICAL CENTER, 1453 East Bert Kouns Industrial Loop, Shreveport,
Louisiana, Zip 71105–6050, tel. 318/681–5000; Isaac Palmer, Chief Executive
Officer) **A**1 2 5 10 **F**3 11 12 13 15 17 18 20 22 24 26 28 29 30 31 32 34 35
40 45 46 47 48 49 50 53 54 55 56 57 58 59 61 64 70 72 73 74 75 76 77 78
79 80 81 82 84 85 86 87 90 93 96 97 102 107 108 110 111 114 115 119
120 121 123 124 126 130 131 132 134 135 146 147 148 149 **S** CHRISTUS
Health, Irving, TX
Primary Contact: Isaac Palmer, Chief Executive Officer
CFO: Scott Merryman, Chief Financial Officer
CMO: Marisa Johnson M.D., Vice President Medical Affairs
CIO: Mary Merryman, Regional Director Information Management
CHR: Wendy Chandler, Vice President Human Resources
CNO: Ginger Disante, Chief Nursing Executive
Web address: www.christushealthsb.org
Control: Church operated, Nongovernment, not–for–profit **Service**: General
medical and surgical

Staffed Beds: 185 **Admissions**: 7767 **Census**: 98 **Outpatient Visits**:
128162 **Births**: 629 **Total Expense ($000)**: 174742 **Payroll Expense
($000)**: 48852 **Personnel**: 767

☒ **LIFECARE HOSPITALS OF SHREVEPORT (192011)**, 9320 Linwood Avenue,
Zip 71106–7003; tel. 318/688–8504, (Nonreporting) (Includes LIFECARE
HOSPITALS OF SHREVEPORT–WILLIS KNIGHTON, 8001 Youree Drive, Shreveport,
Louisiana, Zip 71115–2302, tel. 318/681–5000; Keith Cox, Chief Executive
Officer and Administrator; LIFECARE HOSPITALS OF SOUTH SHREVEPORT–WILLIS
KNIGHTON NORTH, 2550 Kings Highway, Shreveport, Louisiana, Zip 71103–3922,
tel. 318/681–5000; Keith Cox, Chief Executive Officer and Administrator) **A**1 10 **S**
LifeCare Management Services, Plano, TX
Primary Contact: Brent Martin, Administrator
Web address: www.lifecare–hospitals.com
Control: Corporation, Investor–owned (for–profit) **Service**: Acute long–term care
hospital

Staffed Beds: 119

☒ **OVERTON BROOKS VETERANS AFFAIRS MEDICAL CENTER**, 510 East
Stoner Avenue, Zip 71101–4295; tel. 318/221–8411, (Nonreporting) **A**1 2 3 5 **S**
Department of Veterans Affairs, Washington, DC
Primary Contact: Richard Crockett, Director
CFO: Kim Lane, Chief Fiscal Service
CIO: Janey Taylor, Chief Information and Technology
CHR: Michael L Palmier, Chief Human Resources Management
Web address: www.shreveport.va.gov/
Control: Veterans Affairs, Government, federal **Service**: General medical and
surgical

Staffed Beds: 100

PHYSICIANS BEHAVIORAL HOSPITAL (194094), 2025 Desoto Street,
Zip 71103–4717; tel. 318/550–0520 (Nonreporting) **A**10
Primary Contact: Allison Cooper, Administrator
Control: Corporation, Investor–owned (for–profit) **Service**: Psychiatric

Staffed Beds: 12

☐ **PROMISE HOSPITAL OF LOUISIANA – SHREVEPORT CAMPUS (192010)**,
1800 Irving Place, Zip 71101–4608; tel. 318/425–4096, (Includes PROMISE
HOSPITAL OF LOUISIANA – BOSSIER CITY CAMPUS, 2525 Viking Drive, Bossier
City, Louisiana, Zip 71111–2103, tel. 318/841–2525) (Nonreporting) **A**1 3 10 **S**
Promise Healthcare, Boca Raton, FL
Primary Contact: Rick Stockton, Chief Executive Officer
Web address: www.promise–shreveport.com
Control: Corporation, Investor–owned (for–profit) **Service**: Acute long–term care
hospital

Staffed Beds: 146

PROMISE SPECIALTY HOSPITAL OF SHREVEPORT See Promise Hospital Of
Louisiana – Shreveport Campus

LA

SHRINERS HOSPITALS FOR CHILDREN–SHREVEPORT (193301), 3100 Samford Avenue, Zip 71103–4289; tel. 318/222–5704 **A**1 3 5 10 **F**34 50 55 59 64 68 77 79 81 85 89 93 94 119 130 131 146 **S** Shriners Hospitals for Children, Tampa, FL
Primary Contact: Garry Kim. Green, FACHE, Administrator
CFO: Clarissa Brown–Smith, Director Fiscal Services
CMO: John A. Fox M.D., Chief of Staff
CIO: Michael Lyons, Regional Information Systems Director
CHR: Rena Arbuthnot, Director Human Resources
CNO: Kathleen A. Redler, Director Patient Care Services
Web address: www.shrinershospitalsforchildren.org/Hospitals/Locations/Shreveport.aspx
Control: Other not–for–profit (including NFP Corporation) **Service**: Children's orthopedic

Staffed Beds: 45 **Admissions:** 247 **Census:** 2 **Outpatient Visits:** 15961 **Births:** 0 **Personnel:** 189

SPECIALISTS HOSPITAL – SHREVEPORT (190278), 1500 Line Avenue, Zip 71101–4639; tel. 318/213–3800 (Nonreporting) **A**10
Primary Contact: Kandi Moore, Administrator
CFO: Daniel Montgomery, Chief Financial Officer
CNO: Mary Virginia Loftus, Chief Nursing Officer
Web address: www.specialistshospitalshreveport.com/
Control: Corporation, Investor–owned (for–profit) **Service**: Orthopedic

Staffed Beds: 15

UNIVERSITY HEALTH SHREVEPORT (190098), 1501 Kings Highway, Zip 71103–4228, Mailing Address: P.O.Box 33932, 71130–3932; tel. 318/675–5000, (Includes CHILDREN'S HOSPITAL OF SHREVEPORT, 1501 Kings Highway, Shreveport, Louisiana, Zip 71103–4228, PO Box 33932, 71130–3932, tel. 318/675–5000) **A**2 3 5 10 **F**3 13 15 16 18 19 20 21 22 23 24 25 26 27 29 30 31 32 34 39 40 41 43 45 46 47 48 49 50 51 54 59 60 61 64 65 66 70 72 73 75 76 77 78 79 81 82 85 87 88 89 93 98 102 104 107 108 109 110 111 112 114 115 116 117 118 119 120 121 123 126 129 130 131 135 146 147 148 **P**1 **S** University Health System, Shreveport, LA
Primary Contact: Mark Randolph, President
COO: Betty Johnson, Associate Administrator
CFO: Harold White, Vice Chancellor
CMO: Kevin Sittig M.D., Senior Associate Dean and Chief Medical Officer
CIO: Marcus Hobgood, Director Information Services
CHR: David Fuqua, Director Human Resources Management
Web address: www.lsuhscshreveport.edu
Control: Other not–for–profit (including NFP Corporation) **Service**: General medical and surgical

Staffed Beds: 395 **Admissions:** 18473 **Census:** 293 **Outpatient Visits:** 312000 **Births:** 1470 **Total Expense ($000):** 571492 **Payroll Expense ($000):** 183427 **Personnel:** 3229

WILLIS–KNIGHTON MEDICAL CENTER (190111), 2600 Greenwood Road, Zip 71103–3908, Mailing Address: P.O.Box 32600, 71130–2600; tel. 318/212–4600, (Includes WILLIS–KNIGHTON PIERREMONT HEALTH CENTER, 8001 Youree Drive, Shreveport, Louisiana, Zip 71115, tel. 318/212–3000; WILLIS–KNIGHTON SOUTH – THE CENTER FOR WOMEN'S HEALTH, 2510 Bert Kouns Industrial Loop, Shreveport, Louisiana, Zip 71118, tel. 318/212–5000; Keri Elrod, Administrator) (Total facility includes 24 beds in nursing home–type unit) **A**1 2 3 5 7 10 **F**3 4 5 7 8 12 13 15 17 18 20 22 24 26 28 29 30 31 32 33 39 40 44 45 46 47 48 49 50 51 52 53 54 55 56 57 59 60 62 63 64 65 66 68 70 72 74 75 76 77 78 79 81 82 84 85 86 87 88 89 90 91 92 93 94 96 97 98 99 100 101 102 103 104 106 107 108 109 110 111 112 114 115 116 117 118 119 120 121 122 123 124 125 127 128 129 130 131 132 134 135 138 139 142 143 144 145 147 148 149 **P**7 **S** Willis–Knighton Health System, Shreveport, LA
Primary Contact: James K. Elrod, FACHE, Chief Executive Officer
COO: Charles D Daigle, Senior Vice President and Chief Operating Officer
CMO: Dan Moller M.D., Chief Medical Officer
CHR: Jaf Fielder, Vice President and Administrator
CNO: Debbie D Olds R.N., MSN, Director of Nursing
Web address: www.wkhs.com
Control: Other not–for–profit (including NFP Corporation) **Service**: General medical and surgical

Staffed Beds: 752 **Admissions:** 43977 **Census:** 506 **Outpatient Visits:** 390389 **Births:** 2732 **Personnel:** 5197

SLIDELL—St. Tammany Parish

NORTHSHORE REGIONAL MEDICAL CENTER See Ochsner Medical Center – North Shore

OCHSNER MEDICAL CENTER – NORTH SHORE (190204), 100 Medical Center Drive, Zip 70461–5520; tel. 985/649–7070 **A**1 10 **F**3 12 15 17 18 20 22 24 26 29 30 31 34 35 38 40 41 44 45 46 49 50 51 57 59 60 61 64 68 70 72 74 75 77 78 79 81 84 85 86 87 88 89 90 91 93 95 96 97 102 107 108 110 111 114 116 117 118 119 126 130 132 135 146 147 148 **S** Ochsner Health System, New Orleans, LA
Primary Contact: John William Bill"". Davis, Chief Executive Officer
CFO: Forrest Whichard, Chief Financial Officer
CMO: James Newcomb M.D., Vice President Medical
CHR: Terri Joseph–Taylor, Chief Human Resource Manager
CNO: Cheryl Woods, Chief Nursing Officer
Web address: www.ochsner.org/locations/ochsner–medical–center–north–shore/
Control: Other not–for–profit (including NFP Corporation) **Service**: General medical and surgical

Staffed Beds: 165 **Admissions:** 4595 **Census:** 59 **Outpatient Visits:** 85629 **Births:** 0 **Total Expense ($000):** 86554 **Payroll Expense ($000):** 34937 **Personnel:** 611

SLIDELL MEMORIAL HOSPITAL (190040), 1001 Gause Boulevard, Zip 70458–2987; tel. 985/280–2200 **A**1 2 3 5 10 **F**3 11 13 15 17 18 20 22 24 26 28 29 30 31 32 34 35 40 45 47 49 54 56 57 59 62 64 65 70 72 75 76 78 79 81 82 85 86 87 90 91 93 96 97 102 107 108 110 111 114 115 116 117 118 119 120 121 124 129 130 132 135 **S** Ochsner Health System, New Orleans, LA
Primary Contact: John William Bill"". Davis, Chief Executive Officer
COO: Bruce Clement, Chief Operating Officer
CFO: Sandy Badinger, Chief Financial Officer
CMO: James Newcomb M.D., Vice President Medical Affairs
CNO: Lynn Strain R.N., MSN, Chief Nursing Officer
Web address: www.slidellmemorial.org
Control: Hospital district or authority, Government, Nonfederal **Service**: General medical and surgical

Staffed Beds: 175 **Admissions:** 7495 **Census:** 81 **Outpatient Visits:** 134178 **Births:** 1340 **Total Expense ($000):** 159555 **Payroll Expense ($000):** 64224

SOUTHERN SURGICAL HOSPITAL (190270), 1700 Lindberg Drive, Zip 70458–8062; tel. 985/641–0600 **A**1 10 **F**3 8 12 17 18 26 29 34 35 45 51 57 59 60 64 67 68 70 75 76 79 80 81 82 85 86 87 89 107 111 114 119 130 131 132 135 **P**5
Primary Contact: Michael J. Pisciotta, Chief Executive Officer
CFO: Michael J Maurin, Chief Financial Officer
CMO: J Gosey M.D., Medical Director
CIO: Buddy Graves, Chief Information Officer
CHR: Lorrie Alfred, Director Human Resources
Web address: www.sshla.com/
Control: Partnership, Investor–owned (for–profit) **Service**: Surgical

Staffed Beds: 37 **Admissions:** 1211 **Census:** 14 **Outpatient Visits:** 5206 **Births:** 0

STERLING SURGICAL HOSPITAL (190256), 989 Robert Boulevard, Zip 70458–2009; tel. 985/690–8200 (Nonreporting) **A**10
Primary Contact: Christopher W. Daniel, Administrator
Web address: www.sterlingsurgical.net/
Control: Corporation, Investor–owned (for–profit) **Service**: Surgical

Staffed Beds: 10

SPRINGHILL—Webster Parish

SPRINGHILL MEDICAL CENTER (190088), 2001 Doctors Drive, Zip 71075–4526, Mailing Address: P.O.Box 920, 71075–0920; tel. 318/539–1000 **A**1 10 20 **F**3 15 18 26 29 30 32 34 35 40 45 47 48 49 50 54 56 57 59 64 65 66 68 70 75 76 81 85 86 87 89 93 97 98 103 107 108 110 111 114 119 127 129 130 131 133 135 146 148 149 **P**6 **S** Willis–Knighton Health System, Shreveport, LA
Primary Contact: Vince Sedminik, Chief Executive Officer
CFO: David Sanders, Chief Financial Officer
CMO: Jerry W. Sessions M.D., Chief Medical Staff
CIO: Brian Griffin, Director Information Services
CHR: Ashley Ortego, Director Human Resources and Marketing
CNO: Dana Jones R.N., Chief Nursing Officer
Web address: www.smccare.com
Control: Other not–for–profit (including NFP Corporation) **Service**: General medical and surgical

Staffed Beds: 58 **Admissions:** 1044 **Census:** 13 **Births:** 0

SULPHUR—Calcasieu Parish

☐ **CORNERSTONE HOSPITAL OF SOUTHWEST LOUISIANA (192013)**, 703 Cypress Street, Zip 70663–5053; tel. 337/310–6000, (Nonreporting) **A**1 10 **S** Cornerstone Healthcare Group, Dallas, TX
Primary Contact: Michael Lombard, President
CFO: Amy Bryant, Chief Financial Officer
Web address: www.chghospitals.com/sulphur/
Control: Partnership, Investor–owned (for–profit) **Service:** Acute long–term care hospital

Staffed Beds: 30

☐ **WEST CALCASIEU CAMERON HOSPITAL (190013)**, 701 Cypress Street, Zip 70663–5000, Mailing Address: P.O.Box 2509, 70664–2509; tel. 337/527–7034 **A**1 10 **F**3 7 8 11 13 15 18 20 22 26 28 29 30 31 34 35 37 38 40 44 45 46 50 51 53 54 57 59 62 65 68 70 75 76 77 78 79 81 85 86 87 89 91 93 94 96 97 107 108 110 111 114 115 118 119 127 129 130 132 134 135 141 145 146 147 148 149
Primary Contact: Janie Fruge, R.N., MSN, FACHE, Chief Executive Officer
CFO: Jobie James, Chief Financial Officer
CIO: Trey Rion, Chief Information Officer
CHR: Christi Kingsley, Vice President Human Resources
CNO: Brenda Quesnel R.N., Vice President of Patient Care and Chief Nursing Officer
Web address: www.wcch.com
Control: Hospital district or authority, Government, Nonfederal **Service:** General medical and surgical

Staffed Beds: 79 Admissions: 2754 Census: 28 Outpatient Visits: 113729 Births: 333 Total Expense ($000): 74602 Payroll Expense ($000): 30658 Personnel: 644

TALLULAH—Madison Parish

MADISON PARISH HOSPITAL (191314), 900 Johnson Street, Zip 71282–4537; tel. 318/574–2374, (Nonreporting) **A**10 18
Primary Contact: Ted Topolewski, Chief Executive Officer
CFO: W Robert Laurents CPA, Chief Financial Officer
CIO: Charles Whitaker, Director Information Technology
CHR: Chasity Whitaker, Administrative Assistant
Web address: www.madisonparishhospital.com
Control: Other not–for–profit (including NFP Corporation) **Service:** General medical and surgical

Staffed Beds: 25

THIBODAUX—Lafourche Parish

☒ △ **THIBODAUX REGIONAL MEDICAL CENTER (190004)**, 602 North Acadia Road, Zip 70301–4847, Mailing Address: P.O.Box 1118, 70302–1118; tel. 985/447–5500 **A**1 2 7 10 **F**3 8 11 12 13 15 18 19 20 22 24 28 29 30 31 32 34 39 40 46 49 50 53 57 59 62 64 70 73 74 75 76 78 79 81 82 85 86 87 89 90 92 93 96 97 98 103 104 107 108 110 111 115 116 117 119 120 121 123 124 126 127 129 130 131 132 134 135 146 147 148 149
Primary Contact: Greg K. Stock, FACHE, Chief Executive Officer
COO: Scott Flowers, Vice President Professional Services
CFO: Steve C Gaubert, Chief Financial Officer
CMO: Allen Vander M.D., Chief Medical Staff
CIO: Bernie Clement, Chief Information Officer
CHR: Eric Degravelle, Director Human Resources
Web address: www.thibodaux.com
Control: Hospital district or authority, Government, Nonfederal **Service:** General medical and surgical

Staffed Beds: 154 Admissions: 8073 Census: 109 Outpatient Visits: 178091 Births: 1142 Total Expense ($000): 156528 Payroll Expense ($000): 66423 Personnel: 1032

VIDALIA—Concordia Parish

☐ **PROMISE HOSPITAL OF MISS LOU (192028)**, 209 Front Street, Zip 71373–2837; tel. 318/336–6500 **A**1 10 **F**1 29 60 64 85 93 130 143 148 **S** Promise Healthcare, Boca Raton, FL
Primary Contact: Michael Harrell, R.N., Chief Executive Officer
COO: Howard B Koslow, President and Chief Executive Officer
CFO: James Hopwood, Chief Financial Officer
CMO: Randy Tillman M.D., Chief Medical Staff
CIO: Robert Greene, Director Information Technology
CHR: Roxan Houghton, Director Human Resources
CNO: Regetta Woods, Chief Nursing Officer and Chief Clinical Officer
Web address: www.promise–misslou.com
Control: Corporation, Investor–owned (for–profit) **Service:** Acute long–term care hospital

Staffed Beds: 40 Admissions: 474 Census: 28 Outpatient Visits: 4424 Births: 0 Personnel: 77

PROMISE HOSPITAL OF MISS LOU(Nonreporting) **A**1 10 **F**1 29 60 64 85 93 130 143 148
COO: Howard B Koslow, President and Chief Executive Officer
CFO: James Hopwood, Chief Financial Officer
CMO: Randy Tillman M.D., Chief Medical Staff
CIO: Robert Greene, Director Information Technology
CHR: Roxan Houghton, Director Human Resources
CNO: Regetta Woods, Chief Nursing Officer and Chief Clinical Officer
Web address: www.promise–misslou.com

VILLE PLATTE—Evangeline Parish

☒ **MERCY REGIONAL MEDICAL CENTER (190167)**, 800 East Main Street, Zip 70586–4618; tel. 337/363–5684, (Nonreporting) (Includes ACADIAN MEDICAL CENTER, 3501 Highway 190, Eunice, Louisiana, Zip 70535–5129, tel. 337/580–7500; Scott M Smith, Chief Executive Officer) **A**1 10 **S** LifePoint Health, Brentwood, TN
Primary Contact: Scott M. Smith, Chief Executive Officer
CFO: Janice G Jones, Interim Chief Financial Officer, Controller and Compliance Officer
CMO: Zebediah Stearns M.D., Chief of Staff
CIO: Courtney Bieber, Director Information Systems
CHR: Cody Ardoin, Director Human Resources
CNO: Sandy Morein, Chief Nursing Officer
Web address: www.mercyregionalmedicalcenter.com
Control: Corporation, Investor–owned (for–profit) **Service:** General medical and surgical

Staffed Beds: 109

VIVIAN—Caddo Parish

NORTH CADDO MEDICAL CENTER (191304), 1000 South Spruce Street, Zip 71082–3232, Mailing Address: P.O.Box 792, 71082–0792; tel. 318/375–3235, (Nonreporting) **A**3 5 10 18
Primary Contact: David C. Jones, Administrator
CFO: Carol Reisz, Chief Financial Officer
CMO: John H Haynes M.D., Jr, Chief of Medical Staff
CIO: Allyson Allums, Director Medical Records
CHR: Lanell Audirsch, Administrative Assistant
Web address: www.northcaddomedicalcenter.com
Control: Hospital district or authority, Government, Nonfederal **Service:** General medical and surgical

Staffed Beds: 27

WEST MONROE—Ouachita Parish

ALLEGIANCE BEHAVIORAL HEALTH CENTERS OF MONROE (194087), 222 Bell Lane, Suite 3, Zip 71291–6302; tel. 318/329–2174, (Includes ALLEGIANCE HEALTH CENTER OF RUSTON, 1401 Ezell Street, Ruston, Louisiana, Zip 71270–7218, tel. 318/255–8085; Chris Young, Chief Executive Officer) (Nonreporting)
Primary Contact: Chris Young, Chief Executive Officer
Web address: www.ahmgt.com
Control: Corporation, Investor–owned (for–profit) **Service:** Psychiatric

Staffed Beds: 38

☐ **CORNERSTONE HOSPITAL–WEST MONROE (192031)**, 6198 Cypress Street, Zip 71291–9010; tel. 318/396–5600 (Nonreporting) **A**1 10 **S** Cornerstone Healthcare Group, Dallas, TX
Primary Contact: Chris Simpson, Chief Executive Officer
COO: Jay Quintana, Vice President Operations
CFO: Kurt Schultz, Chief Financial Officer
CMO: Khaled Shafici M.D., President Medical Staff
CIO: Adam Davis, Chief Information Officer
CHR: Dan Perkins, Corporate Director Human Resources
Web address: www.chghospitals.com/chwm.html
Control: Corporation, Investor–owned (for–profit) **Service:** Acute long–term care hospital

Staffed Beds: 40

Hospital, Medicare Provider Number, Address, Telephone, Approval, Facility, and Physician Codes, Health Care System

★ American Hospital Association (AHA) membership   ○ Healthcare Facilities Accreditation Program   ⇑ Center for Improvement in Healthcare Quality Accreditation
☐ The Joint Commission accreditation   ◇ DNV Healthcare Inc. accreditation   △ Commission on Accreditation of Rehabilitation Facilities (CARF) accreditation

LA

⇑ **GLENWOOD REGIONAL MEDICAL CENTER (190160)**, 503 McMillan Road, Zip 71291–5327; tel. 318/329–4200, (Includes GLENWOOD SURGERY CENTER, 1275 Glenwood Drive, West Monroe, Louisiana, Zip 71291–5539, 503 McMillan Road, 71291–5327, tel. 318/322–1339; Jeremy Tinnerello, MSN, R.N., Chief Executive Officer, Chief Operating Officer) (Total facility includes 14 beds in nursing home–type unit) **A**10 21 **F**3 8 12 13 15 17 18 20 22 24 26 28 29 30 31 34 35 37 38 40 41 45 46 47 48 49 50 51 54 55 56 57 58 59 60 61 62 63 64 68 70 71 72 74 75 76 78 79 81 82 83 84 85 86 87 89 90 91 92 93 94 96 97 98 100 101 102 103 104 105 107 108 110 111 113 114 115 116 117 119 120 121 126 128 129 130 131 132 134 144 146 147 148 149 **S** IASIS Healthcare, Franklin, TN
Primary Contact: Jeremy Tinnerello, MSN, R.N., Chief Executive Officer, Chief Operating Officer
COO: Jeremy Tinnerello MSN, R.N., Chief Executive Officer, Chief Operating Officer
CFO: Lisa Bradley CPA, Chief Financial Officer
CMO: Steve McMahan M.D., Chief Medical Officer
CIO: Ronnie Maxwell, Director Information Systems
CHR: Jan Walker, Director Human Resources
CNO: Daniel P. King MSN, R.N., Chief Nursing Officer
Web address: www.grmc.com
Control: Corporation, Investor–owned (for–profit) **Service**: General medical and surgical

Staffed Beds: 273 **Admissions:** 12769 **Census:** 177 **Outpatient Visits:** 64979 **Births:** 937	

LOUISIANA EXTENDED CARE HOSPITAL WEST MONROE (192055), 503 McMillan Road, 3rd Floor, Zip 71291–5327; tel. 318/329–4378 (Nonreporting) **A**10 **S** LHC Group, Lafayette, LA
Primary Contact: Cleta Munholland, Administrator
Control: Corporation, Investor–owned (for–profit) **Service**: Acute long–term care hospital

Staffed Beds: 18	

WINNFIELD—Winn Parish

□ **SPECIALTY HOSPITAL OF WINNFIELD (192052)**, 915 First Street, Zip 71483–2945; tel. 318/209–4507, (Nonreporting) **A**1 10
Primary Contact: Chuck Jurek, Interim Administrator and Chief Operating Officer
CFO: Chuck Jurek, Business Office Manager
CIO: Shamada Venzant, Manager Health Information
Control: Corporation, Investor–owned (for–profit) **Service**: Acute long–term care hospital

Staffed Beds: 20	

WINN PARISH MEDICAL CENTER (190090), 301 West Boundary Street, Zip 71483–3427, Mailing Address: P.O.Box 152, 71483–0152; tel. 318/648–3000, (Nonreporting) **A**10
Primary Contact: Bryan Bogle, Chief Executive Officer
CFO: Suzette Fatula, Chief Financial Officer
CMO: Mark Shelton, Chief of Staff
CHR: Ashley S Files, Director Human Resources and Public Relations and Marketing
CNO: Toby Wise, Chief Nursing Officer
Web address: www.winnparishmedical.com
Control: Partnership, Investor–owned (for–profit) **Service**: General medical and surgical

Staffed Beds: 60	

WINNSBORO—Franklin Parish

★ **FRANKLIN MEDICAL CENTER (190140)**, 2106 Loop Road, Zip 71295–3344, Mailing Address: P.O.Box 1300, 71295–1300; tel. 318/435–9411, (Nonreporting) **A**3 10
Primary Contact: Blake Kramer, Chief Executive Officer
CFO: William E Page CPA, Chief Financial Officer
CMO: Jay Busby M.D., President Medical Staff
CIO: Judy Ogden, Director Information Technology
Web address: www.fmc–cares.com
Control: Hospital district or authority, Government, Nonfederal **Service**: General medical and surgical

Staffed Beds: 43	

ZACHARY—East Baton Rouge Parish

AMG SPECIALTY HOSPITAL–ZACHARY, 4601 McHugh Road, Zip 70791–5348; tel. 225/683–1600 (Nonreporting) **S** AMG Integrated Healthcare Management, Lafayette, LA
Primary Contact: April Ebeling, Chief Executive Officer
Web address: www.amgzachary.com/
Control: Corporation, Investor–owned (for–profit) **Service**: Acute long–term care hospital

Staffed Beds: 16	

⊞ **LANE REGIONAL MEDICAL CENTER (190020)**, 6300 Main Street, Zip 70791–4037; tel. 225/658–4000, (Total facility includes 38 beds in nursing home–type unit) **A**1 10 **F**3 5 8 11 13 15 18 20 22 26 29 34 35 36 39 40 45 46 50 54 56 57 59 62 64 67 70 73 75 76 77 79 80 81 85 87 90 107 108 110 111 114 115 119 130 144 146 148 **P**6
Primary Contact: Larry Meese, Chief Executive Officer
COO: David Beck, Chief Operating Officer
CFO: Mark Anderson, Chief Financial Officer
CMO: Thomas Trahan M.D., Chief of Medical Staff
CIO: Paul Murphy, Chief Information Officer
CNO: Staci Sullivan R.N., Chief Nursing Officer
Web address: www.lanermc.org
Control: Hospital district or authority, Government, Nonfederal **Service**: General medical and surgical

Staffed Beds: 179 **Admissions:** 4654 **Census:** 96 **Outpatient Visits:** 133385 **Births:** 558 **Total Expense ($000):** 83960 **Payroll Expense ($000):** 34208 **Personnel:** 701	

Many Facility Codes have changed. Please refer to the AHA Guide Code Chart. © 2017 AHA Guide

MAINE

ME

AUGUSTA—Kennebec County

✠ **MAINE VETERANS AFFAIRS MEDICAL CENTER**, 1 VA Center, Zip 04330–6719; tel. 207/623–8411 **A**1 3 **F**3 5 8 18 20 28 29 30 31 33 34 35 36 38 39 40 44 45 54 56 57 58 59 60 61 62 63 64 65 66 68 70 71 74 75 77 78 79 81 82 83 84 85 87 93 94 97 98 100 102 103 104 105 107 108 111 114 115 118 119 127 129 130 132 135 143 146 147 148 149 **P**6 **S** Department of Veterans Affairs, Washington, DC
Primary Contact: Ryan S. Lilly, Director
CFO: Daniel Howard, Chief Financial Officer
CMO: Timothy J Richardson M.D., Chief of Staff
CIO: Richard McNaughton, Chief Information Management Service
CHR: Christine Miller, Chief Human Resources Management Services
Web address: www.maine.va.gov/
Control: Veterans Affairs, Government, federal **Service**: General medical and surgical

Staffed Beds: 167 **Admissions**: 2610 **Census**: 44 **Outpatient Visits**: 459677 **Births**: 0 **Total Expense ($000)**: 319141 **Payroll Expense ($000)**: 95518 **Personnel**: 1478

✠ **MAINEGENERAL MEDICAL CENTER (200039)**, 35 Medical Center Parkway, Zip 4330; tel. 207/626–1000, (Includes MAINEGENERAL MEDICAL CENTER-AUGUSTA CAMPUS, 35 Medical Center Parkway, Augusta, Maine, Zip 04330–9988, tel. 207/626–1000; Chuck Hays, President and Chief Executive Officer) **A**1 2 10 19 **F**2 3 4 5 8 11 12 13 15 17 18 20 28 29 30 31 34 35 36 40 42 44 45 46 47 48 49 50 51 54 55 56 57 58 59 64 65 70 73 74 75 76 77 78 79 81 82 84 85 86 87 89 90 92 93 96 97 98 100 101 102 103 104 107 108 110 115 116 117 118 119 120 121 123 124 126 129 130 131 132 134 135 144 145 146 147 148 **P**8
Primary Contact: Chuck Hays, President and Chief Executive Officer
COO: Paul Stein, Chief Operating Officer
CFO: Terry Brann, Chief Financial Officer
CMO: Steve Diaz M.D., Chief Medical Officer
CIO: Daniel Burgess, Chief Information Officer
CHR: Rebecca Lamey, Vice President Human Resources
CNO: Jennifer Riggs R.N., Chief Nurse Officer
Web address: www.mainegeneral.org
Control: Other not–for–profit (including NFP Corporation) **Service**: General medical and surgical

Staffed Beds: 200 **Admissions**: 9634 **Census**: 156 **Outpatient Visits**: 749080 **Births**: 1023 **Total Expense ($000)**: 451708 **Payroll Expense ($000)**: 188112 **Personnel**: 3117

MAINEGENERAL MEDICAL CENTER–AUGUSTA CAMPUS See Mainegeneral Medical Center

☐ **RIVERVIEW PSYCHIATRIC CENTER (204007)**, 250 Arsenal Street, Zip 04330–5742; tel. 207/624–3900, (Nonreporting) **A**1 10
Primary Contact: Rodney Bouffard, Superintendent
COO: David Lovejoy, Chief Operations Officer
CFO: Samantha Kavanaugh, Chief Financial Officer
CMO: Brendan Kirby M.D., Medical Director
CHR: Aimee Rice, Human Resources Manager
CNO: Roland Pushard, Director of Nursing
Web address: www.state.me.us/dhhs/riverview
Control: State, Government, Nonfederal **Service**: Psychiatric

Staffed Beds: 92

VETERANS AFFAIRS MEDICAL CENTER See Maine Veterans Affairs Medical Center

BANGOR—Penobscot County

☐ **DOROTHEA DIX PSYCHIATRIC CENTER (204004)**, 656 State Street, Zip 04401–5609, Mailing Address: P.O.Box 926, 04402–0926; tel. 207/941–4000, (Nonreporting) **A**1 10
Primary Contact: Carolyn Dimek, Acting Superintendent
CMO: Michelle Gardner M.D., Clinical Director
CHR: Tamra Hanson, Human Resource Manager
CNO: Christine Bellatty, Acting Director of Nursing
Web address: www.maine.gov/dhhs/ddpc/index.shtml
Control: State, Government, Nonfederal **Service**: Psychiatric

Staffed Beds: 51

✠ **EASTERN MAINE MEDICAL CENTER (200033)**, 489 State Street, Zip 04401–6674, Mailing Address: P.O.Box 404, 04402–0404; tel. 207/973–7000 **A**1 2 3 5 10 13 **F**3 11 12 13 15 17 18 19 20 22 24 26 27 28 29 30 31 32 34 36 37 39 40 43 44 45 46 47 48 49 50 51 53 54 55 57 58 59 61 64 70 72 74 75 76 77 78 79 81 82 84 85 86 87 88 89 90 92 93 94 96 97 102 107 108 110 111 114 115 117 118 119 120 121 123 124 126 129 130 131 132 144 145 146 147 148 149 **P**6 **S** Eastern Maine Healthcare Systems, Brewer, ME
Primary Contact: Donna Russell–Cook, FACHE, President
CMO: James Raczek M.D., Sr. Vice President of Operations and Chief Medical Officer
CIO: Catherine Bruno FACHE, Chief Information Officer
CHR: Greg Howat, Vice President Human Resources
Web address: www.emh.org
Control: Other not–for–profit (including NFP Corporation) **Service**: General medical and surgical

Staffed Beds: 367 **Admissions**: 18975 **Census**: 286 **Outpatient Visits**: 519003 **Births**: 1680 **Total Expense ($000)**: 746442 **Payroll Expense ($000)**: 297074 **Personnel**: 3418

✠ **ST. JOSEPH HOSPITAL (200001)**, 360 Broadway, Zip 04401–3979, Mailing Address: P.O.Box 403, 04402–0403; tel. 207/262–1000 **A**1 10 **F**3 8 15 18 29 30 31 35 40 45 48 49 51 55 56 57 64 70 75 79 81 84 85 86 87 97 107 108 110 114 118 119 129 130 132 135 146 147 148 149 **S** Covenant Health, Tewksbury, MA
Primary Contact: Mary Prybylo, President and Chief Executive Officer
CFO: Michael A. Hendrix Jr, Chief Financial Officer
CMO: William Wood M.D., Vice President Medical Affairs
CHR: Paige A Hagerstrom, System Director of Talent Management
CNO: Dianne Swandal R.N., MSN, Vice President Patient Care
Web address: www.sjhhealth.com
Control: Church operated, Nongovernment, not–for–profit **Service**: General medical and surgical

Staffed Beds: 84 **Admissions**: 4112 **Census**: 53 **Outpatient Visits**: 116586 **Births**: 0 **Total Expense ($000)**: 131802 **Payroll Expense ($000)**: 57372 **Personnel**: 809

✠ **THE ACADIA HOSPITAL (204006)**, 268 Stillwater Avenue, Zip 04401–3945, Mailing Address: P.O.Box 422, 04402–0422; tel. 207/973–6100 **A**1 10 **F**5 29 30 50 57 66 68 75 77 87 98 99 100 101 103 104 105 130 132 **P**6 **S** Eastern Maine Healthcare Systems, Brewer, ME
Primary Contact: Scott Oxley, President
CFO: Marie Suitter, Chief Financial Officer
CMO: Anthony Ng M.D., Vice President and Chief Medical Officer
CIO: Jeanne Paradis, Director Information Services
CHR: Paul Bolin, Vice President Human Resources
CNO: Wayne Steller, Vice President Chief Nursing Officer
Web address: www.acadiahospital.org
Control: Other not–for–profit (including NFP Corporation) **Service**: Psychiatric

Staffed Beds: 68 **Admissions**: 1399 **Census**: 56 **Outpatient Visits**: 112918 **Births**: 0 **Total Expense ($000)**: 52586 **Payroll Expense ($000)**: 28386 **Personnel**: 534

BAR HARBOR—Hancock County

★ **MOUNT DESERT ISLAND HOSPITAL (201304)**, 10 Wayman Lane, Zip 04609–1625, Mailing Address: P.O.Box 8, 04609–0008; tel. 207/288–5081 **A**5 10 18 **F**3 5 6 10 11 13 15 28 29 31 34 35 36 39 40 50 54 56 57 59 64 65 70 74 75 76 77 78 79 81 82 84 85 87 91 92 93 97 99 100 101 104 107 108 111 114 119 125 127 130 131 132 133 135 145 146 147 **P**5 6 7
Primary Contact: Arthur J. Blank, President and Chief Executive Officer
CFO: Christina Harding, Vice President Finance
CMO: Stuart Davidson, President Medical Staff
CIO: Bruce Donlin, Director Information Services
CHR: Joanne Harris, Director Human Resources
CNO: Karen Mueller R.N., Chief Nursing Officer
Web address: www.mdihospital.org
Control: Other not–for–profit (including NFP Corporation) **Service**: General medical and surgical

Staffed Beds: 25 **Admissions**: 884 **Census**: 8 **Outpatient Visits**: 183462 **Births**: 100 **Total Expense ($000)**: 51390 **Payroll Expense ($000)**: 23409 **Personnel**: 385

Hospital, Medicare Provider Number, Address, Telephone, Approval, Facility, and Physician Codes, Health Care System

★ American Hospital Association (AHA) membership
☐ The Joint Commission accreditation
○ Healthcare Facilities Accreditation Program
◇ DNV Healthcare Inc. accreditation
⇑ Center for Improvement in Healthcare Quality Accreditation
△ Commission on Accreditation of Rehabilitation Facilities (CARF) accreditation

ME

BELFAST—Waldo County

WALDO COUNTY GENERAL HOSPITAL (201312), 118 Northport Avenue, Zip 04915–6072, Mailing Address: P.O.Box 287, 04915–0287; tel. 207/338–2500, (Nonreporting) **A**10 18 **S** MaineHealth, Portland, ME
Primary Contact: Mark Fourre, Chief Executive Officer
CFO: Linda Drinkwater, Chief Financial Officer
CMO: Kent Clark M.D., Chief Medical Affairs and Quality
CIO: David Felton, Manager Information Systems
CHR: Karen Littlefield, Director Human Resources
CNO: Paula Delahanty, Regional Chief Nursing Officer
Web address: www.wcgh.org
Control: Other not–for–profit (including NFP Corporation) **Service:** General medical and surgical

Staffed Beds: 25

BIDDEFORD—York County

✠ **SOUTHERN MAINE HEALTH CARE – BIDDEFORD MEDICAL CENTER (200019)**, One Medical Center Drive, Zip 04005–9496, Mailing Address: P.O.Box 626, 04005–0626; tel. 207/283–7000, (Includes SOUTHERN MAINE HEALTH CARE – BIDDEFORD MEDICAL CENTER, One Medical Center Drive, Biddeford, Maine, Zip 04005–9496, P.O. Box 626, 04005–0626, tel. 207/283–7000; Edward J McGeachey, President and Chief Executive Officer) (Total facility includes 74 beds in nursing home–type unit) **A**1 2 10 **F**5 6 8 10 11 12 13 15 18 20 22 26 28 29 30 31 33 34 35 40 42 44 45 46 49 50 54 56 57 59 61 64 65 68 70 74 75 76 77 78 79 81 82 84 86 87 89 93 97 98 100 102 103 104 105 107 108 110 111 115 117 119 128 129 130 131 132 135 144 146 147 148 149 **P**6
Primary Contact: Edward J. McGeachey, President and Chief Executive Officer
COO: Patricia Aprile, Chief Operating Officer
CFO: Norman Belair, Senior Vice President and Chief Financial Officer
CMO: Michael Albaum M.D., Senior Vice President and Chief Medical Officer
CIO: Ralph Johnson, Chief Information Officer
CHR: Yvonne McAllister, Senior Director Human Resources
CNO: Joanna Salamone, Senior Vice President Clinical Services and Chief Nursing Officer
Web address: www.smhc.org
Control: Other not–for–profit (including NFP Corporation) **Service:** General medical and surgical

Staffed Beds: 196 **Admissions:** 10103 **Census:** 182 **Outpatient Visits:** 116990 **Births:** 601 **Total Expense ($000):** 269806 **Payroll Expense ($000):** 125961 **Personnel:** 1629

BLUE HILL—Hancock County

★ **BLUE HILL MEMORIAL HOSPITAL (201300)**, 57 Water Street, Zip 04614–5231, Mailing Address: P.O.Box 1029, 04614–1029; tel. 207/374–3400 **A**10 18 **F**8 15 18 28 29 31 32 33 34 35 44 45 50 51 57 59 64 65 66 75 78 79 80 81 82 85 86 87 91 93 96 97 107 110 119 130 132 133 135 146 147 148 **S** Eastern Maine Healthcare Systems, Brewer, ME
Primary Contact: John Ronan, President
CFO: Wendy Jones, Interim Chief Financial Officer
CHR: David Wheaton, Director Human Resources
CNO: Kathy Lirakis R.N., Chief Nursing Officer
Web address: www.bhmh.org
Control: Other not–for–profit (including NFP Corporation) **Service:** General medical and surgical

Staffed Beds: 23 **Admissions:** 643 **Census:** 11 **Outpatient Visits:** 185277 **Births:** 0 **Total Expense ($000):** 38324 **Payroll Expense ($000):** 17230 **Personnel:** 275

BRIDGTON—Cumberland County

★ **BRIDGTON HOSPITAL (201310)**, 10 Hospital Drive, Zip 04009–1148; tel. 207/647–6000 **A**3 10 18 **F**3 7 8 11 13 15 18 29 30 31 34 35 40 43 44 45 50 57 59 64 65 67 68 75 76 77 78 79 80 81 85 87 90 91 93 94 96 97 107 108 110 114 119 128 130 131 132 133 135 143 144 146 148 **P**8 **S** Central Maine Healthcare, Lewiston, ME
Primary Contact: R David. Frum, President
CMO: Alan Verrill M.D., President Medical Staff
CHR: Kirk Miklavic, Director Human Resources
Web address: www.bridgtonhospital.org
Control: Other not–for–profit (including NFP Corporation) **Service:** General medical and surgical

Staffed Beds: 22 **Admissions:** 897 **Census:** 12 **Outpatient Visits:** 159365 **Births:** 107 **Total Expense ($000):** 49069 **Payroll Expense ($000):** 20283 **Personnel:** 299

BRUNSWICK—Cumberland County

✠ **MID COAST HOSPITAL (200021)**, 123 Medical Center Drive, Zip 04011–2652; tel. 207/373–6000 **A**1 2 5 10 **F**3 5 11 12 13 15 18 20 28 29 30 31 32 34 35 36 39 40 41 44 45 46 47 48 51 53 54 56 57 58 59 61 64 66 68 70 74 75 76 77 78 79 81 82 84 85 86 87 89 92 93 97 98 103 105 107 108 110 111 115 118 119 129 130 131 132 134 135 144 146 147 148 **P**6
Primary Contact: Lois N. Skillings, R.N., MSN, President and Chief Executive Officer
COO: Philip A Ortolani, Vice President Operations
CFO: Robert N McCue, Vice President Finance
CMO: Scott Mills M.D., Vice President Medical Staff Administration and Chief Medical Officer
CIO: Gale Stoy, Manager Information Systems
CHR: Coleen M Farrell, Vice President Human Resources
CNO: Deborah MacLeod MS, R.N., Vice President Nursing and Patient Care Services
Web address: www.midcoasthealth.com
Control: Other not–for–profit (including NFP Corporation) **Service:** General medical and surgical

Staffed Beds: 93 **Admissions:** 4911 **Census:** 61 **Outpatient Visits:** 220609 **Births:** 596 **Total Expense ($000):** 174192 **Payroll Expense ($000):** 81429 **Personnel:** 1232

CALAIS—Washington County

★ **CALAIS REGIONAL HOSPITAL (201305)**, 24 Hospital Lane, Zip 04619–1398; tel. 207/454–7521 **A**10 18 **F**3 8 11 13 15 28 29 31 32 34 35 36 40 41 42 45 46 50 54 57 59 62 63 64 65 68 77 79 80 81 82 83 84 85 87 90 93 96 97 107 108 110 111 114 119 127 128 129 130 132 133 146 147 148 149 **S** QHR, Brentwood, TN
Primary Contact: Rodney Boula, Chief Executive Officer
CFO: Nancy Glidden, Chief Financial Officer
CMO: David Feiner M.D., Chief Staff
CIO: Dee Dee Travis, Director Community Relations
CHR: Kristi K Saunders, Director and Compliance Officer
CNO: Erika Marshall, Interim Chief Nursing Officer
Web address: www.calaishospital.com
Control: Other not–for–profit (including NFP Corporation) **Service:** General medical and surgical

Staffed Beds: 25 **Admissions:** 1136 **Census:** 12 **Outpatient Visits:** 39170 **Births:** 60 **Total Expense ($000):** 37227 **Payroll Expense ($000):** 21717 **Personnel:** 252

CARIBOU—Aroostook County

✠ **CARY MEDICAL CENTER (200031)**, 163 Van Buren Road, Suite 1, Zip 04736–3567; tel. 207/498–3111, (Total facility includes 9 beds in nursing home–type unit) **A**1 10 **F**3 8 11 13 15 28 29 31 32 34 35 36 38 40 43 44 51 53 54 56 57 59 61 64 67 68 70 75 76 77 78 79 81 82 84 85 86 87 89 90 93 97 107 108 111 115 118 119 121 130 131 132 133 146 147 148 **S** QHR, Brentwood, TN
Primary Contact: Kris A. Doody, R.N., Chief Executive Officer
COO: Shawn Anderson, Chief Operating Officer
CFO: Galen Dickinson, Chief Financial Officer
CMO: Regen Gallagher D.O., Chief Medical Officer
CIO: Dave Silsbee, Chief Information Officer
CHR: Paula A. Parent, Chief Nursing Officer and Director of Human Resources
CNO: Paula A. Parent, Chief Nursing Officer
Web address: www.carymedicalcenter.org
Control: City, Government, Nonfederal **Service:** General medical and surgical

Staffed Beds: 49 **Admissions:** 1654 **Census:** 29 **Outpatient Visits:** 74575 **Births:** 219 **Total Expense ($000):** 54069 **Payroll Expense ($000):** 21207 **Personnel:** 404

DAMARISCOTTA—Lincoln County

★ **LINCOLNHEALTH (201302)**, 35 Miles Street, Zip 04543–4047; tel. 207/563–1234, (Includes LINCOLNHEALTH MILES CAMPUS, 35 Miles Street, Damariscotta, Maine, Zip 04543–4047, tel. 207/563–1234; James W Donovan, President and Chief Executive Officer; LINCOLNHEALTH ST. ANDREWS CAMPUS, 6 St Andrews Lane, Boothbay Harbor, Maine, Zip 04538–1732, P O Box 417, 04538–0417, tel. 207/633–2121) (Total facility includes 66 beds in nursing home–type unit) **A**10 18 **F**3 11 13 15 29 30 32 34 35 40 43 44 45 50 57 59 64 65 67 70 75 76 79 81 85 86 87 93 96 97 107 108 110 111 114 115 118 119 127 128 130 132 133 135 144 146 147 148 149 **P**6 **S** MaineHealth, Portland, ME
Primary Contact: James W. Donovan, President and Chief Executive Officer
COO: Cynthia Wade R.N., RN, BSN,, Executive Vice President and Chief Operating Officer
CFO: Wayne Printy, Chief Financial Officer and Senior Vice President Finance
CMO: Mark Fourre, Senior Vice President and Chief Medical Officer
CIO: David Felton, Regional Chief Information Officer
CHR: Thomas R Girard, Vice President Human Resources
CNO: Christine Anderson, Chief Nursing Officer and Vice President of Patient Care Services
Web address: www.lchcare.org
Control: Other not–for–profit (including NFP Corporation) **Service:** General medical and surgical

Staffed Beds: 91 **Admissions:** 1993 **Census:** 62 **Outpatient Visits:** 108878 **Births:** 121 **Total Expense ($000):** 75086 **Payroll Expense ($000):** 23359 **Personnel:** 464

Many Facility Codes have changed. Please refer to the AHA Guide Code Chart. © 2017 AHA Guide

DOVER—FOXCROFT—Piscataquis County

★ **MAYO REGIONAL HOSPITAL (201309)**, 897 West Main Street, Zip 04426–1099; tel. 207/564–8401 **A**10 18 **F**3 5 7 8 11 13 15 28 29 30 31 34 35 38 40 45 50 57 59 64 65 71 75 76 77 78 79 80 81 85 86 87 93 96 97 99 104 107 110 111 114 119 127 128 129 130 132 133 135 146 147 148 149
Primary Contact: Marie E. Vienneau, FACHE, President and Chief Executive Officer
CFO: Nancy Glidden, Chief Financial Officer and Vice President Finance
CMO: Challa Reddy M.D., President Medical Staff
CHR: James R Godley, Vice President of Human Resources
CNO: Denise Scuderi, Vice President Patient Care Services
Web address: www.mayohospital.com
Control: Hospital district or authority, Government, Nonfederal **Service:** General medical and surgical

Staffed Beds: 25 **Admissions:** 1280 **Census:** 13 **Outpatient Visits:** 138138 **Births:** 137 **Total Expense ($000):** 50661 **Payroll Expense ($000):** 25408 **Personnel:** 405

ELLSWORTH—Hancock County

⊞ **MAINE COAST MEMORIAL HOSPITAL (200050)**, 50 Union Street, Zip 04605–1599; tel. 207/664–5311 **A**1 10 **F**3 15 18 26 28 29 30 31 34 35 40 45 51 55 57 59 61 64 65 68 70 74 75 76 77 78 79 81 84 85 93 96 97 107 108 111 115 119 129 130 131 132 133 143 145 146 147 148 **S** Eastern Maine Healthcare Systems, Brewer, ME
Primary Contact: John Ronan, President
CFO: Chris Frauenhofer, Chief Financial Officer
CMO: Sheena Whittaker M.D., Chief Medical Officer
CIO: Scott Burtchell, Director Information Systems
CHR: Noah Lundy, Director of Human Resources
CNO: Ardelle Bigos R.N., MSN, Chief Nursing Officer and Vice President Patient Care Services
Web address: www.mainehospital.org
Control: Other not–for–profit (including NFP Corporation) **Service:** General medical and surgical

Staffed Beds: 52 **Admissions:** 643 **Census:** 11 **Personnel:** 574

FARMINGTON—Franklin County

⊞ **FRANKLIN MEMORIAL HOSPITAL (200037)**, 111 Franklin Health Commons, Zip 04938–6144; tel. 207/778–6031 **A**1 5 10 20 **F**3 5 7 8 11 13 15 28 29 30 31 32 34 40 45 46 50 51 54 59 61 64 65 70 75 76 77 78 79 81 83 85 86 87 89 93 94 97 99 101 102 107 108 110 111 115 118 119 129 130 131 135 143 146 147 148 149 **P**1 7 8
Primary Contact: Timothy A. Churchill, Interim Chief Executive Officer
CFO: Wayne Bennett, Chief Financial Officer
CMO: Michael Rowland M.D., Vice President Medical Affairs
CIO: Ralph Johnson, Chief Information Officer
CHR: Joline Hart, Vice President Human Resources
Web address: www.fchn.org
Control: Other not–for–profit (including NFP Corporation) **Service:** General medical and surgical

Staffed Beds: 48 **Admissions:** 2050 **Census:** 19 **Outpatient Visits:** 110637 **Births:** 280 **Personnel:** 547

FORT FAIRFIELD—Aroostook County

COMMUNITY GENERAL HEALTH CENTER See The Aroostook Medical Center, Presque Isle

FORT KENT—Aroostook County

⊞ **NORTHERN MAINE MEDICAL CENTER (200052)**, 194 East Main Street, Zip 04743–1497; tel. 207/834–3155, (Total facility includes 45 beds in nursing home–type unit) **A**1 10 20 **F**3 13 15 29 31 34 40 45 54 57 59 62 64 67 68 70 75 76 77 78 79 81 82 86 87 89 98 99 100 101 102 103 104 107 108 110 111 115 119 127 128 130 131 132 133 135 146 147 **P**6
Primary Contact: Peter Sirois, Chief Executive Officer
CFO: Cindy Daigle, Chief Financial Officer
CMO: Michael Sullivan M.D., Chief Medical Officer
CIO: Adam Landry, Director of Information Systems
CHR: Robin Damboise, Director Human Resources
CNO: Alain Bois R.N., Director of Nursing
Web address: www.nmmc.org
Control: Other not–for–profit (including NFP Corporation) **Service:** General medical and surgical

Staffed Beds: 81 **Admissions:** 1476 **Census:** 62 **Outpatient Visits:** 54307 **Births:** 68 **Total Expense ($000):** 49287 **Payroll Expense ($000):** 26194 **Personnel:** 425

GREENVILLE—Piscataquis County

★ **CHARLES A. DEAN MEMORIAL HOSPITAL (201301)**, 364 Pritham Avenue, Zip 04441–1395, Mailing Address: P.O.Box 1129, 04441–1129; tel. 207/695–5200, (Nonreporting) **A**10 18 **S** Eastern Maine Healthcare Systems, Brewer, ME
Primary Contact: Terri Vieira, Interim President
CFO: Edward Olivier, Chief Financial Officer
CMO: Darin Peck M.D., Chief of Staff
Web address: www.cadean.org
Control: Other not–for–profit (including NFP Corporation) **Service:** General medical and surgical

Staffed Beds: 36

HOULTON—Aroostook County

★ **HOULTON REGIONAL HOSPITAL (201308)**, 20 Hartford Street, Zip 04730–1891; tel. 207/532–9471 **A**10 18 **F**1 3 4 11 13 15 16 17 28 29 30 34 40 43 45 46 50 59 65 67 70 72 73 75 76 77 79 80 81 83 84 85 86 87 88 89 90 93 97 98 107 108 110 111 114 119 127 128 129 130 132 133 146 148 149
Primary Contact: Thomas J. Moakler, Chief Executive Officer
CHR: Vicky Moody, Director Human Resources
Web address: www.houlton.net/hrh
Control: Other not–for–profit (including NFP Corporation) **Service:** General medical and surgical

Staffed Beds: 25 **Admissions:** 1248 **Census:** 15 **Outpatient Visits:** 98376 **Total Expense ($000):** 46941 **Payroll Expense ($000):** 21305 **Personnel:** 348

LEWISTON—Androscoggin County

⊞ △ **CENTRAL MAINE MEDICAL CENTER (200024)**, 300 Main Street, Zip 04240–7027; tel. 207/795–0111 **A**1 2 3 5 7 10 13 **F**3 11 12 13 15 18 19 20 22 24 26 28 29 30 31 32 34 35 36 40 41 43 44 45 46 47 48 49 50 51 52 53 54 55 56 57 58 59 61 64 65 66 67 68 70 71 73 74 75 76 77 78 79 81 82 84 85 86 87 89 90 91 92 93 97 100 101 104 107 108 110 114 115 118 119 120 121 123 124 129 130 131 132 135 143 144 146 147 148 149 150 **P**8 **S** Central Maine Healthcare, Lewiston, ME
Primary Contact: Jeffrey L. Brickman, FACHE, Interim Chief Executive Officer
CFO: David Thompson, Chief Financial Officer
CMO: David Lauver M.D., Chief Division Hospital Based Care
CIO: Denis Tanguay, Chief Information Officer
CHR: Kirk Miklavic, Director, Human Resources
Web address: www.cmmc.org
Control: Other not–for–profit (including NFP Corporation) **Service:** General medical and surgical

Staffed Beds: 190 **Admissions:** 10257 **Census:** 129 **Outpatient Visits:** 754920 **Births:** 673 **Total Expense ($000):** 408185 **Payroll Expense ($000):** 155296 **Personnel:** 1839

⊞ **ST. MARY'S REGIONAL MEDICAL CENTER (200034)**, 93 Campus Avenue, Zip 04240–6030, Mailing Address: P.O.Box 291, 04243–0291; tel. 207/777–8100, (Total facility includes 210 beds in nursing home–type unit) **A**1 2 5 10 **F**3 4 5 7 13 15 17 18 20 28 29 30 31 34 35 36 37 38 39 40 44 45 49 50 53 54 56 57 59 61 64 65 66 68 70 74 75 76 77 78 79 80 81 82 84 85 86 87 89 92 93 97 98 99 100 101 102 103 104 105 107 108 110 111 114 115 118 119 127 128 129 130 131 132 134 135 143 144 146 147 148 149 **P**1 6 **S** Covenant Health, Tewksbury, MA
Primary Contact: Peter J. Holden, Interim President
CFO: Michael Hendrix, Chief Financial Officer
CMO: Christopher Bowe M.D., Chief Medical Officer, Medical Affairs
CIO: Karen Bowling, Chief Information Officer
CHR: Nicole Morin–Scribner, Director Human Resources
CNO: Karen Clark, Vice President Patient Care Services
Web address: www.stmarysmaine.com
Control: Other not–for–profit (including NFP Corporation) **Service:** General medical and surgical

Staffed Beds: 353 **Admissions:** 6765 **Census:** 270 **Outpatient Visits:** 301190 **Births:** 596 **Total Expense ($000):** 167107 **Payroll Expense ($000):** 77763 **Personnel:** 1325

Hospital, Medicare Provider Number, Address, Telephone, Approval, Facility, and Physician Codes, Health Care System

★ American Hospital Association (AHA) membership   ○ Healthcare Facilities Accreditation Program   ⇑ Center for Improvement in Healthcare Quality Accreditation
□ The Joint Commission accreditation   ◇ DNV Healthcare Inc. accreditation   △ Commission on Accreditation of Rehabilitation Facilities (CARF) accreditation

ME

LINCOLN—Penobscot County

★ **PENOBSCOT VALLEY HOSPITAL (201303)**, 7 Transalpine Road, Zip 04457–4222, Mailing Address: P.O.Box 368, 04457–0368; tel. 207/794–3321, (Nonreporting) **A**10 18 **S** QHR, Brentwood, TN
Primary Contact: Gary R. Poquette, FACHE, Chief Executive Officer
CFO: Ann Marie Rush, Chief Financial Officer
CHR: Sarah Loman, Director Human Resources
Web address: www.pvhme.org
Control: Other not–for–profit (including NFP Corporation) **Service**: General medical and surgical

Staffed Beds: 25

MACHIAS—Washington County

★ **DOWN EAST COMMUNITY HOSPITAL (201311)**, 11 Hospital Drive, Zip 04654–3325; tel. 207/255–3356, (Total facility includes 28 beds in nursing home–type unit) **A**10 18 **F**3 13 15 28 29 34 35 40 43 57 59 64 65 75 76 77 79 81 82 83 84 85 89 93 97 107 108 110 111 114 119 127 128 129 130 133 146 147 148
Primary Contact: Dennis Welsh, President and CEO
COO: Steve Lail, Vice President Operations and Chief Operating Officer
CFO: Lynnette Parr, Chief Financial Officer
CMO: Aziz Massaad M.D., Medical Staff President
CHR: Ernestine O Reisman, Vice President Human Resources
CNO: Kevin K McEwan MSN, R.N., Vice President of Patient Care Service and Chief Nursing Officer
Web address: www.dech.org
Control: Other not–for–profit (including NFP Corporation) **Service**: General medical and surgical

Staffed Beds: 53 Admissions: 901 Census: 34 Outpatient Visits: 31074 Births: 153 Total Expense ($000): 40865 Payroll Expense ($000): 18307 Personnel: 267

MARS HILL—Aroostook County

AROOSTOOK HEALTH CENTER See The Aroostook Medical Center, Presque Isle

MILLINOCKET—Penobscot County

★ **MILLINOCKET REGIONAL HOSPITAL (201307)**, 200 Somerset Street, Zip 04462–1298; tel. 207/723–5161 **A**10 18 **F**3 8 11 15 28 29 31 34 35 40 41 45 50 53 56 57 59 64 65 68 75 77 78 79 80 81 85 87 93 97 107 108 110 111 118 119 127 128 130 131 132 133 135 145 148
Primary Contact: Robert Peterson I, Chief Executive Officer
CFO: Catherine LeMay, Vice President Finance
CMO: Daniel Herbert M.D., Medical Administrative Officer
CHR: Lisa Arsenault, Vice President Human Resources and Compliance
CNO: Mary Tatro Esq, Chief Nursing Officer
Web address: www.mrhme.org
Control: Other not–for–profit (including NFP Corporation) **Service**: General medical and surgical

Staffed Beds: 25 Admissions: 621 Census: 9 Outpatient Visits: 27814 Births: 0 Total Expense ($000): 27105 Payroll Expense ($000): 13726 Personnel: 206

NORWAY—Oxford County

★ **STEPHENS MEMORIAL HOSPITAL (201315)**, 181 Main Street, Zip 04268–5664; tel. 207/743–5933 **A**5 10 18 **F**3 7 13 15 28 29 30 31 34 35 40 43 45 57 59 61 64 65 68 75 76 78 79 80 81 85 87 89 93 96 97 102 107 108 110 111 115 119 127 130 132 146 148 149 **S** MaineHealth, Portland, ME
Primary Contact: Timothy A. Churchill, President
CMO: James Eshleman D.O., President Medical Staff
CHR: Roberta Metivier, Vice President Human Resources and Administrator, Western Main Nursing Home
Web address: www.wmhcc.com
Control: Other not–for–profit (including NFP Corporation) **Service**: General medical and surgical

Staffed Beds: 25 Admissions: 1342 Census: 13 Outpatient Visits: 102944 Births: 152 Total Expense ($000): 60382 Payroll Expense ($000): 25360 Personnel: 404

PITTSFIELD—Somerset County

✠ **SEBASTICOOK VALLEY HEALTH (201313)**, 447 North Main Street, Zip 04967–3707; tel. 207/487–4000 **A**1 10 18 **F**3 7 11 15 18 28 29 30 32 34 35 40 45 46 50 51 57 59 64 65 70 75 77 78 79 81 87 93 96 97 104 107 108 111 119 127 129 130 132 133 135 143 146 147 148 **P**6 **S** Eastern Maine Healthcare Systems, Brewer, ME
Primary Contact: Terri Vieira, President and Chief Executive Officer
COO: Michael Peterson FACHE, Chief Operating Officer
CFO: Randal Clark, Vice President Finance
CMO: Robert Schlager M.D., Chief Medical Officer
CIO: Michael Peterson FACHE, Chief Operating Officer
CHR: Tammy Hatch, Manager
Web address: www.sebasticookvalleyhealth.org
Control: Other not–for–profit (including NFP Corporation) **Service**: General medical and surgical

Staffed Beds: 25 Admissions: 822 Census: 13 Outpatient Visits: 78798 Births: 0 Total Expense ($000): 38296 Payroll Expense ($000): 17430 Personnel: 302

PORTLAND—Cumberland County

✠ **MAINE MEDICAL CENTER (200009)**, 22 Bramhall Street, Zip 04102–3175; tel. 207/662–0111, (Includes BARBARA BUSH CHILDREN'S HOSPITAL, 22 Bramhall Street, Portland, Maine, Zip 04102–3134, tel. 207/662–0111; Richard W Petersen, President and Chief Executive Officer; MAINE MEDICAL CENTER, BRIGHTON CAMPUS, 335 Brighton Avenue, Portland, Maine, Zip 04102–9735, P O Box 9735, 04102–9735, tel. 207/879–8000; Richard W Petersen, President and Chief Executive Officer) **A**1 2 3 5 8 10 **F**3 5 6 8 11 12 13 15 16 17 18 19 20 21 22 23 24 25 26 27 28 29 30 31 32 34 35 36 38 40 41 42 43 44 45 46 47 48 49 51 54 55 56 57 58 59 60 61 64 65 66 68 70 72 73 74 75 76 78 79 80 81 82 84 85 86 87 88 89 91 92 97 98 99 100 101 102 103 104 105 107 108 110 111 115 116 117 118 119 120 121 123 124 126 129 130 131 132 134 135 138 141 144 146 147 148 149 **P**6 8 **S** MaineHealth, Portland, ME
Primary Contact: Richard W. Petersen, President and Chief Executive Officer
COO: Jeff Sanders, Senior Vice President, Chief Operating Officer
CFO: Lou Inzana, Senior Vice President and Chief Financial Officer
CMO: Joel Botler M.D., Chief Medical Officer
CHR: Judith M West, Senior Vice President Human Resources and Chief Human Resources Officer
CNO: Marjorie Wiggins, Senior Vice President, Chief Nursing Officer
Web address: www.mmc.org
Control: Other not–for–profit (including NFP Corporation) **Service**: General medical and surgical

Staffed Beds: 637 Admissions: 28484 Census: 405 Outpatient Visits: 288178 Births: 2829 Total Expense ($000): 1114285 Payroll Expense ($000): 450601 Personnel: 7540

✠ **MERCY HOSPITAL OF PORTLAND (200008)**, 144 State Street, Zip 04101–3795; tel. 207/879–3000 **A**1 2 3 10 **F**3 11 13 15 18 20 26 29 30 31 34 35 36 40 44 45 48 49 50 51 54 55 56 57 58 59 61 64 68 70 72 74 75 76 78 79 81 82 84 86 87 93 96 97 100 102 107 108 110 111 114 115 117 119 130 132 135 143 144 146 147 148 149 **P**6 **S** Eastern Maine Healthcare Systems, Brewer, ME
Primary Contact: Charles D. Therrien, President
CFO: Michael Hachey, Senior Vice President and Chief Financial Officer
CIO: Craig Dreher, Chief Information Officer
CHR: Elizabeth B Christensen, Director Human Resources
CNO: Bette Neville R.N., MSN, Vice President and Chief Nursing Officer
Web address: www.mercyhospital.org
Control: Other not–for–profit (including NFP Corporation) **Service**: General medical and surgical

Staffed Beds: 104 Admissions: 5166 Census: 48 Outpatient Visits: 407609 Births: 851 Total Expense ($000): 237583 Payroll Expense ($000): 97450 Personnel: 1017

✠ **NEW ENGLAND REHABILITATION HOSPITAL OF PORTLAND (203025)**, 335 Brighton Avenue, Zip 04102–2363; tel. 207/775–4000 **A**1 3 10 **F**29 34 35 75 79 82 90 93 95 96 131 132 135 146 **S** HEALTHSOUTH Corporation, Birmingham, AL
Primary Contact: Jeanine Chesley, Chief Executive Officer
CFO: James Paladino, Controller
CMO: Thomas Morrione, Medical Director
CHR: Mary Cote, Director Human Resources
CNO: Sharon Kuhrt, Chief Nursing Officer
Web address: www.nerhp.org
Control: Partnership, Investor–owned (for–profit) **Service**: Rehabilitation

Staffed Beds: 90 Admissions: 1919 Census: 66 Outpatient Visits: 9877 Births: 0 Total Expense ($000): 23748 Payroll Expense ($000): 14361 Personnel: 224

PRESQUE ISLE—Aroostook County

✠ **THE AROOSTOOK MEDICAL CENTER (200018)**, 140 Academy Street, Zip 04769–3171, Mailing Address: P.O.Box 151, 04769–0151; tel. 207/768–4000, (Includes AROOSTOOK HEALTH CENTER, 15 Highland Avenue, Mars Hill, Maine, Zip 4758, tel. 207/768–4900; ARTHUR R. GOULD MEMORIAL HOSPITAL, 140 Academy Street, Presque Isle, Maine, Zip 4769, P O Box 151, 4769, tel. 207/768–4000; COMMUNITY GENERAL HEALTH CENTER, 3 Green Street, Fort Fairfield, Maine, Zip 4742, tel. 207/768–4700) (Total facility includes 64 beds in nursing home–type unit) **A**1 10 **F**3 7 8 12 13 15 18 20 28 29 30 31 32 34 35 36 38 40 43 45 46 51 52 53 54 56 57 59 60 61 64 65 67 69 70 74 75 76 77 78 79 80 81 82 84 85 86 87 89 90 91 93 96 97 99 104 107 108 110 114 115 116 117 118 119 120 121 123 128 129 130 131 132 133 134 135 143 146 147 148 149 150 **P6 S** Eastern Maine Healthcare Systems, Brewer, ME
Primary Contact: Gregory La Francois, President
COO: Jay Reynolds M.D., Chief Medical Officer and Chief Clinical Officer
CFO: C Bruce Sandstrom, Vice President and Chief Financial Officer
CMO: Jay Reynolds M.D., Chief Medical Officer and Chief Clinical Officer
CIO: Kyle Johnson, Chief Information Officer
CHR: Joseph Siddiqui, Vice President Human Resources
Web address: www.tamc.org
Control: Other not–for–profit (including NFP Corporation) **Service**: General medical and surgical

Staffed Beds: 114 **Admissions:** 2135 **Census:** 82 **Outpatient Visits:** 207520 **Births:** 214 **Total Expense ($000):** 126049 **Payroll Expense ($000):** 61516 **Personnel:** 835

ROCKPORT—Knox County

☐ **PEN BAY MEDICAL CENTER (200063)**, 6 Glen Cove Drive, Zip 04856–4240; tel. 207/921–8000, (Nonreporting) **A**1 2 5 10 20 **S** MaineHealth, Portland, ME
Primary Contact: Mark A. Biscone, President and Chief Executive Officer
COO: Eric Waters, Vice President Operations
CFO: Maura Kelly, Vice President Fiscal Services
CMO: Dana L Goldsmith M.D., Vice President Medical Affairs
CIO: Brooks Betts, Director Information Systems and Chief Information Officer
CHR: Thomas R Girard, Vice President Human Resources
CNO: Paula Delahanty, Regional Chief Nursing Officer
Web address: www.penbayhealthcare.org
Control: Other not–for–profit (including NFP Corporation) **Service**: General medical and surgical

Staffed Beds: 165

PENOBSCOT BAY MEDICAL CENTER See Pen Bay Medical Center

RUMFORD—Oxford County

★ **RUMFORD HOSPITAL (201306)**, 420 Franklin Street, Zip 04276–2145; tel. 207/369–1000 **A**10 18 **F**3 8 11 13 15 18 28 29 30 31 34 35 40 43 44 45 50 53 57 59 64 65 67 68 75 76 77 78 79 80 81 85 87 89 90 91 93 94 96 97 107 110 114 119 127 128 130 132 133 135 143 144 146 148 **P8 S** Central Maine Healthcare, Lewiston, ME
Primary Contact: R David. Frum, President
CNO: Becky Hall R.N., Director Nursing
Web address: www.rumfordhospital.org
Control: Other not–for–profit (including NFP Corporation) **Service**: General medical and surgical

Staffed Beds: 25 **Admissions:** 1043 **Census:** 13 **Outpatient Visits:** 127721 **Births:** 97 **Total Expense ($000):** 40809 **Payroll Expense ($000):** 16667 **Personnel:** 253

SKOWHEGAN—Somerset County

★ **REDINGTON–FAIRVIEW GENERAL HOSPITAL (201314)**, 46 Fairview Avenue, Zip 4976, Mailing Address: PO Box 468, 04976–0468; tel. 207/474–5121 **A**5 10 18 **F**3 7 11 13 15 18 28 29 30 31 34 35 40 45 47 50 53 56 57 59 65 68 70 74 75 76 77 78 79 81 82 84 85 91 92 93 97 107 108 110 114 115 118 119 130 131 132 133 134 135 146 147 149 **P6**
Primary Contact: Richard Willett, Chief Executive Officer
CFO: Elmer H Doucette, Chief Financial Officer
CMO: Gust Stringos M.D., Medical Staff Director
CHR: Lisa G. Landry, Human Resources Director
CNO: Sherry L Rogers MS, R.N., Chief Nursing Officer
Web address: www.rfgh.net
Control: Other not–for–profit (including NFP Corporation) **Service**: General medical and surgical

Staffed Beds: 25 **Admissions:** 1597 **Census:** 15 **Outpatient Visits:** 55953 **Births:** 150 **Total Expense ($000):** 85370 **Payroll Expense ($000):** 41340 **Personnel:** 592

WATERVILLE—Kennebec County

★ ○ **INLAND HOSPITAL (200041)**, 200 Kennedy Memorial Drive, Zip 04901–4595; tel. 207/861–3000 **A**10 11 **F**3 13 15 18 28 29 30 34 35 40 45 46 50 51 56 57 59 64 68 70 74 75 76 77 79 81 82 85 92 93 97 107 108 109 110 111 115 119 127 129 130 132 146 147 148 149 **P6 S** Eastern Maine Healthcare Systems, Brewer, ME
Primary Contact: John Dalton, President and Chief Executive Officer
COO: Daniel Booth, Vice President Operations and Chief Human Resources Officer
CFO: Dean Bither, Chief Financial Officer
CMO: Michael Palumbo D.O., Vice President Medical Affairs and Chief Education
CIO: Kevin Dieterich, Director Information Services
CHR: Daniel Booth, Vice President Operations
Web address: www.inlandhospital.org
Control: Other not–for–profit (including NFP Corporation) **Service**: General medical and surgical

Staffed Beds: 29 **Admissions:** 1228 **Census:** 13 **Outpatient Visits:** 14575 **Births:** 374 **Total Expense ($000):** 74187 **Payroll Expense ($000):** 31174 **Personnel:** 514

WESTBROOK—Cumberland County

✠ **SPRING HARBOR HOSPITAL (204005)**, 123 Andover Road, Zip 04092–3850; tel. 207/761–2200, (Nonreporting) **A**1 10 **S** MaineHealth, Portland, ME
Primary Contact: Mary Jane Krebs, FACHE, President
CFO: Michael Abbatiello, Chief Financial Officer
CMO: Girard Robinson M.D., Senior Vice President Medical and Clinical Affairs
CIO: Susan Moulton, Director Health Information Management
CHR: Timothy McNulty, Director Human Resources
Web address: www.springharbor.org
Control: Other not–for–profit (including NFP Corporation) **Service**: Psychiatric

Staffed Beds: 88

YORK—York County

★ **YORK HOSPITAL (200020)**, 15 Hospital Drive, Zip 03909–1099; tel. 207/363–4321 **A**10 **F**3 5 8 13 15 18 20 22 26 28 29 30 31 32 34 35 36 37 38 40 42 45 50 53 54 55 57 59 60 62 64 65 68 69 70 71 74 75 76 77 78 79 81 87 89 93 96 97 99 100 102 104 107 108 110 111 114 115 119 126 129 130 131 132 135 143 144 146 148 149 **P6**
Primary Contact: Jud Knox, Chief Executive Officer
CFO: Robin LaBonte, Leader Financial Care
CMO: Lawrence Petrovich M.D., Chief Medical Officer
CIO: Robin LaBonte, Leader Financial Care
CHR: Olivia Chayer, Director, Human Resources
Web address: www.yorkhospital.com
Control: Other not–for–profit (including NFP Corporation) **Service**: General medical and surgical

Staffed Beds: 58 **Admissions:** 2999 **Census:** 32 **Outpatient Visits:** 291005 **Births:** 349 **Total Expense ($000):** 162854 **Payroll Expense ($000):** 77002 **Personnel:** 1029

Hospital, Medicare Provider Number, Address, Telephone, Approval, Facility, and Physician Codes, Health Care System

★ American Hospital Association (AHA) membership
☐ The Joint Commission accreditation
○ Healthcare Facilities Accreditation Program
◇ DNV Healthcare Inc. accreditation
⇑ Center for Improvement in Healthcare Quality Accreditation
△ Commission on Accreditation of Rehabilitation Facilities (CARF) accreditation

MARYLAND

MD

ANNAPOLIS—Anne Arundel County

⊞ **ANNE ARUNDEL MEDICAL CENTER (210023)**, 2001 Medical Parkway, Zip 21401–3019; tel. 443/481–1000, (Total facility includes 40 beds in nursing home–type unit) **A**1 2 3 5 10 **F**3 4 5 6 9 11 12 13 14 15 18 20 22 26 28 29 30 31 32 34 35 36 37 38 39 40 41 44 45 46 47 49 50 51 53 54 55 56 57 58 59 60 61 63 64 65 66 68 70 72 74 75 76 77 78 79 81 82 83 84 85 86 87 89 91 92 93 94 96 99 100 101 102 103 107 108 110 111 114 115 116 117 118 119 120 121 123 124 126 129 130 131 132 134 135 146 147 148 149 150 **P**6 7 8
Primary Contact: Victoria Bayless, President and Chief Executive Officer
COO: Maulik Joshi, Executive Vice President, Integrated Care Delivery and Chief Operating Officer
CFO: Robert Reilly, Vice President and Chief Financial Officer
CMO: Mitchell B Schwartz M.D., Chief Medical Officer
CIO: Barbara Baldwin, Chief Information Officer
CHR: Julie McGovern, Vice President Human Resources
CNO: Barbara S Jacobs MSN, Vice President, Nursing and Chief Nursing Officer
Web address: www.aahs.org
Control: Other not–for–profit (including NFP Corporation) **Service**: General medical and surgical

> **Staffed Beds**: 445 **Admissions**: 27015 **Census**: 292 **Outpatient Visits**: 476950 **Births**: 5743 **Total Expense ($000)**: 518995 **Payroll Expense ($000)**: 196309 **Personnel**: 3885

BALTIMORE—Baltimore City County

⊞ **BON SECOURS BALTIMORE HEALTH SYSTEM (210013)**, 2000 West Baltimore Street, Zip 21223–1558; tel. 410/362–3000 **A**1 10 **F**3 15 18 20 26 29 30 40 44 49 58 59 60 64 66 70 77 78 79 81 84 85 87 97 98 99 100 101 102 103 104 105 107 108 110 111 115 119 130 143 146 148 **S** Bon Secours Health System, Inc., Marriottsville, MD
Primary Contact: Samuel Lee. Ross, M.D., MS, Chief Executive Officer
CFO: Laura Ellison, Chief Financial Officer
CMO: Arsalan Sheikh, Chief of Medicine
CIO: Sanjay Purushotham, Executive Director Information Systems
CHR: Danielle Jorden–Ellis, Director
CNO: Shelly Buck, Chief Nursing Executive and Chief Operating Officer
Web address: www.bonsecoursbaltimore.com
Control: Church operated, Nongovernment, not–for–profit **Service**: General medical and surgical

> **Staffed Beds**: 72 **Admissions**: 3940 **Census**: 49 **Outpatient Visits**: 316956 **Births**: 0 **Total Expense ($000)**: 114507 **Payroll Expense ($000)**: 43714 **Personnel**: 663

FRANKLIN SQUARE HOSPITAL CENTER See Medstar Franklin Square Medical Center

⊞ **GREATER BALTIMORE MEDICAL CENTER (210044)**, 6701 North Charles Street, Zip 21204–6892; tel. 443/849–2000, (Total facility includes 25 beds in nursing home–type unit) **A**1 2 3 5 10 **F**3 8 11 12 13 18 20 22 26 29 30 31 34 35 40 41 44 45 46 47 48 49 50 51 55 56 57 58 59 60 61 63 64 66 68 70 72 73 74 75 76 77 78 79 81 82 83 84 85 86 87 89 92 93 96 97 102 107 108 114 115 119 120 121 123 124 126 128 129 130 132 135 136 142 145 146 147 148 **P**4
Primary Contact: John B. Chessare, M.D., M.P.H., FACHE, President and Chief Executive Officer
COO: Keith R Poisson, Executive Vice President and Chief Operating Officer
CFO: Eric L Melchior, Executive Vice President and Chief Financial Officer
CMO: John R Saunders M.D., Senior Vice President Medical Affairs and Chief Medical Officer
CHR: Deloris Simpson–Tuggle, Vice President Human Resources and Organizational Development and Chief Human Resources Officer
CNO: Jody Porter R.N., Senior Vice President Patient Care Services and Chief Nursing Officer
Web address: www.gbmc.org
Control: Other not–for–profit (including NFP Corporation) **Service**: General medical and surgical

> **Staffed Beds**: 404 **Admissions**: 16699 **Census**: 166 **Outpatient Visits**: 134147 **Births**: 3853 **Total Expense ($000)**: 402045 **Payroll Expense ($000)**: 195279 **Personnel**: 3251

GOOD SAMARITAN HOSPITAL OF MARYLAND See Medstar Good Samaritan Hospital

HARBOR HOSPITAL See Medstar Harbor Hospital

⊞ △ **JOHNS HOPKINS BAYVIEW MEDICAL CENTER (210029)**, 4940 Eastern Avenue, Zip 21224–2780; tel. 410/550–0100 **A**1 3 5 7 8 10 **F**1 2 3 4 5 6 8 9 11 12 13 15 16 17 18 20 22 26 28 29 30 31 32 34 35 36 38 40 41 43 44 45 46 47 48 49 50 51 54 55 56 57 58 59 60 61 64 65 66 68 70 71 72 74 75 76 77 78 79 80 81 82 84 85 86 87 89 90 91 92 93 94 97 98 99 100 101 102 103 104 105 107 110 111 115 117 118 119 120 121 126 129 130 131 132 134 135 141 143 146 147 148 149 **S** Johns Hopkins Health System, Baltimore, MD
Primary Contact: Richard G. Bennett, M.D., President
COO: Charlie Reuland Sc.D., Executive Vice President and Chief Operating Officer
CFO: Carl H Francioli, Vice President Finance
CIO: Sandy Reckert, Director Communications and Public Affairs
CHR: Craig R Brodian, Vice President Human Resources
Web address: www.hopkinsbayview.org
Control: Other not–for–profit (including NFP Corporation) **Service**: General medical and surgical

> **Staffed Beds**: 425 **Admissions**: 19461 **Census**: 317 **Outpatient Visits**: 430632 **Births**: 1297 **Total Expense ($000)**: 543853 **Payroll Expense ($000)**: 182504 **Personnel**: 3075

⊞ △ **JOHNS HOPKINS HOSPITAL (210009)**, 733 North Broadway MRB 104, Zip 21205–1832; tel. 410/955–5000, (Includes JOHNS HOPKINS CHILDREN'S CENTER, 1800 Orleans Street, Baltimore, Maryland, Zip 21287–0010, tel. 410/955–5000) **A**1 2 3 5 7 8 10 **F**3 5 6 7 8 9 11 13 14 15 16 17 18 19 20 21 22 23 24 25 26 27 28 29 30 31 32 34 35 36 38 39 40 41 43 45 46 47 48 49 50 51 52 54 55 56 57 58 59 60 61 63 64 65 66 68 70 72 74 75 76 77 78 79 80 81 82 83 84 85 86 87 88 89 90 92 93 94 96 97 98 99 100 101 102 103 104 105 107 108 110 111 112 114 115 116 117 118 119 120 121 123 124 126 129 130 131 132 134 135 136 137 138 139 140 141 142 143 145 146 147 148 149 150 **S** Johns Hopkins Health System, Baltimore, MD
Primary Contact: Redonda G. Miller, M.D., President
COO: Judy A Reitz Sc.D., Executive Vice President and Chief Operating Officer
CFO: Ronald J Werthman, Senior Vice President Finance, Chief Financial Officer and Treasurer
CIO: Stephanie L Reel, Senior Vice President Information Services
CHR: Bonnie Windsor, Senior Vice President Human Resources
CNO: Deborah Baker, Vice President, Nursing
Web address: www.hopkinsmedicine.org
Control: Other not–for–profit (including NFP Corporation) **Service**: General medical and surgical

> **Staffed Beds**: 1004 **Admissions**: 46593 **Census**: 853 **Outpatient Visits**: 638333 **Births**: 2200 **Total Expense ($000)**: 2318440 **Payroll Expense ($000)**: 598637 **Personnel**: 9970

☐ △ **KENNEDY KRIEGER INSTITUTE (213301)**, 707 North Broadway, Zip 21205–1890; tel. 443/923–9200, (Nonreporting) **A**1 3 5 7 10
Primary Contact: Gary W. Goldstein, M.D., President and Chief Executive Officer
COO: James M Anders Jr, Administrator and Chief Operating Officer
CFO: Michael J Neuman, Vice President Finance
CMO: Michael V Johnston M.D., Chief Medical Officer and Senior Vice President Medical Programs
CIO: Kenneth Davis, Assistant Vice President Information Systems
CHR: Michael Loughran, Vice President Human Resources
Web address: www.kennedykrieger.org
Control: Other not–for–profit (including NFP Corporation) **Service**: Children's other specialty

> **Staffed Beds**: 70

☐ △ **LEVINDALE HEBREW GERIATRIC CENTER AND HOSPITAL (210064)**, 2434 West Belvedere Avenue, Zip 21215–5267; tel. 410/601–2400, (Nonreporting) **A**1 7 10 **S** LifeBridge Health, Baltimore, MD
Primary Contact: Idriz Limaj, Chief Operating Officer and Executive Director
CMO: Susan M Levy M.D., Vice President Medical Affairs
CIO: Tressa Springmann, Vice President and Chief Information Officer
CHR: Cheryl T Boyer, Vice President Human Resources
CNO: Candy Hamner, Vice President and Chief Nursing Officer
Web address: www.sinai–balt.com
Control: Other not–for–profit (including NFP Corporation) **Service**: Acute long–term care hospital

> **Staffed Beds**: 490

MEDSTAR FRANKLIN SQUARE MEDICAL CENTER (210015), 9000 Franklin Square Drive, Zip 21237–3901; tel. 443/777–7000 **A**1 2 3 5 8 10 **F**3 5 11 12 13 15 18 20 22 26 28 29 30 31 32 34 35 36 37 38 39 40 41 44 45 46 47 48 49 50 51 55 56 57 58 59 60 61 64 65 66 68 70 71 72 74 75 77 78 79 81 82 85 86 87 92 93 94 97 98 99 100 101 102 103 104 107 108 109 110 111 115 118 119 126 129 130 131 132 134 135 145 146 147 148 149 **S** MedStar Health, Columbia, MD
Primary Contact: Samuel E. Moskowitz, President
CFO: Robert P Lally Jr, Vice President Finance
CMO: Tony Sclama M.D., Vice President Medical Affairs
CIO: Stephen Mannion, Assistant Vice President Information Systems Customer Service
CNO: Lawrence F Strassner III Ph.D., FACHE, R.N., MS, Senior Vice President Operations and Chief Nursing Officer
Web address: www.medstarfranklin.org
Control: Other not–for–profit (including NFP Corporation) **Service:** General medical and surgical

Staffed Beds: 384 **Admissions:** 20873 **Census:** 264 **Outpatient Visits:** 447944 **Births:** 2821 **Total Expense ($000):** 508340 **Payroll Expense ($000):** 228612 **Personnel:** 2833

△ **MEDSTAR GOOD SAMARITAN HOSPITAL (210056)**, 5601 Loch Raven Boulevard, Zip 21239–2995; tel. 443/444–8000, (Total facility includes 30 beds in nursing home–type unit) **A**1 2 3 5 7 10 **F**3 6 9 11 15 17 18 20 26 28 29 30 31 34 35 36 37 38 40 43 44 45 49 50 51 53 55 56 57 58 59 60 61 64 65 66 68 70 74 75 77 78 79 80 81 82 84 85 86 87 90 91 93 96 97 100 101 103 104 107 108 110 111 114 115 117 118 121 124 128 129 130 131 132 135 143 146 148 149 **P**6 **S** MedStar Health, Columbia, MD
Primary Contact: Bradley Chambers, President and Senior Vice President, MedStar Health
CFO: Deana Stout, Vice President Financial Services
Web address: www.goodsam–md.org
Control: Other not–for–profit (including NFP Corporation) **Service:** General medical and surgical

Staffed Beds: 323 **Admissions:** 10867 **Census:** 169 **Outpatient Visits:** 285402 **Births:** 0 **Total Expense ($000):** 306820 **Payroll Expense ($000):** 129018 **Personnel:** 1748

MEDSTAR HARBOR HOSPITAL (210034), 3001 South Hanover Street, Zip 21225–1290; tel. 410/350–3200 **A**1 2 3 5 10 **F**3 9 11 13 15 18 20 26 29 30 34 35 36 40 43 44 45 46 48 49 50 51 53 55 56 57 58 59 60 61 64 65 66 68 70 72 74 75 76 77 78 79 81 82 84 85 86 87 89 92 93 94 97 102 103 107 108 110 111 114 119 120 121 129 130 131 132 135 146 147 149 **P**6 **S** MedStar Health, Columbia, MD
Primary Contact: Stuart M. Levine, M.D., President and Chief Medical Officer
COO: Jill Donaldson, Vice President Operations
CFO: David R Pitman, Vice President Finance
CMO: Allan Birenberg, Vice President Medical Affairs
CIO: Cynthia Tanebaum, Director Information Services
CHR: Karen Evelius, Director Human Resources
CNO: Lenora Addison, Vice President Patient Care and Nursing
Web address: www.harborhospital.org
Control: Other not–for–profit (including NFP Corporation) **Service:** General medical and surgical

Staffed Beds: 141 **Admissions:** 6891 **Census:** 76 **Outpatient Visits:** 170153 **Births:** 1345 **Total Expense ($000):** 190324 **Payroll Expense ($000):** 76489 **Personnel:** 1002

MEDSTAR UNION MEMORIAL HOSPITAL (210024), 201 East University Parkway, Zip 21218–2895; tel. 410/554–2000 **A**1 2 3 5 10 **F**3 5 8 9 11 15 17 18 20 22 24 26 28 29 30 31 34 35 39 40 41 43 44 45 46 47 51 53 54 55 56 57 58 59 60 61 63 64 65 66 68 70 74 75 77 78 79 80 81 82 84 85 86 87 89 91 92 93 94 96 97 98 100 101 102 103 104 105 107 108 110 114 115 118 119 120 121 123 129 130 131 132 135 142 146 149 **S** MedStar Health, Columbia, MD
Primary Contact: Bradley Chambers, President
COO: Neil MacDonald, Vice President, Operations
CFO: Deana Stout, Vice President, Finance
CMO: Stuart Bell M.D., Vice President, Medical Affairs
CIO: Janet Decker, Assistant Vice President, Information Systems
CHR: Ashley Handwerk, Director, Human Resources
CNO: Karen Owings MSN, Vice President, Patient Care Services
Web address: www.medstarunionmemorial.org
Control: Other not–for–profit (including NFP Corporation) **Service:** General medical and surgical

Staffed Beds: 198 **Admissions:** 11383 **Census:** 153 **Outpatient Visits:** 137270 **Births:** 0 **Total Expense ($000):** 435763 **Payroll Expense ($000):** 169428 **Personnel:** 2032

MERCY MEDICAL CENTER (210008), 301 St Paul Place, Zip 21202–2165; tel. 410/332–9000 **A**1 2 3 10 **F**3 4 8 11 13 14 15 18 20 29 30 31 34 35 36 37 39 40 41 44 45 46 47 48 49 50 51 55 57 58 59 64 65 66 68 70 72 74 75 76 77 78 79 81 82 85 86 87 89 92 93 94 100 102 107 108 110 111 114 115 116 117 118 119 120 121 123 124 126 128 129 130 131 132 135 141 142 143 144 145 146 147 148 149 150 **P**6
Primary Contact: Thomas R. Mullen, President and Chief Executive Officer
COO: Susan D Finlayson MSN, R.N., Senior Vice President of MMC Operations
CFO: Justin Deibel, Senior Vice President and Chief Financial Officer
CMO: Wilma Rowe M.D., Senior Vice President Medical Affairs
CIO: Kathleen Perry, Senior Vice President and Chief Information Officer
CHR: Tammy Janus, Senior Vice President Human Resources
CNO: Kim Bushnell MSN, R.N., Vice President, Patient Care Services
Web address: www.mdmercy.com
Control: Church operated, Nongovernment, not–for–profit **Service:** General medical and surgical

Staffed Beds: 239 **Admissions:** 14447 **Census:** 172 **Outpatient Visits:** 301555 **Births:** 2938 **Total Expense ($000):** 484218 **Payroll Expense ($000):** 170649 **Personnel:** 3541

△ **MT. WASHINGTON PEDIATRIC HOSPITAL (213300)**, 1708 West Rogers Avenue, Zip 21209–4545; tel. 410/578–8600, (Nonreporting) **A**1 3 5 7 10 **S** University of Maryland Medical System, Baltimore, MD
Primary Contact: Sheldon J. Stein, President and Chief Executive Officer
CFO: Mary Miller, Vice President Finance and Business Development
CMO: Richard Katz M.D., Vice President Medical Affairs
CIO: Tim Brady, Director Information Systems
CHR: Thomas J Ellis, Vice President Human Resources
Web address: www.mwph.org
Control: Other not–for–profit (including NFP Corporation) **Service:** Children's other specialty

Staffed Beds: 61

SAINT AGNES HEALTHCARE (210011), 900 Caton Avenue, Zip 21229–5201; tel. 667/234–6000 **A**1 2 3 5 10 **F**3 8 11 12 13 14 15 17 18 20 22 26 28 29 30 31 32 34 35 40 41 44 46 49 50 53 54 55 56 57 58 59 60 61 64 65 68 70 72 74 75 76 77 78 79 81 82 84 85 86 87 88 89 92 93 96 97 100 107 108 110 111 114 115 117 118 119 120 121 123 124 126 129 130 131 132 134 135 144 146 147 148 149 150 **P**6 **S** Ascension Healthcare, Saint Louis, MO
Primary Contact: Keith Vander Kolk, President and Chief Executive Officer
CFO: Scott Furniss, Vice President and Chief Financial Officer
CMO: Nancy Hammond M.D., Vice President, Chief Medical Officer
CHR: James Bobbitt, Vice President Human Resources, Group Ministry Market
CNO: Yolanda Copeland R.N., Senior Vice President Patient Care Services and Chief Nursing Officer
Web address: www.stagnes.org
Control: Church operated, Nongovernment, not–for–profit **Service:** General medical and surgical

Staffed Beds: 367 **Admissions:** 16477 **Census:** 198 **Outpatient Visits:** 508353 **Births:** 2076 **Total Expense ($000):** 431603 **Payroll Expense ($000):** 215654 **Personnel:** 2544

SHEPPARD PRATT HEALTH SYSTEM (214000), 6501 North Charles Street, Zip 21204–6819, Mailing Address: P.O.Box 6815, 21285–6815; tel. 410/938–3000 **A**1 3 5 10 **F**10 30 35 38 56 58 64 75 87 98 99 101 102 103 104 105 106 130 132 135 143 144 146
Primary Contact: Harsh Trivedi, M.D., President and Chief Executive Officer
COO: Armando Colombo, Chief Operating Officer
CFO: Ray R Dziesinski, Vice President and Chief Financial Officer
CMO: Robert Roca M.D., Vice President Medical Affairs
CIO: Matthew Knudsen, Director, Information Systems
CHR: Cathy Doughty, Vice President Human Resources
CNO: Ernestine Y. Cosby, Vice President Clinical Services and Chief Nursing Officer
Web address: www.sheppardpratt.org
Control: Other not–for–profit (including NFP Corporation) **Service:** Psychiatric

Staffed Beds: 336 **Admissions:** 9147 **Census:** 286 **Births:** 0 **Total Expense ($000):** 208973 **Payroll Expense ($000):** 110539 **Personnel:** 2382

MD

Hospital, Medicare Provider Number, Address, Telephone, Approval, Facility, and Physician Codes, Health Care System

★ American Hospital Association (AHA) membership   ○ Healthcare Facilities Accreditation Program   ⇑ Center for Improvement in Healthcare Quality Accreditation
□ The Joint Commission accreditation   ◇ DNV Healthcare Inc. accreditation   △ Commission on Accreditation of Rehabilitation Facilities (CARF) accreditation

MD

⊠ △ **SINAI HOSPITAL OF BALTIMORE (210012)**, 2401 West Belvedere Avenue, Zip 21215–5271; tel. 410/601–9000 **A**1 2 3 5 7 10 **F**3 5 6 8 9 11 12 13 15 17 18 19 20 22 24 26 28 29 30 31 32 34 35 36 38 39 40 41 43 44 45 46 47 48 49 50 51 55 56 57 58 59 60 61 63 64 65 66 68 70 72 73 74 75 76 77 78 79 80 81 82 83 84 85 86 87 88 89 90 92 93 94 95 96 97 98 99 100 101 102 103 104 105 107 108 110 111 113 114 115 116 117 118 119 120 121 123 124 126 129 130 131 132 134 135 143 146 147 **P**6 **S** LifeBridge Health, Baltimore, MD
Primary Contact: Jonathan Ringo, M.D., President and Chief Operating Officer
CFO: David Krajewski, Senior Vice President and Chief Financial Officer
CMO: Daniel C Silverman M.D., Vice President and Chief Medical Officer
CIO: Karen Barker, Vice President and Chief Information Officer
CHR: Cheryl T Boyer, Vice President Human Resources
CNO: Diane Johnson R.N., Vice President Patient Care Services and Chief Nursing Officer
Web address: www.lifebridgehealth.org
Control: Other not–for–profit (including NFP Corporation) **Service**: General medical and surgical

Staffed Beds: 477 Admissions: 20036 Census: 310 Outpatient Visits: 178087 Births: 2083 Total Expense ($000): 725052 Payroll Expense ($000): 307491 Personnel: 4118

☐ **SPRING GROVE HOSPITAL CENTER (214018)**, 55 Wade Avenue, Zip 21228–4663; tel. 410/402–6000, (Nonreporting) **A**1 3 5 10
Primary Contact: David S. Helsel, M.D., Chief Executive Officer
CFO: Edward Swartz, Chief Financial Officer
CMO: Kelly Phillips M.D., M.P.H., Clinical Director and Chief Staff
Web address: www.springgrove.com
Control: State, Government, Nonfederal **Service**: Psychiatric

Staffed Beds: 425

UNION MEMORIAL HOSPITAL See Medstar Union Memorial Hospital

⊠ **UNIVERSITY OF MARYLAND MEDICAL CENTER (210002)**, 22 South Greene Street, Zip 21201–1595; tel. 410/328–8667, (Includes UNIVERSITY OF MARYLAND HOSPITAL FOR CHILDREN, 22 South Greene Street, Baltimore, Maryland, Zip 21201–1544, tel. 800/492–5538) **A**1 2 3 5 8 10 **F**3 5 6 7 8 9 11 12 13 14 15 17 18 19 20 21 22 23 24 25 26 27 28 29 30 31 32 34 35 36 38 39 40 41 43 44 45 46 47 48 49 50 51 52 54 55 56 57 58 59 60 61 64 65 66 68 70 71 72 74 75 76 77 78 79 81 82 84 85 86 87 88 89 92 93 94 97 98 99 100 101 102 103 104 105 106 107 108 109 110 111 114 115 116 117 118 119 120 121 122 123 126 129 130 131 132 134 135 136 137 138 139 140 141 142 143 144 145 146 147 148 149 150 **P**6 **S** University of Maryland Medical System, Baltimore, MD
Primary Contact: Mohan Suntha, M.D., President and Chief Executive Officer
CFO: Keith D Persinger, Senior Vice President Finance and Chief Financial Officer
CMO: Jonathan Gottlieb M.D., Senior Vice President and Chief Medical Officer
CIO: Jon P Burns, Chief Information Officer
CHR: R Keith Allen, Senior Vice President Human Resources
CNO: Lisa Rowen R.N., Senior Vice President and Chief Nursing Officer
Web address: www.umm.edu
Control: Other not–for–profit (including NFP Corporation) **Service**: General medical and surgical

Staffed Beds: 669 Admissions: 27776 Census: 578 Outpatient Visits: 60810 Births: 1535 Total Expense ($000): 1445705 Payroll Expense ($000): 589296 Personnel: 8349

⊠ **UNIVERSITY OF MARYLAND MEDICAL CENTER MIDTOWN CAMPUS (210038)**, 827 Linden Avenue, Zip 21201–4606; tel. 410/225–8000 **A**1 3 5 10 **F**1 5 11 15 18 20 29 30 31 34 35 40 44 45 49 50 56 57 59 60 61 64 65 66 68 70 74 75 77 78 79 81 82 84 87 91 93 94 96 97 98 100 101 102 104 107 108 111 114 115 118 119 129 130 143 146 148 149 **P**7 **S** University of Maryland Medical System, Baltimore, MD
Primary Contact: Mohan Suntha, M.D., President and Chief Executive Officer
COO: Donald Ray, Vice President Operations
CFO: Craig Fleischmann, Vice President Finance
CMO: W Eugene Egerton M.D., Chief Medical Officer
CIO: Jon P Burns, Senior Vice President and Chief Information Officer
CHR: Paula Henderson, Vice President Human Resources
CNO: Lisa Rowen R.N., Chief Nursing Officer
Web address: www.ummidtown.org/
Control: Other not–for–profit (including NFP Corporation) **Service**: General medical and surgical

Staffed Beds: 170 Admissions: 4698 Census: 90 Outpatient Visits: 122365 Births: 0 Total Expense ($000): 191263 Payroll Expense ($000): 72031 Personnel: 1111

⊠ △ **UNIVERSITY OF MARYLAND REHABILITATION & ORTHOPAEDIC INSTITUTE (210058)**, 2200 Kernan Drive, Zip 21207–6697; tel. 410/448–2500 **A**1 3 5 7 10 **F**8 29 34 35 36 39 57 68 74 77 79 81 82 90 91 93 94 95 96 107 131 132 133 143 146 148 149 **S** University of Maryland Medical System, Baltimore, MD
Primary Contact: Cynthia Kelleher, M.P.H., President and Chief Executive Officer
CFO: W Walter Augustin CPA, III, Vice President Financial Services and Chief Financial Officer
CMO: John P. Straumanis M.D., Vice President Medical Affairs and Chief Medical Officer
CIO: Linda Hines, Vice President Information Technology and Information Systems
CHR: Paula Henderson, Vice President Human Resources
CNO: Cheryl D Lee R.N., MSN, Vice President of Patient Care Services and Chief Nursing Officer
Web address: www.umrehabortho.org
Control: Other not–for–profit (including NFP Corporation) **Service**: Rehabilitation

Staffed Beds: 141 Admissions: 2868 Census: 89 Outpatient Visits: 51195 Births: 0 Total Expense ($000): 103856 Payroll Expense ($000): 41290 Personnel: 568

⊠ **VETERANS AFFAIRS MARYLAND HEALTH CARE SYSTEM–BALTIMORE DIVISION**, 10 North Greene Street, Zip 21201–1524; tel. 410/605–7001, (Nonreporting) (Includes VETERANS AFFAIRS MARYLAND HEALTH CARE SYSTEM–PERRY POINT DIVISION, Circle Drive, Perry Point, Maryland, Zip 21902, tel. 410/642–2411; Dennis H Smith, Director) **A**1 2 3 5 8 **S** Department of Veterans Affairs, Washington, DC
Primary Contact: Adam M. Robinson, Director
CFO: MajorTom Scheffler, Chief Fiscal Officer
CMO: Dorothy Snow M.D., Chief of Staff
CIO: Sharon Zielinski, Chief Information Resource Officer
CHR: Jeff Craig, Chief Human Resource Management
Web address: www.maryland.va.gov/
Control: Veterans Affairs, Government, federal **Service**: General medical and surgical

Staffed Beds: 727

BEL AIR—Harford County

⊠ **UNIVERSITY OF MARYLAND UPPER CHESAPEAKE MEDICAL CENTER (210049)**, 500 Upper Chesapeake Drive, Zip 21014–4324; tel. 443/643–1000 **A**1 2 3 10 **F**3 11 13 15 18 20 22 26 28 29 30 31 34 35 36 38 40 41 42 45 46 49 50 51 54 57 59 60 64 65 68 70 71 74 75 76 77 78 79 81 82 84 85 86 87 89 92 93 96 107 108 110 111 114 115 118 119 120 121 124 130 131 143 146 147 **S** University of Maryland Medical System, Baltimore, MD
Primary Contact: Lyle Ernest. Sheldon, FACHE, President and Chief Executive Officer
CFO: Joseph E Hoffman III, Executive Vice President and Chief Financial Officer
CMO: Peggy Vaughan M.D., Senior Vice President Medical Affairs
CIO: Rick Casteel, Vice President Management Information Systems and Chief Information Officer
CHR: Toni M Shivery, Vice President Human Resources
Web address: www.uchs.org
Control: Other not–for–profit (including NFP Corporation) **Service**: General medical and surgical

Staffed Beds: 162 Admissions: 11480 Census: 122 Births: 1339 Total Expense ($000): 261074 Payroll Expense ($000): 103640

BERLIN—Worcester County

⊠ **ATLANTIC GENERAL HOSPITAL (210061)**, 9733 Healthway Drive, Zip 21811–1155; tel. 410/641–1100, (Nonreporting) **A**1 10
Primary Contact: Michael A. Franklin, FACHE, President and Chief Executive Officer
COO: Kim Justice, Vice President Planning and Operations
CFO: Cheryl Nottingham, Chief Financial Officer
CMO: Stephen F Waters M.D., Medical Director
CIO: Andrew Fowler, Vice President Information Services
CHR: Jim Brannon, Vice President Human Resources
CNO: Colleen Wareing, Vice President Patient Care Services
Web address: www.atlanticgeneral.org
Control: Other not–for–profit (including NFP Corporation) **Service**: General medical and surgical

Staffed Beds: 51

BETHESDA—Montgomery County

⊞ **NATIONAL INSTITUTES OF HEALTH CLINICAL CENTER** (Biomedical Research), 9000 Rockville Pike, Building 10, Room 6–2551, Zip 20892–1504; tel. 301/496–4000, (Includes CHILDREN'S INN AT NIH, 7 West Drive, Bethesda, Maryland, Zip 20814–1509, tel. 301/496–5672) **A**1 5 8 **F**3 4 5 14 20 22 26 30 31 36 39 45 53 55 58 59 60 61 64 65 68 70 74 75 77 78 79 81 82 84 85 86 87 89 91 92 93 94 95 96 98 99 100 101 104 105 107 108 111 112 114 115 116 117 118 119 120 121 124 126 129 130 132 135 136 141 142 145 146 148 149 **S** U. S. Indian Health Service, Rockville, MD
Primary Contact: John I. Gallin, M.D., Director
COO: Maureen E Gormley R.N., M.P.H., Chief Operating Officer
CFO: Maria Joyce, Chief Financial Officer
CMO: David K Henderson M.D., Deputy Director Clinical Care
CIO: Jon W McKeeby, Chief Information Officer
CHR: Bonnie Tuma, Human Resources Team Lead
CNO: Clare Hastings R.N., Ph.D., Chief Nurse Officer
Web address: www.clinicalcenter.nih.gov
Control: Public Health Service, Government, Federal **Service:** Other specialty treatment

Staffed Beds: 136 **Admissions:** 5275 **Census:** 127 **Outpatient Visits:** 100148 **Births:** 0 **Total Expense ($000):** 428973 **Payroll Expense ($000):** 178057 **Personnel:** 1800

NATIONAL NAVAL MEDICAL CENTER See Walter Reed National Military Medical Center

⊞ **SUBURBAN HOSPITAL (210022)**, 8600 Old Georgetown Road, Zip 20814–1497; tel. 301/896–3100 **A**1 2 3 5 10 **F**3 5 8 11 15 17 18 20 22 24 26 28 29 30 31 34 35 36 37 38 39 40 41 43 44 45 46 49 50 51 56 57 58 59 60 64 70 71 74 75 77 78 79 81 82 84 85 87 89 92 93 98 99 100 101 102 103 104 105 107 108 110 111 115 118 119 120 121 123 126 130 132 135 146 148 **P**6 **S** Johns Hopkins Health System, Baltimore, MD
Primary Contact: Jacky Schultz, MSN, R.N., President
COO: Joseph Linstrom, Vice President Operations
CFO: Marty Basso, Senior Vice President Finance
CMO: Eric D Dobkin M.D., Vice President Medical Affairs
CIO: Jason Cole, Senior Director, Management Information Systems
CNO: LeighAnn Sidone MSN, R.N., Chief Nursing Officer
Web address: www.suburbanhospital.org
Control: Other not–for–profit (including NFP Corporation) **Service:** General medical and surgical

Staffed Beds: 208 **Admissions:** 13265 **Census:** 158 **Outpatient Visits:** 74249 **Births:** 0 **Total Expense ($000):** 270459 **Payroll Expense ($000):** 100224 **Personnel:** 1431

⊞ **WALTER REED NATIONAL MILITARY MEDICAL CENTER**, 8901 Wisconsin Avenue, Zip 20889–5600; tel. 301/295–4611, (Nonreporting) **A**1 2 3 5 **S** Bureau of Medicine and Surgery, Department of the Navy, Falls Church, VA
Primary Contact: Colonel Michael S. Heimall, Director
CFO: CommanderJoseph Pickel, Director Resource Management
CIO: CommanderCayetano Thornton, Chief Information Officer
CHR: CaptainJaime Carroll, Department Head
Web address: www.wrnmmc.capmed.mil/SitePages/home.aspx
Control: Navy, Government, federal **Service:** General medical and surgical

Staffed Beds: 247

CAMBRIDGE—Dorchester County

☐ **EASTERN SHORE HOSPITAL CENTER (214002)**, 5262 Woods Road, Zip 21613–3796, Mailing Address: P.O.Box 800, 21613–0800; tel. 410/221–2300 **A**1 10 **F**10 11 29 59 75 97 98 100 101 106 135 146 **P**6
Primary Contact: Randy L. Bradford, Chief Executive Officer
COO: William Webb, Assistant Superintendent
CFO: William Webb, Assistant Superintendent
CMO: Evangeline Garcia M.D., Clinical Director
CHR: Cassandra Stanley, Director Personnel
CNO: Lisa Hines, Director Nursing
Web address: www.dhmh.state.md.us/eshc
Control: State, Government, Nonfederal **Service:** Psychiatric

Staffed Beds: 80 **Admissions:** 66 **Census:** 68 **Outpatient Visits:** 0 **Births:** 0 **Total Expense ($000):** 20291 **Payroll Expense ($000):** 11616

⊞ **UNIVERSITY OF MARYLAND SHORE MEDICAL CENTER AT DORCHESTER**, 300 Byrn Street, Zip 21613–1908; tel. 410/228–5511, (Nonreporting) **A**1 **S** University of Maryland Medical System, Baltimore, MD
Primary Contact: Kenneth D. Kozel, FACHE, President and Chief Executive Officer
COO: Robert A Frank, Senior Vice President Operations
CFO: Joanne A Hahey, Senior Vice President and Chief Financial Officer
CMO: William Huffner M.D., Vice President Medical Affairs
CIO: Elizabeth Fish, Chief Information Officer
CHR: Susan Coe, Regional Vice President Human Resources
Web address: www.shorehealth.org
Control: Other not–for–profit (including NFP Corporation) **Service:** General medical and surgical

Staffed Beds: 41

CHESTERTOWN—Kent County

CHESTER RIVER HOSPITAL CENTER See University Of Maryland Shore Medical Center At Chestertown

⊞ **UNIVERSITY OF MARYLAND SHORE MEDICAL CENTER AT CHESTERTOWN (210030)**, 100 Brown Street, Zip 21620–1499; tel. 410/778–3300, (Nonreporting) **A**1 10 **S** University of Maryland Medical System, Baltimore, MD
Primary Contact: Kenneth D. Kozel, FACHE, President and Chief Executive Officer
COO: Robert A Frank, Senior Vice President of Operations
CFO: Joanne A Hahey, Vice President Finance and Chief Financial Officer
CMO: William Huffner M.D., Chief Medical Officer
CIO: Elizabeth Fish, Senior Director Site Executive and Information Technology
CHR: Susan Coe, Vice President Human Resources
CNO: Ruth Ann Jones Ed.D., MSN, R.N., Senior Vice President, Chief Nursing Officer
Web address: www.umms.org/hospitals/shore–health–system.htm
Control: Other not–for–profit (including NFP Corporation) **Service:** General medical and surgical

Staffed Beds: 41

CHEVERLY—Prince George's County

GLADYS SPELLMAN SPECIALTY HOSPITAL AND NURSING CENTER, 2900 Mercy Lane, Zip 20785–1157; tel. 301/618–2010, (Nonreporting)
Primary Contact: Stewart R. Seitz, Chief Executive Officer
CFO: Ketty Taboado, Chief Financial Officer
CMO: Paul A Devore M.D., Medical Director
CHR: Michael Jacobs, Vice President Human Resources
Web address: www.dimensionshealth.org
Control: Corporation, Investor–owned (for–profit) **Service:** Chronic disease

Staffed Beds: 30

☐ **PRINCE GEORGE'S HOSPITAL CENTER (210003)**, 3001 Hospital Drive, Zip 20785–1189; tel. 301/618–2000 **A**1 3 5 10 **F**3 11 13 15 17 18 20 22 24 26 28 29 31 34 35 38 40 42 43 45 46 47 48 50 54 55 56 57 59 60 61 63 64 65 66 68 69 70 72 74 75 76 77 78 79 81 82 84 85 86 87 89 92 93 97 98 100 101 102 103 104 105 107 108 110 111 114 115 118 119 130 131 132 134 135 142 144 146 148 **P**6 **S** Dimensions Healthcare System, Cheverly, MD
Primary Contact: K Singh. Taneja, Chief Operating Officer
CMO: David Goldman M.D., Vice President Medical Affairs and Education
CIO: Don Chenoweth, Chief Information Officer
CHR: Michael Jacobs, Vice President Human Resources
Web address: www.princegeorgeshospital.org
Control: Other not–for–profit (including NFP Corporation) **Service:** General medical and surgical

Staffed Beds: 177 **Admissions:** 12358 **Census:** 176 **Outpatient Visits:** 90547 **Births:** 20/4 **Total Expense ($000):** 280029 **Payroll Expense ($000):** 116990 **Personnel:** 1530

CLINTON—Prince George's County

⊞ **MEDSTAR SOUTHERN MARYLAND HOSPITAL CENTER (210062)**, 7503 Surratts Road, Zip 20735–3358; tel. 301/868–8000, (Total facility includes 20 beds in nursing home–type unit) **A**1 2 10 **F**3 13 15 17 18 20 22 26 28 29 30 31 32 34 35 36 37 39 40 44 45 48 49 50 57 59 64 65 68 70 73 74 75 76 77 78 79 80 81 82 85 86 87 89 91 93 96 98 100 101 102 103 105 107 108 114 115 118 119 126 128 129 130 132 135 143 146 147 148 149 **S** MedStar Health, Columbia, MD
Primary Contact: Christine R. Wray, President
CFO: Daniel Feeley, Interim Chief Financial Officer
CMO: Yvette Johnson–Threat, Vice President Medical Affairs
CIO: Lou Mavromatis, Vice President Information Technology
CHR: Paul Zeller, Vice President Human Resources
CNO: Patricia A Scalfari, Vice President Nursing
Web address: www.medstarsouthernmaryland.org
Control: Other not–for–profit (including NFP Corporation) **Service:** General medical and surgical

Staffed Beds: 255 **Admissions:** 10918 **Census:** 132 **Outpatient Visits:** 164198 **Births:** 1230 **Total Expense ($000):** 242527 **Payroll Expense ($000):** 85984 **Personnel:** 1272

MD

SOUTHERN MARYLAND HOSPITAL CENTER See Medstar Southern Maryland Hospital Center

COLUMBIA—Howard County

✠ **HOWARD COUNTY GENERAL HOSPITAL (210048)**, 5755 Cedar Lane, Zip 21044–2999; tel. 410/740–7890 **A**1 2 3 5 10 **F**3 8 11 13 15 18 20 22 26 28 29 30 31 32 34 35 36 39 40 41 44 45 46 47 49 50 51 55 56 57 58 59 60 61 64 65 68 70 72 74 75 76 77 78 79 81 82 84 85 86 87 89 91 92 93 96 98 100 101 102 103 107 108 110 111 115 119 129 130 131 132 134 135 146 147 148 149 **S** Johns Hopkins Health System, Baltimore, MD
Primary Contact: Steven C. Snelgrove, President
CFO: James Young, Senior Vice President Finance and Chief Financial Officer
CMO: Mohammed Shafeeq Ahmed M.D., Vice President of Medical Affairs and Chief Medical Officer
CHR: Jon Oravec, Vice President, Human Resources
CNO: Karen Davis, Chief Nursing Officer and Vice President, Nursing
Web address: www.hcgh.org
Control: Other not–for–profit (including NFP Corporation) **Service**: General medical and surgical

Staffed Beds: 244 **Admissions**: 17431 **Census**: 191 **Outpatient Visits**: 143230 **Births**: 3597 **Total Expense ($000)**: 250601 **Payroll Expense ($000)**: 96478 **Personnel**: 1593

CRISFIELD—Somerset County

☐ **MCCREADY HEALTH (210045)**, 201 Hall Highway, Zip 21817–1299; tel. 410/968–1200, (Nonreporting) **A**1 10
Primary Contact: Joy A. Strand, Chief Executive Officer
CFO: Gary W Broadwater, Chief Financial Officer
Web address: www.mccreadyfoundation.org
Control: Other not–for–profit (including NFP Corporation) **Service**: General medical and surgical

Staffed Beds: 89

CUMBERLAND—Allegany County

☐ **THOMAS B. FINAN CENTER (214012)**, 10102 Country Club Road SE, Zip 21502–8339, Mailing Address: P.O.Box 1722, 21501–1722; tel. 301/777–2405, (Nonreporting) **A**1 10
Primary Contact: John Cullen, Chief Executive Officer
COO: Craig Alexander, Chief Operating Officer
CFO: Gina Spears, Chief Financial Officer
CMO: David Millis M.D., Clinical Director
CHR: Chris Loney, Director Personnel
CNO: Gayle Walter, Director of Nursing
Web address: www.dhmh.state.md.us
Control: State, Government, Nonfederal **Service**: Psychiatric

Staffed Beds: 80

✠ △ **WESTERN MARYLAND REGIONAL MEDICAL CENTER (210027)**, 12500 Willowbrook Road SE, Zip 21502–6393, Mailing Address: P.O.Box 539, 21501–0539; tel. 240/964–7000, (Total facility includes 88 beds in nursing home–type unit) **A**1 2 7 10 **F**3 5 11 13 14 15 17 18 20 22 24 26 28 29 30 31 32 34 35 40 43 44 45 49 50 53 54 56 57 58 59 60 62 63 64 66 68 70 73 74 75 76 77 78 79 80 81 82 84 85 86 87 89 90 93 94 96 97 98 100 101 102 103 104 107 108 110 111 114 116 117 119 120 121 124 126 128 129 130 132 134 135 144 145 146 148 150 **P**6
Primary Contact: Barry P. Ronan, President and Chief Executive Officer
COO: Nancy D. Adams R.N., Senior Vice President and Chief Operating Officer
CFO: Kimberly S Repac, Senior Vice President and Chief Financial Officer
CMO: Gerald Goldstein M.D., Senior Vice President and Chief Medical Officer
CIO: William J. Byers, Chief Information Officer
CHR: Christopher Bumbaugh, Executive Director Human Resource and Organizational Development
CNO: James M. Karstetter R.N., II, Vice President & Chief Nursing Officer
Web address: www.wmhs.com
Control: Other not–for–profit (including NFP Corporation) **Service**: General medical and surgical

Staffed Beds: 316 **Admissions**: 12038 **Census**: 235 **Outpatient Visits**: 557772 **Births**: 944 **Total Expense ($000)**: 314070 **Payroll Expense ($000)**: 105283 **Personnel**: 1600

EAST NEW MARKET—Dorchester County

WARWICK MANOR BEHAVIORAL HEALTH, 3680 Warwick Road, Zip 21631–1420; tel. 410/943–8108, (Nonreporting)
Primary Contact: L Wesley. Fuhrman, President and Chief Executive Officer
Web address: www.warwickmanor.org/
Control: Corporation, Investor–owned (for–profit) **Service**: Alcoholism and other chemical dependency

Staffed Beds: 42

EASTON—Talbot County

✠ △ **UNIVERSITY OF MARYLAND SHORE MEDICAL CENTER AT EASTON (210037)**, 219 South Washington Street, Zip 21601–2996; tel. 410/822–1000, (Nonreporting) **A**1 2 7 10 **S** University of Maryland Medical System, Baltimore, MD
Primary Contact: Kenneth D. Kozel, FACHE, President and Chief Executive Officer
COO: Robert A Frank, Senior Vice President of Operations
CFO: Joanne A Hahey, Senior Vice President and Chief Financial Officer
CMO: William Huffner M.D., Chief Medical Officer
CIO: Elizabeth Fish, Chief Information Officer
CHR: Susan Coe, Regional Vice President Human Resources
CNO: Ruth Ann Jones Ed.D., MSN, R.N., Senior Vice President, Chief Nursing Officer
Web address: www.shorehealth.org
Control: Other not–for–profit (including NFP Corporation) **Service**: General medical and surgical

Staffed Beds: 132

ELKTON—Cecil County

✠ **UNION HOSPITAL (210032)**, 106 Bow Street, Zip 21921–5596; tel. 410/398–4000 **A**1 2 3 5 10 **F**2 3 11 12 13 15 18 26 29 30 31 34 35 38 40 44 45 46 49 50 51 53 54 57 59 61 64 69 70 74 75 76 77 78 79 81 82 84 85 86 87 89 92 93 97 98 100 102 104 105 107 108 110 111 114 118 119 129 130 131 132 135 146 147 148 149 **P**6
Primary Contact: Richard C. Szumel, M.D., Chief Executive Officer
CFO: Laurie Beyer, Senior Vice President and Chief Financial Officer
CMO: Cydney Teal M.D., Vice President Medical Affairs
CIO: Anne Lara, Chief Information Officer
CHR: Terrence Lovell, Vice President Human Resources
CNO: Katie Boston–Leary, Senior Vice President Patient Care Services
Web address: www.uhcc.com
Control: Other not–for–profit (including NFP Corporation) **Service**: General medical and surgical

Staffed Beds: 109 **Admissions**: 5777 **Census**: 59 **Outpatient Visits**: 142560 **Births**: 642 **Total Expense ($000)**: 152851 **Payroll Expense ($000)**: 67710 **Personnel**: 969

FREDERICK—Frederick County

✠ **FREDERICK REGIONAL HEALTH SYSTEM (210005)**, 400 West Seventh Street, Zip 21701–4593; tel. 240/566–3300, (Nonreporting) **A**1 2 5 10
Primary Contact: Thomas A. Kleinhanzl, President and Chief Executive Officer
COO: John R Verbus, Senior Vice President and Chief Operating Officer
CFO: Michelle K Mahan, Senior Vice President and Chief Financial Officer
CMO: Manuel Casiano M.D., Senior Vice President Medical Affairs
CIO: David Quirke, Vice President Information Services
CNO: Cheryl Cioffi R.N., Senior Vice President Patient Care Services and Chief Nursing Officer
Web address: www.fmh.org
Control: Other not–for–profit (including NFP Corporation) **Service**: General medical and surgical

Staffed Beds: 275

GERMANTOWN—Montgomery County

★ **HOLY CROSS GERMANTOWN HOSPITAL (210065)**, 19801 Observation Drive, Zip 20876–4070; tel. 301/754–7000 **F**3 11 12 13 18 26 29 30 35 39 40 45 46 49 50 59 64 66 68 70 73 74 75 76 77 78 79 81 84 85 86 87 93 97 98 100 102 103 107 108 111 115 118 119 126 130 132 146 147 149 **S** Trinity Health, Livonia, MI
Primary Contact: Doug Ryder, President
Web address: www.holycrosshealth.org/germantown
Control: Church operated, Nongovernment, not–for–profit **Service**: General medical and surgical

Staffed Beds: 101 **Admissions**: 4873 **Census**: 51 **Outpatient Visits**: 55203 **Births**: 739 **Total Expense ($000)**: 86827 **Payroll Expense ($000)**: 29861 **Personnel**: 486

GLEN BURNIE—Anne Arundel County

✠ **UNIVERSITY OF MARYLAND BALTIMORE WASHINGTON MEDICAL CENTER (210043)**, 301 Hospital Drive, Zip 21061–5899; tel. 410/787–4000 **A**1 2 3 5 10 **F**3 11 13 14 15 18 19 20 22 26 28 29 30 31 34 35 37 38 39 40 41 43 44 45 46 48 49 50 54 55 56 57 58 59 60 64 65 68 70 74 75 76 77 78 79 81 82 84 85 86 87 89 93 98 100 101 102 103 104 105 107 111 114 115 118 119 120 121 122 123 124 126 129 130 131 132 135 146 147 148 149 150 **S** University of Maryland Medical System, Baltimore, MD
Primary Contact: Karen E. Olscamp, President and Chief Executive Officer
COO: Kathleen McCollum, Senior Vice President, Clinical Integration and Chief Operating Officer
CFO: Al Pietsch CPA, Senior Vice President and Chief Financial Officer
CMO: Neel Vibhakar M.D., Senior Vice President and Chief Medical Officer
CIO: Jon P Burns, Senior Vice President and Chief Information Officer
CHR: Kathy Poehler, Vice President, Human Resources
CNO: Catherine Whitaker MSN, R.N., Vice President and Chief Nursing Officer
Web address: www.mybwmc.org
Control: Other not–for–profit (including NFP Corporation) **Service**: General medical and surgical

Staffed Beds: 303 **Admissions**: 17650 **Census**: 210 **Outpatient Visits**: 127534 **Births**: 861 **Total Expense ($000)**: 336314 **Payroll Expense ($000)**: 133352 **Personnel**: 2245

Many Facility Codes have changed. Please refer to the AHA Guide Code Chart. © 2017 AHA Guide

MD

HAGERSTOWN—Washington County

☐ **BROOK LANE HEALTH SERVICES (214003)**, 13121 Brook Lane, Zip 21742–1435, Mailing Address: P.O.Box 1945, 21742–1945; tel. 301/733–0330 **A**1 10 **F**5 26 27 30 56 68 98 99 100 101 103 104 105 130 143 146
Primary Contact: R Lynn. Rushing, Chief Executive Officer
COO: Jason Allen, Chief Operating Officer
CFO: David Schey, Chief Financial Officer
CMO: David Gonzalez M.D., Medical Director
CIO: Robert Fritz, Chief Information Officer
CHR: Nicole Twigg, Director Human Resources
CNO: Jason Allen, Director Patient Care Services
Web address: www.brooklane.org
Control: Other not–for–profit (including NFP Corporation) **Service:** Psychiatric

> **Staffed Beds:** 57 **Admissions:** 1998 **Census:** 46 **Births:** 0

☒ △ **MERITUS MEDICAL CENTER (210001)**, 11116 Medical Campus Road, Zip 21742–6710; tel. 301/790–8000 **A**1 2 3 7 10 13 **F**3 5 11 12 13 15 17 18 20 22 26 28 29 30 31 34 35 38 40 43 44 49 51 52 54 56 57 58 59 60 61 62 64 65 70 74 75 76 77 78 79 81 82 83 84 85 86 87 89 90 93 94 96 97 98 99 100 101 102 103 104 105 107 108 111 114 115 118 119 120 121 123 130 131 132 135 143 144 145 146 147 148 **P**6 8
Primary Contact: Joseph P. Ross, President and Chief Executive Officer
CFO: Thomas T Chan, Chief Financial Officer
CMO: Heather Lorenzo M.D., Vice President and Chief Medical Officer
CHR: Laura Minteer, Chief Human Resource Officer
CNO: Melanie M Heuston, Chief Nursing Office
Web address: www.meritushealth.com
Control: Other not–for–profit (including NFP Corporation) **Service:** General medical and surgical

> **Staffed Beds:** 278 **Admissions:** 16060 **Census:** 175 **Outpatient Visits:** 199709 **Births:** 1873 **Total Expense ($000):** 299131 **Payroll Expense ($000):** 97273 **Personnel:** 1695

WASHINGTON COUNTY HEALTH SYSTEM See Meritus Medical Center

☐ △ **WESTERN MARYLAND HOSPITAL CENTER (212002)**, 1500 Pennsylvania Avenue, Zip 21742–3194; tel. 301/745–4200, (Nonreporting) **A**1 7 10
Primary Contact: Michael Reyka, Ph.D., Chief Executive Officer
COO: David Davis, Chief Operating Officer
CFO: Kelly Edmonds, Chief Financial Officer
CMO: Monica Stallworth M.D., Chief of Staff
CIO: Ron Keplinger, Chief Information Officer
CHR: David Davis, Chief Operating Officer
Web address: www.wmhc.us
Control: State, Government, Nonfederal **Service:** Acute long–term care hospital

> **Staffed Beds:** 120

HAVRE DE GRACE—Harford County

☒ **UNIVERSITY OF MARYLAND HARFORD MEMORIAL HOSPITAL (210006)**, 501 South Union Avenue, Zip 21078–3493; tel. 443/843–5000 **A**1 10 **F**3 11 12 15 29 30 31 34 35 36 38 40 42 46 49 50 51 57 59 60 64 65 66 68 70 71 74 75 77 78 79 81 82 84 85 86 87 92 93 96 98 102 103 104 107 108 110 111 114 115 118 119 129 130 131 132 135 146 148 **S** University of Maryland Medical System, Baltimore, MD
Primary Contact: Lyle Ernest. Sheldon, FACHE, President and Chief Executive Officer
CFO: Joseph E Hoffman III, Executive Vice President and Chief Financial Officer
CMO: Peggy Vaughan M.D., Senior Vice President Medical Affairs
CIO: Rick Casteel, Vice President Management Information Systems and Chief Information Officer
CHR: Toni M Shivery, Vice President Human Resources
Web address: www.uchs.org
Control: Other not–for–profit (including NFP Corporation) **Service:** General medical and surgical

> **Staffed Beds:** 49 **Admissions:** 4384 **Census:** 62 **Births:** 0 **Total Expense ($000):** 82722 **Payroll Expense ($000):** 37785

JESSUP—Howard County

☐ **CLIFTON T. PERKINS HOSPITAL CENTER**, 8450 Dorsey Run Road, Zip 20794–9486; tel. 410/724–3000, (Nonreporting) **A**1 3 5
Primary Contact: John Robison, Chief Executive Officer
COO: Thomas D Lewis, Chief Operating Officer
CFO: George Parnel, Chief Financial Officer
CMO: Muhammed Ajanah M.D., Clinical Director
CIO: Chanda Hamilton, Chief Information Officer
CHR: Beverly Stacie, Director Human Resources
Web address: www.dhmh.state.md.us/perkins/
Control: State, Government, Nonfederal **Service:** Psychiatric

> **Staffed Beds:** 250

LA PLATA—Charles County

☒ **UNIVERSITY OF MARYLAND CHARLES REGIONAL MEDICAL CENTER (210035)**, 5 Garrett Avenue, Zip 20646–5960, Mailing Address: P.O.Box 1070, 20646–1070; tel. 301/609–4000 **A**1 2 10 **F**3 11 13 15 28 29 30 31 34 35 36 38 40 44 45 50 51 56 57 59 61 64 70 74 76 77 78 79 81 82 85 86 87 89 91 92 93 107 108 110 111 115 118 119 130 132 135 145 146 148 149 **S** University of Maryland Medical System, Baltimore, MD
Primary Contact: Noel A. Cervino, President and Chief Executive Officer
CFO: Erik Boas, Chief Financial Officer
CMO: Joseph Moser M.D., Chief Medical Officer
CIO: John Czahor, IT Site Executive
CHR: Stacey M Cook MS, Vice President, Human Resources
CNO: Dana Levy, Chief Nursing Officer
Web address: www.charlesregional.org
Control: Other not–for–profit (including NFP Corporation) **Service:** General medical and surgical

> **Staffed Beds:** 110 **Admissions:** 6016 **Census:** 66 **Outpatient Visits:** 78820 **Births:** 874 **Total Expense ($000):** 114047 **Payroll Expense ($000):** 46188 **Personnel:** 743

LANHAM—Prince George's County

☒ **DOCTORS COMMUNITY HOSPITAL (210051)**, 8118 Good Luck Road, Zip 20706–3574; tel. 301/552–8118 **A**1 10 **F**3 8 12 15 18 20 26 28 29 30 31 34 35 40 44 49 50 51 53 54 57 59 64 70 71 75 77 78 79 81 84 85 86 87 90 93 107 108 110 111 114 115 119 120 121 123 126 130 131 132 135 146 **P**6 7
Primary Contact: Philip B. Down, Chief Executive Officer
COO: Paul Grenaldo, Executive Vice President and Chief Operating Officer
CFO: Camille Bash, Chief Financial Officer
CMO: Sunil Madan M.D., Chief Medical Officer and Chief Population Health Officer
CIO: Joyce Hanscome, Chief Information Officer
CHR: Paul Hagens, Vice President Human Resources
Web address: www.dchweb.org
Control: Other not–for–profit (including NFP Corporation) **Service:** General medical and surgical

> **Staffed Beds:** 144 **Admissions:** 9725 **Census:** 141 **Outpatient Visits:** 83757 **Births:** 0 **Total Expense ($000):** 198910 **Payroll Expense ($000):** 89946 **Personnel:** 1252

LAUREL—Prince George's County

☐ △ **LAUREL REGIONAL HOSPITAL (210055)**, 7300 Van Dusen Road, Zip 20707–9463; tel. 301/725–4300 **A**1 7 10 **F**1 3 11 13 15 18 20 29 30 31 34 35 40 46 49 50 51 57 59 60 61 63 64 65 66 68 69 70 74 75 76 77 78 79 80 81 82 84 85 87 90 92 93 98 100 102 103 104 105 107 108 110 111 114 115 118 119 129 130 132 146 148 **P**6 **S** Dimensions Healthcare System, Cheverly, MD
Primary Contact: Trudy Hall, M.D., Vice President Medical Affairs and Interim Chief Executive Officer
CFO: Lisa Goodlett, Senior Vice President and Chief Financial Officer
CMO: Trudy Hall M.D., Vice President Medical Affairs
CIO: David Peterson, Chief Information Officer
CHR: John Peeples, Senior Vice President Human Resources
CNO: June Meyer MSN, R.N., Vice President Chief Nursing Officer
Web address: www.laurelregionalhospital.org
Control: Other not–for–profit (including NFP Corporation) **Service:** General medical and surgical

> **Staffed Beds:** 58 **Admissions:** 4130 **Census:** 68 **Outpatient Visits:** 30183 **Births:** 164 **Total Expense ($000):** 95941 **Payroll Expense ($000):** 40032 **Personnel:** 468

LEONARDTOWN—St. Mary's County

☒ **MEDSTAR ST. MARY'S HOSPITAL (210028)**, 25500 Point Lookout Road, Zip 20650–2015, Mailing Address: PO Box 527, 20650–0527; tel. 301/475–6001 **A**1 2 10 **F**3 11 13 15 18 28 29 30 31 32 34 35 36 39 40 44 45 48 50 51 53 54 57 59 63 64 65 66 68 70 71 74 75 76 77 78 79 81 82 84 85 86 87 89 93 98 100 101 102 103 104 105 107 108 110 111 114 115 118 119 129 130 132 134 135 143 144 146 147 148 149 150 **S** MedStar Health, Columbia, MD
Primary Contact: Christine R. Wray, President
COO: Stephen T. Michaels M.D., Chief Operating Officer and Chief Medical Officer
CIO: Donald Sirk, Director Information Systems
CNO: Elizabeth L Morse, Vice President Nursing and Chief Nursing Officer
Web address: www.medstarstmarys.org
Control: Other not–for–profit (including NFP Corporation) **Service:** General medical and surgical

> **Staffed Beds:** 91 **Admissions:** 7689 **Census:** 76 **Outpatient Visits:** 191026 **Births:** 1283 **Total Expense ($000):** 150572 **Payroll Expense ($000):** 63019 **Personnel:** 1053

Hospital, Medicare Provider Number, Address, Telephone, Approval, Facility, and Physician Codes, Health Care System

★ American Hospital Association (AHA) membership
☐ The Joint Commission accreditation
○ Healthcare Facilities Accreditation Program
◇ DNV Healthcare Inc. accreditation
⇑ Center for Improvement in Healthcare Quality Accreditation
△ Commission on Accreditation of Rehabilitation Facilities (CARF) accreditation

MD

OAKLAND—Garrett County

☒ **GARRETT REGIONAL MEDICAL CENTER (210017)**, 251 North Fourth Street, Zip 21550–1375; tel. 301/533–4000, (Total facility includes 10 beds in nursing home–type unit) **A**1 10 **F**3 11 13 28 29 30 31 32 34 35 38 40 45 50 53 56 57 59 64 65 68 70 75 76 78 79 81 84 85 87 89 102 107 108 114 119 128 130 135 141 144 146 148 **P**6
Primary Contact: Mark G. Boucot, FACHE, President and Chief Executive Officer
CFO: Tracy Lipscomb CPA, Vice President Financial Services and Chief Financial Officer
CMO: Marjorie Fridkin M.D., Chief Medical Officer
CIO: Steven Peterson, Chief Information Officer, Vice President of Operations
CHR: Laura M Waters, Vice President Human Resources
CNO: Kendra Thayer MSN, R.N., Chief Nursing Officer, Vice President Clinical Services
Web address: www.gcmh.com
Control: Other not–for–profit (including NFP Corporation) **Service**: General medical and surgical

Staffed Beds: 59 **Admissions:** 2020 **Census:** 19 **Outpatient Visits:** 76878 **Births:** 333 **Total Expense ($000):** 47661 **Payroll Expense ($000):** 19765 **Personnel:** 351

OLNEY—Montgomery County

☒ **MEDSTAR MONTGOMERY MEDICAL CENTER (210018)**, 18101 Prince Philip Drive, Zip 20832–1512; tel. 301/774–8882 **A**1 2 3 10 **F**3 4 5 11 12 13 15 18 20 26 28 29 30 31 34 35 37 38 40 41 45 46 48 49 50 51 53 55 56 57 59 64 65 68 70 74 75 76 77 78 79 80 81 82 84 85 86 87 89 92 93 98 99 100 102 103 104 105 107 108 111 114 115 118 119 120 121 126 129 130 131 132 134 135 146 147 149 **S** MedStar Health, Columbia, MD
Primary Contact: Thomas J. Senker, FACHE, President
CFO: David A Havrilla, Chief Financial Officer
CMO: Frederick Finelli M.D., Vice President Medical Affairs
CIO: Chistiane Brown, Assistant Vice President
CHR: Kevin Mell, Vice President Operations
CNO: Connie Stone R.N., Chief Nursing Officer
Web address: www.medstarmontgomery.org
Control: Other not–for–profit (including NFP Corporation) **Service**: General medical and surgical

Staffed Beds: 147 **Admissions:** 7119 **Census:** 80 **Outpatient Visits:** 75678 **Births:** 696 **Total Expense ($000):** 151874 **Payroll Expense ($000):** 59301 **Personnel:** 748

OXEN HILL—Prince George's County

☒ **FORT WASHINGTON MEDICAL CENTER (210060)**, 174 Waterfront Street, Suite 225, Zip 20744; tel. 301/292–7000, (Nonreporting) **A**1 10
Primary Contact: Reginald Jones, Interim President and Chief Executive Officer
COO: Al Campbell, Senior Vice President and Chief Operating Officer
CFO: Joseph B Tucker, Senior Vice President and Chief Financial Officer
CMO: Elias Debbas M.D., President Medical Staff
CIO: Fred Ashby, Director Information Technology
CHR: Alexander Morris, Corporate Director Human Resources
CNO: Marjorie Quint–Bouzid, Chief Nursing Officer and Vice President Patient Care Services
Web address: www.fortwashingtonmc.org
Control: Other not–for–profit (including NFP Corporation) **Service**: General medical and surgical

Staffed Beds: 37

PERRY POINT—Cecil County

VETERANS AFFAIRS MARYLAND HEALTH CARE SYSTEM–PERRY POINT DIVISION See Veterans Affairs Maryland Health Care System–Baltimore Division, Baltimore

PRINCE FREDERICK—Calvert County

☒ **CALVERT MEMORIAL HOSPITAL (210039)**, 100 Hospital Road, Zip 20678–4017; tel. 410/535–4000, (Total facility includes 18 beds in nursing home–type unit) **A**1 10 **F**3 8 11 13 18 20 26 28 29 30 31 32 34 35 36 38 39 40 41 45 46 47 48 49 50 51 54 56 57 59 60 64 65 66 68 70 71 74 75 76 77 78 79 81 82 84 85 86 87 89 93 98 99 100 101 102 104 105 106 107 108 111 112 114 115 119 124 127 129 130 132 133 134 135 144 146 147 148 149 **P**4
Primary Contact: Dean Teague, FACHE, Chief Executive Officer
CFO: Robert Kertis, Vice President Finance
CMO: Barbara Estes M.D., Chief of Staff
CIO: Ed Grogan, Vice President Information Services and Chief Information Officer
CHR: Anthony M. Bladen, Vice President Human Resources
CNO: Diane Couchman, Vice President Patient Care Services and Chief Nursing Executive
Web address: www.calverthospital.com
Control: Other not–for–profit (including NFP Corporation) **Service**: General medical and surgical

Staffed Beds: 139 **Admissions:** 5390 **Census:** 67 **Outpatient Visits:** 146208 **Births:** 686 **Total Expense ($000):** 129054 **Payroll Expense ($000):** 54795 **Personnel:** 941

RANDALLSTOWN—Baltimore County

☐ **NORTHWEST HOSPITAL (210040)**, 5401 Old Court Road, Zip 21133–5185; tel. 410/521–2200, (Nonreporting) **A**1 2 3 10 **S** LifeBridge Health, Baltimore, MD
Primary Contact: Brian M. White, President
COO: Kelly Corbi, Chief Operating Officer
CFO: Nancy Kane, Assistant Vice President Finance LifeBridge Health
CMO: Ronald L Ginsberg M.D., Vice President Medical Affairs
CIO: Tressa Springmann, Vice President and Chief Information Officer
CHR: Valerie Brandenburg, Director Human Resources
CNO: Susan L Jalbert R.N., MS, Vice President Patient Care Services and Chief Nursing Officer
Web address: www.lifebridgehealth.org
Control: Other not–for–profit (including NFP Corporation) **Service**: General medical and surgical

Staffed Beds: 253

ROCKVILLE—Montgomery County

☐ **ADVENTIST BEHAVIORAL HEALTH AND WELLNESS SERVICES (214013)**, 14901 Broschart Road, Zip 20850–3318; tel. 301/251–4500, (Nonreporting) **A**1 3 10 **S** Adventist HealthCare, Gaithersburg, MD
Primary Contact: Kevin Young, FACHE, President
CFO: Randy Reimer, Chief Financial Officer
CMO: Peter H Levine M.D., Executive Medical Director Behavioral Health Services
CIO: Kathleen Dyer, Vice President and Chief Information Officer
CHR: Mary Cloutier, Director Human Resources
Web address: www.adventistbehavioralhealth.com
Control: Other not–for–profit (including NFP Corporation) **Service**: Psychiatric

Staffed Beds: 220

☐ △ **ADVENTIST HEALTHCARE PHYSICAL HEALTH AND REHABILITATION (213029)**, 9909 Medical Center Drive, Zip 20850–6361; tel. 240/864–6000, (Nonreporting) **A**1 7 10 **S** Adventist HealthCare, Gaithersburg, MD
Primary Contact: Brent Reitz, President
COO: Jason Makaroff, Chief Operating Officer and Associate Vice President
CMO: Terrence P Sheehan M.D., Medical Director
CHR: Carrie Hibbard, Human Resource Business Partner
CNO: Valerie Summerlin R.N., MS, Chief Nursing Officer
Web address: www.adventistrehab.com
Control: Other not–for–profit (including NFP Corporation) **Service**: Rehabilitation

Staffed Beds: 77

☐ **ADVENTIST HEALTHCARE SHADY GROVE MEDICAL CENTER (210057)**, 9901 Medical Center Drive, Zip 20850–3395; tel. 240/826–6000 **A**1 2 3 10 **F**3 12 13 15 18 20 22 26 28 29 30 31 36 39 40 41 42 45 47 48 50 51 53 55 57 60 61 64 66 68 70 72 74 75 76 77 78 79 81 82 83 84 85 87 89 102 107 108 110 111 114 115 116 117 119 120 121 126 129 130 135 146 148 149 **P**6 8 **S** Adventist HealthCare, Gaithersburg, MD
Primary Contact: John Sackett, President SGMC and Executive Vice President and Chief Operating Officer
COO: Eunmee Shim R.N., MSN, Vice President Operations
CFO: Daniel Cochran, Vice President and Chief Financial Officer
CMO: Kevin Smothers M.D., Vice President Chief Medical Officer
CIO: Christopher Ghion, Vice President and Chief Information Officer
CNO: Joan M Vincent MSN, MS, R.N., Vice President Patient Care Services and Chief Nurse Executive
Web address: www.adventisthealthcare.com
Control: Church operated, Nongovernment, not–for–profit **Service**: General medical and surgical

Staffed Beds: 315 **Admissions:** 17202 **Census:** 187 **Outpatient Visits:** 92598 **Births:** 4655 **Total Expense ($000):** 338053 **Payroll Expense ($000):** 126406 **Personnel:** 2406

POTOMAC RIDGE BEHAVIORAL HEALTH See Adventist Behavioral Health And Wellness Services

SALISBURY—Wicomico County

☒ **DEER'S HEAD HOSPITAL CENTER (212003)**, 351 Deer's Head Hospital Road, Zip 21801–3201, Mailing Address: PO Box 2018, 21802–2018; tel. 410/543–4000, (Total facility includes 61 beds in nursing home–type unit) **A**1 10 **F**1 3 11 28 29 30 44 50 56 57 59 60 61 65 68 75 77 82 84 85 86 87 90 91 93 94 96 128 130 132 135 146 148 149 **P**6
Primary Contact: Mary Beth Waide, JD, MS, R.N., Chief Executive Officer
CFO: Kenneth Waller, Fiscal Administrator
CMO: Michael P. Buchness M.D., Director Medical
CIO: Mac Beattie, Computer Network Specialist
CHR: Luanne G Dashield, Personnel Administrator
CNO: Cheri Porcelli MSN, R.N., Chief Nursing Officer
Web address: www.deershead.org
Control: State, Government, Nonfederal **Service**: Chronic disease

Staffed Beds: 73 **Admissions:** 87 **Census:** 51 **Outpatient Visits:** 10012 **Births:** 0 **Total Expense ($000):** 23902 **Payroll Expense ($000):** 10170 **Personnel:** 232

Many Facility Codes have changed. Please refer to the AHA Guide Code Chart. © 2017 AHA Guide

✠ △ **HEALTHSOUTH CHESAPEAKE REHABILITATION HOSPITAL (213028)**, 220 Tilghman Road, Zip 21804–1921; tel. 410/546–4600, (Nonreporting) **A**1 7 10 **S** HEALTHSOUTH Corporation, Birmingham, AL
Primary Contact: Steven Walas, Chief Executive Officer
CFO: Karen Rounsley, Controller
CHR: Belinda Thompson, Coordinator Human Resources
CNO: Belle Goslee, Chief Nursing Officer
Web address: www.healthsouthchesapeake.com
Control: Corporation, Investor–owned (for–profit) **Service**: Rehabilitation

Staffed Beds: 54

✠ **PENINSULA REGIONAL MEDICAL CENTER (210019)**, 100 East Carroll Street, Zip 21801–5422; tel. 410/546–6400 **A**1 2 3 10 **F**3 11 12 13 15 17 18 20 22 24 26 28 29 30 31 32 34 35 37 40 43 45 46 47 48 49 50 51 53 54 57 58 59 60 61 64 68 70 71 73 74 75 76 77 78 79 81 82 84 85 86 87 89 92 97 98 99 100 102 104 105 107 108 110 111 114 115 118 119 120 121 123 124 126 130 132 135 143 144 145 146 147 148 **P**5 8
Primary Contact: Margaret Nalepa, Ph.D., President and Chief Executive Officer
COO: Cindy Lunsford, Executive Vice President and Chief Operating Officer
CFO: Bruce Ritchie, Vice President of Finance and Chief Financial Officer
CMO: Charles B Silvia M.D., Chief Medical Officer and Vice President Medical Affairs
CIO: Raymond Adkins, Chief Information Officer
CHR: Scott Peterson, Vice President of People and Organizational Development
CNO: Karen C Poisker MSN, Vice President Patient Care Services and Chief Nursing Officer
Web address: www.peninsula.org
Control: Other not–for–profit (including NFP Corporation) **Service**: General medical and surgical

Staffed Beds: 302 **Admissions:** 17023 **Census:** 200 **Outpatient Visits:** 580089 **Births:** 1943 **Total Expense ($000):** 412629 **Payroll Expense ($000):** 165766 **Personnel:** 2489

SILVER SPRING—Montgomery County

✠ **HOLY CROSS HEALTH (210004)**, 1500 Forest Glen Road, Zip 20910–1487; tel. 301/754–7000 **A**1 2 3 5 10 **F**3 11 12 13 15 17 18 19 20 22 26 29 30 31 35 39 40 41 45 46 49 50 56 58 59 60 64 66 68 69 70 72 74 75 76 77 78 79 81 82 84 85 86 87 89 93 97 102 107 108 110 111 115 118 119 120 121 123 124 126 129 130 132 144 146 147 149 **S** Trinity Health, Livonia, MI
Primary Contact: Louis Damiano, Acting President
CFO: Anne Gillis, Chief Financial Officer
CMO: Blair Eig M.D., Senior Vice President Medical Affairs
CIO: Matthew Trimmer, Director Information Services
CHR: J Manuel Ocasio, Vice President Human Resources
CNO: Celia Guarino R.N., MSN, Vice President and Chief Nursing Officer
Web address: www.holycrosshealth.org
Control: Church operated, Nongovernment, not–for–profit **Service**: General medical and surgical

Staffed Beds: 415 **Admissions:** 30838 **Census:** 353 **Outpatient Visits:** 162615 **Births:** 9234 **Total Expense ($000):** 413238 **Payroll Expense ($000):** 182593 **Personnel:** 2492

SILVER SPRING—Prince George's County

SAINT LUKE INSTITUTE, 8901 New Hampshire Avenue, Zip 20903–3611; tel. 301/445–7970, (Nonreporting)
Primary Contact: David Songy, President and Chief Executive Officer
COO: SisterDanile Lynch, Chief Operating Officer
Web address: www.sli.org
Control: Other not–for–profit (including NFP Corporation) **Service**: Psychiatric

Staffed Beds: 24

SYKESVILLE—Carroll County

☐ **SPRINGFIELD HOSPITAL CENTER (214004)**, 6655 Sykesville Road, Zip 21784–7966; tel. 410/970–7000 **A**1 3 10 **F**11 30 35 39 44 50 53 56 57 68 75 77 86 87 98 101 103 130 132 135 146 149 **P**6
Primary Contact: Paula A. Langmead, Chief Executive Officer
COO: Daniel Triplett, Acting Chief Operating Officer
CFO: Keith Hardesty, Chief Financial Officer
CMO: Kim Bright M.D., Clinical Director
CIO: Denise Maskell, Chief Information Officer
CNO: Gloria Merek, Director of Nursing
Web address: www.dhmh.state.md.us/springfield
Control: State, Government, Nonfederal **Service**: Psychiatric

Staffed Beds: 230 **Admissions:** 248 **Census:** 231 **Outpatient Visits:** 0 **Births:** 0 **Total Expense ($000):** 74994 **Payroll Expense ($000):** 40805 **Personnel:** 659

TAKOMA PARK—Montgomery County

☐ △ **ADVENTIST HEALTHCARE WASHINGTON ADVENTIST HOSPITAL (210016)**, 7600 Carroll Avenue, Zip 20912–6392; tel. 301/891–7600, (Nonreporting) **A**1 2 3 5 7 10 **S** Adventist HealthCare, Gaithersburg, MD
Primary Contact: Erik Wangsness, President
Web address: www.adventisthealthcare.com
Control: Other not–for–profit (including NFP Corporation) **Service**: General medical and surgical

Staffed Beds: 252

TOWSON—Baltimore County

✠ **UNIVERSITY OF MARYLAND ST. JOSEPH MEDICAL CENTER (210063)**, 7601 Osler Drive, Zip 21204–7582; tel. 410/337–1000 **A**1 2 3 10 **F**3 11 13 15 17 18 20 22 24 26 28 29 30 31 34 35 36 37 40 41 44 45 46 47 48 49 50 54 55 56 57 58 59 60 61 64 65 66 68 70 71 72 74 75 76 77 78 79 81 82 84 85 86 87 89 91 92 93 97 98 99 100 101 102 103 104 105 107 108 114 115 118 119 120 121 122 123 124 126 129 130 131 132 134 135 144 146 147 148 149 **P**6 **S** University of Maryland Medical System, Baltimore, MD
Primary Contact: Thomas Smyth, President and Chief Executive Officer
COO: Craig Carmichael, Vice President, Operations
CMO: Gail Cunningham, Interim Chief Medical Officer
CIO: Thomas Gronert, Chief Information Officer
CNO: Pamela Jamieson, Vice President Patient Care Services and Chief Nursing Officer
Web address: www.stjosephtowson.com/home.aspx
Control: Other not–for–profit (including NFP Corporation) **Service**: General medical and surgical

Staffed Beds: 276 **Admissions:** 15550 **Census:** 174 **Outpatient Visits:** 109668 **Births:** 2271 **Total Expense ($000):** 330060 **Payroll Expense ($000):** 111186 **Personnel:** 2036

WESTMINSTER—Carroll County

✠ **CARROLL HOSPITAL CENTER (210033)**, 200 Memorial Avenue, Zip 21157–5799; tel. 410/848–3000 **A**1 2 10 **F**3 5 11 13 15 18 19 20 22 26 28 29 30 31 32 34 35 36 37 38 39 40 44 45 46 49 50 51 54 55 56 57 58 59 62 63 64 68 70 74 75 76 77 78 79 81 82 83 84 85 86 87 89 93 94 96 98 99 100 101 102 103 104 105 107 108 109 111 114 115 118 119 120 121 126 129 130 131 132 134 135 145 146 147 148 149 **P**6 8 **S** LifeBridge Health, Baltimore, MD
Primary Contact: Leslie Simmons, FACHE, R.N., President
CFO: Kevin Kelbly, Senior Vice President Finance and Corporate Fiscal Affairs
CMO: Mark Olszyk M.D., Vice President Medical Affairs and Chief Medical Officer
CHR: Holly Phipps Adams, Vice President of Human Resources
CNO: Stephanie Reid R.N., Vice President of Patient Care Services and Chief Nursing Officer
Web address: www.carrollhospitalcenter.org
Control: Other not–for–profit (including NFP Corporation) **Service**: General medical and surgical

Staffed Beds: 143 **Admissions:** 10002 **Census:** 102 **Outpatient Visits:** 167848 **Births:** 1081 **Personnel:** 1621

Hospital, Medicare Provider Number, Address, Telephone, Approval, Facility, and Physician Codes, Health Care System

★ American Hospital Association (AHA) membership
☐ The Joint Commission accreditation
○ Healthcare Facilities Accreditation Program
◇ DNV Healthcare Inc. accreditation
⇑ Center for Improvement in Healthcare Quality Accreditation
△ Commission on Accreditation of Rehabilitation Facilities (CARF) accreditation

MASSACHUSETTS

ATHOL—Worcester County

☐ **ATHOL HOSPITAL (221303)**, 2033 Main Street, Zip 01331–3598;
tel. 978/249–3511, (Nonreporting) **A**1 10 18 **S** Heywood Healthcare, Gardner, MA
Primary Contact: Winfield S. Brown, FACHE, President and Chief Executive Officer
COO: Michael Grimmer, Chief Operating Officer
CFO: Robert Crosby, Chief Financial Officer
CMO: Mohsen Noreldin M.D., President Medical Staff
CIO: Carol Roosa, Vice President Information Services and Chief Information Officer
CNO: Lucille Songer, Chief Nursing Officer
Web address: www.atholhospital.org
Control: Other not–for–profit (including NFP Corporation) **Service**: General medical and surgical

Staffed Beds: 25

ATTLEBORO—Bristol County

☐ **ARBOUR–FULLER HOSPITAL (224021)**, 200 May Street, Zip 02703–5520;
tel. 508/761–8500, (Nonreporting) **A**1 10 **S** Universal Health Services, Inc., King of Prussia, PA
Primary Contact: Rachel Legend, Chief Executive Officer
CFO: James Rollins, Chief Financial Officer
CMO: Aminadav Zakai M.D., Medical Director
CHR: Brian Jenkins, Director Human Resources
Web address: www.arbourhealth.com
Control: Corporation, Investor–owned (for–profit) **Service**: Psychiatric

Staffed Beds: 46

★ ⇑ **STURDY MEMORIAL HOSPITAL (220008)**, 211 Park Street, Zip 02703–3137, Mailing Address: PO Box 2963, 02703–0963; tel. 508/222–5200 **A**2 5 10 21 **F**3 8 12 13 15 18 20 28 29 30 31 32 34 35 36 39 40 44 45 46 49 50 56 57 58 59 61 64 70 74 75 76 77 78 79 81 82 85 86 87 89 93 97 100 107 108 109 110 111 115 118 119 129 130 131 132 134 144 146 147 148 **P**5 6
Primary Contact: Bruce S. Auerbach, M.D., President and Chief Executive Officer
CFO: Joseph Casey, Chief Financial Officer
CMO: Brian Kelly M.D., Vice President Medical Affairs and Medical Director
CHR: Cheryl Barrows, Vice President Human Resources
CNO: Marita Prater MS, R.N., Vice President Patient Care Services
Web address: www.sturdymemorial.org
Control: Other not–for–profit (including NFP Corporation) **Service**: General medical and surgical

Staffed Beds: 128 Admissions: 6595 Census: 74 Outpatient Visits: 221945 Births: 723 Total Expense ($000): 158616 Payroll Expense ($000): 83761 Personnel: 1023

AYER—Middlesex County

☐ **NASHOBA VALLEY MEDICAL CENTER (220098)**, 200 Groton Road, Zip 01432–3300; tel. 978/784–9000, (Nonreporting) **A**1 10 **S** Steward Health Care System, LLC, Boston, MA
Primary Contact: Salvatore Perla, President
CFO: Ben Moll, Assistant Chief Financial Officer
CMO: Michael Older M.D., President Medical Staff
CNO: Cheryl Bonasord, MSN, RN, Vice President and Chief Nursing Officer
Web address: www.nashobamed.com
Control: Corporation, Investor–owned (for–profit) **Service**: General medical and surgical

Staffed Beds: 48

BEDFORD—Middlesex County

⊞ **BEDFORD VETERANS AFFAIRS MEDICAL CENTER, EDITH NOURSE ROGERS MEMORIAL VETERANS HOSPITAL**, 200 Springs Road, Zip 01730–1198;
tel. 781/687–2000 **A**1 3 5 **F**4 5 6 11 18 29 30 34 35 38 39 44 50 53 54 56 57 58 59 61 62 63 64 66 67 74 75 77 82 84 86 87 90 91 93 94 96 97 98 100 101 103 104 105 106 128 130 132 135 143 144 146 147 148 **S** Department of Veterans Affairs, Washington, DC
Primary Contact: Karen Acerra–Williams, Acting Director
COO: Mark Fontaine–Westhart, Associate Director
CFO: Edward Koetting, Chief Financial Officer
CMO: Dan Berlowitz M.D., M.P.H., Acting Chief of Staff
CHR: Robert Colpitts, Chief Human Resource Service
CNO: Mary Ann Petrillo R.N., MSN, Acting Associate Director Nursing and Patient Clinical Services
Web address: www.bedford.va.gov
Control: Veterans Affairs, Government, federal **Service**: Psychiatric

Staffed Beds: 461 Admissions: 1950 Census: 342 Outpatient Visits: 222677 Births: 0 Total Expense ($000): 142400 Payroll Expense ($000): 110000 Personnel: 1479

BELMONT—Middlesex County

⊞ **MCLEAN HOSPITAL (224007)**, 115 Mill Street, Zip 02478–1064; tel. 617/855–2000 **A**1 3 5 10 **F**4 5 29 50 53 56 58 68 77 86 98 99 100 101 103 104 105 106 111 119 130 132 134 146 **P**6 **S** Partners HealthCare System, Inc., Boston, MA
Primary Contact: Scott L. Rauch, M.D., President and Psychiatrist in Chief
COO: Michele L Gougeon, Executive Vice President and Chief Operating Officer
CFO: David A Lagasse, Senior Vice President Fiscal Affairs
CMO: Joseph Gold M.D., Chief Medical Officer
CHR: Lisa D. Pratt, Vice President, Human Resources
CNO: Linda Flaherty R.N., Senior Vice President, Patient Care Services
Web address: www.mcleanhospital.org
Control: Other not–for–profit (including NFP Corporation) **Service**: Psychiatric

Staffed Beds: 217 Admissions: 6052 Census: 180 Outpatient Visits: 50118 Births: 0 Total Expense ($000): 212317 Payroll Expense ($000): 88353 Personnel: 1658

BEVERLY—Essex County

⊞ **BEVERLY HOSPITAL (220033)**, 85 Herrick Street, Zip 01915–1777;
tel. 978/922–3000, (Nonreporting) (Includes ADDISON GILBERT HOSPITAL, 298 Washington Street, Gloucester, Massachusetts, Zip 01930–4887, tel. 978/283–4000) **A**1 2 3 5 10 **S** Lahey Health, Burlington, MA
Primary Contact: Philip M. Cormier, Chief Executive Officer
COO: Pauline Pike, Chief Operating Officer
CFO: Gary P Marlow, Chief Financial Officer
CMO: Peter H Short M.D., Senior Vice President Medical Affairs
CIO: Robert Laramie, Chief Information Officer
CHR: Althea C Lyons, Vice President Human Resources and Development
Web address: www.beverlyhospital.org
Control: Other not–for–profit (including NFP Corporation) **Service**: General medical and surgical

Staffed Beds: 320

BOSTON—Suffolk County

☐ **ARBOUR HOSPITAL (224013)**, 49 Robinwood Avenue, Zip 02130–2156;
tel. 617/522–4400, (Nonreporting) **A**1 10 **S** Universal Health Services, Inc., King of Prussia, PA
Primary Contact: Eric Kennedy, Chief Executive Officer
Web address: www.arbourhealth.com
Control: Other not–for–profit (including NFP Corporation) **Service**: Psychiatric

Staffed Beds: 118

⊞ **BETH ISRAEL DEACONESS MEDICAL CENTER (220086)**, 330 Brookline Avenue, Zip 02215–5491; tel. 617/667–7000 **A**1 2 3 5 8 10 **F**3 6 9 11 12 13 14 15 17 18 20 22 24 26 28 29 30 31 34 35 36 37 38 40 43 44 45 46 47 48 49 50 51 52 53 54 55 56 57 58 59 60 61 63 64 65 66 68 70 71 72 73 74 75 76 77 78 79 81 82 84 85 86 87 92 93 97 98 100 101 102 103 104 107 108 109 110 111 112 113 114 115 116 117 118 119 120 121 123 124 126 129 130 131 132 135 136 138 139 141 142 143 144 145 146 147 148 149 150 **P**8
Primary Contact: Kevin Tabb, M.D., Chief Executive Officer
CFO: Steven P Fischer, Chief Financial Officer
CIO: John Halamka M.D., Chief Information Officer
CHR: Judi Bieber, Senior Vice President Human Resources
CNO: Marsha L. Maurer R.N., MS, Chief Nursing Officer Patient Care Services
Web address: www.bidmc.harvard.edu
Control: Other not–for–profit (including NFP Corporation) **Service**: General medical and surgical

Staffed Beds: 682 Admissions: 35334 Census: 564 Outpatient Visits: 695408 Births: 5161 Total Expense ($000): 1570685 Payroll Expense ($000): 631239 Personnel: 8303

☐ **BOSTON CHILDREN'S HOSPITAL (223302)**, 300 Longwood Avenue, Zip 02115–5737; tel. 617/355–6000 **A**1 3 5 8 10 **F**3 5 8 11 12 14 18 19 20 21 22 23 24 25 26 27 28 29 30 31 32 34 35 36 37 38 39 40 41 43 44 45 46 48 49 50 51 54 55 57 58 59 60 61 62 63 64 65 67 68 72 74 75 77 78 79 80 81 82 83 84 85 86 87 88 89 92 93 94 97 98 99 100 101 102 104 107 108 109 111 112 113 114 115 116 117 118 119 120 121 123 124 126 129 130 131 132 134 135 136 137 138 139 140 141 142 143 144 146 147 148 149 150 **P**3 5
Primary Contact: Sandra L. Fenwick, M.P.H., President and Chief Executive Officer
COO: Kevin B Churchwell M.D., Chief Operating Officer and Executive Vice President Health Affairs
CFO: Douglas M Vanderslice, Senior Vice President and Chief Financial Officer
CIO: Daniel Nigrin M.D., Vice President Information Services and Chief Information Officer
CHR: Inez Stewart, Vice President
Web address: www.childrenshospital.org/
Control: Other not–for–profit (including NFP Corporation) **Service**: Children's general medical and surgical

Staffed Beds: 415 Admissions: 15158 Census: 323 Outpatient Visits: 697539 Births: 0 Total Expense ($000): 1506314 Payroll Expense ($000): 541566 Personnel: 9759

Many Facility Codes have changed. Please refer to the AHA Guide Code Chart.

BOSTON MEDICAL CENTER (220031), 1 Boston Medical Center Place, Zip 02118–2908; tel. 617/638–8000 **A**1 2 3 5 8 10 **F**3 5 8 9 12 13 15 17 18 20 22 24 26 28 29 30 31 32 34 35 36 38 40 41 43 44 45 46 47 48 49 50 54 55 56 57 58 59 60 61 64 65 66 68 70 72 74 75 76 77 78 79 81 82 84 85 86 87 88 89 93 97 99 100 101 102 103 104 107 108 110 111 114 116 117 118 119 120 121 123 124 126 129 130 131 132 134 135 136 138 142 143 144 145 146 147 148 149 150 **P**7
Primary Contact: Kate Walsh, M.P.H., President and Chief Executive Officer
CFO: Ronald E Bartlett, Chief Financial Officer
CMO: Ravin Davidoff M.D., Chief Medical Officer
CHR: Stephanie Lovell, Vice President and General Counsel
Web address: www.bmc.org
Control: Other not–for–profit (including NFP Corporation) **Service**: General medical and surgical

Staffed Beds: 459 **Admissions**: 22421 **Census**: 315 **Outpatient Visits**: 1210079 **Births**: 2721 **Total Expense ($000)**: 1206767 **Payroll Expense ($000)**: 445317 **Personnel**: 6401

BRIGHAM AND WOMEN'S FAULKNER HOSPITAL (220119), 1153 Centre Street, Zip 02130–3446; tel. 617/983–7000 **A**1 3 5 10 **F**3 5 9 11 12 15 17 18 28 29 30 32 34 35 40 41 45 46 47 49 50 51 54 56 57 58 59 64 65 68 70 74 75 77 79 81 82 84 85 86 87 91 93 94 96 98 100 101 102 103 104 105 107 108 110 111 114 115 118 119 126 129 130 131 132 135 145 146 147 148 149 **P**6 **S** Partners HealthCare System, Inc., Boston, MA
Primary Contact: Michael Gustafson, M.D., President
CFO: Gerard Hadley, Vice President Finance for Brigham & Women's Faulkner Hospital and Vice President Finance and Controller
CMO: Margaret M. Duggan M.D., Chief Medical Officer
CIO: Catherine Schroeder, Deputy Chief Information Officer
CHR: Laura Barnett, Executive Director, Human Resources
CNO: Cori Loescher R.N., Interim Chief Nursing Officer
Web address: www.brighamandwomensfaulkner.org/index.asp
Control: Other not–for–profit (including NFP Corporation) **Service**: General medical and surgical

Staffed Beds: 125 **Admissions**: 9282 **Census**: 103 **Outpatient Visits**: 165746 **Births**: 0 **Total Expense ($000)**: 236160 **Payroll Expense ($000)**: 96875 **Personnel**: 1215

BRIGHAM AND WOMEN'S HOSPITAL (220110), 75 Francis Street, Zip 02115–6110; tel. 617/732–5500 **A**1 2 3 5 8 10 **F**3 5 6 8 9 11 12 13 14 15 16 17 18 20 22 24 26 28 29 30 31 32 33 34 35 36 37 38 39 40 41 43 44 45 46 47 48 49 50 51 52 54 55 56 57 58 59 60 61 64 65 66 68 70 71 72 74 75 76 77 78 79 81 82 83 84 85 86 87 92 93 97 99 100 101 102 103 104 105 107 108 110 111 112 114 115 116 117 118 119 120 121 123 124 126 129 130 131 132 133 134 135 136 137 138 140 141 142 143 144 145 146 147 148 149 150 **P**6 **S** Partners HealthCare System, Inc., Boston, MA
Primary Contact: Elizabeth Nabel, M.D., President
COO: Ron Walls M.D., Executive Vice President and Chief Operating Officer
CFO: Christopher Dunleavy, Senior Vice President Finance and Chief Financial Officer
CMO: Stanley Ashley M.D., Senior Vice President Medical Affairs and Chief Medical Officer
CIO: Adam Landman M.D., Chief Information Officer
CHR: Sabrina Williams, Interm Vice President Human Resources
CNO: Madelyn Pearson R.N., Senior Vice President Patient Care Services and Chief Nursing Officer
Web address: www.brighamandwomens.org
Control: Other not–for–profit (including NFP Corporation) **Service**: General medical and surgical

Staffed Beds: 747 **Admissions**: 41472 **Census**: 668 **Outpatient Visits**: 1353198 **Births**: 6336 **Total Expense ($000)**: 2637100 **Payroll Expense ($000)**: 754184 **Personnel**: 13365

CARNEY HOSPITAL (220017), 2100 Dorchester Avenue, Zip 02124–5615; tel. 617/296–4000, (Nonreporting) **A**1 3 5 10 **S** Steward Health Care System, LLC, Boston, MA
Primary Contact: Walter J. Ramos, President
COO: Christian Stroucken, Chief Operating Officer
CFO: David McGrail, Vice President Finance
CMO: Alexander White, Vice President Medical Affairs
CHR: Mary Orlandi, Manager Human Resources
Web address: www.carneyhospital.org
Control: Corporation, Investor–owned (for–profit) **Service**: General medical and surgical

Staffed Beds: 81

DANA–FARBER CANCER INSTITUTE (220162), 450 Brookline Avenue, Zip 02215–5418; tel. 617/632–3000 **A**1 2 3 5 8 10 **F**3 11 15 29 30 31 32 34 35 36 44 50 54 55 56 57 58 59 64 65 66 68 71 75 77 78 82 83 84 85 86 87 99 100 101 104 107 108 110 111 114 115 117 118 119 120 121 123 124 130 132 134 135 146 147 148 149 150 **P**6
Primary Contact: Laurie H. Glimcher, M.D., President and Chief Executive Officer
COO: Dorothy E Puhy, Executive VP and Chief Operating Officer
CIO: Jeffrey R Kessler, Vice President Information Services
CHR: Emily Barclay, Vice President Human Resources
Web address: www.dana–farber.org
Control: Other not–for–profit (including NFP Corporation) **Service**: Cancer

Staffed Beds: 30 **Admissions**: 1286 **Census**: 28 **Outpatient Visits**: 412625 **Births**: 0 **Total Expense ($000)**: 1329715 **Payroll Expense ($000)**: 374057 **Personnel**: 4635

DR. SOLOMON CARTER FULLER MENTAL HEALTH CENTER (224040), 85 East Newton Street, Zip 02118–2340; tel. 617/626–8700 (Nonreporting) **A**3 5 10
Primary Contact: Mary–Louise White, M.D., Chief Operating Officer
Control: Other not–for–profit (including NFP Corporation) **Service**: Psychiatric

Staffed Beds: 32

MASSACHUSETTS EYE AND EAR INFIRMARY (220075), 243 Charles Street, Zip 02114–3002; tel. 617/523–7900 **A**1 3 5 10 **F**3 7 8 11 29 30 31 34 35 36 40 41 44 50 54 55 56 57 58 59 64 65 66 68 74 75 77 78 81 82 85 86 87 89 107 111 114 119 130 132 141 143 144 146 148 149 **P**6
Primary Contact: John R. Fernandez, President and Chief Executive Officer
CFO: CarolAnn Williams, Chief Financial Officer
CIO: Leo Hill, Chief Information Officer
CHR: Martha Pyle Farrell, Vice President Human Resources and General Counsel
Web address: www.masseyeandear.org
Control: Other not–for–profit (including NFP Corporation) **Service**: Eye, ear, nose and throat

Staffed Beds: 41 **Admissions**: 1129 **Census**: 13 **Outpatient Visits**: 413844 **Births**: 0 **Total Expense ($000)**: 260566 **Payroll Expense ($000)**: 71117 **Personnel**: 1824

MASSACHUSETTS GENERAL HOSPITAL (220071), 55 Fruit Street, Zip 02114–2696; tel. 617/726–2000, (Includes MASSGENERAL HOSPITAL FOR CHILDREN, 55 Fruit Street, Boston, Massachusetts, Zip 02114–2621, tel. 888/644–3248) **A**1 3 5 8 10 **F**3 5 6 8 9 11 12 13 14 15 16 17 18 19 20 21 22 23 24 25 26 27 28 29 30 31 32 33 34 35 36 37 38 39 40 41 42 43 44 45 46 47 48 49 50 51 52 53 54 55 56 57 58 59 60 61 62 63 64 65 66 68 70 71 72 73 74 75 76 77 78 79 80 81 82 84 85 86 87 88 89 91 92 93 94 96 97 98 99 100 101 102 103 104 107 108 110 111 112 113 114 115 116 117 118 119 120 121 122 123 124 126 129 130 131 132 134 135 136 137 138 139 140 141 142 143 144 145 146 147 148 149 150 **P**6 7 **S** Partners HealthCare System, Inc., Boston, MA
Primary Contact: Peter L. Slavin, M.D., President
CFO: Sally Mason Boemer, Senior Vice President Finance
CMO: Britain Nicholson M.D., Chief Medical Officer
CIO: Keith Jennings, Chief Information Officer
CHR: Jeff Davis, Senior Vice President Human Resources
CNO: Jeanette R Ives Erickson MS, R.N., Senior Vice President Patient Care and Chief Nurse
Web address: www.massgeneral.org
Control: Other not–for–profit (including NFP Corporation) **Service**: General medical and surgical

Staffed Beds: 1028 **Admissions**: 49799 **Census**: 825 **Outpatient Visits**: 939793 **Births**: 3814 **Total Expense ($000)**: 3529300 **Payroll Expense ($000)**: 1064149 **Personnel**: 17640

NEW ENGLAND BAPTIST HOSPITAL (220088), 125 Parker Hill Avenue, Zip 02120–2847; tel. 617/754–5800 **A**1 3 5 10 **F**3 8 9 14 18 29 30 34 35 37 44 45 50 53 54 57 58 59 64 65 66 70 74 75 77 79 81 82 85 86 87 92 93 97 107 108 111 115 119 130 131 141 146 148
Primary Contact: Trish Hannon, FACHE, R.N., President and Chief Executive Officer
CFO: Thomas Gheringhelli, Senior Vice President, Chief Financial Officer
CHR: Linda Thompson, Senior Vice President, Human Resources and Service Excellence
CNO: Mary Sullivan Smith R.N., MS, Senior Vice President, Chief Operating Officer and Chief Nursing Officer
Web address: www.nebh.org
Control: Other not–for–profit (including NFP Corporation) **Service**: Orthopedic

Staffed Beds: 113 **Admissions**: 8053 **Census**: 63 **Outpatient Visits**: 120885 **Births**: 0 **Total Expense ($000)**: 236117 **Payroll Expense ($000)**: 83617 **Personnel**: 890

MA

Hospital, Medicare Provider Number, Address, Telephone, Approval, Facility, and Physician Codes, Health Care System

★ American Hospital Association (AHA) membership
☐ The Joint Commission accreditation
○ Healthcare Facilities Accreditation Program
◇ DNV Healthcare Inc. accreditation
⇑ Center for Improvement in Healthcare Quality Accreditation
△ Commission on Accreditation of Rehabilitation Facilities (CARF) accreditation

MA

☐ **SHRINERS HOSPITALS FOR CHILDREN–BOSTON (223304)** (Pediatric Burns Orthopaedics Cleft Lip & Palagte), 51 Blossom Street, Zip 02114–2601; tel. 617/722–3000 **A**1 3 5 10 **F**3 16 29 30 34 35 57 64 68 75 77 79 81 85 86 87 93 99 104 130 132 141 143 146 148 149 **S** Shriners Hospitals for Children, Tampa, FL
Primary Contact: John Patrick. ONeill, Administrator
CFO: Maria Chung CPA, Director Fiscal Services
CMO: Matthias B Donelan M.D., Chief of Staff
CIO: Mary Dolan, Regional Director Information Services and HIPAA Security Official
CHR: John Donlin, Regional Director Human Resources – Boston, Erie, and Springfield
Web address: www.shrinershospitalsforchildren.org/Hospitals/Locations/Boston
Control: Other not–for–profit (including NFP Corporation) **Service**: Children's other specialty

Staffed Beds: 14 **Admissions:** 221 **Census:** 7 **Outpatient Visits:** 6384
Births: 0 **Total Expense ($000):** 37185 **Payroll Expense ($000):** 15240
Personnel: 175

✚ **TUFTS MEDICAL CENTER (220116)**, 800 Washington Street, Zip 02111–1552; tel. 617/636–5000 **A**1 2 3 5 8 10 **F**3 12 13 14 15 17 18 19 20 21 22 23 24 25 26 27 28 29 30 31 32 34 35 39 40 41 43 44 45 47 49 50 51 52 55 56 57 58 59 61 64 65 68 70 71 72 74 75 76 77 78 79 81 82 84 85 86 87 88 89 93 97 98 99 100 102 104 107 108 111 114 115 116 117 118 119 120 121 123 124 126 129 130 131 132 134 135 136 137 138 143 146 147 148 149 150 **P**5
Primary Contact: Michael Wagner, M.D., President and Chief Executive Officer
CFO: Kristine Hanscom, Chief Financial Officer
CMO: David Fairchild M.D., Chief Medical Officer
CIO: William Shickolovich, Chief Information Officer
CNO: Therese M. Hudson–Jinks R.N., MSN, Chief Nursing Officer
Web address: www.tuftsmedicalcenter.org
Control: Other not–for–profit (including NFP Corporation) **Service**: General medical and surgical

Staffed Beds: 264 **Admissions:** 16943 **Census:** 265 **Outpatient Visits:** 426452 **Births:** 1298 **Total Expense ($000):** 693239 **Payroll Expense ($000):** 281007 **Personnel:** 4301

BRADFORD—Essex County

✚ **WHITTIER REHABILITATION HOSPITAL (222047)**, 145 Ward Hill Avenue, Zip 01835–6928; tel. 978/372–8000, (Nonreporting) **A**1 10 **S** Whittier Health Network, Haverhill, MA
Primary Contact: Alfred J. Arcidi, M.D., Senior Vice President
Web address: www.whittierhealth.com
Control: Partnership, Investor–owned (for–profit) **Service**: Acute long–term care hospital

Staffed Beds: 60

BRAINTREE—Norfolk County

✚ **HEALTHSOUTH BRAINTREE REHABILITATION HOSPITAL (223027)**, 250 Pond Street, Zip 02184–5351; tel. 781/348–2500 **A**1 3 5 10 **F**29 34 35 57 59 64 74 75 77 78 79 86 87 90 91 92 93 108 119 130 131 132 146 148 149 150 **P**5 **S** HEALTHSOUTH Corporation, Birmingham, AL
Primary Contact: Randy Doherty, CPA, Chief Executive Officer
CFO: Barry Leonard I, Vice President of Finance
CMO: Arthur Williams M.D., Medical Director
CHR: Cathryn Wigman, Director Human Resources
CNO: Jinia Drinkwater R.N., Director Patient Care Services
Web address: www.braintreerehabhospital.com
Control: Corporation, Investor–owned (for–profit) **Service**: Rehabilitation

Staffed Beds: 187 **Admissions:** 2475 **Census:** 89 **Outpatient Visits:** 63433
Births: 0 **Total Expense ($000):** 42253 **Payroll Expense ($000):** 21992
Personnel: 315

BRIDGEWATER—Plymouth County

BRIDGEWATER STATE HOSPITAL, 20 Administration Road, Zip 02324–3201; tel. 508/279–4521, (Nonreporting) **A**3 5
Primary Contact: Daniel Calais Jr, Superintendent
CFO: Diane Wholley, Director Fiscal Services
Control: State, Government, Nonfederal **Service**: Psychiatric

Staffed Beds: 350

BRIGHTON—Suffolk County

CARITAS ST. ELIZABETH'S MEDICAL CENTER See St. Elizabeth's Medical Center

✉ **CURAHEALTH HOSPITAL BOSTON (222045)**, 1515 Commonwealth Avenue, Zip 02135–3617; tel. 617/254–1100, (Nonreporting) **A**1 10 **S** Curahealth Hospitals, Garland, TX
Primary Contact: Susan Downey, R.N., MS, Chief Executive Officer
CFO: Lawrence J Toye, Chief Financial Officer
CMO: Mark Rohrer M.D., Chief Medical Officer
Web address: www.curahealth.com
Control: Corporation, Investor–owned (for–profit) **Service**: Acute long–term care hospital

Staffed Beds: 59

✉ **FRANCISCAN CHILDREN'S (223300)**, 30 Warren Street, Zip 02135–3680; tel. 617/254–3800 **A**1 3 10 **F**1 29 30 38 39 58 59 64 65 68 75 77 81 86 87 90 91 93 97 98 99 100 104 105 106 130 132 146 **P**8
Primary Contact: John D. Nash, FACHE, President and Chief Executive Officer
COO: Donna Polselli, Chief Operating Officer
CFO: Alex Denucci, Chief Financial Officer
CMO: Jane E O'Brien M.D., Medical Director
CIO: Sean McKeon, Director, Information Technology
CHR: Nancy Murphy, Vice President, Human Resources
CNO: Mary Lou Kelleher R.N., MSN, Vice President, Nursing
Web address: www.franciscanhospital.org
Control: Other not–for–profit (including NFP Corporation) **Service**: Children's rehabilitation

Staffed Beds: 74 **Admissions:** 1113 **Census:** 62 **Outpatient Visits:** 36302
Births: 0 **Total Expense ($000):** 56649 **Payroll Expense ($000):** 33926
Personnel: 468

☐ **ST. ELIZABETH'S MEDICAL CENTER (220036)**, 736 Cambridge Street, Zip 02135–2997; tel. 617/789–3000, (Nonreporting) **A**1 2 3 5 8 10 **S** Steward Health Care System, LLC, Boston, MA
Primary Contact: Craig T. Williams, President
CFO: Jeffrey P. Dion, Vice President Finance
CIO: Joseph Schmitt, Chief Information Officer
CHR: Claudia Henderson, Chief Human Resources
Web address: www.semc.org/
Control: Corporation, Investor–owned (for–profit) **Service**: General medical and surgical

Staffed Beds: 338

BROCKTON—Plymouth County

CARITAS GOOD SAMARITAN MEDICAL CENTER See Good Samaritan Medical Center

☐ **GOOD SAMARITAN MEDICAL CENTER (220111)**, 235 North Pearl Street, Zip 02301–1794; tel. 508/427–3000, (Nonreporting) (Includes GOOD SAMARITAN MEDICAL CENTER – CUSHING CAMPUS, 235 North Pearl Street, Brockton, Massachusetts, Zip 02401–1794, tel. 508/427–3000) **A**1 2 3 5 10 **S** Steward Health Care System, LLC, Boston, MA
Primary Contact: John A. Jurczyk, FACHE, Interim President
COO: Donna Rubinate R.N., Chief Operating Officer
CFO: Thomas Whalen, Vice President Finance
CMO: Scott Stewart M.D., Vice President Medical Management
CIO: Lori Caswell, Director Information Technology
CHR: David J Cronin, Regional Vice President Human Resources
Web address: www.stewardhealth.org/Good–Samaritan
Control: Corporation, Investor–owned (for–profit) **Service**: General medical and surgical

Staffed Beds: 190

✉ **SIGNATURE HEALTHCARE BROCKTON HOSPITAL (220052)**, 680 Centre Street, Zip 02302–3395; tel. 508/941–7000, (Total facility includes 29 beds in nursing home–type unit) **A**1 2 3 10 **F**3 11 12 13 15 17 18 20 22 24 28 29 30 31 32 34 35 38 40 45 46 47 48 49 50 51 52 54 55 56 57 58 59 60 61 64 65 66 68 70 73 74 75 76 77 78 79 81 82 84 85 86 87 89 93 97 98 100 102 104 107 108 110 111 114 115 116 117 118 119 120 121 123 124 128 130 131 132 135 143 144 146 147 148 149 **P**6 8
Primary Contact: Kim Norton. Hollon, FACHE, President and Chief Executive Officer
CFO: James Papadakos, Chief Financial Officer
CIO: Gerald Greeley, Chief Information Officer
CHR: David Fisher, Vice President Human Resources
CNO: Kim Walsh, Chief Nursing Officer
Web address: www.signature–healthcare.org
Control: Other not–for–profit (including NFP Corporation) **Service**: General medical and surgical

Staffed Beds: 245 **Admissions:** 11327 **Census:** 138 **Outpatient Visits:** 365572 **Births:** 1101 **Total Expense ($000):** 255524 **Payroll Expense ($000):** 114255 **Personnel:** 1393

Many Facility Codes have changed. Please refer to the AHA Guide Code Chart.   © 2017 AHA Guide

★ **VETERANS AFFAIRS BOSTON HEALTHCARE SYSTEM BROCKTON DIVISION**, 940 Belmont Street, Zip 02301–5596; tel. 508/583–4500, (Nonreporting) (Includes VETERANS AFFAIRS MEDICAL CENTER WEST ROXBURY DIVISION, 1400 VFW Parkway, West Roxbury, Massachusetts, Zip 2132, 1400 VVF Parkway, West Roxbury, Boston, 2132, tel. 617/323–7700; William H Kelleher, Director) **A**3 5 8 **S** Department of Veterans Affairs, Washington, DC
Primary Contact: Vincent Ng, Interim Director
CFO: Joe Costa, Acting Chief Fiscal Officer
Web address: www.boston.va.gov/
Control: Veterans Affairs, Government, federal **Service**: General medical and surgical

Staffed Beds: 375

BROOKLINE—Norfolk County

□ **ARBOUR H. R. I. HOSPITAL (224018)**, 227 Babcock Street, Zip 02446–6799; tel. 617/731–3200, (Nonreporting) **A**1 10 **S** Universal Health Services, Inc., King of Prussia, PA
Primary Contact: Jameson Pinette, Chief Executive Officer
CFO: James Rollins, Chief Financial Officer
CMO: Anthony Raynes M.D., Psychiatrist in Chief
CHR: Kris Munson, Director Human Resources
Web address: www.arbourhealth.com
Control: Corporation, Investor–owned (for–profit) **Service**: Psychiatric

Staffed Beds: 68

BOURNEWOOD HEALTH SYSTEMS (224022), 300 South Street, Zip 02467–3658; tel. 617/469–0300 **A**3 5 10 **F**4 5 98 99 104 105 130 132 149 **P**1
Primary Contact: Marcia Fowler, Chief Executive Officer
CFO: Michael Gale, Chief Financial Officer
CMO: Carmel Heinsohn M.D., Medical Director
CHR: Paula Berardi, Manager Human Resources
Web address: www.bournewood.com
Control: Corporation, Investor–owned (for–profit) **Service**: Psychiatric

Staffed Beds: 90 Admissions: 3740 Census: 87 Outpatient Visits: 10653 Births: 0 Total Expense ($000): 26748 Payroll Expense ($000): 16045 Personnel: 202

BURLINGTON—Middlesex County

⊞ **LAHEY HOSPITAL & MEDICAL CENTER, BURLINGTON (220171)**, 41 Mall Road, Zip 01805–0001; tel. 781/744–5100, (Includes LAHEY MEDICAL CENTER, PEABODY, 1 Essex Center Drive, Peabody, Massachusetts, Zip 01960–2901, tel. 978/538–4000) **A**1 2 3 5 8 10 **F**3 5 6 8 9 11 12 15 17 18 20 22 24 26 28 29 30 31 34 35 36 37 38 40 43 44 45 46 47 48 49 50 51 54 55 56 57 58 59 60 61 63 64 65 68 70 74 75 77 78 79 81 82 84 85 86 87 91 92 93 96 97 100 101 102 103 104 107 108 110 111 114 115 116 117 118 119 120 121 123 124 126 129 130 131 132 135 136 138 139 141 142 144 145 146 147 148 149 **P**6 **S** Lahey Health, Burlington, MA
Primary Contact: Howard R. Grant, JD, M.D., Chief Executive Officer
COO: Richard R Bias, Chief Operating Officer
CFO: Timothy P. O'Connor, Executive Vice President and Chief Financial Officer
CMO: Andrew Villanueva M.D., Interim Chief Medical Officer
CIO: Bruce Metz Ph.D., Senior Vice President and Chief Information Officer
CHR: Elizabeth P. Conrad, Senior Vice President and Chief Human Resource Officer
Web address: www.lahey.org
Control: Other not–for–profit (including NFP Corporation) **Service**: General medical and surgical

Staffed Beds: 345 Admissions: 23644 Census: 298 Outpatient Visits: 793494 Births: 0 Total Expense ($000): 956909 Payroll Expense ($000): 278128 Personnel: 5777

CAMBRIDGE—Middlesex County

⊞ **CAMBRIDGE HEALTH ALLIANCE (220011)**, 1493 Cambridge Street, Zip 02139–1099; tel. 617/665–1000, (Includes CAMBRIDGE HOSPITAL, 1493 Cambridge Street, Cambridge, Massachusetts, Zip 02139–1099, tel. 617/498–1000; SOMERVILLE HOSPITAL, 230 Highland Avenue, Somerville, Massachusetts, Zip 2143, tel. 617/666–4400; WHIDDEN MEMORIAL HOSPITAL, 103 Garland Street, Everett, Massachusetts, Zip 02149–5095, tel. 617/389–6270) **A**1 2 3 5 8 10 **F**2 4 5 8 11 12 13 15 29 30 31 32 34 35 36 38 39 40 42 44 45 46 47 48 49 50 56 57 58 59 61 64 65 66 68 70 75 76 77 78 79 81 82 86 87 93 97 98 99 100 101 102 103 104 107 108 110 111 114 115 119 129 130 131 132 134 135 141 143 145 146 147 148 149 150 **P**6
Primary Contact: Patrick R. Wardell, Chief Executive Officer
CFO: Jill I Batty, Chief Financial Officer
CMO: Assaad Sayah M.D., Chief Medical Officer
CIO: Judith S Klickstein, Chief Information Officer
CHR: Joy U Curtis, Senior Vice President Human Resources
CNO: Elizabeth Cadigan R.N., MSN, Senior Vice President Patient Care Services and Chief Nursing Officer
Web address: www.challiance.org
Control: Hospital district or authority, Government, Nonfederal **Service**: General medical and surgical

Staffed Beds: 274 Admissions: 10687 Census: 153 Outpatient Visits: 712061 Births: 1025 Total Expense ($000): 597976 Payroll Expense ($000): 325270 Personnel: 3449

⊞ **MOUNT AUBURN HOSPITAL (220002)**, 330 Mount Auburn Street, Zip 02138–5597; tel. 617/492–3500 **A**1 2 3 5 8 10 **F**3 5 11 12 13 14 15 17 18 20 22 24 26 28 29 30 31 34 35 36 37 40 45 49 50 51 52 55 56 57 58 59 60 61 62 63 64 65 68 70 73 74 75 76 77 78 79 81 82 86 87 93 97 98 100 101 102 103 104 107 108 110 111 114 115 117 118 119 120 121 123 124 126 129 130 131 132 135 144 145 146 147 **P**5 6 7
Primary Contact: Jeanette G. Clough, President and Chief Executive Officer
COO: Nicholas T Dileso R.N., Chief Operating Officer
CFO: William Sullivan
CIO: Kendall White, Chief Information Officer
CHR: Tom Fabiano, Director Human Resources
CNO: Deborah Baker, Vice President, Patient Care Services
Web address: www.mountauburnhospital.org
Control: Other not–for–profit (including NFP Corporation) **Service**: General medical and surgical

Staffed Beds: 205 Admissions: 11285 Census: 140 Outpatient Visits: 186488 Births: 2700 Total Expense ($000): 318506 Payroll Expense ($000): 145199 Personnel: 2635

SPAULDING HOSPITAL CAMBRIDGE See Spaulding Hospital For Continuing Medical Care Cambridge

⊞ **SPAULDING HOSPITAL FOR CONTINUING MEDICAL CARE CAMBRIDGE (222000)**, 1575 Cambridge Street, Zip 02138–4308; tel. 617/876–4344 **A**1 10 **F**1 7 28 29 30 31 34 35 36 50 54 57 58 60 64 68 77 78 86 91 93 94 95 96 100 130 131 132 146 148 **P**8 **S** Partners HealthCare System, Inc., Boston, MA
Primary Contact: Maureen Banks, FACHE, MS, R.N., President
CFO: Mary Shaughnessy, Vice President Finance
CMO: Jonathon Schwartz M.D., Chief Medical Officer
CIO: John Campbell, Chief Information Officer
CHR: Jack Carroll, Director Human Resources
CNO: Adrienne Sarnecki R.N., Chief Nurse Executive
Web address: www.spauldingnetwork.org
Control: Other not–for–profit (including NFP Corporation) **Service**: Acute long–term care hospital

Staffed Beds: 128 Admissions: 1548 Census: 128 Outpatient Visits: 0 Births: 0 Total Expense ($000): 73606 Payroll Expense ($000): 33387 Personnel: 443

CANTON—Norfolk County

⊞ **PAPPAS REHABILITATION HOSPITAL FOR CHILDREN (222025)**, 3 Randolph Street, Zip 02021–2351; tel. 781/828–2440, (Nonreporting) **A**1 10 **S** Massachusetts Department of Public Health, Boston, MA
Primary Contact: Brian V. Devin, Chief Executive Officer
CFO: Sharon Porter, Chief Financial Officer
CMO: Aruna Sachdev M.D., Medical Director
CIO: Robert Lima, Director Information Systems
CHR: Trish Scully, Manager Employment Services
Web address: www.mhsf.us/
Control: State, Government, Nonfederal **Service**: Children's acute long–term Care

Staffed Beds: 80

CHARLESTOWN—Suffolk County

⊞ △ **SPAULDING REHABILITATION HOSPITAL (223034)**, 300 First Avenue, Zip 02129–3109; tel. 617/952–5000 **A**1 3 5 7 10 **F**3 7 29 30 34 35 36 50 54 57 58 64 68 74 75 77 82 85 86 87 90 91 92 93 94 95 96 100 104 119 129 130 131 132 143 146 148 149 **S** Partners HealthCare System, Inc., Boston, MA
Primary Contact: David E. Storto, President
COO: Maureen Banks FACHE, MS, R.N., Chief Operating Officer
CFO: Mary Shaughnessy, Vice President Finance
CMO: Ross Zafonte D.O., Chief, Physical Medicine and Rehabilitation and Vice President Medical Affairs, Research and Education
CIO: John Campbell, Chief Information Officer
CHR: Russell Averna, Vice President Human Resources
Web address: www.spauldingrehab.org
Control: Other not–for–profit (including NFP Corporation) **Service**: Rehabilitation

Staffed Beds: 132 Admissions: 2299 Census: 126 Outpatient Visits: 296754 Births: 0 Total Expense ($000): 151140 Payroll Expense ($000): 68262 Personnel: 979

MA

CLINTON—Worcester County

★ ⑪ **CLINTON HOSPITAL (220058)**, 201 Highland Street, Zip 01510–1096; tel. 978/368–3000 **A**3 5 10 21 **F**3 11 29 34 35 40 44 50 59 64 68 75 77 79 81 85 93 98 103 107 108 110 115 119 130 146 149 **P**6 **S** UMass Memorial Health Care, Inc., Worcester, MA
Primary Contact: Deborah K. Weymouth, FACHE, President and Chief Executive Officer
CFO: Steven McCue, Chief Financial Officer
CHR: Martha Chiarchiaro, Vice President Human Resources
CNO: Charlene Elie, Vice President Patient Care Services
Web address: www.clintonhospital.org
Control: Other not-for-profit (including NFP Corporation) **Service**: General medical and surgical

> **Staffed Beds**: 41 **Admissions**: 981 **Census**: 24 **Outpatient Visits**: 15064 **Births**: 0 **Total Expense ($000)**: 29185 **Payroll Expense ($000)**: 12573 **Personnel**: 163

CONCORD—Middlesex County

⊞ **EMERSON HOSPITAL (220084)**, 133 Old Road to Nine Acre Corner, Zip 01742–9120; tel. 978/369–1400 **A**1 5 10 **F**3 5 7 8 11 12 13 14 15 17 18 28 29 30 31 32 34 35 36 37 38 40 45 48 49 50 51 54 57 59 60 62 64 65 68 70 72 73 74 75 76 77 78 79 81 82 85 86 87 89 93 98 100 101 102 103 104 105 107 110 111 114 115 119 128 129 130 131 132 135 145 146 148 **P**5 8
Primary Contact: Christine C. Schuster, R.N., President and Chief Executive Officer
CFO: Michael Hachey, Senior Vice President and Chief Financial Officer
CMO: C Gregory Martin M.D., Chief Medical Officer
CIO: Renee Fosberg, Chief Information Officer
CNO: Joyce Welsh R.N., MS, Vice President of Clinical Services and Chief Nursing Officer
Web address: www.emersonhospital.org
Control: Other not-for-profit (including NFP Corporation) **Service**: General medical and surgical

> **Staffed Beds**: 170 **Admissions**: 7657 **Census**: 97 **Outpatient Visits**: 269128 **Births**: 1261 **Total Expense ($000)**: 213607 **Payroll Expense ($000)**: 99457 **Personnel**: 1291

DARTMOUTH—Bristol County

SOUTHCOAST BEHAVIORAL HEALTH (224041), 581 Faunce Corner Road, Zip 02747–1242; tel. 888/210–2475 (Nonreporting) **S** Acadia Healthcare Company, Inc., Franklin, TN
Primary Contact: Kevin R. Burchill, Chief Executive Officer
Web address: www.southcoastbehavioral.com
Control: Corporation, Investor-owned (for-profit) **Service**: Psychiatric

> **Staffed Beds**: 120

EAST SANDWICH—Barnstable County

⊞ △ **SPAULDING REHABILITATION HOSPITAL CAPE COD (223032)**, 311 Service Road, Zip 02537–1370; tel. 508/833–4000 **A**1 7 10 **F**3 28 29 30 32 34 35 36 50 56 60 64 74 75 77 79 82 90 91 92 93 94 96 130 131 132 146 147 148 **P**4 6 **S** Partners HealthCare System, Inc., Boston, MA
Primary Contact: Maureen Banks, FACHE, MS, R.N., President
COO: Stephanie Nadolny, Vice President of Hospital Operations
CFO: Mary Shaughnessy, Vice President Finance
CMO: David Lowell M.D., Chief Medical Officer
CIO: John Campbell, Chief Information Officer
CHR: Russell Averna, Vice President of Human Resources
CNO: Adrienne Sarnecki R.N., Chief Nursing Officer
Web address: www.spauldingrehab.org
Control: State, Government, Nonfederal **Service**: Rehabilitation

> **Staffed Beds**: 60 **Admissions**: 1185 **Census**: 45 **Outpatient Visits**: 114948 **Births**: 0 **Total Expense ($000)**: 40918 **Payroll Expense ($000)**: 22450 **Personnel**: 350

EVERETT—Middlesex County

WHIDDEN MEMORIAL HOSPITAL See Cambridge Health Alliance

FALL RIVER—Bristol County

CHARLTON MEMORIAL HOSPITAL See Southcoast Hospitals Group

☐ **DR. J. CORRIGAN MENTAL HEALTH CENTER (224028)**, 49 Hillside Street, Zip 02720–5266; tel. 508/235–7200 (Nonreporting) **A**1 10 **S** Massachusetts Department of Mental Health, Boston, MA
Primary Contact: Frank O'Reilly, Director
Control: State, Government, Nonfederal **Service**: Psychiatric

> **Staffed Beds**: 16

☐ **SAINT ANNE'S HOSPITAL (220020)**, 795 Middle Street, Zip 02721–1798; tel. 508/674–5741, (Nonreporting) **A**1 2 10 **S** Steward Health Care System, LLC, Boston, MA
Primary Contact: Michael Bushell, President
CMO: John Conlon M.D., Chief Medical Officer
CIO: Julie Berry, Chief Information Officer
CHR: Sandra Dellicker, Director of Human Resources
CNO: Carole Billington R.N., MSN, Vice President Operations, Chief Nursing Officer
Web address: www.saintanneshospital.org
Control: Corporation, Investor-owned (for-profit) **Service**: General medical and surgical

> **Staffed Beds**: 160

⊞ **SOUTHCOAST HOSPITALS GROUP (220074)**, 363 Highland Avenue, Zip 02720–3703; tel. 508/679–3131, (Includes CHARLTON MEMORIAL HOSPITAL, 363 Highland Avenue, Fall River, Massachusetts, Zip 02720–3703, tel. 508/679–3131; Keith A Hovan, R.N., President and Chief Executive Officer; ST. LUKE'S HOSPITAL, 101 Page Street, New Bedford, Massachusetts, Zip 2740, tel. 508/997–1515; Keith A Hovan, R.N., President and Chief Executive Officer; TOBEY HOSPITAL, 43 High Street, Wareham, Massachusetts, Zip 2571, tel. 508/295–0880; Keith A Hovan, R.N., President and Chief Executive Officer) **A**1 2 10 **F**3 8 11 12 13 15 17 18 20 22 24 26 28 29 30 31 34 35 37 40 41 44 45 46 47 48 49 50 51 54 56 57 58 59 60 61 64 65 68 70 71 73 74 75 76 77 78 79 81 82 83 84 85 86 87 89 90 91 92 93 95 96 100 101 102 103 107 108 110 111 114 115 116 117 118 119 120 121 123 124 126 130 131 132 134 135 144 146 147 148 149 **P**5 6
Primary Contact: Keith A. Hovan, R.N., President and Chief Executive Officer
COO: Renee Clark, Senior Vice President and Chief Operating Officer
CFO: Wade Broughman, Chief Financial Officer
CMO: Robert Caldas D.O., Chief Medical Officer
CIO: Jim Feen, Senior Vice President and Chief Information Officer
CHR: David DeJesus, Senior Vice President Human Resources
CNO: Timothy D. Eixenberger, Chief Nursing Officer
Web address: www.southcoast.org
Control: Other not-for-profit (including NFP Corporation) **Service**: General medical and surgical

> **Staffed Beds**: 684 **Admissions**: 34476 **Census**: 411 **Outpatient Visits**: 890169 **Births**: 3315 **Total Expense ($000)**: 753007 **Payroll Expense ($000)**: 320152 **Personnel**: 4121

FALMOUTH—Barnstable County

⊞ **FALMOUTH HOSPITAL (220135)**, 100 Ter Heun Drive, Zip 02540–2599; tel. 508/548–5300 **A**1 2 10 **F**3 8 11 13 15 18 28 29 30 34 35 36 38 40 45 50 53 54 57 58 59 61 64 65 68 70 74 75 76 77 79 81 82 85 86 87 89 93 96 100 101 102 107 108 110 111 115 118 119 129 130 131 132 135 143 144 146 147 148 149 **P**6 8 **S** Cape Cod Healthcare, Inc., Hyannis, MA
Primary Contact: Michael K. Lauf, President and Chief Executive Officer
COO: Lori Jewett R.N., Vice President of Nursing and Chief Operating Officer
CFO: Michael Connors, Senior Vice President and Chief Financial Officer
CMO: Alex Heard M.D., Chief Medical Officer
CIO: Jeanne M. Fallon, Chief Information Officer
CHR: Emily Schorer, Vice President, Human Resources
CNO: Lori Jewett R.N., Vice President of Nursing and Chief Operating Officer
Web address: www.capecodhealth.org
Control: Other not-for-profit (including NFP Corporation) **Service**: General medical and surgical

> **Staffed Beds**: 95 **Admissions**: 5933 **Census**: 64 **Outpatient Visits**: 156586 **Births**: 414 **Total Expense ($000)**: 149340 **Payroll Expense ($000)**: 68611 **Personnel**: 531

FRAMINGHAM—Middlesex County

⊞ **METROWEST MEDICAL CENTER (220175)**, 115 Lincoln Street, Zip 01702–6342; tel. 508/383–1000, (Includes FRAMINGHAM UNION HOSPITAL, 115 Lincoln Street, Framingham, Massachusetts, Zip 1702, tel. 508/383–1000; LEONARD MORSE HOSPITAL, 67 Union Street, Natick, Massachusetts, Zip 1760, tel. 508/650–7000) **A**1 2 3 5 10 **F**3 5 12 13 14 15 18 20 22 26 28 29 30 31 32 34 35 36 40 41 44 45 49 50 54 56 57 59 61 62 63 64 65 68 70 73 74 75 76 77 78 79 81 84 85 87 89 93 97 98 99 100 102 103 104 105 107 108 110 114 115 118 119 120 121 129 130 131 132 134 135 143 146 147 148 149 **S** TENET Healthcare Corporation, Dallas, TX
Primary Contact: Jeffrey Liebman, Market Chief Executive Officer
CHR: Rebecca Heffernan, Director Human Resources
CNO: Donna T Gemme R.N., Chief Nursing Officer Vice President Patient Care Services
Web address: www.mwmc.com
Control: Corporation, Investor-owned (for-profit) **Service**: General medical and surgical

> **Staffed Beds**: 160 **Admissions**: 10749 **Census**: 151 **Outpatient Visits**: 352871 **Births**: 1037 **Total Expense ($000)**: 248958 **Payroll Expense ($000)**: 113402

Many Facility Codes have changed. Please refer to the AHA Guide Code Chart.
© 2017 AHA Guide

MA

MA

LEEDS—Hampshire County

⊞ **VETERANS AFFAIRS CENTRAL WESTERN MASSACHUSETTS HEALTHCARE SYSTEM**, 421 North Main Street, Zip 01053–9764; tel. 413/582–3000, (Nonreporting) **A**1 5 **S** Department of Veterans Affairs, Washington, DC
Primary Contact: John P. Collins, FACHE, Medical Center Director
COO: Joyce Fredrick, Associate Director
CFO: Andrew McMahon, Chief Fiscal Officer
CMO: Neil Nusbaum M.D., Chief of Staff
CIO: Michael Marley, Chief Information Officer
CHR: Pablo Feliciano, Manager Human Resources
Web address: www.centralwesternmass.va.gov/
Control: Veterans Affairs, Government, federal **Service**: Psychiatric

Staffed Beds: 117

LEOMINSTER—Worcester County

⊞ **HEALTHALLIANCE HOSPITALS (220001)**, 60 Hospital Road, Zip 01453–2205; tel. 978/466–2000 **A**1 2 3 5 10 **F**3 5 13 15 28 29 30 31 34 35 36 40 45 46 47 49 50 51 54 57 59 60 62 63 64 66 68 70 74 75 76 77 78 79 80 81 82 83 84 85 89 91 92 93 97 104 107 108 110 114 115 118 119 127 130 131 132 133 135 144 146 149 **P**6 **S** UMass Memorial Health Care, Inc., Worcester, MA
Primary Contact: Deborah K. Weymouth, FACHE, President and Chief Executive Officer
COO: Paul MacKinnon R.N., Chief Operating Officer
CFO: John Bronhard, Chief Financial Officer
CMO: Daniel H O'Leary M.D., Chief Medical Officer
CNO: Mary Fortunato–Habib, Chief Nursing Officer
Web address: www.healthalliance.com
Control: Other not–for–profit (including NFP Corporation) **Service**: General medical and surgical

Staffed Beds: 103 **Admissions**: 6733 **Census**: 71 **Outpatient Visits**: 276549 **Births**: 861 **Total Expense ($000)**: 173754 **Payroll Expense ($000)**: 71584 **Personnel**: 912

LOWELL—Middlesex County

⊞ **LOWELL GENERAL HOSPITAL (220063)**, 295 Varnum Avenue, Zip 01854–2134; tel. 978/937–6000, (Includes LOWELL GENERAL HOSPITAL, SAINTS CAMPUS, 1 Hospital Drive, Lowell, Massachusetts, Zip 01852–1311, 295 Varnum Ave, 01854–2134, tel. 978/458–1411; Normand E. Deschene, FACHE, Chief Executive Officer) **A**1 2 3 5 10 **F**3 8 11 12 13 15 18 20 22 26 28 29 30 31 32 34 35 36 38 40 41 43 44 45 46 47 48 49 50 51 54 55 56 57 58 59 60 61 62 63 64 65 66 68 70 73 74 75 76 77 78 79 81 82 84 85 86 87 89 93 97 107 108 110 114 115 118 119 120 121 123 124 126 129 130 131 132 134 135 144 146 147 149 150 **P**5 6 8
Primary Contact: Joseph White, FACHE, President and Chief Executive Officer
COO: Amy J Hoey R.N., MS, Executive Vice President and Chief Operating Officer
CFO: Susan Green, Senior Vice President Finance, Chief Financial Officer
CMO: David Pickul M.D., Chief Medical Officer, Circle Health
CIO: Brian Sandager, Chief Information Officer
CHR: Sabrina M Granville, Senior Vice President and Chief Human Resources Officer
CNO: Cecelia Lynch R.N., MS, Vice President Patient Care Services and Chief Nursing Officer
Web address: www.lowellgeneral.org
Control: Other not–for–profit (including NFP Corporation) **Service**: General medical and surgical

Staffed Beds: 310 **Admissions**: 19609 **Census**: 220 **Outpatient Visits**: 552877 **Births**: 2329 **Total Expense ($000)**: 431761 **Payroll Expense ($000)**: 175899 **Personnel**: 2604

SAINTS MEDICAL CENTER See Lowell General Hospital, Saints Campus

LUDLOW—Hampden County

⊞ **HEALTHSOUTH REHABILITATION HOSPITAL OF WESTERN MASSACHUSETTS (223030)**, 222 State Street, Zip 01056–3437; tel. 413/308–3300 **A**1 10 **F**29 64 90 93 94 96 132 **P**5 **S** HEALTHSOUTH Corporation, Birmingham, AL
Primary Contact: John R. Hunt, Chief Executive Officer
CFO: John Flaherty, Chief Financial Officer
CMO: Adnan Dahdul M.D., Medical Director
CHR: Mary Mazza, Director Human Resources
CNO: Deborah Santos R.N., Chief Nursing Officer
Web address: www.healthsouthrehab.org
Control: Individual, Investor–owned (for–profit) **Service**: Rehabilitation

Staffed Beds: 53 **Admissions**: 1276 **Census**: 47 **Outpatient Visits**: 10400 **Births**: 0 **Total Expense ($000)**: 21708 **Payroll Expense ($000)**: 9781 **Personnel**: 161

LYNN—Essex County

UNION CAMPUS See North Shore Medical Center, Miami

UNION HOSPITAL See Union Campus

MARLBOROUGH—Middlesex County

⊞ **UMASS MEMORIAL–MARLBOROUGH HOSPITAL (220049)**, 157 Union ST, Zip 01752–1297; tel. 508/481–5000 **A**1 3 5 10 **F**3 11 15 18 24 28 29 30 34 35 40 49 50 51 53 57 68 70 77 79 81 82 85 93 98 100 101 105 107 115 119 132 146 147 149 **S** UMass Memorial Health Care, Inc., Worcester, MA
Primary Contact: Steven P. Roach, FACHE, President and Chief Executive Officer
COO: John Kelly R.N., Chief Nursing Officer and Chief Operating Officer
CFO: Steven McCue, Chief Financial Officer
CMO: Habib Sioufi M.D., Chief Medical Officer
CHR: Francis Meringolo, Vice President Human Resources
CNO: John Kelly R.N., Chief Nursing Officer and Chief Operating Officer
Web address: www.marlboroughhospital.org
Control: Other not–for–profit (including NFP Corporation) **Service**: General medical and surgical

Staffed Beds: 67 **Admissions**: 3612 **Census**: 44 **Outpatient Visits**: 28513 **Births**: 0 **Total Expense ($000)**: 79338 **Payroll Expense ($000)**: 31456 **Personnel**: 433

MEDFORD—Middlesex County

LAWRENCE MEMORIAL HOSPITAL OF MEDFORD See Hallmark Health System, Melrose

MELROSE—Middlesex County

⊞ **HALLMARK HEALTH SYSTEM (220070)**, 585 Lebanon Street, Zip 02176–3225; tel. 781/979–3000, (Includes LAWRENCE MEMORIAL HOSPITAL OF MEDFORD, 170 Governors Avenue, Medford, Massachusetts, Zip 02155–1643, tel. 781/306–6000; MELROSE–WAKEFIELD HOSPITAL, 585 Lebanon Street, Melrose, Massachusetts, Zip 2176, tel. 781/979–3000; Michael V Sack, FACHE, Chief Executive Officer) **A**1 2 3 10 **F**2 3 11 12 13 15 18 20 22 26 28 29 30 31 34 35 38 40 41 45 46 47 49 50 51 54 55 56 57 58 59 60 61 62 63 64 65 68 70 72 74 75 77 78 79 81 82 84 85 86 87 93 97 98 100 101 102 103 104 107 108 110 111 114 115 116 117 118 119 120 121 123 124 129 130 131 132 135 144 146 147 148 149 **P**5 6
Primary Contact: Alan G. Macdonald, President and Chief Executive Officer
COO: William J. Doherty M.D., Executive Vice President and Chief Operating Officer
CFO: James A Nania, System Vice President and Chief Financial Officer
CMO: Steven Sbardella M.D., Chief Medical Officer
CIO: Carol Ann Dresser, Vice President Information Services and Chief Information Officer
CHR: David P. Ryan, Vice President Human Resources
Web address: www.hallmarkhealth.org
Control: Other not–for–profit (including NFP Corporation) **Service**: General medical and surgical

Staffed Beds: 267 **Admissions**: 10297 **Census**: 142 **Outpatient Visits**: 535497 **Births**: 943 **Total Expense ($000)**: 265652 **Payroll Expense ($000)**: 129414

METHUEN—Essex County

☐ **HOLY FAMILY HOSPITAL (220080)**, 70 East Street, Zip 01844–4597; tel. 978/687–0151, (Nonreporting) (Includes HOLY FAMILY HOSPITAL AT MERRIMACK VALLEY, 140 Lincoln Avenue, Haverhill, Massachusetts, Zip 01830–6798, tel. 978/374–2000; Craig A Jesiolowski, FACHE, President) **A**1 2 10 **S** Steward Health Care System, LLC, Boston, MA
Primary Contact: Craig A. Jesiolowski, FACHE, President
COO: Martha M McDrury R.N., Chief Operating Officer and Chief Nursing Officer
CFO: Kevin Kilday, Vice President Finance
CHR: Patricia Gauron, Director Human Resources
CNO: Christine M. Basil, MSN, RN, Chief Operating Officer and Chief Nursing Officer
Web address: www.stewardhealth.org/Holy–Family–Hospital
Control: Corporation, Investor–owned (for–profit) **Service**: General medical and surgical

Staffed Beds: 329

Many Facility Codes have changed. Please refer to the AHA Guide Code Chart. © 2017 AHA Guide

MILFORD—Worcester County

✠ **MILFORD REGIONAL MEDICAL CENTER (220090)**, 14 Prospect Street, Zip 01757–3003; tel. 508/473–1190, (Includes WHITINSVILLE MEDICAL CENTER, 18 Granite Street, Whitinsville, Massachusetts, Zip 1588, tel. 508/234–6311) **A**1 2 3 5 10 **F**3 11 12 13 15 18 20 28 29 30 31 32 34 35 40 41 45 46 47 48 49 50 51 52 57 59 64 65 68 70 74 75 76 77 79 80 81 82 84 85 86 87 89 93 107 108 110 115 118 119 124 126 130 131 132 134 135 144 146 147 148 149 **P**6
Primary Contact: Edward Kelly, Chief Executive Officer and President
COO: Peggy Novick, Vice President, Clinical Support and Outpatient Services
CFO: Jeanne Lynskey, Vice President and Chief Financial Officer
CMO: Mary Czymbor, Chief Medical Officer
CIO: Nicole Heim, Chief Information Officer
CHR: Linda Greason, Vice President Human Resources
CNO: Nancy Tomaso, Vice President, Patient Care Services
Web address: www.milfordregional.org
Control: Other not–for–profit (including NFP Corporation) **Service:** General medical and surgical

Staffed Beds: 145 **Admissions:** 7911 **Census:** 76 **Outpatient Visits:** 512573 **Births:** 963 **Total Expense ($000):** 206836 **Payroll Expense ($000):** 98120 **Personnel:** 1626

MILTON—Norfolk County

☐ **BETH ISRAEL DEACONESS HOSPITAL–MILTON (220108)**, 199 Reedsdale Road, Zip 02186–3926; tel. 617/696–4600 **A**1 10 **F**12 15 17 18 26 28 29 30 34 35 37 40 41 50 51 56 57 59 64 68 70 74 75 77 79 81 82 85 87 93 107 108 110 111 115 119 126 129 130 131 132 146 147 148 149
Primary Contact: Richard W. Fernandez, President and Chief Executive Officer
CIO: Jean Fernandez, Chief Information Officer
CHR: Kathleen Harrington, Vice President Human Resources
Web address: www.miltonhospital.org
Control: Other not–for–profit (including NFP Corporation) **Service:** General medical and surgical

Staffed Beds: 88 **Admissions:** 7212 **Census:** 67 **Outpatient Visits:** 137295 **Births:** 0 **Total Expense ($000):** 101107 **Payroll Expense ($000):** 44192 **Personnel:** 623

NANTUCKET—Nantucket County

✠ **NANTUCKET COTTAGE HOSPITAL (220177)**, 57 Prospect Street, Zip 02554–2799; tel. 508/825–8100 **A**1 10 **F**13 15 28 29 31 35 40 45 50 57 59 60 64 68 70 75 76 77 78 79 81 84 85 86 87 89 93 100 102 107 110 111 115 119 130 132 133 147 148 **P**5 **S** Partners HealthCare System, Inc., Boston, MA
Primary Contact: Margot Hartmann, M.D., Ph.D., President and Chief Executive Officer
COO: Jim Kelly, Chief Operating Officer
CFO: David J Burke, Director Finance and Chief Financial Officer
CMO: Jock Lawrason M.D., Chief Medical Officer
CIO: Terry Hughes, Director Information Systems
CHR: Susan Partridge, Director Human Resources
CNO: Bonnie J Kester R.N., MSN, Vice President Patient Care Services and Chief Nursing Officer
Web address: www.nantuckethospital.org
Control: Other not–for–profit (including NFP Corporation) **Service:** General medical and surgical

Staffed Beds: 19 **Admissions:** 777 **Census:** 5 **Outpatient Visits:** 35472 **Births:** 159 **Total Expense ($000):** 47579 **Payroll Expense ($000):** 17558 **Personnel:** 209

NATICK—Middlesex County

LEONARD MORSE HOSPITAL See Metrowest Medical Center, Framingham

NEEDHAM—Norfolk County

☐ **BETH ISRAEL DEACONESS HOSPITAL–NEEDHAM CAMPUS (220083)**, 148 Chestnut Street, Zip 2492; tel. 781/453–3000 **A**1 2 3 **F**3 15 18 29 30 34 35 40 45 49 50 51 54 59 60 64 65 68 69 70 74 75 77 79 81 82 85 87 93 100 102 107 108 110 111 115 118 119 129 130 131 144 145 146 148 149
Primary Contact: John M. Fogarty, President and Chief Executive Officer
CFO: Brian Smith, Chief Financial Officer
CMO: Peter Ostrow M.D., President Medical Staff
Web address: www.bidneedham.org/
Control: Other not–for–profit (including NFP Corporation) **Service:** General medical and surgical

Staffed Beds: 45 **Admissions:** 2423 **Census:** 30 **Outpatient Visits:** 180311 **Births:** 0 **Total Expense ($000):** 80125 **Payroll Expense ($000):** 32480 **Personnel:** 542

NEW BEDFORD—Bristol County

ST. LUKE'S HOSPITAL See Southcoast Hospitals Group, Fall River

✠ **VIBRA HOSPITAL OF SOUTHEASTERN MASSACHUSETTS (222043)**, 4499 Acushnet Avenue, Zip 02745–4707; tel. 508/995–6900 **A**1 10 **F**1 12 18 28 29 50 56 57 64 74 75 77 79 87 93 94 96 101 103 104 130 135 146 148 **P**6 **S** Vibra Healthcare, Mechanicsburg, PA
Primary Contact: Edward B. Leary, Chief Executive Officer
CFO: Cheryl Perry, Chief Financial Officer
CMO: Albert Loerinc M.D., Medical Director
CHR: Ilene Mirabella, Director Human Resources
CNO: Emmanuel Berthil, Chief Clinical Officer
Web address: www.newbedfordrehab.com
Control: Corporation, Investor–owned (for–profit) **Service:** Children's acute long–term Care

Staffed Beds: 90 **Admissions:** 586 **Census:** 72 **Outpatient Visits:** 3747 **Births:** 0 **Total Expense ($000):** 25027 **Payroll Expense ($000):** 15178 **Personnel:** 159

NEWBURYPORT—Essex County

✠ **ANNA JAQUES HOSPITAL (220029)**, 25 Highland Avenue, Zip 01950–3894; tel. 978/463–1000 **A**1 10 **F**3 8 13 14 15 18 20 26 28 29 31 34 37 40 43 45 46 50 59 64 65 70 75 76 77 78 79 80 81 82 85 89 92 93 98 99 102 105 107 108 110 111 115 116 117 118 119 129 130 135 146 148 149 **P**5 8
Primary Contact: Mark L. Goldstein, President and Chief Executive Officer
CFO: Kevin Kilday, Chief Financial Officer
CMO: Gail Fayre M.D., Medical Director
CIO: Robert Buchanan, Chief Information Officer
CHR: Stephen Salvo, Vice President Human Resources
CNO: Richard Maki R.N., Vice President Nursing and Chief Nursing Officer
Web address: www.ajh.org
Control: Other not–for–profit (including NFP Corporation) **Service:** General medical and surgical

Staffed Beds: 123 **Admissions:** 6371 **Census:** 73 **Outpatient Visits:** 269088 **Births:** 693 **Total Expense ($000):** 122248 **Payroll Expense ($000):** 55310 **Personnel:** 730

NEWTON LOWER FALLS—Middlesex County

✠ **NEWTON–WELLESLEY HOSPITAL (220101)**, 2014 Washington Street, Zip 02462–1699; tel. 617/243–6000, (Includes MASSGENERAL FOR CHILDREN AT NEWTON–WELLESLEY HOSPITAL, 2000 Washington Street, Newton, Massachusetts, Zip 02462–1650, tel. 617/243–6585) **A**1 2 3 5 10 **F**3 8 11 12 13 15 17 18 26 28 29 30 31 32 34 35 36 40 41 44 45 46 47 48 49 50 52 53 54 55 56 57 58 59 60 63 64 65 68 70 74 75 76 77 78 79 81 82 84 85 86 87 89 93 97 98 99 100 101 102 107 108 110 111 114 115 117 118 119 121 129 130 131 132 134 135 144 145 146 147 148 149 150 **P**1 6 **S** Partners HealthCare System, Inc., Boston, MA
Primary Contact: Michael R. Jaff, D.O., President
CFO: Jeffrey P. Dion, Vice President Finance and Chief Financial Officer
CMO: Timothy Foster, Acting Chief Medical Officer
CIO: Beth Downie, Chief Information Officer
CHR: Beth Taylor, Vice President, Human Resources
Web address: www.nwh.org
Control: Other not–for–profit (including NFP Corporation) **Service:** General medical and surgical

Staffed Beds: 264 **Admissions:** 15032 **Census:** 166 **Outpatient Visits:** 539598 **Births:** 3991 **Total Expense ($000):** 439246 **Payroll Expense ($000):** 194921 **Personnel:** 2422

NORTHAMPTON—Hampshire County

✠ **COOLEY DICKINSON HOSPITAL (220015)**, 30 Locust Street, Zip 01060–2093, Mailing Address: P.O.Box 5001, 01061–5001; tel. 413/582–2000 **A**1 2 10 **F**3 11 13 14 15 18 20 26 28 29 30 31 34 35 38 39 40 49 50 51 54 55 57 59 60 61 64 68 70 74 75 76 78 79 80 81 82 85 86 87 89 93 96 98 100 102 107 108 110 111 114 115 119 120 121 123 126 130 131 132 134 135 144 146 147 148 149 **P**8 **S** Partners HealthCare System, Inc., Boston, MA
Primary Contact: Joanne Marqusee, President and Chief Executive Officer
CFO: Laurie Lamoureux, Director of Finance
CMO: Mark Novotny M.D., Chief Medical Officer
CIO: Lee Martinez, Chief Information Officer
CHR: Lori A Kerwood, Director Human Resources
Web address: www.cooleydickinson.org
Control: Other not–for–profit (including NFP Corporation) **Service:** General medical and surgical

Staffed Beds: 74 **Admissions:** 6617 **Census:** 80 **Outpatient Visits:** 241551 **Births:** 596 **Total Expense ($000):** 170036 **Payroll Expense ($000):** 72273

MA

NORWOOD—Norfolk County

☐ **NORWOOD HOSPITAL (220126)**, 800 Washington Street, Zip 02062–3487;
tel. 781/769–4000, (Nonreporting) **A**1 2 5 10 **S** Steward Health Care System,
LLC, Boston, MA
Primary Contact: Kimberly S. Bassett, R.N., President
COO: William P Fleming, Chief Operating Officer
CFO: Mark Johnson, Chief Financial Officer
CHR: Kimberly Brosnan, Director Human Resources
CNO: Mary Kinneman R.N., MSN, Chief Nursing Officer, Vice President Patient Care
Services
Web address: www.norwood–hospital.org
Control: Corporation, Investor–owned (for–profit) **Service**: General medical and
surgical

Staffed Beds: 188

OAK BLUFFS—Dukes County

✠ **MARTHA'S VINEYARD HOSPITAL (221300)**, One Hospital Road, Zip 2557,
Mailing Address: P.O.Box 1477, 02557–1477; tel. 508/693–0410 **A**1 10 18 **F**3 8
13 15 28 29 30 31 39 40 45 50 57 59 60 64 69 70 75 76 78 79 81 82 85 86
87 89 93 97 107 110 111 115 119 120 130 133 135 146 147 **P**6 **S** Partners
HealthCare System, Inc., Boston, MA
Primary Contact: Timothy Walsh, Interim President and Chief Executive Officer
CFO: Edward Olivier, Chief Financial Officer
CMO: Pieter Pil M.D., Chief Medical Staff
CHR: Christine Gould, Director Human Resources
CNO: Carol A Bardwell R.N., MSN, Chief Nurse Executive
Web address: www.mvhospital.com/
Control: Other not–for–profit (including NFP Corporation) **Service**: General
medical and surgical

Staffed Beds: 25 Admissions: 1342 Census: 17 Outpatient Visits: 134398
Births: 121 Total Expense ($000): 77379 Payroll Expense ($000): 35579
Personnel: 385

PALMER—Hampden County

✠ **BAYSTATE WING HOSPITAL (220030)**, 40 Wright Street, Zip 01069–1138;
tel. 413/283–7651 **A**1 5 10 **F**3 5 11 15 18 29 30 31 33 34 35 37 38 40 42 45
47 49 50 51 54 56 59 60 61 64 65 68 70 74 79 81 82 85 87 89 93 97 98 99
100 101 102 103 104 107 108 109 110 115 118 119 129 130 131 132 146
147 148 **P**6 **S** Baystate Health, Inc., Springfield, MA
Primary Contact: Michael Francis. Moran, President and Chief Administrative Officer
CFO: Keary T Allicon, Vice President Finance and Chief Financial Officer
CMO: David L Maguire M.D., Vice President Medical Affairs
CIO: Kenneth Riley, Director Information Systems
CHR: Thomas Guilfoil, Director Human Resources
Web address: www.baystatewinghospital.org/
Control: Other not–for–profit (including NFP Corporation) **Service**: General
medical and surgical

Staffed Beds: 74 Admissions: 2794 Census: 43 Outpatient Visits: 199498
Births: 0 Total Expense ($000): 82000 Payroll Expense ($000): 37464
Personnel: 627

PEABODY—Essex County

✠ **CURAHEALTH BOSTON NORTH SHORE (222044)**, 15 King Street, Zip 01960–
4379; tel. 978/531–2900, (Nonreporting) **A**1 10 **S** Curahealth Hospitals, Garland,
TX
Primary Contact: Amber Hester, Chief Executive Officer
CMO: M Akbarian M.D., Medical Director
CHR: Jan Pray, Coordinator Payroll and Benefits
CNO: Michelle Mastin, Chief Clinical Officer
Web address: www.curahealth.com
Control: Corporation, Investor–owned (for–profit) **Service**: Acute long–term care
hospital

Staffed Beds: 50

PEMBROKE—Plymouth County

PEMBROKE HOSPITAL, 199 Oak Street, Zip 02359–1953; tel. 781/829–7000,
(Nonreporting) **S** Universal Health Services, Inc., King of Prussia, PA
Primary Contact: Raymond Robinson, Chief Executive Officer
CFO: Diane Airosus, Chief Financial Officer
CMO: Gary Jacobson M.D., Chief Medical Officer
Web address: www.arbourhealth.com/organizations/pembroke–hospital/
Control: Partnership, Investor–owned (for–profit) **Service**: Psychiatric

Staffed Beds: 115

PITTSFIELD—Berkshire County

✠ **BERKSHIRE MEDICAL CENTER (220046)**, 725 North ST, Zip 01201–4124,
Mailing Address: 725 North Street, 01201–4124; tel. 413/447–2000, (Includes
HILLCREST HOSPITAL, 165 Tor Court, Pittsfield, Massachusetts, Zip 01201–3099,
Box 1155, 01202–1155, tel. 413/443–4761) **A**1 2 3 5 8 10 12 13 **F**3 4 5 8 12
13 14 15 17 18 20 26 28 29 30 31 32 34 35 37 38 39 40 42 43 44 45 46 48
49 50 51 53 54 55 56 57 58 59 60 61 62 63 64 65 68 70 71 74 75 76 77 78
79 81 82 83 85 86 87 89 90 92 93 94 98 99 100 101 102 103 104 105 107
108 110 111 112 114 115 116 117 118 119 120 121 122 123 124 126 129
130 131 132 134 135 144 145 146 147 148 149 150 **P**6 **S** Berkshire Health
Systems, Inc., Pittsfield, MA
Primary Contact: David E. Phelps, President and Chief Executive Officer
COO: Diane Kelly, Chief Operating Officer
CFO: Darlene Rodowicz, Chief Financial Officer
CIO: William Young, Chief Information Officer
CHR: Arthur D Milano, Vice President Human Resources
CNO: Brenda E Cadorette, Chief Nursing Officer
Web address: www.berkshirehealthsystems.org
Control: Other not–for–profit (including NFP Corporation) **Service**: General
medical and surgical

Staffed Beds: 275 Admissions: 14216 Census: 175 Outpatient Visits:
131050 Births: 772 Total Expense ($000): 439370 Payroll Expense
($000): 200080 Personnel: 2564

PLYMOUTH—Plymouth County

✠ **BETH ISRAEL DEACONESS HOSPITAL PLYMOUTH (220060)**, 275 Sandwich
Street, Zip 02360–2196; tel. 508/746–2000 **A**1 2 5 10 **F**3 13 15 17 18 20 22
26 28 29 30 31 34 35 36 37 40 44 45 51 57 58 59 61 64 68 70 74 75 76 77
78 79 81 82 85 86 87 89 93 96 98 100 102 103 104 107 108 109 110 111
115 117 118 119 120 121 123 126 129 130 131 132 134 135 143 146 147
148 149
Primary Contact: Kevin B. Coughlin, Chief Executive Officer
CFO: Jason Radzevich, Vice President Finance
CIO: Ronald Rutherford, Chief Information Officer
CHR: Lisa Berry–Barbosa, Vice President Human Resources
CNO: Donna Doherty R.N., Vice President of Nursing and Chief Nursing Officer
Web address: www.bidplymouth.org
Control: Other not–for–profit (including NFP Corporation) **Service**: General
medical and surgical

Staffed Beds: 150 Admissions: 10010 Census: 122 Outpatient Visits:
325713 Births: 770

POCASSET—Barnstable County

☐ **CAPE COD & ISLAND COMMUNITY MENTAL HEALTH CENTER (224031)**,
830 County Road, Zip 02559–2110; tel. 508/564–9600 (Nonreporting) **A**1 10
Primary Contact: Steven Jochim, Administrator
Control: Other not–for–profit (including NFP Corporation) **Service**: Psychiatric

Staffed Beds: 24

ROCHDALE—Worcester County

VIBRA HOSPITAL OF WESTERN MASSACHUSETTS–CENTRAL CAMPUS See
Vibra Hospital Of Western Massachusetts, Springfield

ROSLINDALE—Suffolk County

★ △ **HEBREW REHABILITATION CENTER (222007)**, 1200 Centre Street,
Zip 02131–1097; tel. 617/363–8000, (Total facility includes 675 beds in nursing
home–type unit) **A**7 10 **F**1 2 6 18 29 30 35 39 50 58 59 60 64 65 68 69 75 77
82 83 84 93 97 100 103 104 119 128 130 132 143 146 148 149 **P**6
Primary Contact: Mary K. Moscato, FACHE, President
COO: Brian Murphy, Senior Director Admissions and Referral Services
CFO: Lise Paul, Vice President Reimbursement and Network Planning
CMO: Helen Chen M.D., Chief Medical Officer
CIO: Eric Rogers, Chief Information Officer
CHR: Deborah Lemmerman, Chief People Officer
CNO: Tammy B. Retalic R.N., MS, Chief Nursing Officer
Web address: www.hebrewseniorlife.org
Control: Other not–for–profit (including NFP Corporation) **Service**: Acute long–
term care hospital

Staffed Beds: 725 Admissions: 1335 Census: 680 Outpatient Visits:
63762 Births: 0 Total Expense ($000): 131377 Payroll Expense ($000):
77584 Personnel: 984

Many Facility Codes have changed. Please refer to the AHA Guide Code Chart. © 2017 AHA Guide

SALEM—Essex County

NORTH SHORE CHILDREN'S HOSPITAL See Massgeneral For Children At North Shore Medical Center

☒ **NORTH SHORE MEDICAL CENTER (220035)**, 81 Highland Avenue, Zip 01970–2714; tel. 978/741-1200, (Includes MASSGENERAL FOR CHILDREN AT NORTH SHORE MEDICAL CENTER, 57 Highland Avenue, Salem, Massachusetts, Zip 01970–6508, tel. 978/745–2100; SALEM CAMPUS, 81 Highland Avenue, Salem, Massachusetts, Zip 1970, tel. 978/741–1200; Robert G Norton, President; UNION CAMPUS, 500 Lynnfield Street, Lynn, Massachusetts, Zip 01904–1487, tel. 781/581–9200; Robert G Norton, President) **A**1 3 5 10 **F**5 12 13 15 17 18 20 22 24 26 28 29 30 32 34 35 36 38 40 41 43 45 46 48 49 50 51 55 57 59 60 63 64 68 70 73 74 75 76 77 79 81 82 84 85 86 87 89 92 93 98 99 100 101 102 103 104 105 107 108 110 111 114 115 119 129 130 132 135 143 146 147 148 149 150 **P**6 8 **S** Partners HealthCare System, Inc., Boston, MA
Primary Contact: David J. Roberts, M.D., President
CFO: Sally Mason Boemer, Chief Financial Officer
CMO: Mitchell S Rein M.D., Chief Medical Officer
CIO: Fran X. Hinckley, Chief Information Officer
CHR: Arthur Bowes, Senior Vice President Human Resources
CNO: Cheryl Bhima Merrill MSN, R.N., Senior Vice President Patient Care Services and Chief Nursing Officer
Web address: www.nsmc.partners.org/
Control: Other not–for–profit (including NFP Corporation) **Service**: General medical and surgical

| Staffed Beds: 406 | Admissions: 17758 | Census: 247 | Outpatient Visits: 639452 | Births: 1284 | Total Expense ($000): 465178 | Payroll Expense ($000): 205585 | Personnel: 2355 |

SALEM HOSPITAL See Salem Campus

SOMERVILLE—Middlesex County

SOMERVILLE HOSPITAL See Cambridge Health Alliance, Cambridge

SOUTH WEYMOUTH—Norfolk County

☒ **SOUTH SHORE HOSPITAL (220100)**, 55 Fogg Road, Zip 02190–2432; tel. 781/624–8000 **A**1 2 3 5 10 **F**3 7 11 13 15 17 18 20 22 24 26 28 29 30 31 32 34 35 36 37 40 41 43 44 45 46 49 50 51 53 54 55 57 58 59 60 62 63 64 65 68 70 72 73 74 75 76 78 79 81 82 84 85 86 87 89 91 92 93 96 107 108 110 111 114 115 118 119 124 126 129 130 132 134 135 143 146 147 148 149 150 **P**1
Primary Contact: Gene E. Green, M.D., Chief Executive Officer
COO: Joseph Cahill, Executive Vice President and Chief Operating Officer
CFO: Michael Cullen, Senior Vice President and Chief Financial Officer
CMO: John Stevenson M.D., Senior Vice President and Chief Medical Officer
CIO: Del Dixon, Chief Information Officer
CHR: Robert Wheeler, Vice President Human Resources
Web address: www.southshorehospital.org
Control: Other not–for–profit (including NFP Corporation) **Service**: General medical and surgical

| Staffed Beds: 387 | Admissions: 25188 | Census: 286 | Outpatient Visits: 598572 | Births: 3497 | Total Expense ($000): 552661 | Payroll Expense ($000): 279429 | Personnel: 3744 |

SOUTHBRIDGE—Worcester County

☒ **HARRINGTON HOSPITAL (220019)**, 100 South Street, Zip 01550–4051; tel. 508/765–9771 **A**1 2 5 10 **F**3 5 8 11 13 15 17 18 19 28 29 30 31 32 34 35 38 39 40 42 45 48 49 50 51 54 57 59 61 64 65 68 70 71 74 75 76 77 78 79 81 82 85 86 87 89 92 93 94 96 98 99 100 101 102 103 104 105 107 108 110 111 114 115 117 118 119 129 130 131 132 134 135 145 146 147 148 149
Primary Contact: Edward H. Moore, President and Chief Executive Officer
COO: Kristin Morales, Chief Operating Officer
CFO: Thomas Sullivan, Vice President Fiscal Services
CMO: Arthur Russo M.D., Director Medical Affairs
CIO: Harry Lemieux, Chief Information Officer
CHR: Christopher Canniff, Executive Director, Human Resources
CNO: Thomas W. Hijeck R.N., MS, Vice President Nursing Services and Chief Nursing Officer
Web address: www.harringtonhospital.org
Control: Other not–for–profit (including NFP Corporation) **Service**: General medical and surgical

| Staffed Beds: 130 | Admissions: 3897 | Census: 45 | Births: 210 |

SPRINGFIELD—Hampden County

☒ **BAYSTATE MEDICAL CENTER (220077)**, 759 Chestnut Street, Zip 01199–0001; tel. 413/794–0000, (Includes BAYSTATE CHILDREN'S HOSPITAL, 759 Chestnut Street, Springfield, Massachusetts, Zip 01199–1001, tel. 413/794–0000; Mark A. Keroack, M.D., M.P.H., President and Chief Executive Officer, Baystate Health) **A**1 3 5 8 10 **F**3 8 12 13 14 15 17 18 19 20 22 24 26 28 29 30 31 32 34 35 37 38 40 41 43 44 45 46 47 48 49 50 51 52 54 55 56 57 58 59 60 61 64 65 66 68 70 72 74 75 76 77 78 79 80 81 82 83 84 85 86 87 88 89 92 93 96 97 98 99 100 101 103 104 105 107 108 110 111 114 115 118 119 120 121 123 124 126 129 130 131 132 135 138 143 145 146 147 148 149 **P**8 **S** Baystate Health, Inc., Springfield, MA
Primary Contact: Nancy Shendell–Falk, President
COO: Tejas Gandhi Ph.D., Chief Operating Officer
CFO: Dennis Chalke, Senior Vice President, Chief Financial Officer and Treasurer
CMO: Andrew Artenstein M.D., Chief Physician Executive, Chief Academic Officer and President, Baystate Medical Practices
CIO: Joel L. Vengco MS, Vice President, Chief Information Officer
CHR: Paula C Squires, Senior Vice President, Chief Human Resources Officer and Chief Human Resources Officer
CNO: Nancy Shendell–Falik R.N., Senior Vice President, Chief Operating Officer and Chief Nursing Officer
Web address: www.baystatehealth.org/bmc
Control: Other not–for–profit (including NFP Corporation) **Service**: General medical and surgical

| Staffed Beds: 713 | Admissions: 37498 | Census: 518 | Outpatient Visits: 888230 | Births: 3837 | Total Expense ($000): 1116035 | Payroll Expense ($000): 414624 | Personnel: 7388 |

KINDRED HOSPITAL PARK VIEW See Vibra Hospital Of Western Massachusetts

☒ △ **MERCY MEDICAL CENTER (220066)**, 271 Carew Street, Zip 01104–2398, Mailing Address: P.O.Box 9012, 01102–9012; tel. 413/748–9000 **A**1 2 7 10 **F**3 4 5 8 12 13 14 15 18 20 26 29 30 31 34 35 38 40 44 45 46 47 48 49 50 51 54 55 56 57 58 59 62 64 68 70 74 75 76 77 78 79 81 82 83 84 85 86 87 89 90 91 92 93 96 98 99 100 101 102 103 104 105 106 107 108 110 111 113 114 115 116 117 118 119 120 121 123 124 126 130 131 132 134 135 143 146 147 148 **S** Trinity Health, Livonia, MI
Primary Contact: Mary Elizabeth. O'Brien, President
CFO: Thomas W. Robert, Senior Vice President of Finance and Chief Financial Officer
CIO: Joan Methe, Chief Information Officer
CHR: Leonard F Pansa, Senior Vice President Human Resources and Administrative Services
CNO: Sharon Adams R.N., Senior Vice President Patient Care Services and Chief Quality Officer
Web address: www.mercycares.com
Control: Other not–for–profit (including NFP Corporation) **Service**: General medical and surgical

| Staffed Beds: 333 | Admissions: 15136 | Census: 206 | Outpatient Visits: 582037 | Births: 1319 | Total Expense ($000): 268912 | Payroll Expense ($000): 103977 | Personnel: 314 |

☐ **SHRINERS HOSPITALS FOR CHILDREN–SPRINGFIELD (223303)**, 516 Carew Street, Zip 01104–2396; tel. 413/787–2000 **A**1 3 5 10 **F**3 29 32 34 35 50 55 58 59 64 66 68 71 74 75 77 79 81 85 86 89 91 92 93 94 119 130 131 143 146 **P**1 **S** Shriners Hospitals for Children, Tampa, FL
Primary Contact: H Lee. Kirk Jr, FACHE, Administrator
CFO: Richard Fulkerson, Director Fiscal Services
CMO: David M Drvaric M.D., Chief of Staff
CIO: Eric Kamens, Regional Director Information Systems
CHR: John Donlin, Director Human Resources
CNO: Diane Brunelle MSN, R.N., Director Patient Care Services and Chief Nursing Officer
Web address: www.shrinershospitalsforchildren.org/Hospitals/Locations/Springfield.aspx
Control: Other not–for–profit (including NFP Corporation) **Service**: Children's orthopedic

| Staffed Beds: 10 | Admissions: 89 | Census: 1 | Outpatient Visits: 13381 | Births: 0 | Total Expense ($000): 18377 | Payroll Expense ($000): 9507 | Personnel: 154 |

Hospital, Medicare Provider Number, Address, Telephone, Approval, Facility, and Physician Codes, Health Care System
★ American Hospital Association (AHA) membership ○ Healthcare Facilities Accreditation Program ⇑ Center for Improvement in Healthcare Quality Accreditation
☐ The Joint Commission accreditation ◇ DNV Healthcare Inc. accreditation △ Commission on Accreditation of Rehabilitation Facilities (CARF) accreditation

MA

✉ **VIBRA HOSPITAL OF WESTERN MASSACHUSETTS (222046)**, 1400 State Street, Zip 01109–2550; tel. 413/726–6700, (Includes VIBRA HOSPITAL OF WESTERN MASSACHUSETTS–CENTRAL CAMPUS, 111 Huntoon Memorial Highway, Rochdale, Massachusetts, Zip 1542, tel. 508/892–6000; Scott MacLean, Administrator) (Total facility includes 28 beds in nursing home–type unit) **A**1 10 **F**3 29 50 75 80 82 96 98 128 130 148 **P**7 **S** Vibra Healthcare, Mechanicsburg, PA
Primary Contact: Edward B. Leary, Interim Chief Executive Officer
CFO: Anna Dyrkacz, Chief Financial Officer
CHR: Donna Ciarefella, Director Human Resources
Web address: www.vhwmass.com
Control: Corporation, Investor–owned (for–profit) **Service**: Acute long–term care hospital

Staffed Beds: 174 Admissions: 532 Census: 75 Outpatient Visits: 0 Births: 0 Personnel: 233

STOCKBRIDGE—Berkshire County

✉ **AUSTEN RIGGS CENTER**, 25 Main Street, Zip 1262, Mailing Address: P.O.Box 962, 01262–0962; tel. 413/298–5511, (Nonreporting) **A**1 3 5
Primary Contact: Andrew Gerber, M.D., Ph.D., Medical Director and Chief Executive Officer
COO: Chauncey Collins, Chief Operating Officer and Chief Financial Officer
CFO: Chauncey Collins, Chief Operating Officer and Chief Financial Officer
CIO: Ave Schwartz, Chief Information Officer
CHR: Bertha Mary Connelley, Director Human Resources
CNO: Barbara Turner, Director of Nursing
Web address: www.austenriggs.org
Control: Other not–for–profit (including NFP Corporation) **Service**: Psychiatric

Staffed Beds: 74

STOUGHTON—Norfolk County

✉ **CURAHEALTH STOUGHTON (222002)**, 909 Sumner Street, 1st Floor, Zip 02072–3396; tel. 781/297–8200, (Nonreporting) **A**1 10 **S** Curahealth Hospitals, Garland, TX
Primary Contact: Robert A. Gundersen, Market Chief Executive Officer
Web address: www.curahealth.com
Control: Corporation, Investor–owned (for–profit) **Service**: Acute long–term care hospital

Staffed Beds: 111

☐ **NEW ENGLAND SINAI HOSPITAL AND REHABILITATION CENTER (222027)**, 150 York Street, Zip 02072–1881; tel. 781/344–0600, (Nonreporting) **A**1 3 5 10 **S** Steward Health Care System, LLC, Boston, MA
Primary Contact: Mary Beth. Urquhart, Interim President, Vice President Patient Care Services and Chief Nursing Officer
CFO: Victoria Lobban, Vice President Finance
CMO: Lawrence S Hotes M.D., Chief Medical Officer
CIO: Michael West, Manager Systems Account
CHR: Julie Burke, Director Human Resources
CNO: Mary Beth Urquhart, Vice President Patient Care Services and Director of Quality
Web address: www.newenglandsinai.org
Control: Other not–for–profit (including NFP Corporation) **Service**: Acute long–term care hospital

Staffed Beds: 212

TAUNTON—Bristol County

☐ **MORTON HOSPITAL AND MEDICAL CENTER (220073)**, 88 Washington Street, Zip 02780–2465; tel. 508/828–7000, (Nonreporting) **A**1 2 10 **S** Steward Health Care System, LLC, Boston, MA
Primary Contact: Deborah Bitsoli, CPA, President
COO: Donna Maher R.N., Chief Operating Officer
CFO: Heidi Taylor, Chief Financial Officer
CMO: Charles Thayer M.D., Chief Medical Officer
CNO: Lisa Coggins, Chief Nursing Officer
Web address: www.mortonhospital.org
Control: Other not–for–profit (including NFP Corporation) **Service**: General medical and surgical

Staffed Beds: 153

☐ **TAUNTON STATE HOSPITAL (224001)**, 60 Hodges Avenue Extension, Zip 02780–3034, Mailing Address: PO Box 4007, 02780–0997; tel. 508/977–3000, (Nonreporting) **A**1 10 **S** Massachusetts Department of Mental Health, Boston, MA
Primary Contact: Joyce O Connor, Chief Operating Officer
CHR: Trish Scully, Director Human Resources
Control: State, Government, Nonfederal **Service**: Psychiatric

Staffed Beds: 45

TEWKSBURY—Middlesex County

☐ **TEWKSBURY HOSPITAL (222003)**, 365 East Street, Zip 01876–1998; tel. 978/851–7321, (Nonreporting) **A**1 3 10 **S** Massachusetts Department of Public Health, Boston, MA
Primary Contact: Debra Tosti, Chief Executive Officer
COO: Betsy L Schwechheimer, Chief Operating Officer
CFO: Maureen DiPalma, Chief Financial Officer
CMO: James DeVita M.D., Chief Medical Officer
CNO: Janice E Bishop R.N., Chief Nursing Officer
Web address: www.mass.gov
Control: State, Government, Nonfederal **Service**: Acute long–term care hospital

Staffed Beds: 381

WALTHAM—Middlesex County

☐ **WALDEN BEHAVIORAL CARE (224038)**, 9 Hope Avenue, Zip 02453–2741; tel. 781/647–6700 **A**1 10 **F**98 99 101 104 105 106 **P**6
Primary Contact: Stuart Koman, Ph.D., President and Chief Executive Officer
COO: Paula Vass, Vice President Clinical Operations
CFO: Lawrence Behan, Vice President Administration and Finance, Chief Financial Officer
CMO: James Greenblatt M.D., Chief Medical Officer, Vice President Medical Clinical Services
CIO: Lawrence Behan, Vice President Administration and Finance, Chief Financial Officer
CHR: Carol Pender, Assistant Vice President Human Resources
CNO: Stephen Reider R.N., Director of Nursing, Assistant Vice President Patient Care Services
Web address: www.waldenbehavioralcare.com/
Control: Partnership, Investor–owned (for–profit) **Service**: Psychiatric

Staffed Beds: 69 Admissions: 3909 Census: 62 Outpatient Visits: 28361 Births: 0 Total Expense ($000): 28262 Payroll Expense ($000): 14266 Personnel: 289

WAREHAM—Plymouth County

TOBEY HOSPITAL See Southcoast Hospitals Group, Fall River

WEST ROXBURY—Suffolk County

★ △ **VETERANS AFFAIRS BOSTON HEALTHCARE SYSTEM**, 1400 VFW Parkway, Zip 02132–4927; tel. 617/323–7700, (Nonreporting) **A**3 5 7 8 **S** Department of Veterans Affairs, Washington, DC
Primary Contact: Vincent Ng, Director
CFO: Joe Costa, Chief Financial Officer
CMO: Brian Hoffman M.D., Chief Medical Services
CIO: David M Goodman Ph.D., Chief Information Officer
CHR: William Warfield, Chief Human Resources Management
Web address: www.boston.va.gov/
Control: Veterans Affairs, Government, federal **Service**: General medical and surgical

Staffed Beds: 361

VETERANS AFFAIRS MEDICAL CENTER WEST ROXBURY DIVISION See Veterans Affairs Boston Healthcare System Brockton Division, Brockton

WESTBOROUGH—Worcester County

☐ **WHITTIER REHABILITATION HOSPITAL (222048)**, 150 Flanders Road, Zip 01581–1017; tel. 508/871–2000 (Nonreporting) **A**1 10 **S** Whittier Health Network, Haverhill, MA
Primary Contact: Alfred J. Arcidi, M.D., Senior Vice President
Web address: www.whittierhealth.com
Control: Partnership, Investor–owned (for–profit) **Service**: Acute long–term care hospital

Staffed Beds: 74

WESTFIELD—Hampden County

✉ **BAYSTATE NOBLE HOSPITAL (220065)**, 115 West Silver Street, Zip 01085–3628; tel. 413/568–2811 **A**1 2 5 10 **F**8 14 15 18 28 29 30 31 34 40 57 59 66 70 75 77 78 79 80 81 86 89 90 93 98 100 101 102 103 104 105 107 108 110 111 115 116 117 119 130 132 144 146 147 148 **P**8 **S** Baystate Health, Inc., Springfield, MA
Primary Contact: Ronald Bryant, President
CFO: John Shaver, Chief Financial Officer
CMO: Stanley Strzempko M.D., Vice President Medical Affairs and Chief Medical Officer
CIO: Steven Cummings, Chief Operating Officer and Chief Information Officer
CHR: Joanne Ollson, Vice President Human Resources
Web address: www.baystatehealth.org/locations/noble-hospital
Control: Other not–for–profit (including NFP Corporation) **Service**: General medical and surgical

Staffed Beds: 97 Admissions: 2999 Census: 45 Outpatient Visits: 104761 Births: 0 Total Expense ($000): 57898 Payroll Expense ($000): 27136 Personnel: 330

☐ **WESTERN MASSACHUSETTS HOSPITAL (222023)**, 91 East Mountain Road, Zip 01085–1801; tel. 413/562–4131, (Nonreporting) **A**1 10 **S** Massachusetts Department of Public Health, Boston, MA
Primary Contact: Valenda M. Liptak, Chief Executive Officer
CMO: Chabilal Neergheen M.D., Medical Director
CHR: James E Duggan, Director Human Resources
Web address: www.mass.gov/eohhs/gov/departments/dph/programs/western–massachusetts–hospital.html
Control: State, Government, Nonfederal **Service**: Acute long–term care hospital

Staffed Beds: 70

WHITINSVILLE—Worcester County

WHITINSVILLE MEDICAL CENTER See Milford Regional Medical Center, Milford

WINCHESTER—Middlesex County

✠ **WINCHESTER HOSPITAL (220105)**, 41 Highland Avenue, Zip 01890–1496; tel. 781/729–9000 **A**1 2 3 5 10 **F**3 8 12 13 15 18 26 28 29 30 31 32 34 35 36 38 40 41 44 45 46 49 50 51 54 55 56 57 59 62 64 70 73 74 75 76 77 78 79 81 82 85 86 87 89 91 92 93 107 108 110 114 115 118 119 120 121 126 129 130 131 132 135 144 145 146 147 148 149 **S** Lahey Health, Burlington, MA
Primary Contact: Dale M. Lodge, Chief Executive Officer
CFO: Matthew Woods, Vice President Finance
CMO: Richard Iseke M.D., Vice President Medical Affairs
CHR: Stephanie M Bettinelli, Vice President of Human Resources
CNO: Kathy Schuler R.N., MS, Vice President of Patient Care Services
Web address: www.winchesterhospital.org
Control: Other not–for–profit (including NFP Corporation) **Service**: General medical and surgical

Staffed Beds: 197 Admissions: 11043 Census: 120 Outpatient Visits: 536050 Births: 2196 Total Expense ($000): 271918 Payroll Expense ($000): 116076 Personnel: 1766

WOBURN—Middlesex County

✠ **HEALTHSOUTH NEW ENGLAND REHABILITATION HOSPITAL (223026)**, Two Rehabilitation Way, Zip 01801–6098; tel. 781/935–5050 **A**1 3 10 **F**28 29 30 34 58 59 64 75 77 82 86 90 91 93 94 96 100 101 103 104 132 146 148 **S** HEALTHSOUTH Corporation, Birmingham, AL
Primary Contact: Laura Ames, Chief Executive Officer
CFO: Lester Felege, Controller
CHR: Annamarie Cronin, Director Human Resources
Web address: www.newenglandrehab.com
Control: Corporation, Investor–owned (for–profit) **Service**: Rehabilitation

Staffed Beds: 210 Admissions: 2760 Census: 102 Outpatient Visits: 25743 Births: 0 Total Expense ($000): 42130 Payroll Expense ($000): 20326 Personnel: 452

WORCESTER—Worcester County

ADCARE HOSPITAL OF WORCESTER (220062), 107 Lincoln Street, Zip 01605–2499; tel. 508/799–9000, (Nonreporting) **A**3 5 10
Primary Contact: David W. Hillis, Chairman and Chief Executive Officer
COO: Jeffrey W Hillis, Chief Operating Officer
CFO: Christine Judycki–Crepeault, Chief Financial Officer
CMO: Ronald F Pike M.D., Medical Director
CHR: Joan L. Bertrand, Vice President Human Resources
CNO: Judith Richards, Director of Nursing
Web address: www.adcare.com
Control: Other not–for–profit (including NFP Corporation) **Service**: Alcoholism and other chemical dependency

Staffed Beds: 114

✠ **FAIRLAWN REHABILITATION HOSPITAL (223029)**, 189 May Street, Zip 01602–4339; tel. 508/791–6351 **A**1 3 5 10 **F**3 28 29 34 35 56 57 59 60 64 74 75 77 79 82 86 87 90 91 93 95 96 130 132 135 **P**8 **S** HEALTHSOUTH Corporation, Birmingham, AL
Primary Contact: Mary Lou D'Avino, Chief Executive Officer
CFO: John Flaherty, Controller
CMO: Debra Twehous, Medical Director
CHR: Rosalie Lawless, Director Human Resources
CNO: Sonja Cooley–Johnson, Chief Nursing Officer
Web address: www.fairlawnrehab.org
Control: Corporation, Investor–owned (for–profit) **Service**: Rehabilitation

Staffed Beds: 110 Admissions: 2477 Census: 88 Outpatient Visits: 10935 Births: 0

✠ **SAINT VINCENT HOSPITAL (220176)**, 123 Summer Street, Zip 01608—1216; tel. 508/363–5000 **A**1 2 5 10 **F**3 8 12 13 15 17 18 20 22 24 26 28 29 30 31 34 35 36 38 40 45 46 48 49 50 54 55 56 57 59 60 64 68 70 74 75 76 77 78 79 81 82 84 85 86 87 92 93 97 98 100 101 102 105 107 108 110 111 114 115 116 117 119 120 121 124 126 129 130 131 132 135 144 146 147 **P**5 **S** TENET Healthcare Corporation, Dallas, TX
Primary Contact: Jeffrey M. Welch, Market Chief Executive Officer
CFO: Peter D'Elia, Chief Financial Officer
CMO: Douglas Waite M.D., Chief Medical Officer
CHR: Jan Peters, Vice President Human Resources
CNO: JoAnn Piedrafite R.N., Chief Nursing Officer
Web address: www.stvincenthospital.com
Control: Corporation, Investor–owned (for–profit) **Service**: General medical and surgical

Staffed Beds: 283 Admissions: 17622 Census: 201 Outpatient Visits: 252721 Births: 1928 Total Expense ($000): 375848 Payroll Expense ($000): 149152 Personnel: 1752

✠ **UMASS MEMORIAL MEDICAL CENTER (220163)**, 119 Belmont Street, Zip 01605—2982; tel. 508/334–1000, (Includes HAHNEMANN CAMPUS, 281 Lincoln Street, Worcester, Massachusetts, Zip 1605, tel. 508/334–1000; MEMORIAL CAMPUS, 119 Belmont Street, Worcester, Massachusetts, Zip 1605, tel. 508/334–1000; UMASS MEMORIAL CHILDREN'S MEDICAL CENTER, 55 Lake Avenue North, Worcester, Massachusetts, Zip 01655–0002, tel. 508/334–1000; UNIVERSITY CAMPUS, 55 Lake Avenue North, Worcester, Massachusetts, Zip 01655–0002, tel. 508/334–1000) **A**1 2 3 5 8 10 **F**3 5 6 7 8 9 12 13 14 15 16 17 18 19 20 22 24 26 29 30 31 32 38 40 41 43 45 46 47 48 49 50 51 52 54 55 56 58 59 60 61 64 65 68 70 71 72 73 74 75 76 77 78 79 81 82 84 85 86 87 88 89 92 93 97 98 99 100 101 102 103 104 105 107 108 110 114 115 118 119 120 121 123 124 126 127 130 131 132 135 136 138 139 142 145 146 147 148 149 150 **P**5 6 **S** UMass Memorial Health Care, Inc., Worcester, MA
Primary Contact: Patrick L. Muldoon, FACHE, President
COO: Andrew Sussman M.D., Chief Operating Officer
CFO: Therese Day, Chief Financial Officer
CMO: Stephen E Tosi M.D., Chief Medical Officer
CIO: George Brenkle, Chief Information Officer
CNO: Lisa Colombo R.N., Senior Vice President Patient Care Services and Chief Nursing Officer
Web address: www.umassmemorial.org
Control: Other not–for–profit (including NFP Corporation) **Service**: General medical and surgical

Staffed Beds: 662 Admissions: 38444 Census: 570 Outpatient Visits: 1019503 Births: 3918 Total Expense ($000): 1573928 Payroll Expense ($000): 524323 Personnel: 7718

☐ **WORCESTER RECOVERY CENTER AND HOSPITAL (224032)**, 309 Belmont Street, Zip 01604—1695; tel. 508/368–3300, (Nonreporting) **A**1 3 5 10 **S** Massachusetts Department of Mental Health, Boston, MA
Primary Contact: Anthony Riccitelli, Chief Operating Officer
COO: Anthony Riccitelli, Chief Operating Officer
CIO: Ron Medciros, Director Applied Information Technology
Control: State, Government, Nonfederal **Service**: Psychiatric

Staffed Beds: 126

MA

Hospital, Medicare Provider Number, Address, Telephone, Approval, Facility, and Physician Codes, Health Care System

★ American Hospital Association (AHA) membership   ◯ Healthcare Facilities Accreditation Program   ⇑ Center for Improvement in Healthcare Quality Accreditation
☐ The Joint Commission accreditation   ◇ DNV Healthcare Inc. accreditation   △ Commission on Accreditation of Rehabilitation Facilities (CARF) accreditation

MICHIGAN

MI

ADRIAN—Lenawee County

★ ○ **PROMEDICA BIXBY HOSPITAL (230005)**, 818 Riverside Avenue, Zip 49221–1446; tel. 517/265–0900 **A**2 10 11 **F**3 11 13 15 18 28 29 30 34 35 40 45 46 49 50 51 55 57 59 64 67 68 70 74 75 76 78 79 81 82 84 85 87 91 92 93 100 102 107 108 110 111 115 116 117 118 119 120 121 123 126 130 131 132 135 145 146 148 149 **P**6 8 **S** ProMedica Health System, Toledo, OH
Primary Contact: Julie Yaroch, D.O., President
CFO: Bernie Nawrocki, Administrative Director Finance
CIO: Stephanie Sonnenberg, Director Information Technology
CHR: Cathy J Davis, Director Human Resources
CNO: Kathryn M Greenlee R.N., Vice President, Clinical Services/CNO
Web address: www.promedica.org
Control: Other not–for–profit (including NFP Corporation) **Service**: General medical and surgical

Staffed Beds: 66 **Admissions:** 3969 **Census:** 35 **Outpatient Visits:** 144899 **Births:** 638 **Total Expense ($000):** 77082 **Payroll Expense ($000):** 25698 **Personnel:** 421	

ALLEGAN—Allegan County

★ ⇑ **ALLEGAN GENERAL HOSPITAL (231328)**, 555 Linn Street, Zip 49010–1524; tel. 269/673–8424 **A**3 10 18 21 **F**3 12 15 28 29 31 34 35 40 45 47 48 50 57 59 62 70 75 77 78 79 81 82 85 86 87 96 99 100 101 104 107 108 110 114 119 127 129 130 131 132 135 146 149 **S** QHR, Brentwood, TN
Primary Contact: Gerald J. Barbini, President and Chief Executive Officer
CFO: Richard Harning, Vice President Finance and Chief Financial Officer
CMO: Nabil Nouna M.D., Chief of Staff
CIO: David Federinko, Chief Information Officer
CHR: Denise A Eberth, Chief Human Resources Officer
CNO: Kathy Chapman R.N., Chief Clinical Officer and Vice President of Patient Services
Web address: www.aghosp.org
Control: Other not–for–profit (including NFP Corporation) **Service**: General medical and surgical

Staffed Beds: 25 **Admissions:** 842 **Census:** 7 **Outpatient Visits:** 79240 **Births:** 0 **Total Expense ($000):** 45878 **Payroll Expense ($000):** 16428 **Personnel:** 255	

ALMA—Gratiot County

GRATIOT MEDICAL CENTER See Midmichigan Medical Center–Gratiot

⊞ △ **MIDMICHIGAN MEDICAL CENTER–GRATIOT (230030)**, 300 East Warwick Drive, Zip 48801–1014; tel. 989/463–1101 **A**1 5 7 10 **F**3 11 12 13 15 18 20 28 29 31 34 35 40 45 50 51 56 57 59 61 64 65 68 70 74 76 77 78 79 81 85 86 87 89 90 92 93 96 97 98 100 101 102 103 104 105 107 108 110 111 115 117 118 119 127 129 130 132 135 144 145 146 147 148 149 **S** MidMichigan Health, Midland, MI
Primary Contact: Gregory H. Rogers, Interim President
CFO: Jeff Provenzano, Vice President and Chief Financial Officer
CNO: Robin Whitmore, Chief Nursing Officer
Web address: www.midmichigan.org/gratiot
Control: Other not–for–profit (including NFP Corporation) **Service**: General medical and surgical

Staffed Beds: 79 **Admissions:** 4103 **Census:** 53 **Outpatient Visits:** 145030 **Births:** 472 **Total Expense ($000):** 102197 **Payroll Expense ($000):** 29649 **Personnel:** 583	

ALPENA—Alpena County

⊞ **MIDMICHIGAN MEDICAL CENTER – ALPENA (230036)**, 1501 West Chisholm Street, Zip 49707–1401; tel. 989/356–7000 **A**1 2 10 **F**3 11 13 15 20 26 28 29 31 34 35 40 44 45 46 47 48 49 50 59 62 64 65 70 71 73 74 75 76 77 78 79 81 82 85 86 87 90 92 93 96 97 98 99 100 101 102 103 104 106 107 108 110 111 114 115 118 119 129 130 131 132 135 146 147 148 **P**6 **S** MidMichigan Health, Midland, MI
Primary Contact: Karmon T. Bjella, President
COO: Charles H Sherwin, Vice President of Business Development and Clinical Services
CFO: George J Smart, Vice President Finance and Information Technology
CMO: Richard Bates, Vice President of Medical Affairs
CHR: Diane Shields, Chief Human Resources Officer
CNO: Charles H Sherwin, Chief Nursing Officer
Web address: www.alpenaregionalmedicalcenter.org
Control: Other not–for–profit (including NFP Corporation) **Service**: General medical and surgical

Staffed Beds: 125 **Admissions:** 4622 **Census:** 54 **Outpatient Visits:** 236801 **Births:** 393 **Total Expense ($000):** 132024 **Payroll Expense ($000):** 52206 **Personnel:** 889	

ANN ARBOR—Washtenaw County

⊞ **MICHIGAN MEDICINE (230046)**, 1500 East Medical Center Drive, Zip 48109; tel. 734/936–4000, (Includes C. S. MOTT CHILDREN'S HOSPITAL, 1540 East Hospital Drive, Ann Arbor, Michigan, Zip 48109–5475, tel. 734/936–4000; Paul A King, Executive Director) **A**1 2 3 5 8 10 **F**3 5 6 8 9 11 12 13 15 16 17 18 19 20 21 22 23 24 25 26 27 28 29 30 31 32 34 35 36 37 38 39 40 41 43 44 45 46 47 48 49 50 51 52 53 54 55 56 57 58 59 60 61 62 64 65 66 68 69 70 72 74 75 76 77 78 79 80 81 82 84 85 86 87 88 89 90 91 92 93 94 95 97 98 99 100 101 102 103 104 107 108 110 111 112 114 115 116 117 118 119 120 121 123 124 126 127 129 130 131 132 134 135 136 137 138 139 140 141 142 145 146 147 148 149 150 **P**1
Primary Contact: David Spahlinger, M.D., President
COO: Tony Denton JD, Senior Vice President and Chief Operating Officer
CFO: Paul Castillo, Chief Financial Officer
CMO: Jeffrey Desmond M.D., Chief Medical Officer
CIO: Andrew Rosenberg M.D., Chief Information Officer
CHR: Joseph Fournier, Chief Human Resources Officer
CNO: Marge Calarco, Chief Nursing Executive
Web address: www.med.umich.edu
Control: Other not–for–profit (including NFP Corporation) **Service**: General medical and surgical

Staffed Beds: 976 **Admissions:** 50322 **Census:** 820 **Outpatient Visits:** 2372793 **Births:** 4608 **Total Expense ($000):** 2889597 **Payroll Expense ($000):** 1081599 **Personnel:** 15920	

⊞ **VETERANS AFFAIRS ANN ARBOR HEALTHCARE SYSTEM**, 2215 Fuller Road, Zip 48105–2399; tel. 734/769–7100 **A**1 2 3 5 8 **F**1 3 4 5 12 16 17 18 20 22 24 26 28 29 30 31 34 35 36 38 39 40 45 46 48 49 50 54 56 57 58 59 60 61 62 63 64 65 67 68 70 71 72 73 74 75 76 77 78 79 80 81 82 83 84 85 86 87 88 89 90 91 92 93 94 96 97 98 100 101 102 103 104 105 107 108 111 114 115 116 117 118 119 120 121 123 126 128 129 130 132 135 143 144 146 147 148 149 **P**6 **S** Department of Veterans Affairs, Washington, DC
Primary Contact: Andrew Pacyna, FACHE, Acting Director
COO: Himanshu Singh M.D., Associate Director
CFO: Joel Wallinga, Chief Financial Officer
CMO: Eric Young M.D., Chief of Staff
CIO: Rob Whitehurst, Chief, Office of Information and Technology
CHR: Stephanie Hunter, Chief Human Resources Officer
CNO: Stacey Breedveld R.N., MSN, Associate Director for Patient Care
Web address: www.annarbor.va.gov
Control: Veterans Affairs, Government, federal **Service**: General medical and surgical

Staffed Beds: 109 **Admissions:** 5843 **Census:** 109 **Outpatient Visits:** 637532 **Births:** 0 **Total Expense ($000):** 504702 **Payroll Expense ($000):** 214363 **Personnel:** 3103	

AUBURN HILLS—Oakland County

☐ **HAVENWYCK HOSPITAL (234023)**, 1525 University Drive, Zip 48326–2673; tel. 248/373–9200 **A**1 10 **F**98 99 102 103 105 106 130 **P**8 **S** Universal Health Services, Inc., King of Prussia, PA
Primary Contact: Diane Henneman, Chief Executive Officer
COO: Julie Szyska, Chief Operating Officer
CFO: Steve Sacharski, Chief Financial Officer
CMO: Hani Mekhael M.D., Chief Staff
CHR: Amy Giannosa, Director Human Resources
CNO: Mitzi Sawicki, Director of Nursing
Web address: www.havenwyckhospital.com
Control: Corporation, Investor–owned (for–profit) **Service**: Psychiatric

Staffed Beds: 235 **Admissions:** 6989 **Census:** 195 **Outpatient Visits:** 5254 **Births:** 0 **Total Expense ($000):** 45729 **Payroll Expense ($000):** 17917 **Personnel:** 416	

BAD AXE—Huron County

HURON MEDICAL CENTER (230118), 1100 South Van Dyke Road, Zip 48413–9615; tel. 989/269–9521 **A**5 10 20 **F**3 11 13 14 15 18 20 28 29 31 32 34 35 40 45 53 56 57 59 64 70 74 75 76 77 78 79 81 82 85 90 93 97 107 108 114 119 126 127 130 132 134 135 144 146 148 149 **P**6
Primary Contact: Jeffery Longbrake, President and Chief Executive Officer
CFO: Bill Castle, Chief Financial Officer
CMO: Christopher Gong M.D., Chief Staff
CHR: Nancy Bouck, Director Human Resources
CNO: Carrie Franzel, Chief Nursing Officer
Web address: www.huronmedicalcenter.org
Control: Other not–for–profit (including NFP Corporation) **Service**: General medical and surgical

Staffed Beds: 35 **Admissions:** 1605 **Census:** 12 **Outpatient Visits:** 50307 **Births:** 436 **Total Expense ($000):** 44922 **Payroll Expense ($000):** 17240 **Personnel:** 316	

Many Facility Codes have changed. Please refer to the AHA Guide Code Chart. © 2017 AHA Guide

BATTLE CREEK—Calhoun County

⊞ **BATTLE CREEK VETERANS AFFAIRS MEDICAL CENTER**, 5500 Armstrong Road, Zip 49037–7314; tel. 269/966–5600, (Total facility includes 75 beds in nursing home–type unit) **A**1 3 5 **F**3 4 5 7 12 18 29 30 33 34 35 36 38 39 50 53 54 56 57 58 59 61 62 63 64 65 68 74 75 77 82 83 84 86 87 91 93 94 96 97 98 100 101 102 103 104 106 107 108 111 114 115 119 127 128 130 132 135 143 144 146 147 148 **S** Department of Veterans Affairs, Washington, DC
Primary Contact: Mary Beth Skupien, Director
COO: Edward G. Dornoff, Associate Director
CFO: James M. Rupert, Chief Fiscal Services
CMO: Wilfredo Rodriguez M.D., Chief of Staff
CIO: Scott Hershberger, Acting Chief Information Management Services
CHR: Palma Simkins, Chief Human Resources Management Services
CNO: Kay Bower, Associate Director for Patient Care Services
Web address: www.battlecreek.va.gov/
Control: Veterans Affairs, Government, federal **Service:** Psychiatric

Staffed Beds: 242 **Admissions:** 1753 **Census:** 191 **Outpatient Visits:** 563374 **Births:** 0 **Personnel:** 1525

⊞ **BRONSON BATTLE CREEK (230075)**, 300 North Avenue, Zip 49017–3307; tel. 269/245–8000, (Includes FIELDSTONE CENTER, 165 North Washington Avenue, Battle Creek, Michigan, Zip 49037, tel. 269/245–8570; MAIN CAMPUS, 300 North Avenue, Battle Creek, Michigan, Zip 49017, tel. 616/966–8000) **A**1 2 10 **F**3 4 5 6 9 11 12 15 18 20 26 28 29 30 31 34 35 36 38 40 44 45 46 49 50 51 54 55 56 57 58 59 60 61 63 64 65 66 68 70 71 74 75 76 77 78 79 81 82 83 84 85 86 87 90 92 93 97 98 100 101 102 103 104 107 108 110 111 115 117 119 126 129 130 131 132 134 135 143 144 146 147 148 149 **P**6 **S** Bronson Healthcare Group, Kalamazoo, MI
Primary Contact: Frank J. Sardone, President and Chief Executive Officer
COO: James E. Mckernan, Chief Operating Officer
CMO: Daniel Stewart M.D., Vice President Medical Affairs
CHR: John Hayden, Senior Vice President and Human Resources Officer
CNO: Susan Watson MSN, R.N., Vice President
Web address: www.bronsonhealth.com
Control: Other not–for–profit (including NFP Corporation) **Service:** General medical and surgical

Staffed Beds: 198 **Admissions:** 8913 **Census:** 108 **Outpatient Visits:** 516725 **Births:** 811 **Total Expense ($000):** 231376 **Payroll Expense ($000):** 118066 **Personnel:** 1464

⊞ **SELECT SPECIALTY HOSPITAL–BATTLE CREEK (232035)**, 300 North Avenue, Zip 49017–3307; tel. 269/245–4675, (Nonreporting) **A**1 10 **S** Select Medical Corporation, Mechanicsburg, PA
Primary Contact: Robert Mach, Chief Executive Officer
Web address: www.battlecreek.selectspecialtyhospitals.com/
Control: Corporation, Investor–owned (for–profit) **Service:** Acute long–term care hospital

Staffed Beds: 25

VETERANS AFFAIRS MEDICAL CENTER See Battle Creek Veterans Affairs Medical Center

BAY CITY—Bay County

☐ △ **MCLAREN BAY REGION (230041)**, 1900 Columbus Avenue, Zip 48708–6831; tel. 989/894–3000, (Includes MCLAREN BAY REGION–WEST CAMPUS, 3250 East Midland Road, Bay City, Michigan, Zip 48706, tel. 989/667–6750) **A**1 2 3 5 7 10 12 13 **F**3 7 11 13 15 17 18 20 22 24 26 28 29 30 31 32 34 35 36 38 40 44 45 46 47 48 49 50 54 57 58 59 64 65 68 70 73 74 75 76 78 79 81 82 85 86 87 89 90 92 93 96 97 98 100 102 103 107 108 110 111 114 115 119 120 121 123 124 129 130 131 132 135 141 143 144 146 147 148 **S** McLaren Health Care Corporation, Flint, MI
Primary Contact: Clarence Sevillian, President and Chief Executive Officer
CMO: Jason White M.D., Chief Medical Officer
CIO: Ronald Strachan, Chief Information Officer
CHR: Carolyn Potter, Vice President Human Resources
CNO: Ellen E Talbott R.N., MSN, Vice President Patient Care Services
Web address: www.bayregional.org
Control: Other not–for–profit (including NFP Corporation) **Service:** General medical and surgical

Staffed Beds: 338 **Admissions:** 14979 **Census:** 196 **Outpatient Visits:** 312755 **Births:** 842 **Total Expense ($000):** 279065 **Payroll Expense ($000):** 122599 **Personnel:** 2094

○ **MCLAREN BAY SPECIAL CARE (232020)**, 3250 East Midland Road, Suite 1, Zip 48706–2835; tel. 989/667–6802 **A**10 11 **F**1 3 29 79 87 96 148 **S** McLaren Health Care Corporation, Flint, MI
Primary Contact: Cheryl A. Burzynski, MSN, President
CMO: Janet Sutton M.D., Medical Director
CIO: Greg Jacobs, Manager
CHR: Carolyn Potter, Vice President Human Resources
Web address: www.bayspecialcare.org
Control: Other not–for–profit (including NFP Corporation) **Service:** Acute long–term care hospital

Staffed Beds: 21 **Admissions:** 352 **Census:** 17 **Outpatient Visits:** 0 **Births:** 0 **Total Expense ($000):** 7139 **Payroll Expense ($000):** 3413 **Personnel:** 36

BIG RAPIDS—Mecosta County

⊞ **SPECTRUM HEALTH BIG RAPIDS HOSPITAL (230093)**, 605 Oak Street, Zip 49307–2099; tel. 231/796–8691 **A**1 5 10 20 **F**3 8 13 15 17 28 29 33 34 35 40 45 53 59 62 63 64 65 70 75 76 77 79 81 85 86 87 89 91 93 96 97 107 108 110 111 115 119 124 127 129 130 131 135 146 147 148 149 **P**6 **S** Spectrum Health, Grand Rapids, MI
Primary Contact: Mary Kay VanDriel, President
COO: Catherine Rybicki, Vice President Physician Services and Chief Operating Officer
CFO: Thomas Khoerl, Vice President Finance
CMO: Christopher Skinner, Chief of Staff
CIO: Patrick Whiteside, Manager Information Services
CHR: Ricky Green, Senior Human Resources Business Partner
CNO: Caroline A Ring, Chief Nursing Officer
Web address: www.mcmcbr.com
Control: Other not–for–profit (including NFP Corporation) **Service:** General medical and surgical

Staffed Beds: 49 **Admissions:** 1972 **Census:** 15 **Outpatient Visits:** 456819 **Births:** 602 **Total Expense ($000):** 66736 **Payroll Expense ($000):** 25101 **Personnel:** 468

BRIGHTON—Livingston County

★ **BRIGHTON CENTER FOR RECOVERY (230279)**, 12851 Grand River Road, Zip 48116–8506; tel. 810/227–1211 **A**10 **F**4 5 34 35 38 44 68 75 104 130 132 135 146 149 150 **S** Ascension Healthcare, Saint Louis, MO
Primary Contact: Raymond A. Waller, Director
COO: Raymond A. Waller, Director
CFO: Marie Allard, Finance Manager
CMO: Ismael David Yanga M.D., Chief Medical Officer
CIO: Frank Sanzone, Manager Information Technology
CHR: Marney Daugherty, Worklife Services Consultant
CNO: Barbara Shoup R.N., Chief Nursing Officer
Web address: www.brightonrecovery.org
Control: Church operated, Nongovernment, not–for–profit **Service:** Alcoholism and other chemical dependency

Staffed Beds: 99 **Admissions:** 3937 **Census:** 86 **Outpatient Visits:** 18957 **Births:** 0 **Total Expense ($000):** 15266 **Payroll Expense ($000):** 7650 **Personnel:** 132

CADILLAC—Wexford County

⊞ **MUNSON HEALTHCARE CADILLAC HOSPITAL (230081)**, 400 Hobart Street, Zip 49601–2389; tel. 231/876–7200 **A**1 10 20 **F**3 11 13 15 18 28 29 30 31 34 35 40 44 45 50 51 59 64 68 70 76 77 78 79 81 85 87 93 97 107 111 114 115 116 119 127 129 130 132 146 **P**8 **S** Munson Healthcare, Traverse City, MI
Primary Contact: Tonya Smith, President
COO: Michael Zdrodowski, Vice President of Operations and Ambulatory Services
CFO: Kristin Ellis, Controller
CMO: Joe Santangelo M.D., Vice President of Medical Affairs
CIO: Randi Terry, Site Director Management Information Systems
CHR: Kelley Whittington–Geppert, Director Human Resources
CNO: Kathryn Bandfield–Keough, Vice President Patient Care Services
Web address: www.mercyhealthcadillac.com/welcome–cadillac
Control: Other not–for–profit (including NFP Corporation) **Service:** General medical and surgical

Staffed Beds: 97 **Admissions:** 3536 **Census:** 31 **Outpatient Visits:** 144135 **Births:** 374 **Total Expense ($000):** 81221 **Payroll Expense ($000):** 32651 **Personnel:** 603

MI

Hospital, Medicare Provider Number, Address, Telephone, Approval, Facility, and Physician Codes, Health Care System

★ American Hospital Association (AHA) membership
☐ The Joint Commission accreditation
○ Healthcare Facilities Accreditation Program
◇ DNV Healthcare Inc. accreditation
⇑ Center for Improvement in Healthcare Quality Accreditation
△ Commission on Accreditation of Rehabilitation Facilities (CARF) accreditation

CARO—Tuscola County

☐ **CARO CENTER (234025)**, 2000 Chambers Road, Zip 48723–9296; tel. 989/673–3191, (Nonreporting) **A**1 10
Primary Contact: Rose Laskowski, R.N., Director
COO: Rose Laskowski R.N., Director
CFO: Mary Jo Drzewiecki–Burger, Administrative Manager
CMO: William Clark M.D., Chief Clinical Affairs
CIO: Michele Wills, Registered Health Information Administrator
CHR: Barbara Frank, Human Resource Specialist
Control: State, Government, Nonfederal **Service:** Psychiatric

Staffed Beds: 193

★ **CARO COMMUNITY HOSPITAL (231329)**, 401 North Hooper Street, Zip 48723–1476, Mailing Address: P.O.Box 435, 48723–0435; tel. 989/673–3141 **A**5 10 18 **F**3 11 15 29 34 40 45 46 50 57 59 65 75 81 82 85 87 89 92 93 97 107 108 110 115 119 129 130 131 135 146 147 149
Primary Contact: Marc Augsburger, R.N., President and Chief Executive Officer
CFO: Ron Srebinski, Chief Financial Officer
CMO: T Gard Adams M.D., Chief of Staff
CHR: Allyson Joyce, Vice President Human Resources
CNO: Kelly Whittaker, Vice President Nursing
Web address: www.cch-mi.org
Control: Other not–for–profit (including NFP Corporation) **Service:** General medical and surgical

Staffed Beds: 25 **Admissions:** 207 **Census:** 1 **Outpatient Visits:** 26344
Births: 0 **Total Expense ($000):** 13961 **Payroll Expense ($000):** 5996
Personnel: 95

CARSON CITY—Montcalm County

★ ○ **SPARROW CARSON HOSPITAL (230208)**, 406 East Elm Street, Zip 48811–9693, Mailing Address: P.O.Box 879, 48811–0879; tel. 989/584–3131 **A**3 5 10 11 19 **F**3 11 13 15 30 31 34 35 40 45 46 50 57 59 62 64 65 68 70 75 76 78 79 81 82 93 97 107 108 110 111 115 119 126 127 130 131 132 135 146 147 148 **P**8 **S** Sparrow Health System, Lansing, MI
Primary Contact: Matthew J. Thompson, FACHE, President and Chief Executive Officer
CFO: Richard Reid, Vice President Chief Finance Officer
CMO: Robert Seals D.O., Medical Director
CIO: Richard Terry, Vice President & Chief Information Officer
CHR: Georgette Russell, Vice President of Talent & Organizational Effectiveness
Web address: www.carsoncityhospital.com
Control: Other not–for–profit (including NFP Corporation) **Service:** General medical and surgical

Staffed Beds: 48 **Admissions:** 1166 **Census:** 10 **Outpatient Visits:** 67468
Births: 329 **Total Expense ($000):** 47405 **Payroll Expense ($000):** 26707
Personnel: 465

CASS CITY—Tuscola County

★ **HILLS & DALES GENERAL HOSPITAL (231316)**, 4675 Hill Street, Zip 48726–1099; tel. 989/872–2121 **A**5 10 18 **F**3 11 15 29 30 31 32 34 35 40 45 46 53 56 57 59 61 64 68 74 75 77 79 81 82 86 87 93 97 107 108 109 110 115 118 119 127 129 130 131 132 133 135 144 146 147 148 149 **P**6
Primary Contact: Jean Anthony, R.N., President and Chief Executive Officer
CFO: Kenneth Baranski, Chief Financial Officer
CMO: Donald Robbins M.D., Jr, Chief Staff
CNO: Jennifer TerBush, Vice President, Patient Services
Web address: www.hdghmi.org
Control: Other not–for–profit (including NFP Corporation) **Service:** General medical and surgical

Staffed Beds: 25 **Admissions:** 517 **Census:** 6 **Outpatient Visits:** 99477
Births: 0 **Total Expense ($000):** 30069 **Payroll Expense ($000):** 13894
Personnel: 257

CHARLEVOIX—Charlevoix County

⊞ **MUNSON HEALTHCARE CHARLEVOIX HOSPITAL (231322)**, 14700 Lake Shore Drive, Zip 49720–1999; tel. 231/547–4024, (Data for 213 days) **A**1 5 10 18 **F**11 12 15 28 29 30 31 32 34 35 40 45 46 48 50 57 59 64 65 75 77 79 81 86 87 93 97 99 100 101 104 107 111 115 119 124 127 129 130 131 132 133 135 144 146 147 **P**6 **S** Munson Healthcare, Traverse City, MI
Primary Contact: Joanne Schroeder, President
COO: Christine Wilhelm, Chief Operating Officer
CFO: Robert Zimmerman, Vice President Financial Services
CMO: Craig Boss M.D., Chief Medical Officer
CIO: David Priest, Director Information Systems
CHR: Patty Fitzgerald, Staff Services
CNO: Bernadette Green Cole R.N., Chief Nursing Officer
Web address: www.cah.org
Control: Other not–for–profit (including NFP Corporation) **Service:** General medical and surgical

Staffed Beds: 25 **Admissions:** 516 **Census:** 6 **Outpatient Visits:** 23047
Births: 129 **Total Expense ($000):** 26248 **Payroll Expense ($000):** 12245
Personnel: 331

CHARLOTTE—Eaton County

⊞ **HAYES GREEN BEACH MEMORIAL HOSPITAL (231327)**, 321 East Harris Street, Zip 48813–1629; tel. 517/543–1050 **A**1 10 18 **F**3 7 11 15 18 26 28 29 34 35 36 40 45 46 50 53 59 64 65 68 69 75 77 79 81 82 85 87 89 92 93 97 107 108 110 111 114 118 119 129 130 131 132 135 143 144 146 147 148 149 **P**6 **S** QHR, Brentwood, TN
Primary Contact: Matthew Rush, FACHE, President and Chief Executive Officer
CFO: Kim Capps, Chief Financial Officer
CMO: Hugh Lindsey M.D., Chief Medical Officer
CIO: Kevin Neugent, Chief Information Officer
CHR: Jennifer C Bucienski, Vice President Human Resources
CNO: Maureen Hillary, Chief Nursing Officer
Web address: www.hgbhealth.com
Control: Other not–for–profit (including NFP Corporation) **Service:** General medical and surgical

Staffed Beds: 25 **Admissions:** 675 **Census:** 5 **Outpatient Visits:** 163519
Births: 0 **Total Expense ($000):** 49300 **Payroll Expense ($000):** 21000
Personnel: 378

CHELSEA—Washtenaw County

⊞ **ST. JOSEPH MERCY CHELSEA (230259)**, 775 South Main Street, Zip 48118–1383; tel. 734/593–6000 **A**1 3 5 10 **F**3 5 8 11 15 18 28 29 30 31 34 35 40 45 50 51 56 57 59 62 64 65 70 74 75 77 78 79 81 82 84 85 86 87 90 91 92 93 97 98 99 100 101 102 103 104 107 110 111 112 119 120 121 129 130 131 132 134 135 146 147 149 **P**6 **S** Trinity Health, Livonia, MI
Primary Contact: Nancy Kay. Graebner, President and Chief Executive Officer
CFO: Barb Fielder, Vice President Finance
CMO: Randall T Forsch M.D., M.P.H., Chief Medical Officer
CHR: Jeremy Stephens, Vice President and Chief Human Resources Officer
CNO: Kathy M. Brubaker R.N., MSN, Vice President and Chief Nursing Officer
Web address: www.cch.org
Control: Church operated, Nongovernment, not–for–profit **Service:** General medical and surgical

Staffed Beds: 96 **Admissions:** 5494 **Census:** 47 **Outpatient Visits:** 285462
Births: 0 **Total Expense ($000):** 142769 **Payroll Expense ($000):** 59088
Personnel: 752

CLARE—Clare County

⊞ **MIDMICHIGAN MEDICAL CENTER–CLARE (230180)**, 703 North McEwan Street, Zip 48617–1440; tel. 989/802–5000 **A**1 5 10 **F**3 11 15 18 20 28 29 30 34 35 40 45 50 53 57 58 59 61 64 75 77 79 80 81 85 87 91 93 97 107 108 110 111 115 118 119 127 129 130 132 135 144 146 **S** MidMichigan Health, Midland, MI
Primary Contact: Raymond Stover, President and Chief Executive Officer
CFO: Jeff Provenzano, Vice President and Chief Financial Officer
CMO: David Bremer D.O., Chief of Staff
CIO: Michael Larson, Vice President Chief Information Officer
CNO: Glenn King R.N., MSN, Vice President, Chief Nursing Officer
Web address: www.midmichigan.org
Control: Other not–for–profit (including NFP Corporation) **Service:** General medical and surgical

Staffed Beds: 49 **Admissions:** 1081 **Census:** 8 **Outpatient Visits:** 109427
Births: 0 **Total Expense ($000):** 47221 **Payroll Expense ($000):** 13507
Personnel: 289

CLINTON TOWNSHIP—Macomb County

⊞ **HENRY FORD MACOMB HOSPITALS (230047)**, 15855 19 Mile Road, Zip 48038–6324; tel. 586/263–2300, (Includes HENRY FORD MACOMB HOSPITAL – MOUNT CLEMENS CAMPUS, 215 North Avenue, Mount Clemens, Michigan, Zip 48043, tel. 586/466–9300; ST. JOSEPH'S MERCY HOSPITAL–WEST, 15855 19 Mile Road, Clinton Township, Michigan, Zip 48038, tel. 586/263–2707; ST. JOSEPH'S MERCY–NORTH, 80650 North Van Dyke, Romeo, Michigan, Zip 48065, tel. 810/798–3551) **A**1 2 3 10 13 **F**3 7 11 12 13 15 18 20 22 24 26 28 29 30 31 32 34 35 36 38 40 41 42 43 44 45 46 47 49 50 51 54 56 57 58 59 60 61 62 63 64 65 66 68 69 70 73 74 75 76 77 78 79 81 82 84 85 86 87 89 90 92 93 96 97 98 100 101 102 103 107 108 110 111 114 115 116 117 118 119 120 121 123 124 126 129 130 131 132 134 135 144 146 147 148 149 150 **P**6 8 **S** Henry Ford Health System, Detroit, MI
Primary Contact: Barbara W. Rossmann, R.N., President and Chief Executive Officer
COO: Gary Beaulac, Chief Operating Officer
CFO: Terry Goodbalian, Vice President Finance and Chief Financial Officer
CMO: Charles Kelly D.O., Vice President Medical Affairs and Chief Medical Officer
CHR: Joel Gibson, Vice President Human Resources
Web address: www.henryfordmacomb.com
Control: Other not–for–profit (including NFP Corporation) **Service:** General medical and surgical

Staffed Beds: 439 **Admissions:** 20514 **Census:** 281 **Outpatient Visits:** 623911 **Births:** 1689 **Total Expense ($000):** 460725 **Payroll Expense ($000):** 175083 **Personnel:** 2696

MI

COLDWATER—Branch County

⊞ **COMMUNITY HEALTH CENTER OF BRANCH COUNTY (230022)**, 274 East Chicago Street, Zip 49036–2041; tel. 517/279–5400 **A**1 10 13 19 **F**3 8 11 13 15 28 29 30 31 34 40 43 45 50 57 59 62 63 64 70 74 75 76 77 78 79 81 85 87 91 92 93 96 97 98 100 101 102 106 107 108 110 111 115 119 127 129 130 132 146 **P**6
Primary Contact: Randy DeGroot, President and Chief Executive Officer
COO: Mary R Rose R.N., Chief Clinical Officer
CFO: Amy Crouch, Chief Financial Officer
CMO: Joudat Daoud M.D., Chief of Staff
CIO: Joel Lederman, Director Information Systems
CHR: Amy Jensen, Director Human Resources
Web address: www.chcbc.com
Control: County, Government, Nonfederal **Service**: General medical and surgical

Staffed Beds: 62 **Admissions**: 2836 **Census**: 29 **Outpatient Visits**: 142059 **Births**: 248 **Total Expense ($000)**: 65864 **Payroll Expense ($000)**: 28177 **Personnel**: 458

COMMERCE TOWNSHIP—Oakland County

⊞ **DMC HURON VALLEY–SINAI HOSPITAL (230277)**, 1 William Carls Drive, Zip 48382–2201; tel. 248/937–3300 **A**1 3 5 10 **F**3 11 12 13 15 18 20 22 26 28 29 30 31 34 35 37 39 40 44 45 46 47 48 49 50 51 53 57 58 59 61 64 65 70 73 74 75 76 77 78 79 81 82 85 86 87 89 93 96 107 108 110 111 114 115 116 117 118 119 121 123 124 126 129 130 131 132 135 141 145 146 147 148 149 150 **P**1 6 **S** TENET Healthcare Corporation, Dallas, TX
Primary Contact: Karima Bentounsi, Interim Chief Executive Officer
COO: Samuel Pieh, Chief Operating Officer
CFO: William Lantzy, Chief Financial Officer
CHR: Nicole Williams, Director of Human Resources Operations
CNO: Lori Stallings–Sicard R.N., Chief Nursing Officer
Web address: www.hvsh.org
Control: Corporation, Investor–owned (for–profit) **Service**: General medical and surgical

Staffed Beds: 156 **Admissions**: 8679 **Census**: 85 **Outpatient Visits**: 94706 **Births**: 1136 **Total Expense ($000)**: 166206 **Payroll Expense ($000)**: 57185 **Personnel**: 836

DEARBORN—Wayne County

⊞ **BEAUMONT HOSPITAL–DEARBORN (230020)**, 18101 Oakwood Boulevard, Zip 48124–4089, Mailing Address: P.O.Box 2500, 48123–2500; tel. 313/593–7000 **A**1 2 3 5 10 **F**3 11 12 13 15 17 18 19 20 22 24 26 28 29 30 31 32 34 35 37 38 39 40 41 43 44 45 46 47 49 50 52 54 55 56 57 58 59 60 61 64 65 68 70 72 74 75 76 77 78 79 81 82 84 85 86 87 89 92 93 96 97 100 102 107 108 110 111 114 115 117 118 119 120 121 123 124 126 129 130 131 132 135 146 147 149 **P**6 8 **S** Beaumont Health, Southfield, MI
Primary Contact: Kelly C. Smith, Senior Vice President and Division President
COO: Carolyn Wilson, Chief Operating Officer
CFO: Timothy Jodway, Chief Financial Administrator
CMO: Paolo G Marciano M.D., Chief Medical Officer
CIO: Subra Sripada, Executive Vice President, Chief Transformation Officer and Chief Information Officer
CHR: Sherry Huffman, Administrator Human Resources
CNO: Mary Ellen Kochis MSN, R.N., Administrator Nursing Operations
Web address: www.beaumont.org
Control: Other not–for–profit (including NFP Corporation) **Service**: General medical and surgical

Staffed Beds: 632 **Admissions**: 31056 **Census**: 429 **Outpatient Visits**: 250912 **Births**: 4275 **Total Expense ($000)**: 630740 **Payroll Expense ($000)**: 237398 **Personnel**: 3537

DECKERVILLE—Sanilac County

DECKERVILLE COMMUNITY HOSPITAL (231311), 3559 Pine Street, Zip 48427–7703, Mailing Address: P.O.Box 126, 48427–0126; tel. 810/376–2835, (Nonreporting) **A**10 18
Primary Contact: Angela McConnachie, Chief Executive Officer and Chief Nursing Officer
CFO: Valerie Bryant, Chief Financial Officer
CMO: Bassam Afaneh M.D., Chief of Staff
Web address: www.deckervillehosp.org
Control: Other not–for–profit (including NFP Corporation) **Service**: General medical and surgical

Staffed Beds: 15

DETROIT—Wayne County

BCA STONECREST HOSPITAL See Stonecrest Center

⊞ △ **DMC – CHILDREN'S HOSPITAL OF MICHIGAN (233300)**, 3901 Beaubien Street, Zip 48201–2119; tel. 313/745–5437 **A**1 3 5 7 10 **F**3 7 8 11 16 17 18 19 20 21 22 23 24 25 26 27 29 30 31 32 34 35 37 38 39 40 41 42 43 44 45 48 49 50 51 54 55 57 58 59 60 61 64 65 66 72 74 75 77 78 79 80 81 82 84 85 86 87 88 89 90 91 92 93 95 96 97 99 100 107 108 111 114 115 116 117 119 120 121 123 124 129 130 131 132 134 136 137 138 139 141 146 148 149 150 **P**1 6 **S** TENET Healthcare Corporation, Dallas, TX
Primary Contact: Luanne T. Ewald, Interim Chief Executive Officer
COO: Monique Butler, Chief Operating Officer
CMO: Rudolph Valentini M.D., Chief Medical Officer
CHR: Walter Tetteh, Director Human Resources
CNO: Claudine N Hoppen MSN, Interim Chief Nursing Officer
Web address: www.chmkids.org
Control: Corporation, Investor–owned (for–profit) **Service**: Children's general medical and surgical

Staffed Beds: 224 **Admissions**: 11479 **Census**: 153 **Outpatient Visits**: 314290 **Births**: 0 **Total Expense ($000)**: 363247 **Payroll Expense ($000)**: 134194 **Personnel**: 2048

⊞ **DMC – DETROIT RECEIVING HOSPITAL (230273)**, 4201 Saint Antoine Street, Zip 48201–2153; tel. 313/745–3000 **A**1 3 5 10 **F**3 16 17 18 29 30 34 35 38 39 40 43 44 49 50 56 57 58 59 60 61 64 65 66 67 70 74 75 77 79 81 82 84 85 86 87 93 97 98 100 102 103 104 107 114 115 119 129 130 131 132 135 141 144 145 146 148 149 150 **P**1 6 **S** TENET Healthcare Corporation, Dallas, TX
Primary Contact: Scott Steiner, FACHE, Chief Executive Officer
COO: Tina Wood, Chief Operations Officer
CFO: Bridgett Feagin, Chief Financial Officer
CMO: Patricia Wilkerson–Uddyback M.D., Chief Medical Officer
CIO: Michael LeRoy, Senior Vice President and Chief Information Officer
CNO: Sheri Testani, Chief Nursing Officer
Web address: www.dmc.org
Control: Corporation, Investor–owned (for–profit) **Service**: General medical and surgical

Staffed Beds: 185 **Admissions**: 13596 **Census**: 177 **Outpatient Visits**: 142670 **Births**: 0 **Total Expense ($000)**: 261642 **Payroll Expense ($000)**: 92460 **Personnel**: 1473

⊞ △ **DMC – REHABILITATION INSTITUTE OF MICHIGAN (233027)**, 261 Mack Avenue, Zip 48201–2495; tel. 313/745–1203 **A**1 3 5 7 10 **F**3 11 28 29 30 34 35 44 50 53 54 58 59 64 65 75 82 86 87 90 91 92 93 95 96 119 130 131 132 134 146 149 **P**1 6 **S** TENET Healthcare Corporation, Dallas, TX
Primary Contact: William Restum, Chief Executive Officer
COO: Patty Jobbitt, Chief Operating Officer
CFO: Dan Babb, Chief Financial Officer
CMO: Ali Bitar M.D., Vice President Medical Affairs
CHR: Paul Sturgis, Director Human Resources
CNO: Julia Libcke R.N., MSN, VP Patient Care Services
Web address: www.rimrehab.org
Control: Corporation, Investor–owned (for–profit) **Service**: Rehabilitation

Staffed Beds: 69 **Admissions**: 1312 **Census**: 57 **Outpatient Visits**: 244251 **Births**: 0 **Total Expense ($000)**: 74512 **Payroll Expense ($000)**: 38469 **Personnel**: 575

⊞ **DMC – SINAI–GRACE HOSPITAL (230024)**, 6071 West Outer Drive, Zip 48235–2679; tel. 313/966–3300 **A**1 3 5 10 12 13 **F**3 8 11 13 15 18 20 22 24 26 28 29 30 31 32 34 35 37 38 39 40 43 44 45 49 50 51 53 54 55 57 58 59 60 61 64 65 66 70 72 74 75 76 77 78 79 80 81 82 84 85 86 87 90 93 96 97 98 100 102 104 107 108 110 111 114 115 117 118 119 120 121 123 126 129 130 131 132 134 135 141 144 146 147 148 149 150 **P**1 6 **S** TENET Healthcare Corporation, Dallas, TX
Primary Contact: Conrad Mallett Jr., Chief Executive Officer
COO: London Quicci, Chief Operating Officer
CFO: Michael Prusatis, Vice President Finance
CMO: Matthew Griffin M.D., Vice President Medical Affairs
CHR: Paulette Griffin, Director Human Resources
Web address: www.sinaigrace.org
Control: Corporation, Investor–owned (for–profit) **Service**: General medical and surgical

Staffed Beds: 301 **Admissions**: 20130 **Census**: 257 **Outpatient Visits**: 220085 **Births**: 1276 **Total Expense ($000)**: 337903 **Payroll Expense ($000)**: 129384 **Personnel**: 1927

MI

DMC HARPER UNIVERSITY HOSPITAL (230104), 3990 John 'R' Street, Zip 48201–2018; tel. 313/745–8040, (Includes DMC HUTZEL WOMEN'S HOSPITAL, 3980 John R Street, Detroit, Michigan, Zip 48201, tel. 313/745–7555; Scott Steiner, FACHE, Chief Executive Officer) **A**1 3 5 10 **F**3 9 11 12 13 15 18 20 22 24 26 28 29 30 34 35 37 40 43 44 45 46 47 48 49 50 51 52 54 55 57 58 59 60 61 64 65 66 70 72 74 75 76 77 78 79 81 82 84 85 86 87 93 97 100 107 108 111 115 118 119 126 130 131 132 134 135 138 141 145 146 147 148 149 150 **P**1 6 **S** TENET Healthcare Corporation, Dallas, TX
Primary Contact: Scott Steiner, FACHE, Chief Executive Officer
COO: Tina Wood, Chief Operating Officer
CFO: Bridgett Feagin, Chief Financial Officer
CMO: Patricia Wilkerson–Uddyback M.D., Chief Medical Officer
CIO: Michael LeRoy, Senior Vice President and Chief Information Officer
CHR: Deloris Hunt, Corporate Vice President Human Resources
CNO: Christine Bowen R.N., Chief Nursing Officer
Web address: www.harperhospital.org
Control: Corporation, Investor–owned (for–profit) **Service:** General medical and surgical

Staffed Beds: 364 Admissions: 22385 Census: 268 Outpatient Visits: 215749 Births: 4114 Total Expense ($000): 490944 Payroll Expense ($000): 150948 Personnel: 2407

HARPER UNIVERSITY HOSPITAL See DMC Harper University Hospital

HENRY FORD HOSPITAL (230053), 2799 West Grand Boulevard, Zip 48202–2608; tel. 313/916–2600 **A**1 2 3 5 8 10 **F**3 4 5 6 8 9 11 12 13 15 17 18 19 20 22 24 26 28 29 30 31 32 33 34 35 36 38 40 41 42 43 44 45 46 47 48 49 50 51 52 53 54 55 56 57 58 59 60 61 62 63 64 65 66 70 71 72 73 74 75 76 77 78 79 80 81 82 83 84 85 86 87 91 92 93 96 97 99 100 101 102 103 104 105 107 108 110 111 112 113 114 115 116 117 118 119 120 121 123 124 126 129 130 131 132 134 135 136 137 138 139 140 141 142 144 145 146 147 148 149 150 **P**6 **S** Henry Ford Health System, Detroit, MI
Primary Contact: John Popovich, M.D., President and Chief Executive Officer
COO: Veronica Hall R.N., Chief Operating Officer
CFO: Joseph Schmitt III, Senior Vice President Finance and Chief Financial Officer
CMO: John Popovich M.D., President and Chief Executive Officer
CIO: Mary Alice Annecharico, System Vice President and Chief Information Officer
CHR: Kathy Oswald, Senior Vice President and Chief Human Resources Officer
CNO: Gwen Gnam R.N., MSN, Chief Nursing Officer
Web address: www.henryfordhealth.org
Control: Other not–for–profit (including NFP Corporation) **Service:** General medical and surgical

Staffed Beds: 725 Admissions: 36432 Census: 545 Outpatient Visits: 3071110 Births: 2540 Total Expense ($000): 1891679 Payroll Expense ($000): 936783 Personnel: 12692

JOHN D. DINGELL VETERANS AFFAIRS MEDICAL CENTER, 4646 John 'R' Street, Zip 48201–1932; tel. 313/576–1000, (Total facility includes 44 beds in nursing home–type unit) **A**1 2 3 5 7 **F**3 5 8 9 11 12 18 20 26 28 29 30 31 34 35 36 37 38 39 40 44 45 46 49 50 54 56 57 58 59 60 61 62 63 64 65 66 67 70 74 75 77 78 79 81 82 83 84 85 86 87 90 91 92 93 94 97 98 100 101 102 103 104 105 107 108 111 114 115 118 119 121 123 126 127 128 129 130 132 135 143 146 147 148 149 **P**6 **S** Department of Veterans Affairs, Washington, DC
Primary Contact: Pamela J. Reeves, M.D., Director
COO: Annette Walker, Associate Director
CFO: Sherry Riedel, Chief Financial Management Service
CMO: Scott Gruber M.D., Chief of Staff
CIO: Jonathan Small, Chief Operations Information and Technology
CHR: Kathleen Osinski, Chief Human Resources Service
CNO: Belina Brown–Tezera MSN, Associate Director Patient Care Services
Web address: www.detroit.va.gov/
Control: Veterans Affairs, Government, federal **Service:** General medical and surgical

Staffed Beds: 216 Admissions: 5104 Census: 94 Outpatient Visits: 547422 Births: 0 Total Expense ($000): 394819 Payroll Expense ($000): 160458 Personnel: 1851

KARMANOS CANCER CENTER (230297), 4100 John 'R' Street, Zip 48201–2013; tel. 313/576–8670 **A**1 2 3 5 10 **F**3 8 14 15 29 30 33 39 44 45 46 47 48 49 50 51 54 55 57 58 59 60 63 64 65 68 70 74 75 78 79 81 82 83 84 85 86 87 100 107 108 110 111 113 114 115 116 117 118 119 120 121 123 124 126 130 132 135 136 146 147 148 149 **P**6 8
Primary Contact: Gerold Bepler, M.D., Ph.D., President and Chief Executive Officer
CFO: Brian Gamble, Chief Financial Officer
CMO: George Yoo M.D., Chief Medical Officer
CIO: Scott McCarter, Chief Information Officer
CHR: David Jansen, Vice President Human Resources
Web address: www.karmanos.org
Control: Other not–for–profit (including NFP Corporation) **Service:** Cancer

Staffed Beds: 84 Admissions: 3288 Census: 69 Outpatient Visits: 147863 Births: 0 Total Expense ($000): 252479 Payroll Expense ($000): 57433 Personnel: 999

KINDRED HOSPITAL DETROIT (232027), 4777 East Outer Drive, Zip 48234–3241; tel. 313/369–5800 **A**1 10 **F**1 3 29 34 35 57 60 62 107 114 148 **S** Kindred Healthcare, Louisville, KY
Primary Contact: Mary Hoskins, Chief Executive Officer
CFO: Clayton Kubacki, Controller
CMO: Kevin Potts M.D., Medical Director
CHR: Karen McGrail, District Director Human Resource
Web address: www.kindreddetroit.com/
Control: Corporation, Investor–owned (for–profit) **Service:** Acute long–term care hospital

Staffed Beds: 77 Admissions: 512 Census: 34 Outpatient Visits: 0 Births: 0 Total Expense ($000): 19762 Payroll Expense ($000): 7845

SELECT SPECIALTY HOSPITAL–NORTHWEST DETROIT (232032), 6071 West Outer Drive, Zip 48235–2624; tel. 313/966–4747, (Nonreporting) **A**1 10 **S** Select Medical Corporation, Mechanicsburg, PA
Primary Contact: Marilouise Riska, Chief Executive Officer
Web address: www.selectspecialtyhospitals.com/company/locations/northwestdetroit.aspx
Control: Corporation, Investor–owned (for–profit) **Service:** Acute long–term care hospital

Staffed Beds: 36

ST. JOHN HOSPITAL AND MEDICAL CENTER (230165), 22101 Moross Road, Zip 48236–2148; tel. 313/343–4000 **A**1 2 3 5 8 10 **F**3 8 9 11 12 13 14 15 17 18 20 24 26 28 29 30 31 32 34 35 36 37 38 39 40 41 42 43 44 45 46 47 48 49 50 54 55 56 57 58 59 60 61 63 64 65 66 68 70 72 74 75 76 77 78 79 80 81 82 84 85 86 87 88 89 90 91 92 93 95 96 97 98 100 101 102 103 107 108 110 111 114 115 116 117 118 119 120 121 123 124 126 130 131 132 135 138 141 143 144 146 147 148 149 150 **S** Ascension Healthcare, Saint Louis, MO
Primary Contact: Robert E. Hoban, President
COO: Brant Russell R.N., Chief Operating Officer
CMO: Kevin Grady M.D., Chief Medical Officer
CIO: Ralph Tenney, Chief Information Officer
CHR: Joanne E Tuscany, Director Human Resources
Web address: www.stjohnprovidence.org/stjohnhospital/
Control: Church operated, Nongovernment, not–for–profit **Service:** General medical and surgical

Staffed Beds: 586 Admissions: 28306 Census: 394 Outpatient Visits: 1032535 Births: 2965 Total Expense ($000): 774345 Payroll Expense ($000): 271752 Personnel: 3550

STONECREST CENTER (234038), 15000 Gratiot Avenue, Zip 48205–1973; tel. 313/245–0600 **A**1 10 **F**98 99 100 101 103 130 149 **S** Acadia Healthcare Company, Inc., Franklin, TN
Primary Contact: Steve Savage, Chief Executive Officer
Web address: www.stonecrestcenter.com
Control: Corporation, Investor–owned (for–profit) **Service:** Psychiatric

Staffed Beds: 125 Admissions: 3790 Census: 112 Outpatient Visits: 0 Births: 0 Total Expense ($000): 25374 Payroll Expense ($000): 11599 Personnel: 283

TRIUMPH HOSPITAL DETROIT See Kindred Hospital Detroit

DOWAGIAC—Cass County

BORGESS–LEE MEMORIAL HOSPITAL (231315), 420 West High Street, Zip 49047–1943; tel. 269/782–8681 **A**1 10 18 **F**3 11 15 18 28 29 30 31 34 35 40 41 50 54 57 59 64 65 68 70 75 77 78 79 81 85 86 87 93 97 100 104 107 108 110 114 119 127 128 130 132 133 135 146 148 149 **P**6 **S** Ascension Healthcare, Saint Louis, MO
Primary Contact: John E. Ryder, Chief Operating Officer
COO: John E. Ryder, Chief Operating Officer
CFO: Damon Sorensen, Chief Financial Officer
CMO: Robert Hill M.D., Chief Medical Officer
CIO: James Keller, Chief Information Officer
CHR: Robert Bauer, Director Human Resources
Web address: www.borgess.com
Control: Church operated, Nongovernment, not–for–profit **Service:** General medical and surgical

Staffed Beds: 25 Admissions: 359 Census: 3 Outpatient Visits: 105067 Births: 0 Total Expense ($000): 24867 Payroll Expense ($000): 11987 Personnel: 172

Many Facility Codes have changed. Please refer to the AHA Guide Code Chart.

© 2017 AHA Guide

EAST CHINA—St. Clair County

⊞ **ST. JOHN RIVER DISTRICT HOSPITAL (230241)**, 4100 River Road, Zip 48054–2909; tel. 810/329–7111 **A**1 3 10 **F**3 7 11 13 15 18 20 29 30 34 35 36 39 40 44 45 49 50 57 59 60 63 64 65 68 70 75 76 77 79 80 81 82 84 85 86 87 92 93 97 107 108 110 111 115 116 117 119 129 130 132 141 146 147 148 149 150 **S** Ascension Healthcare, Saint Louis, MO
Primary Contact: Kim Ronnisch, R.N., Vice President Nursing and Operations
CMO: H Lee Bacheldor D.O., Chief Medical Officer
CHR: Dawn Beindit, Labor Relations Partner
Web address: www.stjohnprovidence.org/RiverDistrict/
Control: Church operated, Nongovernment, not–for–profit **Service:** General medical and surgical

Staffed Beds: 68 **Admissions:** 1744 **Census:** 14 **Outpatient Visits:** 52201 **Births:** 323 **Total Expense ($000):** 39342 **Payroll Expense ($000):** 17741 **Personnel:** 249

EATON RAPIDS—Eaton County

★ ⇑ **EATON RAPIDS MEDICAL CENTER (231324)**, 1500 South Main Street, Zip 48827–1952, Mailing Address: P.O.Box 130, 48827–0130; tel. 517/663–2671 **A**10 18 21 **F**3 11 15 29 34 35 38 40 41 50 53 57 59 64 65 66 68 75 77 81 86 87 91 93 97 107 110 112 114 119 127 129 130 131 132 133 144 146 149
Primary Contact: Timothy Johnson, President and Chief Executive Officer
CFO: Shari Glynn, Vice President Finance and Chief Financial Officer
CMO: Ashok K Gupta M.D., Chief of Staff
CIO: Mark Rodge, Director Information Systems
CHR: Laurie Field, Director Human Resources
Web address: www.eatonrapidsmedicalcenter.org
Control: Other not–for–profit (including NFP Corporation) **Service:** General medical and surgical

Staffed Beds: 20 **Admissions:** 531 **Census:** 6 **Outpatient Visits:** 69310 **Births:** 0 **Total Expense ($000):** 24013 **Payroll Expense ($000):** 10649 **Personnel:** 199

ESCANABA—Delta County

⊞ **OSF ST. FRANCIS HOSPITAL AND MEDICAL GROUP (231337)**, 3401 Ludington Street, Zip 49829–1377; tel. 906/786–3311 **A**1 10 18 **F**3 11 13 15 18 28 29 30 31 34 35 40 44 45 46 53 56 57 59 62 63 64 65 66 68 70 75 77 78 79 81 83 84 85 86 92 93 96 97 107 108 110 111 115 119 127 129 130 131 132 133 144 146 147 148 149 **S** OSF Healthcare System, Peoria, IL
Primary Contact: David Lord, President
COO: Kelly Jefferson, Vice President, Operations
CFO: Fred Wagner, Chief Financial Officer
CMO: Mark Povich D.O., Medical Director
CIO: Mark Irving, Manager Management Information Systems
CHR: Elizabeth Zorza, Assistant Administrator
CNO: Joy Hopkins, Vice President Patient Care Services
Web address: www.osfstfrancis.org
Control: Church operated, Nongovernment, not–for–profit **Service:** General medical and surgical

Staffed Beds: 25 **Admissions:** 1897 **Census:** 15 **Outpatient Visits:** 110998 **Births:** 301 **Total Expense ($000):** 81788 **Payroll Expense ($000):** 24112 **Personnel:** 375

FARMINGTON HILLS—Oakland County

★ ○ **BEAUMONT HOSPITAL – FARMINGTON HILLS (230151)**, 28050 Grand River Avenue, Zip 48336–5933; tel. 248/471–8000 **A**2 3 10 11 12 13 **F**3 8 11 13 15 18 20 22 26 28 29 30 31 32 34 35 36 38 39 40 41 43 44 45 46 47 48 49 50 51 54 56 57 58 59 60 61 63 64 65 68 70 74 75 76 77 78 79 81 82 83 84 85 87 89 90 92 93 94 96 97 98 100 101 102 103 107 108 110 111 114 115 119 120 121 123 124 126 129 130 131 132 134 135 144 146 147 148 149 **P**1 6 **S** Beaumont Health, Southfield, MI
Primary Contact: Constance O'Malley, President
COO: Carolyn Wilson R.N., Chief Operating Officer
CFO: Barbara Hrit, Controller
CMO: Michael Rebock, Chief Medical Officer
CIO: Subra Sripada, Executive Vice President, Chief Transportation Officer and Chief Information Officer
CHR: Dalph Watson, Director of Human Resources
CNO: Kim Guesman R.N., Chief Nursing Officer
Web address: www.beaumont.org
Control: Other not–for–profit (including NFP Corporation) **Service:** General medical and surgical

Staffed Beds: 330 **Admissions:** 14592 **Census:** 211 **Outpatient Visits:** 441213 **Births:** 656 **Total Expense ($000):** 348272 **Payroll Expense ($000):** 160773 **Personnel:** 2292

FERNDALE—Oakland County

⊞ **HENRY FORD KINGSWOOD HOSPITAL (234011)**, 10300 West Eight Mile Road, Zip 48220–2100; tel. 248/398–3200 **A**1 10 **F**29 30 32 34 35 44 50 56 57 59 68 75 77 82 86 87 98 99 101 103 130 134 135 **P**6 **S** Henry Ford Health System, Detroit, MI
Primary Contact: DoreeAnn V. Espiritu, M.D., Interim Chair, Behavioral Health Services
CMO: Robert Lagrou D.O., Medical Director
CNO: Cheryl Taylor R.N., Director of Nursing
Web address: www.henryford.com
Control: Other not–for–profit (including NFP Corporation) **Service:** Psychiatric

Staffed Beds: 101 **Admissions:** 3817 **Census:** 64 **Outpatient Visits:** 0 **Births:** 0 **Total Expense ($000):** 23219 **Payroll Expense ($000):** 15545 **Personnel:** 259

FLINT—Genesee County

⊞ **HURLEY MEDICAL CENTER (230132)**, One Hurley Plaza, Zip 48503–5993; tel. 810/262–6887, (Includes HURLEY CHILDREN'S HOSPITAL, 1 Hurley Plaza, Flint, Michigan, Zip 48503–5902, tel. 313/745–7555) **A**1 2 3 5 8 10 **F**3 5 11 12 13 15 16 17 18 19 20 22 26 28 29 30 31 32 35 39 40 41 43 45 46 49 50 52 54 55 56 57 58 59 61 64 66 70 72 74 75 76 77 78 79 80 81 82 84 85 86 87 88 89 90 93 96 97 98 100 101 102 103 104 107 108 110 111 114 115 118 119 120 121 123 124 126 129 130 131 132 135 141 143 144 146 147 148 Primary Contact: Melany Gavulic, President & Chief Executive Officer
COO: Melany Gavulic, Senior Vice President Operations & COO
CFO: Cass Wisniewski, Interim Chief Financial Officer
CMO: Michael Jaggi D.O., Vice President and Chief Medical Officer
CIO: Gary Townsend, Chief Information Officer
CHR: Beth Brophy, Interim VP for Human Resources
CNO: Teresa Bourque, Sr. Administrator for Nursing/Chief Nurse
Web address: www.hurleymc.com
Control: City, Government, Nonfederal **Service:** General medical and surgical

Staffed Beds: 418 **Admissions:** 19394 **Census:** 277 **Outpatient Visits:** 483893 **Births:** 2699 **Total Expense ($000):** 419003 **Payroll Expense ($000):** 171793 **Personnel:** 2484

☐ **MCLAREN FLINT (230141)**, 401 South Ballenger Highway, Zip 48532–3685; tel. 810/342–2000 **A**1 2 3 5 8 10 **F**3 5 8 11 12 13 15 17 18 20 22 24 26 28 29 30 31 32 34 35 36 38 39 40 43 44 45 46 49 50 53 54 55 56 57 58 59 60 61 64 68 70 74 75 76 77 78 79 81 82 85 86 87 90 91 93 96 97 98 99 100 101 102 103 104 105 107 108 111 114 115 118 119 120 121 123 124 126 129 130 131 132 135 141 144 146 147 148 149 **P**6 7 **S** McLaren Health Care Corporation, Flint, MI
Primary Contact: Chad M. Grant, President
COO: Brent Wheeler, Vice President Ancillary and Support Services
CFO: Fred Korte, Chief Financial Officer
CMO: Binesh Patel M.D., Chief Medical Officer
CIO: Ronald Strachan, Chief Information Officer
CHR: Rachelle Hulett, Vice President Human Resources
CNO: Diane Kallas, Vice President of Nursing Services
Web address: www.mclarenregional.org
Control: Other not–for–profit (including NFP Corporation) **Service:** General medical and surgical

Staffed Beds: 348 **Admissions:** 19394 **Census:** 254 **Outpatient Visits:** 347005 **Births:** 614 **Total Expense ($000):** 420029 **Payroll Expense ($000):** 184529 **Personnel:** 2208

⊞ **SELECT SPECIALTY HOSPITAL–FLINT (232012)**, 401 South Ballenger Highway, 5th Floor Central, Zip 48532–3638; tel. 810/342–4545, (Nonreporting) **A**1 10 **S** Select Medical Corporation, Mechanicsburg, PA
Primary Contact: Christina DeBlouw, Chief Executive Officer
CMO: Jitendra P. Katneni M.D., Medical Director
CHR: Gayle Barthel, Coordinator Human Resources
CNO: Kathleen Gallardo, Chief Nursing Officer
Web address: www.selectspecialtyhospitals.com/company/locations/flint.aspx
Control: Corporation, Investor–owned (for–profit) **Service:** Acute long–term care hospital

Staffed Beds: 26

Hospital, Medicare Provider Number, Address, Telephone, Approval, Facility, and Physician Codes, Health Care System

★ American Hospital Association (AHA) membership ○ Healthcare Facilities Accreditation Program ⇑ Center for Improvement in Healthcare Quality Accreditation
☐ The Joint Commission accreditation ◇ DNV Healthcare Inc. accreditation △ Commission on Accreditation of Rehabilitation Facilities (CARF) accreditation

© 2017 AHA Guide *Many Facility Codes have changed. Please refer to the AHA Guide Code Chart.* Hospitals **A319**

MI

FRANKFORT—Benzie County

★ **PAUL OLIVER MEMORIAL HOSPITAL (231300)**, 224 Park Avenue, Zip 49635–9658; tel. 231/352–2200, (Total facility includes 39 beds in nursing home–type unit) **A**10 18 **F**11 15 28 30 34 35 40 45 50 53 57 59 60 64 75 77 81 86 87 93 107 110 111 115 119 129 130 132 133 143 146 148 **S** Munson Healthcare, Traverse City, MI
Primary Contact: Peter Marinoff, President
CMO: George Ryckman D.O., Chief of Staff
CHR: Julie Banktson, Manager Human Resources
Web address: www.munsonhealthcare.org
Control: Other not–for–profit (including NFP Corporation) **Service:** General medical and surgical

Staffed Beds: 47 **Admissions:** 114 **Census:** 34 **Outpatient Visits:** 55745 **Births:** 0 **Total Expense ($000):** 17056 **Payroll Expense ($000):** 6370 **Personnel:** 131	

FREMONT—Newaygo County

✠ **SPECTRUM HEALTH GERBER MEMORIAL (230106)**, 212 South Sullivan Avenue, Zip 49412–1548; tel. 231/924–3300 **A**1 3 10 18 **F**3 11 13 15 28 29 31 32 34 35 36 40 43 45 47 50 53 59 64 68 70 75 76 77 78 79 81 86 87 93 96 107 108 110 111 115 118 119 127 129 130 131 132 135 146 147 **S** Spectrum Health, Grand Rapids, MI
Primary Contact: Randall Stasik, President
COO: Janice Stone, Chief Operating Officer
CFO: Kevin Nichols, Controller
CMO: Nicholas Kuhl M.D., Chief of Staff
CIO: Dave Mitchell, Manager Information Services
CHR: Christine Schurkamp, Senior Human Resources Business Partner
CNO: Meleah Mariani, Chief Nursing Officer
Web address: www.spectrumhealth.org
Control: Other not–for–profit (including NFP Corporation) **Service:** General medical and surgical

Staffed Beds: 25 **Admissions:** 2141 **Census:** 14 **Outpatient Visits:** 154618 **Births:** 514 **Total Expense ($000):** 84405 **Payroll Expense ($000):** 28345 **Personnel:** 584	

GARDEN CITY—Wayne County

★ ○ **GARDEN CITY HOSPITAL (230244)**, 6245 Inkster Road, Zip 48135–4001; tel. 734/421–3300 **A**3 10 11 12 13 **F**3 4 11 13 15 17 18 20 22 26 28 29 31 34 35 36 40 43 44 45 46 47 49 50 59 62 64 65 68 70 71 74 75 76 77 78 79 80 81 82 85 87 89 90 91 92 93 96 107 109 110 111 112 114 115 119 129 130 131 132 135 143 146 147 148 149 **P**6 **S** Prime Healthcare, Ontario, CA
Primary Contact: Saju George, Chief Executive Officer
CFO: Gina Butcher, Chief Financial Officer
CMO: H. Rex Reuttinger D.O., Chief Medical Officer, Administration
CIO: Randall Sanborn, Director Information Systems
CHR: Josie Ciccone, Director, Human Resources
Web address: www.gch.org
Control: Corporation, Investor–owned (for–profit) **Service:** General medical and surgical

Staffed Beds: 176 **Admissions:** 9846 **Census:** 106 **Outpatient Visits:** 104714 **Births:** 781 **Total Expense ($000):** 140920 **Payroll Expense ($000):** 53457 **Personnel:** 942	

GAYLORD—Otsego County

✠ **OTSEGO MEMORIAL HOSPITAL (230133)**, 825 North Center Avenue, Zip 49735–1592; tel. 989/731–2100, (Total facility includes 34 beds in nursing home–type unit) **A**1 5 10 20 **F**3 13 15 28 29 31 32 34 35 36 40 43 44 45 46 49 50 51 54 56 57 59 64 65 70 74 75 76 77 78 79 81 82 85 86 87 93 96 97 100 104 107 108 110 111 115 118 119 124 126 127 128 130 131 132 134 135 144 146 147 148 149 **P**6
Primary Contact: Thomas R. Lemon, Chief Executive Officer
COO: James Flickema, Vice President Market Development
CFO: Robert Courtois, Vice President Finance
CMO: Kevin Smith D.O., Chief of Staff
CIO: Timothy Hella, Chief Information Officer
CHR: Terra Deming, Director Human Resources
CNO: Diane Fisher R.N., VP, Patient Care Services
Web address: www.myomh.org
Control: Other not–for–profit (including NFP Corporation) **Service:** General medical and surgical

Staffed Beds: 80 **Admissions:** 2214 **Census:** 48 **Outpatient Visits:** 293645 **Births:** 382 **Total Expense ($000):** 90519 **Payroll Expense ($000):** 45906 **Personnel:** 700	

GLADWIN—Gladwin County

✠ **MIDMICHIGAN MEDICAL CENTER–GLADWIN (231325)**, 515 Quarter Street, Zip 48624–1959; tel. 989/426–9286 **A**1 5 10 18 **F**3 11 15 18 28 29 30 31 34 35 40 45 53 57 59 64 75 77 81 85 86 93 97 107 108 110 111 114 118 119 127 129 130 132 135 144 146 **S** MidMichigan Health, Midland, MI
Primary Contact: Raymond Stover, President and Chief Executive Officer
CFO: Jeff Provenzano, Vice President and Chief Financial Officer
CMO: Cheryl Loubert M.D., Chief Medical Staff
CIO: Dan Waltz, Vice President and Chief Information Officer
CNO: Glenn King R.N., MSN, Vice President and Chief Nursing Officer
Web address: www.midmichigan.org
Control: Other not–for–profit (including NFP Corporation) **Service:** General medical and surgical

Staffed Beds: 25 **Admissions:** 562 **Census:** 4 **Outpatient Visits:** 55887 **Births:** 0 **Total Expense ($000):** 26862 **Payroll Expense ($000):** 8147 **Personnel:** 156	

GRAND BLANC—Genesee County

✠ **GENESYS REGIONAL MEDICAL CENTER (230197)**, One Genesys Parkway, Zip 48439–8066; tel. 810/606–5000, (Total facility includes 12 beds in nursing home–type unit) **A**1 3 5 10 12 13 **F**3 11 15 18 20 22 24 26 28 29 30 31 32 34 35 40 43 44 45 46 47 48 49 50 51 57 58 60 61 64 68 70 73 74 75 76 78 79 81 82 84 85 86 87 89 90 91 92 96 97 102 107 108 111 114 115 117 118 119 126 128 129 130 132 135 145 146 147 148 **P**1 6 7 **S** Ascension Healthcare, Saint Louis, MO
Primary Contact: Chris Palazzolo, President and Chief Executive Officer
COO: Joy Finkenbiner, Vice President, Operations
CFO: Nancy Haywood, Chief Financial Officer
CMO: Charles Husson, Regional Chief Medical Officer
CIO: Daniel Stross, Chief Information Officer
CNO: Julie A Gorczyca R.N., Chief Nursing Officer
Web address: www.genesys.org
Control: Church operated, Nongovernment, not–for–profit **Service:** General medical and surgical

Staffed Beds: 427 **Admissions:** 21039 **Census:** 276 **Outpatient Visits:** 531724 **Births:** 1791 **Total Expense ($000):** 402987 **Payroll Expense ($000):** 179844 **Personnel:** 2864	

GRAND HAVEN—Ottawa County

★ ⇑ **NORTH OTTAWA COMMUNITY HOSPITAL (230174)**, 1309 Sheldon Road, Zip 49417–2488; tel. 616/842–3600 **A**10 21 **F**3 7 11 12 13 15 29 30 34 35 40 43 45 50 51 57 59 61 62 63 64 65 68 70 74 75 76 79 81 83 84 86 87 89 97 107 108 115 119 126 128 129 130 131 132 135 143 144 146 147 148 149 **P**6
Primary Contact: Shelleye Yaklin, President and Chief Executive Officer
CFO: Donald J Longpre, Vice President Finance and Chief Financial Officer
CMO: Haney Assaad, Vice President Medical Affairs
CIO: Joe Abbott, Director Information Systems
CHR: Carla Wallis, Director Human Resources
CNO: Cindy Van Kampen, Chief Nursing Officer
Web address: www.noch.org
Control: Other not–for–profit (including NFP Corporation) **Service:** General medical and surgical

Staffed Beds: 58 **Admissions:** 1558 **Census:** 12 **Outpatient Visits:** 126431 **Births:** 331 **Total Expense ($000):** 71643 **Payroll Expense ($000):** 27227 **Personnel:** 523	

GRAND RAPIDS—Kent County

☐ **FOREST VIEW PSYCHIATRIC HOSPITAL (234030)**, 1055 Medical Park Drive SE, Zip 49546–3607; tel. 616/942–9610 **A**1 10 **F**87 98 99 100 101 102 103 104 105 130 132 **S** Universal Health Services, Inc., King of Prussia, PA
Primary Contact: Andrew Hotaling, Chief Executive Officer
CFO: Andre Pierre, Chief Financial Officer
CMO: James VanHaren M.D., Medical Director
CHR: Mike Henderson, Director Human Resources
CNO: Jo ell Harris, Director of Nursing
Web address: www.forestviewhospital.com
Control: Corporation, Investor–owned (for–profit) **Service:** Psychiatric

Staffed Beds: 108 **Admissions:** 3243 **Census:** 89 **Outpatient Visits:** 14438 **Births:** 0 **Total Expense ($000):** 21088 **Payroll Expense ($000):** 9373 **Personnel:** 170	

✠ **GREAT LAKES SPECIALTY HOSPITAL–GRAND RAPIDS (232026)**, 200 SE Jefferson Avenue, 5th Floor, Zip 49503–4502; tel. 616/965–8650, (Nonreporting) **A**1 10 **S** Select Medical Corporation, Mechanicsburg, PA
Primary Contact: Jevne Conover, Chief Executive Officer
CMO: Mark J Ivey M.D., Medical Director
CNO: Tracie Bauman R.N., Chief Nursing Officer
Web address: www.selectmedicalcorp.com
Control: Corporation, Investor–owned (for–profit) **Service:** Acute long–term care hospital

Staffed Beds: 20

LIFECARE HOSPITALS OF WESTERN MICHIGAN See Great Lakes Specialty Hospital–Grand Rapids

✠ △ **MARY FREE BED REHABILITATION HOSPITAL (233026)**, 235 Wealthy Street SE, Zip 49503–5247; tel. 616/840–8000 **A**1 3 5 7 10 **F**2 30 34 54 56 57 58 62 64 68 75 77 78 79 82 86 90 91 92 93 94 95 96 100 104 119 128 130 131 132 143 146 **P**6
Primary Contact: Kent Riddle, Chief Executive Officer
CFO: Randall DeNeff, Vice President Finance
CMO: Michael Jakubowski M.D., Chief Medical Officer
CIO: Jeff Burns, Manager of Information Technology
CNO: Ingrid Cheslek R.N., Chief Nursing Officer
Web address: www.maryfreebed.com
Control: Other not–for–profit (including NFP Corporation) **Service:** Rehabilitation

Staffed Beds: 140 **Admissions:** 1628 **Census:** 79 **Outpatient Visits:** 85221 **Births:** 0 **Total Expense ($000):** 74064 **Payroll Expense ($000):** 43720 **Personnel:** 926

✠ **MERCY HEALTH SAINT MARY'S (230059)**, 200 Jefferson Avenue SE, Zip 49503–4598; tel. 616/685–5000, (Includes MERCY HEALTH ROCKFORD, 6050 Northland Drive NE, Rockford, Michigan, Zip 49341–9244, tel. 616/685–7950) **A**1 2 3 5 10 **F**3 13 15 18 20 22 26 28 29 30 34 35 36 37 39 40 42 43 44 45 46 48 49 50 54 55 56 57 58 59 61 64 65 66 68 70 72 74 75 76 77 78 79 80 81 82 83 84 85 86 87 97 98 100 102 105 107 108 110 111 114 115 116 117 118 119 120 121 123 124 126 129 130 132 135 138 144 146 148 149 **P**6 8 **S** Trinity Health, Livonia, MI
Primary Contact: Bill Manns, President
COO: Randall J Wagner, Chief Operating Officer
CFO: Steve Eavenson, Vice President Finance
CMO: Rolland Mambourg M.D., Vice President Medical Affairs
CIO: Jim Keller, Site Director Information Services
CHR: Thomas L Karel, Vice President Organization and Talent Effectiveness
CNO: Elizabeth A Murphy R.N., FACHE, Vice President for Patient Care Services
Web address: www.mercyhealthsaintmarys.org
Control: Church operated, Nongovernment, not–for–profit **Service:** General medical and surgical

Staffed Beds: 371 **Admissions:** 22102 **Census:** 285 **Outpatient Visits:** 1104710 **Births:** 2230 **Total Expense ($000):** 528720 **Payroll Expense ($000):** 176930 **Personnel:** 3479

✠ **PINE REST CHRISTIAN MENTAL HEALTH SERVICES (234006)**, 300 68th Street SE, Zip 49548–6927, Mailing Address: P.O.Box 165, 49501–0165; tel. 616/455–5000 **A**1 3 5 10 **F**4 5 6 29 30 32 34 35 38 56 58 59 66 68 75 77 82 86 87 98 99 100 101 102 103 104 105 106 130 132 134 135 146 147 149 150 **P**6
Primary Contact: Mark C. Eastburg, Ph.D., President and Chief Executive Officer
COO: Robert Nykamp, Vice President and Chief Operating Officer
CFO: Paul H Karsten, Vice President Finance and Chief Financial Officer
CMO: Alan Armstrong M.D., Chief Medical Officer
Web address: www.pinerest.org
Control: Other not–for–profit (including NFP Corporation) **Service:** Psychiatric

Staffed Beds: 451 **Admissions:** 6226 **Census:** 167 **Outpatient Visits:** 327728 **Births:** 0 **Total Expense ($000):** 133260 **Payroll Expense ($000):** 77010 **Personnel:** 1388

✠ **SPECTRUM HEALTH – BUTTERWORTH HOSPITAL (230038)**, 100 Michigan Street NE, Zip 49503–2560; tel. 616/774–7444, (Includes HELEN DEVOS CHILDREN'S HOSPITAL, 100 Michigan Street NE, Grand Rapids, Michigan, Zip 49503–2560, tel. 616/391–9000; Robert Connors, M.D., President; SPECTRUM HEALTH – BLODGETT CAMPUS, 1840 Wealthy Street SE, Grand Rapids, Michigan, Zip 49506–2921, tel. 616/774–7444; Julie Wolowitz, Vice President, Imaging, Lab; SPECTRUM HEALTH, 100 Michigan Street NE, Grand Rapids, Michigan, Zip 49503–2551, tel. 616/391–1774; Christina Freese Decker, FACHE, President, Spectrum Health Hospital Group) **A**1 2 3 5 8 10 **F**3 8 9 11 12 13 15 16 17 18 19 20 21 22 23 24 25 26 27 28 29 30 31 32 34 35 36 37 38 40 41 43 44 45 46 47 48 49 50 51 52 54 55 56 57 58 59 60 61 64 65 66 68 70 71 72 73 74 75 76 77 78 79 80 81 82 84 85 86 87 88 89 90 93 96 100 101 102 107 108 110 111 112 114 115 116 117 118 119 120 121 123 124 126 130 131 132 134 135 136 137 138 140 145 146 147 148 149 **P**6 8 **S** Spectrum Health, Grand Rapids, MI
Primary Contact: Gwen L. Sandefur, President, Spectrum Health Hospital Group
CFO: Doug Welday, Senior Vice President Finance
CMO: David Krhovsky M.D., Vice President, Medical Affairs
CIO: Jason Joseph, Vice President, Information Services
CHR: Ovell Barbee, Senior Vice President, Human Resources
CNO: Shawn Ulreich R.N., MSN, Vice President Clinical Operations and Chief Nursing Executive
Web address: www.spectrumhealth.org
Control: Other not–for–profit (including NFP Corporation) **Service:** General medical and surgical

Staffed Beds: 1126 **Admissions:** 58921 **Census:** 777 **Outpatient Visits:** 1442177 **Births:** 7617 **Total Expense ($000):** 1816388 **Payroll Expense ($000):** 496766 **Personnel:** 8670

✠ △ **SPECTRUM HEALTH SPECIAL CARE HOSPITAL (232029)**, 750 Fuller Avenue NE, Zip 49503–1995; tel. 616/486–3000, (Nonreporting) **A**1 7 10 **S** Spectrum Health, Grand Rapids, MI
Primary Contact: Chad Tuttle, President
COO: Linda Joel, Vice President Operations
CFO: Larry Oberst, Vice President Finance
CMO: Peter Sholler M.D., Medical Director
CIO: Mary Nader, Director Information Technology
CHR: Mark Pakkala, Director Human Resources
CNO: Jennifer Groeneweg R.N., Director of Nursing
Web address: www.spectrum–health.org
Control: Other not–for–profit (including NFP Corporation) **Service:** Acute long–term care hospital

Staffed Beds: 36

GRAYLING—Crawford County

✠ **MUNSON HEALTHCARE GRAYLING HOSPITAL (230058)**, 1100 East Michigan Avenue, Zip 49738–1312; tel. 989/348–5461, (Total facility includes 39 beds in nursing home–type unit) **A**1 5 10 20 **F**3 11 13 15 28 29 30 32 34 35 36 38 40 44 45 50 51 53 54 56 57 58 59 60 64 65 66 70 75 76 77 78 79 81 85 86 87 93 97 107 108 111 115 119 127 129 130 131 135 146 147 148 **P**8 **S** Munson Healthcare, Traverse City, MI
Primary Contact: Stephanie J. Riemer, President
COO: Kirsten Korth–White, Vice President Physician Network and Ambulatory Service
CFO: Lori Shively, Vice President of Finance
CMO: Vince Schultz M.D., Chief Medical Officer
CHR: Kirsten Korth–White, Vice President Physician Network and Ambulatory Services
CNO: Carla Gardner, Director of Nursing
Web address: www.mercygrayling.munsonhealthcare.org/
Control: Other not–for–profit (including NFP Corporation) **Service:** General medical and surgical

Staffed Beds: 110 **Admissions:** 3045 **Census:** 58 **Outpatient Visits:** 136927 **Births:** 312 **Total Expense ($000):** 77909 **Payroll Expense ($000):** 33220 **Personnel:** 551

MI

Hospital, Medicare Provider Number, Address, Telephone, Approval, Facility, and Physician Codes, Health Care System

★ American Hospital Association (AHA) membership ○ Healthcare Facilities Accreditation Program ⇑ Center for Improvement in Healthcare Quality Accreditation
□ The Joint Commission accreditation ◇ DNV Healthcare Inc. accreditation △ Commission on Accreditation of Rehabilitation Facilities (CARF) accreditation

MI

GREENVILLE—Montcalm County

⊞ **SPECTRUM HEALTH UNITED HOSPITAL (230035)**, 615 South Bower Street, Zip 48838–2614; tel. 616/754–4691, (Includes SPECTRUM HEALTH KELSEY HOSPITAL, 418 Washington Avenue, Lakeview, Michigan, Zip 48850, tel. 989/352–7211) (Total facility includes 70 beds in nursing home–type unit) **A**1 10 **F**3 8 11 13 15 18 19 28 29 30 31 32 34 35 40 41 43 44 45 46 50 54 57 59 64 65 66 68 70 71 75 76 77 78 79 81 85 87 89 93 96 97 107 108 110 111 115 119 124 127 128 129 130 132 133 134 135 143 146 147 148 **P**6 **S** Spectrum Health, Grand Rapids, MI
Primary Contact: Andrea M. Leslie, MSN, R.N., President
COO: Priscilla Mahar, Chief Clinical Officer
CFO: Ryan K Johnson, Vice President Finance
CMO: Kevin O'Connor D.O., President Medical Staff
CIO: David Dutmers, Manager Technology Information System
CHR: Mary Fenske, Human Resource Business Partner
Web address: www.spectrumhealth.org/
Control: Other not–for–profit (including NFP Corporation) **Service**: General medical and surgical

Staffed Beds: 116 **Admissions**: 3156 **Census**: 88 **Outpatient Visits**: 195537 **Births**: 473 **Total Expense ($000)**: 95645 **Payroll Expense ($000)**: 37390 **Personnel**: 821

GROSSE POINTE—Wayne County

⊞ **BEAUMONT HOSPITAL – GROSSE POINTE (230089)**, 468 Cadieux Road, Zip 48230–1507; tel. 313/473–1000 **A**1 2 3 5 10 **F**3 6 11 12 13 15 18 20 22 26 28 29 30 31 32 34 35 36 39 40 43 44 45 46 47 48 49 50 51 53 54 55 56 57 58 59 60 61 63 64 65 68 69 70 71 74 75 76 77 78 79 80 81 82 84 85 86 87 91 92 93 94 96 97 100 102 107 108 110 111 114 115 116 117 118 119 126 129 130 131 132 134 135 145 146 147 148 149 **P**1 6 **S** Beaumont Health, Southfield, MI
Primary Contact: Richard P. Swaine, President
COO: Carolyn Wilson R.N., Chief Operating Officer
CFO: Maria Miller, Controller
CMO: Donna Hoban M.D., Senior Vice President and Chief Medical Officer
CIO: Subra Sripada, Executive Vice President, Chief Transportation Officer and Chief Information Officer
CHR: Pandora Walker, Director, Human Resources
CNO: Anne Stewart, Vice President and Chief Nursing Officer
Web address: www.beaumont.org
Control: Other not–for–profit (including NFP Corporation) **Service**: General medical and surgical

Staffed Beds: 280 **Admissions**: 12349 **Census**: 130 **Outpatient Visits**: 350417 **Births**: 748 **Total Expense ($000)**: 190285 **Payroll Expense ($000)**: 71460 **Personnel**: 1483

⊞ **SELECT SPECIALTY HOSPITAL–GROSSE POINTE (232038)**, 468 Cadieux Road, 3 North East, Zip 48230–1507; tel. 313/473–6131, (Nonreporting) **A**1 10 **S** Select Medical Corporation, Mechanicsburg, PA
Primary Contact: Zaahra Butt, Chief Executive Officer
Web address: www.grossepointe.selectspecialtyhospitals.com/
Control: Corporation, Investor–owned (for–profit) **Service**: Acute long–term care hospital

Staffed Beds: 30

HANCOCK—Houghton County

⊞ **UP HEALTH SYSTEM–PORTAGE (230108)**, 500 Campus Drive, Zip 49930–1569; tel. 906/483–1000, (Total facility includes 60 beds in nursing home–type unit) **A**1 5 10 20 **F**3 8 11 13 15 26 27 29 30 31 32 34 35 40 43 50 53 56 57 59 60 62 63 64 65 67 68 70 75 76 77 78 79 81 84 85 86 87 89 90 93 94 97 107 108 110 111 115 119 129 130 131 132 133 144 145 146 148 **P**6 **S** LifePoint Health, Brentwood, TN
Primary Contact: Jeff Lang, President
CFO: Steve Bishop, Chief Financial Officer
CMO: Mary Beth Hines D.O., Chief Medical Officer
CHR: Robbyn Lucier, Director Human Resources
Web address: www.portagehealth.org
Control: Corporation, Investor–owned (for–profit) **Service**: General medical and surgical

Staffed Beds: 96 **Admissions**: 1405 **Census**: 73 **Outpatient Visits**: 90575 **Births**: 275 **Total Expense ($000)**: 75275 **Payroll Expense ($000)**: 31764 **Personnel**: 634

HARBOR BEACH—Huron County

HARBOR BEACH COMMUNITY HOSPITAL (231313), 210 South First Street, Zip 48441–1236; tel. 989/479–3201, (Nonreporting) **A**5 10 18
Primary Contact: Paul Clabuesch, President and Chief Executive Officer
CFO: Jill Wehner, Vice President Financial Services
CMO: Richard Lloyd D.O., Chief of Staff
CIO: Tami Nickrand, Director Information Technology
CHR: Tina Osantoski, Director Human Resources
CNO: Deb Geiger, Executive Director of Acute Care
Web address: www.hbch.org
Control: Other not–for–profit (including NFP Corporation) **Service**: General medical and surgical

Staffed Beds: 54

HASTINGS—Barry County

⊞ **SPECTRUM HEALTH PENNOCK (230040)**, 1009 West Green Street, Zip 49058–1710; tel. 269/945–3451 **A**1 10 **F**3 11 13 15 29 30 32 34 35 36 39 40 44 45 50 53 54 56 57 59 62 63 64 65 68 70 74 75 76 77 79 81 82 84 85 86 87 89 91 92 93 96 97 107 108 110 111 115 119 125 126 127 130 131 132 135 144 146 147 148 **P**6 8 **S** Spectrum Health, Grand Rapids, MI
Primary Contact: Sheryl Lewis. Blake, FACHE, President
COO: Carla Wilson–Neil FACHE, Chief Operating Officer
CFO: Deidre Weller CPA, Controller
CMO: Douglas Smendik M.D., Chief Medical Officer
CIO: Teri VanTongeren, Director Information Services
CHR: Sherri Thrasher, Executive Human Resources Partner
CNO: Steve Marzolf R.N., Chief Nursing Officer
Web address: www.spectrumhealth.org
Control: Other not–for–profit (including NFP Corporation) **Service**: General medical and surgical

Staffed Beds: 39 **Admissions**: 2393 **Census**: 22 **Outpatient Visits**: 429899 **Births**: 306 **Total Expense ($000)**: 73810 **Payroll Expense ($000)**: 33878 **Personnel**: 508

HILLSDALE—Hillsdale County

★ ○ **HILLSDALE HOSPITAL (230037)**, 168 South Howell Street, Zip 49242–2081; tel. 517/437–4451, (Total facility includes 39 beds in nursing home–type unit) **A**10 11 12 13 19 **F**3 11 12 13 15 28 29 31 34 35 38 40 45 46 48 49 50 57 59 62 70 74 75 76 78 79 81 82 87 93 97 98 102 107 110 111 115 119 127 128 130 131 132 135 146 147 148 **P**6 8
Primary Contact: Duke Anderson, President and Chief Executive Officer
CFO: Valerie Fetters, Chief Financial Officer
CMO: Dan McCance D.O., Chief of Staff
CIO: Sheila Puffenberger, Manager Information Technology
CHR: Stacy Mellon, Manager Human Resource
CNO: Julie Walters, Chief Nursing Officer
Web address: www.hillsdalehospital.com
Control: Other not–for–profit (including NFP Corporation) **Service**: General medical and surgical

Staffed Beds: 93 **Admissions**: 2959 **Census**: 57 **Outpatient Visits**: 102594 **Births**: 328 **Total Expense ($000)**: 62640 **Payroll Expense ($000)**: 22362 **Personnel**: 407

HOLLAND—Ottawa County

★ ⇑ **HOLLAND HOSPITAL (230072)**, 602 Michigan Avenue, Zip 49423–4999; tel. 616/392–5141, (Nonreporting) **A**10 21
Primary Contact: Dale Sowders, President and Chief Executive Officer
CFO: Terry L Steele, Vice President Finance and Chief Financial Officer
CMO: William Vandervliet M.D., Vice President Medical Affairs
CIO: Randy J Paruch, Director, Information Systems
CHR: Michael Matthews, Vice President Human Resources
CNO: Patti J VanDort MSN, R.N., Vice President Nursing/Chief Nursing Officer
Web address: www.hollandhospital.org
Control: Other not–for–profit (including NFP Corporation) **Service**: General medical and surgical

Staffed Beds: 130

HOWELL—Livingston County

⊞ **ST. JOSEPH MERCY LIVINGSTON HOSPITAL (230069)**, 620 Byron Road, Zip 48843–1093; tel. 517/545–6000 **A**1 3 5 10 13 **F**3 5 8 11 12 15 18 28 29 30 31 34 35 40 41 42 45 50 51 54 56 57 59 62 63 64 65 66 68 70 74 75 77 78 79 81 82 84 85 86 87 93 97 100 104 107 108 110 111 115 117 118 119 120 121 123 129 130 131 132 134 135 141 145 146 147 148 149 **P**1 **S** Trinity Health, Livonia, MI
Primary Contact: John F. O'Malley, FACHE, President
COO: Robin Damschroder, Chief Operating Officer
CFO: Kathy O'Connor, Vice President Finance and Controller
CMO: Rosalie Tocco–Bradley Ph.D., M.D., Chief Medical Officer
CIO: Frank Rademacher, Director, Information Systems
CHR: Tonia Schemer, Interim Chief Human Resources
CNO: Joyce Young Ph.D., R.N., Vice President, Patient Services and Chief Nursing Officer
Web address: www.stjoeslivingston.org/livingston
Control: Church operated, Nongovernment, not–for–profit **Service**: General medical and surgical

Staffed Beds: 38 **Admissions**: 2535 **Census**: 22 **Outpatient Visits**: 279942 **Births**: 0 **Total Expense ($000)**: 106003 **Payroll Expense ($000)**: 34576 **Personnel**: 548

Many Facility Codes have changed. Please refer to the AHA Guide Code Chart. © 2017 AHA Guide

IONIA—Ionia County

☒ **SPARROW IONIA HOSPITAL (231331)**, 3565 South State Road, Zip 48846–1870; tel. 616/523–1400 **A**1 10 18 **F**3 12 15 18 29 31 34 35 40 45 50 54 57 59 64 65 68 70 75 77 78 79 81 85 93 107 108 110 111 115 119 127 129 130 131 146 148 **P**6 **S** Sparrow Health System, Lansing, MI
Primary Contact: William Roeser, President and Chief Executive Officer
COO: Kevin A Price, Vice President and Chief Operating Officer
CFO: Mark Brisboe, VP and Chief Financial Officer
CMO: Amy Jentz M.D., Chief of Staff
CIO: Bob Neal, Information Technology
CHR: Debbie Olsen, Human Resource Partner
Web address: www.sparrow.org/sparrowionia
Control: Other not–for–profit (including NFP Corporation) **Service**: General medical and surgical

Staffed Beds: 22 **Admissions**: 743 **Census**: 6 **Outpatient Visits**: 155715
Births: 2 **Total Expense ($000)**: 44948 **Payroll Expense ($000)**: 19550
Personnel: 278

IRON MOUNTAIN—Dickinson County

☒ **DICKINSON COUNTY HEALTHCARE SYSTEM (230055)**, 1721 South Stephenson Avenue, Zip 49801–3637; tel. 906/774–1313 **A**1 10 20 **F**3 11 13 15 18 28 29 30 31 34 35 40 45 46 50 53 59 62 64 65 70 75 76 77 78 79 80 81 85 87 89 91 92 93 96 107 108 110 111 114 115 118 119 120 121 127 129 130 131 132 133 144 145 146 147 148 149 **P**6
Primary Contact: John Schon, Administrator and Chief Executive Officer
COO: Peggy Freeman, Chief Physicians Services Officer
CFO: Eileen Sparpana, Chief Financial Officer
CMO: Don Kube M.D., Chief of Staff
CIO: Dean Decremer, Information Systems Manager
CHR: Paula Swartout, Human Resources Manager
CNO: Susan Hadley R.N., MS, Chief Nursing Officer
Web address: www.dchs.org
Control: County, Government, Nonfederal **Service**: General medical and surgical

Staffed Beds: 96 **Admissions**: 2691 **Census**: 25 **Outpatient Visits**: 290065
Births: 455 **Total Expense ($000)**: 114444 **Payroll Expense ($000)**: 46347
Personnel: 645

☒ **OSCAR G. JOHNSON VETERANS AFFAIRS MEDICAL CENTER**, 325 East 'H' Street, Zip 49801–4792; tel. 906/774–3300, (Nonreporting) **A**1 **S** Department of Veterans Affairs, Washington, DC
Primary Contact: James W. Rice, Director
Web address: www.ironmountain.va.gov/
Control: Veterans Affairs, Government, federal **Service**: General medical and surgical

Staffed Beds: 17

VETERANS AFFAIRS MEDICAL CENTER See Oscar G. Johnson Veterans Affairs Medical Center

IRON RIVER—Iron County

☒ **ASPIRUS IRON RIVER HOSPITALS & CLINICS, INC. (231318)**, 1400 West Ice Lake Road, Zip 49935–9526; tel. 906/265–6121 **A**1 10 18 **F**11 15 28 29 31 32 34 35 40 43 50 54 56 57 59 60 63 64 70 75 77 78 79 81 86 87 89 93 97 107 111 115 119 128 130 131 132 133 135 144 145 146 147 148 **S** Aspirus, Inc., Wausau, WI
Primary Contact: Connie L. Koutouzos, R.N., MSN, Chief Executive Officer
CFO: Glenn E Dobson, Vice President, Finance and Chief Financial Officer
CMO: Nasseem Rizkalla M.D., Chief Medical Officer
CHR: Carol Bastianello, Director Human Resources
CNO: Nancy Lynn Ponozzo MSN, R.N., Chief Nursing Officer
Web address: www.aspirus.org
Control: Other not–for–profit (including NFP Corporation) **Service**: General medical and surgical

Staffed Beds: 12 **Admissions**: 776 **Census**: 7 **Outpatient Visits**: 59935
Births: 0 **Total Expense ($000)**: 41739 **Payroll Expense ($000)**: 14398
Personnel: 232

IRONWOOD—Gogebic County

☒ **ASPIRUS IRONWOOD HOSITAL & CLINICS, INC. (231333)**, N10561 Grand View Lane, Zip 49938–9622; tel. 906/932–2525 **A**1 10 18 **F**3 11 13 15 28 29 31 34 35 40 50 56 57 59 62 64 65 70 75 77 78 79 81 85 93 97 107 110 114 115 119 127 129 130 132 133 135 146 147 148 **P**6 **S** Aspirus, Inc., Wausau, WI
Primary Contact: Paula L. Chermside, Chief Executive Officer
COO: Paula L Chermside, Chief Executive Officer
CFO: Shane Jacques, Regional Chief Financial Officer
CMO: Chris Pogliano M.D., Chief Medical Staff
CIO: John Steenport, Information Systems Manager
CHR: Keri Van Epern, Manager Human Resources
CNO: Grace Tousignant R.N., MSN, Chief Nursing Officer
Web address: www.aspirus.org
Control: Other not–for–profit (including NFP Corporation) **Service**: General medical and surgical

Staffed Beds: 25 **Admissions**: 1066 **Census**: 10 **Outpatient Visits**: 64406
Births: 128 **Total Expense ($000)**: 57448 **Payroll Expense ($000)**: 23045
Personnel: 232

ISHPEMING—Marquette County

★ **UP HEALTH SYSTEM–BELL (231321)**, 901 Lakeshore Drive, Zip 49849–1367; tel. 906/486–4431 **A**10 18 **F**3 11 13 15 29 30 34 40 50 53 57 59 64 65 68 70 75 76 77 79 81 82 85 87 92 93 96 97 107 108 110 119 129 133 135 144 146 147 **P**6 **S** LifePoint Health, Brentwood, TN
Primary Contact: Mitchell D. Leckelt, Chief Executive Officer
CFO: Teresa J Perry, Chief Financial Officer
CMO: Douglas LaBelle M.D., Chief Medical Officer
CIO: Mike Brady, Director Information Technology
CHR: Tami Ketchem, Human Resource Director
CNO: Sandra McGovern, Chief Nursing Officer
Web address: www.bellhospital.org
Control: Corporation, Investor–owned (for–profit) **Service**: General medical and surgical

Staffed Beds: 25 **Admissions**: 1106 **Census**: 9 **Outpatient Visits**: 56399
Births: 301 **Total Expense ($000)**: 36428 **Payroll Expense ($000)**: 13607
Personnel: 214

JACKSON—Jackson County

☒ **CARELINK OF JACKSON (232036)**, 110 North Elm Avenue, Zip 49202–3595; tel. 517/787–1440 **A**1 10 **F**1 3 29 30 31 50 57 60 77 85 87 130 146 148
Primary Contact: J Mark. Fall, Chief Executive Officer
COO: Charlotte Hyatt MSN, R.N., Chief Operating Officer and Chief Nursing Officer
CFO: Dale L Friesen, Chief Financial Officer
CMO: Robert Albertson M.D., Chief Medical Officer
CNO: Charlotte Hyatt MSN, R.N., Chief Operating Officer and Chief Nursing Officer
Web address: www.carelinkofjackson.org
Control: Other not–for–profit (including NFP Corporation) **Service**: Acute long–term care hospital

Staffed Beds: 44 **Admissions**: 409 **Census**: 31 **Outpatient Visits**: 0 **Births**: 0
Total Expense ($000): 15476 **Payroll Expense ($000)**: 5775 **Personnel**: 119

DUANE L. WATERS HOSPITAL, 3857 Cooper Street, Zip 49201–7521; tel. 517/780–5600, (Nonreporting)
Primary Contact: Carol Griffes, Administrator
Control: State, Government, Nonfederal **Service**: Hospital unit of an institution (prison hospital, college infirmary, etc.)

Staffed Beds: 150

☒ **HENRY FORD ALLEGIANCE HEALTH (230092)**, 205 North East Avenue, Zip 49201–1753; tel. 517/788–4800 **A**1 2 3 5 10 12 13 **F**3 4 5 8 9 11 13 15 17 18 20 22 24 26 28 29 30 31 34 35 38 40 44 45 46 47 48 49 50 51 53 56 57 58 59 61 62 64 65 68 69 70 71 73 74 75 76 77 78 79 81 82 84 85 87 89 92 93 96 98 99 100 101 102 103 104 105 106 107 108 110 111 114 115 119 121 123 126 128 129 130 131 132 135 146 147 148 149 **P**6 **S** Henry Ford Health System, Detroit, MI
Primary Contact: Georgia R. Fojtasek, R.N., President and Chief Executive Officer
COO: Ondrea Bates, Senior Vice President, Operations and Continuum of Care
CMO: Ray King M.D., Senior Vice President and Chief Medical Officer
CIO: Aaron Wootton, Vice President Health Information Systems
CHR: Patricia Seagram, Vice President Human Resources
CNO: Wendy Boersma R.N., Vice President and Chief Nursing Officer
Web address: www.allegiancehealth.org
Control: Other not–for–profit (including NFP Corporation) **Service**: General medical and surgical

Staffed Beds: 327 **Admissions**: 17447 **Census**: 208 **Outpatient Visits**: 492187 **Births**: 1617 **Total Expense ($000)**: 501574 **Payroll Expense ($000)**: 229869 **Personnel**: 3620

KALAMAZOO—Kalamazoo County

☒ △ **BORGESS MEDICAL CENTER (230117)**, 1521 Gull Road, Zip 49048–1640; tel. 269/226–7000, (Includes BORGESS–PIPP HOSPITAL, 411 Naomi Street, Plainwell, Michigan, Zip 49080–1222, tel. 269/685–6811; John E. Ryder, Administrator and Chief Operating Officer) **A**1 3 5 7 10 12 13 **F**3 7 8 9 11 12 13 15 17 18 20 22 24 26 28 29 30 31 32 33 34 35 36 37 38 39 40 43 44 45 46 47 49 50 53 54 56 57 58 59 60 61 64 68 70 74 75 76 77 78 79 81 82 83 84 85 86 87 90 91 92 93 94 96 97 98 99 100 101 102 103 104 105 107 108 110 114 118 119 126 129 130 131 132 135 144 146 147 148 149 **P**3 6 8 **S** Ascension Healthcare, Saint Louis, MO
Primary Contact: Kathlene A. Young, MS, FACHE, Chief Executive Officer
COO: Mark Anthony, Executive Vice President and Chief Operating Officer
CFO: Damon Sorensen, Chief Financial Officer
CMO: Robert Hill M.D., Vice President Medical Staff Affairs
CHR: Laura Lentenbrink, Vice President, Human Resources
CNO: Lori J Brown R.N., FACHE, Vice President and Chief Nursing Executive
Web address: www.borgess.com
Control: Church operated, Nongovernment, not–for–profit **Service**: General medical and surgical

Staffed Beds: 422 **Admissions**: 19036 **Census**: 245 **Outpatient Visits**: 395138 **Births**: 1279 **Total Expense ($000)**: 386978 **Payroll Expense ($000)**: 148622 **Personnel**: 2733

☒ **BRONSON METHODIST HOSPITAL (230017)**, 601 John Street, Zip 49007–5346; tel. 269/341–6000, (Includes BRONSON VICKSBURG HOSPITAL, 13326 North Boulevard, Vicksburg, Michigan, Zip 49097–1099, tel. 269/649–2321; Frank J Sardone, President and Chief Executive Officer; CHILDREN'S HOSPITAL AT BRONSON, 601 John Street, Kalamazoo, Michigan, Zip 49007–5341, tel. 269/341–7654) **A**1 3 5 10 12 13 **F**3 8 9 11 12 15 16 17 18 19 20 22 24 26 28 29 30 31 34 35 37 39 40 41 43 44 45 46 47 48 49 50 51 54 55 56 57 58 59 60 61 63 64 65 66 68 70 71 72 74 75 76 77 78 79 80 81 82 83 84 85 86 87 88 89 90 92 93 97 102 107 108 110 111 115 117 119 126 129 130 131 132 134 135 141 143 144 146 147 148 149 **P**6 **S** Bronson Healthcare Group, Kalamazoo, MI
Primary Contact: Frank J. Sardone, President and Chief Executive Officer
COO: Kenneth L Taft, Executive Vice President and Chief Operating Officer
CMO: Scott Larson M.D., Vice President Medical Affairs and Chief Medical Officer
CHR: John Hayden, Vice President and Chief Human Resources Officer
CNO: Denise Neely R.N., Vice President and Chief Nursing Officer
Web address: www.bronsonhealth.com
Control: Other not–for–profit (including NFP Corporation) **Service**: General medical and surgical

Staffed Beds: 415 **Admissions**: 23027 **Census**: 288 **Outpatient Visits**: 1009349 **Births**: 3765 **Total Expense ($000)**: 746379 **Payroll Expense ($000)**: 357250 **Personnel**: 3697

☐ **KALAMAZOO PSYCHIATRIC HOSPITAL (234026)**, 1312 Oakland Drive, Zip 49008–1205; tel. 269/337–3000 **A**1 10 12 13 **F**3 39 50 53 56 65 75 77 86 87 97 98 101 103 130 132 135 143 146 148 149 **P**6
Primary Contact: Jill A. Krause, Director
CMO: V.R. Kanaparti M.D., Director Medical Services
CIO: Brian Bayer, Information Technology Site Leader
CHR: Holly Hiday, Director Human Resources
CNO: Kathleen Millard, Acting Director Nursing
Control: State, Government, Nonfederal **Service**: Psychiatric

Staffed Beds: 203 **Admissions**: 159 **Census**: 134 **Outpatient Visits**: 0 **Births**: 0 **Total Expense ($000)**: 58709 **Payroll Expense ($000)**: 28004 **Personnel**: 454

KALKASKA—Kalkaska County

★ **KALKASKA MEMORIAL HEALTH CENTER (231301)**, 419 South Coral Street, Zip 49646–2503; tel. 231/258–7500, (Total facility includes 104 beds in nursing home–type unit) **A**10 18 **F**2 10 15 28 34 35 40 44 45 50 53 56 57 59 60 64 65 66 79 81 84 87 93 97 107 110 111 115 119 127 128 129 130 132 134 143 144 146 147 148 **S** Munson Healthcare, Traverse City, MI
Primary Contact: Kevin L. Rogols, FACHE, Administrator
CHR: Kimberly Babcock, Administrative Director of Operations
CNO: Christine Bissonette R.N., Service Line Director for Acute Services
Web address: www.munsonhealthcare.org
Control: Hospital district or authority, Government, Nonfederal **Service**: General medical and surgical

Staffed Beds: 112 **Admissions**: 249 **Census**: 81 **Outpatient Visits**: 76623 **Births**: 0 **Total Expense ($000)**: 37805 **Payroll Expense ($000)**: 17021 **Personnel**: 280

LAKEVIEW—Montcalm County

SPECTRUM HEALTH KELSEY HOSPITAL See Spectrum Health United Hospital, Greenville

L'ANSE—L'Anse County

☐ **BARAGA COUNTY MEMORIAL HOSPITAL (231307)**, 18341 U.S. Highway 41, Zip 49946–8024; tel. 906/524–3300 **A**1 10 18 **F**3 11 15 28 31 34 35 40 45 50 53 57 59 62 63 64 74 75 77 78 79 81 82 84 85 89 93 107 108 110 114 118 119 127 130 132 133 146 **P**6
Primary Contact: Margie Hale, R.N., MSN, Chief Executive Officer
CFO: Gail Jestila–Peltola, Chief Financial Officer
CMO: Sharon Gilliland, Chief of Staff
CIO: Taylor Makela, Director Information Technology
CHR: Janelle E Beeler, Human Resource Manager
CNO: Bonny Cotter, Chief Nursing Officer
Web address: www.bcmh.org
Control: County, Government, Nonfederal **Service**: General medical and surgical

Staffed Beds: 15 **Admissions**: 540 **Census**: 7 **Outpatient Visits**: 23935 **Births**: 1 **Total Expense ($000)**: 21977 **Payroll Expense ($000)**: 8245 **Personnel**: 122

LANSING—Ingham County

○ **MCLAREN GREATER LANSING (230167)**, 401 West Greenlawn Avenue, Zip 48910–2819; tel. 517/975–6000, (Nonreporting) (Includes MCLAREN GREATER LANSING, 401 West Greenlawn Avenue, Lansing, Michigan, Zip 48910–2819, tel. 517/795–6000; MCLAREN ORTHOPEDIC HOSPITAL, 2727 South Pennsylvania Avenue, Lansing, Michigan, Zip 48910–3490, tel. 517/975–6000; Thomas Mee, R.N., President and Chief Executive Officer) **A**2 3 5 10 11 13 **S** McLaren Health Care Corporation, Flint, MI
Primary Contact: Thomas Mee, R.N., President and Chief Executive Officer
CFO: Dale Thompson, Chief Financial Officer
CMO: Linda Peterson M.D., Vice President Medical Affairs
CHR: Amy Dorr, Vice President Human Resources
CNO: Camille Jensen R.N., Chief Nursing Officer
Web address: www.mclaren.org
Control: Other not–for–profit (including NFP Corporation) **Service**: General medical and surgical

Staffed Beds: 321

☒ △ **SPARROW HOSPITAL (230230)**, 1215 East Michigan Avenue, Zip 48912–1811; tel. 517/364–1000, (Includes SPARROW CHILDREN'S CENTER, 1215 East Michigan Avenue, Lansing, Michigan, Zip 48912–1811, tel. 517/364–1000) **A**1 2 3 5 7 8 10 12 13 **F**3 5 11 12 13 15 17 18 20 22 24 26 28 29 30 31 34 35 36 38 40 41 43 44 45 46 49 50 51 54 56 57 58 59 60 63 64 65 66 67 70 72 74 75 76 77 78 79 81 82 84 85 86 87 88 89 90 91 92 93 94 96 97 98 99 100 101 102 103 104 105 107 108 109 110 114 115 116 117 118 119 120 121 123 124 126 128 129 130 131 132 135 144 146 147 148 149 **P**1 6 **S** Sparrow Health System, Lansing, MI
Primary Contact: Dennis A. Swan, JD, FACHE, President and Chief Executive Officer
COO: Joseph Ruth, Executive Vice President and Chief Operating Officer
CFO: Paula Reichle, Senior Vice President and Chief Operating Officer
CMO: Brian D. Schroeder M.D., Senior Vice President and Chief Medical Officer
CIO: Thomas Bres, Senior Vice President and Chief Administrative Officer
CHR: Paul Sturgis, Vice President and Chief Human Resources Officer
CNO: Mary Lou Wesley R.N., Senior Vice President and Chief Nursing Officer
Web address: www.sparrow.org
Control: Other not–for–profit (including NFP Corporation) **Service**: General medical and surgical

Staffed Beds: 652 **Admissions**: 34503 **Census**: 473 **Outpatient Visits**: 811239 **Births**: 4389 **Total Expense ($000)**: 911243 **Payroll Expense ($000)**: 430010 **Personnel**: 5745

★ ○ **SPARROW SPECIALTY HOSPITAL (232037)**, 8 West Sparrow Hospital Tower, Zip 48912; tel. 517/364–4840 **A**10 11 **F**1 3 29 30 60 68 85 100 101 119 130 148 **S** Sparrow Health System, Lansing, MI
Primary Contact: Lou Little, President and Chief Executive Officer
CFO: David Przybylski, Controller
CMO: Paul Entler D.O., Medical Director
CHR: Paul Sturgis, Chief Human Resource Officer
CNO: Tina Gross MSN, R.N., Chief Nursing Officer
Web address: www.sparrowspecialty.org
Control: Other not–for–profit (including NFP Corporation) **Service**: Acute long–term care hospital

Staffed Beds: 30 **Admissions**: 334 **Census**: 25 **Outpatient Visits**: 0 **Births**: 0 **Total Expense ($000)**: 13379 **Payroll Expense ($000)**: 6166 **Personnel**: 96

LAPEER—Lapeer County

○ **MCLAREN LAPEER REGION (230193)**, 1375 North Main Street, Zip 48446–1350; tel. 810/667–5500, (Total facility includes 19 beds in nursing home–type unit) **A**2 10 11 **F**3 13 15 18 20 28 29 30 31 34 35 40 43 45 49 50 51 54 56 59 61 64 68 70 74 75 76 77 78 79 81 82 85 87 92 93 97 98 100 101 102 107 108 110 111 114 115 119 128 129 130 135 143 144 146 148 149 **S** McLaren Health Care Corporation, Flint, MI
Primary Contact: Chris Candela, President and Chief Executive Officer
CFO: Mary Beth Callahan, Chief Financial Officer
CMO: Gary Salem M.D., Vice President Medical Affairs
CIO: Gayle Consiglio, Chief Information Officer
CHR: Amy Dorr, Vice President Human Resources
Web address: www.lapeerregional.org
Control: Other not–for–profit (including NFP Corporation) **Service:** General medical and surgical

Staffed Beds: 159 **Admissions:** 6869 **Census:** 89 **Outpatient Visits:** 146559 **Births:** 282 **Total Expense ($000):** 110894 **Payroll Expense ($000):** 49817 **Personnel:** 609

LAURIUM—Houghton County

✠ **ASPIRUS KEWEENAW HOSPITAL, INC. (231319)**, 205 Osceola Street, Zip 49913–2134; tel. 906/337–6500 **A**1 10 18 **F**3 7 11 13 15 17 18 28 29 30 31 34 35 36 40 45 52 53 56 57 59 61 64 65 66 70 75 76 77 78 79 81 85 87 89 91 92 93 97 107 108 110 111 115 118 119 127 129 130 131 132 133 135 146 147 148 **P**6 **S** Aspirus, Inc., Wausau, WI
Primary Contact: Michael Hauswirth, Chief Executive Officer
CFO: Shane Jacques, Regional Chief Financial Officer – U.P.
CMO: Michael Luoma M.D., Chief of Staff
CIO: Dave Olsson, Director of Marketing
CHR: Chad Rowe, Human Resource Director
CNO: Grace Tousignant R.N., MSN, Chief Nursing Officer
Web address: www.aspirus.org
Control: Other not–for–profit (including NFP Corporation) **Service:** General medical and surgical

Staffed Beds: 25 **Admissions:** 1154 **Census:** 9 **Outpatient Visits:** 42404 **Births:** 134 **Total Expense ($000):** 50874 **Payroll Expense ($000):** 19760 **Personnel:** 297

LINCOLN PARK—Wayne County

✠ **VIBRA HOSPITAL OF SOUTHEASTERN MICHIGAN, LLC (232019)**, 26400 West Outer Drive, Zip 48146–2088; tel. 313/386–2000 (Nonreporting) **A**1 10 **S** Vibra Healthcare, Mechanicsburg, PA
Primary Contact: Denise Wayne, Chief Executive Officer
COO: Cindy Brassinger, Chief Operating Officer
CFO: Douglas Morris, Chief Financial Officer
CHR: Karen D Gray, Director Human Resources
Web address: www.vhsemichigan.com/
Control: Corporation, Investor–owned (for–profit) **Service:** Acute long–term care hospital

Staffed Beds: 220

LIVONIA—Wayne County

✠ **ST. MARY MERCY HOSPITAL (230002)**, 36475 Five Mile Road, Zip 48154–1988; tel. 734/655–4800 **A**1 2 3 10 12 13 **F**3 4 5 12 13 15 18 20 22 26 28 29 30 31 34 35 36 38 40 43 44 45 46 47 49 50 51 53 56 57 58 59 63 64 68 70 74 75 76 78 79 81 84 85 87 90 93 97 98 100 101 102 103 104 107 108 110 111 114 115 116 117 118 119 120 121 126 129 130 131 132 135 143 145 146 147 148 149 **P**6 **S** Trinity Health, Livonia, MI
Primary Contact: David A. Spivey, President and Chief Executive Officer
CFO: Mike Samyn, Vice President, Finance and Chief Financial Officer
CIO: Janet Yim, Director Information Services
CHR: Kenneth Antczak, Vice President Human Resources
Web address: www.stmarymercy.org
Control: Church operated, Nongovernment, not–for–profit **Service:** General medical and surgical

Staffed Beds: 303 **Admissions:** 17318 **Census:** 196 **Outpatient Visits:** 274726 **Births:** 852 **Total Expense ($000):** 276994 **Payroll Expense ($000):** 118054 **Personnel:** 1604

LUDINGTON—Mason County

★ ⇑ **SPECTRUM HEALTH LUDINGTON HOSPITAL (230110)**, One Atkinson Drive, Zip 49431–1906; tel. 231/843–2591 **A**10 20 21 **F**8 11 13 15 28 29 31 32 34 35 40 41 45 49 50 54 57 59 64 65 68 70 75 76 77 78 79 81 82 85 86 87 92 93 98 100 102 103 104 107 108 110 111 114 115 118 119 127 129 130 131 132 135 146 147 148 149 **S** Spectrum Health, Grand Rapids, MI
Primary Contact: Randall Kelley, FACHE, President
CFO: Kerri Nelson, Chief Financial Officer
CMO: Steve Strbich D.O., Chief of Staff
CIO: Jeremy Vronko, Manager, Information Services
CHR: Jill Vasquez, Manager Human Resources
CNO: Helen Johnson R.N., MSN, Vice President Patient Services
Web address: www.mmcwm.com
Control: Other not–for–profit (including NFP Corporation) **Service:** General medical and surgical

Staffed Beds: 44 **Admissions:** 2368 **Census:** 25 **Outpatient Visits:** 99554 **Births:** 340 **Total Expense ($000):** 82006 **Payroll Expense ($000):** 26567 **Personnel:** 474

MANISTEE—Manistee County

MUNSON HEALTHCARE MANISTEE HOSPITAL (230303), 1465 East Parkdale Avenue, Zip 49660–9709; tel. 231/398–1100 **A**10 20 **F**3 7 11 13 15 28 29 31 34 35 39 40 44 45 48 50 51 53 54 59 64 74 77 78 79 80 81 85 92 93 96 97 107 108 110 111 115 118 119 127 129 131 141 146 147 148 149 **P**6 **S** Munson Healthcare, Traverse City, MI
Primary Contact: James Barker, Chief Executive Officer
COO: Donn J Lemmer, Chief Financial Officer and Chief Operating Officer
CFO: Donn J Lemmer, Chief Financial Officer and Chief Operating Officer
CMO: Marion Fuller, Chief of Staff
CHR: Kim Weckesser, Director Human Resources
CNO: Thomas Kane R.N., Vice President Patient Services and Chief Nursing Officer
Web address: www.westshoremedcenter.org
Control: County, Government, Nonfederal **Service:** General medical and surgical

Staffed Beds: 45 **Admissions:** 1467 **Census:** 14 **Outpatient Visits:** 94130 **Births:** 207 **Total Expense ($000):** 66059 **Payroll Expense ($000):** 24510 **Personnel:** 318

MANISTIQUE—Schoolcraft County

★ **SCHOOLCRAFT MEMORIAL HOSPITAL (231303)**, 7870W US Highway 2, Zip 49854–8992; tel. 906/341–3200 **A**10 18 **F**3 11 15 28 29 30 31 32 34 35 40 41 50 53 56 57 59 62 63 64 65 68 70 75 77 78 79 81 85 93 97 107 108 110 114 118 119 127 129 130 132 133 144 146 147 148 **P**6
Primary Contact: Robert Crumb, Chief Executive Officer
CMO: John P Galey M.D., Chief Medical Officer
CIO: Kent La Croix, Chief Information Officer
CHR: Fawn Freeborn, Human Resources Generalist
CNO: Cindy Olli R.N., Chief Nursing Officer
Web address: www.scmh.org
Control: County, Government, Nonfederal **Service:** General medical and surgical

Staffed Beds: 12 **Admissions:** 392 **Census:** 4 **Outpatient Visits:** 40362 **Births:** 0 **Total Expense ($000):** 29641 **Payroll Expense ($000):** 13439 **Personnel:** 211

MARLETTE—Sanilac County

MARLETTE REGIONAL HOSPITAL (231330), 2770 Main Street, Zip 48453–1141, Mailing Address: P.O.Box 307, 48453–0307; tel. 989/635–4000, (Nonreporting) **A**5 10 18
Primary Contact: Daniel Babcock, Chief Executive Officer
CFO: James L Singles, Chief Financial Officer
CMO: Daniel Kulick M.D., Chief of Staff
CIO: Paul Gugel, Manager Information Technology
CHR: Connie Kennedy, Director Human Resources
CNO: Hilda Hebberd R.N., MSN, Senior Director Clinical Services
Web address: www.marletteregionalhospital.org
Control: Other not–for–profit (including NFP Corporation) **Service:** General medical and surgical

Staffed Beds: 74

Hospital, Medicare Provider Number, Address, Telephone, Approval, Facility, and Physician Codes, Health Care System

★ American Hospital Association (AHA) membership ○ Healthcare Facilities Accreditation Program ⇑ Center for Improvement in Healthcare Quality Accreditation
☐ The Joint Commission accreditation ◇ DNV Healthcare Inc. accreditation △ Commission on Accreditation of Rehabilitation Facilities (CARF) accreditation

MARQUETTE—Marquette County

✠ **UP HEALTH SYSTEM–MARQUETTE (230054)**, 580 West College Avenue, Zip 49855–2736; tel. 906/228–9440 **A**1 2 3 5 10 13 **F**3 4 5 7 8 11 12 13 14 15 17 18 19 20 22 24 26 28 29 30 31 32 34 35 37 38 40 43 45 46 49 50 51 53 55 56 57 58 59 60 62 63 64 65 68 70 72 74 75 76 77 78 79 81 82 84 85 86 87 89 90 93 94 98 100 101 104 106 107 108 110 111 114 115 116 118 119 120 121 123 124 127 129 130 131 132 135 145 147 148 149 **P**6 **S** Duke LifePoint Healthcare, Brentwood, TN
Primary Contact: Brian Sinotte, Chief Executive Officer
COO: Steven Salyer, Chief Operating Officer
CFO: Steve Embree, Chief Financial Officer
CMO: Tom Noren M.D., Chief Medical Officer
CIO: Doug Stacy, Director Information Technology
CHR: Ruth Solinski, Senior Director Human Resources
Web address: www.mgh.org
Control: Corporation, Investor–owned (for–profit) **Service**: General medical and surgical

> **Staffed Beds**: 268 **Admissions**: 10186 **Census**: 136 **Outpatient Visits**: 193259 **Births**: 616 **Total Expense ($000)**: 344340 **Payroll Expense ($000)**: 127771 **Personnel**: 1714

MARSHALL—Calhoun County

★ ⇑ **OAKLAWN HOSPITAL (230217)**, 200 North Madison Street, Zip 49068–1199; tel. 269/781–4271, (Nonreporting) **A**10 21
Primary Contact: Ginger Williams, M.D., FACHE, President and Chief Executive Officer
COO: Sharon Thomas–Boyd, Chief Operating Officer
CFO: Gregg M Beeg FACHE, Chief Financial Officer
CIO: Mac McClurkan, Chief Information Officer
CNO: Theresa Dawson MSN, R.N., Chief Nursing Officer
Web address: www.oaklawnhospital.org
Control: Other not–for–profit (including NFP Corporation) **Service**: General medical and surgical

> **Staffed Beds**: 78

MIDLAND—Midland County

✠ **MIDMICHIGAN MEDICAL CENTER–MIDLAND (230222)**, 4000 Wellness Drive, Zip 48670–2000; tel. 989/839–3000 **A**1 2 3 5 10 **F**3 7 8 11 12 13 15 17 18 19 20 22 24 26 28 29 30 31 32 34 35 37 40 43 45 46 47 48 49 50 51 53 54 55 56 57 58 59 60 61 62 63 64 65 68 70 71 74 75 77 78 79 80 81 82 84 85 86 87 91 92 93 94 96 97 98 100 101 102 103 104 107 108 109 110 111 114 115 116 117 118 119 120 121 122 123 124 126 127 129 130 131 132 135 143 144 146 147 148 149 **S** MidMichigan Health, Midland, MI
Primary Contact: Gregory H. Rogers, President
CFO: Scott D Currie, Vice President and Chief Financial Officer
CMO: Margueritte Kuhn M.D., Vice President Medical Affairs
CIO: C Harlan Goodrich, Vice President and Chief Information Officer
CNO: Jan Penney R.N., Vice President and Chief Nursing Officer
Web address: www.midmichigan.org
Control: Other not–for–profit (including NFP Corporation) **Service**: General medical and surgical

> **Staffed Beds**: 304 **Admissions**: 12540 **Census**: 130 **Outpatient Visits**: 273139 **Births**: 1249 **Total Expense ($000)**: 367483 **Payroll Expense ($000)**: 107556 **Personnel**: 1896

MONROE—Monroe County

✠ **PROMEDICA MONROE REGIONAL HOSPITAL (230099)**, 718 North Macomb Street, Zip 48162–7815; tel. 734/240–8400 **A**1 2 3 10 13 **F**3 5 8 11 13 15 18 20 21 28 29 30 34 35 38 40 41 44 45 46 49 50 51 54 56 57 59 65 66 69 70 71 74 75 76 77 78 79 81 85 86 87 89 92 93 97 98 99 100 101 102 103 104 107 108 109 110 111 113 114 115 116 123 126 129 130 131 132 135 145 146 147 148 **S** ProMedica Health System, Toledo, OH
Primary Contact: Daniel Schwanke, Interim President
CMO: Gary L. Moorman D.O., Chief Medical Officer and Senior Vice President Medical Affairs
CNO: Pamela A Urbanski R.N., MSN, Chief Nursing Officer, Senior Vice President, Patient Care Services
Web address: www.promedica.org
Control: Other not–for–profit (including NFP Corporation) **Service**: General medical and surgical

> **Staffed Beds**: 152 **Admissions**: 7619 **Census**: 84 **Outpatient Visits**: 156595 **Births**: 800 **Total Expense ($000)**: 146243 **Payroll Expense ($000)**: 52289 **Personnel**: 1156

MOUNT CLEMENS—Macomb County

MCLAREN MACOMB (230227), 1000 Harrington Boulevard, Zip 48043–2992; tel. 586/493–8000 **A**2 10 12 13 **F**3 8 11 12 13 14 15 18 19 20 22 24 26 28 29 30 31 34 35 36 37 40 41 43 45 46 47 48 49 50 51 54 55 56 59 62 63 64 65 66 68 70 71 74 75 76 77 78 79 81 82 85 87 89 91 92 93 94 96 100 102 107 110 114 118 119 120 121 122 123 124 126 129 130 131 132 135 144 145 146 147 148 **P**8 **S** McLaren Health Care Corporation, Flint, MI
Primary Contact: Thomas M. Brisse, President and Chief Executive Officer
COO: Sue Durst R.N., MS, Vice President Plant Operations
CFO: Brian Baluntanski, Chief Financial Officer
CMO: Dennis J. Cunningham M.D., Chief Medical Officer
Web address: www.mclaren.org/macomb/macomb.aspx
Control: Other not–for–profit (including NFP Corporation) **Service**: General medical and surgical

> **Staffed Beds**: 288 **Admissions**: 15044 **Census**: 164 **Outpatient Visits**: 163556 **Births**: 1073 **Total Expense ($000)**: 308883 **Payroll Expense ($000)**: 128334 **Personnel**: 1860

✠ **SELECT SPECIALTY HOSPITAL–MACOMB COUNTY (232023)**, 215 North Avenue, Zip 48043–1700; tel. 586/307–9000, (Nonreporting) **A**1 10 **S** Select Medical Corporation, Mechanicsburg, PA
Primary Contact: Jon P. O'Malley, Chief Executive Officer
CFO: Sharon Ryan, Regional Controller
CMO: Arsenio V Deleon M.D., Chief Medical Officer
CHR: Katelyn Andre, Human Resource Coordinator
CNO: Lydia Alaszewski, Chief Nursing Officer
Web address: www.macomb.selectspecialtyhospitals.com/
Control: Corporation, Investor–owned (for–profit) **Service**: Acute long–term care hospital

> **Staffed Beds**: 36

MOUNT PLEASANT—Isabella County

☐ **MCLAREN CENTRAL MICHIGAN (230080)**, 1221 South Drive, Zip 48858–3257; tel. 989/772–6700 **A**1 2 5 10 19 **F**3 12 13 15 18 20 22 26 28 29 30 31 34 35 40 44 45 48 49 50 51 54 57 59 62 64 65 68 70 74 75 76 77 78 79 81 82 85 86 87 89 96 97 107 108 110 111 114 117 118 119 120 121 123 124 129 130 131 132 144 145 146 147 148 **S** McLaren Health Care Corporation, Flint, MI
Primary Contact: William P. Lawrence, President and Chief Executive Officer
CFO: Gregg Beeg, Chief Financial Officer
CMO: Ashok Vashishta M.D., Vice President Medical Affairs
CIO: Nicolette Zalud, Customer Site Manager
CHR: Carolyn Potter, Vice President Human Resources
CNO: Sheri Myers, Vice President Patient Care Services
Web address: www.cmch.org
Control: Other not–for–profit (including NFP Corporation) **Service**: General medical and surgical

> **Staffed Beds**: 78 **Admissions**: 3335 **Census**: 25 **Outpatient Visits**: 129422 **Births**: 526 **Total Expense ($000)**: 86689 **Payroll Expense ($000)**: 35132 **Personnel**: 515

MUNISING—Alger County

MUNISING MEMORIAL HOSPITAL (231308), 1500 Sand Point Road, Zip 49862–1406; tel. 906/387–4110, (Nonreporting) **A**10 18
Primary Contact: Kevin P. Calhoun, Chief Executive Officer
CFO: Wendy Rautio, Chief Financial Officer
CMO: Christine Krueger M.D., Chief of Staff
CHR: Melissa Hall, Human Resources
CNO: Andrea Wills R.N., Chief Nursing Executive
Web address: www.munisingmemorial.org
Control: Other not–for–profit (including NFP Corporation) **Service**: General medical and surgical

> **Staffed Beds**: 25

Many Facility Codes have changed. Please refer to the AHA Guide Code Chart. © 2017 AHA Guide

MI

MUSKEGON—Muskegon County

⊞ **MERCY HEALTH HACKLEY CAMPUS (230066)**, 1700 Clinton Street, Zip 49442–5502, Mailing Address: P.O.Box 3302, 49443–3302; tel. 231/726–3511, (Includes MERCY HEALTH, GENERAL CAMPUS, 1700 Oak Avenue, Muskegon, Michigan, Zip 49442, tel. 231/672–3311; Greg Loomis, Interim President and Chief Operating Officer; MERCY HEALTH, MERCY CAMPUS, 1500 East Sherman Boulevard, Muskegon, Michigan, Zip 49444–1849, tel. 231/672–2000; Greg Loomis, President) **A**1 2 10 13 **F**3 7 11 12 13 15 20 22 24 26 28 29 30 35 36 40 43 45 49 50 51 53 54 56 57 59 61 64 68 70 76 77 79 81 82 84 85 87 89 90 91 93 96 97 98 100 101 102 103 104 105 106 107 108 110 111 114 115 118 119 122 123 124 127 129 130 131 132 144 146 147 148 149 **P**6 8 **S** Trinity Health, Livonia, MI
Primary Contact: Greg Loomis, President
CFO: Gary Allore, Chief Financial Officer
CMO: F. Remington Sprague M.D., Chief Medical Officer
CIO: William Stefl, Director Information Systems
CNO: Kimberly Maguire R.N., Chief Nursing Officer
Web address: www.mercyhealthmuskegon.com
Control: Other not–for–profit (including NFP Corporation) **Service**: General medical and surgical

Staffed Beds: 401 **Admissions**: 18374 **Census**: 203 **Outpatient Visits**: 1016591 **Births**: 1963 **Total Expense ($000)**: 498874 **Payroll Expense ($000)**: 219849 **Personnel**: 3304

⊞ **SELECT SPECIALTY HOSPITAL–MUSKEGON (232021)**, 1700 Clinton Street, 3 South, Zip 49442–5502; tel. 231/728–5811, (Nonreporting) **A**1 10 **S** Select Medical Corporation, Mechanicsburg, PA
Primary Contact: Sharon Purkis, Administrator
Web address: www.greatlakesspecialtyhospital.com
Control: Corporation, Investor–owned (for–profit) **Service**: Acute long–term care hospital

Staffed Beds: 31

SELECT SPECIALTY HOSPITAL–WESTERN MICHIGAN See Select Specialty Hospital–Muskegon

NEW BALTIMORE—Macomb County

HARBOR OAKS HOSPITAL (234021), 35031 23 Mile Road, Zip 48047–3649; tel. 586/725–5777, (Nonreporting) **A**10 **S** Acadia Healthcare Company, Inc., Franklin, TN
Primary Contact: Sari Abromovich, Chief Executive Officer
CFO: Michael Ferguson, Chief Financial Officer
CMO: James D. Adamo M.D., Medical Director
CHR: Zena Ridley, Director Human Resources
CNO: Leeann Duncan, Director Patient Care Services
Web address: www.harboroaks.com
Control: Corporation, Investor–owned (for–profit) **Service**: Psychiatric

Staffed Beds: 45

NEWBERRY—Luce County

★ ⇧ **HELEN NEWBERRY JOY HOSPITAL (231304)**, 502 West Harrie Street, Zip 49868–1209; tel. 906/293–9200, (Total facility includes 39 beds in nursing home–type unit) **A**10 18 21 **F**3 15 28 29 31 34 35 40 45 53 57 59 64 65 75 78 81 87 93 97 107 108 111 114 118 119 127 128 129 130 131 132 133 143 144 148 **P**6
Primary Contact: Scott Pillion, Chief Executive Officer
CFO: Hunter Nostrant, Chief Financial Officer
CMO: Michael Gregory Beaulieu M.D., Chief Medical Officer
CIO: Howard Bliss, Director of Information Systems
CNO: Deborah Baker, Chief Nursing Officer
Web address: www.hnjh.org
Control: County, Government, Nonfederal **Service**: General medical and surgical

Staffed Beds: 64 **Admissions**: 526 **Census**: 45 **Outpatient Visits**: 36951 **Births**: 0 **Total Expense ($000)**: 34865 **Payroll Expense ($000)**: 14456 **Personnel**: 276

NORTHVILLE—Wayne County

☐ **HAWTHORN CENTER**, 18471 Haggerty Road, Zip 48168–9575; tel. 248/735–6771, (Nonreporting) **A**1 3
Primary Contact: George Mellows, Facility Director
CIO: Robert W Bailey, Chief Information Officer
Web address: www.michigan.gov
Control: State, Government, Nonfederal **Service**: Children's hospital psychiatric

Staffed Beds: 69

NOVI—Oakland County

PROVIDENCE – PROVIDENCE PARK HOSPITAL, NOVI CAMPUS See Providence–Providence Park Hospitals, Southfield

ONTONAGON—Ontonagon County

⊞ **ASPIRUS ONTONAGON HOSPITAL, INC. (231309)**, 601 South Seventh Street, Zip 49953–1459; tel. 906/884–8000, (Total facility includes 46 beds in nursing home–type unit) **A**1 10 18 **F**3 15 28 29 31 34 35 40 41 45 47 53 56 59 64 65 68 75 77 78 79 81 85 87 90 93 94 97 107 110 114 119 127 128 131 132 133 147 149 **P**6 **S** Aspirus, Inc., Wausau, WI
Primary Contact: Michael Hauswirth, Chief Executive Officer
CMO: Richard Chaltry M.D., Director Medical Staff
CHR: Gina Linna, Manager Human Resources
CNO: Deanna Wilson, VP Patient Care Services/Site Manager
Web address: www.aspirus.org
Control: Other not–for–profit (including NFP Corporation) **Service**: General medical and surgical

Staffed Beds: 64 **Admissions**: 232 **Census**: 43 **Outpatient Visits**: 14216 **Births**: 0 **Total Expense ($000)**: 15289 **Payroll Expense ($000)**: 5678 **Personnel**: 71

OWOSSO—Shiawassee County

⊞ **MEMORIAL HEALTHCARE (230121)**, 826 West King Street, Zip 48867–2120; tel. 989/723–5211, (Total facility includes 32 beds in nursing home–type unit) **A**1 2 5 10 **F**11 13 15 28 29 30 31 32 34 35 36 38 40 45 50 51 56 57 59 62 63 64 65 69 70 74 75 76 77 78 79 81 82 85 87 89 93 97 98 100 101 102 107 108 110 111 115 119 127 128 129 130 131 132 143 144 146 147 148 **P**6 7
Primary Contact: Brian Long, FACHE, President and Chief Executive Officer
COO: Tim Susterich, Chief Financial Officer and Chief Operating Officer
CFO: Tim Susterich, Chief Financial Officer and Chief Operating Officer
CMO: Wael Salman M.D., Vice President Medical Affairs
CIO: Tom Kurtz, Vice President Information Services and Chief Information Officer
CNO: Jim Nemeth, Senior Vice President of Patient Care Services and Chief Nursing Officer
Web address: www.memorialhealthcare.org
Control: Other not–for–profit (including NFP Corporation) **Service**: General medical and surgical

Staffed Beds: 149 **Admissions**: 3794 **Census**: 77 **Outpatient Visits**: 418425 **Births**: 425 **Total Expense ($000)**: 127639 **Payroll Expense ($000)**: 59437 **Personnel**: 1019

PAW PAW—Van Buren County

⊞ **BRONSON LAKEVIEW HOSPITAL (231332)**, 408 Hazen Street, Zip 49079–1019, Mailing Address: P.O.Box 209, 49079–0209; tel. 269/657–3141 **A**1 10 18 **F**3 6 9 11 12 15 29 30 34 35 36 40 44 50 55 56 57 58 59 64 65 66 68 71 74 75 77 79 81 82 83 84 85 86 87 90 93 97 98 100 101 102 103 107 110 111 115 119 127 129 130 132 135 143 146 147 148 149 **P**6 **S** Bronson Healthcare Group, Kalamazoo, MI
Primary Contact: Kirk Richardson, R.N., Vice President, Chief Operating Officer, and Chief Nursing Officer
COO: Kirk Richardson R.N., Vice President, Chief Operating Officer, and Chief Nursing Officer
CFO: Becky East CPA, Senior Vice President, Chief Financial Officer
CMO: Matthew Dommer M.D., Chief Medical Officer
CIO: Paul Peabody, Vice President Information Technology and Chief Information Officer
CHR: John Hayden, Senior Vice President and Chief Human Resources Officer
CNO: Kirk Richardson R.N., Vice President, Chief Operating Officer, and Chief Nursing Officer
Web address: www.bronsonhealth.com/lakeview
Control: Other not–for–profit (including NFP Corporation) **Service**: General medical and surgical

Staffed Beds: 35 **Admissions**: 793 **Census**: 12 **Outpatient Visits**: 96643 **Births**: 0 **Total Expense ($000)**: 47412 **Payroll Expense ($000)**: 25618 **Personnel**: 298

MI

Hospital, Medicare Provider Number, Address, Telephone, Approval, Facility, and Physician Codes, Health Care System

★ American Hospital Association (AHA) membership
☐ The Joint Commission accreditation
○ Healthcare Facilities Accreditation Program
◇ DNV Healthcare Inc. accreditation
⇧ Center for Improvement in Healthcare Quality Accreditation
△ Commission on Accreditation of Rehabilitation Facilities (CARF) accreditation

PETOSKEY—Emmet County

☐ **MCLAREN NORTHERN MICHIGAN (230105)**, 416 Connable Avenue, Zip 49770–2297; tel. 231/487–4000 **A**1 2 5 10 **F**3 13 15 17 18 20 22 24 26 28 29 30 31 32 34 35 36 38 40 42 44 45 48 49 50 51 53 57 58 59 60 64 68 70 74 75 76 77 78 79 81 82 85 86 87 89 90 91 93 94 96 107 108 110 111 114 115 119 120 121 123 124 129 130 132 135 146 148 149 **S** McLaren Health Care Corporation, Flint, MI
Primary Contact: David M. Zechman, FACHE, President and Chief Executive Officer
CFO: David Bellamy, Chief Financial Officer
CMO: Kirk Lufkin M.D., VPMA
CIO: David Bellamy, Chief Financial Officer
CHR: Gene Kaminski, Vice President Human Resources and Hospitality Services
CNO: Jennifer Woods R.N., MSN, Chief Nursing Officer
Web address: www.northernhealth.org
Control: Other not–for–profit (including NFP Corporation) **Service**: General medical and surgical

Staffed Beds: 188 Admissions: 10102 Census: 108 Outpatient Visits: 188342 Births: 569 Total Expense ($000): 229467 Payroll Expense ($000): 78023 Personnel: 1308

PIGEON—Huron County

☒ **SCHEURER HOSPITAL (231310)**, 170 North Caseville Road, Zip 48755–9781; tel. 989/453–3223, (Total facility includes 19 beds in nursing home–type unit) **A**1 5 10 18 **F**3 7 8 10 11 15 28 29 30 31 32 34 35 40 44 45 50 53 54 56 57 59 64 65 68 69 75 77 78 79 81 85 86 87 91 93 97 107 108 110 115 119 125 127 130 131 132 133 134 144 146 149 **P**6
Primary Contact: Terrance Lerash, President and Chief Executive Officer
CFO: Terry Lutz, Chief Financial Officer
CMO: Ross Ramsey M.D., Chief of Staff
CIO: Carleen Giddings, Information Technology System Leader
CHR: Gregory S. Foy, Human Resources System Leader
CNO: Kendra Kretzschmer, Patient Care System Leader
Web address: www.scheurer.org
Control: Other not–for–profit (including NFP Corporation) **Service**: General medical and surgical

Staffed Beds: 44 Admissions: 580 Census: 28 Outpatient Visits: 45594 Births: 0 Total Expense ($000): 40557 Payroll Expense ($000): 19451 Personnel: 351

PONTIAC—Oakland County

☐ **DOCTORS' HOSPITAL OF MICHIGAN (230013)**, 461 West Huron Street, Zip 48341–1601; tel. 248/857–7200, (Nonreporting) **A**1 3 10
Primary Contact: Robert Barrow, Chief Executive Officer
COO: Dennis Franks, Vice President Operations
CFO: Dennis Franks, Interim Chief Financial Officer
CMO: Ray Breitenbach M.D., Chief of Staff
CIO: Albert Sinisi, Director Information Systems
Web address: www.dhofm.com
Control: Other not–for–profit (including NFP Corporation) **Service**: General medical and surgical

Staffed Beds: 106

☐ ○ **MCLAREN OAKLAND (230207)**, 50 North Perry Street, Zip 48342–2253; tel. 248/338–5000, (Total facility includes 120 beds in nursing home–type unit) **A**1 2 3 10 11 12 13 **F**3 4 7 8 11 12 14 15 18 20 24 26 28 29 30 31 32 33 34 35 36 40 42 43 44 45 50 53 54 57 59 62 63 64 65 66 68 70 74 75 77 78 79 81 82 85 90 92 93 94 98 103 107 108 111 114 118 119 124 128 129 130 131 132 135 136 137 138 139 140 141 142 143 144 146 148 **P**4 8 **S** McLaren Health Care Corporation, Flint, MI
Primary Contact: Chad M. Grant, President and Chief Executive Officer
COO: Nicholle Mehr, Vice President Operations
CFO: Matthew LeGault, Chief Financial Officer
CMO: Steven Calkin D.O., Vice President Medical Affairs
CIO: Darin Boka, Chief Information Officer
CHR: Dwan Cosby, Manager Human Resources
CNO: Calandra Anderson, Vice President Patient Care and Chief Nursing Officer
Web address: www.mclaren.org/oakland
Control: Other not–for–profit (including NFP Corporation) **Service**: General medical and surgical

Staffed Beds: 263 Admissions: 5625 Census: 197 Outpatient Visits: 182199 Births: 0 Total Expense ($000): 180440 Payroll Expense ($000): 71874 Personnel: 1235

PIONEER SPECIALTY HOSPITAL (230304), 50 North Perry Street, 6th Floor, Zip 48342–2217; tel. 248/338–5430 (Nonreporting)
Primary Contact: Anu Locricchio, Chief Executive Officer
Web address: www.pioneerspecialtyhospital.com
Control: Individual, Investor–owned (for–profit) **Service**: Acute long–term care hospital

Staffed Beds: 30

☒ **SELECT SPECIALTY HOSPITAL–PONTIAC (232030)**, 44405 Woodward Avenue, 8th Floor, Zip 48341–5023; tel. 248/452–5252, (Nonreporting) **A**1 10 **S** Select Medical Corporation, Mechanicsburg, PA
Primary Contact: Peggy Kingston, Chief Executive Officer
CMO: Fadi Salloum M.D., Medical Director
CNO: Cathy Boyd, Chief Nursing Officer
Web address: www.selectspecialtyhospitals.com/company/locations/pontiac.aspx
Control: Corporation, Investor–owned (for–profit) **Service**: Acute long–term care hospital

Staffed Beds: 30

☒ **ST. JOSEPH MERCY OAKLAND (230029)**, 44405 Woodward Avenue, Zip 48341–5023; tel. 248/858–3000 **A**1 2 3 5 10 13 **F**3 8 11 12 13 15 17 18 20 22 24 26 28 29 30 31 34 35 36 39 40 41 43 44 45 46 48 49 50 53 54 55 56 57 58 59 61 64 65 66 68 70 72 74 75 76 77 78 79 81 82 84 85 86 87 89 90 93 94 96 97 98 100 102 103 105 107 108 110 111 114 115 119 126 129 130 131 132 135 144 146 147 148 149 150 **P**6 **S** Trinity Health, Livonia, MI
Primary Contact: Shannon Striebich, Chief Executive Officer
CFO: Michael Gusho, Chief Financial Officer
CMO: Michael Smith M.D., Vice President Medical Affairs
CIO: Robert Jones, Director Management Information Systems
CHR: Ane McNeil, Vice President Human Resources
CNO: Douglas R Dascenzo MSN, R.N., Chief Nursing Officer
Web address: www.stjoesoakland.com
Control: Church operated, Nongovernment, not–for–profit **Service**: General medical and surgical

Staffed Beds: 422 Admissions: 19307 Census: 251 Outpatient Visits: 364954 Births: 1865 Total Expense ($000): 400545 Payroll Expense ($000): 155316 Personnel: 2449

PORT HURON—St. Clair County

☒ **LAKE HURON MEDICAL CENTER (230031)**, 2601 Electric Avenue, Zip 48060–6518; tel. 810/985–1500 **A**1 2 10 **F**3 12 15 18 20 28 29 30 31 34 35 37 40 45 49 50 54 56 57 58 59 61 64 66 70 74 75 77 78 79 81 82 85 86 87 90 91 93 96 97 107 108 110 114 118 119 120 121 123 130 131 132 135 144 146 147 148 149 **P**6 8 **S** Prime Healthcare, Ontario, CA
Primary Contact: Jay De los Reyes, Chief Executive Officer
COO: Ken Sanger R.N., Chief Nursing Officer and Chief Operations Officer
CFO: Chris Fulks, Vice President Finance
CMO: Sridhar Reddy M.D., Chief Medical Officer
CIO: Jefferey Wagner, Director, Information Technology
CHR: Debra A Seifert, Director Human Resources
CNO: Ken Sanger R.N., Chief Nursing Officer and Chief Operations Officer
Web address: www.mymercy.us
Control: Corporation, Investor–owned (for–profit) **Service**: General medical and surgical

Staffed Beds: 119 Admissions: 4601 Census: 48 Outpatient Visits: 111890 Births: 0 Total Expense ($000): 73741 Payroll Expense ($000): 29160 Personnel: 521

☒ **MCLAREN PORT HURON (230216)**, 1221 Pine Grove Avenue, Zip 48060–3511; tel. 810/987–5000 **A**1 2 10 **F**1 3 4 5 11 12 13 15 16 17 18 20 22 24 26 28 29 30 31 32 34 35 36 39 40 43 44 45 46 48 49 50 51 54 56 57 58 59 61 64 65 66 67 68 70 71 72 73 74 75 76 77 78 79 80 81 82 84 85 86 87 88 89 90 92 93 94 96 97 98 99 100 101 102 103 104 107 108 110 111 114 115 116 117 118 119 120 121 126 128 129 130 131 132 134 135 144 145 146 147 148 149 **P**6 **S** McLaren Health Care Corporation, Flint, MI
Primary Contact: Jennifer Montgomery, R.N., FACHE, President and Chief Executive Officer
COO: John Liston, Chief Operating Officer
CFO: Bridget Sholtis, Chief Financial Officer
CMO: Michael W Tawney D.O., Vice President Medical Affairs
CIO: Abby Bishop, Chief Information Officer
CHR: Doris A Seidl, Vice President Human Resources
CNO: Christine R Sansom, Chief Nursing Officer
Web address: www.porthuronhospital.org
Control: Other not–for–profit (including NFP Corporation) **Service**: General medical and surgical

Staffed Beds: 186 Admissions: 11061 Census: 118 Outpatient Visits: 206215 Births: 1057 Total Expense ($000): 172153 Payroll Expense ($000): 69759 Personnel: 1155

MI

REED CITY—Osceola County

✠ **SPECTRUM HEALTH REED CITY HOSPITAL (231323)**, 300 North Patterson Road, Zip 49677–8041, Mailing Address: P.O.Box 75, 49677–0075; tel. 231/832–3271, (Total facility includes 50 beds in nursing home–type unit) **A**1 5 10 18 **F**3 8 15 28 29 31 34 35 40 45 53 54 57 59 64 65 70 75 77 78 79 81 84 85 86 87 93 96 97 107 108 110 111 115 119 120 121 123 124 127 128 129 130 131 133 146 147 149 **P**6 **S** Spectrum Health, Grand Rapids, MI
Primary Contact: Mary Kay VanDriel, President
COO: Cathy Rybicki, Chief Operating Officer
CFO: Thomas Knoerl, Vice President Finance
CMO: Thomas Campana M.D., Chief of Staff
CIO: Brandi Johnson, Site Manager Technology Information Systems
CHR: Kris Miller, Senior Human Resources Business Partner
Web address: www.spectrumhealth.org/reedcity
Control: Other not–for–profit (including NFP Corporation) **Service:** General medical and surgical

Staffed Beds: 75 **Admissions:** 868 **Census:** 56 **Outpatient Visits:** 311963 **Births:** 0 **Total Expense ($000):** 56322 **Payroll Expense ($000):** 18026 **Personnel:** 363

ROCHESTER—Oakland County

✠ △ **CRITTENTON HOSPITAL MEDICAL CENTER (230254)**, 1101 West University Drive, Zip 48307–1831; tel. 248/652–5000, (Nonreporting) **A**1 3 5 7 10 **S** Ascension Healthcare, Saint Louis, MO
Primary Contact: Margaret Dimond, Ph.D., President and Chief Executive Officer
CFO: Donna Kopinski, Chief Financial Officer
CMO: Sheryl Wissman M.D., Chief Medical Officer
CIO: Ralph Tenney, Chief Information Officer
CHR: Ann Vano, Vice President, Human Resources
Web address: www.crittenton.com
Control: Other not–for–profit (including NFP Corporation) **Service:** General medical and surgical

Staffed Beds: 254

ROMEO—Macomb County

ST. JOSEPH'S MERCY–NORTH See Henry Ford Macomb Hospitals, Clinton Township

ROYAL OAK—Oakland County

✠ **BEAUMONT HOSPITAL – ROYAL OAK (230130)**, 3601 West Thirteen Mile Road, Zip 48073–6712; tel. 248/898–5000, (Includes BEAUMONT CHILDREN'S HOSPITAL, 3601 West 13 Mile Road, Royal Oak, Michigan, Zip 48073–6712, tel. 248/898–5000) **A**1 2 3 5 8 10 **F**3 6 8 11 12 13 15 17 18 19 20 22 24 26 28 29 30 31 32 34 35 36 37 38 39 40 41 43 44 45 46 47 48 49 50 51 54 55 56 57 58 59 60 61 62 63 64 65 66 70 71 72 73 74 75 76 77 78 79 80 81 82 83 84 85 86 87 88 89 90 91 92 93 94 95 96 97 98 99 100 101 102 103 104 105 107 108 109 110 111 114 115 116 117 118 119 120 121 123 124 126 129 130 131 132 134 135 138 139 141 142 143 144 145 146 147 148 149 150 **P**1 6 **S** Beaumont Health, Southfield, MI
Primary Contact: Rosanna Morris, Hospital President
COO: Carolyn Wilson R.N., Chief Operating Officer
CFO: John Kerndl, Executive Vice President and Chief Financial Officer
CMO: Leslie Rocher, Senior Vice President and Chief Medical Officer
CIO: Subra Sripada, Executive Vice President, Chief Transportation Officer and Chief Information Officer
CHR: Michael L Dixon, Director, Human Resources
CNO: Maureen Bowman, Vice President and Chief Nursing Officer
Web address: www.beaumont.org
Control: Other not–for–profit (including NFP Corporation) **Service:** General medical and surgical

Staffed Beds: 1100 **Admissions:** 61407 **Census:** 861 **Outpatient Visits:** 1556665 **Births:** 6626 **Total Expense ($000):** 1211201 **Payroll Expense ($000):** 460861 **Personnel:** 9364

SAGINAW—Saginaw County

✠ **ALEDA E. LUTZ VETERANS AFFAIRS MEDICAL CENTER**, 1500 Weiss Street, Zip 48602–5298; tel. 989/497–2500, (Total facility includes 81 beds in nursing home–type unit) **A**1 3 **F**3 5 8 11 12 15 18 29 30 31 34 35 36 38 39 44 45 50 53 54 56 57 58 59 61 63 64 68 74 75 77 78 81 82 83 84 85 86 87 93 94 97 100 101 102 103 104 107 108 119 127 128 130 131 132 133 135 136 137 138 139 140 141 142 143 144 146 147 148 149 **P**6 **S** Department of Veterans Affairs, Washington, DC
Primary Contact: Ginny L. Creasman, Director
COO: Stephanie Young, Associate Director
CFO: Jeff Drew, Fiscal Officer
CMO: Gregory Movsesian M.D., Acting Chief of Staff
CIO: Angie Schmus, Chief Information Technology
CHR: Thomas Stredney, Chief Human Resources Management Service
CNO: Penny Holland, Associate Director for Patient Care Services
Web address: www.saginaw.va.gov/
Control: Veterans Affairs, Government, federal **Service:** General medical and surgical

Staffed Beds: 89 **Admissions:** 1038 **Census:** 39 **Outpatient Visits:** 430408 **Births:** 0 **Total Expense ($000):** 194494 **Payroll Expense ($000):** 101749 **Personnel:** 1138

★ ○ △ **COVENANT HEALTHCARE (230070)**, 1447 North Harrison Street, Zip 48602–4727; tel. 989/583–0000, (Includes COVENANT MEDICAL CENTER–COOPER, 700 Cooper Avenue, Saginaw, Michigan, Zip 48602–5399, tel. 989/583–0000; Edward Bruff, President and Chief Executive Officer; COVENANT MEDICAL CENTER–HARRISON, 1447 North Harrison Street, Saginaw, Michigan, Zip 48602–4785, tel. 989/583–0000; Edward Bruff, President and Chief Executive Officer) (Total facility includes 20 beds in nursing home–type unit) **A**2 3 5 7 10 11 **F**3 8 11 12 13 15 17 18 19 20 22 24 25 26 27 28 29 30 31 35 36 40 41 42 43 45 46 47 48 49 50 54 57 58 59 60 61 62 63 64 65 70 72 74 75 76 77 78 79 81 82 83 84 86 87 88 89 90 91 92 93 94 97 107 108 110 111 113 114 115 118 119 120 121 123 124 126 128 129 130 131 132 135 143 144 146 147 148 **P**7 8
Primary Contact: Edward Bruff, President and Chief Executive Officer
COO: Daniel M George, Executive Vice President, Operations
CFO: Kevin Albosta, Vice President, Chief Financial Officer
CMO: John Kosanovich M.D., Executive Vice President Physician Enterprise and Chief Executive Officer, Covenant Medical Group
CHR: Kevin Birchmeier, Director Human Resources
CNO: Beth Charlton, Vice President Patient Services and Chief Nursing Officer
Web address: www.covenanthealthcare.com
Control: Other not–for–profit (including NFP Corporation) **Service:** General medical and surgical

Staffed Beds: 532 **Admissions:** 27778 **Census:** 401 **Outpatient Visits:** 444610 **Births:** 3103 **Total Expense ($000):** 571986 **Payroll Expense ($000):** 249287 **Personnel:** 4197

☐ **HEALTHSOURCE SAGINAW, INC. (230275)**, 3340 Hospital Road, Zip 48603–9622; tel. 989/790–7700, (Total facility includes 213 beds in nursing home–type unit) **A**1 5 10 **F**4 5 64 66 90 91 93 98 99 100 101 102 104 128 130 143 146 **P**6
Primary Contact: Lisa Lapham, President and Chief Executive Officer
CFO: Glen Chipman, Chief Financial Officer
CMO: Daniel Duffy D.O., Chief Medical Director
CIO: Greg Sieg, Director Information Technology
CHR: Krystal Hadaway, Director Human Resources
CNO: Susan Graham R.N., Nurse Executive
Web address: www.healthsourcesaginaw.org
Control: Other not–for–profit (including NFP Corporation) **Service:** Psychiatric

Staffed Beds: 343 **Admissions:** 4175 **Census:** 281 **Outpatient Visits:** 11107 **Births:** 0 **Total Expense ($000):** 49108 **Payroll Expense ($000):** 23044 **Personnel:** 625

✠ **SELECT SPECIALTY HOSPITAL–SAGINAW (232033)**, 1447 North Harrison Street, 8th Floor, Zip 48602–4785; tel. 989/583–4235, (Nonreporting) **A**1 10 **S** Select Medical Corporation, Mechanicsburg, PA
Primary Contact: Matthew J. Campbell, Chief Executive Officer
Web address: www.selectspecialtyhospitals.com/company/locations/saginaw.aspx
Control: Corporation, Investor–owned (for–profit) **Service:** Acute long–term care hospital

Staffed Beds: 32

MI

Hospital, Medicare Provider Number, Address, Telephone, Approval, Facility, and Physician Codes, Health Care System

★ American Hospital Association (AHA) membership
☐ The Joint Commission accreditation
○ Healthcare Facilities Accreditation Program
◇ DNV Healthcare Inc. accreditation
⇑ Center for Improvement in Healthcare Quality Accreditation
△ Commission on Accreditation of Rehabilitation Facilities (CARF) accreditation

MI

✠ **ST. MARY'S OF MICHIGAN (230077)**, 800 South Washington Avenue, Zip 48601–2594; tel. 989/907–8000 **A**1 2 3 5 10 **F**2 3 11 12 15 17 18 20 22 24 26 28 29 30 31 34 35 40 42 43 44 45 49 50 54 57 58 59 64 66 68 70 74 77 78 79 80 81 82 84 85 86 87 92 93 96 97 100 102 107 108 110 111 114 115 118 119 120 121 123 124 126 129 130 132 146 149 **P**6 8 **S** Ascension Healthcare, Saint Louis, MO
Primary Contact: Chris Palazzolo, Health System President and Chief Executive Officer Mid–Michigan
CFO: Nancy Haywood, Chief Financial Officer
CMO: Raghu Sarvepalli M.D., Vice President of Medical Affairs
CIO: Daniel Stross, Chief Information Officer
CHR: Paula Coffee, Director Human Resources
CNO: Bernie Jore, Chief Nursing Officer
Web address: www.stmarysofmichigan.org
Control: Church operated, Nongovernment, not–for–profit **Service**: General medical and surgical

Staffed Beds: 232 **Admissions**: 9801 **Census**: 135 **Outpatient Visits**: 203507 **Births**: 0 **Total Expense ($000)**: 257579 **Payroll Expense ($000)**: 101503 **Personnel**: 1389

SAINT IGNACE—Mackinac County

★ ⇑ **MACKINAC STRAITS HEALTH SYSTEM, INC. (231306)**, 1140 North State Street, Zip 49781–1048; tel. 906/643–8585, (Total facility includes 48 beds in nursing home–type unit) **A**10 18 21 **F**8 15 28 29 31 32 40 42 43 45 51 54 56 59 64 65 74 75 77 78 79 81 91 93 97 107 110 111 114 119 127 128 130 133 135 144 146 147 148
Primary Contact: Karen Cheeseman, Chief Executive Officer
CFO: Jason Anderson, Chief Financial Officer
CMO: Matthew Bowes M.D., Chief of Staff
CNO: Dawn Stageman–Tyrer R.N., Chief Nursing Officer
Web address: www.mackinacstraitshealth.org
Control: Other not–for–profit (including NFP Corporation) **Service**: General medical and surgical

Staffed Beds: 63 **Admissions**: 300 **Census**: 49 **Outpatient Visits**: 35479 **Births**: 0 **Total Expense ($000)**: 39749 **Payroll Expense ($000)**: 13721 **Personnel**: 185

SAINT JOHNS—Clinton County

✠ **SPARROW CLINTON HOSPITAL (231326)**, 805 South Oakland Street, Zip 48879–2253; tel. 989/227–3400 **A**1 10 18 **F**3 11 15 18 31 32 34 35 40 45 50 53 57 59 64 68 70 75 77 78 79 81 85 93 107 108 110 111 114 119 129 130 131 133 146 148 149 **P**6 **S** Sparrow Health System, Lansing, MI
Primary Contact: Edward Bruun, President and Chief Executive Officer
COO: Kevin A Price, Vice President and Chief Operating Officer
CFO: Mark Brisboe, VP and Chief Financial Officer
CMO: Christopher Beal M.D., Chief of Staff
CNO: Beth Ann Daugherty R.N., M.P.H., Vice President Care Services and Chief Nursing Executive
Web address: www.sparrowclinton.org
Control: Other not–for–profit (including NFP Corporation) **Service**: General medical and surgical

Staffed Beds: 25 **Admissions**: 754 **Census**: 6 **Outpatient Visits**: 85771 **Births**: 0 **Total Expense ($000)**: 39911 **Payroll Expense ($000)**: 14508 **Personnel**: 221

SAINT JOSEPH—Berrien County

✠ **LAKELAND MEDICAL CENTER, ST. JOSEPH (230021)**, 1234 Napier Avenue, Zip 49085–2158; tel. 269/983–8300, (Nonreporting) (Includes LAKELAND HOSPITAL, NILES, 31 North Saint Joseph Avenue, Niles, Michigan, Zip 49120, tel. 269/683–5510; Debra Johnson, R.N., Chief Administrator) **A**1 2 10 13 **S** Lakeland Health, Saint Joseph, MI
Primary Contact: Loren Hamel, M.D., President and Chief Executive Officer
CFO: Timothy Calhoun, Vice President Finance and Chief Financial Officer
CMO: Stephen Hempel M.D., Interim Medical Staff
CIO: Emily Gallay, Vice President and Chief Information Officer
Web address: www.lakelandhealth.org
Control: Other not–for–profit (including NFP Corporation) **Service**: General medical and surgical

Staffed Beds: 303

SALINE—Washtenaw County

☐ **CENTER FOR FORENSIC PSYCHIATRY (234041)**, 8303 Platt Rd, Zip 48176–9773, Mailing Address: P.O.Box 2060, Ann Arbor, 48106–2060; tel. 734/429–2531 (Nonreporting) **A**1 10
Primary Contact: Diane Heisel, Acting Director
Web address: www.michigan.gov
Control: County, Government, Nonfederal **Service**: Psychiatric

Staffed Beds: 210

SANDUSKY—Sanilac County

MCKENZIE HEALTH SYSTEM (231314), 120 North Delaware Street, Zip 48471–1087; tel. 810/648–3770, (Nonreporting) **A**10 18
Primary Contact: Steve Barnett, President and Chief Executive Officer
COO: Billi Jo Hennika, Vice President Operations
CFO: Amy Ruedisueli, Vice President of Finance
CMO: Michael Merkler, Chief of Staff
CHR: Carrie Krampits, Director Human Resources
CNO: Patricia Schafsnitz, Director of Nursing Services
Web address: www.mckenziehealth.org
Control: Other not–for–profit (including NFP Corporation) **Service**: General medical and surgical

Staffed Beds: 25

SAULT SAINTE MARIE—Chippewa County

★ ⇑ **WAR MEMORIAL HOSPITAL (230239)**, 500 Osborn Boulevard, Zip 49783–1884; tel. 906/635–4460, (Total facility includes 51 beds in nursing home–type unit) **A**5 10 20 21 **F**3 11 12 13 15 18 28 29 30 31 34 35 36 38 40 43 44 50 51 53 54 56 57 59 60 61 64 65 66 68 70 74 75 76 77 78 79 81 82 85 87 92 93 96 97 98 100 101 103 104 107 108 110 111 115 119 127 128 129 130 131 132 133 135 143 144 146 147 148 **P**6
Primary Contact: David B. Jahn, President and Chief Executive Officer
COO: Marla Bunker, Vice President Nursing and Chief Operating Officer
CFO: Kevin Kalchik, Chief Financial Officer
CMO: Paula Rechner M.D., Chief Medical Officer
CIO: Sandy DePlonty, Senior Director Clinical Services
CHR: Susan Sliger, Director Human Resources
CNO: Marla Bunker, Vice President Nursing and Chief Operating Officer
Web address: www.warmemorialhospital.org
Control: Other not–for–profit (including NFP Corporation) **Service**: General medical and surgical

Staffed Beds: 133 **Admissions**: 3298 **Census**: 89 **Outpatient Visits**: 181598 **Births**: 325 **Total Expense ($000)**: 104225 **Payroll Expense ($000)**: 47530 **Personnel**: 853

SHELBY—Oceana County

✠ **MERCY HEALTH, LAKESHORE CAMPUS (231320)**, 72 South State Street, Zip 49455–1299; tel. 231/861–2156 **A**1 10 18 **F**3 11 15 29 30 34 35 40 45 47 50 57 59 68 81 83 84 85 87 89 97 107 110 111 114 119 127 129 131 132 146 **S** Trinity Health, Livonia, MI
Primary Contact: Jay Bryan, President and Chief Executive Officer
CFO: Mark Gross, Senior Business Director Finance
Web address: www.mercyhealthmuskegon.com
Control: Other not–for–profit (including NFP Corporation) **Service**: General medical and surgical

Staffed Beds: 24 **Admissions**: 284 **Census**: 3 **Outpatient Visits**: 82289 **Births**: 0 **Total Expense ($000)**: 24441 **Payroll Expense ($000)**: 12775 **Personnel**: 192

SHERIDAN—Montcalm County

★ **SHERIDAN COMMUNITY HOSPITAL (231312)**, 301 North Main Street, Zip 48884–9235, Mailing Address: P.O.Box 279, 48884–0279; tel. 989/291–3261, (Nonreporting) **A**5 10 18
Primary Contact: Randolph K. Flechsig, Administrator
COO: Steve Scott, Chief Operating Officer
CFO: Randolph K Flechsig, Administrator
CMO: Maria Charlotte Alvarez M.D., Chief of Staff
CIO: David Bussler, Chief Information Officer
CHR: Sharon Bowers R.N., Manager of Community, Public and Employee Relations
CNO: Kim Christensen, Interim Chief Nursing Executive
Web address: www.sheridanhospital.com
Control: Other not–for–profit (including NFP Corporation) **Service**: General medical and surgical

Staffed Beds: 22

MI

SOUTH HAVEN—Van Buren County

☒ **BRONSON SOUTH HAVEN HOSPITAL (230085)**, 955 South Bailey Avenue, Zip 49090–6743; tel. 269/637–5271 **A**1 10 **F**3 11 15 18 28 29 30 31 34 35 36 40 41 45 50 53 54 57 59 62 65 68 70 75 77 78 79 81 82 85 86 87 89 91 93 96 97 107 108 110 111 114 115 117 119 127 129 130 131 132 135 144 146 148 149 **P**4 **S** Bronson Healthcare Group, Kalamazoo, MI
Primary Contact: Joanne Schroeder, President and Chief Executive Officer
CFO: Mark Gross, Executive Vice President and Chief Financial Officer
CMO: Allan Caudill M.D., Chief of Staff
CIO: Dennis Sorenson, Supervisor Information Technology
CHR: Kim Wise, Director Human Resources
CNO: Donna Cassidy, Chief Nursing Executive
Web address: www.sh–hs.org
Control: Hospital district or authority, Government, Nonfederal **Service**: General medical and surgical

Staffed Beds: 49 Admissions: 667 Census: 5 Outpatient Visits: 143605 Births: 0 Total Expense ($000): 43261 Payroll Expense ($000): 20158 Personnel: 268

SOUTH HAVEN COMMUNITY HOSPITAL See Bronson South Haven Hospital

SOUTHFIELD—Oakland County

★ ○ **OAKLAND REGIONAL HOSPITAL (230301)**, 22401 Foster Winter Drive, Zip 48075–3724; tel. 248/423–5100, (Total facility includes 26 beds in nursing home–type unit) **A**10 11 **F**12 45 64 79 81 82 85 87 90 93 111 115 119 128 130 149
Primary Contact: Amelia Jones, Chief Operating Officer and Acting Chief Executive Officer
COO: Amelia Jones, Chief Operating Officer
CMO: John Jack Ryan M.D., Chief Medical Officer
CIO: William Moncrief, ORH IT Client Executive
CHR: Gordon Meyer, Director Human Resources
CNO: Lola Evans, Director of Nursing
Web address: www.oaklandregionalhospital.com
Control: Corporation, Investor–owned (for–profit) **Service**: General medical and surgical

Staffed Beds: 71 Admissions: 635 Census: 21 Outpatient Visits: 10057 Births: 0 Total Expense ($000): 26517 Payroll Expense ($000): 7229 Personnel: 157

☒ **PROVIDENCE–PROVIDENCE PARK HOSPITALS (230019)**, 16001 West Nine Mile Road, Zip 48075; tel. 248/849–3400, (Includes PROVIDENCE – PROVIDENCE PARK HOSPITAL, NOVI CAMPUS, 47601 Grand River Avebue, Novi, Michigan, Zip 48374–1233, tel. 248/465–4100; Joseph R Hurshe, President) **A**1 2 3 5 10 **F**3 5 8 9 11 12 13 15 17 18 20 22 24 26 28 29 30 31 34 35 36 38 39 40 43 44 45 46 47 48 49 50 51 54 55 56 57 58 59 60 61 63 64 65 66 68 70 72 74 75 76 77 78 79 80 81 82 84 85 86 87 89 90 92 93 97 98 100 101 102 103 105 107 108 110 111 114 115 116 117 118 119 120 121 123 124 126 129 130 131 132 135 141 143 146 147 148 149 150 **S** Ascension Healthcare, Saint Louis, MO
Primary Contact: Joseph R. Hurshe, President
CFO: Douglas Winner, Chief Financial Officer, Acute Care Operations
CHR: Ann Vano, Vice President Human Resources
Web address: www.ascension.org/michigan
Control: Church operated, Nongovernment, not–for–profit **Service**: General medical and surgical

Staffed Beds: 635 Admissions: 33150 Census: 409 Outpatient Visits: 318865 Births: 3809 Total Expense ($000): 681100 Payroll Expense ($000): 248474 Personnel: 3542

☒ **STRAITH HOSPITAL FOR SPECIAL SURGERY (230071)**, 23901 Lahser Road, Zip 48033–6035; tel. 248/357–3360, (Nonreporting) **A**1 10
Primary Contact: Jan Rys, Chief Executive Officer
CFO: Bradley Bescoe, Chief Financial Officer
CNO: Michelle Holder, Nurse Executive
Web address: www.straith.org/
Control: Other not–for–profit (including NFP Corporation) **Service**: Surgical

Staffed Beds: 24

STANDISH—Arenac County

☒ **ST. MARY'S OF MICHIGAN STANDISH HOSPITAL (231305)**, 805 West Cedar Street, Zip 48658–9526; tel. 989/846–4521, (Nonreporting) **A**1 5 10 18 **S** Ascension Healthcare, Saint Louis, MO
Primary Contact: Chris Palazzolo, President and Chief Executive Officer
CFO: Tony Doud, Controller
CMO: Jaya Sankaran M.D., Chief of Staff
CIO: Tammy Copes, Director Information Systems
CHR: Renee Reetz, Director Human Resources
Web address: www.stmarysofmichigan.org/standish
Control: Other not–for–profit (including NFP Corporation) **Service**: General medical and surgical

Staffed Beds: 64

STURGIS—St. Joseph County

★ ⇑ **STURGIS HOSPITAL (230096)**, 916 Myrtle Street, Zip 49091–2326; tel. 269/651–7824 **A**10 21 **F**3 11 13 15 28 29 30 31 34 35 40 49 50 57 59 62 63 64 65 68 70 75 76 77 79 81 82 85 87 89 93 97 102 107 108 110 115 118 119 127 129 130 132 144 145 146 147 148 149 **P**6 **S** QHR, Brentwood, TN
Primary Contact: Robert J. LaBarge, President and Chief Executive Officer
CFO: Robert J. Morin, Vice President Finance and Chief Financial Officer
CMO: Bharat Vakharia M.D., President Medical Staff
CIO: Rita Denison, Director of Information Systems
CHR: Mary Kay Schultz, Director Human Resources
CNO: Charlotte J Pavilanis R.N., Vice President of Clinical Services and Chief Nursing Officer
Web address: www.sturgishospital.com
Control: Other not–for–profit (including NFP Corporation) **Service**: General medical and surgical

Staffed Beds: 49 Admissions: 1497 Census: 11 Outpatient Visits: 161602 Births: 354 Total Expense ($000): 48757 Payroll Expense ($000): 21665 Personnel: 284

TAWAS CITY—Iosco County

☒ **ST. JOSEPH HEALTH SYSTEM (230100)**, 200 Hemlock Street, Zip 48763–9237, Mailing Address: P.O.Box 659, 48764–0659; tel. 989/362–3411, (Nonreporting) **A**1 10 20 **S** Ascension Healthcare, Saint Louis, MO
Primary Contact: Ann M. Balfour, R.N., President
CFO: Tony Doud, Controller
CIO: Daniel Stross, Chief Information Officer
CHR: Nancy Bodenner, Director Human Resources
Web address: www.sjhsys.org
Control: Other not–for–profit (including NFP Corporation) **Service**: General medical and surgical

Staffed Beds: 20

TAYLOR—Wayne County

☒ **BEAUMONT HOSPITAL – TAYLOR (230270)**, 10000 Telegraph Road, Zip 48180–3330; tel. 313/295–5000 **A**1 3 5 10 **F**3 11 15 29 30 34 35 37 38 39 40 44 46 49 50 56 57 59 61 64 65 68 70 74 75 79 81 82 85 86 87 90 92 93 96 98 100 101 102 103 104 105 107 108 111 114 117 118 119 130 131 132 135 146 148 149 **P**6 8 **S** Beaumont Health, Southfield, MI
Primary Contact: Lee Ann Odom, Division President
COO: Carolyn Wilson R.N., Chief Operating Officer
CFO: Mark Deming, Administrator, Finance and Support
CMO: Kassem Charara, Chief Medical Officer
CIO: Subra Sripada, Exec. Vice President, Chief Transformation Officer and Chief Information Officer
CHR: Karen Krolicki, Director, Human Resources
CNO: Kristine Marie Donahue, Administrator, Clinical Operations
Web address: www.beaumont.org
Control: Other not–for–profit (including NFP Corporation) **Service**: General medical and surgical

Staffed Beds: 189 Admissions: 7380 Census: 123 Outpatient Visits: 77500 Births: 0 Total Expense ($000): 135759 Payroll Expense ($000): 58956 Personnel: 987

Hospital, Medicare Provider Number, Address, Telephone, Approval, Facility, and Physician Codes, Health Care System

★ American Hospital Association (AHA) membership
□ The Joint Commission accreditation
○ Healthcare Facilities Accreditation Program
◇ DNV Healthcare Inc. accreditation
⇑ Center for Improvement in Healthcare Quality Accreditation
△ Commission on Accreditation of Rehabilitation Facilities (CARF) accreditation

TECUMSEH—Lenawee County

★ **PROMEDICA HERRICK HOSPITAL (231334)**, 500 East Pottawatamie Street, Zip 49286–2018; tel. 517/424–3000, (Total facility includes 25 beds in nursing home–type unit) **A**10 18 **F**3 5 11 15 29 30 40 43 45 46 53 64 68 74 75 77 79 81 85 91 92 93 98 100 101 102 104 107 108 110 114 119 128 129 130 132 135 145 146 147 149 **P**6 8 **S** ProMedica Health System, Toledo, OH
Primary Contact: Julie Yaroch, D.O., President
CFO: Bernie Nawrocki, Administrative Director Finance
CIO: Stephanie Sonnenberg, Director Information Technology
CHR: Cathy J Davis, Director Human Resources
CNO: Kathryn M Greenlee R.N., Vice President, Clinical Services/CNO
Web address: www.promedica.org
Control: Other not–for–profit (including NFP Corporation) **Service:** General medical and surgical

Staffed Beds: 60 **Admissions:** 567 **Census:** 33 **Outpatient Visits:** 39401 **Total Expense ($000):** 29191 **Payroll Expense ($000):** 8948 **Personnel:** 128

THREE RIVERS—St. Joseph County

★ ○ △ **THREE RIVERS HEALTH (230015)**, 701 South Health Parkway, Zip 49093–8352; tel. 269/278–1145, (Nonreporting) **A**7 10 11 **S** QHR, Brentwood, TN
Primary Contact: William B. Russell, Chief Executive Officer
COO: Laurie Herbert, Vice President Operations
CFO: Steve Andrews, Chief Financial Officer
CIO: Dave Parks, Chief Information Officer
Web address: www.threerivershealth.org
Control: Hospital district or authority, Government, Nonfederal **Service:** General medical and surgical

Staffed Beds: 35

TRAVERSE CITY—Grand Traverse County

⊞ **MUNSON MEDICAL CENTER (230097)**, 1105 Sixth Street, Zip 49684–2386; tel. 231/935–5000 **A**1 2 3 4 5 10 13 **F**3 4 5 6 11 12 13 15 17 18 22 26 28 29 30 31 32 34 35 36 38 39 40 43 44 45 47 48 49 50 53 54 55 56 57 58 59 60 61 62 63 64 65 68 70 71 72 74 75 76 77 78 79 81 82 84 85 86 87 89 90 92 93 94 96 97 98 100 101 102 103 104 105 107 108 110 111 115 116 117 118 119 120 121 123 124 126 129 130 131 132 133 141 142 143 144 145 146 147 148 149 **P**6 **S** Munson Healthcare, Traverse City, MI
Primary Contact: Alfred E. Pilong Jr, FACHE, President, Munson Medical Center and Chief Operating Officer, Munson Healthcare
COO: Derk F Pronger, Chief Operating Officer
CFO: Mark A Helper, Vice President, Chief Financial Officer
CMO: David S McGreaham M.D., Vice President Medical Affairs
CIO: Christopher J Podges, Chief Information Officer and Vice President Outpatient and Retail Services
CHR: Suzanne K Peters, Vice President Human Resources
CNO: Loraine Frank–Lightfoot R.N., Vice President, Patient Care Services and Chief Nursing Officer
Web address: www.munsonhealthcare.org
Control: Other not–for–profit (including NFP Corporation) **Service:** General medical and surgical

Staffed Beds: 391 **Admissions:** 22025 **Census:** 278 **Outpatient Visits:** 553354 **Births:** 1922 **Total Expense ($000):** 544595 **Payroll Expense ($000):** 207284 **Personnel:** 2950

TRENTON—Wayne County

⊞ **BEAUMONT HOSPITAL – TRENTON (230176)**, 5450 Fort Street, Zip 48183–4625; tel. 734/671–3800 **A**1 3 10 12 13 **F**3 8 11 13 15 18 20 22 26 28 29 30 34 35 38 39 40 42 43 44 45 46 47 49 50 51 56 57 59 60 61 62 63 64 65 68 70 74 75 76 78 79 80 81 82 85 87 91 92 93 100 102 107 108 110 111 115 117 118 119 130 131 132 135 146 147 148 149 150 **P**6 8 **S** Beaumont Health, Southfield, MI
Primary Contact: Chris Stesney–Ridenour, President
COO: Carolyn Wilson R.N., Chief Operating Officer
CFO: Paul Lauzau, Controller
CMO: Jonathan Kaper, Chief Medical Officer
CIO: Subra Sripada, Executive Vice President, Chief Transformation Officer and Chief Information Officer
CHR: Juliet Hafford, Director Human Resources
CNO: Susan G Schulz, Director Patient Care Services
Web address: www.beaumont.org
Control: Other not–for–profit (including NFP Corporation) **Service:** General medical and surgical

Staffed Beds: 173 **Admissions:** 8928 **Census:** 99 **Outpatient Visits:** 98106 **Births:** 502 **Total Expense ($000):** 155366 **Payroll Expense ($000):** 57925 **Personnel:** 803

TROY—Oakland County

⊞ **BEAUMONT HOSPITAL – TROY (230269)**, 44201 Dequindre Road, Zip 48085–1117; tel. 248/964–5000 **A**1 2 3 5 10 13 **F**3 8 11 12 13 15 17 18 19 20 22 24 26 28 29 30 31 32 34 35 36 39 40 41 43 44 45 46 47 48 49 50 51 53 54 55 56 57 58 59 60 61 62 63 64 65 66 68 70 71 72 74 75 76 77 78 79 80 81 82 84 85 86 87 89 90 91 92 93 94 96 97 100 102 107 108 109 110 111 114 115 116 117 118 119 120 121 123 124 126 129 130 132 135 141 142 143 145 146 147 148 149 **P**1 6 **S** Beaumont Health, Southfield, MI
Primary Contact: Nancy Susick, MSN, President
COO: Carolyn Wilson R.N., Chief Operating Officer
CFO: Mark Leonard, Vice President Finance
CMO: James Lynch, Senior Vice President and Chief Medical Officer
CIO: Subra Sripada, Executive Vice President, Chief Transportation Officer and Chief Information Officer
CHR: Lisa Ouelette, Director Human Resources
CNO: Debra Guido–Allen, Vice President and Chief Nursing Officer
Web address: www.beaumont.org
Control: Other not–for–profit (including NFP Corporation) **Service:** General medical and surgical

Staffed Beds: 520 **Admissions:** 35877 **Census:** 395 **Outpatient Visits:** 961026 **Births:** 3750 **Total Expense ($000):** 539719 **Payroll Expense ($000):** 217119 **Personnel:** 3540

VICKSBURG—Kalamazoo County

BRONSON VICKSBURG HOSPITAL See Bronson Methodist Hospital, Kalamazoo

WARREN—Macomb County

☐ **BEHAVIORAL CENTER OF MICHIGAN (234042)**, 4050 East 12 Mile Road, Zip 48092–2534; tel. 586/261–2266 **A**1 10 **F**29 38 66 75 98 101 102 103 104 105 130 132 135 149 150 **P**4 5 6
Primary Contact: Ryan Gunabalan, Chief Executive Officer
COO: Efren Lusterio, Director of Nursing
CFO: Mark Corey, Chief Financial Officer
CMO: Eleanor Medina M.D., Chief Medical Officer
CIO: Kashmira Khade, Coordinator Non–Clinical Services
CHR: Erin R Youngblood, Chief Human Resources Officer
Web address: www.behavioralcenter.com
Control: Corporation, Investor–owned (for–profit) **Service:** Psychiatric

Staffed Beds: 42 **Admissions:** 1400 **Census:** 5 **Outpatient Visits:** 0 **Births:** 0 **Personnel:** 171

☐ **SOUTHEAST MICHIGAN SURGICAL HOSPITAL (230264)**, 21230 Dequindre, Zip 48091–2287; tel. 586/427–1000, (Nonreporting) **A**1 10 **S** National Surgical Healthcare, Chicago, IL
Primary Contact: Barry Cullen, Chief Executive Officer
CMO: Benjamin Paolucci D.O., Chief of Staff
CHR: Dawn Meiers, Coordinator Medical Staff and Personnel Services
Web address: www.nshinc.com
Control: Corporation, Investor–owned (for–profit) **Service:** Surgical

Staffed Beds: 13

⊞ **ST. JOHN MACOMB–OAKLAND HOSPITAL (230195)**, 11800 East 12 Mile Road, Zip 48093–3472; tel. 586/573–5000, (Includes ST. JOHN MACOMB–OAKLAND HOSPITAL, MADISON HEIGHTS CAMPUS, 27351 Dequindre, Madison Heights, Michigan, Zip 48071–3487, tel. 248/967–7000; Terry Hamilton, President; ST. JOHN MACOMB–OAKLAND HOSPITAL, WARREN CAMPUS, 11800 East Twelve Mile Road, Warren, Michigan, Zip 48093–3472, tel. 586/573–5000; Terry Hamilton, President) **A**1 2 3 10 12 13 **F**3 11 12 13 15 17 18 20 22 24 26 28 29 30 31 34 35 36 38 39 40 43 44 45 46 47 48 49 50 51 56 57 58 59 60 61 63 64 65 68 70 74 75 76 77 78 79 80 81 82 84 85 86 87 90 91 92 93 95 96 97 98 100 101 102 103 105 107 108 111 115 116 117 118 119 121 123 126 129 130 131 132 135 141 143 146 147 148 149 150 **S** Ascension Healthcare, Saint Louis, MO
Primary Contact: Terry Hamilton, President
COO: William Mott, Chief Operating Officer
CFO: Patrick McGuire, Chief Financial Officer, Michigan Market
CMO: Gary L Berg D.O., Chief Medical Officer
CIO: Ralph Tenney, Chief Information Officer
CHR: Joanne E Tuscany, Senior Director Human Resources
Web address: www.stjohnprovidence.org/macomb–oakland/
Control: Church operated, Nongovernment, not–for–profit **Service:** General medical and surgical

Staffed Beds: 535 **Admissions:** 25386 **Census:** 358 **Outpatient Visits:** 495089 **Births:** 844 **Total Expense ($000):** 392230 **Payroll Expense ($000):** 158707 **Personnel:** 2698

Many Facility Codes have changed. Please refer to the AHA Guide Code Chart. © 2017 AHA Guide

WATERVLIET—Berrien County

COMMUNITY HOSPITAL See Lakeland Hospital, Watervliet

☒ △ **LAKELAND HOSPITAL, WATERVLIET (230078)**, 400 Medical Park Drive, Zip 49098–9225; tel. 269/463–3111 **A**1 7 10 **F**3 11 15 29 30 34 35 38 40 45 50 54 57 59 64 68 75 77 79 81 86 87 90 93 94 96 97 107 119 127 130 131 132 135 144 146 148 149 **S** Lakeland Health, Saint Joseph, MI
Primary Contact: Ray Cruse, Chief Executive Officer
CFO: Timothy Calhoun, Vice President Finance, Chief Financial Officer
CIO: Norma Tirado, Vice President, Human Resources and Health Information Technology
CHR: Norma Tirado, Vice President, Human Resources and Health Information Technology
CNO: Connie Harmon, Director of Nursing
Control: Other not-for-profit (including NFP Corporation) **Service**: General medical and surgical

Staffed Beds: 38 Admissions: 586 Census: 9 Outpatient Visits: 138955 Births: 2 Total Expense ($000): 36802 Payroll Expense ($000): 16441 Personnel: 255

WAYNE—Wayne County

☒ **BEAUMONT HOSPITAL – WAYNE (230142)**, 33155 Annapolis Street, Zip 48184–2405; tel. 734/467–4000 **A**1 3 10 **F**3 11 12 13 15 18 20 22 26 28 29 30 31 34 35 38 40 42 43 44 45 46 47 49 50 57 59 60 61 64 65 68 70 74 75 76 77 78 79 81 82 84 85 86 87 91 92 93 96 100 102 107 108 110 111 115 118 126 130 131 132 134 135 143 146 147 148 149 **P**6 8 **S** Beaumont Health, Southfield, MI
Primary Contact: Eric W. Widner, Division President
COO: Carolyn Wilson R.N., Chief Operating Officer
CFO: Jacqueline Nash, Controller
CMO: Ashok Jain M.D., Senior Vice President and Chief Medical Officer
CIO: Subra Sripada, Executive Vice President, Chief Transformation Officer and Chief Information Officer
CHR: Robert L James, Director Human Resources
CNO: Diane L Hartley, Director of Patient Care Services
Web address: www.beaumont.org
Control: Other not-for-profit (including NFP Corporation) **Service**: General medical and surgical

Staffed Beds: 185 Admissions: 8533 Census: 82 Outpatient Visits: 53890 Births: 897 Total Expense ($000): 168647 Payroll Expense ($000): 75307 Personnel: 1059

WEST BLOOMFIELD—Oakland County

☒ **HENRY FORD WEST BLOOMFIELD HOSPITAL (230302)**, 6777 West Maple Road, Zip 48322–3013; tel. 248/661–4100 **A**1 2 10 **F**3 6 11 12 13 15 18 20 22 26 28 29 30 31 32 34 35 36 37 38 40 41 44 45 46 49 50 51 53 55 56 57 58 59 60 61 62 63 64 65 66 68 70 73 74 75 76 77 78 79 80 81 82 84 85 86 87 89 92 93 97 100 101 102 103 107 108 110 111 114 115 117 118 119 120 121 123 124 126 130 131 132 135 146 147 148 149 150 **P**6 **S** Henry Ford Health System, Detroit, MI
Primary Contact: Lynn M. Torossian, President and Chief Executive Officer
COO: Karen Harris R.N., Chief Nursing and Operations Officer
CFO: Terry Goodbalian, Regional Chief Financial Officer
CMO: Betty Chu M.D., Chief Medical Officer and Vice President of Medical Affairs
CIO: Mary Alice Annecharico, System Vice President and Chief Information Officer
CNO: Karen Harris R.N., Chief Nursing and Operations Officer
Web address: www.henryford.com
Control: Other not-for-profit (including NFP Corporation) **Service**: General medical and surgical

Staffed Beds: 212 Admissions: 12775 Census: 132 Outpatient Visits: 218636 Births: 2069 Total Expense ($000): 272281 Payroll Expense ($000): 104539 Personnel: 1908

WEST BRANCH—Ogemaw County

★ ○ **WEST BRANCH REGIONAL MEDICAL CENTER (230095)**, 2463 South M–30, Zip 48661–1199; tel. 989/345–3660 **A**5 10 11 20 **F**3 11 15 17 20 28 29 30 34 35 40 50 57 59 63 64 75 77 79 81 93 97 107 111 115 117 119 130 135 146 148 **P**6
Primary Contact: Robert McGrail, Chief Executive Officer
CFO: Kathy Kohr, Chief Financial Officer
CMO: Mark Weber M.D., President Medical Staff
CHR: Kent Allen, Director Human Resources
CNO: Nicole Gillette R.N., Chief Nursing Officer
Web address: www.wbrmc.com
Control: Other not-for-profit (including NFP Corporation) **Service**: General medical and surgical

Staffed Beds: 88 Admissions: 2556 Census: 27 Outpatient Visits: 63429 Births: 0 Total Expense ($000): 46081 Payroll Expense ($000): 14086 Personnel: 319

WESTLAND—Wayne County

☐ **WALTER P. REUTHER PSYCHIATRIC HOSPITAL (234035)**, 30901 Palmer Road, Zip 48186–5389; tel. 734/367–8400, (Nonreporting) **A**1 10
Primary Contact: Richard T. Young, FACHE, Director
CMO: H. Bandla M.D., Chief Clinical Affairs
CHR: Deborah Moore, Director Human Resources
CNO: E. McDade R.N., MS, Ph.D.,
Web address: www.mhweb.org/wayne/reuther.htm
Control: State, Government, Nonfederal **Service**: Psychiatric

Staffed Beds: 239

WYANDOTTE—Wayne County

☒ △ **HENRY FORD WYANDOTTE HOSPITAL (230146)**, 2333 Biddle Avenue, Zip 48192–4668; tel. 734/246–6000 **A**1 3 7 10 12 13 **F**3 5 8 11 12 13 15 18 20 22 26 28 29 30 31 32 34 35 36 38 40 41 42 43 44 45 46 47 49 50 51 54 56 57 58 59 60 61 62 63 64 65 66 68 70 73 74 75 76 77 78 79 80 81 82 84 85 86 87 90 92 93 96 97 98 100 101 102 103 107 108 110 111 114 115 116 117 118 119 126 129 130 131 132 135 144 146 147 148 149 **P**6 **S** Henry Ford Health System, Detroit, MI
Primary Contact: Denise Brooks-Williams, President and Chief Executive Officer
CFO: Terry Goodbalian, Vice President, Finance and Chief Financial Officer
CMO: Dennis R Lemanski D.O., Senior Vice President Medical Affairs and Medical Education/CMO
CIO: Mary Alice Annecharico, System Vice President and Chief Information Officer
CNO: Josephine Sclafani Wahl R.N., MS, FACHE, VP, Patient Care Services & CNO
Web address: www.henryfordhealth.org
Control: Other not-for-profit (including NFP Corporation) **Service**: General medical and surgical

Staffed Beds: 343 Admissions: 16052 Census: 217 Outpatient Visits: 413773 Births: 1658 Total Expense ($000): 300001 Payroll Expense ($000): 124319 Personnel: 1880

☒ **SELECT SPECIALTY HOSPITAL–DOWNRIVER (232031)**, 2333 Biddle Avenue, 8th Floor, Zip 48192–4668; tel. 734/246–5500, (Nonreporting) **A**1 10 **S** Select Medical Corporation, Mechanicsburg, PA
Primary Contact: John Ponczocha, Chief Executive Officer
CMO: Roderick Boyer M.D., Medical Director
CHR: Barb Wierzbicki, Manager Human Resources
CNO: Angela Kudla MSN, R.N., Chief Nursing Officer
Web address: www.downriver.selectspecialtyhospitals.com/
Control: Corporation, Investor–owned (for–profit) **Service**: Acute long–term care hospital

Staffed Beds: 35

WYOMING—Kent County

★ ○ **METRO HEALTH HOSPITAL (230236)**, 5900 Byron Center Avenue SW, Zip 49519–9606, Mailing Address: P.O.Box 916, 49509–0916; tel. 616/252–7200 **A**3 5 10 11 12 13 **F**3 12 13 15 18 20 22 26 28 29 30 31 34 35 40 43 44 45 48 49 50 54 57 58 59 64 65 66 70 71 74 75 76 77 78 79 80 81 82 85 86 87 92 94 97 107 108 110 111 115 119 126 129 130 131 132 135 144 146 147 148 **P**8
Primary Contact: Michael D. Faas, President and Chief Executive Officer
CFO: Kris Kurtz, Controller
CIO: William Lewkowski, Executive Vice President Information Services and Chief Information Officer
Web address: www.metrohealth.net
Control: Other not-for-profit (including NFP Corporation) **Service**: General medical and surgical

Staffed Beds: 208 Admissions: 9362 Census: 109 Outpatient Visits: 511421 Births: 1533 Total Expense ($000): 338460 Payroll Expense ($000): 114322 Personnel: 2191

YPSILANTI—Washtenaw County

☐ **FOREST HEALTH MEDICAL CENTER (230144)**, 135 South Prospect Street, Zip 48198–7914; tel. 734/547–4700 **A**1 10 **F**12 30 64 74 75 79 81 82 85 111 119 130 132 149
Primary Contact: Trevor J. Dyksterhouse, President
COO: Andrea Walrath, Chief Operating Officer
CFO: David Althoen, Director Financial Planning and Analysis
CMO: Jason Adams M.D., Medical Staff President
CIO: Andrea Walrath, Chief Operating Officer
CHR: Amy Mohr, Coordinator Human Resources
Web address: www.fhmc–mi.com
Control: Corporation, Investor–owned (for–profit) **Service**: General medical and surgical

Staffed Beds: 24 Admissions: 1055 Census: 5 Outpatient Visits: 14302 Births: 0 Personnel: 48

MI

Hospital, Medicare Provider Number, Address, Telephone, Approval, Facility, and Physician Codes, Health Care System

★ American Hospital Association (AHA) membership   ○ Healthcare Facilities Accreditation Program   ⇑ Center for Improvement in Healthcare Quality Accreditation
☐ The Joint Commission accreditation   ◇ DNV Healthcare Inc. accreditation   △ Commission on Accreditation of Rehabilitation Facilities (CARF) accreditation

⊞ **SELECT SPECIALTY HOSPITAL–ANN ARBOR (232024)**, 5301 East Huron River Drive, 5th Floor, Zip 48197–1051; tel. 734/712–6751, (Nonreporting) **A**1 10 **S** Select Medical Corporation, Mechanicsburg, PA
Primary Contact: Bryan Cutliff, Chief Executive Officer
CMO: Hamid Halimi M.D., Medical Director
CHR: Leah Warshaw, Coordinator Human Resources
CNO: Tim Varney R.N., Chief Nursing Officer
Web address: www.annarbor.selectspecialtyhospitals.com/
Control: Corporation, Investor–owned (for–profit) **Service**: Acute long–term care hospital

Staffed Beds: 36

★ **ST. JOSEPH MERCY ANN ARBOR (230156)**, 5301 Mcauley Drive, Zip 48197–1051, Mailing Address: P.O.Box 995, Ann Arbor, 48106–0995; tel. 734/712–3456 **A**2 3 5 10 **F**3 4 5 6 8 9 11 12 13 15 17 18 20 22 24 26 28 29 30 31 32 34 35 36 37 38 40 41 43 44 45 46 47 48 49 50 51 53 54 55 56 57 58 59 61 63 64 65 66 68 70 71 72 73 74 75 76 77 78 79 80 81 82 83 84 85 86 87 89 90 91 92 93 94 95 96 97 98 99 100 101 102 103 104 105 107 108 109 110 111 114 115 118 119 120 121 123 124 126 129 130 131 132 134 135 141 143 144 146 147 148 149 **P**1 **S** Trinity Health, Livonia, MI
Primary Contact: David Brooks, President
CFO: Kathy O'Connor, Vice President Finance
CMO: Rosalie Tocco–Bradley Ph.D., M.D., Chief Medical Officer
CIO: Frank Rademacher, Senior Director Information Systems
CNO: Joyce Young Ph.D., R.N., Vice President, Patient Services and Chief Nursing Officer
Web address: www.sjmercyhealth.org
Control: Church operated, Nongovernment, not–for–profit **Service**: General medical and surgical

Staffed Beds: 483 **Admissions:** 31390 **Census:** 386 **Outpatient Visits:** 1082861 **Births:** 3747 **Total Expense ($000):** 750838 **Payroll Expense ($000):** 270925 **Personnel:** 5568

ZEELAND—Ottawa County

⊞ **SPECTRUM HEALTH ZEELAND COMMUNITY HOSPITAL (230003)**, 8333 Felch Street, Zip 49464–2608; tel. 616/772–4644 **A**1 10 **F**3 12 13 15 18 29 32 34 35 39 40 43 45 46 47 50 57 59 64 65 68 69 70 74 75 76 78 79 81 85 86 87 89 91 92 93 97 107 108 110 111 115 118 119 129 130 132 134 135 144 146 147 **S** Spectrum Health, Grand Rapids, MI
Primary Contact: Ron Lewis, President
CFO: Ryan J. Powers, Vice President Finance
CMO: Ruel R. Lirio M.D., Clinical Physician Advisor
CIO: Imran Syed, Manager Technology Information Services
CHR: Jennifer F Becksvoort, Senior Human Resource Business Partner
CNO: Jane Czerew, Vice President Clinical Services and Quality
Web address: www.spectrumhealth.org/zeeland
Control: Other not–for–profit (including NFP Corporation) **Service**: General medical and surgical

Staffed Beds: 50 **Admissions:** 2462 **Census:** 19 **Outpatient Visits:** 98064 **Births:** 522 **Total Expense ($000):** 51522 **Payroll Expense ($000):** 18053 **Personnel:** 358

ZEELAND COMMUNITY HOSPITAL See Spectrum Health Zeeland Community Hospital

MINNESOTA

ADA—Norman County

BRIDGES MEDICAL CENTER See Essentia Health ADA

★ **ESSENTIA HEALTH ADA (241313)**, 201 9th Street West, Zip 56510–1279;
tel. 218/784–5000, (Nonreporting) **A**10 18 **S** Essentia Health, Duluth, MN
Primary Contact: Erin Stoltman, Administrator
CMO: Jeff Peterson M.D., Chief of Staff
CHR: Shayla Hennenberg, Director Human Resources
Web address: www.essentiahealth.org
Control: Other not–for–profit (including NFP Corporation) **Service**: General
medical and surgical

Staffed Beds: 14

AITKIN—Aitkin County

✠ **RIVERWOOD HEALTHCARE CENTER (241305)**, 200 Bunker Hill Drive,
Zip 56431–1865; tel. 218/927–2121 **A**1 2 10 18 **F**3 8 11 13 15 28 29 31 32
34 35 40 43 45 53 54 56 57 59 64 65 70 75 76 77 78 79 81 82 86 87 93 97
104 107 110 111 114 119 127 129 130 131 132 133 135 144 145 146 147
148 149 **P**6
Primary Contact: Chad D. Cooper, Chief Executive Officer
COO: Cindi Sorensen–Baker, Chief Operating Officer
CFO: Casey R Johnson, Chief Financial Officer
CMO: Mark Heggem M.D., Chief Medical Officer
CIO: Daryl Kallevig, Chief Information Officer
CHR: Cindi Hills, Director Human Resources
CNO: Kristine Layne R.N., Chief Nursing Officer
Web address: www.riverwoodhealthcare.org
Control: Other not–for–profit (including NFP Corporation) **Service**: General
medical and surgical

Staffed Beds: 25 Admissions: 1161 Census: 11 Outpatient Visits: 70266
Births: 75 Total Expense ($000): 56844 Payroll Expense ($000): 22236
Personnel: 326

ALBERT LEA—Freeborn County

☐ **MAYO CLINIC HEALTH SYSTEM IN ALBERT LEA (240043)**, 404 West Fountain
Street, Zip 56007–2473; tel. 507/373–2384, (Nonreporting) **A**1 3 5 10 20 **S**
Mayo Clinic, Rochester, MN
Primary Contact: Mark Ciota, M.D., Chief Executive Officer
CFO: Sheri Dankert, Chief Financial Officer
CMO: John Grzybowski M.D., Medical Director
CHR: Monica Fleegel, Director Human Resources
CNO: Lori Routh R.N., Nurse Administrator
Web address: www.almedcenter.org
Control: Other not–for–profit (including NFP Corporation) **Service**: General
medical and surgical

Staffed Beds: 129

ALEXANDRIA—Sherburne County

☐ **COMMUNITY BEHAVIORAL HEALTH HOSPITAL – ALEXANDRIA (244012)**,
1610 8th Avenue East, Zip 56308–2472; tel. 320/335–6201 (Nonreporting) **A**1
10 **S** Minnesota Department of Human Services, Saint Paul, MN
Primary Contact: Jennifer Westrum, Administrator
CFO: Shirley Jacobson, Chief Financial Officer
Web address: www.health.state.mn.us
Control: State, Government, Nonfederal **Service**: Psychiatric

Staffed Beds: 16

ALEXANDRIA—Douglas County

★ ○ **DOUGLAS COUNTY HOSPITAL (240030)**, 111 17th Avenue East,
Zip 56308–3798; tel. 320/762–1511 **A**2 10 11 **F**3 8 11 13 15 28 29 30 31 32
34 35 36 40 43 45 50 57 61 64 65 68 70 76 77 78 79 81 82 85 86 87 89 91
93 97 107 108 111 115 117 118 119 129 130 131 132 135 144 146 149 **P**6
Primary Contact: Carl P. Vaagenes, Chief Executive Officer
CFO: Nate Meyer, Director Finance
CHR: Shelly Gompf, Director Human Resources
Web address: www.dchospital.com
Control: County, Government, Nonfederal **Service**: General medical and surgical

Staffed Beds: 99 Admissions: 3409 Census: 30 Outpatient Visits: 67684
Births: 664 Total Expense ($000): 136883 Payroll Expense ($000): 41955
Personnel: 628

ANNANDALE—Wright County

☐ **COMMUNITY BEHAVIORAL HEALTH HOSPITAL – ANNANDALE (244011)**,
400 Annandale Boulevard, Zip 55302–3141; tel. 651/259–3850 (Nonreporting)
A1 10 **S** Minnesota Department of Human Services, Saint Paul, MN
Primary Contact: James P. Kelly, FACHE, Administrator
CMO: Shabeer A Ahmed M.D., Clinical Director
CNO: Lennetta M Reynolds, Administrative Supervisor
Web address: www.health.state.mn.us
Control: State, Government, Nonfederal **Service**: Psychiatric

Staffed Beds: 16

ANOKA—Anoka County

☐ **ANOKA–METROPOLITAN REGIONAL TREATMENT CENTER (244002)**, 3301
Seventh Avenue, Zip 55303–4516, Mailing Address: 3301 Seventh Avenue North,
55303–4516; tel. 651/431–5000, (Nonreporting) **A**1 10 **S** Minnesota Department
of Human Services, Saint Paul, MN
Primary Contact: Wade Brost, Executive Director
Web address: www.health.state.mn.us
Control: State, Government, Nonfederal **Service**: Psychiatric

Staffed Beds: 200

APPLETON—Swift County

★ **APPLETON AREA HEALTH SERVICES (241341)**, 30 South Behl Street,
Zip 56208–1699; tel. 320/289–2422, (Nonreporting) **A**10 18
Primary Contact: Kathy Johnson, Interim Chief Executive Officer
CFO: Anne Kells, Interim Chief Financial Officer
Web address: www.appletonareahealth.com
Control: City, Government, Nonfederal **Service**: General medical and surgical

Staffed Beds: 15

ARLINGTON—Sibley County

★ ⇑ **RIDGEVIEW SIBLEY MEDICAL CENTER (241311)**, 601 West Chandler
Street, Zip 55307–2127; tel. 507/964–2271, (Nonreporting) **A**10 18 21 **S**
Ridgeview Medical Center, Waconia, MN
Primary Contact: Todd Sandberg, Chief Executive Officer
CFO: Darla Anderson, Chief Financial Officer
CMO: Ehtaisham Mohammed M.D., Chief Medical Officer
CIO: Chris Bulau, Manager Information Technology
CHR: Sara Christiansen, Interim Director Human Resources
CNO: Sandy Domeier, Director Patient Care Services
Web address: www.sibleymedical.org
Control: City, Government, Nonfederal **Service**: General medical and surgical

Staffed Beds: 16

AURORA—St. Louis County

★ **ESSENTIA HEALTH NORTHERN PINES MEDICAL CENTER (241340)**, 5211
Highway 110, Zip 55705–1599; tel. 218/229–2211, (Total facility includes 50
beds in nursing home–type unit) **A**10 18 **F**28 29 34 38 40 50 56 57 59 65 75 79
81 82 87 91 93 96 97 99 100 101 102 103 104 105 106 107 128 130 133
135 148 149 150 **P**6 **S** Essentia Health, Duluth, MN
Primary Contact: Laura Ackman, Chief Operating Officer and Administrator
CFO: Kevin Boren, Chief Financial Officer
CMO: Michelle Oman D.O., Chief Medical Officer
CHR: Kim Carlson, Director Human Resources
CNO: Cindy Loe R.N., Director of Nursing
Web address: www.essentiahealth.org/NorthernPines/FindaClinic/Essentia–
HealthNorthern–Pines–36.aspx
Control: Other not–for–profit (including NFP Corporation) **Service**: General
medical and surgical

Staffed Beds: 58 Admissions: 181 Census: 38 Outpatient Visits: 19612
Births: 0 Total Expense ($000): 15013 Payroll Expense ($000): 7632
Personnel: 117

WHITE COMMUNITY HOSPITAL See Essentia Health Northern Pines Medical
Center

MN

Hospital, Medicare Provider Number, Address, Telephone, Approval, Facility, and Physician Codes, Health Care System

★ American Hospital Association (AHA) membership   ○ Healthcare Facilities Accreditation Program   ⇑ Center for Improvement in Healthcare Quality Accreditation
☐ The Joint Commission accreditation   ◇ DNV Healthcare Inc. accreditation   △ Commission on Accreditation of Rehabilitation Facilities (CARF) accreditation

AUSTIN—Mower County

MAYO CLINIC HEALTH SYSTEM–ALBERT LEA AND AUSTIN (240117), 1000 First Drive NW, Zip 55912–2904; tel. 507/433–7351 **A**3 5 **F**3 5 11 13 15 18 28 29 30 31 34 35 40 43 45 50 52 56 57 59 61 62 63 64 65 70 74 75 76 77 78 79 81 82 84 86 87 93 96 97 98 99 100 101 102 103 104 105 106 107 110 111 115 118 119 129 130 131 132 135 143 144 146 147 148 149 **P**6 **S** Mayo Clinic, Rochester, MN
Primary Contact: Mark Ciota, M.D., Chief Executive Officer
CFO: Sheri Dankert, Vice President Finance
CMO: Cynthia Dube M.D., Medical Director
CIO: Tammy Kritzer, Vice President Clinic Operations
CHR: Rodney Nording, Vice President Organizational Support
CNO: Lori Routh R.N., Nurse Administrator
Web address: www.austinmedicalcenter.org
Control: Other not–for–profit (including NFP Corporation) **Service**: General medical and surgical

Staffed Beds: 69 Admissions: 4234 Census: 40 Outpatient Visits: 314029 Births: 747 Personnel: 1222

BAGLEY—Clearwater County

★ **SANFORD BAGLEY MEDICAL CENTER (241328)**, 203 Fourth Street NW, Zip 56621–8307; tel. 218/694–6501 **A**10 18 **F**3 7 15 28 34 40 45 53 59 65 66 75 77 79 81 87 89 93 97 104 107 114 119 127 128 133 143 149 150 **P**6 **S** Sanford Health, Sioux Falls, SD
Primary Contact: Robert Belanger, Chief Executive Officer
CMO: Andre Spence, Chief Medical Staff
CNO: Stephanie McKnight, Hospital Nursing Manager
Web address: www.sanfordhealth.org
Control: Other not–for–profit (including NFP Corporation) **Service**: General medical and surgical

Staffed Beds: 8 Admissions: 108 Census: 1 Outpatient Visits: 20709 Births: 0 Total Expense ($000): 10341 Payroll Expense ($000): 4914 Personnel: 78

BAUDETTE—Lake Of The Woods County

★ **CHI LAKEWOOD HEALTH (241301)**, 600 Main Avenue South, Zip 56623–2855; tel. 218/634–2120, (Nonreporting) **A**10 18 **S** Catholic Health Initiatives, Englewood, CO
Primary Contact: Benjamin Koppelman, Interim President
CFO: Jay Ross, Vice President of Finance
CMO: Justin Quo, Chief of Staff
CIO: Dan Leadbetter, Information Technology Systems Site Lead
CHR: Lois Slick, Director Human Resources
CNO: Danielle Abel, Vice President of Patient Care Services
Web address: www.lakewoodhealthcenter.org
Control: Church operated, Nongovernment, not–for–profit **Service**: General medical and surgical

Staffed Beds: 55

BAXTER—Crow Wing County

☐ **COMMUNITY BEHAVIORAL HEALTH HOSPITAL – BAXTER (244015)**, 14241 Grand Oaks Drive, Zip 56425–8749; tel. 218/316–3101 (Nonreporting) **A**1 10 **S** Minnesota Department of Human Services, Saint Paul, MN
Primary Contact: Richard G. Slieter Jr, Administrator
Control: State, Government, Nonfederal **Service**: Psychiatric

Staffed Beds: 16

BEMIDJI—Beltrami County

☐ **COMMUNITY BEHAVIORAL HEALTH HOSPITAL – BEMIDJI (244014)**, 800 Bemidji Avenue North, Zip 56601–3054; tel. 218/308–2400 (Nonreporting) **A**1 10 **S** Minnesota Department of Human Services, Saint Paul, MN
Primary Contact: Larry A. Laudon, Administrator
Control: State, Government, Nonfederal **Service**: Psychiatric

Staffed Beds: 16

NORTH COUNTRY REGIONAL HOSPITAL See Sanford Bemidji Medical Center

★ **SANFORD BEMIDJI MEDICAL CENTER (240100)**, 1300 Anne Street NW, Zip 56601–5103; tel. 218/751–5430, (Total facility includes 78 beds in nursing home–type unit) **A**2 10 **F**3 7 8 10 11 13 14 15 18 20 22 28 29 30 31 34 35 40 43 44 45 46 49 50 51 53 54 55 56 57 58 59 60 62 63 64 65 66 68 70 74 75 76 77 78 79 81 82 85 86 87 90 93 96 97 103 104 107 108 110 111 114 115 117 119 120 121 123 124 125 126 127 128 129 130 131 132 133 135 141 142 143 144 145 146 147 148 149 150 **P**6 **S** Sanford Health, Sioux Falls, SD
Primary Contact: Bryan Nermoe, President
CFO: Craig Boyer, Vice President Finance
CMO: Daniel DeKrey M.D., Chief of Staff
CIO: Dan Moffatt, Chief Information Officer
Web address: www.nchs.com
Control: Other not–for–profit (including NFP Corporation) **Service**: General medical and surgical

Staffed Beds: 196 Admissions: 5684 Census: 135 Outpatient Visits: 281554 Births: 959 Total Expense ($000): 146333 Payroll Expense ($000): 52662 Personnel: 1040

BENSON—Swift County

★ **SWIFT COUNTY – BENSON HEALTH SERVICES (241365)**, 1815 Wisconsin Avenue, Zip 56215–1653; tel. 320/843–1311, (Nonreporting) **A**10 18
Primary Contact: Kurt Waldbillig, Chief Executive Officer
CFO: Jayne Thielke, Chief Financial Officer
CMO: Richard Horecka, Chief Medical Officer
CIO: Jayne Thielke, Chief Financial Officer
CHR: Naomi Sands, Administrative Assistant and Manager Human Resources
Web address: www.scbh.org
Control: Hospital district or authority, Government, Nonfederal **Service**: General medical and surgical

Staffed Beds: 18

BIGFORK—Itasca County

★ **BIGFORK VALLEY HOSPITAL (241316)**, 258 Pine Tree Drive, Zip 56628, Mailing Address: P.O.Box 258, 56628–0258; tel. 218/743–3177, (Total facility includes 47 beds in nursing home–type unit) **A**10 18 **F**2 3 8 10 11 15 28 29 31 33 34 35 40 45 53 56 57 59 62 64 77 79 80 81 82 85 89 90 92 93 97 110 119 125 128 130 132 133 143 146 148 149
Primary Contact: Aaron Saude, Chief Executive Officer
CFO: Christine Lokken, Director of Finance
CMO: Edwin Anderson M.D., Chief of Staff and Chief Medical Officer
CIO: Amanda Niemala, Director of Information Services
CHR: Angela Kleffman, Director of Ancillary Services
CNO: Nancy Probst R.N., Chief Nursing Officer
Web address: www.bigforkvalley.org
Control: Hospital district or authority, Government, Nonfederal **Service**: General medical and surgical

Staffed Beds: 67 Admissions: 367 Census: 46 Outpatient Visits: 21380 Total Expense ($000): 23926 Payroll Expense ($000): 8477 Personnel: 176

BLUE EARTH—Faribault County

⊞ **UNITED HOSPITAL DISTRICT (241369)**, 515 South Moore Street, Zip 56013–2158, Mailing Address: P.O.Box 160, 56013–0160; tel. 507/526–3273 **A**1 10 18 **F**3 5 7 8 11 13 15 17 28 29 30 34 35 40 43 45 47 48 50 53 56 57 59 62 63 64 65 68 69 70 75 76 77 79 81 82 85 86 89 91 93 96 97 107 110 111 114 115 119 129 130 132 133 135 144 146 148 149 **P**6
Primary Contact: Richard M. Ash, Chief Executive Officer
CFO: Patrick Justin, Chief Financial Officer
CMO: Bob Karp M.D., Chief Medical Officer
CIO: Mary Hynes, Manager Information Services
CHR: Shanna Gudahl, Manager Human Resources
CNO: Candace Arends R.N., Chief Nursing Officer
Web address: www.uhd.org
Control: Other not–for–profit (including NFP Corporation) **Service**: General medical and surgical

Staffed Beds: 25 Admissions: 599 Census: 7 Outpatient Visits: 55082 Births: 70 Total Expense ($000): 30254 Payroll Expense ($000): 12113 Personnel: 180

BRAINERD—Crow Wing County

⊞ **ESSENTIA HEALTH ST. JOSEPH'S MEDICAL CENTER (240075)**, 523 North Third Street, Zip 56401–3098; tel. 218/829–2861 **A**1 2 10 **F**3 4 5 11 13 15 17 18 20 22 26 28 29 30 31 32 34 35 40 43 45 49 50 51 54 57 59 64 65 70 74 75 76 77 78 81 82 86 87 89 91 93 96 97 98 100 102 107 111 118 119 126 130 131 132 135 144 146 148 **P**6 **S** Essentia Health, Duluth, MN
Primary Contact: Adam Rees, President
COO: Mike Larson, Chief Operating Officer
CFO: Dave Pilot, Chief Financial Officer
CMO: Peter Henry M.D., Chief Medical Officer
CIO: Pam Marlatt, Business Systems Director
CHR: Sarah Carlson, Director Human Resources
CNO: Patricia DeLong, Chief Nursing Officer
Web address: www.essentiahealth.org
Control: Church operated, Nongovernment, not–for–profit **Service**: General medical and surgical

Staffed Beds: 136 **Admissions**: 4941 **Census**: 51 **Outpatient Visits**: 324822 **Births**: 478 **Total Expense ($000)**: 176455 **Payroll Expense ($000)**: 79423 **Personnel**: 958

ST. JOSEPH'S MEDICAL CENTER See Essentia Health St. Joseph's Medical Center

BRECKENRIDGE—Wilkin County

★ **CHI ST. FRANCIS HEALTH (241377)**, 2400 St Francis Drive, Zip 56520–1025; tel. 218/643–3000, (Total facility includes 80 beds in nursing home–type unit) **A**5 10 18 **F**3 8 11 13 15 28 29 30 34 35 38 40 43 45 50 56 57 59 64 65 75 79 81 87 93 96 97 99 100 101 103 104 107 110 111 115 119 125 127 128 129 130 131 132 133 146 **S** Catholic Health Initiatives, Englewood, CO
Primary Contact: David A. Nelson, President
CFO: Becky Thompson, Chief Financial Officer
CHR: Gail Grant, Director Human Resources
Web address: www.sfcare.org
Control: Church operated, Nongovernment, not–for–profit **Service**: General medical and surgical

Staffed Beds: 105 **Admissions**: 681 **Census**: 83 **Outpatient Visits**: 18988 **Births**: 124 **Total Expense ($000)**: 29459 **Payroll Expense ($000)**: 11666 **Personnel**: 92

BROOKLYN PARK—Hennepin County

PRAIRIECARE – BROOKLYN PARK (244016), 9400 Zane Avenue North, Zip 55443, Mailing Address: 12915 63rd Avenue North, Maple Grove, 55369–6001; tel. 763/383–5800 (Nonreporting)
Primary Contact: Stephen Setterburg, M.D., President
Web address: www.prairie–care.com
Control: Investor–owned (for–profit) **Service**: Psychiatric

Staffed Beds: 50

BUFFALO—Wright County

⊞ **BUFFALO HOSPITAL (240076)**, 303 Catlin Street, Zip 55313–1947; tel. 763/682–1212 **A**1 10 **F**3 11 13 15 18 28 29 30 31 32 34 35 36 40 43 44 45 50 53 57 59 64 75 76 77 78 79 80 81 85 86 87 93 107 110 111 114 118 119 129 130 131 132 135 146 148 149 150 **S** Allina Health, Minneapolis, MN
Primary Contact: Jennifer Myster, President
COO: Heather Johnson, Director of Finance, Operations and Business Development
CFO: Heather Johnson, Director of Finance, Operations and Business Development
CMO: Corey Martin M.D., Director Medical Affairs
CIO: Jonathan Cloutier, Manager, Information Services
CHR: Leah Schmoyer, Human Resources Director
CNO: Gretchen A Frederick R.N., Director Patient Care Services
Web address: www.buffalohospital.org
Control: Other not–for–profit (including NFP Corporation) **Service**: General medical and surgical

Staffed Beds: 44 **Admissions**: 2286 **Census**: 16 **Outpatient Visits**: 77255 **Births**: 638 **Total Expense ($000)**: 69284 **Payroll Expense ($000)**: 28220 **Personnel**: 336

BURNSVILLE—Dakota County

⊞ **FAIRVIEW RIDGES HOSPITAL (240207)**, 201 East Nicollet Boulevard, Zip 55337–5799; tel. 952/892–2000 **A**1 2 3 5 10 **F**3 13 15 18 19 20 22 28 29 30 31 34 40 41 43 44 45 46 49 50 52 55 57 59 64 65 68 70 72 74 75 76 77 78 79 81 82 84 85 87 89 93 100 107 108 110 111 114 115 116 117 118 119 126 130 132 134 146 148 **P**6 **S** Fairview Health Services, Minneapolis, MN
Primary Contact: Patrick Belland, President
COO: Brian A Knapp, Vice President Operations
CFO: Alan Lem, Vice President Finance
CMO: John Stoltenberg M.D., Vice President Medical Affairs
CHR: Michelle LeDell, Director Human Resource
CNO: Julie Sethney R.N., Vice President Patient Care
Web address: www.fairview.org
Control: Other not–for–profit (including NFP Corporation) **Service**: General medical and surgical

Staffed Beds: 162 **Admissions**: 10807 **Census**: 115 **Outpatient Visits**: 118822 **Births**: 2355 **Total Expense ($000)**: 193881 **Payroll Expense ($000)**: 93447 **Personnel**: 1005

CAMBRIDGE—Isanti County

⊞ **CAMBRIDGE MEDICAL CENTER (240020)**, 701 South Dellwood Street, Zip 55008–1920; tel. 763/689–7700 **A**1 2 10 **F**3 4 5 11 13 14 15 18 28 29 30 31 32 34 35 38 40 43 45 50 55 56 57 59 61 64 65 69 70 74 75 76 77 78 79 81 82 85 86 87 89 93 97 98 99 100 101 102 103 104 107 108 111 114 119 125 129 130 131 132 134 135 144 145 146 147 148 149 **P**5 6 **S** Allina Health, Minneapolis, MN
Primary Contact: Gary Shaw, President
CFO: Nancy Treacy, Director Finance
CHR: Diane Rasmussen, Director Human Resources
CNO: Sherri Abrahamson–Baty, Director Patient Care Services
Web address: www.allina.com/ahs/cambridge.nsf
Control: Other not–for–profit (including NFP Corporation) **Service**: General medical and surgical

Staffed Beds: 75 **Admissions**: 2886 **Census**: 33 **Outpatient Visits**: 90683 **Births**: 357 **Total Expense ($000)**: 77580 **Payroll Expense ($000)**: 33049 **Personnel**: 631

CANBY—Yellow Medicine County

★ **SANFORD CANBY MEDICAL CENTER (241347)**, 112 St Olaf Avenue South, Zip 56220–1433; tel. 507/223–7277, (Total facility includes 58 beds in nursing home–type unit) **A**10 18 **F**3 7 10 11 13 15 28 29 31 34 35 39 40 45 46 53 56 59 60 62 64 65 70 71 75 79 81 85 89 92 93 107 110 119 127 128 130 132 133 135 144 149 **P**6 **S** Sanford Health, Sioux Falls, SD
Primary Contact: Lori Sisk, R.N., Chief Executive Officer
CFO: Allison Nelson, Chief Financial Officer
CMO: Maritza Lopez M.D., Chief of Staff
CIO: Cheryl L Ferguson, Associate Administrator
Web address: www.sanfordcanby.org
Control: Other not–for–profit (including NFP Corporation) **Service**: General medical and surgical

Staffed Beds: 93 **Admissions**: 364 **Census**: 53 **Outpatient Visits**: 34520 **Births**: 0 **Total Expense ($000)**: 20713 **Payroll Expense ($000)**: 9763 **Personnel**: 190

CANNON FALLS—Goodhue County

☐ **MAYO CLINIC HEALTH SYSTEM IN CANNON FALLS (241346)**, 32021 County Road 24 Boulevard, Zip 55009–1898; tel. 507/263–4221 **A**1 10 18 **F**3 11 15 18 28 29 34 35 40 45 57 59 64 67 69 74 75 77 79 81 87 93 97 104 107 111 115 119 130 133 149 **P**6 **S** Mayo Clinic, Rochester, MN
Primary Contact: Thomas J. Witt, M.D., President and Chief Executive Officer
COO: Glenn Christian, Administrator
CFO: Edward A Tusa, Chief Financial Officer
CMO: Tarlochan Turna M.D., Medical Director
CHR: Mary Garlets, Director Human Resources
Web address: www.mayoclinichealthsystem.org/locations/cannon-falls
Control: Other not–for–profit (including NFP Corporation) **Service**: General medical and surgical

Staffed Beds: 15 **Admissions**: 484 **Census**: 15 **Outpatient Visits**: 21739 **Births**: 0 **Personnel**: 118

MN

CASS LAKE—Cass County

★ **U.S. PUBLIC HEALTH SERVICE INDIAN HOSPITAL (241358)**, 425 7th Street North West, Zip 56633; tel. 218/335–3200, (Nonreporting) **A**5 10 18 **S** U. S. Indian Health Service, Rockville, MD
Primary Contact: Louis P. Erdrich, Acting Chief Executive Officer
CMO: Antonio Guimaraes M.D., Clinical Director
CHR: Terrance Lascano, Administrative Officer
CNO: Roberta A Williams, Director of Nursing
Web address: www.ihs.gov
Control: PHS, Indian Service, Government, federal **Service**: General medical and surgical

Staffed Beds: 9

CLOQUET—Carlton County

★ **COMMUNITY MEMORIAL HOSPITAL (241364)**, 512 Skyline Boulevard, Zip 55720–1199; tel. 218/879–4641, (Nonreporting) **A**10 18
Primary Contact: Rick Breuer, Chief Executive Officer and Administrator
CFO: Brad Anderson, Chief Financial Officer
CIO: Sam Jacobson, Director Management Information Systems
Web address: www.cloquethospital.com
Control: Other not-for-profit (including NFP Corporation) **Service**: General medical and surgical

Staffed Beds: 113

COOK—St. Louis County

★ **COOK HOSPITAL AND CONVALESCENT NURSING CARE UNIT (241312)**, 10 Fifth Street SE, Zip 55723–9745; tel. 218/666–5945, (Total facility includes 28 beds in nursing home–type unit) **A**10 18 **F**2 3 11 15 28 29 35 40 43 50 53 56 57 64 77 81 93 96 107 110 111 119 128 130 133 148 149
Primary Contact: Teresa Debevec, Chief Executive Officer
CFO: Kaylee S Hoard, Chief Financial Officer
Web address: www.cookhospital.org
Control: Hospital district or authority, Government, Nonfederal **Service**: General medical and surgical

Staffed Beds: 42 **Admissions**: 260 **Census**: 28 **Outpatient Visits**: 16852 **Births**: 0 **Total Expense ($000)**: 13595 **Payroll Expense ($000)**: 5806 **Personnel**: 105

COON RAPIDS—Anoka County

✉ ⇑ **MERCY HOSPITAL (240115)**, 4050 Coon Rapids Boulevard, Zip 55433–2586; tel. 763/236–6000, (Includes UNITY HOSPITAL, 550 Osborne Road NE, Fridley, Minnesota, Zip 55432–2799, tel. 763/236–5000; Helen J Strike, R.N., President) **A**1 2 3 5 10 21 **F**3 4 5 8 11 12 13 17 18 20 22 24 26 28 29 30 31 34 35 36 37 38 40 43 45 46 49 50 53 55 56 57 59 64 65 68 69 70 74 75 76 77 78 79 81 82 85 86 87 93 96 97 98 99 100 101 102 103 104 105 107 108 111 114 115 119 126 130 131 132 135 145 146 147 148 **S** Allina Health, Minneapolis, MN
Primary Contact: Sara J. Criger, President
CFO: Gerald Pietz, Vice President Finance
CMO: Ryan Else M.D., Vice President Medical Affairs
CIO: Susan Heichert, Chief Information Officer
CHR: Nancy Watson, Director Human Resources
CNO: MariBeth Olson R.N., Vice President Patient Care Services
Web address: www.allinamercy.org
Control: Other not-for-profit (including NFP Corporation) **Service**: General medical and surgical

Staffed Beds: 430 **Admissions**: 30191 **Census**: 305 **Outpatient Visits**: 237833 **Births**: 3181 **Total Expense ($000)**: 608755 **Payroll Expense ($000)**: 229856 **Personnel**: 2292

CROOKSTON—Polk County

✉ **RIVERVIEW HEALTH (241320)**, 323 South Minnesota Street, Zip 56716–1601; tel. 218/281–9200, (Total facility includes 24 beds in nursing home–type unit) **A**1 5 10 18 **F**2 3 5 6 11 13 15 28 29 34 35 36 40 45 46 47 48 49 56 57 59 62 65 66 69 70 76 77 79 81 82 85 87 93 94 96 97 99 107 108 110 111 112 115 119 127 128 129 130 132 133 135 144 145 146 147
Primary Contact: Carrie Michalski, President and Chief Executive Officer
COO: Chris Bruggeman, Chief Operating Officer
CFO: Betty Arvidson, Chief Financial Officer
CMO: Colin Fennell M.D., Chief Medical Officer
CIO: Nichole Beauchane, Director Information Technology
CHR: Jean Tate, Vice President Human Resources
CNO: April Grunhovd, Chief Nursing Officer
Web address: www.riverviewhealth.org
Control: Other not-for-profit (including NFP Corporation) **Service**: General medical and surgical

Staffed Beds: 49 **Admissions**: 869 **Census**: 30

CROSBY—Crow Wing County

✉ **CUYUNA REGIONAL MEDICAL CENTER (241353)**, 320 East Main Street, Zip 56441–1690; tel. 218/546–7000, (Total facility includes 117 beds in nursing home–type unit) **A**1 2 3 5 10 18 **F**3 7 12 13 15 18 28 29 31 34 35 40 45 46 47 48 49 50 51 56 57 59 62 63 64 65 68 70 75 76 77 78 79 81 82 84 85 86 87 91 92 93 94 97 99 100 101 103 104 107 110 111 115 116 117 118 119 124 127 128 130 131 132 133 143 144 146 147 148 149 150 **P**6
Primary Contact: Kyle Bauer, Chief Executive Officer and Chief Financial Officer
COO: Amy Hart, Chief Operating Officer
CFO: Kyle Bauer, Chief Executive Officer and Chief Financial Officer
CMO: Robert Westin M.D., Chief Medical Officer
CHR: Caity Eggen, Chief Human Resource Officer
CNO: Renee Steffin, Chief Nursing Officer
Web address: www.cuyunamed.org
Control: Hospital district or authority, Government, Nonfederal **Service**: General medical and surgical

Staffed Beds: 142 **Admissions**: 2255 **Census**: 107 **Outpatient Visits**: 166864 **Births**: 276 **Total Expense ($000)**: 108731 **Payroll Expense ($000)**: 40056 **Personnel**: 669

DAWSON—Lac Qui Parle County

JOHNSON MEMORIAL HEALTH SERVICES (241314), 1282 Walnut Street, Zip 56232–2333; tel. 320/769–4323, (Total facility includes 56 beds in nursing home–type unit) **A**10 18 **F**3 7 8 10 11 12 15 28 31 32 34 40 41 42 43 45 50 56 57 59 62 64 65 66 69 71 75 77 81 93 97 107 110 111 115 119 127 128 129 130 133 135 145 147 148 **P**6
Primary Contact: Stacey Lee, CPA, JD, Chief Executive Officer
COO: Lori Andreas, Chief Operating Officer
CFO: Crystal Bothun, Chief Financial Officer
CMO: Ayaz Virji M.D., Chief of Staff
CIO: Derrick Ochsendorf, Manager Information Technology and Systems
CHR: Megan Lynch, Manager Human Resources
CNO: Lori Andreas, Director Patient Care Services
Web address: www.jmhsmn.org
Control: Hospital district or authority, Government, Nonfederal **Service**: General medical and surgical

Staffed Beds: 76 **Admissions**: 161 **Census**: 53 **Outpatient Visits**: 10152 **Births**: 0 **Total Expense ($000)**: 15775 **Payroll Expense ($000)**: 8165 **Personnel**: 151

DEER RIVER—Itasca County

★ **ESSENTIA HEALTH–DEER RIVER (241360)**, 115 10th Avenue NE, Zip 56636–8795; tel. 218/246–2900, (Total facility includes 32 beds in nursing home–type unit) **A**10 18 **F**3 7 11 12 13 15 28 29 31 34 35 40 45 46 50 56 57 59 62 64 65 70 71 74 75 76 77 79 81 82 85 91 92 93 96 97 107 108 110 115 118 119 125 128 130 131 133 135 143 146 147 148 149 **P**6 **S** Essentia Health, Duluth, MN
Primary Contact: Marsha Green, Chief Executive Officer
CMO: David Goodall M.D., Chief Medical Staff
CHR: Brittany Mohler, Director Human Resources
Web address: www.essentiahealth.org
Control: Other not-for-profit (including NFP Corporation) **Service**: General medical and surgical

Staffed Beds: 52 **Admissions**: 424 **Census**: 31 **Outpatient Visits**: 49870 **Births**: 75 **Total Expense ($000)**: 28005 **Payroll Expense ($000)**: 13603 **Personnel**: 205

DETROIT LAKES—Becker County

✉ **ESSENTIA HEALTH ST. MARY'S – DETROIT LAKES (240101)**, 1027 Washington Avenue, Zip 56501–3409; tel. 218/847–5611, (Total facility includes 96 beds in nursing home–type unit) **A**1 5 10 20 **F**7 10 11 13 15 18 28 29 30 31 34 35 40 41 43 45 56 57 59 62 64 65 70 75 76 77 79 81 87 89 93 97 104 107 110 111 114 115 119 125 127 128 130 131 132 135 144 146 147 148 149 **S** Essentia Health, Duluth, MN
Primary Contact: Peter Jacobson, President
CMO: Rich Vetter M.D., Associate Chief
CIO: Ken Gilles, Associate Chief Information Officer
CHR: Diane Sundrud, Human Resource Service Partner
CNO: Kay Larson R.N., Chief Nursing Officer
Web address: www.essentiahealth.org
Control: Other not-for-profit (including NFP Corporation) **Service**: General medical and surgical

Staffed Beds: 131 **Admissions**: 2387 **Census**: 99 **Outpatient Visits**: 278699 **Births**: 497 **Total Expense ($000)**: 106729 **Payroll Expense ($000)**: 50693 **Personnel**: 665

ST. MARY'S INNOVIS HEALTH See Essentia Health St. Mary's – Detroit Lakes

Many Facility Codes have changed. Please refer to the AHA Guide Code Chart. © 2017 AHA Guide

DULUTH—St. Louis County

✠ △ **ESSENTIA HEALTH DULUTH (240019)**, 502 East Second Street, Zip 55805–1982; tel. 218/727–8762 **A**1 3 5 7 10 **F**3 5 11 12 15 16 29 30 31 32 34 35 49 50 51 52 54 55 56 57 59 61 64 65 70 74 75 77 78 79 81 82 84 85 86 87 90 91 92 93 94 96 97 98 99 100 101 103 104 105 107 108 110 111 114 115 116 117 118 119 120 121 123 124 130 131 132 134 135 141 144 146 147 148 149 **P**6 **S** Essentia Health, Duluth, MN
Primary Contact: James Garvey, Senior Vice President Hospital Practice, Essentia Health East
CFO: Kevin Boren, Chief Financial Officer
CMO: Hugh Renier M.D., Vice President Medical Affairs
CIO: Dennis Dassenko, Chief Information Officer
CHR: Diane Davidson, Senior Vice President Human Resources
CNO: Sandee Carlson, Director of Nursing
Web address: www.smdcmedicalcenter.org
Control: Other not–for–profit (including NFP Corporation) **Service:** General medical and surgical

Staffed Beds: 154 **Admissions:** 3049 **Census:** 71 **Outpatient Visits:** 535099 **Births:** 14 **Total Expense ($000):** 395112 **Payroll Expense ($000):** 214629 **Personnel:** 2089

✠ **ESSENTIA HEALTH ST. MARY'S MEDICAL CENTER (240002)**, 407 East Third Street, Zip 55805–1984; tel. 218/786–4000, (Includes ST. MARY'S CHILDREN'S HOSPITAL, 407 East Third Street, Duluth, Minnesota, Zip 55805–1950, tel. 218/786–5437) **A**1 2 3 5 10 **F**3 11 12 13 17 18 20 22 24 26 28 29 30 34 35 37 38 40 41 43 45 46 47 48 49 50 57 59 63 65 67 70 72 74 76 78 79 81 83 84 85 86 87 88 89 91 102 107 108 111 115 119 126 129 130 132 135 141 146 149 **P**6 **S** Essentia Health, Duluth, MN
Primary Contact: James Garvey, Senior Vice President Hospital Practice, Essentia Health East
CMO: Hugh Renier M.D., Vice President Medical Affairs
CIO: Tess Jettergren, Director Clinical Informatics
CHR: Glen Porter, Vice President Human Resources
Web address: www.essentiahealth.org/StMarysMedicalCenter/FindaClinic/Essentia–HealthSt–Marys–Medical–Center–46.aspx
Control: Other not–for–profit (including NFP Corporation) **Service:** General medical and surgical

Staffed Beds: 327 **Admissions:** 17958 **Census:** 216 **Outpatient Visits:** 131303 **Births:** 1295 **Total Expense ($000):** 377708 **Payroll Expense ($000):** 155533 **Personnel:** 2126

SMDC MEDICAL CENTER See Essentia Health Duluth

★ △ ⇑ **ST. LUKE'S HOSPITAL (240047)**, 915 East First Street, Zip 55805–2193; tel. 218/249–5555 **A**2 3 7 10 21 **F**3 8 9 11 12 13 15 18 20 22 24 26 28 29 30 31 34 35 39 40 43 45 46 47 48 49 51 53 54 57 58 59 60 61 62 63 64 65 70 74 75 76 77 78 79 81 82 83 84 85 86 87 89 90 91 92 93 97 98 99 100 102 104 107 108 110 114 115 118 119 120 121 123 124 126 129 130 131 132 144 145 146 147 148 149 **P**6
Primary Contact: John Strange, President and Chief Executive Officer
CFO: Eric Lohn, Vice President and Chief Financial Officer
CMO: Gary Peterson M.D., Vice President Medical Affairs and Chief Medical Officer
CIO: Clark Averill, Director Information Technology
CHR: Marla Halvorson, Director Human Resources
CNO: Susan Hamel, Chief Nursing Officer
Web address: www.slhduluth.com
Control: Other not–for–profit (including NFP Corporation) **Service:** General medical and surgical

Staffed Beds: 267 **Admissions:** 10463 **Census:** 151 **Outpatient Visits:** 754856 **Births:** 785 **Total Expense ($000):** 413808 **Payroll Expense ($000):** 200638 **Personnel:** 2186

ST. MARY'S MEDICAL CENTER See Essentia Health St. Mary's Medical Center

EDINA—Hennepin County

✠ ⇑ **FAIRVIEW SOUTHDALE HOSPITAL (240078)**, 6401 France Avenue South, Zip 55435–2199; tel. 952/924–5000 **A**1 2 3 5 10 21 **F**3 5 8 11 12 13 15 17 18 20 22 24 26 28 29 30 31 34 35 38 39 40 43 45 46 49 50 51 55 56 57 59 60 64 65 68 70 74 75 76 77 78 79 81 82 83 84 85 87 92 93 94 96 98 100 102 107 108 110 111 114 115 116 117 118 119 121 124 126 129 130 131 132 134 135 146 147 148 149 150 **P**6 **S** Fairview Health Services, Minneapolis, MN
Primary Contact: Bradley Beard, Regional President
CFO: Alan Lem, Vice President Finance
CHR: Michelle LeDell, Director Human Resources
Web address: www.fairview.org
Control: Other not–for–profit (including NFP Corporation) **Service:** General medical and surgical

Staffed Beds: 317 **Admissions:** 17367 **Census:** 199 **Outpatient Visits:** 129187 **Births:** 3023 **Total Expense ($000):** 401249 **Payroll Expense ($000):** 161047 **Personnel:** 1731

ELBOW LAKE—Grant County

ELEAH MEDICAL CENTER See Prairie Ridge Hospital And Health Services

★ **PRAIRIE RIDGE HOSPITAL AND HEALTH SERVICES (241379)**, 1411 Highway 79 E, Zip 56531–4611; tel. 218/685–7300 **A**10 18 **F**3 7 18 24 26 28 34 40 43 45 48 59 64 79 81 93 96 107 114 121 132 133 135 148 149 **P**5
Primary Contact: Jim Gingerich, Chief Executive Officer
CFO: Loraine Martineau, Controller
CMO: Phillip Walter Holmes M.D., Chief of Staff
CNO: Alycia Athey, Director of Nursing
Web address: www.prairiehealth.org
Control: Other not–for–profit (including NFP Corporation) **Service:** General medical and surgical

Staffed Beds: 9 **Admissions:** 141 **Census:** 2 **Outpatient Visits:** 32004 **Births:** 0 **Total Expense ($000):** 17988 **Payroll Expense ($000):** 4969 **Personnel:** 103

ELY—St. Louis County

★ **ELY–BLOOMENSON COMMUNITY HOSPITAL (241318)**, 328 West Conan Street, Zip 55731–1198; tel. 218/365–3271 **A**10 18 **F**3 15 28 31 40 45 53 62 64 81 107 110 119 130 133 148 149 **P**6
Primary Contact: John Fossum, Chief Executive Officer
CFO: Scott Kellerman, Chief Financial Officer
CHR: Rochelle Sjoberg, Director Human Resources
CNO: Becky Gaulke, Chief Nursing Officer
Web address: www.ebch.org
Control: Other not–for–profit (including NFP Corporation) **Service:** General medical and surgical

Staffed Beds: 21 **Admissions:** 236 **Census:** 2 **Outpatient Visits:** 3497 **Births:** 0 **Total Expense ($000):** 15989 **Payroll Expense ($000):** 5423 **Personnel:** 92

FAIRMONT—Martin County

☐ **MAYO CLINIC HEALTH SYSTEM IN FAIRMONT (240166)**, 800 Medical Center Drive, Zip 56031–4575; tel. 507/238–8100, (Total facility includes 40 beds in nursing home–type unit) **A**1 10 20 **F**3 12 13 15 18 28 29 30 31 34 36 40 43 45 56 57 59 64 65 68 74 75 76 77 78 79 81 82 84 85 86 87 92 93 97 99 100 101 103 104 107 108 110 111 115 118 119 128 129 130 132 133 144 146 148 149 **P**6 **S** Mayo Clinic, Rochester, MN
Primary Contact: Robert Bartingale, Administrator
COO: Gayle B Hansen R.N., Chief Operating Officer
CFO: Brian Suter, Chief Financial Officer
CMO: Rufus Rodriguez M.D., Medical Director
Web address: www.fairmontmedicalcenter.org
Control: Other not–for–profit (including NFP Corporation) **Service:** General medical and surgical

Staffed Beds: 63 **Admissions:** 1884 **Census:** 45 **Outpatient Visits:** 100299 **Births:** 228 **Personnel:** 341

FARIBAULT—Rice County

★ **DISTRICT ONE HOSPITAL (240071)**, 200 State Avenue, Zip 55021–6345; tel. 507/334–6451, (Nonreporting) **A**2 10 **S** Allina Health, Minneapolis, MN
Primary Contact: Stephen J. Pribyl, FACHE, President
COO: Rick Miller, Director, Operations and Finance
CFO: Rick Miller, Chief Financial Officer
CMO: Amy Elliott M.D., Director Medical Affairs
Web address: www.allinahealth.org/District–One–Hospital/
Control: Hospital district or authority, Government, Nonfederal **Service:** General medical and surgical

Staffed Beds: 42

FERGUS FALLS—Otter Tail County

☐ **COMMUNITY BEHAVIORAL HEALTH HOSPITAL – FERGUS FALLS (244013)**, 1801 West Alcott Avenue, Zip 56537–2661, Mailing Address: P.O.Box 478, 56538–0478; tel. 218/332–5001, (Nonreporting) **A**1 10 **S** Minnesota Department of Human Services, Saint Paul, MN
Primary Contact: Brenda Schleske, Administrator
Control: State, Government, Nonfederal **Service:** Psychiatric

Staffed Beds: 16

MN

Hospital, Medicare Provider Number, Address, Telephone, Approval, Facility, and Physician Codes, Health Care System

★ American Hospital Association (AHA) membership
☐ The Joint Commission accreditation
○ Healthcare Facilities Accreditation Program
◇ DNV Healthcare Inc. accreditation
⇑ Center for Improvement in Healthcare Quality Accreditation
△ Commission on Accreditation of Rehabilitation Facilities (CARF) accreditation

⊞ △ **LAKE REGION HEALTHCARE (240052)**, 712 South Cascade Street, Zip 56537–2900, Mailing Address: P.O.Box 728, 56538–0728; tel. 218/736–8000 **A**1 7 10 20 **F**3 10 11 13 15 17 18 26 28 29 30 31 32 34 35 36 40 43 44 45 50 51 53 54 56 57 58 59 61 64 65 70 74 75 76 77 78 79 81 82 84 85 86 87 89 90 92 93 94 96 97 98 100 101 102 103 104 107 108 110 111 115 118 119 120 121 123 130 131 132 135 144 146 147 148
Primary Contact: Kyle Richards, Chief Executive Officer
CFO: Brett Longtin, Chief Financial Officer
CMO: Greg Smith, Chief Medical Officer
CIO: Wade A Jyrkas, Director Computer Information Systems
CHR: Kim Blank, Director Human Resources
CNO: Lucia E Anderson, Senior Vice President Operations and Chief Nurse Executive
Web address: www.lrhc.org
Control: Other not–for–profit (including NFP Corporation) **Service**: General medical and surgical

> **Staffed Beds: 108 Admissions: 2609 Census: 29 Outpatient Visits:** 59070
> **Births: 302 Total Expense ($000): 120285 Payroll Expense ($000):** 41114
> **Personnel: 763**

FOSSTON—Polk County

★ **ESSENTIA HEALTH FOSSTON (241357)**, 900 Hilligoss Boulevard SE, Zip 56542–1599; tel. 218/435–1133, (Total facility includes 50 beds in nursing home–type unit) **A**10 18 **F**3 7 10 11 13 15 18 28 29 31 34 35 40 43 44 50 56 57 59 62 63 65 68 70 75 76 77 78 79 80 81 82 84 85 87 93 97 99 104 107 110 114 127 128 129 130 131 132 133 135 146 148 149 **P**6 **S** Essentia Health, Duluth, MN
Primary Contact: Kevin Gish, Administrator and Vice President
CFO: Kim Bodensteiner, Chief Financial Officer
CHR: Diane Sundrud, Director Human Resources
Web address: www.essentiahealth.org
Control: Other not–for–profit (including NFP Corporation) **Service**: General medical and surgical

> **Staffed Beds: 74 Admissions: 534 Census: 42 Outpatient Visits:** 57540
> **Births: 99 Total Expense ($000): 26288 Payroll Expense ($000):** 13249
> **Personnel: 222**

FIRST CARE MEDICAL SERVICES See Essentia Health Fosston

GLENCOE—Mcleod County

★ **GLENCOE REGIONAL HEALTH SERVICES (241355)**, 1805 Hennepin Avenue North, Zip 55336–1416; tel. 320/864–3121, (Total facility includes 110 beds in nursing home–type unit) **A**10 18 **F**3 11 13 15 28 29 31 34 40 43 45 48 50 56 64 68 75 76 77 78 79 81 85 86 87 89 93 97 107 111 115 118 119 125 128 130 132 133 135 144 146 148 149 **P**6 **S** HealthPartners, Bloomington, MN
Primary Contact: Jon D. Braband, FACHE, President and Chief Executive Officer
CFO: John C Doidge, Vice President Finance
CMO: John H Bergseng D.O., Vice President Medical Affairs
CIO: Ryan Lake, Director Medical Imaging and Information Technology
CHR: Jill Hatlestad, Vice President Human Resources and Marketing
CNO: Patricia Henderson R.N., Vice President Nursing and Clinical Services
Web address: www.grhsonline.org
Control: Other not–for–profit (including NFP Corporation) **Service**: General medical and surgical

> **Staffed Beds: 135 Admissions: 1004 Census: 104 Outpatient Visits:** 26177 **Births: 172 Total Expense ($000): 57508 Payroll Expense ($000):** 27703 **Personnel: 400**

GLENWOOD—Pope County

★ **GLACIAL RIDGE HEALTH SYSTEM (241376)**, 10 Fourth Avenue SE, Zip 56334–1898; tel. 320/634–4521 **A**10 18 **F**7 11 12 13 15 17 28 31 34 35 40 41 43 53 59 62 63 64 75 76 79 81 93 107 110 111 114 119 127 130 133 146 148 149 **P**6
Primary Contact: Kirk A. Stensrud, Chief Executive Officer
CFO: Kyle Chase, Chief Financial Officer
CMO: Gustave Mellgren M.D., Chief of Staff
CIO: Jeff Ofstedal, Manager Information Technology
CHR: Gordon Paulson, Manager Human Resources
CNO: Lynn Flesner, Director of Nursing
Web address: www.glacialridge.org
Control: Hospital district or authority, Government, Nonfederal **Service**: General medical and surgical

> **Staffed Beds: 19 Admissions: 825 Census: 9 Outpatient Visits:** 17355
> **Births: 60 Total Expense ($000): 31398 Payroll Expense ($000):** 15140
> **Personnel: 257**

GOLDEN VALLEY—Hennepin County

⊞ **REGENCY HOSPITAL OF MINNEAPOLIS (242005)**, 1300 Hidden Lakes Parkway, Zip 55422–4286; tel. 763/588–2750, (Nonreporting) **A**1 10 **S** Select Medical Corporation, Mechanicsburg, PA
Primary Contact: Marshall E. Smith, Chief Executive Officer
CMO: Alaka Nagaraj M.D., Medical Director
CNO: Caren Gaytko, Chief Nursing Officer
Web address: www.regencyhospital.com
Control: Corporation, Investor–owned (for–profit) **Service**: Acute long–term care hospital

> **Staffed Beds: 92**

GRACEVILLE—Big Stone County

★ **ESSENTIA HEALTH–GRACEVILLE (241321)**, 115 West Second Street, Zip 56240–4845, Mailing Address: P.O.Box 157, 56240–0157; tel. 320/748–7223, (Nonreporting) **A**10 18 **S** Essentia Health, Duluth, MN
Primary Contact: Julie Rosenberg, Administrator
CMO: Arthur Van Vranken M.D., Chief Medical Officer
CIO: Brad Tostenson, Chief Information Officer
CHR: Jenny Lee, Human Resources Generalist
CNO: Jill Johnsrud, Director of Nursing
Web address: www.essentiahealth.org/HolyTrinityHospital/FindaClinic/Essentia–HealthHoly–Trinity–Hospital–96.aspx
Control: Other not–for–profit (including NFP Corporation) **Service**: General medical and surgical

> **Staffed Beds: 60**

GRACEVILLE HEALTH CENTER See Essentia Health–Graceville

GRAND MARAIS—Cook County

★ **NORTH SHORE HEALTH (241317)**, 515 5th Avenue West, Zip 55604–3017; tel. 218/387–3040, (Total facility includes 37 beds in nursing home–type unit) **A**10 18 **F**3 7 11 15 28 40 45 50 56 59 62 64 75 84 85 89 93 107 110 111 115 119 128 130 133 148 149
Primary Contact: Kimber L. Wraalstad, FACHE, Administrator
CFO: Vera Schumann, Director of Finance and Controller
CMO: Milan Schmidt, Medical Director
CIO: Greg Johnson, IT Coordinator
CHR: Robert Willis, Director Human Resources
CNO: Bridget Sobieck, Director of Nursing
Web address: www.nshorehospital.com
Control: Hospital district or authority, Government, Nonfederal **Service**: General medical and surgical

> **Staffed Beds: 53 Admissions: 196 Census: 31 Outpatient Visits:** 11159
> **Births: 2 Total Expense ($000): 15064 Payroll Expense ($000):** 5979
> **Personnel: 114**

GRAND RAPIDS—Itasca County

⊞ **GRAND ITASCA CLINIC AND HOSPITAL (240064)**, 1601 Golf Course Road, Zip 55744–8648; tel. 218/326–5000, (Nonreporting) **A**1 10 20 **S** Fairview Health Services, Minneapolis, MN
Primary Contact: Michael Youso, Chief Executive Officer
CFO: Sarah S Gustafson, Vice President of Finance
CHR: Julie Schmidt, Director Human Resources
CNO: Sue Skinner, Vice President of Patient Care Services
Web address: www.granditasca.org
Control: Other not–for–profit (including NFP Corporation) **Service**: General medical and surgical

> **Staffed Beds: 31**

GRANITE FALLS—Yellow Medicine County

★ **GRANITE FALLS MUNICIPAL HOSPITAL AND MANOR (241343)**, 345 Tenth Avenue, Zip 56241–1499; tel. 320/564–3111, (Nonreporting) **A**10 18
Primary Contact: Thomas Kooiman, Chief Executive Officer
CFO: Val Hoffman, Chief Financial Officer
CIO: Kris Wilke, Manager Health Information
CHR: Sue Tollefson, Coordinator Payroll Personnel
CNO: Patty Massman, Director of Nursing
Web address: www.granitefallshealthcare.com
Control: City, Government, Nonfederal **Service**: General medical and surgical

> **Staffed Beds: 82**

MN

Many Facility Codes have changed. Please refer to the AHA Guide Code Chart. © 2017 AHA Guide

HALLOCK—Kittson County

★ **KITTSON MEMORIAL HEALTHCARE CENTER (241336)**, 1010 South
Birch Street, Zip 56728–4215, Mailing Address: P.O.Box 700, 56728–0700;
tel. 218/843–3612, (Nonreporting) **A**10 18
Primary Contact: Ashley Rivera, Chief Financial Officer and Chief Executive Officer
CFO: Todd Christensen, Chief Financial Officer
CMO: Thomas Lohstreter M.D., Chief of Staff
CIO: Holly Knutson, Manager Information Technology
CHR: Carlene Cole, Manager Human Resources
CNO: Tawnya Sorenson, Director of Nursing
Web address: www.kmhc.net
Control: Other not–for–profit (including NFP Corporation) **Service**: General
medical and surgical

Staffed Beds: 75

HASTINGS—Dakota County

⊞ **REGINA HOSPITAL (240059)**, 1175 Nininger Road, Zip 55033–1098;
tel. 651/480–4100 **A**1 10 **F**3 8 11 13 15 28 29 30 34 35 40 43 45 46 50 57
59 75 76 77 79 80 81 87 93 103 107 110 111 114 119 129 130 132 145 146
148 149 **S** Allina Health, Minneapolis, MN
Primary Contact: Thomas R. Thompson, President
CFO: Andy Rolling, Director of Finance
CMO: James Noreen M.D., Chief Medical Officer
Web address: www.reginamedical.org
Control: Other not–for–profit (including NFP Corporation) **Service**: General
medical and surgical

Staffed Beds: 29 Admissions: 1657 Census: 19 Outpatient Visits: 50940
Births: 248 Total Expense ($000): 47841 Payroll Expense ($000): 18727
Personnel: 266

HENDRICKS—Lincoln County

★ **HENDRICKS COMMUNITY HOSPITAL ASSOCIATION (241339)**, 503 East
Lincoln Street, Zip 56136–9598, Mailing Address: P.O.Box 106, 56136–0106;
tel. 507/275–3134, (Total facility includes 58 beds in nursing home–type unit) **A**10
18 **F**2 3 7 10 11 15 17 28 29 31 34 35 40 50 59 62 63 70 81 89 93 107 125
127 128 130 132 133 146 148
Primary Contact: Jeffrey Gollaher, Chief Executive Officer
CMO: Tabb McCluskey M.D., Chief Medical Officer
CHR: Lynn R Olson, Director Human Resources
Web address: www.hendrickshosp.org
Control: Other not–for–profit (including NFP Corporation) **Service**: General
medical and surgical

Staffed Beds: 70 Admissions: 178 Census: 59 Outpatient Visits: 11935
Births: 0 Total Expense ($000): 12857 Payroll Expense ($000): 7150
Personnel: 108

HIBBING—St. Louis County

⊞ **RANGE REGIONAL HEALTH SERVICES (240040)**, 750 East 34th Street,
Zip 55746–4600; tel. 218/262–4881 **A**1 2 10 **F**3 6 11 13 15 17 28 29 30 31
33 34 35 40 43 50 57 62 63 64 65 68 70 75 76 77 78 79 81 82 84 85 87
89 93 94 97 98 99 100 102 104 105 107 108 110 111 115 117 118 119
120 121 129 130 131 132 135 143 144 146 148 149 **P**6 **S** Fairview Health
Services, Minneapolis, MN
Primary Contact: Debra K. Boardman, FACHE, President and Chief Executive
Officer
COO: Patrick Sharp, Chief Operating Officer
CFO: Tom Fink, Vice President Regional Finance Officer
CMO: Susan Rudberg M.D., Chief Medical Officer
CIO: Jessica Valento, Director Information Systems
CHR: Mitchell S Vincent, Vice President Organizational Support
CNO: Connie Harle, Chief Nursing Officer
Web address: www.range.fairview.org
Control: Other not–for–profit (including NFP Corporation) **Service**: General
medical and surgical

Staffed Beds: 72 Admissions: 2403 Census: 35 Outpatient Visits: 48404
Births: 351 Total Expense ($000): 113081 Payroll Expense ($000): 57919
Personnel: 847

HUTCHINSON—Mcleod County

⊞ **HUTCHINSON HEALTH (240187)**, 1095 Highway 15 South, Zip 55350–3182;
tel. 320/234–5000 **A**1 10 20 **F**3 5 11 13 15 28 29 31 34 35 36 38 40 43 45
47 56 57 59 64 65 69 70 75 76 77 78 79 81 82 85 86 87 93 96 97 98 99 100
103 104 107 110 111 115 119 127 129 130 131 132 144 146 147 148 149
P6 **S** Allina Health, Minneapolis, MN
Primary Contact: Steven Mulder, M.D., President and Chief Executive Officer
COO: Glen Kegley, Chief Operating Officer
CFO: Pamela Larson, Division Director Financial Services
CMO: Brian Pollman, Chief Medical Officer
CIO: Jim Lyons, Chief Clinic Officer
CHR: Rebecca Streich, Manager Human Resources and Education Manager
CNO: Terry J. Graner R.N., Chief Nursing Officer
Web address: www.hutchhealth.com
Control: Other not–for–profit (including NFP Corporation) **Service**: General
medical and surgical

Staffed Beds: 49 Admissions: 2017 Census: 22 Outpatient Visits: 223713
Births: 285 Total Expense ($000): 86605 Payroll Expense ($000): 32479
Personnel: 480

INTERNATIONAL FALLS—Koochiching County

☐ **RAINY LAKE MEDICAL CENTER (241322)**, 1400 Highway 71, Zip 56649–
2189; tel. 218/283–4481, (Nonreporting) **A**1 10 18
Primary Contact: Bonnie Erickson, Chief Executive Officer
CFO: Melissa Marcotte, Chief Financial Officer
CIO: Michael Blesi, Director Information Technology
CNO: Donita Ettestad R.N., MS, Chief Nursing Officer
Web address: www.rainylakemedical.com
Control: Other not–for–profit (including NFP Corporation) **Service**: General
medical and surgical

Staffed Beds: 25

JACKSON—Jackson County

★ **SANFORD JACKSON MEDICAL CENTER (241315)**, 1430 North Highway,
Zip 56143–1093; tel. 507/847–2420 **A**10 18 **F**1 3 15 18 28 29 31 34 35 40
41 43 45 56 57 59 64 65 66 67 68 75 77 78 79 81 82 85 86 87 89 93 97
107 108 110 111 114 118 119 127 128 129 132 133 148 149 **P**6 **S** Sanford
Health, Sioux Falls, SD
Primary Contact: Dawn Schnell, Chief Nursing Officer and Interim Senior Director
CFO: Gail Eike, Chief Financial Officer
CMO: SisterMarie Paul Lockerd M.D., Chief Medical Officer
CNO: Dawn Schnell, Chief Nursing Officer
Web address: www.sanfordjackson.org
Control: Other not–for–profit (including NFP Corporation) **Service**: General
medical and surgical

Staffed Beds: 14 Admissions: 168 Census: 2 Outpatient Visits: 25939
Births: 0 Total Expense ($000): 9016 Payroll Expense ($000): 3814
Personnel: 66

LAKE CITY—Goodhue County

☐ **MAYO CLINIC HEALTH SYSTEM IN LAKE CITY (241338)**, 500 West Grant
Street, Zip 55041–1143; tel. 651/345–3321, (Total facility includes 90 beds in
nursing home–type unit) **A**1 10 18 **F**15 18 28 29 30 34 35 40 45 57 59 64 67
69 75 79 81 87 92 93 97 107 110 111 114 119 128 130 132 133 146 148
149 **P**6 **S** Mayo Clinic, Rochester, MN
Primary Contact: Thomas J. Witt, M.D., President and Chief Executive Officer
CFO: David Biren, Chief Financial Officer
CMO: Dennis Spano M.D., Medical Director
CHR: Jacqueline Ryan, Director Human Resources
Web address: www.lakecitymedicalcenter.org
Control: Other not–for–profit (including NFP Corporation) **Service**: General
medical and surgical

Staffed Beds: 101 Admissions: 752 Census: 99 Outpatient Visits: 52737
Births: 0 Personnel: 142

MN

LE SUEUR—Le Sueur County

★ **RIDGEVIEW LE SUEUR MEDICAL CENTER (241375)**, 621 South Fourth Street, Zip 56058–2298; tel. 507/665–3375, (Nonreporting) **A**10 18 **S** Ridgeview Medical Center, Waconia, MN
Primary Contact: Pam Williams, Vice President
CFO: Patricia Schlegel, Executive Director Finance
CMO: Carolyn Stelter M.D., Chief of Staff
CHR: Bonnie Barnhardt, Executive Director Human Resources
CNO: Kim Putz R.N., Director, Nursing Hospital
Web address: www.mvhc.org
Control: Other not–for–profit (including NFP Corporation) **Service**: General medical and surgical

Staffed Beds: 64

LITCHFIELD—Meeker County

★ **MEEKER MEMORIAL HOSPITAL (241366)**, 612 South Sibley Avenue, Zip 55355–3398; tel. 320/693–4500 **A**10 18 **F**11 13 15 28 29 31 34 40 43 45 57 59 70 75 77 78 81 93 107 110 111 114 119 130 133 146 148 149
Primary Contact: Kyle R. Rasmussen, Chief Executive Officer
CFO: Stephen Plaisance, Chief Financial Officer
CMO: Tim Peterson M.D., Chief of Staff
CIO: Troy Bruning, Director Information Technology
CHR: Cindi Twardy, Manager Human Resources
CNO: Joan Bitz, Chief Nursing Officer
Web address: www.meekermemorial.org
Control: County, Government, Nonfederal **Service**: General medical and surgical

Staffed Beds: 38 Admissions: 930 Census: 13 Outpatient Visits: 29381
Births: 160 Total Expense ($000): 31449 Payroll Expense ($000): 11140
Personnel: 169

LITTLE FALLS—Morrison County

⊞ **CHI ST. GABRIEL'S HEALTH (241370)**, 815 Second Street SE, Zip 56345–3596; tel. 320/632–5441, (Nonreporting) **A**1 10 18 **S** Catholic Health Initiatives, Englewood, CO
Primary Contact: Lee Boyles, President
CFO: Steve Smith, Assistant Vice President Finance
CMO: Susan Okoniewski M.D., Chief of Staff
Web address: www.stgabriels.com
Control: Church operated, Nongovernment, not–for–profit **Service**: General medical and surgical

Staffed Beds: 25

LONG PRAIRIE—Todd County

★ **CENTRACARE HEALTH–LONG PRAIRIE (241326)**, 20 Ninth Street SE, Zip 56347–1404; tel. 320/732–2141, (Nonreporting) **A**3 5 10 18 **S** CentraCare Health, Saint Cloud, MN
Primary Contact: Daniel J. Swenson, FACHE, Administrator
CFO: Larry Knutson, Director Finance
CMO: Rene Eldidy M.D., Chief of Staff
Web address: www.centracare.com
Control: Other not–for–profit (including NFP Corporation) **Service**: General medical and surgical

Staffed Beds: 20

LONG PRAIRIE MEMORIAL HOSPITAL AND HOME See Centracare Health–Long Prairie

LUVERNE—Rock County

★ **SANFORD LUVERNE MEDICAL CENTER (241371)**, 1600 North Kniss Avenue, Zip 56156–1067; tel. 507/283–2321 **A**10 18 **F**3 4 5 7 8 11 13 15 18 19 28 29 31 32 34 35 40 43 45 56 57 59 63 64 65 67 68 74 75 76 77 78 79 81 82 83 84 85 86 87 90 93 96 97 107 111 114 118 119 128 129 131 132 133 135 146 147 148 149 **P**6 **S** Sanford Health, Sioux Falls, SD
Primary Contact: Tammy Loosbrock, Chief Executive Officer
COO: Nancy E Drenth R.N., Director Ancillary Services
CFO: Stanley Knobloch, Director Fiscal Services
CMO: Judy S Chesley M.D., Chief of Staff
CNO: Nyla H Sandbulte R.N., Director of Nursing
Web address: www.sanfordluverne.org
Control: Other not–for–profit (including NFP Corporation) **Service**: General medical and surgical

Staffed Beds: 25 Admissions: 546 Census: 6 Outpatient Visits: 31483
Births: 78 Total Expense ($000): 23250 Payroll Expense ($000): 9829
Personnel: 155

MADELIA—Watonwan County

⊞ **MADELIA COMMUNITY HOSPITAL (241323)**, 121 Drew Avenue SE, Zip 56062–1899; tel. 507/642–3255 **A**1 5 10 18 **F**3 11 13 15 34 35 40 57 59 62 64 68 69 75 76 77 81 84 85 86 93 102 107 110 114 128 130 132 133 144 145 149
Primary Contact: Candace Fenske, Chief Executive Officer
CFO: Donna M Klinkner, Chief Financial Officer
CMO: Todd Gavin, Chief Medical Officer
CIO: Valerie Juhl, Director of Health
CHR: Donna M Klinkner, Chief Financial Officer
CNO: Deidre Hruby, Director of Patient Care
Web address: www.mchospital.org
Control: Other not–for–profit (including NFP Corporation) **Service**: General medical and surgical

Staffed Beds: 21 Admissions: 209 Census: 3 Outpatient Visits: 9430
Births: 0 Total Expense ($000): 11329 Payroll Expense ($000): 4413
Personnel: 68

MADISON—Lac Qui Parle County

★ **MADISON HEALTHCARE SERVICES (241372)**, 900 Second Avenue, Zip 56256–1006; tel. 320/598–7556 **A**10 18 **F**10 11 15 28 29 30 34 40 43 57 59 62 64 65 77 78 79 81 82 84 93 97 107 110 111 119 127 130 132 133 145 147 149 **P**5
Primary Contact: Erik Bjerke, Chief Executive Officer
CFO: Carol Borgerson, Business Office Manager and Chief Financial Officer
CIO: Jerry Harberts, Information Technologist
CHR: Allen Anderson, Director Human Resources
Web address: www.mlhmn.org/
Control: Other not–for–profit (including NFP Corporation) **Service**: General medical and surgical

Staffed Beds: 12 Admissions: 183 Census: 2 Outpatient Visits: 12905
Births: 3 Total Expense ($000): 10300 Payroll Expense ($000): 3846
Personnel: 55

MAHNOMEN—Mahnomen County

★ **MAHNOMEN HEALTH CENTER (241300)**, 414 West Jefferson Avenue, Zip 56557–4912, Mailing Address: P.O.Box 396, 56557–0396; tel. 218/935–2511, (Total facility includes 32 beds in nursing home–type unit) **A**10 18 **F**2 3 7 11 15 34 40 43 57 59 62 110 128 130 132 133 146 149 **S** Sanford Health, Sioux Falls, SD
Primary Contact: Dale K. Kruger, Chief Executive Officer
CFO: Mary Pazdernik, Chief Financial Officer
CMO: Anju Gurung M.D., Chief Medical Officer
CHR: Kristi Stall, Chief Human Resources Officer
Web address: www.mahnomenhealthcenter.com
Control: City–county, Government, Nonfederal **Service**: General medical and surgical

Staffed Beds: 50 Admissions: 102 Census: 28 Outpatient Visits: 17488
Births: 0 Total Expense ($000): 8907 Payroll Expense ($000): 3066
Personnel: 77

MANKATO—Blue Earth County

⊞ **MAYO CLINIC HEALTH SYSTEM IN MANKATO (240093)**, 1025 Marsh Street, Zip 56001–4752; tel. 507/625–4031 **A**1 3 5 10 13 **F**3 7 11 12 13 15 18 19 20 22 26 28 29 30 31 33 34 35 36 38 40 41 43 45 49 53 54 56 57 58 59 60 61 63 64 65 66 68 70 73 74 75 76 77 78 79 81 82 83 84 85 87 89 91 92 93 97 98 99 100 102 103 104 107 108 110 111 114 115 118 119 120 121 126 127 129 130 131 132 135 144 146 147 148 149 **P**6 **S** Mayo Clinic, Rochester, MN
Primary Contact: James Hebl, Regional Vice President
CFO: James Tarasovitch, Chief Financial Officer
CMO: Susan Pearson M.D., Chief Medical Officer
CIO: Sarah Daniels, Vice President, Information Technology
CHR: Beth Dittbenner, Regional Director, Human Resources
Web address: www.isj–mhs.org
Control: Other not–for–profit (including NFP Corporation) **Service**: General medical and surgical

Staffed Beds: 168 Admissions: 10147 Census: 97 Outpatient Visits: 280304 Births: 1387 Personnel: 1665

Many Facility Codes have changed. Please refer to the AHA Guide Code Chart.

© 2017 AHA Guide

MN

MAPLE GROVE—Hennepin County

✠ ⇑ **MAPLE GROVE HOSPITAL (240214)**, 9875 Hospital Drive, Zip 55369–4648; tel. 763/581–1000 **A**1 3 10 21 **F**3 13 15 18 29 30 40 43 45 47 53 60 68 70 72 76 77 79 81 84 85 89 100 102 107 108 111 115 118 119 126 130 146 148 149 **P**8 **S** North Memorial Health Care, Robbinsdale, MN
Primary Contact: Andrew S. Cochrane, Chief Executive Officer
CFO: Aaron Bloomquist, Chief Financial Officer
CMO: Pamela Doorenbos, Medical Director, Medical Affairs
CHR: Rebecca A Thiesfeld Rauen, Director Human Resources
CNO: Faith Zwirchitz, Director Nursing and Professional Practice
Web address: www.maplegrovehospital.org
Control: Other not–for–profit (including NFP Corporation) **Service**: General medical and surgical

Staffed Beds: 108 **Admissions**: 8991 **Census**: 63 **Outpatient Visits**: 209718 **Births**: 4623 **Total Expense ($000)**: 155630 **Payroll Expense ($000)**: 53177 **Personnel**: 652

MAPLEWOOD—Ramsey County

✠ **ST. JOHN'S HOSPITAL (240210)**, 1575 Beam Avenue, Zip 55109–1126; tel. 651/232–7000 **A**1 3 5 10 **F**3 13 15 17 18 28 29 30 31 34 35 36 37 38 40 43 44 45 46 49 50 51 55 57 59 61 63 64 68 70 72 74 75 76 77 78 79 81 82 85 86 87 89 93 96 97 100 102 104 107 108 110 111 114 115 116 117 118 119 121 123 126 129 130 131 132 135 146 147 148 149 **P**8 **S** Fairview Health Services, Minneapolis, MN
Primary Contact: Catherine Barr, Senior Vice President and Chief Operating Officer
COO: Brian Gager, Vice President Operations, Acute Care Hospitals
CMO: Kevin C. Garrett M.D., Chief Medical Officer
CIO: Joanne Sundquist, Chief Information Officer
CHR: Dawn Kessler, Senior Vice President Human Resources
CNO: Debra J Hurd R.N., MS, Vice President Nursing Acute Care
Web address: www.stjohnshospital–mn.org
Control: Other not–for–profit (including NFP Corporation) **Service**: General medical and surgical

Staffed Beds: 198 **Admissions**: 11730 **Census**: 100 **Outpatient Visits**: 115504 **Births**: 2362 **Total Expense ($000)**: 235902 **Payroll Expense ($000)**: 89356 **Personnel**: 931

MARSHALL—Lyon County

★ **AVERA MARSHALL REGIONAL MEDICAL CENTER (241359)**, 300 South Bruce Street, Zip 56258–3900; tel. 507/532–9661, (Nonreporting) **A**10 18 **S** Avera Health, Sioux Falls, SD
Primary Contact: Mary B. Maertens, FACHE, President and Chief Executive Officer
CFO: Sharon Williams, Vice President Finance and Information Technology
CMO: Edward Woiske M.D., Chief Medical Officer
CIO: Sharon Williams, Vice President Finance and Information Technology
CHR: Sonya J Kayser, Human Resources Officer
CNO: Dodie Derynck, Chief Nursing Officer
Web address: www.avera.org
Control: City, Government, Nonfederal **Service**: General medical and surgical

Staffed Beds: 111

MELROSE—Stearns County

★ **CENTRACARE HEALTH–MELROSE (241330)**, 525 Main Street West, Zip 56352–1043; tel. 320/256–4231, (Total facility includes 75 beds in nursing home–type unit) **A**10 18 **F**2 6 7 10 13 15 28 30 34 35 40 56 57 59 75 76 77 78 79 81 85 89 93 99 103 107 110 114 115 118 121 122 125 127 128 129 130 132 133 146 148 **S** CentraCare Health, Saint Cloud, MN
Primary Contact: Gerry Gilbertson, FACHE, Administrator
COO: Gerry Gilbertson FACHE, Administrator
CFO: Adam Paulson, Director Finance
CMO: Dante Beretta M.D., Chief of Staff
CIO: Janet Kruzel, Business Office Manager
CHR: Joyce Chan, Chief Human Resources Officer
CNO: Keri Wimmer R.N., Patient Care Director
Web address: www.centracare.com
Control: Other not–for–profit (including NFP Corporation) **Service**: General medical and surgical

Staffed Beds: 93 **Admissions**: 566 **Census**: 79 **Payroll Expense ($000)**: 13265 **Personnel**: 207

MINNEAPOLIS—Hennepin County

✠ ⇑ **ABBOTT NORTHWESTERN HOSPITAL (240057)**, 800 East 28th Street, Zip 55407–3799; tel. 612/863–4000, (Includes SISTER KENNY REHABILITATION INSTITUTE, 810 East 27th Street, Minneapolis, Minnesota, Zip 55407, tel. 612/874–4000) (Total facility includes 44 beds in nursing home–type unit) **A**1 2 3 5 10 21 **F**3 8 9 12 13 15 17 18 19 20 22 24 26 28 29 30 31 34 35 36 38 39 40 41 42 43 44 45 46 47 48 49 50 51 52 53 54 55 56 57 58 59 60 61 63 64 65 66 68 70 71 74 75 76 77 78 79 81 82 83 84 85 86 87 90 91 92 93 94 95 96 97 98 99 100 101 102 103 104 105 107 108 109 110 111 112 113 114 115 116 117 118 119 120 121 123 124 126 128 129 130 131 132 135 136 137 138 141 143 144 145 146 147 148 149 **P**6 **S** Allina Health, Minneapolis, MN
Primary Contact: Thomas O'Connor, Interim Chief Executive Officer
CFO: Brian Weinreis, Vice President Operations and Finance
CMO: Penny Ann Wheeler M.D., President and Chief Medical Officer
CIO: Susan Heichert, Senior Vice President and Chief Information Officer
CHR: Margaret Butler, Vice President Human Resources
Web address: www.abbottnorthwestern.com
Control: Other not–for–profit (including NFP Corporation) **Service**: General medical and surgical

Staffed Beds: 675 **Admissions**: 36315 **Census**: 455 **Outpatient Visits**: 493711 **Births**: 5241 **Total Expense ($000)**: 1141943 **Payroll Expense ($000)**: 487588 **Personnel**: 4140

✠ **CHILDREN'S HOSPITALS AND CLINICS OF MINNESOTA (243302)**, 2525 Chicago Avenue South, Zip 55404–4518; tel. 612/813–6100, (Includes CHILDREN'S HOSPITALS AND CLINICS OF MINNESOTA, 345 North Smith Avenue, Saint Paul, Minnesota, Zip 55102–2346, tel. 651/220–6000; Robert Bonar Jr, Chief Executive Officer) **A**1 3 5 10 **F**3 8 9 17 18 19 20 21 22 23 24 25 26 27 28 29 30 31 32 34 35 36 38 39 40 43 45 50 51 54 55 57 58 59 61 62 63 64 65 68 71 72 73 74 75 77 78 79 80 81 82 84 85 86 87 88 89 92 93 97 99 100 101 102 104 107 108 111 112 114 115 119 129 130 131 132 134 135 136 143 145 146 148
Primary Contact: Robert Bonar Jr, Chief Executive Officer
COO: David S Overman, President and Chief Operating Officer
CFO: Rebecca Woitalewicz, Chief Financial Officer
CMO: Emily Chapman, Chief Medical Officer
CIO: Jeffrey D Young, Chief Information Officer
CHR: Samantha Hanson, Chief Human Resources Officer
CNO: Roxanne Fernandes R.N., Chief Nursing Officer
Web address: www.childrensmn.org
Control: Other not–for–profit (including NFP Corporation) **Service**: Children's general medical and surgical

Staffed Beds: 429 **Admissions**: 14588 **Census**: 290 **Outpatient Visits**: 447731 **Births**: 0 **Total Expense ($000)**: 833800

FAIRVIEW RIVERSIDE HOSPITAL See University Of Minnesota Medical Center, Fairview

☐ △ **HENNEPIN COUNTY MEDICAL CENTER (240004)**, 701 Park Avenue South, Zip 55415–1829; tel. 612/873–3000, (Includes HCMC DEPARTMENT OF PEDIATRICS, 701 Park Avenue, Minneapolis, Minnesota, Zip 55415–1623, tel. 612/873–2064) **A**1 2 3 5 7 8 10 **F**3 5 7 12 13 15 16 18 20 22 24 26 28 29 30 31 32 33 34 35 36 38 39 40 41 43 44 45 46 47 48 49 50 51 53 54 55 56 57 58 59 60 61 62 63 64 65 66 68 70 72 74 75 76 77 78 79 81 82 84 85 86 87 88 89 90 92 93 94 96 97 98 99 100 101 102 103 104 105 107 108 110 111 112 114 115 117 118 119 120 121 129 130 131 132 134 135 138 141 144 145 146 147 148 149 150 **P**6
Primary Contact: Jon Pryor, M.D., Chief Executive Officer
CFO: Larry Kryzaniak, Chief Financial Officer
CMO: William Heegaard M.D., Chief Medical Officer
CIO: Nancy Garrett, Chief Analytics and Information Technology Officer
CHR: Walter Chesley, Senior Vice President Human Resources
CNO: Kathy R Wilde R.N., Chief Nursing Officer
Web address: www.hcmc.org
Control: County, Government, Nonfederal **Service**: General medical and surgical

Staffed Beds: 461 **Admissions**: 23528 **Census**: 354 **Outpatient Visits**: 718207 **Births**: 1979 **Total Expense ($000)**: 1015357 **Payroll Expense ($000)**: 538664 **Personnel**: 5840

⊠ △ **MINNEAPOLIS VETERANS AFFAIRS HEALTH CARE SYSTEM**, One Veterans Drive, Zip 55417–2399; tel. 612/725–2000 **A**1 2 3 5 7 8 **F**1 2 3 5 8 9 12 15 18 20 22 24 26 28 29 30 31 33 35 36 38 39 40 46 47 49 52 53 56 57 58 59 60 61 62 63 64 65 70 74 75 77 78 79 80 81 82 83 84 85 86 87 90 91 92 93 94 95 96 97 98 100 101 102 103 104 105 107 108 109 110 111 112 113 114 115 116 117 118 119 120 121 122 123 124 126 127 130 131 132 135 143 144 146 147 148 149 **S** Department of Veterans Affairs, Washington, DC
Primary Contact: Patrick J. Kelly, FACHE, Director
COO: Kurt Thielen, Associate Director
CFO: LeAnn Stomberg, Chief Financial Officer
CMO: Kent Crossley M.D., Chief of Staff
CIO: Brian Bornick, Chief Information Officer
CHR: Torn Johnson, Chief Human Resource Officer
CNO: Helen Pearlman, Nurse Executive
Web address: www.minneapolis.va.gov
Control: Veterans Affairs, Government, federal **Service:** General medical and surgical

Staffed Beds: 309 **Admissions:** 8689 **Census:** 199 **Outpatient Visits:** 903280 **Births:** 0

⊠ **PHILLIPS EYE INSTITUTE (240196)**, 2215 Park Avenue, Zip 55404–3756; tel. 612/775–8800, (Nonreporting) **A**1 10 **S** Allina Health, Minneapolis, MN
Primary Contact: Daniel S. Conrad, M.D., President
CFO: Chris Verdon, Director Finance
CMO: Emmett Carpel M.D., Medical Director and Chief of Staff
CNO: Margaret Watry, Director of Patient Care Services and Nurse Executive
Web address: www.allinahealth.org/ahs/pei.nsf/
Control: Other not–for–profit (including NFP Corporation) **Service:** Eye, ear, nose and throat

Staffed Beds: 8

☐ **SHRINERS HOSPITALS FOR CHILDREN–TWIN CITIES (243303)**, 2025 East River Parkway, Zip 55414–3696; tel. 612/596–6100, (Nonreporting) **A**1 3 5 10 **S** Shriners Hospitals for Children, Tampa, FL
Primary Contact: Charles C. Lobeck, Administrator
CMO: Kenneth Guidera M.D., Chief of Staff
CHR: Karen Frigen, Director Human Resources
Web address: www.shrinershospitalsforchildren.org/Hospitals/Locations/twincities.aspx
Control: Other not–for–profit (including NFP Corporation) **Service:** Children's orthopedic

Staffed Beds: 40

SISTER KENNY REHABILITATION INSTITUTE See Abbott Northwestern Hospital

ST. MARY'S HOSPITAL AND REHABILITATION CENTER See University Of Minnesota Medical Center, Fairview

UNIVERSITY OF MINNESOTA HOSPITAL AND CLINIC See University Of Minnesota Medical Center, Fairview

⊠ **UNIVERSITY OF MINNESOTA MEDICAL CENTER, FAIRVIEW (240080)**, 2450 Riverside Avenue, Zip 55454–1400; tel. 612/672–6000, (Includes FAIRVIEW RIVERSIDE HOSPITAL, 2312 South Sixth Street, Minneapolis, Minnesota, Zip 55454, tel. 612/371–6300; ST. MARY'S HOSPITAL AND REHABILITATION CENTER, 2414 South Seventh Street, Minneapolis, Minnesota, Zip 55454, tel. 612/338–2229; UNIVERSITY OF MINNESOTA HOSPITAL AND CLINIC, 420 SE Delaware Street, Minneapolis, Minnesota, Zip 55455–0392, tel. 612/626–3000; UNIVERSITY OF MINNESOTA MASONIC CHILDREN'S HOSPITAL, 420 Delaware Street, SE, Minneapolis, Minnesota, Zip 55455–0341, tel. 612/543–7866) (Total facility includes 20 beds in nursing home–type unit) **A**1 3 5 8 10 **F**2 3 4 5 9 11 12 13 15 17 18 19 20 21 22 23 24 25 26 27 28 29 30 31 32 33 34 35 36 37 38 39 40 41 43 44 45 46 47 48 49 50 51 54 55 56 57 58 59 60 61 64 65 68 70 72 74 75 76 77 78 79 80 81 82 84 85 86 87 88 89 90 91 92 97 98 99 100 101 102 103 104 105 106 107 108 109 110 111 112 113 114 115 116 117 118 119 120 121 123 124 126 128 129 130 131 132 134 135 136 137 138 139 140 141 142 145 146 147 148 149 **P**5 **S** Fairview Health Services, Minneapolis, MN
Primary Contact: David Murphy, Interim Chief Executive Officer
CFO: John Doherty, Vice President Finance
CMO: Barbara Gold M.D., Chief Medical Officer
CHR: Don Moschkau, Senior Director Human Resources
Web address: www.fairview.org
Control: Other not–for–profit (including NFP Corporation) **Service:** General medical and surgical

Staffed Beds: 860 **Admissions:** 32470 **Census:** 616 **Outpatient Visits:** 575043 **Births:** 2415 **Total Expense ($000):** 1502695 **Payroll Expense ($000):** 547919 **Personnel:** 7794

VETERANS AFFAIRS MEDICAL CENTER See Minneapolis Veterans Affairs Health Care System

---

MONTEVIDEO—Chippewa County

★ **CHIPPEWA COUNTY–MONTEVIDEO HOSPITAL (241325)**, 824 North 11th Street, Zip 56265–1683; tel. 320/269–8877, (Nonreporting) **A**10 18
Primary Contact: Charles E. Bruhn, Interim Chief Executive Officer
CFO: Darlene Boike, Chief Financial Officer
CIO: Jeff Plemel, Director Health Information
CHR: Vonnie Erickson, Human Resource Manager
CNO: Terry Anderson R.N., Director of Nursing Services
Web address: www.montevideomedical.com
Control: City–county, Government, Nonfederal **Service:** General medical and surgical

Staffed Beds: 25

MONTICELLO—Wright County

⊠ **CENTRACARE HEALTH–MONTICELLO (241362)**, 1013 Hart Boulevard, Zip 55362–8230; tel. 763/295–2945, (Total facility includes 89 beds in nursing home–type unit) **A**1 5 10 18 **F**3 7 11 13 15 30 31 34 35 40 45 50 57 59 66 68 69 70 76 78 79 81 85 90 96 97 107 110 111 114 117 119 120 121 123 128 129 130 132 133 146 148 149 **S** CentraCare Health, Saint Cloud, MN
Primary Contact: Mary Ellen Wells, FACHE, Administrator
CFO: Kristine Hammer, Director of Finance
CMO: John Hering M.D., Chief Medical Officer
CNO: Lynn Christian R.N., MSN, Division Director, Acute Care Nursing
Web address: www.centracare.com
Control: Other not–for–profit (including NFP Corporation) **Service:** General medical and surgical

Staffed Beds: 126 **Admissions:** 1602 **Census:** 93 **Outpatient Visits:** 15638 **Births:** 244 **Total Expense ($000):** 67399 **Payroll Expense ($000):** 31310 **Personnel:** 344

MOOSE LAKE—Carlton County

★ **MERCY HOSPITAL (241350)**, 4572 County Road 61, Zip 55767–9405; tel. 218/485–4481 **A**10 18 **F**3 7 8 11 13 15 28 29 31 34 35 40 43 45 46 53 57 59 62 64 68 70 75 76 77 79 81 85 86 87 93 107 111 114 119 130 131 132 133 135 143 144 146 148 149 **P**5
Primary Contact: Michael Delfs, Chief Executive Officer
CHR: Sonya Towle, Director Human Resources
CNO: Donita Korpela R.N., Director of Patient Care Services
Web address: www.mercymooselake.org
Control: Hospital district or authority, Government, Nonfederal **Service:** General medical and surgical

Staffed Beds: 25 **Admissions:** 741 **Census:** 7 **Outpatient Visits:** 33191 **Births:** 121 **Total Expense ($000):** 33781 **Payroll Expense ($000):** 13900 **Personnel:** 188

MORA—Kanabec County

⊠ **FIRSTLIGHT HEALTH SYSTEM (241367)**, 301 South Highway 65 South, Zip 55051–1899; tel. 320/679–1212 **A**1 10 18 **F**3 7 11 12 13 15 28 30 31 34 35 40 43 51 53 57 59 70 75 76 77 78 79 81 84 85 87 93 94 107 110 111 115 118 119 127 130 131 132 133 135 144 146 148 149
Primary Contact: Randy Ulseth, Chief Executive Officer
COO: Sandy Zutz–Wiczek, Chief Operating Officer
CFO: Gordy Forbort, Chief Financial Officer
CIO: Becky Gallik, Information Systems Manager
CHR: Kim Carlson, Senior Vice President Human Resources
CNO: Diane Bankers, Senior Vice President, Nursing Services
Web address: www.firstlighthealthsystem.org
Control: County, Government, Nonfederal **Service:** General medical and surgical

Staffed Beds: 25 **Admissions:** 1231 **Census:** 9 **Outpatient Visits:** 35400 **Births:** 143 **Total Expense ($000):** 70874 **Payroll Expense ($000):** 23350 **Personnel:** 389

MORRIS—Stevens County

★ **STEVENS COMMUNITY MEDICAL CENTER (241363)**, 400 East First Street, Zip 56267–1408; tel. 320/589–1313 **A**10 18 **F**3 11 13 15 28 29 31 34 35 40 44 45 50 54 57 59 64 70 75 76 77 79 81 85 86 87 89 97 107 110 111 115 119 130 131 132 135 146 148 149 **P**6
Primary Contact: Jason Breuer, President and Chief Executive Officer
CFO: Kerrie Erickson, Vice President of Finance
CIO: Kerrie Erickson, Vice President of Finance
CHR: Karla Larson, Director Human Resources
Web address: www.scmcinc.com
Control: Other not–for–profit (including NFP Corporation) **Service:** General medical and surgical

Staffed Beds: 25 **Admissions:** 829 **Census:** 7 **Outpatient Visits:** 71885 **Births:** 89 **Total Expense ($000):** 37054 **Payroll Expense ($000):** 17188 **Personnel:** 246

NEW PRAGUE—Scott County

☐ **MAYO CLINIC HEALTH SYSTEM IN NEW PRAGUE (241361)**, 301 Second Street NE, Zip 56071–1799; tel. 952/758–4431 **A**1 10 18 **F**11 13 15 28 29 30 31 34 35 36 40 43 45 46 53 57 59 64 68 74 75 76 77 78 79 81 82 85 87 93 97 107 108 110 111 114 116 117 119 125 128 129 130 131 132 133 146 147 149 **P**6 **S** Mayo Clinic, Rochester, MN
Primary Contact: Mary J. Klimp, FACHE, Administrator
Web address: www.mayoclinichealthsystem.org/locations/new–prague
Control: Other not–for–profit (including NFP Corporation) **Service:** General medical and surgical

Staffed Beds: 25 **Admissions:** 772 **Census:** 11 **Outpatient Visits:** 62378 **Births:** 150 **Personnel:** 197

NEW ULM—Brown County

⊞ **NEW ULM MEDICAL CENTER (241378)**, 1324 Fifth Street North, Zip 56073–1553; tel. 507/217–5000 **A**1 10 18 **F**3 4 5 8 13 15 28 29 31 32 34 35 36 40 43 45 50 55 56 57 59 64 65 68 70 75 76 77 78 79 81 82 84 85 87 89 93 94 97 98 99 100 101 102 103 104 107 108 111 114 119 129 130 131 132 135 144 146 148 149 **S** Allina Health, Minneapolis, MN
Primary Contact: Toby Freier, President
CFO: Steve Schneider, Manager Behavioral Services and Director Operations
CMO: Daniel Holmberg M.D., Director of Medical Affairs
CHR: Anne Makepeace, Director Human Resources
CNO: Jennifer Brehmer, Director of Patient Care
Web address: www.newulmmedicalcenter.com
Control: Other not–for–profit (including NFP Corporation) **Service:** General medical and surgical

Staffed Beds: 45 **Admissions:** 2169 **Census:** 19 **Outpatient Visits:** 108671 **Births:** 318 **Personnel:** 392

NORTHFIELD—Dakota County

★ **NORTHFIELD HOSPITAL (240014)**, 2000 North Avenue, Zip 55057–1498; tel. 507/646–1000, (Total facility includes 40 beds in nursing home–type unit) **A**10 **F**3 7 11 13 15 30 31 40 43 59 62 63 64 68 69 70 75 76 77 78 79 81 85 87 89 93 107 110 111 115 119 128 130 131 132 133 144 146 149 **P**6
Primary Contact: Steve Underdahl, President and Chief Executive Officer
COO: Jerry Ehn, Chief Operating Officer
CFO: Scott D Edin, Vice President, Finance and Chief Financial Officer
CMO: Jeff Meland M.D., Vice President, Chief Medical Officer
CHR: Vicki Stevens, Human Resources Executive
CNO: Tammy A. Hayes R.N., MS, Chief Nurse Executive and Long Term Care Administrator
Web address: www.northfieldhospital.org
Control: City, Government, Nonfederal **Service:** General medical and surgical

Staffed Beds: 77 **Admissions:** 2009 **Census:** 51 **Outpatient Visits:** 137928 **Births:** 573 **Total Expense ($000):** 102065 **Payroll Expense ($000):** 44317 **Personnel:** 556

OLIVIA—Renville County

★ **RC HOSPITAL AND CLINICS (241306)**, 100 Healthy Way, Zip 56277–1117; tel. 320/523–1261 **A**10 18 **F**3 8 15 17 28 29 34 35 40 41 43 45 46 57 59 63 64 65 68 70 75 76 77 79 81 82 85 86 89 93 94 96 97 107 111 114 119 127 129 131 132 133 146 148 149
Primary Contact: Nathan Blad, Chief Executive Officer
CFO: Nathan Blad, Chief Financial Officer
CIO: Cherry Weigel, Director Health Information Management
Web address: www.rchospital.com
Control: County, Government, Nonfederal **Service:** General medical and surgical

Staffed Beds: 16 **Admissions:** 429 **Census:** 5 **Outpatient Visits:** 65676 **Births:** 59 **Total Expense ($000):** 26034 **Payroll Expense ($000):** 10202 **Personnel:** 152

ONAMIA—Mille Lacs County

★ **MILLE LACS HEALTH SYSTEM (241356)**, 200 North Elm Street, Zip 56359–7901; tel. 320/532–3154, (Total facility includes 57 beds in nursing home–type unit) **A**10 18 **F**7 11 15 28 29 31 33 34 40 43 45 50 59 62 63 64 75 77 81 85 93 98 103 107 110 114 115 127 129 130 132 133 135 144 149 **P**6
Primary Contact: Bill Nelson, Chief Executive Officer
COO: Kim Kucera, Chief Operating Officer
CFO: John Unzen, Chief Financial Officer
CMO: Thomas H Bracken M.D., Vice President Medical Affairs
Web address: www.mlhealth.org
Control: Other not–for–profit (including NFP Corporation) **Service:** General medical and surgical

Staffed Beds: 85 **Admissions:** 810 **Census:** 61 **Outpatient Visits:** 24229 **Births:** 4 **Total Expense ($000):** 40146 **Payroll Expense ($000):** 19468 **Personnel:** 333

ORTONVILLE—Big Stone County

★ **ORTONVILLE AREA HEALTH SERVICES (241342)**, 450 Eastvold Avenue, Zip 56278–1133; tel. 320/839–2502, (Total facility includes 51 beds in nursing home–type unit) **A**5 10 18 **F**2 3 6 7 8 10 11 13 15 18 19 20 21 28 29 30 31 32 34 36 40 44 45 46 47 50 56 59 60 62 63 64 65 68 69 74 75 76 77 78 79 81 85 86 89 93 94 96 97 100 101 107 110 111 112 114 115 116 117 118 119 125 127 128 129 130 131 132 133 135 143 147 148 149 **P**4 **S** Sanford Health, Sioux Falls, SD
Primary Contact: David Rogers, Chief Executive Officer
CFO: Kevin Benson, Chief Financial Officer
CMO: Stacy Longnecker, Chief of Staff
CIO: Barbara Voecks, Chief Information Officer
CHR: Kim McCrea, Chief Human Resources Officer
CNO: Jennifer Wiik, Chief Nursing Officer
Web address: www.oahs.us
Control: City, Government, Nonfederal **Service:** General medical and surgical

Staffed Beds: 102 **Admissions:** 554 **Census:** 55 **Outpatient Visits:** 23380 **Births:** 88 **Total Expense ($000):** 19695 **Payroll Expense ($000):** 9560 **Personnel:** 205

OWATONNA—Steele County

⊞ **OWATONNA HOSPITAL (240069)**, 2250 NW 26th Street, Zip 55060–5503; tel. 507/451–3850 **A**1 10 **F**11 13 28 29 34 35 40 57 76 77 79 80 81 89 93 98 100 101 102 103 107 108 119 129 130 131 145 149 **S** Allina Health, Minneapolis, MN
Primary Contact: David L. Albrecht, President
COO: Mark T Gillen, Director of Operations
CFO: Mark T Gillen, Director Finance and Operations
CHR: Sarah Stumme, Director Human Resources
CNO: Anne Draeger, Chief Nursing Officer
Web address: www.owatonnahospital.com
Control: Other not–for–profit (including NFP Corporation) **Service:** General medical and surgical

Staffed Beds: 43 **Admissions:** 2518 **Census:** 25 **Outpatient Visits:** 40194 **Births:** 478 **Total Expense ($000):** 50330 **Payroll Expense ($000):** 18397 **Personnel:** 224

PARK RAPIDS—Hubbard County

⊞ **CHI ST. JOSEPH'S HEALTH (241380)**, 600 Pleasant Avenue, Zip 56470–1431; tel. 218/732–3311 **A**1 5 10 18 **F**3 11 12 13 15 28 29 30 32 34 35 39 40 43 45 47 50 57 59 63 64 65 70 75 76 77 79 81 82 84 85 93 107 108 110 115 118 129 130 131 132 133 134 146 149 150 **S** Catholic Health Initiatives, Englewood, CO
Primary Contact: Benjamin Koppelman, President
CFO: Jay Ross, Chief Financial Officer
CMO: Darryl Beehler D.O., Chief of Staff
CHR: John Tormanen, Director Mission and Human Resources
CNO: Deb Haagenson R.N., Vice President of Patient Care
Web address: www.sjahs.org
Control: Church operated, Nongovernment, not–for–profit **Service:** General medical and surgical

Staffed Beds: 25 **Admissions:** 1377 **Census:** 13 **Outpatient Visits:** 43711 **Births:** 102 **Total Expense ($000):** 42915 **Payroll Expense ($000):** 16863 **Personnel:** 237

PAYNESVILLE—Stearns County

★ **CENTRACARE HEALTH–PAYNESVILLE (241349)**, 200 West 1st Street, Zip 56362–1496; tel. 320/243–3767, (Total facility includes 52 beds in nursing home–type unit) **A**10 18 **F**2 7 10 11 13 15 28 31 34 40 43 45 50 56 57 64 65 70 71 81 82 85 93 107 110 111 115 119 125 127 128 130 133 145 146 148 149 **S** CentraCare Health, Saint Cloud, MN
Primary Contact: Jason Carlson, Administrator
CFO: Jennifer Holtz, Director Finance
CMO: Timothy Malling M.D., Chief of Staff
CHR: Paulette Hagen, Human Resources and Administrative Services Director
CNO: Rachel A Walz, Director Patient Care
Web address: www.centracare.com
Control: Other not–for–profit (including NFP Corporation) **Service:** General medical and surgical

Staffed Beds: 82 **Admissions:** 534 **Census:** 55 **Outpatient Visits:** 32888 **Births:** 77 **Total Expense ($000):** 38002 **Payroll Expense ($000):** 18335 **Personnel:** 150

Hospital, Medicare Provider Number, Address, Telephone, Approval, Facility, and Physician Codes, Health Care System

★ American Hospital Association (AHA) membership   ○ Healthcare Facilities Accreditation Program   ⇑ Center for Improvement in Healthcare Quality Accreditation
☐ The Joint Commission accreditation   ◇ DNV Healthcare Inc. accreditation   △ Commission on Accreditation of Rehabilitation Facilities (CARF) accreditation

PERHAM—Otter Tail County

⊞ **PERHAM HEALTH (241373)**, 1000 Coney Street West, Zip 56573–1108; tel. 218/347–4500, (Total facility includes 96 beds in nursing home–type unit) **A**1 10 18 **F**2 3 8 10 13 15 28 29 30 33 34 35 36 40 43 45 50 56 57 59 62 64 69 75 76 77 81 85 86 89 93 97 104 107 110 111 115 119 125 128 130 131 132 133 144 146 147 148 149 **S** Sanford Health, Sioux Falls, SD
Primary Contact: Chuck Hofius, Chief Executive Officer
CFO: Brad D Wurgler, Chief Financial Officer
CMO: Tim Studer, President Medical Staff
CIO: Jim Rieber, Director Information Systems
CNO: Bonnie Johnson R.N., Vice President of Patient Services
Web address: www.perhamhealth.org
Control: Hospital district or authority, Government, Nonfederal **Service:** General medical and surgical

Staffed Beds: 121 **Admissions:** 743 **Census:** 97 **Outpatient Visits:** 332535
Births: 176 **Total Expense ($000):** 49332 **Payroll Expense ($000):** 22842
Personnel: 229

PIPESTONE—Pipestone County

★ **PIPESTONE COUNTY MEDICAL CENTER AVERA (241374)**, 916 4th Avenue SW, Zip 56164–1890; tel. 507/825–5811 **A**10 18 **F**8 13 15 28 29 31 34 35 40 45 46 47 48 50 53 56 57 59 62 63 64 65 68 75 76 77 79 81 82 85 93 97 107 110 111 115 119 130 131 132 133 135 146 148 149 **P**6 **S** Avera Health, Sioux Falls, SD
Primary Contact: Bradley D. Burris, Chief Executive Officer
CFO: Dave Keeler, Chief Financial Officer
CHR: Judy Raschke, Director Human Resources
CNO: Jessica Smidt R.N., Director of Nursing
Web address: www.pcmchealth.org
Control: County, Government, Nonfederal **Service:** General medical and surgical

Staffed Beds: 25 **Admissions:** 420 **Census:** 3 **Outpatient Visits:** 32593
Births: 77 **Total Expense ($000):** 26871 **Payroll Expense ($000):** 9163
Personnel: 200

PRINCETON—Sherburne County

⊞ **FAIRVIEW NORTHLAND MEDICAL CENTER (240141)**, 911 Northland Drive, Zip 55371–2173; tel. 763/389–1313 **A**1 5 10 **F**3 8 11 13 15 18 28 29 30 31 32 34 35 36 40 41 45 46 50 57 59 64 70 75 76 77 78 79 81 85 86 87 89 91 93 94 100 107 110 111 115 119 130 131 132 146 147 148 149 **P**6 **S** Fairview Health Services, Minneapolis, MN
Primary Contact: John W. Herman, President
CFO: Kim Ericson, Vice President Finance
CMO: Greg Schoen M.D., Regional Medical Director
CHR: Erich Spencer, Chief Human Resource Officer
CNO: Karen Whiley R.N., Vice President Patient Care Services
Web address: www.northland.fairview.org
Control: Other not–for–profit (including NFP Corporation) **Service:** General medical and surgical

Staffed Beds: 20 **Admissions:** 1720 **Census:** 14 **Outpatient Visits:** 48823
Births: 429 **Total Expense ($000):** 55660 **Payroll Expense ($000):** 26583
Personnel: 245

RED LAKE—Beltrami County

☐ **RED LAKE INDIAN HEALTH SERVICE HOSPITAL (240206)**, 24760 Hospital Drive, Zip 56671, Mailing Address: P.O.Box 497, 56671–0497; tel. 218/679–3912, (Nonreporting) **A**1 10 **S** U. S. Indian Health Service, Rockville, MD
Primary Contact: Norine Smith, Chief Executive Officer
CMO: Paul Ditmanson M.D., Clinical Director
CNO: Mary Ann Cook R.N., Director of Nursing
Web address: www.rlnnredlakehospital.com/
Control: PHS, Indian Service, Government, federal **Service:** General medical and surgical

Staffed Beds: 19

RED WING—Goodhue County

☐ **MAYO CLINIC HEALTH SYSTEM IN RED WING (240018)**, 701 Hewitt Boulevard, Zip 55066–2848, Mailing Address: P.O.Box 95, 55066–0095; tel. 651/267–5000 **A**1 3 10 **F**3 11 13 15 18 28 29 30 31 34 35 36 40 43 45 57 59 62 63 64 70 74 75 76 77 78 79 81 87 93 94 96 97 99 100 104 107 111 115 119 129 130 131 132 146 147 149 **P**6 **S** Mayo Clinic, Rochester, MN
Primary Contact: Thomas J. Witt, M.D., President and Chief Executive Officer
CMO: Jack Alexander M.D., Chief Medical Officer
CHR: Kim Trittin, Manager Human Resources
Web address: www.mayoclinichealthsystem.org/locations/red–wing
Control: Other not–for–profit (including NFP Corporation) **Service:** General medical and surgical

Staffed Beds: 22 **Admissions:** 2029 **Census:** 13 **Outpatient Visits:** 117396
Births: 337 **Personnel:** 501

REDWOOD FALLS—Redwood County

★ **REDWOOD AREA HOSPITAL (241351)**, 100 Fallwood Road, Zip 56283–1828; tel. 507/637–4500 **A**10 18 **F**2 3 11 13 15 29 31 34 35 40 45 46 57 59 62 63 75 76 77 79 81 84 93 107 111 115 119 129 130 131 133 146 148 149
Primary Contact: Bryan Lydick, Chief Executive Officer
CFO: Thomas Richard, Director Budget and Revenue Cycle
CIO: Tom Balko, Manager Information Systems
CHR: Jody Rindfleisch, Manager Human Resources
CNO: Dawn Allen R.N., Chief Clinical Officer
Web address: www.redwoodareahospital.org
Control: City–county, Government, Nonfederal **Service:** General medical and surgical

Staffed Beds: 25 **Admissions:** 522 **Census:** 5 **Outpatient Visits:** 21300
Births: 84 **Total Expense ($000):** 24260 **Payroll Expense ($000):** 8886
Personnel: 136

ROBBINSDALE—Hennepin County

★ △ ⇑ **NORTH MEMORIAL MEDICAL CENTER (240001)**, 3300 Oakdale Avenue North, Zip 55422–2926; tel. 763/520–5200, (Nonreporting) **A**2 3 5 7 10 21 **S** North Memorial Health Care, Robbinsdale, MN
Primary Contact: Jeff Wicklander, President
COO: Laura Latt, Vice President of Operations
CFO: Aaron Bloomquist, Chief Financial Officer
CIO: Patrick Taffe, Vice President Information Services
CHR: David Abrams, Vice President Human Resources
CNO: Kelly Lynn White, Vice President of Patient Care and Chief Nursing Officer
Web address: www.northmemorial.com
Control: Other not–for–profit (including NFP Corporation) **Service:** General medical and surgical

Staffed Beds: 355

ROCHESTER—Olmsted County

☐ **COMMUNITY BEHAVIORAL HEALTH HOSPITAL – ROCHESTER (244017)**, 251 Wood Lake Drive SE, Zip 55904–5530; tel. 507/206–2561 (Nonreporting) **A**1 10 **S** Minnesota Department of Human Services, Saint Paul, MN
Primary Contact: Stephanie Juhl, Administrator
CFO: Shirley Jacobson, Chief Financial Officer
CMO: Peter S Millen, Chief Medical Officer MHSATS
CIO: Thomas Baden Jr, Chief Information Officer
CHR: Connie Jones, Director Human Resources
CNO: Pamela R Bajari R.N., Nurse Executive MHSATS
Web address: www.health.state.mn.us
Control: State, Government, Nonfederal **Service:** Psychiatric

Staffed Beds: 16

⊞ △ **MAYO CLINIC HOSPITAL – ROCHESTER (240010)**, 1216 Second Street SW, Zip 55902–1906; tel. 507/255–5123, (Includes MAYO CLINIC HOSPITAL – METHODIST CAMPUS, 201 West Center Street, Rochester, Minnesota, Zip 55902–3084, tel. 507/266–7890; MAYO CLINIC HOSPITAL – SAINT MARYS CAMPUS, 1216 Second Street SW, Rochester, Minnesota, Zip 55902–1970, tel. 507/255–5123; F. Kenneth Ackerman, Chair, Hospital Operation; MAYO EUGENIO LITTA CHILDREN'S HOSPITAL, 200 First Street, SW, Rochester, Minnesota, Zip 55905–0001, tel. 507/255–5123) **A**1 2 3 5 7 8 10 20 **F**3 5 6 8 9 11 12 13 14 15 17 18 19 20 21 22 23 24 25 26 27 28 29 30 31 34 35 36 37 38 39 40 41 43 44 45 46 47 48 49 50 51 52 53 54 55 56 57 58 59 60 61 63 64 65 68 70 71 72 73 74 75 76 77 78 79 80 81 82 84 85 86 87 88 89 90 91 92 93 94 95 96 97 98 99 100 101 102 103 104 105 106 107 108 110 111 112 114 115 116 117 118 119 120 121 122 124 126 130 132 134 135 136 137 138 139 140 141 142 143 145 146 147 148 149 150 **P**6 **S** Mayo Clinic, Rochester, MN
Primary Contact: F. Kenneth. Ackerman, Hospital Administrator
COO: Jeffrey W Bolton, Chief Administrative Officer
CFO: Kedrick D. Adkins, Chief Financial Officer
CMO: Amy W. Williams M.D., Chief Medical Officer
CIO: Christopher Ross, Chief Information Technology Officer
CHR: Cathryn Fraser, Chief Human Resources Officer
CNO: Pamela O. Johnson MS, R.N., Chief Nursing Officer
Web address: www.mayoclinic.org
Control: Other not–for–profit (including NFP Corporation) **Service:** General medical and surgical

Staffed Beds: 1259 **Admissions:** 56079 **Census:** 847 **Outpatient Visits:** 294299 **Births:** 2385 **Personnel:** 31158

MN

★ ⇑ **OLMSTED MEDICAL CENTER (240006)**, 1650 Fourth Street SE,
Zip 55904–4717, Mailing Address: 210 Ninth Street SE, 55904–6756;
tel. 507/288–3443 **A**10 21 **F**3 11 12 13 15 18 26 28 29 30 34 40 44 45 46 50
51 53 54 57 58 59 64 65 68 74 75 76 77 79 80 81 82 84 85 86 87 92 93 97
100 102 104 107 108 110 111 115 119 129 130 131 132 135 146 147 148
149 **P**6
Primary Contact: Tim W. Weir, Chief Executive Officer
CFO: Kevin A Higgins, Chief Financial Officer
CIO: Susan M Schuett, Chief Information Officer
CHR: Tom Hunsberger, Director Human Resources
CNO: Susan Klenner, Chief Nursing Officer and Vice President of Hospital
Operations
Web address: www.olmmed.org
Control: Other not–for–profit (including NFP Corporation) **Service:** General
medical and surgical

Staffed Beds: 42 **Admissions:** 2178 **Census:** 14 **Outpatient Visits:** 356834
Births: 968 **Total Expense ($000):** 178657 **Payroll Expense ($000):** 89476

ROSEAU—Roseau County

⊞ **LIFECARE MEDICAL CENTER (241344)**, 715 Delmore Drive, Zip 56751–1599;
tel. 218/463–2500, (Total facility includes 90 beds in nursing home–type unit) **A**1
5 10 18 **F**3 7 10 11 13 15 28 29 30 31 32 34 35 36 40 43 45 53 56 57 59 62
63 64 65 68 75 76 77 81 82 84 85 86 93 104 107 110 111 115 118 119 128
129 130 132 133 135 144 146 147 148 149 **P**6
Primary Contact: Keith Okeson, President and Chief Executive Officer
COO: Susan C Lisell, Vice President of Clinical Services
CFO: Cathy Huss, Chief Financial Officer
CIO: Kevin Schumacher, Director of Information Systems
CHR: Kristy S McFarlane, Director Human Resources
CNO: Roxanne Fabian, Director of Nursing–Acute Care
Web address: www.lifecaremedicalcenter.org
Control: Other not–for–profit (including NFP Corporation) **Service:** General
medical and surgical

Staffed Beds: 115 **Admissions:** 777 **Census:** 95 **Outpatient Visits:** 42103
Births: 180 **Total Expense ($000):** 41052 **Payroll Expense ($000):** 18425
Personnel: 269

SAINT CLOUD—Stearns County

⊞ △ **ST. CLOUD HOSPITAL (240036)**, 1406 Sixth Avenue North, Zip 56303–
1901; tel. 320/251–2700 **A**1 2 3 5 7 10 20 **F**3 5 11 12 13 14 15 17 18 19 20
22 24 26 27 28 29 30 31 32 34 35 36 37 38 39 40 43 44 45 46 47 48 49 50
51 54 56 57 58 59 60 61 62 63 64 66 68 69 70 72 74 75 76 77 78 79 80 81
82 84 85 86 87 88 89 90 92 93 96 97 98 99 100 101 102 103 104 105 106
107 108 110 111 115 117 118 119 120 121 123 126 129 130 131 132 134
135 141 144 145 146 147 148 149 150 **P**6 **S** CentraCare Health, Saint Cloud,
MN
Primary Contact: Craig J. Broman, FACHE, President
COO: Linda A Chmielewski R.N., Vice President Operations
CFO: Greg Klugherz, Vice President Corporate Services and Chief Financial Officer
CMO: Mark Matthias M.D., Vice President of Medical Affairs
CIO: Amy Porwoll, Vice President of Information Systems
CHR: Duane Rasmusson, Vice President Human Resources
CNO: Linda A Chmielewski R.N., Vice President Operations
Web address: www.centracare.com
Control: Other not–for–profit (including NFP Corporation) **Service:** General
medical and surgical

Staffed Beds: 487 **Admissions:** 26617 **Census:** 323 **Outpatient Visits:**
512989 **Births:** 2592 **Total Expense ($000):** 702566 **Payroll Expense
($000):** 302529 **Personnel:** 5047

⊞ **ST. CLOUD VETERANS AFFAIRS HEALTH CARE SYSTEM**, 4801 Veterans
Drive, Zip 56303–2099; tel. 320/252–1670, (Nonreporting) **A**1 **S** Department of
Veterans Affairs, Washington, DC
Primary Contact: Stephen Black, MS, Health Care System Director
COO: Barry I Bahl, Director
CFO: Joseph Schmitz, Chief Financial Officer
CMO: Susan Markstrom M.D., Chief of Staff
CIO: Denise Hanson, Information Technology Specialist
CHR: Lisa Rosendahl, Director Human Resources
CNO: Meri Hauge R.N., MSN, Associate Director of Patient Care Services and
Nurse Executive
Web address: www.stcloud.va.gov
Control: Veterans Affairs, Government, federal **Service:** Psychiatric

Staffed Beds: 388

VETERANS AFFAIRS MEDICAL CENTER See St. Cloud Veterans Affairs Health
Care System

SAINT JAMES—Watonwan County

☐ **MAYO CLINIC HEALTH SYSTEM IN SAINT JAMES (241333)**, 1101 Moulton
and Parsons Drive, Zip 56081–5550; tel. 507/375–3261 **A**1 10 18 **F**3 15 18 28
34 35 40 43 53 57 59 64 75 81 86 87 97 107 110 114 119 128 129 130 132
133 144 146 148 149 **P**6 **S** Mayo Clinic, Rochester, MN
Primary Contact: Amy Long, Administrator
COO: Richard Grace, Chief Administrative Officer
CFO: James Tarasovich, Chief Financial Officer
CMO: Jennifer Langbehn, Medical Director
CIO: Thomas Borowski, Chief Information Officer
CHR: Gayle B Hansen R.N., Chief Integration Officer
Web address: www.mayoclinichealthsystem.org/locations/st-james
Control: Other not–for–profit (including NFP Corporation) **Service:** General
medical and surgical

Staffed Beds: 13 **Admissions:** 202 **Census:** 5 **Outpatient Visits:** 21620
Births: 0 **Personnel:** 70

SAINT LOUIS PARK—Hennepin County

☐ **PARK NICOLLET METHODIST HOSPITAL (240053)**, 6500 Excelsior Boulevard,
Zip 55426–4702, Mailing Address: Minneapolis, tel. 952/993–5000 **A**1 2 3 5 10
F3 8 11 12 13 15 17 18 20 22 24 26 28 29 30 31 34 38 40 43 44 45 46 47
49 50 51 53 55 56 57 58 59 62 63 64 68 70 71 73 74 75 76 77 78 79 81
82 83 84 85 86 87 89 93 94 100 102 107 108 111 114 115 117 119 120
121 123 124 126 129 130 132 145 146 147 148 149 **P**6 **S** HealthPartners,
Bloomington, MN
Primary Contact: Roxanna L. Gapstur, Ph.D., R.N., President
COO: Michael Kaupa, Executive Vice President and Chief Operating Officer
CFO: Sheila McMillan, Chief Financial Officer
CMO: Steven Connelly M.D., President and Chief Medical Officer
CIO: Julie Flaschenriem, Chief Information Officer
CHR: Paul Dominski, Vice President Human Resources
Web address: www.parknicollet.com
Control: Other not–for–profit (including NFP Corporation) **Service:** General
medical and surgical

Staffed Beds: 420 **Admissions:** 22642 **Census:** 224 **Outpatient Visits:**
59738 **Births:** 3128 **Total Expense ($000):** 517569 **Payroll Expense
($000):** 216211 **Personnel:** 3028

SAINT PAUL—Ramsey County

⊞ **BETHESDA HOSPITAL (242004)**, 559 Capitol Boulevard, Zip 55103–2101;
tel. 651/232–2000 **A**1 3 5 10 **F**1 3 6 11 29 30 38 44 50 53 56 64 68 74 75 85
86 87 91 93 100 101 103 104 105 107 119 130 132 146 148 **P**8 **S** Fairview
Health Services, Minneapolis, MN
Primary Contact: Catherine Barr, Senior Vice President and Chief Operating Officer
COO: Eric Nelson, Vice President, Ambulatory Services
CFO: Douglas Davenport, Chief Financial Officer
CMO: Kevin C. Garrett M.D., Chief Medical Officer
CIO: Joanne Sunquist, Chief Information Officer
CNO: Linda Barnhart, Vice President and Chief Nursing Officer
Web address: www.healtheast.org
Control: Other not–for–profit (including NFP Corporation) **Service:** Acute long–
term care hospital

Staffed Beds: 114 **Admissions:** 1289 **Census:** 97 **Outpatient Visits:** 6168
Births: 0 **Total Expense ($000):** 81025 **Payroll Expense ($000):** 37753
Personnel: 412

⊞ △ **GILLETTE CHILDREN'S SPECIALTY HEALTHCARE (243300)**, 200
University Avenue East, Zip 55101–2507; tel. 651/291–2848 **A**1 3 5 7 10 **F**3 29
34 35 36 39 43 50 54 64 68 74 79 81 82 83 84 85 86 87 88 89 90 91 92 93
94 95 96 107 111 115 119 127 129 130 146 148 149 **P**6
Primary Contact: Barbara Walczyk–Joers, President and Chief Executive Officer
CFO: James Haddican, Chief Financial Officer, Vice President Finance
CMO: Steven Koop M.D., Chief Medical Officer, Medical Director
CIO: Timothy Getsay, Chief Information Officer, Vice President of Performance &
Information Mgmt
CHR: Kit Brady, Vice President Human Resources, Education and Guest Experience
CNO: Karen Brill R.N., Chief Nursing Officer, Vice President Care
Web address: www.gillettechildrens.org
Control: Other not–for–profit (including NFP Corporation) **Service:** Children's
general medical and surgical

Staffed Beds: 60 **Admissions:** 2260 **Census:** 30 **Outpatient Visits:** 150983
Births: 0 **Total Expense ($000):** 232325 **Payroll Expense ($000):** 108689
Personnel: 1089

MN

Hospital, Medicare Provider Number, Address, Telephone, Approval, Facility, and Physician Codes, Health Care System

★ American Hospital Association (AHA) membership
☐ The Joint Commission accreditation
○ Healthcare Facilities Accreditation Program
◇ DNV Healthcare Inc. accreditation
⇑ Center for Improvement in Healthcare Quality Accreditation
△ Commission on Accreditation of Rehabilitation Facilities (CARF) accreditation

MN

☐ △ **REGIONS HOSPITAL (240106)**, 640 Jackson Street, Zip 55101–2595; tel. 651/254–3456 **A**1 2 3 5 7 8 10 **F**3 4 5 7 8 13 15 16 17 18 20 22 24 26 28 29 30 31 34 35 36 38 40 42 43 45 46 47 48 49 50 51 53 54 55 56 57 58 59 60 64 65 68 70 71 72 74 75 76 77 78 79 81 82 84 85 86 87 88 90 92 93 96 98 100 101 102 103 104 105 106 107 108 109 110 111 112 114 115 116 117 119 120 121 122 124 126 129 130 131 132 135 143 146 147 148 149 **S** HealthPartners, Bloomington, MN
Primary Contact: Megan Remark, President and Chief Executive Officer
CFO: Heidi Conrad, Vice President and Chief Financial Officer
CMO: Charles Fazio, Chief Health Officer and Medical Director Health Plan
CIO: Kim LaReau, Vice President and Chief Information Officer
CHR: Kim Egan, Executive Director Human Resources
CNO: Chris Boese, Vice President and Chief Nursing Officer
Web address: www.regionshospital.com
Control: Other not-for-profit (including NFP Corporation) **Service**: General medical and surgical

Staffed Beds: 463 Admissions: 26037 **Census:** 354 **Outpatient Visits:** 149076 **Births:** 2429 **Total Expense ($000):** 720055 **Payroll Expense ($000):** 346797 **Personnel:** 3762

☒ **ST. JOSEPH'S HOSPITAL (240063)**, 45 West 10th Street, Zip 55102–1053; tel. 651/232–3000 **A**1 2 3 5 10 **F**3 4 5 12 13 15 17 18 20 22 24 26 28 29 30 35 36 37 38 40 43 44 49 50 58 61 63 64 68 70 73 74 75 76 77 79 81 84 85 86 87 92 93 96 97 98 100 101 102 103 104 105 107 108 110 111 114 115 118 119 120 121 124 130 132 146 148 149 **P**8 **S** Fairview Health Services, Minneapolis, MN
Primary Contact: Catherine Barr, Senior Vice President and Chief Operating Officer
COO: Brian Gager, Vice President, Acute Care Operations
CMO: Kevin C. Garrett M.D., Chief Medical Officer
CIO: Joanne Sunquist, Information System, Senior Vice President and Chief Information Officer
CHR: Dawn Kessler, Senior Vice President Human Resources
CNO: Debra J Hurd R.N., MS, Vice President Nursing
Web address: www.healtheast.org
Control: Other not-for-profit (including NFP Corporation) **Service**: General medical and surgical

Staffed Beds: 246 Admissions: 10767 **Census:** 149 **Outpatient Visits:** 51240 **Births:** 699 **Total Expense ($000):** 267519 **Payroll Expense ($000):** 99552 **Personnel:** 1131

☒ △ ⇑ **UNITED HOSPITAL (240038)**, 333 North Smith Avenue, Zip 55102–2389; tel. 651/241–8000 **A**1 2 3 5 10 **F**3 8 12 13 15 17 18 20 22 24 26 28 29 30 31 34 35 36 37 40 43 46 47 49 51 53 56 58 60 61 64 65 70 74 75 76 77 78 79 81 82 85 87 90 91 92 93 97 98 99 100 101 102 103 104 105 107 108 110 111 112 113 114 115 118 119 120 121 123 124 126 129 130 132 146 148 **P**6 **S** Allina Health, Minneapolis, MN
Primary Contact: Thomas O'Connor, President
CFO: John Bien, Vice President Finance
CMO: Alison Peterson, Vice President Medical Affairs
CIO: Susan Heichert, Senior Vice President
CHR: James McGlade, Director Human Resources
CNO: Mandy Richards R.N., MSN, Vice President Patient Care
Web address: www.allina.com
Control: Other not-for-profit (including NFP Corporation) **Service**: General medical and surgical

Staffed Beds: 371 Admissions: 23004 **Census:** 266 **Outpatient Visits:** 180299 **Births:** 3562 **Total Expense ($000):** 531808 **Payroll Expense ($000):** 209011 **Personnel:** 2437

SAINT PETER—Nicollet County

★ ⇑ **RIVER'S EDGE HOSPITAL AND CLINIC (241334)**, 1900 North Sunrise Drive, Zip 56082–5376; tel. 507/931–2200, (Nonreporting) **A**10 18 21
Primary Contact: George A. Rohrich, FACHE, Chief Executive Officer
CFO: Lori Zook, Chief Financial Officer
CIO: Kevin Schaefer, Manager Information Services
CHR: Jackie Kimmet, Chief Human Resource Officer
CNO: Paula Meskan R.N., Chief Nursing Officer
Web address: www.rehc.org
Control: City, Government, Nonfederal **Service**: General medical and surgical

Staffed Beds: 17

SANDSTONE—Pine County

★ **ESSENTIA HEALTH SANDSTONE (241309)**, 705 Lundorff Drive, Zip 55072–5009; tel. 320/245–2212, (Total facility includes 22 beds in nursing home–type unit) **A**10 18 **F**7 11 12 15 28 29 30 34 35 40 45 59 64 65 75 77 80 81 85 87 91 92 93 107 110 114 128 130 132 133 135 143 144 148 149 **P**5 6 **S** Essentia Health, Duluth, MN
Primary Contact: Michael D. Hedrix, Administrator and President
CMO: Sarah Aldredge M.D., Chief Medical Officer
Web address: www.pinemedicalcenter.org
Control: Hospital district or authority, Government, Nonfederal **Service**: General medical and surgical

Staffed Beds: 33 Admissions: 225 **Census:** 33 **Outpatient Visits:** 13103 **Births:** 0 **Total Expense ($000):** 17810 **Payroll Expense ($000):** 8132 **Personnel:** 142

SAUK CENTRE—Stearns County

★ **CENTRACARE HEALTH–SAUK CENTRE (241368)**, 425 North Elm Street, Zip 56378–1010; tel. 320/352–2221, (Nonreporting) **A**3 5 10 18 **S** CentraCare Health, Saint Cloud, MN
Primary Contact: Delano Christianson, Administrator
CFO: Delano Christianson, Administrator
Web address: www.centracare.com/hospitals/sauk_centre/index.html
Control: City, Government, Nonfederal **Service**: General medical and surgical

Staffed Beds: 85

SHAKOPEE—Scott County

☒ **ST. FRANCIS REGIONAL MEDICAL CENTER (240104)**, 1455 St Francis Avenue, Zip 55379–3380; tel. 952/428–3000 **A**1 2 5 10 **F**3 12 13 15 28 29 30 31 34 35 36 38 40 41 43 45 46 50 57 58 59 64 68 75 77 78 79 80 81 82 84 86 87 93 107 108 110 111 114 117 118 119 124 129 130 131 132 144 146 147 148 **S** Allina Health, Minneapolis, MN
Primary Contact: Mike McMahan, President
CFO: Cynthia Vincent, Vice President Finance and Operations
CMO: Monte Johnson, Vice President, Medical Affairs
CIO: Joe Delveaux, Manager Information Services
CHR: Ann Glaves, Vice President Human Resources
CNO: Debora Ryan R.N., Vice President Patient Care
Web address: www.stfrancis–shakopee.com
Control: Other not-for-profit (including NFP Corporation) **Service**: General medical and surgical

Staffed Beds: 85 Admissions: 5823 **Census:** 43 **Outpatient Visits:** 125250 **Births:** 1261 **Total Expense ($000):** 131779 **Payroll Expense ($000):** 49393 **Personnel:** 545

SLAYTON—Murray County

★ **MURRAY COUNTY MEDICAL CENTER (241319)**, 2042 Juniper Avenue, Zip 56172–1017; tel. 507/836–6111, (Nonreporting) **A**10 18 **S** Sanford Health, Sioux Falls, SD
Primary Contact: Dennis Goebel, Chief Executive Officer
CFO: Renee Logan, Chief Financial Officer
CMO: Joyce Tarbet M.D., Chief Medical Officer
CIO: Justin Keller, Chief Information Officer
CHR: Nancy Andert, Director Human Resources
CNO: Lorrie Mortensen R.N., MSN, Chief Patient Services
Web address: www.murraycountymed.org
Control: County, Government, Nonfederal **Service**: General medical and surgical

Staffed Beds: 18

SLEEPY EYE—Brown County

SLEEPY EYE MEDICAL CENTER (241327), 400 Fourth Avenue NW, Zip 56085–1109, Mailing Address: P.O.Box 323, 56085–0323; tel. 507/794–3571 **A**10 18 **F**13 15 28 29 34 40 41 45 57 59 64 65 81 107 110 114 127 130 133 144 148 149 **P**6
Primary Contact: Kevin Sellheim, Administrator
CHR: Connie Dahlberg, Director Business and Employee
CNO: Karee Schmiesing, Director of Nursing
Web address: www.semedicalcenter.org
Control: City, Government, Nonfederal **Service**: General medical and surgical

Staffed Beds: 16 Admissions: 295 **Census:** 2 **Outpatient Visits:** 12666 **Births:** 47 **Total Expense ($000):** 12523 **Payroll Expense ($000):** 5857 **Personnel:** 99

SPRINGFIELD—Brown County

☐ **MAYO CLINIC HEALTH SYSTEM IN SPRINGFIELD (241352)**, 625 North Jackson Avenue, Zip 56087–1714, Mailing Address: P.O.Box 146, 56087–0146; tel. 507/723–6201 **A**1 10 18 **F**3 15 28 29 32 34 35 40 45 57 59 64 65 75 81 85 89 93 97 107 110 114 128 133 135 146 148 149 **P**6 **S** Mayo Clinic, Rochester, MN
Primary Contact: Scott D. Thoreson, FACHE, Administrator
CFO: James Tarasovich, Chief Financial Officer
CMO: Jennifer White, Chief of Staff
Web address: www.mayoclinichealthsystem.org
Control: Other not-for-profit (including NFP Corporation) **Service**: General medical and surgical

Staffed Beds: 23 Admissions: 332 **Census:** 4 **Outpatient Visits:** 14438 **Births:** 0 **Personnel:** 62

Many Facility Codes have changed. Please refer to the AHA Guide Code Chart. © 2017 AHA Guide

STAPLES—Todd County

LAKEWOOD HEALTH SYSTEM (241329), 49725 County 83, Zip 56479–5280; tel. 218/894–1515, (Total facility includes 100 beds in nursing home–type unit) **A**10 18 **F**1 3 4 6 7 8 10 11 12 13 15 16 17 28 29 30 31 34 35 36 39 40 43 50 52 53 56 57 59 62 63 64 65 67 68 70 72 73 75 76 77 78 79 80 81 82 84 85 86 87 88 89 90 93 97 98 99 100 101 102 103 104 105 107 110 114 119 125 127 128 129 130 131 132 133 135 143 146 147 148 149 **P**7
Primary Contact: Tim Rice, President and Chief Executive Officer
CMO: John Halfen M.D., Medical Director
CHR: Janet Jacobson, Director Human Resources
CNO: Teresa Fisher, Chief Nursing Officer
Web address: www.lakewoodhealthsystem.com
Control: Other not–for–profit (including NFP Corporation) **Service**: General medical and surgical

Staffed Beds: 135 **Admissions**: 1697 **Census**: 119 **Outpatient Visits**: 126922 **Births**: 477 **Total Expense ($000)**: 96946 **Payroll Expense ($000)**: 40117 **Personnel**: 708	

STILLWATER—Washington County

⌖ **LAKEVIEW HOSPITAL (240066)**, 927 Churchill Street West, Zip 55082–6605; tel. 651/439–5330 **A**1 3 5 10 **F**3 7 8 13 15 18 26 28 29 30 31 34 35 36 40 43 45 50 62 63 64 68 70 72 73 75 76 77 78 79 81 84 85 87 89 90 91 92 96 107 108 110 111 115 118 119 129 130 132 135 146 147 149 **S** HealthPartners, Bloomington, MN
Primary Contact: Theodore Wegleitner, Chief Executive Officer and President
CFO: Douglas E Johnson, Chief Financial Officer
CMO: Thomas Anderson, Vice President Medical Affairs
CIO: Emad Awwad, Director Care Delivery Sites Information Systems and Technology
CHR: Angy Duchesneau, Senior Director Human Resources
CNO: Robbi Hagelberg, Vice President Nursing Services and Chief Nursing Officer
Web address: www.lakeview.org
Control: Other not–for–profit (including NFP Corporation) **Service**: General medical and surgical

Staffed Beds: 54 **Admissions**: 3909 **Census**: 30 **Outpatient Visits**: 60653 **Births**: 578 **Total Expense ($000)**: 101371 **Payroll Expense ($000)**: 44480 **Personnel**: 540	

THIEF RIVER FALLS—Pennington County

MERITCARE THIEF RIVER FALLS NORTHWEST MEDICAL CENTER See Sanford Medical Center Thief River Falls

★ **SANFORD MEDICAL CENTER THIEF RIVER FALLS (241381)**, 3001 Sanford Parkway, Zip 56701–2700; tel. 218/681–4240 **A**10 18 **F**3 8 11 13 15 28 29 31 32 33 34 35 39 40 43 45 50 53 64 65 68 70 74 78 79 81 82 85 86 87 93 94 107 110 111 115 119 129 130 131 132 133 135 144 146 147 148 **P**6 **S** Sanford Health, Sioux Falls, SD
Primary Contact: Brian J. Carlson, FACHE, Chief Executive Officer
COO: Rob Lovejoy, Chief Operating Officer
CFO: Todd Christensen, Executive Director Fiscal Services
CMO: Ashok Patel M.D., Chief of Staff
CHR: Rob Lovejoy, Chief Operating Officer
CNO: Janell Hudson, Chief Clinical Officer
Web address: www.sanfordhealth.org
Control: Other not–for–profit (including NFP Corporation) **Service**: General medical and surgical

Staffed Beds: 25 **Admissions**: 1177 **Census**: 9 **Outpatient Visits**: 99479 **Births**: 288 **Total Expense ($000)**: 65237 **Payroll Expense ($000)**: 27368 **Personnel**: 474	

SANFORD THIEF RIVER FALLS BEHAVIORAL HEALTH CENTER, 120 LaBree Avenue South, Zip 56701–2819, Mailing Address: 3001 Sanford Parkway, 56701–2819; tel. 218/683–4349 **F**50 64 98 99 100 101 104 106 **P**6 **S** Sanford Health, Sioux Falls, SD
Primary Contact: Brian J. Carlson, FACHE, Chief Executive Officer
COO: Rob Lovejoy, Chief Operating Officer
CFO: Todd Christensen, Executive Director Finance
Web address: www.sanfordhealth.org/Locations/1766896362
Control: Other not–for–profit (including NFP Corporation) **Service**: Psychiatric

Staffed Beds: 16 **Admissions**: 399 **Census**: 8 **Outpatient Visits**: 750 **Births**: 0 **Total Expense ($000)**: 9527 **Payroll Expense ($000)**: 4851 **Personnel**: 103	

TRACY—Lyon County

★ **SANFORD TRACY MEDICAL CENTER (241303)**, 251 Fifth Street East, Zip 56175–1536; tel. 507/629–8400 **A**10 18 **F**3 28 29 31 32 34 40 41 42 43 45 50 56 57 59 62 64 65 68 77 81 85 87 89 91 93 97 107 108 111 114 125 127 129 130 131 132 133 135 143 149 **S** Sanford Health, Sioux Falls, SD
Primary Contact: Stacy Barstad, Chief Executive Officer
CMO: Muhammad Ali M.D., Chief Medical Officer
CIO: Janet Theisen, Chief Information Officer
CHR: Becky Foster, Employee Relations Specialist
CNO: Jeri Schons R.N., Chief Nursing Officer
Web address: www.sanfordtracy.org
Control: Other not–for–profit (including NFP Corporation) **Service**: General medical and surgical

Staffed Beds: 25 **Admissions**: 91 **Census**: 1 **Outpatient Visits**: 17864 **Births**: 0 **Total Expense ($000)**: 10392 **Payroll Expense ($000)**: 4094 **Personnel**: 84	

TWO HARBORS—Lake County

LAKE VIEW HOSPITAL (241308), 325 11th Avenue, Zip 55616–1360; tel. 218/834–7300 **A**10 18 **F**15 28 29 34 40 43 50 53 59 63 64 75 77 81 82 84 93 97 107 115 119 130 133 135 144 148 149
Primary Contact: Greg Ruberg, President and Chief Executive Officer
CFO: Eric Lohn, Chief Financial Officer
Web address: www.lvmhospital.com
Control: Other not–for–profit (including NFP Corporation) **Service**: General medical and surgical

Staffed Beds: 16 **Admissions**: 278 **Census**: 7 **Outpatient Visits**: 33526 **Births**: 0 **Total Expense ($000)**: 14068 **Payroll Expense ($000)**: 5850 **Personnel**: 93	

TYLER—Lincoln County

AVERA TYLER HOSPITAL (241348), 240 Willow Street, Zip 56178–1166; tel. 507/247–5521, (Nonreporting) **A**10 18 **S** Avera Health, Sioux Falls, SD
Primary Contact: Allen Anderson, Chief Executive Officer
Web address: www.avera.org
Control: Other not–for–profit (including NFP Corporation) **Service**: General medical and surgical

Staffed Beds: 25	

VIRGINIA—St. Louis County

⌖ △ **ESSENTIA HEALTH–VIRGINIA (240084)**, 901 Ninth Street North, Zip 55792–2398; tel. 218/741–3340, (Total facility includes 90 beds in nursing home–type unit) **A**1 7 10 **F**3 11 13 15 17 18 28 29 30 31 34 35 40 41 43 45 47 48 56 59 63 64 65 70 75 76 77 81 84 85 87 89 90 96 97 107 108 110 111 115 119 124 128 129 130 132 135 144 146 147 148 149 **P**6 **S** Essentia Health, Duluth, MN
Primary Contact: Sam Stone, Administrative and Chief Operating Officer
CFO: Steven Feltman CPA, Chief Financial Officer
CMO: Michelle Oman D.O., Chief Medical Officer
Web address: www.essentiahealth.org
Control: Other not–for–profit (including NFP Corporation) **Service**: General medical and surgical

Staffed Beds: 150 **Admissions**: 1637 **Census**: 94 **Outpatient Visits**: 117429 **Births**: 247 **Total Expense ($000)**: 78668 **Payroll Expense ($000)**: 37468 **Personnel**: 488	

WABASHA—Wabasha County

★ **SAINT ELIZABETH'S MEDICAL CENTER (241335)**, 1200 Grant Boulevard West, Zip 55981–1042; tel. 651/565–4531, (Total facility includes 146 beds in nursing home–type unit) **A**10 18 **F**2 6 10 11 12 15 28 29 30 34 35 40 43 45 46 49 50 53 56 59 62 64 65 75 77 78 79 81 85 86 93 94 107 110 114 119 125 128 130 133 135 143 144 145 146 148 **S** Ascension Healthcare, Saint Louis, MO
Primary Contact: Thomas Crowley, President and Chief Executive Officer
CFO: John Wolfe, Chief Financial Officer
CMO: Brian E. Kelly M.D., President Medical Staff
CHR: Jim Root, Vice President Human Resources
CNO: Kathy Lueders R.N., Director of Nursing–Acute Care
Web address: www.stelizabethswabasha.org
Control: Church operated, Nongovernment, not–for–profit **Service**: General medical and surgical

Staffed Beds: 164 **Admissions**: 398 **Census**: 131 **Outpatient Visits**: 22741 **Births**: 0 **Total Expense ($000)**: 29186 **Payroll Expense ($000)**: 13162 **Personnel**: 231	

MN

Hospital, Medicare Provider Number, Address, Telephone, Approval, Facility, and Physician Codes, Health Care System

★ American Hospital Association (AHA) membership ○ Healthcare Facilities Accreditation Program ⇑ Center for Improvement in Healthcare Quality Accreditation
☐ The Joint Commission accreditation ◇ DNV Healthcare Inc. accreditation △ Commission on Accreditation of Rehabilitation Facilities (CARF) accreditation

WACONIA—Carver County

★ ⇑ **RIDGEVIEW MEDICAL CENTER (240056)**, 500 South Maple Street, Zip 55387–1791; tel. 952/442–2191 **A2** 10 21 **F3** 7 12 13 15 18 20 22 28 29 30 31 32 34 35 36 38 40 41 42 43 45 46 48 49 54 57 58 59 62 63 64 65 70 73 74 75 76 77 78 79 80 81 82 84 85 86 87 89 93 96 103 107 108 110 111 114 115 118 119 126 127 129 130 131 132 135 144 146 147 148 149 **P6 S** Ridgeview Medical Center, Waconia, MN
Primary Contact: Michael Phelps, President and Chief Executive Officer
CFO: Gordon Gablenz, Vice President Finance
CIO: Tamara Korbel, Director Management Information Systems
CHR: Sarah M Hastings, Executive Director
Web address: www.ridgeviewmedical.org
Control: Other not–for–profit (including NFP Corporation) **Service**: General medical and surgical

Staffed Beds: 108 Admissions: 5048 Census: 63 Outpatient Visits: 279707 **Births:** 1233 **Total Expense ($000):** 238422 **Payroll Expense ($000):** 116377 **Personnel:** 1421

WADENA—Wadena County

☒ **TRI–COUNTY HOSPITAL (241354)**, 415 Jefferson Street North, Zip 56482–1297; tel. 218/631–3510 **A1** 10 18 **F3** 7 11 13 15 17 28 31 34 35 40 43 50 54 57 59 64 65 68 70 75 76 77 81 85 86 87 89 93 99 104 107 108 110 111 114 115 118 119 127 129 130 131 132 133 135 146 147 148 149 **P6**
Primary Contact: Joel Beiswenger, Chief Executive Officer
CFO: Kim Aagard, Chief Financial Officer
CMO: John Pate M.D., Chief Medical Officer
CIO: Bill Blaha, Manager Information Technology
CHR: Bryan Pederson, Human Resources Manager
CNO: Kathy Kleen, Chief Nursing Officer
Web address: www.tchc.org
Control: Other not–for–profit (including NFP Corporation) **Service**: General medical and surgical

Staffed Beds: 25 Admissions: 765 Census: 6 Outpatient Visits: 129293 **Births:** 153 **Total Expense ($000):** 57994 **Payroll Expense ($000):** 22996 **Personnel:** 372

WARREN—Marshall County

★ **NORTH VALLEY HEALTH CENTER (241337)**, 300 West Good Samaritan Drive, Zip 56762; tel. 218/745–4211, (Nonreporting) **A**10 18
Primary Contact: Jon E. Linnell, Interim Chief Executive Officer
CFO: Mitchell Kotrba, Chief Financial Officer
CNO: Sara Marie Kazmierczak R.N., Director of Nursing
Web address: www.northvalleyhealth.org
Control: Other not–for–profit (including NFP Corporation) **Service**: General medical and surgical

Staffed Beds: 20

WASECA—Waseca County

☐ **MAYO CLINIC HEALTH SYSTEM IN WASECA (241345)**, 501 North State Street, Zip 56093–2811; tel. 507/835–1210 **A1** 3 5 10 18 **F3** 11 15 18 28 29 30 34 35 40 45 53 57 59 64 65 74 75 77 81 82 85 86 87 93 97 107 110 114 119 128 130 132 133 144 146 148 149 **P6 S** Mayo Clinic, Rochester, MN
Primary Contact: Thomas Borowski, Administrator
CMO: Christopher Schimming M.D., Medical Director
Web address: www.mayoclinichealthsystem.org
Control: Other not–for–profit (including NFP Corporation) **Service**: General medical and surgical

Staffed Beds: 25 Admissions: 238 Census: 7 Outpatient Visits: 27950 **Births:** 0 **Personnel:** 100

WESTBROOK—Cottonwood County

★ **SANFORD WESTBROOK MEDICAL CENTER (241302)**, 920 Bell Avenue, Zip 56183–9669, Mailing Address: P.O.Box 188, 56183–0188; tel. 507/274–6121 **A**10 18 **F3** 29 31 34 35 40 42 43 56 57 59 62 64 65 68 71 75 77 81 85 86 87 89 91 93 97 99 100 101 102 103 104 107 108 114 125 127 130 131 132 133 135 143 **P6 S** Sanford Health, Sioux Falls, SD
Primary Contact: Stacy Barstad, Chief Executive Officer
COO: Gordon Kopperud, Director Operations
CIO: Janet Theisen, Chief Information Officer
CHR: Becky Foster, Employee Relations Specialist
Web address: www.sanfordwestbrook.org
Control: Other not–for–profit (including NFP Corporation) **Service**: General medical and surgical

Staffed Beds: 6 Admissions: 98 Census: 1 Outpatient Visits: 11143 **Births:** 0 **Total Expense ($000):** 6729 **Payroll Expense ($000):** 2488 **Personnel:** 40

WHEATON—Traverse County

★ **SANFORD WHEATON MEDICAL CENTER (241304)**, 401 12th Street North, Zip 56296–1099; tel. 320/563–8226 **A**10 18 **F3** 7 11 15 18 28 29 30 34 40 43 45 57 59 64 65 81 86 97 107 111 114 119 127 128 132 133 **P6 S** Sanford Health, Sioux Falls, SD
Primary Contact: JoAnn M. Foltz, R.N., Chief Executive Officer
CFO: Shane Ayres, Chief Financial Officer
CHR: Brenda Petersen, Human Resources
CNO: Chelsie Falk, Chief Nursing Officer
Web address: www.sanfordhealth.org
Control: Other not–for–profit (including NFP Corporation) **Service**: General medical and surgical

Staffed Beds: 15 Admissions: 82 Census: 1 Outpatient Visits: 14909 **Births:** 0 **Total Expense ($000):** 7357 **Payroll Expense ($000):** 3149 **Personnel:** 52

WILLMAR—Kandiyohi County

☐ **CHILD AND ADOLESCENT BEHAVIORAL HEALTH SERVICES (244005)**, 1701 Technology Drive Northeast, Zip 56201–2275; tel. 320/231–5421 (Nonreporting) **A**1 10
Primary Contact: Jacquelyn Sammons, R.N., Supervisor
Web address: www.dhs.state.mn.us
Control: County, Government, Nonfederal **Service**: Psychiatric

Staffed Beds: 16

☒ **RICE MEMORIAL HOSPITAL (240088)**, 301 Becker Avenue SW, Zip 56201–3395; tel. 320/235–4543, (Total facility includes 78 beds in nursing home–type unit) **A**1 2 10 **F3** 7 11 12 13 28 29 30 34 35 39 40 43 45 47 48 49 50 57 59 60 63 64 65 68 70 73 75 76 78 79 81 82 85 86 87 89 90 93 98 100 101 102 103 104 105 107 108 111 115 118 119 121 128 130 132 143 146 147 148 149 150
Primary Contact: Michael Schramm, Chief Executive Officer
CFO: Bill Fenske, Chief Financial Officer
CMO: Kenneth Flowe M.D., Chief Medical Officer
CIO: Teri Beyer, Chief Information Officer, Quality
CNO: Wendy Ulferts R.N., Chief Nursing Officer
Web address: www.ricehospital.com
Control: City, Government, Nonfederal **Service**: General medical and surgical

Staffed Beds: 184 Admissions: 3846 Census: 106 Outpatient Visits: 76332 **Births:** 747 **Total Expense ($000):** 110581 **Payroll Expense ($000):** 45801 **Personnel:** 551

WINDOM—Cottonwood County

★ **WINDOM AREA HOSPITAL (241332)**, 2150 Hospital Drive, Zip 56101–0339, Mailing Address: P.O.Box 339, 56101–0339; tel. 507/831–2400 **A**10 18 **F**11 13 15 28 31 34 35 40 45 53 57 64 76 77 81 93 107 114 119 130 133 148 149 **S** Sanford Health, Sioux Falls, SD
Primary Contact: Shelby Medina, Chief Executive Officer
CFO: Kim Armstrong, Chief Financial Officer
CIO: Lori Ling, Information Technician
CHR: Emily Masters, Director Human Resources and Marketing
CNO: Kari Witte, Director Patient Care
Web address: www.windomareahospital.com
Control: City, Government, Nonfederal **Service**: General medical and surgical

Staffed Beds: 18 Admissions: 339 Census: 3 Outpatient Visits: 34773 **Births:** 102 **Total Expense ($000):** 15591 **Payroll Expense ($000):** 6009 **Personnel:** 110

WINONA—Winona County

★ **WINONA HEALTH (240044)**, 855 Mankato Avenue, Zip 55987–4868, Mailing Address: P.O.Box 5600, 55987–0600; tel. 507/454–3650 **A**2 10 20 **F**11 13 15 28 29 30 31 32 34 35 38 40 43 50 53 56 57 59 60 61 70 74 75 76 77 78 79 81 82 84 85 86 87 89 93 96 97 98 99 100 101 102 103 104 107 108 110 111 115 118 119 127 129 130 131 132 135 144 146 147 148
Primary Contact: Rachelle H. Schultz, Ed.D., President and Chief Executive Officer
CFO: Jan Brosnahan, Chief Financial Officer
CMO: Dan Parker M.D., Chief of Staff
CIO: Polly Peterson, Information Technology Director
CHR: Ashley Anderson, Manager Human Resources
Web address: www.winonahealth.org
Control: Other not–for–profit (including NFP Corporation) **Service**: General medical and surgical

Staffed Beds: 53 Admissions: 2352 Census: 23 Outpatient Visits: 223980 **Births:** 339 **Total Expense ($000):** 122272 **Payroll Expense ($000):** 52747 **Personnel:** 772

MN

WOODBURY—Washington County

✠ **WOODWINDS HEALTH CAMPUS (240213)**, 1925 Woodwinds Drive, Zip 55125–4445; tel. 651/232–0228 **A**1 5 10 **F**3 13 15 28 29 30 31 34 35 36 37 38 40 43 44 49 50 57 59 61 63 64 68 70 74 75 76 77 78 79 81 85 86 87 93 96 97 100 102 104 107 108 110 111 115 118 119 120 121 124 130 132 146 149 **P**8 **S** Fairview Health Services, Minneapolis, MN
Primary Contact: Catherine Barr, President, East Region
COO: Lia Chistiansen, Vice President, Hospital Operations
CFO: Dan Fromm, Chief Financial Officer
CMO: Kevin C. Garrett M.D., Medical Executive, East Region
CIO: Joanne Sunquist, Chief Information Officer
CHR: Carolyn Jacobson, Chief Human Resource Officer
CNO: Debra J Hurd R.N., MS, Vice President and Chief Nursing Officer
Web address: www.woodwinds.org
Control: Other not–for–profit (including NFP Corporation) **Service**: General medical and surgical

Staffed Beds: 86 **Admissions**: 7408 **Census**: 54 **Outpatient Visits**: 92560 **Births**: 1673 **Total Expense ($000)**: 134578 **Payroll Expense ($000)**: 48423 **Personnel**: 481

WORTHINGTON—Nobles County

SANFORD REGIONAL HOSPITAL WORTHINGTON See Sanford Worthington Medical Center

★ **SANFORD WORTHINGTON MEDICAL CENTER (240022)**, 1018 Sixth Avenue, Zip 56187–2202, Mailing Address: P.O.Box 997, 56187–0997; tel. 507/372–2941 **A**10 20 **F**3 7 11 13 15 18 19 26 27 28 31 34 35 40 43 45 50 57 59 60 62 64 68 69 70 75 78 79 81 85 86 93 97 107 110 111 114 116 119 120 121 126 129 130 131 132 135 144 146 147 148 149 **S** Sanford Health, Sioux Falls, SD
Primary Contact: Jennifer . Weg, MS, R.N., Chief Executive Officer
CFO: Linda Wagner, Chief Financial Officer
CMO: Charles Dike M.D., Chief of Staff
CIO: Brad Klassen, Information Technology Coordinator
CNO: Gwen Post R.N., Chief Nursing Officer
Web address: www.sanfordhealth.org
Control: Other not–for–profit (including NFP Corporation) **Service**: General medical and surgical

Staffed Beds: 48 **Admissions**: 1195 **Census**: 9 **Outpatient Visits**: 70382 **Births**: 456 **Total Expense ($000)**: 48401 **Payroll Expense ($000)**: 22947 **Personnel**: 215

WYOMING—Chisago County

✠ **FAIRVIEW LAKES HEALTH SERVICES (240050)**, 5200 Fairview Boulevard, Zip 55092–8013; tel. 651/982–7000 **A**1 10 **F**3 8 11 13 15 18 28 29 30 32 34 35 40 41 45 51 57 59 64 65 68 70 75 76 81 85 87 89 91 93 96 107 110 111 115 119 130 131 132 134 144 146 147 148 149 **P**6 **S** Fairview Health Services, Minneapolis, MN
Primary Contact: John W. Herman, President
CFO: Kim Ericson, Vice President Finance
CMO: David Milbrandt M.D., Vice President Medical Affairs
CNO: Margaret J Swanson, Chief Nursing Officer
Web address: www.fairview.org/
Control: Other not–for–profit (including NFP Corporation) **Service**: General medical and surgical

Staffed Beds: 33 **Admissions**: 2842 **Census**: 23 **Outpatient Visits**: 82937 **Births**: 659 **Total Expense ($000)**: 74685 **Payroll Expense ($000)**: 40984 **Personnel**: 429

MISSISSIPPI

ABERDEEN—Monroe County

★ ⇑ **PIONEER COMMUNITY HOSPITAL OF ABERDEEN (251302)**, 400 South Chestnut Street, Zip 39730–3335, Mailing Address: P.O.Box 548, 39730–0548; tel. 662/369–2455 **A**10 18 21 **F**3 8 10 11 29 35 39 40 45 53 56 75 77 81 85 86 87 93 96 97 98 100 101 102 103 104 105 106 107 112 115 119 125 127 130 131 133 135 143 146 **S** Pioneer Health Services, Magee, MS
Primary Contact: Christopher Chandler, Chief Executive Officer
CFO: Julie Gieger, Chief Financial Officer
CMO: Kevin Hayes M.D., Chief of Staff
CHR: Lee Rob, Director Human Resources
Web address: www.pchaberdeen.com
Control: Corporation, Investor–owned (for–profit) **Service**: General medical and surgical

Staffed Beds: 25 **Admissions**: 829 **Census**: 19 **Outpatient Visits**: 14094
Births: 0 **Total Expense ($000)**: 16442 **Payroll Expense ($000)**: 8035
Personnel: 160

ACKERMAN—Choctaw County

⇑ **CHOCTAW REGIONAL MEDICAL CENTER (251334)**, 8613 Highway 12, Zip 39735–8708; tel. 662/285–6235, (Total facility includes 60 beds in nursing home–type unit) **A**10 18 21 **F**3 29 34 40 43 50 57 58 65 77 87 90 93 104 107 114 119 127 130 133 **P**4
Primary Contact: Jamie Rodgers, Interim Chief Executive Officer
Control: County, Government, Nonfederal **Service**: General medical and surgical

Staffed Beds: 75 **Admissions**: 367 **Census**: 65 **Outpatient Visits**: 19654
Births: 0 **Total Expense ($000)**: 19828 **Payroll Expense ($000)**: 10185
Personnel: 219

AMORY—Monroe County

⊞ **GILMORE MEMORIAL HOSPITAL (250025)**, 1105 Earl Frye Boulevard, Zip 38821–5500, Mailing Address: P.O.Box 459, 38821–0459; tel. 662/256–7111 **A**1 10 **F**3 13 15 17 18 29 32 34 35 40 41 43 45 49 50 53 55 57 59 64 65 68 70 72 73 75 76 77 81 85 86 87 88 89 90 107 108 110 111 114 115 119 126 130 135 146 147 **P**8 **S** Curae Health, Clinton, TN
Primary Contact: J Allen. Tyra, Chief Executive
COO: Carol Upton, Regional Area Practice Manager
CFO: Bert Pickard, Chief Financial Officer
CMO: William Rogers, Chief Medical Officer
CIO: Jeff Wideman, Director Information Systems
CHR: Angie L Weaver, Director Human Resources
Web address: www.gilmorehealth.com
Control: Corporation, Investor–owned (for–profit) **Service**: General medical and surgical

Staffed Beds: 95 **Admissions**: 2601 **Census**: 26 **Outpatient Visits**: 57880
Births: 623 **Total Expense ($000)**: 35269 **Payroll Expense ($000)**: 12342
Personnel: 242

BATESVILLE—Panola County

★ **PANOLA MEDICAL CENTER (250128)**, 303 Medical Center Drive, Zip 38606–8608; tel. 662/563–5611 **A**10 **F**3 4 5 11 12 13 15 18 19 28 29 30 32 34 35 38 40 43 45 48 50 56 57 59 64 65 68 70 76 77 81 85 87 89 97 98 100 101 102 103 104 107 108 114 119 127 129 130 132 146 147 **S** Curae Health, Clinton, TN
Primary Contact: Travis Sisson, Chief Executive Officer
COO: Vince Brummett, Director Administrative Services
CMO: Michael R. Hovens M.D., Chief Medical Officer
CIO: Will Morris, Director Information Technology
CHR: Arthur A Wasek, Director Human Resources
Web address: www.trilakesmc.com
Control: Corporation, Investor–owned (for–profit) **Service**: General medical and surgical

Staffed Beds: 112 **Admissions**: 2746 **Census**: 37 **Outpatient Visits**: 26154
Births: 268 **Total Expense ($000)**: 33050 **Payroll Expense ($000)**: 12674
Personnel: 298

BAY SAINT LOUIS—Hancock County

⊞ **HANCOCK MEDICAL CENTER (250162)**, 149 Drinkwater Boulevard, Zip 39520–1658, Mailing Address: 149 Drinkwater Road, 39520–1658; tel. 228/467–8600 **A**1 10 **F**3 13 15 17 18 28 29 34 35 39 40 43 45 54 57 59 64 65 70 75 76 77 79 81 85 86 87 89 90 93 97 107 108 110 111 114 115 118 119 127 129 130 131 146 147 **S** Ochsner Health System, New Orleans, LA
Primary Contact: Alan Hodges, Chief Executive Officer
CFO: Thomas Ramsey, Chief Financial Officer
CIO: Craig Hodges, Director Information Services
CHR: Cathy Benvenutti, Human Resource Director
CNO: Virginia Kenny, Chief Nursing Officer
Web address: www.hmc.org
Control: County, Government, Nonfederal **Service**: General medical and surgical

Staffed Beds: 102 **Admissions**: 1833 **Census**: 16 **Outpatient Visits**: 45299
Births: 219 **Total Expense ($000)**: 37146 **Payroll Expense ($000)**: 16176
Personnel: 260

BAY SPRINGS—Jasper County

★ **JASPER GENERAL HOSPITAL (250018)**, 15 'A' South Sixth Street, Zip 39422–9738, Mailing Address: P.O.Box 527, 39422–0527; tel. 601/764–2101, (Total facility includes 110 beds in nursing home–type unit) **A**10 **F**10 55 59 62 64 108 119 128 130 133
Primary Contact: Clinton Eaves, Administrator
CFO: Steve Green, Comptroller
CMO: A K Lay M.D., Jr, Chief Medical Officer
CHR: Beth Gable, Administrative Assistant
CNO: Becky Ulmer R.N., Director of Nursing
Web address: www.jaspergeneralhospital.com
Control: County, Government, Nonfederal **Service**: General medical and surgical

Staffed Beds: 126 **Admissions**: 143 **Census**: 116 **Outpatient Visits**: 0
Births: 0 **Total Expense ($000)**: 9100 **Payroll Expense ($000)**: 5922
Personnel: 183

BILOXI—Harrison County

⊞ **MERIT HEALTH BILOXI (250007)**, 150 Reynoir Street, Zip 39530–4199, Mailing Address: P.O.Box 128, 39533–0128; tel. 228/432–1571, (Nonreporting) **A**1 10 **S** Community Health Systems, Inc., Franklin, TN
Primary Contact: Robert Calhoun, Chief Executive Officer
COO: Tonda V. Haigler, Chief Operating Officer
CFO: Charles Brinkley III, Chief Financial Officer
CMO: George Loukatos M.D., President Medical Staff Affairs
CIO: George Bickel, Director, Information Systems
CNO: James Wells, Chief Nursing Officer
Web address: www.merithealthbiloxi.com
Control: Corporation, Investor–owned (for–profit) **Service**: General medical and surgical

Staffed Beds: 198

⊞ **VETERANS AFFAIRS GULF COAST VETERANS HEALTH CARE SYSTEM**, 400 Veterans Avenue, Zip 39531–2410; tel. 228/523–5000, (Nonreporting) **A**1 3 5 **S** Department of Veterans Affairs, Washington, DC
Primary Contact: Christopher M. Saslo, Acting Director
COO: Alexander Murray, Interim Associate Director
CFO: John D Williams Jr, Chief Financial Officer
CMO: Kenneth B Simon M.D., Chief of Staff
CIO: David D Wagner, Chief Information Management Service
CHR: Andrew Roberts, Interim Chief Human Resources Officer
CNO: Deatosha D. Haynes, Interim Associates Director for Patient
Web address: www.biloxi.va.gov/
Control: Veterans Affairs, Government, federal **Service**: General medical and surgical

Staffed Beds: 392

BOONEVILLE—Prentiss County

⊞ **BAPTIST MEMORIAL HOSPITAL–BOONEVILLE (250044)**, 100 Hospital Street, Zip 38829–3359; tel. 662/720–5000 **A**1 10 **F**3 15 17 29 34 35 40 43 56 57 59 63 68 70 74 75 77 81 85 86 87 89 90 93 98 103 107 108 111 115 118 119 129 130 132 133 145 146 **S** Baptist Memorial Health Care Corporation, Memphis, TN
Primary Contact: James Grantham, Administrator and Chief Executive Officer
CFO: Donavan Leonard, Chief Financial Officer
CMO: Nathan Baldwin M.D., President Medical Staff
CIO: Linda Chaffin, Director Medical Review
CHR: Shannon Bolen, Director Human Resources
Web address: www.bmhcc.org/booneville
Control: Other not–for–profit (including NFP Corporation) **Service**: General medical and surgical

Staffed Beds: 66 **Admissions**: 993 **Census**: 18 **Outpatient Visits**: 25186
Births: 0 **Total Expense ($000)**: 18736 **Payroll Expense ($000)**: 8137
Personnel: 173

BRANDON—Rankin County

✠ **MERIT HEALTH RANKIN (250096)**, 350 Crossgates Boulevard, Zip 39042–2698; tel. 601/825–2811 **A**1 5 10 **F**3 6 15 17 29 30 34 40 43 45 50 57 59 64 70 78 79 81 85 87 90 93 97 98 103 106 107 108 109 110 111 112 114 119 129 130 146 **P**8 **S** Community Health Systems, Inc., Franklin, TN
Primary Contact: L Dwayne. Blaylock, Chief Executive Officer
CFO: Christy Wilson, Chief Financial Officer
CMO: Edward Rigdon M.D., Chief Medical Officer
CIO: Heather Holmes, Director Health Information Systems
CHR: Joy M Hutson, Director Human Resources
CNO: Jacqueline C Sullins R.N., Chief Nursing Officer
Web address: www.crossgatesriveroaks.com
Control: Corporation, Investor–owned (for–profit) **Service**: General medical and surgical

Staffed Beds: 134 **Admissions**: 2257 **Census**: 35 **Outpatient Visits**: 60129
Births: 0 **Total Expense ($000)**: 50779 **Payroll Expense ($000)**: 13855
Personnel: 287

BROOKHAVEN—Lincoln County

★ ⇑ **KING'S DAUGHTERS MEDICAL CENTER (250057)**, 427 Highway 51 North, Zip 39601–2350, Mailing Address: P.O.Box 948, 39602–0948; tel. 601/833–6011 **A**10 20 21 **F**3 7 11 13 15 17 29 34 35 40 41 45 53 54 57 59 64 65 68 70 73 74 75 76 77 79 80 81 82 86 89 93 96 97 107 108 110 111 114 115 119 126 129 130 131 132 143 146 147 149 **S** QHR, Brentwood, TN
Primary Contact: Alvin Hoover, FACHE, Chief Executive Officer
COO: Tom Hood, Chief Operating Officer
CFO: Randy B Pirtle, Chief Financial Officer
CMO: Richard Rushing, Chief of Staff
CIO: Carl Smith, Director Information Systems
CHR: Celine H Craig, Director Human Resources
CNO: Cheri Walker R.N., Chief Nursing Officer
Web address: www.kdmc.org
Control: Other not–for–profit (including NFP Corporation) **Service**: General medical and surgical

Staffed Beds: 79 **Admissions**: 4190 **Census**: 31 **Outpatient Visits**: 133349
Births: 627 **Total Expense ($000)**: 84016 **Payroll Expense ($000)**: 34928
Personnel: 620

CALHOUN CITY—Calhoun County

★ **BAPTIST MEMORIAL HOSPITAL – CALHOUN (251331)**, 140 Burke–Calhoun City Road, Zip 38916–9690; tel. 662/628–6611, (Total facility includes 120 beds in nursing home–type unit) **A**10 18 **F**7 40 43 64 68 81 87 89 93 103 107 119 128 130 133 **S** Baptist Memorial Health Care Corporation, Memphis, TN
Primary Contact: James P. Franklin, Administrator
CFO: Kenneth Conley, Chief Financial Officer
CMO: Bruce Longest M.D., President Medical Staff
Web address: www.baptistonline.org/calhoun/
Control: Other not–for–profit (including NFP Corporation) **Service**: General medical and surgical

Staffed Beds: 145 **Admissions**: 376 **Census**: 106 **Births**: 0 **Total Expense ($000)**: 17456 **Payroll Expense ($000)**: 7654 **Personnel**: 198

CANTON—Madison County

✠ **MERIT HEALTH MADISON (250038)**, 161 River Oaks Drive, Zip 39046–5375, Mailing Address: PO Box 1607, 39046–5375; tel. 601/855–4000 **A**1 10 **F**13 15 29 35 40 43 70 73 76 81 82 87 89 108 119 130 146 **P**8 **S** Community Health Systems, Inc., Franklin, TN
Primary Contact: Britton Phelps, Chief Executive Officer
CFO: Shea Sutherland, Chief Financial Officer
CMO: Vibha Vig, Chief of Staff
CIO: Rick Hartzog, Chief Information Officer
CHR: Jackie Williams, Director Human Resources
CNO: Terri Meadows, Chief Nursing Executive
Web address: www.merithealthmadison.com
Control: Corporation, Investor–owned (for–profit) **Service**: General medical and surgical

Staffed Beds: 43 **Admissions**: 1263 **Census**: 12 **Outpatient Visits**: 39766
Births: 271 **Total Expense ($000)**: 30998 **Payroll Expense ($000)**: 12083
Personnel: 223

CARTHAGE—Leake County

★ **BAPTIST MEDICAL CENTER LEAKE (251315)**, 1100 Highway 16 E, Zip 39051–3809, Mailing Address: P.O.Box 909, 39051–0909; tel. 601/267–1100 **A**10 18 **F**3 15 29 32 34 35 40 41 43 46 57 59 65 66 81 87 107 108 110 111 114 119 127 130 133 135 146 **P**6 **S** Baptist Memorial Health Care Corporation, Memphis, TN
Primary Contact: Daryl W. Weaver, Chief Executive Officer
COO: C Gerald Cotton, Interim Chief Operating Officer
CFO: David Jackson, Chief Financial Officer
CMO: Doug Perry M.D., Chief of Staff
Web address: www.mbhs.com/locations/baptist–medical–center–leake/
Control: Other not–for–profit (including NFP Corporation) **Service**: General medical and surgical

Staffed Beds: 25 **Admissions**: 836 **Census**: 18 **Outpatient Visits**: 24861
Births: 3 **Personnel**: 142

CENTREVILLE—Wilkinson County

✠ **FIELD MEMORIAL COMMUNITY HOSPITAL (251309)**, 178 Highway 24, Zip 39631–4171; tel. 601/645–5221 **A**1 10 18 **F**15 18 29 30 34 39 40 43 45 57 59 61 64 75 77 81 89 90 93 107 108 114 118 119 127 130 133 135 148 **P**6
Primary Contact: Chad Netterville, Administrator
CFO: Bryan N Stevens, Chief Financial Officer
CIO: Locke Wheeles, Information Technology Manager
CHR: Dana McNabb, Human Resources Manager
CNO: Robin Walker, Chief Nursing Officer
Web address: www.fmch.org
Control: County, Government, Nonfederal **Service**: General medical and surgical

Staffed Beds: 16 **Admissions**: 537 **Census**: 10 **Outpatient Visits**: 15905
Births: 0 **Total Expense ($000)**: 17973 **Payroll Expense ($000)**: 7724
Personnel: 157

CHARLESTON—Tallahatchie County

⇑ **TALLAHATCHIE GENERAL HOSPITAL (251304)**, 201 South Market, Zip 38921–2236, Mailing Address: P.O.Box 230, 38921–0240; tel. 662/647–5535, (Total facility includes 98 beds in nursing home–type unit) **A**10 18 21 **F**29 34 40 42 43 53 57 64 86 87 93 107 114 127 128 130 133 135 143 **P**6
Primary Contact: Jim Blackwood, Chief Executive Officer
CFO: Sammie Bell Jr, Chief Financial Officer
Control: County, Government, Nonfederal **Service**: General medical and surgical

Staffed Beds: 116 **Admissions**: 425 **Census**: 97 **Births**: 0 **Total Expense ($000)**: 31248 **Payroll Expense ($000)**: 15003 **Personnel**: 362

CLARKSDALE—Coahoma County

✠ **MERIT HEALTH NORTHWEST MISSISSIPPI (250042)**, 1970 Hospital Drive, Zip 38614–7202, Mailing Address: P.O.Box 1218, 38614–1218; tel. 662/627–3211 **A**1 10 19 **F**3 13 15 18 20 22 28 29 30 31 34 35 40 43 45 46 49 50 57 59 64 70 73 74 76 79 81 85 89 105 107 108 110 111 114 115 118 119 126 130 131 132 **P**8 **S** Community Health Systems, Inc., Franklin, TN
Primary Contact: Joel Southern, R.N., MSN, Chief Executive Officer
CFO: Charles H. Hester CPA, Jr, Chief Financial Officer
CMO: Maha Wasef M.D., Chief of Staff
CIO: Patricia Keenum, Health Information Management Systems Officer
CNO: Steven W Brackeen R.N., Chief Nursing Officer
Web address: www.merithealthnorthwestms.com
Control: Corporation, Investor–owned (for–profit) **Service**: General medical and surgical

Staffed Beds: 181 **Admissions**: 3161 **Census**: 35 **Outpatient Visits**: 54689
Births: 690 **Personnel**: 362

CLEVELAND—Bolivar County

✠ **BOLIVAR MEDICAL CENTER (250093)**, 901 East Sunflower Road, Zip 38732–2833, Mailing Address: P.O.Box 1380, 38732–1380; tel. 662/846–0061, (Total facility includes 35 beds in nursing home–type unit) **A**1 10 20 **F**13 15 24 25 29 30 35 39 40 43 56 60 70 73 76 81 82 87 88 89 93 98 103 107 108 111 116 118 119 128 130 132 133 146 148 **S** LifePoint Health, Brentwood, TN
Primary Contact: Robert L. Marshall Jr, FACHE, Chief Executive Officer
CMO: Mark Blackwood M.D., Chief of Staff
CIO: Cagri Sapmaz, Information Technology Director
CHR: Ben Bufkin, Human Resource Director
CNO: Joann McCollum, Chief Nursing Officer
Web address: www.bolivarmedical.com
Control: Corporation, Investor–owned (for–profit) **Service**: General medical and surgical

Staffed Beds: 129 **Admissions**: 3163 **Census**: 69 **Births**: 406 **Personnel**: 398

Hospital, Medicare Provider Number, Address, Telephone, Approval, Facility, and Physician Codes, Health Care System

★ American Hospital Association (AHA) membership   ○ Healthcare Facilities Accreditation Program   ⇑ Center for Improvement in Healthcare Quality Accreditation
□ The Joint Commission accreditation   ◇ DNV Healthcare Inc. accreditation   △ Commission on Accreditation of Rehabilitation Facilities (CARF) accreditation

COLLINS—Covington County

★ ⇑ **COVINGTON COUNTY HOSPITAL (251325)**, 701 South Holly Avenue, Zip 39428–3899, Mailing Address: P.O.Box 1149, 39428–1149; tel. 601/765–6711, (Total facility includes 60 beds in nursing home–type unit) **A**10 18 21 **F**3 7 29 34 35 40 43 45 50 54 57 59 64 65 66 68 81 89 93 94 98 103 104 107 114 119 127 128 133 135 143 144 146 147
Primary Contact: Gregg Gibbes, Chief Executive Officer
CFO: Kirstie Evans, Chief Financial Officer
CMO: Word Johnston, Medical Director
CIO: Ransom Jones, Information Technology Director
CHR: Beverly K Ponder, Executive Assistant and Human Resources Coordinator
CNO: Martha Lynn Scott, Chief Patient Care Officer
Web address: www.covingtoncountyhospital.com
Control: County, Government, Nonfederal **Service:** General medical and surgical

Staffed Beds: 95 **Admissions:** 538 **Census:** 70 **Outpatient Visits:** 25433 **Births:** 0 **Total Expense ($000):** 28221 **Payroll Expense ($000):** 9890 **Personnel:** 197

COLUMBIA—Marion County

MARION GENERAL HOSPITAL (250085), 1560 Sumrall Road, Zip 39429–2654, Mailing Address: P.O.Box 630, 39429–0630; tel. 601/736–6303 **A**10 **F**11 29 35 39 40 43 61 70 75 81 87 90 93 97 107 108 111 118 119 130 133 144 146
Primary Contact: Bryan K. Maxie, Administrator
CMO: Mark Stevens M.D., Chief Medical Staff
CIO: Donny Bracey, Director Information Services
CNO: Patricia Reid, Director of Nursing
Control: County, Government, Nonfederal **Service:** General medical and surgical

Staffed Beds: 49 **Admissions:** 973 **Census:** 21 **Outpatient Visits:** 28792 **Births:** 0 **Total Expense ($000):** 15575 **Payroll Expense ($000):** 6829 **Personnel:** 139

COLUMBUS—Lowndes County

✉ **BAPTIST MEMORIAL HOSPITAL–GOLDEN TRIANGLE (250100)**, 2520 Fifth Street North, Zip 39705–2095, Mailing Address: P.O.Box 1307, 39703–1307; tel. 662/244–1000 **A**1 10 19 **F**3 4 5 7 11 13 15 17 18 20 22 24 28 29 31 34 38 39 43 43 45 49 51 57 59 61 64 70 73 75 76 77 79 80 81 84 85 87 88 89 91 93 94 96 98 100 102 104 105 106 107 108 109 110 111 114 115 116 117 118 119 120 121 123 124 126 129 130 132 134 146 147 **P**6 **S** Baptist Memorial Health Care Corporation, Memphis, TN
Primary Contact: Paul Cade, Administrator and Chief Executive Officer
CFO: David Webb, Chief Financial Officer
CMO: John E Reed M.D., Medical Director
CIO: Sheila Bardwell, Director Information Systems
CHR: Bob McCallister, Director Human Resources
CNO: Mary Ellen Sumrall, Chief Nursing Officer
Web address: www.baptistonline.org/golden-triangle/
Control: Other not–for–profit (including NFP Corporation) **Service:** General medical and surgical

Staffed Beds: 236 **Admissions:** 8885 **Census:** 99 **Outpatient Visits:** 128518 **Births:** 927 **Total Expense ($000):** 112965 **Payroll Expense ($000):** 43915 **Personnel:** 917

CORINTH—Alcorn County

☐ **MAGNOLIA REGIONAL HEALTH CENTER (250009)**, 611 Alcorn Drive, Zip 38834–9321; tel. 662/293–1000 **A**1 10 13 19 **F**13 15 17 22 24 29 35 39 40 43 51 53 62 63 70 75 76 77 78 81 82 86 87 89 93 98 100 101 102 103 107 108 111 116 118 119 127 130 131 132 143 146 147 **P**7 8
Primary Contact: Ronny Humes, Chief Executive Officer
COO: Angela Nowlin R.N., FACHE, Senior VP, Operations
CFO: Brian Craven, Senior Vice President Finance
CMO: Felton Combest M.D., Vice President Medical Affairs
CIO: David Parker, VP Information Technology
CHR: Regenia Brown, Vice President Human Resources
CNO: Pam B Wallis MSN, Vice President Nursing Services
Web address: www.mrhc.org
Control: City–county, Government, Nonfederal **Service:** General medical and surgical

Staffed Beds: 200 **Admissions:** 8679 **Census:** 100 **Outpatient Visits:** 167997 **Births:** 665 **Personnel:** 1379

DE KALB—Kemper County

JOHN C. STENNIS MEMORIAL HOSPITAL (251335), 14365 Highway 16 West, Zip 39328–7974; tel. 769/486–1000 **A**10 18 **F**29 40 43 75 107 119 127 133 **P**6 **S** Rush Health Systems, Meridian, MS
Primary Contact: Justin Palmer, Administrator
Web address: www.johncstennismemorialhospital.com/jcsmh/
Control: Other not–for–profit (including NFP Corporation) **Service:** General medical and surgical

Staffed Beds: 25 **Admissions:** 358 **Census:** 8 **Outpatient Visits:** 6353 **Births:** 0 **Total Expense ($000):** 12420 **Payroll Expense ($000):** 2836 **Personnel:** 174

EUPORA—Webster County

✚ **NORTH MISSISSIPPI MEDICAL CENTER–EUPORA (250020)**, 70 Medical Plaza, Zip 39744–4018; tel. 662/258–6221, (Total facility includes 35 beds in nursing home–type unit) **A**1 10 20 **F**3 7 11 24 28 29 32 34 35 40 41 43 50 53 57 59 64 65 68 71 84 86 87 89 90 93 97 107 114 119 129 130 131 132 133 146 **S** North Mississippi Health Services, Inc., Tupelo, MS
Primary Contact: Wes Sigler, Administrator
CFO: Adonna Mitchell, Director Fiscal Services
CMO: Christy Vowell D.O., Chief of Staff
CIO: Helen Reed, Director Health Information
CHR: Dorothy Castle, Director Human Resources
Web address: www.nmhs.net/eupora
Control: Other not–for–profit (including NFP Corporation) **Service:** General medical and surgical

Staffed Beds: 73 **Admissions:** 1001 **Census:** 44 **Outpatient Visits:** 42593 **Births:** 0 **Total Expense ($000):** 23208 **Payroll Expense ($000):** 11380 **Personnel:** 191

FAYETTE—Jefferson County

★ **JEFFERSON COUNTY HOSPITAL (250060)**, 870 South Main Street, Zip 39069–5695, Mailing Address: P.O.Box 577, 39069–0577; tel. 601/786–3401 **A**10 **F**3 40 42 105 106 130
Primary Contact: Ada Wilson, R.N., Interim Chief Executive Officer
CMO: Khar Omolara M.D., Chief Medical Staff
CHR: Patricia Selmon, Director Public Relations and Chief Human Resources
Control: County, Government, Nonfederal **Service:** General medical and surgical

Staffed Beds: 30 **Admissions:** 213 **Census:** 5 **Outpatient Visits:** 21832 **Births:** 0 **Personnel:** 93

FLOWOOD—Rankin County

✚ **MERIT HEALTH RIVER OAKS (250138)**, 1030 River Oaks Drive, Zip 39232–9553, Mailing Address: P.O.Box 5100, Jackson, 39296–5100; tel. 601/932–1030 **A**1 3 10 **F**3 11 12 13 15 18 20 29 30 31 35 39 40 43 45 49 51 60 61 63 70 72 73 74 75 76 77 78 79 81 82 85 87 89 93 107 108 110 111 115 119 126 130 144 146 147 **P**5 **S** Community Health Systems, Inc., Franklin, TN
Primary Contact: L Dwayne. Blaylock, Chief Executive Officer
COO: Heather Sistrunk R.N., Chief Operating Officer
CFO: Brad Sinclair, Chief Financial Officer
CIO: Pat Jones, Director Information Systems
CHR: Warren Weed, Director Human Resources
CNO: Sherry P Cook R.N., MSN, Chief Nursing Executive
Web address: www.riveroakshosp.com
Control: Corporation, Investor–owned (for–profit) **Service:** General medical and surgical

Staffed Beds: 158 **Admissions:** 4590 **Census:** 57 **Births:** 1562 **Total Expense ($000):** 101841 **Payroll Expense ($000):** 32095 **Personnel:** 568

✚ **MERIT HEALTH WOMAN'S HOSPITAL (250136)**, 1026 North Flowood Drive, Zip 39232–9532, Mailing Address: 1026 North Flowood Drive, 39232; tel. 601/932–1000, (Nonreporting) **A**1 10 **S** Community Health Systems, Inc., Franklin, TN
Primary Contact: Sherry J. Pitts, Chief Executive Officer
CFO: Nick Renda, Chief Financial Officer
CMO: Ed Barham M.D., Chief of Staff
CHR: Warren Weed, Director Associate Relations
CNO: Linda Atwood, Chief Nursing Officer
Web address: www.merithealthwomanshospital.com
Control: Corporation, Investor–owned (for–profit) **Service:** Obstetrics and gynecology

Staffed Beds: 60

FOREST—Scott County

★ ⇑ **LACKEY MEMORIAL HOSPITAL (251300)**, 330 Broad Street, Zip 39074–3508, Mailing Address: P.O.Box 428, 39074–0428; tel. 601/469–4151, (Total facility includes 20 beds in nursing home–type unit) **A**10 18 21 **F**3 8 11 15 18 29 34 35 38 40 41 43 45 50 54 55 56 57 59 64 65 66 68 81 86 87 89 92 97 98 103 104 106 107 108 110 111 114 119 127 128 130 133 143 **P**6
Primary Contact: Sydney Sawyer, R.N., Chief Executive Officer
CFO: Julie Gieger, Chief Financial Officer
CMO: John Paul Lee M.D., Chief of Staff
CIO: Eddie Pope, Chief Information Officer
CHR: Donn Paul, Chief Human Resources
Web address: www.lackeymemorialhospital.com
Control: Other not–for–profit (including NFP Corporation) **Service:** General medical and surgical

Staffed Beds: 45 **Admissions:** 1079 **Census:** 32 **Outpatient Visits:** 21651 **Births:** 0 **Personnel:** 211

MS

Many Facility Codes have changed. Please refer to the AHA Guide Code Chart. © 2017 AHA Guide

GREENVILLE—Washington County

★ ⇑ **ALLEGIANCE SPECIALTY HOSPITAL OF GREENVILLE (252013)**, 300 South Washington Avenue, 3rd Floor, Zip 38701–4719; tel. 662/332–7344 **A**10 21 **F**1 3 29 34 57 85 87 130 148 **S** Allegiance Health Management, Shreveport, LA
Primary Contact: Vernail Herzog, Chief Executive Officer
CMO: Parvez Karim M.D., Chief Medical Officer
CIO: Sharon Scott, Health Information Director
CHR: Sharon Taylor, Human Resources Director
CNO: John Read, Chief Nursing Officer
Web address: www.ahmgt.com
Control: Corporation, Investor–owned (for–profit) **Service**: Acute long–term care hospital

Staffed Beds: 39 **Admissions**: 443 **Census**: 22 **Outpatient Visits**: 0 **Births**: 0
Total Expense ($000): 10441 **Payroll Expense ($000)**: 4159 **Personnel**: 109

★ **DELTA REGIONAL MEDICAL CENTER (250082)**, 1400 East Union Street, Zip 38704–5247; tel. 662/378–3783, (Includes THE KING'S DAUGHTERS HOSPITAL, 300 Washington Avenue, Greenville, Mississippi, Zip 38701–3614, P O Box 1857, 38702–1857, tel. 662/378–2020; Scott Christensen, Chief Executive Officer) **A**10 19 **F**3 4 11 13 15 18 20 22 28 29 31 34 35 39 40 43 45 47 50 55 57 59 60 62 63 64 65 68 70 72 73 75 76 78 79 81 85 87 89 90 92 93 96 97 98 100 102 103 104 107 108 110 111 115 116 118 119 124 127 129 130 131 132 144 145 146 147 149
Primary Contact: Scott Christensen, Chief Executive Officer
CFO: C Thomas Moore, Chief Financial Officer
CIO: Andy Altenburger, Chief Information Officer
CHR: Chrissy Nicholson, Vice President Human Resources
CNO: Amy Walker, Chief Nursing Officer
Web address: www.deltaregional.com
Control: County, Government, Nonfederal **Service**: General medical and surgical

Staffed Beds: 171 **Admissions**: 6591 **Census**: 82 **Outpatient Visits**: 103797 **Births**: 699 **Total Expense ($000)**: 118289 **Payroll Expense ($000)**: 50156 **Personnel**: 876

GREENWOOD—Leflore County

AMG SPECIALTY HOSPITAL–GREENWOOD (252010), 1401 River Road Floor 2, Zip 38930–4030; tel. 662/459–2681 **A**10 **F**1 3 18 34 50 59 130 **S** AMG Integrated Healthcare Management, Lafayette, LA
Primary Contact: Jennifer Wallace, Chief Executive Officer
CMO: Gutti Rao M.D., Medical Director
CNO: Brenda Small, Chief Clinical Officer
Web address: www.amggreenwood.com/
Control: Corporation, Investor–owned (for–profit) **Service**: Acute long–term care hospital

Staffed Beds: 40 **Admissions**: 307 **Census**: 20 **Outpatient Visits**: 0 **Births**: 0
Total Expense ($000): 8749 **Payroll Expense ($000)**: 3600 **Personnel**: 73

☐ △ **GREENWOOD LEFLORE HOSPITAL (250099)**, 1401 River Road, Zip 38930–4030, Mailing Address: Drawer 1410, 38935–1410; tel. 662/459–7000 **A**1 7 10 19 **F**3 13 15 17 18 19 20 34 35 39 40 43 44 45 46 50 53 56 57 58 59 64 65 70 74 75 76 79 81 82 85 86 87 89 90 93 96 98 103 106 107 108 109 110 111 114 118 119 120 121 129 130 132 146 147 149 **P**6 8
Primary Contact: James H. Jackson Jr, Executive Director
COO: Dodie McElmurray, Chief Operating Officer
CFO: Dawne Holmes, Chief Financial Officer
CMO: Gutti Rao M.D., Chief of Staff
CIO: Mark S Hutson, Chief Information Officer
CHR: Key Britt, Associate Director
CNO: Rebecca Edwards, Chief Nursing Officer
Web address: www.glh.org
Control: City–county, Government, Nonfederal **Service**: General medical and surgical

Staffed Beds: 208 **Admissions**: 6090 **Census**: 75 **Outpatient Visits**: 163407 **Births**: 516 **Total Expense ($000)**: 126082 **Payroll Expense ($000)**: 58874 **Personnel**: 871

GRENADA—Grenada County

★ ⇑ **UNIVERSITY OF MISSISSIPPI MEDICAL CENTER GRENADA (250168)**, 960 Avent Drive, Zip 38901–5230; tel. 662/227–7000 **A**10 21 **F**3 7 8 11 13 15 17 29 30 32 34 35 39 40 43 45 53 57 59 60 62 64 65 70 73 76 77 79 80 81 82 85 87 89 90 93 94 96 97 98 103 107 108 110 111 115 116 118 119 127 130 143 146 147 **P**6 **S** University Hospitals and Health System, Jackson, MS
Primary Contact: Donald Hutson, Chief Executive Officer
COO: Molly B. Brown, Chief Operating Officer
CFO: Scott Whittemore, Chief Financial Officer
CIO: John Farrish, Health Information Director
CHR: Claudette Hathcock, Administrative Director Human Resources
Web address: www.ummchealth.com/grenada
Control: State, Government, Nonfederal **Service**: General medical and surgical

Staffed Beds: 93 **Admissions**: 2583 **Census**: 32 **Outpatient Visits**: 58722 **Births**: 433 **Total Expense ($000)**: 41793 **Payroll Expense ($000)**: 24780 **Personnel**: 412

GULFPORT—Harrison County

⊞ **GARDEN PARK MEDICAL CENTER (250123)**, 15200 Community Road, Zip 39503–3085, Mailing Address: P.O. Box 1240, 39502–1240; tel. 228/575–7000 **A**1 10 **F**3 9 12 13 15 29 34 35 37 40 41 43 45 46 49 57 59 64 65 70 74 76 79 81 85 86 89 90 98 103 107 108 109 110 111 112 115 118 119 126 147 149 **S** HCA Healthcare, Nashville, TN
Primary Contact: Randy Rogers, FACHE, Chief Executive Officer
COO: Regina Ramazani, Chief Operating Officer
CFO: Regina Ramazani, Chief Financial Officer
CMO: T. Paul Mace, Chief Medical Officer
CIO: Chris Oubre, Information Technology Director
CHR: Michael Pocchiari, Director Human Resources
CNO: Cheryl Thompson, Chief Nursing Officer
Web address: www.gpmedical.com
Control: Corporation, Investor–owned (for–profit) **Service**: General medical and surgical

Staffed Beds: 130 **Admissions**: 3788 **Census**: 48 **Outpatient Visits**: 65035 **Births**: 408 **Total Expense ($000)**: 71584 **Payroll Expense ($000)**: 23950 **Personnel**: 332

⊞ △ **MEMORIAL HOSPITAL AT GULFPORT (250019)**, 4500 13th Street, Zip 39501–2569, Mailing Address: P.O. Box 1810, 39502–1810; tel. 228/867–4000, (Includes MEMORIAL BEHAVIORAL HEALTH, 11150 Highway 49 North, Gulfport, Mississippi, Zip 39503–4110, tel. 228/831–1700; Michael A Zieman, Administrator) **A**1 2 3 7 10 **F**2 3 4 11 12 13 15 17 18 20 22 24 28 29 31 34 35 40 43 44 45 46 48 49 50 53 54 57 59 64 65 68 70 71 72 73 74 76 77 78 79 80 81 84 85 87 89 90 92 93 95 96 98 99 100 101 102 104 105 107 108 110 111 114 115 116 117 118 119 120 121 123 124 126 130 132 145 146 149 **P**8
Primary Contact: Gary G. Marchand, President and Chief Executive Officer
COO: Kent Nicaud, Chief Operating Officer
CFO: Jeffrey T Steiner, Vice President Finance
CMO: Larry Couvillon M.D., Chief Medical Officer
CIO: Gene Thomas, Vice President, Information Systems, Chief Information Officer
CHR: Cathy Wood, Vice President, Human Resources
CNO: Jennifer Dumal R.N., Chief Operating Officer of Clinical and Chief Nursing Officer
Web address: www.gulfportmemorial.com
Control: City–county, Government, Nonfederal **Service**: General medical and surgical

Staffed Beds: 445 **Admissions**: 16496 **Census**: 242 **Outpatient Visits**: 658320 **Births**: 1510 **Total Expense ($000)**: 457160 **Payroll Expense ($000)**: 206534 **Personnel**: 3191

⊞ **SELECT SPECIALTY HOSPITAL–GULFPORT (252005)**, 1520 Broad Avenue, Suite 300, Zip 39501–3601; tel. 228/575–7500 **A**1 10 **F**1 29 75 82 87 90 **S** Select Medical Corporation, Mechanicsburg, PA
Primary Contact: John O'Keefe, Chief Executive Officer
Web address: www.selectspecialtyhospitals.com/company/locations/gulfcoast.aspx
Control: Corporation, Investor–owned (for–profit) **Service**: Acute long–term care hospital

Staffed Beds: 61 **Admissions**: 386 **Census**: 27 **Outpatient Visits**: 0 **Births**: 0 **Personnel**: 140

HATTIESBURG—Forrest County

★ △ ⇑ **FORREST GENERAL HOSPITAL (250078)**, 6051 U S Highway 49, Zip 39401–7200, Mailing Address: P.O. Box 16389, 39404–6389; tel. 601/288–7000 **A**2 3 5 7 10 19 21 **F**3 4 5 12 13 15 17 18 20 22 24 28 29 31 34 35 37 39 40 43 45 46 47 48 49 53 57 58 59 62 63 64 68 70 72 73 75 76 77 79 81 84 85 86 87 89 90 91 92 93 95 96 98 99 100 101 102 103 104 105 106 107 108 111 114 115 118 119 120 121 123 124 126 128 130 132 146 147 149 **P**1
Primary Contact: Evan S. Dillard, M.P.H., FACHE, President and Chief Executive Officer
COO: Douglas A Jones, Chief Operating Officer
CFO: Andy Woodard, Chief Financial Officer
CMO: Steven E Farrell M.D., Chief Medical Officer
CHR: Troy P Daniels, Chief Human Resources Officer
CNO: Micah Rehm, Chief Nursing Officer
Web address: www.forrestgeneral.com
Control: County, Government, Nonfederal **Service**: General medical and surgical

Staffed Beds: 512 **Admissions**: 28759 **Census**: 360 **Outpatient Visits**: 149476 **Births**: 2403 **Total Expense ($000)**: 414644 **Payroll Expense ($000)**: 152485 **Personnel**: 3177

MS

Hospital, Medicare Provider Number, Address, Telephone, Approval, Facility, and Physician Codes, Health Care System

★ American Hospital Association (AHA) membership   ○ Healthcare Facilities Accreditation Program   ⇑ Center for Improvement in Healthcare Quality Accreditation
☐ The Joint Commission accreditation   ◇ DNV Healthcare Inc. accreditation   △ Commission on Accreditation of Rehabilitation Facilities (CARF) accreditation

⊞ **REGENCY HOSPITAL OF HATTIESBURG (252009)**, 6051 U S Highway 49, 5th Floor, Zip 39401–6031; tel. 601/288–8510 **A**1 10 **F**1 **S** Select Medical Corporation, Mechanicsburg, PA
Primary Contact: William Heath, Chief Executive Officer
CMO: Ralph Kahler M.D., Medical Director
CHR: Joseph Worley, Human Resources Coordinator
Web address: www.hattiesburg.regencyhospital.com/
Control: Corporation, Investor–owned (for–profit) **Service**: Acute long–term care hospital

Staffed Beds: 33 **Admissions**: 403 **Census**: 28 **Outpatient Visits**: 0 **Births**: 0
Total Expense ($000): 14751 **Payroll Expense ($000)**: 5938 **Personnel**: 115

HATTIESBURG—Lamar County

⊞ **MERIT HEALTH WESLEY (250094)**, 5001 Hardy Street, Zip 39402–1308, Mailing Address: P.O.Box 16509, 39404–6509; tel. 601/268–8000 **A**1 10 19 **F**3 8 11 12 13 15 17 18 20 22 24 26 28 29 30 32 34 35 37 39 40 41 43 45 46 49 53 54 57 58 59 60 61 64 65 70 71 72 73 74 75 76 77 78 79 81 82 85 87 89 90 91 93 96 97 103 107 108 110 111 114 115 117 118 119 126 129 130 132 135 146 148 **S** Community Health Systems, Inc., Franklin, TN
Primary Contact: Michael Neuendorf, Chief Executive Officer
CFO: Randy Humphrey, Chief Financial Officer
CMO: William Reno M.D., III, President Medical Staff
CHR: Terry Trigg, Director Human Resources
Web address: www.wesley.com
Control: Corporation, Investor–owned (for–profit) **Service**: General medical and surgical

Staffed Beds: 211 **Admissions**: 7043 **Census**: 97 **Outpatient Visits**: 81490
Births: 1287 **Personnel**: 848

HAZLEHURST—Copiah County

★ **COPIAH COUNTY MEDICAL CENTER (251327)**, 27190 Highway 28, Zip 39083–2228, Mailing Address: P.O.Box 889, 39083–0889; tel. 601/574–7000 **A**10 18 **F**15 18 29 35 39 40 45 51 59 64 77 81 93 104 107 110 111 115 119 133
Primary Contact: Benjamin Lott, Chief Executive Officer
CFO: Bryan N Stevens, Interim Chief Financial Officer
CNO: Alison Mathis, Chief Nursing Officer
Web address: www.myccmc.org/
Control: County, Government, Nonfederal **Service**: General medical and surgical

Staffed Beds: 25 **Admissions**: 760 **Census**: 13 **Outpatient Visits**: 15431
Births: 0 **Total Expense ($000)**: 13289 **Payroll Expense ($000)**: 4861
Personnel: 158

HOLLY SPRINGS—Marshall County

ALLIANCE HEALTHCARE SYSTEM (250012), 1430 Highway 4 East, Zip 38635–2140, Mailing Address: P.O.Box 6000, 38634–6000; tel. 662/252–1212 **A**10 20 **F**15 29 35 40 43 75 81 87 89 98 103 107 119 130 132 133 143
Primary Contact: Perry E. Williams Sr, Administrator and Chief Executive Officer
COO: Cecelia Bost, Chief Operating Officer
CFO: William F Magee, Chief Financial Officer
CMO: Subbu Rayudu M.D., Chief of Staff
CIO: Saul Mbenga, Manager Information Technology
CHR: Judy Eggers, Manager Human Resources
Web address: www.alliancehealth.us
Control: Corporation, Investor–owned (for–profit) **Service**: General medical and surgical

Staffed Beds: 40 **Admissions**: 622 **Census**: 12 **Outpatient Visits**: 5872
Births: 0 **Total Expense ($000)**: 9870 **Payroll Expense ($000)**: 4077
Personnel: 95

HOUSTON—Chickasaw County

TRACE REGIONAL HOSPITAL (250017), Highway 8 East, Zip 38851–9396, Mailing Address: P.O.Box 626, 38851–0626; tel. 662/456–3700 **A**10 **F**3 11 15 30 34 35 45 57 59 61 64 66 75 82 90 91 93 98 101 102 103 107 111 119 127 130 133 135 146 148 **P**6 **S** Sunlink Health Systems, Atlanta, GA
Primary Contact: Gary L. Staten, Chief Executive Officer
CFO: Pamela W Cook, Chief Financial Officer
CMO: Bill Brohawn, Chief of Staff
CHR: Sherry Craig, Director Human Resources
CNO: Marianne Johnson, Chief Nursing Officer
Web address: www.traceregional.com
Control: Corporation, Investor–owned (for–profit) **Service**: General medical and surgical

Staffed Beds: 84 **Admissions**: 593 **Census**: 20 **Outpatient Visits**: 11148
Births: 0 **Total Expense ($000)**: 13981 **Payroll Expense ($000)**: 8558
Personnel: 171

INDIANOLA—Sunflower County

★ **SOUTH SUNFLOWER COUNTY HOSPITAL (250095)**, 121 East Baker Street, Zip 38751–2498; tel. 662/887–5235 **A**10 20 **F**13 40 43 76 80 81 107 110 111 119 127 130 133 **P**8
Primary Contact: Courtney Phillips, Chief Executive Officer
COO: Holly H. Sparks, Chief Clinical Officer
CFO: Katie Yates, Chief Financial Officer
CMO: John H. Jones, Chief of Staff
CIO: Benjamin Rosenthal, Information Systems Director
CHR: Meredith Taylor, Controller
Web address: www.southsunflower.com
Control: County, Government, Nonfederal **Service**: General medical and surgical

Staffed Beds: 48 **Admissions**: 1196 **Census**: 14 **Births**: 100 **Total Expense ($000)**: 16025 **Payroll Expense ($000)**: 5597 **Personnel**: 109

IUKA—Tishomingo County

⊞ **NORTH MISSISSIPPI MEDICAL CENTER–IUKA (250002)**, 1777 Curtis Drive, Zip 38852–1001, Mailing Address: P.O.Box 860, 38852–0860; tel. 662/423–6051 **A**1 10 **F**7 15 29 34 35 40 53 57 64 65 68 75 80 82 86 87 89 90 91 93 107 108 111 119 130 132 133 134 146 **S** North Mississippi Health Services, Inc., Tupelo, MS
Primary Contact: Fred A. Truesdale Jr, Administrator
CFO: Betty Moore, Business Manager
CMO: Margaret Glynn M.D., Chief Medical Officer
CIO: Fred A Truesdale Jr, Administrator
CHR: Jane Chamblee, Manager Human Resources
Web address: www.nmhs.net
Control: Other not–for–profit (including NFP Corporation) **Service**: General medical and surgical

Staffed Beds: 48 **Admissions**: 634 **Census**: 6 **Outpatient Visits**: 24808
Births: 0 **Total Expense ($000)**: 12225 **Payroll Expense ($000)**: 7449
Personnel: 153

JACKSON—Hinds County

☐ **BRENTWOOD BEHAVIORAL HEALTHCARE OF MISSISSIPPI (254007)**, 3531 East Lakeland Drive, Zip 39232–8839; tel. 601/936–2024 **A**1 10 **F**35 98 99 101 102 104 105 130 132 134 **S** Universal Health Services, Inc., King of Prussia, PA
Primary Contact: Michael J. Carney, Chief Executive Officer
Web address: www.brentwoodjackson.com
Control: Corporation, Investor–owned (for–profit) **Service**: Psychiatric

Staffed Beds: 105 **Admissions**: 2771 **Census**: 71 **Outpatient Visits**: 3895
Births: 0 **Personnel**: 220

⊞ **G.V. (SONNY) MONTGOMERY VETERANS AFFAIRS MEDICAL CENTER**, 1500 East Woodrow Wilson Drive, Zip 39216–5199; tel. 601/362–4471, (Nonreporting) **A**1 3 5 **S** Department of Veterans Affairs, Washington, DC
Primary Contact: David M. Walker, M.D., Medical Center Director
COO: Jed Fillingim, Acting Chief Operating Officer and Associate Director
CFO: Joy Willis, Acting Chief Fiscal Service
CMO: Kent Kirchner M.D., Chief of Staff
CIO: Robert Wolak, Chief Information Resource Management Service
CHR: Sam Evans, Chief Human Resources Management
Web address: www.jackson.va.gov/
Control: Veterans Affairs, Government, federal **Service**: General medical and surgical

Staffed Beds: 323

⊞ **MERIT HEALTH CENTRAL (250072)**, 1850 Chadwick Drive, Zip 39204–3479, Mailing Address: P.O.Box 59001, 39284–9001; tel. 601/376–1000 **A**1 3 10 **F**4 13 15 16 17 29 35 40 43 70 72 75 76 77 78 81 86 87 89 90 93 97 98 100 102 107 108 111 116 118 119 130 132 146 **S** Community Health Systems, Inc., Franklin, TN
Primary Contact: Barry Moss, Chief Executive Officer
CFO: Justin Stroud, Chief Financial Officer
CMO: Greg Oden, Chief Medical Officer
CIO: Tracy Holifield, Director Information Systems
CHR: Sean Jones, Director Human Resources
CNO: Laura Knight, Chief Nursing Officer
Web address: www.merithealthcentral.com/
Control: Corporation, Investor–owned (for–profit) **Service**: General medical and surgical

Staffed Beds: 319 **Admissions**: 8262 **Census**: 110 **Births**: 794 **Personnel**: 851

Many Facility Codes have changed. Please refer to the AHA Guide Code Chart.
© 2017 AHA Guide

MS

✠ △ **METHODIST REHABILITATION CENTER (250152)**, 1350 Woodrow Wilson Drive, Zip 39216–5198; tel. 601/981–2611, (Total facility includes 60 beds in nursing home–type unit) **A**1 3 5 7 10 **F**35 81 82 86 87 90 93 119 130 131 132 146
Primary Contact: Mark A. Adams, President and Chief Executive Officer
COO: Joseph M Morette, Executive Vice President
CFO: Gary Armstrong, Executive Vice President
CIO: Gary Armstrong, Executive Vice President
CHR: Steve Hope, Vice President Corporate Services
Web address: www.methodistrehab.org
Control: Other not–for–profit (including NFP Corporation) **Service:** Rehabilitation

Staffed Beds: 184 Admissions: 1288 Census: 114 Outpatient Visits: 54170 Births: 0 Total Expense ($000): 42791 Payroll Expense ($000): 26291 Personnel: 586

✠ **MISSISSIPPI BAPTIST MEDICAL CENTER (250102)**, 1225 North State Street, Zip 39202–2064; tel. 601/968–1000 **A**1 2 3 5 10 **F**3 5 8 11 12 13 15 17 18 19 20 22 24 26 27 28 29 30 31 34 35 36 40 43 44 45 46 47 48 49 50 51 52 53 54 55 57 59 60 64 65 68 70 71 72 74 75 76 78 79 80 81 85 86 89 91 92 93 94 98 100 103 107 108 109 110 111 113 114 115 116 117 118 119 126 130 132 144 145 146 147 **S** Baptist Memorial Health Care Corporation, Memphis, TN
Primary Contact: Bobbie K. Ware, R.N., FACHE, Chief Executive Officer
COO: Bobbie K. Ware R.N., FACHE, Vice President Patient Care and Chief Nursing Officer
CFO: William Thompson, Chief Financial Officer
CMO: Michael Maples M.D., Vice President and Chief Medical Officer
CIO: Steve M Stanic, Vice President and Chief Information Officer
CHR: Lee Ann Foreman, Vice President Human Resources
CNO: Bobbie K. Ware R.N., FACHE, Vice President Patient Care and Chief Nursing Officer
Web address: www.mbhs.org
Control: Other not–for–profit (including NFP Corporation) **Service:** General medical and surgical

Staffed Beds: 483 Admissions: 20147 Census: 268 Outpatient Visits: 235866 Births: 1715 Total Expense ($000): 243325 Payroll Expense ($000): 130663 Personnel: 2640

✠ **SELECT SPECIALTY HOSPITAL – BELHAVEN (252003)**, 1225 North State Street, Zip 39202–2097, Mailing Address: P.O.Box 23695, 39225–3695; tel. 601/968–1000 **A**1 10 **F**1 3 29 56 61 82 130 **S** Select Medical Corporation, Mechanicsburg, PA
Primary Contact: Robert Shannon. Canard, Chief Executive Officer
CFO: Russell W York, Vice President and Chief Financial Officer
CMO: Holland M Addison M.D., Medical Director
CIO: Steve M Stanic, Vice President and Chief Information Officer
CHR: Lee Ann Foreman, Vice President Human Resources
Web address: www.mbhs.org
Control: Corporation, Investor–owned (for–profit) **Service:** Acute long–term care hospital

Staffed Beds: 25 Admissions: 227 Census: 20 Outpatient Visits: 0 Births: 0 Total Expense ($000): 16939 Payroll Expense ($000): 6476 Personnel: 108

✠ **SELECT SPECIALTY HOSPITAL–JACKSON (252007)**, 5903 Ridgewood Road, Suite 100, Zip 39211–3700; tel. 601/899–3800 **A**1 10 **F**1 107 119 **P**7 **S** Select Medical Corporation, Mechanicsburg, PA
Primary Contact: Chandler Ewing, Chief Executive Officer
CFO: Melissa Smith, Controller
CIO: Jacqueline Barnes, Manager Health Information
CHR: Vicki Watson, Manager Human Resources
Web address: www.selectspecialtyhospitals.com/company/locations/jackson.aspx
Control: Corporation, Investor–owned (for–profit) **Service:** Acute long–term care hospital

Staffed Beds: 53 Admissions: 589 Census: 41 Outpatient Visits: 0 Births: 0 Total Expense ($000): 15519 Payroll Expense ($000): 10188 Personnel: 216

✠ **ST. DOMINIC–JACKSON MEMORIAL HOSPITAL (250048)**, 969 Lakeland Drive, Zip 39216–4606; tel. 601/200–2000 **A**1 2 3 5 10 **F**3 4 11 12 13 15 17 18 20 22 24 28 29 31 34 35 36 37 38 40 43 46 47 49 50 51 53 57 58 61 64 65 68 70 72 73 74 75 76 77 79 80 81 84 85 89 90 92 93 96 97 98 100 101 102 103 106 107 108 109 110 111 114 115 116 117 118 119 120 121 123 124 126 131 147 **P**6 8
Primary Contact: Lester K. Diamond, President
CFO: Sam Scott, Vice President Financial Services
CMO: Eric A McVey M.D., Executive Vice President Medical Affairs and Quality
CIO: Keith Van Camp, Vice President Information Services
CHR: Frank Lenior, Vice President Human Resources
CNO: Theresa Horne, NEA–BC MS, MSN, Vice President Patient Care Services
Web address: www.stdom.com
Control: Church operated, Nongovernment, not–for–profit **Service:** General medical and surgical

Staffed Beds: 535 Admissions: 37941 Census: 394 Outpatient Visits: 210305 Births: 1477 Total Expense ($000): 460654 Payroll Expense ($000): 194467 Personnel: 3007

✠ △ **UNIVERSITY OF MISSISSIPPI MEDICAL CENTER (250001)**, 2500 North State Street, Zip 39216–4505; tel. 601/984–1000, (Includes BLAIR E. BATSON HOSPITAL FOR CHILDREN, 2500 North State State Room W019, Jackson, Mississippi, Zip 39216–4500, tel. 601/984–1000; CHILDREN'S HEALTHCARE OF MISSISSIPPI, 2500 North State Street, Jackson, Mississippi, Zip 39216–4500, tel. 601/984–1000) **A**1 2 3 5 7 8 10 13 **F**3 6 7 11 12 13 15 17 18 19 20 21 22 23 24 25 28 29 31 32 34 35 38 39 40 41 43 45 46 47 48 49 50 52 53 54 55 56 57 58 59 60 61 64 65 66 68 70 71 72 73 74 75 76 77 79 80 81 82 84 85 86 87 88 89 90 92 93 94 96 97 98 99 100 101 102 103 104 107 108 110 111 112 114 115 116 117 118 119 120 121 123 124 126 129 130 131 132 134 136 137 138 139 142 143 144 146 147 149 **P**6 **S** University Hospitals and Health System, Jackson, MS
Primary Contact: Kevin S. Cook, Chief Executive Officer
CFO: Dan Janicak, Chief Financial Officer
CMO: William H Cleland M.D., Chief Medical Officer
CHR: Michael Estes, Director Human Resources
Web address: www.umc.edu
Control: State, Government, Nonfederal **Service:** General medical and surgical

Staffed Beds: 680 Admissions: 30886 Census: 551 Outpatient Visits: 518414 Births: 2131 Total Expense ($000): 710193 Payroll Expense ($000): 265777 Personnel: 4616

KEESLER AFB—Harrison County

✠ **U.S. AIR FORCE MEDICAL CENTER KEESLER**, 301 Fisher Street, Room 1A132, Zip 39534–2519; tel. 228/376–2550, (Nonreporting) **A**1 2 3 5 **S** Department of the Air Force, Washington, DC
Primary Contact: Colonel Thomas Harrell, M.D., Commander
COO: Brigadier GeneralJames Dougherty, Commander
CFO: MajorBrenda Yi, Director Medical Resource Management and Chief Financial Officer
CMO: ColonelJames Gasque M.D., Chief Hospital Services
CIO: MajorSamuel Silverthorne, Chief Information Officer
CHR: MajorBrenda Yi, Director Medical Resource Management and Chief Financial Officer
Web address: www.keesler.af.mil
Control: Air Force, Government, federal **Service:** General medical and surgical

Staffed Beds: 56

KOSCIUSKO—Attala County

★ ⇧ **BAPTIST MEDICAL CENTER ATTALA (251336)**, 220 Highway 12 West, Zip 39090–3208, Mailing Address: P.O.Box 887, 39090–0887; tel. 662/289–4311 **A**10 18 21 **F**3 15 29 34 35 40 56 57 59 63 64 65 81 85 89 90 92 93 103 107 108 110 115 116 118 119 130 133 148 **S** Baptist Memorial Health Care Corporation, Memphis, TN
Primary Contact: Sean Johnson, Interim Chief Executive Officer
CHR: Stephanie Washington, Human Resources Director
CNO: Allison Schuler R.N., Chief Nursing Officer
Web address: www.mbhs.org/locations/baptist–medical–center–attala/
Control: Other not–for–profit (including NFP Corporation) **Service:** General medical and surgical

Staffed Beds: 25 Admissions: 723 Census: 12 Births: 0 Total Expense ($000): 12057 Payroll Expense ($000): 4754 Personnel: 122

Hospital, Medicare Provider Number, Address, Telephone, Approval, Facility, and Physician Codes, Health Care System

★ American Hospital Association (AHA) membership   ○ Healthcare Facilities Accreditation Program   ⇧ Center for Improvement in Healthcare Quality Accreditation
□ The Joint Commission accreditation   ◇ DNV Healthcare Inc. accreditation   △ Commission on Accreditation of Rehabilitation Facilities (CARF) accreditation

LAUREL—Jones County

★ ⇑ **SOUTH CENTRAL REGIONAL MEDICAL CENTER (250058)**, 1220 Jefferson Street, Zip 39440–4374, Mailing Address: P.O.Box 607, 39441–0607; tel. 601/426–4000, (Total facility includes 260 beds in nursing home–type unit) **A**10 21 **F**3 4 7 10 11 12 13 15 17 18 20 28 29 31 32 34 35 39 40 41 43 45 46 47 48 49 50 51 53 54 57 59 62 63 64 65 68 70 71 73 74 75 76 77 78 79 81 82 84 85 86 87 89 90 93 100 102 104 105 107 108 109 110 111 115 117 119 126 128 129 130 131 132 134 143 144 146 147 **P**6
Primary Contact: G Douglas Higginbotham, President and Chief Executive Officer
CFO: Tom Canizaro, Vice President and Chief Financial Officer
CIO: Dell Blakeney, Vice President and Chief Information Officer
CHR: Janet Staples, Vice President Human Resources
CNO: Beth W Endom R.N., MSN, Vice President and Chief Nursing Officer
Web address: www.scrmc.com
Control: County, Government, Nonfederal **Service**: General medical and surgical

Staffed Beds: 410 **Admissions**: 7605 **Census**: 328 **Outpatient Visits**: 88401 **Births**: 916 **Total Expense ($000)**: 149941 **Payroll Expense ($000)**: 74116 **Personnel**: 1607

LEAKESVILLE—Greene County

GREENE COUNTY HOSPITAL (251329), 1017 Jackson Avenue, Zip 39451–9105; tel. 601/394–4139 **A**10 18 **F**40 43 107 133
Primary Contact: Deborah Berry, Director of Operations
CFO: Debbie Brannan, Chief Financial Officer
CMO: Larry Henderson M.D., Medical Director
CHR: Carla Shows, Payroll Clerk
Web address: www.georgeregional.com
Control: County, Government, Nonfederal **Service**: General medical and surgical

Staffed Beds: 7 **Admissions**: 154 **Census**: 5 **Births**: 0 **Total Expense ($000)**: 5924 **Payroll Expense ($000)**: 2026 **Personnel**: 46

LEXINGTON—Holmes County

⊞ **UNIVERSITY OF MISSISSIPPI MEDICAL CENTER HOLMES COUNTY (251319)**, 239 Bowling Green Road, Zip 39095–5167; tel. 601/496–5200 **A**1 10 18 **F**3 11 15 29 34 40 43 45 50 56 57 59 64 86 87 89 93 104 107 108 114 118 119 127 130 133 146 **P**6 **S** University Hospitals and Health System, Jackson, MS
Primary Contact: Donald Hutson, Chief Executive Officer
COO: Paige Lawrence, Assistant Administrator
CFO: Scott Whittemore, Chief Financial Officer
CMO: Mark Smothers M.D., Chief Medical Officer
CIO: Sammuel Townsend, LAN Administrator
CHR: Claudette Hathcock, Human Resources Director
Web address: www.ummchealth.com/holmes/
Control: State, Government, Nonfederal **Service**: General medical and surgical

Staffed Beds: 25 **Admissions**: 356 **Census**: 6 **Births**: 0 **Total Expense ($000)**: 10278 **Payroll Expense ($000)**: 6931 **Personnel**: 97

LOUISVILLE—Winston County

WINSTON MEDICAL CENTER (250027), 562 East Main Street, Zip 39339–2742, Mailing Address: P.O.Box 967, 39339–0967; tel. 662/773–6211, (Total facility includes 74 beds in nursing home–type unit) **A**10 20 **F**15 29 34 35 40 43 57 59 65 89 93 103 107 110 114 119 127 128 130 133 146
Primary Contact: Paul S. Black, Interim Administrator
Web address: www.winstonmedical.org
Control: Other not–for–profit (including NFP Corporation) **Service**: General medical and surgical

Staffed Beds: 91 **Admissions**: 894 **Census**: 83 **Outpatient Visits**: 24814 **Births**: 0 **Total Expense ($000)**: 19029 **Payroll Expense ($000)**: 7991 **Personnel**: 216

LUCEDALE—George County

GEORGE REGIONAL HOSPITAL (250036), 859 Winter Street, Zip 39452–6603, Mailing Address: P.O.Box 607, 39452–0607; tel. 601/947–3161 **A**10 20 **F**3 11 13 15 18 29 30 34 35 40 43 45 47 48 49 53 54 57 59 65 68 70 76 77 81 82 86 87 93 97 100 107 108 111 119 127 129 130 133 135 146 148 **P**8
Primary Contact: Greg Havard, Chief Executive Officer
CFO: Debbie Brannan, Chief Financial Officer
CMO: Jay Pinkerton, Chief Medical Officer
CIO: Anthoney Fryfogle, Chief Information Officer
CHR: Carla Shows, Human Resource and Payroll Clerk
CNO: Tabatha Pinter, Director of Nursing
Web address: www.georgeregional.com
Control: County, Government, Nonfederal **Service**: General medical and surgical

Staffed Beds: 48 **Admissions**: 1006 **Census**: 9 **Outpatient Visits**: 43704 **Births**: 249 **Total Expense ($000)**: 22645 **Payroll Expense ($000)**: 12218 **Personnel**: 326

MACON—Noxubee County

NOXUBEE GENERAL HOSPITAL (251307), 606 North Jefferson Street, Zip 39341–2242, Mailing Address: P.O.Box 480, 39341–0480; tel. 662/726–4231, (Total facility includes 60 beds in nursing home–type unit) **A**10 18 **F**40 89 107 127 128 130 133
Primary Contact: Danny H. McKay, Administrator
Web address: www.noxubeecountyms.com/quality–of–life–noxubee–mississipp/health–care–noxubee–mississippi/
Control: County, Government, Nonfederal **Service**: General medical and surgical

Staffed Beds: 85 **Admissions**: 625 **Census**: 64 **Births**: 0 **Total Expense ($000)**: 14342 **Payroll Expense ($000)**: 7954 **Personnel**: 183

MAGEE—Simpson County

★ **MAGEE GENERAL HOSPITAL (250124)**, 300 Third Avenue SE, Zip 39111–3698; tel. 601/849–5070 **A**10 **F**13 15 29 35 40 43 81 89 97 107 108 111 119 130 133 146
Primary Contact: Amy Tolliver, Administrator
CMO: Kelli Smith M.D., Chief of Staff
CIO: Kirby Craft, Chief Information Officer
CHR: Steve Beckham, Director Human Resources
CNO: Cindy McIntyre R.N., Administrative Director Clinical Services
Web address: www.mghosp.org
Control: Other not–for–profit (including NFP Corporation) **Service**: General medical and surgical

Staffed Beds: 64 **Admissions**: 1095 **Census**: 18 **Births**: 109 **Personnel**: 196

MAGNOLIA—Pike County

BEACHAM MEMORIAL HOSPITAL (250049), 205 North Cherry Street, Zip 39652–2819, Mailing Address: P.O.Box 351, 39652–0351; tel. 601/783–2351 **A**10 **F**3 34 35 36 57 59 65 68 98 100 101 103 107 114 127 130 133 146 148
Primary Contact: Jason Reed, Chief Executive Officer
CMO: Lucius Lampton M.D., Medical Director
CHR: Jackie McKenzie, Director Administrative Services
Web address: www.beachammemorial.org
Control: Other not–for–profit (including NFP Corporation) **Service**: General medical and surgical

Staffed Beds: 31 **Admissions**: 1205 **Census**: 19 **Outpatient Visits**: 0 **Births**: 0 **Personnel**: 44

MCCOMB—Pike County

★ ⇑ **SOUTHWEST MISSISSIPPI REGIONAL MEDICAL CENTER (250097)**, 215 Marion Avenue, Zip 39648–2705, Mailing Address: P.O.Box 1307, 39649–1307; tel. 601/249–5500, (Nonreporting) **A**10 19 21 **S** Southwest Health Systems, Mccomb, MS
Primary Contact: Norman M. Price, FACHE, Chief Executive Officer
COO: Richard Williams, Chief Operating Officer
CFO: Charla Rowley, Chief Financial Officer
CMO: Kevin Richardson M.D., Chief of Staff
CIO: Ron Noreen, Director, Information Services
CHR: Don Haskins, Administrative Director Human Resources
CNO: Michelle Gough MSN, RN–B, Chief Nursing Officer
Web address: www.smrmc.com
Control: Hospital district or authority, Government, Nonfederal **Service**: General medical and surgical

Staffed Beds: 143

MEADVILLE—Franklin County

FRANKLIN COUNTY MEMORIAL HOSPITAL (251330), 40 Union Church Road, Zip 39653–8336, Mailing Address: P.O.Box 636, 39653–0636; tel. 601/384–5801 **A**10 18 **F**29 35 39 40 43 56 86 93 103 104 107 119 127 130 133 143 148 **P**6
Primary Contact: Mike Boleware, Administrator
Web address: www.fcmh.net
Control: County, Government, Nonfederal **Service**: General medical and surgical

Staffed Beds: 25 **Admissions**: 346 **Census**: 16 **Births**: 0 **Personnel**: 196

MENDENHALL—Simpson County

SIMPSON GENERAL HOSPITAL (251317), 1842 Simpson Highway 149, Zip 39114–3438; tel. 601/847–2221 **A**10 18 **F**3 11 29 30 34 35 40 43 44 54 56 57 59 61 64 65 66 68 81 85 86 87 93 98 100 101 102 103 104 107 114 119 127 130 132 133 134 143 146 **P**5
Primary Contact: Randall Neely, Chief Executive Officer
COO: Al Gary, COO
CFO: Al Gary, COO
CMO: Chip Holbrook M.D., Chief of Staff
CIO: David Welch, Director Information Technology
CHR: Randall Neely, CEO
CNO: Sharon Burnham, Director of Nursing
Web address: www.simpsongeneralhospital.com
Control: Other not–for–profit (including NFP Corporation) **Service**: General medical and surgical

Staffed Beds: 35 **Admissions**: 642 **Census**: 11 **Outpatient Visits**: 12551 **Births**: 0 **Total Expense ($000)**: 12660 **Payroll Expense ($000)**: 8088 **Personnel**: 176

MS

MERIDIAN—Lauderdale County

☐ **ALLIANCE HEALTH CENTER (250151)**, 5000 Highway 39 North, Zip 39301–1021; tel. 601/483–6211 **A**1 10 **F**4 32 34 35 36 38 54 57 59 64 71 86 87 98 99 101 102 103 105 106 135 **P**6 **S** Universal Health Services, Inc., King of Prussia, PA
Primary Contact: Jay Shehi, Chief Executive Officer
CFO: Robert Jackson, Chief Financial Officer
CMO: Terry Jordan M.D., Chief of Staff
CIO: Brenda Smith, Director Financial Services
CHR: Shrea Johnson, Director Human Resources
Web address: www.alliancehealthcenter.com
Control: Corporation, Investor–owned (for–profit) **Service:** Psychiatric

Staffed Beds: 154 **Admissions:** 2812 **Census:** 103 **Outpatient Visits:** 0 **Births:** 0 **Total Expense ($000):** 25525 **Payroll Expense ($000):** 8309 **Personnel:** 319

⊞ **ANDERSON REGIONAL HEALTH SYSTEM (250104)**, 2124 14th Street, Zip 39301–4040; tel. 601/553–6000 **A**1 2 10 19 **F**3 13 15 17 18 20 24 28 29 31 32 34 35 40 43 45 48 49 50 53 57 59 64 65 68 70 72 73 74 75 76 77 78 79 80 81 86 87 88 89 90 92 93 94 96 98 107 109 110 111 113 114 116 117 119 121 126 129 130 131 132 146 **P**7 8
Primary Contact: John G. Anderson, FACHE, President and Chief Executive Officer
CFO: Steven Brown, Vice President Finance
CMO: Scot Bell, Chief Medical Officer
CHR: Joel Windham, Vice President Human Resources
CNO: Matt Edwards, Vice President Nursing Services and Chief Nursing Officer
Web address: www.andersonregional.org
Control: Other not–for–profit (including NFP Corporation) **Service:** General medical and surgical

Staffed Beds: 260 **Admissions:** 12730 **Census:** 157 **Outpatient Visits:** 139274 **Births:** 1218 **Total Expense ($000):** 147996 **Payroll Expense ($000):** 49913 **Personnel:** 912

☐ △ **ANDERSON REGIONAL HEALTH SYSTEM SOUTH (250081)**, 1102 Constitution Avenue, Zip 39301–4001; tel. 601/553–6000 **A**1 7 10 19 **F**29 35 60 81 82 86 87 90 92 94 96 97 103 119 130 132 133 146 **P**7 8
Primary Contact: John G. Anderson, FACHE, President and Chief Executive Officer
CFO: Steven Brown, Vice President Finance
CIO: Steve Taylor, Chief Information Officer
CHR: Joel Windham, Vice President Human Resources
CNO: Betty Cryer R.N., Administrator/Chief Nursing Officer
Web address: www.andersonregional.org
Control: Other not–for–profit (including NFP Corporation) **Service:** General medical and surgical

Staffed Beds: 69 **Admissions:** 1239 **Census:** 44 **Outpatient Visits:** 35955 **Births:** 0 **Total Expense ($000):** 20351 **Payroll Expense ($000):** 6161 **Personnel:** 170

☐ **EAST MISSISSIPPI STATE HOSPITAL**, 1818 College Drive, Zip 39307, Mailing Address: Box 4128, West Station, 39304–4128; tel. 601/482–6186, (Total facility includes 210 beds in nursing home–type unit) **A**1 **F**4 29 34 38 39 59 82 86 87 98 99 103 106 128 130 143 146 149 **S** Mississippi State Department of Mental Health, Jackson, MS
Primary Contact: Charles Carlisle, Director
CFO: Geri Doggett, Director Business
CMO: Gloria Gomez M.D., Medical Director
CIO: Scotty Taylor, Information Technology Director
CHR: Shearmaine Calaway, Director Human Resources
CNO: Diane Nobles, Nurse Executive
Web address: www.emsh.state.ms.us
Control: State, Government, Nonfederal **Service:** Psychiatric

Staffed Beds: 335 **Admissions:** 1004 **Census:** 328 **Outpatient Visits:** 0 **Births:** 0 **Total Expense ($000):** 58365 **Payroll Expense ($000):** 29335 **Personnel:** 867

⊞ **REGENCY HOSPITAL OF MERIDIAN (252006)**, 1102 Constitution Avenue, 2nd Floor, Zip 39301–4001; tel. 601/484–7900 **A**1 10 **F**1 **S** Select Medical Corporation, Mechanicsburg, PA
Primary Contact: Clifton Quinn, Chief Executive Officer
Web address: www.regencyhospital.com
Control: Corporation, Investor–owned (for–profit) **Service:** Acute long–term care hospital

Staffed Beds: 40 **Admissions:** 363 **Census:** 26 **Outpatient Visits:** 0 **Births:** 0 **Total Expense ($000):** 12133 **Payroll Expense ($000):** 5684 **Personnel:** 112

RILEY HOSPITAL See Anderson Regional Health System South

★ ⇧ **RUSH FOUNDATION HOSPITAL (250069)**, 1314 19th Avenue, Zip 39301–4195; tel. 601/483–0011 **A**10 19 21 **F**13 15 17 22 24 29 35 39 40 43 70 72 73 76 77 81 82 86 89 90 93 97 107 108 118 119 130 131 146 147 **P**3 8 **S** Rush Health Systems, Meridian, MS
Primary Contact: Larkin Kennedy, Chief Executive Officer
COO: Jason Payne, Executive Vice President and Chief Operating Officer
CMO: W Scot Bell M.D., Chief Medical Officer
CIO: Angela Sherrill, Corporate Director Information System
CHR: Donnie Smith, Director Human Resources
CNO: Casey Bland, Director of Nursing
Web address: www.rushhealthsystems.org/rfh/
Control: Other not–for–profit (including NFP Corporation) **Service:** General medical and surgical

Staffed Beds: 182 **Admissions:** 6510 **Census:** 72 **Outpatient Visits:** 167847 **Births:** 1974 **Total Expense ($000):** 133298 **Payroll Expense ($000):** 39493 **Personnel:** 766

SPECIALTY HOSPITAL OF MERIDIAN (252004), 1314 19th Avenue, Zip 39301–4116; tel. 601/703–4211 **A**10 **F**1 3 18 20 34 50 57 59 68 74 79 85 87 94 96 112 133 144 145 149 **S** Rush Health Systems, Meridian, MS
Primary Contact: Elizabeth C. Mitchell, Chief Executive Officer and Chief Operating Officer
COO: Elizabeth C Mitchell, Chief Operating Officer
CFO: Christopher Rush, Chief Financial Officer
CMO: John Johnston, Chief Medical Officer
CIO: Angela Sherrill, Corporate Director Information System
CHR: Donnie Smith, Director of Human Resources
CNO: Kawanda Johnson, Director of Nursing
Web address: www.specialtyhospitalofmeridian.com/shm/
Control: Other not–for–profit (including NFP Corporation) **Service:** Acute long–term care hospital

Staffed Beds: 49 **Admissions:** 592 **Census:** 44 **Outpatient Visits:** 0 **Births:** 0 **Personnel:** 143

MONTICELLO—Lawrence County

LAWRENCE COUNTY HOSPITAL (251305), Highway 84 East, Zip 39654–0788, Mailing Address: P.O.Box 788, 39654–0788; tel. 601/587–4051 **A**10 18 **F**3 18 34 40 43 50 57 59 64 68 87 107 115 117 119 133 **S** Southwest Health Systems, Mccomb, MS
Primary Contact: Semmes Ross Jr, Administrator
CFO: Jennifer Moak, Business Office Manager
Web address: www.smrmc.com
Control: County, Government, Nonfederal **Service:** General medical and surgical

Staffed Beds: 25 **Admissions:** 493 **Census:** 11 **Outpatient Visits:** 6395 **Births:** 0 **Personnel:** 110

MORTON—Scott County

SCOTT REGIONAL HOSPITAL (251323), 317 Highway 13 South, Zip 39117–3353, Mailing Address: P.O.Box 259, 39117–0259; tel. 601/732–6301 **A**10 18 **F**3 30 35 40 43 55 57 77 81 89 93 107 111 112 114 119 127 130 133 **S** Rush Health Systems, Meridian, MS
Primary Contact: Heather Davis, Administrator
CFO: Paul S Black, Chief Financial Officer
CHR: Amy Sugg, Director Human Resources
Web address: www.scottregional.org/srh/
Control: Other not–for–profit (including NFP Corporation) **Service:** General medical and surgical

Staffed Beds: 25 **Admissions:** 375 **Census:** 8 **Outpatient Visits:** 9829 **Births:** 1 **Total Expense ($000):** 8289 **Payroll Expense ($000):** 4003 **Personnel:** 134

NATCHEZ—Adams County

⊞ △ **MERIT HEALTH NATCHEZ (250084)**, 54 Seargent 'S' Prentiss Drive, Zip 39120–4726; tel. 601/443–2100 **A**1 7 10 **F**13 15 17 29 35 40 43 60 70 73 75 76 77 78 81 82 86 87 88 89 90 93 98 103 107 108 111 116 118 119 130 131 132 134 146 147 **P**5 **S** Community Health Systems, Inc., Franklin, TN
Primary Contact: Eric Robinson, Chief Executive Officer
CFO: Charles Mack, Vice President Finance and Chief Financial Officer
CMO: Leslie England, Chief of Staff
CIO: Leslie Makoro, Director Information management Systems
CHR: Jean E Juchnowicz, Director Human Resources
Web address: www.natchezregional.com
Control: Corporation, Investor–owned (for–profit) **Service:** General medical and surgical

Staffed Beds: 136 **Admissions:** 4074 **Census:** 54 **Outpatient Visits:** 54911 **Births:** 715 **Total Expense ($000):** 83136 **Payroll Expense ($000):** 24065 **Personnel:** 441

MS

Hospital, Medicare Provider Number, Address, Telephone, Approval, Facility, and Physician Codes, Health Care System

★ American Hospital Association (AHA) membership ○ Healthcare Facilities Accreditation Program ⇧ Center for Improvement in Healthcare Quality Accreditation
☐ The Joint Commission accreditation ◇ DNV Healthcare Inc. accreditation △ Commission on Accreditation of Rehabilitation Facilities (CARF) accreditation

© 2017 AHA Guide   *Many Facility Codes have changed. Please refer to the AHA Guide Code Chart.*   Hospitals **A359**

NEW ALBANY—Union County

✠ **BAPTIST MEMORIAL HOSPITAL–UNION COUNTY (250006)**, 200 Highway 30 West, Zip 38652–3112; tel. 662/538–7631 **A**1 10 **F**3 7 11 13 15 17 29 31 34 35 40 45 51 57 59 64 70 75 76 77 79 81 84 85 86 87 89 90 91 92 93 94 96 107 108 110 111 114 115 118 119 124 130 132 133 146 147 149 **S** Baptist Memorial Health Care Corporation, Memphis, TN
Primary Contact: Walter Grace, Chief Executive Officer and Administrator
CFO: Kim High, Chief Financial Officer
CMO: Justin Lohmeier M.D., Chief of Staff
CIO: Missy Coltharp, Director
CHR: Lori Goode, Director Human Resources
CNO: Randy White, Chief Nursing Officer
Web address: www.baptistonline.org/union–county/
Control: Other not–for–profit (including NFP Corporation) **Service**: General medical and surgical

Staffed Beds: 153 **Admissions**: 3206 **Census**: 26 **Outpatient Visits**: 63274 **Births**: 988 **Total Expense ($000)**: 52039 **Payroll Expense ($000)**: 19595 **Personnel**: 343

OCEAN SPRINGS—Jackson County

OCEAN SPRINGS HOSPITAL See Singing River Health System, Pascagoula

OLIVE BRANCH—Desoto County

☐ **METHODIST OLIVE BRANCH HOSPITAL (250167)**, 4250 Bethel Road, Zip 38654–8737; tel. 662/932–9000 **A**1 10 **F**3 4 15 16 17 20 22 24 25 29 34 35 40 43 57 59 62 63 64 68 70 74 76 77 79 80 81 82 86 87 88 89 90 93 107 108 109 110 111 114 119 130 132 144 146 147 **P**8 **S** Methodist Le Bonheur Healthcare, Memphis, TN
Primary Contact: David G. Baytos, Chief Executive Officer
CFO: Kris Sanders, Chief Financial Officer
CHR: Robin Mathis, Director of Human Resources
CNO: Annelise Jensen, Chief Nursing Officer
Web address: www.methodisthealth.org/olivebranch
Control: Other not–for–profit (including NFP Corporation) **Service**: General medical and surgical

Staffed Beds: 67 **Admissions**: 1782 **Census**: 17 **Births**: 327 **Personnel**: 350

☐ **PARKWOOD BEHAVIORAL HEALTH SYSTEM (254005)**, 8135 Goodman Road, Zip 38654–2103; tel. 662/895–4900, (Total facility includes 40 beds in nursing home–type unit) **A**1 10 **F**4 5 29 34 35 54 57 64 71 75 82 86 87 98 99 100 101 102 103 104 105 106 130 135 **P**5 **S** Universal Health Services, Inc., King of Prussia, PA
Primary Contact: Ethan Permenter, Chief Executive Officer
CFO: David Denegri, Chief Financial Officer
CMO: Paul King M.D., Medical Director
CHR: Julie Dorman, Human Resources Director
CNO: Alicia Plunkett, Chief Nurse Executive
Web address: www.parkwoodbhs.com
Control: Corporation, Investor–owned (for–profit) **Service**: Psychiatric

Staffed Beds: 148 **Admissions**: 3088 **Census**: 109 **Outpatient Visits**: 5209 **Births**: 0 **Personnel**: 151

OXFORD—Lafayette County

✠ △ **BAPTIST MEMORIAL HOSPITAL–NORTH MISSISSIPPI (250034)**, 2301 South Lamar Boulevard, Zip 38655–5373, Mailing Address: P.O.Box 946, 38655–6002; tel. 662/232–8100 **A**1 2 7 10 19 **F**3 7 11 12 13 15 17 18 20 22 24 25 28 29 31 34 35 40 43 45 46 47 48 49 54 57 59 64 65 70 73 74 76 79 81 84 85 86 87 89 90 91 93 96 107 108 110 111 114 115 116 117 118 119 120 121 123 124 126 129 130 132 146 **S** Baptist Memorial Health Care Corporation, Memphis, TN
Primary Contact: William C. Henning, Administrator and Chief Executive Officer
CFO: Dana Williams, Chief Financial Officer
CMO: Dennis P Morgan, Chief of Staff
CIO: Linda Britt, Director Information Systems
CHR: Debbie Swan, Director Human Resources
CNO: Mark Ottens, Chief Nursing Officer
Web address: www.baptistonline.org/north–mississippi/
Control: Other not–for–profit (including NFP Corporation) **Service**: General medical and surgical

Staffed Beds: 172 **Admissions**: 7747 **Census**: 90 **Outpatient Visits**: 83134 **Births**: 812 **Personnel**: 702

PASCAGOULA—Jackson County

☐ △ **SINGING RIVER HEALTH SYSTEM (250040)**, 2809 Denny Avenue, Zip 39581–5301; tel. 228/809–5000, (Includes OCEAN SPRINGS HOSPITAL, 3109 Bienville Boulevard, Ocean Springs, Mississippi, Zip 39564–4361, tel. 228/818–1111; Heath Thompson, R.N., Administrator; SINGING RIVER HOSPITAL, 2809 Denny Avenue, Pascagoula, Mississippi, Zip 39581–5301, tel. 228/809–5000; Laurin St. Pe', Administrator – Singing River Hospital) **A**1 2 7 10 **F**3 11 13 15 17 18 19 20 21 22 24 26 28 29 30 31 38 39 40 41 43 44 45 47 48 49 53 54 61 64 70 72 73 74 76 78 80 81 82 83 84 85 86 87 88 89 90 92 94 95 96 98 99 100 101 102 103 104 106 107 108 110 111 114 115 118 119 120 121 123 124 126 127 129 130 135 144 145 146 148 **P**8
Primary Contact: Kevin Holland, Chief Executive Officer
COO: Lee Bond, Chief Operating Officer
CFO: Sandra Albrecht, Interim Chief Financial Officer
CMO: Randy Roth, Chief Medical Officer
CHR: Craig Summerlin, Chief Human Resources Officer
CNO: Susan Russell, Chief Nursing Officer
Web address: www.singingriverhealthsystem.com
Control: County, Government, Nonfederal **Service**: General medical and surgical

Staffed Beds: 376 **Admissions**: 16240 **Census**: 196 **Outpatient Visits**: 202238 **Births**: 1451 **Total Expense ($000)**: 329548 **Payroll Expense ($000)**: 126334 **Personnel**: 2084

PHILADELPHIA—Neshoba County

⇑ **CHOCTAW HEALTH CENTER (250127)**, 210 Hospital Circle, Zip 39350–6781; tel. 601/656–2211, (Nonreporting) **A**10 21
Primary Contact: Tina Scott, Acting Health Director
CFO: Myrna Hancock, Director Financial Services
CMO: Juantina Johnson, Chief of Staff
CIO: Raymond Willis, IT Manager
CHR: Anna Denson, Human Resources Specialist
CNO: Regina Isaac, Director of Nursing
Web address: www.choctaw.org
Control: Public Health Service, Government, Federal **Service**: General medical and surgical

Staffed Beds: 35

NESHOBA COUNTY GENERAL HOSPITAL (250043), 1001 Holland Avenue, Zip 39350–2161, Mailing Address: P.O.Box 648, 39350–0648; tel. 601/663–1200, (Total facility includes 160 beds in nursing home–type unit) **A**10 20 **F**3 6 7 11 15 29 31 32 34 38 40 43 45 57 59 64 65 79 81 82 89 90 92 93 96 103 104 106 107 108 110 111 115 118 119 128 129 130 132 133 143 144 146 149
Primary Contact: Lee McCall, Chief Executive Officer
CFO: Scott McNair, Chief Financial Officer
CMO: Jessica Myers, Medical Director
CHR: Hedda Stewart, Director Human Resources
CNO: Scott Breazeale, Chief Nursing Officer
Web address: www.neshobageneral.com
Control: County, Government, Nonfederal **Service**: General medical and surgical

Staffed Beds: 208 **Admissions**: 1777 **Census**: 174 **Births**: 0 **Total Expense ($000)**: 43470 **Payroll Expense ($000)**: 21964 **Personnel**: 497

PICAYUNE—Pearl River County

HIGHLAND COMMUNITY HOSPITAL (250117), 130 Highland Parkway, Zip 39466–5574, Mailing Address: P.O.Box 909, 39466–0909; tel. 601/358–9400 **A**10 **F**3 13 15 18 29 34 40 43 45 56 57 59 64 65 70 75 76 81 86 87 89 93 103 106 107 108 110 111 119 130 131 146 147
Primary Contact: Mark Stockstill, R.N., Administrator
CMO: Robert Lopez, Chief Medical Officer
CHR: Cynthia Render–Leach, Director Human Resources
CNO: Kim Varnado R.N., Chief Nursing Officer
Web address: www.highlandch.com
Control: County, Government, Nonfederal **Service**: General medical and surgical

Staffed Beds: 60 **Admissions**: 1864 **Census**: 20 **Outpatient Visits**: 51452 **Births**: 304 **Total Expense ($000)**: 38866 **Payroll Expense ($000)**: 15605 **Personnel**: 297

PONTOTOC—Pontotoc County

✠ **NORTH MISSISSIPPI MEDICAL CENTER–PONTOTOC (251308)**, 176 South Main Street, Zip 38863–3311, Mailing Address: P.O.Box 790, 38863–0790; tel. 662/488–7640, (Total facility includes 44 beds in nursing home–type unit) **A**1 10 18 **F**3 11 34 35 40 43 57 65 68 82 83 84 86 87 93 104 107 114 119 128 130 133 146 **S** North Mississippi Health Services, Inc., Tupelo, MS
Primary Contact: Leslia Carter, Administrator
CFO: M Denise Heard, Director Business Services
CHR: P. Marie Barnes, Director, Human Resources
CNO: Cathy Waldrop, Director, Hospital Nursing Services
Web address: www.nmhs.net
Control: Other not–for–profit (including NFP Corporation) **Service**: General medical and surgical

Staffed Beds: 69 **Admissions**: 554 **Census**: 64 **Births**: 0 **Personnel**: 181

Many Facility Codes have changed. Please refer to the AHA Guide Code Chart. © 2017 AHA Guide

MS

POPLARVILLE—Pearl River County

★ **PEARL RIVER COUNTY HOSPITAL (251333)**, 305 West Moody Street, Zip 39470–7338, Mailing Address: P.O.Box 392, 39470–0392; tel. 601/795–4543 **A**10 18 **F**3 35 40 43 64 65 119 127 130 133 146
CNO: Lisa Brown, Director of Nursing
CEO: James Williams, Chief Executive Officer
Web address: www.prc-med.com/
Control: County, Government, Nonfederal **Service**: General medical and surgical

Staffed Beds: 24 **Admissions:** 24 **Census:** 1 **Outpatient Visits:** 15469 **Births:** 0 **Total Expense ($000):** 19192 **Payroll Expense ($000):** 10222 **Personnel:** 220

PORT GIBSON—Claiborne County

CLAIBORNE COUNTY MEDICAL CENTER (251320), 123 McComb Avenue, Zip 39150–2915, Mailing Address: P.O.Box 1004, 39150–1004; tel. 601/437–5141 **A**10 18 **F**40 43 89 98 100 101 103 104 105 107 119 130 133
Primary Contact: Ada Ratliff, Chief Executive Officer
CFO: Linda Caho–Mooney, Chief Financial Officer
CIO: Ada Ratliff, Chief Information Officer
Control: County, Government, Nonfederal **Service**: General medical and surgical

Staffed Beds: 22 **Admissions:** 578 **Census:** 5 **Births:** 0 **Total Expense ($000):** 11799 **Payroll Expense ($000):** 5231 **Personnel:** 128

PRENTISS—Jefferson Davis County

JEFFERSON DAVIS COMMUNITY HOSPITAL (251326), 1102 Rose Street, Zip 39474–5200, Mailing Address: P.O.Box 1288, 39474–1288; tel. 601/792–4276, (Total facility includes 60 beds in nursing home–type unit) **A**10 18 **F**3 35 40 43 53 56 57 59 64 86 87 89 93 98 103 104 106 107 115 119 128 130 132 133
Primary Contact: Jimmy Graves, Interim Chief Executive Officer
CHR: Diane Daughdrill, Director Human Resources
Web address: www.jdchospital.com
Control: County, Government, Nonfederal **Service**: General medical and surgical

Staffed Beds: 95 **Admissions:** 346 **Census:** 56 **Outpatient Visits:** 11718 **Births:** 0 **Total Expense ($000):** 8638 **Payroll Expense ($000):** 3180

PURVIS—Lamar County

☐ **SOUTH MISSISSIPPI STATE HOSPITAL (254008)**, 823 Highway 589, Zip 39475–4194; tel. 601/794–0100 **A**1 10 **F**3 98 106 130 146 **S** Mississippi State Department of Mental Health, Jackson, MS
Primary Contact: Sabrina Young, Director
CFO: Andy Tucker, Chief Financial Officer
CMO: Allen Harris M.D., Clinical Director
CIO: Sabrina Young, Administrative Support Director
CHR: Kelly Reid, Human Resources Director
CNO: Pam Brinson, Nurse Executive
Web address: www.smsh.state.ms.us
Control: State, Government, Nonfederal **Service**: Psychiatric

Staffed Beds: 50 **Admissions:** 693 **Census:** 46 **Outpatient Visits:** 0 **Births:** 0 **Total Expense ($000):** 8055 **Payroll Expense ($000):** 4187 **Personnel:** 89

QUITMAN—Clarke County

H. C. WATKINS MEMORIAL HOSPITAL (251316), 605 South Archusa Avenue, Zip 39355–2331; tel. 601/776–6925 **A**10 18 **F**29 40 43 81 89 104 107 127 130 133 **P**6 **S** Rush Health Systems, Meridian, MS
Primary Contact: Michael Nester, Administrator
CFO: Paul S Black, Controller
CMO: O Wayne Byrd M.D., Chief of Staff
CIO: Melinda Smith, Chief Information Systems
CHR: Leigh Moore, Administrative Assistant Human Resources
Web address: www.watkinsmemorialhospital.com/hcwmh/
Control: Other not-for-profit (including NFP Corporation) **Service**: General medical and surgical

Staffed Beds: 25 **Admissions:** 441 **Census:** 12 **Births:** 0 **Personnel:** 182

RALEIGH—Smith County

PATIENTS CHOICE MEDICAL CENTER OF SMITH COUNTY (250163), 347 Magnolia Drive, Zip 39153–6011; tel. 601/782–9997 **A**10 **F**5 22 98 99 103 131 **P**6
Primary Contact: Tim Cockrell, Chief Executive Officer
Control: Corporation, Investor-owned (for-profit) **Service**: General medical and surgical

Staffed Beds: 20 **Admissions:** 156 **Census:** 6 **Births:** 0

RICHTON—Perry County

PERRY COUNTY GENERAL HOSPITAL (251306), 206 Bay Avenue, Zip 39476–2941; tel. 601/788–6316 **A**10 18 **F**3 34 40 57 59 64 65 107 119 127 130 133 146
Primary Contact: David Paris, Chief Executive Officer
Web address: www.pcghospital.com/
Control: Partnership, Investor-owned (for-profit) **Service**: General medical and surgical

Staffed Beds: 22 **Admissions:** 165 **Census:** 4 **Outpatient Visits:** 9709 **Births:** 0 **Total Expense ($000):** 4398 **Payroll Expense ($000):** 2445 **Personnel:** 61

RIPLEY—Tippah County

★ **TIPPAH COUNTY HOSPITAL (250010)**, 1005 City Avenue North, Zip 38663–1414, Mailing Address: P.O.Box 499, 38663–0499; tel. 662/837–9221, (Total facility includes 40 beds in nursing home–type unit) **A**10 20 **F**29 40 43 53 81 90 93 98 103 107 119 128 130 131 133 **P**1
Primary Contact: Patrick Chapman, Ed.D., Chief Executive Officer
CFO: Stephanie McAlister, Controller
CMO: Troy Cappleman M.D., Chief of Staff
CHR: Heather Taylor, Human Resources Manager
CNO: Carol Anne Hurt, Chief Nursing Officer
Web address: www.tippahcountyhospital.com/
Control: County, Government, Nonfederal **Service**: General medical and surgical

Staffed Beds: 65 **Admissions:** 556 **Census:** 45 **Outpatient Visits:** 13568 **Births:** 0 **Total Expense ($000):** 11869 **Payroll Expense ($000):** 4847 **Personnel:** 193

ROLLING FORK—Sharkey County

SHARKEY–ISSAQUENA COMMUNITY HOSPITAL (250079), 108 South Fourth Street, Zip 39159–5146, Mailing Address: P.O.Box 339, 39159–0339; tel. 662/873–4395 **A**10 **F**40 53 56 98 103 104 105 107 133
Primary Contact: Jerry Keever, Administrator
Control: County, Government, Nonfederal **Service**: General medical and surgical

Staffed Beds: 29 **Admissions:** 552 **Census:** 9 **Births:** 0 **Total Expense ($000):** 8089 **Payroll Expense ($000):** 3348 **Personnel:** 71

RULEVILLE—Sunflower County

★ **NORTH SUNFLOWER MEDICAL CENTER (251318)**, 840 North Oak Avenue, Zip 38771–3227, Mailing Address: P.O.Box 369, 38771–0369; tel. 662/756–2711, (Total facility includes 60 beds in nursing home–type unit) **A**10 18 **F**15 28 29 32 34 35 40 43 45 53 56 59 63 64 65 66 68 74 75 77 81 82 84 85 87 90 93 97 100 103 104 107 110 115 119 128 129 130 132 133 134 143 147 149 **P**6
Primary Contact: Sam Miller, Chief Executive Officer
COO: Rodney Clark, Chief Operating Officer
CFO: Nickie Moore, Chief Financial Officer
CMO: Bennie B Wright M.D., Chief of Staff
CIO: Roger Goss, Director, Information Services
CHR: Robbie Taylor, Director Human Resources
CNO: Lisa Miller R.N., Director of Nursing
Web address: www.northsunflower.com
Control: County, Government, Nonfederal **Service**: General medical and surgical

Staffed Beds: 95 **Admissions:** 888 **Census:** 69 **Outpatient Visits:** 47959 **Births:** 0 **Total Expense ($000):** 61725 **Payroll Expense ($000):** 26254 **Personnel:** 555

SENATOBIA—Tate County

☐ **NORTH OAK REGIONAL MEDICAL CENTER (250126)**, 401 Getwell Drive, Zip 38668–2213, Mailing Address: P.O.Box 648, 38668–0648; tel. 662/562–3100 **A**1 10 **F**3 29 34 35 40 43 45 56 57 64 81 86 98 103 107 114 119 130 132
Primary Contact: Sonja Graham, Chief Executive Officer
CHR: Vickie Barksdale, Manager Human Resources
Web address: www.northoakregional.com/
Control: Corporation, Investor-owned (for-profit) **Service**: General medical and surgical

Staffed Beds: 41 **Admissions:** 834 **Census:** 12 **Outpatient Visits:** 10858 **Births:** 0 **Personnel:** 125

MS

SOUTHAVEN—Desoto County

☒ △ **BAPTIST MEMORIAL HOSPITAL–DESOTO (250141)**, 7601 Southcrest Parkway, Zip 38671–4742; tel. 662/772–4000 **A**1 3 7 10 **F**3 7 9 11 13 15 17 18 20 22 24 28 29 31 35 39 40 43 44 45 46 47 48 49 50 57 59 60 68 70 73 74 75 76 77 79 80 81 82 84 85 86 87 90 93 96 107 108 109 110 111 114 115 116 117 118 119 120 121 123 124 126 129 130 131 132 143 144 146 147 **P**7 **S** Baptist Memorial Health Care Corporation, Memphis, TN
Primary Contact: James Huffman, Chief Executive Officer and Administrator
CFO: Joe McWherter, Chief Financial Officer
CMO: Joann Wood M.D., Chief Medical Officer
CHR: Walter Banks, Director Human Resources
Web address: www.baptistonline.org/desoto/
Control: Other not–for–profit (including NFP Corporation) **Service**: General medical and surgical

Staffed Beds: 195 **Admissions:** 15644 **Census:** 191 **Outpatient Visits:** 123427 **Births:** 1642 **Total Expense ($000):** 244907 **Payroll Expense ($000):** 87589 **Personnel:** 1199

STARKVILLE—Oktibbeha County

★ ⇑ **OCH REGIONAL MEDICAL CENTER (250050)**, 400 Hospital Road, Zip 39759–2163, Mailing Address: P.O.Box 1506, 39760–1506; tel. 662/323–4320 **A**10 21 **F**3 7 11 13 15 17 28 29 32 34 35 40 41 43 45 47 48 51 53 57 59 61 64 65 70 73 74 75 76 77 79 81 82 87 88 89 90 93 94 97 98 107 108 110 111 114 115 118 119 126 129 130 131 132 133 146 147 **P**6
Primary Contact: Richard G. Hilton, Administrator and Chief Executive Officer
COO: Mike Andrews, Associate Administrator and Chief Operating Officer
CFO: Susan Russell, Chief Financial Officer
CIO: Chamath Wijewardane, Director Information Technology
CHR: Mike Andrews, Associate Administrator and Chief Operating Officer
CNO: Martha Fulcher MSN, Chief Nursing Officer
Web address: www.och.org
Control: County, Government, Nonfederal **Service**: General medical and surgical

Staffed Beds: 96 **Admissions:** 2507 **Census:** 25 **Outpatient Visits:** 241638 **Births:** 940 **Total Expense ($000):** 72625 **Payroll Expense ($000):** 35736 **Personnel:** 603

TUPELO—Lee County

☒ △ **NORTH MISSISSIPPI MEDICAL CENTER – TUPELO (250004)**, 830 South Gloster Street, Zip 38801–4934; tel. 662/377–3000, (Total facility includes 107 beds in nursing home–type unit) **A**1 2 3 5 7 10 **F**3 4 5 7 11 12 13 15 17 18 19 20 22 24 26 28 29 30 31 32 34 35 37 38 40 41 43 44 46 47 48 49 50 51 53 56 57 58 59 61 62 63 64 66 68 70 71 72 73 74 75 76 77 78 79 81 83 84 85 86 87 89 90 91 92 93 96 97 98 100 101 103 104 106 107 108 109 110 111 112 113 114 115 116 117 118 119 120 121 122 123 124 126 128 129 130 131 132 134 135 146 147 148 **P**7 **S** North Mississippi Health Services, Inc., Tupelo, MS
Primary Contact: David C. Wilson, Chief Executive Officer
CFO: Joseph A Reppert, Executive Vice President and Chief Financial Officer
CHR: Rodger Brown, Vice President Human Resources
Web address: www.nmhs.net
Control: Other not–for–profit (including NFP Corporation) **Service**: General medical and surgical

Staffed Beds: 747 **Admissions:** 26631 **Census:** 507 **Outpatient Visits:** 262253 **Births:** 2179 **Personnel:** 4747

☐ **NORTH MISSISSIPPI STATE HOSPITAL (254009)**, 1937 Briar Ridge Road, Zip 38804–5963; tel. 662/690–4200 **A**1 10 **F**3 29 30 34 87 98 101 106 130 143 146 **S** Mississippi State Department of Mental Health, Jackson, MS
Primary Contact: Paul A. Callens, Ph.D., Director
CFO: Joe Rials, Director Fiscal Services
CMO: Ken Lippincott M.D., Chief of Staff
CIO: James Wilhite, Director Systems Information
Web address: www.nmsh.state.ms.us
Control: State, Government, Nonfederal **Service**: Psychiatric

Staffed Beds: 50 **Admissions:** 577 **Census:** 46 **Outpatient Visits:** 0 **Births:** 0 **Personnel:** 101

TYLERTOWN—Walthall County

★ **WALTHALL COUNTY GENERAL HOSPITAL (251324)**, 100 Hospital Drive, Zip 39667–2099; tel. 601/876–2122 **A**10 18 **F**40 43 81 89 93 107 111 119 127 130 133 146
Primary Contact: Bryan K. Maxie, Administrator
Web address: www.walthallhospitalms.org
Control: County, Government, Nonfederal **Service**: General medical and surgical

Staffed Beds: 25 **Admissions:** 363 **Census:** 7 **Outpatient Visits:** 16640 **Births:** 0 **Total Expense ($000):** 9179 **Payroll Expense ($000):** 4508 **Personnel:** 82

UNION—Newton County

LAIRD HOSPITAL (251322), 25117 Highway 15, Zip 39365–9099; tel. 601/774–8214 **A**10 18 **F**29 35 40 43 81 87 89 93 104 107 119 130 132 133 146 **S** Rush Health Systems, Meridian, MS
Primary Contact: Thomas G. Bartlett III, Administrator
COO: Morris A Reece, EVP/COO
CFO: Jennifer Flint, Chief Financial Officer
CMO: John Mutziger M.D., Chief Medical Officer
CIO: Angela Sherrill, Chief Information Officer
CHR: Donnie Smith, Chief Human Resources Officer
CNO: Pam Rigdon, Director Nursing
Web address: www.lairdhospital.com/lh/
Control: Other not–for–profit (including NFP Corporation) **Service**: General medical and surgical

Staffed Beds: 25 **Admissions:** 454 **Census:** 10 **Outpatient Visits:** 14161 **Births:** 0 **Total Expense ($000):** 17354 **Payroll Expense ($000):** 5027 **Personnel:** 246

VICKSBURG—Warren County

☒ **MERIT HEALTH RIVER REGION (250031)**, 2100 Highway 61 North, Zip 39183–8211, Mailing Address: P.O.Box 590, 39181–0590; tel. 601/883–5000, (Includes RIVER REGION WEST CAMPUS, 1111 North Frontage Road, Vicksburg, Mississippi, Zip 39180–5102, tel. 601/883–5000) **A**1 10 **F**3 4 11 13 15 17 18 19 20 22 24 28 29 34 35 38 39 40 43 49 50 51 56 59 60 64 68 70 73 74 75 76 77 79 81 82 85 87 89 90 93 97 98 103 107 108 110 111 115 118 119 126 130 131 132 146 147 149 **S** Community Health Systems, Inc., Franklin, TN
Primary Contact: Benjamin Richaud, Interim Chief Executive Officer
CFO: John Milazzo, Chief Financial Officer
CMO: W Briggs Hopson M.D., Clinical Medical Director
CIO: J B White, Director Information Systems
CHR: Hal Harrington, Vice President Human Resources
Web address: www.riverregion.com
Control: Corporation, Investor–owned (for–profit) **Service**: General medical and surgical

Staffed Beds: 361 **Admissions:** 7308 **Census:** 111 **Outpatient Visits:** 146212 **Births:** 668 **Total Expense ($000):** 157166 **Payroll Expense ($000):** 32400 **Personnel:** 909

PROMISE HOSPITAL OF VICKSBURG (252008), 1111 North Frontage Road, 2nd Floor, Zip 39180–5102; tel. 601/619–3526 **A**10 **F**1 3 11 29 77 148 **S** Promise Healthcare, Boca Raton, FL
Primary Contact: Michael Harrell, R.N., Chief Executive Officer
COO: Dawn Posey, Chief Operating Officer
CFO: Christopher A Stegall, Regional Chief Financial Officer and Chief Operating Officer
CMO: Daniel Edney M.D., Chief of Staff
CIO: Barbara Whiting, Director Health Information Management
CHR: Debbie Carson, Director Human Resources
Web address: www.promise–vicksburg.com
Control: Corporation, Investor–owned (for–profit) **Service**: Acute long–term care hospital

Staffed Beds: 33 **Admissions:** 370 **Census:** 27 **Outpatient Visits:** 0 **Births:** 0 **Personnel:** 88

WATER VALLEY—Yalobusha County

★ **YALOBUSHA GENERAL HOSPITAL (250061)**, 630 South Main, Zip 38965–3468, Mailing Address: P.O.Box 728, 38965–0728; tel. 662/473–1411, (Total facility includes 122 beds in nursing home–type unit) **A**10 **F**3 7 15 29 33 34 59 65 107 110 114 119 128 130 133 143 146 **P**6
Primary Contact: Terry Varner, Administrator
COO: Ashlee Langdon, Controller
CHR: Katie Rotenberry–Baggett, Administrative Assistant and Human Resources
Web address: www.yalobushageneral.com/
Control: County, Government, Nonfederal **Service**: General medical and surgical

Staffed Beds: 148 **Admissions:** 781 **Census:** 134 **Outpatient Visits:** 0 **Births:** 0 **Total Expense ($000):** 21885 **Payroll Expense ($000):** 14343 **Personnel:** 196

WAYNESBORO—Wayne County

⇑ **WAYNE GENERAL HOSPITAL (250077)**, 950 Matthew Drive, Zip 39367–2590, Mailing Address: P.O.Box 1249, 39367–1249; tel. 601/735–5151 **A**10 20 21 **F**13 15 29 40 43 53 62 63 70 75 76 81 86 89 93 107 108 111 119 127 130 132 133 146
Primary Contact: Kathy Waddell, Administrator
Web address: www.waynegeneralhospital.org
Control: County, Government, Nonfederal **Service**: General medical and surgical

Staffed Beds: 80 **Admissions:** 1993 **Census:** 28 **Outpatient Visits:** 34186 **Births:** 187 **Personnel:** 357

Many Facility Codes have changed. Please refer to the AHA Guide Code Chart. © 2017 AHA Guide

WEST POINT—Clay County

☒ **NORTH MISSISSIPPI MEDICAL CENTER–WEST POINT (250067)**, 835 Medical Center Drive, Zip 39773–9320; tel. 662/495–2300 **A**1 10 **F**3 11 13 15 17 28 29 31 32 34 35 40 42 43 45 48 53 57 59 64 65 70 73 75 76 79 80 81 85 86 87 89 90 97 107 108 109 110 114 119 120 129 130 132 133 143 145 146 147 **S** North Mississippi Health Services, Inc., Tupelo, MS
Primary Contact: Barry L. Keel, Administration
CFO: Kay Lawler, Business Office Manager
CMO: B Keith Watson M.D., Chief Medical Staff
CIO: Stacie Griggs, MIS Analyst
CHR: Brenda Johnson, Director Human Resources
CNO: Jane Windle R.N., Director of Nurses
Web address: www.nmhs.net/westpoint
Control: Other not–for–profit (including NFP Corporation) **Service**: General medical and surgical

Staffed Beds: 60 **Admissions**: 1369 **Census**: 16 **Outpatient Visits**: 44408
Births: 304 **Total Expense ($000)**: 32875 **Payroll Expense ($000)**: 12864
Personnel: 241

WHITFIELD—Rankin County

☒ **MISSISSIPPI STATE HOSPITAL (254010)**, 3550 Highway 468 West, Zip 39193–5529, Mailing Address: P.O.Box 157–A, 39193–0157; tel. 601/351–8000, (Includes WHITFIELD MEDICAL SURGICAL HOSPITAL, P O Box 157A, Whitfield, Mississippi, Zip 39193–0157, tel. 601/351–8023) **A**1 3 10 **F**3 4 24 25 29 32 39 50 55 56 59 65 68 74 75 86 87 98 100 101 103 104 107 115 119 128 130 143 146 149 **P**1 **S** Mississippi State Department of Mental Health, Jackson, MS
Primary Contact: James G. Chastain, FACHE, Director
COO: Kelly R Breland CPA, Director Support Services
CFO: Alicia Harris, Director Fiscal Services
CMO: Duncan Stone D.D.S., Chief Medical Staff
CIO: Bart Uharriet, Director Information Services
CHR: Katie Storr, Director of Human Resources
CNO: Jackie Yates R.N., Nurse Executive
Web address: www.msh.state.ms.us
Control: State, Government, Nonfederal **Service**: Psychiatric

Staffed Beds: 506 **Admissions**: 2184 **Census**: 360 **Outpatient Visits**: 3311
Births: 0 **Total Expense ($000)**: 134347 **Payroll Expense ($000)**: 86576
Personnel: 1123

WIGGINS—Stone County

STONE COUNTY HOSPITAL (251303), 1434 East Central Avenue, Zip 39577–9602; tel. 601/928–6600 **A**10 18 **F**3 7 29 34 35 40 43 46 57 59 64 81 82 89 97 112 114 115 119 130 133 143 146
Primary Contact: Lynn Truelove, Chief Executive Officer
Web address: www.schospital.net/
Control: Corporation, Investor–owned (for–profit) **Service**: General medical and surgical

Staffed Beds: 25 **Admissions**: 577 **Census**: 17 **Outpatient Visits**: 23927
Births: 0 **Personnel**: 171

WINONA—Montgomery County

TYLER HOLMES MEMORIAL HOSPITAL (251312), 409 Tyler Holmes Drive, Zip 38967–1599; tel. 662/283–4114 **A**10 18 **F**3 11 34 35 40 41 43 50 57 59 87 104 107 111 114 119 130 133 **P**8
Primary Contact: Eddie Rutherford, Administrator
CFO: Cori Bailey, Accountant
CHR: Becky Corley, Director Human Resources
Control: County, Government, Nonfederal **Service**: General medical and surgical

Staffed Beds: 25 **Admissions**: 473 **Census**: 10 **Outpatient Visits**: 12145
Births: 0 **Total Expense ($000)**: 12483 **Payroll Expense ($000)**: 6218
Personnel: 134

YAZOO CITY—Yazoo County

★ **BAPTIST MEDICAL CENTER YAZOO (251313)**, 823 Grand Avenue, Zip 39194–3233; tel. 662/746–2261 **A**10 18 **F**8 11 15 29 30 40 53 54 56 81 93 97 107 110 111 114 119 133 **S** Baptist Memorial Health Care Corporation, Memphis, TN
Primary Contact: Sean Johnson, Chief Executive Officer
COO: Marsha Jones R.N., Director Nursing
CFO: James L Miller, Chief Financial Officer
CMO: Marion Sigrest M.D., Chief of Staff
CIO: Benton D Estes, Materials Management
CHR: Stephanie Washington, Director Community Relations and Human Resources
CNO: Marsha Jones R.N., Director of Nursing
Web address: www.kdhyazoo.com
Control: Other not–for–profit (including NFP Corporation) **Service**: General medical and surgical

Staffed Beds: 25 **Admissions**: 855 **Census**: 11 **Outpatient Visits**: 30095
Births: 3 **Total Expense ($000)**: 16624 **Payroll Expense ($000)**: 9491
Personnel: 174

MS

Hospital, Medicare Provider Number, Address, Telephone, Approval, Facility, and Physician Codes, Health Care System

★ American Hospital Association (AHA) membership   ○ Healthcare Facilities Accreditation Program   ⇑ Center for Improvement in Healthcare Quality Accreditation
□ The Joint Commission accreditation   ◇ DNV Healthcare Inc. accreditation   △ Commission on Accreditation of Rehabilitation Facilities (CARF) accreditation

MISSOURI

ALBANY—Gentry County

★ **NORTHWEST MEDICAL CENTER (261328)**, 705 North College Street, Zip 64402–1433; tel. 660/726–3941 **A**10 18 **F**3 11 15 18 28 29 34 35 40 44 45 50 56 57 59 62 64 65 68 74 75 77 79 81 85 86 87 90 93 97 104 107 108 110 111 114 118 119 127 128 130 131 133 135 148 149 **P**6
Primary Contact: Jon D. Doolittle, Regional President
COO: Nate Blackford, Chief Operating Officer
CMO: Angelia Martin M.D., Chief of Staff
CIO: James Crouch, Vice President Technical Services
CHR: Vickie Cline, Director Human Resources
CNO: Miranda Floyd R.N., Chief Nursing Officer
Web address: www.northwestmedicalcenter.org
Control: Other not-for-profit (including NFP Corporation) **Service**: General medical and surgical

Staffed Beds: 25 **Admissions**: 436 **Census**: 6 **Outpatient Visits**: 45756
Births: 0 **Total Expense ($000)**: 17339 **Payroll Expense ($000)**: 7684
Personnel: 136

APPLETON CITY—St. Clair County

★ **ELLETT MEMORIAL HOSPITAL (261301)**, 610 North Ohio Avenue, Zip 64724–1609, Mailing Address: P.O.Box 6, 64724–0006; tel. 660/476–2111 **A**10 18 **F**3 7 11 18 34 40 45 50 57 59 64 77 79 81 97 107 111 114 119 127 129 133 143 **P**6
Primary Contact: Melissa Fletcher, Chief Executive Officer
CMO: Richard R Dailey D.O., President Medical Staff
CIO: Gina Raybourn, Director Health Information
CHR: Cathy Grishow, Director Human Resources
CNO: Laura Smith, Interim Chief Nursing Officer and Director of Infection Control
Web address: www.ellettmemorial.com
Control: Hospital district or authority, Government, Nonfederal **Service**: General medical and surgical

Staffed Beds: 12 **Admissions**: 229 **Census**: 4 **Outpatient Visits**: 12299
Births: 0 **Total Expense ($000)**: 8965 **Payroll Expense ($000)**: 3236
Personnel: 87

AURORA—Lawrence County

⊞ **MERCY HOSPITAL AURORA (261316)**, 500 Porter Street, Zip 65605–2365; tel. 417/678–2122 **A**1 10 18 **F**3 11 13 15 28 29 30 34 35 40 41 45 50 57 59 64 65 75 76 77 81 85 86 87 89 92 93 94 96 107 108 110 111 114 119 129 132 133 135 148 149 **P**6 **S** Mercy, Chesterfield, MO
Primary Contact: Douglas M. Stroemel, Administrator Mercy Hospital Aurora and Mercy Hospital Cassville
CFO: Sherry Clouse Day CPA, Vice President Finance and Regional Chief Financial Officer
CMO: Christie Hurt M.D., Chief of Staff and Medical Director
CHR: George Roden, Vice President Human Resources
CNO: Nicki Gamet R.N., Vice President and Chief Nursing Officer
Web address: www.stjohns.com/aboutus/aurora.aspx
Control: Church operated, Nongovernment, not-for-profit **Service**: General medical and surgical

Staffed Beds: 25 **Admissions**: 670 **Census**: 6 **Outpatient Visits**: 31538
Births: 275 **Total Expense ($000)**: 18453 **Payroll Expense ($000)**: 8656
Personnel: 146

BELTON—Cass County

⊞ **BELTON REGIONAL MEDICAL CENTER (260214)**, 17065 South 71 Highway, Zip 64012–4631; tel. 816/348–1200 **A**1 2 10 **F**3 15 18 20 29 30 31 34 35 37 40 43 45 57 59 65 68 70 74 75 77 78 79 81 82 85 87 90 93 107 108 110 111 114 115 118 119 129 130 131 132 146 **P**5 **S** HCA Healthcare, Nashville, TN
Primary Contact: Todd Krass, Chief Executive Officer
COO: Patrick Avila, Chief Operating Officer
CFO: Ronnie Thompson, Chief Financial Officer
CMO: Douglas Bradley M.D., Chief Medical Officer
CIO: Sarah Richardson, Director Information Systems
CHR: Jessica Sulzen, Director Human Resources
CNO: Karen Lee MSN, R.N., Chief Nursing Officer
Web address: www.beltonregionalmedicalcenter.com
Control: Corporation, Investor-owned (for-profit) **Service**: General medical and surgical

Staffed Beds: 48 **Admissions**: 3043 **Census**: 26 **Outpatient Visits**: 105128
Births: 0 **Total Expense ($000)**: 56555 **Payroll Expense ($000)**: 17976
Personnel: 200

RESEARCH BELTON HOSPITAL See Belton Regional Medical Center

BETHANY—Harrison County

★ **HARRISON COUNTY COMMUNITY HOSPITAL (261312)**, 2600 Miller Street, Zip 64424–2701, Mailing Address: P.O.Box 428, 64424–0428; tel. 660/425–2211 **A**10 18 **F**3 11 15 28 29 34 40 41 44 45 50 53 54 57 59 62 64 67 74 75 77 79 81 82 87 89 90 92 93 96 97 98 102 103 104 107 108 110 111 115 119 127 128 129 130 131 133 135 143 147 148 149 **P**5
Primary Contact: Tina Gillespie, Chief Executive Officer
CFO: Lee Ann Miles, Chief Financial Officer
CMO: Terry E. Hall, Chief of Staff
CIO: Will Holt, Director Information Technology
CHR: Cathie Chalfant, Director Human Resources
CNO: Crystal Hicks R.N., Chief Nursing Officer
Web address: www.hcchospital.org
Control: Hospital district or authority, Government, Nonfederal **Service**: General medical and surgical

Staffed Beds: 19 **Admissions**: 413 **Census**: 6 **Outpatient Visits**: 74246
Births: 0 **Total Expense ($000)**: 24300 **Payroll Expense ($000)**: 10315
Personnel: 233

BLUE SPRINGS—Jackson County

⊞ **ST. MARY'S MEDICAL CENTER (260193)**, 201 Northwest R D Mize Road, Zip 64014–2518; tel. 816/228–5900 **A**1 10 13 **F**3 8 15 18 20 22 28 29 30 34 35 40 49 50 53 57 59 60 64 68 70 74 77 78 79 80 81 82 83 84 85 87 90 93 96 107 108 110 111 113 114 115 119 123 129 130 131 135 143 145 146 148 **P**6 **S** Prime Healthcare, Ontario, CA
Primary Contact: Debra Ohnoutka, Chief Executive Officer
Web address: www.stmaryskc.com/
Control: Corporation, Investor-owned (for-profit) **Service**: General medical and surgical

Staffed Beds: 88 **Admissions**: 5644 **Census**: 57 **Outpatient Visits**: 71381
Births: 0 **Total Expense ($000)**: 86360 **Payroll Expense ($000)**: 30262
Personnel: 483

BOLIVAR—Polk County

⊞ **CITIZENS MEMORIAL HOSPITAL (260195)**, 1500 North Oakland Avenue, Zip 65613–3011; tel. 417/326–6000 **A**1 10 20 **F**3 7 11 13 15 18 20 22 26 28 29 31 34 36 40 43 44 50 51 54 56 57 59 64 66 70 74 75 76 77 78 79 80 81 82 84 85 86 87 89 90 93 94 96 97 98 100 102 103 104 107 108 110 111 115 117 119 127 128 129 130 131 132 133 135 146 147 148 149 **P**6
Primary Contact: Donald J. Babb, Chief Executive Officer
COO: Jeff Miller, Chief Operating Officer
CFO: Gary D Fullbright, Comptroller
CMO: Ronald A. Evans M.D., Chief Medical Officer
CIO: Denni McColm, Chief Information Officer
CHR: Jeremy MacLaughlin, Director Human Resources
CNO: Lesa Stock R.N., Chief Clinical Officer
Web address: www.citizensmemorial.com
Control: Hospital district or authority, Government, Nonfederal **Service**: General medical and surgical

Staffed Beds: 72 **Admissions**: 3342 **Census**: 29 **Outpatient Visits**: 360802
Births: 521 **Total Expense ($000)**: 142118 **Payroll Expense ($000)**: 64807 **Personnel**: 1077

BONNE TERRE—St. Francois County

★ **PARKLAND HEALTH CENTER-BONNE TERRE (261315)**, 7245 Raider Road, Zip 63628, Mailing Address: 1101 West Liberty Street, Farmington, 63640; tel. 573/358–1400 **A**10 18 **F**3 11 29 30 31 34 35 40 50 53 57 59 64 65 75 77 78 86 90 93 107 129 130 146 149 **P**8 **S** BJC HealthCare, Saint Louis, MO
Primary Contact: Steven R. Marler, Administrator
CFO: Cheri L Goldsmith, Director Financial Services
CHR: Sheri Graham, Director Human Resources and Administrative Services
Web address: www.parklandhealthcenter.org
Control: Other not-for-profit (including NFP Corporation)
Service: General medical and surgical

Staffed Beds: 3 **Admissions**: 22 **Census**: 1 **Outpatient Visits**: 25687
Births: 0 **Personnel**: 60

Many Facility Codes have changed. Please refer to the AHA Guide Code Chart. © 2017 AHA Guide

MO

BOONVILLE—Cooper County

★ **COOPER COUNTY MEMORIAL HOSPITAL (260004)**, 17651 'B' Highway, Zip 65233–2839, Mailing Address: P.O.Box 88, 65233–0088; tel. 660/882–7461, (Total facility includes 14 beds in nursing home–type unit) **A**10 20 **F**3 7 11 29 34 35 40 45 53 57 59 64 67 68 75 79 81 85 89 93 94 107 111 114 119 127 128 130 131 132 133 135 146 148 **S** Rural Community Hospitals of America, Kansas City, MO
Primary Contact: Mark Hirshberg, Interim Chief Executive Officer
CFO: Patricia Nowlin, Director Accounting
CMO: Mona Brownfield M.D., Chief Medical Staff
CIO: Bill Fletcher, Director Information Technology
CHR: Patricia Nowlin, Director Human Resources
CNO: Nancy Fredrich R.N., Chief Clinical Officer
Web address: www.coopercmh.com
Control: County, Government, Nonfederal **Service**: General medical and surgical

Staffed Beds: 32 **Admissions:** 330 **Census:** 17 **Outpatient Visits:** 30433 **Births:** 0 **Total Expense ($000):** 14984 **Payroll Expense ($000):** 6552 **Personnel:** 135

BRANSON—Taney County

★ △ ⇑ **COX MEDICAL CENTER BRANSON (260094)**, 251 Skaggs Road, Zip 65616–2031, Mailing Address: P.O.Box 650, 65615–0650; tel. 417/335–7000 **A**7 10 21 **F**3 8 13 15 17 18 20 22 26 28 29 31 32 34 35 40 41 44 45 46 47 50 53 56 57 59 60 61 62 63 64 65 66 68 70 74 75 76 77 78 79 80 81 82 84 85 86 87 89 90 93 97 98 100 103 106 107 108 110 111 114 117 119 120 121 123 127 129 130 131 132 135 143 144 146 147 148 149 150 **P**6 **S** CoxHealth, Springfield, MO
Primary Contact: William K. Mahoney, FACHE, President and Chief Executive Officer
CFO: David Strong, Chief Financial Officer/Vice President Finance
CMO: James Duff M.D., Chief Medical Officer
CHR: Carol Murrow, Vice President Business Development
Web address: www.coxhealth.com
Control: Other not-for-profit (including NFP Corporation) **Service**: General medical and surgical

Staffed Beds: 115 **Admissions:** 6670 **Census:** 80 **Outpatient Visits:** 299304 **Births:** 581 **Total Expense ($000):** 166549 **Payroll Expense ($000):** 58854 **Personnel:** 1096

BRIDGETON—St. Louis County

⊞ △ **SSM HEALTH DEPAUL HOSPITAL - ST. LOUIS (260104)**, 12303 De Paul Drive, Zip 63044–2512; tel. 314/344–6000, (Total facility includes 52 beds in nursing home–type unit) **A**1 2 5 7 10 **F**3 4 5 11 12 13 16 17 18 20 22 24 26 28 29 30 31 34 35 36 38 40 43 44 45 49 50 51 53 55 56 57 58 59 60 61 64 68 70 73 74 75 76 78 79 81 82 84 85 86 87 89 98 99 100 101 102 104 105 107 108 110 111 114 115 117 118 119 120 121 126 128 130 132 135 144 146 147 148 **P**6 **S** SSM Health, Saint Louis, MO
Primary Contact: Sean Hogan, FACHE, President
COO: Tina Garrison, Vice President Operations
CFO: Hal Holder, Director Finance
CMO: John Moore M.D., Vice President Medical Affairs
CIO: Scott Feldmann, Director Information Technology
CHR: Gloria Reed, Leader Human Resources
CNO: Shelly L. Cordum R.N., MSN, Vice President Nursing and Chief Nursing Officer
Web address: www.ssmdepaul.com
Control: Church operated, Nongovernment, not-for-profit
Service: General medical and surgical

Staffed Beds: 507 **Admissions:** 23121 **Census:** 348 **Outpatient Visits:** 270636 **Births:** 972 **Total Expense ($000):** 387930 **Payroll Expense ($000):** 125087 **Personnel:** 1974

BROOKFIELD—Linn County

GENERAL JOHN J. PERSHING MEMORIAL HOSPITAL (261307), 130 East Lockling Avenue, Zip 64628–2337, Mailing Address: P.O.Box 408, 64628–0408; tel. 660/258–2222 **A**10 18 **F**11 15 28 29 34 36 40 57 59 64 75 77 81 85 87 89 93 97 107 111 114 119 127 129 130 133 146 149 **P**6
Primary Contact: Phil Hamilton, R.N., Chief Executive Officer
CFO: Gary R Tandy, Chief Financial Officer
CMO: B K Knowles D.O., Chief of Staff
CIO: Elaine Sutton, Chief Information Officer
CHR: Amy Sayre, Director Human Resources
Web address: www.phsmo.org
Control: Other not-for-profit (including NFP Corporation)
Service: General medical and surgical

Staffed Beds: 25 **Admissions:** 441 **Census:** 6 **Outpatient Visits:** 56563 **Births:** 0 **Total Expense ($000):** 15924 **Payroll Expense ($000):** 6355 **Personnel:** 156

BUTLER—Bates County

★ **BATES COUNTY MEMORIAL HOSPITAL (260034)**, 615 West Nursery Street, Zip 64730–1840, Mailing Address: P.O.Box 370, 64730–0370; tel. 660/200–7000 **A**10 20 **F**3 7 11 15 28 29 30 31 34 40 45 50 59 64 68 70 77 78 79 81 87 90 93 107 108 109 110 111 115 118 119 127 129 130 132 133 **P**5 6
Primary Contact: John P. Bustle, M.D., Interim Chief Executive Officer
CFO: Terri Floyd, Chief Financial Officer
CMO: William F. Joyce D.O., Chief of Staff
CIO: Marcia Cook, Director Information Technology
CHR: Melinda R Jackson, Director Human Resources
CNO: Rebecca Tarver, Chief Nursing Officer
Web address: www.bcmhospital.com
Control: County, Government, Nonfederal **Service**: General medical and surgical

Staffed Beds: 49 **Admissions:** 846 **Census:** 10 **Outpatient Visits:** 77436 **Births:** 0 **Total Expense ($000):** 36064 **Payroll Expense ($000):** 13644 **Personnel:** 266

CAMERON—Clinton County

CAMERON REGIONAL MEDICAL CENTER (260057), 1600 East Evergreen, Zip 64429–2400, Mailing Address: P.O.Box 557, 64429–0557; tel. 816/632–2101 **A**3 5 10 **F**3 11 12 13 15 28 29 30 31 34 35 39 40 46 47 49 56 57 59 61 62 63 64 67 70 74 75 76 77 78 79 81 82 84 85 86 87 89 90 98 100 104 107 110 111 115 119 128 129 130 131 133 143 146 147 148 **P**6
Primary Contact: Joseph F. Abrutz Jr, Administrator
CFO: Rosa Patti, Chief Financial Officer
CIO: Bill Walser, Coordinator Technology
CHR: Pat Bestgen, Manager Human Resources
Web address: www.cameronregional.org
Control: Other not-for-profit (including NFP Corporation) **Service**: General medical and surgical

Staffed Beds: 58 **Admissions:** 1973 **Census:** 31 **Outpatient Visits:** 315644 **Births:** 128 **Total Expense ($000):** 57020 **Payroll Expense ($000):** 25485 **Personnel:** 392

CAPE GIRARDEAU—Cape Girardeau County

☐ **LANDMARK HOSPITAL OF CAPE GIRARDEAU (262015)**, 3255 Independence Street, Zip 63701–4914; tel. 573/335–1091 **A**1 10 22 **F**1 3 29 148 **S** Landmark Hospitals, Cape Girardeau, MO
Primary Contact: Donna Mansard, Chief Executive Officer
COO: Michael L Norman, Executive Vice President and Chief Operating Officer
CFO: Richard H Hogan CPA, Chief Financial Officer
CMO: William Fritsch M.D., Medical Director
CIO: Renee Hesselrode, Director Health Information Management
CHR: Angela Kisner, Director Human Resources and Coordinator Medical Staff
Web address: www.landmarkhospitals.com
Control: Corporation, Investor-owned (for-profit) **Service**: Acute long-term care hospital

Staffed Beds: 30 **Admissions:** 329 **Census:** 22 **Outpatient Visits:** 0 **Births:** 0 **Total Expense ($000):** 11478 **Payroll Expense ($000):** 4501 **Personnel:** 75

⊞ **SAINT FRANCIS MEDICAL CENTER (260183)**, 211 St Francis Drive, Zip 63703–5049; tel. 573/331–3000 **A**1 2 10 19 **F**3 9 11 12 13 15 17 18 20 22 24 26 28 29 30 31 32 34 35 39 40 43 44 45 46 47 48 49 50 53 54 56 57 58 59 60 61 62 63 64 65 68 70 72 73 74 75 76 77 78 79 80 81 82 83 84 85 86 87 89 90 91 92 93 96 97 107 110 111 114 115 117 118 119 120 121 123 124 126 127 129 130 131 132 135 141 142 143 144 145 146 147 148 **P**6
Primary Contact: Maryann Reese, R.N., FACHE, President and Chief Executive Officer
CFO: Tony Balsano, Vice President Finance
CMO: James Schell M.D., Vice President Medical Affairs
CIO: Edward E Duryee, Director Information Systems
CHR: Teri Kreitzer, Director Human Resources
CNO: Jeannie Fadler R.N., Vice President Patient Care Services
Web address: www.sfmc.net
Control: Church operated, Nongovernment, not-for-profit
Service: General medical and surgical

Staffed Beds: 289 **Admissions:** 12008 **Census:** 160 **Outpatient Visits:** 673464 **Births:** 907 **Total Expense ($000):** 454197 **Payroll Expense ($000):** 176843 **Personnel:** 2446

MO

MO

☒ **SOUTHEAST HOSPITAL (260110)**, 1701 Lacey Street, Zip 63701–5230; tel. 573/334–4822 **A**1 10 19 **F**3 11 13 15 17 18 20 22 24 26 28 29 30 31 32 34 35 40 44 45 48 50 51 53 54 57 58 59 60 61 62 63 64 65 70 72 73 74 75 76 77 78 79 80 81 82 84 85 86 87 88 89 90 92 93 96 97 98 100 102 107 108 110 111 114 115 117 119 120 121 123 124 126 127 129 130 131 132 135 146 147 148 149 **P**6 **S** SoutheastHEALTH, Cape Girardeau, MO
Primary Contact: Kenneth Bateman, CPA, President and Chief Executive Officer
COO: Sylvia Moore, Vice President and Chief Operating Officer
CFO: Bruce Fairbanks, Vice President and Chief Financial Officer
CMO: Matt Shoemaker D.O., Vice President and Chief Medical Officer
CIO: Mike Dozier, Chief Information Officer
CHR: Lincoln Scott, Vice President Human Resources
CNO: Judy Aslin MSN, R.N., Vice President and Chief Nursing Officer
Web address: www.sehealth.org/
Control: Other not-for-profit (including NFP Corporation) **Service**: General medical and surgical

> **Staffed Beds**: 209 **Admissions**: 9115 **Census**: 109 **Outpatient Visits**: 419957 **Births**: 957 **Total Expense ($000)**: 308707 **Payroll Expense ($000)**: 116701 **Personnel**: 1895

CARROLLTON—Carroll County

★ **CARROLL COUNTY MEMORIAL HOSPITAL (261332)**, 1502 North Jefferson Street, Zip 64633–1948; tel. 660/542–1695 **A**10 18 **F**3 11 15 28 29 30 31 32 34 35 38 40 45 50 53 56 57 59 62 64 65 69 74 75 77 78 79 81 86 87 90 91 92 93 96 103 104 107 108 110 111 114 119 125 127 129 130 131 132 133 143 146 148 149 **P**6
Primary Contact: Jeff A. Tindle, Chief Executive Officer
COO: Tim Braun, Assistant Administrator
CFO: Amy Ireland, Chief Financial Officer
CMO: Richard Smith, Chief of Staff
CIO: Bill Bollinger, Chief Information Officer
CHR: Michael Schubach, Director Human Resources
CNO: Jeanne Rector, Chief Nursing Officer
Web address: www.carrollcountyhospital.org
Control: Other not-for-profit (including NFP Corporation) **Service**: General medical and surgical

> **Staffed Beds**: 25 **Admissions**: 282 **Census**: 5 **Outpatient Visits**: 52153 **Births**: 0 **Total Expense ($000)**: 18766 **Payroll Expense ($000)**: 7900 **Personnel**: 184

CARTHAGE—Jasper County

★ **MERCY HOSPITAL CARTHAGE (260228)**, 3125 Dr Russell Smith Way, Zip 64836–7402; tel. 417/358–8121 **A**10 18 **F**3 7 11 15 28 29 30 31 34 35 40 45 50 53 57 59 62 64 67 68 69 75 79 81 89 98 104 107 110 111 115 119 127 129 130 131 132 133 135 146 147 **P**6 **S** Mercy, Chesterfield, MO
Primary Contact: Scott Watson, Administrator
CFO: Douglas Culver, Chief Financial Officer
CIO: Cheryl Lease-Homeyer, Lead Information Technology Business Partner
CHR: Colette St. Peter, Senior Manager Human Resources
Web address: www.mercy.net
Control: Church operated, Nongovernment, not-for-profit
Service: General medical and surgical

> **Staffed Beds**: 13 **Admissions**: 812 **Census**: 12 **Outpatient Visits**: 103900 **Births**: 0 **Total Expense ($000)**: 44389 **Payroll Expense ($000)**: 16619 **Personnel**: 227

CASSVILLE—Barry County

☒ **MERCY HOSPITAL CASSVILLE (261317)**, 94 Main Street, Zip 65625–1610; tel. 417/847–6000 **A**1 10 18 **F**3 11 15 28 29 30 34 40 41 45 50 53 57 59 64 65 75 77 81 85 86 87 89 92 93 94 96 103 107 110 111 114 119 132 133 135 148 149 **P**6 **S** Mercy, Chesterfield, MO
Primary Contact: Douglas M. Stroemel, President
CFO: Sherry Clouse Day CPA, Chief Financial Officer
CMO: Jamie Zengotita M.D., Chief Medical Staff
CHR: George Roden, Vice President Human Resources
CNO: Nicki Gamet R.N., Chief Nursing Officer
Web address: www.mercy.net/northwestar/practice/mercy-hospital-cassville
Control: Church operated, Nongovernment, not-for-profit
Service: General medical and surgical

> **Staffed Beds**: 18 **Admissions**: 314 **Census**: 3 **Outpatient Visits**: 30936 **Births**: 0 **Total Expense ($000)**: 14774 **Payroll Expense ($000)**: 6734 **Personnel**: 100

CHESTERFIELD—St. Louis County

☐ △ **MERCY REHABILITATION HOSPITAL ST. LOUIS (263029)**, 14561 North Outer Forty Road, Zip 63017; tel. 314/881–4000 **A**1 7 10 **F**16 29 30 90 130 132 148 **S** Kindred Healthcare, Louisville, KY
Primary Contact: Donna M. Flannery, Chief Executive Officer
CMO: Siresha Samudrala M.D., Medical Director
Web address: www.stjohnsmercyrehab.com
Control: Partnership, Investor-owned (for-profit) **Service**: Rehabilitation

> **Staffed Beds**: 90 **Admissions**: 1731 **Census**: 63 **Outpatient Visits**: 0 **Births**: 0 **Total Expense ($000)**: 27231 **Payroll Expense ($000)**: 13151 **Personnel**: 236

☒ **ST. LUKE'S HOSPITAL (260179)**, 232 South Woods Mill Road, Zip 63017–3417; tel. 314/434–1500, (Total facility includes 140 beds in nursing home–type unit) **A**1 2 3 10 **F**3 10 11 13 15 17 18 20 22 24 26 28 29 30 31 32 34 35 36 38 39 40 41 42 44 45 46 49 50 52 53 54 55 56 57 58 59 60 61 62 63 64 65 66 68 69 70 71 73 74 75 76 77 78 79 81 82 83 84 85 86 87 89 90 93 97 107 108 110 111 114 115 117 118 119 120 121 123 124 126 128 129 130 131 132 135 144 145 146 147 148 149 **P**6 8
Primary Contact: Christine M. Candio, R.N., FACHE, President and Chief Executive Officer
COO: Donald L Miller FACHE, Vice President, Operations
CFO: Scott H. Johnson, Vice President Finance and Chief Financial Officer
CIO: William Meyers, Chief Information Officer
CHR: Janette Taaffe, Vice President, Human Resource
CNO: Diane Ray R.N., Vice President and Chief Nursing Officer Patient Services
Web address: www.stlukes-stl.com
Control: Church operated, Nongovernment, not-for-profit **Service**: General medical and surgical

> **Staffed Beds**: 539 **Admissions**: 14787 **Census**: 270 **Outpatient Visits**: 982578 **Births**: 1901 **Total Expense ($000)**: 498935 **Payroll Expense ($000)**: 220514 **Personnel**: 2998

☒ △ **ST. LUKE'S REHABILITATION HOSPITAL (263030)**, 14709 Olive Boulevard, Zip 63017–2221; tel. 314/317–5700 **A**1 7 10 **F**3 12 18 28 29 34 75 79 90 96 100 130 132 148
Primary Contact: Christopher Baechle, Chief Executive Officer
Web address: www.khrehabstluke.com
Control: Partnership, Investor-owned (for-profit) **Service**: Rehabilitation

> **Staffed Beds**: 35 **Admissions**: 669 **Census**: 23 **Outpatient Visits**: 0 **Births**: 0 **Total Expense ($000)**: 8845 **Payroll Expense ($000)**: 5148 **Personnel**: 47

CHILLICOTHE—Livingston County

☒ **HEDRICK MEDICAL CENTER (261321)**, 2799 North Washington Street, Zip 64601–2902; tel. 660/646–1480 **A**1 10 18 **F**3 11 13 15 18 28 29 30 31 34 35 39 40 41 43 44 45 50 54 57 59 64 65 68 69 70 74 75 76 77 78 79 81 85 86 87 89 90 92 93 96 97 100 104 107 108 110 111 115 118 119 127 128 129 130 131 133 146 147 148 **P**6 **S** Saint Luke's Health System, Kansas City, MO
Primary Contact: Steven M. Schieber, FACHE, Chief Executive Officer
CHR: Lisa Hecker, Director Human Resources
CNO: Catherine Hamilton, Chief Nursing Officer
Web address: www.saintlukeskc.org
Control: Other not-for-profit (including NFP Corporation) **Service**: General medical and surgical

> **Staffed Beds**: 25 **Admissions**: 1177 **Census**: 14 **Outpatient Visits**: 104485 **Births**: 231 **Total Expense ($000)**: 43710 **Payroll Expense ($000)**: 16931 **Personnel**: 291

CLINTON—Henry County

☒ **GOLDEN VALLEY MEMORIAL HEALTHCARE (260175)**, 1600 North Second Street, Zip 64735–1192; tel. 660/885–5511 **A**1 10 **F**3 7 11 13 15 17 18 28 29 30 31 34 35 40 45 47 48 49 53 57 59 61 62 64 68 70 74 75 76 77 78 79 81 85 86 87 89 90 93 96 107 108 111 115 118 127 128 129 130 131 132 133 143 146 147 148 149
Primary Contact: Craig Thompson, Chief Executive Officer
CFO: Tammy R Nadler, Chief Financial Officer
CIO: Mike Gaul, Director Information Technology
CHR: Greg Shannon, Chief Human Resources Officer
CNO: Mark David Mattes R.N., MS, Assistant Administrator/Patient Care Services
Web address: www.gvmh.org
Control: Hospital district or authority, Government, Nonfederal **Service**: General medical and surgical

> **Staffed Beds**: 55 **Admissions**: 2223 **Census**: 20 **Outpatient Visits**: 296452 **Births**: 0 **Total Expense ($000)**: 84701 **Payroll Expense ($000)**: 38789 **Personnel**: 673

COLUMBIA—Boone County

☒ **BOONE HOSPITAL CENTER (260068)**, 1600 East Broadway, Zip 65201–5844; tel. 573/815–8000 **A**1 2 3 5 10 **F**3 7 11 12 13 15 17 18 20 22 24 26 28 29 31 34 35 36 40 45 46 47 48 49 50 51 53 54 56 57 59 60 61 64 65 68 70 71 72 73 74 75 76 77 78 79 80 81 82 84 85 86 87 89 90 93 96 107 108 110 111 115 117 118 119 126 129 130 131 132 135 145 146 147 148 149 **S** BJC HealthCare, Saint Louis, MO
Primary Contact: James J. Sinek, FACHE, President
CFO: Randy Morrow, Vice President and Chief Operating Officer
CMO: Jerry Kennett M.D., Chief Medical Officer
CHR: Michelle Zvanut, Vice President Human Resources
Web address: www.boone.org
Control: Other not-for-profit (including NFP Corporation) **Service**: General medical and surgical

> **Staffed Beds**: 311 **Admissions**: 14787 **Census**: 181 **Outpatient Visits**: 173773 **Births**: 1791 **Total Expense ($000)**: 315156 **Payroll Expense ($000)**: 89085 **Personnel**: 1471

ELLIS FISCHEL CANCER CENTER See University Of Missouri Health Care

Many Facility Codes have changed. Please refer to the AHA Guide Code Chart.
© 2017 AHA Guide

⊞ **HARRY S. TRUMAN MEMORIAL VETERANS HOSPITAL**, 800 Hospital Drive, Zip 65201–5275; tel. 573/814–6000, (Nonreporting) **A**1 3 5 **S** Department of Veterans Affairs, Washington, DC
Primary Contact: David Isaacks, Director
COO: Robert G Ritter FACHE, Associate Director
CFO: Deborah Henderson, Acting Chief Financial Officer
CMO: Lana Zerrer M.D., Chief of Staff
CIO: Donna Krause, Chief Information Officer
CHR: Jimmy Powell, Manager Human Resources
Web address: www.columbiamo.va.gov
Control: Veterans Affairs, Government, federal **Service**: General medical and surgical

> **Staffed Beds**: 123

⊞ **HOWARD A. RUSK REHABILITATION CENTER (263027)**, 315 Business Loop 70 West, Zip 65203–3248; tel. 573/817–2703 **A**1 3 5 10 **F**29 34 58 68 75 90 91 94 95 96 132 134 143 148 **S** HEALTHSOUTH Corporation, Birmingham, AL
Primary Contact: John M. Dawes, FACHE, Chief Executive Officer
CFO: Jeff Reese, Chief Financial Officer
CMO: Gregory Worsowicz M.D., Medical Director
CHR: Robin Prater, Director Human Resources
CNO: Lori Mann R.N., MSN, Chief Nursing Officer
Web address: www.ruskrehab.com
Control: Partnership, Investor-owned (for-profit) **Service**: Rehabilitation

> **Staffed Beds**: 60 **Admissions**: 1102 **Census**: 43 **Outpatient Visits**: 0
> **Births**: 0 **Total Expense ($000)**: 19296 **Payroll Expense ($000)**: 8756
> **Personnel**: 150

LANDMARK HOSPITAL OF COLUMBIA (262020), 604 Old 63 North, Zip 65201–6308; tel. 573/499–6600 **A**3 5 10 22 **F**1 60 70 83 148 **P**5 **S** Landmark Hospitals, Cape Girardeau, MO
Primary Contact: Jerry Deller, Chief Executive Officer
Web address: www.landmarkhospitals.com
Control: Corporation, Investor-owned (for-profit) **Service**: Acute long-term care hospital

> **Staffed Beds**: 42 **Admissions**: 300 **Census**: 24 **Outpatient Visits**: 0
> **Births**: 0 **Total Expense ($000)**: 14087 **Payroll Expense ($000)**: 4503
> **Personnel**: 52

⊞ **UNIVERSITY OF MISSOURI HEALTH CARE (260141)**, One Hospital Drive, Zip 65212–0001; tel. 573/882–4141, (Includes ELLIS FISCHEL CANCER CENTER, 115 Business Loop 70 West, Columbia, Missouri, Zip 65203, tel. 573/882–5460; WOMEN'S AND CHILDREN'S HOSPITAL, 404 Keene Street, Columbia, Missouri, Zip 65201–6626, tel. 573/875–9000; Keri Simon, Executive Director) **A**1 2 3 5 8 10 **F**3 4 7 9 11 12 13 15 16 17 18 19 20 22 24 26 28 29 30 31 32 34 35 37 38 39 40 41 42 43 44 45 46 47 48 49 50 51 52 53 54 55 56 57 58 59 60 61 64 65 66 68 70 71 72 73 74 75 76 77 78 79 80 81 82 83 84 85 86 87 88 89 91 92 93 97 98 99 100 101 102 103 104 107 108 110 111 114 115 116 117 118 119 120 121 123 124 126 127 129 130 131 132 134 135 138 141 142 143 144 146 147 148 **P**1 6 **S** University of Missouri Health Care, Columbia, MO
Primary Contact: Jonathan W. Curtright, Chief Executive Officer and Chief Operating Officer
CFO: Kevin Necas, Chief Financial Officer
CMO: Stevan Whitt M.D., Chief Medical Officer
CHR: Sue Kopfle, Chief Human Resources Officer
Web address: www.muhealth.org
Control: State, Government, Nonfederal **Service**: General medical and surgical

> **Staffed Beds**: 569 **Admissions**: 26277 **Census**: 366 **Outpatient Visits**: 939845 **Births**: 2058 **Total Expense ($000)**: 800751 **Payroll Expense ($000)**: 247144 **Personnel**: 4987

CRYSTAL CITY—Jefferson County

⊞ △ **MERCY HOSPITAL JEFFERSON (260023)**, Highway 61 South, Zip 63019, Mailing Address: P.O.Box 350, 63019–0350; tel. 636/933–1000 **A**1 7 10 **F**3 4 5 8 11 12 13 15 18 20 22 24 26 28 29 30 31 34 35 40 44 45 49 50 51 53 54 57 59 60 62 63 64 68 70 74 75 76 77 78 79 81 82 84 85 86 87 89 90 93 96 97 98 100 101 102 103 104 107 108 110 111 114 115 116 117 118 119 129 130 131 132 135 143 144 146 147 148 149 **P**6 8 **S** Mercy, Chesterfield, MO
Primary Contact: Eric Ammons, President
COO: Michele C Meyer, Vice President of Operations
CMO: Mark Briete M.D., Vice President Medical Affairs
CIO: Jan Poneta, Director Information Services
CHR: Saundra G Turner, Director Human Resources
Web address: www.mercy.net/crystalcitymo
Control: Other not-for-profit (including NFP Corporation) **Service**: General medical and surgical

> **Staffed Beds**: 205 **Admissions**: 9647 **Census**: 124 **Outpatient Visits**: 184589 **Births**: 406 **Total Expense ($000)**: 151597 **Payroll Expense ($000)**: 57169 **Personnel**: 1004

DEXTER—Stoddard County

SOUTHEAST HEALTH CENTER OF STODDARD COUNTY (260160), 1200 North One Mile Road, Zip 63841–1000; tel. 573/624–5566 **A**10 **F**3 11 15 28 29 31 34 39 40 45 59 62 65 70 75 77 78 81 85 89 90 93 97 107 108 111 115 118 119 127 129 130 133 135 146 **P**6 **S** SoutheastHEALTH, Cape Girardeau, MO
Primary Contact: Sue Ann Williams, Chief Executive Officer
Web address: www.sehealth.org
Control: Other not-for-profit (including NFP Corporation) **Service**: General medical and surgical

> **Staffed Beds**: 16 **Admissions**: 765 **Census**: 5 **Outpatient Visits**: 108113
> **Births**: 0 **Total Expense ($000)**: 22959 **Payroll Expense ($000)**: 9885
> **Personnel**: 176

DONIPHAN—Ripley County

★ **SOUTHEAST HEALTH CENTER OF RIPLEY COUNTY (260080)**, 109 Plum Street, Zip 63935–1299; tel. 573/996–2141 **A**10 **F**3 29 34 35 40 59 62 64 65 93 97 107 111 115 119 127 129 130 133 149 **P**6 **S** SoutheastHEALTH, Cape Girardeau, MO
Primary Contact: Cheryl Lynne. Barton, R.N., Chief Executive Officer
CFO: Rickie Maples, Interim Chief Financial Officer
CMO: Ureej Mansoor M.D., Chief of Staff
CIO: Riley March, Manager Information Technology
CHR: Peggy Teasdale, Director Human Resources
Web address: www.sehealth.org/southeast-health-center-of-ripley-county/SoutheastHEALTH.aspx?nd=41
Control: Other not-for-profit (including NFP Corporation) **Service**: General medical and surgical

> **Staffed Beds**: 10 **Admissions**: 311 **Census**: 2 **Outpatient Visits**: 45601
> **Births**: 0 **Total Expense ($000)**: 10581 **Payroll Expense ($000)**: 4318
> **Personnel**: 87

EL DORADO SPRINGS—Cedar County

CEDAR COUNTY MEMORIAL HOSPITAL (261323), 1401 South Park Street, Zip 64744–2037; tel. 417/876–2511 **A**10 18 **F**11 15 18 28 29 30 34 35 40 45 53 56 57 59 62 64 65 74 77 81 85 87 89 90 93 102 103 107 110 111 114 119 127 129 130 133 146 147 148 149 **P**6
Primary Contact: Jana Witt, Chief Executive Officer
CFO: Carla Gilbert, Director Finance
CMO: Rick Casey D.O., Chief Medical Staff
CIO: Lois Willmore, Supervisor Health Information Management
CHR: Diana Pyle, Director Human Resources and Executive Assistant to Chief Executive Officer
CNO: Drew Alexander, Chief Nursing Officer
Web address: www.cedarcountyhospital.org
Control: County, Government, Nonfederal **Service**: General medical and surgical

> **Staffed Beds**: 25 **Admissions**: 310 **Census**: 6 **Outpatient Visits**: 31025
> **Births**: 0 **Total Expense ($000)**: 12295 **Payroll Expense ($000)**: 4418
> **Personnel**: 115

EXCELSIOR SPRINGS—Clay County

★ **EXCELSIOR SPRINGS HOSPITAL (261322)**, 1700 Rainbow Boulevard, Zip 64024–1190; tel. 816/630–6081, (Total facility includes 80 beds in nursing home–type unit) **A**10 18 **F**3 10 11 15 18 29 30 31 32 34 35 39 40 45 49 56 57 59 62 63 64 67 68 70 75 77 78 79 81 82 84 85 86 87 89 90 93 102 107 108 110 111 114 117 118 119 125 128 129 130 133 143 146 147
Primary Contact: Kristen DeHart, Chief Executive Officer
CFO: Dennis Hartman, Chief Financial Officer
CMO: Manoch Kuangparichat M.D., President Medical Staff
CIO: Alicia Harrison, Data Management Officer
CHR: Joni Schwan, Director Human Resources
Web address: www.esmc.org
Control: City, Government, Nonfederal **Service**: General medical and surgical

> **Staffed Beds**: 105 **Admissions**: 378 **Census**: 67 **Outpatient Visits**: 33891
> **Births**: 0 **Total Expense ($000)**: 27355 **Payroll Expense ($000)**: 11360
> **Personnel**: 245

Hospital, Medicare Provider Number, Address, Telephone, Approval, Facility, and Physician Codes, Health Care System

★ American Hospital Association (AHA) membership
□ The Joint Commission accreditation
○ Healthcare Facilities Accreditation Program
◇ DNV Healthcare Inc. accreditation
⇑ Center for Improvement in Healthcare Quality Accreditation
△ Commission on Accreditation of Rehabilitation Facilities (CARF) accreditation

FAIRFAX—Atchison County

⇧ **COMMUNITY HOSPITAL ASSOCIATION** See Community Hospital-Fairfax

★ ⇧ **COMMUNITY HOSPITAL-FAIRFAX (261303)**, 26136 US Highway 59, Zip 64446–9105, Mailing Address: P.O.Box 107, 64446–0107; tel. 660/686–2211 **A**10 18 21 **F**3 11 13 15 18 28 29 30 34 40 45 50 57 59 62 64 75 76 79 81 85 87 89 90 93 96 97 101 103 104 107 111 119 130 131 132 133 148 149
Primary Contact: Roger W. Steinkruger, Chief Executive Officer
CFO: Jon Davis, Chief Financial Officer
CIO: Chris Hedlund, Director Information Systems
CHR: Amber Durr, Human Resources Executive
CNO: Julie L Jones, Chief Nursing Officer
Web address: www.fairfaxmed.com
Control: Other not-for-profit (including NFP Corporation) **Service:** General medical and surgical

Staffed Beds: 18 **Admissions:** 494 **Census:** 6 **Outpatient Visits:** 20851
Births: 45 **Total Expense ($000):** 14548 **Payroll Expense ($000):** 5088
Personnel: 105

FARMINGTON—St. Francois County

✉ **PARKLAND HEALTH CENTER - FARMINGTON COMMUNITY (260163)**, 1101 West Liberty Street, Zip 63640–1921; tel. 573/756–6451 **A**1 10 **F**3 4 11 13 15 18 28 29 30 34 35 40 45 46 49 50 53 57 59 65 68 69 70 75 76 77 79 81 85 86 87 93 98 103 107 108 111 115 118 119 130 135 143 146 147 148 149 **P**6 **S** BJC HealthCare, Saint Louis, MO
Primary Contact: Thomas P. Karl, President
COO: Steven R Marler, Assistant Administrator
CFO: Cheri L Goldsmith, Director Financial Services
CMO: Jamesy Smith D.O., Chief of Staff
CHR: Sheri Graham, Director Human Resources and Administrative Services
Web address: www.parklandhealthcenter.org
Control: Other not-for-profit (including NFP Corporation) **Service:** General medical and surgical

Staffed Beds: 103 **Admissions:** 4124 **Census:** 36 **Outpatient Visits:** 94431
Births: 739 **Total Expense ($000):** 98306 **Payroll Expense ($000):** 39721
Personnel: 501

☐ **SOUTHEAST MISSOURI MENTAL HEALTH CENTER (264005)**, 1010 West Columbia Street, Zip 63640–2997; tel. 573/218–6792 **A**1 10 **F**4 11 30 39 53 65 75 77 86 87 97 98 101 103 106 130 132 135 143 146
Primary Contact: Julie Inman, Regional Executive Officer
CMO: Jay Englehart M.D., Medical Director
CHR: Mark Remspecher, Director Human Resources
Web address: www.dmh.missouri.gov/southeast/
Control: State, Government, Nonfederal **Service:** Psychiatric

Staffed Beds: 323 **Admissions:** 51 **Census:** 304 **Outpatient Visits:** 0
Births: 0 **Total Expense ($000):** 62466 **Payroll Expense ($000):** 33552
Personnel: 903

FENTON—St. Louis County

✉ **SSM HEALTH ST. CLARE HOSPITAL - FENTON (260081)**, 1015 Bowles Avenue, Zip 63026–2394; tel. 636/496–2000 **A**1 10 **F**3 11 13 15 17 18 20 22 24 28 29 30 31 34 35 40 41 44 45 49 50 51 53 54 56 57 58 59 61 64 70 73 74 75 76 78 79 81 82 84 85 86 87 89 100 102 103 107 108 110 111 115 117 119 120 121 124 130 132 135 143 144 146 147 148 **P**6 8 **S** SSM Health, Saint Louis, MO
Primary Contact: Ellis Hawkins, President
COO: Lee Bernstein, Regional Executive Vice President and Chief Operating Officer
CFO: Hal Holder, Regional Chief Financial Officer-Hospital Operations
CMO: Timothy J Pratt M.D., Vice President Medical Affairs and Chief Medical Officer
CIO: Michael Paasch, Vice President, Regional Chief Information Officer
CHR: Renee Roach, System Vice President, Human Resources
CNO: Wayne Laramie, Vice President Nursing
Web address: www.ssmstclare.com
Control: Church operated, Nongovernment, not-for-profit **Service:** General medical and surgical

Staffed Beds: 184 **Admissions:** 10761 **Census:** 117 **Outpatient Visits:** 141612 **Births:** 1107 **Total Expense ($000):** 191351 **Payroll Expense ($000):** 61384 **Personnel:** 927

FORT LEONARD WOOD—Pulaski County

✉ **GENERAL LEONARD WOOD ARMY COMMUNITY HOSPITAL**, 4430 Missouri Avenue, Zip 65473–8952, Mailing Address: PO Box 4430, 65473–8952; tel. 573/596–0414, (Nonreporting) **A**1 3 **S** Department of the Army, Office of the Surgeon General, Falls Church, VA
Primary Contact: Colonel Christian Meko, Hospital Commander
CFO: MajorMichael Hogan, Chief Resource Management
CMO: Lieutenant ColonelJohn Lowery M.D., Deputy Commander Clinical Services
CHR: MajorSandra Roper, Chief Human Resources
Web address: www.glwach.amedd.army.mil/
Control: Army, Government, federal **Service:** General medical and surgical

Staffed Beds: 42

FREDERICKTOWN—Madison County

MADISON MEDICAL CENTER (261302), 611 West Main Street, Zip 63645–1111; tel. 573/783–3341, (Total facility includes 80 beds in nursing–type unit) **A**10 18 **F**6 11 15 18 28 31 35 40 45 59 62 64 67 70 74 77 78 79 81 85 87 92 93 97 103 107 111 119 127 128 130 133 146
Primary Contact: Lisa Twidwell, Administrator
CMO: P A George M.D., Chief of Staff
CHR: Jennifer Penuel, Director Human Resources
Web address: www.madisonmedicalcenter.net
Control: County, Government, Nonfederal **Service:** General medical and surgical

Staffed Beds: 97 **Admissions:** 393 **Census:** 72 **Outpatient Visits:** 54651
Births: 0 **Total Expense ($000):** 18938 **Payroll Expense ($000):** 9282
Personnel: 243

FULTON—Callaway County

☐ **FULTON MEDICAL CENTER (260209)**, 10 South Hospital Drive, Zip 65251–2510; tel. 573/642–3376, **A**1 3 5 10 11 29 33 40 45 48 54 75 79 85 93 97 103 107 108 110 114 119 127 130
Primary Contact: Mike Powell, Chief Executive Officer
COO: Isabel Schmedemann R.N., Chief Nursing Officer and Chief Operating Officer
CNO: Isabel Schmedemann R.N., Chief Nursing Officer and Chief Operating Officer
Web address: www.fultonmed.com
Control: Corporation, Investor-owned (for-profit) **Service:** General medical and surgical

Staffed Beds: 37 **Admissions:** 352 **Census:** 11 **Outpatient Visits:** 31897
Births: 0 **Total Expense ($000):** 16630 **Payroll Expense ($000):** 6228

☐ **FULTON STATE HOSPITAL (264004)**, 600 East Fifth Street, Zip 65251–1753; tel. 573/592–4100 **A**1 3 5 10 **F**3 4 11 29 30 39 44 50 53 56 57 58 59 65 75 77 82 86 87 98 100 101 102 103 130 132 135 143 146 149 **P**6
Primary Contact: Robert Reitz, Ph.D., Chief Executive Officer
COO: Anthony Menditto Ph.D., Interim Chief Operating Officer
CFO: Forrest Bud"" H Smith Jr, Chief Financial Officer
CMO: Sanjiv Sethi M.D., Medical Director
CIO: Thomas Gillespie, Chief Information Officer
CHR: Lori Hollinger, Manager Human Resources
CNO: Sherry Lee, Chief Nurse Executive
Web address: www.dmh.missouri.gov/fulton
Control: State, Government, Nonfederal **Service:** Psychiatric

Staffed Beds: 401 **Admissions:** 169 **Census:** 398 **Outpatient Visits:** 0
Births: 0 **Total Expense ($000):** 97554 **Payroll Expense ($000):** 49211
Personnel: 1210

HANNIBAL—Marion County

✉ **HANNIBAL REGIONAL HOSPITAL (260025)**, 6000 Hospital Drive, Zip 63401–6887, Mailing Address: P.O.Box 551, 63401–0551; tel. 573/248–1300 **A**1 2 10 **F**3 13 15 20 22 26 28 29 31 34 35 40 45 47 49 51 57 59 62 64 68 70 74 75 76 78 79 81 85 86 87 89 90 92 107 108 110 111 114 115 117 118 119 120 121 123 124 129 130 132 135 148 **P**1
Primary Contact: C Todd. Ahrens, President and Chief Executive Officer
CFO: Roger J Dix, Vice President Finance
CMO: Bryson McHardy M.D., President Medical Staff
CIO: Jeff W. Evans, Vice President Information and Technology
CHR: Susan R Wathen, Vice President Human Resources
Web address: www.hrhonline.org
Control: Other not-for-profit (including NFP Corporation) **Service:** General medical and surgical

Staffed Beds: 99 **Admissions:** 4081 **Census:** 44 **Outpatient Visits:** 147147
Births: 617 **Total Expense ($000):** 123963 **Payroll Expense ($000):** 53444 **Personnel:** 723

HARRISONVILLE—Cass County

✉ **CASS REGIONAL MEDICAL CENTER (261324)**, 2800 East Rock Haven Road, Zip 64701–4411; tel. 816/380–3474 **A**1 10 18 **F**3 11 12 15 17 18 28 29 30 31 32 34 35 40 43 44 45 46 48 50 54 56 57 59 64 65 66 70 74 75 77 78 79 81 82 84 85 86 92 93 96 97 98 107 111 114 115 119 127 129 130 131 132 133 135 146 147 148 149 **P**6
Primary Contact: John Christopher. Lang, Chief Executive Officer
CFO: Brent Probasco, Chief Financial Officer
CIO: Lester Vohs, Manager Information Systems
CHR: Carla Wallen, Manager Human Resources
CNO: Twila Buckner R.N., Chief Nursing Officer
Web address: www.cassregional.org
Control: County, Government, Nonfederal **Service:** General medical and surgical

Staffed Beds: 35 **Admissions:** 1100 **Census:** 16 **Outpatient Visits:** 110070
Births: 0 **Total Expense ($000):** 62650 **Payroll Expense ($000):** 23992
Personnel: 368

MO

Many Facility Codes have changed. Please refer to the AHA Guide Code Chart. © 2017 AHA Guide

HAYTI—Pemiscot County

PEMISCOT MEMORIAL HEALTH SYSTEM (260070), 946 East Reed Street, Zip 63851–1245, Mailing Address: P.O.Box 489, 63851–0489; tel. 573/359–1372, (Total facility includes 66 beds in nursing home–type unit) **A**10 **F**3 4 11 15 17 28 29 30 34 39 40 50 57 59 64 67 68 70 75 79 81 82 85 87 89 90 93 97 98 99 103 104 107 111 119 127 128 130 133 143 144 146 149 **P**6
Primary Contact: Jim Marshall, Chief Executive Officer and Administrator
CFO: Kerry L Noble, Chief Financial Officer
CHR: Jackie Powell, Director Human Resources
Web address: www.pemiscot.org/
Control: County, Government, Nonfederal **Service**: General medical and surgical

Staffed Beds: 167 **Admissions**: 1455 **Census**: 68 **Outpatient Visits**: 26834 **Births**: 0 **Total Expense ($000)**: 33716 **Payroll Expense ($000)**: 16108 **Personnel**: 431

HERMANN—Gasconade County

HERMANN AREA DISTRICT HOSPITAL (261314), 509 West 18th Street, Zip 65041–1547, Mailing Address: P.O.Box 470, 65041–0470; tel. 573/486–2191 **A**10 18 **F**3 11 15 18 28 29 34 35 40 41 44 45 53 56 57 59 62 64 67 69 71 75 77 78 81 85 86 87 89 90 93 96 97 104 107 110 111 114 119 128 143 146 **P**6
Primary Contact: Dan McKinney, Administrator
COO: Matt Siebert, Assistant Administrator Ancillary Services
CFO: Christine Lewis, Controller
CMO: Michael Rothermich M.D., Chief of Staff
CIO: Jeffrey Wehmeyer, Director Information Technology
CHR: Brandon Hughes, Director Human Resources
CNO: Sue Daller R.N., Assistant Administrator Nursing
Web address: www.hadh.org
Control: Hospital district or authority, Government, Nonfederal **Service**: General medical and surgical

Staffed Beds: 24 **Admissions**: 466 **Census**: 12 **Outpatient Visits**: 60138 **Births**: 0 **Total Expense ($000)**: 19257 **Payroll Expense ($000)**: 9348 **Personnel**: 219

HOUSTON—Texas County

TEXAS COUNTY MEMORIAL HOSPITAL (260024), 1333 South Sam Houston Boulevard, Zip 65483–2046; tel. 417/967–3311 **A**10 20 **F**3 7 13 15 28 29 34 40 45 57 59 62 63 64 70 76 81 85 86 89 93 97 107 110 111 115 119 127 129 130 133 143 148 149 **P**6
Primary Contact: Wesley E. Murray, Chief Executive Officer
CFO: Linda Pamperien, Chief Financial Officer
CMO: Charles Mueller M.D., Chief of Staff
CHR: Anita Kuhn, Controller
Web address: www.tcmh.org
Control: County, Government, Nonfederal **Service**: General medical and surgical

Staffed Beds: 47 **Admissions**: 1348 **Census**: 14 **Outpatient Visits**: 104695 **Births**: 206 **Total Expense ($000)**: 31214 **Payroll Expense ($000)**: 15120 **Personnel**: 337

INDEPENDENCE—Jackson County

CENTERPOINT MEDICAL CENTER (260095), 19600 East 39th Street, Zip 64057–2301; tel. 816/698-7000 **A**1 2 10 **F**3 8 12 13 15 18 20 22 24 26 28 29 30 31 34 35 38 40 43 46 47 48 49 50 52 54 55 57 59 60 64 68 70 72 74 75 76 77 78 79 80 81 82 85 86 87 92 93 107 108 110 111 114 115 117 118 119 120 121 123 126 129 130 131 132 144 145 146 147 148 149 **S** HCA Healthcare, Nashville, TN
Primary Contact: David R. Williams, Chief Executive Officer
COO: Phil Buttell, Chief Operating Officer
CFO: James H Brown, Chief Financial Officer
CMO: Christopher Sullivan M.D., Chief Medical Officer
CIO: Carl Sifers, Director Information Technology and System Services
CHR: Kyla Stoltz, Vice President Human Resources
CNO: Lynn Barrett, Chief Nursing Officer
Web address: www.centerpointmedical.com
Control: Corporation, Investor-owned (for-profit) **Service**: General medical and surgical

Staffed Beds: 221 **Admissions**: 15603 **Census**: 167 **Outpatient Visits**: 158448 **Births**: 1425 **Total Expense ($000)**: 238487 **Payroll Expense ($000)**: 76688 **Personnel**: 1011

JEFFERSON CITY—Cole County

CAPITAL REGION MEDICAL CENTER (260047), 1125 Madison Street, Zip 65101–5200, Mailing Address: P.O. Box 1128, 65102–1128; tel. 573/632–5000 **A**1 3 5 10 12 13 **F**3 5 11 13 15 17 18 20 22 24 26 28 29 30 31 32 34 35 36 38 40 45 47 48 53 54 57 59 61 62 64 65 66 70 73 74 75 76 77 78 79 80 81 85 87 89 90 92 93 94 97 100 107 108 110 111 114 115 118 119 120 121 123 132 134 146 147 148 149 150 **P**2 6 **S** University of Missouri Health Care, Columbia, MO
Primary Contact: Gaspare Calvaruso, President
COO: Janet Weckenborg, Vice President Operations
CFO: Tom Luebbering, Vice President Finance
CMO: Mitchell Godbee, Chief of Staff
CIO: Jason Cecil, Vice President, Information
CHR: Sarah Morrow, Vice President Human Resources
Web address: www.crmc.org
Control: Other not-for-profit (including NFP Corporation) **Service**: General medical and surgical

Staffed Beds: 114 **Admissions**: 4782 **Census**: 50 **Outpatient Visits**: 459866 **Births**: 658 **Total Expense ($000)**: 181307 **Payroll Expense ($000)**: 80285 **Personnel**: 1252

SSM HEALTH ST. MARY'S HOSPITAL - JEFFERSON CITY (260011), 2505 Mission Drive, Zip 65109; tel. 573/681–3000 **A**1 10 19 **F**3 4 5 11 12 13 15 17 18 20 22 24 28 29 30 31 34 40 45 46 47 48 49 50 51 54 57 59 60 64 68 70 73 74 75 76 77 78 79 81 82 85 86 87 89 93 96 98 100 101 102 104 107 108 110 111 115 118 119 120 121 122 123 127 129 130 131 132 135 141 144 146 147 148 149 150 **P**6 **S** SSM Health, Saint Louis, MO
Primary Contact: R Brent. VanConia, President
CFO: James Stratton, Vice President Finance
CMO: Stephen Stewart M.D., Vice President Medical Affairs
CHR: Susan Mankoski, Vice President Human Resources
CNO: Alice M Chatley R.N., MSN, Vice President Acute Care Services
Web address: www.lethealingbegin.com
Control: Church operated, Nongovernment, not-for-profit **Service**: General medical and surgical

Staffed Beds: 139 **Admissions**: 7111 **Census**: 75 **Outpatient Visits**: 221222 **Births**: 912 **Total Expense ($000)**: 172937 **Payroll Expense ($000)**: 51563 **Personnel**: 898

JOPLIN—Newton County

FREEMAN HEALTH SYSTEM (260137), 1102 West 32nd Street, Zip 64804–3503; tel. 417/347–1111, (Includes FREEMAN HOSPITAL EAST, 932 East 34th Street, Joplin, Missouri, Zip 64804–3999, 1102 West 32nd Street, 64804–3999, tel. 417/347–1111; Paula F Baker, President and Chief Executive Officer) **A**10 11 13 **F**3 8 11 12 13 15 17 18 20 22 24 26 28 30 31 34 35 40 42 43 44 45 46 47 48 49 50 54 56 57 59 60 61 62 64 65 68 70 72 73 74 75 76 77 78 79 81 82 84 85 86 87 89 90 93 96 97 98 100 102 103 107 108 110 111 115 117 119 120 121 124 129 130 131 132 144 145 146 147 148 **P**1 6 **S** Freeman Health System, Joplin, MO
Primary Contact: Paula F. Baker, President and Chief Executive Officer
CFO: Steve W Graddy, Chief Financial Officer
CMO: Saba Habis M.D., Chief Medical Officer
CIO: Skip Rollins, Chief Information Officer
CHR: Mary Frerer, Chief Human Resources Officer
CNO: Jeffrey Carrier R.N., Chief Clinical Officer
Web address: www.freemanhealth.com
Control: Other not-for-profit (including NFP Corporation) **Service**: General medical and surgical

Staffed Beds: 391 **Admissions**: 17123 **Census**: 243 **Outpatient Visits**: 760612 **Births**: 2096 **Total Expense ($000)**: 475759 **Payroll Expense ($000)**: 219165 **Personnel**: 3198

LANDMARK HOSPITAL OF JOPLIN (262016), 2040 West 32nd Street, Zip 64804–3512; tel. 417/627–1300 **A**10 22 **F**1 3 44 60 75 83 87 90 119 130 148 **S** Landmark Hospitals, Cape Girardeau, MO
Primary Contact: Kevin J. Clement, Chief Executive Officer
CMO: Jack Rhoads M.D., Medical Director
CHR: Janice Nordstrom, Director Human Resources
CNO: Stephanie Slater-Nesuold, Director of Nursing
Web address: www.landmarkhospitals.com
Control: Corporation, Investor-owned (for-profit) **Service**: Acute long-term care hospital

Staffed Beds: 30 **Admissions**: 343 **Census**: 23 **Outpatient Visits**: 0 **Births**: 0 **Total Expense ($000)**: 13110 **Payroll Expense ($000)**: 5336

MO

Hospital, Medicare Provider Number, Address, Telephone, Approval, Facility, and Physician Codes, Health Care System

★ American Hospital Association (AHA) membership ◯ Healthcare Facilities Accreditation Program ⇑ Center for Improvement in Healthcare Quality Accreditation
☐ The Joint Commission accreditation ◇ DNV Healthcare Inc. accreditation △ Commission on Accreditation of Rehabilitation Facilities (CARF) accreditation

© 2017 AHA Guide *Many Facility Codes have changed. Please refer to the AHA Guide Code Chart.* Hospitals **A369**

✠ **MERCY HOSPITAL JOPLIN (260001)**, 100 Mercy Way, Zip 64804–1626; tel. 417/781–2727, (Includes ST. JOHN'S REHABILITATION CENTER, 2727 McClelland Boulevard, Joplin, Missouri, Zip 64804, tel. 417/659–6716) **A**1 2 10 13 **F**3 5 7 11 12 13 15 17 18 19 20 22 24 26 28 29 30 31 34 35 38 39 40 43 44 45 46 47 48 49 50 54 57 58 59 60 61 62 63 64 65 66 68 70 72 73 74 75 76 77 78 79 81 82 84 85 86 87 89 93 94 97 98 100 101 102 103 104 105 107 110 111 114 115 117 118 119 120 121 123 124 126 127 129 130 131 132 135 144 146 147 148 **P**6 **S** Mercy, Chesterfield, MO
Primary Contact: Gary W. Pulsipher, President and Chief Executive Officer
COO: Michele Stewart R.N., Chief Operating Officer
CFO: Shelly Hunter, Chief Financial Officer
CHR: Timothy Murphy, Vice President Human Resources
CNO: Dennis Manley R.N., Chief Nursing Officer
Web address: www.mercy.net/joplinmo
Control: Church operated, Nongovernment, not-for-profit **Service:** General medical and surgical

Staffed Beds: 240 **Admissions:** 9351 **Census:** 135 **Outpatient Visits:** 269450 **Births:** 1100 **Total Expense ($000):** 240288 **Payroll Expense ($000):** 89792 **Personnel:** 1368	

KANSAS CITY—Clay County

SIGNATURE PSYCHIATRIC HOSPITAL (264030), 2900 Clay Edwards Drive, Zip 64116–3235; tel. 816/691–5101 **F**2 34 59 98 101 102 103 104 105 130 132
Primary Contact: Lisa St. Aubyn, Chief Executive Officer
CFO: Tariq F Malik CPA, Chief Financial Officer
CMO: Azfar Malik M.D., Chief Medical Officer
CIO: Mike Solom, Director Information Technology
CHR: Sheila Shipley, Human Resources Educator
Web address: www.signaturepsychiatrichospitalkc.com
Control: Corporation, Investor-owned (for-profit) **Service:** Psychiatric

Staffed Beds: 24 **Admissions:** 1271 **Census:** 21 **Outpatient Visits:** 0 **Births:** 0 **Total Expense ($000):** 6799 **Payroll Expense ($000):** 3423 **Personnel:** 62	

KANSAS CITY—Jackson County

☐ **CENTER FOR BEHAVIORAL MEDICINE (264008)**, 1000 East 24th Street, Zip 64108–2776; tel. 816/512–7000, (Total facility includes 68 beds in nursing home–type unit) **A**1 3 5 10 **F**4 29 35 36 38 50 53 86 87 98 128
Primary Contact: Denise Norbury, Regional Chief Executive Officer
COO: Jeanette Simmons, Chief Operating Officer
CFO: Randy Riley, Chief Financial Officer
CMO: Nashaat Boutros M.D., Clinical Director
CIO: Robert Curren, Director Information Technology
CHR: Silva Ward, Director Human Resources
CNO: John Tucker, Chief Nursing Executive
Web address: www.dmhonline.dmh.state.mo.us
Control: State, Government, Nonfederal **Service:** Psychiatric

Staffed Beds: 133 **Admissions:** 75 **Census:** 120 **Outpatient Visits:** 0 **Births:** 0 **Total Expense ($000):** 24081 **Payroll Expense ($000):** 13222 **Personnel:** 391	

✠ **CHILDREN'S MERCY HOSPITAL KANSAS CITY (263302)**, 2401 Gillham Road, Zip 64108–4619; tel. 816/234–3000 **A**1 2 3 5 8 10 **F**3 7 8 9 11 12 16 19 20 21 22 23 24 25 26 27 29 30 31 32 34 35 36 39 40 41 43 44 48 50 54 55 57 58 59 60 61 62 64 65 68 72 73 74 75 77 78 79 81 82 84 85 86 87 88 89 90 91 92 93 94 96 97 100 101 104 107 108 111 115 117 118 119 130 131 132 134 136 137 138 139 141 142 144 146 148 149 150 **P**6
Primary Contact: Randall L. O'Donnell, Ph.D., President and Chief Executive Officer
COO: Jo W Stueve, Executive Vice President and Co-Chief Operating Officer
CFO: Sandra A J Lawrence, Executive Vice President and Chief Financial Officer
CMO: Charles Roberts M.D., Executive Vice President and Executive Medical Director
CIO: Jean Ann Breedlove, Chief Information Officer
CNO: Cheri Hunt R.N., Vice President Patient Care Services and Chief Nursing Officer
Web address: www.childrensmercy.org
Control: Other not-for-profit (including NFP Corporation) **Service:** Children's general medical and surgical

Staffed Beds: 301 **Admissions:** 11771 **Census:** 221 **Outpatient Visits:** 442079 **Births:** 154 **Total Expense ($000):** 1050629 **Payroll Expense ($000):** 513982 **Personnel:** 5506	

✠ **KANSAS CITY VETERANS AFFAIRS MEDICAL CENTER**, 4801 East Linwood Boulevard, Zip 64128–2226; tel. 816/861–4700, (Nonreporting) **A**1 2 3 5 **S** Department of Veterans Affairs, Washington, DC
Primary Contact: Kathleen R. Fogarty, MS, Director
CFO: Bryan Bieri, Manager Finance
CMO: Ahmad Batrash, Chief of Staff
CIO: Eddie Johnson, Chief Information Technology Officer
CHR: Kathi Nippert, Acting Chief Human Resources Officer
Web address: www.kansascity.va.gov/
Control: Veterans Affairs, Government, federal **Service:** General medical and surgical

Staffed Beds: 157	

✠ **KINDRED HOSPITAL KANSAS CITY (262011)**, 8701 Troost Avenue, Zip 64131–2767; tel. 816/995–2000 **A**1 10 **F**1 18 29 56 70 82 85 100 107 130 143 148 **S** Kindred Healthcare, Louisville, KY
Primary Contact: Jason Grundstrom, Interim Chief Executive Officer
CFO: Brett Stevenson, Controller
Web address: www.kindredhospitalkc.com
Control: Corporation, Investor-owned (for-profit) **Service:** Acute long-term care hospital

Staffed Beds: 55 **Admissions:** 404 **Census:** 45 **Outpatient Visits:** 0 **Births:** 0 **Total Expense ($000):** 31848 **Payroll Expense ($000):** 10412 **Personnel:** 124	

✠ **KINDRED HOSPITAL NORTHLAND (262018)**, 500 Northwest 68th Street, Zip 64118–2455; tel. 816/420–6300 **A**1 10 **F**1 3 28 29 80 82 85 90 130 135 142 148 149 **S** Kindred Healthcare, Louisville, KY
Primary Contact: Jason Grundstrom, Chief Executive Officer
CFO: Brett Stevenson, Controller
CMO: Sean R Muldoon M.D., Senior Vice President and Chief Medical Officer-Kindred Healthcare, Hospital Division
CNO: Laura Inge, Chief Clinical Officer
Web address: www.khnorthland.com
Control: Corporation, Investor-owned (for-profit) **Service:** Acute long-term care hospital

Staffed Beds: 35 **Admissions:** 406 **Census:** 31 **Outpatient Visits:** 0 **Births:** 0 **Total Expense ($000):** 17949 **Payroll Expense ($000):** 7083 **Personnel:** 118	

NORTHLAND LTAC HOSPITAL See Kindred Hospital Northland

✠ **RESEARCH MEDICAL CENTER (260027)**, 2316 East Meyer Boulevard, Zip 64132–1136; tel. 816/276–4000, (Includes RESEARCH PSYCHIATRIC CENTER, 2323 East 63rd Street, Kansas City, Missouri, Zip 64130–3462, tel. 816/444–8161; Shannon Griggs, Interim Chief Executive Officer) **A**1 2 3 5 10 **F**3 4 5 8 11 13 15 16 17 18 20 22 24 26 28 29 30 31 34 35 38 39 40 42 43 44 45 46 47 49 50 52 53 54 55 57 58 59 60 61 64 68 70 72 73 74 75 76 77 78 79 81 82 84 85 86 87 90 91 93 94 96 97 98 99 100 101 102 103 104 105 107 108 110 111 112 114 115 116 117 118 119 120 121 122 124 126 129 130 131 132 134 135 138 142 143 146 147 148 149 **S** HCA Healthcare, Nashville, TN
Primary Contact: Jacqueline DeSouza, Chief Executive Officer
COO: Eric Becker, Chief Operating Officer
CFO: Susan Shreeve, Chief Financial Officer
CMO: James Bower M.D., Chief Medical Officer
CIO: Shawn Kegley, Director Information Services
CHR: Charlotte O'Neal, Vice President Human Resources
Web address: www.researchmedicalcenter.com
Control: Corporation, Investor-owned (for-profit) **Service:** General medical and surgical

Staffed Beds: 456 **Admissions:** 19779 **Census:** 304 **Outpatient Visits:** 172437 **Births:** 1074 **Total Expense ($000):** 436802 **Payroll Expense ($000):** 126869 **Personnel:** 2245	

✠ **SAINT LUKE'S HOSPITAL OF KANSAS CITY (260138)**, 4401 Wornall Road, Zip 64111–3220; tel. 816/932–3800, (Includes CRITTENTON CHILDREN'S CENTER, 10918 Elm Avenue, Kansas City, Missouri, Zip 64134–4108, tel. 816/765–6600; Janine Hron, Chief Executive Officer) **A**1 2 3 5 8 10 **F**3 5 6 8 9 11 12 13 15 17 18 20 22 24 25 26 28 29 30 31 32 34 35 36 37 38 39 40 43 44 45 46 47 48 49 50 55 56 57 58 59 60 61 64 65 66 68 70 71 72 73 74 75 76 77 78 79 80 81 82 84 85 86 87 89 90 91 92 93 94 95 96 97 98 99 100 101 102 103 104 106 107 108 110 111 114 115 116 117 118 119 120 121 123 124 126 129 130 131 132 134 135 137 138 139 141 145 146 147 148 149 **P**6 **S** Saint Luke's Health System, Kansas City, MO
Primary Contact: Jani L. Johnson, R.N., MSN, Chief Executive Officer
COO: Brad Simmons, Chief Operating Officer
CFO: Amy Nachtigal, Chief Financial Officer
CMO: Peter Holt M.D., Director Medical Affairs
CIO: Deborah Gash, Chief Information Officer
CHR: Doris Rogers, Vice President Human Resources
CNO: Debra Wilson, Vice President and Chief Nursing Officer
Web address: www.saint-lukes.org
Control: Church operated, Nongovernment, not-for-profit **Service:** General medical and surgical

Staffed Beds: 501 **Admissions:** 22571 **Census:** 361 **Outpatient Visits:** 258498 **Births:** 2517 **Total Expense ($000):** 710211 **Payroll Expense ($000):** 184777 **Personnel:** 3110	

Many Facility Codes have changed. Please refer to the AHA Guide Code Chart.

© 2017 AHA Guide

⊞ **SELECT SPECIALTY HOSPITAL-WESTERN MISSOURI (262014)**, 2316 East Meyer Boulevard, 3 West, Zip 64132–1136; tel. 816/276–3300 **A1** 10 **F1** 3 29 148 **S** Select Medical Corporation, Mechanicsburg, PA
Primary Contact: Kerry McLane, Interim Chief Executive Officer
Web address: www.westernmissouri.selectspecialtyhospitals.com/
Control: Corporation, Investor-owned (for-profit) **Service:** Acute long-term care hospital

Staffed Beds: 34 **Admissions:** 333 **Census:** 24 **Outpatient Visits:** 0
Births: 0 **Total Expense ($000):** 14265 **Payroll Expense ($000):** 5975
Personnel: 91

⊞ **ST. JOSEPH MEDICAL CENTER (260085)**, 1000 Carondelet Drive, Zip 64114–4673; tel. 816/942–4400 **A1** 2 3 10 **F3** 11 12 13 15 17 18 20 22 24 26 28 29 30 31 34 35 40 45 47 49 50 51 57 58 59 60 64 68 70 72 74 75 76 77 78 79 80 81 82 84 85 87 90 93 96 107 108 110 111 114 115 116 118 119 129 130 132 146 147 148 **P6 S** Prime Healthcare, Ontario, CA
Primary Contact: Jodi Fincher, Administrator
CFO: Debra Cartwright, Chief Financial Officer
CMO: Tommy Ko M.D., Chief Medical Officer
CIO: Cheryl Johnson, Regional Chief Information Officer
CHR: Donna Sumner, Director, Human Resources and Organizational Development
CNO: Greg Simpson, Chief Nursing Officer
Web address: www.stjosephkc.com/
Control: Individual, Investor-owned (for-profit) **Service:** General medical and surgical

Staffed Beds: 185 **Admissions:** 7804 **Census:** 94 **Outpatient Visits:** 98157
Births: 444 **Total Expense ($000):** 174542 **Payroll Expense ($000):** 53707 **Personnel:** 1013

⊞ **TRUMAN MEDICAL CENTER-HOSPITAL HILL (260048)**, 2301 Holmes Street, Zip 64108–2640; tel. 816/404–1000 **A1** 2 3 5 8 10 13 **F3** 4 5 8 11 12 13 14 15 17 20 22 26 28 29 30 31 34 35 36 37 38 39 40 41 43 44 45 46 48 49 50 52 53 55 57 58 59 61 64 65 66 68 70 71 72 73 74 75 76 77 78 79 81 82 84 85 86 90 93 94 97 98 99 100 101 102 103 104 107 108 110 111 114 115 119 129 130 131 132 134 135 143 146 147 148 **P5 6 S** Truman Medical Centers, Kansas City, MO
Primary Contact: Charlie Shields, President and Chief Executive Officer
CFO: Allen Johnson, Chief Financial Officer
CMO: Mark Steele M.D., Chief Medical Officer
CIO: Mitzi Cardenas, Chief Information Officer
CHR: Marcos DeLeon, Vice President Community Engagement
Web address: www.trumed.org
Control: Other not-for-profit (including NFP Corporation) **Service:** General medical and surgical

Staffed Beds: 249 **Admissions:** 14519 **Census:** 199 **Outpatient Visits:** 621092 **Births:** 1759 **Total Expense ($000):** 375884 **Payroll Expense ($000):** 135608 **Personnel:** 2468

⊞ **TRUMAN MEDICAL CENTER-LAKEWOOD (260102)**, 7900 Lee's Summit Road, Zip 64139–1236; tel. 816/404–7000, (Total facility includes 188 beds in nursing home–type unit) **A1** 3 5 10 **F3** 4 5 6 11 13 15 18 29 30 32 34 35 36 38 39 40 44 45 50 53 56 57 58 59 64 65 66 67 68 70 71 72 74 75 76 77 78 79 81 85 86 87 89 90 92 93 94 97 98 99 100 101 102 103 104 107 112 115 119 126 128 129 130 131 132 134 135 143 146 147 **P5 6 S** Truman Medical Centers, Kansas City, MO
Primary Contact: Lynette Wheeler, MSN, Chief Operating Officer
CFO: Allen Johnson, Chief Financial Officer
CMO: Mark Steele M.D., Chief Medical Officer
CIO: Mitzi Cardenas, Chief Information Officer
CHR: Marcos DeLeon, Vice President Community Engagement
CNO: Amy Peters R.N., Chief Nursing Officer
Web address: www.trumed.org
Control: Other not-for-profit (including NFP Corporation) **Service:** General medical and surgical

Staffed Beds: 298 **Admissions:** 4426 **Census:** 222 **Outpatient Visits:** 424597 **Births:** 1412 **Total Expense ($000):** 140357 **Payroll Expense ($000):** 58991 **Personnel:** 1005

⊞ **TWO RIVERS BEHAVIORAL HEALTH SYSTEM (264017)**, 5121 Raytown Road, Zip 64133–2141; tel. 816/382–6300 **A1** 10 **F4** 5 34 75 98 99 101 102 103 104 105 130 132 143 149 **P6 S** Universal Health Services, Inc., King of Prussia, PA
Primary Contact: Greg Shannon, Interim Chief Executive Officer
CFO: Teresa Martin, Chief Financial Officer
CMO: Shahbaz Khan M.D., Medical Director
CHR: Diane Peoples, Director Human Resources
CNO: Kristie Baker, Chief Nursing Officer
Web address: www.tworivershospital.com
Control: Corporation, Investor-owned (for-profit) **Service:** Psychiatric

Staffed Beds: 105 **Admissions:** 2508 **Census:** 38 **Outpatient Visits:** 0
Births: 0 **Total Expense ($000):** 16376 **Payroll Expense ($000):** 7991
Personnel: 138

VETERANS AFFAIRS MEDICAL CENTER See Kansas City Veterans Affairs Medical Center

KANSAS CITY—Platte County

⊞ **SAINT LUKE'S NORTH HOSPITAL - BARRY ROAD (260062)**, 5830 NW Barry Road, Zip 64154–2778; tel. 816/891–6000, (Includes SAINT LUKE'S NORTH HOSPITAL-SMITHVILLE CAMPUS, 601 South 169 Highway, Smithville, Missouri, Zip 64089–9317, tel. 816/532–3700; Adele Ducharme, MSN, R.N., Interim Chief Executive Officer) **A1** 2 10 **F3** 11 13 15 18 20 22 26 28 29 30 31 34 35 36 38 40 44 45 46 49 50 53 57 58 59 60 64 65 69 70 73 74 75 76 77 78 79 80 81 82 84 85 86 87 89 90 92 93 96 98 99 100 101 102 103 107 108 110 111 114 115 116 117 118 119 129 130 131 132 135 141 143 146 147 148 149 **S** Saint Luke's Health System, Kansas City, MO
Primary Contact: Adele Ducharme, MSN, R.N., Interim Chief Executive Officer
CFO: Julie Murphy, Chief Financial Officer
CMO: Leonardo J Lozada M.D., Chief Physician Executive
CIO: LaDonna Seger, Director Information Services
CHR: Donna Kunz, System Director Human Resources
CNO: Amy Brummer R.N., MSN, Chief Nursing Officer
Web address: www.saint-lukes.org
Control: Church operated, Nongovernment, not-for-profit **Service:** General medical and surgical

Staffed Beds: 141 **Admissions:** 7565 **Census:** 83 **Outpatient Visits:** 92121
Births: 829 **Total Expense ($000):** 128581 **Payroll Expense ($000):** 40088 **Personnel:** 653

KENNETT—Dunklin County

⊞ **TWIN RIVERS REGIONAL MEDICAL CENTER (260015)**, 1301 First Street, Zip 63857–2508, Mailing Address: P.O.Box 728, 63857–0728; tel. 573/888–4522 **A1** 10 **F3** 11 13 15 18 29 30 31 35 40 50 56 57 59 60 64 68 70 75 76 78 79 81 85 89 90 98 99 100 101 102 103 104 107 108 110 111 114 115 117 119 127 129 130 135 147 148 149 **P5 S** Community Health Systems, Inc., Franklin, TN
Primary Contact: Christian Jones, Chief Executive Officer
CFO: Michelle Beachman, Chief Financial Officer
CHR: Mark Niemeier, Director Human Resources
CNO: Judy Haney, Chief Nursing Officer
Web address: www.twinriversregional.com
Control: Corporation, Investor-owned (for-profit) **Service:** General medical and surgical

Staffed Beds: 100 **Admissions:** 2820 **Census:** 27 **Outpatient Visits:** 75716
Births: 358 **Total Expense ($000):** 45994 **Payroll Expense ($000):** 13663
Personnel: 280

KIRKSVILLE—Adair County

★ ○ **NORTHEAST REGIONAL MEDICAL CENTER (260022)**, 315 South Osteopathy, Zip 63501–6401, Mailing Address: P.O.Box C8502, 63501–8599; tel. 660/785–1000 **A3** 10 11 12 13 **F3** 13 15 18 20 22 24 28 29 30 34 35 36 40 43 45 46 48 49 50 53 57 59 60 62 64 68 70 73 74 75 76 77 79 81 82 85 86 87 89 90 93 107 108 110 111 115 119 127 129 130 131 132 133 135 146 147 148 **P5 S** Community Health Systems, Inc., Franklin, TN
Primary Contact: Ranee C. Brayton, FACHE, R.N., MSN, Chief Executive Officer
CFO: Carol Cross CPA, Chief Financial Officer
CMO: Brent Speak, Chief of Staff
CIO: Chad Tatro, Supervisor Information Systems
CHR: Jim Bergman, Director Human Resources
CNO: Mary Knudsen, Chief Nursing Officer
Web address: www.nermc.com
Control: Corporation, Investor-owned (for-profit) **Service:** General medical and surgical

Staffed Beds: 93 **Admissions:** 2449 **Census:** 27 **Outpatient Visits:** 81197
Births: 504 **Total Expense ($000):** 51120 **Payroll Expense ($000):** 18804
Personnel: 415

MO

Hospital, Medicare Provider Number, Address, Telephone, Approval, Facility, and Physician Codes, Health Care System

★ American Hospital Association (AHA) membership   ○ Healthcare Facilities Accreditation Program   ⇑ Center for Improvement in Healthcare Quality Accreditation
□ The Joint Commission accreditation   ◇ DNV Healthcare Inc. accreditation   △ Commission on Accreditation of Rehabilitation Facilities (CARF) accreditation

MO

LAKE SAINT LOUIS—St. Charles County

✠ **SSM HEALTH ST. JOSEPH HOSPITAL - LAKE SAINT LOUIS (260200)**, 100 Medical Plaza, Zip 63367–1366; tel. 636/625–5200 **A**1 2 10 **F**3 11 13 15 17 18 20 22 28 29 30 31 34 35 36 38 40 41 43 44 49 50 51 53 54 55 56 57 59 60 61 64 68 70 73 74 75 76 78 79 81 82 84 85 86 87 89 102 107 108 110 111 114 115 117 119 129 130 132 135 145 146 147 148 149 **P**6 8 **S** SSM Health, Saint Louis, MO
Primary Contact: Lisle Wescott, President
COO: Lee Bernstein, Regional Executive Vice President of Hospital and Chief Operating Officer
CFO: Hal Holder, Regional Chief Financial Officer
CMO: Michael Handler M.D., Vice President Medical Affairs and Chief Medical Officer
CIO: Sharon Gardner, Manager Information Systems
CHR: Renee Roach, System Vice President
CNO: Janet K. Pestle R.N., MSN, Vice President Nursing and Chief Nursing Officer
Web address: www.ssmstjoseph.com
Control: Church operated, Nongovernment, not-for-profit **Service**: General medical and surgical

Staffed Beds: 119 **Admissions:** 8591 **Census:** 91 **Outpatient Visits:** 175590 **Births:** 921 **Total Expense ($000):** 150207 **Payroll Expense ($000):** 55022 **Personnel:** 806

LAMAR—Barton County

BARTON COUNTY MEMORIAL HOSPITAL (261325), 29 NW First Lane, Zip 64759–8105; tel. 417/681–5100 **A**10 18 **F**3 11 15 18 28 30 34 35 36 40 44 45 50 57 59 64 65 68 74 75 77 79 81 84 85 86 87 89 90 92 93 97 107 108 110 111 114 119 127 128 129 130 132 133 135 146 148 149
Primary Contact: Wendy Duvall, Chief Executive Officer
CIO: Brad Butler, Network Administrator
CHR: Sheila Boice, Director Human Resources
CNO: Marlys Buckner, Chief Nursing Officer
Web address: www.bcmh.net
Control: County, Government, Nonfederal **Service**: General medical and surgical

Staffed Beds: 25 **Admissions:** 736 **Census:** 8 **Outpatient Visits:** 43568 **Births:** 0 **Total Expense ($000):** 18008 **Payroll Expense ($000):** 7386 **Personnel:** 153

LEBANON—Laclede County

✠ **MERCY HOSPITAL LEBANON (260059)**, 100 Hospital Drive, Zip 65536–9210; tel. 417/533–6100 **A**1 10 20 **F**3 11 13 15 28 29 30 31 35 36 40 45 47 50 51 53 57 59 64 65 68 70 71 74 75 76 77 78 79 81 82 83 85 86 87 89 90 93 94 102 107 108 110 111 114 119 129 130 131 132 135 146 147 148 149 **P**6 **S** Mercy, Chesterfield, MO
Primary Contact: Scott W. Childers, Administrator
CFO: Douglas M Hoban, Vice President and Chief Financial Officer
CNO: Judy O'Connor-Snyder, Chief Nursing Officer
Web address: www.mercy.net/practice/mercy-hospital-lebanon
Control: Church operated, Nongovernment, not-for-profit **Service**: General medical and surgical

Staffed Beds: 58 **Admissions:** 2283 **Census:** 17 **Outpatient Visits:** 135675 **Births:** 379 **Total Expense ($000):** 69761 **Payroll Expense ($000):** 27170 **Personnel:** 465

LEE'S SUMMIT—Jackson County

✠ **LEE'S SUMMIT MEDICAL CENTER (260190)**, 2100 SE Blue Parkway, Zip 64063–1007; tel. 816/282–5000 **A**1 10 **F**3 15 18 20 22 28 29 30 31 34 40 43 49 57 59 60 64 65 68 69 70 74 75 77 78 79 81 82 84 85 87 93 107 108 109 110 111 115 119 126 129 130 131 132 145 146 148 149 **S** HCA Healthcare, Nashville, TN
Primary Contact: Matt Sogard, Chief Executive Officer
CFO: John Heurtin, Chief Financial Officer
CIO: Andrew Beechy, Manager Information Technology Systems
CHR: Linda Duncan, Director Human Resources
CNO: Paige Baker MSN, R.N., Chief Nursing Officer
Web address: www.leessummitmedicalcenter.com
Control: Corporation, Investor-owned (for-profit) **Service**: General medical and surgical

Staffed Beds: 64 **Admissions:** 3946 **Census:** 37 **Outpatient Visits:** 103328 **Births:** 0 **Total Expense ($000):** 90785 **Payroll Expense ($000):** 35222 **Personnel:** 303

SAINT LUKE'S EAST HOSPITAL (260216)

✠ **SAINT LUKE'S EAST HOSPITAL (260216)**, 100 NE Saint Luke's Boulevard, Zip 64086–6000; tel. 816/347–5000 **A**1 10 **F**3 13 15 18 20 22 26 28 29 30 31 34 35 38 40 43 44 45 46 49 50 56 57 58 59 60 64 65 70 71 72 73 74 75 76 77 78 79 80 81 82 84 85 86 87 90 91 92 93 94 96 100 102 107 108 110 111 114 115 117 118 119 121 123 126 129 130 131 132 135 145 146 147 148 149 **S** Saint Luke's Health System, Kansas City, MO
Primary Contact: Ron Baker, FACHE, Chief Executive Officer
CFO: Joseph P Stasi, Chief Financial Officer
CHR: John Clabaugh, Director Human Resources
CNO: Gloria Solis R.N., MSN, Chief Nursing Officer
Web address: www.saintlukeskc.org
Control: Church operated, Nongovernment, not-for-profit **Service**: General medical and surgical

Staffed Beds: 203 **Admissions:** 12738 **Census:** 132 **Outpatient Visits:** 146013 **Births:** 2159 **Total Expense ($000):** 215108 **Payroll Expense ($000):** 59417 **Personnel:** 961

LEXINGTON—Lafayette County

✠ **LAFAYETTE REGIONAL HEALTH CENTER (261320)**, 1500 State Street, Zip 64067–1107; tel. 660/259–2203 **A**1 10 18 **F**11 15 29 31 40 64 68 70 75 78 79 81 85 93 107 110 111 114 116 119 127 129 130 133 147 149 **P**6 **S** HCA Healthcare, Nashville, TN
Primary Contact: Darrel Box, Chief Executive Officer
COO: Daniel Astleford, Vice President Operations
CFO: Teri James, Chief Financial Officer
CIO: Keith Richcreek, Manager Technical Services
CHR: Stephen Davidson, Director Human Resources
CNO: Kim Leakey R.N., Chief Nursing Officer
Web address: www.lafayetteregionalhealthcenter.com
Control: Corporation, Investor-owned (for-profit) **Service**: General medical and surgical

Staffed Beds: 25 **Admissions:** 960 **Census:** 9 **Outpatient Visits:** 66333 **Births:** 0 **Total Expense ($000):** 27371 **Payroll Expense ($000):** 9256 **Personnel:** 190

LIBERTY—Clay County

✠ **LIBERTY HOSPITAL (260177)**, 2525 Glenn Hendren Drive, Zip 64068–9600, Mailing Address: P.O.Box 1002, 64069–1002; tel. 816/781–7200 **A**1 2 10 **F**3 8 9 11 13 15 17 18 20 22 24 28 29 30 31 34 35 37 40 43 44 45 46 47 49 51 53 54 59 61 62 63 64 65 68 69 70 73 74 75 76 77 78 79 80 81 82 83 84 85 86 87 89 90 92 93 96 97 107 108 110 111 114 115 117 118 119 126 129 130 131 135 144 146 147 148
Primary Contact: David Feess, President and Chief Executive Officer
CFO: Dan Williams, Vice President Finance and Support
CMO: Robert Haas M.D., Chief Medical Officer
CIO: Paul Klehn, Chief Information Technology Officer
CHR: Nancy E Cattell, Vice President Human Resources
CNO: Shirley Heintz R.N., MS, Vice President Patient Care
Web address: www.Libertyhospital.org
Control: Hospital district or authority, Government, Nonfederal **Service**: General medical and surgical

Staffed Beds: 225 **Admissions:** 8632 **Census:** 91 **Outpatient Visits:** 287678 **Births:** 1147 **Total Expense ($000):** 190683 **Payroll Expense ($000):** 88933 **Personnel:** 1231

LOUISIANA—Pike County

✠ **PIKE COUNTY MEMORIAL HOSPITAL (261333)**, 2305 Georgia Street, Zip 63353–2559; tel. 573/754–5531 **A**1 10 18 **F**3 7 11 15 18 28 29 30 34 35 40 45 50 53 54 56 57 59 64 65 68 74 75 77 79 81 85 86 87 89 90 93 97 100 107 110 114 127 130 131 132 133 147 148 149
Primary Contact: Justin Selle, Chief Executive Officer
CFO: Ann Tran, Chief Financial Officer
CIO: Jeremy Gruen, Director Information Systems
CHR: Connie Bair, Human Resources Assistant
CNO: Judith Prater, Director of Nursing
Web address: www.pcmh-mo.org
Control: County, Government, Nonfederal **Service**: General medical and surgical

Staffed Beds: 25 **Admissions:** 459 **Census:** 6 **Outpatient Visits:** 40414 **Births:** 0 **Total Expense ($000):** 17089 **Payroll Expense ($000):** 7554 **Personnel:** 164

Many Facility Codes have changed. Please refer to the AHA Guide Code Chart. © 2017 AHA Guide

MACON—Macon County

★ **SAMARITAN HOSPITAL (261313)**, 1205 North Missouri Street, Zip 63552–2095; tel. 660/385–8700 **A**10 18 F3 7 8 11 31 34 35 40 45 46 53 56 57 59 63 64 65 68 71 74 75 77 78 79 81 82 84 85 86 87 89 90 93 94 107 111 115 119 127 128 129 130 133 143 146 148 **P**5
Primary Contact: Bernard A. Orman Jr, FACHE, Chief Executive Officer
CFO: Susan Spencer, Chief Financial Officer
CHR: Suzanne Britt, Director Human Resources
Web address: www.samaritanhospital.net
Control: County, Government, Nonfederal **Service:** General medical and surgical

Staffed Beds: 25 Admissions: 813 Census: 15 Outpatient Visits: 63130 Births: 0 Total Expense ($000): 27097 Payroll Expense ($000): 9390 Personnel: 202

MARSHALL—Saline County

★ **FITZGIBBON HOSPITAL (260142)**, 2305 South 65 Highway, Zip 65340–0250, Mailing Address: P.O.Box 250, 65340–0250; tel. 660/886–7431 **A**5 10 20 F3 11 13 15 30 31 33 34 35 40 45 50 57 59 62 63 64 68 70 74 75 76 77 78 79 81 82 85 87 89 90 93 98 103 104 107 110 111 115 117 118 119 120 121 127 128 129 130 131 132 133 143 146 147 148
Primary Contact: Darin L. Haug, D.O., President and Chief Executive Officer
COO: Angela P. Littrell CPA, Chief Financial Officer and Chief Operating Officer
CFO: Angela P. Littrell CPA, Chief Financial Officer and Chief Operating Officer
CMO: Darin L. Haug D.O., President & Chief Executive Officer
CIO: Tom Jones, Chief Information Officer
CHR: Jessica Henderson, Employee Relations Specialist
CNO: Angela Igo MSN, R.N., Chief Nursing Officer
Web address: www.fitzgibbon.org
Control: Other not-for-profit (including NFP Corporation) **Service:** General medical and surgical

Staffed Beds: 52 Admissions: 1838 Census: 17 Outpatient Visits: 117604 Births: 244 Total Expense ($000): 51765 Payroll Expense ($000): 23052 Personnel: 475

MARYLAND HEIGHTS—St. Louis County

★ **RANKEN JORDAN PEDIATRIC BRIDGE HOSPITAL (263303)**, 11365 Dorsett Road, Zip 63043–3411; tel. 314/872–6400 **A**3 10 F1 3 12 29 30 32 34 35 44 50 68 86 87 89 90 91 92 93 94 96 98 99 104 130 132 146 148 149 **P**6
Primary Contact: Laureen K. Tanner, R.N., MSN, FACHE, President and Chief Executive Officer
COO: Brett Moorehouse FACHE, Vice President and Chief Operating Officer
CFO: Jean Bardwell, Vice President and Chief Financial Officer
CMO: Nicholas Holekamp M.D., Chief Medical Officer
CIO: Jean Bardwell, Vice President and Chief Financial Officer
CHR: Thomas M Irvin, Administrator Human Resources
CNO: Laureen K Tanner R.N., MSN, FACHE, President and Chief Executive Officer
Web address: www.rankenjordan.org
Control: Other not-for-profit (including NFP Corporation) **Service:** Children's rehabilitation

Staffed Beds: 34 Admissions: 291 Census: 29 Outpatient Visits: 7342 Births: 0 Total Expense ($000): 29789 Payroll Expense ($000): 15438 Personnel: 255

MARYVILLE—Nodaway County

⊞ **SSM HEALTH ST. FRANCIS HOSPITAL - MARYVILLE (260050)**, 2016 South Main Street, Zip 64468–2655; tel. 660/562–2600 **A**1 10 20 F3 11 13 15 18 19 30 34 35 38 40 45 57 59 64 65 68 70 75 76 77 79 81 82 84 85 86 89 90 93 96 97 98 102 103 104 107 110 111 115 117 118 119 127 128 130 131 132 133 135 149 **P**6 **S** SSM Health, Saint Louis, MO
Primary Contact: Michael A. Baumgartner, President
COO: Frank Grispino, Vice President Operations
CFO: Jocelyn Skidmore, Director Finance
CMO: Shirley Harris M.D., President Medical Staff
CIO: Dave Lewis, Director Information Services
CHR: Krista Barcus, Human Resources Leader
CNO: Debbie Hoffman, Vice President Patient Services
Web address: www.ssmhealthstfrancis.com
Control: Church operated, Nongovernment, not-for-profit **Service:** General medical and surgical

Staffed Beds: 56 Admissions: 1506 Census: 17 Outpatient Visits: 128896 Births: 286 Total Expense ($000): 63186 Payroll Expense ($000): 26309 Personnel: 390

MEMPHIS—Scotland County

★ **SCOTLAND COUNTY HOSPITAL (261310)**, 450 Sigler Avenue, Zip 63555–1726, Mailing Address: 450 E Sigler Avenue, 63555–1726; tel. 660/465–8511 **A**10 18 F3 7 8 9 11 13 15 18 28 29 30 31 32 33 34 35 39 40 45 46 47 48 50 56 57 59 64 65 67 70 75 76 77 78 79 81 82 85 86 87 89 90 97 107 119 127 128 130 131 132 135 146 147 148 **P**6
Primary Contact: Randy Tobler, M.D., Chief Executive Officer
CFO: Sheryl Templeton, Chief Financial Officer
CMO: Randy Tobler M.D., Chief Medical Officer
CIO: Ken McMinn, Director Information Technology
CHR: Missy Smith, Coordinator Human Resources
CNO: Carla Cook, Director of Nursing
Web address: www.scotlandcountyhospital.com
Control: Hospital district or authority, Government, Nonfederal **Service:** General medical and surgical

Staffed Beds: 25 Admissions: 634 Census: 10 Outpatient Visits: 104067 Births: 124 Total Expense ($000): 22535 Payroll Expense ($000): 9881 Personnel: 182

SCOTLAND COUNTY MEMORIAL HOSPITAL See Scotland County Hospital

MEXICO—Audrain County

⊞ **SSM HEALTH ST. MARY'S HOSPITAL - AUDRAIN (260064)**, 620 East Monroe Street, Zip 65265–2919; tel. 573/582–5000 **A**1 2 10 F3 11 13 15 18 20 22 26 28 29 30 31 34 40 45 54 57 59 64 65 70 73 74 75 76 77 78 79 81 82 85 86 87 89 90 93 98 103 107 108 110 111 115 118 119 121 123 127 129 130 131 132 144 146 147 149 **P**6 **S** SSM Health, Saint Louis, MO
Primary Contact: Donna K. Jacobs, FACHE, President
CFO: James Stratton, Regional Vice President Finance
CMO: Diane Jacobi, Chief of Staff
CIO: Dawn Evans, Manager Information Technology
CHR: Christy Smiley, Leader Human Resources
CNO: Kari Wilson R.N., Vice President Patient Care Services and Chief Nursing Officer
Web address: www.ssmhealthmidmo.com
Control: Church operated, Nongovernment, not-for-profit **Service:** General medical and surgical

Staffed Beds: 51 Admissions: 1853 Census: 17 Outpatient Visits: 123857 Births: 240 Total Expense ($000): 63340 Payroll Expense ($000): 22952 Personnel: 387

MILAN—Sullivan County

★ **SULLIVAN COUNTY MEMORIAL HOSPITAL (261306)**, 630 West Third Street, Zip 63556–1076; tel. 660/265–4212, (Total facility includes 14 beds in nursing home–type unit) **A**10 18 F28 29 32 33 34 40 57 59 64 65 67 68 77 79 87 93 97 99 103 104 107 111 114 119 127 128 130 133 147 148 149 **P**5 6
Primary Contact: Jerry Dover, Chief Executive Officer
COO: Amy J Michael, Chief Operating Officer
CMO: Dale Essmyer M.D., Chief of Staff
CIO: Vern Johnson, Director Information Technology
CHR: Billie Ryals, Director Human Resources
CNO: Carol Fordyce, Director Patient Care Services
Web address: www.scmhospital.org
Control: County, Government, Nonfederal **Service:** General medical and surgical

Staffed Beds: 29 Admissions: 160 Census: 21 Outpatient Visits: 26436 Births: 0 Total Expense ($000): 10217 Payroll Expense ($000): 2977 Personnel: 68

MOBERLY—Randolph County

⊞ **MOBERLY REGIONAL MEDICAL CENTER (260074)**, 1515 Union Avenue, Zip 65270–9449; tel. 660/263–8400 **A**1 10 20 F3 18 20 22 26 28 29 30 34 35 38 39 40 44 45 50 51 53 54 56 57 59 64 65 70 74 75 77 79 81 82 85 86 87 89 93 94 97 98 100 103 107 108 111 115 118 119 127 128 129 130 133 135 146 149 **P**5 **S** Community Health Systems, Inc., Franklin, TN
Primary Contact: Ranee C. Brayton, FACHE, R.N., MSN, Chief Executive Officer
COO: Tracey Matheis, Chief Operating Officer
CFO: Tracey Matheis, Chief Financial Officer
CMO: Heather Gessling M.D., Chief Medical Officer
CHR: Michael Turner, Director Human Resources
CNO: Jennifer Dunkin, Chief Nursing Officer
Web address: www.moberlyhospital.com
Control: Corporation, Investor-owned (for-profit) **Service:** General medical and surgical

Staffed Beds: 101 Admissions: 1331 Census: 19 Outpatient Visits: 55343 Births: 0 Total Expense ($000): 49578 Payroll Expense ($000): 13747 Personnel: 261

MO

Hospital, Medicare Provider Number, Address, Telephone, Approval, Facility, and Physician Codes, Health Care System

★ American Hospital Association (AHA) membership
□ The Joint Commission accreditation
○ Healthcare Facilities Accreditation Program
◇ DNV Healthcare Inc. accreditation
⇑ Center for Improvement in Healthcare Quality Accreditation
△ Commission on Accreditation of Rehabilitation Facilities (CARF) accreditation

MONETT—Barry County

⇧ **COX MONETT HOSPITAL (261329)**, 801 North Lincoln Avenue, Zip 65708–1641; tel. 417/235–3144 **A**10 18 21 **F**3 11 13 15 28 29 30 32 34 35 40 45 50 56 57 59 64 76 77 81 85 89 90 93 107 111 114 119 127 128 129 130 131 133 135 144 146 147 **P**3 6 **S** CoxHealth, Springfield, MO
Primary Contact: Darren Bass, President
CFO: Josh Powell, Facility Controller
CMO: Frank Romero M.D., Vice President Medical Affairs and Chief Medical Officer
CHR: Debra Isenmann, Human Resources Generalist
CNO: Bev Eli, Chief Nursing Officer
Web address: www.coxhealth.com
Control: Other not-for-profit (including NFP Corporation) **Service**: General medical and surgical

Staffed Beds: 25 **Admissions**: 849 **Census**: 7 **Outpatient Visits**: 92992 **Births**: 266 **Total Expense ($000)**: 33559 **Payroll Expense ($000)**: 15992 **Personnel**: 310

MOUNTAIN VIEW—Howell County

⊞ **MERCY ST. FRANCIS HOSPITAL (261335)**, 100 West Highway 60, Zip 65548–7125; tel. 417/934–7000 **A**1 10 18 **F**3 11 15 28 29 30 34 40 45 50 57 59 64 65 75 77 81 85 89 90 93 107 110 111 114 119 129 131 132 133 148 **P**6 **S** Mercy, Chesterfield, MO
Primary Contact: Cynthia Weatherford, Administrator and Director of Nursing
CFO: Sherry Clouse Day CPA, Chief Financial Officer
CMO: Barry Spoon M.D., Chief of Staff
CHR: Tracy Smith, Director Human Resources
Web address: www.stjohns.com/aboutus/stfrancis.aspx
Control: Church operated, Nongovernment, not-for-profit **Service**: General medical and surgical

Staffed Beds: 20 **Admissions**: 288 **Census**: 4 **Outpatient Visits**: 26021 **Births**: 0 **Total Expense ($000)**: 14517 **Payroll Expense ($000)**: 6512 **Personnel**: 94

NEOSHO—Newton County

★ **FREEMAN NEOSHO HOSPITAL (261331)**, 113 West Hickory Street, Zip 64850–1705; tel. 417/455–4352 **A**10 18 **F**3 11 15 28 29 30 34 35 40 44 45 47 56 57 59 64 68 70 75 77 79 81 84 85 86 87 90 93 97 107 110 111 114 119 130 131 132 133 146 147 148 **P**1 6 **S** Freeman Health System, Joplin, MO
Primary Contact: Renee Denton, Chief Operating Officer
CFO: Steve W Graddy, Chief Financial Officer
CMO: Rodney McFarland M.D., Medical Director
CIO: Sue Annesser, Director Information Systems
CHR: Mary Frerer, Chief Human Resources Officer
Web address: www.freemanhealth.com
Control: Other not-for-profit (including NFP Corporation) **Service**: General medical and surgical

Staffed Beds: 25 **Admissions**: 970 **Census**: 11 **Outpatient Visits**: 78834 **Births**: 0 **Total Expense ($000)**: 26588 **Payroll Expense ($000)**: 11689 **Personnel**: 191

NEVADA—Vernon County

☐ **HEARTLAND BEHAVIORAL HEALTH SERVICES**, 1500 West Ashland Street, Zip 64772–1710; tel. 417/667–2666 **A**1 **F**98 99 101 106 **S** Universal Health Services, Inc., King of Prussia, PA
Primary Contact: Alyson Wysong-Harder, Chief Executive Officer
CFO: Bryan Bishop, Chief Financial Officer
CMO: Ahmad Tarar M.D., Medical Director
CHR: Carri Compton-Ogle, Administrative Officer
CNO: Nathan Taylor, Director of Nursing
Web address: www.heartlandbehavioral.com
Control: Corporation, Investor-owned (for-profit) **Service**: Psychiatric

Staffed Beds: 69 **Admissions**: 1926 **Census**: 41 **Outpatient Visits**: 0 **Births**: 0 **Total Expense ($000)**: 14142 **Payroll Expense ($000)**: 7691 **Personnel**: 132

⊞ **NEVADA REGIONAL MEDICAL CENTER (260061)**, 800 South Ash Street, Zip 64772–3223; tel. 417/667–3355 **A**1 10 **F**3 11 13 15 26 27 28 29 30 31 32 34 35 39 40 41 45 50 54 57 59 62 63 64 65 66 70 74 75 76 77 78 79 81 82 83 84 85 86 87 89 90 91 93 94 96 98 101 102 103 104 107 111 115 119 127 129 130 131 132 133 135 143 144 146 147 148 **S** QHR, Brentwood, TN
Primary Contact: Kevin Leeper, Chief Executive Officer
CFO: Mike Harbor, Chief Financial Officer
CMO: Russ Kemm M.D., Chief Medical Officer
CIO: Marci Hardin, Manager Information Technology
CHR: Heather Brockmeyer, Human Resource Administrative Officer
CNO: Cory Vokoun, Chief Nursing Officer
Web address: www.nrmchealth.com
Control: City, Government, Nonfederal **Service**: General medical and surgical

Staffed Beds: 71 **Admissions**: 2129 **Census**: 26 **Outpatient Visits**: 69875 **Births**: 299 **Total Expense ($000)**: 39619 **Payroll Expense ($000)**: 14590 **Personnel**: 296

NORTH KANSAS CITY—Clay County

⊞ **NORTH KANSAS CITY HOSPITAL (260096)**, 2800 Clay Edwards Drive, Zip 64116–3220; tel. 816/691–2000 **A**1 2 3 5 10 **F**3 11 12 13 15 17 18 20 22 24 26 28 29 30 31 34 35 37 40 43 44 45 46 47 48 49 50 51 53 54 57 58 59 60 62 64 70 72 74 75 76 77 78 79 80 81 82 83 84 85 86 87 89 90 93 96 100 107 108 110 111 114 115 116 117 118 119 120 121 123 124 126 129 130 132 135 146 147 148 149
Primary Contact: Peggy Schmitt, President and Chief Executive Officer
COO: Jody Abbott, Senior Vice President and Chief Operating Officer
CFO: Jim McNey, Senior Vice President Finance and Chief Financial Officer
CMO: Gary L Carter M.D., Vice President and Chief Medical Officer
CIO: Paul Foelsch, Vice President and Chief Information Technology Officer
CHR: Dawn Bryant, Vice President Human Resources
CNO: Sarah G Oakley, Vice President Nursing
Web address: www.nkch.org
Control: City, Government, Nonfederal **Service**: General medical and surgical

Staffed Beds: 413 **Admissions**: 21588 **Census**: 282 **Outpatient Visits**: 252598 **Births**: 1578 **Total Expense ($000)**: 458314 **Payroll Expense ($000)**: 169641 **Personnel**: 2619

O'FALLON—St. Charles County

⊞ **PROGRESS WEST HOSPITAL (260219)**, Two Progress Point Parkway, Zip 63368–2208; tel. 636/344–1000 **A**1 10 **F**3 13 15 18 20 22 26 29 30 34 35 40 41 45 49 51 57 59 60 70 76 77 79 81 85 86 87 89 107 108 110 111 115 118 119 130 135 146 148 149 **S** BJC HealthCare, Saint Louis, MO
Primary Contact: Chris Watts, President
CFO: Glen Schwaegel, Chief Financial Officer
CMO: Dane Glueck M.D., Chief of Staff
CHR: Michael J Miller, Director Human Resources
CNO: Jill Skyles R.N., Vice President Patient Care Services and Chief Nurse Executive
Web address: www.progresswest.org
Control: Other not-for-profit (including NFP Corporation) **Service**: General medical and surgical

Staffed Beds: 44 **Admissions**: 3164 **Census**: 29 **Outpatient Visits**: 52600 **Births**: 772 **Total Expense ($000)**: 71846 **Payroll Expense ($000)**: 26449 **Personnel**: 319

OSAGE BEACH—Camden County

⊞ **LAKE REGIONAL HEALTH SYSTEM (260186)**, 54 Hospital Drive, Zip 65065–3050; tel. 573/348–8000, (Total facility includes 16 beds in nursing home–type unit) **A**1 2 10 **F**3 11 12 13 15 17 18 20 22 24 28 29 30 31 32 34 35 38 39 40 43 44 48 49 50 51 53 57 59 60 62 64 65 68 70 73 74 75 76 77 78 79 81 82 84 85 86 87 89 93 96 107 108 111 114 115 118 119 120 121 122 123 124 127 128 129 130 131 132 135 144 145 146 148 149 150 **P**6
Primary Contact: Dane W. Henry, Chief Executive Officer
COO: Kevin G McRoberts FACHE, Senior Vice President of Operations
CFO: David Halsell, Senior Vice President and Chief Financial Officer
CMO: Robert Hyatt M.D., Senior Vice President Medical Affairs
CIO: Scott Poest, Chief Information Officer
CHR: Tom Williams, Vice President Human Resources
CNO: Janice L Dungan, Senior Vice President Clinical Services
Web address: www.lakeregional.com
Control: Other not-for-profit (including NFP Corporation) **Service**: General medical and surgical

Staffed Beds: 116 **Admissions**: 4540 **Census**: 54 **Outpatient Visits**: 310831 **Births**: 591 **Total Expense ($000)**: 173484 **Payroll Expense ($000)**: 68946 **Personnel**: 1119

☐ **OSAGE BEACH CENTER FOR COGNITIVE DISORDERS**, 840 Passover Road, Zip 65065; tel. 573/302–0319 **A**1 **F**29 50 56 68 74 75 86 87 98 101 103 130 135 149 **P**6
Primary Contact: Lorri Steffen, Chief Executive Officer and Administrator
Web address: www.osagebeachccd.com
Control: Partnership, Investor-owned (for-profit) **Service**: Psychiatric

Staffed Beds: 14 **Admissions**: 387 **Census**: 10 **Outpatient Visits**: 0 **Births**: 0 **Total Expense ($000)**: 4369 **Payroll Expense ($000)**: 1552 **Personnel**: 31

MO

Many Facility Codes have changed. Please refer to the AHA Guide Code Chart. © 2017 AHA Guide

PERRYVILLE—Perry County

☒ **PERRY COUNTY MEMORIAL HOSPITAL (261311)**, 434 North West Street,
Zip 63775–1398; tel. 573/547–2536 **A**1 10 18 **F**3 7 8 11 13 15 28 29 30 31
34 35 40 44 48 51 53 54 56 57 59 62 64 66 68 75 76 77 78 79 81 85 87 89
90 92 93 97 100 101 102 103 104 107 111 115 117 119 129 130 131 132
133 135 143 144 145 146 147 148
Primary Contact: Patrick E. Carron, FACHE, President and Chief Executive Officer
CFO: Randall Wolf, Vice President Finance
CMO: Michael Steele M.D., Chief of Staff
CIO: Ron Heuring, Director Information Systems
CHR: Christopher Wibbenmeyer, Director Human Resources
Web address: www.pchmo.org
Control: Other not-for-profit (including NFP Corporation) **Service**: General medical
and surgical

Staffed Beds: 25 **Admissions**: 933 **Census**: 11 **Outpatient Visits**: 50428
Births: 136 **Total Expense ($000)**: 35309 **Payroll Expense ($000)**: 13892
Personnel: 310

PILOT KNOB—Iron County

IRON COUNTY MEDICAL CENTER (261336), 301 North Highway 21,
Zip 63663–0548, Mailing Address: P.O.Box 548, 63663–0548; tel. 573/546–
1260 **A**10 18 **F**3 11 15 18 29 34 35 38 40 44 45 57 59 64 66 79 81 82 89 90
93 96 97 100 102 104 107 111 114 119 127 129 130 133 148 **P**6
Primary Contact: Joshua Gilmore, Chief Executive Officer
COO: Cyndi Basler, Chief Operating Officer
CFO: Justin Lattimore, Chief Financial Officer
CNO: Cindy Finley, Chief Nursing Officer
Web address: www.icmedcenter.org/
Control: Hospital district or authority, Government, Nonfederal **Service**: General
medical and surgical

Staffed Beds: 15 **Admissions**: 230 **Census**: 4 **Outpatient Visits**: 23202
Births: 0 **Personnel**: 124

POPLAR BLUFF—Butler County

☒ **BLACK RIVER MEDICAL CENTER (260227)**, 217 Physicians Park Drive,
Zip 63901–3956; tel. 573/727–9080 **A**1 10 **F**3 15 29 34 39 40 45 57 59 64 65
81 86 107 108 110 111 115 118 119 135 149
Primary Contact: Christy Shawan, Chief Executive Officer
CFO: Phillip Crocker, Accounting Specialist
CMO: Christopher Pinderski M.D., Medical Director of Emergency Room
CIO: TJ Mcmeans, Information Technology Technician
CHR: Denyce Keele, Administrative Assistant and Human Resources Coordinator
CNO: E. Kay Fox, Director of Nursing
Web address: www.blackrivermedical.com
Control: Other not-for-profit (including NFP Corporation) **Service**: General medical
and surgical

Staffed Beds: 8 **Admissions**: 806 **Census**: 4 **Outpatient Visits**: 10559
Births: 0 **Total Expense ($000)**: 20743 **Payroll Expense ($000)**: 5447
Personnel: 124

☒ **JOHN J. PERSHING VETERANS AFFAIRS MEDICAL CENTER**, 1500 North
Westwood Boulevard, Zip 63901–3318; tel. 573/686–4151, (Nonreporting) **A**1 **S**
Department of Veterans Affairs, Washington, DC
Primary Contact: Patricia Ten Haaf, R.N., MSN, Ph.D., Director
COO: Seth Barlage, Associate Medical Center Director
CFO: Kristy Siebert, Manager Finance
CMO: Vijayachandran Nair M.D., Chief of Staff
CIO: Michael Gustin, Information Technology
CHR: Genise Denton, Manager Human Resources
CNO: Elizabeth A Smith, Director of Nursing
Web address: www.poplarbluff.va.gov
Control: Veterans Affairs, Government, federal **Service**: General medical and
surgical

Staffed Beds: 58

☒ **POPLAR BLUFF REGIONAL MEDICAL CENTER (260119)**, 3100 Oak Grove
Road, Zip 63901, Mailing Address: P.O.Box 88, 63902–0088; tel. 573/776–
2000, (Includes POPLAR BLUFF REGIONAL MEDICAL CENTER-SOUTH CAMPUS,
621 Pine Boulevard, Poplar Bluff, Missouri, Zip 63901, tel. 573/785–7721) **A**1
2 10 **F**3 11 13 15 17 18 20 22 24 29 30 31 34 35 40 45 46 49 50 51 53 54
57 59 60 64 65 68 70 74 75 76 77 78 79 80 81 82 85 87 89 90 93 98 102
107 108 111 114 117 118 119 120 121 126 127 130 131 132 146 148 **S**
Community Health Systems, Inc., Franklin, TN
Primary Contact: Larry Rodgers, Chief Executive Officer
COO: Buddy Daniels, Chief Operating Officer
CFO: Steve Dorris, Chief Financial Officer
CMO: Steve Pu D.O., Chief Medical Officer
CIO: Gary Dollins, Director Management Information Systems
CHR: Denise Rushin, Director Human Resources
CNO: Melissa A Samuelson R.N., Chief Nurse Executive
Web address: www.poplarbluffregional.com
Control: Individual, Investor-owned (for-profit) **Service**: General medical and
surgical

Staffed Beds: 252 **Admissions**: 10831 **Census**: 118 **Outpatient Visits**:
99462 **Births**: 1455 **Total Expense ($000)**: 188579 **Payroll Expense
($000)**: 41892 **Personnel**: 1042

POTOSI—Washington County

★ **WASHINGTON COUNTY MEMORIAL HOSPITAL (261308)**, 300 Health Way,
Zip 63664–1420; tel. 573/438–5451 **A**10 18 **F**3 11 15 28 29 33 34 35 40 45
57 59 64 65 74 75 77 79 81 87 90 93 97 98 104 106 107 108 110 111 114
119 127 129 130 133 144 145 146 147 148 **P**6
Primary Contact: Michele C. Meyer, Interim Chief Executive Officer
CFO: Yvonne Fourez, Chief Financial Officer
CMO: Jonathan Borchers M.D., Chief Medical Officer
CIO: Jim Smith, Director Information Systems
CHR: Christy Aubuchon, Director Personnel
CNO: Beverly Williams R.N., Chief Nursing Officer
Web address: www.wcmhosp.org
Control: County, Government, Nonfederal **Service**: General medical and surgical

Staffed Beds: 25 **Admissions**: 785 **Census**: 8 **Outpatient Visits**: 79843
Births: 0 **Total Expense ($000)**: 24100 **Payroll Expense ($000)**: 11044
Personnel: 211

RICHMOND—Ray County

★ **RAY COUNTY MEMORIAL HOSPITAL (261327)**, 904 Wollard Boulevard,
Zip 64085–2229; tel. 816/470–5432 **A**10 18 **F**3 11 15 29 31 40 45 56 57 62
64 68 74 75 78 79 81 82 85 87 93 103 107 108 110 111 115 117 119 130
133 146
Primary Contact: Earl Nielsen. Sheehy, Chief Executive Officer
CFO: Donald Harr, Controller
CHR: Donna Strain, Director Human Resources
Web address: www.raycountyhospital.com
Control: County, Government, Nonfederal **Service**: General medical and surgical

Staffed Beds: 25 **Admissions**: 728 **Census**: 9 **Outpatient Visits**: 17504
Births: 0 **Total Expense ($000)**: 21932 **Payroll Expense ($000)**: 9920
Personnel: 218

RICHMOND HEIGHTS—St. Louis County

☒ △ **SSM SELECT REHABILITATION HOSPITAL (263031)**, 1027 Bellevue
Avenue, 3rd Floor, Zip 63117–1851, Mailing Address: 1027 Bellevue Avenue,
63117–1851; tel. 314/768–5300, (Nonreporting) (Includes SSM HEALTH
REHABILITATION HOSPITAL - LAKE SAINT LOUIS, 100 Medical Plaza, Fifth Floor,
Lake Saint Louis, Missouri, Zip 63367–1366, tel. 636/755–6500; Robert Pritts,
Chief Executive Officer and Market Executive; SSM SELECT REHABILITATION
HOSPITAL, 12380 De Paul Drive, Bridgeton, Missouri, Zip 63044–2511,
tel. 314/447–9700; Timothy Wadman, Chief Executive Officer) **A**1 7 10 **S** Select
Medical Corporation, Mechanicsburg, PA
Primary Contact: Robert Pritts, Chief Executive Officer
Web address: www.ssm-select.com
Control: Corporation, Investor-owned (for-profit) **Service**: Rehabilitation

Staffed Beds: 95

MO

ROLLA—Phelps County

△ **PHELPS COUNTY REGIONAL MEDICAL CENTER (260017)**, 1000 West Tenth Street, Zip 65401–2905; tel. 573/458–8899, (Total facility includes 20 beds in nursing home–type unit) **A**1 2 7 10 **F**3 7 8 11 13 15 18 20 22 26 28 29 30 31 34 35 39 40 45 47 49 50 51 54 56 57 58 59 60 62 63 68 70 73 74 75 76 77 78 79 81 82 84 85 86 87 89 90 93 96 98 100 101 102 103 104 107 108 110 111 114 115 117 118 119 120 121 127 128 129 130 132 135 143 146 147 148 149 **P**6
Primary Contact: Edward Clayton, Chief Executive Officer
CMO: Donald James D.O., Chief Medical Officer
CIO: Jeff McKune, Chief Health Informatics Officer
CHR: Frank A Lazzaro III, Chief Human Resources Officer
CNO: Keri S. Brookshire-Heavin, Chief Nurse Executive
Web address: www.pcrmc.com
Control: County, Government, Nonfederal **Service**: General medical and surgical

Staffed Beds: 181 **Admissions:** 6112 **Census:** 82 **Outpatient Visits:** 408542 **Births:** 831 **Total Expense ($000):** 223213 **Payroll Expense ($000):** 97256 **Personnel:** 1221

SAINT CHARLES—St. Charles County

CENTERPOINTE HOSPITAL (264012), 4801 Weldon Spring Parkway, Zip 63304–9101; tel. 636/441–7300 **A**1 10 **F**4 5 34 35 38 44 54 80 87 98 99 100 101 102 103 104 105 106 143
Primary Contact: Susan Mathis, MSN, R.N., Chief Executive Officer
CFO: Tom Croffut, Chief Financial Officer
CMO: Azfar Malik M.D., Chief Medical Officer
CIO: Jennifer Bourn, Director, Health Information Services and Medical Staff Services
CHR: Kelli White, Director, Human Resources
Web address: www.centerpointehospital.com
Control: Corporation, Investor-owned (for-profit) **Service**: Psychiatric

Staffed Beds: 150 **Admissions:** 4683 **Census:** 104 **Outpatient Visits:** 0 **Births:** 0 **Total Expense ($000):** 39519 **Payroll Expense ($000):** 17275 **Personnel:** 346

SELECT SPECIALTY HOSPITAL-ST. LOUIS (262013), 300 First Capitol Drive, Unit 1, Zip 63301–2844; tel. 636/947–5010 **A**1 10 **F**1 29 74 75 148 **S** Select Medical Corporation, Mechanicsburg, PA
Primary Contact: Jeff Denney, Chief Executive Officer
Web address: www.selectspecialtyhospitals.com/company/locations/stlouis.aspx
Control: Corporation, Investor-owned (for-profit) **Service**: Acute long-term care hospital

Staffed Beds: 33 **Admissions:** 333 **Census:** 27 **Outpatient Visits:** 0 **Births:** 0 **Total Expense ($000):** 16681 **Payroll Expense ($000):** 7347 **Personnel:** 91

SSM HEALTH ST. JOSEPH - ST. CHARLES (260005), 300 First Capitol Drive, Zip 63301–2844; tel. 636/947–5000, (Includes SSM HEALTH ST. JOSEPH - WENTZVILLE, 500 Medical Drive, Wentzville, Missouri, Zip 63385–3421, tel. 636/327–1000) **A**1 2 10 **F**3 4 11 13 15 17 18 20 22 24 26 28 29 30 31 34 35 38 40 41 42 43 44 45 46 49 50 53 54 55 56 57 58 59 60 64 68 70 73 74 75 76 78 79 81 82 84 85 86 87 90 96 97 98 99 100 101 102 103 104 105 107 108 110 111 114 118 119 120 121 129 130 132 135 144 146 147 148 **P**6 8 **S** SSM Health, Saint Louis, MO
Primary Contact: Michael E. Bowers, President
COO: Lee Bernstein, Regional Executive Vice President and Chief Operating Officer
CFO: Karen Rewerts, System Vice President Finance
CIO: Margaret Feilner, Director Information Services
CHR: Debbie G Walkenhorst, System Vice President Talent Management
Web address: www.ssmstjoseph.com
Control: Church operated, Nongovernment, not-for-profit **Service**: General medical and surgical

Staffed Beds: 341 **Admissions:** 14067 **Census:** 202 **Outpatient Visits:** 208090 **Births:** 733 **Total Expense ($000):** 238033 **Payroll Expense ($000):** 84643 **Personnel:** 1296

SAINT JOSEPH—Buchanan County

★ **LONG-TERM ACUTE CARE HOSPITAL, MOSAIC LIFE CARE AT ST. JOSEPH (262019)**, 5325 Faraon Street, Zip 64506–3488; tel. 816/271–6000 **A**10 **F**1 3 29 85 130 148 149 150
Primary Contact: Dana Anderson, Administrator
CNO: Douglas Schmitz, Director of Nursing
Web address: www.mymosaiclifecare.org/General/Long-Term-Acute-Care-Hospital/
Control: Other not-for-profit (including NFP Corporation) **Service**: Acute long-term care hospital

Staffed Beds: 41 **Admissions:** 262 **Census:** 21 **Outpatient Visits:** 0 **Births:** 0 **Total Expense ($000):** 11141 **Payroll Expense ($000):** 3406 **Personnel:** 57

MOSAIC LIFE CARE AT ST. JOSEPH (260006), 5325 Faraon Street, Zip 64506–3488; tel. 816/271–6000 **A**1 2 10 20 **F**3 8 9 11 12 13 15 17 18 20 22 24 26 28 29 30 31 32 33 34 35 36 40 43 45 46 48 49 50 53 54 57 58 59 62 63 64 65 70 74 75 76 77 78 79 80 81 82 84 85 86 87 89 90 92 93 94 96 97 98 102 103 104 107 108 110 111 114 115 118 119 120 121 123 129 130 131 134 135 143 144 146 147 148 149 150 **P**6
Primary Contact: Samuel Mark. Laney, M.D., Chief Executive Officer
COO: Curt Kretzinger, Chief Operating Officer
CFO: Dwain Stilson, Chief Financial Officer
CIO: Brennan Lehman, Chief Information Officer
CHR: Michael Pulido, Chief Administrative Officer
Web address: www.mymosaiclifecare.org/Main/Location/st-joseph-mo/mosaic-life-care-at-st.joseph/
Control: Other not-for-profit (including NFP Corporation) **Service**: General medical and surgical

Staffed Beds: 352 **Admissions:** 15371 **Census:** 179 **Outpatient Visits:** 1179326 **Births:** 1600 **Total Expense ($000):** 570103 **Payroll Expense ($000):** 256836 **Personnel:** 3393

☐ **NORTHWEST MISSOURI PSYCHIATRIC REHABILITATION CENTER (264007)**, 3505 Frederick Avenue, Zip 64506–2914; tel. 816/387–2300 **A**1 3 10 **F**4 29 30 34 58 59 65 68 75 77 86 87 97 98 101 102 103 130 132 135 143 146 **P**6
Primary Contact: Denise Norbury, Regional Executive Officer
COO: Mary Attebury, Chief Operating Officer
CFO: Randy Riley, Fiscal and Administrative Manager
CMO: James B Reynolds M.D., Medical Director
CIO: Robert Curren, Western Region Chief Information Technology Officer
CHR: Mary Blakey Gorman, Director Human Resources
CNO: Pam Nold, Chief Nurse Executive
Web address: www.dmh.mo.gov
Control: State, Government, Nonfederal **Service**: Psychiatric

Staffed Beds: 108 **Admissions:** 73 **Census:** 107 **Outpatient Visits:** 0 **Births:** 0 **Total Expense ($000):** 23305 **Payroll Expense ($000):** 11559 **Personnel:** 299

SAINT LOUIS—St. Louis City County

BARNES-JEWISH HOSPITAL (260032), 1 Barnes-Jewish Hospital Plaza, Zip 63110–1003; tel. 314/747–3000, (Includes BARNES-JEWISH HOSPITAL PSYCHIATRIC SUPPORT CENTER, 5355 Delmar Boulevard, Saint Louis, Missouri, Zip 63112–3146, tel. 314/273–0040; John M Eiler, Ph.D., President) (Total facility includes 120 beds in nursing home–type unit) **A**1 2 3 5 8 10 **F**3 4 6 8 9 11 12 13 14 15 16 17 18 20 22 24 26 28 29 30 31 34 35 36 37 38 39 40 43 44 45 46 47 48 49 50 51 52 53 54 55 56 57 58 59 60 61 63 64 65 66 68 70 71 73 74 75 76 77 78 79 80 81 82 84 85 86 87 89 90 91 92 93 94 95 96 97 98 99 100 101 102 103 104 105 107 108 109 110 111 112 114 115 116 117 118 119 120 121 122 123 124 126 128 129 130 131 132 134 135 136 137 138 139 140 141 142 143 144 145 146 147 148 149 **P**6 **S** BJC HealthCare, Saint Louis, MO
Primary Contact: Robert W. Cannon, President
CFO: Mark Krieger, Vice President and Chief Financial Officer
CMO: John Lynch M.D., Vice President and Chief Medical Officer
CIO: Jerry Vuchak, Vice President Information Systems
CHR: John Beatty, Vice President Human Resources
CNO: Coreen Vlodarchyk R.N., Vice President, Patient Care Services and Chief Nursing Officer
Web address: www.barnesjewish.org
Control: Other not-for-profit (including NFP Corporation) **Service**: General medical and surgical

Staffed Beds: 1414 **Admissions:** 55110 **Census:** 969 **Outpatient Visits:** 768947 **Births:** 3347 **Total Expense ($000):** 1893416 **Payroll Expense ($000):** 605304 **Personnel:** 11014

BARNES-JEWISH WEST COUNTY HOSPITAL (260162), 12634 Olive Boulevard, Zip 63141–6337; tel. 314/996–8000 **A**1 3 5 10 **F**3 12 15 18 29 34 35 40 45 46 47 49 50 51 57 59 60 64 65 70 74 75 77 78 79 81 82 85 90 93 107 110 111 114 115 119 120 121 123 126 129 130 131 142 145 146 148 149 **S** BJC HealthCare, Saint Louis, MO
Primary Contact: Trisha Lollo, President
CFO: Diane M Glen, Assistant Administrator
CMO: Sam B Bhayani M.D., Chief Medical Officer
CIO: Jerry Vuchak, Vice President Information Systems
CNO: Yoany Finetti R.N., Chief Nursing Officer
Web address: www.barnesjewishwestcounty.org
Control: Other not-for-profit (including NFP Corporation) **Service**: General medical and surgical

Staffed Beds: 77 **Admissions:** 2491 **Census:** 17 **Outpatient Visits:** 149908 **Births:** 0 **Total Expense ($000):** 109584 **Payroll Expense ($000):** 35046 **Personnel:** 448

MO

✠ **CHRISTIAN HOSPITAL (260180)**, 11133 Dunn Road, Zip 63136–6119; tel. 314/653–5000 **A**1 2 3 10 **F**3 4 5 7 8 11 15 17 18 20 22 24 26 28 29 30 31 34 35 36 38 40 42 44 45 46 47 49 50 53 56 57 58 59 60 63 64 65 68 69 70 74 75 77 78 79 80 81 82 83 84 85 86 87 90 92 93 94 96 107 108 109 110 111 112 113 114 115 116 117 118 119 120 121 123 126 129 130 132 135 143 146 147 148 149 **P**6 **S** BJC HealthCare, Saint Louis, MO
Primary Contact: Rick Stevens, President
CMO: Sebastian Rueckert M.D., Chief Medical Officer
CIO: Michael Kelly, Vice President
CHR: Bryan Hartwick, Vice President Human Resources
CNO: Jennifer Cordia, Vice President and Chief Nursing Executive
Web address: www.christianhospital.org
Control: Other not-for-profit (including NFP Corporation) **Service**: General medical and surgical

> **Staffed Beds:** 220 **Admissions:** 12101 **Census:** 188 **Outpatient Visits:** 307688 **Births:** 0 **Total Expense ($000):** 297291 **Payroll Expense ($000):** 116938 **Personnel:** 1657

✠ **DES PERES HOSPITAL (260176)**, 2345 Dougherty Ferry Road, Zip 63122–3313; tel. 314/966–9100 **A**1 3 5 10 12 13 **F**3 12 15 18 20 22 24 26 29 34 35 36 37 40 44 48 49 50 56 58 59 60 64 68 69 70 75 77 79 81 85 86 87 93 107 108 110 111 115 119 126 130 132 143 146 149 **S** TENET Healthcare Corporation, Dallas, TX
Primary Contact: David E. Loving, Chief Executive Officer
COO: Alex Lovshin, Chief Operating Officer
CFO: Rhonda Rogers, Chief Financial Officer
CMO: Karen Webb M.D., Chief Medical Officer
CIO: Kay Hannon, Director Information Systems
CHR: Kathaleen Clutts, Chief Human Resources Officer
CNO: Mary Ann Hampton R.N., MSN, Chief Nursing Officer
Web address: www.despereshospital.com
Control: Corporation, Investor-owned (for-profit) **Service**: General medical and surgical

> **Staffed Beds:** 88 **Admissions:** 4571 **Census:** 40 **Outpatient Visits:** 28168 **Births:** 0 **Total Expense ($000):** 111676 **Payroll Expense ($000):** 32002 **Personnel:** 500

☐ **HAWTHORN CHILDREN PSYCHIATRIC HOSPITAL (264028)**, 1901 Pennsylvania, Zip 63133–1325, Mailing Address: 1901 Pennsylvania Avenue, 63133–1325; tel. 314/512–7800 **A**1 3 10 **F** 99, 106
Primary Contact: Laurent D. Javois, Regional Executive Officer
COO: Marcia F Ford, Chief Operating Officer
CFO: James D Martin, Chief Financial Officer
CMO: Joshua Calhoun M.D., Medical Director
CHR: Michael McFarlane, Director Human Resource
CNO: Melody Chilese, Chief Nurse Executive
Web address: www.dmh.missouri.gov/hcph/
Control: State, Government, Nonfederal **Service**: Intellectual disabilities

> **Staffed Beds:** 323 **Admissions:** 6 **Census:** 6 **Outpatient Visits:** 0 **Births:** 0 **Total Expense ($000):** 15078 **Payroll Expense ($000):** 8847

✠ **KINDRED HOSPITAL-ST. LOUIS (262010)**, 4930 Lindell Boulevard, Zip 63108–1510; tel. 314/361–8700, (Includes KINDRED HOSPITAL ST. LOUIS-ST. ANTHONY'S, 10018 Kennerly Road, 3rd Floor, Saint Louis, Missouri, Zip 63128, tel. 314/525–8100; Jan Turk, Interim Administrator) **A**1 10 **F**1 5 29 67 70 128 148 **S** Kindred Healthcare, Louisville, KY
Primary Contact: Jan Turk, Interim Administrator
COO: Dakota Redd R.N., Chief Clinical Officer
CFO: Maureen Roach, Senior Chief Financial Officer
CMO: Michael Holtzman M.D., Medical Director
CIO: Thomas C Christman, Director Plant Operations
CHR: Cindy Sander, Coordinator Human Resources
Web address: www.kindredstlouis.com/
Control: Corporation, Investor-owned (for-profit) **Service**: Acute long-term care hospital

> **Staffed Beds:** 98 **Admissions:** 685 **Census:** 50 **Outpatient Visits:** 0 **Births:** 0 **Total Expense ($000):** 30648 **Payroll Expense ($000):** 13188 **Personnel:** 187

✠ **MERCY HOSPITAL ST. LOUIS (260020)**, 615 South New Ballas Road, Zip 63141–8277; tel. 314/251–6000, (Includes MERCY CHILDREN'S HOSPITAL ST. LOUIS, 615 South New Ballas Road, Saint Louis, Missouri, Zip 63141–8221, tel. 314/251–6000) (Total facility includes 15 beds in nursing home–type unit) **A**1 2 3 5 8 10 **F**1 3 4 5 8 11 12 13 14 15 16 17 18 19 20 22 24 25 26 27 28 29 30 31 32 33 34 35 36 38 39 40 41 43 45 46 47 48 49 50 51 52 53 54 55 56 57 58 59 60 61 64 66 67 68 69 70 71 72 73 74 75 76 77 78 79 80 81 82 84 85 86 87 88 89 90 92 93 94 96 98 99 100 101 102 103 104 105 106 107 108 110 111 114 115 116 117 118 119 120 121 123 124 126 128 129 130 131 132 134 135 143 144 146 147 148 149 **P**6 8 **S** Mercy, Chesterfield, MO
Primary Contact: Stephen Mackin, President
CFO: Cheryl Matejka, Chief Financial Officer
CMO: Paul Hintze M.D., Vice President Medical Affairs
CIO: Eugene Roth, Vice President Information Services
CHR: Rocky Ruello, Vice President Human Resources
Web address: www.mercy.net/stlouismo
Control: Other not-for-profit (including NFP Corporation) **Service**: General medical and surgical

> **Staffed Beds:** 831 **Admissions:** 40656 **Census:** 558 **Outpatient Visits:** 1118326 **Births:** 8940 **Total Expense ($000):** 874806 **Payroll Expense ($000):** 311143 **Personnel:** 4959

☐ **METROPOLITAN ST. LOUIS PSYCHIATRIC CENTER (264025)**, 5351 Delmar, Zip 63112–3198; tel. 314/877–0501, **A**1 3 10 **F** 11, 30, 106, 146, 149
Primary Contact: Laurent D. Javois, Regional Executive Officer
COO: Michael Bruce Anderson Ph.D., Chief Operating Officer
CFO: James D Martin, Chief Financial Officer
CMO: Roy Wilson M.D., Medical Director
CHR: Michael McFarlane, Director Human Resources
CNO: Sarah Jones, Chief Nurse Executive
Web address: www.dmh.missouri.gov/mpc
Control: State, Government, Nonfederal **Service**: Psychiatric

> **Staffed Beds:** 50 **Admissions:** 24 **Census:** 24 **Outpatient Visits:** 0 **Births:** 0 **Total Expense ($000):** 13772 **Payroll Expense ($000):** 6959 **Personnel:** 190

✠ **MISSOURI BAPTIST MEDICAL CENTER (260108)**, 3015 North Ballas Road, Zip 63131–2329; tel. 314/996–5000 **A**1 2 3 5 10 **F**3 11 13 14 15 17 18 20 22 24 26 28 29 30 31 32 34 35 36 40 41 45 46 48 49 50 51 54 56 57 58 59 60 63 64 65 68 70 71 72 74 75 76 77 78 79 81 82 83 84 85 86 87 89 90 92 93 94 96 97 102 107 108 110 111 114 115 116 117 118 119 120 121 123 124 126 130 132 135 145 146 147 148 149 150 **P**6 **S** BJC HealthCare, Saint Louis, MO
Primary Contact: John Antes, President
COO: Michael Kelly, Vice President Operations
CFO: Amy Desart, Vice President, Chief Financial Officer
CMO: Mitchell Botney M.D., Vice President Medical Affairs and Chief Medical Officer
CIO: Tracie Johnson, Director Information Services
CHR: Cyndy Donato, Vice President, Human Resources
CNO: Tim Mislan MS, Vice President and Chief Nurse Executive
Web address: www.missouribaptist.org
Control: Other not-for-profit (including NFP Corporation) **Service**: General medical and surgical

> **Staffed Beds:** 489 **Admissions:** 20607 **Census:** 251 **Outpatient Visits:** 367350 **Births:** 3936 **Total Expense ($000):** 567332 **Payroll Expense ($000):** 187201 **Personnel:** 2469

☐ **SHRINERS HOSPITALS FOR CHILDREN-ST. LOUIS (263304)**, 4400 Clayton Avenue, Zip 63110–1624; tel. 314/432–3600 **A**1 3 5 10 **F**3 29 58 64 74 75 79 81 85 86 87 89 93 94 130 131 146 **S** Shriners Hospitals for Children, Tampa, FL
Primary Contact: John Gloss, FACHE, Administrator
CFO: Sandra K. Lawson, Interim Director Fiscal Services
CMO: Perry L Schoenecker M.D., Chief of Staff
CIO: Jeanne Hall, Director Information Systems
CHR: Mark Venable, Interim Director Human Resources
Web address: www.shrinershospitalsforchildren.org/Hospitals/Locations/Stlouis.aspx
Control: Other not-for-profit (including NFP Corporation) **Service**: Children's orthopedic

> **Staffed Beds:** 12 **Admissions:** 292 **Census:** 2 **Outpatient Visits:** 9004 **Births:** 0 **Total Expense ($000):** 25234 **Payroll Expense ($000):** 8161 **Personnel:** 141

MO

Hospital, Medicare Provider Number, Address, Telephone, Approval, Facility, and Physician Codes, Health Care System

★ American Hospital Association (AHA) membership
☐ The Joint Commission accreditation
○ Healthcare Facilities Accreditation Program
◇ DNV Healthcare Inc. accreditation
⇑ Center for Improvement in Healthcare Quality Accreditation
△ Commission on Accreditation of Rehabilitation Facilities (CARF) accreditation

★ **SSM CARDINAL GLENNON CHILDREN'S HOSPITAL (269807)**, 1465 South Grand Boulevard, Zip 63104–1095; tel. 314/577–5600 **A**3 5 10 **F**3 11 19 21 23 25 27 29 30 31 32 34 35 38 39 40 41 43 44 45 46 47 48 49 50 54 55 57 59 60 61 64 66 68 72 73 74 75 77 78 79 80 81 82 84 85 86 87 88 89 90 93 94 97 99 100 101 102 104 107 108 111 115 118 119 124 127 129 130 131 132 134 136 137 138 139 141 142 146 148 **P**6 8 **S** SSM Health, Saint Louis, MO
Primary Contact: Steven Burghart, President
CFO: Karen Rewerts, System Vice President of Finance
CMO: John Peter M.D., Vice President Medical Affairs
CIO: Michael Paasch, Regional Vice President and Chief Information Officer
CHR: Debbie G Walkenhorst, Network Vice President
Web address: www.cardinalglennon.com
Control: Church operated, Nongovernment, not-for-profit **Service:** Children's general medical and surgical

Staffed Beds: 176 Admissions: 7585 Census: 146 Outpatient Visits: 244032 Births: 0 Total Expense ($000): 338860 Payroll Expense ($000): 104019 Personnel: 1638

✉ **SSM HEALTH SAINT LOUIS UNIVERSITY HOSPITAL (260105)**, 3635 Vista at Grand Boulevard, Zip 63110–0250, Mailing Address: P.O.Box 15250, 63110–0250; tel. 314/577–8000, (Includes SSM HEALTH SAINT LOUIS UNIVERSITY HOSPITAL-SOUTH, 1755 South Grand Boulevard, Saint Louis, Missouri, Zip 63104–1540, tel. 314/577–6027; Raymond Alvey, Chief Financial Officer) **A**1 2 3 5 8 10 **F**3 4 6 7 8 9 11 14 15 17 18 20 22 24 26 28 29 30 31 34 35 36 37 38 39 40 43 44 45 46 47 48 49 50 51 55 56 57 58 59 60 61 63 64 65 68 70 74 75 77 78 79 81 82 84 85 86 87 90 91 92 93 94 96 97 98 100 101 102 103 104 107 108 110 111 112 113 114 115 116 117 118 119 121 123 124 126 129 130 131 132 135 136 138 139 141 142 146 147 148 149 150 **P**1 6 **S** SSM Health, Saint Louis, MO
Primary Contact: Kathleen R. Becker, M.P.H., JD, President
COO: Robert William Hoefer FACHE, Chief Operating Officer
CFO: Raymond Alvey, Chief Financial Officer
CMO: Nirav Patel M.D., Interim Chief Medical Officer
CIO: Patrick Brennan, Director Information System Technology
Web address: www.sluhospital.com
Control: Church operated, Nongovernment, not-for-profit **Service:** General medical and surgical

Staffed Beds: 356 Admissions: 16900 Census: 276 Outpatient Visits: 158635 Births: 0 Total Expense ($000): 488327 Payroll Expense ($000): 127987 Personnel: 1661

★ **SSM HEALTH ST. MARY'S HOSPITAL - ST. LOUIS (260091)**, 6420 Clayton Road, Zip 63117–1811, Mailing Address: Richmond Heights, tel. 314/768–8000 **A**2 5 **F**3 4 13 15 17 18 20 22 24 26 28 29 30 31 34 35 37 38 40 44 45 46 48 49 50 51 55 56 57 58 59 60 61 64 66 70 72 73 74 75 76 78 79 81 82 84 85 86 87 97 98 100 101 102 103 104 105 107 108 110 111 114 115 119 120 121 126 129 130 132 135 143 144 146 147 148 149 **P**6 8 **S** SSM Health, Saint Louis, MO
Primary Contact: Travis Capers, FACHE, President
CFO: Karen Rewerts, System Vice President of Finance
CMO: Stephen Kelly M.D., Chief Medical Officer
CIO: Michael Paasch, Regional Chief Information Officer
Web address: www.stmarys-stlouis.com
Control: Church operated, Nongovernment, not-for-profit **Service:** General medical and surgical

Staffed Beds: 381 Admissions: 18671 Census: 265 Outpatient Visits: 246125 Births: 3456 Total Expense ($000): 359919 Payroll Expense ($000): 119022 Personnel: 1864

☐ **ST. ALEXIUS HOSPITAL - BROADWAY CAMPUS (260210)**, 3933 South Broadway, Zip 63118–4601; tel. 314/865–7000, (Includes SOUTHPOINTE HOSPITAL, 2639 Miami Street, Saint Louis, Missouri, Zip 63118–3929, tel. 314/772–1456; ST. ALEXIUS HOSPITAL - FOREST PARK CAMPUS, 6150 Oakland Avenue, Saint Louis, Missouri, Zip 63139–3215, tel. 314/768–3000; Michael J. Motte, Chief Executive Officer) **A**1 5 10 **F**3 12 15 20 29 30 35 38 39 40 56 57 59 60 68 70 74 77 78 79 81 86 87 98 101 102 103 104 107 108 111 118 119 130 143 146 148 **P**6 **S** Success Healthcare, Boca Raton, FL
Primary Contact: Michael J. Motte, Chief Executive Officer
CFO: Matthew Brandt, Chief Financial Officer
Web address: www.stalexiushospital.com
Control: Corporation, Investor-owned (for-profit) **Service:** General medical and surgical

Staffed Beds: 189 Admissions: 3760 Census: 107 Outpatient Visits: 30082 Births: 0 Total Expense ($000): 62350 Payroll Expense ($000): 34797 Personnel: 674

✉ △ **ST. ANTHONY'S MEDICAL CENTER (260077)**, 10010 Kennerly Road, Zip 63128–2106; tel. 314/525–1000 **A**1 2 3 5 7 10 **F**3 4 5 11 12 13 15 17 18 20 22 24 26 28 29 30 31 34 35 36 38 40 41 43 47 48 49 50 51 53 54 56 57 58 59 60 61 62 63 64 65 66 70 73 74 75 76 77 78 79 80 81 82 84 85 86 87 90 91 92 93 94 95 96 97 98 99 100 101 102 103 104 105 107 108 110 111 114 115 116 117 118 119 120 121 122 123 124 126 129 130 131 132 143 144 146 147 148 149 **P**6 **S** Mercy, Chesterfield, MO
Primary Contact: Michael McCurry, President
COO: Bill Hoefer, Chief Operating Officer
CFO: Brent Singer, Chief Financial Officer
CMO: Rajesh Swaminathan M.D., Chief Medical Officer
CIO: Jim Weldon, Chief Information Officer
CNO: Russell Schroeder, Chief Nursing Officer
Web address: www.stanthonysmedcenter.com
Control: Other not-for-profit (including NFP Corporation) **Service:** General medical and surgical

Staffed Beds: 550 Admissions: 25305 Census: 317 Outpatient Visits: 741192 Births: 1058 Total Expense ($000): 495972 Payroll Expense ($000): 222964 Personnel: 3110

ST. JOHN'S MERCY CHILDREN'S HOSPITAL See Mercy Children's Hospital St. Louis

ST. JOHN'S MERCY MEDICAL CENTER See Mercy Hospital St. Louis

✉ △ **ST. LOUIS CHILDREN'S HOSPITAL (263301)**, One Children's Place, Zip 63110–1002; tel. 314/454–6000 **A**1 3 5 7 8 10 **F**3 5 7 8 11 16 17 19 20 21 22 23 25 26 27 29 30 31 32 34 35 38 39 40 41 43 44 45 46 47 48 49 50 54 57 58 59 60 61 62 63 64 65 68 71 72 74 75 77 78 79 81 82 83 84 85 86 87 88 89 90 91 92 93 95 96 99 100 101 102 104 107 108 109 111 112 114 115 119 129 130 131 132 134 135 136 137 138 139 140 141 142 143 145 146 148 149 150 **S** BJC HealthCare, Saint Louis, MO
Primary Contact: Joan Magruder, President
CFO: Michele McKee, Vice President and Chief Financial Officer
CMO: F Sessions Cole M.D., Chief Medical Officer
Web address: www.stlouischildrens.org
Control: Other not-for-profit (including NFP Corporation) **Service:** Children's general medical and surgical

Staffed Beds: 280 Admissions: 10469 Census: 213 Outpatient Visits: 325441 Births: 0 Total Expense ($000): 572663 Payroll Expense ($000): 204315 Personnel: 2743

☐ **ST. LOUIS PSYCHIATRIC REHABILITATION CENTER (264010)**, 5300 Arsenal Street, Zip 63139–1463; tel. 314/877–6501 **A**1 10 **F**11 30 39 65 68 75 86 87 98 100 101 106 130 143 146
Primary Contact: Laurent D. Javois, Chief Executive Officer
COO: Felix T Vincenz, Chief Operating Officer
CFO: James D Martin, Chief Financial Officer
CMO: Roy Wilson M.D., Medical Director
CHR: Michael McFarlane, Chief Human Resource Officer
CNO: Deborah Mokry, Chief Nurse Executive
Web address: www.dmh.missouri.gov
Control: State, Government, Nonfederal **Service:** Psychiatric

Staffed Beds: 180 Admissions: 41 Census: 180 Outpatient Visits: 0 Births: 0 Total Expense ($000): 35245 Payroll Expense ($000): 18259 Personnel: 512

✉ △ **THE REHABILITATION INSTITUTE OF ST. LOUIS (263028)**, 4455 Duncan Avenue, Zip 63110–1111; tel. 314/658–3800 **A**1 3 7 10 **F**29 44 56 58 60 64 68 74 75 79 82 87 90 91 93 94 100 130 132 143 146 148 149 150 **S** HEALTHSOUTH Corporation, Birmingham, AL
Primary Contact: Tara Diebling, Chief Executive Officer
CFO: Tara Diebling, Chief Executive Officer
CMO: David Carr M.D., Physician Medical Director
CHR: Heather Savage, Director Human Resources
CNO: Angelina Sherman R.N., MSN, Chief Nursing Officer
Web address: www.rehabinstitutestl.com
Control: Partnership, Investor-owned (for-profit) **Service:** Rehabilitation

Staffed Beds: 96 Admissions: 1951 Census: 77 Outpatient Visits: 38046 Births: 0 Total Expense ($000): 36620 Payroll Expense ($000): 17660 Personnel: 258

MO

Many Facility Codes have changed. Please refer to the AHA Guide Code Chart. © 2017 AHA Guide

✠ △ **VETERANS AFFAIRS ST. LOUIS HEALTH CARE SYSTEM**, 915 North Grand, Zip 63106–1621; tel. 314/652–4100, (Nonreporting) **A**1 3 5 7 **S** Department of Veterans Affairs, Washington, DC
Primary Contact: Keith D. Repko, Director
CFO: Karen Westerheide, Chief Financial Officer
CIO: Steve Warmbold, Director Information Management Service Line
CHR: Marie Lewis, Human Resources Liaison
CNO: Richard Holt R.N., Associate Director Patient Care Services
Web address: www.stlouis.va.gov/
Control: Veterans Affairs, Government, federal **Service:** General medical and surgical

Staffed Beds: 356

SAINT PETERS—St. Charles County

✠ **BARNES-JEWISH ST. PETERS HOSPITAL (260191)**, 10 Hospital Drive, Zip 63376–1659; tel. 636/916–9000 **A**1 3 5 10 **F**3 11 15 18 20 22 26 28 29 30 31 34 35 40 45 46 49 51 57 59 64 70 75 77 78 79 81 85 86 93 107 108 110 111 115 118 119 120 121 123 129 130 132 135 146 147 148 149 **S** BJC HealthCare, Saint Louis, MO
Primary Contact: Chris Watts, President
CFO: Glen Schwaegel, Vice President and Chief Financial Officer
CMO: Feliipe Orellana, Chief Medical Officer
CIO: Cindy Gross, Director of Finance
CHR: Michael J Miller, Director Human Resources
CNO: Jill Skyles R.N., Vice President Patient Care Services and Chief Nurse Executive
Web address: www.bjsph.org/
Control: Other not-for-profit (including NFP Corporation) **Service:** General medical and surgical

Staffed Beds: 101 Admissions: 4939 Census: 56 Outpatient Visits: 90644 Births: 0 Total Expense ($000): 117031 Payroll Expense ($000): 40946 Personnel: 537

SALEM—Dent County

★ **SALEM MEMORIAL DISTRICT HOSPITAL (261318)**, Highway 72 North, Zip 65560–0774, Mailing Address: P.O.Box 774, 65560–0774; tel. 573/729–6626, (Total facility includes 18 beds in nursing home–type unit) **A**10 18 **F**3 7 11 29 30 34 40 59 60 62 67 75 81 85 87 89 107 115 119 127 128 130 133 135 146
Primary Contact: Kasey Lucas, Chief Executive Officer, Hospital Administrator
CFO: Becky Cunningham, Controller
CMO: John Demorlis M.D., Chief Medical Staff
CHR: Jodie Gorman, Director Human Resources
Web address: www.smdh.net
Control: Hospital district or authority, Government, Nonfederal **Service:** General medical and surgical

Staffed Beds: 43 Admissions: 591 Census: 24 Outpatient Visits: 34400 Births: 0 Total Expense ($000): 20316 Payroll Expense ($000): 8561 Personnel: 195

SEDALIA—Pettis County

✠ **BOTHWELL REGIONAL HEALTH CENTER (260009)**, 601 East 14th Street, Zip 65301–5972, Mailing Address: P.O.Box 1706, 65302–1706; tel. 660/826–8833, (Total facility includes 10 beds in nursing home–type unit) **A**1 10 **F**3 9 11 13 14 15 18 20 22 28 29 30 31 34 35 39 40 51 54 56 57 59 60 64 65 68 70 73 74 75 76 77 78 79 80 81 82 84 85 86 87 89 92 93 107 108 110 111 114 115 116 117 118 119 120 121 123 124 127 128 129 130 131 132 135 146 147 148
Primary Contact: James A. Robertson Jr, President and Chief Executive Officer
COO: Thomas Bailey, Chief Operating Officer
CIO: Tom Fairfax, Director Information Systems
CHR: Deb Clemmer, Vice President Human Resources
CNO: Regina W Crow R.N., Chief Nursing Officer
Web address: www.brhc.org
Control: City, Government, Nonfederal **Service:** General medical and surgical

Staffed Beds: 137 Admissions: 4918 Census: 61 Outpatient Visits: 126615 Births: 449 Total Expense ($000): 102103 Payroll Expense ($000): 37865 Personnel: 710

SIKESTON—Scott County

☐ **MISSOURI DELTA MEDICAL CENTER (260113)**, 1008 North Main Street, Zip 63801–5044; tel. 573/471–1600 **A**1 10 **F**3 13 15 18 28 29 30 31 34 35 37 40 50 51 53 54 56 57 59 60 62 64 68 70 74 75 76 77 78 79 81 82 84 85 86 87 89 90 93 97 98 103 107 108 109 110 111 115 116 117 118 119 126 127 129 130 131 132 144 146 147 148 149
Primary Contact: Jason Schrumpf, President
CFO: Greg Carda, Vice President Finance
Web address: www.missouridelta.com
Control: Other not-for-profit (including NFP Corporation) **Service:** General medical and surgical

Staffed Beds: 110 Admissions: 4056 Census: 52 Outpatient Visits: 223456 Births: 385 Total Expense ($000): 96264 Payroll Expense ($000): 41351 Personnel: 753

SPRINGFIELD—Greene County

★ ⇑ **COX MEDICAL CENTERS (260040)**, 1423 North Jefferson Street, Zip 65802–1988; tel. 417/269–3000, (Includes COX MEDICAL CENTER NORTH, 1423 North Jefferson Avenue, Springfield, Missouri, Zip 65802, tel. 417/269–3000; COX MEDICAL CENTER SOUTH, 3801 South National Avenue, Springfield, Missouri, Zip 65807, tel. 417/269–6000) **A**3 5 10 21 **F**3 4 5 7 11 12 13 15 17 18 19 20 22 24 26 28 29 30 31 32 34 35 38 39 40 41 42 43 44 45 46 47 48 49 50 51 52 53 54 55 56 57 58 59 60 61 62 64 65 68 69 70 71 72 74 75 76 77 78 79 80 81 82 84 85 86 87 88 89 90 92 93 94 95 96 97 98 99 100 101 102 103 104 107 108 111 114 115 116 117 118 119 120 121 124 126 127 128 129 130 131 132 134 135 143 144 146 147 148 149 150 **P**3 6 **S** CoxHealth, Springfield, MO
Primary Contact: Steven D. Edwards, President and Chief Executive Officer
CFO: Jacob McWay, Senior Vice President and Chief Financial Officer
CMO: Frank Romero M.D., Chief Medical Officer
CIO: Bruce Robison, Vice President and Chief Information Officer
CHR: John Hursh, Vice President Human Resources
CNO: Karen Kramer R.N., Vice President and System Chief Nursing Officer
Web address: www.coxhealth.com
Control: Other not-for-profit (including NFP Corporation) **Service:** General medical and surgical

Staffed Beds: 625 Admissions: 33329 Census: 445 Outpatient Visits: 1493801 Births: 3458 Total Expense ($000): 961351 Payroll Expense ($000): 317884 Personnel: 7461

☐ **LAKELAND BEHAVIORAL HEALTH SYSTEM (264024)**, 440 South Market Street, Zip 65806–2026; tel. 417/865–5581 **A**1 10 **F**98 99 103 106 130 **S** Acadia Healthcare Company, Inc., Franklin, TN
Primary Contact: Nathan Duncan, Chief Executive Officer
COO: Randy Fox, Director Performance Improvement and Risk Management
CFO: Rick Crump, Chief Financial Officer
CMO: Richard Aiken M.D., Medical Director
CIO: Brad Strothkamp, Chief Information Systems
CHR: Dave England, Director Human Resources
Web address: www.lakeland-hospital.com
Control: Corporation, Investor-owned (for-profit) **Service:** Psychiatric

Staffed Beds: 122 Admissions: 1584 Census: 107 Outpatient Visits: 0 Births: 0 Total Expense ($000): 24705 Payroll Expense ($000): 13325 Personnel: 328

✠ **MERCY HOSPITAL SPRINGFIELD (260065)**, 1235 East Cherokee Street, Zip 65804–2263; tel. 417/820–2000, (Includes MERCY CHILDREN'S HOSPITAL SPRINGFIELD, 1235 East Cherokee Street, Springfield, Missouri, Zip 65804–2203, tel. 417/820–2000; MERCY ORTHOPEDIC HOSPITAL SPRINGFIELD, 3050 East Riverbluff Boulevard, Ozark, Missouri, Zip 65721, tel. 417/820–5611; Robert Steele, M.D., President) (Total facility includes 97 beds in nursing home–type unit) **A**1 3 5 10 **F**3 4 5 7 8 9 11 12 13 14 15 16 17 18 19 20 22 24 26 28 29 30 31 32 34 35 36 37 38 39 40 43 44 45 46 49 50 51 54 55 56 57 58 59 60 61 62 63 64 65 66 67 68 70 71 72 73 74 75 76 77 78 79 81 82 84 85 86 87 88 89 90 91 92 93 94 96 97 98 100 101 102 103 104 107 108 110 111 114 115 117 118 119 120 121 123 124 126 127 128 129 130 131 132 134 135 143 146 147 148 149 150 **P**6 8 **S** Mercy, Chesterfield, MO
Primary Contact: Alan Scarrow, M.D., President
COO: Jay Guffey, Senior Vice President and Chief Operating Officer
CFO: Scott Reynolds, Vice President Finance
CMO: Allan Allphin M.D., Chief of Staff
CIO: Lori Sturgill, Vice President Business Partnership
CHR: Tanya Maricn, Interim Vice President Human Resources
Web address: www.mercy.net/springfieldmo
Control: Church operated, Nongovernment, not-for-profit **Service:** General medical and surgical

Staffed Beds: 741 Admissions: 34782 Census: 460 Outpatient Visits: 601919 Births: 2937 Total Expense ($000): 961239 Payroll Expense ($000): 341317 Personnel: 7958

MO

Hospital, Medicare Provider Number, Address, Telephone, Approval, Facility, and Physician Codes, Health Care System

★ American Hospital Association (AHA) membership   ◯ Healthcare Facilities Accreditation Program   ⇑ Center for Improvement in Healthcare Quality Accreditation
☐ The Joint Commission accreditation   ◇ DNV Healthcare Inc. accreditation   △ Commission on Accreditation of Rehabilitation Facilities (CARF) accreditation

---

☐ **MERCY REHABILITION HOSPITAL SPRINGFIELD (263032)**, 5904 South Southwood Road, Zip 65804–5234; tel. 417/227–9000 **A**1 10 **F**29 30 90 130 132 148
Primary Contact: Bruce Eady, Chief Executive Officer
CFO: Melissa Campbell, Controller
CMO: Hollis Bell M.D., Medical Director
CHR: Sarah Eiffert, Director Human Resources
CNO: Jennifer Friedline R.N., Director of Nursing
Web address: www.mercy.net
Control: Partnership, Investor-owned (for-profit) **Service**: Rehabilitation

Staffed Beds: 60 Admissions: 1251 Census: 41 Outpatient Visits: 0
Births: 0 Total Expense ($000): 15510 Payroll Expense ($000): 7093
Personnel: 152

⊞ **SELECT SPECIALTY HOSPITAL-SPRINGFIELD (262017)**, 1630 East Primrose Street, Zip 65804–7929; tel. 417/885–4700, **A**1 10 **F** 1 3 29 45 85 107 114 148 **S** Select Medical Corporation, Mechanicsburg, PA
Primary Contact: Jeff Denney, Chief Executive Officer
CHR: Tonya Eddington, Coordinator Human Resources
Web address: www.selectspecialtyhospitals.com/company/locations/springfield.aspx
Control: Corporation, Investor-owned (for-profit) **Service**: Acute long-term care hospital

Staffed Beds: 44 Admissions: 413 Census: 31 Outpatient Visits: 0
Births: 0 Total Expense ($000): 19043 Payroll Expense ($000): 8165
Personnel: 169

STE GENEVIEVE—Ste. Genevieve County

★ **STE. GENEVIEVE COUNTY MEMORIAL HOSPITAL (261330)**, 800 Ste Genevieve Drive, Zip 63670–1434; tel. 573/883–2751 **A**10 18 **F**2 3 11 13 14 15 18 28 29 31 34 35 39 40 50 53 56 57 59 62 64 65 66 68 75 76 77 78 79 81 82 85 86 87 89 92 93 107 110 111 115 119 124 127 129 130 131 132 133 135 145 146 147 148 **P**6
Primary Contact: Thomas Keim, Chief Executive Officer
CFO: Susan Eckenfels, Chief Financial Officer
CMO: Joseph Sharlow M.D., Chief of Staff
CHR: Sarah Jo Kelley, Director Human Resources
CNO: Rita Brumfield R.N., MSN, Chief Nursing Officer
Web address: www.stegenevievehospital.org
Control: County, Government, Nonfederal **Service**: General medical and surgical

Staffed Beds: 25 Admissions: 908 Census: 10 Outpatient Visits: 109555
Births: 152 Total Expense ($000): 42452 Payroll Expense ($000): 17934
Personnel: 328

SULLIVAN—Crawford County

★ **MISSOURI BAPTIST SULLIVAN HOSPITAL (261337)**, 751 Sappington Bridge Road, Zip 63080–2354; tel. 573/468–4186 **A**10 18 **F**3 4 7 11 13 15 28 29 30 31 34 35 40 53 56 57 59 63 64 65 70 75 76 77 78 79 81 82 83 84 85 86 87 89 90 93 97 98 102 103 104 107 111 115 119 127 129 130 131 132 133 146 148 **S** BJC HealthCare, Saint Louis, MO
Primary Contact: Tony Schwarm, President
CFO: Angela Wilks, Finance Director
CMO: Alison Baker M.D., Chief of Staff
CHR: Kathleen Reed, Manager Human Resources
CNO: Carmen J Bartolotta, Chief Nursing Officer
Web address: www.missouribaptistsullivan.org
Control: Other not-for-profit (including NFP Corporation) **Service**: General medical and surgical

Staffed Beds: 35 Admissions: 2043 Census: 25 Outpatient Visits: 101183
Births: 271 Total Expense ($000): 49293 Payroll Expense ($000): 20221
Personnel: 348

SWEET SPRINGS—Saline County

I-70 COMMUNITY HOSPITAL (261334), 105 Hospital Drive, Zip 65351–2229; tel. 660/335–4700 **A**10 18 **F**3 11 29 32 34 35 40 45 57 59 64 65 68 75 77 79 81 83 87 89 90 93 102 107 111 127 128 130 133 143 148 **S** Rural Community Hospitals of America, Kansas City, MO
Primary Contact: Jeff Bloemker, Chief Executive Officer
CFO: Cathy Berube, Chief Financial Officer
CMO: Deborah Herrmann M.D., Chief of Staff
CIO: Diane Swift, Director Medical Records
CHR: Tina Bredehoeft, Human Resources
CNO: Nancy Gardner, Chief Nursing Officer
Web address: www.i70medcenter.com
Control: Corporation, Investor-owned (for-profit) **Service**: General medical and surgical

Staffed Beds: 11 Admissions: 121 Census: 2 Outpatient Visits: 11203
Births: 0 Total Expense ($000): 8462 Payroll Expense ($000): 3495
Personnel: 51

TRENTON—Grundy County

★ **WRIGHT MEMORIAL HOSPITAL (261309)**, 191 Iowa Boulevard, Zip 64683–8343; tel. 660/358–5700 **A**10 18 **F**3 11 15 28 29 30 31 34 35 40 45 50 56 57 58 59 64 68 75 77 78 79 81 82 84 85 87 89 90 93 102 104 107 108 110 111 115 119 127 129 130 133 146 148 149 **P**6 **S** Saint Luke's Health System, Kansas City, MO
Primary Contact: Gary W. Jordan, FACHE, Chief Executive Officer
CFO: Leslie Reed, Chief Financial Officer
CMO: Gerald C Zabielski M.D., Chief Medical Staff
CHR: Jenny Donovan, Director Human Resources
Web address: www.saintlukeshealthsystem.org
Control: Other not-for-profit (including NFP Corporation) **Service**: General medical and surgical

Staffed Beds: 15 Admissions: 662 Census: 8 Outpatient Visits: 75240
Births: 195 Total Expense ($000): 31065 Payroll Expense ($000): 11214
Personnel: 159

TROY—Lincoln County

⊞ **MERCY HOSPITAL LINCOLN (261319)**, 1000 East Cherry Street, Zip 63379–1513; tel. 636/528–8551 **A**1 10 18 **F**3 11 15 17 18 28 29 30 34 35 40 44 45 50 51 57 59 62 64 65 68 70 75 77 79 81 85 86 87 89 90 93 104 107 110 111 113 114 119 127 129 130 131 132 133 135 144 146 149 **P**6 8 **S** Mercy, Chesterfield, MO
Primary Contact: Anthony Rothermich, Administrator
CFO: Mark Thorn FACHE, Executive Director, Finance
CIO: Travis Boyd, Manager, Information Technology
CHR: Mary Kay Kunza, Manager Human Resources
Web address: www.mercy.net
Control: Other not-for-profit (including NFP Corporation) **Service**: General medical and surgical

Staffed Beds: 25 Admissions: 872 Census: 9 Outpatient Visits: 105147
Births: 0 Total Expense ($000): 31429 Payroll Expense ($000): 14167
Personnel: 245

UNIONVILLE—Putnam County

PUTNAM COUNTY MEMORIAL HOSPITAL (261305), 1926 Oak Street, Zip 63565–1180, Mailing Address: P.O. Box 389, 63565–0389; tel. 660/947–2411 **A**10 18 **F**3 15 18 28 29 34 35 40 45 50 57 59 75 77 81 85 90 93 97 98 102 104 105 107 111 112 115 119 127 128 129 130 133 135 143 145 147 148 149 **P**5
Primary Contact: David Byrns, Chief Executive Officer
COO: Jerry Cummings, Chief Operating Officer
CMO: Dawn Ann Fairley M.D., Chief of Staff
CHR: Debbie Douglas, Director Human Resources
CNO: Gayle Pickens, Chief Nursing Officer
Web address: www.pcmhosp.com
Control: County, Government, Nonfederal **Service**: General medical and surgical

Staffed Beds: 25 Admissions: 205 Census: 10 Outpatient Visits: 15901
Births: 0 Total Expense ($000): 11413 Payroll Expense ($000): 4854
Personnel: 89

WARRENSBURG—Johnson County

⊞ **WESTERN MISSOURI MEDICAL CENTER (260097)**, 403 Burkarth Road, Zip 64093–3101; tel. 660/747–2500 **A**1 10 20 **F**3 8 11 12 13 15 17 18 28 29 30 31 32 34 35 40 43 45 47 56 57 59 61 64 65 68 70 74 75 76 77 78 79 81 82 85 89 90 93 98 102 103 107 108 110 111 115 117 118 119 127 129 130 131 132 133 135 144 146 147 148 **P**6
Primary Contact: Darinda Reberry, MSN, R.N., President and Chief Executive Officer
CFO: Terri Bradley CPA, Vice President Financial Services and Chief Financial Officer
CIO: Bill Ladd, Director Information Services
CHR: Dennis Long, Director Human Resources
CNO: Jennifer Koepke R.N., Vice President of Patient Care Services and Chief Nursing Officer
Web address: www.wmmc.com
Control: County, Government, Nonfederal **Service**: General medical and surgical

Staffed Beds: 72 Admissions: 2789 Census: 24 Outpatient Visits: 172728
Births: 689 Total Expense ($000): 88008 Payroll Expense ($000): 33547
Personnel: 647

MO

WASHINGTON—Franklin County

☒ **MERCY HOSPITAL WASHINGTON (260052)**, 901 East Fifth Street, Zip 63090–3127; tel. 636/239–8000 **A**1 10 **F**3 8 11 12 13 14 15 17 18 20 22 26 28 29 30 31 32 34 35 39 40 43 44 46 48 49 50 51 52 53 54 57 59 61 64 66 68 69 70 73 74 75 76 77 78 79 80 81 82 84 85 87 89 90 93 94 96 97 98 99 100 101 104 105 107 108 110 111 114 116 117 118 119 120 121 123 127 129 130 131 132 134 135 143 144 146 147 **P**6 8 **S** Mercy, Chesterfield, MO
Primary Contact: Eric J. Eoloff, President
COO: Joan Frost R.N., Chief Operating Officer
CFO: Cheryl Matejka, Chief Financial Officer
CMO: Thomas Riechers M.D., Chief Medical Staff
CIO: Michael McCreary, Chief of Services
CHR: Barbara Grayson, Vice President Human Resources
CNO: Stacy Blankenship, Chief Nursing Officer
Web address: www.mercy.net
Control: Other not-for-profit (including NFP Corporation) **Service**: General medical and surgical

Staffed Beds: 148 **Admissions:** 5923 **Census:** 52 **Outpatient Visits:** 333841 **Births:** 861 **Total Expense ($000):** 151219 **Payroll Expense ($000):** 58218 **Personnel:** 796

WENTZVILLE—St. Charles County

SSM HEALTH ST. JOSEPH - WENTZVILLE See Ssm Health St. Joseph - St. Charles, Saint Charles

WEST PLAINS—Howell County

☒ **OZARKS MEDICAL CENTER (260078)**, 1100 Kentucky Avenue, Zip 65775–2029, Mailing Address: P.O.Box 1100, 65775–1100; tel. 417/256–9111 **A**1 10 **F**2 3 5 11 13 15 17 18 20 22 24 28 29 30 31 34 38 40 44 45 49 50 57 59 61 62 63 64 68 70 74 75 76 77 78 79 81 82 84 85 86 87 89 90 91 93 94 98 99 100 101 102 103 104 107 108 110 111 115 118 119 120 121 127 129 130 131 132 135 144 145 146 147 148 **P**8
Primary Contact: Thomas Keller, President and Chief Executive Officer
COO: Pamela R. Lee, Chief Operating Officer
CFO: Kim Thompson, Vice President and Chief Financial Officer
CMO: Walter R Holloway, Chief Medical Officer
CIO: John Wilcox, Chief Information Officer
CHR: Connie Schott, Vice President, Human Resources
CNO: Kurt Abbey, Chief Nursing Officer
Web address: www.ozarksmedicalcenter.com
Control: Other not-for-profit (including NFP Corporation) **Service**: General medical and surgical

Staffed Beds: 103 **Admissions:** 5326 **Census:** 50 **Outpatient Visits:** 546721 **Births:** 599 **Total Expense ($000):** 141672 **Payroll Expense ($000):** 62080 **Personnel:** 1008

WINDSOR—Henry County

☐ **ROYAL OAKS HOSPITAL (264020)**, 307 North Main, Zip 65360–1449; tel. 660/647–2182 **A**1 3 5 10 **F**4 35 59 98 99 100 101 102 103 135 149 150 **P**6
Primary Contact: Alan W. Greiman, Chief Executive Officer and President
CFO: Jake Matthew Krafve, Chief Financial Officer
CMO: Syed Arshad Husain M.D., Executive Vice President and Chief Medical Officer
CIO: Richard Colvert, Chief Information Officer
CHR: Diane Coletta, Vice President Human Resources
CNO: Erin Allee R.N., Director of Nursing
Web address: www.compasshealthnetwork.org
Control: Other not-for-profit (including NFP Corporation) **Service**: Psychiatric

Staffed Beds: 41 **Admissions:** 1331 **Census:** 27 **Outpatient Visits:** 0 **Births:** 0 **Total Expense ($000):** 13493 **Payroll Expense ($000):** 6870 **Personnel:** 161

MO

MONTANA

ANACONDA—Deer Lodge County

★ **COMMUNITY HOSPITAL OF ANACONDA (271335)**, 401 West Pennsylvania Street, Zip 59711; tel. 406/563–8500, (Total facility includes 32 beds in nursing home–type unit) **A**10 18 **F**3 8 11 13 15 29 30 31 34 35 40 45 50 54 57 59 62 63 64 74 75 76 77 78 79 81 82 87 93 97 99 104 107 111 114 116 119 128 130 133 135 143 144 146 148 **P**6
Primary Contact: Steve McNeece, President and Chief Executive Officer
CFO: Laura Austin, Vice President Finance and Chief Financial Officer
CMO: Freddy Bartoletti M.D., Chief of Staff
CHR: Meg Hickey-Boynton, Director Human Resources and Marketing
CNO: Jamie Johnson R.N., Vice President Nursing
Web address: www.communityhospitalofanaconda.org
Control: Other not-for-profit (including NFP Corporation) **Service**: General medical and surgical

Staffed Beds: 87 Admissions: 1287 Census: 46 Outpatient Visits: 76945 Births: 222 Total Expense ($000): 61367 Payroll Expense ($000): 26519 Personnel: 358

BAKER—Fallon County

FALLON MEDICAL COMPLEX (271301), 202 South 4th Street West, Zip 59313–9156, Mailing Address: P.O.Box 820, 59313–0820; tel. 406/778–3331, (Total facility includes 15 beds in nursing home–type unit) **A**10 18 **F**11 15 32 34 40 56 57 59 62 64 65 66 68 69 75 93 97 107 110 114 119 127 128 130 133 146 148 149 **P**6
Primary Contact: David Espeland, Chief Executive Officer
CFO: Selena Nelson, Chief Financial Officer
CMO: Darryl Espeland D.O., Chief Medical Staff
CIO: Susan Stevens, Information Technology Specialist
CHR: Theresa Myers, Personnel Director
CNO: Susan Lunde R.N., Director of Nursing
Web address: www.fallonmedical.org
Control: Other not-for-profit (including NFP Corporation) **Service**: General medical and surgical

Staffed Beds: 40 Admissions: 191 Census: 19 Outpatient Visits: 18090 Births: 0 Total Expense ($000): 9869 Payroll Expense ($000): 4278 Personnel: 82

BIG SANDY—Chouteau County

★ **BIG SANDY MEDICAL CENTER (271311)**, 166 Montana Avenue East, Zip 59520–8474, Mailing Address: P.O.Box 530, 59520–0530; tel. 406/378–2188, (Total facility includes 22 beds in nursing home–type unit) **A**10 18 **F**40 64 93 127 128 133
Primary Contact: Leah Griffith, Chief Executive Officer
CFO: Nora Grubb, Chief Financial Officer
Web address: www.bsmc.org
Control: Other not-for-profit (including NFP Corporation) **Service**: General medical and surgical

Staffed Beds: 30 Admissions: 49 Census: 18 Outpatient Visits: 3803 Births: 0 Total Expense ($000): 3262 Payroll Expense ($000): 1736 Personnel: 30

BIG SKY—Gallatin County

BOZEMAN HEALTH BIG SKY MEDICAL CENTER, 334 Town Center Avenue, Zip 59716, Mailing Address: P.O. Box 161529, 59716–1529; tel. 406/995–6995 (Nonreporting)
Primary Contact: Tracy Reamy, Administrator
Web address: www.bigskymedicalcenter.org/
Control: Other not-for-profit (including NFP Corporation) **Service**: General medical and surgical

Staffed Beds: 4

BIG TIMBER—Sweet Grass County

★ **PIONEER MEDICAL CENTER (271313)**, 301 West Seventh Avenue, Zip 59011–7893, Mailing Address: P.O.Box 1228, 59011–1228; tel. 406/932–4603 **A**10 18 **F**2 7 10 28 29 34 35 40 45 57 59 63 64 65 69 75 77 93 97 107 114 119 127 130 131 132 133 **P**6
Primary Contact: Gary Hamilton, Interim Chief Executive Officer
CFO: Kyle Gee, Chief Financial Officer
CMO: Benjamin P Bullington M.D., Chief of Staff
CHR: Miki Gregorich, Director Human Resources
CNO: Randi Pike, Director of Nursing
Web address: www.pmcmt.org/
Control: Other not-for-profit (including NFP Corporation) **Service**: General medical and surgical

Staffed Beds: 25 Admissions: 183 Census: 42 Outpatient Visits: 10001 Births: 0 Total Expense ($000): 7244 Payroll Expense ($000): 2852 Personnel: 106

BILLINGS—Yellowstone County

☐ **ADVANCED CARE HOSPITAL OF MONTANA (272001)**, 3528 Gabel Road, Zip 59102–7307; tel. 406/373–8000 (Nonreporting) **A**1 10 **S** Ernest Health, Inc., Albuquerque, NM
Primary Contact: Judi Powers, Chief Executive Officer
Web address: www.achm.ernesthealth.com
Control: Corporation, Investor-owned (for-profit) **Service**: Acute long-term care hospital

Staffed Beds: 40

⊞ **BILLINGS CLINIC (270004)**, 2800 10th Avenue North, Zip 59101–0703, Mailing Address: P.O.Box 37000, 59107–7000; tel. 406/657–4000, (Total facility includes 125 beds in nursing home–type unit) **A**1 2 3 10 19 **F**3 7 8 9 10 11 12 13 15 17 18 19 20 22 24 26 27 28 29 30 31 32 34 35 36 38 40 41 43 44 45 46 48 49 50 51 52 54 55 56 57 58 59 60 61 62 63 64 65 66 68 70 71 72 74 75 76 77 78 79 81 82 84 85 86 87 89 91 92 93 97 98 99 100 101 102 103 104 105 107 108 110 111 114 115 116 117 118 119 120 121 124 126 128 129 130 131 132 134 135 143 146 147 148 **P**6
Primary Contact: Randall K. Gibb, M.D., Chief Executive Officer
CFO: Connie F Prewitt, Chief Financial Officer
CMO: Randall K. Gibb M.D., Chief Executive Officer
CIO: Chris E Stevens, Chief Information Officer
CHR: Karla Stauffer, Executive Director People Resources
CNO: Lu Byrd R.N., MSN, Vice President Hospital Operations and Chief Nursing Officer
Web address: www.billingsclinic.com
Control: Other not-for-profit (including NFP Corporation) **Service**: General medical and surgical

Staffed Beds: 400 Admissions: 15609 Census: 269 Outpatient Visits: 851749 Births: 1278 Total Expense ($000): 602306 Payroll Expense ($000): 302017 Personnel: 3587

⊞ △ **ST. VINCENT HEALTHCARE (270049)**, 1233 North 30th Street, Zip 59101–0165, Mailing Address: P.O.Box 35200, 59107–5200; tel. 406/237–7000 **A**1 2 3 7 10 **F**3 7 11 12 13 15 18 19 20 22 24 26 28 29 30 31 32 34 35 36 37 38 40 43 44 46 47 49 50 51 56 57 58 59 60 61 64 68 70 71 72 74 75 76 77 78 79 81 82 84 85 86 87 88 89 90 92 93 97 99 100 101 103 104 107 108 111 114 115 116 117 118 119 120 121 123 124 126 129 130 131 132 134 135 143 144 145 146 147 148 149 **P**6 **S** SCL Health, Broomfield, CO
Primary Contact: Steve Loveless, President and Chief Executive Officer
CMO: Michael Schweitzer M.D., Chief Medical Officer
CIO: Al Rooney, Director Information Systems
Web address: www.svh-mt.org
Control: Church operated, Nongovernment, not-for-profit **Service**: General medical and surgical

Staffed Beds: 221 Admissions: 11629 Census: 145 Outpatient Visits: 179216 Births: 1631 Total Expense ($000): 337201 Payroll Expense ($000): 107306 Personnel: 1767

BOZEMAN—Gallatin County

⊞ **BOZEMAN HEALTH DEACONESS HOSPITAL (270057)**, 915 Highland Boulevard, Zip 59715–6902; tel. 406/585–5000, (Nonreporting) **A**1 2 10 20 **S** Bozeman Health, Broomfield, CO
Primary Contact: John Hill, President and Chief Executive Officer
CFO: Gordon L Davidson, Chief Financial Officer
CMO: David Chen M.D., Chief Medical Officer
Web address: www.bozemandeaconess.org
Control: Corporation, Investor-owned (for-profit) **Service**: General medical and surgical

Staffed Beds: 86

BUTTE—Silver Bow County

✠ **ST. JAMES HEALTHCARE (270017)**, 400 South Clark Street, Zip 59701–2328; tel. 406/723–2500 **A**1 10 **F**3 11 13 15 18 20 22 26 28 29 30 31 34 35 40 43 45 47 48 49 50 51 56 57 59 64 65 68 70 71 72 75 76 77 78 79 81 82 85 86 87 89 91 92 93 94 97 107 108 110 111 114 115 118 119 120 121 123 126 127 130 131 132 135 146 147 148 149 **S** SCL Health, Broomfield, CO
Primary Contact: Jay Doyle, President and Chief Executive Officer
CFO: David Brain, Interim Vice President Finance
CMO: Dennis Salisbury M.D., Vice President for Medical Affairs
CHR: Trisha Palmer, Director
CNO: Mary Winters, Interim Chief Nursing Officer
Web address: www.stjameshealthcare.org
Control: Other not-for-profit (including NFP Corporation) **Service**: General medical and surgical

Staffed Beds: 67 **Admissions:** 3235 **Census:** 36 **Outpatient Visits:** 58591
Births: 283 **Total Expense ($000):** 99673 **Payroll Expense ($000):** 34710
Personnel: 476

CHESTER—Liberty County

LIBERTY MEDICAL CENTER (271334), 315 West Madison Avenue, Zip 59522, Mailing Address: P.O.Box 705, 59522–0705; tel. 406/759–5181 **A**10 18 **F**2 3 10 11 34 35 40 43 45 56 57 59 64 67 81 86 87 93 97 107 114 119 127 128 130 133 **P**6
Primary Contact: Matthew Waller, Chief Executive Officer
CMO: Gladys Young M.D., Chief of Staff
CHR: Bev Halter, Director Human Resources and Payroll
CNO: Shirley Morkrid, Chief Nursing Officer
Web address: www.lchnh.org
Control: Other not-for-profit (including NFP Corporation) **Service**: General medical and surgical

Staffed Beds: 25 **Admissions:** 34 **Census:** 1 **Outpatient Visits:** 7969
Births: 0 **Total Expense ($000):** 6689 **Payroll Expense ($000):** 3159
Personnel: 87

CHOTEAU—Teton County

BENEFIS TETON MEDICAL CENTER (271307), 915 4th Street North West, Zip 59422–9123; tel. 406/466–5763, (Total facility includes 36 beds in nursing home–type unit) **A**10 18 **F**2 3 34 35 40 41 43 56 57 59 68 77 87 93 107 127 128 133 143 146 **S** Benefis Health System, Great Falls, MT
Primary Contact: Louie King, Chief Executive Officer
Web address: www.tetonmedicalcenter.net
Control: Hospital district or authority, Government, Nonfederal **Service**: General medical and surgical

Staffed Beds: 46 **Admissions:** 168 **Census:** 28 **Outpatient Visits:** 6991
Births: 1

CIRCLE—McCone County

★ **MCCONE COUNTY HEALTH CENTER (271305)**, 605 Sullivan Avenue, Zip 59215, Mailing Address: P.O.Box 48, 59215–0048; tel. 406/485–3381 **A**10 18 **F**2 3 11 34 40 41 57 58 59 65 69 86 87 93 133 135 143 146 149
Primary Contact: Nancy Rosaaen, Chief Executive Officer
CFO: Nancy Rosaaen, Chief Executive Officer
CHR: Jacque Gardner, Administrative Assistant, Clinic Manager, Co-Chief Financial Officer and Chief Human Resources
Web address: www.mcconehealth.org/
Control: County, Government, Nonfederal **Service**: General medical and surgical

Staffed Beds: 25 **Admissions:** 48 **Census:** 23 **Outpatient Visits:** 675
Births: 0 **Total Expense ($000):** 3527 **Payroll Expense ($000):** 1400
Personnel: 37

COLUMBUS—Stillwater County

★ **STILLWATER BILLINGS CLINIC (271330)**, 44 West Fourth Avenue North, Zip 59019–0959, Mailing Address: P.O.Box 959, 59019–0959; tel. 406/322–5316 **A**10 18 **F**3 15 28 32 34 35 40 43 45 50 59 62 64 65 68 75 83 93 107 110 114 127 133 144 **P**1
Primary Contact: Mike Follett, Interim Chief Executive Officer
Web address: www.billingsclinic.com
Control: Other not-for-profit (including NFP Corporation) **Service**: General medical and surgical

Staffed Beds: 10 **Admissions:** 133 **Census:** 2 **Outpatient Visits:** 13443
Births: 0 **Total Expense ($000):** 8962 **Payroll Expense ($000):** 2316
Personnel: 49

CONRAD—Pondera County

PONDERA MEDICAL CENTER (271324), 805 Sunset Boulevard, Zip 59425–1717, Mailing Address: P.O.Box 668, 59425–0668; tel. 406/271–3211, (Total facility includes 59 beds in nursing home–type unit) **A**10 18 **F**3 6 7 11 13 15 28 29 34 35 40 43 53 57 59 62 63 65 66 77 81 87 91 93 97 102 107 111 115 119 127 128 129 130 133 144 146 147 148 **P**6
Primary Contact: Bill O'Leary, Chief Executive Officer
CFO: Brigid Burke, Chief Financial Officer
CMO: Jay Taylor M.D., Chief of Medical Staff
CIO: Sean Kavanagh, Director Information Technology
CHR: Patrick Johnson, Director Human Resources
CNO: Laura Erickson R.N., Chief Nursing Officer
Web address: www.ponderamedical.org
Control: Other not-for-profit (including NFP Corporation) **Service**: General medical and surgical

Staffed Beds: 79 **Admissions:** 109 **Census:** 55 **Outpatient Visits:** 6398
Births: 2 **Total Expense ($000):** 13210 **Payroll Expense ($000):** 6921
Personnel: 194

CROW AGENCY—Big Horn County

CROW/NORTHERN CHEYENNE HOSPITAL (271339), 10110 South 7650 East, Zip 59022–0009, Mailing Address: P.O.Box 9, 59022–0009; tel. 406/638–2626, (Nonreporting) **A**3 10 18 **S** U. S. Indian Health Service, Rockville, MD
Primary Contact: Darren Crowe, Chief Executive Officer
CMO: Jim Upchurch M.D., Chief Medical Officer
CIO: Melanie Falls Down, Site Manager
Web address: www.ihs.gov/billings/healthcarefacilities/crow/
Control: PHS, Indian Service, Government, federal **Service**: General medical and surgical

Staffed Beds: 24

CULBERTSON—Roosevelt County

★ **ROOSEVELT MEDICAL CENTER (271308)**, 818 Second Avenue East, Zip 59218, Mailing Address: P.O.Box 419, 59218–0419; tel. 406/787–6401, (Total facility includes 22 beds in nursing home–type unit) **A**10 18 **F**2 3 7 15 34 35 40 43 50 56 57 59 65 69 77 82 93 97 119 127 128 130 133 143 146 147 **P**6
Primary Contact: Audrey Stromberg, Administrator
CFO: Jennifer Kessner, Financial Director
CMO: Don Helland M.D., Chief Medical Officer
CIO: Brian Fordyce, Director Information Technology
CHR: Elizabeth Raaum, Manger Business Office
CNO: Jessica Schmitz, Director of Nursing
Web address: www.roosmem.org
Control: Other not-for-profit (including NFP Corporation) **Service**: General medical and surgical

Staffed Beds: 25 **Admissions:** 51 **Census:** 22 **Outpatient Visits:** 8375
Births: 0 **Total Expense ($000):** 5618 **Payroll Expense ($000):** 3083
Personnel: 57

CUT BANK—Glacier County

★ **NORTHERN ROCKIES MEDICAL CENTER (271337)**, 802 Second Street SE, Zip 59427–3329; tel. 406/873–2251 **A**10 18 **F**13 40 57 59 65 76 81 93 107 119 127 128 133 149
Primary Contact: Cherie Taylor, Chief Executive Officer
CFO: Treasure Berkram, Chief Financial Officer
CMO: Adron Medley M.D., Chief Medical Staff
CHR: Kandie Lemieux, Administrative Assistant and Director Human Resources
Web address: www.nrmcinc.org
Control: Other not-for-profit (including NFP Corporation) **Service**: General medical and surgical

Staffed Beds: 29 **Admissions:** 239 **Census:** 2 **Outpatient Visits:** 10411
Births: 34 **Total Expense ($000):** 9020 **Payroll Expense ($000):** 5556
Personnel: 82

MT

DEER LODGE—Powell County

DEER LODGE MEDICAL CENTER (271314), 1100 Hollenbeck Lane, Zip 59722–2317; tel. 406/846–2212 **A**10 18 **F**15 30 32 33 34 35 40 45 47 49 50 51 55 56 57 59 64 65 79 81 82 84 85 86 87 91 93 97 107 108 110 119 127 128 133 147 **P**6
Primary Contact: Tony Pfaff, Chief Executive Officer
CFO: Jaena Richards, Chief Financial Officer
CMO: Michelle Corbin M.D., Chief of Staff
CIO: Chris Foster, Director Health Information Management
Web address: www.dlmed.org/
Control: Corporation, Investor-owned (for-profit) **Service:** General medical and surgical

> **Staffed Beds:** 16 **Admissions:** 305 **Census:** 4 **Outpatient Visits:** 9118
> **Births:** 0 **Total Expense ($000):** 10809 **Payroll Expense ($000):** 4452
> **Personnel:** 99

DILLON—Beaverhead County

★ **BARRETT HOSPITAL & HEALTHCARE (271318)**, 600 Mt Highway 91 South, Zip 59725–7379; tel. 406/683–3000 **A**5 10 18 **F**3 13 15 28 31 34 40 45 50 57 59 62 63 64 65 69 75 76 77 79 80 81 83 84 85 87 89 93 96 97 107 110 111 115 119 130 133 135 144 146 **S** HealthTech Management Services, Brentwood, TN
Primary Contact: Ken Westman, Chief Executive Officer
CFO: Dick Achter, Chief Financial Officer
CMO: Carol Kennedy, Chief Clinical Officer
CIO: Dick Achter, Chief Financial Officer
CHR: Geoff Roach, Director Human Resources
Web address: www.barretthospital.org
Control: Hospital district or authority, Government, Nonfederal **Service:** General medical and surgical

> **Staffed Beds:** 18 **Admissions:** 487 **Census:** 4 **Outpatient Visits:** 33205
> **Births:** 70 **Total Expense ($000):** 32068 **Payroll Expense ($000):** 14148
> **Personnel:** 229

EKALAKA—Carter County

DAHL MEMORIAL HEALTHCARE ASSOCIATION (271302), 215 Sandy Street, Zip 59324, Mailing Address: P.O.Box 46, 59324–0046; tel. 406/775–8730 **A**10 18 **F**2 7 40 41 57 59 65 69 127 130 131 133 135 143 146 147 148 **P**6
Primary Contact: Nadine Elmore, Chief Executive Officer
CFO: Nadine Elmore, Chief Executive Officer
CMO: Darryl Espeland D.O., Medical Director
CIO: Davie Ann Barrere, Coordinator Information Technology
CHR: Melissa Matthews, Director Human Resources
CNO: Patricia Rogers, Director of Nursing
Web address: www.dahlmemorial.com
Control: Other not-for-profit (including NFP Corporation) **Service:** General medical and surgical

> **Staffed Beds:** 25 **Admissions:** 61 **Census:** 19 **Outpatient Visits:** 4447
> **Births:** 0 **Total Expense ($000):** 3061 **Payroll Expense ($000):** 1426
> **Personnel:** 35

ENNIS—Madison County

MADISON VALLEY MEDICAL CENTER (271329), 305 North Main Street, Zip 59729–8001; tel. 406/682–4222 **A**10 18 **F**3 8 11 28 29 32 34 35 36 38 40 43 45 46 50 53 56 57 59 64 65 66 71 75 77 87 92 93 94 97 107 114 119 127 128 130 131 132 133 135 148
Primary Contact: Allen Rohrback, Chief Executive Officer
CMO: Cindy Sharp M.D., Chief Medical Officer
CIO: Bo Nix, Chief Information Officer
Web address: www.mvmedcenter.org
Control: Other not-for-profit (including NFP Corporation) **Service:** General medical and surgical

> **Staffed Beds:** 10 **Admissions:** 221 **Census:** 4 **Outpatient Visits:** 5868
> **Births:** 0

FORSYTH—Rosebud County

★ **ROSEBUD HEALTH CARE CENTER (271327)**, 383 North 17th Avenue, Zip 59327–0268, Mailing Address: P.O.Box 268, 59327–0268; tel. 406/346–2161, (Total facility includes 31 beds in nursing home–type unit) **A**10 18 **F**2 30 32 128
Primary Contact: Ryan Tooke, Chief Executive Officer
CMO: William Anderson M.D., Medical Director
CHR: Karla Allies, Director Human Resources
Web address: www.rosebudhealthcare.com/
Control: Other not-for-profit (including NFP Corporation) **Service:** General medical and surgical

> **Staffed Beds:** 55 **Admissions:** 232 **Census:** 26 **Outpatient Visits:** 10526
> **Births:** 0 **Total Expense ($000):** 7166 **Payroll Expense ($000):** 4320

FORT BENTON—Chouteau County

MISSOURI RIVER MEDICAL CENTER (271304), 1501 St Charles Street, Zip 59442–0249, Mailing Address: P.O.Box 249, 59442–0249; tel. 406/622–3331, (Nonreporting) **A**10 18 **S** Benefis Health System, Great Falls, MT
Primary Contact: Louie King, President, Harry Bold Nursing Home Administrator
CMO: Jace Bird M.D., Chief Medical Officer
CIO: Bryan Cartwright, Chief Information Technology Officer
CHR: Carolyn Johnsrud, Manager Human Resources
CNO: Janice Woodhouse, Director of Nursing
Web address: www.mrmcfb.org
Control: Hospital district or authority, Government, Nonfederal **Service:** General medical and surgical

> **Staffed Beds:** 52

FORT HARRISON—Lewis And Clark County

⊞ **VETERANS AFFAIRS MONTANA HEALTH CARE SYSTEM**, 3687 Veterans Drive, Zip 59636–9703, Mailing Address: P.O.Box 1500, 59636–1500; tel. 406/442–6410, (Total facility includes 30 beds in nursing home–type unit) **A**1 **F**3 4 5 7 8 28 29 30 31 33 35 36 38 39 40 44 45 50 51 53 54 55 56 63 64 65 66 70 71 74 75 77 78 79 81 82 83 84 85 87 91 92 93 94 97 100 101 102 103 104 105 106 107 108 111 115 118 119 127 129 130 132 135 143 144 146 147 148 149 **P**6 **S** Department of Veterans Affairs, Washington, DC
Primary Contact: Kathy Berger, Director
CFO: Brian Gustafson, Chief Financial Officer
CMO: Kurt Werner M.D., Chief of Staff
CIO: Paul Gauthier, Chief Information Resources Management
CHR: Aggie Hamilton, Chief Human Resources
Web address: www.montana.va.gov/
Control: Veterans Affairs, Government, federal **Service:** General medical and surgical

> **Staffed Beds:** 94 **Admissions:** 1946 **Census:** 56 **Outpatient Visits:** 433796
> **Births:** 0 **Total Expense ($000):** 342811 **Payroll Expense ($000):** 126233
> **Personnel:** 1139

GLASGOW—Valley County

⊞ **FRANCES MAHON DEACONESS HOSPITAL (271316)**, 621 Third Street South, Zip 59230–2699; tel. 406/228–3500 **A**1 10 18 **F**3 7 11 13 15 28 29 30 31 34 35 40 42 43 53 56 57 59 61 64 70 75 76 78 79 81 82 86 87 89 93 100 102 105 107 108 110 111 114 118 119 127 128 130 131 133 135 145 146 149 **P**6 7
Primary Contact: Randall G. Holom, Chief Executive Officer
COO: Ellen Guttenberg, Chief Operating Officer
CFO: Cami Kalinski, Director Financial Services
CMO: Gordon Bell M.D., Chief of Staff
CIO: David L Nixdorf, Director Support Services
CHR: Charam Orth, Director Human Resources
CNO: Brenda Koessl R.N., Director of Nursing Services
Web address: www.fmdh.org
Control: Other not-for-profit (including NFP Corporation) **Service:** General medical and surgical

> **Staffed Beds:** 25 **Admissions:** 519 **Census:** 4 **Outpatient Visits:** 37566
> **Births:** 143 **Total Expense ($000):** 22291 **Payroll Expense ($000):** 10531
> **Personnel:** 159

GLENDIVE—Dawson County

★ **GLENDIVE MEDICAL CENTER (271332)**, 202 Prospect Drive, Zip 59330–1999; tel. 406/345–3306, (Nonreporting) **A**10 18
Primary Contact: Parker Powell, Chief Executive Officer
CFO: Barbara Markham, Chief Financial Officer
CMO: Joseph M Leal M.D., Jr, Chief of Staff
CIO: Barbara Markham, Chief Financial Officer
CHR: Joetta J Pearcy, Director, Human Resources
Web address: www.gmc.org
Control: Other not-for-profit (including NFP Corporation) **Service:** General medical and surgical

> **Staffed Beds:** 96

MT

GREAT FALLS—Cascade County

△ **BENEFIS HEALTH SYSTEM (270012)**, 1101 26th Street South, Zip 59405–5104; tel. 406/455–5000, (Includes BENEFIS HEALTH CARE-EAST CAMPUS, 1101 26th Street, Great Falls, Montana, Zip 59405, tel. 406/455–5000; BENEFIS HEALTH CARE-WEST CAMPUS, 500 15th Avenue South, Great Falls, Montana, Zip 59405, tel. 406/455–5000) (Total facility includes 237 beds in nursing home–type unit) **A**2 7 10 20 **F**3 4 5 6 10 11 12 13 15 18 20 22 24 26 28 29 30 31 34 35 36 37 38 40 43 45 48 49 50 52 53 54 55 56 57 58 59 61 62 63 64 65 70 71 72 73 74 75 76 77 78 79 81 82 83 84 85 86 87 88 89 90 91 92 93 96 97 98 99 101 102 104 105 107 108 110 111 114 115 116 117 119 120 121 123 124 126 127 128 130 131 132 133 135 141 143 144 145 146 147 148 149 **P**6 **S** Benefis Health System, Great Falls, MT
Primary Contact: John H. Goodnow, Chief Executive Officer
CFO: Forrest Ehlinger, System Chief Financial Officer
CMO: Gregory Tierney M.D., President, BMG and BHS Chief Medical Officer
CIO: Mark Simon, System Chief Information Officer
CNO: Rayn Ginnaty, Vice President Nursing
Web address: www.benefis.org
Control: Other not-for-profit (including NFP Corporation) **Service:** General medical and surgical

Staffed Beds: 502 **Admissions:** 11307 **Census:** 367 **Outpatient Visits:** 496159 **Births:** 1432 **Total Expense ($000):** 389902 **Payroll Expense ($000):** 177442 **Personnel:** 2511

GREAT HALLS HOSPITAL (270086), 1400 29th Street South, Zip 59405–5353; tel. 406/216–8000 **A**10 **F**3 15 18 19 24 26 27 29 30 31 35 38 40 41 45 46 47 51 58 59 65 68 74 77 78 79 81 82 85 86 87 91 92 93 94 107 108 109 110 111 114 115 119 120 121 123 124 126 135 143 144 146 147 148
Primary Contact: Vicki Newmiller, Chief Executive Officer
CFO: Cheryl Cornwell, Chief Financial Officer
CMO: Nicholas Bonfilio M.D., Chief of Staff
Web address: www.gfclinic.com/location/great-falls-clinic-hospital/
Control: Partnership, Investor-owned (for-profit) **Service:** General medical and surgical

Staffed Beds: 20 **Admissions:** 876 **Census:** 9 **Outpatient Visits:** 74304 **Total Expense ($000):** 52058 **Payroll Expense ($000):** 16455 **Personnel:** 268

HAMILTON—Ravalli County

★ **MARCUS DALY MEMORIAL HOSPITAL (271340)**, 1200 Westwood Drive, Zip 59840–2345; tel. 406/363–2211 **A**10 18 **F**3 7 8 11 13 15 17 28 29 30 34 35 40 45 50 57 59 62 63 64 65 70 74 75 76 77 79 81 83 84 89 93 97 102 105 107 110 111 115 119 127 129 130 131 132 133 144 145 146 148
Primary Contact: John M. Bartos, Chief Executive Officer
CFO: Donja Erdman, Chief Financial Officer
CMO: John Moreland M.D., Chief Medical Officer
CIO: Brad Kowalski, Director Information Technology
CHR: Debbie M Morris, Director Human Resources
CNO: Kathy Padilla, Director of Nursing
Web address: www.mdmh.org
Control: Other not-for-profit (including NFP Corporation) **Service:** General medical and surgical

Staffed Beds: 25 **Admissions:** 1642 **Census:** 14 **Outpatient Visits:** 45583 **Births:** 132 **Total Expense ($000):** 56434 **Payroll Expense ($000):** 30728 **Personnel:** 455

HARDIN—Big Horn County

★ **BIG HORN COUNTY MEMORIAL HOSPITAL (271338)**, 17 North Miles Avenue, Zip 59034–2323; tel. 406/665–2310, (Total facility includes 36 beds in nursing home–type unit) **A**10 18 **F**10 11 15 40 43 50 57 59 64 65 68 75 77 81 85 86 87 89 93 107 110 111 114 119 125 128 130 132 133 143 146
Primary Contact: Kristi Gatrell, Chief Executive Officer
CFO: Roxie Cain, Chief Financial Officer
CNO: Kirsten Willoughby, Director of Nursing
Web address: www.bighornhospital.org
Control: Other not-for-profit (including NFP Corporation) **Service:** General medical and surgical

Staffed Beds: 61 **Admissions:** 308 **Census:** 42 **Outpatient Visits:** 8372 **Births:** 8 **Total Expense ($000):** 14179 **Payroll Expense ($000):** 7570 **Personnel:** 153

HARLEM—Blaine County

FORT BELKNAP SERVICE UNIT (271315), 669 Agency Main Street, Zip 59526–9455; tel. 406/353–3100, (Nonreporting) **A**10 18 **S** U. S. Indian Health Service, Rockville, MDPrimary Contact: Gregory Smith, MD
Primary Contact: Gregory Smith, MD
CMO: Ethel L Moore M.D., Director of Medical Affairs
CIO: Mikki Grant, Chief Information Officer
CHR: Charlotte Lamebull, Administrative Officer
CNO: Diana Hunter, Director of Nursing
Web address: www.ihs.gov
Control: PHS, Indian Service, Government, federal **Service:** General medical and surgical

Staffed Beds: 6

HARLOWTON—Wheatland County

★ **WHEATLAND MEMORIAL HEALTHCARE (271321)**, 530 Third Street North West, Zip 59036, Mailing Address: P.O.Box 287, 59036–0287; tel. 406/632–4351, (Nonreporting) **A**10 18
Primary Contact: Hary J. Rutger, Interim Chief Executive Officer
CFO: Doug Lewis, Chief Financial Officer
CMO: Kathy Jutila M.D., Chief of Staff
CIO: Ray Hetherington, Network Administrator
CHR: Peggy Hiner, Director Human Resources
CNO: Lauri Ann Cooney, Director Nursing
Web address: www.wheatlandmemorial.org
Control: Other not-for-profit (including NFP Corporation) **Service:** General medical and surgical

Staffed Beds: 25

HAVRE—Hill County

★ **NORTHERN MONTANA HEALTH CARE (270032)**, 30 13th Street, Zip 59501–5222, Mailing Address: P.O.Box 1231, 59501–1231; tel. 406/265–2211, (Total facility includes 115 beds in nursing home–type unit) **A**10 20 **F**2 5 10 11 13 15 28 29 34 35 36 38 40 43 45 53 56 57 59 60 63 64 68 70 75 76 77 78 79 81 82 84 85 89 93 97 99 101 102 103 104 105 107 108 110 111 115 118 119 127 128 129 130 132 133 135 146 148 **P**6
Primary Contact: David Henry, President and Chief Executive Officer
CFO: Kim Lucke, Vice President Finance
CNO: Eric Koch, Chief Nursing Officer
Web address: www.nmhcare.org
Control: Other not-for-profit (including NFP Corporation) **Service:** General medical and surgical

Staffed Beds: 142 **Admissions:** 1489 **Census:** 103 **Outpatient Visits:** 100990 **Births:** 390 **Total Expense ($000):** 61550 **Payroll Expense ($000):** 32643 **Personnel:** 523

HELENA—Lewis And Clark County

⊞ **SHODAIR CHILDREN'S HOSPITAL (274004)**, 2755 Colonial Drive, Zip 59601–4926, Mailing Address: P.O.Box 5539, 59604–5539; tel. 406/444–7500 **A**1 10 **F**55 98 99 101 104 106 130 149 **P**6
Primary Contact: Craig E. Aasved, Chief Executive Officer
CFO: Ron Wiens, Chief Financial Officer
CMO: Heather Zaluski M.D., President Medical Staff
CIO: Judy Jackson, Director Health Information Management and Privacy Officer
CNO: Christine Bates, Chief Nursing Officer
Web address: www.shodair.org
Control: Other not-for-profit (including NFP Corporation) **Service:** Children's hospital psychiatric

Staffed Beds: 84 **Admissions:** 863 **Census:** 65 **Outpatient Visits:** 2917 **Births:** 0 **Total Expense ($000):** 23034 **Payroll Expense ($000):** 13929 **Personnel:** 267

⊞ **ST. PETER'S HOSPITAL (270003)**, 2475 Broadway, Zip 59601–4928; tel. 406/442–2480 **A**1 2 10 20 **F**3 7 11 13 15 18 20 22 28 29 30 31 34 35 40 43 45 46 49 50 51 54 56 57 59 60 62 63 64 65 70 74 75 76 78 79 81 82 84 85 87 89 92 93 98 100 102 103 107 108 110 111 114 115 116 117 119 120 121 122 129 130 132 133 135 144 146 147 148 **P**6
Primary Contact: Wade C. Johnson, MS, FACHE, Chief Executive Officer
CFO: John Green, Vice President Finance
CHR: Karla Smith, Director Human Resources
CNO: Cheryl Hunt Esq, Chief Nursing Officer
Web address: www.stpetes.org
Control: Other not-for-profit (including NFP Corporation) **Service:** General medical and surgical

Staffed Beds: 123 **Admissions:** 5692 **Census:** 60 **Outpatient Visits:** 471108 **Births:** 812

MT

Hospital, Medicare Provider Number, Address, Telephone, Approval, Facility, and Physician Codes, Health Care System

★ American Hospital Association (AHA) membership   ○ Healthcare Facilities Accreditation Program   ⇑ Center for Improvement in Healthcare Quality Accreditation
□ The Joint Commission accreditation   ◇ DNV Healthcare Inc. accreditation   △ Commission on Accreditation of Rehabilitation Facilities (CARF) accreditation

JORDAN—Garfield County

GARFIELD COUNTY HEALTH CENTER (271310), 332 Leavitt Avenue, Zip 59337, Mailing Address: P.O.Box 389, 59337-0389; tel. 406/557-2500, (Total facility includes 24 beds in nursing home–type unit) **A**10 18 **F**2 7 34 40 42 57 59 64
Primary Contact: Landon Dybaal, Chief Executive Officer
CFO: Charlotte Herbold, Manager Business Officer
CMO: David M. Kidder D.O., Chief Medical Officer
CIO: Charlotte Herbold, Manager Business Officer
CNO: Sarah Nordlund, Director of Nursing
Control: County, Government, Nonfederal **Service**: General medical and surgical

Staffed Beds: 28 Admissions: 18 Census: 17 Outpatient Visits: 624
Births: 0 Total Expense ($000): 2147 Payroll Expense ($000): 1048
Personnel: 22

KALISPELL—Flathead County

HEALTHCENTER NORTHWEST See The Healthcenter

★ △ **KALISPELL REGIONAL HEALTHCARE (270051)**, 310 Sunnyview Lane, Zip 59901-3129; tel. 406/752-5111, (Includes PATHWAYS TREATMENT CENTER, 200 Heritage Way, Kalispell, Montana, Zip 59901, tel. 406/756-3950) **A**2 3 5 7 10 **F**3 4 5 7 8 13 15 18 20 22 24 26 28 29 30 31 35 36 40 43 45 46 49 50 56 57 58 59 62 63 64 68 70 72 74 75 76 77 78 79 81 84 85 86 87 89 98 99 100 101 102 103 104 105 107 108 114 115 118 119 120 121 123 126 129 130 131 132 143 144 145 146 147 148 149 **P**6
Primary Contact: Pamela Martin, Chief Executive Officer
COO: Ted W Hirsch, Senior Executive Director
CFO: Charles T Pearce, Chief Financial and Information Officer
CHR: Deb Wilson, Director Human Resources
Web address: www.krmc.org
Control: Other not-for-profit (including NFP Corporation) **Service**: General medical and surgical

Staffed Beds: 160 Admissions: 7472 Census: 90 Outpatient Visits:
215061 Births: 692 Total Expense ($000): 326498 Payroll Expense
($000): 139027 Personnel: 4780

★ **THE HEALTHCENTER (270087)**, 320 Sunnyview Lane, Zip 59901-3129; tel. 406/751-7550 **A**10 **F**3 8 15 31 36 39 64 68 74 78 79 81 82 85 87 90 93 96 97 100 107 110 111 114 115 117 119 126 147 149 **P**6
Primary Contact: Tate J. Kreitinger, Chief Executive Officer
CFO: Charles T Pearce, Chief Financial and Information Officer
CIO: Charles T Pearce, Chief Financial and Information Officer
CHR: Susan Stevens, Director Human Resources
CNO: Victoria Johnson R.N., Nursing Director of Surgical and Medical Services
Web address: www.krmc.org
Control: Corporation, Investor-owned (for-profit) **Service**: General medical and surgical

Staffed Beds: 30 Admissions: 660 Census: 9 Outpatient Visits: 44874
Births: 0 Personnel: 198

LEWISTOWN—Fergus County

★ **CENTRAL MONTANA MEDICAL CENTER (271345)**, 408 Wendell Avenue, Zip 59457-2261; tel. 406/535-7711 **A**10 18 **F**3 7 11 13 15 28 29 31 34 35 40 43 45 50 53 57 59 62 63 64 65 75 76 77 81 84 85 86 87 89 91 92 93 94 97 107 108 110 111 115 119 129 130 131 132 133 135 146 148 **P**6
Primary Contact: Michael Dowdy, Chief Executive Officer
CFO: Alan Aldrich, Chief Financial Officer
CHR: Torie A Lynch, Manager Human Resources
CNO: Delilah Duffy, Interim Chief Nurse Officer
Web address: www.cmmccares.com
Control: Other not-for-profit (including NFP Corporation) **Service**: General medical and surgical

Staffed Beds: 25 Admissions: 692 Census: 8 Outpatient Visits: 51862
Births: 84 Total Expense ($000): 27939 Payroll Expense ($000): 13953
Personnel: 257

LIBBY—Lincoln County

★ **CABINET PEAKS MEDICAL CENTER (271320)**, 209 Health Park Drive, Zip 59923-2130; tel. 406/283-7000 **A**5 10 18 **F**3 11 13 15 17 28 29 30 31 34 35 40 45 50 56 57 59 64 68 70 75 76 77 79 81 84 85 86 87 89 93 97 102 107 110 111 114 119 128 129 130 131 132 133 135 144 146 147 148 **P**6
Primary Contact: Bruce Whitfield, CPA, Chief Executive Officer and Chief Financial Officer
CFO: Bruce Whitfield CPA, Chief Executive Officer and Chief Financial Officer
CMO: Jay Maloney M.D., Chief of Staff
Web address: www.sjlh.com
Control: Other not-for-profit (including NFP Corporation) **Service**: General medical and surgical

Staffed Beds: 25 Admissions: 807 Census: 8 Outpatient Visits: 33353
Births: 96 Total Expense ($000): 28564 Payroll Expense ($000): 11966
Personnel: 227

LIVINGSTON—Park County

★ **LIVINGSTON HEALTHCARE (271317)**, 320 Alpenglow Lane, Zip 59047-8506; tel. 406/222-3541 **A**5 10 18 **F**3 13 15 17 28 29 31 34 35 36 40 43 45 50 57 59 62 63 64 65 66 67 68 70 75 76 77 78 79 81 82 85 86 87 89 93 100 101 102 104 107 108 110 111 114 119 124 128 129 130 131 133 135 **P**3
Primary Contact: Bren Lowe, Chief Executive Officer
CFO: Ryan Speas, Director Finance
CMO: D. Scott Coleman M.D., Medical Director
CIO: Jody Duran, Manager Information Systems
CHR: Vicki Axtell, Director Human Resources
CNO: Dave Noble, Director of Nursing
Web address: www.livingstonhealthcare.org
Control: Other not-for-profit (including NFP Corporation) **Service**: General medical and surgical

Staffed Beds: 25 Admissions: 1170 Census: 12 Outpatient Visits: 25412
Births: 109 Total Expense ($000): 51025 Payroll Expense ($000): 18104
Personnel: 306

MALTA—Phillips County

★ **PHILLIPS COUNTY HOSPITAL (271312)**, 311 South 8th Avenue East, Zip 59538-0640, Mailing Address: P.O.Box 640, 59538-0640; tel. 406/654-1100 **A**10 18 **F**3 29 31 34 40 41 43 56 57 59 62 66 82 84 90 91 93 107 114 119 127 130 132 133 **P**4
Primary Contact: Ward C. VanWichen, Chief Executive Officer
CFO: Stephanie Denham, Chief Financial Officer and Human Resources Officer
CMO: Ed Medina M.D., Medical Director
CHR: Stephanie Denham, Chief Financial Officer and Human Resources Officer
CNO: Lonna Crowder, Director of Nursing
Web address: www.pchospital.us/
Control: Other not-for-profit (including NFP Corporation) **Service**: General medical and surgical

Staffed Beds: 8 Admissions: 165 Census: 1 Outpatient Visits: 6696
Births: 0 Total Expense ($000): 5793 Payroll Expense ($000): 2752
Personnel: 56

MILES CITY—Custer County

⊞ **HOLY ROSARY HEALTHCARE (271347)**, 2600 Wilson Street, Zip 59301-5094; tel. 406/233-2600, (Total facility includes 65 beds in nursing home–type unit) **A**1 10 18 **F**3 13 15 28 29 30 31 32 34 35 40 48 56 57 59 63 64 65 68 70 75 76 77 78 79 81 84 85 89 93 94 97 99 100 101 103 104 107 108 110 111 115 119 124 127 129 130 131 133 135 143 144 146 147 148 149 **P**6 **S** SCL Health, Broomfield, CO
Primary Contact: Paul Lewis, Chief Executive Officer
CFO: Travis Scheving, Chief Financial Officer
CMO: Michael Bush M.D., Chief Medical Officer
CHR: Cathy Rodenbaugh, Director Human Resources
CNO: Lisa Sanford, VP Patient Care/CNO
Web address: www.holyrosaryhealthcare.org
Control: Church operated, Nongovernment, not-for-profit **Service**: General medical and surgical

Staffed Beds: 90 Admissions: 1249 Census: 56 Outpatient Visits: 29383
Births: 264 Total Expense ($000): 31381 Payroll Expense ($000): 10715
Personnel: 221

MISSOULA—Missoula County

⊞ △ **COMMUNITY MEDICAL CENTER (270023)**, 2827 Fort Missoula Road, Zip 59804-7408; tel. 406/728-4100 **A**1 3 5 7 10 19 **F**3 11 13 15 17 18 20 22 26 28 29 30 31 34 35 37 40 43 46 47 48 49 51 54 57 59 64 65 68 70 72 74 75 76 78 79 81 82 83 84 85 87 88 89 90 91 92 93 94 96 97 107 108 110 111 114 115 116 117 118 119 120 121 123 124 126 130 132 134 135 141 143 144 145 146 147 148 149 **P**6 7 **S** RCCH HealthCare Partners, Brentwood, TN
Primary Contact: Dean French, M.D., Chief Executive Officer
COO: Devin Huntley, Vice President Operations
CFO: David Richhart, Vice President Fiscal Services
CMO: David Lechner M.D., Chief Medical Officer and Vice President Innovation
CNO: Jan Perry R.N., Vice President Patient Care Services
Web address: www.communitymed.org
Control: Corporation, Investor-owned (for-profit) **Service**: General medical and surgical

Staffed Beds: 135 Admissions: 4844 Census: 64 Outpatient Visits:
126062 Births: 1155 Total Expense ($000): 167693 Payroll Expense
($000): 62758 Personnel: 1059

MT

✠ **ST. PATRICK HOSPITAL (270014)**, 500 West Broadway, Zip 59802–4096, Mailing Address: P.O.Box 4587, 59806–4587; tel. 406/543–7271 **A**1 2 3 5 10 19 **F**3 11 12 13 15 18 20 22 24 26 28 29 30 31 34 35 38 40 43 45 46 48 49 50 53 57 58 59 60 61 64 65 68 70 74 75 76 77 78 79 81 82 84 85 86 88 89 90 92 93 96 97 98 99 100 101 102 103 104 105 107 108 109 110 111 113 114 115 116 117 118 119 120 121 123 124 126 127 129 130 131 132 135 141 146 147 148 149 **P4 S** Providence St. Joseph Health, Renton, WA
Primary Contact: Joyce Dombrouski, R.N., Chief Executive Officer
CFO: Kirk Bodlovic, WMSA Chief Financial Officer
CHR: Karyn Trainor, Director Human Resources
CNO: Carol Bensen MSN, R.N., Chief Nursing Officer
Web address: www.montana.providence.org
Control: Church operated, Nongovernment, not-for-profit **Service**: General medical and surgical

Staffed Beds: 200 Admissions: 9988 Census: 129 Outpatient Visits: 312880 **Births:** 458 **Total Expense ($000):** 222883 **Payroll Expense ($000):** 72839 **Personnel:** 1577

PHILIPSBURG—Granite County

★ **GRANITE COUNTY MEDICAL CENTER (271303)**, 310 Sansome Street, Zip 59858–0729, Mailing Address: P.O.Box 729, 59858–0729; tel. 406/859–3271 **A**10 18 **F**2 34 35 39 40 41 54 55 56 57 59 66 68 71 87 91 93 97 99 102 103 104 119 127 133 135 143 146 148 **S** Providence St. Joseph Health, Renton, WA
Primary Contact: Maria Stoppler, Chief Executive Officer
CFO: Susan Ossello, Chief Financial Officer
CMO: John Moore M.D., Medical Director
Web address: www.gcmedcenter.org/
Control: Hospital district or authority, Government, Nonfederal **Service**: General medical and surgical

Staffed Beds: 25 Admissions: 32 Census: 1 Outpatient Visits: 2327 **Births:** 0

PLAINS—Sanders County

★ **CLARK FORK VALLEY HOSPITAL (271323)**, 10 Kruger Road, Zip 59859, Mailing Address: P.O.Box 768, 59859–0768; tel. 406/826–4800, (Total facility includes 28 beds in nursing home–type unit) **A**10 18 **F**3 11 13 15 28 29 30 32 34 35 36 40 43 44 45 50 57 58 59 62 63 64 65 68 70 74 75 76 77 81 82 83 84 85 87 89 91 93 97 107 110 114 118 119 127 128 129 130 132 133 135 143 146 147 148 **P**3 6
Primary Contact: Gregory S. Hanson, M.D., Chief Executive Officer
CFO: Carla A Neiman, Chief Financial Officer
CMO: Ronald Black M.D., Chief Medical Officer
CIO: Carla A Neiman, Chief Financial Officer
CHR: Barry Fowler, Director Human and System Resources
CNO: Lisa Eberhardt, Chief Nursing Officer
Web address: www.cfvh.org
Control: Other not-for-profit (including NFP Corporation) **Service**: General medical and surgical

Staffed Beds: 44 Admissions: 425 Census: 45 Outpatient Visits: 28286 **Births:** 37 **Total Expense ($000):** 18187 **Payroll Expense ($000):** 8272 **Personnel:** 127

PLENTYWOOD—Sheridan County

SHERIDAN MEMORIAL HOSPITAL (271322), 440 West Laurel Avenue, Zip 59254–1596; tel. 406/765–3700, (Total facility includes 78 beds in nursing home–type unit) **A**10 18 **F**3 7 11 13 15 17 29 30 35 40 50 56 59 62 63 64 70 75 77 80 81 87 93 97 107 110 114 119 127 128 130 132 133 145 146 147 148
Primary Contact: Gregory L. Maurer, Chief Executive Officer
CIO: Troy McClymont, Chief Information Technology Officer
Web address: www.sheridanmemorial.net/
Control: Other not-for-profit (including NFP Corporation) **Service**: General medical and surgical

Staffed Beds: 97 Admissions: 230 Census: 38 Outpatient Visits: 17642 **Births:** 0 **Total Expense ($000):** 11555 **Payroll Expense ($000):** 5591

POLSON—Lake County

✠ **PROVIDENCE ST. JOSEPH MEDICAL CENTER (271343)**, 6 Thirteenth Avenue East, Zip 59860–5315, Mailing Address: P.O.Box 1010, 59860–1010; tel. 406/883–5377 **A**1 10 18 **F**3 10 13 15 28 29 30 34 35 40 43 46 50 57 59 64 68 75 76 77 79 81 82 85 87 89 93 97 100 102 107 110 111 114 119 125 127 129 130 131 133 146 147 148 149 **P**6 **S** Providence St. Joseph Health, Renton, WA
Primary Contact: James R. Kiser II, Chief Executive Officer
COO: Colleen Nielsen, Director Operations
CFO: Kirk Bodlovic, Vice President and Chief Financial Officer
CMO: Kelly Bagnell M.D., Chief of Staff
Web address: www.saintjoes.org
Control: Church operated, Nongovernment, not-for-profit **Service**: General medical and surgical

Staffed Beds: 22 Admissions: 700 Census: 6 Outpatient Visits: 84583 **Births:** 129 **Total Expense ($000):** 27612 **Payroll Expense ($000):** 15939 **Personnel:** 193

POPLAR—Richland County

★ **POPLAR COMMUNITY HOSPITAL (271300)**, 211 H Street, Zip 59255–9519, Mailing Address: P.O.Box 38, 59255–0038; tel. 406/768–6100 **A**10 18 **F**3 40 42 43 **P**3 6
Primary Contact: Margaret B. Norgaard, Chief Executive Officer
CHR: Annie Block, Director Human Resources
Web address: www.nemhs.net
Control: Other not-for-profit (including NFP Corporation) **Service**: General medical and surgical

Staffed Beds: 20 Admissions: 117 Census: 3 Outpatient Visits: 7432 **Births:** 3 **Total Expense ($000):** 9204 **Payroll Expense ($000):** 4993 **Personnel:** 87

RED LODGE—Carbon County

★ **BEARTOOTH BILLINGS CLINIC (271326)**, 2525 North Broadway Avenue, Zip 59068–9222, Mailing Address: P.O.Box 590, 59068–0590; tel. 406/446–2345 **A**10 18 **F**3 11 15 18 28 29 34 35 40 43 44 45 50 56 57 59 62 63 64 65 68 75 77 81 84 85 86 87 91 93 94 96 97 107 110 114 119 130 131 133 135 146 147 148 **P**6
Primary Contact: Kelley Evans, Chief Administrative Officer
CFO: Kyle Gee, Chief Financial Officer
CMO: William George M.D., Chief of Staff
CHR: Katie Nordstrom, Director Human Resources
CNO: Bridgett Chartier, Director of Nursing
Web address: www.beartoothbillingsclinic.org
Control: Other not-for-profit (including NFP Corporation) **Service**: General medical and surgical

Staffed Beds: 10 Admissions: 134 Census: 1 Outpatient Visits: 59717 **Births:** 0 **Total Expense ($000):** 13587 **Payroll Expense ($000):** 4683 **Personnel:** 104

RONAN—Lake County

★ **ST. LUKE COMMUNITY HEALTHCARE (271325)**, 107 Sixth Avenue SW, Zip 59864–2634; tel. 406/676–4441, (Total facility includes 75 beds in nursing home–type unit) **A**10 18 **F**2 13 15 28 29 34 40 43 45 53 54 56 57 59 61 64 65 68 75 76 79 81 85 93 97 107 108 110 111 115 119 127 128 129 130 131 132 133 135 144 145 147 **P**6
Primary Contact: Steve J. Todd, Chief Executive Officer
COO: Sarah Teaff, Chief Operating Officer
CFO: Paul Soukup, Chief Financial Officer
CMO: Edred T. Vizcarra M.D., Chief of Staff
CHR: Theresa L. Jones, Manager Human Resources
CNO: Leah Emerson, Director of Nursing
Web address: www.stlukehealthcare.org
Control: Other not-for-profit (including NFP Corporation) **Service**: General medical and surgical

Staffed Beds: 100 Admissions: 1033 Census: 58 Outpatient Visits: 85076 **Births:** 160 **Total Expense ($000):** 35767 **Payroll Expense ($000):** 18154 **Personnel:** 323

MT

Hospital, Medicare Provider Number, Address, Telephone, Approval, Facility, and Physician Codes, Health Care System

★ American Hospital Association (AHA) membership ○ Healthcare Facilities Accreditation Program ⇧ Center for Improvement in Healthcare Quality Accreditation
☐ The Joint Commission accreditation ◇ DNV Healthcare Inc. accreditation △ Commission on Accreditation of Rehabilitation Facilities (CARF) accreditation

ROUNDUP—Musselshell County

★ **ROUNDUP MEMORIAL HEALTHCARE (271346)**, 1202 Third Street West, Zip 59072–1816, Mailing Address: P.O.Box 40, 59072–0040; tel. 406/323–2301 **A**10 18 **F**11 29 30 34 35 40 45 50 57 59 65 66 85 87 97 102 107 119 127 130 132 133 146
Primary Contact: Bradley Howell, Chief Executive Officer
CFO: Kyle Gee, Regional Vice President Financial Operations
CMO: Mark Ward M.D., Chief of Staff
CHR: Michelle Clement, Executive Assistant/Human Resources Director
CNO: Emily Shoup, Director Nursing Services
Web address: www.rmhmt.org/
Control: Other not-for-profit (including NFP Corporation) **Service**: General medical and surgical

Staffed Beds: 25 **Admissions:** 143 **Census:** 18 **Outpatient Visits:** 10516
Births: 0

SAINT MARY—Glacier County

U.S. PUBLIC HEALTH SERVICE BLACKFEET COMMUNITY HOSPITAL (270074), 760 New Hospital Circle, Zip 59417–0760, Mailing Address: P.O.Box 760, Browning, 59417–0760; tel. 406/338–6100, (Nonreporting) **A**5 10 **S** U. S. Indian Health Service, Rockville, MD
Primary Contact: Garland Stiffarm, Acting Chief Executive Officer
CFO: Cleo Main, Finance Officer
CMO: Neil Sun Rhodes M.D., Chief Medical Officer
CNO: Susan Head, Director Nursing Services
Web address: www.ihs.gov
Control: PHS, Indian Service, Government, federal **Service**: General medical and surgical

Staffed Beds: 25

SCOBEY—Daniels County

DANIELS MEMORIAL HEALTHCARE CENTER (271342), 105 Fifth Avenue East, Zip 59263, Mailing Address: P.O.Box 400, 59263–0400; tel. 406/487–2296, (Total facility includes 30 beds in nursing home–type unit) **A**10 18 **F**2 11 29 34 35 40 50 56 59 64 65 67 69 75 77 85 86 87 91 93 97 107 114 119 127 130 133 143 146 148 **P**6
Primary Contact: David Ryerse, Chief Executive Officer
CMO: Don Sawdey M.D., Medical Director
CHR: Edith Huda, Director Human Resources
CNO: Kathy Ware, Director of Nursing
Web address: www.danielsmemorialhealthcare.org
Control: Hospital district or authority, Government, Nonfederal **Service**: General medical and surgical

Staffed Beds: 54 **Admissions:** 132 **Census:** 28 **Outpatient Visits:** 4889
Births: 0 **Total Expense ($000):** 7738 **Payroll Expense ($000):** 3137
Personnel: 89

SHELBY—Toole County

★ **MARIAS MEDICAL CENTER (271328)**, 640 Park Drive, Zip 59474–1663, Mailing Address: P.O.Box 915, 59474–0915; tel. 406/434–3200 **A**10 18 **F**3 11 13 15 17 28 29 34 40 41 53 56 57 59 65 70 76 77 81 83 85 87 89 91 93 102 107 110 114 119 129 130 133 146
Primary Contact: Jessica Brusven, Chief Executive Officer
CFO: Melissa Ostberg, Chief Financial Officer
CMO: Melanie Hardy D.O., Chief of Staff
CIO: Jayce Yarn, Director Information Technology
CHR: Cindy Lamb, Director Human Resources
CNO: Tamra Fender, Chief Nursing Officer
Web address: www.mmcmt.org
Control: County, Government, Nonfederal **Service**: General medical and surgical

Staffed Beds: 21 **Admissions:** 181 **Census:** 20 **Outpatient Visits:** 7595
Births: 31 **Total Expense ($000):** 12091 **Payroll Expense ($000):** 3714
Personnel: 89

SHERIDAN—Madison County

★ **RUBY VALLEY HOSPITAL (271319)**, 220 East Crofoot Street, Zip 59749–7714, Mailing Address: P.O.Box 336, 59749–0336; tel. 406/842–5453 **A**10 18 **F**2 11 29 34 35 38 40 43 56 57 59 64 65 66 75 82 86 90 91 93 97 107 114 127 128 130 133 135 147 148 149 **P**3 6
Primary Contact: John H. Semingson, Chief Executive Officer
CFO: Dennis Holschbach, Chief Financial Officer
CMO: Roman Hendrickson M.D., Medical Director
CHR: Jenny Rohrback, Director Human Resource
CNO: Brenda Green, Director of Nursing
Web address: www.rubyvalleyhospital.com/
Control: Hospital district or authority, Government, Nonfederal **Service**: General medical and surgical

Staffed Beds: 8 **Admissions:** 143 **Census:** 2 **Outpatient Visits:** 5021
Births: 0 **Total Expense ($000):** 5980 **Payroll Expense ($000):** 3276
Personnel: 64

SIDNEY—Richland County

★ **SIDNEY HEALTH CENTER (271344)**, 216 14th Avenue SW, Zip 59270–3586; tel. 406/488–2100, (Total facility includes 56 beds in nursing home–type unit) **A**10 18 **F**2 3 13 15 17 28 30 31 34 35 40 41 45 50 56 59 62 63 64 68 70 75 76 78 79 81 82 84 85 86 87 89 93 96 97 107 108 110 111 115 119 120 121 122 123 124 128 129 133 144 145 146 147 148 149 **P**6
Primary Contact: Richard Haraldson, Chief Executive Officer
CFO: Tina Montgomery, Chief Financial Officer
CMO: Rajohn Karanjai M.D., Chief Medical Officer
CIO: Brian Fay, Director Information Systems
CHR: Lisa Aisenbrey, Administrator Human Resources and Support Services
Web address: www.sidneyhealth.org
Control: Other not-for-profit (including NFP Corporation) **Service**: General medical and surgical

Staffed Beds: 81 **Admissions:** 1665 **Census:** 60 **Outpatient Visits:** 48213
Births: 117 **Total Expense ($000):** 58604 **Payroll Expense ($000):** 21621
Personnel: 343

SUPERIOR—Mineral County

MINERAL COMMUNITY HOSPITAL (271331), 1208 6th Avenue East, Zip 59872–9618; tel. 406/822–4841 **A**10 18 **F**10 29 40 57 69 75 77 81 93 107 110 114 119 133 143
Primary Contact: Ronald M. Gleason, Chief Executive Officer
CFO: Cliff Case, Chief Financial Officer
CMO: Roger Pafford M.D., Medical Director
CHR: Stacy Conrow-Ververis, Director Human Resources
CNO: Jenifer Mitchell R.N., Director of Nursing Services
Web address: www.mineralcommunityhospital.com/
Control: Other not-for-profit (including NFP Corporation) **Service**: General medical and surgical

Staffed Beds: 25 **Admissions:** 123 **Census:** 15 **Outpatient Visits:** 5537
Births: 0 **Total Expense ($000):** 5820 **Payroll Expense ($000):** 3137
Personnel: 63

TERRY—Prairie County

PRAIRIE COMMUNITY HEALTH CENTER See Prairie Community Hospital

★ **PRAIRIE COMMUNITY HOSPITAL (271309)**, 312 South Adams Avenue, Zip 59349–0156, Mailing Address: P.O.Box 156, 59349–0156; tel. 406/635–5511 **A**10 18 **F**1 2 34 40 41 57 59 64 65 67 69 75 87 90 93 127 128 133 135 146 148 **P**6
Primary Contact: Laurie Lea Durham, Chief Executive Officer
CFO: Laurie Chandler, Financial Officer
CIO: Laurie Chandler, Chairman
CNO: Susan Morgan, Director of Nursing Services
Web address: www.prairiecommunityhospital.org/
Control: Hospital district or authority, Government, Nonfederal **Service**: General medical and surgical

Staffed Beds: 22 **Admissions:** 64 **Census:** 20 **Outpatient Visits:** 3883
Births: 0 **Total Expense ($000):** 2713 **Payroll Expense ($000):** 1136
Personnel: 37

MT

TOWNSEND—Broadwater County

BROADWATER HEALTH CENTER (271333), 110 North Oak Street, Zip 59644–2306; tel. 406/266–3186 **A**10 18 **F**3 7 9 15 29 32 34 40 41 43 50 53 54 55 57 59 64 66 71 75 77 79 87 91 93 97 107 111 128 130 131 133 135 143 144 146 147 148
Primary Contact: Kyle Hopstad, Chief Executive Officer
CFO: Jennifer Clowes, Chief Financial Officer
CMO: Carol Bridges M.D., Medical Director
CHR: April Campbell, Director Human Resources
CNO: Fran Wright, Director of Nursing
Web address: www.broadwaterhealthcenter.com
Control: Other not-for-profit (including NFP Corporation) **Service**: General medical and surgical

Staffed Beds: 41 **Admissions:** 74 **Census:** 2 **Outpatient Visits:** 967
Births: 0

WARM SPRINGS—Deer Lodge County

MONTANA STATE HOSPITAL (274086), 100 Garnet Way, Zip 59756–9705, Mailing Address: P.O.Box 300, tel. 406/693–7000 **A**10 **F**39 98
Primary Contact: Jay Pottenger, Administrator
CFO: Tracey Thun, Director Business and Support Services
CMO: Thomas Gray M.D., Medical Director
CIO: Melinda Bridgewater, Director, Information Services
CHR: Todd Thun, Director Human Resources
CNO: Dave Olson, Director of Nursing
Web address: www.msh.mt.gov
Control: State, Government, Nonfederal **Service**: Psychiatric

Staffed Beds: 288 **Admissions:** 768 **Census:** 244 **Outpatient Visits:** 0
Births: 0 **Total Expense ($000):** 44254 **Payroll Expense ($000):** 20698
Personnel: 498

WHITE SULPHUR SPRINGS—Meagher County

MOUNTAINVIEW MEDICAL CENTER (271306), 16 West Main Street, Zip 59645–9036, Mailing Address: P.O.Box 'Q', 59645–0817; tel. 406/547–3321 **A**10 18 **F**3 11 34 35 40 56 57 59 64 65 82 93 97 107 114 119 127 133 148 **P**3
Primary Contact: Rob Brandt, Chief Executive Officer
Web address: www.mvmc.org
Control: Other not-for-profit (including NFP Corporation) **Service**: General medical and surgical

Staffed Beds: 21 **Admissions:** 116 **Census:** 3 **Outpatient Visits:** 3546
Births: 0 **Total Expense ($000):** 5122 **Payroll Expense ($000):** 2666

WHITEFISH—Flathead County

★ **NORTH VALLEY HOSPITAL (271336)**, 1600 Hospital Way, Zip 59937–7849; tel. 406/863–3500 **A**10 18 **F**3 11 13 15 28 29 30 31 34 35 37 40 43 45 50 51 54 55 56 59 64 65 68 70 75 76 79 81 84 85 86 87 97 99 103 104 107 110 111 114 119 126 127 129 130 131 132 133 135 144 146 148 **P**6
Primary Contact: Chris Thomas, Chief Executive Officer
COO: Christina Bogers, Chief Clinical Officer
CFO: Arebi Garsa, Interim Chief Financial Officer
CMO: Jason Cohen M.D., Chief Medical Officer
CIO: Michael Barnes, Chief Information Officer
CHR: Joseph Schmier, Interim Director Human Resources
Web address: www.nvhosp.org
Control: Other not-for-profit (including NFP Corporation) **Service**: General medical and surgical

Staffed Beds: 25 **Admissions:** 1696 **Census:** 12 **Outpatient Visits:** 73570
Births: 571 **Total Expense ($000):** 53502 **Payroll Expense ($000):** 19663
Personnel: 305

WOLF POINT—Roosevelt County

★ **TRINITY HOSPITAL (271341)**, 315 Knapp Street, Zip 59201–1826; tel. 406/653–6500, (Total facility includes 60 beds in nursing home–type unit) **A**10 **F**3 6 7 8 13 15 29 31 32 34 40 42 43 45 50 56 57 59 64 70 75 76 78 81 92 110 119 120 125 127 128 130 133 143 145 **P**5
Primary Contact: Margaret B. Norgaard, Chief Executive Officer
Web address: www.nemhs.net
Control: Other not-for-profit (including NFP Corporation) **Service**: General medical and surgical

Staffed Beds: 82 **Admissions:** 411 **Census:** 55 **Outpatient Visits:** 13583
Births: 148 **Total Expense ($000):** 20153 **Payroll Expense ($000):** 10772
Personnel: 202

MT

Hospital, Medicare Provider Number, Address, Telephone, Approval, Facility, and Physician Codes, Health Care System

★ American Hospital Association (AHA) membership
□ The Joint Commission accreditation
○ Healthcare Facilities Accreditation Program
◇ DNV Healthcare Inc. accreditation
⇑ Center for Improvement in Healthcare Quality Accreditation
△ Commission on Accreditation of Rehabilitation Facilities (CARF) accreditation

NEBRASKA

AINSWORTH—Brown County

BROWN COUNTY HOSPITAL (281325), 945 East Zero Street, Zip 69210–1547; tel. 402/387–2800, (Nonreporting) **A**10 18
Primary Contact: Shannon Sorensen, Chief Executive Officer
CFO: Lisa Wood, Chief Financial Officer
CMO: Melvin Campbell M.D., Medical Staff Chairman
CIO: Mike Depko, Director Information Technology
CHR: Lisa Fischer, Director Human Resources
CNO: Matt Lentz R.N., Director of Patient Services
Web address: www.browncountyhospital.org
Control: County, Government, Nonfederal **Service**: General medical and surgical

Staffed Beds: 18

ALBION—Boone County

★ **BOONE COUNTY HEALTH CENTER (281334)**, 723 West Fairview Street, Zip 68620–1725, Mailing Address: P.O.Box 151, 68620–0151; tel. 402/395–2191 **A**3 5 10 18 **F**13 26 31 34 35 40 43 57 62 64 68 75 77 78 81 93 107 110 111 114 119 130 131 132 134 **P**5
Primary Contact: Tanya Sharp, President and Chief Executive Officer
CFO: Rita Liss, Vice President Fiscal Services and Chief Financial Officer
CMO: Lynette Kramer M.D., Chief Medical Officer
CIO: Larry Zoucha, Chief Information Officer
CHR: Jennifer Beierman, Director Human Resources
CNO: Cindy Lesiak, Vice President Patient Care Services and Director of Nursing
Web address: www.boonecohealth.org
Control: County, Government, Nonfederal **Service**: General medical and surgical

Staffed Beds: 25 **Admissions**: 774 **Census**: 8 **Outpatient Visits**: 6950
Births: 93

ALLIANCE—Box Butte County

✠ **BOX BUTTE GENERAL HOSPITAL (281360)**, 2101 Box Butte Avenue, Zip 69301–4445, Mailing Address: P.O.Box 810, 69301–0810; tel. 308/762–6660 **A**1 3 5 10 18 **F**3 5 11 13 15 28 29 32 34 35 36 38 40 43 47 48 50 53 57 59 60 64 68 69 75 77 78 79 81 82 85 86 87 92 93 97 100 101 104 107 108 111 114 116 118 119 127 129 130 131 132 133 134 135 146 148
Primary Contact: Lori Mazanec, Interim Chief Executive Officer
COO: Lori Mazanec, Chief Operating Officer
CFO: Tracy E Jatczak CPA, Chief Financial Officer
CHR: Lisa L Hillyer, Human Resources Manager
CNO: Carolyn Jones R.N., MSN, Chief Nursing Officer
Web address: www.bbgh.org
Control: County, Government, Nonfederal **Service**: General medical and surgical

Staffed Beds: 25 **Admissions**: 876 **Census**: 8 **Outpatient Visits**: 34844
Births: 89 **Total Expense ($000)**: 36907 **Payroll Expense ($000)**: 13840
Personnel: 255

ALMA—Harlan County

★ **HARLAN COUNTY HEALTH SYSTEM (281300)**, 717 North Brown Street, Zip 68920–2132, Mailing Address: P.O.Box 836, 68920–0836; tel. 308/928–2151 **A**10 18 **F**1 3 4 11 15 16 17 29 30 31 40 45 46 50 57 59 64 67 70 72 73 80 81 85 86 88 89 90 93 98 107 110 114 119 127 128 130 132 133 135 146 147 **P**6 **S** Great Plains Health Alliance, Inc., Wichita, KS
Primary Contact: Manuela Wolf, R.N., Chief Executive Officer
CFO: Sue Lans, Comptroller
CMO: Cameron Knackstedt D.O., Chief Medical Staff
CIO: Michael Andrews, Coordinator Information Systems
CHR: Ana Schluntz, Director of Human Resources
CNO: Elizabeth Miller, Director of Nursing
Web address: www.harlancountyhealth.com
Control: County, Government, Nonfederal **Service**: General medical and surgical

Staffed Beds: 19 **Admissions**: 135 **Census**: 3 **Outpatient Visits**: 18061
Births: 0 **Total Expense ($000)**: 8663 **Payroll Expense ($000)**: 3677
Personnel: 81

ATKINSON—Holt County

WEST HOLT MEDICAL SERVICES (281343), 406 West Neely Street, Zip 68713–4801; tel. 402/925–2811, (Nonreporting) **A**10 18 **S** Faith Regional Health Services, Norfolk, NE
Primary Contact: Bradley D. Pfeifer, FACHE, Chief Executive Officer
CFO: Karen Nollette, Chief Financial Officer
CMO: John Tubbs M.D., Chief of Staff
CIO: Mark Johnson, Chief Information Officer
CHR: Margaret Linse, Administrative Secretary and Director Human Resources
CNO: Tana O'Neill R.N., Chief Nursing Officer
Web address: www.westholtmed.org
Control: Other not-for-profit (including NFP Corporation) **Service**: General medical and surgical

Staffed Beds: 17

AUBURN—Nemaha County

★ ⇑ **NEMAHA COUNTY HOSPITAL (281324)**, 2022 13th Street, Zip 68305–1799; tel. 402/274–4366 **A**10 18 21 **F**3 7 12 15 28 29 30 31 34 35 40 43 62 64 68 74 75 77 78 79 81 82 85 86 87 93 94 107 110 111 114 117 119 128 129 130 131 133 135 141 147 148 149
Primary Contact: Marty Fattig, Chief Executive Officer
COO: Kermit Moore R.N., Chief Operating Officer and Chief Nursing Officer
CFO: Stacy Taylor, Chief Financial Officer
CHR: Susan Shupp, Chief Human Resources Officer
Web address: www.nchnet.org
Control: County, Government, Nonfederal **Service**: General medical and surgical

Staffed Beds: 16 **Admissions**: 223 **Census**: 3 **Outpatient Visits**: 18872
Births: 0 **Total Expense ($000)**: 11790 **Payroll Expense ($000)**: 5020
Personnel: 88

AURORA—Hamilton County

★ **MEMORIAL COMMUNITY HEALTH (281320)**, 1423 Seventh Street, Zip 68818–1197; tel. 402/694–3171, (Total facility includes 47 beds in nursing home–type unit) **A**10 18 **F**10 11 13 15 28 29 31 34 35 40 41 43 45 50 51 57 59 64 65 67 75 76 77 78 79 81 82 85 86 87 93 94 97 107 108 110 114 119 130 131 132 133 146 **P**6
Primary Contact: Diane R. Keller, Chief Executive Officer
CFO: Phil Fendt, Chief Financial Officer
CMO: Jeff Muilenburg, Chief of Staff
CIO: Brad Tiede, Director Information Systems
CHR: Laura Teichmeier, Director Human Resources
CNO: Lindy Mosel, Director of Nursing
Web address: www.memorialcommunityhealth.org
Control: Other not-for-profit (including NFP Corporation) **Service**: General medical and surgical

Staffed Beds: 63 **Admissions**: 295 **Census**: 44 **Outpatient Visits**: 24412
Births: 44 **Total Expense ($000)**: 22535 **Payroll Expense ($000)**: 10544
Personnel: 224

MEMORIAL HOSPITAL See Memorial Community Health

BASSETT—Rock County

ROCK COUNTY HOSPITAL (281333), 102 East South Street, Zip 68714–5508; tel. 402/684–3366, (Total facility includes 30 beds in nursing home–type unit) **A**10 18 **F**7 11 15 28 40 53 57 81 84 107 110 127 128 133
Primary Contact: Stacey A. Knox, Administrator
CMO: John Tubbs M.D., Chief of Staff
CIO: Cal Alder, Director Information Technology
CHR: Jackie Carpenter, Office Manager
CNO: Katie Aase, Director of Nursing
Web address: www.rockcountyhospital.com
Control: County, Government, Nonfederal **Service**: General medical and surgical

Staffed Beds: 54 **Admissions**: 158 **Census**: 30 **Outpatient Visits**: 5870
Births: 0 **Total Expense ($000)**: 9548 **Payroll Expense ($000)**: 3478
Personnel: 96

NE

BEATRICE—Gage County

☒ **BEATRICE COMMUNITY HOSPITAL AND HEALTH CENTER (281364)**, 4800 Hospital Parkway, Zip 68310–6906, Mailing Address: P.O.Box 278, 68310–0278; tel. 402/228–3344 **A**1 10 18 **F**3 13 15 28 29 31 34 35 40 45 57 62 63 64 65 68 69 70 75 76 78 79 81 82 84 85 87 93 107 110 111 114 119 127 129 130 131 132 133 135 146 147 149
Primary Contact: John T Findley, M.D., Chief Medical Officer and Interim Chief Executive Officer
CFO: Alan W Streeter, Chief Financial Officer
CMO: John T Findley M.D., Chief Medical Officer
CHR: Kathryn G. Humble, Chief Human Resources Officer
CNO: Arlinda K Ament R.N., Interim Chief Nursing Officer
Web address: www.beatricecommunityhospital.com
Control: Other not-for-profit (including NFP Corporation) **Service**: General medical and surgical

Staffed Beds: 25 **Admissions**: 981 **Census**: 9 **Outpatient Visits**: 204105
Births: 219 **Total Expense ($000)**: 68232 **Payroll Expense ($000)**: 31493
Personnel: 474

BELLEVUE—Sarpy County

MADONNA REHABILITATION SPECIALTY HOSPITAL (280136), 2500 Bellevue Medical Center Drive, Fourth Floor, Zip 68123–1591; tel. 402/401–3000 (Nonreporting)
Primary Contact: Paul Dongilli Jr, Ph.D., FACHE, President and Chief Executive Officer
Web address: www.madonna.org
Control: Other not-for-profit (including NFP Corporation) **Service**: General medical and surgical

Staffed Beds: 32

☐ **NEBRASKA MEDICINE - BELLEVUE (280132)**, 2500 Bellevue Medical Center Drive, Zip 68123–1591; tel. 402/763–3000 **A**1 3 5 10 **F**3 13 15 18 20 22 28 29 30 31 34 35 40 41 44 45 47 48 49 50 51 53 55 57 58 59 60 63 64 65 68 70 74 75 76 77 78 79 81 82 85 86 87 91 92 93 96 97 107 108 110 111 114 119 130 131 132 135 141 143 144 145 146 147 148 149
Primary Contact: Matt E. Pospisil, Vice President Perioperative Services
CFO: Stephanie Daubert, Chief Financial Officer
CMO: Jeffrey D. Akerson M.D., Chief Medical Officer
CIO: Brian Lancaster, Executive Director Information Management
CNO: Ray D. Dial, Director of Nursing
Web address: www.nebraskamed.com
Control: Other not-for-profit (including NFP Corporation) **Service**: General medical and surgical

Staffed Beds: 55 **Admissions**: 4072 **Census**: 35 **Outpatient Visits**: 111667
Births: 740 **Total Expense ($000)**: 65057 **Payroll Expense ($000)**: 24456
Personnel: 378

BENKELMAN—Dundy County

★ **DUNDY COUNTY HOSPITAL (281340)**, 1313 North Cheyenne Street, Zip 69021–3074, Mailing Address: P.O.Box 626, 69021–0626; tel. 308/423–2204, (Nonreporting) **A**10 18
Primary Contact: Rita A. Jones, Chief Executive Officer
COO: Wendy Elkins, Director Operations
CFO: Renee Fink CPA, Chief Financial Officer
CMO: Jose Garcia M.D., Chief Medical Staff
CIO: David Craw, Coordinator Information Technology
CHR: Sandy Noffsinger, Executive Assistant, Risk Manager and Director Marketing
CNO: Laken Vrbas R.N., Director of Nursing
Web address: www.dchbenkelman.com
Control: County, Government, Nonfederal **Service**: General medical and surgical

Staffed Beds: 14

BLAIR—Washington County

★ **MEMORIAL COMMUNITY HOSPITAL AND HEALTH SYSTEM (281359)**, 810 North 22nd Street, Zip 68008–1199, Mailing Address: P.O.Box 250, 68008–0250; tel. 402/426–2182, (Nonreporting) **A**10 18
Primary Contact: Tim Plante, MSN, R.N., President and Chief Executive Officer
CMO: John F Simonson M.D., President Medical Staff
CHR: Kristine Nielsen, Manager Human Resources
CNO: Laura Stawniak R.N., Chief Nursing Executive
Web address: www.mchhs.org
Control: Other not-for-profit (including NFP Corporation) **Service**: General medical and surgical

Staffed Beds: 25

BRIDGEPORT—Morrill County

MORRILL COUNTY COMMUNITY HOSPITAL (281318), 1313 'S' Street, Zip 69336–0579; tel. 308/262–1616 **A**10 18 **F**7 28 32 34 35 40 43 57 59 62 64 65 69 77 81 82 90 93 97 107 108 111 112 119 120 121 122 123 124 127 129 130 133 135 144 148 **P**6
Primary Contact: Robin Stuart, Chief Executive Officer
CFO: Connie Christensen, Chief Financial Officer
CMO: John Post M.D., Medical Director
CIO: Lori Shengle, Director Information Technology
CHR: Rhea Basa, Director Human Resources
CNO: Sylvia Marie Lichius R.N., Chief Nursing Officer
Web address: www.morrillcountyhospital.org
Control: County, Government, Nonfederal **Service**: General medical and surgical

Staffed Beds: 20 **Admissions**: 150 **Census**: 1 **Outpatient Visits**: 4500
Births: 0

BROKEN BOW—Custer County

JENNIE M. MELHAM MEMORIAL MEDICAL CENTER (281365), 145 Memorial Drive, Zip 68822–1378, Mailing Address: P.O.Box 250, 68822–0250; tel. 308/872–4100, (Total facility includes 50 beds in nursing home–type unit) **A**10 18 **F**3 10 11 13 15 28 31 34 40 43 45 53 57 59 67 79 81 107 110 115 119 125 129 130 133
Primary Contact: Michael J. Steckler, President and Chief Executive Officer
CFO: Tim Schuckman, Chief Financial Officer
CIO: Tim Schuckman, Chief Financial Officer
CHR: Teri Sell, Payroll and Personnel Coordinator
CNO: Shelly Amsberry, Director of Nursing
Web address: www.brokenbow-ne.com/community/healthcare/melham.htm
Control: Other not-for-profit (including NFP Corporation) **Service**: General medical and surgical

Staffed Beds: 73 **Admissions**: 456 **Census**: 43 **Outpatient Visits**: 13462
Births: 78 **Total Expense ($000)**: 16557 **Payroll Expense ($000)**: 6821
Personnel: 120

CALLAWAY—Custer County

★ **CALLAWAY DISTRICT HOSPITAL (281335)**, 211 East Kimball, Zip 68825–2589, Mailing Address: P.O.Box 100, 68825–0100; tel. 308/836–2228, (Nonreporting) **A**10 18
Primary Contact: Marvin Neth, Chief Executive Officer
CFO: Brett Eggleston, Chief Financial Officer
CHR: Carol Koch, Manager Human Resources
Web address: www.callawayhospital.org
Control: Hospital district or authority, Government, Nonfederal **Service**: General medical and surgical

Staffed Beds: 12

CAMBRIDGE—Furnas County

★ **TRI VALLEY HEALTH SYSTEM (281348)**, 1305 West Highway 6 and 34, Zip 69022–0488, Mailing Address: P.O.Box 488, 69022–0488; tel. 308/697–3329, (Total facility includes 32 beds in nursing home–type unit) **A**10 18 **F**3 8 10 11 13 15 28 29 30 31 32 34 35 40 41 45 46 53 56 57 59 64 65 67 68 69 71 75 76 77 78 79 81 82 86 87 91 93 107 110 115 116 119 125 127 128 129 130 131 132 133 135 143 145 146 147 148 **P**6
Primary Contact: Deborah L. Herzberg, R.N., MS, FACHE, Chief Executive Officer
COO: Keith Luedders, Chief Operations Officer
CFO: Diana Rippe, Chief Financial Officer
CMO: Lennie Deaver M.D., Chief of Staff
CIO: Ciprian Galarneau, Director Information Systems
CHR: Tammy Claussen, Chief Human Resource Officer
CNO: Melissa Bodkins R.N., Chief Clinical Officer
Web address: www.trivalleyhealth.com
Control: Other not-for-profit (including NFP Corporation) **Service**: General medical and surgical

Staffed Beds: 52 **Admissions**: 453 **Census**: 34 **Outpatient Visits**: 14378
Births: 52 **Total Expense ($000)**: 21075 **Payroll Expense ($000)**: 8269
Personnel: 150

CENTRAL CITY—Merrick County

★ **MERRICK MEDICAL CENTER (281328)**, 1715 26th Street, Zip 68826–9620; tel. 308/946–3015, (Nonreporting) **A**10 18 **S** Bryan Health, Lincoln, NE
Primary Contact: Julie Murray, Chief Executive Officer
CHR: Shauna Graham, Director of Professional Services Human Resources, Marketing Foundation
Web address: www.lmchealth.com
Control: County, Government, Nonfederal **Service**: General medical and surgical

Staffed Beds: 65

NE

Hospital, Medicare Provider Number, Address, Telephone, Approval, Facility, and Physician Codes, Health Care System

★ American Hospital Association (AHA) membership
☐ The Joint Commission accreditation
○ Healthcare Facilities Accreditation Program
◇ DNV Healthcare Inc. accreditation
⇑ Center for Improvement in Healthcare Quality Accreditation
△ Commission on Accreditation of Rehabilitation Facilities (CARF) accreditation

CHADRON—Dawes County

★ **CHADRON COMMUNITY HOSPITAL AND HEALTH SERVICES (281341)**, 825 Centennial Drive, Zip 69337–9400; tel. 308/432–5586 **A**10 18 **F**3 7 10 11 12 13 14 15 28 29 31 34 35 40 43 44 45 57 59 60 62 63 64 65 68 70 77 78 79 81 82 86 87 91 93 94 96 107 110 111 114 119 125 127 130 131 132 133 143 146 149
Primary Contact: Anna Turman, Interim Chief Executive Officer
COO: Anna Turman, Chief Operating Officer
CFO: Russ Bohnenkamp, Chief Financial Officer
CMO: Ed Pelton, Chief of Staff
CIO: Anna Turman, Chief Information Officer
CHR: Ellen Krueger, Director Human Resources
CNO: Cheryl Cassiday R.N., Director of Nursing
Web address: www.chadronhospital.com
Control: Other not-for-profit (including NFP Corporation) **Service**: General medical and surgical

Staffed Beds: 25 **Admissions**: 519 **Census**: 4 **Outpatient Visits**: 24606 **Births**: 122 **Total Expense ($000)**: 23158 **Payroll Expense ($000)**: 8722 **Personnel**: 186

COLUMBUS—Platte County

✠ **COLUMBUS COMMUNITY HOSPITAL (280111)**, 4600 38th Street, Zip 68601–1664, Mailing Address: P.O.Box 1800, 68602–1800; tel. 402/564–7118, (Nonreporting) **A**1 10 20
Primary Contact: Michael T. Hansen, FACHE, President and Chief Executive Officer
COO: James P Goulet, Vice President Operations
CFO: Chad Van Cleave, Chief Financial Officer
CMO: Mark Howerter M.D., President Medical Staff
CIO: Cheryl Tira, Director Information Systems
CHR: Scott E Messersmith, Director Human Resources
CNO: Linda K Walline R.N., Ph.D., MSN, Vice President Nursing
Web address: www.columbushosp.org
Control: Other not-for-profit (including NFP Corporation) **Service**: General medical and surgical

Staffed Beds: 51

COZAD—Dawson County

★ **COZAD COMMUNITY HEALTH SYSTEM (281327)**, 300 East 12th Street, Zip 69130–1505, Mailing Address: P.O.Box 108, 69130–0108; tel. 308/784–2261 **A**3 5 10 18 **F**3 10 13 15 28 30 31 34 35 40 43 50 53 56 57 59 62 63 68 70 75 76 77 81 82 84 86 93 94 97 107 110 114 119 127 128 129 130 131 132 133 135 146 148 149 **P**6
Primary Contact: Lyle E. Davis, Administrator
Web address: www.cozadhealthcare.com
Control: Hospital district or authority, Government, Nonfederal **Service**: General medical and surgical

Staffed Beds: 20 **Admissions**: 384 **Census**: 4 **Outpatient Visits**: 8530 **Births**: 83 **Total Expense ($000)**: 13945 **Payroll Expense ($000)**: 6527 **Personnel**: 137

CREIGHTON—Knox County

★ **AVERA CREIGHTON HOSPITAL (281331)**, 1503 Main Street, Zip 68729–3007, Mailing Address: P.O.Box 186, 68729–0186; tel. 402/358–5700, (Total facility includes 47 beds in nursing home–type unit) **A**10 18 **F**8 11 15 28 29 31 34 35 40 45 46 50 53 56 57 59 64 65 75 76 77 78 81 84 90 93 107 110 127 128 130 131 133 146 147 148 **P**2 **S** Avera Health, Sioux Falls, SD
Primary Contact: Todd Consbruck, Chief Executive Officer
CHR: Jane E Miller, Director Human Resources
CNO: Jean M Henes R.N., MSN, RN-B, Director of Nursing
Web address: www.avera.org/creighton/
Control: Other not-for-profit (including NFP Corporation) **Service**: General medical and surgical

Staffed Beds: 64 **Admissions**: 159 **Census**: 42 **Outpatient Visits**: 10010 **Births**: 0 **Total Expense ($000)**: 10871 **Payroll Expense ($000)**: 4940 **Personnel**: 111

CRETE—Saline County

★ **CRETE AREA MEDICAL CENTER (281354)**, 2910 Betten Drive, Zip 68333–3084, Mailing Address: P.O.Box 220, 68333–0220; tel. 402/826–2102, (Nonreporting) **A**10 18 **S** Bryan Health, Lincoln, NE
Primary Contact: Rebekah Mussman, Chief Executive Officer
CFO: Doug Kucera, Chief Financial Officer
CMO: Amy Vertin M.D., Chief of Staff
CIO: Drew Kotil, Director Information Technology
CHR: Bobbie Wilson, Director Human Resources
CNO: Jeaniffr P. Snide, Chief Nursing Officer
Web address: www.creteareamedicalcenter.com
Control: Other not-for-profit (including NFP Corporation) **Service**: General medical and surgical

Staffed Beds: 24

DAVID CITY—Butler County

★ **BUTLER COUNTY HEALTH CARE CENTER (281332)**, 372 South Ninth Street, Zip 68632–2116; tel. 402/367–1200, (Nonreporting) **A**5 10 18
Primary Contact: Donald T. Naiberk, Administrator
CFO: Jodi Prochaska, Chief Financial Officer
CMO: Victor Thoendel M.D., Chief Medical Officer
CIO: Cindy Neesen, Director of Information Technology
CHR: Andra Vandenberg, Director Human Resources
CNO: Sue M Birkel R.N., Director of Nursing
Web address: www.bchccnet.org
Control: County, Government, Nonfederal **Service**: General medical and surgical

Staffed Beds: 20

ELKHORN—Douglas County

METHODIST WOMEN'S HOSPITAL See Nebraska Methodist Hospital, Omaha

FAIRBURY—Jefferson County

★ **JEFFERSON COMMUNITY HEALTH AND LIFE (281319)**, 2200 'H' Street, Zip 68352–1119, Mailing Address: P.O.Box 277, 68352–0277; tel. 402/729–3351, (Total facility includes 40 beds in nursing home–type unit) **A**10 18 **F**2 3 13 15 28 29 30 31 34 35 40 45 50 53 57 59 62 64 75 76 77 78 79 81 85 86 87 93 107 110 114 119 127 128 130 131 132 133 135 146 149
Primary Contact: Chad Jurgens, Chief Executive Officer
CFO: Chance Klasek CPA, Chief Financial Officer
CIO: Dennis Ahl, Director Information Technology
CHR: Sandra A Bauer, Director Human Resources
Web address: www.jchc.us
Control: Other not-for-profit (including NFP Corporation) **Service**: General medical and surgical

Staffed Beds: 57 **Admissions**: 317 **Census**: 42 **Outpatient Visits**: 27000 **Births**: 23 **Total Expense ($000)**: 18612 **Payroll Expense ($000)**: 8151 **Personnel**: 195

FALLS CITY—Richardson County

★ **COMMUNITY MEDICAL CENTER, INC. (281352)**, 3307 Barada Street, Zip 68355–2470, Mailing Address: P.O.Box 399, 68355–0399; tel. 402/245–2428 **A**10 18 **F**3 13 15 28 31 34 35 40 43 45 59 75 76 78 79 81 85 93 97 107 111 119 127 130 133 135 **P**6
Primary Contact: Ryan C. Larsen, FACHE, Administrator
CFO: Scott Sawyer, Chief Financial Officer
CMO: David E. Borg, Chief of Medical Staff
CIO: Joe Buckminster, Manager Information Technology
CHR: Shannon Weinmann, Human Resources Manager
CNO: Ivy Campbell, Director of Nursing
Web address: www.cmcfc.org
Control: Other not-for-profit (including NFP Corporation) **Service**: General medical and surgical

Staffed Beds: 24 **Admissions**: 780 **Census**: 8 **Outpatient Visits**: 55284 **Births**: 39 **Total Expense ($000)**: 23549 **Payroll Expense ($000)**: 8018 **Personnel**: 170

FRANKLIN—Franklin County

★ **FRANKLIN COUNTY MEMORIAL HOSPITAL (281311)**, 1406 'Q' Street, Zip 68939–0315, Mailing Address: 1406 Q Street, 68939–0315; tel. 308/425–6221, (Nonreporting) **A**10 18
Primary Contact: Theresa Rizzo, Administrator
CFO: Amy Kahrs, Director of Finance
CMO: Linda Mazour M.D., President
CIO: Cathy Webber, Director of Health Information Management
CNO: Kari Yelken R.N., Director of Nursing
Web address: www.fcmh.com
Control: County, Government, Nonfederal **Service**: General medical and surgical

Staffed Beds: 10

FREMONT—Dodge County

✠ **FREMONT HEALTH (280077)**, 450 East 23rd Street, Zip 68025–2387; tel. 402/721–1610, (Total facility includes 112 beds in nursing home–type unit) **A**1 2 3 5 10 20 **F**3 8 11 13 15 17 18 20 22 26 28 29 30 31 34 35 37 40 45 56 57 59 62 63 64 68 70 72 75 76 77 78 79 81 85 86 87 89 93 98 99 100 103 104 107 108 110 111 114 119 120 121 123 124 126 128 129 130 131 132 135 143 146 **P**8
Primary Contact: Patrick M. Booth, FACHE, President and Chief Executive Officer
CFO: Michael Sindelar, Vice President and Chief Financial Officer
CIO: Matt Sakalosky, Director Information Services and Chief Information Officer
CHR: Bethany Childers, Director Human Resources
CNO: Peggy S Kennedy R.N., MS, FACHE, Vice President and Chief Nurse Executive
Web address: www.fremonthealth.com
Control: County, Government, Nonfederal **Service:** General medical and surgical

Staffed Beds: 193 **Admissions:** 3787 **Census:** 115 **Outpatient Visits:** 82089 **Births:** 314 **Total Expense ($000):** 117229 **Payroll Expense ($000):** 50740 **Personnel:** 777

FRIEND—Saline County

FRIEND COMMUNITY HEALTHCARE SYSTEM (281330), 905 Second Street, Zip 68359–1133; tel. 402/947–2541, (Nonreporting) **A**10 18
Primary Contact: Chad Thompson, President and Chief Executive Officer
CFO: Mackenzie Svarc, Finance Director
CMO: Roger Meyer M.D., Chief of Staff
CHR: Shyanne Scholl, Interim Human Resources Director
CNO: Dayna Pulver, Director of Nursing
Web address: www.friendmed.org/
Control: City, Government, Nonfederal **Service:** General medical and surgical

Staffed Beds: 63

GENEVA—Fillmore County

FILLMORE COUNTY HOSPITAL (281301), 1900 'F' Street, Zip 68361–1325, Mailing Address: P.O.Box 193, 68361–0193; tel. 402/759–3167 **A**10 18 **F**3 7 11 13 15 18 28 29 31 34 40 41 45 57 59 64 67 68 69 74 76 77 78 79 81 82 85 89 92 93 94 98 99 101 102 103 104 107 110 111 114 119 128 130 131 132 133 135 143 148 **P**6
Primary Contact: Christopher Nichols, Chief Executive Officer
COO: Debbie Domann, Director of Operations
CFO: Jeanne Ackland, Director of Finance
CMO: Jason Bespalec M.D., Chief of Staff
CIO: Tyler Gewecke, Information Technology Technician
CHR: Abby Tuberville, Human Resource Manager
Web address: www.fhsofgeneva.org
Control: County, Government, Nonfederal **Service:** General medical and surgical

Staffed Beds: 30 **Admissions:** 408 **Census:** 5 **Outpatient Visits:** 16529 **Births:** 38 **Total Expense ($000):** 18693 **Payroll Expense ($000):** 5273 **Personnel:** 129

GENOA—Nance County

GENOA MEDICAL FACILITIES (281312), 706 Ewing Avenue, Zip 68640–3035, Mailing Address: P.O.Box 310, 68640–0310; tel. 402/993–2283, (Total facility includes 39 beds in nursing home–type unit) **A**10 18 **F**3 8 10 28 29 30 34 35 40 41 43 45 46 47 48 49 50 53 56 57 59 64 65 71 75 77 79 81 82 84 92 93 100 101 103 104 107 114 119 128 130 131 132 133 143 146 148 149
Primary Contact: Cory Nelson, Administrator
CFO: Angie Sutton, Chief Financial Officer
CMO: Brian Buhlke M.D., Medical Director
CHR: Brianna Molt, Human Resources Director
CNO: Amanda Roebuck, Director Patient Care Services
Web address: www.genoamedical.org/
Control: City, Government, Nonfederal **Service:** General medical and surgical

Staffed Beds: 58 **Admissions:** 152 **Census:** 30 **Outpatient Visits:** 6258 **Births:** 0 **Total Expense ($000):** 5497 **Payroll Expense ($000):** 2654 **Personnel:** 28

GORDON—Sheridan County

★ **GORDON MEMORIAL HEALTH SERVICES (281358)**, 300 East Eighth Street, Zip 69343–1123; tel. 308/282–0401, (Nonreporting) **A**10 18
Primary Contact: Donald Weidemann, Chief Executive Officer
CFO: Heidi Cushing, Director Finance
CMO: Christopher P. Costa M.D., Chief of Staff
CIO: Ray Waldron, Director Information Technology
CHR: Lisa Woodcock, Director Human Resources
CNO: Megan Heath, Chief Nursing Officer
Web address: www.gordonmemorial.org
Control: Hospital district or authority, Government, Nonfederal **Service:** General medical and surgical

Staffed Beds: 25

GOTHENBURG—Dawson County

★ **GOTHENBURG HEALTH (281313)**, 910 20th Street, Zip 69138–1237, Mailing Address: P.O.Box 469, 69138–0469; tel. 308/537–3661 **A**10 18 **F**3 13 15 28 29 30 31 34 35 36 37 38 40 41 43 45 50 53 57 59 64 65 75 76 77 78 79 81 85 97 107 110 111 115 119 127 128 129 133 147 **P**1
Primary Contact: Mick Brant, FACHE, Chief Executive Officer
CFO: Michael Pracheil, Chief Financial Officer
CMO: Carol Shackleton M.D., Medical Director
CIO: Tinna Therrien, Chief Information Officer and Director Clinical Infomatics
CHR: Jim Imler, Director Human Resources
CNO: Cassie Hilbers R.N., Chief Nursing Officer
Web address: www.gothenburghealth.org
Control: Hospital district or authority, Government, Nonfederal **Service:** General medical and surgical

Staffed Beds: 12 **Admissions:** 312 **Census:** 4 **Outpatient Visits:** 14320 **Births:** 80 **Total Expense ($000):** 17277 **Payroll Expense ($000):** 7528 **Personnel:** 112

GRAND ISLAND—Hall County

✠ **CHI HEALTH SAINT FRANCIS (280023)**, 2620 West Faidley Avenue, Zip 68803–4297, Mailing Address: P.O.Box 9804, 68802–9804; tel. 308/384–4600, (Includes ST. FRANCIS MEDICAL PLAZA, 2116 West Faidley Avenue, Grand Island, Nebraska, Zip 68803, P O Box 9804, 68802, tel. 308/384–4600) **A**1 2 3 5 10 19 **F**3 5 11 12 13 15 17 18 19 20 22 28 30 31 34 35 40 43 45 47 50 51 53 59 60 62 63 64 65 68 70 72 74 75 76 77 78 79 81 82 84 85 89 90 91 97 104 105 110 120 121 123 128 129 130 132 135 145 146 148 **P**8 **S** Catholic Health Initiatives, Englewood, CO
Primary Contact: Edward J. Hannon, FACHE, President
CFO: Lisa Webb, Vice President Operational Finance
CMO: Shu-Ming Wang, MD, Vice President Medical Affairs
CHR: Nancy Wallace, Vice President Human Resources, CHI Health
CNO: Beth Bartlett MSN, R.N., Vice President Nursing
Web address: www.saintfrancisgi.org
Control: Church operated, Nongovernment, not-for-profit **Service:** General medical and surgical

Staffed Beds: 159 **Admissions:** 6144 **Census:** 88 **Outpatient Visits:** 78336 **Births:** 895 **Total Expense ($000):** 136092 **Payroll Expense ($000):** 37939 **Personnel:** 687

GRANT—Perkins County

★ **PERKINS COUNTY HEALTH SERVICES (281356)**, 900 Lincoln Avenue, Zip 69140–3095; tel. 308/352–7200, (Nonreporting) **A**10 18
Primary Contact: James LeBrun, Chief Executive Officer
CFO: Derick Lorentz, Chief Financial Officer
CMO: Ruth Demmel M.D., Chief Medical Officer
CIO: Jennifer Baumgartner, Chief Information Officer
CHR: Julie Bevard, Director Human Resources
CNO: Dana McArtor R.N., Director of Nursing
Web address: www.pchsgrant.com
Control: Hospital district or authority, Government, Nonfederal **Service:** General medical and surgical

Staffed Beds: 20

NE

Hospital, Medicare Provider Number, Address, Telephone, Approval, Facility, and Physician Codes, Health Care System

★ American Hospital Association (AHA) membership ○ Healthcare Facilities Accreditation Program ⇧ Center for Improvement in Healthcare Quality Accreditation
□ The Joint Commission accreditation ◇ DNV Healthcare Inc. accreditation △ Commission on Accreditation of Rehabilitation Facilities (CARF) accreditation

HASTINGS—Adams County

✠ **MARY LANNING HEALTHCARE (280032)**, 715 North St Joseph Avenue, Zip 68901–4497; tel. 402/463–4521, (Nonreporting) **A**1 2 3 10
Primary Contact: Eric A. Barber, President and Chief Executive Officer
COO: Mark Callahan, Chief Operating Officer
CFO: Shawn A Nordby, Chief Financial Officer
CMO: Michael Skoch M.D., Chief Medical Officer
CIO: Lisa Nonneman, Director Information Technology Services
CHR: Bruce E Cutright MS, Vice President Human Resources
CNO: Ronda S Ehly R.N., Chief Nursing Officer
Web address: www.marylanning.org
Control: Other not-for-profit (including NFP Corporation) **Service**: General medical and surgical

Staffed Beds: 148

HEBRON—Thayer County

★ **THAYER COUNTY HEALTH SERVICES (281304)**, 120 Park Avenue, Zip 68370–2019, Mailing Address: P.O.Box 49, 68370–0049; tel. 402/768–6041, (Nonreporting) **A**10 18
Primary Contact: David Burd, Chief Executive Officer
CFO: Doug Wismer, Chief Financial Officer
CMO: Bryan Hubl M.D., Chief of Staff
CIO: Dan Engle, Chief Information Officer
CHR: Tamara Francik, Human Resources Generalist
CNO: Jamie Koch R.N., Director of Nursing
Web address: www.thayercountyhealth.com
Control: County, Government, Nonfederal **Service**: General medical and surgical

Staffed Beds: 19

HENDERSON—York County

HENDERSON HEALTH CARE SERVICES (281308), 1621 Front Street, Zip 68371–8902; tel. 402/723–4512, (Nonreporting) **A**10 18
Primary Contact: Cheryl Brown, Chief Executive Officer
CMO: James M Ohrt M.D., Director Medical Staff
CHR: Lynette Friesen, Manager Human Resources
CNO: Carrie Peterson, Director of Nursing
Web address: www.hendersonhealthcare.org/getpage.php?name=message
Control: Other not-for-profit (including NFP Corporation) **Service**: General medical and surgical

Staffed Beds: 56

HOLDREGE—Phelps County

★ ⇑ **PHELPS MEMORIAL HEALTH CENTER (281362)**, 1215 Tibbals Street, Zip 68949–1255; tel. 308/995–2211, (Nonreporting) **A**10 18 21 **S** QHR, Brentwood, TN
Primary Contact: Mark Harrel, Chief Executive Officer
CFO: Loren D Schroder, Chief Financial Officer
CMO: Stuart Embury M.D., Chief Medical Officer
CIO: Leora Smith, Information System and Health Information Management Team Leader
CHR: Cindy Jackson, Director Human Resources
Web address: www.phelpsmemorial.com
Control: Other not-for-profit (including NFP Corporation) **Service**: General medical and surgical

Staffed Beds: 25

IMPERIAL—Chase County

★ **CHASE COUNTY COMMUNITY HOSPITAL (281351)**, 600 West 12th Street, Zip 69033–3130, Mailing Address: P.O.Box 819, 69033–0819; tel. 308/882–7111 **A**10 18 **F**11 13 15 28 29 30 31 34 35 40 41 42 43 45 57 59 64 75 81 91 93 107 110 114 127 133 **P**6
Primary Contact: Stephen Lewis, Chief Executive Officer
CFO: Abigail Cyboron, Chief Financial Officer
CMO: Jonathan Richman M.D., Chief of Staff
CIO: Jen Harris, Director Health Information Management
CHR: Julie Sharp, Supervisor Human Resources
CNO: Kathy Geier, Director of Nursing
Web address: www.chasecountyhospital.com
Control: County, Government, Nonfederal **Service**: General medical and surgical

Staffed Beds: 22 **Admissions:** 120 **Census:** 2 **Outpatient Visits:** 16314 **Births:** 15 **Total Expense ($000):** 11741 **Payroll Expense ($000):** 4457 **Personnel:** 86

KEARNEY—Buffalo County

✠ **CHI HEALTH GOOD SAMARITAN (280009)**, 10 East 31st Street, Zip 68847–2926, Mailing Address: P.O.Box 1990, 68848–1990; tel. 308/865–7100, (Includes RICHARD H. YOUNG BEHAVIORAL HEALTH CENTER, 1755 Prairie View Place, Kearney, Nebraska, Zip 68848, P O Box 1750, 68848–1705, tel. 308/865–2000; Michelle Hansen, Director) **A**1 2 3 5 10 **F**7 11 12 13 15 17 18 20 22 24 28 29 30 31 34 35 40 41 45 50 53 54 56 57 59 68 69 74 75 76 77 78 79 81 82 84 85 89 90 91 93 97 101 102 104 105 107 108 110 111 112 113 114 115 119 124 126 128 129 130 132 134 135 146 148 149 150 **P**8 **S** Catholic Health Initiatives, Englewood, CO
Primary Contact: Michael H. Schnieders, FACHE, President
CFO: Lisa Webb, Vice President for Operational Finance
CMO: Dennis Edwards M.D., Vice President Medical Affairs
CIO: Katie Gartner, Director Health Information Management
Web address: www.gshs.org
Control: Church operated, Nongovernment, not-for-profit **Service**: General medical and surgical

Staffed Beds: 233 **Admissions:** 8085 **Census:** 122 **Outpatient Visits:** 54119 **Births:** 1016 **Total Expense ($000):** 170174 **Payroll Expense ($000):** 52748 **Personnel:** 787

GOOD SAMARITAN HEALTH SYSTEMS See CHI Health Good Samaritan

★ ○ **KEARNEY REGIONAL MEDICAL CENTER (280134)**, 804 22nd Avenue, Zip 68845–2206; tel. 855/404–5762, (Nonreporting) **A**10 11
Primary Contact: Larry Speicher, Chief Executive Officer
CFO: Steve Regier, Chief Financial Officer
CIO: Travis Gregg, Director Support Services
CHR: Steve Beck MS, Director Human Resources
CNO: Adrienne Carney R.N., Director Nursing and Surgical Services
Web address: www.kearneyregional.com
Control: Partnership, Investor-owned (for-profit) **Service**: General medical and surgical

Staffed Beds: 44

KIMBALL—Kimball County

★ **KIMBALL HEALTH SERVICES (281305)**, 505 South Burg Street, Zip 69145–1398; tel. 308/235–1952, (Nonreporting) **A**10 18
Primary Contact: Ken Hunter, R.N., Chief Executive Officer
CFO: Melissa Prante, Chief Financial Officer
CMO: James Plate M.D., Chief of Staff
CIO: Charles Walker, Director Information Technology
CHR: Jim Imler, Director Human Resources
CNO: Richard Harriger, Director of Emergency Services
Web address: www.kimballhealth.org
Control: County, Government, Nonfederal **Service**: General medical and surgical

Staffed Beds: 10

LEXINGTON—Dawson County

★ ⇑ **LEXINGTON REGIONAL HEALTH CENTER (281361)**, 1201 North Erie Street, Zip 68850–1560, Mailing Address: P.O.Box 980, 68850–0980; tel. 308/324–5651, (Nonreporting) **A**3 5 10 18 21
Primary Contact: Leslie Marsh, Chief Executive Officer
COO: Jim Hain, Chief Operating Officer
CFO: Wade Eschenbrenner, Chief Financial Officer
CMO: Francisca Acosta-Carlson M.D., Chief of Staff
CIO: Robb Hanna, Executive Director Information Technology
CHR: Jill Denker, Executive Director Human Resources
CNO: Nicole Thorell R.N., MSN, Chief Nursing Officer
Web address: www.lexingtonregional.org
Control: Hospital district or authority, Government, Nonfederal **Service**: General medical and surgical

Staffed Beds: 25

NE

Many Facility Codes have changed. Please refer to the AHA Guide Code Chart.

LINCOLN—Lancaster County

✠ △ **BRYAN MEDICAL CENTER (280003)**, 1600 South 48th Street,
Zip 68506–1299; tel. 402/489–0200, (Includes BRYAN MEDICAL CENTER-EAST,
1600 South 48th Street, Lincoln, Nebraska, Zip 68506–1299, tel. 402/489–
0200; BRYAN MEDICAL CENTER-WEST, 2300 South 16th Street, Lincoln,
Nebraska, Zip 68502–3781, tel. 402/475–1011) **A**1 2 7 10 **F**3 4 5 12 13 15 17
18 19 20 22 24 26 28 29 30 31 34 35 37 38 39 40 43 45 46 47 48 49 50 54
56 57 58 59 61 64 68 70 71 72 74 75 76 77 78 79 81 82 84 85 86 87 89 90
92 93 96 98 99 101 102 103 104 105 107 108 110 111 114 115 116 117
118 119 120 123 126 129 130 131 132 135 145 146 147 148 149 **S** Bryan
Health, Lincoln, NE
Primary Contact: John T. Woodrich, President and Chief Operating Officer
CFO: Russell Gronewold, Chief Financial Officer
CMO: John Trapp, Vice President Medical Affairs
CIO: George Carr, Chief Information Officer
CHR: Jan Garvin, Vice President Human Resources
CNO: Lisa M Vail R.N., Chief Nursing Officer and Vice President of Patient Care Services
Web address: www.bryanhealth.com
Control: Other not-for-profit (including NFP Corporation) **Service**: General medical
and surgical

Staffed Beds: 537 **Admissions:** 26037 **Census:** 328 **Outpatient Visits:**
197156 **Births:** 3149 **Total Expense ($000):** 514077 **Payroll Expense
($000):** 185261 **Personnel:** 3036

★ **CHI HEALTH NEBRASKA HEART (280128)**, 7500 South 91st Street, Zip 68526–
9437; tel. 402/327–2700 **A**10 **F**17 18 20 22 24 26 29 30 34 40 45 57 58 59
64 81 107 115 119 130 **P**8 **S** Catholic Health Initiatives, Englewood, CO
Primary Contact: Dan Schonlau, Interim President
CFO: Dan Schonlau, Chief Financial Officer and Vice President of Finance
CMO: Peter Dionisopoulos, Chief Medical Officer
CNO: Jackie Mendoza, Chief Nursing Officer
Web address: www.CHIhealthNebraskaHeart.com
Control: Church operated, Nongovernment, not-for-profit **Service**: Heart

Staffed Beds: 63 **Admissions:** 2014 **Census:** 19 **Outpatient Visits:** 11549 **Total
Expense ($000):** 60167 **Payroll Expense ($000):** 17404 **Personnel:** 283

✠ **CHI HEALTH ST ELIZABETH (280020)**, 555 South 70th Street, Zip 68510–
2494; tel. 402/219–8000 **A**1 2 3 5 10 **F**3 8 11 12 13 15 16 29 30 31 34 35 37
39 40 44 45 46 47 48 49 50 51 53 55 58 59 60 61 64 65 68 70 72 74 75 76
78 79 80 81 84 85 86 87 89 92 107 108 110 111 114 115 116 117 118 119
120 121 123 124 126 129 130 131 132 144 145 146 147 148 **P**8 **S** Catholic
Health Initiatives, Englewood, CO
Primary Contact: Cary Ward, M.D., Chief Medical Officer and Interim President
CFO: Dan Schonlau, Chief Financial Officer and Vice President of Finance
CMO: Michael Ferris M.D., Chief Medical Officer
CIO: Richard Bohaty, Director Information Technology
CHR: Nancy Wallace, Senior Vice President, Chief Human Resources Officer
CNO: Elizabeth A Raetz R.N., MSN, Vice President Nursing and Chief Nursing Officer
Web address: www.saintelizabethonline.com
Control: Other not-for-profit (including NFP Corporation) **Service**: General medical
and surgical

Staffed Beds: 260 **Admissions:** 8737 **Census:** 105 **Outpatient Visits:**
96626 **Births:** 1640 **Total Expense ($000):** 187420 **Payroll Expense
($000):** 56488 **Personnel:** 847

LINCOLN DIVISION See Veterans Affairs Nebraska-Western Iowa Health Care
System - Lincoln

☐ **LINCOLN REGIONAL CENTER (284003)**, West Prospector Place and South
Folsom, Zip 68522–2299, Mailing Address: P.O.Box 94949, 68509–4949; tel.
402/479–5207, (Nonreporting) **A**1 10
Primary Contact: William R. Gibson, Chief Executive Officer
COO: Stacey Werth-Sweeney, Facility Operating Officer
CFO: Randy Willey, Business Manager
CMO: Vijay Dewan M.D., Clinical Director
CHR: Scott Rasmussen, Director Human Resources
Web address: www.hhs.state.ne.us/beh/rc
Control: State, Government, Nonfederal **Service**: Psychiatric

Staffed Beds: 244

LINCOLN SURGICAL HOSPITAL (280127), 1710 South 70th Street, Suite 200,
Zip 68506–1677; tel. 402/484–9090 (Nonreporting) **A**10
Primary Contact: Robb Linafelter, Chief Executive Officer
Web address: www.lincolnsurgery.com
Control: Corporation, Investor-owned (for-profit) **Service**: Surgical

Staffed Beds: 7

△ **MADONNA REHABILITATION HOSPITAL (283025)**, 5401 South Street,
Zip 68506–2134; tel. 402/489–7102, (Nonreporting) **A**7 10
Primary Contact: Paul Dongilli Jr, Ph.D., FACHE, President and Chief Executive
Officer
CFO: Victor J Witkowicz, Senior Vice President and Chief Financial Officer
CMO: Thomas Stadler M.D., Vice President Medical Affairs and Chief Medical
Officer
CIO: David Rolfe, Chief Information Officer
CHR: Lou Ann Manske, Director Human Resources
Web address: www.madonna.org
Control: Other not-for-profit (including NFP Corporation) **Service**: Rehabilitation

Staffed Beds: 308

MADONNA REHABILITATION HOSPITAL (282000), 5401 South Street,
Zip 68506–2150; tel. 402/413–3000 (Nonreporting)
Primary Contact: Paul Dongilli Jr, Ph.D., FACHE, President and Chief Executive
Officer
Web address: www.madonna.org/
Control: Other not-for-profit (including NFP Corporation) **Service**: Acute long-term
care hospital

Staffed Beds: 300

NEBRASKA PENAL AND CORRECTIONAL HOSPITAL, 14th And Pioneer
Streets, Zip 68501, Mailing Address: P.O.Box 94661, 94661; tel. 402/471–3161
(Nonreporting)
Primary Contact: Randy T. Kohl, M.D., Deputy Director, Health Services
Web address: www.corrections.nebraska.gov
Control: State, Government, Nonfederal **Service**: Hospital unit of an institution
(prison hospital, college infirmary, etc.)

Staffed Beds: 12

✠ **SELECT SPECIALTY HOSPITAL - LINCOLN (282002)**, 2300 South 16th Street,
7th Floor, Zip 68502–3704; tel. 402/483–8444 **A**1 10 **F**1 3 29 30 35 50 60 68
97 107 111 115 119 130 148 **P**8 **S** Select Medical Corporation, Mechanicsburg,
PA
Primary Contact: Scott Butterfield, Chief Executive Officer
CHR: Bob Dorsey, Human Resources Coordinator
CNO: Trisha Smolik R.N., MSN, Chief Nursing Officer
Web address: www.selectmedical.com
Control: Corporation, Investor-owned (for-profit) **Service**: Acute long-term care
hospital

Staffed Beds: 24 **Admissions:** 201 **Census:** 14 **Outpatient Visits:** 0
Births: 0

★ **VETERANS AFFAIRS NEBRASKA-WESTERN IOWA HEALTH CARE SYSTEM
- LINCOLN**, 600 South 70th Street, Zip 68510–2493; tel. 402/489–3802,
(Nonreporting) (Includes LINCOLN DIVISION, 600 South 70th Street, Lincoln,
Nebraska, Zip 68510–2493, tel. 402/489–3802) **S** Department of Veterans
Affairs, Washington, DC
Primary Contact: Don Burman, Director
CIO: David Daiker, Chief Information Resource Management
CHR: Dave Peters, Chief Human Resources Officer
Web address: www.nebraska.va.gov/
Control: Veterans Affairs, Government, federal **Service**: General medical and
surgical

Staffed Beds: 132

LYNCH—Boyd County

NIOBRARA VALLEY HOSPITAL (281303), 401 South Fifth Street, Zip 68746–
0118, Mailing Address: P.O.Box 118, 68746–0118; tel. 402/569–2451,
(Nonreporting) **A**10 18 **S** Faith Regional Health Services, Norfolk, NE
Primary Contact: Kelly Kalkowski, Chief Executive Officer
CFO: Martha Nelson, Chief Financial Officer
CMO: James Keil M.D., Chief Medical Officer
CHR: Trudy Nelson, Chief Human Resource Officer
CNO: Debra Dawn Hanzlik R.N., Director of Nursing
Web address: www.nvhcares.org
Control: Other not-for-profit (including NFP Corporation) **Service**: General medical
and surgical

Staffed Beds: 20

NE

Hospital, Medicare Provider Number, Address, Telephone, Approval, Facility, and Physician Codes, Health Care System

★ American Hospital Association (AHA) membership   ○ Healthcare Facilities Accreditation Program   ⇑ Center for Improvement in Healthcare Quality Accreditation
☐ The Joint Commission accreditation   ◇ DNV Healthcare Inc. accreditation   △ Commission on Accreditation of Rehabilitation Facilities (CARF) accreditation

MCCOOK—Red Willow County

★ ⇑ **COMMUNITY HOSPITAL (281363)**, 1301 East 'H' Street, Zip 69001–1328, Mailing Address: P.O.Box 1328, 69001–1328; tel. 308/344–2650 **A**10 18 21 **F**3 11 13 15 28 29 31 34 35 40 41 45 48 50 51 57 62 63 64 75 77 78 79 81 82 85 93 96 107 110 111 114 119 120 121 127 129 130 131 132 133 135 145 146 148
Primary Contact: Troy Bruntz, President and Chief Executive Officer
CFO: Sean Wolfe, Vice President Finance and Chief Financial Officer
CMO: Jason Blomstedt, Chief of Staff
CIO: Lori Beeby, Director Information Systems
CHR: Leanne R Miller, Director Human Resources
CNO: Brad Langdorf R.N., Vice President Clinical Services and Chief Nursing Officer
Web address: www.chmccook.org
Control: Other not-for-profit (including NFP Corporation) **Service:** General medical and surgical

Staffed Beds: 25 **Admissions:** 847 **Census:** 7 **Outpatient Visits:** 31939 **Births:** 133 **Total Expense ($000):** 45009 **Payroll Expense ($000):** 15745 **Personnel:** 247

MINDEN—Kearney County

★ **KEARNEY COUNTY HEALTH SERVICES (281306)**, 727 East First Street, Zip 68959–1705; tel. 308/832–3400, (Total facility includes 34 beds in nursing home–type unit) **A**10 18 **F**3 10 15 28 29 34 40 41 57 59 64 65 67 68 81 97 99 103 104 107 110 115 119 127 128 130 133 145 146 147 148 149 **P**6
Primary Contact: Luke Poore, Chief Executive Officer
CFO: Kayla Rhynalds, Interim Chief Financial Officer
CMO: Douglas Althouse, Chief Medical Staff
CHR: Rebecca L Cooke, Director Human Resources
CNO: Mary Bunger R.N., Director Nursing Services
Web address: www.kchs.org
Control: County, Government, Nonfederal **Service:** General medical and surgical

Staffed Beds: 44 **Admissions:** 157 **Census:** 21 **Outpatient Visits:** 6317 **Births:** 0 **Total Expense ($000):** 9051 **Payroll Expense ($000):** 3408 **Personnel:** 113

NEBRASKA CITY—Otoe County

★ **CHI HEALTH ST. MARY'S (281342)**, 1301 Grundman Boulevard, Zip 68410; tel. 402/873–3321 **A**10 18 **F**3 13 15 18 28 31 34 35 40 43 45 57 59 64 66 68 69 75 78 79 81 82 85 87 97 107 110 111 114 115 118 119 127 128 129 130 132 133 135 146 147 148 **S** Catholic Health Initiatives, Englewood, CO
Primary Contact: Daniel J. Kelly, President
CFO: Tim H Schnack, Vice President Operations Finance
CMO: Jonathan Stelling M.D., Vice President Medical Affairs
CNO: Brenda Jean Sebek R.N., Administrator
Web address: www.chihealthstmarys.com
Control: Church operated, Nongovernment, not-for-profit **Service:** General medical and surgical

Staffed Beds: 18 **Admissions:** 277 **Census:** 3 **Outpatient Visits:** 32834 **Births:** 126

NELIGH—Antelope County

★ **ANTELOPE MEMORIAL HOSPITAL (281326)**, 102 West Ninth Street, Zip 68756–1114, Mailing Address: P.O.Box 229, 68756–0229; tel. 402/887–4151, (Nonreporting) **A**10 18
Primary Contact: Jack W. Green, Administrator
CFO: Martha Nelson, Chief Financial Officer
CMO: Troy Dawson M.D., President Medical Staff
CIO: Kevin Trease, Chief Information Officer
CHR: Mary A Schwager, Director Human Resources
CNO: Merry Sprout R.N., Chief Nursing Officer
Web address: www.amhne.org/
Control: Other not-for-profit (including NFP Corporation) **Service:** General medical and surgical

Staffed Beds: 25

NORFOLK—Madison County

⊠ **FAITH REGIONAL HEALTH SERVICES (280125)**, 2700 West Norfolk Avenue, Zip 68701–4438, Mailing Address: P.O.Box 869, 68702–0869; tel. 402/371–4880, (Includes EAST CAMPUS, 1500 Koenigstein Avenue, Norfolk, Nebraska, Zip 68701, tel. 402/371–3402; WEST CAMPUS, 2700 Norfolk Avenue, Norfolk, Nebraska, Zip 68701, P O Box 869, 68702–0869, tel. 402/371–4880) (Total facility includes 62 beds in nursing home–type unit) **A**1 2 3 5 10 11 13 15 18 20 22 24 26 28 29 30 31 34 35 40 41 43 44 45 46 49 50 53 57 58 59 61 62 63 64 65 67 70 71 73 74 75 76 77 78 79 80 81 82 84 85 86 87 89 90 91 92 93 96 98 102 107 108 110 111 114 115 119 120 121 123 128 129 130 131 132 135 146 147 148 149 **P**6 7 8 **S** Faith Regional Health Services, Norfolk, NE
Primary Contact: Mark D. Klosterman, FACHE, President and Chief Executive Officer
CFO: Johnathan Wilker, Vice President Finance and Chief Financial Officer
CMO: Dean O French M.D., Chief of Staff
CIO: Brian Sterud, Chief Information Officer
CHR: Janet Pinkelman, Director Human Resources
Web address: www.frhs.org
Control: Other not-for-profit (including NFP Corporation) **Service:** General medical and surgical

Staffed Beds: 147 **Admissions:** 4869 **Census:** 126 **Outpatient Visits:** 87960 **Births:** 844 **Total Expense ($000):** 160160 **Payroll Expense ($000):** 49221 **Personnel:** 946

NORTH PLATTE—Lincoln County

⊠ **GREAT PLAINS HEALTH (280065)**, 601 West Leota Street, Zip 69101–6598, Mailing Address: P.O.Box 1167, 69103–1167; tel. 308/568–8000 **A**1 2 3 5 10 **F**3 8 12 13 15 18 20 22 28 29 30 31 34 35 40 43 45 48 50 51 57 59 60 62 63 68 70 73 74 75 76 78 79 81 82 84 85 89 93 98 99 102 103 104 105 107 108 110 111 115 116 117 119 120 121 122 124 129 130 131 132 135 145 146 147 148 **P**8
Primary Contact: Melvin McNea, Chief Executive Officer
CFO: Krystal Claymore, Chief Financial Officer
CIO: Brandon Kelliher, Chief Information Officer
CHR: Jayne Johnson, Director Human Resources
Web address: www.gphealth.org
Control: Other not-for-profit (including NFP Corporation) **Service:** General medical and surgical

Staffed Beds: 114 **Admissions:** 5573 **Census:** 57 **Births:** 553 **Total Expense ($000):** 152892 **Payroll Expense ($000):** 55982

OAKLAND—Burt County

★ **OAKLAND MERCY HOSPITAL (281321)**, 601 East Second Street, Zip 68045–1499; tel. 402/685–5601 **A**10 18 **F**11 15 18 26 28 29 30 34 35 40 43 44 50 57 59 75 81 93 97 107 108 110 114 127 128 132 133 148 **P**6 **S** Trinity Health, Livonia, MI
Primary Contact: John W. Werner, Chief Executive Officer
COO: John W. Werner, Chief Executive Officer
CFO: Terri Mentink, Chief Financial Officer
CMO: Tracie Martin M.D., Chief Medical Officer
CNO: Jayma Brown, Director of Nursing
Web address: www.oaklandhospital.org
Control: Church operated, Nongovernment, not-for-profit **Service:** General medical and surgical

Staffed Beds: 18 **Admissions:** 145 **Census:** 2 **Outpatient Visits:** 5077 **Births:** 0 **Total Expense ($000):** 3855 **Payroll Expense ($000):** 2368 **Personnel:** 36

OGALLALA—Keith County

★ **OGALLALA COMMUNITY HOSPITAL (281355)**, 2601 North Spruce Street, Zip 69153–2465; tel. 308/284–4011, (Nonreporting) **A**10 18 **S** Banner Health, Phoenix, AZ
Primary Contact: Drew H. Dostal, R.N., FACHE, Chief Executive Officer
CFO: Dena Klockman, Chief Financial Officer
CMO: Shane Banks M.D., Chief of Staff
CHR: Patricia Shaner, Interim Chief Human Resources Officer
CNO: Aileen Chandler, Chief Nursing Officer
Web address: www.bannerhealth.com/Locations/Nebraska/Ogallala+Community+Hospital
Control: Other not-for-profit (including NFP Corporation) **Service:** General medical and surgical

Staffed Beds: 18

NE

Many Facility Codes have changed. Please refer to the AHA Guide Code Chart. © 2017 AHA Guide

OMAHA—Douglas County

☐ **BOYS TOWN NATIONAL RESEARCH HOSPITAL (283300)**, 555 North 30th Street, Zip 68131–2198; tel. 402/498–6511 **A**1 3 5 10 **F**3 34 35 58 65 68 79 81 86 87 89 97 99 104 106 107 108 111 119 129 130 131 **P**6
Primary Contact: John K. Arch, FACHE, Director
CFO: Leigh Jean Koinzan, Director Finance
CMO: Edward Kolb M.D., Medical Director
CIO: Ann Ducey, Chief Information Officer
CHR: Michael Gell, Director Human Resources
CNO: Patricia Allgeier R.N., Chief Nursing Officer
Web address: www.boystownhospital.org
Control: Other not-for-profit (including NFP Corporation) **Service:** Children's general medical and surgical

Staffed Beds: 129 **Admissions:** 163 **Census:** 1 **Outpatient Visits:** 216842 **Births:** 0 **Total Expense ($000):** 115281 **Payroll Expense ($000):** 53253 **Personnel:** 912

☒ **CHI HEALTH CREIGHTON UNIVERSITY MEDICAL CENTER - BERGAN MERCY (280060)**, 7500 Mercy Road, Zip 68124–2319; tel. 402/398–6060, (Includes LASTING HOPE RECOVERY CENTER, 415 South 25th Avenue, Omaha, Nebraska, Zip 68131, tel. 402/717–5300; Robin Conyers, Administrator) **A**1 2 3 5 8 10 **F**3 8 11 13 15 17 18 20 22 24 26 28 29 30 31 32 34 35 37 38 40 43 45 46 47 48 49 50 51 53 54 55 56 57 58 59 60 61 62 63 64 65 68 70 72 74 75 76 77 78 79 81 82 83 84 85 86 87 89 92 93 97 98 100 105 107 108 109 110 111 114 115 116 117 118 119 120 121 123 124 126 127 130 131 132 134 143 144 145 146 147 148 **P**8 **S** Catholic Health Initiatives, Englewood, CO
Primary Contact: Kevin J. Nokels, FACHE, Primary
COO: Chris Evans, Vice President Operations
CFO: Tim H Schnack, Vice President Financial Services
CMO: Kevin Reagan M.D., Chief Medical Officer
CIO: Karun Kapur, Chief Information Officer
CHR: Nancy Wallace, Vice President Human Resources
Web address: www.alegent.com/bergan
Control: Church operated, Nongovernment, not-for-profit **Service:** General medical and surgical

Staffed Beds: 308 **Admissions:** 11773 **Census:** 144 **Outpatient Visits:** 109916 **Births:** 3404 **Total Expense ($000):** 246496 **Payroll Expense ($000):** 71800 **Personnel:** 1171

☒ △ **CHI HEALTH IMMANUEL (280081)**, 6901 North 72nd Street, Zip 68122–1799; tel. 402/572–2121 **A**1 2 3 5 7 10 **F**3 4 5 6 11 12 13 15 17 18 20 22 26 28 29 30 31 32 34 35 36 37 38 40 43 45 46 49 50 51 53 55 56 57 58 59 64 68 70 74 75 76 77 78 79 81 82 84 85 86 87 90 91 92 93 94 95 96 97 98 99 100 102 103 105 106 107 108 110 111 114 115 117 118 119 120 121 123 124 126 128 129 130 131 132 136 141 142 146 **P**8 **S** Catholic Health Initiatives, Englewood, CO
Primary Contact: Ann Schumacher, R.N., MSN, FACHE, President
CFO: Tim H Schnack, Chief Financial Officer
CMO: Joseph Hoagbin M.D., Chief Medical Officer
CHR: Nancy Wallace, Vice President Human Resources
Web address: www.alegent.com/immanuel
Control: Church operated, Nongovernment, not-for-profit **Service:** General medical and surgical

Staffed Beds: 289 **Admissions:** 9828 **Census:** 157 **Outpatient Visits:** 112276 **Births:** 468 **Total Expense ($000):** 166883 **Payroll Expense ($000):** 55777 **Personnel:** 907

☒ **CHI HEALTH LAKESIDE (280130)**, 16901 Lakeside Hills Court, Zip 68130–2318; tel. 402/717–8000 **A**1 2 3 5 10 **F**3 8 12 13 15 18 20 22 26 28 29 30 31 32 34 35 36 38 44 45 46 49 53 54 55 56 59 60 61 64 68 70 72 74 75 76 77 78 79 81 82 83 84 85 86 93 94 97 99 100 102 103 104 107 108 110 111 114 115 118 119 120 121 122 123 124 126 129 130 131 132 134 143 146 147 148 **P**8 **S** Catholic Health Initiatives, Englewood, CO
Primary Contact: Kevin Miller, President
COO: Joan E Neuhaus, Division Senior Vice President Chief Operating Officer
CFO: Tyler DeJong, Director, Operational Finance
CMO: Patricia Murdock-Langan M.D., Chief Medical Officer
CIO: Thomas Haley, Information Technology Systems Site Director
CHR: Nancy Wallace, Division Senior Vice President, Chief Human Resource Officer
CNO: Brenda Bergman-Evans, Chief Nursing Officer
Web address: www.CHIhealth.com
Control: Church operated, Nongovernment, not-for-profit **Service:** General medical and surgical

Staffed Beds: 137 **Admissions:** 7155 **Census:** 70 **Outpatient Visits:** 91891 **Births:** 893 **Total Expense ($000):** 117143 **Payroll Expense ($000):** 34988 **Personnel:** 572

☒ **CHILDREN'S HOSPITAL AND MEDICAL CENTER (283301)**, 8200 Dodge St, Zip 68114–4113; tel. 402/955–5400 **A**1 3 5 10 **F**3 7 8 11 12 13 19 21 23 25 27 29 30 31 32 34 35 40 41 43 45 46 47 48 49 50 54 55 58 59 60 62 64 65 68 72 74 75 76 77 78 79 81 82 84 85 87 88 89 92 93 99 104 107 108 111 115 119 126 129 130 131 132 137 144 145 146 148 149 **P**6
Primary Contact: Richard G. Azizkhan, M.D., President and Chief Executive Officer
COO: Kathy L English R.N., MSN, Executive Vice President and Chief Operating Officer
CFO: Amy Hatcher, Chief Financial Officer
CMO: Carl H Gumbiner M.D., Senior Vice President Medical Affairs and Chief Medical Officer
CIO: Mark Stastny, Vice President and Chief Information Officer
CHR: Patricia Schulz, Chief Human Resource Officer
CNO: Debra Arnow R.N., VP Patient Care & Chief Nursing Officer
Web address: www.childrensomaha.org
Control: Other not-for-profit (including NFP Corporation) **Service:** Children's general medical and surgical

Staffed Beds: 140 **Admissions:** 4570 **Census:** 96 **Outpatient Visits:** 370859 **Births:** 9 **Total Expense ($000):** 365848 **Payroll Expense ($000):** 162863 **Personnel:** 2044

★ ○ **DOUGLAS COUNTY COMMUNITY MENTAL HEALTH CENTER (284009)**, 4102 Woolworth Avenue, Zip 68105–1899; tel. 402/444–7000, (Nonreporting) **A**3 5 10 11
Primary Contact: Sherry L. Glasnapp, Director
CFO: DeDe Will, Director Finance
CMO: Sidney A. Kauzlarich M.D., Medical Director
CIO: Dianne Wallace, County Information Manager
CHR: Karen Buche, Chief Human Resource Officer
CNO: Marti Christensen, Director of Psychiatric Nursing
Web address: www.co.douglas.ne.us
Control: County, Government, Nonfederal **Service:** Psychiatric

Staffed Beds: 18

MIDWEST SURGICAL HOSPITAL (280131), 7915 Farnam Drive, Zip 68114–4504; tel. 402/399–1900 (Nonreporting) **A**3 10
Primary Contact: Charles Livingston, Chief Executive Officer
Web address: www.mwsurgicalhospital.com
Control: Corporation, Investor-owned (for-profit) **Service:** Surgical

Staffed Beds: 19

☒ **NEBRASKA MEDICINE - NEBRASKA MEDICAL CENTER (280013)**, 987400 Nebraska Medical Center, Zip 68198–7400; tel. 402/552–2000 **A**1 2 3 5 8 10 **F**3 6 8 9 11 12 13 15 16 17 18 20 22 24 26 28 29 30 31 32 34 35 36 37 38 39 40 41 43 44 45 46 47 48 49 50 51 53 54 55 56 57 58 59 60 61 62 63 64 65 66 68 70 71 72 74 75 76 77 78 79 80 81 82 84 85 86 87 88 89 91 92 93 94 96 97 98 99 100 101 102 103 104 107 108 110 111 113 114 115 116 117 118 119 120 121 123 124 126 127 129 130 131 132 134 135 136 137 138 139 140 141 142 143 144 145 146 147 148 149 **P**5 6 8
Primary Contact: Daniel J. DeBehnke, M.D., Chief Executive Officer
COO: Dennis Bierle, Chief Operating Officer
CFO: Stephanie Daubert, Chief Financial Officer
CMO: Harris Frankel M.D., Interim Chief Medical Officer
CIO: Michael A Ash, Chief Transformation Officer
CHR: Frank Venuto, Chief Human Capital Officer
CNO: Suzanne Langan Nuss M.D., Chief Nursing Officer
Web address: www.nebraskamed.com
Control: Other not-for-profit (including NFP Corporation) **Service:** General medical and surgical

Staffed Beds: 537 **Admissions:** 25548 **Census:** 389 **Outpatient Visits:** 842522 **Births:** 1767 **Total Expense ($000):** 1108486 **Payroll Expense ($000):** 516613 **Personnel:** 6439

NE

Hospital, Medicare Provider Number, Address, Telephone, Approval, Facility, and Physician Codes, Health Care System

★ American Hospital Association (AHA) membership ○ Healthcare Facilities Accreditation Program ⇑ Center for Improvement in Healthcare Quality Accreditation
☐ The Joint Commission accreditation ◇ DNV Healthcare Inc. accreditation △ Commission on Accreditation of Rehabilitation Facilities (CARF) accreditation

✠ △ **NEBRASKA METHODIST HOSPITAL (280040)**, 8303 Dodge Street, Zip 68114–4199; tel. 402/354–4000, (Includes METHODIST WOMEN'S HOSPITAL, 707 North 190th Plaza, Elkhorn, Nebraska, Zip 68022–3974, tel. 402/815–4000; Susan Korth, M.P.H., Ph.D., Vice President and Chief Operating Officer) **A**1 2 3 5 7 10 **F**3 8 11 12 13 15 18 20 22 24 26 28 29 30 31 34 35 40 45 46 47 48 49 50 51 52 53 54 55 56 57 58 59 62 63 64 65 66 68 70 72 74 75 76 77 78 79 80 81 82 83 84 85 86 87 90 91 92 93 96 100 101 104 107 108 110 111 114 115 117 118 119 120 121 123 124 126 129 130 132 135 136 141 143 146 147 148 **S** Nebraska Methodist Health System, Inc., Omaha, NE
Primary Contact: Stephen L. Goeser, FACHE, Executive Vice President and Chief Operations Officer
CFO: Linda K Burt, Corporate Vice President Finance
CMO: William Shiffermiller M.D., Vice President Medical Affairs
CHR: Holly Huerter, Vice President Human Resources
CNO: Teri Tipton MSN, Chief Nursing Officer and Vice President Patient Care Services
Web address: www.bestcare.org
Control: Other not-for-profit (including NFP Corporation) **Service:** General medical and surgical

Staffed Beds: 377 **Admissions:** 18859 **Census:** 262 **Outpatient Visits:** 135461 **Births:** 5219 **Total Expense ($000):** 476025 **Payroll Expense ($000):** 177933 **Personnel:** 2650

✠ **NEBRASKA SPINE HOSPITAL (280133)**, 6901 North 72nd Street, Suite 20300, Zip 68122–1755, Mailing Address: 6901 North 72nd Street, 68122–1709; tel. 402/572–3000, (Nonreporting) **A**1 10
Primary Contact: Cory Kruger, Interim Chief Executive Officer
CNO: Teresa Hawlik MSN, Chief Nurse Executive
Web address: www.nebraskaspinehospital.com
Control: Partnership, Investor-owned (for-profit) **Service:** Orthopedic

Staffed Beds: 34

☐ **ORTHONEBRASKA HOSPITAL (280129)**, 2808 South 143rd Plaza, Zip 68144–5611; tel. 402/609–1600 **A**1 3 5 10 **F**40 42 64 79 81 82 85 93 94 96 107 111 114 119 131 **P**8
Primary Contact: Levi Scheppers, Chief Executive Officer
COO: Mark E Longacre FACHE, Chief Operating Officer
CFO: Anna McCaslin, Chief Financial Officer
CMO: Ian Crabb M.D., Chief Medical Officer
CIO: Tim Pugsley, Chief Information Officer
CHR: Lori L Thompson, Manager Human Resources
CNO: Nancy Laughlin R.N., Chief Nursing Officer
Web address: www.neorthohospital.com
Control: Partnership, Investor-owned (for-profit) **Service:** Orthopedic

Staffed Beds: 24 **Admissions:** 1940 **Census:** 11 **Outpatient Visits:** 63903 **Births:** 0 **Total Expense ($000):** 72322 **Payroll Expense ($000):** 22172 **Personnel:** 272

✠ **SELECT SPECIALTY HOSPITAL-OMAHA (282001)**, 1870 South 75th Street, Zip 68124–1700; tel. 402/361–5700, (Nonreporting) **A**1 10 **S** Select Medical Corporation, Mechanicsburg, PA
Primary Contact: Darrell Jones, Interim Chief Executive Officer
COO: Joel White, Chief Operating Officer
CMO: Guillermo Huerta M.D., Chief Medical Officer
CHR: Laurna Hoss, Human Resource Coordinator
CNO: Amanda Wellman MSN, R.N., Chief Nursing Officer
Web address: www.omaha.selectspecialtyhospitals.com
Control: Corporation, Investor-owned (for-profit) **Service:** Acute long-term care hospital

Staffed Beds: 52

✠ **VETERANS AFFAIRS NEBRASKA-WESTERN IOWA HEALTH CARE SYSTEM**, 4101 Woolworth Avenue, Zip 68105–1873; tel. 402/346–8800, (Nonreporting) **A**1 2 3 5 8 **S** Department of Veterans Affairs, Washington, DC
Primary Contact: Don Burman, Director
COO: Denise Harrison, Associate Director
CFO: Kirk Kay, Chief Financial Officer
CMO: Grace Stringfellow M.D., Chief of Staff
CIO: Jennifer Rosenbalm, Manager Business Office
CHR: Cheryl M DeWispelare, Chief Human Resources Officer
CNO: Eileen M Kingston R.N., Nurse Executive, Associate Director Patient Care
Web address: www.nebraska.va.gov/
Control: Veterans Affairs, Government, federal **Service:** General medical and surgical

Staffed Beds: 137

★ **AVERA ST. ANTHONY'S HOSPITAL (281329)**, 300 North Second Street, Zip 68763–1514, Mailing Address: P.O.Box 270, Oneill, 68763–0270; tel. 402/336–2611 **A**5 10 18 **F**3 8 13 15 18 28 29 30 31 32 34 35 38 40 41 43 44 45 46 48 57 59 60 64 65 68 75 76 77 78 79 81 82 84 86 90 91 93 94 96 97 100 101 107 108 110 111 112 114 119 120 124 127 128 129 130 131 133 135 143 146 148 **P**1 6 **S** Avera Health, Sioux Falls, SD
Primary Contact: Todd Consbruck, President and Chief Executive Officer
CFO: Michael Garman, Chief Financial Officer
CIO: Michael Garman, Chief Financial Officer
CHR: Kathryn Benson, Human Resources Partner
Web address: www.avera.org/st-anthonys
Control: Church operated, Nongovernment, not-for-profit **Service:** General medical and surgical

Staffed Beds: 25 **Admissions:** 901 **Census:** 9 **Outpatient Visits:** 46318 **Births:** 166 **Total Expense ($000):** 35300 **Payroll Expense ($000):** 13211 **Personnel:** 217

★ **VALLEY COUNTY HEALTH SYSTEM (281353)**, 2707 L Street, Zip 68862–1275; tel. 308/728–4200 **A**10 18 **F**7 15 28 31 34 35 40 43 45 46 50 56 57 59 62 63 64 65 68 74 75 77 78 79 81 82 87 93 97 103 107 110 111 115 119 127 128 129 130 133 148
Primary Contact: Nancy Glaubke, Chief Executive Officer
CFO: Ashley Woodward, Director Financial Services
CMO: Jennifer Bengston M.D., Chief Medical Officer
CIO: Shane Molacek, Chief Information Officer
CHR: Danielle Proskocil, Director Human Resources
CNO: Vicki Bredthauer R.N., Director of Nursing
Web address: www.valleycountyhealthsystem.org
Control: County, Government, Nonfederal **Service:** General medical and surgical

Staffed Beds: 16 **Admissions:** 380 **Census:** 2 **Births:** 0 **Total Expense ($000):** 22089 **Payroll Expense ($000):** 8592 **Personnel:** 161

ANNIE JEFFREY MEMORIAL COUNTY HEALTH CENTER (281314), 531 Beebe Street, Zip 68651–5537, Mailing Address: P.O.Box 428, 68651–0428; tel. 402/747–2031 **A**10 18 **F**3 11 13 15 28 29 32 34 35 40 43 45 50 53 57 59 64 75 76 81 107 110 114 119 129 133 135 146 **P**8
Primary Contact: Joseph W. Lohrman, Chief Executive Officer
CFO: Joseph W Lohrman, Chief Executive Officer
CMO: David Jameson M.D., Chief of Staff
CIO: Frank Vrba, Chief Information Officer
CHR: Sue Leif R.N., Director Human Resources
Web address: www.ajhc.org
Control: County, Government, Nonfederal **Service:** General medical and surgical

Staffed Beds: 16 **Admissions:** 153 **Census:** 2 **Outpatient Visits:** 4469 **Births:** 22 **Total Expense ($000):** 6723 **Payroll Expense ($000):** 2477 **Personnel:** 50

★ **REGIONAL WEST GARDEN COUNTY (281310)**, 1100 West Second Street, Zip 69154–6152; tel. 308/772–3283, (Nonreporting) **A**10 18
Primary Contact: William Giles, Chief Executive Officer
CFO: Jennifer Moffat, Staff Accountant
CMO: Steve Boyer M.D., Chief Medical Officer
CHR: Ricca Sanford, Director Human Resources
CNO: Trish Davison R.N., Chief Nursing Officer
Web address: www.gchealth.org
Control: County, Government, Nonfederal **Service:** General medical and surgical

Staffed Beds: 50

★ **OSMOND GENERAL HOSPITAL (281347)**, 402 North Maple Street, Zip 68765–5726, Mailing Address: P.O.Box 429, 68765–0429; tel. 402/748–3393 **A**10 18 **F**3 28 34 40 57 59 64 67 69 81 90 107 127 128 133 143 **P**6
Primary Contact: Lon Knievel, Chief Executive Officer
CFO: Jodi Aschoff, Chief Financial Officer
CMO: David Mwebe M.D., Chief of Staff
CNO: Kristen Colsden, Director of Nursing
Web address: www.osmondhospital.com
Control: Other not-for-profit (including NFP Corporation) **Service:** General medical and surgical

Staffed Beds: 21 **Admissions:** 126 **Census:** 2 **Outpatient Visits:** 4158 **Births:** 0 **Total Expense ($000):** 6915 **Payroll Expense ($000):** 3298 **Personnel:** 62

NE

Many Facility Codes have changed. Please refer to the AHA Guide Code Chart. © 2017 AHA Guide

PAPILLION—Sarpy County

✠ **CHI HEALTH MIDLANDS (280105)**, 11111 South 84th Street, Zip 68046–4122; tel. 402/593–3000 **A**1 2 3 5 10 **F**3 11 15 17 18 20 22 26 28 29 30 34 35 36 38 40 42 43 44 45 46 49 50 51 53 56 57 59 60 61 62 63 64 65 68 70 77 79 81 84 85 86 87 93 97 107 110 111 114 115 117 118 119 129 130 131 132 135 143 146 147 **P**8 **S** Catholic Health Initiatives, Englewood, CO
Primary Contact: Kevin Miller, President
COO: Joan E Neuhaus, Division Senior Vice President, Chief Operating Officer
CFO: Tyler DeJong, Director of Operational Finance
CMO: Patricia Murdock-Langan M.D., Chief Medical Officer
CIO: Thomas Haley, Information Technology Systems Site Director
CHR: Nancy Wallace, Division Senior Vice President, Chief Human Resource Officer
CNO: Brenda Bergman-Evans, Chief Nursing Officer
Web address: www.CHIhealth.com
Control: Church operated, Nongovernment, not-for-profit **Service**: General medical and surgical

Staffed Beds: 28 **Admissions**: 1588 **Census**: 15 **Outpatient Visits**: 40336
Births: 0 **Total Expense ($000)**: 41542 **Payroll Expense ($000)**: 12491
Personnel: 202

PAWNEE CITY—Pawnee County

★ **PAWNEE COUNTY MEMORIAL HOSPITAL AND RURAL HEALTH CLINIC (281302)**, 600 'I' Street, Zip 68420–3001, Mailing Address: P.O.Box 433, 68420–0433; tel. 402/852–2231 **A**10 18 **F**3 7 15 28 29 30 40 43 45 59 81 107 110 119 127 128 130 133 147 **P**6
Primary Contact: Ruth M. Stephens, MSN, R.N., Chief Executive Officer
CFO: Susan Daniels, Chief Financial Officer
CHR: Jennifer Bartels, Director Human Resources
CNO: Kelly Findlay, Director of Nurses
Web address: www.pawneehospital.com
Control: County, Government, Nonfederal **Service**: General medical and surgical

Staffed Beds: 17 **Admissions**: 51 **Census**: 2 **Outpatient Visits**: 1088
Births: 0 **Total Expense ($000)**: 7045 **Payroll Expense ($000)**: 3073
Personnel: 54

PENDER—Thurston County

★ **PENDER COMMUNITY HOSPITAL (281349)**, 100 Hospital Drive, Zip 68047–0100, Mailing Address: P.O.Box 100, 68047–0100; tel. 402/385–3083, (Nonreporting) **A**10 18 **S** Trinity Health, Livonia, MI
Primary Contact: Melissa Kelly, Chief Executive Officer and Chief Financial Officer
CFO: Melissa Kelly, Chief Executive Officer and Chief Financial Officer
CMO: Matt Timm M.D., Medical Director
CIO: Teresa Heise, Coordinator Management Information Systems
CHR: Nancy Suhr, Manager Human Resources
CNO: Katie Peterson R.N., Chief Nursing Officer
Web address: www.pendercommunityhospital.com
Control: Hospital district or authority, Government, Nonfederal **Service**: General medical and surgical

Staffed Beds: 67

PLAINVIEW—Pierce County

★ **CHI HEALTH PLAINVIEW (281346)**, 704 North Third Street, Zip 68769–2047, Mailing Address: P.O.Box 489, 68769–0489; tel. 402/582–4245, (Nonreporting) **A**10 18 **S** Catholic Health Initiatives, Englewood, CO
Primary Contact: Gregory Beckmann, Chief Executive Officer
CFO: Tim H Schnack, Chief Financial Officer
CMO: Steve Peterson M.D., Chief of Staff
CHR: Diane Blair, Human Resources and Admissions
CNO: Debra K Rutledge R.N., Vice President Nursing Services
Web address: www.alegentcreighton.com/plainview-hospital
Control: Church operated, Nongovernment, not-for-profit **Service**: General medical and surgical

Staffed Beds: 8

RED CLOUD—Webster County

WEBSTER COUNTY COMMUNITY HOSPITAL (281316), Sixth Avenue and Franklin Street, Zip 68970–0465, Mailing Address: P.O.Box 465, 68970–0465; tel. 402/746–5600 **A**10 18 **F**3 15 18 28 29 30 32 34 35 40 41 42 45 50 56 57 59 64 65 68 70 75 77 78 79 81 82 83 84 90 93 94 96 97 107 110 111 112 115 119 127 128 129 130 133 135 145 146 147 148 149 150
Primary Contact: Mirya Hallock, Administrator
CFO: Marcia Olson, Business Office Manager
CMO: Amy Springer, Medical Director
CHR: Marcia Olson, Business Office Manager
CNO: Candace Peters R.N., Director of Nursing
Web address: www.websterhospital.org
Control: County, Government, Nonfederal **Service**: General medical and surgical

Staffed Beds: 13 **Admissions**: 152 **Census**: 3 **Outpatient Visits**: 684
Births: 0 **Total Expense ($000)**: 2457 **Payroll Expense ($000)**: 2282
Personnel: 44

SAINT PAUL—Howard County

HOWARD COUNTY COMMUNITY HOSPITAL See Howard County Medical Center

★ **HOWARD COUNTY MEDICAL CENTER (281338)**, 1113 Sherman Street, Zip 68873–1546, Mailing Address: P.O.Box 406, 68873–0406; tel. 308/754–4421, (Nonreporting) **A**10 18
Primary Contact: Arlan D. Johnson, Chief Executive Officer
COO: Jillyn Klein, Chief Operating Officer
CFO: Morgan Meyer, Chief Financial Officer
CMO: Angela Brennan M.D., Chief of Staff
CIO: Cheryl Watson, Chief Information Officer
CHR: Leslie Belzer, Director Human Resources
CNO: Janelle Morgan, Interim Director of Nursing
Web address: www.hcmc.us.com
Control: County, Government, Nonfederal **Service**: General medical and surgical

Staffed Beds: 25

SCHUYLER—Colfax County

★ **CHI HEALTH SCHUYLER (281323)**, 104 West 17th Street, Zip 68661–1304; tel. 402/352–2441, (Nonreporting) **A**10 18 **S** Catholic Health Initiatives, Englewood, CO
Primary Contact: Connie Peters, R.N., President
CFO: Tim H Schnack, Chief Financial Officer
CIO: Kenneth Lawonn, Senior Vice President and Chief Information Officer
CHR: Nancy Wallace, Vice President Human Resources
Web address: www.alegent.org
Control: Church operated, Nongovernment, not-for-profit **Service**: General medical and surgical

Staffed Beds: 25

SCOTTSBLUFF—Scotts Bluff County

✠ △ **REGIONAL WEST MEDICAL CENTER (280061)**, 4021 Avenue 'B', Zip 69361–4695; tel. 308/635–3711, (Nonreporting) **A**1 2 3 5 7 10
Primary Contact: John Mentgen, FACHE, President and Chief Executive Officer
COO: Tadd Greenfield, Executive Vice President and Chief Operating Officer
CFO: Michael F Ickowski, Vice President and Chief Financial Officer
CMO: Lisa Scheppers, Chief Medical Officer
CIO: Montie Hodge, Vice President Information Technology and Chief Information Officer
CHR: Brenda J Forge, Vice President, Human Resources
CNO: Connie Rupp MSN, R.N., Executive Vice President and Chief Nursing Officer
Web address: www.rwhs.org
Control: Other not-for-profit (including NFP Corporation) **Service**: General medical and surgical

Staffed Beds: 107

SEWARD—Seward County

★ **MEMORIAL HEALTH CARE SYSTEMS (281339)**, 300 North Columbia Avenue, Zip 68434–2228; tel. 402/643–2971, (Nonreporting) **A**10 18
Primary Contact: Roger J. Reamer, Chief Executive Officer
CFO: Greg Jerger, Chief Financial Officer
CMO: Joel Gabriel M.D., Medical Director
CIO: Mark Criner, Director Information Technology
CHR: Corey Mann, Director Human Resources
Web address: www.mhcs.us
Control: Other not-for-profit (including NFP Corporation) **Service**: General medical and surgical

Staffed Beds: 25

NE

Hospital, Medicare Provider Number, Address, Telephone, Approval, Facility, and Physician Codes, Health Care System

★ American Hospital Association (AHA) membership
□ The Joint Commission accreditation
○ Healthcare Facilities Accreditation Program
◇ DNV Healthcare Inc. accreditation
⇧ Center for Improvement in Healthcare Quality Accreditation
△ Commission on Accreditation of Rehabilitation Facilities (CARF) accreditation

SIDNEY—Cheyenne County

★ **SIDNEY REGIONAL MEDICAL CENTER (281357)**, 1000 Pole Creek Crossing, Zip 69162–1799; tel. 308/254–5825, (Total facility includes 63 beds in nursing home–type unit) **A**5 10 18 **F**2 10 11 12 13 15 18 26 27 28 29 30 31 34 35 40 41 45 49 50 56 57 59 62 63 64 65 68 70 75 76 77 79 81 84 85 86 87 89 91 92 93 94 97 107 111 115 119 127 129 130 131 132 133 135 143 144 148 **P**6
Primary Contact: Jason Petik, Chief Executive Officer
CMO: Mandy Shaw M.D., Chief of Staff
CIO: Jennifer Brockhaus, Chief Information Officer
CHR: Catherine T Arterburn R.N., Vice President Human Resources
CNO: Julie A Slagle R.N., MSN, Vice President Patient Care Services
Web address: www.sidneyrmc.com
Control: Other not-for-profit (including NFP Corporation) **Service**: General medical and surgical

Staffed Beds: 88 **Admissions**: 743 **Census**: 55 **Outpatient Visits**: 13693 **Births**: 99 **Total Expense ($000)**: 53106 **Payroll Expense ($000)**: 22944 **Personnel**: 354

SUPERIOR—Nuckolls County

★ **BRODSTONE MEMORIAL HOSPITAL (281315)**, 520 East Tenth Street, Zip 68978–1225, Mailing Address: P.O.Box 187, 68978–0187; tel. 402/879–3281 **A**10 18 **F**1 3 4 8 11 13 15 16 17 28 29 30 31 34 35 40 41 57 59 64 65 67 70 72 73 74 75 76 77 79 80 81 82 85 86 87 88 89 90 93 97 98 107 110 111 114 119 127 128 129 130 131 132 133 135 146 148
Primary Contact: John E. Keelan, Chief Executive Officer
COO: Dena C Alvarez R.N., COO & Chief Compliance Officer
CFO: Sandy Borden, Chief Financial Officer
CMO: Timothy Blecha M.D., Medical Director
CIO: Tim Hiatt, Chief Information Officer
CHR: Beth A Schlichtman, Manager Human Resources
CNO: Kori Field, Director of Nursing
Web address: www.brodstonehospital.org
Control: Other not-for-profit (including NFP Corporation) **Service**: General medical and surgical

Staffed Beds: 25 **Admissions**: 437 **Census**: 4 **Outpatient Visits**: 18500 **Births**: 39 **Total Expense ($000)**: 20700 **Payroll Expense ($000)**: 9012

SYRACUSE—Otoe County

★ **COMMUNITY MEMORIAL HOSPITAL (281309)**, 1579 Midland Street, Zip 68446–9732, Mailing Address: P.O.Box N, 68446–0518; tel. 402/269–2011 **A**10 18 **F**1 3 11 15 28 29 40 43 45 53 59 62 64 67 79 81 85 89 90 93 107 110 119 127 128 133
Primary Contact: Michael Harvey, FACHE, President and Chief Executive Officer
CFO: Karrie Beach, Vice President Finance
CMO: Zak Tempelmeyer M.D., Chief Medical Staff
CIO: Matthew Steinblock, Director Information Systems
CHR: Nancy R Brack, Vice President Human Resources
CNO: Pat Howell, Chief Nursing Officer
Web address: www.syracusecmh.org
Control: Hospital district or authority, Government, Nonfederal **Service**: General medical and surgical

Staffed Beds: 10 **Admissions**: 146 **Census**: 2 **Outpatient Visits**: 13039 **Births**: 0 **Total Expense ($000)**: 13851 **Payroll Expense ($000)**: 6400 **Personnel**: 116

TECUMSEH—Johnson County

★ **JOHNSON COUNTY HOSPITAL (281350)**, 202 High Street, Zip 68450–2443, Mailing Address: P.O.Box 599, 68450–0599; tel. 402/335–3361, (Nonreporting) **A**10 18
Primary Contact: Diane Newman, FACHE, Administrator
COO: Diane Newman FACHE, Administrator
CFO: Jennifer Deal, Chief Financial Officer
CMO: Keith Shuey M.D., Chief Medical Staff
CIO: Fred Pooch, Supervisor Information Technology
CHR: Susan Hessheimer, Director Human Resources
CNO: Matthew Snyder R.N., Director of Nursing
Web address: www.jchosp.com
Control: County, Government, Nonfederal **Service**: General medical and surgical

Staffed Beds: 25

VALENTINE—Cherry County

★ **CHERRY COUNTY HOSPITAL (281344)**, 510 North Green Street, Zip 69201–1932, Mailing Address: P.O.Box 410, 69201–0410; tel. 402/376–2525, (Nonreporting) **A**10 18
Primary Contact: Brent A. Peterson, Administrator
CFO: Peggy Snell, Chief Finance Officer
Web address: www.cherrycountyhospital.org
Control: County, Government, Nonfederal **Service**: General medical and surgical

Staffed Beds: 25

WAHOO—Saunders County

★ **SAUNDERS MEDICAL CENTER (281307)**, 1760 County Road J, Zip 68066–4152; tel. 402/443–4191, (Nonreporting) **A**10 18 **S** Bryan Health, Lincoln, NE
Primary Contact: Tyler Toline, FACHE, Chief Executive Officer
COO: Julie A Rezac R.N., Chief Operating Officer
CFO: Chase Manstedt, Chief Financial Officer
CMO: Jared Pehrson M.D., Chief of Staff
CIO: Carrie Stephens, Director Information Technology
CHR: Joanna Peters, Director Human Resources
CNO: Lalah Landers R.N., Director of Nursing
Web address: www.saundersmedicalcenter.com
Control: County, Government, Nonfederal **Service**: General medical and surgical

Staffed Beds: 16

WAYNE—Wayne County

★ **PROVIDENCE MEDICAL CENTER (281345)**, 1200 Providence Road, Zip 68787–1299; tel. 402/375–3800 **A**10 18 **F**3 7 13 15 28 29 30 31 34 35 36 40 50 53 57 59 62 63 64 68 75 76 81 84 85 93 107 110 111 114 119 128 130 132 133 135
Primary Contact: James Frank, CPA, Chief Executive Officer
COO: Kristine A Giese, Chief Operating Officer
CFO: Kim Hixson, Vice President of Financial Officer and Chief Financial Officer
CHR: Jacqueline Ann Backer, Vice President of Human Resources
CNO: Nicole Haglund, Vice President of Nursing Services
Web address: www.providencemedical.com
Control: Other not-for-profit (including NFP Corporation) **Service**: General medical and surgical

Staffed Beds: 25 **Admissions**: 370 **Census**: 5 **Outpatient Visits**: 13724 **Births**: 59 **Total Expense ($000)**: 19337 **Payroll Expense ($000)**: 8116 **Personnel**: 160

WEST POINT—Cuming County

★ **ST. FRANCIS MEMORIAL HOSPITAL (281322)**, 430 North Monitor Street, Zip 68788–1555; tel. 402/372–2404, (Total facility includes 63 beds in nursing home–type unit) **A**10 18 **F**3 6 11 13 15 28 29 30 31 34 35 40 43 45 50 53 57 59 62 63 64 68 75 76 77 78 79 81 82 85 86 90 92 93 94 98 99 100 103 107 111 114 119 127 128 129 130 131 132 133 135 146 147 148 **P**6 **S** Franciscan Sisters of Christian Charity Sponsored Ministries, Inc., Manitowoc, WI
Primary Contact: Jerry Wordekemper, President and Chief Executive Officer
CFO: Dennis Dinslage, Vice President Finance and Chief Financial Officer
CMO: Renae Meyer M.D., Chief Medical Officer
CIO: Jean Meiergerd, Chief Information Officer
CHR: Terri Ridder, Director Human Resources
CNO: Carol Kampschnieder, Vice President Clinical and Regulatory Services
Web address: www.fcswp.org
Control: Church operated, Nongovernment, not-for-profit **Service**: General medical and surgical

Staffed Beds: 88 **Admissions**: 575 **Census**: 54 **Outpatient Visits**: 70863 **Births**: 57 **Total Expense ($000)**: 31930 **Payroll Expense ($000)**: 14760 **Personnel**: 230

WINNEBAGO—Thurston County

☐ ⇑ **U. S. PUBLIC HEALTH SERVICE INDIAN HOSPITAL (280119)**, Highway 7577, Zip 68071; tel. 402/878–2231, (Nonreporting) **A**1 10 21 **S** U. S. Indian Health Service, Rockville, MD
Primary Contact: Gary Wabaunsee, Service Unit Director
CFO: Audrey Parker, Budget Analyst
Web address: www.ihs.gov
Control: PHS, Indian Service, Government, federal **Service**: General medical and surgical

Staffed Beds: 30

YORK—York County

★ **YORK GENERAL (281336)**, 2222 North Lincoln Avenue, Zip 68467–1095; tel. 402/362–6671, (Total facility includes 129 beds in nursing home–type unit) **A**10 18 **F**3 10 11 12 13 15 28 29 31 34 35 40 45 53 56 57 59 60 62 64 68 70 75 76 77 78 79 81 82 85 86 87 89 93 96 107 108 110 111 115 117 118 119 125 128 129 130 131 132 133 145 146 148
Primary Contact: James P. Ulrich Jr, Chief Executive Officer
COO: Jenny Obermier, Senior Vice President, Chief Operating Officer and Chief Nursing Officer
CFO: Bob McQuistan, Vice President Finance
CMO: Ye Ye, Chief of Staff
CIO: Chris Kraft, Director Information Systems
CHR: Cathy Norquest, Director Human Resources
CNO: Jenny Obermier, Senior Vice President, Chief Operating Officer and Chief Nursing Officer
Web address: www.yorkgeneral.org
Control: Other not-for-profit (including NFP Corporation) **Service**: General medical and surgical

Staffed Beds: 154 **Admissions**: 1009 **Census**: 119 **Outpatient Visits**: 40096 **Births**: 82 **Total Expense ($000)**: 40934 **Payroll Expense ($000)**: 18722 **Personnel**: 403

NE

Many Facility Codes have changed. Please refer to the AHA Guide Code Chart.

NEVADA

BATTLE MOUNTAIN—Lander County

BATTLE MOUNTAIN GENERAL HOSPITAL (291303), 535 South Humboldt Street, Zip 89820–1988; tel. 775/635–2550, (Nonreporting) **A**10 18
Primary Contact: Kelley Price, R.N., Interim Chief Executive Officer
CFO: Cindy Fagg, Fiscal Officer
CMO: Mark S. Meyers M.D., Chief of Staff
CIO: Terry Dunn, Director Information Technology
CHR: Lori Sherbondy, Director Human Resources
CNO: Kelley Price R.N., Chief Nursing Officer
Web address: www.bmgh.org
Control: Hospital district or authority, Government, Nonfederal **Service**: General medical and surgical

Staffed Beds: 7

BOULDER CITY—Clark County

BOULDER CITY HOSPITAL (291309), 901 Adams Boulevard, Zip 89005–2213; tel. 702/293–4111, (Nonreporting) **A**10 18
Primary Contact: Thomas Maher, Chief Executive Officer and Administrator
CFO: Douglas Lewis, Chief Financial Officer
CMO: Herve Bezard M.D., Chief of Staff
CHR: Belinda McGraw, Director Human Resources
CNO: Andre Pastian R.N., MSN, Chief Nursing Officer
Web address: www.bouldercityhospital.org
Control: Other not-for-profit (including NFP Corporation) **Service**: General medical and surgical

Staffed Beds: 25

CALIENTE—Lincoln County

GROVER C. DILS MEDICAL CENTER (291312), 700 North Spring Street, Zip 89008, Mailing Address: P.O.Box 1010, 89008–1010; tel. 775/726–3171 (Nonreporting) **A**10 18
Primary Contact: Jason Bleak, Administrator and Chief Executive Officer
COO: Jason Bleak, Administrator and Chief Executive Officer
CFO: Sherlyn Fackrell, Finance Controller
CMO: R William Katschke M.D., Jr, Medical Director
CHR: Rozanne Mangum, Administrative Assistant and Director Human Resources
Web address: www.gcdmc.org
Control: Other not-for-profit (including NFP Corporation) **Service**: Other specialty treatment

Staffed Beds: 20

CARSON CITY—Carson City County

CARSON TAHOE CONTINUING CARE HOSPITAL (292008), 775 Fleischmann Way, 2nd Floor, Zip 89703–2995; tel. 775/445–7795 **A**10 **F**1 3 29 68 85 130 148
Primary Contact: Kelly Wilcher, Chief Executive Officer
CFO: Ann Beck, Vice President and Chief Financial Officer
CMO: Jose Aguirre M.D., Medical Director
CHR: Angie Rodriguez, Human Resource Manager
CNO: Kristin Madsen, Chief Nursing Officer
Web address: www.carsontahoe.com
Control: Other not-for-profit (including NFP Corporation) **Service**: Acute long-term care hospital

Staffed Beds: 29 Admissions: 334 Census: 22 Outpatient Visits: 0 Births: 0 Total Expense ($000): 12571 Payroll Expense ($000): 5134 Personnel: 65

CARSON TAHOE HEALTH (290019), 1600 Medical Parkway, Zip 89703–4625, Mailing Address: P.O.Box 2168, 89702–2168; tel. 775/445–8672, (Includes SIERRA SURGERY HOSPITAL, 1400 Medical Parkway, Carson City, Nevada, Zip 89703–4624, tel. 775/883–1700; Ken Doran, Interim Chief Executive Officer) **A**1 2 5 10 22 **F**3 5 8 11 13 15 17 18 20 22 24 26 28 29 30 31 34 35 38 40 42 46 47 49 50 51 54 56 57 59 64 65 68 70 74 75 76 77 78 79 81 82 85 86 87 89 93 96 98 99 100 101 102 103 104 105 107 108 110 111 115 116 117 118 119 130 132 135 144 146 147 148 149
Primary Contact: Edward L. Epperson, Chief Executive Officer
COO: Michelle L Joy, Chief Operating Officer
CFO: Ann Beck, Vice President Finance
CMO: Jeffrey Sanders M.D., Chief of Staff
CHR: Jim Lewandowski, Interim Director of Human Resources
CNO: Anna Anders, Vice President and Chief Nursing Officer
Web address: www.carsontahoe.com
Control: Other not-for-profit (including NFP Corporation) **Service**: General medical and surgical

Staffed Beds: 211 Admissions: 12489 Census: 148 Outpatient Visits: 296085 Births: 921 Total Expense ($000): 246975 Payroll Expense ($000): 83600 Personnel: 1305

ELKO—Elko County

NORTHEASTERN NEVADA REGIONAL HOSPITAL (290008), 2001 Errecart Boulevard, Zip 89801–8333; tel. 775/738–5151 **A**1 10 20 **F**3 8 11 13 15 18 20 22 28 29 30 31 34 38 40 41 45 46 50 51 57 59 60 68 70 75 77 79 81 85 93 102 107 108 111 114 115 119 129 148 **S** LifePoint Health, Brentwood, TN
Primary Contact: Richard L. Palagi, Chief Executive Officer
CFO: Grant Trollope, Chief Financial Officer
CIO: Jeff Morgan, Director Information Systems
CHR: Laura Elliott, Director Human Resources
Web address: www.nnrhospital.com
Control: Corporation, Investor-owned (for-profit) **Service**: General medical and surgical

Staffed Beds: 50 Admissions: 1956 Census: 15 Outpatient Visits: 53722 Births: 435 Total Expense ($000): 53987 Payroll Expense ($000): 22219 Personnel: 241

ELY—White Pine County

WILLIAM BEE RIRIE HOSPITAL (291302), 1500 Avenue 'H', Zip 89301–2699; tel. 775/289–3001, (Nonreporting) **A**1 10 18
Primary Contact: Matthew Walker, Chief Executive Officer and Administrator
CMO: G N Christensen M.D., Chief Medical Officer
CIO: Destin Brandis, Chief Information Officer
CHR: Vicki Pereace, Manager Human Resources
Web address: www.wbrhely.org/getpage.php?name=index
Control: Hospital district or authority, Government, Nonfederal **Service**: General medical and surgical

Staffed Beds: 15

FALLON—Churchill County

BANNER CHURCHILL COMMUNITY HOSPITAL (290006), 801 East Williams Avenue, Zip 89406–3052; tel. 775/423–3151 **A**1 10 18 20 **F**3 7 11 13 15 29 31 34 35 40 41 45 50 57 59 65 68 70 75 76 79 81 85 86 87 93 97 107 108 110 111 115 119 129 130 146 **S** Banner Health, Phoenix, AZ
Primary Contact: Robert H. Carnahan II, R.N., Chief Executive Officer
CFO: Steve Fraker, Chief Financial Officer
CMO: Tedd McDonald M.D., Chief Medical Officer
CHR: Darlene Hanefeld, Chief Human Resources Officer
Web address: www.bannerhealth.com/churchill
Control: Other not-for-profit (including NFP Corporation) **Service**: General medical and surgical

Staffed Beds: 25 Admissions: 1379 Census: 13 Births: 279 Total Expense ($000): 36222 Payroll Expense ($000): 15851 Personnel: 257

NV

Hospital, Medicare Provider Number, Address, Telephone, Approval, Facility, and Physician Codes, Health Care System

★ American Hospital Association (AHA) membership   ○ Healthcare Facilities Accreditation Program   ⇑ Center for Improvement in Healthcare Quality Accreditation
□ The Joint Commission accreditation   ◇ DNV Healthcare Inc. accreditation   △ Commission on Accreditation of Rehabilitation Facilities (CARF) accreditation

GARDNERVILLE—Douglas County

★ **CARSON VALLEY MEDICAL CENTER (291306)**, 1107 Highway 395, Zip 89410; tel. 775/782–1500 **A**3 10 18 **F**3 15 18 29 30 31 34 35 40 45 46 47 48 50 56 57 59 64 65 66 68 70 75 77 78 79 81 82 85 87 93 103 104 107 108 110 111 115 119 127 128 129 130 132 133 144 146 148 149 **P**6
Primary Contact: Preston Becker, Chief Executive Officer
COO: Linda Lilleboe R.N., MSN, Director Operations
CFO: Mike Ellis, Chief Financial Officer
CMO: Evan Easley M.D., Chief Medical Officer
CIO: Jason Roberts, Director Information System
CHR: Lisa Tremaine, Manager Human Resources
CNO: Kathy Cocking R.N., Director of Clinical Services
Web address: www.cvmchospital.org
Control: Other not-for-profit (including NFP Corporation) **Service:** General medical and surgical

Staffed Beds: 23 **Admissions:** 1104 **Census:** 10 **Outpatient Visits:** 81463
Births: 0 **Total Expense ($000):** 48055 **Payroll Expense ($000):** 17310
Personnel: 331

HAWTHORNE—Mineral County

MOUNT GRANT GENERAL HOSPITAL (291300), First and 'A' Street, Zip 89415, Mailing Address: P.O.Box 1510, 89415–1510; tel. 775/945–2461, (Nonreporting) **A**10 18
Primary Contact: Richard Munger, Administrator
Web address: www.mtgrantgenhospital.org/
Control: Other not-for-profit (including NFP Corporation) **Service:** General medical and surgical

Staffed Beds: 11

HENDERSON—Clark County

☒ **HEALTHSOUTH REHABILITATION HOSPITAL - HENDERSON (293032)**, 10301 Jeffreys Street, Zip 89052–3922; tel. 702/939–9400, (Nonreporting) **A**1 10 **S** HEALTHSOUTH Corporation, Birmingham, AL
Primary Contact: Samantha Billig, Chief Executive Officer
CFO: Robert Bollard, Chief Financial Officer
Web address: www.hendersonrehabhospital.com
Control: Corporation, Investor-owned (for-profit) **Service:** Rehabilitation

Staffed Beds: 90

HENDERSON HOSPITAL, 1050 West Galleria Drive, Zip 89011; tel. 702/963–7000 **S** Universal Health Services, Inc., King of Prussia, PA (Nonreporting)
Primary Contact: Samuel Kaufman, Chief Executive Officer
CNO: Tina Coker MSN, Chief Nursing Officer
Web address: www.hendersonhospital.com/
Control: Investor-owned (for-profit) **Service:** General medical and surgical

Staffed Beds: 145

☒ **KINDRED HOSPITAL LAS VEGAS-SAHARA (292002)**, 102 East Mead Parkway, 3rd Floor, Zip 89015; tel. 702/871–1418, (Nonreporting) (Includes KINDRED HOSPITAL-FLAMINGO, 2250 East Flamingo Road, Las Vegas, Nevada, Zip 89119, tel. 702/871–1418) **A**1 10 **S** Kindred Healthcare, Louisville, KY
Primary Contact: Doug McCoy, Chief Executive Officer
CFO: William Lysaght, Chief Financial Officer
CMO: Paul Stewart M.D., Medical Director
CHR: Jim Sturgeon, Area Director Human Resources
Web address: www.kindredhospitallvs.com/
Control: Corporation, Investor-owned (for-profit) **Service:** Acute long-term care hospital

Staffed Beds: 238

SEVEN HILLS HOSPITAL (294012), 3021 West Horizon Ridge Parkway, Zip 89052–3990; tel. 702/646–5000 **A**10 **F**4 29 56 98 99 101 103 104 105 130 132 143 **P**8 **S** Acadia Healthcare Company, Inc., Franklin, TN
Primary Contact: Christopher West, Chief Executive Officer
CFO: Mars Patricio Jr, Chief Financial Officer
CMO: Jonathan Wirjo M.D., Medical Director
CIO: Jessica Raub, Director Health Information Management
CHR: Teresa Sulit, Director of Human Resources
CNO: Rustin Park, Director of Nursing
Web address: www.sevenhillsbi.com
Control: Corporation, Investor-owned (for-profit) **Service:** Psychiatric

Staffed Beds: 134 **Admissions:** 6000 **Census:** 107 **Outpatient Visits:** 6068
Births: 0 **Total Expense ($000):** 12103

☒ **ST. ROSE DOMINICAN HOSPITALS - ROSE DE LIMA CAMPUS (290012)**, 102 East Lake Mead Parkway, Zip 89015–5524; tel. 702/616–5000 **A**1 10 **F**3 8 12 15 18 20 29 30 31 32 34 35 38 40 44 45 49 50 57 59 61 62 63 64 65 68 70 74 75 77 78 79 80 81 82 84 85 86 87 90 91 95 96 102 107 110 111 115 119 130 131 132 133 143 146 147 148 149 **S** Dignity Health, San Francisco, CA
Primary Contact: Teressa Conley, President and Chief Executive Officer
COO: Teressa Conley, Vice President and Chief Operating Officer
CFO: Kevin Walters, Chief Financial Officer
CMO: Stephen K Jones M.D., Vice President Medical Staff Affairs
Web address: www.strosehospitals.org
Control: Church operated, Nongovernment, not-for-profit **Service:** General medical and surgical

Staffed Beds: 110 **Admissions:** 4770 **Census:** 75 **Outpatient Visits:** 44118
Births: 0 **Total Expense ($000):** 155703 **Payroll Expense ($000):** 64358
Personnel: 652

☒ **ST. ROSE DOMINICAN HOSPITALS - SIENA CAMPUS (290045)**, 3001 St Rose Parkway, Zip 89052; tel. 702/616–5000 **A**1 3 5 10 **F**3 7 8 13 15 18 19 20 22 24 26 28 29 30 31 32 34 35 38 40 41 43 44 45 46 50 51 57 59 61 62 63 64 68 70 72 74 75 78 79 80 81 82 84 85 87 88 89 93 102 107 108 111 115 116 117 119 126 130 131 132 135 146 147 148 149 **S** Dignity Health, San Francisco, CA
Primary Contact: Eugene Bassett, President and Chief Executive Officer
COO: Kimberly Shaw, Chief Operating Officer
CFO: Brian Kleven, Chief Financial Officer
CMO: Robert Pretzlaff M.D., Chief Medical Officer
CIO: Russ Patterson, Director Information Technology
CHR: Linda Gerstenberger, Vice President Human Resources
CNO: Cathleen Hamel, Chief Nurse Executive
Web address: www.strosehospitals.com
Control: Church operated, Nongovernment, not-for-profit **Service:** General medical and surgical

Staffed Beds: 326 **Admissions:** 16930 **Census:** 227 **Outpatient Visits:** 92007 **Births:** 3567 **Total Expense ($000):** 417103 **Payroll Expense ($000):** 172491 **Personnel:** 2033

INCLINE VILLAGE—Washoe County

★ **INCLINE VILLAGE COMMUNITY HOSPITAL (291301)**, 880 Alder Avenue, Zip 89451–8335; tel. 775/833–4100, (Nonreporting) **A**3 5 10 18 **S** Tahoe Forest Health System, Truckee, CA
Primary Contact: Judy Newland, R.N., Chief Nursing Officer
CFO: Crystal Betts, Chief Financial Officer
CIO: Mark Griffiths, Director Management Information Systems
CHR: Jayne O'Flanagan, Director Human Resources
Web address: www.tfhd.com
Control: Hospital district or authority, Government, Nonfederal **Service:** General medical and surgical

Staffed Beds: 6

LAS VEGAS—Clark County

AMG SPECIALTY HOSPITAL - LAS VEGAS (292007), 4015 Mcleod Drive, Zip 89121–4305; tel. 702/433–2200 (Nonreporting) **A**10 **S** AMG Integrated Healthcare Management, Lafayette, LA
Primary Contact: William Fox, Chief Executive Officer
CMO: Anthony Pollard D.O., Chief Medical Officer
Web address: www.amgihm.com/locations/#map_top
Control: Partnership, Investor-owned (for-profit) **Service:** Acute long-term care hospital

Staffed Beds: 24

☐ **CENTENNIAL HILLS HOSPITAL MEDICAL CENTER (290054)**, 6900 North Durango Drive, Zip 89149–4409; tel. 702/835–9700 (Nonreporting) **A**1 10 **S** Universal Health Services, Inc., King of Prussia, PA
Primary Contact: Sajit Pullarkat, Chief Executive Officer and Managing Director
Web address: www.centennialhillshospital.com
Control: Corporation, Investor-owned (for-profit) **Service:** General medical and surgical

Staffed Beds: 165

☒ **COMPLEX CARE HOSPITAL AT TENAYA (292006)**, 2500 North Tenaya, Zip 89128–0482; tel. 702/562–2021, (Nonreporting) **A**1 10 **S** LifeCare Management Services, Plano, TX
Primary Contact: Matt Archer, Chief Executive Officer
COO: Paul D'Ambrosio, Chief Operating Officer
CFO: Anna Rich, Chief Financial Officer
CMO: C Dean Milne D.O., Medical Director
CIO: Lynn Tunson, Manager Medical Records
CHR: Belinda McGraw, Director Human Resources
CNO: Robin Wolf, Chief Nursing Officer
Web address: www.lifecare-hospitals.com
Control: Corporation, Investor-owned (for-profit) **Service:** Acute long-term care hospital

Staffed Beds: 70

NV

Many Facility Codes have changed. Please refer to the AHA Guide Code Chart. © 2017 AHA Guide

DESERT PARKWAY BEHAVIORAL HEALTHCARE HOSPITAL (294013), 3247 South Maryland Parkway, Zip 89109–2412; tel. 702/776–3500 **F**4 5 29 35 50 98 99 104 105 **S** Signature Healthcare Services, Corona, CA
Primary Contact: Steve Shell, Chief Executive Officer
Control: State, Government, Nonfederal **Service:** Psychiatric

Staffed Beds: 83 **Admissions:** 3113 **Census:** 71 **Outpatient Visits:** 0
Births: 0 **Total Expense ($000):** 20168 **Payroll Expense ($000):** 10215
Personnel: 156

☐ **DESERT SPRINGS HOSPITAL MEDICAL CENTER (290022)**, 2075 East Flamingo Road, Zip 89119–5121; tel. 702/733–8800, (Nonreporting) **A**1 10 **S** Universal Health Services, Inc., King of Prussia, PA
Primary Contact: Ryan Jensen, Chief Executive Officer
CFO: George Wiley, Chief Financial Officer
CMO: Golam Choudhury, Chief of Staff
CIO: Alan Woratschek, System Director of Information Services
CNO: Elena McNutt, Chief Nursing Officer
Web address: www.desertspringshospital.com
Control: Corporation, Investor-owned (for-profit) **Service:** General medical and surgical

Staffed Beds: 346

DESERT WILLOW TREATMENT CENTER, 6171 West Charleston Boulevard, Zip 89146–1126; tel. 702/486–8900 **A**3 5 **F**29 98 99 106 **P**6
Primary Contact: Linda Santangelo, Ph.D., Director
Control: State, Government, Nonfederal **Service:** Children's hospital psychiatric

Staffed Beds: 58 **Admissions:** 176 **Census:** 28 **Outpatient Visits:** 0
Births: 0 **Total Expense ($000):** 9879

HARMON MEDICAL AND REHABILITATION HOSPITAL (290042), 2170 East Harmon Avenue, Zip 89119–7840; tel. 702/794–0100 (Nonreporting) **A**10 **S** Fundamental Long Term Care Holdings, LLC, Sparks Glencoe, MD
Primary Contact: Bonnie Essex. Hillegass, Chief Executive Officer
Control: Corporation, Investor-owned (for-profit) **Service:** Rehabilitation

Staffed Beds: 118

✠ **HEALTHSOUTH DESERT CANYON REHABILITATION HOSPITAL (293033)**, 9175 West Oquendo Road, Zip 89148–1234; tel. 702/252–7342 **A**1 10 **F**3 29 60 75 77 78 79 86 90 91 93 95 96 130 132 146 148 149 **S** HEALTHSOUTH Corporation, Birmingham, AL
Primary Contact: Andrea Davis, Chief Executive Officer
CMO: Bevins Chue M.D., Medical Director
CNO: Timothy Murphy R.N., Chief Nursing Officer
Web address: www.healthsouthdesertcanyon.com
Control: Corporation, Investor-owned (for-profit) **Service:** Rehabilitation

Staffed Beds: 50 **Admissions:** 1208 **Census:** 40 **Outpatient Visits:** 3904
Births: 0 **Total Expense ($000):** 14336 **Payroll Expense ($000):** 9560

✠ **HEALTHSOUTH REHABILITATION HOSPITAL-LAS VEGAS (293026)**, 1250 South Valley View Boulevard, Zip 89102–1861; tel. 702/877–8898, (Nonreporting) **A**1 10 **S** HEALTHSOUTH Corporation, Birmingham, AL
Primary Contact: Michael Ward, Chief Executive Officer
CFO: Daniel Lai, Controller
CMO: John D. Reneau, Medical Director
CHR: Debra Tafoya, Director Human Resources
CNO: Susan Ramirez, Chief Nursing Officer
Web address: www.healthsouthlasvegas.com
Control: Corporation, Investor-owned (for-profit) **Service:** Rehabilitation

Staffed Beds: 79

☐ **HORIZON SPECIALTY HOSPITAL (292003)**, 640 Desert Lane, Zip 89106–4207; tel. 702/382–3155, (Nonreporting) **A**1 10 **S** Fundamental Long Term Care Holdings, LLC, Sparks Glencoe, MD
Primary Contact: Darrin Cook, Chief Executive Officer and Administrator
CFO: Darnell Bennett, Director Finance
CMO: Syed Rahman M.D., Chief of Staff
CIO: Azena Ansi, Manager Health Information Management
CHR: Melvin Layugan, Director Human Resources
Web address: www.horizonspecialtyhosp.com/
Control: Corporation, Investor-owned (for-profit) **Service:** Acute long-term care hospital

Staffed Beds: 49

☐ **MONTEVISTA HOSPITAL (294009)**, 5900 West Rochelle Avenue, Zip 89103–3327; tel. 702/364–1111, (Nonreporting) **A**1 10 **S** Strategic Behavioral Health, LLC, Memphis, TN
Primary Contact: Charlene Arnett, Chief Executive Officer
CMO: William Bauer M.D., Medical Director
CHR: Carol Nelson, Director Human Resources
Web address: www.montevistahospital.com
Control: Corporation, Investor-owned (for-profit) **Service:** Psychiatric

Staffed Beds: 90

MOUNTAIN'S EDGE HOSPITAL (290056), 8656 West Patrick Lane, Zip 89148–5043; tel. 702/777–7100 (Nonreporting)
Primary Contact: Melissa War, Chief Executive Officer
Web address: www.mountainsedgehospital.com/
Control: Other not-for-profit (including NFP Corporation) **Service:** General medical and surgical

Staffed Beds: 130

✠ **MOUNTAINVIEW HOSPITAL (290039)**, 3100 North Tenaya Way, Zip 89128–0436; tel. 702/255–5000, (Nonreporting) **A**1 3 5 10 **S** HCA Healthcare, Nashville, TN
Primary Contact: Jeremy Bradshaw, Chief Executive Officer
CFO: Lana Arad, Chief Financial Officer
CMO: Jack Collier M.D., Chief of Staff
CHR: Robert Nettles, Director Human Resources
CNO: Natalie Ransom, Chief Nursing Officer
Web address: www.mountainview-hospital.com
Control: Corporation, Investor-owned (for-profit) **Service:** General medical and surgical

Staffed Beds: 340

☐ **RED ROCK BEHAVIORAL HOSPITAL (294008)**, 5975 West Twain Avenue, Zip 89103–1237; tel. 702/214–8099 (Nonreporting) **A**1 10 **S** Strategic Behavioral Health, LLC, Memphis, TN
Primary Contact: Richard Failla, Chief Executive Officer
Web address: www.redrockhospital.com
Control: Other not-for-profit (including NFP Corporation) **Service:** Psychiatric

Staffed Beds: 21

✠ **SOUTHERN HILLS HOSPITAL AND MEDICAL CENTER (290047)**, 9300 West Sunset Road, Zip 89148–4844; tel. 702/880–2100, (Nonreporting) **A**1 10 **S** HCA Healthcare, Nashville, TN
Primary Contact: Adam Rudd, Chief Executive Officer
CFO: Jennifer Le, Chief Financial Officer
CMO: Eric Ramos M.D., Division Chief Medical Officer
CIO: Joe Grandiosi, Director Information Technology
CHR: Brian Wood, Director Human Resources
CNO: Maura Wright, Chief Nursing Officer
Web address: www.southernhillshospital.com
Control: Corporation, Investor-owned (for-profit) **Service:** General medical and surgical

Staffed Beds: 134

☐ **SOUTHERN NEVADA ADULT MENTAL HEALTH SERVICES (294002)**, 6161 West Charleston Boulevard, Zip 89146–1126; tel. 702/486–6000 **A**1 3 5 10 **F**34 86 87 98 101 106 130 135 149
Primary Contact: Chelsea Szklany, Hospital Administrator
Web address: www.mhds.state.nv.us
Control: State, Government, Nonfederal **Service:** Psychiatric

Staffed Beds: 289 **Admissions:** 2754 **Census:** 166 **Outpatient Visits:** 0
Births: 0 **Total Expense ($000):** 74416 **Payroll Expense ($000):** 34573
Personnel: 323

☐ **SPRING MOUNTAIN SAHARA (294010)**, 5460 West Sahara, Zip 89146–3307; tel. 702/216–8900 **A**1 10 **F**29 56 64 98 103 104 130 **S** Universal Health Services, Inc., King of Prussia, PA
Primary Contact: Alan Eaks, Chief Executive Officer and Managing Director
Web address: www.springmountainsahara.com
Control: Corporation, Investor-owned (for-profit) **Service:** Psychiatric

Staffed Beds: 30 **Admissions:** 719 **Census:** 19 **Outpatient Visits:** 1235
Births: 0 **Total Expense ($000):** 6037 **Payroll Expense ($000):** 2775
Personnel: 53

NV

Hospital, Medicare Provider Number, Address, Telephone, Approval, Facility, and Physician Codes, Health Care System

★ American Hospital Association (AHA) membership ☐ The Joint Commission accreditation ○ Healthcare Facilities Accreditation Program ◇ DNV Healthcare Inc. accreditation ⇧ Center for Improvement in Healthcare Quality Accreditation △ Commission on Accreditation of Rehabilitation Facilities (CARF) accreditation

☐ **SPRING MOUNTAIN TREATMENT CENTER (294011)**, 7000 West Spring Mountain Road, Zip 89117–3816; tel. 702/873–2400 **A**1 10 **F**29 98 99 105 130 **S** Universal Health Services, Inc., King of Prussia, PA
Primary Contact: C Alan. Eaks, Chief Executive Officer and Managing Director
Web address: www.springmountaintreatmentcenter.com/
Control: Corporation, Investor-owned (for-profit) **Service**: Psychiatric

Staffed Beds: 110 **Admissions**: 4753 **Census**: 84 **Outpatient Visits**: 28
Births: 0 **Total Expense ($000)**: 19856 **Payroll Expense ($000)**: 9094
Personnel: 160

☐ **SPRING VALLEY HOSPITAL MEDICAL CENTER (290046)**, 5400 South Rainbow Boulevard, Zip 89118–1859; tel. 702/853–3000 (Nonreporting) **A**1 3 10 **S** Universal Health Services, Inc., King of Prussia, PA
Primary Contact: Leonard Freehof, Chief Executive Officer and Managing Director
COO: Matthew Wheelus, Chief Operating Officer
CFO: Carl Caley, Chief Financial Officer
CMO: S. Daniel M.D., Chief Medical Officer
CHR: Angelique Ford, Administrator Human Resources
CNO: Margaret Covelli R.N., Chief Nursing Officer
Web address: www.springvalleyhospital.com
Control: Corporation, Investor-owned (for-profit) **Service**: General medical and surgical

Staffed Beds: 169

⊞ **ST. ROSE DOMINICAN HOSPITALS - SAN MARTIN CAMPUS (290053)**, 8280 West Warm Springs Road, Zip 89113–3612; tel. 702/492–8000 **A**1 10 **F**3 8 13 15 18 19 20 22 24 26 28 29 30 31 34 35 38 40 44 45 47 49 50 57 59 61 62 63 64 68 70 72 74 75 76 77 78 79 80 81 84 85 86 87 93 102 107 108 110 111 115 119 126 130 131 132 135 146 147 148 149 **S** Dignity Health, San Francisco, CA
Primary Contact: Lawrence Barnard, President and Chief Executive Officer
CFO: Dev Ramsamy, Chief Financial Officer
CMO: Robert Pretzlaff M.D., Chief Medical Officer
CIO: Russ Patterson, Site Manager Information Technology
CHR: Linda Gerstenberger, Vice President Human Resources
CNO: Katherine Raymond, Chief Nursing Officer
Web address: www.strosehospitals.org
Control: Church operated, Nongovernment, not-for-profit **Service**: General medical and surgical

Staffed Beds: 147 **Admissions**: 7110 **Census**: 96 **Outpatient Visits**: 37508
Births: 1330 **Total Expense ($000)**: 194230 **Payroll Expense ($000)**: 69967 **Personnel**: 683

☐ **SUMMERLIN HOSPITAL MEDICAL CENTER (290041)**, 657 Town Center Drive, Zip 89144–6367; tel. 702/233–7000, (Nonreporting) **A**1 10 **S** Universal Health Services, Inc., King of Prussia, PA
Primary Contact: Robert S. Freymuller, Chief Executive Officer
Web address: www.summerlinhospital.com
Control: Corporation, Investor-owned (for-profit) **Service**: General medical and surgical

Staffed Beds: 148

⊞ △ **SUNRISE HOSPITAL AND MEDICAL CENTER (290003)**, 3186 Maryland Parkway, Zip 89109–2306, Mailing Address: P.O.Box 98530, 89193; tel. 702/731–8000, (Nonreporting) **A**1 2 3 5 7 10 **S** HCA Healthcare, Nashville, TN
Primary Contact: Todd Sklamberg, President
CFO: Daniel Perritt, Chief Financial Officer
CMO: Katherine Keeley M.D., Chief of Staff
CIO: Alan Burt, Director Information Services
Web address: www.sunrisehospital.com
Control: Corporation, Investor-owned (for-profit) **Service**: General medical and surgical

Staffed Beds: 664

⊞ **UNIVERSITY MEDICAL CENTER (290007)**, 1800 West Charleston Boulevard, Zip 89102–2386; tel. 702/383–2000, (Nonreporting) (Includes CHILDREN'S HOSPITAL OF NEVADA AT UMC, 800 Hope Place, Las Vegas, Nevada, Zip 89106, tel. 702/383–2000) **A**1 2 3 5 10
Primary Contact: Mason VanHouweling, Chief Executive Officer
COO: Kurt Houser, Chief Operating Officer
CFO: Stephanie Merrill, Chief Financial Officer
CIO: Ernie McKinley, Chief Information Officer
CHR: John Espinoza, Chief Human Resources Officer
CNO: Debra Fox, Chief Nursing Officer
Web address: www.umcsn.com
Control: County, Government, Nonfederal **Service**: General medical and surgical

Staffed Beds: 541

☐ **VALLEY HOSPITAL MEDICAL CENTER (290021)**, 620 Shadow Lane, Zip 89106–4119; tel. 702/388–4000, (Nonreporting) **A**1 3 10 **S** Universal Health Services, Inc., King of Prussia, PA
Primary Contact: Elaine Glaser, Chief Executive Officer
CFO: Betsy A Sponsler, Chief Financial Officer
CMO: Dost Wattoo M.D., Chief of Staff
CIO: Tom Schoenig, Regional Director Information Services
CHR: Dana Thorne, Administrator Human Resources
Web address: www.valleyhospital.net
Control: Corporation, Investor-owned (for-profit) **Service**: General medical and surgical

Staffed Beds: 365

LOVELOCK—Pershing County

★ **PERSHING GENERAL HOSPITAL (291304)**, 855 Sixth Street, Zip 89419, Mailing Address: P.O.Box 661, 89419–0661; tel. 775/273–2621, (Total facility includes 25 beds in nursing home–type unit) **A**10 18 **F**29 32 34 35 40 50 59 64 65 66 68 82 87 93 97 107 114 119 127 128 130 133 146 148
Primary Contact: Patty Bianchi, Chief Executive Officer
CFO: Marjorie Skinner, Director Finance
CMO: Yousri Gadallah M.D., Chief Medical Officer
CIO: Jim Weeldreyer, Manager Information Technology
CHR: Cynthia Hixenbaugh, Director Human Resources
Web address: www.pershinghospital.org
Control: Hospital district or authority, Government, Nonfederal **Service**: General medical and surgical

Staffed Beds: 38 **Admissions**: 55 **Census**: 22 **Outpatient Visits**: 17987
Births: 1 **Total Expense ($000)**: 9809 **Payroll Expense ($000)**: 4719
Personnel: 89

MESQUITE—Clark County

⊞ **MESA VIEW REGIONAL HOSPITAL (291307)**, 1299 Bertha Howe Avenue, Zip 89027–7500; tel. 702/346–8040 **A**1 10 18 **F**3 11 13 15 18 29 30 34 35 40 45 46 51 56 57 59 64 70 75 76 79 81 85 87 107 108 110 111 114 119 130 132 133 135 146 147 148 **P**7 **S** Quorum Health, Brentwood, TN
Primary Contact: Patricia Holden, Chief Executive Officer
CFO: Mitchell Fransen, Chief Financial Officer
CHR: Steve Siegrist, Director of Human Resources
CNO: Nancy K Seck, Chief Nursing Officer
Web address: www.mesaviewhospital.com
Control: Corporation, Investor-owned (for-profit) **Service**: General medical and surgical

Staffed Beds: 25 **Admissions**: 715 **Census**: 6 **Outpatient Visits**: 33544
Births: 100 **Total Expense ($000)**: 27421 **Payroll Expense ($000)**: 12641
Personnel: 164

NELLIS AFB—Clark County

⊞ **MIKE O'CALLAGHAN FEDERAL HOSPITAL**, 4700 Las Vegas Boulevard North, Suite 2419, Zip 89191–6600; tel. 702/653–2000, (Nonreporting) **A**1 3 5 **S** Department of the Air Force, Washington, DC
Primary Contact: Colonel Christian Benjamin, USAF, MC, Commander
COO: ColonelLinnes L Chester USAF, MSC, Administrator
CFO: MajorKari Turkal-Barrett, Flight Commander Resource Management Officer
CMO: Lieutenant ColonelMarkham Brown M.D., Chief Medical Staff
CIO: MajorKevin Seeley, Chief Information Officer
Web address: www.nellis.af.mil/
Control: Air Force, Government, federal **Service**: General medical and surgical

Staffed Beds: 46

NORTH LAS VEGAS—Clark County

★ ⇑ **NORTH VISTA HOSPITAL (290005)**, 1409 East Lake Mead Boulevard, Zip 89030–7197; tel. 702/649–7711, (Nonreporting) **A**10 21 **S** Prime Healthcare, Ontario, CA
Primary Contact: Vincenzo Variale, Chief Executive Officer
CFO: Peter S Miller, Chief Financial Officer
CHR: Abayomi Fibiyi, Chief Human Resources Officer
CNO: Joanna Young R.N., Chief Nursing Officer
Web address: www.northvistahospital.com
Control: Corporation, Investor-owned (for-profit) **Service**: General medical and surgical

Staffed Beds: 177

NV

Many Facility Codes have changed. Please refer to the AHA Guide Code Chart. © 2017 AHA Guide

⊞ **VETERANS AFFAIRS SOUTHERN NEVADA HEALTHCARE SYSTEM**, 6900 North Pecos Road, Zip 89086–4400; tel. 702/791–9000 **A**1 5 **F**3 5 8 12 15 18 20 22 28 29 30 31 33 34 35 36 38 39 40 44 45 47 48 50 51 54 56 57 58 59 60 61 62 64 65 66 68 70 74 75 77 78 79 81 82 84 85 86 87 91 92 93 94 97 98 100 101 102 103 104 105 106 107 108 110 111 114 115 116 117 118 119 127 130 132 135 143 144 146 147 148 149 **S** Department of Veterans Affairs, Washington, DC
Primary Contact: Peggy W. Kearns, MS, FACHE, Executive Director
CFO: Richard O Hays, Chief Fiscal Service
CMO: Ramanujam Komanduri M.D., Chief of Staff
Web address: www.lasvegas.va.gov/
Control: Veterans Affairs, Government, federal **Service:** General medical and surgical

Staffed Beds: 90 **Admissions:** 6017 **Census:** 78 **Outpatient Visits:** 857295 **Births:** 0 **Total Expense ($000):** 552716 **Payroll Expense ($000):** 202700 **Personnel:** 2235

PAHRUMP—Nye County

★ **DESERT VIEW HOSPITAL (291311)**, 360 South Lola Lane, Zip 89048–0884; tel. 775/751–7500, (Nonreporting) **A**10 18 **S** Universal Health Services, Inc., King of Prussia, PA
Primary Contact: Susan Davila, Chief Executive Officer
CFO: Ryan Eggleston, Chief Financial Officer
CMO: Fredric Siegel M.D., Chief of Staff
CIO: Chad Andres, Chief Information Officer
CHR: Lisa Doty, Manager Human Resources
CNO: Markeeta Araujo, Chief Nursing Officer
Web address: www.desertviewhospital.com
Control: Corporation, Investor-owned (for-profit) **Service:** General medical and surgical

Staffed Beds: 25

DESERT VIEW REGIONAL MEDICAL CENTER See Desert View Hospital

RENO—Washoe County

⊞ **RENOWN REGIONAL MEDICAL CENTER (290001)**, 1155 Mill Street, Zip 89502–1576; tel. 775/982–4100, (Includes RENOWN CHILDREN'S HOSPITAL, 1155 Mill Street, Reno, Nevada, Zip 89502–1576, tel. 775/982–5437) **A**1 2 3 5 10 **F**3 5 11 13 15 17 18 19 20 21 22 23 24 25 26 27 28 29 30 31 32 34 35 40 41 43 45 46 48 49 54 56 57 58 59 61 64 65 66 68 70 72 73 74 75 76 77 78 79 80 81 85 86 87 88 89 92 99 100 101 102 103 104 105 107 108 111 114 115 118 119 120 121 123 124 126 130 131 132 135 146 148 149 **S** Renown Health, Reno, NV
Primary Contact: Erik Olson, Chief Executive Officer
COO: Sy Johnson, Executive Vice President, Chief Operating Officer
CFO: Sam King, Chief Financial Officer
CMO: Charles Johnson M.D., Chief of Staff
CIO: Charles Scully, Chief Information Officer
CHR: Michelle Sanchez-Bickley, Vice President Human Resources
Web address: www.renown.org
Control: Other not-for-profit (including NFP Corporation) **Service:** General medical and surgical

Staffed Beds: 643 **Admissions:** 28083 **Census:** 418 **Outpatient Visits:** 479499 **Births:** 4063 **Total Expense ($000):** 562368 **Payroll Expense ($000):** 189845 **Personnel:** 2585

★ △ **RENOWN REHABILITATION HOSPITAL**, 1495 Mill Street, Zip 89502–1479; tel. 775/982–3500 **A**3 5 7 **F**29 54 77 82 90 93 95 96 143 148 **S** Renown Health, Reno, NV
Primary Contact: Chris Nicholas, Chief Executive Officer
CFO: Dawn Ahner, Chief Financial Officer
CIO: Ronald Fuschillo, Chief Information Officer
CHR: Michelle Sanchez-Bickley, Vice President Human Resources
CNO: Melodie Osborn, Chief Nursing Officer
Web address: www.renown.org
Control: Other not-for-profit (including NFP Corporation) **Service:** Rehabilitation

Staffed Beds: 62 **Admissions:** 807 **Census:** 37 **Outpatient Visits:** 20466 **Births:** 0 **Total Expense ($000):** 20959 **Payroll Expense ($000):** 10227 **Personnel:** 149

⊞ **RENOWN SOUTH MEADOWS MEDICAL CENTER (290049)**, 10101 Double 'R' Boulevard, Zip 89521–5931; tel. 775/982–7000 **A**1 3 5 10 **F**8 10 12 29 30 35 39 40 46 68 70 74 75 79 81 82 85 87 93 97 107 108 111 119 125 130 131 146 **S** Renown Health, Reno, NV
Primary Contact: Siri Nelson, Chief Executive Officer
COO: Sy Johnson, Executive Vice President, Chief Operating Officer
CFO: Gina Nelson, Chief Financial Officer
CMO: Dennis Rochier, Chief Medical Officer
CIO: Ronald Fuschillo, Chief Information Officer
CHR: Michelle Sanchez-Bickley, Vice President Human Resources
CNO: Melodie Osborn, Chief Nursing Officer
Web address: www.renown.org
Control: Other not-for-profit (including NFP Corporation) **Service:** General medical and surgical

Staffed Beds: 76 **Admissions:** 3087 **Census:** 26 **Outpatient Visits:** 66965 **Births:** 0 **Total Expense ($000):** 67803 **Payroll Expense ($000):** 21710 **Personnel:** 313

⊞ **SAINT MARY'S REGIONAL MEDICAL CENTER (290009)**, 235 West Sixth Street, Zip 89503–4548; tel. 775/770–3000 **A**1 2 3 5 10 **F**3 11 12 13 15 17 18 20 22 24 26 28 29 30 31 34 35 36 40 45 46 47 49 50 51 53 54 56 57 59 62 63 64 65 68 70 72 74 75 76 77 78 79 81 82 84 85 86 87 89 91 92 93 94 95 96 97 107 108 110 111 114 115 119 120 121 123 124 126 129 130 132 143 144 146 147 148 **S** Prime Healthcare, Ontario, CA
Primary Contact: Helen Lidholm, Chief Executive Officer
CFO: John R Deakyne, Chief Financial Officer
CIO: Cindy Mullins, Director Information Technology
CHR: David Milovich, Vice President Human Resources
Web address: www.saintmarysreno.org
Control: Corporation, Investor-owned (for-profit) **Service:** General medical and surgical

Staffed Beds: 293 **Admissions:** 15182 **Census:** 164 **Outpatient Visits:** 151581 **Births:** 1989 **Total Expense ($000):** 282366 **Payroll Expense ($000):** 96146 **Personnel:** 1613

⊞ **VETERANS AFFAIRS SIERRA NEVADA HEALTH CARE SYSTEM**, 975 Kirman Avenue, Zip 89502–0993; tel. 775/786–7200, (Total facility includes 60 beds in nursing home–type unit) **A**1 3 5 **F**1 3 5 18 20 22 29 30 31 33 34 35 36 38 39 40 44 45 46 47 50 54 56 57 58 59 60 61 62 63 64 65 66 68 70 74 75 77 78 79 81 82 83 84 85 86 87 91 92 93 94 96 97 98 100 101 102 103 104 107 108 111 114 115 119 127 129 130 132 135 143 146 147 148 149 **P**6 **S** Department of Veterans Affairs, Washington, DC
Primary Contact: Lisa M. Howard, Director
COO: Lisa M Howard, Associate Director
CFO: Kelly Manson, Chief Financial Officer
CMO: Steven Brilliant M.D., Chief of Staff
CIO: Jack Smith, Acting Chief Information Resources Management Service
CHR: Debbie Jenkins, Chief Human Resources Management Service
Web address: www.reno.va.gov/
Control: Veterans Affairs, Government, federal **Service:** General medical and surgical

Staffed Beds: 124 **Admissions:** 3694 **Census:** 106 **Outpatient Visits:** 432402 **Births:** 0 **Total Expense ($000):** 291874 **Payroll Expense ($000):** 106743 **Personnel:** 1539

☐ **WEST HILLS HOSPITAL (294003)**, 1240 East Ninth Street, Zip 89512–2964; tel. 775/323–0478, (Nonreporting) **A**1 10 **S** Universal Health Services, Inc., King of Prussia, PA
Primary Contact: Allison Zednicek, Chief Executive Officer
CMO: Philip Rich M.D., Chief Medical Officer
CHR: Don Gay, Director Human Resources
Web address: www.westhillshospital.net
Control: Corporation, Investor-owned (for-profit) **Service:** Psychiatric

Staffed Beds: 190

WILLOW SPRINGS CENTER, 690 Edison Way, Zip 89502–4135; tel. 775/858–3303, (Nonreporting) **A**3 5
Primary Contact: Chris Farley, Interim Chief Executive Officer and Managing Director
CMO: Dana Arlien M.D., Chief Medical Officer
CNO: Sam McCord, Chief Nursing Officer
Web address: www.willowspringscenter.com
Control: Corporation, Investor-owned (for-profit) **Service:** Children's hospital psychiatric

Staffed Beds: 116

NV

Hospital, Medicare Provider Number, Address, Telephone, Approval, Facility, and Physician Codes, Health Care System

★ American Hospital Association (AHA) membership   ○ Healthcare Facilities Accreditation Program   ⇑ Center for Improvement in Healthcare Quality Accreditation
☐ The Joint Commission accreditation   ◇ DNV Healthcare Inc. accreditation   △ Commission on Accreditation of Rehabilitation Facilities (CARF) accreditation

☐ **NORTHERN NEVADA ADULT MENTAL HEALTH SERVICES (294000)**, 480 Galletti Way, Zip 89431–5564; tel. 775/688–2001 **A**1 3 5 10 **F**29 50 98 103 104 130 149
Primary Contact: Cody Phinney, Administrator
CFO: Elizabeth O'Brien, Chief Financial Officer
CIO: Lois Repass, Quality Assurance Specialist and Coordinator Performance Improvement
Web address: www.mhds.state.nv.us/
Control: State, Government, Nonfederal **Service:** Psychiatric

Staffed Beds: 30 **Admissions:** 869 **Census:** 27 **Outpatient Visits:** 36485 **Births:** 0 **Total Expense ($000):** 19742 **Payroll Expense ($000):** 12657 **Personnel:** 81

☐ **NORTHERN NEVADA MEDICAL CENTER (290032)**, 2375 East Prater Way, Zip 89434–9641; tel. 775/331–7000, (Nonreporting) **A**1 10 **S** Universal Health Services, Inc., King of Prussia, PA
Primary Contact: Alan C. Olive, Chief Executive Officer
COO: Tiffany Coury, Chief Operating Officer
CFO: Ryan Heit, Chief Financial Officer
CHR: Patricia Downs, Director Human Resources
CNO: Carla Adams, Chief Nursing Officer
Web address: www.nnmc.com
Control: Corporation, Investor-owned (for-profit) **Service:** General medical and surgical

Staffed Beds: 108

✠ **TAHOE PACIFIC HOSPITALS (292004)**, 2375 East Prater Way, Zip 89434; tel. 775/355–5600, (Nonreporting) (Includes TAHOE PACIFIC HOSPITALS - WEST, 235 West Sixth Street, 5th Floor, Reno, Nevada, Zip 89503–4548, tel. 775/982–5437; TAHOE PACIFIC HOSPITALS, 10101 Double R Boulevard, Reno, Nevada, Zip 89521–5931, tel. 775/331–1044) **A**1 10 **S** LifeCare Management Services, Plano, TX
Primary Contact: Matt Archer, Chief Executive Officer
COO: Theresa Fegan R.N., Chief Clinical Officer
CFO: Nena Swenson, Financial Manager
CMO: T Brian Callister M.D., Chief Medical Officer
CIO: Kaylene Reeves, Director
CHR: Nelson Coy, Director Human Resources
Web address: www.lifecare-hospitals.com
Control: Corporation, Investor-owned (for-profit) **Service:** Acute long-term care hospital

Staffed Beds: 60

★ **HUMBOLDT GENERAL HOSPITAL (291308)**, 118 East Haskell Street, Zip 89445–3299; tel. 775/623–5222, (Total facility includes 42 beds in nursing home–type unit) **A**3 10 18 **F**3 7 11 13 15 18 28 29 30 34 35 40 45 50 56 57 59 64 65 68 70 75 76 77 81 82 85 86 87 97 103 107 110 111 115 118 119 127 128 130 132 133 135 146 147 148 **P**6
Primary Contact: Darlene Bryan, R.N., Interim Chief Executive Officer and Administrator
CFO: Sandi Lehman, Chief Financial Officer
CMO: Brad Granath M.D., Chief of Staff
CHR: Rose Marie Green, Director Human Resources
CNO: Darlene Bryan R.N., Chief Nursing Officer
Web address: www.hghospital.org
Control: County, Government, Nonfederal **Service:** General medical and surgical

Staffed Beds: 67 **Admissions:** 803 **Census:** 32 **Outpatient Visits:** 29678 **Births:** 267

SOUTH LYON MEDICAL CENTER (290002), 213 South Whitacre, Zip 89447–2561, Mailing Address: P.O.Box 940, 89447–0940; tel. 775/463–2301, (Total facility includes 49 beds in nursing home–type unit) **A**10 20 **F**11 29 34 35 40 50 54 57 59 64 65 67 68 75 83 86 87 90 93 97 107 108 111 119 127 128 130 133 135 146 148
Primary Contact: Toni A. Inserra, Interim Administrator
Web address: www.southlyonmedicalcenter.org
Control: Other not-for-profit (including NFP Corporation) **Service:** General medical and surgical

Staffed Beds: 63 **Admissions:** 147 **Census:** 41 **Outpatient Visits:** 32012 **Total Expense ($000):** 11365 **Payroll Expense ($000):** 6413

NV

NEW HAMPSHIRE

BERLIN—Coos County

★ **ANDROSCOGGIN VALLEY HOSPITAL (301310)**, 59 Page Hill Road, Zip 03570–3531; tel. 603/752-2200, (Data for 274 days)**A**10 18 **F**3 8 11 12 13 15 17 28 29 30 34 40 41 43 45 47 57 59 61 64 67 68 70 74 75 76 77 79 81 82 85 89 92 93 102 107 108 110 115 119 128 129 130 131 132 133 146 147 149 **P**6
Primary Contact: Michael Peterson, FACHE, President
CFO: Jeremy Roberge, Director Reimbursement
CMO: Keith M Shute M.D., Senior Vice President Medical Affairs and Clinical Services
CIO: Linda M Laperle, Vice President Administrative Services
CHR: James A Wheeler, Vice President Human Relations and Community Development
Web address: www.avhnh.org
Control: Other not-for-profit (including NFP Corporation) **Service:** General medical and surgical

Staffed Beds: 25 **Admissions:** 1057 **Census:** 15 **Outpatient Visits:** 53282 **Births:** 75 **Total Expense ($000):** 41510 **Payroll Expense ($000):** 16891 **Personnel:** 307

CLAREMONT—Sullivan County

✠ **VALLEY REGIONAL HOSPITAL (301308)**, 243 Elm Street, Zip 03743–4921; tel. 603/542-7771 **A**1 10 18 **F**2 3 11 14 15 28 29 34 35 38 40 43 45 49 50 51 54 57 59 62 63 64 68 75 77 79 81 83 84 85 87 93 97 107 108 110 114 118 119 130 132 133 135 144 146 147 148 **P**6
Primary Contact: Peter J. Wright, FACHE, Chief Executive Officer
CFO: Jean Shaw, Chief Financial Officer
CMO: Oliver Herfort M.D., Chief Medical Officer
CIO: Patricia Witthaus, Director Information Services
CHR: Cheryl Cavanaugh, Senior Director Human Resources
Web address: www.vrh.org
Control: Other not-for-profit (including NFP Corporation) **Service:** General medical and surgical

Staffed Beds: 25 **Admissions:** 628 **Census:** 8 **Outpatient Visits:** 78201 **Births:** 0 **Total Expense ($000):** 40357 **Payroll Expense ($000):** 17018 **Personnel:** 295

COLEBROOK—Coos County

★ **UPPER CONNECTICUT VALLEY HOSPITAL (301300)**, 181 Corliss Lane, Zip 03576–3207; tel. 603/237-4971 **A**10 18 **F**3 15 29 31 34 35 40 45 50 56 57 59 64 67 68 75 78 79 81 84 85 93 102 107 110 111 114 119 128 130 133 144 146 147 148
Primary Contact: Scott Colby, President
CFO: Celeste Pitts, Chief Financial Officer
CMO: Robert Rose M.D., Chief Medical Officer
CIO: Heather Leighton, Director, Revenue Cycle and Privacy Officer
CHR: Heidi L Saari, Director, Human Resources
CNO: Lindsay Rancourt, Director of Nursing
Web address: www.ucvh.org
Control: Other not-for-profit (including NFP Corporation) **Service:** General medical and surgical

Staffed Beds: 12 **Admissions:** 392 **Census:** 5 **Outpatient Visits:** 18595 **Total Expense ($000):** 15926 **Payroll Expense ($000):** 6156 **Personnel:** 92

CONCORD—Merrimack County

★ ⇑ **CONCORD HOSPITAL (300001)**, 250 Pleasant Street, Zip 03301–2598; tel. 603/225-2711 **A**2 3 5 10 21 **F**3 8 12 13 14 15 17 18 20 22 24 26 28 29 30 31 33 34 35 36 37 38 39 40 42 43 44 45 46 47 48 49 50 51 52 53 54 55 57 58 59 61 64 65 66 68 69 70 71 74 75 76 77 78 79 80 81 82 83 84 85 86 87 89 90 93 97 98 99 100 101 102 103 104 105 107 108 110 111 114 115 118 119 120 121 123 126 129 130 131 132 133 135 144 145 146 147 148 149 **P**6
Primary Contact: Robert P. Steigmeyer, President and Chief Executive Officer
COO: Timothy P. Jones, Chief Operating Officer
CFO: Bruce R. Burns, Chief Financial Officer
CMO: David F. Green M.D., Chief Medical Officer
CIO: Deane Morrison, Chief Information Officer
CHR: Robin A. Moore, Vice President Human Resources
CNO: Amy Dumont R.N., MSN, Chief Nursing Officer
Web address: www.concordhospital.org
Control: Other not-for-profit (including NFP Corporation) **Service:** General medical and surgical

Staffed Beds: 242 **Admissions:** 13647 **Census:** 159 **Outpatient Visits:** 683644 **Births:** 1220 **Total Expense ($000):** 431219 **Payroll Expense ($000):** 207843 **Personnel:** 2779

✠ **HEALTHSOUTH REHABILITATION HOSPITAL (303027)**, 254 Pleasant Street, Zip 03301–2508; tel. 603/226-9800, (Nonreporting) **A**1 10 **S** HEALTHSOUTH Corporation, Birmingham, AL
Primary Contact: Catherine Devaney, Chief Executive Officer
CFO: Diana Lachapelle, Controller
CMO: Muhammad Salmanullah, Chief Medical Director
CHR: Myra Nixon, Director Human Resources
CNO: Joseph Adamski, Chief Nursing Officer
Web address: www.healthsouthrehabconcordnh.com
Control: Corporation, Investor-owned (for-profit) **Service:** Rehabilitation

Staffed Beds: 50

☐ **NEW HAMPSHIRE HOSPITAL (304000)**, 36 Clinton Street, Zip 03301–2359; tel. 603/271-5300 **A**1 3 10 **F**3 29 30 39 56 57 58 65 68 74 75 86 87 91 98 99 101 103 130 135 146 149 **P**4 6
Primary Contact: Donald L. Shumway, Chief Executive Officer
COO: Geoffrey C Souther, Chief Operating Officer
CFO: Jamie Dall, Chief Financial Officer
CIO: David Levesque, Director, Information Systems
CHR: Mark Bussiere, Administrator Human Resources
CNO: Roberta A Vitale-Nolen, Administrator, Patient Care Services
Web address: www.dhhs.nh.gov/dcbcs/nhh/
Control: State, Government, Nonfederal **Service:** Psychiatric

Staffed Beds: 168 **Admissions:** 1930 **Census:** 151 **Outpatient Visits:** 0 **Births:** 0 **Total Expense ($000):** 57383 **Payroll Expense ($000):** 29573 **Personnel:** 596

DERRY—Rockingham County

✠ **PARKLAND MEDICAL CENTER (300017)**, One Parkland Drive, Zip 03038–2750; tel. 603/432-1500, (Nonreporting) **A**1 2 10 **S** HCA Healthcare, Nashville, TN
Primary Contact: Jeff Scionti, Chief Executive Officer
CFO: Jacob Wisemann, Chief Financial Officer
CMO: Edward Yourtee M.D., Chief Medical Officer
CIO: Brad George, Director Information Systems
CHR: Molly Lahti, Director Human Resources
CNO: Eileen Keefe, Chief Nursing Officer
Web address: www.parklandmedicalcenter.com
Control: Corporation, Investor-owned (for-profit)
Service: General medical and surgical

Staffed Beds: 82

DOVER—Strafford County

✠ **WENTWORTH-DOUGLASS HOSPITAL (300018)**, 789 Central Avenue, Zip 3820; tel. 603/742-5252 **A**1 2 10 **F**3 5 8 13 17 18 19 20 22 26 28 29 30 31 32 34 35 36 39 40 41 42 43 44 45 46 47 48 49 50 51 52 53 54 55 57 58 59 61 62 63 64 65 68 70 73 74 75 76 77 78 79 81 82 84 85 86 87 89 92 93 94 96 97 100 101 102 104 107 108 111 114 115 118 119 120 121 123 124 126 129 130 131 132 134 135 143 144 145 146 147 148 149 **P**6 8 **S** Partners HealthCare System, Inc., Boston, MA
Primary Contact: Gregory J. Walker, Chief Executive Officer
COO: Daniel N Dunn, Vice President Operations
CFO: Peter Walcek, Vice President Finance
CMO: Paul Cass D.O., Chief Medical & Clinical Integration Officer
CIO: Jeffrey Pollock, Chief Information Officer
CHR: Erin Flanigan, Vice President Human Resources
CNO: Sheila Woolley R.N., M.P.H., Vice President, Patient Care Services
Web address: www.wdhospital.com
Control: Other not-for-profit (including NFP Corporation)
Service: General medical and surgical

Staffed Beds: 142 **Admissions:** 7082 **Census:** 82 **Outpatient Visits:** 294847 **Births:** 1211 **Total Expense ($000):** 262860 **Payroll Expense ($000):** 104810 **Personnel:** 1527

NH

Hospital, Medicare Provider Number, Address, Telephone, Approval, Facility, and Physician Codes, Health Care System		
★ American Hospital Association (AHA) membership	○ Healthcare Facilities Accreditation Program	⇑ Center for Improvement in Healthcare Quality Accreditation
☐ The Joint Commission accreditation	◇ DNV Healthcare Inc. accreditation	△ Commission on Accreditation of Rehabilitation Facilities (CARF) accreditation

EXETER—Rockingham County

★ ⓕ **EXETER HOSPITAL (300023)**, 5 Alumni Drive, Zip 03833–2128; tel.
603/778–7311 **A**2 10 21 **F**3 8 13 14 15 18 20 22 26 28 29 30 31 32 34 35
36 37 38 40 44 45 46 47 48 49 50 51 52 54 55 57 58 59 64 70 74 75 76 77
78 79 80 81 84 85 86 87 89 93 107 108 110 111 114 115 117 118 119 120
121 123 124 126 129 130 131 132 135 143 144 145 146 147 148 149
Primary Contact: Kevin J. Callahan, President and Chief Executive Officer
CFO: Kevin J O'Leary, Senior Vice President and Chief Financial Officer
CMO: Richard Hollister, President of Medical Staff
CIO: David Briden, Chief Information Officer
CHR: Christopher M Callahan, Vice President Human Resources
CNO: Susan Burns-Tisdale, Senior Vice President Clinical Operations, Interim CNO
Web address: www.ehr.org
Control: Other not-for-profit (including NFP Corporation) **Service**: General medical
and surgical

Staffed Beds: 99 **Admissions**: 5216 **Census**: 57 **Outpatient Visits**: 206201
Births: 651 **Total Expense ($000)**: 195265 **Payroll Expense ($000)**: 71366
Personnel: 1269

FRANKLIN—Merrimack County

★ ⓕ **FRANKLIN REGIONAL HOSPITAL (301306)**, 15 Aiken Avenue, Zip
03235–1299; tel. 603/934–2060 **A**10 18 21 **F**3 5 11 15 18 29 30 34 35 39 40
44 45 46 47 48 49 50 57 58 59 61 64 65 66 68 74 75 77 79 81 82 84 85 87
93 97 98 99 100 101 102 103 107 110 114 119 127 130 131 132 133 135
146 147 148 149 **P**4 6 **S** LRGHealthcare, Laconia, NH
Primary Contact: Kevin Donovan, FACHE, President and CEO
CFO: Henry D Lipman, Senior Vice President, Financial Strategy and External
Relations
CMO: Peter Doane M.D., Chief Medical Officer
CIO: Kevin Irish, Chief Information Officer
CHR: Cass Walker, Vice President Administrative & Support Services
CNO: Patti Strohla R.N., Chief Nursing Officer
Web address: www.lrgh.org
Control: Other not-for-profit (including NFP Corporation) **Service**: General medical
and surgical

Staffed Beds: 31 **Admissions**: 878 **Census**: 17 **Outpatient Visits**: 45098
Births: 0 **Total Expense ($000)**: 34516 **Payroll Expense ($000)**: 16779
Personnel: 156

GREENFIELD—Hillsborough County

CROTCHED MOUNTAIN REHABILITATION CENTER, 1 Verney Drive, Zip
03047–5000; tel. 603/547–3311, (Nonreporting)
Primary Contact: Michael Coughlin, Chief Executive Officer
COO: Michael Redmond, Senior Vice President and Chief Operating Officer
CFO: Thomas Zubricki, Vice President Finance, Chief Financial Officer
CMO: W Carl Cooley M.D., Chief Medical Officer
CIO: Jerry Hunter, Vice President, Information Technology
CHR: Lorrie Rudis, Vice President, Human Resources
Web address: www.cmf.org
Control: Other not-for-profit (including NFP Corporation) **Service**: Rehabilitation

Staffed Beds: 181

HAMPSTEAD—Rockingham County

☐ **HAMPSTEAD HOSPITAL (304001)**, 218 East Road, Zip 03841–2305; tel.
603/329–5311, (Nonreporting) **A**1 10
Primary Contact: Phillip J. Kubiak, President
COO: Cynthia A Gove, Chief Operating Officer
CFO: Cherie Clough-Berry, Vice President, Finance
CMO: Michael Knight M.D., Medical Director
CIO: Sandra J Lucia, Director Health Information and Corporate Compliance Officer
CHR: Lisa M Ryan, Coordinator Human Resources
CNO: Julie D'Apollo R.N., Director of Nursing
Web address: www.hampsteadhospital.com
Control: Corporation, Investor-owned (for-profit) **Service**: Psychiatric

Staffed Beds: 60

KEENE—Cheshire County

⊠ **CHESHIRE MEDICAL CENTER (300019)**, 580 Court Street, Zip 03431–1718;
tel. 603/354–5400 **A**1 2 3 10 **F**3 12 13 15 18 29 30 31 34 35 36 40 41 43
44 45 46 49 50 54 55 56 58 59 61 64 65 68 70 74 75 76 77 78 79 80 81 82
84 85 86 87 89 90 91 92 93 94 96 97 98 100 102 104 107 108 111 115 118
119 120 121 123 129 130 131 132 133 135 146 147 148 149 **P**6
Primary Contact: Don Caruso, M.D., Chief Executive Officer and President
CMO: Don Caruso M.D., Chief Medical Officer
CIO: Peter Malloy, Chief Information Officer
CHR: Julie Green, Vice President Human Resources
CNO: Cynthia Coughlin MS, R.N., Chief Nursing Officer
Web address: www.cheshire-med.com
Control: Other not-for-profit (including NFP Corporation) **Service**: General medical
and surgical

Staffed Beds: 108 **Admissions**: 3919 **Census**: 55 **Outpatient Visits**:
441335 **Births**: 412 **Total Expense ($000)**: 172069 **Payroll Expense
($000)**: 60406 **Personnel**: 1202

LACONIA—Belknap County

★ ⓕ **LAKES REGION GENERAL HOSPITAL (300005)**, 80 Highland Street, Zip
03246–3298; tel. 603/524–3211 **A**10 21 **F**3 8 11 12 13 15 18 28 29 30 31 32
33 34 35 37 39 40 44 45 46 47 48 49 50 53 54 56 57 58 59 61 64 65 66 68
70 74 75 76 77 78 79 81 82 84 85 86 87 93 97 98 99 100 101 102 103 104
107 108 110 115 118 119 120 130 131 132 133 135 144 146 147 148
149 **P**4 6 **S** LRGHealthcare, Laconia, NH
Primary Contact: Kevin Donovan, FACHE, Chief Executive Officer
CFO: Henry D Lipman, Senior Vice President, Financial Strategy and External
Relations
CMO: Peter Doane M.D., Chief Medical Officer
CIO: Kevin Irish, Chief Information Officer
CHR: Cass Walker, Vice President Administrative & Support Services
CNO: Jacqueline Dawe R.N., Chief Nursing Officer
Web address: www.lrgh.org
Control: Other not-for-profit (including NFP Corporation) **Service**: General medical
and surgical

Staffed Beds: 88 **Admissions**: 4701 **Census**: 57 **Outpatient Visits**: 215779
Births: 326 **Total Expense ($000)**: 189536 **Payroll Expense ($000)**: 88064
Personnel: 991

LANCASTER—Coos County

★ **WEEKS MEDICAL CENTER (301303)**, 173 Middle Street, Zip 03584–3508; tel.
603/788–4911 **A**10 18 **F**3 11 15 18 28 29 31 32 34 35 36 40 45 50 51 56 57
59 61 62 63 64 65 66 68 70 75 77 78 79 81 85 86 87 91 92 93 94 97 100
104 107 108 110 111 114 116 117 118 119 127 130 131 132 133 134 135
146 147 148 **P**6
Primary Contact: Michael Lee, President
CMO: Lars Nielson M.D., Chief Medical Officer
CIO: Darrell Bodnar, Director Information
CHR: Linda Rexford, Director Human Resources
CNO: Donna Walker, Chief Nurse Executive
Web address: www.weeksmedical.org
Control: Other not-for-profit (including NFP Corporation) **Service**: General medical
and surgical

Staffed Beds: 25 **Admissions**: 672 **Census**: 8 **Outpatient Visits**: 87840
Births: 0 **Total Expense ($000)**: 43584 **Payroll Expense ($000)**: 23645
Personnel: 271

LEBANON—Grafton County

★ **ALICE PECK DAY MEMORIAL HOSPITAL (301305)**, 10 Alice Peck Day Drive,
Zip 03766–2650; tel. 603/448–3121 **A**10 18 **F**3 11 13 15 29 34 35 36 37 39
40 41 45 47 50 51 54 56 57 59 63 64 65 66 67 75 76 77 79 81 82 83 84 85
93 97 107 110 113 114 115 116 117 119 128 129 130 131 133 135 145 146
147 148 **P**5 6
Primary Contact: Susan E. Mooney, M.D., MS, President and Chief Executive
Officer
CFO: Evalie M Crosby CPA, Vice President Finance and Chief Financial Officer
CMO: Randy Lea M.D., M.P.H., Vice President and Chief Medical Officer
CIO: Kristin Kneisel, Interim Director, Information Services
CHR: Brenda Blair, Vice President Human Resources
CNO: Beverley A Rankin R.N., Vice President & Chief Nursing Officer
Web address: www.alicepeckday.org
Control: Other not-for-profit (including NFP Corporation) **Service**: General medical
and surgical

Staffed Beds: 25 **Admissions**: 1372 **Census**: 14 **Outpatient Visits**: 102144
Births: 263 **Total Expense ($000)**: 62108 **Payroll Expense ($000)**: 34301
Personnel: 356

Many Facility Codes have changed. Please refer to the AHA Guide Code Chart. © 2017 AHA Guide

⊞ **DARTMOUTH-HITCHCOCK MEDICAL CENTER (300003)**, One Medical Center Drive, Zip 03756–0001; tel. 603/650–5000, (Includes CHILDREN'S HOSPITAL AT DARTMOUTH, One Medical Center Drive, Lebanon, New Hampshire, Zip 3756, tel. 603/650–5000) **A**1 3 5 8 10 **F**3 5 6 7 8 9 11 12 13 14 15 17 18 19 20 21 22 23 24 25 26 27 28 29 30 31 32 34 35 36 37 38 39 40 41 43 44 45 46 47 48 49 50 51 52 53 54 55 56 57 58 59 60 61 63 64 65 66 68 70 71 72 74 75 76 77 78 79 80 81 82 84 85 86 87 88 89 91 92 93 94 96 97 98 99 100 101 102 103 104 105 107 108 110 111 112 114 115 116 117 118 119 120 121 123 124 126 129 130 131 132 134 135 136 138 141 142 143 145 146 147 148 149 150 **P**6
Primary Contact: Joanne M. Conroy, M.D., President and Chief Executive Officer
CFO: Daniel Jantzen, Chief Financial Officer
CMO: Alexander de Nesherea M.D., Chief Medical Officer
CHR: Aimee M. Giglio, Chief Human Resources Officer
CNO: Susan A Reeves, Chief Nursing Executive
Web address: www.hitchcock.org
Control: Other not-for-profit (including NFP Corporation) **Service**: General medical and surgical

Staffed Beds: 409 **Admissions**: 20743 **Census**: 325 **Outpatient Visits**: 743128 **Births**: 1193 **Total Expense ($000)**: 1249513 **Payroll Expense ($000)**: 569868 **Personnel**: 6464

LITTLETON—Grafton County

★ **LITTLETON REGIONAL HEALTHCARE (301302)**, 600 Saint Johnsbury Road, Zip 03561–3442; tel. 603/444–9000 **A**10 18 **F**3 11 13 15 18 26 28 29 31 32 34 35 36 38 40 43 44 45 50 56 57 59 64 65 67 70 74 75 76 77 78 79 81 84 85 86 87 89 90 92 93 96 97 107 108 110 111 114 115 118 119 127 128 129 130 131 133 143 146 147 148 **P**6
Primary Contact: Robert Nutter, President
CFO: Robert L Fotter, Chief Financial Officer
CIO: Scott Vachon, Director Information Technology
CHR: Georgene Novak, Director Human Resources
CNO: Linda Gilmore, Chief Nursing Officer/Chief Administrative Officer
Web address: www.littletonhospital.org
Control: Other not-for-profit (including NFP Corporation) **Service**: General medical and surgical

Staffed Beds: 25 **Admissions**: 1545 **Census**: 13 **Outpatient Visits**: 59559 **Births**: 317 **Total Expense ($000)**: 87379 **Payroll Expense ($000)**: 36864 **Personnel**: 367

MANCHESTER—Hillsborough County

⊞ **CATHOLIC MEDICAL CENTER (300034)**, 100 McGregor Street, Zip 03102–3770; tel. 603/668–3545 **A**1 2 3 10 **F**3 9 12 13 15 18 20 22 24 26 28 29 30 31 32 34 35 36 37 38 39 40 41 43 44 46 47 48 49 50 53 57 58 59 60 61 63 64 65 66 70 71 73 74 75 76 77 78 79 80 81 82 83 84 85 86 87 90 92 93 96 100 102 104 107 108 110 111 114 115 118 119 124 126 129 130 131 132 134 135 143 144 146 147 148 149 150 **P**6
Primary Contact: Joseph Pepe, M.D., President and Chief Executive Officer
COO: Alexander J. Walker, Executive Vice President Operations and Strategic Development
CFO: Edward L Dudley III, Executive Vice President and Chief Financial Officer
CMO: William H. Goodman, Vice President Medical Affairs, Chief Medical Officer
CIO: Thomas Della Flora, Vice President and Chief Information Officer
CHR: Merryll Rosenfeld, Vice President, Human Resources
CNO: Robert A Duhaime R.N., Senior Vice President Clinical Operations and Chief Nursing Officer
Web address: www.catholicmedicalcenter.org
Control: Other not-for-profit (including NFP Corporation) **Service**: General medical and surgical

Staffed Beds: 259 **Admissions**: 11382 **Census**: 155 **Outpatient Visits**: 174849 **Births**: 1072 **Total Expense ($000)**: 333727 **Payroll Expense ($000)**: 144441 **Personnel**: 1666

⊞ △ **ELLIOT HOSPITAL (300012)**, One Elliot Way, Zip 03103–3502; tel. 603/669–5300 **A**1 2 3 7 10 **F**3 8 9 12 13 15 18 20 22 26 28 29 30 31 32 34 35 36 37 38 39 40 41 42 43 44 45 46 47 48 49 50 51 53 54 55 56 57 59 62 64 65 68 70 72 74 75 76 77 78 79 81 82 83 84 85 86 87 88 89 91 93 97 98 99 100 101 102 103 104 107 108 110 111 114 115 118 119 120 121 123 124 126 129 130 131 132 134 135 144 146 147 148 149 **P**6
Primary Contact: Douglas F. Dean Jr, Interim Chief Executive Officer
COO: Jean Ten-Haken, Chief Operating Officer
CFO: Richard Elwell, Senior Vice President and Chief Financial Officer
CMO: Greg Baxter M.D., Senior Vice President Medical Affairs and Chief Medical Officer
CIO: Denise Purington, Vice President and Chief Information Officer
CHR: Catherine Bardier, Vice President, Human Resources
Web address: www.elliothospital.org
Control: Other not-for-profit (including NFP Corporation) **Service**: General medical and surgical

Staffed Beds: 266 **Admissions**: 12771 **Census**: 171 **Outpatient Visits**: 518746 **Births**: 1951 **Total Expense ($000)**: 369562 **Payroll Expense ($000)**: 132639 **Personnel**: 2877

★ **MANCHESTER VETERANS AFFAIRS MEDICAL CENTER**, 718 Smyth Road, Zip 03104–4098; tel. 603/624–4366, (Nonreporting) **A**5 **S** Department of Veterans Affairs, Washington, DC
Primary Contact: Alfred Montoya, Director
COO: Richard T Rose, Associate Director
CFO: Frank Ryan, Chief Financial Officer
CMO: Andrew Breuder M.D., Chief of Staff
CIO: John Foote, Chief Information Officer
CHR: Mary Ellen Kenney, Chief Human Services
Web address: www.manchester.va.gov/
Control: Veterans Affairs, Government, federal **Service**: Rehabilitation

Staffed Beds: 90

VETERANS AFFAIRS MEDICAL CENTER See Manchester Veterans Affairs Medical Center

NASHUA—Hillsborough County

★ △ ⇑ **SOUTHERN NEW HAMPSHIRE MEDICAL CENTER (300020)**, 8 Prospect Street, Zip 03060–3925, Mailing Address: P.O.Box 2014, 03061–2014; tel. 603/577–2000 **A**2 3 5 7 10 21 **F**3 11 13 15 18 20 22 26 28 29 30 31 34 35 40 42 43 45 49 50 51 52 57 59 61 65 68 70 72 74 75 76 77 78 79 81 84 85 86 87 89 93 96 98 100 102 104 105 107 110 111 115 118 119 126 129 130 131 132 135 143 146 147 148 149 150 **P**6
Primary Contact: Michael S. Rose, President and Chief Executive Officer
COO: Tate Curti, Senior Vice President and Chief Operating Officer
CFO: Paul Trainor, Senior Vice President Finance and Chief Financial Officer
CMO: Kenneth Howe M.D., Chief Medical Officer
CIO: Andrew Watt M.D., Vice President, Information Technology & Services, Chief Information Officer, Chief Medical Information Officer
CHR: Jacqueline Woolley, Vice President Human Resources
CNO: Cheryl Gagne I, Vice President Patient Care Services and Chief Nursing Officer
Web address: www.snhhs.org
Control: Other not-for-profit (including NFP Corporation) **Service**: General medical and surgical

Staffed Beds: 162 **Admissions**: 7927 **Census**: 96 **Outpatient Visits**: 231876 **Births**: 1240 **Total Expense ($000)**: 187440 **Payroll Expense ($000)**: 91309 **Personnel**: 1502

★ △ ⇑ **ST. JOSEPH HOSPITAL (300011)**, 172 Kinsley Street, Zip 03060–3648; tel. 603/882–3000 **A**2 7 10 21 **F**3 8 13 15 18 20 22 28 29 30 31 32 34 35 36 37 40 43 44 45 46 47 48 49 50 51 54 55 56 57 58 59 61 65 68 70 71 74 75 76 77 78 79 81 82 83 84 85 86 87 89 90 91 92 93 94 96 97 100 102 107 108 109 110 111 115 116 117 118 119 126 129 130 131 132 135 144 145 146 147 148 149 **P**6 8 **S** Covenant Health, Tewksbury, MA
Primary Contact: Richard Boehler, M.D., President and Chief Executive Officer
COO: Pam Duchene R.N., Vice President Patient Care Services
CFO: Richard Plamondon, Vice President Finance and Chief Financial Officer
CIO: Keith A Choinka, Vice President Information Systems and Chief Information Officer
CHR: Jacqueline Woolley, Vice President Human Resources
Web address: www.stjosephhospital.com
Control: Church operated, Nongovernment, not-for-profit **Service**: General medical and surgical

Staffed Beds: 126 **Admissions**: 5384 **Census**: 69 **Outpatient Visits**: 188225 **Births**: 545 **Total Expense ($000)**: 201981 **Payroll Expense ($000)**: 76211 **Personnel**: 1116

NH

Hospital, Medicare Provider Number, Address, Telephone, Approval, Facility, and Physician Codes, Health Care System

★ American Hospital Association (AHA) membership   ○ Healthcare Facilities Accreditation Program   ⇑ Center for Improvement in Healthcare Quality Accreditation
☐ The Joint Commission accreditation   ◇ DNV Healthcare Inc. accreditation   △ Commission on Accreditation of Rehabilitation Facilities (CARF) accreditation

NEW LONDON—Merrimack County

★ **NEW LONDON HOSPITAL (301304)**, 273 County Road, Zip 03257–5736; tel. 603/526–2911 **A**3 10 18 **F**3 7 11 15 18 29 30 31 32 34 40 41 45 50 51 54 56 57 59 64 70 74 75 77 78 79 81 82 84 85 87 89 93 94 97 99 100 102 104 107 110 111 114 119 127 128 130 131 133 134 146 147 148 149 **P**6
Primary Contact: Bruce King, President and Chief Executive Officer
CFO: Lisa Cohen, Chief Financial Officer
CMO: James M. Murphy M.D., Chief Medical Officer Regional Development and Outpatient Services
CIO: David Foss, Chief Information Officer
CHR: Shari Bostwick, Director Human Resources
CNO: Sally K Patton R.N., MS, Chief Nursing Officer
Web address: www.newlondonhospital.org
Control: Other not-for-profit (including NFP Corporation) **Service:** General medical and surgical

Staffed Beds: 25 **Admissions:** 1080 **Census:** 50 **Outpatient Visits:** 109747 **Births:** 0 **Total Expense ($000):** 64583 **Payroll Expense ($000):** 29873 **Personnel:** 414

NORTH CONWAY—Carroll County

★ **MEMORIAL HOSPITAL (301307)**, 3073 White Mountain Highway, Zip 03860–7101; tel. 603/356–5461, (Total facility includes 45 beds in nursing home–type unit) **A**10 18 **F**3 11 13 15 28 29 30 31 32 34 35 36 40 41 45 50 51 59 64 67 68 70 75 76 77 78 79 81 82 85 86 87 90 93 94 96 97 100 101 103 104 107 110 115 119 128 129 130 131 132 133 144 146 147 **P**6 **S** MaineHealth, Portland, ME
Primary Contact: Scott McKinnon, President and Chief Executive Officer
CFO: Diane Maheux, Vice President Finance
CMO: Ray Rabideau M.D., Senior Vice President and Chief Medical Officer
CIO: Curtis Kerbs, Regional Chief Information Officer
CHR: Melanie Sleime, Director Human Resources
CNO: Ethnee Garner R.N., Vice President Patient Care Services
Web address: www.memorialhospitalnh.org
Control: Other not-for-profit (including NFP Corporation) **Service:** General medical and surgical

Staffed Beds: 70 **Admissions:** 1530 **Census:** 60 **Outpatient Visits:** 59940 **Births:** 244 **Total Expense ($000):** 69655 **Payroll Expense ($000):** 28098 **Personnel:** 335

PETERBOROUGH—Hillsborough County

★ **MONADNOCK COMMUNITY HOSPITAL (301309)**, 452 Old Street Road, Zip 03458–1295; tel. 603/924–7191 **A**5 10 18 **F**3 11 13 15 28 29 31 34 35 36 38 40 41 44 50 53 59 64 65 70 74 75 76 77 78 79 81 82 85 86 90 91 92 93 97 98 99 100 101 102 103 104 107 108 110 114 118 119 124 127 128 130 131 132 133 134 135 146 147 148 149 **P**6
Primary Contact: Cynthia McGuire, FACHE, President and Chief Executive Officer
CFO: Richard Scheinblum, Chief Financial Officer
CMO: Michael Lindberg M.D., Chief Medical Officer
CIO: Peter A Johnson, Interim Chief Information Officer
CHR: John Sansone, Vice President, Human Resources
CNO: Vicki Loughery R.N., MS, Chief Nursing Officer
Web address: www.monadnockhospital.org
Control: Other not-for-profit (including NFP Corporation) **Service:** General medical and surgical

Staffed Beds: 25 **Admissions:** 1490 **Census:** 14 **Outpatient Visits:** 79789 **Births:** 353 **Total Expense ($000):** 78089 **Payroll Expense ($000):** 32614 **Personnel:** 464

PLYMOUTH—Grafton County

★ **SPEARE MEMORIAL HOSPITAL (301311)**, 16 Hospital Road, Zip 03264–1199; tel. 603/536–1120 **A**10 18 **F**3 13 15 28 29 30 31 32 34 35 40 45 47 53 54 59 64 70 75 76 77 78 79 81 84 85 93 94 97 107 110 111 113 114 119 127 129 130 131 132 133 146 147 148 **P**8
Primary Contact: Michelle McEwen, President and Chief Executive Officer
CFO: Thomas Lenkowski, Chief Financial Officer
CMO: Joseph Ebner M.D., Chief Medical Officer
CHR: Laurie Bolognani, Human Resources Officer
CNO: Kristine Hering R.N., Chief Nursing Officer
Web address: www.spearehospital.com
Control: Other not-for-profit (including NFP Corporation) **Service:** General medical and surgical

Staffed Beds: 25 **Admissions:** 1336 **Census:** 12 **Outpatient Visits:** 95344 **Births:** 171 **Total Expense ($000):** 53333 **Payroll Expense ($000):** 24688 **Personnel:** 308

PORTSMOUTH—Rockingham County

✉ **PORTSMOUTH REGIONAL HOSPITAL (300029)**, 333 Borthwick Avenue, Zip 03801–7128; tel. 603/436–5110, (Nonreporting) **A**1 2 10 **S** HCA Healthcare, Nashville, TN
Primary Contact: Dean Carucci, Chief Executive Officer
COO: Stuart Hemming, Chief Operating Officer
CFO: Richard Senger, Chief Financial Officer
CMO: Tim Pike M.D., Chief Medical Officer
CIO: Ed Sovetskhy, Director Information Services
CHR: Jackie Brayton, Vice President Human Resources
Web address: www.portsmouthhospital.com
Control: Corporation, Investor-owned (for-profit) **Service:** General medical and surgical

Staffed Beds: 165

ROCHESTER—Strafford County

★ **FRISBIE MEMORIAL HOSPITAL (300014)**, 11 Whitehall Road, Zip 03867–3297; tel. 603/332–5211 **A**10 **F**7 11 13 17 18 20 29 31 34 35 40 45 46 49 50 55 59 68 70 75 76 78 79 81 85 89 91 93 97 98 99 103 104 107 111 114 119 129 130 135 143 144 146 **P**5 8
Primary Contact: John A. Marzinzik, President and Chief Executive Officer
CFO: Robert K. Cochrane, Vice President Finance and Chief Financial Officer
CMO: Jocelyn Caple M.D., Chief Medical Officer
CHR: Christi Green R.N., MS, Vice President, Human Resources
CNO: John Levitow, Vice President Patient Care Services and Chief Nursing Officer
Web address: www.frisbiehospital.com
Control: Other not-for-profit (including NFP Corporation) **Service:** General medical and surgical

Staffed Beds: 96 **Admissions:** 3391 **Census:** 45 **Outpatient Visits:** 127440 **Births:** 329 **Total Expense ($000):** 144523 **Payroll Expense ($000):** 61742 **Personnel:** 911

SALEM—Rockingham County

☐ △ **NORTHEAST REHABILITATION HOSPITAL (303026)**, 70 Butler Street, Zip 03079–3925; tel. 603/893–2900 **A**1 7 10 **F**29 30 62 68 82 87 90 91 93 96 131 133 147 148
Primary Contact: John F. Prochilo Jr, Chief Executive Officer
CFO: Charles D. Champagne, Chief Financial Officer
CMO: A Deniz Ozel M.D., Chief Medical Officer
CHR: Shirley G Lussier, Vice President Human Resources
CNO: Helene Thibodeau R.N., MSN, Vice President Patient Care Services
Web address: www.northeastrehab.com
Control: Corporation, Investor-owned (for-profit) **Service:** Rehabilitation

Staffed Beds: 135 **Admissions:** 3630 **Census:** 118 **Outpatient Visits:** 211739 **Births:** 0 **Total Expense ($000):** 86297 **Payroll Expense ($000):** 49104 **Personnel:** 688

WOLFEBORO—Carroll County

★ **HUGGINS HOSPITAL (301312)**, 240 South Main Street, Zip 03894–4455, Mailing Address: P.O.Box 912, 03894–0912; tel. 603/569–7500 **A**10 18 **F**2 3 10 15 28 29 34 35 36 40 45 50 53 57 59 64 65 68 70 75 79 81 85 86 87 93 96 97 107 108 110 115 119 130 131 132 133 146 147 148 149 **P**6
Primary Contact: Jeremy Roberge, President and Chief Executive Officer
CFO: Jeremy Roberge, Chief Financial Officer
CMO: John Boornazian M.D., Chief Medical Officer
CIO: Pam McGovern, Director Technology
CHR: Laura Stauss, Director of Human Resources
Web address: www.hugginshospital.org
Control: Other not-for-profit (including NFP Corporation) **Service:** General medical and surgical

Staffed Beds: 25 **Admissions:** 848 **Census:** 11 **Outpatient Visits:** 71727 **Births:** 0 **Total Expense ($000):** 54588 **Payroll Expense ($000):** 24273 **Personnel:** 352

WOODSVILLE—Grafton County

★ **COTTAGE HOSPITAL (301301)**, 90 Swiftwater Road, Zip 03785–1421, Mailing Address: P.O.Box 2001, 03785–2001; tel. 603/747–9000, (Nonreporting) **A**10 18
Primary Contact: Maria Ryan, Ph.D., Chief Executive Officer
COO: Lori Hughes R.N., MSN, Chief Nursing Officer, Vice President Operations and Patient Care Services
CFO: Steven L Plant, Chief Financial Officer
CIO: Rick Fredrick, Director Information Technology
CNO: Lori Hughes R.N., MSN, Chief Nursing Officer, Vice President Operations & Patient Care Services
Web address: www.cottagehospital.org
Control: Other not-for-profit (including NFP Corporation) **Service:** General medical and surgical

Staffed Beds: 25

NEW JERSEY

ATLANTIC CITY—Atlantic County

★ ⇑ **ACUITY SPECIALTY HOSPITAL OF NEW JERSEY (312023)**, 1925 Pacific Avenue, 7th Floor, Zip 08401–6713; tel. 609/441–2122, (Nonreporting) **A**10 21 **S** AcuityHealthcare, LP, Charlotte, NC
Primary Contact: Monica Titus, R.N., President and Chief Executive Officer
CFO: Cheryl Lambert, Chief Financial Officer
CHR: Maria Ciro, Director Human Resources
CNO: Kathleen Kerstetter R.N., MSN, Chief Clinical Officer
Web address: www.acuityhealthcare.net
Control: Corporation, Investor-owned (for-profit) **Service:** Acute long-term care hospital

Staffed Beds: 30

⊞ **ATLANTICARE REGIONAL MEDICAL CENTER (310064)**, 1925 Pacific Avenue, Zip 08401–6713; tel. 609/441–8994, (Includes ATLANTICARE REGIONAL MEDICAL CENTER-MAINLAND DIVISION, Jimmie Leeds Road, Pomona, New Jersey, Zip 8240, tel. 609/652–1000) (Data for 274 days)**A**1 2 3 10 13 **F**3 7 11 12 13 15 17 18 20 22 24 26 28 29 30 31 34 35 36 37 38 40 41 42 43 45 46 47 48 49 50 54 55 57 58 59 60 61 64 66 68 70 71 72 73 74 75 76 78 79 81 82 83 84 85 86 87 89 97 98 99 100 102 103 104 105 106 107 108 110 111 114 115 116 117 118 119 120 121 123 124 126 130 132 135 143 146 147 148 149 **P**6 **S** Geisinger Health, Danville, PA
Primary Contact: Lori Herndon, R.N., President and Chief Executive Officer
CFO: Walter Greiner, Chief Financial Officer
CMO: Marilouise Vendetti M.D., Chief Medical Officer
CIO: Christopher A Scanzera, Vice President and Chief Information Officer
CHR: Richard Lovering, Corporate Vice President Human Resources and Organizational Development
CNO: Robyn Begley R.N., Chief Nursing Officer
Web address: www.atlanticare.org
Control: Other not-for-profit (including NFP Corporation) **Service:** General medical and surgical

Staffed Beds: 530 **Admissions:** 21077 **Census:** 346 **Outpatient Visits:** 260465 **Births:** 1483 **Total Expense ($000):** 474189 **Payroll Expense ($000):** 207183 **Personnel:** 3166

BAYONNE—Hudson County

⊞ **CAREPOINT HEALTH BAYONNE MEDICAL CENTER (310025)**, 29th Street & Avenue E, Zip 07002–4699, Mailing Address: 29 East 29 Street, 07002–4699; tel. 201/858–5000, (Nonreporting) **A**1 2 10 12 13 **S** CarePoint Health, Jersey City, NJ
Primary Contact: Catherine Shull. Fernald, MSN, Chief Operating Officer
COO: Catherine Shull Fernald MSN, Chief Operating Officer - Bayonne Medical Center
CFO: Gary Bryant, Chief Financial Officer
CMO: Vijayant Singh M.D., Chief Medical Officer
CIO: Joel Taylor, Chief Information Officer
CHR: Jennifer Dobin, Executive Vice President Human Resources
Web address: www.carepointhealth.org
Control: Corporation, Investor-owned (for-profit) **Service:** General medical and surgical

Staffed Beds: 178

BELLE MEAD—Somerset County

⊞ **CARRIER CLINIC (314012)**, 252 County Route 601, Zip 08502–0147, Mailing Address: P.O.Box 147, 08502–0147; tel. 908/281–1000 **A**1 3 5 10 **F**4 5 30 38 98 99 100 101 102 103 130 132 149 **P**6
Primary Contact: Donald J. Parker, President and Chief Executive Officer
CFO: Randolph Jacobson, Chief Financial Officer
CMO: Umesh Mehta M.D., Interim Chief Medical Officer
CIO: Peter Schwartz, Director of Information Systems
CHR: Trish Toole, Vice President Administrative Services
CNO: Shaun Sweeney, Vice President Patient Care Services
Web address: www.carrierclinic.org
Control: Other not-for-profit (including NFP Corporation) **Service:** Psychiatric

Staffed Beds: 310 **Admissions:** 6468 **Census:** 252 **Outpatient Visits:** 1294 **Births:** 0 **Total Expense ($000):** 72828 **Payroll Expense ($000):** 44804 **Personnel:** 762

EAST MOUNTAIN HOSPITAL (314026), 252 County Route 601, Zip 8502; tel. 908/281–1500 (Nonreporting) **A**10
Primary Contact: Michael Voorhees, MS, Executive Director
CFO: Randolph Jacobson, Chief Financial Officer
CMO: Bohdan Cehelyk M.D., Chief Medical Officer
CIO: Peter Schwartz, Director Information Systems
CHR: Patricia Toole, Vice President Human Resources
CNO: Deborah Charette, Director of Nursing
Web address: www.eastmountainhospital.com
Control: Corporation, Investor-owned (for-profit) **Service:** Psychiatric

Staffed Beds: 16

BELLEVILLE—Essex County

⊞ **CLARA MAASS MEDICAL CENTER (310009)**, One Clara Maass Drive, Zip 07109–3557; tel. 973/450–2000 **A**1 3 5 10 **F**3 4 8 11 12 13 15 16 17 18 19 20 22 28 29 30 31 34 35 36 38 39 40 41 44 45 47 49 50 51 53 55 56 57 58 59 60 63 64 65 66 67 68 70 71 72 73 74 75 77 78 79 81 82 83 84 85 86 87 88 90 92 93 94 96 98 101 102 103 107 108 110 114 115 119 120 121 123 126 128 129 130 131 132 135 143 146 147 148 149 150 **P**6 **S** RWJBarnabas Health, West Orange, NJ
Primary Contact: Mary Ellen Clyne, MSN, Ph.D., R.N., President and Chief Executive Officer
CFO: Nik Alexiades, Chief Financial Officer
CMO: Frank Mazzarella M.D., Chief Medical Officer
CIO: Michael McTigue, Chief Information Officer
CHR: Jim Rolek, Chief Human Resources Officer, Vice President
CNO: Lea Rodriguez R.N., Chief Nursing Officer, Vice President Patient Care Services
Web address: www.barnabashealth.org/hospitals/clara_maass/index.html
Control: Other not-for-profit (including NFP Corporation) **Service:** General medical and surgical

Staffed Beds: 469 **Admissions:** 15472 **Census:** 215 **Outpatient Visits:** 127448 **Births:** 1619 **Total Expense ($000):** 249763 **Payroll Expense ($000):** 108816 **Personnel:** 1358

BERKELEY HEIGHTS—Union County

CORNERSTONE BEHAVIORAL HEALTH HOSPITAL OF UNION COUNTY (314027), 40 Watchung Way, Zip 07922–2600; tel. 908/771–5700 (Nonreporting)
Primary Contact: Michael Flemming, Administrator
Control: County, Government, Nonfederal **Service:** Psychiatric

Staffed Beds: 44

RUNNELLS CENTER FOR REHABILITATION AND HEALTHCARE (315009), 40 Watchung Way, Zip 07922–2618; tel. 908/771–5700, (Nonreporting) **A**10
Primary Contact: Josh Bamberger, Administrator
CFO: Michael Drummond, Chief Financial Officer
CMO: Raymond Lanza D.O., Medical Director
CHR: Greg Hardoby, Director Personnel
CNO: Patricia Spina R.N., Director of Nursing
Web address: www.ucnj.org/runnells
Control: Corporation, Investor-owned (for-profit) **Service:** Rehabilitation

Staffed Beds: 44

BLACKWOOD—Camden County

NORTHBROOK BEHAVIORAL HEALTH HOSPITAL (314018), 425 Woodbury Turnersville Road, Zip 08012–2960; tel. 856/374–6500 (Nonreporting)
Primary Contact: Barbara Loughrey, Administrator
Web address: www.northbrookbhh.com
Control: Corporation, Investor-owned (for-profit) **Service:** Psychiatric

Staffed Beds: 153

Hospital, Medicare Provider Number, Address, Telephone, Approval, Facility, and Physician Codes, Health Care System

★ American Hospital Association (AHA) membership   ○ Healthcare Facilities Accreditation Program   ⇑ Center for Improvement in Healthcare Quality Accreditation
□ The Joint Commission accreditation   ◇ DNV Healthcare Inc. accreditation   △ Commission on Accreditation of Rehabilitation Facilities (CARF) accreditation

NJ

BOONTON TOWNSHIP—Morris County

SAINT CLARE'S HOSPITAL/BOONTON TOWNSHIP See Saint Clare's Health System, Denville

BRICK—Ocean County

⌗ △ **HACKENSACK MERIDIAN HEALTH SHORE REHABILITATION INSTITUTE (313033)**, 425 Jack Martin Boulevard, Zip 08724–7732; tel. 732/836–4500 (Nonreporting) **A**1 7 10 **S** Hackensack Meridian Health, Edison, NJ
Primary Contact: Marci Gietter, Interim Executive Director
CFO: Richard C. Smith, Senior Vice President Finance
CMO: Lisa Luciano D.O., Medical Director
CNO: Maria Clohsey, Director of Nursing
Web address: www.shorerehabilitationinstitute.com
Control: Other not-for-profit (including NFP Corporation) **Service:** Rehabilitation

Staffed Beds: 40

BRICK TOWNSHIP—Ocean County

⌗ **HACKENSACK MERIDIAN HEALTH OCEAN MEDICAL CENTER (310052)**, 425 Jack Martin Boulevard, Zip 08724–7732; tel. 732/840–2200 **A**1 2 10 **F**3 11 12 13 15 17 18 20 22 28 29 30 31 32 34 35 36 38 39 40 41 42 43 44 45 46 47 48 49 50 54 55 56 57 58 59 60 61 63 64 65 66 68 70 71 73 74 75 76 77 78 79 80 81 82 84 85 86 87 92 93 94 96 97 99 100 101 102 103 104 107 108 110 111 114 115 116 117 118 119 120 121 123 124 126 129 130 131 132 134 135 141 144 146 147 148 149 **S** Hackensack Meridian Health, Edison, NJ
Primary Contact: Dean Q. Lin, FACHE, Regional President
COO: Regina Foley R.N., FACHE, Vice President Nursing and Operations
CFO: Robert Palermo, Vice President Finance
CMO: James Clarke M.D., Vice President Medical Affairs and Clinical Effectiveness
CIO: Rebecca Weber, Senior Vice President and Chief Information Officer
CHR: Sherrie String, Senior Vice President Human Resources
Web address: www.meridianhealth.com
Control: Other not-for-profit (including NFP Corporation) **Service:** General medical and surgical

Staffed Beds: 278 Admissions: 14101 Census: 192 Outpatient Visits: 179280 Births: 883 Total Expense ($000): 270621 Payroll Expense ($000): 115697 Personnel: 1546

BRIDGETON—Cumberland County

BRIDGETON HEALTH CENTER See Inspira Medical Center-Vineland, Vineland

BROWNS MILLS—Burlington County

☐ **DEBORAH HEART AND LUNG CENTER (310031)**, 200 Trenton Road, Zip 08015–1705; tel. 609/893–6611, (Nonreporting) **A**1 3 5 10 13
Primary Contact: Joseph Chirichella, President and Chief Executive Officer
COO: Joseph Manni, Executive Vice President and Chief Operating Officer
CFO: R. Grant Leidy, Chief Financial Officer
CMO: Lynn McGrath M.D., Vice President Medical Affairs
CIO: Richard Temple, Chief Information Officer
CHR: Marion Stamopoulos, Vice President Human Resouces
CNO: Rita Zenna R.N., Vice President Patient Care Services
Web address: www.deborah.org
Control: Other not-for-profit (including NFP Corporation) **Service:** Other specialty treatment

Staffed Beds: 89

CAMDEN—Camden County

⌗ **COOPER UNIVERSITY HEALTH CARE (310014)**, One Cooper Plaza, Zip 08103–1489; tel. 856/342–2000, (Includes CHILDEN'S REGIONAL HOSPITAL AT COOPER, Three Cooper Plaza, Camden, New Jersey, Zip 8103, tel. 800/826–6737) **A**1 2 3 5 8 10 **F**3 7 8 11 12 13 15 17 18 19 20 22 24 26 29 30 31 32 34 35 36 37 39 40 41 42 43 44 45 46 47 48 49 50 51 52 54 55 56 57 58 59 60 61 64 65 66 68 70 72 73 74 75 76 78 79 80 81 82 84 85 86 87 88 89 92 93 96 97 98 99 100 101 102 103 104 107 108 110 111 114 115 117 118 119 120 121 123 124 126 129 130 131 132 135 144 146 147 148 149 **P**6
Primary Contact: Adrienne Kirby, Ph.D., FACHE, President and Chief Executive Officer
CFO: Douglas E. Shirley, Senior Executive Vice President and Chief Financial Officer
CMO: Anthony J Mazzarelli JD, M.D., Senior Executive Vice President Chief Physician Executive
CIO: Stephanie Conners, Senior Executive Vice President Chief Operating Officer and Chief Nursing Officer
CHR: Elizabeth Green, Chief Human Resources Officer
Web address: www.cooperhealth.org
Control: Other not-for-profit (including NFP Corporation) **Service:** General medical and surgical

Staffed Beds: 579 Admissions: 28876 Census: 429 Outpatient Visits: 311971 Births: 2083 Total Expense ($000): 842625 Payroll Expense ($000): 302834 Personnel: 5983

⌗ **OUR LADY OF LOURDES MEDICAL CENTER (310029)**, 1600 Haddon Avenue, Zip 08103–3117; tel. 856/757–3500 **A**1 2 3 10 **F**3 7 11 12 13 15 17 18 20 22 24 26 28 29 30 31 32 34 35 36 37 38 40 44 46 47 49 50 55 56 57 58 59 60 61 64 65 66 68 70 72 73 74 75 76 78 79 81 82 84 85 86 87 89 90 95 96 100 107 108 110 111 114 115 118 119 126 130 132 134 135 138 139 142 146 147 148 149 **P**8 **S** Trinity Health, Livonia, MI
Primary Contact: Reginald Blaber, M.D., FACC, President
COO: Mark Nessel, Chief Operating Officer
CFO: Michael Hammond, Chief Financial Officer
CMO: Alan R Pope M.D., Chief Medical Officer
CIO: Maureen Hetu, Chief Information Officer
CHR: Jennifer L Moughan, Chief Human Resources Officer
CNO: Audrey Jadczak R.N., FACHE, Vice President Chief Nursing Officer
Web address: www.lourdesnet.org
Control: Other not-for-profit (including NFP Corporation) **Service:** General medical and surgical

Staffed Beds: 350 Admissions: 12948 Census: 177 Outpatient Visits: 153643 Births: 1016 Total Expense ($000): 300613 Payroll Expense ($000): 107354 Personnel: 2288

CAPE MAY COURT HOUSE—Cape May County

⌗ **CAPE REGIONAL MEDICAL CENTER (310011)**, Two Stone Harbor Boulevard, Zip 08210–9990; tel. 609/463–2000 **A**1 2 10 **F**8 11 12 13 15 18 20 28 29 30 31 34 35 40 44 45 46 49 50 53 57 59 64 70 74 75 76 77 78 79 81 82 84 85 86 87 89 91 93 97 107 111 114 118 119 120 121 123 124 129 130 132 135 143 146 148 149
Primary Contact: Joanne Carrocino, FACHE, President and Chief Executive Officer
CFO: Mark Gill, Vice President Finance and Chief Financial Officer
CMO: Andrea C.S. McCoy M.D., Chief Medical Officer
CIO: Richard Wheatley, Chief Information Officer
CHR: Byron Hunter, Vice President Human Resources
CNO: Deborah Baehser, Vice President Patient Care Services
Web address: www.caperegional.com
Control: Other not-for-profit (including NFP Corporation) **Service:** General medical and surgical

Staffed Beds: 180 Admissions: 6779 Census: 78 Outpatient Visits: 193731 Births: 390 Total Expense ($000): 123577 Payroll Expense ($000): 51927 Personnel: 800

CEDAR GROVE—Essex County

☐ **ESSEX COUNTY HOSPITAL CENTER (314020)**, 204 Grove Avenue, Zip 07009–1436; tel. 973/571–2800, (Nonreporting) **A**1 10
Primary Contact: Frank J. Del Gaudio, Director and Chief Executive Officer
CFO: Jacqueline Campoverde, Business Manager
CMO: Bolivar Pascual M.D., Medical Director
CIO: Vijay Prakash, Information Technology Officer
CHR: Marlon Brown, Human Resources
CNO: Fern Papalia, Director of Nursing
Web address: www.essexcountynj.org
Control: County, Government, Nonfederal **Service:** Psychiatric

Staffed Beds: 180

CHESTER—Morris County

KESSLER INSTITUTE FOR REHABILITATION See Kessler Institute For Rehabilitation, West Orange

DENVILLE—Morris County

⌗ **SAINT CLARE'S HEALTH SYSTEM (310050)**, 25 Pocono Road, Zip 07834–2954; tel. 973/625–6000, (Includes SAINT CLARE'S HEALTH CENTER AT SUSSEX, 20 Walnut Street, Sussex, New Jersey, Zip 7461, tel. 973/702–2200; SAINT CLARE'S HOSPITAL/BOONTON TOWNSHIP, 130 Powerville Road, Boonton Township, New Jersey, Zip 7005, tel. 973/316–1800; SAINT CLARE'S HOSPITAL/DENVILLE, 25 Pocono Road, Denville, New Jersey, Zip 7834, tel. 973/625–6000; SAINT CLARE'S HOSPITAL/DOVER, 400 West Blackwell Street, Dover, New Jersey, Zip 07801–3311, tel. 973/989–3000) (Nonreporting) **A**1 2 10 **S** Prime Healthcare, Ontario, CA
Primary Contact: Brian Finestein, Chief Executive Officer
COO: Joe Nolan, Chief Operating Officer
CFO: Dianne Halford, Chief Financial Officer
CMO: Alma Ratcliffe M.D., Executive Vice President Medical Staff and Business Development
CIO: Tero Caamano, Director Information Technology
CHR: Kay Bryant, Executive Director Human Resources
Web address: www.saintclares.org
Control: Church operated, Nongovernment, not-for-profit **Service:** General medical and surgical

Staffed Beds: 412

SAINT CLARE'S HOSPITAL/DENVILLE See Saint Clare's Health System

Many Facility Codes have changed. Please refer to the AHA Guide Code Chart. © 2017 AHA Guide

DOVER—Morris County

☒ **KINDRED HOSPITAL-NEW JERSEY MORRIS COUNTY (312020)**, 400 West Blackwell Street, Zip 07801–2525; tel. 973/537–3818, (Nonreporting) (Includes KINDRED HOSPITAL NEW JERSEY - RAHWAY, 865 Stone Street, Rahway, New Jersey, Zip 7065, tel. 732/669–8200; Christopher Cannara, Chief Executive Officer; KINDRED HOSPITAL NEW JERSEY - WAYNE, 224 Hamburg Turnpike, Wayne, New Jersey, Zip 7470, tel. 973/636–7200; Alice M O'Connor, Chief Executive Officer) **A**1 10 **S** Kindred Healthcare, Louisville, KY
Primary Contact: Michael A. Pizzano, Chief Executive Officer
COO: Kent Wallace, Chief Operating Officer
CFO: Stephen D. Farber, Chief Financial Officer
CMO: Sean R Muldoon M.D., Chief Medical Officer
Web address: www.khmorriscounty.com/
Control: Corporation, Investor-owned (for-profit) **Service**: Acute long-term care hospital

Staffed Beds: 117

EAST ORANGE—Essex County

☐ **EAST ORANGE GENERAL HOSPITAL (310083)**, 300 Central Avenue, Zip 07018–2897; tel. 973/672–8400, (Nonreporting) **A**1 10 **S** Prospect Medical Holdings, Los Angeles, CA
Primary Contact: Paige Dworak, Interim Chief Executive Officer
CMO: Valentine Burroughs M.D., Chief Medical Officer
CIO: Thomas Ciccarelli, Chief Information Officer
CHR: Chester Banks, Director Human Resources
Web address: www.evh.org
Control: Other not-for-profit (including NFP Corporation) **Service**: General medical and surgical

Staffed Beds: 190

☒ **VETERANS AFFAIRS NEW JERSEY HEALTH CARE SYSTEM**, 385 Tremont Avenue, Zip 07018–1095; tel. 973/676–1000, (Nonreporting) (Includes EAST ORANGE DIVISION, 385 Tremont Avenue, East Orange, New Jersey, Zip 07018–1095, tel. 973/676–1000; LYONS DIVISION, 151 Knollcroft Road, Lyons, New Jersey, Zip 07939–9998, tel. 908/647–0180) **A**1 2 5 **S** Department of Veterans Affairs, Washington, DC
Primary Contact: Vincent F. Immiti, FACHE, Director
CFO: Tyrone Taylor, Chief Financial Officer
CMO: Steven L Lieberman M.D., Chief of Staff
CIO: Kamesha Scarlett, Chief Information Resource Management
CHR: Nancy Hamilton, Chief Human and Learning Resources
CNO: Patrick J Troy R.N., MSN, Associate Director Patient Care Services
Web address: www.newjersey.va.gov/
Control: Veterans Affairs, Government, federal **Service**: Other specialty treatment

Staffed Beds: 439

EDISON—Middlesex County

★ △ **JFK JOHNSON REHABILITATION INSTITUTE**, 65 James Street, Zip 8818; tel. 732/321–7050 **A**7 **F**3 9 28 29 30 35 36 42 50 53 54 64 82 90 91 92 93 94 96 130 131 132 143 149 150 **P**6 **S** JFK Health, Edison, NJ
Primary Contact: Anthony Cuzzola, Vice President and Administrator
COO: Scott Gebhard, Chief Operating Officer
CFO: Richard C. Smith, Chief Financial Officer
CMO: William F. Oser M.D., Chief Medical Officer
CIO: Neal Ganguly, Chief Information Officer
CNO: James Lindquist, Chief Nursing Officer
Web address: www.njrehab.org
Control: Other not-for-profit (including NFP Corporation) **Service**: Rehabilitation

Staffed Beds: 94 Admissions: 1981 Census: 77 Outpatient Visits: 120330 Births: 0 Total Expense ($000): 72969 Payroll Expense ($000): 47905 Personnel: 584

☒ **JFK MEDICAL CENTER (310108)**, 65 James Street, Zip 8818; tel. 732/321–7000 **A**1 2 3 10 **F**3 7 8 11 12 13 14 15 17 18 20 22 26 28 29 30 31 34 35 37 38 39 40 41 42 45 46 47 49 50 51 53 54 56 57 58 59 60 61 63 64 66 68 69 70 73 74 75 77 78 79 81 82 83 84 85 86 87 91 92 93 94 96 97 100 101 102 104 107 108 110 111 113 114 115 116 117 118 119 120 121 124 126 129 130 131 132 135 141 143 144 145 146 147 148 **P**4 5 6 7 **S** JFK Health, Edison, NJ
Primary Contact: Raymond F. Fredericks, President and CEO
COO: Scott Gebhard, Executive VP and Chief Operating Officer
CFO: Richard C. Smith, Senior Vice President and Chief Financial Officer
CMO: William F. Oser M.D., Senior Vice President and Chief Medical Officer
CIO: Indranil Ganguly, Vice President and Chief Information Officer
CHR: Shirley Higgins Bowers, Senior Vice President Human Resources
CNO: James Lindquist, Chief Nursing Officer
Web address: www.jfkmc.org
Control: Other not-for-profit (including NFP Corporation) **Service**: General medical and surgical

Staffed Beds: 345 Admissions: 17799 Census: 246 Outpatient Visits: 280821 Births: 2192 Total Expense ($000): 414259 Payroll Expense ($000): 192568 Personnel: 2887

ELIZABETH—Union County

CAREONE AT TRINITAS REGIONAL MEDICAL CENTER, 225 Williamson Street, Zip 07202–3625; tel. 908/994–5288 (Nonreporting)
Primary Contact: Sharon Bready, R.N., Chief Executive Officer
Web address: www.care-one.com/locations/ltach-careone-at-trinitas-regional-medical-center/
Control: Other not-for-profit (including NFP Corporation) **Service**: Acute long-term care hospital

Staffed Beds: 25

☒ **TRINITAS REGIONAL MEDICAL CENTER (310027)**, 225 Williamson Street, Zip 07202–3625; tel. 908/994–5000, (Includes TRINITAS HOSPITAL, 225 Williamson Street, Elizabeth, New Jersey, Zip 7207, tel. 908/994–5000; Gary S Horan, FACHE, President and Chief Executive Officer; TRINITAS REGIONAL MEDICAL CENTER - NEW POINT CAMPUS, 655 East Jersey Street, Elizabeth, New Jersey, Zip 7206, tel. 908/994–5000; Gary S Horan, FACHE, President and Chief Executive Officer) (Total facility includes 124 beds in nursing home–type unit) **A**1 2 3 5 10 13 **F**3 5 7 8 11 13 15 17 18 20 22 28 29 30 31 32 34 35 36 38 40 44 45 46 48 49 53 55 56 57 58 59 60 61 64 65 66 68 70 73 74 75 76 77 78 79 81 82 84 85 86 87 91 93 97 98 99 100 101 102 103 104 105 106 107 108 110 111 115 117 118 119 120 121 123 124 126 128 129 130 132 134 135 141 143 146 147 148 149 **P**6
Primary Contact: Gary S. Horan, FACHE, President and Chief Executive Officer
CFO: Karen Lumpp, Senior Vice President and Chief Financial Officer
CMO: William McHugh M.D., Medical Director and Chief Medical Officer
CIO: Judy Comitto, Vice President Information Services and Chief Information Officer
CHR: Glenn Nacion, Vice President Human Resources
CNO: Mary McTigue, Vice President Patient Care Services and Chief Nursing Officer
Web address: www.trinitasrmc.com
Control: Other not-for-profit (including NFP Corporation) **Service**: General medical and surgical

Staffed Beds: 461 Admissions: 14895 Census: 369 Outpatient Visits: 436635 Births: 2047 Total Expense ($000): 293155 Payroll Expense ($000): 136254 Personnel: 2314

ELMER—Salem County

★ ⇑ **INSPIRA MEDICAL CENTER-ELMER (310069)**, 501 West Front Street, Zip 08318–2101; tel. 856/363–1000 **A**10 21 **F**3 8 11 12 13 15 18 20 22 28 29 30 34 38 40 42 44 50 57 59 64 68 70 74 75 76 77 78 79 81 82 85 86 87 89 93 107 108 110 111 114 115 117 119 120 121 123 124 130 131 132 134 146 147 148 **S** Inspira Health Network, Mullica Hill, NJ
Primary Contact: John A. DiAngelo, President and Chief Executive Officer
COO: David Yhlen, Chief Operating Officer
CFO: Thomas Baldosaro, Chief Financial Officer
CMO: Steven C Linn M.D., Chief Medical Officer
CIO: Thomas Pacek, Vice President Information Systems and Chief Information Officer
CHR: Erich Florentine, Chief People Officer
CNO: Elizabeth Sheridan, Chief Operating Officer and Chief Nursing Executive
Web address: www.inspirahealthnetwork.org/?id=5281&sid=1
Control: Other not-for-profit (including NFP Corporation) **Service**: General medical and surgical

Staffed Beds: 88 Admissions: 3378 Census: 34 Outpatient Visits: 72106 Births: 315 Total Expense ($000): 61963 Payroll Expense ($000): 26504 Personnel: 268

NJ

Hospital, Medicare Provider Number, Address, Telephone, Approval, Facility, and Physician Codes, Health Care System

★ American Hospital Association (AHA) membership ○ Healthcare Facilities Accreditation Program ⇑ Center for Improvement in Healthcare Quality Accreditation
☐ The Joint Commission accreditation ◇ DNV Healthcare Inc. accreditation △ Commission on Accreditation of Rehabilitation Facilities (CARF) accreditation

ENGLEWOOD—Bergen County

☒ **ENGLEWOOD HOSPITAL AND MEDICAL CENTER (310045)**, 350 Engle Street, Zip 07631–1898; tel. 201/894–3000 **A**1 2 3 5 10 **F**3 7 8 9 11 12 13 15 17 18 19 20 22 24 26 28 29 30 31 32 34 35 36 37 38 40 41 44 45 46 47 48 49 50 51 52 53 54 55 56 57 58 59 60 61 64 65 68 70 72 73 74 75 76 77 78 79 80 81 82 83 84 85 86 87 89 91 92 93 94 96 97 98 100 101 102 103 104 107 108 110 111 114 115 116 117 118 119 120 121 123 124 126 129 130 131 132 133 134 135 143 144 145 146 147 148 149 150 **P**3 5 6
Primary Contact: Warren Geller, President and Chief Executive Officer
CFO: Anthony T Orlando, Senior Vice President Finance
CMO: Michael Harris M.D., Chief Medical Officer
CIO: Dimitri Cruz, Vice President Information Technology
CHR: Patricia Wilson, Senior Vice President Human Resources
CNO: MaryAnn Donohue-Ryan, Vice President Patient Care Services
Web address: www.englewoodhealth.org
Control: Other not-for-profit (including NFP Corporation) **Service:** General medical and surgical

Staffed Beds: 271 **Admissions:** 15289 **Census:** 201 **Outpatient Visits:** 1048146 **Births:** 2567 **Total Expense ($000):** 545667 **Payroll Expense ($000):** 149427 **Personnel:** 2506

FLEMINGTON—Hunterdon County

☒ **HUNTERDON MEDICAL CENTER (310005)**, 2100 Wescott Drive, Zip 08822–4604; tel. 908/788–6100, (Nonreporting) **A**1 2 3 5 10 13
Primary Contact: Robert P. Wise, President and Chief Executive Officer
COO: Lawrence N Grand MS, R.N., Chief Operating Officer
CFO: Gail Kosyla, Chief Financial Officer and Senior Vice President Strategy
CMO: Robert Coates M.D., Vice President, Medical Affairs
CIO: Daniel Morreale, Chief Information Officer
CHR: Violet Kocsis, Chief Human Resources Officer
CNO: Patricia Steingall MS, R.N., Vice President, Patient Care Services
Web address: www.hunterdonhealthcare.org
Control: Other not-for-profit (including NFP Corporation) **Service:** General medical and surgical

Staffed Beds: 186

FREEHOLD—Monmouth County

☒ **CENTRASTATE HEALTHCARE SYSTEM (310111)**, 901 West Main Street, Zip 07728–2549; tel. 732/431–2000 **A**1 2 3 5 10 **F**3 11 12 13 15 18 19 20 28 29 30 31 32 34 35 36 37 38 40 41 45 46 49 56 57 58 59 61 64 65 66 70 73 74 75 76 77 78 79 81 82 84 86 87 89 92 93 97 98 100 101 102 107 108 110 114 118 119 120 121 123 124 126 129 130 131 132 134 135 144 146 147 148 149 **P**1 6
Primary Contact: John Gribbin, FACHE, President and Chief Executive Officer
COO: Thomas W. Scott, Senior Vice President and Chief Operating Officer
CFO: John Dellocono, Senior Vice President and Chief Financial Officer
CMO: Jack H Dworkin M.D., Vice President Medical Affairs and Chief Medical Officer
CIO: John Ulett, Vice President and Chief Information Officer
CHR: Fran Keane, Vice President Human Resources
CNO: Linda W Geisler R.N., FACHE, Vice President Patient Services
Web address: www.centrastate.com
Control: Other not-for-profit (including NFP Corporation) **Service:** General medical and surgical

Staffed Beds: 283 **Admissions:** 13741 **Census:** 166 **Outpatient Visits:** 265351 **Births:** 1322 **Total Expense ($000):** 263786 **Payroll Expense ($000):** 114849 **Personnel:** 1541

HACKENSACK—Bergen County

☒ **HACKENSACK MERIDIAN HEALTH HACKENSACK UNIVERSITY MEDICAL CENTER (319800)**, 30 Prospect Avenue, Zip 07601–1914; tel. 201/996–2000, (Includes THE JOSEPH M. SANZARI CHILDREN'S HOSPITAL, 30 Prospect Avenue, Hackensack, New Jersey, Zip 07601–1914; tel. 201/996–2000) **A**1 2 3 5 8 10 **F**2 3 4 5 6 7 9 10 11 12 13 14 15 16 17 18 19 20 22 24 26 28 29 30 31 32 33 34 35 36 37 38 39 40 41 42 43 44 45 46 47 48 49 50 51 52 53 54 55 56 57 58 59 60 61 63 64 65 66 68 69 70 71 72 73 74 75 76 77 78 79 80 81 82 84 85 86 87 88 89 90 91 92 93 94 96 97 98 99 100 101 102 103 104 105 107 108 109 110 111 112 113 114 115 116 117 118 119 120 121 123 124 126 129 130 131 132 134 135 136 138 141 142 143 144 145 146 147 148 149 150 **P**1 6 7 **S** Hackensack Meridian Health, Edison, NJ
Primary Contact: Ihor S. Sawczuk, M.D., President
CFO: Robert Glenning, Executive Vice President Finance and Chief Financial Officer
CMO: Peter A Gross M.D., Senior Vice President and Chief Medical Officer
CHR: Nancy R Corcoran, Senior Vice President Human Resources and Quality Service
Web address: www.hackensackumc.org
Control: Other not-for-profit (including NFP Corporation) **Service:** General medical and surgical

Staffed Beds: 737 **Admissions:** 74819 **Census:** 579 **Outpatient Visits:** 510623 **Births:** 6498 **Total Expense ($000):** 1603878 **Payroll Expense ($000):** 698978 **Personnel:** 7766

HACKETTSTOWN—Warren County

☒ **HACKETTSTOWN MEDICAL CENTER (310115)**, 651 Willow Grove Street, Zip 07840–1799; tel. 908/852–5100, (Data for 275 days)**A**1 10 **F**3 5 7 11 12 15 18 28 29 30 31 34 35 36 39 40 41 44 45 46 49 50 51 53 56 57 59 60 61 62 64 65 68 70 74 75 77 78 79 81 82 84 85 86 87 91 93 97 102 107 108 110 114 116 117 119 129 130 131 132 135 143 146 147 148 149 150 **P**5 6 **S** Atlantic Health System, Morristown, NJ
Primary Contact: Joseph DiPaolo, FACHE, President, Sussex and Warren Region
COO: Stella Visaggio, Chief Operating Officer
CFO: Robert Peterson, Chief Financial Officer
CMO: Kenneth Janowski M.D., Chief Medical Officer
CIO: Dorothy Cox, Manager Information Systems
CHR: Jeanne Jepson, Director Human Resources
CNO: Linda Ambacher, Interim Chief Nursing Officer
Web address: www.hrmcnj.org
Control: Other not-for-profit (including NFP Corporation) **Service:** General medical and surgical

Staffed Beds: 80 **Admissions:** 3151 **Census:** 48 **Outpatient Visits:** 55418 **Births:** 107 **Total Expense ($000):** 57006 **Payroll Expense ($000):** 25790 **Personnel:** 698

HAMILTON—Mercer County

☒ **ROBERT WOOD JOHNSON UNIVERSITY HOSPITAL AT HAMILTON (310110)**, One Hamilton Health Place, Zip 08690–3599; tel. 609/586–7900, (Nonreporting) **A**1 2 5 10 **S** RWJBarnabas Health, West Orange, NJ
Primary Contact: Richard Freeman, President and Chief Executive Officer
COO: Barbara H Smith, Senior Vice President & Chief Operating Officer
CFO: James M Maher, Senior Vice President and Chief Financial Officer
CMO: Ronald Ryder D.O., President of the Medical Staff
CNO: Lisa Breza R.N., Vice President and Chief Nursing Officer
Web address: www.rwjhamilton.org
Control: Other not-for-profit (including NFP Corporation) **Service:** General medical and surgical

Staffed Beds: 213

HAMMONTON—Camden County

☐ **ANCORA PSYCHIATRIC HOSPITAL (314005)**, 301 Spring Garden Road, Zip 08037–9699; tel. 609/561–1700 **A**1 10 **F**30 39 56 68 75 87 97 98 130 135 143 149 **P**6 **S** Division of Mental Health and Addiction Services, Department of Human Services, State of New Jersey, Trenton, NJ
Primary Contact: Christopher Morrison, Chief Executive Officer
CFO: John Holmes, Business Manager
CMO: David Roat D.O., Medical Director
CIO: Charlene Ruberti, Director Information Technology Development
CHR: Alfred Filipini, Manager Human Resources
CNO: Catherine Jones, Chief Nursing Officer
Web address: www.state.nj.us/humanservices/dmhs/oshm/aph/
Control: State, Government, Nonfederal **Service:** Psychiatric

Staffed Beds: 449 **Admissions:** 643 **Census:** 372 **Outpatient Visits:** 0 **Births:** 0

HOBOKEN—Hudson County

☒ **CAREPOINT HEALTH HOBOKEN UNIVERSITY MEDICAL CENTER (310040)**, 308 Willow Avenue, Zip 07030–3889; tel. 201/418–1000, (Nonreporting) **A**1 3 5 10 **S** CarePoint Health, Jersey City, NJ
Primary Contact: Ann P. Logan, R.N., Ph.D., Chief Operating Officer
COO: Ann P. Logan R.N., Ph.D., Chief Operating Officer
CFO: Vincent Riccitelli, Vice President Finance
CMO: Meika Roberson M.D., Chief Medical Officer
CIO: Joel Taylor, Chief Information Officer
CHR: Roberto Gonzalez, Executive Director Human Resources
CNO: Neena S. Philip R.N., Assistant Vice President Nursing
Web address: www.hobokenumc.com
Control: Corporation, Investor-owned (for-profit) **Service:** General medical and surgical

Staffed Beds: 333

HOLMDEL—Monmouth County

✠ **HACKENSACK MERIDIAN HEALTH BAYSHORE COMMUNITY HOSPITAL (310112)**, 727 North Beers Street, Zip 07733–1598; tel. 732/739–5900 **A**1 2 10 **F**3 11 12 15 18 20 22 28 29 30 31 32 34 35 36 38 39 40 41 43 44 45 46 49 50 51 54 55 56 57 58 59 60 61 63 64 65 66 68 69 70 71 74 75 77 78 79 80 81 82 84 85 86 87 92 93 94 96 97 100 101 102 103 107 108 110 111 114 116 117 118 119 129 130 131 132 134 135 141 144 146 147 148 149 150 **S** Hackensack Meridian Health, Edison, NJ
Primary Contact: Timothy J. Hogan, FACHE, Regional President
CFO: Joseph M Lemaire, Executive Vice President Finance and Partner Company Operations
CMO: Ian Leber M.D., Chief Medical Officer
CIO: Rebecca Weber, Senior Vice President and Chief Information Officer
CHR: Sherrie String, Senior Vice President Human Resources
CNO: Linda Walsh R.N., MSN, Vice President Chief Nursing Executive
Web address: www.bchs.com
Control: Other not-for-profit (including NFP Corporation) **Service**: General medical and surgical

Staffed Beds: 160 **Admissions**: 7240 **Census**: 105 **Outpatient Visits**: 83510 **Births**: 0 **Total Expense ($000)**: 136938 **Payroll Expense ($000)**: 60410 **Personnel**: 922

JERSEY CITY—Hudson County

✠ **CAREPOINT HEALTH CHRIST HOSPITAL (310016)**, 176 Palisade Avenue, Zip 07306–1196, Mailing Address: 176 Palisades Avenue, 07306–1196; tel. 201/795–8200, (Nonreporting) **A**1 10 12 13 **S** CarePoint Health, Jersey City, NJ
Primary Contact: Marie Theresa Duffy, Chief Operating Officer
COO: Marie Theresa Duffy, Chief Operating Officer
CFO: Gary Bryant, Executive Vice President and Chief Financial Officer
CMO: William Holubek M.D., Chief Medical Officer
CHR: Josiane Deroncerey, Director Human Resources
CNO: Denise Cimmino MSN, R.N., Assistant Vice President, Nursing and Patient Care Services
Web address: www.carepointhealth.org
Control: Other not-for-profit (including NFP Corporation) **Service**: General medical and surgical

Staffed Beds: 376

★ ⇑ **JERSEY CITY MEDICAL CENTER (310074)**, 355 Grand Street, Zip 07302–4321; tel. 201/915–2000 **A**3 5 10 13 21 **F**3 5 7 11 12 13 15 17 18 20 22 24 26 29 30 31 34 35 38 39 40 41 43 45 46 47 48 49 50 54 55 56 57 59 60 61 64 65 66 68 70 71 72 73 74 75 76 77 78 79 81 82 84 85 87 89 91 92 93 96 97 98 99 100 101 102 104 105 106 107 108 110 111 112 114 115 119 130 132 135 143 144 146 147 148 149 **S** RWJBarnabas Health, West Orange, NJ
Primary Contact: Joseph F. Scott, FACHE, President and Chief Executive Officer
COO: Michael Prilutsky, Chief Operating Officer
CFO: Paul R Goldberg, Chief Financial Officer
CMO: Kenneth Garay M.D., Chief Medical Officer
CIO: Stephen Li, Vice President Management Information Systems
CHR: Mary Cataudella, Corporate Director Human Resources
Web address: www.barnabashealth.org/Jersey-City-Medical-Center.aspx
Control: Other not-for-profit (including NFP Corporation) **Service**: General medical and surgical

Staffed Beds: 316 **Admissions**: 14862 **Census**: 218 **Outpatient Visits**: 266932 **Births**: 2177 **Total Expense ($000)**: 384165 **Payroll Expense ($000)**: 194661 **Personnel**: 2126

LAKEWOOD—Ocean County

✠ **MONMOUTH MEDICAL CENTER, SOUTHERN CAMPUS (310084)**, 600 River Avenue, Zip 08701–5237; tel. 732/363–1900 **A**1 2 10 **F**3 11 15 18 28 29 30 31 34 35 36 38 40 41 43 44 50 56 57 58 59 60 61 64 68 70 74 75 77 78 79 81 82 86 87 93 96 98 100 101 102 103 107 108 110 111 114 117 119 130 131 132 133 134 146 148 149 **P**6 **S** RWJBarnabas Health, West Orange, NJ
Primary Contact: Frank J. Vozos, M.D., FACS, President and Chief Executive Officer, Barnabas Health Behavioral Health Center
CFO: Joanna Zimmerman, Regional Chief Financial Officer
CMO: Rajesh Mohan M.D., Chief Medical Officer
CIO: Ray Duarte, Director, Information Technology and Services
CHR: Richard Kiernan, Regional Chief Human Resources Officer
CNO: Judy Colorado R.N., Chief Nursing Officer
Web address: www.rwjbarnabashealth.org/monmouth-medical-center-southern-campus.aspx
Control: Other not-for-profit (including NFP Corporation) **Service**: General medical and surgical

Staffed Beds: 124 **Admissions**: 5617 **Census**: 95 **Outpatient Visits**: 80167 **Births**: 0 **Total Expense ($000)**: 106039 **Payroll Expense ($000)**: 44805 **Personnel**: 639

☐ **SPECIALTY HOSPITAL OF CENTRAL JERSEY (312017)**, 600 River Avenue, 4 and 5 West, Zip 08701–5237; tel. 732/942–3588 (Nonreporting) **A**1 10
Primary Contact: Violeta Peters, R.N., Chief Executive Officer
CFO: Kristin Prentiss, Chief Financial Officer
CMO: Howard Lebowitz M.D., Chief Medical Officer
CHR: Mary Pat Napolitano, Director Human Resources
CNO: Judy Boccellato R.N., MSN, Chief Nursing Officer
Web address: www.acutecarehs.com
Control: Corporation, Investor-owned (for-profit) **Service**: Acute long-term care hospital

Staffed Beds: 50

LAWRENCEVILLE—Mercer County

✠ **ST. LAWRENCE REHABILITATION CENTER (313027)**, 2381 Lawrenceville Road, Zip 08648–2025; tel. 609/896–9500, (Total facility includes 56 beds in nursing home–type unit) **A**1 10 **F**34 57 64 90 91 93 96 104 108 119 128 130 132 135 143 146 148 149
Primary Contact: Darlene S. Hanley, R.N., FACHE, President and Chief Executive Officer
COO: Shirley Pukala R.N., Assistant Administrator Operations
CFO: Thomas W Boyle, Chief Financial Officer
CMO: Kevin McGuigan M.D., Medical Director
CIO: Joseph Castronuevo, Director Information Management
CHR: John Levi, Director Human Resources
CNO: Hsiu-chin Brix R.N., Director of Nursing
Web address: www.slrc.org
Control: Church operated, Nongovernment, not-for-profit **Service**: Rehabilitation

Staffed Beds: 116 **Admissions**: 2262 **Census**: 94 **Outpatient Visits**: 21450 **Births**: 0 **Total Expense ($000)**: 36107 **Payroll Expense ($000)**: 20250 **Personnel**: 322

LIVINGSTON—Essex County

✠ **SAINT BARNABAS MEDICAL CENTER (319804)**, 94 Old Short Hills Rd, Zip 07039–5672; tel. 973/322–5000 **A**1 2 3 5 8 10 13 **F**3 8 11 12 13 16 17 18 19 20 22 24 26 28 29 30 31 32 34 35 36 37 38 39 40 41 44 46 47 48 49 50 53 54 55 56 57 58 59 60 61 63 64 65 66 68 69 70 71 72 73 74 75 76 77 78 79 81 82 84 85 86 87 88 89 91 92 93 94 96 97 100 102 103 107 108 111 114 115 118 119 120 121 123 124 126 129 130 131 132 134 135 138 141 142 143 144 146 147 148 149 **P**7 **S** RWJBarnabas Health, West Orange, NJ
Primary Contact: Stephen P. Zieniewicz, FACHE, President and Chief Executive Officer
COO: Patrick Ahearn, Chief Operating Officer and Senior Vice President
CFO: Richard Davis, Chief Financial Officer
CMO: Gregory Rokosz D.O., Senior Vice President Medical and Academic Affairs
CIO: Michael McTigue, Chief Information Officer
CHR: Arnold D Manzo, Vice President Human Resources
CNO: Jennifer A O'Neill R.N., Chief Nursing Officer, Vice President Patient Care Services
Web address: www.barnabashealth.org/hospitals/saint_barnabas/index.html
Control: Other not-for-profit (including NFP Corporation) **Service**: General medical and surgical

Staffed Beds: 545 **Admissions**: 32978 **Census**: 408 **Outpatient Visits**: 289681 **Births**: 5838 **Total Expense ($000)**: 702403 **Payroll Expense ($000)**: 248717 **Personnel**: 3246

LONG BRANCH—Monmouth County

✠ **MONMOUTH MEDICAL CENTER, LONG BRANCH CAMPUS (310075)**, 300 Second Avenue, Zip 07740–6303; tel. 732/222–5200, (Includes CHILDREN'S HOSPITAL AT MONMOUTH MEDICAL CENTER, 300 Second Avenue, Long Branch, New Jersey, Zip 07740–6303, tel. 732/222–5200) **A**1 2 3 5 8 10 **F**3 5 8 9 11 12 13 14 15 17 18 19 20 22 28 29 30 31 32 34 35 38 39 40 41 44 45 46 47 48 49 50 51 52 53 54 55 56 57 58 59 60 61 64 65 66 68 69 70 72 73 74 75 76 77 78 79 81 82 83 84 85 86 87 88 89 97 98 99 100 101 102 103 104 105 106 107 108 109 110 111 114 115 116 118 119 120 121 123 124 126 129 130 131 132 133 134 135 143 144 145 146 147 148 149 **S** RWJBarnabas Health, West Orange, NJ
Primary Contact: Bill Arnold, President and Chief Executive Officer
CMO: Eric Burkett M.D., Vice President Medical Affairs
CIO: Chris Butler, Chief Information Officer
CHR: Richard Kiernan, Vice President Human Resources
CNO: Diann Johnston R.N., MSN, Vice President of Patient Care Services
Web address: www.barnabashealth.org/hospitals/monmouth_medical/index.html
Control: Other not-for-profit (including NFP Corporation) **Service**: General medical and surgical

Staffed Beds: 305 **Admissions**: 16950 **Census**: 201 **Outpatient Visits**: 259294 **Births**: 5412 **Total Expense ($000)**: 366666 **Payroll Expense ($000)**: 137895 **Personnel**: 1794

NJ

Hospital, Medicare Provider Number, Address, Telephone, Approval, Facility, and Physician Codes, Health Care System

★ American Hospital Association (AHA) membership
☐ The Joint Commission accreditation
○ Healthcare Facilities Accreditation Program
◇ DNV Healthcare Inc. accreditation
⇑ Center for Improvement in Healthcare Quality Accreditation
△ Commission on Accreditation of Rehabilitation Facilities (CARF) accreditation

LYONS—Somerset County

LYONS DIVISION See Veterans Affairs New Jersey Health Care System, East Orange

MANAHAWKIN—Ocean County

✠ **HACKENSACK MERIDIAN HEALTH SOUTHERN OCEAN MEDICAL CENTER (310113)**, 1140 Route 72 West, Zip 08050–2499; tel. 609/597–6011, (Total facility includes 20 beds in nursing home–type unit) **A**1 2 10 **F**3 11 12 13 15 18 20 28 29 30 31 32 34 35 36 38 39 40 41 43 44 45 46 48 49 50 51 54 55 56 57 58 59 60 61 63 64 65 66 68 70 71 74 75 76 77 78 79 80 81 82 84 85 86 87 92 93 94 96 97 100 101 102 103 107 108 110 111 114 115 116 117 118 119 120 121 123 128 129 130 131 132 134 135 141 144 145 146 147 148 149 **S** Hackensack Meridian Health, Edison, NJ
Primary Contact: Robert H. Adams Jr, President
COO: Kim Frazee R.N., Vice President Physician and Business Development
CFO: Joseph M Lemaire, Executive Vice President
CMO: Theodore Zaleski M.D., Vice President Clinical Effectiveness
CIO: Rebecca Weber, Senior Vice President and Chief Information Officer
CHR: Susan Tillman-Taylor, Manager Human Resources
CNO: Donna Ciufo R.N., Vice President and Chief Nurse Executive
Web address: www.soch.com
Control: Other not-for-profit (including NFP Corporation) **Service**: General medical and surgical

Staffed Beds: 172 **Admissions**: 7680 **Census**: 93 **Outpatient Visits**: 111745 **Births**: 388 **Total Expense ($000)**: 153529 **Payroll Expense ($000)**: 63215 **Personnel**: 883

MARLTON—Burlington County

✠ △ **KESSLER MARLTON REHABILITATION (313032)**, 92 Brick Road, Zip 08053–2177; tel. 856/988–8778 **A**1 7 10 **F**3 29 50 90 130 132 **P**8 **S** Select Medical Corporation, Mechanicsburg, PA
Primary Contact: Phyllis J. Schlichtmann, Chief Executive Officer
CFO: Stuart Moss, Chief Financial Officer
CMO: Kenneth Wu M.D., Medical Director
CHR: Joanne Cernava, Director Human Resources
CNO: Chris Kreeley, Director Nursing
Web address: www.marltonrehab.com
Control: Corporation, Investor-owned (for-profit) **Service**: Rehabilitation

Staffed Beds: 61 **Admissions**: 1610 **Census**: 52 **Outpatient Visits**: 16025 **Births**: 0

✠ **VIRTUA MARLTON**, 90 Brick Road, Zip 08053–2177; tel. 856/355–6000 **A**1 2 5 **F**3 12 18 20 22 29 30 31 40 45 46 47 49 56 60 64 70 75 77 78 79 81 82 85 87 91 92 107 108 111 114 115 118 119 130 141 146 149 **S** Virtua Health, Marlton, NJ
Primary Contact: Matthew Zuino, Senior Vice President Hospital Services
CFO: Robert Segin, Executive Vice President & Chief Financial Officer
CMO: John Matsinger D.O., Chief Medical Officer
CIO: Thomas Gordon, Chief Information Officer
CHR: Rhonda R Jordan, Chief Human Resources Officer
CNO: Tracy Carlino R.N., Chief Nursing Officer
Web address: www.virtua.org
Control: Other not-for-profit (including NFP Corporation) **Service**: General medical and surgical

Staffed Beds: 189 **Admissions**: 8643 **Census**: 116 **Outpatient Visits**: 46601 **Births**: 0 **Total Expense ($000)**: 164373 **Payroll Expense ($000)**: 52979 **Personnel**: 646

☐ **WEISMAN CHILDREN'S REHABILITATION HOSPITAL (313302)**, 92 Brick Road 3rd Floor, Zip 08053–2177; tel. 856/489–4520 (Nonreporting) **A**1 10
Primary Contact: Michael Rosiak, Chief Operating Officer
COO: Michael Rosiak, Chief Operating Officer
CMO: Connie Domingo M.D., Medical Director
CIO: Darren Pedersen, Coordinator Information Technology
CHR: Jill Koerner, Manager Employee Relations
CNO: Daniel William Pfeffer, Chief Nurse Executive
Web address: www.weismanchildrens.com
Control: Corporation, Investor-owned (for-profit) **Service**: Children's rehabilitation

Staffed Beds: 24

MONTCLAIR—Essex County

✠ **HACKENSACK MERIDIAN HEALTH MOUNTAINSIDE MEDICAL CENTER (310054)**, 1 Bay Avenue, Zip 07042–4898; tel. 973/429–6000 **A**1 2 3 5 10 **F**3 12 13 14 15 17 18 20 22 28 29 30 31 32 34 35 38 39 40 43 44 45 46 48 49 50 51 53 54 55 56 57 58 59 60 64 66 67 68 70 73 74 75 76 77 78 79 80 81 82 84 85 86 87 91 92 93 94 96 97 98 100 101 102 103 104 105 107 108 109 110 111 114 115 116 117 119 120 121 123 124 126 128 129 130 131 132 134 135 141 145 146 147 148 149 **P**5 **S** Ardent Health Services, Nashville, TN
Primary Contact: John A. Fromhold, FACHE, Chief Executive Officer
CFO: Al Aboud CPA, Chief Financial Officer
CMO: Valerie Alluson M.D., Chief Medical Officer
CIO: Max Siu, Chief Information Officer
CHR: Fran Corridon, Vice President Human Resources and Shared Services
CNO: Debbie Regen R.N., Chief Nursing Officer
Web address: www.mountainsidenow.com
Control: Partnership, Investor-owned (for-profit) **Service**: General medical and surgical

Staffed Beds: 202 **Admissions**: 11760 **Census**: 136 **Outpatient Visits**: 102983 **Births**: 923 **Total Expense ($000)**: 205779 **Payroll Expense ($000)**: 84369 **Personnel**: 1286

MORRIS PLAINS—Morris County

☐ **GREYSTONE PARK PSYCHIATRIC HOSPITAL (314016)**, 59 Koch Avenue, Zip 07950–4400; tel. 973/538–1800, (Nonreporting) **A**1 3 5 10 **S** Division of Mental Health and Addiction Services, Department of Human Services, State of New Jersey, Trenton, NJ
Primary Contact: Mary Jo Kurtiak, Chief Executive Officer
COO: Stacey Provenzano, Chief Operating Officer
CFO: Jack Frey, Acting Business Manager
CMO: Cherry Monroy-Miller M.D., Acting Medical Director
CIO: David Saleem, Director Information Technology
CHR: James Frey Jr, Acting Manager Human Resources
CNO: Doreen Sperber-Weiss Ph.D., Chief Nursing Officer
Web address: www.state.nj.us/humanservices/dmhs/oshm/gpph/
Control: State, Government, Nonfederal **Service**: Psychiatric

Staffed Beds: 506

MORRISTOWN—Morris County

✠ **MORRISTOWN MEDICAL CENTER (310015)**, 100 Madison Avenue, Zip 07960–6136; tel. 973/971–5000, (Includes GORYEB CHILDREN'S HOSPITAL, 100 Madison Avenue, Morristown, New Jersey, Zip 07960–6136, tel. 973/971–5000) (Total facility includes 40 beds in nursing home–type unit) **A**1 2 3 5 8 10 13 **F**3 5 6 7 8 9 11 12 13 14 15 17 18 19 20 22 24 26 28 29 30 31 32 33 34 35 36 37 38 39 40 41 43 44 45 46 47 48 49 50 51 52 53 54 55 56 57 58 59 60 61 62 63 64 65 66 68 69 70 71 72 73 74 75 76 77 78 79 81 82 83 84 85 86 87 88 89 90 91 92 93 94 95 96 97 98 100 101 102 103 104 105 107 108 109 110 111 114 115 116 117 118 119 120 121 123 126 128 129 130 131 132 134 135 141 143 144 145 146 147 148 149 150 **P**2 3 5 6 **S** Atlantic Health System, Morristown, NJ
Primary Contact: Trish O'Keefe, Ph.D., R.N., President
CFO: Joseph D'Auria, Director Finance
CMO: Louis Brusco M.D., Chief Medical Officer
CNO: Carol S. Jones MSN, R.N., Interim Chief Nursing Officer
Web address: www.atlantichealth.org/Morristown/
Control: Other not-for-profit (including NFP Corporation) **Service**: General medical and surgical

Staffed Beds: 698 **Admissions**: 38022 **Census**: 574 **Outpatient Visits**: 526946 **Births**: 4441 **Total Expense ($000)**: 1231490 **Payroll Expense ($000)**: 499065 **Personnel**: 6577

MOUNT HOLLY—Burlington County

✠ **VIRTUA MEMORIAL (310057)**, 175 Madison Avenue, Zip 08060–2099; tel. 609/267–0700 **A**1 3 5 10 **F**3 11 12 13 15 18 20 22 28 29 30 31 40 41 45 46 48 49 56 60 70 73 74 75 76 77 78 79 81 82 85 86 87 89 91 92 93 98 102 107 108 110 111 114 115 118 119 120 121 123 126 129 130 143 146 147 149 **S** Virtua Health, Marlton, NJ
Primary Contact: Matthew Zuino, Senior Vice President Hospital Services
CFO: Robert Segin, Chief Financial Officer
CMO: James P Dwyer D.O., Executive Vice President and Chief Medical Officer
CHR: E D Dunn, Vice President Human Resources
Web address: www.virtua.org
Control: Other not-for-profit (including NFP Corporation) **Service**: General medical and surgical

Staffed Beds: 334 **Admissions**: 17552 **Census**: 224 **Outpatient Visits**: 176543 **Births**: 2194 **Total Expense ($000)**: 300220 **Payroll Expense ($000)**: 96806 **Personnel**: 1272

VIRTUA MEMORIAL HOSPITAL BURLINGTON COUNTY See Virtua Memorial

Many Facility Codes have changed. Please refer to the AHA Guide Code Chart. © 2017 AHA Guide

NJ

NEPTUNE—Monmouth County

⊞ **HACKENSACK MERIDIAN HEALTH JERSEY SHORE UNIVERSITY MEDICAL CENTER (310073)**, 1945 Route 33, Zip 07754–0397; tel. 732/775–5500, (Includes K. HOVNANIAN CHILDREN'S HOSPITAL, 1945 State Route 33, Neptune, New Jersey, Zip 07753–4859, tel. 800/560–9990) **A**1 2 3 5 8 10 13 **F**3 4 5 9 11 12 13 15 16 17 18 19 20 22 24 26 28 29 30 31 32 34 35 36 38 39 40 41 43 44 45 46 47 48 49 50 52 54 55 57 58 59 60 61 63 64 65 66 68 70 71 72 73 74 75 76 77 78 79 80 81 82 84 85 86 87 88 89 90 92 93 94 96 97 98 99 100 101 102 103 104 105 107 108 111 114 115 116 117 118 119 120 121 123 126 129 130 131 132 134 135 141 144 145 146 147 148 149 150 **S** Hackensack Meridian Health, Edison, NJ
Primary Contact: Kenneth N. Sable, M.D., President
COO: Robert H Adams, Vice President Operations
CMO: David Kountz M.D., Senior Vice President Medical Affairs
CIO: Rebecca Weber, Senior Vice President and Chief Information Officer
Web address: www.meridianhealth.com
Control: Other not-for-profit (including NFP Corporation) **Service:** General medical and surgical

Staffed Beds: 553 **Admissions:** 24347 **Census:** 372 **Outpatient Visits:** 210858 **Births:** 2167 **Total Expense ($000):** 624012 **Payroll Expense ($000):** 251731 **Personnel:** 3353

NEW BRUNSWICK—Middlesex County

☐ **CHILDREN'S SPECIALIZED HOSPITAL (313300)**, 200 Somerset Street, Zip 08901–1942; tel. 732/258–7000, (Includes CHILDREN'S SPECIALIZED HOSPITAL, 200 Somerset Street, New Brunswick, New Jersey, Zip 08901–1942, tel. 732/258–7134; Warren E. Moore, President and Chief Executive Officer) (Total facility includes 72 beds in nursing home–type unit) **A**1 3 5 10 **F**29 32 35 54 64 65 74 75 77 79 90 91 93 94 97 99 104 130 146 **S** RWJBarnabas Health, West Orange, NJ
Primary Contact: Warren E. Moore, President and Chief Executive Officer
COO: Charles Chianese, Vice President, Chief Operating Officer
CFO: Joseph J Dobosh Jr, Vice President and Chief Financial Officer
CMO: Christopher Haines D.O., Vice President and Chief Medical Officer
CHR: William Dwyer, Vice President and Chief Human Resources Officer
CNO: Bonnie Baloga-Altieri Ph.D., R.N., Vice President Patient Care Services and Chief Nursing Officer
Web address: www.childrens-specialized.org
Control: Other not-for-profit (including NFP Corporation) **Service:** Children's rehabilitation

Staffed Beds: 140 **Admissions:** 589 **Census:** 123 **Outpatient Visits:** 190780 **Births:** 0 **Total Expense ($000):** 137217 **Payroll Expense ($000):** 81618 **Personnel:** 1029

⊞ **ROBERT WOOD JOHNSON UNIVERSITY HOSPITAL (319801)**, 1 Robert Wood Johnson Place, Zip 08901–1928; tel. 732/828–3000, (Includes BRISTOL-MYERS SQUIBB CHILDREN'S HOSPITAL, One Robert Wood Johnson Place, New Brunswick, New Jersey, Zip 8901, P.O. Box 2601, 08903–2601, tel. 732/828–3000) **A**1 2 3 5 8 10 **F**3 6 7 8 9 11 12 13 14 15 17 18 19 20 22 24 26 28 29 30 31 32 34 35 36 37 38 39 40 41 43 44 45 46 47 48 49 50 51 52 53 54 55 56 57 58 59 60 61 62 63 64 65 66 68 70 71 72 73 74 75 76 77 78 79 81 82 83 84 85 86 87 88 89 91 92 93 94 96 97 99 100 102 104 107 108 109 110 111 112 113 114 115 116 117 118 119 120 121 122 123 124 126 129 130 131 132 134 135 136 137 138 141 142 143 145 146 147 148 149 150 **P**3 5 6 **S** RWJBarnabas Health, West Orange, NJ
Primary Contact: John Gantner, President and Chief Executive Officer
COO: Jessie Lee Tucker Ph.D., III, Senior Vice President and Chief Operating Officer
CFO: Brian M Reilly, Chief Financial Officer
CMO: Joshua M Bershad M.D., Senior Vice President Medical Affairs and Chief Medical Officer
CIO: Robert G Irwin, Vice President Information Systems
CHR: Martin S Everhart, Senior Vice President Human Resources
CNO: Lori Colineri MSN, R.N., Senior Vice President Nursing and Chief Nursing Officer
Web address: www.rwjuh.edu
Control: Other not-for-profit (including NFP Corporation) **Service:** General medical and surgical

Staffed Beds: 610 **Admissions:** 30653 **Census:** 517 **Outpatient Visits:** 257916 **Births:** 2535 **Total Expense ($000):** 1049128 **Payroll Expense ($000):** 371872 **Personnel:** 4902

⊞ **SAINT PETER'S UNIVERSITY HOSPITAL (310070)**, 254 Easton Avenue, Zip 08901–1780; tel. 732/745–8600, (Includes THE CHILDREN'S HOSPITAL AT SAINT PETER'S UNIVERSITY, 254 Easton Avenue, New Brunswick, New Jersey, Zip 08901–1766, tel. 732/565–5437) **A**1 2 3 5 8 10 **F**2 3 12 13 15 18 19 20 22 26 27 29 30 31 32 34 35 37 38 39 40 41 44 45 46 49 50 51 54 55 56 57 58 59 60 61 63 64 65 66 68 70 71 72 73 74 75 76 77 78 79 81 82 83 84 85 86 87 88 89 91 92 93 94 96 97 99 100 101 102 103 104 105 107 108 110 111 113 114 115 118 119 120 121 123 124 126 129 130 131 132 134 135 143 145 146 147 148 149 150 **P**6
Primary Contact: Leslie D. Hirsch, FACHE, Interim Chief Executive Officer and President
CFO: Garrick J Stoldt, Vice President and Chief Financial Officer
CIO: Frank DiSanzo, Vice President and Chief Information Officer and Chief Strategy Officer
CHR: Susan Ballestero, Vice President and Chief Human Resources Officer
CNO: Elizabeth Wise R.N., MS, Chief Nursing Officer and Vice President, Patient Care Services
Web address: www.saintpetersuh.com
Control: Church operated, Nongovernment, not-for-profit **Service:** General medical and surgical

Staffed Beds: 350 **Admissions:** 19466 **Census:** 239 **Outpatient Visits:** 248949 **Births:** 5688 **Total Expense ($000):** 453995 **Payroll Expense ($000):** 208604 **Personnel:** 2443

NEWARK—Essex County

⇑ **COLUMBUS HOSPITAL LTACH (312024)**, 495 North Thirteenth Street, Zip 07107–1317; tel. 973/587–7777 (Nonreporting) **A**10 21
Primary Contact: Richard Lipsky, Chairman and Chief Executive Officer
COO: Peter Callaghan, President and Chief Operating Officer
CFO: Alexey Gololobov, Chief Financial Officer
CHR: Patrice Ricciardi, Director Human Resources
CNO: Arthur Kharonov, Vice President Nursing
Web address: www.columbusltach.org
Control: Corporation, Investor-owned (for-profit) **Service:** Acute long-term care hospital

Staffed Beds: 66

⊞ **NEWARK BETH ISRAEL MEDICAL CENTER (319803)**, 201 Lyons Avenue at Osborne Terrace, Zip 07112–2027; tel. 973/926–7000, (Includes CHILDREN'S HOSPITAL OF NEW JERSEY, 201 Lyons Avenue, Newark, New Jersey, Zip 07112–2027, tel. 973/926–7000; Darrell K. Terry Sr, M.P.H., FACHE, President and Chief Executive Officer) **A**1 2 3 5 8 10 12 13 **F**3 15 17 18 19 20 21 22 23 24 25 26 27 28 29 30 31 32 34 35 38 39 40 41 44 45 46 47 48 49 50 51 53 55 56 57 58 59 60 61 64 65 66 68 70 71 72 73 74 75 76 77 78 79 81 82 84 85 86 87 88 89 92 93 94 97 98 99 100 101 102 103 104 105 107 108 109 110 111 114 115 117 118 119 120 121 123 126 129 130 131 132 137 140 141 143 145 146 147 148 149 **P**8 **S** RWJBarnabas Health, West Orange, NJ
Primary Contact: Darrell K. Terry Sr, M.P.H., FACHE, President and Chief Executive Officer
CFO: Douglas A Zehner, Chief Financial Officer
CMO: Jeremias Murillo M.D., Chief Medical Officer
CHR: Zach Lipner, Vice President Human Resources
CNO: Mary Fuhro, Chief Nursing Officer
Web address: www.barnabashealth.org/hospitals/newark_beth_israel/index.html
Control: Other not-for-profit (including NFP Corporation) **Service:** General medical and surgical

Staffed Beds: 360 **Admissions:** 19019 **Census:** 351 **Outpatient Visits:** 297730 **Births:** 3010 **Total Expense ($000):** 570436 **Payroll Expense ($000):** 252525 **Personnel:** 3115

⊞ **SAINT MICHAEL'S MEDICAL CENTER (310096)**, 111 Central Avenue, Zip 07102–1909; tel. 973/877–5350 **A**1 3 5 10 13 **F**3 5 15 17 18 20 22 24 26 29 30 31 34 35 37 40 45 47 49 50 57 58 59 61 64 66 68 70 71 74 75 77 78 79 81 85 87 97 98 100 107 108 109 110 111 114 115 119 121 122 123 126 130 132 143 147 148 149 **S** Prime Healthcare, Ontario, CA
Primary Contact: Robert C. Iannaccone, Chief Executive Officer
COO: Dennis Pettigrew, Chief Operating Officer
CFO: Dennis Pettigrew, Chief Financial Officer
CMO: Joseph DePasquale M.D., Interim Chief Medical Officer
CIO: Tom Addington, Chief Information Officer
CHR: Dennis W. Sparks, Vice President Human Resources
CNO: Johanna Magner, Interim Chief Nursing Officer
Web address: www.smmcnj.org
Control: Corporation, Investor-owned (for-profit) **Service:** General medical and surgical

Staffed Beds: 162 **Admissions:** 7673 **Census:** 94 **Outpatient Visits:** 97135 **Births:** 0 **Total Expense ($000):** 200085 **Payroll Expense ($000):** 78255 **Personnel:** 1093

NJ

Hospital, Medicare Provider Number, Address, Telephone, Approval, Facility, and Physician Codes, Health Care System

★ American Hospital Association (AHA) membership
☐ The Joint Commission accreditation
○ Healthcare Facilities Accreditation Program
◇ DNV Healthcare Inc. accreditation
⇑ Center for Improvement in Healthcare Quality Accreditation
△ Commission on Accreditation of Rehabilitation Facilities (CARF) accreditation

✠ **UNIVERSITY HOSPITAL (310119)**, 150 Bergen Street, Zip 07103–2496;
tel. 973/972–4300 **A**1 2 3 5 10 **F**1 3 4 7 8 11 15 16 17 18 20 22 24 26 28 29
30 31 32 34 35 37 38 39 40 41 43 44 45 46 47 48 49 50 54 55 57 58 59 60
61 64 65 66 67 68 70 71 72 73 74 75 76 77 78 79 80 81 82 84 85 86 87 88
89 90 92 93 96 97 98 100 102 107 108 110 111 114 118 119 120 121 123
124 126 128 130 131 132 134 135 139 141 142 145 146 147 148 149 150
P5
Primary Contact: John N. Kastanis, FACHE, President and Chief Executive Officer
COO: Nancy Hamstra, Chief Operating Officer
CFO: Thomas M Daly CPA, Chief Financial Officer
CMO: Suzanne Atkin M.D., Chief Medical Officer
CIO: Richard Tunnell, Chief Information Officer
CHR: Gerard Garcia, Chief Human Resource Officer
CNO: Carl Kirton Ph.D., Chief Nursing Officer
Web address: www.uhnj.org
Control: State, Government, Nonfederal **Service**: General medical and surgical

Staffed Beds: 519 **Admissions**: 15444 **Census**: 269 **Outpatient Visits**:
262539 **Births**: 1234 **Total Expense ($000)**: 648615 **Payroll Expense
($000)**: 314461 **Personnel**: 3281

NEWTON—Sussex County

✠ **NEWTON MEDICAL CENTER (310028)**, 175 High Street, Zip 07860–1004;
tel. 973/383–2121 **A**1 2 10 **F**3 5 6 7 8 9 11 12 13 14 15 18 19 20 28 29 30
31 32 33 34 35 36 38 39 40 41 44 45 47 49 50 53 54 56 57 58 59 60 61 62 63
64 65 66 68 69 70 71 73 74 75 76 77 78 79 81 82 84 85 86 87 91 92 93 94
95 96 97 98 99 100 101 102 103 104 105 106 107 108 109 110 111 114
118 119 129 130 131 132 134 135 143 144 146 147 148 149 150 **P**3 5 6 **S**
Atlantic Health System, Morristown, NJ
Primary Contact: Joseph DiPaolo, FACHE, President, Sussex and Warren Region
CFO: Kevin Lenahan, Director Corporate Accounting, Budgets, Grants and
Reimbursements
CMO: David Lazarus M.D., Medical Director Clinical Affairs
CIO: Linda Reed, Vice President Information Systems and Chief Information Officer
CHR: Andrew L Kovach, Vice President Human Resources and Chief Administrative
Officer
Web address: www.atlantichealth.org/newton/
Control: Other not-for-profit (including NFP Corporation) **Service**: General medical
and surgical

Staffed Beds: 148 **Admissions**: 7709 **Census**: 96 **Outpatient Visits**:
103035 **Births**: 538 **Total Expense ($000)**: 154988 **Payroll Expense
($000)**: 74946 **Personnel**: 1144

NORTH BERGEN—Hudson County

✠ **HACKENSACK MERIDIAN HEALTH PALISADES MEDICAL CENTER (310003)**,
7600 River Road, Zip 07047–6217; tel. 201/854–5000 **A**1 3 5 10 12 13 **F**3 7
11 12 13 15 17 18 20 28 29 30 31 34 35 38 40 43 44 45 49 50 56 57 59 60
64 68 70 73 74 75 76 77 78 79 80 81 82 84 85 86 87 89 92 93 102 104 107
108 110 111 114 115 119 129 130 132 141 143 145 146 147 148 149 **S**
Hackensack Meridian Health, Edison, NJ
Primary Contact: Anthony Passannante Jr, M.D., Acting President
COO: David J Berkowitz, Vice President and Chief Operating Officer
CFO: John Calandriello, Vice President and Chief Financial Officer
CMO: Suresh Raina M.D., Vice President Medical Staff and Chief Medical Officer
CIO: Albert Porco, Director Management Information Systems
CHR: Donna Cahill, Vice President Human Resources
CNO: Ruben D Fernandez R.N., Vice President and Chief Nursing Officer
Web address: www.palisadesmedical.org
Control: Other not-for-profit (including NFP Corporation) **Service**: General medical
and surgical

Staffed Beds: 228 **Admissions**: 8931 **Census**: 108 **Outpatient Visits**:
111189 **Births**: 1381 **Total Expense ($000)**: 159916 **Payroll Expense
($000)**: 74656 **Personnel**: 1084

PARAMUS—Bergen County

☐ **BERGEN REGIONAL MEDICAL CENTER (310058)**, 230 East Ridgewood
Avenue, Zip 07652–4142; tel. 201/967–4000, (Nonreporting) **A**1 3 10
Primary Contact: Susan Mendelowitz, R.N., FACHE, President, Administrator and
Chief Operating Officer
COO: Susan Mendelowitz R.N., FACHE, Executive Vice President and Chief
Operating Officer
CFO: Connie Magdangal, Executive Vice President and Chief Financial Officer
CMO: Robert M Harris M.D., President Medical and Dental Staff
CIO: Ronald Li, Vice President Management Information Systems
CHR: Guy Mennonna, Senior Vice President Human Resources
Web address: www.bergenregional.com
Control: County, Government, Nonfederal **Service**: Psychiatric

Staffed Beds: 432

PASSAIC—Passaic County

✠ **ST. MARY'S GENERAL HOSPITAL (310006)**, 350 Boulevard, Zip 07055–2840;
tel. 973/365–4300, (Nonreporting) **A**1 10 **S** Prime Healthcare, Ontario, CA
Primary Contact: Edward Condit, President and Chief Executive Officer
CFO: Nicholas Lanza, Controller
CMO: Ronald Poblete M.D., President Medical and Dental Staff
CHR: Cathy Lynch-Kilic, Vice President Human Resources
Web address: www.smh-passaic.org
Control: Other not-for-profit (including NFP Corporation) **Service**: General medical
and surgical

Staffed Beds: 287

PATERSON—Passaic County

★ ⇑ **ST. JOSEPH'S HEALTHCARE SYSTEM (310019)**, 703 Main Street,
Zip 07503–2691; tel. 973/754–2000, (Includes ST. JOSEPH'S CHILDREN'S
HOSPITAL, 703 Main Street, Paterson, New Jersey, Zip 07503–2621,
tel. 973/754–2500; Kevin J Slavin, FACHE, President and Chief Executive Officer;
ST. JOSEPH'S WAYNE HOSPITAL, 224 Hamburg Turnpike, Wayne, New Jersey,
Zip 07470–2100, tel. 973/942–6900; Daniel B Kline, Vice President, Site
Administrator) (Total facility includes 151 beds in nursing home–type unit) **A**2 3 5
10 13 21 **F**3 8 11 12 13 15 17 18 19 20 21 22 23 24 25 26 27 28 29 30 31
32 34 35 36 37 38 39 40 41 43 44 45 46 47 48 49 50 54 55 56 57 58 59 60
61 62 63 64 65 66 68 70 72 73 74 75 76 77 78 79 81 82 83 84 85 86 87 88
89 90 92 93 94 96 97 98 100 101 102 103 104 105 106 107 108 111 114
115 116 117 118 119 126 128 129 130 131 132 134 135 146 147 148 149
150 **P**5
Primary Contact: Kevin J. Slavin, FACHE, President and Chief Executive Officer
COO: Lisa Brady, Senior Vice President and Chief Operating Officer
CFO: David Alexander, Senior Vice President and Chief Financial Officer
CMO: James Labagnara M.D., Vice President Medical Affairs
CIO: Linda Reed, Vice President and Chief Information Officer
CHR: John P Bruno, Vice President Human Resources
CNO: Judy Padula MSN, R.N., Vice President Patient Care Services and Chief
Nursing Officer
Web address: www.stjosephshealth.org
Control: Church operated, Nongovernment, not-for-profit **Service**: General
medical and surgical

Staffed Beds: 700 **Admissions**: 65964 **Census**: 513

PEAPACK—Somerset County

☐ **MATHENY MEDICAL AND EDUCATIONAL CENTER (312014)** (Mentally
complex developmental disabilities), 65 Highland Avenue, Zip 7977, Mailing
Address: P.O.Box 339, 07977–0339; tel. 908/234–0011 **A**1 5 10 **F**2 29 30 32
35 38 39 44 50 59 63 64 68 75 77 79 86 87 89 91 93 94 96 97 99 100 104
130 132 143 146 149 **P**6
Primary Contact: Kendell R. Sprott, M.D., JD, Chief Executive Officer
COO: Christopher King, Director Operations and Administrative Services
CFO: Wayne Guberman, Director Finance
CMO: Gary E Eddey M.D., Medical Director
CIO: Ron Daniel, Manager Information Systems
CHR: Nancy Petrillo, Director Human Resources
Web address: www.matheny.org
Control: Other not-for-profit (including NFP Corporation) **Service**: Other specialty
treatment

Staffed Beds: 101 **Admissions**: 4 **Census**: 98 **Births**: 0

PENNINGTON—Mercer County

✠ **CAPITAL HEALTH MEDICAL CENTER-HOPEWELL (310044)**, 1 Capital Way,
Zip 08534–2520; tel. 609/303–4000 **A**1 2 5 10 **F**3 8 11 12 13 15 18 19 20 22
28 29 30 31 32 34 35 36 40 41 44 45 46 47 48 49 50 51 52 55 57 58 59 60
61 64 65 68 70 72 73 74 75 76 78 79 81 82 84 85 86 87 89 90 93 96 97 107
108 109 110 111 112 114 115 117 118 119 120 121 123 124 126 129 130
132 135 143 145 146 147 148 **P**6 **S** Capital Health, Trenton, NJ
Primary Contact: Al Maghazehe, Ph.D., FACHE, President and Chief Executive
Officer
CFO: Shane Fleming, Chief Financial Officer
CMO: Eugene McMahon, Senior Vice President and Chief Medical Officer
CIO: Eugene Grochala, Vice President Information Systems
CHR: Scott Clemmensen, Vice President Human Resources and Leadership
Enhancement
CNO: Margaret Reiter, Chief Nursing Officer
Web address: www.capitalhealth.org
Control: Other not-for-profit (including NFP Corporation) **Service**: General medical
and surgical

Staffed Beds: 207 **Admissions**: 14332 **Census**: 162 **Outpatient Visits**:
158725 **Births**: 3442 **Personnel**: 1522

NJ

PERTH AMBOY—Middlesex County

☐ **CAREONE AT RARITAN BAY MEDICAL CENTER (312018)**, 530 New Brunswick Avenue, Zip 08861–3654; tel. 732/324–6090 (Nonreporting) **A**1 10
Primary Contact: Sharon Bready, R.N., Chief Executive Officer
CFO: Richard Burguillos, Chief Financial Officer
Web address: www.care-one.com
Control: Corporation, Investor-owned (for-profit) **Service**: Acute long-term care hospital

Staffed Beds: 30

✠ **HACKENSACK MERIDIAN HEALTH RARITAN BAY MEDICAL CENTER (310039)**, 530 New Brunswick Avenue, Zip 08861–3654; tel. 732/442–3700, (Includes OLD BRIDGE DIVISION, One Hospital Plaza, Old Bridge, New Jersey, Zip 8857, tel. 732/360–1000; PERTH AMBOY DIVISION, 530 New Brunswick Avenue, Perth Amboy, New Jersey, Zip 08861–3685, tel. 732/442–3700) **A**1 3 5 10 **F**3 4 5 7 8 11 12 13 15 17 18 20 22 29 30 31 32 34 35 36 38 39 40 43 45 46 47 48 49 50 51 54 56 57 58 59 60 61 63 64 65 66 68 70 73 74 75 76 77 78 79 80 81 82 85 86 87 89 92 93 94 96 97 98 100 101 102 103 104 107 108 110 111 114 115 116 117 119 129 130 131 132 141 143 144 146 147 148 149 **P**6 **S** Hackensack Meridian Health, Edison, NJ
Primary Contact: Michael R. D'Agnes, FACHE, President and Chief Executive Officer
COO: Vincent Costantino, Vice President Operations and Human Resources
CFO: Thomas Shanahan, Chief Financial Officer and Senior Vice President
CMO: Michael Ciencewicki M.D., Vice President Medical Affairs
CHR: Vincent Costantino, Vice President Operations and Human Resources
Web address: www.rbmc.org
Control: Other not-for-profit (including NFP Corporation) **Service**: General medical and surgical

Staffed Beds: 282 **Admissions**: 12706 **Census**: 171 **Outpatient Visits**: 134789 **Births**: 1143 **Total Expense ($000)**: 236846 **Payroll Expense ($000)**: 112841 **Personnel**: 1766

PHILLIPSBURG—Warren County

☐ **ST. LUKE'S HOSPITAL - WARREN CAMPUS (310060)**, 185 Roseberry Street, Zip 08865–1690; tel. 908/859–6700 **A**1 2 3 5 10 13 **F**2 3 8 11 15 18 20 28 29 30 31 34 35 39 40 44 45 48 49 50 51 53 54 56 59 60 61 63 64 65 66 68 70 74 75 77 78 79 81 82 85 86 87 91 92 93 97 100 101 102 103 104 107 108 110 111 115 118 119 124 129 130 131 132 134 146 147 148 149 **S** St. Luke's University Health Network, Bethlehem, PA
Primary Contact: Scott R. Wolfe, CPA, President
COO: Alice Wilson FACHE, Vice President Administration
CMO: Edward Gilkey M.D., Vice President Medical Affairs
CHR: Morgan G Mahl, Director Human Resources
CNO: Gail Newton R.N., MSN, Vice President Patient Care Services
Web address: www.slhn.org
Control: Other not-for-profit (including NFP Corporation) **Service**: General medical and surgical

Staffed Beds: 103 **Admissions**: 3903 **Census**: 53 **Outpatient Visits**: 93315 **Births**: 0 **Total Expense ($000)**: 99433 **Payroll Expense ($000)**: 43038 **Personnel**: 628

PISCATAWAY—Middlesex County

UNIVERSITY BEHAVIORAL HEALTHCARE (314011), 671 Hoes Lane West, Zip 08854–8021; tel. 732/235–5900, (Nonreporting) **A**3 5 10
Primary Contact: Rosemarie Rosati, Interim President and Chief Executive Officer
COO: Rosemarie Rosati, Chief Operating Officer
CFO: Alan Weinkrantz, Chief Financial Officer, Finance
CMO: Theresa Miskimen M.D., Vice President Medical Services
CIO: Adam Levinson, Associate Director, Information Services
CNO: Michele A Miller R.N., MSN, Vice President, Acute and Nursing Services
Web address: www.ubhc.rutgers.edu
Control: State, Government, Nonfederal **Service**: Psychiatric

Staffed Beds: 48

PLAINSBORO—Middlesex County

UNIVERSITY MEDICAL CENTER AT PRINCETON See University Medical Center Of Princeton At Plainsboro

✠ △ **UNIVERSITY MEDICAL CENTER OF PRINCETON AT PLAINSBORO (310010)**, One Plainsboro Road, Zip 08536–1913; tel. 609/853–7100 **A**1 2 3 5 7 10 **F**3 4 5 8 11 12 13 14 15 18 19 20 22 26 28 29 30 31 32 34 35 36 38 39 40 41 45 46 47 48 49 50 51 53 54 55 56 57 58 59 60 61 62 63 64 65 66 68 70 73 74 75 76 77 78 79 81 82 84 85 86 87 89 90 91 92 93 96 97 98 99 100 101 102 103 104 105 107 108 110 111 114 115 116 117 118 119 120 121 123 124 126 129 130 131 132 134 135 143 145 146 147 148
Primary Contact: Barry S. Rabner, President and Chief Executive Officer, Princeton Healthcare System
COO: James Demetriades, Vice President, Operations
CMO: Donald Denny M.D., Senior Vice President, Medical Affairs
CIO: Anne Searle, Chief Information Officer
CHR: Marcia M Telthorster, M.Ed, CCP, Vice President Human Resources
CNO: Barbara Christiano, Vice President, Patient Care Services and Chief Nursing Officer
Web address: www.princetonhcs.org
Control: Other not-for-profit (including NFP Corporation) **Service**: General medical and surgical

Staffed Beds: 355 **Admissions**: 13084 **Census**: 168

POMONA—Atlantic County

ATLANTICARE REGIONAL MEDICAL CENTER-MAINLAND DIVISION See Atlanticare Regional Medical Center, Atlantic City

✠ △ **BACHARACH INSTITUTE FOR REHABILITATION (313030)**, 61 West Jimmie Leeds Road, Zip 08240–9102, Mailing Address: P.O.Box 723, 08240–0723; tel. 609/652–7000, (Nonreporting) **A**1 7 10
Primary Contact: Richard J. Kathrins, Ph.D., President and Chief Executive Officer
CFO: Jeanne Vuksta, Chief Financial Officer
CMO: Craig Anmuth M.D., Medical Director
CIO: Jeff Rees, Director Information Systems
CHR: Diane Croshaw, Vice President Human Resources
Web address: www.bacharach.org
Control: Other not-for-profit (including NFP Corporation) **Service**: Rehabilitation

Staffed Beds: 80

POMPTON PLAINS—Morris County

✠ **CHILTON MEDICAL CENTER (310017)**, 97 West Parkway, Zip 07444–1696; tel. 973/831–5000 **A**1 2 10 **F**3 7 8 9 11 12 13 15 18 20 22 28 29 30 31 32 34 35 36 38 39 40 41 44 45 47 49 50 54 55 56 57 58 59 60 61 62 63 64 65 66 68 70 73 74 75 76 77 78 79 81 82 84 85 86 87 89 93 97 102 107 108 110 111 114 115 116 117 118 119 120 121 123 126 129 130 131 132 134 135 141 143 146 147 148 149 150 **P**3 5 6 **S** Atlantic Health System, Morristown, NJ
Primary Contact: Stephanie L. Schwartz, FACHE, President
CFO: Michael Richetti, Chief Financial Officer
CMO: Charles Ross M.D., Vice President Medical Affairs
CIO: Karen S Smith, Director Information Services
CHR: Julia McGovern, Vice President Human Resources
Web address: www.chiltonmemorial.org
Control: Other not-for-profit (including NFP Corporation) **Service**: General medical and surgical

Staffed Beds: 199 **Admissions**: 8912 **Census**: 119 **Outpatient Visits**: 117231 **Births**: 720 **Total Expense ($000)**: 194622 **Payroll Expense ($000)**: 90894 **Personnel**: 1249

RAHWAY—Union County

KINDRED HOSPITAL NEW JERSEY - RAHWAY See Kindred Hospital-New Jersey Morris County, Dover

✠ **ROBERT WOOD JOHNSON UNIVERSITY HOSPITAL RAHWAY (310024)**, 865 Stone Street, Zip 07065–2797; tel. 732/381–4200 **A**1 10 **F**3 11 15 17 20 29 30 31 34 35 38 40 46 47 49 50 53 56 57 59 64 65 68 70 74 75 77 78 79 81 82 86 87 93 97 100 101 102 107 108 111 117 118 119 129 130 132 134 143 146 147 148 149 **S** RWJBarnabas Health, West Orange, NJ
Primary Contact: Kirk C. Tice, President and Chief Executive Officer
CFO: Peter Bihuniak, Vice President Finance
CMO: Juan Baez M.D., President Medical Staff
CIO: Denine Izzi, Senior Director Information Technology
CHR: Barbara M Mullery, Vice President Administration
CNO: Ann Marie Shears, Vice President Patient Care Services
Web address: www.rwjuhr.com
Control: Other not-for-profit (including NFP Corporation) **Service**: General medical and surgical

Staffed Beds: 122 **Admissions**: 5183 **Census**: 71 **Outpatient Visits**: 73552 **Births**: 0 **Total Expense ($000)**: 111466 **Payroll Expense ($000)**: 45199 **Personnel**: 693

NJ

Hospital, Medicare Provider Number, Address, Telephone, Approval, Facility, and Physician Codes, Health Care System

★ American Hospital Association (AHA) membership
☐ The Joint Commission accreditation
○ Healthcare Facilities Accreditation Program
◇ DNV Healthcare Inc. accreditation
⇑ Center for Improvement in Healthcare Quality Accreditation
△ Commission on Accreditation of Rehabilitation Facilities (CARF) accreditation

RED BANK—Monmouth County

☒ △ **HACKENSACK MERIDIAN HEALTH RIVERVIEW MEDICAL CENTER (310034)**, 1 Riverview Plaza, Zip 07701–1864; tel. 732/741–2700 **A**1 2 7 10 **F**3 4 5 9 11 13 15 18 20 22 28 29 30 31 32 34 35 36 37 38 39 40 41 43 44 45 46 47 49 50 51 54 55 56 57 58 59 60 61 63 64 65 66 68 70 71 73 74 75 76 77 78 79 80 81 82 84 85 86 87 90 91 92 93 94 96 97 98 99 100 101 102 103 104 105 107 108 110 111 114 115 116 117 118 119 120 121 123 124 126 130 131 132 134 135 141 144 145 146 147 148 149 150 **S** Hackensack Meridian Health, Edison, NJ
Primary Contact: Timothy J. Hogan, FACHE, Regional President
COO: Kelly O'Brien, Chief Operating Officer
CFO: Joseph M Lemaire, Executive Vice President Finance
CMO: Joseph Reichman M.D., Vice President Medical Affairs and Clinical Effectiveness
CIO: Rebecca Weber, Senior Vice President Information Technology
CHR: Sherrie String, Senior Vice President Human Resources
CNO: Kathy McKean M.P.H., R.N., Vice President, Chief Nursing Executive
Web address: www.riverviewmedicalcenter.com
Control: Other not-for-profit (including NFP Corporation) **Service**: General medical and surgical

Staffed Beds: 304 Admissions: 12611 **Census:** 176 **Outpatient Visits:** 134012 **Births:** 1310 **Total Expense ($000):** 244868 **Payroll Expense ($000):** 105495 **Personnel:** 1410

RIDGEWOOD—Bergen County

☒ **VALLEY HOSPITAL (310012)**, 223 North Van Dien Avenue, Zip 07450–2726; tel. 201/447–8000 **A**1 2 5 10 **F**3 7 8 11 12 13 15 17 18 19 20 22 24 26 28 29 30 31 32 34 36 37 38 40 41 44 45 46 47 48 49 50 51 52 53 54 55 56 57 58 59 60 61 64 65 66 68 69 70 71 72 73 74 75 76 77 78 79 80 81 82 84 85 86 87 88 89 91 92 93 94 96 97 99 100 101 102 103 107 108 109 110 111 114 115 117 118 119 120 121 123 124 126 129 130 131 132 134 135 141 143 145 146 147 148 149 150 **P**6
Primary Contact: Audrey Meyers, FACHE, President and Chief Executive Officer
COO: Peter Diestel, Senior Vice President and Chief Operating Officer
CFO: Richard Keenan, Senior Vice President Finance and Chief Financial Officer
CMO: Joseph Yallowitz M.D., Vice President Medical Affairs
CIO: Eric R Carey, Vice President Information Systems and Chief Information Officer
CHR: Jose Balderrama, Vice President Human Resources
CNO: Ann Marie Leichman R.N., MSN, Vice President Patient Care Services and Chief Nursing Officer
Web address: www.valleyhealth.com
Control: Other not-for-profit (including NFP Corporation) **Service**: General medical and surgical

Staffed Beds: 446 Admissions: 28632 **Census:** 304 **Outpatient Visits:** 277657 **Births:** 3366 **Total Expense ($000):** 574631 **Payroll Expense ($000):** 241131 **Personnel:** 3231

ROCHELLE PARK—Bergen County

☒ **SELECT SPECIALTY HOSPITAL-NORTHEAST NEW JERSEY (312019)**, 96 Parkway, Zip 07662–4200; tel. 201/221–2352, (Nonreporting) **A**1 10 **S** Select Medical Corporation, Mechanicsburg, PA
Primary Contact: Mary Beth Ray-Simone, Chief Executive Officer
Web address: www.northeastnewjersey.selectspecialtyhospitals.com/about/
Control: Corporation, Investor-owned (for-profit) **Service**: Acute long-term care hospital

Staffed Beds: 62

SADDLE BROOK—Bergen County

KESSLER INSTITUTE FOR REHABILITATION See Kessler Institute For Rehabilitation, West Orange

SALEM—Salem County

☒ **MEMORIAL HOSPITAL OF SALEM COUNTY (310091)**, 310 Woodstown Road, Zip 08079–2080; tel. 856/935–1000, (Nonreporting) **A**1 10 **S** Community Health Systems, Inc., Franklin, TN
Primary Contact: Tammy Torres, R.N., MSN, Chief Executive Officer
CFO: Donald Bevers, Chief Financial Officer
CIO: Brian McCarthy, Director Information Systems
CHR: Victoria A. Bates, Director Human Resources
CNO: Patricia A Scherle, Chief Nursing Officer
Web address: www.salemhospitalnj.org
Control: Corporation, Investor-owned (for-profit) **Service**: General medical and surgical

Staffed Beds: 110

SECAUCUS—Hudson County

HUDSON COUNTY MEADOWVIEW PSYCHIATRIC HOSPITAL (314024), 595 County Avenue, Zip 07094–2605; tel. 201/369–5252 (Nonreporting)
Primary Contact: Joanne Reilly, Administrator
Web address: www.hudsoncountynj.org
Control: County, Government, Nonfederal **Service**: Psychiatric

Staffed Beds: 84

⇑ **LIBERTYHEALTH-MEADOWLANDS HOSPITAL MEDICAL CENTER** See Meadowlands Hospital Medical Center

⇑ **MEADOWLANDS HOSPITAL MEDICAL CENTER (310118)**, 55 Meadowlands Parkway, Zip 07094–2977; tel. 201/392–3100, (Nonreporting) **A**10 12 13 21
Primary Contact: Felicia Karsos, R.N., President and Chief Executive Officer
COO: Lynn McVey, Chief Operating Officer
CMO: Michael Sciarra M.D., Chief Medical Officer
CHR: Elizabeth Garrity, Director Human Resources
CNO: Felicia Karsos R.N., Chief Nursing Officer
Web address: www.meadowlandshospital.org
Control: Partnership, Investor-owned (for-profit) **Service**: General medical and surgical

Staffed Beds: 230

SOMERS POINT—Atlantic County

☐ **SHORE MEDICAL CENTER (310047)**, 100 Medical Center Way, Zip 8244; tel. 609/653–3500, (Nonreporting) **A**1 2 10
Primary Contact: Ronald W. Johnson, FACHE, President and Chief Executive Officer
COO: Linda S Kenwood R.N., MSN, Chief Nursing Officer and Chief Operating Officer
CFO: James T Foley CPA, Vice President and Chief Financial Officer
CMO: Jeanne M Rowe M.D., Chief Medical Officer
CIO: Fred Banner, Chief Information Officer
CHR: Alan L Beatty, Vice President Human Resources
CNO: Linda S Kenwood R.N., MSN, Chief Nursing Officer and Chief Operating Officer
Web address: www.shoremedicalcenter.org
Control: Other not-for-profit (including NFP Corporation) **Service**: General medical and surgical

Staffed Beds: 198

SOMERVILLE—Somerset County

☒ **ROBERT WOOD JOHNSON UNIVERSITY HOSPITAL SOMERSET (310048)**, 110 Rehill Avenue, Zip 08876–2598; tel. 908/685–2200 **A**1 2 3 5 10 **F**3 5 7 8 11 12 13 15 18 20 22 26 28 29 30 31 34 35 36 38 40 44 45 46 47 48 49 50 51 52 55 56 57 58 59 60 61 62 63 64 65 66 68 70 71 73 74 75 76 77 78 79 81 82 83 84 85 86 87 91 92 93 94 97 98 99 100 101 102 103 104 105 107 108 110 111 114 115 116 117 118 119 120 121 123 124 126 129 130 131 132 134 135 143 144 145 146 147 148 149 150 **P**3 5 6 **S** RWJBarnabas Health, West Orange, NJ
Primary Contact: Anthony V. Cava, President
COO: Patrick Delaney, Administrative Director, Operations
CFO: Kenneth Wright, Chief Financial Officer
CMO: Salvatore Moffa M.D., Vice President, Medical Affairs and Chief Medical Officer
CIO: Jordan Ruch, Vice President and Chief Information Officer
CHR: Anastasia Jacobs, Chief Human Resources Officer
CNO: Lynn Kearney, Vice President, Nursing
Web address: www.rwjuh.edu
Control: Other not-for-profit (including NFP Corporation) **Service**: General medical and surgical

Staffed Beds: 285 Admissions: 13157 **Census:** 171 **Outpatient Visits:** 105556 **Births:** 764 **Total Expense ($000):** 548089 **Payroll Expense ($000):** 114194 **Personnel:** 1626

STRATFORD—Camden County

☒ **KENNEDY HEALTH SYSTEM (310086)**, 18 East Laurel Road, Zip 08084–1327; tel. 856/346–6000, (Includes KENNEDY UNIVERSITY HOSPITAL - STRATFORD, 18 East Laurel Road, Stratford, New Jersey, Zip 8084, tel. 609/346–6000; KENNEDY UNIVERSITY HOSPITAL - WASHINGTON TOWNSHIP, 435 Hurffville-Cross Keys Road, Turnersville, New Jersey, Zip 8012, tel. 609/582–2500) **A**1 2 10 **F**3 5 7 8 11 12 13 15 18 20 22 29 30 31 32 34 35 38 39 40 41 44 46 49 50 54 55 56 57 59 60 61 62 64 65 66 70 72 73 74 75 76 77 78 79 81 82 84 85 86 87 89 93 97 98 99 100 101 102 103 104 105 107 108 110 111 114 115 117 118 119 120 121 123 124 126 129 130 131 132 134 143 144 146 147 148 149
Primary Contact: Joseph W. Devine, FACHE, President and Chief Executive Officer
CFO: Glenn Zirbser, Senior Vice President Finance and Chief Financial Officer
CMO: David Condoluci M.D., Senior Vice President and Chief Medical Officer
CIO: Thomas Balcavage, Vice President Chief Patient Safety and Quality Officer
CHR: Anneliese McMenamin, Senior Vice President Information Technology and Program Services
CNO: Helene M Burns MSN, R.N., Chief Nursing Executive
Web address: www.kennedyhealth.org
Control: Other not-for-profit (including NFP Corporation) **Service**: General medical and surgical

Staffed Beds: 527 Admissions: 26634 **Census:** 323 **Outpatient Visits:** 352666 **Births:** 999 **Total Expense ($000):** 511391 **Payroll Expense ($000):** 214841 **Personnel:** 4021

KENNEDY MEMORIAL HOSPITALS-UNIVERSITY MEDICAL CENTER See Kennedy Health System

KENNEDY UNIVERSITY HOSPITAL - STRATFORD See Kennedy Health System

NJ

SUMMIT—Union County

✠ **OVERLOOK MEDICAL CENTER (310051)**, 99 Beauvoir Avenue, Zip 07901–3533; tel. 908/522–2000 **A**1 2 3 5 8 10 13 **F**3 5 6 7 8 9 11 12 13 14 15 17 18 19 20 22 28 29 30 31 32 34 35 36 37 38 39 40 41 42 44 45 46 47 48 49 50 51 52 53 54 55 56 57 58 59 60 61 62 63 64 65 66 68 69 70 71 72 74 75 76 77 78 79 81 82 83 84 85 86 87 89 91 92 93 94 95 96 97 98 99 100 101 102 103 104 105 107 108 109 110 111 113 114 115 116 117 118 119 120 121 123 124 126 129 130 131 132 134 135 141 143 144 145 146 147 148 149 150 **P**3 5 6 **S** Atlantic Health System, Morristown, NJ
Primary Contact: Alan R. Lieber, President
CFO: Kevin Lenahan, Vice President Finance and Chief Financial Officer
CMO: John R Audett M.D., Medical Director Clinical Affairs
CIO: Elizabeth Lindsay-Wood, Interim Chief Information Officer
CNO: Mary Patricia Sullivan R.N., MSN, Chief Nursing Officer
Web address: www.atlantichealth.org/Overlook
Control: Other not-for-profit (including NFP Corporation) **Service**: General medical and surgical

Staffed Beds: 467 Admissions: 21626 Census: 268 Outpatient Visits: 264447 Births: 2558 Total Expense ($000): 714590 Payroll Expense ($000): 318413 Personnel: 3923

☐ **SUMMIT OAKS HOSPITAL (314001)**, 19 Prospect Street, Zip 07901–2530; tel. 908/522–7000, (Nonreporting) **A**1 10 **S** Universal Health Services, Inc., King of Prussia, PA
Primary Contact: Oana Radu, Chief Executive Officer
Web address: www.summitoakshospital.com/
Control: Corporation, Investor-owned (for-profit) **Service**: Psychiatric

Staffed Beds: 90

SUSSEX—Sussex County

SAINT CLARE'S HEALTH CENTER AT SUSSEX See Saint Clare's Health System, Denville

TEANECK—Bergen County

HOLY NAME HOSPITAL See Holy Name Medical Center

✠ **HOLY NAME MEDICAL CENTER (310008)**, 718 Teaneck Road, Zip 07666–4281; tel. 201/833–3000 **A**1 2 5 10 **F**2 3 7 8 11 12 13 15 18 19 20 22 28 29 30 31 32 34 35 36 37 38 39 40 41 44 45 46 47 48 49 50 51 53 54 55 56 57 58 59 60 62 63 64 65 66 68 70 71 73 74 75 76 77 78 79 80 81 82 83 84 85 86 87 89 91 92 93 94 96 97 98 100 101 102 103 107 108 110 111 114 115 116 117 118 119 120 121 123 124 126 129 130 131 132 133 135 143 144 145 146 147 148 149 **P**4 6 7
Primary Contact: Michael Maron, President and Chief Executive Officer
CFO: Ryan Kennedy, Chief Financial Officer
CMO: Adam D Jarrett M.D., Executive Vice President and Chief Medical Officer
CIO: Michael Skvarenina, Assistant Vice President Information Systems
CHR: April Rodgers, Vice President, Human Resources
CNO: Sheryl A Slonim, Executive Vice President and Chief Nursing Officer
Web address: www.holyname.org
Control: Other not-for-profit (including NFP Corporation) **Service**: General medical and surgical

Staffed Beds: 318 Admissions: 18385 Census: 210 Outpatient Visits: 336906 Births: 1190 Total Expense ($000): 333489 Payroll Expense ($000): 144542 Personnel: 2391

TINTON FALLS—Monmouth County

★ **HEALTHSOUTH REHABILITATION HOSPITAL OF TINTON FALLS (313035)**, 2 Centre Plaza, Zip 07724–9744; tel. 732/460–5320, (Nonreporting) **A**10 **S** HEALTHSOUTH Corporation, Birmingham, AL
Primary Contact: Suji Thomas, R.N., MSN, Chief Executive Officer
CFO: Lynne Traister, Controller
CMO: Todd Cooperman M.D., Medical Director
CHR: Anita Saum, Director Human Resources
Web address: www.rehabnj.com
Control: Corporation, Investor-owned (for-profit) **Service**: Rehabilitation

Staffed Beds: 60

TOMS RIVER—Ocean County

✠ **BARNABAS HEALTH BEHAVIORAL HEALTH CENTER (314022)**, 1691 Highway 9, Zip 8754; tel. 732/914–1688 **A**1 10 **F**35 68 98 100 101 103 104 105 **S** RWJBarnabas Health, West Orange, NJ
Primary Contact: Deanna Sperling, President and Chief Executive Officer
Web address: www.barnabashealth.org/hospitals/psychiatric/index.html
Control: Other not-for-profit (including NFP Corporation) **Service**: Psychiatric

Staffed Beds: 40 Admissions: 1304 Census: 31 Outpatient Visits: 7786 Births: 0 Total Expense ($000): 9782 Payroll Expense ($000): 4864 Personnel: 112

✠ **COMMUNITY MEDICAL CENTER (310041)**, 99 Route 37 West, Zip 08755–6423; tel. 732/557–8000 **A**1 2 3 10 **F**3 11 13 15 18 20 22 28 29 30 31 32 34 35 36 38 40 41 43 44 46 48 49 50 54 55 56 57 58 59 60 61 62 63 64 68 69 70 73 74 75 76 77 78 79 81 82 84 85 86 87 89 92 93 96 100 107 108 109 110 111 114 115 118 119 120 121 123 124 126 129 130 131 132 133 134 143 146 147 148 149 **S** RWJBarnabas Health, West Orange, NJ
Primary Contact: Michael Mimoso, FACHE, President and Chief Executive Officer
COO: Patrick Ahearn, Chief Operating Officer
CFO: Thomas Percello, Chief Financial Officer
CMO: Yeshavanth Nayak M.D., Interim Chief Medical Officer
CIO: Shaun Fitzsimmons, Director Information Technology Services
CHR: Vanessa Smith, Chief Human Resources Officer
CNO: Donna Bonacorso, Interim Chief Nursing Officer
Web address: www.barnabashealth.org/hospitals/community_medical/index.html
Control: Other not-for-profit (including NFP Corporation) **Service**: General medical and surgical

Staffed Beds: 353 Admissions: 20920 Census: 295 Outpatient Visits: 262205 Births: 2139 Total Expense ($000): 310959 Payroll Expense ($000): 133646 Personnel: 1847

✠ **HEALTHSOUTH REHABILITATION HOSPITAL OF TOMS RIVER (313029)**, 14 Hospital Drive, Zip 08755–6470; tel. 732/244–3100, (Nonreporting) **A**1 10 **S** HEALTHSOUTH Corporation, Birmingham, AL
Primary Contact: Patricia Ostaszewski, MS, Chief Executive Officer
COO: Patricia Ostaszewski MS, Chief Executive Officer
CFO: Janet Turso, Controller
CMO: Carol Sonatore D.O., Medical Director
CIO: Coleen Rossi, Director Quality Services
CHR: Lori Munyan, Director, Human Resources
CNO: Susan Castor, Chief Nursing Officer
Web address: www.rehabnjtomsriver.com/
Control: Corporation, Investor-owned (for-profit) **Service**: Rehabilitation

Staffed Beds: 92

SAINT BARNABAS BEHAVIORAL HEALTH CENTER See Barnabas Health Behavioral Health Center

TRENTON—Mercer County

✠ **CAPITAL HEALTH REGIONAL MEDICAL CENTER (310092)**, 750 Brunswick Avenue, Zip 08638–4143; tel. 609/394–6000 **A**1 3 5 10 **F**3 7 11 15 18 29 30 32 34 35 40 43 44 45 46 47 48 50 54 57 58 59 60 61 64 65 66 68 70 74 75 77 78 79 81 82 84 85 87 89 93 96 97 98 99 100 101 102 107 108 109 111 112 114 115 118 119 129 130 132 135 143 145 146 147 148 **P**6 **S** Capital Health, Trenton, NJ
Primary Contact: Al Maghazehe, Ph.D., FACHE, President and Chief Executive Officer
CFO: Shane Fleming, Chief Financial Officer
CMO: Eugene McMahon, Senior Vice President and Chief Medical Officer
CIO: Eugene Grochala, Vice President Information Systems
CHR: Scott Clemmensen, Vice President Human Resources and Leadership Enhancement
CNO: Gina Mumolie, Senior Vice President Hospital Administration
Web address: www.capitalhealth.org
Control: Other not-for-profit (including NFP Corporation) **Service**: General medical and surgical

Staffed Beds: 204 Admissions: 7315 Census: 130 Outpatient Visits: 155231 Births: 0 Personnel: 1397

NJ

Hospital, Medicare Provider Number, Address, Telephone, Approval, Facility, and Physician Codes, Health Care System

★ American Hospital Association (AHA) membership
☐ The Joint Commission accreditation
○ Healthcare Facilities Accreditation Program
◇ DNV Healthcare Inc. accreditation
⇑ Center for Improvement in Healthcare Quality Accreditation
△ Commission on Accreditation of Rehabilitation Facilities (CARF) accreditation

© 2017 AHA Guide   *Many Facility Codes have changed. Please refer to the AHA Guide Code Chart.*   Hospitals **A421**

✠ **ST. FRANCIS MEDICAL CENTER (310021)**, 601 Hamilton Avenue, Zip 08629–1986; tel. 609/599–5000, (Nonreporting) **A**1 3 10 **S** Trinity Health, Livonia, MI
Primary Contact: Vincent Costantino, Interim President and Chief Administrative Officer
CFO: Mark Kelly, Vice President Finance
CMO: C James Romano M.D., Chief Medical Officer
CIO: Richard Dowgun, Chief Information Officer
CHR: Laura James, Director Human Resources
CNO: Mary Anne Suttles, Chief Nursing Officer
Web address: www.stfrancismedical.org/
Control: Church operated, Nongovernment, not-for-profit **Service**: General medical and surgical

Staffed Beds: 163

☐ **TRENTON PSYCHIATRIC HOSPITAL (314013)**, Route 29 and Sullivan Way, Zip 08628–3425, Mailing Address: P.O.Box 7500, West Trenton, 08628–0500; tel. 609/633–1500, (Nonreporting) **A**1 3 10 **S** Division of Mental Health and Addiction Services, Department of Human Services, State of New Jersey, Trenton, NJ
Primary Contact: Teresa A. McQuaide, Chief Executive Officer
CFO: Joseph Canale, Business Manager
CMO: Lawrence Rossi M.D., Clinical Director
CIO: Scott Eustace, Director Health Information Technology
CHR: Marybeth Longo, Manager Human Resources
CNO: Colleen Birkhofer, Chief Nursing Officer
Web address: www.state.nj.us/humanservices/dmhs/oshm/tph/
Control: State, Government, Nonfederal **Service**: Psychiatric

Staffed Beds: 431

TURNERSVILLE—Camden County

KENNEDY UNIVERSITY HOSPITAL - WASHINGTON TOWNSHIP See Kennedy Health System, Stratford

VINELAND—Cumberland County

✠ **HEALTHSOUTH REHABILITATION HOSPITAL OF VINELAND (313036)**, 1237 West Sherman Avenue, Zip 08360–6920; tel. 856/696–7100 **A**1 10 **F**29 30 65 75 90 103 130 132 148 149 **S** HEALTHSOUTH Corporation, Birmingham, AL
Primary Contact: Tammy Feuer, Chief Executive Officer
CMO: Eugenio Rocksmith M.D., Medical Director
CHR: Dawn Pearson, Director Human Resources
Web address: www.healthsouthvineland.com
Control: Corporation, Investor-owned (for-profit) **Service**: Rehabilitation

Staffed Beds: 41 **Admissions**: 968 **Census**: 35 **Outpatient Visits**: 0
Births: 0 **Total Expense ($000)**: 12829 **Payroll Expense ($000)**: 7919
Personnel: 140

★ ⇑ **INSPIRA MEDICAL CENTER-VINELAND (310032)**, 1505 West Sherman Avenue, Zip 08360–6912; tel. 856/641–8000, (Includes BRIDGETON HEALTH CENTER, 333 Irving Avenue, Bridgeton, New Jersey, Zip 08302–2100, tel. 856/575–4500) **A**2 3 10 12 13 21 **F**3 8 11 12 13 15 17 18 20 22 28 29 30 34 35 37 38 40 41 42 44 49 50 54 57 59 64 68 70 72 73 74 75 76 77 78 79 81 82 85 86 87 89 93 98 99 100 101 102 103 104 105 107 108 110 111 114 115 117 119 120 121 123 124 126 130 131 132 134 144 146 147 148 **P**8 **S** Inspira Health Network, Mullica Hill, NJ
Primary Contact: John A. DiAngelo, President and Chief Executive Officer
COO: Elizabeth Sheridan, Chief Operating Officer and Chief Nursing Executive
CFO: Thomas Baldosaro, Chief Financial Officer
CMO: Steven C Linn M.D., Chief Medical Officer
CIO: Thomas Pacek, Vice President Information Systems and Chief Information Officer
CHR: Erich Florentine, Chief People Officer
CNO: Elizabeth Sheridan, Chief Operating Officer and Chief Nursing Executive
Web address: www.inspirahealthnetwork.org/?id=5280&sid=1
Control: Other not-for-profit (including NFP Corporation) **Service**: General medical and surgical

Staffed Beds: 335 **Admissions**: 17827 **Census**: 229 **Outpatient Visits**: 263438 **Births**: 1833 **Total Expense ($000)**: 349320 **Payroll Expense ($000)**: 144816 **Personnel**: 1572

VOORHEES—Camden County

✠ **VIRTUA VOORHEES (310022)**, 100 Bowman Drive, Zip 08043–9612; tel. 856/325–3000, (Includes VOORHEES PEDIATRIC FACILITY, 1304 Laurel Oak Road, Voorhees, New Jersey, Zip 08043–4310, tel. 888/873–5437) **A**1 3 5 10 **F**3 11 13 29 30 31 34 35 40 41 45 46 48 49 50 55 58 59 64 66 68 70 72 73 74 75 76 78 79 81 86 87 88 89 90 92 93 107 108 111 115 116 117 119 126 129 130 143 145 146 147 148 149 **S** Virtua Health, Marlton, NJ
Primary Contact: Matthew Zuino, Senior Vice President Hospital Services
COO: Michael S Kotzen, Vice President and Chief Operating Officer
CFO: Robert Rosvold, Director Finance
CMO: James P Dwyer D.O., Executive Vice President and Chief Medical Officer
CIO: Alfred Campanella, Chief Information Officer
Web address: www.virtua.org
Control: Other not-for-profit (including NFP Corporation) **Service**: General medical and surgical

Staffed Beds: 402 **Admissions**: 24755 **Census**: 284 **Outpatient Visits**: 292205 **Births**: 4707 **Total Expense ($000)**: 512726 **Payroll Expense ($000)**: 152090 **Personnel**: 1949

WAYNE—Passaic County

KINDRED HOSPITAL NEW JERSEY - WAYNE See Kindred Hospital-New Jersey Morris County, Dover

WEST ORANGE—Essex County

KESSLER INSTITUTE FOR REHABILITATION See Kessler Institute For Rehabilitation

✠ △ **KESSLER INSTITUTE FOR REHABILITATION (313025)**, 1199 Pleasant Valley Way, Zip 07052–1424; tel. 973/731–3600, (Nonreporting) (Includes KESSLER INSTITUTE FOR REHABILITATION, 1199 Pleasant Valley Way, West Orange, New Jersey, Zip 07052–1424, tel. 973/731–3600; Bonnie Evans, Chief Executive Officer; KESSLER INSTITUTE FOR REHABILITATION, 201 Pleasant Hill Road, Chester, New Jersey, Zip 07930–2141, tel. 973/252–6300; Sue Kida, Chief Executive Officer; KESSLER INSTITUTE FOR REHABILITATION, 300 Market Street, Saddle Brook, New Jersey, Zip 07663–5309, tel. 201/368–6000; Philip J Driscoll Jr, Chief Executive Officer) **A**1 3 5 7 10 **S** Select Medical Corporation, Mechanicsburg, PA
Primary Contact: Sue Kida, President
CMO: Bruce M Gans M.D., Executive Vice President and Chief Medical Officer
CHR: Ken Caldera, Director Human Resources
Web address: www.kessler-rehab.com
Control: Corporation, Investor-owned (for-profit) **Service**: Rehabilitation

Staffed Beds: 336

WESTAMPTON—Burlington County

☐ **HAMPTON BEHAVIORAL HEALTH CENTER (314021)**, 650 Rancocas Road, Zip 08060–5613; tel. 609/267–7000 **A**1 10 **F**30 35 98 99 100 103 104 105 130 132 143 149 **P**6 **S** Universal Health Services, Inc., King of Prussia, PA
Primary Contact: Craig Hilton, Chief Executive Officer and Managing Director
COO: Joanne Wijaya MSN, R.N., Chief Operating Officer and Risk Manager
CFO: Melissa Zinni, Chief Financial Officer
CMO: Anusuya Balasundaram M.D., Medical Director
CHR: Lori DeCelis, Director Human Resources
CNO: Kathleena Cohen MSN, R.N., Director of Nursing
Web address: www.hamptonhospital.com
Control: Corporation, Investor-owned (for-profit) **Service**: Psychiatric

Staffed Beds: 120 **Admissions**: 2621 **Census**: 101 **Outpatient Visits**: 20742 **Births**: 0 **Total Expense ($000)**: 23257 **Payroll Expense ($000)**: 15634 **Personnel**: 305

WESTWOOD—Bergen County

CAREONE AT HACKSENSACK UNIVERSITY MEDICAL CENTER AT PASCACK VALLEY, 250 Old Hook Road, 4 Central, Zip 07675–3123; tel. 201/781–1555 (Nonreporting)
Primary Contact: Sharon Bready, R.N., Chief Executive Officer
Web address: www.care-one.com/locations/ltach-careone-at-hackensack-university-medical-center-pascack-valley/
Control: Other not-for-profit (including NFP Corporation) **Service**: Acute long-term care hospital

Staffed Beds: 25

⊞ **HACKENSACK MERIDIAN HEALTH PASCACK VALLEY MEDICAL CENTER (310130)**, 250 Old Hook Road, Zip 07675–3123; tel. 201/383–1035 **A**1 **F**3 12 13 15 17 18 20 28 29 30 34 35 40 43 44 45 46 47 49 50 51 57 59 60 64 68 70 73 74 75 76 77 78 79 80 81 82 85 87 107 108 110 111 115 119 129 130 135 141 146 147 148 149 **S** Ardent Health Services, Nashville, TN
Primary Contact: Emily L. Holliman, FACHE, Chief Executive Officer
COO: Colleen Smorra, Assistant Administrator
CFO: Jason Pritchard, Chief Financial Officer
CMO: George Lin M.D., Physician Advisor
CIO: Anthony Teri, Director Information Technology
CHR: Theodora Carter, Administrative Director Human Resources
CNO: Susan Giordano R.N., Chief Nursing Officer
Web address: www.hackensackumcpv.com/
Control: Partnership, Investor-owned (for-profit) **Service**: General medical and surgical

Staffed Beds: 128 **Admissions:** 4586 **Census:** 48 **Outpatient Visits:** 24278 **Births:** 240 **Total Expense ($000):** 96898 **Payroll Expense ($000):** 34465 **Personnel:** 483

WILLINGBORO—Burlington County

⊞ **ACUITY SPECIALTY HOSPITAL OF SOUTHERN NEW JERSEY (312022)**, 218 Sunset Road, Zip 08046–1110, Mailing Address: 220 Sunset Road, 08046–1110; tel. 609/835–3650, (Nonreporting) **A**1 10 **S** AcuityHealthcare, LP, Charlotte, NC
Primary Contact: Monica Titus, R.N., Regional Chief Executive Officer
COO: Garrett Arneson FACHE, R.N., Chief Operating Officer
CFO: James Weinstein, Chief Financial Officer
CMO: Edward G. Hamaty D.O., Chief Medical Officer
CHR: Lisa M Sinnott, Director Human Resources
CNO: Kim Fetterolf R.N., Chief Clinical Officer
Web address: www.willingboro.acuityhealthcare.net
Control: Corporation, Investor-owned (for-profit) **Service**: Acute long-term care hospital

Staffed Beds: 69

⊞ **LOURDES MEDICAL CENTER OF BURLINGTON COUNTY (310061)**, 218-A Sunset Road, Zip 08046–1162; tel. 609/835–2900 **A**1 2 3 10 **F**3 7 11 12 15 17 18 29 30 31 34 35 36 38 40 42 44 45 46 47 49 50 55 56 57 59 60 61 64 66 68 70 74 75 78 79 81 82 85 86 87 93 98 100 107 108 109 110 111 114 118 119 129 130 132 135 146 147 148 149 **P**8 **S** Trinity Health, Livonia, MI
Primary Contact: Mark Nessel, Executive Vice President and Chief Operating Officer
CFO: Michael Hammond, Chief Financial Officer
CMO: Alan R Pope M.D., Vice President, Medical Affairs
CIO: Mike Elfert, Director Information Services
CNO: Audrey Jadczak R.N., FACHE, Vice President/Chief Nursing Officer
Web address: www.lourdesnet.org
Control: Other not-for-profit (including NFP Corporation) **Service**: General medical and surgical

Staffed Beds: 169 **Admissions:** 5697 **Census:** 81 **Outpatient Visits:** 127309 **Births:** 0 **Total Expense ($000):** 118677 **Payroll Expense ($000):** 44886 **Personnel:** 552

WOODBURY—Gloucester County

★ ⇑ **INSPIRA MEDICAL CENTER-WOODBURY (310081)**, 509 North Broad Street, Zip 08096–1697; tel. 856/845–0100 **A**3 5 10 21 **F**3 5 11 13 15 18 20 22 26 28 29 30 31 34 35 38 40 41 45 46 47 48 49 50 56 57 58 59 62 64 66 70 73 74 75 77 78 79 80 81 85 86 87 91 92 93 96 97 98 99 100 101 102 104 105 107 110 111 114 115 118 119 129 130 131 132 135 144 146 147 148 149 **P**4 8 **S** Inspira Health Network, Mullica Hill, NJ
Primary Contact: John A. DiAngelo, President and Chief Executive Officer
COO: Patrick B Nolan, Chief Operating Officer
CIO: Robert Mizia, Director Information Systems and Chief Information Officer
CHR: Robert Manestrina, Vice President Human Resources
CNO: Gina Mumolie, Senior Vice President and Chief Nurse Executive
Web address: www.inspirahealthnetwork.org/?id=5282&sid=1
Control: Other not-for-profit (including NFP Corporation) **Service**: General medical and surgical

Staffed Beds: 261 **Admissions:** 9315 **Census:** 115 **Outpatient Visits:** 131053 **Births:** 905 **Total Expense ($000):** 190044 **Payroll Expense ($000):** 83915 **Personnel:** 1035

WYCKOFF—Bergen County

⊞ **CHRISTIAN HEALTH CARE CENTER (314019)**, 301 Sicomac Avenue, Zip 07481–2194; tel. 201/848–5200, (Nonreporting) **A**1 10
Primary Contact: Douglas A. Struyk, CPA, President and Chief Executive Officer
COO: Steve Dumke FACHE, Executive Vice President and Chief Operating Officer
CFO: Kevin Stagg, Executive Vice President Finance and Chief Financial Officer
CMO: Howard Gilman M.D., Medical Executive
CIO: Jennifer D'Angelo, Vice President Information Services
CHR: Bob Zierold, Senior Vice President Human Resources
CNO: Marianne Guerriero, Nurse Executive
Web address: www.chccnj.org
Control: Other not-for-profit (including NFP Corporation) **Service**: Psychiatric

Staffed Beds: 530

NEW MEXICO

ACOMA—Bergen County

☐ **ACOMA-CANONCITO-LAGUNA HOSPITAL (320070)**, 80B Veterans Boulevard, Zip 87034, Mailing Address: P.O.Box 130, San Fidel, 87049–0130; tel. 505/552–5300, (Nonreporting) **A**1 10 **S** U. S. Indian Health Service, Rockville, MD
Primary Contact: Melody Price-Yonts, Chief Executive Officer
Web address: www.ihs.gov/albuquerque/index.cfm?module=dsp_abq_acoma_canoncito_laguna
Control: PHS, Indian Service, Government, federal **Service**: General medical and surgical

Staffed Beds: 6

ALAMOGORDO—Otero County

★ ⇑ **GERALD CHAMPION REGIONAL MEDICAL CENTER (320004)**, 2669 North Scenic Drive, Zip 88310–8799; tel. 575/439–6100 **A**3 10 13 20 21 **F**3 8 11 12 13 18 20 22 26 29 30 31 34 35 38 40 43 44 45 50 51 56 57 58 59 60 64 70 74 75 76 77 78 79 81 82 85 86 87 90 92 96 97 98 100 101 102 103 104 107 108 111 114 115 119 129 130 131 132 145 146 147 148 149 **P**8
Primary Contact: Robert J. Heckert Jr, Chief Executive Officer
CFO: Bashar Naser, Chief Financial Officer
CMO: Lee Saltzgaber, Chief Medical Officer
CIO: Ana Castro, Director Information Technology
CHR: Karen O'Brien, Director Human Resources
CNO: Robert Middleton, Chief Nursing Officer
Web address: www.gcrmc.org
Control: Other not-for-profit (including NFP Corporation) **Service**: General medical and surgical

Staffed Beds: 81 Admissions: 4109 Census: 49 Outpatient Visits: 99623 Births: 545 Total Expense ($000): 120403 Payroll Expense ($000): 45446 Personnel: 733

ALBUQUERQUE—Bernalillo County

☐ **AMG SPECIALTY HOSPITAL-ALBUQUERQUE (322003)**, 235 Elm Street NE, Zip 87102–3672; tel. 505/842–5550 (Nonreporting) **A**1 10 **S** AMG Integrated Healthcare Management, Lafayette, LA
Primary Contact: Ken D'Amico, Chief Executive Officer
CFO: Julie Lenzo, Director Business Office
CMO: Jeffrey Ross M.D., Medical Director
CHR: Robin Stendel-Freels, Coordinator Human Resources
Web address: www.amgalbuquerque.com/
Control: Partnership, Investor-owned (for-profit) **Service**: Acute long-term care hospital

Staffed Beds: 24

☐ **HAVEN BEHAVIORAL SENIOR CARE OF ALBUQUERQUE (324013)**, 5400 Gibson Boulevard SE, 4th Floor, Zip 87108–4729; tel. 505/336–1247 (Nonreporting) **A**1 10
Primary Contact: Sheila McDermott-Lord, Chief Executive Officer
Web address: www.albuquerque.havenbehavioral.com/
Control: Corporation, Investor-owned (for-profit) **Service**: Psychiatric

Staffed Beds: 32

⊞ **HEALTHSOUTH REHABILITATION HOSPITAL OF NEW MEXICO (323027)**, 7000 Jefferson Street NE, Zip 87109–4313; tel. 505/344–9478 **A**1 10 **F**28 29 34 35 56 57 59 60 62 64 74 75 77 79 90 91 93 94 95 96 130 132 143 148 **S** HEALTHSOUTH Corporation, Birmingham, AL
Primary Contact: David S. Nevill, Chief Executive Officer
CFO: Michelle Martinez, Controller
CMO: Angela Walker M.D., Medical Director
CHR: Kristen Hernandez, Director Human Resources
CNO: Karin Jones, Interim Chief Nursing Officer
Web address: www.healthsouthnewmexico.com
Control: Corporation, Investor-owned (for-profit) **Service**: Rehabilitation

Staffed Beds: 87 Admissions: 1648 Census: 59 Births: 0

⊞ **KINDRED HOSPITAL-ALBUQUERQUE (322002)**, 700 High Street NE, Zip 87102–2565; tel. 505/242–4444 **A**1 10 **F**1 3 16 29 30 67 70 75 80 90 91 98 107 130 135 148 **S** Kindred Healthcare, Louisville, KY
Primary Contact: Bud Schawl, Chief Executive Officer
CFO: Sheila Bova, Chief Financial Officer
CMO: Jon Marinaro M.D., Chief Medical Officer
CHR: Donald Whitney, Director Human Resources
CNO: Diane Nelson R.N., Chief Nursing Officer
Web address: www.kindredalbuquerque.com/
Control: Corporation, Investor-owned (for-profit) **Service**: General medical and surgical

Staffed Beds: 61 Admissions: 518 Census: 48 Births: 0

★ ⇑ **LOVELACE MEDICAL CENTER (320009)**, 601 Martin Luther King Avenue NE, Zip 87102–3619; tel. 505/727–8000, (Nonreporting) (Includes HEART HOSPITAL OF NEW MEXICO, 504 Elm Street, Albuquerque, New Mexico, Zip 87102, tel. 505/724–2000; Ronald C Winger, President) **A**3 5 10 21 **S** Ardent Health Services, Nashville, TN
Primary Contact: Troy Greer, Chief Executive Officer
CHR: Helen V Nielsen, Director Human Resources
CNO: Laurie S Bigham R.N., FACHE, Chief Nursing Officer
Web address: www.lovelace.com/albuquerque-hospital/lovelace-medical-center#.UDZ11aDhf48
Control: Corporation, Investor-owned (for-profit) **Service**: General medical and surgical

Staffed Beds: 263

★ △ **LOVELACE REHABILITATION HOSPITAL (323028)**, 505 Elm Street NE, Zip 87102–2500; tel. 505/727–4700, (Nonreporting) **A**5 7 10 **S** Ardent Health Services, Nashville, TN
Primary Contact: Derrick Jones, Chief Executive Officer
CFO: Andrea Solin, Chief Financial Officer
CHR: Helen V Nielsen, Director Human Resources
CNO: Cynthia Rankin, Chief Nursing Officer
Web address: www.lovelace.com
Control: Corporation, Investor-owned (for-profit) **Service**: Rehabilitation

Staffed Beds: 52

★ ⇑ **LOVELACE WESTSIDE HOSPITAL (320074)**, 10501 Golf Course Road NW, Zip 87114–5000, Mailing Address: P.O.Box 25555, 87125–0555; tel. 505/727–8000 **A**5 10 21 **F**3 12 13 15 29 30 34 39 40 41 49 51 57 59 68 70 75 76 79 81 85 93 107 110 111 115 119 130 133 135 146 148 **S** Ardent Health Services, Nashville, TN
Primary Contact: Amy Blasing, Chief Executive Officer
COO: Nancye Cole R.N., Chief Operating Officer
CFO: Andrea Solin, Chief Financial Officer
CNO: Nancye Cole R.N., Chief Nursing Officer and Chief Operating Officer
Web address: www.lovelace.com/albuquerque-hospital/lovelace-westside-hospital#.UDZ1t6Dhf48
Control: Corporation, Investor-owned (for-profit) **Service**: General medical and surgical

Staffed Beds: 80 Admissions: 2636 Census: 22

★ ⇑ **LOVELACE WOMEN'S HOSPITAL (320017)**, 4701 Montgomery Boulevard NE, Zip 87109–1251, Mailing Address: P.O.Box 25555, 87125–0555; tel. 505/727–7800, (Nonreporting) **A**5 10 21 **S** Ardent Health Services, Nashville, TN
Primary Contact: Sheri Milone, Chief Executive Officer and Administrator
COO: Janelle Raborn, Chief Operating Officer
CFO: Joseph Sereno, Chief Financial Officer
CHR: Carol Shelton, Director Human Resources
Web address: www.lovelace.com/albuquerque-hospital/lovelace-womens-hospital#.UDZ17KDhf48
Control: Corporation, Investor-owned (for-profit) **Service**: General medical and surgical

Staffed Beds: 78

⊞ △ **NEW MEXICO VETERANS AFFAIRS HEALTH CARE SYSTEM - RAYMOND G. MURPHY MEDICAL CENTER**, 1501 San Pedro SE, Zip 87108–5153; tel. 505/265–1711, (Nonreporting) **A**1 2 3 5 7 8 **S** Department of Veterans Affairs, Washington, DC
Primary Contact: Andrew Welch, Director
CFO: Michael McNeill, Chief Financial Management
CMO: Meghan Gerety M.D., Chief of Staff
CIO: Ronald Ferrell, Chief Information Officer
CHR: Melvin Hooker, Chief Human Resources
CNO: Tina Prince R.N., Associate Director Patient Care Services, Chief Nursing Officer
Web address: www.albuquerque.va.gov/
Control: Veterans Affairs, Government, federal **Service**: General medical and surgical

Staffed Beds: 203

✠ **PRESBYTERIAN HOSPITAL (320021)**, 1100 Central Avenue SE, Zip 87106–4934, Mailing Address: P.O.Box 26666, 87125–6666; tel. 505/841–1234, (Includes PRESBYTERIAN KASEMAN HOSPITAL, 8300 Constitution Avenue NE, Albuquerque, New Mexico, Zip 87110–7624, P O Box 26666, 87125–6666, tel. 505/291–2000; Doyle Boykin, R.N., MSN, Administrator; PRESBYTERIAN RUST MEDICAL CENTER, 2400 Unser Boulevard SE, Rio Rancho, New Mexico, Zip 87124–4740, tel. 505/253–7878; Jeff McBee, Administrator) **A**1 2 3 5 10 **F**7 8 11 12 13 17 18 19 20 21 22 23 24 25 26 27 28 29 30 31 32 34 35 38 40 42 45 47 48 49 50 51 53 55 56 57 58 59 61 62 63 64 65 68 70 72 74 75 76 77 78 79 80 81 82 84 85 86 87 88 89 91 92 93 96 97 98 99 100 102 103 104 107 108 111 112 114 115 116 117 118 119 121 126 127 128 129 130 131 132 135 138 144 146 147 148 149 **P**6 **S** Presbyterian Healthcare Services, Albuquerque, NM
Primary Contact: Doyle Boykin, R.N., MSN, President
COO: Paul Briggs, Executive Vice President and Chief Operating Officer
CFO: Dale Maxwell, Executive Vice President and Chief Financial Officer
CMO: Jayne McCormick M.D., Chief Medical Officer CDS
CIO: Lee Marley, VP/Information Services Chief Application Officer
CHR: Lee Patchell, Lead Human Resources Business Partner
CNO: Ann L Wright R.N., MSN, Assistant Central Delivery System CNO
Web address: www.phs.org
Control: Other not-for-profit (including NFP Corporation) **Service:** General medical and surgical

Staffed Beds: 616 **Admissions:** 41419 **Census:** 539 **Outpatient Visits:** 2567227 **Births:** 4449 **Total Expense ($000):** 1453738 **Payroll Expense ($000):** 471016 **Personnel:** 5998

TURQUOISE LODGE HOSPITAL, 5901 Zuni Road SE, Zip 87108–3073; tel. 505/841–8978 (Nonreporting)
Primary Contact: Shauna Hartley, Administrator
CFO: Juliette Aragon, Finance Director
CIO: Eric Gurule, Chief Information Officer
CHR: Mario Lechuga, Director Human Resources
CNO: Debra Jane Green R.N., Director of Nursing
Web address: www.health.state.nm.us
Control: State, Government, Nonfederal **Service:** Alcoholism and other chemical dependency

Staffed Beds: 34

✠ **UNIVERSITY OF NEW MEXICO HOSPITALS (320001)**, 2211 Lomas Boulevard NE, Zip 87106–2745; tel. 505/272–2111, (Includes CARRIE TINGLEY HOSPITAL, 1127 University Boulevard NE, Albuquerque, New Mexico, Zip 87102–1715, tel. 505/272–5200; Doris Tinagero, Executive Director; MENTAL HEALTH CENTER, 2600 Marble NE, Albuquerque, New Mexico, Zip 87131–2600, tel. 505/272–2800; UNIVERSITY OF NEW MEXICO Children's hospital psychiatric HOSPITAL, 1001 Yale Boulevard NE, Albuquerque, New Mexico, Zip 87131–3830, tel. 505/272–2890; UNM CHILDREN'S HOSPITAL, 2211 Lomas Boulevard, NE, 3rd Floor of UNM Hospital, Albuquerque, New Mexico, Zip 87106–2745, tel. 505/272–2111) **A**1 2 3 5 8 10 **F**3 8 9 11 13 15 16 18 19 20 21 22 23 24 25 26 27 28 29 30 31 32 34 35 38 40 41 43 44 45 46 47 48 49 50 51 54 56 57 59 60 61 63 64 65 68 70 72 73 74 75 76 77 78 79 81 82 83 84 85 86 87 88 89 90 92 93 94 95 96 97 107 108 109 110 111 114 115 116 117 118 119 121 123 126 129 130 131 132 135 136 138 144 146 147 148 **S** University of New Mexico Hospitals, Albuquerque, NM
Primary Contact: Michael Chicarelli, Interim Chief Executive Officer
CFO: Ella Watt, Chief Financial Officer
CMO: Irene Agostini M.D., Chief Medical Officer
CIO: Dawn Harrington, Chief Information Officer
CHR: Sara Frasch, Chief Human Resource Officer
Web address: www.unm.edu
Control: State, Government, Nonfederal **Service:** General medical and surgical

Staffed Beds: 537 **Admissions:** 28446 **Census:** 419 **Outpatient Visits:** 662047 **Births:** 3024 **Total Expense ($000):** 976157 **Payroll Expense ($000):** 384398 **Personnel:** 6154

ARTESIA—Eddy County

★ **ARTESIA GENERAL HOSPITAL (320030)**, 702 North 13th Street, Zip 88210–1199; tel. 575/748–3333, (Nonreporting) **A**10 20
Primary Contact: Robert C. Tyk, Interim Chief Executive Officer
CFO: Carl Hollingsworth, Chief Financial Officer
CMO: Joe Salgado M.D., Chief of Staff
CHR: Bruce Hinshaw, Director Human Resources
CNO: Wendi Hulett, Chief Nursing Officer
Web address: www.artesiageneral.com
Control: Other not-for-profit (including NFP Corporation) **Service:** General medical and surgical

Staffed Beds: 30

CARLSBAD—Eddy County

✠ **CARLSBAD MEDICAL CENTER (320063)**, 2430 West Pierce Street, Zip 88220–3597; tel. 575/887–4100 **A**1 10 **F**3 11 13 15 18 20 22 29 30 34 35 39 40 41 43 45 46 50 51 54 57 59 64 65 66 74 75 76 77 78 79 81 83 85 86 87 90 91 92 93 107 108 110 111 115 119 120 121 122 123 128 129 135 144 146 147 149 **S** Community Health Systems, Inc., Franklin, TN
Primary Contact: Cathy Hibbs, Chief Executive Officer
CFO: Craig Morse, Chief Financial Officer
CIO: Thomas Motejzik, Director Information Systems
CNO: Connie Shofner, Chief Nursing Officer
Web address: www.carlsbadmedicalcenter.com
Control: Corporation, Investor-owned (for-profit) **Service:** General medical and surgical

Staffed Beds: 115 **Admissions:** 2723 **Census:** 28 **Outpatient Visits:** 66918 **Births:** 427 **Total Expense ($000):** 46542 **Payroll Expense ($000):** 19149 **Personnel:** 277

CLAYTON—Union County

★ **UNION COUNTY GENERAL HOSPITAL (321304)**, 300 Wilson Street, Zip 88415–3304, Mailing Address: P.O.Box 489, 88415–0489; tel. 575/374–2585, (Nonreporting) **A**10 18 **S** Community Hospital Corporation, Plano, TX
Primary Contact: Tammie U. Chavez Stump, R.N., Chief Executive Officer
CFO: Alexander B Altman III, Chief Financial Officer
CMO: Daniel Radunsky M.D., Medical Staff President
CIO: Kelsey Lawrence, Manager Information Technology
CHR: Jill Swagerty, Director Human Resources
CNO: Stacye Bradley R.N., Chief Nursing Officer
Web address: www.ucgh.net/
Control: Other not-for-profit (including NFP Corporation) **Service:** General medical and surgical

Staffed Beds: 21

CLOVIS—Curry County

✠ **PLAINS REGIONAL MEDICAL CENTER (320022)**, 2100 North Doctor Martin Luther King Boulevard, Zip 88101–9412, Mailing Address: P.O.Box 1688, 88102–1688; tel. 575/769–2141 **A**1 10 **F**3 8 11 13 15 20 28 29 30 31 35 39 40 45 47 48 50 51 53 57 58 61 62 63 64 65 68 69 70 75 76 77 78 79 81 84 85 87 89 93 97 107 108 110 111 112 114 115 116 119 120 121 123 129 130 135 146 147 148 149 150 **P**6 **S** Presbyterian Healthcare Services, Albuquerque, NM
Primary Contact: Troy Clark, Interim Administrator
CMO: Brian Willmon M.D., Medical Director
CHR: Cindy Duncan, Manager Human Resources
CNO: Terri A Marney R.N., Director of Nursing
Web address: www.phs.org
Control: Other not-for-profit (including NFP Corporation) **Service:** General medical and surgical

Staffed Beds: 100 **Admissions:** 3667 **Census:** 28 **Outpatient Visits:** 147797 **Births:** 1148 **Total Expense ($000):** 90378 **Payroll Expense ($000):** 31195 **Personnel:** 496

CROWNPOINT—McKinley County

U. S. PUBLIC HEALTH SERVICE INDIAN HOSPITAL (320062), Route 9 and State Road 371, Zip 87313, Mailing Address: P.O.Box 358, 87313–0358; tel. 505/786–5291, (Nonreporting) **A**10 **S** U. S. Indian Health Service, Rockville, MD
Primary Contact: Anslem Roanhorse, Chief Executive Officer
CFO: Darlene Kirk, Manager Finance
CMO: John Johnson M.D., Clinical Director
CIO: Jimmy Burbank, Chief Information Officer
CHR: Christina Bitsilly, Human Resource Specialist
CNO: Alex Daniels, Chief Nurse Executive
Web address: www.ihs.gov
Control: PHS, Indian Service, Government, federal **Service:** General medical and surgical

Staffed Beds: 12

NM

Hospital, Medicare Provider Number, Address, Telephone, Approval, Facility, and Physician Codes, Health Care System

★ American Hospital Association (AHA) membership   ◯ Healthcare Facilities Accreditation Program   ⇑ Center for Improvement in Healthcare Quality Accreditation
□ The Joint Commission accreditation   ◇ DNV Healthcare Inc. accreditation   △ Commission on Accreditation of Rehabilitation Facilities (CARF) accreditation

© 2017 AHA Guide   *Many Facility Codes have changed. Please refer to the AHA Guide Code Chart.*   Hospitals **A425**

DEMING—Luna County

☒ **MIMBRES MEMORIAL HOSPITAL (321309)**, 900 West Ash Street, Zip 88030–4098, Mailing Address: P.O.Box 710, 88031–0710; tel. 575/546–5800, (Nonreporting) **A**1 10 18 **S** Quorum Health, Brentwood, TN
Primary Contact: Kelly Duke, Chief Executive Officer
CFO: Trisha Smith, Chief Financial Officer
CHR: Johanna Gramer, Director Human Resources
CNO: Joy Harrell R.N., Chief Nursing Officer
Web address: www.mimbresmemorial.com
Control: Corporation, Investor-owned (for-profit) **Service**: General medical and surgical

Staffed Beds: 75

ESPANOLA—Rio Arriba County

☒ **PRESBYTERIAN ESPANOLA HOSPITAL (320011)**, 1010 Spruce Street, Zip 87532–2746; tel. 505/753–7111 **A**1 10 20 **F**3 7 8 11 13 15 29 30 32 34 35 40 45 50 51 53 57 59 62 64 68 70 75 76 79 81 85 93 107 108 110 114 115 118 119 129 130 146 149 150 **P**6 **S** Presbyterian Healthcare Services, Albuquerque, NM
Primary Contact: Brenda Romero, Administrator
CFO: Lupe Lucero, Manager Business Office
CMO: Fernando Bayardo M.D., Chief Medical Officer
CHR: Joshua Griffith, Manager Human Resources
CNO: Nancy Santiesteban, Director Patient Care Services
Web address: www.phs.org
Control: Other not-for-profit (including NFP Corporation) **Service**: General medical and surgical

Staffed Beds: 42 Admissions: 2324 Census: 22 Outpatient Visits: 151613 Births: 209 Total Expense ($000): 67020 Payroll Expense ($000): 27279 Personnel: 291

FARMINGTON—San Juan County

☒ ⇑ **SAN JUAN REGIONAL MEDICAL CENTER (320005)**, 801 West Maple Street, Zip 87401–5630; tel. 505/609–2000, (Includes SAN JUAN REGIONAL MEDICAL CENTER REHABILITATION HOSPITAL, 525 South Schwartz Avenue, Farmington, New Mexico, Zip 87401–5955, tel. 505/609–2625; Jeff A. Bourgeois, President and Chief Executive Officer) **A**1 10 21 **F**3 7 8 11 13 15 18 20 22 26 28 29 30 31 32 34 35 39 40 42 43 47 48 49 50 53 54 57 59 60 64 65 68 70 74 75 76 78 79 81 82 85 86 87 89 90 93 96 97 98 99 100 102 107 108 111 112 114 115 118 119 121 130 132 135 143 144 146 148 **P**5 6
Primary Contact: Jeff A. Bourgeois, President and Chief Executive Officer
COO: John Buffington, Chief Operating Officer
CFO: Karen Miller, Chief Financial Officer
CMO: Melania Yeats M.D., Chief Medical Officer
CIO: Sheri Rawlings, Chief Information Officer
CHR: Elizabeth Volkerding, Director Workforce Excellence
CNO: Suzanne E Smith R.N., MSN, Chief Nursing Officer
Web address: www.sanjuanregional.com
Control: Other not-for-profit (including NFP Corporation) **Service**: General medical and surgical

Staffed Beds: 198 Admissions: 9931 Census: 133 Outpatient Visits: 730618 Births: 1174 Total Expense ($000): 294327 Payroll Expense ($000): 140708 Personnel: 1811

GALLUP—Mckinley County

☒ **GALLUP INDIAN MEDICAL CENTER (320061)**, 516 East Nizhoni Boulevard, Zip 87301–5748, Mailing Address: P.O.Box 1337, 87305–1337; tel. 505/722–1000, (Nonreporting) **A**1 5 10 **S** U. S. Indian Health Service, Rockville, MD
Primary Contact: Vida J. Khow, Chief Executive Officer
CFO: Agnes Kee, Financial Manager
CMO: Douglas G Peter M.D., Chief Medical Officer
CIO: Adrian C Haven, Site Manager
CHR: Karen Lee, Director Human Resources
CNO: Selva Thompson R.N., Chief Nurse Executive
Web address: www.ihs.gov/navajo/index.cfm?module=nao_hcc_gallup
Control: PHS, Indian Service, Government, federal **Service**: General medical and surgical

Staffed Beds: 84

★ ⇑ **REHOBOTH MCKINLEY CHRISTIAN HEALTH CARE SERVICES (320038)**, 1901 Red Rock Drive, Zip 87301–5683; tel. 505/863–7000 **A**10 20 21 **F**3 4 5 11 13 15 28 29 30 32 34 35 40 45 50 57 59 62 63 64 65 68 70 74 75 76 77 79 81 82 84 85 86 87 89 93 104 107 108 110 111 115 118 119 129 130 132 135 144 146 149 **P**8
Primary Contact: David Conejo, Chief Executive Officer
COO: William Kiefer, Chief Operating Officer
CFO: John McMullin, Chief Financial Officer
CIO: Randy Myers, Chief Information Officer
CHR: Ronnye Etcitty, Director Human Resources
CNO: Bill Norton, Chief Nursing Officer
Web address: www.rmch.org
Control: Other not-for-profit (including NFP Corporation) **Service**: General medical and surgical

Staffed Beds: 60 Admissions: 2577 Census: 36 Outpatient Visits: 152464 Births: 401 Total Expense ($000): 67400 Payroll Expense ($000): 27621 Personnel: 543

GRANTS—Cibola County

☒ **CIBOLA GENERAL HOSPITAL (321308)**, 1016 East Roosevelt Avenue, Zip 87020–2118; tel. 505/287–4446 **A**1 10 18 **F**3 13 15 29 30 34 40 45 46 50 56 57 59 64 65 66 68 70 75 76 77 81 85 93 97 107 110 115 119 129 130 133 135 147 148 **S** QHR, Brentwood, TN
Primary Contact: Thomas Whelan, Chief Executive Officer
CFO: Ed Brown, Chief Financial Officer
CMO: Janice Shipley M.D., Chief Medical Officer
CIO: Rick Smith, Director Information Services
CHR: Sheila Cox, Director Human Resources
CNO: Glenna Losito R.N., MSN, Chief Nursing Officer
Web address: www.cibolahospital.com
Control: Other not-for-profit (including NFP Corporation) **Service**: General medical and surgical

Staffed Beds: 25 Admissions: 893 Census: 8

HOBBS—Lea County

☒ **LEA REGIONAL MEDICAL CENTER (320065)**, 5419 North Lovington Highway, Zip 88240–9125, Mailing Address: P.O.Box 3000, 88241–9501; tel. 575/492–5000, (Nonreporting) **A**1 10 **S** Community Health Systems, Inc., Franklin, TN
Primary Contact: Timothy Thornell, FACHE, Chief Executive Officer
CFO: Jorge Latibeaudiere, Chief Financial Officer
CMO: Ali Sherif M.D., Chief of Staff
CIO: Terry Purcell, Director Information Services
CHR: Laurie Russell, Director Human Resources
CNO: Patrick A Dunn R.N., Chief Nursing Officer
Web address: www.learegionalmedical.com
Control: Corporation, Investor-owned (for-profit) **Service**: General medical and surgical

Staffed Beds: 195

LAS CRUCES—Dona Ana County

☐ **ADVANCED CARE HOSPITAL OF SOUTHERN NEW MEXICO (322004)**, 4451 East Lohman Avenue, Zip 88011–8267; tel. 575/521–6600 (Nonreporting) **A**1 10 **S** Ernest Health, Inc., Albuquerque, NM
Primary Contact: Claudia Saiz, Chief Operating Officer
Web address: www.achsnm.ernesthealth.com
Control: Corporation, Investor-owned (for-profit) **Service**: Acute long-term care hospital

Staffed Beds: 40

☒ **MEMORIAL MEDICAL CENTER (320018)**, 2450 South Telshor Boulevard, Zip 88011–5076; tel. 575/522–8641 **A**1 2 3 10 13 **F**3 8 11 13 15 17 18 20 22 24 26 28 29 30 31 34 35 40 45 49 50 51 54 57 59 64 65 68 70 72 73 74 75 76 78 79 81 84 87 89 97 98 107 108 109 110 111 114 115 118 119 120 121 122 123 130 146 147 **S** LifePoint Health, Brentwood, TN
Primary Contact: John Harris, Chief Executive Officer
COO: Steven T Ruwoldt, Chief Operating Officer
CFO: Raymond Grenier, Chief Financial Officer
CMO: Bruce San Filippo M.D., Chief Medical Officer
CHR: Laura Pierce, Director Human Resources
CNO: Ann Debooy R.N., Chief Nursing Officer
Web address: www.mmclc.org
Control: Corporation, Investor-owned (for-profit) **Service**: General medical and surgical

Staffed Beds: 173 Admissions: 8347 Census: 108 Outpatient Visits: 168565 Births: 1212 Total Expense ($000): 194609 Payroll Expense ($000): 74595 Personnel: 1145

NM

Many Facility Codes have changed. Please refer to the AHA Guide Code Chart. © 2017 AHA Guide

⊠ **MESILLA VALLEY HOSPITAL (324010)**, 3751 Del Rey Boulevard, Zip 88012–8526; tel. 575/382–3500 **A**1 10 **F**87 98 99 100 101 103 106 **S** Universal Health Services, Inc., King of Prussia, PA
Primary Contact: Dana McRimmon, Interim Chief Executive Officer
CFO: Dana McRimmon, Chief Financial Officer
CMO: Arthur L. Ramirez M.D., Medical Director
CIO: Rebecca Mumpower, Director Marketing
CHR: Linda Moya, Director Human Resources
CNO: Veronica Hughes, Chief Nursing Officer
Web address: www.mesillavalleyhospital.com
Control: Corporation, Investor-owned (for-profit) **Service:** Psychiatric

Staffed Beds: 105 **Admissions:** 2969 **Census:** 115 **Outpatient Visits:** 0 **Births:** 0

⊠ **MOUNTAINVIEW REGIONAL MEDICAL CENTER (320085)**, 4311 East Lohman Avenue, Zip 88011–8255; tel. 575/556–7600, (Nonreporting) **A**1 10 12 13 **S** Community Health Systems, Inc., Franklin, TN
Primary Contact: Denten Park, Chief Executive Officer
COO: Warren Yehl, Chief Operating Officer
CFO: Nathan Crabdree, Chief Financial Officer
CIO: Donald Harlow, Director of Information Services
CHR: Delilah Doss, Director, Human Resources
CNO: Gayle Nash R.N., M.P.H., Chief Nursing Officer
Web address: www.mountainviewregional.com
Control: Corporation, Investor-owned (for-profit) **Service:** General medical and surgical

Staffed Beds: 142

⊠ **REHABILITATION HOSPITAL OF SOUTHERN NEW MEXICO (323032)**, 4441 East Lohman Avenue, Zip 88011–8267; tel. 575/521–6400, (Nonreporting) **A**1 10 **S** Ernest Health, Inc., Albuquerque, NM
Primary Contact: Sabrina Martin, Chief Executive Officer
CFO: Elizabeth Striplin, Chief Financial Officer
CMO: Kimberly Encapera M.D., Medical Director
CIO: Ricky Molina, Director Marketing and Business Development
CHR: Yolanda Mendoza, Director Human Resources
CNO: Carole Carson, Director of Nursing Operations
Web address: www.rhsnm.ernesthealth.com
Control: Corporation, Investor-owned (for-profit) **Service:** Rehabilitation

Staffed Beds: 40

LAS VEGAS—San Miguel County

⊠ **ALTA VISTA REGIONAL HOSPITAL (320003)**, 104 Legion Drive, Zip 87701–4804; tel. 505/426–3500, (Nonreporting) **A**1 10 20 **S** Quorum Health, Brentwood, TN
Primary Contact: Caler O'Rear, Interim Chief Executive Officer
CMO: Nancy Wright M.D., Chief Medical Staff
CIO: Laird Thornton, Director Information Systems
CHR: Michael Freeman, Director Human Resources
CNO: Rhonda Clark, Interim Chief Nursing Officer
Web address: www.altavistaregionalhospital.com
Control: Corporation, Investor-owned (for-profit) **Service:** General medical and surgical

Staffed Beds: 54

☐ **NEW MEXICO BEHAVIORAL HEALTH INSTITUTE AT LAS VEGAS**, 3695 Hot Springs Boulevard, Zip 87701–9549; tel. 505/454–2100, (Nonreporting) **A**1
Primary Contact: Frances Tweed, R.N., Executive Director and Administrator
COO: Charles Jaramillo, Chief Operating Officer
CFO: Darlene Martinez, Director Finance
CMO: Daniel Collins M.D., Clinical Director
CNO: Mabel Arguello-Vasquez R.N., Executive Nurse Administrator
Web address: www.nmbhi.org
Control: State, Government, Nonfederal **Service:** Psychiatric

Staffed Beds: 257

LOS ALAMOS—Los Alamos County

⊠ **LOS ALAMOS MEDICAL CENTER (320033)**, 3917 West Road, Zip 87544–2293; tel. 505/661–9500 **A**1 10 20 **F**3 8 11 13 15 28 29 30 31 34 35 40 45 46 49 50 57 59 64 65 68 70 73 75 76 78 79 81 85 86 87 90 107 108 110 111 115 119 124 129 130 135 143 146 147 148 **P**8 **S** LifePoint Health, Brentwood, TN
Primary Contact: John Whiteside, Chief Executive Officer
CFO: Steve Weingart, Chief Financial Officer
CMO: Barbara Van Eeckhout M.D., Chief of Staff
CIO: Kevin Vigil, Director Information Systems
CHR: Jacqueline Carroll, Director Human Resources
CNO: Tracie Stratton, Chief Nursing Officer
Web address: www.losalamosmedicalcenter.com
Control: Corporation, Investor-owned (for-profit) **Service:** General medical and surgical

Staffed Beds: 29 **Admissions:** 1052 **Census:** 9 **Outpatient Visits:** 54890 **Births:** 223 **Total Expense ($000):** 37888 **Payroll Expense ($000):** 13257 **Personnel:** 283

LOVINGTON—Lea County

★ ⇑ **NOR-LEA HOSPITAL DISTRICT (321305)**, 1600 North Main Avenue, Zip 88260–2871; tel. 575/396–6611 **A**10 18 21 **F**3 9 15 18 26 28 29 30 31 32 34 35 39 40 43 45 46 49 50 51 54 57 59 64 65 66 68 74 75 77 78 81 82 89 92 93 97 100 101 102 103 104 107 108 110 111 115 119 127 129 130 132 133 135 147 148 **P**6
Primary Contact: David B. Shaw, Chief Executive Officer and Administrator
COO: Dan Hamilton, Chief Operating Officer
CFO: Allyson Roberts CPA, Chief Financial Officer
CMO: Ronald Hopkins D.O., Chief of Staff
CIO: Brent Kelley, Director Information Technology
CHR: Angela Carrejo, MPA, Director Human Resources
CNO: Marcia Patterson MSN, R.N., Chief Nursing Officer
Web address: www.norlea.org/
Control: Hospital district or authority, Government, Nonfederal **Service:** General medical and surgical

Staffed Beds: 25 **Admissions:** 488 **Census:** 5 **Births:** 0

MESCALERO—Otero County

☐ **MESCALERO PUBLIC HEALTH SERVICE INDIAN HOSPITAL (320058)**, 318 Abalone Loop, Zip 88340, Mailing Address: Box 210, 88340–0210; tel. 505/464–3801, (Nonreporting) **A**1 10 **S** U. S. Indian Health Service, Rockville, MD
Primary Contact: Dorlynn Simmons, Chief Executive Officer
CFO: Rainey Enjady, Administrative Officer
CIO: Kathy Murphy, Site Manager
Web address: www.ihs.gov
Control: PHS, Indian Service, Government, federal **Service:** General medical and surgical

Staffed Beds: 13

PORTALES—Roosevelt County

⇑ **ROOSEVELT GENERAL HOSPITAL (320084)**, 42121 U S Highway 70, Zip 88130, Mailing Address: P.O.Box 868, 88130–0868; tel. 575/359–1800 (Nonreporting) **A**10 21
CFO: Eva Steven, Chief Financial Officer
CMO: Les Donaldson M.D., Chief of Staff
CHR: Cindy Duncan, Director Human Resources
Web address: www.myrgh.org
Control: Hospital district or authority, Government, Nonfederal **Service:** General medical and surgical

Staffed Beds: 22

RATON—Colfax County

★ **MINERS' COLFAX MEDICAL CENTER (321307)**, 200 Hospital Drive, Zip 87740–2099; tel. 575/445–7700, (Includes MINERS' HOSPITAL OF NEW MEXICO, Hospital Drive, Raton, New Mexico, Zip 87740, Box 1067, 87740, tel. 505/445–2741) **A**10 18 **F**11 13 15 18 34 40 45 46 50 53 54 56 57 58 59 65 70 71 75 76 77 78 81 82 85 86 87 97 107 115 119 127 129 130 132 133 135 146 147 148
Primary Contact: Bo Beames, Interim Chief Executive Officer
CFO: Albino Martinez, Director Budget and Finance
CIO: Richard Laner Jr, Manager Information Systems
CHR: Jamie Johnson, Director Human Resources
Web address: www.minershosp.com
Control: State, Government, Nonfederal **Service:** General medical and surgical

Staffed Beds: 25 **Admissions:** 650 **Census:** 7

NM

Hospital, Medicare Provider Number, Address, Telephone, Approval, Facility, and Physician Codes, Health Care System

★ American Hospital Association (AHA) membership   ○ Healthcare Facilities Accreditation Program   ⇑ Center for Improvement in Healthcare Quality Accreditation
☐ The Joint Commission accreditation   ◇ DNV Healthcare Inc. accreditation   △ Commission on Accreditation of Rehabilitation Facilities (CARF) accreditation

RIO RANCHO—Sandoval County

☐ **UNM SANDOVAL REGIONAL MEDICAL CENTER, INC. (320089)**, 3001 Broadmoor Boulevard NE, Zip 87131; tel. 505/994–7000 **A**1 3 5 10 **F**3 7 15 29 30 35 40 43 45 46 47 48 49 50 70 79 80 81 85 86 87 93 97 98 103 107 108 110 111 114 115 119 126 129 130 143 146 147 **P**8 **S** University of New Mexico Hospitals, Albuquerque, NM
Primary Contact: Jamie A. Silva-Steele, FACHE, R.N., President and Chief Executive Officer
CFO: Darlene Fernandez, Chief Financial Officer
CMO: Robb McLean M.D., Chief Medical Officer
CIO: Matthew Braun, Chief Information Officer
CHR: Correen Bales, Executive Director Human Resources
CNO: Pamela Demarest MSN, R.N., Chief Nursing Officer
Web address: www.hsc.unm.edu/health/locations/sandoval-regional-medical-center.html
Control: Other not-for-profit (including NFP Corporation) **Service:** General medical and surgical

Staffed Beds: 72 **Admissions:** 4544 **Census:** 43 **Outpatient Visits:** 58639 **Births:** 0 **Total Expense ($000):** 91243 **Payroll Expense ($000):** 32450 **Personnel:** 408

ROSWELL—Chaves County

☒ **EASTERN NEW MEXICO MEDICAL CENTER (320006)**, 405 West Country Club Road, Zip 88201–5209; tel. 575/622–8170, (Nonreporting) **A**1 10 19 **S** Community Health Systems, Inc., Franklin, TN
Primary Contact: Rodney Schumacher, Chief Executive Officer
COO: Warren Yehl, Chief Operating Officer
CFO: Leanne Hacker, Chief Financial Officer
CMO: Richard Pinon, Chief Medical Officer
CIO: Deepak Surl, Chief Information Officer
CHR: Sheila Nunez, Director Human Resources
CNO: Kathy Williams, Chief Nursing Officer
Web address: www.enmmc.com
Control: Corporation, Investor-owned (for-profit) **Service:** General medical and surgical

Staffed Beds: 149

★ **LOVELACE REGIONAL HOSPITAL - ROSWELL (320086)**, 117 East 19th Street, Zip 88201–5151; tel. 575/627–7000 **A**10 13 **F**3 13 17 18 22 29 34 40 42 45 57 59 70 76 79 81 82 85 89 90 91 93 111 119 130 146 147 **S** Ardent Health Services, Nashville, TN
Primary Contact: Heather L. Harper, FACHE, Chief Executive Officer
CFO: Veronica Galaviz, Chief Financial Officer
CNO: Rhonda Rauch, Chief Nursing Officer
Web address: www.lovelace.com
Control: Corporation, Investor-owned (for-profit) **Service:** General medical and surgical

Staffed Beds: 26 **Admissions:** 2248 **Census:** 16

☐ **NEW MEXICO REHABILITATION CENTER (323026)**, 72 Gail Harris Street, Zip 88203–8116; tel. 575/347–3400, (Nonreporting) (Includes PECOS VALLEY LODGE, 31 Gail Harris Avenue, Roswell, New Mexico, Zip 88201, tel. 505/347–5491) **A**1 10
Primary Contact: Jose Gurrola, Administrator
CFO: Shirley Donaldson, Chief Financial Officer
CMO: Stephen Dorman M.D., Chief Medical Officer
CIO: Dennis Hoefs, Manager Information Technology
CHR: Teresa Casarez, Director Human Resources
CNO: William Chaltry, Chief Nursing Officer
Control: State, Government, Nonfederal **Service:** Rehabilitation

Staffed Beds: 41

RUIDOSO—Lincoln County

☒ **LINCOLN COUNTY MEDICAL CENTER (321306)**, 211 Sudderth Drive, Zip 88345–6043, Mailing Address: P.O.Box 8000, 88355–8000; tel. 575/257–8200 **A**1 10 18 **F**7 11 13 15 29 30 34 35 39 40 45 46 50 53 56 57 59 64 65 68 70 76 77 79 81 85 87 91 93 97 107 110 111 115 119 127 130 131 132 135 144 146 148 **P**6 **S** Presbyterian Healthcare Services, Albuquerque, NM
Primary Contact: Todd Oberheu, Administrator
CFO: Dudley McCauley, Controller
CMO: Gary Jackson D.O., Medical Director
CHR: Susanne Johnston, Manager Human Resources
Web address: www.phs.org
Control: Other not-for-profit (including NFP Corporation) **Service:** General medical and surgical

Staffed Beds: 25 **Admissions:** 1276 **Census:** 10 **Outpatient Visits:** 89532 **Births:** 227 **Total Expense ($000):** 41841 **Payroll Expense ($000):** 18151 **Personnel:** 251

SANTA FE—Santa Fe County

☒ △ **CHRISTUS ST. VINCENT REGIONAL MEDICAL CENTER (320002)**, 455 St. Michael's Drive, Zip 87505–7663, Mailing Address: P.O.Box 2107, 87505; tel. 505/983–3361, (Includes CHRISTUS ST. VINCENT PHYSICIANS MEDICAL CENTER, 2990 Rodeo Park Drive East, Santa Fe, New Mexico, Zip 87505, tel. 505/428–5400; J. Alex Valdez, JD, President and Chief Executive Officer) **A**1 2 3 7 10 20 **F**8 12 13 15 17 18 19 20 21 22 24 26 28 29 30 31 32 34 35 36 37 38 39 40 41 43 45 46 47 48 49 50 51 53 54 56 57 64 65 66 68 70 73 74 75 77 78 79 81 82 83 84 85 86 87 88 90 91 92 93 97 98 100 101 102 103 104 107 108 109 110 111 112 113 114 115 119 120 121 122 124 126 129 130 131 132 135 143 144 146 147 148 149 150 **S** CHRISTUS Health, Irving, TX
Primary Contact: Patrick Brian. Carrier, President and Chief Executive Officer
COO: Jason Adams, Chief Operating Officer
CFO: Bob Moon, Chief Financial Officer
CMO: John C Beeson M.D., Chief Medical Officer
CIO: Ron Dekeyzer, Regional Director Information Systems
CHR: Pearl Mohnkern, Vice President and Director Human Resources
Web address: www.stvin.org
Control: Other not-for-profit (including NFP Corporation) **Service:** General medical and surgical

Staffed Beds: 219 **Admissions:** 11823 **Census:** 136 **Outpatient Visits:** 141418 **Births:** 1249 **Total Expense ($000):** 371697 **Payroll Expense ($000):** 143807 **Personnel:** 1763

☐ **PHS SANTA FE INDIAN HOSPITAL (320057)**, 1700 Cerrillos Road, Zip 87505–3554; tel. 505/988–9821, (Nonreporting) **A**1 5 10 **S** U. S. Indian Health Service, Rockville, MD
Primary Contact: Leslie Dye, Chief Executive Officer
CMO: Bret Smoker M.D., Clinical Director
CIO: Vernita Jones, Site Manager
Control: PHS, Indian Service, Government, federal **Service:** General medical and surgical

Staffed Beds: 4

SANTA ROSA—Guadalupe County

★ **GUADALUPE COUNTY HOSPITAL (320067)**, 117 Camino de Vida, Zip 88435–2267; tel. 575/472–3417 **A**10 20 **F**3 29 34 35 40 50 57 59 64 65 81 82 87 107 114 119 130 148 **P**5
Primary Contact: Christina Campos, Administrator
CFO: Bret Goebel, Chief Financial Officer
CMO: Randal Brown M.D., Chief of Medical Staff
CIO: Emilio Campos, Deparment Head Information Technology
CHR: Colleen Gallegos, Director Human Resources
CNO: Mandelyn Cordova R.N., Director of Nurses
Web address: www.gchnm.org
Control: County, Government, Nonfederal **Service:** General medical and surgical

Staffed Beds: 10 **Admissions:** 230 **Census:** 2

SANTA TERESA—Dona Ana County

☐ **PEAK BEHAVIORAL HEALTH SERVICES (324012)**, 5065 McNutt Road, Zip 88008–9442; tel. 575/589–3000 **A**1 10 **F**35 59 98 99 100 102 103 105 106 **S** Strategic Behavioral Health, LLC, Memphis, TN
Primary Contact: Peggy Cunningham, Chief Executive Officer
COO: Doug Ginn, Executive Vice President Operations
CFO: Espie Herrara, Chief Financial Officer
CHR: Norma Oaxaca, Director Human Resources
Web address: www.peakbehavioral.com/
Control: Individual, Investor-owned (for-profit) **Service:** Psychiatric

Staffed Beds: 120 **Admissions:** 1919 **Census:** 70 **Outpatient Visits:** 0 **Births:** 0 **Total Expense ($000):** 12847

SHIPROCK—San Juan County

☒ **NORTHERN NAVAJO MEDICAL CENTER (320059)**, Highway 491 North, Zip 87420–0160, Mailing Address: P.O.Box 160, 87420–0160; tel. 505/368–6001 **A**1 10 **F**2 3 8 13 15 29 30 32 34 35 36 38 39 40 44 45 48 50 51 53 54 57 59 61 62 63 64 65 68 70 75 76 77 79 81 82 83 84 85 86 87 89 93 97 99 100 101 102 103 104 105 107 110 115 119 127 130 131 132 134 135 144 147 148 149 150 **S** U. S. Indian Health Service, Rockville, MD
Primary Contact: Fannessa Comer, Chief Executive Officer
CFO: Shawn Morgan, Finance Officer
CMO: Ira Salom M.D., Clinical Director
CIO: Roland Chapman, Chief Information Officer
CHR: Gloria Redhorse-Charley, Director Human Resources
CNO: Lavenia Diswood R.N., Chief Nurse Executive
Web address: www.ihs.gov/
Control: PHS, Indian Service, Government, federal **Service:** General medical and surgical

Staffed Beds: 68 **Admissions:** 1779 **Census:** 19 **Outpatient Visits:** 311510 **Births:** 432 **Total Expense ($000):** 147235 **Payroll Expense ($000):** 71109 **Personnel:** 405

NM

Many Facility Codes have changed. Please refer to the AHA Guide Code Chart. © 2017 AHA Guide

SILVER CITY—Grant County

☐ **GILA REGIONAL MEDICAL CENTER (320016)**, 1313 East 32nd Street,
Zip 88061–7251; tel. 575/538–4000 **A**1 3 10 20 **F**3 11 13 14 15 18 29 30 31
35 40 45 50 51 53 64 68 70 76 77 78 79 81 82 85 87 89 93 97 98 100 102
103 107 110 111 115 119 120 123 129 130 132 148 149
Primary Contact: Taffy J. Arias, Chief Executive Officer
CFO: Craig Stewart, Chief Financial Officer
CIO: David Furnas, Chief Information Officer
CHR: Barbara Barela, Director Human Resources
CNO: Patricia Sheyka, Chief Nursing Officer
Web address: www.grmc.org
Control: County, Government, Nonfederal **Service**: General medical and surgical

Staffed Beds: 47 **Admissions:** 2247 **Census:** 18 **Outpatient Visits:** 69629
Births: 351 **Total Expense ($000):** 75966 **Payroll Expense ($000):** 30805
Personnel: 432

SOCORRO—Socorro County

✠ **SOCORRO GENERAL HOSPITAL (321301)**, 1202 Highway 60 West,
Zip 87801–3914, Mailing Address: P.O.Box 1009, 87801–1009; tel. 575/835–
1140 **A**1 10 18 **F**3 8 11 13 15 29 30 34 40 45 57 59 62 63 64 65 68 75
76 77 81 83 85 91 93 100 103 107 114 130 132 133 134 135 146 147 **P**6 **S**
Presbyterian Healthcare Services, Albuquerque, NM
Primary Contact: Veronica Pound, R.N., Administrator
CFO: Scott Shannon, Director Finance
CMO: Darla Bejnar M.D., Chief Medical Officer
CHR: Pam Miller-Balfour, Director Human Resources
CNO: Veronica Pound R.N., Interim Administrator and Director of Patient Care
Web address: www.phs.org
Control: Other not-for-profit (including NFP Corporation) **Service**: General medical and surgical

Staffed Beds: 18 **Admissions:** 411 **Census:** 4 **Outpatient Visits:** 68069
Births: 107 **Total Expense ($000):** 28443 **Payroll Expense ($000):** 13788
Personnel: 197

TAOS—Taos County

★ ⇧ **HOLY CROSS HOSPITAL (320013)**, 1397 Weimer Road, Zip 87571–6253;
tel. 575/758–8883 **A**3 10 20 21 **F**3 11 13 15 18 29 30 32 34 35 36 40 45 46
50 59 64 68 75 77 79 80 81 85 86 87 90 91 93 97 100 102 107 110 114 115
118 119 130 132 145 146 147 148 149 **P**6 8 **S** QHR, Brentwood, TN
Primary Contact: William D. Patten Jr, Chief Executive Officer
CFO: Steve Rozenboom, Chief Financial Officer
CHR: Judy Marshall, Director Human Resources
CNO: Denise Clark, Chief Nursing Officer
Web address: www.taoshospital.org
Control: Other not-for-profit (including NFP Corporation) **Service**: General medical and surgical

Staffed Beds: 29 **Admissions:** 1565 **Census:** 14 **Outpatient Visits:** 63040
Births: 214 **Total Expense ($000):** 48979 **Payroll Expense ($000):** 20490
Personnel: 335

TRUTH OR CONSEQUENCES—Sierra County

★ ⇧ **SIERRA VISTA HOSPITAL (321300)**, 800 East Ninth Avenue, Zip 87901–
1961; tel. 575/894–2111 **A**10 18 21 **F**7 11 15 16 30 34 40 54 57 59 65 67 93
99 102 104 107 110 127 128 130 133
Primary Contact: Thomas Dandridge, Interim Chief Executive Officer
CFO: Bret Gobel, Chief Financial Officer
CMO: James F Malcolmson M.D., Chief of Staff
CIO: Dan Morrell, Manager Information Systems
CHR: Mindee Holguin, Manager Human Resources
CNO: Palmer Greene R.N., Chief Nursing Officer
Web address: www.svhnm.org
Control: City-county, Government, Nonfederal **Service**: General medical and surgical

Staffed Beds: 15 **Admissions:** 587 **Census:** 6

TUCUMCARI—Quay County

★ **DR. DAN C. TRIGG MEMORIAL HOSPITAL (321302)**, 301 East Miel De
Luna Avenue, Zip 88401–3810, Mailing Address: P.O.Box 608, 88401–0608;
tel. 575/461–7000 **A**10 18 **F**11 15 29 35 38 40 45 59 62 63 64 65 68 81
85 87 97 104 107 110 114 119 130 133 135 146 148 **P**6 **S** Presbyterian
Healthcare Services, Albuquerque, NM
Primary Contact: Troy Clark, Interim Administrator
CMO: Darrell Willis M.D., Chief of Staff
CNO: Vickie Gutierrez, Director of Patient Care
Web address: www.phs.org
Control: Other not-for-profit (including NFP Corporation) **Service**: General medical and surgical

Staffed Beds: 25 **Admissions:** 170 **Census:** 2 **Outpatient Visits:** 45232
Births: 0 **Total Expense ($000):** 20155 **Payroll Expense ($000):** 5598
Personnel: 79

ZUNI—McKinley County

☐ **U. S. PUBLIC HEALTH SERVICE INDIAN HOSPITAL (320060)**, Route 301
North B Street, Zip 87327, Mailing Address: P.O.Box 467, 87327–0467;
tel. 505/782–4431, (Nonreporting) **A**1 10 **S** U. S. Indian Health Service, Rockville,
MD
Primary Contact: Jean Othole, Chief Executive Officer
CFO: Clyde Yatsattie, Administrative Officer
CMO: David Kessler M.D., Clinical Director
CHR: Cynthia Tsalate, Human Resource Specialist
Web address: www.ihs.gov
Control: PHS, Indian Service, Government, federal **Service**: General medical and surgical

Staffed Beds: 32

NM

Hospital, Medicare Provider Number, Address, Telephone, Approval, Facility, and Physician Codes, Health Care System

★ American Hospital Association (AHA) membership   ○ Healthcare Facilities Accreditation Program   ⇧ Center for Improvement in Healthcare Quality Accreditation
☐ The Joint Commission accreditation   ◇ DNV Healthcare Inc. accreditation   △ Commission on Accreditation of Rehabilitation Facilities (CARF) accreditation

NEW YORK

ALBANY—Albany County

☐ **ALBANY MEDICAL CENTER (330013)**, 43 New Scotland Avenue, Zip 12208–3478; tel. 518/262–3125, (Includes ALBANY MEDICAL CENTER SOUTH-CLINICAL CAMPUS, 25 Hackett Boulevard, Albany, New York, Zip 12208–3499, tel. 518/242–1200; Timothy W Duffy, General Director) **A**1 2 3 5 8 10 19 **F**3 6 7 8 11 12 13 15 17 18 19 20 21 22 23 24 25 26 27 28 29 30 31 32 34 35 38 39 40 41 43 44 45 46 47 49 50 51 52 53 54 55 56 57 58 59 60 61 64 65 68 70 72 73 74 75 76 77 78 79 81 82 85 86 87 88 89 90 92 93 96 98 100 102 103 104 105 107 108 109 110 111 114 115 116 117 118 119 120 121 122 123 124 126 130 131 132 135 138 142 145 146 148
Primary Contact: James J. Barba, President and Chief Executive Officer
COO: Bernadette R Pedlow, Senior Vice President Business and Chief Operating Officer
CFO: Frances Spreer-Albert, Chief Financial Officer and Executive Vice President
CMO: Dennis McKenna M.D., Interim Vice President Medical Affairs
CIO: George Hickman, Executive Vice President and Chief Information Officer
Web address: www.amc.edu
Control: Other not-for-profit (including NFP Corporation) **Service**: General medical and surgical

Staffed Beds: 732 **Admissions**: 38841 **Census**: 629 **Outpatient Visits**: 379342 **Births**: 1980 **Total Expense ($000)**: 926535 **Payroll Expense ($000)**: 293671 **Personnel**: 5963

★ **ALBANY MEMORIAL HOSPITAL (330003)**, 600 Northern Boulevard, Zip 12204–1083; tel. 518/471–3221 **A**10 **F**3 8 15 29 30 31 34 40 45 46 49 50 54 57 59 60 63 64 68 70 77 79 81 84 85 87 93 107 111 119 130 135 146 147 148 149 **S** Trinity Health, Livonia, MI
Primary Contact: Virginia L. Golden, Chief Executive Officer
CFO: Lori Santos, Vice President Finance
CMO: Robert Cella M.D., Chief Medical Officer
CHR: Judy Gray, Vice President Human Resources
Web address: www.nehealth.com
Control: Other not-for-profit (including NFP Corporation) **Service**: General medical and surgical

Staffed Beds: 74 **Admissions**: 2910 **Census**: 40 **Births**: 0 **Personnel**: 549

⊞ △ **ALBANY STRATTON VETERANS AFFAIRS MEDICAL CENTER**, 113 Holland Avenue, Zip 12208–3473; tel. 518/626–5000, (Total facility includes 50 beds in nursing home–type unit) **A**1 2 3 5 7 8 **F**2 3 4 5 15 17 18 20 22 28 29 30 31 34 35 39 40 44 45 46 47 49 54 55 56 57 58 59 60 61 62 63 64 65 68 70 74 75 77 78 79 81 82 83 84 85 86 87 91 92 93 94 97 98 100 102 103 104 107 108 110 111 115 117 118 119 120 121 122 123 126 127 128 129 130 132 135 143 146 147 148 149 150 **S** Department of Veterans Affairs, Washington, DC
Primary Contact: Darlene DeLancey, Interim Director
CFO: Gerard Scorzelli, Chief Financial Officer
CMO: Lourdes Irizarry M.D., Chief of Staff
CIO: Ron Diaz, Manager Operations
CHR: Kenneth Kio, Manager Human Resources
CNO: Deborah Spath R.N., MSN, Associate Director Patient and Nurses Services
Web address: www.albany.va.gov/
Control: Veterans Affairs, Government, federal **Service**: General medical and surgical

Staffed Beds: 121 **Admissions**: 2732 **Census**: 46 **Outpatient Visits**: 339913 **Births**: 0 **Total Expense ($000)**: 258559 **Payroll Expense ($000)**: 140400 **Personnel**: 1259

☐ **CAPITAL DISTRICT PSYCHIATRIC CENTER (334046)**, 75 New Scotland Avenue, Zip 12208–3474; tel. 518/549–6000, (Nonreporting) **A**1 3 5 10 **S** New York State Office of Mental Health, Albany, NY
Primary Contact: William Dickson, Executive Director
COO: Catherine McGregor, Deputy Director Facility and Administrative Services
CMO: Kren K Shriver M.D., Clinical Director
CNO: Charlene Puorto, Chief Nursing Officer
Web address: www.omh.ny.gov/omhweb/facilities/cdpc/facility.htm
Control: State, Government, Nonfederal **Service**: Psychiatric

Staffed Beds: 200

⊞ **ST. PETER'S HOSPITAL (330057)**, 315 South Manning Boulevard, Zip 12208–1789; tel. 518/525–1550 **A**1 2 3 5 10 19 **F**4 5 8 11 12 13 15 17 18 19 20 21 22 23 24 26 27 28 29 30 31 34 35 36 37 38 39 40 45 46 47 48 49 50 51 53 54 56 57 59 60 61 62 63 64 65 66 68 69 70 71 72 73 74 75 76 77 78 79 81 82 84 85 86 87 89 92 93 97 107 108 109 110 111 114 115 116 117 118 119 120 121 123 124 126 129 130 132 133 135 143 145 146 147 148 **P**6 **S** Trinity Health, Livonia, MI
Primary Contact: Virginia L. Golden, Chief Executive Officer
CFO: Lori Santos, Chief Financial Officer
CMO: Robert Cella M.D., Chief Medical Officer
CHR: Judy Gray, Vice President Human Resources
CNO: Jane O'Rourke R.N., Chief Nursing Officer, Vice President Operations
Web address: www.sphcs.org
Control: Church operated, Nongovernment, not-for-profit **Service**: General medical and surgical

Staffed Beds: 442 **Admissions**: 25586 **Census**: 368 **Births**: 2728 **Personnel**: 2924

ALEXANDRIA BAY—Jefferson County

★ **RIVER HOSPITAL (331309)**, 4 Fuller Street, Zip 13607–1316; tel. 315/482–2511, (Nonreporting) **A**10 18
Primary Contact: Ben Moore III, President and Chief Executive Officer
COO: William Connor, Assistant Administrator and Director Human Resources
CFO: Traci Mintonye, Chief Financial Officer
CMO: Prasad Yitta M.D., Medical Director
CIO: John Smithers, Network Specialist
CHR: William Connor, Assistant Administrator and Director Human Resources
CNO: Ann Narrow, Director of Nursing
Web address: www.riverhospital.org
Control: Other not-for-profit (including NFP Corporation) **Service**: General medical and surgical

Staffed Beds: 11

AMITYVILLE—Suffolk County

☐ **BRUNSWICK PSYCH CENTER (334026)**, 81 Louden Avenue, Zip 11701–2736; tel. 631/789–7421 (Nonreporting) **A**1 10
Primary Contact: Amarjit Singh, M.D., President and Chief Executive Officer
Control: Corporation, Investor-owned (for-profit) **Service**: Psychiatric

Staffed Beds: 50

⊞ **SOUTH OAKS HOSPITAL (334027)**, 400 Sunrise Highway, Zip 11701–2508; tel. 631/264–4000 **A**1 3 10 **F**4 5 50 53 68 98 99 103 104 105 135 **P**5 6 **S** Northwell Health, New Hyde Park, NY
Primary Contact: Lenny Nartowicz, Executive Director
CMO: Tina Walch M.D., Medical Director
CHR: Irene Calvin, Vice President Human Resources
Web address: www.longislandhome.org
Control: Other not-for-profit (including NFP Corporation) **Service**: Psychiatric

Staffed Beds: 258 **Admissions**: 6143 **Census**: 160 **Outpatient Visits**: 96849 **Births**: 0 **Total Expense ($000)**: 70402 **Payroll Expense ($000)**: 43186 **Personnel**: 742

AMSTERDAM—Montgomery County

⊞ **ST. MARY'S HEALTHCARE (330047)**, 427 Guy Park Avenue, Zip 12010–1054; tel. 518/842–1900, (Includes ST. MARY'S HEALTHCARE, 427 Guy Park Avenue, Amsterdam, New York, Zip 12010–1054, tel. 518/842–1900; Victor Giulianelli, FACHE, President and Chief Executive Officer) (Total facility includes 160 beds in nursing home–type unit) **A**1 10 **F**2 3 4 5 8 11 13 15 17 28 29 30 31 34 35 36 38 40 45 46 49 50 51 54 56 57 59 60 61 65 66 68 70 71 74 75 76 77 78 79 81 84 85 86 87 89 90 93 94 96 97 98 99 100 101 102 103 104 105 106 107 108 110 111 115 118 119 126 127 128 130 131 132 135 144 145 146 147 149 150 **S** Ascension Healthcare, Saint Louis, MO
Primary Contact: Victor Giulianelli, FACHE, President and Chief Executive Officer
COO: Scott Bruce, Vice President Operations
CFO: Rick Henze, Chief Financial Officer
CMO: William Mayer M.D., Vice President Medical Staff Services
CIO: Leigh Chiuminetta, Interim Chief Information Officer
CHR: Albert Turo, Vice President Human Resources
CNO: Michele M Walsh, Chief Nursing Officer
Web address: www.smha.org
Control: Other not-for-profit (including NFP Corporation) **Service**: General medical and surgical

Staffed Beds: 290 **Admissions**: 6866 **Census**: 249 **Outpatient Visits**: 420675 **Births**: 468 **Total Expense ($000)**: 168332 **Payroll Expense ($000)**: 85212 **Personnel**: 1437

NY

ST. MARY'S HEALTHCARE See St. Mary's Healthcare

AUBURN—Cayuga County

⊞ **AUBURN COMMUNITY HOSPITAL (330235)**, 17 Lansing Street, Zip 13021–1943; tel. 315/255–7011, (Total facility includes 80 beds in nursing home–type unit) **A**1 10 20 **F**1 3 12 13 15 18 26 28 29 30 31 34 35 40 42 45 50 51 53 54 55 57 59 60 64 70 76 78 79 81 82 85 89 93 97 98 103 107 108 110 111 115 119 124 129 130 132 135 144 146 147
Primary Contact: Scott A. Berlucchi, FACHE, President and Chief Executive Officer
CFO: Jason Lesch, Chief Financial Officer
CMO: John A. Riccio M.D., Chief Medical Officer
CIO: Chris Ryan, Chief Information Officer
CHR: Linda Daly, Vice President Human Resources
CNO: Tammy Sunderlin, Director of Nursing
Web address: www.auburnhospital.org
Control: Other not-for-profit (including NFP Corporation) **Service:** General medical and surgical

> **Staffed Beds:** 179 **Admissions:** 5244 **Census:** 137 **Outpatient Visits:** 144214 **Births:** 404 **Total Expense ($000):** 114317 **Payroll Expense ($000):** 57627 **Personnel:** 672

BATAVIA—Genesee County

⊞ **UNITED MEMORIAL MEDICAL CENTER (330073)**, 127 North Street, Zip 14020–1631; tel. 585/343–6030, (Includes UNITED MEMORIAL MEDICAL CENTER-BANK STREET, 127 North Street, Batavia, New York, Zip 14020–2260, tel. 716/343–3131; UNITED MEMORIAL MEDICAL CENTER-NORTH STREET, 16 Banks Street, Batavia, New York, Zip 14020–1697, tel. 585/343–6030) **A**1 10 13 **F**3 4 8 13 15 17 18 28 29 30 31 34 35 40 43 49 50 54 57 59 64 65 68 70 75 76 77 78 79 81 82 84 85 86 87 89 93 97 107 111 114 115 119 120 121 122 127 129 130 131 132 135 144 146 147 148 149 **P**5 **S** Rochester Regional Health, Rochester, NY
Primary Contact: Daniel P. Ireland, FACHE, President
CFO: Robert Chiavetta, Vice President Finance
CMO: Michael Merrill M.D., Interim Vice President Medical Affairs
CIO: Kurt Calman, Chief Information Officer
CHR: Sonja Gonyea, Director Human Resources
CNO: Mary Beth Bowen R.N., Vice President Nursing and Chief Nursing Officer
Web address: www.ummc.org
Control: Other not-for-profit (including NFP Corporation) **Service:** General medical and surgical

> **Staffed Beds:** 131 **Admissions:** 4025 **Census:** 48 **Outpatient Visits:** 249413 **Births:** 649 **Total Expense ($000):** 100625 **Payroll Expense ($000):** 40181 **Personnel:** 721

★ **VETERANS AFFAIRS WESTERN NEW YORK HEALTHCARE SYSTEM-BATAVIA DIVISION**, 222 Richmond Avenue, Zip 14020–1288; tel. 585/297–1000, (Nonreporting) **A**5 **S** Department of Veterans Affairs, Washington, DC
Primary Contact: Brian G. Stiller, Director Medical Center
Web address: www.buffalo.va.gov/batavia.asp
Control: Veterans Affairs, Government, federal **Service:** General medical and surgical

> **Staffed Beds:** 128

BATH—Steuben County

⊞ **BATH VETERANS AFFAIRS MEDICAL CENTER**, 76 Veterans Avenue, Zip 14810–0842; tel. 607/664–4000, (Total facility includes 94 beds in nursing home–type unit) **A**1 **F**3 4 5 7 11 12 18 29 30 33 34 35 36 38 39 44 50 53 54 56 57 59 61 62 63 64 65 66 68 71 74 75 77 79 82 83 84 86 87 90 91 93 94 97 100 101 103 104 107 119 127 128 129 130 132 133 135 143 144 146 147 148 149 **P**6 **S** Department of Veterans Affairs, Washington, DC
Primary Contact: Michael J. Swartz, FACHE, Medical Center Director
COO: Kenneth P. Piazza, Associate Director
CFO: Jill Haynes, Financial Coach
CMO: Robert Babcock M.D., Interim Chief of Staff
CHR: Susan DeSalvo, Manager Human Resources
Web address: www.bath.va.gov
Control: Veterans Affairs, Government, federal **Service:** General medical and surgical

> **Staffed Beds:** 274 **Admissions:** 1358 **Census:** 191 **Outpatient Visits:** 171000 **Births:** 0 **Total Expense ($000):** 102005 **Payroll Expense ($000):** 64425 **Personnel:** 720

⇑ **IRA DAVENPORT MEMORIAL HOSPITAL (330144)**, 7571 State Route 54, Zip 14810–9590; tel. 607/776–8500, (Nonreporting) **A**10 21 **S** Arnot Health, Elmira, NY
Primary Contact: Richard C. Cleland, FACHE, Administrator
CFO: Ronald J Kintz, Chief Financial Officer
CMO: Dennis O'Connor M.D., Medical Director
CIO: Gregg Martin, Chief Information Officer
CHR: Dave Stanbro, Director Human Resources
CNO: Linda Donley, Vice President Operations
Web address: www.arnothealth.org
Control: Other not-for-profit (including NFP Corporation) **Service:** General medical and surgical

> **Staffed Beds:** 161

BAY SHORE—Suffolk County

⊞ △ **SOUTHSIDE HOSPITAL (330043)**, 301 East Main Street, Zip 11706–8458; tel. 631/968–3000 **A**1 2 3 5 7 10 **F**3 8 11 13 15 17 18 19 20 22 24 26 28 29 30 31 32 34 35 36 38 40 41 43 44 45 46 49 50 54 55 56 57 58 59 60 61 62 63 64 65 66 68 70 73 74 75 76 77 78 79 80 81 82 84 85 86 87 89 90 93 96 97 100 101 102 103 107 108 110 111 115 118 119 121 123 126 129 130 131 132 135 145 146 147 148 **P**5 6 **S** Northwell Health, New Hyde Park, NY
Primary Contact: Donna Moravick, R.N., MSN, Executive Director
CFO: Robert Power, Associate Executive Director Finance
CMO: Jay Enden M.D., Medical Director
CIO: Lowney Mincy, Director Information Services
CHR: Anne J Barrett, Associate Executive Director Human Resources
Web address: www.southsidehospital.org
Control: Other not-for-profit (including NFP Corporation) **Service:** General medical and surgical

> **Staffed Beds:** 286 **Admissions:** 20168 **Census:** 261 **Outpatient Visits:** 151551 **Births:** 2692 **Total Expense ($000):** 532020 **Payroll Expense ($000):** 268750 **Personnel:** 2646

BELLEROSE—Queens County, See New York City

BETHPAGE—Nassau County

☐ **ST. JOSEPH HOSPITAL (330332)**, 4295 Hempstead Turnpike, Zip 11714–5769; tel. 516/579–6000 **A**1 10 **F**3 8 15 17 18 29 30 31 34 35 39 40 45 46 47 49 50 51 56 57 59 60 64 65 68 69 70 74 75 79 81 82 85 86 87 93 107 108 110 111 114 115 119 129 130 131 132 135 141 146 148 149 **S** Catholic Health Services of Long Island, Rockville Centre, NY
Primary Contact: Peter Scaminaci, Executive Vice President and Chief Administrative Officer
CFO: John Morahan, Vice President Finance
CMO: Howard Sussman M.D., Chief Medical Officer
CHR: Peter Chiacchiaro, Vice President Human Resources
CNO: Barbara Gibbons, Vice President Patient Care Services
Web address: www.stjosephhospital.chsli.org
Control: Other not-for-profit (including NFP Corporation) **Service:** General medical and surgical

> **Staffed Beds:** 128 **Admissions:** 6258 **Census:** 91 **Outpatient Visits:** 41743 **Births:** 0 **Total Expense ($000):** 115774 **Payroll Expense ($000):** 48812 **Personnel:** 664

BINGHAMTON—Broome County

BINGHAMTON GENERAL HOSPITAL See United Health Services Hospitals-Binghamton

☐ **GREATER BINGHAMTON HEALTH CENTER (334012)**, 425 Robinson Street, Zip 13904–1735; tel. 607/724–1391 **A**1 10 **F**29 30 50 54 56 65 66 68 71 75 77 86 98 99 100 101 103 104 105 106 130 132 135 143 146 149 **P**1 **S** New York State Office of Mental Health, Albany, NY
Primary Contact: David Peppel, Executive Director
CFO: Cherry Randall, Business Officer
CHR: Renee O'Brien, Director Human Resources
Web address: www.omh.ny.gov/omhweb/facilities/bipc/facility.htm
Control: State, Government, Nonfederal **Service:** Psychiatric

> **Staffed Beds:** 89 **Admissions:** 353 **Census:** 86 **Outpatient Visits:** 26497 **Births:** 0 **Total Expense ($000):** 51763 **Personnel:** 391

NY

Hospital, Medicare Provider Number, Address, Telephone, Approval, Facility, and Physician Codes, Health Care System

★ American Hospital Association (AHA) membership   ○ Healthcare Facilities Accreditation Program   ⇑ Center for Improvement in Healthcare Quality Accreditation
☐ The Joint Commission accreditation   ◇ DNV Healthcare Inc. accreditation   △ Commission on Accreditation of Rehabilitation Facilities (CARF) accreditation

✠ **OUR LADY OF LOURDES MEMORIAL HOSPITAL, INC. (330011)**, 169 Riverside Drive, Zip 13905–4246; tel. 607/798–5111 **A**1 2 10 13 19 **F**3 11 12 13 15 18 19 28 29 30 31 32 34 35 36 39 40 44 45 46 47 49 50 51 53 54 56 57 59 60 62 63 64 65 66 68 70 71 74 75 76 77 78 79 81 84 85 86 87 89 93 97 99 100 101 103 104 107 108 110 111 114 115 118 119 120 121 123 124 126 127 129 130 131 132 134 135 143 144 145 146 147 148 149 **P**6 **S** Ascension Healthcare, Saint Louis, MO
Primary Contact: Kathryn Connerton, President and Chief Executive Officer
CFO: Sean Mills, Chief Financial Officer
CMO: Richard Blansky M.D., Chief Medical Officer
CIO: Thomas Ellerson, Chief Information Officer
CHR: Mary Hughs, Chief Human Resources Officer
CNO: Deborah Mican, Chief Nursing Officer and Vice President Nursing
Web address: www.lourdes.com
Control: Church operated, Nongovernment, not-for-profit **Service:** General medical and surgical

Staffed Beds: 154 **Admissions:** 9796 **Census:** 107 **Outpatient Visits:** 1603623 **Births:** 1082 **Total Expense ($000):** 316632 **Payroll Expense ($000):** 134179 **Personnel:** 1945

UNITED HEALTH SERVICES HOSPITALS-BINGHAMTON (330394), 10–42 Mitchell Avenue, Zip 13903–1678; tel. 607/763–6000, (Includes BINGHAMTON GENERAL HOSPITAL, 10–42 Mitchell Avenue, Binghamton, New York, Zip 13903, tel. 607/762–2200; John Carrigg, President and Chief Executive Officer; WILSON MEMORIAL REGIONAL MEDICAL CENTER, 33–57 Harrison Street, Johnson City, New York, Zip 13790, tel. 607/763–6000; John Carrigg, President and Chief Executive Officer) (Total facility includes 145 beds in nursing home–type unit) **A**8 10 **F**1 3 4 5 8 11 12 13 15 17 18 20 22 24 26 28 29 30 31 32 33 34 35 38 39 40 43 45 46 47 49 50 51 54 56 57 58 59 61 64 65 68 70 72 74 75 76 77 78 79 81 82 84 85 86 87 89 90 92 93 96 97 98 99 100 101 102 103 104 105 107 108 110 114 115 118 119 120 121 123 124 127 129 130 131 132 135 144 145 146 147 148 149 **P**3 **S** United Health Services, Binghamton, NY
Primary Contact: John Carrigg, President and Chief Executive Officer
COO: John Carrigg, Executive Vice President and Chief Operating Officer
CFO: David MacDougall, Chief Financial Officer
CMO: Rajesh J Dave' M.D., Executive Vice President and Chief Medical Officer
CIO: Susan Carman, Chief Information Officer
CHR: Michael McNally, Vice President Human Resources
CNO: E. Kay Boland R.N., MS, Vice President and Chief Nursing Officer
Web address: www.uhs.net
Control: Other not-for-profit (including NFP Corporation) **Service:** General medical and surgical

Staffed Beds: 464 **Admissions:** 17064 **Census:** 276 **Outpatient Visits:** 1037371 **Births:** 1311 **Total Expense ($000):** 595084 **Payroll Expense ($000):** 212556 **Personnel:** 3954

☐ **PILGRIM PSYCHIATRIC CENTER (334013)**, 998 Crooked Hill Road, Zip 11717–1019; tel. 631/761–3500, (Nonreporting) **A**1 10 **S** New York State Office of Mental Health, Albany, NY
Primary Contact: Kathy O'Keefe, Executive Director
CFO: Florence Corwin, Director for Administration
CMO: Inderjit Singh M.D., Clinical Director
CIO: Douglas Cargonara Ph.D., Chief Information Officer
CHR: Florence Corwin, Director Administration
Web address: www.omh.ny.gov/omhweb/facilities/pgpc/facility.htm
Control: State, Government, Nonfederal **Service:** Psychiatric

Staffed Beds: 569

✠ **NEW YORK-PRESBYTERIAN/LAWRENCE HOSPITAL (330061)**, 55 Palmer Avenue, Zip 10708–3403; tel. 914/787–1000 **A**1 2 3 5 10 **F**3 8 12 13 15 17 18 20 22 26 28 29 30 31 34 35 40 41 45 46 47 48 49 50 51 55 56 57 59 60 62 63 64 65 68 70 72 74 75 77 78 79 81 82 83 84 85 87 93 96 100 107 108 110 111 114 115 116 117 120 121 123 124 126 129 130 131 132 135 144 145 146 148 **P**6 **S** NewYork-Presbyterian, New York, NY
Primary Contact: Michael Fosina, M.P.H., FACHE, President
COO: James Y Lee, Executive Vice President and Chief Operating Officer
CFO: Murray Askinazi, Senior Vice President and Chief Financial Officer
CMO: Werner Roeder M.D., Vice President Medical Affairs
CHR: Tom Mastroianni, Vice President Human Resources
Web address: www.lawrencehealth.org
Control: Other not-for-profit (including NFP Corporation) **Service:** General medical and surgical

Staffed Beds: 208 **Admissions:** 10299 **Census:** 133 **Outpatient Visits:** 180786 **Births:** 1394 **Total Expense ($000):** 243973 **Payroll Expense ($000):** 96891 **Personnel:** 1232

BRYLIN HOSPITALS (334022), 1263 Delaware Avenue, Zip 14209–2402; tel. 716/886–8200, (Nonreporting) **A**10
Primary Contact: Eric D. Pleskow, President and Chief Executive Officer
CFO: E Paul Hettich, Chief Financial Officer
CMO: Maria Cartagena M.D., Chief Medical Officer
CIO: Pawel Wieczorek, Director Information Technology
CHR: Pamela Nicastro, Director Human Resources
Web address: www.brylin.com
Control: Corporation, Investor-owned (for-profit) **Service:** Psychiatric

Staffed Beds: 88

☐ **BUFFALO PSYCHIATRIC CENTER (334052)**, 400 Forest Avenue, Zip 14213–1298; tel. 716/885–2261, (Nonreporting) **A**1 3 5 10 **S** New York State Office of Mental Health, Albany, NY
Primary Contact: Thomas Dodson, Executive Director
COO: Celia Spacone M.D., Director Operations
CFO: Pamela Esposito, Director Administration
CMO: Jeffery Grace M.D., Clinical Director
CIO: Anne Buchheit, Coordinator Mental Health Local Information Systems
CHR: Charles Siewert, Director Human Resources
CNO: Susan Fallis, Chief Nursing Officer
Web address: www.omh.ny.gov
Control: State, Government, Nonfederal **Service:** Psychiatric

Staffed Beds: 240

✠ △ **ERIE COUNTY MEDICAL CENTER (330219)**, 462 Grider Street, Zip 14215–3098; tel. 716/898–3000, (Total facility includes 390 beds in nursing home–type unit) **A**1 3 5 7 10 **F**3 4 5 12 16 17 18 20 29 30 31 33 34 35 38 39 40 43 45 49 50 53 54 56 57 58 59 60 61 63 64 65 66 67 68 70 71 74 75 77 78 79 81 83 84 85 87 90 91 93 94 96 97 98 99 100 101 102 103 104 105 107 110 111 115 119 128 130 131 132 138 146 148 149 **P**6 7
Primary Contact: Thomas J. Quatroche Jr, Chief Executive Officer
COO: Andrew L Davis Jr, Chief Operating Officer
CFO: Michael Sammarco M.D., Chief Financial Officer
CMO: Brian Murray M.D., Medical Director
CIO: Leslie Feidt, Chief Information Officer
CHR: Kathleen O'Hara, Vice President Human Resources
CNO: Karen Ziemianski R.N., MS, Senior Vice President Nursing
Web address: www.ecmc.edu
Control: Hospital district or authority, Government, Nonfederal **Service:** General medical and surgical

Staffed Beds: 890 **Admissions:** 19567 **Census:** 761 **Outpatient Visits:** 316691 **Births:** 0 **Total Expense ($000):** 614395 **Payroll Expense ($000):** 212992 **Personnel:** 3163

△ ⇑ **KALEIDA HEALTH (330005)**, 100 High Street, Zip 14203–1154; tel. 716/859–5600, (Includes DE GRAFF MEMORIAL HOSPITAL, 445 Tremont Street, North Tonawanda, New York, Zip 14120–0750, P O Box 0750, 14120–0750, tel. 716/694–4500; Darcy Craven, President; MILLARD FILLMORE SUBURBAN HOSPITAL, 1540 Maple Road, Williamsville, New York, Zip 14221, tel. 716/688–3100; Darcy Craven, President; WOMEN AND CHILDREN'S HOSPITAL, 219 Bryant Street, Buffalo, New York, Zip 14222–2099, tel. 716/878–7000; Cheryl Klass, President) (Total facility includes 380 beds in nursing home–type unit) **A**3 5 7 10 21 **F**1 2 3 6 8 9 11 12 13 15 17 18 19 20 21 22 24 26 27 28 29 30 31 32 34 35 36 37 38 39 40 41 43 44 45 46 47 48 49 50 51 54 55 56 57 58 59 60 61 62 63 64 65 66 67 68 70 71 72 73 74 75 76 77 78 79 80 81 82 83 84 85 86 87 88 89 90 91 92 93 94 96 97 99 100 101 102 103 104 105 107 108 109 110 111 114 115 118 119 120 124 126 128 130 131 132 134 135 136 143 146 147 148 **P**2 4 5 6 7
Primary Contact: Jody Lomeo, Chief Executive Officer
CFO: Joseph Kessler, Executive Vice President and Chief Financial Officer
CMO: Margaret Paroski M.D., Executive Vice President and Chief Medical Officer
CIO: Francis Meyer, Vice President Information Systems Technology
Web address: www.kaleidahealth.org
Control: Other not-for-profit (including NFP Corporation) **Service:** General medical and surgical

Staffed Beds: 1368 **Admissions:** 50284 **Census:** 1065 **Outpatient Visits:** 673119 **Births:** 5464 **Total Expense ($000):** 1316640 **Payroll Expense ($000):** 572345 **Personnel:** 7850

NY

⊞ **MERCY HOSPITAL (330279)**, 565 Abbott Road, Zip 14220–2095;
tel. 716/826–7000, (Total facility includes 84 beds in nursing home–type unit) **A**1
3 5 10 **F**3 8 13 15 17 18 20 22 24 26 29 30 31 34 35 38 39 40 41 42 44 45
46 48 49 50 54 56 57 59 60 63 64 65 66 68 70 72 73 74 75 76 77 78 79 81
84 85 87 89 90 91 92 93 96 97 100 104 107 108 110 111 114 115 118 119
126 128 129 130 131 132 146 147 148 149 **P**5 6 **S** Catholic Health System,
Buffalo, NY
Primary Contact: Charles J. Urlaub, President and Chief Executive Officer
COO: Eddie Bratko, Chief Operating Officer
CFO: James H Dunlop CPA, Jr, Senior Vice President Finance and Chief Financial
Officer
CMO: Timothy Gabryel M.D., Vice President Medical Affairs and Medical Director
CIO: Michael Galang M.D., Chief Information Officer
CHR: Joseph A Scrivo Jr, Director Human Resources
CNO: Shari McDonald, Vice President Patient Care Services
Web address: www.chsbuffalo.org
Control: Church operated, Nongovernment, not-for-profit **Service:** General
medical and surgical

Staffed Beds: 438 Admissions: 19616 Census: 356 Outpatient Visits:
310035 **Births: 2393 Total Expense ($000): 413883 Payroll Expense**
($000): 169673 Personnel: 1980

☐ **ROSWELL PARK CANCER INSTITUTE (330354)**, Elm and Carlton Streets,
Zip 14263–0001; tel. 716/845–2300 **A**1 2 3 5 8 10 **F**3 14 15 29 30 31 32 34
35 36 38 39 44 45 46 47 49 50 54 55 57 58 59 63 64 65 66 67 70 74 75 77
78 80 81 82 84 85 86 87 89 90 92 93 94 96 97 98 100 104 107 108 110 111
112 114 115 116 117 118 119 120 121 123 124 126 130 132 134 135 136
141 145 146 147 148 149 **P**6
Primary Contact: Candace Johnson, Ph.D., President and Chief Executive Officer
COO: Victor A Filadora M.D., MS, ll, Chief Clinical Services
CFO: Gregory McDonald, Vice President Finance and Chief Financial Officer
CMO: Boris Kuvshinoff M.D., ll, Chief Medical Officer
CIO: Kerry Kerlin, Chief Information Officer
CNO: Margarita Frances Coyne MS, R.N., Interim Chief Nursing Officer
Web address: www.roswellpark.org
Control: Hospital district or authority, Government, Nonfederal **Service:** Cancer

Staffed Beds: 133 Admissions: 4789 Census: 107 Outpatient Visits:
215424 **Births: 0 Total Expense ($000): 723285 Payroll Expense ($000):**
262386 **Personnel: 2983**

⊞ **SISTERS OF CHARITY HOSPITAL OF BUFFALO (330078)**, 2157 Main Street,
Zip 14214–2692; tel. 716/862–1000, (Includes ELIZABETH SETON PEDIATRIC
CENTER, 300 Corporate Boulevard South, Yonkers, New York, Zip 10701–6862,
tel. 914/294–6300; ST. JOSEPH HOSPITAL, 2605 Harlem Road, Cheektowaga,
New York, Zip 14225–4097, tel. 716/891–2400) (Total facility includes 80 beds in
nursing home–type unit) **A**1 2 3 5 10 12 13 **F**2 3 5 8 12 13 15 17 18 28 29 30
31 32 34 35 36 37 38 40 41 42 44 45 46 47 49 50 53 54 55 57 58 59 60 62
63 64 65 66 68 70 72 73 74 75 76 77 78 79 81 82 84 85 87 93 94 96 97 107
108 110 111 114 115 118 119 126 128 129 130 131 132 146 147 148 149
P5 6 **S** Catholic Health System, Buffalo, NY
Primary Contact: Martin Boryszak, President and Chief Executive Officer
COO: John Sperrazza, Chief Operating Officer
CFO: James H Dunlop CPA, Jr, Chief Financial Officer
CMO: Nady Shehata M.D., Vice President Medical Affairs
CIO: Michael Galang M.D., Chief Information Officer
CHR: David DeLorenzo, Senior Director Human Resources
CNO: Mary E Dillon MS, R.N., Vice President Patient Care Services
Web address: www.chsbuffalo.org
Control: Church operated, Nongovernment, not-for-profit **Service:** General
medical and surgical

Staffed Beds: 454 Admissions: 15980 Census: 289 Outpatient Visits:
710540 **Births: 3359 Total Expense ($000): 325915 Payroll Expense**
($000): 145760 Personnel: 1929

⊞ **VETERANS AFFAIRS WESTERN NEW YORK HEALTHCARE SYSTEM-**
BUFFALO DIVISION, 3495 Bailey Avenue, Zip 14215–1129; tel. 716/834–9200,
(Nonreporting) **A**1 3 5 8 **S** Department of Veterans Affairs, Washington, DC
Primary Contact: Brian G. Stiller, Director Medical Center
CFO: Susan Gage, Financial Manager
CMO: Ali El-Solh M.D., Interim Chief of Staff
CIO: Margaret Senker, Chief Information Officer
Web address: www.buffalo.va.gov/index.asp
Control: Veterans Affairs, Government, federal **Service:** General medical and
surgical

Staffed Beds: 113

WOMEN AND CHILDREN'S HOSPITAL See Kaleida Health

★ **GROVER M. HERMANN HOSPITAL (331303)**, 8881 Route 97, Zip 12723;
tel. 845/887–5530 **A**10 18 **F**3 11 15 29 30 34 35 40 50 57 59 64 65 68 75
85 93 97 107 130 132 133 146 150 **S** Greater Hudson Valley Health System,
Middletown, NY
Primary Contact: Rolland Bojo, R.N., Administrator
Web address: www.crmcny.org
Control: Other not-for-profit (including NFP Corporation) **Service:** General medical
and surgical

Staffed Beds: 25 Admissions: 90 Census: 3 Outpatient Visits: 14006
Births: 0 Total Expense ($000): 5214 Payroll Expense ($000): 2539
Personnel: 41

★ **CANANDAIGUA VETERANS AFFAIRS MEDICAL CENTER**, 400 Fort Hill Avenue,
Zip 14424–1159; tel. 585/394–2000, (Nonreporting) **A**3 5 **S** Department of
Veterans Affairs, Washington, DC
Primary Contact: Michael J. Swartz, FACHE, Medical Center Director
CMO: Robert Babcock M.D., Chief of Staff
CIO: Bob Corrado, Chief Information Officer
Web address: www.canandaigua.va.gov/
Control: Veterans Affairs, Government, federal **Service:** Psychiatric

Staffed Beds: 196

⊞ **F. F. THOMPSON HOSPITAL (330074)**, 350 Parrish Street, Zip 14424–1731;
tel. 585/396–6000, (Total facility includes 178 beds in nursing home–type unit)
A1 10 **F**3 8 11 13 15 17 18 28 29 30 32 33 34 35 38 40 43 44 45 46 49 50
54 56 57 59 60 64 68 70 75 76 77 79 81 84 85 86 87 89 91 93 95 96 97 107
108 110 111 115 118 119 125 126 128 129 130 131 132 135 144 145 146
147 148 149 **S** University of Rochester Medical Center, Rochester, NY
Primary Contact: Michael Stapleton, President and Chief Executive Officer
COO: Kurt Koczent, Executive Vice President and Chief Operating Officer
CFO: Mark Prunoske, Chief Financial Officer and Senior Vice President Finance
CMO: David Baum M.D., Senior Vice President Medical Services
CIO: Mark Halladay, Director Information Services
CHR: Jennifer DeVault, Vice President Associate Services
CNO: Hazel Robertshaw R.N., Ph.D., Chief Nursing Officer, Vice President Patient
Services
Web address: www.thompsonhealth.com
Control: Other not-for-profit (including NFP Corporation) **Service:** General medical
and surgical

Staffed Beds: 291 Admissions: 5396 Census: 227 Outpatient Visits:
267514 **Births: 692 Total Expense ($000): 138807 Payroll Expense**
($000): 63882 Personnel: 1311

THOMPSON HEALTH See F. F. Thompson Hospital

ARMS ACRES, 75 Seminary Hill Road, Zip 10512–1921; tel. 845/225–3400,
(Nonreporting)
Primary Contact: Patrice Wallace-Moore, Chief Executive Officer and Executive Director
CFO: Jason Burczeuski, Controller
CMO: Fred Hesse M.D., Medical Director
CIO: Dolores Watson, Director Health Information Management
CHR: Kim Halpin, Director Human Resources
CNO: Barbara Klein R.N., Director of Nursing
Web address: www.armsacres.com
Control: Corporation, Investor-owned (for-profit) **Service:** Alcoholism and other
chemical dependency

Staffed Beds: 146

☐ **PUTNAM HOSPITAL CENTER (330273)**, 670 Stoneleigh Avenue, Zip 10512–
3997; tel. 845/279–5711 **A**1 2 10 **F**3 8 12 13 15 18 28 29 30 31 34 35 37
38 40 41 45 46 49 55 56 57 59 61 64 65 68 70 74 75 76 77 78 79 81 82 83
84 85 87 89 91 92 93 94 98 100 101 102 103 104 105 107 108 110 111
114 118 119 120 121 126 129 130 131 132 143 146 149 **P**6 **S** Health Quest
Systems, Inc., LaGrangeville, NY
Primary Contact: Peter Kelly, President
CFO: Joseph Hart, Director Finance and Support Services
CNO: Luanne Convery, Vice President Patient Care Services
Web address: www.healthquest.org/carmel/putnam-hospital-center.aspx
Control: Other not-for-profit (including NFP Corporation) **Service:** General medical
and surgical

Staffed Beds: 164 Admissions: 6578 Census: 80 Outpatient Visits:
120780 **Births: 424 Total Expense ($000): 158268 Payroll Expense**
($000): 52380 Personnel: 728

NY

CARTHAGE—Jefferson County

⊞ **CARTHAGE AREA HOSPITAL (331318)**, 1001 West Street, Zip 13619–9703; tel. 315/493–1000, (Nonreporting) **A**1 10 18
Primary Contact: Richard Duvall, Chief Executive Officer
CFO: Rob Bloom, Chief Financial Officer
CMO: Mirza Ashraf M.D., Medical Director
CIO: Joe Virkler, Chief Information Officer
CHR: Cathy Siedlecki, Director Human Resources
CNO: Susan Kellogg, Administrator Patient Care Services
Web address: www.carthagehospital.com
Control: Other not-for-profit (including NFP Corporation) **Service**: General medical and surgical

Staffed Beds: 55

CLIFTON SPRINGS—Ontario County

★ ⇑ **CLIFTON SPRINGS HOSPITAL AND CLINIC (330265)**, 2 Coulter Road, Zip 14432–1189; tel. 315/462–9561, (Total facility includes 108 beds in nursing home–type unit) **A**10 21 **F**4 5 11 15 28 29 30 31 34 35 36 38 40 45 48 49 50 51 57 59 60 64 65 68 70 75 77 78 79 81 82 87 93 97 98 100 102 104 107 110 111 115 116 117 119 124 128 130 132 146 148 149 **P**5 6 **S** Rochester Regional Health, Rochester, NY
Primary Contact: Dustin Riccio, M.D., President
CFO: Sharon Kelley, Chief Financial Officer
CIO: Joel Majauskas, Chief Information Officer
CHR: Kathy Babb, Manager Human Resources
CNO: Donna P Smith R.N., Vice President Chief Operating Officer and Chief Nursing Officer
Web address: www.cliftonspringshospital.org
Control: Other not-for-profit (including NFP Corporation) **Service**: General medical and surgical

Staffed Beds: 214 Admissions: 2551 Census: 153 Outpatient Visits: 105507 Births: 0 Total Expense ($000): 60765 Payroll Expense ($000): 28296 Personnel: 566

COBLESKILL—Schoharie County

⊞ **COBLESKILL REGIONAL HOSPITAL (330268)**, 178 Grandview Drive, Zip 12043–5144; tel. 518/254–3456, (Nonreporting) **A**1 10 20 **S** Bassett Healthcare Network, Cooperstown, NY
Primary Contact: Eric H. Stein, FACHE, President and Chief Executive Officer
CFO: Leanna Jensen, Vice President Finance and Chief Financial Officer
CMO: Roy Korn M.D., Medical Director
CIO: Bridgette West, Director Patient Access Services
CNO: Susan Oakes Ferrucci MS, Vice President Patient Services and Chief Nursing Officer
Web address: www.cobleskillhospital.org
Control: Other not-for-profit (including NFP Corporation) **Service**: General medical and surgical

Staffed Beds: 40

COOPERSTOWN—Otsego County

⊞ **BASSETT MEDICAL CENTER (330136)**, One Atwell Road, Zip 13326–1394; tel. 607/547–3456, (Nonreporting) **A**1 2 3 5 8 10 **S** Bassett Healthcare Network, Cooperstown, NY
Primary Contact: Vance Brown, M.D., President and Chief Executive Officer
COO: Ronette Wiley R.N., Executive Vice President and Chief Operating Officer
CFO: Michael A. Tengeres, Corporate Vice President and Chief Financial Officer
CMO: William W LeCates M.D., Vice President Medical Affairs and Medical Director
CIO: Scott C Groom, Vice President Information Services and Chief Information Officer
CHR: Sara Z Albright, Vice President Human Resources
CNO: Judi Brendle, Vice President Clinical Support and Chief Nursing Officer
Web address: www.bassett.org
Control: Other not-for-profit (including NFP Corporation) **Service**: General medical and surgical

Staffed Beds: 152

CORNING—Steuben County

⊞ **GUTHRIE CORNING HOSPITAL (330277)**, One Guthrie Drive, Zip 14830–3696; tel. 607/937–7200, (Nonreporting) **A**1 10 **S** Guthrie Clinic, Sayre, PA
Primary Contact: Garrett W. Hoover, FACHE, President
CFO: Francis M Macafee, Vice President Finance and Chief Financial Officer
CMO: Chris Wentzel M.D., Interim Medical Director
CHR: Laura Manning, Administrative Director
CNO: Deb Raupers MSN, R.N., Chief Nursing Officer
Web address: www.corninghospital.com
Control: Other not-for-profit (including NFP Corporation) **Service**: General medical and surgical

Staffed Beds: 82

CORNWALL—Orange County

ST. LUKE'S CORNWALL HOSPITAL - CORNWALL CAMPUS See St. Luke's Cornwall Hospital

CORTLAND—Cortland County

⊞ **CORTLAND REGIONAL MEDICAL CENTER (330175)**, 134 Homer Avenue, Zip 13045–1206; tel. 607/756–3500, (Total facility includes 82 beds in nursing home–type unit) **A**1 10 20 **F**2 3 8 11 13 15 18 28 29 30 31 34 35 40 44 45 49 50 54 56 57 59 62 64 70 75 76 77 78 79 81 82 85 86 87 91 93 96 98 100 102 103 107 108 110 111 114 115 118 119 128 130 131 132 133 135 146 147 148 149 150 **P**6
Primary Contact: Mark Webster, President and Chief Executive Officer
COO: Tracy Gates, Vice President Operations and Chief Operating Officer
CFO: Denise Wrinn, Vice President Finance and Chief Financial Officer
CMO: Roger Scott D.O., Vice President Medical Affairs and Chief Medical Officer
CIO: Robert J Duthe, Director Information Systems and Chief Information Officer
CHR: Bonita N Lindberg, Director Human Resources
CNO: Mary Wright, Vice President Nursing Services and Chief Nursing Officer
Web address: www.cortlandregional.org
Control: Other not-for-profit (including NFP Corporation) **Service**: General medical and surgical

Staffed Beds: 172 Admissions: 3654 Census: 114 Outpatient Visits: 122119 Births: 454 Total Expense ($000): 84939 Payroll Expense ($000): 36746 Personnel: 657

CORTLANDT MANOR—Westchester County

⊞ **NEW YORK-PRESBYTERIAN/HUDSON VALLEY HOSPITAL (330267)**, 1980 Crompond Road, Zip 10567–4182; tel. 914/737–9000 **A**1 10 **F**3 8 11 12 13 15 18 28 29 30 31 34 35 36 37 40 41 45 46 47 49 53 54 56 57 59 64 70 73 74 75 76 77 78 79 81 82 85 87 89 91 93 94 96 102 107 108 110 111 114 115 119 120 124 130 131 132 145 146 147 148 149 **P**6 **S** NewYork-Presbyterian, New York, NY
Primary Contact: Stacey Petrower, President
COO: Deborah Neuendorf, Vice President Administration
CFO: Mark Webster, Vice President Finance
CMO: William Higgins M.D., Vice President Medical Affairs
CIO: Bud Sorbello, Director Management Information Systems
CHR: Jeane L Costella, Vice President
CNO: Kathleen Webster R.N., MSN, Vice President Patient Services
Web address: www.hvhc.org
Control: Other not-for-profit (including NFP Corporation) **Service**: General medical and surgical

Staffed Beds: 128 Admissions: 8163 Census: 93 Outpatient Visits: 153056 Births: 749 Total Expense ($000): 179925 Payroll Expense ($000): 79014 Personnel: 981

CUBA—Allegany County

CUBA MEMORIAL HOSPITAL (331301), 140 West Main Street, Zip 14727–1398; tel. 585/968–2000, (Nonreporting) **A**10 18
Primary Contact: Andrew Boser, Chief Executive Officer
CFO: Jack Ormond, Chief Financial Officer
Web address: www.cubamemorialhospital.com
Control: Other not-for-profit (including NFP Corporation) **Service**: General medical and surgical

Staffed Beds: 81

DANSVILLE—Livingston County

⊞ **NICHOLAS H. NOYES MEMORIAL HOSPITAL (330238)**, 111 Clara Barton Street, Zip 14437–9503; tel. 585/335–6001 **A**1 10 **F**3 8 11 13 15 29 31 32 34 35 40 45 47 49 50 51 54 57 59 60 64 68 70 75 76 79 81 82 84 85 93 99 100 102 104 107 108 110 115 119 130 131 132 133 144 146 **P**5 **S** University of Rochester Medical Center, Rochester, NY
Primary Contact: Amy Pollard, R.N., President and Chief Executive Officer
CFO: Jay T Maslyn, Chief Financial Officer
CMO: Douglas Mayhle M.D., Medical Director
CIO: John Dorak, Chief Information Officer
CNO: Tamara West R.N., MSN, Vice President Patient Care
Web address: www.noyes-health.org
Control: Other not-for-profit (including NFP Corporation) **Service**: General medical and surgical

Staffed Beds: 40 Admissions: 2364 Census: 23

NY

DELHI—Delaware County

⊞ **O'CONNOR HOSPITAL (331305)**, 460 Andes Road, State Route 28, Zip 13753–7407; tel. 607/746–0300 **A**1 10 18 **F**15 29 34 35 40 45 46 50 56 57 59 64 65 75 77 79 81 85 86 87 91 92 93 96 107 110 119 130 131 132 133 135 147 149 **S** Bassett Healthcare Network, Cooperstown, NY
Primary Contact: Scott Bonderoff, President
CFO: Sue E. Andrews, Chief Financial Officer
CMO: Peter L Sosnow, Medical Director
CHR: Barbara Green, Director Human Resources
CNO: Debra Neale R.N., Chief Nursing Officer
Web address: www.bassett.org
Control: Other not-for-profit (including NFP Corporation) **Service:** General medical and surgical

Staffed Beds: 16 **Admissions:** 285 **Census:** 6 **Outpatient Visits:** 30815 **Births:** 0 **Personnel:** 147

DIX HILLS—Suffolk County

☐ **SAGAMORE Children's hospital psychiatric CENTER**, 197 Half Hollow Road, Zip 11746–5861; tel. 631/370–1700 **A**1 **F**38 39 50 54 64 71 98 99 104 105 130 132 149 **P**1 **S** New York State Office of Mental Health, Albany, NY
Primary Contact: Kathy O'Keefe, Interim Executive Director
COO: Cathy Stein, Chief Inpatient Services
CFO: Jane Alexander, Director Facility Administrative Services
CIO: Bryan Doherty, Management Information Technology Services I
CHR: Nancy Angell, Associate Administrator Personnel
CNO: Sandra King, Chief Nursing Officer
Web address: www.omh.ny.gov
Control: State, Government, Nonfederal **Service:** Children's hospital psychiatric

Staffed Beds: 54 **Admissions:** 178 **Census:** 39 **Outpatient Visits:** 5000 **Births:** 0 **Total Expense ($000):** 22900 **Payroll Expense ($000):** 15600 **Personnel:** 260

DUNKIRK—Chautauqua County

⇑ **BROOKS MEMORIAL HOSPITAL (330229)**, 529 Central Avenue, Zip 14048–2599; tel. 716/366–1111 **A**10 21 **F**15 18 28 29 34 35 40 41 50 59 60 68 69 70 76 79 81 82 84 85 87 93 107 108 110 111 115 119 130 131 135 146
Primary Contact: Mary E. LaRowe, FACHE, President and Chief Executive Officer
CFO: Jeffrey H. Morgan, Vice President Finance and Chief Financial Officer
CIO: Kevin Kimball, Director Information Technology
CHR: Tracie Luther, Director Employee and Labor Relations
CNO: Jodi Witherell, Vice President Patient Care and Quality
Web address: www.brookshospital.org
Control: Other not-for-profit (including NFP Corporation) **Service:** General medical and surgical

Staffed Beds: 65 **Admissions:** 2192 **Census:** 21 **Outpatient Visits:** 115000 **Births:** 449 **Total Expense ($000):** 46741 **Payroll Expense ($000):** 16789 **Personnel:** 332

EAST MEADOW—Nassau County

⊞ **NASSAU UNIVERSITY MEDICAL CENTER (330027)**, 2201 Hempstead Turnpike, Zip 11554–1859; tel. 516/572–0123, (Nonreporting) **A**1 3 5 10 12 13
Primary Contact: Victor Politi, M.D., President and Chief Executive Officer
COO: Harold E McDonald, Deputy Executive Director and Senior Vice President Administration
CFO: John P Maher, Executive Vice President and Chief Financial Officer
CMO: Victor Scarmato M.D., Acting Medical Director
CIO: Farooq Ajmal, Vice President and Chief Information Officer
CHR: Maureen Roarty, Executive Vice President Human Resources
CNO: Kathy Skarka MSN, R.N., Executive Vice President Patient Care Services
Web address: www.nuhealth.net
Control: Hospital district or authority, Government, Nonfederal **Service:** General medical and surgical

Staffed Beds: 481

ELIZABETHTOWN—Essex County

⊞ **THE UNIVERSITY OF VERMONT HEALTH NETWORK ELIZABETHTOWN COMMUNITY HOSPITAL (331302)**, 75 Park Street, Zip 12932, Mailing Address: P.O.Box 277, 12932–0277; tel. 518/873–6377 **A**1 10 18 **F**3 7 11 15 28 29 30 31 34 35 40 44 45 46 50 53 57 64 65 68 75 77 78 81 86 87 90 93 96 97 107 110 115 119 127 130 132 133 142 145 146 147 **P**6
Primary Contact: John R. Remillard, Interim Chief Executive Officer
COO: Matthew Nolan, Chief Operating Officer
CFO: Alan Chardavoyne, Chief Financial Officer
CMO: Rob DeMuro M.D., Chief Medical Officer
CIO: Darrin Goodrow, Chief Information Officer
CHR: Michelle Meachem, Director Human Resources
CNO: Julie Tromblee R.N., Chief Nursing Officer
Web address: www.ech.org
Control: Other not-for-profit (including NFP Corporation) **Service:** General medical and surgical

Staffed Beds: 25 **Admissions:** 484 **Census:** 10 **Outpatient Visits:** 53864 **Births:** 0 **Total Expense ($000):** 25274 **Payroll Expense ($000):** 12698 **Personnel:** 160

ELLENVILLE—Ulster County

★ **ELLENVILLE REGIONAL HOSPITAL (331310)**, 10 Healthy Way, Zip 12428–5612; tel. 845/647–6400, (Nonreporting) **A**10 18
Primary Contact: Steven L. Kelley, President and Chief Executive Officer
CFO: Robert Rue, Chief Financial Officer
CMO: Walter Sperling M.D., Medical Director
CHR: Deborah Briggs, Vice President Human Resources, Marketing, Volunteer Services and Community Relations
CNO: Ann Marie Guntlow, Chief Nursing Officer
Web address: www.ellenvilleregional.org
Control: Other not-for-profit (including NFP Corporation) **Service:** General medical and surgical

Staffed Beds: 25

ELMHURST—Queens County, See New York City

ELMIRA—Chemung County

★ ⇑ **ARNOT OGDEN MEDICAL CENTER (330090)**, 600 Roe Avenue, Zip 14905–1629; tel. 607/737–4100, (Nonreporting) **A**2 3 10 12 13 21 **S** Arnot Health, Elmira, NY
Primary Contact: Jonathan I. Lawrence, System Chief Operating Officer
CFO: Ronald J Kintz, Vice President and Treasurer
CMO: Kenneth Herzl-Betz M.D., Chief Medical Officer
CIO: Gregg Martin, Chief Information Officer
CHR: Dave Stanbro, Director Human Resources
CNO: Sandra Mac"" McCarthy, Chief Nursing Officer
Web address: www.arnothealth.org
Control: Other not-for-profit (including NFP Corporation) **Service:** General medical and surgical

Staffed Beds: 176

☐ **ELMIRA PSYCHIATRIC CENTER (334045)**, 100 Washington Street, Zip 14901–2898; tel. 607/737–4739, (Nonreporting) **A**1 3 10 **S** New York State Office of Mental Health, Albany, NY
Primary Contact: David Peppel, Executive Director
COO: Karen Patterson, Deputy Director Operations
CFO: J. Paul Bedzyk, Deputy Director Administration
CMO: Kurt Hahn M.D., Acting Clinical Director
CIO: Jeremy Newcomer, Director Information Services
CHR: Patricia Santulli, Director Human Resources
CNO: Pam Seeley, Chief Nursing Officer
Web address: www.omh.ny.gov/omhweb/facilities/elpc/facility.htm
Control: State, Government, Nonfederal **Service:** Psychiatric

Staffed Beds: 100

⇑ **ST. JOSEPH'S HOSPITAL (330108)**, 555 St. Joseph's Boulevard, Zip 14901–3223; tel. 607/733–6541, (Nonreporting) **A**10 21 **S** Arnot Health, Elmira, NY
Primary Contact: Joseph Braunscheidel, Administrator
CFO: Ronald J Kintz, Senior Vice President Finance and Chief Financial Officer
CMO: Kenneth Herzl-Betz M.D., Chief Medical Officer and Senior Vice President Medical Affairs
CIO: Gregg Martin, Chief Information Officer
CHR: Dave Stanbro, Director Human Resources
CNO: Sandra Mac"" McCarthy, Chief Nursing Officer
Web address: www.arnothealth.org
Control: Other not-for-profit (including NFP Corporation) **Service:** General medical and surgical

Staffed Beds: 141

NY

Hospital, Medicare Provider Number, Address, Telephone, Approval, Facility, and Physician Codes, Health Care System

★ American Hospital Association (AHA) membership
☐ The Joint Commission accreditation
○ Healthcare Facilities Accreditation Program
◇ DNV Healthcare Inc. accreditation
⇑ Center for Improvement in Healthcare Quality Accreditation
△ Commission on Accreditation of Rehabilitation Facilities (CARF) accreditation

FAR ROCKAWAY—Queens County, See New York City

FLUSHING—Queens County, See New York City

FOREST HILLS—Queens County, See New York City

FRESH MEADOWS—Queens County

CORNERSTONE OF MEDICAL ARTS CENTER HOSPITAL, 159–05 Union Turnpike, Zip 11366–1950; tel. 212/755–0200, (Nonreporting)
Primary Contact: Thomas C. Puzo, President and Chief Executive Officer
CFO: Jeff OniFather, Chief Financial Officer
CMO: Sami Kaddouri M.D., Medical Director
CHR: Gloria Burtch, Director Human Resources
Web address: www.cornerstoneny.com
Control: Corporation, Investor-owned (for-profit) **Service**: Alcoholism and other chemical dependency

Staffed Beds: 162

GENEVA—Ontario County

⊞ **GENEVA GENERAL HOSPITAL (330058)**, 196 North Street, Zip 14456–1694; tel. 315/787–4000 **A**1 3 10 **F**3 8 11 13 15 17 18 28 29 31 32 34 35 40 45 50 54 57 59 60 61 64 66 69 70 74 75 76 77 79 81 85 86 87 90 92 93 96 97 107 108 110 111 115 118 119 128 129 130 131 132 135 146 147 **P**6 **S** Finger Lakes Health, Geneva, NY
Primary Contact: Jose Acevedo, M.D., President and Chief Executive Officer
COO: Frank Korich, Senior Vice President, Operations
CFO: Pamela Johnson, Treasurer and Chief Financial Officer
CMO: Jason Feinberg M.D., Vice President Medical Affairs and Chief Medical Officer
CIO: Guy W Mosher III, Manager Information Systems
CHR: Patrick R Boyle, Vice President Human Resources
CNO: Eileen Gage R.N., Vice President Nursing
Web address: www.flhealth.org
Control: Other not-for-profit (including NFP Corporation) **Service**: General medical and surgical

Staffed Beds: 132 Admissions: 3778 Census: 48 Outpatient Visits: 504846 Births: 0 Total Expense ($000): 91488 Payroll Expense ($000): 50488 Personnel: 773

GLEN COVE—Nassau County

⊞ **GLEN COVE HOSPITAL (330181)**, 101 St Andrews Lane, Zip 11542–2254; tel. 516/674–7300 **A**1 2 3 5 10 **F**3 8 9 11 15 17 18 28 29 30 31 32 33 34 35 36 38 39 40 43 45 46 47 48 49 50 51 54 55 56 57 58 59 60 61 63 64 65 66 68 69 70 74 75 77 78 79 81 82 84 85 86 87 90 91 92 93 94 96 97 100 102 103 104 107 108 110 111 115 118 119 121 130 131 132 135 143 146 147 **P**5 6 **S** Northwell Health, New Hyde Park, NY
Primary Contact: Susan Kwiatek, R.N., Executive Director
COO: Michele Frankel, Associate Executive Director Finance
CFO: Michele Frankel, Associate Executive Director Finance
CMO: Barbara Barnett M.D., Medical Director
CHR: Thomas Salvo, Associate Executive Director Human Resources
CNO: Cathy Sheerin R.N., MS, Director Patient Care Services
Web address: www.northshorelij.com
Control: Other not-for-profit (including NFP Corporation) **Service**: General medical and surgical

Staffed Beds: 119 Admissions: 4572 Census: 87 Outpatient Visits: 76445 Births: 0 Total Expense ($000): 137774 Payroll Expense ($000): 73755 Personnel: 665

GLEN OAKS—Queens County, See New York City

GLENS FALLS—Warren County

⊞ **GLENS FALLS HOSPITAL (330191)**, 100 Park Street, Zip 12801–4413; tel. 518/926–1000 **A**1 2 5 10 **F**3 5 8 11 13 15 17 18 20 22 26 28 29 30 31 32 34 35 36 37 38 39 40 43 44 45 46 47 49 50 53 54 57 59 60 64 68 70 71 73 74 75 76 77 78 79 81 82 84 85 86 87 89 90 92 93 96 97 98 99 100 102 103 104 105 107 108 110 114 115 118 119 120 121 123 124 126 127 129 130 132 135 144 145 146 147 148 **P**6
Primary Contact: Dianne Shugrue, President and Chief Executive Officer
COO: Paul Scimeca, Senior Vice President Operations and Chief Operating Officer
CFO: Mitchell Amado, Senior Vice President Finance and Chief Financial Officer
CMO: Benjamin Katz M.D., Vice President Medical Affairs
CIO: John Kelleher, Vice President Information Technology and Chief Information Officer
CHR: Kyle Brock, Vice President Human Resources
CNO: Donna Kirker R.N., MS, Vice President Patient Services and Chief Nursing Officer
Web address: www.glensfallshospital.org
Control: Other not-for-profit (including NFP Corporation) **Service**: General medical and surgical

Staffed Beds: 275 Admissions: 13163 Census: 191 Outpatient Visits: 731420 Births: 1225 Total Expense ($000): 335633 Payroll Expense ($000): 156360 Personnel: 2240

GLENVILLE—Schenectady County

CONIFER PARK, 79 Glenridge Road, Zip 12302–4523; tel. 518/399–6446, (Nonreporting)
Primary Contact: Jeanne Gluchowski, Executive Director
COO: Jeanne Gluchowski, Executive Director
CFO: Jason Burczeuski, Controller
CMO: John Melbourne M.D., Medical Director
CIO: Amy Kentera, Chief Information Officer
CHR: Maureen Fowler, Director Human Resources
Web address: www.coniferpark.com/
Control: Corporation, Investor-owned (for-profit) **Service**: Alcoholism and other chemical dependency

Staffed Beds: 225

GLOVERSVILLE—Fulton County

★ ⇑ **NATHAN LITTAUER HOSPITAL AND NURSING HOME (330276)**, 99 East State Street, Zip 12078–1203; tel. 518/725–8621, (Total facility includes 84 beds in nursing home–type unit) **A**5 10 21 **F**3 8 11 13 15 18 28 29 30 31 32 34 35 36 37 40 45 50 53 54 57 59 61 64 65 70 74 75 76 77 78 79 81 82 85 86 87 89 93 97 107 108 110 115 118 119 128 130 131 132 135 144 145 146 147 **P**6
Primary Contact: Laurence E. Kelly, President and Chief Executive Officer
CFO: Michael Ostrander, Chief Financial Officer
CMO: Frederick Goldberg M.D., Vice President Medical Affairs and Chief Medical Officer
CIO: Martin Brown, Vice President Information Services and Chief Information Officer
CHR: Lana Wydra, Vice President Human Resources
CNO: Stephanie Fishel, Vice President Patient Care Services and Chief Nursing Officer
Web address: www.nlh.org
Control: Other not-for-profit (including NFP Corporation) **Service**: General medical and surgical

Staffed Beds: 158 Admissions: 2307 Census: 104 Outpatient Visits: 253008 Births: 312 Total Expense ($000): 94757 Payroll Expense ($000): 48977 Personnel: 767

GOUVERNEUR—St. Lawrence County

★ ⇑ **GOUVERNEUR HOSPITAL (331315)**, 77 West Barney Street, Zip 13642–1040; tel. 315/287–1000 **A**10 18 21 **F**3 8 11 15 29 34 40 45 50 57 59 64 81 87 89 93 107 111 119 129 130 133 149 **P**6 **S** St. Lawrence Health System, Potsdam, NY
Primary Contact: David Bender, Chief Executive Officer
CFO: Richard T Lang, Chief Financial Officer
CMO: George Dodds M.D., Medical Director
CHR: Suzan McDermott, Director, Human Resources
CNO: Jennifer Shaver, Director of Nursing
Web address: www.gvnrhospital.org
Control: Other not-for-profit (including NFP Corporation) **Service**: General medical and surgical

Staffed Beds: 25 Admissions: 490 Census: 8 Outpatient Visits: 43147 Births: 0 Total Expense ($000): 18423 Payroll Expense ($000): 8479 Personnel: 165

GREENPORT—Suffolk County

⊞ **EASTERN LONG ISLAND HOSPITAL (330088)**, 201 Manor Place, Zip 11944–1298; tel. 631/477–1000 **A**1 10 **F**3 4 5 8 11 14 17 18 28 29 34 35 38 40 45 47 49 53 56 59 64 65 68 70 74 78 79 81 82 85 93 97 98 100 102 103 106 107 110 111 119 130 132 135 146
Primary Contact: Paul J. Connor III, President and Chief Executive Officer
CFO: Robert A Ragona, Senior Vice President Finance and Chief Financial Officer
CMO: Lloyd Simon M.D., Medical Director
CIO: Dan Scotto, Director Information Technology
CHR: Frank Dumont, Assistant Vice President Human Resources and Corporate Compliance
CNO: D Patricia Pispisa, Executive Vice President Patient Care Services
Web address: www.elih.org
Control: Other not-for-profit (including NFP Corporation) **Service**: General medical and surgical

Staffed Beds: 90 Admissions: 2583 Census: 47 Outpatient Visits: 43682 Births: 0 Total Expense ($000): 51202 Payroll Expense ($000): 24212 Personnel: 326

NY

Many Facility Codes have changed. Please refer to the AHA Guide Code Chart. © 2017 AHA Guide

HAMILTON—Madison County

✠ **COMMUNITY MEMORIAL HOSPITAL (331316)**, 150 Broad Street, Zip 13346–9518; tel. 315/824–1100 **A**1 10 18 **F**3 11 15 18 26 29 40 45 54 57 59 64 79 81 85 89 93 102 107 108 111 114 119 127 130 133 135 144 146
Primary Contact: Sean Fadale, President and Chief Executive Officer
CFO: Christopher W Graham, Chief Financial Officer
CMO: Robert Delorme, Vice President Medical Affairs
CHR: Jennifer Montana, Manager Human Resources
CNO: Denise Hummer R.N., Vice President Administrative Services
Web address: www.communitymemorial.org
Control: Other not-for-profit (including NFP Corporation) **Service:** General medical and surgical

Staffed Beds: 25 **Admissions:** 1422 **Census:** 9 **Births:** 0 **Total Expense ($000):** 42593 **Payroll Expense ($000):** 16430 **Personnel:** 273

HARRIS—Sullivan County

✠ **CATSKILL REGIONAL MEDICAL CENTER (330386)**, 68 Harris Bushville Road, Zip 12742–5030, Mailing Address: P.O.Box 800, 12742–0800; tel. 845/794–3300, (Total facility includes 64 beds in nursing home–type unit) **A**1 2 10 **F**2 3 8 11 12 13 15 17 29 30 31 34 35 38 40 45 50 51 56 57 59 64 65 66 68 70 75 76 78 79 81 85 86 87 89 93 96 97 98 99 100 101 102 103 104 107 108 111 115 119 127 128 130 132 135 146 147 148 150 **S** Greater Hudson Valley Health System, Middletown, NY
Primary Contact: Jonathan Schiller, Chief Executive Officer
CFO: Rick Caprico, Chief Financial Officer
CMO: Gerard Galarneau M.D., Regional Chief Medical Officer
CIO: Brian Tew, Chief Information Officer
CNO: Rolland Bojo R.N., Chief Nursing Officer, Administrator Patient Care and Services
Web address: www.crmcny.org
Control: Other not-for-profit (including NFP Corporation) **Service:** General medical and surgical

Staffed Beds: 165 **Admissions:** 4107 **Census:** 109 **Outpatient Visits:** 73275 **Births:** 586 **Total Expense ($000):** 82086 **Payroll Expense ($000):** 34646 **Personnel:** 622

HOLLISWOOD—Queens County, See New York City

HORNELL—Steuben County

✠ **ST. JAMES MERCY HOSPITAL (330151)**, 411 Canisteo Street, Zip 14843–2197; tel. 607/324–8000, (Total facility includes 112 beds in nursing home–type unit) **A**1 10 20 **F**1 3 12 15 28 29 30 34 35 38 40 44 45 50 51 54 64 77 79 81 85 87 91 92 93 94 95 96 107 108 110 114 118 119 130 132 144 146 149
Primary Contact: Jennifer Sullivan, President and Chief Executive Officer
CFO: Stan Konopko, Chief Financial Officer
CMO: John Carroll M.D., Chief Medical Officer
CIO: Jason Soles, Manager Information Systems
CHR: Jennifer Spike, Director Human Resources
CNO: Kathleen Brodbeck MSN, RN-B, Chief Nursing Officer
Web address: www.stjamesmercy.org
Control: Other not-for-profit (including NFP Corporation) **Service:** General medical and surgical

Staffed Beds: 127 **Admissions:** 874 **Census:** 37 **Outpatient Visits:** 104151 **Births:** 0 **Total Expense ($000):** 31614 **Payroll Expense ($000):** 11400 **Personnel:** 358

HUDSON—Columbia County

★ **COLUMBIA MEMORIAL HOSPITAL (330094)**, 71 Prospect Avenue, Zip 12534–2907; tel. 518/828–7601 **A**10 19 **F**8 11 13 15 18 26 29 32 34 35 39 40 45 49 50 54 59 61 63 64 68 70 71 75 76 77 79 81 82 87 89 93 97 98 100 102 103 104 105 107 108 110 111 115 116 119 127 129 130 131 144 146 147
Primary Contact: Jay P. Cahalan, Chief Executive Officer
COO: Karen Tassey FACHE, Chief Operating Officer
CFO: Bryan Mahoney, Chief Financial Officer
CMO: Lawrence Perl M.D., Chief Medical Officer
CIO: Bonnie Ratliff, Chief Information Officer
CNO: Mary Ellen Plass MS, R.N., Senior Vice President and Chief Nursing Officer
Web address: www.columbiamemorialhealth.org
Control: Other not-for-profit (including NFP Corporation) **Service:** General medical and surgical

Staffed Beds: 192 **Admissions:** 5500 **Census:** 89 **Outpatient Visits:** 447000 **Births:** 390 **Total Expense ($000):** 156127 **Payroll Expense ($000):** 78832 **Personnel:** 1435

HUNTINGTON—Suffolk County

✠ **HUNTINGTON HOSPITAL (330045)**, 270 Park Avenue, Zip 11743–2799; tel. 631/351–2200 **A**1 2 3 10 **F**3 8 11 12 13 15 17 18 20 22 26 29 30 31 32 34 35 36 37 38 40 41 43 44 45 46 47 48 49 50 51 54 55 56 57 58 59 60 61 63 64 65 66 68 69 70 73 74 75 76 78 79 81 82 84 85 86 87 89 91 97 98 100 101 102 103 107 108 110 111 114 115 118 119 126 130 132 146 147 148 149 150 **P**5 6 **S** Northwell Health, New Hyde Park, NY
Primary Contact: Gerard Brogan Jr, M.D., Executive Director
CFO: Michael Fagan, Chief Financial Officer
CMO: Michael Grosso M.D., Senior Vice President Medical Affairs
CIO: Linda Fischer, Director Information Services
CHR: Donna Cice, Vice President Human Resources
CNO: Susan Knoepffler R.N., Vice President Nursing
Web address: www.hunthosp.org
Control: Other not-for-profit (including NFP Corporation) **Service:** General medical and surgical

Staffed Beds: 290 **Admissions:** 16564 **Census:** 215 **Outpatient Visits:** 110000 **Births:** 1298 **Total Expense ($000):** 400929 **Payroll Expense ($000):** 190760 **Personnel:** 1791

IRVING—Chautauqua County

⇑ **TLC HEALTH NETWORK - LAKE SHORE HOSPITAL**, 845 Route 5 and 20, Zip 14081–9716; tel. 716/951–7000, (Nonreporting) **A**21
Primary Contact: John P. Galati, Chief Executive Officer
CFO: John Eichner, Vice President Finance
CMO: James Wild M.D., Medical Director
CIO: Raymond Manning, Director Information Technology
CHR: Shannon Bobseine, Manager Human Resources
CNO: Patricia Dole, Vice President Patient Care Services
Web address: www.tlchealth.org
Control: Other not-for-profit (including NFP Corporation) **Service:** General medical and surgical

Staffed Beds: 200

ITHACA—Tompkins County

✠ **CAYUGA MEDICAL CENTER AT ITHACA (330307)**, 101 Dates Drive, Zip 14850–1342; tel. 607/274–4011 **A**1 2 5 10 **F**3 8 12 13 15 18 20 22 28 29 30 31 34 35 38 40 41 45 48 49 50 51 54 57 59 61 64 68 70 72 74 75 76 77 78 79 81 82 84 85 86 87 90 92 93 98 99 100 101 102 103 107 108 110 111 114 115 116 117 118 119 121 129 130 131 132 133 135 144 145 146 147 148 149 **P**6 **S** Cayuga Health System, Ithaca, NY
Primary Contact: John B. Rudd, President and Chief Executive Officer
CFO: John Collett, Vice President and Chief Financial Officer
CMO: David M Evelyn M.D., Vice President Medical Affairs
CIO: Brett Mello, Chief Information Officer
CHR: Brian Forrest, Vice President Human Resources
CNO: Deb Raupers MSN, R.N., Vice President Patient Services and Chief Nursing Officer
Web address: www.cayugamed.org
Control: Other not-for-profit (including NFP Corporation) **Service:** General medical and surgical

Staffed Beds: 193 **Admissions:** 6551 **Census:** 78 **Outpatient Visits:** 263996 **Births:** 898 **Total Expense ($000):** 189014 **Payroll Expense ($000):** 70540 **Personnel:** 1429

JACKSON HEIGHTS—Queens County, See New York City

JAMAICA—Queens County, See New York City

JAMESTOWN—Chautauqua County

✠ **UPMC CHAUTAUQUA WCA (330239)**, 207 Foote Avenue, Zip 14701–7077, Mailing Address: P.O.Box 840, 14702–0840; tel. 716/487–0141 **A**1 2 10 **F**3 4 8 11 12 13 15 18 19 20 28 29 31 34 35 38 40 45 46 57 59 64 68 69 70 74 75 76 77 78 79 81 82 83 84 85 86 87 89 90 92 93 94 96 98 99 100 101 102 103 104 107 108 110 111 116 119 121 126 129 130 131 132 135 141 146 147 148 149 **S** UPMC, Pittsburgh, PA
Primary Contact: Betsy T. Wright, President and Chief Executive Officer
CMO: Marlene Garone M.D., Vice President Medical Affairs and Medical Director
CIO: Keith Robison, Chief Information Officer
CHR: Karen Bohall, Director Human Resources
Web address: www.wcahospital.org
Control: Other not-for-profit (including NFP Corporation) **Service:** General medical and surgical

Staffed Beds: 197 **Admissions:** 6684 **Census:** 99 **Outpatient Visits:** 278874 **Births:** 611 **Total Expense ($000):** 110998 **Payroll Expense ($000):** 43114 **Personnel:** 809

NY

JOHNSON CITY—Broome County

WILSON MEMORIAL REGIONAL MEDICAL CENTER See United Health Services Hospitals-Binghamton, Binghamton

KATONAH—Westchester County

☐ **FOUR WINDS HOSPITAL (334002)**, 800 Cross River Road, Zip 10536–3549; tel. 914/763–8151 (Nonreporting) **A**1 10
Primary Contact: Martin A. Buccolo, Ph.D., Chief Executive Officer
COO: Moira Morrissey, Chief Operating Officer and General Counsel
CFO: Barry S Weinstein, Chief Financial Officer
CMO: Jonathan Bauman M.D., Chief Medical Officer
CIO: Barry S Weinstein, Chief Financial Officer
CHR: Susan Cusano, Director Human Resources
Web address: www.fourwindshospital.com
Control: Partnership, Investor-owned (for-profit) **Service**: Psychiatric

Staffed Beds: 181

KENMORE—Erie County

☒ **KENMORE MERCY HOSPITAL (330102)**, 2950 Elmwood Avenue, Zip 14217–1390, Mailing Address: 2950 Elmwood Avenue, Room 4024, 14217–1390; tel. 716/447–6100, (Total facility includes 160 beds in nursing home–type unit) **A**1 3 10 **F**3 11 15 17 18 29 30 31 34 35 37 38 40 41 44 45 49 50 53 54 57 59 60 63 64 65 66 68 70 74 75 77 78 79 81 83 84 85 87 90 93 96 97 107 108 110 114 115 119 126 128 129 130 131 132 146 147 148 149 **P**5 6 **S** Catholic Health System, Buffalo, NY
Primary Contact: James M. Millard, President and Chief Executive Officer
COO: Walter Ludwig, Chief Operating Officer
CFO: James H Dunlop CPA, Jr, Executive Vice President and Chief Financial Officer
CMO: James Fitzpatrick M.D., Vice President Medical Affairs
CHR: Laura Cianflone, Director Human Resources
CNO: Cheryl Hayes, Vice President Patient Care Services
Web address: www.chsbuffalo.org
Control: Church operated, Nongovernment, not-for-profit **Service**: General medical and surgical

Staffed Beds: 288 **Admissions**: 9469 **Census**: 218 **Outpatient Visits**: 129591 **Births**: 0 **Total Expense ($000)**: 168853 **Payroll Expense ($000)**: 70113 **Personnel**: 956

KINGSTON—Ulster County

⇑ **BENEDICTINE HOSPITAL** See Health Alliance Hospital - Mary's Avenue Campus

⇑ **HEALTH ALLIANCE HOSPITAL - BROADWAY CAMPUS (330004)**, 396 Broadway, Zip 12401–4692; tel. 845/331–3131, (Nonreporting) **A**3 10 19 21 **S** WMCHealth, Valhalla, NY
Primary Contact: David Scarpino, President and Chief Executive Officer
COO: Robert Seidman, Chief Operating Officer
CFO: Steven J Haas, Chief Financial Officer
CMO: Frank Ehrlich M.D., Chief Medical Officer
CIO: John Finch, Vice President Information Services
CHR: Greg M Howard, Director Human Resource
Web address: www.hahv.org
Control: Other not-for-profit (including NFP Corporation) **Service**: General medical and surgical

Staffed Beds: 150

⇑ **HEALTH ALLIANCE HOSPITAL - MARY'S AVENUE CAMPUS (330224)**, 105 Marys Avenue, Zip 12401–5894; tel. 845/338–2500, (Nonreporting) **A**2 10 19 21 **S** WMCHealth, Valhalla, NY
Primary Contact: David Scarpino, President and Chief Executive Officer
COO: Robert Seidman, Chief Operating Officer
CFO: Steven J Haas, Chief Financial Officer
CMO: Frank Ehrlich M.D., Chief Medical Officer
CIO: John Finch, Chief Information and Community Officer
CHR: Greg M Howard, Vice President Human Resources
Web address: www.hahv.org
Control: Other not-for-profit (including NFP Corporation) **Service**: General medical and surgical

Staffed Beds: 120

⇑ **KINGSTON HOSPITAL** See Health Alliance Hospital - Broadway Campus

LEWISTON—Niagara County

☒ **MOUNT ST. MARY'S HOSPITAL AND HEALTH CENTER (330188)**, 5300 Military Road, Zip 14092–1903; tel. 716/297–4800 **A**1 10 **F**3 4 11 13 15 17 18 28 29 30 34 35 40 41 44 45 49 50 51 54 56 57 59 60 64 65 66 68 70 74 75 76 77 79 81 84 85 87 89 92 93 97 107 108 110 111 114 115 119 130 143 146 147 148 149 **P**5 6 **S** Catholic Health System, Buffalo, NY
Primary Contact: Gary C. Tucker, President and Chief Executive Officer
CFO: Stephen Franko, Vice President Finance and Chief Financial Officer
CMO: Domonic F Falsetti M.D., Chief of Staff and Medical Director
CHR: Deborah J Serafin, Vice President Human Resources
CNO: Jessica Visser R.N., Vice President Patient Care Services and Chief Nursing Officer
Web address: www.msmh.org
Control: Church operated, Nongovernment, not-for-profit **Service**: General medical and surgical

Staffed Beds: 129 **Admissions**: 5311 **Census**: 73 **Outpatient Visits**: 175680 **Births**: 373 **Total Expense ($000)**: 98899 **Payroll Expense ($000)**: 50047 **Personnel**: 676

LITTLE FALLS—Herkimer County

★ **LITTLE FALLS HOSPITAL (331311)**, 140 Burwell Street, Zip 13365–1725; tel. 315/823–1000, (Nonreporting) **A**10 18 **S** Bassett Healthcare Network, Cooperstown, NY
Primary Contact: Michael L. Ogden, President and Chief Executive Officer
CFO: James Vielkind, Chief Financial Officer
CMO: Louis Oceguera M.D., Medical Director
CIO: Duane Merry, Chief Information Officer
CHR: Christine Pirri, Vice President Human Resources
CNO: Heidi Camardello, Vice President Patient Care Services and Chief Nursing Officer
Web address: www.bassett.org
Control: Other not-for-profit (including NFP Corporation) **Service**: General medical and surgical

Staffed Beds: 59

LITTLE NECK—Queens County, See New York City

LOCKPORT—Niagara County

★ **EASTERN NIAGARA HOSPITAL (330163)**, 521 East Avenue, Zip 14094–3299; tel. 716/514–5700, (Includes EASTERN NIAGARA HOSPITAL LOCKPORT, 521 East Avenue, Lockport, New York, Zip 14094–3299, tel. 716/514–5700; EASTERN NIAGARA HOSPITAL NEWFANE, 2600 William Street, Newfane, New York, Zip 14108–1093, tel. 716/778–5111) **A**10 13 **F**3 4 8 13 15 18 19 28 29 30 31 34 40 45 46 47 48 49 50 51 54 57 59 60 63 65 68 70 74 75 76 77 79 81 82 83 84 85 87 89 93 94 97 98 99 100 102 107 108 110 111 115 119 126 130 132 135 144 146 147 148
Primary Contact: Clare A. Haar, Chief Executive Officer
COO: David J Di Bacco, Chief Operating Officer
CMO: Bruce J Cusenz M.D., Medical Director
CHR: Joseph Farrauto, Director Human Resources
CNO: Mary Beth Campo MS, R.N., Director of Nursing
Web address: www.enhs.org
Control: Other not-for-profit (including NFP Corporation) **Service**: General medical and surgical

Staffed Beds: 125 **Admissions**: 4398 **Census**: 77 **Births**: 346 **Total Expense ($000)**: 62935 **Payroll Expense ($000)**: 28738

LONG ISLAND CITY—Queens County, See New York City

LOWVILLE—Lewis County

☒ **LEWIS COUNTY GENERAL HOSPITAL (331317)**, 7785 North State Street, Zip 13367–1297; tel. 315/376–5200, (Nonreporting) **A**1 10 18
Primary Contact: Gerald Cayer, Chief Executive Officer
COO: Michele Prince, Chief Operating Officer
CFO: Jeffrey Hellinger, Interim Chief Financial Officer
CMO: Catherine Williams M.D., Medical Director
CIO: Rob Uttendorfsky, Director Information Management
CHR: James Swords, Director Human Resources
CNO: Jennifer Shaver, Director of Nursing
Web address: www.lcgh.net
Control: County, Government, Nonfederal **Service**: General medical and surgical

Staffed Beds: 185

Many Facility Codes have changed. Please refer to the AHA Guide Code Chart. © 2017 AHA Guide

MALONE—Franklin County

THE UNIVERSITY OF VERMONT HEALTH NETWORK - ALICE HYDE MEDICAL CENTER (330084), 133 Park Street, Zip 12953–1243, Mailing Address: P.O.Box 729, 12953–0729; tel. 518/483–3000, (Total facility includes 135 beds in nursing home–type unit) **A**1 10 20 **F**3 10 11 13 15 17 18 28 29 31 34 36 39 40 45 50 57 59 64 68 70 75 76 77 78 79 81 82 84 85 86 87 90 92 93 96 97 100 107 108 110 111 115 117 119 121 127 128 129 130 131 132 135 146 147 148 149 **P**6
Primary Contact: Stephens M. Mundy, Interim President
COO: Matthew Jones, Senior Director Support Services and Facilities
CFO: Sean Curtin, Chief Financial Officer
CMO: William Latreille M.D., Chief Medical Officer
CIO: Darrin Goodrow, Chief Information Officer
CHR: Emily Campbell, Senior Director Human Resources
CNO: Julie Marshall, Chief Nursing Officer
Web address: www.UVMHealth.org/AHMC
Control: Other not-for-profit (including NFP Corporation) **Service**: General medical and surgical

Staffed Beds: 225 **Admissions:** 2051 **Census:** 148 **Outpatient Visits:** 199540 **Births:** 225 **Total Expense ($000):** 87541 **Payroll Expense ($000):** 44364 **Personnel:** 658

MANHASSET—Nassau County

NORTH SHORE UNIVERSITY HOSPITAL (330106), 300 Community Drive, Zip 11030–3816; tel. 516/562–0100 **A**1 2 3 5 8 10 **F**3 6 7 8 9 11 12 13 14 15 17 18 20 22 24 26 28 29 30 31 34 35 36 37 38 39 40 41 43 44 45 46 47 48 49 50 51 52 54 55 56 57 58 59 60 61 62 63 64 65 66 68 69 70 71 72 73 74 75 76 77 78 79 80 81 82 83 84 85 86 87 91 92 93 94 97 99 100 101 102 103 104 107 108 110 111 112 114 115 117 118 119 120 121 123 126 129 130 131 132 134 135 136 138 141 142 143 144 145 146 147 148 149 150 **P**5 6 **S** Northwell Health, New Hyde Park, NY
Primary Contact: Alessandro Bellucci, M.D., Executive Director
CFO: Frank Rizzo, Chief Financial Officer, Central Region
CMO: Michael Gitman M.D., Medical Director
CIO: Nympha Meindel R.N., Chief Information Officer
CHR: Debra Bierman, Associate Executive Director Human Resources
CNO: Kerri Scanlon MSN, Chief Nursing Officer
Web address: www.northwell.edu/find-care/locations/north-shore-university-hospital
Control: Other not-for-profit (including NFP Corporation) **Service**: General medical and surgical

Staffed Beds: 738 **Admissions:** 48314 **Census:** 764 **Outpatient Visits:** 940426 **Births:** 6755 **Total Expense ($000):** 2115362 **Payroll Expense ($000):** 1065950 **Personnel:** 11381

MANHATTAN—New York County, See New York City

MARCY—Oneida County

CENTRAL NEW YORK PSYCHIATRIC CENTER, 9005 Old River Road, Zip 13403–3000, Mailing Address: P.O.Box 300, 13403–0300; tel. 315/765–3600, (Nonreporting) **A**1 **S** New York State Office of Mental Health, Albany, NY
Primary Contact: Maureen Bosco, Executive Director
Web address: www.omh.ny.gov
Control: State, Government, Nonfederal **Service**: Psychiatric

Staffed Beds: 226

MARGARETVILLE—Delaware County

MARGARETVILLE HOSPITAL (331304), 42084 State Highway 28, Zip 12455–2820; tel. 845/586–2631, (Nonreporting) **A**10 18 21 **S** WMCHealth, Valhalla, NY
Primary Contact: Mark Pohar, Executive Director
CHR: Linda Mead, Director Human Resources
Web address: www.margaretvillehospital.org
Control: Other not-for-profit (including NFP Corporation) **Service**: General medical and surgical

Staffed Beds: 15

MASSENA—St. Lawrence County

MASSENA MEMORIAL HOSPITAL (330223), One Hospital Drive, Zip 13662–1097; tel. 315/764–1711, (Nonreporting) **A**1 10 20
Primary Contact: Robert G. Wolleben, Chief Executive Officer
CFO: Patrick M Facteau, Chief Financial Officer
CMO: Nimesh Desai M.D., Medical Director
CIO: Jana Grose, Chief Information Officer
CHR: Jonnie Dorothy, Senior Director Human Resources
CNO: Ralene North, Chief Nurse Executive
Web address: www.massenahospital.org
Control: City, Government, Nonfederal **Service**: General medical and surgical

Staffed Beds: 50

MEDINA—Orleans County

★ △ ⇑ **MEDINA MEMORIAL HOSPITAL (331319)**, 200 Ohio Street, Zip 14103–1095; tel. 585/798–2000, (Total facility includes 30 beds in nursing home–type unit) **A**7 10 18 21 **F**3 11 15 18 24 26 29 34 35 40 45 46 50 51 53 54 57 59 60 62 64 68 70 75 77 79 81 85 86 87 90 91 92 93 96 97 107 108 110 111 115 118 119 128 129 130 132 133 135 144 146 148 149
Primary Contact: Wendy Jacobson, President and Chief Executive Officer
CFO: David Britton, Interim Chief Financial Officer
CMO: Joseph Misiti M.D., President Medical Staff
CHR: Mary Williams, Director Human Resources
Web address: www.medinamemorial.org
Control: Other not-for-profit (including NFP Corporation) **Service**: General medical and surgical

Staffed Beds: 64 **Admissions:** 753 **Census:** 41 **Outpatient Visits:** 60342 **Births:** 0 **Total Expense ($000):** 29981 **Payroll Expense ($000):** 14714 **Personnel:** 269

MIDDLETOWN—Orange County

ORANGE REGIONAL MEDICAL CENTER (330126), 707 East Main Street, Zip 10940–2650; tel. 845/333–1000 **A**1 2 7 10 12 13 **F**8 11 12 13 15 17 18 20 22 26 28 29 30 31 34 35 36 40 41 43 45 46 47 48 49 50 51 54 57 58 59 60 63 64 65 68 70 72 74 75 76 77 78 79 81 82 83 84 85 86 87 89 90 91 93 94 96 97 98 99 100 101 102 103 104 107 108 110 111 114 115 116 117 119 120 121 122 123 124 126 129 130 132 135 144 146 148 149 150 **S** Greater Hudson Valley Health System, Middletown, NY
Primary Contact: Scott Batulis, President and Chief Executive Officer
COO: Timothy P Selz, Vice President
CFO: Mitch Amodo, Vice President and Chief Financial Officer
CMO: James Oxley D.O., Vice President Medical Affairs
CHR: Deborah Carr, Vice President Human Resources
Web address: www.ormc.org
Control: Other not-for-profit (including NFP Corporation) **Service**: General medical and surgical

Staffed Beds: 345 **Admissions:** 21766 **Census:** 297 **Outpatient Visits:** 829824 **Births:** 1750 **Total Expense ($000):** 434240 **Payroll Expense ($000):** 166194 **Personnel:** 1579

MINEOLA—Nassau County

NYU WINTHROP HOSPITAL (330167), 259 First Street, Zip 11501–3957; tel. 516/663–0333, (Includes CHILDREN'S MEDICAL CENTER, 259 First Street, Mineola, New York, Zip 11501–3957, tel. 516/663–0333) **A**1 2 3 5 8 10 **F**3 5 6 8 9 11 12 13 14 15 17 18 19 20 22 24 26 28 29 30 31 32 34 35 36 37 38 39 40 41 43 44 45 46 47 48 49 50 51 52 54 55 56 57 58 59 60 61 62 63 64 65 66 68 70 72 73 74 75 76 77 78 79 81 82 84 85 86 87 88 89 92 93 94 97 99 100 101 102 103 104 107 108 110 111 114 115 116 117 118 119 120 121 123 124 126 129 130 131 132 134 135 141 142 144 145 146 147 148 149 150 **P**5 6 7 8 **S** NYU Langone Health, New York, NY
Primary Contact: John F. Collins, President and Chief Executive Officer
COO: Garry Schwall, Chief Operating Officer
CFO: Palmira Cataliotti, Senior Vice President, Chief Financial Officer and Treasurer
CMO: Michael Ammazzalorso M.D., Chief Medical Officer
CIO: Nicholas Casabona, Chief Information Officer
CHR: Stacey Pfeffer, Senior Vice President Human Resources
CNO: Valerie Terzano MSN, R.N., Senior Vice President Nursing
Web address: www.winthrop.org
Control: Other not-for-profit (including NFP Corporation) **Service**: General medical and surgical

Staffed Beds: 511 **Admissions:** 32012 **Census:** 452 **Outpatient Visits:** 443848 **Births:** 5014 **Total Expense ($000):** 1359442 **Payroll Expense ($000):** 686150 **Personnel:** 7874

MONTOUR FALLS—Schuyler County

SCHUYLER HOSPITAL (331313), 220 Steuben Street, Zip 14865–9709; tel. 607/535–7121, (Total facility includes 120 beds in nursing home–type unit) **A**1 10 18 **F**3 11 14 15 29 30 34 35 40 45 59 64 70 75 77 81 82 85 87 91 92 93 94 97 107 110 111 114 119 128 129 130 133 135 146 149 **P**6 **S** Cayuga Health System, Ithaca, NY
Primary Contact: James B. Watson, President
CMO: Michael Eisman M.D., Medical Director
CHR: Troy Preston, Director Human Resources
Web address: www.schuylerhospital.org
Control: Other not-for-profit (including NFP Corporation) **Service**: General medical and surgical

Staffed Beds: 145 **Admissions:** 797 **Census:** 117 **Outpatient Visits:** 61289 **Births:** 0 **Total Expense ($000):** 32548 **Payroll Expense ($000):** 17602 **Personnel:** 333

NY

Hospital, Medicare Provider Number, Address, Telephone, Approval, Facility, and Physician Codes, Health Care System

★ American Hospital Association (AHA) membership
☐ The Joint Commission accreditation
○ Healthcare Facilities Accreditation Program
◇ DNV Healthcare Inc. accreditation
⇑ Center for Improvement in Healthcare Quality Accreditation
△ Commission on Accreditation of Rehabilitation Facilities (CARF) accreditation

MONTROSE—Westchester County

VETERANS AFFAIRS HUDSON VALLEY HEALTH CARE SYSTEM, 2094 Albany Post Road, Zip 10548–1454, Mailing Address: P.O.Box 100, 10548–0100; tel. 914/737–4400, (Includes VETERAN AFFAIRS HUDSON VALLEY HEALTH CARE SYSTEM-CASTLE POINT CAMPUS, 41 Castle Point Road, Wappingers, New York, Zip 12590, tel. 914/831–2000; VETERANS AFFAIRS HUDSON VALLEY HEALTH CARE SYSTEM-MONTROSE CAMPUS, 2094 Albany Post Road, Montrose, New York, Zip 10548, tel. 914/737–4400) **A**1 3 5 **F**1 3 4 5 7 8 12 15 18 20 22 24 26 28 29 30 31 34 35 36 37 38 39 44 45 46 47 48 49 53 54 56 57 58 59 60 61 63 65 66 67 68 71 74 75 77 78 79 81 82 84 86 87 90 93 94 97 98 100 101 102 103 104 105 106 107 108 109 111 112 113 114 115 116 117 118 119 120 122 123 124 127 128 130 132 135 143 144 145 146 147 148 149 **P**6 **S** Department of Veterans Affairs, Washington, DC
Primary Contact: Margaret B. Caplan, Director
COO: John M Grady, Associate Director
CFO: John Walsh, Chief Fiscal Services
CMO: Joanne J Malina M.D., Chief of Staff
CIO: Thomas Rooney, Chief Information Resource Management
CHR: Dardanella Russell, Chief Human Resources Management Service
Web address: www.hudsonvalley.va.gov/
Control: Veterans Affairs, Government, federal **Service:** Psychiatric

Staffed Beds: 577 **Admissions:** 1505 **Census:** 236 **Outpatient Visits:** 381622 **Births:** 0 **Total Expense ($000):** 271556 **Payroll Expense ($000):** 121280 **Personnel:** 1450

MOUNT KISCO—Westchester County

NORTHERN WESTCHESTER HOSPITAL (330162), 400 East Main Street, Zip 10549–3477, Mailing Address: 400 East Main Street, G-02, 10549–3477; tel. 914/666–1200 **A**1 2 10 **F**3 7 8 12 13 15 17 18 28 29 30 31 32 34 35 36 37 40 43 46 47 48 49 50 51 54 55 56 57 59 60 61 64 65 68 70 72 73 74 75 76 78 79 81 82 84 85 86 87 89 91 92 93 97 98 99 100 101 102 103 107 108 109 110 111 114 115 118 119 120 121 123 124 126 129 130 131 132 135 146 147 148 **P**5 6 **S** Northwell Health, New Hyde Park, NY
Primary Contact: Joel Seligman, President and Chief Executive Officer
CFO: John Partenza, Vice President and Treasurer
CMO: Marla Koroly M.D., Chief Medical Officer and Senior Vice President Medical Affairs
CIO: Sue Prince, Director Information Systems
CHR: Kerry Flynn Barrett, Vice President Human Resources
CNO: Lauraine Szekely R.N., Senior Vice President, Patient Care
Web address: www.nwhc.net
Control: Other not-for-profit (including NFP Corporation) **Service:** General medical and surgical

Staffed Beds: 195 **Admissions:** 9433 **Census:** 118 **Outpatient Visits:** 148963 **Births:** 1582 **Total Expense ($000):** 256767 **Payroll Expense ($000):** 114794 **Personnel:** 1333

MOUNT VERNON—Westchester County

MONTEFIORE MOUNT VERNON (330086), 12 North Seventh Avenue, Zip 10550–2098; tel. 914/664–8000 **A**1 3 5 10 **F**3 14 15 18 29 30 31 34 35 40 45 50 59 60 61 64 65 66 68 70 74 75 77 78 79 81 84 85 86 87 92 93 97 98 100 102 104 107 110 111 114 119 130 146 147 **P**5 **S** Montefiore Health System, Bronx, NY
Primary Contact: Jaccel Kouns, R.N., MS, Vice President and Executive Director
CFO: Albert M Farina, Chief Financial Officer
CMO: Gary Ishkanian M.D., Vice President Medical Affairs
CIO: Barbara Cooke, Director Health Information Systems
CHR: Dennis H Ashley, Vice President Human Resources
Web address: www.montefiorehealthsystem.org/landing.cfm?id=17
Control: Other not-for-profit (including NFP Corporation) **Service:** General medical and surgical

Staffed Beds: 63 **Admissions:** 3332 **Census:** 62 **Outpatient Visits:** 138501 **Births:** 0 **Total Expense ($000):** 85005 **Payroll Expense ($000):** 37197 **Personnel:** 563

NEW HAMPTON—Orange County

MID-HUDSON FORENSIC PSYCHIATRIC CENTER (334061), Route 17M, Zip 10958, Mailing Address: P.O.Box 158, 10958–0158; tel. 845/374–8700 **A**1 3 10 **F**39 68 77 87 98 130 135 **S** New York State Office of Mental Health, Albany, NY
Primary Contact: Joseph Freebern, Executive Director
COO: Kristin Orlando, Director Operations
Web address: www.omh.ny.gov
Control: State, Government, Nonfederal **Service:** Psychiatric

Staffed Beds: 285 **Admissions:** 298 **Census:** 254 **Outpatient Visits:** 0 **Births:** 0 **Total Expense ($000):** 89875 **Payroll Expense ($000):** 48850 **Personnel:** 551

NEW HYDE PARK—Queens County, See New York City

NEW ROCHELLE—Westchester County

MONTEFIORE NEW ROCHELLE (330184), 16 Guion Place, Zip 10801–5502; tel. 914/632–5000, (Total facility includes 150 beds in nursing home–type unit) **A**1 2 3 5 10 **F**2 3 8 12 13 15 18 28 29 30 31 32 34 35 37 40 45 50 55 59 64 65 66 68 70 72 74 75 76 77 78 79 81 82 84 85 86 87 89 90 92 93 97 100 107 108 110 114 119 128 130 132 146 **P**5 **S** Montefiore Health System, Bronx, NY
Primary Contact: Anthony Alfano, Vice President Executive Director
COO: John P. Mamangakis, Senior Vice President
CFO: Albert M Farina, Senior Vice President and Chief Financial Officer
CMO: Richard Barone M.D., Medical Director
CIO: Barbara Cooke, Director Health Information Systems
CHR: Dennis H Ashley, Vice President Human Resources
CNO: Pamela M Dupuis R.N., Senior Vice President Patient Care Services
Web address: www.montefiorehealthsystem.org
Control: Other not-for-profit (including NFP Corporation) **Service:** General medical and surgical

Staffed Beds: 298 **Admissions:** 7317 **Census:** 228 **Outpatient Visits:** 99180 **Births:** 1111 **Total Expense ($000):** 196355 **Payroll Expense ($000):** 89577 **Personnel:** 1292

NEW YORK (Includes all hospitals located within the five boroughs)
BRONX - Bronx County (Mailing Address - Bronx)
BROOKLYN - Kings County (Mailing Address - Brooklyn)
MANHATTAN - New York County (Mailing Address - New York)
QUEENS - Queens County (Mailing Addresses - Bellerose, Elmhurst, Far Rockaway, Flushing, Forest Hills, Glen Oaks, Holliswood, Jackson Heights, Jamaica, Little Neck, Long Island City, New Hyde Park, and Queens Village)
RICHMOND VALLEY - Richmond County (Mailing Address - Staten Island)

BETH ISRAEL MEDICAL CENTER See Mount Sinai Beth Israel

BETH ISRAEL MEDICAL CENTER-KINGS HIGHWAY DIVISION See Mount Sinai Beth Israel Brooklyn

BRONX-LEBANON HOSPITAL CENTER HEALTH CARE SYSTEM (330009), 1276 Fulton Avenue, Zip 10456–3499; tel. 718/590–1800, (Includes BRONX-LEBANON SPECIAL CARE CENTER, 1265 Fulton Avenue, Bronx, New York, Zip 10465, tel. 718/579–7000; Octavio Marin, Vice President Long Term Care and Ambulatory Care Services; CONCOURSE DIVISION, 1650 Grand Concourse, Bronx, New York, Zip 10457, 1276 Fulton Ave, 10456–3402, tel. 718/590–1800; Miguel A Fuentes Jr, President and Chief Executive Officer; FULTON DIVISION, 1276 Fulton Avenue, Bronx, New York, Zip 10456, 1650 Grand Concourse, 10457–7606, tel. 718/590–1800; Miguel A Fuentes Jr, President and Chief Executive Officer; HIGHBRIDGE WOODYCREST CENTER, 936 Woodycrest Avenue, Bronx, New York, Zip 10452, tel. 718/579–8875; Leonardo Vicent III, Executive Director) (Total facility includes 330 beds in nursing home–type unit) **A**1 3 5 10 **F**3 4 8 9 11 12 13 15 17 18 19 20 21 22 26 28 29 30 31 32 34 35 37 38 39 40 41 44 45 46 47 48 49 50 51 52 54 55 56 57 58 59 60 61 64 65 66 68 70 71 72 73 74 75 76 77 78 79 81 82 83 84 85 86 87 88 89 91 92 93 95 96 97 98 99 100 101 102 103 104 105 106 107 108 110 111 118 119 126 128 129 130 131 132 133 134 135 143 144 145 146 147 148 149 150 **P**6
Primary Contact: Miguel A. Fuentes Jr, President and Chief Executive Officer
CFO: Victor DeMarco, Chief Financial Officer
CMO: Milton A Gumbs M.D., Vice President and Medical Director
CIO: Ivan Durbak, Chief Information Officer
CHR: Selena Griffin-Mahon, Assistant Vice President Human Resources
CNO: Patricia Cahill R.N., Vice President, Patient Care Services and Chief Nursing Officer
Web address: www.bronxcare.org
Control: Other not-for-profit (including NFP Corporation) **Service:** General medical and surgical

Staffed Beds: 972 **Admissions:** 31012 **Census:** 780 **Outpatient Visits:** 1145655 **Births:** 2094 **Total Expense ($000):** 804996 **Payroll Expense ($000):** 381718 **Personnel:** 4173

BRONX PSYCHIATRIC CENTER (334053), 1500 Waters Place, Zip 10461–2796; tel. 718/931–0600, (Nonreporting) **A**1 3 5 10 **S** New York State Office of Mental Health, Albany, NY
Primary Contact: Anita Daniels, Director
CFO: Robert Erway, Director for Administration
Web address: www.omh.ny.gov
Control: State, Government, Nonfederal **Service:** Psychiatric

Staffed Beds: 450

Many Facility Codes have changed. Please refer to the AHA Guide Code Chart.

☐ **BROOKDALE HOSPITAL MEDICAL CENTER (330233)**, 125 Worth Street, 4th Fl Ste 418, Zip 10013, Mailing Address: One Brookdale Plaza, Brooklyn, 11212–3139; tel. 718/240–5000, (Nonreporting) **A**1 3 5 10
Primary Contact: Dominick Stanzione, President and Chief Executive Officer
CFO: James Porter, Chief Financial Officer
CMO: Estevan Garcia M.D., Chief Medical Officer
CIO: David Reitzel, Chief Information Officer
CHR: Margaret M Brubaker, Senior Vice President Human Resources
Web address: www.brookdalehospital.org
Control: Other not-for-profit (including NFP Corporation) **Service:** General medical and surgical

Staffed Beds: 789

☐ **BROOKLYN HOSPITAL CENTER (330056)**, 121 DeKalb Avenue, Zip 11201–5425; tel. 718/250–8000 **A**1 3 5 10 **F**3 4 7 8 12 13 15 17 18 19 20 26 29 30 31 32 34 35 39 40 41 45 46 47 48 49 50 52 54 55 56 57 58 59 60 61 63 64 65 68 70 72 74 75 76 77 78 79 81 82 83 84 85 86 87 88 89 90 93 94 97 100 101 103 107 109 110 111 112 114 115 116 117 119 120 121 122 123 129 130 131 132 133 134 135 143 144 145 146 147 148 149 150
Primary Contact: Gary G. Terrinoni, President and Chief Executive Officer
COO: John Gupta, Executive Vice President and Chief Operating Officer
CIO: Irene Farrelly, Vice President and Chief Information Officer
CHR: Ira Warm, Senior Vice President Human Resources
Web address: www.tbh.org
Control: Other not-for-profit (including NFP Corporation) **Service:** General medical and surgical

Staffed Beds: 297 Admissions: 14702 **Census:** 214 **Outpatient Visits:** 340408 **Births:** 2099 **Total Expense ($000):** 420612 **Payroll Expense ($000):** 217278 **Personnel:** 4288

✦ **CALVARY HOSPITAL (332006)**, 1740 Eastchester Road, Zip 10461–2392; tel. 718/863–6900 **A**1 3 5 10 **F**1 29 30 35 39 62 63 64 68 74 78 82 84 87 119 121 130 132 134 146 148 149 **P**6
Primary Contact: Frank A. Calamari, President and Chief Executive Officer
COO: Richard J Kutilek, Chief Operating Officer
CFO: Andrew Greco, Chief Financial Officer
CMO: Michael J Brescia M.D., Executive Medical Director
CIO: Patrick Martin, Director Information Systems
CHR: Michael T Troncone, Chief Human Resources Officer
CNO: Margaret Pelkowski R.N., Vice President Patient Care Services
Web address: www.calvaryhospital.org
Control: Church operated, Nongovernment, not-for-profit **Service:** Acute long-term care hospital

Staffed Beds: 225 Admissions: 2886 **Census:** 216 **Outpatient Visits:** 121147 **Births:** 0 **Total Expense ($000):** 118938 **Payroll Expense ($000):** 62733 **Personnel:** 874

COLER-GOLDWATER SPECIALTY HOSPITAL AND NURSING FACILITY See Nyc Health + Hospitals / Carter

CONCOURSE DIVISION See Bronx-Lebanon Hospital Center Health Care System

☐ **CREEDMOOR PSYCHIATRIC CENTER (334004)**, 79–25 Winchester Boulevard, Zip 11427–2128; tel. 718/264–3600, (Nonreporting) **A**1 3 10 **S** New York State Office of Mental Health, Albany, NY
Primary Contact: Ann Marie. Barbarotta, Executive Director
CFO: Viodelda Ho-Shing, Deputy Director Administration
CIO: Ed Yunusov, Chief Information Officer
CHR: Adrienne Jones, Director Human Resources
CNO: Marie S Jean-Louis R.N., Chief Nursing Officer
Web address: www.omh.ny.gov
Control: State, Government, Nonfederal **Service:** Psychiatric

Staffed Beds: 380

✦ **FLUSHING HOSPITAL MEDICAL CENTER (330193)**, 4500 Parsons Boulevard, Zip 11355–2205; tel. 718/670–5000 **A**1 3 5 10 **F**3 4 5 7 8 12 13 15 17 18 19 29 30 31 32 34 35 36 39 40 41 45 49 50 51 55 56 57 59 60 61 64 65 68 70 71 72 73 74 75 76 77 78 79 81 82 84 85 87 89 91 92 93 97 98 100 101 103 104 107 110 111 114 119 126 128 130 132 135 146 147 148 149 150 **P**5 **S** MediSys Health Network, Jamaica, NY
Primary Contact: Bruce J. Flanz, President and Chief Executive Officer
COO: Robert V Levine, Executive Vice President and Chief Operating Officer
CFO: Mounir F Doss, Executive Vice President and Chief Financial Officer
CMO: Siamack Nemazie M.D., Medical Director, Patient Safety Officer
CIO: Tony Gatto, Director Management Information Systems
CHR: Sheila Garvey, Vice President Human Resources
Web address: www.flushinghospital.org
Control: Other not-for-profit (including NFP Corporation) **Service:** General medical and surgical

Staffed Beds: 299 Admissions: 15552 **Census:** 245 **Outpatient Visits:** 152083 **Births:** 3126 **Total Expense ($000):** 618376 **Payroll Expense ($000):** 125087 **Personnel:** 1721

FULTON DIVISION See Bronx-Lebanon Hospital Center Health Care System

☐ **GRACIE SQUARE HOSPITAL (334048)**, 420 East 76th Street, Zip 10021–3396; tel. 212/988–4400, (Nonreporting) **A**1 10
Primary Contact: David Wyman, President and Chief Executive Officer
Web address: www.nygsh.org
Control: Other not-for-profit (including NFP Corporation) **Service:** Psychiatric

Staffed Beds: 157

HENRY J. CARTER SPECIALTY HOSPITAL & NURSING FACILITY See NYC Health + Hospitals / Carter

✦ **HOSPITAL FOR SPECIAL SURGERY (330270)**, 535 East 70th Street, Zip 10021–4898, Mailing Address: 535 East 70th Street, Belaire 10–08, 10021–4898; tel. 212/606–1000 **A**1 3 5 8 10 **F**3 8 9 29 30 32 33 34 35 36 37 38 43 44 50 53 54 56 57 58 59 64 66 68 70 74 75 77 79 80 81 82 84 85 86 87 89 92 93 94 97 100 107 109 111 114 115 116 117 119 121 123 126 130 131 132 134 141 142 146 147 148 149 **P**8
Primary Contact: Louis A. Shapiro, President and Chief Executive Officer
COO: Lisa Goldstein, Executive Vice President and Chief Operating Officer
CFO: Stacey Malakoff, Executive Vice President and Chief Financial Officer
CMO: Todd Albert M.D., Surgeon-in-Chief and Medical Director
CIO: Jamie Nelson, Vice President and Chief Information Officer
CHR: Bruce Slawitsky, Vice President Human Resources
CNO: Stephanie J Goldberg MSN, R.N., Senior Vice President and Chief Nursing Officer
Web address: www.hss.edu
Control: Other not-for-profit (including NFP Corporation) **Service:** Orthopedic

Staffed Beds: 209 Admissions: 15812 **Census:** 145 **Outpatient Visits:** 411876 **Births:** 0 **Total Expense ($000):** 982111 **Payroll Expense ($000):** 431597 **Personnel:** 4309

☐ **INTERFAITH MEDICAL CENTER (330397)**, 1545 Atlantic Avenue, Zip 11213–1122; tel. 718/613–4000, (Nonreporting) **A**1 3 5 10
Primary Contact: LaRay Brown, President and Chief Executive Officer
CMO: Jochanan Weisenfreund M.D., Senior Vice President Academic and Medical Affairs
CIO: Mark Lederman, Chief Information Officer
CHR: Venra Mathurin, Vice President Human Resources
Web address: www.interfaithmedical.com
Control: Other not-for-profit (including NFP Corporation) **Service:** General medical and surgical

Staffed Beds: 277

JACK D WEILER HOSPITAL OF ALBERT EINSTEIN COLLEGE OF MEDICINE See Montefiore Medical Center

✦ **JAMAICA HOSPITAL MEDICAL CENTER (330014)**, 8900 Van Wyck Expressway, Zip 11418–2832; tel. 718/206–6000, (Total facility includes 228 beds in nursing home–type unit) **A**1 3 5 10 13 **F**1 3 7 11 13 15 17 18 19 20 22 26 29 30 31 32 34 35 36 38 39 40 41 43 44 45 49 50 52 53 54 55 56 57 58 59 60 61 62 64 65 66 68 70 71 72 73 74 75 76 77 78 79 81 82 83 84 85 86 87 89 90 92 93 96 97 98 99 100 101 102 103 104 107 108 110 111 114 115 118 119 128 129 130 131 132 134 135 143 144 146 147 149 150 **P**5 7 8 **S** MediSys Health Network, Jamaica, NY
Primary Contact: Bruce J. Flanz, President and Chief Executive Officer
COO: William Lynch, Executive Vice President and Chief Operating Officer
CFO: Mounir F Doss, Executive Vice President and Chief Financial Officer
CMO: Antonietta Morisco M.D., Medical Director, Chairman Anesthesiology
CIO: Sami Boshut, Chief Information Officer
CHR: Trina Cornet JD, Vice President Human Resources
CNO: Kathleen Scher Ed.D., R.N., Chief Nursing Officer
Web address: www.Jamaicahospital.org
Control: Other not-for-profit (including NFP Corporation) **Service:** General medical and surgical

Staffed Beds: 668 Admissions: 23472 **Census:** 549 **Outpatient Visits:** 368690 **Births:** 2277 **Total Expense ($000):** 700032 **Payroll Expense ($000):** 258849 **Personnel:** 3356

NY

☒ △ **JAMES J. PETERS VETERANS AFFAIRS MEDICAL CENTER**, 130 West
Kingsbridge Road, Zip 10468–3904; tel. 718/584–9000, (Nonreporting) **A**1 2 3 5
7 8 **S** Department of Veterans Affairs, Washington, DC
Primary Contact: Erik Langhoff, M.D., Ph.D., Director
CFO: Gregory Angelo, Chief Fiscal Program
CMO: Clive Rosendorff M.D., Chief Medical Program
CIO: Linda Bund, Chief Information Officer and Director Education
CHR: Peter Tinker, Chief Human Resources Officer
CNO: Kathleen Capitulo Ph.D., R.N., Chief Nurse Executive
Web address: www.bronx.va.gov/
Control: Veterans Affairs, Government, federal **Service:** General medical and
surgical

Staffed Beds: 325

☐ **KINGSBORO PSYCHIATRIC CENTER (334063)**, 681 Clarkson Avenue,
Zip 11203–2125; tel. 718/221–7395, (Nonreporting) **A**1 3 5 10 **S** New York
State Office of Mental Health, Albany, NY
Primary Contact: Deborah Parchment, Executive Director
CFO: Yinusa Awolowo, Business Officer
CMO: Jeffery Lucey M.D., Clinical Director
CIO: George Gavora, Director Program Evaluation
CHR: Vera Thompson, Director Human Resources
CNO: Deborah Denigris, Chief Nursing Officer
Web address: www.omh.ny.gov/omhweb/facilities/kbpc/facility/htm
Control: State, Government, Nonfederal **Service:** Psychiatric

Staffed Beds: 290

☐ △ **KINGSBROOK JEWISH MEDICAL CENTER (330201)**, 585 Schenectady
Avenue, Zip 11203–1891; tel. 718/604–5000, (Nonreporting) **A**1 3 5 7 10
Primary Contact: Linda Brady, M.D., President and Chief Executive Officer
COO: Robert Dubicki, Executive Vice President and Chief Operating Officer
CFO: John Schmitt, Senior Vice President and Chief Financial Officer
CMO: Sibte Burney M.D., Senior Vice President Medical Affairs and Chief Medical
Officer
CIO: Daniel Morreale, Vice President and Chief Information Officer
CHR: John McKeon, Vice President Human Resources
CNO: Jane Lederer R.N., Ed.D., Vice President and Chief Nursing Officer
Web address: www.kingsbrook.org
Control: Other not-for-profit (including NFP Corporation) **Service:** General medical
and surgical

Staffed Beds: 748

KIRBY FORENSIC PSYCHIATRIC CENTER (334060), 600 East 125th Street,
Zip 10035–6000; tel. 646/672–5800 (Nonreporting) **S** New York State Office of
Mental Health, Albany, NY
Primary Contact: Vincent Miccoli, Executive Director
Web address: www.omh.ny.gov/omhweb/facilities/krpc/
Control: Other not-for-profit (including NFP Corporation) **Service:** Psychiatric

Staffed Beds: 193

☒ **LENOX HILL HOSPITAL (330119)**, 100 East 77th Street, Zip 10075–1850;
tel. 212/434–2000, (Includes MANHATTAN EYE, EAR AND THROAT HOSPITAL,
210 East 64th Street, New York, New York, Zip 10021–9885, tel. 212/838–9200;
Philip P Rosenthal, Executive Director) **A**1 3 5 8 10 **F**3 7 8 9 11 12 13 14 15 17
18 20 22 24 26 29 30 31 32 34 35 36 37 39 40 42 43 44 45 46 47 48 49 50
51 52 54 55 56 57 58 59 60 61 62 63 64 65 66 68 70 72 74 75 76 77 78 79
81 82 84 85 86 87 89 91 92 93 94 97 98 99 100 101 102 103 104 107 108
110 111 115 116 117 118 119 120 121 123 124 126 129 130 131 132 135
141 143 146 147 148 **P**5 6 **S** Northwell Health, New Hyde Park, NY
Primary Contact: Dennis Connors, Executive Director
CMO: Marc L Napp M.D., Vice President Medical Affairs
CIO: Beth Dituro, Divisional Chief Information Officer
Web address: www.lenoxhillhospital.org
Control: Other not-for-profit (including NFP Corporation) **Service:** General medical
and surgical

Staffed Beds: 441 **Admissions:** 28540 **Census:** 327 **Outpatient Visits:**
243607 **Births:** 4059 **Total Expense ($000):** 1148325 **Payroll Expense
($000):** 557868 **Personnel:** 4435

☒ **LONG ISLAND JEWISH MEDICAL CENTER (330195)**, 270–05 76th Avenue,
Zip 11040–1496; tel. 718/470–7000, (Includes LONG ISLAND JEWISH
FOREST HILLS, 102–01 66th Road, Forest Hills, New York, Zip 11375–2029,
tel. 718/830–4000; Susan Browning, Executive Director; LONG ISLAND JEWISH
VALLEY STREAM, 900 Franklin Avenue, Valley Stream, New York, Zip 11580–
2190, tel. 516/256–6000; Stephen Bello, Executive Director; MANHASSET
AMBULATORY CARE PAVILION, 1554 Northern Boulevard, Manhasset, New York,
Zip 11030, tel. 516/365–2070; STEVEN AND ALEXANDRA COHEN CHILDREN'S
MEDICAL CENTER OF NEW YORK, 270–05 76th Avenue, New Hyde Park, New
York, Zip 11040, tel. 718/470–3000; ZUCKER HILLSIDE HOSPITAL, 75–59 263rd
Street, Glen Oaks, New York, Zip 11004, tel. 718/470–8000) **A**1 2 3 5 8 10 13
F2 3 5 6 7 8 9 11 12 13 14 15 17 18 19 20 21 22 23 24 25 26 27 28 29 30
31 32 34 35 38 39 40 41 42 43 44 45 46 47 48 49 50 51 52 53 54 55 56 57
58 59 60 61 62 63 64 65 66 67 68 70 72 73 74 75 76 77 78 79 80 81 82 84
85 86 87 88 89 92 93 97 98 99 100 101 102 103 104 105 106 107 108 109
110 111 114 115 116 117 118 119 120 121 123 124 126 129 130 131 132
134 135 136 141 142 143 144 145 146 147 148 149 **P**5 6 **S** Northwell Health,
New Hyde Park, NY
Primary Contact: Michael Goldberg, Executive Director
CIO: John Bosco, Senior Vice President and Chief Information Officer
CHR: Ronald W Stone, Regional Chief Human Resource Officer
Web address: www.lij.edu
Control: Other not-for-profit (including NFP Corporation) **Service:** General medical
and surgical

Staffed Beds: 1220 **Admissions:** 80794 **Census:** 1263 **Outpatient Visits:**
1042489 **Births:** 10816 **Total Expense ($000):** 2481755 **Payroll Expense
($000):** 1214135 **Personnel:** 13623

☒ **MAIMONIDES MEDICAL CENTER (330194)**, 4802 Tenth Avenue, Zip 11219–
2916; tel. 718/283–6000, (Includes MAIMONIDES INFANTS AND CHILDREN'S
HOSPITAL OF BROOKLYN, 4802 Tenth Avenue, Brooklyn, New York, Zip 11219–
2916, tel. 718/283–6000) **A**1 2 3 5 8 10 12 13 **F**2 3 7 8 9 11 12 13 14 15 17
18 19 20 22 24 26 28 29 30 31 32 34 35 38 39 40 41 43 44 45 46 47 48 49
50 51 52 54 55 56 57 58 59 60 61 64 65 66 68 70 72 73 74 75 76 77 78 79
81 82 84 85 86 87 88 89 91 92 93 96 97 98 99 100 101 102 103 104 107
108 110 111 114 115 117 118 119 120 121 123 124 126 129 130 131 132
135 145 146 147 148 **P**5 6
Primary Contact: Kenneth Gibbs, President and Chief Executive Officer
COO: Mark McDougle, Executive Vice President and Chief Operating Officer
CFO: Robert Naldi, Chief Financial Officer
CMO: Samuel Kopel M.D., Medical Director
CIO: Walter Fahey, Chief Information Officer
Web address: www.maimonidesmed.org/
Control: Other not-for-profit (including NFP Corporation) **Service:** General medical
and surgical

Staffed Beds: 598 **Admissions:** 36646 **Census:** 550 **Outpatient Visits:**
519917 **Births:** 8421 **Total Expense ($000):** 1180524 **Payroll Expense
($000):** 571343 **Personnel:** 5704

☐ **MANHATTAN PSYCHIATRIC CENTER-WARD'S ISLAND (334054)**, 600 East
125th Street, Zip 10035–6000; tel. 646/672–6767, (Nonreporting) **A**1 3 5 10 **S**
New York State Office of Mental Health, Albany, NY
Primary Contact: Vincent Miccoli, Executive Director
Web address: www.omh.ny.gov
Control: State, Government, Nonfederal **Service:** Psychiatric

Staffed Beds: 745

☒ **MEMORIAL SLOAN-KETTERING CANCER CENTER (330154)**, 1275 York
Avenue, Zip 10065–6007; tel. 212/639–2000 **A**1 2 3 5 8 10 **F**3 8 11 14 15 29
31 32 34 35 36 37 39 44 45 46 47 48 49 50 54 55 56 57 58 59 60 61 64 66
68 70 74 75 77 78 79 81 82 84 85 86 87 88 89 92 93 94 96 99 100 103 104
107 108 110 111 112 114 115 117 118 119 120 121 123 124 126 130 132
135 136 142 143 144 145 146 147 148 149 **P**6
Primary Contact: Craig B. Thompson, M.D., President and Chief Executive Officer
COO: Ned Groves, Executive Vice President and Administrator
CFO: Michael Gutnick, Executive Vice President and Chief Financial Officer
CMO: Jose Baselga M.D., Physician-in-Chief
CIO: Patricia Skarulis, Senior Vice President and Chief Information Systems Officer
CHR: Kerry Bessey, Senior Vice President and Chief Human Resources Officer
CNO: Elizabeth Nelkin McCormick MSN, R.N., Senior Vice President and Chief
Nursing Officer
Web address: www.mskcc.org
Control: Other not-for-profit (including NFP Corporation) **Service:** Cancer

Staffed Beds: 473 **Admissions:** 23079 **Census:** 436 **Outpatient Visits:**
1610580 **Births:** 0 **Total Expense ($000):** 3044670 **Payroll Expense
($000):** 1206202 **Personnel:** 15563

NY

☒ **MONTEFIORE MEDICAL CENTER (339807)**, 111 East 210th Street, Zip 10467–2401; tel. 718/920–4321, (Includes CHILDREN'S HOSPITAL OF MONTEFIORE, 3415 Bainbridge Avenue, Bronx, New York, Zip 10467–2403, tel. 718/741–2426; JACK D WEILER HOSPITAL OF ALBERT EINSTEIN COLLEGE OF MEDICINE, 1825 Eastchester Road, Bronx, New York, Zip 10461–2373, tel. 718/904–2000; MONTEFIORE MEDICAL CENTER - NORTH DIVISION, 600 East 233rd Street, Bronx, New York, Zip 10466–2697, tel. 718/920–9000) **A**1 2 3 5 8 10 **F**3 5 6 7 8 9 12 13 14 15 17 18 19 20 21 22 23 24 25 26 27 28 29 30 31 32 34 35 36 37 38 39 40 41 42 44 45 46 47 48 49 50 51 52 54 55 56 57 58 59 60 61 62 63 64 65 66 68 70 71 72 73 74 75 76 77 78 79 80 81 82 83 84 85 86 87 88 89 90 92 93 94 97 98 99 100 101 102 103 104 107 108 110 111 114 115 117 118 119 120 121 123 124 126 129 130 131 132 134 135 136 137 138 139 141 143 144 145 146 147 148 149 150 **P**5 6 **S** Montefiore Health System, Bronx, NY
Primary Contact: Steven M. Safyer, M.D., President and Chief Executive Officer
COO: Philip O. Ozuah M.D., Ph.D., Executive Vice President and Chief Operating Officer
CFO: Colleen M Blye, Executive Vice President and Chief Financial Officer
CMO: Gary Kalkut M.D., Senior Vice President and Chief Medical Officer
CIO: Jack Wolf, Vice President Information Systems
Web address: www.montefiore.org
Control: Other not-for-profit (including NFP Corporation) **Service**: General medical and surgical

> **Staffed Beds:** 1519 **Admissions:** 88931 **Census:** 1367 **Outpatient Visits:** 1640349 **Births:** 6318 **Total Expense ($000):** 3888560 **Payroll Expense ($000):** 1728174 **Personnel:** 18459

MORGAN STANLEY CHILDREN'S HOSPITAL OF NEW YORK-PRESBYTERIAN See New York-Presbyterian Hospital

☒ **MOUNT SINAI BETH ISRAEL (330169)**, First Avenue and 16th Street, Zip 10003–3803; tel. 212/420–2000, (Includes MOUNT SINAI BETH ISRAEL BROOKLYN, 3201 Kings Highway, Brooklyn, New York, Zip 11234, tel. 718/252–3000; Lin H Mo, M.P.H., President) **A**1 2 3 5 8 10 **F**3 4 5 7 8 9 11 12 13 14 15 17 18 19 20 22 24 26 29 30 31 32 34 35 36 38 39 40 41 43 44 45 46 47 48 49 50 51 54 55 56 57 58 59 60 61 62 63 64 65 66 68 70 72 74 75 76 77 78 79 80 81 82 83 84 85 86 87 88 89 92 93 94 97 98 99 100 101 103 104 107 108 110 111 114 115 117 118 119 120 121 123 124 126 130 131 132 134 135 143 144 145 146 147 148 149 150 **P**5 6 **S** Mount Sinai Health System, New York, NY
Primary Contact: Jeremy Boal, M.D., President
COO: Kevin Molloy, Senior Vice President and Chief Operating Officer
CFO: Donald Scanlon, Chief Corporate Services, Mount Sinai Health System
CIO: Kumar Chatani, Senior Vice President and Chief Information Officer Mount Sinai Health System
CHR: Jane Maksoud R.N., Senior Vice President Human Resources and Labor Relations, Mount Sinai Health System
CNO: Mary Walsh R.N., MSN, Vice President Patient Care Services and Chief Nursing Officer
Web address: www.bethisraelny.org
Control: Other not-for-profit (including NFP Corporation) **Service**: General medical and surgical

> **Staffed Beds:** 633 **Admissions:** 38117 **Census:** 588 **Outpatient Visits:** 361165 **Births:** 3034 **Total Expense ($000):** 1198458 **Payroll Expense ($000):** 445283 **Personnel:** 6521

☒ △ **MOUNT SINAI HOSPITAL (330024)**, One Gustave L Levy Place, Zip 10029–0310; tel. 212/241–6500, (Includes KRAVIS CHILDREN'S HOSPITAL, 1184 Fifth Avenue, New York, New York, Zip 10029–6503, One Gustave L Levy Place, 10029–0312, tel. 212/241–9500; MOUNT SINAI QUEENS, 25–10 30th Avenue, Long Island City, New York, Zip 11102–2448, tel. 718/932–1000; Caryn A Schwab, Executive Director) **A**1 2 5 7 8 10 **F**1 3 4 6 7 8 9 11 12 13 14 15 17 18 19 20 21 22 23 24 25 26 27 28 29 30 31 32 34 35 36 37 38 39 40 41 43 44 45 46 47 48 49 50 51 52 54 55 56 57 58 59 60 61 63 64 65 66 67 68 70 71 72 73 74 75 77 78 79 80 81 82 83 84 85 86 87 88 89 90 91 92 93 94 95 96 97 98 99 100 101 102 103 104 105 107 108 110 111 114 115 116 117 118 119 120 121 123 124 126 128 129 130 131 132 134 135 136 137 138 139 141 142 143 144 145 146 147 148 149 150 **P**5 6 **S** Mount Sinai Health System, New York, NY
Primary Contact: David L. Reich, M.D., President and Chief Operating Officer
COO: David L Reich M.D., President and Chief Operating Officer
CFO: Donald Scanlon, Chief Financial Officer
CMO: Vicki LoPachin M.D., Chief Medical Officer
CIO: Kumar Chatani, Senior Vice President and Chief Information Officer Mount Sinai Health System
CHR: Jane Maksoud R.N., Senior Vice President Human Resources and Labor Relations
Web address: www.mountsinai.org
Control: Other not-for-profit (including NFP Corporation) **Service**: General medical and surgical

> **Staffed Beds:** 1132 **Admissions:** 58994 **Census:** 964 **Outpatient Visits:** 968608 **Births:** 7905 **Total Expense ($000):** 2208521 **Payroll Expense ($000):** 838868 **Personnel:** 10072

☒ **MOUNT SINAI WEST (330046)**, 1111 Amsterdam Avenue, Zip 10025–1716; tel. 212/523–4000, (Includes MOUNT SINAI WEST HOSPITAL, 1000 Tenth Avenue, New York, New York, Zip 10019, tel. 212/523–4000; Evan Flatow, M.D., President) **A**1 2 3 5 8 10 **F**3 4 5 7 8 11 12 13 17 18 20 22 24 26 29 30 32 34 35 36 38 39 40 41 43 44 45 46 48 49 50 51 52 54 55 56 57 58 59 60 61 62 63 64 65 66 68 70 72 74 75 76 77 78 79 81 82 84 85 86 87 90 92 93 94 96 97 98 99 100 101 102 103 104 107 108 110 111 114 115 119 120 121 123 124 126 130 131 132 135 143 144 145 146 147 148 149 150 **P**5 6 **S** Mount Sinai Health System, New York, NY
Primary Contact: Arthur A. Gianelli, M.P.H., President
COO: Kevin Molloy, Senior Vice President and Chief Operating Officer
CFO: Donald Scanlon, Chief Corporate Services, Mount Sinai Health System
CIO: Kumar Chatani, Chief Information Officer, Mount Sinai Health System
CHR: Jane Maksoud R.N., Senior Vice President Human Resources and Labor Relations, Mount Sinai Health System
CNO: Mary Walsh R.N., MSN, Vice President Patient Care Services and Chief Nursing Officer
Web address: www.stlukeshospitalnyc.org
Control: Other not-for-profit (including NFP Corporation) **Service**: General medical and surgical

> **Staffed Beds:** 668 **Admissions:** 33364 **Census:** 537 **Outpatient Visits:** 493658 **Births:** 4603 **Total Expense ($000):** 1080892 **Payroll Expense ($000):** 443656 **Personnel:** 5478

MOUNT SINAI WEST HOSPITAL See Mount Sinai West

☐ **NEW YORK CITY CHILDREN'S CENTER**, 74–03 Commonwealth Boulevard, Zip 11426–1890; tel. 718/264–4506, (Nonreporting) (Includes BRONX Children's hospital psychiatric CENTER, 1000 Waters Place, Bronx, New York, Zip 10461–2799, tel. 718/239–3600; BROOKLYN Children's hospital psychiatric CENTER, 1819 Bergen Street, Brooklyn, New York, Zip 11233–4513, tel. 718/221–4500) **A**1 **S** New York State Office of Mental Health, Albany, NY
Primary Contact: Anita Daniels, Executive Director
CMO: David M Rube M.D., Clinical Director
CIO: Ed Yunusov, Coordinator Facility Information Center
Web address: www.omh.ny.gov/omhweb/facilities/nyccc/
Control: State, Government, Nonfederal **Service**: Children's hospital psychiatric

> **Staffed Beds:** 84

☐ **NEW YORK COMMUNITY HOSPITAL (330019)**, 2525 Kings Highway, Zip 11229–1705; tel. 718/692–5300, (Nonreporting) **A**1 5 10
Primary Contact: Barry Stern, President and Chief Executive Officer
COO: Una E Morrissey R.N., MSN, Senior Vice President Operations, Chief Operating Officer and Chief Nursing Officer
CFO: Leonardo Tamburello, Chief Financial Officer
CMO: Herbert Rader M.D., Advisor for Medical Affairs
CIO: Edward B. Stolyar D.O., Divisional Chief Informational Officer
CHR: Raquel Collado, Vice President Human Resources
CNO: Una E Morrissey R.N., MSN, Senior Vice President Operations, Chief Operating Officer and Chief Nursing Officer
Web address: www.nych.com
Control: Other not-for-profit (including NFP Corporation) **Service**: General medical and surgical

> **Staffed Beds:** 127

☒ **NEW YORK EYE AND EAR INFIRMARY OF MOUNT SINAI (330100)**, 310 East 14th Street, Zip 10003–4201; tel. 212/979–4000 **A**1 3 5 8 10 **F**3 11 29 30 34 35 44 50 57 58 59 64 66 68 74 81 82 85 86 87 91 92 93 94 97 107 114 119 129 130 132 146 **S** Mount Sinai Health System, New York, NY
Primary Contact: James Tsai, M.D., President
COO: Allan Fine, Chief Operating Officer
CFO: Donald Scanlon, Chief Corporate Services, Mount Sinai Health System
CIO: Kumar Chatani, Chief Information Officer, Mount Sinai Health System
CHR: Jane Maksoud R.N., Senior Vice President Human Resources and Labor Relations, Mount Sinai Health System
CNO: Sonja Tennaro Ed.D., FACHE, Senior Vice President Clinical Operations
Web address: www.nyee.edu
Control: Other not-for-profit (including NFP Corporation) **Service**: Eye, ear, nose and throat

> **Staffed Beds:** 32 **Admissions:** 329 **Census:** 2 **Outpatient Visits:** 193743 **Births:** 0 **Total Expense ($000):** 169659 **Payroll Expense ($000):** 81368 **Personnel:** 871

NY

Hospital, Medicare Provider Number, Address, Telephone, Approval, Facility, and Physician Codes, Health Care System

★ American Hospital Association (AHA) membership   ○ Healthcare Facilities Accreditation Program   ⇑ Center for Improvement in Healthcare Quality Accreditation
☐ The Joint Commission accreditation   ◇ DNV Healthcare Inc. accreditation   △ Commission on Accreditation of Rehabilitation Facilities (CARF) accreditation

---

⊠ △ **NEW YORK-PRESBYTERIAN HOSPITAL (330101)**, 525 East 68th Street, Zip 10065–4870; tel. 212/746–5454, (Includes MORGAN STANLEY CHILDREN'S HOSPITAL OF NEW YORK-PRESBYTERIAN, 3959 Broadway, New York, New York, Zip 10032–3784, tel. 212/305–2500; NEW YORK PRESBYTERIAN LOWER MANHATTAN HOSPITAL, 170 William Street, New York, New York, Zip 10038–2649, tel. 212/312–5000; Robert E Kelly, M.D., President; NEW YORK-PRESBYTERIAN HOSPITAL, WESTCHESTER DIVISION, 21 Bloomingdale Road, White Plains, New York, New York, Zip 10605, tel. 914/682–9100; NEW YORK-PRESBYTERIAN HOSPITAL/WEILL CORNELL MEDICAL CENTER, 525 East 68th Street, New York, New York, Zip 10021–4885, tel. 212/746–5454; NEW YORK-PRESBYTERIAN/COLUMBIA UNIVERSITY MEDICAL CENTER, 161 Fort Washington Avenue, New York, New York, Zip 10032, tel. 212/305–2500; PAYNE WHITNEY PSYCHIATRIC CLINIC, 525 East 68th Street, New York, New York, Zip 10021, tel. 212/746–3800; PHYLLIS AND DAVID KOMANSKY CENTER FOR CHILDREN'S HEALTH, 525 East 68th Street, New York, New York, Zip 10065–4870, tel. 212/746–5454; THE ALLEN PAVILION, 5141 Broadway, New York, New York, Zip 10032, tel. 212/932–5000) **A**1 2 3 5 7 8 10 **F**3 4 5 6 7 8 9 11 12 13 14 15 16 17 18 19 20 21 22 23 24 25 26 27 28 29 30 31 32 34 35 36 37 38 39 40 41 43 44 45 46 47 48 49 50 51 52 53 54 55 56 57 58 59 60 61 63 64 65 66 68 69 70 71 72 73 74 75 76 77 78 79 80 81 82 84 85 86 87 88 89 90 91 92 93 94 96 97 98 99 100 101 102 103 104 105 107 108 110 111 112 114 115 116 117 118 119 120 121 123 124 126 127 129 130 131 132 134 135 136 137 138 139 140 141 142 143 144 145 146 147 148 149 150 **S** NewYork-Presbyterian, New York, NY
Primary Contact: Steven J. Corwin, M.D., President and Chief Executive Officer
CFO: Phyllis R Lantos, Executive Vice President, Corporate Chief Financial Officer and Treasurer
CMO: Laura Forese M.D., M.P.H., Executive Vice President and Chief Medical Officer
CIO: Aurelia Boyer, Senior Vice President and Chief Information Officer
CHR: G Thomas Ferguson, Senior Vice President and Chief Human Resources Officer
CNO: Rosemary Ventura M.D., Chief Nursing Informatics Officer
Web address: www.nyp.org
Control: Other not-for-profit (including NFP Corporation) **Service**: General medical and surgical

Staffed Beds: 2338 **Admissions**: 111446 **Census**: 2000 **Outpatient Visits**: 2207215 **Births**: 15248 **Total Expense ($000)**: 4927836 **Payroll Expense ($000)**: 2370432 **Personnel**: 22219

⊠ **NEW YORK-PRESBYTERIAN QUEENS (330055)**, 56–45 Main Street, Zip 11355–5045; tel. 718/670–1231 **A**1 2 3 5 10 **F**3 7 11 12 13 14 15 17 18 19 20 22 24 26 28 29 30 31 32 34 35 39 40 41 43 44 45 46 47 49 50 51 52 54 55 56 57 58 59 60 61 63 64 65 66 67 72 73 74 75 76 77 78 79 80 81 82 83 84 85 87 89 91 92 93 96 97 100 101 107 108 110 111 114 115 116 117 118 119 120 121 123 126 130 131 145 146 147 148 **P**6 **S** NewYork-Presbyterian, New York, NY
Primary Contact: Jaclyn Mucaria, President
COO: Robert Blenderman, Senior Vice President and Chief Operating Officer
CFO: Kevin J Ward, Vice President and Chief Financial Officer
CMO: Amir Jaffer M.D., Senior Vice President Medical Affairs
CIO: Mark Greaker, Chief Information Officer
CHR: Lorraine Orlando, Vice President Human Resources
CNO: Alan M. Levin MSN, R.N., Chief Nursing Officer
Web address: www.nyhq.org
Control: Other not-for-profit (including NFP Corporation) **Service**: General medical and surgical

Staffed Beds: 483 **Admissions**: 28042 **Census**: 439 **Outpatient Visits**: 434209 **Births**: 4356 **Total Expense ($000)**: 659081 **Payroll Expense ($000)**: 399729 **Personnel**: 4032

⊠ **NEW YORK-PRESBYTERIAN BROOKLYN METHODIST HOSPITAL (330236)**, 506 Sixth Street, Zip 11215–3609; tel. 718/780–3000 **A**1 2 3 5 8 10 **F**3 6 7 8 9 11 12 13 15 17 18 19 20 22 24 26 29 30 31 32 33 34 35 36 39 40 41 43 44 45 46 47 48 49 50 51 52 54 55 56 57 58 59 61 64 65 66 68 70 72 73 74 75 76 77 78 79 81 82 84 85 87 88 89 90 91 92 93 95 96 97 98 100 102 103 107 108 109 110 111 112 114 115 118 120 121 123 124 126 129 130 131 132 144 145 146 147 148 149 **P**6 7 **S** New York-Presbyterian, New York, NY
Primary Contact: Richard Liebowitz, M.D., President
COO: Lauren Yedvab, Chief Operating Officer
CFO: Michael Fagan, Senior Vice President Finance
CMO: Steven Silber M.D., Senior Vice President Medical Affairs
CIO: Rick Plisko, Director information Systems
CHR: Dennis Buchanan, Vice President Human Resources
CNO: Rebecca L Flood R.N., MS, Senior Vice President Nursing
Web address: www.nym.org
Control: Other not-for-profit (including NFP Corporation) **Service**: General medical and surgical

Staffed Beds: 591 **Admissions**: 37200 **Census**: 543 **Outpatient Visits**: 560451 **Births**: 5743 **Total Expense ($000)**: 906893 **Payroll Expense ($000)**: 408322 **Personnel**: 4408

☐ **NEW YORK STATE PSYCHIATRIC INSTITUTE (334009)**, 1051 Riverside Drive, Zip 10032–1007; tel. 646/774–5000, (Nonreporting) **A**1 3 5 10 **S** New York State Office of Mental Health, Albany, NY
Primary Contact: Jeffrey A. Lieberman, M.D., Executive Director
COO: Janelle Dierkens, Chief Administration Officer
CFO: Jonathan Segal, Chief Financial Officer
CMO: David Lowenthal M.D., Clinical Director
CIO: Joseph Grun, Chief Information Officer
CHR: Rebecca Dechabert, Acting Director Personnel
Web address: www.nyspi.org
Control: State, Government, Nonfederal **Service**: Psychiatric

Staffed Beds: 58

⊠ **NYC HEALTH + HOSPITALS / BELLEVUE (330204)**, 462 First Avenue, Zip 10016–9198; tel. 212/562–4141 **A**1 3 5 10 **F**3 4 5 8 11 12 13 15 17 18 19 20 22 24 26 28 29 30 31 34 35 36 37 38 39 40 41 43 45 46 47 48 49 50 52 53 55 56 57 58 59 61 64 65 66 68 70 71 72 73 74 75 76 77 78 79 81 82 84 85 86 87 88 89 90 91 92 93 94 96 97 98 99 100 101 102 103 104 105 107 108 110 111 114 115 118 119 126 130 132 134 135 143 144 146 147 148 149 **S** NYC Health + Hospitals, New York, NY
Primary Contact: William Hicks, Chief Executive Officer
COO: Michael Rawlings, Interim Chief Operating Officer
CFO: Jay Weinmann, Chief Financial Officer
CMO: Nate Link M.D., Medical Director
CIO: Tonguc Yaman, Deputy Chief Information Officer
CHR: Howard Kritz, Director Human Resources
CNO: Kim K Mendez Ed.D., R.N., Chief Nurse Officer
Web address: www.nyc.gov/bellevue
Control: City, Government, Nonfederal **Service**: General medical and surgical

Staffed Beds: 796 **Admissions**: 28342 **Census**: 651 **Outpatient Visits**: 589329 **Births**: 1496 **Total Expense ($000)**: 958663 **Payroll Expense ($000)**: 335997 **Personnel**: 4673

⊠ **NYC HEALTH + HOSPITALS / CARTER (332008)**, 1752 Park Avenue, Zip 10035; tel. 646/686–0000, (Includes COLER REHABILITATION AND NURSING CARE CENTER, 900 Main Street, Roosevelt Island, New York, New York, Zip 10044, tel. 212/848–6300; Robert K. Hughes, Chief Executive Officer; HENRY J. CARTER SPECIALTY HOSPITAL & NURSING FACILITY, 1752 Park Avenue, New York, New York, Zip 10035, tel. 646/686–0000; Floyd R Long, Chief Executive Officer) (Total facility includes 164 beds in nursing home–type unit) **A**1 10 **F**1 3 11 28 29 30 39 56 58 68 74 75 77 79 84 85 87 100 103 107 114 119 128 130 132 135 146 148 149 **P**4 **S** NYC Health + Hospitals, New York, NY
Primary Contact: Floyd R. Long, Chief Executive Officer
CFO: Manuela Brito, Chief Financial Officer Post Acute Care
CMO: Vasudeva Raju M.D., Suffix, Chief, Long Term Acute Care Medicine
CIO: Steve ONeill, Chief Information Officer
CHR: Jamie Grecco, Director Human Resources Post Acute
CNO: Stanlee Richards R.N., Chief Nurse Executive
Web address: www.nychealthandhospitals.org/Carter
Control: City, Government, Nonfederal **Service**: Acute long-term care hospital

Staffed Beds: 365 **Admissions**: 433 **Census**: 301 **Outpatient Visits**: 0 **Births**: 0 **Total Expense ($000)**: 161794 **Payroll Expense ($000)**: 57940 **Personnel**: 827

⊠ **NYC HEALTH + HOSPITALS / CONEY ISLAND (330196)**, 2601 Ocean Parkway, Zip 11235–7795; tel. 718/616–3000 **A**1 3 5 10 12 13 **F**3 4 5 13 15 17 18 20 29 30 31 34 39 40 41 44 45 48 49 50 51 54 55 56 57 58 59 60 61 64 65 66 68 70 71 72 73 74 75 76 77 78 79 81 82 83 84 85 87 89 90 91 92 93 94 96 97 98 99 100 102 103 104 107 108 110 111 114 115 118 119 129 130 132 134 135 143 146 147 148 149 150 **S** NYC Health + Hospitals, New York, NY
Primary Contact: Anthony Rajkumar, Chief Executive Officer
COO: Mei Kong, Chief Operating Officer
CMO: Wehbeh Wehbeh M.D., Chief Medical Officer
CIO: Robert Kee, Chief Information Officer
CHR: Andrew Campbell, Associate Executive Director
CNO: Patricia Ruiz R.N., Chief Nursing Officer
Web address: www.nyc.gov/html/hhc/html/facilities/coneyisland.shtml
Control: City, Government, Nonfederal **Service**: General medical and surgical

Staffed Beds: 371 **Admissions**: 14323 **Census**: 307 **Outpatient Visits**: 338349 **Births**: 1236 **Total Expense ($000)**: 502784 **Payroll Expense ($000)**: 190469 **Personnel**: 3210

✠ **NYC HEALTH + HOSPITALS / ELMHURST (330128)**, 79–01 Broadway, Zip 11373–1329; tel. 718/334–4000 **A**1 2 3 5 10 **F**3 5 8 9 13 14 15 17 18 20 22 26 29 30 31 32 34 35 38 40 41 43 44 45 49 50 51 53 54 55 56 57 58 59 60 61 64 65 66 68 70 72 73 74 75 76 77 78 79 81 82 83 84 85 86 87 89 90 92 93 96 97 98 99 100 101 102 103 104 105 107 108 110 111 115 119 121 126 130 131 132 134 135 143 146 147 149 150 **P**6 **S** NYC Health + Hospitals, New York, NY
Primary Contact: Israel Rocha, Chief Executive Officer
COO: Wayne Zimmermann, Chief Operating Officer
CMO: Jasmin Moshirpur M.D., Dean and Medical Director
CIO: Vincent Smith, Chief Information Officer
CHR: Jeannith Michelen, Associate Executive Director
CNO: Joann Bernadette Gull, Chief Nursing Officer
Web address: www.nyc.gov/html/hhc/ehc/html/home/home.shtml
Control: City, Government, Nonfederal **Service**: General medical and surgical

Staffed Beds: 545 Admissions: 18766 Census: 408 Outpatient Visits: 630468 Births: 2903 Total Expense ($000): 696869 Payroll Expense ($000): 250247 Personnel: 2912

✠ △ **NYC HEALTH + HOSPITALS / HARLEM (330240)**, 506 Lenox Avenue, Zip 10037–1802; tel. 212/939–1000 **A**1 3 5 7 10 **F**3 4 5 8 11 12 13 15 16 17 18 19 20 29 30 32 34 35 38 39 40 41 43 44 45 46 47 48 49 50 52 53 55 57 58 59 60 61 64 65 68 70 71 72 73 74 75 76 77 79 81 82 84 85 86 87 88 89 90 93 94 96 97 98 99 100 101 102 103 104 107 108 110 111 114 115 118 119 130 132 134 135 141 144 146 147 148 149 150 **S** NYC Health + Hospitals, New York, NY
Primary Contact: Ebone' Carrington, Interim Executive Director
COO: Ebone' Carrington, Chief Operating Officer
Web address: www.nyc.gov/html/hhc/harlem
Control: City, Government, Nonfederal **Service**: General medical and surgical

Staffed Beds: 257 Admissions: 13234 Census: 203 Outpatient Visits: 313111 Births: 935 Total Expense ($000): 491129 Payroll Expense ($000): 169063 Personnel: 2543

✠ **NYC HEALTH + HOSPITALS / JACOBI (330127)**, 1400 Pelham Parkway South, Zip 10461–1197; tel. 718/918–5000 **A**1 3 5 10 **F**3 4 5 8 11 12 13 15 16 17 18 20 26 29 30 31 32 34 35 38 39 40 41 43 44 45 46 47 49 50 51 55 56 57 58 59 60 61 64 65 66 70 72 73 74 75 76 77 78 79 80 81 82 84 85 87 88 89 90 92 93 94 96 97 98 99 100 101 102 103 104 107 108 110 111 114 115 118 119 130 131 132 134 135 144 146 147 148 149 150 **P**6 **S** NYC Health + Hospitals, New York, NY
Primary Contact: Christopher Mastromanno, Interim Chief Executive Officer
COO: Christopher Mastromanno, Chief Operating Officer
CFO: Ellen Barlis, Chief Financial Officer
CMO: Michael Zinaman M.D., Acting Chief Medical Officer
CIO: Md Alam, Chief Information Officer
CHR: Jamie Grecco, Chief Human Resource Executive
CNO: Suzanne Pennacchio, Chief Nursing Officer
Web address: www.nyc.gov/html/hhc/jacobi/home.html
Control: City, Government, Nonfederal **Service**: General medical and surgical

Staffed Beds: 441 Admissions: 18694 Census: 361 Outpatient Visits: 429938 Births: 1835 Total Expense ($000): 771512 Payroll Expense ($000): 266982 Personnel: 3521

✠ **NYC HEALTH + HOSPITALS / KINGS COUNTY (330202)**, 451 Clarkson Avenue, Zip 11203–2097; tel. 718/245–3131 **A**1 3 5 10 **F**3 4 5 8 9 11 12 13 15 17 18 19 20 24 26 28 29 30 31 32 34 35 38 39 40 41 43 45 46 47 49 50 51 52 53 56 57 58 59 60 61 64 65 66 68 70 71 72 73 74 75 76 77 78 79 81 82 84 85 86 87 88 89 90 91 92 93 94 97 98 99 100 101 102 103 104 105 106 107 108 110 111 114 115 116 119 120 121 123 129 130 131 132 134 135 143 144 145 146 147 148 149 **P**6 **S** NYC Health + Hospitals, New York, NY
Primary Contact: Ernest Baptiste, Executive Director
COO: Robert R Miller II, Chief Operating Officer
CFO: Julian John, Chief Financial Officer
CMO: Ghassan Jamaleddine M.D., Medical Director
CIO: Dino Civan, Chief Information Officer
CHR: Michelle Emmons, Associate Executive Director
CNO: Opal Sinclair-Chung R.N., MS, Chief Nursing Officer, Deputy Executive Director
Web address: www.nyc.gov/html/hhc/kchc/html/home/home.shtml
Control: City, Government, Nonfederal **Service**: General medical and surgical

Staffed Beds: 599 Admissions: 22754 Census: 502 Outpatient Visits: 685692 Births: 2114 Total Expense ($000): 869601 Payroll Expense ($000): 393776 Personnel: 5018

✠ **NYC HEALTH + HOSPITALS / LINCOLN (330080)**, 234 East 149th Street, Zip 10451–5504, Mailing Address: 234 East 149th Street, Room 923, 10451–5504; tel. 718/579–5700 **A**1 2 3 5 10 **F**3 5 8 11 13 15 17 18 19 29 30 31 32 34 35 38 39 40 41 43 45 50 55 59 60 61 64 65 68 70 71 72 73 74 75 76 77 78 79 81 82 84 85 86 87 88 89 93 97 98 99 100 101 102 103 104 107 108 110 111 114 115 119 121 123 130 132 134 135 143 144 146 147 148 **P**4 **S** NYC Health + Hospitals, New York, NY
Primary Contact: Milton Nunez, Executive Director
CFO: Caswell Samms, Network Chief Financial Officer
CMO: Melissa Schori M.D., Medical Director
CIO: Maricar Barrameda, Chief Information Officer
CHR: Jeannith Michelen, Senior Associate Executive Director
Web address: www.nyc.gov/html/hhc/lincoln/
Control: City, Government, Nonfederal **Service**: General medical and surgical

Staffed Beds: 317 Admissions: 20922 Census: 281 Outpatient Visits: 554185 Births: 2124 Total Expense ($000): 641899 Payroll Expense ($000): 233219 Personnel: 3478

✠ **NYC HEALTH + HOSPITALS / METROPOLITAN (330199)**, 1901 First Avenue, Zip 10029–7404; tel. 212/423–6262 **A**1 3 5 10 **F**3 4 8 9 11 13 15 17 18 28 29 30 31 32 34 35 38 39 40 41 44 45 46 48 49 50 51 53 54 55 56 57 58 59 60 61 64 65 66 68 70 72 73 74 75 76 77 78 79 81 82 84 85 86 87 89 90 92 93 94 96 97 98 99 100 101 102 103 104 107 108 110 111 114 119 130 131 132 134 135 144 146 147 148 149 **S** NYC Health + Hospitals, New York, NY
Primary Contact: Alina Moran, Chief Executive Officer
COO: William Norberto Wang M.D., Chief Operating Officer
CFO: Tracy V. Green, Chief Financial Officer
CMO: John T Pellicone M.D., Chief Medical Officer
CIO: Md Alam, Chief Information Officer
CHR: April Alexander, Director Human Resources
CNO: Noreen Brennan, Chief Nursing Officer
Web address: www.nyc.gov/html/hhc/mhc/html/home/home.shtml
Control: City, Government, Nonfederal **Service**: General medical and surgical

Staffed Beds: 317 Admissions: 12091 Census: 221 Outpatient Visits: 403189 Births: 963 Total Expense ($000): 388318 Payroll Expense ($000): 145797 Personnel: 1907

✠ **NYC HEALTH + HOSPITALS / NORTH CENTRAL BRONX (330385)**, 3424 Kossuth Avenue, Zip 10467–2489; tel. 718/519–3500 **A**1 3 5 10 **F**3 5 8 11 12 13 15 18 28 29 30 32 34 35 38 39 40 41 43 44 45 46 48 50 51 55 56 57 58 59 60 61 64 65 66 68 70 72 73 74 75 76 77 78 79 80 81 82 84 85 87 89 92 93 94 96 97 98 99 100 101 102 103 104 105 107 108 110 111 115 119 130 131 132 135 144 146 147 148 **P**6 **S** NYC Health + Hospitals, New York, NY
Primary Contact: Maureen Pode, Co-Interim Executive Director
COO: Sheldon McLeod, Chief Operating Officer
CFO: Kathy Garramone, Chief Financial Officer
CMO: Joseph Skarzynski M.D., Medical Director
CIO: Diane Carr, Chief Information Officer
CHR: Dolores Leite, Chief Human Resource Executive
CNO: Elizabeth Gerdts, Chief Nursing Officer
Web address: www.nyc.gov/html/hhc/ncbh/html/home/home.shtml
Control: City, Government, Nonfederal **Service**: General medical and surgical

Staffed Beds: 202 Admissions: 6602 Census: 119 Outpatient Visits: 213793 Births: 1199 Total Expense ($000): 217113 Payroll Expense ($000): 79411 Personnel: 1173

✠ **NYC HEALTH + HOSPITALS / QUEENS (330231)**, 82–68 164th Street, Zip 11432–1104; tel. 718/883–3000 **A**1 2 3 5 10 **F**3 5 7 8 9 11 13 14 15 18 28 29 30 31 32 34 35 38 39 40 41 45 46 47 49 50 51 52 53 54 55 56 58 59 60 61 64 65 66 68 70 71 72 73 74 75 76 77 78 79 81 82 84 85 86 87 90 91 92 93 94 97 98 99 100 101 102 103 104 105 107 108 109 110 111 114 115 116 117 118 119 120 121 122 124 129 130 132 133 135 146 147 148 149 **P**6 **S** NYC Health + Hospitals, New York, NY
Primary Contact: Christopher Roker, Chief Executive Officer
COO: Dona Green, Chief Operating Officer
CFO: Brian Stacey, Chief Financial Officer
CMO: Jasmin Moshirpur M.D., Chief Medical Officer
CIO: Vincent Smith, Chief Information Officer
CHR: Jeannith Michelen, Senior Associate Executive Director
CNO: Joan Gabriele, Deputy Executive Director
Web address: www.nyc.gov/html/hhc/qhc/html/home/home.shtml
Control: City, Government, Nonfederal **Service**: General medical and surgical

Staffed Beds: 253 Admissions: 12067 Census: 204 Outpatient Visits: 412716 Births: 1619 Total Expense ($000): 465144 Payroll Expense ($000): 159135 Personnel: 2032

NY

Hospital, Medicare Provider Number, Address, Telephone, Approval, Facility, and Physician Codes, Health Care System

★ American Hospital Association (AHA) membership
□ The Joint Commission accreditation
○ Healthcare Facilities Accreditation Program
◇ DNV Healthcare Inc. accreditation
⇑ Center for Improvement in Healthcare Quality Accreditation
△ Commission on Accreditation of Rehabilitation Facilities (CARF) accreditation

✠ **NYC HEALTH + HOSPITALS / WOODHULL (330396)**, 760 Broadway, Zip 11206–5383; tel. 718/963–8000 **A**1 3 5 10 **F**3 4 5 11 13 15 18 19 29 30 31 32 34 35 36 38 39 40 41 42 43 44 45 46 49 50 54 55 56 57 59 60 61 62 64 65 68 70 71 72 73 74 75 76 77 78 79 80 81 82 84 87 89 91 92 93 94 97 98 99 100 102 103 104 107 108 110 111 115 118 119 130 131 132 135 143 145 146 147 148 149 **P**6 **S** NYC Health + Hospitals, New York, NY
Primary Contact: Gregory Calliste, Ph.D., FACHE, Chief Executive Officer
COO: Eve Borzon R.N., Chief Operating Officer
CFO: Erika Soiman CPA, Chief Financial Officer
CMO: Edward Fishkin M.D., Medical Director
CHR: Irma Suarez, Deputy Executive Director
CNO: Angela Imelda Edwards R.N., Chief Nurse Executive
Web address: www.nyc.gov/html/hhc
Control: City-county, Government, Nonfederal **Service**: General medical and surgical

Staffed Beds: 305 Admissions: 11179 Census: 235 Outpatient Visits: 471073 Births: 1663 Total Expense ($000): 486045 Payroll Expense ($000): 182490 Personnel: 2910

NYU HOSPITAL FOR JOINT DISEASES See NYU Langone Orthopedic Hospital

✠ **NYU LANGONE HOSPITALS (330214)**, 550 First Avenue, Zip 10016–6402; tel. 212/263–7300, (Includes HASSENFELD CHILDRENS HOSPITAL OF NEW YORK AT NYU LANGONE MEDICAL CENTER, 550 First Avenue, New York, New York, Zip 10016–6401, tel. 212/263–7300; NYU LANGONE HOSPITAL-BROOKLYN, 150 55th Street, Brooklyn, New York, Zip 11220–2559, tel. 718/630–7000; Bret Rudy, M.D., Executive Director and Senior Vice President; NYU LANGONE ORTHOPEDIC HOSPITAL, 301 East 17th Street, New York, New York, Zip 10003–3890, tel. 212/598–6000; David A Dibner, FACHE, Senior Vice President Hospital Operations and Musculoskeletal Strategic Areas; RUSK INSTITUTE AT NYU-HJD, 301 E 17th ST, New York, New York, Zip 10003–3804, tel. 212/598–6000; David A Dibner, FACHE, Senior Vice President Hospital Operations and Musculoskeletal Strategic Areas) **A**1 2 3 5 8 10 **F**3 5 6 11 12 13 15 17 18 19 20 21 22 23 24 25 26 27 28 29 30 31 32 33 34 35 36 37 38 39 40 41 42 43 44 45 46 47 48 49 50 51 52 53 54 55 56 57 58 59 60 61 63 64 65 66 68 70 72 73 74 75 76 77 78 79 80 81 82 84 85 86 87 88 89 90 91 92 93 94 95 96 97 98 99 100 101 102 103 104 107 108 110 111 113 114 115 116 117 118 119 120 121 123 124 126 129 130 131 132 134 135 136 138 139 141 142 145 146 147 148 149 150 **P**5 6 **S** NYU Langone Health, New York, NY
Primary Contact: Robert I. Grossman, M.D., Chief Executive Officer
COO: Robert Press M.D., Senior Vice President, Vice Dean and Chief Hospital Operations
CFO: Michael Burke, Senior Vice President and Corporate Chief Financial Officer
CMO: Fritz Francois M.D., Chief Medical Officer
CIO: Nader Mherabi, Senior Vice President and Vice Dean, Chief Information Officer
CHR: Nancy Sanchez, Senior Vice President and Vice Dean Human Resources
CNO: Kimberly S Glassman Ph.D., R.N., Chief Nursing Officer
Web address: www.nyumedicalcenter.org
Control: Other not-for-profit (including NFP Corporation) **Service**: General medical and surgical

Staffed Beds: 1104 Admissions: 60086 Census: 827 Outpatient Visits: 1702373 Births: 10041 Total Expense ($000): 3604338 Payroll Expense ($000): 1217761 Personnel: 16199

PAYNE WHITNEY PSYCHIATRIC CLINIC See New York-Presbyterian Hospital

QUEENS Children's hospital psychiatric CENTER See New York City Chi ldren's Center

✠ **RICHMOND UNIVERSITY MEDICAL CENTER (330028)**, 355 Bard Avenue, Zip 10310–1664; tel. 718/818–1234, (Nonreporting) **A**1 2 3 5 10
Primary Contact: Daniel J. Messina, Ph.D., FACHE, President and Chief Executive Officer
CMO: Edward Arsura M.D., Chief Medical Officer
CHR: Patricia Caldari, Vice President
Web address: www.rumcsi.org
Control: Other not-for-profit (including NFP Corporation) **Service**: General medical and surgical

Staffed Beds: 374

☐ **ROCKEFELLER UNIVERSITY HOSPITAL (330387)**, 1230 York Avenue, Zip 10065–6399; tel. 212/327–8000, (Nonreporting) **A**1 10
Primary Contact: James G. Krueger, M.D., Ph.D., Chief Executive Officer
CMO: Barbara O'Sullivan M.D., M.P.H., Medical Director
Web address: www.rucares.org
Control: Other not-for-profit (including NFP Corporation) **Service**: Other specialty treatment

Staffed Beds: 40

ROOSEVELT HOSPITAL See Mount Sinai West Hospital

☐ **SOUTH BEACH PSYCHIATRIC CENTER (334043)**, 777 Seaview Avenue, Zip 10305–3409; tel. 718/667–2300, (Nonreporting) **A**1 3 10 **S** New York State Office of Mental Health, Albany, NY
Primary Contact: Doreen Piazza, Acting Executive Director
CHR: George Bouquio, Director Human Resources
Web address: www.omh.ny.gov/omhweb/facilities/sbpc/facility.htm
Control: State, Government, Nonfederal **Service**: Psychiatric

Staffed Beds: 340

✠ **ST. BARNABAS HOSPITAL (330399)**, 4422 Third Avenue, Zip 10457–2545; tel. 718/960–9000, (Total facility includes 199 beds in nursing home–type unit) **A**1 3 5 10 12 13 **F**3 4 5 11 13 15 18 19 20 22 26 29 30 31 32 34 35 36 38 39 40 41 43 44 45 46 47 49 50 51 54 55 56 57 58 59 60 61 64 65 66 68 70 71 72 74 75 76 77 78 79 81 82 83 84 85 86 87 89 91 92 93 94 97 98 99 100 101 102 103 104 107 108 109 110 111 114 115 117 118 119 123 128 129 130 131 132 134 135 143 146 147 148 149 150 **P**6
Primary Contact: David A. Perlstein, M.D., President and Chief Executive Officer
COO: Len Walsh, Executive Vice President and Chief Operating Officer
CFO: Todd Gorlewski, Senior Vice President and Chief Financial Officer
CIO: Jitendra Barmecha M.D., M.P.H., Senior Vice President and Chief Information Officer
CHR: Marc Wolf, Assistant Vice President Human Resources
CNO: Denise Richardson R.N., MSN, Senior Vice President and Chief Nursing Officer
Web address: www.sbhny.org
Control: Other not-for-profit (including NFP Corporation) **Service**: General medical and surgical

Staffed Beds: 621 Admissions: 14230 Census: 377 Outpatient Visits: 582021 Births: 1000 Total Expense ($000): 433560 Payroll Expense ($000): 187279

☐ **ST. JOHN'S EPISCOPAL HOSPITAL-SOUTH SHORE (330395)**, 327 Beach 19th Street, Zip 11691–4423; tel. 718/869–7000 **A**1 3 5 10 13 **F**3 12 13 15 17 18 19 29 30 31 32 34 35 38 40 41 45 49 50 54 55 56 57 59 60 61 64 65 68 70 73 74 75 76 77 78 79 81 82 84 85 87 89 92 93 97 98 99 100 101 102 103 104 107 108 110 111 114 118 119 130 132 134 135 141 146 148
Primary Contact: Gerard W. Walsh, Chief Executive Officer
COO: Patrick L Sullivan, Chief Operating Officer
CFO: Kathleen Garcia, Controller
CMO: Raymond Pastore M.D., Chief Medical Officer
CIO: Michael J Piro, Chief Information Officer
CHR: Roger Franco, Director Human Resources
Web address: www.ehs.org
Control: State, Government, Nonfederal **Service**: General medical and surgical

Staffed Beds: 213 Admissions: 8425 Census: 153 Outpatient Visits: 122742 Total Expense ($000): 205014 Payroll Expense ($000): 102078 Personnel: 1316

✠ △ **STATEN ISLAND UNIVERSITY HOSPITAL (330160)**, 475 Seaview Avenue, Zip 10305–3436; tel. 718/226–9000 **A**1 2 3 5 7 8 10 **F**3 4 5 7 8 11 12 13 14 15 16 17 18 19 20 22 24 26 28 29 30 31 32 34 35 36 38 39 40 41 43 44 45 46 47 48 49 50 51 52 54 55 56 57 60 61 63 64 65 66 68 70 72 73 74 75 76 77 78 79 81 82 84 85 86 87 88 89 90 92 93 94 95 96 97 98 100 101 102 103 104 105 107 108 110 111 114 115 116 117 118 119 120 121 123 124 126 129 130 131 132 134 135 145 146 147 148 **P**5 6 **S** Northwell Health, New Hyde Park, NY
Primary Contact: Donna Proske, MS, R.N., Executive Director
CFO: Thomas Reca Sr., Deputy Executive Director and Chief Financial Officer
CMO: Theodore Maniatis M.D., Medical Director
CIO: Kathy Kania, Chief Information Officer
CHR: Margaret DiAlto, Regional Chief Human Resource Officer
CNO: Dian I Johnson MSN, Chief Nurse Executive
Web address: www.siuh.edu
Control: Other not-for-profit (including NFP Corporation) **Service**: General medical and surgical

Staffed Beds: 634 Admissions: 39295 Census: 573 Outpatient Visits: 940889 Births: 2927 Total Expense ($000): 866796 Payroll Expense ($000): 387668 Personnel: 5276

STEVEN AND ALEXANDRA COHEN CHILDREN'S MEDICAL CENTER OF NEW YORK See Long Island Jewish Medical Center

NY

SUNY DOWNSTATE MEDICAL CENTER UNIVERSITY HOSPITAL (330350), 450 Clarkson Avenue, Zip 11203–2012, Mailing Address: 450 Clarkson Avenue, MSC#75, 11203–2012; tel. 718/270–1000, (Includes UNIVERSITY HOSPITAL OF BROOKLYN AT LONG ISLAND COLLEGE HOSPITAL, 339 Hicks Street, Brooklyn, New York, Zip 11201–5509, tel. 718/780–1000; George P Caralis, Interim Chief Executive Officer) **A**1 3 5 8 10 **F**8 13 14 15 17 18 19 20 21 22 23 24 25 26 27 28 29 30 31 32 34 35 36 37 38 39 40 41 42 44 45 46 47 48 49 50 51 52 53 54 55 56 57 58 59 60 61 64 65 66 68 70 72 73 74 75 77 78 79 80 81 82 84 86 87 88 90 91 92 93 94 97 104 107 108 111 112 114 115 116 117 118 119 120 121 122 123 124 126 129 130 131 132 138 143 144 146 147 149 150 **P**6
Primary Contact: William P. Walsh, Senior Vice President Hospital Affairs and Managing Director
COO: Patricia A Winston FACHE, MS, R.N., Vice President, Chief Administrative Officer and Chief Operating Officer
CFO: Richard B. Miller Ph.D., Vice President Hospital Affairs and Chief Financial Officer
CMO: Michael Lucchesi M.D., Chief Medical Officer; Chair, Emergency Medicine
CIO: Dilip Nath Sc.D., Associate Chief Information Officer
CHR: Maria Silas, Manager Human Resources
CNO: Margaret G. Jackson R.N., Vice President Patient Care Services and Chief Nursing Officer
Web address: www.downstate.edu
Control: State, Government, Nonfederal **Service:** General medical and surgical

Staffed Beds: 323 **Admissions:** 12338 **Census:** 226 **Outpatient Visits:** 319239 **Births:** 798 **Total Expense ($000):** 548810 **Payroll Expense ($000):** 258629 **Personnel:** 2644

TERENCE CARDINAL COOKE HEALTH CARE CENTER (332022), 1249 Fifth Avenue, Zip 10029–4413; tel. 212/360–1000 (Nonreporting) **A**10
Primary Contact: Mitch Marsh, Interim Executive Director
COO: Neil Pollack, Senior Administrator
CFO: Ann Marie Covone, Senior Vice President and Chief Financial Officer
CMO: Anthony Lechich M.D., Chief Medical Officer
CIO: Mitze Amoroso, Chief Information Officer
CHR: Hugo A Pizarro, Vice President Human Resources
CNO: Monica McGibbon, Chief Nursing Officer
Web address: www.tcchcc.org/
Control: Church operated, Nongovernment, not-for-profit **Service:** Acute long-term care hospital

Staffed Beds: 28

THE ALLEN PAVILION See New York-Presbyterian Hospital

VETERANS AFFAIRS MEDICAL CENTER See James J. Peters Veterans Affairs Medical Center

VETERANS AFFAIRS NEW YORK HARBOR HEALTHCARE SYSTEM, 800 Poly Place, Zip 11209–7104; tel. 718/630–3500, (Nonreporting) (Includes VETERANS AFFAIRS NEW YORK HARBOR HEALTHCARE SYSTEM - MANHATTAN CAMPUS, 423 East 23rd Street, New York, New York, Zip 10010–5050, tel. 212/686–7500) **A**1 2 3 5 **S** Department of Veterans Affairs, Washington, DC
Primary Contact: Martina A. Parauda, Director
CFO: Daniel Downey, Chief Fiscal Service
CIO: Maria Schay, Chief Information Officer
Web address: www.nyharbor.va.gov
Control: Veterans Affairs, Government, federal **Service:** General medical and surgical

Staffed Beds: 522

WYCKOFF HEIGHTS MEDICAL CENTER (330221), 374 Stockholm Street, Zip 11237–4006; tel. 718/963–7272 **A**1 3 5 10 12 13 **F**3 7 8 9 12 13 15 18 19 20 26 29 30 31 34 35 39 40 41 44 45 50 54 56 57 61 64 65 68 70 72 73 74 75 76 78 79 81 82 85 86 87 89 90 92 93 94 97 102 107 108 109 110 111 114 115 118 119 120 121 123 124 130 132 134 143 146 147 148
Primary Contact: Ramon J. Rodriguez, President and Chief Executive Officer
COO: David Rock, Executive Vice President and Chief Operating Officer
CFO: Frank A Vutrano, Chief Financial Officer
CMO: Gustavo Del Toro M.D., Chief Medical Officer
CIO: Jebashini Jesurasa, Vice President, Chief Information Technology Officer
CHR: Margaret E Cornelius, Vice President Human Resources
CNO: Catherine A Gallogly-Simon R.N., MS, Chief Nursing Officer
Web address: www.wyckoffhospital.org
Control: Other not-for-profit (including NFP Corporation) **Service:** General medical and surgical

Staffed Beds: 276 **Admissions:** 13956 **Census:** 162

ZUCKER HILLSIDE HOSPITAL See Long Island Jewish Medical Center, New Hyde Park

NEWARK-WAYNE COMMUNITY HOSPITAL (330030), 1200 Driving Park Avenue, Zip 14513–1057, Mailing Address: P.O.Box 111, 14513–0111; tel. 315/332–2022, (Total facility includes 180 beds in nursing home–type unit) **A**1 10 **F**2 3 6 8 11 13 15 28 29 30 34 35 38 40 44 50 54 55 56 57 59 61 64 68 70 74 75 76 77 79 80 81 85 86 87 90 93 97 98 100 102 103 107 110 111 114 118 119 126 128 130 131 132 135 143 146 147 148 149 **P**5 6 7 **S** Rochester Regional Health, Rochester, NY
Primary Contact: Dustin Riccio, M.D., President Eastern Region
CFO: Tom Crilly, Executive Vice President, Chief Financial Officer, Rochester Regional Health
CMO: Robert Mayo M.D., Executive Vice President, Chief Medical Officer, Rochester Regional Health
CIO: John Glynn, Executive Vice President, Chief Information Officer, Rochester Regional Health
CHR: Janine Schue, Executive Vice President, Chief Human Resources Officer, Rochester Regional Health
CNO: Theresa Glessner, Chief Nursing Officer, Eastern Region
Web address: www.rochesterregional.org
Control: Other not-for-profit (including NFP Corporation) **Service:** General medical and surgical

Staffed Beds: 280 **Admissions:** 5850 **Census:** 232 **Outpatient Visits:** 150888 **Births:** 793 **Total Expense ($000):** 96665 **Payroll Expense ($000):** 46966 **Personnel:** 750

ST. LUKE'S CORNWALL HOSPITAL (330264), 70 Dubois Street, Zip 12550–4851; tel. 845/561–4400, (Includes ST. LUKE'S CORNWALL HOSPITAL - CORNWALL CAMPUS, 19 Laurel Avenue, Cornwall, New York, Zip 12518–1499, tel. 845/534–7711; ST. LUKE'S CORNWALL HOSPITAL - NEWBURGH CAMPUS, 70 Dubois Street, Newburgh, New York, Zip 12550–4898, tel. 845/561–4400; Joan Cusack-McGuirk, Interim President and Chief Executive Officer) **A**1 2 10 **F**3 11 12 13 15 18 20 22 26 28 29 31 34 35 37 40 43 46 49 51 54 57 59 60 61 64 70 72 74 75 76 77 78 79 81 82 84 85 86 87 89 93 100 102 107 108 110 114 115 118 119 120 121 123 124 126 129 130 131 132 146 147 149
Primary Contact: Joan Cusack-McGuirk, Interim President and Chief Executive Officer
CFO: Thomas Gibney, Senior Vice President and Chief Financial Officer
CMO: Christine Jelalian M.D., Medical Director
CIO: Dwayne Simmons, Interim Chief Information Officer
CHR: Daniel Bengyak, Vice President, Human Resources
CNO: Margaret Deyo-Allers, Vice President, Chief Nursing Officer
Web address: www.stlukescornwallhospital.org
Control: Other not-for-profit (including NFP Corporation) **Service:** General medical and surgical

Staffed Beds: 128 **Admissions:** 9651 **Census:** 127 **Outpatient Visits:** 192276 **Births:** 750 **Total Expense ($000):** 194018 **Payroll Expense ($000):** 67709 **Personnel:** 1011

NIAGARA FALLS MEMORIAL MEDICAL CENTER (330065), 621 Tenth Street, Zip 14301–1813, Mailing Address: P.O.Box 708, 14302–0708; tel. 716/278–4000, (Nonreporting) **A**3 5 10 11 13
Primary Contact: Joseph A. Ruffolo, President and Chief Executive Officer
CMO: Fatma Patel M.D., Vice President Medical Affairs
CIO: Diane Martin-Pratt, Director Information Systems
CNO: JoAnn Pellegrino, MS, RN, Vice President and Chief Nursing Officer
Web address: www.nfmmc.com
Control: Other not-for-profit (including NFP Corporation) **Service:** General medical and surgical

Staffed Beds: 288

DE GRAFF MEMORIAL HOSPITAL See Kaleida Health, Buffalo

NY

NORTHPORT—Suffolk County

☒ △ **NORTHPORT VETERANS AFFAIRS MEDICAL CENTER**, 79 Middleville Road, Zip 11768–2200; tel. 631/261–4400, (Total facility includes 134 beds in nursing home–type unit) **A**1 2 3 5 7 **F**1 3 4 5 8 9 18 20 28 29 30 31 34 35 36 39 40 45 49 50 51 52 53 54 56 57 58 59 60 61 62 63 64 65 68 70 71 74 75 77 78 79 81 82 83 84 85 86 87 92 93 94 96 97 98 100 101 102 103 104 105 106 107 108 109 111 114 116 118 119 120 121 127 129 130 132 133 135 143 144 146 147 148 149 150 **S** Department of Veterans Affairs, Washington, DC
Primary Contact: D. Scott. Guermonprez, FACHE, Director
COO: Michael McCully, Chief Operating Officer
CFO: Mary Pat Hessman, Chief Fiscal
CMO: Mark Kaufman M.D., Chief of Staff
CIO: Robert Ziskin, Chief Information Officer
CHR: Wilmino Sainbert, Chief Human Resources Management Service
Web address: www.northport.va.gov/index.asp
Control: Veterans Affairs, Government, federal **Service:** General medical and surgical

Staffed Beds: 254 **Admissions:** 3343 **Census:** 172 **Outpatient Visits:** 409224
Births: 0 **Personnel:** 1754

NORWICH—Chenango County

★ ○ **UHS CHENANGO MEMORIAL HOSPITAL (330033)**, 179 North Broad Street, Zip 13815–1097; tel. 607/337–4111, (Total facility includes 80 beds in nursing home–type unit) **A**10 11 **F**3 8 11 13 15 17 18 29 32 34 35 38 39 40 45 47 50 54 56 57 59 61 64 65 68 70 75 76 77 79 81 82 85 86 87 89 93 97 107 108 110 111 115 119 127 128 130 132 133 146 147 148 149 **P**6 **S** United Health Services, Binghamton, NY
Primary Contact: Drake M. Lamen, M.D., President, Chief Executive Officer and Chief Medical Officer
COO: Christina A Kisacky, Vice President, Operations
CFO: Peggy Swartwood, Assistant Vice President, Finance and Controller
CIO: Richard Stone, Manager, Technical Services
CHR: Anne L English, Director Human Resources
CNO: David Finney R.N., Vice President Nursing
Web address: www.uhs.net/cmh
Control: Other not-for-profit (including NFP Corporation) **Service:** General medical and surgical

Staffed Beds: 138 **Admissions:** 1449 **Census:** 80 **Outpatient Visits:** 268032
Births: 266 **Total Expense ($000):** 68853 **Payroll Expense ($000):** 19918
Personnel: 417

NYACK—Rockland County

☐ **NYACK HOSPITAL (330104)**, 160 North Midland Avenue, Zip 10960–1998; tel. 845/348–2000 **A**1 2 5 10 **F**4 5 8 11 12 14 15 17 18 19 20 29 30 31 34 40 43 45 46 49 62 70 73 75 76 77 78 79 81 82 83 84 85 86 87 89 93 98 99 102 103 107 108 111 118 119 129 130 135 146 148 **S** Montefiore Health System, Bronx, NY
Primary Contact: Mark Geller, M.D., President and Chief Executive Officer
COO: John Volanto, Vice President, Chief Operating Officer
CFO: John Burke, Chief Financial Officer
CMO: Anthony Matejicka D.O., M.P.H., Vice President, Chief Medical Officer
CHR: Mary K Shinick, Vice President Human Resources
CNO: Kathleen Lunney MS, R.N., Vice President Patient Care Services and Chief Nursing Officer
Web address: www.nyackhospital.org
Control: Other not-for-profit (including NFP Corporation) **Service:** General medical and surgical

Staffed Beds: 245 **Admissions:** 11336 **Census:** 166 **Outpatient Visits:** 162039
Births: 1948 **Total Expense ($000):** 243460 **Payroll Expense ($000):** 102105
Personnel: 1367

OCEANSIDE—Nassau County

☒ **SOUTH NASSAU COMMUNITIES HOSPITAL (330198)**, One Healthy Way, Zip 11572–1551; tel. 516/632–3000 **A**1 2 3 5 10 12 13 **F**3 5 11 12 13 15 17 18 20 22 26 28 29 30 31 34 35 37 38 40 42 43 44 45 46 47 49 50 54 55 56 57 58 59 60 62 64 66 68 69 70 73 74 75 76 77 78 79 81 82 83 84 85 86 87 89 91 92 93 97 98 99 100 102 103 104 105 107 108 109 110 111 114 115 117 118 119 120 121 123 124 126 128 129 130 131 132 135 145 146 148 149 **P**8
Primary Contact: Richard J. Murphy, President and Chief Executive Officer
CFO: Mark A. Bogen, Senior Vice President and Chief Financial Officer
CMO: Adhi Sharma M.D., Chief Medical Officer
CIO: John Mertz, Chief Information Officer
CHR: Paul D Giordano, Vice President Human Resources
CNO: Sue Penque R.N., Ph.D., Senior Vice President and Chief Nursing Officer
Web address: www.southnassau.org
Control: Other not-for-profit (including NFP Corporation) **Service:** General medical and surgical

Staffed Beds: 387 **Admissions:** 20843 **Census:** 324 **Outpatient Visits:** 349727 **Births:** 1944 **Total Expense ($000):** 498677 **Payroll Expense ($000):** 244083 **Personnel:** 2914

OGDENSBURG—St. Lawrence County

★ ⇑ **CLAXTON-HEPBURN MEDICAL CENTER (330211)**, 214 King Street, Zip 13669–1142; tel. 315/393–3600, (Nonreporting) **A**2 10 20 21
Primary Contact: Nathan Howell, President and Chief Executive Officer
COO: Vicki Perrine FACHE, Chief Operating Officer
CFO: Kelley Tiernan, Chief Financial Officer
CIO: James Flood, Director Information Systems
CHR: Lou-Ann McNally, Executive Director Human Resources and Staff Development
CNO: David Ferris, Chief Nursing Officer and Vice President Patient Care Services
Web address: www.claxtonhepburn.org
Control: Other not-for-profit (including NFP Corporation) **Service:** General medical and surgical

Staffed Beds: 97

☐ **ST. LAWRENCE PSYCHIATRIC CENTER (334003)**, 1 Chimney Point Drive, Zip 13669–2291; tel. 315/541–2001, (Nonreporting) **A**1 3 10 **S** New York State Office of Mental Health, Albany, NY
Primary Contact: Timothy Farrell, Executive Director
CMO: Harishankar Sanghi M.D., Clinical Director
CHR: Rosie Turnbull, Director Human Resources
Web address: www.omh.ny.gov/omhweb/facilities/slpc/facility.htm
Control: State, Government, Nonfederal **Service:** Psychiatric

Staffed Beds: 146

OLEAN—Cattaraugus County

☒ **OLEAN GENERAL HOSPITAL (330103)**, 515 Main Street, Zip 14760–1513; tel. 716/373–2600 **A**1 3 5 10 19 **F**3 8 11 13 15 17 18 20 22 28 29 30 31 34 35 38 39 40 45 46 47 48 49 50 51 54 57 58 59 60 61 62 64 65 70 71 74 75 76 77 78 79 81 82 83 84 85 86 87 89 91 92 93 94 96 97 98 100 101 102 103 107 108 109 110 111 114 115 116 117 118 119 120 121 123 127 129 130 131 132 133 134 135 143 144 145 146 147 148 149 **P**6 8 **S** Upper Allegheny Health System, Olean, NY
Primary Contact: Timothy J. Finan, FACHE, President and Chief Executive Officer
COO: Jeff S Zewe R.N., Senior Vice President, Chief Operating Officer
CFO: Richard G Braun CPA, Jr, Senior Vice President and Chief Financial Officer
CMO: William Mills M.D., Senior Vice President Quality and Professional Affairs
CIO: Jason Yaworsky, Senior Vice President Information Systems and Chief Information Officer
CHR: Timothy M McNamara, Senior Vice President Human Resources
CNO: Vi-Anne Antrum, Chief Nursing Officer
Web address: www.ogh.org
Control: Other not-for-profit (including NFP Corporation) **Service:** General medical and surgical

Staffed Beds: 186 **Admissions:** 5637 **Census:** 77 **Outpatient Visits:** 208108
Births: 756 **Total Expense ($000):** 115691 **Payroll Expense ($000):** 44012
Personnel: 833

ONEIDA—Madison County

☒ **ONEIDA HEALTHCARE (330115)**, 321 Genesee Street, Zip 13421–2611; tel. 315/363–6000, (Total facility includes 160 beds in nursing home–type unit) **A**1 10 **F**3 11 13 15 18 29 34 40 45 49 50 54 57 59 64 65 68 70 74 75 76 77 79 81 85 86 87 89 92 93 97 107 108 110 111 115 117 118 119 126 128 129 130 135 146 149 **P**6 8
Primary Contact: Gene Morreale, President and Chief Executive Officer
COO: Mary Parry, Vice President Operations and Chief Operating Officer
CMO: Dan J. Vick M.D., Vice President of Medical Affairs and Chief Medical Officer
CIO: Mary McGuirl, Director Information Systems
CHR: Michael Fifield, Vice President Human Resources
CNO: Janis Kohlbrenner R.N., Ph.D., Vice President Clinical Services and Chief Nursing Officer
Web address: www.oneidahealthcare.org
Control: Other not-for-profit (including NFP Corporation) **Service:** General medical and surgical

Staffed Beds: 231 **Admissions:** 3101 **Census:** 179 **Outpatient Visits:** 193735 **Births:** 483 **Total Expense ($000):** 95277 **Payroll Expense ($000):** 44667 **Personnel:** 677

NY

Many Facility Codes have changed. Please refer to the AHA Guide Code Chart. © 2017 AHA Guide

ONEONTA—Otsego County

★ ⇑ **AURELIA OSBORN FOX MEMORIAL HOSPITAL (330085)**, 1 Norton
Avenue, Zip 13820–2629; tel. 607/432–2000, (Total facility includes 131 beds in
nursing home–type unit) **A**10 21 **F**2 3 11 13 15 26 28 29 30 34 35 39 40 45 46
47 48 51 53 54 56 57 59 64 65 68 75 77 81 85 86 87 93 96 97 104 107 108
110 111 115 118 119 120 121 123 128 129 130 135 146 147 **P**6 **S** Bassett
Healthcare Network, Cooperstown, NY
Primary Contact: Jeff Joyner, President
COO: Gary Smith, Chief Operating Officer
CFO: Mark J. Wright, Chief Financial Officer
CMO: Reginald Q. Knight, Chief Medical Officer
CHR: Jennie Gliha, Chief Human Resource Officer
CNO: Joan MacDonald R.N., MSN, Chief Nursing Officer
Web address: www.bassett.org/ao-fox-hospital/
Control: Other not-for-profit (including NFP Corporation) **Service**: General medical
and surgical

Staffed Beds: 191 Admissions: 2410 Census: 152 Outpatient Visits:
167553 **Births:** 149 **Total Expense ($000):** 80106 **Payroll Expense ($000):**
34039 **Personnel:** 695

ORANGEBURG—Rockland County

☐ **ROCKLAND Children's hospital psychiatric CENTER**, 599 Convent Road,
Zip 10962–1162; tel. 845/359–7400, (Nonreporting) **A**1 3 5 **S** New York State
Office of Mental Health, Albany, NY
Primary Contact: Christopher Tavella, Acting Executive Director
COO: Kenneth Perrotte, Director Operations
CFO: Peter Gorey, Administrative Coordinator
CMO: Sadhana Sardana M.D., Clinical Director
CIO: Mary Pivonka, Director Quality Management
Web address: www.omh.ny.gov/
Control: State, Government, Nonfederal **Service**: Children's hospital psychiatric

Staffed Beds: 54

☐ **ROCKLAND PSYCHIATRIC CENTER (334015)**, 140 Old Orangeburg Road,
Zip 10962–1157; tel. 845/359–1000, (Nonreporting) **A**1 3 5 10 **S** New York
State Office of Mental Health, Albany, NY
Primary Contact: Christopher Tavella, Executive Director
Web address: www.omh.ny.gov/
Control: State, Government, Nonfederal **Service**: Psychiatric

Staffed Beds: 525

OSSINING—Westchester County

OSSINING CORRECTIONAL FACILITIES HOSPITAL, 354 Hunter Street,
Zip 10562–5498; tel. 914/941–0108, (Nonreporting) **A**3
Primary Contact: Riza Ferdous, Health Services Director
Control: State, Government, Nonfederal **Service**: Hospital unit of an institution
(prison hospital, college infirmary, etc.)

Staffed Beds: 25

OSWEGO—Oswego County

✚ **OSWEGO HOSPITAL (330218)**, 110 West Sixth Street, Zip 13126–2507;
tel. 315/349–5511 **A**1 3 10 20 **F**2 3 11 13 15 18 29 34 37 38 40 41 45 49 50
51 57 59 62 70 75 77 79 81 85 86 87 93 97 98 99 100 101 102 104 107 108
110 111 114 115 118 119 130 131 132 135 144 146 **P**6
Primary Contact: Michael Harlovic, R.N., President and Chief Executive Officer
COO: Allison A.N. Duggan FACS, Chief Operating Officer
CFO: Eric Campbell, Chief Financial Officer
CMO: Renato Mandanas M.D., Chief Medical Officer
CIO: Barry W. Ryle, Chief Information Officer
CHR: James E Marco Jr, Interim Vice President, Human Resources
CNO: Valerie Favata R.N., MS, Chief Nursing Officer
Web address: www.oswegohealth.org
Control: Other not-for-profit (including NFP Corporation) **Service**: General medical
and surgical

Staffed Beds: 97 Admissions: 4154 Census: 56 Outpatient Visits: 343294
Births: 572 **Total Expense ($000):** 110546 **Payroll Expense ($000):** 53867
Personnel: 899

PATCHOGUE—Suffolk County

★ ⇑ **BROOKHAVEN MEMORIAL HOSPITAL MEDICAL CENTER (330141)**, 101
Hospital Road, Zip 11772–4897; tel. 631/714–2941 **A**3 10 12 13 21 **F**12 15 17
18 20 22 24 26 28 29 30 31 34 35 40 43 45 46 47 49 50 51 54 57 59 60 62
63 64 66 68 70 74 75 78 79 80 81 82 83 84 85 97 98 99 100 102 103 104
107 110 111 114 115 116 117 119 129 130 131 132 135 146 147 148 **P**6
Primary Contact: Richard T. Margulis, President and Chief Executive Officer
COO: Ron Stephenson, Chief Operating Officer
CFO: Brenda Farrell, Vice President Finance
CMO: Nejat Zeyneloglu, Vice President and Chief Quality Medical Officer
CIO: Joseph Wood, Vice President and Chief Information Officer
CHR: Susan C Hever, Director Human Resources
Web address: www.bmhmc.org
Control: Other not-for-profit (including NFP Corporation) **Service**: General medical
and surgical

Staffed Beds: 247 Admissions: 12162 Census: 224 Outpatient Visits:
151437 **Births:** 0 **Total Expense ($000):** 273768 **Payroll Expense ($000):**
124638 **Personnel:** 1775

PENN YAN—Yates County

**SOLDIERS AND SAILORS MEMORIAL HOSPITAL OF YATES COUNTY
(331314)**, 418 North Main Street, Zip 14527–1085; tel. 315/531–2000 **A**10 18
F2 3 11 15 18 28 29 34 35 38 40 45 54 56 57 59 64 65 66 68 70 75 81 87
91 93 97 98 100 101 102 103 104 107 110 114 119 128 130 132 133 135
146 147 **P**6 **S** Finger Lakes Health, Geneva, NY
Primary Contact: Jose Acevedo, M.D., President and Chief Executive Officer
COO: Lina Brennan, Site Administrator
CFO: Pamela Johnson, Treasurer and Chief Financial Officer
CMO: Jason Feinberg M.D., Vice President Medical Affairs and Chief Medical Officer
CIO: Guy W Mosher III, Manager Information Systems
CHR: Patrick R Boyle, Vice President Human Resources
CNO: Eileen Gage R.N., Vice President Nursing
Web address: www.flhealth.org
Control: Other not-for-profit (including NFP Corporation) **Service**: General medical
and surgical

Staffed Beds: 186 Admissions: 936 Census: 145 Outpatient Visits: 157712
Births: 0 **Total Expense ($000):** 28992 **Payroll Expense ($000):** 16397
Personnel: 328

PLAINVIEW—Nassau County

✚ **PLAINVIEW HOSPITAL (330331)**, 888 Old Country Road, Zip 11803–4978;
tel. 516/719–3000 **A**1 3 10 12 13 **F**3 8 9 15 17 18 29 30 31 34 35 36 38 40
43 44 45 46 49 50 51 57 58 59 60 63 64 65 68 69 71 74 75 78 79 81 84 85
86 87 97 100 101 102 107 108 110 111 114 115 119 130 132 135 146 148
P5 6 **S** Northwell Health, New Hyde Park, NY
Primary Contact: Michael Fener, Executive Director
CMO: Alan Mensch M.D., Senior Vice President Medical Affairs
CIO: Nicholas O'Connor, Vice President and Chief Information Officer
Web address: www.northshorelij.com
Control: Other not-for-profit (including NFP Corporation) **Service**: General medical
and surgical

Staffed Beds: 158 Admissions: 8728 Census: 119 Outpatient Visits:
61190 **Births:** 0 **Total Expense ($000):** 215747 **Payroll Expense ($000):**
106440 **Personnel:** 1115

PLATTSBURGH—Clinton County

✚ **THE UNIVERSITY OF VERMONT HEALTH NETWORK-CHAMPLAIN VALLEY
PHYSICIANS HOSPITAL (330250)**, 75 Beekman Street, Zip 12901–1438;
tel. 518/561–2000, (Total facility includes 54 beds in nursing home–type unit) **A**1
2 3 10 **F**3 7 8 11 13 14 15 18 20 22 26 28 29 30 31 34 35 36 38 40 41 43 45
46 49 50 53 56 58 59 64 68 70 76 77 78 79 81 83 84 85 87 89 93 94 96 98
99 102 107 108 110 111 114 115 116 117 118 119 120 121 123 126 128
130 132 143 144 145 146 147 148 149 **P**6
Primary Contact: Stephens M. Mundy, President and Chief Executive Officer
COO: Michelle Lebeau, Senior Vice President, Chief Operating Officer, Chief
Nursing Officer
CFO: Joyce Rafferty, Vice President Finance
CMO: Kent Hall M.D., Vice President and Chief Medical Officer
CIO: Wouter Rietsema M.D., Chief Quality and Information Officer
CHR: Dean Civitello, Vice President, Human Resources, Public Relations and
Development
CNO: Michelle Lebeau, Senior Vice President, Chief Operating Officer, Chief
Nursing Officer
Web address: www.UVMHealth.org/CVPH
Control: Other not-for-profit (including NFP Corporation) **Service**: General medical
and surgical

Staffed Beds: 247 Admissions: 8987 Census: 192 Outpatient Visits:
365527 **Births:** 899 **Total Expense ($000):** 311787 **Payroll Expense
($000):** 155041 **Personnel:** 1986

NY

Hospital, Medicare Provider Number, Address, Telephone, Approval, Facility, and Physician Codes, Health Care System

★ American Hospital Association (AHA) membership   ○ Healthcare Facilities Accreditation Program   ⇑ Center for Improvement in Healthcare Quality Accreditation
☐ The Joint Commission accreditation   ◇ DNV Healthcare Inc. accreditation   △ Commission on Accreditation of Rehabilitation Facilities (CARF) accreditation

PORT JEFFERSON—Suffolk County

☒ **JOHN T. MATHER MEMORIAL HOSPITAL (330185)**, 75 North Country Road, Zip 11777–2190; tel. 631/473–1320 **A**1 2 3 10 **F**5 8 11 12 14 15 17 18 29 34 35 36 37 38 40 44 45 46 49 51 55 56 57 59 60 64 65 69 70 74 75 77 78 79 81 82 84 85 86 87 91 93 98 99 100 101 102 103 104 105 107 108 110 111 114 115 118 119 120 124 126 129 130 132 146 147 148 **P**6
Primary Contact: Kenneth D. Roberts, President
COO: Kevin J Murray, Senior Vice President
CFO: Joseph Wisnoski, Chief Financial Officer
CMO: Joan Faro M.D., Chief Medical Officer
CIO: Thomas Heiman, Vice President Information Services and Chief Information Officer
CHR: Diane Marotta, Vice President Human Resources
CNO: Marie Mulligan R.N., MSN, Vice President Nursing
Web address: www.matherhospital.com
Control: Other not-for-profit (including NFP Corporation) **Service**: General medical and surgical

Staffed Beds: 248 **Admissions**: 11980 **Census**: 183 **Outpatient Visits**: 170643 **Births**: 0 **Total Expense ($000)**: 350048 **Payroll Expense ($000)**: 163355 **Personnel**: 2174

☐ △ **ST. CHARLES HOSPITAL (330246)**, 200 Belle Terre Road, Zip 11777–1928; tel. 631/474–6000 **A**1 2 3 7 10 **F**3 4 5 8 11 12 13 15 17 28 29 30 31 32 34 35 37 39 40 41 44 45 46 48 50 54 57 58 59 64 65 66 68 69 70 72 73 74 75 76 77 78 79 80 81 82 84 85 86 87 89 90 91 92 93 96 97 107 108 110 111 115 118 119 126 129 130 131 132 134 135 136 141 142 146 149 **P**5 6 **S** Catholic Health Services of Long Island, Rockville Centre, NY
Primary Contact: James O'Connor, Executive Vice President and Chief Administrative Officer
COO: Ronald Weingartner, Vice President Administration
CFO: Kathleen Vasil, Vice President Finance
CMO: Michael Sauter M.D., Chief Medical Officer
CIO: Felix Pabon-Ramirez, Chief Information Officer
CNO: Nicolette Fiore-Lopez R.N., Chief Nursing Officer
Web address: www.stcharleshospital.chsli.org
Control: Church operated, Nongovernment, not-for-profit **Service**: General medical and surgical

Staffed Beds: 243 **Admissions**: 9198 **Census**: 173 **Outpatient Visits**: 25540 **Births**: 1083 **Total Expense ($000)**: 228570 **Payroll Expense ($000)**: 103321 **Personnel**: 1218

PORT JERVIS—Orange County

☒ **BON SECOURS COMMUNITY HOSPITAL (330135)**, 160 East Main Street, Zip 12771–2245, Mailing Address: P.O.Box 1014, 12771–0268; tel. 845/858–7000, (Nonreporting) **A**1 10 **S** WMCHealth, Valhalla, NY
Primary Contact: Mary Leahy, M.D., Chief Executive Officer
COO: Gaynor Rosenstein, Vice President Operations
CMO: Jeffrey Auerbach D.O., Medical Director
CHR: Kim Hirkaler, Director Human Resources
Web address: www.bonsecourscommunityhosp.org
Control: Church operated, Nongovernment, not-for-profit **Service**: General medical and surgical

Staffed Beds: 187

POTSDAM—St. Lawrence County

★ ⇑ **CANTON-POTSDAM HOSPITAL (330197)**, 50 Leroy Street, Zip 13676–1799; tel. 315/265–3300, (Nonreporting) **A**10 20 21 **S** St. Lawrence Health System, Potsdam, NY
Primary Contact: David B. Acker, FACHE, President and Chief Executive Officer
CFO: Richard Jacobs, Vice President Finance and Chief Financial Officer
CMO: Robert T Rogers M.D., II, Medical Director
CIO: Jorge C Grillo, Chief Information Officer
CHR: Darlene Lewis, Vice President Human Resources
CNO: Jan Carroll MSN, M.P.H., R.N., Chief Nursing Officer
Web address: www.cphospital.org
Control: Other not-for-profit (including NFP Corporation) **Service**: General medical and surgical

Staffed Beds: 94

POUGHKEEPSIE—Dutchess County

☐ **VASSAR BROTHERS MEDICAL CENTER (330023)**, 45 Reade Place, Zip 12601–3947; tel. 845/454–8500 **A**1 2 10 **F**3 8 11 12 13 15 17 18 20 22 24 26 28 29 30 31 34 35 36 37 40 43 44 45 46 47 48 49 50 51 54 55 57 58 59 60 68 70 72 73 74 75 76 77 78 79 81 82 84 85 86 87 89 92 93 97 99 100 107 108 109 110 111 114 115 117 118 119 120 121 123 124 126 129 130 131 132 135 146 147 148 149 **S** Health Quest Systems, Inc., LaGrangeville, NY
Primary Contact: Ann McMackin, President
CFO: Tony Perugino, Director Finance
CMO: Michael Doyle M.D., Vice President Medical Affairs
CNO: Loretta Bogolin MSN, R.N., Chief Nursing Officer and Vice President Care Services
Web address: www.health-quest.org
Control: Other not-for-profit (including NFP Corporation) **Service**: General medical and surgical

Staffed Beds: 365 **Admissions**: 21122 **Census**: 289 **Outpatient Visits**: 314822 **Births**: 2114 **Total Expense ($000)**: 523957 **Payroll Expense ($000)**: 155599 **Personnel**: 1964

QUEENS—Queens County, See New York City

QUEENS VILLAGE—Queens County, See New York City

RHINEBECK—Dutchess County

☐ △ **NORTHERN DUTCHESS HOSPITAL (330049)**, 6511 Springbrook Avenue, Zip 12572–3709, Mailing Address: P.O.Box 5002, 12572–5002; tel. 845/876–3001 **A**1 7 10 **F**3 11 13 15 18 28 29 34 35 36 37 40 45 50 53 56 64 68 70 74 75 76 77 78 79 81 82 84 85 87 90 93 100 107 108 110 111 115 118 119 125 126 129 130 146 147 148 149 **S** Health Quest Systems, Inc., LaGrangeville, NY
Primary Contact: Denise George, R.N., President
CFO: Alan Mossoff, Director Finance
CMO: John Sabia M.D., Vice President Medical Affairs
CNO: Pamela Rhodes R.N., Vice President Patient Care Services and Chief Nursing Officer
Web address: www.health-quest.org/home_nd.cfm?id=9
Control: Other not-for-profit (including NFP Corporation) **Service**: General medical and surgical

Staffed Beds: 68 **Admissions**: 4511 **Census**: 51 **Outpatient Visits**: 117231 **Births**: 906 **Total Expense ($000)**: 93528 **Payroll Expense ($000)**: 32356 **Personnel**: 534

RICHMOND VALLEY—Richmond County, See New York City

RIVERHEAD—Suffolk County

☒ **PECONIC BAY MEDICAL CENTER (330107)**, 1300 Roanoke Avenue, Zip 11901–2031; tel. 631/548–6000 **A**1 3 10 12 13 **F**3 7 8 11 12 13 15 18 29 30 31 34 35 40 45 46 47 49 50 54 57 59 60 61 62 64 68 70 74 75 76 77 78 79 80 81 82 84 85 86 87 91 92 93 94 96 97 107 108 110 111 115 118 119 126 130 131 132 143 146 147 148 149 **P**5 6 **S** Northwell Health, New Hyde Park, NY
Primary Contact: Andrew J. Mitchell, President and Chief Executive Officer
COO: Ronald McManus, Senior Vice President Clinical Services and Business Entities
CFO: Michael F. O'Donnell CPA, Chief Financial Officer
CMO: Richard Kubiak M.D., Vice President Medical Affairs
CIO: Arthur Crowe, Director Information Systems
CHR: Monica Chestnut-Rauls, Vice President Human Resources
CNO: Gerard Zunno R.N., Vice President Patient Care Services
Web address: www.pbmchealth.org
Control: Other not-for-profit (including NFP Corporation) **Service**: General medical and surgical

Staffed Beds: 94 **Admissions**: 7947 **Census**: 84 **Outpatient Visits**: 102653 **Births**: 310 **Total Expense ($000)**: 167768 **Payroll Expense ($000)**: 68865 **Personnel**: 991

ROCHESTER—Monroe County

☒ **HIGHLAND HOSPITAL (330164)**, 1000 South Avenue, Zip 14620–2733; tel. 585/473–2200 **A**1 3 5 10 19 **F**3 12 13 15 24 29 30 31 34 35 37 40 44 45 46 47 49 50 54 55 56 57 58 59 60 63 64 65 66 68 70 74 75 76 77 78 79 81 83 84 85 86 87 91 93 97 100 107 108 110 111 114 115 118 119 120 121 123 126 130 132 134 135 141 145 146 147 148 149 **P**5 6 **S** University of Rochester Medical Center, Rochester, NY
Primary Contact: Steven I. Goldstein, President and Chief Executive Officer
COO: Cindy Becker, Vice President and Chief Operating Officer
CFO: Adam Anolik, Chief Financial Officer
CMO: Raymond Mayewski M.D., Chief Medical Officer
CIO: Tom Barnett, Chief Information Officer
CHR: Amy Taney, Chief Human Resource Officer
CNO: Jamie Philpott R.N., Interim Chief Nursing Officer
Web address: www.urmc.rochester.edu/highland
Control: Other not-for-profit (including NFP Corporation) **Service**: General medical and surgical

Staffed Beds: 261 **Admissions**: 15744 **Census**: 196 **Outpatient Visits**: 424509 **Births**: 2998 **Total Expense ($000)**: 329692 **Payroll Expense ($000)**: 154306 **Personnel**: 2179

NY

Many Facility Codes have changed. Please refer to the AHA Guide Code Chart. © 2017 AHA Guide

⊞ **ROCHESTER GENERAL HOSPITAL (330125)**, 1425 Portland Avenue, Zip 14621–3099; tel. 585/922–4000 **A**1 2 3 5 10 **F**3 5 8 9 11 12 13 15 17 18 20 22 24 26 28 29 30 31 32 34 35 38 39 40 41 44 45 47 49 50 51 54 55 56 57 58 59 60 61 63 64 65 66 68 70 73 74 75 76 77 78 79 80 81 82 84 85 86 87 89 90 92 93 96 97 98 99 100 101 102 103 104 107 108 110 111 114 115 116 117 118 119 120 121 123 124 126 130 131 132 134 135 145 146 147 148 149 **P**5 6 7 **S** Rochester Regional Health, Rochester, NY
Primary Contact: Nancy Tinsley, President
CMO: Robert Mayo M.D., Chief Medical Officer
CIO: John Glynn, Chief Information Officer
CHR: Janine Schue, Senior Vice President Human Resources
CNO: Cheryl Sheridan R.N., Senior Vice President Patient Care Services
Web address: www.rochestergeneral.org
Control: Other not-for-profit (including NFP Corporation) **Service:** General medical and surgical

Staffed Beds: 520 **Admissions:** 30460 **Census:** 433 **Outpatient Visits:** 1713916 **Births:** 2133 **Total Expense ($000):** 924985 **Payroll Expense ($000):** 455899 **Personnel:** 6409

☐ **ROCHESTER PSYCHIATRIC CENTER (334020)**, 1111 Elmwood Avenue, Zip 14620–3005; tel. 585/241–1200, (Nonreporting) **A**1 3 5 10 **S** New York State Office of Mental Health, Albany, NY
Primary Contact: Philip Griffin, Director of Operations
COO: Joseph Coffey, Director Facility Administration
CFO: Rosanne Minnis, Business Officer
CMO: Laurence Guttmacher M.D., Clinical Director
CIO: Lori Hintz, Coordinator Information Systems
CHR: Colomba Misseritti, Director Human Resources
CNO: Christopher Kirisits, Chief Nursing Officer
Web address: www.omh.ny.gov/omhweb/facilities/ropc/facility.htm
Control: State, Government, Nonfederal **Service:** Psychiatric

Staffed Beds: 180

⊞ △ **STRONG MEMORIAL HOSPITAL OF THE UNIVERSITY OF ROCHESTER (330285)**, 601 Elmwood Avenue, Zip 14642–0002, Mailing Address: 601 Elmwood Avenue, Box 612, 14642–0002; tel. 585/275–2100, (Includes GOLISANO CHILDREN'S HOSPITAL, 601 Elmwood Avenue, Rochester, New York, Zip 14610, tel. 585/275–2182) **A**1 2 3 5 7 8 10 19 **F**3 5 6 8 9 11 12 13 14 15 16 17 18 19 20 21 22 23 24 25 26 27 28 29 30 31 32 33 34 35 36 38 39 40 41 42 43 44 45 46 47 48 49 50 51 52 53 54 55 56 57 58 59 60 61 63 64 65 66 68 70 71 72 73 74 75 76 77 78 79 81 82 83 84 85 86 87 88 89 90 91 92 93 94 95 96 97 98 99 100 101 102 103 104 105 107 108 110 111 114 115 116 117 118 119 120 121 123 124 126 127 129 130 131 132 134 135 136 137 138 139 141 142 143 144 145 146 147 148 149 150 **P**6 **S** University of Rochester Medical Center, Rochester, NY
Primary Contact: Steven I. Goldstein, President and Chief Executive Officer
COO: Kathleen M Parrinello Ph.D., Chief Operating Officer
CFO: David L. Kirshner, Chief Financial Officer
CMO: Raymond Mayewski M.D., Chief Medical Officer
CIO: D Jerome Powell M.D., Chief Information Officer
CHR: Charles J Murphy, Associate Vice President Human Resources
Web address: www.urmc.rochester.edu
Control: Other not-for-profit (including NFP Corporation) **Service:** General medical and surgical

Staffed Beds: 835 **Admissions:** 37579 **Census:** 762 **Outpatient Visits:** 1547758 **Births:** 2896 **Total Expense ($000):** 1488702 **Payroll Expense ($000):** 598878 **Personnel:** 10400

⊞ **UNITY HOSPITAL (330226)**, 1555 Long Pond Road, Zip 14626–4182; tel. 585/723–7000, (Total facility includes 120 beds in nursing home–type unit) **A**1 3 5 10 **F**3 4 5 13 15 18 20 22 26 28 29 30 31 33 34 35 38 39 40 44 45 46 47 48 49 50 52 55 56 57 59 60 61 63 64 65 66 67 70 71 73 74 75 76 77 78 79 80 81 82 84 85 86 87 90 91 92 93 96 97 98 100 102 104 107 108 118 119 126 128 129 130 131 132 134 135 141 144 146 147 148 149 **P**5 6 **S** Rochester Regional Health, Rochester, NY
Primary Contact: Douglas Stewart, PsyD, President
COO: Stewart C Putnam, Executive Vice President and Chief Operating Officer
CFO: Tom Crilly, Executive Vice President and Chief Financial Officer
CMO: James Haley M.D., Senior Vice President and Chief Medical Officer
CIO: John Glynn, Senior Vice President and Chief Information Officer
CHR: Maryalice Keller, Vice President Brand and Talent Management
CNO: Jane McCormack R.N., MSN, Vice President, Chief Nursing Officer and Nursing and Patient Care Services
Web address: www.unityhealth.org
Control: Other not-for-profit (including NFP Corporation) **Service:** General medical and surgical

Staffed Beds: 487 **Admissions:** 16700 **Census:** 377 **Outpatient Visits:** 816005 **Births:** 1572 **Total Expense ($000):** 449464 **Payroll Expense ($000):** 227400 **Personnel:** 4253

ROCKVILLE CENTRE—Nassau County

☐ **MERCY MEDICAL CENTER (330259)**, 1000 North Village Avenue, Zip 11570–1000; tel. 516/705–2525 **A**1 2 3 10 13 **F**3 5 8 12 13 15 20 26 29 30 31 34 35 37 38 40 41 43 45 46 48 49 50 51 56 57 58 59 60 64 65 66 68 70 72 74 75 76 77 78 79 81 82 84 85 87 90 92 93 94 96 97 98 100 102 103 104 105 107 108 110 111 115 119 129 130 131 132 135 141 142 143 146 147 148 **P**5 **S** Catholic Health Services of Long Island, Rockville Centre, NY
Primary Contact: Ronald Steimel, Executive Vice President and Chief Administrative Officer
CFO: William C Armstrong, Senior Vice President and Chief Financial Officer
CMO: John Reilly M.D., Vice President Medical Affairs and Chief Medical Officer
CIO: Marcy Dunn, Vice President Information Services and Chief Information Officer
CHR: Allison Cianciotto Croyle, Vice President of Human Resources
CNO: Beth Vlahavas R.N., MSN, Vice President Patient Care Services and Chief Nursing Officer
Web address: www.mercymedicalcenter.chsli.org
Control: Church operated, Nongovernment, not-for-profit **Service:** General medical and surgical

Staffed Beds: 191 **Admissions:** 9872 **Census:** 186 **Outpatient Visits:** 114583 **Births:** 999 **Total Expense ($000):** 214136 **Payroll Expense ($000):** 98608 **Personnel:** 1124

ROME—Oneida County

★ ○ **ROME MEMORIAL HOSPITAL (330215)**, 1500 North James Street, Zip 13440–2844; tel. 315/338–7000, (Total facility includes 82 beds in nursing home–type unit) **A**10 11 **F**3 5 8 11 13 15 17 18 26 28 29 30 34 40 41 45 47 48 49 50 54 56 57 59 64 68 70 74 76 77 78 79 80 81 85 86 87 89 93 98 100 101 102 103 104 107 108 109 110 111 112 113 114 115 116 117 119 120 121 122 123 124 128 129 130 132 135 143 144 146 147 148
Primary Contact: David W. Lundquist, President and Chief Executive Officer
CFO: Dewey R Rowlands, Vice President and Chief Financial Officer
CMO: Ankur Desai, Interim Chief Medical officer
CIO: Bruce Peterson, Chief Information Officer
CHR: Regina Chambers, Vice President Human Resource
CNO: Durinda Durr, Vice President Clinical Services and Chief Nursing Officer
Web address: www.romehospital.org
Control: Other not-for-profit (including NFP Corporation) **Service:** General medical and surgical

Staffed Beds: 203 **Admissions:** 3716 **Census:** 123 **Outpatient Visits:** 164643 **Births:** 522 **Total Expense ($000):** 80559 **Payroll Expense ($000):** 38542 **Personnel:** 808

ROSLYN—Nassau County

⊞ **ST. FRANCIS HOSPITAL, THE HEART CENTER (330182)**, 100 Port Washington Boulevard, Zip 11576–1353; tel. 516/562–6000 **A**1 3 10 **F**3 7 11 12 15 17 18 19 20 21 22 23 24 26 27 28 29 30 31 34 35 36 37 38 39 40 44 45 46 47 49 50 53 54 55 56 57 58 59 60 61 62 63 64 65 66 68 70 71 72 74 75 77 78 79 81 82 83 84 85 86 87 88 89 93 97 100 102 107 108 109 110 111 114 115 116 117 118 119 120 121 123 126 130 131 132 135 141 145 146 147 148 149 **P**6 **S** Catholic Health Services of Long Island, Rockville Centre, NY
Primary Contact: Ruth Hennessey, Executive Vice President and Chief Administrative Officer
CFO: William C Armstrong, Vice President and Chief Financial Officer
CMO: Jack Soterakis M.D., Executive Vice President Medical Affairs
CIO: Marcy Dunn, Vice President Information Services and Chief Information Officer
CHR: Barbara Fierro, Director, Human Resources
CNO: Ann S Cella R.N., Senior Vice President, Patient Care Services
Web address: www.stfrancisheartcenter.com/index.html
Control: Church operated, Nongovernment, not-for-profit **Service:** General medical and surgical

Staffed Beds: 306 **Admissions:** 16429 **Census:** 279 **Outpatient Visits:** 203988 **Births:** 0 **Total Expense ($000):** 752402 **Payroll Expense ($000):** 356830 **Personnel:** 3040

Hospital, Medicare Provider Number, Address, Telephone, Approval, Facility, and Physician Codes, Health Care System

★ American Hospital Association (AHA) membership
☐ The Joint Commission accreditation
○ Healthcare Facilities Accreditation Program
◇ DNV Healthcare Inc. accreditation
⇑ Center for Improvement in Healthcare Quality Accreditation
△ Commission on Accreditation of Rehabilitation Facilities (CARF) accreditation

SARANAC LAKE—Franklin County

★ ○ **ADIRONDACK HEALTH (330079)**, 2233 State Route 86, Zip 12983–5644, Mailing Address: P.O.Box 471, 12983–0471; tel. 518/891–4141, (Total facility includes 60 beds in nursing home–type unit) **A**5 10 11 **F**3 8 9 12 13 15 18 28 29 30 31 34 35 37 38 39 40 41 42 43 45 46 49 50 53 54 56 57 59 60 64 70 71 74 75 76 77 78 79 81 82 84 85 86 89 90 92 93 94 97 98 102 103 104 107 108 110 111 114 116 119 127 128 129 130 131 132 135 146 147 148 **P**6 **S** HealthTech Management Services, Brentwood, TN
Primary Contact: Sylvia Getman, President and Chief Executive Officer
COO: Patti Hammond, Chief Operating Officer
CFO: Tristan Glanville, Chief Financial Officer
CMO: Joahd Toure' M.D., Chief Medical Officer
CHR: Michael D Lee, Chief Human Resources Officer
CNO: Linda McClarigan R.N., Chief Nursing Officer
Web address: www.adirondackhealth.org
Control: Other not-for-profit (including NFP Corporation) **Service**: General medical and surgical

Staffed Beds: 120 **Admissions:** 2365 **Census:** 131 **Outpatient Visits:** 135225 **Births:** 157 **Total Expense ($000):** 101144 **Payroll Expense ($000):** 48174 **Personnel:** 903

SARATOGA SPRINGS—Saratoga County

□ **FOUR WINDS HOSPITAL (334049)**, 30 Crescent Avenue, Zip 12866–5142; tel. 518/584–3600 (Nonreporting) **A**1 10
Primary Contact: Samuel A. Bastien IV, Ph.D., Chief Executive Officer
CFO: Juanita Wheeler-Moore, Director Financial Services
CMO: Kevin P. Martin M.D., Chief Medical Officer
CIO: Susan Snowdon, Director Information Technology
CHR: Susan M Kirchner, Director Human Resources
CNO: James Colamaria, Director of Nursing
Web address: www.fourwindshospital.com
Control: Corporation, Investor-owned (for-profit) **Service**: Children's hospital psychiatric

Staffed Beds: 83

⊞ **SARATOGA HOSPITAL (330222)**, 211 Church Street, Zip 12866–1003; tel. 518/587–3222 **A**1 2 5 10 **F**3 8 11 12 13 15 18 20 22 26 28 29 30 31 34 35 37 40 42 44 46 47 49 50 54 57 59 60 64 66 68 70 74 75 76 77 78 79 81 82 84 85 87 92 93 96 97 98 100 101 102 104 105 107 108 110 111 114 117 119 120 121 126 127 128 129 130 131 132 133 141 143 144 146 147 **P**6
Primary Contact: Angelo G. Calbone, President and Chief Executive Officer
CFO: Gary Foster, Vice President and Chief Financial Officer
CMO: Richard Falivena D.O., M.P.H., Vice President and Chief Medical Officer
CIO: John Mangona, Vice President, Chief Information Officer and Compliance Officer
CHR: Jeffrey M Methven, Vice President Ambulatory Services and Chief Human Resources Officer
CNO: Mary Jo LaPosta Ph.D., R.N., Senior Vice President Patient Care and Organizational Excellence
Web address: www.saratogacare.org
Control: Other not-for-profit (including NFP Corporation) **Service**: General medical and surgical

Staffed Beds: 207 **Admissions:** 9323 **Census:** 130

SCHENECTADY—Schenectady County

⊞ **ELLIS HOSPITAL (330153)**, 1101 Nott Street, Zip 12308–2425; tel. 518/243–4000, (Includes BELLEVUE WOMAN'S CARE CENTER, 2210 Troy Road, Schenectady, New York, Zip 12309–4797, tel. 518/346–9400; ELLIS HOSPITAL HEALTH CENTER, 600 McClellan Street, Schenectady, New York, Zip 12304–1090, tel. 518/382–2000) (Total facility includes 82 beds in nursing home–type unit) **A**1 3 5 10 13 **F**8 11 12 13 15 17 18 20 22 24 26 28 29 30 31 34 35 38 39 40 44 45 46 47 48 49 50 51 54 59 61 62 64 65 68 70 72 74 75 76 77 78 79 81 82 84 85 86 87 89 90 93 97 98 99 100 102 103 104 107 110 111 114 115 119 120 121 126 128 129 130 131 132 143 144 146 147 148 149 **P**6
Primary Contact: Paul A. Milton, Acting President and Chief Executive Officer
COO: Paul A Milton, Executive Vice President and Chief Operating Officer
CFO: Marc Mesick, Vice President and Chief Financial Officer
CMO: David Liebers M.D., Chief Medical Officer and Vice President Medical Affairs
CIO: Ron McKinnon, Chief Information Officer
CHR: Joseph Giansante, Vice President Human Resources
Web address: www.ellismedicine.org
Control: Other not-for-profit (including NFP Corporation) **Service**: General medical and surgical

Staffed Beds: 436 **Admissions:** 18599 **Census:** 322 **Outpatient Visits:** 592909 **Births:** 2660 **Total Expense ($000):** 412846 **Payroll Expense ($000):** 209923 **Personnel:** 2942

ELLIS HOSPITAL HEALTH CENTER See Ellis Hospital

ELLIS HOSPITAL MCCLELLAN CAMPUS See Ellis Hospital Health Center

⊞ △ **SUNNYVIEW REHABILITATION HOSPITAL (330406)**, 1270 Belmont Avenue, Zip 12308–2104; tel. 518/382–4500, (Nonreporting) **A**1 3 5 7 10 **S** Trinity Health, Livonia, MI
Primary Contact: Edward Eisenman, Chief Executive Officer
CFO: Kristin Signor, Director Finance
CMO: Lynne T Nicolson M.D., Medical Director
CIO: Patrick Clark, Manager Information Technology
CHR: Meghan Glowa, Director Human Resources
Web address: www.sunnyview.org
Control: Other not-for-profit (including NFP Corporation) **Service**: Rehabilitation

Staffed Beds: 115

SLEEPY HOLLOW—Westchester County

⊞ **PHELPS MEMORIAL HOSPITAL CENTER (330261)**, 701 North Broadway, Zip 10591–1020; tel. 914/366–3000 **A**1 2 3 5 10 **F**3 4 5 8 9 11 13 14 15 17 18 28 29 30 31 34 35 37 39 40 45 46 47 48 49 50 53 55 56 57 58 59 60 61 63 64 65 68 70 74 75 76 77 78 79 81 82 84 85 86 87 89 90 91 92 93 94 96 97 98 100 101 102 103 104 107 108 110 111 114 115 118 119 129 130 131 132 135 141 143 145 146 147 148 **P**5 6 **S** Northwell Health, New Hyde Park, NY
Primary Contact: Daniel Blum, President
CFO: Vincent DeSantis, Vice President Finance
CHR: Jussi Maijala, Vice President, Human Resources
CNO: Mary McDermott MSN, MS, R.N., Senior Vice President Patient Care Services and Chief Nursing Officer
Web address: www.phelpshospital.org
Control: Other not-for-profit (including NFP Corporation) **Service**: General medical and surgical

Staffed Beds: 158 **Admissions:** 6941 **Census:** 131 **Outpatient Visits:** 176933 **Births:** 928 **Total Expense ($000):** 250508 **Payroll Expense ($000):** 135165 **Personnel:** 1416

SMITHTOWN—Suffolk County

□ **ST. CATHERINE OF SIENA MEDICAL CENTER (330401)**, 50 Route 25-A, Zip 11787–1348; tel. 631/862–3000, (Nonreporting) **A**1 10 **S** Catholic Health Services of Long Island, Rockville Centre, NY
Primary Contact: Paul J. Rowland, Executive Vice President and Chief Administrative Officer
CFO: John Pohlman, Vice President Finance and Administration
CMO: Jason Golbin M.D., Chief Medical Officer
CNO: Mary Jane Finnegan, Chief Nursing Officer
Web address: www.stcatherines.chsli.org/
Control: Church operated, Nongovernment, not-for-profit **Service**: General medical and surgical

Staffed Beds: 503

SPRINGVILLE—Erie County

BERTRAND CHAFFEE HOSPITAL (330111), 224 East Main Street, Zip 14141–1497; tel. 716/592–2871, (Nonreporting) **A**10
Primary Contact: Nils Gunnersen, Administrator
CMO: J Matthew Baker M.D., President Medical Staff
CHR: Mary Beth Brown, Director Human Resources
Web address: www.chaffeehospitalandhome.com
Control: Other not-for-profit (including NFP Corporation) **Service**: General medical and surgical

Staffed Beds: 24

STAR LAKE—St. Lawrence County

★ **CLIFTON-FINE HOSPITAL (331307)**, 1014 Oswegatchie Trail, Zip 13690–3143; tel. 315/848–3351, (Nonreporting) **A**10 18
Primary Contact: Robert L. Seamon, Chief Executive Officer
CFO: Nancy Russell, Chief Financial Officer
CMO: David Welch M.D., Medical Director
CIO: Devin Rice, Director Information Systems
CNO: Michelle Bristol, Director of Nursing
Web address: www.cliftonfinehospital.org
Control: Other not-for-profit (including NFP Corporation) **Service**: General medical and surgical

Staffed Beds: 20

NY

Many Facility Codes have changed. Please refer to the AHA Guide Code Chart. © 2017 AHA Guide

STATEN ISLAND—Richmond County, See New York City

STONY BROOK—Suffolk County

✣ **STONY BROOK UNIVERSITY HOSPITAL (330393)**, State University of New York, Zip 11794–8410; tel. 631/444–1077, (Includes STONY BROOK CHILDREN'S HOSPITAL, 100 Nicolls Road, Stony Brook, New York, Zip 11794–0001, tel. 631/444–4000; STONY BROOK SOUTHAMPTON HOSPITAL, 240 Meeting House Lane, Southampton, New York, Zip 11968–5090, tel. 631/726–8200; Robert S Chaloner, Chief Administrative Officer) **A**1 2 5 8 10 **F**3 6 7 8 9 11 12 13 14 15 16 17 18 19 20 22 24 26 28 29 30 31 32 34 35 36 37 38 39 40 41 43 44 45 46 47 48 49 50 51 52 53 54 55 56 57 58 59 60 61 63 64 65 66 68 70 72 73 74 75 76 77 78 79 81 82 84 85 86 87 88 89 91 92 93 96 97 98 99 100 101 102 103 104 105 107 108 110 111 114 115 116 117 118 119 120 121 122 123 124 126 129 130 131 132 134 135 136 138 141 143 145 146 147 148 149 150 **P**1 6
Primary Contact: L. Reuven. Pasternak, M.D., M.P.H., Vice President for Health System and Chief Executive Officer
COO: Carol Gomes FACHE, Chief Operating Officer
CFO: Gary E Bie CPA, Chief Financial Officer
CMO: Joseph H. Laver M.D., Chief Medical Officer
CIO: Jim Murry, Chief Information Officer
CHR: Luis de Onis, Interim Chief Human Resources Officer
CNO: Mary Ann T Donohue Ph.D., R.N., Chief Patient Care Services Officer
Web address: www.stonybrookmedicalcenter.org
Control: State, Government, Nonfederal **Service**: General medical and surgical

Staffed Beds: 603 **Admissions:** 32117 **Census:** 515 **Outpatient Visits:** 403711 **Births:** 3094 **Total Expense ($000):** 1150599 **Payroll Expense ($000):** 491539 **Personnel:** 5592

SUFFERN—Rockland County

✣ **GOOD SAMARITAN REGIONAL MEDICAL CENTER (330158)**, 255 Lafayette Avenue, Zip 10901–4869; tel. 845/368–5000, (Nonreporting) **A**1 2 10 **S** WMCHealth, Valhalla, NY
Primary Contact: Mary Leahy, M.D., Chief Executive Officer
COO: Gerry Durney, Chief Operating Officer
CMO: Rodney W Williams M.D., JD, MS, Vice President Medical Affairs
CIO: Deborah K Marshall, Vice President Public Relations
CHR: Pamela Tarulli, Senior Vice President Human Resources
Web address: www.goodsamhosp.org
Control: Church operated, Nongovernment, not-for-profit **Service**: General medical and surgical

Staffed Beds: 308

SYOSSET—Nassau County

★ **SYOSSET HOSPITAL**, 221 Jericho Turnpike, Zip 11791–4515; tel. 516/496–6500 **A**3 **F**3 8 12 15 18 29 30 31 34 35 36 38 40 43 44 45 50 57 58 59 60 62 63 64 65 68 70 74 78 79 81 82 84 85 87 97 98 100 101 102 107 108 114 119 126 130 132 135 146 **P**5 6 **S** Northwell Health, New Hyde Park, NY
Primary Contact: Michael Fener, Executive Director
COO: Mark J Solazzo, Regional Chief Operating Officer
CFO: Richard Reilly, Deputy Executive Director
CMO: Randolph DiLorenzo M.D., Medical Director
CHR: Andrew S Goldberg, Associate Executive Director
Web address: www.northshorelij.com
Control: Other not-for-profit (including NFP Corporation) **Service**: General medical and surgical

Staffed Beds: 75 **Admissions:** 3951 **Census:** 58 **Outpatient Visits:** 60427 **Births:** 0 **Total Expense ($000):** 176934 **Payroll Expense ($000):** 93795 **Personnel:** 748

SYRACUSE—Onondaga County

COMMUNITY-GENERAL HOSPITAL OF GREATER SYRACUSE See Upstate University Hospital At Community General

★ ⇑ **CROUSE HEALTH (330203)**, 736 Irving Avenue, Zip 13210–1690; tel. 315/470–7375 **A**3 5 10 21 **F**3 4 5 8 11 12 13 15 18 19 22 23 26 27 29 31 34 35 36 37 40 49 50 53 58 59 60 64 66 68 70 72 73 74 75 76 77 78 79 81 83 84 86 87 89 91 93 96 107 108 110 112 114 115 116 117 118 119 126 129 130 131 132 135 144 145 146 147 148 149 150
Primary Contact: Kimberly Boynton, President and Chief Executive Officer
CFO: Kelli Harris, Chief Financial Officer
CMO: Seth Kronenberg M.D., Chief Medical Officer
CIO: Kim Rose, Chief Information Technology
CHR: John Bergemann, Director Human Resources
CNO: Betty O'Connor, Chief Nursing Officer
Web address: www.crouse.org
Control: Other not-for-profit (including NFP Corporation) **Service**: General medical and surgical

Staffed Beds: 487 **Admissions:** 19686 **Census:** 303 **Outpatient Visits:** 439753 **Births:** 3989 **Total Expense ($000):** 421059 **Payroll Expense ($000):** 173439 **Personnel:** 1894

□ **RICHARD H. HUTCHINGS PSYCHIATRIC CENTER (334001)**, 620 Madison Street, Zip 13210–2319; tel. 315/426–3632, (Nonreporting) **A**1 3 5 10 **S** New York State Office of Mental Health, Albany, NY
Primary Contact: Colleen A. Sawyer, R.N., MSN, Executive Director
CFO: Robert Stapleton, Director Administration
CMO: Mark Cattalani M.D., Clinical Director
CIO: Neil Nemi, Administrator Facility Information Center
CHR: Katherine Herron, Director Human Resources
Web address: www.omh.ny.gov
Control: State, Government, Nonfederal **Service**: Psychiatric

Staffed Beds: 131

★ ⇑ **ST. JOSEPH'S HOSPITAL HEALTH CENTER (330140)**, 301 Prospect Avenue, Zip 13203–1807; tel. 315/448–5111 **A**3 5 10 21 **F**2 3 5 8 11 12 13 14 15 17 18 20 22 24 26 28 29 30 31 34 35 36 37 38 39 40 45 46 47 48 49 50 51 54 56 57 58 59 60 62 64 65 66 68 70 71 72 73 74 75 76 77 78 79 81 82 83 84 85 87 92 93 94 97 98 99 100 101 102 103 104 106 107 108 110 111 114 115 118 119 126 129 130 131 132 135 144 145 146 147 148 **S** Trinity Health, Livonia, MI
Primary Contact: Leslie Paul. Luke, President and Chief Executive Officer
COO: Mary W Brown, Senior Vice President Operations
CFO: Meredith Price, Vice President Fiscal Services and Chief Financial Officer
CMO: Joseph W Spinale D.O., Chief Medical Officer
CIO: Charles Fennell, Vice President Information Management
CHR: Sallie Biittner, Vice President Human Resources
CNO: AnneMarie Czyz R.N., MS, Ed.D., Senior Vice President Operations, Chief Operating Officer and Chief Nursing Officer
Web address: www.sjhsyr.org
Control: Other not-for-profit (including NFP Corporation) **Service**: General medical and surgical

Staffed Beds: 431 **Admissions:** 24787 **Census:** 349

✣ △ **SYRACUSE VETERANS AFFAIRS MEDICAL CENTER**, 800 Irving Avenue, Zip 13210–2716; tel. 315/425–4400, (Nonreporting) **A**1 3 5 7 8 **S** Department of Veterans Affairs, Washington, DC
Primary Contact: Judy A. Hayman, Ph.D., Interim Director
CFO: Deborah Angell, Chief Financial Officer
CMO: Syed Asif Ali M.D., Chief of Staff
CIO: James Stenson, Chief Information Officer
CHR: Mark Antinelli, Manager Human Resources
CNO: Cheryl Czajkowski, Associate Director Patient and Nursing Services
Web address: www.syracuse.va.gov/
Control: Veterans Affairs, Government, federal **Service**: General medical and surgical

Staffed Beds: 161

★ ⇑ **UPSTATE UNIVERSITY HOSPITAL (330241)**, 750 East Adams Street, Zip 13210–2342; tel. 315/464–5540, (Includes GOLISANO CHILDREN'S HOSPITAL, 750 East Adams Street, Syracuse, New York, Zip 13210–2342, tel. 315/464–4570; UPSTATE UNIVERSITY HOSPITAL AT COMMUNITY GENERAL, 4900 Broad Road, Syracuse, New York, Zip 13215–2293, tel. 315/492–5011) **A**2 3 8 10 21 **F**3 6 9 12 13 15 16 17 18 19 20 21 22 23 24 25 26 27 28 29 30 31 33 34 35 36 37 38 39 40 41 43 44 45 46 47 48 49 50 51 52 53 54 55 56 57 58 59 61 64 65 66 68 70 74 76 78 79 81 82 84 85 86 87 88 89 90 92 93 95 96 97 98 99 100 101 102 104 107 108 109 110 111 112 114 115 118 119 120 121 123 124 126 128 129 130 131 132 135 136 138 141 142 145 146 147 148 149 150 **P**4
Primary Contact: Steven M. Scott, Interim Chief Executive Officer
CFO: Stuart M Wright CPA, Chief Financial Officer
CMO: Anthony Weiss M.D., Medical Director
CIO: Terry Wagner, Chief Information Officer
CHR: Eric Frost, Associate Vice President Human Resources
CNO: Nancy E Page MS, R.N., Interim Chief Nursing Officer
Web address: www.upstate.edu/hospital
Control: State, Government, Nonfederal **Service**: General medical and surgical

Staffed Beds: 630 **Admissions:** 30521 **Census:** 475 **Outpatient Visits:** 718066 **Births:** 1029 **Total Expense ($000):** 956747 **Payroll Expense ($000):** 345841 **Personnel:** 5069

VETERANS AFFAIRS MEDICAL CENTER See Syracuse Veterans Affairs Medical Center

NY

Hospital, Medicare Provider Number, Address, Telephone, Approval, Facility, and Physician Codes, Health Care System

★ American Hospital Association (AHA) membership
□ The Joint Commission accreditation
○ Healthcare Facilities Accreditation Program
◇ DNV Healthcare Inc. accreditation
⇑ Center for Improvement in Healthcare Quality Accreditation
△ Commission on Accreditation of Rehabilitation Facilities (CARF) accreditation

TICONDEROGA—Essex County

★ **MOSES LUDINGTON HOSPITAL (331306)**, 1019 Wicker Street, Zip 12883–1097; tel. 518/585–2831 **A**10 18 **F**11 15 40 57 67 68 77 90 93 107 114 119 128 133
Primary Contact: John R. Remillard, Interim Chief Executive Officer
CFO: Alan Chardavoyne, Chief Financial Officer
CIO: Darrin Goodrow, Chief Information Officer
CHR: Tamara Evens, Director Human Resources
Web address: www.interlakeshealth.com
Control: Other not-for-profit (including NFP Corporation) **Service**: General medical and surgical

Staffed Beds: 15 **Admissions**: 84 **Census**: 1 **Outpatient Visits**: 6541 **Births**: 0
Total Expense ($000): 10469 **Payroll Expense ($000)**: 4200 **Personnel**: 97

TROY—Rensselaer County

★ **SAMARITAN HOSPITAL (330180)**, 2215 Burdett Avenue, Zip 12180–2475; tel. 518/271–3300, (Nonreporting) **A**3 10 **S** Trinity Health, Livonia, MI
Primary Contact: Norman E. Dascher Jr, Chief Executive Officer
CFO: Daniel A Kochie CPA, Chief Financial Officer
CMO: Daniel C Silverman M.D., Chief Medical Officer, Acute Care Troy
CIO: Karen LeBlanc, Director, Applications
CNO: Jacqueline Priore, Chief Nursing Officer
Web address: www.nehealth.com
Control: Other not-for-profit (including NFP Corporation) **Service**: General medical and surgical

Staffed Beds: 212

★ **ST. MARY'S HOSPITAL (330232)**, 1300 Massachusetts Avenue, Zip 12180–1695; tel. 518/268–5000, (Nonreporting) (Includes SETON HEALTH SYSTEM-ST. MARY'S HOSPITAL, 1300 Massachusetts Avenue, Troy, New York, Zip 12180, tel. 518/272–5000) **A**10 **S** Trinity Health, Livonia, MI
Primary Contact: Norman E. Dascher Jr, Chief Executive Officer
CFO: Daniel A Kochie CPA, Chief Financial Officer
CMO: Daniel C Silverman M.D., Chief Medical Officer
CHR: Barbara McCandless, Vice President Human Resources
CNO: Carol Crucetti R.N., Chief Nursing Officer
Web address: www.setonhealth.org
Control: Church operated, Nongovernment, not-for-profit **Service**: General medical and surgical

Staffed Beds: 173

UTICA—Oneida County

★ △ ⇑ **FAXTON ST. LUKE'S HEALTHCARE (330044)**, 1656 Champlin Avenue, Zip 13502–4830, Mailing Address: P.O.Box 479, 13503–0479; tel. 315/624–6000, (Includes FAXTON CAMPUS, 1676 Sunset Avenue, Utica, New York, Zip 13502–5475, tel. 315/624–6000; ST. LUKE'S CAMPUS, 1656 Champlin Avenue, Utica, New York, Zip 13502–4830, P O Box 479, 13503–0479, tel. 315/624–6000) **A**2 3 7 10 21 **F**2 3 11 12 13 15 28 29 30 31 34 35 36 39 40 45 46 47 48 49 50 51 53 54 56 57 58 59 60 62 64 65 66 68 70 73 74 75 76 77 78 79 80 81 84 85 86 87 89 90 92 93 97 98 102 103 104 107 108 110 114 115 116 117 118 119 120 121 123 124 127 130 131 132 135 141 143 144 146 147 148 **P**6
Primary Contact: Scott H. Perra, FACHE, President and Chief Executive Officer
COO: Robert Scholefield MS, R.N., Executive Vice President and Chief Operating Officer
CFO: Louis Aiello, Senior Vice President and Chief Financial Officer
CMO: Michael F Trevisani M.D., Senior Vice President and Chief Medical Officer
CIO: John Lynch, Vice President and Chief Information Officer
CHR: Jack Davis, Vice President Human Resources
CNO: Angela Belmont R.N., Interim Chief Nursing Officer
Web address: www.mvhealthsystem.org
Control: Other not-for-profit (including NFP Corporation) **Service**: General medical and surgical

Staffed Beds: 278 **Admissions**: 13129 **Census**: 178 **Outpatient Visits**: 483339 **Births**: 1869 **Total Expense ($000)**: 285292 **Payroll Expense ($000)**: 137718 **Personnel**: 2161

☐ **MOHAWK VALLEY PSYCHIATRIC CENTER (334021)**, 1400 Noyes Street, Zip 13502–3854; tel. 315/738–3800, (Nonreporting) **A**1 10 **S** New York State Office of Mental Health, Albany, NY
Primary Contact: Colleen A. Sawyer, R.N., MSN, Executive Director
Web address: www.omh.ny.gov/omhweb/facilities/mvpc/facility.htm
Control: State, Government, Nonfederal **Service**: Psychiatric

Staffed Beds: 614

★ ⇑ **ST. ELIZABETH MEDICAL CENTER (330245)**, 2209 Genesee Street, Zip 13501–5999; tel. 315/798–8100 **A**3 10 13 21 **F**3 11 15 17 18 20 22 24 26 29 30 32 34 35 36 37 40 43 45 50 54 57 58 59 61 62 65 66 68 70 74 75 77 78 79 80 81 84 85 87 89 92 93 97 98 102 103 107 108 110 114 115 119 126 127 129 130 131 132 135 141 146 147 148 149 150 **P**6 **S** Sisters of Saint Francis, Albany, NY
Primary Contact: Scott H. Perra, FACHE, Chief Executive Officer
COO: Robert Scholefield MS, R.N., Chief Operating Officer
CFO: Louis Aiello, Chief Financial Officer
CMO: Albert D'Accurzio M.D., Medical Director
CIO: Robert Gillette, Chief Information Officer
CHR: Patrick Buckley, Vice President Human Resources
CNO: Varinya Sheppard R.N., Chief Nursing Officer
Web address: www.stemc.org
Control: Church operated, Nongovernment, not-for-profit **Service**: General medical and surgical

Staffed Beds: 181 **Admissions**: 10323 **Census**: 144 **Outpatient Visits**: 451824 **Births**: 0 **Total Expense ($000)**: 217041 **Payroll Expense ($000)**: 103020 **Personnel**: 1640

ST. LUKE'S CAMPUS See Faxton St. Luke's Healthcare

VALHALLA—Westchester County

⊞ **BLYTHEDALE CHILDREN'S HOSPITAL (333301)**, 95 Bradhurst Avenue, Zip 10595–1697; tel. 914/592–7555, (Nonreporting) **A**1 3 10
Primary Contact: Larry L. Levine, President and Chief Executive Officer
COO: Maureen Desimone, Chief Operating Officer
CFO: John Canning, Chief Financial Officer
CMO: Joelle Mast Ph.D., M.D., Chief Medical Officer
CHR: Ronald Gallo, Director Human Resources
Web address: www.blythedale.org
Control: Other not-for-profit (including NFP Corporation) **Service**: Children's rehabilitation

Staffed Beds: 92

⇑ **WESTCHESTER MEDICAL CENTER (330234)**, 100 Woods Road, Zip 10595–1530; tel. 914/493–7000, (Includes MARIA FARERI CHILDREN'S HOSPITAL, 100 Woods Road, Valhalla, New York, Zip 10595–1652, tel. 866/962–7337; MIDHUDSON REGIONAL HOSPITAL OF WESTCHESTER REGIONAL CENTER, 241 North Road, Poughkeepsie, New York, Zip 12601–1154, tel. 845/483–5000; Paul S Hochenberg, Executive Director) **A**2 3 5 8 10 21 **F**3 4 5 8 12 13 14 15 16 17 18 19 20 21 22 23 24 25 26 27 28 29 30 31 32 34 35 36 37 38 39 40 41 43 44 45 46 47 48 49 50 51 52 54 55 56 57 58 59 60 61 62 64 65 66 68 70 71 72 73 74 75 76 77 78 79 80 81 82 84 85 86 87 88 89 90 91 92 93 94 97 98 99 100 101 102 103 104 107 108 110 111 114 115 116 117 118 119 120 121 123 124 126 129 130 131 132 134 135 136 137 138 139 141 142 145 146 147 148 149 **P**6 **S** WMCHealth, Valhalla, NY
Primary Contact: Michael D. Israel, President and Chief Executive Officer
COO: Gary F Brudnicki, Senior Executive Vice President, Chief Operating Officer and Chief Financial Officer
CFO: Gary F Brudnicki, Senior Executive Vice President, Chief Operating Officer and Chief Financial Officer
CMO: Renee Garrick M.D., Executive Medical Director
CIO: John Moustakakis, Senior Vice President Information Systems and Chief Information Officer
CHR: Jordy Rabinowitz, Senior Vice President Human Resources Operations
CNO: Patricia A. Wrobbel, Senior Vice President and Chief Nurse Executive
Web address: www.wmchealth.org
Control: Hospital district or authority, Government, Nonfederal **Service**: General medical and surgical

Staffed Beds: 867 **Admissions**: 27601 **Census**: 629 **Outpatient Visits**: 137231 **Births**: 827 **Total Expense ($000)**: 1335521 **Payroll Expense ($000)**: 294728 **Personnel**: 3459

WALTON—Delaware County

UHS DELAWARE VALLEY HOSPITAL (331312), 1 Titus Place, Zip 13856–1498; tel. 607/865–2100 **A**10 18 **F**3 4 5 11 15 18 28 29 34 35 40 45 50 57 59 64 75 77 85 87 93 97 107 110 114 119 130 131 133 146 147 148 **S** United Health Services, Binghamton, NY
Primary Contact: Paul Summers, President and Chief Executive Officer
CFO: Paul Summers, Chief Financial Officer
CMO: John Giannone M.D., Chief Medical Officer
CIO: James Armstrong, Manager Information Technology
CHR: Paul Summers, Chief Human Resources Officer
CNO: Victoria Conkling, Vice President Patient Care Services and Chief Nursing Officer
Web address: www.uhs.net/locations/
Control: Other not-for-profit (including NFP Corporation) **Service**: General medical and surgical

Staffed Beds: 25 **Admissions**: 525 **Census**: 11 **Outpatient Visits**: 161072 **Births**: 0 **Total Expense ($000)**: 21185 **Payroll Expense ($000)**: 7199 **Personnel**: 155

NY

Many Facility Codes have changed. Please refer to the AHA Guide Code Chart.
© 2017 AHA Guide

WAPPINGERS—Dutchess County

VETERAN AFFAIRS HUDSON VALLEY HEALTH CARE SYSTEM-CASTLE POINT CAMPUS See Veterans Affairs Hudson Valley Health Care System, Montrose

WARSAW—Wyoming County

☐ **WYOMING COUNTY COMMUNITY HOSPITAL (330008)**, 400 North Main Street, Zip 14569–1025; tel. 585/786–2233, (Nonreporting) **A**1 10 20
Primary Contact: Donald T. Eichenauer, Chief Executive Officer
COO: Michael Corcimiglia, Chief Operating Officer
CFO: James T. Cullen III, Director Finance
CMO: Bilal Ahmed M.D., Medical Director
CIO: Jane Beechler, Director Healthcare Information Systems
CHR: Peter J Bendyna, Director Human Resources
CNO: Connie Almeter, Director of Nursing
Web address: www.wcchs.net
Control: County, Government, Nonfederal **Service:** General medical and surgical

Staffed Beds: 75

WARWICK—Orange County

✠ **ST. ANTHONY COMMUNITY HOSPITAL (330205)**, 15 Maple Avenue, Zip 10990–1028; tel. 845/986–2276, (Nonreporting) **A**1 10 **S** WMCHealth, Valhalla, NY
Primary Contact: Mary Leahy, M.D., Chief Executive Officer
Web address: www.stanthonycommunityhosp.org
Control: Church operated, Nongovernment, not-for-profit **Service:** General medical and surgical

Staffed Beds: 73

WATERTOWN—Jefferson County

✠ **SAMARITAN MEDICAL CENTER (330157)**, 830 Washington Street, Zip 13601–4034; tel. 315/785–4000 **A**1 3 10 12 13 20 **F**3 5 8 13 15 18 28 29 30 31 35 40 49 50 51 57 60 62 64 68 70 73 74 75 76 77 78 79 81 82 87 89 90 93 97 98 99 100 102 103 104 107 108 111 114 115 116 119 120 121 126 127 129 130 135 146 147 148 **P**6
Primary Contact: Thomas H. Carman, President and Chief Executive Officer
CFO: Sean Mills, Chief Financial Officer
CMO: Mario Victoria M.D., Vice President, Medical Affairs
CIO: M Andrew Short, Vice President Information Services
CHR: Thomas Shatraw, Director Human Resources
CNO: Kimberly Thibert R.N., MSN, Vice President Patient Care Services and Chief Nursing Officer
Web address: www.samaritanhealth.com
Control: Other not-for-profit (including NFP Corporation) **Service:** General medical and surgical

Staffed Beds: 211 **Admissions:** 8413 **Census:** 128 **Outpatient Visits:** 290219 **Births:** 1509 **Total Expense ($000):** 202046 **Payroll Expense ($000):** 96007 **Personnel:** 1317

WELLSVILLE—Allegany County

✠ **JONES MEMORIAL HOSPITAL (330096)**, 191 North Main Street, Zip 14895–1150, Mailing Address: P.O.Box 72, 14895–0072; tel. 585/593–1100 **A**1 10 20 **F**3 8 11 13 15 17 28 29 30 31 34 35 36 40 43 50 57 59 61 64 68 70 75 76 77 78 79 81 85 89 93 97 107 110 114 119 129 131 132 133 146 147 149 **S** University of Rochester Medical Center, Rochester, NY
Primary Contact: Eva Benedict, R.N., President and Chief Executive Officer
CFO: James Helms, Vice President Finance
CMO: William Coch M.D., Medical Director
CIO: James Helms, Vice President Finance
CHR: Brenda Sobeck, Director of Human Resources
CNO: Donna Bliven, Vice President Patient Care Services and Chief Nursing Officer
Web address: www.jmhny.org
Control: Other not-for-profit (including NFP Corporation) **Service:** General medical and surgical

Staffed Beds: 33 **Admissions:** 1607 **Census:** 17 **Outpatient Visits:** 132029 **Births:** 420 **Total Expense ($000):** 39105 **Payroll Expense ($000):** 18413 **Personnel:** 328

WEST HAVERSTRAW—Rockland County

☐ △ **HELEN HAYES HOSPITAL (330405)**, Route 9W, Zip 10993–1127; tel. 845/786–4000, (Nonreporting) **A**1 3 5 7 10
Primary Contact: Edmund Coletti, Chief Executive Officer
COO: Kathleen Martucci, Chief Operating Officer
CFO: Lori A. Meszler, Chief Financial Officer
CIO: Virgil Ennis, Chief Information Officer
CHR: Patrick J. Ryan, Chief Human Resources Officer
Web address: www.helenhayeshospital.org
Control: State, Government, Nonfederal **Service:** Rehabilitation

Staffed Beds: 155

WEST ISLIP—Suffolk County

✠ **GOOD SAMARITAN HOSPITAL MEDICAL CENTER (330286)**, 1000 Montauk Highway, Zip 11795–4927; tel. 631/376–3000, (Total facility includes 100 beds in nursing home–type unit) **A**1 2 3 5 10 12 13 **F**3 8 11 12 13 15 17 18 19 20 22 24 26 28 29 30 31 32 34 35 40 41 43 45 46 47 48 49 50 54 55 56 57 59 64 65 66 68 70 72 73 74 75 76 77 78 79 81 82 84 85 86 87 88 89 91 93 94 96 97 99 100 102 107 108 110 111 114 115 117 118 119 120 121 123 124 126 128 129 130 131 132 146 147 **S** Catholic Health Services of Long Island, Rockville Centre, NY
Primary Contact: Thomas Ockers, Executive Vice President and Chief Administrative Officer
CFO: Dan Macksood, Regional Senior Vice President and Chief Financial Officer
CMO: Jerome Weiner M.D., Senior Vice President Medical Affairs
CIO: Marcy Dunn, Vice President Information Services and Chief Information Officer
CHR: Lori Spina, Vice President Human Resources
Web address: www.good-samaritan-hospital.org
Control: Church operated, Nongovernment, not-for-profit **Service:** General medical and surgical

Staffed Beds: 506 **Admissions:** 25429 **Census:** 474 **Outpatient Visits:** 214751 **Births:** 2655 **Total Expense ($000):** 625837 **Payroll Expense ($000):** 279033

WEST POINT—Orange County

✠ **KELLER ARMY COMMUNITY HOSPITAL**, 900 Washington Road, Zip 10996–1197, Mailing Address: U S Military Academy, Building 900, 10996–1197; tel. 845/938–5169, (Nonreporting) **A**1 3 5 **S** Department of the Army, Office of the Surgeon General, Falls Church, VA
Primary Contact: Colonel Eric B. Sones, Commander
CIO: Patrick McGuinness, Chief Information Management
CHR: Margaret Greco, Chief Human Resources
Web address: www.kach.amedd.army.mil/SitePages/Home.aspx
Control: Army, Government, federal **Service:** General medical and surgical

Staffed Beds: 20

WEST SENECA—Erie County

☐ **WESTERN NEW YORK CHILDREN'S HOSPITAL PSYCHIATRIC CENTER**, 1010 East and West Road, Zip 14224–3602; tel. 716/677–7000 **A**1 3 5 **F**32 34 38 54 59 64 75 77 98 99 100 101 104 130 132 134 135 142 146 149 **S** New York State Office of Mental Health, Albany, NY
Primary Contact: Kathe Hayes, Executive Director
COO: David Privett, Deputy Director
CMO: Patrick Stein M.D., Clinical Director
CIO: Dan Hrubiak, Associate Computer Program Analyst
CHR: Charles Siewert, Director Human Resources
Web address: www.omh.ny.gov
Control: State, Government, Nonfederal **Service:** Children's hospital psychiatric

Staffed Beds: 46 **Admissions:** 171 **Census:** 38 **Outpatient Visits:** 2143 **Births:** 0 **Personnel:** 178

NY

Hospitals, U.S. / NEW YORK

WESTFIELD—Chautauqua County

★ **WESTFIELD MEMORIAL HOSPITAL (330166)**, 189 East Main Street,
Zip 14787–1195; tel. 716/326–4921, (Nonreporting) **A**10 **S** Allegheny Health
Network, Pittsburgh, PA
Primary Contact: Christopher Clark, D.O., President and Chief Executive Officer
COO: Patricia Ballman, Director
CFO: Tina Gowen, System Controller
CMO: Russell Elwell M.D., Medical Director
CIO: Cindy Harper, Manager Patient Data
Web address: www.wmhinc.org
Control: Other not-for-profit (including NFP Corporation) **Service**: General medical
and surgical

Staffed Beds: 4

WHITE PLAINS—Westchester County

✠ △ **BURKE REHABILITATION HOSPITAL (330404)**, 785 Mamaroneck Avenue,
Zip 10605–2523; tel. 914/597–2500 **A**1 3 5 7 10 **F**11 28 29 30 34 35 53 54
57 58 59 74 75 77 87 90 92 93 94 95 96 100 104 130 131 132 133 146 148
149 **S** Montefiore Health System, Bronx, NY
Primary Contact: Jeffrey Menkes, President and Chief Executive Officer
COO: Brian M Swift, Senior Administrator Plant Operations
CFO: John Stewart, Director Finance
CIO: Cathy Dwyer, Senior Administrator Information Systems
CHR: Annette Bucci, Senior Administrator Human Resources
CNO: Marie Spencer, Chief Nursing Officer and Senior Administrator
Web address: www.burke.org
Control: Other not-for-profit (including NFP Corporation) **Service**: Rehabilitation

Staffed Beds: 150 Admissions: 2306 Census: 116 Outpatient Visits:
116605 Births: 0 Total Expense ($000): 75885 Payroll Expense ($000):
45372 Personnel: 548

NEW YORK-PRESBYTERIAN HOSPITAL, WESTCHESTER DIVISION See New
York-Presbyterian Hospital, New York

✠ **WHITE PLAINS HOSPITAL CENTER (330304)**, 41 East Post Road, Zip 10601–
4699; tel. 914/681–0600 **A**1 2 3 5 10 **F**3 11 12 13 14 15 17 18 20 22 26 29
30 31 32 34 35 36 38 40 41 43 44 45 46 47 49 50 51 54 55 56 57 58 59 60
61 63 64 65 66 68 70 72 73 74 75 77 78 79 81 82 84 85 86 87 92 93 97 99
100 101 102 104 107 108 110 111 115 116 117 118 119 120 121 122 123
126 129 130 131 132 135 144 145 146 147 148 149 **P**5 6 **S** Montefiore Health
System, Bronx, NY
Primary Contact: Susan Fox, President and Chief Executive Officer
COO: Edward F Leonard, Executive Vice President and Chief Operating Officer
CFO: Joseph Guarracino, Senior Vice President and Chief Financial Officer
CMO: Michael Palumbo M.D., Executive Vice President and Medical Director
CIO: Elizabeth King, Director
CHR: John Sanchez, Vice President Human Resources
CNO: Leigh McMahon MS, R.N., Senior Vice President Patient Care Services and
Chief Nursing Officer
Web address: www.wphospital.org
Control: Other not-for-profit (including NFP Corporation) **Service**: General medical
and surgical

Staffed Beds: 292 Admissions: 16285 Census: 194 Outpatient Visits:
391072 Births: 1876 Total Expense ($000): 512970 Payroll Expense
($000): 251505 Personnel: 2615

WILLIAMSVILLE—Erie County

MILLARD FILLMORE SUBURBAN HOSPITAL See Kaleida Health, Buffalo

YONKERS—Westchester County

ANDRUS PAVILION See St. John's Riverside Hospital

✠ **SAINT JOSEPH'S MEDICAL CENTER (330006)**, 127 South Broadway,
Zip 10701–4006; tel. 914/378–7000, (Total facility includes 200 beds in nursing
home–type unit) **A**1 3 5 10 **F**2 3 4 5 8 11 15 18 29 30 31 34 35 38 39 40 45
47 48 49 54 56 57 58 59 60 61 62 64 68 70 74 75 77 78 79 81 82 85 87 89
93 94 97 98 99 100 101 102 103 104 105 106 107 108 110 111 115 118
119 128 130 132 134 135 143 144 146 **P**5 8
Primary Contact: Michael J. Spicer, President and Chief Executive Officer
COO: Frances Casola, Senior Vice President Operations
CFO: Frank Hagan, Senior Vice President Finance
CMO: James Neuendorf M.D., Medical Director
CIO: Deborah Di Bernardo, Chief Information Officer
CHR: Dean Civitello, Vice President Human Resources
CNO: Margaret M Cusumano R.N., MSN, Vice President Patient Care Services and
Chief Nursing Officer
Web address: www.saintjosephs.org
Control: Other not-for-profit (including NFP Corporation) **Service**: General medical
and surgical

Staffed Beds: 473 Admissions: 7412 Census: 396 Births: 0 Total Expense
($000): 257206 Payroll Expense ($000): 117829 Personnel: 1640

☐ **ST. JOHN'S RIVERSIDE HOSPITAL (330208)**, 967 North Broadway,
Zip 10701–1399; tel. 914/964–4444, (Includes ANDRUS PAVILION, 967 North
Broadway, Yonkers, New York, Zip 10701–1399, tel. 914/964–4444; ST. JOHN'S
RIVERSIDE HOSPITAL - PARK CARE PAVILION, Two Park Avenue, Yonkers, New York,
Zip 10703–3497, tel. 914/964–7300; ST. JOHN'S RIVERSIDE HOSPITAL - DOBBS
FERRY PAVILION, 128 Ashford Avenue, Dobbs Ferry, New York, Zip 10522–1896,
tel. 914/693–0700) **A**1 2 3 10 **F**3 4 5 8 11 12 13 15 18 29 30 31 34 35 36 37
40 41 45 49 50 51 52 55 56 57 59 60 61 64 68 70 73 74 76 77 78 79 81 82
83 84 85 90 93 97 107 108 110 111 114 115 118 119 124 126 129 130 131
132 135 136 143 146 147 148 149
Primary Contact: Ronald J. Corti, President and Chief Executive Officer
COO: Lynn M. Nelson R.N., R.N., Chief Nursing Officer and Chief Operating Officer
CFO: Dennis M. Keane, Vice President Finance and Chief Financial Officer
CMO: Paul Antonecchia M.D., Vice President Medical Affairs and Chief Medical
Officer
CIO: Peter Weidner, Director Information Technology
CHR: Marc Leff, Vice President Human Resources
CNO: Lynn M. Nelson R.N., R.N., Chief Nursing Officer and Chief Operating Officer
Web address: www.riversidehealth.org
Control: Other not-for-profit (including NFP Corporation) **Service**: General medical
and surgical

Staffed Beds: 338 Admissions: 17029 Census: 249 Outpatient Visits:
226241 Births: 1196 Total Expense ($000): 251302 Payroll Expense
($000): 113783 Personnel: 1475

NY

A456 Hospitals   *Many Facility Codes have changed. Please refer to the AHA Guide Code Chart.*   © 2017 AHA Guide

NORTH CAROLINA

AHOSKIE—Hertford County

☒ **VIDANT ROANOKE–CHOWAN HOSPITAL (340099)**, 500 South Academy Street, Zip 27910–3261, Mailing Address: P.O.Box 1385, 27910–1385; tel. 252/209–3000 **A**1 10 20 **F**3 11 13 15 28 29 30 31 34 35 40 43 44 45 53 56 57 59 64 68 70 75 76 77 78 79 81 82 85 86 87 89 92 98 100 101 102 103 107 108 110 111 114 119 121 123 129 130 132 146 148 149 **S** Vidant Health, Greenville, NC
Primary Contact: Patrick Heins, President
CFO: Jon Graham, Chief Finance Officer
CMO: David Lingle, Directors Council Chairman and Chief of Staff
CHR: Debbie Sisler, Director, Human Resource
CNO: Judy Bruno, Chief Nursing Officer
Web address: www.vidanthealth.com
Control: Other not–for–profit (including NFP Corporation) **Service**: General medical and surgical

> **Staffed Beds:** 70 **Admissions:** 4424 **Census:** 56 **Outpatient Visits:** 68296 **Births:** 333 **Total Expense ($000):** 68308 **Payroll Expense ($000):** 26300 **Personnel:** 525

ALBEMARLE—Stanly County

☒ **CAROLINAS HEALTHCARE SYSTEM STANLY (340119)**, 301 Yadkin Street, Zip 28001–3441, Mailing Address: P.O.Box 1489, 28002–1489; tel. 704/984–4000 **A**1 2 10 **F**3 11 13 15 18 28 29 30 31 34 35 39 40 45 46 49 57 59 61 62 63 64 68 70 74 75 76 77 78 79 81 82 85 86 87 89 91 93 98 100 101 102 103 107 108 110 111 114 115 118 119 120 121 123 129 130 131 132 144 146 147 148 149 **S** Carolinas HealthCare System, Charlotte, NC
Primary Contact: Brian Freeman, President
CFO: Nick Samilo, Vice President Fiscal Services and Chief Financial Officer
CMO: Paul D'Amico M.D., Chief of Staff
CNO: Judy Doran R.N., Vice President of Hospital Services and Chief Nurse Executive
Web address: www.stanly.org
Control: Hospital district or authority, Government, Nonfederal **Service**: General medical and surgical

> **Staffed Beds:** 109 **Admissions:** 3850 **Census:** 40 **Outpatient Visits:** 77952 **Births:** 543 **Total Expense ($000):** 77371 **Payroll Expense ($000):** 31020 **Personnel:** 499

ASHEBORO—Randolph County

☒ **RANDOLPH HOSPITAL (340123)**, 364 White Oak Street, Zip 27203–5400, Mailing Address: P.O.Box 1048, 27204–1048; tel. 336/625–5151 **A**1 2 10 **F**3 8 13 15 18 28 29 30 31 34 35 37 40 45 48 49 50 53 56 57 58 59 61 62 64 68 70 74 75 76 77 78 79 80 81 83 84 85 86 87 89 91 92 93 94 96 97 107 109 110 111 114 115 119 120 121 123 130 131 132 135 143 146 148 **P**6 **S** Carolinas HealthCare System, Charlotte, NC
Primary Contact: Steven E. Eblin, Chief Executive Officer / President
CMO: Charles West M.D., Chief Medical Officer
CIO: Angela Burgess, Chief Information Officer
Web address: www.randolphhospital.org
Control: Other not–for–profit (including NFP Corporation) **Service**: General medical and surgical

> **Staffed Beds:** 101 **Admissions:** 5148 **Census:** 47 **Outpatient Visits:** 101245 **Births:** 759 **Total Expense ($000):** 97216 **Payroll Expense ($000):** 40178 **Personnel:** 911

ASHEVILLE—Buncombe County

★ **ASHEVILLE SPECIALTY HOSPITAL (342017)**, 428 Biltmore Avenue, 4th Floor, Zip 28801–4502; tel. 828/213–5400, (Nonreporting) **A**3 10 **S** Mission Health System, Asheville, NC
Primary Contact: Julie A. Dikos, MSN, R.N., President and Chief Executive Officer
CFO: Gregg Dixon, Chief Financial Officer
CMO: Ronnie Jacobs M.D., Chief Medical Officer
CIO: Megan Serzan, Director of Quality, Compliance, Risk & Safety
CNO: Josephine Picker MSN, R.N., Director of Nursing
Web address: www.missionhospitals.org/acute–care
Control: Partnership, Investor–owned (for–profit) **Service**: Acute long–term care hospital

> **Staffed Beds:** 32

☒ △ **CAREPARTNERS HEALTH SERVICES (343025)**, 68 Sweeten Creek Road, Zip 28803–2318, Mailing Address: P.O.Box 15025, 28813–0025; tel. 828/277–4800, (Nonreporting) **A**1 3 7 10 **S** Mission Health System, Asheville, NC
Primary Contact: Tracy Buchanan, Chief Executive Officer and President
CFO: Gregg Dixon, Chief Financial Officer
CMO: Michael Parmer, Chief Medical Officer
CIO: Jennifer Scott, Director of Informatics
CHR: Katy Pless, Director of Human Resources
CNO: Cathleen Adams, Chief Nursing Officer
Web address: www.carepartners.org
Control: Other not–for–profit (including NFP Corporation) **Service**: Rehabilitation

> **Staffed Beds:** 80

☒ **CHARLES GEORGE VETERANS AFFAIRS MEDICAL CENTER**, 1100 Tunnel Road, Zip 28805–2087; tel. 828/298–7911, (Total facility includes 73 beds in nursing home–type unit) **A**1 3 5 **F**3 4 5 12 18 20 22 24 26 28 29 30 31 34 35 36 38 39 40 45 49 50 54 56 57 58 59 61 62 63 64 65 68 70 74 75 77 78 79 81 82 83 84 85 86 87 91 92 93 94 97 98 100 101 102 103 104 107 108 111 114 115 119 128 130 132 135 145 146 147 148 149 **S** Department of Veterans Affairs, Washington, DC
Primary Contact: Cynthia Breyfogle, FACHE, Director
CFO: Margaret Wilkes, Chief Fiscal Officer
CMO: Webster Carl Bazemore M.D., Interim Chief of Staff
CIO: Carla McLendon, Director Information Resource Management Services
CHR: James Sitlinger, Chief Human Resources Management
CNO: David Przestrzelski, Associate Director, Patient Care Services and Chief Nursing Executive
Web address: www.asheville.va.gov/
Control: Veterans Affairs, Government, federal **Service**: General medical and surgical

> **Staffed Beds:** 174 **Admissions:** 5001 **Census:** 133 **Outpatient Visits:** 533965 **Births:** 0 **Total Expense ($000):** 361844 **Payroll Expense ($000):** 150947 **Personnel:** 1747

☒ **MISSION HOSPITAL (340002)**, 509 Biltmore Avenue, Zip 28801–4690; tel. 828/213–1111, (Includes MISSION CHILDREN'S HOSPITAL, 509 Biltmore Avenue, Asheville, North Carolina, Zip 28801–4601, tel. 828/213–1111; MISSION HOSPITAL – ST. JOSEPH'S CAMPUS, 428 Biltmore Avenue, Asheville, North Carolina, Zip 28801–9839, tel. 828/213–1111; MISSION HOSPITAL, 509 Biltmore Avenue, Asheville, North Carolina, Zip 28801–4690, tel. 828/213–1111; Jill Hoggard Green, Ph.D., R.N., President) **A**1 2 3 5 10 **F**3 7 8 11 12 13 15 17 18 19 20 22 24 26 28 29 30 31 33 34 36 37 39 40 43 44 45 46 47 48 49 50 51 53 54 55 56 57 58 59 60 61 64 65 68 70 71 72 73 74 75 76 77 78 79 80 81 82 84 85 86 87 88 89 91 92 93 95 96 97 98 99 100 101 102 103 104 105 107 108 110 111 114 115 116 117 118 119 120 121 123 124 126 129 130 131 132 134 135 141 142 143 146 147 148 149 **S** Mission Health System, Asheville, NC
Primary Contact: Jill Hoggard Green, Ph.D., R.N., President
CFO: Paul L McDowell, Deputy Chief Financial Officer
CMO: William Hathaway M.D., Chief Medical Officer
CIO: Jon Brown, Chief Information Officer
CHR: Sheila M Meadows, Chief Human Resources Officer
CNO: Karen M Olsen R.N., Chief Nursing Officer
Web address: www.mission–health.org
Control: Other not–for–profit (including NFP Corporation) **Service**: General medical and surgical

> **Staffed Beds:** 763 **Admissions:** 38391 **Census:** 566 **Outpatient Visits:** 545932 **Births:** 4151 **Total Expense ($000):** 1073529 **Payroll Expense ($000):** 299504 **Personnel:** 5293

BERMUDA RUN—Davie County

★ **WAKE FOREST BAPTIST HEALTH–DAVIE MEDICAL CENTER (341313)**, 329 NC Highway 801 North, Zip 27006; tel. 336/998–1300 **A**10 **F**3 15 28 29 30 34 35 40 50 57 59 64 68 74 75 77 79 81 83 107 115 119 129 130 131 133 146 **S** Wake Forest Baptist Health, Winston–Salem, NC
Primary Contact: Chad J. Brown, M.P.H., President
CFO: Danny Squires, Chief Financial Officer
CMO: Bret Nicks M.D., Chief Medical Officer and Chief of Staff
CIO: William Showalter, Senior Vice President and Chief Information Officer, Information Technology Services
CHR: Jennifer Bandy, Human Resource Business Partner
CNO: Susan T. Bachmeier MSN, R.N., Chief Nursing Officer
Web address: www.wakehealth.edu/Davie–Medical–Center
Control: Other not–for–profit (including NFP Corporation) **Service**: General medical and surgical

> **Staffed Beds:** 25 **Admissions:** 151 **Census:** 14 **Outpatient Visits:** 45375 **Births:** 0 **Total Expense ($000):** 35090 **Payroll Expense ($000):** 11509 **Personnel:** 190

Hospital, Medicare Provider Number, Address, Telephone, Approval, Facility, and Physician Codes, Health Care System

★ American Hospital Association (AHA) membership
□ The Joint Commission accreditation
○ Healthcare Facilities Accreditation Program
◇ DNV Healthcare Inc. accreditation
⇑ Center for Improvement in Healthcare Quality Accreditation
△ Commission on Accreditation of Rehabilitation Facilities (CARF) accreditation

NC

BLACK MOUNTAIN—Buncombe County

☒ **JULIAN F. KEITH ALCOHOL AND DRUG ABUSE TREATMENT CENTER (344023)**, 201 Tabernacle Road, Zip 28711–2599; tel. 828/669–3400, (Nonreporting) **A**10
Primary Contact: W Douglas. Baker, Director
CFO: Jackie Maurer, Fiscal Officer
CMO: Anthony Burnett M.D., Medical Director
CHR: Faye Hamlin, Manager Human Resources
Web address: www.jfkadatc.net
Control: State, Government, Nonfederal **Service**: Alcoholism and other chemical dependency

Staffed Beds: 80

BOLIVIA—Brunswick County

☒ **NOVANT HEALTH BRUNSWICK MEDICAL CENTER (340158)**, 240 Hospital Drive NE, Zip 28422–8346; tel. 910/721–1000 **A**1 10 **F**3 13 15 18 26 28 29 30 34 35 40 45 46 57 59 64 70 71 75 76 79 80 81 82 85 87 93 107 108 110 111 114 118 119 126 130 132 135 141 145 146 147 148 **S** Novant Health, Winston Salem, NC
Primary Contact: Shelbourn Stevens, President and Chief Operating Officer
CFO: Fred M Hargett, Executive Vice President and Chief Financial Officer
CMO: Thomas Zweng, Executive Vice President and Chief Medical Officer
CIO: David B Garrett, Senior Vice President and Chief Information Officer
CHR: Janet Smith-Hill, Executive Vice President and Chief Human Resources Officer
CNO: Lorna J Ward MSN, R.N., Chief Nursing Officer
Web address: www.novanthealth.org
Control: Other not–for–profit (including NFP Corporation) **Service**: General medical and surgical

Staffed Beds: 54 Admissions: 4550 Census: 44 Outpatient Visits: 114100 Births: 475 Total Expense ($000): 85978 Payroll Expense ($000): 24339 Personnel: 430

BOONE—Watauga County

☒ **WATAUGA MEDICAL CENTER (340051)**, 336 Deerfield Road, Zip 28607–5008, Mailing Address: P.O.Box 2600, 28607–2600; tel. 828/262–4100 **A**1 2 10 **F**3 5 13 15 17 18 20 22 26 28 29 30 31 32 34 35 38 40 44 45 46 47 48 49 50 53 54 57 59 64 70 73 75 76 77 78 81 82 84 85 86 87 91 92 93 96 107 108 110 111 114 115 118 119 120 121 122 123 124 129 130 131 132 135 144 145 146 147 148 149 **P**6 **S** Appalachian Regional Healthcare System, Boone, NC
Primary Contact: Charles Mantooth, President and Chief Executive Officer
CFO: Kevin B May, Chief Financial Officer
CMO: Herman A Godwin M.D., Jr, Senior Vice President and Medical Director
CIO: Mike Quinto, Chief Information Officer
CHR: Amy J Crabbe, Senior Vice President Human Resources
Web address: www.apprhs.org/contact–us
Control: Other not–for–profit (including NFP Corporation) **Service**: General medical and surgical

Staffed Beds: 99 Admissions: 3873 Census: 35 Outpatient Visits: 126341 Births: 614 Total Expense ($000): 116810 Payroll Expense ($000): 37513 Personnel: 620

BREVARD—Transylvania County

☒ **TRANSYLVANIA REGIONAL HOSPITAL (341319)**, 260 Hospital Drive, Zip 28712–3378; tel. 828/884–9111, (Total facility includes 10 beds in nursing home–type unit) **A**1 3 10 18 **F**3 11 15 18 28 29 30 31 34 35 40 45 49 53 54 56 64 70 75 77 78 79 80 81 85 97 107 108 110 111 114 119 128 129 130 133 135 146 147 **P**6 **S** Mission Health System, Asheville, NC
Primary Contact: Michele Pilon, President and Chief Nursing Officer
CFO: Theresa M Parker, Regional Finance Director
CMO: Mark Lemel, Chief of Staff
CIO: Ed Coye, Director Information Technology
CHR: Susan Stevens, Human Resources Strategic Business Partner
CNO: Melina Arrowood, Interim President and Chief Nursing Officer
Web address: www.trhospital.org
Control: Other not–for–profit (including NFP Corporation) **Service**: General medical and surgical

Staffed Beds: 40 Admissions: 1728 Census: 20 Outpatient Visits: 105214 Births: 0 Total Expense ($000): 64957 Payroll Expense ($000): 26869 Personnel: 395

BRYSON CITY—Swain County

★ **SWAIN COMMUNITY HOSPITAL (341305)**, 45 Plateau Street, Zip 28713–4200; tel. 828/488–2155 **A**10 18 **F**8 11 15 29 30 35 40 44 57 59 62 63 68 75 77 81 82 84 85 91 93 103 107 119 130 133 146 148 149 **S** Duke LifePoint Healthcare, Brentwood, TN
Primary Contact: Steve Heatherly, Chief Executive Officer
CMO: David Zimmerman M.D., Chief of Staff
Web address: www.westcare.org
Control: Corporation, Investor–owned (for–profit) **Service**: General medical and surgical

Staffed Beds: 25 Admissions: 418 Census: 4 Outpatient Visits: 39772 Births: 0 Total Expense ($000): 14177 Payroll Expense ($000): 5069 Personnel: 84

BURGAW—Pender County

☒ **PENDER MEMORIAL HOSPITAL (341307)**, 507 East Freemont Street, Zip 28425–5131; tel. 910/259–5451, (Total facility includes 43 beds in nursing home–type unit) **A**1 10 18 **F**3 11 15 29 34 35 40 45 54 56 57 59 62 64 81 85 87 93 96 107 110 114 119 128 130 133 143 146 148 149 **S** New Hanover Regional Medical Center, Wilmington, NC
Primary Contact: Ruth Glaser, President
CFO: Morrison Hall, Chief Financial Officer
CMO: Heather Davis M.D., Chief of Staff
CIO: Ashley Hernandez, Chief Information Technology Officer
CHR: Lori McKoy, Business Partner
CNO: Cynthia Faulkner R.N., Chief Nursing Executive
Web address: www.pendermemorial.org
Control: County, Government, Nonfederal **Service**: General medical and surgical

Staffed Beds: 68 Admissions: 746 Census: 44 Outpatient Visits: 44200 Births: 2 Total Expense ($000): 23197 Payroll Expense ($000): 7351 Personnel: 188

BURLINGTON—Alamance County

☒ **ALAMANCE REGIONAL MEDICAL CENTER (340070)**, 1240 Huffman Mill Road, Zip 27215–8700, Mailing Address: P.O.Box 202, 27216–0202; tel. 336/538–7000 **A**1 2 10 **F**3 8 9 12 13 15 18 20 22 24 26 28 29 30 31 32 34 35 36 38 39 40 44 45 46 47 49 50 53 54 56 57 58 59 60 64 66 68 70 73 74 75 76 77 78 79 81 82 84 85 86 87 89 91 93 94 96 97 98 100 101 102 103 107 108 110 111 114 117 118 119 120 121 123 126 130 131 132 135 144 145 146 147 148 **P**6 **S** Cone Health, Greensboro, NC
Primary Contact: Preston W. Hammock, President
CFO: Rex Street, Senior Vice President and Chief Financial Officer
CMO: Andrew Lamb M.D., Chief of Staff
CIO: Terri Andrews, Director Information Technology
CNO: Theresa M Brodrick R.N., MSN, Ph.D., Chief Nursing Officer
Web address: www.armc.com
Control: Other not–for–profit (including NFP Corporation) **Service**: General medical and surgical

Staffed Beds: 218 Admissions: 10786 Census: 115 Outpatient Visits: 203038 Births: 1290 Total Expense ($000): 246151 Payroll Expense ($000): 73970 Personnel: 1507

BUTNER—Granville County

☐ **CENTRAL REGIONAL HOSPITAL (344004)**, 300 Veazey Road, Zip 27509–1668; tel. 919/764–2000 (Nonreporting) **A**1 3 5 10
Primary Contact: Walter Edwin. Beal, Chief Executive Officer
COO: Cliff Hood, Chief Operating Officer
CFO: Pamela Richardson, Business Manager
CMO: Alan Cook, Chief Medical Officer
CIO: Joe Thurber, Director Information Technology
CHR: Kathleen Tardif, Director of Human Resources
CNO: Diana Holmes, Chief Nursing Officer
Control: State, Government, Nonfederal **Service**: Psychiatric

Staffed Beds: 382

CAMP LEJEUNE—Onslow County

☒ **NAVAL HOSPITAL CAMP LEJEUNE**, 100 Brewster Boulevard, Zip 28547–2538, Mailing Address: P.O.Box 10100, 28547–0100; tel. 910/450–4300, (Nonreporting) **A**1 3 5 **S** Bureau of Medicine and Surgery, Department of the Navy, Falls Church, VA
Primary Contact: Captain Rick Freedman, Commanding Officer
Web address: www.med.navy.mil/sites/nhcl/Pages/default.aspx
Control: Navy, Government, federal **Service**: General medical and surgical

Staffed Beds: 117

CARY—Wake County

☒ **WAKEMED CARY HOSPITAL (340173)**, 1900 Kildaire Farm Road, Zip 27518–6616; tel. 919/350–8000 **A**1 10 **F**3 7 12 13 15 18 20 28 29 30 31 35 40 42 44 45 46 48 49 50 54 61 64 68 70 73 74 75 76 77 79 81 82 85 86 92 107 110 111 114 115 118 119 126 129 130 132 146 147 **P**6 **S** WakeMed Health & Hospitals, Raleigh, NC
Primary Contact: Donald R. Gintzig, President and Chief Executive Officer
COO: Denise Wilder Warren R.N., Executive Vice President and Chief Operating Officer
CMO: West Paul M.D., Ph.D., Senior Vice President, Chief Quality and Medical Staff Officer
CIO: Denton Arledge, Vice President and Chief Information Officer
CHR: Jeanene R Martin M.P.H., Senior Vice President Human Resources and Chief People Officer
CNO: Cindy Boily MSN, R.N., Senior Vice President and Chief Nursing Officer
Web address: www.wakemed.org
Control: Other not–for–profit (including NFP Corporation) **Service**: General medical and surgical

Staffed Beds: 156 Admissions: 10456 Census: 111 Outpatient Visits: 262845 Births: 2305 Total Expense ($000): 173825 Payroll Expense ($000): 63091 Personnel: 1062

CHAPEL HILL—Orange County

☒ △ **UNIVERSITY OF NORTH CAROLINA HOSPITALS (340061)**, 101 Manning Drive, Zip 27514–4220; tel. 984/974–1000, (Includes N.C. WOMEN'S HOSPITAL, 101 Manning Drive, Chapel Hill, North Carolina, Zip 27514–4220, tel. 984/974–1000; Gary L Park, President; NORTH CAROLINA CHILDREN'S HOSPITAL, 101 Manning Drive, Chapel Hill, North Carolina, Zip 27514–4220, tel. 984/974–1000; NORTH CAROLINA NEUROSCIENCES HOSPITAL, University Campus, Chapel Hill, North Carolina, Zip 27514, tel. 984/974–1000; UNC HEALTH CARE HILLSBOROUGH CAMPUS, 430 Waterstone Drive, Hillsborough, North Carolina, Zip 27278–9078, tel. 984/215–2000; Gary L Park, Chief Executive Officer; UNC LINEBERGER COMPREHENSIVE CANCER CENTER, 450 West Drive, Chapel Hill, North Carolina, Zip 27599–5020, tel. 919/966–3036) **A**1 2 3 5 7 8 10 **F**3 4 5 7 8 9 11 12 13 14 15 16 17 18 19 20 21 22 23 24 25 26 27 28 29 30 31 32 34 35 36 38 39 40 41 43 44 45 46 47 48 49 50 52 53 54 55 56 57 58 59 60 61 62 63 64 65 66 68 70 72 73 74 75 76 77 78 79 80 81 82 84 85 86 87 88 89 90 91 92 93 96 97 98 99 100 101 102 103 104 105 106 107 108 110 111 114 115 116 117 118 119 120 121 123 124 126 129 130 131 132 134 135 136 137 138 139 140 141 142 143 144 145 146 147 148 149 150 **S** UNC Health Care, Chapel Hill, NC
Primary Contact: Gary L. Park, President
CFO: Christopher Ellington, Executive Vice President and Chief Financial Officer
CMO: Tony Lindsey M.D., Chief of Staff
CIO: Tracy Parham
CHR: Scott Doak, System Vice President, Human Resources
CNO: Catherine Madigan, Chief Nursing Officer
Web address: www.unchealthcare.org
Control: State, Government, Nonfederal **Service:** General medical and surgical

Staffed Beds: 929 **Admissions:** 39091 **Census:** 734 **Outpatient Visits:** 1025408 **Births:** 3545 **Total Expense ($000):** 1368665 **Payroll Expense ($000):** 482607 **Personnel:** 8690

CHARLOTTE—Mecklenburg County

☒ **CAROLINAS CONTINUECARE HOSPITAL AT PINEVILLE (342015)**, 10648 Park Road, Zip 28210; tel. 704/667–8050 **A**1 5 10 **F**1 3 18 20 29 34 35 59 65 68 74 75 77 82 84 85 91 130 148 **P**5 **S** Community Hospital Corporation, Plano, TX
Primary Contact: Derek Murzyn, Market Chief Executive Officer
CFO: Joanne Tyo, Chief Financial Officer
CMO: Joseph Lang M.D., Chief of Staff
CHR: Doug Gallagher, Director Human Resources
CNO: Teshia Davis, Chief Clinical Officer
Web address: www.continuecare.org/pineville/
Control: Other not–for–profit (including NFP Corporation) **Service:** Acute long–term care hospital

Staffed Beds: 40 **Admissions:** 466 **Census:** 33 **Outpatient Visits:** 0 **Births:** 0 **Total Expense ($000):** 18990 **Payroll Expense ($000):** 7859 **Personnel:** 135

★ **CAROLINAS CONTINUECARE HOSPITAL AT UNIVERSITY (340189)**, 8800 North Tryon Street, Zip 28262–3300; tel. 704/863–8300 (Nonreporting) **S** Community Hospital Corporation, Plano, TX
Primary Contact: Derek Murzyn, Chief Executive Officer
Web address: www.continuecare.org/charlotte//
Control: Other not–for–profit (including NFP Corporation) **Service:** Acute long–term care hospital

Staffed Beds: 35

☒ △ **CAROLINAS HEALTHCARE SYSTEM PINEVILLE (340098)**, 10628 Park Road, Zip 28210–8407; tel. 704/667–1000 **A**1 2 3 7 10 **F**3 13 17 18 20 22 24 26 28 29 30 31 40 42 45 49 50 51 64 68 70 73 74 75 76 77 78 79 81 82 84 86 87 90 91 92 93 100 107 108 111 114 115 119 126 129 130 132 135 146 147 148 149 **S** Carolinas HealthCare System, Charlotte, NC
Primary Contact: Christopher R. Hummer, President
Web address: www.carolinashealthcare.org/pineville
Control: Hospital district or authority, Government, Nonfederal **Service:** General medical and surgical

Staffed Beds: 235 **Admissions:** 16152 **Census:** 192 **Outpatient Visits:** 168043 **Births:** 2491 **Total Expense ($000):** 291389 **Payroll Expense ($000):** 97230 **Personnel:** 1414

☒ **CAROLINAS HEALTHCARE SYSTEM UNIVERSITY (340166)**, 8800 North Tryon Street, Zip 28262–3300, Mailing Address: P.O.Box 560727, 28256–0727; tel. 704/863–6000 **A**1 2 10 22 **F**3 8 13 15 18 20 26 29 30 31 34 40 42 43 44 45 46 49 50 51 57 59 60 64 65 68 70 72 74 75 76 78 79 83 84 85 86 87 93 107 111 114 115 118 119 126 129 130 145 146 148 149 150 **S** Carolinas HealthCare System, Charlotte, NC
Primary Contact: William H. Leonard, President
CFO: Greg A Gombar, Chief Financial Officer
CIO: John Knox, Senior Vice President and Chief Information Officer
Web address: www.carolinashealthcare.org/university
Control: Hospital district or authority, Government, Nonfederal **Service:** General medical and surgical

Staffed Beds: 100 **Admissions:** 5992 **Census:** 62 **Outpatient Visits:** 153342 **Births:** 1515 **Total Expense ($000):** 146846 **Payroll Expense ($000):** 50936 **Personnel:** 749

☒ △ **CAROLINAS MEDICAL CENTER (340113)**, 1000 Blythe Boulevard, Zip 28203–5871, Mailing Address: P.O.Box 32861, 28232–2861; tel. 704/355–2000, (Includes CAROLINAS MEDICAL CENTER–MERCY, 2001 Vail Avenue, Charlotte, North Carolina, Zip 28207–1289, tel. 704/304–5000; Scott Jones, Vice President and Facility Executive; LEVINE CHILDREN'S HOSPITAL, 1000 Blythe Boulevard, Charlotte, North Carolina, Zip 28203, tel. 704/381–2000) **A**1 2 3 5 7 8 10 **F**3 4 5 6 7 8 12 13 15 17 18 19 20 21 22 23 24 25 26 27 28 29 30 31 32 34 35 36 37 38 39 40 41 42 43 44 45 46 47 48 49 50 52 54 55 56 57 58 59 60 61 62 64 65 66 68 70 71 72 73 74 75 76 77 78 79 80 81 82 83 84 85 86 87 88 89 90 93 96 97 98 99 100 101 102 103 104 105 107 111 114 115 116 117 118 119 120 121 123 124 126 129 130 131 132 134 135 136 137 138 139 141 142 143 145 146 147 148 **S** Carolinas HealthCare System, Charlotte, NC
Primary Contact: Spencer Lilly, President
CFO: Greg A Gombar, Chief Financial Officer
CMO: Roger A Ray M.D., Executive Vice President and Chief Medical Officer
CIO: Craig D Richardville, Senior Vice President and Chief Information and Analytics Officer
CHR: Debra Plousha–Moore, Senior Vice President Human Resources
Web address: www.carolinashealthcare.org/cmc
Control: Hospital district or authority, Government, Nonfederal **Service:** General medical and surgical

Staffed Beds: 1212 **Admissions:** 61270 **Census:** 971 **Outpatient Visits:** 1030938 **Births:** 7121 **Total Expense ($000):** 1965274 **Payroll Expense ($000):** 595327 **Personnel:** 8652

☒ △ **CAROLINAS REHABILITATION (343026)**, 1100 Blythe Boulevard, Zip 28203–5864; tel. 704/355–4300 **A**1 3 7 10 **F**3 29 30 60 64 74 76 82 89 90 93 107 111 119 129 131 146 148 **P**1 **S** Carolinas HealthCare System, Charlotte, NC
Primary Contact: Robert G. Larrison Jr, President
CFO: William Hopkins, Director Finance
CMO: William Bockenek M.D., Chief Medical Officer
CIO: Craig D Richardville, Chief Information and Analytics Officer
CHR: Deonca Leach, Director, Human Resources
CNO: Susan Chase, Vice President
Web address: www.carolinashealthcare.org/rehabilitation
Control: Other not–for–profit (including NFP Corporation) **Service:** Rehabilitation

Staffed Beds: 157 **Admissions:** 2693 **Census:** 117 **Outpatient Visits:** 82855 **Births:** 0 **Total Expense ($000):** 90330 **Payroll Expense ($000):** 39555 **Personnel:** 634

★ **NOVANT HEALTH CHARLOTTE ORTHOPAEDIC HOSPITAL (340153)**, 1901 Randolph Road, Zip 28207–1195; tel. 704/316–2000, (Total facility includes 16 beds in nursing home–type unit) **A**10 **F**3 11 29 30 37 44 50 51 64 75 79 81 82 86 87 107 111 114 118 119 128 130 131 132 141 146 **S** Novant Health, Winston Salem, NC
Primary Contact: Jason Bernd, Vice President
CFO: Fred M Hargett, Executive Vice President and Chief Financial Officer
CMO: Thomas Zweng, Executive Vice President and Chief Medical Officer
CIO: David B Garrett, Senior Vice President and Chief Information Officer
CHR: Janet Smith–Hill, Executive Vice Presideent and Chief Human Resource Officer
CNO: Kelli S Sadler Bell R.N., Vice President, Chief Nursing Officer
Web address: www.novanthealth.org
Control: Other not–for–profit (including NFP Corporation) **Service:** Orthopedic

Staffed Beds: 31 **Admissions:** 3044 **Census:** 27 **Outpatient Visits:** 21227 **Births:** 0 **Total Expense ($000):** 89774 **Payroll Expense ($000):** 18289 **Personnel:** 271

Hospital, Medicare Provider Number, Address, Telephone, Approval, Facility, and Physician Codes, Health Care System

★ American Hospital Association (AHA) membership   ○ Healthcare Facilities Accreditation Program   ⇑ Center for Improvement in Healthcare Quality Accreditation
☐ The Joint Commission accreditation   ◇ DNV Healthcare Inc. accreditation   △ Commission on Accreditation of Rehabilitation Facilities (CARF) accreditation

NC

✠ **NOVANT HEALTH PRESBYTERIAN MEDICAL CENTER (340053)**, 200 Hawthorne Lane, Zip 28204–2528, Mailing Address: P.O.Box 33549, 28233–3549; tel. 704/384–4000, (Includes PRESBYTERIAN HEMBY CHILDREN'S HOSPITAL, 200 Hawthorne Lane, Charlotte, North Carolina, Zip 28204–2515, tel. 704/384–5134) **A**1 2 3 10 **F**3 5 11 12 13 17 18 19 20 22 24 26 28 29 30 31 32 34 35 36 38 40 41 43 45 46 47 48 49 54 55 56 57 58 59 60 61 63 64 65 67 70 71 72 74 75 76 77 78 79 81 82 84 85 86 87 88 89 91 92 93 98 99 100 101 102 103 104 105 107 108 110 111 114 115 116 117 118 119 120 121 123 124 126 129 130 131 132 135 141 142 145 146 147 148 149 **S** Novant Health, Winston Salem, NC
Primary Contact: Paula Vincent, MSN, President and Chief Operating Officer
CFO: Fred M Hargett, Executive Vice President and Chief Financial Officer
CMO: Thomas Zweng, Executive Vice President and Chief Medical Officer
CIO: David B Garrett, Senior Vice President Information Technology
CHR: Janet Smith–Hill, Senior Vice President Human Resources
CNO: Kelli S Sadler Bell R.N., Vice President, Chief Nursing Officer
Web address: www.novanthealth.org
Control: Other not–for–profit (including NFP Corporation) **Service:** General medical and surgical

Staffed Beds: 440 **Admissions:** 26933 **Census:** 390 **Outpatient Visits:** 424332 **Births:** 5097 **Total Expense ($000):** 609953 **Payroll Expense ($000):** 184484 **Personnel:** 2859

PRESBYTERIAN HOSPITAL See Novant Health Presbyterian Medical Center

PRESBYTERIAN–ORTHOPAEDIC HOSPITAL See Novant Health Charlotte Orthopaedic Hospital

STRATEGIC BEHAVIORAL HEALTH – CHARLOTTE (344031), 1715 Sharon Road West, Zip 28210–5663; tel. 704/944–0650 (Nonreporting) **S** Strategic Behavioral Health, LLC, Memphis, TN
Primary Contact: George G. Boykin, Chief Executive Officer
Web address: www.sbcharlotte.com/
Control: Corporation, Investor–owned (for–profit) **Service:** Children's hospital psychiatric

Staffed Beds: 60

CHEROKEE—Swain County

✠ **CHEROKEE INDIAN HOSPITAL (340156)**, 1 Hospital Road, Zip 28719; tel. 828/497–9163, (Nonreporting) **A**1 3 10
Primary Contact: Casey Cooper, Chief Executive Officer
COO: Beth Greene, Chief Operating Officer
CFO: Chrissy Arch, Chief Financial Officer
CMO: Michael E Toedt M.D., Director Clinical Services
CIO: Anthony Taylor, Manager Information Technology
Web address: www.cherokeehospital.org
Control: Other not–for–profit (including NFP Corporation) **Service:** General medical and surgical

Staffed Beds: 15

CLINTON—Sampson County

✠ **SAMPSON REGIONAL MEDICAL CENTER (340024)**, 607 Beaman Street, Zip 28328–2697, Mailing Address: P.O.Box 260, 28329–0260; tel. 910/592–8511 **A**1 10 12 13 **F**3 13 14 15 29 34 35 40 45 46 47 50 51 53 57 59 62 64 68 70 75 76 77 79 81 82 85 86 89 91 93 107 110 111 114 119 130 132 133 144 146 148
Primary Contact: Shawn Howerton, M.D., Chief Executive Officer and President, Medical Staff
COO: Geraldine H Shipp, Director of Risk Management
CFO: Jerry Heinzman, Senior Vice President and Chief Financial Officer
CMO: Shawn Howerton M.D., Chief Executive Officer and President, Medical Staff
CIO: Kelly Lucas, Chief Information Officer
CHR: Michael W. Gilpin, Vice President Human Resources
CNO: Allison H Taylor R.N., Chief Nursing Officer and Vice President Clinical Services
Web address: www.sampsonrmc.org
Control: County, Government, Nonfederal **Service:** General medical and surgical

Staffed Beds: 83 **Admissions:** 2970 **Census:** 38 **Outpatient Visits:** 74400 **Births:** 423 **Total Expense ($000):** 60609 **Payroll Expense ($000):** 24761 **Personnel:** 487

CLYDE—Haywood County

✠ **HAYWOOD REGIONAL MEDICAL CENTER (340184)**, 262 Leroy George Drive, Zip 28721–7430; tel. 828/456–7311 **A**1 3 10 **F**3 11 13 15 18 20 28 29 30 31 34 35 38 40 44 45 46 50 51 53 54 57 59 62 63 64 65 68 70 71 74 75 76 77 78 79 81 82 84 85 86 87 93 98 100 101 102 107 108 111 114 118 119 129 130 131 132 144 146 147 148 149 **P**8 **S** Duke LifePoint Healthcare, Brentwood, TN
Primary Contact: Rod Harkleroad, R.N., Chief Executive Officer
COO: Teresa Reynolds, Chief Operating Officer
CFO: Rose Coyne, Interim CFO
CMO: Tyson Smith M.D., Chief Medical Officer
CIO: Greg Copen, Chief Information Officer
CHR: Janet Millsaps, Vice President Human Resources
Web address: www.haymed.org
Control: Corporation, Investor–owned (for–profit) **Service:** General medical and surgical

Staffed Beds: 146 **Admissions:** 5609 **Census:** 62 **Outpatient Visits:** 272089 **Births:** 220 **Total Expense ($000):** 93538 **Payroll Expense ($000):** 31407 **Personnel:** 899

COLUMBUS—Polk County

✠ **ST. LUKE'S HOSPITAL (341322)**, 101 Hospital Drive, Zip 28722–6418; tel. 828/894–3311 **A**1 10 18 **F**3 11 15 29 30 34 35 40 45 56 57 59 64 70 75 77 79 81 82 85 87 93 98 103 104 107 108 115 119 130 133 135 146 **P**6 **S** Carolinas HealthCare System, Charlotte, NC
Primary Contact: James B. Bross, President
CFO: Elizabeth Presnell, Assistant Vice President of Finance
CMO: James Holleman M.D., Chief of Staff
CIO: Nick Whichard, Chief Information Officer
CHR: Amy Norville, Vice President Support Services
CNO: Cathy Moore, Chief Nursing Officer
Web address: www.saintlukeshospital.com
Control: Other not–for–profit (including NFP Corporation) **Service:** General medical and surgical

Staffed Beds: 35 **Admissions:** 1599 **Census:** 22 **Outpatient Visits:** 23732 **Births:** 0 **Total Expense ($000):** 29628 **Payroll Expense ($000):** 12273 **Personnel:** 298

CONCORD—Cabarrus County

✠ **CAROLINAS HEALTHCARE SYSTEM NORTHEAST (340001)**, 920 Church Street North, Zip 28025–2983; tel. 704/403–3000 **A**1 2 3 10 **F**3 5 6 8 9 11 12 13 15 17 18 20 22 24 26 28 29 30 32 34 36 37 38 40 42 43 44 45 46 47 48 49 50 51 53 55 56 57 58 59 60 61 64 65 68 70 71 72 73 74 75 76 78 79 81 82 84 85 86 87 88 89 93 97 98 99 100 102 103 104 105 107 108 110 111 114 115 116 117 118 119 120 121 124 126 129 130 131 132 135 145 146 147 148 149 150 **P**6 **S** Carolinas HealthCare System, Charlotte, NC
Primary Contact: Phyllis A. Wingate, FACHE, President
COO: Bill Hubbard, Vice President, Operations
CFO: Rodney Ball, Vice President Finance
CMO: Dan Hagler M.D., Vice President and Chief Medical Officer
CIO: Lisa Sykes, Manager, Information Services
CHR: Lesley Chambless, Assistant Vice President Workforce Relations
CNO: Kate Grew MSN, R.N., Vice President/Chief Nurse Executive
Web address: www.carolinashealthcare.org/northeast
Control: Hospital district or authority, Government, Nonfederal **Service:** General medical and surgical

Staffed Beds: 455 **Admissions:** 21753 **Census:** 270 **Outpatient Visits:** 364913 **Births:** 2844 **Total Expense ($000):** 458694 **Payroll Expense ($000):** 156704 **Personnel:** 2553

DANBURY—Stokes County

★ ⇑ **LIFEBRITE COMMUNITY HOSPITAL OF STOKES (341317)**, 1570 NC 8 & 89 Highway North, Zip 27016, Mailing Address: P.O.Box 10, 27016–0010; tel. 336/593–2831, (Nonreporting) **A**10 18 21
Primary Contact: Pamela P. Tillman, Administrator
CFO: Warren S. Binderman, Chief Financial Officer
CMO: Samuel C Newsome M.D., Chief of Staff
CIO: Ada Ashley, HIM Director
CHR: Lee Sykes, Human Resources Director
CNO: Amanda Parks, Chief Nursing Officer
Web address: www.lifebritestokes.com
Control: Corporation, Investor–owned (for–profit) **Service:** General medical and surgical

Staffed Beds: 65

NC

DUNN—Harnett County

☐ **HARNETT HEALTH SYSTEM (340071)**, 800 Tilghman Drive, Zip 28334–5599, Mailing Address: P.O.Box 1706, 28335–1706; tel. 910/892–1000, (Includes CENTRAL HARTNETT HOSPITAL, 215 Brightwater Drive, Lillington, North Carolina, Zip 27546, tel. 910/892–1000) **A**1 10 12 13 **F**3 11 13 15 18 28 29 30 34 35 39 40 45 50 56 57 59 70 73 75 76 77 79 81 85 86 87 89 92 93 96 102 107 108 110 111 114 118 119 130 146 148 **S** Cape Fear Valley Health System, Fayetteville, NC
Primary Contact: Kevin Jackson, Interim Chief Executive Officer
COO: Kenneth E Bryan FACHE, President and Chief Executive Officer
CFO: Lynn Lambert, Chief Financial Officer
CIO: Tim Krieger, Director Information Systems
CHR: Sondra Davis, Vice President Human Resources & System Development
CNO: Vicki Allen R.N., MS, Vice President Patient Care Services and Chief Nursing Officer
Web address: www.myharnetthealth.org/
Control: Other not–for–profit (including NFP Corporation) **Service:** General medical and surgical

Staffed Beds: 96 **Admissions:** 5981 **Census:** 68 **Outpatient Visits:** 116842 **Births:** 567 **Total Expense ($000):** 99252 **Payroll Expense ($000):** 40566 **Personnel:** 739

DURHAM—Durham County

⊞ **DUKE REGIONAL HOSPITAL (340155)**, 3643 North Roxboro Street, Zip 27704–2763; tel. 919/470–4000 **A**1 3 5 10 **F**3 8 11 12 13 15 17 18 20 22 24 26 29 30 31 34 35 40 41 44 45 47 48 50 51 57 58 59 60 64 66 68 70 73 74 75 76 77 78 79 80 81 82 84 85 86 87 90 93 96 98 100 102 107 108 110 111 115 118 119 120 121 123 124 126 130 131 132 135 146 147 148 149 **P**6 **S** Duke University Health System, Durham, NC
Primary Contact: Kathleen B. Galbraith, FACHE, President
COO: A. Mitch Babb, Vice President, Operations
CFO: Jonathan B Hoy, Chief Financial Officer
CMO: Barbara Griffith M.D., Chief Medical Officer
CIO: Terry Mears, Director Information Systems
CHR: Dexter Nolley, Chief Human Resources Officer
CNO: Victoria K Orto R.N., Chief Nursing and Patient Care Services Officer
Web address: www.dukehealth.org
Control: Other not–for–profit (including NFP Corporation) **Service:** General medical and surgical

Staffed Beds: 202 **Admissions:** 15792 **Census:** 202 **Outpatient Visits:** 123234 **Births:** 2396 **Total Expense ($000):** 294501 **Payroll Expense ($000):** 130914 **Personnel:** 1890

⊞ **DUKE UNIVERSITY HOSPITAL (340030)**, 2301 Erwin Road, Zip 27705–4699, Mailing Address: P.O.Box 3814, 27710–3708; tel. 919/684–8111, (Includes DUKE CHILDREN'S HOSPITAL & HEALTH CENTER, 2301 Erwin Road, Durham, North Carolina, Zip 27710–0001, PO Box 3708, 27702, tel. 919/684–8111) **A**1 2 3 5 8 10 **F**3 5 6 7 8 9 11 12 13 15 17 18 19 20 21 22 23 24 25 26 27 28 29 30 31 32 34 35 37 39 40 41 43 44 45 46 47 48 49 50 51 52 53 54 55 56 57 58 59 60 61 64 65 66 68 70 72 73 74 75 76 77 78 79 80 81 82 84 85 86 87 88 89 91 92 93 94 96 97 98 99 100 101 102 103 104 107 108 110 111 112 114 115 116 117 118 119 120 121 123 124 126 127 129 130 131 132 134 135 136 137 138 139 140 141 142 145 146 147 148 149 **P**1 **S** Duke University Health System, Durham, NC
Primary Contact: Kevin W. Sowers, R.N., MSN, President
COO: Carolyn Carpenter, Chief Operating Officer
CFO: Sabrina Olsen, Chief Financial Officer
CMO: Lisa C Pickett M.D., Chief Medical Officer
CIO: Jeffrey Ferranti M.D., Chief Information Officer
CHR: Deborah Page, Chief Human Resources Officer
CNO: Mary Ann Fuchs R.N., Vice President Patient Care and System Chief Nurse Executive
Web address: www.dukehealth.org
Control: Other not–for–profit (including NFP Corporation) **Service:** General medical and surgical

Staffed Beds: 925 **Admissions:** 41408 **Census:** 763 **Outpatient Visits:** 1119151 **Births:** 3274 **Total Expense ($000):** 2153349 **Payroll Expense ($000):** 691222 **Personnel:** 10362

DURHAM REGIONAL HOSPITAL See Duke Regional Hospital

⊞ **DURHAM VETERANS AFFAIRS MEDICAL CENTER**, 508 Fulton Street, Zip 27705–3897; tel. 919/286–0411, (Total facility includes 100 beds in nursing home–type unit) **A**1 3 5 8 **F**3 5 8 10 15 17 18 20 22 24 26 28 30 31 35 37 38 39 40 45 46 47 48 49 51 54 55 56 58 59 60 61 62 63 64 65 66 68 70 71 74 75 77 78 79 81 82 83 84 85 87 91 92 93 94 96 97 98 100 102 104 107 108 109 110 111 112 115 116 117 118 119 120 121 123 124 126 128 129 130 132 135 136 137 138 139 140 141 146 147 148 149 **S** Department of Veterans Affairs, Washington, DC
Primary Contact: DeAnne Seekins, Director
COO: Sara Haigh, Associate Director
CFO: David Kuboushek, Chief, Fiscal Service
CMO: John D Shelburne M.D., Chief of Staff
CIO: Toby Dickerson, Chief Information Resources Management Services
CHR: Jerry Freeman, Chief, Human Resources Management Services
CNO: Gregory S Eagerton Ph.D., R.N., Nurse Executive
Web address: www.durham.va.gov/
Control: Veterans Affairs, Government, federal **Service:** General medical and surgical

Staffed Beds: 251 **Admissions:** 7013 **Census:** 189 **Outpatient Visits:** 381818 **Births:** 0 **Total Expense ($000):** 622430 **Payroll Expense ($000):** 282772 **Personnel:** 3179

☐ **NORTH CAROLINA SPECIALTY HOSPITAL (340049)**, 3916 Ben Franklin Boulevard, Zip 27704–2383, Mailing Address: PO Box 15819, 27704–2383; tel. 919/956–9300 **A**1 10 **F**3 29 30 51 64 79 81 82 85 86 87 107 119 126 130 131 148 **S** National Surgical Healthcare, Chicago, IL
Primary Contact: Randi L. Shults, Chief Executive Officer
CFO: Bill Wilson, Chief Financial Officer
CMO: David Musante M.D., Medical Director
CHR: Sarah Bohlin, Human Resources Director
CNO: John Medlin, Chief Nursing Officer
Web address: www.ncspecialty.com
Control: Partnership, Investor–owned (for–profit) **Service:** Surgical

Staffed Beds: 18 **Admissions:** 1651 **Census:** 10 **Outpatient Visits:** 11700 **Births:** 0 **Total Expense ($000):** 43042 **Payroll Expense ($000):** 11426 **Personnel:** 199

⊞ **SELECT SPECIALTY HOSPITAL–DURHAM (342018)**, 3643 North Roxboro Road, 6th Floor, Zip 27704–2702; tel. 919/470–9159, (Nonreporting) **A**1 10 **S** Select Medical Corporation, Mechanicsburg, PA
Primary Contact: Jennifer Rawley, PharmD, Chief Executive Officer
CHR: Michael Stinson, Human Resources Coordinator
CNO: Cole Oren R.N., Chief Nursing Officer
Web address: www.selectspecialtyhospitals.com/company/locations/durham.aspx
Control: Corporation, Investor–owned (for–profit) **Service:** Acute long–term care hospital

Staffed Beds: 30

EDEN—Rockingham County

★ ⇑ **MOREHEAD MEMORIAL HOSPITAL (340060)**, 117 East King's Highway, Zip 27288–5201; tel. 336/623–9711, (Total facility includes 121 beds in nursing home–type unit) **A**2 10 21 **F**3 11 13 15 18 26 29 30 34 35 40 45 47 48 49 50 57 59 64 68 70 74 76 77 78 79 81 82 85 87 89 90 93 107 108 110 111 114 118 119 122 123 128 129 130 132 143 144 146 147 148 **P**6
Primary Contact: Dana Weston, Chief Executive Officer
CFO: Raymond C. Owings, Interim Chief Financial Officer
CIO: Wade Williams, Chief Information Officer
CHR: Tom Stevens, Director Personnel
CNO: JoAnn P. Smith R.N., Chief Nursing Officer, and Vice President Patient Care Services
Web address: www.morehead.org
Control: Other not–for–profit (including NFP Corporation) **Service:** General medical and surgical

Staffed Beds: 188 **Admissions:** 3335 **Census:** 132 **Outpatient Visits:** 171858 **Births:** 524 **Total Expense ($000):** 80167 **Payroll Expense ($000):** 31460 **Personnel:** 522

Hospital, Medicare Provider Number, Address, Telephone, Approval, Facility, and Physician Codes, Health Care System

★ American Hospital Association (AHA) membership
☐ The Joint Commission accreditation
○ Healthcare Facilities Accreditation Program
◇ DNV Healthcare Inc. accreditation
⇑ Center for Improvement in Healthcare Quality Accreditation
△ Commission on Accreditation of Rehabilitation Facilities (CARF) accreditation

NC

EDENTON—Chowan County

☒ **VIDANT CHOWAN HOSPITAL (341318)**, 211 Virginia Road, Zip 27932–9668; Mailing Address: P.O.Box 629, 27932–0629; tel. 252/482–8451 **A**1 3 10 18 **F**3 11 13 15 18 19 28 29 30 31 34 35 40 45 46 57 59 64 70 74 75 76 77 78 79 81 82 85 93 107 108 110 111 114 119 130 132 135 146 147 148 **S** Vidant Health, Greenville, NC
Primary Contact: Jeffrey Sackrison, President
CFO: Brian Harvill, Vice President Financial Services
CMO: William Hope IV, Chief of Medical Staff
CIO: Brian White, Director Strategic Operations
CHR: Nicole Spell, Director Human Resources
CNO: Cindy Coker, Vice President, Patient Care Services
Web address: www.vidanthealth.com
Control: Other not–for–profit (including NFP Corporation) **Service:** General medical and surgical

Staffed Beds: 19 **Admissions:** 1479 **Census:** 14 **Outpatient Visits:** 41957 **Births:** 322 **Total Expense ($000):** 41734 **Payroll Expense ($000):** 14860 **Personnel:** 312	

ELIZABETH CITY—Pasquotank County

★ ⇑ **SENTARA ALBEMARLE MEDICAL CENTER (340109)**, 1144 North Road Street, Zip 27909–3473, Mailing Address: P.O.Box 1587, 27906–1587; tel. 252/335–0531 **A**10 21 **F**3 11 13 15 17 18 20 22 28 29 30 31 34 35 36 37 38 39 40 41 44 45 46 47 48 49 50 51 53 54 55 56 57 58 59 60 61 64 65 68 70 74 75 76 77 78 79 81 84 85 86 87 91 92 93 94 96 100 102 103 107 108 110 111 114 116 117 118 119 126 129 130 131 132 135 142 144 145 146 147 148 149 **P**6 **S** Sentara Healthcare, Norfolk, VA
Primary Contact: Coleen F. Santa Ana, President
CFO: Craig Lewis, Chief Financial Officer
CMO: Charles Nicholson, Vice President, Medical Affairs
CHR: Deborah Ferguson, Director, Human Resources
CNO: Jaime Carroll R.N., Vice President Nursing
Web address: www.albemarlehealth.org
Control: Other not–for–profit (including NFP Corporation) **Service:** General medical and surgical

Staffed Beds: 83 **Admissions:** 5303 **Census:** 59 **Outpatient Visits:** 128929 **Births:** 563 **Total Expense ($000):** 100027 **Payroll Expense ($000):** 36049 **Personnel:** 663	

ELIZABETHTOWN—Bladen County

BLADEN COUNTY HOSPITAL See Cape Fear Valley – Bladen County Hospital

☒ **CAPE FEAR VALLEY – BLADEN COUNTY HOSPITAL (341315)**, 501 South Poplar Street, Zip 28337–9375, Mailing Address: P.O.Box 398, 28337–0398; tel. 910/862–5100, (Nonreporting) **A**1 10 18 **S** Cape Fear Valley Health System, Fayetteville, NC
Primary Contact: Roxie Cannon. Wells, M.D., Chief Executive Officer
CFO: Stephen Fife, Chief Financial Officer
CMO: Pearly Graham Hoskins M.D., President Medical Staff
CIO: Craig Kellum, Director Management Information Systems
CHR: Ginger Parks, Director Human Resources
CNO: Diana Harris, Chief Nursing Officer
Web address: www.bchn.org
Control: County, Government, Nonfederal **Service:** General medical and surgical

Staffed Beds: 25	

ELKIN—Surry County

☒ **HUGH CHATHAM MEMORIAL HOSPITAL (340097)**, 180 Parkwood Drive, Zip 28621–2430, Mailing Address: P.O.Box 560, 28621–0560; tel. 336/527–7000 **A**1 10 **F**3 11 13 15 28 29 30 34 40 45 49 53 57 59 62 64 70 74 75 76 77 79 81 85 87 93 96 107 108 110 111 118 119 120 121 125 127 130 131 132 133 135 144 146 147 148 149 **P**6 **S** Alliant Management Services, Louisville, KY
Primary Contact: Paul Hammes, Chief Executive Officer
COO: Mary Blackburn, Vice President Operations and Chief Practice Officer
CFO: Donald E Trippel, Chief Financial Officer
CMO: Dominick Carbone M.D., Chief of Staff
CIO: Lee Powe, Director Management Information Systems
CHR: Kathy Poteate, Interim Director Human Resources
CNO: Paula Moore R.N., Chief Clinical Officer
Web address: www.hughchatham.org
Control: Other not–for–profit (including NFP Corporation) **Service:** General medical and surgical

Staffed Beds: 81 **Admissions:** 4095 **Census:** 42 **Outpatient Visits:** 72307 **Births:** 523 **Total Expense ($000):** 63619 **Payroll Expense ($000):** 22941 **Personnel:** 707	

FAYETTEVILLE—Cumberland County

☒ △ **CAPE FEAR VALLEY MEDICAL CENTER (340028)**, 1638 Owen Drive, Zip 28304–3431, Mailing Address: P.O.Box 2000, 28302–2000; tel. 910/615–4000, (Includes BEHAVIORAL HEALTH CARE OF CAPE FEAR VALLEY HEALTH SYSTEM, 711 Executive Place, Fayetteville, North Carolina, Zip 28301, tel. 910/615–3700; CAPE FEAR VALLEY REHABILITATION CENTER, 1638 Owen Drive, Fayetteville, North Carolina, Zip 28304, tel. 910/615–4000) **A**1 2 3 5 7 10 12 13 **F**3 4 5 7 12 13 14 15 17 18 20 22 24 26 28 29 30 31 34 35 38 39 40 41 43 44 46 49 53 54 55 56 57 59 60 61 64 65 68 70 72 73 74 75 76 77 78 79 81 82 85 86 87 88 89 90 91 92 93 96 97 98 99 100 101 102 103 104 105 106 107 108 109 110 111 114 115 116 117 118 119 120 121 122 123 124 126 127 129 130 132 135 143 144 146 147 148 149 150 **P**6 **S** Cape Fear Valley Health System, Fayetteville, NC
Primary Contact: Michael Nagowski, Chief Executive Officer
COO: Daniel R Weatherly, Chief Operating Officer
CFO: Sandra Williams, Chief Financial Officer
CMO: Samuel A Fleishman M.D., Chief Medical Officer
CIO: Phillip E. Wood Jr, Chief Information Officer
CHR: William B Pryor, Chief Human Resources Officer
CNO: Deborah Marshburn R.N., Chief Nursing Executive
Web address: www.capefearvalley.com
Control: Other not–for–profit (including NFP Corporation) **Service:** General medical and surgical

Staffed Beds: 612 **Admissions:** 30663 **Census:** 428 **Outpatient Visits:** 260242 **Births:** 4678 **Total Expense ($000):** 642856 **Payroll Expense ($000):** 316193 **Personnel:** 4560	

☒ **FAYETTEVILLE VETERANS AFFAIRS MEDICAL CENTER**, 2300 Ramsey Street, Zip 28301–3899; tel. 910/488–2120, (Nonreporting) **A**1 3 5 **S** Department of Veterans Affairs, Washington, DC
Primary Contact: Elizabeth Goolsby, Director
COO: James Galkowski, Associate Director for Operations
CFO: Patrick Bullard, Chief Financial Officer
CMO: Greg Antoine M.D., Chief of Staff
CIO: Kenneth Williams, Chief Information Officer
CHR: Joseph Whaley, Chief, Human Resources Management Service
CNO: Joyce Alexander–Hines R.N., MSN, Associate Director, Patient Care Services
Web address: www.fayettevillenc.va.gov
Control: Veterans Affairs, Government, federal **Service:** General medical and surgical

Staffed Beds: 58	

☐ **HIGHSMITH–RAINEY SPECIALTY HOSPITAL (342014)**, 150 Robeson Street, Zip 28301–5570; tel. 910/615–1000 **A**1 10 **F**1 3 11 29 30 35 39 50 51 58 68 70 81 85 107 114 119 130 144 146 148 149 150 **P**6 **S** Cape Fear Valley Health System, Fayetteville, NC
Primary Contact: Kevin Jackson, On Site Administrator
Web address: www.capefearvalley.com
Control: Other not–for–profit (including NFP Corporation) **Service:** Acute long–term care hospital

Staffed Beds: 60 **Admissions:** 303 **Census:** 46 **Outpatient Visits:** 35783 **Births:** 0 **Total Expense ($000):** 36857 **Payroll Expense ($000):** 21255 **Personnel:** 305	

VETERANS AFFAIRS MEDICAL CENTER See Fayetteville Veterans Affairs Medical Center

FORT BRAGG—Cumberland County

☒ **WOMACK ARMY MEDICAL CENTER**, 2817 Reilly Road, Zip 28310–7302; tel. 910/907–6000, (Nonreporting) **A**1 3 5 **S** Department of the Army, Office of the Surgeon General, Falls Church, VA
Primary Contact: Colonel Lance C. Raney, Commander
CIO: Mary Peters, Chief Information Officer
Web address: www.wamc.amedd.army.mil/
Control: Army, Government, federal **Service:** General medical and surgical

Staffed Beds: 156	

FRANKLIN—Macon County

☒ **ANGEL MEDICAL CENTER (341326)**, 120 Riverview Street, Zip 28734–2612, Mailing Address: P.O.Box 1209, 28744–0569; tel. 828/524–8411 **A**1 3 10 18 **F**3 11 13 15 18 28 29 30 31 34 35 40 44 45 47 49 50 54 57 59 64 70 77 78 79 81 85 86 87 93 96 97 107 108 110 111 114 119 127 130 131 132 133 135 144 146 147 148 149 **S** Mission Health System, Asheville, NC
Primary Contact: Karen S. Gorby, R.N., MSN, FACHE, President and Chief Nursing Officer
COO: Martin Wadewitz, Chief Operations Officer/ Vice President, Operations
CFO: George Kimbro, Vice President Finance
CIO: Ed Coye, Director Information Technology Mission Health System Hospitals
CHR: Teresa Mallonee, Director Human Resources
Web address: www.angelmed.org
Control: Other not–for–profit (including NFP Corporation) **Service:** General medical and surgical

Staffed Beds: 43 **Admissions:** 1950 **Census:** 18 **Outpatient Visits:** 118225 **Births:** 400 **Total Expense ($000):** 59343 **Payroll Expense ($000):** 15645 **Personnel:** 330	

NC

Many Facility Codes have changed. Please refer to the AHA Guide Code Chart. © 2017 AHA Guide

GARNER—Wake County

☐ **STRATEGIC BEHAVIORAL HEALTH – RALEIGH (344028)**, 3200 Waterfield Drive, Zip 27529–7727; tel. 919/800–4400 (Nonreporting) **A**1 10 **S** Strategic Behavioral Health, LLC, Memphis, TN
Primary Contact: Matt Doyle, Chief Executive Officer
CMO: Karen Miles M.D., Medical Director
CHR: Christina Meeker, Director Human Resources
CNO: Shawanna Royal R.N., Director Nursing
Web address: www.sbcraleigh.com/
Control: Corporation, Investor–owned (for–profit) **Service**: Children's hospital psychiatric

Staffed Beds: 50

GASTONIA—Gaston County

⊞ **CAROMONT REGIONAL MEDICAL CENTER (340032)**, 2525 Court Drive, Zip 28054–2140, Mailing Address: P.O.Box 1747, 28053–1747; tel. 704/834–2000 **A**1 2 10 **F**3 13 15 17 18 20 22 24 26 28 29 30 31 34 35 40 41 42 43 44 45 46 48 49 50 53 54 55 57 58 59 60 64 68 70 71 72 73 74 75 76 78 79 81 82 83 84 87 89 91 92 93 94 96 98 99 100 101 102 104 107 108 110 111 114 115 116 117 118 119 120 121 123 124 126 129 130 131 132 135 146 147 148 **P**4
Primary Contact: Chris Peek, Chief Executive Officer
COO: Kathleen Besson, Executive Vice President and Chief Operating Officer
CFO: David O'Connor, Executive Vice President and Chief Financial Officer
CMO: Todd Davis M.D., Vice President Medical Affairs, Patient Safety Officer
CIO: Mike Johnson, Vice President, Chief Information Officer
CHR: Elizabeth McCraw, Vice President, Human Resources
CNO: Scott E Wells MSN, R.N., Vice President Patient Care Services
Web address: www.caromont.org
Control: Other not–for–profit (including NFP Corporation) **Service**: General medical and surgical

Staffed Beds: 423 **Admissions**: 20684 **Census**: 258 **Outpatient Visits**: 399145 **Births**: 2001 **Total Expense ($000)**: 375958 **Payroll Expense ($000)**: 150446 **Personnel**: 2914

GASTON MEMORIAL HOSPITAL See Caromont Regional Medical Center

GOLDSBORO—Wayne County

☐ **CHERRY HOSPITAL (344026)**, 1401 West Ash Street, Zip 27530–1057; tel. 919/947–7000 **A**1 3 10 **F**30 39 98 99 103 130 143 146
Primary Contact: J. Luckey. Welsh Jr, Chief Executive Officer
CFO: Susie Sherrod Sanders, Chief Financial Officer
CMO: Jim Mayo M.D., Clinical Director
CIO: Mike Letchworth, Manager Information Systems
CHR: Carol Thornton, Director Human Resources
CNO: Debbie Wall, Chief Nursing Officer
Web address: www.cherryhospital.org
Control: State, Government, Nonfederal **Service**: Psychiatric

Staffed Beds: 197 **Admissions**: 607 **Census**: 175 **Outpatient Visits**: 441 **Births**: 0 **Total Expense ($000)**: 82344 **Payroll Expense ($000)**: 51598 **Personnel**: 1006

⊞ **WAYNE MEMORIAL HOSPITAL (340010)**, 2700 Wayne Memorial Drive, Zip 27534–9494, Mailing Address: P.O.Box 8001, 27533–8001; tel. 919/736–1110, (Data for 274 days)**A**1 10 **F**3 8 13 15 18 20 22 28 29 30 31 34 35 39 40 47 49 50 57 58 59 60 64 65 68 70 71 73 74 76 77 78 79 80 81 85 86 89 92 93 96 98 100 101 102 103 107 108 110 111 114 118 119 126 129 130 132 134 135 142 143 145 146 147 148 149 **P**6 **S** UNC Health Care, Chapel Hill, NC
Primary Contact: Janie Jaberg, FACHE, President and Chief Executive Officer
COO: Thomas A Bradshaw, Vice President Operations
CFO: Rebecca W Craig, Vice President and Chief Financial Officer
CIO: Lori Cole, Director Information Technology
CHR: Richard K Rogers, FACHE, SPHR, CHHR FACHE, Vice President Human Resources
CNO: Shirley S Harkey, FACHE R.N., Vice President, Patient Services
Web address: www.waynehealth.org
Control: Other not–for–profit (including NFP Corporation) **Service**: General medical and surgical

Staffed Beds: 274 **Admissions**: 8047 **Census**: 134 **Outpatient Visits**: 111234 **Births**: 998 **Total Expense ($000)**: 165658 **Payroll Expense ($000)**: 63789 **Personnel**: 1619

GREENSBORO—Guilford County

⊞ **KINDRED HOSPITAL–GREENSBORO (342012)**, 2401 Southside Boulevard, Zip 27406–3311; tel. 336/271–2800 **A**1 10 **F**1 3 29 30 35 39 75 77 81 91 105 107 114 130 **S** Kindred Healthcare, Louisville, KY
Primary Contact: Chad Lovett, Chief Executive Officer
CFO: Anthony Grate, Controller
CMO: Saad Amin, Medical Director Hospital
CIO: Little Shuford, Health Information Manager
CNO: Anne Correll, Chief Clinical Officer
Web address: www.khgreensboro.com
Control: Corporation, Investor–owned (for–profit) **Service**: Acute long–term care hospital

Staffed Beds: 101 **Admissions**: 586 **Census**: 56 **Births**: 0 **Total Expense ($000)**: 30417 **Payroll Expense ($000)**: 11681

⊞ △ **MOSES H. CONE MEMORIAL HOSPITAL (340091)**, 1200 North Elm Street, Zip 27401–1020; tel. 336/832–7000, (Includes ANNIE PENN HOSPITAL, 618 South Main Street, Reidsville, North Carolina, Zip 27320–5094, tel. 336/951–4000; Cynthia B Farrand, President; BEHAVIORAL HEALTH CENTER, 700 Walter Reed Drive, Greensboro, North Carolina, Zip 27403–1129, tel. 336/832–9600; Debbie Cunningham, R.N., Senior Vice President, Cone Health and President, Maternal, Child and Behavioral Health Services; CONE HEALTH, 1200 North Elm Street, Greensboro, North Carolina, Zip 27401, tel. 336/832–7000; Judith A Schanel, R.N., MSN, FACHE, Chief Operating Officer; WESLEY LONG COMMUNITY HOSPITAL, 501 North Elam Avenue, Greensboro, North Carolina, Zip 27403, tel. 336/832–1000; Paul A Jeffrey, President; WOMEN'S HOSPITAL OF GREENSBORO, 801 Green Valley Road, Greensboro, North Carolina, Zip 27408, tel. 336/832–6500; Debbie Cunningham, R.N., President) (Total facility includes 92 beds in nursing home–type unit) **A**1 2 3 5 7 10 **F**3 5 7 8 11 12 13 15 17 18 19 20 22 24 26 28 29 30 31 32 34 35 36 37 39 40 41 42 43 44 45 46 47 49 50 54 55 56 57 58 59 60 61 63 64 66 68 70 72 74 75 76 77 78 79 80 81 82 83 84 85 86 87 88 89 90 92 93 95 96 97 98 99 100 101 102 103 104 105 107 108 111 114 115 117 118 119 120 121 123 124 126 128 129 130 131 132 134 135 144 145 146 147 148 **P**8 **S** Cone Health, Greensboro, NC
Primary Contact: Mickey Foster, President
CFO: Jeffrey Jones, Chief Financial Officer
CMO: William Bowman M.D., Vice President Medical Affairs
CIO: Steve Horsley, Vice President and Chief Information Officer
CHR: Noel F Burt Ph.D., Chief Human Resources Officer
CNO: Ann Marie Madden R.N., Vice President of Patient Care Services and Chief Nursing Officer
Web address: www.conehealth.com/locations/moses-cone-hospital/
Control: Other not–for–profit (including NFP Corporation) **Service**: General medical and surgical

Staffed Beds: 935 **Admissions**: 51578 **Census**: 663 **Outpatient Visits**: 835374 **Births**: 5990 **Total Expense ($000)**: 1308815 **Payroll Expense ($000)**: 472429 **Personnel**: 8848

⊞ **SELECT SPECIALTY HOSPITAL–GREENSBORO (342020)**, 1200 North Elm Street, 5th Floor, Zip 27401–1004; tel. 336/832–8571, (Nonreporting) **A**1 10 **S** Select Medical Corporation, Mechanicsburg, PA
Primary Contact: Deana Knight, Chief Executive Officer
CHR: Karen Tracey, Chief Human Resources
CNO: Robin Clark, Chief Nursing Officer
Web address: www.selectspecialtyhospitals.com/company/locations/greensboro.aspx
Control: Corporation, Investor–owned (for–profit) **Service**: Acute long–term care hospital

Staffed Beds: 30

GREENVILLE—Pitt County

PITT COUNTY MEMORIAL HOSPITAL See Vidant Medical Center

⊞ △ **VIDANT MEDICAL CENTER (340040)**, 2100 Stantonsburg Road, Zip 27834–2818, Mailing Address: P.O.Box 6028, 27835–6028; tel. 252/847–4100, (Includes JAMES AND CONNIE MAYNARD CHILDREN'S HOSPITAL, 2101 Stantonsburg Road, Greenville, North Carolina, Zip 27834–2817, tel. 252/847–5712; UNIVERSITY HEALTH SYSTEMS CHILDREN'S HOSPITAL, 2100 Stantonsburg Road, Greenville, North Carolina, Zip 27834–2818, PO Box 6028, 27835–6028, tel. 252/847–4100) **A**1 2 3 5 7 8 10 **F**3 7 12 13 14 17 18 19 20 21 22 23 24 25 26 27 29 30 31 34 35 38 40 41 42 43 44 45 46 47 48 49 50 51 52 55 56 57 58 59 60 61 64 65 68 70 72 73 74 75 76 77 78 79 80 81 82 83 84 85 86 87 88 89 90 92 93 94 95 96 97 98 100 101 102 103 104 107 108 111 114 115 116 117 118 119 124 126 129 130 131 132 134 135 138 139 143 145 146 147 148 149 150 **P**6 **S** Vidant Health, Greenville, NC
Primary Contact: William Brian. Floyd, President
CFO: David S Hughes, Chief Financial Officer
CMO: Paul Shackelford M.D., Chief Medical Officer
CIO: Donnette Herring, Chief Information Officer
CHR: Tyree Walker, Chief Human Resources Officer
CNO: Linda D Hofler Ph.D., R.N., FACHE, Senior Vice President, Nurse Executive
Web address: www.vidanthealth.com/
Control: Other not–for–profit (including NFP Corporation) **Service**: General medical and surgical

Staffed Beds: 909 **Admissions**: 37733 **Census**: 656 **Outpatient Visits**: 407301 **Births**: 3790 **Total Expense ($000)**: 977315 **Payroll Expense ($000)**: 347404 **Personnel**: 6188

Hospital, Medicare Provider Number, Address, Telephone, Approval, Facility, and Physician Codes, Health Care System

★ American Hospital Association (AHA) membership   ○ Healthcare Facilities Accreditation Program   ⇑ Center for Improvement in Healthcare Quality Accreditation
☐ The Joint Commission accreditation   ◇ DNV Healthcare Inc. accreditation   △ Commission on Accreditation of Rehabilitation Facilities (CARF) accreditation

NC

WALTER B. JONES ALCOHOL AND DRUG ABUSE TREATMENT CENTER (344024), 2577 West Fifth Street, Zip 27834–7813; tel. 252/830–3426, (Nonreporting) **A**3 10
Primary Contact: Ben Gregory, Chief Executive Officer
CFO: Roy Carlton, Chief Financial Officer
CMO: Sonya Longest M.D., Chief Medical Officer
CIO: Jed Hayn, Chief Information Officer
CHR: Amy Marion, Chief Human Resource Officer
CNO: Linda Roy R.N., Chief Nursing Officer
Web address: www.ncdhhs.gov
Control: State, Government, Nonfederal **Service:** Alcoholism and other chemical dependency

Staffed Beds: 80

HAMLET—Richmond County

FIRSTHEALTH MOORE REGIONAL HOSPITAL – HAMLET (340106), 1000 West Hamlet Avenue, Zip 28345–4522, Mailing Address: P.O.Box 1109, 28345–1109; tel. 910/205–8000, (Nonreporting) **A**1 10 **S** FirstHealth of the Carolinas, Pinehurst, NC
Primary Contact: John J. Jackson, Chief Executive Officer
CFO: Patrick Sloan, Chief Financial Officer
CMO: Charlita Mangrum M.D., Chief of Staff
CIO: Regina Yingling, Supervisor
CHR: Della Connor, Director Human Resource
CNO: Brenda Ewing, Chief Nursing Officer
Web address: www.sandhillsregional.com
Control: Corporation, Investor–owned (for–profit) **Service:** General medical and surgical

Staffed Beds: 64

HENDERSON—Vance County

MARIA PARHAM MEDICAL CENTER (340132), 566 Ruin Creek Road, Zip 27536–2927; tel. 252/438–4143 **A**1 2 3 10 **F**3 11 13 15 18 20 28 29 30 31 34 39 40 44 45 46 48 49 50 54 57 59 60 64 68 70 74 75 76 77 78 79 81 82 85 86 87 90 91 92 93 94 96 97 102 107 108 110 111 114 118 119 120 121 123 129 130 131 132 135 146 147 148 **P**6 **S** Duke LifePoint Healthcare, Brentwood, TN
Primary Contact: Bert Beard, Chief Executive Officer
CFO: Jim Chatman, Chief Financial Officer
CIO: Randy Williams, Director Management Information Systems
Web address: www.mariaparham.com
Control: Corporation, Investor–owned (for–profit) **Service:** General medical and surgical

Staffed Beds: 102 Admissions: 5252 Census: 62 Outpatient Visits: 133545 Births: 521

HENDERSONVILLE—Henderson County

★ ⇑ **MARGARET R. PARDEE MEMORIAL HOSPITAL (340017)**, 800 North Justice Street, Zip 28791–3410; tel. 828/696–1000 **A**2 3 10 21 **F**3 4 5 11 13 15 18 22 28 29 30 31 34 35 36 38 39 40 44 45 46 47 48 49 50 54 56 57 58 59 62 63 65 68 69 70 74 75 76 77 78 79 81 82 85 86 87 89 93 94 97 98 100 101 102 103 104 107 108 110 111 114 115 118 119 120 121 123 129 130 131 132 135 143 144 146 147 148 149 **P**6 **S** UNC Health Care, Chapel Hill, NC
Primary Contact: James M. Kirby II, President and Chief Executive Officer
CFO: Andrew Wampler, Chief Financial Officer
CMO: Robert Kiskaddon M.D., Chief Medical Officer
CHR: Hope Reynolds, Vice President, Human Resources and Service Excellence
CNO: Denise Lucas R.N., MSN, Vice President Clinical Services and Chief Nursing Officer
Web address: www.pardeehospital.org
Control: County, Government, Nonfederal **Service:** General medical and surgical

Staffed Beds: 142 Admissions: 7647 Census: 79 Outpatient Visits: 272984 Births: 328 Total Expense ($000): 205012 Payroll Expense ($000): 72019 Personnel: 1165

PARK RIDGE HEALTH (340023), 100 Hospital Drive, Zip 28792–5272; tel. 828/684–8501 **A**1 2 3 10 11 19 **F**3 11 13 15 18 26 28 29 30 31 32 34 35 39 40 45 46 47 48 49 50 54 59 62 65 68 70 71 74 75 76 77 78 79 80 81 82 85 87 93 97 98 101 102 103 104 105 107 108 110 111 114 115 117 118 119 129 130 131 132 135 142 146 147 148 **P**6 **S** Adventist Health System Sunbelt Health Care Corporation, Altamonte Springs, FL
Primary Contact: Jimm Bunch, President and Chief Executive Officer
CFO: Wendi Barber, Vice President Finance and Chief Financial Officer
CMO: Carlo Mainardi M.D., Vice President Medical Affairs and Chief Medical Officer
CIO: Lee Strickland, Regional Director Information Technology
CHR: Sharon J Campbell, Director, Human Resources
CNO: Roland Eugene Joy Jr, Vice President and Chief Nursing Officer
Web address: www.parkridgehealth.org
Control: Other not–for–profit (including NFP Corporation) **Service:** General medical and surgical

Staffed Beds: 95 Admissions: 3839 Census: 49 Outpatient Visits: 337751 Births: 647 Total Expense ($000): 155187 Payroll Expense ($000): 64562 Personnel: 1080

HICKORY—Catawba County

⊞ △ **CATAWBA VALLEY MEDICAL CENTER (340143)**, 810 Fairgrove Church Road SE, Zip 28602–9643; tel. 828/326–3000 **A**1 2 5 7 10 **F**3 11 12 13 15 18 20 22 26 28 29 30 31 33 34 35 39 40 44 45 49 50 51 53 54 56 57 58 59 61 64 65 68 70 71 73 74 75 76 77 78 79 81 84 85 86 87 89 90 91 92 93 96 97 98 100 101 102 103 104 107 108 109 110 111 114 115 117 118 119 120 121 122 123 124 126 129 130 131 132 135 143 144 145 146 147 148 149 **P**3 8
Primary Contact: J Anthony. Rose, President and Chief Executive Officer
COO: Edward L Beard R.N., Chief Operating Officer and Chief Nursing Officer
CFO: Kimberly Crews, Vice President and Chief Financial Officer
CMO: Andrew Chesson, Chief Medical Officer
CIO: Tim Blanchat, Chief Information Officer
CHR: Phyllis M Johnston, Vice President
CNO: Edward L Beard R.N., Chief Operating Officer and Chief Nursing Officer
Web address: www.catawbavalleymc.org
Control: County, Government, Nonfederal **Service:** General medical and surgical

Staffed Beds: 250 Admissions: 10704 Census: 140 Outpatient Visits: 235995 Births: 2032 Total Expense ($000): 251254 Payroll Expense ($000): 111138 Personnel: 1575

⊞ **FRYE REGIONAL MEDICAL CENTER (340116)**, 420 North Center Street, Zip 28601–5049; tel. 828/315–5000, (Includes FRYE REGIONAL MEDICAL CENTER–SOUTH CAMPUS, One Third Avenue NW, Hickory, North Carolina, Zip 28601, 420 North Center St., 28603, tel. 828/315–5777) **A**1 2 10 **F**3 11 12 13 15 17 18 20 22 24 26 28 29 30 31 34 35 37 40 44 45 46 49 54 57 59 64 70 72 74 75 76 77 78 79 81 82 85 86 87 89 90 93 96 98 101 103 107 108 110 111 114 115 118 119 128 129 130 131 132 144 146 147 148 **P**6 **S** Duke LifePoint Healthcare, Brentwood, TN
Primary Contact: Garfield Atchison, Chief Executive Officer
COO: Chris Fensterle, Chief Operating Officer
CFO: Jamey Stoner, Chief Financial Officer
CNO: Michelle Dickerson, Chief Nursing Officer
Web address: www.fryemedctr.com
Control: Corporation, Investor–owned (for–profit) **Service:** General medical and surgical

Staffed Beds: 256 Admissions: 10916 Census: 168 Outpatient Visits: 97579 Personnel: 1374

HIGH POINT—Guilford County

⊞ △ **HIGH POINT REGIONAL HEALTH SYSTEM (340004)**, 601 North Elm Street, Zip 27262–4398, Mailing Address: P.O.Box HP–5, 27261–1899; tel. 336/878–6000 **A**1 7 10 **F**3 4 5 7 8 11 12 13 15 17 18 20 22 24 26 28 29 30 34 35 38 39 40 44 45 47 48 49 50 51 53 54 55 57 58 59 60 61 62 64 66 68 70 71 73 74 75 76 77 78 79 80 81 82 84 85 86 87 90 91 92 93 96 97 98 100 101 102 103 104 105 107 108 109 110 111 114 115 118 119 120 121 123 124 126 129 130 131 132 135 144 145 146 147 148 149 150 **P**6 **S** UNC Health Care, Chapel Hill, NC
Primary Contact: Ernest L. Bovio Jr, Chief Executive Officer
COO: Gregory W Taylor M.D., Vice President and Chief Operating Officer
CMO: L Dale Williams M.D., Vice President and Chief Medical Director
CIO: Nancy Waters, Interim Chief Information Officer
CHR: Katherine Burns, Vice President Human Resources
CNO: Tammi Erving–Mengel R.N., MSN, Vice President, Chief Nursing Officer
Web address: www.highpointregional.com
Control: Other not–for–profit (including NFP Corporation) **Service:** General medical and surgical

Staffed Beds: 335 Admissions: 15826 Census: 187 Outpatient Visits: 248668 Births: 1438 Total Expense ($000): 258928 Payroll Expense ($000): 96041 Personnel: 2243

HIGHLANDS—Macon County

⊞ **HIGHLANDS–CASHIERS HOSPITAL (341316)**, 190 Hospital Drive, Zip 28741–7600, Mailing Address: P O Drawer 190, 28741–0190; tel. 828/526–1200, (Total facility includes 80 beds in nursing home–type unit) **A**1 10 18 **F**3 11 15 28 29 30 34 35 40 45 46 47 48 53 56 57 59 64 65 74 75 77 79 81 91 97 107 108 110 111 113 119 128 130 133 146 **P**6 **S** Mission Health System, Asheville, NC
Primary Contact: Jacqueline Medland, MS, Ph.D., President and Chief Nursing Officer
CFO: Lena Cochran, Director of Finance
CHR: Ruby Rowland, Strategic Partner
CNO: Cindy Pierson, Interim Chief Nursing Officer
Web address: www.hchospital.org
Control: Other not–for–profit (including NFP Corporation) **Service:** General medical and surgical

Staffed Beds: 104 Admissions: 355 Census: 65 Outpatient Visits: 34830 Births: 0 Total Expense ($000): 22317 Payroll Expense ($000): 5827 Personnel: 88

NC

Many Facility Codes have changed. Please refer to the AHA Guide Code Chart. © 2017 AHA Guide

HUNTERSVILLE—Mecklenburg County

⊞ **NOVANT HEALTH HUNTERSVILLE MEDICAL CENTER (340183)**, 10030 Gilead Road, Zip 28078–7545, Mailing Address: P.O.Box 3508, 28070–3508; tel. 704/316–4000 **A**1 2 3 10 13 **F**3 13 18 26 29 30 31 34 35 40 45 49 50 57 59 63 67 68 70 72 74 75 76 77 78 79 81 84 85 86 87 92 93 102 107 108 111 115 118 119 126 130 135 145 146 147 **S** Novant Health, Winston Salem, NC
Primary Contact: Mike Riley, President and Chief Operating Officer
CFO: Fred M Hargett, Executive Vice President and Chief Financial Officer
CMO: Thomas Zweng, Executive Vice President and Chief Medical Officer
CIO: David B Garrett, Senior Vice President and Chief Information Officer
CHR: Janet Smith–Hill, Executive Vice President and Chief Human Resources
CNO: Katrina King R.N., Senior Director, Nursing
Web address: www.novanthealth.org
Control: Other not–for–profit (including NFP Corporation) **Service**: General medical and surgical

Staffed Beds: 91 **Admissions:** 6664 **Census:** 61 **Outpatient Visits:** 140707 **Births:** 1459 **Total Expense ($000):** 121619 **Payroll Expense ($000):** 34464 **Personnel:** 523

JACKSONVILLE—Onslow County

☐ **BRYNN MARR HOSPITAL (344016)**, 192 Village Drive, Zip 28546–7299; tel. 910/577–1400, (Nonreporting) **A**1 10 **S** Universal Health Services, Inc., King of Prussia, PA
Primary Contact: Jay Kortemeyer, Chief Executive Officer
CFO: David Warmerdam, Chief Financial Officer
CMO: Ashraf Mikhail M.D., Medical Director
CIO: Amy Black, Risk Manager/PI Director
CHR: Jennifer Gier, Director Human Resources
CNO: Sheila Maraan, Director of Nursing
Web address: www.brynnmarr.org
Control: Corporation, Investor–owned (for–profit) **Service**: Psychiatric

Staffed Beds: 99

⊞ **ONSLOW MEMORIAL HOSPITAL (340042)**, 317 Western Boulevard, Zip 28546–6379, Mailing Address: P.O.Box 1358, 28541–1358; tel. 910/577–2345 **A**1 2 10 20 **F**3 8 11 13 15 19 20 28 29 34 35 40 45 46 47 48 49 54 57 59 60 64 68 70 72 73 75 76 77 79 81 82 84 85 86 87 89 93 96 107 108 110 111 114 115 117 118 119 126 131 132 135 146 147 148 **P**7
Primary Contact: Penney Burlingame Deal, FACHE, R.N., Chief Executive Officer
CFO: Roy Smith, Chief Financial Officer
CMO: Scott Johnston, Chief of Staff
CIO: Rob Lowe, Director, Healthcare Information Management
CHR: Taylor Flowers, Senior Vice President Human Resources
CNO: Regina Lanier R.N., Senior Vice President and Chief Nursing Officer
Web address: www.onslow.org
Control: Hospital district or authority, Government, Nonfederal **Service**: General medical and surgical

Staffed Beds: 149 **Admissions:** 7074 **Census:** 80 **Outpatient Visits:** 139157 **Births:** 1566 **Total Expense ($000):** 137777 **Payroll Expense ($000):** 51165 **Personnel:** 922

JEFFERSON—Ashe County

⊞ **ASHE MEMORIAL HOSPITAL (341325)**, 200 Hospital Avenue, Zip 28640–9244; tel. 336/846–7101 **A**1 10 18 **F**3 11 13 15 28 30 31 34 35 40 45 48 56 57 59 64 75 76 77 78 79 80 81 85 86 89 91 93 102 107 108 110 111 114 118 119 127 130 132 133 135 141 142 146 147 **S** Novant Health, Winston Salem, NC
Primary Contact: Laura Lambeth, Chief Executive Officer
COO: Joe Thore, Chief Operating Officer
CFO: Charles Wright, Chief Financial Officer
CMO: Jayne Leonard M.D., Family Medicine
CIO: William Baldwin, Chief Information Officer
CHR: Lana Smith, Human Resources Director
CNO: Sara Houser, Chief Nursing Officer
Web address: www.ashememorial.org
Control: Other not–for–profit (including NFP Corporation) **Service**: General medical and surgical

Staffed Beds: 25 **Admissions:** 1197 **Census:** 11 **Outpatient Visits:** 71176 **Births:** 120 **Total Expense ($000):** 28781 **Payroll Expense ($000):** 13603 **Personnel:** 266

KENANSVILLE—Duplin County

⊞ **VIDANT DUPLIN HOSPITAL (340120)**, 401 North Main Street, Zip 28349–8801, Mailing Address: P.O.Box 278, 28349–0278; tel. 910/296–0941 **A**1 10 **F**3 11 13 15 18 19 29 30 31 34 35 39 40 45 56 57 59 68 70 75 76 77 78 79 81 91 93 97 98 101 102 103 107 108 110 111 115 119 129 130 131 132 135 146 147 **S** Vidant Health, Greenville, NC
Primary Contact: Jay Briley, President
COO: Matthew Gitzinger, Director of Operations
CFO: Lucinda Crawford, Vice President Financial Services
CMO: Dyrek Miller M.D., Chief Medical Staff
CIO: Lucinda Crawford, Vice President Financial Services
CHR: Pansy Chase, Director Human Resources
CNO: Sue O. Taylor, Vice President Nursing
Web address: www.vidanthealth.com
Control: Other not–for–profit (including NFP Corporation) **Service**: General medical and surgical

Staffed Beds: 48 **Admissions:** 3179 **Census:** 44 **Outpatient Visits:** 47549 **Births:** 496 **Total Expense ($000):** 46149 **Payroll Expense ($000):** 18704 **Personnel:** 404

KINGS MOUNTAIN—Cleveland County

★ **CAROLINAS CONTINUECARE HOSPITAL AT KINGS MOUNTAIN (342019)**, 706 West King Street, 2nd Floor, Zip 28086–2708, Mailing Address: P.O.Box 159, 28086–0159; tel. 980/487–5520 **F**1 3 29 34 35 59 86 87 130 148 **S** Community Hospital Corporation, Plano, TX
Primary Contact: Derek Murzyn, Chief Executive Officer
CFO: Lisa Young CPA, Chief Financial Officer
Web address: www.continuecare.org/kings–mountain/
Control: Other not–for–profit (including NFP Corporation) **Service**: Acute long–term care hospital

Staffed Beds: 28 **Admissions:** 234 **Census:** 17 **Outpatient Visits:** 0 **Births:** 0 **Total Expense ($000):** 8711 **Payroll Expense ($000):** 3556 **Personnel:** 69

⊞ **CAROLINAS HEALTHCARE SYSTEM KINGS MOUNTAIN (340037)**, 706 West King Street, Zip 28086–2708; tel. 980/487–5000 **A**1 10 **F**3 4 15 29 30 34 40 45 49 59 70 79 81 82 85 93 98 107 110 111 115 119 130 133 146 148 149 **S** Carolinas HealthCare System, Charlotte, NC
Primary Contact: Brian Gwyn, President and Chief Executive Officer
CFO: Terry Edwards, Controller
CHR: Debra Kale, Director Human Resources
Web address: www.clevelandregional.org/kings–mountain–hospital.html
Control: Hospital district or authority, Government, Nonfederal **Service**: General medical and surgical

Staffed Beds: 59 **Admissions:** 2675 **Census:** 35 **Outpatient Visits:** 57987 **Births:** 0 **Total Expense ($000):** 39547 **Payroll Expense ($000):** 15107 **Personnel:** 262

KINSTON—Lenoir County

☐ **UNC LENOIR HEALTHCARE (340027)**, 100 Airport Road, Zip 28501–1634, Mailing Address: P.O.Box 1678, 28503–1678; tel. 252/522–7000 **A**1 10 **F**3 8 11 12 13 18 20 22 28 29 30 31 34 35 38 40 43 45 47 48 49 50 53 56 57 59 60 61 64 65 68 70 74 75 76 77 78 79 81 82 85 86 87 89 90 93 102 107 108 111 114 115 118 119 120 121 129 130 131 132 134 135 143 145 146 147 148 **S** UNC Health Care, Chapel Hill, NC
Primary Contact: Gary E. Black, President and Chief Executive Officer
CFO: Sarah Mayo, Vice President Financial Services
CMO: John Herlong, Medical Staff President
CIO: Karl Vanderstouw, Vice President Information Systems
CHR: Jim Dobbins, Vice President Human Resources
CNO: Laurel Molloy, Vice President Nursing and Rehab Services
Web address: www.lenoirmemorial.org
Control: Other not–for–profit (including NFP Corporation) **Service**: General medical and surgical

Staffed Beds: 155 **Admissions:** 5205 **Census:** 71 **Outpatient Visits:** 94392 **Births:** 376 **Total Expense ($000):** 99632 **Payroll Expense ($000):** 43528 **Personnel:** 827

Hospital, Medicare Provider Number, Address, Telephone, Approval, Facility, and Physician Codes, Health Care System

★ American Hospital Association (AHA) membership   ○ Healthcare Facilities Accreditation Program   ⇑ Center for Improvement in Healthcare Quality Accreditation
☐ The Joint Commission accreditation   ◇ DNV Healthcare Inc. accreditation   △ Commission on Accreditation of Rehabilitation Facilities (CARF) accreditation

NC

LAURINBURG—Scotland County

✠ **SCOTLAND HEALTH CARE SYSTEM (340008)**, 500 Lauchwood Drive, Zip 28352–5599; tel. 910/291–7000 **A**1 2 3 10 **F**3 11 13 15 18 28 29 31 34 37 40 45 54 57 59 64 66 70 71 73 74 75 76 77 78 79 81 85 86 87 89 90 92 93 96 97 107 110 111 114 115 119 120 121 123 127 130 132 135 143 144 145 146 147 148 149 **S** Carolinas HealthCare System, Charlotte, NC
Primary Contact: Gregory C. Wood, President and Chief Executive Officer
CFO: Matthew Pracht, Vice President Finance
CMO: Cheryl Davis M.D., Chief Medical Officer
CIO: Gary Liuzzo, Director Information Systems
CHR: Ann Locklear, Vice President, Human Resources
CNO: Camille Utter R.N., Chief Nursing Officer
Web address: www.scotlandhealth.org
Control: Other not–for–profit (including NFP Corporation) **Service**: General medical and surgical

Staffed Beds: 104 **Admissions**: 5096 **Census**: 51 **Outpatient Visits**: 138647 **Births**: 676 **Total Expense ($000)**: 132690 **Payroll Expense ($000)**: 43941 **Personnel**: 927

LELAND—Brunswick County

☐ **STRATEGIC BEHAVIORAL HEALTH – WILMINGTON (344030)**, 2050 Mercantile Drive, Zip 28451–4053; tel. 910/371–2500 **A**1 10 **F**56 98 99 101 103 106 **S** Strategic Behavioral Health, LLC, Memphis, TN
Primary Contact: Daniel Kern, Chief Executive Officer
CHR: Kelly Pace, Director Human Resource
CNO: Brooke Cook, Director of Nursing
Web address: www.sbcwilmington.com/
Control: Corporation, Investor–owned (for–profit) **Service**: Psychiatric

Staffed Beds: 112 **Admissions**: 563 **Census**: 13 **Outpatient Visits**: 0 **Births**: 0 **Total Expense ($000)**: 12543 **Payroll Expense ($000)**: 7622 **Personnel**: 260

LENOIR—Caldwell County

✠ **CALDWELL UNC HEALTH CARE (340041)**, 321 Mulberry Street SW, Zip 28645–5720, Mailing Address: P.O.Box 1890, 28645–1890; tel. 828/757–5100 **A**1 10 **F**3 8 11 13 15 18 20 22 29 31 34 35 37 40 45 46 48 49 50 53 54 55 57 59 64 65 70 75 76 77 78 79 81 82 85 86 87 93 97 107 108 109 110 111 114 119 120 121 122 123 129 132 135 145 146 147 148 149 **P**6 **S** UNC Health Care, Chapel Hill, NC
Primary Contact: Laura J. Easton, President and Chief Executive Officer
COO: Rebecca T Smith, Chief Operating Officer and Chief Nursing Officer
CFO: Shawn Hartley, Chief Financial Officer
CMO: David Lowry M.D., Chief Medical Officer
CIO: Deborah Purcell, Director of Information Technology
CHR: Laura J Easton, President and Chief Executive Officer
CNO: Rebecca T Smith, Chief Operating Officer and Chief Nursing Officer
Web address: www.caldwellmemorial.org
Control: Other not–for–profit (including NFP Corporation) **Service**: General medical and surgical

Staffed Beds: 82 **Admissions**: 3694 **Census**: 48 **Outpatient Visits**: 81879 **Births**: 324 **Total Expense ($000)**: 107431 **Payroll Expense ($000)**: 46392 **Personnel**: 753

LEXINGTON—Davidson County

LEXINGTON MEMORIAL HOSPITAL See Wake Forest Baptist Health–Lexington Medical Center

✠ **WAKE FOREST BAPTIST HEALTH–LEXINGTON MEDICAL CENTER (340096)**, 250 Hospital Drive, Zip 27292–6728, Mailing Address: P.O.Box 1817, 27293–1817; tel. 336/248–5161 **A**1 3 10 **F**3 13 15 18 28 29 30 31 34 35 39 40 45 46 50 57 58 59 61 64 65 68 70 74 75 76 78 79 81 82 85 87 91 92 93 97 102 107 108 110 111 115 119 120 121 123 129 130 131 146 147 148 **S** Wake Forest Baptist Health, Winston–Salem, NC
Primary Contact: William B. James, FACHE, President
CFO: Danny Squires, Vice President and Chief Financial Officer
CMO: Raghava Nagaraj, Chief Medical Officer
CIO: Dee Emon R.N., Chief Information Officer
CNO: Clyde A. Bristow MSN, R.N., III, Senior Director Nursing and Clinical Services, Chief Nursing Officer
Web address: www.lexington.wakehealth.edu
Control: Other not–for–profit (including NFP Corporation) **Service**: General medical and surgical

Staffed Beds: 85 **Admissions**: 3134 **Census**: 25 **Outpatient Visits**: 122364 **Births**: 471 **Total Expense ($000)**: 73618 **Payroll Expense ($000)**: 29858 **Personnel**: 537

LINCOLNTON—Lincoln County

✠ **CAROLINAS HEALTHCARE SYSTEM LINCOLN (340145)**, 433 McAlister Road, Zip 28092–4147, Mailing Address: PO Box 677, 28093–0677; tel. 980/212–2000 **A**1 10 **F**3 8 11 13 15 18 28 29 30 31 34 40 44 45 50 51 57 59 64 68 70 73 74 75 76 77 78 79 81 82 84 85 87 91 93 94 96 107 108 114 115 118 119 129 130 131 132 135 146 148 149 150 **S** Carolinas HealthCare System, Charlotte, NC
Primary Contact: Peter W. Acker, President and Chief Executive Officer
COO: Teresa C Watson, Vice President Administration
CFO: Jarrett L Morris, Controller
CMO: Vineet Goel, Chief Medical Officer
CIO: Jarrett L Morris, Controller and Chief Information Officer
CHR: Lesley Chambless, Assistant Vice President Human Resources
CNO: Elaine S Haynes R.N., MSN, Vice President Patient Services and Chief Nursing Executive
Web address: www.carolinashealthcare.org/lincoln
Control: Hospital district or authority, Government, Nonfederal **Service**: General medical and surgical

Staffed Beds: 101 **Admissions**: 4308 **Census**: 46 **Outpatient Visits**: 99759 **Births**: 467 **Total Expense ($000)**: 101004 **Payroll Expense ($000)**: 32877 **Personnel**: 537

LUMBERTON—Robeson County

★ ⇑ **SOUTHEASTERN HEALTH (340050)**, 300 West 27th Street, Zip 28358–3075, Mailing Address: P.O.Box 1408, 28359–1408; tel. 910/671–5000, (Total facility includes 115 beds in nursing home–type unit) **A**2 10 12 13 21 **F**3 5 7 8 9 12 13 15 17 18 20 22 24 28 29 30 31 34 35 37 40 45 48 49 50 53 54 57 59 60 61 62 63 64 67 68 70 71 72 73 74 75 76 77 78 79 80 81 82 83 84 85 87 89 92 93 98 102 103 107 108 111 112 113 114 115 118 119 120 121 126 127 128 129 130 131 132 135 143 144 146 147 148 **P**6
Primary Contact: Joann Anderson, President and Chief Executive Officer
CFO: C Thomas Johnson III, Vice President Finance and Chief Financial Officer
CMO: Barry Williamson, President Medical Staff
CIO: Eric Harper, Chief Information Officer
CHR: Susan Hayes, Director Human Resources
CNO: Renae Taylor, Chief Nursing Officer
Web address: www.srmc.org
Control: Other not–for–profit (including NFP Corporation) **Service**: General medical and surgical

Staffed Beds: 385 **Admissions**: 15529 **Census**: 301 **Outpatient Visits**: 425568 **Births**: 1415 **Total Expense ($000)**: 313669 **Payroll Expense ($000)**: 125896

MARION—Mcdowell County

✠ **MCDOWELL HOSPITAL (340087)**, 430 Rankin Drive, Zip 28752–6568, Mailing Address: P.O.Box 730, 28752–0730; tel. 828/659–5000 **A**1 10 **F**3 13 15 28 29 30 31 34 35 39 40 45 54 57 59 64 70 76 77 78 79 81 82 85 87 91 93 97 107 108 110 111 115 119 127 129 130 131 132 135 144 146 147 148 149 **S** Mission Health System, Asheville, NC
Primary Contact: Carol C. Wolfenbarger, FACHE, MSN, President and Chief Executive Officer
CFO: Clint Stewart, Regional Director of Finance East
CMO: Rex Henderson M.D., Chief of Staff
CIO: Pam Blevins R.N., Director Information Technology Member Hospitals Mission
CHR: Tonya Revels, Senior Strategic Business Partner
CNO: Kathy Hefner, Chief Nursing Officer
Web address: www.mission–health.org
Control: Other not–for–profit (including NFP Corporation) **Service**: General medical and surgical

Staffed Beds: 49 **Admissions**: 1944 **Census**: 20 **Outpatient Visits**: 179580 **Births**: 177 **Total Expense ($000)**: 56861 **Payroll Expense ($000)**: 28296 **Personnel**: 368

MATTHEWS—Mecklenburg County

✠ **NOVANT HEALTH MATTHEWS MEDICAL CENTER (340171)**, 1500 Matthews Township Parkway, Zip 28105–4656; tel. 704/384–6500 **A**1 2 10 **F**3 11 12 13 15 18 20 22 26 28 29 30 31 34 35 36 40 45 49 56 57 59 63 64 67 70 73 75 76 77 78 79 81 82 83 84 85 86 87 92 93 107 110 111 114 115 118 119 126 129 130 132 141 144 145 146 147 148 149 **S** Novant Health, Winston Salem, NC
Primary Contact: Roland R. Bibeau, President and Chief Operating Officer
CFO: Fred M Hargett, Executive Vice President and Chief Financial Officer
CMO: Thomas Zweng, Executive Vice President and Chief Medical Officer
CIO: David B Garrett, Senior Vice President and Chief Information Officer
CHR: Janet Smith-Hill, Executive Vice President and Chief HR Officer
CNO: Tracy B Forster R.N., Senior Director of Nursing
Web address: www.novanthealth.org
Control: Other not–for–profit (including NFP Corporation) **Service**: General medical and surgical

Staffed Beds: 117 **Admissions**: 10135 **Census**: 105 **Outpatient Visits**: 180852 **Births**: 2221 **Total Expense ($000)**: 152848 **Payroll Expense ($000)**: 46128 **Personnel**: 719

NC

Many Facility Codes have changed. Please refer to the AHA Guide Code Chart. © 2017 AHA Guide

MONROE—Union County

✠ **CAROLINAS HEALTHCARE SYSTEM UNION (340130)**, 600 Hospital Drive, Zip 28112–6000, Mailing Address: P.O.Box 5003, 28111–5003; tel. 980/993–3100, (Total facility includes 70 beds in nursing home–type unit) **A**1 2 3 10 **F**3 4 5 8 11 13 18 20 22 26 27 28 29 30 31 34 35 39 40 42 45 49 53 56 57 59 60 64 66 70 73 74 75 76 77 78 79 81 82 83 84 85 86 87 89 93 97 102 107 108 111 114 115 117 118 119 120 121 123 128 129 130 132 135 146 147 148 **S** Carolinas HealthCare System, Charlotte, NC
Primary Contact: Michael Lutes, President
COO: Dave Anderson FACHE, Vice President Administration
CFO: John G Moore, Vice President and Chief Financial Officer
CMO: Craig M Slater M.D., Chief Medical Officer
CIO: Lisa Sykes, Director Information Services
CHR: Rhonda McFarland, Director Human Resources
CNO: Denise White MSN, Chief Nurse Executive
Web address: www.carolinashealthcare.org/union
Control: Hospital district or authority, Government, Nonfederal **Service:** General medical and surgical

Staffed Beds: 236 **Admissions:** 9001 **Census:** 150 **Outpatient Visits:** 168006 **Births:** 1164 **Total Expense ($000):** 199760 **Payroll Expense ($000):** 63784 **Personnel:** 989

MOORESVILLE—Iredell County

✠ **LAKE NORMAN REGIONAL MEDICAL CENTER (340129)**, 171 Fairview Road, Zip 28117–9500, Mailing Address: P.O.Box 3250, 28117–3250; tel. 704/660–4000 **A**1 2 10 19 **F**3 8 11 12 13 15 18 20 29 30 31 34 35 37 40 41 45 46 47 48 49 50 51 56 57 59 60 61 62 64 65 68 70 72 73 74 75 76 77 78 79 81 82 84 85 86 87 93 96 97 100 107 108 110 111 114 115 116 117 118 119 129 130 131 132 135 145 146 147 148 **P**8 **S** Community Health Systems, Inc., Franklin, TN
Primary Contact: Stephen L. Midkiff, Chief Executive Officer
CFO: Claire Polk, Chief Financial Officer
CHR: Stephanie Williams, Market Director Human Resources
CNO: Marie Marks, Chief Nursing Officer
Web address: www.lnrmc.com
Control: Corporation, Investor–owned (for–profit) **Service:** General medical and surgical

Staffed Beds: 123 **Admissions:** 4640 **Census:** 42 **Outpatient Visits:** 73587 **Births:** 870

MOREHEAD CITY—Carteret County

✠ **CARTERET HEALTH CARE (340142)**, 3500 Arendell Street, Zip 28557–2901, Mailing Address: P.O.Box 1619, 28557–1619; tel. 252/499–6000 **A**1 2 10 **F**3 7 11 12 13 15 18 20 28 29 30 31 34 35 37 40 45 46 54 57 59 62 63 64 65 68 70 74 75 76 77 78 79 81 82 84 85 86 87 89 91 93 97 107 108 110 111 114 115 118 119 120 121 123 129 130 132 135 143 145 146 148
Primary Contact: Richard A. Brvenik, President
CFO: Joanie King, Chief Financial Officer
CMO: Donald Pocock, Vice–President Medical Affairs
CIO: Kyle Marek, Chief Information Officer
CHR: Elizabeth Beswick, Vice President Human Resources and Public Relations
Web address: www.carterethealth.org
Control: County, Government, Nonfederal **Service:** General medical and surgical

Staffed Beds: 99 **Admissions:** 5523 **Census:** 65 **Outpatient Visits:** 130666 **Births:** 702 **Total Expense ($000):** 128539 **Payroll Expense ($000):** 50811 **Personnel:** 892

MORGANTON—Burke County

☐ **BROUGHTON HOSPITAL (344025)**, 1000 South Sterling Street, Zip 28655–3999; tel. 828/433–2111, (Nonreporting) **A**1 3 5 10
Primary Contact: Vivian Streater, Co–Acting Chief Executive Officer
CFO: Bea Tullis, Chief Financial Officer and Budget Officer
CMO: George Krebs M.D., Chief Medical Officer
CIO: Darin Kiracofe, Director Information Resource Management
CHR: Jean Buchanan, Director Human Resources
CNO: Vivian Streater, Chief Nursing Officer and Co–Acting Chief Executive Officer
Web address: www.ncdhhs.gov/dsohf/broughton
Control: State, Government, Nonfederal **Service:** Psychiatric

Staffed Beds: 297

✠ **CAROLINAS HEALTHCARE SYSTEM BLUE RIDGE (340075)**, 2201 South Sterling Street, Zip 28655–4058; tel. 828/580–5000, (Includes CAROLINAS HEALTHCARE SYSTEM – BLUE RIDGE – MORGANTON, 2201 South Sterling Street, Morganton, North Carolina, Zip 28655–4058, tel. 828/580–5000; VALDESE GENERAL HOSPITAL, 720 Malcolm Boulevard, Valdese, North Carolina, Zip 28690–2872, P O Box 700, 28690–0700, tel. 828/874–2251) **A**1 2 10 13 **F**3 13 15 18 20 22 28 29 30 31 34 35 40 42 45 49 50 53 56 57 59 64 68 69 70 71 72 76 77 78 81 82 85 86 87 93 96 97 98 107 108 110 111 114 115 119 120 121 123 130 131 132 146 147 148 **S** Carolinas HealthCare System, Charlotte, NC
Primary Contact: Kathy C. Bailey, Ph.D., FACHE, President and Chief Executive Officer
CFO: Robert G Fritts, Chief Financial Officer and Senior Vice President
CMO: Joe Mazzola D.O., Senior Vice President Medical Affairs and Chief Medical Officer
CHR: Thomas Eure, Vice President Administration
Web address: www.blueridgehealth.org
Control: Other not–for–profit (including NFP Corporation) **Service:** General medical and surgical

Staffed Beds: 156 **Admissions:** 7841 **Census:** 93 **Outpatient Visits:** 164296 **Births:** 893 **Total Expense ($000):** 197456 **Payroll Expense ($000):** 70731 **Personnel:** 1177

MOUNT AIRY—Surry County

✠ **NORTHERN HOSPITAL OF SURRY COUNTY (340003)**, 830 Rockford Street, Zip 27030–5365, Mailing Address: P.O.Box 1101, 27030–1101; tel. 336/719–7000, (Total facility includes 33 beds in nursing home–type unit) **A**1 10 **F**3 13 15 18 29 30 31 34 35 40 45 50 51 53 54 56 57 59 64 65 67 70 75 76 77 79 80 81 82 85 86 87 89 97 107 108 110 111 114 115 118 119 128 130 131 132 133 135 145 146 147 149 **P**6 **S** QHR, Brentwood, TN
Primary Contact: Ned Hill, President and Chief Executive Officer
CFO: Andrea Hickling, Vice President of Finance and Chief Financial Officer
CMO: Druery DeVore, Chief of Medical Staff
CIO: Rodney Bond, Director of Information Technology
CHR: Julia Nelson, Vice President of Human Resources
CNO: Robin Hodgin R.N., Vice President of Patient Services and Chief Nursing Officer
Web address: www.northernhospital.com
Control: Hospital district or authority, Government, Nonfederal **Service:** General medical and surgical

Staffed Beds: 108 **Admissions:** 3912 **Census:** 66 **Outpatient Visits:** 126115 **Births:** 377 **Total Expense ($000):** 89046 **Payroll Expense ($000):** 37680 **Personnel:** 720

MURPHY—Cherokee County

✠ **MURPHY MEDICAL CENTER (341328)**, 3990 U S Highway 64 East Alt, Zip 28906–7917; tel. 828/837–8161, (Total facility includes 134 beds in nursing home–type unit) **A**1 10 18 **F**3 6 13 15 28 29 30 34 35 40 41 45 50 53 57 62 63 64 68 70 76 77 79 81 84 87 93 97 102 107 110 111 114 115 127 128 130 133 144 146 148 **S** Carolinas HealthCare System, Charlotte, NC
Primary Contact: Michael Stevenson, Chief Executive Officer
COO: Toni Lovingood, Chief Operating Officer
CFO: Steve Gilgen, Chief Financial Officer
CMO: Jeffrey H Martin M.D., Chief of Staff
CIO: Connie Stalcup, Manager Information Systems
CHR: Russ Paine, Human Resources Officer
CNO: Teresa Bowleg R.N., Chief Nursing Officer
Web address: www.murphymedical.org
Control: Other not–for–profit (including NFP Corporation) **Service:** General medical and surgical

Staffed Beds: 159 **Admissions:** 2240 **Census:** 115 **Outpatient Visits:** 375467 **Births:** 127 **Total Expense ($000):** 63373 **Payroll Expense ($000):** 26629

NAGS HEAD—Dare County

✠ **THE OUTER BANKS HOSPITAL (341324)**, 4800 South Croatan Highway, Zip 27959–9704; tel. 252/449–4500 **A**1 2 10 18 **F**3 13 15 28 29 30 31 34 35 36 38 40 45 50 51 54 57 59 64 65 68 71 75 76 77 78 79 81 82 84 85 86 87 93 100 107 108 109 110 111 114 115 118 119 120 121 129 130 133 135 141 144 146 147 149 **P**5 **S** Vidant Health, Greenville, NC
Primary Contact: Ronald A. Sloan, FACHE, President
CFO: Todd Warlitner, Vice President Business Operations
CMO: Roger Lever M.D., President Medical Staff
CHR: Mary Kelley, Director Human Resources
CNO: Marcia Bryant R.N., Vice President, Clinical Operations
Web address: www.theouterbankshospital.com
Control: Other not–for–profit (including NFP Corporation) **Service:** General medical and surgical

Staffed Beds: 21 **Admissions:** 1121 **Census:** 7 **Outpatient Visits:** 40437 **Births:** 355 **Total Expense ($000):** 65410 **Payroll Expense ($000):** 18803 **Personnel:** 351

NEW BERN—Craven County

☒ △ **CAROLINAEAST HEALTH SYSTEM (340131)**, 2000 Neuse Boulevard, Zip 28560–3499, Mailing Address: P.O.Box 12157, 28561–2157; tel. 252/633–8111 **A**1 2 7 10 20 **F**3 7 8 11 13 15 17 18 20 22 24 26 28 29 30 31 34 35 40 42 45 47 48 49 53 54 57 59 62 64 67 68 70 74 75 76 77 78 79 81 85 86 87 89 90 91 92 93 94 96 98 100 101 102 103 104 105 107 108 110 111 113 114 115 116 117 118 119 120 121 123 126 129 130 132 135 143 146 147 148 **P**6
Primary Contact: G Raymond. Leggett III, President and Chief Executive Officer
CFO: Tammy M Sherron, Vice President Finance
CMO: Ronald B May M.D., Vice President Medical Affairs
CIO: Ronald B May M.D., Vice President Medical Affairs
CHR: Bruce A Martin, Vice President Human Resources
CNO: Rosanne Leahy, Vice President Nursing Services
Web address: www.carolinaeasthealth.com
Control: Hospital district or authority, Government, Nonfederal **Service**: General medical and surgical

Staffed Beds: 205 **Admissions:** 12763 **Census:** 176 **Outpatient Visits:** 179412 **Births:** 1190 **Total Expense ($000):** 259038 **Payroll Expense ($000):** 94652 **Personnel:** 1784

NEWLAND—Avery County

☒ **CHARLES A. CANNON MEMORIAL HOSPITAL (341323)**, 434 Hospital Drive, Zip 28646, Mailing Address: P.O.Box 767, Linville, 28646–0767; tel. 828/737–7000 **A**1 10 18 **F**11 15 28 29 30 40 45 64 68 70 81 85 93 98 99 100 102 104 107 110 115 119 130 133 135 146 149 **S** Appalachian Regional Healthcare System, Boone, NC
Primary Contact: Carmen Lacey, MSN, R.N., President
CFO: Kevin B May, System Director Finance
CMO: Thomas M Haizlip M.D., Jr, Chief of Staff
CIO: Nathan White, Chief Information Officer
CHR: Amy J Crabbe, Vice President People Services
CNO: Carmen Lacey MSN, R.N., President and Director of Patient Care Services
Web address: www.apprhs.org/locations/cannon–memorial–hospital
Control: Other not–for–profit (including NFP Corporation) **Service**: General medical and surgical

Staffed Beds: 35 **Admissions:** 1310 **Census:** 15 **Outpatient Visits:** 28989 **Births:** 0 **Total Expense ($000):** 22639 **Payroll Expense ($000):** 8976 **Personnel:** 166

NORTH WILKESBORO—Wilkes County

☒ **WAKE FOREST BAPTIST HEALTH – WILKES MEDICAL CENTER (340064)**, 1370 West 'D' Street, Zip 28659–3506, Mailing Address: P.O.Box 609, 28659–0609; tel. 336/651–8100, (Total facility includes 10 beds in nursing home–type unit) **A**1 10 **F**3 11 13 15 18 29 30 34 35 40 45 49 57 59 60 64 67 68 70 74 76 77 79 81 82 85 87 92 93 107 108 110 111 114 115 119 124 128 130 146 **S** Wake Forest Baptist Health, Winston–Salem, NC
Primary Contact: J Gene. Faile, Chief Executive Officer and President
CFO: Barry Wald, Chief Financial Officer
CMO: Richard Barber M.D., Chief Medical Officer
CIO: William Hofman, Manager Information Technology
CHR: Vanya Baker, Director
CNO: Sandy Sheppard, Vice President Patient Services
Web address: www.wilkesregional.com/
Control: City, Government, Nonfederal **Service**: General medical and surgical

Staffed Beds: 91 **Admissions:** 4212 **Census:** 44 **Outpatient Visits:** 105232 **Births:** 467 **Total Expense ($000):** 75932 **Payroll Expense ($000):** 28116 **Personnel:** 634

OXFORD—Granville County

☒ **GRANVILLE HEALTH SYSTEM (340127)**, 1010 College Street, Zip 27565–2507, Mailing Address: P.O.Box 947, 27565–0947; tel. 919/690–3000, (Total facility includes 80 beds in nursing home–type unit) **A**1 10 **F**2 3 7 11 13 15 18 19 29 30 34 35 38 39 40 45 50 54 55 56 57 59 64 66 70 75 76 77 78 79 81 82 85 86 93 99 100 101 103 104 107 108 110 111 114 118 119 124 127 128 129 130 132 133 143 144 146 147 148 **P**3 6 8
Primary Contact: L Lee. Isley, FACHE, Ph.D., Chief Executive Officer
COO: Cristina Rigsbee Carroll, Chief Operating Officer
CFO: Jeffery Armstrong CPA, Chief Financial Officer
CMO: Richard Pacca M.D., Chief of Staff
CIO: Geoff Tanthorey, Director, Information Systems
CHR: Scott Thomas, Administrative Director Human Resources and Communications
CNO: Bill Hughes, Chief Nursing Officer
Web address: www.ghshospital.org
Control: County, Government, Nonfederal **Service**: General medical and surgical

Staffed Beds: 142 **Admissions:** 2259 **Census:** 90 **Outpatient Visits:** 54408 **Births:** 269 **Total Expense ($000):** 58194 **Payroll Expense ($000):** 26292 **Personnel:** 534

PINEHURST—Moore County

☒ △ **FIRSTHEALTH MOORE REGIONAL HOSPITAL (340115)**, 155 Memorial Drive, Zip 28374–8710, Mailing Address: P.O.Box 3000, 28374–3000; tel. 910/715–1000 **A**1 2 7 10 13 19 **F**3 4 5 11 12 13 15 17 18 20 22 24 26 28 29 30 31 34 35 40 44 45 46 47 48 49 50 51 53 54 55 56 57 58 59 60 64 65 68 70 72 74 75 76 77 78 79 81 82 86 87 89 90 91 93 96 98 99 100 101 102 103 104 105 107 108 111 114 115 118 119 120 121 124 126 129 130 132 134 135 143 146 147 148 **S** FirstHealth of the Carolinas, Pinehurst, NC
Primary Contact: David J. Kilarski, FACHE, Chief Executive Officer
COO: Brian Canfield, Chief Operating Officer
CFO: Lynn S DeJaco, Chief Financial Officer
CMO: John F Krahnert M.D., Chief Medical Officer
CIO: David B Dillehunt, Chief Information Officer
CHR: Daniel F Biediger, Vice President Human Resources
CNO: Karen Robeano R.N., Chief Nursing Officer and Vice President Patient Care Services
Web address: www.firsthealth.org
Control: Other not–for–profit (including NFP Corporation) **Service**: General medical and surgical

Staffed Beds: 372 **Admissions:** 22878 **Census:** 278 **Outpatient Visits:** 196335 **Births:** 1979 **Total Expense ($000):** 396689 **Payroll Expense ($000):** 163292 **Personnel:** 3280

PLYMOUTH—Washington County

⇑ **WASHINGTON COUNTY HOSPITAL (341314)**, 958 U S Highway 64 East, Zip 27962–9591, Mailing Address: PO Box 707, 27962–9591; tel. 252/793–4135, (Nonreporting) **A**10 18 21 **F**3 11 15 28 29 30 34 35 39 40 50 58 68 81 85 107 110 114 119 130 146 149 150 **S** Rural Community Hospitals of America, Kansas City, MO
Primary Contact: Al Arrowood, Interim President
CMO: Robert Venable M.D., Chief Medical Staff
CIO: Christina Craft, Director Information Systems
CNO: Kimberly Manning, Chief Nursing Officer
Control: County, Government, Nonfederal **Service**: General medical and surgical

Staffed Beds: 25

RAEFORD—Hoke County

HOKE HOSPITAL (340188), 210 Medical Pavilion Drive, Zip 28376–9111; tel. 910/904–8000 **S** Cape Fear Valley Health System, Fayetteville, NC
Primary Contact: Roxie Cannon. Wells, M.D., President
Web address: www.capefearvalley.com
Control: Other not–for–profit (including NFP Corporation) **Service**: General medical and surgical

Staffed Beds: 41 **Admissions:** 1302 **Census:** 10 **Outpatient Visits:** 49219 **Births:** 0 **Total Expense ($000):** 34166 **Payroll Expense ($000):** 14424

RALEIGH—Wake County

CENTRAL PRISON HOSPITAL, 1300 Western Boulevard, Zip 27606–2148; tel. 919/743–2440, (Nonreporting) **A**3
Primary Contact: Dean Doering, Chief Executive Officer
CMO: Olushola Metiko M.D., Medical Director
CHR: Bruce McKinney, Business Officer, Administrative Services
CNO: Cindy J McLean R.N., MSN, Director of Nursing
Web address: www.ncdps.gov/index2.cfm?a=000003,002240,002381,002252
Control: State, Government, Nonfederal **Service**: Hospital unit of an institution (prison hospital, college infirmary, etc.)

Staffed Beds: 230

☒ **DUKE RALEIGH HOSPITAL (340073)**, 3400 Wake Forest Road, Zip 27609–7373; tel. 919/954–3000 **A**1 2 3 10 **F**3 11 12 15 18 20 22 26 28 29 30 31 34 35 36 39 40 44 45 46 47 49 50 51 53 55 57 58 59 60 64 68 70 74 75 77 78 79 80 81 82 84 85 87 92 93 94 96 100 101 102 103 104 107 108 110 111 114 115 117 118 119 120 121 123 126 129 130 131 132 146 148 149 **P**6 **S** Duke University Health System, Durham, NC
Primary Contact: David Zaas, M.D., Chief Executive Officer
COO: Brian Sloan, Chief Operating Officer
CMO: Ted Kunstling M.D., Chief Medical Officer
CIO: Janis Curtis, Interim Director Information Technology
CHR: Donald K Barnes, Chief Human Resources Officer
Web address: www.dukehealthraleigh.org
Control: Other not–for–profit (including NFP Corporation) **Service**: General medical and surgical

Staffed Beds: 159 **Admissions:** 8967 **Census:** 102 **Outpatient Visits:** 190846 **Births:** 0 **Total Expense ($000):** 347634 **Payroll Expense ($000):** 90414 **Personnel:** 1507

NC

Many Facility Codes have changed. Please refer to the AHA Guide Code Chart.
© 2017 AHA Guide

Hospitals, U.S. / NORTH CAROLINA

☐ **HOLLY HILL HOSPITAL (344014)**, 3019 Falstaff Road, Zip 27610–1812; tel. 919/250–7000 **A**1 10 **F**4 5 29 38 56 68 98 99 103 105 **S** Universal Health Services, Inc., King of Prussia, PA
Primary Contact: Amanda Johanson, Chief Executive Officer
COO: Jessica Knudsen, Chief Operating Officer and Director Performance Improvement and Risk Management
CFO: Ron Howard, Chief Financial Officer
CMO: Thomas Cornwall M.D., Medical Director
CHR: Ebuni McFall–Roberts, Director Human Resources
CNO: Michael Hartley MS, Chief Nursing Officer
Web address: www.hollyhillhospital.com
Control: Corporation, Investor–owned (for–profit) **Service:** Psychiatric

Staffed Beds: 228 **Admissions:** 8047 **Census:** 196 **Outpatient Visits:** 6078 **Births:** 0 **Total Expense ($000):** 42559 **Payroll Expense ($000):** 18911 **Personnel:** 435

LARRY B. ZIEVERINK, SR. ALCOHOLISM TREATMENT CENTER, 3000 Falstaff Road, Zip 27610–1897; tel. 919/250–1500, (Nonreporting)
Primary Contact: Martin D. Woodward, Director Acute Care Services
COO: Martin D Woodward, Director Acute Care Services
CFO: Paul Gross, Human Services and Finance Officer
CMO: Enrique Lopez M.D., Medical Director
CIO: Wil A Glenn, Director Communications
Web address: www.wakegov.com/county/family/atc
Control: County, Government, Nonfederal **Service:** Alcoholism and other chemical dependency

Staffed Beds: 34

☒ **UNC REX HEALTH CARE (340114)**, 4420 Lake Boone Trail, Zip 27607–6599; tel. 919/784–3100, (Total facility includes 227 beds in nursing home–type unit) **A**1 2 3 5 10 **F**3 7 8 11 12 13 14 15 17 18 20 22 24 26 28 29 30 31 34 35 36 40 44 45 46 47 48 49 50 53 54 56 57 58 59 60 62 64 65 66 68 70 71 72 73 74 75 76 77 78 79 81 82 84 85 86 87 89 92 93 96 97 100 102 107 108 110 111 114 115 116 117 118 119 120 121 123 126 128 129 130 131 132 135 142 143 144 145 146 147 148 149 **P**6 **S** UNC Health Care, Chapel Hill, NC
Primary Contact: Stephen W. Burriss, President
COO: Sue Sandberg R.N., Chief Operating Officer
CFO: Andrew Zukowski, Chief Financial Officer
CMO: Linda H. Butler M.D., Chief Medical Officer
CIO: Tracy Parham, Health Care System Chief Information Officer
CHR: Scott Doak, Vice President, Human Resources
CNO: ColonelJoel Ray MSN, Vice President and Chief Nursing Officer
Web address: www.rexhealth.com
Control: Other not–for–profit (including NFP Corporation) **Service:** General medical and surgical

Staffed Beds: 660 **Admissions:** 28753 **Census:** 515 **Outpatient Visits:** 856952 **Births:** 5624 **Total Expense ($000):** 880969 **Payroll Expense ($000):** 352253 **Personnel:** 5052

☒ △ **WAKEMED RALEIGH CAMPUS (340069)**, 3000 New Bern Avenue, Zip 27610–1295; tel. 919/350–8000, (Includes WAKEMED NORTH FAMILY HEALTH AND WOMEN'S HOSPITAL, 10000 Falls Of Neuse Road, Raleigh, North Carolina, Zip 27614–7838, tel. 919/350–8000; Sherri De Shazo, R.N., Senior Vice President and Hospital Administrator) **A**1 3 5 7 10 **F**3 7 8 12 13 15 17 18 20 22 24 26 28 29 30 31 32 34 35 37 38 40 41 42 43 44 45 46 48 49 50 53 54 56 57 58 59 60 61 62 64 65 66 68 70 71 72 73 74 75 76 77 78 79 80 81 85 86 87 88 89 90 92 93 95 96 97 107 110 111 114 115 118 119 126 130 131 132 135 143 144 146 147 148 **P**6 **S** WakeMed Health & Hospitals, Raleigh, NC
Primary Contact: Donald R. Gintzig, President and Chief Executive Officer
COO: Denise Wilder Warren R.N., Executive Vice President and Chief Operating Officer
CMO: West Paul M.D., Ph.D., Senior Vice President and Chief Quality and Medical Staff Officer
CIO: Peter Marks, Vice President & Chief Information Officer
CHR: Jeanene R Martin M.P.H., Senior Vice President Human Resources
CNO: Cindy Boily MSN, R.N., Senior Vice President and Chief Nursing Officer
Web address: www.wakemed.org
Control: Other not–for–profit (including NFP Corporation) **Service:** General medical and surgical

Staffed Beds: 681 **Admissions:** 30362 **Census:** 508 **Outpatient Visits:** 1407577 **Births:** 5549 **Total Expense ($000):** 946804 **Payroll Expense ($000):** 511737 **Personnel:** 6911

REIDSVILLE—Rockingham County

ANNIE PENN HOSPITAL See Moses H. Cone Memorial Hospital, Greensboro

ROANOKE RAPIDS—Halifax County

☒ **HALIFAX REGIONAL MEDICAL CENTER (340151)**, 250 Smith Church Road, Zip 27870–4914, Mailing Address: P.O.Box 1089, 27870–1089; tel. 252/535–8011 **A**1 10 20 **F**3 11 13 15 18 20 22 29 31 34 35 40 45 50 57 59 64 65 68 70 76 77 78 79 81 82 85 86 87 91 93 98 100 101 102 103 106 107 108 110 111 114 115 119 124 127 129 130 132 144 146 147 148 149 **P**6 **S** Novant Health, Winston Salem, NC
Primary Contact: William Mahone, President and Chief Executive Officer
CFO: Sherry Jensen, Chief Financial Officer
CIO: Robert Gordon, Manager Information Systems
CHR: Thomas Mastroianni, Administrative Director of Human Resources
CNO: Karen Daniels MSN, R.N., Chief Nursing Officer
Web address: www.halifaxmedicalcenter.org
Control: Other not–for–profit (including NFP Corporation) **Service:** General medical and surgical

Staffed Beds: 142 **Admissions:** 5797 **Census:** 73 **Outpatient Visits:** 73486 **Births:** 639 **Total Expense ($000):** 84298 **Payroll Expense ($000):** 33453 **Personnel:** 798

ROCKINGHAM—Richmond County

★ **FIRSTHEALTH RICHMOND MEMORIAL HOSPITAL (340035)**, 925 Long Drive, Zip 28379–4835; tel. 910/417–3000, (Nonreporting) **S** FirstHealth of the Carolinas, Pinehurst, NC
Primary Contact: John J. Jackson, President
COO: Allison G. Duckworth R.N., FACHE, Chief Operating Officer and Chief Nursing Officer
CFO: John D Price, Chief Financial Officer
CMO: Matthew Vreeland M.D., Chief Medical Officer
Web address: www.firsthealth.org
Control: Other not–for–profit (including NFP Corporation) **Service:** General medical and surgical

Staffed Beds: 91

ROCKY MOUNT—Nash County

☒ **LIFECARE HOSPITALS OF NORTH CAROLINA (342013)**, 1051 Noell Lane, Zip 27804–1761; tel. 252/451–2300, (Nonreporting) **A**1 10 **S** LifeCare Management Services, Plano, TX
Primary Contact: Robyn Perkerson, R.N., Administrator
COO: Robyn Perkerson R.N., Administrator
CMO: Daniel Crocker M.D., Chief Medical Officer
CHR: Vicky Goode, Director Human Resources
CNO: Brandee Chappell, Director of Nursing
Web address: www.lifecare–hospitals.com
Control: Corporation, Investor–owned (for–profit) **Service:** Acute long–term care hospital

Staffed Beds: 41

☒ **NASH HEALTH CARE SYSTEMS (340147)**, 2460 Curtis Ellis Drive, Zip 27804–2237; tel. 252/962–8000 **A**1 2 10 **F**3 4 11 12 13 15 18 20 22 28 29 30 31 34 35 38 40 41 44 45 48 49 50 54 55 57 59 60 63 64 70 73 74 75 76 77 78 79 80 81 82 84 85 86 87 89 90 93 96 98 100 101 102 107 108 110 111 114 115 117 118 119 120 121 123 126 127 129 130 131 132 135 146 147 148 **P**6 **S** UNC Health Care, Chapel Hill, NC
Primary Contact: Ian B. Buchanan, Interim Chief Executive Officer
COO: Brad Weisner, Executive Vice President and Chief Operating Officer
CFO: David Paugh, Senior Vice President and Chief Financial Officer
CMO: Meera Kelley M.D., Senior Vice President and Chief Medical Officer
CHR: Katie Davison, Executive Director, Human Resources
CNO: Crystal Hayden MSN, R.N., Senior Vice President and Chief Nursing Officer
Web address: www.nhcs.org
Control: Hospital district or authority, Government, Nonfederal **Service:** General medical and surgical

Staffed Beds: 303 **Admissions:** 12473 **Census:** 173 **Outpatient Visits:** 178396 **Births:** 993 **Total Expense ($000):** 226816 **Payroll Expense ($000):** 90630 **Personnel:** 1607

Hospital, Medicare Provider Number, Address, Telephone, Approval, Facility, and Physician Codes, Health Care System

★ American Hospital Association (AHA) membership ☐ The Joint Commission accreditation ○ Healthcare Facilities Accreditation Program ◇ DNV Healthcare Inc. accreditation ⇑ Center for Improvement in Healthcare Quality Accreditation △ Commission on Accreditation of Rehabilitation Facilities (CARF) accreditation

NC

© 2017 AHA Guide   *Many Facility Codes have changed. Please refer to the AHA Guide Code Chart.*   Hospitals **A469**

ROXBORO—Person County

⊞ **PERSON MEMORIAL HOSPITAL (340159)**, 615 Ridge Road, Zip 27573–4629; tel. 336/599–2121, (Total facility includes 60 beds in nursing home–type unit) **A**1 10 **F**3 11 15 18 28 29 34 40 45 57 59 64 70 75 77 79 81 85 87 93 96 97 107 108 110 111 114 119 128 130 132 146 149 **P**6 **S** Duke LifePoint Healthcare, Brentwood, TN
Primary Contact: David Ziolkowski, Chief Executive Officer
CFO: Jessi Ayers, Chief Financial Officer
CIO: Rhonda M. Elliott, Director Information Technology and Meaningful Use
CHR: Mary Barksdale, Director Human Resources
CNO: Lynn Peoples, Interim Chief Nursing Officer
Web address: www.personhospital.com
Control: Partnership, Investor–owned (for–profit) **Service:** General medical and surgical

Staffed Beds: 98 **Admissions:** 1400 **Census:** 60 **Outpatient Visits:** 23445 **Births:** 0 **Total Expense ($000):** 31889 **Payroll Expense ($000):** 10085 **Personnel:** 248

RUTHERFORDTON—Rutherford County

⊞ **RUTHERFORD REGIONAL HEALTH SYSTEM (340013)**, 288 South Ridgecrest Avenue, Zip 28139–2838; tel. 828/286–5000 **A**1 2 10 **F**3 13 15 18 20 28 29 30 31 34 35 40 45 48 49 50 57 59 64 70 74 75 76 77 78 79 81 85 86 87 89 93 97 98 100 101 102 104 106 107 108 110 111 114 115 118 119 130 131 132 135 146 147 149 **S** Duke LifePoint Healthcare, Brentwood, TN
Primary Contact: Rebecca Segal, Chief Executive Officer
COO: John Domansky, Vice President Operations
CFO: Jeff Rush, Chief Financial Officer
CIO: Tommy Finley, Chief Information Officer
CHR: Robin B Callas R.N., Vice President Human Resources
Web address: www.rutherfordhosp.org
Control: Partnership, Investor–owned (for–profit) **Service:** General medical and surgical

Staffed Beds: 112 **Admissions:** 4007 **Census:** 54 **Outpatient Visits:** 168718 **Births:** 418 **Total Expense ($000):** 76456 **Payroll Expense ($000):** 32791 **Personnel:** 659

SALISBURY—Rowan County

⊞ **NOVANT HEALTH ROWAN MEDICAL CENTER (340015)**, 612 Mocksville Avenue, Zip 28144–2799; tel. 704/210–5000 **A**1 2 10 19 **F**3 8 11 12 13 15 18 20 22 26 28 29 30 31 32 34 35 37 39 40 44 45 49 50 53 56 57 59 60 64 65 68 70 71 73 74 75 76 77 78 79 81 84 85 86 87 90 91 92 93 94 98 100 101 102 103 107 108 110 111 114 115 118 119 120 121 123 124 126 130 131 132 135 141 142 146 147 148 149 150 **S** Novant Health, Winston Salem, NC
Primary Contact: Dari Caldwell, R.N., Ph.D., FACHE, President and Chief Operating Officer
CFO: Fred M Hargett, Executive Vice President and Chief Financial Officer
CMO: Thomas Zweng, Executive Vice President and Chief Medical Officer
CIO: David B Garrett, Senior Vice President and Chief Information Officer
CHR: Janet Smith–Hill, Executive Vice President and Chief Human Resource Officer
CNO: Cora Greene, Senior Director, Chief Nursing Officer
Web address: www.novanthealth.org/rowan–medical–center.aspx
Control: Other not–for–profit (including NFP Corporation) **Service:** General medical and surgical

Staffed Beds: 149 **Admissions:** 9326 **Census:** 136 **Outpatient Visits:** 125863 **Births:** 767 **Total Expense ($000):** 189372 **Payroll Expense ($000):** 59068 **Personnel:** 917

VETERANS AFFAIRS MEDICAL CENTER See W. G. (Bill) Heffner Veterans Affairs Medical Center

⊞ **W. G. (BILL) HEFFNER VETERANS AFFAIRS MEDICAL CENTER**, 1601 Brenner Avenue, Zip 28144–2559; tel. 704/638–9000, (Nonreporting) **A**1 3 5 **S** Department of Veterans Affairs, Washington, DC
Primary Contact: Kaye Green, FACHE, Director
CFO: Steve Patil, Chief Financial Officer
CIO: Deborah Gunn, Chief Information Officer
CHR: Sandra Fischer, Director Human Resources
Web address: www.salisbury.va.gov
Control: Veterans Affairs, Government, federal **Service:** Psychiatric

Staffed Beds: 171

SANFORD—Lee County

⊞ **CENTRAL CAROLINA HOSPITAL (340020)**, 1135 Carthage Street, Zip 27330–4162; tel. 919/774–2100, (Nonreporting) **A**1 10 **S** Duke LifePoint Healthcare, Brentwood, TN
Primary Contact: John Maxwell, Chief Executive Officer
CFO: Debbie Kyzar, Chief Financial Officer
CIO: Jimmy Whitaker, Director Information Systems
CHR: Deanna Lamb, Director Human Resources
CNO: Mary Florit, Interim Chief Nursing Officer
Web address: www.centralcarolinahosp.com
Control: Corporation, Investor–owned (for–profit) **Service:** General medical and surgical

Staffed Beds: 137

SCOTLAND NECK—Halifax County

★ **OUR COMMUNITY HOSPITAL (341302)**, 921 Junior High Road, Zip 27874–0405, Mailing Address: Box 405, 27874–0405; tel. 252/826–4144, (Nonreporting) **A**10 18
Primary Contact: Thomas K. Majure, Administrator
CFO: Sarah Diversi, Chief Financial Officer
CMO: Cornelius Artis M.D., Chief Medical Officer
CIO: Dana Mobley, Chief Information Officer
CNO: Claudia Giddings R.N., Chief Nursing Officer
Web address: www.och–bltc.org
Control: Other not–for–profit (including NFP Corporation) **Service:** General medical and surgical

Staffed Beds: 75

SHELBY—Cleveland County

⊞ **CAROLINAS HEALTHCARE SYSTEM CLEVELAND (340021)**, 201 East Grover Street, Zip 28150–3917; tel. 980/487–3000 **A**1 2 10 19 **F**3 8 13 15 18 20 28 29 30 31 32 34 35 39 40 43 45 47 48 49 50 51 53 56 57 59 64 65 70 74 75 76 77 78 79 80 81 85 86 87 89 93 102 107 108 110 111 114 115 118 119 121 123 126 129 130 131 132 135 143 145 146 147 148 149 **S** Carolinas HealthCare System, Charlotte, NC
Primary Contact: Brian Gwyn, President and Chief Executive Officer
COO: Brian Gwyn, President Chief Operating Officer
CFO: Christine M Martin, Vice President and Chief Financial Officer
CMO: Charles M Tomlinson M.D., Chief Medical Officer
CIO: Craig D Richardville, Chief Information and Analytics Officer
CHR: Debra Kale, Vice President Human Resources
CNO: Veronica Poole–Adams R.N., Vice President, Chief Operating Officer and Chief Nursing Executive
Web address: www.clevelandregional.org
Control: Hospital district or authority, Government, Nonfederal **Service:** General medical and surgical

Staffed Beds: 161 **Admissions:** 7373 **Census:** 80 **Outpatient Visits:** 142237 **Births:** 1064 **Total Expense ($000):** 171811 **Payroll Expense ($000):** 54709 **Personnel:** 925

SILER CITY—Chatham County

⊞ **CHATHAM HOSPITAL (341311)**, 475 Progress Boulevard, Zip 27344–6787, Mailing Address: P.O.Box 649, 27344–0649; tel. 919/799–4000 **A**1 10 18 **F**3 15 18 26 28 29 30 34 35 39 40 45 46 57 59 68 70 75 77 81 85 92 93 107 110 111 114 119 130 133 135 **S** UNC Health Care, Chapel Hill, NC
Primary Contact: Robert A. Enders Jr, President
CFO: Jeff LeGay, Chief Financial Officer
CMO: Andrew Hannapel, Chief Medical Officer
CIO: Deborah Taylor, Chief Information Officer
CHR: Jodie Sartor Solow, Director of Human Resources
CNO: Tammy Needham, Chief Nursing Officer
Web address: www.chathamhospital.org
Control: Other not–for–profit (including NFP Corporation) **Service:** General medical and surgical

Staffed Beds: 25 **Admissions:** 883 **Census:** 14 **Outpatient Visits:** 35024 **Births:** 0 **Total Expense ($000):** 32137 **Payroll Expense ($000):** 9582 **Personnel:** 157

SMITHFIELD—Johnston County

⊞ **JOHNSTON HEALTH (340090)**, 509 North Bright Leaf Blvd, Zip 27577–4407, Mailing Address: P.O.Box 1376, 27577–1376; tel. 919/934–8171 **A**1 2 10 **F**3 11 13 15 17 18 20 22 26 28 29 30 31 32 34 35 40 42 45 49 50 53 57 59 61 62 63 64 66 68 70 73 74 75 76 79 81 85 86 87 89 92 93 97 98 100 107 108 110 111 115 119 120 121 126 130 132 144 146 147 148 149 **S** UNC Health Care, Chapel Hill, NC
Primary Contact: Charles W. Elliott Jr, Chief Executive Officer
COO: Ruth Marler, Chief Nursing Officer and Chief Operating Officer
CFO: Edward A Klein, Chief Financial Officer
CMO: Peter Charvat, Chief Medical Officer
CIO: Teresa Chappell, Chief Information Officer
CHR: Timothy A Hays, Vice President Human Resources
CNO: Ruth Marler, Chief Nursing Officer and Chief Operating Officer
Web address: www.johnstonhealth.org
Control: Hospital district or authority, Government, Nonfederal **Service:** General medical and surgical

Staffed Beds: 153 **Admissions:** 10078 **Census:** 117 **Outpatient Visits:** 153181 **Births:** 1534 **Total Expense ($000):** 193411 **Payroll Expense ($000):** 75580 **Personnel:** 1315

Many Facility Codes have changed. Please refer to the AHA Guide Code Chart. © 2017 AHA Guide

NC

SOUTHPORT—Brunswick County

⊞ **J. ARTHUR DOSHER MEMORIAL HOSPITAL (341327)**, 924 North Howe Street, Zip 28461–3099; tel. 910/457–3800, (Total facility includes 57 beds in nursing home–type unit) **A**1 10 18 **F**3 11 15 28 30 34 35 40 45 47 50 54 57 59 64 68 75 77 79 81 91 93 97 107 110 111 114 115 118 119 127 128 129 130 131 132 133 144 146 148 149 **P**6
Primary Contact: Thomas R. Siemers, Chief Executive Officer
COO: Carol Northup R.N., Chief Nursing Officer and Chief Operating Officer
CFO: Daniel J. Porter, Senior Vice President and Chief Financial Officer
CIO: Susan Shomaker, Director Information Management Systems
CHR: Deanna Parker, Director Human Resources
CNO: Carol Northup R.N., Chief Nursing Officer and Chief Operating Officer
Web address: www.dosher.org
Control: Hospital district or authority, Government, Nonfederal **Service**: General medical and surgical

> **Staffed Beds:** 89 **Admissions:** 914 **Census:** 31 **Outpatient Visits:** 66191 **Births:** 0 **Total Expense ($000):** 42837 **Payroll Expense ($000):** 17058 **Personnel:** 249

SPARTA—Alleghany County

⊞ **ALLEGHANY MEMORIAL HOSPITAL (341320)**, 233 Doctors Street, Zip 28675–9247; tel. 336/372–5511 **A**1 10 18 **F**3 15 18 28 29 30 34 35 40 43 45 59 64 67 70 77 78 79 81 82 87 90 93 97 107 111 114 119 129 130 131 133 135 146
Primary Contact: Craig James, President
CFO: Brett Liverman, Chief Financial Officer
CMO: Joe Arocha, Chief of Staff
CIO: Darlene Keith, Chief Information Systems
CHR: Courtney Bennett, Human Resource Manager
CNO: Wendy Orton, Chief Nursing Officer
Web address: www.amhsparta.org
Control: Other not–for–profit (including NFP Corporation) **Service**: General medical and surgical

> **Staffed Beds:** 25 **Admissions:** 459 **Census:** 4 **Outpatient Visits:** 26481 **Births:** 0 **Total Expense ($000):** 12695 **Payroll Expense ($000):** 5405 **Personnel:** 152

SPRUCE PINE—Mitchell County

⊞ **BLUE RIDGE REGIONAL HOSPITAL (341329)**, 125 Hospital Drive, Zip 28777–3035; tel. 828/765–4201, (Includes BLUE RIDGE MEDICAL CENTER – YANCEY CAMPUS, 800 Medical Campus Drive, Burnsville, North Carolina, Zip 28714–9010, tel. 828/682–0200) **A**1 10 18 **F**3 13 15 17 28 29 30 31 34 35 40 43 45 46 50 53 54 57 59 64 66 70 75 76 77 78 79 81 82 85 87 90 93 96 97 107 108 111 114 118 119 127 128 129 130 131 132 133 135 146 147 148 **P**6 **S** Mission Health System, Asheville, NC
Primary Contact: Rebecca W. Carter, MSN, R.N., FACHE, Chief Executive Officer and Chief Nursing Officer
CFO: Clint Stewart, Chief Financial Officer
CMO: Jennifer Larson M.D., Chief of Staff
CIO: Pam Blevins R.N., Director, Clinical Informatics
CNO: Rebecca W Carter MSN, R.N., FACHE, Chief Executive Officer and Chief Nursing Officer
Web address: www.spchospital.org
Control: Other not–for–profit (including NFP Corporation) **Service**: General medical and surgical

> **Staffed Beds:** 42 **Admissions:** 1244 **Census:** 11 **Outpatient Visits:** 116847 **Births:** 169 **Total Expense ($000):** 44426 **Payroll Expense ($000):** 21464

STATESVILLE—Iredell County

⊞ **DAVIS REGIONAL MEDICAL CENTER (340144)**, 218 Old Mocksville Road, Zip 28625–1930, Mailing Address: P.O.Box 1823, 28687–1823; tel. 704/873–0281 **A**1 10 19 **F**13 15 17 18 20 26 28 29 34 40 43 49 50 51 53 56 57 59 60 70 73 76 77 78 79 81 82 84 85 86 87 89 90 92 93 94 98 102 103 107 108 110 111 115 119 126 129 130 131 132 146 147 148 **S** Community Health Systems, Inc., Franklin, TN
Primary Contact: Matthew Banks, Chief Executive Officer
CFO: Hugh Tobin, Chief Financial Officer
CMO: Christopher Lariscy M.D., Chief of Staff
CIO: Janie Stikeleather, Director Marketing and Community Relations
CHR: Christine McKenzie, Director Human Resources
CNO: Janice S Martin R.N., Chief Nursing Officer
Web address: www.davisregional.com
Control: Corporation, Investor–owned (for–profit) **Service**: General medical and surgical

> **Staffed Beds:** 130 **Admissions:** 3578 **Census:** 47

IREDELL HEALTH SYSTEM (340039), 557 Brookdale Drive, Zip 28677–4107,
⊞ **IREDELL HEALTH SYSTEM (340039)**, 557 Brookdale Drive, Zip 28677–4107, Mailing Address: P.O.Box 1828, 28687–1828; tel. 704/873–5661, (Total facility includes 48 beds in nursing home–type unit) **A**1 2 10 **F**3 11 13 15 17 18 20 22 28 29 30 31 32 34 35 40 41 45 47 49 50 56 57 58 59 60 62 64 68 70 74 75 76 77 78 79 81 82 85 86 87 89 91 93 97 107 108 111 114 115 117 118 119 120 121 123 127 128 129 130 132 135 146 147 148 **P**6
Primary Contact: Ed Rush, President and Chief Executive Officer
COO: John Snow, Vice President Ancillary and Support Services
CFO: Skip Smith, Vice President Finance
CMO: Brent Warren, President Medical Staff
CIO: Kyle Smith, Director Information Systems
CHR: Cindy Smale, Director, Human Resources
CNO: Becky Quate, Vice President Nursing and Patient Care Services
Web address: www.iredellhealth.org
Control: Other not–for–profit (including NFP Corporation) **Service**: General medical and surgical

> **Staffed Beds:** 203 **Admissions:** 8105 **Census:** 114 **Outpatient Visits:** 122848 **Births:** 690 **Total Expense ($000):** 162118 **Payroll Expense ($000):** 71829 **Personnel:** 1584

SYLVA—Jackson County

⊞ **HARRIS REGIONAL HOSPITAL (340016)**, 68 Hospital Road, Zip 28779–2722; tel. 828/586–7000 **A**1 10 **F**3 7 8 11 13 15 28 29 30 31 34 35 40 46 50 54 62 63 64 68 70 72 75 76 77 78 79 81 82 84 85 86 87 89 93 107 108 110 111 114 119 120 121 129 130 131 135 143 144 146 147 148 149 **S** Duke LifePoint Healthcare, Brentwood, TN
Primary Contact: Steve Heatherly, Chief Executive Officer
CHR: Janet Millsaps, Chief Human Resources Officer
Web address: www.westcare.org
Control: Corporation, Investor–owned (for–profit) **Service**: General medical and surgical

> **Staffed Beds:** 86 **Admissions:** 3422 **Census:** 34 **Outpatient Visits:** 221238 **Births:** 405 **Total Expense ($000):** 65405 **Payroll Expense ($000):** 22100 **Personnel:** 748

TARBORO—Edgecombe County

⊞ △ **VIDANT EDGECOMBE HOSPITAL (340107)**, 111 Hospital Drive, Zip 27886–2011; tel. 252/641–7700 **A**1 2 3 7 10 **F**3 11 13 15 18 28 29 30 31 34 35 40 45 50 57 59 60 70 73 75 78 79 81 82 85 87 90 92 93 96 107 110 111 119 127 130 131 132 135 145 146 **S** Vidant Health, Greenville, NC
Primary Contact: Wendell H. Baker Jr, President
CFO: Charles Alford, Vice President Financial Services
CMO: Barry Bunn M.D., Chief of Staff
CHR: David Prafka Ed.D., Director of Human Resources
Web address: www.vidanthealth.com/edgecombe/default.aspx
Control: Other not–for–profit (including NFP Corporation) **Service**: General medical and surgical

> **Staffed Beds:** 94 **Admissions:** 3690 **Census:** 44 **Outpatient Visits:** 76489 **Births:** 439 **Total Expense ($000):** 70125 **Payroll Expense ($000):** 24501 **Personnel:** 463

THOMASVILLE—Davidson County

⊞ ⇑ **NOVANT HEALTH THOMASVILLE MEDICAL CENTER (340085)**, 207 Old Lexington Road, Zip 27360–3428, Mailing Address: P.O.Box 789, 27361–0789; tel. 336/472–2000 **A**1 3 10 21 **F**3 8 11 13 15 18 26 28 29 30 34 35 38 40 44 45 50 53 56 57 59 64 66 68 70 74 75 76 77 78 79 81 82 83 84 85 86 87 89 91 92 93 98 100 102 103 104 107 108 110 111 114 115 119 126 129 130 131 132 135 141 146 147 148 149 **S** Novant Health, Winston Salem, NC
Primary Contact: Jon D. Applebaum, President and Chief Operating Officer
CFO: Fred M Hargett, Executive Vice President and Chief Financial Officer
CMO: Thomas Zweng, Executive Vice President and Chief Medical Officer
CIO: David B Garrett, Senior Vice President and Chief Information Officer
CHR: Janet Smith-Hill, Executive Vice Presideent and Chief Human Resource Officer
CNO: Nancy Pearson MSN, R.N., Director, Nursing
Web address: www.thomasvillemedicalcenter.org
Control: Other not–for–profit (including NFP Corporation) **Service**: General medical and surgical

> **Staffed Beds:** 87 **Admissions:** 4564 **Census:** 74 **Outpatient Visits:** 107112 **Births:** 695 **Total Expense ($000):** 85634 **Payroll Expense ($000):** 29133 **Personnel:** 470

Hospital, Medicare Provider Number, Address, Telephone, Approval, Facility, and Physician Codes, Health Care System

★ American Hospital Association (AHA) membership
□ The Joint Commission accreditation
○ Healthcare Facilities Accreditation Program
◇ DNV Healthcare Inc. accreditation
⇑ Center for Improvement in Healthcare Quality Accreditation
△ Commission on Accreditation of Rehabilitation Facilities (CARF) accreditation

NC

TROY—Montgomery County

⊞ **FIRSTHEALTH MONTGOMERY MEMORIAL HOSPITAL (341303)**, 520 Allen Street, Zip 27371–2802; tel. 910/571–5000, (Nonreporting) **A**1 10 18 **S** FirstHealth of the Carolinas, Pinehurst, NC
Primary Contact: Beth Walker, R.N., President
CFO: Bryan Hawkins, Controller
CIO: David B Dillehunt, Chief Information Officer
CHR: Tina H Thompson, Coordinator Human Resources
CNO: Pam Gaddy, Director, Patient Care Services and Chief Nursing Officer
Web address: www.firsthealth.org
Control: Other not–for–profit (including NFP Corporation) **Service:** General medical and surgical

Staffed Beds: 25

WADESBORO—Anson County

⊞ **CAROLINAS HEALTHCARE SYSTEM ANSON (340084)**, 2301 US Highway 74 W, Zip 28170–7554, Mailing Address: 2301 U.S Highway 74 West, 28170; tel. 704/994–4500 **A**1 10 **F**15 18 28 29 34 35 40 57 59 64 71 77 81 86 87 93 97 107 110 114 119 129 130 131 132 135 145 146 **S** Carolinas HealthCare System, Charlotte, NC
Primary Contact: Gary A. Henderson, Administrator
CFO: Jeff Griffin, Assistant Vice President Finance
CMO: Edward Blasko, Chief of Staff
CIO: Lisa Sykes, IS/Communications Director
CHR: Rhonda McFarland, Director Human Resources
CNO: Denise White MSN, Chief Nurse Executive
Web address: www.carolinashealthcare.org/anson
Control: Hospital district or authority, Government, Nonfederal **Service:** General medical and surgical

Staffed Beds: 15 Admissions: 142 Census: 1 Outpatient Visits: 30273 Births: 0 Total Expense ($000): 16320 Payroll Expense ($000): 6231 Personnel: 108

WASHINGTON—Beaufort County

BEAUFORT COUNTY HOSPITAL See Vidant Beaufort Hospital

⊞ **VIDANT BEAUFORT HOSPITAL (340186)**, 628 East 12th Street, Zip 27889–3409; tel. 252/975–4100 **A**1 3 10 **F**3 5 9 13 15 26 27 28 29 30 31 34 35 36 38 40 49 53 57 59 64 65 69 70 75 76 77 78 79 81 82 85 86 87 93 97 98 99 100 101 102 104 107 108 109 111 115 118 119 129 130 132 135 143 144 145 146 **S** Vidant Health, Greenville, NC
Primary Contact: Harvey Case, President
CFO: Lucinda Crawford, Vice President of Patient Care Services
CMO: James Egbert, Chief of Staff
CHR: Jenny Brown, Director of Human Resources
CNO: Lou Montana–Rhodes, Vice President of Patient Care Services
Web address: www.vidanthealth.com
Control: Hospital district or authority, Government, Nonfederal **Service:** General medical and surgical

Staffed Beds: 84 Admissions: 3321 Census: 45 Outpatient Visits: 53269 Births: 256 Total Expense ($000): 67124 Payroll Expense ($000): 21809 Personnel: 483

WHITEVILLE—Columbus County

⊞ **COLUMBUS REGIONAL HEALTHCARE SYSTEM (340068)**, 500 Jefferson Street, Zip 28472–3634; tel. 910/642–8011 **A**1 10 19 **F**11 13 15 28 29 30 31 34 35 40 45 46 47 48 49 50 57 59 65 68 70 71 74 75 76 77 78 79 81 85 86 87 89 91 92 93 94 97 107 108 110 111 114 115 118 119 126 129 130 132 146 148 149 150 **P**7 **S** Carolinas HealthCare System, Charlotte, NC
Primary Contact: Carla Hollis, President and Chief Executive Officer
CFO: Carl Biber, Vice President Finance
CMO: Samuel N Wheatley, Chief Medical Officer
CIO: Lisa Ward, Director Management Information Systems
CHR: Andrea West MS, Vice President of Human Resources
CNO: Terri Veneziano, Interim Chief Nursing Officer
Web address: www.crhealthcare.org/
Control: Other not–for–profit (including NFP Corporation) **Service:** General medical and surgical

Staffed Beds: 92 Admissions: 3963 Census: 44 Outpatient Visits: 122955 Births: 375 Total Expense ($000): 85902 Payroll Expense ($000): 35504 Personnel: 532

WILLIAMSTON—Martin County

⊞ **MARTIN GENERAL HOSPITAL (340133)**, 310 South McCaskey Road, Zip 27892–2150, Mailing Address: P.O.Box 1128, 27892–1128; tel. 252/809–6300, (Nonreporting) **A**1 10 **S** Quorum Health, Brentwood, TN
Primary Contact: John Jacobson, Interim Chief Executive Officer
CFO: John Jacobson, Chief Financial Officer
CIO: James Griffin, Manager Information Systems
CHR: Rebecca Edwards, Director Human Resources
CNO: Gregory Hornick MSN, Chief Nursing Officer
Web address: www.martingeneral.com
Control: Corporation, Investor–owned (for–profit) **Service:** General medical and surgical

Staffed Beds: 49

WILMINGTON—New Hanover County

⊞ △ **NEW HANOVER REGIONAL MEDICAL CENTER (340141)**, 2131 South 17th Street, Zip 28401–7483, Mailing Address: P.O.Box 9000, 28402–9000; tel. 910/343–7000, (Includes CAPE FEAR HOSPITAL, 5301 Wrightsville Avenue, Wilmington, North Carolina, Zip 28403–6599, tel. 910/452–8100) **A**1 2 3 5 7 10 13 20 **F**3 7 8 11 12 13 15 17 18 20 22 24 26 28 29 30 31 34 35 36 37 39 40 42 43 44 45 46 47 48 49 50 53 54 56 57 58 59 60 61 64 65 66 68 70 72 73 74 75 76 77 78 79 80 81 82 84 85 86 87 88 89 90 92 93 94 96 97 98 100 101 102 103 107 108 110 111 114 115 117 118 119 121 123 126 130 131 132 135 144 146 147 148 149 **S** New Hanover Regional Medical Center, Wilmington, NC
Primary Contact: Andre Boyd Sr, Executive Vice President, Hospital Division
CFO: Edwin J Ollie, Executive Vice President and Chief Financial Officer
CMO: Sam Spicer M.D., Vice President Medical Affairs
CIO: Avery Cloud, Vice President and Chief Information Officer
CHR: Keith A Strawn, Vice President Human Resources
CNO: Mary Ellen Bonczek R.N., Chief Nursing Executive
Web address: www.nhrmc.org
Control: County, Government, Nonfederal **Service:** General medical and surgical

Staffed Beds: 685 Admissions: 39890 Census: 543 Outpatient Visits: 386002 Births: 4016 Total Expense ($000): 834548 Payroll Expense ($000): 312583 Personnel: 4833

WILMINGTON TREATMENT CENTER (340168), 2520 Troy Drive, Zip 28401–7643; tel. 910/762–2727, (Nonreporting) **A**10 **S** CRC Health Group, Inc., Cupertino, CA
Primary Contact: Robert Pitts, Executive Director
COO: Paige Bottom, Director Operations
CFO: Virginia Powell, Director Finance
CMO: Patrick Martin M.D., Medical Director
Web address: www.wilmtreatment.com
Control: Corporation, Investor–owned (for–profit) **Service:** Alcoholism and other chemical dependency

Staffed Beds: 44

WILSON—Wilson County

TRIANGLE EAST NURSING CARE CENTER See Wilmed Nursing Care Center

⊞ **WILSON MEDICAL CENTER (340126)**, 1705 Tarboro Street, SW, Zip 27893–3428; tel. 252/399–8040, (Total facility includes 90 beds in nursing home–type unit) **A**1 2 10 19 **F**3 11 13 15 18 19 20 22 26 28 29 30 31 34 35 39 40 45 47 48 49 50 57 60 64 70 73 74 75 76 77 78 79 81 82 83 84 85 86 87 89 92 93 94 97 102 103 107 108 110 111 114 115 118 119 120 121 123 128 129 130 132 135 146 148 **S** Duke LifePoint Healthcare, Brentwood, TN
Primary Contact: William E. Caldwell Jr, Chief Executive Officer
CMO: Rick Guarino M.D., Vice President Medical Affairs
CIO: Brian Dietrick, Director Information Systems
CHR: Denise O'Hara, Director Human Resources
Web address: www.wilmed.org
Control: Corporation, Investor–owned (for–profit) **Service:** General medical and surgical

Staffed Beds: 220 Admissions: 7192 Census: 159 Outpatient Visits: 53902 Births: 928 Total Expense ($000): 107226 Payroll Expense ($000): 45868 Personnel: 950

Many Facility Codes have changed. Please refer to the AHA Guide Code Chart. © 2017 AHA Guide

WINDSOR—Bertie County

⊠ **VIDANT BERTIE HOSPITAL (341304)**, 1403 South King Street, Zip 27983–9666, Mailing Address: P.O.Box 40, 27983–0040; tel. 252/794–6600 **A**1 10 18 **F**3 15 29 30 34 35 40 45 46 47 48 49 57 59 64 77 79 81 82 93 94 97 107 110 114 119 127 132 135 146 148 **S** Vidant Health, Greenville, NC
Primary Contact: Jeffrey Sackrison, President
CFO: Brian Harvill, Vice President Financial Services
CMO: William Ballance, Chief of Medical Staff
CIO: Brian White, Director Strategic Planning
CHR: Nicole Spell, Director Human Resources
CNO: Silvia Rose, Director Patient Care Services
Web address: www.vidanthealth.com
Control: Other not–for–profit (including NFP Corporation) **Service**: General medical and surgical

Staffed Beds: 6 **Admissions**: 414 **Census**: 4 **Outpatient Visits**: 25052
Births: 0 **Total Expense ($000)**: 17020 **Payroll Expense ($000)**: 7436
Personnel: 104

WINSTON SALEM—Forsyth County

BRENNER CHILDREN'S HOSPITAL & HEALTH SERVICES See Wake Forest Baptist Medical Center

WINSTON—SALEM-Forsyth County

MEDICAL PARK HOSPITAL See Novant Health Medical Park Hospital

⊠ △ **NOVANT HEALTH FORSYTH MEDICAL CENTER (340014)**, 3333 Silas Creek Parkway, Zip 27103–3090; tel. 336/718–5000, (Includes KERNERSVILLE MEDICAL CENTER, 2911750 Kernersville Medical Parkway, Kernersville, North Carolina, Zip 27284–2932, Mailing Address: 1750 Kernersville Medical Parkway, Zip 27284–2932, tel. 336/564–4000; Chad Setliff, President and Chief Operating Officer; NOVANT HEALTH CLEMMONS MEDICAL CENTER, 6915 Village Medical Circle, Clemmons, North Carolina, Zip 27012–8002, tel. 336/893–1000; Chad Setliff, President and Chief Operating Officer) **A**1 2 3 5 7 10 **F**3 12 13 14 15 17 18 20 22 24 26 28 29 30 31 32 34 35 37 38 40 42 45 46 49 50 53 54 56 57 58 59 60 61 64 65 66 67 70 71 72 74 75 76 77 78 79 80 81 82 83 84 85 86 87 89 90 93 98 100 101 102 103 104 105 107 108 109 111 112 114 115 116 117 118 119 120 121 123 124 126 129 130 131 132 135 141 143 146 147 148 149 **S** Novant Health, Winston Salem, NC
Primary Contact: Sean M. Sanz, President and Chief Operating Officer
CFO: Fred M Hargett, Executive Vice President and Chief Financial Officer
CMO: Thomas Zweng, Executive Vice President and Chief Medical Officer
CIO: David B Garrett, Senior Vice President and Chief Information Officer
CHR: Janet Smith–Hill, Senior Vice President Human Resources
CNO: Janet L Bright, Vice President, Chief Nursing Officer
Web address: www.novanthealth.org
Control: Other not–for–profit (including NFP Corporation) **Service**: General medical and surgical

Staffed Beds: 740 **Admissions**: 43292 **Census**: 657 **Outpatient Visits**: 428319 **Births**: 6499 **Total Expense ($000)**: 787374 **Payroll Expense ($000)**: 240465 **Personnel**: 3890

⊠ **NOVANT HEALTH MEDICAL PARK HOSPITAL (340148)**, 1950 South Hawthorne Road, Zip 27103–3993; tel. 336/718–0600 **A**1 2 10 **F**3 29 35 39 64 74 78 79 81 85 126 130 131 135 141 146 **S** Novant Health, Winston Salem, NC
Primary Contact: Kirsten Royster, President and Chief Operating Officer
CFO: Fred M Hargett, Executive Vice President and Chief Financial Officer
CMO: Thomas Zweng, Executive Vice President and Chief Medical Officer
CIO: David B Garrett, Senior Vice President and Chief Information Officer
CHR: Janet Smith–Hill, Executive Vice President and Chief Human Resource Officer
CNO: Carol A Smith R.N., Director Operations and Nursing
Web address: www.novanthealth.org
Control: Other not–for–profit (including NFP Corporation) **Service**: General medical and surgical

Staffed Beds: 21 **Admissions**: 902 **Census**: 9 **Outpatient Visits**: 34994
Births: 0 **Total Expense ($000)**: 53199 **Payroll Expense ($000)**: 12058
Personnel: 194

☐ **OLD VINEYARD BEHAVIORAL HEALTH SERVICES (344007)**, 3637 Old Vineyard Road, Zip 27104–4842; tel. 336/794–3550 **A**1 10 **F**4 29 40 50 75 87 98 99 101 102 103 104 105 130 149 **S** Universal Health Services, Inc., King of Prussia, PA
Primary Contact: Kevin Patton, Chief Executive Officer
CFO: Ernest C Priddy III, Chief Financial Officer
CMO: Raj Thotakura M.D., Medical Director
CHR: Jackie Pennino, Director Human Resources
CNO: Susan Evans, Chief Nursing Officer
Web address: www.oldvineyardbhs.com
Control: Corporation, Investor–owned (for–profit) **Service**: Psychiatric

Staffed Beds: 104 **Admissions**: 4201 **Census**: 104 **Outpatient Visits**: 11017 **Births**: 0 **Total Expense ($000)**: 20480 **Payroll Expense ($000)**: 10295 **Personnel**: 168

⊠ **WAKE FOREST BAPTIST MEDICAL CENTER (340047)**, Medical Center Boulevard, Zip 27157–0001; tel. 336/716–2011, (Includes BRENNER CHILDREN'S HOSPITAL & HEALTH SERVICES, Medical Center Boulevard, Winston Salem, North Carolina, Zip 27157, Mailing Address: One Medical Center Boulevard, Zip 27157, tel. 336/716–2255) **A**1 2 3 5 8 10 **F**3 5 6 7 9 11 12 15 16 17 18 19 20 21 22 23 24 25 26 27 28 29 30 31 32 34 35 36 37 40 41 43 44 45 46 47 48 49 50 52 53 54 55 56 57 58 59 60 61 62 64 65 66 67 68 70 72 73 74 75 77 78 79 80 81 82 84 85 86 87 88 89 90 92 93 96 97 98 99 100 101 102 103 104 107 108 110 111 113 114 115 116 117 118 119 120 121 123 124 126 129 130 131 132 135 136 137 138 141 142 143 144 145 146 147 148 149 **P**6 **S** Wake Forest Baptist Health, Winston–Salem, NC
Primary Contact: Julie Ann. Freischlag, M.D., Chief Executive Officer
CMO: Russell M Howerton M.D., Chief Medical Officer
CHR: Cheryl Locke, Vice President and Chief Human Resource Officer
Web address: www.wakehealth.edu
Control: Other not–for–profit (including NFP Corporation) **Service**: General medical and surgical

Staffed Beds: 812 **Admissions**: 40810 **Census**: 671 **Outpatient Visits**: 941254 **Births**: 8 **Total Expense ($000)**: 1412915 **Payroll Expense ($000)**: 475045 **Personnel**: 9146

NORTH DAKOTA

ASHLEY—Mcintosh County

★ **ASHLEY MEDICAL CENTER (351322)**, 612 North Center Avenue, Zip 58413–7013, Mailing Address: P.O.Box 450, 58413–0450; tel. 701/288–3433, (Nonreporting) **A**10 18
Primary Contact: Holly Wolff, Chief Executive Officer
CMO: Udom Tinsa M.D., Medical Director
Web address: www.amctoday.org
Control: Other not–for–profit (including NFP Corporation) **Service:** General medical and surgical

Staffed Beds: 64

BELCOURT—Rolette County

☐ **INDIAN HEALTH SERVICE – QUENTIN N. BURDICK MEMORIAL HEALTH CARE FACILITY (350063)**, 1300 Hospital Loop, Zip 58316, Mailing Address: P.O.Box 160, 58316–0160; tel. 701/477–6111, (Nonreporting) **A**1 5 10 **S** U. S. Indian Health Service, Rockville, MD
Primary Contact: Shelly Harris, Chief Executive Officer
CFO: Deland Davis, Chief Financial Officer
CMO: Vernon Azure, Clinical Director
CIO: Chance Wilkie, Information Technology Specialist
CHR: Donna Belgarde, Human Resources Specialist
CNO: Lynelle Hunt, Director of Nursing
Web address: www.ihs.gov
Control: PHS, Indian Service, Government, federal **Service:** General medical and surgical

Staffed Beds: 27

BISMARCK—Burleigh County

✛ **CHI ST. ALEXIUS HEALTH (350002)**, 900 East Broadway, Zip 58501–4586, Mailing Address: P.O.Box 5510, 58506–5510; tel. 701/530–7000, (Total facility includes 19 beds in nursing home–type unit) **A**1 2 3 5 10 **F**3 8 9 11 12 13 15 17 18 19 20 21 22 23 24 25 26 28 29 30 31 32 34 35 38 40 43 45 46 49 53 56 57 58 59 60 62 63 64 65 68 70 72 73 74 75 76 77 78 79 81 82 83 84 85 87 88 89 91 92 93 94 96 97 98 99 100 101 102 103 104 105 106 107 110 111 114 115 117 118 119 126 128 129 130 131 132 135 146 147 148 149 150 **P**8 **S** Catholic Health Initiatives, Englewood, CO
Primary Contact: Kurt Schley, Market Chief Executive Officer
CFO: Susan Sisk, Chief Financial Officer
CMO: Shiraz Hyder M.D., Director Medical Affairs
CIO: Todd Bortke, Director Information Systems
CHR: Tom Gregg, Vice President Human Resources
CNO: Rosanne Schmidt R.N., Chief Nursing Officer
Web address: www.st.alexius.org
Control: Church operated, Nongovernment, not–for–profit **Service:** General medical and surgical

Staffed Beds: 237 Admissions: 10359 Census: 126 Outpatient Visits: 177159 Births: 1590 Total Expense ($000): 435168 Payroll Expense ($000): 97831 Personnel: 1952

✛ △ **SANFORD BISMARCK (350015)**, 300 North Seventh Street, Zip 58501–4439, Mailing Address: P.O.Box 5525, 58506–5525; tel. 701/323–6000 **A**1 2 3 5 7 10 19 **F**3 7 9 11 12 13 15 17 18 20 22 24 26 28 29 30 34 35 36 37 38 40 43 44 45 48 49 50 51 52 53 54 55 56 57 58 59 60 61 62 63 64 66 68 69 70 72 73 74 75 77 78 79 81 82 85 86 87 88 89 90 91 92 93 96 97 98 99 100 101 102 103 104 105 107 108 110 111 114 115 116 117 118 119 126 128 129 130 131 132 135 138 144 146 147 148 149 150 **P**6 **S** Sanford Health, Sioux Falls, SD
Primary Contact: Craig Lambrecht, M.D., President
COO: Al Hurley, Clinic Chief Operating Officer
CFO: Kirk Cristy, Chief Financial Officer
CMO: Chris Meeker M.D., Chief Medical Officer
CHR: Scott D Boehm, Executive Vice President Human Resources and Facilities
CNO: Jan Kamphuis Ph.D., R.N., Executive Vice President and Chief Nurse Executive
Web address: www.bismarck.sanfordhealth.org/
Control: Other not–for–profit (including NFP Corporation) **Service:** General medical and surgical

Staffed Beds: 208 Admissions: 10785 Census: 137 Outpatient Visits: 202879 Births: 1088 Total Expense ($000): 439947 Payroll Expense ($000): 211263 Personnel: 2538

SANFORD HEALTH See Sanford Bismarck

BOTTINEAU—Bottineau County

ST. ANDREW'S HEALTH CENTER (351307), 316 Ohmer Street, Zip 58318–1045; tel. 701/228–9300 **A**5 10 18 **F**3 15 28 29 30 34 35 40 43 57 59 81 93 107 108 110 125 127 130 132 133 143 144 146 149 **P**5 **S** Sisters of Mary of the Presentation Health System, Fargo, ND
Primary Contact: Jodi Atkinson, President and Chief Executive Officer
CFO: Sean Rinkenberger, Chief Financial Officer
CMO: Jessica Skjolden M.D., Chief of Staff
CHR: Brenda Arneson, Administrative Assistant
CNO: Karla Spence, Director of Nursing
Web address: www.standrewshealth.com
Control: Church operated, Nongovernment, not–for–profit **Service:** General medical and surgical

Staffed Beds: 25 Admissions: 140 Census: 18 Outpatient Visits: 8650 Births: 0 Total Expense ($000): 8753 Payroll Expense ($000): 3738 Personnel: 97

BOWMAN—Bowman County

SOUTHWEST HEALTHCARE SERVICES (351313), 802 2nd Street Northwest, Zip 58623–4483, Mailing Address: P O Drawer 'C', 58623; tel. 701/523–5265, (Nonreporting) **A**10 18
Primary Contact: John Michael. Osse, Interim Chief Executive Officer
Web address: www.swhealthcare.net
Control: Other not–for–profit (including NFP Corporation) **Service:** General medical and surgical

Staffed Beds: 55

CANDO—Towner County

★ **TOWNER COUNTY MEDICAL CENTER (351331)**, State Highway 281 North, Zip 58324, Mailing Address: P.O.Box 688, 58324–0688; tel. 701/968–4411, (Total facility includes 30 beds in nursing home–type unit) **A**5 10 18 **F**8 15 18 29 31 32 33 34 35 40 43 45 50 53 54 57 59 65 68 75 78 81 82 83 85 86 89 93 97 107 110 114 125 127 128 129 130 133 135 143 144 147 148
Primary Contact: Ben Bucher, Chief Executive Officer
CFO: Tammy Larson, Chief Financial Officer
CMO: Russ Petty M.D., Chief of Staff
CIO: David Fite, Director Information Technology
CHR: Pat Klingenberg, Director Human Resources
Web address: www.tcmedcenter.org
Control: Other not–for–profit (including NFP Corporation) **Service:** General medical and surgical

Staffed Beds: 50 Admissions: 197 Census: 33 Outpatient Visits: 12749 Births: 0 Total Expense ($000): 6627 Payroll Expense ($000): 2405 Personnel: 96

CARRINGTON—Foster County

★ **CHI ST ALEXIUS HEALTH CARRINGTON MEDICAL CENTER (351318)**, 800 North Fourth Street, Zip 58421–1217, Mailing Address: P.O.Box 461, 58421–0461; tel. 701/652–3141 **A**5 10 18 **F**7 11 15 28 30 34 40 45 46 75 81 87 107 108 110 114 119 124 127 133 143 146 **P**6 **S** Catholic Health Initiatives, Englewood, CO
Primary Contact: Mariann Doeling, R.N., President
COO: Brenda Rask, Vice President Operations
CFO: Kurt Sargent CPA, Vice President, Operational Finance
CIO: Keith Stauffer, Regional Chief Information Officer
CHR: Carol Risovi, Human Resources
CNO: Jodi Lynn Hovdenes, Vice President of Patient Care
Web address: www.carringtonhealthcenter.org
Control: Other not–for–profit (including NFP Corporation) **Service:** General medical and surgical

Staffed Beds: 25 Admissions: 355 Census: 4 Outpatient Visits: 20434 Births: 0 Total Expense ($000): 11522 Payroll Expense ($000): 3358 Personnel: 95

CAVALIER—Pembina County

★ **PEMBINA COUNTY MEMORIAL HOSPITAL AND WEDGEWOOD MANOR (351319)**, 301 Mountain Street East, Zip 58220–4015, Mailing Address: P.O.Box 380, 58220–0380; tel. 701/265–8461, (Total facility includes 50 beds in nursing home–type unit) **A**5 10 18 **F**2 3 28 29 31 40 42 43 45 56 59 65 68 78 81 82 84 87 93 97 107 114 119 127 128 130 131 132 133 135 146
Primary Contact: Lisa LeTexier, Interim Chief Executive Officer
CMO: K S Sumra M.D., Chief of Staff
CIO: Robert Heidt, Director Information Systems
Web address: www.cavalierhospital.com
Control: Other not–for–profit (including NFP Corporation) **Service:** General medical and surgical

Staffed Beds: 70 Admissions: 703 Census: 45 Outpatient Visits: 20999 Births: 0 Total Expense ($000): 13763 Payroll Expense ($000): 5076 Personnel: 174

Many Facility Codes have changed. Please refer to the AHA Guide Code Chart. © 2017 AHA Guide

COOPERSTOWN—Griggs County

★ **COOPERSTOWN MEDICAL CENTER (351306)**, 1200 Roberts Avenue, Zip 58425–7101; tel. 701/797–2221, (Nonreporting) **A**10 18
Primary Contact: Nikki Johnson, Interim Chief Executive Officer
CMO: Jeffrey Peterson M.D., Medical Director
CHR: Pamela VenHuizen, Chief Human Resources Officer
Web address: www.coopermc.com
Control: Other not–for–profit (including NFP Corporation) **Service:** General medical and surgical

Staffed Beds: 62

CROSBY—Divide County

★ **ST. LUKE'S MEDICAL CENTER (351325)**, 702 First Street Southwest, Zip 58730–3329, Mailing Address: P.O.Box 10, 58730–0010; tel. 701/965–6384, (Nonreporting) **A**10 18
Primary Contact: Cody Barnhart, Chief Executive Officer
Web address: www.dcstlukes.org/
Control: Other not–for–profit (including NFP Corporation) **Service:** General medical and surgical

Staffed Beds: 15

DEVILS LAKE—Ramsey County

⊞ **CHI ST. ALEXIUS HEALTH DEVILS LAKE HOSPITAL (351333)**, 1031 Seventh Street NE, Zip 58301–2798; tel. 701/662–2131 **A**1 5 10 18 **F**3 11 13 28 29 30 34 35 40 43 45 50 57 70 75 76 81 85 87 93 107 108 111 115 119 130 131 133 146 148 149 150 **S** Catholic Health Initiatives, Englewood, CO
Primary Contact: Andrew Lankowicz, FACHE, President
CFO: Kurt Sargent CPA, Vice President Operational Finance
CMO: Richard Johnson M.D., Chief of Medical Staff
CHR: Bonnie Mattern, Director Human Resources
CNO: Aaron Johnson, Vice President Patient Care Services and Chief Nursing Officer
Web address: www.mercyhospitaldl.com
Control: Other not–for–profit (including NFP Corporation) **Service:** General medical and surgical

Staffed Beds: 25 **Admissions:** 873 **Census:** 11 **Outpatient Visits:** 21414 **Births:** 330 **Total Expense ($000):** 20227 **Payroll Expense ($000):** 8656 **Personnel:** 129

DICKINSON—Stark County

⊞ **CHI ST. ALEXIUS HEALTH – DICKINSON MEDICAL CENTER (351336)**, 2500 Fairway Street, Zip 58601–4399; tel. 701/456–4000 **A**1 5 10 18 **F**3 8 11 13 15 28 29 30 34 35 40 53 57 59 64 70 75 76 79 81 84 85 86 87 89 97 107 108 111 114 119 127 129 130 132 133 146 149 **S** Catholic Health Initiatives, Englewood, CO
Primary Contact: Reed Reyman, President
CFO: Stephanie Franken, Vice President Operational Finance
CHR: Denise Lutz, Chief Human Resources Officer
CNO: DeeAnna Opstedahl R.N., Vice President Patient Care Services
Web address: www.stjoeshospital.org
Control: Church operated, Nongovernment, not–for–profit **Service:** General medical and surgical

Staffed Beds: 25 **Admissions:** 2001 **Census:** 16 **Outpatient Visits:** 51463 **Births:** 703 **Total Expense ($000):** 64142 **Payroll Expense ($000):** 25157 **Personnel:** 288

ELGIN—Grant County

★ **JACOBSON MEMORIAL HOSPITAL CARE CENTER (351314)**, 601 East Street North, Zip 58533–7105, Mailing Address: P.O.Box 367, 58533–0367; tel. 701/584–2792 **A**10 18 **F**15 28 34 40 41 43 50 56 57 59 69 75 77 90 93 97 107 110 111 119 127 128 130 131 133 146 147 148
Primary Contact: Theo Stoller, Chief Executive Officer
CFO: Scott Ostenson, Chief Financial Officer
CMO: Deepak Goyal M.D., Chief of Staff
CHR: Rynae Golke, Director Human Resources
CNO: Connie Gustafson, Director of Nursing
Web address: www.jacobsonhospital.org
Control: Other not–for–profit (including NFP Corporation) **Service:** General medical and surgical

Staffed Beds: 30 **Admissions:** 169 **Census:** 22 **Outpatient Visits:** 7641 **Births:** 0 **Total Expense ($000):** 6808 **Payroll Expense ($000):** 2434 **Personnel:** 52

FARGO—Cass County

⊞ **ESSENTIA HEALTH FARGO (350070)**, 3000 32nd Avenue South, Zip 58103–6132; tel. 701/364–8000 **A**1 2 3 5 10 **F**3 9 11 12 13 15 17 18 20 22 24 25 26 28 29 30 31 32 33 34 35 38 40 41 43 44 45 46 47 48 49 50 51 56 57 58 59 60 61 64 65 70 72 74 75 76 77 78 79 81 82 83 84 85 86 87 89 91 92 93 97 107 108 109 110 111 112 113 114 115 116 117 118 119 120 121 122 123 124 126 129 130 131 132 135 144 145 146 147 148 **P**6 **S** Essentia Health, Duluth, MN
Primary Contact: Timothy Sayler, Chief Operating Officer
COO: Timothy Sayler, Chief Operating Officer
CFO: Dennis Fuhrman, Vice President Finance
CMO: Michael Briggs M.D., Chief Medical Officer
CIO: Ken Gilles, Chief Information Officer
CHR: Keith Wahlund, Vice President Human Resources
Web address: www.essentiahealth.com
Control: Other not–for–profit (including NFP Corporation) **Service:** General medical and surgical

Staffed Beds: 133 **Admissions:** 8632 **Census:** 105 **Outpatient Visits:** 147859 **Births:** 1424 **Total Expense ($000):** 349503 **Payroll Expense ($000):** 152825 **Personnel:** 1926

⊞ **FARGO VETERANS AFFAIRS HEALTH CARE SYSTEM**, 2101 Elm Street North, Zip 58102–2498; tel. 701/232–3241 **A**1 3 5 **F**3 5 8 11 12 18 29 30 31 33 34 35 36 38 39 40 44 45 50 54 56 57 58 59 60 61 62 63 64 65 70 71 74 75 77 78 79 81 82 83 84 85 86 87 93 94 96 97 98 99 100 101 102 103 104 107 111 114 115 119 120 127 128 129 130 132 133 135 136 137 138 139 140 141 142 143 144 146 148 149 150 **P**6 **S** Department of Veterans Affairs, Washington, DC
Primary Contact: Lavonne Liversage, Director
COO: Dale DeKrey MS, Associate Director Operations and Resources
CFO: Roger Sayler, Finance Officer
CMO: J Brian Hancock M.D., Chief of Staff
CIO: Raymond Nelson, Acting Chief Information Resource Management
CHR: Jason Wells, Chief Human Resources Management Service
CNO: Julie Bruhn R.N., MS, Associate Director Patient Care and Nurse Executive
Web address: www.fargo.va.gov/
Control: Veterans Affairs, Government, federal **Service:** General medical and surgical

Staffed Beds: 65 **Admissions:** 2644 **Census:** 21 **Outpatient Visits:** 215063 **Births:** 0 **Total Expense ($000):** 240071 **Payroll Expense ($000):** 74089 **Personnel:** 1203

INNOVIS HEALTH See Essentia Health Fargo
KINDRED HOSPITAL FARGO See Vibra Hospital Of Fargo
MERITCARE MEDICAL CENTER See Sanford Medical Center Fargo

⊞ **PRAIRIE ST. JOHN'S (354004)**, 510 4th Street South, Zip 58103–1914; tel. 701/476–7200, (Nonreporting) **A**1 10 **S** Universal Health Services, Inc., King of Prussia, PA
Primary Contact: Jeff Herman, Chief Executive Officer
COO: Jennifer Faul, Chief Operating Officer
CFO: Tom Eide, Chief Financial Officer
CMO: Eduardo Meza M.D., Medical Director
CHR: Michelle A Parkinson, Director Human Resources
CNO: Jacki Toppen, Director of Nursing
Web address: www.prairie–stjohns.com
Control: Partnership, Investor–owned (for–profit) **Service:** Psychiatric

Staffed Beds: 94

⊞ △ **SANFORD MEDICAL CENTER FARGO (350011)**, 801 Broadway North, Zip 58122–3641; tel. 701/234–2000, (Includes SANFORD SOUTH UNIVERSITY, 1720 South University Drive, Fargo, North Dakota, Zip 58103–4994, tel. 701/234–2000; Nate White, Executive Vice President) **A**1 2 3 5 7 8 10 19 **F**3 7 8 9 11 12 13 15 17 18 19 20 21 22 23 24 25 26 27 28 29 30 31 32 33 34 35 36 37 38 39 40 43 44 45 46 47 48 49 50 51 52 53 54 55 56 57 58 59 60 61 62 63 64 65 66 68 70 71 72 73 74 75 76 78 79 80 81 82 83 84 85 86 87 88 89 90 91 92 93 94 96 97 98 99 100 101 102 103 104 105 107 111 112 114 115 116 117 118 119 120 121 123 124 126 129 130 131 132 135 138 141 142 143 144 145 146 147 148 149 150 **P**6 **S** Sanford Health, Sioux Falls, SD
Primary Contact: Nate White, Executive Vice President
COO: Susan Jarvis, Vice President Operations
CFO: Tiffany Lawrence, Vice President of Finance
CMO: Douglas Griffin M.D., Vice President Medical Officer
CIO: Arlyn Broekhuis, Chief Information Officer
CHR: Bill Gassen, Chief Human Resource Officer
CNO: Roberta Young, Vice President Nursing
Web address: www.sanfordhealth.org
Control: Other not–for–profit (including NFP Corporation) **Service:** General medical and surgical

Staffed Beds: 490 **Admissions:** 22965 **Census:** 351 **Outpatient Visits:** 429068 **Births:** 2765 **Total Expense ($000):** 932923 **Payroll Expense ($000):** 400229 **Personnel:** 4632

Hospital, Medicare Provider Number, Address, Telephone, Approval, Facility, and Physician Codes, Health Care System

★ American Hospital Association (AHA) membership
□ The Joint Commission accreditation
○ Healthcare Facilities Accreditation Program
◇ DNV Healthcare Inc. accreditation
⇑ Center for Improvement in Healthcare Quality Accreditation
△ Commission on Accreditation of Rehabilitation Facilities (CARF) accreditation

© 2017 AHA Guide   *Many Facility Codes have changed. Please refer to the AHA Guide Code Chart.*   Hospitals **A475**

VETERANS AFFAIRS HEALTH CARE SYSTEM See Fargo Veterans Affairs Health Care System

✠ **VIBRA HOSPITAL OF FARGO (352004)**, 1720 University Drive South, Zip 58103–4940; tel. 701/241–9099, (Nonreporting) **A**1 10 **S** Vibra Healthcare, Mechanicsburg, PA
Primary Contact: Custer Huseby, Chief Executive Officer
Web address: www.vhfargo.com
Control: Corporation, Investor–owned (for–profit) **Service**: Acute long–term care hospital

Staffed Beds: 31

FORT YATES—Sioux County

⇑ **STANDING ROCK SERVICE UNIT, FORT YATES HOSPITAL, INDIAN HEALTH SERVICE, DHHS (350064)**, 10 North River Road, Zip 58538, Mailing Address: P.O.Box 'J', 58538; tel. 701/854–3831, (Nonreporting) **A**5 10 21 **S** U. S. Indian Health Service, Rockville, MD
Primary Contact: Jana Gipp, Chief Executive Officer
CFO: Byron Wilcox, Chief Financial Management Officer
CMO: Sara Jumping Eagle, Clinical Director
CNO: Joelle Keepseagle, Director of Nursing
Web address: www.ihs.gov
Control: PHS, Indian Service, Government, federal **Service**: General medical and surgical

Staffed Beds: 14

GARRISON—Mclean County

★ **CHI ST. ALEXIUS HEALTH GARRISON (351303)**, 407 Third Avenue SE, Zip 58540–7235; tel. 701/463–2275, (Nonreporting) **A**5 10 18 **S** Catholic Health Initiatives, Englewood, CO
Primary Contact: Tod Graeber, Administrator
CMO: Vern Harchenko M.D., Chief of Staff
CNO: Beth Hetletved, Director of Nurses
Web address: www.garrisonmh.com
Control: Other not–for–profit (including NFP Corporation) **Service**: General medical and surgical

Staffed Beds: 50

GRAFTON—Walsh County

★ **UNITY MEDICAL CENTER (351320)**, 164 West 13th Street, Zip 58237–1896; tel. 701/352–1620, (Nonreporting) **A**5 10 18
Primary Contact: Alan O'Neil, Chief Executive Officer
CFO: Rachel Ray, Chief Financial Officer
Web address: www.unitymedcenter.com
Control: Other not–for–profit (including NFP Corporation) **Service**: General medical and surgical

Staffed Beds: 14

GRAND FORKS—Grand Forks County

✠ △ **ALTRU HEALTH SYSTEM (350019)**, 1200 South Columbia Road, Zip 58201–4036, Mailing Address: P.O.Box 6002, 58206–6002; tel. 701/780–5000, (Includes ALTRU HOSPITAL, 1200 South Columbia Road, Grand Forks, North Dakota, Zip 58201, PO Box 6002, 58206–6002, tel. 701/780–5000; David R Molmen, M.P.H., Chief Executive Officer; ALTRU REHABILITATION CENTER, 1300 South Columbia Road, Grand Forks, North Dakota, Zip 58201, tel. 701/780–2311; David R Molmen, M.P.H., Chief Executive Officer) **A**1 2 3 5 7 10 20 **F**3 7 8 11 12 13 14 15 18 20 22 24 26 28 29 30 31 32 33 34 35 36 37 38 40 43 44 45 48 49 50 52 53 55 56 57 58 59 60 61 62 63 64 65 68 69 70 71 72 74 75 77 78 79 81 82 83 84 85 86 87 90 91 92 93 94 96 97 98 99 100 101 102 103 104 105 107 108 110 111 114 115 117 119 121 123 124 125 129 130 131 132 135 143 144 145 146 147 148 **P**6
Primary Contact: David R. Molmen, M.P.H., Chief Executive Officer
COO: Brad Wehe, Chief Operating Officer
CFO: Dwight Thompson, Chief Financial Officer
CMO: Colleen Swank, Chief Medical Officer
CIO: Mark Waind, Chief Information Officer
CHR: Kellee J Fisk, Chief People Officer
CNO: Margaret M Reed R.N., Chief Nursing Officer
Web address: www.altru.org
Control: Other not–for–profit (including NFP Corporation) **Service**: General medical and surgical

Staffed Beds: 305 Admissions: 11823 Census: 180 Outpatient Visits: 947756 Births: 1805 Total Expense ($000): 543256 Payroll Expense ($000): 278200 Personnel: 3382

⇑ **RED RIVER BEHAVIORAL HEALTH SYSTEM (354005)**, 1451 44th Avenue South Unit A, Zip 58201–3434; tel. 701/772–2500 (Nonreporting) **A**10 21
Primary Contact: John Baker, Chief Executive Officer
CFO: Michelle Currie, Chief Financial Officer
CHR: Amanda Altendorf, Chief Human Resources and Quality Management
Web address: www.redriverbhs.com
Control: Corporation, Investor–owned (for–profit) **Service**: Psychiatric

Staffed Beds: 70

HARVEY—Wells County

★ **ST. ALOISIUS MEDICAL CENTER (351327)**, 325 East Brewster Street, Zip 58341–1653; tel. 701/324–4651, (Total facility includes 95 beds in nursing home–type unit) **A**5 10 18 **F**15 28 30 40 45 53 56 57 59 77 81 93 107 110 114 125 128 130 131 132 133 146 147 **S** Sisters of Mary of the Presentation Health System, Fargo, ND
Primary Contact: Mike Zwicker, Chief Executive Officer
CFO: Sandra Teubner, Chief Financial Officer
Web address: www.staloisius.com
Control: Church operated, Nongovernment, not–for–profit **Service**: General medical and surgical

Staffed Beds: 120 Admissions: 257 Census: 88 Outpatient Visits: 7656 Births: 0 Total Expense ($000): 16762 Payroll Expense ($000): 6437 Personnel: 198

HAZEN—Mercer County

★ **SAKAKAWEA MEDICAL CENTER (351310)**, 510 Eighth Avenue NE, Zip 58545–4637; tel. 701/748–2225, (Nonreporting) **A**5 10 18
Primary Contact: Darrold Bertsch, Chief Executive Officer
CFO: Renae Snyder, Chief Financial Officer
CHR: Laurie Miller, Administrative Assistant
CNO: Marcie Schulz, Director Patient Care
Web address: www.sakmedcenter.com
Control: Other not–for–profit (including NFP Corporation) **Service**: General medical and surgical

Staffed Beds: 18

HETTINGER—Adams County

WEST RIVER REGIONAL MEDICAL CENTER (351330), 1000 Highway 12, Zip 58639–7530; tel. 701/567–4561, (Nonreporting) **A**3 5 10 18
Primary Contact: Matthew Shahan, Chief Executive Officer
CFO: Nathan Stadheim, Chief Financial Officer
CMO: Jennifer Shefield M.D., Chief of Staff
CIO: Julia Gochenour, Manager Information Systems
CHR: Tera Fried, Manager Human Resources
CNO: Barbara Stadheim, Chief Nursing Officer
Web address: www.wrhs.com
Control: Other not–for–profit (including NFP Corporation) **Service**: General medical and surgical

Staffed Beds: 25

HILLSBORO—Traill County

★ **SANFORD HILLSBORO MEDICAL CENTER (351329)**, 12 Third Street SE, Zip 58045–4840, Mailing Address: P.O.Box 609, 58045–0609; tel. 701/636–3200, (Total facility includes 36 beds in nursing home–type unit) **A**5 10 18 **F**7 10 11 34 35 40 64 65 68 75 81 93 97 103 125 128 130 131 133 143 146 148 **P**6 **S** Sanford Health, Sioux Falls, SD
Primary Contact: Jac McTaggart, Chief Executive Officer
CFO: Scott Awalt, Chief Financial Officer
CMO: Charles J Breen M.D., Medical Director
CHR: Jenny Jacobson, Manager Human Resources
Web address: www.hillsboromedicalcenter.com
Control: Other not–for–profit (including NFP Corporation) **Service**: General medical and surgical

Staffed Beds: 52 Admissions: 206 Census: 39 Outpatient Visits: 15995 Total Expense ($000): 10387 Payroll Expense ($000): 4910 Personnel: 75

JAMESTOWN—Stutsman County

✠ **JAMESTOWN REGIONAL MEDICAL CENTER (351335)**, 2422 20th Street SW, Zip 58401–6201; tel. 701/252–1050 **A**1 5 10 18 **F**3 11 13 15 28 29 31 34 35 40 43 45 50 53 57 59 62 63 64 68 70 75 77 78 79 81 82 84 85 86 87 93 107 108 110 111 115 118 119 130 131 132 133 135 146 148 149
Primary Contact: K C. DeBoer, President and Chief Executive Officer
COO: Ricki Ramlo, Chief Operating Officer and Human Resources
CFO: Brandon Vaughan, Chief Financial Officer and Vice President Finance
CMO: Derek Brickner, President Medical Staff
CIO: Jeff Gunkel, Chief Information Officer
CHR: Ricki Ramlo, Chief Operating Officer and Human Resources
CNO: Trisha Jungels R.N., Chief Nursing Officer and Vice President Clinical Services
Web address: www.jamestownhospital.com
Control: Other not–for–profit (including NFP Corporation) **Service**: General medical and surgical

Staffed Beds: 25 Admissions: 1062 Census: 12 Outpatient Visits: 32501 Births: 337 Total Expense ($000): 43015 Payroll Expense ($000): 16427 Personnel: 312

Many Facility Codes have changed. Please refer to the AHA Guide Code Chart. © 2017 AHA Guide

☐ **NORTH DAKOTA STATE HOSPITAL (354003)**, 2605 Circle Drive SE, Zip 58401–6905; tel. 701/253–3964, (Nonreporting) **A**1 3 5 10
Primary Contact: Rosalie Etherington, Superintendent and Chief Executive Officer
COO: Ken Schulz, Chief Operating Officer
CMO: Eduardo Yabut M.D., Medical Director
CIO: Amy Shape, Information Technology
CNO: Leah Schulz, Director of Nursing
Web address: www.nd.gov/
Control: State, Government, Nonfederal **Service**: Psychiatric

Staffed Beds: 140

KENMARE—Ward County

★ **KENMARE COMMUNITY HOSPITAL (351305)**, 317 First Avenue NW, Zip 58746–7104, Mailing Address: P.O.Box 697, 58746–0697; tel. 701/385–4296, (Nonreporting) **A**10 18
Primary Contact: Danielle Alsadon, Clinic/Hospital Manager
COO: Bev Heninger, Director of Nursing
CFO: Dennis Empey, Chief Financial Officer
CMO: Buki Oni M.D., Chief Medical Officer
CIO: David Wanner, Director Information Technology
CHR: Ranae Ehlke, Administrative Secretary and Coordinator Risk Management and Human Resources
CNO: Bev Heninger, Director of Nursing
Web address: www.kenmarend.net/hospital.htm
Control: Corporation, Investor–owned (for–profit) **Service**: General medical and surgical

Staffed Beds: 25

LANGDON—Cavalier County

★ **CAVALIER COUNTY MEMORIAL HOSPITAL AND CLINICS (351323)**, 909 Second Street, Zip 58249–2407; tel. 701/256–6100, (Nonreporting) **A**5 10 18
Primary Contact: Christopher D. Wyatt, Chief Executive Officer
COO: Darla Roder, Chief Operating Officer
CFO: Richard Fromme, Chief Financial Officer
CMO: Suresh Patel M.D., Chief Medical Officer
CHR: Nicole Walker, Human Resource Officer
CNO: Jamie Nienhuis, Chief Nursing Officer
Web address: www.cavaliercountyhospital.com
Control: Other not–for–profit (including NFP Corporation) **Service**: General medical and surgical

Staffed Beds: 20

LINTON—Emmons County

LINTON HOSPITAL (351328), 518 North Broadway, Zip 58552–7308, Mailing Address: P.O.Box 850, 58552–0850; tel. 701/254–4511, (Nonreporting) **A**5 10 18
Primary Contact: Robert O. Black, Chief Executive Officer
CMO: John Knecht, Chief Medical Staff
CHR: Sue Meidinger, Manager Business Office
Web address: www.lintonhospital.com
Control: Other not–for–profit (including NFP Corporation) **Service**: General medical and surgical

Staffed Beds: 14

LISBON—Ransom County

★ **CHI LISBON HEALTH (351311)**, 905 Main Street, Zip 58054–4334, Mailing Address: P.O.Box 353, 58054–0353; tel. 701/683–6400 **A**5 10 18 **F**3 15 28 29 30 31 34 40 45 56 57 59 64 67 79 81 85 107 114 119 128 130 133 150 **P**3 **S** Catholic Health Initiatives, Englewood, CO
Primary Contact: Peggy Reinke, R.N., Administrator
COO: Sheri Heinisch, Compliance Officer
CFO: Amber Stowman, Controller
CHR: Janet Froemke, Human Resources Officer
Web address: www.lisbonhospital.com
Control: Church operated, Nongovernment, not–for–profit **Service**: General medical and surgical

Staffed Beds: 25 Admissions: 298 Census: 14 Outpatient Visits: 10935 Births: 0

MANDAN—Morton County

TRIUMPH HOSPITAL – CENTRAL DAKOTAS See Vibra Hospital Of Central Dakotas
⊞ **VIBRA HOSPITAL OF CENTRAL DAKOTAS (352005)**, 1000 18th Street NW, Zip 58554–1612; tel. 701/667–2000, (Nonreporting) **A**1 10 **S** Vibra Healthcare, Mechanicsburg, PA
Primary Contact: Glynda Troyo–Sauviac, Chief Executive Officer
Web address: www.vhcentraldakotas.com
Control: Corporation, Investor–owned (for–profit) **Service**: Acute long–term care hospital

Staffed Beds: 41

MAYVILLE—Traill County

MERITCARE MAYVILLE UNION HOSPITAL See Sanford Mayville Medical Center
★ **SANFORD MAYVILLE MEDICAL CENTER (351309)**, 42 Sixth Avenue SE, Zip 58257–1598; tel. 701/786–3800 **A**5 10 18 **F**7 40 43 45 50 65 77 81 93 97 107 119 128 129 130 133 **P**6 **S** Sanford Health, Sioux Falls, SD
Primary Contact: Roger Baier, Chief Executive Officer
CFO: Shauna Slabik, Chief Financial Officer
CMO: Jane Ostlig, Chief Medical Officer
Web address: www.unionhospital.com
Control: Other not–for–profit (including NFP Corporation) **Service**: General medical and surgical

Staffed Beds: 18 Admissions: 211 Census: 3 Outpatient Visits: 21333 Births: 0 **Total Expense ($000):** 8690 **Payroll Expense ($000):** 4250 **Personnel:** 62

MCVILLE—Nelson County

NELSON COUNTY HEALTH SYSTEM (351308), 200 Main Street, Zip 58254, Mailing Address: P.O.Box 367, 58254–0367; tel. 701/322–4328, (Nonreporting) **A**10 18
Primary Contact: Cathy Swenson, Chief Executive Officer
CFO: Steve Forde, Chief Financial Officer
CMO: Erling Martinson M.D., Medical Director
Web address: www.nelsoncountyhealthsystem.org
Control: Other not–for–profit (including NFP Corporation) **Service**: General medical and surgical

Staffed Beds: 58

MINOT—Ward County

⊞ △ **TRINITY HEALTH (350006)**, One Burdick Expressway West, Zip 58701–4406, Mailing Address: P.O.Box 5020, 58702–5020; tel. 701/857–5766, (Includes TRINITY HOSPITAL–ST. JOSEPH'S, 407 3rd Street SE, Minot, North Dakota, Zip 58702–5001, tel. 701/857–2000) (Total facility includes 215 beds in nursing home–type unit) **A**1 2 3 5 7 10 **F**3 4 5 7 8 11 13 15 17 18 20 22 24 28 29 31 34 35 36 38 40 43 45 46 49 50 54 55 56 57 58 59 60 62 63 64 65 68 70 72 73 74 75 76 77 78 79 80 81 82 85 86 87 89 90 91 92 93 94 96 97 98 99 100 101 102 103 104 105 107 108 110 111 114 115 116 117 118 119 120 121 123 124 126 127 128 129 130 131 132 133 143 144 146 147 148
Primary Contact: John M. Kutch, President
CFO: Dennis Empey, Chief Financial Officer
CIO: David Wanner, Chief Information Officer
CHR: Paul Simonson, Vice President
Web address: www.trinityhealth.org
Control: Other not–for–profit (including NFP Corporation) **Service**: General medical and surgical

Staffed Beds: 615 Admissions: 11048 Census: 332 Outpatient Visits: 193608 Births: 1687 **Total Expense ($000):** 431003 **Payroll Expense ($000):** 210426 **Personnel:** 1575

NORTHWOOD—Grand Forks County

★ **NORTHWOOD DEACONESS HEALTH CENTER (351312)**, 4 North Park Street, Zip 58267–4102, Mailing Address: P.O.Box 190, 58267–0190; tel. 701/587–6060, (Nonreporting) **A**5 10 18 **S** Sanford Health, Sioux Falls, SD
Primary Contact: Pete Antonson, Chief Executive Officer
CMO: Jon Berg M.D., Chief of Staff
CIO: Chad Peterson, Chief Information Officer
Web address: www.ndhc.net
Control: Church operated, Nongovernment, not–for–profit **Service**: General medical and surgical

Staffed Beds: 73

OAKES—Dickey County

★ **CHI OAKES HOSPITAL (351315)**, 1200 North Seventh Street, Zip 58474–2502; tel. 701/742–3291, (Nonreporting) **A**5 10 18 **S** Catholic Health Initiatives, Englewood, CO
Primary Contact: Becki Thompson, President
CFO: Bethany Smith, Director of Finance
CMO: Katie O'Brien–Paradis M.D., Chief Medical Officer
CHR: Julie Entzminger, Manager Human Resources
CNO: Kimberly A. Ketterling R.N., Vice President of Nursing
Web address: www.oakeshospital.com
Control: Other not–for–profit (including NFP Corporation) **Service**: General medical and surgical

Staffed Beds: 20

Hospital, Medicare Provider Number, Address, Telephone, Approval, Facility, and Physician Codes, Health Care System
★ American Hospital Association (AHA) membership   ○ Healthcare Facilities Accreditation Program   ⇑ Center for Improvement in Healthcare Quality Accreditation ☐ The Joint Commission accreditation   ◇ DNV Healthcare Inc. accreditation   △ Commission on Accreditation of Rehabilitation Facilities (CARF) accreditation

PARK RIVER—Walsh County

★ **FIRST CARE HEALTH CENTER (351326)**, 115 Vivian Street, Zip 58270–4540, Mailing Address: PO Box I, 58270–0708; tel. 701/284–7500 **A**5 10 18 **F**11 15 28 29 30 31 34 35 40 45 50 59 64 65 68 77 78 79 81 93 104 107 110 111 114 119 127 130 133 135 **P**6
Primary Contact: Brandon Mickelson, Chief Executive Officer
CFO: Layne Ensrude, Chief Financial Officer
CMO: Joel Johnson M.D., Chief Medical Staff
CNO: Lori Seim R.N., Director Nursing Services
Web address: www.firstcarehc.com
Control: Other not–for–profit (including NFP Corporation) **Service:** General medical and surgical

Staffed Beds: 14 Admissions: 320 Census: 6 Outpatient Visits: 29152 Births: 0 Total Expense ($000): 10890 Payroll Expense ($000): 4137 Personnel: 81

ROLLA—Rolette County

PRESENTATION MEDICAL CENTER (351316), 213 Second Avenue NE, Zip 58367–7153, Mailing Address: P.O.Box 759, 58367–0759; tel. 701/477–3161 **A**5 10 18 **F**1 4 11 15 16 17 18 28 29 30 31 34 40 41 43 45 57 59 63 64 66 67 70 72 73 76 80 81 87 88 89 90 93 97 98 107 110 114 115 119 127 128 129 133 135 146 149 **P**6 **S** Sisters of Mary of the Presentation Health System, Fargo, ND
Primary Contact: Mark Kerr, Chief Executive Officer
CFO: Paula Wilkie, Chief Financial Officer
CMO: Roy Cordy M.D., President Medical Staff
CHR: Tara Okerson, Director Human Resources
Web address: www.pmc–rolla.com
Control: Church operated, Nongovernment, not–for–profit **Service:** General medical and surgical

Staffed Beds: 25 Admissions: 103 Census: 6 Outpatient Visits: 9625 Births: 0 Total Expense ($000): 9950 Payroll Expense ($000): 3698 Personnel: 80

RUGBY—Pierce County

★ **HEART OF AMERICA MEDICAL CENTER (351332)**, 800 Main Avenue South, Zip 58368–2198; tel. 701/776–5261, (Total facility includes 60 beds in nursing home–type unit) **A**5 10 18 **F**17 28 29 30 31 40 43 45 46 50 53 54 56 59 63 64 65 67 75 77 81 93 97 107 110 111 114 119 127 128 129 130 132 133 143 **P**6
Primary Contact: Patrick J. Branco, Chief Executive Officer
CFO: Bonnie Kuehnemund, Comptroller
CIO: Jeremy Schonebery, Director Information Technology
Web address: www.hamc.com
Control: Other not–for–profit (including NFP Corporation) **Service:** General medical and surgical

Staffed Beds: 85 Admissions: 361 Census: 56 Outpatient Visits: 2840 Births: 0 Total Expense ($000): 23946 Payroll Expense ($000): 12741 Personnel: 246

STANLEY—Mountrail County

★ **MOUNTRAIL COUNTY MEDICAL CENTER (351301)**, 615 6th Street SE, Zip 58784–4444, Mailing Address: P.O.Box 399, 58784–0399; tel. 701/628–2424, (Nonreporting) **A**10 18
Primary Contact: Rockford Zastoupil, Administrator
CFO: Susan Weston CPA, Chief Financial Officer
CMO: Marla Longmuir M.D., Chief Medical Officer
CIO: Kathy Janssen, Director Medical Records
CHR: Alisha McMahon, Director Human Resources
CNO: Belinda Moen R.N., MSN, Interim Director of Nursing
Web address: www.stanleyhealth.org
Control: Other not–for–profit (including NFP Corporation) **Service:** General medical and surgical

Staffed Beds: 11

TIOGA—Williams County

★ **TIOGA MEDICAL CENTER (351300)**, 810 North Welo Street, Zip 58852–7157, Mailing Address: P.O.Box 159, 58852–0159; tel. 701/664–3305, (Nonreporting) **A**5 10 18
Primary Contact: Randall K. Pederson, Chief Executive Officer
CMO: Swami P Gade M.D., Medical Director
CHR: Mary Ann Holm, Office Clerk
Web address: www.tiogahealth.org
Control: Other not–for–profit (including NFP Corporation) **Service:** General medical and surgical

Staffed Beds: 55

TURTLE LAKE—McLean County

★ **COMMUNITY MEMORIAL HOSPITAL (351304)**, 220 Fifth Avenue, Zip 58575–4005, Mailing Address: P.O.Box 280, 58575–0280; tel. 701/448–2331, (Nonreporting) **A**10 18 **S** Catholic Health Initiatives, Englewood, CO
Primary Contact: Tod Graeber, Administrator
CFO: Janet Kurle, Chief Financial Officer
CNO: Jason Landenberger, Director of Nursing
Web address: www.wrtc.com/cullum/hospital
Control: Church operated, Nongovernment, not–for–profit **Service:** General medical and surgical

Staffed Beds: 25

VALLEY CITY—Barnes County

★ **CHI MERCY HEALTH (351324)**, 570 Chautauqua Boulevard, Zip 58072–3199; tel. 701/845–6400 **A**10 18 **F**11 15 28 29 30 34 40 45 48 50 64 65 68 77 81 82 89 93 107 108 111 115 119 129 130 133 149 150 **S** Catholic Health Initiatives, Englewood, CO
Primary Contact: Keith E. Heuser, President
CFO: Cyndee Thormodson, Vice President, Operational Finance
CHR: Sheri Sweere, Division Director Human Resources
Web address: www.mercyhospitalvalleycity.org
Control: Church operated, Nongovernment, not–for–profit **Service:** General medical and surgical

Staffed Beds: 19 Admissions: 398 Census: 8 Outpatient Visits: 12755 Births: 0 Total Expense ($000): 12075 Payroll Expense ($000): 4168 Personnel: 47

WATFORD CITY—Mckenzie County

★ **MCKENZIE COUNTY HEALTHCARE SYSTEM (351302)**, 516 North Main Street, Zip 58854–7310; tel. 701/842–3000 **A**10 18 **F**3 11 28 29 34 40 43 45 50 57 59 64 65 67 68 77 81 85 87 93 94 97 107 114 119 127 128 129 131 133 146
Primary Contact: Daniel R. Kelly, Chief Executive Officer
COO: Michael Curtis, Chief Administrative Officer
CFO: Kenneth Cox, Interim Chief Financial Officer
CMO: Gary Ramage M.D., Chief Medical Officer
CIO: Karn Pederson, Manager Health Information Management
CHR: Amy Gonzales, Director of Human Resources
CNO: Cheryl Faulkner, Director of Nursing
Web address: www.mckenziehealth.com
Control: Other not–for–profit (including NFP Corporation) **Service:** General medical and surgical

Staffed Beds: 24 Admissions: 45 Census: 1 Outpatient Visits: 4527 Births: 0 Total Expense ($000): 16882 Payroll Expense ($000): 6724 Personnel: 87

WILLISTON—Williams County

⊞ **CHI ST. ALEXIUS HEALTH – WILLISTON MEDICAL CENTER (351334)**, 1301 15th Avenue West, Zip 58801–3896; tel. 701/774–7400 **A**1 3 10 18 **F**3 11 18 26 28 29 30 31 34 35 40 43 45 46 47 50 51 56 59 64 65 70 74 75 76 77 78 79 81 82 85 87 91 93 97 99 102 107 108 111 114 115 118 119 120 121 129 130 132 133 135 146 147 148 149 **P**4 **S** Catholic Health Initiatives, Englewood, CO
Primary Contact: Dan Bjerknes, Market Leader
CMO: Brett Vibeto M.D., Chief of Staff
CIO: Jeff Rust, Information Technology Systems Site Manager
CHR: Dan Bjerknes, Director Human Resources
CNO: Lori Hahn, Vice President Nursing Services
Web address: www.mercy–williston.org
Control: Church operated, Nongovernment, not–for–profit **Service:** General medical and surgical

Staffed Beds: 25 Admissions: 1878 Census: 13 Outpatient Visits: 68912 Births: 850 Total Expense ($000): 82781 Payroll Expense ($000): 38203 Personnel: 317

WISHEK—Mcintosh County

★ **WISHEK COMMUNITY HOSPITAL AND CLINICS (351321)**, 1007 Fourth Avenue South, Zip 58495–7527, Mailing Address: P.O.Box 647, 58495–0647; tel. 701/452–2326 **A**5 10 18 **F**3 7 11 15 17 18 28 29 32 34 35 36 40 42 44 45 50 53 56 57 59 64 65 68 75 81 83 87 91 92 93 97 107 114 127 128 130 131 133 143 146 147 148 149 **P**6
Primary Contact: Beverly Vilhauer, Chief Executive Officer
CFO: Megan Rath, Chief Financial Officer
CMO: Joseph Thirumalareddy M.D., Chief of Staff
CIO: Kari Buchholz, Director Health Information Management
CHR: Shar Bauer, Executive Secretary
Web address: www.wishekhospital.com
Control: Other not–for–profit (including NFP Corporation) **Service:** General medical and surgical

Staffed Beds: 19 Admissions: 199 Census: 2 Outpatient Visits: 9225 Births: 0 Total Expense ($000): 7293 Payroll Expense ($000): 2974 Personnel: 71

OHIO

AKRON—Summit County

✠ **AKRON CHILDREN'S HOSPITAL (363303)**, One Perkins Square, Zip 44308–1063; tel. 330/543–1000 **A**1 2 3 5 8 10 **F**3 7 11 13 16 18 19 20 21 22 23 25 26 27 29 30 31 32 33 34 35 36 38 39 40 41 43 44 48 50 54 55 57 58 59 60 61 62 63 64 65 66 68 72 73 74 75 76 77 78 79 81 82 84 85 86 87 88 89 91 92 93 94 96 97 98 99 100 101 102 104 105 107 108 111 112 114 115 116 117 118 119 129 130 131 132 134 135 136 141 143 144 146 148 149 **P**6
Primary Contact: William H. Considine, President
COO: Lisa Aurilio R.N., MSN, Chief Operating Officer
CFO: Michael Trainer, Chief Financial Officer
CMO: Robert McGregor M.D., Chief Medical Officer
CIO: Harun Rashid, Vice President and Chief Information Officer
CHR: Bernett Williams, Interim Chief Human Resource Officer
CNO: Christine Young MSN, R.N., Vice President of Patient Services and Chief Nursing Officer
Web address: www.akronchildrens.org
Control: Other not–for–profit (including NFP Corporation) **Service:** Children's general medical and surgical

Staffed Beds: 446 **Admissions:** 9654 **Census:** 204 **Outpatient Visits:** 1015526 **Births:** 0 **Total Expense ($000):** 746088 **Payroll Expense ($000):** 372785 **Personnel:** 4904

✠ **CLEVELAND CLINIC AKRON GENERAL (360027)**, 1 Akron General Avenue, Zip 44307–2433; tel. 330/344–6000 **A**1 2 3 5 8 10 **F**3 5 8 11 12 13 14 15 17 18 20 22 24 26 28 29 30 31 32 34 35 36 37 38 40 42 43 44 45 46 47 48 49 50 51 52 53 54 55 56 57 58 59 60 61 62 63 64 65 66 68 70 71 72 74 75 76 77 78 79 81 82 84 85 86 87 91 92 93 94 96 97 98 100 101 102 103 104 105 107 108 110 111 112 114 115 117 118 119 120 121 123 124 126 129 130 131 132 134 135 138 144 145 146 147 148 **S** Cleveland Clinic Health System, Cleveland, OH
Primary Contact: Alan Papa, President
CFO: Dave Frigo, Vice President Financial Planning and Treasury
CMO: David Peter M.D., Senior Vice President Medical Affairs and Chief Medical Director
CIO: David Fiser, Vice President and Chief Information Officer
CHR: Don Corpora, Executive Vice President and Chief Human Resources Officer
CNO: Cherie M Guster R.N., MSN,   Senior Vice President and Chief Nursing Officer
Web address: www.akrongeneral.org
Control: Other not–for–profit (including NFP Corporation) **Service:** General medical and surgical

Staffed Beds: 439 **Admissions:** 23945 **Census:** 298 **Outpatient Visits:** 649185 **Births:** 2828 **Total Expense ($000):** 551774 **Payroll Expense ($000):** 221055 **Personnel:** 2973

✠ **SELECT SPECIALTY HOSPITAL–AKRON (362027)**, 200 East Market Street, Zip 44308–2015; tel. 330/761–7500, (Nonreporting) **A**1 10 **S** Select Medical Corporation, Mechanicsburg, PA
Primary Contact: Sonda Burns, Chief Executive Officer
Web address: www.selectspecialtyhospitals.com/company/locations/akron.aspx
Control: Corporation, Investor–owned (for–profit) **Service:** Acute long–term care hospital

Staffed Beds: 60

SUMMA AKRON CITY HOSPITAL See Summa Health System

SUMMA HEALTH SYSTEM See Summa Health System

✠ **SUMMA HEALTH SYSTEM (360020)**, 525 East Market Street, Zip 44304–1619; tel. 330/375–3000, (Includes SUMMA AKRON CITY HOSPITAL, 525 East Market Street, Akron, Ohio, Zip 44309–2090, P O Box 2090, 44309–2090, tel. 330/375–3000; SUMMA HEALTH SYSTEM BARBERTON HOSPITAL, 155 Fifth Street NE, Barberton, Ohio, Zip 44203–3332, tel. 330/615–3000; Michael Hughes, M.D., President, Summa Health System Barberton; SUMMA SAINT THOMAS HOSPITAL, 444 North Main Street, Akron, Ohio, Zip 44310, tel. 330/375–3000) **A**1 2 5 8 10 13 **F**3 4 5 6 8 11 12 13 15 17 18 20 22 24 26 28 29 30 31 33 34 35 36 38 39 40 42 43 44 45 46 47 49 50 51 53 54 56 57 58 59 60 61 62 63 64 65 66 68 70 71 74 75 76 77 78 79 80 81 82 83 84 85 86 87 92 93 96 97 98 100 101 102 103 104 105 107 108 110 111 114 115 116 117 118 119 120 121 123 124 126 129 130 131 132 134 135 144 146 147 148 149 **P**6 8 **S** Summa Health, Akron, OH
Primary Contact: David Custodio, M.D., President Summa Health System Akron
CMO: Erik N Steele D.O., Senior Vice President and Chief Medical Officer
CIO: Greg Kall, Chief Information Officer
CHR: Kyle Klawitter, Vice President Human Resources
Web address: www.summahealth.org
Control: Other not–for–profit (including NFP Corporation) **Service:** General medical and surgical

Staffed Beds: 661 **Admissions:** 34544 **Census:** 436 **Outpatient Visits:** 506504 **Births:** 3871 **Total Expense ($000):** 815326 **Payroll Expense ($000):** 259441 **Personnel:** 6620

□ △ **SUMMA REHAB HOSPITAL (363035)**, 29 North Adams Street, Zip 44304–1641; tel. 330/572–7300 (Nonreporting) **A**1 7 10 **S** Summa Health, Akron, OH
Primary Contact: Cheryl Henthorn, Chief Executive Officer
Web address: www.summarehabhospital.com/
Control: Corporation, Investor–owned (for–profit) **Service:** Rehabilitation

Staffed Beds: 60

SUMMA SAINT THOMAS HOSPITAL See Summa Health System

ALLIANCE—Stark County

○ **ALLIANCE COMMUNITY HOSPITAL (360131)**, 200 East State Street, Zip 44601–4936; tel. 330/596–6000, (Total facility includes 78 beds in nursing home–type unit) **A**2 5 10 11 **F**3 8 11 13 15 28 29 30 31 34 35 36 40 45 49 50 51 56 57 59 60 62 63 64 68 69 70 74 75 76 77 79 81 82 84 85 86 87 90 93 96 98 103 107 108 110 111 114 115 117 118 119 128 129 130 132 135 143 144 146 147 148 **P**5 7 8
Primary Contact: Stanley W. Jonas, Chief Executive Officer
COO: Dale W. Wells, Chief Financial and Operating Officer
CFO: Dale W. Wells, Chief Financial and Operating Officer
CMO: Ashraf Ahmed M.D., Senior Vice President Physician and Hospital Services
CIO: David W Shroades, Vice President Technology Services
CHR: Nicole L Russ, Director Colleague Relations
CNO: Amy Antonacci MSN, R.N., Vice President Nursing Services
Web address: www.achosp.org
Control: Other not–for–profit (including NFP Corporation) **Service:** General medical and surgical

Staffed Beds: 202 **Admissions:** 3199 **Census:** 102 **Outpatient Visits:** 179853 **Births:** 140 **Total Expense ($000):** 92235 **Payroll Expense ($000):** 40005 **Personnel:** 803

AMHERST—Lorain County

□ **SPECIALTY HOSPITAL OF LORAIN (362025)**, 254 Cleveland Avenue, Zip 44001–1620; tel. 440/988–6260, (Nonreporting) **A**1 10
Primary Contact: Rajive Khanna, Chief Executive Officer
COO: Susan Adams, Chief Nursing Officer and Chief Operating Officer
CNO: Susan Adams, Chief Nursing Officer and Chief Operating Officer
Control: Other not–for–profit (including NFP Corporation) **Service:** Acute long–term care hospital

Staffed Beds: 30

OH

ARCHBOLD—Fulton County

ARCHBOLD HOSPITAL See Community Hospitals And Wellness Centers, Bryan

ASHLAND—Ashland County

✠ **UNIVERSITY HOSPITALS SAMARITAN MEDICAL CENTER (360002)**, 1025 Center Street, Zip 44805–4011; tel. 419/289–0491 **A**1 5 10 **F**11 13 15 18 20 28 29 30 31 34 35 40 45 50 51 57 59 62 64 68 75 76 77 78 79 81 82 86 87 93 96 107 111 114 119 129 130 131 132 135 146 147 148 149 **S** University Hospitals, Cleveland, OH
Primary Contact: Karen McNeil, President
CFO: Mary Griest, Vice President Finance and Chief Financial Officer
CMO: Philip Myers M.D., Vice President Medical Affairs
CIO: Kathleen Metcalf, Chief Information Officer
CHR: Alyce Legg, Vice President Human Resources
CNO: Karin Schwan, Chief Nursing Officer, Vice President Patient Care Services
Web address: www.samaritanhospital.org
Control: Other not–for–profit (including NFP Corporation) **Service**: General medical and surgical

Staffed Beds: 38 Admissions: 2292 Census: 18 Outpatient Visits: 134412 Births: 360 Total Expense ($000): 71425 Payroll Expense ($000): 26689 Personnel: 512

ASHTABULA—Ashtabula County

✠ **ASHTABULA COUNTY MEDICAL CENTER (360125)**, 2420 Lake Avenue, Zip 44004–4954; tel. 440/997–2262, (Total facility includes 15 beds in nursing home–type unit) **A**1 5 10 20 **F**3 11 13 15 18 19 20 26 28 29 30 31 34 40 44 45 49 51 53 54 57 59 61 62 63 64 68 70 74 76 78 79 81 82 85 87 89 92 93 97 98 100 102 103 104 107 108 110 111 114 116 117 118 119 128 129 130 131 132 135 144 146 147 148 149 **P**4 6 7 8
Primary Contact: Michael J. Habowski, President and Chief Executive Officer
COO: Lewis Hutchison, Vice President Operations and Quality
CFO: Donald L Kepner, Chief Financial Officer
CMO: Jude Cauwenberg M.D., Chief of Staff
CIO: Jared Swiger, Director Information Systems
CHR: Jonathan Forbes, Director Human Resources
CNO: Ken Frame, Chief Nursing Officer
Web address: www.acmchealth.org
Control: Other not–for–profit (including NFP Corporation) **Service**: General medical and surgical

Staffed Beds: 151 Admissions: 6104 Census: 70 Outpatient Visits: 267188 Births: 358 Total Expense ($000): 124203 Payroll Expense ($000): 57074 Personnel: 864

ATHENS—Athens County

☐ **APPALACHIAN BEHAVIORAL HEALTHCARE (364015)**, 100 Hospital Drive, Zip 45701–2301; tel. 740/594–5000, (Nonreporting) **A**1 10 **S** Ohio Department of Mental Health, Columbus, OH
Primary Contact: Jane E. Krason, R.N., Chief Executive Officer
COO: Kelly Sole, Chief Operating Officer
CMO: Mark F McGee M.D., Chief Clinical Officer
CHR: Donovan Workman, Director Human Capital Management
CNO: Karen Durniat–Sushrstedt, Nurse Executive
Web address: www.mh.state.oh.us
Control: State, Government, Nonfederal **Service**: Psychiatric

Staffed Beds: 224

✠ **O'BLENESS MEMORIAL HOSPITAL (360014)**, 55 Hospital Drive, Zip 45701–2302; tel. 740/593–5551, (Nonreporting) **A**1 10 12 13 **S** OhioHealth, Columbus, OH
Primary Contact: Mark R. Seckinger, President
CFO: Robert Melaragno, Vice President Finance
CIO: Kristine Barr, Vice President Communication Services
CHR: Sandie Leasure, Senior Vice President Human Resources
CNO: Sandy Wood MSN, R.N., Vice President Patient Services and Chief Nursing Officer
Web address: www.obleness.org
Control: Other not–for–profit (including NFP Corporation) **Service**: General medical and surgical

Staffed Beds: 64

AVON—Lorain County

★ **CLEVELAND CLINIC AVON HOSPITAL**, 33300 Cleveland Clinic Boulevard, Zip 44011; tel. 440/695–5000, (Data for 47 days) **F**3 15 18 20 29 30 34 35 45 51 60 64 68 70 74 75 79 81 82 85 87 92 100 107 108 111 115 119 130 146 148 **S** Cleveland Clinic Health System, Cleveland, OH
Primary Contact: Rebecca Starck, M.D., President
Web address: www.my.clevelandclinic.org
Control: Other not–for–profit (including NFP Corporation) **Service**: General medical and surgical

Staffed Beds: 126 Admissions: 482 Census: 35 Outpatient Visits: 830 Births: 0 Total Expense ($000): 19824 Payroll Expense ($000): 10038 Personnel: 541

★ **CLEVELAND CLINIC REHABILITATION HOSPITAL (363038)**, 33355 Health Campus Boulevard, Zip 44011; tel. 440/937–9099 (Nonreporting) **A**3 **S** Select Medical Corporation, Mechanicsburg, PA
Primary Contact: Sam Bayoumy, Chief Executive Officer
Web address: www.my.clevelandclinic.org
Control: Partnership, Investor–owned (for–profit) **Service**: Rehabilitation

Staffed Beds: 60

UH AVON REHABILITATION HOSPITAL (363039), 37900 Chester Road, Zip 44011–1044; tel. 440/695–7100, (Data for 300 days) **F**29 75 90 91 96 **S** Kindred Healthcare, Louisville, KY
Primary Contact: Andrew Goldfrach, Chief Executive Officer
CFO: Jason DiGuilio, Controller
CHR: Abby Hoag, Director, Human Resources
CNO: Katie Kasper, Chief Clinical Officer
Web address: www.uhhospitals.org/uh–avon–rehabilitation–hospital
Control: Partnership, Investor–owned (for–profit) **Service**: Rehabilitation

Staffed Beds: 50 Admissions: 460 Census: 19 Outpatient Visits: 0 Births: 0

BARNESVILLE—Belmont County

✠ **BARNESVILLE HOSPITAL (361321)**, 639 West Main Street, Zip 43713–1039, Mailing Address: P.O.Box 309, 43713–0309; tel. 740/425–3941, (Nonreporting) **A**1 10 18
Primary Contact: David D. Phillips, Chief Executive Officer and Administrator
CFO: Willie Cooper–Lohr, Chief Financial Officer
CMO: David J Hilliard D.O., Chief of Staff
CHR: Beth K. Brill, Senior Director Human Resources
CNO: Cynthia Touvelle R.N., Senior Director Care Management and Chief Nursing Officer
Web address: www.barnesvillehospital.com
Control: Other not–for–profit (including NFP Corporation) **Service**: General medical and surgical

Staffed Beds: 25

BATAVIA—Clermont County

✠ **MERCY HEALTH – CLERMONT HOSPITAL (360236)**, 3000 Hospital Drive, Zip 45103–1921; tel. 513/732–8200, (Nonreporting) **A**1 2 10 **S** Mercy Health, Cincinnati, OH
Primary Contact: Ken James, President and Chief Executive Officer of East Market
CFO: Philip Wheeler, Director Finance
CMO: Parma Hariharan M.D., Chief of Staff
CHR: Angie Ferrell, Director Human Resources
CNO: Gayle Heintzelman R.N., Site Administrator and Chief Nursing Officer
Web address: www.e-mercy.com
Control: Church operated, Nongovernment, not–for–profit **Service**: General medical and surgical

Staffed Beds: 119

BEACHWOOD—Cuyahoga County

UH REHABILITATION HOSPITAL (363036), 23333 Harvard Road, Zip 44122–6232; tel. 216/593–2200 (Nonreporting) **S** Kindred Healthcare, Louisville, KY
Primary Contact: Mirza Baig, M.D., Medical Director
Web address: www.uhhospitals.org
Control: Corporation, Investor–owned (for–profit) **Service**: Rehabilitation

Staffed Beds: 50

✠ **UNIVERSITY HOSPITALS AHUJA MEDICAL CENTER (360359)**, 3999 Richmond Road, Zip 44122–6046; tel. 216/593–5500 **A**1 3 10 **F**3 5 15 18 20 22 24 26 28 29 30 34 35 36 40 41 42 45 46 47 48 50 51 56 57 59 60 61 65 68 70 74 75 77 79 80 81 82 85 87 91 93 107 108 109 110 111 115 119 126 130 131 144 145 146 148 149 **S** University Hospitals, Cleveland, OH
Primary Contact: Susan V. Juris, President
Web address: www.uhhospitals.org/ahuja/tabid/7051/uhahujamedicalcenter.aspx
Control: Other not–for–profit (including NFP Corporation) **Service**: General medical and surgical

Staffed Beds: 138 Admissions: 8671 Census: 93 Outpatient Visits: 177845 Births: 0 Total Expense ($000): 168061 Payroll Expense ($000): 56723 Personnel: 967

BEAVERCREEK—Greene County

★ ○ **SOIN MEDICAL CENTER (360360)**, 3535 Pentagon Boulevard, Zip 45431–1705; tel. 937/702–4000 **A**2 3 10 11 **F**3 11 13 18 20 22 29 30 31 34 35 38 39 40 43 44 45 46 47 48 50 51 53 56 57 59 60 61 64 66 68 70 73 74 75 76 77 78 79 81 82 85 86 87 102 107 108 111 114 115 116 117 118 119 126 130 132 135 146 148 149 **S** Kettering Health Network, Dayton, OH
Primary Contact: Rick A. Dodds, President
COO: Ron D Connovich, Chief Financial Officer and Chief Operating Officer
CFO: Ron D Connovich, Chief Financial Officer and Chief Operating Officer
CMO: David Small M.D., Chief Medical Officer
CIO: Andy Lehman, Vice President Information Systems
CNO: Belinda Mallett R.N., MS, Vice President, Patient Care and Clinical Services
Web address: www.khnetwork.org/soin
Control: Church operated, Nongovernment, not–for–profit **Service**: General medical and surgical

Staffed Beds: 133 **Admissions**: 6658 **Census**: 64 **Outpatient Visits**: 73325 **Births**: 595 **Total Expense ($000)**: 165005 **Payroll Expense ($000)**: 60977 **Personnel**: 699

BELLAIRE—Belmont County

☐ **BELMONT COMMUNITY HOSPITAL (360153)**, 4697 Harrison Street, Zip 43906–1338, Mailing Address: P.O.Box 653, 43906–0653; tel. 740/671–1200, (Nonreporting) **A**1 10
Primary Contact: John DeBlasis, Vice President
CFO: James B Murdy, Chief Financial Officer
CMO: Jeffrey A Patey M.D., Chief of Staff
CHR: Serge Gentile, Director Human Resources
Web address: www.wheelinghospital.org/facilities/bch/
Control: Other not–for–profit (including NFP Corporation) **Service**: General medical and surgical

Staffed Beds: 66

BELLEFONTAINE—Logan County

★ ⇑ **MARY RUTAN HOSPITAL (360197)**, 205 Palmer Avenue, Zip 43311–2281; tel. 937/592–4015 **A**5 10 20 21 **F**3 11 12 13 14 15 18 20 28 29 30 31 32 34 50 51 54 57 59 64 66 68 70 74 75 76 77 79 81 82 85 86 87 89 107 108 110 111 115 119 129 130 132 133 135 146 147 149
Primary Contact: Mandy C. Goble, President and Chief Executive Officer
CFO: Steven Brown, Vice President Fiscal Affairs
CMO: Grant Varian M.D., Medical Director
CIO: Robert Reynolds, Director Information Systems
CHR: Vickie L Crumley, Chief Human Resources Officer
CNO: Frank Gliha, Vice President of Patient Care
Web address: www.maryrutan.org
Control: Other not–for–profit (including NFP Corporation) **Service**: General medical and surgical

Staffed Beds: 46 **Admissions**: 1610 **Census**: 13 **Outpatient Visits**: 117130 **Births**: 351 **Total Expense ($000)**: 91402 **Payroll Expense ($000)**: 41405 **Personnel**: 595

BELLEVUE—Sandusky County

⊞ **BELLEVUE HOSPITAL (360107)**, 1400 West Main Street, Zip 44811–9088, Mailing Address: P.O.Box 8004, 44811–8004; tel. 419/483–4040 **A**1 5 10 **F**3 13 15 28 29 30 31 34 35 40 41 45 46 50 53 56 57 59 61 68 70 74 75 76 77 79 81 82 85 89 93 107 110 111 115 118 119 127 129 130 131 132 133 135 143 144 146 147 148 149 **P**8
Primary Contact: Michael Winthrop, President
CFO: Timothy Buit, Executive Vice President and Chief Financial Officer
CMO: Donald Smith, President Medical Staff
CIO: Kim Stults, Director, Information Systems
CHR: Lisa M. Sartain, Vice President, Human Resources
CNO: Sara Brokaw, Vice President Patient Care Services
Web address: www.bellevuehospital.com
Control: Other not–for–profit (including NFP Corporation) **Service**: General medical and surgical

Staffed Beds: 50 **Admissions**: 1347 **Census**: 11 **Outpatient Visits**: 85966 **Births**: 351 **Total Expense ($000)**: 45807 **Payroll Expense ($000)**: 17136 **Personnel**: 353

BLUFFTON—Allen County

★ **BLUFFTON HOSPITAL (361322)**, 139 Garau Street, Zip 45817–1027; tel. 419/358–9010 **A**10 18 **F**3 8 11 13 15 18 40 45 54 57 59 63 64 68 70 76 77 79 81 82 91 93 107 110 114 119 127 133 146 148 **P**5 **S** Blanchard Valley Health System, Findlay, OH
Primary Contact: Christine Keller, Chief Administrative Officer
CFO: David Cytlak, Vice President Finance
CMO: William H Kose M.D., Vice President Quality and Medical Affairs
CIO: David Cytlak, Vice President Finance
CHR: Ryan Fisher, Director Human Resources
CNO: Barbara J. Pasztor R.N., Vice President Nursing and Patient Care Services
Web address: www.bvhealthsystem.org/
Control: Other not–for–profit (including NFP Corporation) **Service**: General medical and surgical

Staffed Beds: 25 **Admissions**: 372 **Census**: 2 **Outpatient Visits**: 35751 **Births**: 246 **Total Expense ($000)**: 13308 **Payroll Expense ($000)**: 8789 **Personnel**: 115

BOARDMAN—Mahoning County

MAHONING VALLEY HOSPITAL See Vibra Hospital Of Mahoning Valley

⊞ **MERCY HEALTH – ST. ELIZABETH BOARDMAN HOSPITAL (360276)**, 8401 Market Street, Zip 44512–6777; tel. 330/729–2929 **A**1 3 10 13 **F**3 8 11 13 15 18 29 30 31 34 35 37 40 45 46 49 50 59 60 68 70 74 75 76 77 78 79 81 84 87 93 107 108 110 111 114 115 116 117 118 119 120 121 123 129 130 131 146 147 148 149 **S** Mercy Health, Cincinnati, OH
Primary Contact: Eugenia Aubel, President
CMO: Heath Dorion, Physician Administrator
CIO: Maureen Kordupel, Director Information Technology Relationship Manager
CHR: Molly Seals, System Vice President, Human Resources Program Delivery and Youngstown Market
CNO: Stacie Call, Chief Nursing Officer
Web address: www.ehealthconnection.com/regions/youngstown/content/show_facility.asp?facility_id=190
Control: Church operated, Nongovernment, not–for–profit **Service**: General medical and surgical

Staffed Beds: 217 **Admissions**: 13961 **Census**: 141 **Outpatient Visits**: 121832 **Births**: 2750 **Total Expense ($000)**: 161997 **Payroll Expense ($000)**: 48943 **Personnel**: 768

⊞ **SELECT SPECIALTY HOSPITAL – BOARDMAN (360363)**, 8401 Market Street, 7 South, Zip 44512–6725; tel. 330/729–1750 (Nonreporting) **A**1 10 **S** Select Medical Corporation, Mechanicsburg, PA
Primary Contact: Varun Chauhan, Chief Executive Officer
Web address: www.selectspecialtyhospitals.com/
Control: Corporation, Investor–owned (for–profit) **Service**: Acute long–term care hospital

Staffed Beds: 24

⊞ **VIBRA HOSPITAL OF MAHONING VALLEY (362023)**, 8049 South Avenue, Zip 44512–6154; tel. 330/726–5000, (Includes VIBRA HOSPITAL OF MAHONING VALLEY–TRUMBULL CAMPUS, 1350 E Market Street, 9th Floor, Warren, Ohio, Zip 44483–6608, tel. 330/675–5555; Nathan Mast, Chief Executive Officer) **A**1 10 **F**1 3 29 30 130 148 **S** Vibra Healthcare, Mechanicsburg, PA
Primary Contact: Nathan Mast, Chief Executive Officer
CMO: Lawrence Goldstein M.D., Chief Medical Officer
Web address: www.vhmvalley.com
Control: Corporation, Investor–owned (for–profit) **Service**: Acute long–term care hospital

Staffed Beds: 42 **Admissions**: 409 **Census**: 27 **Outpatient Visits**: 0 **Births**: 0 **Total Expense ($000)**: 15452 **Payroll Expense ($000)**: 5930 **Personnel**: 126

Hospital, Medicare Provider Number, Address, Telephone, Approval, Facility, and Physician Codes, Health Care System

★ American Hospital Association (AHA) membership
☐ The Joint Commission accreditation
○ Healthcare Facilities Accreditation Program
◇ DNV Healthcare Inc. accreditation
⇑ Center for Improvement in Healthcare Quality Accreditation
△ Commission on Accreditation of Rehabilitation Facilities (CARF) accreditation

OH

BOWLING GREEN—Wood County

✠ **WOOD COUNTY HOSPITAL (360029)**, 950 West Wooster Street, Zip 43402–2603; tel. 419/354–8900 **A**1 5 10 **F**3 11 12 13 15 17 18 28 29 30 31 32 34 35 40 44 45 50 57 59 64 65 68 69 70 74 75 76 77 78 79 81 82 85 87 89 93 107 108 110 111 114 115 118 119 120 121 123 124 129 130 131 132 135 144 146 147 148 **P**6 8
Primary Contact: Stanley R. Korducki, President
CFO: Karol Bortel, Vice President Financial Services
CMO: Shawn Stansbery M.D., Chief of Staff
CIO: Joanne White, Chief Information Officer
CHR: Michael Ford, Vice President Patient Services
CNO: Sandra Beidelschies MSN, R.N., Vice President Patient Services
Web address: www.woodcountyhospital.org
Control: Other not–for–profit (including NFP Corporation) **Service**: General medical and surgical

Staffed Beds: 108 **Admissions**: 2593 **Census**: 26 **Outpatient Visits**: 112717 **Births**: 334 **Total Expense ($000)**: 84602 **Payroll Expense ($000)**: 31756 **Personnel**: 617

BRYAN—Williams County

☐ **COMMUNITY HOSPITALS AND WELLNESS CENTERS (360121)**, 433 West High Street, Zip 43506–1679; tel. 419/636–1131, (Nonreporting) (Includes ARCHBOLD HOSPITAL, 121 Westfield Drive, Archbold, Ohio, Zip 43502, tel. 419/445–4415; BRYAN HOSPITAL, 433 West High Street, Bryan, Ohio, Zip 43506, tel. 419/636–1131; MONTPELIER HOSPITAL, 909 East Snyder Avenue, Montpelier, Ohio, Zip 43543, tel. 419/485–3154) **A**1 2 5 10
Primary Contact: Philip L. Ennen, Vice President and Chief Executive Officer
CFO: Leroy P Feather, Vice President Finance
CIO: Greg Slattery, Vice President Information
CHR: Mary Ann Potts, Director Personnel
Web address: www.chwchospital.com
Control: Other not–for–profit (including NFP Corporation) **Service**: General medical and surgical

Staffed Beds: 113

BUCYRUS—Crawford County

★ ⇑ **BUCYRUS COMMUNITY HOSPITAL (361316)**, 629 North Sandusky Avenue, Zip 44820–1821; tel. 419/562–4677, (Nonreporting) **A**5 10 18 21 **S** Avita Health System, Galion, OH
Primary Contact: Jerome Morasko, Chief Executive Officer
COO: Andy Daniels, Chief Operating Officer
CMO: Michael A Johnson M.D., Chief of Staff
CIO: Joann Riedlinger, Vice President Nursing and Manager Information Systems
CHR: Jeanne Perkins, Vice President Nursing and Interim Manager Human Resources
Web address: www.bchonline.org
Control: Other not–for–profit (including NFP Corporation) **Service**: General medical and surgical

Staffed Beds: 25

CADIZ—Harrison County

✠ **HARRISON COMMUNITY HOSPITAL (361311)**, 951 East Market Street, Zip 43907–9799; tel. 740/942–4631 **A**1 10 18 **F**7 11 15 18 28 29 30 31 34 35 40 45 47 50 51 53 57 59 62 64 65 68 75 77 78 79 81 82 85 86 87 93 97 107 108 110 111 114 119 129 130 132 133 135 143 146 147 148 149
Primary Contact: Clifford K. Harmon, Chief Executive Officer
CFO: Donald Huelskamp, Interim Chief Financial Officer
CMO: Siripurapu Prasad, Chief of Staff
CIO: Will Combs, Director Information Technology
CHR: Peter Giordano, Senior Director Human Resources
CNO: Janis Olinski R.N., Vice President Clinical Services
Web address: www.harrisoncommunity.com
Control: Other not–for–profit (including NFP Corporation) **Service**: General medical and surgical

Staffed Beds: 25 **Admissions**: 216 **Census**: 3 **Outpatient Visits**: 30141 **Births**: 0 **Total Expense ($000)**: 17926 **Payroll Expense ($000)**: 6601 **Personnel**: 144

CAMBRIDGE—Guernsey County

CAMBRIDGE BEHAVIORAL HOSPITAL (364027), 66755 State Street, Zip 43725–8757; tel. 740/432–4906 (Nonreporting)
Primary Contact: Pamela Braden, Administrator
Web address: www.cbhohio.com
Control: Corporation, Investor–owned (for–profit) **Service**: Psychiatric

Staffed Beds: 66

SOUTHEASTERN OHIO REGIONAL MEDICAL CENTER (360203)

✠ **SOUTHEASTERN OHIO REGIONAL MEDICAL CENTER (360203)**, 1341 North Clark Street, Zip 43725–9614, Mailing Address: P.O.Box 610, 43725–0610; tel. 740/439–8000 **A**1 2 3 10 20 **F**3 11 13 15 28 29 30 31 32 34 35 40 43 44 45 48 49 50 51 57 59 60 62 64 66 68 70 75 76 77 78 79 81 83 84 85 86 87 89 90 91 93 96 107 108 110 111 114 115 118 119 120 121 123 130 131 132 135 146 147 148 149 **P**6 8
Primary Contact: Raymond M. Chorey, President and Chief Executive Officer
CFO: Timothy R. Evancho, Chief Financial Officer
CMO: E Edwin Conaway M.D., Vice President Medical Affairs and Chief Medical Officer
CIO: Kevin Ludwigsen, Chief Information Officer
CHR: Steven Michael Brooks, Vice President Human Resources
CNO: Angela S Long, Vice President Clinical Services and Chief Nursing Officer
Web address: www.seormc.org
Control: Other not–for–profit (including NFP Corporation) **Service**: General medical and surgical

Staffed Beds: 95 **Admissions**: 3386 **Census**: 31 **Outpatient Visits**: 138746 **Births**: 409 **Total Expense ($000)**: 89317 **Payroll Expense ($000)**: 31597 **Personnel**: 689

CANAL WINCHESTER—Fairfield County

☐ **DILEY RIDGE MEDICAL CENTER (360358)**, 7911 Diley Road, Zip 43110–9653; tel. 614/838–7911 **A**1 10 **F**3 15 29 30 35 40 50 54 64 68 85 87 107 110 111 114 119 130 147
Primary Contact: Jodi Wilson, President and Chief Operating Officer
COO: Jodi Wilson, President and Chief Operating Officer
Web address: www.dileyridgemedicalcenter.com
Control: Other not–for–profit (including NFP Corporation) **Service**: General medical and surgical

Staffed Beds: 10 **Admissions**: 30 **Census**: 10 **Outpatient Visits**: 52574 **Births**: 0 **Total Expense ($000)**: 12936 **Payroll Expense ($000)**: 4758 **Personnel**: 72

CANTON—Stark County

✠ △ **AULTMAN HOSPITAL (360084)**, 2600 Sixth Street SW, Zip 44710–1702; tel. 330/452–9911, (Includes AULTMAN HOSPITAL PEDIATRIC SERVICES, 2600 Sixth Street, SW, Canton, Ohio, Zip 44710–1702, tel. 330/363–5455) (Total facility includes 60 beds in nursing home–type unit) **A**1 2 3 5 7 10 **F**3 7 8 11 12 13 14 15 17 18 20 22 24 26 28 29 30 31 34 35 39 40 43 44 45 48 49 50 51 53 54 55 56 57 58 59 60 61 62 63 64 68 70 71 72 74 75 76 77 78 79 81 82 83 84 85 86 87 89 90 93 96 97 98 102 103 104 105 106 107 108 109 110 111 114 115 117 118 119 120 121 123 127 128 129 130 131 132 133 134 135 143 144 145 146 147 148 149 150 **P**6 **S** Aultman Health Foundation, Canton, OH
Primary Contact: Edward J. Roth III, President and Chief Executive Officer
CFO: Mark Wright, Vice President
CMO: Allison Oprandi M.D., Chief Medical Officer
CIO: Liz Getz, Chief Information Officer
CHR: Sue Olivera, Vice President
CNO: Anne Gunther, DNP R.N., MSN, Chief Nursing Officer
Web address: www.aultman.com
Control: Other not–for–profit (including NFP Corporation) **Service**: General medical and surgical

Staffed Beds: 532 **Admissions**: 22959 **Census**: 336 **Outpatient Visits**: 470680 **Births**: 2761 **Total Expense ($000)**: 439819 **Payroll Expense ($000)**: 172485 **Personnel**: 4226

☐ **AULTMAN SPECIALTY HOSPITAL (362032)**, 2600 Sixth Street, SW, Zip 44710–1702; tel. 330/363–4000 (Nonreporting) **A**1 10 **S** Aultman Health Foundation, Canton, OH
Primary Contact: Terry Regula, Chief Executive Officer
CFO: Mark Wright, Chief Financial Officer
CMO: George Kefalas, Chief Medical Officer
Web address: www.aultman.org
Control: Other not–for–profit (including NFP Corporation) **Service**: Acute long–term care hospital

Staffed Beds: 30

✠ △ **MERCY MEDICAL CENTER (360070)**, 1320 Mercy Drive NW, Zip 44708–2641; tel. 330/489–1000 **A**1 2 3 5 7 10 **F**3 11 13 15 17 18 20 22 24 26 28 29 30 31 34 35 39 40 43 44 46 48 49 50 51 53 54 57 58 59 60 61 62 63 64 66 68 70 72 74 75 76 77 78 79 80 81 82 84 85 86 87 89 90 91 92 93 96 97 107 108 110 111 114 115 116 117 118 119 120 121 123 124 126 129 130 131 132 135 144 146 147 148 149 150 **P**6 7 **S** Sisters of Charity Health System, Cleveland, OH
Primary Contact: Paul C. Hiltz, FACHE, Interim Chief Executive Officer
COO: David D Cemate FACHE, Senior Vice President and Chief Operating Officer
CFO: David K Stewart, Senior Vice President and Chief Financial Officer
CMO: David Gormsen D.O., Vice President and Chief Medical Officer
CIO: Trevor Clere, Director Information Technology
CHR: Patti Bresnahan, Director Human Resources
CNO: Barbara Yingling R.N., Vice President Patient Care Services and Chief Nursing Officer
Web address: www.cantonmercy.org
Control: Other not–for–profit (including NFP Corporation) **Service**: General medical and surgical

Staffed Beds: 329 **Admissions**: 14765 **Census**: 200 **Outpatient Visits**: 630521 **Births**: 1593 **Total Expense ($000)**: 323647 **Payroll Expense ($000)**: 136004 **Personnel**: 2365

Many Facility Codes have changed. Please refer to the AHA Guide Code Chart. © 2017 AHA Guide

⌘ **SELECT SPECIALTY HOSPITAL–CANTON (362016)**, 1320 Mercy Drive NW, 6th Floor, Zip 44708–2614; tel. 330/489–8189, (Nonreporting) **A**1 10 **S** Select Medical Corporation, Mechanicsburg, PA
Primary Contact: Dawne Wheeler, Chief Executive Officer
Web address: www.selectspecialtyhospitals.com/company/locations/canton.aspx
Control: Corporation, Investor–owned (for–profit) **Service:** Acute long–term care hospital

Staffed Beds: 30

CHARDON—Geauga County

☐ **HEATHERHILL CARE COMMUNITIES (362014)**, 12340 Bass Lake Road, Zip 44024–8327; tel. 440/285–4040, (Nonreporting) **A**1 10
Primary Contact: Jim Homa, Chief Executive Officer
COO: Lisa Deering, Administrator
CFO: Valerie Love, Manager Business Office
CMO: Beejadi Makunda M.D., Chief Medical Officer
CHR: Pam McCall, Director Human Resources
CNO: Alice Harvey, Director of Nursing
Web address: www.heatherhill.com
Control: Other not–for–profit (including NFP Corporation) **Service:** Acute long–term care hospital

Staffed Beds: 214

⌘ **UNIVERSITY HOSPITALS GEAUGA MEDICAL CENTER (360192)**, 13207 Ravenna Road, Zip 44024–7032; tel. 440/269–6000 **A**1 2 3 10 **F**3 8 11 12 13 15 18 20 22 26 28 29 30 31 32 34 35 36 38 39 40 41 43 44 47 49 50 51 54 56 57 58 59 60 62 63 64 65 68 70 74 75 76 77 78 79 81 82 84 85 86 87 91 92 93 96 97 98 100 101 102 107 108 109 110 111 114 115 116 117 118 119 120 121 123 124 129 130 131 132 134 135 143 145 146 147 148 149 **S** University Hospitals, Cleveland, OH
Primary Contact: M Steven. Jones, President
COO: M Steven Jones, President
CFO: Paul Amantea, Director Finance
CMO: David Kosnosky M.D., Chief Medical Officer
CIO: Lou Ciraldo, Information Services Representative
CHR: Danialle Lynce, Manager Human Resources
CNO: Peggy A Kuhar R.N., MSN, Chief Nursing Officer
Web address: www.uhhospitals.org/geauga/
Control: Other not–for–profit (including NFP Corporation) **Service:** General medical and surgical

Staffed Beds: 142 **Admissions:** 7939 **Census:** 87 **Outpatient Visits:** 146399 **Births:** 1021 **Total Expense ($000):** 135971 **Payroll Expense ($000):** 44325 **Personnel:** 807

CHILLICOTHE—Ross County

⌘ **ADENA MEDICAL CENTER (360159)**, 272 Hospital Road, Zip 45601–9031; tel. 740/779–7500 **A**1 2 3 5 10 12 13 19 **F**3 5 8 13 15 18 20 22 24 26 28 29 30 31 32 34 35 38 40 41 45 46 48 49 50 51 54 57 59 62 63 64 66 70 73 74 75 76 77 78 79 81 82 83 84 85 87 89 91 93 96 97 98 99 100 101 102 103 104 107 108 111 114 115 119 120 121 123 126 127 129 130 131 132 133 135 144 146 147 148 **P**6 **S** Adena Health System, Chillicothe, OH
Primary Contact: Jeff Graham, President and Chief Executive Officer
COO: Eric Cecava, Chief Operating Officer
CFO: Robert Rosenberger, Chief Financial Officer
CMO: John Fortney, Senior System Medical Advisor
CIO: Linn Weimer, Chief Information Officer
CHR: Jay D. Justice, Chief Human Resource Officer
Web address: www.adena.org
Control: Other not–for–profit (including NFP Corporation) **Service:** General medical and surgical

Staffed Beds: 189 **Admissions:** 8876 **Census:** 89 **Outpatient Visits:** 641659 **Births:** 945 **Total Expense ($000):** 342168 **Payroll Expense ($000):** 106337 **Personnel:** 2264

⌘ **CHILLICOTHE VETERANS AFFAIRS MEDICAL CENTER**, 17273 State Route 104, Zip 45601–9718; tel. 740/773–1141, (Total facility includes 162 beds in nursing home–type unit) **A**1 3 5 **F**3 5 12 18 28 29 30 33 34 35 36 38 39 44 45 47 50 53 54 56 57 59 61 62 63 64 65 67 68 74 75 77 79 80 82 84 86 87 92 93 94 96 97 98 100 101 102 103 104 105 106 107 108 111 119 127 128 129 130 132 135 143 144 146 147 148 149 **P**6 **S** Department of Veterans Affairs, Washington, DC
Primary Contact: Keith Sullivan, Director
CFO: Rick Deckard, Chief Fiscal Service
CMO: Deborah Meesig M.D., Chief of Staff
CIO: William Gawler, Chief Information Officer
CHR: Angela Young, Human Resources Officer
Web address: www.chillicothe.va.gov/
Control: Veterans Affairs, Government, federal **Service:** General medical and surgical

Staffed Beds: 295 **Admissions:** 3087 **Census:** 237 **Outpatient Visits:** 411235 **Births:** 0 **Total Expense ($000):** 213419 **Payroll Expense ($000):** 98724 **Personnel:** 1424

VETERANS AFFAIRS MEDICAL CENTER See Chillicothe Veterans Affairs Medical Center

CINCINNATI—Hamilton County

⌘ **BETHESDA NORTH HOSPITAL (360179)**, 10500 Montgomery Road, Zip 45242–4402; tel. 513/865–1111, (Includes BETHESDA BUTLER HOSPITAL, 3125 Hamilton Mason Road, Hamilton, Ohio, Zip 45011–5307, tel. 513/894–8888; Chuck Brown, Administrator) **A**1 3 5 10 **F**3 5 8 9 11 12 13 15 17 18 20 22 24 26 28 29 30 31 34 35 36 37 38 39 40 41 42 43 44 45 46 47 48 49 50 53 54 55 56 57 58 59 61 63 64 65 66 68 70 71 73 74 75 76 77 78 79 81 82 83 84 85 86 87 91 92 93 94 96 97 99 100 101 102 103 104 107 108 110 111 114 115 116 117 118 119 120 121 123 124 126 129 130 131 132 134 135 141 143 144 145 146 147 148 149 **P**6 8
Primary Contact: Barbara Boyne, Executive Director, Operations
COO: Jenny Oliphant, Executive Vice President and Chief Operating Officer
CFO: Michael Crofton, Senior Vice President and Chief Financial Officer
CMO: Georges Feghali M.D., Senior Vice President Quality and Chief Medical Officer
CIO: Rick Moore, Chief Information Officer
CHR: Walter L McLarty, Chief Human Resources Officer
CNO: Mary Irvin R.N., MSN, Senior Vice President and Chief Nursing Officer
Web address: www.trihealth.com
Control: Other not–for–profit (including NFP Corporation) **Service:** General medical and surgical

Staffed Beds: 352 **Admissions:** 22565 **Census:** 252 **Outpatient Visits:** 357708 **Births:** 4217 **Total Expense ($000):** 491509 **Payroll Expense ($000):** 168338 **Personnel:** 3164

BRIDGEWELL HOSPITAL OF CINCINNATI (364046), 5500 Verulam Avenue, Zip 45213–2418; tel. 513/531–6444 (Nonreporting) **A**10
Primary Contact: Glenna Coffey, R.N., Chief Operating Officer
CNO: Doug Eppley, Director of Nursing
Web address: www.bridgewellhospitals.com
Control: Corporation, Investor–owned (for–profit) **Service:** Psychiatric

Staffed Beds: 48

☐ △ **CHRIST HOSPITAL (360163)**, 2139 Auburn Avenue, Zip 45219–2906; tel. 513/585–2000 **A**1 2 3 5 7 10 **F**1 3 6 8 9 12 13 15 17 18 20 22 24 26 28 29 30 31 34 35 36 37 38 39 40 44 45 46 47 48 49 50 51 53 54 55 56 57 58 59 60 61 64 65 66 68 70 73 74 75 76 77 78 79 80 81 82 83 84 85 86 87 90 92 93 94 96 97 98 99 100 101 102 103 104 107 108 109 110 111 114 115 116 117 118 119 120 121 123 124 126 129 130 131 132 135 138 141 143 144 145 146 147 148 149
Primary Contact: Michael Keating, President and Chief Executive Officer
COO: Victor DiPilla, Vice President and Chief Business Development Officer
CMO: Bernard B Gawne M.D., Vice President and Chief Medical Officer
CIO: Alex Vaillancourt, Chief Information Officer
CHR: Rick Tolson, Chief Administrative Officer and Chief Human Resources Officer
CNO: Deborah Marie Hayes R.N., MS, Chief Hospital Officer and Chief Nursing Officer
Web address: www.thechristhospital.com
Control: Other not–for–profit (including NFP Corporation) **Service:** General medical and surgical

Staffed Beds: 527 **Admissions:** 23132 **Census:** 284 **Outpatient Visits:** 579915 **Births:** 3201 **Total Expense ($000):** 629103 **Payroll Expense ($000):** 218217 **Personnel:** 3745

⌘ △ **CINCINNATI CHILDREN'S HOSPITAL MEDICAL CENTER (363300)**, 3333 Burnet Avenue MLC 8006, Zip 45229–3039, Mailing Address: 3333 Burnet Avenue, 45229–3039; tel. 513/636–4200, (Includes CHILDREN'S HOSPITAL, Elland and Bethesda Avenues, Cincinnati, Ohio, Zip 45229, tel. 513/894–8888) **A**1 2 3 5 7 8 10 **F**3 7 9 11 12 17 18 19 20 21 22 23 24 25 26 27 28 29 30 31 32 34 35 36 37 38 39 40 41 42 43 44 45 46 48 49 50 51 54 55 57 58 59 60 61 62 63 64 65 66 68 72 74 75 76 77 78 79 81 82 84 85 86 87 88 89 90 91 92 93 94 95 96 97 98 99 100 101 102 104 105 106 107 108 111 112 113 115 117 118 119 120 122 126 129 131 132 133 134 135 136 137 138 139 140 141 142 144 145 146 148 149 150 **P**1
Primary Contact: Michael Fisher, President and Chief Executive Officer
CIO: Marianne Speight, Vice President Information System and Chief Information Officer
Web address: www.cincinnatichildrens.org
Control: Other not–for–profit (including NFP Corporation) **Service:** Children's general medical and surgical

Staffed Beds: 609 **Admissions:** 19684 **Census:** 420 **Outpatient Visits:** 1281733 **Births:** 15 **Total Expense ($000):** 2097151 **Payroll Expense ($000):** 1080585 **Personnel:** 12835

Hospital, Medicare Provider Number, Address, Telephone, Approval, Facility, and Physician Codes, Health Care System

★ American Hospital Association (AHA) membership
☐ The Joint Commission accreditation
○ Healthcare Facilities Accreditation Program
◇ DNV Healthcare Inc. accreditation
⇑ Center for Improvement in Healthcare Quality Accreditation
△ Commission on Accreditation of Rehabilitation Facilities (CARF) accreditation

OH

✠ **CINCINNATI VETERANS AFFAIRS MEDICAL CENTER**, 3200 Vine Street, Zip 45220–2288; tel. 513/475–6300, (Nonreporting) **A**1 2 3 5 **S** Department of Veterans Affairs, Washington, DC
Primary Contact: Colonel Vivian T. Hutson, Director
COO: David Ninneman, Associate Director
CFO: Sandra Selvidge, Chief Fiscal Service
CIO: Vique Caro, Chief Information Officer
CHR: Sandra Stenger, Acting Chief Human Resources
CNO: Katheryn Cook R.N., Nurse Executive
Web address: www.cincinnati.va.gov/
Control: Veterans Affairs, Government, federal **Service:** General medical and surgical

Staffed Beds: 268

✠ **DANIEL DRAKE CENTER FOR POST ACUTE CARE (362004)**, 151 West Galbraith Road, Zip 45216–1015; tel. 513/418–2500, (Nonreporting) **A**1 3 5 10 **S** UC Health, Cincinnati, OH
Primary Contact: Amy Schroyer, Vice President Administration and Senior Site Executive
CFO: Duane Pifko, Interim Director Financial Services
Web address: www.uchealth.com/danieldrakecenter/
Control: Other not–for–profit (including NFP Corporation) **Service:** Acute long–term care hospital

Staffed Beds: 202

✠ **GOOD SAMARITAN HOSPITAL (360134)**, 375 Dixmyth Avenue, Zip 45220–2489; tel. 513/862–1400 **A**1 2 3 5 8 10 **F**3 5 6 8 9 11 12 13 15 17 18 20 22 24 26 28 29 30 31 34 35 36 37 38 39 40 41 42 44 45 46 47 48 49 50 53 54 55 56 57 58 59 61 63 64 65 66 68 70 71 72 74 75 76 77 78 79 81 82 83 84 85 86 87 91 92 93 94 96 97 98 99 100 101 102 103 104 105 107 108 110 111 114 115 116 117 118 119 120 121 123 124 126 129 130 131 132 134 135 141 143 144 145 146 147 148 149 **P**6 8 **S** Catholic Health Initiatives, Englewood, CO
Primary Contact: Jamie Easterling, Executive Director, Operations
COO: Gerald P Oliphant, Executive Vice President and Chief Operating Officer
CFO: Michael Crofton, Chief Financial Officer
CMO: Georges Feghali M.D., Senior Vice President Quality and Chief Medical Officer
CIO: Rick Moore, Chief Information Officer
CHR: Walter L McLarty, Chief Human Resources Officer
Web address: www.trihealth.com
Control: Church operated, Nongovernment, not–for–profit **Service:** General medical and surgical

Staffed Beds: 476 Admissions: 22810 Census: 315 Outpatient Visits: 288175 Births: 5405 Total Expense ($000): 509668 Payroll Expense ($000): 174329 Personnel: 2714

✠ **HEALTHSOUTH REHABILITATION HOSPITAL AT DRAKE (363034)**, 151 West Galbraith Road, Zip 45216–1015; tel. 513/418–5600, (Includes HEALTHSOUTH REHABILITATION HOSPITAL OF CINCINNATI AT NORWOOD, 4953 Section Avenue, Cincinnati, Ohio, Zip 45212–2120, tel. 513/712–9200; Ryan Smokovitz, Chief Executive Officer) **A**1 3 10 **F**29 31 34 35 56 74 90 91 92 130 148 **S** HEALTHSOUTH Corporation, Birmingham, AL
Primary Contact: Ryan Smokovitz, Chief Executive Officer
CFO: Scott Corder, Controller
CMO: Mark Goddard M.D., Medical Director
CHR: Jason Sparks, Director, Human Resources
CNO: Kathy McNally, Chief Nursing Officer
Web address: www.healthsouthatdrake.com
Control: Corporation, Investor–owned (for–profit) **Service:** Rehabilitation

Staffed Beds: 60 Admissions: 1147 Census: 46 Outpatient Visits: 0 Births: 0 Total Expense ($000): 17867 Payroll Expense ($000): 9399 Personnel: 135

✠ **MERCY HEALTH – ANDERSON HOSPITAL (360001)**, 7500 State Road, Zip 45255–2492; tel. 513/624–4500, (Nonreporting) **A**1 2 3 10 **S** Mercy Health, Cincinnati, OH
Primary Contact: Ken James, President and Chief Executive Officer of East Market
COO: Katherine Edrington R.N., Administrator
CFO: Patrick A Kowalski, Chief Financial Officer
CMO: Dan Roth M.D., Vice President Medical Affairs
CIO: Matt Eversole, Regional Vice President Information Services
CHR: Angie Ferrell, Director Human Resources
Web address: www.e–mercy.com
Control: Church operated, Nongovernment, not–for–profit **Service:** General medical and surgical

Staffed Beds: 188

✠ **MERCY HEALTH – WEST HOSPITAL (360234)**, 3300 Mercy Health Boulevard, Zip 45211; tel. 513/215–5000, (Nonreporting) **A**1 2 10 **S** Mercy Health, Cincinnati, OH
Primary Contact: Michael Kramer, Chief Executive Officer
COO: Jason Asic, Chief Operating Officer
CFO: Kyle Klein, Assistant Chief Financial Officer
CMO: Creighton Wright M.D., Vice President Medical Administration
CHR: Bridget Mentzel, Director Human Resources
CNO: Stephanie Meade, MSN, Chief Nursing Officer
Web address: www.e–mercy.com/west–hospital
Control: Church operated, Nongovernment, not–for–profit **Service:** General medical and surgical

Staffed Beds: 250

✠ **SELECT SPECIALTY HOSPITAL – CINCINNATI NORTH (362034)**, 10500 Montgomery Road, Zip 45242–4402; tel. 513/865–5300, (Nonreporting) **A**1 10 **S** Select Medical Corporation, Mechanicsburg, PA
Primary Contact: Susan Glenn, Chief Executive Officer
CMO: Sunil Dama M.D., Medical Director
CHR: Elizabeth M Wilson, Coordinator Human Resources
Web address: www.cincinnatinorth.selectspecialtyhospitals.com/
Control: Corporation, Investor–owned (for–profit) **Service:** Acute long–term care hospital

Staffed Beds: 41

✠ **SELECT SPECIALTY HOSPITAL–CINCINNATI (362019)**, 375 Dixmyth Avenue, 15th Floor, Zip 45220–2475; tel. 513/862–4444, (Nonreporting) **A**1 10 **S** Select Medical Corporation, Mechanicsburg, PA
Primary Contact: David D. Muggli, FACHE, Chief Executive Officer
CMO: Brian Boster M.D., Medical Director
CNO: Bobbi Schmidt, Chief Nursing Officer
Web address: www.selectspecialtyhospitals.com/company/locations/cincinnati.aspx
Control: Corporation, Investor–owned (for–profit) **Service:** Acute long–term care hospital

Staffed Beds: 36

☐ **SHRINERS HOSPITALS FOR CHILDREN–CINCINNATI (363308)**, 3229 Burnet Avenue, Zip 45229–3095; tel. 513/872–6000, (Nonreporting) **A**1 3 10 **S** Shriners Hospitals for Children, Tampa, FL
Primary Contact: Mark D. Shugarman, Administrator
CFO: Susan Harris, Director Fiscal Services
CMO: Petra Warner, Interim Chief of Staff
CIO: David Brian, Chief Information Officer
CHR: Debra A Felder, Director Human Resources
Web address: www.shrinershospitalsforchildren.org/Hospitals/Locations/Cincinnati.aspx
Control: Other not–for–profit (including NFP Corporation) **Service:** Children's other specialty

Staffed Beds: 30

✠ **SUMMIT BEHAVIORAL HEALTHCARE (364035)**, 1101 Summit Road, Zip 45237–2652; tel. 513/948–3600, (Nonreporting) **A**1 3 10 **S** Ohio Department of Mental Health, Columbus, OH
Primary Contact: Elizabeth Banks, Chief Executive Officer
COO: Steven Burns, Director Fiscal Services
CFO: Steven Burns, Director Fiscal Services
CMO: Patrick McCullough M.D., Chief Medical Services
CIO: Eric Bradley, Director Computer Information Services
CHR: Bobbie Carrelli, Director Human Resources
CNO: Kathy A. Smith MSN, R.N., Nurse Executive
Web address: www.mh.state.oh.us/
Control: State, Government, Nonfederal **Service:** Psychiatric

Staffed Beds: 291

✠ **THE JEWISH HOSPITAL – MERCY HEALTH (360016)**, 4777 East Galbraith Road, Zip 45236–2725; tel. 513/686–3000, (Nonreporting) **A**1 2 3 5 10 **S** Mercy Health, Cincinnati, OH
Primary Contact: Patricia Davis–Hagens, R.N., Central Market Leader and President
COO: Jack Hill, Chief Operating Officer and Administrator
Web address: www.jewishhospitalcincinnati.com/
Control: Other not–for–profit (including NFP Corporation) **Service:** General medical and surgical

Staffed Beds: 209

Many Facility Codes have changed. Please refer to the AHA Guide Code Chart. © 2017 AHA Guide

□ **TRIHEALTH EVENDALE HOSPITAL (360362)**, 3155 Glendale Milford Road, Zip 45241–3134; tel. 513/454–2222 **A**1 2 10 **F**3 8 29 30 34 35 44 46 50 57 59 64 68 70 75 79 81 82 85 86 87 107 111 115 119 130 131 143 146 149 **P**6 8
Primary Contact: Kelvin Hanger, Chief Executive Officer
CFO: Michael Crofton, Chief Financial Officer
Web address: www.evendalemedical.com
Control: Other not–for–profit (including NFP Corporation) **Service:** Surgical

Staffed Beds: 6 **Admissions:** 606 **Census:** 3 **Outpatient Visits:** 34536 **Births:** 0 **Total Expense ($000):** 46978 **Payroll Expense ($000):** 13668 **Personnel:** 184

★ **TRIHEALTH REHABILITATION HOSPITAL (363041)**, 2155 Dana Avenue, Zip 45207; tel. 513/601–0600 (Nonreporting) **S** Select Medical Corporation, Mechanicsburg, PA
Primary Contact: Mark Asnen, Chief Executive Officer
Web address: www.trihealthrehab.com
Control: Corporation, Investor–owned (for–profit) **Service:** Rehabilitation

Staffed Beds: 60

⊞ **UNIVERSITY OF CINCINNATI MEDICAL CENTER (360003)**, 234 Goodman Street, Zip 45219–2316; tel. 513/584–1000 **A**1 2 3 5 8 10 **F**3 7 9 11 12 13 15 16 17 18 20 22 24 26 29 30 33 34 35 36 37 38 39 40 41 43 44 45 46 47 48 49 50 51 53 54 55 56 57 58 59 60 61 63 64 66 68 70 71 72 74 75 76 77 78 79 80 81 82 84 85 86 87 91 92 97 98 100 101 102 103 104 107 108 110 111 112 114 115 116 117 118 119 120 121 123 124 126 129 130 131 132 134 135 136 137 138 139 141 142 145 146 147 148 149 150 **P**6 **S** UC Health, Cincinnati, OH
Primary Contact: Jennifer Jackson, R.N., MSN, Chief Administrative Officer, Chief Nursing Officer and Vice President
CFO: Matthew Nealon, Vice President, Chief Financial Officer
CMO: Bill Hurford, Chief Medical Officer
CIO: Jay Brown, Vice President and Chief Information Officer
CHR: Clarence Pauley, Senior Vice President and Chief Human Resources Officer
CNO: Jennifer Jackson R.N., MSN, Vice President and Chief Nursing Officer
Web address: www.uchealth.com/university-of-cincinnati-medical-center/
Control: Other not–for–profit (including NFP Corporation) **Service:** General medical and surgical

Staffed Beds: 592 **Admissions:** 28549 **Census:** 446 **Outpatient Visits:** 644377 **Births:** 2274 **Total Expense ($000):** 881922 **Payroll Expense ($000):** 272747 **Personnel:** 4536

VETERANS AFFAIRS MEDICAL CENTER See Cincinnati Veterans Affairs Medical Center

CIRCLEVILLE—Pickaway County

⊞ **BERGER HEALTH SYSTEM (360170)**, 600 North Pickaway Street, Zip 43113–1447; tel. 740/474–2126 **A**1 5 10 **F**3 13 15 18 20 28 29 30 31 34 35 40 45 46 50 54 59 63 64 70 76 77 78 81 85 87 92 93 96 107 108 110 111 115 119 124 129 130 131 132 135 146 148
Primary Contact: Tim A. Colburn, President and Chief Executive Officer
CFO: Richard Filler, Chief Financial Officer
CMO: Jill Barno M.D., Chief Medical Officer
CIO: Andy Chileski, Chief Information Officer and Vice President Facilities
CHR: Richard Filler, Chief Human Resource Officer
CNO: Kristin Day Gardner, Chief Nursing Officer
Web address: www.bergerhealth.com
Control: City–county, Government, Nonfederal **Service:** General medical and surgical

Staffed Beds: 56 **Admissions:** 2446 **Census:** 16 **Outpatient Visits:** 115055 **Births:** 356 **Total Expense ($000):** 71727 **Payroll Expense ($000):** 23114 **Personnel:** 431

CLEVELAND—Cuyahoga County

⊞ **CLEVELAND CLINIC (360180)**, 9500 Euclid Avenue, Zip 44195–5108; tel. 216/444–2200, (Includes CLEVELAND CLINIC CHILDREN'S HOSPITAL, 9500 Euclid Avenue, Cleveland, Ohio, Zip 44103, tel. 800/223–2273) **A**1 3 5 8 10 **F**3 6 7 8 9 12 13 14 15 17 18 19 20 21 22 23 24 25 26 27 28 29 30 31 32 33 34 35 36 37 38 39 40 42 44 45 46 47 48 49 50 51 52 53 54 55 56 57 58 59 60 61 62 63 64 65 66 68 70 71 72 74 75 76 77 78 79 80 81 82 83 84 85 86 87 88 89 90 91 92 93 94 96 97 100 101 103 104 107 108 109 110 111 112 113 114 115 116 117 118 119 120 121 123 124 126 129 130 131 132 134 135 136 137 138 139 140 141 142 143 144 145 146 147 148 149 **P**6 **S** Cleveland Clinic Health System, Cleveland, OH
Primary Contact: Delos Cosgrove, M.D., President and Chief Executive Officer
CFO: Steven Glass, Chief Financial Officer
CMO: Joseph Hahn M.D., Chief of Staff
CIO: C Martin Harris M.D., Chief Information Officer
CNO: Katherine Hancock R.N., Executive Chief Nursing Officer
Web address: www.clevelandclinic.org
Control: Other not–for–profit (including NFP Corporation) **Service:** General medical and surgical

Staffed Beds: 1280 **Admissions:** 52423 **Census:** 997 **Outpatient Visits:** 6033971 **Births:** 214 **Total Expense ($000):** 5297989 **Payroll Expense ($000):** 2612281 **Personnel:** 29191

⊞ △ **CLEVELAND CLINIC CHILDREN'S HOSPITAL FOR REHABILITATION (363304)**, 2801 Martin Luther King Jr Drive, Zip 44104–3865; tel. 216/448–6400 **A**1 3 7 10 **F**28 29 30 32 34 35 36 44 50 60 74 75 79 80 82 90 91 93 94 96 99 100 130 131 132 143 146 148 **S** Cleveland Clinic Health System, Cleveland, OH
Primary Contact: Michael J. McHugh, M.D., Medical Director
COO: Alec G Kulik, Administrator
CFO: Debra Nyikes, Director Finance and Chief Financial Officer
CMO: Roberta Bauer M.D., Acting Chair Medical Staff
CIO: C Martin Harris M.D., Chief Information Officer
CHR: Jan Hlahol, Manager Human Resources
Web address: www.my.clevelandclinic.org/childrens–hospital/default.aspx
Control: Other not–for–profit (including NFP Corporation) **Service:** Children's rehabilitation

Staffed Beds: 25 **Admissions:** 227 **Census:** 14 **Outpatient Visits:** 100048 **Births:** 0 **Total Expense ($000):** 43195 **Payroll Expense ($000):** 25244 **Personnel:** 527

⊞ **CLEVELAND CLINIC FAIRVIEW HOSPITAL (360077)**, 18101 Lorain Avenue, Zip 44111–5656; tel. 216/476–7000 **A**1 2 5 10 13 **F**3 8 12 13 15 17 18 19 20 22 24 26 28 29 30 31 34 35 36 40 41 43 45 46 47 49 50 51 53 55 57 58 59 60 64 65 66 68 69 70 71 72 73 74 75 76 77 78 79 80 81 82 85 86 87 89 92 93 97 98 99 100 107 108 110 111 114 115 117 118 119 120 121 123 124 126 130 131 132 135 143 146 147 148 149 150 **S** Cleveland Clinic Health System, Cleveland, OH
Primary Contact: Neil Smith, D.O., President
COO: John C Mills, Senior Vice President Operations
CFO: Ankit Chhabra, Director Finance
CMO: Brent Burkey M.D., Chief Medical Officer
CIO: C Martin Harris M.D., Chief Information Officer
CHR: Ann Beatty, Director Human Resources
CNO: Deborah C Small MSN, R.N., Vice President Patient Care Services and Chief Nursing Officer
Web address: www.fairviewhospital.org
Control: Other not–for–profit (including NFP Corporation) **Service:** General medical and surgical

Staffed Beds: 451 **Admissions:** 25383 **Census:** 297 **Outpatient Visits:** 239374 **Births:** 5081 **Total Expense ($000):** 394700 **Payroll Expense ($000):** 152965 **Personnel:** 2221

□ **GRACE HOSPITAL (362015)**, 2307 West 14th Street, Zip 44113–3698; tel. 216/687–1500, (Nonreporting) **A**1 10
Primary Contact: Rajive Khanna, Chief Executive Officer
COO: Rajive Khanna, Chief Executive Officer
CFO: Michelle Hennis, Administrative Director Financial Services
CMO: John Nickels M.D., President Medical Staff
CNO: Barbara Moran R.N., Director Patient Care Services and Chief Nursing Officer
Web address: www.gracehospital.org
Control: Other not–for–profit (including NFP Corporation) **Service:** Acute long–term care hospital

Staffed Beds: 87

Hospital, Medicare Provider Number, Address, Telephone, Approval, Facility, and Physician Codes, Health Care System

★ American Hospital Association (AHA) membership
□ The Joint Commission accreditation
○ Healthcare Facilities Accreditation Program
◇ DNV Healthcare Inc. accreditation
⇑ Center for Improvement in Healthcare Quality Accreditation
△ Commission on Accreditation of Rehabilitation Facilities (CARF) accreditation

© 2017 AHA Guide   *Many Facility Codes have changed. Please refer to the AHA Guide Code Chart.*   Hospitals **A485**

OH

✠ **HILLCREST HOSPITAL (360230)**, 6780 Mayfield Road, Zip 44124–2203; tel. 440/312–4500 **A**1 2 3 10 **F**3 12 13 15 17 18 20 22 24 26 28 29 30 31 34 35 36 37 38 40 41 43 46 49 50 51 53 54 55 56 57 59 60 64 65 68 69 70 72 74 75 76 77 78 79 81 82 84 85 86 89 93 97 99 100 107 108 110 111 114 115 116 117 118 119 120 121 126 129 130 131 132 135 143 145 146 147 148 **S** Cleveland Clinic Health System, Cleveland, OH
Primary Contact: Donald Ford, M.D., Interim President
Web address: www.hillcresthospital.org
Control: Other not–for–profit (including NFP Corporation) **Service:** General medical and surgical

Staffed Beds: 453 Admissions: 22574 Census: 297 Outpatient Visits: 227041 Births: 4459 Total Expense ($000): 378370 Payroll Expense ($000): 135373 Personnel: 2128

✠ △ **LOUIS STOKES CLEVELAND VETERANS AFFAIRS MEDICAL CENTER**, 10701 East Boulevard, Zip 44106–1702; tel. 216/791–3800, (Total facility includes 123 beds in nursing home–type unit) **A**1 2 3 5 7 8 **F**3 4 5 8 9 10 12 15 17 18 20 22 24 26 28 29 30 31 33 34 35 36 38 39 40 44 45 46 47 48 49 50 51 53 54 55 56 57 58 59 60 61 62 63 64 65 67 68 70 71 74 75 77 78 79 80 81 82 83 84 85 86 87 90 91 92 93 94 95 96 97 98 100 101 102 103 104 105 106 107 110 111 113 116 117 119 120 121 126 127 128 129 130 132 135 143 146 147 148 149 150 **S** Department of Veterans Affairs, Washington, DC
Primary Contact: Susan Fuehrer, Director
CFO: Michael Pappas, Chief Fiscal Service Officer
CMO: Murray Altose M.D., Chief of Staff
CIO: Steve Gaj, Facility Chief Information Officer
CHR: Charles Franks, Chief Human Resources
CNO: Innette Mary Sarduy M.P.H., R.N., Associate Director Patient Care Services and Nurse Executive
Web address: www.cleveland.va.gov/
Control: Veterans Affairs, Government, federal **Service:** General medical and surgical

Staffed Beds: 576 Admissions: 9938 Census: 488 Outpatient Visits: 1284645 Births: 0 Personnel: 4952

✠ **LUTHERAN HOSPITAL (360087)**, 1730 West 25th Street, Zip 44113–3170; tel. 216/696–4300 **A**1 3 10 **F**3 4 5 15 29 30 34 35 37 40 45 50 56 57 58 59 60 64 65 68 70 74 75 77 79 81 82 85 86 87 93 94 98 99 102 103 104 105 107 108 110 111 114 115 119 130 131 132 143 146 148 149 **S** Cleveland Clinic Health System, Cleveland, OH
Primary Contact: Donald A. Malone Jr, President
COO: Matthew Mattner, Chief Operating Officer
CFO: Don Urbancsik, Director Finance
CMO: Ronald Golovan M.D., Vice President Medical Operations
CIO: C Martin Harris M.D., Chief Information Officer
CHR: Judith Santora, Chief Human Resource Officer
CNO: Janet Schuster, Chief Nursing Officer
Web address: www.lutheranhospital.org
Control: Other not–for–profit (including NFP Corporation) **Service:** General medical and surgical

Staffed Beds: 194 Admissions: 9039 Census: 112 Outpatient Visits: 70537 Births: 0 Total Expense ($000): 106356 Payroll Expense ($000): 45022 Personnel: 652

✠ △ **METROHEALTH MEDICAL CENTER (360059)**, 2500 MetroHealth Drive, Zip 44109–1998; tel. 216/778–7800, (Total facility includes 135 beds in nursing home–type unit) **A**1 2 3 5 7 8 10 13 **F**3 5 6 7 8 9 11 12 13 15 16 17 18 19 20 22 24 26 27 28 29 30 31 32 34 35 36 38 39 40 42 43 44 45 46 47 48 49 50 51 52 53 54 55 56 57 58 59 60 61 63 64 65 66 68 70 71 72 74 75 76 77 78 79 80 81 82 83 84 85 86 87 88 89 90 91 92 93 94 95 96 97 98 99 100 101 102 103 104 105 107 108 110 111 114 115 116 117 118 119 120 121 123 124 126 128 129 130 131 132 134 135 143 144 146 147 148 149 150 **P**6
Primary Contact: Akram Boutros, M.D., FACHE, President and Chief Executive Officer
COO: Daniel Lewis, Executive Vice President and Chief Operating Officer
CFO: Craig Richmond, Senior Vice President and Chief Financial Officer
CMO: Alfred Connors M.D., Executive Vice President and Chief Quality Officer and Interim Chief Medical Officer
CIO: Don Reichert, Vice President Associate Chief Information Officer
CHR: Debbie Warman, Vice President Human Resources
CNO: Melissa Kline, Chief Nursing Officer
Web address: www.metrohealth.org
Control: County, Government, Nonfederal **Service:** General medical and surgical

Staffed Beds: 715 Admissions: 24165 Census: 493 Outpatient Visits: 1341453 Births: 3073 Total Expense ($000): 1047431 Payroll Expense ($000): 548750 Personnel: 6514

SELECT SPECIALTY HOSPITAL – CLEVELAND FAIRHILL See Select Specialty Hospital – Cleveland Gateway

★ **SELECT SPECIALTY HOSPITAL – CLEVELAND GATEWAY (362026)**, 2351 East 22nd Street, 7th Floor, Zip 44115–3111; tel. 216/363–2671, (Nonreporting) (Includes SELECT SPECIALTY HOSPITAL – CLEVELAND FAIRHILL, 11900 Fairhill Road, Cleveland, Ohio, Zip 44120–1062, tel. 216/983–8030; Steve Jakubcanin, Executive Director) **A**3 10 **S** Select Medical Corporation, Mechanicsburg, PA
Primary Contact: Cheryl G. Gentry, Interim Chief Executive Officer
Web address: www.selectspecialtyhospitals.com/
Control: Corporation, Investor–owned (for–profit) **Service:** Acute long–term care hospital

Staffed Beds: 143

☐ **ST. VINCENT CHARITY MEDICAL CENTER (360037)**, 2351 East 22nd Street, Zip 44115–3111; tel. 216/861–6200 **A**1 2 3 5 10 **F**3 4 5 8 12 15 17 18 20 22 24 28 29 30 31 33 34 35 36 37 38 39 40 44 45 50 54 56 57 58 59 60 61 62 64 65 66 68 70 74 75 77 78 79 81 84 85 86 87 93 94 97 98 100 102 103 107 108 110 111 118 119 126 129 130 131 132 144 146 148 **P**4 **S** Sisters of Charity Health System, Cleveland, OH
Primary Contact: David F. Perse, M.D., President and Chief Executive Officer
COO: Joan Ross, Senior Vice President and Chief Operating Officer
CFO: John Rusnaczyk, Senior Vice President and Chief Financial Officer
CMO: Joseph A. Sopko M.D., Chief Medical Officer
CIO: Robin Stursa, Chief Information Officer
CHR: Ted Monczewski, Vice President Human Resources
CNO: Beverly Lozar, Chief Nursing Executive
Web address: www.stvincentcharity.com/
Control: Other not–for–profit (including NFP Corporation) **Service:** General medical and surgical

Staffed Beds: 208 Admissions: 8559 Census: 113 Outpatient Visits: 153975 Births: 0 Total Expense ($000): 156777 Payroll Expense ($000): 64464 Personnel: 1002

✠ **UH REGIONAL HOSPITALS (360075)**, 27100 Chardon Road, Zip 44143–1116; tel. 440/585–6500, (Includes UNIVERSITY HOSPITALS BEDFORD MEDICAL CENTER, 44 Blaine Avenue, Cleveland, Ohio, Zip 44146–2709, tel. 440/735–3900; UNIVERSITY HOSPITALS RICHMOND MEDICAL CENTER, 27100 Chardon Road, Cleveland, Ohio, Zip 44143–1116, tel. 440/585–6500) **A**1 3 10 12 13 **F**8 14 15 18 20 26 29 30 34 35 40 50 57 59 60 64 65 66 68 70 74 75 77 78 79 81 82 84 85 86 87 91 92 93 96 97 100 105 106 107 108 109 110 111 114 116 117 118 119 129 130 131 132 133 135 143 146 147 148 149 **S** University Hospitals, Cleveland, OH
Primary Contact: Brian Monter, MSN, R.N., President
CFO: Scott Platz, Director Finance
CMO: Rosemary Leeming M.D., Chief Medical Officer
CHR: Stephanie W Neonakis, Manager Human Resources
CNO: Michelle Giltner, Interim Chief Nursing Officer
Web address: www.uhhospitals.org
Control: Other not–for–profit (including NFP Corporation) **Service:** General medical and surgical

Staffed Beds: 101 Admissions: 4987 Census: 52 Outpatient Visits: 138969 Births: 0 Total Expense ($000): 113707 Payroll Expense ($000): 44800 Personnel: 817

✠ **UNIVERSITY HOSPITALS CLEVELAND MEDICAL CENTER (360137)**, 11100 Euclid Avenue, Zip 44106–1716; tel. 216/844–1000, (Includes HANNA HOUSE SKILLED NURSING FACILITY, 11100 Euclid Avenue, Cleveland, Ohio, Zip 44106, tel. 216/844–3911; RAINBOW BABIES AND CHILDREN'S HOSPITAL, 2101 Adelbert Road, Cleveland, Ohio, Zip 44106–2624, tel. 216/844–3911; Patricia DePompei, President; UNIVERSITY MACDONALD WOMEN'S HOSPITAL, 2101 Adelbert Road, Cleveland, Ohio, Zip 44106–2624, tel. 216/844–3911; Patricia DePompei, President) (Total facility includes 38 beds in nursing home–type unit) **A**1 2 3 5 8 10 **F**3 5 6 8 9 11 12 13 14 15 17 18 19 20 21 22 23 24 25 26 27 28 29 30 31 32 34 35 36 37 38 39 40 41 42 43 44 45 46 47 48 49 50 51 52 53 54 55 56 57 58 59 60 61 62 63 64 65 66 68 70 71 72 73 74 75 76 77 78 79 80 81 82 83 84 85 86 87 88 89 91 92 93 94 96 97 98 99 100 101 102 103 104 105 107 108 109 110 111 112 114 115 116 117 118 119 120 121 122 123 124 126 128 129 130 131 132 133 135 136 137 138 139 140 141 142 143 144 145 146 147 148 149 **P**6 7 **S** University Hospitals, Cleveland, OH
Primary Contact: Daniel I. Simon, M.D., President
COO: Ron Dziedzicki R.N., Chief Operating Officer
CFO: Sonia Salvino, Vice President Finance
CIO: Sue Schade, Interim Chief Information Officer
CHR: Julie Chester, Vice President Human Resources
CNO: Jean Blake, Chief Nursing Officer
Web address: www.UHhospitals.org
Control: Other not–for–profit (including NFP Corporation) **Service:** General medical and surgical

Staffed Beds: 836 Admissions: 41497 Census: 673 Outpatient Visits: 494560 Births: 4049 Total Expense ($000): 1406028 Payroll Expense ($000): 498526 Personnel: 8948

VETERANS AFFAIRS MEDICAL CENTER See Louis Stokes Cleveland Veterans Affairs Medical Center

Many Facility Codes have changed. Please refer to the AHA Guide Code Chart.   © 2017 AHA Guide

OH

COLDWATER—Mercer County

⊠ **MERCER HEALTH (360058)**, 800 West Main Street, Zip 45828–1698;
tel. 419/678–2341 **A**1 10 **F**7 11 12 13 15 18 28 29 30 31 34 35 40 44 45 47
50 51 54 57 59 61 62 64 65 70 75 77 78 79 81 82 85 87 92 93 94 95 97 107
108 110 111 114 118 119 130 131 132 133 134 135 143 144 145 146 147
148 149 150 **P**3
Primary Contact: Lisa R. Klenke, R.N., Chief Executive Officer
CFO: George Boyles, Senior Vice President of Finance and Chief Financial Officer
CMO: James Reichert, Chief Medical Officer
CIO: DeWayne Marsee, Director Information Systems
CHR: Jon Dingledine, Senior Director Human Resources and Support Services
CNO: Cindy Liette, Vice President Patient Care Services
Web address: www.mercer–health.com
Control: Hospital district or authority, Government, Nonfederal **Service**: General
medical and surgical

Staffed Beds: 60 **Admissions**: 1722 **Census**: 15 **Outpatient Visits**: 123558
Births: 350 **Total Expense ($000)**: 50449 **Payroll Expense ($000)**: 17421
Personnel: 388

COLUMBUS—Franklin County

⊠ **JAMES CANCER HOSPITAL AND SOLOVE RESEARCH INSTITUTE (360242)**,
460 West Tenth Avenue, Zip 43210–1240; tel. 614/293–3300 **A**1 2 3 5 10 **F**3
15 29 30 31 32 34 35 36 37 38 39 44 46 47 48 49 50 52 54 55 57 58 59
61 64 66 68 70 71 74 75 77 78 79 81 82 84 85 86 87 93 97 100 107 108
110 111 112 114 115 116 117 118 119 120 121 123 124 126 130 132 134
135 136 141 143 144 145 146 147 148 149 **P**6 **S** Ohio State University Health
System, Columbus, OH
Primary Contact: Michael Caligiuri, M.D., Chief Executive Officer
COO: Jeff Walker, Chief Operating Officer
CFO: Bell Julian, Associate Executive Director and Chief Financial Officer
CIO: Michael Townsend, Chief Information Officer
CHR: Jill Hannah, Director Human Resources
CNO: Kris M Kipp, Executive Director, Patient Services and Chief Nursing Officer
Web address: www.cancer.osu.edu/
Control: State, Government, Nonfederal **Service**: Cancer

Staffed Beds: 306 **Admissions**: 13780 **Census**: 257 **Outpatient Visits**:
391035 **Births**: 0 **Total Expense ($000)**: 901033 **Payroll Expense ($000)**:
216644 **Personnel**: 3956

⊠ **MOUNT CARMEL (360035)**, 793 West State Street, Zip 43222–1551;
tel. 614/234–5000, (Includes MOUNT CARMEL EAST HOSPITAL, 6001 East Broad
Street, Columbus, Ohio, Zip 43213, tel. 614/234–6000; Brinsley Lewis, FACHE,
President; MOUNT CARMEL WEST HOSPITAL, 793 West State Street, Columbus, Ohio,
Zip 43222, tel. 614/234–5000) **A**1 4 2 3 5 10 **F**3 11 12 13 15 17 18 20 22 26
28 29 30 31 34 35 37 40 42 43 44 45 46 47 48 49 50 51 54 55 57 58 59 61 63
64 65 66 68 70 72 74 75 76 77 78 79 81 82 83 84 85 86 87 90 91 92 93 96 97
98 100 101 102 103 104 107 108 109 110 111 114 115 116 117 118 119 120
121 123 124 126 130 131 132 145 146 147 148 **P**6 8 **S** Trinity Health, Livonia, MI
Primary Contact: Sean McKibben, President and Chief Operating Officer
COO: Mary R Trimmer, Interim Chief Operating Officer
CFO: Keith T Coleman, Chief Financial Officer
Web address: www.mountcarmelhealth.com
Control: Church operated, Nongovernment, not–for–profit **Service**: General
medical and surgical

Staffed Beds: 749 **Admissions**: 36795 **Census**: 461 **Outpatient Visits**:
373160 **Births**: 3486 **Total Expense ($000)**: 752709 **Payroll Expense
($000)**: 250996 **Personnel**: 3909

⊠ △ **NATIONWIDE CHILDREN'S HOSPITAL (363305)**, 700 Children's Drive,
Zip 43205–2664; tel. 614/722–2000 **A**1 2 3 5 7 10 **F**3 7 8 12 16 17 18 19 20
21 22 23 24 25 26 27 28 29 30 31 32 34 35 36 38 39 40 41 43 44 45 47 48
50 51 52 53 54 55 57 58 59 60 61 62 63 64 65 66 68 71 72 74 75 77 78 79
81 82 83 84 85 86 87 88 89 90 92 93 94 96 97 98 99 100 101 102 104 105
107 108 111 112 114 115 116 117 118 119 126 127 129 130 131 132 133
134 135 136 137 138 140 141 143 144 145 146 148 149 150 **P**8
Primary Contact: Steve Allen, M.D., Chief Executive Officer
COO: Rick Miller, President and Chief Operating Officer
CFO: Tim Robinson, Executive Vice President, Chief Financial and Administrative
Officer and Treasurer
CMO: Richard Brilli M.D., Chief Medical Officer
CIO: Denise Zabawski, Vice President Information Services and Chief Information Officer
Web address: www.nationwidechildrens.org
Control: Other not–for–profit (including NFP Corporation) **Service**: Children's
general medical and surgical

Staffed Beds: 616 **Admissions**: 17857 **Census**: 438 **Outpatient Visits**:
1255566 **Births**: 0 **Total Expense ($000)**: 1152204 **Payroll Expense
($000)**: 523135 **Personnel**: 8486

□ **OHIO HOSPITAL FOR PSYCHIATRY (364041)**, 880 Greenlawn Avenue,
Zip 43223–2616; tel. 614/449–9664 (Nonreporting) **A**1 10 **S** Acadia Healthcare
Company, Inc., Franklin, TN
Primary Contact: Stanley Frank, Chief Executive Officer
COO: Shannon Robbins, Chief Operating Officer
CFO: Steve Snyder, Chief Financial Officer
CMO: Richard Nockowitz M.D., Medical Director
CNO: Jayne Zink, Director of Nursing
Web address: www.ohiohospitalforpsychiatry.com/
Control: Corporation, Investor–owned (for–profit) **Service**: Children's hospital
psychiatric

Staffed Beds: 90

⊠ △ **OHIO STATE UNIVERSITY WEXNER MEDICAL CENTER (360085)**,
370 West 9th Avenue, Zip 43210–1238; tel. 614/293–8000, (Includes OHIO
STATE UNIVERSITY HOSPITALS EAST, 1492 East Broad Street, Columbus, Ohio,
Zip 43205–1546, tel. 614/257–3000) **A**1 3 5 7 8 10 **F**3 4 5 6 8 9 11 12 13 15
16 17 18 20 22 24 26 28 29 30 31 33 34 35 36 37 38 39 40 43 44 45 46 47
48 49 50 51 52 53 54 55 56 57 58 59 60 61 64 65 66 68 70 72 73 74 75 76
77 78 79 80 81 82 84 85 86 87 90 91 92 93 94 95 96 97 98 99 100 101 102
103 104 105 107 108 110 111 112 113 114 115 118 119 126 129 130 131
132 134 135 137 138 139 140 141 142 143 144 145 146 147 148 149 **P**6 **S**
Ohio State University Health System, Columbus, OH
Primary Contact: David P. McQuaid, FACHE, Chief Operating Officer
COO: David P McQuaid FACHE, Chief Operating Officer
CMO: Andrew Thomas M.D., Chief Medical Officer
CIO: Phyllis Teater, Chief Information Officer
CHR: Kim Shumate, Human Resources Officer
CNO: Mary G Nash Ph.D., R.N., Chief Nursing Officer
Web address: www.medicalcenter.osu.edu
Control: State, Government, Nonfederal **Service**: General medical and surgical

Staffed Beds: 971 **Admissions**: 45578 **Census**: 763 **Outpatient Visits**:
1333141 **Births**: 4971 **Total Expense ($000)**: 1434906 **Payroll Expense
($000)**: 432118 **Personnel**: 10448

⊠ **OHIOHEALTH DOCTORS HOSPITAL (360152)**, 5100 West Broad Street,
Zip 43228–1607; tel. 614/544–1000 **A**1 2 3 5 10 12 13 **F**3 13 15 17 18 20 22
24 26 28 29 30 31 34 35 36 40 45 46 47 48 49 50 57 58 59 64 65 66 68 70
72 74 75 76 77 78 81 82 84 85 87 90 92 93 97 100 107 109 110 111 114
115 116 117 119 120 121 123 126 130 131 135 145 146 147 148 **P**1 3 6 **S**
OhioHealth, Columbus, OH
Primary Contact: Michael L. Reichfield, President
CFO: Troy Hammett, Vice President and Chief Financial Officer
CMO: Dean Colwell D.O., Vice President Medical Affairs
CIO: Michael Krouse, Chief Information Officer
CHR: David Sullivan, Director Human Resources
Web address: www.ohiohealth.com
Control: Church operated, Nongovernment, not–for–profit **Service**: General
medical and surgical

Staffed Beds: 243 **Admissions**: 8843 **Census**: 93 **Outpatient Visits**:
242711 **Births**: 917 **Total Expense ($000)**: 206182 **Payroll Expense
($000)**: 90285 **Personnel**: 1277

⊠ **OHIOHEALTH GRANT MEDICAL CENTER (360017)**, 111 South Grant Avenue,
Zip 43215–1898; tel. 614/566–9000 **A**1 2 3 5 8 10 **F**3 7 8 9 11 13 15 17 18
20 22 24 26 28 29 30 31 35 36 37 40 42 43 45 46 47 48 49 50 53 54 56 57
58 59 60 61 64 66 67 68 70 72 74 75 76 78 79 81 82 83 84 85 86 87 97
100 102 107 108 109 110 111 114 115 116 117 119 120 121 123 124 126
129 130 131 132 135 143 144 146 147 148 149 150 **P**1 3 6 **S** OhioHealth,
Columbus, OH
Primary Contact: Michael Lawson, President and Chief Operating Officer
COO: Kevin Lutz DPM, Chief Operating Officer, Grant
CFO: Heather Brandon, Vice President of Finance, Grant
CMO: Michael Ezzie, Director of Medical Education and Interim Vice President of
Medical Affairs
CIO: Michael Krouse, Chief Information Officer
CHR: Qiana Williams, Director, Human Resource Business Partner, Grant
CNO: Sharon Neenan R.N., Interim Chief Nursing Officer, Grant
Web address: www.ohiohealth.com
Control: Church operated, Nongovernment, not–for–profit **Service**: General
medical and surgical

Staffed Beds: 445 **Admissions**: 21594 **Census**: 278 **Outpatient Visits**:
91176 **Births**: 2556 **Total Expense ($000)**: 527505 **Payroll Expense
($000)**: 205842 **Personnel**: 2846

Hospital, Medicare Provider Number, Address, Telephone, Approval, Facility, and Physician Codes, Health Care System

★ American Hospital Association (AHA) membership ○ Healthcare Facilities Accreditation Program ⇑ Center for Improvement in Healthcare Quality Accreditation
□ The Joint Commission accreditation ◇ DNV Healthcare Inc. accreditation △ Commission on Accreditation of Rehabilitation Facilities (CARF) accreditation

OH

✠ **OHIOHEALTH REHABILITATION HOSPITAL (363037)**, 1087 Dennison Avenue, 4th Floor, Zip 43201–3201; tel. 614/484–9600, (Nonreporting) **A**1 10 **S** Select Medical Corporation, Mechanicsburg, PA
Primary Contact: Eric Yap, Chief Executive Officer
CFO: Ted Bolcavage, Vice President Division Controller, Inpatient
CMO: Lisa Lombard, Chief Medical Officer
CHR: Josette Alexander, Director, Human Resources
CNO: Graydon Todd Auckerman, Chief Nursing Officer
Web address: www.ohiohealth–rehab.com
Control: Partnership, Investor–owned (for-profit) **Service:** Rehabilitation

Staffed Beds: 44

✠ **OHIOHEALTH RIVERSIDE METHODIST HOSPITAL (360006)**, 3535 Olentangy River Road, Zip 43214–3998; tel. 614/566–5000 **A**1 2 3 5 8 10 **F**3 5 7 8 11 12 13 14 15 17 18 20 21 22 24 26 28 29 30 31 33 34 35 36 37 38 39 40 43 44 45 46 47 48 49 50 51 53 54 55 56 57 58 59 60 61 62 63 64 65 66 67 68 69 70 71 72 73 74 75 76 77 78 79 80 81 82 83 84 85 86 87 90 91 92 93 94 96 97 98 100 102 103 104 105 107 108 110 111 114 115 116 117 118 119 120 121 123 124 126 129 130 132 135 143 144 145 146 147 148 **P**1 3 6 **S** OhioHealth, Columbus, OH
Primary Contact: Brian Jepson, President
COO: Elizabeth Brill M.D., Chief Operating Officer
CFO: Peter Bury, Vice President Finance
CMO: Thomas Harmon M.D., Vice President Medical Affairs
CIO: Michael Krouse, Chief Information Officer
CHR: Shereen Solaiman, Vice President Human Resources
CNO: Lisa Gossett MSN, R.N., Chief Nursing Officer
Web address: www.ohiohealth.com
Control: Church operated, Nongovernment, not–for–profit **Service:** General medical and surgical

Staffed Beds: 820 Admissions: 46107 Census: 552 Outpatient Visits: 814486 Births: 6655 Total Expense ($000): 970546 Payroll Expense ($000): 405380 Personnel: 5889

✠ **REGENCY HOSPITAL OF COLUMBUS (362037)**, 1430 South High Street, Zip 43207–1045; tel. 614/456–0300, (Nonreporting) (Includes SELECT SPECIALTY HOSPITAL – COLUMBUS EAST, 1492 East Broad Street, 6th Floor, Columbus, Ohio, Zip 43205–1546; tel. 614/685–1703; Lisa J. Pettrey, MSN, R.N., Interim Chief Executive Officer) **A**1 10 **S** Select Medical Corporation, Mechanicsburg, PA
Primary Contact: Kindra Marks, Chief Executive Officer
Web address: www.regencyhospital.com/
Control: Corporation, Investor–owned (for-profit) **Service:** Acute long–term care hospital

Staffed Beds: 66

✠ **SELECT SPECIALTY HOSPITAL–COLUMBUS (362022)**, 1087 Dennison Avenue, Zip 43201–3201; tel. 614/258–9000, (Nonreporting) (Includes SELECT SPECIALTY HOSPITAL–COLUMBUS, MOUNT CARMEL CAMPUS, 793 West State Street, Columbus, Ohio, Zip 43222–1551, tel. 614/234–0950) **A**1 10 **S** Select Medical Corporation, Mechanicsburg, PA
Primary Contact: Lisa J. Pettrey, MSN, R.N., Chief Executive Officer
CMO: Victoria Ruff M.D., Medical Director
CHR: Charles Pankowski, Manager Human Resources
Web address: www.selectspecialtyhospitals.com/company/locations/columbus.aspx
Control: Corporation, Investor–owned (for-profit) **Service:** Acute long–term care hospital

Staffed Beds: 186

SELECT SPECIALTY HOSPITAL–COLUMBUS, MOUNT CARMEL CAMPUS See Select Specialty Hospital–Columbus

SEQUEL POMEGRANATE HEALTH SYSTEMS (364045), 765 Pierce Drive, Zip 43223, Mailing Address: 975 Pierce Avenue, 43227; tel. 614/223–1650 (Nonreporting)
Primary Contact: Angela Nickell, Executive Director
Web address: www.pomegranatehealthsystems.com
Control: Other not–for–profit (including NFP Corporation) **Service:** Psychiatric

Staffed Beds: 90

☐ **TWIN VALLEY BEHAVIORAL HEALTHCARE (364007)**, 2200 West Broad Street, Zip 43223–1297; tel. 614/752–0333, (Nonreporting) **A**1 3 10 **S** Ohio Department of Mental Health, Columbus, OH
Primary Contact: Veronica Lofton, Acting Chief Executive Officer
COO: David Blahnik, Chief Operating Officer
CFO: Tracy Gladen, Chief Financial Officer
CMO: R Alan Freeland M.D., Chief Clinical Officer
CIO: Missy McGarvey, Chief Information Officer
CHR: Marcia McKeen, Director Human Resources
CNO: Michael Breakwell R.N., Nurse Executive
Web address: www.mh.state.oh.us/ibhs/bhos/tvbh.html
Control: State, Government, Nonfederal **Service:** Psychiatric

Staffed Beds: 228

✠ **LAKE HEALTH (360098)**, 7590 Auburn Road, Zip 44077–9176; tel. 440/953–9600, (Includes TRIPOINT MEDICAL CENTER, 7590 Auburn Road, Concord Township, Ohio, Zip 44077, tel. 614/234–0950; Cynthia Moore–Hardy, FACHE, President and Chief Executive Officer) **A**1 10 **F**3 5 11 12 13 15 18 20 22 24 26 28 29 30 34 35 36 40 42 44 45 50 51 53 54 56 57 58 59 60 62 63 64 65 68 70 75 76 77 79 81 82 84 85 86 87 90 93 97 98 103 107 108 110 111 112 113 114 115 116 117 119 120 121 122 123 124 126 129 130 131 132 133 135 143 144 146 147 148 **P**1
Primary Contact: Cynthia Moore–Hardy, FACHE, President and Chief Executive Officer
CFO: Robert B Tracz CPA, Senior Vice President and Chief Financial Officer
CMO: John Baniewicz M.D., Chief Medical Officer
CIO: Gerald Peters, Vice President Information Technologies and Chief Information Officer
CHR: Craig J Ghidotti, Vice President Human Resources
CNO: Mary L Ogrinc R.N., MS, Chief Nursing Officer, Senior Vice President Patient Care Services
Web address: www.lakehealth.org
Control: Other not–for–profit (including NFP Corporation) **Service:** General medical and surgical

Staffed Beds: 352 Admissions: 17189 Census: 190 Outpatient Visits: 485183 Births: 1814 Total Expense ($000): 355594 Payroll Expense ($000): 124817 Personnel: 2351

✠ **UNIVERSITY HOSPITALS CONNEAUT MEDICAL CENTER (361308)**, 158 West Main Road, Zip 44030–2039; tel. 440/593–1131 **A**1 10 18 **F**3 7 11 15 18 28 29 31 34 35 37 40 45 56 57 59 64 68 70 75 77 78 79 81 82 85 86 87 93 107 110 111 115 119 130 132 133 135 143 144 146 147 148 149 **S** University Hospitals, Cleveland, OH
Primary Contact: M Steven. Jones, President
COO: Jason Glowczewski, Chief Operating Officer
CFO: Lara Eggleston, Finance Manager
CMO: Abirammy Sundaramoorthy M.D., Chief Medical Officer
CIO: Kirsten Hale, Coordinator Health Information Services
CHR: Danialle Lynce, Business Partner Human Resources
CNO: Ashley Fertig, Chief Nursing Officer
Web address: www.uhhospitals.org
Control: Other not–for–profit (including NFP Corporation) **Service:** General medical and surgical

Staffed Beds: 25 Admissions: 555 Census: 5 Outpatient Visits: 34623 Births: 0 Total Expense ($000): 28803 Payroll Expense ($000): 10056 Personnel: 171

✠ **COSHOCTON REGIONAL MEDICAL CENTER (360109)**, 1460 Orange Street, Zip 43812–2229, Mailing Address: P.O.Box 1330, 43812–6330; tel. 740/622–6411, (Data for 61 days) **A**1 5 10 20 **F**3 15 20 28 29 30 31 34 35 40 42 45 46 47 57 59 64 68 70 75 77 78 79 81 82 85 86 87 90 92 93 96 97 107 111 115 119 132 144 147 149 **P**3 **S** Prime Healthcare, Ontario, CA
Primary Contact: Stephanie Conn, Administrator and Chief Nursing Officer
CFO: Robin Nichols, Chief Financial Officer
CMO: Tammy S Alverson M.D., Chief of Staff
CIO: Seth Peterson, Director Information Services
CHR: Rick Davis, Chief Operating Officer and Support Services
Web address: www.ccmh.com
Control: Other not–for–profit (including NFP Corporation) **Service:** General medical and surgical

Staffed Beds: 44 Admissions: 362 Census: 18 Outpatient Visits: 17646 Births: 0 Total Expense ($000): 9708 Payroll Expense ($000): 3349 Personnel: 344

CUYAHOGA FALLS GENERAL HOSPITAL See Summa Western Reserve Hospital

✠ △ **EDWIN SHAW REHAB (360241)**, 330 Broadway Street East, Zip 44221–3312; tel. 330/436–0910 **A**1 5 7 10 **F**5 29 34 35 57 90 93 96 130 132 135 146 **S** Cleveland Clinic Health System, Cleveland, OH
Primary Contact: Geoffrey Hall, Chief Executive Officer
CFO: Dave Frigo, Chief Financial Officer
CMO: Anthony Hayek D.O., Medical Director
CHR: Heather Saus, Human Resource Generalist
Web address: www.edwinshaw.com
Control: Other not–for–profit (including NFP Corporation) **Service:** Rehabilitation

Staffed Beds: 35 Admissions: 754 Census: 27 Outpatient Visits: 35346 Births: 0 Total Expense ($000): 15689 Payroll Expense ($000): 9278 Personnel: 147

Many Facility Codes have changed. Please refer to the AHA Guide Code Chart.

OH

○ **SUMMA WESTERN RESERVE HOSPITAL (360150)**, 1900 23rd Street, Zip 44223–1499; tel. 330/971–7000 **A**3 10 11 13 **F**3 8 11 18 26 29 30 31 32 33 34 35 36 38 40 44 45 47 49 50 51 54 57 59 60 64 65 66 68 70 74 75 77 78 79 81 82 84 85 86 87 92 93 94 96 97 107 108 111 114 115 119 129 130 132 135 144 146 148 **P**6 8 **S** Summa Health, Akron, OH
Primary Contact: Robert Kent, D.O., President and Chief Executive Officer
CFO: Jill Hiner, Vice President and Chief Financial Officer
CMO: Charles Feunning M.D., President Medical Staff
CHR: Heather Milicevic, Director Human Resources
Web address: www.westernreservehospital.org
Control: Partnership, Investor–owned (for–profit) **Service**: General medical and surgical

Staffed Beds: 83 **Admissions**: 3721 **Census**: 40 **Outpatient Visits**: 129593 **Births**: 0 **Total Expense ($000)**: 119827 **Payroll Expense ($000)**: 41694 **Personnel**: 779

DAYTON—Montgomery County

☐ **ACCESS HOSPITAL DAYTON (364050)**, 2611 Wayne Avenue, Zip 45420–1833; tel. 937/256–7802 (Nonreporting) **A**1 10
Primary Contact: Belinda Stevens, Chief Executive Officer
Web address: www.accesshospital.com/
Control: Corporation, Investor–owned (for–profit) **Service**: Psychiatric

Staffed Beds: 28

☐ **CHILDREN'S MEDICAL CENTER (363306)**, One Children's Plaza, Zip 45404–1815; tel. 937/641–3000 **A**1 2 3 5 10 **F**3 7 11 19 21 29 30 31 32 34 35 39 40 41 42 43 44 45 50 54 55 57 58 59 60 61 62 63 64 65 66 68 72 74 75 77 78 79 81 82 84 85 86 87 88 89 93 97 100 101 104 107 111 115 119 129 130 131 132 134 135 144 146 **P**6
Primary Contact: Deborah A. Feldman, President and Chief Executive Officer
COO: Matthew P Graybill, Vice President, Human Resources and Chief Administrative Officer
CFO: Chris Bergman, Chief Financial Officer
CMO: Adam Mezoff M.D., Vice President and Chief Medical Officer
CIO: Beth Fredette, Chief Information Officer
Web address: www.childrensdayton.org
Control: Other not–for–profit (including NFP Corporation) **Service**: Children's general medical and surgical

Staffed Beds: 133 **Admissions**: 7221 **Census**: 81 **Outpatient Visits**: 314641 **Births**: 0 **Total Expense ($000)**: 239546 **Payroll Expense ($000)**: 99990 **Personnel**: 2325

⊠ △ **DAYTON VETERANS AFFAIRS MEDICAL CENTER**, 4100 West Third Street, Zip 45428–9000; tel. 937/268–6511, (Nonreporting) **A**1 3 5 7 8 **S** Department of Veterans Affairs, Washington, DC
Primary Contact: Glenn A. Costie, FACHE, Director
CFO: Shannon Rappach, Chief Fiscal Services
CMO: James Hardy D.O., Chief of Staff
CIO: Susan Sherer, Chief Information Resource Management
CHR: Rolanda Watkins, Chief Human Resources Management Service
CNO: Penelope Franklin Gorsuch, Associate Director Patient Care Services
Web address: www.dayton.va.gov/
Control: Veterans Affairs, Government, federal **Service**: General medical and surgical

Staffed Beds: 486

⊠ **GOOD SAMARITAN HOSPITAL (360052)**, 2222 Philadelphia Drive, Zip 45406–1813; tel. 937/734–2612 **A**1 2 3 5 10 **F**3 5 13 15 17 18 20 22 24 26 28 29 30 31 34 35 36 37 38 40 41 42 44 45 46 50 54 56 57 58 59 60 61 64 68 70 73 74 75 76 77 78 79 80 81 82 85 86 87 92 93 96 100 101 102 104 107 108 110 111 114 115 117 118 119 126 129 130 131 132 141 145 146 147 148 149 150 **S** Catholic Health Initiatives, Englewood, CO
Primary Contact: Eloise Broner, President and Chief Executive Officer
COO: Mary E Garman MS, R.N., Chief Operating Officer
CMO: Jennifer Hauler D.O., Chief Medical Officer
CHR: Barbara A Johnson, System Vice President and Chief Human Resources Officer
CNO: Christie Gray, Chief Nursing Officer
Web address: www.goodsamdayton.org
Control: Other not–for–profit (including NFP Corporation) **Service**: General medical and surgical

Staffed Beds: 346 **Admissions**: 13494 **Census**: 152 **Outpatient Visits**: 255156 **Births**: 941 **Total Expense ($000)**: 355087 **Payroll Expense ($000)**: 140206 **Personnel**: 2210

★ ○ **GRANDVIEW MEDICAL CENTER (360133)**, 405 West Grand Avenue, Zip 45405–4796; tel. 937/723–3200, (Includes SOUTHVIEW MEDICAL CENTER, 1997 Miamisburg–Centerville Road, Dayton, Ohio, Zip 45459–3800; tel. 937/439–6000; Richard Manchur, President) **A**2 3 10 11 12 13 **F**3 11 12 13 15 18 20 22 24 28 29 30 31 34 35 36 38 39 40 42 43 44 45 47 48 49 50 51 53 54 56 57 58 59 60 61 64 65 66 68 70 73 74 75 76 77 78 79 81 82 85 86 87 93 96 97 98 100 101 102 103 104 105 107 108 110 111 114 115 116 117 118 119 120 121 123 124 129 130 131 132 135 141 144 145 146 147 148 149 **S** Kettering Health Network, Dayton, OH
Primary Contact: Rebecca Lewis, President
CFO: Luis Chanaga, Chief Financial Officer
CMO: Paul Martin, Chief Medical Officer
CIO: Andy Lehman, Senior Vice President Technology and Analytics
CHR: Keith Jenkins, Director, Human Resources
CNO: Ronda Brandstater, Vice President Patient Care
Web address: www.ketteringhealth.org/grandview/
Control: Church operated, Nongovernment, not–for–profit **Service**: General medical and surgical

Staffed Beds: 282 **Admissions**: 12433 **Census**: 150 **Outpatient Visits**: 396309 **Births**: 1867 **Total Expense ($000)**: 475189 **Payroll Expense ($000)**: 183800 **Personnel**: 1584

☐ **HAVEN BEHAVIORAL SENIOR CARE OF DAYTON (364048)**, One Elizabeth Place, 4th Floor Southwest Tower, Zip 45417–3445; tel. 937/234–0100 (Nonreporting) **A**1 10 **S** Haven Behavioral Healthcare, Nashville, TN
Primary Contact: Keith Kuhn, Chief Executive Officer
CMO: Amita Patel M.D., Medical Director
CNO: Cheryl Meyer MSN, Director of Nursing
Web address: www.havenbehavioraldayton.com/
Control: Corporation, Investor–owned (for–profit) **Service**: Psychiatric

Staffed Beds: 32

⊠ **HEALTHSOUTH REHABILITATION HOSPITAL OF DAYTON (363033)**, One Elizabeth Place, Zip 45417–3445; tel. 937/424–8200 **A**1 10 **F**29 90 94 96 148 **P**5 **S** HEALTHSOUTH Corporation, Birmingham, AL
Primary Contact: Lynne Blinco, Chief Executive Officer
Web address: www.reliantdayton.com
Control: Corporation, Investor–owned (for–profit) **Service**: Rehabilitation

Staffed Beds: 50 **Admissions**: 621 **Census**: 20 **Outpatient Visits**: 0 **Births**: 0 **Total Expense ($000)**: 7594 **Payroll Expense ($000)**: 4972 **Personnel**: 84

⊠ **KINDRED HOSPITAL–DAYTON (362033)**, 707 South Edwin C Moses Boulevard, Zip 45417–3462; tel. 937/222–5963, (Nonreporting) **A**1 10 **S** Kindred Healthcare, Louisville, KY
Primary Contact: Phillip Underwood, Chief Executive Officer
CMO: Felipe Rubio M.D., Medical Director
Web address: www.khdayton.com
Control: Corporation, Investor–owned (for–profit) **Service**: Acute long–term care hospital

Staffed Beds: 67

⊠ △ **MIAMI VALLEY HOSPITAL (360051)**, One Wyoming Street, Zip 45409–2793; tel. 937/208–8000, (Includes MIAMI VALLEY HOSPITAL SOUTH, 2400 Miami Valley Drive, Centerville, Ohio, Zip 45459–4774, tel. 937/438–2400) **A**1 2 3 5 7 10 **F**3 5 7 12 13 15 16 17 18 20 22 24 26 28 29 30 31 34 35 37 39 40 41 42 43 44 45 46 47 48 49 50 53 54 55 56 57 58 59 60 61 64 65 68 70 72 73 74 75 76 77 78 79 81 82 85 86 87 90 91 92 93 95 96 98 100 101 102 103 104 107 108 110 111 114 115 117 118 119 120 121 123 126 129 130 131 132 134 135 141 145 146 147 148 **P**8 **S** Premier Health, Dayton, OH
Primary Contact: Mikki Clancy, Chief Operating Officer
COO: Mikki Clancy, Chief Operating Officer
CFO: Thomas M Duncan, Executive Vice President and Chief Financial Officer
CMO: Mark Williams M.D., Vice President and Chief Medical Officer
CIO: Gary Ginter, System Vice President and Chief Information Officer
CHR: Barbara A Johnson, System Vice President and Chief Human Resources Officer
CNO: Jolyn M Angus R.N., Chief Nursing Officer
Web address: www.miamivalleyhospital.org
Control: Other not–for–profit (including NFP Corporation) **Service**: General medical and surgical

Staffed Beds: 845 **Admissions**: 33170 **Census**: 397 **Outpatient Visits**: 344612 **Births**: 4848 **Total Expense ($000)**: 816565 **Payroll Expense ($000)**: 308094 **Personnel**: 5463

OH

☐ ○ **THE MEDICAL CENTER AT ELIZABETH PLACE (360274)**, One Elizabeth Place, Zip 45417–3445; tel. 937/660–3100 (Nonreporting) **A**1 10 11
Primary Contact: Alexander M. Rintoul, Chief Executive Officer
Web address: www.regentsurgicalhealth.com/Partner+Centers/Medical+Center+at+Elizabeth+Place
Control: Partnership, Investor–owned (for–profit) **Service:** General medical and surgical

Staffed Beds: 26

VETERANS AFFAIRS MEDICAL CENTER See Dayton Veterans Affairs Medical Center

DEFIANCE—Defiance County

☒ **MERCY HOSPITAL OF DEFIANCE (360270)**, 1404 East Second Street, Zip 43512–2440; tel. 419/782–8444, (Nonreporting) **A**1 10 **S** Mercy Health, Cincinnati, OH
Primary Contact: B Lynn. Detterman, President and Chief Executive Officer
COO: Kerry Knuth, Chief Operating Officer
CFO: James Puffenberger, Vice President and Chief Financial Officer
CMO: Jeffrey Pruitt M.D., Chief of Staff
CHR: Susan Pscodna, Director Human Resources
CNO: Sonya Selhorst R.N., Administrator and Chief Nursing Officer
Web address: www.ehealthconnection.com/regions/toledo/
Control: Partnership, Investor–owned (for–profit) **Service:** General medical and surgical

Staffed Beds: 23

☒ **PROMEDICA DEFIANCE REGIONAL HOSPITAL (361328)**, 1200 Ralston Avenue, Zip 43512–1396; tel. 419/783–6955 **A**1 5 10 18 **F**3 11 13 15 18 20 28 31 32 34 40 43 55 57 59 64 66 68 70 75 76 77 78 79 81 82 85 86 87 93 98 100 101 102 103 104 105 107 108 110 111 114 118 119 129 130 132 135 144 146 147 148 **S** ProMedica Health System, Toledo, OH
Primary Contact: Neeraj Kanwal, M.D., President
CFO: Ken Swint, Director Finance
CMO: Stanislaw Dajczak M.D., Chief of Staff
CIO: Patricia Swint, Director Information Management Systems
CHR: Carrie Miller, Director Human Resources
Web address: www.promedica.org
Control: Other not–for–profit (including NFP Corporation) **Service:** General medical and surgical

Staffed Beds: 35 Admissions: 1931 Census: 17 Outpatient Visits: 90271 Births: 468 Total Expense ($000): 55058 Payroll Expense ($000): 14789 Personnel: 260

DELAWARE—Delaware County

☒ **OHIOHEALTH GRADY MEMORIAL HOSPITAL (360210)**, 561 West Central Avenue, Zip 43015–1410; tel. 740/615–1000 **A**1 2 10 **F**3 13 15 17 18 20 26 28 29 30 31 34 35 40 45 46 48 50 54 57 58 59 60 63 64 66 68 75 76 77 78 79 81 85 86 87 92 93 96 97 102 107 108 109 110 111 114 119 124 129 130 131 132 134 135 146 147 148 149 **P**1 3 6 **S** OhioHealth, Columbus, OH
Primary Contact: Steve Bunyard, President
COO: Anna Hensley, Chief Operating Officer
CFO: David Hensel, Director Financial Operations
CMO: Barbara Evert M.D., Vice President Medical Affairs
CIO: Michael Krouse, Chief Information Officer Information Services
CHR: Victoria L. Matlack, Director and Human Resources Business Partner
CNO: Elizabeth Anne Biegler R.N., Chief Nursing Officer
Web address: www.ohiohealth.com
Control: Church operated, Nongovernment, not–for–profit **Service:** General medical and surgical

Staffed Beds: 59 Admissions: 2160 Census: 20 Outpatient Visits: 103605 Births: 208 Total Expense ($000): 77963 Payroll Expense ($000): 31954 Personnel: 427

DENNISON—Tuscarawas County

☐ **TEN LAKES CENTER (364042)**, 819 North First Street, 3rd Floor, Zip 44621–1003; tel. 740/922–7499 (Nonreporting) **A**1 10 **S** Acadia Healthcare Company, Inc., Franklin, TN
Primary Contact: Debra C. Gardner, R.N., MSN, Administrator
Web address: www.tenlakescenter.com/
Control: Corporation, Investor–owned (for–profit) **Service:** Psychiatric

Staffed Beds: 16

☒ **TRINITY HOSPITAL TWIN CITY (361302)**, 819 North First Street, Zip 44621–1098; tel. 740/922–2800 **A**1 10 18 **F**11 15 18 19 28 29 30 34 35 40 45 50 57 59 64 70 75 77 81 85 86 87 89 93 97 107 114 119 127 128 129 130 132 133 146 147 148 **P**4 **S** Catholic Health Initiatives, Englewood, CO
Primary Contact: Teresa Gagliardi, R.N., Chief Nursing Officer and Interim Chief Executive Officer
CMO: Tim McKnight M.D., Chief of Staff
CHR: Bianca Love, Assistant Administrator Human Resources
CNO: Teresa Gagliardi R.N., Chief Nursing Officer
Web address: www.trinitytwincity.org
Control: Church operated, Nongovernment, not–for–profit **Service:** General medical and surgical

Staffed Beds: 12 Admissions: 209 Census: 2 Outpatient Visits: 45038 Births: 0 Total Expense ($000): 22521 Payroll Expense ($000): 10165 Personnel: 206

DOVER—Tuscarawas County

★ △ ⇑ **UNION HOSPITAL (360010)**, 659 Boulevard, Zip 44622–2077; tel. 330/343–3311 **A**7 10 19 21 **F**3 8 11 13 15 18 28 29 34 35 40 50 53 54 57 59 62 64 70 74 75 76 77 79 80 81 82 85 86 90 91 93 105 107 108 110 111 115 119 124 129 130 131 132 135 144 146 148 149 **P**6
Primary Contact: Bruce James, Chief Executive Officer
CFO: Eugene A Thorn III, Vice President Finance and Chief Financial Officer
CMO: Todd Meyerhoefer M.D., Vice President Medical Affairs
CIO: David Baumgardner, Director Information Management
CHR: Darwin K Smith, Vice President Human Resources
CNO: Diana Boyd, Vice President Nursing
Web address: www.unionhospital.org
Control: Other not–for–profit (including NFP Corporation) **Service:** General medical and surgical

Staffed Beds: 159 Admissions: 5077 Census: 54 Outpatient Visits: 266474 Births: 657 Total Expense ($000): 117239 Payroll Expense ($000): 49777 Personnel: 989

DUBLIN—Franklin County

☐ **COLUMBUS DUBLIN SPRINGS (364049)**, 7625 Hospital Drive, Zip 43016–9649; tel. 614/717–1800 (Nonreporting) **A**1 10
Primary Contact: Garry W. Hoyes, Chief Executive Officer
COO: Merissa McKinstry, Chief Operating Officer
CFO: Alexis Barbour, Director Finance
CMO: Mark Blair M.D., Medical Director
CHR: Tam Wisler, Director Human Resources
CNO: Melissa Patton MSN, Director of Nursing
Web address: www.dublinsprings.com/
Control: Corporation, Investor–owned (for–profit) **Service:** Psychiatric

Staffed Beds: 72

☒ **OHIOHEALTH DUBLIN METHODIST HOSPITAL (360348)**, 7500 Hospital Drive, Zip 43016–8518; tel. 614/544–8000 **A**1 2 3 10 **F**3 13 15 18 20 22 28 29 34 40 45 46 57 59 62 68 70 76 77 79 81 82 85 87 97 107 110 111 126 129 130 131 132 135 146 147 148 149 **P**1 3 6 **S** OhioHealth, Columbus, OH
Primary Contact: Steve Bunyard, President
COO: Anna Hensley, Chief Operating Officer
CFO: Keely Pummel, Director, Financial Operations
CMO: Barbara Evert M.D., Vice President Medical Affairs
CIO: Michael Krouse, Senior Vice President Chief Information Officer
CHR: Victoria L. Matlack, Director and Human Resources Business Partner
CNO: Elizabeth Anne Biegler R.N., Chief Nursing Officer
Web address: www.ohiohealth.com
Control: Church operated, Nongovernment, not–for–profit **Service:** General medical and surgical

Staffed Beds: 120 Admissions: 6950 Census: 49 Outpatient Visits: 116261 Births: 2401 Total Expense ($000): 156172 Payroll Expense ($000): 54967 Personnel: 687

EAST LIVERPOOL—Columbiana County

☒ **EAST LIVERPOOL CITY HOSPITAL (360096)**, 425 West Fifth Street, Zip 43920–2498; tel. 330/385–7200, (Nonreporting) **A**1 10 13 **S** Prime Healthcare, Ontario, CA
Primary Contact: Keith Richardson, President and Chief Executive Officer
CFO: Kyle Johnson, Vice President Finance
CMO: Steve LaTulippe, President Medical Staff
CIO: Frank Mader, Director Information Services
CHR: Teri Pasco, Director Human Resources
CNO: Stacie Call R.N., Vice President Patient Care and Chief Nursing Officer
Web address: www.elch.org
Control: Other not–for–profit (including NFP Corporation) **Service:** General medical and surgical

Staffed Beds: 120

ELYRIA—Lorain County

☒ **UNIVERSITY HOSPITALS ELYRIA MEDICAL CENTER (360145)**, 630 East River Street, Zip 44035–5902; tel. 440/329–7500 **A**1 2 10 13 **F**3 11 12 13 15 17 18 20 22 24 26 28 29 30 31 32 34 35 36 37 40 41 42 44 45 46 49 50 53 54 57 59 60 62 64 68 70 73 74 75 77 78 79 81 82 85 86 87 91 92 93 94 98 100 102 107 108 110 111 114 115 116 117 118 119 126 129 130 131 132 133 135 146 147 148 149 **S** University Hospitals, Cleveland, OH
Primary Contact: Charlotte Wray, MSN, President
CFO: David A Cook, Vice President and Chief Financial Officer
CHR: Daniel Miller, Vice President Human Resources
CNO: Sandra Jean Kantelas, Chief Nursing Officer
Web address: www.emh–healthcare.org
Control: Other not–for–profit (including NFP Corporation) **Service:** General medical and surgical

Staffed Beds: 237 **Admissions:** 10194 **Census:** 117 **Outpatient Visits:** 428578 **Births:** 762 **Total Expense ($000):** 202138 **Payroll Expense ($000):** 72483 **Personnel:** 1331	

EUCLID—Cuyahoga County

☒ **EUCLID HOSPITAL (360082)**, 18901 Lake Shore Boulevard, Zip 44119–1090; tel. 216/531–9000, (Total facility includes 40 beds in nursing home–type unit) **A**1 3 10 **F**3 15 17 18 26 28 29 30 34 35 40 45 47 50 51 56 57 59 60 64 70 74 75 77 79 81 82 85 87 90 91 93 94 96 98 100 102 103 107 108 111 114 118 119 128 130 131 146 148 **S** Cleveland Clinic Health System, Cleveland, OH
Primary Contact: Daniel Napierkowski, M.D., President
COO: Rich Lea, Vice President Operations
CFO: Don Urbancsik, Director Finance
CMO: John Bertsch M.D., Chief of Staff
CHR: Gloria Donnelly, Director Human Resources
CNO: Dawn A Bailey R.N., Vice President Nursing and Chief Nursing Officer
Web address: www.euclidhospital.org
Control: Other not–for–profit (including NFP Corporation) **Service:** General medical and surgical

Staffed Beds: 221 **Admissions:** 6871 **Census:** 127 **Outpatient Visits:** 105784 **Births:** 0 **Total Expense ($000):** 114955 **Payroll Expense ($000):** 49948 **Personnel:** 705	

FAIRFIELD—Butler County

☒ △ **MERCY HEALTH – FAIRFIELD HOSPITAL (360056)**, 3000 Mack Road, Zip 45014–5335; tel. 513/870–7000, (Nonreporting) **A**1 2 7 10 **S** Mercy Health, Cincinnati, OH
Primary Contact: Thomas S. Urban, Market Leader and President
COO: Justin Krueger, Chief Operating Officer
CFO: Robin Yon, Site Finance Director
CMO: John Kennedy M.D., Vice President Medical Affairs
CIO: Yousuf Ahmad, Divisional Senior Vice President and Chief Network Transformation Officer
CHR: Maggie Lund, Divisional Senior Vice President Human Resources
Web address: www.e–mercy.com
Control: Church operated, Nongovernment, not–for–profit **Service:** General medical and surgical

Staffed Beds: 236	

FINDLAY—Hancock County

☒ **BLANCHARD VALLEY HOSPITAL (360095)**, 1900 South Main Street, Zip 45840–1214; tel. 419/423–4500, (Includes BLANCHARD VALLEY HOSPITAL, 1900 South Main Street, Findlay, Ohio, Zip 45840, tel. 419/423–4500) **A**1 2 5 10 19 **F**3 11 13 15 17 18 20 22 24 26 28 29 30 31 34 35 40 41 43 44 45 48 49 50 54 55 57 58 59 60 64 65 68 70 73 74 76 77 78 79 81 82 83 84 85 86 87 91 93 96 97 98 101 103 104 107 108 110 111 114 115 117 118 119 120 121 124 126 129 130 131 132 135 146 147 148 149 **P**5 **S** Blanchard Valley Health System, Findlay, OH
Primary Contact: Scott C. Malaney, FACHE, President and Chief Executive Officer
CFO: David Cytlak, Chief Financial Officer
CMO: Michael Denike D.O., Vice President, Medical Affairs
CIO: David Cytlak, Chief Financial Officer
CHR: Ryan Fisher, Director of Human Resources
CNO: Barbara J. Pasztor R.N., Vice President Patient Care Services and Chief Nursing Officer
Web address: www.bvhealthsystem.org
Control: Other not–for–profit (including NFP Corporation) **Service:** General medical and surgical

Staffed Beds: 159 **Admissions:** 7196 **Census:** 65 **Outpatient Visits:** 270434 **Births:** 1270 **Total Expense ($000):** 176879 **Payroll Expense ($000):** 84854 **Personnel:** 1336	

FOSTORIA—Hancock County

☒ **PROMEDICA FOSTORIA COMMUNITY HOSPITAL (361318)**, 501 Van Buren Street, Zip 44830–1534, Mailing Address: P.O.Box 907, 44830–0907; tel. 419/435–7734 **A**1 5 10 18 **F**3 11 15 28 29 31 34 35 40 45 46 55 57 59 60 62 64 66 68 70 75 78 79 81 82 85 86 87 89 93 94 96 97 107 108 110 111 115 117 119 128 129 130 131 132 133 135 144 146 149 **P**7 **S** ProMedica Health System, Toledo, OH
Primary Contact: Pamela Jensen, FACHE, President
COO: Tom Borer, Vice President Operations
CFO: Ken Swint, Vice President Finance and Chief Financial Officer
CMO: Terrence Fondessy M.D., Vice President Medical Affairs
CIO: Rose Ann Laureto, Chief Information Officer
CNO: Paula Grieb R.N., Chief Nursing Officer
Web address: www.promedica.org
Control: Other not–for–profit (including NFP Corporation) **Service:** General medical and surgical

Staffed Beds: 25 **Admissions:** 574 **Census:** 4 **Outpatient Visits:** 50228 **Births:** 0 **Total Expense ($000):** 36162 **Payroll Expense ($000):** 8363 **Personnel:** 176	

FREMONT—Sandusky County

☒ **PROMEDICA MEMORIAL HOSPITAL (360156)**, 715 South Taft Avenue, Zip 43420–3237; tel. 419/332–7321 **A**1 10 **F**3 7 11 13 14 15 18 19 28 29 30 31 34 35 38 40 44 45 46 47 48 50 51 53 56 57 59 61 64 65 70 74 75 77 78 79 80 81 82 84 85 86 87 89 91 92 93 96 97 107 108 110 111 114 115 119 123 129 130 131 132 135 141 142 146 147 148 149 **P**1 5 6 **S** ProMedica Health System, Toledo, OH
Primary Contact: Pamela Jensen, FACHE, President
CFO: David Brewer, Chief Financial Officer
CHR: Warrenette Parthemore, Director Human Resources
CNO: Jodi Rucker, Chief Nursing Officer
Web address: www.promedica.org
Control: Other not–for–profit (including NFP Corporation) **Service:** General medical and surgical

Staffed Beds: 49 **Admissions:** 1130 **Census:** 10 **Outpatient Visits:** 82827 **Births:** 251 **Total Expense ($000):** 59232 **Payroll Expense ($000):** 14549 **Personnel:** 262	

GAHANNA—Franklin County

THE WOODS AT PARKSIDE (360247), 349 Olde Ridenour Road, Zip 43230–2528; tel. 614/471–2552, (Nonreporting) **A**10
Primary Contact: Harry Nguyen, Medical Director
Web address: www.thewoodsatparkside.com
Control: Partnership, Investor–owned (for–profit) **Service:** Alcoholism and other chemical dependency

Staffed Beds: 50	

GALION—Crawford County

★ ⇑ **GALION COMMUNITY HOSPITAL (361325)**, 269 Portland Way South, Zip 44833–2399; tel. 419/468–4841, (Nonreporting) **A**10 18 21 **S** Avita Health System, Galion, OH
Primary Contact: Jerome Morasko, President and Chief Executive Officer
CIO: Andy Daniels, Vice President Non–Clinical Operations and Information Systems
CHR: Traci L Oswald, Vice President Human Resources
Web address: www.avitahs.org
Control: Other not–for–profit (including NFP Corporation) **Service:** General medical and surgical

Staffed Beds: 35	

GALLIPOLIS—Gallia County

☐ △ **HOLZER MEDICAL CENTER (360054)**, 100 Jackson Pike, Zip 45631–1563; tel. 740/446–5000, (Nonreporting) **A**1 2 3 5 7 10 13 19 **S** Holzer Health System, Jackson, OH
Primary Contact: Michael Canady, M.D., Interim Chief Executive Officer
CFO: Kenneth G Payne, Chief Financial Officer
CMO: John Viall M.D., Vice President Medical Affairs
CIO: John Allen, Chief Information Officer
CHR: Lisa B Halley, Vice President Human Resources
Web address: www.holzer.org
Control: Other not–for–profit (including NFP Corporation) **Service:** General medical and surgical

Staffed Beds: 181	

Hospital, Medicare Provider Number, Address, Telephone, Approval, Facility, and Physician Codes, Health Care System

★ American Hospital Association (AHA) membership   ○ Healthcare Facilities Accreditation Program   ⇑ Center for Improvement in Healthcare Quality Accreditation
☐ The Joint Commission accreditation   ◇ DNV Healthcare Inc. accreditation   △ Commission on Accreditation of Rehabilitation Facilities (CARF) accreditation

© 2017 AHA Guide   *Many Facility Codes have changed. Please refer to the AHA Guide Code Chart.*   Hospitals **A491**

OH

GARFIELD HEIGHTS—Cuyahoga County

☒ **MARYMOUNT HOSPITAL (360143)**, 12300 McCracken Road, Zip 44125–2975; tel. 216/581–0500 **A**1 2 3 10 **F**3 7 8 11 15 18 28 29 30 31 34 35 38 39 40 44 50 51 53 54 56 57 59 60 62 63 64 65 68 70 74 75 77 78 79 81 82 85 86 87 92 93 96 97 98 100 102 103 104 107 108 110 111 114 115 116 118 119 124 129 131 132 135 143 144 146 147 148 **S** Cleveland Clinic Health System, Cleveland, OH
Primary Contact: Richard Parker, M.D., President
COO: Mark Nussbaum, Vice President Operations
CFO: Mike Stilgenbauer, Director Finance
CMO: Douglas Kohler M.D., Vice President Medical Operations
CIO: Ralph A Cagna, Director Information Technology Operations, Cleveland Clinic Health System South Market
CHR: Judith Santora, Human Resources Business Partner
CNO: Barbara Zinner, Chief Nursing Officer
Web address: www.marymount.org
Control: Other not–for–profit (including NFP Corporation) **Service**: General medical and surgical

> **Staffed Beds**: 226 **Admissions**: 8712 **Census**: 132 **Outpatient Visits**: 108214 **Births**: 0 **Total Expense ($000)**: 164325 **Payroll Expense ($000)**: 62139 **Personnel**: 923

GENEVA—Ashtabula County

☒ **UNIVERSITY HOSPITALS GENEVA MEDICAL CENTER (361307)**, 870 West Main Street, Zip 44041–1295; tel. 440/466–1141 **A**1 10 18 **F**3 5 7 11 15 18 29 34 35 40 46 51 56 57 59 60 64 68 70 75 77 78 79 81 82 85 86 87 91 93 107 110 111 115 116 119 129 130 132 133 135 143 146 147 148 149 **S** University Hospitals, Cleveland, OH
Primary Contact: M Steven. Jones, President
COO: Jason Glowczewski, Chief Operating Officer
CFO: Lara Eggleston, Finance Manager
CMO: Amitabh Goel M.D., Chief Medical Officer
CIO: Kirsten Hale, Coordinator Health Informations Systems and Coding
CHR: Danialle Lynce, Business Partner Human Resources
CNO: Ashley Fertig, Chief Nursing Officer
Web address: www.uhhs.com
Control: Other not–for–profit (including NFP Corporation) **Service**: General medical and surgical

> **Staffed Beds**: 25 **Admissions**: 1253 **Census**: 13 **Outpatient Visits**: 61287 **Births**: 0 **Total Expense ($000)**: 38469 **Payroll Expense ($000)**: 13827 **Personnel**: 248

GREEN SPRINGS—Sandusky County

☐ **ELMWOOD HEALTHCARE CENTER AT THE SPRINGS (362007)**, 401 North Broadway, Zip 44836–9653; tel. 419/639–2626, (Nonreporting) **A**1 10
Primary Contact: Kathy Hunt, Chief Executive Officer
CFO: Douglas Morris, Chief Financial Officer
CMO: John Yuhas D.O., Medical Director
CHR: Joan E Schmidt, Director Human Resources
Web address: www.sfhcc.org
Control: Church operated, Nongovernment, not–for–profit **Service**: Acute long–term care hospital

> **Staffed Beds**: 186

GREENFIELD—Highland County

☐ △ **ADENA GREENFIELD MEDICAL CENTER (361304)**, 550 Mirabeau Street, Zip 45123–1617; tel. 937/981–9400 **A**1 7 10 18 **F**3 15 18 29 30 34 35 40 41 45 50 54 59 68 81 93 107 108 110 114 118 119 130 133 135 146 148 **P**6 **S** Adena Health System, Chillicothe, OH
Primary Contact: Kathy Dye, Interim Administrator
CFO: Ralph W Sorrell Sr., Chief Financial Officer
CIO: Marcus Bost, Director Information Services and Chief Information Officer
CHR: Brandt Lippert, Vice President Human Resources
Web address: www.adena.org
Control: Other not–for–profit (including NFP Corporation) **Service**: General medical and surgical

> **Staffed Beds**: 25 **Admissions**: 343 **Census**: 7 **Outpatient Visits**: 42783 **Births**: 0 **Total Expense ($000)**: 16799 **Payroll Expense ($000)**: 5796 **Personnel**: 113

GREENVILLE—Darke County

★ ○ **WAYNE HEALTHCARE (360044)**, 835 Sweitzer Street, Zip 45331–1077; tel. 937/548–1141 **A**2 10 11 **F**3 8 11 13 15 28 29 30 31 34 35 39 40 41 45 57 59 64 65 70 75 76 77 78 79 81 82 84 85 86 89 93 98 103 107 108 110 111 114 117 118 119 124 129 130 131 132 135 141 146 147 148 149 **P**1
Primary Contact: Wayne G. Deschambeau, President and Chief Executive Officer
COO: Jeffrey R. Subler, Vice President Support Services
CFO: Dennis Lockard, Vice President Fiscal Services and Chief Financial Officer
CMO: Tom Brown M.D., President Medical Staff
CIO: Shelton Monger, Director Information Technology
CHR: Peggy Schwartz, Vice President Human Resources
CNO: Kimberlee Freeman R.N., MSN, Vice President Patient Care Services and Chief Nursing Officer
Web address: www.waynehealthcare.org
Control: Other not–for–profit (including NFP Corporation) **Service**: General medical and surgical

> **Staffed Beds**: 53 **Admissions**: 1594 **Census**: 13 **Outpatient Visits**: 82833 **Births**: 322 **Total Expense ($000)**: 53608 **Payroll Expense ($000)**: 18525 **Personnel**: 385

HAMILTON—Butler County

★ ○ **FORT HAMILTON HOSPITAL (360132)**, 630 Eaton Avenue, Zip 45013–2770; tel. 513/867–2000 **A**2 10 11 **F**3 11 13 15 18 20 22 24 28 29 30 31 34 35 40 45 49 50 54 59 60 64 68 70 73 74 75 76 77 78 79 81 82 85 86 87 93 98 99 100 105 107 108 110 111 114 115 116 117 119 120 121 124 129 130 131 135 144 146 147 148 149 **S** Kettering Health Network, Dayton, OH
Primary Contact: Michael Mewhirter, President
CFO: William Villegas, Vice President Finance
CMO: Marcus Romanello, Chief Medical Officer
CIO: Andy Lehman, Senior Vice President Technology and Analytics
CHR: Joseph Geigle, Director Human Resources
CNO: Carol Applegeet MSN, R.N., Vice President and Chief Nursing Officer
Web address: www.khnetwork.org/forthamilton
Control: Church operated, Nongovernment, not–for–profit **Service**: General medical and surgical

> **Staffed Beds**: 164 **Admissions**: 8242 **Census**: 87 **Outpatient Visits**: 115825 **Births**: 693 **Total Expense ($000)**: 155982 **Payroll Expense ($000)**: 68280 **Personnel**: 792

HICKSVILLE—Defiance County

☐ **COMMUNITY MEMORIAL HOSPITAL (361301)**, 208 North Columbus Street, Zip 43526–1299; tel. 419/542–6692, (Nonreporting) **A**1 10 18
Primary Contact: Michelle Waggoner, Chief Executive Officer
CFO: Steve Caryer, Chief Financial Officer
CNO: Jane Zachrich, Chief Nursing Officer
Web address: www.cmhosp.com
Control: Hospital district or authority, Government, Nonfederal **Service**: General medical and surgical

> **Staffed Beds**: 25

HILLSBORO—Highland County

☒ **HIGHLAND DISTRICT HOSPITAL (361332)**, 1275 North High Street, Zip 45133–8273; tel. 937/393–6100 **A**1 10 18 **F**3 11 13 15 29 30 31 34 35 40 45 47 49 50 57 59 62 64 74 76 77 78 79 81 85 86 87 92 93 94 96 98 103 107 110 111 115 118 119 127 130 131 132 133 135 146 148 149 **P**3
Primary Contact: Randal P. Lennartz, CPA, President and Chief Executive Officer
COO: Timothy Parry R.N., Chief Operating Officer
CMO: Ron Zile M.D., Chief of Staff
CIO: Tim Bogard, Manager Information Technology
CHR: Melanie Wymer, Director Human Resources
CNO: Pam Barnett R.N., Director of Nursing
Web address: www.hdh.org
Control: Hospital district or authority, Government, Nonfederal **Service**: General medical and surgical

> **Staffed Beds**: 25 **Admissions**: 1671 **Census**: 16 **Outpatient Visits**: 77624 **Births**: 281 **Total Expense ($000)**: 37158 **Payroll Expense ($000)**: 15540 **Personnel**: 342

JACKSON—Jackson County

☐ **HOLZER MEDICAL CENTER – JACKSON (361320)**, 500 Burlington Road, Zip 45640–9360; tel. 740/288–4625 (Nonreporting) **A**1 10 18 **S** Holzer Health System, Jackson, OH
Primary Contact: Michael Canady, M.D., Interim Chief Executive Officer
CFO: Kevin Yeager, Vice President Fiscal Services
CMO: Nimal Dutla M.D., Chief Medical Staff
CHR: Sandy Carlisle, Manager Human Resources
Web address: www.holzer.org
Control: Other not–for–profit (including NFP Corporation) **Service**: General medical and surgical

> **Staffed Beds**: 24

Many Facility Codes have changed. Please refer to the AHA Guide Code Chart. © 2017 AHA Guide

OH

KENTON—Hardin County

☒ **OHIOHEALTH HARDIN MEMORIAL HOSPITAL (361315)**, 921 East Franklin Street, Zip 43326–2099; tel. 419/673–0761, (Nonreporting) **A**1 10 18 **S** OhioHealth, Columbus, OH
Primary Contact: Ron Snyder, Chief Operating Officer
Web address: www.hardinmemorial.org
Control: Other not–for–profit (including NFP Corporation) **Service**: General medical and surgical

Staffed Beds: 25

KETTERING—Montgomery County

★ ○ △ **KETTERING MEDICAL CENTER (360079)**, 3535 Southern Boulevard, Zip 45429–1221; tel. 937/298–4331 **A**2 3 5 7 8 10 11 **F**3 8 11 13 15 17 18 20 22 24 26 28 29 30 31 34 35 36 37 38 39 40 43 44 45 46 47 48 49 50 51 52 53 54 55 56 57 58 59 60 61 62 64 65 66 68 70 71 72 74 75 76 77 78 79 81 82 84 85 86 87 90 91 92 93 96 97 102 107 108 110 111 114 115 116 117 118 119 120 121 123 124 126 129 130 131 132 135 141 145 146 147 148 149 **S** Kettering Health Network, Dayton, OH
Primary Contact: Roy G. Chew, Ph.D., President
CFO: Steven Chavez, Vice President Finance and Operations
CMO: Robert T. Smith M.D., Chief Medical Officer
CIO: Andy Lehman, Senior Vice President Technology and Analytics
CHR: Derek Morgan, Vice President Human Resources
CNO: Brenda Kuhn Ph.D., R.N., FACHE, Chief Nursing Officer
Web address: www.ketteringhealth.org/kettering
Control: Church operated, Nongovernment, not–for–profit **Service**: General medical and surgical

Staffed Beds: 396 Admissions: 22305 Census: 263 Outpatient Visits: 270237 Births: 2420 Total Expense ($000): 681037 Payroll Expense ($000): 269002 Personnel: 2758

LANCASTER—Fairfield County

☒ **FAIRFIELD MEDICAL CENTER (360072)**, 401 North Ewing Street, Zip 43130–3371; tel. 740/687–8000 **A**1 2 3 5 10 13 **F**3 8 11 12 13 15 18 20 22 24 26 28 29 30 31 34 35 38 40 44 45 48 49 50 53 54 57 59 64 70 74 75 76 77 78 79 81 82 83 84 85 87 89 93 96 97 98 102 104 107 108 110 111 114 115 118 119 129 130 131 132 135 145 146 147 148 149
Primary Contact: John R. Janoso, Chief Executive Officer
CFO: Sky Gettys, Chief Financial Officer
CMO: Terrence Welsh, Chief Medical Administrator
CIO: Martha Buckley, Chief Medical Informatics Officer
CHR: Debra L Palmer MS, R.N., Chief Human Resources Officer and Corporate Compliance Officer
CNO: Helen Harding, Chief Nursing Officer
Web address: www.fmchealth.org
Control: Other not–for–profit (including NFP Corporation) **Service**: General medical and surgical

Staffed Beds: 222 Admissions: 10088 Census: 102 Outpatient Visits: 268163 Births: 944 Total Expense ($000): 243775 Payroll Expense ($000): 91933 Personnel: 2143

LIMA—Allen County

☒ **INSTITUTE FOR ORTHOPAEDIC SURGERY (360263)**, 801 Medical Drive, Suite B, Zip 45804–4030; tel. 419/224–7586, (Nonreporting) **A**1 10 **S** Mercy Health, Cincinnati, OH
Primary Contact: Mark McDonald, M.D., President and Chief Executive Officer
CMO: Mark McDonald M.D., President and Chief Executive Officer
CHR: Pat Farmer, Coordinator Human Resources and Safety Officer
Web address: www.ioshospital.org
Control: Partnership, Investor–owned (for–profit) **Service**: Orthopedic

Staffed Beds: 3

☒ **KINDRED HOSPITAL LIMA (362020)**, 730 West Market Street, 6th Floor, Zip 45801–4602; tel. 419/224–1888, (Nonreporting) **A**1 10 **S** Kindred Healthcare, Louisville, KY
Primary Contact: Susan Krinke, Chief Executive Officer
Web address: www.khlima.com
Control: Corporation, Investor–owned (for–profit) **Service**: Acute long–term care hospital

Staffed Beds: 26

☒ △ **LIMA MEMORIAL HEALTH SYSTEM (360009)**, 1001 Bellefontaine Avenue, Zip 45804–2899; tel. 419/228–3335, (Total facility includes 17 beds in nursing home–type unit) **A**1 2 7 10 **F**3 11 13 15 17 18 20 22 24 26 28 29 30 31 34 35 36 40 41 43 45 46 47 48 49 50 54 57 59 60 62 63 64 68 70 73 74 75 76 77 78 79 81 82 84 85 86 89 90 93 96 107 108 110 111 114 115 119 121 126 128 130 131 132 135 146 147 148 149 **P**8
Primary Contact: Michael D. Swick, President and Chief Executive Officer
COO: Robert Armstrong, Senior Vice President and Chief Operating Officer
CFO: John Fischbach, Vice President of Finance, Chief Financial Officer
CMO: Kha H. Tran M.D., Vice President Medical Affairs
CIO: KC Williams, Director, MIS Operations
CHR: Denise G Kiraly, Director, Human Resources and Organization Development
CNO: Ann–Marie J Pohl R.N., MSN, Vice President and Chief Nursing Officer
Web address: www.limamemorial.org
Control: Other not–for–profit (including NFP Corporation) **Service**: General medical and surgical

Staffed Beds: 217 Admissions: 6501 Census: 80 Outpatient Visits: 250748 Births: 535 Total Expense ($000): 171158 Payroll Expense ($000): 61650 Personnel: 1420

OAKWOOD CORRECTIONAL FACILITY, 3200 North West Street, Zip 45801–2000; tel. 419/225–8052, (Nonreporting)
Primary Contact: Ed Sheldon, Warden and Chief Executive Officer
CFO: Thomas Ferry, Business Administrator
CHR: Glenda Turner, Director Personnel
Web address: www.drc.state.oh.us/public/ocf.htm
Control: State, Government, Nonfederal **Service**: Psychiatric

Staffed Beds: 61

☒ △ **ST. RITA'S MEDICAL CENTER (360066)**, 730 West Market Street, Zip 45801–4602; tel. 419/227–3361, (Nonreporting) **A**1 2 7 10 **S** Mercy Health, Cincinnati, OH
Primary Contact: Robert O. Baxter, Regional Chief Executive Officer, Lima
COO: Ronda Lehman PharmD, Chief Operating Officer, SRPS
CFO: Tim Rieger, Chief Financial Officer
CMO: Kevin Casey M.D., Chief Clinical Officer
CHR: Will Cason, Vice President Human Resources
CNO: Jodi Pahl, Chief Nurse Executive
Web address: www.stritas.org
Control: Church operated, Nongovernment, not–for–profit **Service**: General medical and surgical

Staffed Beds: 415

TRIUMPH HOSPITAL LIMA See Kindred Hospital Lima

LODI—Medina County

☒ **LODI COMMUNITY HOSPITAL (361303)**, 225 Elyria Street, Zip 44254–1096; tel. 330/948–1222 **A**1 10 18 **F**3 15 18 28 29 30 34 35 40 44 45 51 57 59 64 65 75 77 81 93 96 97 107 111 114 129 130 133 135 146 147 **S** Cleveland Clinic Health System, Cleveland, OH
Primary Contact: Dana Kocsis, Vice President, Nursing and Operations
COO: Dana Kocsis, Vice President Nursing and Operations
CFO: Dave Frigo, Director Finance and Controller
CMO: David Peter M.D., Senior Vice President Medical Affairs and Chief Medical Officer
CIO: Robb Baldauf, Coordinator Information Systems
CHR: Lynn Moraca, Director Human Resources
CNO: Dana Kocsis, Vice President, Nursing and Operations
Web address: www.lodihospital.org
Control: Other not–for–profit (including NFP Corporation) **Service**: General medical and surgical

Staffed Beds: 20 Admissions: 222 Census: 5 Outpatient Visits: 36518 Births: 0 Total Expense ($000): 13725 Payroll Expense ($000): 6503 Personnel: 103

Hospital, Medicare Provider Number, Address, Telephone, Approval, Facility, and Physician Codes, Health Care System

★ American Hospital Association (AHA) membership ○ Healthcare Facilities Accreditation Program ⇑ Center for Improvement in Healthcare Quality Accreditation
□ The Joint Commission accreditation ◇ DNV Healthcare Inc. accreditation △ Commission on Accreditation of Rehabilitation Facilities (CARF) accreditation

OH

LOGAN—Hocking County

✠ **HOCKING VALLEY COMMUNITY HOSPITAL (361330)**, 601 State Route 664 North, Zip 43138–8541, Mailing Address: P.O.Box 966, 43138–0966; tel. 740/380–8000 **A**1 10 18 **F**3 8 11 15 28 29 31 34 40 56 57 59 64 70 75 77 78 79 81 82 85 86 87 93 98 103 107 111 114 118 119 129 130 133 135 144 146 147 148 **P**1
Primary Contact: Julie Stuck, R.N., Chief Executive Officer
CFO: Julie E Grow, Chief Financial Officer
CMO: Duane Mast M.D., Medical Director
CIO: John Burgess, Director Information Services
CHR: Robert F Schmidt, Director Human Resources
CNO: Janelle Hicks R.N., Vice President Patient Services
Web address: www.hvch.org
Control: County, Government, Nonfederal **Service**: General medical and surgical

Staffed Beds: 35 **Admissions**: 1063 **Census**: 17 **Outpatient Visits**: 113644 **Births**: 0 **Total Expense ($000)**: 35862 **Payroll Expense ($000)**: 12957 **Personnel**: 253

LONDON—Madison County

✠ **MADISON HEALTH (360189)**, 210 North Main Street, Zip 43140–1115; tel. 740/845–7000 **A**1 10 **F**3 11 13 15 18 29 30 31 34 35 40 45 50 53 57 64 68 70 75 76 77 78 79 81 85 87 89 93 97 107 108 110 111 114 118 119 129 130 132 135 146 **P**6
Primary Contact: Dana E. Engle, Chief Executive Officer
CFO: Michael Browning, Chief Financial Officer
CMO: Bernard Oppong D.O., Chief of Staff
CIO: Dennis Vogt, Director Information Technology
CHR: Becky Rozell, Chief Human Resources Officer
CNO: Jennifer Piccione, Chief Nursing and Clinical Services Officer
Web address: www.madison–health.com
Control: Other not–for–profit (including NFP Corporation) **Service**: General medical and surgical

Staffed Beds: 55 **Admissions**: 1125 **Census**: 10 **Outpatient Visits**: 47999 **Births**: 227 **Total Expense ($000)**: 39580 **Payroll Expense ($000)**: 15470 **Personnel**: 328

LORAIN—Lorain County

CLEARVISTA HEALTH AND WELLNESS (364052), 3364 Kolbe Road, Zip 44053–1628; tel. 440/960–7960 (Nonreporting)
Primary Contact: John Sannuto, Chief Executive Officer
Web address: www.clearvistahealth.com
Control: Corporation, Investor–owned (for–profit) **Service**: Psychiatric

Staffed Beds: 30

✠ △ **MERCY REGIONAL MEDICAL CENTER (360172)**, 3700 Kolbe Road, Zip 44053–1697; tel. 440/960–4000, (Nonreporting) **A**1 2 7 10 **S** Mercy Health, Cincinnati, OH
Primary Contact: Edwin M. Oley, President and Chief Executive Officer
COO: Robert Tonkinson, Chief Operating Officer and Chief Financial Officer
CFO: Robert Tonkinson, Chief Operating Officer and Chief Financial Officer
CMO: Sam El–Dalati M.D., Chief Medical Officer
CHR: JC Fischer, Director Human Resources
CNO: Catherine Walsh, Interim Nursing Executive
Web address: www.community–health–partners.com
Control: Church operated, Nongovernment, not–for–profit **Service**: General medical and surgical

Staffed Beds: 259

MANSFIELD—Richland County

✠ **KINDRED HOSPITAL OF CENTRAL OHIO (362021)**, 335 Glessner Avenue, 5th Floor, Zip 44903–2269; tel. 419/526–0777 **A**1 10 **F**1 3 29 148 **P**7 **S** Kindred Healthcare, Louisville, KY
Primary Contact: Jeffrey Paul. Weier, Chief Executive Officer
Web address: www.khcentralohio.com/
Control: Corporation, Investor–owned (for–profit) **Service**: Acute long–term care hospital

Staffed Beds: 33 **Admissions**: 296 **Census**: 22 **Outpatient Visits**: 0 **Births**: 0 **Personnel**: 98

MEDCENTRAL – MANSFIELD HOSPITAL See Ohiohealth Medcentral Mansfield Hospital

✠ **OHIOHEALTH MEDCENTRAL MANSFIELD HOSPITAL (360118)**, 335 Glessner Avenue, Zip 44903–2265; tel. 419/526–8000, (Includes MANSFIELD HOSPITAL, 335 Glessner Avenue, Mansfield, Ohio, Zip 44903–2265, tel. 419/526–8000) **A**1 2 5 10 **F**3 5 8 11 13 15 17 18 20 22 24 26 28 29 30 31 32 34 35 38 39 40 43 44 45 46 47 48 49 50 51 53 54 55 56 57 58 59 61 62 63 64 65 68 70 73 74 75 76 77 78 79 81 82 83 84 85 86 87 89 90 92 93 96 98 99 100 101 102 103 104 105 107 108 110 111 114 115 116 117 118 119 120 121 122 123 124 126 129 130 131 132 133 135 144 146 147 148 149 150 **S** OhioHealth, Columbus, OH
Primary Contact: Jean Halpin, President
CFO: Michael Bichimer, Acting Vice President of Finance
CMO: Terry Weston M.D., Vice President Physician Services
CIO: Cindy Sheets, Vice President Information Systems and Chief Information Officer
CHR: Beth Hildreth, Vice President Human Resources
CNO: Pam Crawford R.N., Ph.D., Vice President of Nursing and Chief Nursing Officer
Web address: www.medcentral.org
Control: Other not–for–profit (including NFP Corporation) **Service**: General medical and surgical

Staffed Beds: 243 **Admissions**: 11600 **Census**: 140 **Outpatient Visits**: 343100 **Births**: 927 **Total Expense ($000)**: 234273 **Payroll Expense ($000)**: 92240 **Personnel**: 1719

MARIETTA—Washington County

★ ○ **MARIETTA MEMORIAL HOSPITAL (360147)**, 401 Matthew Street, Zip 45750–1699; tel. 740/374–1400, (Nonreporting) **A**2 3 5 10 11 13 **S** Memorial Health System, Marietta, OH
Primary Contact: J Scott. Cantley, President and Chief Executive Officer
CFO: Eric L Young, Vice President Finance and Chief Financial Officer
CMO: Matthew Macatol M.D., President Medical Staff
CIO: Andy Altenburger, Chief Information Officer
CHR: Dee Ann Gehlauf, Senior Vice President Business and Organization Development
Web address: www.mhsystem.org
Control: Other not–for–profit (including NFP Corporation) **Service**: General medical and surgical

Staffed Beds: 152

★ △ **SELBY GENERAL HOSPITAL (361319)**, 1106 Colegate Drive, Zip 45750–1323; tel. 740/568–2000 **A**7 10 18 **F**3 11 29 40 41 45 68 69 74 77 79 81 85 87 89 90 91 92 97 100 107 114 116 117 119 130 133 135 146 **S** Memorial Health System, Marietta, OH
Primary Contact: Stephen Smith, President
CFO: Eric L Young, Chief Financial Officer
CMO: David Spears D.O., Chief of Staff
CHR: Tricia A Engfehr, Chief Human Resources
CNO: Misti Spencer, Director Inpatient Services
Web address: www.selbygeneral.org
Control: Other not–for–profit (including NFP Corporation) **Service**: General medical and surgical

Staffed Beds: 35 **Admissions**: 1497 **Census**: 18 **Outpatient Visits**: 25157 **Births**: 0 **Total Expense ($000)**: 42804 **Payroll Expense ($000)**: 12556 **Personnel**: 160

MARION—Marion County

✠ **OHIOHEALTH MARION GENERAL HOSPITAL (360011)**, 1000 McKinley Park Drive, Zip 43302–6397; tel. 740/383–8400 **A**1 2 10 19 **F**3 8 13 15 18 20 22 24 26 28 29 30 31 35 40 53 54 57 59 60 62 63 64 68 70 72 73 74 75 76 77 78 79 81 82 87 89 91 93 94 98 104 105 107 111 114 116 119 126 129 130 132 135 146 147 148 149 **P**1 6 **S** OhioHealth, Columbus, OH
Primary Contact: Bruce P. Hagen, President
CIO: Chris King, Director Information Services
CHR: Gianna Ferrarotti, Director Human Resources North Region
Web address: www.ohiohealth.com/mariongeneral
Control: Other not–for–profit (including NFP Corporation) **Service**: General medical and surgical

Staffed Beds: 161 **Admissions**: 7049 **Census**: 74 **Outpatient Visits**: 213335 **Births**: 880 **Total Expense ($000)**: 175631 **Payroll Expense ($000)**: 65815 **Personnel**: 1180

Many Facility Codes have changed. Please refer to the AHA Guide Code Chart. © 2017 AHA Guide

MARTINS FERRY—Belmont County

☐ **EAST OHIO REGIONAL HOSPITAL (360080)**, 90 North Fourth Street, Zip 43935–1648; tel. 740/633–1100, (Total facility includes 50 beds in nursing home–type unit) **A**1 3 10 **F**3 8 11 15 20 28 29 30 31 34 35 37 40 43 44 45 54 57 59 64 68 70 74 75 77 79 81 82 85 87 107 108 110 111 114 115 118 119 128 129 130 131 132 133 135 146 148 149 150 **P**6 **S** Alecto Healthcare, Irvine, CA
Primary Contact: Bernie Albertini, Chief Administrative Officer
COO: Bernie Albertini, Chief Administrative Officer
CFO: Lisa M. Simon, Senior Vice President Chief Financial Officer
CIO: Lisa M. Simon, Senior Vice President Chief Financial Officer
CHR: Robert Wright, Senior Human Resource Advisor
CNO: Christine Kerwood, Chief Nursing Officer
Web address: www.ovmc-eorh.com
Control: Other not–for–profit (including NFP Corporation) **Service:** General medical and surgical

Staffed Beds: 120 **Admissions:** 2303 **Census:** 60 **Outpatient Visits:** 127556 **Births:** 0 **Total Expense ($000):** 63636 **Payroll Expense ($000):** 23094 **Personnel:** 453

MARYSVILLE—Union County

★ ⇧ **MEMORIAL HEALTH (360092)**, 500 London Avenue, Zip 43040–1594; tel. 937/644–6115 **A**5 10 21 **F**3 8 11 13 15 18 20 22 28 29 30 31 32 34 35 40 45 48 49 50 51 53 54 57 59 62 69 74 75 76 77 78 79 80 81 82 85 86 87 91 92 93 96 107 108 110 111 114 115 118 119 120 129 130 131 132 135 144 145 146 148 149 **P**6
Primary Contact: Olas A. Hubbs III, FACHE, President and Chief Executive Officer
COO: Laurie A Whittington, Chief Operating Officer
CFO: Jeffrey Ehlers, Chief Financial Officer
CMO: Matthew Hazelbaker M.D., President Medical Staff
CIO: Carl Zani, Chief Technology Director
CHR: Larry C Schleeter, Chief Human Resources Officer
CNO: Robin Slattman, Chief Nursing Officer
Web address: www.memorialhosp.org
Control: County, Government, Nonfederal **Service:** General medical and surgical

Staffed Beds: 76 **Admissions:** 1546 **Census:** 12 **Outpatient Visits:** 122569 **Births:** 531 **Total Expense ($000):** 97191 **Payroll Expense ($000):** 35758 **Personnel:** 549

MASON—Warren County

☐ **LINDNER CENTER OF HOPE (364044)**, 4075 Old Western Row Road, Zip 45040–3104; tel. 513/536–0311, (Nonreporting) **A**1 2 3 10
Primary Contact: Paul Keck, M.D., President and Chief Executive Officer
COO: Brian Owens, Chief Operating Officer
CFO: David McAdams, Chief Financial Officer
CIO: Cliff McClintick, Chief Information Officer
CHR: Debbie A Strawser, Director Human Resources
Web address: www.lindnercenterofhope.org
Control: Other not–for–profit (including NFP Corporation) **Service:** Psychiatric

Staffed Beds: 48

MASSILLON—Stark County

★ ○ **AFFINITY MEDICAL CENTER (360151)**, 875 Eighth Street NE, Zip 44646–8503, Mailing Address: P.O.Box 4805, 44648–0805; tel. 330/832–8761, (Nonreporting) **A**10 11 13 **S** Quorum Health, Brentwood, TN
Primary Contact: John Walsh, Chief Executive Officer
COO: Elizabeth Ann Pruitt, Chief Operating Officer
CFO: James Hutchinson CPA, Chief Financial Officer
Web address: www.affinitymedicalcenter.com
Control: Corporation, Investor–owned (for–profit) **Service:** General medical and surgical

Staffed Beds: 112

☐ **HEARTLAND BEHAVIORAL HEALTHCARE (364031)**, 3000 Erie Stree South, Zip 44646–7993, Mailing Address: 3000 Erie Street South, 44646–7976; tel. 330/833–3135, (Nonreporting) **A**1 5 10 **S** Ohio Department of Mental Health, Columbus, OH
Primary Contact: Jeffrey Sims, Chief Executive Officer
CFO: Patricia Eddleman, Fiscal Officer
CMO: Steven Thomson M.D., Medical Director
CIO: Robert Hobart, Director Management Information Systems
CHR: Jerald Wilhite, Administrator Human Resources
Web address: www.mh.state.oh.us/lbhs/bhos/hoh.html
Control: State, Government, Nonfederal **Service:** Psychiatric

Staffed Beds: 130

MAUMEE—Lucas County

☐ **ARROWHEAD BEHAVIORAL HEALTH HOSPITAL (364036)**, 1725 Timber Line Road, Zip 43537–4015; tel. 419/891–9333, (Nonreporting) **A**1 10 **S** Universal Health Services, Inc., King of Prussia, PA
Primary Contact: Joseph Denicola, Chief Executive Officer and Managing Director
CFO: Allison Duncan, Chief Financial Officer
CMO: Kenneth Adler M.D., Medical Director
CIO: Peggy Montgomery, Director Medical Records
CHR: Dawn Bosworth, Director Human Resources
CNO: Anita Zych, Director of Nursing
Web address: www.arrowheadbehavioral.com
Control: Corporation, Investor–owned (for–profit) **Service:** Psychiatric

Staffed Beds: 42

★ ⇧ **ST. LUKE'S HOSPITAL (360090)**, 5901 Monclova Road, Zip 43537–1899; tel. 419/893–5911 **A**3 5 10 21 **F**3 8 11 13 15 17 18 20 22 24 26 28 29 30 31 34 35 40 45 46 48 49 57 59 64 68 70 74 76 77 78 79 81 82 85 86 87 92 93 100 107 108 111 114 115 118 119 126 129 130 131 132 135 143 145 146 147 148 149 150
Primary Contact: Daniel L. Wakeman, President
CMO: Stephen Bazeley M.D., Vice President Medical Affairs
CIO: Patricia Swint, Director Information Technology
CHR: Connie Sessler, Director Human Resources
CNO: Jill A. Trosin R.N., MSN, Vice President Patient Care Services, Chief Nursing Officer
Web address: www.stlukeshospital.com
Control: Other not–for–profit (including NFP Corporation) **Service:** General medical and surgical

Staffed Beds: 170 **Admissions:** 9858 **Census:** 105 **Outpatient Visits:** 183138 **Births:** 760 **Total Expense ($000):** 180789 **Payroll Expense ($000):** 61065 **Personnel:** 1233

MEDINA—Medina County

⊞ **CLEVELAND CLINIC, MEDINA HOSPITAL (360091)**, 1000 East Washington Street, Zip 44256–2170; tel. 330/725–1000 **A**1 2 3 5 10 **F**3 7 8 13 15 18 20 28 29 30 31 34 35 40 47 49 50 51 57 59 60 64 70 74 75 76 77 78 79 81 82 85 86 93 96 107 111 114 117 119 129 130 131 132 133 135 146 147 148 **S** Cleveland Clinic Health System, Cleveland, OH
Primary Contact: Richard K. Shewbridge, M.D., President
COO: Vicky Snyder, Chief Operating Officer
CFO: Becky Molnar, Director of Finance
CIO: Frank Longley, Business Partner Information Technology
CHR: Tracie Curtis, Business Partner Human Resources
CNO: Mary Kennedy R.N., Chief Nursing Officer
Web address: www.medinahospital.org
Control: Other not–for–profit (including NFP Corporation) **Service:** General medical and surgical

Staffed Beds: 136 **Admissions:** 6329 **Census:** 68 **Outpatient Visits:** 103556 **Births:** 830 **Total Expense ($000):** 111154 **Payroll Expense ($000):** 42069 **Personnel:** 642

MIAMISBURG—Montgomery County

⊞ **LIFECARE HOSPITAL OF DAYTON (362028)**, 4000 Miamisburg–Centerville Road, Zip 45342–7615; tel. 937/384–8300, (Nonreporting) **A**1 10 **F**3 11 12 15 18 20 28 29 30 31 34 35 36 38 40 42 44 45 47 48 49 50 53 54 56 57 58 59 60 61 64 65 66 68 70 74 75 77 78 79 81 82 84 85 86 87 91 92 93 97 98 99 100 101 102 103 104 105 107 108 110 111 114 115 118 119 129 130 131 132 134 135 141 145 146 148 149 **S** LifeCare Management Services, Plano, TX
Primary Contact: William Bryant, Chief Executive Officer
CMO: Richard Gregg M.D., Medical Director
CHR: Pam Fannin, Coordinator Human Resources
Web address: www.lifecare–hospitals.com
Control: Corporation, Investor–owned (for–profit) **Service:** Acute long–term care hospital

Staffed Beds: 44

Hospital, Medicare Provider Number, Address, Telephone, Approval, Facility, and Physician Codes, Health Care System

★ American Hospital Association (AHA) membership
☐ The Joint Commission accreditation
○ Healthcare Facilities Accreditation Program
◇ DNV Healthcare Inc. accreditation
⇧ Center for Improvement in Healthcare Quality Accreditation
△ Commission on Accreditation of Rehabilitation Facilities (CARF) accreditation

Many Facility Codes have changed. Please refer to the AHA Guide Code Chart.

OH

★ ○ **SYCAMORE MEDICAL CENTER (360239)**, 4000 Miamisburg–Centerville Road, Zip 45342–7615; tel. 937/866–0551, (Includes KETTERING BEHAVIORAL MEDICAL CENTER, 5350 Lamme Road, Dayton, Ohio, Zip 45439, tel. 937/534–4600; Jason Brown, Director) **A**10 11 **F**3 5 7 8 11 13 15 18 20 22 24 26 28 29 30 31 32 34 35 36 37 38 39 40 42 43 44 45 46 49 50 51 53 54 56 57 59 60 62 63 64 65 68 70 74 75 76 77 78 79 81 82 84 85 86 87 90 92 93 94 98 99 100 101 102 103 104 105 107 108 110 111 114 115 118 119 120 121 123 126 129 130 131 132 134 135 143 146 147 148 149 **S** Kettering Health Network, Dayton, OH
Primary Contact: Walter Sackett, President
CFO: Terry M Burns, Chief Financial Officer
CMO: Robert T. Smith M.D., Chief Medical Officer
CIO: Andy Lehman, Senior Vice President Technology and Analytics
CHR: Derek Morgan, Vice President Human Resources
CNO: Julie S. Vincent R.N., MSN, Chief Nursing Officer
Web address: www.khnetwork.org/sycamore
Control: Church operated, Nongovernment, not–for–profit **Service**: General medical and surgical

Staffed Beds: 202 Admissions: 9490 Census: 100 Outpatient Visits: 148690 Births: 0 Total Expense ($000): 175705 Payroll Expense ($000): 73690 Personnel: 712

MIDDLE POINT—Van Wert County

□ **RIDGEVIEW BEHAVIORAL HOSPITAL (364047)**, 17872 Lincoln Highway, Zip 45863–9700; tel. 419/968–2950 (Nonreporting) **A**1 10
Primary Contact: Pat Tracy, Administrator
Web address: www.ridgeviewhospital.net/
Control: Corporation, Investor–owned (for–profit) **Service**: Psychiatric

Staffed Beds: 40

MIDDLEBURG HEIGHTS—Cuyahoga County

□ **SOUTHWEST GENERAL HEALTH CENTER (360155)**, 18697 Bagley Road, Zip 44130–3497; tel. 440/816–8000 **A**1 2 3 5 10 **P**6
Primary Contact: William A. Young Jr, President and Chief Executive Officer
COO: Bradley W. Rauh, Vice President, Chief Operating Officer
CFO: Mary Ann Freas, Senior Vice President and Chief Financial Officer
CMO: Marilyn McNamara M.D., Chief Medical Officer
CIO: Alec Williams, Chief Information Officer
CHR: Judy Murphy, Vice President Human Resources
CNO: Martha F. Bauschka R.N., Vice President and Chief Nursing Officer
Web address: www.swgeneral.com
Control: Other not–for–profit (including NFP Corporation) **Service**: General medical and surgical

Staffed Beds: 252 Admissions: 14730 Census: 180 Outpatient Visits: 407995 Births: 1065 Total Expense ($000): 299915 Payroll Expense ($000): 109281 Personnel: 2014

MIDDLETOWN—Warren County

✠ △ **ATRIUM MEDICAL CENTER (360076)**, One Medical Center Drive, Zip 45005–1066; tel. 513/424–2111 **A**1 2 3 7 10 **F**3 8 11 13 15 17 18 20 22 24 26 28 29 30 31 32 34 35 36 38 40 41 42 43 44 45 46 47 48 49 50 54 56 57 59 61 64 65 66 68 70 71 73 74 75 76 77 78 79 80 81 82 85 86 87 90 91 92 93 96 98 100 101 102 103 107 108 110 111 114 115 117 118 119 126 130 131 132 135 141 145 146 147 148 149 **S** Premier Health, Dayton, OH
Primary Contact: Michael Uhl, President
CMO: Matthew Reeves D.O., Esq, Chief Medical Officer
CHR: Ted Ripperger, Administrative Director Human Resources
CNO: Marquita Turner, Chief Operating Officer and Chief Nursing Officer
Web address: www.PremierHealth.com
Control: Other not–for–profit (including NFP Corporation) **Service**: General medical and surgical

Staffed Beds: 284 Admissions: 8858 Census: 100 Outpatient Visits: 112415 Births: 901 Total Expense ($000): 254209 Payroll Expense ($000): 90165 Personnel: 1429

MILLERSBURG—Holmes County

POMERENE HOSPITAL (360148), 981 Wooster Road, Zip 44654–1094; tel. 330/763–2001 **A**10 22 **F**3 11 13 15 18 29 30 34 35 40 45 50 53 55 57 58 59 68 70 75 76 79 81 85 86 87 89 93 107 108 110 115 119 127 130 131 132 135 143 144 146 149
Primary Contact: Tony Snyder, Administrator and Chief Executive Officer
CFO: Jason Justus, Vice President Finance and Chief Financial Officer
CMO: Yasser Omran M.D., President Medical Staff
CIO: Mark Jacobs, Director Information Services
CHR: Kim Croft R.N., Executive Director Human Resources
CNO: Nicole Kolacz, Vice President Patient Services
Web address: www.pomerenehospital.org
Control: Other not–for–profit (including NFP Corporation) **Service**: General medical and surgical

Staffed Beds: 41 Admissions: 1412 Census: 14 Outpatient Visits: 42841 Births: 549 Total Expense ($000): 27981 Payroll Expense ($000): 11269 Personnel: 265

MONTPELIER—Williams County

COMMUNITY HOSPITALS AND WELLNESS CENTERS–MONTPELIER (361327), 909 East Snyder Avenue, Zip 43543–1251; tel. 419/385–3154 (Nonreporting) **A**10 18 **F**3 5 11 13 15 18 20 22 26 28 29 31 34 35 38 40 44 45 48 50 53 57 59 64 69 70 75 76 77 78 79 81 82 83 84 85 86 87 93 94 96 97 107 108 110 111 114 115 118 119 120 121 122 129 130 131 132 144 146 147 149 150
Primary Contact: Philip L. Ennen, President and Chief Executive Officer
Web address: www.chwchospital.com
Control: Corporation, Investor–owned (for–profit) **Service**: General medical and surgical

Staffed Beds: 35

MONTPELIER HOSPITAL See Community Hospitals And Wellness Centers, Bryan

MOUNT GILEAD—Morrow County

✠ **MORROW COUNTY HOSPITAL (361313)**, 651 West Marion Road, Zip 43338–1027; tel. 419/946–5015, (Nonreporting) **A**1 5 10 18 **S** OhioHealth, Columbus, OH
Primary Contact: Chad J. Miller, President and Chief Executive Officer
CFO: Joe Schueler, Chief Financial Officer
Web address: www.morrowcountyhospital.com
Control: County, Government, Nonfederal **Service**: General medical and surgical

Staffed Beds: 23

MOUNT VERNON—Knox County

✠ **KNOX COMMUNITY HOSPITAL (360040)**, 1330 Coshocton Road, Zip 43050–1495; tel. 740/393–9000 **A**1 2 10 20 **P**6 **S** QHR, Brentwood, TN
Primary Contact: Bruce D. White, Chief Executive Officer
COO: Bruce M Behner, Chief Operating Officer
CFO: Michael Ambrosiani, Chief Financial Officer
CMO: Jeffrey Northup D.O., Chief Medical Officer
CIO: Kwi Holland, Vice President Information Services
CHR: Lisa Bragg, Vice President Human Resources
CNO: James Middleton MSN, R.N., Chief Nursing Officer
Web address: www.knoxcommhosp.org
Control: Other not–for–profit (including NFP Corporation) **Service**: General medical and surgical

Staffed Beds: 65 Admissions: 3166 Census: 27 Outpatient Visits: 150443 Births: 401 Total Expense ($000): 139841 Payroll Expense ($000): 61857 Personnel: 902

NAPOLEON—Henry County

★ ⇧ **HENRY COUNTY HOSPITAL (361309)**, 1600 East Riverview Avenue, Zip 43545–9399; tel. 419/592–4015 **A**5 10 18 21 **F**3 5 11 13 15 28 29 30 31 34 35 36 40 45 50 53 57 59 64 65 68 70 75 76 77 78 79 81 82 85 86 87 93 99 100 101 104 107 108 110 114 119 130 132 133 135 146 149
Primary Contact: Kimberly Hupp. Bordenkircher, Chief Executive Officer
CFO: Diane Walther, Controller
CIO: William Grimm, Chief Information Officer
CHR: Jennifer A Fisher, Manager Human Resources
CNO: Patricia Frank, Chief Nursing Officer
Web address: www.henrycountyhospital.org
Control: Other not–for–profit (including NFP Corporation) **Service**: General medical and surgical

Staffed Beds: 25 Admissions: 774 Census: 8 Outpatient Visits: 63310 Births: 138 Total Expense ($000): 28405 Payroll Expense ($000): 11541 Personnel: 191

NEW ALBANY—Franklin County

✠ **MOUNT CARMEL NEW ALBANY SURGICAL HOSPITAL (360266)**, 7333 Smith's Mill Road, Zip 43054–9291; tel. 614/775–6600 **A**1 5 10 **F**3 29 34 35 44 57 58 59 64 65 68 74 75 79 81 85 86 87 91 107 111 114 119 146 **P**6 8 **S** Trinity Health, Livonia, MI
Primary Contact: Diane Doucette, R.N., President
Web address: www.mountcarmelhealth.com
Control: Church operated, Nongovernment, not–for–profit **Service**: Surgical

Staffed Beds: 60 Admissions: 4286 Census: 19 Outpatient Visits: 14259 Births: 0 Total Expense ($000): 85057 Payroll Expense ($000): 14690 Personnel: 222

NEWARK—Licking County

☐ **LICKING MEMORIAL HOSPITAL (360218)**, 1320 West Main Street, Zip 43055–3699; tel. 740/348–4000 **A**1 2 10 **F**3 4 5 13 15 18 20 22 28 29 30 31 32 34 35 40 41 45 46 48 49 50 53 57 59 62 64 65 68 70 74 75 76 77 78 79 81 82 84 85 86 87 89 90 92 93 97 98 100 101 102 104 106 107 108 110 111 114 115 118 119 130 132 135 144 146 147 148 **P**6
Primary Contact: Robert A. Montagnese, President and Chief Executive Officer
CFO: Cindy Webster, Vice President Financial Services
CMO: Craig Cairns M.D., Vice President Medical Affairs
CIO: Sallie Arnett, Vice President Information Systems
CHR: Anne Peterson, Vice President Human Resources and Support Services
Web address: www.lmhealth.org
Control: Other not–for–profit (including NFP Corporation) **Service:** General medical and surgical

Staffed Beds: 199 **Admissions:** 7730 **Census:** 75 **Outpatient Visits:** 319794 **Births:** 1100 **Total Expense ($000):** 173110 **Payroll Expense ($000):** 71071 **Personnel:** 1452

⊞ **SELECT SPECIALTY HOSPITAL OF SOUTHEAST OHIO (362031)**, 2000 Tamarack Road, Zip 43055; tel. 740/588–7888, (Nonreporting) **A**1 10 **S** Select Medical Corporation, Mechanicsburg, PA
Primary Contact: Linda Supplee, Chief Executive Officer
CMO: Armand Bermudez M.D., Medical Director
CHR: Jacqueline Nezbeth, Human Resources Officer
CNO: Taryn Vierling, Chief Nursing Officer
Web address: www.selectspecialtyhospitals.com/company/locations/zanesville.aspx
Control: Corporation, Investor–owned (for–profit) **Service:** Acute long–term care hospital

Staffed Beds: 35

NORTHFIELD—Summit County

☐ **NORTHCOAST BEHAVIORAL HEALTHCARE (364011)**, 1756 Sagamore Road, Zip 44067–1086; tel. 330/467–7131 **A**1 10 **F**30 53 65 75 77 98 106 130 132 135 **S** Ohio Department of Mental Health, Columbus, OH
Primary Contact: Douglas W. Kern, Chief Executive Officer
CIO: Karl Donenwirth, Vice President Information Services
Web address: www.mha.ohio.gov
Control: State, Government, Nonfederal **Service:** Psychiatric

Staffed Beds: 258 **Admissions:** 1601 **Census:** 218 **Outpatient Visits:** 0 **Births:** 0 **Total Expense ($000):** 46295 **Payroll Expense ($000):** 31091 **Personnel:** 419

NORWALK—Huron County

★ ○ **FISHER–TITUS MEDICAL CENTER (360065)**, 272 Benedict Avenue, Zip 44857–2374; tel. 419/668–8101, (Total facility includes 69 beds in nursing home–type unit) **A**2 3 5 10 11 19 **F**3 10 13 15 18 20 28 29 31 34 35 36 39 40 43 45 49 50 51 54 57 59 62 64 68 70 74 75 76 78 79 81 85 86 87 92 93 94 96 107 108 110 111 115 118 119 126 128 129 130 131 132 135 143 146 147 148 **P**6 8
Primary Contact: Lorna Strayer, President and Chief Executive Officer
COO: Lorna Strayer, Executive Vice President
CFO: Duane L Woods Jr, Chief Financial Officer
CMO: Shankar Kurra M.D., Senior Vice President Medical Affairs
CIO: John Britton, Vice President Information Services
CHR: Phillip Annarino, Vice President Human Resources
CNO: Suzanne Inglis MSN, FACHE, Senior Vice President Nursing Services
Web address: www.fisher–titus.org
Control: Other not–for–profit (including NFP Corporation) **Service:** General medical and surgical

Staffed Beds: 147 **Admissions:** 4237 **Census:** 96 **Outpatient Visits:** 177028 **Births:** 642 **Total Expense ($000):** 115136 **Payroll Expense ($000):** 46149 **Personnel:** 880

OBERLIN—Lorain County

⊞ **MERCY ALLEN HOSPITAL (361306)**, 200 West Lorain Street, Zip 44074–1077; tel. 440/775–1211, (Nonreporting) **A**1 10 18 **S** Mercy Health, Cincinnati, OH
Primary Contact: Joseph Sober, President
COO: Robert Tonkinson, Chief Operating Officer and Chief Financial Officer
CFO: Robert Tonkinson, Chief Operating Officer and Chief Financial Officer
CMO: Vamsee Amirneni M.D., Chief of Staff
CNO: Catherine Walsh, Interim Chief Nursing Officer
Web address: www.mercyonline.org/mercy_allen_hospital.aspx
Control: Other not–for–profit (including NFP Corporation) **Service:** General medical and surgical

Staffed Beds: 25

ONTARIO—Richland County

★ **AVITA ONTARIO HOSPITAL (360365)**, 715 Richland Mall, Zip 44906–3802; tel. 567/307–7666 (Nonreporting) **S** Avita Health System, Galion, OH
Primary Contact: Jerome Morasko, President and Chief Executive Officer
CFO: D. Eric Draime, Vice President and Chief Financial Officer
CIO: Alex Reed, Chief Information Officer
CHR: Traci L Oswald, Vice President, Chief Human Resources
CNO: Kathy Durflinger R.N., Vice President and Chief Nursing Officer
Web address: www.avitahealth.org
Control: Other not–for–profit (including NFP Corporation) **Service:** Acute long–term care hospital

Staffed Beds: 26

OREGON—Lucas County

⊞ △ **MERCY HEALTH – ST. CHARLES HOSPITAL (360081)**, 2600 Navarre Avenue, Zip 43616–3297; tel. 419/696–7200 **A**1 2 3 7 10 **F**3 11 13 15 18 28 29 30 31 34 35 40 43 44 46 48 49 51 56 57 59 60 64 66 68 70 74 75 76 77 78 79 81 82 85 86 87 90 91 92 93 97 98 100 102 103 104 105 107 108 110 111 114 115 118 119 120 121 123 126 129 130 132 135 146 147 148 149 **P**8 **S** Mercy Health, Cincinnati, OH
Primary Contact: Jeffrey Dempsey, President and Chief Operating Officer
COO: Jeffrey Dempsey, President and Chief Executive Officer
CFO: Mark Thompson, Market Chief Financial Officer Northern Region and Chief Financial Officer
CMO: Riaz Chaudhry M.D., Chief Medical Officer
CIO: Rebecca S Sykes, Senior Vice President Resource Management, Chief Information Officer
CHR: Maggie A. Lund, System Vice President Human Resource Market and Labor
CNO: Craig Albers, Vice President Patient Care and Chief Nursing Officer
Web address: www.mercyweb.org
Control: Church operated, Nongovernment, not–for–profit **Service:** General medical and surgical

Staffed Beds: 279 **Admissions:** 10578 **Census:** 148 **Outpatient Visits:** 151201 **Births:** 484 **Personnel:** 917

⊞ **PROMEDICA BAY PARK HOSPITAL (360259)**, 2801 Bay Park Drive, Zip 43616–4920; tel. 419/690–7900 **A**1 10 **F**3 11 13 15 18 28 29 30 31 34 35 49 50 54 57 58 59 64 68 70 75 76 77 78 79 81 82 85 86 92 93 97 107 108 110 111 114 118 119 124 126 129 130 131 132 134 135 146 147 148 **S** ProMedica Health System, Toledo, OH
Primary Contact: Arturo Polizzi, President
COO: Darrell Wachowiak, Associate Vice President Operations
CFO: Scott Fought, Vice President Finance
CMO: David Lindstrom M.D., Vice President Medical Affairs
CIO: Rose Ann Laureto, Corporate Vice President Information Resources
CHR: Kara Zimmerly, Manager Human Resources
CNO: Paula Grieb R.N., Vice President Patient Care Service and Chief Nursing Officer
Web address: www.promedica.org
Control: Other not–for–profit (including NFP Corporation) **Service:** General medical and surgical

Staffed Beds: 44 **Admissions:** 3147 **Census:** 31 **Outpatient Visits:** 98605 **Births:** 595 **Total Expense ($000):** 72840 **Payroll Expense ($000):** 22898 **Personnel:** 357

ST. CHARLES MERCY HOSPITAL See Mercy Health – St. Charles Hospital

ORRVILLE—Wayne County

⊞ **AULTMAN ORRVILLE HOSPITAL (361323)**, 832 South Main Street, Zip 44667–2208; tel. 330/682–3010 **A**1 10 18 **F**3 8 11 12 13 14 15 28 29 30 34 35 40 45 50 51 53 55 57 59 68 70 75 76 77 79 81 82 85 86 87 93 108 110 111 115 118 119 127 129 130 131 132 133 135 143 146 147 149 150 **P**6 **S** Aultman Health Foundation, Canton, OH
Primary Contact: Marchelle Suppan, DPM, President and Chief Executive Officer
CFO: Adam Luntz, Chief Financial Officer
CIO: Vince Logozzo, Director Information Technology
CHR: Jennifer Kessel, Assistant Vice President, Operations and Human Resources
CNO: Angela McGee, Vice President Nursing Services
Web address: www.aultmanorrville.org
Control: Other not–for–profit (including NFP Corporation) **Service:** General medical and surgical

Staffed Beds: 25 **Admissions:** 943 **Census:** 6 **Outpatient Visits:** 36132 **Births:** 518 **Total Expense ($000):** 23083 **Payroll Expense ($000):** 9203 **Personnel:** 201

OH

OXFORD—Butler County

★ ○ **MCCULLOUGH–HYDE MEMORIAL HOSPITAL/TRIHEALTH (360046)**, 110 North Poplar Street, Zip 45056–1292; tel. 513/523–2111 **A2** 10 11 **F3** 11 13 15 18 26 28 29 30 31 34 35 36 40 45 47 50 57 59 68 69 70 76 77 78 79 81 82 85 93 107 108 110 111 114 119 124 129 130 131 144 146 147 **P6**
Primary Contact: Brett Kirkpatrick, Executive Director
CFO: John R Clements, Chief Financial Officer
CMO: Amy Spivey, Chief Medical Officer
CIO: Kathy Dickman, Director Information Technology
CHR: Sharon Hancock, Chief Human Resources Officer
CNO: Pamela Collins, Vice President Chief Patient Services Officer
Web address: www.mhmh.org
Control: Other not–for–profit (including NFP Corporation) **Service**: General medical and surgical

Staffed Beds: 45 Admissions: 1731 **Census:** 15 **Outpatient Visits:** 60836 **Births:** 393 **Total Expense ($000):** 52243 **Payroll Expense ($000):** 21650 **Personnel:** 332

PARMA—Cuyahoga County

✉ △ **UNIVERSITY HOSPITALS PARMA MEDICAL CENTER (360041)**, 7007 Powers Boulevard, Zip 44129–5495; tel. 440/743–3000 **A1** 2 7 10 13 **F2** 3 10 11 12 13 15 17 18 20 22 24 26 28 29 30 31 34 35 36 40 44 45 49 50 51 53 55 56 57 58 59 62 63 64 65 68 69 70 71 74 75 76 77 78 79 81 82 85 86 87 90 93 96 98 100 101 103 107 108 111 114 115 116 117 118 119 120 121 126 130 131 132 135 143 146 147 148 149 **S** University Hospitals, Cleveland, OH
Primary Contact: Peter U. Bergmann, President
COO: Kristi M Sink, Chief Operating Officer
CMO: Christopher Loyke, Chief Medical Officer
CHR: Daniel Miller, Human Resources Business Partner
Web address: www.uhhospitals.org/parma
Control: Other not–for–profit (including NFP Corporation) **Service**: General medical and surgical

Staffed Beds: 265 Admissions: 10384 **Census:** 133 **Outpatient Visits:** 366142 **Births:** 500 **Total Expense ($000):** 180646 **Payroll Expense ($000):** 66448 **Personnel:** 1183

PAULDING—Paulding County

□ **PAULDING COUNTY HOSPITAL (361300)**, 1035 West Wayne Street, Zip 45879–1544; tel. 419/399–4080, (Nonreporting) **A1** 10 18
Primary Contact: Randy Ruge, Chief Executive Officer
COO: Randy Ruge, Chief Operating Officer
CFO: Rob Goshia, Chief Financial Officer
CMO: Wendell J Spangler M.D., Chief of Staff
CIO: Dan Kaufman, Director Information Services
CHR: Melanie Rittenour, Director Human Resources
Web address: www.pauldingcountyhospital.com
Control: County, Government, Nonfederal **Service**: General medical and surgical

Staffed Beds: 25

PORT CLINTON—Ottawa County

✉ **MAGRUDER MEMORIAL HOSPITAL (361314)**, 615 Fulton Street, Zip 43452–2001; tel. 419/734–3131 **A1** 5 10 18 **F3** 11 15 18 28 29 31 34 35 40 44 45 46 48 50 53 57 59 64 65 70 75 77 78 79 81 82 85 86 87 89 93 107 108 110 115 118 119 129 130 131 132 133 135 144 146 147 148 149 **P6** 8
Primary Contact: J Todd. Almendinger, President and Chief Executive Officer
COO: Nick Marsico, Vice President and Chief Operating Officer
CFO: Ronald Weiner, Vice President Finance and Chief Financial Officer
CMO: Barry Cover M.D., Medical Director
CIO: Charles Dellick, Director Information Technology
CHR: Jason Kraus, Director Human Resources
Web address: www.magruderhospital.com
Control: Other not–for–profit (including NFP Corporation) **Service**: General medical and surgical

Staffed Beds: 25 Admissions: 505 **Census:** 5 **Outpatient Visits:** 83618 **Births:** 0 **Total Expense ($000):** 51206 **Payroll Expense ($000):** 20231 **Personnel:** 359

PORTSMOUTH—Scioto County

KING'S DAUGHTERS MEDICAL CENTER OHIO (360361), 2001 Scioto Trail, Zip 45662–2845; tel. 740/991–4000 **F3** 18 20 29 30 34 40 45 46 49 51 57 59 64 65 66 68 70 75 79 81 82 85 107 108 111 115 119 129 144 146 149
Primary Contact: Kim Grooms, Administrator
Web address: www.kdmcohio.com/
Control: Other not–for–profit (including NFP Corporation) **Service**: General medical and surgical

Staffed Beds: 10 Admissions: 213 **Census:** 1 **Outpatient Visits:** 54688 **Births:** 0 **Total Expense ($000):** 21014 **Payroll Expense ($000):** 6270

SOUTHERN OHIO MEDICAL CENTER (360008), 1805 27th Street,

✉ △ **SOUTHERN OHIO MEDICAL CENTER (360008)**, 1805 27th Street, Zip 45662–2640; tel. 740/356–5000 **A1** 2 3 5 7 10 13 **F3** 11 13 15 17 18 20 22 24 26 28 29 30 31 34 35 37 38 40 41 44 45 46 47 48 49 50 53 54 57 59 62 63 64 65 68 70 74 75 76 77 78 79 81 82 84 85 86 87 89 90 92 97 98 100 101 102 103 104 107 108 109 110 111 114 115 116 117 118 119 120 121 122 123 124 129 130 131 132 135 144 145 146 147 **P3**
Primary Contact: Randal M. Arnett, President and Chief Executive Officer
CFO: Dean Wray, Vice President Finance
CMO: Kendall Stewart M.D., Chief Medical Officer
CIO: Brent Richard, Administrative Director Information Systems
CHR: Vicki Noel, Vice President Human Resources
CNO: Claudia L Burchett R.N., Vice President of Patient Services
Web address: www.somc.org
Control: Other not–for–profit (including NFP Corporation) **Service**: General medical and surgical

Staffed Beds: 248 Admissions: 12742 **Census:** 163 **Outpatient Visits:** 405658 **Total Expense ($000):** 285011 **Payroll Expense ($000):** 108591 **Personnel:** 2353

PROCTORVILLE—Lawrence County

□ **THREE GABLES SURGERY CENTER (360261)**, 5897 County Road 107, Zip 45669–8852, Mailing Address: P.O.Box 490, 45669–0490; tel. 740/886–9911 (Nonreporting) **A1** 10
Primary Contact: Tony Aluise, Chief Executive Officer
Web address: www.threegablessurgery.com
Control: Partnership, Investor–owned (for–profit) **Service**: Surgical

Staffed Beds: 8

RAVENNA—Portage County

✉ **UH PORTAGE MEDICAL CENTER (360078)**, 6847 North Chestnut Street, Zip 44266–3929, Mailing Address: P.O.Box 1204, 44266–1204; tel. 330/297–0811 **A1** 2 5 10 **F3** 11 13 15 18 20 22 26 28 29 30 34 35 39 40 42 43 44 45 46 47 48 49 50 51 54 56 57 58 59 60 63 64 65 68 70 74 75 76 77 78 79 81 82 84 85 87 92 93 100 107 108 109 110 111 115 117 119 129 130 131 132 135 143 144 145 146 147 148 149 **S** University Hospitals, Cleveland, OH
Primary Contact: M Steven. Jones, President
CFO: Jen Hahn, Finance Manager
CMO: Benjamin Prestegaard, Chief Medical Officer
CIO: Rhonda Smith, Applications Support Manager
CHR: Neil Everett, Vice President Human Resources
Web address: www.uhportage.org
Control: Other not–for–profit (including NFP Corporation) **Service**: General medical and surgical

Staffed Beds: 117 Admissions: 5580 **Census:** 64 **Outpatient Visits:** 169883 **Births:** 639 **Total Expense ($000):** 112328 **Payroll Expense ($000):** 40498 **Personnel:** 736

ROCK CREEK—Ashtabula County

GLENBEIGH HOSPITAL AND OUTPATIENT CENTERS (360245), 2863 Route 45, Zip 44084, Mailing Address: P.O.Box 298, 44084–0298; tel. 440/563–3400 **A10 F4** 5 29 30 34 36 53 54 57 75 86 87 100 130 132 135 149
Primary Contact: Patricia Weston–Hall, Chief Executive Officer
CFO: Phil Pawlowski, Chief Financial Officer
CIO: Linda Advey, Manager Information Systems
CHR: Shirley Deary, Director Human Resources
Web address: www.glenbeigh.com
Control: Other not–for–profit (including NFP Corporation) **Service**: Alcoholism and other chemical dependency

Staffed Beds: 114 Admissions: 3207 **Census:** 91 **Outpatient Visits:** 89951 **Births:** 0 **Total Expense ($000):** 21351 **Payroll Expense ($000):** 9877 **Personnel:** 229

SAINT MARYS—Auglaize County

⇑ **JOINT TOWNSHIP DISTRICT MEMORIAL HOSPITAL (360032)**, 200 St Clair Street, Zip 45885–2400; tel. 419/394–3335, (Total facility includes 13 beds in nursing home–type unit) **A10** 21 **F3** 7 8 11 12 13 15 28 29 30 32 34 35 36 40 41 45 47 51 53 57 59 62 63 64 70 74 75 76 77 79 81 82 83 84 85 87 90 93 107 108 110 115 119 124 128 129 130 131 132 143 144 146 147 148
Primary Contact: Kevin W. Harlan, President
CFO: Jeffrey W Vossler, Chief Financial Officer
CIO: Joshua Miller, Director Information Systems
CHR: Art Swain, Vice President Support Services
CNO: Debra McKee R.N., Chief Clinical Officer and Chief Nursing Officer
Web address: www.grandlakehealth.org
Control: Other not–for–profit (including NFP Corporation) **Service**: General medical and surgical

Staffed Beds: 53 Admissions: 1749 **Census:** 13 **Outpatient Visits:** 77055 **Births:** 308 **Total Expense ($000):** 66350 **Payroll Expense ($000):** 19809 **Personnel:** 520

Many Facility Codes have changed. Please refer to the AHA Guide Code Chart. © 2017 AHA Guide

SALEM—Columbiana County

☒ **SALEM REGIONAL MEDICAL CENTER (360185)**, 1995 East State Street, Zip 44460–2423; tel. 330/332–1551, (Total facility includes 15 beds in nursing home–type unit) **A**1 5 10 **F**3 13 15 18 29 30 31 34 35 40 45 47 48 49 51 54 57 59 64 70 74 75 76 77 78 79 81 82 85 86 87 92 93 104 105 107 108 109 110 111 115 116 117 118 119 128 129 130 132 145 146 148 149
Primary Contact: Anita Hackstedde, M.D., President and Chief Executive Officer
COO: Keith Meredith, Chief Operating Officer
CFO: Mike Giangardella, Vice President Finance and Administration
CMO: Anita Hackstedde M.D., Vice President Medical Affairs
CIO: Mark L'Italien, Director Information Services
CHR: Barb Hirst R.N., Vice President Human Resources and Chief Nursing Officer
CNO: Barb Hirst R.N., Vice President Human Resources and Chief Nursing Officer
Web address: www.salemregional.com
Control: Other not–for–profit (including NFP Corporation) **Service:** General medical and surgical

Staffed Beds: 116 **Admissions:** 4142 **Census:** 53 **Outpatient Visits:** 90356 **Births:** 408 **Total Expense ($000):** 102322 **Payroll Expense ($000):** 37562 **Personnel:** 834

SANDUSKY—Erie County

○ **FIRELANDS REGIONAL HEALTH SYSTEM (360025)**, 1111 Hayes Avenue, Zip 44870–3323; tel. 419/557–7400, (Includes FIRELANDS REGIONAL MEDICAL CENTER – MAIN CAMPUS, 1111 Hayes Avenue, Sandusky, Ohio, Zip 44870, tel. 419/557–7400; FIRELANDS REGIONAL MEDICAL CENTER SOUTH CAMPUS, 1912 Hayes Avenue, Sandusky, Ohio, Zip 44870–4736, tel. 419/557–7000) **A**2 3 10 11 12 13 19 **F**3 5 8 11 12 13 15 18 20 22 24 28 29 31 34 35 36 38 40 43 45 46 48 49 50 51 54 57 58 59 60 62 64 68 70 74 75 76 77 78 79 80 81 82 85 86 87 89 90 92 93 96 98 99 100 101 102 103 104 105 107 108 110 111 115 117 118 119 120 121 123 124 129 130 131 132 135 143 145 146 147 148 149 150 **P**8
Primary Contact: Martin Tursky, President and Chief Executive Officer
CFO: Daniel J Moncher, Vice President and Chief Financial Officer
CMO: Brenda Violette M.D., Director Medical Staff
CIO: Robert Ayres, Director Information Systems
CHR: James Sennish, Vice President Human Resources
Web address: www.firelands.com
Control: Other not–for–profit (including NFP Corporation) **Service:** General medical and surgical

Staffed Beds: 239 **Admissions:** 8945 **Census:** 120 **Outpatient Visits:** 336968 **Births:** 740 **Total Expense ($000):** 236670 **Payroll Expense ($000):** 96232 **Personnel:** 1825

SEAMAN—Adams County

☒ **ADAMS COUNTY REGIONAL MEDICAL CENTER (361326)**, 230 Medical Center Drive, Zip 45679–8002; tel. 937/386–3400 **A**1 10 18 **F**3 11 15 28 29 30 31 34 35 40 45 49 50 53 57 59 64 65 68 75 77 78 79 81 82 85 86 91 93 107 108 110 111 115 119 129 130 132 133 135 146 148
Primary Contact: Bill May, President and Chief Executive Officer
CFO: Pete Dagenbach, Chief Financial Officer
CHR: Heather Hoop, Human Resources Generalist
CNO: Sharon Ashley MSN, Chief Nursing Officer
Web address: www.acrmc.com
Control: County, Government, Nonfederal **Service:** General medical and surgical

Staffed Beds: 25 **Admissions:** 804 **Census:** 8 **Outpatient Visits:** 51686 **Births:** 0 **Total Expense ($000):** 23383 **Payroll Expense ($000):** 7980 **Personnel:** 173

SHELBY—Richland County

★ **OHIOHEALTH MEDCENTRAL SHELBY HOSPITAL (361324)**, 199 West Main Street, Zip 44875–1490; tel. 419/342–5015 **A**10 18 **F**3 11 13 15 18 29 30 31 34 35 40 57 59 64 68 69 70 75 76 78 79 81 93 107 108 110 115 118 119 130 133 146 149 **S** OhioHealth, Columbus, OH
Primary Contact: Jean Halpin, President
CNO: Trish DelGreco, Director of Nursing
Web address: www.medcentral.org/body.cfm?id=153
Control: Other not–for–profit (including NFP Corporation) **Service:** General medical and surgical

Staffed Beds: 25 **Admissions:** 1040 **Census:** 10 **Outpatient Visits:** 54378 **Births:** 135 **Total Expense ($000):** 24222 **Payroll Expense ($000):** 8286 **Personnel:** 246

SIDNEY—Shelby County

★ ○ **WILSON MEMORIAL HOSPITAL (360013)**, 915 West Michigan Street, Zip 45365–2491; tel. 937/498–2311 **A**10 11 **F**3 7 11 13 15 20 28 29 30 34 40 45 49 51 56 57 59 62 63 64 68 70 75 76 77 79 81 82 85 86 87 89 93 97 98 103 107 108 111 115 118 119 129 130 131 132 135 144 146 147 **P**6
Primary Contact: Mark J. Dooley, Chief Executive Officer
COO: Craig Lannoye, Vice President Operations
CFO: Julie Covault, Vice President Finance
CMO: Robert J McDevitt M.D., Chief of Staff
CIO: Larry Meyers, Chief Information Officer
CHR: John Eve, Vice President Human Resources and Education
CNO: Linda Maurer, Vice President Patient Care Services
Web address: www.wilsonhospital.com
Control: Other not–for–profit (including NFP Corporation) **Service:** General medical and surgical

Staffed Beds: 71 **Admissions:** 2348 **Census:** 26 **Outpatient Visits:** 219347 **Births:** 701 **Total Expense ($000):** 77232 **Payroll Expense ($000):** 29038 **Personnel:** 687

SPRINGFIELD—Clark County

☐ **MENTAL HEALTH SERVICES FOR CLARK AND MADISON COUNTIES (364040)**, 474 North Yellow Springs Street, Zip 45504–2463; tel. 937/399–9500 (Nonreporting) **A**1 10
Primary Contact: Curt Gillespie, Chief Executive Officer
Web address: www.mhscc.org
Control: County, Government, Nonfederal **Service:** Psychiatric

Staffed Beds: 16

☐ **OHIO VALLEY SURGICAL HOSPITAL (360355)**, 100 West Main Street, Zip 45502–1312; tel. 937/521–3900 (Nonreporting) **A**1 10
Primary Contact: Steve Eisentrager, President
CFO: Amanda martin, Manager Human Resources
CMO: Thales Pavlatos, Medical Director
CIO: Jonathan Bisdorf, Director Information Technology
CNO: Beth Lizza, Chief Nursing Officer
Web address: www.ovsurgical.com/
Control: Partnership, Investor–owned (for–profit) **Service:** Surgical

Staffed Beds: 24

☒ **SPRINGFIELD REGIONAL MEDICAL CENTER (360086)**, 100 Medical Center Drive, Zip 45504–2687; tel. 937/523–1000, (Nonreporting) **A**1 2 3 10 **S** Mercy Health, Cincinnati, OH
Primary Contact: Matthew T. Caldwell, President and Chief Executive Officer
COO: Gary Hagens, Chief Operating Officer and Chief Medical Officer
CFO: William J. Kusnierz, Vice President and Chief Financial Officer
CMO: Gary Hagens, Chief Operating Officer and Chief Medical Officer
CIO: Denise Craven, Director Information Systems Relationship Management
CNO: Sherry Nelson JD, MS, R.N., Chief Nursing Officer
Web address: www.community–mercy.org
Control: Church operated, Nongovernment, not–for–profit **Service:** General medical and surgical

Staffed Beds: 259

STEUBENVILLE—Jefferson County

☒ **ACUITY SPECIALTY HOSPITALS OHIO VALLEY (362035)**, 380 Summit Avenue, 3rd Floor, Zip 43952–2667; tel. 740/283–7600, (Includes ACUITY SPECIALTY HOSPITALS OHIO VALLEY AT BELMONT, 4697 Harrison Street, Bellaire, Ohio, Zip 43906–1338, tel. 740/671–2086) **A**1 10 **F**1 3 29 34 57 85 91 148 **S** AcuityHealthcare, LP, Charlotte, NC
Primary Contact: Judy K. Weaver, MS, Chief Executive Officer
Web address: www.acuityhealthcare.net
Control: Partnership, Investor–owned (for–profit) **Service:** Acute long–term care hospital

Staffed Beds: 52 **Admissions:** 669 **Census:** 48 **Outpatient Visits:** 0 **Births:** 0 **Total Expense ($000):** 26207 **Payroll Expense ($000):** 11058 **Personnel:** 148

LIFE LINE HOSPITAL (362039), 200 School Street, Zip 43953–9610; tel. 740/346–2600 (Nonreporting) **A**10
Primary Contact: Patricia Cross, Chief Executive Officer
Web address: www.llhospital.com
Control: Partnership, Investor–owned (for–profit) **Service:** Acute long–term care hospital

Staffed Beds: 30

Hospital, Medicare Provider Number, Address, Telephone, Approval, Facility, and Physician Codes, Health Care System

★ American Hospital Association (AHA) membership
☐ The Joint Commission accreditation
○ Healthcare Facilities Accreditation Program
◇ DNV Healthcare Inc. accreditation
⇧ Center for Improvement in Healthcare Quality Accreditation
△ Commission on Accreditation of Rehabilitation Facilities (CARF) accreditation

OH

TRINITY HEALTH SYSTEM (360211), 380 Summit Avenue, Zip 43952–2699; tel. 740/283–7000, (Includes TRINITY MEDICAL CENTER EAST, 380 Summit Avenue, Steubenville, Ohio, Zip 43952–2699, tel. 740/283–7000; TRINITY MEDICAL CENTER WEST, 4000 Johnson Road, Steubenville, Ohio, Zip 43952–2393, tel. 740/264–8000) (Data for 182 days)**A**1 2 10 13 **F**3 4 5 12 13 15 17 18 20 22 24 26 28 29 30 31 32 33 34 35 38 40 46 47 48 49 51 54 56 57 59 62 64 65 70 74 75 76 77 78 79 81 82 85 86 87 89 90 91 92 93 94 96 97 98 99 100 101 102 103 104 105 107 108 110 111 114 115 117 118 119 120 121 123 126 128 129 130 131 132 135 144 146 147 148 149 **P**6 **S** Catholic Health Initiatives, Englewood, CO
Primary Contact: Matthew Grimshaw, Market Chief Executive Officer
COO: JoAnn M Mulrooney R.N., Chief Operating Officer
CFO: Dave Werkin, Vice President Finance and Chief Financial Officer
CMO: Gray Goncz, Vice President of Medical Affairs
CIO: Tom Kiger, Director Information Systems
CHR: Lewis C Musso, Vice President Human Resources
Web address: www.trinityhealth.com
Control: Other not–for–profit (including NFP Corporation) **Service:** General medical and surgical

Staffed Beds: 320 **Admissions:** 4861 **Census:** 163 **Outpatient Visits:** 142468 **Births:** 268 **Total Expense ($000):** 117227 **Payroll Expense ($000):** 41856	

SYLVANIA—Lucas County

△ **PROMEDICA FLOWER HOSPITAL (360074)**, 5200 Harroun Road, Zip 43560–2196; tel. 419/824–1444 **A**1 2 3 5 7 10 **F**3 11 12 13 15 18 28 29 30 31 34 36 38 40 47 48 49 50 54 57 59 64 65 67 68 70 75 76 77 78 79 81 82 84 85 86 87 90 91 92 93 96 97 98 100 101 102 103 107 108 109 110 111 114 116 117 118 119 120 121 123 124 126 129 130 131 132 146 147 **S** ProMedica Health System, Toledo, OH
Primary Contact: Arturo Polizzi, President
CFO: Michael Browning, Chief Financial Officer
CMO: John Evanoff M.D., Vice President Medical Affairs
CIO: Lori Johnston, Chief Information Officer
CHR: Karen Strauss, Chief Human Resources Officer
CNO: Maurine Weis MSN, R.N., Vice President Nursing and Chief Nursing Officer
Web address: www.promedica.org
Control: Other not–for–profit (including NFP Corporation) **Service:** General medical and surgical

Staffed Beds: 295 **Admissions:** 11020 **Census:** 157 **Outpatient Visits:** 169761 **Births:** 843 **Total Expense ($000):** 217226 **Payroll Expense ($000):** 67951 **Personnel:** 1072	

REGENCY HOSPITAL OF TOLEDO (362036), 5220 Alexis Road, Zip 43560–2504; tel. 419/318–5700, (Nonreporting) **A**1 5 10 **S** Select Medical Corporation, Mechanicsburg, PA
Primary Contact: Gary Zaciewski, Chief Executive Officer
Web address: www.regencyhospital.com
Control: Corporation, Investor–owned (for–profit) **Service:** Acute long–term care hospital

Staffed Beds: 45	

TIFFIN—Seneca County

MERCY TIFFIN HOSPITAL (360089), 45 St Lawrence Drive, Zip 44883–8310; tel. 419/455–7000 **A**1 2 10 **F**3 12 13 15 18 19 20 28 29 30 31 34 35 36 40 46 49 50 51 56 57 59 62 64 68 70 74 75 76 77 78 79 81 82 83 84 85 86 87 89 93 97 107 108 110 111 115 118 119 129 130 132 133 134 135 145 146 147 148 149 **S** Mercy Health, Cincinnati, OH
Primary Contact: B Lynn. Detterman, President and Chief Executive Officer
CFO: Cynthia Dennison, Assistant Chief Financial Officer 3
CMO: Steven Bruhl, Chief Medical Officer
CHR: Diana Olson, Director Human Resources
CNO: Anne Zimmerman, Senior Director Patient Care Services and Chief Nursing Officer
Web address: www.mercyweb.org
Control: Church operated, Nongovernment, not–for–profit **Service:** General medical and surgical

Staffed Beds: 46 **Admissions:** 2007 **Census:** 16 **Outpatient Visits:** 87610 **Births:** 394 **Total Expense ($000):** 58884 **Payroll Expense ($000):** 12877 **Personnel:** 329	

TOLEDO—Lucas County

☐ **ADVANCED SPECIALTY HOSPITAL OF TOLEDO (362038)**, 1015 Garden Lake Parkway, Zip 43614–2779; tel. 419/381–0037 (Nonreporting) **A**1 3 10
Primary Contact: Kim Burkholder–McNutt, Chief Executive Officer
CFO: Troy Holmes, Director Finance
CMO: B Sarroui M.D., Chief of Staff
CHR: Lauren Avigdor, Director Human Resources
CNO: Bridgett Mitchell, Chief Clinical Officer
Web address: www.advancedspecialtyhospitals.com
Control: Corporation, Investor–owned (for–profit) **Service:** Acute long–term care hospital

Staffed Beds: 25	

MERCY ST. ANNE HOSPITAL (360262), 3404 West Sylvania Avenue, Zip 43623–4467; tel. 419/407–2663 **A**1 2 3 10 **F**3 8 15 17 18 20 22 24 28 29 30 31 34 35 36 38 40 42 45 54 56 57 59 64 65 68 70 74 75 78 79 81 82 84 85 86 87 92 102 107 108 110 111 115 119 126 129 130 132 135 146 147 149 **P**8 **S** Mercy Health, Cincinnati, OH
Primary Contact: Bradley J. Bertke, President and Chief Operating Officer
CFO: Michael Whipple, Chief Financial Officer
CMO: Herbert Stockard M.D., Chief Medical Officer
CIO: Rebecca S Sykes, Chief Information Officer
CNO: Barb Dianda–Martin, Chief Nursing Officer
Web address: www.mercyweb.org
Control: Church operated, Nongovernment, not–for–profit **Service:** General medical and surgical

Staffed Beds: 96 **Admissions:** 4875 **Census:** 51 **Outpatient Visits:** 183489 **Births:** 0 **Personnel:** 594	

MERCY ST. VINCENT MEDICAL CENTER (360112), 2213 Cherry Street, Zip 43608–2691; tel. 419/251–3232, (Includes MERCY CHILDREN'S HOSPITAL, 2213 Cherry Street, Toledo, Ohio, Zip 43608–2691, tel. 419/251–8000) **A**1 2 3 5 10 13 **F**3 7 8 11 12 13 15 16 18 19 20 21 22 23 24 25 26 29 30 31 32 34 35 37 38 39 40 41 42 43 44 45 46 48 49 50 51 53 54 55 56 57 58 59 60 61 64 65 66 68 70 72 74 75 76 77 78 79 81 82 83 84 85 86 87 88 89 92 93 97 107 108 110 111 114 115 118 119 126 129 130 131 132 134 135 146 147 148 **P**8 **S** Mercy Health, Cincinnati, OH
Primary Contact: Jeffrey Dempsey, President
CMO: Thomas Welch M.D., Chief Medical Officer
CHR: Gary George, Senior Vice President Human Resources
CNO: Barbara Martin, Chief Nursing Officer
Web address: www.mercyweb.org
Control: Church operated, Nongovernment, not–for–profit **Service:** General medical and surgical

Staffed Beds: 351 **Admissions:** 16708 **Census:** 207 **Outpatient Visits:** 233972 **Births:** 1375 **Personnel:** 2175	

☐ **NORTHWEST OHIO PSYCHIATRIC HOSPITAL (364014)**, 930 Detroit Avenue, Zip 43614–2701; tel. 419/381–1881 (Nonreporting) **A**1 3 10 **S** Ohio Department of Mental Health, Columbus, OH
Primary Contact: Tamara Junge, Chief Executive Officer
CMO: Thomas Osinowo M.D., Chief Clinical Officer
CIO: Michael Carter, Administrator Information Technology
CHR: Lois Mason–Williams, Director of Human Resources
CNO: Deb Duris, Director of Nursing
Web address: www.mh.state.oh.us/
Control: State, Government, Nonfederal **Service:** Psychiatric

Staffed Beds: 114	

PROMEDICA TOLEDO HOSPITAL (360068), 2142 North Cove Boulevard, Zip 43606–3896; tel. 419/291–4000, (Includes PROMEDICA WILDWOOD ORTHOPAEDIC AND SPINE HOSPITAL, 2901 North Reynolds Road, Toledo, Ohio, Zip 43615, tel. 419/578–7700; Arturo Polizzi, President; TOLEDO CHILDREN'S HOSPITAL, 2142 North Cove Boulevard, Toledo, Ohio, Zip 43606, tel. 419/251–8000) (Total facility includes 35 beds in nursing home–type unit) **A**1 2 3 5 10 13 **F**3 7 8 11 12 13 15 17 18 20 22 24 26 29 30 31 32 34 36 38 40 41 43 48 49 50 51 53 54 55 57 58 59 60 64 65 67 70 72 74 75 76 77 78 79 81 82 84 85 86 87 88 89 91 92 93 94 96 97 98 99 100 101 102 104 105 107 108 111 114 115 118 119 126 128 129 130 131 132 134 135 143 144 146 147 148 150 **S** ProMedica Health System, Toledo, OH
Primary Contact: Arturo Polizzi, President
CMO: Khurram Kamran M.D., Vice President Medical Affairs
CIO: Rose Ann Laureto, Chief Information Officer
CHR: Arturo Polizzi, Chief Human Resources Officer
Web address: www.promedica.org
Control: Other not–for–profit (including NFP Corporation) **Service:** General medical and surgical

Staffed Beds: 595 **Admissions:** 31963 **Census:** 433 **Outpatient Visits:** 702093 **Births:** 3747 **Total Expense ($000):** 781751 **Payroll Expense ($000):** 238262 **Personnel:** 3940	

REHABILITATION HOSPITAL OF NORTHWEST OHIO, 1455 West Medical Loop, Zip 43614; tel. 419/214–6600 (Nonreporting) **A**3 **S** Ernest Health, Inc., Albuquerque, NM
Primary Contact: Scott Williams, Chief Executive Officer
Control: Corporation, Investor–owned (for–profit) **Service:** Rehabilitation

Staffed Beds: 40	

Many Facility Codes have changed. Please refer to the AHA Guide Code Chart. © 2017 AHA Guide

✠ **THE UNIVERSITY OF TOLEDO MEDICAL CENTER (360048)**, 3000 Arlington Avenue, Zip 43614–2595; tel. 419/383–4000 **A**1 2 3 5 8 10 **F**3 8 11 15 17 18 20 22 24 26 28 29 30 31 32 34 35 36 37 38 39 40 43 44 45 46 47 48 49 50 51 53 54 55 57 58 59 60 61 64 65 68 70 74 75 77 78 79 81 82 84 85 86 87 90 91 92 93 94 96 97 98 99 100 101 102 103 104 105 107 108 110 111 114 115 116 117 118 119 120 121 123 124 126 129 130 131 132 134 135 138 146 147 148 149
Primary Contact: Daniel Barbee, Chief Executive Officer
CMO: Linda Speer M.D., Interim Chief Medical Officer
CIO: William McCreary, Vice President and Chief Information Officer
CHR: Jovita Thomas–Williams, Associate Vice President Human Resources
CNO: Moneca Smith, Chief Nursing Officer
Web address: www.utoledo.edu
Control: State, Government, Nonfederal **Service**: General medical and surgical

Staffed Beds: 267 **Admissions**: 11509 **Census**: 176 **Outpatient Visits**: 332267 **Births**: 0 **Total Expense ($000)**: 307418 **Payroll Expense ($000)**: 121340 **Personnel**: 2374

TROY—Miami County

✠ △ **UPPER VALLEY MEDICAL CENTER (360174)**, 3130 North County Road 25A, Zip 45373–1309; tel. 937/440–4000 **A**1 2 5 7 10 **F**3 13 15 18 20 28 29 30 31 34 35 36 38 40 41 44 45 48 49 50 54 55 56 57 58 59 60 61 64 65 68 70 73 74 75 76 77 78 79 80 81 85 86 87 90 92 93 96 98 100 101 102 103 104 107 108 110 111 114 115 118 119 126 129 130 131 132 135 141 145 146 147 148 149 **S** Premier Health, Dayton, OH
Primary Contact: Rebecca Rice, FACHE, Chief Executive Officer
CFO: Tim Snider, Senior Vice President for Finance
CMO: Jennifer Hauler D.O., Chief Medical Officer
CIO: James Kaiser, Site Director Information Technology
CHR: Kathy Boerger, Director Human Resources
CNO: Terry Fry R.N., Chief Nursing Officer
Web address: www.uvmc.com
Control: Other not–for–profit (including NFP Corporation) **Service**: General medical and surgical

Staffed Beds: 157 **Admissions**: 6734 **Census**: 65 **Outpatient Visits**: 83954 **Births**: 683 **Total Expense ($000)**: 141320 **Payroll Expense ($000)**: 60110 **Personnel**: 1009

UPPER SANDUSKY—Wyandot County

★ **WYANDOT MEMORIAL HOSPITAL (361329)**, 885 North Sandusky Avenue, Zip 43351–1098; tel. 419/294–4991 **A**10 18 **F**3 11 13 15 17 18 28 29 30 31 34 35 40 45 46 50 53 57 59 64 65 74 75 76 77 78 79 81 82 85 86 87 89 92 93 97 107 108 110 111 115 116 117 118 119 124 129 130 132 133 135 144 146 148 149 **P**6
Primary Contact: Joseph A. D'Ettorre, Chief Executive Officer
COO: Ty Shaull, Chief Operating Officer
CFO: Alan H Yeates, Vice President Fiscal Services
CHR: Vickie Underwood, Director Human Resources
CNO: Marty Gray R.N., Director of Nursing
Web address: www.wyandotmemorial.org
Control: Hospital district or authority, Government, Nonfederal **Service**: General medical and surgical

Staffed Beds: 25 **Admissions**: 873 **Census**: 11 **Outpatient Visits**: 65018 **Births**: 128 **Total Expense ($000)**: 42022 **Payroll Expense ($000)**: 15060 **Personnel**: 224

URBANA—Champaign County

★ **MERCY MEMORIAL HOSPITAL (361312)**, 904 Scioto Street, Zip 43078–2200; tel. 937/653–5231, (Nonreporting) **A**10 18 **S** Mercy Health, Cincinnati, OH
Primary Contact: Matthew T. Caldwell, President and Chief Executive Officer
Web address: www.health–partners.org
Control: Church operated, Nongovernment, not–for–profit **Service**: General medical and surgical

Staffed Beds: 25

VAN WERT—Van Wert County

✠ **VAN WERT COUNTY HOSPITAL (360071)**, 1250 South Washington Street, Zip 45891–2599; tel. 419/238–2390 **A**1 5 10 **F**8 13 15 28 29 34 35 40 48 50 53 54 57 59 62 64 70 76 77 79 81 85 87 89 91 93 107 108 113 119 127 129 130 135 146 **P**7 8
Primary Contact: James W. Pope, FACHE, President and Chief Executive Officer
CFO: Michael T Holliday, Vice President Fiscal and Administrative Services
CMO: Charles Hoehn, President, Medical Staff
CIO: Brett Taylor, Manager Information
CNO: Shelia Kay Brokenshire, Vice President of Nursing
Web address: www.vanwerthospital.org
Control: Other not–for–profit (including NFP Corporation) **Service**: General medical and surgical

Staffed Beds: 34 **Admissions**: 743 **Census**: 8 **Outpatient Visits**: 126995 **Births**: 150 **Total Expense ($000)**: 38989 **Payroll Expense ($000)**: 11177 **Personnel**: 321

WARREN—Trumbull County

✠ △ **HILLSIDE REHABILITATION HOSPITAL (363026)**, 8747 Squires Lane NE, Zip 44484–1649; tel. 330/841–3700, (Nonreporting) **A**1 5 7 10 **S** Steward Health Care System, LLC, Boston, MA
Primary Contact: Linda Case, Administrator
CMO: Joseph Cerimele D.O., Medical Director
CIO: Barry Fitts, Chief Information Officer
CHR: Jody Roman, Chief Human Resource Officer
CNO: Susan Joy, Chief Nursing Officer
Web address: www.valleycareofohio.steward.org
Control: Corporation, Investor–owned (for–profit) **Service**: Rehabilitation

Staffed Beds: 65

✠ **MERCY HEALTH – ST. JOSEPH WARREN HOSPITAL (360161)**, 667 Eastland Avenue SE, Zip 44484–4531, Mailing Address: 627 Eastland Avenue, 44484–4531; tel. 330/841–4000 **A**1 2 3 10 13 **F**3 5 8 11 12 13 15 28 29 30 31 34 35 40 42 43 45 46 49 50 51 54 58 59 64 66 67 68 70 74 75 76 77 78 79 81 82 83 84 85 87 89 92 93 102 107 108 109 110 111 114 115 116 117 118 119 120 121 123 124 126 129 130 135 144 146 147 148 149 **S** Mercy Health, Cincinnati, OH
Primary Contact: Kathy Cook, FACHE, MSN, President
COO: Donald E. Koenig Jr, Chief Operating Officer
CMO: Nicholas Kreatsoulas, Vice President Medical Affairs
Web address: www.hmpartners.org
Control: Church operated, Nongovernment, not–for–profit **Service**: General medical and surgical

Staffed Beds: 136 **Admissions**: 8215 **Census**: 93 **Outpatient Visits**: 191696 **Births**: 890 **Total Expense ($000)**: 150526 **Payroll Expense ($000)**: 44324 **Personnel**: 637

✠ **TRUMBULL MEMORIAL HOSPITAL (360055)**, 1350 East Market Street, Zip 44483–6628; tel. 330/841–9011, (Nonreporting) **A**1 2 5 10 **S** Steward Health Care System, LLC, Boston, MA
Primary Contact: Ronald L. Bierman, Chief Executive Officer
CMO: Thomas L James M.D., Chief Medical Officer
CIO: Barry Fitts, Chief Information Officer
CHR: Robert Sincich, Vice President Human Resources
CNO: Melissa Bennett, Chief Nursing Officer
Web address: www.trumbullmemorial.org/?_ga=2.209137234.1564767671.1497292183–315051339.1497292183
Control: Corporation, Investor–owned (for–profit) **Service**: General medical and surgical

Staffed Beds: 292

WARRENSVILLE HEIGHTS—Cuyahoga County

REGENCY HOSPITAL CLEVELAND EAST(Nonreporting) (Includes REGENCY HOSPITAL OF CLEVELAND – WEST, 6990 Engle Road, Middleburg Heights, Ohio, Zip 44130–3420, tel. 440/202–4200; Timothy Rolsen, Chief Executive Officer) **A**1 10
Web address: www.regencyhospital.com/
✠ **REGENCY HOSPITAL CLEVELAND EAST (362029)**, 4200 Interchange Corporate Center Road, Zip 44128–5631; tel. 216/910–3800, (Nonreporting) (Includes REGENCY HOSPITAL OF CLEVELAND – WEST, 6990 Engle Road, Middleburg Heights, Ohio, Zip 44130–3420, tel. 440/202–4200; Timothy Rolsen, Chief Executive Officer) **A**1 10 **S** Select Medical Corporation, Mechanicsburg, PA
Primary Contact: Thomas Knoske, Chief Executive Officer
Web address: www.regencyhospital.com/
Control: Corporation, Investor–owned (for–profit) **Service**: Acute long–term care hospital

Staffed Beds: 87

✠ **SOUTH POINTE HOSPITAL (360144)**, 20000 Harvard Road, Zip 44122–6805; tel. 216/491–6000 **A**1 2 3 10 13 **F**3 15 18 26 28 29 30 31 34 35 36 38 39 40 44 50 51 54 55 56 57 58 59 60 61 64 65 66 68 70 74 75 77 78 79 81 82 84 85 86 87 92 93 97 100 102 107 108 110 111 119 130 131 132 135 143 144 145 146 148 **S** Cleveland Clinic Health System, Cleveland, OH
Primary Contact: Robert S. Juhasz, D.O., President
COO: Andrea Jacobs, Chief Operating Officer
CFO: Lindsay Bird, Director Finance
CMO: Arun Gupta M.D., Vice President Medical Affairs
CIO: Ralph A Cagna, Director Information Technology
CHR: Doris A. Zajec, Director Human Resources
Web address: www.southpointehospital.com
Control: Other not–for–profit (including NFP Corporation) **Service**: General medical and surgical

Staffed Beds: 173 **Admissions**: 6346 **Census**: 84 **Outpatient Visits**: 112924 **Births**: 0 **Total Expense ($000)**: 126364 **Payroll Expense ($000)**: 50215 **Personnel**: 778

Hospital, Medicare Provider Number, Address, Telephone, Approval, Facility, and Physician Codes, Health Care System

★ American Hospital Association (AHA) membership
□ The Joint Commission accreditation
○ Healthcare Facilities Accreditation Program
◇ DNV Healthcare Inc. accreditation
⇑ Center for Improvement in Healthcare Quality Accreditation
△ Commission on Accreditation of Rehabilitation Facilities (CARF) accreditation

OH

WASHINGTON COURT HOUSE—Fayette County

☒ **FAYETTE COUNTY MEMORIAL HOSPITAL (361331)**, 1430 Columbus Avenue, Zip 43160–1791; tel. 740/335–1210, **A**1 10 18
Primary Contact: D Michael. Diener, Chief Executive Officer
COO: Emily Johnson M.D., Chief of Staff
CFO: Trent Lemle, Chief Financial Officer
CIO: Bruce Denen, Manager Data Processing
CHR: Earlene Christensen, Director Human Resources
CNO: Tammie Wilson R.N., MSN, Chief Nursing Officer
Web address: www.fcmh.org
Control: County, Government, Nonfederal **Service**: General medical and surgical

Staffed Beds: 25 **Admissions**: 1005 **Census**: 12

WAUSEON—Fulton County

☒ **FULTON COUNTY HEALTH CENTER (361333)**, 725 South Shoop Avenue, Zip 43567–1701; tel. 419/335–2015, (Total facility includes 71 beds in nursing home–type unit) **A**1 2 5 10 18 **F**3 8 11 12 13 15 18 26 28 29 31 34 40 53 57 59 67 69 70 75 76 77 78 79 81 87 89 93 98 101 102 103 104 105 107 108 111 115 118 119 128 129 130 131 132 135 146 148 149
Primary Contact: Patti Finn, Chief Executive Officer
COO: Patti Finn, Chief Executive Officer
CFO: Jenee Seibert, Director Finance
CIO: Larry Hefflinger, Director Information Systems
CHR: Kristy Snyder, Director Human Resources
CNO: Tiffany Siegel, Chief Nursing Officer
Web address: www.fultoncountyhealthcenter.org
Control: Other not–for–profit (including NFP Corporation) **Service**: General medical and surgical

Staffed Beds: 106 **Admissions**: 1524 **Census**: 79 **Outpatient Visits**: 183993 **Births**: 226 **Total Expense ($000)**: 64268 **Payroll Expense ($000)**: 23586 **Personnel**: 686

WAVERLY—Pike County

ADENA PIKE MEDICAL CENTER (360047), 100 Dawn Lane, Zip 45690–9138; tel. 740/947–2186 **A**10 18 **F**3 18 29 30 34 35 40 41 45 50 57 59 79 81 82 86 93 104 107 108 114 118 130 131 133 135 146 **P**6 **S** Adena Health System, Chillicothe, OH
Primary Contact: David M. Zanni, Administrator
COO: Eric Cecava, Chief Operating Officer
CFO: Lisa Carlson, Chief Financial Officer
CMO: John Fortney, Chief Medical Officer
CIO: Tom Bialorucki, Chief Information Officer
CHR: Jay D. Justice, Chief Human Resources Officer
CNO: Kathy Dye, Chief Nursing Officer
Web address: www.adena.org
Control: Other not–for–profit (including NFP Corporation) **Service**: General medical and surgical

Staffed Beds: 25 **Admissions**: 475 **Census**: 5 **Outpatient Visits**: 33760 **Births**: 0 **Total Expense ($000)**: 16123 **Payroll Expense ($000)**: 6510 **Personnel**: 136

WEST CHESTER—Butler County

☐ **BECKETT SPRINGS (364051)**, 8614 Shepherd Farm Drive, Zip 45069; tel. 513/942–9500 (Nonreporting) **A**1 10
Primary Contact: Phil Sheridan, Chief Executive Officer
Web address: www.springstone.com/hospitals.stmhl
Control: Corporation, Investor–owned (for–profit) **Service**: Psychiatric

Staffed Beds: 48

☒ **WEST CHESTER HOSPITAL (360354)**, 7700 University Drive, Zip 45069–2505; tel. 513/298–3000, (Includes WEST CHESTER HOSPITAL SURGICAL CENTER, 7750 University Court, West Chester, Ohio, Zip 45069, tel. 513/475–8300; Tom G Daskalakis, Chief Administrative Officer) **A**1 3 10 **F**3 9 12 13 15 18 20 22 26 29 30 31 34 35 37 38 40 41 43 44 45 46 47 48 49 50 51 54 57 58 59 60 61 63 64 68 70 73 74 75 76 77 78 79 80 81 82 84 85 86 87 91 92 100 107 108 110 111 114 115 116 117 119 126 129 130 131 132 134 135 141 145 146 147 148 149 150 **P**6 **S** UC Health, Cincinnati, OH
Primary Contact: Tom G. Daskalakis, Chief Administrative Officer
CFO: Karen Shadowens, Director Finance and Chief Financial Officer
CIO: Jay Brown, Senior Vice President, Chief Information Officer
CHR: Jack Talbot, Director, Human Resources
CNO: Patrick Baker R.N., Vice President, Chief Nursing Officer
Web address: www.uchealth.com/westchesterhospital
Control: Other not–for–profit (including NFP Corporation) **Service**: General medical and surgical

Staffed Beds: 182 **Admissions**: 9091 **Census**: 96 **Outpatient Visits**: 223822 **Births**: 676 **Total Expense ($000)**: 188853 **Payroll Expense ($000)**: 58438 **Personnel**: 976

WESTERVILLE—Franklin County

☒ **MOUNT CARMEL ST. ANN'S (360012)**, 500 South Cleveland Avenue, Zip 43081–8998; tel. 614/898–4000 **A**1 2 3 5 10 **F**3 11 13 15 18 20 22 24 26 28 29 30 31 34 35 37 40 44 45 47 48 49 50 51 54 55 57 58 59 61 63 64 65 66 68 70 74 75 76 77 78 79 81 85 86 87 91 93 96 97 100 101 102 107 108 109 110 111 114 115 116 118 119 120 121 123 124 126 130 131 132 145 146 147 148 **P**6 8 **S** Trinity Health, Livonia, MI
Primary Contact: Kim Unhee, President
Web address: www.mountcarmelhealth.com
Control: Church operated, Nongovernment, not–for–profit **Service**: General medical and surgical

Staffed Beds: 281 **Admissions**: 21182 **Census**: 169 **Outpatient Visits**: 163582 **Births**: 4235 **Total Expense ($000)**: 298180 **Payroll Expense ($000)**: 98038 **Personnel**: 1493

WESTLAKE—Cuyahoga County

☒ **ST. JOHN MEDICAL CENTER (360123)**, 29000 Center Ridge Road, Zip 44145–5293; tel. 440/835–8000 **A**1 2 3 10 13 **F**3 8 13 15 17 18 20 22 24 26 28 29 30 31 34 35 39 40 43 44 45 46 47 49 50 51 54 56 57 59 64 65 68 70 71 74 75 76 78 79 80 81 84 85 86 87 89 92 93 100 107 108 110 111 114 115 119 130 132 143 144 146 147 149 **S** University Hospitals, Cleveland, OH
Primary Contact: Robert G. David, President
CFO: Allen R Tracy, Senior Vice President and Chief Financial Officer
CMO: Michael Dobrovich M.D., Chief Medical Officer
CIO: James H Carroll, Chief Information Officer
CHR: Gary Lazroff, Vice President Human Resources
Web address: www.sjws.net
Control: Other not–for–profit (including NFP Corporation) **Service**: General medical and surgical

Staffed Beds: 191 **Admissions**: 9891 **Census**: 94 **Outpatient Visits**: 199865 **Births**: 882 **Total Expense ($000)**: 150702 **Payroll Expense ($000)**: 62021 **Personnel**: 965

ST. JOHN WEST SHORE HOSPITAL See St. John Medical Center

WILLARD—Huron County

☒ **MERCY HEALTH – WILLARD HOSPITAL (361310)**, 1100 Neal Zick Road, Zip 44890–9287; tel. 419/964–5000 **A**1 10 18 **F**3 5 7 15 18 28 29 30 31 34 35 40 46 57 59 68 70 74 75 77 78 79 81 84 85 87 89 93 107 111 114 119 129 130 131 132 133 135 143 145 146 147 149 **S** Mercy Health, Cincinnati, OH
Primary Contact: B Lynn. Detterman, President and Chief Executive Officer
CMO: Christopher Bohach DPM, Chief of Staff
CHR: Diana Olson, Chief Human Resources Officer
Web address: www.mercyweb.org
Control: Church operated, Nongovernment, not–for–profit **Service**: General medical and surgical

Staffed Beds: 20 **Admissions**: 574 **Census**: 7 **Outpatient Visits**: 41066 **Births**: 0 **Total Expense ($000)**: 27280 **Payroll Expense ($000)**: 7148 **Personnel**: 162

WILLOUGHBY—Lake County

☐ **WINDSOR–LAURELWOOD CENTER FOR BEHAVIORAL MEDICINE (364029)**, 35900 Euclid Avenue, Zip 44094–4648; tel. 440/953–3000 **A**1 10 **F**4 5 64 98 99 100 101 103 104 105 130 132 143 **P**5 6 **S** Universal Health Services, Inc., King of Prussia, PA
Primary Contact: Ric McAllister, Chief Executive Officer
COO: Brenda Bailey, Assistant Administrator
CFO: Robin Stough, Chief Financial Officer
CMO: Leonard Barley M.D., Chief Medical Officer
CIO: Cory Wheatcraft, Information Technology and Purchasing Officer
CHR: Pam Connell, Manager Human Resources
CNO: Debra Schaefer, Chief Nursing Officer
Web address: www.windsorlaurelwood.com
Control: Corporation, Investor–owned (for–profit) **Service**: Psychiatric

Staffed Beds: 159 **Admissions**: 4936 **Census**: 121 **Outpatient Visits**: 11714 **Births**: 0 **Total Expense ($000)**: 32168 **Payroll Expense ($000)**: 13103

WILMINGTON—Clinton County

☐ **CLINTON MEMORIAL HOSPITAL (360175)**, 610 West Main Street, Zip 45177–2125; tel. 937/382–6611, (Nonreporting) **A**1 2 5 10 **S** RCCH HealthCare Partners, Brentwood, TN
Primary Contact: Gregory A. Nielsen, FACHE, Chief Executive Officer
CFO: Bradley Boggus, Chief Financial Officer
CIO: Ray Doherty, Director Information Technology
CHR: Jan Blair, Director Human Resources
CNO: Sheila Martin, Chief Nursing Officer
Web address: www.cmhregional.com
Control: Corporation, Investor–owned (for–profit) **Service**: General medical and surgical

Staffed Beds: 102

Many Facility Codes have changed. Please refer to the AHA Guide Code Chart. © 2017 AHA Guide

WOOSTER—Wayne County

△ ⇑ **WOOSTER COMMUNITY HOSPITAL (360036)**, 1761 Beall Avenue, Zip 44691–2342; tel. 330/263–8100, (Nonreporting) **A**2 5 7 10 19 21 **S** QHR, Brentwood, TN
Primary Contact: William E. Sheron, Chief Executive Officer
Web address: www.woosterhospital.org
Control: City, Government, Nonfederal **Service:** General medical and surgical

Staffed Beds: 152

WRIGHT—PATTERSON AFB–Greene County

⊠ **WRIGHT PATTERSON MEDICAL CENTER**, 4881 Sugar Maple Drive, Zip 45433–5529; tel. 937/257–9144, (Nonreporting) **A**1 2 3 5 **S** Department of the Air Force, Washington, DC
Primary Contact: Colonel Brent J. Erickson, Administrator
COO: ColonelBrent J Erickson, Administrator
CFO: MajorKelly Lesnick, Resource Manager Flight Commander
CMO: Gregory Sweitzer, Chief Medical Officer
CIO: John Beighle, Flight Chief Medical Information Systems
CHR: Hubert Chatman, Chief Civilian Personnel
CNO: ColonelDaniel Gerke, Chief Nursing Officer
Web address: www.wpafb.af.mil/units/wpmc/
Control: Air Force, Government, federal **Service:** General medical and surgical

Staffed Beds: 62

XENIA—Greene County

★ ○ **GREENE MEMORIAL HOSPITAL (360026)**, 1141 North Monroe Drive, Zip 45385–1600; tel. 937/352–2000 **A**2 5 10 11 **F**3 11 15 18 28 29 30 31 34 35 38 40 43 44 45 46 48 50 51 53 54 56 57 59 61 64 68 70 74 75 77 78 79 81 82 85 86 87 91 93 96 102 107 108 110 111 114 118 119 127 129 130 132 135 146 148 **S** Kettering Health Network, Dayton, OH
Primary Contact: Rick A. Dodds, President
CFO: Ron D Connovich, Chief Financial Officer
CMO: David Small M.D., Chief Medical Officer
CIO: Andy Lehman, Senior Vice President Technology & Analytics
CHR: Jeff Jones, Director Human Resources
CNO: Brenda Kuhn Ph.D., R.N., FACHE, Chief Nursing Officer
Web address: www.ketteringhealth.org/greene
Control: Church operated, Nongovernment, not–for–profit **Service:** General medical and surgical

Staffed Beds: 49 Admissions: 2399 Census: 25 Outpatient Visits: 98548 Births: 0 Total Expense ($000): 62124 Payroll Expense ($000): 26161 Personnel: 297

YOUNGSTOWN—Mahoning County

⊠ △ **MERCY HEALTH – ST. ELIZABETH YOUNGSTOWN HOSPITAL (360064)**, 1044 Belmont Avenue, Zip 44504–1096, Mailing Address: P.O.Box 1790, 44501–1790; tel. 330/746–7211 **A**1 2 3 5 7 10 **F**1 3 7 8 11 14 15 17 18 20 22 24 26 28 29 30 31 34 35 37 39 40 42 43 44 45 46 49 50 51 53 54 56 57 58 59 60 61 64 66 68 70 71 74 75 77 78 79 81 82 84 85 86 87 88 89 90 92 93 96 97 98 100 101 102 103 104 105 107 110 111 114 115 116 117 118 119 120 121 123 126 129 130 131 132 135 143 146 147 148 149 **S** Mercy Health, Cincinnati, OH
Primary Contact: Donald E. Kline, President and Chief Executive Officer
COO: Donald E. Koenig Jr, Executive Vice President and Regional Chief Operating Officer, President, St. Elizabeth Youngstown Hospital
CFO: Anthony Seminaro, Chief Financial Officer
CMO: Nicholas Kreatsoulas, Senior Vice President and Chief Medical Officer and Chief Quality Officer
CIO: Maureen Kordupel, Director Relationship Manager
CHR: Molly Seals, System Vice President, HR Program Delivery
CNO: Catherine L. Tolbert FACHE, MSN, R.N., Chief Nursing Officer
Web address: www.mercy.com
Control: Church operated, Nongovernment, not–for–profit **Service:** General medical and surgical

Staffed Beds: 379 Admissions: 18319 Census: 256 Outpatient Visits: 295601 Births: 0 Total Expense ($000): 328543 Payroll Expense ($000): 100898 Personnel: 1909

NORTHSIDE MEDICAL CENTER See Northside Medical Center

⊠ **SELECT SPECIALTY HOSPITAL–YOUNGSTOWN (362024)**, 1044 Belmont Avenue, Zip 44504–1006; tel. 330/480–2349, (Nonreporting) (Includes SELECT SPECIALTY HOSPITAL–YOUNGSTOWN, BOARDMAN CAMPUS, 667 Eastland Avenue SE, Warren, Ohio, Zip 44484–4503, tel. 330/729–1700) **A**1 10 **S** Select Medical Corporation, Mechanicsburg, PA
Primary Contact: Jodi Costello, Chief Executive Officer
Web address: www.selectspecialtyhospitals.com/company/locations/youngstown.aspx
Control: Corporation, Investor–owned (for–profit) **Service:** Acute long–term care hospital

Staffed Beds: 56

☐ **SURGICAL HOSPITAL AT SOUTHWOODS (360352)**, 7630 Southern Boulevard, Zip 44512–5633; tel. 330/729–8000 (Nonreporting) **A**1 10
Primary Contact: Ed Muransky, Owner
Web address: www.surgeryatsouthwoods.com/
Control: Individual, Investor–owned (for–profit) **Service:** Surgical

Staffed Beds: 12

YOUNGSTOWN—Trumbull County

☐ **BELMONT PINES HOSPITAL (364038)**, 615 Churchill–Hubbard Road, Zip 44505–1379; tel. 330/759–2700, (Nonreporting) **A**1 10 **S** Universal Health Services, Inc., King of Prussia, PA
Primary Contact: Lisa Cocca, Chief Executive Officer
CFO: Robin Stough, Chief Financial Officer
CMO: Phillip Maiden M.D., Medical Director
Web address: www.belmontpines.com
Control: Corporation, Investor–owned (for–profit) **Service:** Psychiatric

Staffed Beds: 96

⊠ **NORTHSIDE MEDICAL CENTER (360141)**, 500 Gypsy Lane, Zip 44504–1315; tel. 330/884–1000, (Nonreporting) (Includes NORTHSIDE MEDICAL CENTER, 500 Gypsy Lane, Youngstown, Ohio, Zip 44501–0240, tel. 330/747–1444) **A**1 3 5 10 **S** Steward Health Care System, LLC, Boston, MA
Primary Contact: K Robert. Bauer Jr, Interim Chief Executive Officer
CMO: Jay Osborne M.D., Senior Vice President Medical Affairs
CHR: Lavern H Carrera, Senior Vice President Human Resources
Web address: www.northsidemedicalcenter.net
Control: Corporation, Investor–owned (for–profit) **Service:** General medical and surgical

Staffed Beds: 373

ZANESVILLE—Muskingum County

★ ○ **GENESIS HEALTHCARE SYSTEM (360039)**, 2951 Maple Avenue, Zip 43701–1406; tel. 740/454–5000, (Includes BETHESDA HOSPITAL, 2951 Maple Avenue, Zanesville, Ohio, Zip 43701–1465, tel. 614/454–4000; GOOD SAMARITAN MEDICAL AND REHABILITATION CENTER, 800 Forest Avenue, Zanesville, Ohio, Zip 43701–2881, tel. 614/454–5000) **A**2 5 10 11 **F**3 5 8 9 11 13 15 17 18 20 22 24 26 28 29 30 31 32 34 35 40 43 44 45 46 47 48 50 51 54 57 58 59 60 63 64 65 68 70 73 74 75 76 77 78 79 81 82 84 85 86 87 89 91 92 93 94 96 98 99 100 101 102 103 104 105 107 108 109 110 111 114 115 116 117 118 119 120 121 123 124 126 129 130 131 132 135 144 146 147 148 **P**6 8 **S** Franciscan Sisters of Christian Charity Sponsored Ministries, Inc., Manitowoc, WI
Primary Contact: Matthew J. Perry, President and Chief Executive Officer
COO: Richard S Helsper, Chief Operating Officer
CFO: Paul Masterson, Chief Financial Officer
CMO: Dan Scheerer M.D., Chief Medical Officer
CIO: Edmund J Romito, Chief Information Officer
CHR: Dianna LeVeck, Chief Human Resources Officer
CNO: Abby Nguyen R.N., Chief Nursing Officer
Web address: www.genesishcs.org
Control: Other not–for–profit (including NFP Corporation) **Service:** General medical and surgical

Staffed Beds: 321 Admissions: 14200 Census: 161 Outpatient Visits: 440049 Births: 1557 Total Expense ($000): 345569 Payroll Expense ($000): 120951 Personnel: 2836

OK

OKLAHOMA

ADA—Pontotoc County

☒ **CHICKASAW NATION MEDICAL CENTER (370180)**, 1921 Stonecipher Drive, Zip 74820–3439; tel. 580/436–3980 **A**1 10 13 **F**3 5 7 8 13 15 18 29 30 34 38 39 40 43 45 50 53 54 57 58 59 60 61 64 65 66 68 69 70 75 76 79 81 82 85 86 87 89 91 92 93 97 99 100 104 107 110 111 115 119 127 130 132 135 143 144 146 147 148
Primary Contact: Judy Goforth. Parker, Ph.D., Secretary of Health
CFO: Marty Wafford, Under Secretary of Support and Programs
CMO: Richard McClain M.D., Chief Medical Officer
CIO: Desiree Traylor, Chief Information Officer
CHR: Jalinda Kelley, Secretary of Interior Services
CNO: Jerod Waters, Chief Nursing Officer
Web address: www.chickasaw.net
Control: PHS, Indian Service, Government, federal **Service**: General medical and surgical

Staffed Beds: 72 Admissions: 4497 Census: 34 Outpatient Visits: 594055 Births: 912 Total Expense ($000): 217899 Payroll Expense ($000): 95355 Personnel: 537

☒ **MERCY HOSPITAL ADA (370020)**, 430 North Monte Vista, Zip 74820–4610; tel. 580/332–2323 **A**1 2 3 10 **F**3 7 11 13 15 18 29 30 31 34 35 40 43 44 45 49 50 59 64 68 69 70 72 75 76 77 78 79 81 82 85 86 87 89 90 91 93 98 100 101 103 107 108 110 111 114 116 117 119 120 121 124 127 129 130 131 132 133 146 148 149 **P**6 **S** Mercy, Chesterfield, MO
Primary Contact: Lori Wightman, R.N., MSN, FACHE, President
COO: Daniel J Coats, Vice President Operations
CFO: Mary Garber, Vice President Finance
CMO: Imtiaz Ahmed, Chief of Staff
CHR: Katrina Godfrey, Director Human Resources
CNO: Karen Sweeney MSN, R.N., Vice President, Chief Nursing Officer
Web address: www.mercy.net/ada
Control: Church operated, Nongovernment, not–for–profit
Service: General medical and surgical

Staffed Beds: 156 Admissions: 3491 Census: 51 Outpatient Visits: 90950 Births: 543 Total Expense ($000): 79419 Payroll Expense ($000): 35020 Personnel: 581

☐ **ROLLING HILLS HOSPITAL (374016)**, 1000 Rolling Hills Lane, Zip 74820–9415; tel. 580/436–3600 **A**1 10 **F**98 101 102 103 106 135 **P**6 **S** Acadia Healthcare Company, Inc., Franklin, TN
Primary Contact: Anthony Guild, Chief Executive Officer
CMO: Robert Morton M.D., Medical Director
CIO: Sherry Barnes, Director Health Information and Quality Management
CHR: Timothy Blackwell, Manager Human Resources
Web address: www.rollinghillshospital.com
Control: Corporation, Investor–owned (for–profit) **Service**: Psychiatric

Staffed Beds: 92 Admissions: 1628 Census: 72 Outpatient Visits: 0 Births: 0 Total Expense ($000): 14301 Payroll Expense ($000): 6742 Personnel: 156

ALTUS—Jackson County

☒ **JACKSON COUNTY MEMORIAL HOSPITAL (370022)**, 1200 East Pecan Street, Zip 73521–6192, Mailing Address: P.O.Box 8190, 73522–8190; tel. 580/379–5000 **A**1 3 10 **F**3 10 11 13 15 29 30 34 35 40 43 45 49 56 57 59 62 63 64 65 70 75 76 77 79 81 85 86 87 93 100 101 103 104 107 110 111 114 119 129 130 131 132 133 135 145 146 147 148 149 **P**6
Primary Contact: Steve L. Hartgraves, President and Chief Executive Officer
COO: Casey D. Miranda, Executive Vice President and Chief Operating Officer
CFO: Nancy Davidson, Senior Vice President and Chief Financial Officer
CMO: M. George Zakhary M.D., Chief of Staff
CIO: Dena Daniel, Director Information Systems
CHR: Richard Pope, Vice President Human Resources
CNO: Kay Bolding R.N., MS, Vice President Patient Care Services and Chief Nursing Officer
Web address: www.jcmh.com
Control: Hospital district or authority, Government, Nonfederal **Service**: General medical and surgical

Staffed Beds: 49 Admissions: 2573 Census: 25 Outpatient Visits: 147821 Births: 447 Total Expense ($000): 66774 Payroll Expense ($000): 33340 Personnel: 649

ALVA—Woods County

☒ **SHARE MEDICAL CENTER (370080)**, 800 Share Drive, Zip 73717–3618, Mailing Address: P.O.Box 727, 73717–0727; tel. 580/327–2800, (Total facility includes 65 beds in nursing home–type unit) **A**10 20 **F**3 15 29 30 40 45 57 59 64 65 67 69 81 87 93 97 100 104 107 110 119 129 130 133 146 148 149
Primary Contact: Kandice K. Allen, R.N., Chief Executive Officer
CFO: Kevin O'Brien, Chief Financial Officer
CMO: Elizabeth Kinzic M.D., Chief of Staff
CIO: Alan Vaughan, Director Information Technology
CHR: Mary Herold, Director Human Resources
CNO: Regina Wilson R.N., Director of Nursing
Web address: www.smcok.com
Control: Hospital district or authority, Government, Nonfederal **Service**: General medical and surgical

Staffed Beds: 90 Admissions: 313 Census: 53 Outpatient Visits: 20612 Births: 0 Total Expense ($000): 13072 Payroll Expense ($000): 5699

ANADARKO—Caddo County

PHYSICIANS' HOSPITAL IN ANADARKO (371314), 1002 Central Boulevard East, Zip 73005–4496; tel. 405/247–2551 **A**10 18 **F**1 3 4 8 11 16 17 29 30 34 35 40 41 45 47 57 64 65 67 70 73 76 77 81 82 85 88 89 90 93 98 107 114 128 130 133 146 149 **S** First Physicians Capital Group, Inc., Oklahoma City, OK
Primary Contact: Travis A. Villani, FACHE, Chief Executive Officer and Administrator
Web address: www.anadarkohospital.com
Control: Other not–for–profit (including NFP Corporation) **Service**: General medical and surgical

Staffed Beds: 25 Admissions: 196 Census: 7 Outpatient Visits: 9625 Births: 3 Personnel: 76

ANTLERS—Pushmataha County

PUSHMATAHA HOSPITAL (370083), 510 East Main Street, Zip 74523–3262, Mailing Address: P.O.Box 518, 74523–0518; tel. 580/298–3341 **A**10 **F**3 8 11 34 39 40 45 57 59 64 65 81 107 119 133
Primary Contact: Nick Rowland, Chief Executive Officer
COO: Nick Rowland, Chief Operating Officer
CFO: Rory Ward, Chief Financial Officer
CMO: G Wayne Flatt D.O., Chief Medical Director
CHR: Paula Schalski, Director Human Resources
CNO: Marla Barnes, Director of Nursing
Web address: www.pushhospital.com
Control: City–county, Government, Nonfederal **Service**: General medical and surgical

Staffed Beds: 23 Admissions: 451 Census: 4 Births: 0

ARDMORE—Carter County

☒ **MERCY HOSPITAL ARDMORE (370047)**, 1011 14th Avenue NW, Zip 73401–1828; tel. 580/223–5400 **A**1 10 **F**3 11 13 15 18 20 22 28 29 30 31 34 35 40 43 44 45 47 48 49 50 57 59 62 64 68 70 74 75 76 77 78 79 81 82 84 85 86 87 89 90 93 98 103 107 108 110 111 114 117 118 119 120 121 123 126 129 130 146 148 149 **P**6 **S** Mercy, Chesterfield, MO
Primary Contact: Daryle Voss, FACHE, President and Chief Executive Officer
CFO: Karen Hendren, Vice President of Finance and Operations
CMO: Pam Kimbrough M.D., Vice President Medical Affairs
CHR: Melinda Sharum, Director Human Resources
CNO: Debra Pender MS, R.N., Vice President Nursing
Web address: www.mercyok.net
Control: Church operated, Nongovernment, not–for–profit **Service**: General medical and surgical

Staffed Beds: 190 Admissions: 6627 Census: 80 Outpatient Visits: 124490 Births: 872 Total Expense ($000): 136302 Payroll Expense ($000): 50417 Personnel: 807

ATOKA—Atoka County

ATOKA COUNTY MEDICAL CENTER (371300), 1590 West Liberty Road, Zip 74525–1621, Mailing Address: PO Box 1107, 74525–1621; tel. 580/889–3333, (Nonreporting) **A**10 18
Primary Contact: Traci Walker, Chief Executive Officer
CMO: Ted Rowland, Chief of Medical Staff
CHR: Stacy Sharp, Coordinator Human Resources
CNO: David Lively, Chief Nursing Officer
Web address: www.atokamedicalcenter.org
Control: Hospital district or authority, Government, Nonfederal **Service**: General medical and surgical

Staffed Beds: 25

Many Facility Codes have changed. Please refer to the AHA Guide Code Chart. © 2017 AHA Guide

BARTLESVILLE—Washington County

★ ⇧ **JANE PHILLIPS MEDICAL CENTER (370018)**, 3500 East Frank Phillips Boulevard, Zip 74006–2411; tel. 918/333–7200 **A**3 5 10 21 **F**3 8 11 13 15 17 18 20 22 24 28 29 30 31 34 35 40 43 46 49 50 51 53 57 58 59 60 61 64 68 70 74 75 76 77 78 79 81 82 84 85 86 87 90 92 93 96 98 102 103 107 111 114 115 116 117 118 119 121 123 127 129 130 131 135 143 145 146 147 148 **P**4 **S** Ascension Healthcare, Saint Louis, MO
Primary Contact: Mike Moore, President and Chief Operating Officer
CFO: James Brasel, Chief Financial Officer
CMO: Paul McQuillen M.D., Chief Medical Officer
CIO: Rob Poole, Director
CNO: Angie Bidleman, Chief Nursing Officer
Web address: www.jpmc.org
Control: Church operated, Nongovernment, not–for–profit **Service:** General medical and surgical

Staffed Beds: 114 **Admissions:** 4749 **Census:** 49 **Outpatient Visits:** 83565 **Births:** 611 **Total Expense ($000):** 101447 **Payroll Expense ($000):** 33402 **Personnel:** 563

BEAVER—Beaver County

BEAVER COUNTY MEMORIAL HOSPITAL (371322), 212 East Eighth Street, Zip 73932, Mailing Address: P.O.Box 640, 73932–0640; tel. 580/625–4551, (Nonreporting) **A**10 18
Primary Contact: Alissa Schlessman, Administrator
CMO: Gary Mathews M.D., Medical Doctor
CHR: Karla Leisher, Business Office Manager
Web address: www.beavercountyhospitalauthority.com
Control: Hospital district or authority, Government, Nonfederal **Service:** General medical and surgical

Staffed Beds: 24

BETHANY—Oklahoma County

△ **THE CHILDREN'S CENTER REHABILITATION HOSPITAL (373302)**, 6800 NW 39th Expressway, Zip 73008–2513; tel. 405/789–6711 **A**3 5 7 10 **F**1 29 30 34 35 39 53 58 59 68 74 75 79 84 87 90 91 93 96 107 130 132 146 148 149 **P**6
Primary Contact: Albert Gray, Chief Executive Officer
Web address: www.tccokc.org
Control: Other not–for–profit (including NFP Corporation) **Service:** Children's general medical and surgical

Staffed Beds: 120 **Admissions:** 124 **Census:** 96 **Outpatient Visits:** 12106 **Total Expense ($000):** 36773 **Payroll Expense ($000):** 22249 **Personnel:** 522

BLACKWELL—Kay County

⊠ **BLACKWELL REGIONAL HOSPITAL (370030)**, 710 South 13th Street, Zip 74631–3700; tel. 580/363–2311 **A**1 10 **F**3 15 29 30 34 40 41 43 50 56 57 59 64 68 79 81 85 86 87 91 93 107 110 114 119 133 146 **P**5 6 **S** Community Health Systems, Inc., Franklin, TN
Primary Contact: Joyce Daniel, Chief Executive Officer and Chief Nursing Officer
CFO: Jacob Easson, Chief Financial Officer
CMO: Jeffery Shuart M.D., Chief of Staff
CHR: Tonya Criner, Human Resource Lead
CNO: Joyce Daniel, Chief Executive Officer and Chief Nursing Officer
Web address: www.blackwellregional.org
Control: Corporation, Investor–owned (for–profit) **Service:** General medical and surgical

Staffed Beds: 49 **Admissions:** 242 **Census:** 2

BOISE CITY—Cimarron County

CIMARRON MEMORIAL HOSPITAL (371307), 100 South Ellis Street, Zip 73933, Mailing Address: P.O.Box 1059, 73933–1059; tel. 580/544–2501, (Nonreporting) **A**10 18
Primary Contact: Tim Beard, Chief Executive Officer
CFO: Jamie Jacoby, Chief Financial Officer
CIO: Tim Beard, Director, Information Technology
CNO: Barbara Carter, Chief Nursing Officer
Web address: www.cimarronmemorialhospital.org
Control: County, Government, Nonfederal **Service:** General medical and surgical

Staffed Beds: 25

BRISTOW—Creek County

BRISTOW MEDICAL CENTER (370041), 700 West 7th Avenue, Suite 6, Zip 74010–2302; tel. 918/367–2215, (Nonreporting) **A**10
Primary Contact: Jan Winter–Clark, Chief Executive Officer
CFO: Robin Van Vickle, Chief Financial Officer
Web address: www.bristowmedcenter.com
Control: Corporation, Investor–owned (for–profit) **Service:** General medical and surgical

Staffed Beds: 30

BROKEN ARROW—Tulsa County

★ **ST. JOHN BROKEN ARROW (370235)**, 1000 West Boise Circle, Zip 74012–4900; tel. 918/994–8100 **A**10 **F**3 11 14 15 18 29 30 34 35 37 40 43 45 50 57 59 64 65 68 74 79 81 84 85 87 94 107 108 110 111 114 115 119 130 132 135 143 146 **P**1 5 **S** Ascension Healthcare, Saint Louis, MO
Primary Contact: David L. Phillips, Chief Operating Officer
CFO: Katie Caughman, Chief Financial Officer
CMO: Jason Lepak M.D., Medical Director
CNO: Dwan Borens, Chief Nursing Officer
Web address: www.stjohnbrokenarrow.com
Control: Church operated, Nongovernment, not–for–profit **Service:** General medical and surgical

Staffed Beds: 44 **Admissions:** 2675 **Census:** 17 **Outpatient Visits:** 108136 **Births:** 0 **Total Expense ($000):** 53907 **Payroll Expense ($000):** 12794 **Personnel:** 227

BUFFALO—Harper County

★ **HARPER COUNTY COMMUNITY HOSPITAL (371324)**, Highway 64 North, Zip 73834, Mailing Address: P.O.Box 60, 73834–0060; tel. 580/735–2555, (Nonreporting) **A**10 18
Primary Contact: Georganna Buss, Chief Executive Officer
COO: Pam Dodd, Chief Operating Officer
CFO: Lisa Oakley, Chief Financial Officer
CNO: Melissa Madrid R.N., Chief Nursing Officer
Web address: www.hcchospital.com/
Control: County, Government, Nonfederal **Service:** General medical and surgical

Staffed Beds: 16

CARNEGIE—Caddo County

CARNEGIE TRI–COUNTY MUNICIPAL HOSPITAL (371334), 102 North Broadway, Zip 73015, Mailing Address: P.O.Box 97, 73015–0097; tel. 580/654–1050 **A**10 18 **F**29 40 43 67 68 93 97 107 119 128 130 133 149 **S** First Physicians Capital Group, Inc., Oklahoma City, OK
Primary Contact: Doris Brown, Chief Executive Officer and Administrator
Web address: www.carnegiehospital.org/
Control: Other not–for–profit (including NFP Corporation) **Service:** General medical and surgical

Staffed Beds: 15 **Admissions:** 232 **Census:** 2 **Outpatient Visits:** 1933

CHEYENNE—Roger Mills County

★ **ROGER MILLS MEMORIAL HOSPITAL (371303)**, 501 South L.L. Males, Zip 73628, Mailing Address: P.O. Box 219, 73628; tel. 580/497–3336 **A**10 18 **F**3 7 34 40 57 59 64 65 93 107 115 133 **P**6
Primary Contact: Cynthia Duncan, Chief Executive Officer
Web address: www.rmmhonline.com
Control: Hospital district or authority, Government, Nonfederal **Service:** General medical and surgical

Staffed Beds: 15 **Admissions:** 36 **Census:** 1 **Outpatient Visits:** 3833 **Births:** 0 **Total Expense ($000):** 5417 **Payroll Expense ($000):** 2533 **Personnel:** 43

CHICKASHA—Grady County

★ **GRADY MEMORIAL HOSPITAL (370054)**, 2220 West Iowa Avenue, Zip 73018–2738; tel. 405/224–2300 **A**10 **F**3 8 11 15 17 29 30 34 35 40 43 45 57 59 65 66 70 79 81 82 85 87 89 91 93 107 110 111 114 115 119 127 128 130 131 132 133 144 146 147 149 **P**6
Primary Contact: Warren K. Spellman, Chief Executive Officer
CFO: Jackie McAdoo, Chief Financial Officer
CMO: Mitch Coppedge M.D., Chief Medical Officer
CIO: Mike Townsend, Interim Director Health Information Systems
CHR: Rebel Rutledge, Director Human Resources
CNO: Cathy Groseclose, Vice President Patient Care Services
Web address: www.gradymem.org
Control: Hospital district or authority, Government, Nonfederal **Service:** General medical and surgical

Staffed Beds: 39 **Admissions:** 1083 **Census:** 10 **Outpatient Visits:** 65308 **Births:** 0 **Total Expense ($000):** 34716 **Payroll Expense ($000):** 18067 **Personnel:** 289

OK

Hospital, Medicare Provider Number, Address, Telephone, Approval, Facility, and Physician Codes, Health Care System

★ American Hospital Association (AHA) membership
☐ The Joint Commission accreditation
○ Healthcare Facilities Accreditation Program
◇ DNV Healthcare Inc. accreditation
⇧ Center for Improvement in Healthcare Quality Accreditation
△ Commission on Accreditation of Rehabilitation Facilities (CARF) accreditation

OK

CLAREMORE—Rogers County

☐ **CLAREMORE INDIAN HOSPITAL (370173)**, 101 South Moore Avenue, Zip 74017–5091; tel. 918/342–6200, (Nonreporting) **A**1 10 **S** U. S. Indian Health Service, Rockville, MD
Primary Contact: George Valliere, Chief Executive Officer
CFO: LaLana Spears, Supervisor Accounting
CMO: Gary Lang M.D., Clinical Director
CIO: David Ponder, Information Technology Officer
CHR: Quinn Proctor, Director Human Resources
CNO: Alonna Adair–Triplett, Chief Nurse Executive
Web address: www.ihs.gov
Control: PHS, Indian Service, Government, federal **Service**: General medical and surgical

Staffed Beds: 44

★ ⇑ **HILLCREST HOSPITAL CLAREMORE (370039)**, 1202 North Muskogee Place, Zip 74017–3036; tel. 918/341–2556 **A**10 21 **F**3 6 11 13 15 18 20 22 26 28 29 30 34 35 37 40 45 49 51 59 64 70 74 77 79 81 82 85 86 87 93 98 103 107 108 110 111 119 126 129 130 131 133 135 145 146 147 148 **P**6 **S** Ardent Health Services, Nashville, TN
Primary Contact: David Chaussard, Chief Executive Officer
CFO: Brandon Bullard, Chief Financial Officer
CIO: Celeste Rodden, Chief Information Officer
CHR: Pat Goad, Director Human Resources
CNO: Randy Walker, Chief Nursing Officer
Web address: www.hillcrestclaremore.com
Control: Corporation, Investor–owned (for–profit) **Service**: General medical and surgical

Staffed Beds: 67 Admissions: 2719 Census: 29 Outpatient Visits: 41442 Births: 673 Total Expense ($000): 49228 Payroll Expense ($000): 16654 Personnel: 310

CLEVELAND—Pawnee County

★ **CLEVELAND AREA HOSPITAL (371320)**, 1401 West Pawnee Street, Zip 74020–3019; tel. 918/358–2501 **A**10 18 **F**15 29 34 35 40 43 57 59 64 75 77 87 89 91 92 93 97 102 103 107 119 128 130 133 **P**6
Primary Contact: Edred Benton, Chief Executive Officer and Chief Operating Officer
COO: Edred Benton, Chief Executive Officer and Chief Operating Officer
CMO: Jason Sims M.D., Chief Medical Officer
CHR: Sherry Brown, Director Human Resources
Web address: www.clevelandareahospital.com
Control: Hospital district or authority, Government, Nonfederal **Service**: General medical and surgical

Staffed Beds: 14 Admissions: 156 Census: 4 Outpatient Visits: 12957 Births: 1 Total Expense ($000): 10587 Payroll Expense ($000): 6006 Personnel: 100

CLINTON—Custer County

✠ **ALLIANCEHEALTH CLINTON (370029)**, 100 North 30th Street, Zip 73601–3117; tel. 580/323–2363, (Nonreporting) **A**1 10 **S** Community Health Systems, Inc., Franklin, TN
Primary Contact: Cameron Lewis, Chief Executive Officer
CFO: Jay Johnson, Chief Financial Officer
CHR: Julie Graumann, Director
CNO: Kimberly Todd, Chief Nursing Officer
Web address: www.alliancehealthclinton.com
Control: Partnership, Investor–owned (for–profit) **Service**: General medical and surgical

Staffed Beds: 49

COALGATE—Coal County

★ **COAL COUNTY GENERAL HOSPITAL (371319)**, 6 North Covington Street, Zip 74538–2002, Mailing Address: P.O.Box 326, 74538–0326; tel. 580/927–2327, (Total facility includes 75 beds in nursing home–type unit) **A**10 18 **F**40 107 119 128 133
Primary Contact: Billy Johnson, Chief Executive Officer
CFO: Diane Downard, Chief Financial Officer
CMO: R.J Helton D.O., Chief of Staff
CIO: Matt Balliett, Chief Information Officer
CHR: Cyndie Martin, Director
CNO: Farra Ybarra R.N., Chief Nursing Officer
Web address: www.hillcrest.com
Control: Hospital district or authority, Government, Nonfederal **Service**: General medical and surgical

Staffed Beds: 95 Admissions: 880 Census: 74 Outpatient Visits: 5988 Births: 0 Total Expense ($000): 5184 Payroll Expense ($000): 2078 Personnel: 58

CORDELL—Washita County

★ **CORDELL MEMORIAL HOSPITAL (371325)**, 1220 North Glenn English Street, Zip 73632–2010; tel. 580/832–3339, (Nonreporting) **A**10 18
Primary Contact: Landon Hise, Chief Executive Officer
CFO: Sue Kelley, Chief Financial Officer
Web address: www.cordellmemorialhospital.com
Control: City, Government, Nonfederal **Service**: General medical and surgical

Staffed Beds: 25

CUSHING—Payne County

★ **HILLCREST HOSPITAL CUSHING (370099)**, 1027 East Cherry Street, Zip 74023–4101; tel. 918/225–2915 **A**10 **F**11 13 15 18 29 30 31 34 35 40 43 44 45 46 50 51 56 57 59 64 65 66 68 70 71 75 76 81 82 86 87 93 94 97 98 100 101 102 103 106 107 110 111 114 115 119 128 129 130 131 143 145 146 147 148 **S** Ardent Health Services, Nashville, TN
Primary Contact: Kevin Hawk, Chief Executive Officer
CFO: Joseph Mendoza, Chief Financial Officer
CHR: Bethany Leininger, Manager Human Resource
CNO: Tina Petersen, Chief Nursing Officer
Web address: www.hillcrestcushing.com/
Control: Corporation, Investor–owned (for–profit) **Service**: General medical and surgical

Staffed Beds: 99 Admissions: 1813 Census: 20 Outpatient Visits: 17159 Births: 219 Total Expense ($000): 23362 Payroll Expense ($000): 8931 Personnel: 165

DRUMRIGHT—Creek County

DRUMRIGHT REGIONAL HOSPITAL (371331), 610 West Bypass, Zip 74030–5957; tel. 918/382–2300 **A**10 18 **F**3 11 18 29 40 45 56 59 64 65 68 77 81 85 91 92 93 103 107 114 119 127 128 129 130 132 133 146 **P**6 **S** Rural Community Hospitals of America, Kansas City, MO
Primary Contact: Tracy Byers, Chief Executive Officer
CFO: Mark Conrath, Chief Financial Officer
Web address: www.drumrighthospital.com/
Control: Corporation, Investor–owned (for–profit) **Service**: General medical and surgical

Staffed Beds: 15 Admissions: 462 Census: 5 Outpatient Visits: 14726 Births: 0

DUNCAN—Stephens County

✠ **DUNCAN REGIONAL HOSPITAL (370023)**, 1407 North Whisenant Drive, Zip 73533–1650, Mailing Address: P.O.Box 2000, 73534–2000; tel. 580/252–5300, (Total facility includes 16 beds in nursing home–type unit) **A**1 3 5 10 20 **F**3 11 13 15 18 28 29 30 34 35 40 43 45 50 57 59 62 63 64 70 75 76 77 79 81 85 86 87 89 90 93 96 98 103 104 107 108 110 111 114 115 119 128 129 130 131 132 141 142 143 145 146 147 148 **S** Duncan Regional Hospital, Duncan, OK
Primary Contact: Jay R. Johnson, FACHE, President and Chief Executive Officer
CFO: Douglas R Volinski, Vice President and Chief Financial Officer
CMO: Che' Miller M.D., Chief of Staff
CIO: Roger Neal, Vice President Operations
CHR: Mark Rhoades, Vice President and Chief Human Resources Officer
CNO: Cindy Rauh R.N., Vice President and Chief Nursing Officer
Web address: www.duncanregional.com
Control: Other not–for–profit (including NFP Corporation) **Service**: General medical and surgical

Staffed Beds: 117 Admissions: 4324 Census: 52 Outpatient Visits: 254912 Births: 641 Total Expense ($000): 103217 Payroll Expense ($000): 45767 Personnel: 800

DURANT—Bryan County

✠ **ALLIANCEHEALTH DURANT (370014)**, 1800 University Boulevard, Zip 74701–3006, Mailing Address: P.O.Box 1207, 74702–1207; tel. 580/924–3080 **A**1 5 10 13 19 **F**3 8 11 13 15 17 18 20 22 28 29 30 34 35 39 40 43 45 50 51 56 57 59 70 74 75 76 77 79 80 81 82 85 86 89 97 102 107 108 110 111 115 119 126 129 130 135 145 146 147 148 **P**8 **S** Community Health Systems, Inc., Franklin, TN
Primary Contact: Jeffrey S. Tarrant, FACHE, Chief Executive Officer
CFO: Cindy Rios, Chief Financial Officer
CMO: Kevin Gordon M.D., Chief of Staff
CIO: Katy Stinson, Director Information Services
Web address: www.alliancehealthdurant.com/
Control: Corporation, Investor–owned (for–profit) **Service**: General medical and surgical

Staffed Beds: 140 Admissions: 5272 Census: 50 Outpatient Visits: 63459 Births: 1006 Total Expense ($000): 62435 Payroll Expense ($000): 22436 Personnel: 396

OK

EDMOND—Oklahoma County

☐ **AMG SPECIALTY HOSPITAL–EDMOND (372005)**, 1100 East Ninth Street, Zip 73034–5755; tel. 405/341–8150, (Nonreporting) **A**1 10 **S** AMG Integrated Healthcare Management, Lafayette, LA
Primary Contact: Ricky Higdon, Chief Executive Officer
CFO: Rowena Davidson, Manager Business Office
CMO: Brian Levy M.D., Medical Director
CHR: Pam Grimes, Director Human Resources
Web address: www.amgedmond.com/
Control: Corporation, Investor–owned (for–profit) **Service**: Acute long–term care hospital

Staffed Beds: 37

EDMOND MEDICAL CENTER See OU Medical Center Edmond

⊞ **INTEGRIS HEALTH EDMOND (370236)**, 4801 Integris Parkway, Zip 73034–8864; tel. 405/657–3000 **A**1 10 **F**3 8 11 13 15 18 20 22 29 30 34 35 40 43 45 46 47 49 53 54 57 59 60 64 68 70 74 76 77 78 79 81 82 85 87 93 97 100 102 107 108 110 111 114 115 119 130 131 132 135 146 147 148 **P**6 7 **S** INTEGRIS Health, Oklahoma City, OK
Primary Contact: Avilla Williams, MS, President
CNO: Angela K Kamermayer MS, Chief Nursing Officer
Web address: www.integrisok.com/edmond
Control: Other not–for–profit (including NFP Corporation) **Service**: General medical and surgical

Staffed Beds: 40 **Admissions**: 2679 **Census**: 26 **Outpatient Visits**: 35132
Births: 606 **Total Expense ($000)**: 54789 **Payroll Expense ($000)**: 15347
Personnel: 237

OU MEDICAL CENTER EDMOND See OU Medical Center, Oklahoma City

★ **SUMMIT MEDICAL CENTER (370225)**, 1800 S Renaissance Boulevard, Zip 73013–3023; tel. 405/359–2400 **A**10 **F**3 12 29 40 41 45 54 64 70 75 79 81 82 85 107 111 119 127 129 148 149
Primary Contact: Curtis Summers, Chief Executive Officer
Web address: www.summitmedcenter.com/
Control: Individual, Investor–owned (for–profit) **Service**: General medical and surgical

Staffed Beds: 9 **Admissions**: 242 **Census**: 2 **Outpatient Visits**: 22935
Births: 0 **Total Expense ($000)**: 47648 **Payroll Expense ($000)**: 11731
Personnel: 268

EL RENO—Canadian County

★ **MERCY HOSPITAL EL RENO (370011)**, 2115 Parkview Drive, Zip 73036–2199; tel. 405/262–2640 **A**10 **F**3 7 11 29 30 35 40 44 45 50 62 64 68 77 79 81 82 85 93 107 111 114 119 132 146 148 149 **P**6 **S** Mercy, Chesterfield, MO
Primary Contact: Cindy Carmichael, Administrator
CMO: Michael Dean Sullivan M.D., Chief of Staff
CIO: Karen Heldreth, Director Data Processing
CHR: Wendy Ward, Director Human Resources
Web address: www.mercyok.net
Control: Church operated, Nongovernment, not–for–profit **Service**: General medical and surgical

Staffed Beds: 48 **Admissions**: 449 **Census**: 4 **Outpatient Visits**: 22743
Births: 0 **Total Expense ($000)**: 12058 **Payroll Expense ($000)**: 6850
Personnel: 109

PARKVIEW HOSPITAL See Mercy Hospital El Reno

ELK CITY—Beckham County

⊞ **GREAT PLAINS REGIONAL MEDICAL CENTER (370019)**, 1801 West Third Street, Zip 73644–5145, Mailing Address: P.O.Box 2339, 73648–2339; tel. 580/225–2511 **A**1 3 10 **F**3 11 13 15 18 28 29 30 31 34 35 40 43 47 50 51 56 57 59 62 64 68 70 75 76 77 78 79 81 85 87 89 91 93 96 98 100 101 102 103 107 108 110 111 115 118 119 120 121 123 129 130 131 132 133 135 146 147 148 149
Primary Contact: Corey Lively, Chief Executive Officer
CFO: Monica Scott, Chief Financial Officer
CMO: Craig Phelps M.D., Chief of Staff
CIO: Terry Price, Director Information Technology
CHR: Misty Carter, Vice President Human Resources and Ancillary Services
CNO: Debra D. Morris R.N., MSN, Chief Nursing Officer
Web address: www.gprmc-ok.com
Control: Other not–for–profit (including NFP Corporation) **Service**: General medical and surgical

Staffed Beds: 46 **Admissions**: 1842 **Census**: 21 **Outpatient Visits**: 54913
Births: 364 **Total Expense ($000)**: 47558 **Payroll Expense ($000)**: 17333
Personnel: 389

ENID—Garfield County

INTEGRIS BASS BEHAVIORAL HEALTH SYSTEM See Integris Bass Meadowlake

⊞ **INTEGRIS BASS BAPTIST HEALTH CENTER (370016)**, 600 South Monroe Street, Zip 73701–7211, Mailing Address: P.O.Box 3168, 73702–3168; tel. 580/233–2300, (Includes INTEGRIS BASS MEADOWLAKE, 2216 South Van Buren Street, Enid, Oklahoma, Zip 73703–8299, tel. 580/234–2220) **A**1 10 13 19 **F**3 11 13 15 17 18 20 22 24 28 29 30 31 35 40 43 45 49 57 62 68 70 74 75 76 77 78 79 81 85 98 99 103 107 108 111 114 117 118 119 120 121 127 128 129 132 144 146 147 148 **S** INTEGRIS Health, Oklahoma City, OK
Primary Contact: Edward Herrman, R.N., FACHE, President
CFO: Duane Miller, Chief Financial Officer
CNO: Cynthia Leathers R.N., Chief Nursing Officer
Web address: www.integris-health.com
Control: Other not–for–profit (including NFP Corporation) **Service**: General medical and surgical

Staffed Beds: 167 **Admissions**: 4492 **Census**: 81 **Personnel**: 527

☐ **INTEGRIS BASS PAVILION (372016)**, 401 South Third Street, Zip 73701–5737; tel. 580/249–4260 **A**1 10 **F**11 29 30 40 43 68 75 77 82 85 93 132 146 148
Primary Contact: Edward Herrman, R.N., FACHE, President
CHR: Kerri Johnson, Human Resources Operations Consultant
CNO: Sherry Dunlay, Vice President Chief Nursing Officer
Web address: www.integris-health.com/integris/en-us/locations/bass-enid
Control: Other not–for–profit (including NFP Corporation) **Service**: General medical and surgical

Staffed Beds: 24 **Admissions**: 133 **Census**: 9 **Outpatient Visits**: 0 **Births**: 0
Personnel: 48

☐ △ **ST. MARY'S REGIONAL MEDICAL CENTER (370026)**, 305 South Fifth Street, Zip 73701–5899, Mailing Address: P.O.Box 232, 73702–0232; tel. 580/233–6100 **A**1 7 10 **F**3 11 13 15 18 20 22 26 28 29 30 31 34 35 37 39 40 43 45 49 51 53 54 56 57 59 60 64 68 69 70 73 74 75 76 77 78 79 80 81 82 85 86 87 90 91 92 93 96 98 100 101 102 103 104 107 108 110 111 114 115 118 119 129 130 131 132 135 146 147 **P**6 **S** Universal Health Services, Inc., King of Prussia, PA
Primary Contact: Stanley D. Tatum, FACHE, Chief Executive Officer
COO: Krista Roberts, Chief Operating Officer
CFO: David Jamin, Chief Financial Officer
CMO: Michael Pontious M.D., Chief of Staff
CIO: Tracy Andersen, Chief Information Officer
CHR: David Camp, Director Human Resources
CNO: Douglas W Coffey R.N., MSN, Chief Nursing Officer
Web address: www.stmarysregional.com
Control: Corporation, Investor–owned (for–profit) **Service**: General medical and surgical

Staffed Beds: 164 **Admissions**: 4752 **Census**: 62 **Outpatient Visits**: 94523
Births: 345 **Total Expense ($000)**: 80066 **Payroll Expense ($000)**: 32773
Personnel: 489

FAIRFAX—Osage County

FAIRFAX COMMUNITY HOSPITAL (371318), 40 Hospital Road, Zip 74637–5084; tel. 918/642–3291 **A**10 18 **F**3 29 40 45 57 77 93 107 117 129 133 **S** Rural Community Hospitals of America, Kansas City, MO
Primary Contact: Tina Steele, Chief Executive Officer and Chief Financial Officer
COO: Linda Thompson, Chief Operating Officer
CFO: Tina Steele, Chief Executive Officer and Chief Financial Officer
CMO: Arman Janloo M.D., Chief Medical Staff
CIO: Lisa Drymon, Manager
CHR: Sharon Binkley, Director Human Resources
Control: Corporation, Investor–owned (for–profit) **Service**: General medical and surgical

Staffed Beds: 15 **Admissions**: 184 **Census**: 4 **Outpatient Visits**: 5500
Births: 0 **Total Expense ($000)**: 5942 **Payroll Expense ($000)**: 3107
Personnel: 47

FAIRFAX MEMORIAL HOSPITAL See Fairfax Community Hospital

Hospital, Medicare Provider Number, Address, Telephone, Approval, Facility, and Physician Codes, Health Care System

★ American Hospital Association (AHA) membership
☐ The Joint Commission accreditation
○ Healthcare Facilities Accreditation Program
◇ DNV Healthcare Inc. accreditation
⇑ Center for Improvement in Healthcare Quality Accreditation
△ Commission on Accreditation of Rehabilitation Facilities (CARF) accreditation

OK

FAIRVIEW—Major County

FAIRVIEW REGIONAL MEDICAL CENTER (371329), 523 East State Road, Zip 73737–1453, Mailing Address: P.O.Box 548, 73737–0548; tel. 580/227–3721 **A**10 18 **F**3 28 34 35 40 43 45 57 59 64 65 68 69 75 77 81 84 85 91 93 107 114 127 128 130 131 132 135 146 149 **P**5 6
Primary Contact: Roger Knak, Administrator and Chief Executive Officer
CMO: John Stephen Price M.D., Chief of Staff
CIO: Bob Maynard, Chief Information Officer
CHR: Elisabeth Hughes, Director Human Resources and Community Relations
CNO: Tamara Eitzen, Chief Nursing Officer
Web address: www.fairviewregionalmedicalcenter.com
Control: Hospital district or authority, Government, Nonfederal **Service**: General medical and surgical

Staffed Beds: 25 **Admissions:** 205 **Census:** 3 **Outpatient Visits:** 9718
Births: 0 **Total Expense ($000):** 6927 **Payroll Expense ($000):** 3186
Personnel: 63

FORT SUPPLY—Major County

NORTHWEST CENTER FOR BEHAVIORAL HEALTH (374001), 1 Mi East Highway 270, Zip 73841, Mailing Address: 1222 10th Street, Suite 211, Woodward, 73801–3156; tel. 580/766–2311 **A**3 10 **F**98 104 106 130 135 149 **P**6 **S** Oklahoma Department of Mental Health and Substance Abuse Services, Oklahoma City, OK
Primary Contact: Trudy Hoffman, Executive Director
Web address: www.ncbhok.org/
Control: State, Government, Nonfederal **Service**: Psychiatric

Staffed Beds: 24 **Admissions:** 505 **Census:** 16 **Outpatient Visits:** 62435
Births: 0 **Total Expense ($000):** 12901 **Payroll Expense ($000):** 6330
Personnel: 176

GROVE—Delaware County

✠ **INTEGRIS GROVE HOSPITAL (370113)**, 1001 East 18th Street, Zip 74344–2907; tel. 918/786–2243 **A**1 10 20 **F**3 7 11 13 15 18 20 22 29 30 34 35 40 43 45 54 57 59 62 64 70 76 77 79 81 85 93 107 108 109 110 111 115 119 125 146 147 **S** INTEGRIS Health, Oklahoma City, OK
Primary Contact: Chris Hammes, Interim President
CFO: Stacie Mason, Vice President and Chief Financial Officer
CMO: Kyle Schauf M.D., President Medical Staff
CNO: Brandi Stewart R.N., Vice President and Chief Nursing Officer
Web address: www.integris–health.com
Control: Other not–for–profit (including NFP Corporation) **Service**: General medical and surgical

Staffed Beds: 58 **Admissions:** 1865 **Census:** 15 **Outpatient Visits:** 37312
Births: 305 **Total Expense ($000):** 48889 **Payroll Expense ($000):** 12328
Personnel: 210

GUTHRIE—Logan County

★ **MERCY HOSPITAL LOGAN COUNTY (371317)**, 200 South Academy Road, Zip 73044–8727, Mailing Address: P.O.Box 1017, 73044–1017; tel. 405/282–6700 **A**10 18 **F**3 15 29 30 34 35 40 44 50 57 59 68 75 77 87 93 107 110 111 114 119 127 129 130 131 133 144 146 148 149 **P**6 **S** Mercy, Chesterfield, MO
Primary Contact: Joshua Tucker, Administrator
CMO: Jignesh Veragiwala, Chief of Staff
CHR: Mary Jo Messelt, Senior Human Resources Manager
CNO: Kim Williams R.N., Director of Nursing
Web address: www.mercy.net
Control: Church operated, Nongovernment, not–for–profit **Service**: General medical and surgical

Staffed Beds: 25 **Admissions:** 680 **Census:** 10 **Outpatient Visits:** 55051
Births: 0 **Total Expense ($000):** 17054 **Payroll Expense ($000):** 10179
Personnel: 158

GUYMON—Texas County

★ **MEMORIAL HOSPITAL OF TEXAS COUNTY (370138)**, 520 Medical Drive, Zip 73942–4438; tel. 580/338–6515, (Nonreporting) **A**10 20
Primary Contact: Dondie Rodgers, Interim Chief Nursing Officer
CFO: Michele Reust, Controller
CIO: Sheldon Spence, Director of Revenue Cycle, IT
CHR: Sarah Wagner, Human Resources Officer
CNO: Dondie Rodgers, Interim Chief Nursing Officer
Web address: www.mhtcguymon.org
Control: County, Government, Nonfederal **Service**: General medical and surgical

Staffed Beds: 14

HEALDTON—Carter County

★ **MERCY HOSPITAL HEALDTON (371310)**, 918 South 8th Street, Zip 73438–0928, Mailing Address: P.O.Box 928, 73438–0928; tel. 580/229–0701 **A**10 18 **F**3 29 34 35 40 43 44 57 64 68 107 114 127 133 146 149 **S** Mercy, Chesterfield, MO
Primary Contact: Jeremy A. Jones, Administrator
CMO: Mark Newey D.O., Chief of Staff
CHR: Melinda Sharum, Director Human Resources
Web address: www.mercyok.com
Control: Church operated, Nongovernment, not–for–profit **Service**: General medical and surgical

Staffed Beds: 22 **Admissions:** 225 **Census:** 6 **Outpatient Visits:** 8812
Births: 0 **Total Expense ($000):** 5801 **Payroll Expense ($000):** 3319
Personnel: 61

HENRYETTA—Okmulgee County

★ **HILLCREST HOSPITAL HENRYETTA (370183)**, 2401 West Main Street, Zip 74437–3893, Mailing Address: P.O.Box 1269, 74437–1269; tel. 918/650–1100 **A**10 **F**3 15 18 29 40 45 54 56 64 65 79 81 85 87 93 98 102 103 107 110 111 114 119 129 130 131 133 143 147 148 **P**6 **S** Ardent Health Services, Nashville, TN
Primary Contact: Dee Renshaw, Chief Executive Officer
CFO: Joseph Mendoza, Chief Financial Officer
CHR: Sheree Snyder, Manager Human Resources
CNO: April Secor R.N., Chief Nursing Officer
Web address: www.hillcresthenryetta.com/
Control: Corporation, Investor–owned (for–profit) **Service**: General medical and surgical

Staffed Beds: 41 **Admissions:** 964 **Census:** 16 **Outpatient Visits:** 12942
Births: 0 **Total Expense ($000):** 16100 **Payroll Expense ($000):** 6086
Personnel: 121

HOBART—Kiowa County

★ **ELKVIEW GENERAL HOSPITAL (370153)**, 429 West Elm Street, Zip 73651–1615; tel. 580/726–1900 **A**10 20 **F**3 15 28 29 31 34 35 40 45 56 59 62 79 81 85 89 93 107 108 110 111 115 118 119 129 133 146 148 **P**6
Primary Contact: Lisa Hart, Chief Executive Officer
CFO: Amy Harmon, Chief Financial Officer
CMO: William Sims M.D., Medical Director
CIO: Dennis Tarver, Director Information Technology
CHR: Sharon Moad, Human Resources Director Health Information Management
CNO: Debbie Norman MSN, R.N., Chief Nursing Officer
Web address: www.elkviewhospital.com
Control: Hospital district or authority, Government, Nonfederal **Service**: General medical and surgical

Staffed Beds: 38 **Admissions:** 826 **Census:** 8 **Outpatient Visits:** 11126
Births: 1 **Total Expense ($000):** 13384 **Payroll Expense ($000):** 6701
Personnel: 120

HOLDENVILLE—Hughes County

★ **HOLDENVILLE GENERAL HOSPITAL (371321)**, 100 McDougal Drive, Zip 74848–2822; tel. 405/379–4200 **A**10 18 **F**3 11 29 30 34 40 45 57 59 64 65 79 81 97 107 111 115 119 127 133 146 **P**3
Primary Contact: Roberta Jeffrey, Chief Executive Officer
CFO: Drew Johnson, Chief Financial Officer
CMO: Tom Osborn D.O., Chief Medical Staff
CIO: Mike Combs, Manager Information Technology
CHR: Heather Heard, Director Human Resources
CNO: Jackie Smith R.N., Chief Nursing Officer
Web address: www.holdenvillegeneral.org
Control: City, Government, Nonfederal **Service**: General medical and surgical

Staffed Beds: 25 **Admissions:** 534 **Census:** 8 **Outpatient Visits:** 45703
Births: 0

HOLLIS—Harmon County

HARMON MEMORIAL HOSPITAL (370036), 400 East Chestnut Street, Zip 73550–2030, Mailing Address: P.O.Box 791, 73550–0791; tel. 580/688–3363, (Nonreporting) **A**10 20
Primary Contact: Sheila Lewis, Administrator
CFO: Willie Mae Copeland, Chief Financial Officer
CMO: Akram Abraham M.D., Chief of Staff
CHR: Abbey Welch, Director Human Resources
Control: Hospital district or authority, Government, Nonfederal **Service**: General medical and surgical

Staffed Beds: 31

Many Facility Codes have changed. Please refer to the AHA Guide Code Chart. © 2017 AHA Guide

OK

HUGO—Choctaw County

CHOCTAW MEMORIAL HOSPITAL (370100), 1405 East Kirk Street,
Zip 74743–3603; tel. 580/317–9500, (Nonreporting) **A**10
Primary Contact: Marcia O'Connor, Chief Executive Officer
CIO: Andy Richmond, Director Information Technology
CHR: Darlene Galyon, Director Human Resources
Web address: www.choctawmemorial.com
Control: Hospital district or authority, Government, Nonfederal **Service**: General
medical and surgical

Staffed Beds: 32

IDABEL—Mccurtain County

MCCURTAIN MEMORIAL HOSPITAL (370048), 1301 Lincoln Road, Zip 74745–
7341; tel. 580/286–7623 **A**10 20 **F**3 11 13 15 28 29 30 34 40 45 49 53 59 62
64 70 75 76 81 87 93 98 103 107 110 111 114 119 130 132 148 149 **P**6 8
Primary Contact: Jahni Tapley, JD, Chief Executive Officer
CFO: Ray B Whitmore, Chief Financial Officer
CMO: Michael C West M.D., Chief of Staff
CIO: Dana A Stowell, Chief Information Officer
CNO: Pam Johnson R.N., Chief Nursing Officer
Web address: www.mmhok.com
Control: Other not–for–profit (including NFP Corporation) **Service**: General
medical and surgical

Staffed Beds: 77 **Admissions**: 1132 **Census**: 11 **Outpatient Visits**: 28780 **Births**: 212 **Total Expense ($000)**: 17720 **Payroll Expense ($000)**: 9213 **Personnel**: 192

KINGFISHER—Kingfisher County

★ **MERCY HOSPITAL KINGFISHER (371313)**, 1000 Kingfisher Regional Hospital
Drive, Zip 73750–3528, Mailing Address: P.O.Box 59, 73750–0059; tel.
405/375–3141 **A**10 18 **F**3 11 15 29 30 34 35 40 43 45 50 59 68 75 77 79
81 85 87 93 107 110 111 114 119 129 132 133 146 148 149 **P**6 **S** Mercy,
Chesterfield, MO
Primary Contact: Brian Denton, Administrator
CMO: Brett Krablin M.D., Chief of Staff
CIO: Chad Kliewer, Information Technology Specialist
CHR: Carolyn Bjerke, Director Human Resources
CNO: Hannah Powell, Chief Nursing Officer
Web address: www.kingfisherhospital.com
Control: Church operated, Nongovernment, not–for–profit **Service**: General
medical and surgical

Staffed Beds: 25 **Admissions**: 376 **Census**: 5 **Outpatient Visits**: 19309 **Births**: 0 **Total Expense ($000)**: 12210 **Payroll Expense ($000)**: 5907 **Personnel**: 99

LAWTON—Comanche County

☒ △ **COMANCHE COUNTY MEMORIAL HOSPITAL (370056)**, 3401 West Gore
Boulevard, Zip 73505–6332, Mailing Address: P.O.Box 129, 73502–0129; tel.
580/355–8620, (Total facility includes 135 beds in nursing home–type unit) **A**1 2 3
5 7 10 13 **F**3 6 7 8 11 12 13 15 17 18 20 22 24 26 28 29 30 31 32 34 35 40 43
45 46 47 48 49 50 51 54 56 57 58 59 62 63 64 65 66 68 70 72 74 75 77 78 79
80 81 82 84 85 86 90 91 92 93 96 97 98 103 104 107 108 110 111 114 115
116 117 119 121 127 128 131 132 134 135 143 146 147 148 **P**6
Primary Contact: Brent Smith, Chief Executive Officer
CFO: George Kruger CPA, Chief Financial Officer
CMO: Scott Michener M.D., Chief Medical Officer
CIO: James Wellman, Senior Director Information Services
CHR: Donna Wade, Senior Director Human Resources
CNO: Chris Ward, Chief Nursing Officer
Web address: www.ccmhonline.com
Control: Hospital district or authority, Government, Nonfederal **Service**: General
medical and surgical

Staffed Beds: 362 **Admissions**: 9221 **Census**: 249 **Outpatient Visits**: 176168 **Births**: 1299 **Total Expense ($000)**: 262372 **Payroll Expense ($000)**: 103210 **Personnel**: 1555

JIM TALIAFERRO COMMUNITY MENTAL HEALTH (374008), 602 SW 38th
Street, Zip 73505; tel. 580/248–5780 **A**3 10 **F**4 5 29 34 35 36 38 44 53 59 64
66 68 71 87 98 99 100 101 102 103 104 106 130 134
Primary Contact: Brenda Ototivo, Executive Director
Web address: www.odmhsas.org
Control: State, Government, Nonfederal **Service**: Psychiatric

Staffed Beds: 22 **Admissions**: 526 **Census**: 12 **Outpatient Visits**: 5225 **Births**: 0 **Total Expense ($000)**: 9874 **Payroll Expense ($000)**: 4890 **Personnel**: 134

☐ **LAWTON INDIAN HOSPITAL (370170)**, 1515 Lawrie Tatum Road, Zip 73507–
3099; tel. 580/353–0350, (Nonreporting) **A**1 10 **S** U. S. Indian Health Service,
Rockville, MD
Primary Contact: Travis Scott, Chief Executive Officer
COO: John Bear, Hospital Administrator Officer and Supervisor Human Resources
CFO: Sarabeth Sahmaunt, Supervisory Accountant
CMO: Richard Chadek M.D., Clinical Director
CIO: William R Harris, Chief Information Officer
CHR: John Bear, Hospital Administrator Officer and Supervisor Human Resources
CNO: Lenora Littledeer R.N., Director of Nursing
Web address: www.ihs.gov
Control: PHS, Indian Service, Government, federal **Service**: General medical and
surgical

Staffed Beds: 26

☐ △ **SOUTHWESTERN MEDICAL CENTER (370097)**, 5602 SW Lee Boulevard,
Zip 73505–9635; tel. 580/531–4700 **A**1 3 5 7 10 **F**3 8 13 29 30 34 38 40 41
43 45 47 49 50 51 57 59 60 64 65 67 68 70 74 76 77 78 79 81 85 87 89 90
91 92 93 98 99 100 101 102 104 106 107 108 111 114 118 119 127 129
130 131 133 135 146 147 148 **P**6 **S** RCCH HealthCare Partners, Brentwood, TN
Primary Contact: Randy Butler, Interim Chief Executive Officer
CFO: Wayne Colson, Chief Financial Officer
CMO: Aryan Kadivar M.D., Chief Medical Officer
CIO: Kent Lewis, Director Information Services
CHR: Danny Hale, Director Human Resources
CNO: Jayne Thomas, Chief Nursing Officer
Web address: www.swmconline.com
Control: Corporation, Investor–owned (for–profit) **Service**: General medical and
surgical

Staffed Beds: 178 **Admissions**: 4605 **Census**: 87 **Outpatient Visits**: 59871 **Births**: 560 **Total Expense ($000)**: 83599 **Payroll Expense ($000)**: 35642 **Personnel**: 512

LINDSAY—Garvin County

LINDSAY MUNICIPAL HOSPITAL (370214), Highway 19 West, Zip 73052,
Mailing Address: P.O.Box 888, 73052–0888; tel. 405/756–1404 (Nonreporting)
A10
Primary Contact: Jeff Walraven, Chief Executive Officer
Control: City, Government, Nonfederal **Service**: General medical and surgical

Staffed Beds: 26

MADILL—Marshall County

☒ **ALLIANCEHEALTH MADILL (371326)**, 901 South Fifth Avenue, Zip 73446–
3640, Mailing Address: P.O.Box 827, 73446–0827; tel. 580/795–3384 **A**1 10 18
F3 11 29 30 34 35 40 45 59 64 81 87 93 107 114 119 130 133 135 146 **P**5
S Community Health Systems, Inc., Franklin, TN
Primary Contact: Minnie Burkhardt, Chief Executive Officer
CFO: Thomas Briggs, Chief Financial Officer
CMO: Heidi Haislip M.D., Chief of Staff
CHR: D.J. Shawn, Director Human Resources
CNO: Carol Wright, Chief Nursing Officer
Web address: www.myalliancehealth.com
Control: Corporation, Investor–owned (for–profit) **Service**: General medical and
surgical

Staffed Beds: 21 **Admissions**: 290 **Census**: 3 **Outpatient Visits**: 13143 **Births**: 0 **Total Expense ($000)**: 8827 **Payroll Expense ($000)**: 3710 **Personnel**: 64

MANGUM—Greer County

MANGUM REGIONAL MEDICAL CENTER (371330), One Wickersham Drive,
Zip 73554–9116, Mailing Address: P.O.Box 280, 73554–0280; tel. 580/782–
3353 **A**10 18 **F**29 40 41 45 57 68 81 82 85 93 107 111 114 119 127 128 133
148 149 150 **P**6
Primary Contact: Larry Troxell, Chief Executive Officer
COO: Danny Avery, Chief Financial Officer and Chief Operating Officer
CIO: Gregg Burnam, Chief Information Officer and Manager Business Office
Web address: www.qmhealth.org/
Control: Individual, Investor–owned (for–profit) **Service**: General medical and
surgical

Staffed Beds: 25 **Admissions**: 273 **Census**: 3 **Outpatient Visits**: 10000 **Births**: 0

Hospital, Medicare Provider Number, Address, Telephone, Approval, Facility, and Physician Codes, Health Care System

★ American Hospital Association (AHA) membership
☐ The Joint Commission accreditation
○ Healthcare Facilities Accreditation Program
◇ DNV Healthcare Inc. accreditation
⇑ Center for Improvement in Healthcare Quality Accreditation
△ Commission on Accreditation of Rehabilitation Facilities (CARF) accreditation

© 2017 AHA Guide *Many Facility Codes have changed. Please refer to the AHA Guide Code Chart.* Hospitals **A509**

OK

MARIETTA—Love County

★ **MERCY HEALTH LOVE COUNTY (371306)**, 300 Wanda Street, Zip 73448–1200; tel. 580/276–3347 **A**10 18 **F**3 7 11 29 34 40 43 44 50 57 59 77 87 107 114 119 127 133 135 146 148 149 **S** Mercy, Chesterfield, MO
Primary Contact: Richard Barker, Administrator and Chief Executive Officer
CMO: J T O'Connor M.D., Medical Director
CIO: Connie Graham, Public Information Officer
Web address: www.mercyhealthlovecounty.com
Control: Church operated, Nongovernment, not–for–profit **Service**: General medical and surgical

Staffed Beds: 25 **Admissions**: 255 **Census**: 6 **Outpatient Visits**: 15929 **Births**: 0 **Total Expense ($000)**: 14720 **Payroll Expense ($000)**: 8440 **Personnel**: 148

MCALESTER—Pittsburg County

CARL ALBERT COMMUNITY MENTAL HEALTH CENTER (374006), 1101 East Monroe Avenue, Zip 74501–4826; tel. 918/426–7800, (Nonreporting) **A**10
Primary Contact: Debbie Moran, Executive Director
CFO: Konnie Taylor, Chief Financial Officer
CMO: William Mings M.D., Medical Director
CHR: Judy Allen, Human Resource Specialist
Web address: www.odmhsas.org
Control: State, Government, Nonfederal **Service**: Psychiatric

Staffed Beds: 15

★ △ ⇑ **MCALESTER REGIONAL HEALTH CENTER (370034)**, One East Clark Bass Boulevard, Zip 74501–4267, Mailing Address: P.O.Box 1228, 74502–1228; tel. 918/426–1800 **A**7 10 13 21 **F**3 10 11 13 15 18 20 22 26 29 30 34 35 40 43 45 49 50 51 53 54 56 57 59 61 62 63 64 66 68 69 70 75 76 77 79 81 82 85 86 87 90 91 92 93 107 108 109 110 111 114 115 116 117 118 119 125 128 129 130 131 132 135 144 146 147 148 **P**6
Primary Contact: David N. Keith, FACHE, President and Chief Executive Officer
CFO: Darryl Linnington, Chief Financial Officer
CIO: Jason Bray, Chief Information Officer
CHR: Scott Lowe, Director Human Resource
CNO: Kimberly Dawn Stout, Chief Nursing Officer
Web address: www.mrhcok.com
Control: City, Government, Nonfederal **Service**: General medical and surgical

Staffed Beds: 191 **Admissions**: 4378 **Census**: 49 **Outpatient Visits**: 86385 **Births**: 444 **Total Expense ($000)**: 83868 **Payroll Expense ($000)**: 35165 **Personnel**: 686

MIAMI—Ottawa County

⊞ **INTEGRIS MIAMI HOSPITAL (370004)**, 200 Second Avenue SW, Zip 74354–6830; tel. 918/542–6611 **A**1 10 20 **F**7 8 11 13 15 18 20 22 26 28 29 30 34 35 40 45 51 57 59 62 63 70 75 76 77 79 81 85 89 93 98 100 103 104 107 108 110 111 115 119 125 129 130 131 132 135 144 146 147 148 **S** INTEGRIS Health, Oklahoma City, OK
Primary Contact: Jonas Rabel, President
CFO: Valerie Reeves, Chief Financial Officer
CMO: Elaine Mader M.D., Chief of Staff
CHR: Jamil Haynes, Regional Director Human Resources
CNO: Lisa Halstead, Chief Nursing Officer
Web address: www.integrisok.com/miami–hospital
Control: Other not–for–profit (including NFP Corporation) **Service**: General medical and surgical

Staffed Beds: 84 **Admissions**: 2106 **Census**: 24 **Outpatient Visits**: 40420 **Births**: 294 **Total Expense ($000)**: 47413 **Payroll Expense ($000)**: 14994 **Personnel**: 267

★ **WILLOW CREST HOSPITAL (374017)**, 130 'A' Street SW, Zip 74354–6800; tel. 918/542–1836 **A**10 **F**29 75 98 99 101 102 106 130 **P**6
Primary Contact: Shari Murphree, Chief Executive Officer
COO: Steven Goodman, Chief Operating Officer
CFO: Cindy Bell, Director Finance
CMO: Mark Elkington M.D., Chief Medical Officer
CIO: Steven Goodman, Chief Operating Officer
CHR: Kathy Henderson, Director Human Resources
CNO: Kassi Davis, Director Patient Care Services
Web address: www.willowcresthospital.com
Control: Partnership, Investor–owned (for–profit) **Service**: Children's hospital psychiatric

Staffed Beds: 75 **Admissions**: 652 **Census**: 48 **Outpatient Visits**: 0 **Births**: 0 **Total Expense ($000)**: 9681 **Payroll Expense ($000)**: 5302 **Personnel**: 130

MIDWEST CITY—Oklahoma County

⊞ **ALLIANCEHEALTH MIDWEST (370094)**, 2825 Parklawn Drive, Zip 73110–4258; tel. 405/610–4411 **A**1 3 5 10 **F**3 7 8 11 13 14 15 17 18 20 22 26 29 30 31 34 40 43 45 46 49 50 57 59 64 70 74 76 77 78 79 80 81 85 86 87 89 91 93 98 100 101 102 103 107 108 110 111 114 115 119 126 130 132 135 143 146 147 **P**5 **S** Community Health Systems, Inc., Franklin, TN
Primary Contact: Clay Franklin, Chief Executive Officer
COO: Lisa Ellis, Chief Operating Officer
CFO: Cynthia Gray, Interim Chief Financial Officer
CMO: Rockey Talley M.D., Chief Medical Officer
CHR: Dana Leach, Director Human Resources
CNO: Jaconna Joni"" Tiller, Chief Nursing Officer
Web address: www.myalliancehealth.com
Control: Corporation, Investor–owned (for–profit) **Service**: General medical and surgical

Staffed Beds: 255 **Admissions**: 8822 **Census**: 117 **Outpatient Visits**: 92138 **Births**: 585 **Total Expense ($000)**: 128291 **Payroll Expense ($000)**: 42669 **Personnel**: 762

⊞ **MIDWEST CITY SPECIALTY HOSPITAL (372012)**, 8210 National Avenue, Zip 73110–8518; tel. 405/739–0800 **A**1 10 **F**1 3 29 40 82 83 84 85 86 130 135 148 149 **S** Concord Healthcare Group, Lakewood, NJ
Primary Contact: Bobby Snyder, Chief Executive Officer
CFO: Veronica Scott, Business Office Manager
CHR: Anna Emamghoraishi, Human Resources
CNO: Jason Farris, Chief Nursing Officer
Web address: www.midwestcityspecialtyhospital.com/
Control: Individual, Investor–owned (for–profit) **Service**: Acute long–term care hospital

Staffed Beds: 31 **Admissions**: 361 **Census**: 19

MOORE—Cleveland County

NORMAN REGIONAL MOORE See Norman Regional Health System, Norman

MUSKOGEE—Muskogee County

CORNERSTONE HOSPITAL OF OKLAHOMA–MUSKOGEE (372022), 351 South 40th Street, Zip 74401–4916; tel. 918/682–6161, (Includes CORNERSTONE HOSPITAL OF OKLAHOMA–BROKEN ARROW, 1000 West Boise Circle, Third Floor, Broken Arrow, Oklahoma, Zip 74012–4900, 1000 West Boise Circle, 74012–4900, tel. 918/994–8300; Craig Koele, Chief Executive Officer) (Nonreporting) **A**10 22 **S** Cornerstone Healthcare Group, Dallas, TX
Primary Contact: Craig Koele, Chief Executive Officer
CMO: Jeremiah Rutherford, Chief Medical Officer
Web address: www.chghospitals.com/muskogee/
Control: Corporation, Investor–owned (for–profit) **Service**: Acute long–term care hospital

Staffed Beds: 41

EASTAR HEALTH SYSTEM, EAST CAMPUS See Saint Francis Hospital Muskogee

⊞ △ **JACK C. MONTGOMERY VETERANS AFFAIRS MEDICAL CENTER**, 1011 Honor Heights Drive, Zip 74401–1318; tel. 918/577–3000 **A**1 2 3 5 7 **F**3 5 18 28 29 30 31 34 35 38 39 40 44 45 46 50 54 56 57 58 59 61 62 63 64 65 68 70 71 74 75 77 78 79 81 82 83 84 85 86 87 90 91 93 94 96 97 98 100 101 102 103 104 105 107 108 111 114 118 119 130 132 135 146 147 148 149 **P**6 **S** Department of Veterans Affairs, Washington, DC
Primary Contact: Mark E. Morgan, Medical Center Director
CFO: Dwight Beal, Chief Fiscal Services
CMO: Thomas D Schneider D.O., Chief of Staff
CNO: Bonnie Pierce MSN, R.N., Associate Director for Patient Care Services
Web address: www.muskogee.va.gov
Control: Veterans Affairs, Government, federal **Service**: General medical and surgical

Staffed Beds: 89 **Admissions**: 3637 **Census**: 51 **Outpatient Visits**: 459367 **Births**: 0

MUSKOGEE REGIONAL MEDICAL CENTER See Saint Francis Hospital Muskogee

Many Facility Codes have changed. Please refer to the AHA Guide Code Chart. © 2017 AHA Guide

⊞ **SAINT FRANCIS HOSPITAL MUSKOGEE (370025)**, 300 Rockefeller Drive, Zip 74401–5081; tel. 918/682–5501, (Includes EASTAR HEALTH SYSTEM, EAST CAMPUS, 2900 North Main Street, Muskogee, Oklahoma, Zip 74401–4078, tel. 918/687–7777) **A**1 2 10 19 **F**3 8 11 13 15 18 20 22 29 30 31 34 35 37 40 43 44 45 46 47 48 50 51 53 56 57 59 64 70 73 74 75 76 78 79 81 82 85 86 87 89 90 92 96 98 100 101 102 103 107 108 110 111 114 115 119 120 121 123 124 130 131 135 146 147 148 149 **S** RCCH HealthCare Partners, Brentwood, TN
Primary Contact: Anthony R. Young, Chief Executive Officer
COO: Tony Capuano, Chief Operating Officer
CFO: Scott Bailey, Chief Financial Officer
CMO: Jay Gregory M.D., Chief Medical Officer
CIO: James Tolbert, Director Information Systems
CHR: Bill Peterson, Director Human Resources
CNO: James Wells R.N., Chief Nursing Officer
Web address: www.saintfrancis.com/muskogee/Pages/default.aspx
Control: Corporation, Investor–owned (for–profit) **Service:** General medical and surgical

Staffed Beds: 175 Admissions: 9161 Census: 129 Outpatient Visits: 76886 Births: 725 Total Expense ($000): 126982 Payroll Expense ($000): 43880 Personnel: 863

NORMAN—Cleveland County

☐ **GRIFFIN MEMORIAL HOSPITAL (374000)**, 900 East Main Street, Zip 73071–5305, Mailing Address: P.O.Box 151, 73070–0151; tel. 405/573–6600 **A**1 3 5 10 **F**4 29 30 98 102 103 130 132 135 149 **P**6 **S** Oklahoma Department of Mental Health and Substance Abuse Services, Oklahoma City, OK
Primary Contact: Lori Jordan, Executive Director
CFO: Cheryl Cupps, Director Finance
CMO: Clayton Morris, Medical Director
CNO: Mike Abla, Director of Nursing
Web address: www.odmhsas.org
Control: State, Government, Nonfederal **Service:** Psychiatric

Staffed Beds: 120 Admissions: 1214 Census: 106 Outpatient Visits: 594 Births: 0 Total Expense ($000): 26189 Payroll Expense ($000): 11874 Personnel: 332

J. D. MCCARTY CENTER FOR CHILDREN WITH DEVELOPMENTAL DISABILITIES (373300), 2002 East Robinson, Zip 73071–7420; tel. 405/307–2800 **A**10 **F**3 29 35 64 65 75 77 87 90 91 93 119 130 134 135 146
Primary Contact: Vicki Kuestersteffen, Director and Chief Executive Officer
CFO: Erik Paulson, Director of Finance
CMO: Thomas Thurston M.D., Medical Director
CIO: Jeffery Setzer, Administrator Information Systems
CHR: Tina Martinez, Director Human Resources
Web address: www.jdmc.org
Control: State, Government, Nonfederal **Service:** Children's rehabilitation

Staffed Beds: 36 Admissions: 208 Census: 33 Outpatient Visits: 11420 Births: 0 Total Expense ($000): 20978 Payroll Expense ($000): 8872 Personnel: 229

⊞ △ **NORMAN REGIONAL HEALTH SYSTEM (370008)**, 3300 HealthPlex Parkway, Zip 73072, Mailing Address: P.O.Box 1308, 73070–1308; tel. 405/515–1000, (Includes NORMAN REGIONAL HOSPITAL, 901 North Porter Street, Norman, Oklahoma, Zip 73071–6482, P O Box 1308, 73070–1308, tel. 405/307–1000; Richie Splitt, FACHE, President and Chief Executive Office; NORMAN REGIONAL MOORE, 700 South Telephone Road, Moore, Oklahoma, Zip 73160, tel. 405/793–9355; Richie Splitt, FACHE, President and Chief Executive Officer) **A**1 7 10 13 **F**3 7 11 12 13 15 17 18 20 22 24 28 29 30 31 32 34 35 36 37 39 40 42 43 44 45 47 48 49 50 53 54 55 56 57 58 59 63 64 65 69 70 72 74 75 77 78 79 80 81 82 83 84 85 86 87 90 93 94 96 97 98 100 101 102 103 104 107 110 111 114 115 117 118 119 120 123 126 127 129 130 131 132 135 143 145 146 147 148 **P**5 6 8
Primary Contact: Richie Splitt, FACHE, President and Chief Executive Officer
COO: John Manfredo, Chief Operating Officer
CFO: Ken Hopkins, Vice President Finance and Chief Financial Officer
CMO: Aaron Boyd M.D., Chief Medical Officer
CIO: Danny Kelley, Administrative Director, Health Information Technology
CHR: Jim Beyer, Administrative Director Human Resources
Web address: www.normanregional.com
Control: Hospital district or authority, Government, Nonfederal **Service:** General medical and surgical

Staffed Beds: 387 Admissions: 15886 Census: 196 Outpatient Visits: 365444 Births: 2755 Total Expense ($000): 358207 Payroll Expense ($000): 163701 Personnel: 2772

NOWATA—Nowata County

★ **JANE PHILLIPS NOWATA HEALTH CENTER (371305)**, 237 South Locust Street, Zip 74048–3660; tel. 918/273–3102 **A**10 18 **F**3 29 30 34 35 40 50 57 64 68 107 114 119 128 133 146 **P**5 **S** Ascension Healthcare, Saint Louis, MO
Primary Contact: Jason McCauley, Administrator
CMO: David Caughell M.D., Chief of Staff
Web address: www.jpmc.org
Control: Church operated, Nongovernment, not–for–profit **Service:** General medical and surgical

Staffed Beds: 15 Admissions: 166 Census: 5 Outpatient Visits: 13436 Births: 0 Total Expense ($000): 4716 Payroll Expense ($000): 2210 Personnel: 46

OKEENE—Blaine County

★ **OKEENE MUNICIPAL HOSPITAL (371327)**, 207 East 'F' Street, Zip 73763–9441, Mailing Address: P.O.Box 489, 73763–0489; tel. 580/822–4417 **A**10 18 **F**3 29 34 40 50 59 64 65 68 85 93 97 107 130 132 133 135 **P**6
Primary Contact: Shelly Dunham, Chief Executive Officer
COO: Tammi Jantzen, Chief Operating Officer
CFO: Sandra Lamle, Chief Financial Officer
CMO: George S. Stenger D.O., Chief of Staff
CHR: Barbara Creps, Director Human Resources and Accounting
CNO: Tamara Fischer, Chief Nursing Officer
Web address: www.okeenehospital.com
Control: Hospital district or authority, Government, Nonfederal **Service:** General medical and surgical

Staffed Beds: 17 Admissions: 127 Census: 3 Outpatient Visits: 20284 Births: 0 Total Expense ($000): 6753 Payroll Expense ($000): 2767 Personnel: 57

OKEMAH—Okfuskee County

★ ⇑ **CREEK NATION COMMUNITY HOSPITAL (371333)**, 309 North 14th Street, Zip 74859–2028; tel. 918/623–1424, (Nonreporting) **A**10 18 21
Primary Contact: Sheryl Sharber–Howell, Administrator
COO: Rhonda Beaver, Chief Operating Officer
CFO: Tyler McIntosh, Chief Financial Officer
CMO: Lawrence Vark M.D., Chief Medical Officer
CIO: Robert Coffee, Chief Information Officer
CHR: Russell B Torbett, Director Human Resources
CNO: Annette James R.N., MSN, Chief Nursing Officer
Web address: www.creekhealth.org
Control: Other not–for–profit (including NFP Corporation) **Service:** General medical and surgical

Staffed Beds: 18

OKLAHOMA CITY—Cleveland County

⇑ **COMMUNITY HOSPITAL (370203)**, 3100 SW 89th Street, Zip 73159–7900; tel. 405/378–3755 **A**10 21 **F**29 37 40 45 70 77 79 81 82 85 86 87 93 94 107 111 114 115 119 126 129 130 135 146 149 **P**2 6
Primary Contact: Debbie Kearns, Chief Executive Officer
Web address: www.communityhospitalokc.com
Control: Partnership, Investor–owned (for–profit) **Service:** General medical and surgical

Staffed Beds: 45 Admissions: 2370 Census: 8 Outpatient Visits: 96056 Births: 0 Total Expense ($000): 103419 Payroll Expense ($000): 26084 Personnel: 497

OKLAHOMA CITY—Oklahoma County

⊞ △ **ALLIANCEHEALTH DEACONESS (370032)**, 5501 North Portland Avenue, Zip 73112–2099; tel. 405/604–6000, (Nonreporting) **A**1 3 5 7 10 **S** Community Health Systems, Inc., Franklin, TN
Primary Contact: Devon Hyde, Chief Executive Officer
COO: Brett Kirkham, Chief Operating Officer
CIO: Don Bandy, Director Information Technology
CHR: Ellen Gifford, Director Human Resources
CNO: Jayne Thomas, Chief Nursing Officer
Web address: www.deaconessokc.com
Control: Partnership, Investor–owned (for–profit) **Service:** General medical and surgical

Staffed Beds: 238

Hospital, Medicare Provider Number, Address, Telephone, Approval, Facility, and Physician Codes, Health Care System

★ American Hospital Association (AHA) membership   ◯ Healthcare Facilities Accreditation Program   ⇑ Center for Improvement in Healthcare Quality Accreditation
☐ The Joint Commission accreditation   ◇ DNV Healthcare Inc. accreditation   △ Commission on Accreditation of Rehabilitation Facilities (CARF) accreditation

OK

☐ **CEDAR RIDGE HOSPITAL (374023)**, 6501 NE 50th Street, Zip 73141–9118; tel. 405/605–6111, (Includes BETHANY BEHAVIORAL HEALTH, 7600 NW 23rd Street, Bethany, Oklahoma, Zip 73008–4944, tel. 405/792–5360; Heather Joseph, Chief Executive Officer) **A**1 10 **F**98 99 102 103 106 130 149 **P**6 **S** Universal Health Services, Inc., King of Prussia, PA
Primary Contact: Heather Joseph, Chief Executive Officer
Web address: www.cedarridgebhs.com
Control: Corporation, Investor–owned (for–profit) **Service**: Psychiatric

Staffed Beds: 172 **Admissions**: 2909 **Census**: 97 **Outpatient Visits**: 0 **Births**: 0 **Total Expense ($000)**: 21329 **Payroll Expense ($000)**: 9951 **Personnel**: 209

CHILDREN'S HOSPITAL OF OKLAHOMA See OU Medical Center

☒ **CURAHEALTH HOSPITAL OKLAHOMA CITY (372004)**, 1407 North Robinson Avenue, Zip 73103–4823; tel. 405/232–8000, (Nonreporting) (Includes CURAHEALTH OKLAHOMA, 2129 SW 59th Street, Oklahoma City, Oklahoma, Zip 73119, tel. 405/713–5955; Brenda Hood, Chief Executive Officer) **A**1 5 10 **S** Curahealth Hospitals, Garland, TX
Primary Contact: Brenda Hood, Chief Executive Officer
Web address: www.curahealth.com
Control: Corporation, Investor–owned (for–profit) **Service**: Acute long–term care hospital

Staffed Beds: 93

EVERETT TOWER See OU Medical Center

☒ △ **INTEGRIS BAPTIST MEDICAL CENTER (370028)**, 3300 NW Expressway, Zip 73112–4418; tel. 405/949–3011, (Includes INTEGRIS MENTAL HEALTH SYSTEM–SPENCER, 2601 North Spencer Road, Spencer, Oklahoma, Zip 73084–3699, P O Box 11137, Oklahoma City, 73136–0137, tel. 405/717–9800) **A**1 2 3 5 7 10 **F**3 8 11 12 13 15 16 17 18 20 22 24 26 28 29 30 31 32 34 35 36 38 39 40 43 44 45 46 47 49 50 51 54 55 57 58 59 60 62 63 64 68 70 71 72 74 75 76 77 78 79 80 81 82 84 85 86 87 88 89 90 92 93 96 97 98 99 100 101 102 104 105 106 107 108 109 110 111 114 115 116 118 119 120 121 123 124 126 129 130 131 132 133 134 135 137 138 139 140 141 142 146 147 148 149 **P**6 7 **S** INTEGRIS Health, Oklahoma City, OK
Primary Contact: Timothy J. Johnsen, MS, President
CFO: David R Hadley, Managing Director and Chief Financial Officer
CMO: James P White M.D., Chief Medical Officer
CIO: Mark Pasquale, Chief Information Officer
CHR: Jason L Eliot, Vice President Human Resources
Web address: www.integrisok.com
Control: Other not–for–profit (including NFP Corporation) **Service**: General medical and surgical

Staffed Beds: 662 **Admissions**: 23488 **Census**: 427 **Outpatient Visits**: 163722 **Births**: 2844 **Total Expense ($000)**: 702595 **Payroll Expense ($000)**: 193233 **Personnel**: 2296

☒ △ **INTEGRIS SOUTHWEST MEDICAL CENTER (370106)**, 4401 South Western, Zip 73109–3413; tel. 405/636–7000 **A**1 2 3 7 10 13 **F**3 11 13 15 18 20 22 24 26 28 29 30 31 34 35 40 43 44 45 47 49 50 51 57 58 59 60 64 68 70 74 75 76 77 78 79 80 81 82 85 86 87 90 91 92 93 95 96 97 98 100 102 107 108 110 111 114 115 118 119 120 121 123 124 126 129 130 131 132 133 135 143 146 147 148 **S** INTEGRIS Health, Oklahoma City, OK
Primary Contact: Jordan Cash, President
CFO: Dan Davis, Managing Director and Chief Financial Officer
CMO: Philip Mosca M.D., President, Medical Staff
CIO: Mark Pasquale, Chief Information Officer
CHR: Lynn Ketch, Regional Director Integris Southwest Medical Center
CNO: Marva Harrison R.N., Vice President and Chief Nursing Officer
Web address: www.integrisok.com
Control: Other not–for–profit (including NFP Corporation) **Service**: General medical and surgical

Staffed Beds: 303 **Admissions**: 11790 **Census**: 196 **Outpatient Visits**: 134206 **Births**: 1370 **Total Expense ($000)**: 246539 **Payroll Expense ($000)**: 75789 **Personnel**: 1125

☒ **LAKESIDE WOMEN'S HOSPITAL (370199)**, 11200 North Portland Avenue, Zip 73120–5045; tel. 405/936–1500 **A**1 10 **F**3 12 13 15 30 35 40 45 59 64 73 76 81 85 87 110 119 126 130 132 147 **P**6 **S** INTEGRIS Health, Oklahoma City, OK
Primary Contact: Kelley Brewer, R.N., MSN, President
CFO: Darla McCallister, Chief Financial Officer
CMO: Margaret Hall M.D., Chief Medical Officer
Web address: www.lakeside–wh.net
Control: Corporation, Investor–owned (for–profit) **Service**: Obstetrics and gynecology

Staffed Beds: 23 **Admissions**: 1504 **Census**: 10 **Outpatient Visits**: 4385 **Births**: 1416 **Total Expense ($000)**: 21545 **Payroll Expense ($000)**: 7904 **Personnel**: 135

MCBRIDE ORTHOPEDIC HOSPITAL (370222), 9600 Broadway Extension, Zip 73114–7408; tel. 405/486–2100 **A**3 5 10 **F**3 29 34 40 64 68 77 79 81 82 85 86 87 107 111 114 119 126 130 131 146 149 **P**2 6
Primary Contact: Mark Galliart, Chief Executive Officer
CFO: Greg Gisler, Chief Financial Officer
CNO: Krista Reyna, Chief Nursing Officer
Web address: www.mcboh.com
Control: Corporation, Investor–owned (for–profit) **Service**: Orthopedic

Staffed Beds: 60 **Admissions**: 3739 **Census**: 30 **Outpatient Visits**: 150255 **Births**: 0 **Total Expense ($000)**: 129557 **Payroll Expense ($000)**: 52149 **Personnel**: 706

☒ **MERCY HOSPITAL OKLAHOMA CITY (370013)**, 4300 West Memorial Road, Zip 73120–8362; tel. 405/755–1515 **A**1 2 3 5 10 **F**3 11 13 15 28 29 30 31 32 34 35 40 43 44 45 46 47 48 49 50 53 55 57 58 59 60 61 62 63 64 65 68 69 70 72 74 75 76 77 78 79 81 82 83 84 85 86 87 89 90 91 92 93 94 96 100 101 107 108 110 111 114 115 117 118 119 120 121 124 126 129 130 131 132 134 135 143 146 147 148 149 **P**6 **S** Mercy, Chesterfield, MO
Primary Contact: Jim Gebhart Jr, FACHE, President
COO: Aaron Steffens, Chief Operating Officer
CFO: Jon Vitiello, Senior Vice President, Finance Operations and Analytics
CIO: Ellen Stephens, Vice President Information Services
CHR: Becky J Payton, Vice President Human Resources
Web address: www.mercyok.net
Control: Church operated, Nongovernment, not–for–profit **Service**: General medical and surgical

Staffed Beds: 369 **Admissions**: 15496 **Census**: 207 **Outpatient Visits**: 313519 **Births**: 3511 **Total Expense ($000)**: 402225 **Payroll Expense ($000)**: 136169 **Personnel**: 2323

☐ △ **MERCY REHABILITATION HOSPITAL OKLAHOMA CITY (373033)**, 5401 West Memorial Rd, Zip 73142–2026; tel. 405/752–3935 **A**1 7 10 **F**3 28 29 30 87 90 91 96 130 148
Primary Contact: Sharon Smeltzer, Chief Executive Officer
Control: Partnership, Investor–owned (for–profit) **Service**: Rehabilitation

Staffed Beds: 50 **Admissions**: 1167 **Census**: 41 **Outpatient Visits**: 0 **Births**: 0 **Total Expense ($000)**: 15217 **Payroll Expense ($000)**: 7629 **Personnel**: 133

⇑ **NORTHWEST SURGICAL HOSPITAL (370192)**, 9204 North May Avenue, Zip 73120–4419; tel. 405/848–1918 **A**10 21 **F**3 29 40 75 77 79 81 82 85 86 87 107 111 119 130 135 149 **P**2
Primary Contact: Debbie Kearns, Chief Executive Officer
CFO: Cindy Thompson, Chief Financial Officer
CMO: Jimmy Conway M.D., President Medical Staff
Web address: www.nwsurgicalokc.com/
Control: Partnership, Investor–owned (for–profit) **Service**: General medical and surgical

Staffed Beds: 9 **Admissions**: 269 **Census**: 1 **Outpatient Visits**: 12149 **Births**: 0 **Total Expense ($000)**: 13873 **Payroll Expense ($000)**: 2747 **Personnel**: 40

OAKWOOD SPRINGS, 13101 Memorial Springs Court, Zip 73114–2226; tel. 405/438–3000 (Nonreporting)
Primary Contact: Michael A. Truman, Chief Executive Officer
Web address: www.springstone.com/hospitals/hospital–listing.stml#Oakwood%20Springs
Control: Investor–owned (for–profit) **Service**: Psychiatric

Staffed Beds: 72

☐ **OKLAHOMA CENTER FOR ORTHOPEDIC AND MULTI–SPECIALTY SURGERY (370212)**, 8100 South Walker, Suite C, Zip 73139–9402, Mailing Address: P.O.Box 890609, 73189–0609; tel. 405/602–6500 **A**1 10 **F**3 8 12 29 34 35 37 39 40 45 47 48 54 57 59 64 74 79 82 85 86 93 94 97 107 111 129 131 148 149 **P**6 **S** United Surgical Partners International, Addison, TX
Primary Contact: Mike Kimzey, Chief Executive Officer and Administrator
COO: Jeff Bibb, Chief Operating Officer
CFO: Amy Taylor, Chief Financial Officer
CHR: Emily Phipps, Director Human Resources
CNO: Jolena Wyer R.N., Chief Nursing Officer
Web address: www.ocomhospital.com
Control: Partnership, Investor–owned (for–profit) **Service**: Orthopedic

Staffed Beds: 14 **Admissions**: 807 **Census**: 5 **Outpatient Visits**: 40528 **Births**: 0 **Total Expense ($000)**: 52613 **Payroll Expense ($000)**: 14389 **Personnel**: 251

Many Facility Codes have changed. Please refer to the AHA Guide Code Chart. © 2017 AHA Guide

⊞ △ **OKLAHOMA CITY VETERANS AFFAIRS MEDICAL CENTER**, 921 NE 13th Street, Zip 73104–5028; tel. 405/456–1000, (Nonreporting) **A**1 2 3 5 7 8 **S** Department of Veterans Affairs, Washington, DC
Primary Contact: Wade Vlosich, Director
CFO: Michele Pipgrass, Chief Fiscal Service
CMO: Mark Huycke M.D., Chief of Staff
CIO: David Buckley, Acting Chief Information Management Services
CHR: Kyle Inhofe, Chief Human Resources Officer
CNO: Donna Delise, Associate Director Patient Care Services
Web address: www.oklahoma.va.gov
Control: Veterans Affairs, Government, federal **Service**: General medical and surgical

Staffed Beds: 192

⇑ **OKLAHOMA HEART HOSPITAL (370215)**, 4050 West Memorial Road, Zip 73120–8382; tel. 405/608–3200 **A**10 21 **F**17 18 20 22 24 26 28 29 30 34 35 40 50 59 64 68 74 75 81 85 86 87 100 102 107 108 111 114 115 116 117 118 119 126 127 130 135 146 **P**3 6
Primary Contact: John Harvey, M.D., Chief Executive Officer
COO: Peggy Tipton, Chief Operating Officer and Chief Nursing Officer
CFO: Carol Walker, Chief Financial Officer
CMO: John Harvey M.D., Chief Executive Officer
CIO: Michelle Mullins, Chief Information Officer
CHR: Katherine Wynn, Director Human Resource
Web address: www.okheart.com
Control: Corporation, Investor–owned (for–profit) **Service**: Heart

Staffed Beds: 94 **Admissions**: 6592 **Census**: 76 **Outpatient Visits**: 261375 **Births**: 0 **Total Expense ($000)**: 213952 **Payroll Expense ($000)**: 85036 **Personnel**: 1543

⇑ **OKLAHOMA HEART HOSPITAL SOUTH CAMPUS (370234)**, 5200 East I–240 Service Road, Zip 73135; tel. 405/628–6000 **A**10 21 **F**17 18 20 22 24 26 28 29 30 34 35 40 50 53 59 64 66 68 74 75 81 82 85 87 100 107 111 115 116 117 118 119 126 130 135 146 **P**3 6
Primary Contact: John Harvey, M.D., Chief Executive Officer
Web address: www.okheart.com
Control: Corporation, Investor–owned (for–profit) **Service**: Heart

Staffed Beds: 44 **Admissions**: 3961 **Census**: 41 **Outpatient Visits**: 54549 **Births**: 0 **Total Expense ($000)**: 123135 **Payroll Expense ($000)**: 44043 **Personnel**: 501

⇑ **OKLAHOMA SPINE HOSPITAL (370206)**, 14101 Parkway Commons Drive, Zip 73134–6012; tel. 405/749–2700 (Nonreporting) **A**10 21
Primary Contact: Kevin Blaylock, Chief Executive Officer
Web address: www.oklahomaspine.com
Control: Corporation, Investor–owned (for–profit) **Service**: Surgical

Staffed Beds: 12

ONECORE HEALTH (370220), 1044 SW 44th Street, Suite 350, Zip 73109–3609; tel. 405/631–3085 **A**10 **F**3 15 40 54 59 64 74 79 81 82 85 86 87 107 110 111 114 119 149
Primary Contact: Steve Hockert, Chief Executive Officer
CMO: Joel L Frazier M.D., Medical Director
CNO: Teresa Carter, Vice President Patient Care Services
Web address: www.onecorehealth.com
Control: Corporation, Investor–owned (for–profit) **Service**: Orthopedic

Staffed Beds: 8 **Admissions**: 232 **Census**: 1 **Outpatient Visits**: 8712 **Births**: 0 **Total Expense ($000)**: 13863 **Payroll Expense ($000)**: 3272 **Personnel**: 67

⊞ **OU MEDICAL CENTER (370093)**, 1200 Everett Drive, Zip 73104–5047, Mailing Address: P.O.Box 26307, 73126–0307; tel. 405/271–3636, (Includes CHILDREN'S HOSPITAL OF OKLAHOMA, 940 NE 13th Street, Oklahoma City, Oklahoma, Zip 73104, P O Box 26307, 73126, tel. 405/271–6165; EVERETT TOWER, 1200 Everett Drive, Oklahoma City, Oklahoma, Zip 73104, tel. 405/271–4700; OU MEDICAL CENTER EDMOND, 1 South Bryant Avenue, Edmond, Oklahoma, Zip 73034–6309, tel. 405/341–6100; PRESBYTERIAN TOWER, 700 NE 13th Street, Oklahoma City, Oklahoma, Zip 73104–5070, tel. 405/271–5100) **A**1 2 3 5 8 10 **F**3 8 11 12 13 15 17 18 19 20 21 22 23 24 25 26 27 28 29 30 31 32 34 35 37 38 39 40 41 43 45 46 47 48 49 50 51 52 55 56 57 58 59 60 61 63 64 65 66 68 70 71 72 73 74 75 76 77 78 79 81 82 84 85 86 87 88 89 91 92 93 94 96 97 98 99 100 102 103 105 107 108 110 111 114 115 116 117 118 119 120 121 123 124 126 129 130 131 132 135 136 138 142 145 146 147 148 **S** HCA Healthcare, Nashville, TN
Primary Contact: Charles Spicer, President and Chief Executive Officer
COO: Kristina Wallace R.N., Chief Operating Officer
CFO: Mike Reese, Chief Financial Officer
CMO: Curt Steinhart M.D., Chief Medical Officer
CIO: Larry Forsyth, Director Information Services
CHR: Jed M Liuzza, Chief Human Resources Officer
Web address: www.oumedicine.com/oumedicalcenter
Control: Corporation, Investor–owned (for–profit) **Service**: General medical and surgical

Staffed Beds: 735 **Admissions**: 33880 **Census**: 584 **Outpatient Visits**: 330238 **Births**: 4104 **Total Expense ($000)**: 841662 **Payroll Expense ($000)**: 232080 **Personnel**: 3443

PRESBYTERIAN TOWER See OU Medical Center

⊞ **SELECT SPECIALTY HOSPITAL–OKLAHOMA CITY (372009)**, 3524 NW 56th Street, Zip 73112–4518; tel. 405/606–6700 **A**1 10 **F**1 3 12 29 74 75 79 87 107 119 130 148 **S** Select Medical Corporation, Mechanicsburg, PA
Primary Contact: Connie Strickland, Chief Executive Officer
Web address: www.oklahomacity.selectspecialtyhospitals.com/
Control: Corporation, Investor–owned (for–profit) **Service**: Acute long–term care hospital

Staffed Beds: 72 **Admissions**: 741 **Census**: 53 **Outpatient Visits**: 0 **Births**: 0 **Total Expense ($000)**: 29060 **Payroll Expense ($000)**: 12758 **Personnel**: 236

⊞ **ST. ANTHONY HOSPITAL (370037)**, 1000 North Lee Street, Zip 73102–1080, Mailing Address: P.O.Box 205, 73101–0205; tel. 405/272–7000, (Includes BONE AND JOINT HOSPITAL, 1111 North Dewey Avenue, Oklahoma City, Oklahoma, Zip 73103–2609, tel. 405/272–9671; Tammy Powell, FACHE, M.P.H., President; ST. ANTHONY SOUTH, 2129 SW 59th Street, Oklahoma City, Oklahoma, Zip 73119–7001, tel. 405/713–5700) **A**1 2 3 5 10 12 13 **F**3 4 5 7 8 11 12 13 15 17 18 20 22 24 26 28 29 30 31 34 35 36 37 40 42 43 45 46 47 48 49 50 54 56 57 58 59 64 67 70 71 74 76 77 78 79 81 82 84 85 86 87 89 90 91 92 93 96 97 98 99 100 101 102 103 104 105 106 107 108 110 111 114 115 117 118 119 120 121 123 124 126 127 129 130 131 132 136 144 146 147 148 149 **S** SSM Health, Saint Louis, MO
Primary Contact: Tammy Powell, FACHE, M.P.H., President
COO: Marti Jourden FACHE, Chief Quality Officer
CFO: Shasta Manuel, Executive Director Finance
CMO: Kersey Winfree M.D., Chief Medical Officer
CIO: Kevin Olson, Director Information Systems
CHR: Cynthia Brundise, Vice President Human Resources
Web address: www.saintsok.com
Control: Church operated, Nongovernment, not–for–profit **Service**: General medical and surgical

Staffed Beds: 624 **Admissions**: 22919 **Census**: 455 **Outpatient Visits**: 342813 **Births**: 1044 **Total Expense ($000)**: 459702 **Payroll Expense ($000)**: 144685 **Personnel**: 2436

□ **SURGICAL HOSPITAL OF OKLAHOMA (370201)**, 100 SE 59th Street, Zip 73129–3616; tel. 405/634–9300 **A**1 10 **F**3 40 81 111 129
Primary Contact: Phil Ross, Chief Executive Officer
CNO: Cindy Ridge Braly MAAL, R.N., Chief Nursing Officer
Web address: www.sh–ok.com/
Control: Partnership, Investor–owned (for–profit) **Service**: General medical and surgical

Staffed Beds: 12 **Admissions**: 181 **Census**: 1 **Outpatient Visits**: 6070 **Births**: 0 **Total Expense ($000)**: 14182 **Payroll Expense ($000)**: 3731 **Personnel**: 70

Hospital, Medicare Provider Number, Address, Telephone, Approval, Facility, and Physician Codes, Health Care System

★ American Hospital Association (AHA) membership
□ The Joint Commission accreditation
○ Healthcare Facilities Accreditation Program
◇ DNV Healthcare Inc. accreditation
⇑ Center for Improvement in Healthcare Quality Accreditation
△ Commission on Accreditation of Rehabilitation Facilities (CARF) accreditation

OK

✠ **VALIR REHABILITATION HOSPITAL (373025)**, 700 NW Seventh Street, Zip 73102–1212; tel. 405/236–3131 **A**1 10 **F**3 28 29 30 34 40 50 53 54 56 57 59 64 77 82 85 86 87 90 91 93 96 100 130 131 132 135 143 148 **P**1
Primary Contact: Tom Tucker, Chief Executive Officer
COO: Ginger Castleberry, Corporate Risk Manager, Quality and Patient Safety
CFO: Scott Brown, Chief Financial Officer
CMO: Tonya Washburn M.D., Medical Director
CIO: Mark Dickey, Director Business Development
CHR: Bill Turner, Vice President Human Resources
Web address: www.valir.com
Control: Partnership, Investor–owned (for–profit) **Service**: Rehabilitation

Staffed Beds: 49 **Admissions:** 967 **Census:** 31 **Outpatient Visits:** 3458 **Births:** 0 **Total Expense ($000):** 14861 **Payroll Expense ($000):** 8663 **Personnel:** 186	

VETERANS AFFAIRS MEDICAL CENTER See Oklahoma City Veterans Affairs Medical Center

OKMULGEE—Okmulgee County

★ **MUSCOGEE CREEK NATION MEDICAL CENTER (370057)**, 1401 Morris Drive, Zip 74447–6429, Mailing Address: P.O.Box 1038, 74447–1038; tel. 918/756–4233 **A**10 **F**7 11 15 29 34 40 43 50 56 57 59 81 83 85 87 89 98 103 107 108 111 115 119 128 130 133 146 **P**6
Primary Contact: Greg Martin, Administrator
CFO: John W Crawford, Chief Financial Officer
CMO: Michael Sandlin M.D., Chief of Staff
CHR: Stacey R. Burton, Director Human Resources
Web address: www.creekhealth.org/medical–center/
Control: PHS, Indian Service, Government, federal **Service**: General medical and surgical

Staffed Beds: 45 **Admissions:** 624 **Census:** 9 **Outpatient Visits:** 28378 **Births:** 0 **Total Expense ($000):** 25697 **Payroll Expense ($000):** 10939 **Personnel:** 175	

MUSCOGEE CREEK NATION PHYSICAL REHABILITATION CENTER (372023), 1401 Morris Drive, Zip 74447–6429, Mailing Address: P.O.Box 1038, 74447–1938; tel. 918/756–4233 (Nonreporting)
Primary Contact: Greg Martin, Administrator
Control: Other not–for–profit (including NFP Corporation) **Service**: Acute long–term care hospital

Staffed Beds: 12	

OWASSO—Tulsa County

★ **BAILEY MEDICAL CENTER (370228)**, 10502 North 110th East Avenue, Zip 74055–6655; tel. 918/376–8000 **A**10 **F**3 12 13 15 18 29 34 40 45 51 57 70 75 76 77 79 81 85 107 108 110 111 115 119 129 132 146 147 149 **S** Ardent Health Services, Nashville, TN
Primary Contact: Keith Mason, Chief Executive Officer
CFO: Brandon Bullard, Chief Financial Officer
CHR: Tandy Groves, Coordinator Human Resources
Web address: www.baileymedicalcenter.com
Control: Corporation, Investor–owned (for–profit) **Service**: General medical and surgical

Staffed Beds: 37 **Admissions:** 1402 **Census:** 8 **Outpatient Visits:** 32894 **Births:** 390 **Total Expense ($000):** 34786 **Payroll Expense ($000):** 11903 **Personnel:** 193	

★ **ST. JOHN OWASSO (370227)**, 12451 East 100th Street North, Zip 74055–4600; tel. 918/274–5000 **A**10 **F**3 11 13 15 18 29 30 34 35 40 43 45 57 59 64 68 76 79 81 85 87 93 107 108 110 111 114 115 119 130 131 132 146 149 **P**5 6 **S** Ascension Healthcare, Saint Louis, MO
Primary Contact: David L. Phillips, President and Chief Operating Officer
CFO: Katie Caughman, Chief Financial Officer
CMO: Tim Hepner M.D., Chief Medical Officer
CIO: Mike Reeves, Chief Information Officer
CNO: Dan Hall R.N., Chief Operating Officer
Web address: www.stjohnowasso.com
Control: Church operated, Nongovernment, not–for–profit **Service**: General medical and surgical

Staffed Beds: 45 **Admissions:** 1913 **Census:** 12 **Outpatient Visits:** 108120 **Births:** 497 **Total Expense ($000):** 29812 **Payroll Expense ($000):** 9783 **Personnel:** 170	

PAULS VALLEY—Garvin County

★ **PAULS VALLEY GENERAL HOSPITAL (370156)**, 100 Valley Drive, Zip 73075–6613, Mailing Address: P.O.Box 368, 73075–0368; tel. 405/238–5501 **A**10 20 **F**3 7 10 11 15 29 30 40 45 57 59 63 64 65 77 81 82 84 87 89 93 107 111 114 117 119 129 130 132 133 146 147 148 149 **P**3
Primary Contact: Nathan Staggs, Chief Executive Officer
CFO: Dale Semar, Controller
CIO: Rusty Weaver, Manager Information Technology
CHR: Stephanie Dancer, Manager Human Resources
CNO: Kari Howard, Interim Director of Nursing
Web address: www.pvgh.net
Control: City, Government, Nonfederal **Service**: General medical and surgical

Staffed Beds: 53 **Admissions:** 493 **Census:** 4 **Outpatient Visits:** 21959 **Births:** 0 **Total Expense ($000):** 16054 **Payroll Expense ($000):** 6581 **Personnel:** 149	

PAWHUSKA—Osage County

★ **PAWHUSKA HOSPITAL (371309)**, 1101 East 15th Street, Zip 74056–1920; tel. 918/287–3232, (Nonreporting) **A**10 18
Primary Contact: Godwin Feh, Interim Administrator
CMO: Mike Priest M.D., Chief of Staff
Control: City, Government, Nonfederal **Service**: General medical and surgical

Staffed Beds: 15	

PERRY—Noble County

★ ⇑ **PERRY MEMORIAL HOSPITAL (370139)**, 501 North 14th Street, Zip 73077–5099; tel. 580/336–3541 **A**10 20 21 **F**3 11 15 28 29 34 35 40 45 57 59 62 64 65 67 81 85 90 93 97 107 114 127 128 131 133 146 148 149 **P**6 **S** QHR, Brentwood, TN
Primary Contact: Daniel Odegaard, FACHE, Chief Executive Officer
CFO: Courtney Kozikuski, Chief Financial Officer
CMO: Michael Hartwig M.D., Chief of Staff
CIO: Randy Taylor, Chief Information Technology Officer
CHR: Deb Ellis, Director Human Resources
CNO: Jeannie Carey R.N., Director Patient Care
Web address: www.pmh–ok.org
Control: Hospital district or authority, Government, Nonfederal **Service**: General medical and surgical

Staffed Beds: 26 **Admissions:** 290 **Census:** 4 **Outpatient Visits:** 25033 **Births:** 0 **Total Expense ($000):** 8786 **Payroll Expense ($000):** 3913 **Personnel:** 92	

PONCA CITY—Kay County

✠ **ALLIANCEHEALTH PONCA CITY (370006)**, 1900 North 14th Street, Zip 74601–2099; tel. 580/765–3321 **A**1 10 19 **F**3 13 15 18 20 28 29 30 34 35 40 43 45 46 50 51 53 57 59 64 65 66 68 69 70 72 74 75 76 77 78 79 81 82 85 89 90 91 93 97 107 108 110 111 115 119 129 130 131 132 133 145 146 147 148 149 **P**6 **S** Community Health Systems, Inc., Franklin, TN
Primary Contact: Christopher Mendoza, Chief Executive Officer
CFO: Sheryl Schmidtberger, Chief Financial Officer
CIO: William Gazaway, Information Technology Security Officer
CHR: Calvin Hodges, Director Human Resources
CNO: Jeanne Stara R.N., MSN, Chief Nursing Officer
Web address: www.AllianceHealthPoncaCity.com
Control: Corporation, Investor–owned (for–profit) **Service**: General medical and surgical

Staffed Beds: 74 **Admissions:** 2689 **Census:** 24 **Outpatient Visits:** 59874 **Births:** 530 **Total Expense ($000):** 52367 **Payroll Expense ($000):** 21726 **Personnel:** 394	

POTEAU—Le Flore County

★ ⇑ **EASTERN OKLAHOMA MEDICAL CENTER (370040)**, 105 Wall Street, Zip 74953–4433, Mailing Address: P.O.Box 1148, 74953–1148; tel. 918/647–8161, (Nonreporting) **A**10 18 21
Primary Contact: Shaun Keef, Chief Executive Officer and Chief Financial Officer
CFO: Shaun Keef, Chief Executive Officer and Chief Financial Officer
CMO: Dennis Carter M.D., Chief of Staff
CIO: Michael C Huggins, Administrator Network System
Web address: www.eomchospital.com
Control: County, Government, Nonfederal **Service**: General medical and surgical

Staffed Beds: 59	

PRAGUE—Lincoln County

PRAGUE COMMUNITY HOSPITAL (371301), 1322 Klabzuba Avenue, Zip 74864–9005, Mailing Address: P.O.Box S, 74864–1090; tel. 405/567–4922 **A**10 18 **F**3 29 34 40 43 45 55 57 59 64 65 68 81 93 97 107 111 114 119 127 128 130 133 148 **P**6 **S** Rural Community Hospitals of America, Kansas City, MO
Primary Contact: Randy Simmons, Chief Executive Officer
CFO: Doug Erickson, Chief Financial Officer
CMO: Darryl Jackson D.O., Chief of Staff
CIO: Rhonda Whitnum, Director Health Improvement Management
CHR: Angie Brezny, Director Human Resources
Web address: www.praguehospital.com
Control: Corporation, Investor–owned (for–profit) **Service:** General medical and surgical

Staffed Beds: 15 **Admissions:** 103 **Census:** 3 **Outpatient Visits:** 17802 **Births:** 0 **Total Expense ($000):** 4748 **Payroll Expense ($000):** 3152 **Personnel:** 51

PRYOR—Mayes County

✠ **HILLCREST HOSPITAL PRYOR (370015)**, 111 North Bailey Street, Zip 74361–4201; tel. 918/825–1600, (Nonreporting) **A**1 10 **S** Ardent Health Services, Nashville, TN
Primary Contact: Douglas K. Weaver, FACHE, Chief Executive Officer
CMO: Jason Joice M.D., Chief Medical Staff
CHR: Pamela A Guthrie, Chief Human Resources Officer
CNO: Mary Ozment, Chief Nursing Officer
Web address: www.hillcrestpryor.com/
Control: Partnership, Investor–owned (for–profit) **Service:** General medical and surgical

Staffed Beds: 24

PURCELL—McClain County

PURCELL MUNICIPAL HOSPITAL (370158), 1500 North Green Avenue, Zip 73080–1699, Mailing Address: P.O.Box 511, 73080–0511; tel. 405/527–6524 **A**10 **F**3 11 18 29 30 34 35 40 45 48 57 59 64 65 75 79 81 82 86 87 89 114 119 130 132 133 144
Primary Contact: Kem Scully, Chief Executive Officer and Chief Nursing Officer
CMO: David Bryan Dye M.D., Chief Medical Officer
CIO: Jennifer Coates, Coordinator Information Technology
CHR: Tara Selfridge, Manager Human Resources
CNO: Kem Scully, Chief Executive Officer and Chief Nursing Officer
Web address: www.purcellhospital.com
Control: City, Government, Nonfederal **Service:** General medical and surgical

Staffed Beds: 28 **Admissions:** 688 **Census:** 7 **Outpatient Visits:** 46319 **Births:** 0 **Total Expense ($000):** 11637 **Payroll Expense ($000):** 5296 **Personnel:** 114

SALLISAW—Sequoyah County

NORTHEASTERN HEALTH SYSTEM SEQUOYAH (370112), 213 East Redwood Street, Zip 74955–2811, Mailing Address: P.O.Box 505, 74955–0505; tel. 918/774–1100 **A**10 **F**3 8 11 14 15 18 29 30 32 34 35 40 43 45 49 50 57 59 62 63 64 65 70 77 81 84 86 87 91 93 107 111 114 115 119 128 129 130 132 133 146 147 148 149 **P**5
Primary Contact: Julie Ward, Chief Executive Officer
CMO: Jennifer Scoufos M.D., Chief of Staff
CIO: Gary McClanahan, Chief Information Officer
CHR: Shayna Brooke Roberts, Director Human Resources
CNO: Ozalina Martinez R.N., Director of Nursing
Web address: www.sequoyahmemorial.com/home.php
Control: Hospital district or authority, Government, Nonfederal **Service:** General medical and surgical

Staffed Beds: 26 **Admissions:** 610 **Census:** 9 **Births:** 0 **Personnel:** 159

SAPULPA—Creek County

★ **ST. JOHN SAPULPA (371312)**, 519 South Division Street, Zip 74066–4501, Mailing Address: P.O.Box 1368, 74067–1368; tel. 918/224–4280 **A**10 18 **F**3 8 11 14 29 30 34 35 40 45 57 59 64 68 79 81 85 86 87 107 111 119 128 130 132 133 135 143 149 **P**5 6 **S** Ascension Healthcare, Saint Louis, MO
Primary Contact: Ron Hoffman, Chief Operating Officer
COO: Ron Hoffman, Chief Operating Officer
CFO: John W Crawford, Chief Financial Officer
CMO: Jason Lepak M.D., Medical Director
CNO: Kelly Johnson R.N., Chief Nursing Officer
Web address: www.stjohnhealthsystem.com/sapulpa
Control: Church operated, Nongovernment, not–for–profit **Service:** General medical and surgical

Staffed Beds: 25 **Admissions:** 815 **Census:** 15 **Outpatient Visits:** 36161 **Births:** 0 **Total Expense ($000):** 22089 **Payroll Expense ($000):** 6790 **Personnel:** 118

SAYRE—Beckham County

SAYRE MEMORIAL HOSPITAL, 911 Hospital Drive, Zip 73662–1206; tel. 580/928–5541 (Nonreporting)
Primary Contact: , R.N.
Control: Other not–for–profit (including NFP Corporation) **Service:** General medical and surgical

Staffed Beds: 25

SEILING—Dewey County

★ **SEILING MUNICIPAL HOSPITAL (371332)**, Highway 60 NE, Zip 73663, Mailing Address: P.O.Box 720, 73663–0720; tel. 580/922–7361 **A**10 18 **F**7 28 32 34 40 56 57 59 65 77 82 86 93 97 107 127 128 133 135 147 148 **P**5
Primary Contact: Jennifer Coons, Chief Executive Officer
CFO: Nancy Freed, Chief Financial Officer
CMO: Kenneth Duffy M.D., Medical Director
CHR: Sandy Landreth, Director Human Resources
Web address: www.seilinghospital.com
Control: City, Government, Nonfederal **Service:** General medical and surgical

Staffed Beds: 18 **Admissions:** 133 **Census:** 1 **Outpatient Visits:** 3628 **Births:** 0 **Total Expense ($000):** 3409 **Payroll Expense ($000):** 1699 **Personnel:** 32

SEMINOLE—Seminole County

✠ **ALLIANCEHEALTH SEMINOLE (370229)**, 2401 Wrangler Boulevard, Zip 74868–1917; tel. 405/303–4000 **A**1 10 **F**3 11 15 18 29 30 34 40 41 43 44 45 46 47 48 49 50 57 59 64 65 68 79 81 87 89 91 92 93 96 97 107 108 109 110 111 112 114 115 119 129 133 146 147 148 **P**5 **S** Community Health Systems, Inc., Franklin, TN
Primary Contact: Adam Bracks, Chief Executive Officer
CMO: Nikki Chawla M.D., Medical Director
CHR: Lori Friend, Human Resources Director
CNO: Barbara Lewis, Chief Nursing Officer
Web address: www.alliancehealthseminole.com/
Control: Corporation, Investor–owned (for–profit) **Service:** General medical and surgical

Staffed Beds: 32 **Admissions:** 674 **Census:** 6 **Outpatient Visits:** 22927 **Births:** 4

SHATTUCK—Ellis County

★ **NEWMAN MEMORIAL HOSPITAL (370007)**, 905 South Main Street, Zip 73858–9205; tel. 580/938–2551 **A**10 18 20 **F**3 40 45 81 82 107 114
Primary Contact: Ed Majors, Chief Executive Officer
CFO: Kellcie Skinner, Controller
CMO: Danna Stuart M.D., Chief Medical Officer
CIO: Robert Neal, Manager Information Technology Services
CNO: Rylee Casper R.N., Chief Nursing Officer
Web address: www.newmanmemorialhospital.org
Control: City, Government, Nonfederal **Service:** General medical and surgical

Staffed Beds: 15 **Admissions:** 157 **Census:** 1 **Births:** 0

SHAWNEE—Pottawatomie County

CORNERSTONE HOSPITAL OF OKLAHOMA–SHAWNEE (372019), 1900 Gordon Cooper Drive, 2nd Floor, Zip 74801–8603, Mailing Address: P.O.Box 1245, 74802–1245; tel. 405/395–5800 (Nonreporting) **A**10 **S** Cornerstone Healthcare Group, Dallas, TX
Primary Contact: Elizabeth Waytula, Chief Executive Officer
COO: Cindy Linck, Chief Nursing Officer
CMO: Rakesh Shrivastava M.D., Chief Medical Officer
Web address: www.chghospitals.com/shawnee/
Control: Corporation, Investor–owned (for–profit) **Service:** Acute long–term care hospital

Staffed Beds: 34

Hospital, Medicare Provider Number, Address, Telephone, Approval, Facility, and Physician Codes, Health Care System

★ American Hospital Association (AHA) membership
☐ The Joint Commission accreditation
○ Healthcare Facilities Accreditation Program
◇ DNV Healthcare Inc. accreditation
⇑ Center for Improvement in Healthcare Quality Accreditation
△ Commission on Accreditation of Rehabilitation Facilities (CARF) accreditation

OK

⊠ **ST. ANTHONY SHAWNEE HOSPITAL (370149)**, 1102 West MacArthur Street, Zip 74804–1744; tel. 405/273–2270 **A**1 10 19 **F**3 11 13 15 18 20 22 29 30 31 34 35 40 43 45 50 57 59 60 64 65 68 69 70 75 76 77 78 79 81 82 84 87 94 107 110 111 114 115 119 121 123 129 130 131 132 135 144 146 147 148 **P**6 **S** SSM Health, Saint Louis, MO
Primary Contact: Charles E. Skillings, President and Chief Executive Officer
COO: Angela Mohr R.N., MS, Vice President Nursing and Chief Operating Officer
CFO: Jennifer Pierce, Administrative Director of Finance
CMO: Gaynell Anderson M.D., Medical Director
CHR: Michael Spears, Human Resource Leader
CNO: Angela Mohr R.N., MS, Vice President Nursing and Chief Operating Officer
Web address: www.stanthonyshawnee.com
Control: Other not–for–profit (including NFP Corporation) **Service**: General medical and surgical

Staffed Beds: 70 **Admissions:** 3775 **Census:** 33 **Outpatient Visits:** 113565 **Births:** 798 **Total Expense ($000):** 76659 **Payroll Expense ($000):** 25206 **Personnel:** 532

UNITY HEALTH CENTER See St. Anthony Shawnee Hospital

SPENCER—Oklahoma County

INTEGRIS MENTAL HEALTH SYSTEM–SPENCER See Integris Baptist Medical Center, Oklahoma City

STIGLER—Haskell County

HASKELL COUNTY COMMUNITY HOSPITAL (371335), 401 Northwest 'H' Street, Zip 74462–1625; tel. 918/967–4682 **A**10 18 **F**3 11 34 40 50 57 64 65 67 83 84 86 87 89 90 91 92 93 94 97 107 114 119 128 130 133 **S** Rural Community Hospitals of America, Kansas City, MO
Primary Contact: Donald E. Buchanan, Chief Executive Officer
CMO: Stephen Woodson D.O., Chief of Staff
CIO: Steve Hurst, Information Technology Specialist
Web address: www.haskellhospital.com
Control: Corporation, Investor–owned (for–profit) **Service**: General medical and surgical

Staffed Beds: 20 **Admissions:** 288 **Census:** 7 **Outpatient Visits:** 7764 **Births:** 0 **Total Expense ($000):** 6830 **Payroll Expense ($000):** 3690 **Personnel:** 82

HASKELL COUNTY HEALTHCARE SYSTEM See Haskell County Community Hospital

STILLWATER—Payne County

★ ⇑ **STILLWATER MEDICAL CENTER (370049)**, 1323 West Sixth Avenue, Zip 74074–4399, Mailing Address: P.O.Box 2408, 74076–2408; tel. 405/372–1480 **A**3 5 10 21 **F**3 8 13 15 18 20 22 28 29 31 34 35 40 43 45 46 47 48 49 50 51 53 57 59 62 64 65 68 69 70 74 75 76 78 79 81 82 85 87 90 91 93 94 97 107 108 110 111 115 119 126 129 130 131 132 135 144 146 147 148 149 **P**4 6
Primary Contact: Denise Webber, President and Chief Executive Officer
CFO: Alan Lovelace, Vice President and Chief Financial Officer
CMO: Steve Cummings M.D., Chief of Medical Staff
CIO: Chris Roark, Chief Information Officer
CHR: Keith Hufnagel, Director Human Resources
CNO: Elizabeth Michael R.N., MS, Vice President Patient Care Services and Chief Nursing Officer
Web address: www.stillwater–medical.org
Control: Hospital district or authority, Government, Nonfederal **Service**: General medical and surgical

Staffed Beds: 97 **Admissions:** 3559 **Census:** 35 **Outpatient Visits:** 127582 **Births:** 844 **Total Expense ($000):** 154133 **Payroll Expense ($000):** 65369 **Personnel:** 1086

STILWELL—Adair County

STILWELL MEMORIAL HOSPITAL (370178), 1401 West Locust, Zip 74960–3275, Mailing Address: P.O.Box 272, 74960–0272; tel. 918/696–3101, (Nonreporting) **A**10
Primary Contact: Alan L. Adams, Administrator
Web address: www.stilwellmemorialhospital.com
Control: Corporation, Investor–owned (for–profit) **Service**: General medical and surgical

Staffed Beds: 30

STROUD—Lincoln County

STROUD REGIONAL MEDICAL CENTER (371316), Highway 66 West, Zip 74079, Mailing Address: P.O.Box 530, 74079–0530; tel. 918/968–3571 **A**10 18 **F**29 30 34 35 40 41 45 57 59 68 93 107 114 119 128 130 133 143 148 149 **P**5 **S** First Physicians Capital Group, Inc., Oklahoma City, OK
Primary Contact: Ed Dyer, Chief Executive Officer
CFO: Richard E Rentsch, President
CMO: Ken Darvin M.D., Chief of Staff
CIO: Donna Buchanan, Director Nursing
CHR: Leannette Raffety, Administrative Generalist
Web address: www.stroudhospital.com/
Control: Other not–for–profit (including NFP Corporation) **Service**: General medical and surgical

Staffed Beds: 25 **Admissions:** 174 **Census:** 5 **Births:** 0 **Personnel:** 85

SULPHUR—Murray County

★ **ARBUCKLE MEMORIAL HOSPITAL (371328)**, 2011 West Broadway Street, Zip 73086–4221, Mailing Address: P.O. Box 1109, 73086–8109; tel. 580/622–2161 **A**10 18 **F**3 11 29 32 40 45 56 57 81 87 93 107 119 133 135 148 **P**6 **S** Mercy, Chesterfield, MO
Primary Contact: Darin Farrell, Administrator
CFO: Denise Welch, Chief Financial Officer
CMO: Ryan Oden D.O., Chief of Staff
CIO: Tiffany Sands, Manager Health Information
CHR: Sallie Tomlinson, Manager Human Resources
CNO: Sarah Freehill, Chief Nursing Officer
Web address: www.arbucklehospital.com/
Control: County, Government, Nonfederal **Service**: General medical and surgical

Staffed Beds: 13 **Admissions:** 526 **Census:** 12 **Outpatient Visits:** 26503 **Total Expense ($000):** 14014 **Payroll Expense ($000):** 7634 **Personnel:** 122

TAHLEQUAH—Cherokee County

★ ⇑ **CHEROKEE NATION W.W. HASTINGS INDIAN HOSPITAL (370171)**, 100 South Bliss Avenue, Zip 74464–2512; tel. 918/458–3100, (Nonreporting) **A**10 21
Primary Contact: Brian Hail, Chief Executive Officer
COO: Mitchell Thornbrugh, Administrative Officer
CMO: Douglas Nolan M.D., Medical Director
CIO: Mitchell Thornbrugh, Acting Chief Information Officer
CNO: Valerie J Rogers, Director of Nursing
Web address: www.cherokee.org
Control: Public Health Service, Public, Federal **Service**: General medical and surgical

Staffed Beds: 58

★ **NORTHEASTERN HEALTH SYSTEM (370089)**, 1400 East Downing Street, Zip 74464–3324, Mailing Address: P.O.Box 1008, 74465–1008; tel. 918/456–0641 **A**10 13 20 **F**3 7 11 13 15 17 18 20 22 24 28 29 30 31 34 35 39 40 43 45 46 47 49 51 57 59 60 64 68 70 75 76 77 78 79 80 81 82 85 87 89 90 93 97 98 103 107 108 110 111 114 115 116 117 118 119 120 121 123 129 130 135 144 146 147 148 **P**6
Primary Contact: James T. Berry, FACHE, Executive Vice President and Administrator
COO: Mark McCroskey, Vice President Operations
CFO: Julie Ward, Vice President Finance
CIO: Julie Ward, Vice President Finance
CHR: Phyllis Smith, Vice President Human Resources
CNO: Donna Dallis R.N., Vice President Patient Care
Web address: www.nhs–ok.org/
Control: City, Government, Nonfederal **Service**: General medical and surgical

Staffed Beds: 90 **Admissions:** 3612 **Census:** 42 **Outpatient Visits:** 163364 **Births:** 301 **Total Expense ($000):** 100796 **Payroll Expense ($000):** 34457 **Personnel:** 913

TALIHINA—Latimer County

⊠ **CHOCTAW NATION HEALTH CARE CENTER (370172)**, One Choctaw Way, Zip 74571–2022; tel. 918/567–7000 **A**1 10 13 **F**3 4 5 7 12 13 15 18 29 34 35 38 39 40 45 50 53 54 56 57 58 59 64 65 68 71 74 75 76 79 81 87 89 91 93 97 107 110 111 119 127 129 130 135 141 142 143 144 146 147 148 149
Primary Contact: Todd Hallmark, Chief Executive Officer
COO: Todd Hallmark, Chief Operating Officer
CMO: Jason Hill M.D., Chief Medical Officer
CIO: Dwane Sorrells, Chief Information Officer
CHR: Jami Beckwith, Director Human Resources
CNO: Lisa Isaac, Chief Nursing Officer
Web address: www.cnhsa.com
Control: PHS, Indian Service, Government, federal **Service**: General medical and surgical

Staffed Beds: 44 **Admissions:** 1358 **Census:** 11 **Outpatient Visits:** 211452 **Births:** 500 **Personnel:** 1538

Many Facility Codes have changed. Please refer to the AHA Guide Code Chart. © 2017 AHA Guide

OK

TISHOMINGO—Johnston County

JOHNSTON MEMORIAL HOSPITAL See Mercy Hospital Tishomingo

★ **MERCY HOSPITAL TISHOMINGO (371304)**, 1000 South Byrd Street, Zip 73460–3299; tel. 580/371–2327 **A**10 18 **F**3 29 40 43 44 68 85 107 108 114 133 149 **S** Mercy, Chesterfield, MO
Primary Contact: Gary Sharum, Administrator
CFO: Lisa Dowling, Manager Finance
CHR: Arlita Hummelke, Manager Human Resources
Web address: www.mercy.net/
Control: Church operated, Nongovernment, not–for–profit **Service**: General medical and surgical

Staffed Beds: 25 **Admissions**: 273 **Census**: 5 **Outpatient Visits**: 5002 **Births**: 0 **Total Expense ($000)**: 6224 **Payroll Expense ($000)**: 3318 **Personnel**: 52

TULSA—Tulsa County

AMG SPECIALTY HOSPITAL–TULSA (372011), 2408 East 81st Street, Suite 2800, Zip 74104–6510; tel. 918/710–3620, (Includes CONTINUOUS CARE CENTERS OF OKLAHOMA, 744 West Ninth Floor, Tulsa, Oklahoma, Zip 74127, tel. 918/599–4604) **A**10 **S** AMG Integrated Healthcare Management, Lafayette, LA
Primary Contact: Kelly Rose, R.N., Chief Executive Officer
COO: Mike Harris, Chief Operating Officer
CFO: Basil Wyatt, Chief Financial Officer
CMO: Mark Myers M.D., Chief Medical Officer
CIO: Dana Jetton, Chief Information Officer
CHR: Donna Nagel, Director Human Resources
Web address: www.amgoftulsa.com/
Control: Other not–for–profit (including NFP Corporation) **Service**: Acute long–term care hospital

Staffed Beds: 46

△ **BROOKHAVEN HOSPITAL (374012)**, 201 South Garnett Road, Zip 74128–1805; tel. 918/438–4257 **A**7 10 **F**4 5 29 30 38 74 75 77 98 104 106 130 132
Primary Contact: Rolf B. Gainer, Ph.D., Chief Executive Officer
CFO: Kenneth Pierce, Chief Financial Officer
CMO: Mark Gage D.O., Medical Director
CHR: Heather Dudley, Director Administrative Services
CNO: Debbie Jones, Director of Nursing
Web address: www.brookhavenhospital.com
Control: Corporation, Investor–owned (for–profit) **Service**: Psychiatric

Staffed Beds: 64 **Admissions**: 986 **Census**: 52 **Outpatient Visits**: 2498 **Births**: 0 **Total Expense ($000)**: 11033 **Payroll Expense ($000)**: 6672 **Personnel**: 187

CONTINUOUS CARE CENTERS OF TULSA See AMG Specialty Hospital–Tulsa

⊞ ⇑ **HILLCREST HOSPITAL – SOUTH (370202)**, 8801 South 101st East Avenue, Zip 74133–5716; tel. 918/294–4000 **A**1 10 21 **F**3 13 15 18 20 22 24 26 28 29 34 40 43 47 49 51 64 76 79 81 85 86 87 91 93 97 107 108 110 111 114 115 119 126 129 130 131 146 147 148 **S** Ardent Health Services, Nashville, TN
Primary Contact: Lynn M. Mergen, Chief Executive Officer
COO: Matthew Morgan, Associate Administrator
CFO: James Washecka, Chief Financial Officer
CMO: David L. Pohl M.D., Chief of Staff
CIO: David Graser, Vice President and Chief Information Officer
CHR: Rachel Steward, Director Human Resources
CNO: Dava Baldridge R.N., Chief Nursing Officer
Web address: www.southcresthospital.com
Control: Corporation, Investor–owned (for–profit) **Service**: General medical and surgical

Staffed Beds: 160 **Admissions**: 7886 **Census**: 96 **Outpatient Visits**: 87141 **Births**: 1197 **Total Expense ($000)**: 132020 **Payroll Expense ($000)**: 42269 **Personnel**: 654

★ ⇑ **HILLCREST MEDICAL CENTER (370001)**, 1120 South Utica Avenue, Zip 74104–4090; tel. 918/579–1000 **A**3 5 10 21 **F**3 11 13 15 16 17 18 20 22 24 26 28 29 30 31 34 37 40 43 45 46 47 48 49 50 51 53 57 58 59 60 64 68 70 72 74 75 76 78 79 80 81 83 84 85 86 87 90 93 98 100 107 108 110 111 114 115 116 117 118 119 120 121 123 124 126 129 130 131 135 145 146 147 148 **S** Ardent Health Services, Nashville, TN
Primary Contact: Kevin J. Gross, FACHE, Chief Executive Officer
COO: Farron Sneed, Chief Operating Officer
CFO: Donald Baker CPA, Chief Financial Officer
CIO: Richard Gomez, Assistant Vice President Information Technology Division
CHR: Donald Morris, Vice President Human Resources
CNO: Jodi Simmons, Chief Nursing Officer
Web address: www.hillcrestmedicalcenter.com
Control: Corporation, Investor–owned (for–profit) **Service**: General medical and surgical

Staffed Beds: 508 **Admissions**: 23766 **Census**: 332 **Outpatient Visits**: 133871 **Births**: 3029 **Total Expense ($000)**: 419373 **Payroll Expense ($000)**: 128743 **Personnel**: 2141

⊞ **LAUREATE PSYCHIATRIC CLINIC AND HOSPITAL (374020)**, 6655 South Yale Avenue, Zip 74136–3329; tel. 918/481–4000 **A**1 3 5 10 **F**4 5 40 98 99 100 101 102 103 104 105 106 146 **P**6 **S** Saint Francis Health System, Tulsa, OK
Primary Contact: Michele A. Keeling, Senior Vice President and Administrator
CFO: Eric Schick, Senior Vice President, Chief Administrative Officer and Chief Financial Officer
CMO: Mark I Frost M.D., Senior Vice President Medical Affairs
CNO: Lynn A. Sund, Senior Vice President, Administrator and Chief Nursing Executive
Web address: www.laureate.com
Control: Other not–for–profit (including NFP Corporation) **Service**: Psychiatric

Staffed Beds: 90 **Admissions**: 2759 **Census**: 69 **Outpatient Visits**: 57981 **Births**: 0 **Total Expense ($000)**: 33992 **Payroll Expense ($000)**: 19424 **Personnel**: 375

MEADOWBROOK SPECIALTY HOSPITAL OF TULSA See Post Acute Medical Specialty Hospital Of Tulsa

○ **OKLAHOMA STATE UNIVERSITY MEDICAL CENTER (370078)**, 744 West Ninth Street, Zip 74127–9020; tel. 918/599–1000, (Nonreporting) **A**3 10 11 12 13
Primary Contact: Matthew Adams, Administrator
COO: Jeff Stroup, Chief Operating Officer
CFO: Sara Bradley, Chief Financial Officer
CMO: Damon Baker D.O., Chief Medical Officer
CIO: Heidi Holmes, Chief Information Officer
CNO: Joy Upshaw, Chief Nursing Officer
Web address: www.osumc.net
Control: City, Government, Nonfederal **Service**: General medical and surgical

Staffed Beds: 191

OKLAHOMA SURGICAL HOSPITAL (370210), 2408 East 81st Street, Suite 300, Zip 74137–4215; tel. 918/477–5000 **A**3 5 10 **F**3 12 29 30 34 35 37 40 41 44 45 50 51 58 64 65 68 74 75 77 79 81 82 85 86 87 93 94 107 108 111 114 119 126 130 131 148 149 **P**2
Primary Contact: Rick Ferguson, Chief Executive Officer
CFO: Dub Cleland, Chief Financial Officer
Web address: www.oklahomasurgicalhospital.com
Control: Partnership, Investor–owned (for–profit) **Service**: Surgical

Staffed Beds: 49 **Admissions**: 3961 **Census**: 23 **Outpatient Visits**: 36243 **Births**: 0 **Total Expense ($000)**: 91424 **Payroll Expense ($000)**: 20112 **Personnel**: 525

★ **PAM REHABILITATION HOSPITAL OF TULSA**, 10020 East 91st Street, Zip 74133; tel. 918/893–2400 (Nonreporting) **S** Post Acute Medical, LLC, Enola, PA
Primary Contact: Jerry Elenbaas, Chief Executive Officer and Division President
CNO: Charles Myers, Chief Nursing Officer
Web address: www.warmsprings.org/our–facilities/outpatient–rehabilitation
Control: Investor–owned (for–profit) **Service**: Rehabilitation

Staffed Beds: 41

PARKSIDE PSYCHIATRIC HOSPITAL AND CLINIC (374021), 1620 East 12th Street, Zip 74120–5407; tel. 918/582–2131 **A**3 5 10 **F**3 5 35 38 59 98 99 102 103 104 105 106 146 149 150
Primary Contact: Debra Moore–Jones, Chief Executive Officer
CFO: Saunya Moore, Chief Financial Officer
CMO: Marvin Jin M.D., Medical Director
CIO: Joe Vitali, Director Information Technology
CHR: David Patterson, Director Human Resources
Web address: www.parksideinc.org
Control: Other not–for–profit (including NFP Corporation) **Service**: Psychiatric

Staffed Beds: 60 **Admissions**: 1794 **Census**: 59 **Outpatient Visits**: 20992 **Births**: 0 **Total Expense ($000)**: 13901 **Payroll Expense ($000)**: 7787

Hospital, Medicare Provider Number, Address, Telephone, Approval, Facility, and Physician Codes, Health Care System

★ American Hospital Association (AHA) membership
□ The Joint Commission accreditation
○ Healthcare Facilities Accreditation Program
◇ DNV Healthcare Inc. accreditation
⇑ Center for Improvement in Healthcare Quality Accreditation
△ Commission on Accreditation of Rehabilitation Facilities (CARF) accreditation

○ **PINNACLE SPECIALTY HOSPITAL (370233)**, 2408 East 81st Street, Suite 600, Zip 74137–4200; tel. 918/392–2780 (Nonreporting) **A**10 11
Primary Contact: Marc Cravens, Interim Chief Executive Officer
CFO: Marc Cravens, Chief Financial Officer
CHR: Roberta Wagle, Director Human Resources
CNO: Jill Voelkel, Chief Nursing Officer
Web address: www.pinnaclespecialtyhospital.com/
Control: Partnership, Investor–owned (for–profit) **Service:** General medical and surgical

Staffed Beds: 4

☒ **POST ACUTE MEDICAL SPECIALTY HOSPITAL OF TULSA (372018)**, 3219 South 79th East Avenue, Zip 74145–1343; tel. 918/663–8183 **A**1 10 **F**1 3 29 40 45 60 68 70 75 87 94 107 108 114 130 143 148 **S** Post Acute Medical, LLC, Enola, PA
Primary Contact: Lee A. Simpson Jr, Chief Executive Officer
CFO: Lee A Simpson Jr, Chief Executive Officer
Web address: www.postacutetulsa.com
Control: Corporation, Investor–owned (for–profit) **Service:** Acute long–term care hospital

Staffed Beds: 60 **Admissions:** 606 **Census:** 37 **Outpatient Visits:** 5 **Births:** 0 **Total Expense ($000):** 18494 **Payroll Expense ($000):** 6864 **Personnel:** 166

SAINT FRANCIS HEART HOSPITAL See Saint Francis Hospital

☒ **SAINT FRANCIS HOSPITAL (370091)**, 6161 South Yale Avenue, Zip 74136–1902; tel. 918/494–2200, (Includes CHILDREN'S HOSPITAL AT SAINT FRANCIS, 6161 South Yale Avenue, Tulsa, Oklahoma, Zip 74136–1902, tel. 918/502–6714; Shannon M. Filosa, Executive Director Women's and Children; SAINT FRANCIS HEART HOSPITAL, 6151 South Yale Avenue, Tulsa, Oklahoma, Zip 74136–1902, tel. 918/494–1817; Douglas Williams, Vice President, Saint Francis Heart Hospital) **A**1 2 3 5 10 **F**3 7 8 11 12 13 15 19 20 21 22 23 24 25 26 27 28 29 30 31 32 35 37 39 40 41 43 44 45 46 47 48 49 50 51 54 55 56 57 58 59 60 61 64 66 68 70 72 73 74 75 76 77 78 79 80 81 82 83 84 85 86 87 88 89 90 92 93 100 102 107 108 110 111 114 115 116 117 118 119 120 121 123 124 126 129 130 131 132 135 136 138 141 146 147 148 **P**6 **S** Saint Francis Health System, Tulsa, OK
Primary Contact: Jake Henry Jr, Chief Executive Officer and President, Saint Francis Health System
COO: Barry L Steichen, Executive Vice President and Chief Operating Officer, Saint Francis Health System
CFO: Eric Schick, Senior Vice President and Chief Financial Officer, Saint Francis Health System
CMO: Mark I Frost M.D., Senior Vice President Medical Affairs, Saint Francis Health System
CIO: Meridith Coburn, Vice President Information Services
CHR: Maria E. Isquierdo, Executive Director, Human Resources
CNO: Lynn A. Sund, Senior Vice President, Chief Nurse Executive, Saint Francis Health System and Administrator, Saint Francis Hospital
Web address: www.saintfrancis.com
Control: Other not–for–profit (including NFP Corporation) **Service:** General medical and surgical

Staffed Beds: 871 **Admissions:** 44946 **Census:** 648 **Outpatient Visits:** 389574 **Births:** 4128 **Total Expense ($000):** 799943 **Payroll Expense ($000):** 298897 **Personnel:** 5134

☒ **SAINT FRANCIS HOSPITAL SOUTH (370218)**, 10501 East 91st Street, Zip 74133–5790; tel. 918/307–6010 **A**1 10 **F**11 13 15 18 20 22 26 29 30 34 35 37 39 40 44 48 49 50 51 57 58 60 61 64 68 70 72 75 76 79 80 81 82 85 87 107 108 110 111 114 115 118 119 130 146 148 **P**6 **S** Saint Francis Health System, Tulsa, OK
Primary Contact: David S. Weil, Senior Vice President and Administrator
COO: Barry L Steichen, Executive Vice President and Chief Operating Officer
CFO: Eric Schick, Chief Financial Officer
CMO: Mark I Frost M.D., Senior Vice President Medical Affairs
CIO: Meridith Coburn, Vice President, Information Systems
CHR: Maria E. Isquierdo, Executive Director, Human Resources
CNO: Lynn A. Sund, Chief Nursing Executive
Web address: www.saintfrancis.com/south/
Control: Other not–for–profit (including NFP Corporation) **Service:** General medical and surgical

Staffed Beds: 84 **Admissions:** 4419 **Census:** 45 **Outpatient Visits:** 73866 **Births:** 1088 **Total Expense ($000):** 71872 **Payroll Expense ($000):** 27519 **Personnel:** 452

☒ **SELECT SPECIALTY HOSPITAL–TULSA MIDTOWN (372007)**, 1125 South Trenton Avenue, 3rd Floor, Zip 74120–5418; tel. 918/579–7300 **A**1 10 **F**1 3 29 75 85 87 130 148 **S** Select Medical Corporation, Mechanicsburg, PA
Primary Contact: Raymond Carnevale, Interim Chief Executive Officer
CMO: E Joe Schelbar M.D., Medical Director
CNO: Connie Ryan, Chief Nursing Officer
Web address: www.tulsa.selectspecialtyhospitals.com/
Control: Corporation, Investor–owned (for–profit) **Service:** Acute long–term care hospital

Staffed Beds: 56 **Admissions:** 324 **Census:** 23 **Outpatient Visits:** 0 **Births:** 0 **Total Expense ($000):** 13702 **Payroll Expense ($000):** 6316 **Personnel:** 87

☐ **SHADOW MOUNTAIN BEHAVIORAL HEALTH SYSTEM (374024)**, 6262 South Sheridan Road, Zip 74133–4055; tel. 918/492–8200, (Nonreporting) **A**1 5 **S** Universal Health Services, Inc., King of Prussia, PA
Primary Contact: Mike Kistler, Chief Executive Officer
CFO: Kirt Penrod, Chief Financial Officer
CMO: K. Michael Saliba M.D., Medical Director
CHR: Jordan Cooke, Director Human Resources
Web address: www.shadowmountainbhs.com
Control: Corporation, Investor–owned (for–profit) **Service:** Children's hospital psychiatric

Staffed Beds: 226

☐ **SOUTHWESTERN REGIONAL MEDICAL CENTER (370190)**, 10109 East 79th Street, Zip 74133–4564; tel. 918/286–5000 **A**1 2 5 10 **F**3 15 29 30 31 34 35 36 40 44 45 46 47 49 50 53 57 58 59 64 67 70 75 77 78 81 82 84 85 86 87 93 97 100 107 108 110 111 114 116 117 118 119 120 121 123 124 126 130 132 135 143 145 146 148 **P**6 **S** Cancer Treatment Centers of America, Schaumburg, IL
Primary Contact: Jay Foley, Interim President and Chief Executive Officer
COO: Jay Foley, Chief Operating Officer
CFO: David Hedges, Chief Financial Officer
CMO: Daniel Nader D.O., Chief of Staff
CIO: Craig Olson, Director Information Technology
CHR: Ryan Crawford, Director Talent
CNO: Denise Geuder, Vice President Patient Care Service and Chief Nursing Officer
Web address: www.cancercenter.com
Control: Corporation, Investor–owned (for–profit) **Service:** Cancer

Staffed Beds: 40 **Admissions:** 683 **Census:** 13 **Outpatient Visits:** 47011 **Births:** 0 **Personnel:** 576

☒ **ST. JOHN MEDICAL CENTER (370114)**, 1923 South Utica Avenue, Zip 74104–6502; tel. 918/744–2345 **A**1 2 3 5 10 **F**3 8 9 11 12 13 14 15 17 18 19 20 22 24 26 28 29 30 31 34 35 37 39 40 43 45 47 48 50 51 53 54 56 57 58 59 60 61 63 64 65 66 68 70 72 73 74 75 76 77 78 79 80 81 82 83 84 85 86 87 88 89 90 92 93 94 96 97 100 104 107 108 110 111 114 115 116 117 118 119 120 121 123 124 126 129 130 131 132 135 138 141 143 145 146 147 148 149 **P**1 5 **S** Ascension Healthcare, Saint Louis, MO
Primary Contact: Jeffrey D. Nowlin, President and Chief Operating Officer
COO: Jeffrey D Nowlin, President and Chief Operating Officer
CFO: Wayne Walthall, Vice President and Chief Financial Officer
CMO: William Allred M.D., Vice President Medical Affairs
CIO: Mike Reeves, Vice President
CHR: John Page Bachman, Corporate Vice President
CNO: Pamela Kiser R.N., MS, Chief Nursing Executive and Vice President of Nursing
Web address: www.sjmc.org
Control: Church operated, Nongovernment, not–for–profit **Service:** General medical and surgical

Staffed Beds: 527 **Admissions:** 32971 **Census:** 438 **Outpatient Visits:** 272071 **Births:** 2434 **Total Expense ($000):** 501136 **Payroll Expense ($000):** 141697 **Personnel:** 2556

ST. JOHN REHABILITATION HOSPITAL, 1819 East 19th Street, 5th Floor, Zip 74104–5407; tel. 918/744–2338 (Nonreporting) **S** HEALTHSOUTH Corporation, Birmingham, AL
Primary Contact: David Nicholas, Chief Executive Officer
Web address: www.stjohnrehab.com
Control: Corporation, Investor–owned (for–profit) **Service:** Rehabilitation

Staffed Beds: 22

☒ **TULSA SPINE AND SPECIALTY HOSPITAL (370216)**, 6901 South Olympia Avenue, Zip 74132–1843; tel. 918/388–5701, (Nonreporting) **A**1 10 **S** Ardent Health Services, Nashville, TN
Primary Contact: Terry L. Woodbeck, Chief Executive Officer
CFO: Thom Biby, Chief Financial Officer
CMO: David Fell M.D., Chief Medical Officer
Web address: www.tulsaspinehospital.com
Control: Corporation, Investor–owned (for–profit) **Service:** General medical and surgical

Staffed Beds: 21

Many Facility Codes have changed. Please refer to the AHA Guide Code Chart. © 2017 AHA Guide

VINITA—Craig County

OKLAHOMA FORENSIC CENTER, 24800 South 4420 Road, Zip 74301–5544, Mailing Address: P.O.Box 69, 74301–0069; tel. 918/256–7841 **A**3 **F**39 98 106 **P**5 6 **S** Oklahoma Department of Mental Health and Substance Abuse Services, Oklahoma City, OK
Primary Contact: Kevan Finley, Chief Executive Officer
CFO: Miriam Harris, Director Finance
CMO: Satwant Tandon M.D., Director of Clinical Services
CIO: Kevin Marble, Director Information Technology
CHR: Julie Jacobs, Director Human Resources
CNO: Glenda Satterwhite, Director of Nursing
Web address: www.odmhsas.org
Control: State, Government, Nonfederal **Service**: Psychiatric

Staffed Beds: 200 Admissions: 263 Census: 184 Outpatient Visits: 0
Births: 0 Total Expense ($000): 17485 Payroll Expense ($000): 8570
Personnel: 229

★ **SAINT FRANCIS HOSPITAL VINITA (370065)**, 735 North Foreman Street, Zip 74301–1418, Mailing Address: P.O.Box 326, 74301–0326; tel. 918/256–7551, (Nonreporting) **A**10 20 **S** Saint Francis Health System, Tulsa, OK
Primary Contact: Todd Schuster, Administrator
CMO: Ed Allensworth M.D., Medical Director
CHR: Darlene R Nolte, Chief Human Resource Officer
CNO: Ann Carr R.N., Chief Nursing Officer
Web address: www.saintfrancis.com/vinita/Pages/default.aspx
Control: Other not–for–profit (including NFP Corporation) **Service**: General medical and surgical

Staffed Beds: 55

WAGONER—Wagoner County

WAGONER COMMUNITY HOSPITAL (370166), 1200 West Cherokee Street, Zip 74467–4624, Mailing Address: P.O.Box 407, 74477–0407; tel. 918/485–5514 **A**10 **F**3 11 15 18 28 29 30 34 39 40 41 45 50 51 57 59 64 65 68 70 75 79 81 82 85 87 89 98 102 107 108 110 111 115 118 119 129 130 131 135 146 147 148 149
Primary Contact: Jimmy Leopard, FACHE, Chief Executive Officer
COO: Louise Dodson R.N., Chief Operating Officer and Chief Nursing Officer
CFO: Rebecca Sharp, Chief Financial Officer
CMO: Casey Hanna M.D., Chief of Staff
CIO: Jim Riley, Director Information Technology
CHR: Barnetta Pofahl, Director Human Resources
CNO: Louise Dodson R.N., Chief Nursing Officer
Web address: www.wagonerhospital.com
Control: Hospital district or authority, Government, Nonfederal **Service**: General medical and surgical

Staffed Beds: 100 Admissions: 2273 Census: 33 Outpatient Visits: 24794
Births: 0 Total Expense ($000): 19819 Payroll Expense ($000): 9302
Personnel: 185

WATONGA—Blaine County

★ **MERCY HOSPITAL WATONGA (371302)**, 500 North Clarence Nash Boulevard, Zip 73772–2845, Mailing Address: P.O.Box 370, 73772–0370; tel. 580/623–7211 **A**10 18 **F**3 11 29 30 34 40 43 50 57 59 64 68 75 85 87 93 107 114 119 130 132 133 135 149 **P**6 **S** Mercy, Chesterfield, MO
Primary Contact: Bobby Stitt, R.N., Administrator
CFO: Patricia Dianne Robertson, Chief Financial Officer
CHR: Mary Jo Messelt, Manager Human Resources
Web address: www.mercy.net/watongaok/practice/mercy–hospital–watonga
Control: Church operated, Nongovernment, not–for–profit **Service**: General medical and surgical

Staffed Beds: 17 Admissions: 241 Census: 3 Outpatient Visits: 9287
Births: 0 Total Expense ($000): 6496 Payroll Expense ($000): 3773
Personnel: 46

WAURIKA—Jefferson County

★ **JEFFERSON COUNTY HOSPITAL (371311)**, Highway 70 and 81, Zip 73573–3075, Mailing Address: P.O.Box 90, 73573–0090; tel. 580/228–2344 **A**10 18 **F**11 40 43 64 93 107 119 127 129 133 146 **P**6 **S** Duncan Regional Hospital, Duncan, OK
Primary Contact: Richard Gillespie, Chief Executive Officer
CFO: Richard Tallon, Chief Financial Officer
CMO: Rob Linzman D.O., Chief of Staff
CIO: Nikki McGahey, Information Officer
Web address: www.jeffersoncountyhospital.net
Control: Hospital district or authority, Government, Nonfederal **Service**: General medical and surgical

Staffed Beds: 25 Admissions: 98 Census: 1 Outpatient Visits: 7715
Births: 0

WEATHERFORD—Custer County

★ **WEATHERFORD REGIONAL HOSPITAL (371323)**, 3701 East Main Street, Zip 73096–3309; tel. 580/772–5551 **A**10 18 **F**3 11 13 15 29 34 40 42 43 45 64 68 75 76 77 81 86 87 93 107 108 110 111 115 119 130 133 135 144 146 147 148 **P**6 7
Primary Contact: Debbie Howe, Chief Executive Officer
CFO: Stephanie Helton, Chief Financial Officer
CMO: Jonathan Ray Long M.D., Chief of Staff
CIO: Amy Outhier, Director Health Information Management
CHR: Tawnya Paden, Director Human Resources
CNO: Delvin Mast R.N., Director of Nursing
Web address: www.weatherfordhospital.com
Control: Hospital district or authority, Government, Nonfederal **Service**: General medical and surgical

Staffed Beds: 22 Admissions: 627 Census: 6 Outpatient Visits: 56504
Births: 161 Total Expense ($000): 18471 Payroll Expense ($000): 7242
Personnel: 144

WILBURTON—Latimer County

LATIMER COUNTY GENERAL HOSPITAL (370072), 806 Highway 2 North, Zip 74578–3698; tel. 918/465–2391, (Nonreporting) **A**10
Primary Contact: Nicholas Weston, Administrator and Chief Executive Officer
CMO: Richard Valbuena M.D., Medical Director
CHR: Rachel Chinnock, Chief Human Resources Officer
Web address: www.lcghok.com/
Control: County, Government, Nonfederal **Service**: General medical and surgical

Staffed Beds: 33

WOODWARD—Woodward County

⊠ **ALLIANCEHEALTH WOODWARD (370002)**, 900 17th Street, Zip 73801–2448; tel. 580/256–5511 **A**1 10 20 **F**3 13 15 29 30 31 34 40 43 45 50 57 59 64 68 70 75 76 77 79 81 82 85 93 107 108 110 111 115 119 124 127 129 130 131 133 135 146 149 **S** Community Health Systems, Inc., Franklin, TN
Primary Contact: Ross Korkmas, Chief Executive Officer
CFO: Tom Earley, Chief Financial Officer
CIO: Larry Churchill, Director Information Services
CHR: Melinda Brock, Director Human Resources
CNO: Kimberly N Arnold R.N., Chief Nursing Officer and Interim Chief Quality Officer
Web address: www.woodwardhospital.com
Control: Corporation, Investor–owned (for–profit) **Service**: General medical and surgical

Staffed Beds: 40 Admissions: 1503 Census: 13 Outpatient Visits: 91251
Births: 341

YUKON—Canadian County

⊠ **INTEGRIS CANADIAN VALLEY HOSPITAL (370211)**, 1201 Health Center Parkway, Zip 73099–6381; tel. 405/717–6800 **A**1 10 **F**3 11 13 15 18 20 22 29 30 34 40 44 45 46 49 52 57 59 60 64 68 70 76 79 81 87 107 108 110 111 115 118 119 130 135 145 146 148 **P**8 **S** INTEGRIS Health, Oklahoma City, OK
Primary Contact: Rex Van Meter, President
COO: Cindy White CPA, Vice President of Operations
CFO: Errol Mitchell, Chief Financial Officer
CHR: Lynn Ketch, Human Resources Recruiter Generalist
CNO: Teresa Gray, Chief Nursing Officer and Assistant Vice President
Web address: www.integris–health.com
Control: Other not–for–profit (including NFP Corporation) **Service**: General medical and surgical

Staffed Beds: 75 Admissions: 2628 Census: 23 Outpatient Visits: 49986
Births: 829 Total Expense ($000): 54420 Payroll Expense ($000): 17043
Personnel: 239

Hospital, Medicare Provider Number, Address, Telephone, Approval, Facility, and Physician Codes, Health Care System

★ American Hospital Association (AHA) membership
☐ The Joint Commission accreditation
○ Healthcare Facilities Accreditation Program
◇ DNV Healthcare Inc. accreditation
⇑ Center for Improvement in Healthcare Quality Accreditation
△ Commission on Accreditation of Rehabilitation Facilities (CARF) accreditation

OREGON

ALBANY—Linn County

★ ⫟ **SAMARITAN ALBANY GENERAL HOSPITAL (380022)**, 1046 Sixth Avenue, SW, Zip 97321–1999; tel. 541/812–4000 **A**10 21 **F**3 5 11 13 15 18 28 29 30 31 34 35 36 37 40 43 45 47 49 53 54 57 59 61 63 64 67 68 70 73 74 76 77 78 79 81 84 85 86 87 89 92 93 97 104 107 108 110 111 114 116 117 119 129 130 131 132 135 144 145 146 147 148 149 150 **P**6 **S** Samaritan Health Services, Corvallis, OR
Primary Contact: David G. Triebes, Chief Executive Officer
CFO: Daniel B Smith, Vice President Finance
Web address: www.samhealth.org
Control: Other not–for–profit (including NFP Corporation) **Service**: General medical and surgical

Staffed Beds: 70 **Admissions**: 2590 **Census**: 23 **Outpatient Visits**: 304786 **Births**: 541 **Total Expense ($000)**: 173887 **Payroll Expense ($000)**: 73843 **Personnel**: 825

ASHLAND—Jackson County

★ ⫟ **ASANTE ASHLAND COMMUNITY HOSPITAL (380005)**, 280 Maple Street, Zip 97520–1593; tel. 541/201–4000 **A**10 21 **F**3 11 13 15 29 30 34 35 36 40 43 48 49 50 59 62 64 65 70 75 76 79 81 82 84 85 86 87 93 97 107 110 114 119 130 132 135 143 145 146 147 148 **P**6 **S** Asante Health System, Medford, OR
Primary Contact: Sheila Clough, Chief Executive Officer
CFO: Patrick Hocking, Chief Financial Officer
CMO: Bill Steinsick M.D., Chief Medical Staff
CIO: Mark Hetz, Chief Information Officer
CHR: Gregg Edwards, Vice President Human Resources
CNO: Susan Montgomery, Chief Nursing Officer
Web address: www.ashlandhospital.org
Control: Other not–for–profit (including NFP Corporation) **Service**: General medical and surgical

Staffed Beds: 36 **Admissions**: 1350 **Census**: 12 **Outpatient Visits**: 49989 **Births**: 290 **Total Expense ($000)**: 52769 **Payroll Expense ($000)**: 17626 **Personnel**: 270

ASTORIA—Clatsop County

★ **COLUMBIA MEMORIAL HOSPITAL (381320)**, 2111 Exchange Street, Zip 97103–3329; tel. 503/325–4321 **A**5 10 18 **F**3 8 11 13 15 18 19 28 29 30 31 34 35 36 40 43 44 46 50 51 57 58 59 63 64 68 70 75 76 77 78 79 81 85 86 87 89 91 93 97 107 108 110 111 114 115 119 130 131 132 133 134 135 143 144 146 147 148 **P**5 8
Primary Contact: Erik Thorsen, Chief Executive Officer
CFO: Stephanie D Brenden, Vice President Finance
CMO: Bruce Bobek, President Professional Staff
CIO: Galina Gandy, Vice President Information Technology
CHR: Lucy G Dupree, Director Human Resources
CNO: Trece Gurrad, Vice President Patient Care Services
Web address: www.columbiamemorial.org
Control: Other not–for–profit (including NFP Corporation) **Service**: General medical and surgical

Staffed Beds: 25 **Admissions**: 1587 **Census**: 13 **Outpatient Visits**: 191682 **Births**: 344 **Total Expense ($000)**: 95275 **Payroll Expense ($000)**: 39004 **Personnel**: 533

BAKER CITY—Baker County

⊞ **SAINT ALPHONSUS MEDICAL CENTER – BAKER CITY (381315)**, 3325 Pocahontas Road, Zip 97814–1464; tel. 541/523–6461 **A**1 10 18 **F**3 11 13 15 29 31 34 35 36 37 40 43 44 45 50 59 70 75 76 77 79 81 82 83 85 91 93 97 107 110 115 119 127 128 129 131 133 143 144 146 147 148 **P**6 **S** Trinity Health, Livonia, MI
Primary Contact: Phil Harrop, President
CFO: Robert D Wehling, Interim Chief Financial Officer
CHR: Jerry Nickell, Vice President Human Resource and Mission
Web address: www.saintalphonsus.org/bakercity
Control: Other not–for–profit (including NFP Corporation) **Service**: General medical and surgical

Staffed Beds: 25 **Admissions**: 702 **Census**: 7 **Outpatient Visits**: 45903 **Births**: 107 **Total Expense ($000)**: 32360 **Payroll Expense ($000)**: 14212 **Personnel**: 186

ST. ELIZABETH HEALTH SERVICES See Saint Alphonsus Medical Center – Baker City

BANDON—Coos County

★ **SOUTHERN COOS HOSPITAL AND HEALTH CENTER (381304)**, 900 11th Street SE, Zip 97411–9114; tel. 541/347–2426 **A**10 18 **F**3 11 15 29 34 35 40 45 50 57 59 64 65 75 81 82 85 87 97 107 110 119 132 133 135 146 148 149 **P**6
Primary Contact: JoDee Tittle, Chief Executive Officer
CFO: Robin Triplett, Chief Financial Officer
CIO: Mandy Calvert, Director Information Systems
CHR: Cyndy Vollmer, Director Human Resources
CNO: Carol Meijer, Chief Nursing Officer
Web address: www.southerncoos.org
Control: Hospital district or authority, Government, Nonfederal **Service**: General medical and surgical

Staffed Beds: 19 **Admissions**: 233 **Census**: 2 **Outpatient Visits**: 51151 **Births**: 0 **Total Expense ($000)**: 17334 **Payroll Expense ($000)**: 7030 **Personnel**: 105

BEND—Deschutes County

⊞ **ST. CHARLES BEND (380047)**, 2500 NE Neff Road, Zip 97701–6015; tel. 541/382–4321 **A**1 2 3 5 10 19 **F**3 8 11 12 13 15 18 19 20 21 22 24 26 28 29 30 31 34 35 36 37 38 40 42 43 44 45 46 47 49 50 51 54 57 58 59 60 62 63 64 65 67 68 70 72 74 75 76 77 78 79 81 82 84 85 86 87 89 90 91 92 93 97 98 99 100 101 102 104 107 108 111 112 114 115 119 120 121 122 124 126 129 130 132 135 142 144 146 147 148 149 **P**6 **S** St. Charles Health System, Inc., Bend, OR
Primary Contact: Iman Simmons, Chief Operating Officer and Interim President
CFO: Jennifer Welander CPA, Senior Vice President Finance and Chief Financial Officer
CMO: Jeffrey Absalon M.D., Chief Physician Officer
CIO: Jerimiah Brickhouse, Chief Information Officer
CHR: Rebecca Berry, Vice President Human Resources
CNO: Karen Reed R.N., MSN, Chief Nursing Officer
Web address: www.stcharleshealthcare.org
Control: Other not–for–profit (including NFP Corporation) **Service**: General medical and surgical

Staffed Beds: 249 **Admissions**: 16349 **Census**: 178 **Outpatient Visits**: 122340 **Births**: 1772 **Total Expense ($000)**: 393748 **Payroll Expense ($000)**: 181695 **Personnel**: 2819

BURNS—Harney County

★ **HARNEY DISTRICT HOSPITAL (381307)**, 557 West Washington Street, Zip 97720–1497; tel. 541/573–7281 **A**3 10 18 **F**3 7 13 15 29 31 34 35 40 43 45 50 53 57 59 64 65 70 75 76 78 81 82 85 86 93 107 111 114 119 127 129 131 132 133 146 149 **P**6
Primary Contact: Dan Grigg, Chief Executive Officer
CFO: Catherine White, Chief Financial Officer
CMO: Sarah Laiosa M.D., Chief Medical Staff
CIO: Tanya Strong, Manager Information Technology
CHR: Sammie Masterson, Director Human Resources
CNO: Deana Altman, Interim Chief Nursing Officer
Web address: www.harneydh.com
Control: Hospital district or authority, Government, Nonfederal **Service**: General medical and surgical

Staffed Beds: 20 **Admissions**: 379 **Census**: 4 **Outpatient Visits**: 41503 **Births**: 63 **Total Expense ($000)**: 22816 **Payroll Expense ($000)**: 10732 **Personnel**: 157

CLACKAMAS—Clackamas County

⊞ ⫟ **KAISER SUNNYSIDE MEDICAL CENTER (380091)**, 10180 SE Sunnyside Road, Zip 97015–8970; tel. 503/652–2880 **A**1 2 3 5 10 21 **F**3 11 12 13 15 17 18 20 22 24 26 29 30 31 34 35 40 45 46 47 49 51 60 61 64 65 68 70 72 74 75 76 77 78 79 81 84 85 86 87 93 94 97 102 107 108 110 111 114 115 118 119 130 135 141 146 147 148 149 **P**6 **S** Kaiser Foundation Hospitals, Oakland, CA
Primary Contact: Justin N. Evander, Administrator and Chief Operating Officer
CFO: Justin N. Evander, Chief Financial Officer
CMO: Richard Hunt M.D., Chief Operating Officer
CIO: Mark A Burmester, Vice President Strategy and Communications
CHR: Rich Smith, Vice President Human Resources
CNO: Lauren M Bridge R.N., Chief Nursing Officer
Web address: www.kaiserpermanente.org
Control: Other not–for–profit (including NFP Corporation) **Service**: General medical and surgical

Staffed Beds: 302 **Admissions**: 18177 **Census**: 193 **Outpatient Visits**: 65485 **Births**: 2380 **Total Expense ($000)**: 390832 **Payroll Expense ($000)**: 158576 **Personnel**: 2063

Many Facility Codes have changed. Please refer to the AHA Guide Code Chart. © 2017 AHA Guide

COOS BAY—Coos County

⊠ **BAY AREA HOSPITAL (380090)**, 1775 Thompson Road, Zip 97420–2198; tel.
541/269–8111 **A**1 2 3 5 10 **F**3 11 12 13 15 18 20 22 26 28 29 31 34 35 40
43 45 46 48 50 51 57 59 62 68 70 73 74 75 76 77 78 79 81 84 85 89 91 92
93 98 99 100 101 102 104 107 108 110 111 115 118 119 120 121 123 126
129 130 132 135 146 147 148 149
Primary Contact: Paul Janke, FACHE, President and Chief Executive Officer
COO: Ben Pfau, Chief Facility and Information Officer
CFO: Sam Patterson, Chief Financial Officer
CIO: Bob Adams, Director Information Services
CHR: Suzie Q McDaniel, Chief Human Resource Officer
Web address: www.bayareahospital.org
Control: Hospital district or authority, Government, Nonfederal **Service**: General
medical and surgical

Staffed Beds: 130 **Admissions**: 5799 **Census**: 64 **Outpatient Visits**: 90663
Births: 678 **Total Expense ($000)**: 168619 **Payroll Expense ($000)**:
63940 **Personnel**: 867

COQUILLE—Coos County

★ **COQUILLE VALLEY HOSPITAL (381312)**, 940 East Fifth Street, Zip 97423–
1699; tel. 541/396–3101 **A**10 18 **F**3 8 11 15 29 34 35 40 43 45 50 57 59 62
64 67 70 75 79 81 82 85 86 87 97 107 110 111 114 118 119 128 132 133
135 146 148 149 **P**6
Primary Contact: David J. Ameen, Interim Chief Executive Officer
CFO: Jim Basch, Chief Financial Officer
CMO: James Sinnott M.D., Chief Medical Staff
CIO: Curt Carpenter, Manager Information Technology
CHR: Monte Johnston, Manager Human Resources
Web address: www.cvhospital.org
Control: Hospital district or authority, Government, Nonfederal **Service**: General
medical and surgical

Staffed Beds: 17 **Admissions**: 616 **Census**: 5 **Outpatient Visits**: 23768
Births: 0 **Total Expense ($000)**: 26053 **Payroll Expense ($000)**: 12226
Personnel: 176

CORVALLIS—Benton County

★ ⇧ **GOOD SAMARITAN REGIONAL MEDICAL CENTER (380014)**, 3600 NW
Samaritan Drive, Zip 97330–3737, Mailing Address: P.O.Box 1068, 97339–1068;
tel. 541/768–5111 **A**2 10 12 13 19 21 **F**3 11 12 13 15 17 18 20 22 24 26 28
29 30 31 34 35 36 37 40 43 46 47 49 53 54 56 57 58 59 61 62 64 68 70 73
74 76 77 78 79 81 82 84 85 86 87 89 92 93 97 98 99 100 101 102 103 104
107 108 110 111 114 115 116 117 118 119 120 121 123 124 126 129 130
131 132 135 144 146 147 148 149 **P**6 **S** Samaritan Health Services, Corvallis,
OR
Primary Contact: Becky A. Pape, R.N., Chief Executive Officer
CFO: Daniel B Smith, Vice President Finance
CIO: Bob Power, Vice President Information Services
CHR: Doug Boysen, Chief Legal Counsel and Vice President Human Resources
CNO: William Howden, Vice President Nursing
Web address: www.samhealth.org
Control: Other not–for–profit (including NFP Corporation) **Service**: General
medical and surgical

Staffed Beds: 182 **Admissions**: 9528 **Census**: 120 **Outpatient Visits**:
419862 **Births**: 1090 **Total Expense ($000)**: 408077 **Payroll Expense
($000)**: 162304 **Personnel**: 1748

COTTAGE GROVE—Lane County

★ **PEACEHEALTH COTTAGE GROVE COMMUNITY MEDICAL CENTER
(381301)**, 1515 Village Drive, Zip 97424–9700; tel. 541/942–0511 **A**10 18 **F**3
11 15 29 32 34 35 38 40 44 50 59 64 65 66 68 75 91 93 97 99 102 107 110
115 119 127 130 132 133 146 148 **P**6 **S** PeaceHealth, Vancouver, WA
Primary Contact: Tim Herrmann, R.N., Administrator
Web address: www.peacehealth.org
Control: Church operated, Nongovernment, not–for–profit **Service**: General
medical and surgical

Staffed Beds: 14 **Admissions**: 408 **Census**: 3 **Outpatient Visits**: 36321
Births: 0 **Total Expense ($000)**: 33953 **Payroll Expense ($000)**: 11727
Personnel: 130

DALLAS—Polk County

SALEM HEALTH WEST VALLEY (381308), 525 SE Washington Street,
Zip 97338–2834, Mailing Address: P.O.Box 378, 97338–0378; tel. 503/623–
8301 **A**10 18 **F**3 15 35 40 50 59 64 75 79 81 85 93 97 107 108 110 111 114
119 131 132 133 143 146 148 **P**6 **S** Salem Health, Salem, OR
Primary Contact: Bruce C. Rodgers, Chief Administrative Officer
CFO: James Parr, Chief Financial Officer
CMO: Ralph Yates D.O., Chief Medical Officer
CHR: Laurie C Barr, Vice President Human Resources
CNO: Sarah Horn, Chief Nursing Officer
Web address: www.salemhealth.org/wvh/
Control: Other not–for–profit (including NFP Corporation) **Service**: General
medical and surgical

Staffed Beds: 6 **Admissions**: 122 **Census**: 1 **Outpatient Visits**: 67485
Births: 0 **Total Expense ($000)**: 23130 **Payroll Expense ($000)**: 11399
Personnel: 128

ENTERPRISE—Wallowa County

★ **WALLOWA MEMORIAL HOSPITAL (381306)**, 601 Medical Parkway, Zip 97828–
5124; tel. 541/426–3111 **A**3 5 10 18 **F**3 7 11 13 15 29 30 31 34 35 40 43 45
46 56 57 59 62 64 68 75 76 78 79 81 82 85 87 93 97 102 107 110 115 119
127 128 131 132 133 134 135 143 145 148 149 **P**6
Primary Contact: Larry Davy, Chief Executive Officer
CFO: Dan Jessup, Chief Financial Officer
CMO: Keith DeYoung M.D., Chief Medical Staff
CIO: John Straughan, Director Information Technology
CHR: Linda Childers, Director Human Resources
CNO: Jenni Word R.N., Chief Nursing Officer
Web address: www.wchcd.org
Control: Hospital district or authority, Government, Nonfederal **Service**: General
medical and surgical

Staffed Beds: 25 **Admissions**: 602 **Census**: 7 **Outpatient Visits**: 20645
Births: 56 **Total Expense ($000)**: 20039 **Payroll Expense ($000)**: 8417
Personnel: 142

EUGENE—Lane County

★ △ ⇧ **PEACEHEALTH SACRED HEART MEDICAL CENTER UNIVERSITY
DISTRICT (380033)**, 1255 Hilyard Street, Zip 97401–3700, Mailing Address:
P.O.Box 10905, 97440–2905; tel. 541/686–7300 **A**7 10 21 **F**3 29 30 31
38 40 43 56 62 63 68 84 90 93 98 102 105 107 115 130 146 148 **P**6 **S**
PeaceHealth, Vancouver, WA
Primary Contact: Mary Anne McMurren, R.N., Chief Administrative Officer
CFO: Wendy Apland, Interim Chief Financial Officer
CMO: Bill Moshofsky M.D., Chief of Staff
CIO: Donn McMillan, Chief Information Officer
CHR: Craig Mills, Vice President Human Resources
Web address: www.peacehealth.org
Control: Church operated, Nongovernment, not–for–profit **Service**: General
medical and surgical

Staffed Beds: 104 **Admissions**: 2708 **Census**: 60 **Outpatient Visits**:
109005 **Births**: 0 **Total Expense ($000)**: 123652 **Payroll Expense ($000)**:
44444 **Personnel**: 386

FLORENCE—Lane County

★ ⇧ **PEACEHEALTH PEACE HARBOR MEDICAL CENTER (381316)**, 400 Ninth
Street, Zip 97439–7398; tel. 541/997–8412 **A**10 18 21 **F**3 8 11 13 15 28 29
30 34 38 40 43 45 50 54 57 59 62 63 65 66 68 70 75 76 77 79 81 84 85 87
93 97 99 100 102 104 107 108 110 111 115 119 130 132 133 135 144 147
148 149 **P**6 **S** PeaceHealth, Vancouver, WA
Primary Contact: Rick Yecny, Chief Executive Officer and Chief Mission Officer
CMO: Ron Shearer M.D., Regional Medical Director
CIO: Ginni Boughal, Director Health Information and Information Technology
CHR: Don Bourland, Vice President Human Resources
Web address: www.peacehealth.org
Control: Church operated, Nongovernment, not–for–profit **Service**: General
medical and surgical

Staffed Beds: 21 **Admissions**: 1077 **Census**: 9 **Outpatient Visits**: 99687
Births: 63 **Total Expense ($000)**: 76528 **Payroll Expense ($000)**: 33332
Personnel: 173

Hospital, Medicare Provider Number, Address, Telephone, Approval, Facility, and Physician Codes, Health Care System

★ American Hospital Association (AHA) membership
□ The Joint Commission accreditation
○ Healthcare Facilities Accreditation Program
◇ DNV Healthcare Inc. accreditation
⇧ Center for Improvement in Healthcare Quality Accreditation
△ Commission on Accreditation of Rehabilitation Facilities (CARF) accreditation

OR

FOREST GROVE—Washington County

TUALITY FOREST GROVE HOSPITAL See Tuality Healthcare, Hillsboro

GOLD BEACH—Curry County

★ ⇑ **CURRY GENERAL HOSPITAL (381322)**, 94220 Fourth Street, Zip 97444–7756; tel. 541/247–3000 **A**10 18 21 **F**3 8 10 11 13 15 28 29 34 40 43 50 54 59 64 70 75 79 81 82 85 87 89 97 107 114 119 127 128 133 135 144 147 148 149 **P**6
Primary Contact: Virginia Razo, Chief Executive Officer
CFO: Carl Gerlach, Chief Financial Officer
CMO: Reginald Williams M.D., Medical Staff President
CIO: Kristina Martin, Chief Information Officer
CNO: Barbara A Hannon R.N., Interim Chief Nursing Officer and Chief Clinical Officer
Web address: www.curryhealthnetwork.com
Control: Hospital district or authority, Government, Nonfederal **Service:** General medical and surgical

Staffed Beds: 16 **Admissions:** 495 **Census:** 5 **Outpatient Visits:** 91684 **Births:** 37 **Total Expense ($000):** 38291 **Payroll Expense ($000):** 17676 **Personnel:** 215

GRANTS PASS—Josephine County

★ ⇑ **ASANTE THREE RIVERS MEDICAL CENTER (380002)**, 500 SW Ramsey Avenue, Zip 97527–5554; tel. 541/472–7000 **A**3 10 21 **F**11 13 15 29 30 31 34 35 40 43 45 46 50 57 59 64 65 70 75 76 78 81 87 93 97 107 110 111 118 119 129 130 132 135 143 144 146 147 148 **P**6 **S** Asante Health System, Medford, OR
Primary Contact: Win Howard, Chief Executive Officer
COO: David Kinyon, Vice President of Operations and Outpatient Services
CFO: Patrick Hocking, Chief Financial Officer
CMO: Eric Loeliger, Vice President of Medical Affairs
CIO: Mark Hetz, Chief Information Officer
CHR: Gregg Edwards, Chief People Officer
Web address: www.asante.org/trmc/
Control: Other not–for–profit (including NFP Corporation) **Service:** General medical and surgical

Staffed Beds: 111 **Admissions:** 6966 **Census:** 66 **Outpatient Visits:** 259610 **Births:** 771 **Total Expense ($000):** 151436 **Payroll Expense ($000):** 57834 **Personnel:** 957

GRESHAM—Multnomah County

✠ **LEGACY MOUNT HOOD MEDICAL CENTER (380025)**, 24800 SE Stark, Zip 97030–3378; tel. 503/667–1122 **A**1 2 10 **F**3 11 13 15 18 20 26 28 29 30 31 32 34 35 38 40 44 45 46 48 49 50 51 57 59 60 64 68 70 74 75 76 77 78 79 81 85 86 87 93 100 101 102 107 108 110 111 114 115 118 119 120 121 123 126 129 130 132 146 147 148 149 **P**6 **S** Legacy Health, Portland, OR
Primary Contact: Gretchen Nichols, R.N., President
COO: Michael Newcomb D.O., Senior Vice President and Chief Operating Officer
CFO: Linda Hoff, Senior Vice President and Chief Financial Officer
CMO: Lewis Low M.D., Chief Medical Officer
CIO: John Jay Kenagy Ph.D., Senior Vice President and Chief Information Officer
CHR: Sonja Steves, Senior Vice President Human Resources
CNO: Marcia Soderling R.N., Hospital Nurse Executive
Web address: www.legacyhealth.org
Control: Other not–for–profit (including NFP Corporation) **Service:** General medical and surgical

Staffed Beds: 94 **Admissions:** 6294 **Census:** 64 **Outpatient Visits:** 132455 **Births:** 1009 **Total Expense ($000):** 137173 **Payroll Expense ($000):** 52593 **Personnel:** 594

HEPPNER—Morrow County

PIONEER MEMORIAL HOSPITAL (381310), 564 East Pioneer Drive, Zip 97836–7318, Mailing Address: P.O.Box 9, 97836–0009; tel. 541/676–9133 **A**10 18 **F**3 7 17 34 35 40 43 45 50 57 59 62 63 64 66 68 75 81 97 107 119 127 133 147 148 **P**6
Primary Contact: Robert Houser, FACHE, Chief Executive Officer
CFO: Nicole Mahoney, Chief Financial Officer
CIO: Shawn Cutsforth, Information Systems Officer
CHR: Patti Allstott, Administrative Coordinator Human Resources and Grant Writer
Web address: www.morrowcountyhealthdistrict.org
Control: Hospital district or authority, Government, Nonfederal **Service:** General medical and surgical

Staffed Beds: 21 **Admissions:** 106 **Census:** 8 **Outpatient Visits:** 5573 **Births:** 0 **Total Expense ($000):** 9959 **Payroll Expense ($000):** 5213 **Personnel:** 72

HERMISTON—Umatilla County

★ ⇑ **GOOD SHEPHERD HEALTH CARE SYSTEM (381325)**, 610 NW 11th Street, Zip 97838–6601; tel. 541/667–3400 **A**10 18 21 **F**3 11 13 15 28 29 30 34 35 37 40 43 45 46 50 53 57 59 62 63 64 65 68 70 75 76 77 78 79 81 82 85 86 89 97 107 108 110 111 115 119 126 127 131 132 133 135 141 143 146 147 148 149
Primary Contact: Dennis E. Burke, President and Chief Executive Officer
COO: Jim Schlenker, Chief Operating Officer
CFO: Jan D Peter, Vice President Fiscal Services and Chief Financial Officer
CMO: Gary Trupp, President Medical Staff
CIO: Rob Rizk, Director Information Technology
CHR: Kelly B. Sanders, Vice President Human Resources
CNO: Theresa Brock, Vice President Nursing
Web address: www.gshealth.org
Control: Other not–for–profit (including NFP Corporation) **Service:** General medical and surgical

Staffed Beds: 25 **Admissions:** 1791 **Census:** 12 **Outpatient Visits:** 56055 **Births:** 442 **Total Expense ($000):** 70358 **Payroll Expense ($000):** 32311 **Personnel:** 565

HILLSBORO—Washington County

✠ **KAISER FOUNDATION HOSPITAL WESTSIDE MEDICAL CENTER (380103)**, 2875 NW Stucki Avenue, Zip 97124–5806; tel. 971/310–1000 **A**1 10 **F**3 13 15 29 30 31 34 35 40 45 46 47 49 51 59 60 61 64 65 68 70 74 75 76 77 79 81 84 85 86 87 93 96 97 102 107 108 110 111 114 115 118 119 126 130 135 141 146 147 148 149 **P**6 **S** Kaiser Foundation Hospitals, Oakland, CA
Primary Contact: Brantley Dettmer, Administrator and Chief Operating Officer
CMO: Carol Unitan M.D., Chief Medical Officer
CIO: Charles Stearns, Area Information Officer
CHR: Rich Smith, Vice President Human Resources
CNO: Janet Lee Reeder R.N., Chief Nurse Executive
Web address: www.kp.org
Control: Other not–for–profit (including NFP Corporation) **Service:** General medical and surgical

Staffed Beds: 122 **Admissions:** 8184 **Census:** 62 **Outpatient Visits:** 38244 **Births:** 1440 **Total Expense ($000):** 162111 **Payroll Expense ($000):** 65476 **Personnel:** 852

✠ **TUALITY HEALTHCARE (380021)**, 335 SE Eighth Avenue, Zip 97123–4246; tel. 503/681–1111, (Includes TUALITY COMMUNITY HOSPITAL, 335 SE Eighth Avenue, Hillsboro, Oregon, Zip 97123, P O Box 309, 97123, tel. 503/681–1111; Manuel S Berman, FACHE, President and Chief Executive Officer; TUALITY FOREST GROVE HOSPITAL, 1809 Maple Street, Forest Grove, Oregon, Zip 97116–1995, tel. 503/357–2173; Manuel S Berman, FACHE, President and Chief Executive Officer) **A**1 5 10 **F**1 3 4 11 13 15 16 17 18 20 22 24 26 28 29 30 31 32 34 35 36 40 44 45 47 49 50 53 54 56 57 59 62 64 67 68 70 71 72 73 74 75 76 77 78 79 80 81 82 85 86 87 88 89 90 92 93 97 98 100 103 104 107 108 110 111 114 115 118 119 128 129 130 131 132 135 143 144 145 146 147 148 **P**1 6
Primary Contact: Manuel S. Berman, FACHE, President and Chief Executive Officer
COO: Steven P Krautscheid, Ancillary Services Administrator
CFO: Tim Fleischmann, Chief Financial Officer
CMO: Stuart Currie, Chief Medical Officer
CIO: Sonney Sapra, Director Information Systems and Chief Information Officer
CHR: Cheryl Gebhart, Chief Human Resources Officer
CNO: Eunice A Rech MSN, Chief Clinical Officer and Administrator of Quality Services
Web address: www.tuality.org
Control: Other not–for–profit (including NFP Corporation) **Service:** General medical and surgical

Staffed Beds: 148 **Admissions:** 4076 **Census:** 53 **Outpatient Visits:** 238773 **Births:** 739 **Total Expense ($000):** 181822 **Payroll Expense ($000):** 88959 **Personnel:** 1138

HOOD RIVER—Hood River County

✠ **PROVIDENCE HOOD RIVER MEMORIAL HOSPITAL (381318)**, 810 12th Street, Zip 97031–1587, Mailing Address: P.O.Box 149, 97031–0055; tel. 541/386–3911 **A**1 3 10 18 **F**3 5 9 10 11 12 13 15 18 28 29 30 31 34 35 36 40 43 45 47 48 53 54 56 57 59 60 64 65 68 70 75 77 78 79 81 82 84 85 86 89 92 97 99 100 101 102 104 107 108 110 111 114 118 119 125 130 131 132 133 134 135 143 146 147 148 149 **P**6 **S** Providence St. Joseph Health, Renton, WA
Primary Contact: Jeanette Vieira, Chief Executive
CHR: Jami McCaslin, Director Human Resources
Web address: www.providence.org/hoodriver
Control: Church operated, Nongovernment, not–for–profit **Service:** General medical and surgical

Staffed Beds: 25 **Admissions:** 1518 **Census:** 11 **Outpatient Visits:** 171353 **Births:** 398 **Total Expense ($000):** 93309 **Payroll Expense ($000):** 30806 **Personnel:** 405

JOHN DAY—Grant County

★ **BLUE MOUNTAIN HOSPITAL (381305)**, 170 Ford Road, Zip 97845–2009; tel. 541/575–1311, (Total facility includes 29 beds in nursing home–type unit) **A**3 5 10 18 **F**3 7 11 13 15 29 30 34 35 36 40 41 43 45 50 57 59 62 63 64 67 68 70 75 76 81 82 86 87 93 97 107 110 111 114 119 127 130 131 132 133 135 143 144 145 146 148 **P**6 **S** HealthTech Management Services, Brentwood, TN
Primary Contact: Derek Daly, Chief Executive Officer
CMO: Keith Thomas M.D., Chief of Staff
CIO: Sean Tsao, Director Information Technology
CHR: Verlene Davis, Director Human Resources
CNO: Les McLeod, Director of Nursing Services
Web address: www.bluemountainhospital.org
Control: Hospital district or authority, Government, Nonfederal **Service:** General medical and surgical

Staffed Beds: 45 **Admissions:** 388 **Census:** 25 **Outpatient Visits:** 26473 **Births:** 36 **Total Expense ($000):** 21400 **Payroll Expense ($000):** 10710 **Personnel:** 160	

KLAMATH FALLS—Klamath County

★ ⇑ **SKY LAKES MEDICAL CENTER (380050)**, 2865 Daggett Avenue, Zip 97601–1106; tel. 541/882–6311 **A**2 3 5 10 21 **F**2 3 8 11 13 15 18 20 22 29 30 31 34 35 37 40 43 44 45 46 47 48 50 51 53 54 56 57 59 61 62 64 68 70 71 75 76 77 78 79 81 84 85 86 87 92 93 94 96 97 100 102 107 108 110 111 114 115 116 117 118 119 120 121 123 130 131 132 134 135 141 142 143 144 145 146 148 149 **P**6
Primary Contact: Paul R. Stewart, President and Chief Executive Officer
CFO: Richard Rico, Vice President and Chief Financial Officer
CMO: Grant Niskanen M.D., Vice President Medical Affairs
CHR: Don York, Vice President and Chief Human Resource Officer
CNO: Annette E. Cole R.N., MSN, Vice President and Chief Nursing Officer
Web address: www.skylakes.org
Control: Other not–for–profit (including NFP Corporation) **Service:** General medical and surgical

Staffed Beds: 105 **Admissions:** 5132 **Census:** 52 **Outpatient Visits:** 369781 **Births:** 800 **Total Expense ($000):** 226064 **Payroll Expense ($000):** 81783 **Personnel:** 1191	

LA GRANDE—Union County

⊞ **GRANDE RONDE HOSPITAL (381321)**, 900 Sunset Drive, Zip 97850–1387, Mailing Address: P.O.Box 3290, 97850–7290; tel. 541/963–8421 **A**1 10 18 **F**3 8 11 13 15 17 29 30 31 34 35 37 39 40 41 43 44 45 46 50 53 54 59 62 63 64 66 70 74 75 76 78 79 81 82 84 85 86 87 89 92 93 96 97 107 108 110 111 114 118 119 128 129 130 131 132 133 135 144 146 147 148 149 **P**6
Primary Contact: James A. Mattes, President and Chief Executive Officer
CFO: Wade Weis, Chief Financial Officer and Senior Director Finance
CMO: Aaron Spracklen M.D., Professional Staff President
CIO: Parhez Sattar, Senior Director Information Technology
CHR: Kristi Puckett, Director Human Resources
Web address: www.grh.org
Control: Other not–for–profit (including NFP Corporation) **Service:** General medical and surgical

Staffed Beds: 25 **Admissions:** 1426 **Census:** 13 **Outpatient Visits:** 137337 **Births:** 253 **Total Expense ($000):** 79751 **Payroll Expense ($000):** 44255 **Personnel:** 602	

LAKEVIEW—Lake County

★ **LAKE DISTRICT HOSPITAL (381309)**, 700 South 'J' Street, Zip 97630–1679; tel. 541/947–2114 **A**5 10 18 **F**3 13 15 18 29 30 31 34 35 40 45 46 57 59 62 63 64 68 76 77 78 79 81 82 84 85 87 90 93 107 111 115 119 127 129 130 132 133 135 146 148 149 **P**6
Primary Contact: Charles B. Tveit, Chief Executive Officer
CFO: Cheryl J Cornwell, Chief Financial Officer
CMO: Stephen Hussey M.D., Chief of Staff
CIO: Steven Vance, Information Technology Director
CHR: Lesley Hanson, Director Human Resources
CNO: Teresa Squires R.N., Chief Nursing Officer
Web address: www.lakehealthdistrict.org
Control: Hospital district or authority, Government, Nonfederal **Service:** General medical and surgical

Staffed Beds: 24 **Admissions:** 491 **Census:** 8 **Outpatient Visits:** 34301 **Births:** 60 **Total Expense ($000):** 24411 **Payroll Expense ($000):** 9962 **Personnel:** 196	

LEBANON—Linn County

★ ⇑ **SAMARITAN LEBANON COMMUNITY HOSPITAL (381323)**, 525 North Santiam Highway, Zip 97355–4363, Mailing Address: P.O.Box 739, 97355–0739; tel. 541/258–2101 **A**10 18 21 **F**3 10 11 13 15 28 29 30 31 34 35 40 43 44 45 46 47 53 59 64 68 70 75 76 78 79 81 85 86 87 89 92 93 97 107 108 110 111 114 116 117 118 119 125 130 131 132 135 144 146 147 148 149 **P**6 **S** Samaritan Health Services, Corvallis, OR
Primary Contact: Marty Cahill, Chief Executive Officer
CFO: Daniel B Smith, Vice President Finance
CMO: Alan Blake M.D., President Medical Staff
CIO: Robert Power, Vice President Information Services
CHR: Connie Erwin, Manager
CNO: Wendie Wunderwald R.N., Vice President Patient Care Services
Web address: www.samhealth.org
Control: Other not–for–profit (including NFP Corporation) **Service:** General medical and surgical

Staffed Beds: 25 **Admissions:** 1712 **Census:** 15 **Outpatient Visits:** 228475 **Births:** 316 **Total Expense ($000):** 114146 **Payroll Expense ($000):** 50289 **Personnel:** 610	

LINCOLN CITY—Lincoln County

★ ⇑ **SAMARITAN NORTH LINCOLN HOSPITAL (381302)**, 3043 NE 28th Street, Zip 97367–4518, Mailing Address: P.O.Box 767, 97367–0767; tel. 541/994–3661 **A**10 18 21 **F**3 8 11 13 15 26 29 30 31 34 35 40 44 45 51 57 58 59 62 63 64 68 70 71 75 76 77 78 79 81 85 87 93 97 104 107 108 110 111 116 117 118 119 127 130 132 133 135 144 146 147 148 149 **P**6 **S** Samaritan Health Services, Corvallis, OR
Primary Contact: Lesley Ogden, M.D., Chief Executive Officer
CFO: Kathryn Doksum, Director Finance
CMO: Raj Baman D.O., President Medical Staff
CHR: Gina Tapp, Director Human Resources
CNO: Virginia Riffle, Vice President Patient Care Services
Web address: www.samhealth.org
Control: Other not–for–profit (including NFP Corporation) **Service:** General medical and surgical

Staffed Beds: 25 **Admissions:** 1024 **Census:** 10 **Outpatient Visits:** 103121 **Births:** 150 **Total Expense ($000):** 59840 **Payroll Expense ($000):** 29629 **Personnel:** 313	

MADRAS—Jefferson County

★ **ST. CHARLES MADRAS (381324)**, 470 NE 'A' Street, Zip 97741–1844; tel. 541/475–3882 **A**10 18 **F**3 13 15 29 30 34 35 40 43 45 50 57 59 62 63 64 67 68 70 75 76 77 79 81 85 87 89 90 91 98 107 110 115 119 127 128 132 133 135 146 148 **P**6 **S** St. Charles Health System, Inc., Bend, OR
Primary Contact: John Bishop, President
Web address: www.stcharleshealthcare.org/Our-Locations/Madras
Control: Other not–for–profit (including NFP Corporation) **Service:** General medical and surgical

Staffed Beds: 23 **Admissions:** 715 **Census:** 7 **Outpatient Visits:** 23273 **Births:** 147 **Total Expense ($000):** 26894 **Payroll Expense ($000):** 17644 **Personnel:** 172	

MCMINNVILLE—Yamhill County

☐ **WILLAMETTE VALLEY MEDICAL CENTER (380071)**, 2700 SE Stratus Avenue, Zip 97128–6255; tel. 503/472–6131 **A**1 2 10 **F**3 11 12 13 15 18 20 24 26 27 28 29 30 31 34 35 40 41 43 45 46 48 50 51 56 57 58 59 60 64 65 70 74 75 76 77 78 79 81 82 84 85 86 87 91 92 93 98 103 107 108 110 111 114 115 118 119 120 123 124 130 131 132 135 146 147 148 **P**6 **S** RCCH HealthCare Partners, Brentwood, TN
Primary Contact: Peter A. Hofstetter, Chief Executive Officer
CFO: Meredith Nelson, Chief Financial Officer
CIO: Diane Farrow, Manager Information Technology and Systems
CHR: Lisa Clark, Director Human Resources
CNO: Connie Pullen R.N., Chief Nursing Officer
Web address: www.wvmcweb.com
Control: Corporation, Investor–owned (for–profit) **Service:** General medical and surgical

Staffed Beds: 88 **Admissions:** 3462 **Census:** 37 **Outpatient Visits:** 111845 **Births:** 510 **Total Expense ($000):** 79128 **Payroll Expense ($000):** 31085 **Personnel:** 510	

OR

Hospital, Medicare Provider Number, Address, Telephone, Approval, Facility, and Physician Codes, Health Care System

★ American Hospital Association (AHA) membership   ○ Healthcare Facilities Accreditation Program   ⇑ Center for Improvement in Healthcare Quality Accreditation
☐ The Joint Commission accreditation   ◇ DNV Healthcare Inc. accreditation   △ Commission on Accreditation of Rehabilitation Facilities (CARF) accreditation

---

MEDFORD—Jackson County

★ ⇧ **ASANTE ROGUE REGIONAL MEDICAL CENTER (380018)**, 2825 East Barnett Road, Zip 97504–8332; tel. 541/789–7000 **A**2 3 10 21 **F**11 12 13 15 17 18 20 22 24 26 28 29 30 31 32 34 35 37 40 43 45 46 50 51 57 58 59 60 63 64 65 70 72 74 75 76 78 79 81 82 85 86 87 89 90 93 94 96 97 98 100 102 107 108 110 111 112 115 119 120 121 122 126 129 130 132 135 143 146 147 148 **P**6 **S** Asante Health System, Medford, OR
Primary Contact: Scott A. Kelly, Chief Executive Officer
COO: Kristi Blackhurst, Interim Vice President Operations
CFO: Patrick Hocking, Chief Financial Officer
CMO: Jamie Grebosky M.D., Vice President of Medical Affairs
CIO: Mark Hetz, Chief Information Officer
CHR: Gregg Edwards, Chief People Officer
Web address: www.asante.org
Control: Other not-for-profit (including NFP Corporation) **Service:** General medical and surgical

Staffed Beds: 320 **Admissions:** 16549 **Census:** 229 **Outpatient Visits:** 413494 **Births:** 1714 **Total Expense ($000):** 434179 **Payroll Expense ($000):** 144135 **Personnel:** 2449

⊞ **PROVIDENCE MEDFORD MEDICAL CENTER (380075)**, 1111 Crater Lake Avenue, Zip 97504–6241; tel. 541/732–5000 **A**1 2 10 **F**3 11 13 15 17 18 20 22 28 29 30 31 32 34 35 40 43 45 49 50 55 56 57 59 61 64 68 70 74 75 76 77 78 79 81 82 84 85 86 87 90 91 92 93 96 97 102 107 110 114 115 118 119 120 121 123 124 126 129 130 131 132 146 147 148 **P**6 **S** Providence St. Joseph Health, Renton, WA
Primary Contact: Cindy Mayo, R.N., FACHE, Chief Executive
COO: Chris Pizzi, Chief Operating Officer and Chief Financial Officer
CFO: Chris Pizzi, Chief Operating Officer and Chief Financial Officer
CHR: Julie Levison, Director Human Resources
CNO: Sherri Steele, Chief Nursing Officer
Web address: www.providence.org
Control: Church operated, Nongovernment, not-for-profit **Service:** General medical and surgical

Staffed Beds: 138 **Admissions:** 6800 **Census:** 75 **Outpatient Visits:** 335900 **Births:** 431 **Total Expense ($000):** 214626 **Payroll Expense ($000):** 61365 **Personnel:** 883

MILWAUKIE—Clackamas County

⊞ **PROVIDENCE MILWAUKIE HOSPITAL (380082)**, 10150 SE 32nd Avenue, Zip 97222–6516; tel. 503/513–8300 **A**1 3 5 10 **F**3 15 18 29 30 34 35 36 39 40 44 45 46 50 53 54 57 59 63 64 68 70 71 74 75 77 79 81 82 84 85 87 89 91 92 93 97 98 100 102 103 105 107 108 110 111 114 115 119 129 130 131 132 133 135 146 147 148 **P**6 **S** Providence St. Joseph Health, Renton, WA
Primary Contact: Keith Hyde, Chief Executive
COO: Sherri Paris, Chief Operating Officer
CFO: Sheila Waldron, Finance Manager
CHR: Julie Smith, Senior Human Resources Strategic Partner
CNO: Lisa Halvorsen, Chief Nurse Executive
Web address: www.providence.org
Control: Church operated, Nongovernment, not-for-profit **Service:** General medical and surgical

Staffed Beds: 52 **Admissions:** 2722 **Census:** 26 **Outpatient Visits:** 229738 **Births:** 0 **Total Expense ($000):** 101945 **Payroll Expense ($000):** 33376 **Personnel:** 433

NEWBERG—Yamhill County

⊞ **PROVIDENCE NEWBERG MEDICAL CENTER (380037)**, 1001 Providence Drive, Zip 97132–7485; tel. 503/537–1555 **A**1 10 **F**3 11 13 15 18 20 29 30 34 35 40 45 46 47 49 50 51 57 59 60 64 68 70 75 76 77 79 81 84 85 87 93 100 107 108 110 111 114 118 119 129 130 132 135 146 147 148 **P**6 **S** Providence St. Joseph Health, Renton, WA
Primary Contact: Lorinda Van Zanten, MSN, Chief Executive
CFO: Jack R Sumner, Assistant Administrator Finance
CMO: George Weghorst M.D., Chief Medical Officer
CIO: Laureen O'Brien, Chief Information Officer
CHR: Cheryl Gebhart, Director Human Resources Providence Health Plan and Providence Medical Group
Web address: www.phsor.org
Control: Church operated, Nongovernment, not-for-profit **Service:** General medical and surgical

Staffed Beds: 40 **Admissions:** 2679 **Census:** 23 **Outpatient Visits:** 241475 **Births:** 521 **Total Expense ($000):** 104696 **Payroll Expense ($000):** 31490 **Personnel:** 417

NEWPORT—Lincoln County

★ ⇧ **SAMARITAN PACIFIC COMMUNITIES HOSPITAL (381314)**, 930 SW Abbey Street, Zip 97365–4820, Mailing Address: P.O.Box 945, 97365–0072; tel. 541/265–2244 **A**10 18 21 **F**3 8 11 13 15 26 28 29 30 31 34 35 40 44 45 47 53 54 62 63 64 68 70 75 76 77 78 79 81 82 85 86 87 92 93 97 107 110 111 114 119 127 129 130 132 133 135 144 146 147 148 149 **P**6 **S** Samaritan Health Services, Corvallis, OR
Primary Contact: Lesley Ogden, M.D., Chief Executive Officer
CFO: Daniel B Smith, Chief Financial Officer
CIO: Robert Power, Chief Information Officer
CHR: Gina Tapp, Director Human Resources
CNO: Lorie Williams R.N., Vice President Nursing
Web address: www.samhealth.org
Control: Other not-for-profit (including NFP Corporation) **Service:** General medical and surgical

Staffed Beds: 25 **Admissions:** 1282 **Census:** 12 **Outpatient Visits:** 152815 **Births:** 214 **Total Expense ($000):** 89452 **Payroll Expense ($000):** 39799 **Personnel:** 408

ONTARIO—Malheur County

HOLY ROSARY MEDICAL CENTER See Saint Alphonsus Medical Center – Ontario

⊞ **SAINT ALPHONSUS MEDICAL CENTER – ONTARIO (380052)**, 351 SW Ninth Street, Zip 97914–2693; tel. 541/881–7000 **A**1 3 5 10 20 **F**3 11 13 15 29 30 31 32 34 35 39 40 43 44 45 46 50 54 56 57 59 64 65 68 70 75 76 77 78 79 81 82 83 85 87 93 97 107 108 110 111 114 118 119 127 129 130 131 132 135 141 142 144 146 147 148 149 **P**6 **S** Trinity Health, Livonia, MI
Primary Contact: Kenneth Hart, President
CFO: Lannie Checketts, Chief Financial Officer
CMO: Paul Gering M.D., Vice President Medical Affairs
CHR: Stefanie Thiel, Senior Human Resources Business Partner
CNO: Dina Ellwanger R.N., Chief Nursing Officer
Web address: www.saintalphonsus.org/ontario
Control: Church operated, Nongovernment, not-for-profit **Service:** General medical and surgical

Staffed Beds: 38 **Admissions:** 2254 **Census:** 17 **Outpatient Visits:** 74594 **Births:** 488 **Total Expense ($000):** 68329 **Payroll Expense ($000):** 25562 **Personnel:** 434

OREGON CITY—Clackamas County

⊞ **PROVIDENCE WILLAMETTE FALLS MEDICAL CENTER (380038)**, 1500 Division Street, Zip 97045–1597; tel. 503/656–1631 **A**1 10 **F**13 15 29 30 34 35 36 40 44 45 46 50 53 54 57 59 63 64 68 70 74 75 76 77 78 79 81 82 84 85 87 91 92 93 97 98 99 100 107 108 111 114 119 130 131 132 133 135 146 147 **P**6 **S** Providence St. Joseph Health, Renton, WA
Primary Contact: Russ Reinhard, Chief Executive
COO: Patricia A Markesino FACHE, Chief Nurse Executive and Chief Operating Officer
CFO: Elizabeth Sublette, Director Finance
CMO: James Watkins M.D., President Medical Staff
CHR: Joann M Pfister, Director Human Resources
CNO: Jessica Bailey-Oetker, Director Quality and Medical Staff
Web address: www.providence.org/pwfmc
Control: Church operated, Nongovernment, not-for-profit **Service:** General medical and surgical

Staffed Beds: 111 **Admissions:** 4803 **Census:** 47 **Outpatient Visits:** 177272 **Births:** 1035 **Total Expense ($000):** 125722 **Payroll Expense ($000):** 40908 **Personnel:** 504

PENDLETON—Umatilla County

⊞ **CHI ST. ANTHONY HOSPITAL (381319)**, 2801 St Anthony Way, Zip 97801–3800; tel. 541/276–5121 **A**1 10 18 **F**3 11 13 15 18 29 30 31 35 40 43 45 50 51 53 54 57 59 62 63 64 65 68 70 75 77 78 79 81 85 86 87 91 93 97 107 108 110 111 114 118 119 127 129 130 131 132 133 134 135 146 147 149 **P**6 **S** Catholic Health Initiatives, Englewood, CO
Primary Contact: Harold S. Geller, Chief Executive Officer
CFO: Scott Attridge, Chief Financial Officer
CMO: John McBee, Chief of Staff
CHR: Janeen K Reding, Director Human Resources
CNO: Joyce Bailey, Vice President Patient Care
Web address: www.sahpendleton.org
Control: Church operated, Nongovernment, not-for-profit **Service:** General medical and surgical

Staffed Beds: 25 **Admissions:** 1435 **Census:** 12 **Outpatient Visits:** 74667 **Births:** 300 **Total Expense ($000):** 60646 **Payroll Expense ($000):** 22538 **Personnel:** 273

Many Facility Codes have changed. Please refer to the AHA Guide Code Chart. © 2017 AHA Guide

OR

OR

PORTLAND—Multnomah County

ADVENTIST MEDICAL CENTER–PORTLAND (380060), 10123 SE Market Street, Zip 97216–2599; tel. 503/257–2500 **A**1 2 5 10 **F**3 9 11 13 15 17 18 20 22 24 26 28 29 30 31 34 35 36 37 40 44 45 46 49 54 57 58 59 64 70 71 74 75 76 77 78 79 81 82 84 85 86 93 94 98 100 102 107 108 110 111 114 115 118 119 120 121 123 126 129 130 131 132 135 144 146 147 148 **P**6 7 **S** Adventist Health, Roseville, CA
Primary Contact: David Russell, President and Chief Executive Officer
CFO: V Mark Perry, Chief Financial Officer
CMO: Wesley E Rippey M.D., Chief Medical Officer
CHR: Shane Voshell, Director Human Resources
CNO: Ellen Tryon R.N., Chief Nursing Officer
Web address: www.adventisthealthnw.com
Control: Church operated, Nongovernment, not–for–profit **Service**: General medical and surgical

Staffed Beds: 242 Admissions: 10302 Census: 113 Outpatient Visits: 374418 Births: 950 Total Expense ($000): 342437 Payroll Expense ($000): 125143 Personnel: 1558

GOOD SAMARITAN HOSPITAL AND MEDICAL CENTER See Legacy Good Samaritan Medical Center

△ ⇑ **LEGACY EMANUEL MEDICAL CENTER (380007)**, 2801 North Gantenbein Avenue, Zip 97227–1674; tel. 503/413–2200, (Includes RANDALL CHILDREN'S HOSPITAL, 2801 North Gantenbein Avenue, Portland, Oregon, Zip 97227–1623, tel. 503/413–2200) **A**1 2 3 5 7 10 21 **F**3 7 11 13 15 16 17 18 19 20 21 22 23 24 25 26 27 29 30 31 32 34 35 37 38 39 40 41 43 44 45 46 47 48 49 50 51 54 55 56 57 59 60 61 64 65 66 68 72 74 75 76 77 78 79 80 81 83 84 85 86 87 88 89 93 97 98 99 100 101 102 107 108 110 111 114 115 116 127 130 131 132 135 144 146 147 148 149 **P**6 **S** Legacy Health, Portland, OR
Primary Contact: Lori Morgan, M.D., Chief Administrative Officer
CHR: Sonja Steves, Senior Vice President Human Resources and Marketing
Web address: www.legacyhealth.org
Control: Other not–for–profit (including NFP Corporation) **Service**: General medical and surgical

Staffed Beds: 427 Admissions: 18927 Census: 306 Outpatient Visits: 399635 Births: 2043 Total Expense ($000): 776633 Payroll Expense ($000): 366258 Personnel: 2960

LEGACY GOOD SAMARITAN MEDICAL CENTER (380017), 1015 NW 22nd Avenue, Zip 97210–3099; tel. 503/413–7711, (Includes GOOD SAMARITAN HOSPITAL AND MEDICAL CENTER, 1015 NW 22nd Avenue, Portland, Oregon, Zip 97210, tel. 503/229–7711; REHABILITATION INSTITUTE OF OREGON, 2010 NW Kearney Street, Portland, Oregon, Zip 97209, tel. 503/226–3774) **A**1 2 3 5 10 **F**3 8 11 12 15 18 20 22 24 26 28 29 30 31 34 35 38 40 44 45 46 47 48 49 50 51 55 56 57 58 59 60 61 64 65 68 70 74 75 76 77 78 79 80 81 82 83 84 85 86 87 90 91 93 94 96 97 98 100 101 102 103 107 108 110 111 114 115 116 117 118 119 120 121 123 124 126 129 130 131 135 138 142 143 144 145 146 147 148 149 **P**6 **S** Legacy Health, Portland, OR
Primary Contact: Jonathan Avery, Chief Administrative Officer
CIO: C Matthew Calais, Senior Vice President and Chief Information Officer
CHR: Sonja Steves, Vice President Marketing
CNO: Cindy Evans R.N., MS, Chief Nursing Officer
Web address: www.legacyhealth.org
Control: Other not–for–profit (including NFP Corporation) **Service**: General medical and surgical

Staffed Beds: 239 Admissions: 10419 Census: 146 Outpatient Visits: 200515 Births: 1114 Total Expense ($000): 314174 Payroll Expense ($000): 118346 Personnel: 1324

OHSU HOSPITAL (380009), 3181 SW Sam Jackson Park Road, Zip 97239–3098; tel. 503/494–8311, (Includes DOERNBECHER CHILDREN'S HOSPITAL, 700 SW Campus Drive, Portland, Oregon, Zip 97239, tel. 503/494–8811; Timothy Goldfarb, Interim Chief Executive Officer) **A**1 2 3 5 8 10 **F**3 5 6 8 9 12 13 15 17 18 19 20 21 22 23 24 25 26 27 28 29 30 31 32 33 34 35 36 37 38 39 40 41 43 44 45 46 47 48 49 50 51 52 53 54 55 56 57 58 59 60 61 64 66 68 70 71 72 74 75 76 77 78 79 81 82 84 85 86 87 88 89 90 91 92 93 95 96 97 98 100 103 104 107 108 109 110 111 112 114 115 116 117 118 119 120 121 123 124 126 127 129 130 131 132 134 135 136 137 138 139 141 145 146 147 148 **P**1
Primary Contact: Mitchell L. Wasden, Ed.D., Chief Executive Officer
COO: Cynthia M Grueber, Senior Vice President and Chief Operating Officer
CFO: Diana Gernhart, Senior Vice President and Hospital Chief Financial Officer
CMO: Michael Bonazzola M.D., Interim Chief Medical Officer
CIO: Bridget Barnes, Vice President and Chief Information Officer
CHR: Dan Forbes, Vice President Human Resources
CNO: Dana Bjarnason Ph.D., R.N., Vice President and Chief Nursing Officer
Web address: www.ohsu.edu
Control: Hospital district or authority, Government, Nonfederal **Service**: General medical and surgical

Staffed Beds: 573 Admissions: 29834 Census: 469 Outpatient Visits: 856291 Births: 2471 Total Expense ($000): 1527249 Payroll Expense ($000): 523720 Personnel: 7191

PROVIDENCE PORTLAND MEDICAL CENTER (380061), 4805 NE Glisan Street, Zip 97213–2933; tel. 503/215–5526 **A**1 2 3 5 10 **F**3 4 5 13 15 18 20 22 24 26 29 30 31 34 35 36 37 38 40 44 45 46 49 50 51 53 54 55 56 57 58 59 60 61 62 63 64 68 70 72 73 74 75 76 77 78 79 81 82 84 85 86 87 90 92 93 97 98 100 102 103 104 105 107 108 109 110 111 114 116 117 118 119 121 123 124 126 129 130 131 132 133 135 136 145 146 147 148 **P**6 **S** Providence St. Joseph Health, Renton, WA
Primary Contact: Paul Gaden, Chief Executive Officer
COO: Krista Farnham, Chief Operating Officer
CFO: Eric Olson, Chief Financial Officer
CMO: Robert Wells M.D., Chief Medical Officer
CIO: Mark Premo, Senior Director HC Intelligence
CHR: Jeannie Mikulic, Director Human Resources
CNO: Mary T McFadden MSN, R.N., Chief Nurse Executive
Web address: www.providence.org
Control: Church operated, Nongovernment, not–for–profit **Service**: General medical and surgical

Staffed Beds: 427 Admissions: 20948 Census: 295 Outpatient Visits: 1337066 Births: 2806 Total Expense ($000): 781022 Payroll Expense ($000): 232284 Personnel: 2840

REHABILITATION INSTITUTE OF OREGON See Legacy Good Samaritan Medical Center

☐ **SHRINERS HOSPITALS FOR CHILDREN–PORTLAND (383300)**, 3101 SW Sam Jackson Park Road, Zip 97239–3009; tel. 503/241–5090 **A**1 3 5 10 **F**3 29 34 35 37 50 53 58 64 68 75 77 79 81 85 86 87 91 93 94 130 131 132 134 146 148 **P**6 **S** Shriners Hospitals for Children, Tampa, FL
Primary Contact: J Craig. Patchin, Administrator
CFO: Mark Knudsen, Director Fiscal Services
CMO: Michael Aiona M.D., Chief of Staff
CIO: Carl Montante, Director Information Systems and Information Technology
CHR: Rhonda Smith, Director Human Resources
CNO: Suzanne Diers R.N., Director Patient Care Services
Web address: www.shrinershospitalsforchildren.org/Hospitals/Locations/Portland.aspx
Control: Other not–for–profit (including NFP Corporation) **Service**: Children's general medical and surgical

Staffed Beds: 12 Admissions: 366 Census: 5 Outpatient Visits: 12349 Births: 0 Total Expense ($000): 37028 Payroll Expense ($000): 19899 Personnel: 237

VA PORTLAND HEALTHCARE SYSTEM, 3710 SW U S Veterans Hospital Road, Zip 97239–2964, Mailing Address: 3710 SW US Veterans Hospital Road, 97207–1034; tel. 503/220–8262, (Total facility includes 67 beds in nursing home–type unit) **A**1 2 3 5 8 **F**1 3 5 8 10 12 18 20 22 24 26 28 29 30 31 35 36 38 39 40 46 54 58 59 60 61 62 64 65 66 68 70 74 75 78 79 81 82 84 86 87 91 93 94 97 98 102 104 105 107 111 115 116 117 118 119 127 129 130 132 135 138 139 145 146 147 148 149 **S** Department of Veterans Affairs, Washington, DC
Primary Contact: Michael W. Fisher, Director
CFO: Josh Wiseman, Chief Financial Officer
CMO: Sahana Misra, Acting Chief of Staff
CHR: Karla Azcuy, Acting Chief Human Resources Officer
CNO: Kathleen Chapman Esq, Deputy Director, Patient Care Services
Web address: www.portland.va.gov/
Control: Veterans Affairs, Government, federal **Service**: General medical and surgical

Staffed Beds: 176 Admissions: 9371 Census: 167 Outpatient Visits: 934597 Births: 0 Total Expense ($000): 815763 Payroll Expense ($000): 600000

VETERANS AFFAIRS MEDICAL CENTER See VA Portland Healthcare System

VIBRA SPECIALTY HOSPITAL OF PORTLAND (382004), 10300 NE Hancock Street, Zip 97220–3831; tel. 503/257–5500 (Nonreporting) **A**1 10 **S** Vibra Healthcare, Mechanicsburg, PA
Primary Contact: Victor Jackson, Chief Executive Officer
CFO: Stephanie Lawrence, Chief Financial Officer
CMO: Cynthia Wallace M.D., Medical Director
CIO: Marie Roof, Executive Vice President Information Systems
CHR: Kellie Bernert–Yap, Director Human Resources
CNO: Susan E Brooker R.N., Chief Clinical Officer
Web address: www.vshportland.com
Control: Corporation, Investor–owned (for–profit) **Service**: Acute long–term care hospital

Staffed Beds: 68

Hospital, Medicare Provider Number, Address, Telephone, Approval, Facility, and Physician Codes, Health Care System

★ American Hospital Association (AHA) membership
☐ The Joint Commission accreditation
○ Healthcare Facilities Accreditation Program
◇ DNV Healthcare Inc. accreditation
⇑ Center for Improvement in Healthcare Quality Accreditation
△ Commission on Accreditation of Rehabilitation Facilities (CARF) accreditation

OR

PORTLAND—Washington County

☐ **CEDAR HILLS HOSPITAL (384012)**, 10300 SW Eastridge Street, Zip 97225–5004; tel. 503/944–5000 (Nonreporting) **A**1 10 **S** Universal Health Services, Inc., King of Prussia, PA
Primary Contact: Elizabeth Hutter, Chief Executive Officer
Web address: www.cedarhillshospital.com
Control: Corporation, Investor–owned (for–profit) **Service**: Psychiatric

Staffed Beds: 78

☐ **CEDAR HILLS HOSPITAL (384012)**, 10300 SW Eastridge Street, Zip 97225–5004; tel. 503/944–5000 (Nonreporting) **A**1 10 **S** Universal Health Services, Inc., King of Prussia, PA
Primary Contact: Elizabeth Hutter, Chief Executive Officer
Web address: www.cedarhillshospital.com
Control: Corporation, Investor–owned (for–profit) **Service**: Psychiatric

Staffed Beds: 78

⊠ **PROVIDENCE ST. VINCENT MEDICAL CENTER (380004)**, 9205 SW Barnes Road, Zip 97225–6661; tel. 503/216–1234, (Includes CHILDREN AT PROVIDENCE ST. VINCENT, 9205 SW Barnes Road, Portland, Oregon, Zip 97225–6603, tel. 503/216–4400) **A**1 2 3 5 10 **F**3 5 13 15 17 18 20 22 24 26 28 29 30 31 34 35 36 37 38 40 41 44 45 46 47 48 49 50 53 54 56 57 58 59 60 61 64 65 70 72 74 75 76 77 78 79 81 82 84 85 86 87 88 89 91 92 93 99 100 102 103 104 105 107 108 109 110 111 112 114 115 116 117 118 119 120 121 123 126 129 130 131 132 133 135 146 147 148 **P**6 **S** Providence St. Joseph Health, Renton, WA
Primary Contact: Janice Burger, Chief Executive
COO: Nancy Roberts, Chief Operating Officer
CFO: Scott Pfister, Director Finance
Web address: www.providence.org/portland/hospitals
Control: Church operated, Nongovernment, not–for–profit **Service**: General medical and surgical

Staffed Beds: 487 **Admissions**: 25882 **Census**: 319 **Outpatient Visits**: 891440 **Births**: 3978 **Total Expense ($000)**: 781173 **Payroll Expense ($000)**: 226963 **Personnel**: 2827

PRINEVILLE—Crook County

★ **ST. CHARLES PRINEVILLE (381313)**, 384 SE Combs Flat Road, Zip 97754–1206; tel. 541/447–6254 **A**10 18 **F**3 11 15 29 30 34 35 40 43 45 50 59 64 65 68 70 75 77 79 81 82 84 85 86 87 93 97 100 107 110 115 119 127 128 130 132 133 135 146 **P**6 **S** St. Charles Health System, Inc., Bend, OR
Primary Contact: John Bishop, President
CFO: Karen Shepard, Senior Vice President and Chief Financial Officer
CMO: Michel Boileau M.D., Chief Clinical Officer
CHR: Rebecca Berry, Senior Director Human Resources
Web address: www.stcharleshealthcare.org
Control: Other not–for–profit (including NFP Corporation) **Service**: General medical and surgical

Staffed Beds: 18 **Admissions**: 709 **Census**: 6 **Outpatient Visits**: 36351 **Births**: 0 **Total Expense ($000)**: 26737 **Payroll Expense ($000)**: 16829 **Personnel**: 203

REDMOND—Deschutes County

⊠ **ST. CHARLES REDMOND (380040)**, 1253 NW Canal Boulevard, Zip 97756–1395; tel. 541/548–8131 **A**1 10 20 **F**3 12 13 29 30 31 34 35 40 43 44 45 47 51 54 59 62 63 64 70 75 76 78 81 84 85 87 91 93 97 107 115 119 129 130 132 135 145 146 147 149 **P**6 **S** St. Charles Health System, Inc., Bend, OR
Primary Contact: Iman Simmons, Chief Operating Officer and Interim President
CFO: Jennifer Welander CPA, Senior Vice President Finance and Chief Financial Officer
CMO: Jeffrey Absalon M.D., Chief Physician Officer
CIO: Jerimiah Brickhouse, Chief Information Officer
CHR: Rebecca Berry, Vice President Human Resources
CNO: Karen Reed R.N., MSN, Chief Nursing Officer
Web address: www.stcharleshealthcare.org
Control: Other not–for–profit (including NFP Corporation) **Service**: General medical and surgical

Staffed Beds: 49 **Admissions**: 2528 **Census**: 20 **Outpatient Visits**: 52836 **Births**: 417 **Total Expense ($000)**: 64730 **Payroll Expense ($000)**: 41577 **Personnel**: 444

REEDSPORT—Douglas County

LOWER UMPQUA HOSPITAL DISTRICT (381311), 600 Ranch Road, Zip 97467–1795; tel. 541/271–2171 **A**10 18 **F**3 7 11 15 29 34 35 40 43 45 46 50 57 64 70 75 77 79 81 82 85 87 93 97 107 108 115 119 127 130 132 133 143 144 148 **P**6
Primary Contact: Ryan Fowler, Chief Administrative Officer
CMO: Ronald Vail M.D., Chief of Staff
CIO: Timothy Picou, Manager Information Technology
Web address: www.lowerumpquahospital.com
Control: Hospital district or authority, Government, Nonfederal **Service**: General medical and surgical

Staffed Beds: 20 **Admissions**: 351 **Census**: 4 **Outpatient Visits**: 18282 **Births**: 0 **Total Expense ($000)**: 25604 **Payroll Expense ($000)**: 10790 **Personnel**: 147

ROSEBURG—Douglas County

⊠ **MERCY MEDICAL CENTER (380027)**, 2700 Stewart Parkway, Zip 97471–1281; tel. 541/673–0611 **A**1 10 **F**3 8 11 13 15 17 18 19 20 21 22 23 24 25 26 27 28 29 30 31 32 34 35 37 38 40 43 44 45 46 47 48 49 50 51 54 56 57 59 60 61 62 63 64 65 68 70 74 75 76 77 78 79 81 82 83 84 85 86 87 89 93 96 102 107 108 110 111 114 115 118 119 129 130 132 135 143 146 147 148 149 **S** Catholic Health Initiatives, Englewood, CO
Primary Contact: Kelly C. Morgan, President and Chief Executive Officer
COO: Debbie Boswell, Chief Operating Officer and Chief Nursing Officer
CFO: Doug Klebe, Vice President Operational Finance
CMO: Jason Gray M.D., Chief Medical Officer
CIO: Kathleen Nickel, Director Communications
CHR: Debora Lightcap, Director Human Resources
CNO: Debbie Boswell, Chief Operating Officer and Chief Nursing Officer
Web address: www.mercyrose.org
Control: Church operated, Nongovernment, not–for–profit **Service**: General medical and surgical

Staffed Beds: 140 **Admissions**: 7203 **Census**: 79 **Outpatient Visits**: 399005 **Births**: 898 **Total Expense ($000)**: 174207 **Payroll Expense ($000)**: 62312 **Personnel**: 804

⊠ **VETERANS AFFAIRS ROSEBURG HEALTHCARE SYSTEM**, 913 NW Garden Valley Boulevard, Zip 97471–6513; tel. 541/440–1000, (Nonreporting) **A**1 **S** Department of Veterans Affairs, Washington, DC
Primary Contact: Douglas V. Paxton, Director
COO: Steven Broskey, Associate Director
CHR: Larry Mentzer, Chief Human Resources Officer
CNO: Tracy Weistreich Ph.D., R.N., Associate Director Patient Care Services/Nurse Executive
Web address: www.roseburg.va.gov/
Control: Veterans Affairs, Government, federal **Service**: General medical and surgical

Staffed Beds: 88

SALEM—Marion County

☐ **OREGON STATE HOSPITAL (384008)**, 2600 Center Street NE, Zip 97301–2682; tel. 503/945–2870 **A**1 3 5 10 **F**3 29 30 39 50 53 56 57 58 59 61 65 68 75 77 79 82 83 84 86 87 91 92 96 97 98 100 101 102 103 106 130 132 135 143 146 148 149
Primary Contact: Greg Roberts, Superintendent
Web address: www.oregon.gov/OHA/amh/osh/
Control: State, Government, Nonfederal **Service**: Psychiatric

Staffed Beds: 669 **Admissions**: 952 **Census**: 602 **Outpatient Visits**: 0 **Births**: 0

⊠ **SALEM HOSPITAL (380051)**, 890 Oak Street SE, Zip 97301–3959, Mailing Address: P.O.Box 14001, 97309–5014; tel. 503/561–5200, (Includes PSYCHIATRIC MEDICINE CENTER, 1127 Oak Street SE, Salem, Oregon, Zip 97301, P O Box 14001, 97309–5014, tel. 503/216–4400; REGIONAL REHABILITATION CENTER, 2561 Center Street NE, Salem, Oregon, Zip 97301, P O Box 14001, 97309–5014, tel. 503/370–5986) **A**1 2 5 10 **F**3 11 12 13 15 17 18 20 22 24 26 28 29 30 31 34 35 36 37 38 40 43 45 46 47 48 49 50 53 54 55 56 57 58 59 64 67 68 70 72 74 75 76 77 78 79 81 82 84 85 86 87 89 90 91 92 93 94 95 96 97 98 102 103 105 106 107 108 109 110 111 112 113 114 115 116 117 118 119 120 121 122 123 124 126 129 130 131 132 135 145 146 147 148 **P**6 **S** Salem Health, Salem, OR
Primary Contact: Cheryl R. Nester Wolfe, President and Chief Executive Officer
COO: Bahaa Wanly, Interim Chief Operating Officer
CFO: James Parr, Chief Financial Officer
CMO: Ralph Yates D.O., Chief Medical Officer
CIO: Leah Mitchell R.N., Interim Chief Information Officer
CHR: Laurie C Barr, Vice President Human Resources
CNO: Sarah Horn, Chief Nursing Officer
Web address: www.salemhealth.org
Control: Other not–for–profit (including NFP Corporation) **Service**: General medical and surgical

Staffed Beds: 440 **Admissions**: 24929 **Census**: 300 **Outpatient Visits**: 395953 **Births**: 3485 **Total Expense ($000)**: 659689 **Payroll Expense ($000)**: 286546 **Personnel**: 3582

Many Facility Codes have changed. Please refer to the AHA Guide Code Chart. © 2017 AHA Guide

SEASIDE—Clatsop County

⊞ **PROVIDENCE SEASIDE HOSPITAL (381303)**, 725 South Wahanna Road, Zip 97138–7735; tel. 503/717–7000 **A**1 10 18 **F**3 12 13 15 18 29 30 31 32 34 35 40 45 46 56 57 59 61 64 65 66 70 75 78 79 81 82 83 84 85 86 87 91 92 93 97 107 108 110 111 114 119 127 130 132 133 135 143 146 147 148 **P**6 **S** Providence St. Joseph Health, Renton, WA
Primary Contact: Kendall Sawa, R.N., Chief Executive Officer
COO: Debbie Glass, Interim Chief Operating Officer
CFO: Pamela Cooper, Director Finance
CMO: Susan Heineck M.D., President Professional Staff
CHR: Theresa Osburne, Human Resources Strategic Partners
CNO: Janiece Zauner, Chief Nursing Officer
Web address: www.providence.org
Control: Church operated, Nongovernment, not–for–profit **Service:** General medical and surgical

> **Staffed Beds:** 25 **Admissions:** 1062 **Census:** 9 **Outpatient Visits:** 146625 **Births:** 100 **Total Expense ($000):** 67763 **Payroll Expense ($000):** 27340 **Personnel:** 345

SILVERTON—Marion County

⊞ **LEGACY SILVERTON MEDICAL CENTER (380029)**, 342 Fairview Street, Zip 97381–1993; tel. 503/873–1500 **A**1 5 10 **F**3 11 13 15 20 26 28 29 30 34 35 40 43 47 50 54 57 59 64 65 66 70 75 76 77 79 81 85 86 87 89 102 104 107 108 110 111 114 115 119 124 127 130 131 132 133 135 143 144 146 147 148 149 **P**8 **S** Legacy Health, Portland, OR
Primary Contact: Sarah Fronza, President
COO: Karen Brady, Vice President, Chief Nursing Officer
CFO: Daniel Jessup, Chief Financial Officer
CMO: Joseph Huang M.D., Chief Medical and Quality Officer
CIO: Karen Brady, Vice President, Chief Nursing Officer
CHR: Natalie Britton, Director Human Resources
CNO: Karen Brady, Vice President, Chief Nursing Officer
Web address: www.silvertonhealth.org
Control: Other not–for–profit (including NFP Corporation) **Service:** General medical and surgical

> **Staffed Beds:** 48 **Admissions:** 2937 **Census:** 20 **Outpatient Visits:** 179681 **Births:** 1473 **Total Expense ($000):** 115761 **Payroll Expense ($000):** 57057 **Personnel:** 709

SPRINGFIELD—Lane County

⊞ **MCKENZIE–WILLAMETTE MEDICAL CENTER (380020)**, 1460 'G' Street, Zip 97477–4197; tel. 541/726–4400 **A**1 10 **F**3 11 13 17 18 20 22 24 26 28 29 30 31 34 35 39 40 41 43 45 46 47 49 50 57 59 70 73 76 78 79 81 82 85 87 89 93 107 108 111 115 118 119 126 129 130 132 146 147 148 **P**6 **S** Quorum Health, Brentwood, TN
Primary Contact: Chad Campbell, Chief Executive Officer
CFO: Rosanne Devault, Chief Financial Officer
CIO: David Blomquist, Director Information Technology
CHR: Megan A O'Leary, Vice President Human Resources and Rehabilitation Services
Web address: www.mckweb.com
Control: Corporation, Investor–owned (for–profit) **Service:** General medical and surgical

> **Staffed Beds:** 113 **Admissions:** 8011 **Census:** 81 **Outpatient Visits:** 93654 **Births:** 1079 **Total Expense ($000):** 149999 **Payroll Expense ($000):** 53799 **Personnel:** 686

★ ⇑ **PEACEHEALTH SACRED HEART MEDICAL CENTER AT RIVERBEND (380102)**, 3333 Riverbend Drive, Zip 97477–8800; tel. 541/222–7300 **A**10 21 **F**3 11 12 13 19 20 21 22 24 26 28 29 30 31 37 38 40 43 45 46 47 49 51 57 60 64 68 70 72 74 75 76 78 79 81 84 85 89 93 102 107 108 111 115 118 119 124 126 129 130 146 148 **P**6 **S** PeaceHealth, Vancouver, WA
Primary Contact: Rand O'Leary, FACHE, Chief Executive, Oregon Network
COO: Shannon Surber, Chief Operating Officer
CHR: Marie F Stehmer, Senior Director of Human Resources
Web address: www.peacehealth.org
Control: Church operated, Nongovernment, not–for–profit **Service:** General medical and surgical

> **Staffed Beds:** 379 **Admissions:** 23520 **Census:** 296 **Outpatient Visits:** 106253 **Births:** 2506 **Total Expense ($000):** 560810 **Payroll Expense ($000):** 177211 **Personnel:** 2466

STAYTON—Marion County

⊞ **SANTIAM HOSPITAL (380056)**, 1401 North 10th Avenue, Zip 97383–1399; tel. 503/769–2175 **A**1 10 **F**3 7 11 13 15 16 17 29 30 40 41 43 50 65 70 72 73 76 80 81 85 87 88 89 90 98 107 111 115 119 128 130 133 135 143 **P**8
Primary Contact: Terry L. Fletchall, President and Chief Executive Officer
COO: Maggie Hudson, Chief Financial and Operations Officer
CFO: Rachael Seeder, Controller
CMO: Amy Sutkus M.D., Medical Staff President
CIO: Trace Jacobs, Director Information Technology
CNO: Janet Dow R.N., Chief Nursing Officer
Web address: www.santiamhospital.org
Control: Other not–for–profit (including NFP Corporation) **Service:** General medical and surgical

> **Staffed Beds:** 40 **Admissions:** 927 **Census:** 9 **Outpatient Visits:** 43121 **Births:** 86 **Total Expense ($000):** 45065 **Payroll Expense ($000):** 21857 **Personnel:** 279

THE DALLES—Wasco County

⊞ △ **MID–COLUMBIA MEDICAL CENTER (380001)**, 1700 East 19th Street, Zip 97058–3317; tel. 541/296–1111 **A**1 2 7 10 **F**3 11 13 15 18 20 28 29 30 31 32 34 35 36 40 41 43 45 46 50 57 59 62 65 66 68 70 75 76 77 78 79 81 82 83 84 86 87 89 90 91 92 93 99 100 101 104 107 108 110 111 114 118 119 120 121 123 127 129 130 131 132 133 135 146 147 148 149 **P**6
Primary Contact: Dennis M. Knox, Chief Executive Officer
CFO: Don Arbon, Vice President Finance
CMO: Judy Richardson M.D., President Medical Staff
CIO: Erick Larson, Vice President and Chief Information Officer
CHR: Christine Espy, Division Director
CNO: Felicia M Adams MS, Chief Nursing Officer
Web address: www.mcmc.net
Control: Other not–for–profit (including NFP Corporation) **Service:** General medical and surgical

> **Staffed Beds:** 45 **Admissions:** 2113 **Census:** 18 **Outpatient Visits:** 114556 **Births:** 275 **Total Expense ($000):** 103803 **Payroll Expense ($000):** 47449 **Personnel:** 633

TILLAMOOK—Tillamook County

⊞ **TILLAMOOK REGIONAL MEDICAL CENTER (381317)**, 1000 Third Street, Zip 97141–3430; tel. 503/842–4444 **A**1 10 18 **F**2 3 7 13 15 17 18 29 30 31 33 34 35 37 40 43 45 50 57 59 64 65 68 75 76 77 78 79 81 82 85 87 93 94 97 102 107 108 110 111 115 119 127 129 130 132 133 134 135 144 146 147 148 149 **P**6 **S** Adventist Health, Roseville, CA
Primary Contact: David Butler, President and Chief Executive Officer
CFO: Walt Larson, Vice President Finance
CMO: Mark Bowman M.D., President Medical Staff
CNO: Kathy Saxon R.N., Vice President Patient Care Services
Web address: www.tillamookregionalmc.com
Control: Church operated, Nongovernment, not–for–profit **Service:** General medical and surgical

> **Staffed Beds:** 25 **Admissions:** 1408 **Census:** 13 **Outpatient Visits:** 134465 **Births:** 183 **Total Expense ($000):** 72994 **Payroll Expense ($000):** 30633 **Personnel:** 386

TUALATIN—Clackamas County

⊞ **LEGACY MERIDIAN PARK MEDICAL CENTER (380089)**, 19300 SW 65th Avenue, Zip 97062–9741; tel. 503/692–1212 **A**1 2 10 **F**3 11 13 15 18 20 22 28 29 30 31 32 34 35 38 40 44 45 46 49 50 51 56 57 59 60 64 68 70 74 75 76 77 78 79 80 81 85 86 87 91 93 97 107 108 110 111 114 115 116 117 118 119 120 121 126 129 130 132 145 146 147 148 149 **P**6 **S** Legacy Health, Portland, OR
Primary Contact: Allyson Anderson, President
COO: Michael Newcomb D.O., Senior Vice President and Chief Operating Officer
CMO: Lewis Low M.D., Senior Vice President and Chief Medical Officer
CIO: John Jay Kenagy Ph.D., Senior Vice President and Chief Information Officer
CHR: Sonja Steves, Vice President Human Resources and Marketing
CNO: Carol Bradley MSN, R.N., Senior Vice President and Chief Nursing Officer
Web address: www.legacyhealth.org
Control: Other not–for–profit (including NFP Corporation) **Service:** General medical and surgical

> **Staffed Beds:** 130 **Admissions:** 8812 **Census:** 82 **Outpatient Visits:** 235355 **Births:** 1086 **Total Expense ($000):** 199409 **Payroll Expense ($000):** 71987 **Personnel:** 800

OR

Hospital, Medicare Provider Number, Address, Telephone, Approval, Facility, and Physician Codes, Health Care System

★ American Hospital Association (AHA) membership
□ The Joint Commission accreditation
○ Healthcare Facilities Accreditation Program
◇ DNV Healthcare Inc. accreditation
⇑ Center for Improvement in Healthcare Quality Accreditation
△ Commission on Accreditation of Rehabilitation Facilities (CARF) accreditation

PENNSYLVANIA

ABINGTON—Montgomery County

✠ **ABINGTON HOSPITAL (390231)**, 1200 Old York Road, Zip 19001–3720; tel. 215/481–2000 **A**1 2 3 5 10 13 **F**3 6 8 9 11 12 13 15 17 18 20 22 24 26 28 29 30 31 32 34 35 36 37 38 39 40 43 44 45 46 47 48 49 50 52 53 54 55 56 57 58 59 61 62 63 64 65 66 68 70 72 73 74 75 76 77 78 79 80 81 82 84 85 86 87 89 90 91 92 93 94 96 97 98 99 100 101 102 103 104 107 108 110 111 114 115 118 119 120 121 123 124 126 129 130 131 132 135 144 145 146 147 148 149 150 **P**6 **S** Jefferson Health, Philadelphia, PA
Primary Contact: Margaret M. McGoldrick, President
COO: Eileen Jameson, Chief Operating Officer
CFO: Michael Walsh, Senior Vice President Finance and Chief Financial Officer
CMO: Gerard M. Cleary M.D., Senior Vice President, Chief of Staff and Chief Medical Officer
CIO: Daniel P. Walsh, Vice President, Information Systems and Technology Northern Division
CHR: Meghan Patton, Vice President Human Resources
CNO: Theresa Reilly MSN, R.N., Senior Vice President Patient Services and Chief Nursing Officer
Web address: www.abingtonhealth.org
Control: Other not–for–profit (including NFP Corporation) **Service:** General medical and surgical

Staffed Beds: 618 **Admissions:** 28888 **Census:** 363 **Outpatient Visits:** 597916 **Births:** 4770 **Total Expense ($000):** 723369 **Payroll Expense ($000):** 349917 **Personnel:** 4217

ALLENTOWN—Lehigh County

☐ △ **GOOD SHEPHERD REHABILITATION HOSPITAL (393035)**, 850 South 5th Street, Zip 18103–3308; tel. 610/776–3299 **A**1 3 5 7 10 **F**28 29 30 32 34 35 36 53 54 56 57 58 59 64 65 66 68 74 75 82 86 87 90 91 93 94 95 100 107 111 119 130 131 132 143 146 147 148 **P**1 **S** Good Shepherd Rehabilitation Network, Allentown, PA
Primary Contact: John Kristel, President and Chief Executive Officer
CFO: Ronald J. Petula, Chief Financial Officer
Web address: www.goodshepherdrehab.org
Control: Other not–for–profit (including NFP Corporation) **Service:** Rehabilitation

Staffed Beds: 106 **Admissions:** 1394 **Census:** 72 **Outpatient Visits:** 237392 **Births:** 0 **Total Expense ($000):** 87362 **Payroll Expense ($000):** 35793 **Personnel:** 827

✠ **LEHIGH VALLEY HOSPITAL (390133)**, 1200 South Cedar Crest Boulevard, Zip 18103–6248, Mailing Address: P.O.Box 689, 18105–1556; tel. 610/402–8000, (Includes LEHIGH VALLEY HEALTH NETWORK PEDITATRICS, 1200 South Cedar Crest Boulevard, Allentown, Pennsylvania, Zip 18103–6202, P.O. Box 689, 18105, tel. 484/862–3131) **A**1 2 3 5 8 10 **F**3 6 7 8 12 13 15 16 17 18 19 20 22 24 26 28 29 30 31 32 33 34 35 36 37 38 39 40 41 43 44 45 46 47 48 49 50 51 53 54 55 56 57 58 59 60 61 62 63 64 65 66 68 70 71 72 74 76 77 78 79 80 81 82 84 85 87 88 89 90 92 93 96 97 98 99 100 101 102 104 105 106 107 108 110 114 115 116 117 118 119 120 121 123 124 126 128 129 130 131 132 134 135 138 141 142 143 144 145 146 147 148 149 **P**5 6 8 **S** Lehigh Valley Health Network, Allentown, PA
Primary Contact: Brian A. Nester, D.O., President and Chief Executive Officer
COO: Terry Ann Capuano R.N., MSN, FACHE, Executive Vice President and Chief Operating Officer
CFO: Edward O'Dea, Executive Vice President and Chief Financial Officer
CMO: Thomas V. Whalen M.D., Chief Medical Officer
CIO: Michael N. Minear, Senior Vice President and Chief Information Officer
CHR: Deborah A. Patrick, Senior Vice President Human Resources
CNO: Marie Kim Jordan R.N., Senior Vice President and Chief Nursing Officer
Web address: www.lvhn.org
Control: Other not–for–profit (including NFP Corporation) **Service:** General medical and surgical

Staffed Beds: 877 **Admissions:** 43173 **Census:** 673 **Outpatient Visits:** 500506 **Births:** 4439 **Total Expense ($000):** 1349795 **Payroll Expense ($000):** 455281 **Personnel:** 7209

☐ △ **SACRED HEART HOSPITAL (390197)**, 421 West Chew Street, Zip 18102–3490; tel. 610/776–4500, (Total facility includes 22 beds in nursing home–type unit) **A**1 3 5 7 10 **F**3 11 12 13 15 18 20 22 24 28 29 30 31 32 34 35 38 39 40 43 45 46 47 49 50 56 57 59 61 64 66 68 74 75 76 77 78 79 80 81 82 84 85 87 91 92 93 97 98 100 101 102 103 107 108 110 111 114 115 117 118 119 121 128 129 130 132 135 143 146 147 148 **P**8
Primary Contact: John L. Nespoli, Chief Executive Officer
CMO: Farrokh Sadr M.D., Chief Medical Officer
CIO: Tracy Burkhart, Vice President Information Services
CHR: Joseph Mikitka, Vice President Human Resources
Web address: www.shh.org
Control: Other not–for–profit (including NFP Corporation) **Service:** General medical and surgical

Staffed Beds: 125 **Admissions:** 4990 **Census:** 108 **Outpatient Visits:** 164072 **Births:** 273 **Total Expense ($000):** 99377 **Payroll Expense ($000):** 36053 **Personnel:** 803

ST LUKE'S HOSPITAL – ALLENTOWN CAMPUS See St. Luke's University Hospital – Bethlehem Campus, Bethlehem

☐ **SURGICAL SPECIALTY CENTER AT COORDINATED HEALTH (390321)**, 1503 North Cedar Crest Boulevard, Zip 18104–2302; tel. 610/861–8080 (Nonreporting) **A**1 10
Primary Contact: Emil Dilorio, M.D., Chief Executive Officer
Web address: www.coordinatedhealth.com
Control: Other not–for–profit (including NFP Corporation) **Service:** Surgical

Staffed Beds: 20

ALTOONA—Blair County

ALTOONA REGIONAL HEALTH SYSTEM See UPMC Altoona

✠ **HEALTHSOUTH REHABILITATION HOSPITAL OF ALTOONA (393040)**, 2005 Valley View Boulevard, Zip 16602–4598; tel. 814/944–3535 **A**1 10 **F**28 29 34 64 74 75 82 90 91 93 94 96 130 131 **P**5 **S** HEALTHSOUTH Corporation, Birmingham, AL
Primary Contact: Scott Filler, Chief Executive Officer
CFO: George Berger, Controller
CMO: Rakesh Patel D.O., Medical Director
CIO: Kathleen Edwards, Manager Information Systems Operation
CHR: Christine Filer, Director Human Resources
CNO: Mary Gen Boyles, Chief Nursing Officer
Web address: www.healthsouthaltoona.com
Control: Corporation, Investor–owned (for–profit) **Service:** Rehabilitation

Staffed Beds: 80 **Admissions:** 1349 **Census:** 45 **Births:** 0

✠ **JAMES E. VAN ZANDT VETERANS AFFAIRS MEDICAL CENTER**, 2907 Pleasant Valley Boulevard, Zip 16602–4305; tel. 877/626–2500, (Nonreporting) **A**1 **S** Department of Veterans Affairs, Washington, DC
Primary Contact: Charles Thilges, Director
CFO: Carl Parrish, Chief Fiscal Service
CMO: Santha Kurian M.D., Chief of Staff
CIO: Michael Hynoski, Chief Information Resource Management
CHR: Gina Dunio, Chief Human Resources
Web address: www.altoona.va.gov/
Control: Veterans Affairs, Government, federal **Service:** General medical and surgical

Staffed Beds: 68

✠ **UPMC ALTOONA (390073)**, 620 Howard Avenue, Zip 16601–4804; tel. 814/889–2011 **A**1 2 3 5 10 12 13 **F**3 5 8 11 12 13 15 17 18 20 22 24 26 28 29 30 31 34 35 37 38 39 40 43 44 45 47 48 49 50 51 54 56 57 59 60 61 64 65 66 68 70 73 74 75 76 77 78 79 81 83 84 85 86 87 89 91 92 93 97 98 100 101 102 103 107 108 110 111 114 115 117 118 119 120 121 123 126 129 130 131 132 135 146 147 148 149 **P**6 **S** UPMC, Pittsburgh, PA
Primary Contact: Gerald Murray, President
COO: Ron McConnell, Chief Operating Officer
CFO: Betsy Kreuz, Chief Financial Officer
CMO: Linnane Batzel M.D., Senior Vice President Quality and Medical Affairs and Chief Medical Officer
CIO: Dale Fuller, Vice President and Chief Information Officer
CHR: Michelle A Speck, Vice President Human Resources
CNO: Chris Rickens R.N., MS, Senior Vice President and Chief Nursing Officer
Web address: www.altoonaregional.org
Control: Other not–for–profit (including NFP Corporation) **Service:** General medical and surgical

Staffed Beds: 342 **Admissions:** 17754 **Census:** 232 **Outpatient Visits:** 313773 **Births:** 859 **Total Expense ($000):** 381539 **Payroll Expense ($000):** 136421 **Personnel:** 2054

Many Facility Codes have changed. Please refer to the AHA Guide Code Chart.
© 2017 AHA Guide

AMBLER—Montgomery County

☐ **HORSHAM CLINIC (394034)**, 722 East Butler Pike, Zip 19002–2310; tel. 215/643–7800 **A**1 3 5 10 **F**5 98 99 100 102 105 **S** Universal Health Services, Inc., King of Prussia, PA
Primary Contact: Phyllis Weisfield, Chief Executive Officer and Managing Director
CFO: Christian Owen, Chief Operating Officer
CMO: James B Congdon M.D., Medical Director
CIO: Suzanne Scholz, Director Medical Records
CHR: Kathleen Nichelson, Director Human Resources
CNO: Calvin Litka R.N., Director of Nursing
Web address: www.horshamclinic.com
Control: Corporation, Investor–owned (for–profit) **Service**: Psychiatric

Staffed Beds: 206 **Admissions**: 5880 **Census**: 191 **Outpatient Visits**: 0
Births: 0 **Total Expense ($000)**: 41620 **Payroll Expense ($000)**: 20125

BEAVER—Beaver County

✚ **CURAHEALTH HERITAGE VALLEY (392043)**, 1000 Dutch Ridge Road, Zip 15009–9727; tel. 724/773–8480, (Nonreporting) **A**1 10 **S** Curahealth Hospitals, Garland, TX
Primary Contact: Janie Rosenberger–Slampack, Chief Executive Officer
CFO: Kevin Varley, Chief Financial Officer
CMO: Jeffrey Erukhimou M.D., Medical Director
Web address: www.curahealth.com
Control: Corporation, Investor–owned (for–profit) **Service**: Acute long–term care hospital

Staffed Beds: 35

☐ **HERITAGE VALLEY HEALTH SYSTEM (390036)**, 1000 Dutch Ridge Road, Zip 15009–9727; tel. 724/728–7000 **A**1 3 10 13 **F**3 11 13 14 15 18 20 22 24 26 28 29 30 32 34 35 38 40 46 49 50 53 54 55 57 59 60 64 66 70 73 74 75 76 77 78 79 81 82 84 85 86 89 90 92 93 96 97 98 100 101 102 103 104 107 108 110 111 115 116 118 119 120 121 129 130 131 132 135 145 147 148 **P**6 **S** Heritage Valley Health System, Beaver, PA
Primary Contact: Norman F. Mitry, President and Chief Executive Officer
CFO: Bryan J Randall, Vice President Finance and Chief Financial Officer
CMO: John Cinicola M.D., Chief Medical Officer
CIO: David Carleton, Chief Information Officer
CHR: Bruce Edwards, Vice President Human Resources
CNO: Marcia L Ferrero MS, Chief Nursing Officer
Web address: www.heritagevalley.org
Control: Other not–for–profit (including NFP Corporation) **Service**: General medical and surgical

Staffed Beds: 271 **Admissions**: 13455 **Census**: 159 **Births**: 1080

BENSALEM—Bucks County

LIVENGRIN FOUNDATION, 4833 Hulmeville Road, Zip 19020–3099; tel. 215/638–5200, (Nonreporting)
Primary Contact: Richard M. Pine, President and Chief Executive Officer
CFO: James D Flis, Chief Financial Officer
CMO: William J Lorman Ph.D., Clinical Director
CIO: William Miller, Coordinator Management Information Systems
Web address: www.livengrin.org
Control: Other not–for–profit (including NFP Corporation) **Service**: Alcoholism and other chemical dependency

Staffed Beds: 76

☐ **ROTHMAN SPECIALTY HOSPITAL (390322)**, 3300 Tillman Drive, Zip 19020–2071; tel. 215/244–7400 **A**1 3 10 **F**29 79 81 82 85 89 141 146
Primary Contact: Kelly Doyle, Chief Executive Officer
Web address: www.rothmanspecialtyhospital.com/
Control: Partnership, Investor–owned (for–profit) **Service**: Surgical

Staffed Beds: 24 **Admissions**: 2017 **Census**: 7 **Births**: 0

BERWICK—Columbia County

✚ **BERWICK HOSPITAL CENTER (390072)**, 701 East 16th Street, Zip 18603–2397; tel. 570/759–5000, (Nonreporting) **A**1 10 **S** Community Health Systems, Inc., Franklin, TN
Primary Contact: Diane Ljungquist, R.N., MS, Chief Executive Officer
CFO: Whitney Holloway, Chief Financial Officer
CMO: John A. Guerriero, Chief of Staff
CIO: Kerry Yeager, Director Information Technology
CHR: Jackie Ridall, Director Human Resources
CNO: Doreen Kolojejechick, Chief Nursing Officer
Web address: www.berwick–hospital.com
Control: Corporation, Investor–owned (for–profit) **Service**: General medical and surgical

Staffed Beds: 101

BETHLEHEM—Northampton County

☐ **COORDINATED HEALTH–BETHLEHEM (390314)**, 2310 Highland Avenue, Zip 18020–8920, Mailing Address: 2300 Highland Avenue, 18020; tel. 610/861–8080 **A**1 3 10 **F**3 29 34 64 79 81 82 85 111 115 119 124 130 131 141 148
Primary Contact: Laurie H. Gombert, Administrator
Web address: www.coordinatedhealth.com
Control: Corporation, Investor–owned (for–profit) **Service**: Orthopedic

Staffed Beds: 20 **Admissions**: 1226 **Census**: 7 **Outpatient Visits**: 6461
Births: 0 **Total Expense ($000)**: 21385 **Payroll Expense ($000)**: 5779
Personnel: 124

BETHLEHEM—Lehigh County

✚ △ **GOOD SHEPHERD SPECIALTY HOSPITAL (392033)**, 2545 Schoenersville Road, 4th Floor, Zip 18017–7300; tel. 484/884–5051 **A**1 7 10 **F**1 3 29 30 36 77 85 87 91 95 130 148 **P**5 **S** Good Shepherd Rehabilitation Network, Allentown, PA
Primary Contact: Susan Ferguson, Administrator
CFO: Ronald J. Petula, Chief Financial Officer
CIO: Michael Cirba, Chief Information Officer
CHR: Kristen Melan, Director Human Resources Administration
CNO: Samuel Miranda Jr, Chief Nursing Officer
Web address: www.goodshepherdrehab.org
Control: Other not–for–profit (including NFP Corporation) **Service**: Acute long–term care hospital

Staffed Beds: 32 **Admissions**: 347 **Census**: 25 **Outpatient Visits**: 0
Births: 0 **Total Expense ($000)**: 15267 **Payroll Expense ($000)**: 5210
Personnel: 83

✚ **LEHIGH VALLEY HOSPITAL–MUHLENBERG (390263)**, 2545 Schoenersville Road, Zip 18017–7300; tel. 484/884–2200 **A**1 2 3 10 12 13 **F**3 7 8 11 15 17 18 20 22 24 28 29 30 31 34 35 36 37 38 39 40 44 45 46 49 50 51 53 54 57 58 59 60 61 62 63 64 65 68 70 74 77 78 79 80 81 82 84 85 86 87 90 92 93 97 100 102 105 107 108 110 111 115 118 119 126 129 130 131 132 134 135 141 143 146 148 149 **P**5 6 8 **S** Lehigh Valley Health Network, Allentown, PA
Primary Contact: Brian A. Nester, D.O., President and Chief Executive Officer
COO: Terry Ann Capuano R.N., MSN, FACHE, Executive Vice President and Chief Operating Officer
CFO: Edward O'Dea, Executive Vice President and Chief Financial Officer
CMO: Thomas V. Whalen M.D., Executive Vice President and Chief Medical Officer
CIO: Michael N. Minear, Senior Vice President and Chief Information Officer
CHR: Deborah A. Patrick, Senior Vice President Human Resources
CNO: Marie Kim Jordan R.N., Senior Vice President, Chief Nursing Officer
Web address: www.lvhn.org
Control: Other not–for–profit (including NFP Corporation) **Service**: General medical and surgical

Staffed Beds: 158 **Admissions**: 9605 **Census**: 123 **Outpatient Visits**: 199377 **Births**: 0 **Total Expense ($000)**: 220521 **Payroll Expense ($000)**: 81269 **Personnel**: 1264

☐ △ **ST. LUKE'S UNIVERSITY HOSPITAL – BETHLEHEM CAMPUS (390049)**, 801 Ostrum Street, Zip 18015–1065; tel. 484/526–4000, (Includes ST LUKE'S HOSPITAL – ALLENTOWN CAMPUS, 1736 Hamilton Street, Allentown, Pennsylvania, Zip 18104–5656, tel. 610/628–8300) **A**1 2 3 7 8 10 12 13 **F**3 9 11 12 13 15 17 18 19 20 22 24 26 27 28 29 30 31 32 34 35 36 37 38 39 40 42 43 44 45 46 47 48 49 50 51 52 53 54 55 56 57 58 59 60 61 63 64 65 66 68 70 71 72 73 74 75 76 77 78 79 81 82 84 85 86 87 89 90 92 93 96 97 98 99 100 101 102 103 104 105 107 108 109 110 111 115 117 118 119 120 121 123 124 126 129 130 131 132 133 134 135 144 145 146 147 148 149 **S** St. Luke's University Health Network, Bethlehem, PA
Primary Contact: Carol Kuplen, R.N., MSN, President and Chief Executive Officer
CFO: Tom Lichtenwalner, Vice President Finance
CMO: Jeffrey Jahre M.D., Vice President Medical and Academic Affairs
CIO: Chad Brisendine, Chief Information Officer
CHR: Robert Zimmel, Senior Vice President Human Resources
Web address: www.slhn–lehighvalley.org
Control: Other not–for–profit (including NFP Corporation) **Service**: General medical and surgical

Staffed Beds: 540 **Admissions**: 27436 **Census**: 365 **Outpatient Visits**: 540307 **Births**: 3770 **Total Expense ($000)**: 577416 **Payroll Expense ($000)**: 241096 **Personnel**: 4409

Hospital, Medicare Provider Number, Address, Telephone, Approval, Facility, and Physician Codes, Health Care System

★ American Hospital Association (AHA) membership
☐ The Joint Commission accreditation
○ Healthcare Facilities Accreditation Program
◇ DNV Healthcare Inc. accreditation
⇑ Center for Improvement in Healthcare Quality Accreditation
△ Commission on Accreditation of Rehabilitation Facilities (CARF) accreditation

PA

PA

BLOOMSBURG—Columbia County

★ **GEISINGER–BLOOMSBURG HOSPITAL (390003)**, 549 Fair Street, Zip 17815–1419; tel. 570/387–2100 **A**3 10 **F**8 11 13 15 20 26 27 28 29 30 32 34 35 36 38 39 40 41 44 45 46 50 51 53 55 56 57 59 62 63 65 68 70 74 75 76 79 81 85 86 87 91 92 93 97 98 100 101 102 103 104 107 108 110 111 115 119 130 131 132 144 145 146 147 148 149 150 **P**6 **S** Geisinger Health, Danville, PA
Primary Contact: Lissa Bryan–Smith, Chief Administrative Officer
COO: Joseph M DeVito, Vice President Finance and Chief Operating Officer
CFO: Joseph M DeVito, Vice President Finance and Chief Operating Officer
CMO: James Joseph M.D., President Medical Staff
CIO: Thomas Wray, Director Information
CHR: Mary Lenzini Howe, Vice President Human Resources
Web address: www.bloomhealth.net
Control: Other not–for–profit (including NFP Corporation) **Service**: General medical and surgical

Staffed Beds: 72 **Admissions:** 2547 **Census:** 30 **Outpatient Visits:** 70554 **Births:** 286 **Total Expense ($000):** 39888 **Payroll Expense ($000):** 13958 **Personnel:** 317	

BRADFORD—Mckean County

☐ **BRADFORD REGIONAL MEDICAL CENTER (390118)**, 116 Interstate Parkway, Zip 16701–1036; tel. 814/368–4143, (Total facility includes 95 beds in nursing home–type unit) **A**1 10 **F**3 5 11 13 15 18 20 28 29 30 31 34 35 38 39 40 45 47 49 50 53 54 56 57 59 64 65 70 75 76 77 78 79 81 82 83 84 85 86 87 93 94 96 97 98 100 101 102 103 104 105 107 108 110 111 114 117 118 119 127 128 129 130 131 132 135 146 147 148 149 **P**6 8 **S** Upper Allegheny Health System, Olean, NY
Primary Contact: Timothy J. Finan, FACHE, President and Chief Executive Officer
COO: Jeff S Zewe R.N., Chief Operating Officer
CFO: Richard G Braun CPA, Jr, Senior Vice President and Chief Financial Officer
CMO: William Mills M.D., Senior Vice President Quality and Professional Affairs
CIO: Jason Yaworsky, Chief Information Officer
CHR: Timothy M McNamara, Senior Vice President Human Resources
Web address: www.brmc.com
Control: Other not–for–profit (including NFP Corporation) **Service**: General medical and surgical

Staffed Beds: 182 **Admissions:** 2796 **Census:** 119 **Outpatient Visits:** 134282 **Births:** 177 **Total Expense ($000):** 67343 **Payroll Expense ($000):** 26798 **Personnel:** 484	

BRISTOL—Bucks County

⊞ **LOWER BUCKS HOSPITAL (390070)**, 501 Bath Road, Zip 19007–3190; tel. 215/785–9200, (Nonreporting) **A**1 10 13 **S** Prime Healthcare, Ontario, CA
Primary Contact: Linda J. Grass, Chief Executive Officer
CMO: Sanjay Bhatia, Chief Medical Officer
CIO: Steve Kane, Director Information Technology
CNO: Pat Bain, Chief Nursing Officer
Web address: www.lowerbuckshosp.com
Control: Other not–for–profit (including NFP Corporation) **Service**: General medical and surgical

Staffed Beds: 138	

BROOKVILLE—Jefferson County

PENN HIGHLANDS BROOKVILLE (391312), 100 Hospital Road, Zip 15825–1367; tel. 814/849–2312 **A**10 18 **F**3 11 15 18 28 29 30 34 35 39 40 45 46 57 59 62 64 65 75 77 81 82 85 86 93 98 102 103 104 107 108 110 114 118 119 127 129 130 131 132 133 145 146
Primary Contact: Julianne Peer, President
CFO: Jessica Park, Director Accounting
CMO: Timothy Pendleton M.D., President Medical Staff
CIO: Thomas Johnson, Director Information Systems
CHR: Rebecca Edwards, Chief Human Resources Officer
CNO: Debra A. Thomas, Vice President of Patient Care Services and Chief Nursing Officer
Web address: www.phhealthcare.org/
Control: Other not–for–profit (including NFP Corporation) **Service**: General medical and surgical

Staffed Beds: 35 **Admissions:** 1080 **Census:** 18 **Births:** 0	

BRYN MAWR—Montgomery County

⊞ **BRYN MAWR HOSPITAL (390139)**, 130 South Bryn Mawr Avenue, Zip 19010–3160; tel. 484/337–3000 **A**1 2 3 5 10 13 **F**3 5 11 12 13 15 17 18 20 22 24 26 28 29 30 31 34 35 36 37 38 39 40 41 44 45 46 48 49 50 54 55 56 57 58 59 63 64 65 70 72 74 75 76 78 79 80 81 82 84 85 86 87 89 92 97 98 99 100 101 102 103 104 105 107 108 110 111 114 115 118 119 120 124 126 129 130 131 134 135 141 146 147 148 149 **S** Main Line Health, Ontario, CA
Primary Contact: Andrea F. Gilbert, FACHE, President
COO: Andrea F Gilbert FACHE, President
CFO: Michael J Buongiorno, Executive Vice President Finance and Chief Financial Officer
CMO: Andrew J Norton M.D., Chief Medical Officer
CIO: Karen A Thomas, Vice President and Chief Information Officer
CHR: Terry Dougherty, Director Human Resources
CNO: Barbara A Wadsworth MSN, R.N., FACHE, Chief Nursing Officer
Web address: www.brynmawrhospital.org
Control: Other not–for–profit (including NFP Corporation) **Service**: General medical and surgical

Staffed Beds: 287 **Admissions:** 13521 **Census:** 156 **Outpatient Visits:** 267086 **Births:** 1598 **Total Expense ($000):** 312312 **Payroll Expense ($000):** 104998 **Personnel:** 1558	

BUTLER—Butler County

★ **BUTLER HEALTH SYSTEM (390168)**, 1 Hospital Way, Zip 16001–4697; tel. 724/283–6666, (Total facility includes 25 beds in nursing home–type unit) **A**2 10 **F**3 4 5 12 13 15 18 20 22 24 26 28 29 31 32 35 40 45 57 59 70 74 76 77 79 81 82 85 87 93 98 100 103 107 108 111 114 118 119 128 129 130 132 135 146 147 148 149 **P**6
Primary Contact: Ken DeFurio, President and Chief Executive Officer
COO: Stephanie Roskovski, Chief Operating Officer
CFO: Anne Krebs, Chief Financial Officer
CMO: John C Reefer M.D., Director
CIO: Thomas McGill, Chief Information Officer
CHR: Thomas A Genevro, Vice President Human Resources
CNO: Karen A Allen R.N., Chief Nursing Officer
Web address: www.butlerhealthsystem.org
Control: Other not–for–profit (including NFP Corporation) **Service**: General medical and surgical

Staffed Beds: 288 **Admissions:** 12082 **Census:** 169 **Outpatient Visits:** 516086 **Births:** 951 **Total Expense ($000):** 220367 **Payroll Expense ($000):** 86079 **Personnel:** 1505	

CAMP HILL—Cumberland County

⊞ **GEISINGER HOLY SPIRIT (390004)**, 503 North 21st Street, Zip 17011–2204; tel. 717/763–2100 **A**1 10 **F**3 8 11 13 14 15 17 18 20 22 24 26 28 29 30 31 34 35 37 38 40 43 44 45 46 48 49 50 54 55 57 58 59 60 64 65 70 71 72 74 75 76 77 78 79 81 82 84 85 86 87 89 93 98 99 100 101 102 103 104 105 106 107 108 110 111 114 115 117 119 120 121 124 126 129 130 132 134 135 146 147 148 149 **P**6 **S** Geisinger Health, Danville, PA
Primary Contact: Kyle C. Snyder, Chief Administrative Officer
COO: Richard Schaffner, Senior Vice President and Chief Operating Officer
CFO: Manuel J Evans, Senior Vice President Finance and Chief Financial Officer
CMO: Joseph Torchia M.D., Senior Vice President Medical Affairs and Chief Medical Officer
CIO: Edith Dees, Vice President Information Services and Chief Information Officer
CHR: William Shartle, Senior Vice President Human Resources
CNO: Lisa F Torchia NEA–BC MSN, R.N., Vice President and Chief Nursing Officer
Web address: www.hsh.org
Control: Other not–for–profit (including NFP Corporation) **Service**: General medical and surgical

Staffed Beds: 295 **Admissions:** 10384 **Census:** 143 **Outpatient Visits:** 243418 **Births:** 1170 **Total Expense ($000):** 283623 **Payroll Expense ($000):** 111700 **Personnel:** 2287	

⊞ **SELECT SPECIALTY HOSPITAL–CENTRAL PENNSYLVANIA (392039)**, 503 North 21st Street, 5th Floor, Zip 17011–2204; tel. 717/972–4575, (Includes SELECT SPECIALTY HOSPITAL–HARRISBURG, 111 South Front Street, Alex Grass Building, 5th Floor, Harrisburg, Pennsylvania, Zip 17101, tel. 717/724–6603; John E Simodejka, Marketing Chief Executive Officer; SELECT SPECIALTY HOSPITAL–YORK, 1001 South George Street, York, Pennsylvania, Zip 17403–3676, tel. 717/851–2661; Marcia Medlin, Chief Executive Officer) **A**1 10 **F**1 3 5 12 28 29 30 31 34 38 39 45 46 47 48 49 50 57 63 74 75 78 79 82 84 87 100 107 108 109 110 111 112 113 114 115 116 117 118 119 130 133 **S** Select Medical Corporation, Mechanicsburg, PA
Primary Contact: John E. Simodejka, Chief Executive Officer
Web address: www.camphill.selectspecialtyhospitals.com/
Control: Corporation, Investor–owned (for–profit) **Service**: Acute long–term care hospital

Staffed Beds: 92 **Admissions:** 891 **Census:** 64 **Births:** 0	

Many Facility Codes have changed. Please refer to the AHA Guide Code Chart. © 2017 AHA Guide

STATE CORRECTIONAL INSTITUTION AT CAMP HILL, 2500 Lisburn Road, Zip 17011–8005, Mailing Address: P.O.Box 200, 17001–0200; tel. 717/737–4531, (Nonreporting)
Primary Contact: Beth Herb, Administrator
Web address: www.cor.state.pa.us/
Control: State, Government, Nonfederal **Service**: Hospital unit of an institution (prison hospital, college infirmary, etc.)

Staffed Beds: 34

CANONSBURG—Washington County

✠ **CANONSBURG HOSPITAL (390160)**, 100 Medical Boulevard, Zip 15317–9762; tel. 724/745–6100 **A**1 10 **F**3 7 11 15 18 29 30 34 35 38 40 44 45 46 47 49 50 53 54 57 64 70 74 75 77 79 81 84 85 86 87 90 93 96 97 102 107 108 110 111 114 118 119 129 130 131 132 135 143 146 148 149 **S** Allegheny Health Network, Pittsburgh, PA
Primary Contact: Louise Urban, R.N., President and Chief Executive Officer
CMO: Thomas B Corkery D.O., Chief Medical Officer
CIO: David Vincent, Director Information Systems
CHR: Martha L Clister, Director Human Resources
Web address: www.wpahs.org
Control: Other not–for–profit (including NFP Corporation) **Service**: General medical and surgical

Staffed Beds: 104 Admissions: 2295 Census: 28 Outpatient Visits: 63320 Births: 1 Total Expense ($000): 51651 Payroll Expense ($000): 16060 Personnel: 354

CARLISLE—Cumberland County

✠ **CARLISLE REGIONAL MEDICAL CENTER (390058)**, 361 Alexander Spring Road, Zip 17015–6940; tel. 717/249–1212 **A**1 10 **F**3 8 11 12 13 14 15 18 20 29 30 31 34 38 40 45 46 47 48 49 50 51 53 56 57 59 60 64 65 68 70 73 74 75 76 78 79 81 82 85 86 87 90 91 92 93 94 107 108 109 110 111 112 114 115 116 117 119 120 121 123 124 126 129 130 132 141 142 146 147 148 **P**5 **S** UPMC Pinnacle, Harrisburg, PA
Primary Contact: David P. Steitz, Chief Executive Officer
CFO: Mark Reyngoudt, Chief Financial Officer
CMO: Ivan' Sola', President Medical Staff
CIO: Sherry Aby, Director Information Management
CHR: Sylvia Rockwood, Director Human Resources
CNO: Ann M. Spade, Chief Nursing Executive
Web address: www.carlislermc.com/default.aspx
Control: Corporation, Investor–owned (for–profit) **Service**: General medical and surgical

Staffed Beds: 65 Admissions: 3827 Census: 39 Births: 446

CENTRE HALL—Centre County

✠ **MEADOWS PSYCHIATRIC CENTER (394040)**, 132 The Meadows Drive, Zip 16828–9231; tel. 814/364–2161 **A**1 10 **F**29 38 40 98 99 103 135 **S** Universal Health Services, Inc., King of Prussia, PA
Primary Contact: Ann Wayne, Chief Executive Officer
CFO: David Witt, Chief Financial Officer
CMO: Craig Richman M.D., Medical Director
CHR: Mary Jane Schreffler, Director Human Resources
CNO: Dana Thies, Director of Nursing
Web address: www.themeadows.net
Control: Corporation, Investor–owned (for–profit) **Service**: Psychiatric

Staffed Beds: 107 Admissions: 2732 Census: 96 Outpatient Visits: 2864 Births: 0 Personnel: 197

CHAMBERSBURG—Franklin County

✠ **CHAMBERSBURG HOSPITAL (390151)**, 112 North Seventh Street, Zip 17201–1720; tel. 717/267–3000 **A**1 2 3 5 10 19 **F**3 11 12 13 15 17 18 20 22 26 28 29 30 31 34 35 39 40 44 45 49 50 54 56 57 58 59 61 64 65 68 70 72 74 75 76 77 79 81 85 86 87 90 91 93 94 98 100 102 103 104 107 108 110 111 114 115 118 119 126 129 130 131 132 135 144 146 147 148 149 **P**8 **S** Summit Health, Chambersburg, PA
Primary Contact: Patrick W. O'Donnell, CPA, President and Chief Executive Officer
COO: John P Massimilla FACHE, Vice President and Chief Operating Officer
CFO: Kimberly Rzomp, Vice President and Chief Financial Officer
CMO: Thomas Anderson M.D., Vice President Medical Affairs
CIO: Michele Zeigler, Vice President and Chief Information Officer
CHR: Cathy A. Puhl, Vice President Human Resources
CNO: Sherri Stahl R.N., Senior Vice President Hospital Services
Web address: www.summithealth.org
Control: Other not–for–profit (including NFP Corporation) **Service**: General medical and surgical

Staffed Beds: 257 Admissions: 12834 Census: 144 Outpatient Visits: 389325 Births: 1334 Total Expense ($000): 278853 Payroll Expense ($000): 120425 Personnel: 1569

CLARION—Clarion County

★ ○ **CLARION HOSPITAL (390093)**, One Hospital Drive, Zip 16214–8501; tel. 814/226–9500 **A**10 11 12 13 **F**3 7 11 13 15 29 30 31 35 40 48 49 51 57 59 64 70 77 78 79 81 82 84 85 90 107 108 111 115 119 129 130 132 133 135 145 146 148 **S** QHR, Brentwood, TN
Primary Contact: Byron Quinton, Chief Executive Officer
CFO: Vincent M Lamorella, Chief Financial Officer
CMO: Janice Semeyn D.O., President, Medical Staff
CIO: James Confer, Manager Information Systems
CHR: Brooke Divins, Manager Human Resources
CNO: Leslie Walters MSN, Chief Nursing Officer
Web address: www.clarionhospital.org
Control: Other not–for–profit (including NFP Corporation) **Service**: General medical and surgical

Staffed Beds: 66 Admissions: 1803 Census: 19 Outpatient Visits: 157854 Births: 117 Total Expense ($000): 52728 Payroll Expense ($000): 18750 Personnel: 463

□ **CLARION PSYCHIATRIC CENTER (394043)**, 2 Hospital Drive, Zip 16214–8502; tel. 814/226–9545 **A**1 10 **F**98 99 101 102 105 **P**6 **S** Universal Health Services, Inc., King of Prussia, PA
Primary Contact: Michael Post, Chief Executive Officer
CFO: Shelly Rhoades, Chief Financial Officer
CMO: Jeffrey Moll M.D., Medical Director
CHR: Dianne C Bilunka, Director Human Resources
CNO: Rhonda Massa, Director of Nursing
Web address: www.clarioncenter.com
Control: Individual, Investor–owned (for–profit) **Service**: Psychiatric

Staffed Beds: 74 Admissions: 1999 Census: 70 Outpatient Visits: 0 Births: 0

CLARKS SUMMIT—Lackawanna County

CLARKS SUMMIT STATE HOSPITAL (394012), 1451 Hillside Drive, Zip 18411–9504; tel. 570/586–2011 **A**10 **F**29 39 57 77 91 98 130 135 143 146 **P**6
Primary Contact: Monica Bradbury, Chief Executive Officer
COO: Gordon Weber, Chief Operating Officer
CMO: David Waibel M.D., Medical Director
CHR: William Abda, Chief Human Resources Officer
Web address: www.dpw.state.pa.us/
Control: State, Government, Nonfederal **Service**: Psychiatric

Staffed Beds: 210 Admissions: 79 Census: 197 Outpatient Visits: 0 Births: 0

CLEARFIELD—Clearfield County

PENN HIGHLANDS CLEARFIELD (390052), 809 Turnpike Avenue, Zip 16830–1232, Mailing Address: P.O.Box 992, 16830–0992; tel. 814/765–5341 **A**10 **F**3 8 11 14 15 18 28 29 30 32 34 40 45 50 57 59 62 63 68 75 77 79 81 82 84 85 86 87 93 97 98 103 104 107 108 110 111 115 118 119 130 131 132 133 146 148
Primary Contact: Gary Macioce, President
CFO: William Cain, Controller
CMO: Kevin L Tyler M.D., President Medical Staff
CHR: James G Glade, Director Human Resources
CNO: Kathy Bedger, Chief Nursing Officer
Web address: www.phhealthcare.org
Control: Other not–for–profit (including NFP Corporation) **Service**: General medical and surgical

Staffed Beds: 50 Admissions: 1875 Census: 22 Outpatient Visits: 143903 Births: 0 Total Expense ($000): 45258 Payroll Expense ($000): 17544 Personnel: 329

COALDALE—Schuylkill County

□ **ST. LUKE'S HOSPITAL – MINERS CAMPUS (390183)**, 360 West Ruddle Street, Zip 18218–1027; tel. 570/645–2131, (Total facility includes 48 beds in nursing home–type unit) **A**1 2 10 **F**3 15 18 28 29 31 34 35 40 43 45 46 49 50 51 53 54 56 57 59 60 63 64 65 68 70 75 77 78 79 81 85 86 93 107 108 110 111 115 118 119 127 128 129 130 131 132 145 146 148 149 **P**6 8 **S** St. Luke's University Health Network, Bethlehem, PA
Primary Contact: William E. Moyer, President
COO: Joel Fagerstrom, Executive Vice President and Chief Operating Officer
CFO: Michele Levitz, Director Finance
CIO: Chad Brisendine, Vice President and Chief Information Officer
CHR: Susan Van Why, Director Human Resources
CNO: Kimberly Sargent, Vice President Patient Services
Web address: www.slhn.org
Control: Other not–for–profit (including NFP Corporation) **Service**: General medical and surgical

Staffed Beds: 92 Admissions: 1980 Census: 65 Outpatient Visits: 86632 Births: 0 Total Expense ($000): 47676 Payroll Expense ($000): 20659 Personnel: 291

PA

Hospital, Medicare Provider Number, Address, Telephone, Approval, Facility, and Physician Codes, Health Care System

★ American Hospital Association (AHA) membership
□ The Joint Commission accreditation
○ Healthcare Facilities Accreditation Program
◇ DNV Healthcare Inc. accreditation
⇑ Center for Improvement in Healthcare Quality Accreditation
△ Commission on Accreditation of Rehabilitation Facilities (CARF) accreditation

PA

COATESVILLE—Chester County

✠ **BRANDYWINE HOSPITAL (390076)**, 201 Reeceville Road, Zip 19320–1536;
tel. 610/383–8000 **A**1 10 **F**3 12 15 17 18 20 22 24 26 28 29 31 34 35 40 45
46 50 51 54 56 59 60 62 64 69 70 74 75 77 78 79 81 82 92 93 98 103 104
106 107 108 110 111 114 115 116 117 119 126 129 132 146 147 148 **S**
Community Health Systems, Inc., Franklin, TN
Primary Contact: W. Jeffrey. Hunt, Chief Executive Officer
COO: Jill Tillman, Assistant Chief Executive Officer
CFO: Jay Graham, Interim Chief Financial Officer
Web address: www.brandywinehospital.com
Control: Corporation, Investor–owned (for–profit) **Service**: General medical and
surgical

Staffed Beds: 169 **Admissions**: 6399 **Census**: 98 **Births**: 0

✠ **COATESVILLE VETERANS AFFAIRS MEDICAL CENTER**, 1400 Black Horse Hill
Road, Zip 19320–2040; tel. 610/384–7711, (Nonreporting) **A**1 3 5 **S** Department
of Veterans Affairs, Washington, DC
Primary Contact: Carla Sivek, Director
CFO: Tony Wolfgang, Chief Financial Officer
CMO: Sheila Chellappa M.D., Chief of Staff
CIO: Ryan McGettigan, Chief Information Officer
CHR: Andrew Sutton, Chief Human Resources Officer
CNO: Nancy A. Schmid R.N., MS, Associate Director Patient Care Services
Web address: www.coatesville.va.gov/
Control: Veterans Affairs, Government, federal **Service**: Alcoholism and other
chemical dependency

Staffed Beds: 118

VETERANS AFFAIRS MEDICAL CENTER See Coatesville Veterans Affairs
Medical Center

CONNELLSVILLE—Fayette County

HIGHLANDS HOSPITAL (390184), 401 East Murphy Avenue, Zip 15425–2700;
tel. 724/628–1500 **A**10 **F**3 11 15 26 27 29 30 34 35 39 40 44 45 46 49 50 53
54 56 57 59 61 64 65 70 74 75 79 81 82 85 86 87 89 97 98 99 100 102 103
104 107 108 111 115 119 129 130 131 132 146
Primary Contact: Michelle P. Cunningham, Chief Executive Officer
CFO: John Andursky, Chief Financial Officer
CMO: Richard Grimaldi, President Medical Staff
CIO: John Andursky, Chief Financial Officer
CHR: Mary June Krosoff, Chief Human Resources Officer
CNO: Tammy Donaldson, Director of Nursing
Web address: www.highlandshospital.org
Control: Other not–for–profit (including NFP Corporation) **Service**: General
medical and surgical

Staffed Beds: 64 **Admissions**: 2298 **Census**: 26 **Outpatient Visits**: 59779
Births: 0 **Total Expense ($000)**: 25390 **Payroll Expense ($000)**: 11426
Personnel: 265

CORRY—Erie County

CORRY MEMORIAL HOSPITAL (391308), 965 Shamrock Lane, Zip 16407; tel.
814/664–4641, (Nonreporting) **A**10 18
Primary Contact: Barbara Nichols, R.N., President and Chief Executive Officer
CFO: Michael Heller, Chief Financial Officer
CMO: Paul McGeehan M.D., Chief Medical Staff
CIO: Andrew Jackman, Director Information Technology
CHR: Sharon Kimmy, Coordinator Human Resources
Web address: www.corryhospital.com
Control: Other not–for–profit (including NFP Corporation) **Service**: General
medical and surgical

Staffed Beds: 25

COUDERSPORT—Potter County

✠ **COLE MEMORIAL (391313)**, 1001 East Second Street, Zip 16915–8161; tel.
814/274–9300, (Total facility includes 44 beds in nursing home–type unit) **A**1 10
18 **F**3 10 13 15 28 29 30 31 35 39 40 45 49 53 57 59 62 63 64 68 70 76 77
78 79 81 82 85 87 92 93 98 103 107 108 110 111 115 119 121 127 128 129
130 131 132 133 146 147 148 **P**6
Primary Contact: Edward C. Pitchford, President and Chief Executive Officer
CFO: Ron Rapp, Vice President Finance
CMO: Brenda Wahlers M.D., Chief of Staff
CHR: James Evens, Executive Director, Human Resources and General Services
CNO: Emily Ann Bunnell, Chief Nurse Executive, Senior Director of Acute Care
Web address: www.colememorial.org/
Control: Other not–for–profit (including NFP Corporation) **Service**: General
medical and surgical

Staffed Beds: 79 **Admissions**: 1788 **Census**: 55 **Outpatient Visits**: 238076
Births: 196 **Total Expense ($000)**: 84367 **Payroll Expense ($000)**: 28619
Personnel: 493

CRANBERRY—Butler County

UPMC PASSAVANT CRANBERRY See UPMC Passavant, Pittsburgh

DANVILLE—Montour County

DANVILLE STATE HOSPITAL (394004), 200 State Hospital Drive, Zip 17821–
9198; tel. 570/271–4500 **A**3 10 **F**30 39 65 75 77 98 106 130 135 146 **P**6
Primary Contact: Theresa Long, Chief Executive Officer
COO: Thomas J Burk, Chief Operating Officer
CFO: Patricia Riegert, Director Fiscal Services
CMO: Vikrant Mittal M.D., Chief Medical Officer
CHR: Thomas J Burk, Chief Operating Officer
CNO: Brenda Lahout, Chief Nurse Executive
Web address: www.dpw.state.pa.us/foradults/statehospitals/danvillestatehospital/
index.htm
Control: State, Government, Nonfederal **Service**: Psychiatric

Staffed Beds: 161 **Admissions**: 69 **Census**: 162 **Outpatient Visits**: 0
Births: 0 **Total Expense ($000)**: 41940 **Payroll Expense ($000)**: 19182
Personnel: 380

✠ **GEISINGER HEALTHSOUTH REHABILITATION HOSPITAL (393047)**, 2
Rehab Lane, Zip 17821–8498; tel. 570/271–6733, (Nonreporting) **A**1 10 **S**
HEALTHSOUTH Corporation, Birmingham, AL
Primary Contact: Lorie Dillon, Chief Executive Officer
CFO: Sally Shipierski, Controller
CMO: Greg Burke M.D., Medical Director
CHR: Christian Shirley, Director Human Resources
Web address: www.geisingerhealthsouth.com
Control: Corporation, Investor–owned (for–profit) **Service**: Rehabilitation

Staffed Beds: 42

✠ **GEISINGER MEDICAL CENTER (390006)**, 100 North Academy Avenue,
Zip 17822–2201; tel. 570/271–6211, (Includes GEISINGER–SHAMOKIN AREA
COMMUNITY HOSPITAL, 4200 Hospital Road, Coal Township, Pennsylvania,
Zip 17866–9697, tel. 570/644–4200; Sam Balukoff, Interim Administrator) **A**1 2 3
5 8 10 13 19 **F**3 8 9 11 12 13 14 15 17 18 19 20 21 22 23 24 25 26 27 28 29
30 31 32 34 35 36 37 39 40 41 43 44 45 46 47 48 49 50 51 52 53 54 55 56 57
58 59 60 61 63 64 65 66 67 68 69 70 71 72 73 74 75 76 77 78 79 80 81 82 84
85 86 87 88 89 92 93 94 96 97 98 99 100 101 102 103 104 105 107 108 110
111 114 115 117 119 120 121 123 124 126 129 130 131 132 135 136 138
139 141 143 145 146 147 148 149 150 **P**6 **S** Geisinger Health, Danville, PA
Primary Contact: Thomas P. Sokola, Chief Administrative Officer
CFO: Kevin F Brennan CPA, Executive Vice President and Chief Financial Officer
CMO: Albert Bothe M.D., Jr, Chief Medical Officer
CIO: Frank Richards, Chief Information Officer
CHR: Amy Brayford, Chief Human Resources Officer
CNO: Susan M Hallick R.N., Executive Vice President and Chief Nursing Officer
Web address: www.geisinger.org
Control: Other not–for–profit (including NFP Corporation) **Service**: General
medical and surgical

Staffed Beds: 547 **Admissions**: 30140 **Census**: 410 **Outpatient Visits**:
1015009 **Births**: 1784 **Total Expense ($000)**: 1028944 **Payroll Expense
($000)**: 279801 **Personnel**: 4616

✠ **SELECT SPECIALTY HOSPITAL–DANVILLE (392047)**, 100 North Academy
Avenue, 3rd Floor, Zip 17822–3050; tel. 570/214–9653, (Nonreporting) **A**1 10 **S**
Select Medical Corporation, Mechanicsburg, PA
Primary Contact: Brian Mann, Chief Executive Officer
Web address: www.selectspecialtyhospitals.com/company/locations/danville.aspx
Control: Corporation, Investor–owned (for–profit) **Service**: Acute long–term care hospital

Staffed Beds: 30

DARBY—Delaware County

✠ △ **MERCY FITZGERALD HOSPITAL (390156)**, 1500 Lansdowne Avenue,
Zip 19023–1200; tel. 610/237–4000, (Includes MERCY FITZGERALD HOSPITAL,
1500 South Lansdowne Avenue, Darby, Pennsylvania, Zip 19023, tel. 610/237–
4000; MERCY PHILADELPHIA HOSPITAL, 501 South 54th Street, Philadelphia,
Pennsylvania, Zip 19143, tel. 215/748–9000; Susan Cusack, Executive Director)
A1 2 3 5 7 10 12 13 **F**3 4 11 12 15 18 20 22 24 26 28 29 30 31 34 35 38 40
45 46 49 50 51 54 55 57 58 59 61 64 66 70 75 77 78 79 81 82 85 86 87 90
91 92 93 97 98 100 101 102 103 107 108 110 111 114 115 118 119 120 121
123 124 130 132 135 145 146 147 148 149 150 **S** Trinity Health, Livonia, MI
Primary Contact: Susan Cusack, Executive Director
COO: Ruth Thomas, Chief Operating Officer
CFO: Don Snenk, Chief Financial Officer
CMO: Jeff Komins M.D., Chief Medical Officer
CIO: Jeff Byda, Vice President Information Technology
Web address: www.mercyhealth.org
Control: Other not–for–profit (including NFP Corporation) **Service**: General
medical and surgical

Staffed Beds: 343 **Admissions**: 8717 **Census**: 206 **Outpatient Visits**:
252538 **Births**: 0 **Total Expense ($000)**: 329650 **Payroll Expense ($000)**:
138681 **Personnel**: 2037

DOWNINGTOWN—Chester County

★ **ST. JOHN VIANNEY HOSPITAL**, 151 Woodbine Road, Zip 19335–3057; tel. 610/269–2600 **F**4 29 30 75 98 106 149 **P**5
Primary Contact: David Shellenberger, President
CMO: James MacFadyen M.D., Medical Director
Web address: www.sjvcenter.org
Control: Church operated, Nongovernment, not–for–profit **Service**: Psychiatric

Staffed Beds: 47 **Admissions**: 134 **Census**: 40 **Outpatient Visits**: 0 **Births**: 0 **Total Expense ($000)**: 8222 **Payroll Expense ($000)**: 4515 **Personnel**: 61

DOYLESTOWN—Bucks County

⊞ △ **DOYLESTOWN HOSPITAL (390203)**, 595 West State Street, Zip 18901–2597; tel. 215/345–2200 **A**1 2 3 5 7 10 **F**3 8 10 13 15 17 18 20 22 24 26 28 29 30 31 32 34 35 40 45 46 49 50 51 54 56 57 58 59 62 63 64 70 73 74 75 76 77 78 79 81 85 86 87 89 92 93 94 96 107 108 110 111 114 115 118 119 124 126 130 131 132 141 146 147 149 **P**2 5 7 8
Primary Contact: James L. Brexler, President and Chief Executive Officer
COO: Eleanor Wilson R.N., MSN, Vice President and Chief Operating Officer
CFO: Daniel Upton, Vice President and Chief Financial Officer
CMO: Scott S Levy M.D., Vice President and Chief Medical Officer
CIO: Richard Lang Ed.D., Vice President and Chief Information Officer
CHR: Barbara Hebel, Vice President Human Resources
CNO: Patricia A Stover, Administrator Nursing
Web address: www.doylestownhealth.org
Control: Other not–for–profit (including NFP Corporation) **Service**: General medical and surgical

Staffed Beds: 232 **Admissions**: 12372 **Census**: 130 **Outpatient Visits**: 309510 **Births**: 1226 **Total Expense ($000)**: 245428 **Payroll Expense ($000)**: 99454 **Personnel**: 1856

☐ **FOUNDATIONS BEHAVIORAL HEALTH (394038)**, 833 East Butler Avenue, Zip 18901–2280; tel. 215/345–0444 **A**1 10 **F**98 99 100 101 102 105 106 **S** Universal Health Services, Inc., King of Prussia, PA
Primary Contact: Gina Fusco, Chief Executive Officer
Web address: www.fbh.com
Control: Corporation, Investor–owned (for–profit) **Service**: Children's hospital psychiatric

Staffed Beds: 58 **Admissions**: 1105 **Census**: 49 **Outpatient Visits**: 0 **Births**: 0

DREXEL HILL—Delaware County

☐ **DELAWARE COUNTY MEMORIAL HOSPITAL (390081)**, 501 North Lansdowne Avenue, Zip 19026–1114; tel. 610/284–8100 **A**1 2 3 5 10 **F**3 7 8 9 11 12 13 15 17 18 29 30 31 34 35 36 40 44 46 47 50 51 55 56 57 58 59 60 61 62 63 64 65 66 68 72 74 75 76 77 78 79 81 82 84 85 86 87 90 92 93 94 96 97 100 107 108 109 110 111 114 115 116 117 118 119 120 121 123 124 129 130 131 132 134 135 143 146 147 148 **P**6 **S** Prospect Medical Holdings, Los Angeles, CA
Primary Contact: Robert Haffey, R.N., President
CFO: Richard I Bennett, Senior Vice President and Chief Financial Officer
CMO: Seth Malin M.D., President Medical and Dental Staff
CIO: Robert E Wilson, Vice President and Chief Information Officer
Web address: www.crozer.org
Control: Other not–for–profit (including NFP Corporation) **Service**: General medical and surgical

Staffed Beds: 168 **Admissions**: 6591 **Census**: 83 **Births**: 1059

DUBOIS—Clearfield County

☐ **PENN HIGHLANDS DUBOIS (390086)**, 100 Hospital Avenue, Zip 15801–1440, Mailing Address: P.O.Box 447, 15801–0447; tel. 814/371–2200 **A**1 10 19 **F**5 11 13 15 17 18 19 20 22 24 26 27 28 29 30 31 34 35 40 49 51 54 55 57 58 59 62 63 64 70 72 74 76 77 78 81 82 85 89 90 93 97 98 99 104 107 108 111 115 116 117 119 120 121 122 129 130 131 132 133 135 146 147 148
Primary Contact: John Sutika, President
CFO: Brian S Kline, Vice President and Chief Financial Officer
CMO: Gary Dugan M.D., Vice President Medical Affairs
CHR: Robert J McKee, Vice President Human Resources
Web address: www.drmc.org
Control: Other not–for–profit (including NFP Corporation) **Service**: General medical and surgical

Staffed Beds: 219 **Admissions**: 8665 **Census**: 99 **Births**: 1109

EAGLEVILLE—Montgomery County

★ **EAGLEVILLE HOSPITAL (390278)**, 100 Eagleville Road, Zip 19403–1829, Mailing Address: P.O.Box 45, 19408–0045; tel. 610/539–6000 **A**5 10 **F**4 29 34 35 50 61 68 75 86 98 100 101 103 130 132 134 143 146 147 **P**6
Primary Contact: Maureen King. Pollock, Chief Executive Officer
COO: Eugene J. Ott Jr, Chief Operating Officer
CFO: Alfred P Salvitti, Chief Financial Officer
CMO: Robert Wilson D.O., Director Medical Services
CIO: Richard R Mitchell, Director Information Technology
CHR: Zoe Yousaitis, Director Human Resources
Web address: www.eaglevillehospital.org
Control: Other not–for–profit (including NFP Corporation) **Service**: Alcoholism and other chemical dependency

Staffed Beds: 83 **Admissions**: 2353 **Census**: 46 **Outpatient Visits**: 0 **Births**: 0

EAST NORRITON—Montgomery County

☐ **EINSTEIN MEDICAL CENTER MONTGOMERY (390329)**, 559 West Germantown Pike, Zip 19403–4250; tel. 484/622–1000 **A**1 2 3 10 **F**3 11 12 13 15 18 20 22 24 26 29 30 31 34 35 40 45 46 49 55 57 59 62 63 64 68 70 72 74 75 76 78 79 80 81 82 84 85 87 92 100 107 108 110 111 115 117 119 120 121 123 126 129 130 131 132 135 146 147 149 **S** Einstein Healthcare Network, Philadelphia, PA
Primary Contact: Beth Duffy, Chief Operating Officer
COO: Beth Duffy, Chief Operating Officer
CFO: David Ertel, Chief Financial Officer
CMO: Robert Czincila D.O., Medical Staff President
CIO: Brenda West, Assistant Vice President, Information Services
CHR: Lynne R Kornblatt, Chief Human Resources Officer
CNO: AnnMarie Papa R.N., Vice President and Chief Nursing Officer
Control: Other not–for–profit (including NFP Corporation) **Service**: General medical and surgical

Staffed Beds: 171 **Admissions**: 10022 **Census**: 115 **Outpatient Visits**: 195072 **Births**: 2171 **Total Expense ($000)**: 199370 **Payroll Expense ($000)**: 65174 **Personnel**: 1316

EAST STROUDSBURG—Monroe County

⊞ △ **LEHIGH VALLEY HOSPITAL – POCONO (390201)**, 206 East Brown Street, Zip 18301–3006; tel. 570/421–4000 **A**1 2 7 10 **F**3 7 11 12 13 14 15 17 18 20 22 24 26 28 29 30 31 32 34 35 36 38 39 40 41 43 45 47 48 49 50 54 55 56 57 59 61 62 63 64 65 66 68 70 72 74 75 77 78 79 81 82 84 85 86 87 92 93 94 96 97 98 100 101 102 103 107 108 110 111 114 115 116 117 118 119 120 121 123 124 126 127 130 132 134 135 144 146 147 148 149 **P**6 7 **S** Lehigh Valley Health Network, Allentown, PA
Primary Contact: Elizabeth Wise, President and Chief Executive Officer
CFO: Michael Wilk, Senior President Financial Services and Chief Financial Officer
CMO: William K Cors M.D., Vice President and Chief Medical Quality Officer
CIO: Ferd Feola, Chief Information Officer
CHR: Lynn M Lansdowne, Vice President Human Resources
Web address: www.pmchealthsystem.org
Control: Other not–for–profit (including NFP Corporation) **Service**: General medical and surgical

Staffed Beds: 239 **Admissions**: 12056 **Census**: 135 **Outpatient Visits**: 182390 **Births**: 1049 **Total Expense ($000)**: 241220 **Payroll Expense ($000)**: 91093 **Personnel**: 1531

EASTON—Northampton County

⊞ **EASTON HOSPITAL (390162)**, 250 South 21st Street, Zip 18042–3892; tel. 610/250–4000 **A**1 2 3 5 10 **F**3 12 13 15 17 18 20 22 24 26 28 29 30 31 34 35 45 46 47 48 49 50 51 56 57 58 59 60 64 67 70 72 76 78 79 81 82 85 87 89 90 98 103 107 108 109 110 111 114 115 116 117 118 119 120 121 124 126 129 130 132 135 146 148 **S** Steward Health Care System, LLC, Boston, MA
Primary Contact: Jeffery Snyder, President
COO: Ron Ziobro, Chief Operating Officer
CFO: Steven Clark, Chief Financial Officer
CMO: Roman Tuma, Chief Medical Officer
CIO: Don Lutz, Director Information Technology
CHR: Tanya Segal, Director
CNO: Karen Vadyak, Chief Nursing Officer
Web address: www.easton–hospital.com
Control: Corporation, Investor–owned (for–profit) **Service**: General medical and surgical

Staffed Beds: 196 **Admissions**: 6969 **Census**: 94 **Births**: 426

Hospital, Medicare Provider Number, Address, Telephone, Approval, Facility, and Physician Codes, Health Care System

★ American Hospital Association (AHA) membership
☐ The Joint Commission accreditation
○ Healthcare Facilities Accreditation Program
◇ DNV Healthcare Inc. accreditation
⇧ Center for Improvement in Healthcare Quality Accreditation
△ Commission on Accreditation of Rehabilitation Facilities (CARF) accreditation

☐ **ST. LUKE'S HOSPITAL – ANDERSON CAMPUS (390326)**, 1872 Riverside Circle, Zip 18045–5669; tel. 484/503–3000 **A**1 2 3 10 **F**3 11 15 18 20 22 24 26 29 30 31 34 35 38 40 44 45 46 49 50 51 53 54 55 57 59 60 63 64 68 70 71 74 75 77 78 79 81 82 84 85 86 87 92 93 96 100 102 107 108 110 111 115 118 119 120 121 123 124 130 132 144 145 146 149 **S** St. Luke's University Health Network, Bethlehem, PA
Primary Contact: Edward Nawrocki, President
CMO: Justin P Psaila M.D., Vice President Medical Affairs
CNO: Darla Frack R.N., RN, Vice President, Patient Services
Web address: www.mystlukesonline.org
Control: Other not–for–profit (including NFP Corporation) **Service:** General medical and surgical

Staffed Beds: 108 **Admissions:** 6450 **Census:** 71 **Outpatient Visits:** 193552 **Births:** 0 **Total Expense ($000):** 141573 **Payroll Expense ($000):** 47031 **Personnel:** 632

ELLWOOD CITY—Lawrence County

ELLWOOD CITY HOSPITAL (390008), 724 Pershing Street, Zip 16117–1474; tel. 724/752–0081, (Nonreporting) **A**10
Primary Contact: Beverly Annarumo, R.N., MSN, President
CFO: Christopher M Little, Vice President and Chief Financial Officer
CIO: Connie Cunningham, Chief Information Officer
CHR: Paul Landman, Director Human Resources
CNO: Della Stabryla, Director of Nursing
Web address: www.TheEllwoodCityHospital.org
Control: Other not–for–profit (including NFP Corporation) **Service:** General medical and surgical

Staffed Beds: 95

EPHRATA—Lancaster County

☒ **WELLSPAN EPHRATA COMMUNITY HOSPITAL (390225)**, 169 Martin Avenue, Zip 17522–1724, Mailing Address: P.O.Box 1002, 17522–1002; tel. 717/733–0311 **A**1 2 10 **F**3 12 13 15 18 20 28 29 30 31 34 35 36 40 45 49 50 51 54 57 59 60 61 62 64 69 70 72 74 75 76 77 78 79 80 81 82 85 87 89 90 91 97 98 99 100 101 102 103 107 108 110 111 114 115 116 117 118 119 120 121 129 130 131 132 135 144 146 147 148 149 **P**6 8 **S** WellSpan Health, York, PA
CFO: David Kreider, Controller
CMO: Mark Jacobson D.O., Vice President Medical Affairs
CIO: Leon John Jabour, Regional Chief Information Officer
CHR: Jana Salaki, Regional Director Human Resources
CNO: Tina Citro R.N., Chief Nursing Officer, Vice President, Patient Services
Web address: www.wellspan.org
Control: Other not–for–profit (including NFP Corporation) **Service:** General medical and surgical

Staffed Beds: 130 **Admissions:** 6189 **Census:** 72 **Outpatient Visits:** 357524 **Births:** 797 **Total Expense ($000):** 187606 **Payroll Expense ($000):** 55634 **Personnel:** 981

ERIE—Erie County

☒ **ERIE VETERANS AFFAIRS MEDICAL CENTER**, 135 East 38th Street, Zip 16504–1559; tel. 814/860–2576, (Total facility includes 45 beds in nursing home–type unit) **A**1 **F**3 5 8 29 30 31 33 34 35 36 38 39 45 54 55 56 57 59 61 62 63 64 65 68 74 75 77 78 79 81 82 83 84 85 86 87 91 93 94 97 100 101 102 103 104 107 114 119 127 128 130 132 133 143 144 146 147 148 149 **P**6 **S** Department of Veterans Affairs, Washington, DC
Primary Contact: John Gennaro, FACHE, Director
CFO: Joann Pritchard, Chief Financial Officer
CMO: Anthony Behm D.O., Chief of Staff
CIO: Jonathan Seale, Chief Information Officer
CHR: Lynn Nies, Human Resources Officer
CNO: Dorene M. Sommers, Associate Director Patient Care Services
Web address: www.erie.va.gov/
Control: Veterans Affairs, Government, federal **Service:** General medical and surgical

Staffed Beds: 52 **Admissions:** 512 **Census:** 41 **Outpatient Visits:** 262272 **Births:** 0 **Total Expense ($000):** 147240 **Payroll Expense ($000):** 66947 **Personnel:** 747

HAMOT MEDICAL CENTER See UPMC Hamot

☒ **HEALTHSOUTH REHABILITATION HOSPITAL OF ERIE (393046)**, 143 East Second Street, Zip 16507–1501; tel. 814/878–1200 **A**1 10 **F**29 34 90 91 95 96 132 **S** HEALTHSOUTH Corporation, Birmingham, AL
Primary Contact: John Papalia, Chief Executive Officer
CFO: Lori Gibbens, Controller
CMO: Douglas Grisier D.O., Medical Director
CIO: Sharon Zielinski, Manager Health Information
CHR: William Robinson, Director Human Resources
CNO: Evelyn Armstrong, Chief Nursing Officer
Web address: www.healthsoutherie.com
Control: Corporation, Investor–owned (for–profit) **Service:** Rehabilitation

Staffed Beds: 100 **Admissions:** 1825 **Census:** 68 **Outpatient Visits:** 0 **Births:** 0

○ **LECOM HEALTH MILLCREEK COMMUNITY HOSPITAL (390198)**, 5515 Peach Street, Zip 16509–2695; tel. 814/864–4031, (Nonreporting) **A**3 10 11 12 13
Primary Contact: Mary L. Eckert, President and Chief Executive Officer
CFO: Richard P Olinger, Chief Financial Officer
CMO: James Y Lin D.O., Chief of Staff
CIO: Cheryl Girardier, Director Information Technology
CHR: Polly Momeyer, Manager Human Resources
CNO: Katie Agresti R.N., Director Patient Care Services
Web address: www.millcreekcommunityhospital.com
Control: Other not–for–profit (including NFP Corporation) **Service:** General medical and surgical

Staffed Beds: 168

☒ **SAINT VINCENT HOSPITAL (390009)**, 232 West 25th Street, Zip 16544–0002; tel. 814/452–5000 **A**1 2 3 5 10 12 13 **F**3 8 11 12 13 15 17 18 20 22 24 26 28 29 30 31 34 35 36 38 39 40 44 45 46 47 48 49 50 51 54 56 57 58 59 60 61 64 65 70 71 72 74 75 76 77 78 79 80 81 82 84 85 86 87 89 90 92 93 94 96 98 100 101 102 103 107 108 110 111 115 118 119 121 123 124 126 129 130 132 135 141 146 147 149 **S** Allegheny Health Network, Pittsburgh, PA
Primary Contact: Christopher Clark, D.O., President and Chief Executive Officer
COO: Jason Roeback, Chief Operating Officer
CFO: Al Mansfield, Chief Financial Officer
CIO: Richard B Ong, Chief Information Officer
CHR: Johnie M Atkinson, Chief Human Resources Officer
CNO: Maureen C Chadwick R.N., Chief Nursing Officer
Web address: www.svhs.org
Control: Other not–for–profit (including NFP Corporation) **Service:** General medical and surgical

Staffed Beds: 400 **Admissions:** 14074 **Census:** 278 **Outpatient Visits:** 204884 **Births:** 1028 **Total Expense ($000):** 264731 **Payroll Expense ($000):** 79797 **Personnel:** 1779

☒ **SELECT SPECIALTY HOSPITAL–ERIE (392037)**, 252 West 11th Street, Zip 16501–1702; tel. 814/874–5300, (Nonreporting) **A**1 10 **S** Select Medical Corporation, Mechanicsburg, PA
Primary Contact: Thomas Fucci, FACHE, Chief Executive Officer
CNO: Keith Christiansen, Chief Nursing Officer
Web address: www.erie.selectspecialtyhospitals.com/
Control: Corporation, Investor–owned (for–profit) **Service:** Acute long–term care hospital

Staffed Beds: 50

☐ **UPMC HAMOT (390063)**, 201 State Street, Zip 16550–0002; tel. 814/877–6000 **A**1 2 3 5 8 10 13 **F**3 9 12 13 15 17 18 20 22 24 26 28 29 30 31 34 35 36 37 38 39 40 43 44 45 46 47 48 49 50 51 56 57 58 59 60 61 62 63 64 65 66 68 70 72 74 75 76 77 78 79 80 81 82 84 85 86 87 89 92 93 96 97 99 100 101 102 103 104 106 107 108 109 110 111 114 115 118 119 124 126 129 130 131 132 134 135 138 141 147 148 149 150 **P**6 **S** UPMC, Pittsburgh, PA
Primary Contact: David Gibbons, President
CFO: Stephen M Danch, Chief Financial Officer
CMO: Richard Long M.D., Chief Medical Officer
CIO: Lisa D McChesney R.N., Senior Director Information Systems
CNO: James E Donnelly, Chief Nursing Officer and Vice President Patient Care Services
Web address: www.upmc.com/locations/hospitals/hamot
Control: Other not–for–profit (including NFP Corporation) **Service:** General medical and surgical

Staffed Beds: 302 **Admissions:** 20495 **Census:** 245 **Outpatient Visits:** 215791 **Births:** 2336 **Total Expense ($000):** 329043 **Payroll Expense ($000):** 95903 **Personnel:** 1909

VETERANS AFFAIRS MEDICAL CENTER See ERIE Veterans Affairs Medical Center

Many Facility Codes have changed. Please refer to the AHA Guide Code Chart. © 2017 AHA Guide

PA

EVERETT—Bedford County

☐ **UPMC BEDFORD MEMORIAL (390117)**, 10455 Lincoln Highway, Zip 15537–7046; tel. 814/623–6161 **A**1 10 20 **F**3 8 11 13 15 18 28 29 30 31 34 35 36 39 40 41 45 50 51 56 57 59 61 64 65 68 70 74 75 76 77 78 79 81 85 86 87 89 93 102 104 107 108 110 111 114 119 129 130 131 132 133 135 146 147 149 **P**6 **S** UPMC, Pittsburgh, PA
Primary Contact: Gerald Murray, President
CFO: Mario Wilfong, Vice President Finance and Administration
CIO: Mark Wiley, Manager Information Systems Development
CHR: Michelle A Speck, Vice President Human Resources
CNO: Paula Thomas R.N., MSN, Vice President Patient Services
Web address: www.upmcbedfordmemorial.com
Control: Other not–for–profit (including NFP Corporation) **Service**: General medical and surgical

> **Staffed Beds**: 27 **Admissions**: 1365 **Census**: 10 **Outpatient Visits**: 114872 **Births**: 293 **Total Expense ($000)**: 56096 **Payroll Expense ($000)**: 14354 **Personnel**: 256

FARRELL—Mercer County

SHENANGO VALLEY CAMPUS See UPMC Horizon

☐ ○ **UPMC HORIZON (390178)**, 2200 Memorial Drive, Zip 16121–1357; tel. 724/588–2100, (Includes GREENVILLE CAMPUS, 110 North Main Street, Greenville, Pennsylvania, Zip 16125–1795, tel. 724/588–2100; SHENANGO VALLEY CAMPUS, 2200 Memorial Drive, Farrell, Pennsylvania, Zip 16121–1398, tel. 724/981–3500) **A**1 10 11 13 **F**3 11 12 13 15 18 26 28 29 30 31 32 34 35 39 40 43 44 45 46 49 50 53 54 56 57 59 61 64 65 68 70 73 74 75 76 77 78 79 81 82 85 86 87 90 92 97 100 107 110 111 114 115 118 119 120 129 130 131 132 133 135 146 147 148 149 **S** UPMC, Pittsburgh, PA
Primary Contact: Donald R. Owrey, President
CFO: David Shulik, Vice President and Chief Financial Officer
CMO: Samuel Daisley D.O., Vice President Medical Affairs
CHR: Connie Mayle, Vice President Administrative Services
Web address: www.upmc.com
Control: Other not–for–profit (including NFP Corporation) **Service**: General medical and surgical

> **Staffed Beds**: 121 **Admissions**: 6182 **Census**: 71 **Outpatient Visits**: 218383 **Births**: 1107 **Total Expense ($000)**: 153820 **Payroll Expense ($000)**: 38533 **Personnel**: 664

FORT WASHINGTON—Montgomery County

☐ **BROOKE GLEN BEHAVIORAL HOSPITAL (394049)**, 7170 Lafayette Avenue, Zip 19034–2301; tel. 215/641–5300, (Nonreporting) **A**1 5 10 **S** Universal Health Services, Inc., King of Prussia, PA
Primary Contact: Neil Callahan, Chief Executive Officer
COO: William R Mason, Chief Operating Officer
CFO: Robert Zagerman, Chief Financial Officer
CMO: Chand Nair M.D., Medical Director
CHR: Dawn Kownacki, Director Human Resources
Web address: www.brookeglenhospital.com
Control: Corporation, Investor–owned (for–profit) **Service**: Psychiatric

> **Staffed Beds**: 146

GETTYSBURG—Adams County

✠ **WELLSPAN GETTYSBURG HOSPITAL (390065)**, 147 Gettys Street, Zip 17325–2534; tel. 717/334–2121 **A**1 3 10 **F**3 8 11 13 15 18 20 26 28 29 30 31 35 40 46 49 50 51 54 56 59 64 65 68 70 74 75 76 78 79 81 82 84 85 87 92 93 102 107 108 110 111 114 117 118 119 120 121 123 129 130 131 132 134 135 146 147 148 149 **S** WellSpan Health, York, PA
Primary Contact: Jane E. Hyde, President
COO: Joseph H Edgar, Senior Vice President Operations
CMO: Charles Marley D.O., Vice President Medical Affairs
CIO: Robin Kimple, Director Information Services
CHR: Kim Brister, Director Human Resources
Web address: www.wellspan.org
Control: Other not–for–profit (including NFP Corporation) **Service**: General medical and surgical

> **Staffed Beds**: 76 **Admissions**: 3888 **Census**: 42 **Outpatient Visits**: 195875 **Births**: 531 **Total Expense ($000)**: 148103 **Payroll Expense ($000)**: 39427 **Personnel**: 662

GREENSBURG—Westmoreland County

☐ **EXCELA HEALTH WESTMORELAND HOSPITAL (390145)**, 532 West Pittsburgh Street, Zip 15601–2282; tel. 724/832–4000 **A**1 3 10 **F**3 5 8 11 12 13 15 17 18 20 22 24 26 28 29 30 31 34 35 38 40 44 45 46 48 49 50 51 54 56 57 59 61 64 65 68 70 73 74 75 76 77 78 79 81 82 84 85 86 87 89 90 92 93 96 98 100 102 103 104 105 107 108 110 111 114 115 118 119 126 129 130 131 132 134 135 143 146 147 148 **S** Excela Health, Greensburg, PA
Primary Contact: Ronald H. Ott, President
COO: Michael D Busch, Executive Vice President and Chief Operating Officer
CFO: Jeffrey T Curry, Executive Vice President and Chief Financial Officer
CMO: Jerome Granato M.D., Senior Vice President and Chief Medical Officer
CIO: David Gawaluck, Vice President and Chief Information Officer
CHR: John Caverno, Chief Human Resources Officer
CNO: Helen K Burns Ph.D., R.N., Senior Vice President and Chief Nursing Officer
Web address: www.excelahealth.org
Control: Other not–for–profit (including NFP Corporation) **Service**: General medical and surgical

> **Staffed Beds**: 270 **Admissions**: 15156 **Census**: 189 **Births**: 1229

GROVE CITY—Mercer County

GROVE CITY MEDICAL CENTER (390266), 631 North Broad Street Extension, Zip 16127–4603; tel. 724/450–7000, (Total facility includes 20 beds in nursing home–type unit) **A**10 **F**3 15 20 26 28 29 31 34 35 40 45 46 49 51 57 59 64 70 75 78 79 81 82 87 91 92 93 107 108 110 111 115 117 119 128 129 130 132 146 148 149 **P**6
Primary Contact: Robert Jackson Jr, Chief Executive Officer
CFO: David Poland, Chief Financial Officer
CMO: Daniel Ferguson, Chief of Staff
CIO: Philip Swartwood, Director Information Systems
CHR: Donald Henley, Vice President Human Resources
CNO: Anthony Bono Jr, Chief Nursing Officer
Web address: www.gcmcpa.org
Control: Other not–for–profit (including NFP Corporation) **Service**: General medical and surgical

> **Staffed Beds**: 55 **Admissions**: 1967 **Census**: 28 **Outpatient Visits**: 100578 **Births**: 0 **Total Expense ($000)**: 44879 **Payroll Expense ($000)**: 17123 **Personnel**: 372

HANOVER—York County

✠ **HANOVER HOSPITAL (390233)**, 300 Highland Avenue, Zip 17331–2297; tel. 717/316–3711 **A**1 10 **F**3 11 13 15 18 20 22 26 28 29 30 31 34 35 36 40 44 45 49 50 53 54 57 59 61 62 64 65 75 76 77 78 79 81 84 85 86 87 89 93 94 96 107 108 110 111 115 118 119 129 130 131 132 134 135 144 146 147 148 149 150
Primary Contact: Michael W. Gaskins, President and Chief Executive Officer
COO: Michael A Hockenberry, Senior Vice President and Chief Operating Officer
CFO: Donna L. Muller, Interim Chief Financial Officer
CMO: Michael H Ader M.D., Vice President Medical Affairs
CIO: William C. Tandy, Chief Information Officer
CHR: Christine Miller, General Counsel and Vice President Human Resources
CNO: M Patricia Saunders R.N., MS, Vice President Nursing
Web address: www.hanoverhospital.org
Control: Other not–for–profit (including NFP Corporation) **Service**: General medical and surgical

> **Staffed Beds**: 93 **Admissions**: 5822 **Census**: 63 **Outpatient Visits**: 220091 **Births**: 591 **Total Expense ($000)**: 151702 **Payroll Expense ($000)**: 58955 **Personnel**: 998

HARRISBURG—Dauphin County

✠ **HELEN M. SIMPSON REHABILITATION HOSPITAL (393056)**, 4300 Londonderry Road, Zip 17109–5317; tel. 717/920–4300 (Nonreporting) **A**1 **S** Select Medical Corporation, Mechanicsburg, PA
Primary Contact: Mark Freeburn, Chief Executive Officer
Web address: www.simpson–rehab.com/
Control: Corporation, Investor–owned (for–profit) **Service**: Rehabilitation

> **Staffed Beds**: 55

PA

⊞ **PENNSYLVANIA PSYCHIATRIC INSTITUTE (394051)**, 2501 North Third Street, Zip 17110–1904; tel. 717/782–6420 **A**1 3 5 10 **F**34 35 50 56 57 59 64 87 98 99 103 104 105 130 132 143 146 149
Primary Contact: William Daly, Chief Executive Officer
CFO: Robert Fotter, Chief Financial Officer
CHR: Wanda Geesey, Director Human Resources
CNO: Teresa Terry–Williams, Chief Nursing Officer
CMO: Elisabeth J. Kunkel, MD, Chief Medical Officer
Web address: www.ppimhs.org/
Control: Other not–for–profit (including NFP Corporation) **Service**: Psychiatric

| Staffed Beds: 72 Admissions: 2080 Census: 59 Births: 0 |

PINNACLEHEALTH AT COMMUNITY GENERAL OSTEOPATHIC HOSPITAL See Pinnacle Health Harrisburg Hospital

☐ **PINNACLEHEALTH HARRISBURG HOSPITAL (390067)**, 111 South Front Street, Zip 17101–2010, Mailing Address: P.O.Box 8700, 17105–8700; tel. 717/231–8900, (Includes PINNACLEHEALTH AT COMMUNITY GENERAL OSTEOPATHIC HOSPITAL, 4300 Londonderry Road, Harrisburg, Pennsylvania, Zip 17109–5397, P O Box 3000, 17105–3000, tel. 717/652–3000; PINNACLEHEALTH AT HARRISBURG HOSPITAL, 111 South Front Street, Harrisburg, Pennsylvania, Zip 17101–2099, tel. 717/782–3131; PINNACLEHEALTH WEST SHORE HOSPITAL, 1995 Technology Parkway, Mechanicsburg, Pennsylvania, Zip 17050–8522, tel. 717/791–2600) **A**1 2 3 5 10 12 13 **F**3 7 8 11 12 13 14 15 17 18 19 20 22 24 26 27 28 29 30 31 32 34 35 36 37 38 40 44 45 46 47 48 49 50 52 53 54 55 56 57 58 59 60 61 64 65 66 68 70 72 74 75 76 77 78 79 81 82 84 85 86 87 89 93 97 100 101 102 103 104 107 108 110 111 114 115 116 117 118 119 120 121 123 124 126 129 130 131 132 134 138 141 142 143 144 145 146 147 148 149 **P**6 **S** UPMC Pinnacle, Harrisburg, PA
Primary Contact: Philip Guarneschelli, Interim Chief Executive Officer
COO: Philip Guarneschelli, Senior Vice President and Chief Operating Officer
CFO: William H Pugh, Senior Vice President Corporate Finance and Chief Financial Officer
CMO: Nirmal Joshi M.D., Senior Vice President Medical Affairs and Chief Medical Officer
CHR: Ann H Gormley, Senior Vice President Human Resources
CNO: Susan Comp, Senior Vice President and Chief Nursing Officer
Web address: www.pinnaclehealth.org
Control: Other not–for–profit (including NFP Corporation) **Service**: General medical and surgical

| Staffed Beds: 627 Admissions: 33339 Census: 433 Outpatient Visits: 867407 Births: 3957 Total Expense ($000): 780363 Payroll Expense ($000): 269829 Personnel: 5323 |

SELECT SPECIALTY HOSPITAL–HARRISBURG See Select Specialty Hospital–Central Pennsylvania, Camp Hill

HASTINGS—Cambria County

★ **CONEMAUGH MINERS MEDICAL CENTER (390130)**, 290 Haida Avenue, Zip 16646–5610, Mailing Address: P.O.Box 689, 16646–0689; tel. 814/247–3100 **A**10 20 **F**3 15 18 29 30 31 35 36 40 45 48 50 56 59 64 70 75 78 79 81 86 92 93 96 97 102 107 108 110 119 129 130 133 144 148 **P**8 **S** Duke LifePoint Healthcare, Brentwood, TN
Primary Contact: Timothy Harclerode, Chief Executive Officer
COO: Debbie Spells–Wilson R.N., Chief Operating Officer and Chief Nursing Officer
CFO: Linda Fanale, Chief Financial Officer
CMO: Susan Williams M.D., Chief Medical Officer
CIO: Joe Dado, Chief Information Officer
CNO: Debbie Spells–Wilson R.N., Chief Operating Officer and Chief Nursing Officer
Web address: www.conemaugh.org
Control: Corporation, Investor–owned (for–profit) **Service**: General medical and surgical

| Staffed Beds: 30 Admissions: 417 Census: 5 Outpatient Visits: 35084 Births: 0 Total Expense ($000): 16197 Payroll Expense ($000): 5385 Personnel: 113 |

HAZLETON—Luzerne County

★ ○ **LEHIGH VALLEY HOSPITAL – HAZLETON (390185)**, 700 East Broad Street, Zip 18201–6897; tel. 570/501–4000 **A**10 11 **F**3 8 11 12 13 15 18 28 29 31 33 34 35 40 43 50 53 54 57 59 60 62 64 68 69 70 75 76 77 78 79 81 82 85 86 87 89 90 93 107 108 110 111 114 117 118 119 124 129 130 131 132 135 143 144 146 147 148 **P**6 **S** Lehigh Valley Health Network, Allentown, PA
Primary Contact: John R. Fletcher, President
CFO: William Bauer, Vice President Finance and Chief Financial Officer
CMO: Anthony Valente M.D., Vice President Medical Affairs
CIO: Carl Shoener, Chief Information Officer
Web address: www.lvhn.org/hazleton/
Control: Other not–for–profit (including NFP Corporation) **Service**: General medical and surgical

| Staffed Beds: 120 Admissions: 6887 Census: 87 Outpatient Visits: 166495 Births: 736 Total Expense ($000): 111047 Payroll Expense ($000): 43789 Personnel: 724 |

HERSHEY—Dauphin County

⊞ **PENN STATE MILTON S. HERSHEY MEDICAL CENTER (390256)**, 500 University Drive, Zip 17033–2360, Mailing Address: P.O.Box 850, 17033–0850; tel. 717/531–8521, (Includes PENN STATE CHILDREN'S HOSPITAL, 500 University Drive, Hershey, Pennsylvania, Zip 17033–2360, tel. 717/531–8521) **A**1 2 3 5 8 10 **F**3 5 6 7 8 9 11 12 13 14 15 17 18 19 20 21 22 23 24 25 26 27 28 29 30 31 32 34 35 36 37 38 40 41 43 44 45 46 47 48 49 50 51 52 53 54 55 56 57 58 59 60 61 64 65 66 68 70 71 72 73 74 75 76 77 78 79 80 81 82 84 85 86 87 88 89 91 92 93 95 96 97 99 100 101 102 103 104 105 106 107 108 109 110 111 114 115 116 117 118 119 120 121 123 124 126 129 130 131 132 134 135 136 137 138 139 141 142 143 144 145 146 147 148 149 150 **P**6 **S** Penn State Hershey Health System, Hershey, PA
Primary Contact: A. Craig. Hillemeier, M.D., Chief Executive Officer
COO: Stephen M. Massini, Chief Operating Officer
CFO: Stephen M. Massini, Chief Financial Officer
CMO: Thomas Tracy Jr, Chief Medical Officer
CIO: Rod Dykehouse, Chief Information Officer
CHR: David Swift, Chief Human Resources Officer
CNO: Judy N. Himes MSN, R.N., Chief Nursing Officer
Web address: www.pennstatehershey.org/
Control: Other not–for–profit (including NFP Corporation) **Service**: General medical and surgical

| Staffed Beds: 527 Admissions: 26754 Census: 444 Outpatient Visits: 1062280 Births: 2044 Total Expense ($000): 1309810 Payroll Expense ($000): 445041 Personnel: 9000 |

HONESDALE—Wayne County

★ ⇑ **WAYNE MEMORIAL HOSPITAL (390125)**, 601 Park Street, Zip 18431–1498; tel. 570/253–8100 **A**10 20 21 **F**3 11 13 15 18 20 22 28 29 30 31 34 35 36 37 39 40 45 46 48 49 50 51 53 54 56 57 59 61 62 63 64 65 75 76 77 78 79 81 86 90 92 93 99 100 101 102 103 104 107 108 110 111 115 116 117 119 124 129 130 131 132 133 134 135 146 147 148
Primary Contact: David L. Hoff, Chief Executive Officer
COO: John Conte, Director Facility Services and Real Estate
CFO: Michael J Clifford, Director Finance
CMO: William Dewar M.D., Chief of Staff
CIO: Tom Hoffman, Manager Information Systems
CHR: Elizabeth McDonald, Director Human Resources
CNO: Jim Pettinato, Director Patient Care Services
Web address: www.wmh.org
Control: Other not–for–profit (including NFP Corporation) **Service**: General medical and surgical

| Staffed Beds: 87 Admissions: 3857 Census: 43 Outpatient Visits: 157822 Births: 466 Total Expense ($000): 84802 Payroll Expense ($000): 33354 Personnel: 616 |

HUMMELSTOWN—Dauphin County

⊞ △ **PENN STATE HERSHEY REHABILITATION HOSPITAL (393053)**, 1135 Old West Chocolate Avenue, Zip 17036; tel. 717/832–2600, (Nonreporting) **A**1 3 7 10 **S** Select Medical Corporation, Mechanicsburg, PA
Primary Contact: Michelle Von Arx, Chief Executive Officer
CMO: Brenda Mallory M.D., Medical Director
Web address: www.psh–rehab.com
Control: Corporation, Investor–owned (for–profit) **Service**: Rehabilitation

| Staffed Beds: 76 |

HUNTINGDON—Huntingdon County

⊞ **J. C. BLAIR MEMORIAL HOSPITAL (390056)**, 1225 Warm Springs Avenue, Zip 16652–2398; tel. 814/643–2290 **A**1 10 20 **F**3 11 13 15 18 29 34 35 40 45 50 53 55 57 59 64 68 70 75 76 77 79 81 85 86 87 89 96 98 100 102 103 107 108 110 111 114 116 117 118 119 129 130 132 133 135 146 147 148
Primary Contact: Adam Dimm, Chief Executive Officer
COO: Adam Dimm, Chief Executive Officer
CFO: Deborah A Shughart, Vice President and Chief Financial Officer
CMO: James Hayden M.D., Chief Medical Officer
CIO: Armen Arakelian, Chief Information Officer
CHR: Susan Hess, Director Human Resources
CNO: Joye Gingrich, Director Patient Care Services and Chief Nursing Officer
Web address: www.jcblair.org
Control: Other not–for–profit (including NFP Corporation) **Service**: General medical and surgical

| Staffed Beds: 75 Admissions: 2171 Census: 24 Outpatient Visits: 102737 Births: 214 Total Expense ($000): 48150 Payroll Expense ($000): 21923 Personnel: 437 |

PA

INDIANA—Indiana County

★ **INDIANA REGIONAL MEDICAL CENTER (390173)**, 835 Hospital Road, Zip 15701–3629, Mailing Address: P.O.Box 788, 15701–0788; tel. 724/357-7000 **A**2 10 20 22 **F**3 11 15 18 20 22 28 29 31 34 35 40 44 45 46 47 49 53 56 57 59 64 65 70 71 74 75 76 77 78 79 81 82 83 84 85 87 90 91 98 102 103 107 108 111 114 115 118 119 120 123 124 129 130 132 144 146 147 148 149
Primary Contact: Stephen A. Wolfe, President and Chief Executive Officer
COO: Dominic Paccapaniccia, Chief Operating Officer
CFO: Robert Gongaware, Senior Vice President Finance
CMO: Bruce A Bush M.D., Senior Vice President Medical Affairs
CIO: Mark Volovic, Vice President and Chief Information Officer
CHR: James W Kinneer, Vice President Organizational Development
CNO: Cindy L Virgil MSN, R.N., Senior Vice President Patient Care Services
Web address: www.indianarmc.org
Control: Other not–for–profit (including NFP Corporation) **Service:** General medical and surgical

Staffed Beds: 166 **Admissions:** 7286 **Census:** 85 **Outpatient Visits:** 266305 **Births:** 597 **Total Expense ($000):** 139878 **Payroll Expense ($000):** 61103 **Personnel:** 942

JEFFERSON HILLS—Allegheny County

⊞ **JEFFERSON HOSPITAL (390265)**, 565 Coal Valley Road, Zip 15025–3703, Mailing Address: Box 18119, Pittsburgh, 15236–0119; tel. 412/469-5000 **A**1 2 10 **F**1 3 4 8 11 12 13 15 17 18 20 22 24 26 28 29 30 31 34 35 38 40 44 45 46 47 48 49 50 51 54 57 59 60 64 67 70 72 73 74 75 76 77 78 79 80 81 84 85 86 87 88 89 90 97 98 100 102 104 107 108 110 111 115 117 118 119 126 128 129 130 131 132 135 146 147 148 149 **P**6 **S** Allegheny Health Network, Pittsburgh, PA
Primary Contact: Louise Urban, R.N., President and Chief Executive Officer
CMO: Richard F Collins M.D., Executive Vice President and Chief Medical Officer
CIO: James Witenske, Chief Information Officer
CNO: Kimberley Finnerty MSN, R.N., Chief Nursing Officer
Web address: www.jeffersonregional.com
Control: Other not–for–profit (including NFP Corporation) **Service:** General medical and surgical

Staffed Beds: 341 **Admissions:** 14812 **Census:** 181 **Outpatient Visits:** 248369 **Births:** 920 **Total Expense ($000):** 303653 **Payroll Expense ($000):** 114306 **Personnel:** 1519

JERSEY SHORE—Lycoming County

⊞ **JERSEY SHORE HOSPITAL (391300)**, 1020 Thompson Street, Zip 17740–1794; tel. 570/398-0100 **A**1 10 18 **F**3 15 18 28 29 30 34 35 40 45 46 47 48 50 57 59 75 77 79 81 82 85 93 107 108 109 110 111 115 119 129 130 133 135 144 **S** Geisinger Health, Danville, PA
Primary Contact: David A. Shannon, President and Chief Executive Officer
CFO: Mark Rice CPA, Chief Financial Officer
CMO: Stephen Goykovich D.O., Chief Medical Officer
CIO: Christine Haas, Chief Information Officer
CHR: Joan Rounsley, Director Human Resources
CNO: Paulette Nish, Chief Nursing Officer
Web address: www.jsh.org
Control: Other not–for–profit (including NFP Corporation) **Service:** General medical and surgical

Staffed Beds: 25 **Admissions:** 767 **Census:** 8 **Outpatient Visits:** 84450 **Births:** 0 **Total Expense ($000):** 24828 **Payroll Expense ($000):** 10485 **Personnel:** 217

JOHNSTOWN—Cambria County

⊞ △ **CONEMAUGH MEMORIAL MEDICAL CENTER (390110)**, 1086 Franklin Street, Zip 15905–4398; tel. 814/534-9000, (Includes MEMORIAL MEDICAL CENTER – LEE CAMPUS, 320 Main Street, Johnstown, Pennsylvania, Zip 15901–1601, tel. 814/533-0123) **A**1 3 7 10 12 13 **F**3 5 8 12 13 15 17 18 20 22 24 26 27 28 29 30 31 34 35 36 37 39 40 43 45 46 49 50 51 53 54 55 56 57 58 59 61 62 63 64 65 68 70 72 74 75 76 77 78 79 81 82 83 84 85 86 87 89 90 91 92 93 96 97 98 99 100 101 102 103 104 105 107 108 109 110 111 114 115 118 119 124 126 127 128 129 130 132 134 135 144 145 146 147 148 149 150 **S** Duke LifePoint Healthcare, Brentwood, TN
Primary Contact: Steven E. Tucker, Chief Executive Officer
COO: Steven E Tucker, Chief Executive Officer
CMO: Susan Williams M.D., Chief Medical Officer
CIO: Joe Dado, Chief Information Officer
CNO: Claudia Rager R.N., Vice President Patient Care Services
Web address: www.conemaugh.org
Control: Corporation, Investor–owned (for–profit) **Service:** General medical and surgical

Staffed Beds: 539 **Admissions:** 20332 **Census:** 298 **Outpatient Visits:** 451378 **Births:** 1567 **Total Expense ($000):** 383666 **Payroll Expense ($000):** 156758 **Personnel:** 2971

MEMORIAL MEDICAL CENTER – LEE CAMPUS See Conemaugh Memorial Medical Center

⊞ **SELECT SPECIALTY HOSPITAL–JOHNSTOWN (392031)**, 320 Main Street, 3rd Floor, Zip 15901–1601; tel. 814/534-7300, (Nonreporting) **A**1 10 **S** Select Medical Corporation, Mechanicsburg, PA
Primary Contact: Kelly Blake, Chief Executive Officer
CMO: Gary Davidson M.D., Medical Director
Web address: www.selectspecialtyhospitals.com/company/locations/johnstown.aspx
Control: Corporation, Investor–owned (for–profit) **Service:** Acute long–term care hospital

Staffed Beds: 39

KANE—Mckean County

UPMC KANE (390104), 4372 Route 6, Zip 16735–3060; tel. 814/837-8585 **A**10 20 **F**3 11 15 17 18 28 29 30 34 35 40 41 45 46 50 53 57 59 62 64 65 70 75 77 79 81 82 85 89 91 93 107 108 110 111 115 118 119 128 130 132 133 135 145 146 147 149 **P**4 **S** UPMC, Pittsburgh, PA
Primary Contact: J Gary. Rhodes, FACHE, Chief Executive Officer
CFO: Angela Hadzega, Chief Financial Officer
CMO: Linda Rettger M.D., President Medical Staff
CIO: Deano Cherry, Chief Information Officer
CHR: Marsha Keller, Director Human Resources
CNO: Pam Bray, Director of Nursing and Director Inpatient Services
Web address: www.kanehosp.com
Control: Other not–for–profit (including NFP Corporation) **Service:** General medical and surgical

Staffed Beds: 31 **Admissions:** 601 **Census:** 7 **Outpatient Visits:** 78850 **Births:** 0 **Total Expense ($000):** 20909 **Payroll Expense ($000):** 10532 **Personnel:** 187

KINGSTON—Luzerne County

⊞ **FIRST HOSPITAL WYOMING VALLEY (394039)**, 562 Wyoming Avenue, Zip 18704–3721; tel. 570/552-3900 **A**1 3 10 **F**98 99 103 105 130 **P**6 **S** Community Health Systems, Inc., Franklin, TN
Primary Contact: Eugene Boylan, Chief Executive Officer
CFO: Kelly Knorr, Chief Financial Officer
CMO: David Liskov M.D., Medical Director
CNO: Rhonda Moffitt Sod, Chief Nursing Officer
Web address: www.commonwealthhealth.net/locations/first–hospital
Control: Corporation, Investor–owned (for–profit) **Service:** Psychiatric

Staffed Beds: 149 **Admissions:** 4099 **Census:** 107 **Outpatient Visits:** 0 **Births:** 0 **Personnel:** 112

KITTANNING—Armstrong County

⇑ **ACMH HOSPITAL (390163)**, One Nolte Drive, Zip 16201–7111; tel. 724/543-8500, (Total facility includes 17 beds in nursing home–type unit) **A**2 10 19 21 **F**3 11 13 15 17 18 20 22 26 28 29 30 34 35 40 45 47 49 59 70 74 75 76 77 78 79 81 82 85 90 93 98 102 103 107 108 110 111 112 114 119 120 127 128 129 130 131 132 135 136 141 142 146 148 149
Primary Contact: John I. Lewis, President and Chief Executive Officer
CFO: Patrick Burns, Vice President Finance
CMO: Harold Altman M.D., Chief Medical Officer
CIO: Dianne Emminger, Vice President Information Services
CHR: Anne Remaley, Vice President Human Resources
Web address: www.acmh.org
Control: Other not–for–profit (including NFP Corporation) **Service:** General medical and surgical

Staffed Beds: 165 **Admissions:** 5303 **Census:** 68 **Outpatient Visits:** 267717 **Births:** 457 **Total Expense ($000):** 100819 **Payroll Expense ($000):** 44920 **Personnel:** 852

PA

LANCASTER—Lancaster County

⊞ **LANCASTER GENERAL HOSPITAL (390100)**, 555 North Duke Street, Zip 17602–2250; tel. 717/544–5511 **A**1 2 3 5 10 **F**3 7 8 11 12 13 14 15 17 18 20 22 24 26 28 29 30 31 32 34 35 36 38 39 40 43 44 45 46 47 49 50 54 55 56 57 58 59 60 61 64 65 66 68 70 72 73 74 75 76 77 78 79 80 81 82 84 85 86 87 89 91 92 93 94 96 97 98 100 102 103 104 107 108 110 114 115 118 119 120 121 123 124 126 129 130 132 135 141 142 145 146 147 148 149 150 **P**6 **S** University of Pennsylvania Health System, Philadelphia, PA
Primary Contact: Jan L. Bergen, President and Chief Executive Officer
CFO: Dennis Roemer, Executive Vice President and Chief Financial Officer
CMO: Lee M Duke M.D., II, Senior Vice President and Chief Physician Executive
CIO: Gary Davidson, Senior Vice President and Chief Information Officer
CHR: Regina Mingle, Senior Vice President and Chief Leadership Officer
CNO: Lanyce Roldan, Interim Chief Nursing Officer
Web address: www.lancastergeneralhealth.org
Control: Other not–for–profit (including NFP Corporation) **Service:** General medical and surgical

Staffed Beds: 630 **Admissions:** 31954 **Census:** 390 **Outpatient Visits:** 1575325 **Births:** 4232 **Total Expense ($000):** 856048 **Payroll Expense ($000):** 349009 **Personnel:** 4935

⊞ **LANCASTER REGIONAL MEDICAL CENTERS (390061)**, 250 College Avenue, Zip 17603–3363, Mailing Address: P.O.Box 3434, 17604–3434; tel. 717/291–8211 **A**1 3 10 **F**3 15 18 20 22 24 26 28 29 30 31 34 35 37 40 45 46 47 48 49 50 51 56 57 59 64 68 70 74 75 77 78 79 81 82 84 85 87 90 91 92 93 96 98 100 101 102 103 107 108 110 111 114 119 121 126 129 130 131 135 146 **S** UPMC Pinnacle, Harrisburg, PA
Primary Contact: Brooks Turkel, Chief Executive Officer
CFO: Mike Johnson, Chief Financial Officer
CMO: N. A. Mastropietro M.D., Medical Director
CHR: Brian Hoffman, Director Human Resources
CNO: Michelle Reaser R.N., Chief Nursing Executive
Web address: www.lancasterregional.com
Control: Corporation, Investor–owned (for–profit) **Service:** General medical and surgical

Staffed Beds: 150 **Admissions:** 4009 **Census:** 63 **Births:** 0

☐ **LANCASTER REHABILITATION HOSPITAL (393054)**, 675 Good Drive, Zip 17601–2426; tel. 717/406–3000 (Nonreporting) **A**1 10
Primary Contact: Tammy L. Derk, Chief Executive Officer
CFO: David Stark, Chief Financial Officer
CHR: Lisa Andrews, Director Human Resources
Web address: www.lancastergeneral.org
Control: Corporation, Investor–owned (for–profit) **Service:** Rehabilitation

Staffed Beds: 10

LANGHORNE—Bucks County

☐ **BARIX CLINICS OF PENNSYLVANIA (390302)**, 280 Middletown Boulevard, Zip 19047–1816; tel. 267/572–3100 (Nonreporting) **A**1 10
Primary Contact: Tony Adams, President
Web address: www.barixclinics.com
Control: Partnership, Investor–owned (for–profit) **Service:** Surgical

Staffed Beds: 40

BUCKS COUNTY CAMPUS See ARIA – Jefferson Health, Philadelphia

⊞ **ST. MARY MEDICAL CENTER (390258)**, 1201 Langhorne–Newtown Road, Zip 19047–1201; tel. 215/710–2000 **A**1 2 3 10 **F**2 7 12 15 17 18 20 22 24 26 28 29 30 31 32 34 35 36 40 41 43 53 55 56 57 58 59 64 66 70 72 74 75 76 77 78 79 81 82 84 86 87 89 91 92 93 94 107 108 110 111 114 115 116 117 118 119 120 121 123 124 126 129 130 132 135 146 147 148 **S** Trinity Health, Livonia, MI
Primary Contact: James L. Woodward, President and Chief Executive Officer
COO: Jeffrey N Yarmel, Chief Operating Officer
CFO: Daniel Confalone, Chief Financial Officer and Vice President Finance
CMO: Lawrence Brilliant M.D., Vice President and Chief Medical Officer
CIO: Bonnie Buehler, Chief Information Officer
CHR: Mary Sweeney, Vice President Colleague Services and Development
CNO: Sharon Brown R.N., MSN, Vice President Patient Care and Chief Nursing Officer
Web address: www.stmaryhealthcare.org
Control: Church operated, Nongovernment, not–for–profit **Service:** General medical and surgical

Staffed Beds: 307 **Admissions:** 22226 **Census:** 242 **Outpatient Visits:** 307223 **Births:** 2328 **Total Expense ($000):** 388559 **Payroll Expense ($000):** 149651 **Personnel:** 2106

ST. MARY REHABILITATION HOSPITAL (393055), 1201 Langhorne Newtown Road, Zip 19047–1201, Mailing Address: 1208 Langhorne Newtown Road, 19047–1234; tel. 267/560–1111 (Nonreporting) **S** Kindred Healthcare, Louisville, KY
Primary Contact: Lisa Haney, Chief Executive Officer
Web address: www.stmaryhealthcare.org
Control: Church operated, Nongovernment, not–for–profit **Service:** Rehabilitation

Staffed Beds: 50

LANSDALE—Montgomery County

⊞ **ABINGTON–LANSDALE HOSPITAL JEFFERSON HEALTH (390012)**, 100 Medical Campus Drive, Zip 19446–1200; tel. 215/368–2100 **A**1 10 **F**2 3 11 15 18 28 29 30 32 34 35 36 37 40 44 45 49 50 53 54 56 57 59 63 64 65 66 68 70 74 75 77 79 81 82 84 85 86 87 90 93 96 97 107 110 111 114 115 119 129 130 131 132 135 146 147 148 149 150 **P**6 **S** Jefferson Health, Philadelphia, PA
Primary Contact: Gary R. Candia, Ph.D., FACHE, Chief Administrative Officer
COO: Katie Farrell, Chief Operating Officer
CFO: Michael Walsh, Senior Vice President Finance and Chief Financial Officer
CMO: Michel Taupin M.D., Chief Medical Officer
CIO: Alison Ferren, Vice President Information Technology and Chief Information Officer
CHR: Meghan Patton, Vice President Human Resources
CNO: Kelly Cummings, Chief Nursing Officer
Web address: www.abingtonhealth.org/find–a–location/abington–lansdale–hospital/#.V5dyVVL9yk4
Control: Other not–for–profit (including NFP Corporation) **Service:** General medical and surgical

Staffed Beds: 127 **Admissions:** 5892 **Census:** 55 **Outpatient Visits:** 77222 **Births:** 0 **Total Expense ($000):** 82249 **Payroll Expense ($000):** 31571 **Personnel:** 361

LATROBE—Westmoreland County

☐ **EXCELA LATROBE AREA HOSPITAL (390219)**, One Mellon Way, Zip 15650–1096; tel. 724/537–1000 **A**1 2 3 5 10 13 **F**3 7 8 12 15 18 28 29 30 34 35 40 44 45 48 49 50 51 54 57 59 64 65 68 70 74 75 77 78 79 81 82 85 86 87 92 93 96 97 98 99 100 101 102 104 107 108 110 111 114 115 117 118 119 126 130 132 134 135 143 146 147 **P**6 **S** Excela Health, Greensburg, PA
Primary Contact: Michael D. Busch, Executive Vice President and Chief Operating Officer
COO: Michael D Busch, Executive Vice President and Chief Operating Officer
CMO: Carol J. Fox M.D., Senior Vice President and Chief Medical Officer
CIO: David Gawaluck, Vice President and Chief Information Officer
CHR: Laurie English, Senior Vice President and Chief Human Resource Officer
CNO: Helen K Burns Ph.D., R.N., Senior Vice President and Chief Nursing Officer
Web address: www.excelahealth.org
Control: Other not–for–profit (including NFP Corporation) **Service:** General medical and surgical

Staffed Beds: 114 **Admissions:** 6810 **Census:** 71 **Births:** 0

⊞ **SELECT SPECIALTY HOSPITAL–LAUREL HIGHLANDS (392036)**, One Mellon Way, 3rd Floor, Zip 15650–1197; tel. 724/539–3870, (Nonreporting) **A**1 10 **S** Select Medical Corporation, Mechanicsburg, PA
Primary Contact: Lauren Donahoe, Chief Executive Officer
Web address: www.laurelhighlands.selectspecialtyhospitals.com/
Control: Corporation, Investor–owned (for–profit) **Service:** Acute long–term care hospital

Staffed Beds: 40

LEBANON—Lebanon County

⊞ **LEBANON VETERANS AFFAIRS MEDICAL CENTER**, 1700 South Lincoln Avenue, Zip 17042–7529; tel. 717/272–6621, (Nonreporting) **A**1 3 5 **S** Department of Veterans Affairs, Washington, DC
Primary Contact: Margaret G. Wilson, R.N., MSN, Acting Director
CFO: Geoffrey Smith, Chief Financial Officer
CMO: Kanan Chatterjee M.D., Chief of Staff
CIO: Andru Ditzler, Chief Information Officer
CHR: Cindy Shiner, Manager Human Resources
Web address: www.lebanon.va.gov
Control: Veterans Affairs, Government, federal **Service:** General medical and surgical

Staffed Beds: 213

VETERANS AFFAIRS MEDICAL CENTER See Lebanon Veterans Affairs Medical Center

☒ **WELLSPAN GOOD SAMARITAN HOSPITAL (390066)**, Fourth and Walnut Streets, Zip 17042–1281, Mailing Address: P.O.Box 1281, 17042–1281; tel. 717/270–7500, (Total facility includes 19 beds in nursing home–type unit) **A**1 3 5 10 13 **F**3 8 11 13 14 15 17 18 20 22 24 26 28 29 30 31 34 35 40 45 49 50 51 57 58 59 62 63 64 67 68 70 74 75 76 77 78 79 80 81 82 85 87 89 90 91 92 93 94 96 97 107 110 111 114 115 116 117 118 119 120 121 124 126 129 130 132 135 145 146 148 149 **P**8 **S** WellSpan Health, York, PA
Primary Contact: Thomas R. Harlow, FACHE, President
COO: Kimberly Feeman, Senior Vice President and Chief Operating Officer
CMO: Robert D Shaver M.D., Vice President Medical Affairs
CIO: Leon John Jabour, Regional Chief Information Officer
CHR: Denise M Garman, Director Human Resources
CNO: Jacquelyn M Gould MS, R.N., Vice President Patient Care Services and Chief Nursing Officer
Web address: www.gshleb.org
Control: Other not–for–profit (including NFP Corporation) **Service:** General medical and surgical

Staffed Beds: 157 **Admissions:** 7450 **Census:** 101 **Outpatient Visits:** 262255 **Births:** 722 **Total Expense ($000):** 190268 **Payroll Expense ($000):** 65013 **Personnel:** 1272

LEHIGHTON—Carbon County

☒ △ **BLUE MOUNTAIN HOSPITAL (390194)**, 211 North 12th Street, Zip 18235–1138; tel. 610/377–1300, (Includes BLUE MOUNTAIN HOSPITAL PALMERTON CAMPUS, 135 Lafayette Avenue, Palmerton, Pennsylvania, Zip 18071–1596, tel. 610/826–3141; Andrew E Harris, Chief Executive Officer) (Total facility includes 91 beds in nursing home–type unit) **A**1 7 10 **F**2 3 11 12 15 28 29 30 34 35 40 46 47 49 50 56 57 59 62 64 65 68 70 74 75 77 79 81 82 85 87 90 93 94 97 98 102 103 107 108 110 111 114 116 117 119 124 128 129 130 132 133 135 146 147 148 **S** Blue Mountain Health System, Lehighton, PA
Primary Contact: Andrew E. Harris, Chief Executive Officer
CFO: Andrea Andrae, Chief Financial Officer
CMO: Dennis Kondash D.O., Vice President Medical Affairs
CIO: Steve Kinkaid, Director Information Systems
CHR: Terrance J Purcell, Vice President Support Services and Ambulatory Care
CNO: Dorothy Patzek, Vice President Nursing
Web address: www.blmtn.org
Control: Other not–for–profit (including NFP Corporation) **Service:** General medical and surgical

Staffed Beds: 250 **Admissions:** 5004 **Census:** 164 **Outpatient Visits:** 108415 **Births:** 0 **Total Expense ($000):** 93938 **Payroll Expense ($000):** 40523 **Personnel:** 870

LEWISBURG—Union County

⇑ **EVANGELICAL COMMUNITY HOSPITAL (390013)**, One Hospital Drive, Zip 17837–9350; tel. 570/522–2000 **A**10 19 21 **F**3 8 11 12 13 15 18 20 22 28 29 30 31 34 35 40 43 45 49 50 51 53 54 57 59 63 64 65 68 74 75 76 77 78 79 81 82 84 85 86 87 90 91 92 93 94 96 97 107 108 110 111 114 115 116 117 118 119 129 130 131 132 135 144 146 147 148 **P**7
Primary Contact: Kendra A. Aucker, President and Chief Executive Officer
COO: Kendra A. Aucker, Vice President Operations
CFO: Jim Stopper CPA, Chief Financial Officer
CMO: J Lawrence Ginsburg M.D., Vice President Medical Affairs
CIO: Dale Moyer, Vice President Information Systems
CHR: Angela Hummel, Vice President Human Resources
CNO: Tamara F. Persing MHA, BSN,, Chief Nursing Officer
Web address: www.evanhospital.com
Control: Other not–for–profit (including NFP Corporation) **Service:** General medical and surgical

Staffed Beds: 132 **Admissions:** 5713 **Census:** 52 **Outpatient Visits:** 292556 **Births:** 924 **Total Expense ($000):** 151710 **Payroll Expense ($000):** 62673 **Personnel:** 1303

U. S. PENITENTIARY INFIRMARY, Route 7, Zip 17837–9303; tel. 570/523–1251, (Nonreporting)
Primary Contact: Steve Brown, Health Services Director
Control: Department of Justice, Government, federal **Service:** Hospital unit of an institution (prison hospital, college infirmary, etc.)

Staffed Beds: 17

LEWISTOWN—Mifflin County

☒ **GEISINGER–LEWISTOWN HOSPITAL (390048)**, 400 Highland Avenue, Zip 17044–1198; tel. 717/248–5411 **A**1 2 3 10 **F**3 11 12 13 15 17 18 19 28 29 30 31 34 35 40 45 46 49 50 51 57 59 64 68 70 71 74 75 76 78 79 81 82 83 85 86 87 97 98 99 100 101 102 103 107 108 110 111 114 115 116 117 118 119 120 121 123 124 130 132 135 146 147 148 149 **S** Geisinger Health, Danville, PA
Primary Contact: Kirk E. Thomas, Vice President Operations
COO: Kirk E Thomas, Vice President Operations
CFO: Kristy Hine, Associate Vice President Finance
CMO: Michael T Hegstrom M.D., Chief Medical Officer
CIO: Ronald M Cowan, Vice President Information Systems
CHR: N Sue Reinke, Vice President Human Resources
CNO: Christine W Mathews R.N., MSN, Vice President Nursing Services
Web address: www.geisinger.org
Control: Other not–for–profit (including NFP Corporation) **Service:** General medical and surgical

Staffed Beds: 123 **Admissions:** 4696 **Census:** 52 **Outpatient Visits:** 147339 **Births:** 502 **Total Expense ($000):** 98925 **Payroll Expense ($000):** 38267 **Personnel:** 773

LITITZ—Lancaster County

☒ **HEART OF LANCASTER REGIONAL MEDICAL CENTER (390068)**, 1500 Highlands Drive, Zip 17543–7694; tel. 717/625–5000 **A**1 3 10 13 **F**2 12 13 15 18 29 30 31 34 35 44 45 47 49 50 57 59 60 64 68 70 72 74 75 76 77 79 81 82 85 87 89 107 108 110 111 115 119 126 130 146 147 148 **S** UPMC Pinnacle, Harrisburg, PA
Primary Contact: Deborah J. Willwerth, R.N., MSN, Chief Executive Officer
CIO: David Fisher, Director Information Systems
Web address: www.heartoflancaster.com
Control: Corporation, Investor–owned (for–profit) **Service:** General medical and surgical

Staffed Beds: 148 **Admissions:** 2756 **Census:** 27 **Births:** 1018

LOCK HAVEN—Clinton County

☒ **LOCK HAVEN HOSPITAL (390071)**, 24 Cree Drive, Zip 17745–2699; tel. 570/893–5000, (Nonreporting) **A**1 10 **S** Quorum Health, Brentwood, TN
Primary Contact: Steven T. Davis, Chief Executive Officer
CFO: Jennifer Lesher, Chief Financial Officer
CMO: Rajesh Patel M.D., Chief of Staff
CIO: Judy Chapman, Interim Director Information Systems
CHR: Courtney Kunes, Director Human Resources
Web address: www.lockhavenhospital.com
Control: Corporation, Investor–owned (for–profit) **Service:** General medical and surgical

Staffed Beds: 20

MALVERN—Chester County

☒ △ **BRYN MAWR REHABILITATION HOSPITAL (393025)**, 414 Paoli Pike, Zip 19355–3300, Mailing Address: P.O.Box 3007, 19355–0707; tel. 484/596–5400 **A**1 3 7 10 **F**3 11 28 29 30 34 35 36 44 50 65 71 75 82 86 87 90 91 92 93 95 96 119 130 131 132 143 146 **P**5 **S** Main Line Health, Brentwood, TN
Primary Contact: Donna Phillips, President
CFO: Dave Schmotzer, Chief Financial Officer
CMO: John Kraus M.D., Chief Medical Officer
CIO: Karen A Thomas, Chief Information Officer
Web address: www.brynmawrrehab.org
Control: Other not–for–profit (including NFP Corporation) **Service:** Rehabilitation

Staffed Beds: 148 **Admissions:** 2137 **Census:** 91 **Outpatient Visits:** 71993 **Births:** 0 **Total Expense ($000):** 68321 **Payroll Expense ($000):** 36564 **Personnel:** 534

DEVEREUX CHILDREN'S BEHAVIORAL HEALTH CENTER, 655 Sugartown Road, Zip 19355–3303, Mailing Address: 655 Sugartown Rd, 19355–3303; tel. 800/345–1292 **F**29 34 35 38 59 86 98 99 106 149 150 **P**6 **S** Devereux, Villanova, PA
Primary Contact: David E. Woodward, Executive Director
CFO: Tim Evans, Assistant Financial Director
CMO: Jacquelyn Zavodnick M.D., Medical Director
CIO: MaryLou Hettinger, Director Quality Management
CHR: Sean Maher, Director Human Resources
CNO: Deanna Reiss, Hospital Director of Nursing
Web address: www.devereux.org
Control: Other not–for–profit (including NFP Corporation) **Service:** Children's hospital psychiatric

Staffed Beds: 49 **Admissions:** 523 **Census:** 32 **Outpatient Visits:** 15 **Births:** 0 **Total Expense ($000):** 7305 **Payroll Expense ($000):** 4098 **Personnel:** 92

PA

MALVERN INSTITUTE, 940 King Road, Zip 19355–3166; tel. 610/647–0330, (Nonreporting)
Primary Contact: Scott Weisenberger, Chief Executive Officer
CFO: Janet Corley, Accountant
Web address: www.malverninstitute.com
Control: Corporation, Investor–owned (for–profit) **Service**: Alcoholism and other chemical dependency

Staffed Beds: 40

MC CONNELLSBURG—Fulton County

★ **FULTON COUNTY MEDICAL CENTER (391303)**, 214 Peach Orchard Road, Zip 17233–8559; tel. 717/485–3155, (Total facility includes 67 beds in nursing home–type unit) **A**10 18 **F**3 11 12 15 18 28 29 30 34 35 40 46 50 57 59 62 64 70 75 77 78 79 81 87 91 93 97 107 108 110 111 115 118 119 128 129 130 132 133 135 146 147 148
Primary Contact: Jason F. Hawkins, President and Chief Executive Officer
COO: William Buterbaugh, Director Support Services
CFO: Deborah A Shughart, Vice President and Chief Financial Officer
CMO: Sharon E Martin M.D., Ph.D., President Medical Staff
CIO: Armen Arakelian, Chief Information Officer
CHR: Cheryl Rose, Human Resources Director
Web address: www.fcmcpa.org
Control: Other not–for–profit (including NFP Corporation) **Service**: General medical and surgical

Staffed Beds: 88 **Admissions**: 798 **Census**: 76 **Outpatient Visits**: 60270 **Births**: 0 **Total Expense ($000)**: 46681 **Payroll Expense ($000)**: 22536 **Personnel**: 344

MCKEES ROCKS—Allegheny County

✠ **OHIO VALLEY HOSPITAL (390157)**, 25 Heckel Road, Zip 15136–1694; tel. 412/777–6161 **A**1 10 **F**3 10 15 18 20 29 30 40 45 46 49 51 59 65 70 74 75 77 79 81 82 85 87 90 92 93 98 103 104 107 108 111 118 119 126 129 130 143 146 148 149 **P**6
Primary Contact: David W. Scott, President and Chief Executive Officer
CFO: Jack Nelson, Vice President Finance and Chief Financial Officer
CHR: Erin J Frohnhofer, Vice President Human Resources
CNO: Paulette Bingham, Director Nursing Services
Web address: www.ohiovalleyhospital.org
Control: Other not–for–profit (including NFP Corporation) **Service**: General medical and surgical

Staffed Beds: 124 **Admissions**: 3352 **Census**: 55 **Outpatient Visits**: 101755 **Births**: 0 **Total Expense ($000)**: 62162 **Payroll Expense ($000)**: 21806 **Personnel**: 400

MCKEESPORT—Allegheny County

✠ **SELECT SPECIALTY HOSPITAL–MCKEESPORT (392045)**, 1500 Fifth Avenue, 6th Floor, Zip 15132–2422; tel. 412/664–2900 **A**1 10 **F**3 91 92 97 130 148 **S** Select Medical Corporation, Mechanicsburg, PA
Primary Contact: Angela Merryman, Chief Executive Officer
Web address: www.mckeesport.selectspecialtyhospitals.com/
Control: Corporation, Investor–owned (for–profit) **Service**: Acute long–term care hospital

Staffed Beds: 30 **Admissions**: 261 **Census**: 20 **Outpatient Visits**: 0 **Births**: 0

☐ **UPMC MCKEESPORT (390002)**, 1500 Fifth Avenue, Zip 15132–2422; tel. 412/664–2000, (Total facility includes 24 beds in nursing home–type unit) **A**1 3 5 10 13 **F**3 8 11 15 18 20 22 28 29 30 31 34 35 37 40 46 49 50 54 56 57 59 60 61 62 64 65 66 68 70 74 75 77 78 79 81 84 85 86 87 90 91 96 97 98 100 101 102 103 107 111 114 115 118 119 121 128 130 131 132 135 143 146 148 **P**6 **S** UPMC, Pittsburgh, PA
Primary Contact: Mark Sevco, President
COO: Amy Bush, Vice President Operations
CFO: Christopher Stockhausen, Chief Financial Officer
CMO: R Curtis Waligura D.O., Vice President Medical Affairs, Chief Medical Officer
CIO: Terri Keeling, Vice President Information Systems
CHR: Kelli Reale, Vice President Human Resources
CNO: Leeanna McKibben R.N., MSN, Vice President Patient Services and Chief Nursing Officer
Web address: www.mckeesport.upmc.com
Control: Other not–for–profit (including NFP Corporation) **Service**: General medical and surgical

Staffed Beds: 174 **Admissions**: 7545 **Census**: 120 **Outpatient Visits**: 124923 **Births**: 0 **Total Expense ($000)**: 136331 **Payroll Expense ($000)**: 40702 **Personnel**: 605

MEADOWBROOK—Montgomery County

⇑ **HOLY REDEEMER HOSPITAL (390097)**, 1648 Huntingdon Pike, Zip 19046–8001; tel. 215/947–3000, (Total facility includes 21 beds in nursing home–type unit) **A**2 3 5 10 21 **F**3 13 15 17 18 20 22 29 30 31 32 34 35 36 39 40 41 44 45 46 49 50 51 53 54 55 56 57 58 59 61 62 63 64 68 69 70 72 74 75 76 77 78 79 81 82 84 85 86 87 92 93 96 98 100 103 104 107 108 109 110 114 115 116 117 118 119 120 121 123 128 129 130 131 132 135 141 143 146 147 148 149
Primary Contact: Michael B. Laign, President and Chief Executive Officer
CFO: Russell R Wagner, Executive Vice President and Chief Financial Officer
CMO: Henry D. Unger M.D., Senior Vice President and Chief Medical Officer
CIO: Donald F. Friel, Executive Vice President
CHR: Joseph J Cassidy, Vice President
CNO: Anne Catino MS, R.N., Vice President and Chief Nursing Officer
Web address: www.holyredeemer.com
Control: Other not–for–profit (including NFP Corporation) **Service**: General medical and surgical

Staffed Beds: 250 **Admissions**: 10207 **Census**: 134 **Outpatient Visits**: 309198 **Births**: 2638 **Total Expense ($000)**: 187566 **Payroll Expense ($000)**: 70742 **Personnel**: 1289

MEADVILLE—Crawford County

★ ⇑ **MEADVILLE MEDICAL CENTER (390113)**, 751 Liberty Street, Zip 16335–2559; tel. 814/333–5000, (Total facility includes 32 beds in nursing home–type unit) **A**2 10 12 13 21 **F**3 4 5 11 13 15 18 20 22 28 29 30 31 35 36 38 39 40 43 45 46 49 53 57 59 63 64 66 68 70 74 75 76 77 78 79 81 82 84 85 86 87 89 90 91 93 98 99 102 103 104 107 110 111 114 115 118 119 120 128 129 130 131 132 146 147 148 149 **P**6 7 **S** Meadville Medical Center, Meadville, PA
Primary Contact: Philip E. Pandolph, FACHE, Chief Executive Officer
CFO: Renato Suntay, Chief Financial Officer
CMO: Denise Johnson M.D., Medical Director
CIO: Young Vu, Chief Information Officer
CHR: Greg Maras, Vice President Human Resources
CNO: MaryAnn Hewston R.N., Chief Nurse Executive
Web address: www.mmchs.org
Control: Other not–for–profit (including NFP Corporation) **Service**: General medical and surgical

Staffed Beds: 210 **Admissions**: 6961 **Census**: 96 **Outpatient Visits**: 261131 **Births**: 574 **Total Expense ($000)**: 177249 **Payroll Expense ($000)**: 68862 **Personnel**: 1303

MECHANICSBURG—Cumberland County

HEALTHSOUTH REGIONAL SPECIALTY HOSPITAL See Lifecare Hospitals Of Mechanicsburg

✠ **HEALTHSOUTH REHABILITATION HOSPITAL OF MECHANICSBURG (393031)**, 175 Lancaster Boulevard, Zip 17055–3562; tel. 717/691–3700 **A**1 10 **F**28 29 34 54 57 59 64 68 75 77 79 82 90 91 92 93 94 95 96 130 132 146 148 **S** HEALTHSOUTH Corporation, Birmingham, AL
Primary Contact: Jarvis Ford, Chief Executive Officer
CMO: Michael Lupinacci M.D., Medical Director
CHR: David Staskin, Director Human Resources
Web address: www.healthsouthpa.com
Control: Corporation, Investor–owned (for–profit) **Service**: Rehabilitation

Staffed Beds: 75 **Admissions**: 1242 **Census**: 41 **Births**: 0

✠ **LIFECARE HOSPITALS OF MECHANICSBURG (392038)**, 4950 Wilson Lane, Zip 17055–4442; tel. 717/697–7706 **A**1 10 **F**1 3 29 60 77 91 **P**5 **S** LifeCare Management Services, Plano, TX
Primary Contact: Mary Ellen Kable, Chief Executive Officer
CMO: Michael Gluck M.D., Medical Director
CHR: Jennifer Rashford, Manager Human Resources
CNO: Alicia Kuntz, Nurse Manager
Web address: www.lifecare–hospitals.com/hospital.php?id=20
Control: Corporation, Investor–owned (for–profit) **Service**: Acute long–term care hospital

Staffed Beds: 68 **Admissions**: 358 **Census**: 23 **Outpatient Visits**: 0 **Births**: 0

Many Facility Codes have changed. Please refer to the AHA Guide Code Chart. © 2017 AHA Guide

MEDIA—Delaware County

✠ **RIDDLE HOSPITAL (390222)**, 1068 West Baltimore Pike, Zip 19063–5177; tel. 484/227–9400, (Total facility includes 23 beds in nursing home–type unit) **A**1 2 3 10 **F**3 7 11 13 15 18 20 22 26 28 29 30 31 34 35 36 37 38 40 41 44 45 46 49 50 53 54 55 56 57 58 59 63 64 65 70 72 74 75 76 78 79 80 81 82 84 85 86 87 92 97 100 102 103 107 108 110 111 114 115 118 119 120 124 128 129 130 131 132 135 141 143 145 146 147 148 149 **S** Main Line Health, Plano, TX
Primary Contact: Gary L. Perecko, President
COO: Jeshahnton Essex, Vice President of Administration
CFO: Ed McKillip, Director of Finance
CMO: David Thomas, President Medical Staff
CHR: Mary Louise Ciciretti, Director Human Resources
CNO: Rosemary H Wurster, Vice President Patient Care Services
Web address: www.riddlehospital.org
Control: Other not–for–profit (including NFP Corporation) **Service**: General medical and surgical

Staffed Beds: 227 **Admissions**: 10582 **Census**: 140 **Outpatient Visits**: 97634 **Births**: 972 **Total Expense ($000)**: 180528 **Payroll Expense ($000)**: 64352 **Personnel**: 960

RIDDLE MEMORIAL HOSPITAL See Riddle Hospital

MEYERSDALE—Somerset County

★ **CONEMAUGH MEYERSDALE MEDICAL CENTER (391302)**, 200 Hospital Drive, Zip 15552–1249; tel. 814/634–5911 **A**10 18 **F**29 34 40 64 75 81 107 114 119 127 130 132 133 146 148 **S** Duke LifePoint Healthcare, Brentwood, TN
Primary Contact: Heather Smith, President
CMO: Dwayne Platt M.D., Chief Medical Officer
Web address: www.conemaugh.org
Control: Corporation, Investor–owned (for–profit) **Service**: General medical and surgical

Staffed Beds: 20 **Admissions**: 324 **Census**: 5 **Outpatient Visits**: 47534 **Births**: 0 **Total Expense ($000)**: 14283 **Payroll Expense ($000)**: 4753 **Personnel**: 104

MONONGAHELA—Washington County

✠ **MONONGAHELA VALLEY HOSPITAL (390147)**, 1163 Country Club Road, Zip 15063–1095; tel. 724/258–1000 **A**1 2 10 **F**3 8 9 11 12 15 17 18 20 22 28 29 30 31 32 34 35 40 45 48 49 50 51 54 55 56 57 59 61 64 68 70 74 75 77 78 79 80 81 82 85 86 87 89 90 92 93 96 98 100 101 102 103 107 108 110 111 114 115 118 119 120 121 123 124 129 130 131 132 134 135 146 147 148 149 **P**7 8
Primary Contact: Louis J. Panza Jr, President and Chief Executive Officer
COO: Patrick J Alberts, Senior Vice President and Chief Operating Officer
CFO: Daniel F Simmons, Senior Vice President and Treasurer
CMO: L. Douglas Pepper M.D., President, Medical Staff
CIO: Matt Rashilla, Chief Information and Application Manager
CHR: Louis Goodman, Senior Vice President Human Resources
CNO: Mary Lou Murt R.N., Senior Vice President Nursing
Web address: www.monvalleyhospital.com
Control: Other not–for–profit (including NFP Corporation) **Service**: General medical and surgical

Staffed Beds: 210 **Admissions**: 7250 **Census**: 105 **Outpatient Visits**: 301597 **Births**: 0 **Total Expense ($000)**: 131782 **Payroll Expense ($000)**: 54321 **Personnel**: 1024

MONROEVILLE—Allegheny County

✠ **FORBES HOSPITAL (390267)**, 2570 Haymaker Road, Zip 15146–3513; tel. 412/858–2000 **A**1 2 3 5 10 **F**3 7 8 11 13 15 17 18 20 22 24 26 28 29 30 31 34 35 36 38 40 43 44 46 49 50 54 55 57 58 59 64 65 69 70 73 74 75 76 77 78 79 80 81 82 84 85 86 87 89 90 93 96 98 100 101 102 103 107 108 110 111 115 118 119 126 130 132 135 146 147 148 149 **P**6 **S** Allegheny Health Network, Pittsburgh, PA
Primary Contact: Mark Rubino, M.D., President
CFO: Tom Hipkiss, Vice President Finance
CMO: Mark Rubino M.D., Chief Medical Officer
CIO: Sharon Lewis, Director Information Systems
CHR: Georgia Redding, Director Human Resources
CNO: Amber Egyud R.N., Vice President Chief Nursing Officer
Web address: www.ahn.org
Control: Other not–for–profit (including NFP Corporation) **Service**: General medical and surgical

Staffed Beds: 315 **Admissions**: 14353 **Census**: 196 **Outpatient Visits**: 141149 **Births**: 1289 **Total Expense ($000)**: 219868 **Payroll Expense ($000)**: 72200 **Personnel**: 1228

UPMC EAST (390328), 2775 Mosside Boulevard, Zip 15146–2760; tel. 412/357–3000 **A**10 **F**3 18 20 22 26 28 29 30 31 34 35 40 45 46 49 50 57 59 60 62 64 68 70 74 75 77 78 79 81 84 85 87 90 91 92 96 100 107 108 111 115 119 120 121 122 123 130 132 135 146 148 **S** UPMC, Pittsburgh, PA
Primary Contact: Mark Sevco, President
CNO: Tamra Minton R.N., MSN, Vice President Patient Care Services and Chief Nursing Officer
Web address: www.upmc.com/locations/hospitals/east/Pages/default.aspx
Control: Other not–for–profit (including NFP Corporation) **Service**: General medical and surgical

Staffed Beds: 155 **Admissions**: 7653 **Census**: 102 **Outpatient Visits**: 85124 **Births**: 0 **Total Expense ($000)**: 130724 **Payroll Expense ($000)**: 37418 **Personnel**: 619

WESTERN PENNSYLVANIA HOSPITAL – FORBES REGIONAL CAMPUS See Forbes Hospital

MONTROSE—Susquehanna County

✠ **ENDLESS MOUNTAIN HEALTH SYSTEMS (391306)**, 100 Hospital Drive, Zip 18801–6402; tel. 570/278–3801 **A**10 18 **F**3 15 34 40 44 45 50 53 57 59 64 65 77 79 81 85 93 107 110 111 114 119 130 132 133 135 146 **P**4
Primary Contact: Loren Stone, Chief Executive Officer
CIO: Gary Passmore, Chief Information Officer
CHR: Paula Anderson, Administrative Director Human Resources
Web address: www.endlesscare.org
Control: Other not–for–profit (including NFP Corporation) **Service**: General medical and surgical

Staffed Beds: 25 **Admissions**: 811 **Census**: 9 **Births**: 0

MOUNT GRETNA—Lebanon County

✠ **WELLSPAN PHILHAVEN (394020)**, 283 South Butler Road, Zip 17064–6085, Mailing Address: P.O.Box 550, 17064–0550; tel. 717/273–8871 **A**1 10 **F**30 98 99 100 101 102 103 104 105 106 130 146 **P**6 **S** WellSpan Health, York, PA
Primary Contact: Phil Hess, Chief Executive Officer
COO: Phil Hess, Chief Executive Officer
CFO: Matt Rogers, Chief Financial Officer
CMO: Francis D Sparrow M.D., Medical Director
CIO: Lori Nolt, Director Information Technology
CHR: Denis Orthaus, Director Human Resources
CNO: Heidi McMullan R.N., Chief Nursing Officer
Web address: www.philhaven.org
Control: Church operated, Nongovernment, not–for–profit **Service**: Psychiatric

Staffed Beds: 103 **Admissions**: 2476 **Census**: 94 **Outpatient Visits**: 121234 **Births**: 0 **Total Expense ($000)**: 64106 **Payroll Expense ($000)**: 42623 **Personnel**: 969

MOUNT PLEASANT—Westmoreland County

☐ **EXCELA FRICK HOSPITAL (390217)**, 508 South Church Street, Zip 15666–1790; tel. 724/547–1500 **A**1 10 **F**3 8 12 15 28 29 30 34 35 40 45 49 51 57 59 64 65 68 70 75 77 78 79 81 85 86 87 93 96 107 108 110 111 114 118 119 129 130 132 135 143 146 148 **S** Excela Health, Greensburg, PA
Primary Contact: Michael D. Busch, Executive Vice President and Chief Operating Officer
COO: Michael D Busch, Executive Vice President and Chief Operating Officer
CFO: Jeffrey T Curry, Executive Vice President and Chief Financial Officer
CMO: Jerome Granato M.D., Senior Vice President and Chief Medical Officer
CIO: David Gawaluck, Vice President and Chief Information Officer
CHR: John Caverno, Chief Human Resources Officer
CNO: Helen K Burns Ph.D., R.N., Senior Vice President and Chief Nursing Officer
Web address: www.excelahealth.org/PatientsandVisitors/HospitalsFacilities/Hospitals/Frick.aspx
Control: Other not–for–profit (including NFP Corporation) **Service**: General medical and surgical

Staffed Beds: 33 **Admissions**: 2240 **Census**: 23 **Births**: 0

PA

Hospital, Medicare Provider Number, Address, Telephone, Approval, Facility, and Physician Codes, Health Care System		
★ American Hospital Association (AHA) membership	○ Healthcare Facilities Accreditation Program	⇑ Center for Improvement in Healthcare Quality Accreditation
☐ The Joint Commission accreditation	◇ DNV Healthcare Inc. accreditation	△ Commission on Accreditation of Rehabilitation Facilities (CARF) accreditation

MUNCY—Lycoming County

★ **MUNCY VALLEY HOSPITAL (391301)**, 215 East Water Street, Zip 17756–8700; tel. 570/546–8282, (Total facility includes 136 beds in nursing home–type unit) **A**3 10 18 **F**6 11 34 40 44 50 56 57 59 64 68 81 86 87 93 107 108 119 128 130 133 144 146 **P**7 **S** UPMC Susquehanna, Williamsport, PA
Primary Contact: Christine Ballard, President and Chief Executive Officer
CFO: Eric Pohjala, Executive Vice President and Chief Financial Officer
CIO: Timothy E Schoener, Chief Information Officer
CHR: Donald Wilver Jr, Vice President Human Resources
CNO: C Cynthia Whipple, Director of Nursing
Web address: www.susquehannahealth.org
Control: Other not–for–profit (including NFP Corporation) **Service**: General medical and surgical

Staffed Beds: 156 **Admissions**: 844 **Census**: 134 **Outpatient Visits**: 25252 **Births**: 0 **Total Expense ($000)**: 41847 **Payroll Expense ($000)**: 13549 **Personnel**: 259

NATRONA HEIGHTS—Allegheny County

⊞ **ALLEGHENY VALLEY HOSPITAL (390032)**, 1301 Carlisle Street, Zip 15065–1152; tel. 724/224–5100 **A**1 2 3 10 **F**3 11 15 17 18 24 28 29 30 31 34 35 38 39 40 44 45 47 49 50 54 56 57 58 59 64 65 70 74 75 77 78 79 80 81 84 85 86 87 92 93 96 98 100 101 102 103 107 108 110 111 115 118 119 121 123 124 126 129 130 132 135 144 146 147 148 149 **S** Allegheny Health Network, Pittsburgh, PA
Primary Contact: William Englert, Chief Executive Officer
CFO: James A Kanuch, Vice President Finance
CMO: Suzanne M. Labriola D.O., Chief Medical Officer
CIO: Linda Fergus, Manager Information Technology
CHR: Cindy Moser, Director Human Resources
Web address: www.wpahs.org
Control: Other not–for–profit (including NFP Corporation) **Service**: General medical and surgical

Staffed Beds: 200 **Admissions**: 5579 **Census**: 71 **Outpatient Visits**: 193890 **Births**: 0 **Total Expense ($000)**: 113802 **Payroll Expense ($000)**: 37308 **Personnel**: 761

NEW CASTLE—Lawrence County

☐ **UPMC JAMESON HOSPITAL (390016)**, 1211 Wilmington Avenue, Zip 16105–2516; tel. 724/658–9001, (Total facility includes 20 beds in nursing home–type unit) **A**1 10 19 **F**3 8 11 15 18 20 22 28 29 30 32 34 35 40 41 45 46 49 57 59 63 64 65 70 74 75 76 77 79 81 82 85 86 90 92 93 96 98 100 101 102 103 105 107 108 110 111 114 115 118 119 128 129 130 146 147 **S** UPMC, Pittsburgh, PA
Primary Contact: Donald R. Owrey, President
CFO: James Aubel, Chief Financial Officer
CMO: Robert McGann M.D., President Medical Staff
CIO: Frank Divito, Manager Information Systems
CHR: Neil A Chessin, Vice President
CNO: Barbara Bernardi R.N., Nurse Executive
Web address: www.jamesonhealth.org
Control: Other not–for–profit (including NFP Corporation) **Service**: General medical and surgical

Staffed Beds: 238 **Admissions**: 6168 **Census**: 88 **Outpatient Visits**: 288521 **Births**: 30 **Total Expense ($000)**: 102766 **Payroll Expense ($000)**: 42102 **Personnel**: 901

NORRISTOWN—Montgomery County

☐ **MONTGOMERY COUNTY EMERGENCY SERVICE (394033)**, 50 Beech Drive, Zip 19403–5421; tel. 610/279–6100 **A**1 10 **F**4 5 7 29 35 38 50 64 98 99 100 101 102 103 104 130 **P**6
Primary Contact: William Myers, Chief Executive Officer
CMO: Deepraj Singh M.D., Medical Director
CHR: Byanka Meacham, Director Human Resources
CNO: Naomi Finkel, Nurse Executive
Web address: www.mces.org
Control: Other not–for–profit (including NFP Corporation) **Service**: Psychiatric

Staffed Beds: 81 **Admissions**: 1783 **Census**: 54 **Outpatient Visits**: 2174 **Births**: 0 **Total Expense ($000)**: 17213 **Payroll Expense ($000)**: 10363 **Personnel**: 180

NORRISTOWN STATE HOSPITAL (394001), 1001 Sterigere Street, Zip 19401–5300; tel. 610/270–1000 **A**10 **F**30 35 38 39 53 59 65 75 77 98 101 102 103 130 135 146 149 **P**6
Primary Contact: Edna I. McCutcheon, Chief Executive Officer
COO: Gary Raisner, Chief Operating Officer
CMO: Mia Marcovici M.D., Chief Medical Officer
CHR: Richard Szczurowski, Director Human Resources
CNO: Taryn Mason–Jones, Chief Nurse Executive
Control: State, Government, Nonfederal **Service**: Psychiatric

Staffed Beds: 259 **Admissions**: 108 **Census**: 250 **Outpatient Visits**: 112 **Births**: 0 **Total Expense ($000)**: 70651 **Payroll Expense ($000)**: 35860 **Personnel**: 542

⊞ **SUBURBAN COMMUNITY HOSPITAL (390116)**, 2701 DeKalb Pike, Zip 19401–1820; tel. 610/278–2000 **A**1 2 3 10 12 13 **F**3 12 15 18 28 29 30 31 34 40 45 46 50 54 56 57 59 64 70 74 75 77 78 79 81 82 85 87 93 96 98 103 107 108 110 111 114 115 118 119 120 121 126 129 130 132 135 146 147 **S** Prime Healthcare, Ontario, CA
Primary Contact: Peter J. Adamo, Chief Executive Officer
COO: Joseph Schofield, Chief Operating Officer
CFO: Joseph Marino, Chief Financial Officer
CMO: Andrea D Pedano D.O., Chief Medical Officer
CIO: Jason Wayne, Network Administrator
CHR: Gretchen Pendleton, Director Human Resources
CNO: Mary Ellen Rauner R.N., Chief Nursing Officer
Web address: www.suburbanhosp.org
Control: Church operated, Nongovernment, not–for–profit **Service**: General medical and surgical

Staffed Beds: 126 **Admissions**: 3465 **Census**: 42 **Births**: 0

☐ **VALLEY FORGE MEDICAL CENTER AND HOSPITAL (390272)**, 1033 West Germantown Pike, Zip 19403–3905; tel. 610/539–8500 **A**1 10 **F**3 4 29 61 68 75 82 100 130 132 148 149 **P**6
Primary Contact: Marian W. Colcher, President and Chief Executive Officer
CFO: Gregg Y Slocum, Chief Financial Officer
CMO: Robert E Colcher M.D., Medical Director
CHR: Frederick D Jackes, Assistant Administrator and Director Human Resources
Web address: www.vfmc.net
Control: Corporation, Investor–owned (for–profit) **Service**: Alcoholism and other chemical dependency

Staffed Beds: 50 **Admissions**: 1534 **Census**: 47 **Outpatient Visits**: 0 **Births**: 0

OAKDALE—Allegheny County

⊞ **CURAHEALTH PITTSBURGH (392028)**, 7777 Steubenville Pike, Zip 15071–3409; tel. 412/494–5500, (Nonreporting) **A**1 10 **S** Curahealth Hospitals, Garland, TX
Primary Contact: Janie Rosenberger–Slampack, Market Chief Executive Officer
CFO: Kevin Varley, Chief Financial Officer
CMO: Ravi Alagar M.D., Medical Director
Web address: www.curahealth.com
Control: Corporation, Investor–owned (for–profit) **Service**: Acute long–term care hospital

Staffed Beds: 63

OREFIELD—Lehigh County

KIDSPEACE CHILDREN'S HOSPITAL (394047), 5300 Kids Peace Drive, Zip 18069–2044; tel. 610/799–7900 **F**29 39 59 98 99 100 101 105 130 **P**7
Primary Contact: William R. Isemann, President and Chief Executive Officer
CFO: Michael Callan, Executive Vice President and Chief Financial Officer
CMO: Matthew Koval M.D., Vice President Medical Affairs
CIO: Joan Lesko, Director Technical Support and Services
CHR: Sheila Rulli, Director Human Resources
CNO: Tamara Wasilick, Director Operations
Web address: www.kidspeace.org
Control: Other not–for–profit (including NFP Corporation) **Service**: Children's hospital psychiatric

Staffed Beds: 120 **Admissions**: 2308 **Census**: 82 **Outpatient Visits**: 0 **Births**: 0 **Total Expense ($000)**: 26785 **Payroll Expense ($000)**: 11301 **Personnel**: 189

PAOLI—Chester County

⊞ **PAOLI HOSPITAL (390153)**, 255 West Lancaster Avenue, Zip 19301–1763; tel. 484/565–1000 **A**1 2 3 10 **F**3 5 11 13 15 18 20 22 24 26 28 29 30 31 32 34 35 36 38 39 40 41 43 44 45 46 47 48 49 50 54 55 56 57 59 63 64 65 70 72 74 75 76 78 79 80 81 82 84 85 86 87 92 97 99 100 101 102 103 104 105 107 108 110 111 114 115 118 119 120 121 123 124 126 129 130 131 132 134 135 141 144 146 147 148 149 150 **S** Main Line Health, Garland, TX
Primary Contact: James Paradis, President
CFO: John Doyle, Vice President Finance
CMO: Andrew J Norton M.D., Chief Medical Officer
CIO: Karen A Thomas, Vice President and Chief Information Officer
CHR: Deborah Fedora, Director Human Resources
Web address: www.mainlinehealth.org
Control: Other not–for–profit (including NFP Corporation) **Service**: General medical and surgical

Staffed Beds: 231 **Admissions**: 13166 **Census**: 135 **Outpatient Visits**: 299445 **Births**: 2106 **Total Expense ($000)**: 269629 **Payroll Expense ($000)**: 84547 **Personnel**: 1153

PHILADELPHIA—Philadelphia County

ALBERT EINSTEIN MEDICAL CENTER See Einstein Medical Center Philadelphia

⊞ △ **ARIA – JEFFERSON HEALTH (390115)**, 10800 Knights Road, Zip 19114–4200; tel. 215/612–4101, (Includes BUCKS COUNTY CAMPUS, 380 North Oxford Valley Road, Langhorne, Pennsylvania, Zip 19047–8399, tel. 215/949–5000; FRANKFORD CAMPUS, Frankford Avenue and Wakeling Street, Philadelphia, Pennsylvania, Zip 19124, tel. 215/831–2000) **A**1 3 5 7 10 13 **F**3 5 11 12 15 17 18 20 22 24 26 28 29 30 31 34 35 39 40 43 44 45 46 48 49 53 54 56 57 59 61 62 64 65 66 68 70 74 75 77 78 79 80 81 82 85 86 87 91 92 93 94 100 102 107 108 109 110 111 114 115 116 117 118 119 120 121 123 124 126 127 129 130 131 132 135 143 144 145 146 147 148 149 **P**6 **S** Jefferson Health, Philadelphia, PA
Primary Contact: Kathleen Kinslow, Ed.D., Chief Executive Officer
COO: Sandra Gomberg, Chief Operating Officer
CFO: William Degnan, Vice President Finance
CMO: Stanton Segal M.D., Chief Medical Officer
CIO: Daniel P. Walsh, Chief Information Officer
CHR: Dorinda Carolina, Chief Human Resources Officer
CNO: Michelle E Conley R.N., Chief Nursing Officer
Web address: www.ariahealth.org
Control: Other not–for–profit (including NFP Corporation) **Service:** General medical and surgical

Staffed Beds: 464 **Admissions:** 24541 **Census:** 306 **Outpatient Visits:** 307097 **Births:** 0 **Total Expense ($000):** 454361 **Payroll Expense ($000):** 182466 **Personnel:** 3137

☐ **BELMONT BEHAVIORAL HOSPITAL (394023)**, 4200 Monument Road, Zip 19131–1625; tel. 215/877–2000 **A**1 3 5 10 **F**4 5 29 77 86 87 98 99 103 104 105 130 146 149 **P**6 **S** Acadia Healthcare Company, Inc., Franklin, TN
Primary Contact: Mark Schor, Chief Executive Officer
CFO: Guy Romaniello, Director Fiscal Services
CMO: Richard Jaffe M.D., Medical Director
CHR: Jenna Pacini, Human Resources Specialist
CNO: Nona Fain Ph.D., R.N., Director of Nursing
Web address: www.einstein.edu/locations/belmont–behavioral–health/
Control: Individual, Investor–owned (for–profit) **Service:** Psychiatric

Staffed Beds: 171 **Admissions:** 4209 **Census:** 143 **Outpatient Visits:** 65946 **Births:** 0 **Personnel:** 364

⊞ **CHESTNUT HILL HOSPITAL (390026)**, 8835 Germantown Avenue, Zip 19118–2718; tel. 215/248–8200, (Nonreporting) **A**1 3 5 10 **S** Community Health Systems, Inc., Franklin, TN
Primary Contact: John D. Cacciamani, M.D., Chief Executive Officer
CFO: Marc Costner, Chief Financial Officer
CMO: John Scanlon DPM, Chief Medical Officer
CHR: Marilyn DiCicco, Director Human Resources
CNO: Teresa M Kelly MSN, R.N., Chief Nursing Officer
Web address: www.chhealthsystem.com
Control: Corporation, Investor–owned (for–profit) **Service:** General medical and surgical

Staffed Beds: 212

☐ **CHILDREN'S HOSPITAL OF PHILADELPHIA (393303)**, 3401 Civic Center Boulevard, Zip 19104–4319; tel. 215/590–1000 **A**1 3 5 8 10 **F**3 7 8 11 12 13 17 18 19 20 21 22 23 24 25 26 27 28 29 30 31 32 33 34 35 36 37 38 39 40 41 43 44 45 46 48 50 53 54 55 57 58 59 60 61 62 64 65 66 68 71 72 74 75 76 77 78 79 81 82 83 84 85 86 87 88 89 90 91 92 93 95 96 97 99 100 101 102 104 107 108 111 112 113 114 115 116 117 118 119 126 129 130 131 132 134 136 137 138 139 140 141 142 143 144 146 148 149 150 **P**6
Primary Contact: Madeline Bell, President and Chief Executive Officer
COO: Douglas G Hock, Executive Vice President and Chief Operating Officer
CFO: Thomas Todorow, Chief Financial Officer and Executive Vice President
CMO: Jan Boswinkel M.D., Vice President Medical Operations and Chief Safety Officer
CHR: Robert Croner, Senior Vice President and Chief Human Resources Officer
CNO: Paula M Agosto R.N., MSN, Senior Vice President and Chief Nursing Officer
Web address: www.chop.edu
Control: Other not–for–profit (including NFP Corporation) **Service:** Children's general medical and surgical

Staffed Beds: 546 **Admissions:** 29301 **Census:** 434 **Outpatient Visits:** 1290614 **Births:** 463 **Total Expense ($000):** 1893347 **Payroll Expense ($000):** 844740 **Personnel:** 10668

☐ **EASTERN REGIONAL MEDICAL CENTER (390312)**, 1331 East Wyoming Avenue, Zip 19124–3808; tel. 215/537–7400 **A**1 2 3 10 **F**3 15 29 30 31 33 34 35 36 45 46 47 48 49 50 55 56 57 58 59 64 65 68 70 75 78 79 80 81 82 84 85 86 87 91 93 96 100 101 103 104 107 108 109 110 111 114 115 116 118 119 121 123 124 126 129 131 132 135 136 143 144 146 147 148 149 **P**6 **S** Cancer Treatment Centers of America, Schaumburg, IL
Primary Contact: Nancy Hesse, MSN, R.N., President and Chief Executive Officer
COO: Kristin Mullen, Chief Operating Officer
CFO: Jeffrey Ryan, Senior Vice President, Finance and Business Development
CMO: Steven B. Standiford M.D., Chief of Staff
CIO: Kristin Darby, Chief Information Officer
CHR: Ronald Gilg, Assistant Vice President Talent
CNO: Joanne McGovern MSN, R.N., Chief Nursing Officer
Web address: www.cancercenter.com
Control: Corporation, Investor–owned (for–profit) **Service:** Cancer

Staffed Beds: 56 **Admissions:** 928 **Census:** 18 **Outpatient Visits:** 75652 **Births:** 0 **Personnel:** 558

☐ **EINSTEIN MEDICAL CENTER PHILADELPHIA (390142)**, 5501 Old York Road, Zip 19141–3098; tel. 215/456–7890, (Includes EINSTEIN MEDICAL CENTER ELKINS PARK, 60 Township Line Road, Elkins Park, Pennsylvania, Zip 19027–2220, tel. 215/663–6000; Barry R Freedman, President and Chief Executive Officer) (Total facility includes 39 beds in nursing home–type unit) **A**1 2 3 5 8 10 13 **F**3 8 11 12 13 15 17 18 20 22 24 26 28 29 30 31 32 34 35 36 37 38 39 40 41 43 44 45 46 47 48 49 51 54 55 56 57 58 59 61 64 65 66 68 70 72 73 74 75 76 77 78 79 81 82 84 85 86 87 90 91 92 93 95 97 98 99 100 101 102 103 104 107 108 110 111 114 115 119 120 121 123 124 126 128 129 130 131 132 138 139 142 143 145 146 147 148 149 150 **P**6 **S** Einstein Healthcare Network, Philadelphia, PA
Primary Contact: Barry R. Freedman, President and Chief Executive Officer
COO: Ruth Lefton, Chief Operating Officer
CFO: Gerard Blaney, Vice President Finance and Interim Chief Financial Officer
CMO: Steven Sivak M.D., Chief Medical Officer, Einstein Physicians Philadelphia
CIO: Brenda West, Vice President, Information Services and Interim Chief Information Officer
CHR: Lynne R Kornblatt, Chief Human Resources Officer
CNO: Jill Stunkard R.N., MSN, Associate Chief Nurse Executive and Interim Chief Nursing Officer
Web address: www.einstein.edu
Control: Other not–for–profit (including NFP Corporation) **Service:** General medical and surgical

Staffed Beds: 489 **Admissions:** 26267 **Census:** 489 **Outpatient Visits:** 574592 **Births:** 2789 **Total Expense ($000):** 779952 **Payroll Expense ($000):** 340881 **Personnel:** 4928

☐ **FAIRMOUNT BEHAVIORAL HEALTH SYSTEM (394027)**, 561 Fairthorne Avenue, Zip 19128–2499; tel. 215/487–4000 **A**1 10 **F**4 98 99 102 105 130 **P**6 **S** Universal Health Services, Inc., King of Prussia, PA
Primary Contact: Lisa M. McConlogue, MSN, Ph.D., Chief Executive Officer and Managing Director
CFO: Anthony Tortella, Chief Financial Officer
CMO: Silvia Gratz D.O., Chief Medical Officer
CIO: Anthony Tortella, Chief Financial Officer
CHR: Brendan Aurand, Director, Human Resources
CNO: Wanda Nolasco, Chief Nursing Officer
Web address: www.fairmountbhs.com
Control: Corporation, Investor–owned (for–profit) **Service:** Psychiatric

Staffed Beds: 235 **Admissions:** 5639 **Census:** 222 **Births:** 0

⊞ **FOX CHASE CANCER CENTER–AMERICAN ONCOLOGIC HOSPITAL (390196)**, 333 Cottman Avenue, Zip 19111–2434; tel. 215/728–6900 **A**1 2 3 5 10 **F**3 11 15 29 30 31 34 35 36 45 46 47 49 50 55 57 58 59 60 61 63 64 68 70 71 75 77 78 79 81 82 84 85 86 87 93 100 104 107 108 109 110 111 114 115 116 117 118 119 120 121 123 124 126 130 132 135 136 144 145 146 147 148 149 **P**6 **S** Temple University Health System, Philadelphia, PA
Primary Contact: Richard Fisher, M.D., President and Chief Executive Officer
COO: Judith Lynn Bachman, Chief Operating Officer
CFO: Anthony J Diasio, Chief Financial Officer
CMO: James Helstrom, Chief Medical Officer
CIO: Michael Sweeney, Chief Information Officer
CNO: Anne Jadwin, Chief Nursing Officer
Web address: www.fccc.org
Control: Other not–for–profit (including NFP Corporation) **Service:** Cancer

Staffed Beds: 67 **Admissions:** 4229 **Census:** 64 **Outpatient Visits:** 105111 **Births:** 0 **Total Expense ($000):** 275030 **Payroll Expense ($000):** 79651 **Personnel:** 1431

Hospital, Medicare Provider Number, Address, Telephone, Approval, Facility, and Physician Codes, Health Care System

★ American Hospital Association (AHA) membership
☐ The Joint Commission accreditation
○ Healthcare Facilities Accreditation Program
◇ DNV Healthcare Inc. accreditation
⇑ Center for Improvement in Healthcare Quality Accreditation
△ Commission on Accreditation of Rehabilitation Facilities (CARF) accreditation

FRIENDS HOSPITAL (394008), 4641 Roosevelt Boulevard, Zip 19124–2343; tel. 215/831–4600 **A**1 3 5 10 **F**30 68 87 98 99 101 102 103 130 132 **P**1 **S** Universal Health Services, Inc., King of Prussia, PA
Primary Contact: Michael S. McDonald Jr, Chief Executive Officer
COO: Diane Carugati, Chief Operating Officer
CFO: Michael Terwilliger, Chief Financial Officer
CMO: Marc Rothman M.D., Medical Director
CIO: John Healy, Manager Information Technology
CHR: Paul Cavanaugh, Director Human Resources
Web address: www.friendshospital.com
Control: Corporation, Investor–owned (for–profit) **Service:** Psychiatric

Staffed Beds: 192 Admissions: 4737 Census: 163 Births: 0

GOOD SHEPHERD PENN PARTNERS SPECIALTY HOSPITAL AT RITTENHOUSE (392050), 1800 Lombard Street, Zip 19146–1414; tel. 877/969–7342 **A**1 10 **F**1 3 28 29 30 34 35 44 50 57 58 60 64 68 75 77 84 85 86 87 90 91 93 94 95 96 100 130 131 132 148 **P**6
Primary Contact: Laura Porter, Executive Director
CFO: Ronald J. Petula, Vice President Finance
CMO: Michael Grippi M.D., Chief Medical Officer
CHR: Jana Romano, Manager Human Resources
CNO: Lawanda Goehring MSN, Chief Nursing Officer
Web address: www.phillyrehab.com
Control: Other not–for–profit (including NFP Corporation) **Service:** Acute long–term care hospital

Staffed Beds: 38 Admissions: 270 Census: 21 Outpatient Visits: 169472 Births: 0 Total Expense ($000): 43911 Payroll Expense ($000): 20179

HAHNEMANN UNIVERSITY HOSPITAL (390290), 230 North Broad Street, Zip 19102–1192; tel. 215/762–7000 **A**1 2 3 5 8 10 13 **F**3 12 13 14 15 17 18 20 22 24 26 28 29 31 34 35 44 45 46 48 49 50 51 58 59 60 61 65 68 70 72 74 75 76 78 79 80 81 82 85 92 94 95 96 97 98 100 101 102 103 105 107 108 109 110 111 112 113 114 115 116 117 118 119 120 121 123 124 126 130 132 135 136 137 138 139 147 148 149 **P**6 **S** TENET Healthcare Corporation, Dallas, TX
Primary Contact: Michael P. Halter, Chief Executive Officer
COO: Barbara Boston, Interim Chief Operating Officer
CFO: Richard Imbimbo, Chief Financial Officer
CMO: George Amrom M.D., Vice President Medical Affairs
CIO: Irv Fisher, Director, Information Services
CHR: Ayanna Weber Esq, Chief Human Resources Officer
CNO: Rosemary Dunn R.N., Chief Nursing Officer
Web address: www.hahnemannhospital.com
Control: Corporation, Investor–owned (for–profit) **Service:** General medical and surgical

Staffed Beds: 496 Admissions: 18355 Census: 268 Outpatient Visits: 118241 Births: 1908 Personnel: 2536

HAVEN BEHAVIORAL HOSPITAL OF PHILADELPHIA (394053), 3300 Henry Avenue, Zip 19129–1121, Mailing Address: 3301 Scotts Lane, Four Falls Building, 19129; tel. 215/791–6821 (Nonreporting) **S** Haven Behavioral Healthcare, Nashville, TN
Primary Contact: Lisa M. Olander, Chief Executive Officer
Web address: www.philadelphia.havenbehavioral.com
Control: Investor–owned (for–profit) **Service:** Psychiatric

Staffed Beds: 36

HOSPITAL OF THE UNIVERSITY OF PENNSYLVANIA (390111), 3400 Spruce Street, Zip 19104–4206; tel. 215/662–4000, (Includes SCHEIE EYE INSTITUTE OF THE HOSPITAL OF THE UNIVERSITY OF PENNSYLVANIA, 3400 Civic Center Blvd FL 3, West Pavilion, 3rd Floor, Philadelphia, Pennsylvania, 19104–5127, tel. 215/662–8100; Sheara Hollin, Chief Operating Officer) **A**1 2 5 7 8 10 **F**3 6 7 9 11 12 13 15 17 18 20 22 24 26 29 30 31 34 35 36 38 39 40 44 45 46 47 48 49 50 51 52 54 55 56 57 58 59 60 61 62 63 64 65 66 68 70 72 73 74 75 76 77 78 79 80 81 82 84 85 86 87 90 91 93 94 95 97 100 102 103 104 107 108 110 111 115 117 118 119 121 122 123 126 129 130 131 132 134 135 136 137 138 139 140 141 142 145 146 147 148 149 150 **P**6 **S** University of Pennsylvania Health System, Philadelphia, PA
Primary Contact: Regina Cunningham, Ph.D., R.N., Chief Executive Officer
COO: Carolyn Jackson, Chief Operating Officer
CFO: Joseph M Huber, Chief Financial Officer
CMO: Patrick J Brennan M.D., Senior Vice President and Chief Medical Officer
CIO: Michael Restuccia, Chief Information Officer
CHR: Denise J. Mariotti, Chief Human Resource Officer
Web address: www.pennmedicine.org
Control: Other not–for–profit (including NFP Corporation) **Service:** General medical and surgical

Staffed Beds: 788 Admissions: 34691 Census: 679 Outpatient Visits: 1690429 Births: 4078 Total Expense ($000): 2364364 Payroll Expense ($000): 939928 Personnel: 13326

JEANES HOSPITAL (390080), 7600 Central Avenue, Zip 19111–2499; tel. 215/728–2000 **A**1 3 5 10 **F**3 11 12 15 17 18 20 22 24 26 28 29 30 31 34 35 40 44 45 49 50 51 56 57 59 60 61 62 65 68 70 74 75 77 78 79 81 82 84 85 86 87 91 92 93 96 107 108 110 111 114 115 118 119 129 130 132 135 146 147 148 149 **S** Temple University Health System, Philadelphia, PA
Primary Contact: Marc P. Hurowitz, D.O., President and Chief Executive Officer
COO: Judith Lynn Bachman, Chief Operating Officer
CFO: Ray Lefton, Chief Financial Officer
CMO: Rebecca Armbruster M.D., Chief Medical Officer
CIO: Michael Sweeney, Chief Informatics Officer
CHR: Beverly Sherbondy, Assistant Vice President, Human Resources
CNO: Denise Anne Lavery Frasca MSN, R.N., Vice President Patient Care Services and Chief Nursing Officer
Web address: www.jeanes.com
Control: Other not–for–profit (including NFP Corporation) **Service:** General medical and surgical

Staffed Beds: 146 Admissions: 7314 Census: 85 Outpatient Visits: 132874 Births: 0 Total Expense ($000): 157731 Payroll Expense ($000): 60784 Personnel: 903

KENSINGTON HOSPITAL (390025), 136 West Diamond Street, Zip 19122–1721; tel. 215/426–8100, (Nonreporting) **A**1 10
Primary Contact: Eileen Hause, Chief Executive Officer
CFO: Kenneth Biddle, Controller
CMO: Luis F Vera M.D., Medical Director
CHR: Maria Dimichele, Administrative Assistant
CNO: Aleyamma John R.N., Director of Nursing
Control: State, Government, Nonfederal **Service:** General medical and surgical

Staffed Beds: 33

KINDRED HOSPITAL SOUTH PHILADELPHIA (392046), 1930 South Broad Street, Zip 19145–2328; tel. 267/570–5200, (Nonreporting) **A**1 10 **S** Kindred Healthcare, Louisville, KY
Primary Contact: Michele S. Basile, Chief Executive Officer
COO: Diane K. White MSN, R.N., Chief Clinical Officer
CFO: Kevin Varley, Chief Financial Officer
CMO: James Dovnarsky M.D., Director Pulmonary Medical
CHR: Amy Cain, District Director Human Resources
CNO: Diane K. White MSN, R.N., Chief Clinical Officer
Web address: www.khsouthphilly.com
Control: Corporation, Investor–owned (for–profit) **Service:** Acute long–term care hospital

Staffed Beds: 58

KINDRED HOSPITAL–PHILADELPHIA (392027), 6129 Palmetto Street, Zip 19111–5729; tel. 215/722–8555, (Includes KINDRED HOSPITAL PHILADELPHIA – HAVERTOWN, 2000 Old West Chester Pike, Havertown, Pennsylvania, Zip 19083–2712, tel. 610/536–2100; Margaret M Murphy, Chief Executive Officer) **A**1 10 **F**1 3 18 28 29 30 35 45 50 60 62 63 65 68 70 74 75 77 84 85 86 87 90 96 98 130 143 145 146 148 **S** Kindred Healthcare, Louisville, KY
Primary Contact: Michael Bass, Chief Executive Officer
COO: Sandra Collins, Chief Clinical Officer
CFO: Thomas A McMullen, Chief Financial Officer
Web address: www.kindredphila.com/
Control: Corporation, Investor–owned (for–profit) **Service:** Acute long–term care hospital

Staffed Beds: 52 Admissions: 336 Census: 26 Outpatient Visits: 0 Births: 0 Total Expense ($000): 18247 Payroll Expense ($000): 7755 Personnel: 117

KIRKBRIDE CENTER (394007), 111 North 49th Street, Zip 19139–2718; tel. 215/471–2600 (Nonreporting) **A**1 10
Primary Contact: Marlene Douglas–Walsh, Chief Executive Officer
Web address: www.kirkbridecenter.com
Control: Partnership, Investor–owned (for–profit) **Service:** Psychiatric

Staffed Beds: 205

MAGEE REHABILITATION HOSPITAL (393038), 1513 Race Street, Zip 19102–1177; tel. 215/587–3000 **A**1 3 5 7 10 **F**2 29 30 34 35 50 60 64 68 74 75 77 79 82 86 90 91 92 93 94 95 96 130 132 146 148 **P**6
Primary Contact: Jack A. Carroll, Ph.D., President and Chief Executive Officer
CFO: Stephen DeStefano, Chief Financial Officer
CMO: Guy Fried M.D., Chief Medical Officer
CIO: Shawna White, Chief Information Officer
CHR: Cindy Tobin–Payne, Director
Web address: www.mageerehab.org
Control: Other not–for–profit (including NFP Corporation) **Service:** Rehabilitation

Staffed Beds: 96 Admissions: 952 Census: 70 Births: 0

MERCY PHILADELPHIA HOSPITAL See Mercy Fitzgerald Hospital, Darby

METHODIST HOSPITAL See Thomas Jefferson University Hospitals

⊞ △ **NAZARETH HOSPITAL (390204)**, 2601 Holme Avenue, Zip 19152–2096; tel. 215/335–6000, (Total facility includes 28 beds in nursing home–type unit) **A**1 3 7 10 **F**3 12 15 18 20 22 29 30 31 34 35 37 39 40 45 46 49 50 53 56 57 58 59 64 65 70 74 75 77 78 79 80 81 82 84 85 86 87 90 93 97 100 107 108 110 111 114 115 117 118 119 120 121 128 130 131 132 135 146 147 148 149 **P**7 **S** Trinity Health, Livonia, MI
Primary Contact: Nancy Cherone, Executive Director and Administrator
CFO: David Wajda, Chief Financial Officer
CMO: Mathew Matthew M.D., Chief Medical Officer
CIO: Terry O'Neil, Chief Information Technology
CHR: Kathleen M Pries, Director Human Resources
CNO: Michael Beshel R.N., Vice President Patient Care and Chief Nursing Officer
Web address: www.nazarethhospital.org
Control: Other not–for–profit (including NFP Corporation) **Service**: General medical and surgical

Staffed Beds: 162 **Admissions**: 7434 **Census**: 107 **Outpatient Visits**: 127943 **Births**: 0 **Total Expense ($000)**: 140501 **Payroll Expense ($000)**: 56299 **Personnel**: 902

NORTH PHILADELPHIA HEALTH SYSTEM (390132), 801 West Girard Ave, Zip 19122–4212, Mailing Address: 801 West Girard Avenue, 19122–4212; tel. 215/787–9000, (Nonreporting) (Includes GIRARD MEDICAL CENTER, Girard Avenue at Eighth Street, Philadelphia, Pennsylvania, Zip 19122, tel. 215/787–2000; George J Walmsley III, CPA, President and Chief Executive Officer) **A**10
Primary Contact: George J. Walmsley III, CPA, President and Chief Executive Officer
CFO: Ronald Kaplan, Chief Financial Officer
CIO: Tony Iero, Director Management Information Systems
CHR: James Gloner, Senior Vice President
Web address: www.nphs.com
Control: Other not–for–profit (including NFP Corporation) **Service**: General medical and surgical

Staffed Beds: 315

PENN PRESBYTERIAN MEDICAL CENTER (390223), 51 North 39th Street, Zip 19104–2699; tel. 215/662–8000, (Total facility includes 25 beds in nursing home–type unit) **A**1 2 3 5 10 **F**3 4 5 7 8 9 11 12 15 17 18 20 21 22 24 26 29 30 31 32 34 35 36 37 38 39 40 43 44 45 46 49 50 51 52 54 56 57 58 59 60 61 62 63 64 65 66 68 70 74 75 77 78 79 81 82 84 85 86 87 92 94 96 97 98 100 101 104 105 107 108 110 111 114 115 118 119 126 128 130 131 132 134 135 141 142 146 147 148 149 150 **P**6 **S** University of Pennsylvania Health System, Philadelphia, PA
Primary Contact: Michele M. Volpe, Chief Executive Officer
COO: Robert J Russell, Associate Executive Director Operations
CFO: Anthony Zumpano, Chief Financial Officer
CMO: Kevin Fosnocht M.D., Chief Medical Officer and Associate Executive Director
CIO: Theresa Hiltunen, Entity Information Officer
CHR: Margorie Michele, Chief Human Resources Officer
CNO: James R Ballinghoff MSN, R.N., Chief Nursing Officer and Associate Executive Director
Web address: www.pennmedicine.org/pmc/
Control: Other not–for–profit (including NFP Corporation) **Service**: General medical and surgical

Staffed Beds: 365 **Admissions**: 17218 **Census**: 269 **Outpatient Visits**: 253744 **Births**: 0 **Total Expense ($000)**: 571925 **Payroll Expense ($000)**: 213359 **Personnel**: 2365

PENNSYLVANIA HOSPITAL (390226), 800 Spruce Street, Zip 19107–6192; tel. 215/829–3000 **A**1 2 3 5 10 13 **F**3 7 8 11 12 13 15 17 18 20 22 24 26 29 30 31 34 35 36 37 38 39 40 44 45 46 49 50 51 52 54 55 56 57 58 59 60 61 62 63 64 68 70 72 74 75 76 77 78 79 80 81 82 84 85 86 87 92 96 97 98 99 100 101 102 103 104 107 108 110 111 114 115 116 117 118 119 120 121 123 124 126 129 130 131 132 135 141 142 145 146 147 148 149 150 **P**6 **S** University of Pennsylvania Health System, Philadelphia, PA
Primary Contact: Theresa M. Larivee, Chief Executive Officer
CFO: Frank Anastasi, Chief Financial Officer
CMO: Daniel Feinberg M.D., Chief Medical Officer
CIO: Kwon Lee, Chief Information Officer
CNO: Mary Margaret Del Guidice R.N., Chief Nursing Officer
Web address: www.pahosp.com
Control: Other not–for–profit (including NFP Corporation) **Service**: General medical and surgical

Staffed Beds: 415 **Admissions**: 19705 **Census**: 275 **Outpatient Visits**: 317466 **Births**: 5197 **Total Expense ($000)**: 594172 **Payroll Expense ($000)**: 192103 **Personnel**: 2432

⊞ △ **PHILADELPHIA VETERANS AFFAIRS MEDICAL CENTER**, 3900 Woodland Avenue, Zip 19104–4594; tel. 215/823–5800, (Total facility includes 135 beds in nursing home–type unit) **A**1 2 5 7 8 **F**1 3 4 5 6 8 9 11 15 18 20 22 24 26 28 29 30 31 34 35 38 39 40 42 43 44 45 46 47 48 49 50 51 54 55 56 57 58 59 60 61 62 63 64 65 66 67 70 74 75 77 78 79 80 81 82 83 84 85 86 87 89 90 91 92 93 94 96 97 98 99 100 101 102 103 104 105 106 107 108 109 110 111 112 114 115 116 117 118 119 120 121 122 123 124 126 128 129 130 132 134 135 144 145 146 147 148 149 **S** Department of Veterans Affairs, Washington, DC
Primary Contact: Daniel Hendee, Director
COO: Jeffrey Beiler, Associate Director
CFO: Graciela McDaniel, Chief Financial Officer
CMO: Dave Oslin M.D., Chief of Staff
CIO: Adrienne Ficchi, Vice President Information Management
CHR: Gerald Morelli, Director Human Resources
Web address: www.philadelphia.va.gov/
Control: Veterans Affairs, Government, federal **Service**: General medical and surgical

Staffed Beds: 291 **Admissions**: 4627 **Census**: 125 **Outpatient Visits**: 410276 **Births**: 0 **Total Expense ($000)**: 574152 **Payroll Expense ($000)**: 198105 **Personnel**: 2513

⊞ **ROXBOROUGH MEMORIAL HOSPITAL (390304)**, 5800 Ridge Avenue, Zip 19128–1737; tel. 215/483–9900 **A**1 3 10 **F**3 15 18 24 29 31 34 40 44 49 50 56 57 59 65 68 70 74 77 78 79 81 82 84 85 90 93 96 98 103 104 107 108 110 111 116 119 129 130 143 146 148 **S** Prime Healthcare, Ontario, CA
Primary Contact: Peter J. Adamo, Chief Executive Officer
CFO: Thomas Reinboth, Chief Financial Officer
CHR: Michael Henrici, Associate Administrator
Web address: www.roxboroughmemorial.com
Control: Corporation, Investor–owned (for–profit) **Service**: General medical and surgical

Staffed Beds: 140 **Admissions**: 4604 **Census**: 58 **Births**: 0

⊞ **SHRINERS HOSPITALS FOR CHILDREN–PHILADELPHIA (393309)**, 3551 North Broad Street, Zip 19140–4160; tel. 215/430–4000 **A**1 3 5 10 **F**29 35 57 58 64 65 68 74 75 77 79 81 82 85 88 89 91 92 93 94 95 96 119 130 131 132 143 146 149 **S** Shriners Hospitals for Children, Tampa, FL
Primary Contact: Ed Myers, Administrator
CFO: Mario Salvati, Director Fiscal Services
CMO: Scott Kozin M.D., Chief of Staff
CHR: Megan Hauser, Director Human Resources
CNO: Cindy Max, Chief Nursing Officer
Web address: www.shrinershospitalsforchildren.org/Hospitals/Locations/Philadelphia.aspx
Control: Other not–for–profit (including NFP Corporation) **Service**: Children's orthopedic

Staffed Beds: 39 **Admissions**: 530 **Census**: 11 **Outpatient Visits**: 10969 **Births**: 0 **Total Expense ($000)**: 50014 **Payroll Expense ($000)**: 23217 **Personnel**: 287

⊞ **ST. CHRISTOPHER'S HOSPITAL FOR CHILDREN (393307)**, 3601 A Street, Zip 19134–1043; tel. 215/427–5000 **A**1 3 5 8 10 **F**3 7 16 17 19 21 23 25 27 29 30 31 32 34 35 39 40 41 43 44 48 49 50 54 55 58 59 60 61 64 68 70 71 72 73 74 75 77 78 79 80 81 82 83 84 87 88 89 93 97 99 100 101 102 107 111 119 129 130 131 132 134 136 138 143 144 146 **P**6 **S** TENET Healthcare Corporation, Dallas, TX
Primary Contact: James B. Burke, FACHE, Interim Chief Executive Officer
COO: Maria Scenna, Chief Operating Officer
CFO: George Rizzuto CPA, Chief Financial Officer
CMO: Barbara Hoffman M.D., Chief Medical Officer
CIO: Robert Taylor, Director Information Services
CHR: Stephen W Krouse, Chief Human Resource Officer
CNO: Heidi Baur R.N., MS, Chief Nursing Officer
Web address: www.stchristophershospital.com
Control: Corporation, Investor–owned (for–profit) **Service**: Children's general medical and surgical

Staffed Beds: 189 **Admissions**: 8953 **Census**: 101 **Births**: 0

PA

⊞ TEMPLE UNIVERSITY HOSPITAL (390027), 3401 North Broad Street, Zip 19140–5103; tel. 215/707–2000, (Includes TEMPLE UNIVERSITY HOSPITAL – EPISCOPAL DIVISION, 100 East Lehigh Avenue, Philadelphia, Pennsylvania, Zip 19125–1098, tel. 215/427–7000; Kathleen Barron, Executive Director) **A**1 2 3 5 8 10 **F**3 8 11 12 13 14 15 16 17 18 20 22 24 26 28 29 30 31 34 35 37 38 40 41 43 44 45 46 47 48 49 50 53 54 55 56 57 58 59 60 61 64 68 70 72 73 74 75 76 77 78 79 80 81 82 83 84 85 86 87 90 92 93 94 96 97 98 100 101 102 104 107 108 109 110 111 112 114 115 118 119 120 121 123 124 126 129 130 131 132 135 136 137 138 139 140 141 142 146 147 148 **S** Temple University Health System, Philadelphia, PA
Primary Contact: Verdi Disesa, M.D., President and Chief Executive Officer
COO: Rosemary Nolan R.N., MSN, JD, Chief Operating Officer
CFO: Gerald P Oetzel, Chief Financial Officer
CMO: Herbert Cushing M.D., Chief Medical Officer
CIO: David Kamowski, Vice President and Chief Information Officer
CHR: John Lasky Jr, Vice President, Chief Human Resources Officer
CNO: Elizabeth J Craig MSN, Chief Nursing Officer and Vice President Patient Services
Web address: www.tuh.templehealth.org/content/default.htm
Control: Other not–for–profit (including NFP Corporation) **Service**: General medical and surgical

> **Staffed Beds:** 722 **Admissions:** 35872 **Census:** 559 **Outpatient Visits:** 348096 **Births:** 2849 **Total Expense ($000):** 1016154 **Payroll Expense ($000):** 347249 **Personnel:** 4511

⊞ △ THOMAS JEFFERSON UNIVERSITY HOSPITALS (390174), 111 South 11th Street, Zip 19107–5084; tel. 215/955–6000, (Includes METHODIST HOSPITAL, 2301 South Broad Street, Philadelphia, Pennsylvania, Zip 19148, tel. 215/952–9000; Stephen K Klasko, M.D., President and Chief Executive Officer) **A**1 2 3 5 7 8 10 **F**3 5 6 7 8 9 11 12 13 14 15 17 18 20 22 24 26 28 29 30 31 34 35 36 37 38 39 40 43 44 45 46 47 48 49 50 52 53 54 55 56 57 58 59 61 64 65 66 68 70 72 74 75 76 77 78 79 80 81 82 84 85 86 87 89 90 92 93 94 96 97 98 100 101 102 103 104 107 108 110 111 114 115 116 118 119 120 121 123 124 126 129 130 131 132 134 135 136 137 138 139 141 142 144 145 146 147 148 149 150 **P**2 6 8 **S** Jefferson Health, Philadelphia, PA
Primary Contact: Richard Webster, R.N., President
CFO: Neil Lubarsky, Senior Vice President, Finance and Chief Financial Officer
CMO: Anne Docimo M.D., Executive Vice President and Chief Medical Officer, Jefferson Health
CIO: Praveen Chopra, Executive Vice President and Chief Information and Transformative Innovative Environment Officer
CHR: Jeffrey Stevens, Senior Vice President and Chief Human Resource Officer
CNO: Mary Ann McGinley Ph.D., Senior Vice President, Patient Services and Chief Nursing Officer
Web address: www.jefferson.edu
Control: Other not–for–profit (including NFP Corporation) **Service**: General medical and surgical

> **Staffed Beds:** 886 **Admissions:** 42928 **Census:** 640 **Outpatient Visits:** 494722 **Births:** 1918 **Total Expense ($000):** 1522052 **Payroll Expense ($000):** 477932 **Personnel:** 7452

TRIUMPH HOSPITAL PHILADELPHIA See Kindred Hospital South Philadelphia

VETERANS AFFAIRS MEDICAL CENTER See Philadelphia Veterans Affairs Medical Center

PHOENIXVILLE—Chester County

⊞ △ PHOENIXVILLE HOSPITAL (390127), 140 Nutt Road, Zip 19460–3900, Mailing Address: P.O.Box 3001, 19460–0916; tel. 610/983–1000 **A**1 2 7 10 **F**3 8 13 15 18 20 22 24 26 28 29 31 32 34 35 36 38 39 40 45 49 50 51 55 56 57 59 61 64 68 69 70 72 74 75 76 77 78 79 81 82 85 86 87 93 102 107 108 111 114 115 117 118 119 126 130 132 134 135 146 147 **S** Community Health Systems, Inc., Franklin, TN
Primary Contact: Stephen M. Tullman, Chief Executive Officer
CFO: David Paulosky, Chief Financial Officer
CMO: David Stepansky M.D., Chief Medical Officer
CIO: Terry Murphy, Director Information Services
CHR: Denise Chiolo, Chief Human Resources Officer
CNO: Sarah Strzelecki Ed.D., R.N., Chief Nursing Officer
Web address: www.phoenixvillehospital.com
Control: Corporation, Investor–owned (for–profit) **Service**: General medical and surgical

> **Staffed Beds:** 139 **Admissions:** 6773 **Census:** 84 **Outpatient Visits:** 96739 **Births:** 859 **Total Expense ($000):** 155620 **Payroll Expense ($000):** 47575 **Personnel:** 784

PITTSBURGH—Allegheny County

⊞ ALLEGHENY GENERAL HOSPITAL (390050), 320 East North Avenue, Zip 15212–4756; tel. 412/359–3131 **A**1 2 3 5 8 10 12 13 **F**3 8 11 12 15 17 18 20 21 24 26 28 29 30 31 34 35 36 37 38 39 40 43 44 45 46 47 48 49 50 53 54 57 58 59 61 64 65 70 74 75 77 78 79 80 81 82 84 85 86 87 89 92 93 96 100 102 104 105 107 108 110 111 115 117 118 119 121 123 124 126 130 131 132 135 137 138 139 146 147 148 149 **P**6 **S** Allegheny Health Network, Pittsburgh, PA
Primary Contact: Jeffrey Cohen, M.D., President
COO: Duke Rupert, Chief Operating Officer
CFO: Richard W Fries, Vice President Finance
CMO: Tony Farah M.D., President Medical Staff
CIO: John Foley, Chief Information Officer
Web address: www.wpahs.org/locations/allegheny–general–hospital
Control: Other not–for–profit (including NFP Corporation) **Service**: General medical and surgical

> **Staffed Beds:** 524 **Admissions:** 23856 **Census:** 347 **Outpatient Visits:** 348725 **Births:** 0 **Total Expense ($000):** 718597 **Payroll Expense ($000):** 195181 **Personnel:** 3649

□ CHILDREN'S HOSPITAL OF PITTSBURGH OF UPMC (393302), One Children's Hospital Drive, Zip 15224–1334; tel. 412/692–5325 **A**1 3 5 10 **F**3 8 12 17 19 21 22 23 24 25 27 28 29 30 31 32 34 35 36 38 39 40 41 43 45 46 48 49 50 53 54 55 57 58 59 60 61 64 65 66 68 71 72 74 75 77 78 79 81 82 84 86 87 88 89 90 91 92 93 97 100 107 108 109 111 114 115 116 117 118 119 120 121 123 124 126 127 129 130 131 132 134 135 136 137 138 139 140 141 142 143 144 146 150 **S** UPMC, Pittsburgh, PA
Primary Contact: Christopher A. Gessner, President
CFO: Nicholas J. Barcellona, Chief Financial Officer
CMO: Brian Martin, Vice President Medical Affairs
CIO: Srinivasan Suresh M.D., Chief Medical Information Officer
CHR: Rhonda Larimore, Vice President, Human Resources
CNO: Diane Hupp R.N., Vice President Support Services and Patient Care Services
Web address: www.chp.edu
Control: Other not–for–profit (including NFP Corporation) **Service**: Children's general medical and surgical

> **Staffed Beds:** 305 **Admissions:** 12549 **Census:** 220 **Outpatient Visits:** 324125 **Births:** 0 **Total Expense ($000):** 606523 **Payroll Expense ($000):** 150635 **Personnel:** 2665

EYE AND EAR HOSPITAL OF PITTSBURGH See UPMC Presbyterian Shadyside

⊞ HEALTHSOUTH HARMARVILLE REHABILITATION HOSPITAL (393027), 320 Guys Run Road, Zip 15238–0460, Mailing Address: P.O.Box 11460, 15238–0460; tel. 412/828–1300 **A**1 3 10 **F**29 62 75 77 79 86 90 93 95 96 132 148 149 **S** HEALTHSOUTH Corporation, Birmingham, AL
Primary Contact: Mark Van Volkenburg, Chief Executive Officer
CFO: Daniel A Vrana, Controller
CMO: Thomas Franz M.D., Medical Director
CHR: Eric Larson, Director Human Resources
Web address: www.healthsouthharmarville.com
Control: Corporation, Investor–owned (for–profit) **Service**: Rehabilitation

> **Staffed Beds:** 162 **Admissions:** 1557 **Census:** 68 **Outpatient Visits:** 7344 **Births:** 0 **Total Expense ($000):** 25390 **Payroll Expense ($000):** 12984 **Personnel:** 244

⊞ LIFECARE HOSPITALS OF PITTSBURGH (392024), 225 Penn Avenue, Zip 15221–2148; tel. 412/247–2424, (Nonreporting) (Includes LIFECARE HOSPITALS OF PITTSBURGH – SUBURBAN CAMPUS, 100 South Jackson Avenue, 4th Floor, Pittsburgh, Pennsylvania, Zip 15202–3428, tel. 215/952–9000) **A**1 10 **S** LifeCare Management Services, Plano, TX
Primary Contact: Trisha Niemuth, Market Chief Executive Officer
CFO: Nikki Aykul, Manager Business Office
CMO: Steven Sotos M.D., President Medical Staff
CIO: George Fitzgerald, Regional Director Information Systems
CHR: Robin F Arslanpay, Director Human Resources
Web address: www.lifecare–hospitals.com
Control: Corporation, Investor–owned (for–profit) **Service**: Acute long–term care hospital

> **Staffed Beds:** 236

Many Facility Codes have changed. Please refer to the AHA Guide Code Chart.

© 2017 AHA Guide

⊞ **MAGEE–WOMENS HOSPITAL OF UPMC (390114)**, 300 Halket Street, Zip 15213–3108; tel. 412/641–1000, (Total facility includes 20 beds in nursing home–type unit) **A**1 2 3 5 10 **F**3 11 12 13 15 29 30 31 34 35 40 43 44 45 46 49 52 54 55 56 57 59 64 65 66 68 70 72 74 75 76 77 78 79 80 81 82 84 85 86 87 91 97 107 108 110 111 115 117 119 120 121 123 126 128 130 131 132 134 135 146 147 148 149 150 **S** UPMC, Pittsburgh, PA
Primary Contact: Leslie C. Davis, President
COO: Lou Baverso, Vice President Operations
CFO: Eileen Simmons, Chief Financial Officer
CMO: Dennis English M.D., Vice President Medical Affairs
CHR: Rhonda Larimore, Vice President Human Resources
CNO: Maribeth McLaughlin R.N., Vice President Patient Care Services
Web address: www.magee.edu
Control: Other not–for–profit (including NFP Corporation) **Service**: Obstetrics and gynecology

Staffed Beds: 321 **Admissions**: 19069 **Census**: 234 **Outpatient Visits**: 592966 **Births**: 9453 **Total Expense ($000)**: 800470 **Payroll Expense ($000)**: 134802 **Personnel**: 2352

⊞ **SELECT SPECIALTY HOSPITAL–PITTSBURGH/UPMC (392044)**, 200 Lothrop Street, E824, Zip 15213–2536; tel. 412/586–9800 **A**1 10 **F**1 3 29 36 65 85 86 87 91 148 **S** Select Medical Corporation, Mechanicsburg, PA
Primary Contact: Yvonne Kughn, Chief Executive Officer
CMO: Michael Donahue M.D., Medical Director
CHR: Prudence Sloan, Coordinator Human Resources
CNO: Eli Babich, Chief Nursing Officer
Web address: www.pittsburghupmc.selectspecialtyhospitals.com/
Control: Corporation, Investor–owned (for–profit) **Service**: Acute long–term care hospital

Staffed Beds: 32 **Admissions**: 312 **Census**: 25 **Outpatient Visits**: 0 **Births**: 0

☐ **SOUTHWOOD PSYCHIATRIC HOSPITAL**, 2575 Boyce Plaza Road, Zip 15241–3925; tel. 412/257–2290, (Nonreporting) **A**1 **S** Acadia Healthcare Company, Inc., Franklin, TN
Primary Contact: Stephen J. Quigley, Chief Executive Officer
CFO: Frank Urban, Chief Financial Officer
CMO: Allan W Clark M.D., Medical Director
CHR: Erin J Frohnhofer, Director Human Resources
Web address: www.southwoodhospital.com
Control: Corporation, Investor–owned (for–profit) **Service**: Children's hospital psychiatric

Staffed Beds: 156

⊞ **ST. CLAIR HOSPITAL (390228)**, 1000 Bower Hill Road, Zip 15243–1873; tel. 412/942–4000 **A**1 2 3 10 **F**3 8 11 12 14 15 17 18 20 24 26 28 29 30 31 34 35 37 40 42 45 46 49 51 53 54 57 59 60 63 64 67 68 70 73 74 75 76 77 78 79 81 82 84 85 86 87 89 91 92 93 96 98 100 102 104 105 107 108 110 111 114 115 119 126 129 130 131 132 135 143 144 146 147 148 149
Primary Contact: James M. Collins, President and Chief Executive Officer
COO: Michael J Flanagan, Senior Vice President and Chief Operating Officer
CFO: Richard C Chesnos, Senior Vice President Finance and Chief Financial Officer
CMO: G Alan Yeasted M.D., Senior Vice President and Chief Medical Officer
CIO: Richard Schaeffer, Vice President Information Systems and Chief Information Officer
CHR: Andrea Kalina, Vice President External Affairs and Chief Human Resources Officer
CNO: Joan Massella, Administrative Vice President and Chief Nursing Officer
Web address: www.stclair.org
Control: Other not–for–profit (including NFP Corporation) **Service**: General medical and surgical

Staffed Beds: 301 **Admissions**: 16344 **Census**: 189 **Outpatient Visits**: 315522 **Births**: 1495 **Total Expense ($000)**: 261398 **Payroll Expense ($000)**: 98635 **Personnel**: 1752

★ **THE CHILDREN'S HOME OF PITTSBURGH (393304)**, 5324 Penn Avenue, Zip 15224–1733; tel. 412/441–4884 **A**10 **F**19 63 77 83 86 89 132 146
Primary Contact: Pamela R. Schanwald, Chief Executive Officer
COO: Kimberly Reblock M.D., Chief Operating Officer
CFO: Kimberly A Phillips, Chief Financial Officer
CMO: Frederick C Sherman M.D., Chief Medical Officer
Web address: www.childrenshomepgh.org
Control: Other not–for–profit (including NFP Corporation) **Service**: Children's general medical and surgical

Staffed Beds: 30 **Admissions**: 411 **Census**: 22 **Outpatient Visits**: 0 **Births**: 0

★ **THE CHILDREN'S INSTITUTE OF PITTSBURGH (393308)**, 1405 Shady Avenue, Zip 15217–1350; tel. 412/420–2400 **A**3 10 **F**3 29 30 34 54 57 58 59 64 74 75 79 82 85 86 87 90 91 93 96 97 98 99 100 101 104 107 130 131 132 146 148 149 **P**6
Primary Contact: David K. Miles, President and Chief Executive Officer
COO: Stacey Vaccaro, Chief Operating Officer
CFO: John Jubas, Vice President Finance
CMO: Matthew Masiello M.D., Chief Medical Officer
CIO: Sharon Dorogy, Chief Information Officer
CHR: Linda M Allen, Vice President Human Resources
Web address: www.amazingkids.org
Control: Other not–for–profit (including NFP Corporation) **Service**: Children's rehabilitation

Staffed Beds: 62 **Admissions**: 274 **Census**: 19 **Outpatient Visits**: 59629 **Births**: 0 **Total Expense ($000)**: 29836 **Payroll Expense ($000)**: 16396 **Personnel**: 305

☐ **UPMC MERCY (390028)**, 1400 Locust Street, Zip 15219–5166; tel. 412/232–8111 **A**1 3 5 10 12 13 **F**3 4 8 13 16 17 18 20 22 24 26 28 29 30 31 32 34 35 36 39 40 43 44 45 49 50 51 54 56 57 58 59 60 61 64 65 66 68 70 72 74 75 76 77 78 79 81 82 84 85 86 87 90 91 92 93 94 95 96 97 98 100 101 102 107 108 111 114 115 116 118 119 126 129 130 132 135 141 142 146 147 148 **P**6 **S** UPMC, Pittsburgh, PA
Primary Contact: Michael A. Grace, President
COO: Julie Hecker, Vice President, Operations
CFO: Eileen Simmons, Chief Financial Officer, UPMC Hospital Network
CIO: Kevin Conway, Chief Information Officer
CHR: Tracey Stange Kolo, Vice President, Human Resources
CNO: Leeanna McKibben R.N., MSN, Vice President Patient Services and Chief Nursing Officer
Web address: www.upmc.com/HospitalsFacilities/HFHome/Hospitals/Mercy/
Control: Other not–for–profit (including NFP Corporation) **Service**: General medical and surgical

Staffed Beds: 482 **Admissions**: 19027 **Census**: 330 **Outpatient Visits**: 189296 **Births**: 1069 **Total Expense ($000)**: 393406 **Payroll Expense ($000)**: 122575 **Personnel**: 2266

UPMC MONTEFIORE See UPMC Presbyterian Shadyside

☐ **UPMC PASSAVANT (390107)**, 9100 Babcock Boulevard, Zip 15237–5815; tel. 412/748–6700, (Includes UPMC PASSAVANT CRANBERRY, One St Francis Way, Cranberry, Pennsylvania, Zip 16066, tel. 724/772–5300; Teresa G Petrick, President) **A**1 2 3 5 10 **F**3 8 11 15 17 18 20 22 24 26 28 29 30 31 34 35 40 45 46 47 48 49 51 54 56 57 58 59 64 68 70 74 75 77 78 79 81 82 84 85 86 87 90 92 96 100 107 108 109 110 111 114 115 117 118 119 120 121 123 126 129 130 132 135 143 146 147 148 **S** UPMC, Pittsburgh, PA
Primary Contact: David T. Martin, President
CFO: Thomas M Newman, Chief Financial Officer
CMO: James W Boyle M.D., Chief Medical Officer
CNO: Susan E Hoolahan R.N., MSN, Vice President Patient Care Services and Chief Nursing Officer
Web address: www.upmc.edu/passavant
Control: Other not–for–profit (including NFP Corporation) **Service**: General medical and surgical

Staffed Beds: 286 **Admissions**: 15371 **Census**: 215 **Outpatient Visits**: 283347 **Births**: 0 **Total Expense ($000)**: 344258 **Payroll Expense ($000)**: 89640 **Personnel**: 1559

☐ **UPMC PRESBYTERIAN SHADYSIDE (390164)**, 200 Lothrop Street, Zip 15213–2536; tel. 412/647–2345, (Includes EYE AND EAR HOSPITAL OF PITTSBURGH, 200 Lothrop Street, Pittsburgh, Pennsylvania, Zip 15213–2592, tel. 412/647–2345; UPMC MONTEFIORE, 3459 Fifth Avenue, Pittsburgh, Pennsylvania, Zip 15213, tel. 412/647–2345; John Innocenti Sr, President and Chief Executive Officer; UPMC PRESBYTERIAN HOSPITAL, 200 Lothrop Street, Pittsburgh, Pennsylvania, Zip 15213, tel. 412/647–2345; UPMC SHADYSIDE, 5230 Centre Avenue, Pittsburgh, Pennsylvania, Zip 15232–1381, tel. 412/623–2121; WESTERN PSYCHIATRIC INSTITUTE AND CLINIC, 3811 O'Hara Street, Pittsburgh, Pennsylvania, Zip 15213–2593, tel. 412/624–2100) (Total facility includes 30 beds in nursing home–type unit) **A**1 2 5 8 10 12 13 **F**2 3 5 6 7 8 9 10 11 12 14 15 17 18 19 20 22 24 25 26 29 30 31 32 33 34 35 36 37 38 39 40 43 44 45 46 47 48 49 50 51 52 53 54 55 56 57 58 59 60 61 62 63 64 65 66 68 69 70 71 74 75 77 78 79 81 82 83 84 85 86 87 90 91 92 93 94 97 98 99 100 101 102 103 104 105 106 107 108 109 110 111 112 113 114 115 116 117 118 119 120 121 123 124 126 128 129 130 131 132 134 135 136 137 138 139 140 141 142 143 144 145 146 147 148 149 150 **P**6 **S** UPMC, Pittsburgh, PA
Primary Contact: John Innocenti Sr, President and Chief Executive Officer
CFO: Eileen Simmons, Chief Financial Officer
CMO: Margaret Reidy M.D., Vice President Medical Affairs
CHR: Kathryn Devine, Vice President Human Resources
Web address: www.upmc.edu
Control: Other not–for–profit (including NFP Corporation) **Service**: General medical and surgical

Staffed Beds: 1452 **Admissions**: 59284 **Census**: 1177 **Outpatient Visits**: 1012672 **Births**: 0 **Total Expense ($000)**: 1957528 **Payroll Expense ($000)**: 486349 **Personnel**: 9479

☐ **UPMC ST. MARGARET (390102)**, 815 Freeport Road, Zip 15215–3301; tel. 412/784–4000 **A**1 2 3 5 10 13 **F**3 6 7 8 9 11 15 18 20 29 30 31 34 35 40 44 45 49 50 51 54 56 57 58 59 60 61 63 64 65 68 70 74 75 77 78 79 81 82 84 85 86 87 90 96 97 102 103 104 107 108 111 114 115 119 120 121 123 129 130 131 132 134 135 144 146 **S** UPMC, Pittsburgh, PA
Primary Contact: David J. Patton, President
COO: Merle Taylor, Vice President Operations
CFO: Thomas M Newman, Vice President Finance
CMO: John Lagnese M.D., Vice President Medical Affairs
CIO: Charles M Rudek, Chief Information Officer
CHR: Tracey Stange Kolo, Vice President Human Resources
CNO: Mary C Barkhymer R.N., MSN, Vice President Patient Care Services and Chief Nursing Officer
Web address: www.upmc.com/locations/hospitals/st-margaret/Pages/default.aspx
Control: Other not–for–profit (including NFP Corporation) **Service:** General medical and surgical

Staffed Beds: 206 Admissions: 11336 **Census:** 160 **Outpatient Visits:** 161662 **Births:** 0 **Total Expense ($000):** 225992 **Payroll Expense ($000):** 61604 **Personnel:** 1137

☒ △ **VETERANS AFFAIRS PITTSBURGH HEALTHCARE SYSTEM,** University Drive, Zip 15240–1001; tel. 866/482–7488, (Includes VETERANS AFFAIRS MEDICAL CENTER, 7180 Highland Drive, Pittsburgh, Pennsylvania, Zip 15206–1297, tel. 412/365–4900; VETERANS AFFAIRS MEDICAL CENTER, University Drive 'C', Pittsburgh, Pennsylvania, Zip 15240–1001, tel. 412/688–6000) (Total facility includes 225 beds in nursing home–type unit) **A**1 3 5 7 8 **F**2 3 4 5 6 7 8 9 10 11 12 15 18 20 22 24 26 29 30 31 33 34 35 36 37 38 39 40 42 43 44 45 46 47 48 49 50 52 53 54 56 57 58 59 60 61 62 63 64 65 67 68 70 71 74 75 77 78 79 80 81 82 83 84 85 86 87 90 91 92 93 94 96 97 98 100 101 102 103 104 105 106 107 108 111 114 115 116 117 118 119 126 127 128 129 130 132 133 135 136 138 139 141 142 143 144 146 147 148 149 150 **P**6 **S** Department of Veterans Affairs, Washington, DC
Primary Contact: Karin L. McGraw, MSN, FACHE, Director
CMO: Ali Sonel M.D., Chief of Staff
CIO: John Kovac, Facility Chief Information Officer
CHR: Amber Mesoras, Chief Human Resources Officer
CNO: Ira Richmond, Associate Director Patient Care Services
Web address: www.pittsburgh.va.gov/
Control: Veterans Affairs, Government, federal **Service:** General medical and surgical

Staffed Beds: 549 Admissions: 10096 **Census:** 414 **Births:** 0

☒ **WEST PENN HOSPITAL (390090)**, 4800 Friendship Avenue, Zip 15224–1722; tel. 412/578–5000 **A**1 2 3 5 8 10 **F**3 8 11 12 13 15 16 17 18 20 22 24 26 29 30 31 34 35 37 38 39 40 44 45 46 47 48 49 50 51 54 57 58 59 64 65 66 70 72 74 75 76 77 78 79 80 81 82 84 85 86 87 89 90 97 100 102 107 108 110 111 115 118 119 120 121 123 124 126 129 130 132 135 136 141 142 145 146 147 148 149 **P**6 **S** Allegheny Health Network, Pittsburgh, PA
Primary Contact: Ronald J. Andro, President and Chief Executive Officer
CFO: James A Kanuch, Vice President Finance
CMO: I William Goldfarb, Chief Medical Officer
CIO: Jacqueline Dailey, Chief Information Officer
CHR: Sally Carozza, Director Human Resources
CNO: Paula A Lacher MSN, R.N., Chief Nursing Officer
Web address: www.wpahs.org
Control: Other not–for–profit (including NFP Corporation) **Service:** General medical and surgical

Staffed Beds: 317 Admissions: 12239 **Census:** 168 **Outpatient Visits:** 107957 **Births:** 4047 **Total Expense ($000):** 363352 **Payroll Expense ($000):** 88015 **Personnel:** 1559

WESTERN PSYCHIATRIC INSTITUTE AND CLINIC See UPMC Presbyterian Shadyside

PLEASANT GAP—Centre County

☒ **HEALTHSOUTH NITTANY VALLEY REHABILITATION HOSPITAL (393039)**, 550 West College Avenue, Zip 16823–7401; tel. 814/359–3421 **A**1 10 **F**29 34 44 59 60 64 90 93 148 **S** HEALTHSOUTH Corporation, Birmingham, AL
Primary Contact: Susan Hartman, Chief Executive Officer
CFO: Alan M Phillips, Controller
CMO: Richard Allatt M.D., Medical Director
CHR: Michelle Katz, Director Human Resources
CNO: Penny Frownfelter, Chief Nursing Officer
Web address: www.nittanyvalleyrehab.com
Control: Corporation, Investor–owned (for–profit) **Service:** Rehabilitation

Staffed Beds: 73 Admissions: 1358 **Census:** 45 **Births:** 0

POTTSTOWN—Montgomery County

☒ **POTTSTOWN MEMORIAL MEDICAL CENTER (390123)**, 1600 East High Street, Zip 19464–5093; tel. 610/327–7000 **A**1 2 10 **F**3 7 12 13 15 18 20 29 30 31 34 35 38 40 44 45 48 49 50 51 54 57 59 64 68 70 74 75 76 77 78 79 80 81 82 85 87 89 92 93 97 98 100 103 107 108 110 111 114 117 118 119 120 121 123 131 132 135 146 147 148 **P**6 **S** Community Health Systems, Inc., Franklin, TN
Primary Contact: Richard Newell, Chief Executive Officer
CFO: Debbie Konarski, Interim Chief Financial Officer
CMO: Richard F Saylor M.D., Chief Medical Officer
CIO: Ron Peterson, Chief Information Officer
CHR: Ruta Ore, Director Human Resources
Web address: www.pottstownmemorial.com
Control: Corporation, Investor–owned (for–profit) **Service:** General medical and surgical

Staffed Beds: 232 Admissions: 8286 **Census:** 103 **Outpatient Visits:** 100239 **Births:** 438 **Total Expense ($000):** 144202 **Payroll Expense ($000):** 52608 **Personnel:** 829

POTTSVILLE—Schuylkill County

☒ △ **LEHIGH VALLEY HOSPITAL – SCHUYLKILL EAST NORWEGIAN STREET (390031)**, 700 East Norwegian Street, Zip 17901–2710; tel. 570/621–4000 **A**1 7 10 **F**3 5 11 15 18 29 30 31 34 40 45 49 56 57 59 64 70 74 75 77 78 79 81 85 86 90 93 98 100 103 107 108 109 110 115 117 118 119 130 132 135 146 147 148 149 **P**6 **S** Lehigh Valley Health Network, Allentown, PA
Primary Contact: William Reppy, President
CFO: Diane Boris, Vice President and Chief Financial Officer
CIO: Tina Zanis, Director Information Technology
CHR: Martin Treasure, Director Human Resources
CNO: Darnell F Furer MS, R.N., Vice President of Patient Care Services
Web address: www.schuylkillhealth.com
Control: Other not–for–profit (including NFP Corporation) **Service:** General medical and surgical

Staffed Beds: 109 Admissions: 3804 **Census:** 59 **Outpatient Visits:** 94509 **Births:** 0 **Total Expense ($000):** 55033 **Payroll Expense ($000):** 24597 **Personnel:** 492

☒ **LEHIGH VALLEY HOSPITAL – SCHUYLKILL SOUTH JACKSON STREET (390030)**, 420 South Jackson Street, Zip 17901–3625; tel. 570/621–5000 **A**1 10 19 **F**3 11 13 15 18 19 28 29 30 31 32 34 35 38 40 45 49 51 56 57 59 62 64 70 74 75 76 77 78 79 81 82 85 86 89 92 93 96 98 99 100 101 102 107 108 110 111 115 118 119 124 126 129 130 132 146 147 149 **P**6 **S** Lehigh Valley Health Network, Allentown, PA
Primary Contact: William Reppy, President
CFO: Diane Boris, Chief Financial Officer
CIO: Tina Zanis, Director Information Systems
CHR: Martin Treasure, Director Human Resources
CNO: Darnell F Furer MS, R.N., Vice President Patient Care Services and Chief Nursing Officer
Web address: www.schuylkillhealth.com
Control: Other not–for–profit (including NFP Corporation) **Service:** General medical and surgical

Staffed Beds: 179 Admissions: 4556 **Census:** 66 **Outpatient Visits:** 105057 **Births:** 728 **Total Expense ($000):** 78529 **Payroll Expense ($000):** 34619 **Personnel:** 653

PUNXSUTAWNEY—Jefferson County

PUNXSUTAWNEY AREA HOSPITAL (390199), 81 Hillcrest Drive, Zip 15767–2616; tel. 814/938–1800 **A**10 20 **F**3 13 15 26 29 30 34 35 40 44 45 46 48 50 51 57 59 62 64 70 74 75 76 77 78 79 81 85 86 87 92 93 96 100 104 107 108 110 111 115 118 119 127 130 132 133 146 147 148 149 **P**6
Primary Contact: Daniel D. Blough Jr, Chief Executive Officer
CFO: Jack Sisk, Chief Financial Officer
CMO: Dajani Zuhd M.D., President Medical Staff
CIO: Chuck States, Director Information Systems
CHR: Barbara Kostok, Manager Human Resources
CNO: Paula Spack R.N., MSN, Vice President Nursing
Web address: www.pah.org
Control: Other not–for–profit (including NFP Corporation) **Service:** General medical and surgical

Staffed Beds: 49 Admissions: 1347 **Census:** 18 **Outpatient Visits:** 73029 **Births:** 125 **Total Expense ($000):** 34446 **Payroll Expense ($000):** 16829 **Personnel:** 341

Many Facility Codes have changed. Please refer to the AHA Guide Code Chart.   © 2017 AHA Guide

PA

QUAKERTOWN—Bucks County

☐ **ST. LUKE'S HOSPITAL – QUAKERTOWN CAMPUS (390035)**, 1021 Park Avenue, Zip 18951–1573; tel. 215/538–4500 **A**1 2 3 10 **F**3 15 18 28 29 30 31 34 35 38 40 42 43 44 45 49 50 51 54 56 57 59 63 64 65 68 70 71 74 75 77 78 79 81 82 85 86 87 92 93 98 100 102 103 107 108 109 110 111 115 118 119 129 130 131 132 135 144 146 148 149 **S** St. Luke's University Health Network, Bethlehem, PA
Primary Contact: Edward Nawrocki, President
CFO: Theresa Corrado, Director Finance
CMO: Thomas Filipowicz M.D., Medical Director
CIO: Chad Brisendine, Chief Information Officer
CHR: Shelley Maley, Director Human Resources
Web address: www.slhhn.org
Control: Other not–for–profit (including NFP Corporation) **Service:** General medical and surgical

Staffed Beds: 57 **Admissions:** 2806 **Census:** 36 **Outpatient Visits:** 82251 **Births:** 0 **Total Expense ($000):** 61366 **Payroll Expense ($000):** 24329 **Personnel:** 312

READING—Berks County

☐ **HAVEN BEHAVIORAL HOSPITAL OF EASTERN PENNSYLVANIA (394052)**, 145 North 6th Street, 3rd Floor, Zip 19601–3096; tel. 610/406–4340 (Nonreporting) **A**1 10 **S** Haven Behavioral Healthcare, Nashville, TN
Primary Contact: Bryan W. Lett, Chief Executive Officer
CMO: Mark Putnam M.D., Medical Director
CHR: Kathy Copenhaver, Director Human Resources
Web address: www.havenbehavioral.com/
Control: Corporation, Investor–owned (for–profit) **Service:** Psychiatric

Staffed Beds: 48

✠ **HEALTHSOUTH READING REHABILITATION HOSPITAL (393026)**, 1623 Morgantown Road, Zip 19607–9455; tel. 610/796–6000, (Nonreporting) **A**1 10 **S** HEALTHSOUTH Corporation, Birmingham, AL
Primary Contact: Amy Teal, Chief Executive Officer
CFO: Jason Pulaski, Controller
CMO: Patti Brown M.D., Medical Director
CHR: Edward Werner, Director Human Resources
CNO: Margaret Montgomery, Chief Nursing Officer
Web address: www.healthsouthreading.com
Control: Corporation, Investor–owned (for–profit) **Service:** Rehabilitation

Staffed Beds: 60

✠ **PENN STATE HEALTH ST. JOSEPH (390096)**, 2500 Bernville Road, Zip 19605–9453, Mailing Address: P.O.Box 316, 19603–0316; tel. 610/378–2000, (Includes PENN STATE HEALTH ST. JOSEPH – DOWNTOWN CAMPUS, 145 North Sixth Street, Reading, Pennsylvania, Zip 19601, P O Box 316, 19603–0316, tel. 610/378–2000; John R Morahan, President and Chief Executive Officer) **A**1 2 10 12 13 **F**3 13 15 18 20 22 24 26 28 29 30 31 32 34 35 39 40 44 45 46 49 50 51 53 54 57 58 59 64 66 68 70 72 74 75 76 77 78 79 81 82 84 85 87 89 93 97 107 108 111 113 114 115 116 117 118 119 120 121 130 131 132 135 144 146 147 148 149 **P**1 6 **S** Penn State Hershey Health System, Hershey, PA
Primary Contact: John R. Morahan, President and Chief Executive Officer
CFO: Courtney Coffman, Vice President, Finance and Chief Financial Officer
CMO: Christopher Newman M.D., Vice President Medical Affairs and Chief Medical Officer
CIO: Amanda Klopp, Director, Innovation and Clinical Integration
CHR: Scott Mengle, Vice President Human Resources
CNO: Sharon Strohecker R.N., MSN, Vice President Clinical Operations and Chief Nursing Officer
Web address: www.thefutureofhealthcare.org
Control: Other not–for–profit (including NFP Corporation) **Service:** General medical and surgical

Staffed Beds: 180 **Admissions:** 7503 **Census:** 97 **Outpatient Visits:** 259704 **Births:** 730 **Total Expense ($000):** 201559 **Payroll Expense ($000):** 33617 **Personnel:** 1183

RENOVO—Clinton County

BUCKTAIL MEDICAL CENTER (391304), 1001 Pine Street, Zip 17764–1620; tel. 570/923–1000, (Total facility includes 43 beds in nursing home–type unit) **A**10 18 **F**3 7 11 34 54 56 57 55 66 69 77 97 127 128 130 133 143 146 **P**6
Primary Contact: Timothy Reeves, Administrator
CFO: Wendy Janerella, Controller
CMO: Alvin Berlot M.D., Medical Director
Web address: www.bucktailmed.org
Control: Other not–for–profit (including NFP Corporation) **Service:** General medical and surgical

Staffed Beds: 64 **Admissions:** 230 **Census:** 41 **Outpatient Visits:** 9759 **Births:** 0 **Total Expense ($000):** 6531 **Payroll Expense ($000):** 2714 **Personnel:** 90

RIDLEY PARK—Delaware County

TAYLOR HOSPITAL See Crozer–Chester Medical Center, Upland

ROARING SPRING—Blair County

✠ **CONEMAUGH NASON MEDICAL CENTER (390062)**, 105 Nason Drive, Zip 16673–1202; tel. 814/224–2141 **A**1 10 **F**3 11 13 15 18 19 29 30 34 35 40 45 50 56 57 59 62 64 65 70 74 75 76 77 79 81 85 87 91 107 108 110 111 114 119 124 130 146 147 148 **S** LifePoint Health, Brentwood, TN
Primary Contact: Timothy Harclerode, Chief Executive Officer
CFO: Kimberly Semelsberger CPA, Chief Financial Officer
CHR: Lorie Smith, Director Human Resources
Web address: www.nasonhospital.com
Control: Corporation, Investor–owned (for–profit) **Service:** General medical and surgical

Staffed Beds: 45 **Admissions:** 1809 **Census:** 14 **Outpatient Visits:** 75128 **Births:** 397 **Total Expense ($000):** 32206 **Payroll Expense ($000):** 13283 **Personnel:** 250

ROYERSFORD—Montgomery County

⇑ **PHYSICIANS CARE SURGICAL HOSPITAL (390324)**, 454 Enterprise Drive, Zip 19468–1200; tel. 610/495–3330 **A**10 21 **F**3
Primary Contact: Christopher Doyle, Chief Executive Officer
Web address: www.phycarehospital.com
Control: Corporation, Investor–owned (for–profit) **Service:** Surgical

Staffed Beds: 12 **Admissions:** 1021 **Census:** 4 **Outpatient Visits:** 5283 **Births:** 0 **Personnel:** 76

SAINT MARYS—Elk County

PENN HIGHLANDS ELK (391315), 763 Johnsonburg Road, Zip 15857–3498; tel. 814/788–8000, (Total facility includes 138 beds in nursing home–type unit) **A**10 18 **F**2 3 6 8 11 13 15 28 29 30 34 35 40 44 45 56 57 59 62 63 65 75 76 77 79 80 81 82 84 85 86 87 93 98 100 103 107 108 110 111 115 118 119 124 128 129 130 131 132 133 135 146 147 148
Primary Contact: Bradley Chapman, President
CFO: Laurie MacDonald, Vice President Finance
CMO: David Johe M.D., President Medical Staff
CIO: Mary Ann Schwabenbauer, Director Information Technology
CHR: Seanna D'Amore, Director Human Resources
Web address: www.phhealthcare.org
Control: Other not–for–profit (including NFP Corporation) **Service:** General medical and surgical

Staffed Beds: 173 **Admissions:** 2095 **Census:** 146 **Outpatient Visits:** 145190 **Births:** 210 **Total Expense ($000):** 55285 **Payroll Expense ($000):** 22418 **Personnel:** 489

SAYRE—Bradford County

✠ **GUTHRIE ROBERT PACKER HOSPITAL (390079)**, 1 Guthrie Square, Zip 18840–1698; tel. 570/888–6666 **A**1 2 3 5 10 12 13 19 **F**3 11 12 13 15 17 18 20 22 24 26 28 29 30 31 34 37 38 40 43 45 46 47 48 49 50 51 57 58 59 61 64 70 73 74 75 76 78 79 81 82 84 85 86 87 89 91 92 93 96 98 99 100 101 102 103 105 107 108 110 111 114 115 116 117 118 119 120 121 123 126 129 130 132 141 142 145 146 148 149 150 **S** Guthrie Clinic, Sayre, PA
Primary Contact: Paul G. VerValin, Interim President
CFO: Scott Silvestri, Chief Financial Officer, Hospital Financial Operations
CMO: Brian Fillipo M.D., Chief Medical Officer
CIO: Burt Robles, Vice President Information Services
CHR: Frank Pinkosky, Senior Vice President
CNO: Catherine Mohr R.N., MSN, Chief Nursing Officer
Web address: www.guthrie.org/location/robert–packer–hospital
Control: Other not–for–profit (including NFP Corporation) **Service:** General medical and surgical

Staffed Beds: 254 **Admissions:** 13969 **Census:** 174 **Outpatient Visits:** 147353 **Births:** 848 **Total Expense ($000):** 286133 **Payroll Expense ($000):** 83959 **Personnel:** 1319

PA

☐ △ **ALLIED SERVICES REHABILITATION HOSPITAL (393030)**, 475 Morgan Highway, Zip 18508–2605, Mailing Address: P.O.Box 1103, 18501–1103; tel. 570/348–1300 **A**1 7 10 **F**11 29 34 53 56 59 64 74 75 77 78 79 86 87 90 91 93 94 96 130 143 146
Primary Contact: Karen Kearney, Vice President Inpatient Rehabilitation Services
CFO: Michael Avvisato, Senior Vice President and Chief Financial Officer
CMO: Gregory Basting M.D., Vice President Medical Affairs
CIO: John Regula, Chief Information Officer
CHR: Judy P Oprisko, Vice President
CNO: Jeana Sluck R.N., Executive Director Nursing Clinical Inpatient Departments
Web address: www.allied–services.org
Control: Other not–for–profit (including NFP Corporation) **Service**: Rehabilitation

> **Staffed Beds: 117 Admissions: 1402 Census: 43 Births: 0**

COMMUNITY MEDICAL CENTER HEALTHCARE SYSTEM See Geisinger–Community Medical Center

✠ **GEISINGER–COMMUNITY MEDICAL CENTER (390001)**, 1800 Mulberry Street, Zip 18510–2369; tel. 570/703–8000 **A**1 2 3 5 10 **F**3 11 12 15 18 20 22 24 26 29 30 31 34 35 39 40 43 44 45 46 47 49 54 57 59 64 68 74 75 77 78 79 80 81 82 84 85 86 87 89 93 94 98 107 108 110 111 114 115 117 118 119 126 129 130 131 132 145 146 147 148 149 **P**6 **S** Geisinger Health, Danville, PA
Primary Contact: Anthony Aquilina, D.O., Regional President
CFO: Edward Chabalowski, Chief Financial Officer
CMO: Anthony Aquilina D.O., Chief Medical Officer
CHR: Lois Wolfe, Director Human Resources
Web address: www.geisinger.org/for–patients/locations–directions/gcmc/
Control: Other not–for–profit (including NFP Corporation) **Service**: General medical and surgical

> **Staffed Beds: 293 Admissions: 12531 Census: 159 Outpatient Visits: 281147 Births: 0 Total Expense ($000): 227254 Payroll Expense ($000): 84161 Personnel: 1376**

MERCY HOSPITAL OF SCRANTON See Regional Hospital Of Scranton

✠ △ **MOSES TAYLOR HOSPITAL (390119)**, 700 Quincy Avenue, Zip 18510–1724; tel. 570/770–5000 **A**1 3 5 7 10 **F**3 7 13 15 18 29 30 31 34 40 44 45 49 50 51 54 56 57 59 60 61 62 64 65 66 68 70 72 74 75 76 77 78 79 81 85 86 87 89 92 93 98 103 107 108 110 111 114 116 119 124 129 130 132 135 146 147 **P**6 **S** Community Health Systems, Inc., Franklin, TN
Primary Contact: Justin Davis, Chief Executive Officer
CFO: Thomas Bisignani, Chief Financial Officer
CMO: Mary Sewatsky M.D., Chief Medical Officer
CHR: Elizabeth Leo, Chief Human Resources Officer
CNO: Patricia Seliga R.N., Chief Nursing Officer
Web address: www.mth.org
Control: Corporation, Investor–owned (for–profit) **Service**: General medical and surgical

> **Staffed Beds: 213 Admissions: 9069 Census: 119 Outpatient Visits: 186520 Births: 2518 Total Expense ($000): 155106 Payroll Expense ($000): 44907 Personnel: 807**

✠ △ **REGIONAL HOSPITAL OF SCRANTON (390237)**, 746 Jefferson Avenue, Zip 18510–1624; tel. 570/348–7100 **A**1 2 3 5 7 10 12 **F**7 8 11 12 15 17 18 20 22 24 26 28 29 30 31 34 35 39 40 44 45 46 47 48 49 50 51 53 54 57 58 59 60 61 64 65 66 68 70 74 75 77 78 79 81 85 86 87 91 92 93 97 107 108 109 110 111 112 113 114 115 116 117 118 119 120 121 122 123 124 126 130 132 143 144 145 146 147 148 149 **P**6 **S** Community Health Systems, Inc., Franklin, TN
Primary Contact: Justin Davis, Chief Executive Officer
CFO: Stephen Franko, Vice President Finance and Chief Financial Officer
CMO: Anthony Yanni M.D., Vice President Medical Affairs
CIO: Jorge Coronel, Chief Information Officer
Web address: www.regionalhospitalofscranton.net
Control: Corporation, Investor–owned (for–profit) **Service**: General medical and surgical

> **Staffed Beds: 186 Admissions: 8342 Census: 113 Outpatient Visits: 109745 Births: 0 Total Expense ($000): 162428 Payroll Expense ($000): 50430 Personnel: 953**

✠ **GRAND VIEW HEALTH (390057)**, 700 Lawn Avenue, Zip 18960–1548, Mailing Address: P.O.Box 902, 18960–0902; tel. 215/453–4000 **A**1 2 10 **F**3 7 11 12 13 15 18 28 29 31 34 35 40 44 45 46 47 48 49 50 51 54 56 57 59 61 62 63 64 65 66 68 70 71 72 74 75 76 77 78 79 81 84 85 86 87 89 90 93 96 97 107 108 110 111 114 115 117 119 120 121 123 130 131 132 135 141 143 144 146 147 148 149 **P**6
Primary Contact: Jean M. Keeler, President and Chief Executive Officer
COO: J Mark Horne, Senior Vice President, Ambulatory Services and Chief Operating Officer
CFO: Michael Keen, Senior Vice President and Chief Financial Officer
CMO: Jane Ferry M.D., Vice President Medical Affairs
CIO: Jane Doll Loveless, Vice President, Chief Information Officer
CNO: Kathleen Burkey R.N., MSN, Vice President, Patient Care Service and Chief Nursing Officer
Web address: www.gvh.org
Control: Other not–for–profit (including NFP Corporation) **Service**: General medical and surgical

> **Staffed Beds: 194 Admissions: 7853 Census: 94 Outpatient Visits: 324314 Births: 1259 Total Expense ($000): 188316 Payroll Expense ($000): 99526 Personnel: 1459**

☐ **UPMC NORTHWEST (390091)**, 100 Fairfield Drive, Zip 16346–2130; tel. 814/676–7600, (Total facility includes 16 beds in nursing home–type unit) **A**1 2 3 10 19 **F**3 11 13 15 18 20 28 29 31 34 35 40 44 45 46 47 50 56 57 59 63 64 65 68 70 74 75 76 77 78 79 81 82 84 85 86 87 89 90 93 96 98 100 101 102 103 107 108 110 111 114 115 118 119 121 123 128 130 131 132 135 141 142 146 147 148 149 **S** UPMC, Pittsburgh, PA
Primary Contact: Brian Durniok, President
COO: Brian Durniok, Vice President Operations
CFO: Bradley Dinger, Financial Representative
CMO: David McCandless, Vice President Medical Affairs
CHR: Brian Durniok, Vice President Human Resources
CNO: Daniel Shearn R.N., MSN, Vice President Patient Services and Chief Nursing Officer
Web address: www.upmc.com/locations/hospitals/northwest/Pages/default.aspx
Control: Other not–for–profit (including NFP Corporation) **Service**: General medical and surgical

> **Staffed Beds: 128 Admissions: 6450 Census: 84 Outpatient Visits: 140653 Births: 725 Total Expense ($000): 100163 Payroll Expense ($000): 29404 Personnel: 619**

✠ **HEALTHSOUTH REHABILITATION HOSPITAL OF SEWICKLEY (393045)**, 303 Camp Meeting Road, Zip 15143–8322; tel. 412/741–9500 **A**1 10 **F**29 34 56 57 59 60 62 64 65 74 75 87 90 91 92 93 95 96 100 132 146 148 **S** HEALTHSOUTH Corporation, Birmingham, AL
Primary Contact: Leah Laffey, R.N., Chief Executive Officer
CFO: Daniel A Vrana, Area Controller
CMO: Shelana Gibbs–McElvy M.D., Medical Director
CIO: Jamie Smith, Supervisor Health Information Management Systems
CHR: Melissa Coleman, Director Human Resources
CNO: Christie Ryan, Chief Nursing Officer
Web address: www.healthsouthsewickley.com
Control: Corporation, Investor–owned (for–profit) **Service**: Rehabilitation

> **Staffed Beds: 44 Admissions: 927 Census: 37 Outpatient Visits: 3845 Births: 0 Total Expense ($000): 12543 Payroll Expense ($000): 6199 Personnel: 116**

☐ **SEWICKLEY VALLEY HOSPITAL, (A DIVISION OF VALLEY MEDICAL FACILITIES) (390037)**, 720 Blackburn Road, Zip 15143–1459; tel. 412/741–6600 **A**1 10 **F**3 8 11 12 13 14 15 18 20 28 29 30 32 34 35 38 40 46 49 50 53 54 55 57 59 60 64 70 74 75 76 77 78 79 81 82 84 85 86 90 92 93 96 97 98 100 101 102 103 104 107 108 109 110 111 115 118 119 120 121 126 129 130 132 135 145 **P**6 **S** Heritage Valley Health System, Beaver, PA
Primary Contact: Norman F. Mitry, President and Chief Executive Officer
CFO: Bryan J Randall, Vice President Finance and Chief Financial Officer
CMO: John Cinicola M.D., Chief Medical Officer
CIO: David Carleton, Chief Information Officer
CHR: Bruce Edwards, Vice President Human Resources
CNO: Linda Homyk, Chief Nursing Officer
Web address: www.heritagevalley.org
Control: Other not–for–profit (including NFP Corporation) **Service**: General medical and surgical

> **Staffed Beds: 179 Admissions: 7966 Census: 88 Births: 710**

Many Facility Codes have changed. Please refer to the AHA Guide Code Chart. © 2017 AHA Guide

SHARON—Mercer County

⊠ **SHARON REGIONAL HEALTH SYSTEM (390211)**, 740 East State Street, Zip 16146–3395; tel. 724/983–3911, (Nonreporting) **A**1 10 19 **S** Steward Health Care System, LLC, Boston, MA
Primary Contact: Joseph G. Hugar, President
CFO: Jeffrey Chrobak, Vice President Finance and Chief Financial Officer
CHR: John Davidson, Vice President Human Resources
Web address: www.sharonregional.com
Control: Corporation, Investor–owned (for–profit) **Service:** General medical and surgical

Staffed Beds: 218

SHICKSHINNY—Luzerne County

HUNTINGTON CREEK RECOVERY CENTER, 890 Bethel Road, Zip 18655; tel. 570/864–3116, (Nonreporting)
Primary Contact: Robert Norris, Chief Executive Officer
Web address: www.clearbrookinc.com
Control: Other not–for–profit (including NFP Corporation) **Service:** Alcoholism and other chemical dependency

Staffed Beds: 65

SHIPPENSBURG—Franklin County

☐ **ROXBURY TREATMENT CENTER (394050)**, 601 Roxbury Road, Zip 17257–9302; tel. 800/648–4673 (Nonreporting) **A**1 10 **S** Universal Health Services, Inc., King of Prussia, PA
Primary Contact: Shauna Mogerman, Chief Executive Officer
Web address: www.roxburyhospital.com
Control: Corporation, Investor–owned (for–profit) **Service:** Psychiatric

Staffed Beds: 94

SOMERSET—Somerset County

★ **SOMERSET HOSPITAL (390039)**, 225 South Center Avenue, Zip 15501–2088; tel. 814/443–5000 **A**10 20 **F**3 8 11 13 15 17 18 20 22 26 28 29 30 32 34 35 40 45 47 49 50 53 57 59 62 63 64 68 74 76 77 79 80 81 82 84 85 86 87 89 93 97 98 100 103 104 107 108 111 115 119 129 130 131 132 133 135 141 146 147 148 149
Primary Contact: Craig M. Saylor, Interim CEO
COO: Andy Rush, Senior Vice President and Chief Operating Officer
CFO: Matthew Kociola, Senior Vice President and Chief Financial Officer
CIO: Jonathan Bauer, Director Information Systems
CHR: Mark P Frick, Senior Vice President Human Resources
CNO: Suellen Lichtenfels, Vice President and Chief Nursing Officer
Web address: www.somersethospital.com
Control: Other not–for–profit (including NFP Corporation) **Service:** General medical and surgical

Staffed Beds: 111 **Admissions:** 3222 **Census:** 40 **Outpatient Visits:** 142677 **Births:** 347 **Total Expense ($000):** 69167 **Payroll Expense ($000):** 25909 **Personnel:** 545

SPRINGFIELD—Delaware County

SPRINGFIELD HOSPITAL See Crozer–Chester Medical Center, Upland

STATE COLLEGE—Centre County

⊠ **MOUNT NITTANY MEDICAL CENTER (390268)**, 1800 East Park Avenue, Zip 16803–6797; tel. 814/231–7000 **A**1 2 3 5 10 **F**3 7 8 13 15 17 20 22 26 28 29 30 31 35 40 46 49 51 57 59 64 68 70 73 74 75 76 77 78 79 80 81 82 84 85 87 89 93 98 100 101 102 107 108 111 114 115 118 119 121 126 129 130 132 135 143 146 148 149
Primary Contact: Kathleen Rhine, President and Chief Executive Officer
CFO: Randy E Tewksbury, Senior Vice President Finance and Chief Financial Officer
CIO: Wayne Thompson, Executive Vice President and Chief Information Officer
CHR: Gerald P Dittmann, Vice President Human Resources
Web address: www.mountnittany.org
Control: Other not–for–profit (including NFP Corporation) **Service:** General medical and surgical

Staffed Beds: 260 **Admissions:** 14046 **Census:** 143 **Outpatient Visits:** 322083 **Births:** 1362 **Total Expense ($000):** 379448 **Payroll Expense ($000):** 162998 **Personnel:** 1498

SUNBURY—Northumberland County

⊠ **SUNBURY COMMUNITY HOSPITAL AND OUTPATIENT CENTER (390084)**, 350 North Eleventh Street, Zip 17801–1611; tel. 570/286–3333, (Nonreporting) **A**1 10 **S** Quorum Health, Brentwood, TN
Primary Contact: Robert D. Williams, Chief Executive Officer
CFO: James J. Pachucki Jr, Chief Financial Officer
CMO: Charles C Pagana M.D., Chief Medical Officer
CIO: Fax Rector III, Director Information Technology
CHR: Talia Beatty, Director Human Resources
CNO: Catharine L Keister, Chief Nursing Officer
Web address: www.sunburyhospital.com
Control: Other not–for–profit (including NFP Corporation) **Service:** General medical and surgical

Staffed Beds: 76

SUSQUEHANNA—Susquehanna County

BARNES–KASSON COUNTY HOSPITAL (391309), 2872 Turnpike Street, Zip 18847–2771; tel. 570/853–3135, (Nonreporting) **A**10 18
Primary Contact: Sara F. Adornato, Executive Director
CFO: Kelli R Kane, Director of Finance
CMO: Pravinchandra Patel M.D., Chief Medical Officer
CIO: Eric Detwiler, Director Information Technology
Web address: www.barnes–kasson.org
Control: Other not–for–profit (including NFP Corporation) **Service:** General medical and surgical

Staffed Beds: 83

TITUSVILLE—Crawford County

★ **TITUSVILLE AREA HOSPITAL (391314)**, 406 West Oak Street, Zip 16354–1404; tel. 814/827–1851 **A**10 18 **F**3 8 11 15 18 28 29 30 31 34 35 40 45 50 51 57 59 64 68 70 75 78 79 81 82 85 86 87 89 93 107 108 110 111 115 119 130 133 145 **P**4 **S** Meadville Medical Center, Meadville, PA
Primary Contact: Lee Clinton, FACHE, Chief Executive Officer
CFO: Jill Neely, Chief Financial Officer
CMO: William Sonnenberg M.D., President Medical Staff
CIO: Karen Humes, Chief Information Officer
CHR: Jeffrey Saintz, Vice President Human Resources
CNO: Brenda Burnett, Vice President Patient Care Services and Chief Nursing Officer
Web address: www.titusvillehospital.org
Control: Other not–for–profit (including NFP Corporation) **Service:** General medical and surgical

Staffed Beds: 25 **Admissions:** 919 **Census:** 11 **Outpatient Visits:** 51618 **Births:** 0 **Total Expense ($000):** 26065 **Payroll Expense ($000):** 10143 **Personnel:** 219

TORRANCE—Westmoreland County

TORRANCE STATE HOSPITAL (394026), Torrance Road, Zip 15779–0111, Mailing Address: P.O.Box 111, 15779–0111; tel. 724/459–8000 **A**10 **F**39 75 98 130 135 143 146 147 148
Primary Contact: Edna I. McCutcheon, Chief Executive Officer
COO: R Brad Snyder, Chief Operating Officer
CFO: Michael Yahner, Chief Financial Officer
CMO: Herbert G Chissell M.D., Chief Medical Officer
Web address: www.dpw.state.pa.us
Control: State, Government, Nonfederal **Service:** Psychiatric

Staffed Beds: 328 **Admissions:** 248 **Census:** 304 **Outpatient Visits:** 0 **Births:** 0

TOWANDA—Bradford County

★ **GUTHRIE TOWANDA MEMORIAL HOSPITAL (390236)**, 91 Hospital Drive, Zip 18848–9702; tel. 570/265–2191, (Total facility includes 160 beds in nursing home–type unit) **A**10 **F**3 7 10 11 28 29 34 35 36 40 50 57 59 64 70 75 77 79 81 82 84 85 87 93 107 108 111 115 119 128 129 130 133 135 143 146 **S** Guthrie Clinic, Sayre, PA
Primary Contact: Staci Covey, R.N., MS, President
CMO: Joseph Cama M.D., President Medical Staff
CIO: Karen Brown, Manager Information Technology
CHR: Linda Berry, Vice President Human Resources
CNO: Lynn Dibble, Vice President Patient Care Services
Web address: www.memorialhospital.org
Control: Other not–for–profit (including NFP Corporation) **Service:** General medical and surgical

Staffed Beds: 195 **Admissions:** 1102 **Census:** 146 **Outpatient Visits:** 49686 **Births:** 0 **Total Expense ($000):** 31933 **Payroll Expense ($000):** 14041 **Personnel:** 253

PA

TRANSFER—Mercer County

EDGEWOOD SURGICAL HOSPITAL (390307), 239 Edgewood Drive Extension, Zip 16154–1817; tel. 724/646–0400 (Nonreporting) **A**10
Primary Contact: Lloyd Scarrow, FACHE, Chief Executive Officer
Web address: www.edgewoodsurgical.com
Control: Corporation, Investor–owned (for–profit) **Service:** Surgical

Staffed Beds: 10

TROY—Bradford County

★ **TROY COMMUNITY HOSPITAL (391305)**, 275 Guthrie Drive, Zip 16947; tel. 570/297–2121 **A**10 18 **F**3 11 15 28 29 30 34 40 43 45 50 57 64 75 81 82 85 87 93 96 107 110 111 119 129 130 133 135 146 148 **S** Guthrie Clinic, Sayre, PA
Primary Contact: Staci Covey, R.N., MS, President
CFO: Bernie Smith, Chief Financial Officer
CMO: Vance A Good M.D., Chief Medical Staff
CIO: Dale Swingle, Vice President Information Services
CHR: Frank Pinkosky, Executive Vice President
CNO: Lori Barnett R.N., MSN, Chief Nursing Officer
Web address: www.guthrie.org
Control: Other not–for–profit (including NFP Corporation) **Service:** General medical and surgical

Staffed Beds: 25 **Admissions:** 947 **Census:** 18 **Outpatient Visits:** 33695 **Births:** 0 **Total Expense ($000):** 19569 **Payroll Expense ($000):** 5968 **Personnel:** 139

TUNKHANNOCK—Bradford County

✠ **TYLER MEMORIAL HOSPITAL (390192)**, 5950 State Route 6, Zip 18657–7905; tel. 570/836–2161 **A**1 10 **F**15 18 20 22 24 26 28 29 30 31 34 35 40 50 54 56 58 60 62 64 70 75 77 78 79 81 82 86 87 89 92 93 107 108 110 111 119 120 121 129 130 133 146 147 148 **S** Community Health Systems, Inc., Franklin, TN
Primary Contact: Ann Marie. Stevens, R.N., Chief Executive Officer
CFO: Robert Stiekes, Chief Financial Officer
CMO: Terrance Chilson, Chief of Staff
CNO: Maribeth Angeli, Chief Nursing Officer
Web address: www.tylermemorialhospital.net
Control: Corporation, Investor–owned (for–profit) **Service:** General medical and surgical

Staffed Beds: 44 **Admissions:** 587 **Census:** 5 **Births:** 0

TYRONE—Blair County

TYRONE HOSPITAL (391307), 187 Hospital Drive, Zip 16686–1808; tel. 814/684–1255 **A**10 18 **F**3 15 40 70 75 77 79 81 82 93 107 119 130 133 146
Primary Contact: Joseph J. Peluso, Chief Executive Officer
CFO: Todd Dieffenbach, Chief Financial Officer
CMO: Kelly Biggs M.D., Chief Medical Officer
CHR: Rosemary Jorden Best, Director Human Resources
CNO: Sharon Fisher R.N., Chief Nursing Officer
Web address: www.tyronehospital.org
Control: Other not–for–profit (including NFP Corporation) **Service:** General medical and surgical

Staffed Beds: 25 **Admissions:** 816 **Census:** 5 **Births:** 0

UNIONTOWN—Fayette County

✠ **UNIONTOWN HOSPITAL (390041)**, 500 West Berkeley Street, Zip 15401–5596; tel. 724/430–5000 **A**1 10 **F**3 11 12 13 15 18 20 22 29 30 34 35 40 45 49 51 54 57 59 64 70 73 74 75 76 77 78 79 81 89 90 92 96 102 107 108 110 111 114 115 118 119 130 132 146 148 149
Primary Contact: Steven P. Handy, CPA, Chief Executive Officer
CHR: James Proud, Vice President Human Resources and Marketing
CNO: Betty Ann Rock, Vice President Nursing and Chief Nursing Officer
Web address: www.uniontownhospital.com
Control: Other not–for–profit (including NFP Corporation) **Service:** General medical and surgical

Staffed Beds: 142 **Admissions:** 8220 **Census:** 91 **Outpatient Visits:** 218491 **Births:** 888 **Total Expense ($000):** 125644 **Payroll Expense ($000):** 42527 **Personnel:** 996

UPLAND—Delaware County

☐ **CROZER–CHESTER MEDICAL CENTER (390180)**, One Medical Center Boulevard, Zip 19013–3995; tel. 610/447–2000, (Includes SPRINGFIELD HOSPITAL, 190 West Sproul Road, Springfield, Pennsylvania, Zip 19064–2097, tel. 610/328–8700; TAYLOR HOSPITAL, 175 East Chester Pike, Ridley Park, Pennsylvania, Zip 19078–2212, tel. 610/595–6000) **A**1 2 3 5 10 12 13 **F**2 3 5 6 7 8 11 12 13 14 15 16 17 18 20 22 24 26 28 29 30 31 32 34 35 36 37 38 40 41 42 43 44 45 46 47 48 49 50 51 52 54 55 56 57 58 59 61 62 63 64 65 66 68 70 72 74 75 76 77 78 79 81 82 83 84 85 86 87 89 90 92 93 94 96 97 98 99 100 101 102 103 104 105 107 108 109 110 111 114 115 116 117 118 119 120 121 123 124 126 129 130 131 132 134 135 138 143 145 146 147 148 **P**6 **S** Prospect Medical Holdings, Los Angeles, CA
Primary Contact: Michael Curran, President
CMO: Sat Arora M.D., President Medical and Dental Staff
CIO: Robert E Wilson, Vice President and Chief Information Officer
Web address: www.crozer.org
Control: Other not–for–profit (including NFP Corporation) **Service:** General medical and surgical

Staffed Beds: 384 **Admissions:** 18598 **Census:** 258 **Births:** 1332

WARREN—Warren County

WARREN GENERAL HOSPITAL (390146), Two Crescent Park West, Zip 16365–0068, Mailing Address: P.O.Box 68, 16365–0068; tel. 814/723–4973 **A**10 **F**4 11 13 15 28 29 30 31 34 35 39 40 44 45 47 50 51 57 59 62 63 64 70 75 76 77 78 79 81 84 85 86 87 89 92 93 96 97 98 99 100 103 107 108 110 111 114 117 119 120 121 130 131 133 144 146 **P**6
Primary Contact: Richard Allen, Chief Executive Officer
COO: Randy California, Chief Operating Officer
CFO: Julie Jacobs, Chief Financial Officer
CMO: John Maljovec M.D., Medical Director
CIO: Helen Rosequist, Manager Information Systems
CHR: Matthew Franklin, Director Human Resources
CNO: Joe Akif, Chief Clinical Officer and Chief Nursing Officer
Web address: www.wgh.org
Control: Other not–for–profit (including NFP Corporation) **Service:** General medical and surgical

Staffed Beds: 87 **Admissions:** 3040 **Census:** 34 **Births:** 342

WARREN STATE HOSPITAL (394016), 33 Main Drive, Zip 16365–5001; tel. 814/723–5500 **A**10 **F**4 39 50 56 75 77 82 98 100 101 103 128 130 132 135 143 146 149 **P**6
Primary Contact: Charlotte M. Uber, Chief Executive Officer
COO: Ronnie Cropper, Chief Operating Officer
CFO: Terry Crambes, Manager Finance
CMO: Asha Prabhu M.D., Chief Medical Officer
CIO: Karen Byler, Information Technology Generalist
CHR: Nancy Saullo, Director Human Resources
CNO: Sara Flasher, Chief Nurse Executive
Web address: www.dpw.pa.gov
Control: State, Government, Nonfederal **Service:** Psychiatric

Staffed Beds: 152 **Admissions:** 81 **Census:** 146 **Outpatient Visits:** 0 **Births:** 0 **Total Expense ($000):** 47295 **Payroll Expense ($000):** 20161 **Personnel:** 394

WASHINGTON—Washington County

☐ **ADVANCED SURGICAL HOSPITAL (390323)**, 100 Trich Drive Suite 1, Zip 15301–5990; tel. 724/884–0710 **A**1 10 **F**64 77 79 81 82 93 111 129
Primary Contact: Anne S. Hast, R.N., Chief Executive Officer
CFO: Diane Hritz, Chief Financial Officer
CNO: Anne S Hast R.N., Director of Nursing
Web address: www.ashospital.net
Control: Partnership, Investor–owned (for–profit) **Service:** Orthopedic

Staffed Beds: 14 **Admissions:** 617 **Census:** 4 **Births:** 0

✠ **WASHINGTON HOSPITAL (390042)**, 155 Wilson Avenue, Zip 15301–3398; tel. 724/225–7000 **A**1 3 5 10 13 **F**3 5 11 12 13 15 18 20 22 24 26 28 29 30 31 32 34 35 36 38 39 40 45 46 49 50 53 54 56 57 59 60 61 64 65 70 74 75 76 77 78 79 81 82 84 85 86 89 90 91 92 93 94 96 97 98 100 101 102 103 107 108 110 111 114 115 118 119 126 127 130 131 132 134 135 146 147 148 **P**1 7 **S** Washington Health System, Washington, PA
Primary Contact: Gary B. Weinstein, President and Chief Executive Officer
COO: Brook Ward, Executive Vice President
CFO: Alisa Rucker, Vice President Finance and Chief Financial Officer
CMO: Paul T Cullen M.D., Vice President Medical Affairs
CIO: Rodney Louk, Vice President Information Systems
CHR: Barbara A McCullough, Vice President Human Resources
CNO: Karen A Bray R.N., MSN, Vice President Patient Care Services
Web address: www.washingtonhospital.org
Control: Other not–for–profit (including NFP Corporation) **Service:** General medical and surgical

Staffed Beds: 206 **Admissions:** 12021 **Census:** 144 **Outpatient Visits:** 714803 **Births:** 947 **Total Expense ($000):** 225060 **Payroll Expense ($000):** 101987 **Personnel:** 1540

Many Facility Codes have changed. Please refer to the AHA Guide Code Chart.

WAYNESBORO—Franklin County

✠ **WAYNESBORO HOSPITAL (390138)**, 501 East Main Street, Zip 17268–2394; tel. 717/765–4000 **A**1 10 **F**3 11 13 15 29 30 34 40 44 45 49 50 54 56 57 59 61 64 65 68 74 75 76 77 79 81 85 86 87 91 93 94 100 107 108 110 111 115 118 119 129 130 131 132 133 135 146 147 148 149 150 **P**8 **S** Summit Health, Chambersburg, PA
Primary Contact: Melissa Dubrow, Chief Operating Officer
COO: Melissa Dubrow, Vice President and Chief Operating Officer
CFO: Kimberly Rzomp, Vice President Finance
CMO: Thomas Anderson M.D., Vice President Medical Affairs
CIO: Michele Zeigler, Vice President Information Services
CHR: Jennifer Knight, Manager Human Resources
CNO: Jill Keller R.N., MSN, Vice President for Nursing Services, Quality and Risk Management
Web address: www.summithealth.org
Control: Other not–for–profit (including NFP Corporation) **Service**: General medical and surgical

Staffed Beds: 56 **Admissions**: 2651 **Census**: 21 **Outpatient Visits**: 100473
Births: 435 **Total Expense ($000)**: 55126 **Payroll Expense ($000)**: 25934
Personnel: 403

WAYNESBURG—Greene County

✠ **WASHINGTON HEALTH SYSTEM GREENE (390150)**, 350 Bonar Avenue, Zip 15370–1608; tel. 724/627–3101 **A**1 10 **F**11 15 29 30 34 35 40 44 45 51 57 59 64 81 85 87 98 103 104 107 108 110 111 114 119 130 133 135 146 **S** Washington Health System, Washington, PA
Primary Contact: Terry Wiltrout, President
COO: Janel Mudry, Chief Operating Officer
CMO: Jamie Boris M.D., President Medical Staff
CIO: Leslie Hayhurst, Director Information Systems
CHR: Patricia Marshall, Assistant Administrator Human Resources
Web address: www.southwestregionalmedical.com/
Control: Other not–for–profit (including NFP Corporation) **Service**: General medical and surgical

Staffed Beds: 49 **Admissions**: 1743 **Census**: 25 **Outpatient Visits**: 18757
Births: 0 **Total Expense ($000)**: 27919 **Payroll Expense ($000)**: 13219
Personnel: 227

WELLSBORO—Tioga County

✠ **SOLDIERS AND SAILORS MEMORIAL HOSPITAL (390043)**, 32–36 Central Avenue, Zip 16901–1899; tel. 570/724–1631 **A**1 10 20 **F**3 11 13 15 17 28 31 34 40 44 45 48 49 64 65 70 75 76 78 79 81 85 93 104 107 108 110 111 115 118 119 129 130 146 **P**7 **S** UPMC Susquehanna, Williamsport, PA
Primary Contact: Janie Hilfiger, Chief Administrative Officer
CFO: Eric Pohjala, Chief Financial Officer
CMO: Walter Laibinis M.D., Chief Medical Officer
CIO: Timothy E Schoener, Senior Vice President and Chief Information Officer
CHR: Christine Ballard, Vice President Human Resources
CNO: Matt Romania, Director of Nursing
Web address: www.susquehannahealth.org
Control: Other not–for–profit (including NFP Corporation) **Service**: General medical and surgical

Staffed Beds: 67 **Admissions**: 1767 **Census**: 18 **Outpatient Visits**: 105251
Births: 264 **Total Expense ($000)**: 57667 **Payroll Expense ($000)**: 22428
Personnel: 357

WERNERSVILLE—Berks County

WERNERSVILLE STATE HOSPITAL (394014), 160 Main Street, Zip 19565–9490; tel. 610/678–3411 **A**10 **F**30 39 75 77 98 103 130 135 146
Primary Contact: Andrea Kepler, Chief Executive Officer
COO: Cheryl Benson, Chief Operating Officer
CMO: Dale K Adair M.D., Chief Medical Officer
CIO: William Edwards, Information Technology Generalist
CHR: Melvin McMinn, Director Human Resources
Web address: www.dpw.state.pa.us/
Control: State, Government, Nonfederal **Service**: Psychiatric

Staffed Beds: 266 **Admissions**: 74 **Census**: 257 **Outpatient Visits**: 0
Births: 0 **Total Expense ($000)**: 67798 **Personnel**: 565

WEST CHESTER—Chester County

✠ **LIFECARE HOSPITALS OF CHESTER COUNTY (392048)**, 400 East Marshall Street, Zip 19380–5412; tel. 484/826–0400 **A**1 10 **F**1 77 79 130 148 **P**5 **S** LifeCare Management Services, Plano, TX
Primary Contact: Janet Biedron, R.N., Chief Executive Officer
CMO: Raj Patel M.D., Medical Director
CHR: Evan Ganley, Manager Human Resources
CNO: Bonnie Barclay, Chief Nursing Officer
Web address: www.lifecare–hospitals.com
Control: Corporation, Investor–owned (for–profit) **Service**: Acute long–term care hospital

Staffed Beds: 39 **Admissions**: 349 **Census**: 25 **Outpatient Visits**: 0
Births: 0

✠ **PENN MEDICINE CHESTER COUNTY HOSPITAL (390179)**, 701 East Marshall Street, Zip 19380–4412; tel. 610/431–5000 **A**1 2 3 5 10 **F**1 3 4 11 13 15 17 18 20 22 24 26 28 29 30 31 34 35 36 39 40 44 45 46 49 50 51 54 55 57 58 59 60 62 63 64 68 70 72 73 74 75 76 77 78 79 80 81 82 84 85 86 87 89 90 91 92 93 98 107 108 110 111 114 115 116 117 119 120 121 126 128 130 131 132 135 146 147 148 149 **S** University of Pennsylvania Health System, Philadelphia, PA
Primary Contact: Michael J. Duncan, President and Chief Executive Officer
COO: Michael Barber, Chief Operating Officer
CFO: Kenneth E Flickinger, Chief Financial Officer
CMO: Richard D Donze D.O., Senior Vice President Medical Affairs
CIO: Karen Pinsky M.D., Chief Medical Information Officer
CHR: Jacqueline Felicetti, Chief Human Resource Officer
CNO: Angela R. Coladonato DNP, RN, NEA–BC MSN, R.N., Chief Nursing Officer
Web address: www.chestercountyhospital.org
Control: Other not–for–profit (including NFP Corporation) **Service**: General medical and surgical

Staffed Beds: 248 **Admissions**: 13920 **Census**: 128 **Outpatient Visits**: 256113 **Births**: 2568 **Total Expense ($000)**: 260167 **Payroll Expense ($000)**: 114145 **Personnel**: 1803

WEST GROVE—Chester County

✠ **JENNERSVILLE REGIONAL HOSPITAL (390220)**, 1015 West Baltimore Pike, Zip 19390–9459; tel. 610/869–1000 **A**1 2 10 **F**3 15 18 29 40 45 49 50 51 57 59 70 74 75 79 81 82 85 87 92 93 107 108 110 111 115 119 130 131 132 133 146 147 149 **P**6 **S** Community Health Systems, Inc., Franklin, TN
Primary Contact: Matt Shelak, Interim Chief Executive Officer
CFO: Tracey Claxton, Chief Financial Officer
CMO: Tracy Carmellini M.D., Chief of Staff
CHR: Debra Basquill, Director Human Resources
CNO: David Schmidt R.N., Chief Nursing Officer
Web address: www.jennersville.com
Control: Corporation, Investor–owned (for–profit) **Service**: General medical and surgical

Staffed Beds: 63 **Admissions**: 2798 **Census**: 26 **Outpatient Visits**: 55561
Births: 249 **Total Expense ($000)**: 56143 **Payroll Expense ($000)**: 19479
Personnel: 239

WEST READING—Berks County

✠ **READING HOSPITAL (390044)**, Sixth Avenue and Spruce Street, Zip 19611–1428, Mailing Address: P.O.Box 16052, 19612–6052; tel. 610/988–8000 **A**1 2 3 5 8 10 12 13 **F**3 5 7 11 12 13 15 18 20 22 24 26 28 29 30 31 32 34 35 37 40 41 42 43 44 45 46 48 49 50 54 56 57 58 59 60 61 62 70 72 73 74 75 76 77 78 79 81 82 85 86 87 89 92 93 94 96 97 98 99 100 101 102 103 104 105 106 107 108 110 111 114 115 116 117 118 119 120 121 123 124 125 126 128 129 130 131 132 135 144 146 147 148 **P**5 8
Primary Contact: Clinton Matthews, President and Chief Executive Officer
CFO: Richard W Jones, Chief Financial Officer
CMO: M. Joseph Grennan M.D., Jr, Senior Vice President and Chief Medical Officer
CIO: Jayashree Raman, Vice President and Chief Information Officer
CNO: Mary Christine Agnew R.N., MS, Vice President and Chief Nursing Officer
Web address: www.readinghospital.org
Control: Other not–for–profit (including NFP Corporation) **Service**: General medical and surgical

Staffed Beds: 714 **Admissions**: 32662 **Census**: 471 **Outpatient Visits**: 1026037 **Births**: 3683 **Total Expense ($000)**: 794834 **Payroll Expense ($000)**: 317562 **Personnel**: 4855

Hospital, Medicare Provider Number, Address, Telephone, Approval, Facility, and Physician Codes, Health Care System

★ American Hospital Association (AHA) membership
□ The Joint Commission accreditation
○ Healthcare Facilities Accreditation Program
◇ DNV Healthcare Inc. accreditation
⇑ Center for Improvement in Healthcare Quality Accreditation
△ Commission on Accreditation of Rehabilitation Facilities (CARF) accreditation

PA

WILKES BARRE—Luzerne County

⊞ **GEISINGER WYOMING VALLEY MEDICAL CENTER (390270)**, 1000 East Mountain Boulevard, Zip 18711–0027; tel. 570/808–7300 **A**1 2 3 5 10 13 **F**2 3 6 11 12 13 15 18 19 20 22 24 26 28 29 30 31 34 35 37 39 40 43 44 45 46 47 48 49 52 53 54 56 57 59 61 64 68 70 71 72 74 75 76 77 78 79 80 81 82 84 85 86 87 89 90 93 94 96 97 100 107 108 110 111 114 115 117 118 119 120 121 123 124 126 129 130 131 132 143 144 145 146 147 148 149 **P**6 **S** Geisinger Health, Danville, PA
Primary Contact: Anthony Aquilina, D.O., Regional President
CFO: Thomas A Bielecki, Chief Financial Officer
CMO: Steven Pierdon M.D., Executive Vice President and Chief Medical Officer
CIO: Frank Richards, Chief Information Officer
CHR: Margaret Heffers, Assistant Vice President Human Resources
Web address: www.geisinger.org
Control: Other not–for–profit (including NFP Corporation) **Service:** General medical and surgical

Staffed Beds: 256 **Admissions:** 15997 **Census:** 196 **Outpatient Visits:** 777622 **Births:** 1546 **Total Expense ($000):** 447346 **Payroll Expense ($000):** 104744 **Personnel:** 2148	

★ **PAM SPECIALTY HOSPITAL OF WILKES–BARRE (392025)**, 575 North River Street, 7th Floor, Zip 18702–2634; tel. 570/208–3310 (Nonreporting) **S** Post Acute Medical, LLC, Enola, PA
Primary Contact: Salvatore Aquilina, Chief Executive Officer
Web address: www.warmsprings.org/our–facilities/hospitals/post–acute–medical–specialty–hospital–wilkes–barre/
Control: Corporation, Investor–owned (for–profit) **Service:** Acute long–term care hospital

Staffed Beds: 36	

WILKES—BARRE–Luzerne County

☐ △ **JOHN HEINZ INSTITUTE OF REHABILITATION MEDICINE (393036)**, 150 Mundy Street, Zip 18702–6830; tel. 570/826–3800, (Total facility includes 21 beds in nursing home–type unit) **A**1 7 10 **F**3 11 29 30 32 35 54 57 59 62 64 68 75 77 82 86 90 91 92 93 130 131 132 143 146 148
Primary Contact: Karen Kearney, Vice President Inpatient Rehabilitation Services
CFO: Mike Avvisato, Vice President and Chief Financial Officer
CMO: Gregory Basting M.D., Vice President Medical Affairs
CIO: John Regula, Chief Information Officer
CHR: Judy P Oprisko, Vice President Human Resources
CNO: Maria Berlyn, Assistant Vice President Nursing Services
Web address: www.allied–services.org
Control: Other not–for–profit (including NFP Corporation) **Service:** Rehabilitation

Staffed Beds: 71 **Admissions:** 1241 **Census:** 44 **Births:** 0	

VETERANS AFFAIRS MEDICAL CENTER See Wilkes–Barre Veterans Affairs Medical Center

★ △ **WILKES–BARRE GENERAL HOSPITAL (390137)**, 575 North River Street, Zip 18764–0001; tel. 570/829–8111, (Includes WILKES–BARRE GENERAL HOSPITAL, 575 North River Street, Wilkes–Barre, Pennsylvania, Zip 18764, tel. 570/829–8111) **A**2 3 5 7 10 **F**3 8 12 13 15 17 18 20 22 24 26 28 29 30 31 34 37 40 44 45 46 47 48 49 50 51 53 54 56 57 59 61 64 66 70 73 74 75 76 78 79 81 82 83 84 85 86 87 89 90 91 92 93 96 107 108 110 111 112 114 115 116 117 118 119 120 121 123 124 126 129 130 132 145 146 147 148 149 **S** Community Health Systems, Inc., Franklin, TN
Primary Contact: Cornelio R. Catena, President and Chief Executive Officer
COO: Robert P Hoffman, Vice President and Director Patient Care Services
CFO: Maggie Koehler, Senior Vice President and Chief Financial Officer
CMO: Ragupathy Veluswamy M.D., Vice President Medical Affairs
CIO: Chris Galanda, Chief Information Officer
CHR: James Carmody, Vice President Human Resources
Web address: www.wvhc.org
Control: Corporation, Investor–owned (for–profit) **Service:** General medical and surgical

Staffed Beds: 374 **Admissions:** 13497 **Census:** 187 **Outpatient Visits:** 502633 **Births:** 1106 **Total Expense ($000):** 286139 **Payroll Expense ($000):** 83229 **Personnel:** 1405	

⊞ **WILKES–BARRE VETERANS AFFAIRS MEDICAL CENTER**, 1111 East End Boulevard, Zip 18711–0030; tel. 570/824–3521, (Total facility includes 105 beds in nursing home–type unit) **A**1 2 3 5 **F**3 4 5 18 20 26 29 30 31 34 35 36 38 39 40 44 50 54 55 56 57 58 59 60 61 62 63 64 65 70 74 75 77 78 79 81 82 83 84 85 86 87 90 93 94 97 98 100 101 102 103 104 105 106 107 111 115 116 117 118 119 127 128 129 130 132 135 143 146 147 148 149 150 **S** Department of Veterans Affairs, Washington, DC
Primary Contact: Russell E. Lloyd, Director
COO: Joesph P. Sharon, Associate Director
CFO: Donald E Foote, Fiscal Officer
CMO: Mirza Z Ali M.D., Chief of Staff
CIO: David Longmore, Chief Information Officer
CHR: Dawn P DeMorrow, Chief Human Resources Service
Web address: www.va.gov/vamcwb
Control: Veterans Affairs, Government, federal **Service:** General medical and surgical

Staffed Beds: 165 **Admissions:** 3219 **Census:** 119 **Outpatient Visits:** 397418 **Births:** 0 **Total Expense ($000):** 258989 **Payroll Expense ($000):** 94553 **Personnel:** 1292	

WYOMING VALLEY HEALTH CARE SYSTEM See Wilkes–Barre General Hospital

WILLIAMSPORT—Lycoming County

★ **DIVINE PROVIDENCE HOSPITAL (394048)**, 1100 Grampian Boulevard, Zip 17701–1995; tel. 570/326–8000 **A**3 10 **F**11 15 31 35 38 44 50 51 53 54 55 56 59 62 63 64 68 75 77 78 79 81 82 83 84 86 87 93 98 99 100 103 107 108 110 111 115 120 121 129 130 131 132 134 146 147 148 **P**7 **S** UPMC Susquehanna, Williamsport, PA
Primary Contact: Robert E. Kane, Chief Administrative Officer
COO: Neil G Armstrong FACHE, Vice President and Chief Operating Officer
Web address: www.susquehannahealth.org
Control: Other not–for–profit (including NFP Corporation) **Service:** Psychiatric

Staffed Beds: 31 **Admissions:** 637 **Census:** 15 **Outpatient Visits:** 322991 **Births:** 0 **Total Expense ($000):** 88013 **Payroll Expense ($000):** 23570 **Personnel:** 215	

WILLIAMSPORT HOSPITAL AND MEDICAL CENTER See Williamsport Regional Medical Center

⊞ **WILLIAMSPORT REGIONAL MEDICAL CENTER (390045)**, 700 High Street, Zip 17701–3100; tel. 570/321–1000 **A**1 2 5 10 13 **F**3 7 9 11 12 13 15 17 18 20 22 24 26 28 29 30 32 34 35 37 38 40 44 45 46 47 48 49 50 51 52 53 54 56 57 58 59 60 61 65 68 70 73 74 75 76 77 79 81 85 86 87 89 90 91 92 93 94 96 97 107 108 110 111 114 115 116 117 118 119 120 121 123 124 126 130 132 134 135 143 144 146 147 **P**7 **S** UPMC Susquehanna, Williamsport, PA
Primary Contact: Jan E. Fisher, Executive Vice President, Chief Operating Officer and Chief Administrative Officer
COO: Jan E Fisher, Executive Vice President, Chief Operating Officer and Chief Administrative Officer
CFO: Eric Pohjala, Executive Vice President and Chief Financial Officer
CIO: Timothy E Schoener, Vice President and Chief Information Officer
CHR: Christine Ballard, Vice President Human Resources
CNO: Lori A Beucler, MSN, RN, BS–NE, FACHE R.N., Vice President and Chief Nursing Officer
Web address: www.susquehannahealth.org
Control: Other not–for–profit (including NFP Corporation) **Service:** General medical and surgical

Staffed Beds: 220 **Admissions:** 11551 **Census:** 134 **Outpatient Visits:** 92675 **Births:** 1130 **Total Expense ($000):** 297387 **Payroll Expense ($000):** 100450 **Personnel:** 1439	

WINDBER—Somerset County

★ **CHAN SOON–SHIONG MEDICAL CENTER (390112)**, 600 Somerset Avenue, Zip 15963–1331; tel. 814/467–3000 **A**10 **F**3 11 12 15 18 28 29 30 34 35 36 40 45 53 55 56 57 58 59 62 63 70 75 79 81 83 84 85 93 107 108 110 111 114 118 119 129 130 131 132 135 146 147
Primary Contact: Thomas M. Kurtz, President and Chief Executive Officer
CFO: Richard Sukenik CPA, Vice President Finance and Chief Financial Officer
CMO: Kim Marley M.D., Chief Medical Officer
CIO: Renee Adams, Director Information Technology
CHR: Jamie Brock, Director Human Resources
CNO: Michelle Hamula, Director of Nursing and Quality
Web address: www.windbercare.org
Control: Other not–for–profit (including NFP Corporation) **Service:** General medical and surgical

Staffed Beds: 54 **Admissions:** 997 **Census:** 7 **Outpatient Visits:** 93571 **Births:** 0 **Total Expense ($000):** 41051 **Payroll Expense ($000):** 16928 **Personnel:** 351	

WYNNEWOOD—Montgomery County

LANKENAU HOSPITAL See Lankenau Medical Center

☒ **LANKENAU MEDICAL CENTER (390195)**, 100 Lancaster Avenue West, Zip 19096–3411; tel. 484/476–2000, (Total facility includes 22 beds in nursing home–type unit) **A**1 2 3 5 8 10 12 13 **F**3 11 13 15 17 18 20 22 24 26 28 29 30 31 32 34 35 36 37 38 39 40 41 44 45 46 47 48 49 50 54 55 56 57 58 59 63 64 65 66 70 72 73 74 75 76 78 79 80 81 82 84 85 86 87 92 97 100 102 103 107 108 110 111 114 115 119 120 121 124 126 128 129 130 131 132 135 138 146 148 149 **S** Main Line Health, Williamsport, PA
Primary Contact: Phillip D. Robinson, President
COO: John Schwarz, Vice President Administration
CFO: Michael J Buongiorno, Vice President Finance
CMO: Robert Benz M.D., Chief Medical Officer
CIO: Karen A Thomas, Acting Vice President and Chief Information Officer
CHR: Paul Yakulis MS, R.N., Senior Vice President Human Resources
CNO: Margaret Iacobacci, Vice President Patient Care
Web address: www.mainlinehealth.org
Control: Other not–for–profit (including NFP Corporation) **Service**: General medical and surgical

Staffed Beds: 392 Admissions: 17599 Census: 236 Outpatient Visits: 327465 Births: 2824 Total Expense ($000): 473045 Payroll Expense ($000): 142125 Personnel: 2390

WYOMISSING—Berks County

READING HEALTH REHABILITATION HOSPITAL, 2802 Papermill Road, Zip 19610–1065; tel. 484/628–2388 (Nonreporting)
Primary Contact: Clinton Matthews, President and Chief Executive Officer
Web address: www.readinghealth.org/locations/locations–module/reading–health–rehabilitation–hospital–2802–papermill–road–wyomissing–pa–19610–889615952/
Control: Other not–for–profit (including NFP Corporation) **Service**: Rehabilitation

Staffed Beds: 112

☒ **SURGICAL INSTITUTE OF READING (390316)**, 2752 Century Boulevard, Zip 19610–3345; tel. 610/378–8800 **A**1 10 **F**3 8 29 45 68 79 81 82 85 86 107 114
Primary Contact: James Bennett, Chief Executive Officer
CFO: Cheryl Peterson, Business Office Manager
CHR: Megan Schaffer, Administrative Assistant
Web address: www.sireading.com
Control: Partnership, Investor–owned (for–profit) **Service**: Surgical

Staffed Beds: 15 Admissions: 863 Census: 5 Outpatient Visits: 15816 Births: 0 Total Expense ($000): 31104 Payroll Expense ($000): 8903 Personnel: 170

YORK—York County

☒ **HEALTHSOUTH REHABILITATION HOSPITAL OF YORK (393037)**, 1850 Normandie Drive, Zip 17408–1534; tel. 717/767–6941, (Nonreporting) **A**1 10 **S** HEALTHSOUTH Corporation, Birmingham, AL
Primary Contact: Steven Alwine, Chief Executive Officer
CFO: Joyce Henry, Controller
CMO: Bruce Sicilia M.D., Medical Director
CIO: Laura Emig, Director Marketing Operations
CHR: Bradley Teahl, Director Human Resources
CNO: Julie Scott, Chief Nursing Officer
Web address: www.healthsouthyork.com
Control: Corporation, Investor–owned (for–profit) **Service**: Rehabilitation

Staffed Beds: 90

★ ○ **MEMORIAL HOSPITAL (390101)**, 325 South Belmont Street, Zip 17403–2609, Mailing Address: P.O.Box 15118, 17405–7118; tel. 717/843–8623 **A**10 11 13 **F**3 7 8 13 15 18 20 22 26 29 30 31 34 35 40 45 47 48 49 50 51 54 56 57 58 59 60 64 65 66 68 70 75 76 77 78 79 81 84 85 93 97 107 108 111 116 117 118 119 126 129 130 132 135 146 147 **P**6 **S** UPMC Pinnacle, Harrisburg, PA
Primary Contact: Sally J. Dixon, Chief Executive Officer
CIO: James Mahoney, Chief Information Officer
CHR: Corey Hudak, Director Human Resources
CNO: Susan Gordon R.N., Chief Nursing Officer
Web address: www.mhyork.org
Control: Other not–for–profit (including NFP Corporation) **Service**: General medical and surgical

Staffed Beds: 100 Admissions: 4501 Census: 40 Births: 551

☒ **OSS ORTHOPAEDIC HOSPITAL (390325)**, 1861 Powder Mill Road, Zip 17402–4723; tel. 717/718–2000 **A**1 10 **F**3 29 34 62 64 79 81 82 85 86 87 92 94 107 111 114 119 130 131 135 144 148 **P**1 2 6
Primary Contact: Joseph Alhadeff, M.D., President
COO: Cynthia Page FACHE, Chief Operating Officer
CFO: Dale Bushey, Chief Financial Officer
CMO: Todd A. Curran M.D., President Medical Staff
CIO: Tricia Wolf, Director Information Technology
CHR: Maureen M Putnam, Director Human Resources
CNO: Debra Garton R.N., Chief Nursing Officer
Web address: www.osshealth.com
Control: Partnership, Investor–owned (for–profit) **Service**: Orthopedic

Staffed Beds: 30 Admissions: 1603 Census: 11 Births: 0

SELECT SPECIALTY HOSPITAL–YORK See Select Specialty Hospital–Central Pennsylvania, Camp Hill

☒ △ **WELLSPAN YORK HOSPITAL (390046)**, 1001 South George Street, Zip 17403–3645; tel. 717/851–2345, (Includes WELLSPAN SURGERY AND REHABILLITATION HOSPITAL, 55 Monument Road, York, Pennsylvania, Zip 17403–5023, tel. 717/812–6100; Barbara Yarrish, R.N., President) **A**1 2 3 5 7 8 10 12 13 **F**3 7 11 12 13 14 15 17 18 20 22 24 26 28 29 30 31 34 35 39 40 43 44 45 46 48 49 50 54 55 56 57 58 59 60 61 64 65 66 68 70 72 74 75 76 77 78 79 81 82 84 85 86 87 89 92 93 96 97 98 100 101 102 103 104 107 108 110 111 114 115 117 118 119 120 121 123 124 126 129 130 131 132 135 146 147 148 **S** WellSpan Health, York, PA
Primary Contact: Keith D. Noll, President
COO: Raymond Rosen FACHE, Vice President Operations
CFO: Michael F O'Connor, Senior Vice President Finance
CMO: Peter M Hartmann M.D., Vice President Medical Affairs
CIO: R Hal Baker M.D., Vice President and Chief Information Officer
CHR: Robert J Batory, Vice President Human Resources
CNO: Astrid Davis R.N., Chief Nursing Officer
Web address: www.wellspan.org
Control: Other not–for–profit (including NFP Corporation) **Service**: General medical and surgical

Staffed Beds: 556 Admissions: 30342 Census: 427 Births: 3095

RHODE ISLAND

CRANSTON—Providence County

☐ **ELEANOR SLATER HOSPITAL (412001)**, 111 Howard Avenue, Zip 02920–0269, Mailing Address: P.O.Box 8269, 02920–0269; tel. 401/462–3085 **A**1 3 10 **F**1 74 77 98
Primary Contact: Paul J. Despres, Chief Executive Officer
CMO: Charlene Tate M.D., Chief Medical Staff and Clinical Services
Web address: www.bhddh.ri.gov/esh/
Control: State, Government, Nonfederal **Service:** Acute long–term care hospital

> **Staffed Beds:** 284 **Admissions:** 445 **Census:** 273 **Outpatient Visits:** 0
> **Births:** 0 **Total Expense ($000):** 110000 **Personnel:** 757

EAST PROVIDENCE—Providence County

☐ **EMMA PENDLETON BRADLEY HOSPITAL (414003)**, 1011 Veterans Memorial Parkway, Zip 02915–5099; tel. 401/432–1000 **A**1 3 5 10 **F**3 29 34 35 38 57 58 62 64 68 77 86 87 98 99 100 101 104 105 106 130 132 134 **S** Lifespan Corporation, Providence, RI
Primary Contact: Daniel J. Wall, President and Chief Executive Officer
CFO: Mamie Wakefield, Vice President Finance and Chief Financial Officer
CMO: Henry T Sachs M.D., III, Medical Director
CIO: Carole Cotter, Senior Vice President and Chief Information Officer
CHR: Rob Duval, Chief Human Resources Officer
CNO: Vareen O'Keefe Domaleski MS, R.N., Vice Patient Care Services and Chief Nursing Officer
Web address: www.lifespan.org
Control: Other not–for–profit (including NFP Corporation) **Service:** Children's hospital psychiatric

> **Staffed Beds:** 60 **Admissions:** 1428 **Census:** 63 **Outpatient Visits:** 5641
> **Births:** 0 **Total Expense ($000):** 67727 **Payroll Expense ($000):** 38234
> **Personnel:** 551

NEWPORT—Newport County

☐ △ **NEWPORT HOSPITAL (410006)**, 11 Friendship Street, Zip 02840–2299; tel. 401/846–6400 **A**1 2 3 7 10 **F**3 8 11 13 15 18 28 29 30 31 34 35 40 45 49 50 51 53 54 56 57 59 60 64 68 70 74 75 76 77 78 79 81 82 85 86 87 90 91 92 93 96 97 98 99 100 102 103 104 105 107 108 110 111 114 118 119 129 130 132 133 135 143 146 147 148 **P**6 **S** Lifespan Corporation, Providence, RI
Primary Contact: Crista F. Durand, President
CFO: Frank J Byrne, Vice President Finance
CMO: Thomas E. McGue M.D., Vice President Medical Affairs and Chief Medical Officer
CHR: Barbara J. Arcangeli, Vice President Human Resources
CNO: Orla Brandos MSN, R.N., Vice President of Patient Care Services and Chief Nursing Officer
Web address: www.newporthospital.org
Control: Other not–for–profit (including NFP Corporation) **Service:** General medical and surgical

> **Staffed Beds:** 119 **Admissions:** 4714 **Census:** 61 **Outpatient Visits:** 80046
> **Births:** 445 **Total Expense ($000):** 105328 **Payroll Expense ($000):**
> 45759 **Personnel:** 609

NORTH PROVIDENCE—Providence County

☐ △ **ST. JOSEPH HEALTH SERVICES OF RHODE ISLAND (410005)**, 200 High Service Avenue, Zip 02904–5199; tel. 401/456–3000, (Nonreporting) (Includes OUR LADY OF FATIMA HOSPITAL, 200 High Service Avenue, North Providence, Rhode Island, Zip 2904, tel. 401/456–3000; Thomas Hughes, President; ST. JOSEPH HOSPITAL FOR SPECIALTY CARE, 21 Peace Street, Providence, Rhode Island, Zip 2907, tel. 401/456–3000) **A**1 7 10 **S** Prospect Medical Holdings, Los Angeles, CA
Primary Contact: John J. Holiver, Chief Executive Officer
CFO: Michael E Conklin Jr, Chief Financial Officer
CIO: Susan Cerrone Abely, Chief Information Officer
CHR: Darlene Souza, Vice President
CNO: Patricia A Nadle R.N., Chief Nursing Officer
Web address: www.saintjosephri.com
Control: Other not–for–profit (including NFP Corporation) **Service:** General medical and surgical

> **Staffed Beds:** 125

NORTH SMITHFIELD—Providence County

LANDMARK MEDICAL CENTER–FOGARTY UNIT See Landmark Medical Center, Woonsocket

⊞ **REHABILITATION HOSPITAL OF RHODE ISLAND (413025)**, 116 Eddie Dowling Highway, Zip 02896–7327; tel. 401/766–0800 (Nonreporting) **A**1 10 **S** Prime Healthcare, Ontario, CA
Primary Contact: Michael Souza, Chief Executive Officer
COO: Demetra Ouellette, Chief Operating Officer
CFO: Thomas Klessens, Chief Financial Officer
CMO: Khin Yin, Medical Director
CIO: Vincent Larosa, Director of Information Technology Services
CHR: Gail Gosselin, Director Human Resources
CNO: Kathy Keeling, Director of Nursing
Web address: www.rhri.net
Control: Corporation, Investor–owned (for–profit) **Service:** Rehabilitation

> **Staffed Beds:** 70

PAWTUCKET—Providence County

⊞ △ **MEMORIAL HOSPITAL OF RHODE ISLAND (410001)**, 111 Brewster Street, Zip 02860–4499; tel. 401/729–2000, (Nonreporting) **A**1 3 5 7 8 10 **S** Care New England Health System, Providence, RI
Primary Contact: Michael J. Dacey, M.D., President
CFO: James M. Burke, Senior Vice President Finance
CMO: Joseph Diaz M.D., Chief Medical Officer
CHR: Lisa D. Pratt, Vice President Human Resources
CNO: Eileen Dobbing R.N., Senior Vice President for Patient Care Services
Web address: www.mhri.org
Control: Other not–for–profit (including NFP Corporation) **Service:** General medical and surgical

> **Staffed Beds:** 152

PROVIDENCE—Providence County

⊞ **BUTLER HOSPITAL (414000)**, 345 Blackstone Boulevard, Zip 02906–4829; tel. 401/455–6200, (Nonreporting) **A**1 3 5 10 **S** Care New England Health System, Providence, RI
Primary Contact: Lawrence Price, M.D., President and Chief Operating Officer
COO: Lawrence Price M.D., President and Chief Operating Officer
CFO: Bonnie Baker, Vice President Finance and Chief Financial Officer
CMO: James Sullivan M.D., Chief Medical Officer
CIO: Summa Gaddam, Chief Information Officer
CHR: Timothy Bigelow, Director Human Resources
CNO: Mary Leveillee, Senior Vice President Patient Care Services and Chief Nursing Officer
Web address: www.butler.org
Control: Other not–for–profit (including NFP Corporation) **Service:** Psychiatric

> **Staffed Beds:** 143

☐ **MIRIAM HOSPITAL (410012)**, 164 Summit Avenue, Zip 02906–2853; tel. 401/793–2500 **A**1 2 3 5 8 10 **F**3 8 11 12 15 18 20 22 26 28 29 30 31 34 35 40 44 45 46 49 50 53 54 56 57 58 59 60 61 64 65 66 67 68 70 74 75 77 78 79 81 82 84 85 87 92 93 97 100 103 107 108 110 111 114 115 118 119 126 130 132 135 143 146 147 148 **P**3 6 **S** Lifespan Corporation, Providence, RI
Primary Contact: Arthur J. Sampson, FACHE, President
COO: Maria Ducharme R.N., Senior Vice President Patient Care Services and Chief Nursing Officer
CFO: Mamie Wakefield, Chief Financial Officer
CMO: G. Dean Roye M.D., Senior Vice President of Medical Affairs and Chief Medical Officer
CIO: Carole Cotter, Vice President and Chief Information Officer
CHR: Nancy McMahon, Vice President Human Resources
Web address: www.lifespan.org
Control: Other not–for–profit (including NFP Corporation) **Service:** General medical and surgical

> **Staffed Beds:** 247 **Admissions:** 17551 **Census:** 182 **Outpatient Visits:**
> 196107 **Births:** 0 **Total Expense ($000):** 432274 **Payroll Expense ($000):**
> 180802 **Personnel:** 2352

Many Facility Codes have changed. Please refer to the AHA Guide Code Chart. © 2017 AHA Guide

☒ **PROVIDENCE VETERANS AFFAIRS MEDICAL CENTER**, 830 Chalkstone Avenue, Zip 02908–4799; tel. 401/273–7100 **A**1 2 3 5 **F**3 5 8 12 18 29 30 31 34 35 37 38 39 40 44 45 46 47 48 49 50 51 53 54 55 56 57 58 59 60 61 62 63 64 65 68 70 74 75 77 78 79 81 82 84 85 86 87 91 92 93 94 97 98 100 101 102 103 104 107 108 111 114 115 118 119 126 130 132 135 143 144 145 146 147 148 149 150 **S** Department of Veterans Affairs, Washington, DC
Primary Contact: Susan MacKenzie, Ph.D., Director
COO: Erin Clare Sears, Associate Director of Operations
CMO: Satish C Sharma M.D., Chief of Staff
Web address: www.providence.va.gov/
Control: Veterans Affairs, Government, federal **Service**: General medical and surgical

Staffed Beds: 73 **Admissions**: 3307 **Census**: 47 **Outpatient Visits**: 466490
Births: 0 **Total Expense ($000)**: 283213 **Personnel**: 1506

☐ **RHODE ISLAND HOSPITAL (410007)**, 593 Eddy Street, Zip 02903–4900; tel. 401/444–4000, (Includes HASBRO CHILDREN'S HOSPITAL, 593 Eddy Street, Providence, Rhode Island, Zip 02903–4923, tel. 401/444–4000) **A**1 2 3 5 8 10 **F**3 6 7 8 11 15 16 17 18 19 20 21 22 23 24 26 29 30 31 33 34 35 38 39 40 41 43 44 45 46 47 48 49 50 51 53 54 55 56 57 58 59 60 61 64 65 66 67 68 70 74 75 77 78 79 81 82 84 85 86 87 88 89 90 92 93 94 97 98 99 100 101 102 103 104 105 107 108 110 111 114 115 116 117 118 119 120 121 123 124 126 129 130 131 132 133 134 135 138 142 143 145 146 147 148 **P**3 6 **S** Lifespan Corporation, Providence, RI
Primary Contact: Margaret M. Van Bree, Dr.PH, President
COO: Fredrick Macri, Executive Vice President
CFO: Mamie Wakefield, Senior Vice President and Chief Financial Officer
CMO: John B Murphy M.D., Vice President Medical Affairs and Chief Medical Officer
CIO: Carole Cotter, Senior Vice President and Chief Information Officer
CHR: Louis J Sperling, Vice President Human Resources
Web address: www.rhodeislandhospital.org/
Control: Other not–for–profit (including NFP Corporation) **Service**: General medical and surgical

Staffed Beds: 679 **Admissions**: 36770 **Census**: 528 **Outpatient Visits**: 494904 **Births**: 0 **Total Expense ($000)**: 1254603 **Payroll Expense ($000)**: 527828 **Personnel**: 6051

☒ **ROGER WILLIAMS MEDICAL CENTER (410004)**, 825 Chalkstone Avenue, Zip 02908–4735; tel. 401/456–2000, (Nonreporting) **A**1 2 3 5 10 **S** Prospect Medical Holdings, Los Angeles, CA
Primary Contact: Demetra Ouellette, President
CFO: Addy Kane, Chief Financial Officer
CMO: Elaine Jones M.D., President Medical Staff
CIO: Susan Cerrone Abely, Vice President and Chief Information Officer
Web address: www.rwmc.org/
Control: Other not–for–profit (including NFP Corporation) **Service**: General medical and surgical

Staffed Beds: 86

ST. JOSEPH HOSPITAL FOR SPECIALTY CARE See St. Joseph Health Services Of Rhode Island, North Providence

VETERANS AFFAIRS MEDICAL CENTER See Providence Veterans Affairs Medical Center

☒ **WOMEN & INFANTS HOSPITAL OF RHODE ISLAND (410010)**, 101 Dudley Street, Zip 02905–2499; tel. 401/274–1100 **A**1 2 3 5 8 10 **F**3 5 11 13 15 29 30 31 33 34 35 36 38 40 44 45 50 52 54 55 57 58 59 63 64 65 66 68 71 72 74 75 76 77 78 81 82 84 85 86 87 93 97 100 101 102 104 105 107 110 111 114 119 126 130 132 134 135 143 146 147 149 150 **P**6 **S** Care New England Health System, Providence, RI
Primary Contact: Diane Rafferty, Interim Chief Executive Officer
CFO: Robert W Pacheco, Vice President Finance
CMO: Raymond Powrie M.D., Senior Vice President Quality and Clinical Effectiveness
CHR: Paul F Heffernan, Vice President Human Resources
Web address: www.womenandinfants.org
Control: Other not–for–profit (including NFP Corporation) **Service**: Obstetrics and gynecology

Staffed Beds: 247 **Admissions**: 11722 **Census**: 155 **Outpatient Visits**: 337535 **Births**: 9034 **Total Expense ($000)**: 487699 **Payroll Expense ($000)**: 187911 **Personnel**: 1789

☐ **SOUTH COUNTY HOSPITAL (410008)**, 100 Kenyon Avenue, Zip 02879–4299; tel. 401/782–8000 **A**1 2 10 **F**3 13 15 18 20 28 29 30 31 34 35 36 37 40 44 45 46 47 49 50 51 53 54 56 57 59 60 61 64 65 68 70 74 77 78 79 81 85 86 87 103 107 108 110 111 114 119 126 129 130 131 135 141 145 146 149 **P**6
Primary Contact: Louis R. Giancola, President and Chief Executive Officer
CFO: Thomas Breen, Vice President and Chief Financial Officer
CMO: John Russell Corcoran, Vice President Medical Affairs
CIO: Gary Croteau, Assistant Vice President and Chief Information Officer
CHR: Maggie Thomas, Vice President Human Resources and Practice Management
CNO: Anne Schmidt, Vice President of Patient Care Services and Chief Nursing Officer
Web address: www.schospital.com
Control: Other not–for–profit (including NFP Corporation) **Service**: General medical and surgical

Staffed Beds: 85 **Admissions**: 4730 **Census**: 47 **Outpatient Visits**: 210604 **Births**: 642 **Total Expense ($000)**: 159880 **Payroll Expense ($000)**: 68234 **Personnel**: 906

☒ △ **KENT COUNTY MEMORIAL HOSPITAL (410009)**, 455 Tollgate Road, Zip 02886–2770; tel. 401/737–7000 **A**1 3 5 7 10 13 **F**3 8 11 12 13 15 17 18 20 22 26 29 30 31 34 35 36 40 44 45 46 47 48 49 50 51 56 57 58 59 60 61 63 64 65 68 70 73 74 75 76 77 78 79 81 82 84 85 86 87 90 93 94 96 97 98 99 100 102 103 107 108 110 111 114 115 116 118 119 126 129 130 131 132 143 146 147 148 149 **S** Care New England Health System, Providence, RI
Primary Contact: Michael J. Dacey, M.D., President and Chief Operating Officer
COO: Michael J Dacey M.D., President and Chief Operating Officer
CFO: James M. Burke, Vice President Finance, Chief Nursing Executive Medical Surgical Hospitals
CIO: Sumalatha Gaddam, Senior Vice President and Chief Information Officer
CHR: Marilyn J Walsh, Vice President Human Resources
CNO: Rebecca Burke R.N., MS, Senior Vice President and Chief Nursing Officer
Web address: www.kentri.org
Control: Other not–for–profit (including NFP Corporation) **Service**: General medical and surgical

Staffed Beds: 318 **Admissions**: 14106 **Census**: 196 **Outpatient Visits**: 278629 **Births**: 818 **Total Expense ($000)**: 374162 **Payroll Expense ($000)**: 151999 **Personnel**: 1768

☒ **WESTERLY HOSPITAL (410013)**, 25 Wells Street, Zip 02891–2934; tel. 401/596–6000 **A**1 2 10 **F**3 11 14 15 18 20 26 28 29 30 31 34 35 40 44 48 49 51 57 59 60 64 68 70 75 78 79 81 85 86 87 93 94 107 108 110 111 115 118 119 130 132 135 146 148 149 **P**3 **S** Yale New Haven Health, New Haven, CT
Primary Contact: Patrick Green, FACHE, President and Chief Executive Officer
CFO: Seth Van Essendelft, Vice President and Chief Financial Officer
CMO: Oliver Mayorga M.D., Chief Medical Officer
CIO: Kimberly Kalajainen, Vice President, Operations and Information Technology, Chief Information Officer
CHR: Donna Epps, Vice President, Chief Human Resource Officer
CNO: Lauren Williams MS, Vice President Patient Care Services and Chief Nursing Officer
Web address: www.westerlyhospital.org
Control: Other not–for–profit (including NFP Corporation) **Service**: General medical and surgical

Staffed Beds: 39 **Admissions**: 2480 **Census**: 29 **Outpatient Visits**: 114325 **Births**: 0 **Total Expense ($000)**: 69868 **Payroll Expense ($000)**: 28702 **Personnel**: 380

☒ **LANDMARK MEDICAL CENTER (410011)**, 115 Cass Avenue, Zip 02895–4731; tel. 401/769–4100, (Nonreporting) (Includes LANDMARK MEDICAL CENTER–FOGARTY UNIT, Eddie Dowling Highway, North Smithfield, Rhode Island, Zip 2896, Woonsocket, tel. 401/766–0800; LANDMARK MEDICAL CENTER–WOONSOCKET UNIT, 115 Cass Avenue, Woonsocket, Rhode Island, Zip 2895, tel. 401/769–4100) **A**1 2 10 **S** Prime Healthcare, Ontario, CA
Primary Contact: Michael Souza, Chief Executive Officer
CFO: Thomas Klessens, Chief Financial Officer
CMO: Glenn Fort, Chief Medical Officer
CIO: Vincent Larosa, Director of Information Systems
CHR: Gail Gosselin, Director Human Resources
CNO: Carol Conley, Chief Nursing Officer
Web address: www.landmarkmedcenter.com
Control: Corporation, Investor–owned (for–profit) **Service**: General medical and surgical

Staffed Beds: 140

Hospital, Medicare Provider Number, Address, Telephone, Approval, Facility, and Physician Codes, Health Care System

★ American Hospital Association (AHA) membership
☐ The Joint Commission accreditation
○ Healthcare Facilities Accreditation Program
◇ DNV Healthcare Inc. accreditation
⇑ Center for Improvement in Healthcare Quality Accreditation
△ Commission on Accreditation of Rehabilitation Facilities (CARF) accreditation

SOUTH CAROLINA

ABBEVILLE—Abbeville County

★ ⇑ **ABBEVILLE AREA MEDICAL CENTER (421301)**, 420 Thomson Circle, Zip 29620–5656, Mailing Address: P.O.Box 887, 29620–0887; tel. 864/366–5011 **A**10 18 21 **F**3 15 29 30 35 40 51 53 56 57 59 62 67 70 74 75 77 81 85 87 89 90 94 103 107 108 110 114 119 127 128 129 130 132 133 135 146 147 148 **P**5 **S** QHR, Brentwood, TN
Primary Contact: Howard D. Turner, Chief Executive Officer
CFO: Timothy Wren, Chief Financial Officer
CMO: Christopher Ceraldi M.D., Chief of Staff
CIO: Tim Stewart, Chief Information Officer
CHR: Alice Rigney, Chief Human Resources Officer
CNO: Ernest Shock, Chief Nursing Officer
Web address: www.abbevilleareamc.com
Control: County, Government, Nonfederal **Service**: General medical and surgical

Staffed Beds: 25 **Admissions**: 613 **Census**: 9 **Outpatient Visits**: 30518 **Births**: 0 **Total Expense ($000)**: 41717 **Payroll Expense ($000)**: 19734 **Personnel**: 395

AIKEN—Aiken County

☐ **AIKEN REGIONAL MEDICAL CENTERS (420082)**, 302 University Parkway, Zip 29801–6302; tel. 803/641–5000, (Includes AURORA PAVILION, 655 Medical Park Drive, Aiken, South Carolina, Zip 29801, tel. 803/641–5900) **A**1 3 5 10 **F**1 3 4 5 11 12 15 18 20 22 24 29 30 31 34 35 40 46 49 56 57 58 59 64 70 73 74 76 77 78 79 80 81 85 86 87 89 98 99 100 101 102 103 104 105 107 108 110 111 114 115 119 121 123 128 129 130 131 132 135 146 147 148 **S** Universal Health Services, Inc., King of Prussia, PA
Primary Contact: Vance V. Reynolds, FACHE, CPA, Chief Executive Officer
COO: Matt Merrifield, Chief Operating Officer
Web address: www.aikenregional.com
Control: Corporation, Investor–owned (for–profit) **Service**: General medical and surgical

Staffed Beds: 271 **Admissions**: 11948 **Census**: 162 **Outpatient Visits**: 141757 **Births**: 1058 **Personnel**: 824

ANDERSON—Anderson County

⊞ **ANMED HEALTH MEDICAL CENTER (420027)**, 800 North Fant Street, Zip 29621–5793; tel. 864/512–1000, (Includes ANMED HEALTH WOMEN'S AND CHILDREN'S HOSPITAL, 2000 East Greenville Street, Anderson, South Carolina, Zip 29621, tel. 864/512–1000; William T Manson III, Chief Executive Officer) **A**1 2 3 5 10 **F**3 4 5 8 11 12 13 14 15 17 18 20 22 24 26 28 29 30 31 34 35 37 39 40 43 45 46 48 49 50 51 53 54 56 57 58 59 60 61 62 64 65 68 70 71 73 74 75 76 77 78 79 80 81 84 85 86 87 89 90 91 97 98 100 101 102 103 104 105 107 108 110 111 114 115 117 118 119 121 123 127 129 130 131 132 135 144 146 147 148 149 **P**2 6 **S** AnMed Health, Anderson, SC
Primary Contact: William T. Manson III, Chief Executive Officer
CFO: Christine Pearson, Vice President Finance and Chief Financial Officer
CMO: Thomas Kayrouz M.D., Chief Medical Officer
CIO: Marty Stewart, Director Information Services
CHR: Richard Walter Grooms Jr, Chief Human Resources Officer
CNO: Tina M Jury MSN, Executive Vice President Hospital Operations and Chief Nursing Officer
Web address: www.anmedhealth.org
Control: Other not–for–profit (including NFP Corporation) **Service**: General medical and surgical

Staffed Beds: 400 **Admissions**: 19698 **Census**: 272 **Outpatient Visits**: 920391 **Births**: 1807 **Total Expense ($000)**: 564547 **Payroll Expense ($000)**: 207467 **Personnel**: 4014

⊞ **ANMED HEALTH REHABILITATION HOSPITAL (423029)**, 1 Spring Back Way, Zip 29621–2676; tel. 864/716–2600 **A**1 10 **F**3 29 30 56 57 60 68 74 75 79 90 91 93 94 95 96 **S** HEALTHSOUTH Corporation, Birmingham, AL
Primary Contact: Denise R. Murray, Chief Executive Officer
CFO: Julie Saylors, Controller
CMO: William Vogentiz M.D., Medical Director
CHR: Tara Myers, Director Human Resources
CNO: Carmella Burton, Chief Nursing Officer
Web address: www.anmedrehab.com
Control: Corporation, Investor–owned (for–profit) **Service**: Rehabilitation

Staffed Beds: 60 **Admissions**: 1473 **Census**: 48 **Births**: 0 **Total Expense ($000)**: 15587 **Payroll Expense ($000)**: 8776 **Personnel**: 199

☐ **PATRICK B. HARRIS PSYCHIATRIC HOSPITAL (424011)**, 130 Highway 252, Zip 29621–5054; tel. 864/231–2600 **A**1 3 5 10 **F**98 100 101 102 103 106 130 143 146
Primary Contact: John Fletcher, Chief Executive Officer
Web address: www.patrickbharris.com/
Control: State, Government, Nonfederal **Service**: Psychiatric

Staffed Beds: 110 **Admissions**: 449 **Census**: 109 **Outpatient Visits**: 0 **Births**: 0 **Personnel**: 292

BEAUFORT—Beaufort County

⊞ **BEAUFORT MEMORIAL HOSPITAL (420067)**, 955 Ribaut Road, Zip 29902–5441; tel. 843/522–5200 **A**1 2 10 **F**3 11 12 13 15 18 20 22 28 29 30 31 32 34 35 40 43 45 49 50 51 53 54 57 59 60 64 65 69 70 71 73 74 75 76 77 78 79 81 85 86 87 89 90 93 94 97 98 100 101 102 103 104 107 108 111 114 115 117 119 120 121 126 127 130 132 134 135 145 146 147 148
Primary Contact: Edmond Russell. Baxley III, President and Chief Executive Officer
CFO: Ken Miller, Chief Financial Officer
CMO: Kurt Gambla D.O., Chief Medical Officer
CIO: Edward Ricks, Vice President and Chief Information Officer
CHR: Doug Douglas, Interim Vice President Human Resources
CNO: Karen Carroll MSN, R.N., Vice President and Chief Nursing Officer
Web address: www.bmhsc.org
Control: County, Government, Nonfederal **Service**: General medical and surgical

Staffed Beds: 197 **Admissions**: 10708 **Census**: 122 **Outpatient Visits**: 184062

⊞ **NAVAL HOSPITAL BEAUFORT**, 1 Pinckney Boulevard, Zip 29902–6122; tel. 843/228–5301, (Nonreporting) **A**1 5 **S** Bureau of Medicine and Surgery, Department of the Navy, Falls Church, VA
Primary Contact: Lieutenant Commander Willie Brown, Director Administration
Web address: www.med.navy.mil/sites/nhbeaufort/Pages/Welcome_Page.aspx
Control: Navy, Government, federal **Service**: General medical and surgical

Staffed Beds: 20

CAMDEN—Kershaw County

⊞ **KERSHAWHEALTH (420048)**, 1315 Roberts Street, Zip 29020–3737, Mailing Address: P.O.Box 7003, 29021–7003; tel. 803/432–4311 **A**1 10 **F**3 11 13 15 18 20 24 28 29 30 31 32 34 35 40 44 45 49 50 51 54 57 59 61 62 63 64 66 68 70 75 76 77 78 79 81 85 86 87 89 90 94 97 107 108 110 111 114 115 118 119 127 129 130 132 144 146 147 148 **S** RCCH HealthCare Partners, Brentwood, TN
Primary Contact: Terry Gunn, FACHE, Chief Executive Officer
COO: Susan R Burroughs FACHE, Chief Operating Officer
CFO: Mike Bunch, Executive Vice President, Chief Operating Officer and Chief Financial Officer
CMO: Tallulah Holmstrom, Chief Medical Officer
CIO: Diane Arrants, Chief Information Officer
CHR: Angela F Nettles, Director Human Resources
Web address: www.kershawhealth.com
Control: Corporation, Investor–owned (for–profit) **Service**: General medical and surgical

Staffed Beds: 119 **Admissions**: 4091 **Census**: 47 **Outpatient Visits**: 77776 **Births**: 286 **Total Expense ($000)**: 87679 **Payroll Expense ($000)**: 38016 **Personnel**: 772

CHARLESTON—Charleston County

⊞ **BON SECOURS ST. FRANCIS HOSPITAL (420065)**, 2095 Henry Tecklenburg Drive, Zip 29414–5733; tel. 843/402–1000 **A**1 10 **F**3 7 12 13 14 15 28 29 30 31 34 35 40 45 46 47 48 49 50 51 56 57 59 64 68 70 73 74 75 76 77 78 79 80 81 82 84 85 86 87 89 93 94 100 102 107 108 110 111 114 115 117 118 119 120 121 123 130 131 132 145 146 147 148 149 **S** Carolinas HealthCare System, Charlotte, NC
Primary Contact: Stephen D. Porter, Chief Executive Officer
CFO: Bret Johnson, Chief Financial Officer
CMO: Steven D Shapiro M.D., Chief Medical Officer
CIO: Michael Taylor, Chief Information Officer
CNO: Pennie Peralta R.N., VP, Nursing & Chief Nursing Officer
Web address: www.rsfh.com/
Control: Other not–for–profit (including NFP Corporation) **Service**: General medical and surgical

Staffed Beds: 173 **Admissions**: 9142 **Census**: 96 **Outpatient Visits**: 168432 **Births**: 2625 **Total Expense ($000)**: 178532 **Payroll Expense ($000)**: 55522 **Personnel**: 1074

SC

✠ **HEALTHSOUTH REHABILITATION HOSPITAL OF CHARLESTON (423027)**, 9181 Medcom Street, Zip 29406–9168; tel. 843/820–7777 **A**1 10 **F**90 94 96 **S** HEALTHSOUTH Corporation, Birmingham, AL
Primary Contact: Michele M. Skripps, R.N., Chief Executive Officer
CFO: Beckye Lariviere, Controller
CMO: William Livesay D.O., Jr, Medical Director
CHR: Traxler Littlejohn, Human Resources Director
CNO: Patricia Simon, Chief Nursing Officer
Web address: www.healthsouthcharleston.com
Control: Corporation, Investor–owned (for–profit) **Service:** Rehabilitation

Staffed Beds: 49 **Admissions:** 1059 **Census:** 39 **Outpatient Visits:** 6213 **Births:** 0 **Total Expense ($000):** 17018 **Payroll Expense ($000):** 7401 **Personnel:** 153

✠ **MUSC MEDICAL CENTER OF MEDICAL UNIVERSITY OF SOUTH CAROLINA (420004)**, 169 Ashley Avenue, Zip 29425–8905; tel. 843/792–2300, (Includes CHILDREN'S HOSPITAL OF SOUTH CAROLINA AT MUSC, 171 Ashley Avenue, Charleston, South Carolina, Zip 29425–8908, tel. 843/792–1414; Patrick J Cawley, M.D., Chief Executive Officer, MUSC Health and Vice President for Health Affairs, University) **A**1 2 3 5 8 10 **F**3 4 5 6 7 8 9 11 12 13 14 15 16 17 18 19 20 21 22 23 24 25 26 27 28 29 30 31 32 34 35 36 37 38 39 40 41 43 44 45 46 47 48 49 50 51 52 53 54 55 56 57 58 59 60 61 64 65 66 67 68 70 71 72 73 74 75 76 77 78 79 80 81 82 84 85 86 87 88 89 91 92 93 94 97 98 99 100 101 102 103 104 105 106 107 108 109 110 111 114 115 116 117 118 119 120 121 123 124 126 129 130 131 132 134 135 136 137 138 139 140 141 142 144 145 146 147 148 149 150
Primary Contact: Patrick J. Cawley, M.D., Chief Executive Officer, MUSC Health and Vice President for Health Affairs, University
COO: Matthew Wain, Chief Operating Officer
CFO: Stephen Hargett, Administrator Finance and Support Services
CMO: Daniel Handel M.D., Chief Medical Officer
CIO: Michael Caputo, Chief Information Officer
CHR: Darrick Paul, Chief People Officer
CNO: Jerry A Mansfield Ph.D., R.N., Executive Chief Nursing Officer & Chief Patient Experience Officer
Web address: www.muschealth.com
Control: State, Government, Nonfederal **Service:** General medical and surgical

Staffed Beds: 779 **Admissions:** 35134 **Census:** 620 **Outpatient Visits:** 1078156 **Births:** 2640 **Total Expense ($000):** 1349127 **Payroll Expense ($000):** 458667 **Personnel:** 7030

☐ **PALMETTO LOWCOUNTRY BEHAVIORAL HEALTH (424006)**, 2777 Speissegger Drive, Zip 29405–8229; tel. 843/747–5830 **A**1 10 **F**4 5 64 98 99 102 103 104 105 **S** Universal Health Services, Inc., King of Prussia, PA
Primary Contact: Clint Hauger, Chief Executive Officer
CFO: Stan Markowski, Chief Financial Officer
CMO: Steven Lopez M.D., Chief Medical Officer
CHR: Sheila Simpson, Vice President Human Resources
CNO: Jo Good, Director of Nursing
Web address: www.palmettobehavioralhealth.com
Control: Corporation, Investor–owned (for–profit) **Service:** Psychiatric

Staffed Beds: 100 **Admissions:** 2817 **Census:** 63 **Outpatient Visits:** 3638 **Births:** 0 **Personnel:** 164

✠ **RALPH H. JOHNSON VETERANS AFFAIRS MEDICAL CENTER**, 109 Bee Street, Zip 29401–5799; tel. 843/577–5011, (Nonreporting) **A**1 2 3 5 8 **S** Department of Veterans Affairs, Washington, DC
Primary Contact: Scott R. Isaacks, FACHE, Director and Chief Executive Officer
CFO: Cassandra Helfer, Chief Financial Officer
CMO: Florence N. Hutchison M.D., Chief of Staff
CIO: LaBon Hardy, Chief Information Officer
CHR: Renae A. Jacobson, Human Resources Officer
CNO: Garett E. Schreier R.N., Associate Director, Nursing and Patient Care Services
Web address: www.charleston.va.gov/
Control: Veterans Affairs, Government, federal **Service:** General medical and surgical

Staffed Beds: 98

✠ △ **ROPER ST. FRANCIS (420087)**, 316 Calhoun Street, Zip 29401–1125; tel. 843/724–2000 **A**1 2 3 5 7 10 **F**3 7 8 9 14 15 17 18 20 22 24 26 28 29 30 31 34 35 37 40 42 43 45 49 50 51 53 54 55 56 57 58 59 60 61 62 63 64 65 67 68 69 70 74 75 77 78 79 80 81 82 84 85 86 87 90 92 93 94 95 96 102 107 108 110 111 114 115 118 119 120 121 123 124 126 129 130 131 132 135 136 143 146 147 148 149 **S** Carolinas HealthCare System, Charlotte, NC
Primary Contact: Matthew J. Severance, FACHE, Chief Executive Officer
CFO: Bret Johnson, Chief Financial Officer
CMO: Steven D Shapiro M.D., Vice President Medical Affairs
CIO: Melinda H. Cardell, Interim Vice President and Chief Information Officer
CHR: Melanie Stith, Vice President Human Resources
CNO: Carolyn Viall Donohue MSN, R.N., Vice President Nursing
Web address: www.rsfh.com/
Control: Other not–for–profit (including NFP Corporation) **Service:** General medical and surgical

Staffed Beds: 300 **Admissions:** 13672 **Census:** 200 **Outpatient Visits:** 219166 **Births:** 0 **Total Expense ($000):** 348785 **Payroll Expense ($000):** 108141 **Personnel:** 2040

✠ **TRIDENT MEDICAL CENTER (420079)**, 9330 Medical Plaza Drive, Zip 29406–9195; tel. 843/797–7000, (Includes MONCKS CORNER MEDICAL CENTER, 401 North Live Oak Drive, Highway 17A, Moncks Corner, South Carolina, Zip 29461–5603, tel. 843/761–8721; SUMMERVILLE MEDICAL CENTER, 295 Midland Parkway, Summerville, South Carolina, Zip 29485–8104, tel. 843/832–5000) **A**1 2 3 5 10 **F**3 8 12 13 15 16 18 20 22 24 26 28 29 30 31 34 35 40 41 42 43 45 46 47 48 49 50 54 55 56 57 59 60 61 64 70 72 73 74 75 76 77 78 79 80 81 84 85 86 87 88 89 90 93 94 98 100 102 105 107 108 110 111 114 115 116 117 118 119 120 121 123 126 130 131 132 135 145 146 147 148 **S** HCA Healthcare, Nashville, TN
Primary Contact: Todd Gallati, FACHE, President and Chief Executive Officer
CFO: Teresa Finch, Chief Financial Officer
CIO: Susan Murray, Director Information Services
CHR: Joe B Hill Jr, Vice President Human Resources
Web address: www.tridenthealthsystem.com
Control: Corporation, Investor–owned (for–profit) **Service:** General medical and surgical

Staffed Beds: 421 **Admissions:** 24230 **Census:** 285 **Outpatient Visits:** 347293 **Births:** 2984 **Personnel:** 1836

CHERAW—Chesterfield County

⇑ **MCLEOD HEALTH CHERAW (420107)**, 711 Chesterfield Highway, Zip 29520–7002; tel. 843/537–7881 **A**10 21 **F**3 13 15 18 28 29 30 34 35 40 45 56 57 59 68 70 76 79 80 81 85 86 87 89 102 107 108 111 114 118 119 128 130 132 133 135 **P**3 **S** McLeod Health, Florence, SC
Primary Contact: Mib Scoggins, Chief Executive Officer
CFO: Louis Anderson, Chief Financial Officer
CMO: David Bersinger M.D., Chief of Staff
CIO: Jim Spencer, Director Information System
Web address: www.chesterfieldgeneral.com
Control: Other not–for–profit (including NFP Corporation) **Service:** General medical and surgical

Staffed Beds: 52 **Admissions:** 1825 **Census:** 17 **Outpatient Visits:** 33675 **Births:** 196 **Total Expense ($000):** 34852 **Payroll Expense ($000):** 11956 **Personnel:** 181

CHESTER—Chester County

✠ **CHESTER REGIONAL MEDICAL CENTER (420019)**, 1 Medical Park Drive, Zip 29706–9769; tel. 803/581–3151 **A**1 10 **F**15 28 29 34 35 40 50 56 57 59 70 75 77 79 81 85 86 87 89 90 94 107 108 110 111 119 128 129 130 131 132 135 **S** Community Health Systems, Inc., Franklin, TN
Primary Contact: Page H. Vaughan, Chief Executive Officer
CFO: Tracey Claxton, Chief Financial Officer
CMO: Terry Dodge M.D., Chief of Staff
CIO: Shaw Laird, Chief Information Officer
CHR: Karen Chapman, Director Human Resources
CNO: Betty Griffin, Interim Chief Nursing Officer
Web address: www.chesterregional.com
Control: Corporation, Investor–owned (for–profit) **Service:** General medical and surgical

Staffed Beds: 36 **Admissions:** 997 **Census:** 8 **Outpatient Visits:** 52335 **Births:** 0

SC

SC

CLINTON—Laurens County

⊞ **GREENVILLE HEALTH SYSTEM – LAURENS COUNTY MEMORIAL HOSPITAL (420038)**, 22725 Highway 76 East, Zip 29325–7527, Mailing Address: P O Drawer 976, 29325–0976; tel. 864/833–9100, (Includes GHS – LAURENS COUNTY MEMORIAL HOSPITAL, 22725 Highway 76 E, PO Drawer 976, Clinton, South Carolina, Zip 29325–7527, PO Box 976, 29325–0976, tel. 803/833–9100; Justin Benfield, Southern Region Chief Operating Officer) (Total facility includes 14 beds in nursing home–type unit) **A**1 5 10 20 **F**1 3 13 15 18 28 30 40 45 46 59 70 76 79 80 81 87 89 107 110 111 114 115 119 128 132 147 **P**6 **S** Greenville Health System, Greenville, SC
Primary Contact: Justin Benfield, Southern Region Chief Operating Officer
CFO: Michael Norrick, Director of Campus Operations
CMO: Vincent Green, Medical Director
CIO: Kathleen Anderson, Director, Acute Clinical Systems
CHR: Cathy M Rogers, Manager Human Resources
CNO: Kay Swisher, Chief Nursing Officer
Web address: www.ghs.org/laurens
Control: Other not–for–profit (including NFP Corporation) **Service**: General medical and surgical

Staffed Beds: 71 **Admissions:** 2890 **Census:** 37 **Outpatient Visits:** 67857 **Births:** 333 **Total Expense ($000):** 64574 **Payroll Expense ($000):** 18358 **Personnel:** 311

WHITTEN CENTER, Highway 76 East, Zip 29325, Mailing Address: P.O.Box 239, 29325–0239; tel. 864/833–2733, (Nonreporting)
Primary Contact: Wes Leonard, Chief Executive Officer
Control: State, Government, Nonfederal **Service**: Intellectual disabilities

Staffed Beds: 22

COLUMBIA—Laurens County

★ **CONTINUECARE HOSPITAL AT PALMETTO HEALTH BAPTIST (422006)**, Taylor at Marion Street, Zip 29220, Mailing Address: PO BOX 11069, 29211–1069; tel. 803/296–3757 (Nonreporting) **A**10 **S** Community Hospital Corporation, Plano, TX
Primary Contact: Thomas P. Harlan, Chief Executive Officer
Web address: www.continuecare.org/palmetto//
Control: Other not–for–profit (including NFP Corporation) **Service**: Acute long–term care hospital

Staffed Beds: 35

COLUMBIA—Lexington County

⊞ **PALMETTO HEALTH BAPTIST PARKRIDGE (420106)**, 400 Palmetto Health Parkway, Zip 29212–1760, Mailing Address: P.O. BOX 2266, 29202–2266; tel. 803/907–7000 **A**1 10 **F**3 8 13 15 29 30 31 34 35 40 45 46 50 55 57 59 64 68 70 71 75 76 77 78 81 86 87 90 93 94 97 107 110 111 115 119 130 132 143 144 146 147 **S** Palmetto Health, Columbia, SC
Primary Contact: Sarah Kirby, R.N., MSN, FACHE, Chief Operating Officer
Web address: www.palmettohealth.org
Control: Other not–for–profit (including NFP Corporation) **Service**: General medical and surgical

Staffed Beds: 69 **Admissions:** 4676 **Census:** 52 **Outpatient Visits:** 100586 **Births:** 649 **Total Expense ($000):** 114547 **Payroll Expense ($000):** 39685 **Personnel:** 886

COLUMBIA—Richland County

EARLE E. MORRIS ALCOHOL AND DRUG TREATMENT CENTER, 610 Faison Drive, Zip 29203–3218; tel. 803/935–7100 **F**4 29 39 53 61 67 74 75 87 98 130 132 146
Primary Contact: George McConnell, Director
Web address: www.state.sc.us/dmh/morris_village/
Control: State, Government, Nonfederal **Service**: Alcoholism and other chemical dependency

Staffed Beds: 96 **Admissions:** 1391 **Census:** 95 **Outpatient Visits:** 0 **Births:** 0 **Personnel:** 180

☐ **G. WERBER BRYAN PSYCHIATRIC HOSPITAL (424005)**, 220 Faison Drive, Zip 29203–3210; tel. 803/935–7140 **A**1 3 10 **F**1 4 30 50 74 75 97 98 101 103 128 130 132 135 146
Primary Contact: Stuart Shields, Director
COO: Jaclyn Upfield, Chief Operating Officer
CIO: Sam Livingston, Information Resource Consultant
CHR: Kim Church, Manager Human Resources
Web address: www.scdmh.org
Control: State, Government, Nonfederal **Service**: Psychiatric

Staffed Beds: 157 **Admissions:** 227 **Census:** 142 **Outpatient Visits:** 0 **Births:** 0 **Personnel:** 395

⊞ **HEALTHSOUTH REHABILITATION HOSPITAL OF COLUMBIA (423025)**, 2935 Colonial Drive, Zip 29203–6811; tel. 803/254–7777 **A**1 10 **F**29 50 53 60 64 77 90 91 92 93 94 95 96 97 119 **S** HEALTHSOUTH Corporation, Birmingham, AL
Primary Contact: Catherine Landis, R.N., Chief Executive Officer
CFO: Jessica Burriss, Chief Financial Officer
CMO: Devin Troyer M.D., Medical Director
CHR: Luanne Burton, Director Human Resources
CNO: April Brooks, Chief Nursing Officer
Web address: www.healthsouthcolumbia.com
Control: Corporation, Investor–owned (for–profit) **Service**: Rehabilitation

Staffed Beds: 96 **Admissions:** 1825 **Census:** 65 **Outpatient Visits:** 12431 **Births:** 0 **Total Expense ($000):** 20147 **Payroll Expense ($000):** 11291

⊞ **PALMETTO HEALTH BAPTIST (420086)**, Taylor at Marion Street, Zip 29220–0001; tel. 803/296–5010, (Total facility includes 22 beds in nursing home–type unit) **A**1 2 3 5 10 **F**1 3 5 7 11 12 13 15 18 20 29 30 31 34 35 38 40 45 47 48 49 51 54 57 59 61 62 63 64 65 66 68 70 71 72 73 74 75 76 77 78 79 80 81 82 83 84 85 86 87 89 90 93 94 97 98 99 100 101 102 103 104 105 107 108 110 111 114 115 117 118 119 124 128 130 132 145 146 147 148 **S** Palmetto Health, Columbia, SC
Primary Contact: Gregory B. Gattman, Chief Operating Officer
COO: James M Bridges, Executive Vice President and Chief Operating Officer
CFO: Paul K Duane, Chief Financial Officer and Office of Health Reform
CMO: Mark J Mayson M.D., Medical Director
CIO: Michelle Edwards, Executive Vice President Information Technology
CHR: Trip Gregory, Senior Vice President Human Resources
Web address: www.palmettohealth.org
Control: Other not–for–profit (including NFP Corporation) **Service**: General medical and surgical

Staffed Beds: 400 **Admissions:** 20671 **Census:** 265 **Outpatient Visits:** 211752 **Births:** 3179 **Total Expense ($000):** 325057 **Payroll Expense ($000):** 131610 **Personnel:** 2513

⊞ **PALMETTO HEALTH RICHLAND (420018)**, Five Richland Medical Park Drive, Zip 29203–6897; tel. 803/434–7000, (Includes PALMETTO HEALTH CHILDREN'S HOSPITAL, Five Richland Medical Park Dr, Columbia, South Carolina, Zip 29203–6863, tel. 803/434–6882) **A**1 2 3 5 8 10 **F**1 2 3 4 5 7 11 13 15 17 18 19 20 21 22 24 28 29 30 31 32 34 35 39 40 41 43 45 46 50 54 55 56 57 58 59 60 61 64 65 66 68 70 71 72 73 74 75 76 77 78 79 81 86 87 88 89 90 93 94 97 98 99 100 101 102 103 104 105 107 110 111 114 115 119 121 126 128 129 130 131 132 134 135 143 146 147 148 **S** Palmetto Health, Columbia, SC
Primary Contact: Jay Hamm, R.N., FACHE, Chief Operating Officer
CFO: Paul K Duane, Chief Financial Officer and Office of Health Reform
CMO: Eric Brown M.D., Physician Executive
CNO: Carole A Siegfried MSN, R.N., Campus Nurse Executive
Web address: www.palmettohealth.org
Control: Other not–for–profit (including NFP Corporation) **Service**: General medical and surgical

Staffed Beds: 671 **Admissions:** 30962 **Census:** 564 **Outpatient Visits:** 586682 **Births:** 2412 **Total Expense ($000):** 775516 **Payroll Expense ($000):** 306886 **Personnel:** 5445

★ ⇑ **PROVIDENCE HOSPITAL (420026)**, 2435 Forest Drive, Zip 29204–2098; tel. 803/865–4500, (Includes PROVIDENCE HOSPITAL NORTHEAST, 120 Gateway Corporate Boulevard, Columbia, South Carolina, Zip 29203–9611, tel. 803/865–4500; Ryan Hall, Vice President) **A**10 21 **F**3 8 11 17 18 20 22 24 26 28 29 30 34 35 38 40 44 45 49 50 53 54 56 57 58 59 61 63 64 68 70 74 75 79 80 81 83 84 85 86 87 90 92 93 94 100 107 108 111 114 115 118 119 129 130 131 132 141 146 147 148 **P**5 **S** LifePoint Health, Brentwood, TN
Primary Contact: Scott Campbell, Market Chief Executive Officer
COO: W. Carl Martin, Chief Operating Officer
CFO: Pamela Gallagher, Chief Financial Officer
CMO: Wayne Sribnick M.D., Senior Vice President and Chief Medical Officer
CIO: Lib Cumbee, Director Information Systems
CHR: Justin A Lofurno, Director Human Resources
Web address: www.sistersofcharityhealth.org/health–care/providence–hospitals/
Control: Corporation, Investor–owned (for–profit) **Service**: General medical and surgical

Staffed Beds: 247 **Admissions:** 9241 **Census:** 121 **Outpatient Visits:** 105055 **Births:** 0 **Total Expense ($000):** 210050 **Payroll Expense ($000):** 67200 **Personnel:** 1169

PROVIDENCE HOSPITAL NORTHEAST See Providence Hospital

SOUTH CAROLINA DEPARTMENT OF CORRECTIONS HOSPITAL, 4344 Broad River Road, Zip 29210–4098; tel. 803/896–8567 (Nonreporting)
Primary Contact: John Solomon, M.D., Director
Web address: www.doc.sc.gov/
Control: State, Government, Nonfederal **Service**: Hospital unit of an institution (prison hospital, college infirmary, etc.)

Staffed Beds: 70

☐ **WILLIAM S. HALL PSYCHIATRIC INSTITUTE (424003)**, 1800 Colonial Drive, Zip 29203–6827; tel. 803/898–1693 **A**1 3 5 10 **F**4 30 74 75 98 99 130 146
Primary Contact: Angela Forand, Director
COO: Doug Glover, Controller
CFO: Doug Glover, Controller
CMO: Phyllis Bryant–Mobley M.D., Director Medical Services
CIO: Mesa Foard, Director Information technology
CHR: Kim Church, Manager Human Resources
Web address: www.scdmh.org
Control: State, Government, Nonfederal **Service:** Psychiatric

Staffed Beds: 37 **Admissions:** 534 **Census:** 32 **Outpatient Visits:** 0 **Births:** 0 **Personnel:** 220

⊠ △ **WM. JENNINGS BRYAN DORN VETERANS AFFAIRS MEDICAL CENTER**, 6439 Garners Ferry Road, Zip 29209–1639; tel. 803/776–4000, (Nonreporting) **A**1 2 3 5 7 8 **S** Department of Veterans Affairs, Washington, DC
Primary Contact: David Omura, Interim Director
COO: David Omura, Associate Director
CMO: Bernard L. DeKoning M.D., Chief of Staff
CIO: Steve Chalphant, Director Information Management Service Line
CHR: Phyllis Jones, Chief Human Resources
CNO: Ruth W. Mustard R.N., MSN, Associate Director Nursing and Patient Services
Web address: www.columbiasc.va.gov/
Control: Veterans Affairs, Government, federal **Service:** General medical and surgical

Staffed Beds: 216

CONWAY—Horry County

★ ⇧ **CONWAY MEDICAL CENTER (420049)**, 300 Singleton Ridge Road, Zip 29526–9142, Mailing Address: P.O.Box 829, 29528–0829; tel. 843/347–7111, (Total facility includes 88 beds in nursing home–type unit) **A**10 21 **F**1 3 8 11 13 15 18 20 26 28 29 30 34 35 40 43 45 46 49 50 51 57 59 60 61 68 70 71 73 75 76 77 79 81 83 84 85 86 87 89 90 93 94 100 102 107 108 110 111 114 115 118 119 128 129 130 132 135 145 146 147 148 149 150 **P**6
Primary Contact: Philip A. Clayton, President and Chief Executive Officer
CFO: Bret A. Barr, Executive Vice President and Chief Financial Officer
CMO: Paul McKinley Richardson Jr, Vice President, Medical Affairs
CIO: David Crutchfield, Vice President, Information Services & Chief Information Officer
CHR: Matthew J. Securro, Vice President, Human Resources
CNO: Tony L. Minshew, Vice President, Patient Care Services
Web address: www.conwaymedicalcenter.com
Control: Other not–for–profit (including NFP Corporation) **Service:** General medical and surgical

Staffed Beds: 262 **Admissions:** 9741 **Census:** 176 **Outpatient Visits:** 169538 **Births:** 1465 **Total Expense ($000):** 154432 **Payroll Expense ($000):** 55279 **Personnel:** 1021

☐ **LIGHTHOUSE CARE CENTER OF CONWAY (424002)**, 152 Waccamaw Medical Park Drive, Zip 29526–8901; tel. 843/347–8871 **A**1 10 **F**4 98 99 101 102 103 106 130 **S** Universal Health Services, Inc., King of Prussia, PA
Primary Contact: Thomas L. Ryba, Chief Executive Officer
CFO: Gabrielle Gale, Chief Financial Officer
CMO: Adedapo Oduwole M.D., Medical Director
CIO: Gabrielle Gale, Chief Financial Officer
CHR: Lois Woodall, Director Human Resources
Web address: www.lighthousecarecenterofconway.com/
Control: Corporation, Investor–owned (for–profit) **Service:** Psychiatric

Staffed Beds: 87 **Admissions:** 3106 **Census:** 71 **Outpatient Visits:** 0 **Births:** 0 **Personnel:** 178

DARLINGTON—Darlington County

⇧ **MCLEOD MEDICAL CENTER–DARLINGTON (420057)**, 701 Cashua Ferry Road, Zip 29532–8488, Mailing Address: P.O.Box 1859, 29540; tel. 843/395–1100 **A**10 21 **F**1 3 4 15 34 35 38 56 57 59 61 64 67 68 77 85 94 97 98 100 101 103 104 107 110 114 119 127 128 130 133 135 147 148 **P**3 **S** McLeod Health, Florence, SC
Primary Contact: Tim Smoak, Administrator
Web address: www.mcleodhealth.org
Control: Other not–for–profit (including NFP Corporation) **Service:** General medical and surgical

Staffed Beds: 42 **Admissions:** 1334 **Census:** 58 **Outpatient Visits:** 8363 **Births:** 0 **Total Expense ($000):** 12099 **Personnel:** 112

DILLON—Dillon County

⇧ **MCLEOD MEDICAL CENTER DILLON (420005)**, 301 East Jackson Street, Zip 29536–2509, Mailing Address: P.O.Box 1327, 29536–1327; tel. 843/774–4111 **A**10 21 **F**3 11 13 15 28 29 30 34 35 40 50 57 59 64 68 70 75 76 79 81 82 85 87 89 90 94 107 111 114 119 130 132 134 135 146 147 148 149 **P**3 **S** McLeod Health, Florence, SC
Primary Contact: Joan Ervin, Administrator
CFO: Fulton Ervin, Senior Vice President and Chief Financial Officer
CMO: Walter B Blum M.D., Chief of Staff
CIO: Jenean Blackmon, Assistant Vice President and Chief Information Officer
CHR: Cynthia Causey, Associate Administrator Human and Mission Services
Web address: www.mcleodhealth.org
Control: Other not–for–profit (including NFP Corporation) **Service:** General medical and surgical

Staffed Beds: 58 **Admissions:** 2561 **Census:** 23 **Outpatient Visits:** 87042 **Births:** 265 **Total Expense ($000):** 41517 **Payroll Expense ($000):** 17557 **Personnel:** 284

EASLEY—Pickens County

⊠ **BAPTIST EASLEY HOSPITAL (420015)**, 200 Fleetwood Drive, Zip 29640–2022, Mailing Address: P.O.Box 2129, 29641–2129; tel. 864/442–7200 **A**1 5 10 **F**3 11 13 15 20 28 29 30 34 35 39 40 56 57 59 64 70 76 79 81 85 86 87 89 107 108 111 114 115 119 124 130 132 146 147
Primary Contact: Todd Walker, President
CFO: Kathleen Stapleton, Chief Financial Officer
CIO: Cynthia Ellenburg, Director Health Information Services
CHR: Richard B Posey, Director Human Resources
CNO: Mary Ann Hunter, Director Nursing Services
Web address: www.baptisteasley.org
Control: Other not–for–profit (including NFP Corporation) **Service:** General medical and surgical

Staffed Beds: 89 **Admissions:** 3256 **Census:** 37 **Outpatient Visits:** 106836 **Births:** 437 **Total Expense ($000):** 77615 **Payroll Expense ($000):** 28303 **Personnel:** 676

EDGEFIELD—Edgefield County

★ **EDGEFIELD COUNTY HOSPITAL (421304)**, 300 Ridge Medical Plaza, Zip 29824–4525, Mailing Address: PO Box 590, 29824–4525; tel. 803/637–3174 **A**10 18 **F**3 28 29 34 35 40 45 59 65 68 77 79 81 84 90 93 94 107 115 119 127 128 130 133 146 **P**1
Primary Contact: Carlos Milanes, Chief Executive Officer
CFO: Lori Jacobs, Chief Financial Officer
CMO: W Hugh Morgan M.D., Chief Medical Staff
CIO: Juli Corley, Chief Information Officer
CHR: Theresa Stover, Chief Human Resource Officer
CNO: Cheryl Faust, Chief Nursing Officer
Web address: www.myech.org
Control: County, Government, Nonfederal **Service:** General medical and surgical

Staffed Beds: 25 **Admissions:** 280 **Census:** 7 **Outpatient Visits:** 13698 **Births:** 0 **Personnel:** 143

FAIRFAX—Allendale County

★ **ALLENDALE COUNTY HOSPITAL (421300)**, 1787 Allendale Fairfax Highway, Zip 29827–9133, Mailing Address: P.O.Box 218, 29827–0218; tel. 803/632–3311, (Nonreporting) **A**10 18
Primary Contact: Lari Gooding, Chief Executive Officer
Web address: www.achospital.org
Control: County, Government, Nonfederal **Service:** General medical and surgical

Staffed Beds: 69

FLORENCE—Florence County

⊠ △ **CAROLINAS HOSPITAL SYSTEM (420091)**, 805 Pamplico Highway, Zip 29505–6050, Mailing Address: P.O.Box 100550, 29502–0550; tel. 843/674–5000 **A**1 7 10 **F**4 5 6 8 13 15 17 18 20 22 24 26 28 29 30 31 34 35 40 41 43 45 53 56 57 59 60 63 64 67 70 72 73 76 77 78 79 81 87 88 89 90 94 107 110 111 114 115 116 117 119 121 128 129 132 135 145 146 147 148 **S** Community Health Systems, Inc., Franklin, TN
Primary Contact: Gary Malaer, Chief Executive Officer
CFO: Loren Rials, Chief Financial Officer
CMO: Kevin Shea M.D., Chief of Staff
CIO: Lynn Northcutt, Chief Information Officer
CHR: Donna Damico, Director Human Resources
Web address: www.carolinashospital.com
Control: Corporation, Investor–owned (for–profit) **Service:** General medical and surgical

Staffed Beds: 416 **Admissions:** 12694 **Census:** 183 **Births:** 706 **Total Expense ($000):** 181184 **Payroll Expense ($000):** 57465

SC

Hospital, Medicare Provider Number, Address, Telephone, Approval, Facility, and Physician Codes, Health Care System

★ American Hospital Association (AHA) membership
☐ The Joint Commission accreditation
○ Healthcare Facilities Accreditation Program
◇ DNV Healthcare Inc. accreditation
⇧ Center for Improvement in Healthcare Quality Accreditation
△ Commission on Accreditation of Rehabilitation Facilities (CARF) accreditation

✠ **HEALTHSOUTH REHABILITATION HOSPITAL OF FLORENCE (423026)**, 900 East Cheves Street, Zip 29506–2704; tel. 843/679–9000 **A**1 10 **F**9 28 29 34 35 56 57 59 75 77 82 86 87 90 91 92 93 94 95 96 130 131 132 148 **S** HEALTHSOUTH Corporation, Birmingham, AL
Primary Contact: Brian Nunn, R.N., Chief Executive Officer
CFO: Robert Wheeler, Controller
CMO: Adora Matthews M.D., Medical Director
CHR: Susan Trantham, Director Human Resources
Web address: www.healthsouthflorence.com
Control: Corporation, Investor–owned (for–profit) **Service:** Rehabilitation

Staffed Beds: 88 **Admissions:** 1182 **Census:** 45 **Outpatient Visits:** 0
Births: 0 **Total Expense ($000):** 14421 **Payroll Expense ($000):** 7960
Personnel: 165

★ ⇑ **MCLEOD REGIONAL MEDICAL CENTER (420051)**, 555 East Cheves Street, Zip 29506–2617, Mailing Address: P.O.Box 100551, 29502–0551; tel. 843/777–2000 **A**2 3 5 10 21 **F**1 3 7 8 11 13 15 17 18 19 20 22 24 26 28 29 30 31 32 34 35 37 39 40 43 44 45 46 47 48 49 50 51 53 54 56 57 58 59 60 61 62 63 64 65 66 67 68 70 71 72 73 74 75 76 77 78 79 80 81 82 84 85 86 87 88 89 92 94 96 97 100 102 107 108 110 111 112 114 115 116 117 118 119 120 121 124 126 128 129 130 131 132 135 143 145 146 147 148 149 150 **P**3 **S** McLeod Health, Florence, SC
Primary Contact: Robert L. Colones, President and Chief Executive Officer
COO: Ron Boring, Senior Vice President and Chief Operating Officer
CFO: Fulton Ervin, Chief Financial Officer
CMO: Alva W Whitehead M.D., Vice President Medical Services
CIO: Jenean Blackmon, Associate Vice President and Chief Information Officer
CHR: Jeannette Glenn, Vice President Human Resources, Education and Training
Web address: www.mcleodhealth.org
Control: Other not–for–profit (including NFP Corporation) **Service:** General medical and surgical

Staffed Beds: 541 **Admissions:** 25996 **Census:** 357 **Outpatient Visits:** 233021 **Births:** 2120 **Total Expense ($000):** 581634 **Payroll Expense ($000):** 199551 **Personnel:** 3052

✠ **REGENCY HOSPITAL OF FLORENCE (422007)**, 121 East Cedar Street, 4th Floor, Zip 29506–2576; tel. 843/661–3471 **A**1 10 **F**1 3 29 34 35 57 58 77 80 85 90 100 130 148 **S** Select Medical Corporation, Mechanicsburg, PA
Primary Contact: Amy Metz, Chief Executive Officer
CMO: Stephen Dersch M.D., President Medical Staff
CHR: Tina Stokes, Manager Human Resources
Web address: www.regencyhospital.com
Control: Corporation, Investor–owned (for–profit) **Service:** Acute long–term care hospital

Staffed Beds: 40 **Admissions:** 434 **Census:** 33 **Outpatient Visits:** 0 **Births:** 0 **Personnel:** 157

FORT JACKSON—Richland County

✠ **MONCRIEF ARMY COMMUNITY HOSPITAL**, 4500 Stuart Street, Zip 29207–5700; tel. 803/751–2160, (Nonreporting) **A**1 3 5 **S** Department of the Army, Office of the Surgeon General, Falls Church, VA
Primary Contact: Colonel Traci Crawford, R.N., Commander
Web address: www.moncrief.amedd.army.mil
Control: Army, Government, federal **Service:** General medical and surgical

Staffed Beds: 60

GAFFNEY—Cherokee County

✠ **MARY BLACK HEALTH SYSTEM – GAFFNEY (420043)**, 1530 North Limestone Street, Zip 29340–4738; tel. 864/487–4271 **A**1 10 **F**3 11 13 15 18 19 29 34 35 40 45 46 51 57 59 64 65 67 70 75 76 79 81 82 85 86 87 89 107 108 110 111 113 119 129 130 131 132 135 145 146 147 148 **S** Community Health Systems, Inc., Franklin, TN
Primary Contact: Joshua Self, Chief Executive Officer
COO: Leslie Glover, Director Operations
CFO: Christine Poplawski, Chief Financial Officer
CMO: Frank Phillips M.D., Chief of Staff
CIO: Richard Bledsoe, Director Information Systems
CHR: Connie Gibson R.N., Director Human Resources
Web address: www.maryblackgaffney.com/mary–black–gaffney/home.aspx
Control: Corporation, Investor–owned (for–profit) **Service:** General medical and surgical

Staffed Beds: 125 **Admissions:** 2532 **Census:** 26 **Births:** 262 **Personnel:** 264

GEORGETOWN—Georgetown County

✠ **TIDELANDS GEORGETOWN MEMORIAL HOSPITAL (420020)**, 606 Black River Road, Zip 29440–3368, Mailing Address: Drawer 421718, 29442–4203; tel. 843/527–7000 **A**1 3 5 10 19 **F**3 8 11 12 13 15 17 18 20 22 26 28 29 30 31 32 34 35 39 40 45 50 51 53 54 56 57 59 60 61 64 65 68 70 73 74 75 76 77 78 79 81 82 84 85 86 87 89 90 93 94 97 100 102 107 108 110 111 115 118 119 130 131 132 135 146 147 148 **S** QHR, Brentwood, TN
Primary Contact: Bruce P. Bailey, Chief Executive Officer
COO: Gayle L Resetar, Vice President and Chief Operating Officer
CFO: Elizabeth S. Ward, Chief Financial Officer
CHR: James F Harper, Senior Vice President and Chief Human Resources Officer
Web address: www.tidelandsgeorgetownmemorial.org
Control: Other not–for–profit (including NFP Corporation) **Service:** General medical and surgical

Staffed Beds: 136 **Admissions:** 4056 **Census:** 45 **Outpatient Visits:** 190773 **Births:** 247 **Total Expense ($000):** 129090 **Payroll Expense ($000):** 49340 **Personnel:** 891

GREENVILLE—Greenville County

✠ △ **BON SECOURS ST. FRANCIS HEALTH SYSTEM (420023)**, One St Francis Drive, Zip 29601–3207; tel. 864/255–1000, (Includes ST. FRANCIS EASTSIDE, 125 Commonwealth Drive, Greenville, South Carolina, Zip 29615–4812, tel. 864/675–4000) **A**1 2 7 10 **F**3 8 12 13 14 15 17 18 20 22 24 26 28 29 30 31 34 35 36 39 40 44 45 46 47 48 49 50 51 53 54 55 57 58 59 60 61 62 63 64 66 68 69 70 71 73 74 75 76 77 78 79 80 81 82 83 84 85 86 87 89 90 94 96 97 107 108 110 111 114 115 118 119 124 126 129 130 132 135 136 141 146 147 **P**6 **S** Bon Secours Health System, Inc., Marriottsville, MD
Primary Contact: Craig McCoy, Chief Executive Officer
COO: Daniel Duggan, Chief Operating Officer
CFO: Ronnie Hyatt, Senior Vice President Finance and Chief Financial Officer
CMO: Saria Saccoio M.D., Chief Medical Officer
CIO: Rita Hooker, Administrative Director Information Services
CHR: Fernando Fleites, Senior Vice President Human Resources
CNO: Teri Ficicchy R.N., MSN, Chief Nursing Officer
Web address: www.stfrancishealth.org
Control: Other not–for–profit (including NFP Corporation) **Service:** General medical and surgical

Staffed Beds: 396 **Admissions:** 19073 **Census:** 220 **Outpatient Visits:** 192553 **Births:** 2143 **Total Expense ($000):** 389104 **Payroll Expense ($000):** 127313 **Personnel:** 2347

✠ △ **GHS GREENVILLE MEMORIAL HOSPITAL (420078)**, 701 Grove Road, Zip 29605–4295; tel. 864/455–7000, (Includes GHS CHILDREN'S HOSPITAL, 701 Grove Road, Greenville, South Carolina, Zip 29605–5611, tel. 864/455–7000; MARSHALL I. PICKENS HOSPITAL, 701 Grove Road, Greenville, South Carolina, Zip 29605–5601, tel. 864/455–8988; ROGER C. PEACE REHABILITATION HOSPITAL, 701 Grove Road, Greenville, South Carolina, Zip 29605–4295, tel. 864/455–7000) (Total facility includes 15 beds in nursing home–type unit) **A**1 2 3 5 7 8 10 **F**1 3 4 5 11 13 15 17 18 19 20 22 24 26 27 28 29 30 31 34 35 36 38 39 40 41 43 44 45 46 47 48 49 50 51 52 53 54 56 57 58 59 61 64 65 66 68 70 72 73 74 75 76 77 78 79 81 82 83 84 85 86 87 88 89 90 92 93 94 96 97 98 99 100 101 102 103 104 105 106 107 108 110 111 114 115 116 117 118 119 120 121 123 124 126 128 129 130 132 134 135 136 141 142 145 146 147 148 **P**6 **S** Greenville Health System, Greenville, SC
Primary Contact: Paul F. Johnson, Vice President and Chief Operating Officer Central Region
COO: Greg Rusnak, Executive Vice President and Chief Operating Officer
CFO: Terri Newsom, Vice President of Finance and Chief Financial Officer
CMO: Angelo Sinopoli M.D., Vice President Clinical Integration and Chief Medical Officer
CIO: Rich Rogers, Vice President Information Services
CHR: Doug Dorman, Vice President Human Resources
CNO: Michelle T Smith R.N., MSN, FACHE, Vice President Nursing Chief Nursing Officer Chief Experience Officer
Web address: www.ghs.org
Control: Other not–for–profit (including NFP Corporation) **Service:** General medical and surgical

Staffed Beds: 769 **Admissions:** 32084 **Census:** 597 **Outpatient Visits:** 662681 **Births:** 5522 **Total Expense ($000):** 962303 **Payroll Expense ($000):** 261871 **Personnel:** 5678

✠ **PATEWOOD MEMORIAL HOSPITAL (420102)**, 175 Patewood Drive, Zip 29615–3570; tel. 864/797–1000 **A**1 5 10 **F**3 11 29 30 37 45 50 64 74 77 79 80 81 85 130 135 146 **P**6 **S** Greenville Health System, Greenville, SC
Primary Contact: Tim Brookshire, FACHE, Interim Chief Operating Officer
Web address: www.ghs.org/patewood
Control: Other not–for–profit (including NFP Corporation) **Service:** Surgical

Staffed Beds: 72 **Admissions:** 1123 **Census:** 6 **Outpatient Visits:** 6973 **Births:** 0 **Total Expense ($000):** 84097 **Payroll Expense ($000):** 22471 **Personnel:** 168

SC

Many Facility Codes have changed. Please refer to the AHA Guide Code Chart. © 2017 AHA Guide

✠ **REGENCY HOSPITAL OF GREENVILLE (422009)**, One St Francis Drive, 4th Floor, Zip 29601–3955; tel. 864/255–1438 **A**1 10 **F**1 3 29 60 75 77 85 97 **S** Select Medical Corporation, Mechanicsburg, PA
Primary Contact: Paige Beauregard, Chief Executive Officer
Web address: www.regencyhospital.com
Control: Corporation, Investor–owned (for–profit) **Service:** Acute long–term care hospital

> **Staffed Beds:** 32 **Admissions:** 283 **Census:** 21 **Outpatient Visits:** 0 **Births:** 0 **Personnel:** 137

☐ **SHRINERS HOSPITALS FOR CHILDREN–GREENVILLE (423300)**, 950 West Faris Road, Zip 29605–4277; tel. 864/271–3444 **A**1 3 5 10 **F**29 59 64 68 75 77 79 81 85 87 89 90 93 94 130 131 146 148 **P**6 **S** Shriners Hospitals for Children, Tampa, FL
Primary Contact: Randall R. Romberger, Administrator
CFO: John Conti, Director Finance
CMO: J. Michael Wattenbarger M.D., Chief of Staff
CHR: Willis E Tisdale, Director Human Resources
CNO: Allison Leigh Windas, Director of Patient Care Services
Web address: www.greenvilleshrinershospital.org
Control: Other not–for–profit (including NFP Corporation) **Service:** Children's orthopedic

> **Staffed Beds:** 15 **Admissions:** 229 **Census:** 1 **Outpatient Visits:** 18720 **Births:** 0 **Personnel:** 176

GREENWOOD—Greenwood County

☐ **GREENWOOD REGIONAL REHABILITATION HOSPITAL (423030)**, 1530 Parkway, Zip 29646–4027; tel. 864/330–9070, (Total facility includes 12 beds in nursing home–type unit) **A**1 10 **F**3 29 75 90 128 130 132 143 148 **S** Ernest Health, Inc., Albuquerque, NM
Primary Contact: Kristin Manske, Chief Executive Officer
CFO: Charity Walker, Controller and Regional Business Officer Manager
CMO: Cam Monda D.O., Medical Director
CNO: Teresa Nabors, Director of Nursing
Web address: www.grrh.ernesthealth.com
Control: Corporation, Investor–owned (for–profit) **Service:** Rehabilitation

> **Staffed Beds:** 54 **Admissions:** 1085 **Census:** 39 **Outpatient Visits:** 0 **Births:** 0 **Personnel:** 219

★ ⇑ **SELF REGIONAL HEALTHCARE (420071)**, 1325 Spring Street, Zip 29646–3860; tel. 864/725–4111 **A**2 3 5 10 21 **F**3 8 11 13 15 17 18 20 22 24 26 28 29 30 31 32 34 35 39 40 43 44 45 46 48 49 50 51 53 57 58 59 60 61 62 64 68 70 72 73 74 75 76 77 78 79 80 81 82 85 86 87 89 90 91 94 96 97 98 102 103 107 108 110 111 114 115 119 120 121 123 124 129 130 131 132 134 135 146 147 148 149 **P**5 8
Primary Contact: James A. Pfeiffer, FACHE, President and Chief Executive Officer
CFO: Timothy Evans, Vice President and Chief Financial Officer
CMO: F Gregory Mappin M.D., Vice President Medical Affairs and Chief Medical Officer
CIO: Andy Hartung, Director Information Systems
CHR: Michael Dixon, Director Human Resources
CNO: Linda Russell, Vice President and Chief Nursing Officer
Web address: www.selfregional.org
Control: County, Government, Nonfederal **Service:** General medical and surgical

> **Staffed Beds:** 322 **Admissions:** 11477 **Census:** 146 **Outpatient Visits:** 339214 **Births:** 1389 **Total Expense ($000):** 298865 **Payroll Expense ($000):** 102968 **Personnel:** 1887

GREER—Greenville County

☐ **CAROLINA CENTER FOR BEHAVIORAL HEALTH (424010)**, 2700 East Phillips Road, Zip 29650–4816; tel. 864/235–2335 **A**1 10 **F**4 98 99 100 101 102 103 104 105 **S** Universal Health Services, Inc., King of Prussia, PA
Primary Contact: John Willingham, Chief Executive Officer and Managing Director
COO: Greg Schlangen R.N., Chief Operating Officer
CFO: James P Boynton Jr, Chief Financial Officer
CMO: Gergana Dimitrova M.D., Medical Director
CHR: George Hammett, Director Human Resources
CNO: Jennifer Daigle R.N., Director of Nursing and Utilization Review
Web address: www.thecarolinacenter.com
Control: Corporation, Investor–owned (for–profit) **Service:** Psychiatric

> **Staffed Beds:** 109 **Admissions:** 4058 **Census:** 111 **Outpatient Visits:** 0 **Births:** 0 **Personnel:** 264

✠ **GHS GREER MEMORIAL HOSPITAL (420033)**, 830 South Buncombe Road, Zip 29650–2400; tel. 864/797–8000 **A**1 5 10 **F**3 11 13 15 18 28 29 30 34 35 40 44 45 49 50 51 57 59 64 65 68 70 76 77 79 81 85 87 89 94 107 110 111 114 119 129 130 146 147 148 **P**6 **S** Greenville Health System, Greenville, SC
Primary Contact: John F. Mansure, FACHE, President
Web address: www.ghs.org
Control: Other not–for–profit (including NFP Corporation) **Service:** General medical and surgical

> **Staffed Beds:** 70 **Admissions:** 3729 **Census:** 29 **Outpatient Visits:** 107729 **Births:** 679 **Total Expense ($000):** 80976 **Payroll Expense ($000):** 24162 **Personnel:** 387

GREER—Spartanburg County

★ ⇑ **PELHAM MEDICAL CENTER (420103)**, 250 Westmoreland Road, Zip 29651–9013; tel. 864/530–6000 **A**10 21 **F**3 11 15 18 20 26 29 30 34 35 37 40 45 49 50 54 57 59 64 68 70 74 75 77 79 81 82 84 85 86 87 90 94 107 108 110 111 114 115 118 119 130 146 148 149 **S** Spartanburg Regional Healthcare System, Spartanburg, SC
Primary Contact: Anthony Kouskolekas, FACHE, President
CNO: Connie Spykerman, Chief Nursing Officer
Web address: www.pelhammedicalcenter.com
Control: Hospital district or authority, Government, Nonfederal **Service:** General medical and surgical

> **Staffed Beds:** 46 **Admissions:** 2972 **Census:** 29 **Outpatient Visits:** 49644 **Births:** 0 **Total Expense ($000):** 61875 **Payroll Expense ($000):** 21809 **Personnel:** 608

HARDEEVILLE—Jasper County

✠ **COASTAL CAROLINA HOSPITAL (420101)**, 1000 Medical Center Drive, Zip 29927–3446; tel. 843/784–8000 **A**1 10 **F**3 11 13 15 28 29 30 34 35 40 45 46 47 48 49 57 59 64 70 74 75 76 77 79 81 85 90 93 94 107 108 110 111 115 119 126 127 132 135 146 147 148 **S** TENET Healthcare Corporation, Dallas, TX
Primary Contact: Joel Taylor, Chief Executive Officer
CFO: Ronald J. Groteluschen, Chief Financial Officer
CIO: Cheryl Grant, Director Information Systems
CHR: Darlene E. Nester, Market Chief Human Resources Officer
CNO: Patricia A. Feilmeier, Interim Chief Nursing Officer
Web address: www.coastalhospital.com
Control: Corporation, Investor–owned (for–profit) **Service:** General medical and surgical

> **Staffed Beds:** 35 **Admissions:** 3005 **Census:** 27 **Outpatient Visits:** 44791 **Births:** 654 **Total Expense ($000):** 46934 **Payroll Expense ($000):** 15771 **Personnel:** 282

HARTSVILLE—Darlington County

☐ ○ **CAROLINA PINES REGIONAL MEDICAL CENTER (420010)**, 1304 West Bobo Newsom Highway, Zip 29550–4710; tel. 843/339–2100 **A**1 10 11 **F**3 11 13 15 20 28 29 30 34 35 40 43 46 49 57 64 70 73 75 76 79 81 82 85 86 87 89 90 93 107 108 110 111 114 115 118 119 129 130 131 132 135 146 147 148 **S** RCCH HealthCare Partners, Brentwood, TN
Primary Contact: William Little, Chief Executive Officer
COO: Susan C Shugart, Chief Operating Officer
CFO: Rodney VanDonkelaar, Chief Financial Officer
CMO: Tallulah Holmstrom, Chief Medical Officer
CIO: Denise Barefoot, Director of Information Technology
CHR: Charlotte Adams, Director of Human Resources
CNO: Danny Wharton, Chief Nursing Officer
Web address: www.cprmc.com
Control: Corporation, Investor–owned (for–profit) **Service:** General medical and surgical

> **Staffed Beds:** 120 **Admissions:** 4248 **Census:** 38 **Outpatient Visits:** 101487 **Births:** 578

SC

HILTON HEAD ISLAND—Beaufort County

⊞ **HILTON HEAD HOSPITAL (420080)**, 25 Hospital Center Boulevard, Zip 29926–2738; tel. 843/681–6122 **A**1 10 20 **F**3 11 13 17 18 20 22 24 26 28 29 30 34 35 37 40 45 46 48 49 50 51 53 54 57 59 60 61 64 65 68 70 74 76 77 78 79 81 85 86 89 94 96 107 108 110 111 114 115 119 126 130 131 132 135 146 147 148 **S** TENET Healthcare Corporation, Dallas, TX
Primary Contact: Jeremy L. Clark, Market Chief Executive Officer
CFO: Cassie Ball, Chief Financial Officer
CMO: Glenn Neil Love M.D., Medical Director
CIO: Stephen Brendler, Director Information Systems
CHR: Darlene E. Nester, Chief Human Resources Officer
Web address: www.hiltonheadregional.com
Control: Partnership, Investor–owned (for–profit) **Service**: General medical and surgical

Staffed Beds: 93 **Admissions**: 5778 **Census**: 58 **Outpatient Visits**: 85991 **Births**: 463 **Total Expense ($000)**: 98377 **Payroll Expense ($000)**: 26723 **Personnel**: 502

LAKE CITY—Florence County

★ **LAKE CITY COMMUNITY HOSPITAL (420066)**, 258 N Ron McNair Boulevard, Zip 29560–2462, Mailing Address: P.O.Box 1479, 29560–1479; tel. 843/374–2036 **A**10 **F**3 11 15 28 29 34 35 40 50 53 56 57 59 61 64 65 69 75 77 79 81 85 86 87 93 94 107 108 110 111 113 114 119 127 130 132 144 146
Primary Contact: Michael Faucett, Chief Operating Officer
COO: Michael Faucett, Chief Operating Officer
CMO: Stephen Askins M.D., Chief of Staff
CIO: David Moon Jr, Director Information Systems
CHR: Anne Poston, Director of Human Resources/Compliance
CNO: Renate Browder R.N., Director of Nursing
Web address: www.lcchospital.org
Control: Hospital district or authority, Government, Nonfederal **Service**: General medical and surgical

Staffed Beds: 26 **Admissions**: 875 **Census**: 11 **Outpatient Visits**: 45455 **Births**: 0 **Total Expense ($000)**: 15119 **Payroll Expense ($000)**: 7458 **Personnel**: 213

LANCASTER—Lancaster County

☐ **REBOUND BEHAVIORAL HEALTH (044014)**, 134 East Rebound Road, Zip 29720–7712; tel. 877/959–5063 (Nonreporting) **A**1 **S** Acadia Healthcare Company, Inc., Franklin, TN
Primary Contact: Patricia Hamilton, Chief Executive Officer
Web address: www.reboundbehavioralhealth.com
Control: Corporation, Investor–owned (for–profit) **Service**: Psychiatric

Staffed Beds: 42

⊞ **SPRINGS MEMORIAL HOSPITAL (420036)**, 800 West Meeting Street, Zip 29720–2298; tel. 803/286–1214, (Total facility includes 14 beds in nursing home–type unit) **A**1 5 10 **F**3 8 11 13 15 17 18 20 29 30 31 34 35 40 47 48 49 51 57 59 60 63 64 68 70 73 74 75 76 77 78 79 80 81 85 89 90 93 94 98 102 103 107 108 110 111 114 115 118 119 128 129 130 131 132 135 146 147 148 **S** Community Health Systems, Inc., Franklin, TN
Primary Contact: Page Vaughan, Chief Executive Officer
COO: Richard Warrin, Chief Operating Officer
CFO: Holt Smith, Chief Financial Officer
CMO: Douglas Tiedt M.D., Chief of Staff
CIO: Chrys Steele, Director Information Systems
CHR: Trent Elmore, Director Human Resources
CNO: Karen Martin, Chief Nursing Officer
Web address: www.springsmemorial.com
Control: Corporation, Investor–owned (for–profit) **Service**: General medical and surgical

Staffed Beds: 176 **Admissions**: 6191 **Census**: 90 **Outpatient Visits**: 35682 **Births**: 579 **Total Expense ($000)**: 103846 **Payroll Expense ($000)**: 31551 **Personnel**: 604

LORIS—Horry County

⇑ **MCLEOD LORIS SEACOAST HOSPITAL (420105)**, 3655 Mitchell Street, Zip 29569–2827; tel. 843/716–7000, (Includes MCLEOD SEACOAST, 4000 Highway 9 East, Little River, South Carolina, Zip 29566–7833, tel. 843/390–8100) **A**10 21 **F**3 11 13 15 17 18 20 28 29 30 31 32 34 35 40 44 50 53 57 58 59 60 63 64 68 70 74 75 76 77 78 79 81 82 85 86 87 89 90 94 96 102 107 108 110 111 115 118 119 130 131 132 134 135 143 146 148 149 **P**3 **S** McLeod Health, Florence, SC
Primary Contact: Edward D. Tinsley III, Chief Executive Officer
COO: Arnold Green, Senior Vice President and Chief Operating Officer
CFO: Fred O Todd, Senior Vice President Finance
CMO: James N Craigie M.D., Vice President Medical Affairs
CHR: Teresa Pougnaud, Vice President Human Resources
Web address: www.mcleodhealth.org
Control: Other not–for–profit (including NFP Corporation) **Service**: General medical and surgical

Staffed Beds: 155 **Admissions**: 5283 **Census**: 50 **Outpatient Visits**: 107977 **Births**: 440 **Total Expense ($000)**: 119352 **Payroll Expense ($000)**: 40072 **Personnel**: 338

MANNING—Clarendon County

★ ⇑ **MCLEOD HEALTH CLARENDON (420069)**, 10 Hospital Street, Zip 29102–3153, Mailing Address: P.O. Box 550, 29102–0550; tel. 803/433–3000 **A**10 21 **F**3 7 13 15 18 26 28 29 34 35 40 45 50 51 53 54 56 59 62 64 65 70 75 76 77 79 81 85 87 90 91 93 94 96 97 107 108 110 111 114 119 127 128 129 130 132 133 135 143 146 147 148 149 **P**3 **S** McLeod Health, Florence, SC
Primary contact:
Primary Contact: Rachel T. Gainey
COO: Paul Schumacher, Chief Operating Officer
CFO: John Shaughnessy, Chief Financial Officer
CMO: Catherine Rabon M.D., Chief Medical Officer
CIO: Pat Kolb, Manager Information Technology
CHR: Gail A Richbourg, Director Human Resources
CNO: Natalie Davis R.N., Interim Chief Nursing Officer
Web address: www.clarendonhealth.com
Control: Other not–for–profit (including NFP Corporation) **Service**: General medical and surgical

Staffed Beds: 31 **Admissions**: 2267 **Census**: 28 **Births**: 357 **Total Expense ($000)**: 49749 **Payroll Expense ($000)**: 21877 **Personnel**: 605

MOUNT PLEASANT—Charleston County

⊞ **EAST COOPER MEDICAL CENTER (420089)**, 2000 Hospital Drive, Zip 29464–3764; tel. 843/881–0100 **A**1 3 5 10 **F**3 13 15 18 29 31 34 35 40 43 46 51 57 59 60 64 68 70 73 74 75 76 77 78 79 80 81 82 84 85 86 90 92 93 94 100 102 107 108 110 111 114 115 119 126 129 130 131 132 135 146 147 148 **S** TENET Healthcare Corporation, Dallas, TX
Primary Contact: Patrick Downes, Chief Executive Officer
COO: Ramona Pickens, Chief Operating Officer
CFO: Patrick C Bolander, Chief Financial Officer
CMO: Kevin Keenan M.D., Physician Advisor
CIO: Michael Foster, Director Information Systems
CHR: Tracy Hunter, Chief Human Resources Officer
CNO: Patrick Beaver MSN, R.N., Chief Nursing Officer
Web address: www.eastcoopermedctr.com
Control: Corporation, Investor–owned (for–profit) **Service**: General medical and surgical

Staffed Beds: 140 **Admissions**: 5427 **Census**: 45 **Outpatient Visits**: 52895 **Births**: 1553 **Total Expense ($000)**: 116792 **Payroll Expense ($000)**: 31029 **Personnel**: 492

EAST COOPER REGIONAL MEDICAL CENTER See East Cooper Medical Center

⊞ **ROPER ST. FRANCIS MOUNT PLEASANT HOSPITAL (420104)**, 3500 Highway 17 North, Zip 29466–9123, Mailing Address: 3500 North Highway 17, 29466–9123; tel. 843/606–7000 **A**1 10 **F**3 7 13 15 29 30 34 40 45 54 59 68 70 75 76 79 81 84 85 86 87 89 94 102 107 108 110 111 115 118 119 129 143 146 147 148 149 **S** Carolinas HealthCare System, Charlotte, NC
Primary Contact: Anthony Jackson, Chief Executive Officer
CFO: Bret Johnson, Chief Financial Officer
CMO: Steven D Shapiro M.D., Chief Medical Officer
CIO: Melinda H. Cardell, Interim Chief Information Officer
CHR: Melanie Stith, Vice President Human Resources
CNO: Tavia Buck, Chief Nursing Officer
Web address: www.rsfh.com/mount–pleasant–hospital
Control: Other not–for–profit (including NFP Corporation) **Service**: General medical and surgical

Staffed Beds: 50 **Admissions**: 1929 **Census**: 16 **Outpatient Visits**: 44926 **Births**: 551 **Total Expense ($000)**: 59485 **Payroll Expense ($000)**: 15599 **Personnel**: 322

MT. PLEASANT—Mt. Pleasant County

KINDRED HOSPITAL–CHARLESTON See Vibra Hospital Of Charleston

⊞ **VIBRA HOSPITAL OF CHARLESTON (422005)**, 1200 Hospital Drive, Zip 29464; tel. 843/375–4000 **A**1 10 **F**1 3 29 35 85 90 107 114 119 148 **S** Vibra Healthcare, Mechanicsburg, PA
Primary Contact: Daniel C. Dunmyer, Chief Executive Officer
CFO: Julia Smith, Chief Financial Officer
CMO: Athena Beldecos M.D., Medical Director
CHR: Julia Taylor, Area Director Human Resources
Web address: www.vhcharleston.com
Control: Corporation, Investor–owned (for–profit) **Service**: Acute long–term care hospital

Staffed Beds: 59 **Admissions**: 699 **Census**: 38 **Outpatient Visits**: 0 **Births**: 0 **Personnel**: 152

Many Facility Codes have changed. Please refer to the AHA Guide Code Chart. © 2017 AHA Guide

SC

MULLINS—Marion County

⊞ **CAROLINAS HOSPITAL SYSTEM MARION (420055)**, 2829 East Highway 76, Zip 29574–6035, Mailing Address: P O Drawer 1150, Marion, 29571–1150; tel. 843/431–2000, (Total facility includes 92 beds in nursing–home–type unit) **A**1 10 **F**1 3 13 15 28 29 34 40 45 46 53 57 59 60 67 70 72 75 76 77 79 81 82 85 86 89 90 94 107 111 119 128 129 130 131 133 146 148 **S** Community Health Systems, Inc., Franklin, TN
Primary Contact: Parkes Coggins, Chief Executive Officer
CFO: Christopher Green, Chief Financial Officer
CMO: Alvin Abinsay M.D., Chief Medical Staff
CIO: Charlie Grantham, Manager Information Systems
CHR: Kay White, Director Human Resources and Diversity
Web address: www.carolinashospitalmarion.com
Control: Corporation, Investor–owned (for–profit) **Service:** General medical and surgical

Staffed Beds: 216 **Admissions:** 2385 **Census:** 97 **Outpatient Visits:** 47117 **Births:** 245 **Total Expense ($000):** 67150 **Payroll Expense ($000):** 16175 **Personnel:** 240

MARION COUNTY MEDICAL CENTER See Carolinas Hospital System Marion

MURRELLS INLET—Georgetown County

⊞ △ **TIDELANDS WACCAMAW COMMUNITY HOSPITAL (420098)**, 4070 Highway 17 Bypass, Zip 29576–5033, Mailing Address: P O Drawer 3350, 29576–2673; tel. 843/652–1000 **A**1 2 7 10 **F**3 8 11 13 15 17 18 28 29 30 31 32 35 37 39 40 45 50 51 56 60 61 64 65 68 70 73 74 75 76 77 78 79 81 82 84 85 86 87 89 90 93 94 96 97 100 102 107 108 110 111 114 115 118 119 130 131 146 147 148 **S** QHR, Brentwood, TN
Primary Contact: Bruce P. Bailey, Chief Executive Officer
CFO: Elizabeth S. Ward, Chief Financial Officer
Web address: www.tidelandswaccamawcommunity.org
Control: Other not–for–profit (including NFP Corporation) **Service:** General medical and surgical

Staffed Beds: 169 **Admissions:** 7884 **Census:** 102 **Outpatient Visits:** 125850 **Births:** 561 **Total Expense ($000):** 145664 **Payroll Expense ($000):** 33514 **Personnel:** 711

MYRTLE BEACH—Horry County

⊞ **GRAND STRAND REGIONAL MEDICAL CENTER (420085)**, 809 82nd Parkway, Zip 29572–4607; tel. 843/692–1000 **A**1 2 3 5 10 19 **F**3 11 13 15 17 18 20 22 24 26 28 29 30 31 34 35 37 39 40 42 43 46 47 49 50 54 56 57 59 60 64 70 74 75 76 77 78 79 81 82 85 86 87 88 89 90 107 108 110 111 114 115 118 119 126 130 132 135 146 147 **S** HCA Healthcare, Nashville, TN
Primary Contact: Mark E. Sims, Chief Executive Officer
CFO: Turner Wortham, Chief Financial Officer
Web address: www.grandstrandmed.com
Control: Corporation, Investor–owned (for–profit) **Service:** General medical and surgical

Staffed Beds: 303 **Admissions:** 18524 **Census:** 235 **Outpatient Visits:** 176694 **Births:** 937

NEWBERRY—Newberry County

⊞ **NEWBERRY COUNTY MEMORIAL HOSPITAL (420053)**, 2669 Kinard Street, Zip 29108–2911, Mailing Address: P.O.Box 497, 29108–0497; tel. 803/276–7570 **A**1 10 20 **F**3 7 11 13 15 17 28 29 30 31 32 34 35 40 45 47 49 53 56 57 59 64 68 70 75 76 77 78 79 81 82 85 86 87 89 90 93 94 103 104 107 108 109 110 111 114 119 130 133 135 143 146 147 148 **P**6 **S** QHR, Brentwood, TN
Primary Contact: Bruce A. Baldwin, Chief Executive Officer
CFO: Mike Reynolds, Chief Financial Officer
CMO: Mark Davis M.D., Chief of Staff
CIO: David Wolff, Director Information Technology
CHR: Dyan Bowman, Director Human Resources
Web address: www.newberryhospital.org
Control: County, Government, Nonfederal **Service:** General medical and surgical

Staffed Beds: 54 **Admissions:** 1903 **Census:** 20 **Outpatient Visits:** 45119 **Births:** 276 **Total Expense ($000):** 45395 **Payroll Expense ($000):** 16137 **Personnel:** 342

ORANGEBURG—Orangeburg County

⊞ **REGIONAL MEDICAL CENTER (420068)**, 3000 St Matthews Road, Zip 29118–1442; tel. 803/395–2200 **A**1 10 13 **F**3 11 12 13 14 15 17 18 20 28 29 30 31 32 34 35 39 40 43 44 45 46 47 48 49 50 53 57 58 59 60 61 62 64 65 68 70 71 73 74 75 76 77 78 79 81 82 84 85 86 87 89 90 93 94 97 98 100 101 102 103 104 107 108 110 111 114 115 119 121 127 129 130 131 132 134 135 144 146 147 148 **S** QHR, Brentwood, TN
Primary Contact: Bert Whitaker, Interim President and Chief Executive Officer
CFO: Liza Porterfield, Chief Financial Officer
CIO: James Albin, Chief Information Officer
CHR: Howard Harris, Vice President Human Resources
CNO: Mickey Whisenhunt, Interim Chief Nursing Officer
Web address: www.trmchealth.org
Control: County, Government, Nonfederal **Service:** General medical and surgical

Staffed Beds: 283 **Admissions:** 10696 **Census:** 139 **Outpatient Visits:** 215784 **Births:** 910 **Total Expense ($000):** 218691 **Payroll Expense ($000):** 98615 **Personnel:** 1090

☐ **WILLIAM J. MCCORD ADOLESCENT TREATMENT FACILITY (424013)**, 910 Cook Road, Zip 29118–2124, Mailing Address: P.O.Box 1166, 29116–1166; tel. 803/534–2328 **A**1 10 **F**1 4 5 29 34 38 57 61 98 99 128 130 132 134 135
Primary Contact: Michael Dennis, Director
CFO: Laura Murdaugh, Finance Director
CMO: Dorothy Kendall, Medical Director
CNO: Linda Mitchum, Director of Nursing
Web address: www.tccada.com
Control: Other not–for–profit (including NFP Corporation) **Service:** Alcoholism and other chemical dependency

Staffed Beds: 15 **Admissions:** 113 **Census:** 10 **Outpatient Visits:** 0 **Births:** 0 **Personnel:** 22

PICKENS—Pickens County

★ ⇑ **ANMED HEALTH CANNON (420011)**, 123 W G Acker Drive, Zip 29671–2739, Mailing Address: P.O.Box 188, 29671–0188; tel. 864/878–4791 **A**10 21 **F**3 11 15 29 34 40 50 51 56 57 59 61 64 65 70 75 79 81 85 94 97 107 108 110 111 114 119 127 130 135 146 **P**8 **S** AnMed Health, Anderson, SC
Primary Contact: Brandon Clary, Chief Executive Officer
CFO: Will Grant, Chief Financial Officer
CMO: Daniel J Dahlhausen M.D., President of Medical Staff/Chief Medical Officer
CIO: Robert Furr, Director Information Services
CHR: Lisa G Bryant, Director Human Resources
CNO: Donna K Anderson R.N., Chief Nursing Officer
Web address: www.cannonhospital.org
Control: Other not–for–profit (including NFP Corporation) **Service:** General medical and surgical

Staffed Beds: 28 **Admissions:** 644 **Census:** 7 **Outpatient Visits:** 57673 **Births:** 0 **Total Expense ($000):** 21558 **Payroll Expense ($000):** 9664 **Personnel:** 259

ROCK HILL—York County

⊞ **HEALTHSOUTH REHABILITATION HOSPITAL OF ROCK HILL (423028)**, 1795 Dr. Frank Gaston Boulevard, Zip 29732–1190; tel. 803/326–3500 **A**1 10 **F**29 90 95 96 **S** HEALTHSOUTH Corporation, Birmingham, AL
Primary Contact: Deanna Martin, Chief Executive Officer
Web address: www.healthsouthrockhill.com
Control: Corporation, Investor–owned (for–profit) **Service:** Rehabilitation

Staffed Beds: 50 **Admissions:** 1414 **Census:** 47 **Outpatient Visits:** 0 **Births:** 0 **Personnel:** 85

⊞ **PIEDMONT MEDICAL CENTER (420002)**, 222 Herlong Avenue, Zip 29732; tel. 803/329–1234 **A**1 2 10 **F**3 7 11 12 13 15 17 18 20 22 24 26 28 29 30 31 34 35 40 43 45 49 50 57 59 60 64 70 72 73 74 75 76 77 78 79 81 82 85 86 89 90 91 93 98 100 102 107 108 110 111 114 115 118 119 126 130 132 135 146 147 148 **S** TENET Healthcare Corporation, Dallas, TX
Primary Contact: Stephen Gilmore, Interim Chief Executive Officer
CFO: Stephen Gilmore, Chief Financial Officer
CMO: Phil Perry M.D., Regional Chief Medical Officer
CIO: Joel Dean, Director Information Services
CHR: Elizabeth Elich, Vice President Human Resources
Web address: www.piedmontmedicalcenter.com
Control: Corporation, Investor–owned (for–profit) **Service:** General medical and surgical

Staffed Beds: 280 **Admissions:** 14582 **Census:** 179 **Outpatient Visits:** 143276 **Births:** 1637 **Total Expense ($000):** 223506 **Payroll Expense ($000):** 76327 **Personnel:** 1636

SC

Hospital, Medicare Provider Number, Address, Telephone, Approval, Facility, and Physician Codes, Health Care System

★ American Hospital Association (AHA) membership
☐ The Joint Commission accreditation
○ Healthcare Facilities Accreditation Program
◇ DNV Healthcare Inc. accreditation
⇑ Center for Improvement in Healthcare Quality Accreditation
△ Commission on Accreditation of Rehabilitation Facilities (CARF) accreditation

SENECA—Oconee County

✚ **OCONEE MEMORIAL HOSPITAL (420009)**, 298 Memorial Drive, Zip 29672–9499; tel. 864/882–3351, (Total facility includes 120 beds in nursing home–type unit) **A**1 3 5 10 20 **F**1 3 7 11 13 15 17 18 20 28 29 30 31 34 35 39 40 51 54 56 57 59 61 62 63 64 67 70 74 75 76 77 78 79 81 82 84 85 86 87 89 90 94 97 107 108 111 114 119 128 130 132 135 143 146 **P**6 **S** Greenville Health System, Greenville, SC
Primary Contact: Hunter Kome, Campus President
CMO: Conrad K Shuler M.D., Chief Medical Officer
CIO: Jay Hansen, Director Information Services
CNO: Patricia Smith, Chief Nursing Officer
Web address: www.oconeemed.org
Control: Other not–for–profit (including NFP Corporation) **Service:** General medical and surgical

Staffed Beds: 252 **Admissions:** 6420 **Census:** 173 **Outpatient Visits:** 112421 **Births:** 488 **Total Expense ($000):** 108140 **Payroll Expense ($000):** 34939 **Personnel:** 747

SIMPSONVILLE—Greenville County

✚ **GHS HILLCREST MEMORIAL HOSPITAL (420037)**, 729 SE Main Street, Zip 29681–3280; tel. 864/454–6100 **A**1 5 10 **F**3 11 12 15 18 29 34 35 40 44 45 50 57 58 59 61 64 68 70 79 81 85 86 90 107 110 111 114 119 129 130 132 135 146 **P**6 **S** Greenville Health System, Greenville, SC
Primary Contact: Eric Bour, M.D., FACS, President
Web address: www.ghs.org
Control: Other not–for–profit (including NFP Corporation) **Service:** General medical and surgical

Staffed Beds: 43 **Admissions:** 1936 **Census:** 16 **Outpatient Visits:** 70878 **Births:** 0 **Total Expense ($000):** 57998 **Payroll Expense ($000):** 16504 **Personnel:** 244

SPARTANBURG—Spartanburg County

✚ △ **MARY BLACK HEALTH SYSTEM–SPARTANBURG (420083)**, 1700 Skylyn Drive, Zip 29307–1061, Mailing Address: P.O.Box 3217, 29304–3217; tel. 864/573–3000 **A**1 3 5 7 10 **F**3 11 13 15 18 20 29 30 31 34 35 40 45 47 49 50 51 54 56 57 59 60 64 68 70 73 74 76 77 78 79 81 85 89 90 93 94 96 98 102 103 107 108 110 111 114 115 119 126 129 130 135 145 146 147 148 **S** Community Health Systems, Inc., Franklin, TN
Primary Contact: Sean T. Dardeau, FACHE, Chief Executive Officer
COO: Daniel McKinney, Chief Operating Officer
CFO: Brett English, Chief Financial Officer
CMO: Howard Bean M.D., Chief Medical Officer
CIO: John O'Donnell, Director of Information Technology Services
CHR: Lee Ann Roque, Director of Human Resources
CNO: Chanda Flynn R.N., MSN, Chief Nursing Officer
Web address: www.maryblackhealthsystem.com
Control: Corporation, Investor–owned (for–profit) **Service:** General medical and surgical

Staffed Beds: 164 **Admissions:** 6218 **Census:** 79 **Outpatient Visits:** 112782 **Births:** 780 **Personnel:** 905

✚ **SPARTANBURG HOSPITAL FOR RESTORATIVE CARE (422004)**, 389 Serpentine Drive, Zip 29303–3026; tel. 864/560–3280, (Total facility includes 25 beds in nursing home–type unit) **A**1 10 **F**1 29 30 31 35 57 59 60 68 70 75 77 79 82 84 85 87 90 119 128 130 148 149 **S** Spartanburg Regional Healthcare System, Spartanburg, SC
Primary Contact: Anita M. Butler, Chief Executive Officer
Web address: www.srhs.com
Control: Hospital district or authority, Government, Nonfederal **Service:** Acute long–term care hospital

Staffed Beds: 116 **Admissions:** 742 **Census:** 43 **Outpatient Visits:** 0 **Births:** 0 **Total Expense ($000):** 22291 **Payroll Expense ($000):** 11862 **Personnel:** 196

★ ⥣ **SPARTANBURG MEDICAL CENTER (420007)**, 101 East Wood Street, Zip 29303–3040; tel. 864/560–6000 **A**2 3 5 10 13 21 **F**3 7 11 12 13 15 17 18 20 22 24 26 28 29 30 31 34 35 36 37 38 39 40 43 45 46 47 48 49 50 53 54 56 57 58 59 60 61 62 63 64 65 66 68 70 71 72 73 74 75 76 77 78 79 81 82 83 84 85 86 87 88 89 90 94 97 98 99 100 101 102 103 104 105 107 108 110 111 114 115 117 118 119 120 123 124 126 129 130 131 132 135 143 144 145 146 147 148 149 **S** Spartanburg Regional Healthcare System, Spartanburg, SC
Primary Contact: J Philip. Feisal, President and Chief Executive Officer
COO: Mark Aycock, Chief Operating Officer
CFO: Kenneth Meinke, Senior Vice President Administrative Services, Finance and Chief Financial Officer
CMO: Charles Morrow M.D., Chief Medical Officer
CIO: Harold Moore, Chief Information Technology Officer
CHR: Kathy Sinclair, Vice President Human Resources
CNO: Susan Duggar R.N., MSN, Vice President Nursing
Web address: www.spartanburgregional.com
Control: Hospital district or authority, Government, Nonfederal **Service:** General medical and surgical

Staffed Beds: 514 **Admissions:** 34302 **Census:** 436 **Outpatient Visits:** 370333 **Births:** 3033 **Total Expense ($000):** 594793 **Payroll Expense ($000):** 225747 **Personnel:** 5803

SUMTER—Sumter County

✚ **PALMETTO HEALTH TUOMEY (420070)**, 129 North Washington Street, Zip 29150–4983; tel. 803/774–9000, (Total facility includes 18 beds in nursing home–type unit) **A**1 10 19 **F**1 3 13 15 20 28 29 30 31 32 34 35 40 48 49 50 51 54 56 59 60 62 63 64 68 70 71 73 75 76 77 78 79 81 84 85 86 87 89 90 94 102 107 108 110 111 114 117 119 120 121 128 129 130 131 132 135 146 147 148 **S** Palmetto Health, Columbia, SC
Primary Contact: Michelle Logan–Owens, Chief Operating Officer
CFO: Mark Lovell, Vice President and Chief Financial Officer
CMO: Gene Dickerson M.D., Vice President Medical Affairs
CIO: Cheryl Martin, Chief Information Officer
CHR: Letitia Pringle–Miller, Administrative Director
CNO: Terrie Carlton R.N., Vice President & Chief Nursing Officer
Web address: www.tuomey.com
Control: Other not–for–profit (including NFP Corporation) **Service:** General medical and surgical

Staffed Beds: 238 **Admissions:** 7202 **Census:** 187 **Outpatient Visits:** 131393 **Births:** 1260 **Total Expense ($000):** 140678 **Payroll Expense ($000):** 49058 **Personnel:** 1289

TRAVELERS REST—Greenville County

✚ △ **NORTH GREENVILLE HOSPITAL (422008)**, 807 North Main Street, Zip 29690–1551; tel. 864/455–9206 **A**1 5 7 10 **F**1 3 15 29 30 34 35 40 44 50 64 68 75 79 85 86 87 107 110 111 114 119 130 146 148 **P**6
Primary Contact: Adrienne Talbert, Interim Administrator
CMO: Amy Treece M.D., Medical Director
CHR: Carol Bish, Human Resources Coordinator
CNO: Marian Lorraine McVey, Chief Nursing Officer
Web address: www.ghs.org
Control: Other not–for–profit (including NFP Corporation) **Service:** Acute long–term care hospital

Staffed Beds: 28 **Admissions:** 255 **Census:** 20 **Outpatient Visits:** 26118 **Births:** 0 **Total Expense ($000):** 29089 **Payroll Expense ($000):** 8184 **Personnel:** 143

☐ **SPRINGBROOK BEHAVIORAL HEALTH SYSTEM (424007)**, One Havenwood Lane, Zip 29690–9447, Mailing Address: P.O.Box 1005, 29690–1005; tel. 864/834–8013, (Total facility includes 68 beds in nursing home–type unit) **A**1 10 **F**98 99 104 106
Primary Contact: Mike Rowley, Chief Executive Officer
COO: Mary Ann Bennett R.N., Chief Operating Officer and Chief Nursing Officer
CFO: Bart Bennett, Chief Financial Officer
CMO: Mathew Fisher M.D., Medical Director
CIO: Bart Bennett, Chief Information Technology Officer
CHR: Teresa Lipscomb, Director Human Resources
CNO: Mary Ann Bennett R.N., Chief Operating Officer and Chief Nursing Officer
Web address: www.springbrookbehavioral.com
Control: Corporation, Investor–owned (for–profit) **Service:** Psychiatric

Staffed Beds: 112 **Admissions:** 1068 **Census:** 92 **Outpatient Visits:** 0 **Births:** 0 **Personnel:** 260

UNION—Union County

⥣ **UNION MEDICAL CENTER (420039)**, 322 West South Street, Zip 29379–2857, Mailing Address: P.O.Box 789, 29379–0789; tel. 864/301–2000 **A**10 21 **F**1 3 7 11 15 29 30 34 35 40 57 59 64 69 70 75 89 107 111 115 119 129 130 133 135 146 147 149 **S** Spartanburg Regional Healthcare System, Spartanburg, SC
Primary Contact: Paul R. Newhouse, President
CFO: Cindy L. Gault, Chief Financial Officer
CHR: Angie Benfield, Human Resources Generalist
CNO: Beth Lawson, Chief Nursing Officer
Web address: www.spartanburgregional.com/locations/union–medical–center/
Control: Hospital district or authority, Government, Nonfederal **Service:** General medical and surgical

Staffed Beds: 50 **Admissions:** 1037 **Census:** 11 **Outpatient Visits:** 6355 **Births:** 0 **Total Expense ($000):** 28026 **Payroll Expense ($000):** 9837 **Personnel:** 204

VARNVILLE—Hampton County

★ **HAMPTON REGIONAL MEDICAL CENTER (420072)**, 503 Carolina Avenue West, Zip 29944–4735, Mailing Address: P.O.Box 338, 29944–0338; tel. 803/943–2771 **A**10 20 **F**15 17 18 24 28 29 31 34 40 57 59 65 67 70 75 78 79 81 90 93 94 102 107 108 110 111 115 119 127 128 129 133 146
Primary Contact: Dave H. Hamill, President and Chief Executive Officer
Web address: www.hamptonregional.com
Control: Other not–for–profit (including NFP Corporation) **Service:** General medical and surgical

Staffed Beds: 32 **Admissions:** 625 **Census:** 8 **Births:** 4 **Total Expense ($000):** 21235 **Payroll Expense ($000):** 9239

SC

WALTERBORO—Colleton County

⊠ **COLLETON MEDICAL CENTER (420030)**, 501 Robertson Boulevard,
Zip 29488–5714; tel. 843/782–2000 **A**1 10 **F**3 11 13 15 18 26 29 30 32 34
35 36 40 41 45 47 49 56 57 59 60 64 65 68 70 75 76 77 79 81 82 85 86 87
89 90 93 94 96 98 102 107 108 110 111 114 115 119 129 130 131 132 146
147 148 **P**5 **S** HCA Healthcare, Nashville, TN
Primary Contact: Jimmy O. Hiott III, Chief Executive Officer
CFO: Jimmy O. Hiott III, Chief Financial Officer
CMO: Kim Rakes–Stephens M.D., Chief Medical Staff
CIO: Damien Noble, Director Information Technology and System
CHR: Wendy Glass, Director Human Resources
CNO: Anna Jonason Ph.D., R.N., Chief Nursing Officer
Web address: www.colletonmedical.com
Control: Corporation, Investor–owned (for–profit) **Service**: General medical and
surgical

Staffed Beds: 131 **Admissions**: 3941 **Census**: 63 **Outpatient Visits**: 72841
Births: 298 **Total Expense ($000)**: 65888 **Payroll Expense ($000)**: 22967
Personnel: 400

WEST COLUMBIA—Lexington County

★ ⇑ **LEXINGTON MEDICAL CENTER (420073)**, 2720 Sunset Boulevard,
Zip 29169–4810; tel. 803/791–2000 **A**2 3 10 21 **F**3 8 11 12 13 15 18 20 22
24 26 28 29 30 31 32 34 35 38 39 40 43 44 45 48 49 50 53 54 57 58 59 60
61 64 68 70 72 73 74 75 76 77 78 79 80 81 82 85 86 87 89 90 92 93 94 107
108 110 111 114 115 118 119 120 121 123 126 127 129 130 131 132 135
141 142 144 145 146 147 148 **P**6
Primary Contact: Tod Augsburger, President and Chief Executive Officer
COO: Tod Augsburger, Senior Vice President and Chief Operating Officer
CFO: Melinda Kruzner, Chief Financial Officer
CMO: Brent Powers M.D., Vice President/Chief Medical Officer
CIO: Kathleen R Herald, Vice President and Chief Information Officer
CHR: Kathy A Howell, Vice President Human Resources
CNO: Cindy Rohman R.N., MS, Vice President/Chief Nursing Officer
Web address: www.lexmed.com
Control: Hospital district or authority, Government, Nonfederal **Service**: General
medical and surgical

Staffed Beds: 448 **Admissions**: 27419 **Census**: 322 **Outpatient
Visits**: 306183 **Births**: 3388 **Total Expense ($000)**: 584823 **Payroll
Expense ($000)**: 212443 **Personnel**: 3658

☐ **THREE RIVERS BEHAVIORAL HEALTH (424008)**, 2900 Sunset Boulevard,
Zip 29169–3422; tel. 803/796–9911 **A**1 10 **F**4 5 35 98 99 100 101 103 104
105 106 **S** Universal Health Services, Inc., King of Prussia, PA
Primary Contact: Nannette M. Lewis, Chief Executive Officer
CFO: Christopher Jensen, Chief Financial Officer
CMO: Christina Lynn M.D., Medical Director
CHR: Nita Sundberg, Director Human Resources
CNO: Lilly Wing, Chief Nursing Officer
Web address: www.threeriversbehavioral.org
Control: Corporation, Investor–owned (for–profit) **Service**: Psychiatric

Staffed Beds: 122 **Admissions**: 3290 **Census**: 92 **Births**: 0 **Personnel**: 169

WINNSBORO—Fairfield County

☐ **FAIRFIELD MEMORIAL HOSPITAL (421302)**, 102 U S Hwy 321 By–Pass N,
Zip 29180–9251, Mailing Address: P.O.Box 620, 29180–0620; tel. 803/635–
5548 **A**1 5 10 18 **F**3 11 15 28 29 30 34 35 40 50 56 57 59 62 63 64 65 68
75 77 86 87 90 94 102 107 110 111 114 119 127 128 129 130 132 133 135
146 148
Primary Contact: Suzanne C. Doscher, Chief Executive Officer
COO: Darlene Hines
CFO: Timothy Mitchell, Chief Financial Officer
CMO: Roger A Gaddy Jr, Chief Medical Officer
CIO: Donnie Doherty, Director Information Systems
CHR: Kristi Godwin, Interim Human Resource Director
CNO: Starr Connor, Chief Nursing Officer
Web address: www.fairfieldmemorial.com
Control: County, Government, Nonfederal **Service**: General medical and surgical

Staffed Beds: 25 **Admissions**: 118 **Census**: 4 **Outpatient Visits**: 15483
Births: 0

Hospital, Medicare Provider Number, Address, Telephone, Approval, Facility, and Physician Codes, Health Care System

★ American Hospital Association (AHA) membership   ○ Healthcare Facilities Accreditation Program   ⇑ Center for Improvement in Healthcare Quality Accreditation
☐ The Joint Commission accreditation   ◇ DNV Healthcare Inc. accreditation   △ Commission on Accreditation of Rehabilitation Facilities (CARF) accreditation

SOUTH DAKOTA

ABERDEEN—Brown County

★ **AVERA ST. LUKE'S HOSPITAL (430014)**, 305 South State Street, Zip 57401–4527; tel. 605/622–5000, (Total facility includes 137 beds in nursing home–type unit) **A**2 10 19 **F**2 3 5 7 10 11 13 15 17 18 20 22 28 29 30 31 32 34 35 36 39 40 43 45 46 47 48 50 56 57 59 60 61 64 70 71 74 75 76 77 78 79 81 82 84 85 86 87 89 91 92 93 96 97 98 99 100 101 102 103 104 107 108 110 111 114 115 118 119 120 121 125 127 128 129 130 131 132 133 135 144 146 147 148 149 **P**6 **S** Avera Health, Sioux Falls, SD
Primary Contact: Todd Forkel, President and Chief Executive Officer
CFO: Geoff Durst, Vice President Finance
CMO: Shahid Chaudhary M.D., Chief Medical Officer
CIO: Julie Kusler, Manager Information Services
CHR: Tracy L Olson, Human Resource Officer
CNO: Jan Patterson, Chief Nursing Officer
Web address: www.avera.org/st-lukes-hospital/
Control: Church operated, Nongovernment, not-for-profit **Service**: General medical and surgical

Staffed Beds: 212 **Admissions:** 4890 **Census:** 179 **Outpatient Visits:** 189638 **Births:** 492 **Total Expense ($000):** 192942 **Payroll Expense ($000):** 91124 **Personnel:** 1187

DAKOTA PLAINS SURGICAL CENTER (430092), 701 8th Avenue NW, Suite C, Zip 57401–1865; tel. 605/225–3300 (Nonreporting) **A**10
Primary Contact: Charles Livingston, Administrator
Control: Corporation, Investor–owned (for–profit) **Service**: Surgical

Staffed Beds: 15

★ **SANFORD ABERDEEN MEDICAL CENTER (430097)**, 2905 3rd Avenue SE, Zip 57401–5420; tel. 605/626–4200 **A**10 **F**3 12 13 15 18 20 22 28 29 31 34 40 43 45 46 47 48 49 50 55 57 58 59 64 65 68 70 75 76 77 78 79 81 87 89 91 107 111 116 117 119 127 129 130 131 144 146 147 148 149 **P**6 **S** Sanford Health, Sioux Falls, SD
Primary Contact: Ashley M. Erickson, Chief Executive Officer
CFO: Jeffrey Poppen, Chief Financial Officer
CMO: Samuel Nyamu M.D., Chief Medical Officer
CHR: Katie Palmer, Manager Human Resources
CNO: Kila Legrand, Chief Nursing Officer
Web address: www.sanfordaberdeen.org/
Control: Other not-for-profit (including NFP Corporation) **Service**: General medical and surgical

Staffed Beds: 48 **Admissions:** 1447 **Census:** 12 **Outpatient Visits:** 62897 **Births:** 270 **Total Expense ($000):** 70020 **Payroll Expense ($000):** 30556 **Personnel:** 400

ARMOUR—Douglas County

DOUGLAS COUNTY MEMORIAL HOSPITAL (431305), 708 Eighth Street, Zip 57313–2102; tel. 605/724–2159 **A**10 18 **F**3 8 10 28 31 34 40 43 45 46 47 49 53 57 59 62 64 65 68 69 77 81 93 107 114 119 127 133 **P**6
Primary Contact: Heath Brouwer, Administrator
CFO: Dorothy Spease, Manager Business Office
Web address: www.dcmhsd.org
Control: Other not-for-profit (including NFP Corporation) **Service**: General medical and surgical

Staffed Beds: 11 **Admissions:** 160 **Census:** 2 **Outpatient Visits:** 9313 **Births:** 0 **Total Expense ($000):** 8961 **Payroll Expense ($000):** 3895 **Personnel:** 74

BOWDLE—Douglas County

★ **BOWDLE HOSPITAL (431318)**, 8001 West Fifth Street, Zip 57428, Mailing Address: P.O.Box 556, 57428–0556; tel. 605/285–6146, (Nonreporting) **A**10 18
Primary Contact: Sandy Schlechter, Chief Executive Officer
CFO: Brooke Heilman, Chief Financial Officer
CMO: John Ottenbacher, Chief of Staff
CNO: Bobbi Noess, Director of Nursing
Web address: www.bowdlehc.com
Control: City, Government, Nonfederal **Service**: General medical and surgical

Staffed Beds: 50

BRITTON—Marshall County

★ **MARSHALL COUNTY HEALTHCARE CENTER AVERA (431312)**, 413 Ninth Street, Zip 57430–2274; tel. 605/448–2253, (Nonreporting) **A**10 18 **S** Avera Health, Sioux Falls, SD
Primary Contact: Nick Fosness, Chief Executive Officer
Web address: www.avera.org
Control: Other not-for-profit (including NFP Corporation) **Service**: General medical and surgical

Staffed Beds: 18

BROOKINGS—Brookings County

★ **BROOKINGS HEALTH SYSTEM (430008)**, 300 22nd Avenue, Zip 57006–2496; tel. 605/696–9000, (Total facility includes 79 beds in nursing home–type unit) **A**10 20 **F**3 7 8 11 13 28 29 30 31 32 34 40 41 43 45 51 53 57 59 62 63 64 65 70 74 75 76 79 81 82 85 87 92 93 102 107 111 114 118 119 125 126 127 128 129 130 133 135 146 147 148 149
Primary Contact: Jason R. Merkley, Chief Executive Officer
CFO: Steve Lindemann, Chief Financial Officer
CMO: Shelby Eischens, Chief Medical Officer
CHR: September Bessler, Director, Human Resources
CNO: Tammy Hillestad, Chief Nursing Officer
Web address: www.brookingshealth.org
Control: City, Government, Nonfederal **Service**: General medical and surgical

Staffed Beds: 128 **Admissions:** 1255 **Census:** 88 **Outpatient Visits:** 73841 **Births:** 319 **Total Expense ($000):** 56751 **Payroll Expense ($000):** 27442 **Personnel:** 286

BURKE—Gregory County

★ **COMMUNITY MEMORIAL HOSPITAL (431309)**, 809 Jackson Street, Zip 57523–2065, Mailing Address: P.O.Box 319, 57523–0319; tel. 605/775–2621 **A**10 18 **F**3 28 31 34 40 41 42 43 57 62 63 65 68 87 97 107 114 115 127 128 133 148 **S** Sanford Health, Sioux Falls, SD
Primary Contact: Mistie Sachtjen, Chief Executive Officer
CMO: Megan Smith M.D., Chief Medical Staff
CHR: Tami Lyon, Director Human Resources
Web address: www.sanfordhealth.org
Control: Other not-for-profit (including NFP Corporation) **Service**: General medical and surgical

Staffed Beds: 16 **Admissions:** 200 **Census:** 4 **Outpatient Visits:** 3006 **Births:** 0 **Total Expense ($000):** 3034 **Payroll Expense ($000):** 1963 **Personnel:** 57

CANTON—Lincoln County

★ **SANFORD CANTON–INWOOD MEDICAL CENTER (431333)**, 440 North Hiawatha Drive, Zip 57013–5800; tel. 605/764–1400 **A**10 18 **F**7 10 15 28 34 40 45 59 65 71 75 77 81 93 97 104 107 114 119 128 130 133 143 149 150 **P**6 **S** Sanford Health, Sioux Falls, SD
Primary Contact: Scott C. Larson, Chief Executive Officer
CFO: Paul Gerhart, Chief Financial Officer
Web address: www.sanfordcantoninwood.org
Control: Other not-for-profit (including NFP Corporation) **Service**: General medical and surgical

Staffed Beds: 11 **Admissions:** 177 **Census:** 3 **Outpatient Visits:** 18309 **Births:** 0 **Total Expense ($000):** 6682 **Payroll Expense ($000):** 2988 **Personnel:** 75

CHAMBERLAIN—Brule County

★ **SANFORD CHAMBERLAIN MEDICAL CENTER (431329)**, 300 South Byron Boulevard, Zip 57325–9741; tel. 605/234–5511, (Total facility includes 44 beds in nursing home–type unit) **A**10 18 **F**3 8 13 15 18 19 28 29 31 34 35 40 43 50 57 59 68 70 75 76 77 78 81 85 86 87 89 93 100 101 102 104 107 110 114 119 130 131 132 133 148 149 **P**6 **S** Sanford Health, Sioux Falls, SD
Primary Contact: Erica Peterson, Chief Executive Officer
COO: Paul Miller, Director of Operations
CFO: Erica Peterson, Chief Executive Officer and Chief Financial Officer
CMO: Lacey Olson M.D., Chief Medical Staff
CHR: Dorothy Hieb, Director Human Resources
CNO: Sarah Talbott, Chief Nursing Officer
Web address: www.sanfordchamberlain.org
Control: Other not-for-profit (including NFP Corporation) **Service**: General medical and surgical

Staffed Beds: 69 **Admissions:** 532 **Census:** 48 **Outpatient Visits:** 27902 **Births:** 89 **Total Expense ($000):** 21548 **Payroll Expense ($000):** 8902 **Personnel:** 132

Many Facility Codes have changed. Please refer to the AHA Guide Code Chart.   © 2017 AHA Guide

SANFORD MID DAKOTA MEDICAL CENTER See Sanford Chamberlain Medical Center

CLEAR LAKE—Deuel County

★ **SANFORD CLEAR LAKE MEDICAL CENTER (431307)**, 701 Third Avenue South, Zip 57226–2016; tel. 605/874–2141 **A**10 18 **F**3 28 29 34 35 40 43 45 50 53 57 59 62 64 65 68 81 86 87 92 93 97 107 115 119 127 128 133 135 144 147 148 149 **P**6 **S** Sanford Health, Sioux Falls, SD
Primary Contact: Lori Sisk, R.N., Chief Executive Officer
CFO: Allison Nelson, Chief Financial Officer
CMO: Terrance Smith M.D., Chairman Medical Staff
CNO: Stephanie Dobbs, Chief Nursing Officer
Web address: www.sanforddeuelcounty.org
Control: Other not–for–profit (including NFP Corporation) **Service**: General medical and surgical

Staffed Beds: 10 **Admissions:** 213 **Census:** 3 **Outpatient Visits:** 17118 **Births:** 0 **Total Expense ($000):** 6148 **Payroll Expense ($000):** 2843 **Personnel:** 86

CUSTER—Custer County

★ **CUSTER REGIONAL HOSPITAL (431323)**, 1039 Montgomery Street, Zip 57730–1397; tel. 605/673–2229, (Nonreporting) **A**10 18 **S** Regional Health, Rapid City, SD
Primary Contact: Veronica Schmidt, President
Web address: www.regionalhealth.com
Control: Other not–for–profit (including NFP Corporation) **Service**: General medical and surgical

Staffed Beds: 87

DAKOTA DUNES—Union County

SIOUXLAND SURGERY CENTER (430089), 600 North Sioux Point Road, Zip 57049–5000; tel. 605/232–3332 (Nonreporting) **A**10
Primary Contact: Greg Miner, Administrator
Web address: www.siouxlandsurg.com/
Control: Corporation, Investor–owned (for–profit) **Service**: Surgical

Staffed Beds: 40

DE SMET—Kingsbury County

★ **AVERA DE SMET MEMORIAL HOSPITAL (431332)**, 306 Prairie Avenue SW, Zip 57231–2285, Mailing Address: P.O.Box 160, 57231–0160; tel. 605/854–3329, (Nonreporting) **A**10 18 **S** Avera Health, Sioux Falls, SD
Primary Contact: Bryan Breitling, Interim Administrator and Chief Executive Officer
Web address: www.desmetmemorial.org
Control: Other not–for–profit (including NFP Corporation) **Service**: General medical and surgical

Staffed Beds: 6

DEADWOOD—Lawrence County

★ **LEAD–DEADWOOD REGIONAL HOSPITAL (431320)**, 61 Charles Street, Zip 57732–1303; tel. 605/717–6000 **A**10 18 **F**3 7 15 28 29 30 34 40 43 45 59 64 68 69 70 75 77 78 81 85 87 93 97 107 114 119 132 133 **S** Regional Health, Rapid City, SD
Primary Contact: Mark C. Schmidt, President
CMO: Elizabeth Sayler M.D., Chief of Staff
CHR: Kathryn L Shockey, Director Human Resources
Web address: www.regionalhealth.com
Control: State, Government, Nonfederal **Service**: General medical and surgical

Staffed Beds: 9 **Admissions:** 290 **Census:** 6 **Outpatient Visits:** 10982 **Births:** 0 **Total Expense ($000):** 11568 **Payroll Expense ($000):** 6536 **Personnel:** 98

DELL RAPIDS—Minnehaha County

AVERA DELLS AREA HEALTH CENTER See Avera Dells Area Hospital

★ **AVERA DELLS AREA HOSPITAL (431331)**, 909 North Iowa Avenue, Zip 57022–1231; tel. 605/428–5431 **A**10 18 **F**3 11 15 18 28 34 35 40 45 53 57 59 64 65 75 81 86 92 93 94 97 107 110 128 132 133 146 148 **P**6 **S** Avera Health, Sioux Falls, SD
Primary Contact: Scott James. Hargens, Administrator and Chief Executive Officer
CFO: Kory Holt, Division Controller Network Operations
CMO: Demetre Skliris, Chief Medical Officer
CIO: Val Witham, Director of Health Information
CHR: Amy Aukes, Regional Manager of Human Resources
CNO: Karla Carstensen, Director Patient Care
Web address: www.avera.org/dell–rapids/
Control: Other not–for–profit (including NFP Corporation) **Service**: General medical and surgical

Staffed Beds: 23 **Admissions:** 300 **Census:** 4 **Outpatient Visits:** 17797 **Births:** 0 **Total Expense ($000):** 5397 **Payroll Expense ($000):** 2140 **Personnel:** 52

EAGLE BUTTE—Dewey County

⇑ **U. S. PUBLIC HEALTH SERVICE INDIAN HOSPITAL (430083)**, 317 Main Street, Zip 57625–1012, Mailing Address: P.O.Box 1012, 57625–1012; tel. 605/964–7724 **A**10 21 **F**7 13 29 40 50 64 65 66 68 75 82 83 84 86 91 93 97 107 111 114 119 132 135 143 148 **S** U. S. Indian Health Service, Rockville, MD
Primary Contact: Charles Fisher, Chief Executive Officer
CFO: Lisa Deal, Budget Analyst
Web address: www.ihs.gov
Control: PHS, Indian Service, Government, federal **Service**: General medical and surgical

Staffed Beds: 8 **Admissions:** 225 **Census:** 3 **Outpatient Visits:** 80266 **Births:** 17

EUREKA—Mcpherson County

★ **EUREKA COMMUNITY HEALTH SERVICES AVERA (431308)**, 410 Ninth Street, Zip 57437–2182, Mailing Address: P.O.Box 517, 57437–0517; tel. 605/284–2661 **A**10 18 **F**10 28 34 35 40 41 45 59 62 65 81 93 133 **P**4 5 **S** Avera Health, Sioux Falls, SD
Primary Contact: Carmen Weber, Administrator
CFO: Joyce Schwingler, Chief Financial Officer
Web address: www.avera.org
Control: Other not–for–profit (including NFP Corporation) **Service**: General medical and surgical

Staffed Beds: 6 **Admissions:** 69 **Census:** 1 **Outpatient Visits:** 6369 **Births:** 0 **Total Expense ($000):** 2262 **Payroll Expense ($000):** 978 **Personnel:** 31

FAULKTON—Faulk County

FAULKTON AREA MEDICAL CENTER (431301), 1300 Oak Street, Zip 57438–2149, Mailing Address: P.O.Box 100, 57438–0100; tel. 605/598–6263 **A**10 18 **F**3 17 28 29 31 40 45 59 64 77 93 97 107 115 127 128 133
Primary Contact: Jay A. Jahnig, Chief Executive Officer
COO: Jay A Jahnig, Chief Executive Officer
CFO: Susan Miller, Financial Administrator
CMO: K A Bartholomew M.D., Medical Director
CIO: Cheryl Bue, Health Information Transcriptionist
CHR: Blythe Smith, Administrative Assistant
CNO: Shannon Stuwe, Director of Nursing
Web address: www.faulktonmedical.org
Control: Other not–for–profit (including NFP Corporation) **Service**: General medical and surgical

Staffed Beds: 12 **Admissions:** 164 **Census:** 1 **Outpatient Visits:** 12758 **Births:** 0 **Total Expense ($000):** 9099 **Payroll Expense ($000):** 4165 **Personnel:** 74

SD

SD

FLANDREAU—Moody County

★ **AVERA FLANDREAU HOSPITAL (431310)**, 214 North Prairie Street, Zip 57028–1243; tel. 605/997–2433 **A**10 18 **F**3 28 34 35 40 45 57 59 64 65 75 81 86 92 93 97 107 127 128 132 133 146 148 **P**6 **S** Avera Health, Sioux Falls, SD
Primary Contact: Scott James. Hargens, Administrator and Chief Executive Officer
CFO: Kory Holt, Assistant Vice President for Financial Integration
CMO: Scott Peterson M.D., President Medical Staff
CIO: Val Witham, Director Health Information
CHR: Amy Aukes, Human Resources Analyst
Web address: www.avera.org/flandreau–medical/
Control: Other not–for–profit (including NFP Corporation) **Service:** General medical and surgical

Staffed Beds: 18 **Admissions:** 109 **Census:** 1 **Outpatient Visits:** 13558 **Births:** 0 **Total Expense ($000):** 5679 **Payroll Expense ($000):** 2090 **Personnel:** 48

AVERA FLANDREAU MEDICAL CENTER See Avera Flandreau Hospital

FORT MEADE—Meade County

✠ **VETERANS AFFAIRS BLACK HILLS HEALTH CARE SYSTEM**, 113 Comanche Road, Zip 57741–1099; tel. 605/347–2511, (Nonreporting) (Includes VETERANS AFFAIRS MEDICAL CENTER HOT SPRINGS CAMPUS, 500 North Fifth Street, Hot Springs, South Dakota, Zip 57747, tel. 605/745–2052) **A**1 5 **S** Department of Veterans Affairs, Washington, DC
Primary Contact: Sandra Horsman, Director
CFO: Joseph Ferris, Chief Financial Officer
CHR: Denis Sullivan, Chief Human Resources Management
Web address: www.blackhills.va.gov/
Control: Veterans Affairs, Government, federal **Service:** General medical and surgical

Staffed Beds: 243

FREEMAN—Hutchinson County

★ **FREEMAN REGIONAL HEALTH SERVICES (431313)**, 510 East Eighth Street, Zip 57029–2086, Mailing Address: P.O.Box 370, 57029–0370; tel. 605/925–4000, (Total facility includes 56 beds in nursing home–type unit) **A**10 18 **F**2 3 6 11 15 28 30 34 35 40 43 45 49 54 56 57 59 64 65 68 69 70 75 77 79 81 82 86 93 97 107 114 119 125 127 128 130 132 133 146 **P**6
Primary Contact: Nicholas R. Brandner, Chief Executive Officer
CFO: Mark Miller, Chief Financial Officer
Web address: www.freemanregional.com
Control: Other not–for–profit (including NFP Corporation) **Service:** General medical and surgical

Staffed Beds: 81 **Admissions:** 214 **Census:** 58 **Outpatient Visits:** 11659 **Births:** 0 **Total Expense ($000):** 10550 **Payroll Expense ($000):** 4637 **Personnel:** 118

GETTYSBURG—Potter County

★ **AVERA GETTYSBURG HOSPITAL (431302)**, 606 East Garfield Avenue, Zip 57442–1398; tel. 605/765–2480, (Nonreporting) **A**10 18 **S** Avera Health, Sioux Falls, SD
Primary Contact: Robert L. Sheckler, Administrator
Web address: www.avera.org/st–marys–pierre/gettysburg–hospital/
Control: Church operated, Nongovernment, not–for–profit **Service:** General medical and surgical

Staffed Beds: 55

GREGORY—Gregory County

★ **AVERA GREGORY HOSPITAL (431338)**, 400 Park Avenue, Zip 57533–1302, Mailing Address: P.O.Box 408, 57533–0408; tel. 605/835–8394, (Total facility includes 40 beds in nursing home–type unit) **A**10 18 **F**8 15 28 29 31 34 35 40 42 45 54 59 60 64 75 77 84 91 93 97 107 108 110 114 127 128 132 133 135 **P**6 **S** Avera Health, Sioux Falls, SD
Primary Contact: Anthony Timanus, Chief Executive Officer
CFO: Trish Keiser, Comptroller
CMO: Rich Kafka M.D., Chief Medical Officer
CIO: Justin Keegan, Director Support Services
CHR: Carol Postulka, Administrative Coordinator
Web address: www.gregoryhealthcare.org
Control: Other not–for–profit (including NFP Corporation) **Service:** General medical and surgical

Staffed Beds: 65 **Admissions:** 590 **Census:** 45 **Outpatient Visits:** 12720 **Births:** 0 **Total Expense ($000):** 11663 **Payroll Expense ($000):** 4611 **Personnel:** 37

HOT SPRINGS—Fall River County

★ **FALL RIVER HOSPITAL (431322)**, 1201 Highway 71 South, Zip 57747–8800; tel. 605/745–3159, (Total facility includes 48 beds in nursing home–type unit) **A**10 18 **F**3 28 34 40 43 45 56 57 59 64 65 74 77 81 93 99 100 101 102 103 104 107 111 114 119 127 128 129 130 131 133 146 148 **P**6
Primary Contact: Tricia Uhlir, Chief Executive Officer
CFO: Jesse Naze, Chief Financial Officer
CMO: Rodney Larson M.D., Medical Director
CIO: Dustin Kleinsasser, Information Technology and BioMed
CHR: Cindy Trent, Manager Personnel
Web address: www.frhssd.org
Control: Other not–for–profit (including NFP Corporation) **Service:** General medical and surgical

Staffed Beds: 73 **Admissions:** 425 **Census:** 55 **Outpatient Visits:** 26705 **Births:** 0 **Total Expense ($000):** 18723 **Payroll Expense ($000):** 8582 **Personnel:** 167

VETERANS AFFAIRS MEDICAL CENTER HOT SPRINGS CAMPUS See Veterans Affairs Black Hills Health Care System, Fort Meade

HURON—Beadle County

★ **HURON REGIONAL MEDICAL CENTER (431335)**, 172 Fourth Street SE, Zip 57350–2590; tel. 605/353–6200 **A**10 18 **F**3 11 13 14 15 28 29 31 34 35 40 41 43 45 57 59 60 62 63 64 68 70 75 77 78 79 81 85 86 93 102 107 108 110 111 115 118 119 130 132 133 146 148 **P**6 **S** QHR, Brentwood, TN
Primary Contact: David Dick, Chief Executive Officer
CFO: Marcia Zwanziger, Vice President Finance
CMO: Bill Miner M.D., Chief of Staff
CHR: Rhonda Hanson, Director Human Resources
CNO: Gail Robeson, Vice President Patient Services
Web address: www.huronregional.org
Control: Other not–for–profit (including NFP Corporation) **Service:** General medical and surgical

Staffed Beds: 25 **Admissions:** 1285 **Census:** 12 **Outpatient Visits:** 63102 **Births:** 329 **Total Expense ($000):** 31052 **Payroll Expense ($000):** 14677 **Personnel:** 240

MADISON—Lake County

★ **MADISON COMMUNITY HOSPITAL (431300)**, 323 SW 10th Street, Zip 57042–3200; tel. 605/256–6551 **A**10 18 **F**7 13 15 28 31 34 35 40 41 43 50 57 59 62 64 65 70 75 76 77 81 82 85 87 89 93 97 107 110 111 114 119 129 132 133 135 143 144 145 146 148 **P**6
Primary Contact: Tamara Miller, R.N., Administrator
CFO: Teresa Mallett, Chief Financial Officer
CNO: Charlotte Charles, Director Acute Patient Services
Web address: www.madisonhospital.com
Control: Other not–for–profit (including NFP Corporation) **Service:** General medical and surgical

Staffed Beds: 22 **Admissions:** 510 **Census:** 8 **Outpatient Visits:** 24958 **Births:** 29 **Total Expense ($000):** 23048 **Payroll Expense ($000):** 11284 **Personnel:** 217

MARTIN—Bennett County

BENNETT COUNTY HOSPITAL AND NURSING HOME (431314), 102 Major Allen Street, Zip 57551–6005, Mailing Address: P.O.Box 70, 57551–0070; tel. 605/685–6622, (Total facility includes 8 beds in nursing home–type unit) **A**10 18 **F**7 34 40 50 53 57 59 62 65 66 67 68 77 84 93 107 130 133 143
Primary Contact: Andrew Riggin, Chief Executive Officer
CFO: Jean Kirk, Chief Financial Officer
CMO: Peter Knowles–Smith M.D., Medical Director
CIO: Jean Kirk, Chief Financial Officer
CHR: T J Porter, Director Human Resources
Web address: www.bennettcountyhospital.com/
Control: Other not–for–profit (including NFP Corporation) **Service:** General medical and surgical

Staffed Beds: 62 **Admissions:** 142 **Census:** 36 **Outpatient Visits:** 43479 **Births:** 3 **Total Expense ($000):** 8203 **Payroll Expense ($000):** 3947 **Personnel:** 97

MILBANK—Grant County

★ **MILBANK AREA HOSPITAL AVERA (431326)**, 301 Flynn Drive, Zip 57252–1508; tel. 605/432–4538, (Nonreporting) **A**10 18 **S** Avera Health, Sioux Falls, SD
Primary Contact: Natalie Gauer, Administrator
CMO: Kevin Bjordahl M.D., Chief Medical Officer
CHR: Mona Schafer, Regional Manager Human Resources
Web address: www.averamilbank.org
Control: Other not–for–profit (including NFP Corporation) **Service:** General medical and surgical

Staffed Beds: 25

Many Facility Codes have changed. Please refer to the AHA Guide Code Chart. © 2017 AHA Guide

MILLER—Hand County

★ **AVERA HAND COUNTY MEMORIAL HOSPITAL (431337)**, 300 West Fifth Street, Zip 57362–1238; tel. 605/853–2421 **A**10 18 **F**3 8 11 15 17 28 29 34 35 40 43 45 46 50 53 57 59 64 77 79 81 86 87 93 107 114 119 128 129 132 133 146 148 **S** Avera Health, Sioux Falls, SD
Primary Contact: Bryan Breitling, Administrator
CFO: Debbie Pullman, Director Finance
CMO: Steve Schroeder M.D., Chief of Staff
CIO: Janice Purrington, Coordinator Medical Records
CNO: Teresa E Fanning, Director of Patient Care
Web address: www.avera.org
Control: Other not–for–profit (including NFP Corporation) **Service**: General medical and surgical

> **Staffed Beds**: 9 **Admissions**: 267 **Census**: 3 **Outpatient Visits**: 17996
> **Births**: 0 **Total Expense ($000)**: 7089 **Payroll Expense ($000)**: 3267
> **Personnel**: 59

MITCHELL—Davison County

⊞ **AVERA QUEEN OF PEACE HOSPITAL (430013)**, 525 North Foster, Zip 57301–2999; tel. 605/995–2000, (Total facility includes 109 beds in nursing home–type unit) **A**1 2 10 **F**3 10 13 15 28 29 30 31 34 40 43 45 48 50 51 53 54 57 59 64 69 70 71 75 76 77 78 79 81 82 84 85 86 89 93 94 96 104 107 108 110 111 114 117 118 119 121 123 127 128 129 130 131 132 133 135 146 147 148 **P**6 **S** Avera Health, Sioux Falls, SD
Primary Contact: Thomas A. Clark, Regional President and Chief Executive Officer
CFO: Will Flett, Vice President Finance and Chief Financial Officer
CMO: David Balt D.O., Chief Medical Officer
CIO: Jim Hanson, Director Information Systems
CHR: Rita Lemon, Director Human Resources
CNO: Rochelle Reider, Vice President Patient Care
Web address: www.averaqueenofpeace.org
Control: Church operated, Nongovernment, not–for–profit **Service**: General medical and surgical

> **Staffed Beds**: 180 **Admissions**: 2216 **Census**: 122 **Outpatient Visits**: 131287 **Births**: 482 **Total Expense ($000)**: 95571 **Payroll Expense ($000)**: 44107 **Personnel**: 370

MOBRIDGE—Walworth County

★ **MOBRIDGE REGIONAL HOSPITAL (431325)**, 1401 Tenth Avenue West, Zip 57601–1106, Mailing Address: P.O.Box 580, 57601–0580; tel. 605/845–3692 **A**10 18 **F**3 7 10 11 13 15 17 28 32 34 35 40 43 45 50 56 57 59 62 64 65 70 76 77 81 93 94 97 107 110 114 119 125 127 128 129 130 131 132 133 147 148 **P**6
Primary Contact: John J. Ayoub, FACHE, Chief Executive Officer
COO: Beth Jensen, Director Clinic Operations
CFO: Renae Tisdall, Chief Financial Officer
CMO: Travis Henderson M.D., Chief of Staff
CIO: Lynn Schott, Director Information Technology
CHR: Keri Wientjes, Director Human Resources
CNO: Kristi Voller, Director of Nursing
Web address: www.mobridgehospital.org
Control: Other not–for–profit (including NFP Corporation) **Service**: General medical and surgical

> **Staffed Beds**: 25 **Admissions**: 818 **Census**: 7 **Outpatient Visits**: 56073
> **Births**: 51 **Total Expense ($000)**: 19490 **Payroll Expense ($000)**: 8931
> **Personnel**: 172

PARKSTON—Hutchinson County

★ **AVERA ST. BENEDICT HEALTH CENTER (431330)**, 401 West Glynn Drive, Zip 57366–9605; tel. 605/928–3311, (Total facility includes 74 beds in nursing home–type unit) **A**10 18 **F**2 3 8 10 13 15 28 29 30 31 32 34 35 38 40 45 53 56 57 59 62 64 65 69 75 76 81 82 83 85 86 87 89 107 110 111 115 116 119 128 129 130 131 132 133 135 146 148 **P**6 **S** Avera Health, Sioux Falls, SD
Primary Contact: Gale N. Walker, President and Chief Executive Officer
CFO: Rita Blasius, Assistant Administrator and Chief Financial Officer
CMO: Antoinette VanderPol, Chief of Staff
CIO: Adam Popp, Director Information Systems
CHR: Phyllis Ehler, Director Human Resources
CNO: Denise Muntefering, Vice President Patient Care Services
Web address: www.averastbenedict.org
Control: Church operated, Nongovernment, not–for–profit **Service**: General medical and surgical

> **Staffed Beds**: 99 **Admissions**: 567 **Census**: 80 **Outpatient Visits**: 20955
> **Births**: 49 **Total Expense ($000)**: 20448 **Payroll Expense ($000)**: 10265
> **Personnel**: 176

PHILIP—Haakon County

HANS P. PETERSON MEMORIAL HOSPITAL See Philip Health Services

★ **PHILIP HEALTH SERVICES (431319)**, 503 West Pine Street, Zip 57567–3300, Mailing Address: P.O.Box 790, 57567–0790; tel. 605/859–2511, (Nonreporting) **A**10 18 **S** Regional Health, Rapid City, SD
Primary Contact: Jeremy Schultes, Administrator and Chief Executive Officer
Web address: www.philiphealthservices.com/
Control: Other not–for–profit (including NFP Corporation) **Service**: General medical and surgical

> **Staffed Beds**: 48

PIERRE—Hughes County

⊞ **AVERA ST. MARY'S HOSPITAL (430015)**, 801 East Sioux Avenue, Zip 57501–3323; tel. 605/224–3100, (Nonreporting) **A**1 10 20 **S** Avera Health, Sioux Falls, SD
Primary Contact: Todd Forkel, Interim Chief Executive Officer
CFO: Tom Wagner, Interim Vice President Finance
CMO: Denise Hanisch M.D., Chief of Staff
CIO: Jamie Raske, Information Technology Lead
CHR: Paul Marso, Vice President Human Resources
Web address: www.avera.org/st-marys-pierre/
Control: Other not–for–profit (including NFP Corporation) **Service**: General medical and surgical

> **Staffed Beds**: 164

PINE RIDGE—Shannon County

⇑ **U. S. PUBLIC HEALTH SERVICE INDIAN HOSPITAL (430081)**, East Highway 18, Zip 57770, Mailing Address: P.O.Box 1201, 57770–1201; tel. 605/867–5131 **A**10 21 **F**3 8 13 15 29 32 34 35 38 39 40 41 44 45 50 56 57 59 61 62 64 65 66 68 71 75 76 81 82 87 89 90 91 93 97 99 100 101 102 103 104 107 110 114 119 130 135 143 147 148 149 **S** U. S. Indian Health Service, Rockville, MD
Primary Contact: Ellen Davis, Service Unit Director
CFO: Sophia Conny, Deputy Administrative Officer
CMO: Jan Colton M.D., Acting Clinical Director
CHR: Annabelle Blackbear, Human Resources Specialist
Web address: www.ihs.gov
Control: PHS, Indian Service, Government, federal **Service**: General medical and surgical

> **Staffed Beds**: 45 **Admissions**: 1591 **Census**: 12 **Outpatient Visits**: 149927
> **Births**: 263 **Total Expense ($000)**: 43667 **Payroll Expense ($000)**: 26265
> **Personnel**: 439

PLATTE—Charles Mix County

★ **PLATTE HEALTH CENTER AVERA (431306)**, 601 East Seventh, Zip 57369–2123, Mailing Address: P.O.Box 200, 57369–0200; tel. 605/337–3364, (Total facility includes 44 beds in nursing home–type unit) **A**10 18 **F**3 11 15 28 29 30 31 34 35 40 41 45 56 57 59 62 64 65 66 67 68 69 75 77 78 79 81 87 91 93 97 107 110 115 119 127 128 129 130 131 132 133 146 **S** Avera Health, Sioux Falls, SD
Primary Contact: Mark Burket, Chief Executive Officer
CFO: Jerry Hoffman, Chief Financial Officer
Web address: www.phcavera.org
Control: Other not–for–profit (including NFP Corporation) **Service**: General medical and surgical

> **Staffed Beds**: 61 **Admissions**: 190 **Census**: 45 **Outpatient Visits**: 13040
> **Births**: 3 **Total Expense ($000)**: 9907 **Payroll Expense ($000)**: 4717
> **Personnel**: 125

RAPID CITY—Pennington County

BLACK HILLS SURGICAL HOSPITAL (430091), 216 Anamaria Drive, Zip 57701–7366, Mailing Address: 1868 Lombardy Drive, 57703–4130; tel. 605/721–4900, (Nonreporting) **A**10
Primary Contact: Franklin Shobe, Administrator and Chief Executive Officer
Web address: www.bhsc.com
Control: Partnership, Investor–owned (for–profit) **Service**: Surgical

> **Staffed Beds**: 26

⇑ **INDIAN HEALTH SERVICE HOSPITAL (430082)**, 3200 Canyon Lake Drive, Zip 57702–8197; tel. 605/355–2280, (Nonreporting) **A**10 21 **S** U. S. Indian Health Service, Rockville, MD
Primary Contact: Kevin J. Stiffarm, Chief Executive Officer
Web address: www.ihs.gov
Control: PHS, Indian Service, Government, federal **Service**: General medical and surgical

> **Staffed Beds**: 9

SD

Hospital, Medicare Provider Number, Address, Telephone, Approval, Facility, and Physician Codes, Health Care System

★ American Hospital Association (AHA) membership   ○ Healthcare Facilities Accreditation Program   ⇑ Center for Improvement in Healthcare Quality Accreditation
□ The Joint Commission accreditation   ◇ DNV Healthcare Inc. accreditation   △ Commission on Accreditation of Rehabilitation Facilities (CARF) accreditation

✠ **RAPID CITY REGIONAL HOSPITAL (430077)**, 353 Fairmont Boulevard, Zip 57701–7393, Mailing Address: P.O.Box 6000, 57709–6000; tel. 605/755–1000 **A**1 3 5 10 **F**3 12 13 15 17 18 20 22 24 26 28 29 30 31 34 40 43 46 48 49 51 56 59 60 62 63 64 70 72 74 76 77 78 79 81 82 84 85 87 89 90 92 93 97 98 99 102 103 104 107 108 111 115 118 119 120 121 124 126 129 130 131 144 146 148 149 **P**1 **S** Regional Health, Rapid City, SD
Primary Contact: Paulette Davidson, FACHE, Chief Operating Officer and Interim President
COO: Paulette Davidson FACHE, Chief Operating Officer
CFO: Mark Thompson, Vice President Financial Services
CMO: David Houser M.D., Vice President Medical Affairs
CIO: Richard Latuchie, Vice President Business Development
CHR: Maureen Henson, Vice President Human Resources
Web address: www.regionalhealth.com
Control: Other not–for–profit (including NFP Corporation) **Service:** General medical and surgical

Staffed Beds: 394 **Admissions:** 18392 **Census:** 269 **Outpatient Visits:** 329803 **Total Expense ($000):** 486975 **Payroll Expense ($000):** 198529 **Personnel:** 2300

SAME DAY SURGERY CENTER (430093), 651 Cathedral Drive, Zip 57701–7368; tel. 605/755–9900 (Nonreporting) **A**10
Primary Contact: Doris Fritts, R.N., Executive Director
Web address: www.samedaysurgerycenter.org
Control: Corporation, Investor–owned (for–profit) **Service:** Surgical

Staffed Beds: 8

REDFIELD—Spink County

COMMUNITY MEMORIAL HOSPITAL (431316), 110 West Tenth Avenue, Zip 57469–1520, Mailing Address: P.O.Box 420, 57469–0420; tel. 605/472–1110, (Nonreporting) **A**10 18
Primary Contact: Michael O'Keefe, Interim Chief Executive Officer
CFO: William Boyer, Chief Financial Officer
CHR: Rhonda Stroh, Chief Human Resources Officer
CNO: Julene J Cass R.N., Director of Nursing
Web address: www.redfield–sd.com/hospital.html
Control: City, Government, Nonfederal **Service:** General medical and surgical

Staffed Beds: 18

ROSEBUD—Todd County

⇑ **U. S. PUBLIC HEALTH SERVICE INDIAN HOSPITAL (430084)**, Highway 18, Soldier Creek Road, Zip 57570; tel. 605/747–2231, (Nonreporting) **A**10 21 **S** U. S. Indian Health Service, Rockville, MD
Primary Contact: Kathey Wilson, Acting Chief Executive Officer
COO: Romeo Vivit, Chief Surgeon
CMO: Valerie Parker M.D., Clinical Director
CHR: Michelle Zephier, Human Resource Specialist
Web address: www.ihs.gov
Control: PHS, Indian Service, Government, federal **Service:** General medical and surgical

Staffed Beds: 35

SCOTLAND—Bon Homme County

★ **LANDMANN–JUNGMAN MEMORIAL HOSPITAL AVERA (431317)**, 600 Billars Street, Zip 57059–2026; tel. 605/583–2226 **A**10 18 **F**3 28 34 35 40 43 53 57 59 64 65 67 89 90 93 97 107 114 119 125 128 133 147 148 **S** Avera Health, Sioux Falls, SD
Primary Contact: Melissa Gale, Chief Executive Officer
CFO: Darcy Permann, Manager Business Office
Web address: www.ljmh.org
Control: Other not–for–profit (including NFP Corporation) **Service:** General medical and surgical

Staffed Beds: 25 **Admissions:** 43 **Census:** 1 **Outpatient Visits:** 7569 **Births:** 0 **Total Expense ($000):** 4101 **Payroll Expense ($000):** 1823

SIOUX FALLS—Lincoln County

☐ **AVERA HEART HOSPITAL OF SOUTH DAKOTA (430095)**, 4500 West 69th Street, Zip 57108–8148; tel. 605/977–7000, (Nonreporting) **A**1 3 5 10 **S** Avera Health, Sioux Falls, SD
Primary Contact: Michael Gibbs, President
CFO: Jean White, Vice President Finance
Web address: www.avera.org/heart–hospital
Control: Partnership, Investor–owned (for–profit) **Service:** General medical and surgical

Staffed Beds: 53

SIOUX FALLS—Minnehaha County

✠ △ **AVERA MCKENNAN HOSPITAL AND UNIVERSITY HEALTH CENTER (430016)**, 1325 South Cliff Avenue, Zip 57105–1007, Mailing Address: P.O.Box 5045, 57117–5045; tel. 605/322–8000, (Includes AVERA BEHAVIORAL HEALTH CENTER, 440 West 69th Street, Sioux Falls, South Dakota, Zip 57108, tel. 605/322–4065; Steve Lindquist, Assistant Vice President, Behavioral Health; AVERA CHILDREN'S HOSPITAL, 1325 South Cliff Avenue, Sioux Falls, South Dakota, Zip 57105–1016, PO Box 5045, 57117–5045, tel. 605/322–5437) (Total facility includes 90 beds in nursing home–type unit) **A**1 2 3 5 7 10 **F**3 5 10 11 12 13 15 18 19 20 21 22 23 24 29 30 31 32 34 35 36 38 39 40 41 43 44 46 49 50 53 54 55 56 57 58 59 60 61 63 64 65 66 67 68 70 71 72 74 75 76 77 78 79 81 82 84 85 86 87 88 89 90 92 93 94 96 97 98 99 100 101 102 103 104 105 107 108 110 111 114 115 116 117 118 119 120 121 123 124 125 126 128 129 130 131 132 134 135 136 138 141 142 143 144 145 146 147 148 149 **P**4 **S** Avera Health, Sioux Falls, SD
Primary Contact: David Flicek, President and Chief Executive Officer
COO: Judy Blauwet M.P.H., R.N., Senior Vice President Operations and Chief Nursing Officer
CFO: Julie Norton, Chief Financial Officer
CMO: Michael Elliott M.D., Chief Medical Officer and Senior Vice President of Medical Affairs
CIO: Kristin Gross, Director Information Technology Center
CHR: Lynne D Hagen, Human Resources Officer
CNO: Judy Blauwet M.P.H., R.N., Senior Vice President of Hospital Operations and Chief Nursing Officer
Web address: www.averamckennan.org
Control: Church operated, Nongovernment, not–for–profit **Service:** General medical and surgical

Staffed Beds: 415 **Admissions:** 21637 **Census:** 410 **Outpatient Visits:** 287358 **Births:** 2236 **Total Expense ($000):** 824711 **Payroll Expense ($000):** 345333

CHILDRENS CARE HOSPITAL AND SCHOOL (433300), 2501 West 26th Street, Zip 57105–2498; tel. 605/782–2300, (Nonreporting) **A**10
Primary Contact: David A. Timpe, Interim President and Chief Executive Officer
CFO: John Clark, Chief Financial Officer
CMO: Christiane Maroun M.D., Chief of Staff
CHR: Tiffany Reilly, Director Human Resources
Web address: www.cchs.org
Control: Other not–for–profit (including NFP Corporation) **Service:** Children's rehabilitation

Staffed Beds: 114

✠ △ **SANFORD USD MEDICAL CENTER (430027)**, 1305 West 18th Street, Zip 57105–0496, Mailing Address: P.O.Box 5039, 57117–5039; tel. 605/333–1000, (Includes SANFORD CHILDREN'S HOSPITAL, 1600 West 22nd Street, Sioux Falls, South Dakota, Zip 57105, PO Box 5039, 57117–5039, tel. 605/333–1000) **A**1 2 3 5 7 8 10 **F**3 7 8 9 11 12 13 14 15 17 18 19 20 21 22 23 24 25 26 27 28 29 30 31 32 34 35 36 37 38 40 43 44 45 46 47 48 49 50 51 52 53 54 55 56 57 58 59 60 61 62 63 64 65 66 68 70 71 72 73 74 75 76 77 78 79 80 81 82 83 84 85 86 87 88 89 90 91 92 93 94 96 97 99 100 101 103 104 105 107 108 110 111 114 115 116 117 118 119 120 121 123 124 126 129 130 131 132 134 135 138 141 142 143 144 146 147 148 149 150 **P**6 **S** Sanford Health, Sioux Falls, SD
Primary Contact: Paul A. Hanson, FACHE, President
COO: Brad J. Schipper, Chief Operating Officer
CFO: Merrilee Schultz, Chief Finance
CIO: Arlyn Broekhuis, Vice President and Chief Information Officer
CHR: Evan Burkett, Chief Human Resource Officer
Web address: www.sanfordhealth.org
Control: Other not–for–profit (including NFP Corporation) **Service:** General medical and surgical

Staffed Beds: 500 **Admissions:** 23564 **Census:** 298 **Outpatient Visits:** 508451 **Births:** 3199 **Total Expense ($000):** 795745 **Payroll Expense ($000):** 355516 **Personnel:** 5088

✠ **SELECT SPECIALTY HOSPITAL-SIOUX FALLS (432002)**, 1305 West 18th Street, Zip 57105–0401; tel. 605/312–9500, (Nonreporting) **A**1 10 **S** Select Medical Corporation, Mechanicsburg, PA
Primary Contact: Carol Ulmer, Chief Executive Officer
CNO: Dawn Anderson, Chief Nursing Officer
Web address: www.selectspecialtyhospitals.com/company/locations/siouxfalls.aspx
Control: Corporation, Investor–owned (for–profit) **Service:** Acute long–term care hospital

Staffed Beds: 24

SIOUX FALLS SPECIALTY HOSPITAL (430090), 910 East 20th Street, Zip 57105–1012; tel. 605/334–6730, (Nonreporting) **A**10
Primary Contact: R Blake. Curd, M.D., Chief Executive Officer
CFO: Kyle Goldammer, Chief Financial Officer
Web address: www.sfsurgical.com
Control: Partnership, Investor–owned (for–profit) **Service:** Surgical

Staffed Beds: 35

SD

Many Facility Codes have changed. Please refer to the AHA Guide Code Chart. © 2017 AHA Guide

⊞ **SIOUX FALLS VETERANS AFFAIRS HEALTH CARE SYSTEM**, 2501 West 22nd Street, Zip 57105–1305, Mailing Address: P.O.Box 5046, 57117–5046; tel. 605/336–3230, (Total facility includes 58 beds in nursing home–type unit) **A**1 3 5 **F**3 5 12 18 24 27 29 30 31 33 34 35 36 38 39 40 44 45 50 53 54 56 57 58 59 60 61 62 63 64 65 68 70 74 75 77 78 79 81 82 84 85 86 87 91 92 93 94 97 98 100 101 102 103 104 107 108 111 115 118 119 127 130 132 135 143 146 147 148 149 **P**6 **S** Department of Veterans Affairs, Washington, DC
Primary Contact: Darwin Goodspeed, Director
COO: Sara Ackert, Associate Director
CFO: Daniel Hubbard, Chief Financial Officer
CMO: John M Wempe M.D., Chief of Staff
CIO: Eric Heiser, Chief Information Resource Management
CHR: Betsy Geiver, Chief Human Resources Officer
CNO: Barbara Teal R.N., Associate Director Patient Care Services and Nurse Executive
Web address: www.siouxfalls.va.gov
Control: Veterans Affairs, Government, federal **Service:** General medical and surgical

Staffed Beds: 86 **Admissions:** 2490 **Census:** 77 **Outpatient Visits:** 276350 **Births:** 0 **Total Expense ($000):** 212652 **Payroll Expense ($000):** 76794 **Personnel:** 1205

SISSETON—Roberts County

★ **COTEAU DES PRAIRIES HOSPITAL (431339)**, 205 Orchard Drive, Zip 57262–2398; tel. 605/698–7647, (Nonreporting) **A**10 18
Primary Contact: Michael F. Coyle, Chief Executive Officer
CFO: Larry Moen, Chief Financial Officer
CMO: David Staub M.D., Chief of Staff
CIO: Cheryl Kaufman, Information Technology Technician
CHR: Leslie Hendrickson, Director Human Resources
CNO: Brenda Bostrom, Director of Nursing
Web address: www.cdphospital.com
Control: Other not–for–profit (including NFP Corporation) **Service:** General medical and surgical

Staffed Beds: 25

SPEARFISH—Lawrence County

★ **SPEARFISH REGIONAL HOSPITAL (430048)**, 1440 North Main Street, Zip 57783–1504; tel. 605/644–4000, (Includes SPEARFISH REGIONAL SURGERY CENTER, 1316 N 10th St, Spearfish, South Dakota, Zip 57783–1530, 1316 North 10th Street, 57783–1530, tel. 605/642–3113; Larry W Veitz, President) **A**10 20 **F**3 12 13 15 18 28 29 34 40 57 59 62 63 70 75 76 79 81 82 84 85 89 93 97 107 108 110 111 114 119 127 129 130 131 132 144 146 147 148 **P**6 **S** Regional Health, Rapid City, SD
Primary Contact: Larry W. Veitz, President
CFO: Marcia Olson, Director Finance and Controller
CMO: Christopher Gasbarre D.O., Community Medical Director
CIO: Richard Latuchie, Chief Information Officer
CHR: Patsy Aiken, Coordinator Human Resource
CNO: Suzanne Campbell, Director Patient Services
Web address: www.regionalhealth.com/Our–Locations/Regional–Hospitals/Spearfish–Regional–Hospital.aspx
Control: Other not–for–profit (including NFP Corporation) **Service:** General medical and surgical

Staffed Beds: 35 **Admissions:** 1477 **Census:** 9 **Outpatient Visits:** 162627 **Births:** 451 **Total Expense ($000):** 80077 **Payroll Expense ($000):** 36081 **Personnel:** 498

STURGIS—Meade County

★ **STURGIS REGIONAL HOSPITAL (431321)**, 949 Harmon Street, Zip 57785–2452; tel. 605/720–2400, (Total facility includes 84 beds in nursing home–type unit) **A**10 18 **F**11 15 28 29 40 43 70 77 81 82 93 107 108 110 114 119 128 130 132 133 148 **S** Regional Health, Rapid City, SD
Primary Contact: Mark Schulte, FACHE, President
CFO: Jodie Mitchell, Facility Financial Director
CMO: Constance Stock M.D., Chief Medical Officer
CHR: Ginger Chord, Coordinator Human Resources
CNO: Rikki Plaggemeyer, Director Acute Care Nursing
Web address: www.regionalhealth.com/Our–Locations/Regional–Hospitals/Sturgis–Regional–Hospital.aspx
Control: Other not–for–profit (including NFP Corporation) **Service:** General medical and surgical

Staffed Beds: 109 **Admissions:** 698 **Census:** 95 **Outpatient Visits:** 13862 **Births:** 0 **Total Expense ($000):** 20941 **Payroll Expense ($000):** 10545 **Personnel:** 95

TYNDALL—Bon Homme County

★ **ST. MICHAEL'S HOSPITAL AVERA (431327)**, 410 West 16th Avenue, Zip 57066–2318; tel. 605/589–2152 **A**10 18 **F**3 15 28 31 34 40 43 45 53 57 59 64 65 67 70 75 77 81 86 89 92 93 94 107 110 114 119 127 128 129 131 133 148 **P**6 **S** Avera Health, Sioux Falls, SD
Primary Contact: Carol Deurmier, Chief Executive Officer
CFO: Lisa Ronke, Director Finance
CMO: Melvin Wallinga M.D., Medical Director
Web address: www.stmichaels–bhfp.org
Control: Church operated, Nongovernment, not–for–profit **Service:** General medical and surgical

Staffed Beds: 25 **Admissions:** 191 **Census:** 3 **Outpatient Visits:** 10890 **Births:** 0 **Total Expense ($000):** 8487 **Payroll Expense ($000):** 3222

VERMILLION—Clay County

★ **SANFORD VERMILLION MEDICAL CENTER (431336)**, 20 South Plum Street, Zip 57069–3346; tel. 605/677–3500, (Total facility includes 66 beds in nursing home–type unit) **A**10 18 **F**15 28 29 31 34 35 40 43 45 57 59 67 76 81 91 92 93 97 107 110 114 116 119 125 129 130 131 132 133 135 149 **P**8 **S** Sanford Health, Sioux Falls, SD
Primary Contact: Timothy J. Tracy, Chief Executive Officer
CFO: Valerie Osterberg, Chief Financial Officer
CMO: Roy Mortinsen M.D., Chief of Staff
CIO: Mary C Merrigan, Manager Public Relations
CHR: Cindy Benzel, Manager Human Resources
CNO: Jeff Berens MS, Chief Nursing Officer
Web address: www.sanfordvermillion.org
Control: Other not–for–profit (including NFP Corporation) **Service:** General medical and surgical

Staffed Beds: 114 **Admissions:** 421 **Census:** 70 **Outpatient Visits:** 39414 **Births:** 120 **Total Expense ($000):** 20624 **Payroll Expense ($000):** 8074 **Personnel:** 178

VIBORG—Turner County

★ **PIONEER MEMORIAL HOSPITAL AND HEALTH SERVICES (431328)**, 315 North Washington Street, Zip 57070–2002, Mailing Address: P.O.Box 368, 57070–0368; tel. 605/326–5161, (Total facility includes 52 beds in nursing home–type unit) **A**10 18 **F**6 10 15 28 30 34 40 43 45 53 56 57 59 63 65 69 75 79 81 87 97 107 111 119 125 127 128 130 132 133 **P**6 **S** Sanford Health, Sioux Falls, SD
Primary Contact: Thomas V. Richter, Chief Executive Officer
CFO: Anne Christiansen, Chief Financial Officer
CMO: Syed Shah M.D., Chief of Staff
Web address: www.pioneermemorial.org
Control: Other not–for–profit (including NFP Corporation) **Service:** General medical and surgical

Staffed Beds: 64 **Admissions:** 199 **Census:** 51 **Outpatient Visits:** 29147 **Births:** 0 **Total Expense ($000):** 12096 **Payroll Expense ($000):** 6731 **Personnel:** 146

WAGNER—Charles Mix County

★ **WAGNER COMMUNITY MEMORIAL HOSPITAL AVERA (431315)**, 513 Third Street SW, Zip 57380–9675, Mailing Address: P.O.Box 280, 57380–0280; tel. 605/384–3611 **A**10 18 **F**3 11 15 18 28 31 34 40 43 45 57 59 64 67 70 75 77 81 93 97 107 110 114 119 128 130 133 148 **P**6 **S** Avera Health, Sioux Falls, SD
Primary Contact: Bryan Slaba, Chief Executive Officer
CFO: Lisa Weisser, Supervisor Finance
CHR: Marcia Podzimek, Chief Human Resources Officer
Web address: www.avera.org/wagnerhospital
Control: Other not–for–profit (including NFP Corporation) **Service:** General medical and surgical

Staffed Beds: 20 **Admissions:** 157 **Census:** 1 **Outpatient Visits:** 8255 **Births:** 0 **Total Expense ($000):** 8381 **Payroll Expense ($000):** 3650 **Personnel:** 61

SD

Hospital, Medicare Provider Number, Address, Telephone, Approval, Facility, and Physician Codes, Health Care System

★ American Hospital Association (AHA) membership ○ Healthcare Facilities Accreditation Program ⇧ Center for Improvement in Healthcare Quality Accreditation
□ The Joint Commission accreditation ◇ DNV Healthcare Inc. accreditation △ Commission on Accreditation of Rehabilitation Facilities (CARF) accreditation

WATERTOWN—Codington County

★ **PRAIRIE LAKES HEALTHCARE SYSTEM (430005)**, 401 9th Avenue NW, Zip 57201–1548, Mailing Address: P.O.Box 1210, 57201–6210; tel. 605/882–7000 **A**10 20 **F**3 8 12 13 18 20 22 28 29 30 31 34 35 38 40 43 50 57 58 59 60 62 63 76 77 78 79 80 81 82 83 84 85 87 89 93 107 108 111 114 119 120 121 123 124 130 132 133 146 147 148
Primary Contact: Jill Fuller, R.N., President and Chief Executive Officer
COO: Traci Rabine, Vice President Clinic Operations
CFO: Adam Paul, Chief Financial Officer
CMO: Daniel Flaherty M.D., Chief Medical Staff
CHR: Nathan Lake, Vice President Human Resources
CNO: Shelly Turbak R.N., Chief Nursing Officer
Web address: www.prairielakes.com
Control: Other not–for–profit (including NFP Corporation) **Service**: General medical and surgical

Staffed Beds: 79 **Admissions**: 2799 **Census**: 23 **Births**: 665 **Total Expense ($000)**: 80692 **Payroll Expense ($000)**: 36082 **Personnel**: 502

WEBSTER—Day County

SANFORD WEBSTER MEDICAL CENTER See Sanford Webster Medical Center

★ **SANFORD WEBSTER MEDICAL CENTER (431311)**, 1401 West 1st Street, Zip 57274–1054, Mailing Address: P.O.Box 489, 57274–0489; tel. 605/345–3336 **A**10 18 **F**3 15 28 29 34 35 40 43 57 59 63 64 71 77 81 86 87 91 93 97 107 111 114 119 127 128 130 131 133 148 149 150 **P**6 **S** Sanford Health, Sioux Falls, SD
Primary Contact: Isaac Gerdes, Chief Executive Officer
CFO: Sheryl L Pappas, Chief Financial Officer
Web address: www.sanfordhealth.org
Control: Other not–for–profit (including NFP Corporation) **Service**: General medical and surgical

Staffed Beds: 20 **Admissions**: 201 **Census**: 2 **Outpatient Visits**: 16754 **Births**: 0 **Total Expense ($000)**: 7389 **Payroll Expense ($000)**: 3278 **Personnel**: 57

WESSINGTON SPRINGS—Jerauld County

★ **AVERA WESKOTA MEMORIAL HOSPITAL (431324)**, 604 First Street NE, Zip 57382–2166; tel. 605/539–1201 **A**10 18 **F**3 15 28 31 34 35 40 53 57 59 64 75 77 81 85 93 107 114 119 128 130 131 132 133 **P**5 **S** Avera Health, Sioux Falls, SD
Primary Contact: Gaea Blue, R.N., Administrator and Chief Executive Officer
CFO: Linda Jager, Director Finance
CMO: Thomas Dean M.D., Chief of Staff
CNO: JoAnn Hettinger R.N., Director of Patient Care Services
Web address: www.averaweskota.org
Control: Other not–for–profit (including NFP Corporation) **Service**: General medical and surgical

Staffed Beds: 23 **Admissions**: 143 **Census**: 2 **Outpatient Visits**: 4950 **Births**: 0 **Total Expense ($000)**: 3915 **Payroll Expense ($000)**: 1598 **Personnel**: 26

WINNER—Tripp County

★ **WINNER REGIONAL HEALTHCARE CENTER (431334)**, 745 East Eighth Street, Zip 57580–2631; tel. 605/842–7100, (Total facility includes 79 beds in nursing home–type unit) **A**10 18 **F**1 4 6 11 13 15 16 17 28 29 31 34 35 40 42 43 47 56 57 59 62 64 65 67 68 70 72 73 76 79 80 81 85 88 89 90 91 93 97 98 107 108 127 128 129 130 131 132 133 148 **P**3 **S** Sanford Health, Sioux Falls, SD
Primary Contact: Kevin Coffey, Chief Executive Officer
COO: Debra K. Davis, Director of Operations
CFO: Phil Husher, Chief Financial Officer
CMO: Tony L. Berg M.D., Chief of Staff
CIO: Gary Burrus, Director Information Technology
CHR: Susan Hughes, Interim Director Human Resources
CNO: Julie Hennebold R.N., Interim Chief Nursing Officer
Web address: www.winnerregional.org
Control: Other not–for–profit (including NFP Corporation) **Service**: General medical and surgical

Staffed Beds: 104 **Admissions**: 769 **Census**: 82 **Outpatient Visits**: 9604 **Births**: 235 **Total Expense ($000)**: 22879 **Payroll Expense ($000)**: 7087 **Personnel**: 184

YANKTON—Yankton County

☒ **AVERA SACRED HEART HOSPITAL (430012)**, 501 Summit Avenue, Zip 57078–3855; tel. 605/668–8000, (Total facility includes 187 beds in nursing home–type unit) **A**1 2 3 5 10 **F**2 3 6 8 10 13 15 18 20 28 29 30 31 34 35 39 40 43 45 46 47 48 53 57 59 60 62 63 64 70 71 73 75 76 77 78 79 81 82 84 85 86 87 89 91 93 96 100 103 104 107 108 110 111 114 115 118 119 120 121 125 127 128 129 130 132 133 146 147 148 **P**6 **S** Avera Health, Sioux Falls, SD
Primary Contact: Douglas R. Ekeren, Regional President and Chief Executive Officer
CFO: Jamie Schaefer, Vice President Finance
CIO: Kathy Quinlivan, Director Management Information Systems
CHR: Jane E Miller, Human Resources Officer
CNO: Lindsay Flannery R.N., Vice President Patient Care Services
Web address: www.averasacredheart.com
Control: Church operated, Nongovernment, not–for–profit **Service**: General medical and surgical

Staffed Beds: 293 **Admissions**: 3644 **Census**: 214 **Outpatient Visits**: 85892 **Births**: 629 **Total Expense ($000)**: 101798 **Payroll Expense ($000)**: 40526 **Personnel**: 679

LEWIS AND CLARK SPECIALTY HOSPITAL (430096), 2601 Fox Run Parkway, Zip 57078–5341; tel. 605/665–5100 (Nonreporting) **A**10
Primary Contact: Douglas Doorn, Chief Executive Officer
CFO: Terry Steichen, Business Officer
CHR: Elizabeth Steichen, Human Resources
Web address: www.lewisandclarkspecialty.com
Control: Corporation, Investor–owned (for–profit) **Service**: Surgical

Staffed Beds: 6

TENNESSEE

ASHLAND CITY—Cheatham County

★ **TRISTAR ASHLAND CITY MEDICAL CENTER (441311)**, 313 North Main Street, Zip 37015–1347; tel. 615/792–3030, (Nonreporting) **A**10 18 **S** HCA Healthcare, Nashville, TN
Primary Contact: Darrell White, R.N., Administrator and Chief Nursing Officer
CFO: Joe Bowman, Chief Financial Officer
CMO: Divya Shroff, Chief Medical Officer
CIO: David Archer, Director Information Systems
CNO: Darrell White R.N., Administrator and Chief Nursing Officer
Web address: www.tristarashlandcity.com/
Control: Corporation, Investor–owned (for–profit) **Service**: General medical and surgical

Staffed Beds: 12

ATHENS—Mcminn County

⊞ **STARR REGIONAL MEDICAL CENTER (440068)**, 1114 West Madison Avenue, Zip 37303–4150, Mailing Address: P.O.Box 250, 37371–0250; tel. 423/745–1411, (Nonreporting) **A**1 3 5 10 **S** LifePoint Health, Brentwood, TN
Primary Contact: Mark Nichols, FACHE, Chief Executive Officer
COO: Michael Herr, Chief Operating Officer
CFO: David Alley, Chief Financial Officer
CNO: Teresa Reynolds, Interim Chief Nursing Officer
Web address: www.starrregional.com
Control: Corporation, Investor–owned (for–profit) **Service**: General medical and surgical

Staffed Beds: 63

BARTLETT—Shelby County

⊞ **SAINT FRANCIS HOSPITAL–BARTLETT (440228)**, 2986 Kate Bond Road, Zip 38133–4003; tel. 901/820–7000, (Nonreporting) **A**1 10 **S** TENET Healthcare Corporation, Dallas, TX
Primary Contact: Christopher Locke, Chief Executive Officer
COO: Gwen Bonner, Chief Operating Officer
CFO: Tina Kovacs, Chief Financial Officer
CMO: David Schwartz M.D., Chief Medical Officer
CIO: Mark Lawrence, Director Information Systems
CHR: Adrienne Huntley, Chief Human Resources Officer
CNO: Kris Cherry Ph.D., R.N., Chief Nursing Officer
Web address: www.saintfrancisbartlett.com
Control: Corporation, Investor–owned (for–profit) **Service**: General medical and surgical

Staffed Beds: 156

BOLIVAR—Hardeman County

⊞ **BOLIVAR GENERAL HOSPITAL (440181)**, 650 Nuckolls Road, Zip 38008–1532, Mailing Address: PO Box 509, 38008–0509; tel. 731/658–3100 **A**1 10 **F**3 15 29 30 35 40 44 45 57 59 64 75 81 87 93 107 119 130 132 133 146 149 **S** West Tennessee Healthcare, Jackson, TN
Primary Contact: Ruby Kirby, Administrator
CFO: Terry Swindell, Controller
CMO: Felix Nnaji, Chief Medical Staff
CNO: Angela Lacy, Director of Nursing
Web address: www.wth.net
Control: Hospital district or authority, Government, Nonfederal **Service**: General medical and surgical

Staffed Beds: 21 **Admissions**: 329 **Census**: 3 **Outpatient Visits**: 15786 **Births**: 0 **Total Expense ($000)**: 6941 **Payroll Expense ($000)**: 2705 **Personnel**: 61

☐ **WESTERN MENTAL HEALTH INSTITUTE (444008)**, 11100 Old Highway 64, West, Zip 38008–1554; tel. 731/228–2000, (Nonreporting) **A**1 10
Primary Contact: Roger Pursley, Chief Executive Officer
CFO: Richard Taylor, Chief Financial Officer
CMO: Doug King M.D., Director Clinical Services
CIO: Earl Bates, Director Information Technology
CHR: Barry Young, Director Human Resources
Control: State, Government, Nonfederal **Service**: Psychiatric

Staffed Beds: 247

BRISTOL—Sullivan County

⊞ **SELECT SPECIALTY HOSPITAL–TRI CITIES (442016)**, One Medical Park Boulevard, 5th Floor, Zip 37620–8964; tel. 423/844–5900, (Nonreporting) **A**1 10 **S** Select Medical Corporation, Mechanicsburg, PA
Primary Contact: Jeffrey Radford, Chief Executive Officer
CMO: John Byers M.D., Medical Director
CHR: William G Ison, Human Resources Manager
CNO: Valerie Anderson, Chief Nursing Officer
Web address: www.tricities.selectspecialtyhospitals.com/
Control: Corporation, Investor–owned (for–profit) **Service**: Acute long–term care hospital

Staffed Beds: 33

⊞ **WELLMONT BRISTOL REGIONAL MEDICAL CENTER (440012)**, 1 Medical Park Boulevard, Zip 37620–7430; tel. 423/844–1121 **A**1 2 3 5 10 **F**3 8 11 13 15 17 18 20 22 24 28 29 30 31 34 35 37 38 39 40 43 44 45 46 47 48 49 51 54 56 57 58 59 60 61 63 64 70 73 74 75 76 77 78 79 81 82 83 84 85 86 87 91 92 93 94 96 97 98 100 101 102 103 104 106 107 108 110 111 114 115 118 119 120 121 123 124 126 129 130 131 132 135 144 145 146 147 148 149 **P**1 5 **S** Wellmont Health System, Kingsport, TN
Primary Contact: Greg Neal, FACHE, President
COO: Christopher Brian Hobson, Chief Operating Officer
CFO: Dale Poe, Vice President and Chief Financial Officer, Hospital Division
CMO: Chad Couch, Chief Medical Officer
CIO: Martha O'Regan Chill, Interim Chief Information Officer
CHR: Hamlin J Wilson, Senior Vice President Human Resources
CNO: Timothy Craig Anderson Jr, Chief Nursing Officer
Web address: www.wellmont.org
Control: Other not–for–profit (including NFP Corporation) **Service**: General medical and surgical

Staffed Beds: 296 **Admissions**: 12874 **Census**: 158 **Outpatient Visits**: 130104 **Births**: 872 **Total Expense ($000)**: 224544 **Payroll Expense ($000)**: 59604 **Personnel**: 1539

CAMDEN—Benton County

⊞ **CAMDEN GENERAL HOSPITAL (441316)**, 175 Hospital Drive, Zip 38320–1617; tel. 731/593–6300 **A**1 10 18 **F**3 15 29 30 35 40 44 57 59 64 75 79 81 85 87 93 107 111 119 130 132 133 146 149 **S** West Tennessee Healthcare, Jackson, TN
Primary Contact: Scott Barber, Vice President
CFO: Terry Swindell, Chief Financial Officer
CMO: Jon R. Winter D.O., Chief of Staff
CIO: Jeff Frieling, Vice President Information Systems
CHR: Barry Phillips, Executive Director Human Resources
Web address: www.wth.net
Control: Hospital district or authority, Government, Nonfederal **Service**: General medical and surgical

Staffed Beds: 25 **Admissions**: 329 **Census**: 4 **Outpatient Visits**: 12404 **Births**: 0 **Total Expense ($000)**: 7118 **Payroll Expense ($000)**: 2784 **Personnel**: 67

CARTHAGE—Smith County

⊞ **RIVERVIEW REGIONAL MEDICAL CENTER (441307)**, 158 Hospital Drive, Zip 37030–1096; tel. 615/735–1560 **A**1 10 18 **F**3 11 13 15 29 34 35 40 41 45 50 51 57 59 64 68 70 75 77 79 81 82 86 87 93 98 103 110 111 114 118 119 129 130 131 133 146 149 **S** LifePoint Health, Brentwood, TN
Primary Contact: Michael Herman, Chief Executive Officer
CHR: Gina Anderson, Human Resources Director
CNO: Patricia Anderson, Chief Nursing Officer
Web address: www.myriverviewmedical.com/
Control: Corporation, Investor–owned (for–profit) **Service**: General medical and surgical

Staffed Beds: 35 **Admissions**: 957 **Census**: 15 **Outpatient Visits**: 29138 **Births**: 66 **Total Expense ($000)**: 19554 **Payroll Expense ($000)**: 9126 **Personnel**: 168

TN

CELINA—Clay County

☐ **CUMBERLAND RIVER HOSPITAL (440141)**, 100 Old Jefferson Street, Zip 38551–4040, Mailing Address: P O Box 427, 38551–0427; tel. 931/243–3581, (Nonreporting) **A**1 10 18
Primary Contact: Patricia Strong, Interim Chief Executive Officer
CFO: Patricia Strong, Chief Financial Officer
CMO: Harry Horne D.O., Chief of Staff
CIO: Margie Boone, Registered Health Information Technician
CHR: Angel Lewis, Senior Vice President
CNO: Patsy Marinich, Chief Nursing Officer
Web address: www.cumberlandriverhospital.com
Control: Corporation, Investor–owned (for–profit) **Service**: General medical and surgical

Staffed Beds: 34

CENTERVILLE—Hickman County

☒ **SAINT THOMAS HICKMAN HOSPITAL (441300)**, 135 East Swan Street, Zip 37033–1417; tel. 931/729–4271, (Nonreporting) **A**1 10 18 **S** Ascension Healthcare, Saint Louis, MO
Primary Contact: Jack M. Keller, Chief Executive Officer
COO: Robin Crowell, Chief Nursing Officer and Chief Operating Officer
CMO: Zachary Hutchens M.D., Chief Medical Officer
CHR: Patty Matney, Human Resources Consultant
CNO: Robin Crowell, Chief Nursing Officer and Chief Operating Officer
Web address: www.sths.com/hickman
Control: Other not–for–profit (including NFP Corporation) **Service**: General medical and surgical

Staffed Beds: 65

CHATTANOOGA—Hamilton County

☒ **CHI MEMORIAL (440091)**, 2525 De Sales Avenue, Zip 37404–1161; tel. 423/495–2525, (Includes MEMORIAL HOSPITAL HIXSON, 2051 Hamill Road, Hixson, Tennessee, Zip 37343–4026, tel. 423/495–7100; Larry P Schumacher, R.N., MSN, Chief Executive Officer) **A**1 2 3 10 **F**3 7 8 11 12 15 17 18 20 22 24 26 28 29 30 31 34 35 36 40 43 44 45 46 47 48 49 50 53 54 55 56 57 58 59 60 61 64 67 68 70 71 74 75 77 78 79 81 82 84 85 86 87 93 107 108 110 111 114 115 116 117 118 119 120 121 124 126 129 130 132 135 145 146 147 148 150 **P**3 6 7 8 **S** Catholic Health Initiatives, Englewood, CO
Primary Contact: Larry P. Schumacher, R.N., MSN, Chief Executive Officer
COO: Janelle Reilly, Chief Operating Officer
CFO: Troy Hammett, Chief Financial Officer
CMO: Helen Kuroki, Senior Vice President and Chief Medical Officer
CHR: Brad W Pope, Vice President Human Resources
CNO: Rhonda Poulson, Chief Nursing Officer and Vice President of Clinical Operations
Web address: www.memorial.org
Control: Church operated, Nongovernment, not–for–profit **Service**: General medical and surgical

Staffed Beds: 405 Admissions: 23995 Census: 311 Outpatient Visits: 374724 Births: 0 Total Expense ($000): 508571 Payroll Expense ($000): 140007 Personnel: 2427

☒ **ERLANGER MEDICAL CENTER (440104)**, 975 East Third Street, Zip 37403–2147; tel. 423/778–7000, (Includes ERLANGER EAST HOSPITAL, 1755 Gunbarrel Road, Chattanooga, Tennessee, Zip 37421, tel. 423/778–8700; Phillip E. Jackson, Vice President & CEO; ERLANGER NORTH HOSPITAL, 632 Morrison Springs Road, Chattanooga, Tennessee, Zip 37415, tel. 615/778–3300; Phillip E. Jackson, Vice President and CEO; T. C. THOMPSON CHILDREN'S HOSPITAL, 910 Blackford Street, Chattanooga, Tennessee, Zip 37403, tel. 615/778–6011; Donald Mueller, Vice President and CEO; WILLIE D. MILLER EYE CENTER, 975 East Third Street, Chattanooga, Tennessee, Zip 37403, tel. 615/778–6011) **A**1 2 3 5 8 10 **F**3 5 6 7 8 9 11 12 13 14 15 16 17 18 19 20 21 22 23 24 25 26 27 28 29 30 31 32 34 35 36 37 38 39 40 41 42 43 44 45 46 47 48 49 50 51 52 53 54 55 56 57 58 59 60 61 62 63 64 65 66 68 70 71 72 73 74 75 76 77 78 79 80 81 82 83 84 85 86 87 88 89 91 92 93 94 96 97 98 99 100 101 102 103 104 105 107 108 109 110 111 112 114 115 116 117 118 119 120 121 123 124 126 127 129 130 131 132 133 134 135 138 141 142 143 144 145 146 147 148 149 150 **P**2 4 6 7 **S** Erlanger Health System, Chattanooga, TN
Primary Contact: Kevin M. Spiegel, Chief Executive Officer
COO: Robert M. Brooks FACHE, Executive Vice President, Chief Operating Officer
CFO: J. Britton Tabor, Executive Vice President, Chief Financial Officer
CMO: William L. Jackson M.D., Jr, Executive Vice President, Chief Medical Officer
CIO: David Peterson, Senior Vice President, Chief Technology Officer
CHR: Floyd Chasse, Vice President Human Resources
CNO: Janice C. Keys FACHE, Senior Vice President, Chief Nurse Executive
Web address: www.erlanger.org
Control: Hospital district or authority, Government, Nonfederal **Service**: General medical and surgical

Staffed Beds: 657 Admissions: 35414 Census: 472 Outpatient Visits: 535463 Births: 5604 Total Expense ($000): 747877 Payroll Expense ($000): 304994 Personnel: 5645

ERLANGER WOMEN'S EAST HOSPITAL See Erlanger East Hospital

☒ **HEALTHSOUTH CHATTANOOGA REHABILITATION HOSPITAL (443032)**, 2412 McCallie Avenue, Zip 37404–3398; tel. 423/698–0221, (Nonreporting) **A**1 10 **S** HEALTHSOUTH Corporation, Birmingham, AL
Primary Contact: Scott Rowe, Chief Executive Officer
COO: Scott Rowe, Chief Executive Officer
CFO: Karen Klassen, Controller
CMO: Amjad Munir M.D., Medical Director
CIO: Denise Smith, Director Health Information
CHR: Rebekah McNair, Director Human Resources
CNO: Cinthia Campbell, Chief Nursing Officer
Web address: www.healthsouthchattanooga.com
Control: Corporation, Investor–owned (for–profit) **Service**: Rehabilitation

Staffed Beds: 69

☒ **KINDRED HOSPITAL–CHATTANOOGA (442007)**, 709 Walnut Street, Zip 37402–1916; tel. 423/266–7721 **A**1 10 **F**1 28 **S** Kindred Healthcare, Louisville, KY
Primary Contact: Steve Patterson, Chief Executive Officer
COO: Rick Rheinheimer, Chief Clinical Officer
CFO: Julia Smith, Chief Financial Officer
CMO: Randy Heisser M.D., Medical Director
CHR: Kellie McCampbell, Coordinator Human Resources
CNO: Gigi Johnson, Chief Nursing Officer
Web address: www.kindredchattanooga.com/
Control: Corporation, Investor–owned (for–profit) **Service**: Acute long–term care hospital

Staffed Beds: 39 Admissions: 340 Census: 26 Outpatient Visits: 0 Births: 0 Total Expense ($000): 16436 Payroll Expense ($000): 5229 Personnel: 87

☐ **MOCCASIN BEND MENTAL HEALTH INSTITUTE (444002)**, 100 Moccasin Bend Road, Zip 37405–4415; tel. 423/265–2271 **A**1 10 **F**34 57 59 65 75 77 86 98 101 102 103 130 135
Primary Contact: Mary C. Young, Chief Executive Officer
CFO: Sylvia Harris, Fiscal Director
CMO: Terry R Holmes M.D., Clinical Director
CIO: Mickey Williams, Manager Information Technology
CHR: Cynthia Honeycutt, Director Human Resources
CNO: Charlynne Parson, Nurse Executive
Web address: www.state.tn.us/mental/mhs/mbhmhi/moc.htm
Control: State, Government, Nonfederal **Service**: Psychiatric

Staffed Beds: 150 Admissions: 2921 Census: 130 Outpatient Visits: 0 Births: 0 Total Expense ($000): 35851 Payroll Expense ($000): 17496 Personnel: 446

☒ **PARKRIDGE MEDICAL CENTER (440156)**, 2333 McCallie Avenue, Zip 37404–3258; tel. 423/698–6061, (Includes EAST RIDGE HOSPITAL, 941 Spring Creek Road, East Ridge, Tennessee, Zip 37412, P O Box 91229, 37412–6229, tel. 423/855–3500; Jarrett B. Millsaps Jr, FACHE, Chief Executive Officer; PARKRIDGE EAST HOSPITAL, 941 Spring Creek Road, Chattanooga, Tennessee, Zip 37412–3909, tel. 423/894–7870; Jarrett B. Millsaps Jr, FACHE, Chief Executive Officer; PARKRIDGE VALLEY CHILD AND ADOLESCENT CAMPUS, 2200 Morris Hill Road, Chattanooga, Tennessee, Zip 37421, tel. 423/894–4220; Melissa Arkin, Chief Executive Officer; PARKRIDGE WEST HOSPITAL, 1000 Highway 28, Jasper, Tennessee, Zip 37347–3638, tel. 423/837–9500; Shirley K Scarlatti, Associate Chief Nursing Officer) **A**1 2 3 5 10 **F**3 4 5 13 15 18 20 22 24 26 28 29 30 31 39 40 45 46 49 50 51 55 56 57 58 59 60 62 70 72 75 77 78 79 81 85 90 93 98 99 103 104 105 106 107 108 110 111 114 115 119 120 121 123 124 126 129 130 131 132 146 148 149 **S** HCA Healthcare, Nashville, TN
Primary Contact: Thomas H. Ozburn, Chief Executive Officer
COO: Jim L Coleman Jr, Chief Operating Officer
CFO: Tom Jackson, Chief Financial Officer
CMO: Kevin Lewis M.D., Chief Medical Officer
CIO: David Cornelius, Director Information Systems
CHR: Carole Hoffman, Vice President
CNO: Jerri C Underwood R.N., Chief Nursing Officer
Web address: www.parkridgemedicalcenter.com
Control: Corporation, Investor–owned (for–profit) **Service**: General medical and surgical

Staffed Beds: 464 Admissions: 19158 Census: 313 Outpatient Visits: 166387 Births: 2215 Total Expense ($000): 275146 Payroll Expense ($000): 106151

☒ △ **SISKIN HOSPITAL FOR PHYSICAL REHABILITATION (443025)**, One Siskin Plaza, Zip 37403–1306; tel. 423/634–1200, (Nonreporting) **A**1 7 10
Primary Contact: Carol Sim, President and Chief Executive Officer
CFO: Carol Arnhart, Vice President Finance and Chief Financial Officer
CMO: David N Bowers M.D., Medical Director
CIO: Shane Pilcher, Administrative Director Information Systems
CHR: Kristi Delaney, Director, Human Resources
CNO: Tracy Collings Reed, Vice President Patient Care Services, Chief Nursing Officer
Web address: www.siskinrehab.org
Control: Other not–for–profit (including NFP Corporation) **Service**: Rehabilitation

Staffed Beds: 109

TN

T. C. THOMPSON CHILDREN'S HOSPITAL See Erlanger Medical Center

CLARKSVILLE—Montgomery County

BEHAVIORAL HEALTHCARE CENTER AT CLARKSVILLE (444019), 930 Professional Park Drive, Zip 37040–5136; tel. 931/538–6420 (Nonreporting) **A**10 **S** Tennessee Health Management, Parsons, TN
Primary Contact: Jennifer Robinson, Administrator
CMO: Michael McGhee M.D., Medical Director
CNO: Chrissy Myers R.N., Director of Nursing
Web address: www.bhcclarksville.com
Control: Partnership, Investor–owned (for–profit) **Service**: Psychiatric

Staffed Beds: 26

✠ **TENNOVA HEALTHCARE–CLARKSVILLE (440035)**, 651 Dunlop Lane, Zip 37040–5015, Mailing Address: P.O.Box 31629, 37040–0028; tel. 931/502–1000, (Nonreporting) **A**1 10 **S** Community Health Systems, Inc., Franklin, TN
Primary Contact: Alex Villa, Chief Executive Officer
COO: Shawn Molsberger, Chief Operating Officer
CFO: George Sprinkel, Chief Financial Officer
CMO: Thomas L Ely D.O., Chief Medical Officer
CIO: Scott Greene, Chief Information Officer
CHR: Liza Edmunds, Director Human Resources
CNO: Faye Perry, Chief Nursing Officer
Web address: www.tennova.com/
Control: Partnership, Investor–owned (for–profit) **Service**: General medical and surgical

Staffed Beds: 247

CLEVELAND—Bradley County

✠ **TENNOVA HEALTHCARE – CLEVELAND (440185)**, 2305 Chambliss Avenue NW, Zip 37311–3847, Mailing Address: P.O.Box 3060, 37320–3060; tel. 423/559–6000, (Includes SKYRIDGE MEDICAL CENTER – WESTSIDE CAMPUS, 2800 Westside Drive NW, Cleveland, Tennessee, Zip 37312–3599, tel. 423/339–4100; R Coleman Foss, Chief Executive Officer) **A**1 3 5 10 **F**3 5 13 15 18 20 22 28 29 30 31 32 34 35 36 39 40 44 45 49 50 51 57 58 59 60 68 70 73 74 75 76 77 78 79 81 85 87 89 93 98 104 105 107 108 110 111 114 115 118 119 124 129 135 146 148 149 **S** Community Health Systems, Inc., Franklin, TN
Primary Contact: R Coleman. Foss, Chief Executive Officer
COO: Bernadette De Prez, Chief Operating Officer
CFO: H. Wes Griffith, Chief Financial Officer
CMO: William F Johnson, Chief Medical Officer
CHR: Kristine Godfrey, Director Human Resources
Web address: www.skyridgemedicalcenter.net
Control: Corporation, Investor–owned (for–profit) **Service**: General medical and surgical

Staffed Beds: 185 Admissions: 8818 Census: 105 Outpatient Visits: 93883 Births: 1060 Total Expense ($000): 134949 Payroll Expense ($000): 44875 Personnel: 1092

COLLIERVILLE—Shelby County

★ **BAPTIST MEMORIAL HOSPITAL–COLLIERVILLE (440217)**, 1500 West Poplar Avenue, Zip 38017–0601; tel. 901/861–9400 **A**5 **F**3 7 8 12 15 18 19 20 21 22 23 24 25 26 27 28 29 30 31 32 34 35 36 37 38 40 41 45 46 47 48 49 52 53 55 56 57 58 59 60 61 62 64 65 66 68 70 71 74 75 77 78 79 80 81 82 83 84 85 86 87 92 93 96 107 108 109 110 111 112 113 114 115 116 117 118 119 120 121 123 124 126 129 130 132 135 136 137 143 144 145 146 147 148 **S** Baptist Memorial Health Care Corporation, Memphis, TN
Primary Contact: Lindsay Stencel, Chief Administrative Officer
CFO: Terri Seago, Chief Financial Officer
CIO: Doug Reiselt, Vice President and Chief Information Officer
CHR: Brenda Johnson, Director Human Resources
CNO: Denise Ferguson, Chief Nursing Officer
Web address: www.baptistonline.com/collierville/
Control: Other not–for–profit (including NFP Corporation) **Service**: General medical and surgical

Staffed Beds: 51 Admissions: 2675 Census: 20 Outpatient Visits: 34695 Births: 0 Total Expense ($000): 54729 Payroll Expense ($000): 17873 Personnel: 272

COLUMBIA—Maury County

BEHAVIORAL HEALTHCARE CENTER AT COLUMBIA (440230), 1400 Rosewood Drive, Zip 38401–4878; tel. 931/388–6573 **A**10 **F**29 34 38 56 98 103 135 **S** Tennessee Health Management, Parsons, TN
Primary Contact: Paula Chennault, Administrator
CMO: Rodney Poling M.D., Medical Director
CHR: Pam Brown, Human Resources Manager
CNO: Sheila Ridner R.N., Director of Nursing
Web address: www.thmgt.com/locations/behavioral–healthcare–center–at–columbia
Control: Corporation, Investor–owned (for–profit) **Service**: Psychiatric

Staffed Beds: 16 Admissions: 328 Census: 10 Outpatient Visits: 0 Births: 0 Total Expense ($000): 2552 Payroll Expense ($000): 1467 Personnel: 44

✠ **MAURY REGIONAL HOSPITAL (440073)**, 1224 Trotwood Avenue, Zip 38401–4802; tel. 931/381–1111 **A**1 2 10 19 **F**3 7 8 11 13 15 18 20 22 24 26 28 29 30 31 34 35 37 38 40 41 44 45 46 48 49 50 51 53 54 55 57 58 59 60 62 63 64 66 68 70 73 74 75 76 77 78 79 80 81 82 84 85 86 87 89 91 92 93 96 97 101 107 108 110 111 114 115 116 117 118 119 120 121 123 124 127 129 130 131 132 135 144 146 147 148 149 **S** Maury Regional Health System, Columbia, TN
Primary Contact: H Alan. Watson, FACHE, Chief Executive Officer
COO: Paul Betz FACHE, Chief Operating Officer and Senior Vice President
CFO: Nick Swift, Chief Financial Officer
CMO: Chris Edwards M.D., Chief Medical Officer
CIO: Jim Parcel, Director Information Technology
CHR: Kaye Brewer, Vice President Human Resources
CNO: Deborah Lumpkins MSN, Chief Nursing Officer
Web address: www.mauryregional.com
Control: County, Government, Nonfederal **Service**: General medical and surgical

Staffed Beds: 209 Admissions: 13444 Census: 123 Outpatient Visits: 258528 Births: 1437 Total Expense ($000): 260322 Payroll Expense ($000): 99844 Personnel: 1889

COOKEVILLE—Putnam County

✠ **COOKEVILLE REGIONAL MEDICAL CENTER (440059)**, 1 Medical Center Boulevard, Zip 38501–4294; tel. 931/783–2000 **A**1 2 10 19 **F**3 8 11 12 13 15 17 18 20 22 24 26 28 29 30 31 34 35 40 44 45 49 50 51 54 57 59 62 64 65 68 70 73 74 75 76 77 78 79 81 85 86 87 89 90 93 96 107 108 110 111 114 115 117 118 119 120 121 123 126 129 130 132 135 146 147 148
Primary Contact: Paul Korth, Chief Executive Officer
COO: Scott Williams, Chief Operating Officer
CFO: Paul Korth, Chief Financial Officer
CMO: Jeffrey J Gleason M.D., Chief Medical Officer
CIO: Les Bernstein, Chief Information Officer
CHR: Angel Lewis, Senior Vice President Administration
CNO: Linda Crawford R.N., MSN, Chief Nursing Officer
Web address: www.crmchealth.org
Control: Hospital district or authority, Government, Nonfederal **Service**: General medical and surgical

Staffed Beds: 243 Admissions: 13093 Census: 153 Outpatient Visits: 211956 Births: 1585 Total Expense ($000): 238272 Payroll Expense ($000): 93356

⇑ **TEN BROECK TENNESSEE TREATMENT FACILITY (444022)**, 1 Medical Center Boulevard, 5 West, Zip 38501; tel. 931/783–2570 **A**10 21 **F**4 5 101 103 104 105 **S** United Medical Corporation, Windermere, FL
Primary Contact: Kelly Tripp, Chief Executive Officer
CFO: David Corddry, Chief Financial Officer
CMO: Glenn T. Webb M.D., Medical Director
CHR: Glenda Guy, Director, Health Information Management
CNO: Annasue Collins, Chief Nursing Officer
Web address: www.tenbroeck.com
Control: Corporation, Investor–owned (for–profit) **Service**: Psychiatric

Staffed Beds: 38 Admissions: 1311 Census: 22 Outpatient Visits: 228 Births: 0

COPPERHILL—Polk County

☐ **COPPER BASIN MEDICAL CENTER (441315)**, 144 Medical Center Drive, Zip 37317–5005, Mailing Address: P.O.Box 990, 37317–0990; tel. 423/496–5511, (Nonreporting) **A**1 10 18
Primary Contact: Daniel C. Johnson, Chief Executive Officer
COO: Anna Clark, Chief Operating Officer
CMO: Allen Uhlik M.D., Chief of Staff
CIO: Florence Tichenor, Director Information Technology
CHR: Kathy Pack, Manager Human Resources
CNO: Sonya Standridge, Chief Nursing Officer
Web address: www.copperbasin.org
Control: Other not–for–profit (including NFP Corporation) **Service**: General medical and surgical

Staffed Beds: 25

★ American Hospital Association (AHA) membership	○ Healthcare Facilities Accreditation Program	⇑ Center for Improvement in Healthcare Quality Accreditation
☐ The Joint Commission accreditation	◇ DNV Healthcare Inc. accreditation	△ Commission on Accreditation of Rehabilitation Facilities (CARF) accreditation

Hospital, Medicare Provider Number, Address, Telephone, Approval, Facility, and Physician Codes, Health Care System

© 2017 AHA Guide   *Many Facility Codes have changed. Please refer to the AHA Guide Code Chart.*   Hospitals **A577**

COVINGTON—Tipton County

⊞ **BAPTIST MEMORIAL HOSPITAL–TIPTON (440131)**, 1995 Highway 51 South, Zip 38019–3635; tel. 901/476–2621 **A**1 10 **F**3 11 15 29 30 31 34 35 40 45 55 57 58 59 65 70 74 75 76 77 78 79 81 85 87 89 93 100 107 108 110 111 114 115 119 120 121 130 146 148 **S** Baptist Memorial Health Care Corporation, Memphis, TN
Primary Contact: Samuel Lynd, Administrator and Chief Executive Officer
CFO: Monique Hart, Chief Financial Officer
CMO: Kenneth Afenya M.D., Chief of Staff
CHR: Myra Cousar, Director Human Resources
CNO: Cheryl Furdge Berry, Chief Nursing Officer
Web address: www.baptistonline.org/tipton/
Control: Other not–for–profit (including NFP Corporation) **Service**: General medical and surgical

Staffed Beds: 50 **Admissions:** 1346 **Census:** 9 **Outpatient Visits:** 51394 **Births:** 451 **Total Expense ($000):** 83715 **Payroll Expense ($000):** 17097 **Personnel:** 262

CROSSVILLE—Cumberland County

⊞ **CUMBERLAND MEDICAL CENTER (440009)**, 421 South Main Street, Zip 38555–5031; tel. 931/484–9511 **A**1 2 10 20 **F**3 11 13 15 18 20 22 28 29 30 31 34 35 40 44 45 47 48 49 51 53 57 59 68 70 74 75 76 77 78 79 81 82 85 86 87 93 107 108 110 111 114 119 120 121 129 130 132 135 146 147 148 149 **P**6 **S** Covenant Health, Knoxville, TN
Primary Contact: David V. Bunch, President and Chief Administrative Officer
CFO: April VonAchen, Chief Financial Officer and Vice President Financial Services
CIO: Joe Lowe, Director Management Information Systems
CHR: Charles Sexton, Manager Human Resources
CNO: Rebecca Foster MSN, R.N., Chief Nursing Officer
Web address: www.cmchealthcare.org
Control: Other not–for–profit (including NFP Corporation) **Service**: General medical and surgical

Staffed Beds: 97 **Admissions:** 4595 **Census:** 47 **Outpatient Visits:** 84291 **Births:** 664 **Total Expense ($000):** 72315 **Payroll Expense ($000):** 28979 **Personnel:** 774

DAYTON—Rhea County

⊞ **RHEA MEDICAL CENTER (441310)**, 9400 Rhea County Highway, Zip 37321–7922; tel. 423/775–1121, (Nonreporting) **A**1 10 18 **S** QHR, Brentwood, TN
Primary Contact: David Bixler, Chief Executive Officer
CFO: Harv Sanders, Chief Financial Officer
CMO: Michael Prostko M.D., Chief of Staff
CHR: Peri Meadows, Director Human Resources
Web address: www.rheamedical.org
Control: County, Government, Nonfederal **Service**: General medical and surgical

Staffed Beds: 25

DICKSON—Dickson County

⊞ **TRISTAR HORIZON MEDICAL CENTER (440046)**, 111 Highway 70 East, Zip 37055–2080; tel. 615/446–0446, (Nonreporting) **A**1 2 10 **S** HCA Healthcare, Nashville, TN
Primary Contact: Dustin Greene, Chief Executive Officer
CFO: Clarence Gray, Chief Financial Officer
CIO: Rick Stoker, Director Management Information Systems
CHR: Sheila Kight, Director Human Resources
CNO: Gina Bullington, Chief Nursing Officer
Web address: www.horizonmedicalcenter.com
Control: Corporation, Investor–owned (for–profit) **Service**: General medical and surgical

Staffed Beds: 130

DYERSBURG—Dyer County

⊞ **TENNOVA HEALTHCARE DYERSBURG REGIONAL MEDICAL CENTER (440072)**, 400 East Tickle Street, Zip 38024–3120; tel. 731/285–2410, (Nonreporting) **A**1 10 20 **S** Community Health Systems, Inc., Franklin, TN
Primary Contact: Reba Celsor, Chief Executive Officer
CFO: Meredith Malone, Chief Financial Officer
CMO: Darren Johnson M.D., Chief of Staff
CIO: Russ Shephard, Senior Systems Analyst
CHR: Beverly Ray, Director Human Resources
Web address: www.dyersburgregionalmc.com
Control: Corporation, Investor–owned (for–profit) **Service**: General medical and surgical

Staffed Beds: 120

EAST RIDGE—Hamilton County

EAST RIDGE HOSPITAL See Parkridge Medical Center, Chattanooga

ELIZABETHTON—Carter County

☐ **SYCAMORE SHOALS HOSPITAL (440018)**, 1501 West Elk Avenue, Zip 37643–2874; tel. 423/542–1300 **A**1 10 **F**3 11 15 18 29 30 34 35 40 44 45 48 49 50 53 54 56 57 62 63 64 68 70 75 77 78 79 81 85 87 93 98 103 107 110 111 115 118 119 130 132 135 146 147 148 **S** Mountain States Health Alliance, Johnson City, TN
Primary Contact: Dwayne Taylor, Chief Executive Officer
COO: Melanie Stanton R.N., Chief Nursing Officer
CFO: Chase Wilson, Chief Financial Officer
CMO: Morris H Seligman M.D., Chief Medical Officer and Chief Medical Information Officer
CIO: Paul Merrywell, Chief Information Officer
CHR: Sharon Sheppard, Manager Human Resources
Web address: www.msha.com
Control: Other not–for–profit (including NFP Corporation) **Service**: General medical and surgical

Staffed Beds: 74 **Admissions:** 3678 **Census:** 47 **Outpatient Visits:** 64652 **Births:** 0 **Total Expense ($000):** 41624 **Payroll Expense ($000):** 18122 **Personnel:** 268

ERIN—Houston County

⊞ **HOUSTON COUNTY COMMUNITY HOSPITAL (440232)**, 5001 East Main Street, Zip 37061–4115, Mailing Address: P.O.Box 489, 37061–0489; tel. 931/289–4211, (Nonreporting) **A**1 10
Primary Contact: Mark E. Kimball, Chief Executive Officer
CFO: Kim Pridgen, Chief Financial Officer
CMO: Michael Carter M.D., Chief Medical Officer
CNO: Angie Beard R.N.,
Control: County, Government, Nonfederal **Service**: General medical and surgical

Staffed Beds: 25

ERWIN—Unicoi County

⊞ **UNICOI COUNTY MEMORIAL HOSPITAL (440001)**, 100 Greenway Circle, Zip 37650–2196, Mailing Address: P.O.Box 802, 37650–0802; tel. 423/743–3141, (Total facility includes 46 beds in nursing home–type unit) **A**1 10 **F**11 15 29 30 34 35 40 45 62 64 67 70 75 77 79 81 85 87 107 110 111 115 130 131 146 **S** Mountain States Health Alliance, Johnson City, TN
Primary Contact: Eric Carroll, Chief Executive Officer
CFO: Toni Buchanan, Chief Financial Officer
CMO: Jose Picaza M.D., Chief of Staff
CIO: Maggie Tipton, Chief Information Officer
CHR: Susan Broyles, Director Human Resources and Safety
CNO: Melanie Stanton R.N., Chief Nursing Officer
Web address: www.msha.com
Control: Other not–for–profit (including NFP Corporation) **Service**: General medical and surgical

Staffed Beds: 94 **Admissions:** 705 **Census:** 45 **Outpatient Visits:** 25982 **Births:** 0 **Total Expense ($000):** 13509 **Payroll Expense ($000):** 5613 **Personnel:** 85

FAYETTEVILLE—Lincoln County

⊞ **LINCOLN COUNTY HEALTH SYSTEM (440102)**, 106 Medical Center Boulevard, Zip 37334–2684; tel. 931/438–1100, (Nonreporting) **A**1 10
Primary Contact: Candie Starr, Chief Executive Officer
CFO: Robert Lonis, Chief Financial Officer
CMO: Richard Cline D.O., Chief of Staff
CHR: Wendy Nogler, Director Human Resources
CNO: Vicky Groce, Chief Nursing Officer
Web address: www.lchealthsystem.com
Control: County, Government, Nonfederal **Service**: General medical and surgical

Staffed Beds: 323

FRANKLIN—Williamson County

★ **HEALTHSOUTH REHABILITATION HOSPITAL OF FRANKLIN (443035)**, 1000 Physicians Way, Zip 37067–1471; tel. 615/721–4000 **F**28 29 34 35 53 60 68 75 90 91 94 96 **P**5 **S** HEALTHSOUTH Corporation, Birmingham, AL
Primary Contact: Scott J. Peterson, Chief Executive Officer
CMO: Scott Craig M.D., Medical Director
Web address: www.healthsouthfranklin.com
Control: Corporation, Investor–owned (for–profit) **Service**: Rehabilitation

Staffed Beds: 40 **Admissions:** 454 **Census:** 15 **Outpatient Visits:** 0 **Births:** 0

Many Facility Codes have changed. Please refer to the AHA Guide Code Chart. © 2017 AHA Guide

TN

☐ **ROLLING HILLS HOSPITAL (444007)**, 2014 Quail Hollow Circle, Zip 37067–5967; tel. 615/628–5700 **A**1 10 **F**4 5 34 44 50 54 56 64 68 75 98 99 100 101 102 103 104 105 130 132 135 149 **S** Universal Health Services, Inc., King of Prussia, PA
Primary Contact: Jim Spruyt, Chief Executive Officer
CFO: Chris Leonard, Chief Financial Officer
CMO: James Hart M.D., Medical Director
CHR: Lisa Hodge, Manager, Human Resources
CNO: Laurel Roberts R.N., MSN, Chief Nursing Officer
Web address: www.RollingHillsHospital.org/
Control: Corporation, Investor–owned (for–profit) **Service:** Psychiatric

Staffed Beds: 120 **Admissions:** 3853 **Census:** 83 **Outpatient Visits:** 0
Births: 0 **Total Expense ($000):** 17404 **Payroll Expense ($000):** 10374
Personnel: 340

☐ **WILLIAMSON MEDICAL CENTER (440029)**, 4321 Carothers Parkway, Zip 37067–8542; tel. 615/435–5000 **A**1 2 10 **F**3 7 11 13 15 17 18 20 22 28 29 30 31 34 35 40 41 43 45 49 50 54 57 59 64 67 68 70 72 74 75 76 78 79 80 81 84 85 86 87 93 97 102 107 108 110 111 114 115 118 119 124 126 129 130 132 135 146 148 149
Primary Contact: Donald Webb, Chief Executive Officer
COO: Julie Miller, Chief Operating Officer
CMO: Starling C Evins M.D., Chief of Staff
CIO: Steve Dycus, Director Marketing and Public Relations
CHR: Phyllis Molyneux, Associate Administrator Human Resources and Education
Web address: www.williamsonmedicalcenter.org
Control: County, Government, Nonfederal **Service:** General medical and surgical

Staffed Beds: 185 **Admissions:** 9472 **Census:** 93 **Outpatient Visits:** 118970
Births: 1761 **Total Expense ($000):** 184528 **Payroll Expense ($000):** 75023
Personnel: 1350

GALLATIN—Sumner County

☒ **SUMNER REGIONAL MEDICAL CENTER (440003)**, 555 Hartsville Pike, Zip 37066–2400, Mailing Address: P.O.Box 1558, 37066–1558; tel. 615/452–4210 **A**1 2 3 10 **F**3 11 13 15 18 20 22 26 28 29 30 37 40 41 43 45 49 51 54 57 59 60 68 70 74 75 76 77 78 79 81 82 86 87 89 90 93 98 103 108 110 111 114 115 117 118 119 121 124 126 129 130 131 132 135 146 147 148 **S** LifePoint Health, Brentwood, TN
Primary Contact: Susan M. Peach, R.N., Chief Executive Officer
CIO: Vickie Carter, Information Systems Director
CNO: Anne Melton, Chief Nursing Officer
Web address: www.mysumnermedical.com
Control: Corporation, Investor–owned (for–profit) **Service:** General medical and surgical

Staffed Beds: 110 **Admissions:** 8291 **Census:** 93 **Outpatient Visits:** 115828
Births: 725 **Total Expense ($000):** 119789 **Payroll Expense ($000):** 43316
Personnel: 760

GERMANTOWN—Shelby County

☐ **BAPTIST MEMORIAL REHABILITATION HOSPITAL (443034)**, 1240 South Germantown Road, Zip 38138–2226; tel. 901/275–3300 **A**1 10 **F**3 90 **S** Baptist Memorial Health Care Corporation, Memphis, TN
Primary Contact: Christopher L. Bariola, Chief Executive Officer
CFO: Carlos Mendoza, Controller
CHR: Stacie Schroeppel, Director of Human Resources
CNO: Donna Hale, Director of Nursing
Web address: www.baptistrehab.com
Control: Corporation, Investor–owned (for–profit) **Service:** Rehabilitation

Staffed Beds: 49 **Admissions:** 1147 **Census:** 40 **Outpatient Visits:** 0 **Births:** 0
Total Expense ($000): 16079 **Payroll Expense ($000):** 8444 **Personnel:** 186

METHODIST LE BONHEUR GERMANTOWN HOSPITAL See Methodist Healthcare Memphis Hospitals, Memphis

GREENEVILLE—Greene County

☒ **LAUGHLIN MEMORIAL HOSPITAL (440025)**, 1420 Tusculum Boulevard, Zip 37745–5825; tel. 423/787–5000, (Total facility includes 81 beds in nursing home–type unit) **A**1 2 10 19 **F**3 11 12 13 15 18 20 28 29 31 34 35 46 47 48 49 56 57 59 62 64 66 68 70 73 75 76 77 78 79 81 85 87 88 89 91 93 94 97 107 108 110 111 114 115 118 119 120 121 123 128 129 130 131 132 134 146 147 148 149 **P**6 **S** Mountain States Health Alliance, Johnson City, TN
Primary Contact: Charles H. Whitfield Jr, President and Chief Executive Officer
CFO: Mark Compton, Chief Financial Officer
CMO: Mark Patterson M.D., Chief Medical Officer
CIO: Eric L Garrison, Chief Information Officer
CHR: Robert R Roark, Director Human Resources
CNO: Brenda Cannon R.N., Director of Nursing
Web address: www.laughlinmemorial.org
Control: Other not–for–profit (including NFP Corporation) **Service:** General medical and surgical

Staffed Beds: 152 **Admissions:** 3424 **Census:** 120 **Outpatient Visits:** 96528
Births: 195 **Total Expense ($000):** 72923 **Payroll Expense ($000):** 32625
Personnel: 809

☒ **TAKOMA REGIONAL HOSPITAL (440050)**, 401 Takoma Avenue, Zip 37743–4647; tel. 423/639–3151, (Nonreporting) **A**1 10 **S** Wellmont Health System, Kingsport, TN
Primary Contact: Tammy Albright, President
CFO: Judith Clark, Chief Financial Officer
CMO: Daniel Lewis, Chief Medical Officer
CHR: Jack Lister, Director Human Resources
CNO: Robin Roberts, Executive Director of Patient Services
Web address: www.takoma.org
Control: Church operated, Nongovernment, not–for–profit **Service:** General medical and surgical

Staffed Beds: 32

HARRIMAN—Roane County

☒ **ROANE MEDICAL CENTER (440031)**, 8045 Roane Medical Center Dr, Zip 37748–8333; tel. 865/316–1000 **A**1 10 **F**3 11 15 18 20 28 29 30 40 45 57 59 68 70 81 85 93 107 108 110 111 119 129 130 136 141 142 146 **S** Covenant Health, Knoxville, TN
Primary Contact: Jason B. Pilant, Acting President and Chief Administrative Officer
COO: Jason B Pilant, Chief Operating Officer
CFO: Julie Utterback, Chief Financial Officer
CMO: Mark Browne M.D., Chief Medical Officer
CIO: Mike Ward, Senior Vice President Chief Information Officer
CHR: Randall Carr, Director Human Resources
CNO: Carolyn Shipley, Chief Nursing Officer
Web address: www.roanemedical.com
Control: Other not–for–profit (including NFP Corporation) **Service:** General medical and surgical

Staffed Beds: 52 **Admissions:** 2398 **Census:** 25 **Outpatient Visits:** 65171
Total Expense ($000): 35320 **Payroll Expense ($000):** 12743 **Personnel:** 239

HARTSVILLE—Trousdale County

☒ **TROUSDALE MEDICAL CENTER (441301)**, 500 Church Street, Zip 37074–1744; tel. 615/374–2221, (Nonreporting) **A**1 10 18 **S** LifePoint Health, Brentwood, TN
Primary Contact: Michael Herman, Chief Executive Officer
COO: William D Mize, Chief Operating Officer
CFO: David Wilhoite CPA, Senior Vice President Finance and Chief Financial Officer
CIO: David Young, Senior Vice President Planning and Technology
CHR: Amy Overstreet, Director Human Resources
CNO: Jennifer Holder, Chief Nursing Officer
Web address: www.mytrousdalemedical.com
Control: Corporation, Investor–owned (for–profit) **Service:** General medical and surgical

Staffed Beds: 25

TN

Hospital, Medicare Provider Number, Address, Telephone, Approval, Facility, and Physician Codes, Health Care System

★ American Hospital Association (AHA) membership
☐ The Joint Commission accreditation
○ Healthcare Facilities Accreditation Program
◇ DNV Healthcare Inc. accreditation
⇑ Center for Improvement in Healthcare Quality Accreditation
△ Commission on Accreditation of Rehabilitation Facilities (CARF) accreditation

© 2017 AHA Guide   *Many Facility Codes have changed. Please refer to the AHA Guide Code Chart.*   Hospitals **A579**

HENDERSONVILLE—Sumner County

⊞ **TRISTAR HENDERSONVILLE MEDICAL CENTER (440194)**, 355 New Shackle Island Road, Zip 37075–2479; tel. 615/338–1000, (Nonreporting) **A**1 10 **S** HCA Healthcare, Nashville, TN
Primary Contact: Regina Bartlett, Chief Executive Officer
COO: Cory Darling, Chief Operating Officer
CFO: Jon Baker, Chief Financial Officer
CMO: Jason Thurman, Chief of Staff
CIO: Hal Schultheis, Director Information Systems
CNO: Lisa Gann R.N., Chief Nursing Officer
Web address: www.hendersonvillemedicalcenter.com
Control: Corporation, Investor–owned (for–profit) **Service**: General medical and surgical

Staffed Beds: 96

HERMITAGE—Davidson County

⊞ **TRISTAR SUMMIT MEDICAL CENTER (440150)**, 5655 Frist Boulevard, Zip 37076–2053; tel. 615/316–3000 **A**1 2 10 **F**3 11 13 15 18 20 22 26 28 29 30 31 34 35 37 38 39 40 43 45 46 47 48 49 50 56 57 61 64 70 72 74 75 76 77 78 79 80 81 82 85 87 89 90 93 96 100 107 108 110 111 114 115 118 119 121 123 124 126 129 130 131 135 145 146 147 148 **P**6 **S** HCA Healthcare, Nashville, TN
Primary Contact: Brian Marger, Chief Executive Officer
COO: Greg Caples, Chief Operating Officer
CFO: Bryan Shephard, Chief Financial Officer
CIO: Joel Bain, Director Information Services
CHR: Emily Dye, Vice President Human Resources
CNO: Mary Ann Angle R.N., FACHE, Chief Nursing Officer
Web address: www.summitmedctr.com
Control: Corporation, Investor–owned (for–profit) **Service**: General medical and surgical

Staffed Beds: 196 **Admissions**: 11269 **Census**: 131 **Outpatient Visits**: 126993
Births: 1225 **Total Expense ($000)**: 139720 **Payroll Expense ($000)**: 52296
Personnel: 842

HUNTINGDON—Carroll County

⊞ **BAPTIST MEMORIAL HOSPITAL–HUNTINGDON (440016)**, 631 R.B. Wilson Drive, Zip 38344–1727; tel. 731/986–4461 **A**1 10 **F**3 7 11 15 18 28 29 30 34 35 40 44 50 56 57 59 61 62 63 64 65 68 70 75 77 81 85 86 87 91 93 98 101 102 103 107 108 111 115 118 119 130 132 133 134 145 146 148 149 **S** Baptist Memorial Health Care Corporation, Memphis, TN
Primary Contact: Susan M. Breeden, Administrator and Chief Executive Officer
CFO: Sharron Holland, Chief Financial Officer
CHR: Kim King, Director Human Resources and Public Relations
CNO: Kimberly Sanders, Chief Nursing Officer
Web address: www.baptistonline.org/huntingdon/
Control: Other not–for–profit (including NFP Corporation) **Service**: General medical and surgical

Staffed Beds: 35 **Admissions**: 926 **Census**: 14 **Outpatient Visits**: 16195
Births: 0 **Total Expense ($000)**: 18904 **Payroll Expense ($000)**: 6648
Personnel: 143

JACKSON—Madison County

⊞ △ **JACKSON–MADISON COUNTY GENERAL HOSPITAL (440002)**, 620 Skyline Drive, Zip 38301–3923; tel. 731/541–5000 **A**1 2 3 5 7 10 19 **F**3 7 8 11 13 15 17 18 20 22 24 26 28 29 30 31 34 35 40 42 44 45 46 47 48 49 51 53 55 56 57 58 59 60 63 64 65 68 70 72 74 75 76 77 78 79 80 81 82 83 84 85 86 87 89 90 92 93 94 96 97 107 108 109 110 111 112 114 115 116 117 118 119 120 121 124 126 129 130 131 132 135 145 146 147 148 149 **P**5 8 **S** West Tennessee Healthcare, Jackson, TN
Primary Contact: James E. Ross, President and Chief Executive Officer
CFO: Jeff Blankenship CPA, Vice President and Chief Financial Officer
CMO: David Roberts M.D., Chief Medical Officer
CIO: Jeff Frieling, Vice President and Chief Information Officer
CHR: Wendie Carlson, Chief Human Resources Officer
CNO: Tina Prescott, Vice President, Hospital Services
Web address: www.wth.org
Control: Hospital district or authority, Government, Nonfederal **Service**: General medical and surgical

Staffed Beds: 635 **Admissions**: 29362 **Census**: 474 **Outpatient Visits**: 208832 **Births**: 3107 **Total Expense ($000)**: 600474 **Payroll Expense ($000)**: 223145 **Personnel**: 4245

★ **PATHWAYS OF TENNESSEE (444010)**, 238 Summar Drive, Zip 38301–3906; tel. 731/541–8200 **A**10 **F**4 5 29 35 38 44 57 59 98 99 100 101 102 103 104 132 134 149 150 **S** West Tennessee Healthcare, Jackson, TN
Primary Contact: Pam Henson, Executive Director
CFO: Jeff Blankenship CPA, Chief Financial Officer
CMO: Kevin Turner M.D., Medical Director
CIO: Jeff Frieling, Chief Information Officer
CHR: Wendy Carlson, Director Human Resources
CNO: Angela Hensley, Director of Nursing
Web address: www.wth.net/pathways
Control: Hospital district or authority, Government, Nonfederal **Service**: Psychiatric

Staffed Beds: 25 **Admissions**: 775 **Census**: 9 **Outpatient Visits**: 109043
Births: 0 **Total Expense ($000)**: 15973 **Payroll Expense ($000)**: 8775
Personnel: 205

⊞ **TENNOVA HEALTHCARE REGIONAL HOSPITAL OF JACKSON (440189)**, 367 Hospital Boulevard, Zip 38305–2080; tel. 731/661–2000, (Nonreporting) **A**1 3 10 **S** Community Health Systems, Inc., Franklin, TN
Primary Contact: Damon Brown, Interim Chief Executive Officer
CFO: Richard Read, Chief Financial Officer
CMO: Michael Saridakis M.D., Physician Adviser
CIO: Jimmy Anderson, Director of Information Systems
CHR: Barbara Euler, Director Human Resources
CNO: Jan Zimmer R.N., MS, Chief Nursing Officer
Web address: www.tennova.com/tennova–healthcare/tennova–healthcare–regional–jackson.aspx
Control: Corporation, Investor–owned (for–profit) **Service**: General medical and surgical

Staffed Beds: 134

JAMESTOWN—Fentress County

⊞ **TENNOVA HEALTHCARE–JAMESTOWN (440083)**, 436 Central Ave W, Zip 38556–3031, Mailing Address: P.O.Box 1500, 38556–1500; tel. 931/879–8171, (Nonreporting) **A**1 10 20 **S** Community Health Systems, Inc., Franklin, TN
Primary Contact: Lynette Pritchett, Chief Executive Officer
CMO: Mark Hendrixson M.D., Chief Medical Officer
CIO: Rick Smith, Director Information Systems
CHR: Shelia Russell, Director Human Resources
Web address: www.jamestownregional.org
Control: Corporation, Investor–owned (for–profit) **Service**: General medical and surgical

Staffed Beds: 85

JEFFERSON CITY—Jefferson County

ST. MARY'S JEFFERSON MEMORIAL HOSPITAL See Tennova Healthcare–Jefferson Memorial Hospital

⊞ **TENNOVA HEALTHCARE–JEFFERSON MEMORIAL HOSPITAL (440056)**, 110 Hospital Drive, Zip 37760–5281; tel. 865/471–2500, (Nonreporting) **A**1 10 **S** Community Health Systems, Inc., Franklin, TN
Primary Contact: Colin McRae, Chief Executive Officer
CFO: Roseann M Devault, Chief Financial Officer
CMO: Richard Carter M.D., Chief of Staff
Web address: www.tennova.com/
Control: Corporation, Investor–owned (for–profit) **Service**: General medical and surgical

Staffed Beds: 54

JELLICO—Campbell County

⊞ **JELLICO COMMUNITY HOSPITAL (440180)**, 188 Hospital Lane, Zip 37762–4400; tel. 423/784–7252, (Nonreporting) **A**1 10 **S** Community Hospital Corporation, Plano, TX
Primary Contact: Kim Dowell, R.N., Chief Executive Officer
COO: Pamela Hodge R.N., Chief Nursing Officer and Coordinator Performance Improvement
CFO: Evelyn Ghulum, Chief Financial Officer
CMO: Gregory Wilkens M.D., Chief of Staff
CIO: Derek Brown, Chief Information Officer
CHR: Vince Vannett, Director Human Resources
Web address: www.jellicohospital.com
Control: Other not–for–profit (including NFP Corporation) **Service**: General medical and surgical

Staffed Beds: 31

TN

Many Facility Codes have changed. Please refer to the AHA Guide Code Chart.

JOHNSON CITY—Washington County

✠ **FRANKLIN WOODS COMMUNITY HOSPITAL (440184)**, 300 MedTech Parkway, Zip 37604–2277; tel. 423/302–1000, (Total facility includes 34 beds in nursing home–type unit) **A**1 3 10 **F**3 11 13 29 30 34 35 40 44 45 50 51 56 59 68 70 74 75 76 77 81 85 86 87 91 97 100 107 108 111 114 115 118 119 126 128 130 143 146 147 148 **S** Mountain States Health Alliance, Johnson City, TN
Primary Contact: Lindy P. White, Chief Executive Officer
CFO: Bradley Logan, Chief Financial Officer
CHR: Brooke Graham, Human Resources Manager
CNO: Rhonda Mann, Chief Nursing Officer
Web address: www.msha.com
Control: Other not–for–profit (including NFP Corporation) **Service**: General medical and surgical

Staffed Beds: 80 Admissions: 5167 Census: 49 Outpatient Visits: 50243 Births: 1166 Total Expense ($000): 63798 Payroll Expense ($000): 23044 Personnel: 315

✠ **JOHNSON CITY MEDICAL CENTER (440063)**, 400 North State of Franklin Road, Zip 37604–6094; tel. 423/431–6111, (Includes NISWONGER CHILDREN'S HOSPITAL, 400 North State Of Franklin Road, Johnson City, Tennessee, Zip 37604–6035, tel. 423/431–6111; Lisa Carter, Chief Executive Officer; WOODRIDGE HOSPITAL, 403 State of Franklin Road, Johnson City, Tennessee, Zip 37604–6034, tel. 423/431–7111; Lindy P White, Chief Executive Officer) **A**1 2 3 5 8 10 **F**3 4 5 7 11 12 13 15 17 18 19 20 21 22 24 26 27 28 29 30 31 32 34 35 38 39 40 41 43 44 45 46 47 48 49 50 51 52 53 54 55 56 57 58 59 60 61 62 63 64 68 70 72 74 75 76 77 78 79 81 82 85 86 87 88 89 91 93 97 98 99 100 101 102 103 104 105 107 108 110 111 114 115 117 118 119 120 121 123 124 129 130 131 132 134 135 143 146 147 148 **S** Mountain States Health Alliance, Johnson City, TN
Primary Contact: Melody Trimble, Chief Executive Officer
COO: Tony Benton, Chief Operating Officer
CFO: Richard Boone, Chief Financial Officer
CMO: Clay Runnels, Vice President Chief Medical Officer Washington County
CHR: Barry Tourigny, Human Resources Director
CNO: Dru Malcolm, Vice President and Chief Nursing Officer
Web address: www.msha.com
Control: Other not–for–profit (including NFP Corporation) **Service**: General medical and surgical

Staffed Beds: 585 Admissions: 30320 Census: 427 Outpatient Visits: 274196 Births: 1486 Total Expense ($000): 411831 Payroll Expense ($000): 130407 Personnel: 2094

NORTH SIDE HOSPITAL See Franklin Woods Community Hospital

✠ △ **QUILLEN REHABILITATION HOSPITAL (443033)**, 2511 Wesley Street, Zip 37601–1723; tel. 423/952–1700 **A**1 7 10 **F**29 75 90 91 132 148 **S** HEALTHSOUTH Corporation, Birmingham, AL
Primary Contact: Brian Luff, Chief Executive Officer
CFO: Debbie Wyse, Controller
CHR: Penny Lawson, Human Resource Director
CNO: Lynn Langan, Chief Nursing Officer
Web address: www.quillenrehabilitationhospital.com/
Control: Corporation, Investor–owned (for–profit) **Service**: Rehabilitation

Staffed Beds: 31 Admissions: 634 Census: 22 Outpatient Visits: 0 Births: 0 Total Expense ($000): 9357 Payroll Expense ($000): 4744 Personnel: 85

KINGSPORT—Sullivan County

✠ **HEALTHSOUTH REHABILITATION HOSPITAL (443027)**, 113 Cassel Drive, Zip 37660–3775; tel. 423/246–7240, (Nonreporting) **A**1 10 **S** HEALTHSOUTH Corporation, Birmingham, AL
Primary Contact: Troy Clark, Chief Executive Officer
CFO: Natalie Tilson, Controller
CMO: James P Little M.D., Medical Director
CIO: Natalie Tilson, Controller
CHR: Joyce Jones, Director Human Resources
CNO: Debra Smith, Chief Nursing Officer
Web address: www.healthsouthkingsport.com
Control: Corporation, Investor–owned (for–profit) **Service**: Rehabilitation

Staffed Beds: 50

□ **INDIAN PATH MEDICAL CENTER (440176)**, 2000 Brookside Drive, Zip 37660–4627; tel. 423/857–7000 **A**1 3 10 **F**3 8 11 13 15 18 20 22 26 28 29 30 31 34 35 40 45 46 47 49 50 51 57 59 60 64 65 68 70 73 74 75 76 77 78 79 81 84 85 86 87 91 93 97 107 108 110 111 114 115 116 117 118 119 121 123 129 130 132 135 146 147 **S** Mountain States Health Alliance, Johnson City, TN
Primary Contact: Monty E. McLaurin, Chief Executive Officer, Northwest Market
CFO: Steve Sawyer, Chief Financial Officer
CMO: Mark Wilkinson M.D., Chief Medical Officer
CIO: Jackson Dale, Site Manager Information Systems
CHR: Kevin M Smith, Director Human Resources
CNO: Susan Fannon, Chief Nursing Officer
Web address: www.msha.com
Control: Other not–for–profit (including NFP Corporation) **Service**: General medical and surgical

Staffed Beds: 160 Admissions: 6022 Census: 67 Outpatient Visits: 125954 Births: 846 Total Expense ($000): 88827 Payroll Expense ($000): 31820 Personnel: 466

✠ **WELLMONT HOLSTON VALLEY MEDICAL CENTER (440017)**, 130 West Ravine Street, Zip 37660–3837, Mailing Address: P.O.Box 238, 37662–0238; tel. 423/224–4000, (Nonreporting) **A**1 2 3 5 10 13 19 **S** Wellmont Health System, Kingsport, TN
Primary Contact: Tim Attebery, Chief Executive Officer
COO: Fred L Pelle FACHE, Chief Operating Officer
CFO: Dale Poe, Vice President Finance and Operations
CMO: Daniel Carlson M.D., Chief Medical Officer
CIO: Will Showalter, Senior Vice President Information Technology
CHR: Hamlin J Wilson, Senior Vice President Human Resources
CNO: Kathy Campbell, Interim Chief Nursing Officer
Web address: www.wellmont.org
Control: Other not–for–profit (including NFP Corporation) **Service**: General medical and surgical

Staffed Beds: 345

KNOXVILLE—Knox County

□ **EAST TENNESSEE CHILDREN'S HOSPITAL (443303)**, 2018 Clinch Avenue, Zip 37916–2393, Mailing Address: P.O.Box 15010, 37901–5010; tel. 865/541–8000 **A**1 3 5 10 **F**7 11 19 29 30 31 32 34 35 39 40 41 43 50 55 57 58 59 61 62 64 68 72 74 75 77 78 79 81 82 84 85 86 87 88 89 91 93 97 99 101 104 107 111 115 119 129 130 131 135 146 148 **P**1 7
Primary Contact: Keith D. Goodwin, President and Chief Executive Officer
COO: Rudolph McKinley Jr, Vice President Operations and Chief Operating Officer
CFO: Zane Goodrich, Vice President Finance
CMO: Joe Childs M.D., Vice President Medical Services
CIO: John Hanks, Director Information Systems
CHR: Sue Wilburn, Vice President Human Resources and Organizational Development
CNO: Laura P Barnes MSN, Vice President Patient Care Services and Chief Nursing Officer
Web address: www.etch.com
Control: Other not–for–profit (including NFP Corporation) **Service**: Children's general medical and surgical

Staffed Beds: 152 Admissions: 5799 Census: 101 Outpatient Visits: 168458 Births: 0 Total Expense ($000): 167782 Payroll Expense ($000): 82303 Personnel: 1805

✠ △ **FORT SANDERS REGIONAL MEDICAL CENTER (440125)**, 1901 West Clinch Avenue, Zip 37916–2307; tel. 865/541–1111, (Total facility includes 24 beds in nursing home–type unit) **A**1 2 7 10 19 **F**3 11 12 13 15 17 18 20 22 24 26 28 29 30 31 34 35 40 45 46 47 48 49 50 51 54 55 57 58 59 60 61 64 68 74 75 76 77 78 79 80 81 84 85 86 87 90 91 92 93 94 96 100 102 107 108 110 111 114 115 116 117 118 119 120 121 123 124 126 128 129 130 131 132 135 136 141 142 146 147 148 **S** Covenant Health, Knoxville, TN
Primary Contact: Keith Altshuler, President and Chief Administrative Officer
Web address: www.covenanthealth.com
Control: Other not–for–profit (including NFP Corporation) **Service**: General medical and surgical

Staffed Beds: 384 Admissions: 16585 Census: 241 Outpatient Visits: 226830 Births: 2528 Total Expense ($000): 271669 Payroll Expense ($000): 90751 Personnel: 1495

MERCY MEDICAL CENTER WEST See Tennova Turkey Creek Medical Center

✠ **PARKWEST MEDICAL CENTER (440173)**, 9352 Park West Boulevard, Zip 37923–4325, Mailing Address: P.O.Box 22993, 37933–0993; tel. 865/373–1000 **A**1 2 10 **F**3 13 15 17 18 20 22 24 26 28 29 30 31 34 35 37 40 45 46 47 48 49 50 51 56 58 60 64 68 70 74 75 76 77 78 79 80 81 84 85 87 92 93 98 103 107 108 110 111 115 116 117 118 119 120 121 123 124 126 129 130 131 132 135 141 142 146 147 148 149 **S** Covenant Health, Knoxville, TN
Primary Contact: Neil Heatherly, Chief Executive Officer
COO: Emlyn Cobble, Vice President and Chief Support Officer
CFO: Scott Hamilton, Vice President and Chief Financial Officer
CHR: Randall Carr, Director Human Resources
CNO: Diane Oliver R.N., MSN, Chief Nursing Officer
Web address: www.treatedwell.com/
Control: Other not–for–profit (including NFP Corporation) **Service**: General medical and surgical

| **Staffed Beds**: 297 **Admissions**: 17240 **Census**: 213 **Outpatient Visits**: 184704 **Births**: 1628 **Total Expense ($000)**: 255193 **Payroll Expense ($000)**: 80299 **Personnel**: 1447 |

✠ **SELECT SPECIALTY HOSPITAL–KNOXVILLE (442012)**, 1901 Clinch Avenue, 4th Floor North, Zip 37916–2307; tel. 865/541–2615, (Nonreporting) **A**1 10 **S** Select Medical Corporation, Mechanicsburg, PA
Primary Contact: Rita Wilder, Chief Executive Officer
CFO: David Elledge, Controller
CMO: Jano Janoyan M.D., Medical Director
CHR: Christina Blanton, Administrative Assistant and Human Resources Coordinator
CNO: Danielle Connolly Robbins, Chief Nursing Officer
Web address: www.knoxville.selectspecialtyhospitals.com/
Control: Corporation, Investor–owned (for–profit) **Service**: Acute long–term care hospital

| **Staffed Beds**: 35 |

✠ △ **TENNOVA PHYSICIANS REGIONAL MEDICAL CENTER (440120)**, 900 East Oak Hill Avenue, Zip 37917–4556; tel. 865/545–8000, (Nonreporting) (Includes TENNOVA NORTH KNOXVILLE MEDICAL CENTER, 7565 Dannaher Way, Powell, Tennessee, Zip 37849–4029, tel. 865/859–7000; Clyde Wood, Chief Executive Officer; TENNOVA TURKEY CREEK MEDICAL CENTER, 10820 Parkside Drive, Knoxville, Tennessee, Zip 37922–1956, tel. 865/218–7090; TENNOVA TURKEY CREEK MEDICAL CENTER, 10820 Parkside Drive, Knoxville, Tennessee, Zip 37934–1956, tel. 865/218–7092; Ben Youree, Chief Executive Officer) **A**1 2 7 10 **S** Community Health Systems, Inc., Franklin, TN
Primary Contact: Pamela Beck, Interim Chief Executive Officer
CFO: Rhonda Maynard, Chief Financial Officer
CIO: Tom Lakins, Director Information Systems
CHR: Sarah M Laboranti, Interim Director Human Resources
Web address: www.hma.com/content/physicians–regional–medical–center
Control: Corporation, Investor–owned (for–profit) **Service**: General medical and surgical

| **Staffed Beds**: 223 |

✠ **UNIVERSITY OF TENNESSEE MEDICAL CENTER (440015)**, 1924 Alcoa Highway, Zip 37920–6900; tel. 865/305–9000 **A**1 3 5 8 10 **F**3 6 8 9 11 12 13 15 17 18 20 22 24 26 28 29 30 31 34 35 36 39 40 41 43 44 45 46 47 48 49 50 51 52 53 54 55 56 57 58 59 60 61 64 65 70 71 72 74 75 76 77 78 79 81 82 84 85 86 87 88 91 92 93 94 96 97 100 102 103 107 108 109 110 111 114 115 116 117 118 119 120 121 123 124 126 129 130 131 132 135 138 141 142 144 145 146 147 148 149 150 **P**1 5 6
Primary Contact: Joseph Landsman, President and Chief Executive Officer
COO: David Hall, Senior Vice President and Chief Operating Officer
CFO: Thomas Fisher, Senior Vice President and Chief Financial Officer
CMO: Jerry Epps M.D., Senior Vice President and Chief Medical Officer
CIO: Michael Saad, Vice President and Chief Information Officer
CHR: Julie Simpson, Vice President Human Resources
CNO: Janell Cecil R.N., MSN, Senior Vice President and Chief Nursing Officer
Web address: www.utmedicalcenter.org
Control: Other not–for–profit (including NFP Corporation) **Service**: General medical and surgical

| **Staffed Beds**: 609 **Admissions**: 29350 **Census**: 448 **Outpatient Visits**: 280601 **Births**: 3323 **Total Expense ($000)**: 814214 **Payroll Expense ($000)**: 280879 **Personnel**: 3749 |

LA FOLLETTE—Campbell County

✠ **TENNOVA HEALTHCARE–LAFOLLETTE MEDICAL CENTER (440033)**, 923 East Central Avenue, Zip 37766–2768, Mailing Address: P.O.Box 1301, 37766–1301; tel. 423/907–1200, (Nonreporting) **A**1 10 20 **S** Community Health Systems, Inc., Franklin, TN
Primary Contact: Mark Cain, Chief Executive Officer
COO: Sara Heatherly–Lloyd, Chief Operating Officer
CFO: Michael Cherry, Chief Financial Officer
CMO: George O'Neal Vinsant M.D., Chief Medical Officer
CIO: Dillon Ward, Management Information Systems Specialist
CHR: Bess Stout, Director Human Resources
CNO: Kathy R Myers MS, R.N., Chief Nursing Officer
Web address: www.tennova.com
Control: Corporation, Investor–owned (for–profit) **Service**: General medical and surgical

| **Staffed Beds**: 165 |

LAFAYETTE—Macon County

★ ⇑ **MACON COUNTY GENERAL HOSPITAL (441305)**, 204 Medical Drive, Zip 37083–1799, Mailing Address: P.O.Box 378, 37083–0378; tel. 615/666–2147 **A**10 18 21 **F**3 15 29 30 34 35 40 45 57 59 68 81 87 93 107 110 111 119 128 130 132 133 136 141 142 146 **S** QHR, Brentwood, TN
Primary Contact: Thomas J. Kidd, Chief Executive Officer
Web address: www.mcgh.net
Control: Other not–for–profit (including NFP Corporation) **Service**: General medical and surgical

| **Staffed Beds**: 25 **Admissions**: 774 **Census**: 9 **Outpatient Visits**: 27000 **Births**: 0 **Total Expense ($000)**: 11433 **Payroll Expense ($000)**: 5208 **Personnel**: 126 |

LAWRENCEBURG—Lawrence County

✠ **SOUTHERN TENNESSEE REGIONAL HEALTH SYSTEM–LAWRENCEBURG (440175)**, 1607 South Locust Avenue, Zip 38464–4011, Mailing Address: P.O.Box 847, 38464–0847; tel. 931/762–6571, (Nonreporting) **A**1 10 **S** LifePoint Health, Brentwood, TN
Primary Contact: Jeff Noblin, FACHE, Chief Executive Officer
CFO: Kristie Taylor, Chief Financial Officer
CIO: Jason Weaver, Director Information Systems
CHR: Robert Augustin, Director Human Resources
CNO: Carrie Rogers, Chief Nursing Officer
Web address: www.crocketthospital.com
Control: Corporation, Investor–owned (for–profit) **Service**: General medical and surgical

| **Staffed Beds**: 99 |

LEBANON—Wilson County

✠ **TENNOVA HEALTHCARE–LEBANON (440193)**, 1411 Baddour Parkway, Zip 37087–2513; tel. 615/444–8262, (Nonreporting) (Includes TENNOVA HEALTHCARE–LEBANON MCFARLAND CAMPUS, 500 Park Avenue, Lebanon, Tennessee, Zip 37087–3720, tel. 615/449–0500) **A**1 5 10 **S** Community Health Systems, Inc., Franklin, TN
Primary Contact: Jay Hinesley, FACHE, Chief Executive Officer
CMO: Andrew Jordan M.D., Chief of Staff
CIO: Adrian Fung, Director Information Systems
Web address: www.universitymedicalcenter.com
Control: Corporation, Investor–owned (for–profit) **Service**: General medical and surgical

| **Staffed Beds**: 245 |

LENOIR CITY—Loudon County

✠ **FORT LOUDOUN MEDICAL CENTER (440110)**, 550 Fort Loudoun Medical Center Drive, Zip 37772–5673; tel. 865/271–6000 **A**1 10 **F**3 15 18 28 29 30 34 35 40 50 57 59 68 70 75 77 79 81 85 87 93 102 107 108 110 111 114 118 119 130 135 146 148 **S** Covenant Health, Knoxville, TN
Primary Contact: Jeffrey Feike, President and Chief Administrative Officer
CNO: Teresa Fisher R.N., Chief Nursing Officer
Web address: www.covenanthealth.com
Control: Other not–for–profit (including NFP Corporation) **Service**: General medical and surgical

| **Staffed Beds**: 30 **Admissions**: 1993 **Census**: 24 **Outpatient Visits**: 68156 **Births**: 0 **Total Expense ($000)**: 28746 **Payroll Expense ($000)**: 11886 **Personnel**: 210 |

LEWISBURG—Marshall County

✠ **MARSHALL MEDICAL CENTER (441309)**, 1080 North Ellington Parkway, Zip 37091–2227, Mailing Address: P.O.Box 1609, 37091–1609; tel. 931/359–6241 **A**1 10 18 **F**3 11 15 29 30 34 40 45 50 56 57 59 68 75 77 81 85 86 92 93 104 107 108 110 111 114 119 129 131 132 133 135 146 149 **S** Maury Regional Health System, Columbia, TN
Primary Contact: Phyllis Brown, Chief Executive Officer
CFO: Kyle Jones, Controller
CMO: Tim Nash M.D., Chief of Staff
CHR: Jeff M Pierce, Manager Human Resources
CNO: Karen Martin R.N., MSN, Chief Nursing Officer
Web address: www.mauryregional.com
Control: County, Government, Nonfederal **Service**: General medical and surgical

| **Staffed Beds**: 12 **Admissions**: 310 **Census**: 3 **Outpatient Visits**: 34742 **Births**: 0 **Total Expense ($000)**: 14814 **Payroll Expense ($000)**: 6819 **Personnel**: 127 |

Many Facility Codes have changed. Please refer to the AHA Guide Code Chart. © 2017 AHA Guide

TN

LEXINGTON—Henderson County

☒ **HENDERSON COUNTY COMMUNITY HOSPITAL (440008)**, 200 West Church Street, Zip 38351–2038; tel. 731/968–3646, (Nonreporting) **A**1 10 **S** Quorum Health, Brentwood, TN
Primary Contact: Pamela W. Roberts, Chief Executive Officer
CFO: John Bostwick, Interim Chief Financial Officer
CHR: Linda Durham, Director Human Resources
CNO: Charlene Morgan, Chief Nursing Officer
Web address: www.hendersoncchospital.com
Control: Corporation, Investor–owned (for–profit) **Service**: General medical and surgical

Staffed Beds: 45

LINDEN—Perry County

PERRY COMMUNITY HOSPITAL (440040), 2718 Squirrel Hollow Drive, Zip 37096–3526; tel. 931/589–2121, (Nonreporting) **A**10
Primary Contact: John B. Avery III, Administrator
Control: Other not–for–profit (including NFP Corporation) **Service**: General medical and surgical

Staffed Beds: 53

LIVINGSTON—Overton County

☒ **LIVINGSTON REGIONAL HOSPITAL (440187)**, 315 Oak Street, Zip 38570–1728, Mailing Address: P.O.Box 550, 38570–0550; tel. 931/823–5611 **A**1 10 **F**3 11 13 15 29 30 34 35 40 41 45 57 68 70 75 76 77 81 86 90 93 98 103 108 110 111 114 115 118 119 128 129 130 132 133 146 147 148 150 **S** LifePoint Health, Brentwood, TN
Primary Contact: Timothy W. McGill, Chief Executive Officer
CMO: Donnie Huff M.D., Chief Medical Officer
CIO: Mark Hambridge, Director Information Systems
CNO: Colleen Tuck, Chief Nursing Officer
Web address: www.MyLivingstonHospital.com
Control: Corporation, Investor–owned (for–profit) **Service**: General medical and surgical

Staffed Beds: 82 Admissions: 2418 Census: 33 Outpatient Visits: 29836 Births: 285 Total Expense ($000): 28229 Payroll Expense ($000): 11998 Personnel: 234

LOUISVILLE—Blount County

★ **PENINSULA HOSPITAL**, 2347 Jones Bend Road, Zip 37777–5213, Mailing Address: P.O.Box 2000, 37777–2000; tel. 865/970–9800 **P**6
Primary Contact: Elizabeth P. Clary, R.N., Vice President Behavioral Health
COO: Todd Roberts, Manager Business Operations
CFO: Scott Hamilton, Chief Financial Officer
CMO: Reggie Raman M.D., Medical Director
CIO: Shelby Bowers, Director Marketing and Public Relations
CHR: Anita Rivera, Director Human Resources
CNO: Heather Jett, Director Patient Care Services
Web address: www.peninsula–hospital.org
Control: Other not–for–profit (including NFP Corporation) **Service**: Psychiatric

Staffed Beds: 137 Admissions: 4758 Census: 84 Outpatient Visits: 79576 Births: 0 Total Expense ($000): 31372 Payroll Expense ($000): 15720 Personnel: 282

MANCHESTER—Coffee County

UNITY MEDICAL CENTER (440007), 1001 McArthur Drive, Zip 37355–2455, Mailing Address: P.O.Box 1079, 37349–1079; tel. 931/728–3586, (Nonreporting) **A**10 **F**4 5 29 30 34 35 38 50 64 68 98 99 101 104 130 149 150
Primary Contact: Martha McCormick, Chief Executive Officer
CFO: Pam Jernigan, Chief Financial Officer
CMO: James Van Winkle M.D., Chief of Staff
CIO: Matt Burks, Director Information Technology
CHR: Sherry Holt, Director Human Resources
CNO: Stephanie Byars, Chief Nursing Officer
Web address: www.urmchealthcare.com
Control: Corporation, Investor–owned (for–profit) **Service**: General medical and surgical

Staffed Beds: 36

MARTIN—Weakley County

BEHAVIORAL HEALTHCARE CENTER AT MARTIN (444005), 458 Hannings Lane, Zip 38237–3308; tel. 731/588–2830, (Nonreporting) **A**10 **S** Tennessee Health Management, Parsons, TN
Primary Contact: Carrie Brawley, Administrator
Web address: www.tnhealthmanagement.com/BHC/martin/
Control: Partnership, Investor–owned (for–profit) **Service**: Psychiatric

Staffed Beds: 16

☒ **SPIRE CANE CREEK REHABILITATION HOSPITAL (443030)**, 180 Mount Pelia Road, Zip 38237–3812; tel. 731/587–4231 **A**1 10 **F**3 29 56 75 90 91 94 95 96 130 132 143 148 149 **S** HEALTHSOUTH Corporation, Birmingham, AL
Primary Contact: Rick Johnson, Chief Executive Officer
CFO: Bethany Smith, Controller
CMO: Belinda Merritt M.D., Medical Director
CIO: Jan Trowhill, Director Health Information Management Systems
CHR: Sharon Shihady, Director Human Resources
CNO: Lindsey Rotger, Chief Nursing Officer
Web address: www.healthsouthcanecreek.com
Control: Corporation, Investor–owned (for–profit) **Service**: Rehabilitation

Staffed Beds: 40 Admissions: 839 Census: 29 Outpatient Visits: 0 Births: 0

☒ **TENNOVA HEALTHCARE VOLUNTEER COMMUNITY HOSPITAL (440061)**, 161 Mount Pelia Road, Zip 38237–3811; tel. 731/587–4261, (Nonreporting) **A**1 10 **S** Community Health Systems, Inc., Franklin, TN
Primary Contact: Darrell Blaylock, Chief Executive Officer
CFO: Jason Draper, Chief Financial Officer
CMO: Elizabeth Lund M.D., Chief of Staff
CHR: Tammie Bell, Director Human Resources
CNO: Donna Barfield, Chief Nursing Officer
Web address: www.volunteercommunityhospital.com
Control: Corporation, Investor–owned (for–profit) **Service**: General medical and surgical

Staffed Beds: 65

MARYVILLE—Blount County

☒ **BLOUNT MEMORIAL HOSPITAL (440011)**, 907 East Lamar Alexander Parkway, Zip 37804–5016; tel. 865/983–7211, (Total facility includes 76 beds in nursing home–type unit) **A**1 2 10 **F**3 4 10 11 12 13 15 17 18 20 22 26 28 29 30 31 35 38 40 43 45 46 48 49 53 54 56 57 59 62 63 64 67 70 74 75 76 77 78 79 80 81 84 85 86 87 90 93 96 97 98 99 100 101 102 103 104 105 107 108 110 111 115 117 118 119 120 121 122 123 125 126 128 129 130 131 132 135 144 146 147 148 **P**6
Primary Contact: Don Heinemann, Administrator and Chief Executive Officer
CFO: Jonathan Smith, Assistant Administrator and Chief Financial Officer
CMO: G Harold Naramore M.D., Chief Medical Officer and In house Legal Counsel
CIO: Clay Puckett, Assistant Administrator and Chief Information Officer
CHR: Chris Wilkes MS, Director Human Resources
CNO: Sonya Newman R.N., Chief Nursing Officer
Web address: www.blountmemorial.org
Control: County, Government, Nonfederal **Service**: General medical and surgical

Staffed Beds: 294 Admissions: 12572 Census: 206 Outpatient Visits: 369328 Births: 707 Total Expense ($000): 261323 Payroll Expense ($000): 125255 Personnel: 1974

MC MINNVILLE—Warren County

☒ **SAINT THOMAS RIVER PARK HOSPITAL (440151)**, 1559 Sparta Street, Zip 37110–1316; tel. 931/815–4000, (Nonreporting) **A**1 10 **S** Ascension Healthcare, Saint Louis, MO
Primary Contact: Dale Humphrey, Chief Executive Officer
CFO: Christina Patterson, Chief Financial Officer
CMO: Randal D Rampp M.D., Chief Medical Officer
CIO: Jeff Johnson, Director Information Systems
CHR: Deeann Johnson, Director Human Resources
Web address: www.riverparkhospital.com
Control: Church operated, Nongovernment, not–for–profit **Service**: General medical and surgical

Staffed Beds: 85

TN

Hospital, Medicare Provider Number, Address, Telephone, Approval, Facility, and Physician Codes, Health Care System

★ American Hospital Association (AHA) membership ☐ The Joint Commission accreditation ○ Healthcare Facilities Accreditation Program ◇ DNV Healthcare Inc. accreditation ⇑ Center for Improvement in Healthcare Quality Accreditation △ Commission on Accreditation of Rehabilitation Facilities (CARF) accreditation

© 2017 AHA Guide *Many Facility Codes have changed. Please refer to the AHA Guide Code Chart.* Hospitals **A583**

MCKENZIE—Carroll County

MCKENZIE REGIONAL HOSPITAL (440182), 161 Hospital Drive, Zip 38201–1636; tel. 731/352–5344 **A**1 10 **F**3 13 29 34 40 45 53 57 59 64 76 81 85 89 93 107 110 111 114 115 119 131 133 146 **S** Quorum Health, Brentwood, TN
Primary Contact: Michael Morrical, Chief Executive Officer
CFO: Kevin Harvey, Chief Financial Officer
CHR: Tammie Bell, Director Human Resources
CNO: Penny V Kirby MSN, Chief Nursing Officer
Web address: www.mckenzieregionalhospital.com
Control: Corporation, Investor–owned (for–profit) **Service**: General medical and surgical

> **Staffed Beds**: 35 **Admissions**: 908 **Census**: 6 **Outpatient Visits**: 23659 **Births**: 326 **Total Expense ($000)**: 17428 **Payroll Expense ($000)**: 5945 **Personnel**: 120

MEMPHIS—Shelby County

BAPTIST MEMORIAL HOSPITAL – MEMPHIS (440048), 6019 Walnut Grove Road, Zip 38120–2173; tel. 901/226–5000 **A**1 2 3 5 10 **F**3 6 8 12 17 18 19 20 21 22 23 26 28 29 30 31 34 35 36 37 40 41 45 46 47 48 49 50 53 54 56 57 58 59 60 63 64 65 68 70 74 75 77 78 79 80 81 82 84 85 86 87 91 92 93 107 108 109 111 112 114 115 116 117 118 119 120 121 123 124 126 130 132 135 136 137 143 146 148 **P**8 **S** Baptist Memorial Health Care Corporation, Memphis, TN
Primary Contact: Dana Dye, R.N., Vice President, Administrator and Chief Executive Officer
CFO: Cyndi Pittman, Chief Financial Officer
CMO: Christian C Patrick M.D., Chief Medical Officer
CIO: Doug Reiselt, Vice President and Chief Information Officer
CHR: Jerry Barbaree, Director Human Resources
Web address: www.baptistonline.org/memphis/
Control: Other not–for–profit (including NFP Corporation) **Service**: General medical and surgical

> **Staffed Beds**: 563 **Admissions**: 25468 **Census**: 418 **Outpatient Visits**: 130341 **Births**: 0 **Total Expense ($000)**: 510883 **Payroll Expense ($000)**: 158340 **Personnel**: 2591

★ **BAPTIST MEMORIAL HOSPITAL FOR WOMEN (440222)**, 6225 Humphreys Boulevard, Zip 38120–2373; tel. 901/227–9000 **A**3 **F**3 7 8 12 13 15 29 30 32 34 35 37 38 41 45 46 47 48 49 54 55 56 57 58 59 64 65 68 70 71 72 73 74 75 76 77 78 79 81 82 85 86 87 88 89 107 108 109 110 111 112 114 115 119 124 126 130 132 135 143 146 147 148 **S** Baptist Memorial Health Care Corporation, Memphis, TN
Primary Contact: Kevin R. Hammeran, Chief Executive Officer and Administrator
CFO: Margaret Williams, Chief Financial Officer
CMO: Judi Carney M.D., President Medical Staff
CIO: Melissa Nelson, Assistant Administrator
CHR: Karen Ingram, Director Human Resources
CNO: Carol Thetford, Chief Nursing Officer
Web address: www.baptistonline.org/womens/
Control: Other not–for–profit (including NFP Corporation) **Service**: Obstetrics and gynecology

> **Staffed Beds**: 140 **Admissions**: 7167 **Census**: 80 **Outpatient Visits**: 59358 **Births**: 5051 **Total Expense ($000)**: 94807 **Payroll Expense ($000)**: 36283 **Personnel**: 596

BAPTIST MEMORIAL RESTORATIVE CARE HOSPITAL (442010), 6019 Walnut Grove Road, Zip 38120–2113; tel. 901/226–4200 **A**1 10 **F**1 3 29 68 75 77 130 148 **S** Baptist Memorial Health Care Corporation, Memphis, TN
Primary Contact: Janice Hill, R.N., Administrator
Web address: www.baptistonline.org/restorative–care/
Control: Other not–for–profit (including NFP Corporation) **Service**: Acute long–term care hospital

> **Staffed Beds**: 30 **Admissions**: 214 **Census**: 19 **Outpatient Visits**: 0 **Births**: 0 **Total Expense ($000)**: 15064 **Payroll Expense ($000)**: 4886 **Personnel**: 82

CRESTWYN BEHAVIORAL HEALTH, 9485 Crestwyn Hills Cove, Zip 38125–8515; tel. 901/248–1500 (Nonreporting) **S** Acadia Healthcare Company, Inc., Franklin, TN
Primary Contact: Jeb Stokes, Chief Executive Officer
Web address: www.crestwynbh.com
Control: Corporation, Investor–owned (for–profit) **Service**: Psychiatric

> **Staffed Beds**: 60

DELTA MEDICAL CENTER (440159), 3000 Getwell Road, Zip 38118–2299; tel. 901/369–8100 **A**1 10 **F**5 8 15 18 29 30 38 40 45 56 57 60 81 82 103 104 105 107 111 114 119 129 130 143 147 148 **S** Acadia Healthcare Company, Inc., Franklin, TN
Primary Contact: Phil Willcoxon, Chief Executive Officer
CFO: Mike Reynolds, Chief Financial Officer
CMO: David Richardson M.D., Chief of Staff
CIO: Patrick Duffee, Director Medical Information Systems
CHR: Karyn Erickson, Director Human Resources
CNO: Donna Lanier R.N., Chief Nursing Officer
Web address: www.deltamedcenter.com
Control: Corporation, Investor–owned (for–profit) **Service**: Psychiatric

> **Staffed Beds**: 167 **Admissions**: 3291 **Census**: 103 **Outpatient Visits**: 30706 **Births**: 1 **Total Expense ($000)**: 43315 **Payroll Expense ($000)**: 18915

HEALTHSOUTH REHABILITATION HOSPITAL MEMPHIS–NORTH (443031), 4100 Austin Peay Highway, Zip 38128–2502; tel. 901/213–5400 **A**1 10 **F**3 28 29 34 35 57 59 75 77 82 87 90 91 95 96 130 132 135 148 **S** HEALTHSOUTH Corporation, Birmingham, AL
Primary Contact: Adam Yoe, Chief Executive Officer
CFO: Thaddeus Williams, Controller
CMO: Donald Sullivan M.D., Medical Director
CHR: Adrienne Huntley, Director Human Resources
CNO: Charlotte Boyce, Chief Nursing Officer
Web address: www.healthsouthnorthmemphis.com
Control: Corporation, Investor–owned (for–profit) **Service**: Rehabilitation

> **Staffed Beds**: 50 **Admissions**: 1092 **Census**: 36 **Outpatient Visits**: 0 **Births**: 0 **Total Expense ($000)**: 12946 **Payroll Expense ($000)**: 6340 **Personnel**: 99

HEALTHSOUTH REHABILITATION HOSPITAL OF MEMPHIS (443029), 1282 Union Avenue, Zip 38104–3414; tel. 901/722–2000 **A**1 3 5 10 **F**3 28 29 30 34 60 68 75 90 91 93 96 130 148 149 **S** HEALTHSOUTH Corporation, Birmingham, AL
Primary Contact: Stephanie Bridges, Chief Executive Officer
CFO: Eric Gray, Chief Financial Officer
CMO: Jonathan D Ellen M.D., Medical Director
CHR: Sandra Milburn, Director Human Resources
CNO: Jennifer Ferrell, Chief Nursing Officer
Web address: www.healthsouthmemphis.com
Control: Partnership, Investor–owned (for–profit) **Service**: Rehabilitation

> **Staffed Beds**: 72 **Admissions**: 1373 **Census**: 48 **Outpatient Visits**: 4887 **Births**: 0 **Total Expense ($000)**: 17537 **Payroll Expense ($000)**: 8739 **Personnel**: 177

LAKESIDE BEHAVIORAL HEALTH SYSTEM (444004), 2911 Brunswick Road, Zip 38133–4199; tel. 901/377–4700 **A**1 3 5 10 **F**4 5 34 38 54 56 98 99 100 101 103 104 105 106 130 132 149 **S** Universal Health Services, Inc., King of Prussia, PA
Primary Contact: Joy Golden, Chief Executive Officer
CFO: Thomas Joyner, Chief Financial Officer
CMO: C Hal Brunt M.D., Medical Director
CIO: Jacob Arnett, Chief Information Technology Officer
CHR: Lori Deason, Director
CNO: Scott Thomason, Chief Nursing Officer
Web address: www.lakesidebhs.com
Control: Corporation, Investor–owned (for–profit) **Service**: Psychiatric

> **Staffed Beds**: 345 **Admissions**: 8719 **Census**: 236 **Outpatient Visits**: 21135 **Births**: 0 **Total Expense ($000)**: 41433 **Payroll Expense ($000)**: 21506 **Personnel**: 435

LE BONHEUR CHILDREN'S HOSPITAL See Methodist Healthcare Memphis Hospitals

MEMPHIS MENTAL HEALTH INSTITUTE (444001), 951 Court Ave, Zip 38103–2813, Mailing Address: P.O.Box 63656, 38163–3656; tel. 901/577–1800, (Nonreporting) **A**1 3 5 10
Primary Contact: Josh Carter, Chief Executive Officer
CFO: Donny Hornsby, Director Fiscal Services
CHR: Claudette Seymour, Director Personnel
Web address: www.tn.gov/mental/mhs/mhs2.html
Control: State, Government, Nonfederal **Service**: Psychiatric

> **Staffed Beds**: 55

Many Facility Codes have changed. Please refer to the AHA Guide Code Chart.   © 2017 AHA Guide

TN

⊞ △ **MEMPHIS VETERANS AFFAIRS MEDICAL CENTER**, 1030 Jefferson Avenue, Zip 38104–2193; tel. 901/523–8990, (Nonreporting) **A**1 3 5 7 **S** Department of Veterans Affairs, Washington, DC
Primary Contact: David P. Wood, FACHE, Interim Director
CFO: Kristi Depperman, Chief Financial Officer
CMO: Christopher Marino M.D., Chief of Staff
CIO: Robert Page III, Chief Information and Technology Officer
CHR: Natalie Brown, Chief Human Resources Management Services
CNO: Karen Gillette, Associate Director Patient Care Services
Web address: www.memphis.va.gov/
Control: Veterans Affairs, Government, federal **Service**: General medical and surgical

Staffed Beds: 251

☐ **METHODIST HEALTHCARE MEMPHIS HOSPITALS (440049)**, 1265 Union Avenue, Zip 38104–3415; tel. 901/516–7000, (Includes LE BONHEUR CHILDREN'S HOSPITAL, 848 Adams Avenue, Memphis, Tennessee, Zip 38103, tel. 901/287–5437; Meri Armour, President; METHODIST HEALTHCARE–NORTH HOSPITAL, 3960 New Covington Pike, Memphis, Tennessee, Zip 38128, tel. 901/516–5200; Florence Jones, President; METHODIST HEALTHCARE–SOUTH HOSPITAL, 1300 Wesley Drive, Memphis, Tennessee, Zip 38116, tel. 901/516–3700; David G Baytos, Interim President; METHODIST LE BONHEUR GERMANTOWN HOSPITAL, 7691 Poplar Avenue, Germantown, Tennessee, Zip 38138, tel. 901/516–6000; Diane Ridgway, President) **A**1 2 3 5 8 10 **F**3 7 8 9 11 12 13 15 17 18 19 20 21 22 23 24 25 26 27 28 29 30 31 32 34 35 37 38 39 40 41 43 44 45 46 47 48 49 50 54 55 56 57 58 59 60 61 64 65 68 70 71 72 73 74 75 76 78 79 80 81 82 84 85 86 87 88 89 91 92 93 94 96 97 98 99 100 101 102 103 104 105 107 108 110 111 112 113 114 115 117 118 119 120 121 123 126 129 130 131 132 134 135 136 137 138 139 141 142 143 144 146 147 148 149 150 **P**5 6 8 **S** Methodist Le Bonheur Healthcare, Memphis, TN
Primary Contact: Michael Ugwueke, President and Chief Executive Officer
CFO: Chris McLean, Chief Administrative Officer
CIO: Mark W McMath, Chief Information Officer
CHR: Carol Ross–Spang, Chief Human Resources Officer
CNO: Nikki S Polis Ph.D., Chief Nurse Executive
Web address: www.methodisthealth.org
Control: Other not–for–profit (including NFP Corporation) **Service**: General medical and surgical

Staffed Beds: 1374 Admissions: 61500 Census: 952 Outpatient Visits: 849630 Births: 5387 Total Expense ($000): 1580501 Payroll Expense ($000): 511812 Personnel: 8587

⊞ **REGIONAL ONE HEALTH (440152)**, 877 Jefferson Avenue, Zip 38103–2897; tel. 901/545–7100, (Nonreporting) **A**1 3 5 10
Primary Contact: Reginald W. Coopwood, M.D., President and Chief Executive Officer
COO: Rob Sumter, Executive Vice President and Chief Operating Officer
CFO: Rick Wagers, Senior Executive Vice President and Chief Financial Officer
CIO: Rob Sumter, Executive Vice President and Chief Operation Officer
CHR: Sarah Colley, Senior Vice President Human Resources
CNO: Pam Castleman MSN, Chief Nursing Officer
Web address: www.regionalonehealth.org
Control: Other not–for–profit (including NFP Corporation) **Service**: General medical and surgical

Staffed Beds: 353

REGIONAL ONE HEALTH EXTENDED CARE HOSPITAL (442017), 890 Madison Avenue, Turner Tower, Zip 38103–3409; tel. 901/515–3000 (Nonreporting)
Primary Contact: Mark Kelly, Administrator
CNO: Paula Harrell, Chief Nursing Officer
Web address: www.regionalonehealth.org/extended–care–hospital/
Control: Other not–for–profit (including NFP Corporation) **Service**: Acute long–term care hospital

Staffed Beds: 25

⊞ **SAINT FRANCIS HOSPITAL (440183)**, 5959 Park Avenue, Zip 38119–5198; tel. 901/765–1000 **A**1 3 5 10 **F**3 8 11 12 13 15 17 18 20 22 24 26 28 29 30 31 34 35 38 39 40 44 45 46 47 48 49 50 51 54 56 57 58 59 64 68 70 72 74 75 76 77 78 79 81 82 84 85 86 87 90 93 96 97 98 99 100 101 102 103 104 107 108 110 111 114 115 118 119 121 123 124 126 129 130 131 132 143 146 147 148 **S** TENET Healthcare Corporation, Dallas, TX
Primary Contact: Audrey Gregory, R.N., MSN, Chief Executive Officer
COO: Samuel Pieh, Chief Operating Officer
CFO: Steven Frantz, Chief Financial Officer
CMO: David Schwartz M.D., Chief Medical Officer
CIO: Keith Scarbrough, Director, Information Systems
CHR: Keith Stanhill, Chief Human Resources Officer
CNO: Wanda Jeanne Rook–Peperone, Interim Chief Nursing Officer
Web address: www.saintfrancishosp.com
Control: Corporation, Investor–owned (for–profit) **Service**: General medical and surgical

Staffed Beds: 415 Admissions: 15460 Census: 217 Outpatient Visits: 119786 Births: 1247 Total Expense ($000): 235912 Payroll Expense ($000): 70824 Personnel: 1197

⊞ **SELECT SPECIALTY HOSPITAL–MEMPHIS (442014)**, 5959 Park Avenue, 12th Floor, Zip 38119–5200; tel. 901/765–1245, (Nonreporting) **A**1 10 **S** Select Medical Corporation, Mechanicsburg, PA
Primary Contact: Marcia Taylor, Chief Executive Officer
Web address: www.selectspecialtyhospitals.com/company/locations/memphis.aspx
Control: Corporation, Investor–owned (for–profit) **Service**: Acute long–term care hospital

Staffed Beds: 39

⊞ **ST. JUDE CHILDREN'S RESEARCH HOSPITAL (443302)**, 262 Danny Thomas Place, Zip 38105–3678; tel. 901/595–3300, (Nonreporting) **A**1 3 5 10
Primary Contact: James R. Downing, M.D., Chief Executive Officer
COO: Mary Anna Quinn, Executive Vice President, Chief Administrative Officer
CFO: Patricia Keel, Senior Vice President and Chief Financial Officer
CMO: Ellis Neufeld M.D., Chief Medical Officer
CIO: Darrin Keith Perry, Chief Information Officer and Senior Vice President
CHR: Dana Bottenfield, Vice President Human Resources
CNO: Tiffany Rooks, Interim Chief Nursing Officer
Web address: www.stjude.org
Control: Other not–for–profit (including NFP Corporation) **Service**: Children's other specialty

Staffed Beds: 56

VETERANS AFFAIRS MEDICAL CENTER See Memphis Veterans Affairs Medical Center

MILAN—Gibson County

⊞ **MILAN GENERAL HOSPITAL (440060)**, 4039 Highland Street, Zip 38358–3483; tel. 731/686–1591 **A**1 10 **F**3 15 29 30 35 40 44 45 57 59 64 68 70 81 87 107 110 114 119 130 132 133 146 149 **S** West Tennessee Healthcare, Jackson, TN
Primary Contact: Sherry Scruggs, Administrator
CMO: Joe Appleton M.D., Chief of Surgery
CNO: Carolyn Drake, Director of Nursing
Web address: www.wth.org
Control: Hospital district or authority, Government, Nonfederal **Service**: General medical and surgical

Staffed Beds: 28 Admissions: 568 Census: 6 Outpatient Visits: 14015 Births: 0 Total Expense ($000): 9392 Payroll Expense ($000): 3627 Personnel: 80

MORRISTOWN—Hamblen County

⊞ **LAKEWAY REGIONAL HOSPITAL (440067)**, 726 McFarland Street, Zip 37814–3990; tel. 423/586–2302, (Nonreporting) **A**1 10 19 **S** Community Health Systems, Inc., Franklin, TN
Primary Contact: Steve Simpson, Chief Executive Officer
CMO: Paul Cardali M.D., Chief of Staff
CHR: Deirdre Helton, Director Human Resources
Web address: www.tennova.com
Control: Corporation, Investor–owned (for–profit) **Service**: General medical and surgical

Staffed Beds: 135

TN

Hospital, Medicare Provider Number, Address, Telephone, Approval, Facility, and Physician Codes, Health Care System

★ American Hospital Association (AHA) membership ○ Healthcare Facilities Accreditation Program ⇑ Center for Improvement in Healthcare Quality Accreditation
☐ The Joint Commission accreditation ◇ DNV Healthcare Inc. accreditation △ Commission on Accreditation of Rehabilitation Facilities (CARF) accreditation

© 2017 AHA Guide   *Many Facility Codes have changed. Please refer to the AHA Guide Code Chart.*   Hospitals **A585**

✠ **MORRISTOWN–HAMBLEN HEALTHCARE SYSTEM (440030)**, 908 West Fourth North Street, Zip 37814–3894, Mailing Address: P.O.Box 1178, 37816–1178; tel. 423/492–9000 **A**1 2 5 10 **F**3 11 13 15 18 20 22 26 28 29 30 31 34 35 40 45 46 47 49 50 51 56 57 59 60 64 68 74 76 78 79 80 81 85 93 98 102 103 107 108 110 111 114 115 117 118 119 121 123 129 141 142 146 147 148 **S** Covenant Health, Knoxville, TN
Primary Contact: Gordon Lintz, Chief Administrative Officer
CFO: Amy Herndon, Chief Finance Officer
CIO: Mike Ward, Chief Information Officer
CNO: Wilma Hart–Flynn MSN, Ph.D., R.N., Chief Nursing Officer
Web address: www.morristownhamblen.com
Control: Other not–for–profit (including NFP Corporation) **Service:** General medical and surgical

Staffed Beds: 131 Admissions: 5814 Census: 65 Outpatient Visits: 104608 Births: 900 Total Expense ($000): 76610 Payroll Expense ($000): 28633 Personnel: 533

MOUNTAIN CITY—Johnson County

JOHNSON COUNTY COMMUNITY HOSPITAL (441304), 1901 South Shady Street, Zip 37683–2271; tel. 423/727–1100 **A**5 10 18 **F**3 15 18 28 30 34 35 40 44 50 57 62 64 68 87 93 97 104 107 108 110 111 114 119 127 **S** Mountain States Health Alliance, Johnson City, TN
Primary Contact: Chastity Trivette, Chief Executive Officer
CNO: Helen Pardue, Interim Chief Nursing Officer
Web address: www.msha.com
Control: Other not–for–profit (including NFP Corporation) **Service:** General medical and surgical

Staffed Beds: 2 Admissions: 39 Census: 1 Outpatient Visits: 44083 Births: 0 Total Expense ($000): 8841 Payroll Expense ($000): 4316 Personnel: 53

MOUNTAIN HOME—Johnson County

✠ **JAMES H. QUILLEN VETERANS AFFAIRS MEDICAL CENTER**, Corner of Lamont & Veterans Way, Zip 37684, Mailing Address: P.O.Box 4000, 37684–4000; tel. 423/926–1171, (Nonreporting) **A**1 3 5 **S** Department of Veterans Affairs, Washington, DC
Primary Contact: Dean B. Boros, Medical Center Director
CFO: Sandra Nash, Chief Fiscal Service
CMO: David Hecht M.D., Chief of Staff
CIO: Karen Perry, Chief Information Resource Management Services
CHR: John Henderson, Chief Human Resources Management
CNO: Linda M McConnell R.N., MSN, FACHE, Associate Medical Center Director Patient Care Services
Web address: www.mountainhome.va.gov/
Control: Veterans Affairs, Government, federal **Service:** General medical and surgical

Staffed Beds: 98

MURFREESBORO—Rutherford County

ALVIN C. YORK CAMPUS See Tennessee Valley Healthcare System, Nashville

✠ **SAINT THOMAS RUTHERFORD HOSPITAL (440053)**, 1700 Medical Center Parkway, Zip 37129–2245; tel. 615/396–4100, (Nonreporting) **A**1 2 3 5 10 **S** Ascension Healthcare, Saint Louis, MO
Primary Contact: Gordon B. Ferguson, President and Chief Executive Officer
COO: Elizabeth Lemons, Chief Operating Officer
CFO: Bailey Pratt, Chief Financial Officer
CMO: Scott Corlew M.D., Chief Medical Officer
CHR: Carol Bragdon, Director Human Resources
CNO: Stacey Beaven R.N., Chief Nursing Officer
Web address: www.mtmc.org
Control: Church operated, Nongovernment, not–for–profit **Service:** General medical and surgical

Staffed Beds: 286

□ **TRUSTPOINT HOSPITAL (440231)**, 1009 North Thompson Lane, Zip 37129–4351; tel. 615/867–1111 **A**1 10 **F**29 34 38 56 57 64 77 90 91 93 98 100 101 102 103 104 105 130 132 149 150 **P**6 **S** Acadia Healthcare Company, Inc., Franklin, TN
Primary Contact: Jeffrey Woods, Chief Executive Officer
Web address: www.trustpointhospital.com
Control: Corporation, Investor–owned (for–profit) **Service:** General medical and surgical

Staffed Beds: 101 Admissions: 3319 Census: 85 Outpatient Visits: 3647 Births: 0 Total Expense ($000): 25662 Payroll Expense ($000): 13998 Personnel: 230

NASHVILLE—Davidson County

CENTENNIAL MEDICAL CENTER See Tristar Centennial Medical Center

✠ **CURAHEALTH NASHVILLE (442006)**, 1412 County Hospital Road, Zip 37218–3007; tel. 615/687–2600, (Nonreporting) **A**1 10 **S** Curahealth Hospitals, Garland, TX
Primary Contact: Tom Rone, Chief Executive Officer
CFO: Philip L Jones, Chief Financial Officer
CMO: Clyde Heflin M.D., Chief Medical Officer
Web address: www.curahealth.com
Control: Corporation, Investor–owned (for–profit) **Service:** Acute long–term care hospital

Staffed Beds: 58

□ **MIDDLE TENNESSEE MENTAL HEALTH INSTITUTE (444014)**, 221 Stewarts Ferry Pike, Zip 37214–3325; tel. 615/902–7535 **A**1 3 5 10 **F**3 29 30 75 98 101 102 103 106 130
Primary Contact: Rob Cotterman, Chief Executive Officer
CFO: Mark Stanley, Director Fiscal Services
CMO: Mohammad S Jahan M.D., Clinical Director
CHR: Margie Dunn, Director Human Resources
Web address: www.tn.gov/mental/mhs/mhs2.html
Control: State, Government, Nonfederal **Service:** Psychiatric

Staffed Beds: 207 Admissions: 3818 Census: 174 Outpatient Visits: 0 Births: 0 Total Expense ($000): 48115 Payroll Expense ($000): 25647

MONROE CARELL JR. CHILDREN'S HOSPITAL AT VANDERBILT See Vanderbilt University Medical Center

□ **NASHVILLE GENERAL HOSPITAL (440111)**, 1818 Albion Street, Zip 37208–2918; tel. 615/341–4000, (Nonreporting) **A**1 2 3 5 10
Primary Contact: Joseph Webb, Chief Executive Officer
CFO: Robert Lonis, Interim Chief Financial Officer
CMO: Chike Nzerue M.D., Chief Medical Officer
CIO: Chris Whorley, Chief Information Officer
CHR: Diana Wohlfardt, Director Human Resources
CNO: Leonora Collins, Chief Nursing Officer
Web address: www.nashvillegeneral.org/
Control: City–county, Government, Nonfederal **Service:** General medical and surgical

Staffed Beds: 116

✠ **SAINT THOMAS HOSPITAL FOR SPINAL SURGERY (440218)**, 2011 Murphy Avenue, Suite 400, Zip 37203–2065; tel. 615/341–7500, (Nonreporting) **A**1 10 **S** Ascension Healthcare, Saint Louis, MO
Primary Contact: Kathy Watson, R.N., Administrator and Chief Nursing Officer
CFO: Angie Crow, Director Finance
CMO: Carl Hampf M.D., Chief Medical Officer
COO: Joseph R. Pino, Chief Operating Officer
Web address: www.hospitalforspinalsurgery.com
Control: Partnership, Investor–owned (for–profit) **Service:** General medical and surgical

Staffed Beds: 23

✠ **SAINT THOMAS MIDTOWN HOSPITAL (440133)**, 2000 Church Street, Zip 37236–0002; tel. 615/284–5555, (Nonreporting) **A**1 2 3 5 10 **S** Ascension Healthcare, Saint Louis, MO
Primary Contact: Don King, Chief Executive Officer
COO: Joseph R. Pino, Chief Operating Officer
CFO: Carrie Teaford, Vice President Finance
CMO: William Thompson M.D., Chief Medical Officer
CIO: Jim Drew, Chief Information Officer
CHR: Martha Underwood, Chief Human Resources Officer
Web address: www.sths.com
Control: Other not–for–profit (including NFP Corporation) **Service:** General medical and surgical

Staffed Beds: 425

✠ **SAINT THOMAS WEST HOSPITAL (440082)**, 4220 Harding Road, Zip 37205–2095, Mailing Address: P.O.Box 380, 37202–0380; tel. 615/222–2111, (Nonreporting) **A**1 2 3 5 10 **S** Ascension Healthcare, Saint Louis, MO
Primary Contact: Don King, Chief Executive Officer
COO: Joseph R. Pino, Chief Operating Officer
CFO: Lisa Davis, Vice President Finance
CMO: Dale Batchelor M.D., Chief Medical Officer
CHR: Bud Wood, Chief Human Resources Officer
CNO: Jennifer Elliott, Chief Nursing Officer
Web address: www.stthomas.org
Control: Church operated, Nongovernment, not–for–profit **Service:** General medical and surgical

Staffed Beds: 395

Many Facility Codes have changed. Please refer to the AHA Guide Code Chart.

✠ **SELECT SPECIALTY HOSPITAL–NASHVILLE (442011)**, 2000 Hayes Street, Zip 37203–2318; tel. 615/284–4599, (Nonreporting) **A**1 10 **S** Select Medical Corporation, Mechanicsburg, PA
Primary Contact: Jennifer Causey, Chief Executive Officer
CNO: Karen Cagle, Chief Nursing Officer
Web address: www.selectspecialtyhospitals.com/company/locations/nashville.aspx
Control: Corporation, Investor–owned (for–profit) **Service:** Acute long–term care hospital

Staffed Beds: 70

✠ **TENNESSEE VALLEY HEALTHCARE SYSTEM**, 1310 24th Avenue South, Zip 37212–2637; tel. 615/327–4751, (Nonreporting) (Includes ALVIN C. YORK CAMPUS, 3400 Lebanon Pike, Murfreesboro, Tennessee, Zip 37129–1236, tel. 615/867–6000; NASHVILLE CAMPUS, 1310 24th Avenue South, Nashville, Tennessee, Zip 37212–2637, tel. 615/327–4751) **A**1 3 5 **S** Department of Veterans Affairs, Washington, DC
Primary Contact: Captain Jennifer Vedral–Baron, Health System Director
COO: Suzanne L. Jene, Chief Operating Officer
CFO: Lynn Menthcoast, Chief Fiscal Service
CMO: Roger Jones M.D., Interim Chief of Staff
CIO: Paul Mardy, Chief Information Technology Officer
CHR: Shirley F Pettite, Chief Human Resources Officer
CNO: Janice M Cobb R.N., Chief Nursing Officer
Web address: www.tennesseevalley.va.gov
Control: Veterans Affairs, Government, federal **Service:** General medical and surgical

Staffed Beds: 546

✠ **TRISTAR CENTENNIAL MEDICAL CENTER (440161)**, 2300 Patterson Street, Zip 37203–1528; tel. 615/342–1000, (Nonreporting) (Includes TRISTAR CENTENNIAL WOMEN'S & CHILDREN'S, 2221 Murphy Avenue, Nashville, Tennessee, Zip 37203, tel. 615/342–1000) **A**1 2 3 5 10 **S** HCA Healthcare, Nashville, TN
Primary Contact: Scott A. Cihak, President and Chief Executive Officer
COO: Justin Coury, Chief Operating Officer
CFO: David A Summers, Chief Financial Officer
CHR: Jennifer Burden, Human Resources Director
Web address: www.tristarcentennial.com
Control: Corporation, Investor–owned (for–profit) **Service:** General medical and surgical

Staffed Beds: 650

✠ △ **TRISTAR SKYLINE MEDICAL CENTER (440006)**, 3441 Dickerson Pike, Zip 37207–2539; tel. 615/769–2000, (Nonreporting) (Includes TRISTAR SKYLINE MADISON CAMPUS, 500 Hospital Drive, Madison, Tennessee, Zip 37115–5032, tel. 615/769–5000; Steve Otto, Chief Executive Officer) **A**1 2 3 5 7 10 **S** HCA Healthcare, Nashville, TN
Primary Contact: Steve Otto, Chief Executive Officer
COO: Jason E Boyd, Chief Operating Officer
CFO: Michael Morrison, Chief Financial Officer
CMO: Christopher Conley M.D., President of the Medical Staff
CIO: Troy Sypien, Director Information Technology and Systems
CHR: Robert A Hooper, Director Human Resources
CNO: Laurie Turner, Chief Nursing Officer
Web address: www.tristarskyline.com
Control: Corporation, Investor–owned (for–profit) **Service:** General medical and surgical

Staffed Beds: 295

✠ **TRISTAR SOUTHERN HILLS MEDICAL CENTER (440197)**, 391 Wallace Road, Zip 37211–4859; tel. 615/781–4000, (Nonreporting) **A**1 2 10 **S** HCA Healthcare, Nashville, TN
Primary Contact: Joanna J. Conley, FACHE, Chief Executive Officer
COO: Richard Tumlin, Chief Operating Officer
CFO: John Porada, Chief Financial Officer
CIO: Ronnie Gannon, Director Information Services
CHR: Gary Briggs, Vice President Human Resources
CNO: Chris Staigl, Chief Nursing Officer
Web address: www.tristarsouthernhills.com
Control: Corporation, Investor–owned (for–profit) **Service:** General medical and surgical

Staffed Beds: 87

VANDERBILT PSYCHIATRIC HOSPITAL See Vanderbilt University Medical Center

✠ **VANDERBILT STALLWORTH REHABILITATION HOSPITAL (443028)**, 2201 Childrens Way, Zip 37212–3165; tel. 615/320–7600, (Nonreporting) **A**1 3 5 10 **S** HEALTHSOUTH Corporation, Birmingham, AL
Primary Contact: Jeffrey Palmucci, Chief Executive Officer
CFO: Christine Campbell, Controller
CMO: Jeffery Johns M.D., Medical Director
CHR: Ruth Beasley, Director Human Resources
CNO: Karen Lasher, Chief Nursing Officer
Web address: www.vanderbiltstallworthrehab.com
Control: Corporation, Investor–owned (for–profit) **Service:** Rehabilitation

Staffed Beds: 80

✠ **VANDERBILT UNIVERSITY MEDICAL CENTER (440039)**, 1211 Medical Center Drive, Zip 37232–2102; tel. 615/322–5000, (Includes MONROE CARELL JR. CHILDREN'S HOSPITAL AT VANDERBILT, 2200 Children's Way, Nashville, Tennessee, Zip 37232; tel. 615/936–1000; Luke Gregory, Chief Executive Officer; VANDERBILT PSYCHIATRIC HOSPITAL, 1601 23rd Avenue South, Nashville, Tennessee, Zip 37212–3198, tel. 615/320–7770) **A**1 2 3 5 8 10 **F**3 4 5 6 7 8 9 11 12 13 15 16 17 18 19 20 21 22 23 24 25 26 27 28 29 30 31 32 34 35 36 37 38 39 40 41 43 44 45 46 47 48 49 50 51 52 53 54 55 56 57 58 59 60 61 62 63 64 65 66 68 70 72 74 75 76 77 78 79 80 81 82 83 84 85 86 87 88 89 91 92 93 94 96 97 98 99 100 101 102 103 104 105 107 108 109 110 111 114 115 116 117 118 119 120 121 123 124 126 129 130 131 132 134 135 136 137 138 139 140 141 142 143 144 146 147 148 149 150 **P**2 6 **S** Vanderbilt Health, Nashville, TN
Primary Contact: Jeffrey R. Balsar, President and Chief Executive Officer Vanderbilt Medical Center and Dean, Vanderbilt University Scho
CFO: Cecelia B Moore CPA, Associate Vice Chancellor Finance
CMO: Paul Sternberg M.D., Professor and Chairman
CIO: William Stead, Associate Vice Chancellor Health Affairs, Director Informatics Center and Chief Strategy and Information Officer
CHR: Traci Nordberg, Chief Human Resources Officer
CNO: Pam Jones MSN, R.N., Associate Hospital Director and Chief Nursing Officer
Web address: www.mc.vanderbilt.edu
Control: Other not–for–profit (including NFP Corporation) **Service:** General medical and surgical

Staffed Beds: 1004 **Admissions:** 55778 **Census:** 845 **Outpatient Visits:** 2125663 **Births:** 4191 **Total Expense ($000):** 2200589 **Payroll Expense ($000):** 774922 **Personnel:** 12835

VETERANS AFFAIRS TENNESSEE VALLEY HEALTHCARE SYSTEM See Tennessee Valley Healthcare System

NEWPORT—Cocke County

BAPTIST HOSPITAL OF COCKE COUNTY See Tennova Newport Medical Center

✠ **TENNOVA NEWPORT MEDICAL CENTER (440153)**, 435 Second Street, Zip 37821–3799; tel. 423/625–2200, (Nonreporting) **A**1 10 **S** Community Health Systems, Inc., Franklin, TN
Primary Contact: Trevor Castaneda, Chief Executive Officer
CFO: Jon Richards, Chief Financial Officer
CMO: Larry Mathers M.D., Chief of Staff
CNO: Tonia Hale, Chief Nursing Officer
Web address: www.tennova.com
Control: Corporation, Investor–owned (for–profit) **Service:** General medical and surgical

Staffed Beds: 47

OAK RIDGE—Anderson County

✠ **METHODIST MEDICAL CENTER OF OAK RIDGE (440034)**, 990 Oak Ridge Turnpike, Zip 37830–6976, Mailing Address: P.O.Box 2529, 37831–2529; tel. 865/835–1000 **A**1 2 3 10 **F**3 11 13 15 17 18 20 22 24 26 28 29 30 31 34 35 37 40 45 46 47 48 49 50 51 54 57 58 59 60 64 68 70 74 75 76 77 78 79 80 81 84 85 86 87 92 102 107 108 110 111 114 115 118 119 120 121 123 124 126 129 130 132 135 141 142 146 148 **S** Covenant Health, Knoxville, TN
Primary Contact: Jeremy Biggs, Chief Executive Officer
COO: Connie Martin, Vice President and Chief Support Officer
CFO: Rick Carringer, Vice President and Chief Financial Officer
CMO: Mark Browne M.D., Covenant Health, Senior Vice President and Chief Medical Officer
CIO: Mike Ward, Covenant Health, Senior Vice President and Chief Information Officer
CHR: Rick Akens, Director Human Resources and Labor Relations
CNO: Sue Harris, Vice President and Chief Nursing Officer
Web address: www.mmcoakridge.com
Control: Other not–for–profit (including NFP Corporation) **Service:** General medical and surgical

Staffed Beds: 210 **Admissions:** 10438 **Census:** 127 **Outpatient Visits:** 171264 **Births:** 537 **Total Expense ($000):** 154490 **Payroll Expense ($000):** 55278 **Personnel:** 885

Hospital, Medicare Provider Number, Address, Telephone, Approval, Facility, and Physician Codes, Health Care System

★ American Hospital Association (AHA) membership
☐ The Joint Commission accreditation
○ Healthcare Facilities Accreditation Program
◇ DNV Healthcare Inc. accreditation
⇑ Center for Improvement in Healthcare Quality Accreditation
△ Commission on Accreditation of Rehabilitation Facilities (CARF) accreditation

RIDGEVIEW PSYCHIATRIC HOSPITAL AND CENTER (444003), 240 West Tyrone Road, Zip 37830–6571; tel. 865/482–1076, (Nonreporting) **A**10
Primary Contact: Brian Buuck, Chief Executive Officer
CFO: Mary Claire Duff CPA, Chief Financial Officer
CMO: Renu Bhateja M.D., President Medical Staff
CHR: Julie M Wright, Director Human Resources
Web address: www.ridgeviewresources.com
Control: Other not–for–profit (including NFP Corporation) **Service**: Psychiatric

Staffed Beds: 20

ONEIDA—Scott County

BIG SOUTH FORK MEDICAL CENTER, 18797 Alberta Street, Zip 37841–2127; tel. 423/286–5500 (Nonreporting)
Primary Contact: Tony Taylor, Chief Executive Officer
Control: Other not–for–profit (including NFP Corporation) **Service**: General medical and surgical

Staffed Beds: 25

PARIS—Henry County

✠ **HENRY COUNTY MEDICAL CENTER (440132)**, 301 Tyson Avenue, Zip 38242–4544, Mailing Address: P.O.Box 1030, 38242–1030; tel. 731/642–1220, (Total facility includes 150 beds in nursing home–type unit) **A**1 10 **F**3 7 8 11 13 15 18 20 28 29 30 31 32 34 35 37 40 44 50 51 53 54 57 59 62 63 64 65 67 68 70 71 76 77 78 79 81 82 85 86 87 89 93 98 102 103 107 108 110 111 114 118 119 121 126 128 129 130 131 132 133 135 146 148 **P**6
Primary Contact: Thomas H. Gee, Administrator
CFO: Lisa Casteel, Assistant Administrator and Chief Financial Officer
CIO: Pam Ridley, Director Information Systems
CHR: Edwin L Ledden, Assistant Administrator and Director Human Resources
CNO: Cynthia Whitaker, Chief Nursing Officer
Web address: www.hcmc–tn.org
Control: Hospital district or authority, Government, Nonfederal **Service**: General medical and surgical

Staffed Beds: 251 Admissions: 3828 Census: 120 Outpatient Visits: 133364 Births: 325 Total Expense ($000): 83453 Payroll Expense ($000): 36682 Personnel: 717

PARSONS—Decatur County

☐ **DECATUR COUNTY GENERAL HOSPITAL (440070)**, 969 Tennessee Avenue South, Zip 38363–3700, Mailing Address: P.O.Box 250, 38363–0250; tel. 731/847–3031, (Nonreporting) **A**1 10
Primary Contact: Scott Barber, Chief Executive Officer
CFO: Donna Hayes, Controller
CMO: Tom Hamilton M.D., Chief of Staff
CHR: Shelley Bartholomew, Director Human Resources
Web address: www.dcgh.org
Control: County, Government, Nonfederal **Service**: General medical and surgical

Staffed Beds: 40

PIKEVILLE—Bledsoe County

ERLANGER BLEDSOE HOSPITAL (441306), 71 Wheeler Avenue, Zip 37367, Mailing Address: P.O.Box 699, 37367–0699; tel. 423/447–2112 **A**10 18 **F**3 11 15 18 28 29 30 34 35 38 40 41 42 44 50 54 56 57 59 61 63 64 65 66 68 75 82 84 86 87 92 93 96 97 102 103 107 110 114 119 127 130 131 133 135 144 146 147 148 **P**6 **S** Erlanger Health System, Chattanooga, TN
Primary Contact: Stephanie Boynton, Administrator
CMO: Arturo L Quito M.D., Chief of Staff
CIO: Debbie Rains, Coordinator Health Information Management
CHR: Patsy Brown, Site Coordinator Human Resources
Web address: www.erlanger.org
Control: Hospital district or authority, Government, Nonfederal **Service**: General medical and surgical

Staffed Beds: 25 Admissions: 344 Census: 6 Outpatient Visits: 24751 Births: 3 Total Expense ($000): 13808 Payroll Expense ($000): 5832 Personnel: 102

POWELL—Knox County

MERCY MEDICAL CENTER NORTH See Tennova North Knoxville Medical Center

✠ **SELECT SPECIALTY HOSPITAL–NORTH KNOXVILLE (442015)**, 7557B Dannaher Drive, Suite 145, Zip 37849–3568; tel. 865/512–2450, (Nonreporting) **A**1 10 **S** Select Medical Corporation, Mechanicsburg, PA
Primary Contact: Steve Plumlee, Chief Executive Officer
CFO: David Elledge, Controller
CMO: Jeff Summers M.D., Medical Director
CIO: Steve Plumlee, Chief Executive Officer
CHR: Mallory Wilson, Administrative Assistant and Human Resources Coordinator
CNO: Nancy Johnson, Chief Nursing Officer
Web address: www.northknoxville.selectspecialtyhospitals.com/
Control: Corporation, Investor–owned (for–profit) **Service**: Acute long–term care hospital

Staffed Beds: 33

PULASKI—Giles County

✠ **SOUTHERN TENNESSEE REGIONAL HEALTH SYSTEM–PULASKI (440020)**, 1265 East College Street, Zip 38478–4541; tel. 931/363–7531 **A**1 10 **F**3 4 13 15 17 28 29 30 34 39 40 41 45 50 56 57 59 63 68 70 74 75 76 77 79 81 83 85 89 91 93 98 103 107 111 115 116 117 119 129 130 133 146 147 148 **S** LifePoint Health, Brentwood, TN
Primary Contact: James H. Edmondson, Chief Executive Officer
CFO: Donald Gavin, Chief Financial Officer
CMO: J Michael Windland M.D., Chief of Staff
CIO: Mitzi Foster, Director Information Services
CHR: Jane Petty, Director Human Resources
CNO: Sherry Sands R.N., Chief Nursing Officer
Web address: www.southerntnpulaski.com/
Control: Corporation, Investor–owned (for–profit) **Service**: General medical and surgical

Staffed Beds: 59 Admissions: 1605 Census: 20 Outpatient Visits: 17629 Births: 127 Total Expense ($000): 28306 Payroll Expense ($000): 10734 Personnel: 193

RIPLEY—Lauderdale County

⇑ **LAUDERDALE COMMUNITY HOSPITAL (441314)**, 326 Asbury Avenue, Zip 38063–5577; tel. 731/221–2200, (Nonreporting) **A**10 18 21 **S** Rural Community Hospitals of America, Kansas City, MO
Primary Contact: Michael G. Layfield, Interim Chief Executive Officer
CFO: T J Sheehan, Chief Financial Officer
CMO: Syed A. Zaidi M.D., Chief of Staff
CIO: Jim Vaden, Director Information Systems
CHR: Joan W. Simpson, Manager Human Resources
CNO: Michelle Simpson, Chief Nursing Officer and Quality Leader
Web address: www.lauderdalehospital.com/
Control: Corporation, Investor–owned (for–profit) **Service**: General medical and surgical

Staffed Beds: 25

ROGERSVILLE—Hawkins County

✠ **WELLMONT HAWKINS COUNTY MEMORIAL HOSPITAL (440032)**, 851 Locust Street, Zip 37857–2407, Mailing Address: P.O.Box 130, 37857–0130; tel. 423/921–7000 **A**1 5 10 **F**3 11 15 29 30 31 34 40 45 50 57 59 64 70 75 77 78 79 80 81 82 85 87 93 97 107 108 110 114 119 129 130 133 135 146 **S** Wellmont Health System, Kingsport, TN
Primary Contact: Rebecca Beck, President
CFO: Dale Poe, Vice President and Chief Financial Officer
CHR: Robin Poteete, Manager Human Resources
Web address: www.wellmont.org
Control: Other not–for–profit (including NFP Corporation) **Service**: General medical and surgical

Staffed Beds: 22 Admissions: 856 Census: 8 Outpatient Visits: 36699 Births: 0 Total Expense ($000): 56702 Payroll Expense ($000): 6779 Personnel: 142

SAVANNAH—Hardin County

★ ⇑ **HARDIN MEDICAL CENTER (440109)**, 935 Wayne Road, Zip 38372–1904; tel. 731/926–8000, (Nonreporting) **A**10 21
Primary Contact: Nicholas P. Lewis, Chief Executive Officer
CFO: Leigh Ann Hughes, Chief Financial Officer
CMO: Gilbert M. Thayer M.D., Chief Medical Staff
CIO: Jacob Bomar, Director Information Technology
CNO: Jesse Wint, Director of Nursing
Web address: www.hardinmedicalcenter.org
Control: County, Government, Nonfederal **Service**: General medical and surgical

Staffed Beds: 122

SEVIERVILLE—Sevier County

✠ **LECONTE MEDICAL CENTER (440081)**, 742 Middle Creek Road, Zip 37862–5019, Mailing Address: P.O.Box 8005, 37864–8005; tel. 865/446–7000, (Total facility includes 54 beds in nursing home–type unit) **A**1 5 10 **F**3 11 13 15 18 20 28 29 30 31 34 35 40 45 50 51 53 57 59 61 64 67 68 70 75 76 77 78 79 80 81 85 87 90 93 107 110 111 114 115 119 120 121 123 124 128 129 130 131 135 146 147 149 **S** Covenant Health, Knoxville, TN
Primary Contact: Gaye Jolly, FACHE, Acting President and Chief Administrative Officer
COO: Rick Carringer, Vice President Finance and Support Services
CFO: Rick Carringer, Vice President Finance and Support Services
CMO: Stephen Dill M.D., Chief of Staff
CIO: Amanda Paletz, Director Marketing and Public Relations
CHR: Derek Winkle, Director Human Resources
Web address: www.lecontemedicalcenter.com
Control: Other not–for–profit (including NFP Corporation) **Service**: General medical and surgical

Staffed Beds: 133 Admissions: 5388 Census: 88 Outpatient Visits: 140870 Births: 1067 Total Expense ($000): 95178 Payroll Expense ($000): 28825 Personnel: 482

Many Facility Codes have changed. Please refer to the AHA Guide Code Chart.

© 2017 AHA Guide

TN

SEWANEE—Franklin County

SOUTHERN TENNESSEE REGIONAL HEALTH SYSTEM–SEWANEE See Southern Tennessee Regional Health System–Winchester, Winchester

SHELBYVILLE—Bedford County

✠ **TENNOVA HEALTHCARE-SHELBYVILLE (440137)**, 2835 Highway 231 North, Zip 37160–7327; tel. 931/685–5433 **A**1 10 **F**3 12 13 15 18 29 34 40 45 47 57 59 60 64 70 76 79 81 85 87 89 93 96 102 107 108 110 111 115 119 124 130 131 132 145 146 148 149 **S** Community Health Systems, Inc., Franklin, TN
Primary Contact: Bill Rich, Chief Executive Officer
CFO: Mitchell Frank, Chief Financial Officer
CIO: Jonathon Willis, Director Information Services
CHR: Brian Woods, Director Human Resources
CNO: Vickie Vaughn, Chief Nursing Officer
Web address: www.heritagemedicalcenter.com
Control: Corporation, Investor–owned (for–profit) **Service:** General medical and surgical

> **Staffed Beds:** 49 **Admissions:** 1459 **Census:** 13 **Outpatient Visits:** 41794 **Births:** 1 **Total Expense ($000):** 35551 **Payroll Expense ($000):** 10017 **Personnel:** 236

SMITHVILLE—Dekalb County

✠ **SAINT THOMAS DEKALB HOSPITAL (440148)**, 520 West Main Street, Zip 37166–1138, Mailing Address: P.O.Box 640, 37166–0640; tel. 615/215–5000, (Nonreporting) **A**1 10 **S** Ascension Healthcare, Saint Louis, MO
Primary Contact: Robert Andrew. Wachtel, FACHE, Chief Executive Officer
CFO: Alan Sharp, Chief Financial Officer
CMO: Kimberly Collins M.D., Chief of Staff
CNO: Nancy A Trapp MSN, Director of Nursing
Web address: www.dekalbcommunityhospital.com
Control: Church operated, Nongovernment, not–for–profit **Service:** General medical and surgical

> **Staffed Beds:** 56

SMYRNA—Rutherford County

✠ **TRISTAR STONECREST MEDICAL CENTER (440227)**, 200 StoneCrest Boulevard, Zip 37167–6810; tel. 615/768–2000, (Nonreporting) **A**1 2 10 **S** HCA Healthcare, Nashville, TN
Primary Contact: Louis Caputo, Chief Executive Officer
COO: Andrew Tyrer, Chief Operating Officer
CFO: Joseph E Bowman, Chief Financial Officer
CMO: William Mayfield M.D., Chief of Staff
CHR: Cynthia Adams, Vice President Human Resources
CNO: Amy Cason MSN, Chief Nursing Officer
Web address: www.stonecrestmedical.com
Control: Corporation, Investor–owned (for–profit) **Service:** General medical and surgical

> **Staffed Beds:** 101

SNEEDVILLE—Hancock County

★ **WELLMONT HANCOCK COUNTY HOSPITAL (441313)**, 1519 Main Street, Zip 37869–3657; tel. 423/733–5000 **A**10 18 **F**3 29 30 34 40 50 57 59 85 87 107 108 118 119 133 135 **S** Wellmont Health System, Kingsport, TN
Primary Contact: Rebecca Beck, President
COO: Eric Deaton, Executive Vice President, Chief Operating Officer and Corporate Operating
CFO: Regina Day, Director of Finance
CIO: Martha O'Regan Chill, Interim Chief Information Officer
CHR: Denise Adams, Human Resources Generalist
CNO: Phyllis Dossett, Director of Clinical Services
Web address: www.wellmont.org/Hospitals/Hancock–County–Hospital.aspx
Control: Other not–for–profit (including NFP Corporation) **Service:** General medical and surgical

> **Staffed Beds:** 10 **Admissions:** 227 **Census:** 2 **Outpatient Visits:** 7842 **Births:** 0 **Total Expense ($000):** 5724 **Payroll Expense ($000):** 1725 **Personnel:** 31

SPARTA—White County

✠ **SAINT THOMAS HIGHLANDS HOSPITAL (440192)**, 401 Sewell Road, Zip 38583–1299; tel. 931/738–9211, (Nonreporting) **A**1 10 **S** Ascension Healthcare, Saint Louis, MO
Primary Contact: Robert Andrew. Wachtel, FACHE, Chief Executive Officer
CFO: Rodney VanDonkelaar, Chief Financial Officer
CMO: Robert Knowles M.D., Chief of Staff
CIO: Glenn Wade, Director Information Systems
CHR: Kent Frisbee, Director Human Resources
CNO: Gearline Copeland R.N., Chief Nursing Officer
Web address: www.whitecountyhospital.com
Control: Church operated, Nongovernment, not–for–profit **Service:** General medical and surgical

> **Staffed Beds:** 60

SPRINGFIELD—Robertson County

✠ **NORTHCREST MEDICAL CENTER (440065)**, 100 North Crest Drive, Zip 37172–3961; tel. 615/384–2411, (Nonreporting) **A**1 10
Primary Contact: Randy Davis, Chief Executive Officer
CFO: Kim Pridgen, Chief Financial Officer
CHR: Kimberly Walker, Director of Human Resources
CNO: Angie Beard R.N., Chief Nursing Officer
Web address: www.northcrest.com
Control: Other not–for–profit (including NFP Corporation) **Service:** General medical and surgical

> **Staffed Beds:** 80

SWEETWATER—Monroe County

✠ **SWEETWATER HOSPITAL (440084)**, 304 Wright Street, Zip 37874–2823; tel. 865/213–8200, (Nonreporting) **A**1 10
Primary Contact: Scott Bowman, Administrator
CFO: Debbie Thompson, Chief Financial Officer
CMO: David Norris, Chief Medical Staff
CIO: Tony Sharp, Supervisor Information System
CHR: Lucretia Allen, Director Human Resources
CNO: Andrea Henry, Director of Nursing
Web address: www.sweetwaterhospital.org
Control: Other not–for–profit (including NFP Corporation) **Service:** General medical and surgical

> **Staffed Beds:** 59

TAZEWELL—Claiborne County

✠ **CLAIBORNE MEDICAL CENTER (440057)**, 1850 Old Knoxville Road, Zip 37879–3625; tel. 423/626–4211, (Total facility includes 99 beds in nursing home–type unit) **A**1 10 **F**7 15 18 28 29 30 34 40 57 70 77 81 93 107 110 111 115 119 128 130 146 147 **S** Covenant Health, Knoxville, TN
Primary Contact: Patricia P. Ketterman, R.N., President and Chief Administrative Officer
CFO: Tracee McFarland, Chief Financial Officer
CHR: Susan Stone, Director Human Resources
Web address: www.claibornehospital.org
Control: Other not–for–profit (including NFP Corporation) **Service:** General medical and surgical

> **Staffed Beds:** 132 **Admissions:** 1352 **Census:** 89 **Outpatient Visits:** 39206 **Births:** 0 **Total Expense ($000):** 30841 **Payroll Expense ($000):** 13887 **Personnel:** 356

TULLAHOMA—Coffee County

✠ **TENNOVA HEALTHCARE-HARTON (440144)**, 1801 North Jackson Street, Zip 37388–8259; tel. 931/393–3000, (Nonreporting) **A**1 10 19 **S** Community Health Systems, Inc., Franklin, TN
Primary Contact: Richard Ellis, Chief Executive Officer
CFO: Shaun Adams, Chief Financial Officer
CMO: John D Crabtree M.D., Chief of Staff
CIO: Donald Cooper, Director Information Systems
CHR: Lenore Blackwell, Director Human Resources
Web address: www.hartonmedicalcenter.com
Control: Corporation, Investor–owned (for–profit) **Service:** General medical and surgical

> **Staffed Beds:** 104

TN

UNION CITY—Obion County

☒ **BAPTIST MEMORIAL HOSPITAL–UNION CITY (440130)**, 1201 Bishop Street, Zip 38261–5403, Mailing Address: P.O.Box 310, 38281–0310; tel. 731/885–2410 **A**1 10 **F**7 11 13 15 18 20 26 28 29 30 34 35 40 45 48 50 51 53 57 59 63 64 70 75 76 79 81 82 84 85 86 87 89 91 93 107 108 109 110 111 115 118 119 124 130 132 135 146 **P**3 **S** Baptist Memorial Health Care Corporation, Memphis, TN
Primary Contact: Barry Bondurant, Administrator and Chief Executive Officer
CFO: Mike Perryman, Chief Financial Officer
CMO: Kofi Nuako M.D., President Medical Staff
CIO: David Mercer, Coordinator Information Systems
CHR: Nicky Thomas, Director Human Resources
CNO: Lori Brown, Chief Nursing Officer
Web address: www.baptistonline.org/union-city/
Control: Other not–for–profit (including NFP Corporation) **Service**: General medical and surgical

Staffed Beds: 63 **Admissions:** 2532 **Census:** 22 **Outpatient Visits:** 49823 **Births:** 319 **Total Expense ($000):** 45491 **Payroll Expense ($000):** 15083 **Personnel:** 288

WAVERLY—Humphreys County

THREE RIVERS HOSPITAL (441303), 451 Highway 13 South, Zip 37185–2109, Mailing Address: P.O.Box 437, 37185–0437; tel. 931/296–4203 **A**10 18 **F**3 15 29 34 40 57 59 68 74 81 93 94 97 103 107 110 114 119 130 133 135
Primary Contact: Freda Russell, R.N., Chief Executive Officer and Chief Nursing Officer
CFO: Sandra Patrick, Chief Financial Officer
CMO: George Mathai M.D., Chief of Staff
CIO: Joe Hildreth, Director Information Technology
CHR: Linda Rawlings, Director Human Resources and Personnel
CNO: Freda Russell R.N., Chief Executive Officer and Chief Nursing Officer
Web address: www.threerivershospital.org
Control: Other not–for–profit (including NFP Corporation) **Service**: General medical and surgical

Staffed Beds: 25 **Admissions:** 381 **Census:** 7 **Outpatient Visits:** 23707 **Births:** 0 **Total Expense ($000):** 8036 **Payroll Expense ($000):** 3884 **Personnel:** 114

WAYNESBORO—Wayne County

☒ **WAYNE MEDICAL CENTER (440010)**, 103 J V Mangubat Drive, Zip 38485–2440, Mailing Address: P.O.Box 580, 38485–0580; tel. 931/722–5411, (Nonreporting) **A**1 10 20 **S** Maury Regional Health System, Columbia, TN
Primary Contact: Teresa Grimmett, Chief Executive Officer
CMO: Harish Veeramachaneni M.D., Chief of Staff
CHR: Jeff M Pierce, Manager Human Resources
Web address: www.mauryregional.com
Control: Other not–for–profit (including NFP Corporation) **Service**: General medical and surgical

Staffed Beds: 78

WINCHESTER—Franklin County

☒ **SOUTHERN TENNESSEE REGIONAL HEALTH SYSTEM–WINCHESTER (440058)**, 185 Hospital Road, Zip 37398–2404; tel. 931/967–8200, (Includes SOUTHERN TENNESSEE REGIONAL HEALTH SYSTEM–SEWANEE, 1260 University Avenue, Sewanee, Tennessee, Zip 37375–2303, tel. 931/598–5691; Rob Followell, Chief Executive Officer) (Total facility includes 46 beds in nursing home–type unit) **A**1 10 **F**17 70 76 90 98 128 **S** LifePoint Health, Brentwood, TN
Primary Contact: Rob Followell, Chief Executive Officer
CFO: Steve Moore, Chief Financial Officer
CIO: James Payne, Director Information Systems
CHR: Linda Tipps, Director Human Resources
Web address: www.southerntennessee.com
Control: Corporation, Investor–owned (for–profit) **Service**: General medical and surgical

Staffed Beds: 190 **Admissions:** 4175 **Census:** 64 **Births:** 511

WOODBURY—Cannon County

☒ **SAINT THOMAS STONES RIVER HOSPITAL (440200)**, 324 Doolittle Road, Zip 37190–1139; tel. 615/563–4001, (Nonreporting) **A**1 10 **S** Ascension Healthcare, Saint Louis, MO
Primary Contact: Robert Andrew. Wachtel, FACHE, Chief Executive Officer
CFO: Alan Sharp, Chief Financial Officer
CMO: James Spurlock D.O., Chief of Staff
CNO: Emily Elrod R.N., Director of Nursing
Web address: www.stonesriverhospital.com
Control: Church operated, Nongovernment, not–for–profit **Service**: General medical and surgical

Staffed Beds: 60

Many Facility Codes have changed. Please refer to the AHA Guide Code Chart. © 2017 AHA Guide

TEXAS

ABILENE—Taylor County

⊞ **ABILENE REGIONAL MEDICAL CENTER (450558)**, 6250 US Highway 83, Zip 79606–5299; tel. 325/428–1000, (Total facility includes 25 beds in nursing home–type unit) **A**1 10 **F**8 11 13 15 17 18 20 22 24 26 28 29 30 31 34 35 40 41 43 45 46 49 50 53 56 57 59 64 68 70 72 75 76 77 78 79 81 85 86 87 89 91 93 107 108 110 111 114 115 118 119 126 128 130 132 135 146 147 148 149 **P**3 **S** Community Health Systems, Inc., Franklin, TN
Primary Contact: Michael D. Murphy, FACHE, Chief Executive Officer
COO: Matthew van Leeuwe, Chief Operating Officer
CFO: Ron Bennett, Chief Financial Officer
CMO: Tim Bumann D.O., Chief of Staff
CIO: Dennis Newquist, Director Information Systems
CHR: John J Jeziorske, Director Human Resources
CNO: Jessica Kiehle R.N., Chief Nursing Officer
Web address: www.abileneregional.com
Control: Partnership, Investor–owned (for–profit) **Service**: General medical and surgical

Staffed Beds: 205 **Admissions:** 6012 **Census:** 72 **Outpatient Visits:** 85454 **Births:** 1491 **Total Expense ($000):** 101795 **Payroll Expense ($000):** 36427 **Personnel:** 639

★ **CONTINUECARE HOSPITAL AT HENDRICK MEDICAL CENTER (452029)**, 1900 Pine Street, Zip 79601–2432; tel. 325/670–6251 **A**10 **F**1 3 29 34 35 68 85 87 148 149 **S** Community Hospital Corporation, Plano, TX
Primary Contact: Billy Blasingame, Chief Executive Officer
CFO: Lisa Young CPA, Chief Financial Officer
CHR: Laurie Fields, Director Human Resources
CNO: Sherry Hendricksen R.N., MSN, Chief Nursing Officer
Web address: www.continuecare.org/hendrick/
Control: Other not–for–profit (including NFP Corporation) **Service**: Acute long–term care hospital

Staffed Beds: 23 **Admissions:** 189 **Census:** 15 **Outpatient Visits:** 0 **Births:** 0 **Total Expense ($000):** 7278 **Payroll Expense ($000):** 3626 **Personnel:** 34

⊞ **HEALTHSOUTH REHABILITATION HOSPITAL – ABILENE (673039)**, 6401 Directors Parkway, Zip 79606–5869; tel. 325/691–1600 **A**1 10 **F**3 29 57 59 74 75 77 90 96 130 143 148 **S** HEALTHSOUTH Corporation, Birmingham, AL
Primary Contact: Joe Roberson, Chief Executive Officer
Web address: www.reliantabilene.com
Control: Corporation, Investor–owned (for–profit) **Service**: Rehabilitation

Staffed Beds: 30 **Admissions:** 742 **Census:** 25 **Outpatient Visits:** 0 **Births:** 0 **Total Expense ($000):** 11675 **Payroll Expense ($000):** 5909 **Personnel:** 99

⊞ **HENDRICK HEALTH SYSTEM (450229)**, 1900 Pine Street, Zip 79601–2432; tel. 325/670–2000, (Total facility includes 20 beds in nursing home–type unit) **A**1 10 **F**3 11 12 13 14 15 17 18 20 22 24 26 28 29 30 31 32 34 35 36 39 40 43 44 45 48 49 50 51 53 56 57 59 60 61 62 64 68 70 73 74 75 76 77 78 79 80 81 84 85 86 87 88 89 90 92 93 96 97 102 107 108 110 111 114 115 118 119 121 123 128 129 130 131 132 135 143 146 147 148 149 **P**6 8
Primary Contact: Tim Lancaster, FACHE, President and Chief Executive Officer
CFO: Jeremy Tyler Walker, Vice President and Chief Financial Officer
CIO: Duane Donaway, Director Information Technology
CHR: Susan Wade, Vice President
CNO: Susie Cassle R.N., MSN, Vice President Nursing Services
Web address: www.ehendrick.org
Control: Church operated, Nongovernment, not–for–profit **Service**: General medical and surgical

Staffed Beds: 412 **Admissions:** 16063 **Census:** 239 **Outpatient Visits:** 284898 **Births:** 1230 **Total Expense ($000):** 345379 **Payroll Expense ($000):** 112643 **Personnel:** 2565

⊞ **OCEANS BEHAVIORAL HOSPITAL ABILENE (454122)**, 4225 Woods Place, Zip 79606–5869; tel. 325/691–0030 **A**1 10 **F**29 34 35 98 99 100 101 103 104 130 132 149 **P**6 **S** Oceans Healthcare, Lake Charles, LA
Primary Contact: Stacy Sanford, Chief Executive Officer
Web address: www.oceansabilene.com
Control: Corporation, Investor–owned (for–profit) **Service**: Psychiatric

Staffed Beds: 90 **Admissions:** 751 **Census:** 29 **Outpatient Visits:** 14909 **Births:** 0 **Total Expense ($000):** 6876 **Payroll Expense ($000):** 3499 **Personnel:** 195

ADDISON—Dallas County

⇑ **METHODIST HOSPITAL FOR SURGERY (670073)**, 17101 North Dallas Parkway, Zip 75001–7103; tel. 469/248–3900 **A**10 21 **F**3 29 30 35 40 64 68 70 75 81 85 93 107 111 119 129 146 148
Primary Contact: Daniel L. Gideon, FACHE, President
CFO: Kelly Hayes, Chief Financial Officer
CMO: Robert Fischer M.D., Medical Director
CHR: Erik Leopard, Manager Human Resource
CNO: Patti Griffith R.N., MS, Chief Nursing Officer
Web address: www.methodisthospitalforsurgery.com/
Control: Partnership, Investor–owned (for–profit) **Service**: Surgical

Staffed Beds: 32 **Admissions:** 2620 **Census:** 18 **Outpatient Visits:** 19791 **Births:** 0 **Total Expense ($000):** 126272 **Payroll Expense ($000):** 16806 **Personnel:** 200

ALICE—Jim Wells County

⊞ **CHRISTUS SPOHN HOSPITAL ALICE (450828)**, 2500 East Main Street, Zip 78332–4169; tel. 361/661–8000 **A**1 10 20 **F**3 11 13 15 18 20 22 28 29 30 35 39 40 43 45 46 50 57 59 64 68 70 75 76 77 78 79 81 85 86 87 89 91 93 97 98 102 103 107 108 111 115 119 127 130 146 147 148 **P**8 **S** CHRISTUS Health, Irving, TX
Primary Contact: David LeMonte, Interim President
CFO: Michael Guajardo, Director Finance
CMO: Jerry Liles D.O.,
CHR: Mindy Soliz, Director Human Resources
CNO: Margot Rios R.N., Chief Nursing Officer
Web address: www.christusspohn.org/locations_alice.htm
Control: Church operated, Nongovernment, not–for–profit **Service**: General medical and surgical

Staffed Beds: 73 **Admissions:** 3188 **Census:** 34 **Outpatient Visits:** 50342 **Births:** 398 **Total Expense ($000):** 44724 **Payroll Expense ($000):** 15964 **Personnel:** 226

ALLEN—Collin County

⊞ **POST ACUTE/WARM SPRINGS REHABILITATION HOSPITAL OF ALLEN (673025)**, 1001 Raintree Circle, Zip 75013–4912; tel. 972/908–2015 **A**1 10 **F**3 29 30 34 40 42 56 59 60 74 75 79 87 90 91 94 96 100 130 132 148 **S** Post Acute Medical, LLC, Enola, PA
Primary Contact: Bill Kaupas, Chief Executive Officer
Web address: www.warmsprings.org
Control: Partnership, Investor–owned (for–profit) **Service**: Rehabilitation

Staffed Beds: 39 **Admissions:** 831 **Census:** 26 **Outpatient Visits:** 0 **Births:** 0 **Total Expense ($000):** 13090 **Payroll Expense ($000):** 6467 **Personnel:** 136

⊞ **TEXAS HEALTH PRESBYTERIAN HOSPITAL ALLEN (450840)**, 1105 Central Expressway North, Suite 140, Zip 75013–6103; tel. 972/747–1000 **A**1 10 **F**3 5 13 15 18 20 22 28 29 30 34 35 38 40 43 45 47 49 51 55 57 59 64 65 70 73 74 75 76 78 79 81 89 91 93 98 102 104 105 107 110 111 114 115 118 119 126 130 132 135 146 147 148 **S** Texas Health Resources, Arlington, TX
Primary Contact: Jared Shelton, Chief Executive Officer
COO: Crispin P Hocate, Professional and Support Services Officer
CFO: Lisa Gildon, Group Financial Officer
CMO: Bob Schwab M.D., Chief Medical Officer
CHR: Sharon Chisholm, Entity Human Resource Officer
Web address: www.texashealth.org
Control: Other not–for–profit (including NFP Corporation) **Service**: General medical and surgical

Staffed Beds: 68 **Admissions:** 3541 **Census:** 30 **Outpatient Visits:** 41627 **Births:** 702 **Total Expense ($000):** 79274 **Payroll Expense ($000):** 29752 **Personnel:** 304

TX

Hospital, Medicare Provider Number, Address, Telephone, Approval, Facility, and Physician Codes, Health Care System

★ American Hospital Association (AHA) membership   ○ Healthcare Facilities Accreditation Program   ⇑ Center for Improvement in Healthcare Quality Accreditation
□ The Joint Commission accreditation   ◇ DNV Healthcare Inc. accreditation   △ Commission on Accreditation of Rehabilitation Facilities (CARF) accreditation

ALPINE—Brewster County

⊞ **BIG BEND REGIONAL MEDICAL CENTER (451378)**, 2600 Highway 118 North, Zip 79830–2002; tel. 432/837–3447 **A**1 3 10 18 **F**3 13 29 30 34 35 40 43 45 49 57 59 64 68 70 75 76 77 81 85 93 107 119 132 133 146 147 148 **P**6 **S** Quorum Health, Brentwood, TN
Primary Contact: Diane C. Moore, Chief Executive Officer and Chief Financial Officer
CFO: Diane C. Moore, Chief Executive Officer and Chief Financial Officer
CNO: Keith Ellison, Chief Nursing Officer
Web address: www.bigbendhealthcare.com
Control: Corporation, Investor–owned (for–profit) **Service:** General medical and surgical

Staffed Beds: 25 **Admissions:** 764 **Census:** 7 **Outpatient Visits:** 12683 **Births:** 192 **Total Expense ($000):** 22099 **Payroll Expense ($000):** 7997 **Personnel:** 120	

ALVIN—Brazoria County

ALVIN DIAGNOSTIC AND URGENT CARE CENTER See Clear Lake Regional Medical Center

AMARILLO—Potter County

⊞ **AMARILLO VETERANS AFFAIRS HEALTH CARE SYSTEM**, 6010 West Amarillo Boulevard, Zip 79106–1992; tel. 806/355–9703, (Nonreporting) **A**1 2 3 5 **S** Department of Veterans Affairs, Washington, DC
Primary Contact: Elizabeth Lowery, Interim Director
CIO: Modesto Baca, Chief Information Officer
CHR: Ken Creamer, Chief Human Resource
Web address: www.amarillo.va.gov/
Control: Veterans Affairs, Government, federal **Service:** General medical and surgical

Staffed Beds: 55	

★ ⇑ **BSA HOSPITAL, LLC (450231)**, 1600 Wallace Boulevard, Zip 79106–1799; tel. 806/212–2000 **A**2 3 5 10 21 **F**3 7 8 11 12 13 15 17 18 20 22 24 26 28 29 30 31 34 35 40 45 46 48 49 53 54 56 57 58 59 64 67 70 71 72 74 75 76 77 78 79 81 82 84 85 86 87 88 89 90 91 92 93 96 107 108 109 110 111 114 115 116 117 118 119 120 121 123 124 126 129 130 135 143 145 146 147 148 **S** Ardent Health Services, Nashville, TN
Primary Contact: Bob Williams, President and Chief Executive Officer
COO: Michael Cruz, Senior Vice President Operations
CFO: Lorenzo Olivarez, Senior Vice President and Chief Financial Officer
CMO: Mike Lamanteer M.D., Senior Vice President Medical Affairs
CIO: Lewis Brown, Director Information Technology
CHR: Cheryl L Jones, Vice President Human Resources and Organizational Development
CNO: Belinda D Gibson R.N., Senior Vice President Patient Services
Web address: www.bsahs.org
Control: Corporation, Investor–owned (for–profit) **Service:** General medical and surgical

Staffed Beds: 334 **Admissions:** 20860 **Census:** 247 **Outpatient Visits:** 172357 **Births:** 2114 **Total Expense ($000):** 325890 **Payroll Expense ($000):** 129945 **Personnel:** 1871	

KINDRED HOSPITAL–AMARILLO See Vibra Hospital Of Amarillo

KINDRED REHABILITATION HOSPITAL AMARILLO See Vibra Rehabilitation Hospital Of Amarillo

☐ **NORTHWEST TEXAS HEALTHCARE SYSTEM (450209)**, 1501 South Coulter Avenue, Zip 79106–1770, Mailing Address: P.O.Box 1110, 79105–1110; tel. 806/354–1000, (Includes NORTHWEST CHILDREN'S HOSPITAL, 1501 South Coulter Street, Amarillo, Texas, Zip 79106–1770, tel. 806/354–1000; NORTHWEST PAVILION, 7201 Evans, Amarillo, Texas, Zip 79106, P O Box 1110, 79105–1110, tel. 806/354–1000; NORTHWEST TEXAS SURGERY CENTER, 3501 South Soncy Road Suite 118, Amarillo, Texas, Zip 79119–6405, tel. 806/359–7999; Mark W Crawford, Chief Executive Officer) **A**1 2 3 5 10 **F**3 4 5 8 11 12 13 15 17 18 20 22 24 26 28 29 30 31 32 34 35 37 38 39 40 42 43 44 45 46 48 49 50 54 56 57 59 60 61 64 65 66 68 70 72 74 75 76 77 78 79 80 81 82 84 85 86 87 88 89 90 92 93 94 96 97 98 99 100 101 102 103 104 105 107 108 110 111 115 118 119 126 130 132 135 144 146 147 148 **S** Universal Health Services, Inc., King of Prussia, PA
Primary Contact: Mark W. Crawford, Chief Executive Officer
COO: John McDonald, Chief Operating Officer
CFO: Gene Winters, Chief Financial Officer
CMO: Brian Weis M.D., Chief Medical Officer
CIO: Bach Nguyen, Director Information Systems
CHR: Samuel Lynn, Director Human Resources
Web address: www.nwtexashealthcare.com
Control: Corporation, Investor–owned (for–profit) **Service:** General medical and surgical

Staffed Beds: 409 **Admissions:** 17546 **Census:** 232 **Outpatient Visits:** 214041 **Births:** 2312 **Total Expense ($000):** 286483 **Payroll Expense ($000):** 93186 **Personnel:** 1753	

★ **PHYSICIANS SURGICAL HOSPITAL – QUAIL CREEK (450875)**, 6819 Plum Creek, Zip 79124–1602; tel. 806/354–6100, (Includes PHYSICIANS SURGICAL HOSPITAL – PANHANDLE CAMPUS, 7100 West 9th Avenue, Amarillo, Texas, Zip 79106–1704, tel. 806/212–0247; Brad D. McCall, JD, Chief Executive Officer) **A**10 **F**3 29 30 40 44 68 75 79 81 82 85 130 135 **S** Ardent Health Services, Nashville, TN
Primary Contact: Brad D. McCall, JD, Chief Executive Officer
CFO: Austin Jones CPA, Chief Financial Officer
CMO: Robert Crabtree M.D., Chief of Staff and Medical Director
CNO: Debbie Inman, Chief Nursing Officer
Web address: www.physurg.com
Control: Partnership, Investor–owned (for–profit) **Service:** Surgical

Staffed Beds: 41 **Admissions:** 2158 **Census:** 12 **Outpatient Visits:** 13667 **Births:** 0 **Total Expense ($000):** 48766 **Payroll Expense ($000):** 12134 **Personnel:** 197	

☐ **PLUM CREEK SPECIALTY HOSPITAL (452066)**, 5601 Plum Creek Drive, Zip 79124–1801; tel. 806/351–1000, (Data for 254 days) **A**1 10 **F**1 3 29 40 60 75 85 148 **S** Concord Healthcare Group, Lakewood, NJ
Primary Contact: Bobby Snyder, Interim Chief Executive Officer
Web address: www.plumcreekspecialtyhosp.com/
Control: Corporation, Investor–owned (for–profit) **Service:** Acute long–term care hospital

Staffed Beds: 47 **Admissions:** 154 **Census:** 11 **Outpatient Visits:** 0 **Births:** 0 **Total Expense ($000):** 5968 **Payroll Expense ($000):** 1981 **Personnel:** 29	

SPECIALTY HOSPITAL AT PLUM CREEK See Plum Creek Specialty Hospital

⊞ **VIBRA HOSPITAL OF AMARILLO (452060)**, 7501 Wallace Boulevard, Zip 79124–2150; tel. 806/467–7000 **A**1 10 **F**1 3 29 45 46 50 56 59 60 61 70 74 75 77 79 82 84 85 86 87 91 96 107 114 130 148 **S** Vibra Healthcare, Mechanicsburg, PA
Primary Contact: Becky Burton, R.N., Chief Executive Officer and Market Chief Executive Officer
CFO: Carlene Wright, Chief Financial Officer
CMO: Pablo Rodrigues M.D., Medical Director
CNO: Melany McCarty R.N., Chief Clinical Officer
Web address: www.vhamarillo.com
Control: Corporation, Investor–owned (for–profit) **Service:** Acute long–term care hospital

Staffed Beds: 72 **Admissions:** 758 **Census:** 47 **Outpatient Visits:** 0 **Births:** 0 **Total Expense ($000):** 20223 **Payroll Expense ($000):** 9605 **Personnel:** 181	

⊞ △ **VIBRA REHABILITATION HOSPITAL OF AMARILLO (453096)**, 7200 West 9th Avenue, Zip 79106–1703; tel. 806/468–2900 **A**1 7 10 **F**3 28 29 56 75 77 82 87 90 91 96 107 130 143 148 **S** Vibra Healthcare, Mechanicsburg, PA
Primary Contact: Tammie Tabor, Chief Executive Officer
Web address: www.vrhamarillo.com
Control: Corporation, Investor–owned (for–profit) **Service:** Rehabilitation

Staffed Beds: 44 **Admissions:** 576 **Census:** 18 **Outpatient Visits:** 0 **Births:** 0 **Total Expense ($000):** 7434 **Payroll Expense ($000):** 4739 **Personnel:** 111	

ANAHUAC—Chambers County

★ **BAYSIDE COMMUNITY HOSPITAL (451320)**, 200 Hospital Drive, Zip 77514, Mailing Address: P.O.Box 398, 77514–0398; tel. 409/267–3143 **A**10 18 **F**3 8 11 29 34 35 40 43 45 50 53 54 56 57 59 64 81 86 89 93 107 111 114 119 128 130 133 **P**3
Primary Contact: Steven Gularte, Chief Executive Officer
CFO: Peggy Hamilton, Chief Financial Officer
CMO: Anthony Capili M.D., Chief of Staff
CNO: Christi Morris, Director of Nursing
Web address: www.chambershealth.org/html/bayside_hospital.html
Control: Hospital district or authority, Government, Nonfederal **Service:** General medical and surgical

Staffed Beds: 10 **Admissions:** 150 **Census:** 1 **Outpatient Visits:** 15328 **Births:** 0 **Total Expense ($000):** 18779 **Payroll Expense ($000):** 6209 **Personnel:** 105	

ANDREWS—Andrews County

★ ⇑ **PERMIAN REGIONAL MEDICAL CENTER (450144)**, Northeast By–Pass, Zip 79714, Mailing Address: P.O.Box 2108, 79714–2108; tel. 432/523–2200 **A**3 10 20 21 **F**3 11 13 15 29 34 35 36 38 40 43 44 50 53 56 57 59 62 63 64 65 68 70 73 75 76 77 81 82 84 85 86 87 89 93 97 107 108 110 111 115 119 127 129 130 131 132 133 135 145 146 148 **P**6
Primary Contact: Russell Tippin, Chief Executive Officer and Administrator
CFO: Sandra Cox, Controller
CIO: Dan Smart, Chief Information Management Officer
CHR: Pam McCormick, Director Human Resources
Web address: www.permianregional.com
Control: Hospital district or authority, Government, Nonfederal **Service:** General medical and surgical

Staffed Beds: 44 **Admissions:** 761 **Census:** 5 **Outpatient Visits:** 29016 **Births:** 310 **Total Expense ($000):** 46031 **Payroll Expense ($000):** 21334 **Personnel:** 248	

TX

Many Facility Codes have changed. Please refer to the AHA Guide Code Chart.
© 2017 AHA Guide

ANSON—Jones County

★ **ANSON GENERAL HOSPITAL (450078)**, 101 Avenue 'J', Zip 79501–2198;
tel. 325/823–3231 **A**10 **F**7 11 29 40 75 77 81 93 107 127 133 **P**8
Primary Contact: Terry Amstutz, Chief Executive Officer
CIO: Lynna B Cox, Director Health Information Services
Control: City, Government, Nonfederal **Service**: General medical and surgical

Staffed Beds: 23 Admissions: 320 Census: 5 Outpatient Visits: 7702
Births: 0 Total Expense ($000): 5368 Payroll Expense ($000): 2458
Personnel: 50

ARANSAS PASS—San Patricio County

CARE REGIONAL MEDICAL CENTER (450605), 1711 West Wheeler Avenue,
Zip 78336–4536; tel. 361/758–8585 **A**10 **F**3 4 11 15 18 29 30 34 35 40 44
45 50 56 57 59 64 65 68 70 75 77 78 81 85 86 87 90 93 97 98 101 102 103
107 108 114 119 130 132 133 146 148 149 **P**7
Primary Contact: Sunil Reddy, Chief Executive Officer
CMO: Salim Surani M.D., Chief of Staff
CIO: Greg Palmer, Administrator Information Technology Network
CHR: Kerry L Upton, Administrative Director Human Resources
CNO: Christal Burns R.N., Chief Nursing Officer
Web address: www.crmctx.com
Control: Corporation, Investor–owned (for–profit) **Service**: General medical and surgical

Staffed Beds: 35 Admissions: 798 Census: 11 Outpatient Visits: 24806
Births: 0 Total Expense ($000): 20562 Payroll Expense ($000): 7453
Personnel: 204

NORTH BAY HOSPITAL See Care Regional Medical Center, Atlantic City

ARLINGTON—Tarrant County

☐ **BAYLOR ORTHOPEDIC AND SPINE HOSPITAL AT ARLINGTON (670067)**,
707 Highlander Boulevard, Zip 76015–4319; tel. 817/583–7100 **A**1 10 **F**3 29 40
65 75 79 81 82 85 86 107 111 114
Primary Contact: Allan Beck, Chief Executive Officer
Web address: www.baylorarlington.com/
Control: Partnership, Investor–owned (for–profit) **Service**: General medical and surgical

Staffed Beds: 20 Admissions: 1571 Census: 9 Outpatient Visits: 11612
Births: 0 Total Expense ($000): 56010 Payroll Expense ($000): 10244
Personnel: 136

⊞ **HEALTHSOUTH REHABILITATION HOSPITAL OF ARLINGTON (453040)**, 3200
Matlock Road, Zip 76015–2911; tel. 817/468–4000 **A**1 10 **F**3 29 74 75 77 79
90 91 94 95 96 130 148 **S** HEALTHSOUTH Corporation, Birmingham, AL
Primary Contact: Sheril Appel, Chief Executive Officer
CFO: Kathy Dickerson, Chief Financial Officer
CMO: Todd Daniels M.D., Medical Director
CHR: Nancy Rosiles, Director Human Resources
CNO: David Jones, Chief Nursing Officer
Web address: www.healthsoutharlington.com
Control: Corporation, Investor–owned (for–profit) **Service**: Rehabilitation

Staffed Beds: 83 Admissions: 1701 Census: 57 Outpatient Visits: 0
Births: 0 Total Expense ($000): 25563 Payroll Expense ($000): 11600
Personnel: 221

⊞ **KINDRED HOSPITAL TARRANT COUNTY–ARLINGTON (452028)**, 1000 North
Cooper Street, Zip 76011–5540; tel. 817/548–3400 **A**1 10 **F**1 3 29 30 40 56
57 77 80 82 93 130 148 **S** Kindred Healthcare, Louisville, KY
Primary Contact: Christina Richard, Market Chief Executive Officer
CFO: Jennifer Penland, Controller
CMO: Bernard A McGowen M.D., Medical Director
Web address: www.kindredhospitalarl.com/
Control: Corporation, Investor–owned (for–profit) **Service**: Acute long–term care hospital

Staffed Beds: 55 Admissions: 460 Census: 35 Outpatient Visits: 3477
Births: 0 Total Expense ($000): 16828 Payroll Expense ($000): 8184
Personnel: 130

⊞ **MEDICAL CITY ARLINGTON (450675)**, 3301 Matlock Road, Zip 76015–2908;
tel. 817/465–3241 **A**1 2 3 10 **F**3 11 12 13 17 18 20 22 24 26 28 29 31 34 35
39 40 42 43 45 46 47 48 49 50 57 59 64 70 72 73 74 75 76 78 79 81 82 85
86 87 92 93 107 108 110 111 114 115 119 126 130 131 132 135 146 147
148 149 **S** HCA Healthcare, Nashville, TN
Primary Contact: Keith Zimmerman, Chief Executive Officer
COO: Ben Coogan, Chief Operating Officer
CFO: Jeff Ardemagni, Chief Financial Officer
CMO: Eric Benink M.D., Chief Medical Officer
CIO: Craig Santangelo, Director Information Services
CNO: Cathy McLaughlin R.N., MSN, Chief Nursing Officer
Web address: www.medicalcenterarlington.com
Control: Partnership, Investor–owned (for–profit) **Service**: General medical and surgical

Staffed Beds: 289 Admissions: 15452 Census: 210 Outpatient Visits:
128701 Births: 4305 Total Expense ($000): 202902 Payroll Expense
($000): 74252 Personnel: 1077

☐ **MILLWOOD HOSPITAL (454012)**, 1011 North Cooper Street, Zip 76011–5517;
tel. 817/261–3121 **A**1 10 **F**4 5 29 30 35 54 56 71 75 87 98 99 100 101 102
103 104 105 130 132 135 148 **S** Universal Health Services, Inc., King of Prussia,
PA
Primary Contact: Dwight A. Lacy, Chief Executive Officer
CFO: Jeff Epperson, Chief Financial Officer
CMO: Robert Bennett M.D., Medical Director
CIO: William Jackson, Director Medical Records
CHR: Betty Nuru, Director Human Resources
Web address: www.millwoodhospital.com
Control: Partnership, Investor–owned (for–profit) **Service**: Psychiatric

Staffed Beds: 122 Admissions: 3837 Census: 97 Outpatient Visits: 24806
Births: 0 Total Expense ($000): 27582 Payroll Expense ($000): 12532
Personnel: 264

☐ **SUNDANCE BEHAVIORAL HEALTHCARE (454113)**, 7000 US Highway 287
South, Zip 76001; tel. 817/583–8080, (Includes SUNDANCE BEHAVIORAL
HEALTH HOSPITAL, 2696 West Walnut Street, Garland, Texas, Zip 75042–6441,
tel. 469/440–5566; Scott Blakeley, Chief Executive Officer) **A**1 10 **F**4 5 40 56 98
99 101 102 103 104 105
Primary Contact: Scott Blakeley, Chief Executive Officer
Web address: www.sunbhc.com/
Control: Corporation, Investor–owned (for–profit) **Service**: Psychiatric

Staffed Beds: 232 Admissions: 6325 Census: 137 Outpatient Visits: 4200
Births: 0 Total Expense ($000): 22542 Payroll Expense ($000): 14145
Personnel: 759

⊞ **TEXAS HEALTH ARLINGTON MEMORIAL HOSPITAL (450064)**, 800 West
Randol Mill Road, Zip 76012–2503; tel. 817/548–6100 **A**1 2 10 **F**3 11 12 13 15
18 26 28 29 30 31 34 35 37 40 43 45 46 47 48 49 51 53 54 57 59 60 63 64
65 66 68 70 72 74 75 76 77 78 79 80 81 82 85 86 87 93 98 99 100 101 102
103 104 105 107 108 110 111 114 115 118 119 120 123 124 126 130 131
132 135 145 146 147 148 149 **S** Texas Health Resources, Arlington, TX
Primary Contact: Blake Kretz, FACHE, President
COO: Sandra L Harris R.N., MS, Senior Vice President and Chief Operating Officer
CMO: Robert N Cluck M.D., Vice President and Medical Director
CHR: Yvonne Kyler, Director Human Resources
Web address: www.arlingtonmemorial.org
Control: Other not–for–profit (including NFP Corporation) **Service**: General
medical and surgical

Staffed Beds: 242 Admissions: 13311 Census: 185 Outpatient Visits:
104844 Births: 1970 Total Expense ($000): 252449 Payroll Expense
($000): 105461 Personnel: 1493

☐ **TEXAS HEALTH HEART & VASCULAR HOSPITAL ARLINGTON (670071)**, 811
Wright Street, Zip 76012–4708; tel. 817/960–3500 **A**1 10 **F**3 17 18 20 22 24
26 29 30 34 60 64 65 68 81 85
Primary Contact: William Nesbitt, M.D., President
COO: Sherri Leigh Emerson, Chief Operating Officer
CFO: Kay Mason, Chief Financial Officer
CMO: Baron L Hamman M.D., Chief Medical Officer
CHR: Yvonne Kyler, Director Human Resources
Web address: www.texashealtheartandvascular.org/
Control: Partnership, Investor–owned (for–profit) **Service**: Heart

Staffed Beds: 32 Admissions: 1206 Census: 16 Outpatient Visits: 2758
Births: 0 Total Expense ($000): 44188 Payroll Expense ($000): 10254
Personnel: 114

TX

TEXAS REHABILITATION HOSPITAL OF ARLINGTON (673060), 900 W Arbrook Blvd, Zip 76015; tel. 682/304–6000 **F**3 28 29 34 35 60 65 75 90 91 96 97 130 132 135 148 149
Primary Contact: John Reel, Chief Executive Officer
CFO: Debbie Horn, Controller
CMO: Camelia Mitchell M.D., Medical Director
CHR: Stanley Coleman, Director Human Resources
Web address: www.texasrehabarlington.com
Control: Partnership, Investor–owned (for–profit) **Service:** Rehabilitation

Staffed Beds: 40 Admissions: 892 Census: 31 Outpatient Visits: 0 Births: 0
Total Expense ($000): 11457 Payroll Expense ($000): 6845 Personnel: 147

USMD HOSPITAL AT ARLINGTON (450872), 801 West Interstate 20, Zip 76017–5851; tel. 817/472–3400 **A**1 10 **F**3 12 29 34 35 36 39 40 45 46 49 50 51 57 59 64 70 74 75 78 79 81 82 85 87 107 108 111 114 115 119 124 126 132 **S** USMD Health System, Irving, TX
Primary Contact: Marcia Crim, R.N., MSN, Chief Executive Officer
CFO: Andrew Summers, Chief Financial Officer
CMO: M. Patrick Collini M.D., President Medical Staff
CIO: Bob Rick, Vice President Information Technology
CHR: Bernardo Valle, Vice President Human Resources
CNO: Marcia Crim R.N., MSN, Chief Nursing Officer and Chief Executive Officer
Web address: www.usmdarlington.com
Control: Partnership, Investor–owned (for–profit) **Service:** General medical and surgical

Staffed Beds: 34 Admissions: 1761 Census: 16 Outpatient Visits: 29345
Births: 0 Total Expense ($000): 81108 Payroll Expense ($000): 17853
Personnel: 329

ASPERMONT—Stonewall County

STONEWALL MEMORIAL HOSPITAL (451318), 821 North Broadway, Zip 79502–2029, Mailing Address: P.O.Box 'C', 79502–0902; tel. 940/989–3551 **A**10 18 **F**3 29 34 35 40 41 56 57 59 64 93 97 103 107 114 119 127 128 133 148 **P**5
Primary Contact: Andy Kolb, Chief Executive Officer
COO: Billie Carter, Chief Operating Officer and Assistant Administrator
CFO: Andy Kolb, Chief Executive Officer
CMO: Frederic K Passmann M.D., Chief of Staff
CIO: Billie Carter, Chief Operating Officer and Assistant Administrator
CHR: Andy Kolb, Chief Executive Officer
CNO: Jan Harris R.N., Director of Nursing
Web address: www.smhdhealth.org/
Control: Hospital district or authority, Government, Nonfederal **Service:** General medical and surgical

Staffed Beds: 12 Admissions: 106 Census: 2 Outpatient Visits: 3531
Births: 0 Total Expense ($000): 9557 Payroll Expense ($000): 4417
Personnel: 56

ATHENS—Henderson County

EAST TEXAS MEDICAL CENTER ATHENS (450389), 2000 South Palestine Street, Zip 75751–5610; tel. 903/676–1000 **A**1 10 **F**3 11 13 15 18 20 29 34 40 42 43 45 49 50 70 74 76 78 79 81 85 89 107 108 110 111 114 115 118 119 127 130 132 146 **S** East Texas Medical Center Regional Healthcare System, Tyler, TX
Primary Contact: Jack A. Endres, FACHE, JD, Administrator
CFO: David A Travis, Chief Financial Officer
CHR: Jennifer Rummel, Director Human Resources
CNO: Kevin M Jablonski, Chief Nursing Officer
Web address: www.etmc.org
Control: Other not–for–profit (including NFP Corporation) **Service:** General medical and surgical

Staffed Beds: 127 Admissions: 5000 Census: 48 Outpatient Visits: 92241
Births: 941 Total Expense ($000): 79883 Payroll Expense ($000): 25557
Personnel: 417

AUBREY—Denton County

★ ⇑ **BAYLOR EMERGENCY MEDICAL CENTER AT AUBREY (670062)**, 26791 Highway 380, Zip 76227; tel. 972/347–2525, (Includes BAYLOR EMERGENCY MEDICAL CENTER MURPHY, 511 FM 544, Suite 100, Plano, Texas, Zip 75094, tel. 214/294–6150; Kyle Kirkpatrick, Chief Executive Officer; BAYLOR EMERGENCY MEDICAL CENTERS – COLLEYVILLE, 5500 Colleyville Boulevard, Colleyville, Texas, Zip 76034–5835, tel. 214/294–6350; Kyle Kirkpatrick, Chief Executive Officer; BAYLOR EMERGENCY MEDICAL CENTERS – KELLER, 620 S Main Street, Suite 100, Keller, Texas, Zip 76248–4960, tel. 214/294–6100; Kyle Kirkpatrick, Chief Executive Officer) **A**10 21 **F**3 29 40 75 87 107 119 149 **P**5 **S** Emerus, The Woodlands, TX
Primary Contact: Kyle Kirkpatrick, Chief Executive Officer
CFO: Michael Rzendzian, Chief Financial Officer
CMO: Amynah Kara M.D., Chief Medical Officer
CIO: Trang Dawson, Chief Information Officer
CHR: Larry Guillory, Chief Human Resources Officer
CNO: Daniel Baas R.N., Chief Nursing Officer
Web address: www.bemcataubrey.com
Control: Partnership, Investor–owned (for–profit) **Service:** General medical and surgical

Staffed Beds: 32 Admissions: 190 Census: 1 Outpatient Visits: 33148
Births: 0 Total Expense ($000): 24794 Payroll Expense ($000): 7769
Personnel: 144

AUSTIN—Travis County

☐ **ARISE AUSTIN MEDICAL CENTER (450871)**, 3003 Bee Caves Road, Zip 78746–5542; tel. 512/314–3800 **A**1 10 **F**29 40 59 64 65 68 70 75 79 81 82 85 91 107 111 114 119 126 148
Primary Contact: Shawn G. Strash, Chief Executive Officer
CFO: Lawrence Oldham, Chief Financial Officer
CMO: Robert Wills M.D., Chief Medical Officer
CHR: Marilyn Jennings, Director Human Resources
Web address: www.austinsurgicalhospital.com
Control: Corporation, Investor–owned (for–profit) **Service:** Orthopedic

Staffed Beds: 23 Admissions: 945 Census: 6 Outpatient Visits: 5299
Births: 0 Total Expense ($000): 34156 Payroll Expense ($000): 7666
Personnel: 138

☐ **AUSTIN LAKES HOSPITAL (454069)**, 1025 East 32nd Street, Zip 78705–2714; tel. 512/544–5253 **A**1 5 10 **F**98 103 104 105 130 **S** Universal Health Services, Inc., King of Prussia, PA
Primary Contact: Robert J. Lerma, MS, Chief Executive Officer
CFO: Greg Wysocki, Chief Financial Officer
CMO: Shiva Lam M.D., Executive Medical Director
CHR: Dan Smith, Director Human Resources
CNO: Barbara Powers R.N., Chief Nursing Officer
Web address: www.austinlakeshospital.com
Control: Corporation, Investor–owned (for–profit) **Service:** Psychiatric

Staffed Beds: 58 Admissions: 2663 Census: 47 Outpatient Visits: 6257
Births: 0 Total Expense ($000): 12078 Payroll Expense ($000): 6527
Personnel: 121

☐ **AUSTIN OAKS HOSPITAL (454121)**, 1407 West Stassney Lane, Zip 78745–2947; tel. 512/440–4800 **A**1 10 **F**29 38 64 98 99 100 101 103 104 105 130 **S** Universal Health Services, Inc., King of Prussia, PA
Primary Contact: Steve Kelly, Interim Chief Executive Officer
Web address: www.austinoakshospital.com
Control: Partnership, Investor–owned (for–profit) **Service:** Psychiatric

Staffed Beds: 80 Admissions: 2284 Census: 49 Outpatient Visits: 5124
Births: 0 Total Expense ($000): 11795 Payroll Expense ($000): 6050
Personnel: 124

☐ **AUSTIN STATE HOSPITAL (454084)**, 4110 Guadalupe Street, Zip 78751–4296; tel. 512/452–0381 **A**1 3 5 10 **F**29 30 39 50 56 59 65 68 75 86 98 99 101 103 130 132 143 146 **P**1 **S** Texas Department of State Health Services, Austin, TX
Primary Contact: Alan R. Isaacson, Interim Superintendent
CMO: Ross Taylor M.D., Clinical Director
CIO: Cindy Reed, Director Community Relations
Web address: www.dshs.state.tx.us/mhhospitals/austinsh/default.shtm
Control: State, Government, Nonfederal **Service:** Psychiatric

Staffed Beds: 299 Admissions: 1117 Census: 250 Outpatient Visits: 0
Births: 0 Total Expense ($000): 76396 Payroll Expense ($000): 40170
Personnel: 823

CENTRAL TEXAS REHABILITATION HOSPITAL (673027), 700 West 45th Street, Zip 78751–2800; tel. 512/407–2111 **A**1 3 5 10 **F**3 29 59 74 79 82 90 91 96 130 132 148
Primary Contact: A. Jay. Rimovsky, Chief Executive Officer
CFO: Lisa Donnely, Controller II
CMO: Christopher Garrison M.D., Medical Director
CHR: Trena Robinson, Director, Human Resources
CNO: Lauren Brandt, Chief Clinical Officer
Web address: www.khrehabcentraltexas.com/
Control: Partnership, Investor–owned (for–profit) **Service:** Rehabilitation

Staffed Beds: 50 Admissions: 989 Census: 37 Outpatient Visits: 0 Births: 0
Total Expense ($000): 15013 Payroll Expense ($000): 9007 Personnel: 119

☐ **CORNERSTONE HOSPITAL OF AUSTIN (452034)**, 4207 Burnet Road, Zip 78756–3396; tel. 512/706–1900, (Includes CORNERSTONE HOSPITAL OF AUSTIN, 1005 East 32nd Street, Austin, Texas, Zip 78705, tel. 512/867–5822; Edward J Sherwood, M.D., Chief Executive Officer; CORNERSTONE HOSPITAL OF ROUND ROCK, 4681 College Park Drive, Round Rock, Texas, Zip 78665, tel. 512/533–2525; Edward L Dyer, Chief Executive Officer) **A**1 10 **F**1 3 4 16 17 29 30 45 64 67 70 72 73 75 76 77 80 87 88 89 90 91 98 107 128 148 **S** Cornerstone Healthcare Group, Dallas, TX
Primary Contact: Curt L. Roberts, Chief Executive Officer
CMO: David F. Pohl M.D., Chief of Staff
Web address: www.chghospitals.com/austin/
Control: Corporation, Investor–owned (for–profit) **Service:** Acute long–term care hospital

Staffed Beds: 86 Admissions: 866 Census: 54 Outpatient Visits: 2235
Births: 0 Total Expense ($000): 26001 Payroll Expense ($000): 12509
Personnel: 198

Many Facility Codes have changed. Please refer to the AHA Guide Code Chart.

TX

CROSS CREEK HOSPITAL (454133), 8402 Cross Park Drive, Zip 78754; tel. 512/215–3900 **F**75 98 99 101 102 105 130 135 149 **P**4 5 **S** Acadia Healthcare Company, Inc., Franklin, TN
Primary Contact: Jennifer Miller, Chief Executive Officer
Web address: www.cornerstonehealthcaregroup.com
Control: Corporation, Investor–owned (for–profit) **Service:** Psychiatric

Staffed Beds: 90 **Admissions:** 2311 **Census:** 42 **Outpatient Visits:** 580 **Births:** 0 **Total Expense ($000):** 12641 **Payroll Expense ($000):** 6312 **Personnel:** 128

DELL CHILDREN'S MEDICAL CENTER OF CENTRAL TEXAS (453310), 4900 Mueller Boulevard, Zip 78723–3079; tel. 512/324–0000 **A**1 2 3 5 10 **F**3 11 12 19 21 23 25 27 29 30 31 32 34 35 39 40 41 43 44 46 49 50 53 54 55 58 59 60 61 64 65 68 71 72 74 75 77 78 79 80 81 82 84 85 86 87 88 89 93 99 100 101 104 107 108 111 112 114 115 118 119 126 129 130 131 132 133 135 143 146 148 **P**3 8 **S** Ascension Healthcare, Saint Louis, MO
Primary Contact: Mark W. Shen, M.D., President and Chief Executive Officer
Web address: www.dellchildrens.net
Control: Church operated, Nongovernment, not–for–profit **Service:** Children's general medical and surgical

Staffed Beds: 206 **Admissions:** 9772 **Census:** 113 **Outpatient Visits:** 323248 **Births:** 0 **Total Expense ($000):** 426828 **Payroll Expense ($000):** 153600 **Personnel:** 1960

★ **DELL SETON MEDICAL CENTER AT THE UNIVERSITY OF TEXAS**, 1500 Red River Street, Zip 78701; tel. 512/324–7000 (Nonreporting) **S** Ascension Healthcare, Saint Louis, MO
Primary Contact: Christann Vasquez, President
COO: Debra T. Hernandez, Vice President, Chief Operation Officer and Chief Nursing Officer
CFO: Scott Herndon, Chief Financial Officer, Ministry Market Texas
CMO: Tom Caven M.D., Vice President, Medical Director
CIO: Michael H. Minks, Chief Information Officer VI
CHR: Joe Canales, Vice President Human Resources, Ministry Market Texas
CNO: Debra T. Hernandez, Vice President, Chief Operating Officer and Chief Nursing Officer
Web address: www.seton.net/locations/dell-seton/
Control: Church operated, Nongovernment, not–for–profit **Service:** General medical and surgical

Staffed Beds: 211

HEALTHSOUTH REHABILITATION HOSPITAL – AUSTIN (673054), 330 West Ben White Boulevard, Zip 78704; tel. 512/730–4800 **A**1 10 **F**3 29 75 77 86 87 90 91 94 96 130 148 **S** HEALTHSOUTH Corporation, Birmingham, AL
Primary Contact: Brad Dinsmore, Chief Executive Officer
CNO: Vidette J Forbes R.N., Chief Nursing Officer and Chief Operating Officer
Web address: www.reliantaustin.com
Control: Corporation, Investor–owned (for–profit) **Service:** Rehabilitation

Staffed Beds: 60 **Admissions:** 772 **Census:** 25 **Outpatient Visits:** 0 **Births:** 0 **Total Expense ($000):** 15141 **Payroll Expense ($000):** 5816 **Personnel:** 162

HEALTHSOUTH REHABILITATION HOSPITAL OF AUSTIN (453044), 330 West Ben White Boulevard, Zip 78704; tel. 512/474–5700, (Data for 218 days)**A**1 10 **F**3 29 56 62 74 75 77 79 86 87 90 91 130 132 143 148 **P**5 **S** HEALTHSOUTH Corporation, Birmingham, AL
Primary Contact: Brad Dinsmore, Chief Executive Officer
CFO: Pamela McLaughlin, Chief Financial Officer
CMO: Johnny Shane Ross, Executive Medical Director
Web address: www.healthsouthaustin.com
Control: Corporation, Investor–owned (for–profit) **Service:** Rehabilitation

Staffed Beds: 40 **Admissions:** 426 **Census:** 27 **Outpatient Visits:** 3480 **Births:** 0 **Total Expense ($000):** 9641 **Payroll Expense ($000):** 3816 **Personnel:** 109

☐ **NORTHWEST HILLS SURGICAL HOSPITAL (450808)**, 6818 Austin Center Boulevard, Suite 100, Zip 78731–3199; tel. 512/346–1994 **A**1 5 10 **F**3 40 45 64 75 79 81
Primary Contact: Scott Cullen, Chief Executive Officer
CFO: Jenny Salome, Chief Financial Officer and Assistant Administrator
Web address: www.northwesthillssurgical.com
Control: Partnership, Investor–owned (for–profit) **Service:** General medical and surgical

Staffed Beds: 8 **Admissions:** 461 **Census:** 2 **Outpatient Visits:** 8191 **Births:** 0 **Total Expense ($000):** 26756 **Payroll Expense ($000):** 6161 **Personnel:** 97

⊞ ⇑ **SETON MEDICAL CENTER AUSTIN (450056)**, 1201 West 38th Street, Zip 78705–1006; tel. 512/324–1000 **A**1 2 3 5 10 21 **F**3 11 12 13 15 18 20 22 24 26 28 29 30 31 34 35 40 43 44 45 46 49 50 51 57 58 59 60 61 64 68 70 72 74 75 76 77 78 79 80 81 82 84 85 86 87 93 107 108 111 114 115 119 126 130 131 132 135 137 145 146 147 148 **P**3 8 **S** Ascension Healthcare, Saint Louis, MO
Primary Contact: Katherine Henderson, President
COO: Tad Hatton, Vice President Chief Operating Officer
CFO: Robert Scott Herndon, Vice President Chief Financial Officer
CMO: David W Martin M.D., Vice President Chief Medical Officer
CIO: Michael H. Minks, Chief Information Officer VI
CHR: Joe Canales, Vice President Human Resources
CNO: Elizabeth Steger FACHE, R.N., Chief Nursing Officer
Web address: www.seton.net/locations/smc/
Control: Church operated, Nongovernment, not–for–profit **Service:** General medical and surgical

Staffed Beds: 382 **Admissions:** 20702 **Census:** 276 **Outpatient Visits:** 290312 **Births:** 4814 **Total Expense ($000):** 443998 **Payroll Expense ($000):** 118725 **Personnel:** 1831

⊞ **SETON NORTHWEST HOSPITAL (450867)**, 11113 Research Boulevard, Zip 78759–5236; tel. 512/324–6000 **A**1 2 3 5 10 **F**3 11 12 13 15 18 29 30 31 34 35 36 37 40 43 44 45 47 49 50 51 57 59 64 68 70 73 75 76 77 78 79 81 85 86 87 93 107 111 114 119 130 131 132 135 146 148 **P**3 8 **S** Ascension Healthcare, Saint Louis, MO
Primary Contact: Michelle L. Robertson, R.N., Chief Operating Officer, Texas Market
COO: Margaret E Butler, Vice President Chief Operating Officer, Seton Northwest Hospital
CFO: Scott Herndon, Chief Financial Officer, Texas Market
CMO: Jason Martin M.D., Medical Director
CIO: Michael H. Minks, Chief Information Officer
CHR: Joe Canales, Vice President, Ascension and Human Resources Officer, Texas Market
CNO: Yvonne VanDyke R.N., MSN, Chief Nursing Officer, Texas Market
Web address: www.seton.net
Control: Church operated, Nongovernment, not–for–profit **Service:** General medical and surgical

Staffed Beds: 68 **Admissions:** 5489 **Census:** 48 **Outpatient Visits:** 49382 **Births:** 1388 **Total Expense ($000):** 82448 **Payroll Expense ($000):** 28562 **Personnel:** 323

⊞ **SETON SHOAL CREEK HOSPITAL (454029)**, 3501 Mills Avenue, Zip 78731–6391; tel. 512/324–2000 **A**1 3 5 10 **F**4 5 29 30 56 68 87 98 99 100 101 103 104 130 132 135 146 **P**3 8 **S** Ascension Healthcare, Saint Louis, MO
Primary Contact: Brandy Hart, Executive Director
COO: William Henricks Ph.D., Vice President and Chief Operating Officer
CFO: Robert Scott Herndon, Chief Financial Officer
CMO: Amy E. Walton M.D., Chief Medical Officer
CIO: Michael H. Minks, Chief Information Officer
CHR: Joe Canales, Director Human Resources
Web address: www.seton.net
Control: Church operated, Nongovernment, not–for–profit **Service:** Psychiatric

Staffed Beds: 94 **Admissions:** 3835 **Census:** 63 **Outpatient Visits:** 24728 **Births:** 0 **Total Expense ($000):** 28625 **Payroll Expense ($000):** 13861 **Personnel:** 165

⊞ **SETON SOUTHWEST HOSPITAL (450865)**, 7900 F M 1826, Building 1, Zip 78737–1407; tel. 512/324–9000 **A**1 10 **F**3 11 13 15 28 29 30 34 35 36 40 43 44 45 57 59 64 68 71 72 75 76 79 81 85 87 93 107 110 111 115 119 130 131 132 135 146 147 **P**3 8 **S** Ascension Healthcare, Saint Louis, MO
Primary Contact: Mary Faria, FACHE, Ph.D., Vice President and Chief Operating Officer
Web address: www.seton.net
Control: Church operated, Nongovernment, not–for–profit **Service:** General medical and surgical

Staffed Beds: 33 **Admissions:** 1086 **Census:** 9 **Outpatient Visits:** 29454 **Births:** 773 **Total Expense ($000):** 29799 **Payroll Expense ($000):** 10604 **Personnel:** 88

TX

Hospital, Medicare Provider Number, Address, Telephone, Approval, Facility, and Physician Codes, Health Care System

★ American Hospital Association (AHA) membership ○ Healthcare Facilities Accreditation Program ⇑ Center for Improvement in Healthcare Quality Accreditation
☐ The Joint Commission accreditation ◇ DNV Healthcare Inc. accreditation △ Commission on Accreditation of Rehabilitation Facilities (CARF) accreditation

© 2017 AHA Guide *Many Facility Codes have changed. Please refer to the AHA Guide Code Chart.* Hospitals **A595**

✠ ⇑ **ST. DAVID'S MEDICAL CENTER (450431)**, 919 East 32nd Street, Zip 78705–2709, Mailing Address: P.O.Box 4039, 78765–4039; tel. 512/476–7111, (Includes HEART HOSPITAL OF AUSTIN, 3801 North Lamar Boulevard, Austin, Texas, Zip 78756–4080, tel. 512/407–7000; David Laird, Chief Executive Officer; ST. DAVID'S GEORGETOWN HOSPITAL, 2000 Scenic Drive, Georgetown, Texas, Zip 78626–7726, tel. 512/943–3000; Hugh Brown, Chief Executive Officer; ST. DAVID'S REHABILITATION CENTER, 1005 East 32nd Street, Austin, Texas, Zip 78705–2713, P O Box 4270, 78765–4270, tel. 512/544–5100; Diane Owens, Assistant Administrator) **A**1 2 3 5 10 21 **F**3 8 11 12 13 17 18 20 22 24 26 28 29 30 31 34 35 36 37 39 40 41 42 43 45 46 47 48 49 53 60 61 64 70 72 73 74 75 76 77 78 79 81 84 85 86 87 90 91 93 95 96 107 108 109 110 111 114 115 116 119 126 129 130 131 132 135 146 147 148 149 **P**1 3 6 8 **S** HCA Healthcare, Nashville, TN
Primary Contact: Donald H. Wilkerson, FACHE, Chief Executive Officer
COO: Esther Chung, Chief Operating Officer
CFO: Julie Perez, Chief Financial Officer
CMO: John Marietta M.D., Chief Medical Officer
CIO: Richard Lear, Director Information Systems
CHR: Julie Hajek, Director Human Resources
Web address: www.stdavids.com
Control: Other not–for–profit (including NFP Corporation) **Service:** General medical and surgical

Staffed Beds: 579 **Admissions:** 26476 **Census:** 398 **Outpatient Visits:** 224074 **Births:** 5218 **Total Expense ($000):** 497784 **Payroll Expense ($000):** 157352 **Personnel:** 2509

✠ **ST. DAVID'S NORTH AUSTIN MEDICAL CENTER (459807)**, 12221 North MoPac Expressway, Zip 78758–2496; tel. 512/901–1000 **A**1 2 3 5 10 **F**3 12 13 15 18 20 22 24 26 28 29 30 31 34 35 37 40 41 42 43 45 47 49 53 54 58 59 64 67 70 72 73 74 75 76 77 78 79 81 85 86 87 88 89 90 93 107 108 110 111 114 115 118 119 126 129 130 132 138 144 145 146 147 148 149 **P**1 3 6 8 **S** HCA Healthcare, Nashville, TN
Primary Contact: Thomas W. Jackson, Chief Executive Officer
COO: Sheri Dube, Chief Operating Officer
CFO: Natalie Pack, Chief Financial Officer
CMO: Kenneth W Mitchell M.D., Medical Director
CIO: Marshall Pearson, Director Management Information Systems
CHR: Laura Light, Director Human Resources
Web address: www.northaustin.com
Control: Other not–for–profit (including NFP Corporation) **Service:** General medical and surgical

Staffed Beds: 424 **Admissions:** 20387 **Census:** 280 **Outpatient Visits:** 150076 **Births:** 6808 **Total Expense ($000):** 280848 **Payroll Expense ($000):** 96245 **Personnel:** 1619

✠ **ST. DAVID'S SOUTH AUSTIN MEDICAL CENTER (450713)**, 901 West Ben White Boulevard, Zip 78704–6903; tel. 512/447–2211 **A**1 2 3 5 10 **F**11 12 13 15 17 18 20 22 24 26 28 29 30 31 34 35 37 40 42 43 45 46 48 49 54 56 59 60 64 70 73 74 75 76 77 78 79 80 81 82 84 85 87 93 107 108 110 111 114 115 119 124 126 129 130 132 136 144 145 146 147 148 **P**1 3 6 8 **S** HCA Healthcare, Nashville, TN
Primary Contact: Todd E. Steward, FACHE, Chief Executive Officer
CFO: Wesley D Fountain, Chief Financial Officer
CMO: Albert Gros M.D., Chief Medical Officer
CIO: Richard Lear, Director Information Systems
CHR: Lisa Talbot, Director Human Resources
CNO: Sally A Gillam R.N., Chief Nursing Officer
Web address: www.southaustinmc.com
Control: Other not–for–profit (including NFP Corporation) **Service:** General medical and surgical

Staffed Beds: 291 **Admissions:** 17409 **Census:** 235 **Outpatient Visits:** 146961 **Births:** 1761 **Total Expense ($000):** 250583 **Payroll Expense ($000):** 81070 **Personnel:** 1383

✠ **TEXAS NEUROREHAB CENTER (452038)**, 1106 West Dittmar Road, Building 9, Zip 78745–6328, Mailing Address: P.O.Box 150459, 78715–0459; tel. 512/444–4835 **A**1 10 **F**1 3 29 54 74 75 77 79 93 108 130 148 **P**5 **S** Universal Health Services, Inc., King of Prussia, PA
Primary Contact: Edgar E. Prettyman, PsyD, Chief Executive Officer
COO: Janet Bitner, Chief Operating Officer
CFO: Omar Correa, Chief Financial Officer
CMO: James Boysen M.D., Executive Medical Director
CHR: Colleen Lewis, Director Human Resources
Web address: www.texasneurorehab.com
Control: Partnership, Investor–owned (for–profit) **Service:** Acute long–term care hospital

Staffed Beds: 47 **Admissions:** 523 **Census:** 41 **Outpatient Visits:** 6270 **Births:** 0 **Total Expense ($000):** 12902 **Payroll Expense ($000):** 7655 **Personnel:** 280

☐ **TEXAS STAR RECOVERY (454111)**, 1106 West Dittmar Road, Zip 78745–6328; tel. 512/462–6729 (Nonreporting) **A**1 10
Primary Contact: William Loving, M.D., Medical Director
Web address: www.texasstarrecovery.com
Control: Partnership, Investor–owned (for–profit) **Service:** Psychiatric

Staffed Beds: 28

THE HOSPITAL AT WESTLAKE MEDICAL CENTER (670006), 5656 Bee Caves Road, Suite M302, Zip 78746–5280; tel. 512/327–0000 **A**10 **F**3 18 20 22 26 29 37 39 40 45 51 53 58 59 64 70 75 77 79 81 82 85 93 96 107 108 111 114 119 129 130 131 135 148
Primary Contact: Robin Allen, Chief Executive Officer
CFO: Devon Culbert, Controller
CMO: Tom Burns M.D., Chief of Staff
CHR: Kellie Bryson, Director Human Resources
Web address: www.westlakemedical.com
Control: Partnership, Investor–owned (for–profit) **Service:** General medical and surgical

Staffed Beds: 23 **Admissions:** 943 **Census:** 6 **Outpatient Visits:** 7956 **Births:** 0 **Total Expense ($000):** 39922 **Payroll Expense ($000):** 10608 **Personnel:** 178

AZLE—Tarrant County

✠ **TEXAS HEALTH HARRIS METHODIST HOSPITAL AZLE (450419)**, 108 Denver Trail, Zip 76020–3614; tel. 817/444–8600 **A**1 10 **F**3 11 15 18 29 30 34 35 40 43 45 56 57 59 64 70 75 77 79 81 85 93 107 110 114 119 130 135 146 147 148 149 **S** Texas Health Resources, Arlington, TX
Primary Contact: Bob S. Ellzey, FACHE, President
CFO: Brian Blessing, Chief Financial Officer
CMO: Judy Laviolette M.D., Chief Medical Officer
CIO: Patricia Johnston, Vice President Information Services
CHR: Lance Waring, Director Human Resources
CNO: Valarie Gilbert R.N., Chief Nursing Officer
Web address: www.texashealth.org/Azle
Control: Other not–for–profit (including NFP Corporation) **Service:** General medical and surgical

Staffed Beds: 31 **Admissions:** 1553 **Census:** 14 **Outpatient Visits:** 31819 **Births:** 0 **Total Expense ($000):** 36334 **Payroll Expense ($000):** 15369 **Personnel:** 203

BALLINGER—Runnels County

★ **BALLINGER MEMORIAL HOSPITAL (451310)**, 608 Avenue 'B', Zip 76821–2499, Mailing Address: P.O.Box 617, 76821–0617; tel. 325/365–2531 **A**10 18 **F**3 7 11 29 34 40 43 53 64 65 68 77 93 107 114 119 127 130 133 **P**5
Primary Contact: Rhett D. Fricke, Chief Executive Officer
CFO: Josilyn Peterson, Chief Financial Officer
CHR: Roselyn Hudgens, Director Human Resources
Web address: www.ballingerhospital.org
Control: Hospital district or authority, Government, Nonfederal **Service:** General medical and surgical

Staffed Beds: 16 **Admissions:** 125 **Census:** 3 **Outpatient Visits:** 19747 **Births:** 0 **Total Expense ($000):** 8938 **Payroll Expense ($000):** 3659 **Personnel:** 78

BAY CITY—Matagorda County

✠ **MATAGORDA REGIONAL MEDICAL CENTER (450465)**, 104 7th Street, Zip 77414–4853; tel. 979/245–6383 **A**1 10 20 **F**3 11 12 19 22 28 29 30 32 34 38 39 40 43 45 46 47 50 51 53 56 57 59 64 65 66 68 70 75 76 77 79 81 82 85 86 89 93 98 103 107 108 110 111 114 119 130 132 135 146 147 148 **S** QHR, Brentwood, TN
Primary Contact: Steven L. Smith, Chief Executive Officer
CFO: Bryan Prochnow, Chief Financial Officer
CIO: Beverly Trombatore R.N., Director Managed Information Systems
CHR: Cindy Krebs, District Director Human Resources
CNO: Mike Lee R.N., Chief Nursing Officer
Web address: www.matagordaregional.org
Control: Hospital district or authority, Government, Nonfederal **Service:** General medical and surgical

Staffed Beds: 58 **Admissions:** 2340 **Census:** 27 **Outpatient Visits:** 68086 **Births:** 583 **Total Expense ($000):** 61470 **Payroll Expense ($000):** 21907 **Personnel:** 387

BAYTOWN—Harris County

ALTUS BAYTOWN HOSPITAL (670109), 1626 West Baker Road, Zip 77521–2271; tel. 281/837–7600 **F**3 12 29 40 44 45 49 64 74 79 81 82 85 87 107 108 111 114 116 117 119
Primary Contact: Molly McComas, Administrator
Web address: www.altusbaytownhospital.org
Control: Partnership, Investor–owned (for–profit) **Service:** Surgical

Staffed Beds: 10 **Admissions:** 486 **Census:** 1 **Outpatient Visits:** 2501 **Births:** 0 **Total Expense ($000):** 33337 **Payroll Expense ($000):** 5008 **Personnel:** 91

TX

Many Facility Codes have changed. Please refer to the AHA Guide Code Chart. © 2017 AHA Guide

★ ⇧ **HOUSTON METHODIST SAN JACINTO HOSPITAL (450424)**, 4401 Garth Road, Zip 77521–2122; tel. 281/420–8600, (Includes HOUSTON METHODIST SAN JACINTO HOSPITAL – ALEXANDER, 1700 James Bowie Drive, Baytown, Texas, Zip 77520–3386, 4401 Garth Road, 77520–1451, tel. 281/420–6100; David P. Bernard, FACHE, Chief Executive Officer) (Total facility includes 30 beds in nursing home–type unit) **A**2 3 10 21 **F**3 8 11 12 13 15 18 20 22 24 26 28 29 30 31 34 35 38 40 41 44 45 48 49 50 51 53 57 59 61 64 65 68 70 71 73 74 75 76 77 78 79 81 82 85 86 87 90 91 93 96 97 98 102 103 107 108 110 111 114 115 116 117 118 119 120 121 123 126 128 129 130 131 132 145 146 147 148 149 **S** Houston Methodist, Houston, TX
Primary Contact: David P. Bernard, FACHE, Chief Executive Officer
CFO: Jonathan Sturgis, Chief Financial Officer
CMO: Klaus Thaler FACS, M.D., Chief Medical Officer
CHR: Courtney Lewis, Director Human Resources
CNO: Rebecca Chalupa MSN, R.N., Chief Nursing Officer
Web address: www.houstonmethodist.org
Control: Other not–for–profit (including NFP Corporation) **Service**: General medical and surgical

Staffed Beds: 275 **Admissions:** 12871 **Census:** 184 **Outpatient Visits:** 122387 **Births:** 1609 **Total Expense ($000):** 264432 **Payroll Expense ($000):** 92643 **Personnel:** 1392	

BEAUMONT—Jefferson County

★ **BAPTIST HOSPITALS OF SOUTHEAST TEXAS (450346)**, 3080 College Street, Zip 77701–4689, Mailing Address: P.O.Box 1591, 77704–1591; tel. 409/212–5000, (Includes BAPTIST HOSPITALS OF SOUTHEAST TEXAS FANNIN BEHAVIORAL HEALTH CENTER, 3250 Fannin Street, Beaumont, Texas, Zip 77701, tel. 409/212–7000; David N Parmer, FACHE, Chief Executive Officer) **A**2 10 22 **F**3 4 5 11 12 13 15 17 18 20 22 24 26 28 29 30 31 34 35 40 41 42 43 45 46 49 50 51 55 57 59 60 64 70 72 73 74 75 76 77 78 79 81 85 86 87 88 89 90 93 98 99 101 102 103 104 105 107 108 110 111 114 115 116 117 118 119 120 121 123 124 129 130 131 132 135 144 145 146 147 **P**6 **S** Community Hospital Corporation, Plano, TX
Primary Contact: David N. Parmer, FACHE, Chief Executive Officer
COO: Patrick Shannon, Chief Operating Officer
CFO: Gary Troutman CPA, Chief Financial Officer
CMO: Shariq Ahmad M.D., Chief of Staff
CIO: William Toon, Chief Information Officer
CHR: Hannah Schiesler, Interim Assistant Director Human Resources
CNO: Karen Tomsu MSN, R.N., Chief Nursing Officer
Web address: www.bhset.net
Control: Other not–for–profit (including NFP Corporation) **Service**: General medical and surgical

Staffed Beds: 323 **Admissions:** 16713 **Census:** 195 **Outpatient Visits:** 178308 **Births:** 1546 **Total Expense ($000):** 250875 **Payroll Expense ($000):** 92953 **Personnel:** 1637	

✚ **CHRISTUS DUBUIS HOSPITAL OF BEAUMONT (452042)**, 2830 Calder Avenue, 4th Floor, Zip 77702–1809; tel. 409/899–7680, (Includes CHRISTUS DUBUIS HOSPITAL OF PORT ARTHUR, 3600 Gates Boulevard, 3rd Floor West, Port Arthur, Texas, Zip 77642–3858, tel. 409/989–5300; Tuan Le, Chief Executive Officer) **A**1 10 **F**1 3 18 29 30 31 35 130 148 **S** CHRISTUS Health, Irving, TX
Primary Contact: Tuan Le, Chief Executive Officer
Web address: www.christusdubuis.org/BeaumontandPortArthurSystem–CHRISTUSDubuisHospitalofBeaumont
Control: Church operated, Nongovernment, not–for–profit **Service**: Acute long–term care hospital

Staffed Beds: 51 **Admissions:** 500 **Census:** 37 **Outpatient Visits:** 0 **Births:** 0 **Total Expense ($000):** 17028 **Payroll Expense ($000):** 6500 **Personnel:** 101	

✚ **CHRISTUS SOUTHEAST TEXAS HOSPITAL (450034)**, 2830 Calder Avenue, Zip 77702–1809, Mailing Address: P.O.Box 5405, 77726–5405; tel. 409/892–7171, (Includes CHRISTUS SOUTHEAST TEXAS HOSPITAL–ST. MARY, 3600 Gates Boulevard, Port Arthur, Texas, Zip 77642–3601, P O Box 3696, 77643–3696, tel. 409/985–7431; Wayne Moore, Administrator) **A**1 2 3 10 **F**3 11 12 13 15 17 18 20 22 24 26 28 29 30 31 34 35 36 38 40 43 44 45 46 49 50 51 54 57 59 60 63 64 70 72 74 75 76 77 78 79 81 82 84 85 86 87 89 93 94 107 108 110 111 114 118 119 126 130 131 132 144 146 147 148 149 **P**8 **S** CHRISTUS Health, Irving, TX
Primary Contact: Paul Trevino, Chief Executive Officer
CFO: Shawn Adams, Chief Financial Officer
CMO: Rick Tyler M.D., Vice President Medical Affairs
CIO: Robert Jacobs, Regional Director Information Management
CHR: Charles Foster, Regional Director Human Resources
Web address: www.christushospital.org
Control: Church operated, Nongovernment, not–for–profit **Service**: General medical and surgical

Staffed Beds: 424 **Admissions:** 15372 **Census:** 182 **Outpatient Visits:** 372260 **Births:** 2126 **Total Expense ($000):** 334279 **Payroll Expense ($000):** 102107 **Personnel:** 1580	

CHRISTUS SOUTHEAST TEXAS ORTHOPEDIC SPECIALTY CENTER (670007), 3650 Laurel Street, Zip 77707–2216; tel. 409/838–0346 (Nonreporting) **A**10
Primary Contact: Ryan Miller, FACHE, Administrator and Executive Director
Web address: www.orthodoc.aaos.org/bbji/
Control: Partnership, Investor–owned (for–profit) **Service**: General medical and surgical

Staffed Beds: 6	

KATE DISHMAN REHABILITATION HOSPITAL (673030), 2830 Calder Street, 6th Floor, Zip 77702–1809; tel. 409/899–8380 **F**86 87 90 96 100 **S** CHRISTUS Health, Irving, TX
Primary Contact: David Pipkins, Chief Executive Officer and Administrator
Web address: www.christushospital.org
Control: Partnership, Investor–owned (for–profit) **Service**: Rehabilitation

Staffed Beds: 27 **Admissions:** 379 **Census:** 13 **Outpatient Visits:** 0 **Births:** 0 **Total Expense ($000):** 5783 **Payroll Expense ($000):** 3115 **Personnel:** 59	

☐ **MEDICAL CENTER OF SOUTHEAST TEXAS**, 6025 Metropolitan Drive, Zip 77706–2407; tel. 409/617–7700 (Nonreporting) **A**1 **S** IASIS Healthcare, Franklin, TN
Primary Contact: Becky Ames, Chief Executive Officer
Web address: www.medicalcentersetexas.com/
Control: Other not–for–profit (including NFP Corporation) **Service**: Surgical

Staffed Beds: 17	

MEMORIAL HERMANN BAPTIST FANNIN BEHAVIORAL HEALTH CENTER
See Baptist Hospitals Of Southeast Texas Fannin Behavioral Health Center

✚ **PAM REHABILITATION HOSPITAL OF BEAUMONT (453048)**, 3340 Plaza 10 Boulevard, Zip 77707–2551; tel. 409/835–0835, (Data for 214 days) **A**1 10 **F**3 29 90 96 148 **S** Post Acute Medical, LLC, Enola, PA
Primary Contact: Todd Lorenz, Chief Executive Officer
CMO: Linda C Smith M.D., Medical Director
CHR: Joanna Donica, Director Human Resource
CNO: Barbara Morris R.N., Chief Nursing Officer
Web address: www.postacutemedical.com/our–facilities/outpatient–rehabilitation/rehabilitation–hospital–beaumont/
Control: Partnership, Investor–owned (for–profit) **Service**: Rehabilitation

Staffed Beds: 61 **Admissions:** 318 **Census:** 18 **Outpatient Visits:** 0 **Births:** 0 **Total Expense ($000):** 5609 **Payroll Expense ($000):** 2682 **Personnel:** 97	

BEDFORD—Tarrant County

✚ **HEALTHSOUTH REHABILITATION HOSPITAL – MID–CITIES (673044)**, 2304 State Highway 121, Zip 76021–5985; tel. 817/684–2000 **A**1 10 **F**3 29 90 96 148 **S** HEALTHSOUTH Corporation, Birmingham, AL
Primary Contact: Robert M. Smart, Chief Executive Officer
CFO: Mary Mwaniki, Chief Financial Officer
CMO: Toni Willis M.D., Medical Director
CHR: Christie Moore, Director Human Resources
Web address: www.relianthcp.com
Control: Partnership, Investor–owned (for–profit) **Service**: Rehabilitation

Staffed Beds: 60 **Admissions:** 1400 **Census:** 43 **Outpatient Visits:** 0 **Births:** 0 **Total Expense ($000):** 16806 **Payroll Expense ($000):** 8710 **Personnel:** 166	

✚ **TEXAS HEALTH HARRIS METHODIST HOSPITAL HURST–EULESS–BEDFORD (450639)**, 1600 Hospital Parkway, Zip 76022–6913; tel. 817/685–4000, (Includes TEXAS HEALTH SPRINGWOOD, 1608 Hospital Parkway, Bedford, Texas, Zip 76022, tel. 817/355–7700; Ron Rains, Administrator) **A**1 2 10 **F**9 11 12 13 15 18 20 22 24 28 29 30 31 34 35 40 43 47 49 50 53 57 59 60 64 70 72 74 75 76 78 79 80 81 82 84 86 87 93 107 108 111 114 118 119 126 130 131 132 134 135 146 147 148 **S** Texas Health Resources, Arlington, TX
Primary Contact: Deborah Paganelli, FACHE, President
COO: Alice Landers, Administrative Director Operations
CFO: Jaime James, Entity Finance Officer
CMO: Susann Land M.D., Chief Medical Officer
CHR: Lee Mulvey, Human Resource Officer
CNO: Ray Kelly R.N., MSN, Vice President Chief Nursing Officer
Web address: www.texashealth.org
Control: Other not–for–profit (including NFP Corporation) **Service**: General medical and surgical

Staffed Beds: 190 **Admissions:** 14339 **Census:** 170 **Outpatient Visits:** 83643 **Births:** 2246 **Total Expense ($000):** 242382 **Payroll Expense ($000):** 97582 **Personnel:** 1308	

Hospital, Medicare Provider Number, Address, Telephone, Approval, Facility, and Physician Codes, Health Care System

★ American Hospital Association (AHA) membership
☐ The Joint Commission accreditation
○ Healthcare Facilities Accreditation Program
◇ DNV Healthcare Inc. accreditation
⇧ Center for Improvement in Healthcare Quality Accreditation
△ Commission on Accreditation of Rehabilitation Facilities (CARF) accreditation

TX

BEEVILLE—Bee County

⊞ **CHRISTUS SPOHN HOSPITAL BEEVILLE (450082)**, 1500 East Houston Street, Zip 78102–5312; tel. 361/354–2000 **A**1 10 20 **F**3 11 13 15 29 30 32 34 35 40 43 45 50 53 57 59 63 64 70 75 76 79 81 85 87 93 97 107 108 111 114 115 119 127 130 146 147 148 **P**8 **S** CHRISTUS Health, Irving, TX
Primary Contact: Genifer Rucker, President
Web address: www.christusspohn.org
Control: Church operated, Nongovernment, not–for–profit **Service**: General medical and surgical

Staffed Beds: 49 **Admissions**: 1798 **Census**: 14 **Outpatient Visits**: 40214
Births: 328 **Total Expense ($000)**: 28747 **Payroll Expense ($000)**: 10674
Personnel: 145

BELLAIRE—Harris County

⇑ **FIRST SURGICAL HOSPITAL (670029)**, 4801 Bissonnet, Zip 77401–4028; tel. 713/275–1111 **A**10 21 **F**3 12 29 40 45 48 49 64 65 79 81 82 85 107 119 126 130 **P**5 **S** Nobilis Health Corporation, Houston, TX
Primary Contact: David Kreye, Chief Executive Officer
Web address: www.firststreethospital.com
Control: Other not–for–profit (including NFP Corporation) **Service**: Surgical

Staffed Beds: 19 **Admissions**: 845 **Census**: 4 **Outpatient Visits**: 3350
Births: 0 **Total Expense ($000)**: 93095 **Payroll Expense ($000)**: 11683
Personnel: 149

BELLVILLE—Austin County

BELLVILLE GENERAL HOSPITAL See Chi St. Joseph Health Bellville Hospital

⊞ **CHI ST. JOSEPH HEALTH BELLVILLE HOSPITAL (450253)**, 44 North Cummings Street, Zip 77418–1347, Mailing Address: P.O.Box 977, 77418–0977; tel. 979/413–7400 **A**1 10 **F**3 11 15 29 34 35 40 43 45 50 53 57 59 64 65 68 75 81 87 93 107 110 111 114 119 133 146 **S** Catholic Health Initiatives, Englewood, CO
CMO: Christophe Gay M.D., Chief of Staff
CHR: Jacqueline McEuen, Coordinator Human Resources
Web address: www.st–joseph.org/body.cfm?id=773
Control: Other not–for–profit (including NFP Corporation) **Service**: General medical and surgical

Staffed Beds: 10 **Admissions**: 105 **Census**: 2 **Outpatient Visits**: 18282
Births: 0 **Total Expense ($000)**: 12588 **Payroll Expense ($000)**: 4393
Personnel: 78

BELTON—Bell County

☐ **CEDAR CREST HOSPITAL AND RESIDENTIAL TREATMENT CENTER (454114)**, 3500 I–35 South, Zip 76513; tel. 254/939–2100 **A**1 10 **F**4 29 34 35 59 68 86 87 98 99 100 101 102 103 104 105 106 130 143 **P**4
Primary Contact: Sean Bellinger, Chief Executive Officer
CFO: Melissa West, Chief Financial Officer
CMO: Alejandro Munoz M.D., Chief Medical Officer
CIO: Cesar Osario, Specialist Information Technology
CHR: Allison Liston, Director, Human Resources
CNO: Catherine Reed MSN, R.N., Chief Nursing Officer
Web address: www.cedarcresthospital.com
Control: Corporation, Investor–owned (for–profit) **Service**: Psychiatric

Staffed Beds: 88 **Admissions**: 3094 **Census**: 58 **Outpatient Visits**: 4944
Births: 0 **Total Expense ($000)**: 11878 **Payroll Expense ($000)**: 7196
Personnel: 174

BIG LAKE—Reagan County

★ **REAGAN MEMORIAL HOSPITAL (451301)**, 805 North Main Street, Zip 76932–3999; tel. 325/884–2561 **A**10 18 **F**3 40 43 53 57 89 93 107 114 115 128 130 133 143 **P**5
Primary Contact: Kyle Rockwell, Chief Executive Officer
CMO: Joseph Sudolcan M.D., Medical Director
Web address: www.reaganhealth.com/getpage.php?name=index
Control: Hospital district or authority, Government, Nonfederal **Service**: General medical and surgical

Staffed Beds: 7 **Admissions**: 40 **Census**: 1 **Outpatient Visits**: 4184 **Births**: 0
Total Expense ($000): 9314 **Payroll Expense ($000)**: 4689 **Personnel**: 38

BIG SPRING—Howard County

☐ **BIG SPRING STATE HOSPITAL (454000)**, 1901 North Highway 87, Zip 79720–0283; tel. 432/267–8216 **A**1 3 5 10 **F**3 30 39 50 56 59 61 68 74 75 77 86 87 97 98 101 103 106 130 132 135 146 **P**6 **S** Texas Department of State Health Services, Austin, TX
Primary Contact: Lorie Dunnam, Superintendent
CFO: Adrienne Bides, Assistant Chief Financial Officer and Budget Analyst
CMO: Guido Spangher M.D., Clinical Director
CIO: Elizabeth Correa, Director Information Management
CHR: Traci Phillips, Assistant Superintendent
CNO: Stormy Ward, Chief Nurse Executive
Web address: www.dshs.state.tx.us/mhhospitals/BigSpringSH/default.shtm
Control: State, Government, Nonfederal **Service**: Psychiatric

Staffed Beds: 200 **Admissions**: 278 **Census**: 186 **Outpatient Visits**: 0
Births: 0 **Total Expense ($000)**: 63737 **Payroll Expense ($000)**: 24713
Personnel: 555

⊞ **SCENIC MOUNTAIN MEDICAL CENTER (450653)**, 1601 West 11th Place, Zip 79720–4198; tel. 432/263–1211 **A**1 3 10 20 **F**8 13 15 18 20 22 29 30 34 35 40 43 47 50 57 59 64 65 69 70 75 76 77 79 81 85 87 89 93 107 108 110 111 115 119 129 130 146 147 148 **P**7 **S** Quorum Health, Brentwood, TN
Primary Contact: Emma Krabill, Chief Executive Officer
CFO: Rodger W Bowen M.P.H., Chief Financial Officer
CMO: Keith Ledford M.D., Chief of Staff
CIO: Gene Mills, Director Information Technology
CHR: Deborah Elder, Director Human Resources
CNO: Judy Roever MSN, R.N., Chief Nursing Officer
Web address: www.smmccares.com
Control: Corporation, Investor–owned (for–profit) **Service**: General medical and surgical

Staffed Beds: 62 **Admissions**: 2401 **Census**: 21 **Outpatient Visits**: 31868
Births: 246 **Total Expense ($000)**: 41062 **Payroll Expense ($000)**: 13516
Personnel: 211

★ **WEST TEXAS VETERANS AFFAIRS HEALTH CARE SYSTEM**, 300 Veterans Boulevard, Zip 79720–5500, Mailing Address: Big Springs, tel. 432/263–7361, (Nonreporting) **A**3 5 **S** Department of Veterans Affairs, Washington, DC
Primary Contact: Kalautie JangDhari, Director
CFO: Ray Olivas, Chief Fiscal Service
CMO: Martin Schnier D.O., Chief of Staff
CIO: Mike McKinley, Information Security Officer
CHR: Anna Osborne, Chief Human Resources Management Service
Web address: www.bigspring.va.gov/about/
Control: Veterans Affairs, Government, federal **Service**: General medical and surgical

Staffed Beds: 149

BONHAM—Fannin County

SAM RAYBURN MEMORIAL VETERANS CENTER See Veterans Affairs North Texas Health Care System, Dallas

TMC BONHAM HOSPITAL (451370), 504 Lipscomb Street, Zip 75418–4028; tel. 903/583–8585 **A**10 18 **F**3 11 15 29 30 34 35 40 46 50 57 59 64 65 70 75 81 87 93 107 108 111 118 119 130 133 135
Primary Contact: Harley Smith, Chief Executive Officer
CFO: Jay Hodges, Chief Financial Officer
CMO: Michael Brown D.O., Chief of Staff
CIO: Jack Farguson, Director Information Technology
CHR: Brenda Bagley, Director Human Resources
CNO: William Kiefer, Chief Nursing Officer
Web address: www.redriverregional.com/
Control: Hospital district or authority, Government, Nonfederal **Service**: General medical and surgical

Staffed Beds: 25 **Admissions**: 743 **Census**: 12 **Outpatient Visits**: 17649
Births: 0 **Total Expense ($000)**: 20037 **Payroll Expense ($000)**: 8290
Personnel: 158

BORGER—Hutchinson County

GOLDEN PLAINS COMMUNITY HOSPITAL (451369), 100 Medical Drive, Zip 79007–7579; tel. 806/467–5700 **A**10 18 **F**11 13 15 29 30 34 35 40 43 45 50 54 59 62 64 65 66 68 70 75 76 77 79 81 85 86 87 89 93 107 108 115 119 127 130 131 132 133 146 147 148 **P**6
Primary Contact: Don Bates, Chief Executive Officer
COO: Melody Henderson Ph.D., R.N., Chief Operating Officer and Chief Nursing Officer
CFO: Dina Hermes, Chief Financial Officer
CMO: Tanay M. Patel M.D., Chief of Staff
CHR: Jennifer Harvey, Director Human Resources
Web address: www.goldenplains.org
Control: Corporation, Investor–owned (for–profit) **Service**: General medical and surgical

Staffed Beds: 16 **Admissions**: 842 **Census**: 7 **Outpatient Visits**: 46026
Births: 300 **Total Expense ($000)**: 27243 **Payroll Expense ($000)**: 8466
Personnel: 201

TX

Many Facility Codes have changed. Please refer to the AHA Guide Code Chart. © 2017 AHA Guide

BRADY—Mcculloch County

HEART OF TEXAS MEMORIAL HOSPITAL (451348), 2008 Nine Road, Zip 76825–7210, Mailing Address: P.O.Box 1150, 76825–1150; tel. 325/597–2901 **A**10 18 **F**15 28 40 43 45 64 81 93 107 111 114 119 127 133 **P**4
Primary Contact: Tim Jones, Chief Executive Officer
CFO: Brad Burnett, Chief Financial Officer
CMO: Pete Castro D.O., Chief of Staff
Web address: www.bradyhospital.com/
Control: Other not–for–profit (including NFP Corporation) **Service**: General medical and surgical

Staffed Beds: 25 **Admissions**: 266 **Census**: 3 **Outpatient Visits**: 15909
Births: 0 **Total Expense ($000)**: 14689 **Payroll Expense ($000)**: 3845
Personnel: 99

BRECKENRIDGE—Stephens County

STEPHENS MEMORIAL HOSPITAL (450498), 200 South Geneva Street, Zip 76424–4799; tel. 254/559–2242 **A**10 20 **F**3 7 8 11 15 28 30 34 35 40 43 45 50 53 56 57 59 63 64 68 69 81 85 87 89 93 97 103 107 114 130 133 146 **P**6
Primary Contact: Matthew Kempton, Chief Executive Officer and Administrator
CFO: Samuel Grant, Chief Financial Officer
CMO: Cynthia Perry M.D., Chief of Staff
CIO: Bobby Thompson, Director Information Technology
CHR: Michelle Funderburg, Director Human Resources
CNO: Alicia Whitt R.N., Chief Nursing Officer
Web address: www.smhtx.com
Control: County, Government, Nonfederal **Service**: General medical and surgical

Staffed Beds: 22 **Admissions**: 283 **Census**: 2 **Outpatient Visits**: 13132
Births: 0 **Total Expense ($000)**: 11121 **Payroll Expense ($000)**: 5586
Personnel: 127

BRENHAM—Washington County

⊠ **SCOTT & WHITE HOSPITAL – BRENHAM (450187)**, 700 Medical Parkway, Zip 77833–5498; tel. 979/337–5000 **A**1 10 **F**3 11 13 15 18 29 30 34 35 38 40 43 50 57 59 65 68 70 75 76 77 79 80 81 82 85 87 93 97 102 107 119 130 132 133 135 146 147 148 149 **S** Baylor Scott & White Health, Dallas, TX
Primary Contact: John R. Hughson, Vice President Operations
CFO: Jane Wellmann, Chief Financial Officer
CMO: Michael Schlabach M.D., Chief Medical Officer
CIO: Sharon Schwartz, Director Medical Records
CHR: Virginia Counts, Manager Human Resources
Web address: www.swbrenham.org
Control: Other not–for–profit (including NFP Corporation) **Service**: General medical and surgical

Staffed Beds: 42 **Admissions**: 1285 **Census**: 14 **Outpatient Visits**: 37912
Births: 338 **Total Expense ($000)**: 31459 **Payroll Expense ($000)**: 14034
Personnel: 190

BROWNFIELD—Terry County

★ **BROWNFIELD REGIONAL MEDICAL CENTER (450399)**, 705 East Felt Street, Zip 79316–3439; tel. 806/637–3551 **A**10 20 **F**3 7 13 28 29 30 34 40 43 45 50 53 57 59 62 64 65 68 75 76 80 81 85 86 87 89 90 93 97 102 107 119 127 130 133 135 148 149 **P**4
Primary Contact: Jerry Jasper, Chief Executive Officer
CFO: Grady Paul Gafford, Chief Financial Officer
CIO: Edgar Rivera, Chief Information Officer
CHR: Kelly Barnett, Human Resource Officer
CNO: Chris Beard, Chief Nursing Officer
Web address: www.brownfield–rmc.org
Control: Hospital district or authority, Government, Nonfederal **Service**: General medical and surgical

Staffed Beds: 26 **Admissions**: 696 **Census**: 6 **Outpatient Visits**: 46058
Births: 130 **Total Expense ($000)**: 17349 **Payroll Expense ($000)**: 8151
Personnel: 185

BROWNSVILLE—Cameron County

☐ **SOUTH TEXAS REHABILITATION HOSPITAL (453092)**, 425 East Alton Gloor Boulevard, Zip 78526–3361; tel. 956/554–6000 **A**1 10 **F**28 29 34 35 59 64 75 77 86 87 90 93 94 96 130 132 148 149 **P**6 **S** Ernest Health, Inc., Albuquerque, NM
Primary Contact: Leo Garza, Chief Executive Officer
CFO: Ernest Nash, Chief Financial Officer
CMO: Christopher Wilson M.D., Inpatient Medical Director
CIO: Deborah Alcocer, Chief Information Officer
CHR: Tony Rodriguez, Director Human Resources
CNO: Aaron Cepeda, Director Nursing Operations
Web address: www.strh.ernesthealth.com
Control: Partnership, Investor–owned (for–profit) **Service**: Rehabilitation

Staffed Beds: 40 **Admissions**: 834 **Census**: 32 **Outpatient Visits**: 3736
Births: 0 **Total Expense ($000)**: 14573 **Payroll Expense ($000)**: 6559
Personnel: 113

★ **VALLEY BAPTIST MEDICAL CENTER–BROWNSVILLE (450028)**, 1040 West Jefferson Street, Zip 78520–6338, Mailing Address: P.O.Box 3590, 78523–3590; tel. 956/698–5400, (Total facility includes 11 beds in nursing home–type unit) **A**5 10 **F**3 11 12 13 15 18 20 22 24 26 29 30 34 35 37 40 43 44 45 49 50 51 54 56 57 59 60 63 64 65 68 70 72 74 75 76 77 79 81 82 84 85 87 89 93 98 100 101 102 103 104 105 106 107 108 110 111 112 114 115 119 126 129 130 132 146 147 148 149 **S** TENET Healthcare Corporation, Dallas, TX
Primary Contact: Leslie Bingham, Senior Vice President and Chief Executive Officer
COO: Marisa Aguilar, Chief Operating Officer
CFO: Harvey Torres, Chief Financial Officer
CMO: Jose L Ayala M.D., Chief Medical Officer
CIO: Mary Garrido, Vice President and Regional Chief Information Officer
CNO: Aniceta Mendoza R.N., MSN, Chief Nursing Officer
Web address: www.valleybaptist.net/brownsville/index.htm
Control: Corporation, Investor–owned (for–profit) **Service**: General medical and surgical

Staffed Beds: 262 **Admissions**: 11258 **Census**: 142 **Outpatient Visits**: 76513 **Births**: 2094 **Total Expense ($000)**: 126031 **Payroll Expense ($000)**: 50782 **Personnel**: 707

⊠ **VALLEY REGIONAL MEDICAL CENTER (450662)**, 100A Alton Gloor Boulevard, Zip 78526–3354, Mailing Address: P.O.Box 3710, 78523–3710; tel. 956/350–7101 **A**1 10 **F**3 11 12 13 15 18 20 22 24 26 29 30 31 32 34 35 40 43 44 45 47 49 50 53 57 59 60 61 64 65 68 70 72 73 74 75 76 77 78 79 81 82 84 85 86 87 89 93 107 108 110 111 114 115 118 119 124 130 132 135 146 147 148 149 **P**7 **S** HCA Healthcare, Nashville, TN
Primary Contact: Art Garza, FACHE, Chief Executive Officer
COO: Steven C Hoelscher, Chief Operating Officer
CFO: Marcia Patterson, Chief Financial Officer
CIO: Carlos Leal, Director Information Technology
CHR: Vicky Kahl, Director Human Resources
Web address: www.valleyregionalmedicalcenter.com
Control: Partnership, Investor–owned (for–profit) **Service**: General medical and surgical

Staffed Beds: 214 **Admissions**: 8835 **Census**: 146 **Outpatient Visits**: 68937
Births: 2421 **Total Expense ($000)**: 120284 **Payroll Expense ($000)**: 56034
Personnel: 646

BROWNWOOD—Brown County

⊠ **BROWNWOOD REGIONAL MEDICAL CENTER (450587)**, 1501 Burnet Road, Zip 76801–8520, Mailing Address: P.O.Box 760, 76804–0760; tel. 325/646–8541, (Total facility includes 20 beds in nursing home–type unit) **A**1 10 20 **F**3 11 13 15 18 28 29 30 31 34 35 39 40 45 48 49 50 51 53 54 56 57 59 63 64 68 70 74 75 76 77 78 79 81 82 85 86 87 93 97 98 103 107 108 111 114 119 120 121 123 128 129 130 132 146 147 148 **P**3 8 **S** Community Health Systems, Inc., Franklin, TN
Primary Contact: Claude E Chip"". Camp III, FACHE, Chief Executive Officer
CFO: Joseph Wooldridge, Chief Financial Officer
CMO: Sammy Horton, Chief of Staff
CIO: Jay Smith, Director Information Systems
CHR: Mikeana Bailey, Director Human Resources
CNO: Alicia R. Kayga R.N., Chief Nursing Officer
Web address: www.brmc–cares.com
Control: Partnership, Investor–owned (for–profit) **Service**: General medical and surgical

Staffed Beds: 188 **Admissions**: 3158 **Census**: 38 **Outpatient Visits**: 73041
Births: 656 **Total Expense ($000)**: 66342 **Payroll Expense ($000)**: 21820
Personnel: 468

TX

Hospital, Medicare Provider Number, Address, Telephone, Approval, Facility, and Physician Codes, Health Care System

★ American Hospital Association (AHA) membership
☐ The Joint Commission accreditation
○ Healthcare Facilities Accreditation Program
◇ DNV Healthcare Inc. accreditation
⇑ Center for Improvement in Healthcare Quality Accreditation
△ Commission on Accreditation of Rehabilitation Facilities (CARF) accreditation

BRYAN—Brazos County

⊞ **CHI ST. JOSEPH REGIONAL HEALTH CENTER (450011)**, 2801 Franciscan Drive, Zip 77802–2599; tel. 979/776–3777 **A**1 2 3 5 10 **F**3 7 11 12 13 15 17 18 20 22 24 28 29 30 31 32 34 35 37 40 42 43 44 45 46 48 49 50 53 54 57 59 64 65 68 70 72 74 75 76 77 78 79 80 81 82 84 85 86 87 89 90 93 96 107 110 111 114 118 119 121 123 124 126 127 129 130 131 132 135 143 144 146 148 **S** Catholic Health Initiatives, Englewood, CO
Primary Contact: Rick D. Napper, President and Chief Executive Officer
CFO: Lisa McNair CPA, Senior Vice President and Chief Financial Officer
CIO: John Phillips, Vice President Information Services
CHR: Michael G Costa, Vice President Human Resources
Web address: www.st-joseph.org
Control: Church operated, Nongovernment, not–for–profit **Service:** General medical and surgical

Staffed Beds: 232 **Admissions:** 13948 **Census:** 163 **Outpatient Visits:** 243604 **Births:** 1572 **Total Expense ($000):** 252824 **Payroll Expense ($000):** 92055 **Personnel:** 1532

☐ **THE PHYSICIANS CENTRE HOSPITAL (450834)**, 3131 University Drive East, Zip 77802–3473; tel. 979/731–3100 **A**1 3 10 **F**3 12 15 29 34 35 40 44 45 51 59 64 74 75 77 79 81 82 85 86 87 89 107 111 114 119 130 131 135
Primary Contact: Kori Rich, Chief Executive Officer
CFO: Paul Tannos, Chief Financial Officer
CMO: Barry Solcher M.D., Chief of Staff
CIO: Shawn Clark, Director Information Systems
CHR: LeeAnn Ford, Director Human Resources and Imaging
CNO: Robert Raymond Lemay R.N., Chief Nursing Officer
Web address: www.thephysicianscentre.com
Control: Corporation, Investor–owned (for–profit) **Service:** Surgical

Staffed Beds: 16 **Admissions:** 285 **Census:** 1 **Outpatient Visits:** 7454 **Births:** 0 **Total Expense ($000):** 15476 **Payroll Expense ($000):** 3938 **Personnel:** 87

BURLESON—Tarrant County

⇑ **BAYLOR EMERGENCY MEDICAL CENTERS – BURLESON (670107)**, 12500 South Freeway Suite 100, Zip 76028–7128; tel. 214/294–6250, (Includes BAYLOR EMERGENCY MEDICAL CENTERS – MANSFIELD, 1776 US 287, Suite 100, Mansfield, Texas, Zip 76063, tel. 214/294–6300; Kyle Kirkpatrick, Chief Executive Officer) **A**10 21 **F**3 40 107 119 149 **P**5 **S** Emerus, The Woodlands, TX
Primary Contact: Kyle Kirkpatrick, Chief Executive Officer
Web address: www.bayloremc.com/burleson
Control: Partnership, Investor–owned (for–profit) **Service:** General medical and surgical

Staffed Beds: 16 **Admissions:** 81 **Census:** 1 **Outpatient Visits:** 23305 **Births:** 0 **Total Expense ($000):** 14148 **Payroll Expense ($000):** 4245 **Personnel:** 94

⊞ **TEXAS HEALTH HUGULEY HOSPITAL FORT WORTH SOUTH (450677)**, 11801 South Freeway, Zip 76028–7021, Mailing Address: P.O.Box 6337, Fort Worth, 76115–0337; tel. 817/293–9110 **A**1 10 **F**3 5 8 11 13 15 17 18 20 22 24 26 28 29 30 31 32 34 35 37 38 40 41 43 45 46 48 49 51 53 54 56 57 59 60 64 65 68 70 71 73 74 75 76 77 78 79 80 81 84 85 86 87 91 93 98 100 101 102 103 104 105 107 108 110 111 114 115 118 119 126 130 131 132 135 146 147 148 **S** Adventist Health System Sunbelt Health Care Corporation, Altamonte Springs, FL
Primary Contact: Kenneth A. Finch, President and Chief Executive Officer
CFO: Jesse Sutton, Senior Vice President and Chief Financial Officer
CMO: Edward Laue M.D., Chief Medical Officer
CIO: Thomas Schoenig, Regional Chief Information Officer
CHR: Laura Shepherd, Director Human Resources
CNO: Tammy Ellis FACHE, R.N., Vice President Patient Services
Web address: www.TexasHealthHuguley.org
Control: Church operated, Nongovernment, not–for–profit **Service:** General medical and surgical

Staffed Beds: 177 **Admissions:** 9905 **Census:** 117 **Outpatient Visits:** 131540 **Births:** 1293 **Total Expense ($000):** 164010 **Payroll Expense ($000):** 64787 **Personnel:** 1115

BURNET—Burnet County

⊞ **SETON HIGHLAND LAKES (451365)**, 3201 South Water Street, Zip 78611–4510, Mailing Address: P.O.Box 1219, 78611–7219; tel. 512/715–3000 **A**1 3 10 18 **F**3 11 15 18 28 29 30 34 35 40 43 44 45 50 51 57 59 64 65 66 68 70 71 74 75 77 78 79 81 82 84 85 86 87 91 92 93 97 107 109 110 111 115 118 119 127 130 132 133 135 146 148 **P**3 8 **S** Ascension Healthcare, Saint Louis, MO
Primary Contact: Karen Litterer, R.N., MSN, Administrator and Chief Operating Officer
COO: Karen Litterer R.N., MSN, Administrator and Chief Operating Officer
CFO: Douglas D Waite, Senior Vice President and Chief Financial Officer
CIO: Gerry Lewis, Chief Information Officer
Web address: www.seton.net
Control: Church operated, Nongovernment, not–for–profit **Service:** General medical and surgical

Staffed Beds: 19 **Admissions:** 1698 **Census:** 9 **Outpatient Visits:** 95892 **Births:** 0 **Total Expense ($000):** 44780 **Payroll Expense ($000):** 14060 **Personnel:** 201

CALDWELL—Burleson County

⊞ **CHI ST. JOSEPH HEALTH BURLESON HOSPITAL (451305)**, 1101 Woodson Drive, Zip 77836–1052, Mailing Address: P.O.Box 360, 77836–0360; tel. 979/567–3245 **A**1 10 18 **F**3 7 11 28 29 30 34 35 40 43 57 59 64 93 119 130 133 135 143 **S** Catholic Health Initiatives, Englewood, CO
CFO: Daniel Goggin, Senior Vice President and Chief Financial Officer
CMO: Kristel Leubner D.O., Chief of Staff
CHR: Jackie Stradtman, Director Human Resources
CNO: Heather Page MSN, Director of Nursing
Web address: www.chistjoseph.org/
Control: Church operated, Nongovernment, not–for–profit **Service:** General medical and surgical

Staffed Beds: 12 **Admissions:** 210 **Census:** 5 **Outpatient Visits:** 15501 **Births:** 0 **Total Expense ($000):** 10297 **Payroll Expense ($000):** 4314 **Personnel:** 59

CAMERON—Milam County

⇑ **CAMERON HOSPITAL (670094)**, 806 North Crockett Avenue, Zip 76520–2553; tel. 254/605–1300 **A**21 **F**3 8 40 41 81 107 114 149
Primary Contact: Troy Zinn, Chief Executive Officer
Web address: www.lrhealthcare.com/cameronhospital
Control: Partnership, Investor–owned (for–profit) **Service:** General medical and surgical

Staffed Beds: 10 **Admissions:** 55 **Census:** 1 **Outpatient Visits:** 6660 **Births:** 0 **Total Expense ($000):** 45179 **Payroll Expense ($000):** 10551 **Personnel:** 378

CANADIAN—Hemphill County

HEMPHILL COUNTY HOSPITAL (450578), 1020 South Fourth Street, Zip 79014–3315; tel. 806/323–6422, (Total facility includes 42 beds in nursing home–type unit) **A**10 20 **F**2 7 29 35 40 45 56 57 62 63 64 68 69 87 89 93 97 102 107 108 130 133 146 148
Primary Contact: Christy Francis, Chief Executive Officer
CFO: Bob Ericson, Chief Financial Officer
CMO: G. Anthony Cook M.D., Medical Director
CIO: Brian Goza, Chief Information Officer
CHR: David Troublefield, Chief Communications Officer
CNO: Debra Sappenfield R.N., Chief Nursing Officer
Web address: www.hchdst.org
Control: Hospital district or authority, Government, Nonfederal **Service:** General medical and surgical

Staffed Beds: 61 **Admissions:** 251 **Census:** 27 **Outpatient Visits:** 13586 **Births:** 0 **Total Expense ($000):** 13070 **Payroll Expense ($000):** 5632 **Personnel:** 91

CARRIZO SPRINGS—Dimmit County

★ **DIMMIT REGIONAL HOSPITAL (450620)**, 704 Hospital Drive, Zip 78834–3836, Mailing Address: P.O.Box 1016, 78834–7016; tel. 830/876–2424 **A**10 20 **F**11 13 40 43 45 57 62 64 70 76 81 89 93 107 115 119 144
Primary Contact: Ernest Flores Jr, Chief Executive Officer
CFO: Alma Melendez, Controller
Web address: www.dcmhospital.org
Control: Other not–for–profit (including NFP Corporation) **Service:** General medical and surgical

Staffed Beds: 35 **Admissions:** 904 **Census:** 9 **Outpatient Visits:** 21956 **Births:** 202 **Total Expense ($000):** 19795 **Payroll Expense ($000):** 8843 **Personnel:** 180

CARROLLTON—Denton County

⊞ **BAYLOR SCOTT & WHITE MEDICAL CENTER – CARROLLTON (450730)**, 4343 North Josey Lane, Zip 75010–4691; tel. 972/394–1010 **A**1 2 10 **F**3 11 12 13 15 18 20 22 26 29 30 31 34 35 38 40 41 44 45 46 47 48 49 50 51 56 57 60 61 64 65 66 70 72 74 75 76 77 78 79 81 84 85 87 92 93 102 107 108 109 110 111 112 113 114 115 116 117 118 119 126 129 130 131 132 135 141 146 147 148 **S** Baylor Scott & White Health, Dallas, TX
Primary Contact: Jerri Garrison, Interim President
CFO: James McNatt, Chief Financial Officer
CMO: Matthew Smith M.D., Vice President Medical Affairs and Chief Medical Officer
CIO: Paul Ratcliff, Director Information Services
CHR: Erica Calime, Director Human Resources
CNO: Barbara Vaughn R.N., Chief Nursing Officer
Web address: www.baylorhealth.com
Control: Other not–for–profit (including NFP Corporation) **Service:** General medical and surgical

Staffed Beds: 136 **Admissions:** 5553 **Census:** 69 **Outpatient Visits:** 55689 **Births:** 952 **Total Expense ($000):** 142948 **Payroll Expense ($000):** 49700 **Personnel:** 489

Many Facility Codes have changed. Please refer to the AHA Guide Code Chart. © 2017 AHA Guide

TX

☐ **CARROLLTON SPRINGS (454119)**, 2225 Parker Road, Zip 75010–4711;
tel. 972/242–4114 **A**1 10 **F**4 98 102 103 104 105
Primary Contact: Lance Folske, Chief Executive Officer
Web address: www.carrolltonsprings.com
Control: Corporation, Investor–owned (for–profit) **Service**: Psychiatric

Staffed Beds: 45 **Admissions:** 1630 **Census:** 43 **Outpatient Visits:** 17481
Births: 0 **Total Expense ($000):** 12061 **Payroll Expense ($000):** 7519
Personnel: 148

FIRST TEXAS HOSPITAL, 1401 East Trinity Mills Road, Zip 75006; tel. 972/810–
0700 **F**3 29 30 35 40 42 45 50 68 70 75 79 81 82 85 87 102 107 114 119 130
Primary Contact: Terri Shovald, Chief Executive Officer
Web address: www.firsttexashospital.com/
Control: Corporation, Investor–owned (for–profit) **Service**: General medical and
surgical

Staffed Beds: 28 **Admissions:** 480 **Census:** 8 **Outpatient Visits:** 145569
Births: 0 **Total Expense ($000):** 113745 **Payroll Expense ($000):** 28996
Personnel: 763

⊠ **SELECT SPECIALTY HOSPITAL–DALLAS (452022)**, 2329 West Parker Road,
Zip 75010–4713; **A**1 10 **F**1 3 29 56 74 75 77 85 91 107 114 119 130 135
148 **S** Select Medical Corporation, Mechanicsburg, PA
Primary Contact: Ty Burgess, Chief Executive Officer
Web address: www.firsttexashospital.com/
Control: Corporation, Investor–owned (for–profit) **Service**: Acute long–term care
hospital

Staffed Beds: 60 **Admissions:** 253 **Census:** 19 **Outpatient Visits:** 0 **Births:** 0
Total Expense ($000): 14085 **Payroll Expense ($000):** 6542 **Personnel:** 107

CARTHAGE—Panola County

⊠ **EAST TEXAS MEDICAL CENTER CARTHAGE (450210)**, 409 Cottage Road,
Zip 75633–1466; tel. 903/693–3841 **A**1 10 20 **F**3 8 11 15 28 29 30 34 35 40
43 45 50 57 59 64 65 75 81 85 107 108 110 111 115 119 127 129 145 146
149 150 **S** East Texas Medical Center Regional Healthcare System, Tyler, TX
Primary Contact: Gary Mikeal. Hudson, Administrator
COO: Gary Mikeal Hudson, Administrator
CFO: Phillip A Caron, Chief Financial Officer
CMO: Salah Almohammed, Chief of Staff
CIO: Renee Lawhorn, Director Medical Records
CHR: Amber Cox, Director Human Resources
CNO: Judy Peterson R.N., Chief Nursing Officer
Web address: www.etmc.org
Control: Other not–for–profit (including NFP Corporation) **Service**: General
medical and surgical

Staffed Beds: 23 **Admissions:** 628 **Census:** 5 **Outpatient Visits:** 66754
Births: 0 **Total Expense ($000):** 19338 **Payroll Expense ($000):** 6529
Personnel: 131

CEDAR PARK—Williamson County

★ ⇑ **BAYLOR SCOTT & WHITE EMERGENCY MEDICAL CENTER– CEDAR
PARK (670087)**, 900 East Whitestone Boulevard, Zip 78613–9093;
tel. 512/684–4911 **A**10 21 **F**3 29 40 75 87 107 119 149 **P**5
Primary Contact: Kyle Kirkpatrick, Chief Executive Officer
Web address: www.sweh.org
Control: Partnership, Investor–owned (for–profit) **Service**: General medical and
surgical

Staffed Beds: 8 **Admissions:** 20 **Census:** 1 **Outpatient Visits:** 8637 **Births:** 0
Total Expense ($000): 5321 **Payroll Expense ($000):** 1892 **Personnel:** 38

⊠ **CEDAR PARK REGIONAL MEDICAL CENTER (670043)**, 1401 Medical
Parkway, Zip 78613–7763; tel. 512/528–7000 **A**1 5 10 **F**3 12 15 18 20 22
28 29 34 35 40 43 45 46 47 49 50 54 57 59 64 70 73 74 75 76 77 78 79 81
82 85 87 89 93 107 108 110 111 114 115 118 119 126 129 130 132 135
146 147 148 **S** Community Health Systems, Inc., Franklin, TN
Primary Contact: Brad D. Holland, Chief Executive Officer
COO: Curt M. Junkins, Chief Operating Officer
CFO: Erich Wallschlaeger, Chief Financial Officer
CIO: Brad Hoar, Director Information and Technology
CHR: Jeffery Ward, Director Human Resources
CNO: Krista Baty R.N., Chief Nursing Officer
Web address: www.cedarparkregional.com
Control: Corporation, Investor–owned (for–profit) **Service**: General medical and
surgical

Staffed Beds: 93 **Admissions:** 4819 **Census:** 45 **Outpatient Visits:** 53085
Births: 1117 **Total Expense ($000):** 89312 **Payroll Expense ($000):** 30913
Personnel: 563

CHILDRESS—Childress County

★ **CHILDRESS REGIONAL MEDICAL CENTER (450369)**, Highway 83 North,
Zip 79201–5800, Mailing Address: P.O.Box 1030, 79201–1030; tel. 940/937–6371
A10 20 **F**3 7 8 13 15 29 31 32 34 35 40 43 45 50 56 57 59 60 61 62 63 64 65
66 68 76 77 78 79 81 84 91 92 93 107 111 114 119 127 129 130 133 **P**6
Primary Contact: John Henderson, Chief Executive Officer
COO: Holly Holcomb R.N., Chief Operating Officer
CFO: Kevin Latimer, Chief Financial Officer
CMO: Dustin Pratt M.D., Chief of Staff
CIO: Holly Holcomb R.N., Chie Operating Officer
CHR: Gayle Cannon, Director Human Resources
CNO: Sulynn Mester R.N., Chief Nursing Officer
Web address: www.childresshospital.com
Control: Hospital district or authority, Government, Nonfederal **Service**: General
medical and surgical

Staffed Beds: 35 **Admissions:** 939 **Census:** 7 **Outpatient Visits:** 169859
Births: 211 **Total Expense ($000):** 27647 **Payroll Expense ($000):** 13309
Personnel: 241

CHILLICOTHE—Hardeman County

CHILLICOTHE HOSPITAL DISTRICT (451326), 303 Avenue 'I', Zip 79225,
Mailing Address: P.O.Box 370, 79225–0370; tel. 940/852–5131 **A**10 18 **F**29 34
40 43 57 59 69 81 89 132 133 148 **P**5
Primary Contact: Linda Hall, Administrator and Chief Executive Officer
COO: Linda Hall, Administrator and Chief Executive Officer
CFO: Linda Hall, Administrator and Chief Executive Officer
CMO: Sherry L Wolf M.D., Chief of Medical Staff
CIO: Kathy Busby, Medical Record Technician
CHR: Linda Hall, Administrator and Chief Executive Officer
CNO: Stormy Smith, Chief Nursing Officer
Web address: www.chillhd.org
Control: Hospital district or authority, Government, Nonfederal **Service**: General
medical and surgical

Staffed Beds: 13 **Admissions:** 40 **Census:** 1 **Outpatient Visits:** 7016 **Births:** 0
Total Expense ($000): 2485 **Payroll Expense ($000):** 1004 **Personnel:** 23

CLEBURNE—Johnson County

⊠ **TEXAS HEALTH HARRIS METHODIST HOSPITAL CLEBURNE (450148)**, 201
Walls Drive, Zip 76033–4007; tel. 817/641–2551 **A**1 10 **F**3 11 13 15 18 29 30 32
34 35 40 43 44 47 48 57 59 64 65 66 68 70 75 76 77 79 81 85 89 93 107 108
110 114 119 124 126 130 146 147 148 **S** Texas Health Resources, Arlington, TX
Primary Contact: Lorrie Normand, R.N., President
CFO: Shelly Miland, Group Finance Officer
CMO: Judy Laviolette M.D., Chief Medical Officer
CIO: Brenda Taylor, Director Information Systems
CHR: Marsha Adams, Interim Director Human Resources
CNO: Vicki Brockman R.N., Chief Nursing Officer
Web address: www.texashealth.org
Control: Other not–for–profit (including NFP Corporation) **Service**: General
medical and surgical

Staffed Beds: 92 **Admissions:** 3849 **Census:** 36 **Outpatient Visits:** 45727
Births: 453 **Total Expense ($000):** 67875 **Payroll Expense ($000):** 25888
Personnel: 341

CLEVELAND—Liberty County

CLEVELAND EMERGENCY HOSPITAL, 1017 South Travis Avenue, Zip 77327–
5152; tel. 281/592–5400 (Nonreporting)
Primary Contact: Don Vickers, Chief Executive Officer
Control: Other not–for–profit (including NFP Corporation) **Service**: General
medical and surgical

Staffed Beds: 40

CLIFTON—Bosque County

★ ⇑ **GOODALL–WITCHER HOSPITAL AUTHORITY (450052)**, 101 South Avenue
'T', Zip 76634–1897, Mailing Address: P.O.Box 549, 76634–0549; tel. 254/675–
8322 **A**10 18 21 **F**3 11 13 15 28 29 30 34 35 36 40 43 45 50 53 57 59 62 64
65 68 77 81 93 107 108 114 119 127 130 133 146 147 148 **P**3
Primary Contact: Adam Willmann, President and Chief Executive Officer
CFO: Vicki Gloff, Chief Financial Officer
CMO: Kevin Blanton D.O., Chief of Staff
CHR: Jennie Oldham, Director Human Resources
CNO: Donna Nichols R.N., Chief Nursing Officer
Web address: www.gwhf.org
Control: Hospital district or authority, Government, Nonfederal **Service**: General
medical and surgical

Staffed Beds: 25 **Admissions:** 462 **Census:** 8 **Outpatient Visits:** 53845
Births: 56 **Total Expense ($000):** 19067 **Payroll Expense ($000):** 7814
Personnel: 183

COLEMAN—Coleman County

COLEMAN COUNTY MEDICAL CENTER (451347), 310 South Pecos Street, Zip 76834–4159; tel. 325/625–2135 **A**10 18 **F**3 11 13 28 29 32 34 35 40 41 43 44 45 50 54 56 57 59 62 63 64 65 68 81 83 84 86 87 91 93 97 107 114 127 131 133 144 146 147 148 149 150 **S** Preferred Management Corporation, Shawnee, OK
Primary Contact: Clay Vogel, Administrator and Chief Executive Officer
CMO: Paul Reynolds M.D., Medical Director
CIO: Harvey Ramirez, Chief Information Officer
CHR: Sue Titsworth, Director Human Resources
CNO: Melissa Ereman R.N., Chief Nursing Officer
Web address: www.colemantexas.org/hospital.html
Control: Corporation, Investor–owned (for–profit) **Service**: General medical and surgical

Staffed Beds: 25 **Admissions:** 595 **Census:** 9 **Outpatient Visits:** 20412 **Births:** 19 **Total Expense ($000):** 10857 **Payroll Expense ($000):** 4851 **Personnel:** 116

COLLEGE STATION—Brazos County

COLLEGE STATION MEDICAL CENTER (450299), 1604 Rock Prairie Road, Zip 77845–8345; tel. 979/764–5100 **A**1 3 5 10 **F**3 11 13 15 18 20 22 24 26 28 29 30 31 34 40 43 45 46 49 53 57 61 70 72 74 76 77 78 79 81 82 84 85 87 89 90 91 93 107 108 111 113 115 118 119 126 127 129 130 131 132 135 146 147 148 **P**7 **S** Community Health Systems, Inc., Franklin, TN
Primary Contact: America S. Farrell, FACHE, Chief Executive Officer
COO: Vicky Cha Bridier, Chief Operating Officer
CFO: Kenneth Pannell, Chief Financial Officer
CIO: Daphane Hartman, Director Information Systems
CHR: Sharon Bond, Director Human Resources
CNO: Sherri Welch R.N., Chief Nursing Officer
Web address: www.csmedcenter.com
Control: Corporation, Investor–owned (for–profit) **Service**: General medical and surgical

Staffed Beds: 148 **Admissions:** 4134 **Census:** 41 **Outpatient Visits:** 48465 **Births:** 1108 **Total Expense ($000):** 82418 **Payroll Expense ($000):** 26850 **Personnel:** 529

ROCK PRAIRIE BEHAVIORAL HEALTH (454125), 3550 Normand Drive, Zip 77845–6399; tel. 979/703–8848 **A**1 10 **F**5 29 30 34 35 38 40 57 98 99 101 102 103 105 130 135 **S** Strategic Behavioral Health, LLC, Memphis, TN
Primary Contact: Jackie St. Germain, Chief Executive Officer
CMO: Jason Boley M.D., Medical Director
CHR: MaxAnne Jones, Director Human Resources
Control: Partnership, Investor–owned (for–profit) **Service**: Psychiatric

Staffed Beds: 72 **Admissions:** 1602 **Census:** 39 **Outpatient Visits:** 4015 **Births:** 0 **Total Expense ($000):** 11535 **Payroll Expense ($000):** 5827 **Personnel:** 122

SCOTT & WHITE HOSPITAL – COLLEGE STATION (670088), 700 Scott & White Drive, Zip 77845; tel. 979/207–0100 **A**1 5 10 **F**3 7 12 13 14 15 18 20 22 24 26 28 29 30 31 34 35 40 43 45 46 47 48 49 50 51 56 57 59 61 64 65 68 70 72 73 74 75 76 77 78 79 81 82 83 84 85 87 89 93 94 97 101 102 103 104 107 108 110 111 114 115 116 118 119 123 124 126 129 130 131 145 146 147 148 **S** Baylor Scott & White Health, Dallas, TX
Primary Contact: Jason Jennings, FACHE, Chief Executive Officer
Web address: www.sw.org/location/college–station–hospital
Control: Other not–for–profit (including NFP Corporation) **Service**: General medical and surgical

Staffed Beds: 119 **Admissions:** 5421 **Census:** 52 **Outpatient Visits:** 238911 **Births:** 1284 **Total Expense ($000):** 133960 **Payroll Expense ($000):** 41502 **Personnel:** 880

COLORADO CITY—Mitchell County

★ **MITCHELL COUNTY HOSPITAL (451342)**, 997 West Interstate 20, Zip 79512–2685; tel. 325/728–3431 **A**10 18 **F**3 7 11 28 29 34 35 40 43 45 50 53 57 59 64 65 68 71 81 86 87 93 107 108 109 114 119 127 133 135 146 **P**6
Primary Contact: Robbie Dewberry, Chief Executive Officer
CFO: Joe Wright, Chief Financial Officer
CMO: Dee A Roach M.D., Chief of Staff
CHR: Deana Overton, Director Human Resources
CNO: Donna Goebel M.D., Chief Nursing Officer
Web address: www.mitchellcountyhospital.com
Control: Hospital district or authority, Government, Nonfederal **Service**: General medical and surgical

Staffed Beds: 25 **Admissions:** 367 **Census:** 6 **Outpatient Visits:** 14280 **Births:** 0 **Total Expense ($000):** 14170 **Payroll Expense ($000):** 8500 **Personnel:** 183

COLUMBUS—Colorado County

COLUMBUS COMMUNITY HOSPITAL (450370), 110 Shult Drive, Zip 78934–3010; tel. 979/732–2371 **A**5 10 20 **F**11 13 15 29 35 40 43 57 68 76 79 81 89 107 110 111 114 119 127 130 133 135 149
Primary Contact: James Vanek, Chief Executive Officer
CFO: Regina Wicke, Chief Financial Officer
CMO: Robert Katz M.D., Chief of Staff
CIO: Ashley Mathis, Privacy Officer
CHR: Janie Hammonds, Human Resources Officer
CNO: Jeno Hargrove R.N., Director of Nursing
Web address: www.columbusch.com
Control: Other not–for–profit (including NFP Corporation) **Service**: General medical and surgical

Staffed Beds: 40 **Admissions:** 1055 **Census:** 11 **Outpatient Visits:** 79762 **Births:** 217 **Total Expense ($000):** 27309 **Payroll Expense ($000):** 8296 **Personnel:** 148

COMANCHE—Comanche County

★ **COMANCHE COUNTY MEDICAL CENTER (451382)**, 10201 Highway 16 North, Zip 76442–4462; tel. 254/879–4900 **A**10 18 **F**3 11 15 28 29 30 34 35 40 43 45 50 53 57 59 64 65 75 77 79 81 85 86 87 93 97 107 108 110 111 115 119 127 129 130 131 133 145 146 147 148
Primary Contact: David Freshour, Chief Executive Officer
CFO: David Freshour, Chief Financial Officer
CMO: Guyle Donham M.D., Chief of Staff
CIO: Ismelda Garza, Director Information Systems
CHR: Karen DeLavan, Interim Director Human Resources
CNO: Colleen Jedlicka R.N., JD, Chief Nursing Officer
Web address: www.comanchecmc.org
Control: Other not–for–profit (including NFP Corporation) **Service**: General medical and surgical

Staffed Beds: 23 **Admissions:** 655 **Census:** 7 **Outpatient Visits:** 50723 **Births:** 0 **Total Expense ($000):** 22022 **Payroll Expense ($000):** 6836 **Personnel:** 166

CONROE—Montgomery County

ASPIRE HOSPITAL (454112), 2006 South Loop 336 West, Suite 500, Zip 77304–3315; tel. 936/647–3500 **A**1 10 **F**3 34 54 56 57 59 78 79 87 93 96 98 101 103 105 107 108 111 112 113 114 115 118 119 120 121 123 124 129 130 131 149 **P**6
Primary Contact: Kostas Gotsoulias, Interim Chief Executive Officer
CFO: Bob Gray, Chief Financial Officer
CIO: John Heemann, Vice President and Chief Information Officer
CHR: Angela Walker, Manager Human Resources
CNO: Troy Ryder, Director of Nursing
Web address: www.aspirehospital.com
Control: Partnership, Investor–owned (for–profit) **Service**: Psychiatric

Staffed Beds: 28 **Admissions:** 746 **Census:** 18 **Outpatient Visits:** 13405 **Births:** 0 **Total Expense ($000):** 11005 **Payroll Expense ($000):** 4617 **Personnel:** 76

CHG CORNERSTONE HOSPITAL CONROE (452107), 1500 Grand Lake Drive, Zip 77304–2891; tel. 936/523–1800 **A**1 10 **F**1 3 29 40 70 74 75 77 79 85 86 87 90 91 119 130 148 149 **S** Cornerstone Healthcare Group, Dallas, TX
Primary Contact: Suzanne Kretschmer, Chief Executive Officer
Web address: www.chghospitals.com/conroe/
Control: Partnership, Investor–owned (for–profit) **Service**: Acute long–term care hospital

Staffed Beds: 41 **Admissions:** 477 **Census:** 30 **Outpatient Visits:** 0 **Births:** 0 **Total Expense ($000):** 14668 **Payroll Expense ($000):** 6087 **Personnel:** 85

CONROE REGIONAL MEDICAL CENTER (450222), 504 Medical Boulevard, Zip 77304, Mailing Address: P.O.Box 1538, 77305–1538; tel. 936/539–1111 **A**1 3 10 13 **F**3 11 12 13 15 17 18 20 22 24 26 28 29 31 34 35 40 41 43 45 46 53 54 57 59 64 68 70 72 73 74 75 76 78 79 81 82 85 86 89 90 91 93 107 108 111 114 115 118 119 121 124 129 130 132 135 146 147 148 **S** HCA Healthcare, Nashville, TN
Primary Contact: Matt Davis, FACHE, Chief Executive Officer
COO: Reed Hammond, Chief Operating Officer
CFO: Thomas A Holt, Chief Financial Officer
CMO: Mujtaba Ali–Khan D.O., Chief Medical Officer
CIO: Jeremy Fuller, Director Information Systems
CHR: Diana Howell, Director Human Resources
Web address: www.conroeregional.com/
Control: Partnership, Investor–owned (for–profit) **Service**: General medical and surgical

Staffed Beds: 301 **Admissions:** 15087 **Census:** 203 **Outpatient Visits:** 124916 **Births:** 1309 **Total Expense ($000):** 208527 **Payroll Expense ($000):** 76080 **Personnel:** 1017

Many Facility Codes have changed. Please refer to the AHA Guide Code Chart. © 2017 AHA Guide

TX

✠ **HEALTHSOUTH REHABILITATION HOSPITAL THE WOODLANDS (453059)**, 18550 'IH' 45 South, Zip 77384; tel. 281/364–2000 **A**1 10 **F**3 28 29 34 35 44 57 59 62 65 68 74 75 77 79 82 86 87 90 91 95 96 130 132 148 149 **S** HEALTHSOUTH Corporation, Birmingham, AL
Primary Contact: Jeff Crawford, Chief Executive Officer
CMO: Ben Agana M.D., Medical Director
CHR: Valerie Wells, Manager Human Resources
Web address: www.healthsouththewoodlands.com
Control: Corporation, Investor–owned (for–profit) **Service:** Rehabilitation

Staffed Beds: 84 **Admissions:** 1042 **Census:** 34 **Outpatient Visits:** 0 **Births:** 0
Total Expense ($000): 17352 **Payroll Expense ($000):** 7707 **Personnel:** 147

CORINTH—Denton County

ATRIUM MEDICAL CENTER OF CORINTH (452111), 3305 Corinth Parkway, Zip 76208–5380; tel. 940/270–4100 **A**10 **F**1 3 28 29 40 45 47 60 64 68 70 75 77 81 86 87 96 107 111 114 119 148 **P**2
Primary Contact: Barbara Callaghan, Interim Chief Executive Officer
COO: Kathy Mason, Chief Operating Officer
CFO: Anbu Nachimuthu, Chief Financial Officer
CMO: Jalil Kahn M.D., Chief of Staff
CIO: Wendy Keller, Director Health Information Management
CHR: Melissa Dovel, Manager Human Resources
CNO: Michelle Gray, Nurse Executive
Web address: www.atriumhealthcare.net
Control: Corporation, Investor–owned (for–profit) **Service:** Acute long–term care hospital

Staffed Beds: 60 **Admissions:** 135 **Census:** 7 **Outpatient Visits:** 2265
Births: 0 **Total Expense ($000):** 6238 **Payroll Expense ($000):** 3743

CORPUS CHRISTI—Nueces County

✠ **CHRISTUS SPOHN HOSPITAL CORPUS CHRISTI MEMORIAL (450046)**, 2606 Hospital Boulevard, Zip 78405–1804, Mailing Address: P.O.Box 5280, 78405; tel. 361/902–4000, (Includes CHRISTUS SPOHN HOSPITAL CORPUS CHRISTI SHORELINE, 600 Elizabeth Street, Corpus Christi, Texas, Zip 78404–2235, tel. 361/881–3000; Brian Connor, FACHE, President; CHRISTUS SPOHN HOSPITAL CORPUS CHRISTUS SOUTH, 5950 Saratoga, Corpus Christi, Texas, Zip 78414–4100, tel. 361/985–5000) (Total facility includes 22 beds in nursing home–type unit) **A**1 2 3 5 10 **F**3 11 13 15 17 18 20 22 24 26 28 29 30 31 34 35 37 38 39 40 43 45 46 47 48 49 50 51 53 54 56 57 59 60 64 65 67 70 71 72 74 75 76 77 78 79 81 84 85 87 90 91 92 93 94 96 98 99 100 101 102 103 107 108 111 114 115 118 119 120 121 123 124 126 127 128 130 131 141 142 145 146 147 148 **P**8 **S** CHRISTUS Health, Irving, TX
Primary Contact: Brian Connor, FACHE, President
CFO: Brower Pam, Chief Financial Officer
CMO: Charles T. Volk M.D., Regional Chief Medical Officer
CHR: Mary LaFrancois, Vice President Human Resources
CNO: Jennifer Gentry R.N., Chief Nursing Officer
Web address: www.christusspohn.org
Control: Church operated, Nongovernment, not–for–profit **Service:** General medical and surgical

Staffed Beds: 579 **Admissions:** 30132 **Census:** 448 **Outpatient Visits:** 259256 **Births:** 2598 **Total Expense ($000):** 608635 **Payroll Expense ($000):** 176598 **Personnel:** 2659

✠ **CORPUS CHRISTI MEDICAL CENTER (450788)**, 3315 South Alameda Street, Zip 78411–1883, Mailing Address: P.O.Box 8991, 78468–8991; tel. 361/761–1400, (Includes BAYVIEW BEHAVIORAL HOSPITAL, 6629 Wooldridge Road, Corpus Christi, Texas, Zip 78414, tel. 361/986–9444; CORPUS CHRISTI MEDICAL CENTER BAY AREA, 7101 South Padre Island Drive, Corpus Christi, Texas, Zip 78412–4999, tel. 361/985–1200) **A**1 10 13 **F**3 4 5 11 12 13 15 17 18 20 22 24 26 28 29 31 34 35 37 38 40 42 44 47 49 50 53 57 58 59 64 68 70 72 73 74 75 76 77 78 79 81 82 85 86 87 90 93 97 98 99 100 101 102 103 104 105 107 108 110 111 114 115 118 119 120 121 123 124 126 130 131 132 146 147 148 149 150 **P**3 8 **S** HCA Healthcare, Nashville, TN
Primary Contact: Jay Woodall, FACHE, Chief Executive Officer
CFO: Chris Nicosia, Chief Financial Officer
CMO: Lawrence Brenner M.D., Chief of Staff
CHR: Michael Conwill, Director Human Resources
CNO: Kathleen A Rubano MSN, R.N., Chief Nursing Officer
Web address: www.ccmedicalcenter.com
Control: Partnership, Investor–owned (for–profit) **Service:** General medical and surgical

Staffed Beds: 416 **Admissions:** 19383 **Census:** 254 **Outpatient Visits:** 126603 **Births:** 4521 **Total Expense ($000):** 274690 **Payroll Expense ($000):** 90880 **Personnel:** 1561

✠ △ **DRISCOLL CHILDREN'S HOSPITAL (453301)**, 3533 South Alameda Street, Zip 78411–1785, Mailing Address: P.O.Box 6530, 78466–6530; tel. 361/694–5000 **A**1 3 5 7 10 **F**3 7 11 12 19 21 23 25 27 29 30 31 32 34 35 38 39 40 41 43 49 50 54 55 57 58 59 60 61 64 65 68 72 74 75 77 78 79 81 82 85 86 87 88 89 92 93 97 99 104 107 108 111 115 118 119 130 132 134 138 143 144 146 148 149 150
Primary Contact: Steve Woerner, President and Chief Executive Officer
COO: Donna Quinn, Vice President Operations
CFO: Eric Hamon, Executive Vice President and Chief Financial Officer
CIO: Miguel Perez, III, Chief Information Officer
CHR: Bill Larsen, Vice President Human Resources
CNO: Julie A. Pina, Assistant Vice President Patient Care Services and Chief Nursing Officer
Web address: www.driscollchildrens.org
Control: Other not–for–profit (including NFP Corporation) **Service:** Children's general medical and surgical

Staffed Beds: 162 **Admissions:** 3656 **Census:** 78 **Outpatient Visits:** 166798 **Births:** 0 **Total Expense ($000):** 245663 **Payroll Expense ($000):** 96754 **Personnel:** 2182

KINDRED HOSPITAL–CORPUS CHRISTI See Post Acute Medical Specialty Hospital Of Corpus Christi – South

✠ **POST ACUTE MEDICAL SPECIALTY HOSPITAL OF CORPUS CHRISTI – NORTH (452086)**, 600 Elizabeth Street, 3rd Floor, Zip 78404–2235; tel. 361/881–3223 **A**1 10 **F**1 3 29 75 85 87 91 148 **P**5 **S** Post Acute Medical, LLC, Enola, PA
Primary Contact: Hector Bernal, Chief Executive Officer
Web address: www.postacutemedical.com/our–facilities/hospitals/post–acute–medical–specialty–hospital–corpus–christi/
Control: Corporation, Investor–owned (for–profit) **Service:** Acute long–term care hospital

Staffed Beds: 22 **Admissions:** 346 **Census:** 20 **Outpatient Visits:** 0 **Births:** 0
Total Expense ($000): 10113 **Payroll Expense ($000):** 3979 **Personnel:** 68

✠ **POST ACUTE MEDICAL SPECIALTY HOSPITAL OF CORPUS CHRISTI – SOUTH (452092)**, 6226 Saratoga Boulevard, Zip 78414–3421; tel. 361/986–1600 **A**1 10 **F**1 3 29 34 35 45 59 74 75 77 79 82 86 87 107 130 148 **S** Post Acute Medical, LLC, Enola, PA
Primary Contact: Michael L. Pierce, Chief Executive Officer
CFO: Eva De La Paz, Chief Financial Officer
CHR: Kasey Parkey, Coordinator Payroll and Benefits
Web address: www.postacutemedical.com
Control: Corporation, Investor–owned (for–profit) **Service:** Acute long–term care hospital

Staffed Beds: 74 **Admissions:** 590 **Census:** 37 **Outpatient Visits:** 0 **Births:** 0
Total Expense ($000): 20098 **Payroll Expense ($000):** 8190 **Personnel:** 137

☐ **SOUTH TEXAS SURGICAL HOSPITAL (670061)**, 6130 Parkway Drive, Zip 78414–2455; tel. 361/993–2000 **A**1 3 10 **F**3 29 40 45 54 64 68 75 79 81 82 85 119 126 130 149 **S** National Surgical Healthcare, Chicago, IL
Primary Contact: James Murphy, Chief Executive Officer
CFO: Julie Wittwer, Chief Financial Officer
CMO: Michael Mintz M.D., Chief Medical Officer
CHR: Lory Beth Smith, Manager Human Resource
CNO: Jan O'Donnell, Chief Nursing Officer
Web address: www.southtexassurgicalhospital.com
Control: Partnership, Investor–owned (for–profit) **Service:** Surgical

Staffed Beds: 20 **Admissions:** 836 **Census:** 7 **Outpatient Visits:** 17708 **Births:** 0 **Total Expense ($000):** 35549 **Payroll Expense ($000):** 9642 **Personnel:** 192

CORSICANA—Navarro County

✠ **NAVARRO REGIONAL HOSPITAL (450447)**, 3201 West State Highway 22, Zip 75110–2469; tel. 903/654–6800 **A**1 10 19 **F**3 11 13 15 18 28 29 30 34 35 39 40 43 45 49 50 51 54 57 60 64 68 70 75 76 79 81 82 85 93 107 108 110 111 114 115 119 124 129 132 135 146 148 **P**7 **S** Community Health Systems, Inc., Franklin, TN
Primary Contact: Michael K. Stewart, Chief Executive Officer
CFO: Shea C. Brock, Chief Financial Officer
CIO: Bryan Chilton, Director Information Systems
CHR: Melodee Pugh, Director Human Resources
CNO: Dona E Townsend, Chief Nursing Officer
Web address: www.navarrohospital.com
Control: Partnership, Investor–owned (for–profit) **Service:** General medical and surgical

Staffed Beds: 49 **Admissions:** 2509 **Census:** 21 **Outpatient Visits:** 47872 **Births:** 539 **Total Expense ($000):** 36464 **Payroll Expense ($000):** 14744 **Personnel:** 240

TX

Hospital, Medicare Provider Number, Address, Telephone, Approval, Facility, and Physician Codes, Health Care System

★ American Hospital Association (AHA) membership
☐ The Joint Commission accreditation
○ Healthcare Facilities Accreditation Program
◇ DNV Healthcare Inc. accreditation
⇑ Center for Improvement in Healthcare Quality Accreditation
△ Commission on Accreditation of Rehabilitation Facilities (CARF) accreditation

CRANE—Crane County

★ **CRANE MEMORIAL HOSPITAL (451353)**, 1310 South Alford Street, Zip 79731–3899; tel. 432/558–3555 **A**10 18 **F**3 29 32 34 40 57 59 64 65 68 75 81 86 97 107 114 119 127 133 145 147 148 **P**2 6
Primary Contact: Dianne Yeager, Chief Executive Officer
CFO: Daniel Ibarra, Chief Financial Officer
CMO: Sixta Gumato M.D., Chief Medical Officer
CHR: Becky Esparza, Human Resources
CNO: Pat Touchstone, Chief Nursing Officer
Web address: www.cranememorial.org
Control: Hospital district or authority, Government, Nonfederal **Service:** General medical and surgical

Staffed Beds: 10 **Admissions:** 86 **Census:** 1 **Outpatient Visits:** 9887 **Births:** 0 **Total Expense ($000):** 6583 **Payroll Expense ($000):** 2904 **Personnel:** 51

CROSBYTON—Crosby County

CROSBYTON CLINIC HOSPITAL (451345), 710 West Main Street, Zip 79322–2143; tel. 806/675–2382 **A**10 18 **F**7 10 29 34 40 50 57 59 63 64 68 87 93 119 127 130 133 148 **P**6
Primary Contact: Debra Miller, Administrator
CFO: Cherie Parkhill, Chief Financial Officer
CMO: Steve B Alley M.D., Chief of Staff
CHR: Janie Cantu, Director Human Resources
CNO: Freda Bartlett, Director of Nursing
Web address: www.crosbytonclinichospital.com
Control: Other not–for–profit (including NFP Corporation) **Service:** General medical and surgical

Staffed Beds: 7 **Admissions:** 158 **Census:** 2 **Outpatient Visits:** 16506 **Births:** 0 **Total Expense ($000):** 6424 **Payroll Expense ($000):** 2832 **Personnel:** 78

CUERO—Dewitt County

★ **CUERO COMMUNITY HOSPITAL (450597)**, 2550 North Esplanade Street, Zip 77954–4716; tel. 361/275–6191 **A**10 **F**3 7 11 13 15 29 34 40 43 45 57 59 62 64 68 70 75 76 77 79 81 85 86 93 107 108 110 111 115 118 119 127 129 130 131 **P**6
Primary Contact: Lynn Falcone, Chief Executive Officer
CFO: Greg Pritchett, Chief Financial Officer
CMO: Michael McLeod M.D., Chief Medical Officer
CIO: Arthur Mueller, Director Management Information Systems
CHR: Wanda S Kolodziejcyk, Director Human Resources
CNO: Judith Krupala R.N., Chief Nursing Officer
Web address: www.cuerohospital.org
Control: Hospital district or authority, Government, Nonfederal **Service:** General medical and surgical

Staffed Beds: 29 **Admissions:** 787 **Census:** 8 **Outpatient Visits:** 122289 **Births:** 116 **Total Expense ($000):** 37168 **Payroll Expense ($000):** 16955 **Personnel:** 355

CYPRESS—Harris County

☐ **LONE STAR BEHAVIORAL HEALTH (454118)**, 16303 Grant Road, Zip 77429–1253; tel. 281/516–6200 **A**1 10 **F**98 104 105 149 **P**5
Primary Contact: Nathan Daniel. Ingram, Chief Executive Officer and Owner
Web address: www.lonestarbehavioralhealth.com
Control: Partnership, Investor–owned (for–profit) **Service:** Psychiatric

Staffed Beds: 24 **Admissions:** 515 **Census:** 14 **Outpatient Visits:** 35601 **Births:** 0 **Total Expense ($000):** 6021 **Payroll Expense ($000):** 3707 **Personnel:** 78

☐ **NORTH CYPRESS MEDICAL CENTER (670024)**, 21214 Northwest Freeway, Zip 77429–3373; tel. 832/912–3500 **A**1 10 **F**3 4 5 8 11 12 15 17 18 19 20 22 24 26 28 29 31 34 35 37 39 40 41 42 44 45 46 47 48 49 50 51 53 54 55 56 57 58 59 60 61 64 65 67 70 74 75 77 78 79 80 81 82 84 85 86 87 89 90 91 92 93 96 97 107 108 109 110 111 114 115 116 117 118 119 120 121 123 124 126 129 130 131 132 135 141 142 144 146 148 149
Primary Contact: Robert Behar, M.D., Chief Executive Officer
Web address: www.ncmc–hospital.com
Control: Partnership, Investor–owned (for–profit) **Service:** General medical and surgical

Staffed Beds: 139 **Admissions:** 9669 **Census:** 117 **Outpatient Visits:** 204894 **Births:** 0 **Total Expense ($000):** 227266 **Payroll Expense ($000):** 76403 **Personnel:** 1319

DALHART—Hartley County

COON MEMORIAL HOSPITAL (451331), 1411 Denver Avenue, Zip 79022–4809, Mailing Address: P.O.Box 2014, 79022–6014; tel. 806/244–4571 **A**10 18 **F**3 7 10 11 13 30 34 35 40 43 45 50 53 57 59 62 63 64 65 68 69 71 76 77 79 81 82 83 85 87 93 97 103 107 114 119 125 127 131 133 143 144 146 148 **P**5
Primary Contact: Leroy Schaffner, Chief Executive Officer
CFO: Donny Pettit, Chief Financial Officer
CMO: Randy Herring M.D., Chief of Staff
CIO: Anthony Lovato, Director Information Technology
CHR: Dee Dawn McCormick, Director Personnel and Human Resources
Web address: www.coonmemorial.org
Control: Hospital district or authority, Government, Nonfederal **Service:** General medical and surgical

Staffed Beds: 21 **Admissions:** 350 **Census:** 5 **Outpatient Visits:** 19697 **Births:** 120 **Total Expense ($000):** 28808 **Payroll Expense ($000):** 10527 **Personnel:** 207

DALLAS—Dallas County

✠ **BAYLOR INSTITUTE FOR REHABILITATION (453036)**, 909 North Washington Avenue, Zip 75246–1520; tel. 214/820–9300 **A**1 3 10 **F**3 29 30 34 35 44 62 64 65 68 74 75 77 85 86 87 90 92 93 94 95 96 130 131 132 135 143 148 149
Primary Contact: Fabian Polo, Ph.D., Chief Executive Officer
CMO: Amy Wilson M.D., Medical Director
CHR: Karen Hill, Director Human Resources
CNO: Beth Hudson, Chief Nursing Officer
Web address: www.baylorhealth.com/PhysiciansLocations/BIR/Pages/Default.aspx
Control: Partnership, Investor–owned (for–profit) **Service:** Rehabilitation

Staffed Beds: 89 **Admissions:** 1596 **Census:** 80 **Outpatient Visits:** 217 **Births:** 0 **Total Expense ($000):** 72711 **Payroll Expense ($000):** 45707 **Personnel:** 321

✠ **BAYLOR JACK AND JANE HAMILTON HEART AND VASCULAR HOSPITAL (450851)**, 621 North Hall Street, Suite 150, Zip 75226–1339; tel. 214/820–0600 **A**1 5 10 **F**3 18 20 22 26 28 29 30 34 35 44 50 57 58 59 60 64 68 75 77 81 85 86 87 93 96 107 109 115 119 130 131 132 135 146 149
Primary Contact: Nancy Vish, Ph.D., FACHE, R.N., President
CFO: Julius Wicke III, Vice President Finance and Hospital Financial Officer
CMO: Kevin Wheelan M.D., Medical Director
CHR: Kim Krause, Director Human Resources
Web address: www.baylorhearthospital.com
Control: Partnership, Investor–owned (for–profit) **Service:** Heart

Staffed Beds: 54 **Admissions:** 2248 **Census:** 23 **Outpatient Visits:** 33818 **Births:** 0 **Total Expense ($000):** 117414 **Payroll Expense ($000):** 31882 **Personnel:** 293

✠ **BAYLOR MEDICAL CENTER AT UPTOWN (450422)**, 2727 East Lemmon Avenue, Zip 75204–2895; tel. 214/443–3000 **A**1 3 5 10 **F**29 40 68 77 79 81 82 85 107 111 **P**4 **S** United Surgical Partners International, Addison, TX
Primary Contact: Jon Duckert, FACHE, Chief Executive Officer
CFO: Colene Fielding, Manager Business Office
CMO: Mark Armstrong M.D., Medical Director
CIO: Javier Vela, Director Information Technology
CHR: Emalie Sanchez, Director Human Resources
CNO: Verette Neeb R.N., MSN, Chief Nursing Officer
Web address: www.bmcuptown.com
Control: Partnership, Investor–owned (for–profit) **Service:** General medical and surgical

Staffed Beds: 24 **Admissions:** 1286 **Census:** 6 **Outpatient Visits:** 10113 **Births:** 0 **Total Expense ($000):** 54943 **Payroll Expense ($000):** 11623 **Personnel:** 213

✠ **BAYLOR SCOTT & WHITE MEDICAL CENTER – WHITE ROCK (450678)**, 9440 Poppy Drive, Zip 75218–3694; tel. 214/324–6100 **A**1 10 **F**3 11 12 13 15 17 18 20 22 24 26 28 29 30 31 34 35 37 40 42 45 47 49 50 51 53 56 57 59 64 70 72 73 74 75 76 77 78 79 81 85 93 107 108 110 111 114 115 119 120 124 126 129 130 132 135 144 146 147 148 **S** TENET Healthcare Corporation, Dallas, TX
Primary Contact: Jorge Trevino, Interim Chief Executive Officer
COO: Jorge Trevino, Chief Operations Officer
CFO: Drew Shea, Chief Financial Officer
CMO: William Jones M.D., II, Chief Medical Officer
CHR: Kimberly Harris, Interim Director Human Resources
CNO: Cheryl Nail R.N., Chief Nursing Officer
Web address: www.BaylorScottandWhite.com/WhiteRock
Control: Partnership, Investor–owned (for–profit) **Service:** General medical and surgical

Staffed Beds: 151 **Admissions:** 7474 **Census:** 82 **Outpatient Visits:** 71955 **Births:** 1272 **Total Expense ($000):** 127343 **Payroll Expense ($000):** 45973 **Personnel:** 649

Many Facility Codes have changed. Please refer to the AHA Guide Code Chart. © 2017 AHA Guide

TX

☒ ⇑ **BAYLOR UNIVERSITY MEDICAL CENTER (450021)**, 3500 Gaston Avenue, Zip 75246–2088; tel. 214/820–0111, (Includes A. WEBB ROBERTS HOSPITAL, 3500 Gaston Avenue, Dallas, Texas, Zip 75246–2017, tel. 361/986–9444; ERIK AND MARGARET JONSSON HOSPITAL, 3500 Gaston Avenue, Dallas, Texas, Zip 75246–2017, tel. 361/986–9444; GEORGE W. TRUETT MEMORIAL HOSPITAL, 3500 Gaston Avenue, Dallas, Texas, Zip 75246, tel. 361/986–9444; KARL AND ESTHER HOBLITZELLE MEMORIAL HOSPITAL, 3500 Gaston Avenue, Dallas, Texas, Zip 75246, tel. 361/986–9444) **A**1 2 3 5 8 10 21 **F**3 8 12 13 14 15 17 18 24 29 30 31 34 35 37 38 40 41 43 45 46 47 48 49 50 51 53 54 55 56 57 58 59 60 61 66 68 70 71 72 74 75 76 77 78 79 80 81 82 84 85 87 88 100 101 102 103 107 108 110 111 114 115 116 117 118 119 121 124 126 129 130 131 132 135 136 137 138 139 140 141 142 146 147 148 149 **S** Baylor Scott & White Health, Dallas, TX
Primary Contact: T. Douglas. Lawson, Ph.D., FACHE, President
CFO: Jay Whitfield, Chief Financial Officer
CMO: Brad Lembcke M.D., Vice President Medical Staff Affairs
CHR: Julie Strittmatter, Director Human Resources
CNO: Claudia Wilder R.N., MS, Chief Nursing Executive
Web address: www.baylorhealth.com/PhysiciansLocations/Dallas/Pages/Default.aspx
Control: Other not-for-profit (including NFP Corporation) **Service:** General medical and surgical

Staffed Beds: 859 **Admissions:** 36256 **Census:** 658 **Outpatient Visits:** 242784 **Births:** 4619 **Total Expense ($000):** 1055998 **Payroll Expense ($000):** 342998 **Personnel:** 3751

☒ **CHILDREN'S HEALTH SYSTEM OF TEXAS (453302)**, 1935 Medical District Drive, Zip 75235; tel. 214/456–7000 **A**1 3 5 8 10 **F**3 7 8 11 12 17 19 21 23 25 27 29 30 31 32 34 35 38 39 40 41 43 44 45 46 47 48 49 50 51 54 55 57 58 59 60 61 62 64 65 66 68 72 74 75 77 78 79 81 82 84 85 86 87 88 89 91 92 93 94 97 98 99 100 101 102 104 105 106 107 108 111 114 116 117 118 119 126 127 129 130 131 132 134 136 137 138 139 140 141 142 143 144 145 146 148
Primary Contact: Christopher J. Durovich, President and Chief Executive Officer
COO: David T. Berry, President, System Clinical Operations
CFO: Richard P. Goode, Executive Vice President and Chief Financial Officer
CMO: W. Robert Morrow M.D., Executive Vice President and Chief Medical Officer
CIO: Pamela Arora, Senior Vice President Information Systems
CHR: Kim Besse, Senior Vice President and Chief Human Resource Officer
CNO: Mary Stowe, Senior Vice President and Chief Nursing Officer
Web address: www.childrens.com
Control: Other not-for-profit (including NFP Corporation) **Service:** Children's general medical and surgical

Staffed Beds: 393 **Admissions:** 28321 **Census:** 248 **Outpatient Visits:** 464019 **Births:** 0 **Total Expense ($000):** 947592 **Payroll Expense ($000):** 321213 **Personnel:** 3954

☒ **DALLAS MEDICAL CENTER (450379)**, Seven Medical Parkway, Zip 75234–7823, Mailing Address: P.O.Box 819094, 75381–9094; tel. 972/247–1000 **A**1 10 **F**3 12 13 15 18 20 22 26 29 34 40 44 45 49 51 56 57 59 64 68 70 74 75 76 77 78 79 81 82 84 85 86 93 97 107 108 111 114 116 119 130 131 132 141 142 146 147 148 149 **P**6 **S** Prime Healthcare, Ontario, CA
Primary Contact: J. T. Barnhart, Chief Executive Officer
CFO: Nicholas Geer, Chief Financial Officer
CIO: Mary Jo Tallant–Ball, Director Health Information Systems
CHR: Sheila K Richards, Human Resources Director
CNO: Dawn Beljin R.N., Chief Nursing Officer
Web address: www.dallasmedcenter.com
Control: Corporation, Investor–owned (for–profit) **Service:** General medical and surgical

Staffed Beds: 83 **Admissions:** 3920 **Census:** 37 **Outpatient Visits:** 40850 **Births:** 708 **Total Expense ($000):** 90521 **Payroll Expense ($000):** 26977 **Personnel:** 399

★ ⇑ **FIRST BAPTIST MEDICAL CENTER**, 8111 Meadow Road, Zip 75231; tel. 469/329–3700, (Data for 249 days) **A**21 **F**3 12 29 37 40 45 49 64 70 79 81 82 85 86 87 107 114 119 126 129 130 149 **S** QHR, Brentwood, TN
Primary Contact: Paul Eavenson, Chief Executive Officer
Web address: www.fbmcdallas.com
Control: Corporation, Investor–owned (for–profit) **Service:** Surgical

Staffed Beds: 18 **Admissions:** 424 **Census:** 5 **Outpatient Visits:** 1040 **Births:** 0 **Total Expense ($000):** 18212 **Payroll Expense ($000):** 4227 **Personnel:** 93

☒ **HEALTHSOUTH REHABILITATION HOSPITAL – DALLAS (673043)**, 7930 Northaven Road, Zip 75230–3331; tel. 214/706–8200 **A**1 10 **F**3 29 90 96 128 130 148 **S** HEALTHSOUTH Corporation, Birmingham, AL
Primary Contact: Daniel MacNicol, Chief Executive Officer
CFO: Elizabeth Robertson, Area Controller
CMO: Anna Freed–Sigurdsson M.D., Medical Director
CHR: Lindsay Battles, Director Human Resources
CNO: Elysia Clay, Chief Nursing Officer
Web address: www.healthsouthdallas.com
Control: Corporation, Investor–owned (for–profit) **Service:** Rehabilitation

Staffed Beds: 60 **Admissions:** 1031 **Census:** 35 **Outpatient Visits:** 0 **Births:** 0 **Total Expense ($000):** 17563 **Payroll Expense ($000):** 7939 **Personnel:** 120

☒ **KINDRED HOSPITAL DALLAS CENTRAL (452108)**, 8050 Meadow Road, Zip 75231–3406; tel. 469/232–6500 **A**1 10 **F**1 3 29 75 77 85 87 96 107 114 148 **P**8 **S** Kindred Healthcare, Louisville, KY
Primary Contact: Kyron J. Kooken, MS, Chief Executive Officer
CFO: Robin Fry CPA, Market Controller
CNO: Traci Brewer, Chief Clinical Officer
Web address: www.khdallascentral.com/
Control: Corporation, Investor–owned (for–profit) **Service:** Acute long–term care hospital

Staffed Beds: 60 **Admissions:** 608 **Census:** 49 **Outpatient Visits:** 204 **Births:** 0 **Total Expense ($000):** 28278 **Payroll Expense ($000):** 10225 **Personnel:** 103

☒ **KINDRED HOSPITAL–DALLAS (452015)**, 9525 Greenville Avenue, Zip 75243–4116; tel. 214/355–2600 **A**1 10 **F**1 3 29 70 107 114 130 148 **S** Kindred Healthcare, Louisville, KY
Primary Contact: James Mendez, Chief Executive Officer
CFO: Jean McDowell, Chief Financial Officer
Web address: www.khdallas.com
Control: Corporation, Investor–owned (for–profit) **Service:** Acute long–term care hospital

Staffed Beds: 50 **Admissions:** 540 **Census:** 39 **Outpatient Visits:** 1220 **Births:** 0 **Total Expense ($000):** 22557 **Payroll Expense ($000):** 8152 **Personnel:** 151

☒ **KINDRED HOSPITAL–WHITE ROCK (452071)**, 9440 Poppy Drive, 5th Floor, Zip 75218–3652; tel. 214/324–6562 **A**1 10 **F**1 29 85 86 87 130 148 **S** Kindred Healthcare, Louisville, KY
Primary Contact: Kelly Bailey, Chief Executive Officer and Administrator
COO: Kim Chipman, Chief Clinical Officer
CFO: Jennifer Penland, Controller
CMO: Mark Ferris M.D., Medical Director
CNO: Brenda Perez R.N., MSN, Chief Clinical Officer
Web address: www.khwhiterock.com
Control: Corporation, Investor–owned (for–profit) **Service:** Acute long–term care hospital

Staffed Beds: 25 **Admissions:** 300 **Census:** 21 **Outpatient Visits:** 0 **Births:** 0 **Total Expense ($000):** 10521 **Payroll Expense ($000):** 4643 **Personnel:** 70

☒ **LIFECARE HOSPITALS OF DALLAS (452044)**, 1950 Record Crossing Road, Zip 75235–6223; tel. 214/640–9600, (Includes LIFECARE HOSPITALS OF NORTH TEXAS–FORT WORTH, 6201 Overton Ridge Boulevard, Fort Worth, Texas, Zip 76132–3613, tel. 817/370–6078; Phillip B Douglas, Chairman and Chief Executive Officer; LIFECARE HOSPITALS OF NORTH TEXAS–PLANO, 6800 Preston Road, Plano, Texas, Zip 75024–2505, tel. 214/473–8822; Kathleen Wallace, R.N., MSN, Administrator and Chief Executive Officer) **A**1 10 **F**1 3 29 75 91 107 114 115 119 130 148 **S** LifeCare Management Services, Plano, TX
Primary Contact: Christy Carver, R.N., Chief Executive Officer
CFO: Amie Gratch, Director Financial Services
CMO: Jonathan Weissler M.D., Chief Medical Officer
CHR: Linzie Riley, Interim Human Resource Manager
CNO: Kathy Mason R.N., MSN, Chief Nursing Officer
Web address: www.lifecare–hospitals.com/hospital/dallas
Control: Corporation, Investor–owned (for–profit) **Service:** Acute long–term care hospital

Staffed Beds: 60 **Admissions:** 561 **Census:** 42 **Outpatient Visits:** 0 **Births:** 0 **Total Expense ($000):** 24825 **Payroll Expense ($000):** 10156 **Personnel:** 194

LIFECARE HOSPITALS OF NORTH TEXAS See Lifecare Hospitals Of Dallas

MARY SHIELS HOSPITAL See Baylor Medical Center At Uptown

TX

Hospital, Medicare Provider Number, Address, Telephone, Approval, Facility, and Physician Codes, Health Care System

★ American Hospital Association (AHA) membership   ○ Healthcare Facilities Accreditation Program   ⇑ Center for Improvement in Healthcare Quality Accreditation
□ The Joint Commission accreditation   ◇ DNV Healthcare Inc. accreditation   △ Commission on Accreditation of Rehabilitation Facilities (CARF) accreditation

✠ ⬆ MEDICAL CITY DALLAS (450647), 7777 Forest Lane, Zip 75230–2598; tel. 972/566–7000, (Includes MEDICAL CITY CHILDREN'S HOSPITAL, 7777 Forest Lane, Dallas, Texas, Zip 75230–2505, tel. 972/566–7000; Bill Lee, Chief Executive Officer) **A**1 2 3 5 10 21 **F**3 8 11 12 13 17 18 19 20 21 22 23 24 25 26 27 28 29 30 31 34 35 37 40 41 42 43 44 45 46 47 49 50 51 55 56 57 58 59 60 64 65 68 70 72 73 74 75 76 77 78 79 81 82 84 85 86 87 88 89 90 93 96 107 108 111 114 115 116 117 118 119 124 126 129 130 132 135 136 137 138 141 142 143 146 147 148 149 **P**6 **S** HCA Healthcare, Nashville, TN
Primary Contact: Chris Mowan, Chief Executive Officer
CFO: Mark Atchley, Vice President and Chief Financial Officer
CMO: Kenneth Rothfield M.D., Chief Medical Officer
CIO: Troy Sypien, Director Information Technology and Systems
CHR: Jenifer K Tertel, Director Human Resources
CNO: Joyce M Soule R.N., MSN, Chief Nursing Officer
Web address: www.medicalcityhospital.com
Control: Corporation, Investor–owned (for–profit) **Service**: General medical and surgical

Staffed Beds: 615 **Admissions**: 25322 **Census**: 431 **Outpatient Visits**: 177290 **Births**: 3699 **Total Expense ($000)**: 545428 **Payroll Expense ($000)**: 189327 **Personnel**: 2195

✠ MEDICAL CITY GREEN OAKS HOSPITAL (454094), 7808 Clodus Fields Drive, Zip 75251–2206; tel. 972/991–9504 **A**1 5 10 **F**4 5 29 54 87 98 99 102 103 104 105 130 132 **P**5 **S** HCA Healthcare, Nashville, TN
Primary Contact: Thomas M. Collins, President, Chairman and Chief Executive Officer
COO: Pam Whitley R.N., Chief Operating Officer and Chief Nursing Officer
CMO: Joel Holiner M.D., Executive Medical Director
CIO: Richard Fontenault, Director Information Systems
CHR: Kevin Adkins, Director Human Resources
CNO: Pam Whitley R.N., Chief Nursing Officer and Chief Operating Officer
Web address: www.greenoakspsych.com
Control: Corporation, Investor–owned (for–profit) **Service**: Psychiatric

Staffed Beds: 124 **Admissions**: 4780 **Census**: 122 **Outpatient Visits**: 34298 **Births**: 0 **Total Expense ($000)**: 56549 **Payroll Expense ($000)**: 29777 **Personnel**: 326

✠ METHODIST CHARLTON MEDICAL CENTER (450723), 3500 West Wheatland Road, Zip 75237–3460, Mailing Address: P.O.Box 225357, 75222–5357; tel. 214/947–7777 **A**1 3 10 13 **F**3 11 13 15 18 20 22 24 28 29 30 31 34 35 40 45 46 47 49 50 53 58 59 60 64 66 68 70 74 76 78 79 81 82 84 85 86 87 97 107 108 110 111 114 115 118 119 126 130 131 132 146 148 **P**1 7 **S** Methodist Health System, Dallas, TX
Primary Contact: Fran Laukaitis, R.N., FACHE, President
COO: Pamela Stoyanoff, Executive Vice President and Chief Operating Officer
CFO: Michael J Schaefer, Executive Vice President and Chief Financial Officer
CIO: Pamela McNutt, Vice President Information Systems
CHR: Cheryl Flynn, Senior Vice President Chief Human Resources Officer
Web address: www.methodisthealthsystem.org/charlton
Control: Other not–for–profit (including NFP Corporation) **Service**: General medical and surgical

Staffed Beds: 292 **Admissions**: 11935 **Census**: 166 **Outpatient Visits**: 160097 **Births**: 1924 **Total Expense ($000)**: 237063 **Payroll Expense ($000)**: 108035 **Personnel**: 1512

✠ METHODIST DALLAS MEDICAL CENTER (450051), 1441 North Beckley Avenue, Zip 75203–1201, Mailing Address: P.O.Box 655999, 75265–5999; tel. 214/947–8181 **A**1 2 3 5 10 **F**3 11 12 13 15 18 20 22 24 29 30 31 34 35 37 40 43 45 46 47 48 49 50 53 54 58 59 60 64 66 68 70 72 74 76 78 79 81 82 84 85 87 92 93 97 107 108 110 111 118 119 126 130 132 138 139 142 146 148 149 150 **P**1 7 **S** Methodist Health System, Dallas, TX
Primary Contact: Martin Koonsman, M.D., FACS, President
COO: Pamela Stoyanoff, Executive Vice President and Chief Operating Officer
CFO: Randy Walker, Vice President
CMO: Leslie Cler M.D., Chief Medical Officer
CIO: Pamela McNutt, Senior Vice President and Chief Information Officer
CHR: Jackie Middleton, Vice President Human Resources
Web address: www.methodisthealthsystem.org/Dallas
Control: Other not–for–profit (including NFP Corporation) **Service**: General medical and surgical

Staffed Beds: 390 **Admissions**: 16037 **Census**: 246 **Outpatient Visits**: 160333 **Births**: 2836 **Total Expense ($000)**: 445842 **Payroll Expense ($000)**: 165083 **Personnel**: 2369

☐ METHODIST REHABILITATION HOSPITAL (673031), 3020 West Wheatland Road, Zip 75237–3537; tel. 972/708–8600 **A**1 10 **F**29 30 60 90 91 93 96
Primary Contact: Shari Moore, Chief Executive Officer
CFO: Darline Kennemer, Controller
Web address: www.methodist–rehab.com
Control: Partnership, Investor–owned (for–profit) **Service**: Rehabilitation

Staffed Beds: 40 **Admissions**: 1059 **Census**: 34 **Outpatient Visits**: 10921 **Births**: 0 **Total Expense ($000)**: 15463 **Payroll Expense ($000)**: 8301 **Personnel**: 158

☐ NORTH CENTRAL SURGICAL CENTER (670049), 9301 North Central Expressway, Suite 100, Zip 75231–0802; tel. 214/265–2810 **A**1 10 **F**3 40 45 79 81 82 85 93 96 107 111 115 119
Primary Contact: Thanh Tran, FACHE, Chief Executive Officer
COO: Ben Magestro, Chief Operating Officer
CFO: Mike Quaglieri, Chief Financial Officer
CMO: Stuart Simon M.D., Medical Director
CNO: Katherine Martinez, Chief Nursing Officer
Web address: www.northcentralsurgical.com
Control: Partnership, Investor–owned (for–profit) **Service**: Surgical

Staffed Beds: 30 **Admissions**: 1374 **Census**: 9 **Outpatient Visits**: 19410 **Births**: 0 **Total Expense ($000)**: 67547 **Payroll Expense ($000)**: 15692 **Personnel**: 263

★ OUR CHILDREN'S HOUSE (453308), 1340 Empire Central Drive, Zip 75247–4022; tel. 214/867–6700 **A**3 5 10 **F**3 29 30 35 39 81 89 93 129 130 132 146
Primary Contact: David T. Berry, President, Children's Health Clinical Operations
CMO: Andrew Gelfand M.D., Medical Director
CNO: Kelli Terpstra R.N., Senior Director
Web address: www.childrens.com/och
Control: Other not–for–profit (including NFP Corporation) **Service**: Children's general medical and surgical

Staffed Beds: 39 **Admissions**: 334 **Census**: 22 **Outpatient Visits**: 77050 **Births**: 0 **Total Expense ($000)**: 32682 **Payroll Expense ($000)**: 19122 **Personnel**: 257

✠ PARKLAND HEALTH & HOSPITAL SYSTEM (450015), 5200 Harry Hines Boulevard, Zip 75235–7708; tel. 214/590–8000, (Total facility includes 1840 beds in nursing home–type unit) **A**1 2 3 5 8 10 **F**3 8 9 11 12 13 15 16 17 18 20 22 26 28 29 30 31 34 37 38 39 40 43 46 47 48 49 50 51 54 55 56 57 58 59 60 61 64 65 66 67 68 70 71 72 74 75 76 77 78 79 81 82 83 84 85 86 87 90 91 92 93 94 97 98 99 100 101 102 103 104 105 107 108 110 111 115 116 117 118 119 128 129 130 131 132 134 135 138 141 144 146 147 148 149 150 **P**1
Primary Contact: Fred Cerise, M.D., Chief Executive Officer
COO: David S Lopez FACHE, Executive Vice President and Chief Operating Officer
CFO: Richard Humphrey, Executive Vice President and Chief Financial Officer
CIO: Fernando Martinez, Senior Vice President and Chief Information Officer
CNO: Mary K Eagen R.N., MS, Executive Vice President, Chief Nursing Officer
Web address: www.parklandhospital.com
Control: Hospital district or authority, Government, Nonfederal **Service**: General medical and surgical

Staffed Beds: 2700 **Admissions**: 44591 **Census**: 1944 **Outpatient Visits**: 1288388 **Births**: 11015 **Total Expense ($000)**: 1631499 **Payroll Expense ($000)**: 780521 **Personnel**: 11501

☐ PINE CREEK MEDICAL CENTER (450894), 9032 Harry Hines Boulevard, Zip 75235–1720; tel. 214/231–2273 **A**1 10 **F**3 12 18 24 29 30 34 40 42 45 49 51 64 79 81 82 85 93 107 111 114 149
Primary Contact: Corazon Ramirez, M.D., Chief Executive Officer
CFO: Michael Conroy, Chief Financial Officer
CIO: Kevin Carney, Senior Information Systems Analyst
Web address: www.pinecreekmedicalcenter.com
Control: Partnership, Investor–owned (for–profit) **Service**: Surgical

Staffed Beds: 15 **Admissions**: 1576 **Census**: 9 **Outpatient Visits**: 6383 **Births**: 0 **Total Expense ($000)**: 72432 **Payroll Expense ($000)**: 10934 **Personnel**: 164

☐ PROMISE HOSPITAL OF DALLAS (452067), 7955 Harry Hines Boulevard, Zip 75235–3305; tel. 214/637–0000 **A**1 10 **F**3 29 30 40 64 75 77 91 148 **S** Promise Healthcare, Boca Raton, FL
Primary Contact: Louis P. Bradley Jr, Chief Executive Officer
CFO: Diana B Smith, Chief Financial Officer
CMO: Gary E. Goff M.D., Medical Director
CHR: Ginger Davenport, Director Human Resources
Web address: www.promise–dallas.com/
Control: Corporation, Investor–owned (for–profit) **Service**: Acute long–term care hospital

Staffed Beds: 62 **Admissions**: 350 **Census**: 26 **Outpatient Visits**: 1570 **Births**: 0 **Total Expense ($000)**: 14295 **Payroll Expense ($000)**: 7727 **Personnel**: 88

★ SELECT SPECIALTY HOSPITAL – DALLAS DOWNTOWN (452119), 3500 Gaston Avenue, Floors 3&4 Jonsson, Zip 75246–2017; tel. 469/801–4500 **F**1 3 29 74 77 85 86 87 91 96 148 **S** Select Medical Corporation, Mechanicsburg, PA
Primary Contact: Melody Nagel, Chief Executive Officer
Web address: www.dallasdowntown.selectspecialtyhospitals.com/
Control: Corporation, Investor–owned (for–profit) **Service**: Acute long–term care hospital

Staffed Beds: 46 **Admissions**: 313 **Census**: 22 **Outpatient Visits**: 0 **Births**: 0 **Total Expense ($000)**: 15677 **Payroll Expense ($000)**: 6454 **Personnel**: 87

✣ △ ⇑ **TEXAS HEALTH PRESBYTERIAN HOSPITAL DALLAS (450462)**, 8200 Walnut Hill Lane, Zip 75231–4426; tel. 214/345–6789 **A**1 2 5 7 10 21 **F**3 5 11 12 13 15 17 18 20 22 24 26 28 29 30 31 32 34 35 37 38 40 44 45 46 47 49 50 51 53 54 56 57 58 59 60 61 64 65 66 68 70 72 73 74 75 76 77 78 79 81 84 85 86 87 90 91 92 93 94 95 96 97 98 100 101 102 103 104 105 107 108 110 111 112 114 115 118 119 124 126 129 131 132 135 141 143 144 146 147 148 **P**6 **S** Texas Health Resources, Arlington, TX
Primary Contact: James Berg, FACHE, President
CFO: Brian Craft, Group Finance Officer
CMO: Aurora Estevez M.D., Chief Medical Officer
CIO: Tammy Phillips, Director, Information Systems
CHR: Stacy Miller, Entity Human Resources Officer
CNO: Cole Edmonson R.N., MS, FACHE, Vice President and Chief Nursing Officer
Web address: www.texashealth.org
Control: Other not–for–profit (including NFP Corporation) **Service:** General medical and surgical

Staffed Beds: 617 **Admissions:** 27207 **Census:** 405 **Outpatient Visits:** 152912 **Births:** 5289 **Total Expense ($000):** 625241 **Payroll Expense ($000):** 211071 **Personnel:** 2934

TEXAS HOSPITAL FOR ADVANCED MEDICINE See Dallas Medical Center

☐ **TEXAS INSTITUTE FOR SURGERY AT TEXAS HEALTH PRESBYTERIAN DALLAS (450889)**, 7115 Greenville Avenue, Suite 100, Zip 75231–5100; tel. 214/647–5300 **A**1 10 **F**40 51 64 79 81 82 107 114 115 119
Primary Contact: David Helfer, FACHE, President
CFO: John S Croley, Vice President Business Operations
CMO: Presley Mock M.D., Chief of Staff
CHR: Jennifer Cherrnay Levy, Director Human Resources
CNO: Tammy Jarvis, Vice President Clinical Services and Chief Nursing Officer
Web address: www.texasinstituteforsurgery.com
Control: Partnership, Investor–owned (for–profit) **Service:** General medical and surgical

Staffed Beds: 9 **Admissions:** 471 **Census:** 2 **Outpatient Visits:** 10379 **Births:** 0 **Total Expense ($000):** 52943 **Payroll Expense ($000):** 12533 **Personnel:** 167

✣ **TEXAS SCOTTISH RITE HOSPITAL FOR CHILDREN (453314)**, 2222 Welborn Street, Zip 75219–3924, Mailing Address: P.O.Box 190567, 75219–0567; tel. 214/559–5000 **A**1 3 5 10 **F**3 9 11 29 34 35 50 53 54 58 68 74 75 77 79 81 82 85 86 87 89 92 94 107 111 115 119 130 131 132 146 148 **P**6
Primary Contact: Robert L. Walker, FACHE, President and Chief Executive Officer
CFO: William R Huston, Senior Vice President and Chief Financial Officer
CMO: Daniel J Sucato M.D., MS, Chief of Staff
CIO: Les Clonch, Chief Information Officer
CHR: Connie Wright, Vice President Human Resources
CNO: Debbie A Sayles R.N., Vice President and Chief Nursing Officer
Web address: www.tsrhc.org
Control: Other not–for–profit (including NFP Corporation) **Service:** Children's orthopedic

Staffed Beds: 52 **Admissions:** 482 **Census:** 10 **Outpatient Visits:** 38258 **Births:** 0 **Total Expense ($000):** 176280 **Payroll Expense ($000):** 85677 **Personnel:** 998

☐ **TIMBERLAWN MENTAL HEALTH SYSTEM (454081)**, 4600 Samuell Boulevard, Zip 75228–6800; tel. 214/381–7181 **A**1 5 10 **F**56 59 98 100 101 102 103 130 132 **S** Universal Health Services, Inc., King of Prussia, PA
Primary Contact: Shelah Adams, Chief Executive Officer
COO: Rick Paczkowski, Chief Operating Officer
CFO: Lori Verbeke, Chief Financial Officer
CMO: John Pascoe M.D., Executive Medical Director
CIO: Twila Ragar–Thomas, Director Health Information Management and Quality Improvement
CHR: Winnie Boehnke, Director Human Resources
CNO: Paula Hirschberg R.N., Director of Nursing
Web address: www.timberlawn.com
Control: Corporation, Investor–owned (for–profit) **Service:** Psychiatric

Staffed Beds: 57 **Admissions:** 439 **Census:** 8 **Outpatient Visits:** 0 **Births:** 0 **Personnel:** 70

✣ △ **UNIVERSITY OF TEXAS SOUTHWESTERN MEDICAL CENTER (450766)**, 5323 Harry Hines Boulevard, Zip 75390–9265; tel. 214/648–3111, (Includes UNIVERSITY OF TEXAS SOUTHWESTERN MEDICAL CENTER – ZALE LIPSHY, 5151 Harry Hines Boulevard, Dallas, Texas, Zip 75390–9265, tel. 214/645–8300; Daniel Podolsky, M.D., President) **A**1 2 3 5 7 8 10 **F**3 7 8 11 12 13 15 17 18 20 22 24 26 28 29 30 31 34 35 36 38 39 40 44 45 46 47 48 49 50 52 53 54 55 56 57 58 59 60 61 62 64 65 68 70 71 72 74 75 76 77 78 79 80 81 82 84 85 86 87 90 91 92 93 94 95 96 97 98 99 100 101 102 103 104 107 108 109 110 111 114 115 116 117 118 119 120 121 123 124 126 129 130 131 132 135 136 137 138 139 140 141 142 143 145 146 147 148 149 150 **P**4 6
Primary Contact: John Warner, M.D., Chief Executive Officer
COO: Becky McCulley, Chief Operations Officer
CMO: John Warner M.D., Chief Executive Officer, Interim Chief Medical Officer
CIO: Marc E. Milstein, Vice President Information Resources
CHR: Ivan Thompson, Vice President, Chief Human Resource Officer
CNO: Susan Hernandez R.N., Chief Nurse Executive
Web address: www.utsouthwestern.edu
Control: State, Government, Nonfederal **Service:** General medical and surgical

Staffed Beds: 595 **Admissions:** 24745 **Census:** 398 **Outpatient Visits:** 427045 **Births:** 1887 **Total Expense ($000):** 1067842 **Payroll Expense ($000):** 415502 **Personnel:** 5584

✣ △ **VETERANS AFFAIRS NORTH TEXAS HEALTH CARE SYSTEM**, 4500 South Lancaster Road, Zip 75216–7167; tel. 214/742–8387, (Nonreporting) (Includes SAM RAYBURN MEMORIAL VETERANS CENTER, 1201 East Ninth Street, Bonham, Texas, Zip 75418–4091, tel. 903/583–2111; Angela Nix, Administrator) **A**1 2 3 5 7 **S** Department of Veterans Affairs, Washington, DC
Primary Contact: Kendrick Brown, Interim Director
CFO: Garry Martin, Chief Fiscal
CIO: Lucy Rogers, Chief Information Resource Management Systems
Web address: www.northtexas.va.gov/
Control: Veterans Affairs, Government, federal **Service:** General medical and surgical

Staffed Beds: 875

WILLIAM P. CLEMENTS, JR. UNIVERSITY HOSPITAL (450044), 6201 Harry Hines Boulevard, Zip 75235–5202; tel. 214/633–5555 (Nonreporting) **A**3 5
Primary Contact: Daniel Podolsky, M.D., President
Web address: www.utswmedicine.org/hospitals–clinics/clements/about/faqs/
Control: State, Government, Nonfederal **Service:** General medical and surgical

Staffed Beds: 460

DECATUR—Wise County

✣ **WISE HEALTH SYSTEM (450271)**, 609 Medical Center Drive, Zip 76234–3836; tel. 940/627–5921, (Includes PARKWAY SURGICAL & CARDIOVASCULAR HOSPITAL, 3200 North Tarrant Parkway, Fort Worth, Texas, Zip 76177–8611, tel. 817/502–7300; WISE REGIONAL HEALTH SYSTEM – BRIDGEPORT CAMPUS, 1905 Doctors Hospital Drive, Bridgeport, Texas, Zip 76426–2260, tel. 940/683–0300; WISE REGIONAL HEALTH SYSTEM, EAST CAMPUS DECATUR, 609 Medical Center Drive, Decatur, Texas, Zip 76234–3836, tel. 940/627–5921; WISE REGIONAL HEALTH SYSTEM, WEST CAMPUS DECATUR, 2000 South Fm 51, Decatur, Texas, Zip 76234–3702, tel. 940/627–5921) **A**1 2 10 **F**3 11 12 13 15 17 18 20 22 24 26 28 29 30 31 32 34 40 43 45 47 49 51 53 54 56 57 59 60 64 70 74 75 76 77 78 79 81 85 87 89 90 93 96 97 98 103 104 107 108 110 111 114 115 116 118 119 129 130 131 132 135 144 147 148 149
Primary Contact: Jason Wren, President and Chief Executive Officer
COO: Leon Fuqua, Chief Operating Officer
CFO: Jim Eaton, Chief Financial Officer
CMO: Jason Schuh M.D., Chief of Staff
CIO: Joe Arispe, Director Information Systems
CHR: Mike McQuiston, Administrative Director Human Resources
CNO: Sue Sewell, Chief Nursing Officer
Web address: www.wiseregional.com
Control: Hospital district or authority, Government, Nonfederal **Service:** General medical and surgical

Staffed Beds: 133 **Admissions:** 5022 **Census:** 67 **Outpatient Visits:** 323564 **Births:** 625 **Total Expense ($000):** 327538 **Payroll Expense ($000):** 75074 **Personnel:** 1353

TX

Hospital, Medicare Provider Number, Address, Telephone, Approval, Facility, and Physician Codes, Health Care System

★ American Hospital Association (AHA) membership
☐ The Joint Commission accreditation
○ Healthcare Facilities Accreditation Program
◇ DNV Healthcare Inc. accreditation
⇑ Center for Improvement in Healthcare Quality Accreditation
△ Commission on Accreditation of Rehabilitation Facilities (CARF) accreditation

© 2017 AHA Guide   *Many Facility Codes have changed. Please refer to the AHA Guide Code Chart.*   Hospitals **A607**

DEL RIO—Val Verde County

☒ **VAL VERDE REGIONAL MEDICAL CENTER (450154)**, 801 Bedell Avenue, Zip 78840–4112, Mailing Address: 801 North Bedell Avenue, 78840–4112; tel. 830/775–8566 **A**1 10 20 22 **F**3 7 11 13 15 18 20 29 30 34 35 40 43 46 48 54 57 59 63 73 75 76 77 79 81 82 84 85 87 89 93 96 107 108 110 111 114 119 129 131 132 133 146 147 149
Primary Contact: Xochy Hurtado, FACHE, Chief Executive Officer
CFO: Eddie Read, Interim Chief Financial Officer
CMO: Mohamed Shafiu M.D., Chief of Staff
CIO: Val King, Chief Information Officer
CHR: Leigh Ann Qualia, Director Human Resources
CNO: Kathy Fletcher R.N., MSN, Interim Chief Nursing Officer
Web address: www.vvrmc.org
Control: Hospital district or authority, Government, Nonfederal **Service**: General medical and surgical

Staffed Beds: 80 **Admissions:** 2618 **Census:** 23 **Outpatient Visits:** 88073
Births: 933 **Total Expense ($000):** 60699 **Payroll Expense ($000):** 22332
Personnel: 413

DENISON—Grayson County

☐ **TEXOMA MEDICAL CENTER (450324)**, 5016 South US Highway 75, Zip 75020–4584, Mailing Address: P.O.Box 890, 75021–0890; tel. 903/416–4000, (Includes TMC BEHAVIORAL HEALTH CENTER, 2601 North Cornerstone Drive, Sherman, Texas, Zip 75092–2551, tel. 903/416–3000; Jennifer Wiggins, Chief Executive Officer) **A**1 10 13 **F**3 11 12 13 15 17 18 20 22 24 28 29 30 31 34 35 40 43 45 46 47 48 49 50 53 54 57 59 62 64 70 74 75 76 77 78 79 80 81 82 85 86 87 89 90 91 93 96 98 100 101 102 103 104 105 107 108 110 111 115 118 119 126 132 134 144 145 146 147 148 149 150 **S** Universal Health Services, Inc., King of Prussia, PA
Primary Contact: Ronald T. Seal, Chief Executive Officer
CFO: Gerard Hebert, Chief Financial Officer
CMO: Robert Sanders M.D., Chief Medical Officer
CIO: Lisa Engle, Director Information Technology
CHR: Bill Heinzmann, Director Human Resources
CNO: Andrea Brenn R.N., Chief Nursing Officer
Web address: www.texomamedicalcenter.net
Control: Corporation, Investor–owned (for–profit) **Service**: General medical and surgical

Staffed Beds: 326 **Admissions:** 15324 **Census:** 207 **Outpatient Visits:** 131956 **Births:** 1107 **Total Expense ($000):** 221400 **Payroll Expense ($000):** 90668 **Personnel:** 1746

DENTON—Denton County

☐ **INTEGRITY TRANSITIONAL HOSPITAL (452109)**, 2813 South Mayhill Road, Zip 76208–5910; tel. 940/320–2300 **A**1 10 **F**1 3 29 77 80 82 86 87 91 130 148
Primary Contact: Israel Navarro, Chief Executive Officer
CNO: Michele Andrews, Chief Clinical Officer
Web address: www.ithcare.com
Control: Partnership, Investor–owned (for–profit) **Service**: Acute long–term care hospital

Staffed Beds: 30 **Admissions:** 212 **Census:** 14 **Outpatient Visits:** 1648
Births: 0

☒ **MAYHILL HOSPITAL (670010)**, 2809 South Mayhill Road, Zip 76208–5910; tel. 940/239–3000 **A**1 10 **F**4 5 29 40 56 82 98 101 102 103 104 105 130 **S** Universal Health Services, Inc., King of Prussia, PA
Primary Contact: Dawne Buckley, Interim Chief Executive Officer
CFO: Emmy Adams, Chief Financial Officer
CMO: Asad Islam M.D., Chief Medical Officer
CIO: Kyle Murphy, Director Information Technology
CHR: Patricia Gloria–Barraza, Coordinator Human Resources
Web address: www.mayhillhospital.com
Control: Partnership, Investor–owned (for–profit) **Service**: Psychiatric

Staffed Beds: 59 **Admissions:** 1676 **Census:** 37 **Outpatient Visits:** 2798
Births: 0 **Total Expense ($000):** 10099 **Payroll Expense ($000):** 5004
Personnel: 89

☒ **MEDICAL CITY DENTON (450634)**, 3535 South 1–35 East, Zip 76210; tel. 940/384–3535 **A**1 10 **F**3 15 18 20 22 24 26 28 29 30 34 35 40 43 45 46 47 49 50 57 59 64 70 74 75 76 77 79 81 82 84 85 86 87 93 107 108 110 111 114 115 118 119 126 130 132 144 146 148 149 **S** HCA Healthcare, Nashville, TN
Primary Contact: Steven Edgar, FACHE, President and Chief Executive Officer
COO: Jeffrey T Lawrence, Chief Operating Officer
CFO: Todd Gibson, Chief Financial Officer
CMO: Howard Shaw M.D., Chief Medical Officer
CHR: Stacey Bravo, Vice President Human Resources
CNO: Nicki Roderman, Chief Nursing Officer
Web address: www.dentonregional.com
Control: Partnership, Investor–owned (for–profit) **Service**: General medical and surgical

Staffed Beds: 185 **Admissions:** 9139 **Census:** 120 **Outpatient Visits:** 75476 **Births:** 0 **Total Expense ($000):** 147286 **Payroll Expense ($000):** 50912 **Personnel:** 763

☒ **SELECT REHABILITATION HOSPITAL OF DENTON (673036)**, 2620 Scripture Street, Zip 76201–4315; tel. 940/297–6500 **A**1 10 **F**3 29 60 64 68 74 75 77 79 86 87 90 93 96 132 135 148 149 **P**6 **S** Select Medical Corporation, Mechanicsburg, PA
Primary Contact: Michelle Powell, Chief Executive Officer
CFO: Doug Selsor, Director Finance
CHR: Patsy Martin, Manager Human Resources
CNO: Lee Ann Elliott R.N., Director of Nursing
Web address: www.selectrehab–denton.com/
Control: Partnership, Investor–owned (for–profit) **Service**: Rehabilitation

Staffed Beds: 44 **Admissions:** 849 **Census:** 28 **Outpatient Visits:** 12205
Births: 0 **Total Expense ($000):** 14877 **Payroll Expense ($000):** 8285
Personnel: 99

☒ **TEXAS HEALTH PRESBYTERIAN HOSPITAL DENTON (450743)**, 3000 North I–35, Zip 76201–5119; tel. 940/898–7000 **A**1 10 **F**3 11 12 13 15 17 18 20 22 24 26 28 29 30 31 34 35 40 45 46 48 49 57 59 65 66 68 70 72 74 75 76 78 79 81 82 83 84 85 86 89 93 107 108 110 111 115 118 119 126 129 130 132 135 145 146 147 148 149 **S** Texas Health Resources, Arlington, TX
Primary Contact: Jeff Reecer, FACHE, Chief Executive Officer
CFO: David B Meltzer, Chief Financial Officer
CMO: Timothy Harris M.D., Chief Quality Officer
CIO: Melissa Smart, Communication ad Public Relations Specialist
CHR: Kathy Hardcastle, Director Human Resources
CNO: Deborah Bostic R.N., Chief Nursing Officer
Web address: www.dentonhospital.com
Control: Other not–for–profit (including NFP Corporation) **Service**: General medical and surgical

Staffed Beds: 190 **Admissions:** 11026 **Census:** 129 **Outpatient Visits:** 71933 **Births:** 2468 **Total Expense ($000):** 192256 **Payroll Expense ($000):** 71408 **Personnel:** 946

★ ⇑ **THE HEART HOSPITAL BAYLOR DENTON (450893)**, 2801 South Mayhill Road, Zip 76208–5910, Mailing Address: 1100 Allied Drive, Plano, 76208–5910; tel. 940/220–0600 **A**10 21 **F**3 17 18 20 22 24 26 28 29 30 34 35 40 57 60 64 68 70 71 75 77 81 84 85 87 107 111 115 119 130 132 135 146 148 149
Primary Contact: Mark Valentine, President
COO: Bradley Morgan, Vice President of Operations
CFO: Bryan Nichols, Chief Financial Officer
CMO: Trent Pettijohn M.D., Esq, Chief Medical Officer
CHR: Tracy Stanford, Director Human Resources
CNO: Susan K. Moats R.N., Vice President Patient Care Services and Chief Nursing Officer
Web address: www.denton.thehearthospitalbaylor.com
Control: Partnership, Investor–owned (for–profit) **Service**: Heart

Staffed Beds: 22 **Admissions:** 454 **Census:** 5 **Outpatient Visits:** 5009
Births: 0 **Total Expense ($000):** 32975 **Payroll Expense ($000):** 11450
Personnel: 105

☒ **UNIVERSITY BEHAVIORAL HEALTH OF DENTON (454104)**, 2026 West University Drive, Zip 76201–0644; tel. 940/320–8100 **A**1 10 **F**4 5 34 68 98 99 100 101 102 104 105 149 **S** Universal Health Services, Inc., King of Prussia, PA
Primary Contact: Samantha Castle, Chief Executive Officer
CFO: Ed Sopiarz, Chief Financial Officer
CMO: Atique Khan M.D., Medical Director
CIO: Marsh Smith, Manager Health Information
CHR: Dorie Atherton, Manager Human Resources
CNO: Vicki Stoker, Chief Nursing Officer
Web address: www.ubhdenton.com
Control: Partnership, Investor–owned (for–profit) **Service**: Psychiatric

Staffed Beds: 104 **Admissions:** 2600 **Census:** 70 **Outpatient Visits:** 8629
Births: 0 **Total Expense ($000):** 23798 **Payroll Expense ($000):** 9917
Personnel: 147

DENVER CITY—Yoakum County

★ **YOAKUM COUNTY HOSPITAL (451308)**, 412 Mustang Avenue, Zip 79323–2762, Mailing Address: P.O.Box 1130, 79323–1130; tel. 806/592–2121 **A**10 18 **F**3 11 13 28 34 35 40 43 50 53 57 59 60 62 64 76 81 87 89 93 107 114 119 127 129 133 149 **P**6
Primary Contact: Jerry Osburn, Chief Executive Officer
CFO: Suann Parrish, Chief Financial Officer
CMO: Dan Khan M.D., Chief Medical Officer
CIO: Todd Carrillo, Chief Information Officer
CHR: Teresa Howard, Manager Human Resources
Web address: www.ych.us
Control: County, Government, Nonfederal **Service**: General medical and surgical

Staffed Beds: 22 **Admissions:** 560 **Census:** 5 **Outpatient Visits:** 54127
Births: 260 **Total Expense ($000):** 24822 **Payroll Expense ($000):** 8538
Personnel: 187

DESOTO—Dallas County

☐ **DALLAS BEHAVIORAL HEALTHCARE HOSPITAL (454126)**, 800 Kirnwood Drive, Zip 75115–2000; tel. 855/982–0897 **A**1 **F**4 5 56 87 98 99 100 101 103 104 105 130 **S** Signature Healthcare Services, Corona, CA
Primary Contact: Selene Q. Hammon, Chief Executive Officer
CMO: Rahim Haqqani M.D., Medical Director
CHR: Henry In, Director Human Resources
CNO: Susie Edler R.N., Chief Nursing Officer
Web address: www.dallasbehavioral.com
Control: Individual, Investor–owned (for–profit) **Service**: Psychiatric

Staffed Beds: 116 **Admissions**: 3906 **Census**: 72 **Outpatient Visits**: 5515
Births: 0 **Total Expense ($000)**: 19059 **Payroll Expense ($000)**: 9784
Personnel: 288

☐ **HICKORY TRAIL HOSPITAL (454065)**, 2000 Old Hickory Trail, Zip 75115–2242; tel. 972/298–7323 **A**1 10 **F**4 5 29 38 98 99 100 101 103 104 105 130 **S** Universal Health Services, Inc., King of Prussia, PA
Primary Contact: Kay McKennery, Interim Chief Executive Officer
CFO: Terri Logsdon, Chief Financial Officer
CMO: Manoochehr Khatami M.D., Medical Director
CHR: Sarah Warren, Coordinator Human Resources
Web address: www.hickorytrail.com
Control: Corporation, Investor–owned (for–profit) **Service**: Psychiatric

Staffed Beds: 86 **Admissions**: 2528 **Census**: 54 **Outpatient Visits**: 6613
Births: 0 **Total Expense ($000)**: 15897 **Payroll Expense ($000)**: 7576
Personnel: 158

⊠ **VIBRA SPECIALTY HOSPITAL AT DESOTO (452097)**, 2700 Walker Way, Zip 75115–2088; tel. 972/298–1100 **A**1 10 **F**1 3 29 70 75 77 87 91 107 130 148 **S** Vibra Healthcare, Mechanicsburg, PA
Primary Contact: Thomas Alexander, Chief Executive Officer
CFO: Donald Trimble CPA, Chief Financial Officer
CMO: Ed Dominguez, President Medical Staff
CHR: Tim Lozier, Director Human Resources
CNO: Mae C Weathersby R.N., Chief Clinical Officer
Web address: www.vshdesoto.com
Control: Corporation, Investor–owned (for–profit) **Service**: Acute long–term care hospital

Staffed Beds: 60 **Admissions**: 522 **Census**: 35 **Outpatient Visits**: 0 **Births**: 0
Total Expense ($000): 18848 **Payroll Expense ($000)**: 9002 **Personnel**: 157

DIMMITT—Castro County

★ **PLAINS MEMORIAL HOSPITAL (451350)**, 310 West Halsell Street, Zip 79027–1846, Mailing Address: P.O.Box 278, 79027–0278; tel. 806/647–2191 **A**10 18 **F**3 7 32 34 35 40 43 53 57 59 64 65 69 75 77 85 86 87 93 97 107 114 115 119 127 130 133 135 149 **P**6
Primary Contact: Linda Rasor, R.N., Chief Executive Officer
CFO: Terri Martinez, Chief Financial Officer
CMO: Gary R Hardee M.D., Medical Director
CIO: Terry Young, Chief Information Officer
CHR: Debbie Underwood, Manager Human Resources
CNO: Renee Castillo, Chief Nursing Officer
Web address: www.plainsmemorial.com
Control: Hospital district or authority, Government, Nonfederal **Service**: General medical and surgical

Staffed Beds: 17 **Admissions**: 182 **Census**: 4 **Outpatient Visits**: 22597
Births: 0 **Total Expense ($000)**: 10954 **Payroll Expense ($000)**: 4478
Personnel: 100

DUMAS—Moore County

☐ **MOORE COUNTY HOSPITAL DISTRICT (450221)**, 224 East Second Street, Zip 79029–3808; tel. 806/935–7171 **A**1 10 20 **F**3 7 11 13 15 28 34 35 40 43 46 50 51 57 59 62 63 70 75 79 81 85 86 91 93 107 110 111 115 119 130 131 132 133 135 146 147 148
Primary Contact: Jeff Turner, FACHE, Chief Executive Officer
COO: Ashleigh Wiswell, Chief Operations Officer
CFO: John E. Bailey, Chief Financial Officer
CHR: Kathie Fuston, Director Human Resources
CNO: Ronda Crow, Chief Nursing Officer
Web address: www.mchd.net
Control: Hospital district or authority, Government, Nonfederal **Service**: General medical and surgical

Staffed Beds: 47 **Admissions**: 896 **Census**: 7 **Outpatient Visits**: 41055
Births: 400 **Total Expense ($000)**: 34412 **Payroll Expense ($000)**: 16470
Personnel: 348

EAGLE LAKE—Colorado County

★ **RICE MEDICAL CENTER (451312)**, 600 South Austin Road, Zip 77434–3298, Mailing Address: P.O.Box 277, 77434–0277; tel. 979/234–5571 **A**10 18 **F**3 11 13 15 29 34 40 43 57 59 64 65 70 75 76 77 79 81 107 119 127 133 **P**6
Primary Contact: James D. Janek, Chief Executive Officer
CFO: Brian Mc Bride, Chief Financial Officer
CMO: Russell Thomas M.D., Chief of Staff
CHR: Velma Loya, Administrative Human Resource Coordinator
CNO: Susan Hernandez R.N., Chief Nursing Officer
Web address: www.ricemedicalcenter.net/
Control: Corporation, Investor–owned (for–profit) **Service**: General medical and surgical

Staffed Beds: 15 **Admissions**: 248 **Census**: 3 **Outpatient Visits**: 25010
Births: 36 **Total Expense ($000)**: 12801 **Payroll Expense ($000)**: 3176
Personnel: 81

EAGLE PASS—Maverick County

☐ **FORT DUNCAN REGIONAL MEDICAL CENTER (450092)**, 3333 North Foster Maldonado Boulevard, Zip 78852–5893; tel. 830/773–5321 **A**1 10 20 **F**3 11 13 15 18 20 22 29 40 43 45 57 60 65 68 70 75 76 77 79 81 85 89 90 91 93 107 108 110 111 114 118 119 129 130 146 147 148 **S** Universal Health Services, Inc., King of Prussia, PA
Primary Contact: Eladio Montalvo, Chief Executive Officer
COO: Alan Gonzalez, Chief Operating Officer
CFO: Joel Morales, Chief Financial Officer
CMO: Ruben de los Santos M.D., Chief Medical Officer
CIO: Jose Elias, Director Information Technology
CHR: Daisy Rodriquez, Director Human Resources
CNO: Scott Lethi R.N., FACHE, Chief Nursing Officer
Web address: www.fortduncanmedicalcenter.com
Control: Partnership, Investor–owned (for–profit) **Service**: General medical and surgical

Staffed Beds: 101 **Admissions**: 4392 **Census**: 50 **Outpatient Visits**: 46308
Births: 1163 **Total Expense ($000)**: 53208 **Payroll Expense ($000)**: 21563
Personnel: 335

EASTLAND—Eastland County

EASTLAND MEMORIAL HOSPITAL (450411), 304 South Daugherty Street, Zip 76448–2609, Mailing Address: P.O.Box 897, 76448–0897; tel. 254/629–2601 **A**10 20 **F**7 11 15 28 29 30 34 39 40 43 45 49 50 53 56 57 59 64 65 68 75 81 84 85 86 87 93 107 108 110 111 114 119 128 129 130 131 133 135 146 148 149
Primary Contact: Ted Matthews, Chief Executive Officer
CFO: Jamie Hayden, Chief Financial Officer
CHR: Leisha Hodges, Human Resources Officer
Web address: www.eastlandmemorial.com
Control: Hospital district or authority, Government, Nonfederal **Service**: General medical and surgical

Staffed Beds: 36 **Admissions**: 564 **Census**: 6 **Outpatient Visits**: 21877
Births: 2 **Total Expense ($000)**: 12943 **Payroll Expense ($000)**: 5653
Personnel: 154

EDEN—Concho County

CONCHO COUNTY HOSPITAL (451325), 614 Eaker Street, Zip 76837–0359, Mailing Address: P.O.Box 987, 76837–0987; tel. 325/869–5911 **A**10 18 **F**3 34 40 43 50 53 59 77 87 107 133 146
Primary Contact: Brian Lady, Administrator and Chief Executive Officer
CFO: Melanie Lozano, Chief Financial Officer
CNO: Toby Lehn, Director of Nurses
Web address: www.conchocountyhospital.com/
Control: Hospital district or authority, Government, Nonfederal **Service**: General medical and surgical

Staffed Beds: 16 **Admissions**: 98 **Census**: 1 **Outpatient Visits**: 4375 **Births**: 0
Total Expense ($000): 8349 **Payroll Expense ($000)**: 3150 **Personnel**: 48

TX

EDINBURG—Hidalgo County

CORNERSTONE REGIONAL HOSPITAL (450825), 2302 Cornerstone Boulevard, Zip 78539–8471; tel. 956/618–4444 **A**1 10 **F**3 8 29 34 35 37 39 40 45 46 47 51 57 59 68 74 79 81 82 85 119 126 145 **S** Universal Health Services, Inc., King of Prussia, PA
Primary Contact: Roxanna M. Godinez, Chief Executive Officer
CFO: Janie Alvarez, Accounting Director
CMO: Omar Gomez M.D., Chief of Staff
CHR: Erika Betancourt, Coordinator Human Resources
CNO: Roxanne Reyes, Director of Nursing
Web address: www.cornerstoneregional.com
Control: Partnership, Investor–owned (for–profit) **Service**: Surgical

Staffed Beds: 14 Admissions: 692 Census: 4 Outpatient Visits: 3074 Births: 0 Total Expense ($000): 15153 Payroll Expense ($000): 3940 Personnel: 80

△ **DOCTOR'S HOSPITAL AT RENAISSANCE (450869)**, 5501 South McColl Road, Zip 78539–9152; tel. 956/362–7360 **A**1 2 3 5 7 10 **F**1 3 4 8 9 12 13 15 16 17 18 19 20 22 24 26 28 29 30 31 34 35 38 39 40 41 43 45 46 47 48 49 50 51 52 53 54 55 56 57 58 59 60 64 65 66 67 68 70 71 72 73 74 75 76 77 78 79 80 81 82 83 84 85 86 87 88 89 90 91 92 93 95 96 97 98 99 100 101 102 103 104 105 107 108 109 110 111 112 113 114 115 116 117 118 119 120 121 123 124 126 127 128 130 131 132 135 138 139 144 145 146 147 148 149 **P**3 8
Primary Contact: Carlos Cardenas, M.D., Chief Administrative Officer
COO: Marissa Castaneda, Chief Operating Officer and Director Marketing
CFO: Susan S Turley, Chief Financial Officer
Web address: www.dhr–rgv.com
Control: Partnership, Investor–owned (for–profit) **Service**: General medical and surgical

Staffed Beds: 519 Admissions: 31534 Census: 403 Outpatient Visits: 332585 Births: 8241 Total Expense ($000): 477676 Payroll Expense ($000): 190849 Personnel: 4271

SOUTH TEXAS HEALTH SYSTEM (450119), 1400 West Trenton Road, Zip 78539–9105, Mailing Address: 1102 West Trenton Road, 78539–9105; tel. 956/388–6000, (Includes EDINBURG CHILDREN'S HOSPITAL, 1400 West Trenton Road, Edinburg, Texas, Zip 78539, tel. 956/388–8000; EDINBURG REGIONAL MEDICAL CENTER, 1102 West Trenton Road, Edinburg, Texas, Zip 78539–6199, tel. 956/388–6000; MCALLEN HEART HOSPITAL, 1900 South D Street, McAllen, Texas, Zip 78503, tel. 956/994–2000; Dan Caldwell, Chief Executive Officer; MCALLEN MEDICAL CENTER, 301 West Expressway 83, McAllen, Texas, Zip 78503–3045, tel. 956/632–4000; Todd Mann, Chief Executive Officer; SOUTH TEXAS BEHAVIORAL HEALTH CENTER, 2101 West Trenton Road, Edinburg, Texas, Zip 78539, tel. 956/388–1300; Joe Rodriguez, Chief Executive Officer) **A**1 10 **F**3 4 5 11 12 13 15 17 18 19 20 22 24 26 29 30 31 34 35 38 40 41 42 43 45 46 47 48 49 50 53 56 57 58 59 60 64 68 70 72 74 75 76 77 78 79 81 85 86 87 88 89 90 93 96 97 98 99 100 101 102 103 104 107 108 110 111 114 115 119 126 130 132 135 138 146 148 149 150 **P**6 **S** Universal Health Services, Inc., King of Prussia, PA
Primary Contact: Jennifer Garza, Chief Executive Officer
COO: Jerome M Brooks, Chief Operating Officer
CFO: Carlos Guajardo, Chief Financial Officer
CMO: Yuri Bermudez M.D., Chief of Staff
CIO: Rosie L Mendiola–Balderas, Director Information Systems
CHR: Patricia Mcclelland, Director Human Resources
CNO: Candida Constantine MSN, R.N., Chief Nursing Officer
Web address: www.southtexashealthsystem.com
Control: Partnership, Investor–owned (for–profit) **Service**: General medical and surgical

Staffed Beds: 788 Admissions: 25339 Census: 350 Outpatient Visits: 188773 Births: 1642 Total Expense ($000): 328577 Payroll Expense ($000): 117522 Personnel: 2261

EDNA—Jackson County

★ **JACKSON COUNTY HOSPITAL DISTRICT (451363)**, 1013 South Wells Street, Zip 77957–4098; tel. 361/782–7800 **A**10 18 **F**3 7 15 29 34 35 40 43 44 45 50 53 57 59 62 64 65 68 75 81 87 97 102 107 110 114 119 127 130 133 143 146 **P**8
Primary Contact: Bill Jones, Chief Executive Officer
CFO: Lance Smiga, Chief Financial Officer
CMO: Francisco Ortiz M.D., Chief of Staff
CIO: Jeff Prukop, Director Professional Services
CHR: Donna Coleman, Coordinator Human Resources
CNO: Tammy Zajicek, Director of Nursing
Web address: www.jchd.org
Control: Hospital district or authority, Government, Nonfederal **Service**: General medical and surgical

Staffed Beds: 17 Admissions: 165 Census: 2 Outpatient Visits: 16115 Births: 0 Total Expense ($000): 19803 Payroll Expense ($000): 7597 Personnel: 133

EL CAMPO—Wharton County

EL CAMPO MEMORIAL HOSPITAL (450694), 303 Sandy Corner Road, Zip 77437–9535; tel. 979/543–6251 **A**10 **F**3 11 15 29 34 35 40 43 45 56 57 59 60 64 68 70 77 79 81 85 86 93 97 107 108 110 111 114 119 127 129 130 131 132 148 **P**6
Primary Contact: Nathan Tudor, Chief Executive Officer
CFO: David Mak, Chief Financial Officer
CMO: Thai Huynh M.D., Chief of Medical Staff
CIO: Bill Eller, Director Information Technology
CHR: Ginger Andreas, Coordinator Personnel and Credentialing
CNO: Desiree Cernoch, Director of Nurses
Web address: www.ecmh.org
Control: Other not–for–profit (including NFP Corporation) **Service**: General medical and surgical

Staffed Beds: 25 Admissions: 486 Census: 7 Outpatient Visits: 54246 Births: 0 Total Expense ($000): 19671 Payroll Expense ($000): 7398 Personnel: 138

EL PASO—El Paso County

EAST EL PASO PHYSICIANS MEDICAL CENTER See Foundation Surgical Hospital Of El Paso

EL PASO BEHAVIORAL HEALTH SYSTEM (454109), 1900 Denver Avenue, Zip 79902–3008; tel. 915/544–4000 **A**1 5 10 **F**4 5 56 57 75 86 87 98 99 101 102 103 104 105 130 135 149 150 **S** Universal Health Services, Inc., King of Prussia, PA
Primary Contact: Phillip Sosa, Interim Chief Executive Officer
CFO: Phillip Sosa, Chief Financial Officer
CMO: Arthur L. Ramirez M.D., Medical Director
CIO: Victor Torres, Information Technology Specialist Administrator
CHR: Brenda Holguin, Manager Human Resources
CNO: Susan Brown, Chief Nursing Officer
Web address: www.ubhelpaso.com/
Control: Corporation, Investor–owned (for–profit) **Service**: Psychiatric

Staffed Beds: 163 Admissions: 5791 Census: 144 Outpatient Visits: 35344 Births: 0 Total Expense ($000): 33541 Payroll Expense ($000): 16112 Personnel: 328

EL PASO CHILDREN'S HOSPITAL (453313), 4845 Alameda Avenue, Zip 79905–2705; tel. 915/242–8614 **A**1 3 5 10 **F**3 19 29 30 31 34 35 38 39 40 41 44 45 48 49 50 57 58 59 61 64 68 72 73 74 75 78 79 81 82 85 86 87 88 89 93 96 99 100 111 119 130 132 134 146 148 149 150 **P**6
Primary Contact: Mark J. Amox, President and Chief Executive Officer
COO: Ellen Pitcher, Chief Nursing Officer and Chief Operating Officer
CFO: Andrew Rybolt, Chief Financial Officer
CMO: Bradley Fuhrman M.D., Physician in Chief
CIO: Janina Prada, Director Information Technology
CHR: Marina Estrada, Director Human Resources
CNO: Ellen Pitcher, Chief Nursing Officer and Chief Operating Officer
Web address: www.elpasochildrens.org
Control: Other not–for–profit (including NFP Corporation) **Service**: Children's general medical and surgical

Staffed Beds: 122 Admissions: 3327 Census: 55 Outpatient Visits: 44122 Births: 0 Total Expense ($000): 97536 Payroll Expense ($000): 28129 Personnel: 497

EL PASO LTAC HOSPITAL (452103), 1221 North Cotton Street, Zip 79902–3015; tel. 915/546–5822 **A**10 **F**1 3 7 29 30 34 57 60 75 77 82 84 85 86 87 100 103 119 130 148
Primary Contact: Jose Huerta, Chief Executive Officer
CFO: Eddie Martinez, Chief Financial Officer
CNO: Skylier Blake R.N., Chief Nursing Officer
Control: Partnership, Investor–owned (for–profit) **Service**: Acute long–term care hospital

Staffed Beds: 33 Admissions: 226 Census: 12 Outpatient Visits: 0 Births: 0 Total Expense ($000): 6533 Payroll Expense ($000): 2610 Personnel: 63

EL PASO PSYCHIATRIC CENTER (454100), 4615 Alameda Avenue, Zip 79905–2702; tel. 915/532–2202 **A**1 3 5 10 **F**29 98 99 103 130 135 **P**6 **S** Texas Department of State Health Services, Austin, TX
Primary Contact: Zulema Carrillo, Superintendent
CFO: David Osterhout, Assistant Superintendent and Chief Financial Officer
CMO: Nicolas Baida–Fragoso M.D., Clinical Director
CNO: Raul D. Luna, Chief Nurse Executive
Web address: www.dshs.state.tx.us/mhhospitals/ElPasoPC/default.shtm
Control: State, Government, Nonfederal **Service**: Psychiatric

Staffed Beds: 74 Admissions: 904 Census: 66 Outpatient Visits: 0 Births: 0 Total Expense ($000): 26576 Payroll Expense ($000): 11159 Personnel: 222

Many Facility Codes have changed. Please refer to the AHA Guide Code Chart. © 2017 AHA Guide

TX

☐ **EL PASO SPECIALTY HOSPITAL (450845)**, 1755 Curie Drive, Zip 79902–2919; tel. 915/544–3636 **A**1 3 10 **F**3 29 34 35 40 51 59 64 68 75 79 81 82 85 86 87 107 111 115 130 131 148 **S** National Surgical Healthcare, Chicago, IL
Primary Contact: James Wilcox, Chief Executive Officer
CFO: Greg Watters, Chief Financial Officer
CMO: David Mansfield M.D., Chief of Staff
CNO: Anne Harvey MSN, Chief Nursing Officer
Web address: www.elpasospecialtyhospital.com
Control: Partnership, Investor–owned (for–profit) **Service:** Orthopedic

Staffed Beds: 20 Admissions: 827 Census: 5 Outpatient Visits: 20764 Births: 0 Total Expense ($000): 31780 Payroll Expense ($000): 8268 Personnel: 187

○ **FOUNDATION SURGICAL HOSPITAL OF EL PASO (450877)**, 1416 George Dieter Drive, Zip 79936–7601; tel. 915/598–4240 **A**3 10 11 **F**3 29 40 45 49 79 81 82 85 86 93 107 111 114 119 126 **S** Foundation Surgical Hospital Affiliates, Oklahoma City, OK
Primary Contact: Don Burris, Chief Executive Officer
COO: Marta Contreras, Chief Nursing Officer and Chief Operating Officer
CIO: Louie Aguilera, Director Information Technology
CHR: Grace Beltran, Director Human Resources
CNO: Marta Contreras, Chief Nursing Officer and Chief Operating Officer
Web address: www.physiciansmedcenter.com
Control: Partnership, Investor–owned (for–profit) **Service:** Surgical

Staffed Beds: 20 Admissions: 763 Census: 5 Outpatient Visits: 42441 Births: 0 Total Expense ($000): 47939 Payroll Expense ($000): 8005 Personnel: 192

⊞ **HIGHLANDS REHABILITATION HOSPITAL (453086)**, 1395 George Dieter Drive, Zip 79936–7410; tel. 915/298–7222 **A**1 10 **F**3 29 30 34 57 59 64 74 75 79 86 87 90 93 96 100 130 132 143 146 148 149 **S** Vibra Healthcare, Mechanicsburg, PA
Primary Contact: Craig Johnson, Chief Executive Officer
CHR: Janet Straughan, Manager Human Resources
CNO: Oscar Mendizabal, Chief Nursing Officer
Web address: www.vrhhighlands.com/
Control: Partnership, Investor–owned (for–profit) **Service:** Rehabilitation

Staffed Beds: 41 Admissions: 739 Census: 25 Outpatient Visits: 3551 Births: 0 Total Expense ($000): 15052 Payroll Expense ($000): 6236 Personnel: 105

⊞ **KINDRED HOSPITAL EL PASO (452079)**, 1740 Curie Drive, Zip 79902–2901; tel. 915/351–9044 **A**1 10 **F**1 3 29 45 46 70 75 148 149 **S** Kindred Healthcare, Louisville, KY
Primary Contact: America Jones, R.N., Chief Executive Officer
CFO: Melissa Campa, Controller
CMO: Edward Juarez M.D., Chief Medical Officer
CHR: Laura Anchondo, Administrator Human Resources
Web address: www.khelpaso.com
Control: Corporation, Investor–owned (for–profit) **Service:** Acute long–term care hospital

Staffed Beds: 72 Admissions: 630 Census: 39 Outpatient Visits: 84 Births: 0 Total Expense ($000): 17715 Payroll Expense ($000): 7170 Personnel: 146

⊞ △ **LAS PALMAS MEDICAL CENTER (450107)**, 1801 North Oregon Street, Zip 79902–3591; tel. 915/521–1200, (Includes DEL SOL MEDICAL CENTER, 10301 West Gateway Boulevard, El Paso, Texas, Zip 79925–7798, tel. 915/595–9000; David Shimp, Chief Executive Officer; LAS PALMAS REHABILITATION HOSPITAL, 300 Waymore Drive, El Paso, Texas, Zip 79902–1628, tel. 915/577–2600; Don Karl, Interim Chief Executive Officer) **A**1 3 5 7 10 **F**3 8 11 12 13 15 17 18 19 20 22 24 26 27 28 29 30 34 35 37 38 39 40 41 43 46 47 48 49 50 51 53 54 56 57 58 59 60 64 68 70 72 73 74 75 76 77 78 79 81 82 85 86 87 88 89 90 91 92 93 96 103 107 108 110 111 112 114 115 119 120 121 122 124 126 127 129 130 132 134 135 136 138 143 144 145 146 147 148 149 150 **S** HCA Healthcare, Nashville, TN
Primary Contact: Don Karl, Interim Chief Executive Officer
COO: Don Karl, Chief Operating Officer
CNO: Jerry Gonzalez, Interim Chief Nursing Officer
Web address: www.laspalmashealth.com
Control: Partnership, Investor–owned (for–profit) **Service:** General medical and surgical

Staffed Beds: 509 Admissions: 28497 Census: 390 Outpatient Visits: 151163 Births: 5013 Total Expense ($000): 379768 Payroll Expense ($000): 151096 Personnel: 2276

☐ **MESA HILLS SPECIALTY HOSPITAL (452035)**, 2311 North Oregon Street, 5th Floor, Zip 79902–3216; tel. 915/545–1823 **A**1 10 **F**1 3 29 61 64 65 68 74 75 77 82 85 86 87 97 130 143 148 149 **P**8 **S** Concord Healthcare Group, Lakewood, NJ
Primary Contact: Kathleen Cahill, Chief Executive Officer
COO: Elena Pino, Chief Operating Officer and Chief Nursing Officer
CFO: Priscilla Carter, Chief Financial Officer
Web address: www.specialtyhospitalmesahills.com/
Control: Corporation, Investor–owned (for–profit) **Service:** Acute long–term care hospital

Staffed Beds: 32 Admissions: 303 Census: 22 Outpatient Visits: 0 Births: 0 Total Expense ($000): 6544 Payroll Expense ($000): 3204 Personnel: 122

⊞ **THE HOSPITALS OF PROVIDENCE EAST CAMPUS (670047)**, 3280 Joe Battle Boulevard, Zip 79938–2622; tel. 915/832–2000 **A**1 5 10 **F**3 13 15 18 20 22 26 29 30 31 34 35 37 39 40 41 45 46 47 49 50 57 59 60 63 64 68 70 72 73 74 75 76 77 78 79 81 83 84 85 86 87 89 93 107 108 110 111 115 119 126 130 134 146 147 148 **P**4 **S** TENET Healthcare Corporation, Dallas, TX
Primary Contact: Phillip Young, Chief Executive Officer
COO: Lauren Morton, Chief Operating Officer
Web address: www.sphn.com
Control: Individual, Investor–owned (for–profit) **Service:** General medical and surgical

Staffed Beds: 182 Admissions: 11569 Census: 126 Outpatient Visits: 98815 Births: 2167 Total Expense ($000): 158056 Payroll Expense ($000): 49500 Personnel: 783

⊞ **THE HOSPITALS OF PROVIDENCE MEMORIAL CAMPUS (450002)**, 2001 North Oregon Street, Zip 79902–3368; tel. 915/577–6625, (Includes PROVIDENCE CHILDREN'S HOSPITAL, 2001 North Oregon Street, El Paso, Texas, Zip 79902–3320, tel. 915/577–7746; Sally A. Hurt–Deitch, FACHE, R.N., Market Chief Executive Officer) **A**1 10 **F**3 8 11 12 13 14 15 17 18 19 20 21 22 23 24 25 28 29 31 32 34 35 40 41 42 43 45 46 49 50 51 54 56 57 59 63 64 65 67 70 72 73 74 75 76 77 78 79 81 84 85 86 87 88 89 91 92 93 98 103 107 108 110 111 115 118 119 126 129 130 132 134 145 146 147 148 **S** TENET Healthcare Corporation, Dallas, TX
Primary Contact: Sally A. Hurt–Deitch, FACHE, R.N., Market Chief Executive Officer
COO: Roddex Barlow, Chief Operating Officer
CFO: Charles Handley, Chief Financial Officer
CIO: Ray Davis, Administrative Director
CHR: Stephanie S. Talley, Market Chief Human Resource Officer
CNO: Barbara Vazquez, Chief Nursing Officer
Web address: www.thehospitalsofprovidence.com
Control: Partnership, Investor–owned (for–profit) **Service:** General medical and surgical

Staffed Beds: 409 Admissions: 16717 Census: 201 Outpatient Visits: 147954 Births: 3255 Total Expense ($000): 253964 Payroll Expense ($000): 81518 Personnel: 1306

⊞ **THE HOSPITALS OF PROVIDENCE SIERRA CAMPUS (450668)**, 1625 Medical Center Drive, Zip 79902–5005; tel. 915/747–4000 **A**1 5 10 **F**3 17 18 20 22 24 26 29 30 34 37 40 42 43 45 46 48 49 50 54 57 58 59 60 61 64 65 68 69 70 72 74 75 76 77 78 79 81 82 85 86 90 96 97 107 108 110 111 114 115 118 119 120 124 126 130 132 134 144 145 146 147 148 149 **P**8 **S** TENET Healthcare Corporation, Dallas, TX
Primary Contact: Monica Vargas–Mahar, FACHE, Chief Executive Officer
COO: Benson Chacko, Chief Operating Officer
CFO: Victoria Gonzalez, Chief Financial Officer
CIO: Ray Davis, Administrative Director Information Systems
CHR: Stephanie S. Talley, Chief Human Resource Officer
CNO: Erik Cazares, Chief Nursing Officer
Web address: www.thehospitalsofprovidence.com
Control: Partnership, Investor–owned (for–profit) **Service:** General medical and surgical

Staffed Beds: 225 Admissions: 10267 Census: 131 Outpatient Visits: 103242 Total Expense ($000): 179382 Payroll Expense ($000): 51482 Personnel: 874

TX

Hospital, Medicare Provider Number, Address, Telephone, Approval, Facility, and Physician Codes, Health Care System

★ American Hospital Association (AHA) membership ○ Healthcare Facilities Accreditation Program ⇑ Center for Improvement in Healthcare Quality Accreditation
☐ The Joint Commission accreditation ◇ DNV Healthcare Inc. accreditation △ Commission on Accreditation of Rehabilitation Facilities (CARF) accreditation

★ **THE HOSPITALS OF PROVIDENCE TRANSMOUNTAIN CAMPUS**, 2000 Transmountain Road, Zip 79911; tel. 915/877–8300 (Nonreporting) **S** TENET Healthcare Corporation, Dallas, TX
Primary Contact: Nicholas R. Tejeda, FACHE, Chief Executive Officer
COO: Tasha Hopper, Chief Operating Officer
CFO: David Byrd, Chief Financial Officer
CMO: Gustavo Martell M.D., Chief Medical Officer
CIO: Ray Davis, Chief Information Officer
CHR: Stephanie S. Talley, Chief Human Resource Officer
CNO: Linda B. Lawson, Chief Nursing Officer
Web address: www.thehospitalsofprovidence.com/our–locations/transmountain
Control: Corporation, Investor–owned (for–profit) **Service**: General medical and surgical

Staffed Beds: 106

TRIUMPH HOSPITAL EL PASO See Kindred Hospital El Paso

✠ **UNIVERSITY MEDICAL CENTER OF EL PASO (450024)**, 4815 Alameda Avenue, Zip 79905–2794, Mailing Address: P.O.Box 20009, 79998–0009; tel. 915/544–1200 **A**1 2 3 5 10 **F**3 8 11 13 15 17 18 20 22 24 26 28 29 30 31 34 35 37 40 43 45 46 47 48 49 50 51 53 54 56 57 59 60 61 64 65 68 70 74 75 76 77 78 79 81 82 85 86 87 91 92 93 94 96 97 100 102 107 108 110 111 112 113 114 115 118 119 126 127 130 131 134 143 144 145 146 147 148 149 150 **P**6
Primary Contact: Jacob Cintron, FACHE, President and Chief Executive Officer
COO: Maria Zampini, Chief Operating Officer
CFO: Michael Nunez, Chief Financial Officer
CMO: Joel Hendryx M.D., Chief Medical Officer
CIO: Janina Prada, Director Information Services
CHR: Janice M Harris, Director Human Resources
CNO: Cindy Stout R.N., Chief Nursing Officer
Web address: www.thomasoncares.org
Control: Hospital district or authority, Government, Nonfederal **Service**: General medical and surgical

Staffed Beds: 260 **Admissions**: 14353 **Census**: 177 **Outpatient Visits**: 770087 **Births**: 3439 **Total Expense ($000)**: 608801 **Payroll Expense ($000)**: 147731 **Personnel**: 2545

✠ **WILLIAM BEAUMONT ARMY MEDICAL CENTER**, 5005 North Piedras Street, Zip 79920–5001; tel. 915/742–2121, (Nonreporting) **A**1 2 3 5 **S** Department of the Army, Office of the Surgeon General, Falls Church, VA
Primary Contact: Colonel John A. Smyrski III, Commanding Officer
CIO: MajorRion Koon, Chief Information Management Division
Web address: www.wbamc.amedd.army.mil
Control: Army, Government, federal **Service**: General medical and surgical

Staffed Beds: 209

ELDORADO—Schleicher County

★ **SCHLEICHER COUNTY MEDICAL CENTER (451304)**, 102 North US Highway 277, Zip 76936–4010; tel. 325/853–2507 **A**10 18 **F**34 40 57 59 64 65 66 68 87 93 107 127 133 149 **S** Preferred Management Corporation, Shawnee, OK
Primary Contact: Paul Burke, Administrator
CFO: Larry Stephens, Chief Financial Officer
CMO: Gordy Day M.D., Medical Director
CHR: Beverly Minor, Chief Human Resources
Web address: www.scmc.us
Control: Corporation, Investor–owned (for–profit) **Service**: General medical and surgical

Staffed Beds: 14 **Admissions**: 94 **Census**: 1 **Outpatient Visits**: 6757 **Births**: 0 **Total Expense ($000)**: 4923 **Payroll Expense ($000)**: 2125 **Personnel**: 53

ELECTRA—Wichita County

★ **ELECTRA MEMORIAL HOSPITAL (451343)**, 1207 South Bailey Street, Zip 76360–3221, Mailing Address: P.O.Box 1112, 76360–1112; tel. 940/495–3981 **A**10 18 **F**3 7 11 28 29 32 34 35 40 43 45 53 59 62 64 65 66 75 77 82 86 93 97 107 114 119 127 129 130 131 133 148
Primary Contact: Rebecca J. McCain, Chief Executive Officer
CFO: Ginnie Holmes, Chief Financial Officer
CIO: Brandon Huffstutler, Chief Information Officer
CNO: Kim Gilbert R.N., Chief Nursing Officer
Web address: www.electrahospital.com
Control: Hospital district or authority, Government, Nonfederal **Service**: General medical and surgical

Staffed Beds: 19 **Admissions**: 378 **Census**: 6 **Outpatient Visits**: 22076 **Births**: 0 **Total Expense ($000)**: 16245 **Payroll Expense ($000)**: 8163 **Personnel**: 113

ENNIS—Ellis County

✠ **ENNIS REGIONAL MEDICAL CENTER (450833)**, 2201 West Lampasas Street, Zip 75119–5644; tel. 972/875–0900 **A**1 10 **F**3 11 15 18 29 30 34 35 40 43 45 50 51 57 59 64 65 70 75 77 79 81 82 85 93 107 108 110 111 115 119 146 147 149 **S** LifePoint Health, Brentwood, TN
Primary Contact: Harold L. Siglar, Interim Chief Executive Officer
CFO: Jack Wilcox, Chief Financial Officer
CMO: Raymond W Blair M.D., Jr, Chief of Staff
CHR: Selena Cryer, Director Human Resources
CNO: Edwina A Miner R.N., Chief Nursing Officer
Web address: www.ennisregional.com
Control: Partnership, Investor–owned (for–profit) **Service**: General medical and surgical

Staffed Beds: 58 **Admissions**: 767 **Census**: 7 **Outpatient Visits**: 30282 **Births**: 52 **Total Expense ($000)**: 21366 **Payroll Expense ($000)**: 8287 **Personnel**: 143

FAIRFIELD—Freestone County

★ **FREESTONE MEDICAL CENTER (450658)**, 125 Newman Street, Zip 75840–1499; tel. 903/389–2121 **A**10 20 **F**15 28 34 40 43 45 50 57 59 68 75 81 82 107 110 115 119 127 130 132 **P**7 **S** Community Hospital Corporation, Plano, TX
Primary Contact: Stace D. Holland, Chief Executive Officer
CFO: David A Travis, Chief Financial Officer
CMO: Darryl White M.D., Chief of Staff
CHR: Jennifer Rummel, Director Human Resources
CNO: Tonya Basque, Chief Nursing Officer
Web address: www.freestonemc.com/
Control: Other not–for–profit (including NFP Corporation) **Service**: General medical and surgical

Staffed Beds: 37 **Admissions**: 353 **Census**: 3 **Outpatient Visits**: 41868 **Births**: 0 **Total Expense ($000)**: 11954 **Payroll Expense ($000)**: 3743 **Personnel**: 69

FLORESVILLE—Wilson County

★ **CONNALLY MEMORIAL MEDICAL CENTER (450108)**, 499 10th Street, Zip 78114–3175; tel. 830/393–1300 **A**10 **F**3 15 18 29 34 35 40 43 45 47 49 54 57 59 62 64 70 75 81 82 85 86 87 107 108 110 111 114 119 130 132 133 144 146 148 **P**4 6
Primary Contact: Jeremy Riney, Chief Executive Officer
COO: Bob Gillespie, Chief Operating Officer
CFO: Curtis Rojas, Interim Chief Financial Officer
CMO: Wade Krause M.D., Chief Medical Officer
CIO: Bob Gillespie, Chief Information Technology Officer
CHR: Loretta Y Morgan, Director Human Resources
CNO: Sue Tackitt, Chief Nursing Officer
Web address: www.connallymmc.org
Control: Hospital district or authority, Government, Nonfederal **Service**: General medical and surgical

Staffed Beds: 26 **Admissions**: 971 **Census**: 10 **Outpatient Visits**: 113166 **Births**: 0 **Total Expense ($000)**: 35035 **Payroll Expense ($000)**: 12573 **Personnel**: 363

FLOWER MOUND—Denton County

ICARE REHABILITATION HOSPITAL (673064), 3100 Peters Colony Road, Zip 75022–2949; tel. 214/513–0310 **A**10 **F**3 29 90 93 96
Primary Contact: Gina Tomaseski, Chief Executive Officer
Web address: www.continuumhs.com
Control: State, Government, Nonfederal **Service**: Rehabilitation

Staffed Beds: 41 **Admissions**: 118 **Census**: 4 **Outpatient Visits**: 2000 **Births**: 0 **Total Expense ($000)**: 4173 **Payroll Expense ($000)**: 1963 **Personnel**: 60

☐ **TEXAS HEALTH PRESBYTERIAN HOSPITAL FLOWER MOUND (670068)**, 4400 Long Prairie Road, Zip 75028–1892; tel. 469/322–7000 **A**1 10 **F**3 12 13 15 18 20 29 30 31 34 40 45 49 57 59 70 73 74 75 76 77 78 79 81 82 85 87 91 107 108 110 111 114 115 119 126 130 146 147
Primary Contact: Spencer Turner, FACHE, President
COO: Shelley R Tobey R.N., MS, Chief Operating Officer and Chief Nursing Officer
CFO: Tom Howard, Chief Financial Officer
CHR: Nicole Schweigert, Director Human Resources
CNO: Shelley R Tobey R.N., MS, Chief Operating Officer and Chief Nursing Officer
Web address: www.texashealthflowermound.com/
Control: Partnership, Investor–owned (for–profit) **Service**: General medical and surgical

Staffed Beds: 92 **Admissions**: 5810 **Census**: 56 **Outpatient Visits**: 36142 **Births**: 1868 **Total Expense ($000)**: 114164 **Payroll Expense ($000)**: 40654 **Personnel**: 604

TX

FORT HOOD—Bell County

✠ **CARL R. DARNALL ARMY MEDICAL CENTER**, 36000 Darnall Loop, Zip 76544–5095; tel. 254/288–8000, (Nonreporting) **A**1 2 3 5 **S** Department of the Army, Office of the Surgeon General, Falls Church, VA
Primary Contact: Colonel David R. Gibson, Chief Executive Officer
CHR: Charles Burton, Chief Human Resources
Web address: www.crdamc.amedd.army.mil
Control: Army, Government, federal **Service**: General medical and surgical

Staffed Beds: 109

FORT SAM HOUSTON—Bexar County

✠ **BROOKE ARMY MEDICAL CENTER**, 3851 Roger Brookes Drive, Zip 78234–4501; tel. 210/916–4141, (Nonreporting) **A**1 2 3 5 **S** Department of the Army, Office of the Surgeon General, Falls Church, VA
Primary Contact: Brigadier General Jeffrey Johnson, Commander
CMO: ColonelJoseph P Chozinski M.D., Deputy Commander Clinical Services
CIO: Lieutenant ColonelDavid Broyhill, Chief Information Management
CHR: Rose Juarez, Chief Civilian Personnel Branch
CNO: ColonelSheri Howell, Deputy Commander Nursing
Web address: www.bamc.amedd.army.mil
Control: Army, Government, federal **Service**: General medical and surgical

Staffed Beds: 226

BROOKE ARMY MEDICAL CENTER See Brooke Army Medical Center

FORT STOCKTON—Pecos County

PECOS COUNTY MEMORIAL HOSPITAL (450178), 387 West I H–10, Zip 79735–8912, Mailing Address: P.O.Box 1648, 79735–1648; tel. 432/336–2004 **A**10 20 **F**3 11 13 28 29 30 32 34 35 40 43 45 46 50 53 57 59 62 63 64 65 75 76 81 93 107 111 119 127 130 133 144 146 148 **P**6
Primary Contact: Margaret Davis, Interim Chief Executive Officer
CFO: Anthony Ortiz, Chief Financial Officer
CMO: Subodh Mallik M.D., Chief of Staff
CHR: Malissa Trevino, Director Human Resources
CNO: Gina Kalka R.N., Chief Nursing Officer
Web address: www.pcmhfs.com
Control: County, Government, Nonfederal **Service**: General medical and surgical

Staffed Beds: 25 Admissions: 704 Census: 6 Outpatient Visits: 79945 Births: 150 Total Expense ($000): 28247 Payroll Expense ($000): 13788 Personnel: 239

FORT WORTH—Tarrant County

✠ **BAYLOR ALL SAINTS MEDICAL CENTER AT FORT WORTH (450137)**, 1400 Eighth Avenue, Zip 76104–4192; tel. 817/926–2544 **A**1 2 3 5 10 **F**3 11 12 13 17 18 24 26 28 29 30 31 34 35 38 40 43 45 46 47 49 53 55 59 64 70 72 73 74 75 76 77 78 79 80 81 82 84 86 87 90 96 97 100 101 102 103 104 105 107 108 111 114 115 119 124 126 130 131 132 138 139 142 146 147 148 149 **S** Baylor Scott & White Health, Dallas, TX
Primary Contact: Michael Sanborn, FACHE, MS, President and Chief Executive Officer
COO: Janice L Walker R.N., Chief Operating Officer
CFO: Lucy Catala, Vice President Finance
CMO: Dahlia Hassani, Vice President of Medical Affairs
CIO: Sandy Vaughn, Director Information Services
CHR: Tracy Stanford, Director Human Resources
Web address: www.baylorhealth.com/PhysiciansLocations/AllSaints/Pages/Default.aspx
Control: Other not–for–profit (including NFP Corporation) **Service**: General medical and surgical

Staffed Beds: 371 Admissions: 17743 Census: 237 Outpatient Visits: 68374 Births: 5621 Total Expense ($000): 329973 Payroll Expense ($000): 124249 Personnel: 1231

✠ **BAYLOR INSTITUTE FOR REHABILITATION AT FORT WORTH (673035)**, 6601 Harris Parkway, Zip 76132–6108; **A**1 10 **F**3 28 29 30 64 75 90 93 130 149 **S** Select Medical Corporation, Mechanicsburg, PA
Primary Contact: Victoria Odom. Sanders, FACHE, Chief Executive Officer
CMO: Asher Light M.D., Medical Director
CHR: Nissi Dalton, Manager Human Resources
CNO: Catherine Ewing M.D., Chief Nursing Officer
Web address: www.baylorhealth.com/PhysiciansLocations/BIR/Pages/Default.aspx
Control: Partnership, Investor–owned (for–profit) **Service**: Rehabilitation

Staffed Beds: 42 Admissions: 848 Census: 27 Outpatient Visits: 3623 Births: 0 Total Expense ($000): 16041 Payroll Expense ($000): 8251 Personnel: 126

☐ **BAYLOR SURGICAL HOSPITAL AT FORT WORTH (450880)**, 1800 Park Place Avenue, Zip 76110–1302; tel. 682/703–5600 **A**1 10 **F**3 8 29 40 51 64 70 79 81 82 85 87 107 111 119
Primary Contact: Paul Debona, Chief Executive Officer
CFO: Jane Mathis, Chief Financial Officer
CMO: Bruce Bollinger M.D., Medical Director
CNO: Stacie Merrill, Chief Nursing Officer
Web address: www.mcsh–hospital.com
Control: Partnership, Investor–owned (for–profit) **Service**: General medical and surgical

Staffed Beds: 30 Admissions: 1672 Census: 11 Outpatient Visits: 10997 Births: 0 Total Expense ($000): 79164 Payroll Expense ($000): 14909 Personnel: 226

✠ **COOK CHILDREN'S MEDICAL CENTER (453300)**, 801 Seventh Avenue, Zip 76104–2796; tel. 682/885–4000 **A**1 3 5 10 **F**3 7 8 9 17 19 21 23 25 27 29 30 31 32 34 35 38 39 40 41 43 44 45 46 48 49 50 51 54 55 57 59 60 61 62 63 64 65 68 72 74 75 77 78 79 80 81 82 83 84 85 86 87 88 89 90 91 92 93 94 97 98 99 100 101 102 104 105 107 108 111 112 113 114 115 118 119 129 130 132 133 136 138 144 146 148 149 150 **P**6
Primary Contact: Rick W. Merrill, System President and Chief Executive Officer
CFO: Stephen Kimmel, Chief Financial Officer
CMO: James C Cunningham M.D., Chief Medical Officer
CIO: Theresa Meadows, Chief Information Officer
CNO: Teresa J Clark R.N., MS, Chief Nursing Officer
Web address: www.cookchildrens.org
Control: Other not–for–profit (including NFP Corporation) **Service**: Children's general medical and surgical

Staffed Beds: 369 Admissions: 10947 Census: 211 Outpatient Visits: 337852 Births: 0 Total Expense ($000): 739845 Payroll Expense ($000): 245010 Personnel: 3897

✠ **HEALTHSOUTH CITY VIEW REHABILITATION HOSPITAL (453042)**, 6701 Oakmont Boulevard, Zip 76132–2957; tel. 817/370–4700 **A**1 10 **F**3 29 77 90 91 94 95 96 130 148 **S** HEALTHSOUTH Corporation, Birmingham, AL
Primary Contact: Janell Briscoe, Chief Executive Officer
Web address: www.healthsouthcityview.com
Control: Corporation, Investor–owned (for–profit) **Service**: Rehabilitation

Staffed Beds: 62 Admissions: 1367 Census: 44 Outpatient Visits: 0 Births: 0 Total Expense ($000): 14968 Payroll Expense ($000): 8927 Personnel: 145

✠ **HEALTHSOUTH REHABILITATION HOSPITAL OF FORT WORTH (453041)**, 1212 West Lancaster Avenue, Zip 76102–4510; tel. 817/870–2336 **A**1 10 **F**3 29 60 74 75 77 79 86 90 91 95 96 130 131 148 **S** HEALTHSOUTH Corporation, Birmingham, AL
Primary Contact: Janell Briscoe, Chief Executive Officer
CFO: Sherry Hapney, Chief Financial Officer
CMO: Patrick Donovan M.D., Director Medical Staff
CHR: Tara Kleas, Director Human Resources
Web address: www.healthsouthfortworth.com
Control: Corporation, Investor–owned (for–profit) **Service**: Rehabilitation

Staffed Beds: 60 Admissions: 1078 Census: 37 Outpatient Visits: 0 Total Expense ($000): 14193 Payroll Expense ($000): 7661 Personnel: 141

JOHN PETER SMITH HOSPITAL See JPS Health Network

★ ⇑ **JPS HEALTH NETWORK (450039)**, 1500 South Main Street, Zip 76104–4917; tel. 817/921–3431, (Includes JOHN PETER SMITH HOSPITAL, 1500 South Main Street, Fort Worth, Texas, Zip 76104, tel. 817/921–3431; TRINITY SPRINGS PAVILION, 1500 South Main Street, Fort Worth, Texas, Zip 76104–4917, tel. 817/927–3636; Lily Wong, Director Psychiatry) (Total facility includes 15 beds in nursing home–type unit) **A**2 3 5 8 10 21 **F**3 8 11 13 15 17 18 20 22 24 26 28 29 30 31 32 34 35 36 37 38 39 40 43 44 45 47 49 50 54 55 56 57 58 59 60 61 64 65 66 68 70 72 74 75 76 77 78 79 80 81 82 84 85 86 87 89 91 92 93 97 98 99 100 101 102 103 104 105 107 108 110 111 114 115 118 119 120 121 123 124 126 128 130 131 132 134 135 142 143 144 146 147 148 149
Primary Contact: Robert Earley, President and Chief Executive Officer
CFO: Alan Townsend, Interim Chief Financial Officer
CIO: Melinda Custin, Chief Information Officer
CHR: Nikki Sumpter, Senior Vice President Human Resources
CNO: Wanda V. Peebles, Chief Nursing Officer
Web address: www.jpshealthnet.org
Control: Hospital district or authority, Government, Nonfederal **Service**: General medical and surgical

Staffed Beds: 553 Admissions: 26392 Census: 421 Outpatient Visits: 1173621 Births: 4414 Total Expense ($000): 851190 Payroll Expense ($000): 356836 Personnel: 5673

TX

Hospital, Medicare Provider Number, Address, Telephone, Approval, Facility, and Physician Codes, Health Care System

★ American Hospital Association (AHA) membership ○ Healthcare Facilities Accreditation Program ⇑ Center for Improvement in Healthcare Quality Accreditation
☐ The Joint Commission accreditation ◇ DNV Healthcare Inc. accreditation △ Commission on Accreditation of Rehabilitation Facilities (CARF) accreditation

✠ **KINDRED HOSPITAL–FORT WORTH (452088)**, 815 Eighth Avenue, Zip 76104–2609; tel. 817/332–4812, (Includes KINDRED HOSPITAL TARRANT COUNTY–FORT WORTH SOUTHWEST, 7800 Oakmont Boulevard, Fort Worth, Texas, Zip 76132–4299, tel. 817/346–0094; Anna Rojas, Chief Executive Officer) **A**1 10 **F**3 29 46 48 70 77 79 82 85 107 114 119 130 148 **S** Kindred Healthcare, Louisville, KY
Primary Contact: Anna Rojas, Chief Executive Officer
CFO: Susan Popp, Controller
CMO: Stuart McDonald M.D., President Medical Staff
CIO: Norma Warner, Area Director Health Information Management
CHR: Nicole Newpower, Coordinator Human Resources
Web address: www.kindredfortworth.com/
Control: Corporation, Investor–owned (for–profit) **Service**: Acute long–term care hospital

Staffed Beds: 64 Admissions: 672 Census: 46 Outpatient Visits: 0 Births: 0 Total Expense ($000): 19964 Payroll Expense ($000): 10126 Personnel: 159

★ **MEDICAL CITY ALLIANCE (670103)**, 3101 North Tarrant Parkway, Zip 76177; tel. 817/639–1000 **F**3 11 12 13 15 18 20 22 24 26 29 30 34 35 40 42 45 46 47 48 49 50 54 56 57 59 64 70 72 74 75 76 79 81 82 85 86 87 92 107 108 110 111 114 119 126 130 132 135 145 146 147 148 149 **S** HCA Healthcare, Nashville, TN
Primary Contact: Glenn Wallace, Chief Executive Officer
Web address: www.baylorhealth.com/PhysiciansLocations/BIR/Pages/Default.aspx
Control: Corporation, Investor–owned (for–profit) **Service**: General medical and surgical

Staffed Beds: 55 Admissions: 2520 Census: 28 Outpatient Visits: 32991 Births: 755 Total Expense ($000): 61370 Payroll Expense ($000): 19390 Personnel: 271

✠ **MEDICAL CITY FORT WORTH (450672)**, 900 Eighth Avenue, Zip 76104–3902; tel. 817/336–2100 **A**1 2 3 10 13 **F**3 11 12 17 18 20 22 24 26 28 29 30 31 34 35 40 42 45 46 48 49 53 56 58 64 67 70 74 77 78 79 81 85 87 91 93 107 108 111 114 115 119 126 130 138 145 146 148 **P**8 **S** HCA Healthcare, Nashville, TN
Primary Contact: Jyric Sims, FACHE, Chief Executive Officer
COO: Gregory Haralson FACHE, Chief Operating Officer
CFO: Elia Stokes, Chief Financial Officer
CMO: Terry Loftus M.D., Chief Medical Officer
CIO: Kelley Fredrickson, Director Information Services
CHR: Cyndi Roberts, Director Human Resources
CNO: Damita Williams Ed.D., R.N., MSN, Chief Nursing Officer
Web address: www.medicalcityfortworth.com/about/
Control: Partnership, Investor–owned (for–profit) **Service**: General medical and surgical

Staffed Beds: 212 Admissions: 9930 Census: 151 Outpatient Visits: 51071 Births: 0 Total Expense ($000): 210034 Payroll Expense ($000): 62301 Personnel: 870

☐ **MESA SPRINGS (454124)**, 5560 Mesa Springs Drive, Zip 76123; tel. 817/292–4600 **A**1 10 **F**5 29 54 98 99 101 103 104 105
Primary Contact: Barbara Schmidt, Chief Executive Officer
CFO: Kent Ashley, Chief Financial Officer
CMO: Stewart Keller M.D., Medical Director
CHR: Jill Housand, Director Human Resources
CNO: Ana Ramirez, Director of Nursing
Web address: www.springstone.com/hospitals.stmhl
Control: Corporation, Investor–owned (for–profit) **Service**: Psychiatric

Staffed Beds: 72 Admissions: 2570 Census: 56 Outpatient Visits: 26043 Births: 0 Total Expense ($000): 28219 Payroll Expense ($000): 10095 Personnel: 226

✠ **TEXAS HEALTH HARRIS METHODIST HOSPITAL ALLIANCE (670085)**, 10864 Texas Health Trail, Zip 76244–4897; tel. 682/212–2000 **A**1 10 **F**3 11 12 13 15 18 20 22 24 26 29 30 34 35 40 45 46 48 49 57 59 64 70 72 74 75 76 77 79 81 82 85 86 91 93 107 108 110 111 113 114 115 118 119 130 131 132 135 145 146 147 148 **S** Texas Health Resources, Arlington, TX
Primary Contact: Clint Abernathy, President and Chief Operating Officer
Web address: www.texashealth.org/alliance/Pages/default.aspx
Control: Other not–for–profit (including NFP Corporation) **Service**: General medical and surgical

Staffed Beds: 74 Admissions: 5662 Census: 53 Outpatient Visits: 37403 Births: 1677 Total Expense ($000): 90377 Payroll Expense ($000): 34212 Personnel: 485

✠ △ ⇧ **TEXAS HEALTH HARRIS METHODIST HOSPITAL FORT WORTH (450135)**, 1301 Pennsylvania Avenue, Zip 76104–2122; tel. 817/250–2000 **A**1 2 3 5 7 10 21 **F**3 8 11 12 13 15 17 18 20 22 24 26 28 29 30 31 34 35 36 40 42 43 45 46 47 48 49 53 54 56 57 58 59 60 61 64 65 66 68 70 71 72 74 75 76 77 78 79 81 82 83 84 85 86 87 91 92 93 94 95 96 107 108 110 111 112 114 115 116 117 118 119 120 126 129 130 131 132 135 138 146 147 148 149 150 **S** Texas Health Resources, Arlington, TX
Primary Contact: Lillie Biggins RN, R.N., President
CFO: Shelly Miland, Group Financial Officer
CMO: Joseph Prosser M.D., Chief Medical Officer
CHR: Joseph Condon, Entity Human Resources Officer
CNO: Elaine Nelson R.N., MSN, Chief Nursing Officer
Web address: www.texashealth.org
Control: Other not–for–profit (including NFP Corporation) **Service**: General medical and surgical

Staffed Beds: 640 Admissions: 35728 Census: 536 Outpatient Visits: 201583 Births: 3541 Total Expense ($000): 752345 Payroll Expense ($000): 283219 Personnel: 3605

✠ **TEXAS HEALTH HARRIS METHODIST HOSPITAL SOUTHWEST FORT WORTH (450779)**, 6100 Harris Parkway, Zip 76132–4199; tel. 817/433–5000, (Includes TEXAS HEALTH HOSPITAL CLEARFORK, 5400 Clearfork Main Street, Fort Worth, Texas, Zip 76109–3553, tel. 682/703–5000; Barclay E. Berdan, FACHE, Chief Executive Officer) **A**1 2 10 **F**3 8 11 13 15 18 20 28 29 30 34 35 36 37 40 45 46 47 48 49 50 57 59 60 64 68 70 72 75 76 77 78 79 80 81 84 85 86 87 93 102 107 110 111 114 115 119 126 130 131 146 147 149 **S** Texas Health Resources, Arlington, TX
Primary Contact: Joseph DeLeon, President
CFO: Charlotte Ward, Entity Financial Officer
CMO: Mark Montgomery M.D., Chief Medical Officer
CHR: Leanna W Nalley, Director Human Resources
CNO: Mary Robinson, Chief Nursing Officer and Vice President Patient Care Services
Web address: www.texashealth.org
Control: Other not–for–profit (including NFP Corporation) **Service**: General medical and surgical

Staffed Beds: 247 Admissions: 14805 Census: 143 Outpatient Visits: 93819 Births: 3114 Total Expense ($000): 247723 Payroll Expense ($000): 80820 Personnel: 1014

✠ **TEXAS HEALTH SPECIALTY HOSPITAL (452018)**, 1301 Pennsylvania Avenue, 4th Floor, Zip 76104–2190; tel. 817/250–5500 **A**1 10 **F**1 3 87 130 148 **S** Texas Health Resources, Arlington, TX
Primary Contact: Cheryl Mobley, FACHE, President
CFO: Shelly Miland, Chief Financial Officer
CMO: Michael Thornsberry M.D., Chief Medical Officer
CHR: Joseph Condon, Director Human Resources
CNO: Pam Duffey MSN, R.N., Chief Nursing Officer
Web address: www.texashealth.org
Control: Church operated, Nongovernment, not–for–profit **Service**: Acute long–term care hospital

Staffed Beds: 10 Admissions: 103 Census: 8 Outpatient Visits: 0 Births: 0 Total Expense ($000): 6772 Payroll Expense ($000): 3126 Personnel: 33

☐ △ **TEXAS REHABILITATION HOSPITAL OF FORT WORTH (673048)**, 425 Alabama Avenue, Zip 76104–1022; tel. 817/820–3400 **A**1 7 10 **F**3 29 34 57 74 79 90 91 96 130 132 148 **S** Kindred Healthcare, Louisville, KY
Primary Contact: Russell Bailey, Chief Executive Officer
Web address: www.texasrehabhospital.com/
Control: Corporation, Investor–owned (for–profit) **Service**: Rehabilitation

Staffed Beds: 66 Admissions: 1487 Census: 53 Outpatient Visits: 0 Births: 0 Total Expense ($000): 20050 Payroll Expense ($000): 9639 Personnel: 178

☐ **USMD HOSPITAL AT FORT WORTH (670046)**, 5900 Altamesa Boulevard, Zip 76132–5473; tel. 817/433–9100 **A**1 10 **F**3 29 39 40 51 64 68 81 85 89 107 114 119 130 **S** USMD Health System, Irving, TX
Primary Contact: Stephanie Atkins–Guidry, Administrator and Chief Nursing Officer
CHR: Michelle Speck, Senior Vice President Human Resources
CNO: Stephanie Atkins–Guidry, Administrator and Chief Nursing Officer
Web address: www.usmdfortworth.com/
Control: Partnership, Investor–owned (for–profit) **Service**: General medical and surgical

Staffed Beds: 8 Admissions: 223 Census: 2 Outpatient Visits: 5574 Births: 0 Total Expense ($000): 23930 Payroll Expense ($000): 4547 Personnel: 81

WELLBRIDGE HEALTHCARE OF FORT WORTH (454128), 6200 Overton Ridge Boulevard, Zip 76132–3614; tel. 817/361–1991 **F**98 103 105 **S** Oceans Healthcare, Lake Charles, LA
Primary Contact: Burton Carriker, Chief Executive Officer
Web address: www.oceanshealthcare.com
Control: Corporation, Investor–owned (for–profit) **Service:** Psychiatric

Staffed Beds: 48 **Admissions:** 991 **Census:** 33 **Outpatient Visits:** 5725 **Births:** 0 **Total Expense ($000):** 9798 **Payroll Expense ($000):** 4246 **Personnel:** 69

FREDERICKSBURG—Gillespie County

✠ **HILL COUNTRY MEMORIAL HOSPITAL (450604)**, 1020 South State Highway 16, Zip 78624–4471, Mailing Address: P.O.Box 835, 78624–0835; tel. 830/997–4353 **A**1 10 **F**3 11 13 15 18 20 28 29 30 31 32 34 35 37 40 43 45 49 50 51 53 57 59 62 63 64 68 70 74 75 76 77 78 79 81 82 84 85 86 87 93 96 107 108 110 111 114 115 119 124 129 130 131 132 135 144 146 148 149 **P**8
Primary Contact: Jayne E. Pope, R.N., FACHE, Chief Executive Officer
COO: Mike Reno, Chief Operating Officer
CFO: Mark Jones, Chief Financial Officer
CMO: James R Partin M.D., Chief Medical Director
CIO: John Mason, Chief Information Officer
CHR: Alysha Metzger, Director Human Resources
CNO: Maureen Polivka, Chief Nursing Officer
Web address: www.hillcountrymemorial.org
Control: Other not–for–profit (including NFP Corporation) **Service:** General medical and surgical

Staffed Beds: 57 **Admissions:** 2402 **Census:** 21 **Outpatient Visits:** 92874 **Births:** 471 **Total Expense ($000):** 75537 **Payroll Expense ($000):** 29003 **Personnel:** 479

FRIONA—Parmer County

PARMER COUNTY COMMUNITY HOSPITAL See Parmer Medical Center

★ **PARMER MEDICAL CENTER (451300)**, 1307 Cleveland Street, Zip 79035–1121; tel. 806/250–2754 **A**10 18 **F**11 30 34 35 40 43 57 64 75 77 89 93 107 119 127 130 133 148 **S** Preferred Management Corporation, Shawnee, OK
Primary Contact: Gayla Quillin, Administrator
Web address: www.parmermedicalcenter.com
Control: Other not–for–profit (including NFP Corporation) **Service:** General medical and surgical

Staffed Beds: 15 **Admissions:** 249 **Census:** 5 **Outpatient Visits:** 9850 **Births:** 1 **Total Expense ($000):** 11364 **Payroll Expense ($000):** 4690 **Personnel:** 93

FRISCO—Collin County

✠ **BAYLOR INSTITUTE FOR REHABILITATION AT FRISCO (673046)**, 2990 Legacy Drive, Zip 75034–6066; tel. 469/888–5100 **A**1 10 **F**3 29 30 34 35 64 75 90 91 92 93 96 130 132 148 149 **S** Select Medical Corporation, Mechanicsburg, PA
Primary Contact: Ryan Seymour, Chief Executive Officer
Web address: www.baylorhealth.com/bir
Control: Partnership, Investor–owned (for–profit) **Service:** Rehabilitation

Staffed Beds: 44 **Admissions:** 874 **Census:** 30 **Outpatient Visits:** 11483 **Births:** 0 **Total Expense ($000):** 19279 **Payroll Expense ($000):** 9721 **Personnel:** 104

☐ **BAYLOR MEDICAL CENTER AT FRISCO (450853)**, 5601 Warren Parkway, Zip 75034–4069; tel. 214/407–5000 **A**1 3 5 10 **F**3 13 29 34 40 51 54 57 64 68 72 75 76 79 81 85 87 107 111 114 119 126 129 144 **S** United Surgical Partners International, Addison, TX
Primary Contact: William A. Keaton, Chief Executive Officer
COO: Kevin Coats, Chief Operating Officer and Chief Financial Officer
CFO: Kevin Coats, Chief Financial Officer
CMO: Jimmy Laferney M.D., Vice President Medical Staff Affairs
CIO: Rick Barry, Director Information Systems
CHR: Margaret Garcia, Manager Human Resources
CNO: Randi Elliott MSN, Chief Nursing Officer
Web address: www.bmcf.com
Control: Partnership, Investor–owned (for–profit) **Service:** Surgical

Staffed Beds: 68 **Admissions:** 4880 **Census:** 38 **Outpatient Visits:** 26267 **Births:** 2589 **Total Expense ($000):** 131427 **Payroll Expense ($000):** 44861 **Personnel:** 538

✠ **BAYLOR SCOTT & WHITE MEDICAL CENTER – CENTENNIAL (450885)**, 12505 Lebanon Road, Zip 75035–8298; tel. 972/963–3333 **A**1 10 **F**3 13 15 17 18 20 22 26 29 30 34 35 40 41 45 46 47 48 49 50 51 57 64 65 70 72 74 75 76 77 78 79 81 82 85 89 93 107 110 111 114 115 119 126 132 **S** TENET Healthcare Corporation, Dallas, TX
Primary Contact: Jaikumar Krishnaswamy, Chief Executive Officer
CFO: Blaise Bondi, Chief Financial Officer
CMO: Robert S Hendler M.D., Regional Chief Medical Officer
CIO: Dianne Yarborough, Director of Information Technology
CHR: Stephanie S. Talley, Director Human Resources
CNO: Calee Travis R.N., Chief Nursing Officer
Web address: www.centennialmedcenter.com
Control: Partnership, Investor–owned (for–profit) **Service:** General medical and surgical

Staffed Beds: 106 **Admissions:** 3490 **Census:** 39 **Outpatient Visits:** 32280 **Births:** 650 **Total Expense ($000):** 96443 **Payroll Expense ($000):** 29755 **Personnel:** 339

☐ **HAVEN BEHAVIORAL HOSPITAL OF FRISCO (454134)**, 5680 Frisco Square Boulevard, Suite 3000, Zip 75034–3300; tel. 469/353–2219 **A**1 **F**98 130
Primary Contact: William W. Brattvet, Chief Executive Officer
Web address: www.frisco.havenbehavioral.com/
Control: Corporation, Investor–owned (for–profit) **Service:** Psychiatric

Staffed Beds: 36 **Admissions:** 701 **Census:** 30 **Outpatient Visits:** 0 **Births:** 0 **Total Expense ($000):** 9525 **Payroll Expense ($000):** 4327 **Personnel:** 67

GAINESVILLE—Cooke County

NORTH TEXAS MEDICAL CENTER (450090), 1900 Hospital Boulevard, Zip 76240–2002; tel. 940/665–1751 **A**10 20 **F**3 11 13 15 28 29 34 35 40 43 45 50 59 62 64 68 70 75 76 77 79 81 82 85 86 87 93 107 108 110 111 115 118 119 127 130 132 133 135 146 147 149 **P**5 6
Primary Contact: Christopher Zeringue, Interim Chief Executive Officer
CFO: Melissa Walker CPA, Chief Financial Officer
CHR: Teresa Westover, Director Human Resources
CNO: Audimarie Hayes R.N., Chief Nursing Officer
Web address: www.ntmconline.net
Control: Hospital district or authority, Government, Nonfederal **Service:** General medical and surgical

Staffed Beds: 48 **Admissions:** 1170 **Census:** 12 **Outpatient Visits:** 69569 **Births:** 354 **Total Expense ($000):** 38157 **Payroll Expense ($000):** 15155 **Personnel:** 252

GALVESTON—Galveston County

☐ **SHRINERS HOSPITALS FOR CHILDREN–GALVESTON (453311)** (Burn Care), 815 Market Street, Zip 77550–2725; tel. 409/770–6600 **A**1 3 5 10 **F**3 11 16 29 30 32 34 35 50 64 68 75 77 81 82 85 86 93 99 100 101 104 119 130 132 146 148 **S** Shriners Hospitals for Children, Tampa, FL
Primary Contact: Mary Jaco, Administrator
CFO: Michael B Schimming, Director Financial Services
CMO: David N Herndon M.D., Chief of Staff
CIO: Michael Lyons, Regional Director Information Services
CHR: Robert A Magee, Director Human Resources
CNO: Angel Martinez R.N., RN, BSN,, Director Patient Care Services
Web address: www.shrinershospitalsforchildren.org/Hospitals/Locations/Galveston.aspx
Control: Other not–for–profit (including NFP Corporation) **Service:** Children's other specialty

Staffed Beds: 15 **Admissions:** 181 **Census:** 9 **Outpatient Visits:** 7694 **Births:** 0 **Total Expense ($000):** 34157 **Payroll Expense ($000):** 14331 **Personnel:** 236

TX

Hospital, Medicare Provider Number, Address, Telephone, Approval, Facility, and Physician Codes, Health Care System

★ American Hospital Association (AHA) membership
☐ The Joint Commission accreditation
○ Healthcare Facilities Accreditation Program
◇ DNV Healthcare Inc. accreditation
⇑ Center for Improvement in Healthcare Quality Accreditation
△ Commission on Accreditation of Rehabilitation Facilities (CARF) accreditation

✠ **UNIVERSITY OF TEXAS MEDICAL BRANCH (450018)**, 301 University Boulevard, Zip 77555–0128; tel. 409/772–1011, (Includes ANGLETON DANBURY CAMPUS, 132 East Hospital Drive, Angleton, Texas, Zip 77515–4112, tel. 979/849–7721; Donna K Sollenberger, Executive Vice President and Chief Executive Officer) **A**1 2 3 5 10 **F**3 11 12 13 15 16 17 18 19 20 22 24 26 28 29 30 31 34 35 36 38 39 40 41 43 44 45 46 49 50 51 53 54 55 56 57 58 59 60 61 63 64 65 66 68 70 71 72 73 74 75 76 77 78 79 81 82 84 85 86 87 88 89 92 93 94 96 97 99 100 101 102 103 104 107 108 110 111 112 114 115 116 117 118 119 120 121 123 124 126 129 130 131 132 134 135 137 138 139 141 142 144 145 146 147 148 149 150 **P**6 **S** University of Texas System, Austin, TX
Primary Contact: Donna K. Sollenberger, Executive Vice President and Chief Executive Officer
COO: Deborah A McGrew, Vice President and Chief Operating Officer
CFO: Cheryl A Sadro, Executive Vice President Chief Business and Finance Officer
CIO: Todd Leach, Vice President and Chief Information Officer
CHR: Ronald McKinley Ph.D., Vice President Human Resources and Employee Services
CNO: Annette Macias–Hoag MHA, RN, NEA–BC, Chief Nursing Officer
Web address: www.utmb.edu
Control: State, Government, Nonfederal **Service**: General medical and surgical

Staffed Beds: 603 **Admissions**: 26921 **Census**: 401 **Outpatient Visits**: 1015673 **Births**: 6159 **Total Expense ($000)**: 905925 **Payroll Expense ($000)**: 312125 **Personnel**: 4518

GARLAND—Dallas County

✠ **BAYLOR MEDICAL CENTER AT GARLAND (450280)**, 2300 Marie Curie Drive, Zip 75042–5706; tel. 972/487–5000 **A**1 2 3 5 10 **F**3 11 15 18 20 22 24 26 28 29 30 31 34 35 40 45 47 49 50 54 57 59 60 64 65 66 70 74 75 78 79 81 82 84 86 87 107 108 110 111 114 118 119 126 129 130 132 135 145 146 148 149 **S** Baylor Scott & White Health, Dallas, TX
Primary Contact: Jonas Cole, Interim President
COO: Janice L Walker R.N., Baylor Scott & White Divisional Chief Nursing Executive
CFO: Robert Knowlton, Vice President and Chief Financial Officer
CMO: Steven Arze M.D., Chief Medical Officer and Vice President Medical Affairs
CIO: Michael Larsen, Director Information Systems
CHR: Laura Settles, Director Human Resources
CNO: Janice L Walker R.N., Baylor Scott & White Divisional Chief Nursing Executive
Web address: www.baylorhealth.com/PhysiciansLocations/Garland/Pages/Default.aspx
Control: Partnership, Investor–owned (for–profit) **Service**: General medical and surgical

Staffed Beds: 112 **Admissions**: 7072 **Census**: 83 **Outpatient Visits**: 89822 **Births**: 0 **Total Expense ($000)**: 157726 **Payroll Expense ($000)**: 57305 **Personnel**: 600

GARLAND BEHAVIORAL HOSPITAL (454138), 2300 Marie Curie Boulevard, 5th Floor, Zip 75402; tel. 972/487–5309 **F**98 101 103 **S** Universal Health Services, Inc., King of Prussia, PA
Primary Contact: Scott Cook, Interim Chief Executive Officer
CFO: Scott Cook, Chief Financial Officer
Web address: www.garlandbehavioralhospital.com/
Control: Corporation, Investor–owned (for–profit) **Service**: Psychiatric

Staffed Beds: 72 **Admissions**: 784 **Census**: 16 **Outpatient Visits**: 0 **Births**: 0 **Total Expense ($000)**: 7601 **Payroll Expense ($000)**: 3404 **Personnel**: 75

✠ **SELECT SPECIALTY HOSPITAL – DALLAS GARLAND (452120)**, 2300 Marie Curie Drive, Floors 3E and 3W, Zip 75042–5706; tel. 469/440–5800 **A**1 **F**1 3 29 77 85 86 87 91 130 148 **S** Select Medical Corporation, Mechanicsburg, PA
Primary Contact: Kent R. Helwig, Chief Executive Officer
Web address: www.dallasgarland.selectspecialtyhospitals.com/
Control: Corporation, Investor–owned (for–profit) **Service**: Acute long–term care hospital

Staffed Beds: 40 **Admissions**: 261 **Census**: 19 **Outpatient Visits**: 0 **Births**: 0 **Total Expense ($000)**: 12525 **Payroll Expense ($000)**: 5452 **Personnel**: 75

GATESVILLE—Coryell County

☐ **CORYELL MEMORIAL HOSPITAL (451379)**, 1507 West Main Street, Zip 76528–1098; tel. 254/865–8251 **A**1 10 18 **F**3 7 10 11 15 18 20 28 34 40 43 45 50 57 58 59 61 62 64 65 70 74 79 81 82 84 87 93 97 102 104 107 108 110 111 115 119 125 127 129 130 133 146 **P**6
Primary Contact: David Byrom, Chief Executive Officer
COO: David Byrom, Chief Executive Officer
CFO: Carol Jones, Controller and Manager Business Office
CMO: Diedra Wuenschel D.O., President Medical Staff
CIO: Mike Huckabee, Network Administrator
CHR: Paula Smithhart, Director Human Resources
CNO: Jeanne Griffith, Chief Nursing Officer
Web address: www.cmhos.org
Control: Hospital district or authority, Government, Nonfederal **Service**: General medical and surgical

Staffed Beds: 25 **Admissions**: 871 **Census**: 10 **Outpatient Visits**: 68559 **Births**: 0 **Total Expense ($000)**: 42278 **Payroll Expense ($000)**: 14594 **Personnel**: 398

GEORGETOWN—Williamson County

☐ **GEORGETOWN BEHAVIORAL HEALTH INSTITUTE (454129)**, 3101 South Austin Avenue, Zip 78626–7541; tel. 512/819–1100 **A**1 **F**4 5 56 98 99 102 103 104 105 130 132 135 **S** Signature Healthcare Services, Corona, CA
Primary Contact: Joseph R. Rodriguez, Chief Executive Officer
CFO: Shelli Surcouf, Chief Financial Officer
CHR: Kristi Hynes, Director Human Resources
CNO: Nini Perry, Chief Nursing Officer
Web address: www.georgetownbehavioral.co
Control: Corporation, Investor–owned (for–profit) **Service**: Psychiatric

Staffed Beds: 118 **Admissions**: 2838 **Census**: 66 **Outpatient Visits**: 6651 **Births**: 0 **Total Expense ($000)**: 17335 **Payroll Expense ($000)**: 8985 **Personnel**: 212

★ **ROCK SPRINGS (454127)**, 700 Southeast Inner Loop, Zip 78626; tel. 512/819–9400 **F**98 100 102 104 105
Primary Contact: Keith Furman, Chief Executive Officer
CFO: Jason Guzak, Chief Financial Officer
CHR: Sharon McMurray, Director, Human Resources
CNO: Randall Luce R.N., Director of Nursing
Web address: www.rockspringshealth.com/
Control: Corporation, Investor–owned (for–profit) **Service**: Psychiatric

Staffed Beds: 72 **Admissions**: 1971 **Census**: 46 **Outpatient Visits**: 6901 **Births**: 0 **Total Expense ($000)**: 14093 **Payroll Expense ($000)**: 6797 **Personnel**: 159

GLEN ROSE—Somervell County

☐ **GLEN ROSE MEDICAL CENTER (450451)**, 1021 Holden Street, Zip 76043–4937, Mailing Address: P.O.Box 2099, 76043–2099; tel. 254/897–2215 **A**1 10 **F**2 15 29 34 40 43 45 48 51 56 57 59 65 81 93 103 104 107 108 110 111 119 129 130 132 133 143 146 **P**7
Primary Contact: Ray Reynolds, Chief Executive Officer
CFO: Michael Honea, Chief Financial Officer
CHR: Ladonna Green, Director Human Resources
CNO: Laura Hodnett, Interim Chief Nursing Officer
Web address: www.glenrosemedicalcenter.com
Control: Hospital district or authority, Government, Nonfederal **Service**: General medical and surgical

Staffed Beds: 16 **Admissions**: 424 **Census**: 4 **Outpatient Visits**: 13542 **Births**: 0 **Total Expense ($000)**: 16274 **Payroll Expense ($000)**: 5927 **Personnel**: 142

GONZALES—Gonzales County

★ **MEMORIAL HOSPITAL (450235)**, 1110 Sarah Dewitt Drive, Zip 78629–3311, Mailing Address: P.O.Box 587, 78629–0587; tel. 830/672–7581 **A**10 20 **F**3 11 13 15 29 34 35 38 40 43 53 57 59 62 64 65 68 70 75 76 77 79 81 85 87 93 97 107 110 111 115 119 127 129 130 132 148 **S** QHR, Brentwood, TN
Primary Contact: Charles Norris, Chief Executive Officer
CFO: Patty Stewart, Chief Financial Officer
CMO: Commie Hisey D.O., Chief of Staff
CHR: Joni Leland, Director Human Resources
CNO: Valerie Hohenshell, Director of Clinical Services
Web address: www.gonzaleshealthcare.com
Control: Hospital district or authority, Government, Nonfederal **Service**: General medical and surgical

Staffed Beds: 33 **Admissions**: 682 **Census**: 6 **Outpatient Visits**: 75669 **Births**: 198 **Total Expense ($000)**: 46647 **Payroll Expense ($000)**: 11581 **Personnel**: 256

TX

GRAHAM—Young County

★ **GRAHAM REGIONAL MEDICAL CENTER (450085)**, 1301 Montgomery Road, Zip 76450–4240, Mailing Address: P.O.Box 1390, 76450–1390; tel. 940/549–3400 **A**10 20 **F**3 7 11 15 28 29 40 43 45 50 53 57 59 62 63 75 77 79 81 85 89 93 104 107 111 115 119 127 130 133 135
Primary Contact: Shane Kernell, Chief Executive Officer
CIO: Jeff Clark, Director Information Systems
CHR: Judy Guinn, Chief Human Resources Officer
Web address: www.grahamrmc.com
Control: Hospital district or authority, Government, Nonfederal **Service:** General medical and surgical

Staffed Beds: 17 **Admissions:** 637 **Census:** 6 **Outpatient Visits:** 42363
Births: 0 **Total Expense ($000):** 23190 **Payroll Expense ($000):** 8690
Personnel: 193

GRANBURY—Hood County

⊞ **LAKE GRANBURY MEDICAL CENTER (450596)**, 1310 Paluxy Road, Zip 76048–5555; tel. 817/573–2273 **A**1 10 **F**3 8 11 12 13 15 18 20 22 26 28 29 30 34 37 40 43 45 49 53 57 59 64 68 70 74 75 76 77 79 81 82 85 86 93 107 108 110 111 114 118 119 126 129 133 135 146 147 149 **S** Community Health Systems, Inc., Franklin, TN
Primary Contact: Derrick Cuenca, Chief Executive Officer
CFO: Noe Gutierrez, Chief Financial Officer
CIO: Kevin Myers, Director Information Systems
CHR: Brooke Montoya, Director Human Resources
CNO: Abigail Kendall, Chief Nursing Officer
Web address: www.lakegranburymedicalcenter.com
Control: Corporation, Investor–owned (for–profit) **Service:** General medical and surgical

Staffed Beds: 73 **Admissions:** 2935 **Census:** 25 **Outpatient Visits:** 74754
Births: 575 **Total Expense ($000):** 69896 **Payroll Expense ($000):** 23086
Personnel: 358

GRAND PRAIRIE—Dallas County

⇑ **TEXAS GENERAL HOSPITAL (670083)**, 2709 Hospital Boulevard, Zip 75051–1017; tel. 469/557–9430 **A**10 21 **F**3 18 20 29 34 40 45 46 48 50 57 59 64 70 74 75 79 81 82 85 87 107 108 111 115 119 149 **P**5
Primary Contact: Suleman Hashmi, President and Chief Executive Officer
Web address: www.texasgeneralhospital.com
Control: Partnership, Investor–owned (for–profit) **Service:** General medical and surgical

Staffed Beds: 41 **Admissions:** 533 **Census:** 4 **Outpatient Visits:** 11852
Births: 2 **Total Expense ($000):** 146481 **Payroll Expense ($000):** 13117
Personnel: 262

GRAND SALINE—Van Zandt County

⇑ **TEXAS GENERAL HOSPITAL – VAN ZANDT REGIONAL MEDICAL CENTER**, 707 North Waldrip Street, Zip 75140–1555; tel. 903/717–3300 **A**21 **F**3 34 35 40 45 46 47 57 75 77 81 87 107 114 119 148 149
Primary Contact: Faraz Hashmi, Chief Executive Officer
Control: Partnership, Investor–owned (for–profit) **Service:** General medical and surgical

Staffed Beds: 52 **Admissions:** 58 **Census:** 1 **Outpatient Visits:** 2214 **Births:** 0
Personnel: 29

GRAPEVINE—Tarrant County

⊞ **BAYLOR REGIONAL MEDICAL CENTER AT GRAPEVINE (450563)**, 1650 West College Street, Zip 76051–3565; tel. 817/481–1588 **A**1 2 3 10 **F**3 12 13 15 18 20 22 24 26 28 29 30 31 34 35 40 45 46 47 48 49 56 57 59 64 65 70 72 74 75 76 77 78 79 80 81 82 84 86 87 90 93 107 108 110 111 114 115 119 126 130 131 132 135 145 146 147 149 150 **S** Baylor Scott & White Health, Dallas, TX
Primary Contact: Steven R. Newton, FACHE, President
CFO: Terri Foster, Hospital Finance Officer
CMO: Ron Jensen D.O., Chief Medical Officer and Vice President
CIO: Sandy Vaughn, Director Information Systems
CHR: Donna Stark, Director Human Resources
CNO: Beth P Beckman R.N., Ph.D., Chief Nursing Officer
Web address: www.baylorhealth.com/PhysiciansLocations/Grapevine/Pages/Default.aspx
Control: Other not–for–profit (including NFP Corporation) **Service:** General medical and surgical

Staffed Beds: 270 **Admissions:** 12501 **Census:** 154 **Outpatient Visits:** 63255 **Births:** 2406 **Total Expense ($000):** 207166 **Payroll Expense ($000):** 74716 **Personnel:** 763

☐ **ETHICUS HOSPITAL – GRAPEVINE (452110)**, 4201 William D Tate Avenue, Zip 76051–5736; tel. 817/288–1300 **A**1 10 **F**1 3 29 40 64 75 77 82 85 87 93 96 107 114 119 130 135 148 149
Primary Contact: Roger T. Jenkins, Chief Executive Officer
Web address: www.ethicusgrapevine.com
Control: Partnership, Investor–owned (for–profit) **Service:** Acute long–term care hospital

Staffed Beds: 60 **Admissions:** 349 **Census:** 25 **Outpatient Visits:** 1207
Births: 0 **Total Expense ($000):** 12722 **Payroll Expense ($000):** 7107
Personnel: 121

GREENVILLE—Hunt County

⊞ **GLEN OAKS HOSPITAL (454050)**, 301 Division Street, Zip 75401–4101; tel. 903/454–6000 **A**1 10 **F**4 5 29 34 35 40 50 75 86 87 98 99 100 101 102 103 104 105 132 135 149 **S** Universal Health Services, Inc., King of Prussia, PA
Primary Contact: Ethan Permenter, Corporate Vice President
CFO: Lowell K Hudson, Chief Financial Officer
CHR: Joe Carson, Director Human Resources
Web address: www.glenoakshospital.com
Control: Corporation, Investor–owned (for–profit) **Service:** Psychiatric

Staffed Beds: 54 **Admissions:** 1851 **Census:** 36 **Outpatient Visits:** 2792
Births: 0 **Total Expense ($000):** 9679 **Payroll Expense ($000):** 5075
Personnel: 103

⊞ **HUNT REGIONAL MEDICAL CENTER (450352)**, 4215 Joe Ramsey Boulevard, Zip 75401–7899, Mailing Address: P.O.Box 1059, 75403–1059; tel. 903/408–5000 **A**1 10 **F**3 11 12 13 15 28 29 30 34 37 40 42 43 44 45 46 49 50 53 56 57 59 62 64 65 68 70 71 72 73 74 75 76 77 78 79 81 82 84 85 86 87 90 91 92 93 94 96 98 102 103 104 107 108 110 111 114 119 120 121 123 129 130 132 135 141 143 144 146 147 148 149 **P**1 6 **S** Hunt Regional Healthcare, Greenville, TX
Primary Contact: Richard Carter, District Chief Executive Officer
COO: Michael R Klepin, Administrator
CFO: Lee Boles, Assistant Administrator and Chief Financial Officer
CMO: James H Sandin M.D., Assistant Administrator Medical Affairs
CIO: Richard Montanye, Director Information Systems
CHR: John Heatherly, Assistant Administrator Support Services
CNO: Deborah Clack, Chief Nursing Officer
Web address: www.huntregional.org
Control: Hospital district or authority, Government, Nonfederal **Service:** General medical and surgical

Staffed Beds: 167 **Admissions:** 6520 **Census:** 87 **Outpatient Visits:** 132396 **Births:** 933 **Total Expense ($000):** 138807 **Payroll Expense ($000):** 56085 **Personnel:** 984

GROESBECK—Limestone County

LIMESTONE MEDICAL CENTER (451303), 701 McClintic Drive, Zip 76642–2128; tel. 254/729–3281 **A**10 18 **F**3 7 11 28 29 30 32 34 35 40 41 43 45 57 64 65 68 75 77 84 85 90 93 96 97 104 107 111 115 119 127 129 130 133 135 146 148
Primary Contact: Larry Price, Chief Executive Officer
CFO: Michael F. Williams, Chief Financial Officer
CMO: Jeffrey Rettig D.O., Chief of Staff
CIO: Byong Lee, Chief Information Officer
CHR: Jean Koester, Manager Human Resources
CNO: Jean Wragge, Chief Nursing Officer
Web address: www.lmchospital.com
Control: Hospital district or authority, Government, Nonfederal **Service:** General medical and surgical

Staffed Beds: 15 **Admissions:** 469 **Census:** 7 **Outpatient Visits:** 14096
Births: 0 **Total Expense ($000):** 18899 **Payroll Expense ($000):** 8135
Personnel: 187

HALLETTSVILLE—Lavaca County

LAVACA MEDICAL CENTER (451376), 1400 North Texana Street, Zip 77964–2099; tel. 361/798–3671 **A**10 18 **F**3 11 15 18 29 34 40 41 43 45 47 53 56 57 59 64 65 68 75 77 81 85 86 87 93 107 108 110 111 114 118 119 127 133 135 146 148 149
Primary Contact: Stephen Bowen, Administrator
Control: Hospital district or authority, Government, Nonfederal **Service:** General medical and surgical

Staffed Beds: 25 **Admissions:** 535 **Census:** 7 **Outpatient Visits:** 40903
Births: 0 **Total Expense ($000):** 17433 **Payroll Expense ($000):** 6023
Personnel: 151

TX

Hospital, Medicare Provider Number, Address, Telephone, Approval, Facility, and Physician Codes, Health Care System		
★ American Hospital Association (AHA) membership	○ Healthcare Facilities Accreditation Program	⇑ Center for Improvement in Healthcare Quality Accreditation
☐ The Joint Commission accreditation	◇ DNV Healthcare Inc. accreditation	△ Commission on Accreditation of Rehabilitation Facilities (CARF) accreditation

HAMILTON—Hamilton County

★ ⇑ **HAMILTON GENERAL HOSPITAL (450754)**, 400 North Brown Street, Zip 76531–1518; tel. 254/386–1600 **A**10 20 21 **F**3 7 11 15 28 29 34 40 43 44 45 50 53 56 57 59 64 68 79 80 81 82 85 86 93 97 103 104 107 110 114 119 127 130 132 133
Primary Contact: Grady A. Hooper, Chief Executive Officer
CMO: James R Lee M.D., Chief of Staff
CIO: Chad Reinert, Chief Information Officer
CHR: Keela Payne, Director Human Resources
CNO: Debra Martin, Chief Nursing Officer
Web address: www.hamiltonhospital.org
Control: Hospital district or authority, Government, Nonfederal **Service**: General medical and surgical

Staffed Beds: 42 Admissions: 1027 Census: 10 Outpatient Visits: 67874 Births: 0 Total Expense ($000): 24208 Payroll Expense ($000): 10556 Personnel: 229

HAMLIN—Jones County

HAMLIN MEMORIAL HOSPITAL (450243), 632 Northwest Second Street, Zip 79520–3831, Mailing Address: P.O.Box 400, 79520–0400; tel. 325/576–3646 **A**10 **F**3 7 11 28 29 35 40 43 64 68 69 107 114 127 133 135 146 148 149 **P**5
Primary Contact: Angela Jaco, Chief Executive Officer
CMO: Krishna Sunkavalle M.D., Chief Medical Officer
Control: Hospital district or authority, Government, Nonfederal **Service**: General medical and surgical

Staffed Beds: 23 Admissions: 103 Census: 1 Outpatient Visits: 3380 Births: 0 Total Expense ($000): 3394 Payroll Expense ($000): 1909 Personnel: 45

HARKER HEIGHTS—Bell County

⊠ **SETON MEDICAL CENTER HARKER HEIGHTS (670080)**, 850 West Central Texas Expressway, Zip 76548–1890; tel. 254/690–0900 **A**1 10 **F**3 13 15 18 20 22 26 28 29 30 34 35 40 43 45 50 51 57 59 60 66 70 74 75 76 79 81 91 93 107 108 110 111 115 119 129 130 146 147 148 **P**3 **S** Ardent Health Services, Nashville, TN
Primary Contact: Zach Dieitz, Chief Executive Officer
CFO: John K Sharp, Chief Financial Officer
CHR: Mona Tucker, Director Human Resources
CNO: Pamela Craig R.N., Chief Nursing Officer
Web address: www.setonharkerheights.net
Control: Partnership, Investor–owned (for–profit) **Service**: General medical and surgical

Staffed Beds: 83 Admissions: 3938 Census: 29 Outpatient Visits: 77358 Births: 1033 Total Expense ($000): 72178 Payroll Expense ($000): 22918 Personnel: 327

HARLINGEN—Cameron County

⊠ **HARLINGEN MEDICAL CENTER (450855)**, 5501 South Expressway 77, Zip 78550–3213; tel. 956/365–1000 **A**1 3 5 10 **F**3 12 13 15 17 18 20 22 24 29 30 40 43 49 50 51 57 59 64 68 70 74 75 76 79 81 85 86 107 108 110 111 114 115 118 119 129 130 146 147 148 **S** Prime Healthcare, Ontario, CA
Primary Contact: Brenda Ivory, Chief Executive Officer
CFO: David Glassburn, Vice President Finance and Chief Financial Officer
CMO: Elizabeth Juarez M.D., Chief Medical Officer
CHR: Emmett Craig, Director Human Resources
CNO: Deborah Meeks, Chief Nursing Officer
Web address: www.harlingenmedicalcenter.com
Control: Partnership, Investor–owned (for–profit) **Service**: General medical and surgical

Staffed Beds: 88 Admissions: 5383 Census: 55 Outpatient Visits: 56322 Births: 910 Total Expense ($000): 97015 Payroll Expense ($000): 32135 Personnel: 519

☐ **RIO GRANDE STATE CENTER/SOUTH TEXAS HEALTH CARE SYSTEM (454088)**, 1401 South Rangerville Road, Zip 78552–7638; tel. 956/364–8000, (Includes RIO GRANDE STATE CENTER, 1401 South Rangerville Road, Harlingen, Texas, Zip 78552–7638, tel. 956/364–8000; SOUTH TEXAS HEALTH CARE SYSTEM, 1401 Rangerville Road, Harlingen, Texas, Zip 78552–7609, tel. 956/364–8000) **A**1 3 5 10 **F**30 53 57 65 66 68 75 87 97 98 101 107 119 130 132 135 143 146 147 **P**6 **S** Texas Department of State Health Services, Austin, TX
Primary Contact: Sonia Hernandez–Keeble, Superintendent
CFO: Tom Garza, Director Fiscal and Support
CMO: David Moron M.D., Clinical Director
CIO: Blas Ortiz Jr, Assistant Superintendent and Public Information Officer
CHR: Irma Garcia, Job Coordinator
CNO: Maia Baker MSN, Chief Nurse Executive
Web address: www.dshs.state.tx.us/mhhospitals/RioGrandeSC/default.shtm
Control: State, Government, Nonfederal **Service**: Psychiatric

Staffed Beds: 55 Admissions: 866 Census: 52 Outpatient Visits: 0 Births: 0 Total Expense ($000): 20195 Payroll Expense ($000): 6760 Personnel: 270

SOLARA HOSPITAL HARLINGEN (452101), 508 Victoria Lane, Zip 78550–3225; tel. 956/425–9600, (Includes SOLARA HOSPITAL – BROWNSVILLE CAMPUS, 333 Lorenaly Drive, Brownsville, Texas, Zip 78526–4333, tel. 956/546–0808) **A**10 22 **F**1 29 30 35 40 57 70 85 86 130 148 **S** Cornerstone Healthcare Group, Dallas, TX
Primary Contact: Cary L. Montalvo, Chief Executive Officer
CFO: Kurt Schultz, Chief Financial Officer
CHR: Dan Perkins, Vice President of Human Resources
CNO: Nesa Caldwell, Chief Nursing Officer
Web address: www.chghospitals.com/harlingen/
Control: Partnership, Investor–owned (for–profit) **Service**: Acute long–term care hospital

Staffed Beds: 82 Admissions: 848 Census: 54 Outpatient Visits: 0 Births: 0 Total Expense ($000): 20076 Payroll Expense ($000): 9913 Personnel: 146

⊠ ⇑ **VALLEY BAPTIST MEDICAL CENTER–HARLINGEN (450033)**, 2101 Pease Street, Zip 78550–8307, Mailing Address: P O Drawer 2588, 78551–2588; tel. 956/389–1100 **A**1 3 5 10 21 **F**3 11 12 13 14 15 17 18 20 22 24 26 28 29 30 31 34 35 39 40 43 44 45 46 47 48 49 50 54 56 57 58 59 60 63 64 65 68 70 71 72 73 74 75 76 77 78 79 80 81 82 84 85 86 87 88 89 90 92 93 94 100 103 104 107 108 110 111 112 114 115 119 126 129 130 132 144 146 147 148 **S** TENET Healthcare Corporation, Dallas, TX
Primary Contact: Manuel Vela, President and Chief Executive Officer
COO: Daniel Listi, Chief Operating Officer
CFO: Marco Rodriguez, Chief Financial Officer
CNO: Stephen Hill, Vice President and Chief Nursing Officer
Web address: www.valleybaptist.net/harlingen/index.htm
Control: Corporation, Investor–owned (for–profit) **Service**: General medical and surgical

Staffed Beds: 416 Admissions: 16411 Census: 207 Outpatient Visits: 118764 Births: 2162 Total Expense ($000): 239359 Payroll Expense ($000): 80760 Personnel: 1531

HASKELL—Haskell County

HASKELL MEMORIAL HOSPITAL (451341), 1 North Avenue 'N', Zip 79521–5499, Mailing Address: P.O.Box 1117, 79521–1117; tel. 940/864–2621 **A**10 18 **F**11 28 29 34 35 40 53 54 57 59 64 68 75 77 86 87 93 97 107 119 130 131 133 146 **P**1
Primary Contact: Fran McCown, Administrator
COO: Jeff Lyle, Chief Operating Officer
CHR: Emily Moore, Director Human Resources and Information Technology
CNO: Teri Turner, Chief Nursing Officer
Control: Hospital district or authority, Government, Nonfederal **Service**: General medical and surgical

Staffed Beds: 15 Admissions: 225 Census: 3 Outpatient Visits: 15853 Births: 0 Total Expense ($000): 6849 Payroll Expense ($000): 3077 Personnel: 95

HEMPHILL—Sabine County

☐ **SABINE COUNTY HOSPITAL (451361)**, 2301 Worth Street, Zip 75948–7216, Mailing Address: P.O.Box 750, 75948–0750; tel. 409/787–3300 **A**1 10 18 **F**3 29 34 35 40 43 56 57 65 75 93 107 114 119 127 133 **S** Preferred Management Corporation, Shawnee, OK
Primary Contact: Jerry Howell, Administrator
COO: Mike Easley, Vice President and Chief Operating Officer
CFO: Larry Stephens, Chief Financial Officer
CMO: Vera Luther M.D., Chief of Staff
CIO: Margaret Moore, Director Business Office
CHR: Laura Simpson, Director Human Resources
CNO: Margie Watson MSN, RN–B, Chief Nursing Officer
Web address: www.sabinecountyhospital.com/
Control: Corporation, Investor–owned (for–profit) **Service**: General medical and surgical

Staffed Beds: 25 Admissions: 302 Census: 5 Outpatient Visits: 10038 Births: 0 Total Expense ($000): 8655 Payroll Expense ($000): 3506 Personnel: 81

HENDERSON—Rusk County

⊠ **EAST TEXAS MEDICAL CENTER HENDERSON (450475)**, 300 Wilson Street, Zip 75652–5956; tel. 903/657–7541 **A**1 10 **F**3 8 11 13 15 18 28 29 30 34 35 37 40 43 45 50 57 59 64 65 75 107 108 110 111 115 119 127 129 133 135 145 146 147 148 149 **S** East Texas Medical Center Regional Healthcare System, Tyler, TX
Primary Contact: Mark Leitner, FACHE, Administrator
CFO: Phillip A Caron, Chief Financial Officer
CHR: William Henry, Director Human Resources
CNO: Donna K Stanley R.N., Chief Nursing Officer
Web address: www.etmc.org/etmchenderson/
Control: Other not–for–profit (including NFP Corporation) **Service**: General medical and surgical

Staffed Beds: 41 Admissions: 1455 Census: 13 Outpatient Visits: 54611 Births: 231 Total Expense ($000): 31577 Payroll Expense ($000): 8560 Personnel: 139

TX

Many Facility Codes have changed. Please refer to the AHA Guide Code Chart. © 2017 AHA Guide

HENRIETTA—Clay County

CLAY COUNTY MEMORIAL HOSPITAL (451362), 310 West South Street, Zip 76365–3346; tel. 940/538–5621 **A**10 18 **F**7 8 11 28 34 35 40 50 53 57 62 68 80 81 90 93 107 111 119 130 132 133 144 146 148 **P**5
Primary Contact: Jeff Huskey, Chief Executive Officer and Administrator
CFO: Debra Haehn, Chief Financial Officer
CMO: Lexi Mitchell Sanchez D.O., Chief of Staff
CHR: Linda Burleson, Administrative Secretary
CNO: Kelley McMillion, Chief Nursing Officer
Web address: www.ccmhospital.com
Control: County, Government, Nonfederal **Service:** General medical and surgical

Staffed Beds: 25 **Admissions:** 130 **Census:** 1 **Outpatient Visits:** 7213 **Births:** 0 **Total Expense ($000):** 7766 **Payroll Expense ($000):** 2939 **Personnel:** 83

HEREFORD—Deaf Smith County

HEREFORD REGIONAL MEDICAL CENTER (450155), 540 West 15th Street, Zip 79045–2820; tel. 806/364–2141 **A**10 **F**3 7 11 13 15 29 35 40 43 50 57 59 62 65 70 76 77 81 85 93 107 111 114 119 127 130 133 147 **P**5
Primary Contact: Jeff Barnhart, Chief Executive Officer
COO: Meri Killingsworth, Chief Operating Officer
CNO: Anthony T. Jerina, Chief Nursing Officer
Web address: www.dschd.org/
Control: Hospital district or authority, Government, Nonfederal **Service:** General medical and surgical

Staffed Beds: 39 **Admissions:** 755 **Census:** 7 **Outpatient Visits:** 80544 **Births:** 324 **Total Expense ($000):** 25596 **Payroll Expense ($000):** 8949 **Personnel:** 195

HILLSBORO—Hill County

☒ **HILL REGIONAL HOSPITAL (450192)**, 101 Circle Drive, Zip 76645–2670; tel. 254/580–8500 **A**1 10 20 **F**3 13 15 17 18 19 29 34 35 40 43 45 50 57 59 64 65 68 70 75 76 77 78 81 86 87 88 89 93 107 114 118 119 133 146 147 149 **S** Community Health Systems, Inc., Franklin, TN
Primary Contact: Michael J. Ellis, FACHE, Chief Executive Officer
CFO: Judy Culp, Chief Financial Officer
CHR: Becky Hale, Director Human Resources
Web address: www.chs.net
Control: Corporation, Investor–owned (for–profit) **Service:** General medical and surgical

Staffed Beds: 66 **Admissions:** 950 **Census:** 8 **Outpatient Visits:** 20391 **Births:** 192 **Total Expense ($000):** 28635 **Payroll Expense ($000):** 8644 **Personnel:** 140

HONDO—Medina County

MEDINA COMMUNITY HOSPITAL See Medina Regional Hospital

MEDINA REGIONAL HOSPITAL (451330), 3100 Avenue E, Zip 78861–3599; tel. 830/426–7700 **A**10 18 **F**3 11 13 15 28 29 34 35 40 41 43 45 57 59 64 66 75 76 77 81 82 85 87 93 107 110 111 115 119 127 133 135 145 146 148 **P**4
Primary Contact: Janice Simons, FACHE, Chief Executive Officer
CFO: Kevin Frosch, Chief Financial Officer
CMO: Matthew Windrow M.D., Chief of Staff
CIO: Ken Gallegos, Director Support Services and Information Technology
CHR: Sharon Garcia, Human Resources Representative
CNO: Billie Bell, Chief Nursing Officer
Web address: www.medinahospital.net
Control: Hospital district or authority, Government, Nonfederal **Service:** General medical and surgical

Staffed Beds: 25 **Admissions:** 706 **Census:** 8 **Outpatient Visits:** 102410 **Births:** 124 **Total Expense ($000):** 24956 **Payroll Expense ($000):** 9763 **Personnel:** 225

HOUSTON—Harris County

AD HOSPITAL EAST (670102), 12950 East Freeway, Zip 77015–5710; tel. 713/330–3887 (Nonreporting)
Primary Contact: Robert A. Turner, Chief Executive Officer
Control: Other not–for–profit (including NFP Corporation) **Service:** General medical and surgical

Staffed Beds: 25

☐ **ADVANCED DIAGNOSTICS HOSPITAL (670203)**, 12950 East Freeway, Zip 77015–5710; tel. 713/330–3887, (Data for 345 days)**A**1 **F**3 12 29 40 45 54 64 68 75 79 81 82 85 92 107 111 114 115 119 131 149
Primary Contact: Steve Winnett, Chief Executive Officer
CFO: Carol Files, Chief Financial Officer
CMO: Ian Reynolds, Chief Medical Officer
CIO: Yobi Kasper, Chief Information Officer
CHR: Gabby Myers, Human Resources Director
CNO: David Gonzalez, Chief Clinical Officer
Control: Individual, Investor–owned (for–profit) **Service:** General medical and surgical

Staffed Beds: 4 **Admissions:** 153 **Census:** 1 **Outpatient Visits:** 2123 **Births:** 0 **Total Expense ($000):** 10547 **Payroll Expense ($000):** 3145 **Personnel:** 60

★ ⇧ **BAYLOR ST. LUKE'S MEDICAL CENTER (450193)**, 6720 Bertner Avenue, Zip 77030–2697, Mailing Address: P.O.Box 20269, 77225–0269; tel. 832/355–1000 **A**2 3 5 8 10 21 **F**3 8 11 14 15 17 18 20 22 24 26 28 29 30 31 34 35 36 39 40 42 44 45 46 47 48 49 50 51 54 56 57 58 59 60 61 64 65 66 68 70 71 74 75 77 78 79 80 81 82 84 85 86 87 90 91 92 96 97 100 107 108 110 111 114 115 116 117 118 119 120 121 123 124 126 129 130 132 135 137 138 139 140 145 146 147 148 **P**6 **S** Catholic Health Initiatives, Englewood, CO
Primary Contact: Gay Nord, President
CFO: William Brosius, Vice President and Chief Financial Officer
CIO: James Albin, Chief Information Officer
CHR: Susan Bailey–Newell, Vice President Human Resources
Web address: www.stlukestexas.com
Control: Church operated, Nongovernment, not–for–profit **Service:** General medical and surgical

Staffed Beds: 704 **Admissions:** 24575 **Census:** 493 **Outpatient Visits:** 179300 **Births:** 0 **Total Expense ($000):** 900230 **Payroll Expense ($000):** 324017 **Personnel:** 3256

☒ **BAYLOR ST. LUKE'S MEDICAL CENTER MCNAIR CAMPUS**, One Baylor Plaza, BCM 100, Zip 77030–3411; tel. 713/798–4951 (Nonreporting) **A**1 **S** Catholic Health Initiatives, Englewood, CO
Primary Contact: Michael H. Covert, FACHE, Chief Executive Officer
Web address: www.bcm.edu
Control: Other not–for–profit (including NFP Corporation) **Service:** General medical and surgical

Staffed Beds: 256

☐ **BEHAVIORAL HOSPITAL OF BELLAIRE (454107)**, 5314 Dashwood Drive, Zip 77081–4603; tel. 713/600–9500 **A**1 10 **F**4 5 29 98 99 100 101 103 104 105 130 **S** Universal Health Services, Inc., King of Prussia, PA
Primary Contact: Coleby Wright, Chief Executive Officer
Web address: www.bhbhospital.com
Control: Corporation, Investor–owned (for–profit) **Service:** Psychiatric

Staffed Beds: 122 **Admissions:** 3742 **Census:** 90 **Outpatient Visits:** 4102 **Births:** 0 **Total Expense ($000):** 17601 **Payroll Expense ($000):** 10409 **Personnel:** 181

★ ⇧ **CHI ST. LUKE'S HOSPITAL – THE VINTAGE HOSPITAL (670075)**, 20171 Chasewood Park Drive, Zip 77070–1437; tel. 832/534–5000 **A**10 21 **F**3 11 12 13 15 18 20 22 24 26 29 30 34 35 40 45 49 50 57 59 60 64 68 70 72 75 76 77 79 81 82 85 87 107 108 110 111 114 115 118 119 130 146 147 149 **P**5 **S** Catholic Health Initiatives, Englewood, CO
Primary Contact: Roland Cruickshank, President
Web address: www.stlukesvintage.com/
Control: Church operated, Nongovernment, not–for–profit **Service:** General medical and surgical

Staffed Beds: 78 **Admissions:** 4204 **Census:** 45 **Outpatient Visits:** 25504 **Total Expense ($000):** 86016 **Payroll Expense ($000):** 32328 **Personnel:** 303

CORNERSTONE HOSPITAL–MEDICAL CENTER OF HOUSTON (452055), 2001 Hermann Drive, Zip 77004; tel. 832/649–6200 **A**10 22 **F**1 3 29 31 70 77 85 86 87 119 130 148 149 **S** Cornerstone Healthcare Group, Dallas, TX
Primary Contact: Michael Higginbotham, Chief Executive Officer
Web address: www.chghospitals.com
Control: Corporation, Investor–owned (for–profit) **Service:** Acute long–term care hospital

Staffed Beds: 35 **Admissions:** 369 **Census:** 23 **Outpatient Visits:** 0 **Births:** 0 **Total Expense ($000):** 14102 **Payroll Expense ($000):** 5615 **Personnel:** 84

TX

Hospital, Medicare Provider Number, Address, Telephone, Approval, Facility, and Physician Codes, Health Care System

★ American Hospital Association (AHA) membership
☐ The Joint Commission accreditation
○ Healthcare Facilities Accreditation Program
◇ DNV Healthcare Inc. accreditation
⇧ Center for Improvement in Healthcare Quality Accreditation
△ Commission on Accreditation of Rehabilitation Facilities (CARF) accreditation

☐ **CYPRESS CREEK HOSPITAL (454108)**, 17750 Cali Drive, Zip 77090–2700; tel. 281/586–7600 **A**1 10 **F**4 5 29 30 64 87 98 99 100 102 104 105 130 132 149 **S** Universal Health Services, Inc., King of Prussia, PA
Primary Contact: Brian Brooker, Chief Executive Officer
CFO: Stephen Copeland, Chief Financial Officer
CMO: Marshall Lucas M.D., Medical Director
CIO: James Harmon, Information Technology
CHR: Brenda Dominguez, Director Human Resources
CNO: Michael Smith, Director of Nursing
Web address: www.cypresscreekhospital.com
Control: Corporation, Investor–owned (for–profit) **Service**: Psychiatric

> **Staffed Beds: 96 Admissions: 3675 Census: 87 Outpatient Visits: 8936 Births: 0 Total Expense ($000): 22088 Payroll Expense ($000): 10790 Personnel: 208**

✈ **CYPRESS FAIRBANKS MEDICAL CENTER (450716)**, 10655 Steepletop Drive, Zip 77065–4297; tel. 281/890–4285 **A**1 10 **F**3 11 12 13 15 18 20 22 24 29 30 31 34 35 40 42 43 45 46 47 49 50 57 59 64 65 70 72 74 75 76 77 78 79 81 82 85 87 89 93 107 108 110 111 114 115 119 120 121 124 129 130 132 144 145 146 147 148 **P**8 **S** HCA Healthcare, Nashville, TN
Primary Contact: Naman Mahajan, Interim Chief Executive Officer
CFO: James Wright M.D., Chief Financial Officer
CMO: Arturo Bravo M.D., Chief of Staff
CIO: Donna Cain, Director Information Systems Department
CHR: Linda Creswell, Director Human Resource
CNO: Lisa D. Cox R.N., MSN, Chief Nursing Officer
Web address: www.cyfairhospital.com
Control: Corporation, Investor–owned (for–profit) **Service**: General medical and surgical

> **Staffed Beds: 160 Admissions: 9082 Census: 91 Outpatient Visits: 128050 Births: 3519 Total Expense ($000): 147870 Payroll Expense ($000): 59259 Personnel: 835**

DUBUIS HOSPITAL OF HOUSTON See Cornerstone Hospital–Medical Center Of Houston

FIRST TEXAS HOSPITAL, 9922 Louetta Road, Zip 77070–1468, Mailing Address: 2941 Lake Vista Drive, Lewisville, 75067–3801; tel. 346/206–2300 (Nonreporting)
Primary Contact: Maridel Acosta–Cruz, Chief Executive Officer
Control: Corporation, Investor–owned (for–profit) **Service**: General medical and surgical

> **Staffed Beds: 50**

△ ⇑ **HARRIS HEALTH SYSTEM (450289)**, 2525 Holly Hall Street, Zip 77054–4108, Mailing Address: P.O.Box 66769, 77266–6769; tel. 713/566–6403, (Includes BEN TAUB GENERAL HOSPITAL, 1504 Taub Loop, Houston, Texas, Zip 77030, tel. 713/873–2300; LYNDON B JOHNSON GENERAL HOSPITAL, 5656 Kelley, Houston, Texas, Zip 77026, tel. 713/566–5000; QUENTIN MEASE HOSPITAL, 3601 North MacGregor, Houston, Texas, Zip 77004, tel. 713/873–3700; Jeffrey Webster, Administrator) (Total facility includes 24 beds in nursing home–type unit) **A**2 3 5 7 10 21 **F**3 5 7 8 13 15 17 18 20 22 24 26 29 30 31 32 34 35 39 40 41 43 45 46 49 50 51 54 55 56 57 58 59 60 61 64 65 68 70 71 72 73 74 75 76 77 78 79 81 82 84 87 89 90 91 92 93 94 97 98 99 100 101 102 103 104 107 110 111 112 114 115 118 119 120 121 124 128 129 130 132 134 135 143 144 145 146 147 148 149 150 **P**6
Primary Contact: George V. Masi, Chief Executive Officer
CFO: Michael Norby, Chief Financial Officer
CMO: Fred Sutton M.D., Chief Medical Officer
CIO: Tim Tindle, Chief Information Officer
CHR: Diane Poirot, Vice President Human Resources
CNO: Elizabeth Cloyd R.N., Chief Nurse Executive and Executive Vice President
Web address: www.hchdonline.com
Control: Hospital district or authority, Government, Nonfederal **Service**: General medical and surgical

> **Staffed Beds: 783 Admissions: 36545 Census: 544 Outpatient Visits: 1945934 Births: 6596 Total Expense ($000): 1301033 Payroll Expense ($000): 509966 Personnel: 8576**

⇑ **HEALTHBRIDGE CHILDREN'S HOSPITAL OF HOUSTON (453309)**, 2929 Woodland Park Drive, Zip 77082–2687; tel. 281/293–7774 **A**3 10 21 **F**3 29 74 75 79 85 87 89 91 93 100 130 146 148 **S** Nexus Health Systems, Houston, TX
Primary Contact: Elizabeth E. Fredeboelling, MSN, R.N., Chief Executive Officer
CMO: Robert Yetman M.D., Medical Director
CHR: Guy Murdock, Vice President Human Resources
Web address: www.healthbridgehouston.com/
Control: Partnership, Investor–owned (for–profit) **Service**: Children's general medical and surgical

> **Staffed Beds: 40 Admissions: 214 Census: 25 Outpatient Visits: 282 Births: 0 Total Expense ($000): 15542 Payroll Expense ($000): 6382 Personnel: 98**

✈ **HEALTHSOUTH REHABILITATION HOSPITAL OF CYPRESS (673050)**, 13031 Wortham Center Drive, Zip 77065–5662; tel. 832/280–2500 **A**1 10 **F**3 29 34 57 62 64 75 77 87 90 91 93 95 96 130 132 146 148 149 **S** HEALTHSOUTH Corporation, Birmingham, AL
Primary Contact: Sheila A. Bollier, Chief Executive Officer
CFO: Melissa Haddox, Controller
CMO: Ignazio LaChina M.D., Medical Director
CNO: Roshonda Henry, Chief Nursing Officer
Web address: www.healthsouthcypress.com
Control: Corporation, Investor–owned (for–profit) **Service**: Rehabilitation

> **Staffed Beds: 60 Admissions: 1477 Census: 51 Outpatient Visits: 4120 Births: 0 Total Expense ($000): 16594 Payroll Expense ($000): 10282 Personnel: 183**

✈ **HEALTHSOUTH REHABILITATION HOSPITAL THE VINTAGE (673052)**, 20180 Chasewood Park Drive, Zip 77070–1436; tel. 281/205–5100 **A**1 10 **F**3 29 65 90 91 96 130 148 149 **S** HEALTHSOUTH Corporation, Birmingham, AL
Primary Contact: Jeff Crawford, Chief Executive Officer
CNO: Stanley F Kiebzak R.N., Chief Nursing Officer
Web address: www.reliantnwhouston.com
Control: Corporation, Investor–owned (for–profit) **Service**: Rehabilitation

> **Staffed Beds: 60 Admissions: 1152 Census: 34 Outpatient Visits: 4283 Births: 0 Total Expense ($000): 18646 Payroll Expense ($000): 8280 Personnel: 126**

☐ **HERMANN DRIVE SURGICAL HOSPITAL**, 2001 Hermann Drive, Zip 77004–7643; tel. 713/285–5500 **A**1 **F**3 12 29 40 45 46 64 68 70 74 75 77 81 85 86 89 107 114 **S** Nobilis Health Corporation, Houston, TX
Primary Contact: Michael Torne, Chief Executive Officer
Web address: www.nobilishealth.com/our–facilities/houston/
Control: Corporation, Investor–owned (for–profit) **Service**: Surgical

> **Staffed Beds: 25 Admissions: 975 Census: 5 Outpatient Visits: 1517 Births: 0 Total Expense ($000): 39144 Payroll Expense ($000): 6203 Personnel: 55**

⇑ **HOPEBRIDGE HOSPITAL (670072)**, 5556 Gasmer Drive, Zip 77035–4502; tel. 713/422–2625 **A**10 21 **F**3 29 35 38 64 68 98 99 100 101 103 104 105 130 149 **P**5
Primary Contact: Tim C. Simmons, Chief Executive Officer
Web address: www.hopebridgehealth.com/
Control: Corporation, Investor–owned (for–profit) **Service**: Psychiatric

> **Staffed Beds: 85 Admissions: 1952 Census: 48 Outpatient Visits: 22785 Births: 0 Total Expense ($000): 14440 Payroll Expense ($000): 8727 Personnel: 137**

HOUSTON BEHAVIORAL HEALTHCARE HOSPITAL (454135), 2801 Gessner Road, Zip 77080–2503; tel. 832/834–7710 (Nonreporting) **S** Signature Healthcare Services, Corona, CA
Primary Contact: Roy Hollis, Chief Executive Officer
Web address: www.houstonbehavioralhealth.com/
Control: Individual, Investor–owned (for–profit) **Service**: Psychiatric

> **Staffed Beds: 25**

★ △ ⇑ **HOUSTON METHODIST HOSPITAL (450358)**, 6565 Fannin Street, D200, Zip 77030–2707; tel. 713/790–3311, (Total facility includes 18 beds in nursing home–type unit) **A**2 3 5 7 8 10 21 **F**3 6 8 9 11 12 13 14 15 17 18 20 22 24 26 28 29 30 31 34 35 36 37 38 39 40 41 42 44 45 46 47 48 49 50 51 53 54 55 56 57 58 59 60 61 62 63 64 65 66 67 68 70 73 74 75 76 77 78 79 81 82 84 85 86 87 90 91 92 93 95 96 97 98 100 101 103 104 107 108 110 111 114 115 116 117 118 119 120 121 123 124 126 128 129 130 131 132 135 136 137 138 139 140 141 142 145 146 147 148 149 **P**5 6 **S** Houston Methodist, Houston, TX
Primary Contact: Roberta Schwartz, Ph.D., Executive Vice President
CMO: Robert Phillips M.D., Ph.D., FACC, Executive Vice President and Chief Medical Officer
CIO: Robert K Eardley, Senior Vice President and Chief Information Officer
CNO: Katherine Walsh MS, R.N., Dr.PH, Vice President and Chief Nursing Officer
Web address: www.methodisthealth.com
Control: Other not–for–profit (including NFP Corporation) **Service**: General medical and surgical

> **Staffed Beds: 900 Admissions: 38077 Census: 701 Outpatient Visits: 362787 Births: 978 Total Expense ($000): 1636047 Payroll Expense ($000): 443127 Personnel: 8841**

Many Facility Codes have changed. Please refer to the AHA Guide Code Chart. © 2017 AHA Guide

★ ⇑ **HOUSTON METHODIST WEST HOSPITAL (670077)**, 18500 Katy Freeway, Zip 77094–1110; tel. 832/522–1000 **A**3 10 21 **F**3 13 15 18 20 22 24 26 28 29 30 31 34 35 36 39 40 42 44 45 49 50 51 53 54 57 59 61 63 64 68 70 73 74 75 76 77 78 79 81 82 84 85 87 103 107 108 109 110 111 114 115 117 119 120 121 123 124 126 130 131 132 135 146 147 148 149 **P**6 **S** Houston Methodist, Houston, TX
Primary Contact: Wayne M. Voss, Chief Executive Officer
COO: Peyton Elliott, Vice President Operations
CNO: Victoria Brownewell, Chief Nursing Officer
Web address: www.methodisthealth.com
Control: Other not–for–profit (including NFP Corporation) **Service:** General medical and surgical

Staffed Beds: 193 **Admissions:** 11338 **Census:** 120 **Outpatient Visits:** 133974 **Births:** 2690 **Total Expense ($000):** 247025 **Payroll Expense ($000):** 86721 **Personnel:** 1290

★ ⇑ **HOUSTON METHODIST WILLOWBROOK HOSPITAL (450844)**, 18220 State Highway 249, Zip 77070–4347; tel. 281/477–1000 **A**3 10 21 **F**3 8 11 12 13 15 17 18 20 22 24 26 28 29 30 31 34 35 36 37 40 42 44 45 49 50 53 54 57 59 64 65 70 72 73 74 75 76 77 78 79 81 85 86 87 93 97 102 107 108 110 111 112 115 119 120 121 123 126 129 130 131 132 135 146 147 149 **P**6 **S** Houston Methodist, Houston, TX
Primary Contact: Keith Barber, CPA, Chief Executive Officer
CHR: Elizabeth Acevedo, Director Human Resources
CNO: Nancy C Keenan R.N., Senior Vice President and Chief Nursing Officer
Web address: www.houstonmethodist.org/locations/willowbrook/
Control: Other not–for–profit (including NFP Corporation) **Service:** General medical and surgical

Staffed Beds: 312 **Admissions:** 18314 **Census:** 218 **Outpatient Visits:** 177633 **Births:** 3603 **Total Expense ($000):** 338931 **Payroll Expense ($000):** 121117 **Personnel:** 1849

⊠ **HOUSTON NORTHWEST MEDICAL CENTER (450638)**, 710 Cypress Creek Parkway, Zip 77090–3402; tel. 281/440–1000 **A**1 3 5 10 **F**3 11 12 13 15 18 20 22 24 26 28 29 30 31 34 35 40 43 45 46 49 50 57 59 64 65 70 72 74 75 76 77 78 79 81 82 84 85 86 87 90 91 92 93 96 102 107 108 109 110 111 114 115 117 118 119 126 129 130 132 135 144 145 146 147 148 149 **S** HCA Healthcare, Nashville, TN
Primary Contact: Timothy Puthoff, Chief Executive Officer
COO: Michael Adkins, Chief Operating Officer
CFO: Cameron Pophan, Chief Financial Officer
CIO: Ed Roberson, Director Information Systems
CHR: Melanie R Webb, Director Human Resources
CNO: Cindy Henning R.N., Chief Nursing Officer
Web address: www.hnmc.com
Control: Partnership, Investor–owned (for–profit) **Service:** General medical and surgical

Staffed Beds: 339 **Admissions:** 16551 **Census:** 197 **Outpatient Visits:** 150387 **Births:** 4427 **Total Expense ($000):** 265717 **Payroll Expense ($000):** 98986 **Personnel:** 1397

☐ **INTRACARE NORTH HOSPITAL (454083)**, 1120 Cypress Station Drive, Zip 77090–3031; tel. 281/893–7200 **A**1 10 **F**5 98 99 100 101 103 104 105
Primary Contact: Terry Scovill, Chief Executive Officer
CFO: Fred Chan, Chief Financial Officer
CMO: Javier Ruiz M.D., Medical Director
Web address: www.intracare.org
Control: Other not–for–profit (including NFP Corporation) **Service:** Psychiatric

Staffed Beds: 86 **Admissions:** 2063 **Census:** 51 **Outpatient Visits:** 56267 **Births:** 0 **Total Expense ($000):** 16872 **Payroll Expense ($000):** 7597 **Personnel:** 199

⊠ **KINDRED HOSPITAL HOUSTON MEDICAL CENTER (452023)**, 6441 Main Street, Zip 77030–1596; tel. 713/790–0500 **A**1 3 5 10 **F**1 3 29 30 70 75 77 85 107 130 148 **S** Kindred Healthcare, Louisville, KY
Primary Contact: Robert Stein, Chief Executive Officer
CFO: Sara Langlitz, Controller
Web address: www.khhouston.com/
Control: Corporation, Investor–owned (for–profit) **Service:** Acute long–term care hospital

Staffed Beds: 105 **Admissions:** 964 **Census:** 94 **Outpatient Visits:** 34 **Births:** 0 **Total Expense ($000):** 48827 **Payroll Expense ($000):** 22554

⊠ **KINDRED HOSPITAL–HOUSTON NORTHWEST (452039)**, 11297 Fallbrook Drive, Zip 77065–4292; tel. 281/897–8114, (Includes KINDRED HOSPITAL–BAY AREA, 4801 East Sam Houston Parkway South, Pasadena, Texas, Zip 77505–3955, tel. 281/991–5463; Aleen D. Arabit, Executive Director) **A**1 10 **F**1 3 29 49 57 64 70 77 85 87 107 114 130 148 **P**5 **S** Kindred Healthcare, Louisville, KY
Primary Contact: Aleen D. Arabit, Chief Executive Officer
Web address: www.khhoustonnw.com/
Control: Corporation, Investor–owned (for–profit) **Service:** Acute long–term care hospital

Staffed Beds: 84 **Admissions:** 654 **Census:** 43 **Outpatient Visits:** 266 **Births:** 0 **Total Expense ($000):** 26521 **Payroll Expense ($000):** 9649 **Personnel:** 150

LYNDON B JOHNSON GENERAL HOSPITAL See Harris Health System

⊠ **MEMORIAL HERMANN – TEXAS MEDICAL CENTER (450068)**, 6411 Fannin Street, Zip 77030–1501; tel. 713/704–4000, (Includes CHILDREN'S MEMORIAL HERMANN HOSPITAL, 6411 Fannin, Houston, Texas, Zip 77030, tel. 713/704–5437; MEMORIAL HERMAN CYPRESS, 27700 NW Freeway, Suite 380, Cypress, Texas, Zip 77433, tel. 832/658–3102; Heath Rushing, Senior Vice President and Chief Executive Officer; MEMORIAL HERMANN ORTHOPEDIC AND SPINE HOSPITAL, 5410 West Loop South, Bellaire, Texas, Zip 77401–2103, tel. 713/314–4500; Andrew Knizley, Chief Executive Officer) (Total facility includes 8 beds in nursing home–type unit) **A**1 2 3 5 8 10 **F**3 7 12 15 16 17 18 19 20 21 22 23 24 25 26 27 28 29 30 31 32 34 35 36 37 40 41 43 44 45 46 47 48 49 50 51 55 56 57 58 59 60 61 64 68 70 72 73 74 75 76 77 78 79 81 82 84 85 86 87 88 89 90 91 92 93 96 100 102 107 108 109 110 111 113 114 115 116 118 119 120 121 123 124 126 128 129 130 131 132 133 134 141 142 146 147 148 149 150 **P**5 6 **S** Memorial Hermann Health System, Houston, TX
Primary Contact: Brian Dean, FACHE, Chief Executive Officer
COO: Shawn Cloonan, Executive Vice President and Chief Operating Officer
CFO: William Pack, Chief Financial Officer
CMO: Jeffrey Katz M.D., Chief Medical Officer
CIO: David Bradshaw, Chief Information Officer
CHR: Vivian Kardow, Chief Human Resources Officer
Web address: www.mhhs.org
Control: Other not–for–profit (including NFP Corporation) **Service:** General medical and surgical

Staffed Beds: 1000 **Admissions:** 39196 **Census:** 733 **Outpatient Visits:** 235078 **Births:** 3913 **Total Expense ($000):** 1472946 **Payroll Expense ($000):** 439019 **Personnel:** 5193

⊠ △ **MEMORIAL HERMANN GREATER HEIGHTS HOSPITAL (450184)**, 1635 North Loop West, Zip 77008–1532; tel. 713/867–3380, (Includes MEMORIAL HERMANN PEARLAND MEDICAL CENTER, 16100 South Freeway, Pearland, Texas, Zip 77584–1895, tel. 713/413–5000; Mario J Garner, Ed.D., FACHE, Chief Executive Officer; MEMORIAL HERMANN SOUTHEAST HOSPITAL, 11800 Astoria Boulevard, Houston, Texas, Zip 77089–6041, tel. 281/929–6100; Kyle Price, Interim Chief Executive Officer; MEMORIAL HERMANN SOUTHWEST HOSPITAL, 7600 Beechnut, Houston, Texas, Zip 77074–1850, tel. 713/456–5000; Gregory Haralson, FACHE, Chief Executive Officer; MEMORIAL HERMANN THE WOODLANDS HOSPITAL, 9250 Pinecroft Drive, The Woodlands, Texas, Zip 77380–3225, tel. 281/364–2300) **A**1 2 3 5 7 10 **F**3 8 11 12 13 15 17 18 20 22 24 25 26 28 29 30 31 34 35 36 37 40 41 42 43 44 45 46 47 48 49 50 51 54 55 56 57 58 59 60 64 65 68 69 70 72 73 74 75 76 77 78 79 80 81 82 84 85 86 87 89 90 91 92 93 94 96 101 102 103 107 108 109 110 111 112 114 115 116 117 119 120 121 123 124 126 129 130 131 132 135 143 144 146 147 148 149 **P**5 6 **S** Memorial Hermann Health System, Houston, TX
Primary Contact: Susan Jadlowski, MSN, R.N., Chief Executive Officer
COO: Wesley Tidwell, Chief Operating Officer
CFO: James R Shallock, Chief Financial Officer
CMO: Maurice Leibman M.D., Chief Medical Officer
CIO: David Bradshaw, Chief Information Officer
CNO: Melody Ford Dickerson, Chief Nursing Officer
Web address: www.mhbh.org
Control: Other not–for–profit (including NFP Corporation) **Service:** General medical and surgical

Staffed Beds: 1372 **Admissions:** 63444 **Census:** 842 **Outpatient Visits:** 593012 **Births:** 11032 **Total Expense ($000):** 1244543 **Payroll Expense ($000):** 421813 **Personnel:** 5171

KINDRED HOSPITAL SPRING See Kindred Hospital Tomball

MEMORIAL HERMANN SOUTHEAST HOSPITAL See Memorial Hermann Greater Heights Hospital

MEMORIAL HERMANN SOUTHWEST HOSPITAL See Memorial Hermann Greater Heights Hospital

---

Hospital, Medicare Provider Number, Address, Telephone, Approval, Facility, and Physician Codes, Health Care System

★ American Hospital Association (AHA) membership ○ Healthcare Facilities Accreditation Program ⇑ Center for Improvement in Healthcare Quality Accreditation
☐ The Joint Commission accreditation ◇ DNV Healthcare Inc. accreditation △ Commission on Accreditation of Rehabilitation Facilities (CARF) accreditation

TX

☐ **MENNINGER CLINIC**, 12301 Main Street, Zip 77035–6207; tel. 713/275–5000 **A**1 3 5 **F**30 35 74 98 99 101 104 106 130 132
Primary Contact: C Edward. Coffey, M.D., President, Chief Executive Officer and Chief of Staff
CFO: Tony Gaglio CPA, Senior Vice President and Chief Financial Officer
CIO: M. Justin Coffey, Vice President and Chief Information Officer, Medical Director Center for Brain Stimulation
CHR: Andrea Preisinger, Director Human Resources
CNO: Avni Cirpili, Senior Vice President, Chief Nursing Officer
Web address: www.menningerclinic.com
Control: Other not–for–profit (including NFP Corporation) **Service:** Psychiatric

| Staffed Beds: 102 Admissions: 716 Census: 78 Outpatient Visits: 3367 |
| Births: 0 Total Expense ($000): 59285 Payroll Expense ($000): 26279 |
| Personnel: 358 |

⇑ **METHODIST WEST HOUSTON HOSPITAL** See Houston Methodist West Hospital

⇑ **METHODIST WILLOWBROOK HOSPITAL** See Houston Methodist Willowbrook Hospital

⊠ △ **MICHAEL E. DEBAKEY VETERANS AFFAIRS MEDICAL CENTER**, 2002 Holcombe Boulevard, Zip 77030–4298; tel. 713/791–1414, (Nonreporting) **A**1 3 5 7 8 **S** Department of Veterans Affairs, Washington, DC
Primary Contact: Francisco Vazquez, Director
CFO: Alisa Cooper, Manager Financial Resources
CMO: Jagadeesh S Kalavar M.D., Chief of Staff
CIO: Kevin Lenamond, Information Management Service Line Executive
CHR: Mark Muhammad, Manager Human Resources
CNO: Kelly Ann Irving MSN, RN–B, Associate Director for Patient Care Services
Web address: www.houston.va.gov
Control: Veterans Affairs, Government, federal **Service:** General medical and surgical

| Staffed Beds: 479 |

⊠ **PARK PLAZA HOSPITAL (450659)**, 1313 Hermann Drive, Zip 77004–7092; tel. 713/527–5000 **A**1 2 10 **F**3 12 15 18 20 22 29 31 34 35 40 45 49 50 56 57 59 70 74 78 79 81 85 92 107 108 110 111 114 115 118 119 120 121 123 129 130 132 146 147 148 **S** HCA Healthcare, Nashville, TN
Primary Contact: Steven D. Patonai, Interim Chief Executive Officer
COO: Mary Jo Goodman, Chief Operating Officer
CMO: Robert Brown M.D., Chief Medical Officer
CIO: Terry Janis, Assistant Vice President
CHR: Melanie R Webb, Chief Human Resources Officer
Web address: www.parkplazahospital.com
Control: Partnership, Investor–owned (for–profit) **Service:** General medical and surgical

| Staffed Beds: 139 Admissions: 3435 Census: 53 Outpatient Visits: 33367 |
| Births: 0 Total Expense ($000): 78557 Payroll Expense ($000): 27651 |
| Personnel: 424 |

☐ **PINE VALLEY SPECIALTY HOSPITAL (452043)**, 6160 South Loop East, Zip 77087–1010; tel. 713/640–2400 **A**1 10 **F**1 3 29 75 77 85 87 130 148 **S** Concord Healthcare Group, Lakewood, NJ
Primary Contact: Brent Hanson, Chief Executive Officer
CFO: Betty Priestley, Manager Business Office
CMO: Alfred Louis M.D., Chief Medical Staff
CHR: Laura Garza, Director Human Resources
Web address: www.promise–houston.com
Control: Corporation, Investor–owned (for–profit) **Service:** Acute long–term care hospital

| Staffed Beds: 35 Admissions: 218 Census: 13 Outpatient Visits: 0 Births: 0 |
| Total Expense ($000): 7831 Payroll Expense ($000): 3839 Personnel: 50 |

⊠ **PLAZA SPECIALTY HOSPITAL (452046)**, 1300 Binz Street, Zip 77004–7016; tel. 713/285–1000 **A**1 10 **F**1 3 70 85 87 **P**8 **S** TENET Healthcare Corporation, Dallas, TX
Primary Contact: Richard Andrew. Pletz, Chief Executive Officer
CFO: Charles Handley, Chief Financial Officer
CMO: Wasae S Tabibi M.D., President Medical Staff
CIO: Steve Peacock, Assistant Vice President
Web address: www.plazaspecialtyhospital.com
Control: Corporation, Investor–owned (for–profit) **Service:** Acute long–term care hospital

| Staffed Beds: 46 Admissions: 380 Census: 31 Outpatient Visits: 0 Births: 0 |
| Total Expense ($000): 24659 Payroll Expense ($000): 7963 Personnel: 88 |

PROVIDENCE HOSPITAL OF NORTH HOUSTON, 16750 Red Oak Drive, Zip 77090; tel. 281/453–7110, (Data for 194 days) **F**3 15 37 40 45 48 49 51 64 68 81 82 85 91 107 108 110 111 115 119 129 **P**8
Primary Contact: Stephen Myers, Chief Executive Officer
Control: Partnership, Investor–owned (for–profit) **Service:** General medical and surgical

| Staffed Beds: 16 Admissions: 113 Census: 1 Outpatient Visits: 2447 |
| Births: 0 Total Expense ($000): 11299 Payroll Expense ($000): 2904 |
| Personnel: 118 |

SACRED OAK MEDICAL CENTER, 11500 Space Center Boulevard, Zip 77059–3603; tel. 281/241–6460 (Nonreporting)
Primary Contact: Starsky Bomer, Chief Executive Officer
Web address: www.sacredoakmedical.com/
Control: Other not–for–profit (including NFP Corporation) **Service:** General medical and surgical

| Staffed Beds: 25 |

☐ **SCA HOUSTON HOSPITAL FOR SPECIALIZED SURGERY (450797)**, 5445 La Branch Street, Zip 77004–6835; tel. 713/528–6800 **A**1 10 **F**3 8 40 54 64 79 81 82 85 107 111 119 149
Primary Contact: Mary Whitmeyer, Chief Executive Officer
CFO: Deborah Jones, Controller
Web address: www.scasurgery.com
Control: Partnership, Investor–owned (for–profit) **Service:** Surgical

| Staffed Beds: 7 Admissions: 183 Census: 1 Outpatient Visits: 4266 Births: 0 |
| Total Expense ($000): 16601 Payroll Expense ($000): 4146 Personnel: 174 |

☐ **SHRINERS HOSPITALS FOR CHILDREN–HOUSTON (453312)**, 6977 Main Street, Zip 77030–3701; tel. 713/797–1616 **A**1 3 5 10 **F**3 29 30 35 50 59 64 68 74 75 77 79 81 86 87 89 93 94 96 130 131 132 134 143 146 148 **P**6 **S** Shriners Hospitals for Children, Tampa, FL
Primary Contact: Cathy Moniaci, R.N., MS, Administrator
COO: Cathy Moniaci R.N., MS, Administrator
CFO: Michael B Schimming, Director Fiscal Services
CMO: Douglas A Barnes M.D., Chief of Staff
CHR: Robert A Magee, Director Human Resources
CNO: Jeannie Keith, Director Patient Care Services and Nurse Executive
Web address: www.shrinershospitalsforchildren.org/Locations/houston
Control: Other not–for–profit (including NFP Corporation) **Service:** Children's orthopedic

| Staffed Beds: 40 Admissions: 517 Census: 12 Outpatient Visits: 10262 |
| Births: 0 Total Expense ($000): 28319 Payroll Expense ($000): 15282 |
| Personnel: 173 |

⇑ **ST. JOSEPH MEDICAL CENTER (450035)**, 1401 St Joseph Parkway, Zip 77002–8301; tel. 713/757–1000, (Total facility includes 18 beds in nursing home–type unit) **A**3 5 10 21 **F**3 11 12 13 15 18 20 22 24 26 29 30 31 34 35 40 42 43 45 49 50 51 53 55 57 58 59 60 64 68 70 72 74 75 76 77 78 79 81 82 84 85 86 87 90 93 94 97 98 101 102 103 104 105 107 108 110 111 114 115 116 117 118 119 121 123 124 125 128 129 130 131 132 135 143 144 146 147 148 149 **P**8 **S** IASIS Healthcare, Franklin, TN
Primary Contact: Bryanie W. Swilley Jr, Interim Chief Executive Officer
COO: Laura Fortin R.N., Chief Operating Officer
CIO: Robin Brown, Chief Information Officer and Compliance Officer
CHR: Kris Clatanoff, Director Human Resources
Web address: www.sjmctx.com
Control: Partnership, Investor–owned (for–profit) **Service:** General medical and surgical

| Staffed Beds: 376 Admissions: 14499 Census: 205 Outpatient Visits: |
| 107067 Total Expense ($000): 240902 Payroll Expense ($000): 96134 |
| Personnel: 1271 |

SUN BEHAVIORAL HOUSTON (454139), 7601 Fannin Street, Zip 77054–1905; tel. 713/796–2273 **A**3 **F**98 99 100 101 104 105
Primary Contact: Rick Harding, Chief Executive Officer
CFO: Doug Smith, Chief Financial Officer
CMO: Vernon Walling M.D., Chief Medical Officer
Web address: www.sunhouston.com
Control: Corporation, Investor–owned (for–profit) **Service:** Psychiatric

| Staffed Beds: 60 Admissions: 1108 Census: 22 Outpatient Visits: 525 |
| Births: 0 Total Expense ($000): 11891 Payroll Expense ($000): 6067 |
| Personnel: 153 |

TX

□ △ **TEXAS CHILDREN'S HOSPITAL (453304)**, 6621 Fannin Street,
Zip 77030–2399, Mailing Address: Box 300630, 77230–0630; tel. 832/824–
1000, (Includes TEXAS CHILDREN'S HOSPITAL WEST CAMPUS, 18200 Katy
Freeway, Houston, Texas, Zip 77094–1285, tel. 832/227–1000; Matt Schaefer,
President) **A**1 3 5 7 8 10 **F**3 7 11 12 13 17 19 21 23 25 27 29 30 31 32 34 35
38 39 40 41 42 43 48 49 50 52 54 55 57 58 59 60 61 64 65 68 71 72 73 74
75 76 77 78 79 80 81 84 85 86 87 88 89 90 92 93 94 95 96 97 99 100 101
104 107 108 111 113 114 115 116 117 118 119 126 129 130 131 132 134
136 137 138 139 140 143 146 147 148 149 150
Primary Contact: Mark A. Wallace, FACHE, President and Chief Executive Officer
CMO: Mark W Kline M.D., Physician in Chief
CIO: Myra Davis, Senior Vice President and Chief Information Officer
CHR: Linda W Aldred, Senior Vice President
Web address: www.texaschildrens.org
Control: Other not–for–profit (including NFP Corporation) **Service:** Children's
general medical and surgical

Staffed Beds: 681 **Admissions:** 33950 **Census:** 593 **Outpatient Visits:**
1461359 **Births:** 6001 **Total Expense ($000):** 1794179 **Payroll Expense
($000):** 722297 **Personnel:** 7996

⊞ **TEXAS ORTHOPEDIC HOSPITAL (450804)**, 7401 South Main Street,
Zip 77030–4509; tel. 713/799–8600 **A**1 3 5 10 **F**3 29 30 40 59 64 68
70 79 81 82 85 86 87 93 94 97 107 111 119 146 149 **S** HCA Healthcare,
Nashville, TN
Primary Contact: Eric Becker, Chief Executive Officer
CFO: Blair Callaway, Chief Financial Officer
CMO: Gregory Stocks M.D., Chief of Staff
CNO: Troy Sarver R.N., Chief Nursing Officer
Web address: www.texasorthopedic.com
Control: Partnership, Investor–owned (for–profit) **Service:** Orthopedic

Staffed Beds: 49 **Admissions:** 3687 **Census:** 23 **Outpatient Visits:** 35747
Births: 0 **Total Expense ($000):** 83600 **Payroll Expense ($000):** 24726
Personnel: 378

⇑ **THE METHODIST HOSPITAL** See Houston Methodist Hospital

⊞ △ **TIRR MEMORIAL HERMANN (453025)**, 1333 Moursund Street,
Zip 77030–3405; tel. 713/799–5000 **A**1 3 5 7 10 **F**3 11 29 30 34 35 44 50 54
58 59 60 64 68 74 75 77 79 82 86 87 90 91 93 95 96 97 100 104 107 114
119 129 130 131 132 146 148 149 **P**5 **S** Memorial Hermann Health System,
Houston, TX
Primary Contact: Carl E. Josehart, Chief Executive Officer
COO: Mary Ann Euliarte R.N., Chief Operating Officer and Chief Nursing Officer
CFO: Wayne Gordon, Chief Financial Officer
CMO: Gerard E Francisco M.D., Chief Medical Officer
CIO: Gina Tripp, Director Information Systems
CHR: Vivian Kardow, Chief Human Resources Officer
CNO: Mary Ann Euliarte R.N., Chief Operating Officer and Chief Nursing Officer
Web address: www.memorialhermann.org/locations/tirr.html
Control: Other not–for–profit (including NFP Corporation) **Service:** Rehabilitation

Staffed Beds: 134 **Admissions:** 1265 **Census:** 102 **Outpatient Visits:**
30935 **Births:** 0 **Total Expense ($000):** 118309 **Payroll Expense ($000):**
58401 **Personnel:** 778

□ **TOPS SURGICAL SPECIALTY HOSPITAL (450774)**, 17080 Red Oak Drive,
Zip 77090–2602; tel. 281/539–2900 **A**1 10 **F**3 15 29 40 45 51 79 81 107 **S**
United Surgical Partners International, Addison, TX
Primary Contact: Samuel H. Rossmann, Chief Executive Officer
CFO: Daniel Smith, Chief Financial Officer
CMO: Thomas Barton M.D., Medical Director
CIO: Maud Jones, Manager Medical Records
CHR: Ashley Monzingo, Human Resources, Accounts Payable and Payroll
CNO: Andrea Wappelhorst, Chief Nursing Officer
Web address: www.tops–hospital.com
Control: Partnership, Investor–owned (for–profit) **Service:** General medical and
surgical

Staffed Beds: 15 **Admissions:** 724 **Census:** 4 **Outpatient Visits:** 47114
Births: 0 **Total Expense ($000):** 35475 **Payroll Expense ($000):** 9208
Personnel: 168

TRIUMPH HOSPITAL NORTHWEST See Kindred Hospital Spring

UNITED MEMORIAL MEDICAL CARE (450803), 510 West Tidwell Road,
Zip 77091–4399; tel. 281/618–8500, (Includes DOCTORS HOSPITAL PARKWAY,
233 West Parker Road, Houston, Texas, Zip 77076–2999, tel. 281/765–2600)
A10 22 **F**22 29 40 43 50 64 70 75 79 81 92 107 114 119 130 148
Primary Contact: Farida Moeen, M.D., Chief Executive Officer
COO: Farida Moeen M.D., Chief Executive Officer
CFO: Theresa Eatherly, Chief Financial Officer
CMO: Cesar Ortega M.D., Chief of Staff
CIO: Dell Davis, Director Information Systems
CHR: Carolyn Washington, Director of Human Resources
Web address: www.ummc.care/
Control: Partnership, Investor–owned (for–profit) **Service:** General medical and
surgical

Staffed Beds: 42 **Admissions:** 6102 **Census:** 25 **Outpatient Visits:** 11676
Births: 0 **Total Expense ($000):** 25958 **Payroll Expense ($000):** 10043
Personnel: 272

★ **UNIVERSITY OF TEXAS HARRIS COUNTY PSYCHIATRIC CENTER (454076)**,
2800 South MacGregor Way, Zip 77021–1000, Mailing Address: P.O.Box 20249,
77225–0249; tel. 713/741–7870 **A**5 10 **F**29 30 34 35 57 58 68 75 86 87 98
99 100 101 103 104 106 130 146 **P**6 **S** University of Texas System, Austin, TX
Primary Contact: Jair C. Soares, M.D., Executive Director
COO: Stephen Glazier, Chief Operating Officer
CFO: Lois K. Pierson, Chief Financial Officer
CMO: R Andrew Harper M.D., Medical Director
CHR: Jill Strutton, Director Personnel Systems
CNO: Margaret Pung R.N., Chief Nursing Officer
Web address: www.hcpc.uth.tmc.edu
Control: State, Government, Nonfederal **Service:** Psychiatric

Staffed Beds: 208 **Admissions:** 9583 **Census:** 218 **Outpatient Visits:** 320
Births: 0 **Total Expense ($000):** 53432 **Payroll Expense ($000):** 33316
Personnel: 464

⊞ **UNIVERSITY OF TEXAS M.D. ANDERSON CANCER CENTER (450076)**, 1515
Holcombe Boulevard, Unit 1491, Zip 77030–4000; tel. 713/792–2121 **A**1 2 3
5 8 10 **F**3 8 11 14 15 18 20 22 26 29 30 31 32 34 35 36 37 38 39 40 41 44
45 46 47 49 50 54 55 56 57 58 59 63 64 66 68 70 71 74 75 77 78 79 80 81
82 83 84 85 86 87 88 89 91 92 93 96 97 99 100 101 102 103 104 107 108
110 111 112 114 115 116 117 118 119 120 121 122 123 124 126 129 130
132 134 135 136 141 142 145 146 147 148 149 150 **P**6 **S** University of Texas
System, Austin, TX
Primary Contact: Marshall Hicks, M.D., Interim President
COO: Stephen Hahn, Deputy to the President and Chief Operating Officer
CFO: Benjamin B Melson CPA, Senior Vice President and Chief Financial Officer
CIO: Chris Belmont, Chief Information Officer and Vice President
CHR: Shibu Varghese, Vice President Human Resources
CNO: Barbara L. Summers Ph.D., R.N., Vice President Nursing Practice and Chief
Nursing Officer
Web address: www.mdanderson.org
Control: State, Government, Nonfederal **Service:** Cancer

Staffed Beds: 660 **Admissions:** 27391 **Census:** 541 **Outpatient Visits:**
1388717 **Births:** 0 **Total Expense ($000):** 4270082 **Payroll Expense
($000):** 1868138 **Personnel:** 20871

⊞ **WEST HOUSTON MEDICAL CENTER (450644)**, 12141 Richmond Avenue,
Zip 77082–2499; tel. 281/558–3444 **A**1 10 **F**3 11 12 13 15 18 20 22 24 26 28
29 31 39 40 42 45 46 47 48 49 50 51 56 57 59 60 64 70 73 74 75 76 77 78
79 80 81 82 85 90 93 96 98 102 103 107 110 111 115 116 117 118 119 121
124 126 129 130 132 145 146 147 148 149 **S** HCA Healthcare, Nashville, TN
Primary Contact: Megan Marietta, Chief Executive Officer
COO: Philip Morris, Chief Operating Officer
CFO: Stanley K Nord, Chief Financial Officer
CMO: Magdy Rizk M.D., Chief of Staff
CIO: Sergio Almeida, Director Information Systems
CHR: Carol Melville, Director Human Resources
Web address: www.westhoustonmedical.com
Control: Partnership, Investor–owned (for–profit) **Service:** General medical and
surgical

Staffed Beds: 252 **Admissions:** 12823 **Census:** 184 **Outpatient Visits:**
109827 **Births:** 2981 **Total Expense ($000):** 202748 **Payroll Expense
($000):** 83944 **Personnel:** 1053

TX

Hospital, Medicare Provider Number, Address, Telephone, Approval, Facility, and Physician Codes, Health Care System

★ American Hospital Association (AHA) membership ○ Healthcare Facilities Accreditation Program ⇑ Center for Improvement in Healthcare Quality Accreditation
□ The Joint Commission accreditation ◇ DNV Healthcare Inc. accreditation △ Commission on Accreditation of Rehabilitation Facilities (CARF) accreditation

□ **WEST OAKS HOSPITAL (454026)**, 6500 Hornwood Drive, Zip 77074–5095;
tel. 713/995–0909 **A**1 5 10 **F**5 29 54 56 64 68 98 99 100 101 103 104 105
132 **S** Universal Health Services, Inc., King of Prussia, PA
Primary Contact: Mandy Westerman, Chief Executive Officer
CFO: Rob Tyler, Chief Financial Officer
CMO: Vernon Walling M.D., Executive Medical Director
CIO: James Harmon, Network Administrator
CHR: Janice Webster, Director Human Resources
CNO: Israel Ahaine, Chief Nursing Officer
Web address: www.westoakshospital.com
Control: Corporation, Investor–owned (for–profit) **Service**: Psychiatric

Staffed Beds: 144 Admissions: 5668 Census: 125 Outpatient Visits:
15730 **Births: 0 Total Expense ($000): 26504 Payroll Expense ($000):**
15533 **Personnel: 308**

★ ⇑ **WESTSIDE SURGICAL HOSPITAL**, 4200 Twelve Oaks Drive, Zip 77027;
tel. 713/621–5010 **A**21 **F**3 15 29 34 35 40 45 64 75 79 81 82 85 86 107 110
119 126 132 147 149 **P**7
Primary Contact: Jimmy Wells, Chief Nursing and Administrative Officer
Web address: www.westsidesurgical.net
Control: Corporation, Investor–owned (for–profit) **Service**: Surgical

Staffed Beds: 12 Admissions: 338 Census: 4 Outpatient Visits: 3916
Births: 0 Total Expense ($000): 27683 Payroll Expense ($000): 7324
Personnel: 96

⊞ **WOMAN'S HOSPITAL OF TEXAS (450674)**, 7600 Fannin Street, Zip 77054–1906;
tel. 713/790–1234 **A**1 3 5 10 **F**3 7 8 13 15 19 29 30 34 35 40 41 45 46 50 53
54 55 58 64 65 68 70 71 72 73 75 76 77 78 81 85 86 87 88 89 90 93 100 107
108 110 111 114 119 126 130 132 146 147 **S** HCA Healthcare, Nashville, TN
Primary Contact: Ashley McClellan, FACHE, Chief Executive Officer
CFO: Scott Bentley, Chief Financial Officer
CMO: Eberhard Lotze M.D., Chief Medical Officer
CIO: Emily Le, Director Information Technology and Services
CHR: Arnita Crawford, Director Human Resources
CNO: Holley Tyler R.N., Chief Nursing Officer
Web address: www.womanshospital.com
Control: Partnership, Investor–owned (for–profit) **Service**: Obstetrics and
gynecology

Staffed Beds: 345 Admissions: 17121 Census: 251 Outpatient Visits:
61080 **Births: 11321 Total Expense ($000): 225956 Payroll Expense**
($000): 107694 Personnel: 1209

HUMBLE—Harris County

⊞ **HEALTHSOUTH REHABILITATION HOSPITAL OF HUMBLE, LLC (453029)**,
19002 McKay Drive, Zip 77338–5701; tel. 281/446–6148 **A**1 10 **F**29 56 75
77 82 86 87 90 91 92 95 96 130 132 143 148 149 **P**5 **S** HEALTHSOUTH
Corporation, Birmingham, AL
Primary Contact: Angela L. Simmons, Chief Executive Officer
CFO: Sheila Shepard, Controller
CMO: Emile Mathurin M.D., Jr, Medical Director
CHR: Christy Dixon, Chief Human Resources Officer
CNO: Christie Griffin–Jones R.N., Chief Nursing Officer
Web address: www.healthsouthhumble.com
Control: Corporation, Investor–owned (for–profit) **Service**: Rehabilitation

Staffed Beds: 60 Admissions: 971 Census: 35 Outpatient Visits: 0 Births: 0
Total Expense ($000): 11255 Payroll Expense ($000): 8255 Personnel: 162

⊞ **ICON HOSPITAL (452112)**, 19211 McKay Boulevard, Zip 77338–5502;
tel. 281/883–5500 **A**1 10 **F**1 3 29 40 45 57 64 75 77 82 85 107 114 119 130
146 148 **P**8
Primary Contact: Tony Bonilla, Chief Executive Officer
Web address: www.iconhospitalonline.com/
Control: Partnership, Investor–owned (for–profit) **Service**: Acute long–term care
hospital

Staffed Beds: 32 Admissions: 343 Census: 19 Outpatient Visits: 282
Births: 0 Total Expense ($000): 13857 Payroll Expense ($000): 5906
Personnel: 92

⊞ **KINDRED REHABILITATION HOSPITAL NORTHEAST HOUSTON (673051)**,
18839 McKay Boulevard, Zip 77338–5721; tel. 281/964–6600 **A**1 10 **F**3 29 64
77 90 91 93 130 148 149
Primary Contact: Tracy Wilson, Chief Executive Officer
CFO: Cheryl Csepke, Controller
CMO: Helen Schilling M.D., Medical Director
CHR: Stephanie Williams, Coordinator Human Resources
CNO: Albert J. Chapple R.N., Chief Clinical Officer
Web address: www.khrehabnortheasthouston.com
Control: Corporation, Investor–owned (for–profit) **Service**: Rehabilitation

Staffed Beds: 46 Admissions: 582 Census: 13 Outpatient Visits: 3872
Births: 0 Total Expense ($000): 13158 Payroll Expense ($000): 5583
Personnel: 106

⊞ **MEMORIAL HERMANN NORTHEAST (450684)**, 18951 North Memorial Drive,
Zip 77338–4297; tel. 281/540–7700 **A**1 2 3 5 10 **F**3 11 13 15 18 20 22 24
26 29 30 31 34 35 40 42 44 45 46 49 53 54 57 59 64 65 68 70 72 73 74 75
76 77 78 79 80 81 84 85 87 91 93 100 107 108 109 111 114 115 119 120
121 126 129 130 131 132 135 146 147 148 **P**5 6 **S** Memorial Hermann Health
System, Houston, TX
Primary Contact: Josh Urban, Chief Executive Officer
CFO: Rebecca Tucker, Chief Financial Officer
CMO: Susan Curling M.D., Chief Medical Officer
CHR: Monica Baisden, Director Human Resources
CNO: Linda Stephens R.N., Chief Nursing Officer
Web address: www.memorialhermann.org/locations/northeast/
Control: Other not–for–profit (including NFP Corporation) **Service**: General
medical and surgical

Staffed Beds: 218 Admissions: 12085 Census: 153 Outpatient Visits:
125798 **Births: 1446 Total Expense ($000): 220438 Payroll Expense**
($000): 78502 Personnel: 902

HUNTSVILLE—Walker County

⊞ **HUNTSVILLE MEMORIAL HOSPITAL (450347)**, 110 Memorial Hospital Drive,
Zip 77340–4940, Mailing Address: P.O.Box 4001, 77342–4001; tel. 936/291–
3411 **A**1 10 **F**3 8 11 12 13 15 18 20 22 26 28 29 32 34 35 40 42 43 45 46 47
49 50 53 54 57 59 60 64 65 66 67 68 70 74 75 76 77 79 81 82 85 86 87 89
90 91 92 93 96 97 102 107 108 110 111 114 115 119 126 127 130 131 132
135 146 147 148 149 150
Primary Contact: Shannon Brown, Chief Executive Officer
CFO: Guy Gyros, Chief Financial Officer
CIO: Raul Velez, Director Information Systems
CHR: Brenda Ray, Director Human Resources
CNO: Sheila Ard, Chief Nursing Officer
Web address: www.huntsvillememorial.com
Control: Other not–for–profit (including NFP Corporation) **Service**: General
medical and surgical

Staffed Beds: 98 Admissions: 4703 Census: 55 Outpatient Visits: 106558
Births: 450 Total Expense ($000): 88058 Payroll Expense ($000): 33232
Personnel: 521

IRAAN—Pecos County

IRAAN GENERAL HOSPITAL (451307), 600 349 North, Zip 79744, Mailing
Address: P.O.Box 665, 79744–0665; tel. 432/639–2871 **A**10 18 **F**28 40 43 56
57 59 64 65 75 86 93 104 107 119 127 130 133
Primary Contact: Teresa Callahan, R.N., MSN, Chief Executive Officer
CFO: Tami Burks, Chief Fiscal Services
CMO: Robert W Garcia M.D., Chief Medical Officer
CHR: Cathy Tucker, Director Human Resources
Web address: www.igh–hospital.com
Control: Hospital district or authority, Government, Nonfederal **Service**: General
medical and surgical

Staffed Beds: 14 Admissions: 99 Census: 2 Outpatient Visits: 7813 Births: 0
Total Expense ($000): 9402 Payroll Expense ($000): 3769 Personnel: 57

IRVING—Dallas County

⊞ **BAYLOR SCOTT & WHITE MEDICAL CENTER–IRVING (450079)**, 1901 North
MacArthur Boulevard, Zip 75061–2220; tel. 972/579–8100 **A**1 2 3 5 10 **F**3 8 11
13 15 17 18 20 22 24 26 28 29 30 31 34 35 40 45 46 47 49 54 55 57 58 59
64 65 66 67 70 73 74 75 76 77 78 79 80 81 82 84 85 86 87 90 93 94 100
107 108 110 111 114 115 116 117 118 119 120 121 122 126 129 130 141
143 146 147 148 149 150 **S** Baylor Scott & White Health, Dallas, TX
Primary Contact: Cindy K. Schamp, FACHE, President
CFO: Steve Roussel, Vice President Finance
CMO: Jeffrey Embrey M.D., Chief Medical Officer
CIO: Tim Huffman, Western Region Director, Information Systems Business
Relationships
CHR: Vonetta Fuller–Williams, Director Human Resources Strategic and Business
Services
Web address: www.bswhealth.com
Control: Other not–for–profit (including NFP Corporation) **Service**: General
medical and surgical

Staffed Beds: 233 Admissions: 11025 Census: 143 Outpatient Visits:
98908 **Births: 2055 Total Expense ($000): 219571 Payroll Expense**
($000): 76891 Personnel: 751

TX

Many Facility Codes have changed. Please refer to the AHA Guide Code Chart. © 2017 AHA Guide

☐ **BAYLOR SURGICAL HOSPITAL AT LAS COLINAS (450874)**, 400 West Interstate 635, Zip 75063; tel. 972/868–4000 **A**1 10 **F**3 29 30 40 51 79 81 87 99 100 101 102 103 107 111 119 130 **S** United Surgical Partners International, Addison, TX
Primary Contact: Deonna Unell, Chief Executive Officer
CFO: Gabrielle Holland, Chief Financial Officer
CMO: Scott McGraw M.D., Medical Director
Web address: www.baylorhealth.com/About/Community/Assessments/West/ICSH/Pages/Default.aspx
Control: Partnership, Investor–owned (for–profit) **Service**: General medical and surgical

Staffed Beds: 12 **Admissions**: 849 **Census**: 4 **Outpatient Visits**: 8487 **Births**: 0 **Total Expense ($000)**: 44143 **Payroll Expense ($000)**: 9045 **Personnel**: 186

☒ **MEDICAL CITY LAS COLINAS (450822)**, 6800 North MacArthur Boulevard, Zip 75039–2422; tel. 972/969–2000 **A**1 10 **F**3 8 13 15 18 20 22 24 29 30 31 34 35 37 40 45 46 47 48 49 50 57 59 60 64 68 70 72 74 75 76 77 78 79 81 87 93 100 102 107 108 110 111 114 118 119 126 129 130 147 148 149 **S** HCA Healthcare, Nashville, TN
Primary Contact: Daniela Decell, Chief Executive Officer
COO: Chip Zahn, Chief Operating Officer
CFO: Nick Galt, Chief Financial Officer
Web address: www.lascolinasmedical.com
Control: Corporation, Investor–owned (for–profit) **Service**: General medical and surgical

Staffed Beds: 90 **Admissions**: 4908 **Census**: 47 **Outpatient Visits**: 55291 **Births**: 1670 **Total Expense ($000)**: 77730 **Payroll Expense ($000)**: 26319 **Personnel**: 323

JACKSBORO—Jack County

FAITH COMMUNITY HOSPITAL (450241), 215 Chisholm Trail, Zip 76458–1111; tel. 940/567–6633 **A**10 20 **F**7 11 13 15 28 34 35 40 43 45 57 59 75 76 77 81 93 97 107 114 119 127 130 133 149 **P**6
Primary Contact: Frank Beaman, Chief Executive Officer
COO: Kim Lee, Chief Operating Officer
CFO: Bonnie Blevins R.N., Chief Financial Officer
CMO: Sushil Chokshi M.D., Chief Medical Officer
CIO: Troy McKenzie, Chief information Officer
CHR: Deborah White, Human Resource Coordinator
CNO: Joy Henry R.N., Director Nurses
Web address: www.fchtexas.com
Control: Hospital district or authority, Government, Nonfederal **Service**: General medical and surgical

Staffed Beds: 17 **Admissions**: 230 **Census**: 2 **Outpatient Visits**: 45898 **Births**: 77 **Total Expense ($000)**: 19569 **Payroll Expense ($000)**: 5908 **Personnel**: 134

JACKSONVILLE—Cherokee County

☒ **CHRISTUS MOTHER FRANCES HOSPITAL – JACKSONVILLE (451319)**, 2026 South Jackson, Zip 75766–5822; tel. 903/541–4500 **A**1 10 18 **F**3 15 18 29 30 32 34 35 40 43 45 50 53 56 57 59 64 65 68 79 81 82 85 93 97 107 108 110 111 114 119 129 130 133 145 147 **P**5 6 7 8 **S** CHRISTUS Health, Irving, TX
Primary Contact: Anne Pileggi, Administrator and Associate Vice President
CFO: Elizabeth Pulliam, Chief Financial Officer
CMO: Jane Ragland, President Medical Staff
CIO: Jeff Pearson, Chief Information Officer
CHR: Marsha Ballard, Human Resources
CNO: Jamie Maddox, Chief Nursing Officer
Web address: www.tmfhs.org/jacksonville
Control: Other not–for–profit (including NFP Corporation) **Service**: General medical and surgical

Staffed Beds: 21 **Admissions**: 652 **Census**: 10 **Outpatient Visits**: 70180 **Births**: 0 **Total Expense ($000)**: 34939 **Payroll Expense ($000)**: 8649 **Personnel**: 175

☒ **EAST TEXAS MEDICAL CENTER JACKSONVILLE (450194)**, 501 South Ragsdale Street, Zip 75766–2413; tel. 903/541–5000 **A**1 10 20 **F**3 8 11 13 15 18 26 29 34 35 39 40 43 45 50 57 59 64 65 70 75 76 79 81 82 85 97 107 108 110 111 115 119 127 129 145 146 147 148 **S** East Texas Medical Center Regional Healthcare System, Tyler, TX
Primary Contact: Ruth Cook, R.N., FACHE, MSN, Administrator
CMO: Todd Parrish M.D., Chief of Staff
CHR: Elysia Epperson, Director Human Resources
CNO: Jana Bateman R.N., Chief Nursing Officer
Web address: www.etmc.org
Control: Other not–for–profit (including NFP Corporation) **Service**: General medical and surgical

Staffed Beds: 38 **Admissions**: 1541 **Census**: 12 **Outpatient Visits**: 83877 **Births**: 418 **Total Expense ($000)**: 33665 **Payroll Expense ($000)**: 9997 **Personnel**: 175

JASPER—Jasper County

☒ **CHRISTUS SOUTHEAST TEXAS JASPER MEMORIAL (450573)**, 1275 Marvin Hancock Drive, Zip 75951–4995; tel. 409/384–5461 **A**1 10 **F**3 11 13 15 29 30 34 40 43 50 51 57 59 64 70 76 77 79 81 82 89 107 110 111 114 119 127 130 135 146 149 **P**8 **S** CHRISTUS Health, Irving, TX
Primary Contact: Lance Beus, Administrator
COO: Mark Durand, Assistant Administrator Operations
CFO: Nikki Martin, Chief Financial Officer
CIO: Robert Jacobs, Regional Information Management Executive
CHR: Kay Powell, Director Human Resources
Web address: www.christusjasper.org
Control: Church operated, Nongovernment, not–for–profit **Service**: General medical and surgical

Staffed Beds: 40 **Admissions**: 1366 **Census**: 10 **Outpatient Visits**: 91102 **Births**: 265 **Total Expense ($000)**: 25819 **Payroll Expense ($000)**: 9620 **Personnel**: 146

JOURDANTON—Atascosa County

☒ **METHODIST HOSPITAL SOUTH (450165)**, 1905 Highway 97 East, Zip 78026–1504; tel. 830/769–3515 **A**1 10 20 **F**3 11 13 15 18 29 30 34 35 39 40 43 45 57 59 63 64 68 70 75 76 77 79 81 85 93 107 108 110 111 114 119 129 130 132 133 146 147 148 **P**6 **S** HCA Healthcare, Nashville, TN
Primary Contact: John E. Ulbricht, Chief Executive Officer
CFO: Gary Redmon, Chief Financial Officer
CIO: Rita S Castillo R.N., Chief Quality Officer and Risk Management
Web address: www.sahealth.com/locations/methodisthospitalsouth/
Control: Corporation, Investor–owned (for–profit) **Service**: General medical and surgical

Staffed Beds: 67 **Admissions**: 1640 **Census**: 15 **Outpatient Visits**: 34539 **Births**: 260 **Total Expense ($000)**: 34599 **Payroll Expense ($000)**: 13177 **Personnel**: 222

JUNCTION—Kimble County

KIMBLE HOSPITAL (451306), 349 Reid Road, Zip 76849–3049; tel. 325/446–3321 **A**10 18 **F**3 34 35 40 43 45 56 57 59 65 66 75 93 97 107 114 127 133 146 149 **S** Preferred Management Corporation, Shawnee, OK
Primary Contact: William Barnes, Administrator
COO: Teena Hagood, Chief Nursing Officer
CFO: Larry Stephens, Chief Financial Officer
CMO: Ben Udall M.D., Chief of Staff
CIO: Anna Henry, Chief Information Officer
CHR: Hope Lamb, Manager Human Resources
Web address: www.kimblehospital.org/
Control: Corporation, Investor–owned (for–profit) **Service**: General medical and surgical

Staffed Beds: 15 **Admissions**: 95 **Census**: 1 **Outpatient Visits**: 8299 **Births**: 0 **Total Expense ($000)**: 7075 **Payroll Expense ($000)**: 3023 **Personnel**: 71

TX

Hospital, Medicare Provider Number, Address, Telephone, Approval, Facility, and Physician Codes, Health Care System

★ American Hospital Association (AHA) membership ○ Healthcare Facilities Accreditation Program ⇑ Center for Improvement in Healthcare Quality Accreditation
☐ The Joint Commission accreditation ◇ DNV Healthcare Inc. accreditation △ Commission on Accreditation of Rehabilitation Facilities (CARF) accreditation

KATY—Harris County

⇑ **CHRISTUS ST. CATHERINE HOSPITAL** See Houston Methodist St. Catherine Hospital

★ ⇑ **HOUSTON METHODIST ST. CATHERINE HOSPITAL (452118)**, 701 Fry Road, Zip 77450–2255; tel. 281/599–5700 **A**10 21 **F**1 29 30 35 36 68 75 82 84 86 87 130 132 149 150 **S** Houston Methodist, Houston, TX
Primary Contact: Gary L. Kempf, R.N., Administrator
CFO: Nancy Brock, Chief Financial Officer
CHR: James A Fitch, Director Human Resources
Web address: www.houstonmethodist.org/katy–st–catherine–hospital
Control: Other not–for–profit (including NFP Corporation) **Service:** Acute long–term care hospital

Staffed Beds: 44 **Admissions:** 530 **Census:** 32 **Outpatient Visits:** 0 **Births:** 0 **Total Expense ($000):** 32023 **Payroll Expense ($000):** 12166 **Personnel:** 192

✠ **MEMORIAL HERMANN KATY HOSPITAL (450847)**, 23900 Katy Freeway, Zip 77494–1323; tel. 281/644–7000 **A**1 2 3 5 10 **F**3 8 11 13 15 18 20 22 29 30 34 35 39 40 42 43 45 46 49 50 51 54 57 59 61 64 65 68 69 70 73 74 75 76 77 78 79 80 81 85 87 89 93 102 107 108 110 111 114 119 126 130 131 132 144 145 146 147 149 **P**1 5 6 **S** Memorial Hermann Health System, Houston, TX
Primary Contact: Heath Rushing, Senior Vice President and Chief Executive Officer
CFO: Linda Kulhanek, Chief Financial Officer
Web address: www.memorialhermann.org/locations/katy/
Control: Other not–for–profit (including NFP Corporation) **Service:** General medical and surgical

Staffed Beds: 203 **Admissions:** 9602 **Census:** 98 **Outpatient Visits:** 103668 **Births:** 2307 **Total Expense ($000):** 190310 **Payroll Expense ($000):** 66934 **Personnel:** 667

✠ **MEMORIAL HERMANN REHABILITATION HOSPITAL – KATY (673038)**, 21720 Kingsland Boulevard #102, Zip 77450–2550; **A**1 2 10 **F**3 29 30 64 79 90 92 93 107 111 114 119 129 130 131 148 **P**5 6 **S** Memorial Hermann Health System, Houston, TX
Primary Contact: Carl E. Josehart, Chief Executive Officer
COO: Mary Ann Euliarte R.N., Chief Operating Officer
CFO: Wayne Gordon, Chief Financial Officer
CMO: Shalin Patel M.D., Chief Medical Officer
CIO: David Bradshaw, Chief Information Officer
CHR: Joyce Williams, Consultant Human Resources and Organizational Development
CNO: Mary Ann Euliarte R.N., Chief Nursing Officer
Web address: www.oceanskaty.com/
Control: Partnership, Investor–owned (for–profit) **Service:** Rehabilitation

Staffed Beds: 35 **Admissions:** 597 **Census:** 25 **Outpatient Visits:** 13149 **Births:** 0 **Total Expense ($000):** 21226 **Payroll Expense ($000):** 9521 **Personnel:** 118

OCEANS BEHAVIORAL HOSPITAL KATY (454136), 455 Park Grove Lane, Zip 77450–1572; tel. 281/492–8888 **F**29 34 35 64 98 100 101 103 104 149 **S** Oceans Healthcare, Lake Charles, LA
Primary Contact: Stuart Archer, Chief Executive Officer
Web address: www.oceanskaty.com/
Control: Corporation, Investor–owned (for–profit) **Service:** Psychiatric

Staffed Beds: 48 **Admissions:** 857 **Census:** 33 **Outpatient Visits:** 12524 **Births:** 0 **Total Expense ($000):** 8965 **Payroll Expense ($000):** 3802 **Personnel:** 76

KAUFMAN—Kaufman County

✠ **TEXAS HEALTH PRESBYTERIAN HOSPITAL KAUFMAN (450292)**, 850 Ed Hall Drive, Zip 75142–1861, Mailing Address: P.O.Box 1108, 75142–5401; tel. 972/932–7200 **A**1 10 **F**3 11 15 18 29 30 34 35 40 43 45 53 57 59 64 65 68 70 75 79 81 82 85 86 87 93 100 102 107 108 111 115 118 119 130 132 146 149 **S** Texas Health Resources, Arlington, TX
Primary Contact: Patsy Youngs, President
CMO: Benjamin Bradshaw M.D., President Medical Staff
CHR: Mark J Rainey, Director Human Resources
CNO: Denise Claussen R.N., MSN, Chief Nursing Officer
Web address: www.texashealth.org/Kaufman
Control: Other not–for–profit (including NFP Corporation) **Service:** General medical and surgical

Staffed Beds: 37 **Admissions:** 1707 **Census:** 14 **Outpatient Visits:** 34168 **Births:** 101 **Total Expense ($000):** 36463 **Payroll Expense ($000):** 13621 **Personnel:** 188

KENEDY—Karnes County

★ **OTTO KAISER MEMORIAL HOSPITAL (451364)**, 3349 South Highway 181, Zip 78119–5247; tel. 830/583–3401 **A**10 18 **F**3 11 15 29 30 34 40 45 46 53 57 59 62 64 68 77 81 93 107 111 115 119 133 135 148 **P**8
Primary Contact: David Lee, Chief Executive Officer
CIO: Joseph Wiatrek, Director Information Technology
CHR: Christina Benavides, Director Employee Services
CNO: Vincent Sowell, Chief Nursing Officer
Web address: www.okmh.org/
Control: Hospital district or authority, Government, Nonfederal **Service:** General medical and surgical

Staffed Beds: 25 **Admissions:** 298 **Census:** 4 **Outpatient Visits:** 23427 **Births:** 0 **Total Expense ($000):** 19539 **Payroll Expense ($000):** 8138 **Personnel:** 132

KERMIT—Winkler County

WINKLER COUNTY MEMORIAL HOSPITAL (451314), 821 Jeffee Drive, Zip 79745–4696, Mailing Address: P.O.Box H, 79745–6008; tel. 432/586–5864 **A**10 18 **F**3 32 34 36 40 57 59 64 65 69 93 97 107 114 119 127 133
Primary Contact: Lorenzo Serrano, Chief Executive Officer
CFO: Wannah Hartley, Controller
CMO: K Pham M.D., Chief of Staff
CIO: Keith Palmer, Assistant Administrator
Control: County, Government, Nonfederal **Service:** General medical and surgical

Staffed Beds: 19 **Admissions:** 82 **Census:** 1 **Outpatient Visits:** 6576 **Births:** 0 **Total Expense ($000):** 8764 **Payroll Expense ($000):** 3504 **Personnel:** 73

KERRVILLE—Kerr County

KERRVILLE DIVISION See South Texas Veterans Health Care System, San Antonio

☐ **KERRVILLE STATE HOSPITAL (454014)**, 721 Thompson Drive, Zip 78028–5154; tel. 830/896–2211 **A**1 5 10 **F**11 30 34 39 44 50 56 65 68 75 86 87 97 98 101 103 130 132 135 146 149 **S** Texas Department of State Health Services, Austin, TX
Primary Contact: Leigh Ann Fitzpatrick, Superintendent
CFO: Laurie Harris, Chief Accountant
CMO: Matthew Faubion M.D., Clinical Director
CNO: Amanda McDonald MSN, Chief Nurse Executive
Web address: www.dshs.state.tx.us/mhhospitals/KerrvilleSH/default.shtm
Control: State, Government, Nonfederal **Service:** Psychiatric

Staffed Beds: 202 **Admissions:** 65 **Census:** 191 **Outpatient Visits:** 0 **Births:** 0 **Total Expense ($000):** 24676 **Payroll Expense ($000):** 16329 **Personnel:** 552

✠ **PETERSON REGIONAL MEDICAL CENTER (450007)**, 551 Hill Country Drive, Zip 78028–6085; tel. 830/896–4200 **A**1 10 **F**3 8 11 13 15 18 20 22 26 28 29 30 31 34 35 39 40 44 45 49 51 54 57 59 62 63 64 65 68 70 74 75 76 77 78 79 81 82 84 85 86 87 90 93 96 97 100 107 110 111 114 115 118 119 126 130 131 132 135 144 145 146 147 148 **P**7 8
Primary Contact: J. Patrick. Murray, FACHE, President and Chief Executive Officer
COO: J. Stephen Pautler FACHE, Chief Operating Officer
CFO: Lisa Medovich, Chief Financial Officer
CMO: Thomas Ducker M.D., Chief of Staff
CIO: Richard Cruthirds, Director Information Systems
CHR: Buddy Volpe, Director Human Resources
CNO: Kaeli Dressler R.N., MSN, Chief Nursing Officer
Web address: www.petersonhealth.com
Control: Other not–for–profit (including NFP Corporation) **Service:** General medical and surgical

Staffed Beds: 124 **Admissions:** 4785 **Census:** 60 **Outpatient Visits:** 139160 **Births:** 504 **Total Expense ($000):** 117145 **Payroll Expense ($000):** 50245 **Personnel:** 870

KILGORE—Gregg County

★ ⇑ **ALLEGIANCE SPECIALTY HOSPITAL OF KILGORE (450488)**, 1612 South Henderson Boulevard, Zip 75662–3594; tel. 903/984–3505 **A**10 21 **F**3 29 34 35 54 56 59 75 86 87 98 100 101 103 104 130 **S** Allegiance Health Management, Shreveport, LA
Primary Contact: Karen Ross, Chief Executive Officer
CHR: Michelle Yarbrough, Coordinator Human Resources
CNO: Jackie McDonald, Chief Nursing Officer
Web address: www.ahmgt.com
Control: Corporation, Investor–owned (for–profit) **Service:** Psychiatric

Staffed Beds: 60 **Admissions:** 343 **Census:** 14 **Outpatient Visits:** 12435 **Births:** 0 **Total Expense ($000):** 7867 **Payroll Expense ($000):** 4069 **Personnel:** 94

TX

Many Facility Codes have changed. Please refer to the AHA Guide Code Chart. © 2017 AHA Guide

KILLEEN—Bell County

⊞ **METROPLEX ADVENTIST HOSPITAL (450152)**, 2201 South Clear Creek Road, Zip 76549–4110; tel. 254/526–7523 **A**1 3 10 **F**3 8 11 12 13 15 18 20 22 26 28 29 30 34 35 39 40 43 45 46 48 49 54 57 59 62 65 68 70 71 74 75 76 77 78 79 81 82 83 85 86 87 89 91 93 98 99 100 101 102 103 104 105 107 108 110 111 114 115 118 119 129 130 131 132 135 146 147 148 **P**8 **S** Adventist Health System Sunbelt Health Care Corporation, Altamonte Springs, FL
Primary Contact: Carlyle L E. Walton, FACHE, Chief Executive Officer
CFO: Penny Johnson, Chief Financial Officer
CMO: Frederick Barnett M.D., Chief of Staff
CIO: Dale Koebnick, Director Management Information Systems and Patient Access
CHR: Brenda Coley, Executive Director
Web address: www.mplex.org
Control: Church operated, Nongovernment, not–for–profit **Service:** General medical and surgical

Staffed Beds: 177 **Admissions:** 5890 **Census:** 64 **Outpatient Visits:** 89905 **Births:** 1083 **Total Expense ($000):** 108839 **Payroll Expense ($000):** 44629 **Personnel:** 779

KINGSVILLE—Kleberg County

⊞ **CHRISTUS SPOHN HOSPITAL KLEBERG (450163)**, 1311 General Cavazos Boulevard, Zip 78363–7130; tel. 361/595–1661 **A**1 10 20 **F**3 11 13 15 28 29 30 34 35 40 43 53 54 57 59 64 65 70 75 76 77 79 81 85 86 87 89 93 102 108 110 111 115 119 130 146 **P**8 **S** CHRISTUS Health, Irving, TX
Primary Contact: David LeMonte, Vice President and Chief Operating Officer
CFO: Jessica Pena, Manager Finance
CHR: Mindy Soliz, Director Human Resource Strategy
CNO: LieutenantLaci Lasater R.N., Chief Nursing Officer
Web address: www.christusspohn.org
Control: Church operated, Nongovernment, not–for–profit **Service:** General medical and surgical

Staffed Beds: 50 **Admissions:** 2733 **Census:** 33 **Outpatient Visits:** 36469 **Births:** 274 **Total Expense ($000):** 36799 **Payroll Expense ($000):** 14314 **Personnel:** 200

KINGWOOD—Harris County

☐ **KINGWOOD PINES HOSPITAL (454103)**, 2001 Ladbrook Drive, Zip 77339–3004; tel. 281/404–1001 **A**1 10 **F**4 5 75 86 87 98 99 101 102 103 104 105 130 132 149 **S** Universal Health Services, Inc., King of Prussia, PA
Primary Contact: Shanti Carter, Chief Executive Officer
COO: Grey Mc Kellar, Chief Operating Officer and Director of Performance Improvement and Risk
CFO: Sharon Corum, Chief Financial Officer
CMO: Javier Ruiz M.D., Medical Director
CNO: Kim Wheeler R.N., Director of Nursing
Web address: www.kingwoodpines.com
Control: Corporation, Investor–owned (for–profit) **Service:** Psychiatric

Staffed Beds: 75 **Admissions:** 4099 **Census:** 93 **Outpatient Visits:** 3602 **Births:** 0 **Total Expense ($000):** 22001 **Payroll Expense ($000):** 10887 **Personnel:** 198

KINGWOOD—Montgomery County

⊞ ⇑ **KINGWOOD MEDICAL CENTER (450775)**, 22999 U S Highway 59 North, Zip 77339; tel. 281/348–8000 **A**1 10 21 **F**3 13 15 18 19 20 22 24 26 28 29 31 34 35 40 41 42 45 46 49 57 58 59 67 70 72 74 76 78 79 81 85 86 87 89 90 96 107 108 110 111 114 115 119 126 130 132 146 147 **P**7 **S** HCA Healthcare, Nashville, TN
Primary Contact: Melinda Stephenson, Chief Executive Officer
CFO: Daniel E Davis, Chief Financial Officer
CMO: Eugene Ogrod M.D., Chief Medical Officer
CNO: Kevin Manning, Chief Nursing Officer
Web address: www.kingwoodmedical.com
Control: Corporation, Investor–owned (for–profit) **Service:** General medical and surgical

Staffed Beds: 358 **Admissions:** 17677 **Census:** 259 **Outpatient Visits:** 122756 **Births:** 2729 **Total Expense ($000):** 228533 **Payroll Expense ($000):** 88394 **Personnel:** 1359

KINGWOOD SPECIALTY HOSPITAL See Memorial Hermann Surgical Hospital Kingwood

☐ **MEMORIAL HERMANN SURGICAL HOSPITAL KINGWOOD (670005)**, 300 Kingwood Medical Drive, Zip 77339–6400; tel. 281/312–4000 **A**1 10 **F**3 29 40 45 64 79 81 82 85 86 87 111
Primary Contact: Teal A. Holden, Chief Executive Officer
CFO: Jay Michael Gomez, Chief Financial Officer
CNO: Shawna Fugler R.N., Chief Nursing Officer
Web address: www.memorialhermannkingwood.com
Control: Partnership, Investor–owned (for–profit) **Service:** Surgical

Staffed Beds: 10 **Admissions:** 245 **Census:** 1 **Outpatient Visits:** 9240 **Births:** 0 **Total Expense ($000):** 24908 **Payroll Expense ($000):** 5294 **Personnel:** 99

KNOX CITY—Knox County

KNOX COUNTY HOSPITAL (450746), 701 South Fifth Street, Zip 79529–2107, Mailing Address: P.O.Box 608, 79529–0608; tel. 940/657–3535 **A**10 20 **F**7 11 28 33 34 35 40 43 57 59 62 127 130 133 149 **P**6
Primary Contact: Stephen A. Kuehler, Administrator
CFO: Dan Offutt, Manager Finance
CMO: Ezekiel Duke M.D., Chief of Staff
CNO: Sheila Kuehler R.N., Director of Nursing
Web address: www.knoxcountyhospital–texas.com
Control: Hospital district or authority, Government, Nonfederal **Service:** General medical and surgical

Staffed Beds: 14 **Admissions:** 85 **Census:** 1 **Outpatient Visits:** 31373 **Births:** 0 **Total Expense ($000):** 6701 **Payroll Expense ($000):** 3087 **Personnel:** 75

KYLE—Hays County

⊞ **SETON MEDICAL CENTER HAYS (670056)**, 6001 Kyle Parkway, Zip 78640–6112, Mailing Address: 6001 Kyle Prkway, 78640–6112; tel. 512/504–5000 **A**1 3 5 10 **F**3 11 13 15 18 20 22 24 28 29 30 31 34 35 40 43 44 45 46 49 50 57 59 60 64 65 68 70 72 74 75 76 77 78 79 81 82 84 85 87 93 107 108 110 111 114 115 118 119 129 130 131 135 146 148 **P**3 8 **S** Ascension Healthcare, Saint Louis, MO
Primary Contact: Christopher L. Hartle, President
COO: Neal Kelley, Vice President and Chief Operating Officer
Web address: www.seton.net/locations/seton_medical_center_hays/
Control: Church operated, Nongovernment, not–for–profit **Service:** General medical and surgical

Staffed Beds: 112 **Admissions:** 6676 **Census:** 79 **Outpatient Visits:** 55958 **Births:** 1052 **Total Expense ($000):** 124430 **Payroll Expense ($000):** 35988 **Personnel:** 454

★ **WARM SPRINGS REHABILITATION HOSPITAL OF KYLE (673057)**, 5980 Kyle Parkway, Zip 78640–2400; tel. 512/262–0821 **F**3 29 74 75 79 90 91 93 96 130 131 132 148 **S** Post Acute Medical, LLC, Enola, PA
Primary Contact: Duke Saldivar, FACHE, Chief Executive Officer
Web address: www.warmsprings.org/our–facilities/outpatient–rehabilitation/warm–springs–rehabilitation–center–kyle/
Control: Corporation, Investor–owned (for–profit) **Service:** Rehabilitation

Staffed Beds: 36 **Admissions:** 820 **Census:** 27 **Outpatient Visits:** 13330 **Births:** 0 **Total Expense ($000):** 13990 **Payroll Expense ($000):** 6385 **Personnel:** 143

LA GRANGE—Fayette County

★ **ST. MARK'S MEDICAL CENTER (670004)**, One St Mark's Place, Zip 78945; tel. 979/242–2200 **A**5 10 **F**3 8 11 12 13 15 29 30 34 40 43 45 50 56 57 59 68 70 74 75 76 79 81 82 84 85 87 89 93 107 110 111 114 119 128 129 130 133 145 146 147 **P**6 **S** Community Hospital Corporation, Plano, TX
Primary Contact: Rick J. Montelongo, Chief Executive Officer
COO: Carol Drozd, Chief Operating Officer
CFO: Dennis Boyd, Chief Financial Officer
CMO: Russell Juno M.D., Chief of Staff
CHR: Tammy Oehlke, Director Human Resources
Web address: www.smmctx.org
Control: Other not–for–profit (including NFP Corporation) **Service:** General medical and surgical

Staffed Beds: 65 **Admissions:** 1500 **Census:** 13 **Outpatient Visits:** 49733 **Births:** 205 **Total Expense ($000):** 32184 **Payroll Expense ($000):** 12401 **Personnel:** 187

TX

LAKE JACKSON—Brazoria County

✠ **CHI ST. LUKE'S HEALTH BRAZOSPORT (450072)**, 100 Medical Drive, Zip 77566–5674; tel. 979/297–4411 **A**1 10 **F**3 11 13 15 18 20 22 28 29 30 31 34 37 40 41 43 45 47 48 49 50 51 54 57 59 60 62 64 65 68 70 74 75 76 78 79 81 82 85 86 87 89 90 91 93 94 107 108 110 111 114 117 118 119 120 121 123 129 130 131 132 146 147 148 149 **P**8 **S** Catholic Health Initiatives, Englewood, CO
Primary Contact: Al Guevara Jr, FACHE, President
CFO: Chuck Jeffress, Vice President Fiscal Services
CMO: Michael Gilliand M.D., Chief of Staff
CIO: Todd Edwards, Director Information Management Systems
CHR: Christopher Calia, Vice President Human Resources
CNO: Shannon Haltom, Vice President, Patient Care Services
Web address: www.chistlukesbrazosport.org
Control: Other not–for–profit (including NFP Corporation) **Service**: General medical and surgical

Staffed Beds: 103 **Admissions**: 4329 **Census**: 50 **Outpatient Visits**: 124453 **Births**: 455 **Total Expense ($000)**: 80194 **Payroll Expense ($000)**: 32146 **Personnel**: 602

LAKEWAY—Travis County

✠ △ **VIBRA REHABILITATION HOSPITAL LAKE TRAVIS (673058)**, 2000 Medical Drive, Zip 78734–4200; tel. 512/263–4500 **A**1 7 **F**3 29 90 91 96 119 148 **S** Vibra Healthcare, Mechanicsburg, PA
Primary Contact: Deborah Hopps, R.N., FACHE, Chief Executive Officer
CMO: Maria Elena Arizmendez M.D., Medical Director
CHR: Debbie Belcher, Director Human Resource
CNO: Ramon Austria R.N., Chief Nursing Officer
Web address: www.vrhlaketravis.com
Control: Corporation, Investor–owned (for–profit) **Service**: Rehabilitation

Staffed Beds: 36 **Admissions**: 669 **Census**: 22 **Outpatient Visits**: 0 **Births**: 0 **Total Expense ($000)**: 12997 **Payroll Expense ($000)**: 5533 **Personnel**: 115

LAMESA—Dawson County

MEDICAL ARTS HOSPITAL (450489), 2200 North Bryan Avenue, Zip 79331–2451; tel. 806/872–2183 **A**10 20 **F**3 7 11 13 29 30 35 40 43 45 50 57 59 62 63 64 75 76 81 87 97 107 111 115 119 127 128 130 133 146 148 **P**6
Primary Contact: Letha Stokes, Chief Executive Officer
COO: Jo Beth Smith, Chief Operating Officer
CFO: Jeff Weaver, Chief Financial Officer
CMO: Michael Sprys D.O., Chief of Staff
CHR: Traci Brown, Human Resources Generalist
CNO: Heidi Cobb R.N., Chief Nursing Officer
Web address: www.medicalartshospital.org
Control: Hospital district or authority, Government, Nonfederal **Service**: General medical and surgical

Staffed Beds: 22 **Admissions**: 384 **Census**: 3 **Outpatient Visits**: 81563 **Births**: 134 **Total Expense ($000)**: 23498 **Payroll Expense ($000)**: 9348 **Personnel**: 199

LAMPASAS—Lampasas County

✠ **ROLLINS–BROOK COMMUNITY HOSPITAL (451323)**, 608 North Key Avenue, Zip 76550–1106, Mailing Address: P.O.Box 589, 76550–0032; tel. 512/556–3682 **A**1 10 18 **F**3 8 15 29 35 40 43 45 46 61 81 85 87 93 97 107 110 111 114 119 130 131 133 146 **P**4 **S** Adventist Health System Sunbelt Health Care Corporation, Altamonte Springs, FL
Primary Contact: Ashley Underwood, FACHE, Chief Executive Officer
CFO: Robert Brock, Chief Financial Officer and Vice President
CMO: Don Daniels M.D., Chief Medical Officer
CIO: Carl Elkins, Director Information Technology
CHR: Brenda Coley, Executive Director
CNO: Tammy Rodriguez, Vice President of Patient Care Services
Web address: www.mplex.org
Control: Church operated, Nongovernment, not–for–profit **Service**: General medical and surgical

Staffed Beds: 35 **Admissions**: 603 **Census**: 9 **Outpatient Visits**: 15066 **Births**: 0 **Total Expense ($000)**: 14925 **Payroll Expense ($000)**: 4893 **Personnel**: 84

LANCASTER—Dallas County

⇑ **CRESCENT MEDICAL CENTER LANCASTER (670090)**, 2600 West Pleasant Run Road, Zip 75146–1114; tel. 972/230–8888 **A**10 21 **F**3 29 30 34 40 51 57 60 64 68 70 77 79 81 82 85 104 107 108 111 114 119 129 130 143 148
Primary Contact: Khalid Mahmood, M.D., President and Chairman
Web address: www.cmcl.us/
Control: Partnership, Investor–owned (for–profit) **Service**: General medical and surgical

Staffed Beds: 23 **Admissions**: 397 **Census**: 4 **Outpatient Visits**: 15633 **Births**: 2 **Total Expense ($000)**: 30165 **Payroll Expense ($000)**: 10730 **Personnel**: 168

LAREDO—Webb County

☐ **DOCTORS HOSPITAL OF LAREDO (450643)**, 10700 McPherson Road, Zip 78045–6268; tel. 956/523–2000 **A**1 2 10 **F**3 11 12 13 15 18 20 22 24 26 28 29 31 32 34 35 37 39 40 42 43 45 48 49 50 54 57 59 60 63 64 70 71 72 74 75 76 77 78 79 81 85 87 89 90 91 93 107 108 111 115 119 121 126 129 130 132 146 147 148 **P**5 7 **S** Universal Health Services, Inc., King of Prussia, PA
Primary Contact: James R. Resendez, Chief Executive Officer
COO: Raymond Ramos FACHE, Chief Operating Officer
CFO: Faraz Khan, Chief Financial Officer
CMO: Santiago Gutierrez M.D., Chief Medical Officer
CIO: Maribel Mata, Director Information Services
CHR: Roseann Figueroa, Director Human Resources
CNO: Daman Mott MSN, Chief Nursing Officer
Web address: www.doctorshoslaredo.com
Control: Partnership, Investor–owned (for–profit) **Service**: General medical and surgical

Staffed Beds: 183 **Admissions**: 7903 **Census**: 111 **Outpatient Visits**: 126091 **Births**: 2139 **Total Expense ($000)**: 108858 **Payroll Expense ($000)**: 45931 **Personnel**: 684

✠ **LAREDO MEDICAL CENTER (450029)**, 1700 East Saunders Avenue, Zip 78041–5474, Mailing Address: P.O.Box 2068, 78044–2068; tel. 956/796–5000, (Total facility includes 18 beds in nursing home–type unit) **A**1 10 13 **F**3 8 11 12 13 15 18 20 24 26 28 29 30 31 34 35 40 43 45 46 49 50 51 53 54 57 59 60 64 65 68 70 72 74 75 76 77 78 79 81 85 86 87 89 91 92 93 107 108 110 111 114 119 120 121 123 128 132 135 144 146 147 148 149 **S** Community Health Systems, Inc., Franklin, TN
Primary Contact: Enrique Gallegos, Chief Executive Officer
CIO: Joe Rivera, Chief Information Technology Officer
Web address: www.laredomedical.com
Control: Corporation, Investor–owned (for–profit) **Service**: General medical and surgical

Staffed Beds: 326 **Admissions**: 13868 **Census**: 211 **Outpatient Visits**: 134803 **Births**: 3587 **Total Expense ($000)**: 182446 **Payroll Expense ($000)**: 56510 **Personnel**: 1056

LAREDO REHABILITATION HOSPITAL (673059), 2005a East Bustamante Street, Zip 78041; tel. 956/764–8555 **F**3 29 75 90 91 96 **S** Ernest Health, Inc., Albuquerque, NM
Primary Contact: Larisa Higgins, Administrator and Chief Operating Officer
Web address: www.lrh.ernesthealth.com
Control: Corporation, Investor–owned (for–profit) **Service**: Rehabilitation

Staffed Beds: 20 **Admissions**: 378 **Census**: 16 **Outpatient Visits**: 0 **Births**: 0 **Total Expense ($000)**: 6099 **Payroll Expense ($000)**: 3173 **Personnel**: 51

☐ **LAREDO SPECIALTY HOSPITAL (452096)**, 2005 Bustamente Street, Zip 78041–5470; tel. 956/753–5353 **A**1 10 **F**1 3 29 75 85 91 96 130 148 **S** Ernest Health, Inc., Albuquerque, NM
Primary Contact: Mario Rodriguez, Chief Executive Officer
CFO: Robert Voss, Chief Financial Officer
CMO: Marisa Guerrero, Director Human Resources
Web address: www.lsh.ernesthealth.com
Control: Partnership, Investor–owned (for–profit) **Service**: Acute long–term care hospital

Staffed Beds: 40 **Admissions**: 435 **Census**: 31 **Outpatient Visits**: 3313 **Births**: 0 **Total Expense ($000)**: 19790 **Payroll Expense ($000)**: 6618 **Personnel**: 126

LEAGUE CITY—Galveston County

☐ **DEVEREUX TEXAS TREATMENT NETWORK (454085)**, 1150 Devereux Drive, Zip 77573–2043; tel. 281/335–1000 **A**1 3 10 **F**4 29 32 35 38 53 59 64 75 86 87 98 99 101 106 130 132 134 **S** Devereux, Villanova, PA
Primary Contact: Pamela E. Helm, Executive Director
Web address: www.devereux.org
Control: Other not–for–profit (including NFP Corporation) **Service**: Children's hospital psychiatric

Staffed Beds: 48 **Admissions**: 47 **Census**: 42 **Outpatient Visits**: 0 **Births**: 0 **Total Expense ($000)**: 7992 **Payroll Expense ($000)**: 2803 **Personnel**: 72

LEVELLAND—Hockley County

★ **COVENANT HOSPITAL–LEVELLAND (450755)**, 1900 South College Avenue, Zip 79336–6508; tel. 806/894–4963 **A**10 **F**11 13 15 29 30 34 40 43 45 50 57 59 64 65 68 75 76 77 81 85 87 97 107 110 111 114 115 119 127 133 149 **P**6 **S** Providence St. Joseph Health, Renton, WA
Primary Contact: Bruce White, Administrator
CFO: Newman Wheeler, Chief Financial Officer and Chief Operating Officer
CMO: Harry Weaver M.D., Chief of Staff
CIO: Kevin Elmore, Chief Information Officer
CHR: Tammy Franklin, Manager Personnel and Marketing
CNO: Connie Thomman, Director of Nursing
Web address: www.covenanthospitallevelland.com/
Control: Church operated, Nongovernment, not–for–profit **Service**: General medical and surgical

Staffed Beds: 26 **Admissions**: 796 **Census**: 6 **Outpatient Visits**: 33419
Births: 251 **Total Expense ($000)**: 19956 **Payroll Expense ($000)**: 8168
Personnel: 174

LEWISVILLE—Denton County

✠ **MEDICAL CITY LEWISVILLE (450669)**, 500 West Main, Zip 75057–3699; tel. 972/420–1000 **A**1 2 10 **F**3 13 15 18 20 22 24 26 28 29 30 31 34 35 40 42 43 46 49 50 56 57 59 68 70 72 74 75 76 78 79 81 85 87 89 90 93 96 107 108 110 111 114 118 119 129 130 131 132 135 146 147 148 149 **S** HCA Healthcare, Nashville, TN
Primary Contact: LaSharndra Barbarin, Chief Executive Officer
CFO: Lisa Brodbeck, Chief Financial Officer
CIO: Shirley Archambeault, Chief Information Officer
CHR: Dara Biegert, Vice President Human Resources
CNO: Lynn O'Neill R.N., Chief Nursing Officer
Web address: www.lewisvillemedical.com
Control: Corporation, Investor–owned (for–profit) **Service**: General medical and surgical

Staffed Beds: 166 **Admissions**: 6971 **Census**: 89 **Outpatient Visits**: 84779
Births: 1550 **Total Expense ($000)**: 130720 **Payroll Expense ($000)**: 51582 **Personnel**: 637

LIBERTY—Liberty County

☐ **LIBERTY DAYTON REGIONAL MEDICAL CENTER (451375)**, 1353 North Travis, Zip 77575–3549; tel. 936/336–7316 **A**1 10 18 **F**3 29 40 45 59 64 89 107 114 119 127 128 130 133
Primary Contact: Matt Thornton, Chief Executive Officer
CFO: Hal Mayo, Chief Financial Officer
CMO: Don Callens M.D., Chief Medical Officer
CNO: Cindy Griffin, Chief Nursing Officer
Web address: www.libertydaytonrmc.com
Control: Hospital district or authority, Government, Nonfederal **Service**: General medical and surgical

Staffed Beds: 15 **Admissions**: 155 **Census**: 1 **Outpatient Visits**: 20213
Births: 0 **Total Expense ($000)**: 9768 **Payroll Expense ($000)**: 4329
Personnel: 111

LITTLEFIELD—Lamb County

★ **LAMB HEALTHCARE CENTER (450698)**, 1500 South Sunset, Zip 79339–4899; tel. 806/385–6411 **A**10 20 **F**13 35 40 43 45 50 57 59 64 66 75 76 81 86 87 89 107 114 119 127 132 133 134 146 147 149 **P**6
Primary Contact: Cindy Klein, Chief Executive Officer
CMO: Isabel Molina M.D., Chief Medical Officer
CHR: Joan Williams, Administrative Assistant/Human Resources
CNO: Stacie Styron, Chief Nursing Officer
Web address: www.littlefieldtexas.net/index.php/our–community/lamb–healthcare–center
Control: County, Government, Nonfederal **Service**: General medical and surgical

Staffed Beds: 41 **Admissions**: 309 **Census**: 4 **Outpatient Visits**: 31016
Births: 115 **Total Expense ($000)**: 10851 **Payroll Expense ($000)**: 4462
Personnel: 125

LIVINGSTON—Polk County

✠ **CHI ST. LUKE'S HEALTH MEMORIAL LIVINGSTON (450395)**, 1717 Highway 59 Bypass, Zip 77351–1257, Mailing Address: P.O.Box 1257, 77351–0022; tel. 936/329–8700 **A**1 10 **F**3 11 13 15 29 34 35 40 45 46 50 57 59 62 64 68 70 74 75 76 79 81 85 87 89 107 108 110 111 114 119 129 130 132 146 149 **S** Catholic Health Initiatives, Englewood, CO
Primary Contact: Kristi Froese, R.N., Vice President Clinical Operations
COO: Shawn Barnett, Chief Operating Officer
CFO: Duane Miller, Chief Financial Officer
CMO: Verner Nellsch M.D., Chief of Staff
CIO: Kathy DeFiguieredo, Director, Information Technology
CHR: Heather Jordan, Director Human Resources
CNO: Kristi Froese R.N., Chief Nursing Officer
Web address: www.memorialhealth.org
Control: Other not–for–profit (including NFP Corporation) **Service**: General medical and surgical

Staffed Beds: 66 **Admissions**: 1814 **Census**: 13 **Outpatient Visits**: 54051
Births: 438 **Total Expense ($000)**: 39627 **Payroll Expense ($000)**: 17807
Personnel: 215

LLANO—Llano County

★ **BAYLOR SCOTT & WHITE MEDICAL CENTER – LLANO (450219)**, 200 West Ollie Street, Zip 78643–2628; tel. 325/247–5040 **A**10 20 **F**3 11 13 15 18 20 29 30 31 34 35 40 45 47 59 64 78 79 81 82 85 93 107 114 119 130 131 146 147 149 **S** Baylor Scott & White Health, Dallas, TX
Primary Contact: Timothy A. Ols, FACHE, Chief Executive Officer
COO: Linda Meredith MSN, MS, Chief Operating Officer
CFO: Jason Cole, Director Finance
CMO: Kim Russell M.D., Chief of Staff
CIO: Rodney Lott, Director Management Information Systems and Facility Operations
CHR: Pearl Oestreich, Director Human Resources
CNO: Reta Hunt, Director of Nursing
Web address: www.sw.org/location/llano–hospital
Control: Other not–for–profit (including NFP Corporation) **Service**: General medical and surgical

Staffed Beds: 10 **Admissions**: 265 **Census**: 2 **Outpatient Visits**: 9437
Births: 30 **Total Expense ($000)**: 36577 **Payroll Expense ($000)**: 16772
Personnel: 145

LOCKNEY—Floyd County

★ **W. J. MANGOLD MEMORIAL HOSPITAL (451337)**, 320 North Main Street, Zip 79241–0037, Mailing Address: Box 37, 79241–0037; tel. 806/652–3373 **A**10 18 **F**3 13 35 40 43 45 53 57 59 62 64 65 76 81 85 93 97 107 111 119 127 130 133 148 **P**4
Primary Contact: David Clark, Interim Chief Executive Officer
CFO: Alyssa McCarter, Chief Financial Officer
CMO: Kevin T Stennett M.D., Chief of Staff
CIO: Sam Vanderbeek, Chief Information Officer
CNO: Billie Hendrix R.N., Director of Nursing
Web address: www.mangoldmemorial.org
Control: Hospital district or authority, Government, Nonfederal **Service**: General medical and surgical

Staffed Beds: 25 **Admissions**: 306 **Census**: 4 **Outpatient Visits**: 25863
Births: 27 **Total Expense ($000)**: 10499 **Payroll Expense ($000)**: 4378
Personnel: 107

LONGVIEW—Gregg County

✠ △ **CHRISTUS GOOD SHEPHERD MEDICAL CENTER (450037)**, 700 East Marshall Avenue, Zip 75601–5580; tel. 903/315–1800 **A**1 3 7 10 **F**3 11 12 13 15 18 20 22 24 26 28 29 30 31 32 34 35 37 40 42 43 45 46 49 50 51 53 54 56 57 59 61 63 64 68 70 71 72 73 74 75 76 77 78 79 80 81 82 84 85 86 87 89 90 92 93 97 102 107 108 110 111 114 115 118 119 126 129 130 131 132 135 143 144 146 147 148 149 **S** CHRISTUS Health, Irving, TX
Primary Contact: Todd Hancock, President and Chief Executive Officer
CFO: Tim Pileggi, Interim Chief Financial Officer
CMO: Larry Verfurth D.O., Chief Medical Officer and Senior Vice President
CIO: Chris Blakemore, Interim Chief Information Officer
CHR: Ginger Morrow, Executive Vice President Human Resources
CNO: Patti Bennett, Chief Nursing Officer and Senior Vice President
Web address: www.gsmc.org
Control: Other not–for–profit (including NFP Corporation) **Service**: General medical and surgical

Staffed Beds: 393 **Admissions**: 13949 **Census**: 197 **Outpatient Visits**: 174710 **Births**: 1843 **Total Expense ($000)**: 281044 **Payroll Expense ($000)**: 90888 **Personnel**: 1252

TX

✠ **LONGVIEW REGIONAL MEDICAL CENTER (450702)**, 2901 North Fourth Street, Zip 75605–5191, Mailing Address: P.O.Box 14000, 75607–4000; tel. 903/758–1818, (Total facility includes 15 beds in nursing home–type unit) **A**1 3 10 **F**3 8 11 12 13 15 18 20 22 24 26 28 29 30 31 34 35 37 39 40 43 45 46 47 49 50 57 59 61 64 65 67 70 72 74 75 76 77 78 79 81 85 86 87 89 91 93 107 108 110 111 114 115 118 119 120 126 128 130 146 148 **P**8 **S** Community Health Systems, Inc., Franklin, TN
Primary Contact: Casey Robertson, Chief Executive Officer
COO: Roy Finch, Chief Operating Officer
CFO: Todd Johnson, Chief Financial Officer
CMO: Kenneth McClure M.D., Chief of Staff
CIO: Keith Jarvis, Director Information Systems
CHR: Terry Hardan, Director Human Resources
CNO: Stephanie Foster MSN, R.N., Chief Nursing Officer
Web address: www.longviewregional.com
Control: Partnership, Investor–owned (for–profit) **Service**: General medical and surgical

Staffed Beds: 230 **Admissions**: 9522 **Census**: 112 **Outpatient Visits**: 93985 **Births**: 1885 **Total Expense ($000)**: 158210 **Payroll Expense ($000)**: 53328 **Personnel**: 928

☐ **MAGNOLIA BEHAVIORAL HOSPITAL OF EAST TEXAS**, 22 Bermuda Lane, Zip 75605–2902; tel. 903/291–3456 **A**1 **F**98 100 103 104 105 130 135 149 150
Primary Contact: Allison Debruycker, Administrator
Web address: www.magnoliabehavioralhospital.com/
Control: Corporation, Investor–owned (for–profit) **Service**: Psychiatric

Staffed Beds: 76 **Admissions**: 537 **Census**: 19 **Outpatient Visits**: 1154 **Births**: 0 **Total Expense ($000)**: 6303 **Payroll Expense ($000)**: 3173 **Personnel**: 64

☐ **OCEANS BEHAVIORAL HOSPITAL LONGVIEW (454117)**, 615 Clinic Drive, Zip 75605–5172; tel. 903/212–3105 **A**1 10 **F**29 64 98 100 101 103 104 130 132 149 **S** Oceans Healthcare, Lake Charles, LA
Primary Contact: Lauren Weber, Administrator
Web address: www.oceanslongview.com/
Control: Corporation, Investor–owned (for–profit) **Service**: Psychiatric

Staffed Beds: 24 **Admissions**: 536 **Census**: 20 **Outpatient Visits**: 17409 **Births**: 0 **Total Expense ($000)**: 5142 **Payroll Expense ($000)**: 2562 **Personnel**: 63

✠ **SELECT SPECIALTY HOSPITAL–LONGVIEW (452087)**, 700 East Marshall Avenue, 1st Floor, Zip 75601–5580; tel. 903/315–1100 **A**1 10 **F**1 3 28 29 75 77 85 91 92 130 148 **S** Select Medical Corporation, Mechanicsburg, PA
Primary Contact: Andrew Meade, Chief Executive Officer
Web address: www.longview.selectspecialtyhospitals.com/
Control: Corporation, Investor–owned (for–profit) **Service**: Acute long–term care hospital

Staffed Beds: 32 **Admissions**: 324 **Census**: 23 **Outpatient Visits**: 0 **Births**: 0 **Total Expense ($000)**: 11976 **Payroll Expense ($000)**: 5532 **Personnel**: 105

LUBBOCK—Lubbock County

✠ **COVENANT CHILDREN'S HOSPITAL (453306)**, 4015 22nd Place, Zip 79410; tel. 806/725–1011 **A**1 3 5 10 **F**3 19 21 23 25 27 30 31 32 40 41 43 50 59 72 73 81 89 **P**8 **S** Providence St. Joseph Health, Renton, WA
Primary Contact: Amy Thompson, M.D., Chief Executive Officer
COO: Clay Thomas, Chief Operating Officer
CMO: Scott Robins M.D., Chief Medical Officer
CIO: Jim Reid, Vice President and Chief Information Officer
CHR: Rodney Cates, Senior Vice President Human Resources
Web address: www.covenanthealth.org/About–Us/Facilities/Childrens–Hospital.aspx
Control: Other not–for–profit (including NFP Corporation) **Service**: Children's general medical and surgical

Staffed Beds: 73 **Admissions**: 2004 **Census**: 43 **Outpatient Visits**: 29969 **Births**: 0 **Total Expense ($000)**: 71738 **Payroll Expense ($000)**: 20312 **Personnel**: 212

✠ **COVENANT MEDICAL CENTER (450040)**, 3615 19th Street, Zip 79410–1203, Mailing Address: P.O.Box 1201, 79408–1201; tel. 806/725–0000, (Includes COVENANT MEDICAL CENTER–LAKESIDE, 4000 24th Street, Lubbock, Texas, Zip 79410–1894, tel. 806/725–0000) **A**1 3 10 **F**7 8 15 17 18 19 20 22 23 26 27 28 30 34 35 37 39 40 43 46 47 48 49 50 51 53 54 55 57 58 59 60 61 63 64 65 68 70 71 74 75 76 77 78 79 80 81 82 83 84 85 86 87 90 91 92 93 94 96 98 105 107 108 109 111 114 115 116 117 119 120 121 123 129 130 131 132 135 143 144 146 147 148 **P**6 8 **S** Providence St. Joseph Health, Renton, WA
Primary Contact: Walt Cathey, Chief Executive Officer
CFO: John A Grigson, Vice President and Chief Financial Officer
CMO: Craig Rhyne M.D., FACS, Chief Medical Officer
CIO: Troy Pratt, Information Technology Site Director
CHR: Chris Shaver, Vice President Human Resources
CNO: Karen Baggerly, Chief Nursing Officer and Vice President
Web address: www.covenanthealth.org
Control: Other not–for–profit (including NFP Corporation) **Service**: General medical and surgical

Staffed Beds: 576 **Admissions**: 21770 **Census**: 315 **Outpatient Visits**: 330538 **Births**: 2559 **Total Expense ($000)**: 524356 **Payroll Expense ($000)**: 132403 **Personnel**: 2950

★ **COVENANT SPECIALTY HOSPITAL (452102)**, 3815 20th Street, Zip 79410–1235; tel. 806/725–9200 **A**10 **F**1 3 29 30 31 60 63 68 75 77 78 79 87 119 130 143 148 **S** Providence St. Joseph Health, Renton, WA
Primary Contact: Julie Bell, Interim Chief Executive Officer and Chief Nursing Officer
CFO: John Carigson, Chief Financial Officer
CMO: Naidu Chekuru M.D., Chief Medical Officer
CHR: Chris Shaver, Vice President Human Resources
CNO: Julie Bell, Chief Nursing Officer
Web address: www.covenanthealth.org/view/Facilities/Specialty_Hospital
Control: Partnership, Investor–owned (for–profit) **Service**: Acute long–term care hospital

Staffed Beds: 56 **Admissions**: 363 **Census**: 28 **Outpatient Visits**: 0 **Births**: 0 **Total Expense ($000)**: 17314 **Payroll Expense ($000)**: 6687 **Personnel**: 124

✠ **GRACE MEDICAL CENTER (450162)**, 2412 50th Street, Zip 79412–2494; tel. 806/788–4100 **A**1 10 **F**3 8 11 12 15 29 31 34 35 37 40 44 45 47 49 50 51 59 64 66 70 75 78 79 81 82 85 87 107 108 110 111 114 115 118 119 135 146
Primary Contact: Vanessa Reasoner, Chief Executive Officer
CMO: Howard Beck M.D., Chief of Staff
CIO: Jason Derouen, Director Management Information Systems
CHR: Sally Charles, Coordinator Human Resources
Web address: www.gracehealthsystem.com
Control: Partnership, Investor–owned (for–profit) **Service**: General medical and surgical

Staffed Beds: 43 **Admissions**: 1174 **Census**: 8 **Outpatient Visits**: 103099 **Births**: 0 **Total Expense ($000)**: 62883 **Payroll Expense ($000)**: 11896 **Personnel**: 237

LUBBOCK HEART & SURGICAL HOSPITAL (450876), 4810 North Loop 289, Zip 79416–3025; tel. 806/687–7777 **A**3 5 10 **F**3 17 18 20 22 24 26 29 34 40 45 57 59 79 81 82 85 107 108 115 119 130 131 148
Primary Contact: Mark Hall, Interim Chief Executive Officer
Web address: www.lubbockhsns.com/lubbock–heart/
Control: Partnership, Investor–owned (for–profit) **Service**: General medical and surgical

Staffed Beds: 73 **Admissions**: 3196 **Census**: 30 **Outpatient Visits**: 86782 **Births**: 0 **Total Expense ($000)**: 79697 **Payroll Expense ($000)**: 21647 **Personnel**: 412

☐ **SUNRISE CANYON HOSPITAL (454093)**, 1950 Aspen Ave, Zip 79404–1211, Mailing Address: P.O. Box 2828, 79408–2828; tel. 806/740–1420 **A**1 10 **F**29 35 38 42 61 98 101 130 132 135
Primary Contact: Leonard Valderaz, Administrator
CFO: Jerome Flores, Chief Financial Officer
CMO: Dana Butler M.D., Medical Director
CIO: Wendy Potitadkul, Chief Information Officer
CHR: Barbara McCann, Director Human Resources
Web address: www.starcarelubbock.org
Control: Other not–for–profit (including NFP Corporation) **Service**: Psychiatric

Staffed Beds: 30 **Admissions**: 598 **Census**: 26 **Outpatient Visits**: 0 **Births**: 0 **Total Expense ($000)**: 5624 **Payroll Expense ($000)**: 2277 **Personnel**: 54

☐ **TRUSTPOINT REHABILITATION HOSPITAL OF LUBBOCK (670050)**, 4302A Princeton Street, Zip 79415–1304; tel. 806/749–2222 **A**1 5 10 **F**3 29 34 35 40 56 68 74 75 77 79 85 86 87 90 91 94 96 130 148 **S** Ernest Health, Inc., Albuquerque, NM
Primary Contact: Craig Bragg, Chief Executive Officer
CFO: Crystal Roach, Chief Financial Officer
CNO: John Parsons R.N., Chief Nursing Officer
Web address: www.trustpointhospital.com/
Control: Partnership, Investor–owned (for–profit) **Service**: Rehabilitation

Staffed Beds: 60 **Admissions**: 1150 **Census**: 53 **Outpatient Visits**: 0 **Births**: 0 **Total Expense ($000)**: 22540 **Payroll Expense ($000)**: 10006 **Personnel**: 193

TX

⇑ **UNIVERSITY MEDICAL CENTER (450686)**, 602 Indiana Avenue, Zip 79415–3364, Mailing Address: P.O.Box 5980, 79408–5980; tel. 806/775–8200 **A**2 3 5 10 21 **F**3 7 11 12 13 15 16 17 18 19 20 22 24 26 28 29 30 31 34 35 38 40 41 43 45 46 47 48 49 50 54 55 57 58 59 60 62 64 65 66 68 70 72 74 75 76 77 78 79 80 81 82 83 84 85 86 87 88 89 93 94 96 97 107 108 110 111 114 115 116 117 118 119 120 121 122 123 124 126 127 130 131 132 135 136 141 142 143 144 146 147 148 149 150
Primary Contact: David G. Allison, President and Chief Executive Officer
COO: Mark Funderburk, Executive Vice President and Administrator
CFO: Jeff Dane, Executive Vice President and Chief Financial Officer
CMO: Michael Ragain M.D., Chief Medical Officer and Senior Vice President
CIO: Bill Eubanks, Senior Vice President and Chief Information Officer
CHR: Adrienne Cozart, Vice President Human Resources
CNO: Timothy W. Howell R.N., Senior Vice President and Chief Nursing Officer
Web address: www.umchealthsystem.com
Control: Hospital district or authority, Government, Nonfederal **Service:** General medical and surgical

Staffed Beds: 435 **Admissions:** 30653 **Census:** 372 **Outpatient Visits:** 310859 **Births:** 3102 **Total Expense ($000):** 526849 **Payroll Expense ($000):** 197762 **Personnel:** 3264

LUFKIN—Angelina County

★ **CHI ST. LUKE'S HEALTH MEMORIAL LUFKIN (450211)**, 1201 West Frank Avenue, Zip 75904–3357, Mailing Address: P.O.Box 1447, 75902–1447; tel. 936/634–8111 **A**2 10 19 **F**3 11 12 13 14 15 17 18 20 21 22 23 24 26 28 29 30 31 34 35 37 38 40 44 45 46 47 48 49 50 51 56 57 59 60 61 62 63 64 68 70 71 74 75 76 77 78 79 81 82 83 84 85 86 87 90 91 92 93 97 100 101 102 107 108 110 111 112 114 115 116 117 119 121 126 129 130 132 135 143 144 146 147 148 149 **S** Catholic Health Initiatives, Englewood, CO
Primary Contact: Monte J. Bostwick, Market Chief Executive Officer
CFO: Kristi Gay, Chief Financial Officer
CHR: Tanya Tyler, Vice President Human Resources
Web address: www.memorialhealth.us/centers/lufkin
Control: Other not–for–profit (including NFP Corporation) **Service:** General medical and surgical

Staffed Beds: 217 **Admissions:** 6460 **Census:** 92 **Outpatient Visits:** 83536 **Births:** 274 **Total Expense ($000):** 144864 **Payroll Expense ($000):** 38719 **Personnel:** 781

★ **CHI ST. LUKE'S HEALTH MEMORIAL SPECIALTY HOSPITAL (452031)**, 1201 West Frank Avenue, D5, Zip 75904–3357, Mailing Address: P.O.Box 1447, 75902–1447; tel. 936/639–7530 **A**10 **F**1 3 29 31 50 61 68 74 75 85 86 130 145 149 **S** Catholic Health Initiatives, Englewood, CO
Primary Contact: Darlene Williams, R.N., Administrator
CFO: Duane Miller, Chief Financial Officer
CMO: David Todd M.D., President Medical Staff
CNO: Deborah Burgess R.N., Chief Nursing Officer
Web address: www.memorialhealth.org
Control: Other not–for–profit (including NFP Corporation) **Service:** Acute long–term care hospital

Staffed Beds: 20 **Admissions:** 199 **Census:** 15 **Outpatient Visits:** 0 **Births:** 0 **Total Expense ($000):** 10039 **Payroll Expense ($000):** 5433 **Personnel:** 52

☐ **OCEANS BEHAVIORAL HOSPITAL LUFKIN (454123)**, 302 Gobblers Knob Road, Zip 75904–5419; tel. 936/632–2276 **A**1 10 **F**29 35 64 98 100 101 103 104 130 **S** Oceans Healthcare, Lake Charles, LA
Primary Contact: Frances Dick, Chief Executive Officer
Web address: www.oceanslufkin.com/
Control: Corporation, Investor–owned (for–profit) **Service:** Psychiatric

Staffed Beds: 24 **Admissions:** 421 **Census:** 17 **Outpatient Visits:** 12592 **Births:** 0 **Total Expense ($000):** 4584 **Payroll Expense ($000):** 2194 **Personnel:** 58

☒ **WOODLAND HEIGHTS MEDICAL CENTER (450484)**, 505 South John Redditt Drive, Zip 75904–3157, Mailing Address: P.O.Box 150610, 75904; tel. 936/634–8311 **A**1 10 19 **F**8 11 12 13 15 18 20 22 24 26 28 29 30 34 35 40 41 46 49 50 51 53 57 59 64 68 70 72 74 75 77 78 79 81 82 85 86 87 93 102 107 108 111 114 115 118 119 126 129 130 131 146 147 148 **S** Community Health Systems, Inc., Franklin, TN
Primary Contact: Kyle Swift, Chief Executive Officer
COO: Conner Hickey, Chief Operating Officer
CFO: William Whiddon, Chief Financial Officer
CMO: Imran Nazeer M.D., Chief of Staff
CIO: Kalvin Buckley, Director Information Systems
CHR: Emilie Hobbs, Director Human Resources
CNO: Cathy L Busbee, Chief Nursing Officer
Web address: www.woodlandheights.net
Control: Partnership, Investor–owned (for–profit) **Service:** General medical and surgical

Staffed Beds: 124 **Admissions:** 4870 **Census:** 54 **Outpatient Visits:** 51856 **Births:** 1141 **Total Expense ($000):** 82209 **Payroll Expense ($000):** 30132 **Personnel:** 516

LULING—Caldwell County

☒ **POST ACUTE/WARM SPRINGS SPECIALTY HOSPITAL OF LULING (452062)**, 200 Memorial Drive, Zip 78648–3213; tel. 830/875–8400 **A**1 10 **F**1 3 29 53 64 93 96 130 133 148 **S** Post Acute Medical, LLC, Enola, PA
Primary Contact: Jana Kuykendall, Chief Executive Officer
Web address: www.warmsprings.org
Control: Partnership, Investor–owned (for–profit) **Service:** Acute long–term care hospital

Staffed Beds: 34 **Admissions:** 572 **Census:** 28 **Outpatient Visits:** 11807 **Births:** 0 **Total Expense ($000):** 14990 **Payroll Expense ($000):** 6825 **Personnel:** 145

☒ **SETON EDGAR B. DAVIS HOSPITAL (451371)**, 130 Hays Street, Zip 78648–3207; tel. 830/875–7000 **A**1 10 18 **F**3 7 11 15 18 29 30 31 34 35 40 43 44 45 50 56 57 59 68 71 75 77 78 79 81 85 87 93 97 103 107 110 111 114 119 127 130 133 135 143 146 148 **P**3 8 **S** Ascension Healthcare, Saint Louis, MO
Primary Contact: Apryl Haynes, R.N., Vice President, Chief Operating Officer, Administrator
CMO: Arjun Mohandas M.D., Chief of Staff
CIO: Michael H. Minks, Chief Information Officer
CHR: Joe Canales, Director Human Resources
CNO: Nikki Rivers R.N., Regional Chief Nursing Officer, South Market
Web address: www.seton.net/locations/edgar_davis/
Control: Church operated, Nongovernment, not–for–profit **Service:** General medical and surgical

Staffed Beds: 25 **Admissions:** 582 **Census:** 7 **Outpatient Visits:** 61493 **Births:** 0 **Total Expense ($000):** 23240 **Payroll Expense ($000):** 8865 **Personnel:** 130

WARM SPRINGS SPECIALTY HOSPITAL OF LULING See Post Acute/Warm Springs Specialty Hospital Of Luling

MADISONVILLE—Madison County

☒ **CHI ST. JOSEPH HEALTH MADISON HOSPITAL (451316)**, 100 West Cross Street, Zip 77864–2432, Mailing Address: Box 698, 77864–0698; tel. 936/348–2631 **A**1 10 18 **F**3 7 11 15 30 34 40 43 50 56 57 59 64 68 75 77 93 103 107 110 119 130 133 146 148 **S** Catholic Health Initiatives, Englewood, CO
Primary Contact: , R.N.
CFO: Kris Smith, Controller
CMO: Grover Hubley M.D., President Medical Staff
CIO: Maurita Turner, Team Leader Health Information Systems Services
CNO: Roxanne Hass, Director of Nursing
Web address: www.st–joseph.org
Control: Church operated, Nongovernment, not–for–profit **Service:** General medical and surgical

Staffed Beds: 25 **Admissions:** 233 **Census:** 6 **Outpatient Visits:** 11425 **Births:** 0 **Total Expense ($000):** 10182 **Payroll Expense ($000):** 4438 **Personnel:** 78

MANSFIELD—Tarrant County

☒ **KINDRED HOSPITAL–MANSFIELD (452019)**, 1802 Highway 157 North, Zip 76063–3923; tel. 817/473–6101 **A**1 10 **F**1 3 29 30 45 46 64 70 75 82 85 107 130 132 148 **S** Kindred Healthcare, Louisville, KY
Primary Contact: Susan Schaetti, Chief Executive Officer
CFO: Judy Baker, Chief Financial Officer
Web address: www.kindredmansfield.com
Control: Corporation, Investor–owned (for–profit) **Service:** Acute long–term care hospital

Staffed Beds: 55 **Admissions:** 465 **Census:** 30 **Outpatient Visits:** 295 **Births:** 0 **Total Expense ($000):** 16053 **Payroll Expense ($000):** 6585 **Personnel:** 111

☒ **METHODIST MANSFIELD MEDICAL CENTER (670023)**, 2700 East Broad Street, Zip 76063–5899; tel. 682/622–2000 **A**1 10 **F**3 11 13 15 18 20 22 24 29 30 31 34 35 37 40 45 46 48 49 50 58 59 60 64 68 70 74 76 78 79 81 82 85 87 93 97 107 108 110 111 115 118 119 126 130 132 146 148 **P**1 7 **S** Methodist Health System, Dallas, TX
Primary Contact: John E. Phillips, FACHE, President
CFO: Jary Ganske, Chief Financial Officer
CIO: Pamela McNutt, Senior Vice President and Chief Information Officer
CHR: Judy K Laister, Director, Human Resources
CNO: Nora Frasier R.N., FACHE, Chief Nursing Officer
Web address: www.methodisthealthsystem.org/mansfield
Control: Other not–for–profit (including NFP Corporation) **Service:** General medical and surgical

Staffed Beds: 221 **Admissions:** 9293 **Census:** 114 **Outpatient Visits:** 87057 **Births:** 2002 **Total Expense ($000):** 167453 **Payroll Expense ($000):** 70445 **Personnel:** 906

TX

Hospital, Medicare Provider Number, Address, Telephone, Approval, Facility, and Physician Codes, Health Care System

★ American Hospital Association (AHA) membership
☐ The Joint Commission accreditation
○ Healthcare Facilities Accreditation Program
◇ DNV Healthcare Inc. accreditation
⇑ Center for Improvement in Healthcare Quality Accreditation
△ Commission on Accreditation of Rehabilitation Facilities (CARF) accreditation

MARBLE FALLS—Burnet County

★ **BAYLOR SCOTT & WHITE MEDICAL CENTER – MARBLE FALLS (670108)**, 800 West Highway 71, Zip 78654; tel. 830/201–8000, (Data for 333 days) **F**3 11 13 15 18 20 29 30 31 34 35 40 45 57 59 64 70 76 78 79 81 82 85 93 107 108 110 111 115 119 130 131 146 147 149 **S** Baylor Scott & White Health, Dallas, TX
Primary Contact: Timothy A. Ols, FACHE, President
Web address: www.sw.org/location/marble–falls–hospital
Control: Other not–for–profit (including NFP Corporation) **Service**: General medical and surgical

Staffed Beds: 46 Admissions: 1494 Census: 12 Outpatient Visits: 54984 Births: 305 Total Expense ($000): 50167 Payroll Expense ($000): 19792 Personnel: 293

MARLIN—Falls County

★ **FALLS COMMUNITY HOSPITAL AND CLINIC (450348)**, 322 Coleman Street, Zip 76661–2358, Mailing Address: P.O.Box 60, 76661–0060; tel. 254/803–3561 **A**10 20 **F**3 11 32 33 34 35 36 40 43 53 56 57 59 64 65 66 68 75 82 87 91 93 97 99 103 104 107 114 119 127 129 131 135 146 148
Primary Contact: John Graham, Administrator
COO: Becca Brewer, Chief Operations Officer
CMO: James Scott Crockett M.D., Chief of Staff
CIO: Chris Smith, Chief Information Officer
CHR: Peggy Polster, Manager Personnel and Administrative Assistant
CNO: Tasha Burnett, Director of Nursing
Web address: www.fallshospital.com
Control: Other not–for–profit (including NFP Corporation) **Service**: General medical and surgical

Staffed Beds: 32 Admissions: 354 Census: 3 Outpatient Visits: 72270 Births: 2 Total Expense ($000): 20313 Payroll Expense ($000): 6483 Personnel: 149

MARSHALL—Harrison County

✠ **CHRISTUS GOOD SHEPHERD MEDICAL CENTER-MARSHALL (450032)**, 811 South Washington Avenue, Zip 75670–5336, Mailing Address: P.O.Box 1599, 75671–1599; tel. 903/927–6000 **A**1 3 10 **F**3 11 13 15 18 28 29 30 34 35 40 43 49 50 53 54 57 59 60 64 65 68 70 75 77 79 80 81 86 87 89 90 93 97 102 103 107 110 115 119 129 130 131 132 145 146 147 148 **P**7 8 **S** CHRISTUS Health, Irving, TX
Primary Contact: Russell J. Collier, FACHE, President and Chief Executive Officer
COO: Keith Creel, Vice President Operations
CFO: Michael Cheek, Chief Financial Officer
CMO: Larry Verfurth D.O., Executive Vice President and Chief Medical Officer
CIO: Walter Grimes, Director Information Technology
CHR: Ginger Morrow, Executive Vice President Human Resources
CNO: Keith Kirbow R.N., Vice President and Chief Nursing Officer
Web address: www.gsmcmarshall.org
Control: Other not–for–profit (including NFP Corporation) **Service**: General medical and surgical

Staffed Beds: 140 Admissions: 3843 Census: 42 Outpatient Visits: 161083 Births: 520 Total Expense ($000): 67749 Payroll Expense ($000): 23567 Personnel: 347

MCALLEN—Hidalgo County

✠ **RIO GRANDE REGIONAL HOSPITAL (450711)**, 101 East Ridge Road, Zip 78503–1299; tel. 956/632–6000 **A**1 10 **F**3 8 11 12 13 15 18 19 20 21 22 23 24 25 26 27 29 30 31 34 35 39 40 42 43 45 46 49 50 54 56 57 59 60 64 66 68 70 71 72 73 74 75 76 78 79 81 85 87 88 89 93 107 108 110 111 114 118 119 126 130 132 146 147 148 149 **P**7 **S** HCA Healthcare, Nashville, TN
Primary Contact: Cristina Rivera, Chief Executive Officer
CFO: William Saller, Chief Financial Officer
CHR: Marjorie Whittemore, Director Human Resources
Web address: www.riohealth.com
Control: Partnership, Investor–owned (for–profit) **Service**: General medical and surgical

Staffed Beds: 320 Admissions: 14638 Census: 179 Outpatient Visits: 124507 Births: 2731 Total Expense ($000): 164334 Payroll Expense ($000): 67312 Personnel: 889

SOLARA HOSPITAL MCALLEN (452095), 301 West Expressway 83, 8th Floor, Zip 78503–3045; tel. 956/632–4880 **A**10 22 **F**1 3 29 30 56 57 70 75 77 85 86 87 91 130 148 **S** Cornerstone Healthcare Group, Dallas, TX
Primary Contact: Austin Cleveland, Chief Executive Officer
Web address: www.chghospitals.com/mcallen/
Control: Corporation, Investor–owned (for–profit) **Service**: Acute long–term care hospital

Staffed Beds: 78 Admissions: 551 Census: 38 Outpatient Visits: 0 Births: 0 Total Expense ($000): 18106 Payroll Expense ($000): 7937 Personnel: 109

MCCAMEY—Upton County

★ **MCCAMEY COUNTY HOSPITAL DISTRICT (451309)**, 2500 Highway 305 South, Zip 79752, Mailing Address: P.O.Box 1200, 79752–1200; tel. 432/652–8626, (Total facility includes 30 beds in nursing home–type unit) **A**10 18 **F**3 40 53 59 64 65 66 93 127 128 133
Primary Contact: Jaime Ramirez, Chief Executive Officer
CFO: Jason J Menefee, Chief Financial Officer
CMO: John Bruce Addison D.O., Chief Medical Officer
CIO: Larry Rollins, Supervisor Information Technology
CHR: Ashley Johnson, Director Human Resource
CNO: Erin Mann R.N., Chief Nursing Officer
Web address: www.mccameyhospitaldistrict.org
Control: Hospital district or authority, Government, Nonfederal **Service**: General medical and surgical

Staffed Beds: 44 Admissions: 80 Census: 25 Outpatient Visits: 6374 Births: 0 Total Expense ($000): 13365 Payroll Expense ($000): 4367 Personnel: 76

MCKINNEY—Collin County

✠ **BAYLOR MEDICAL CENTER AT MCKINNEY (670082)**, 5252 West University Drive, Zip 75071–7822; tel. 469/764–1000 **A**1 2 5 10 **F**3 13 15 18 20 22 26 29 30 31 34 35 40 45 46 47 49 50 51 57 59 67 70 72 74 75 76 77 78 79 81 84 85 87 107 110 111 114 115 119 126 130 131 132 146 147 148 **S** Baylor Scott & White Health, Dallas, TX
Primary Contact: Kyle Armstrong, President
COO: Melissa Winter R.N., MSN, Chief Operating Officer and Chief Nursing Officer
CFO: Steve Roussel, Chief Financial Officer
CMO: Jeff Kerr M.D., Chief Medical Officer
CNO: Melissa Winter R.N., MSN, Chief Operating Officer and Chief Nursing Officer
Web address: www.baylorhealth.com/PhysiciansLocations/McKinney/Pages/Default.aspx
Control: Other not–for–profit (including NFP Corporation) **Service**: General medical and surgical

Staffed Beds: 107 Admissions: 7340 Census: 81 Outpatient Visits: 50869 Births: 1981 Total Expense ($000): 143439 Payroll Expense ($000): 48317 Personnel: 488

✠ **MEDICAL CITY MCKINNEY (450403)**, 4500 Medical Center Drive, Zip 75069–1650; tel. 972/547–8000, (Includes WYSONG CAMPUS, 130 South Central Expressway, McKinney, Texas, Zip 75070, tel. 972/548–5300) **A**1 10 **F**3 4 11 13 18 20 22 24 26 28 29 30 34 37 40 42 43 45 49 50 56 57 59 60 64 68 70 72 74 75 76 77 78 79 81 82 85 87 90 91 92 93 94 96 97 98 102 103 107 108 109 111 114 115 119 126 130 131 132 146 147 148 149 **S** HCA Healthcare, Nashville, TN
Primary Contact: Ernest C. Lynch III, FACHE, President and Chief Executive Officer
COO: Andrew Nice, Chief Operating Officer
CFO: Brad Stein, Chief Financial Officer
CMO: Steven Kaster M.D., Chief Medical Officer
CIO: Kevin Fletcher, Director Information Systems
CHR: Alayne Sewick, Vice President Human Resources
CNO: Cassidi Roberts R.N., Chief Nursing Officer
Web address: www.medicalcenterofmckinney.com
Control: Partnership, Investor–owned (for–profit) **Service**: General medical and surgical

Staffed Beds: 222 Admissions: 11663 Census: 170 Outpatient Visits: 76147 Births: 1255 Total Expense ($000): 133359 Payroll Expense ($000): 58597 Personnel: 698

☐ **METHODIST MCKINNEY HOSPITAL (670069)**, 8000 West Eldorado Parkway, Zip 75070–5940; tel. 972/569–2700 **A**1 10 **F**3 29 34 37 40 45 51 75 79 81 82 85 93 107 110 111 119 126 129 130 131
Primary Contact: Joseph Minissale, President
CFO: Mike Conroy, Chief Financial Officer
CIO: Sharon Stark R.N., Manager Clinical Information Systems
CHR: Diana Hume, Manager Human Resources
CNO: Staci Jones R.N., Chief Nursing Officer
Web address: www.methodistmckinneyhospital.com
Control: Partnership, Investor–owned (for–profit) **Service**: Surgical

Staffed Beds: 21 Admissions: 1083 Census: 8 Outpatient Visits: 59973 Births: 0 Total Expense ($000): 58220 Payroll Expense ($000): 10675 Personnel: 174

TX

MESQUITE—Dallas County

⊠ **DALLAS REGIONAL MEDICAL CENTER (450688)**, 1011 North Galloway
Avenue, Zip 75149–2433; tel. 214/320–7000 **A**1 10 **F**3 12 13 15 17 18 20 22
24 26 29 30 34 35 37 39 40 41 43 45 46 49 50 54 56 57 59 64 65 67 68 70
74 75 76 79 80 81 85 87 107 108 110 111 115 119 126 129 130 134 135
146 147 148 149 **S** Prime Healthcare, Ontario, CA
Primary Contact: Glenda Newby, Chief Executive Officer
CMO: Srinivas Gunukula M.D., Chief of Staff
Web address: www.dallasregionalmedicalcenter.com
Control: Individual, Investor–owned (for–profit) **Service**: General medical and
surgical

> **Staffed Beds**: 101 **Admissions**: 5786 **Census**: 60 **Outpatient Visits**: 41916
> **Births**: 536 **Total Expense ($000)**: 83134 **Payroll Expense ($000)**: 37331
> **Personnel**: 494

☐ **MESQUITE REHABILITATION INSTITUTE (673045)**, 1023 North Belt Line Road,
Zip 75149–1788; tel. 972/216–2400 **A**1 10 **F**3 28 29 34 57 59 64 74 75 82 90
91 93 96 130 132 148 **S** Ernest Health, Inc., Albuquerque, NM
Primary Contact: Brian Abraham, Chief Executive Officer
Web address: www.mesquiterehab.ernesthealth.com/
Control: Corporation, Investor–owned (for–profit) **Service**: Rehabilitation

> **Staffed Beds**: 30 **Admissions**: 626 **Census**: 24 **Outpatient Visits**: 3635
> **Births**: 0 **Total Expense ($000)**: 8235 **Payroll Expense ($000)**: 5106
> **Personnel**: 94

☐ **MESQUITE SPECIALTY HOSPITAL (452100)**, 1024 North Galloway Avenue,
Zip 75149–2434; tel. 972/216–2300 **A**1 10 **F**1 3 29 74 75 130 148 149 **S**
Ernest Health, Inc., Albuquerque, NM
Primary Contact: Louis Bradley, Chief Executive Officer
Web address: www.msh.ernesthealth.com
Control: Partnership, Investor–owned (for–profit) **Service**: Acute long–term care
hospital

> **Staffed Beds**: 40 **Admissions**: 428 **Census**: 29 **Outpatient Visits**: 0 **Births**: 0
> **Total Expense ($000)**: 17478 **Payroll Expense ($000)**: 6409 **Personnel**: 151

MEXIA—Limestone County

⊠ **PARKVIEW REGIONAL HOSPITAL (450400)**, 600 South Bonham, Zip 76667–
3603; tel. 254/562–5332 **A**1 10 20 **F**3 11 15 29 30 34 35 40 43 45 51 53 56
57 59 64 65 70 75 77 78 79 81 85 86 87 93 97 98 103 107 108 110 111 114
119 127 130 132 133 146 **P**5 6 **S** LifePoint Health, Brentwood, TN
Primary Contact: Harold L. Siglar, Interim Chief Executive Officer
COO: R. Austin Wratchford, Chief Operating Officer
CFO: Jack Wilcox, Chief Financial Officer
CNO: Edwina J Henry, Assistant Chief Nursing Officer
Web address: www.parkviewregional.com
Control: Partnership, Investor–owned (for–profit) **Service**: General medical and
surgical

> **Staffed Beds**: 58 **Admissions**: 507 **Census**: 7 **Outpatient Visits**: 22857
> **Births**: 0 **Total Expense ($000)**: 16760 **Payroll Expense ($000)**: 7061
> **Personnel**: 149

MIDLAND—Midland County

★ **CONTINUECARE HOSPITAL AT MIDLAND MEMORIAL (452117)**, 4214
Andrews Highway, 3rd Floor, Zip 79703–4822; tel. 432/221–3044 **A**10 22 **F**1 3
29 34 35 79 85 87 148 **S** Community Hospital Corporation, Plano, TX
Primary Contact: Judith Schiros, Chief Executive Officer
Web address: www.continuecare.org/midland/
Control: Other not–for–profit (including NFP Corporation) **Service**: Acute long–
term care hospital

> **Staffed Beds**: 29 **Admissions**: 230 **Census**: 18 **Outpatient Visits**: 0 **Births**: 0
> **Total Expense ($000)**: 10105 **Payroll Expense ($000)**: 4715 **Personnel**: 64

⊠ **HEALTHSOUTH REHABILITATION HOSPITAL MIDLAND–ODESSA (453057)**,
1800 Heritage Boulevard, Zip 79707–9750; tel. 432/520–1600 **A**1 10 **F**3 29 57
59 74 75 77 90 91 96 130 143 148 **S** HEALTHSOUTH Corporation, Birmingham, AL
Primary Contact: Christopher Wortham, Chief Executive Officer
CFO: Vivian Irwin, Chief Financial Officer and Controller
CMO: Mark A Fredrickson M.D., Medical Director
CHR: Tina Parker, Director Human Resources
Web address: www.healthsouthmidland.com
Control: Corporation, Investor–owned (for–profit) **Service**: Rehabilitation

> **Staffed Beds**: 60 **Admissions**: 1353 **Census**: 50 **Outpatient Visits**: 0
> **Births**: 0 **Total Expense ($000)**: 20662 **Payroll Expense ($000)**: 11474
> **Personnel**: 177

★ ⇑ **MIDLAND MEMORIAL HOSPITAL (450133)**, 400 Rosalind Redfern Grover
Parkway, Zip 79701–6499; tel. 432/221–1111, (Includes MIDLAND MEMORIAL
HOSPITAL, 400 Rosalind Redfern Grover Pkwy, Midland, Texas, Zip 79701–5846,
tel. 432/221–1111) **A**3 5 10 21 **F**3 8 11 12 13 15 17 18 20 22 24 26 28 29 30
32 34 35 37 40 43 45 49 50 56 57 59 61 64 68 70 73 74 75 76 77 78 79 81
82 83 84 85 86 87 88 89 93 97 107 108 111 114 115 116 117 118 119 124
126 129 130 131 132 135 145 146 147 148 **P**8
Primary Contact: Russell Meyers, FACHE, President and Chief Executive Officer
COO: Bob Dent R.N., Senior Vice President, Chief Operating Officer and Chief
Nursing Officer
CFO: Stephen Bowerman, Senior Vice President, Chief Financial Officer
CMO: Lawrence Wilson M.D., Vice President, Chief Medical Officer
CIO: Taylor Weems, Vice President, Chief Information Officer
CHR: Roberta SoloRio, Vice President, Chief Human Resource Officer
Web address: www.midland–memorial.com
Control: Hospital district or authority, Government, Nonfederal **Service**: General
medical and surgical

> **Staffed Beds**: 259 **Admissions**: 11649 **Census**: 151 **Outpatient Visits**:
> 146128 **Births**: 2454 **Total Expense ($000)**: 252834 **Payroll Expense
> ($000)**: 101868 **Personnel**: 1694

☐ **OCEANS BEHAVIORAL HEALTH CENTER PERMIAN BASIN (454110)**, 3300
South FM 1788, Zip 79706–2601; tel. 432/561–5915 **A**1 3 10 **F**29 34 35 64 68
98 99 100 101 103 104 130 132 **P**6 **S** Oceans Healthcare, Lake Charles, LA
Primary Contact: Kristin Harris, Interim Chief Executive Officer
Web address: www.oceanspermianbasin.com/
Control: Corporation, Investor–owned (for–profit) **Service**: Psychiatric

> **Staffed Beds**: 58 **Admissions**: 1814 **Census**: 47 **Outpatient Visits**: 7889
> **Births**: 0 **Total Expense ($000)**: 9990 **Payroll Expense ($000)**: 5157
> **Personnel**: 116

MINERAL WELLS—Palo Pinto County

⊠ **PALO PINTO GENERAL HOSPITAL (450565)**, 400 SW 25th Avenue,
Zip 76067–8246; tel. 940/325–7891 **A**1 10 **F**11 13 15 17 18 28 29 32 34 40
43 45 46 51 53 54 57 59 62 63 64 65 66 68 69 71 74 75 76 77 79 81 84 86
87 91 93 107 108 110 111 114 119 127 129 130 131 133 135 146 147 **P**1
Primary Contact: Harris W. Brooks, Chief Executive Officer
CFO: Daniel L. Smith, Chief Financial Officer
CMO: George Thomas M.D., Chief of Staff
CIO: Shane Coleman, Chief Information Officer
CHR: Mary B Braddock, Director Human Resources
CNO: James Fesser, Chief Nursing Officer
Web address: www.ppgh.com
Control: Hospital district or authority, Government, Nonfederal **Service**: General
medical and surgical

> **Staffed Beds**: 42 **Admissions**: 1465 **Census**: 16 **Outpatient Visits**: 96692
> **Births**: 262 **Total Expense ($000)**: 40682 **Payroll Expense ($000)**: 16383
> **Personnel**: 329

MISSION—Hidalgo County

⊠ △ **MISSION REGIONAL MEDICAL CENTER (450176)**, 900 South Bryan
Road, Zip 78572–6613; tel. 956/323–9103 **A**1 7 10 **F**3 11 12 13 15 18 20 22
29 30 31 34 35 40 43 45 46 49 50 51 57 59 60 64 65 66 68 70 72 74 75 76
77 79 81 85 87 89 90 93 96 107 108 110 111 115 119 130 132 146 147 148
P8 **S** Prime Healthcare, Ontario, CA
Primary Contact: Kane A. Dawson, Chief Executive Officer
CFO: Ron Collins, Interim Chief Financial Officer
CMO: Humberto F. Nunez M.D., Chief Medical Officer
CNO: Kennetha Foster, Chief Nursing Officer
Web address: www.missionrmc.org
Control: Other not–for–profit (including NFP Corporation) **Service**: General
medical and surgical

> **Staffed Beds**: 256 **Admissions**: 8825 **Census**: 129 **Outpatient Visits**:
> 76831 **Births**: 2292 **Total Expense ($000)**: 116198 **Payroll Expense
> ($000)**: 53305 **Personnel**: 955

Hospital, Medicare Provider Number, Address, Telephone, Approval, Facility, and Physician Codes, Health Care System

★ American Hospital Association (AHA) membership   ○ Healthcare Facilities Accreditation Program   ⇑ Center for Improvement in Healthcare Quality Accreditation
☐ The Joint Commission accreditation   ◇ DNV Healthcare Inc. accreditation   △ Commission on Accreditation of Rehabilitation Facilities (CARF) accreditation

MONAHANS—Ward County

★ **WARD MEMORIAL HOSPITAL (451373)**, 406 South Gary Street, Zip 79756–4798, Mailing Address: P.O.Box 40, 79756–0040; tel. 432/943–2511 **A**10 18 **F**3 40 43 45 64 65 66 81 82 93 107 114 119 127 131 133 148 **P**6
Primary Contact: Leticia Rodriguez, Chief Executive Officer
CFO: Alison Cooper, Chief Financial Officer
CMO: Htin Thaung M.D., Chief Medical Officer
CIO: David Hargrave, Chief Information Officer
CHR: Corina Subia, Director Human Resources
CNO: Jason Harbin, Director of Nursing
Web address: www.wardmemorial.com
Control: County, Government, Nonfederal **Service:** General medical and surgical

Staffed Beds: 25 **Admissions:** 217 **Census:** 2 **Outpatient Visits:** 59592 **Births:** 0 **Total Expense ($000):** 11540 **Payroll Expense ($000):** 5434 **Personnel:** 95

MORTON—Cochran County

COCHRAN MEMORIAL HOSPITAL (451366), 201 East Grant Street, Zip 79346–3444; tel. 806/266–5565 **A**10 18 **F**34 40 57 59 65 127 149 **P**6
Primary Contact: Larry Turney, Administrator
CFO: Maggie Ramon, Chief Financial Officer
CIO: David Turney, Chief Information Officer
CHR: Amanda Turney, Director Human Resources
CNO: Rosemary Franco, Chief Nursing Officer
Control: Hospital district or authority, Government, Nonfederal **Service:** General medical and surgical

Staffed Beds: 13 **Admissions:** 14 **Census:** 1 **Outpatient Visits:** 5244 **Births:** 0 **Total Expense ($000):** 3837 **Payroll Expense ($000):** 1902 **Personnel:** 49

MOUNT PLEASANT—Titus County

☐ **TITUS REGIONAL MEDICAL CENTER (450080)**, 2001 North Jefferson Avenue, Zip 75455–2398; tel. 903/577–6000 **A**1 10 **F**3 7 11 12 13 15 18 19 20 24 26 28 29 30 34 35 39 40 43 45 47 50 51 53 54 56 57 58 59 64 68 70 73 74 75 76 78 79 81 82 85 89 90 93 97 98 103 107 108 110 111 114 115 117 118 119 121 123 129 130 132 135 147 148 149
Primary Contact: Terry Scoggin, Interim Chief Executive Officer
CFO: Terry Scoggin, Chief Financial Officer
CMO: Chris Burling M.D., Chief of Staff
CIO: Kevin Harris, Director Information Systems
CHR: Tony Piazza, Director Human Resources
CNO: Carol Slider, Chief Nursing Officer
Web address: www.titusregional.com
Control: Hospital district or authority, Government, Nonfederal **Service:** General medical and surgical

Staffed Beds: 64 **Admissions:** 4589 **Census:** 45 **Outpatient Visits:** 227079 **Births:** 1027 **Total Expense ($000):** 76781 **Payroll Expense ($000):** 26360 **Personnel:** 579

MUENSTER—Cooke County

MUENSTER MEMORIAL HOSPITAL (451335), 605 North Maple Street, Zip 76252–2424, Mailing Address: P.O.Box 370, 76252–0370; tel. 940/759–2271 **A**10 18 **F**11 35 40 43 45 53 57 59 62 64 65 75 77 81 93 107 114 119 127 130 133 146 **P**8
Primary Contact: Brian Roland, Chief Executive Officer
CFO: Julie Williams, Chief Financial Officer
CNO: Tiffany Lutkenhaus, Chief Nursing Officer
Web address: www.muensterhospital.com
Control: Hospital district or authority, Government, Nonfederal **Service:** General medical and surgical

Staffed Beds: 18 **Admissions:** 337 **Census:** 7 **Outpatient Visits:** 3648 **Births:** 0 **Total Expense ($000):** 11135 **Payroll Expense ($000):** 4707 **Personnel:** 87

MULESHOE—Bailey County

★ **MULESHOE AREA MEDICAL CENTER (451372)**, 708 South First Street, Zip 79347–3627; tel. 806/272–4524 **A**10 18 **F**3 34 40 50 56 57 59 64 91 93 97 107 119 127 133 **S** Preferred Management Corporation, Shawnee, OK
Primary Contact: Dennis Fleenor, R.N., Administrator
CMO: Bruce Purdy M.D., Chief of Staff
CHR: Suzanne Nichols, Director Human Resources
Web address: www.mahdtx.org
Control: Corporation, Investor–owned (for–profit) **Service:** General medical and surgical

Staffed Beds: 25 **Admissions:** 248 **Census:** 4 **Outpatient Visits:** 12474 **Births:** 0 **Total Expense ($000):** 9366 **Payroll Expense ($000):** 3440 **Personnel:** 98

NACOGDOCHES—Nacogdoches County

☒ **NACOGDOCHES MEDICAL CENTER (450656)**, 4920 NE Stallings Drive, Zip 75965–1200; tel. 936/569–9481 **A**1 2 10 19 **F**3 13 15 17 18 20 22 24 26 29 30 31 34 35 40 42 45 46 49 50 51 54 56 57 59 64 65 68 70 72 74 75 76 77 78 79 81 82 84 85 86 87 89 93 96 97 100 102 107 108 110 111 114 115 118 119 120 121 122 123 126 129 130 131 132 135 141 146 147 **S** TENET Healthcare Corporation, Dallas, TX
Primary Contact: Jeff Patterson, Chief Executive Officer
COO: Philip Koovakada, Chief Operating Officer
CFO: Randy Slack, Chief Financial Officer
CMO: Charles Thompson M.D., Chief Medical Officer
CIO: Teresa Simon, Director Information Systems
CHR: Teresa Farrell, Chief Human Resources Officer
CNO: Mario B Estrella, Chief Nursing Officer
Web address: www.nacmedicalcenter.com
Control: Partnership, Investor–owned (for–profit) **Service:** General medical and surgical

Staffed Beds: 117 **Admissions:** 3878 **Census:** 39 **Outpatient Visits:** 61397 **Births:** 492 **Total Expense ($000):** 65236 **Payroll Expense ($000):** 23055 **Personnel:** 362

☐ **NACOGDOCHES MEMORIAL HOSPITAL (450508)**, 1204 North Mound Street, Zip 75961–4061; tel. 936/564–4611 **A**1 10 19 **F**3 7 11 13 15 18 20 22 24 28 29 30 31 34 35 38 40 43 49 50 57 59 61 64 68 70 74 76 77 78 79 80 81 85 86 89 90 93 96 97 103 107 108 110 111 114 118 119 126 130 131 132 135 146 147 148 **P**6 8
Primary Contact: Gary G. Kendrick, FACHE, Interim Chief Executive Officer
CFO: Jane Ann Bridges, Chief Financial Officer
CNO: Beth Knight, Chief Nursing Officer
Web address: www.nacmem.org
Control: Hospital district or authority, Government, Nonfederal **Service:** General medical and surgical

Staffed Beds: 116 **Admissions:** 4390 **Census:** 59 **Outpatient Visits:** 91892 **Births:** 858 **Total Expense ($000):** 91068 **Payroll Expense ($000):** 33267 **Personnel:** 655

NASSAU BAY—Harris County

★ ⇑ **HOUSTON METHODIST ST. JOHN HOSPITAL (450709)**, 18300 St John Drive, Zip 77058–6302; tel. 281/333–5503 **A**3 5 10 21 **F**3 8 11 12 13 15 18 20 22 24 26 28 29 30 31 34 35 39 40 41 44 45 47 49 50 51 53 54 57 59 60 64 65 68 69 70 73 74 75 76 77 78 79 81 82 84 85 86 87 93 94 96 102 107 108 110 111 115 118 119 130 131 132 135 146 147 148 149 150 **S** Houston Methodist, Houston, TX
Primary Contact: Dan Newman, Chief Executive Officer
CFO: David A Witt, Vice President Finances
CHR: Becky A Merritt, Director Human Resources
Web address: www.houstonmethodist.org/st-john-clear-lake
Control: Other not–for–profit (including NFP Corporation) **Service:** General medical and surgical

Staffed Beds: 111 **Admissions:** 5621 **Census:** 60 **Outpatient Visits:** 132308 **Births:** 419 **Total Expense ($000):** 125790 **Payroll Expense ($000):** 49659 **Personnel:** 715

NAVASOTA—Grimes County

☒ **CHI ST. JOSEPH HEALTH GRIMES HOSPITAL (451322)**, 210 South Judson Street, Zip 77868–3704; tel. 936/825–6585 **A**1 10 18 **F**3 28 29 34 40 43 56 57 59 75 77 93 103 107 111 119 130 132 133 135 146 **S** Catholic Health Initiatives, Englewood, CO
CFO: Daniel Goggin, Senior Vice President and Chief Financial Officer
CMO: Luke P Scamardo M.D., II, Chief of Staff
CIO: Mike Russo, Vice President Information Systems
CHR: Kristina Lee, Director Human Resources
CNO: Cesar Lopez R.N., Director of Nurses
Web address: www.st-joseph.org
Control: Church operated, Nongovernment, not–for–profit **Service:** General medical and surgical

Staffed Beds: 18 **Admissions:** 217 **Census:** 6 **Outpatient Visits:** 17676 **Births:** 0 **Total Expense ($000):** 10474 **Payroll Expense ($000):** 4769 **Personnel:** 88

Many Facility Codes have changed. Please refer to the AHA Guide Code Chart. © 2017 AHA Guide

NEDERLAND—Jefferson County

MID-JEFFERSON EXTENDED CARE HOSPITAL (452083), 2600 Highway 365, Zip 77627-6237; tel. 409/726-8700 **A**10 **F**1 3 29 30 34 35 40 70 74 75 77 79 85 130 148
Primary Contact: Wade Lester, Chief Executive Officer
COO: Wade K Lester, Chief Nursing and Operations Officer
Web address: www.midjeffextendedcare.com/index.php
Control: Corporation, Investor-owned (for-profit) **Service**: Acute long-term care hospital

Staffed Beds: 48 **Admissions**: 656 **Census**: 43 **Outpatient Visits**: 0 **Births**: 0
Total Expense ($000): 16927 **Payroll Expense ($000)**: 8503 **Personnel**: 159

NEW BRAUNFELS—Comal County

GULF STATES LONG TERM ACUTE CARE OF NEW BRAUNFELS See Post Acute/Warm Springs Specialty Hospital Of New Braunfels

☐ **NEW BRAUNFELS REGIONAL REHABILITATION HOSPITAL (673049)**, 2041 Sundance Parkway, Zip 78130-2779; tel. 830/625-6700 **A**1 10 **F**29 34 57 64 90 91 93 130 132 148 **S** Ernest Health, Inc., Albuquerque, NM
Primary Contact: Jessie Smedley, Chief Executive Officer
CFO: Sue Thomsen, Chief Financial Officer
CMO: Maria R Lomba, Medical Director
CHR: Cheryl Smith, Manager Human Resources
CNO: Peggy Schmits, Director, Nursing Operations
Web address: www.nbrrh.ernesthealth.com
Control: Corporation, Investor-owned (for-profit) **Service**: Rehabilitation

Staffed Beds: 40 **Admissions**: 766 **Census**: 30 **Outpatient Visits**: 7637
Births: 0 **Total Expense ($000)**: 13260 **Payroll Expense ($000)**: 6509
Personnel: 141

⊞ **POST ACUTE/WARM SPRINGS SPECIALTY HOSPITAL OF NEW BRAUNFELS (452106)**, 1445 Hanz Drive, Zip 78130-2567; tel. 830/627-7600 **A**1 10 **F**1 3 29 30 34 85 130 148 **S** Post Acute Medical, LLC, Enola, PA
Primary Contact: Shayne Goode, Administrator
Web address: www.warmsprings.org/locations/hos/h1/
Control: Partnership, Investor-owned (for-profit) **Service**: Acute long-term care hospital

Staffed Beds: 40 **Admissions**: 634 **Census**: 29 **Outpatient Visits**: 0 **Births**: 0
Total Expense ($000): 14569 **Payroll Expense ($000)**: 6049 **Personnel**: 103

⊞ **RESOLUTE HEALTH (670098)**, 555 Creekside Crossing, Zip 78130-2594; tel. 830/500-6000 **A**1 10 **F**3 13 15 18 20 22 29 30 34 35 40 45 48 49 50 53 60 64 65 70 72 74 75 76 77 79 81 85 87 107 108 111 114 115 119 126 130 146 147 149 150 **P**8 **S** TENET Healthcare Corporation, Dallas, TX
Primary Contact: Mark L. Bernard, Chief Executive Officer
Web address: www.resolutehealth.com
Control: Corporation, Investor-owned (for-profit) **Service**: General medical and surgical

Staffed Beds: 70 **Admissions**: 3889 **Census**: 36 **Outpatient Visits**: 28223
Births: 615 **Total Expense ($000)**: 84724 **Payroll Expense ($000)**: 21722
Personnel: 351

NOCONA—Montague County

NOCONA GENERAL HOSPITAL (450641), 100 Park Road, Zip 76255-3616; tel. 940/825-3235 **A**10 **F**3 7 11 28 29 30 34 35 40 43 45 50 53 57 59 62 64 68 75 81 82 86 87 93 107 108 114 119 130 133 146 148 **P**5
Primary Contact: Lance Meekins, Chief Executive Officer
CFO: Lance Meekins, Chief Executive Officer
CMO: Chance Dingler M.D., Chief Medical Officer
CHR: Paula Monkres, Administrative Assistant and Director Human Resources
Web address: www.noconageneral.com/
Control: Hospital district or authority, Government, Nonfederal **Service**: General medical and surgical

Staffed Beds: 25 **Admissions**: 563 **Census**: 9 **Outpatient Visits**: 6430
Births: 0 **Total Expense ($000)**: 7675 **Payroll Expense ($000)**: 4010
Personnel: 99

NORTH RICHLAND HILLS—Tarrant County

⊞ **MEDICAL CITY NORTH HILLS (450087)**, 4401 Booth Calloway Road, Zip 76180-7399; tel. 817/255-1000 **A**1 10 **F**3 8 12 15 17 18 20 22 24 28 29 30 31 34 37 40 43 45 49 53 56 57 64 70 74 75 77 78 79 81 84 85 86 87 93 98 103 107 108 110 111 115 118 119 126 130 132 135 146 148 149 **P**3 6 **S** HCA Healthcare, Nashville, TN
Primary Contact: Xavier Villarreal, FACHE, Chief Executive Officer
COO: Nancy L Hill R.N., MSN, Chief Operating Officer
CFO: Nick Galt, Chief Financial Officer
CMO: John McDonald M.D., Chief Medical Officer
CIO: Jason Sims, Facility Information Security Officer
CHR: Cynthia Dang, Vice President Human Resources
CNO: Tracey Smithson MSN, R.N., Chief Nursing Officer
Web address: www.northhillshospital.com
Control: Partnership, Investor-owned (for-profit) **Service**: General medical and surgical

Staffed Beds: 164 **Admissions**: 6687 **Census**: 85 **Outpatient Visits**: 57773
Births: 0 **Total Expense ($000)**: 114090 **Payroll Expense ($000)**: 35316
Personnel: 529

ODESSA—Ector County

★ **CONTINUECARE HOSPITAL AT MEDICAL CENTER (ODESSA) (670111)**, 500 West Fourth Street, 4th Floor, Zip 79761-5001; tel. 432/640-4380 **F**1 3 29 34 35 71 79 85 87 148 **S** Community Hospital Corporation, Plano, TX
Primary Contact: Judith Schiros, Chief Executive Officer
Web address: www.continuecare.org/odessa//
Control: Other not-for-profit (including NFP Corporation) **Service**: Acute long-term care hospital

Staffed Beds: 25 **Admissions**: 67 **Census**: 4 **Outpatient Visits**: 0 **Births**: 0
Total Expense ($000): 3456 **Payroll Expense ($000)**: 1546 **Personnel**: 29

⊞ **MEDICAL CENTER HEALTH SYSTEM (450132)**, 500 West Fourth Street, Zip 79761-5059, Mailing Address: P O Drawer 7239, 79760-7239; tel. 432/640-4000 **A**1 2 3 5 10 **F**3 8 11 12 13 15 17 18 20 22 24 26 28 29 30 31 34 35 39 40 43 45 46 47 48 49 50 53 54 57 59 64 65 66 68 70 71 72 74 75 76 77 78 79 81 85 87 89 90 93 107 111 114 115 116 117 118 119 126 129 130 131 132 135 144 146 147 148 **P**6 8
Primary Contact: William W. Webster, FACHE, President and Chief Executive Officer
COO: Tony Ruiz, Senior Vice President, Chief Operating Officer
CFO: Jon Riggs, Senior Vice President, Chief Financial Officer
CMO: Arun Mathews M.D., Chief Medical Officer (Acute)
CIO: Gary Barnes, Senior Vice President, Chief Information Officer
CHR: Robbi Banks, Vice President, Human Resources
CNO: Chad Dunavan R.N., Vice President, Chief Nursing Officer
Web address: www.mchodessa.com
Control: Hospital district or authority, Government, Nonfederal **Service**: General medical and surgical

Staffed Beds: 368 **Admissions**: 12569 **Census**: 201 **Outpatient Visits**: 352326 **Births**: 1530 **Total Expense ($000)**: 274243 **Payroll Expense ($000)**: 104938 **Personnel**: 1633

MEDICAL CENTER HOSPITAL See Medical Center Health System

⇧ **ODESSA REGIONAL MEDICAL CENTER (450661)**, 520 East Sixth Street, Zip 79761-4565, Mailing Address: P.O.Box 4859, 79760-4859; tel. 432/582-8000 **A**3 5 10 21 **F**3 12 13 15 17 18 20 22 23 24 25 29 34 35 40 43 46 49 50 51 52 55 57 59 60 64 66 72 74 75 76 79 81 82 85 86 87 89 90 91 107 108 111 115 119 124 130 132 146 147 148 **P**8 **S** IASIS Healthcare, Franklin, TN
Primary Contact: Stacey L. Gerig, Chief Executive Officer
CIO: Jimmy Diaz, Director Information Technology
CHR: Jill Sparkman, Director Human Resources
CNO: Levi Ross Stone R.N., Chief Nursing Officer and Chief Operating Officer
Web address: www.odessaregionalmedicalcenter.com
Control: Partnership, Investor-owned (for-profit) **Service**: General medical and surgical

Staffed Beds: 213 **Admissions**: 6189 **Census**: 88 **Outpatient Visits**: 46944
Births: 2663 **Total Expense ($000)**: 118844 **Payroll Expense ($000)**: 41578 **Personnel**: 553

TX

Hospital, Medicare Provider Number, Address, Telephone, Approval, Facility, and Physician Codes, Health Care System

★ American Hospital Association (AHA) membership
☐ The Joint Commission accreditation
○ Healthcare Facilities Accreditation Program
◇ DNV Healthcare Inc. accreditation
⇧ Center for Improvement in Healthcare Quality Accreditation
△ Commission on Accreditation of Rehabilitation Facilities (CARF) accreditation

☐ **ODESSA REGIONAL MEDICAL CENTER SOUTH CAMPUS (670066)**, 900 East 4th Street, Zip 79761–5255; tel. 432/362–9900 (Nonreporting) **A**1 10
Primary Contact: Stacey Gerig, Chief Executive Officer
CMO: Richard Bartlett M.D., Chief Medical Officer
CHR: Gail Knous, Chief Executive Officer and Chief Compliance Officer
Web address: www.bhcodessa.com/
Control: Partnership, Investor–owned (for–profit) **Service:** General medical and surgical

Staffed Beds: 14

OLNEY—Young County

★ **HAMILTON HOSPITAL (451354)**, 901 West Hamilton Street, Zip 76374–1725, Mailing Address: P.O.Box 158, 76374–0158; tel. 940/564–5521 **A**10 18 **F**7 11 13 28 29 30 34 40 43 53 57 76 77 81 86 89 93 107 114 127 129 133 146 148
Primary Contact: Michael H. Huff, Chief Executive Officer
CFO: Coy Noles, Chief Financial Officer Consultant
CMO: Mark L Mankins M.D., Chief of Staff
CIO: Rick Oliver, Information Technology
CHR: Amy Moore, Human Resources
CNO: Samantha Isbell R.N., Chief Nursing Officer
Web address: www.olneyhamiltonhospital.com
Control: Hospital district or authority, Government, Nonfederal **Service:** General medical and surgical

Staffed Beds: 25 **Admissions:** 537 **Census:** 9 **Outpatient Visits:** 16461
Births: 38 **Total Expense ($000):** 16571 **Payroll Expense ($000):** 5169
Personnel: 129

PALACIOS—Matagorda County

PALACIOS COMMUNITY MEDICAL CENTER (451332), 311 Green Street, Zip 77465–3213; tel. 361/972–2511 **A**10 18 **F**29 34 40 41 50 54 57 59 64 65 87 91 93 97 107 119 127 133 146 148 **P**6
Primary Contact: Claude Manning, Chief Executive Officer
COO: Lisa Henderson, Chief Operating Officer
CIO: Angela Yeager, Director Information Technology
CHR: Lisa Henderson, Chief Operations Officer
CNO: Susan Easter, Chief Nursing Officer
Web address: www.palacioshospital.net/
Control: Other not–for–profit (including NFP Corporation) **Service:** General medical and surgical

Staffed Beds: 17 **Admissions:** 111 **Census:** 2 **Outpatient Visits:** 11910
Births: 0 **Total Expense ($000):** 5516 **Payroll Expense ($000):** 2928
Personnel: 43

PALESTINE—Anderson County

✠ **PALESTINE REGIONAL MEDICAL CENTER (453089)**, 2900 S Loop 256, Zip 75801–6958; tel. 903/731–1000, (Nonreporting) **A**1 **S** LifePoint Health, Brentwood, TN
Primary Contact: Roy Finch, Chief Executive Officer
CFO: Celena Brim, Chief Financial Officer
CIO: Rebecca Chou, Directory Information Systems
CHR: Rhonda Beard, Director Human Resources
Web address: www.palestineregional.com
Control: Corporation, Investor–owned (for–profit) **Service:** Rehabilitation

Staffed Beds: 12

✠ **PALESTINE REGIONAL MEDICAL CENTER–EAST (450747)**, 2900 South Loop 256, Zip 75801–6958; tel. 903/731–1000 **A**1 10 **F**3 4 7 11 13 15 18 20 22 26 28 29 30 34 40 43 44 47 48 49 50 51 56 57 59 60 62 63 70 76 79 81 82 85 86 87 89 90 93 96 97 98 100 101 102 103 104 107 108 110 111 114 118 119 129 130 131 146 147 148 **S** LifePoint Health, Brentwood, TN
Primary Contact: Roy Finch, Chief Executive Officer
CFO: Celena Brim, Chief Financial Officer
CIO: Rebecca Chou, Director Information Systems
CHR: Rhonda Beard, Director Human Resources
Web address: www.palestineregional.com
Control: Partnership, Investor–owned (for–profit) **Service:** General medical and surgical

Staffed Beds: 120 **Admissions:** 4074 **Census:** 62 **Outpatient Visits:** 80392
Births: 663 **Total Expense ($000):** 63322 **Payroll Expense ($000):** 29814
Personnel: 482

PAMPA—Gray County

✠ **PAMPA REGIONAL MEDICAL CENTER (450099)**, One Medical Plaza, Zip 79065; tel. 806/665–3721 **A**1 3 10 20 **F**3 11 12 13 15 18 20 22 29 30 34 40 43 45 46 47 48 49 50 51 52 54 56 57 58 59 60 61 63 64 65 66 68 70 75 76 77 79 81 83 84 85 86 87 91 92 93 96 97 98 100 101 103 104 105 107 108 110 111 114 115 119 130 132 134 135 146 147 148 **P**7 **S** Prime Healthcare, Ontario, CA
Primary Contact: Edwin Leon, Chief Executive Officer
CFO: Paul Christenson, Chief Financial Officer
CMO: David Hampton M.D., Chief Medical Staff
CIO: Joy Patton, Chief Information Services
CHR: Debbie Dixon, Director Human Resources
CNO: Catherine Kenney, Chief Nursing Officer
Web address: www.prmctx.com
Control: Other not–for–profit (including NFP Corporation) **Service:** General medical and surgical

Staffed Beds: 72 **Admissions:** 2339 **Census:** 22 **Outpatient Visits:** 42308
Births: 229 **Total Expense ($000):** 41950 **Payroll Expense ($000):** 14798
Personnel: 224

PARIS—Lamar County

★ **CHRISTUS DUBUIS HOSPITAL OF PARIS (452082)**, 820 Clarksville Street, 6th Floor, Zip 75460–6027; tel. 903/737–3600 **A**10 **F**1 3 29 30 85 148 **S** CHRISTUS Health, Irving, TX
Primary Contact: Kathie Reese, R.N., Regional Administrator and Chief Executive Officer
CFO: Michael Murray, Chief Financial Officer
CMO: Devabrata Ganguly M.D., Medical Director
CNO: Janice Cochran R.N., Director Patient Care
Web address: www.christusdubuis.org
Control: Church operated, Nongovernment, not–for–profit **Service:** Acute long–term care hospital

Staffed Beds: 25 **Admissions:** 197 **Census:** 14 **Outpatient Visits:** 0 **Births:** 0
Total Expense ($000): 5542 **Payroll Expense ($000):** 1956 **Personnel:** 39

☐ **PARIS REGIONAL MEDICAL CENTER (450196)**, 865 Deshong Drive, Zip 75460–9313, Mailing Address: P.O.Box 9070, 75461–9070; tel. 903/785–4521, (Includes PARIS REGIONAL MEDICAL CENTER–SOUTH CAMPUS, 820 Clarksville Street, Paris, Texas, Zip 75460–9070, P O Box 9070, 75461–9070, tel. 903/785–4521; PARIS REGIONAL MEDICAL CENTER, 865 Deshong Drive, Paris, Texas, Zip 75462–2097, tel. 903/785–4521) **A**1 10 19 **F**1 3 8 11 13 15 17 18 20 22 24 26 28 29 30 31 34 35 36 39 40 45 49 50 51 55 57 59 60 64 65 66 68 70 72 74 75 76 77 78 79 81 82 85 86 87 89 90 91 93 97 98 102 103 107 108 111 115 119 126 127 130 132 135 145 146 147 148 149 **P**5 **S** RCCH HealthCare Partners, Brentwood, TN
Primary Contact: Steve Hyde, Chief Executive Officer
COO: Patti Monczewski, Chief Operating Officer
CFO: Donald E McDaniel III, Chief Financial Officer
CMO: Richard Bercher M.D., Chief Medical Officer
CHR: Cheryl Perry, Executive Director Human Resources
CNO: Debra Taylor, Chief Nursing Officer
Web address: www.parisregionalmedical.com/
Control: Partnership, Investor–owned (for–profit) **Service:** General medical and surgical

Staffed Beds: 173 **Admissions:** 7699 **Census:** 98 **Outpatient Visits:** 83947
Births: 809 **Total Expense ($000):** 110058 **Payroll Expense ($000):** 38039
Personnel: 677

PASADENA—Harris County

✠ **BAYSHORE MEDICAL CENTER (450097)**, 4000 Spencer Highway, Zip 77504–1202; tel. 713/359–2000, (Includes EAST HOUSTON REGIONAL MEDICAL CENTER, 13111 East Freeway, Houston, Texas, Zip 77015–5820, tel. 713/393–2000; Eric Evans, Chief Executive Officer) **A**1 2 10 **F**3 8 11 12 13 15 17 18 20 22 24 26 28 29 31 34 35 40 41 42 43 45 46 49 50 51 56 57 59 60 64 70 72 74 75 76 77 78 79 81 82 85 90 93 96 98 100 103 104 105 107 108 110 111 114 118 119 121 123 124 129 130 131 132 146 147 148 **S** HCA Healthcare, Nashville, TN
Primary Contact: Jeanna Barnard, FACHE, Chief Executive Officer
CFO: John Armour, Chief Financial Officer
CIO: Clifford Ferguson, Director Information Technology and Systems
Web address: www.bayshoremedical.com
Control: Partnership, Investor–owned (for–profit) **Service:** General medical and surgical

Staffed Beds: 461 **Admissions:** 21635 **Census:** 298 **Outpatient Visits:** 187778 **Births:** 4172 **Total Expense ($000):** 275944 **Payroll Expense ($000):** 113358 **Personnel:** 2264

Many Facility Codes have changed. Please refer to the AHA Guide Code Chart. © 2017 AHA Guide

★ ⇧ **CHI ST. LUKE'S HEALTH – PATIENTS MEDICAL CENTER (670031)**, 4600 East Sam Houston Parkway South, Zip 77505–3948; tel. 713/948–7000 **A**10 21 **F**15 18 20 22 24 29 30 31 35 40 45 46 54 64 70 74 77 81 82 86 87 91 93 94 107 111 114 115 116 117 119 129 130 135 146 147 148 **S** Catholic Health Initiatives, Englewood, CO
Primary Contact: Steven Foster, Chief Executive Officer
Web address: www.stlukestexas.com
Control: Corporation, Investor–owned (for–profit) **Service:** General medical and surgical

Staffed Beds: 61 **Admissions:** 3932 **Census:** 54 **Outpatient Visits:** 34313 **Births:** 0 **Total Expense ($000):** 71128 **Payroll Expense ($000):** 26929 **Personnel:** 386

⇧ **PATIENTS MEDICAL CENTER** See Chi St. Luke's Health – Patients Medical Center

○ **SURGERY SPECIALTY HOSPITALS OF AMERICA (450831)**, 4301B Vista Road, Zip 77504; tel. 713/378–3000 **A**10 11 **F**3 12 29 40 45 68 70 75 79 81 82 107 111 114 119 132 135
Primary Contact: Eric Chan, M.D., Chief Executive Officer
COO: Hemant Khemka, Chief Operating Officer
CFO: Hemant Khemka, Chief Financial Officer
CMO: Xiao H. Li M.D., Chief of Staff
CIO: Ringo Cheng, Director Information Technology
Web address: www.surgeryspecialty.com/
Control: Partnership, Investor–owned (for–profit) **Service:** General medical and surgical

Staffed Beds: 37 **Admissions:** 43 **Census:** 1 **Outpatient Visits:** 1884 **Births:** 0 **Total Expense ($000):** 13627 **Payroll Expense ($000):** 3697 **Personnel:** 88

PEARLAND—Brazoria County

⊞ **PEARLAND MEDICAL CENTER (670106)**, 11100 Shadow Creek Parkway, Zip 77584–7285; tel. 713/770–7000 **A**1 **F**3 13 15 18 20 22 26 29 31 34 35 37 40 41 45 49 50 51 57 59 60 68 73 74 75 76 77 78 79 81 82 85 86 87 107 108 110 111 114 119 126 130 143 146 148 **S** HCA Healthcare, Nashville, TN
Primary Contact: David S. Wagner, FACHE, Chief Executive Officer
Web address: www.pearlandmc.com
Control: Partnership, Investor–owned (for–profit) **Service:** General medical and surgical

Staffed Beds: 34 **Admissions:** 1920 **Census:** 18 **Outpatient Visits:** 23016 **Births:** 264 **Total Expense ($000):** 55282 **Payroll Expense ($000):** 16544 **Personnel:** 232

PEARSALL—Frio County

★ **FRIO REGIONAL HOSPITAL (450293)**, 200 South I H 35, Zip 78061–3998; tel. 830/334–3617 **A**10 **F**3 8 15 29 34 35 40 43 45 53 57 59 62 64 68 77 81 87 107 114 119 130 133 148 **P**6
Primary Contact: Andrew G. Williams, Chief Executive Officer
CMO: Oscar Garza M.D., Chief Medical Staff
CIO: Jacob Flores, Chief Information Officer
CHR: Nancy Ortiz, Director Human Resource and Marketing
CNO: Louisa Martinez, Director of Nursing
Web address: www.frioregionalhospital.com
Control: Other not–for–profit (including NFP Corporation) **Service:** General medical and surgical

Staffed Beds: 22 **Admissions:** 358 **Census:** 4 **Outpatient Visits:** 22163 **Births:** 119 **Total Expense ($000):** 15804 **Payroll Expense ($000):** 6377 **Personnel:** 121

PECOS—Reeves County

REEVES COUNTY HOSPITAL (451377), 2323 Texas Street, Zip 79772–7338; tel. 432/447–3551 **A**10 18 **F**3 11 15 35 40 43 57 60 64 68 70 76 81 87 93 107 110 114 119 127 130 131 133 146 147 148
Primary Contact: Brenda McKinney, Chief Executive Officer
CFO: Bomi Bharucha, Chief Financial Officer
CMO: W J Bang M.D., Chief of Staff
CHR: Nadine Smith, Director Human Resources
CNO: Faye Lease, Director of Nursing
Web address: www.reevescountyhospital.com
Control: Hospital district or authority, Government, Nonfederal **Service:** General medical and surgical

Staffed Beds: 25 **Admissions:** 874 **Census:** 8 **Outpatient Visits:** 55143 **Births:** 138 **Total Expense ($000):** 25097 **Payroll Expense ($000):** 12889 **Personnel:** 210

PERRYTON—Ochiltree County

★ **OCHILTREE GENERAL HOSPITAL (451359)**, 3101 Garrett Drive, Zip 79070–5323; tel. 806/435–3606 **A**10 18 **F**10 11 13 15 30 35 40 43 57 59 62 63 64 69 76 81 85 89 93 107 108 114 119 127 130 133 143 146 147 **P**1
Primary Contact: Robert A. Pascasio, FACHE, Administrator and Chief Executive Officer
CFO: Debbie Blodgett, Director Fiscal Services
CMO: Rex Mann M.D., Chief Medical Officer
CIO: Dyan Harrison, Manager Health Information
CHR: Debbie Beck, Manager Human Resource and Payroll
Web address: www.ochiltreehospital.com
Control: Hospital district or authority, Government, Nonfederal **Service:** General medical and surgical

Staffed Beds: 25 **Admissions:** 499 **Census:** 6 **Outpatient Visits:** 36709 **Births:** 152 **Total Expense ($000):** 16712 **Payroll Expense ($000):** 6857 **Personnel:** 157

PITTSBURG—Camp County

★ **EAST TEXAS MEDICAL CENTER PITTSBURG (451367)**, 2701 Highway 271 North, Zip 75686–1032; tel. 903/946–5000 **A**10 18 **F**3 11 12 28 29 35 40 43 45 50 53 57 59 64 68 70 75 77 81 85 87 89 92 93 97 107 108 111 115 119 127 129 130 133 **P**6 **S** East Texas Medical Center Regional Healthcare System, Tyler, TX
Primary Contact: James Warren. Robicheaux, FACHE, Senior Administrator
CFO: Janet Andersen, Chief Financial Officer
CMO: W R Christensen M.D., Chief of Staff
CIO: Paula Anthony, Vice President Information Services
CHR: Kathy Shelton, Director Human Resources
CNO: Casey Mayben, Chief Nursing Officer
Web address: www.etmc.org/newpittsburg.htm
Control: Other not–for–profit (including NFP Corporation) **Service:** General medical and surgical

Staffed Beds: 25 **Admissions:** 1028 **Census:** 11 **Outpatient Visits:** 90899 **Births:** 0 **Total Expense ($000):** 30188 **Payroll Expense ($000):** 9720 **Personnel:** 187

PLAINVIEW—Hale County

ALLEGIANCE BEHAVIORAL HEALTH CENTER OF PLAINVIEW (454101), 2601 Dimmit Road, Suite 400, Zip 79072–1833; tel. 806/296–9191 **A**10 **F**29 35 56 64 98 101 103 104 149 **S** Allegiance Health Management, Shreveport, LA
Primary Contact: Angie Alexander, Chief Executive Officer
COO: Don Cameron, Chief Operating Officer
CMO: Victor A Gutierrez M.D., Medical Director
CIO: Richard Merk, Executive Vice President
CHR: Richard Merk, Director Human Resources
Web address: www.ahmgt.com
Control: Corporation, Investor–owned (for–profit) **Service:** Psychiatric

Staffed Beds: 20 **Admissions:** 267 **Census:** 11 **Outpatient Visits:** 21503 **Births:** 0 **Total Expense ($000):** 6455 **Payroll Expense ($000):** 2030 **Personnel:** 61

⊞ **COVENANT HOSPITAL PLAINVIEW (450539)**, 2601 Dimmitt Road, Zip 79072–1833; tel. 806/296–5531 **A**1 3 10 20 **F**3 11 12 13 15 18 29 30 32 34 35 38 40 41 43 44 45 46 48 50 51 54 56 57 59 61 64 65 68 70 75 76 77 79 80 81 85 86 87 97 107 108 110 114 119 127 129 130 131 132 135 146 147 148 149 **S** Providence St. Joseph Health, Renton, WA
Primary Contact: Robert Copeland, Interim Chief Executive Officer
COO: Mike McNutt, Assistant Administrator
CFO: Cassie Mogg, Chief Financial Officer
CMO: Sergio Lara M.D., Chief Medical Officer
CNO: Leslie Hackett, Chief Nursing Officer
Web address: www.covenantplainview.org
Control: Church operated, Nongovernment, not–for–profit **Service:** General medical and surgical

Staffed Beds: 68 **Admissions:** 1977 **Census:** 17 **Outpatient Visits:** 86052 **Births:** 447 **Total Expense ($000):** 38514 **Payroll Expense ($000):** 12598 **Personnel:** 315

PLANO—Collin County

✠ **BAYLOR REGIONAL MEDICAL CENTER AT PLANO (450890)**, 4700 Alliance Boulevard, Zip 75093–5323; tel. 469/814–2000 **A**1 2 3 5 10 **F**3 12 15 29 30 31 34 35 40 45 46 47 48 49 54 57 58 59 64 70 74 75 77 78 79 80 81 82 84 85 86 87 107 108 110 111 114 118 119 126 130 131 132 135 145 146 147 148 149 **S** Baylor Scott & White Health, Dallas, TX
Primary Contact: Jerri Garison, R.N., President
COO: Joseph Brown, Vice President Operations
CFO: Deanne Kindered, Vice President Finance
CMO: John Marcucci M.D., Vice President Medical Affairs
CHR: Kriss Gamez, Director Human Resources
Web address: www.baylorhealth.com/PhysiciansLocations/Plano/Pages/Default.aspx
Control: Other not–for–profit (including NFP Corporation) **Service**: General medical and surgical

Staffed Beds: 116 **Admissions**: 6619 **Census**: 90 **Outpatient Visits**: 53524 **Births**: 0 **Total Expense ($000)**: 172832 **Payroll Expense ($000)**: 58553 **Personnel**: 598

CHILDREN'S MEDICAL CENTER PLANO (453316), 7601 Preston Road, Zip 75024–3214; tel. 469/303–7000 **A**3 5 **F**3 88 89 98
Primary Contact: David T. Berry, President, Children's Health Clinical Operations
CIO: Pamela Arora, Senior Vice President and Chief Information Officer
CHR: Kim Besse, Senior Vice President and Chief Human Resource Officer
CNO: Mary Stowe, Senior Vice President and Chief Nursing Officer
Web address: www.childrens.com/location–landing/locations–and–directions/childrens–health–plano
Control: Other not–for–profit (including NFP Corporation) **Service**: Children's general medical and surgical

Staffed Beds: 72 **Admissions**: 6320 **Census**: 27 **Outpatient Visits**: 164698 **Births**: 0 **Total Expense ($000)**: 142988 **Payroll Expense ($000)**: 48302 **Personnel**: 628

✠ **HEALTHSOUTH PLANO REHABILITATION HOSPITAL (453047)**, 2800 West 15th Street, Zip 75075–7526; tel. 972/612–9000 **A**1 10 **F**34 57 59 90 93 95 96 130 132 148 **S** HEALTHSOUTH Corporation, Birmingham, AL
Primary Contact: Jennifer Lynn. Brewer, Chief Executive Officer
CFO: Catrina Madkins, Controller and Chief Financial Officer
CMO: Omar Colon M.D., Medical Director
Web address: www.healthsouthplano.com
Control: Corporation, Investor–owned (for–profit) **Service**: Rehabilitation

Staffed Beds: 83 **Admissions**: 1590 **Census**: 49 **Outpatient Visits**: 8933 **Births**: 0 **Total Expense ($000)**: 20742 **Payroll Expense ($000)**: 11278 **Personnel**: 236

✠ ⇑ **MEDICAL CITY PLANO (450651)**, 3901 West 15th Street, Zip 75075–7738; tel. 972/596–6800, (Includes MEDICAL CENTER FRISCO, 5500 Frisco Square Boulevard, Frisco, Texas, Zip 75034–3305, tel. 214/618–0500; Charles Gressle, Chief Executive Officer) **A**1 2 3 10 13 21 **F**3 12 13 15 16 18 19 20 22 24 26 28 29 30 31 34 35 40 42 43 45 46 47 48 49 51 54 55 57 58 59 60 64 70 72 74 75 76 78 79 81 82 84 85 86 87 90 91 93 107 108 110 111 112 114 115 117 118 119 124 126 130 132 135 145 146 147 148 **P**5 **S** HCA Healthcare, Nashville, TN
Primary Contact: Charles Gressle, Chief Executive Officer
CFO: W Patrick Whitmore, Chief Financial Officer
CMO: Ann Arnold M.D., Medical Director
CIO: Michael Gfeller, Director Information Systems
CHR: Shanna Warren, Director Human Resources
Web address: www.medicalcenterplano.com
Control: Partnership, Investor–owned (for–profit) **Service**: General medical and surgical

Staffed Beds: 390 **Admissions**: 18928 **Census**: 311 **Outpatient Visits**: 137052 **Births**: 2593 **Total Expense ($000)**: 355920 **Payroll Expense ($000)**: 107899 **Personnel**: 1738

☐ **PLANO SPECIALTY HOSPITAL (452054)**, 1621 Coit Road, Zip 75075–6141; tel. 972/758–5200, (Data for 254 days)**A**1 10 **F**1 3 29 75 82 84 85 86 87 96 130 135 148 **S** Concord Healthcare Group, Lakewood, NJ
Primary Contact: Wayne Cook, Chief Executive Officer
CFO: Deanna Lankford, Business Office Manager
CHR: Robbie McCranie, Director Human Resources
Web address: www.specialtyhospital–plano.com
Control: Corporation, Investor–owned (for–profit) **Service**: Acute long–term care hospital

Staffed Beds: 43 **Admissions**: 184 **Census**: 17 **Outpatient Visits**: 0 **Births**: 0 **Total Expense ($000)**: 5973 **Payroll Expense ($000)**: 2797 **Personnel**: 47

ACCEL REHABILITATION HOSPITAL OF PLANO (673055), 2301 Marsh Lane, #200, Zip 75093–8497; tel. 972/899–5510 (Nonreporting)
Primary Contact: Rick Tichenor, Chief Executive Officer
Web address: www.accelrehab.com
Control: Corporation, Investor–owned (for–profit) **Service**: Rehabilitation

Staffed Beds: 48

☐ **TEXAS HEALTH CENTER FOR DIAGNOSTIC & SURGERY (450891)**, 6020 West Parker Road, Suite 100, Zip 75093–8171; tel. 972/403–2700 **A**1 2 10 **F**3 29 40 45 54 64 79 81 82 85 87 107 111 115 119 126 129 149
Primary Contact: Larry Robertson, President
CFO: Douglas Browning, Chief Financial Officer
CHR: Cookie Tedder, Human Resources Manager
CNO: Ellen Baldwin R.N., Chief Nursing Officer
Web address: www.thcds.com
Control: Partnership, Investor–owned (for–profit) **Service**: General medical and surgical

Staffed Beds: 18 **Admissions**: 629 **Census**: 3 **Outpatient Visits**: 15141 **Births**: 0 **Total Expense ($000)**: 52032 **Payroll Expense ($000)**: 12693 **Personnel**: 165

✠ **TEXAS HEALTH PRESBYTERIAN HOSPITAL PLANO (450771)**, 6200 West Parker Road, Zip 75093–8185; tel. 972/981–8000 **A**1 3 10 **F**3 12 13 15 18 20 22 24 26 28 29 30 31 32 34 35 37 38 40 43 44 45 46 49 50 52 53 54 55 57 58 59 60 64 65 68 70 72 74 75 76 77 78 79 81 84 85 86 87 89 93 98 107 108 110 111 114 115 118 119 126 130 131 132 134 135 141 145 146 147 148 149 150 **P**5 **S** Texas Health Resources, Arlington, TX
Primary Contact: Joshua Floren, President
CFO: Lisa Gildon, Vice President and Chief Financial Officer
CMO: Gwen Webster M.D., President Medical Staff
CIO: Susan Anderson, Director Information Systems
CHR: Kelly K Martin, Human Resource Officer
Web address: www.texashealth.org
Control: Other not–for–profit (including NFP Corporation) **Service**: General medical and surgical

Staffed Beds: 371 **Admissions**: 16615 **Census**: 217 **Outpatient Visits**: 97396 **Births**: 4278 **Total Expense ($000)**: 317978 **Payroll Expense ($000)**: 113999 **Personnel**: 1406

✠ **THE HEART HOSPITAL BAYLOR PLANO (670025)**, 1100 Allied Drive, Zip 75093–5348; tel. 469/814–3278 **A**1 3 5 10 **F**3 17 18 20 22 24 26 28 29 30 34 35 40 54 57 58 59 60 64 68 71 75 77 81 84 85 87 107 111 114 115 119 126 130 132 135 146 148 149
Primary Contact: Mark Valentine, President
CFO: Bryan Nichols, Chief Financial Officer
CMO: Trent Pettijohn M.D., Esq, Chief Medical Officer
CHR: Tracy Stanford, Director Human Resources
CNO: Susan K. Moats R.N., Vice President Patient Care Services and Chief Nursing Officer
Web address: www.thehearthospitalbaylor.com
Control: Partnership, Investor–owned (for–profit) **Service**: Heart

Staffed Beds: 116 **Admissions**: 4579 **Census**: 72 **Outpatient Visits**: 27226 **Births**: 0 **Total Expense ($000)**: 208285 **Payroll Expense ($000)**: 65978 **Personnel**: 650

WELLBRIDGE HEALTHCARE GREATER DALLAS (454130), 4301 Mapleshade Lane, Zip 75093–0010; tel. 972/596–5445 (Nonreporting) **S** Oceans Healthcare, Lake Charles, LA
Primary Contact: John Sannuto, Chief Executive Officer
Web address: www.oceansplano.com
Control: Corporation, Investor–owned (for–profit) **Service**: Psychiatric

Staffed Beds: 25

PLANO—Denton County

☐ ⇑ **PLANO SURGICAL HOSPITAL**, 2301 Marsh Lane, Zip 75093–8497; tel. 972/820–2600 **A**1 21 **F**3 29 40 45 46 49 79 81 82 85 87 107 114 149 **S** Nobilis Health Corporation, Houston, TX
Primary Contact: Jay Lindsey, Chief Executive Officer
Web address: www.nobilishealth.com/our–facilities/dallas/
Control: Corporation, Investor–owned (for–profit) **Service**: Surgical

Staffed Beds: 26 **Admissions**: 257 **Census**: 1 **Outpatient Visits**: 1782 **Births**: 0 **Total Expense ($000)**: 62272 **Payroll Expense ($000)**: 7290 **Personnel**: 101

TX

Many Facility Codes have changed. Please refer to the AHA Guide Code Chart.   © 2017 AHA Guide

Hospitals, U.S. / TEXAS

PORT ARTHUR—Jefferson County

DUBUIS HOSPITAL OF PORT ARTHUR See Christus Dubuis Hospital Of Port Arthur

⇑ **THE MEDICAL CENTER OF SOUTHEAST TEXAS (450518)**, 2555 Jimmy Johnson Boulevard, Zip 77640–2007; tel. 409/724–7389 **A**10 21 **F**3 8 11 12 13 15 17 18 20 22 24 26 28 29 30 34 35 40 43 44 45 47 49 50 56 57 59 64 70 72 74 76 77 78 79 81 82 85 86 87 89 90 91 92 93 94 98 101 102 103 104 105 107 108 110 111 114 115 119 121 129 130 132 135 146 147 148 **P**2 **S** IASIS Healthcare, Franklin, TN
Primary Contact: Richard Gonzalez, Chief Executive Officer
COO: Chris McMahon, Chief Operating Officer
CFO: Jason R. Miller, Chief Financial Officer
CMO: Ryan McHugh M.D., Chief of Staff
CIO: Bryan Hebert, Director Information Systems
CHR: Carol Hebert, Director Human Resources
CNO: Debbie Vaughn, Chief Nursing Officer
Web address: www.medicalcentersetexas.com
Control: Partnership, Investor–owned (for–profit) **Service**: General medical and surgical

Staffed Beds: 167 **Admissions:** 8920 **Census:** 113 **Outpatient Visits:** 78858 **Births:** 1543 **Total Expense ($000):** 125278 **Payroll Expense ($000):** 49916 **Personnel:** 784

PORT LAVACA—Calhoun County

★ **MEMORIAL MEDICAL CENTER (451356)**, 815 North Virginia Street, Zip 77979–3025, Mailing Address: P.O.Box 25, 77979–0025; tel. 361/552–6713 **A**10 18 **F**3 11 13 15 18 29 30 32 34 35 40 43 44 45 46 49 50 57 59 64 65 68 70 75 76 77 78 79 81 84 85 86 87 93 107 108 111 115 118 119 127 129 130 132 133 134 135 146 147 148
Primary Contact: Jason Anglin, Chief Executive Officer
COO: Roshanda Gray, Assistant Administrator
CMO: Jeannine Griffin M.D., Chief of Staff
CIO: Adam Besio, Chief Information Officer
CNO: Erin R Clevenger, Chief Nursing Officer and Director of Quality
Web address: www.mmcportlavaca.com
Control: County, Government, Nonfederal **Service**: General medical and surgical

Staffed Beds: 25 **Admissions:** 1142 **Census:** 12 **Outpatient Visits:** 63874 **Births:** 112 **Total Expense ($000):** 27247 **Payroll Expense ($000):** 10292 **Personnel:** 194

QUANAH—Hardeman County

HARDEMAN COUNTY MEMORIAL HOSPITAL (451352), 402 Mercer Street, Zip 79252–4026, Mailing Address: P.O.Box 90, 79252–0090; tel. 940/663–2795 **A**10 18 **F**28 29 34 40 43 50 56 59 62 64 75 77 87 93 100 101 103 104 107 127 130 133 149 **P**5
Primary Contact: Dave Clark, FACHE, Interim Chief Executive Officer
CFO: Tracy Betts, Chief Financial Officer
CMO: Kevin Lane D.O., Chief of Staff
CNO: Dennis Thomas, Chief Nursing Officer
Web address: www.hcmhosp.com/
Control: Hospital district or authority, Government, Nonfederal **Service**: General medical and surgical

Staffed Beds: 18 **Admissions:** 223 **Census:** 4 **Outpatient Visits:** 14760 **Births:** 0 **Total Expense ($000):** 7812 **Payroll Expense ($000):** 3452 **Personnel:** 81

QUITMAN—Wood County

★ **EAST TEXAS MEDICAL CENTER–QUITMAN (451380)**, 117 Winnsboro Street, Zip 75783–2144, Mailing Address: P.O.Box 1000, 75783–1000; tel. 903/763–6300 **A**10 18 **F**3 11 15 29 30 35 40 43 45 50 57 59 64 65 68 79 81 85 87 107 108 110 111 115 119 127 129 130 133 **P**7 **S** East Texas Medical Center Regional Healthcare System, Tyler, TX
Primary Contact: Patrick Swindle, Administrator
CFO: Janet Andersen, Chief Financial Officer
CHR: William Henry, Director Human Resources
CNO: Allicia Settles, Chief Nursing Officer
Web address: www.etmc.org/etmcquitman/
Control: Other not–for–profit (including NFP Corporation) **Service**: General medical and surgical

Staffed Beds: 25 **Admissions:** 1000 **Census:** 11 **Outpatient Visits:** 50293 **Births:** 0 **Total Expense ($000):** 24790 **Payroll Expense ($000):** 7219 **Personnel:** 120

RANKIN—Upton County

★ **RANKIN COUNTY HOSPITAL DISTRICT (451329)**, 1105 Elizabeth Street, Zip 79778, Mailing Address: P.O.Box 327, 79778–0327; tel. 432/693–2443 **A**10 18 **F**3 7 29 32 34 35 40 41 50 53 55 56 57 59 64 65 66 68 75 93 97 107 119 130 131 133 135 147 148 **P**6
Primary Contact: Jim Horton, Chief Executive Officer
CFO: Tami Burks, Comptroller
CMO: Thomas J Curvin M.D., Chief of Staff
Web address: www.rankincountyhospital.com/
Control: Hospital district or authority, Government, Nonfederal **Service**: General medical and surgical

Staffed Beds: 14 **Admissions:** 52 **Census:** 1 **Outpatient Visits:** 8312 **Births:** 0 **Total Expense ($000):** 11383 **Payroll Expense ($000):** 4924 **Personnel:** 71

REFUGIO—Refugio County

REFUGIO COUNTY MEMORIAL HOSPITAL (451317), 107 Swift Street, Zip 78377–2425; tel. 361/526–2321 **A**10 18 **F**3 7 29 40 43 57 61 64 75 81 86 87 93 97 107 119 127 133 **P**6
Primary Contact: Louis R. Willeke, Administrator
Web address: www.refugiohospital.com/
Control: Hospital district or authority, Government, Nonfederal **Service**: General medical and surgical

Staffed Beds: 20 **Admissions:** 76 **Census:** 1 **Outpatient Visits:** 22790 **Births:** 0 **Total Expense ($000):** 14420 **Payroll Expense ($000):** 5449 **Personnel:** 143

RICHARDSON—Collin County

EMINENT MEDICAL CENTER, 1351 West President George Bush Hwy, Zip 75080; tel. 469/910–8800 (Nonreporting)
Primary Contact: Erin Baker, Chief Executive Officer
Web address: www.eminentmedicalcenter.com
Control: Partnership, Investor–owned (for–profit) **Service**: General medical and surgical

Staffed Beds: 25

⊞ **HEALTHSOUTH REHABILITATION HOSPITAL NORTH TEXAS (673029)**, 3351 Waterview Parkway, Zip 75080–1449; tel. 972/398–5700 **A**1 10 **F**3 29 90 93 96 148 149 **S** HEALTHSOUTH Corporation, Birmingham, AL
Primary Contact: Brent Yates, Chief Executive Officer
CFO: Nichole Dykes, Chief Financial Officer
CMO: Richard Jones M.D., Medical Director
CNO: Pam Smith, Chief Nursing Officer
Web address: www.relianthcp.com
Control: Corporation, Investor–owned (for–profit) **Service**: Rehabilitation

Staffed Beds: 50 **Admissions:** 1304 **Census:** 41 **Outpatient Visits:** 259 **Births:** 0 **Total Expense ($000):** 17705 **Payroll Expense ($000):** 9293 **Personnel:** 122

⊞ **METHODIST RICHARDSON MEDICAL CENTER (450537)**, 2831 East President George Bush Highway, Zip 75082–3561; tel. 469/204–1000 **A**1 2 10 **F**3 5 11 13 15 18 20 22 24 29 30 31 34 35 38 40 45 46 49 54 55 56 57 59 64 65 68 70 72 74 75 76 77 78 79 81 82 85 86 87 93 97 98 100 101 102 103 104 105 107 108 109 110 111 112 115 116 117 119 120 121 123 124 126 129 130 131 132 135 146 147 148 **P**1 7 **S** Methodist Health System, Dallas, TX
Primary Contact: E. Kenneth. Hutchenrider Jr, FACHE, President
COO: Robert Simpson, Vice President Operations
CFO: Amy Bodwell, Vice President Finance
CMO: Mark Smith M.D., Chief Medical Officer
CIO: Pamela McNutt, Senior Vice President and Chief Information Officer
CHR: Chris Loyd, Director Human Resources
CNO: Irene T Strejc M.P.H., R.N., Vice President, Nursing
Web address: www.methodisthealthsystem.org/richardson
Control: Other not–for–profit (including NFP Corporation) **Service**: General medical and surgical

Staffed Beds: 266 **Admissions:** 10100 **Census:** 136 **Outpatient Visits:** 86906 **Births:** 1525 **Total Expense ($000):** 202548 **Payroll Expense ($000):** 81620 **Personnel:** 991

RICHMOND—Fort Bend County

☐ **OAKBEND MEDICAL CENTER (450330)**, 1705 Jackson Street, Zip 77469–3289; tel. 281/341–3000, (Includes HOSPITAL FOR SURGICAL EXCELLENCE, 1211 Highway 6, Suite 70, Sugar Land, Texas, Zip 77478–4940, tel. 281/238–3900; Joe Freudenberger, Chief Executive Officer; OAKBEND MEDICAL CENTER WILLIAMS WAY CAMPUS, 22003 Southwest Freeway, Richmond, Texas, Zip 77469–7003, tel. 281/341–2000; Joe Freudenberger, Chief Executive Officer) (Total facility includes 19 beds in nursing home–type unit) **A**1 10 **F**3 13 15 18 20 22 24 26 28 29 30 34 35 40 42 43 45 46 48 49 50 53 56 57 59 70 72 74 75 76 77 78 79 81 85 87 89 97 98 107 110 111 114 115 119 128 129 130 131 146 147 148 **P**6
Primary Contact: Joe Freudenberger, Chief Executive Officer
CFO: Rodney Lenfant, Chief Financial Officer
CMO: Douglas Thibodeaux M.D., Chief Medical Officer
CIO: Tim McCarty, Chief Information Officer
CHR: Eileen Gamboa, Director Human Resources
Web address: www.oakbendmedcenter.org
Control: Hospital district or authority, Government, Nonfederal **Service:** General medical and surgical

Staffed Beds: 205 Admissions: 6482 Census: 92 Outpatient Visits: 81726 Births: 1382 Total Expense ($000): 216995 Payroll Expense ($000): 55517 Personnel: 797

WESTPARK SPRINGS (454131), 6902 South Peek Road, Zip 77407; tel. 832/532–8107 (Nonreporting)
Primary Contact: Jim Serratt, Chief Executive Officer
Web address: www.westparksprings.com/why–westpark–springs/
Control: Other not–for–profit (including NFP Corporation) **Service:** Psychiatric

Staffed Beds: 72

RIO GRANDE CITY—Starr County

★ **STARR COUNTY MEMORIAL HOSPITAL (450654)**, 2753 Hospital Court, Zip 78582–6859, Mailing Address: P.O.Box 78, 78582–0078; tel. 956/487–5561 **A**10 20 **F**7 11 13 15 29 34 35 40 43 45 46 50 57 59 64 65 66 68 75 76 81 89 107 110 111 115 119 127 130 135 145 148 **P**5
Primary Contact: Thalia H. Munoz, R.N., MS, Chief Executive Officer
CFO: Rafael Olivares, Controller
CHR: Amaro Salinas, Assistant Administrator and Human Resource Officer
CNO: Mario Segura, Director of Nursing
Web address: www.starrcountyhospital.com
Control: Hospital district or authority, Government, Nonfederal **Service:** General medical and surgical

Staffed Beds: 47 Admissions: 1195 Census: 11 Outpatient Visits: 36290 Births: 204 Total Expense ($000): 28585 Payroll Expense ($000): 13287 Personnel: 261

ROCKDALE—Milam County

⇑ **ROCKDALE HOSPITAL (451357)**, 1700 Brazos Street, Zip 76567–2517, Mailing Address: Drawer 1010, 76567–1010; tel. 512/446–4500 **A**10 18 21 **F**3 15 18 20 22 26 29 33 34 40 43 45 46 47 50 54 56 57 59 64 65 68 74 75 77 78 79 81 82 84 85 87 91 92 93 97 107 108 110 111 114 116 117 119 127 128 129 130 131 133 135 146 147 148 149
Primary Contact: Jeffrey Madison, FACHE, Chief Executive Officer
CMO: John Weed M.D., III, Medical Director
CHR: Crystal Foley, Director Human Resources
Web address: www.lrhealthcare.com
Control: Partnership, Investor–owned (for–profit) **Service:** General medical and surgical

Staffed Beds: 21 Admissions: 313 Census: 4 Outpatient Visits: 104032 Births: 0 Total Expense ($000): 169159 Payroll Expense ($000): 41533 Personnel: 646

ROCKWALL—Rockwall County

⇑ **BAYLOR EMERGENCY MEDICAL CENTERS – ROCKWALL (670097)**, 1975 Alpha Drive Suite 100, Zip 75087–4951; tel. 214/294–6200 **A**10 21 **F**3 40 107 119 149 **P**5 **S** Emerus, The Woodlands, TX
Primary Contact: Kyle Kirkpatrick, Chief Executive Officer
Web address: www.bayloremc.com/rockwall
Control: Partnership, Investor–owned (for–profit) **Service:** General medical and surgical

Staffed Beds: 8 Admissions: 60 Census: 1 Outpatient Visits: 11252 Births: 0 Total Expense ($000): 6979 Payroll Expense ($000): 2222 Personnel: 43

⊠ **TEXAS HEALTH PRESBYTERIAN HOSPITAL OF ROCKWALL (670044)**, 3150 Horizon Road, Zip 75032–7805; tel. 469/698–1000 **A**1 3 10 **F**3 12 13 15 29 30 34 35 40 42 45 46 47 49 50 54 68 70 75 76 77 79 81 82 84 85 87 107 108 110 111 115 119 126 129 130 146 147
Primary Contact: Cynthia K. Paris, FACHE, R.N., President and Chief Executive Officer
CFO: Jason Linscott CPA, Chief Financial Officer
CMO: Gary Bonacquisti M.D., Chief Medical Officer
CNO: Tami Hawkins R.N., MSN, Vice President Patient Care and Chief Nursing Officer
Web address: www.phrtexas.com
Control: Corporation, Investor–owned (for–profit) **Service:** General medical and surgical

Staffed Beds: 50 Admissions: 4323 Census: 40 Outpatient Visits: 54643 Births: 795 Total Expense ($000): 100645 Payroll Expense ($000): 35815 Personnel: 483

ROTAN—Fisher County

FISHER COUNTY HOSPITAL DISTRICT (451313), 774 State Highway 70 North, Zip 79546–6918, Mailing Address: P O Drawer 'F', 79546–4019; tel. 325/735–2256 **A**10 18 **F**7 28 32 34 35 40 43 50 53 56 57 59 64 66 75 93 97 107 119 127 133 **P**6
Primary Contact: Leanne Martinez, Chief Executive Officer and Administrator
CFO: Debbie Hull, Chief Financial Officer
CMO: Joseph Lampley D.O., Chief of Staff
CHR: Teresa Terry, Director Human Resource, Payroll
CNO: D'Linda Benham, Director of Nursing
Web address: www.fishercountyhospital.com
Control: Hospital district or authority, Government, Nonfederal **Service:** General medical and surgical

Staffed Beds: 13 Admissions: 162 Census: 3 Outpatient Visits: 21594 Births: 0 Total Expense ($000): 9188 Payroll Expense ($000): 4176 Personnel: 81

ROUND ROCK—Williamson County

⊠ **BAYLOR SCOTT & WHITE MEDICAL CENTER – ROUND ROCK (670034)**, 300 University Boulevard, Zip 78665–1032; tel. 512/509–0100, (Includes BAYLOR SCOTT & WHITE MEDICAL CENTER – LAKEWAY, 100 Medical Parkway, Lakeway, Texas, Zip 78738–5621, tel. 512/571–5000; Philippe Bochaton, President) **A**1 3 10 **F**3 11 13 15 18 19 20 22 24 26 28 29 30 31 34 35 36 40 45 46 47 49 50 51 52 54 55 56 57 58 59 60 62 63 64 65 68 74 75 76 77 78 79 81 82 84 85 87 91 92 93 97 99 100 101 103 104 107 108 110 111 114 115 116 119 121 130 131 132 133 135 143 146 147 148 149 **S** Baylor Scott & White Health, Dallas, TX
Primary Contact: Jay Fox, President
COO: Joe Brown, Vice President Operations
CFO: Jason Cole, Regional Chief Financial Officer
CMO: Rob Watson M.D., Chief Medical Officer
CIO: Matthew Chambers, Chief Information Officer
CHR: Mark A. Sherry, Director Human Resources
CNO: Leslie Gembol MSN, R.N., Chief Nursing Officer
Web address: www.sw.org
Control: Other not–for–profit (including NFP Corporation) **Service:** General medical and surgical

Staffed Beds: 101 Admissions: 6408 Census: 62 Outpatient Visits: 548874 Births: 563 Total Expense ($000): 182014 Payroll Expense ($000): 50435 Personnel: 1042

⊠ **HEALTHSOUTH REHABILITATION HOSPITAL ROUND ROCK (673032)**, 1400 Hester's Crossing, Zip 78681–8025; tel. 512/244–4400, (Total facility includes 25 beds in nursing home–type unit) **A**1 10 **F**3 29 90 93 96 128 130 148 149 150 **S** HEALTHSOUTH Corporation, Birmingham, AL
Primary Contact: Jack Boggess, Chief Executive Officer
CFO: Joe Griffin, Controller
CHR: Amelia Leudecke, Director Human Resources
CNO: Stephanie Guerin, Chief Nursing Officer
Web address: www.healthsouthroundrock.com/
Control: Corporation, Investor–owned (for–profit) **Service:** Rehabilitation

Staffed Beds: 75 Admissions: 1740 Census: 60 Outpatient Visits: 4413 Births: 0 Total Expense ($000): 20820 Payroll Expense ($000): 10154 Personnel: 132

TX

Many Facility Codes have changed. Please refer to the AHA Guide Code Chart. © 2017 AHA Guide

⊞ **SETON MEDICAL CENTER WILLIAMSON (670041)**, 201 Seton Parkway, Zip 78665–8000; tel. 512/324–4000 **A**1 2 3 10 **F**3 11 12 13 15 18 20 22 24 26 28 29 30 31 34 35 37 40 43 44 45 46 49 50 51 53 54 57 58 59 60 64 68 70 72 74 75 76 77 78 79 81 82 84 86 87 93 96 100 107 108 110 111 114 115 119 124 126 130 131 132 135 146 147 148 **P**3 8 **S** Ascension Healthcare, Saint Louis, MO
Primary Contact: Christopher L. Hartle, President
CFO: Douglas D Waite, Senior Vice President and Chief Financial Officer
CMO: Hugh V Gilmore M.D., Vice President Medical Affairs
CIO: Gerry Lewis, Chief Information Officer
CHR: Thomas Wilken, Vice President Human Resources
Web address: www.seton.net/williamson
Control: Church operated, Nongovernment, not–for–profit **Service**: General medical and surgical

Staffed Beds: 135 **Admissions**: 7113 **Census**: 89 **Outpatient Visits**: 59927 **Births**: 295 **Total Expense ($000)**: 148081 **Payroll Expense ($000)**: 42081 **Personnel**: 589

⊞ **ST. DAVID'S ROUND ROCK MEDICAL CENTER (450718)**, 2400 Round Rock Avenue, Zip 78681–4097; tel. 512/341–1000 **A**1 2 5 10 **F**3 8 12 13 15 18 20 22 24 26 28 29 30 31 34 35 37 40 42 43 45 49 54 64 67 70 72 74 76 77 78 79 81 85 87 90 91 93 102 107 108 110 111 115 116 117 119 124 126 129 130 132 135 146 147 148 149 **P**1 3 6 8 **S** HCA Healthcare, Nashville, TN
Primary Contact: Jeremy Barclay, Chief Executive Officer
COO: Tad Hatton, Chief Operating Officer
CFO: Cindy Sexton, Chief Financial Officer
CHR: Amy Noak, Director Human Resources
Web address: www.stdavids.com
Control: Other not–for–profit (including NFP Corporation) **Service**: General medical and surgical

Staffed Beds: 171 **Admissions**: 8970 **Census**: 112 **Outpatient Visits**: 69510 **Births**: 1832 **Total Expense ($000)**: 153538 **Payroll Expense ($000)**: 48186 **Personnel**: 747

ROWLETT—Rockwall County

⊞ **BAYLOR SCOTT & WHITE MEDICAL CENTER – LAKE POINTE (450742)**, 6800 Scenic Drive, Zip 75088–4552, Mailing Address: P.O.Box 1550, 75030–1550; tel. 972/412–2273 **A**1 10 **F**3 12 13 15 18 20 22 24 28 29 30 34 35 40 42 45 46 49 50 53 54 57 59 60 64 65 70 72 73 74 75 76 77 78 79 81 82 85 86 87 93 107 108 110 111 114 115 118 119 120 121 126 129 130 131 132 144 146 147 148 **P**2 **S** TENET Healthcare Corporation, Dallas, TX
Primary Contact: Brett D. Lee, Chief Executive Officer
CFO: Becky Speight, Chief Financial Officer
CMO: Larry Dencklau D.O., Chief of Staff
CIO: Mark Slater, Director Information Systems
CHR: David Olmstead, Chief Human Resource Officer – Dallas Market
CNO: Patti Gilliano, Chief Nursing Officer
Web address: www.lakepointemedical.com
Control: Corporation, Investor–owned (for–profit) **Service**: General medical and surgical

Staffed Beds: 112 **Admissions**: 7608 **Census**: 78 **Outpatient Visits**: 110308 **Births**: 1642 **Total Expense ($000)**: 131881 **Payroll Expense ($000)**: 44394 **Personnel**: 823

RUSK—Cherokee County

☐ **RUSK STATE HOSPITAL (454009)**, 805 North Dickinson, Zip 75785–2333, Mailing Address: P.O.Box 318, 75785–0318; tel. 903/683–3421 **A**1 3 10 **F**3 30 39 44 50 68 75 77 86 87 96 98 103 106 130 135 146 148 149 **P**6 **S** Texas Department of State Health Services, Austin, TX
Primary Contact: Brenda Slaton, Superintendent
COO: Lynda Roberson, Senior Program Director
CFO: Rhonda Transier, Financial Officer
CMO: Joe Bates M.D., Clinical Director
CHR: Kendra Brown, Job Requisition Coordinator
Web address: www.dshs.state.tx.us/mhhospitals/RuskSH/default.shtm
Control: State, Government, Nonfederal **Service**: Psychiatric

Staffed Beds: 249 **Admissions**: 405 **Census**: 276 **Outpatient Visits**: 0 **Births**: 0 **Total Expense ($000)**: 38456 **Personnel**: 946

SAN ANGELO—Tom Green County

☐ **RIVER CREST HOSPITAL (454064)**, 1636 Hunters Glen Road, Zip 76901–5016; tel. 325/949–5722 **A**1 10 **F**4 5 29 64 87 98 99 100 101 102 103 104 105 130 132 **S** Universal Health Services, Inc., King of Prussia, PA
Primary Contact: Juana Giralt, Interim Chief Executive Officer
CFO: Juana Giralt, Chief Financial Officer
CMO: Raymond Mays M.D., Medical Director
CHR: Lydia Cardenas, Director Human Resources
CNO: Debra Millsap, Director of Nursing
Web address: www.rivercresthospital.com
Control: Corporation, Investor–owned (for–profit) **Service**: Psychiatric

Staffed Beds: 80 **Admissions**: 3053 **Census**: 55 **Outpatient Visits**: 1078 **Births**: 0 **Total Expense ($000)**: 11994 **Payroll Expense ($000)**: 6167 **Personnel**: 141

⊞ **SAN ANGELO COMMUNITY MEDICAL CENTER (450340)**, 3501 Knickerbocker Road, Zip 76904–7698; tel. 325/949–9511 **A**1 10 **F**3 8 11 13 15 18 20 22 24 26 28 29 30 31 34 35 37 40 43 45 49 51 53 54 57 59 60 63 64 68 70 72 74 75 76 77 78 79 81 82 85 89 93 107 108 110 111 115 118 119 126 129 130 131 135 144 145 146 147 148 **P**8 **S** Community Health Systems, Inc., Franklin, TN
CHR: Lisa Bibb, Director Human Resources
Web address: www.sacmc.com
Control: Partnership, Investor–owned (for–profit) **Service**: General medical and surgical

Staffed Beds: 131 **Admissions**: 4735 **Census**: 48 **Outpatient Visits**: 72415 **Total Expense ($000)**: 95957 **Payroll Expense ($000)**: 30663 **Personnel**: 522

★ **SHANNON MEDICAL CENTER (450571)**, 120 East Harris Street, Zip 76903–5976, Mailing Address: P.O.Box 1879, 76902–1879; tel. 325/653–6741, (Includes SHANNON MEDICAL CENTER– ST. JOHN'S CAMPUS, 2018 Pulliam Street, San Angelo, Texas, Zip 76905–5197, tel. 325/659–7100; Bryan Horner, President and Chief Executive Officer) (Total facility includes 21 beds in nursing home–type unit) **A**3 5 10 22 **F**3 7 8 11 13 15 18 20 22 24 26 28 29 30 31 32 34 35 37 38 40 43 45 47 48 49 50 51 53 54 56 57 58 59 60 61 62 64 68 70 71 72 73 74 75 76 77 78 79 80 81 82 84 85 86 87 89 90 92 93 94 96 98 100 101 102 103 107 108 110 111 114 115 117 119 126 128 130 132 145 146 147 148 149 **P**6
Primary Contact: Shane Plymell, Chief Executive Officer
COO: Shane Plymell, Chief Operating Officer
CFO: Staci Wetz, Chief Financial Officer
CMO: Irvin Zeitler D.O., Vice President Medical Affairs
CIO: Tom Perkins, Chief Information Officer
CHR: Teresa Morgan, Assistant Vice President Human Resources
CNO: Pamela Bradshaw, Chief Nursing Officer
Web address: www.shannonhealth.com
Control: Other not–for–profit (including NFP Corporation) **Service**: General medical and surgical

Staffed Beds: 311 **Admissions**: 12547 **Census**: 177 **Outpatient Visits**: 108627 **Births**: 1135 **Total Expense ($000)**: 256066 **Payroll Expense ($000)**: 93674 **Personnel**: 1679

SAN ANTONIO—Bexar County

⊞ **ACUITY HOSPITAL OF SOUTH TEXAS (452040)**, 718 Lexington Avenue, Zip 78212–4768; tel. 210/572–4600 **A**1 10 **F**1 3 29 40 45 75 85 87 91 107 119 148 149 **S** AcuityHealthcare, LP, Charlotte, NC
Primary Contact: Dorothy J. Elford, Chief Executive Officer
CFO: Merald Manigault, Chief Financial Officer
CMO: Aamir Malik M.D., Chief Medical Officer
CHR: Barbie Gordner, Director Human Resources
CNO: Melissa Low, Chief Clinical Officer
Web address: www.acuitysouthtexas.net
Control: Corporation, Investor–owned (for–profit) **Service**: Acute long–term care hospital

Staffed Beds: 30 **Admissions**: 322 **Census**: 23 **Outpatient Visits**: 0 **Births**: 0 **Total Expense ($000)**: 16056 **Payroll Expense ($000)**: 6926 **Personnel**: 126

TX

⇑ **BAPTIST EMERGENCY HOSPITAL (670078)**, 16088 San Pedro, Zip 78232–2249; tel. 210/402–4092, (Includes BAPTIST EMERGENCY HOSPITAL – HAUSMAN, 8230 North 1604 West, San Antonio, Texas, Zip 78249, tel. 210/572–8885; David Mitchell, Chief Executive Officer; BAPTIST EMERGENCY HOSPITAL – OVERLOOK, 25615 US Highway 281 North, San Antonio, Texas, Zip 78258–7135, tel. 210/572–2911; David Mitchell, Chief Executive Officer; BAPTIST EMERGENCY HOSPITAL – SCHERTZ, 16977 Interstate 35 North, Schertz, Texas, Zip 78154–1466, tel. 210/572–8400; David Mitchell, Chief Executive Officer; BAPTIST EMERGENCY HOSPITAL – WESTOVER HILLS, 10811 Town Center Drive, San Antonio, Texas, Zip 78251–4585, tel. 210/572–0911; David Mitchell, Chief Executive Officer) **A**10 21 **F**3 40 41 42 75 107 119 149 **P**5 **S** Emerus, The Woodlands, TX
Primary Contact: David Mitchell, Interim Chief Executive Officer
Web address: www.baptistemergencyhospital.com
Control: Corporation, Investor–owned (for–profit) **Service:** General medical and surgical

Staffed Beds: 50 **Admissions:** 692 **Census:** 4 **Outpatient Visits:** 79365 **Births:** 0 **Total Expense ($000):** 36395 **Payroll Expense ($000):** 12352 **Personnel:** 327

★ △ ⇑ **BAPTIST MEDICAL CENTER (450058)**, 111 Dallas Street, Zip 78205–1230; tel. 210/297–7000, (Includes MISSION TRAIL BAPTIST HOSPITAL, 3333 Research Plaza, San Antonio, Texas, Zip 78235–5154, tel. 210/297–3000; Eric Schmacker, President; NORTH CENTRAL BAPTIST HOSPITAL, 520 Madison Oak Drive, San Antonio, Texas, Zip 78258–3912, tel. 210/297–4000; NORTHEAST BAPTIST HOSPITAL, 8811 Village Drive, San Antonio, Texas, Zip 78217–5440, tel. 210/297–2000; ST. LUKE'S BAPTIST HOSPITAL, 7930 Floyd Curl Drive, San Antonio, Texas, Zip 78229–0100, tel. 210/297–5000; John E Knox, FACHE, Chief Executive Officer) **A**2 3 5 7 10 21 **F**3 11 12 13 14 15 17 18 19 20 22 24 26 28 29 30 31 35 37 38 40 41 42 43 44 45 46 47 50 54 55 56 57 59 60 64 65 68 70 72 73 74 75 77 78 79 80 81 82 85 86 87 88 90 91 92 93 95 96 98 101 102 103 107 108 111 114 115 116 117 119 124 126 129 130 132 135 145 146 147 148 149 **P**8 **S** TENET Healthcare Corporation, Dallas, TX
Primary Contact: Jonathan Turton, FACHE, President and Chief Executive Officer
COO: Sandy Ethridge, Interim Chief Operating Officer
CMO: Richard Marple M.D., Chief Medical Officer
CIO: Gary Davis, Vice President Information Systems
CHR: Sarah Spinharney, Senior Vice President
CNO: Nelson Tuazon R.N., Chief Nursing Officer
Web address: www.baptisthealthsystem.com
Control: Partnership, Investor–owned (for–profit) **Service:** General medical and surgical

Staffed Beds: 1535 **Admissions:** 65564 **Census:** 798 **Outpatient Visits:** 406814 **Births:** 10657 **Total Expense ($000):** 868342 **Payroll Expense ($000):** 318902 **Personnel:** 5391

TX

⊞ **CHRISTUS SANTA ROSA HEALTH SYSTEM (450237)**, 333 North Santa Rosa Street, Zip 78207–3108, Mailing Address: 100 NE Loop 410 Suite 800, 78216–4749; tel. 210/704–2000, (Nonreporting) (Includes CHILDREN'S HOSPITAL OF SAN ANTONIO, 333 North Santa Rosa Street, San Antonio, Texas, Zip 78207, tel. 210/704–2011; Elias Neujahr, President; CHRISTUS SANTA ROSA HOSPITAL – ALAMO HEIGHTS, 403 Treeline Park Building, San Antonio, Texas, Zip 78209–2042, tel. 216/704–2011; Julie Seale, Administrator; CHRISTUS SANTA ROSA HOSPITAL – NEW BRAUNFELS, 600 North Union Avenue, New Braunfels, Texas, Zip 78130–4191, tel. 830/606–9111; Jim D Wesson, President and Administrator; CHRISTUS SANTA ROSA–MEDICAL CENTER, 2827 Babcock Road, San Antonio, Texas, Zip 78229–4813, tel. 210/705–6300; Ian Thompson Jr, M.D., President) **A**1 3 5 10 **S** CHRISTUS Health, Irving, TX
Primary Contact: Dean Alexander, President and Chief Executive Officer
CFO: Linda Kirks, Vice President and Chief Financial Officer
CMO: Kenneth Davis M.D., Chief Medical Officer
CHR: Crystal H Kohanke, Group Vice President, Human Resources
CNO: Patty Toney R.N., MSN, Chief Nurse Executive
Web address: www.christussantarosa.org
Control: Church operated, Nongovernment, not–for–profit **Service:** General medical and surgical

Staffed Beds: 766

☐ **CLARITY CHILD GUIDANCE CENTER**, 8535 Tom Slick, Zip 78229–3363; tel. 210/616–0300 **A**1 3 5 **F**29 98 99 101 102 104 105 106 130
Primary Contact: Frederick W. Hines, President and Chief Executive Officer
CFO: Michael Bernick, Executive Vice President and Chief Financial Officer
CMO: Soad Michelson M.D., Senior Medical Director
CHR: Gina Massey, Vice President Human Resources
CNO: Carol Carver MSN, R.N., Vice President Patient Services
Web address: www.claritycgc.org
Control: Other not–for–profit (including NFP Corporation) **Service:** Children's hospital psychiatric

Staffed Beds: 66 **Admissions:** 2232 **Census:** 58 **Outpatient Visits:** 20089 **Births:** 0 **Total Expense ($000):** 23756 **Payroll Expense ($000):** 14230 **Personnel:** 290

☐ **CUMBERLAND SURGICAL HOSPITAL (670021)**, 5330 N. Loop 1604 W, Zip 78249; tel. 210/877–8000 (Nonreporting) **A**1 10 **S** Post Acute Medical, LLC, Enola, PA
Primary Contact: Paul B. Abraham, FACHE, Chief Executive Officer
CNO: Lisa Kuopus, Chief Nursing Officer
Web address: www.cumberlandsh.com/
Control: Partnership, Investor–owned (for–profit) **Service:** General medical and surgical

Staffed Beds: 9

⇑ **FOUNDATION SURGICAL HOSPITAL OF SAN ANTONIO (670054)**, 9522 Huebner Road, Zip 78240–1548; tel. 210/478–5400 **A**3 5 10 21 **F**3 12 29 30 35 37 40 44 45 51 53 68 74 75 77 79 81 85 86 87 107 114 119 129 130 132 135 148 **S** Foundation Surgical Hospital Affiliates, Oklahoma City, OK
Primary Contact: Blake W. Hubbard, FACHE, Chief Executive Officer
CNO: Beckie Leonard R.N., Chief Nursing Officer
Web address: www.fshsanantonio.com/bariatric–foundation–surgical.html
Control: Corporation, Investor–owned (for–profit) **Service:** Surgical

Staffed Beds: 20 **Admissions:** 1349 **Census:** 7 **Outpatient Visits:** 3845 **Births:** 0 **Total Expense ($000):** 32810 **Payroll Expense ($000):** 6310 **Personnel:** 90

⊞ **HEALTHSOUTH REHABILITATION INSTITUTE OF SAN ANTONIO (RIOSA) (453031)**, 9119 Cinnamon Hill, Zip 78240–5401; tel. 210/691–0737 **A**1 10 **F**29 90 91 96 130 132 148 **P**5 **S** HEALTHSOUTH Corporation, Birmingham, AL
Primary Contact: Michael Thomas, Chief Executive Officer
CFO: Larry Floyd Spriggs CPA, Controller
CMO: Chaula Rana M.D., Medical Director
CHR: Vanessa Tejada, Director Human Resources
CNO: Matthew D'Ambrosio MSN, R.N., Chief Nursing Officer
Web address: www.hsriosa.com
Control: Corporation, Investor–owned (for–profit) **Service:** Rehabilitation

Staffed Beds: 96 **Admissions:** 1136 **Census:** 59 **Outpatient Visits:** 0 **Births:** 0 **Total Expense ($000):** 19876 **Payroll Expense ($000):** 10888 **Personnel:** 198

⊞ **KINDRED HOSPITAL SAN ANTONIO CENTRAL (452073)**, 111 Dallas Street, 4th Floor, Zip 78205–1201; tel. 210/297–7185, (Data for 179 days) **A**1 10 **F**1 29 148 **P**8 **S** Kindred Healthcare, Louisville, KY
Primary Contact: Kristen Lowe, Interim Chief Executive Officer
Web address: www.kindredsanantoniocentral.com/
Control: Corporation, Investor–owned (for–profit) **Service:** Acute long–term care hospital

Staffed Beds: 44 **Admissions:** 187 **Census:** 29 **Outpatient Visits:** 0 **Births:** 0 **Total Expense ($000):** 9116 **Payroll Expense ($000):** 3620

⊞ **KINDRED HOSPITAL–SAN ANTONIO (452016)**, 3636 Medical Drive, Zip 78229–2183; tel. 210/616–0616 **A**1 10 **F**1 3 29 30 70 75 77 85 87 91 107 130 148 **S** Kindred Healthcare, Louisville, KY
Primary Contact: Kristen Lowe, Chief Executive Officer
CFO: Erin Russell, Controller
CMO: Charles Duncan M.D., Medical Director
CHR: Stanley Richardson, Coordinator Human Resources and Payroll Benefits
Web address: www.khsanantonio.com/
Control: Corporation, Investor–owned (for–profit) **Service:** Acute long–term care hospital

Staffed Beds: 59 **Admissions:** 464 **Census:** 32 **Outpatient Visits:** 0 **Births:** 0 **Total Expense ($000):** 19770 **Payroll Expense ($000):** 7544 **Personnel:** 90

⊞ **LAUREL RIDGE TREATMENT CENTER (454060)**, 17720 Corporate Woods Drive, Zip 78259–3500; tel. 210/491–9400 **A**1 3 10 **F**4 5 29 35 38 75 77 98 99 100 101 103 105 106 130 132 135 **S** Universal Health Services, Inc., King of Prussia, PA
Primary Contact: Jacob Cuellar, M.D., Chief Executive Officer
COO: Karla Ramirez, Chief Operating Officer
CFO: Linda Maenius, Chief Financial Officer
CMO: Benigno J Fernandez M.D., Executive Medical Director
CHR: Brenda Frederick, Director Human Resources
CNO: Kathy Rosetta, Chief Nursing Officer
Web address: www.laurelridgetc.com
Control: Partnership, Investor–owned (for–profit) **Service:** Psychiatric

Staffed Beds: 208 **Admissions:** 7538 **Census:** 178 **Outpatient Visits:** 23377 **Births:** 0 **Total Expense ($000):** 50941 **Payroll Expense ($000):** 21750 **Personnel:** 383

Many Facility Codes have changed. Please refer to the AHA Guide Code Chart. © 2017 AHA Guide

LIFECARE HOSPITALS OF SAN ANTONIO (452059), 8902 Floyd Curl Drive, Zip 78240–1681; tel. 210/690–7000 **A**1 10 **F**1 3 29 45 75 77 85 86 87 96 97 107 114 130 148 149 **S** LifeCare Management Services, Plano, TX
Primary Contact: Michelle Lozano, Chief Executive Officer
CMO: Randall C Bell M.D., Medical Director
CIO: Mike Wattenbarger, Chief Information Officer
Web address: www.lifecare–hospitals.com
Control: Corporation, Investor–owned (for–profit) **Service:** Acute long–term care hospital

Staffed Beds: 62 **Admissions:** 636 **Census:** 54 **Outpatient Visits:** 0 **Births:** 0 **Total Expense ($000):** 26404 **Payroll Expense ($000):** 13280 **Personnel:** 227

METHODIST AMBULATORY SURGERY HOSPITAL – NORTHWEST (450780), 9150 Huebner Road, Suite 100, Zip 78240–1545; tel. 210/575–5000 **A**1 3 10 **F**3 29 40 65 68 79 81 85 87 **P**8 **S** HCA Healthcare, Nashville, TN
Primary Contact: Scott Davis, Chief Executive Officer
CFO: Tim Carr, Chief Financial Officer
CHR: Barry Burns, Vice President
CNO: Cathy Bump R.N., Chief Nursing Officer
Web address: www.sahealth.com
Control: Partnership, Investor–owned (for–profit) **Service:** Surgical

Staffed Beds: 23 **Admissions:** 492 **Census:** 3 **Outpatient Visits:** 5911 **Births:** 0 **Total Expense ($000):** 19277 **Payroll Expense ($000):** 6180 **Personnel:** 101

★ ⇑ **METHODIST HOSPITAL (450388)**, 7700 Floyd Curl Drive, Zip 78229–3993; tel. 210/575–4000, (Includes METHODIST CHILDREN'S HOSPITAL, 7700 Floyd Curl Drive, San Antonio, Texas, Zip 78229–3383, tel. 210/575–7000; Robert Lenza, Chief Executive Officer; METHODIST SPECIALTY AND TRANSPLANT HOSPITAL, 8026 Floyd Curl Drive, San Antonio, Texas, Zip 78229–3915, tel. 210/575–8090; Jeffrey Wilson, Chief Executive Officer; METHODIST TEXSAN HOSPITAL, 6700 IH–10 West, San Antonio, Texas, Zip 78201, tel. 210/736–6700; Scott Davis, Chief Executive Officer; METROPOLITAN METHODIST HOSPITAL, 1310 McCullough Avenue, San Antonio, Texas, Zip 78212–2617, tel. 210/757–2909; Gregory A Seiler, Chief Executive Officer; NORTHEAST METHODIST HOSPITAL, 12412 Judson Road, Live Oak, Texas, Zip 78233–3255, tel. 210/757–5000; Michael D Beaver, Chief Executive Officer) **A**2 3 5 10 21 **F**3 4 5 8 11 12 13 15 17 18 19 20 21 22 23 24 25 26 27 28 29 30 31 34 35 38 40 41 42 43 44 45 46 47 48 49 51 53 54 56 57 58 59 60 64 65 68 70 72 74 75 76 77 78 79 80 81 82 84 85 86 87 88 89 90 93 95 96 98 100 101 102 103 104 105 107 108 111 114 115 119 121 124 126 127 129 130 132 135 136 137 138 139 142 143 145 146 147 148 **P**7 **S** HCA Healthcare, Nashville, TN
Primary Contact: Allen Harrison, Chief Executive Officer
CFO: Nancy Meadows, Chief Financial Officer
CMO: Russell Woodward M.D., Chief Medical Officer
CIO: Eddie Cuellar, Vice President Information Systems
CHR: Nancy Edgar, Vice President Human Resources
Web address: www.sahealth.com
Control: Partnership, Investor–owned (for–profit) **Service:** General medical and surgical

Staffed Beds: 1602 **Admissions:** 80378 **Census:** 1174 **Outpatient Visits:** 470788 **Births:** 9836 **Total Expense ($000):** 1206425 **Payroll Expense ($000):** 436432 **Personnel:** 5763

METHODIST STONE OAK HOSPITAL (670055), 1139 East Sonterra Boulevard, Zip 78258–4347; tel. 210/638–2100 **A**1 3 5 10 **F**3 13 15 18 20 22 24 28 29 30 31 34 35 38 40 41 44 45 46 47 52 56 57 59 60 65 68 70 72 74 75 76 77 78 79 80 81 82 85 87 100 102 103 107 108 111 114 119 126 130 145 146 147 148 149 **S** HCA Healthcare, Nashville, TN
Primary Contact: Marc Strode, Chief Executive Officer
CFO: Gabriel Marrufo, Chief Financial Officer
CNO: Ann M Winn M.D., R.N., FACHE, Chief Nursing Officer
Web address: www.sahealth.com/locations/methodist–stone–oak–hospital/
Control: Partnership, Investor–owned (for–profit) **Service:** General medical and surgical

Staffed Beds: 140 **Admissions:** 11227 **Census:** 126 **Outpatient Visits:** 49442 **Births:** 2012 **Total Expense ($000):** 159112 **Payroll Expense ($000):** 45330 **Personnel:** 667

⇑ **NIX HEALTH CARE SYSTEM (450130)**, 414 Navarro Street, Zip 78205–2516; tel. 210/271–1800 **A**3 5 10 21 **F**3 5 12 15 18 20 22 24 26 29 30 31 34 35 40 44 45 49 50 54 56 57 59 60 62 64 68 70 74 75 78 79 81 82 85 87 90 93 97 98 99 102 103 104 107 108 110 111 114 118 119 129 130 132 142 143 146 147 148 **S** Prospect Medical Holdings, Los Angeles, CA
Primary Contact: Daniel J. Bonk, Chief Executive Officer
CFO: Lester Surrock, Chief Financial Officer
CMO: Dina Goytia–Leos M.D., Chief of Staff
CIO: Adrian Dickreiter, Vice President Technology
CNO: Maria Rose Lopez R.N., Chief of Nursing
Web address: www.nixhealth.com
Control: Corporation, Investor–owned (for–profit) **Service:** General medical and surgical

Staffed Beds: 246 **Admissions:** 8611 **Census:** 143 **Outpatient Visits:** 43529 **Births:** 0 **Total Expense ($000):** 126681 **Payroll Expense ($000):** 40742 **Personnel:** 1154

POST ACUTE/WARM SPRINGS SPECIALTY HOSPITAL OF SAN ANTONIO (452090), 5418 N Loop 1604 W, Zip 78247; tel. 210/921–3550 **A**1 10 **F**1 3 29 30 148 **S** Post Acute Medical, LLC, Enola, PA
Primary Contact: James Asberry, Chief Executive Officer
CNO: Carrie Nims, Director of Nursing
Web address: www.postacutemedical.com
Control: Partnership, Investor–owned (for–profit) **Service:** Acute long–term care hospital

Staffed Beds: 26 **Admissions:** 254 **Census:** 16 **Outpatient Visits:** 0 **Births:** 0 **Total Expense ($000):** 9294 **Payroll Expense ($000):** 3714 **Personnel:** 62

SAN ANTONIO BEHAVIORAL HEALTHCARE HOSPITAL (454132), 8550 Huebner Road, Zip 78240–1803; tel. 877/514–0010 **F**5 98 99 102 104 105 **S** Signature Healthcare Services, Corona, CA
Primary Contact: Kirk Kureska, Chief Executive Officer
Web address: www.sanantoniobehavioral.com
Control: Corporation, Investor–owned (for–profit) **Service:** Psychiatric

Staffed Beds: 108 **Admissions:** 4711 **Census:** 82 **Outpatient Visits:** 3979 **Births:** 0 **Total Expense ($000):** 18948 **Payroll Expense ($000):** 9111 **Personnel:** 173

SAN ANTONIO STATE HOSPITAL (454011), 6711 South New Braunfels, Suite 100, Zip 78223–3006; tel. 210/531–7711 **A**1 3 5 10 **F**30 39 53 56 57 59 68 75 77 86 87 91 98 99 100 101 103 106 130 132 135 146 **P**1 **S** Texas Department of State Health Services, Austin, TX
Primary Contact: Robert C. Arizpe, Superintendent
CFO: Janie Rabago, Chief Accountant
CMO: Terresa Stallworth M.D., Clinical Director
CIO: Chris Stanush, Director Information Management
CHR: Renee Bourland, Human Resources Specialist
CNO: Maria DC Ostrander R.N., MSN, Chief Nurse Executive
Web address: www.dshs.state.tx.us/mhhospitals/SanAntonioSH/default.shtm
Control: State, Government, Nonfederal **Service:** Psychiatric

Staffed Beds: 302 **Admissions:** 1226 **Census:** 262 **Outpatient Visits:** 0 **Births:** 0 **Total Expense ($000):** 76239 **Payroll Expense ($000):** 37232 **Personnel:** 839

★ ○ **SELECT REHABILITATION HOSPITAL OF SAN ANTONIO (673040)**, 19126 Stonehue Road, Zip 78258–3490; tel. 210/482–3400 **A**10 11 **F**3 29 30 75 90 91 96 130 148 149 **S** Select Medical Corporation, Mechanicsburg, PA
Primary Contact: Robert Ward, Chief Executive Officer
Web address: www.sanantonio–rehab.com/
Control: Partnership, Investor–owned (for–profit) **Service:** Rehabilitation

Staffed Beds: 42 **Admissions:** 1028 **Census:** 40 **Outpatient Visits:** 0 **Births:** 0 **Total Expense ($000):** 16658 **Payroll Expense ($000):** 8513 **Personnel:** 163

SOUTH TEXAS SPINE AND SURGICAL HOSPITAL (450856), 18600 Hardy Oak Boulevard, Zip 78258–4206; tel. 210/507–4090 **A**1 3 5 10 **F**3 29 40 41 70 75 77 79 81 82 85 86 87 89 111 **S** National Surgical Healthcare, Chicago, IL
Primary Contact: Thomas Klawiter, Chief Executive Officer
CFO: Sylvia Garcia, Chief Accounting Officer
CHR: Sally Hall, Manager Human Resources
CNO: Jennifer West R.N., Chief Nursing Officer
Web address: www.southtexassurgical.com
Control: Partnership, Investor–owned (for–profit) **Service:** Orthopedic

Staffed Beds: 30 **Admissions:** 1191 **Census:** 8 **Outpatient Visits:** 4208 **Births:** 0 **Total Expense ($000):** 34736 **Payroll Expense ($000):** 7331 **Personnel:** 137

TX

⊞ △ **SOUTH TEXAS VETERANS HEALTH CARE SYSTEM**, 7400 Merton Minter Boulevard, Zip 78229–4404; tel. 210/617–5300, (Nonreporting) (Includes KERRVILLE DIVISION, 3600 Memorial Boulevard, Kerrville, Texas, Zip 78028, tel. 210/896–2020; SAN ANTONIO DIVISION, 7400 Merton Minter Boulevard, San Antonio, Texas, Zip 78284–5799, tel. 210/617–5300) **A**1 3 5 7 8 **S** Department of Veterans Affairs, Washington, DC
Primary Contact: Robert M. Walton, Healthcare System Director
COO: Joe Perez, Associate Director
CFO: Eloisa Salazar, Chief Financial Officer
CMO: Julianne Flynn M.D., Chief of Staff
CIO: Simon Willett, Director Administrative Operations
CHR: Jeffrey Young, Chief Human Resource Officer
CNO: Sharon Millican, Associate Director, Patient Care Services
Web address: www.southtexas.va.gov/
Control: Veterans Affairs, Government, federal **Service:** General medical and surgical

Staffed Beds: 838

⇑ **SOUTHWEST GENERAL HOSPITAL (450697)**, 7400 Barlite Boulevard, Zip 78224–1399; tel. 210/921–2000 **A**10 21 **F**3 12 13 15 18 20 22 24 29 30 35 37 40 43 44 45 46 49 50 51 56 57 59 60 64 65 70 71 72 74 75 76 77 79 80 81 85 87 90 93 96 98 102 103 104 107 108 110 111 114 115 119 126 129 130 132 135 146 147 148 149 **S** IASIS Healthcare, Franklin, TN
Primary Contact: P Craig. Desmond, Chief Executive Officer
COO: Sarah Humme MSN, R.N., Chief Operating Officer
CFO: Colin B. Brooks, Chief Financial Officer
CIO: Debbie Mora, Director
CHR: Christina Rivera, Director Human Resources
CNO: Sarah Humme MSN, R.N., Chief Nursing Officer
Web address: www.swgeneralhospital.com
Control: Corporation, Investor–owned (for–profit) **Service:** General medical and surgical

Staffed Beds: 253 **Admissions:** 9276 **Census:** 132 **Outpatient Visits:** 61960 **Births:** 1677 **Total Expense ($000):** 119662 **Payroll Expense ($000):** 46633 **Personnel:** 713

ST. LUKE'S BAPTIST HOSPITAL See Baptist Medical Center

☐ **TEXAS CENTER FOR INFECTIOUS DISEASE (452033)**, 2303 SE Military Drive, Zip 78223–3597; tel. 210/534–8857 **A**1 3 10 **F**1 3 29 30 50 53 54 61 64 68 75 87 130 132 135 143 146 149 **P**6 **S** Texas Department of State Health Services, Austin, TX
Primary Contact: James N. Elkins, FACHE, Director
CFO: Glenda Armstrong–Huff, Assistant Superintendent
CMO: David Griffith M.D., Medical Director
CIO: Andre Avant, Facility Automation Manager
CHR: Gerald Shackelford, Staff Support Specialist
CNO: Rebecca Sanchez R.N., M.P.H., Director of Nursing
Web address: www.dshs.state.tx.us/tcid/default.shtm
Control: State, Government, Nonfederal **Service:** Tuberculosis and other respiratory diseases

Staffed Beds: 40 **Admissions:** 56 **Census:** 27 **Outpatient Visits:** 1033 **Births:** 0 **Total Expense ($000):** 10425 **Payroll Expense ($000):** 2699 **Personnel:** 146

⊞ **UNIVERSITY HEALTH SYSTEM (450213)**, 4502 Medical Drive, Zip 78229–4493; tel. 210/358–2000, (Includes UNIVERSITY HEALTH CENTER – DOWNTOWN, 4502 Medical Drive, San Antonio, Texas, Zip 78229–4493, tel. 210/358–3400; UNIVERSITY HOSPITAL, 4502 Medical Drive, San Antonio, Texas, Zip 78229–4493, tel. 210/358–4000; Edward Banos, Interim Chief Executive Officer) **A**1 2 3 5 8 10 **F**3 4 7 11 13 14 16 17 18 19 20 21 22 23 24 25 26 27 29 30 31 32 34 35 38 40 41 43 44 45 46 47 48 49 50 51 52 54 55 56 57 58 59 60 61 64 65 66 68 70 72 73 74 75 76 77 78 79 80 81 82 84 85 86 87 88 89 90 92 93 95 98 100 101 107 108 110 111 115 118 119 126 129 130 135 138 139 140 141 142 143 144 145 146 147 148 149 **P**6
Primary Contact: George B. Hernandez Jr, President and Chief Executive Officer
COO: Christann Vasquez, Executive Vice President and Chief Operating Officer
CFO: Peggy Deming, Executive Vice President and Chief Financial Officer
CMO: Bryan Alsip M.D., Executive Vice President, Chief Medical Officer
CIO: Bill Phillips, Vice President Information Services
CHR: Theresa Scepanski, Vice President People and Organizational Development
CNO: Nancy L Ray R.N., Executive Vice President, Chief Nursing Executive
Web address: www.universityhealthsystem.com
Control: Hospital district or authority, Government, Nonfederal **Service:** General medical and surgical

Staffed Beds: 493 **Admissions:** 28201 **Census:** 474 **Outpatient Visits:** 2043113 **Births:** 3217 **Total Expense ($000):** 1144160 **Payroll Expense ($000):** 420696 **Personnel:** 7006

⊞ **WARM SPRINGS REHABILITATION HOSPITAL OF SAN ANTONIO (453035)**, 5101 Medical Drive, Zip 78229–4801; tel. 210/616–0100, (Includes WARM SPRINGS REHABILITATION HOSPITAL OF THOUSAND OAKS, 14747 Jones Maltsberger Road, San Antonio, Texas, Zip 78247–3713, tel. 210/581–5300; Kasondra Kistner, R.N., Chief Executive Officer; WARM SPRINGS REHABILITATION HOSPITAL OF WESTOVER HILLS, 10323 State Highway 151, San Antonio, Texas, Zip 78251–4557, tel. 210/581–5306; Steve Flaherty, Chief Executive Officer) (Total facility includes 10 beds in nursing home–type unit) **A**1 3 5 10 **F**3 11 29 30 57 64 68 74 75 79 82 90 93 94 96 128 130 132 146 148 **S** Post Acute Medical, LLC, Enola, PA
Primary Contact: Debra Bornmann, Chief Executive Officer
CMO: Alex Willingham M.D., Medical Director
CIO: Rick Marek, Vice President Medical Information Systems
CHR: Waynea Finley, System Director Human Resources
Web address: www.postacutemedical.com/our–facilities/hospitals/warm–springs–rehabilitation–hospital–san–antonio/
Control: Partnership, Investor–owned (for–profit) **Service:** Rehabilitation

Staffed Beds: 139 **Admissions:** 2537 **Census:** 91 **Outpatient Visits:** 21182 **Births:** 0 **Total Expense ($000):** 46604 **Payroll Expense ($000):** 23678 **Personnel:** 478

SAN AUGUSTINE—San Augustine County

★ **CHI ST. LUKE'S HEALTH MEMORIAL SAN AUGUSTINE (451360)**, 511 East Hospital Street, Zip 75972–2121, Mailing Address: P.O.Box 658, 75972–0658; tel. 936/275–3446 **A**10 18 **F**29 35 40 57 59 64 102 107 119 132 133 149 **S** Catholic Health Initiatives, Englewood, CO
Primary Contact: Darlene Williams, R.N., Administrator
CFO: Kristi Gay, Chief Financial Officer
Web address: www.memorialhealth.org
Control: Other not–for–profit (including NFP Corporation) **Service:** General medical and surgical

Staffed Beds: 9 **Admissions:** 283 **Census:** 2 **Outpatient Visits:** 11064 **Births:** 9 **Total Expense ($000):** 5950 **Payroll Expense ($000):** 3129 **Personnel:** 45

SAN MARCOS—Hays County

⊞ **CENTRAL TEXAS MEDICAL CENTER (450272)**, 1301 Wonder World Drive, Zip 78666–7544; tel. 512/353–8979 **A**1 10 **F**3 11 13 15 18 20 29 30 32 34 35 39 40 43 44 45 49 50 51 56 57 59 60 62 63 64 65 66 68 70 72 75 76 77 79 80 81 82 85 86 87 92 93 94 98 107 108 109 110 111 114 116 117 118 119 126 129 130 131 132 146 147 148 **P**6 8 **S** Adventist Health System Sunbelt Health Care Corporation, Altamonte Springs, FL
Primary Contact: Anthony Stahl, Ph.D., FACHE, Chief Executive Officer
CFO: Parker Pridgen, Chief Financial Officer
CMO: Lee Johannsen M.D., Chief Medical Officer
CHR: Debbie D Cox, Administrative Director Human Resources
CNO: Elsie Graves, Chief Nursing Officer
Web address: www.ctmc.org
Control: Church operated, Nongovernment, not–for–profit **Service:** General medical and surgical

Staffed Beds: 111 **Admissions:** 3878 **Census:** 40 **Outpatient Visits:** 79156 **Births:** 761 **Total Expense ($000):** 95200 **Payroll Expense ($000):** 32649 **Personnel:** 566

WELLBRIDGE HEALTHCARE OF SAN MARCOS (454137), 1106 North Interstate 35, Zip 78666–7030; tel. 512/353–0194 **F**29 30 35 38 56 75 86 87 98 100 101 103 104 130 135 149 **P**7 **S** Oceans Healthcare, Lake Charles, LA
Primary Contact: Joanne Sundin, Chief Executive Officer
Web address: www.oceanssanmarcos.com
Control: Partnership, Investor–owned (for–profit) **Service:** Psychiatric

Staffed Beds: 24 **Admissions:** 258 **Census:** 17 **Outpatient Visits:** 0 **Births:** 0 **Total Expense ($000):** 5390 **Payroll Expense ($000):** 2542 **Personnel:** 58

SEGUIN—Guadalupe County

⊞ **GUADALUPE REGIONAL MEDICAL CENTER (450104)**, 1215 East Court Street, Zip 78155–5189; tel. 830/379–2411 **A**1 10 **F**3 11 13 15 18 20 22 24 28 29 30 34 35 39 40 43 44 45 46 49 51 53 56 57 58 59 60 61 63 64 65 66 68 70 74 75 76 77 78 79 81 82 84 85 90 93 96 103 104 107 108 110 111 115 119 126 129 132 143 146 148 149 **P**1
Primary Contact: Robert Gerard. Haynes, FACHE, Chief Executive Officer
COO: Sheri Williams, Chief Operating Officer
CFO: Penny Wallace, Chief Financial Officer
CMO: Robert Ryan M.D., Chief Medical Officer
CIO: Steve Ratliff, Director Information Technology
CHR: Fay Bennett, Vice President Employee Services
CNO: Daphne Blake R.N., MSN, Chief Nursing Officer
Web address: www.grmedcenter.com
Control: City–county, Government, Nonfederal **Service:** General medical and surgical

Staffed Beds: 90 **Admissions:** 4016 **Census:** 41 **Outpatient Visits:** 136853 **Births:** 879 **Total Expense ($000):** 91557 **Payroll Expense ($000):** 33661 **Personnel:** 672

SEMINOLE—Gaines County

★ **MEMORIAL HOSPITAL (451358)**, 209 NW Eighth Street, Zip 79360–3447;
tel. 432/758–5811 **A**10 18 **F**3 10 11 13 28 29 30 32 34 35 40 43 45 53 56 57
59 62 63 64 65 75 76 81 87 93 97 102 107 114 119 129 130 131 132 133
143 146 147 148
Primary Contact: James G. Parrish, FACHE, Chief Executive Officer
COO: Heath Mitchell, Chief Operating Officer
CFO: Traci Anderson, Chief Financial Officer
CMO: Michael Watson M.D., Chief of Staff
Web address: www.seminolehospitaldistrict.com
Control: Hospital district or authority, Government, Nonfederal **Service**: General
medical and surgical

Staffed Beds: 25 **Admissions:** 862 **Census:** 8 **Outpatient Visits:** 49953
Births: 423 **Total Expense ($000):** 33090 **Payroll Expense ($000):** 10823
Personnel: 226

SEYMOUR—Baylor County

SEYMOUR HOSPITAL (450586), 200 Stadium Drive, Zip 76380–2344;
tel. 940/889–5572 **A**10 20 **F**3 7 8 11 13 14 28 29 34 36 40 43 45 50 53 56
57 59 62 64 65 66 68 70 75 76 81 85 86 87 89 93 94 100 102 103 104 107
119 127 130 133 135 146 147 148 **P**1
Primary Contact: Leslie Hardin, Chief Executive Officer and Chief Financial Officer
CFO: Leslie Hardin, Chief Executive Officer and Chief Financial Officer
CMO: Kory Lann Martin M.D., Chief of Staff
CHR: Linda Moore, Manager Human Resources
CNO: Julie Smajstrla, Director Nursing
Web address: www.seymourhospital.com/
Control: Hospital district or authority, Government, Nonfederal **Service**: General
medical and surgical

Staffed Beds: 40 **Admissions:** 376 **Census:** 4 **Outpatient Visits:** 36417
Births: 24 **Total Expense ($000):** 36214 **Payroll Expense ($000):** 5634
Personnel: 118

SHAMROCK—Wheeler County

SHAMROCK GENERAL HOSPITAL (451340), 1000 South Main Street,
Zip 79079–2896, Mailing Address: P O Box 511, 79079–0511; tel. 806/256–
2114 **A**10 18 **F**7 11 29 32 34 35 40 43 63 65 68 93 107 119 127 130 133 **P**4
Primary Contact: Wiley M. Fires, Administrator
CFO: Wiley M Fires, Administrator
CHR: Cecille Williams, Assistant Administrator
CNO: Jeanne Crossland, Director of Nursing
Control: Hospital district or authority, Government, Nonfederal **Service**: General
medical and surgical

Staffed Beds: 13 **Admissions:** 93 **Census:** 1 **Outpatient Visits:** 10958
Births: 0 **Total Expense ($000):** 6576 **Payroll Expense ($000):** 3264
Personnel: 72

SHENANDOAH—Montgomery County

⊞ **HEALTHSOUTH REHABILITATION HOSPITAL VISION PARK (673034)**, 117
Vision Park Boulevard, Zip 77384–3001; tel. 936/444–1700 **A**1 10 **F**3 29 65 77
90 91 93 96 130 148 **S** HEALTHSOUTH Corporation, Birmingham, AL
Primary Contact: Jeff Crawford, Chief Executive Officer
CFO: Terri Weiss, Chief Financial Officer
Web address: www.healthsouthvisionpark.com/
Control: Partnership, Investor–owned (for–profit) **Service**: Rehabilitation

Staffed Beds: 41 **Admissions:** 1264 **Census:** 40 **Outpatient Visits:** 8241
Births: 0 **Total Expense ($000):** 21532 **Payroll Expense ($000):** 8597
Personnel: 136

⇑ **NEXUS SPECIALTY HOSPITAL**, 123 Vision Park Boulevard, Zip 77384–3001;
tel. 281/364–0317 **A**21 **F**1 3 70 74 75 77 82 84 85 91 92 93 100 101 107
119 130 132 135 148 **S** Nexus Health Systems, Houston, TX
Primary Contact: Mikael Simpson, Chief Executive Officer
CFO: David Strickler, Chief Financial Officer
CMO: Ather Siddiqi M.D., Medical Director
CIO: Noe Salinas, Vice President Information Technology
CHR: Kevin McAndrews, Vice President Human Resources
CNO: Rhena Anderson, Chief Nursing Officer
Web address: www.nexusspecialty.com
Control: Partnership, Investor–owned (for–profit) **Service**: Acute long–term care
hospital

Staffed Beds: 75 **Admissions:** 582 **Census:** 44 **Outpatient Visits:** 446
Births: 0 **Total Expense ($000):** 25435 **Payroll Expense ($000):** 10661
Personnel: 177

SHERMAN—Grayson County

⇑ **BAYLOR SCOTT & WHITE SURGICAL HOSPITAL AT SHERMAN (670076)**,
3601 North Calais Street, Zip 75090–1785; tel. 903/870–0999 **A**10 21 **F**3
29 37 40 43 45 47 77 81 85 107 111 119 126 131 145 **S** Foundation Surgical
Hospital Affiliates, Oklahoma City, OK
Primary Contact: Marc Devorsetz, Chief Executive Officer
CMO: Curtis Holbrook M.D., Chief Medical Officer
CIO: Grant Hulsey, Director Information Technology
CHR: Terrie Langford, Director Human Resources
CNO: Teresa Dutton R.N., Chief Nursing Officer
Web address: www.heritageparksurgicalhospital.com
Control: Partnership, Investor–owned (for–profit) **Service**: General medical and
surgical

Staffed Beds: 12 **Admissions:** 531 **Census:** 3 **Outpatient Visits:** 23956
Births: 0 **Total Expense ($000):** 42006 **Payroll Expense ($000):** 10372
Personnel: 189

☐ **CARRUS REHABILITATION HOSPITAL (673041)**, 1810 West US Highway 82,
Suite 100, Zip 75092–7069; tel. 903/870–2600 **A**1 10 **F**3 29 40 41 44 65 74
75 77 79 85 86 87 90 91 96 130 **S** Carrus Hospitals, Sherman, TX
Primary Contact: Jon–Michael Rains, Chief Executive Officer
CFO: Michael Exline, Chief Financial Officer
CMO: Jose Matus M.D., Director Medical
CIO: Gary Glenn, Director Information Technology
CHR: Charlene Shupert, Director Staff Services
CNO: Marie Johnson, Chief Nursing Officer
Web address: www.carrushospital.com
Control: Corporation, Investor–owned (for–profit) **Service**: Rehabilitation

Staffed Beds: 24 **Admissions:** 618 **Census:** 22 **Outpatient Visits:** 0 **Births:** 0
Total Expense ($000): 8617 **Payroll Expense ($000):** 3976 **Personnel:** 91

CARRUS SPECIALTY HOSPITAL (452041), 1810 West US Highway 82,
Zip 75092–7069; tel. 903/870–2600 **A**10 **F**1 3 29 40 41 44 56 65 74 75 77 78
79 82 83 85 86 87 91 107 114 129 130 148 **S** Carrus Hospitals, Sherman, TX
Primary Contact: Jon–Michael Rains, Chief Executive Officer
CFO: Michael Exline, Chief Financial Officer
CMO: Nathan Watson M.D., Jr, Chief of Staff
CIO: Gary Glenn, Director Information Technology
CHR: Charlene Shupert, Director Staff Services
CNO: Marie Johnson, Chief Nursing Officer
Web address: www.carrushospital.com
Control: Corporation, Investor–owned (for–profit) **Service**: Acute long–term care
hospital

Staffed Beds: 16 **Admissions:** 237 **Census:** 15 **Outpatient Visits:** 1882
Births: 0 **Total Expense ($000):** 12384 **Payroll Expense ($000):** 4787
Personnel: 124

WILSON N. JONES MEDICAL CENTER See Wilson N. Jones Regional Medical
Center

☐ **WILSON N. JONES REGIONAL MEDICAL CENTER (450469)**, 500 North
Highland Avenue, Zip 75092–7354; tel. 903/870–4611 **A**1 10 **F**3 11 12 13 15
18 20 22 24 26 28 29 30 35 40 41 43 45 53 54 56 57 58 59 61 64 70 74 76
77 78 79 81 84 86 87 93 96 98 100 103 106 107 108 111 118 119 129 130
132 146 147 148 149 **S** Alecto Healthcare, Irvine, CA
Primary Contact: John Rossfeld, Administrator
CFO: Chuck Cave CPA, Chief Financial Officer
CMO: Kenton Schrank M.D., President Medical Staff
CIO: Prabhu Bollu, Director Information Technology
CHR: Bill Barrett, Manager Human Resources
CNO: Tonya Price, Chief Nursing Officer
Web address: www.wnj.org
Control: Corporation, Investor–owned (for–profit) **Service**: General medical and
surgical

Staffed Beds: 108 **Admissions:** 5699 **Census:** 63 **Outpatient Visits:** 33383
Births: 411 **Total Expense ($000):** 79065 **Payroll Expense ($000):** 28152
Personnel: 510

TX

Hospital, Medicare Provider Number, Address, Telephone, Approval, Facility, and Physician Codes, Health Care System

★ American Hospital Association (AHA) membership ○ Healthcare Facilities Accreditation Program ⇑ Center for Improvement in Healthcare Quality Accreditation
☐ The Joint Commission accreditation ◇ DNV Healthcare Inc. accreditation △ Commission on Accreditation of Rehabilitation Facilities (CARF) accreditation

Hospitals, U.S. / TEXAS

SMITHVILLE—Bastrop County

⊞ **SETON SMITHVILLE REGIONAL HOSPITAL (450143)**, 1201 Hill Road,
Zip 78957; tel. 512/237-3214 **A**1 10 **F**3 11 15 29 30 34 40 53 57 64 68 77
79 81 85 87 93 107 110 111 114 119 146 148 **P**3 8 **S** Ascension Healthcare,
Saint Louis, MO
Primary Contact: Christopher L. Hartle, Chief Exeuctive Officer
CFO: Melissa Nordyke, Chief Financial Officer
CHR: Sara Rodriguez, Human Resources
CNO: Christine Laflamme R.N., MSN, Chief Nursing Officer
Web address: www.seton.org
Control: Church operated, Nongovernment, not-for-profit **Service:** General
medical and surgical

Staffed Beds: 5 **Admissions:** 336 **Census:** 2 **Outpatient Visits:** 26918
Births: 0 **Total Expense ($000):** 15755 **Payroll Expense ($000):** 5715
Personnel: 81

SNYDER—Scurry County

⇑ **COGDELL MEMORIAL HOSPITAL (451384)**, 1700 Cogdell Boulevard,
Zip 79549-6198; tel. 325/573-6374 **A**10 18 21 **F**8 11 13 15 18 19 29 30 34
40 43 45 46 47 48 49 50 53 56 57 59 62 64 65 68 75 76 77 79 81 85 86 87
91 92 93 97 107 108 111 115 119 127 130 131 132 133 145 146 147 148
149 **P**6
Primary Contact: Ella Raye. Helms, Chief Executive Officer
CFO: John Everett, Chief Financial Officer
CMO: Robert Rakov M.D., Chief Medical Officer
CHR: Linda Warren, Director Human Resources
Web address: www.cogdellhospital.com
Control: Hospital district or authority, Government, Nonfederal **Service:** General
medical and surgical

Staffed Beds: 25 **Admissions:** 668 **Census:** 6 **Outpatient Visits:** 78143
Births: 188 **Total Expense ($000):** 40365 **Payroll Expense ($000):** 14742
Personnel: 219

SONORA—Sutton County

★ **LILLIAN M. HUDSPETH MEMORIAL HOSPITAL (451324)**, 308 Hudspeth
Avenue, Zip 76950-8003, Mailing Address: P.O.Box 455, 76950-0455;
tel. 325/387-2521 **A**10 18 **F**7 15 18 28 29 30 32 34 35 40 43 44 50 53 57 59
62 63 64 65 66 68 71 75 79 86 87 90 93 96 97 107 110 111 115 119 127
128 131 132 133 135 147 148
Primary Contact: John A. Graves, Chief Executive Officer
CFO: Michelle Schaefer, Chief Financial Officer
CMO: Kristy Edwards M.D., Chief Medical Officer
CNO: Jon–Michael Parker R.N., Chief Nursing Officer
Web address: www.sonora-hospital.org
Control: Hospital district or authority, Government, Nonfederal **Service:** General
medical and surgical

Staffed Beds: 12 **Admissions:** 152 **Census:** 2 **Outpatient Visits:** 8967
Births: 0 **Total Expense ($000):** 10200 **Payroll Expense ($000):** 5013
Personnel: 68

SOUTHLAKE—Tarrant County

★ ○ **METHODIST SOUTHLAKE HOSPITAL**, 421 East State Highway 114,
Zip 76092; tel. 817/865-4400, (Data for 136 days)**A**11 **F**3 12 29 40 45 49 50
51 68 70 75 79 81 82 85 87 107 111 115 119 124 126 130 132 135 149 **S**
Methodist Health System, Dallas, TX
Primary Contact: John McGreevy, FACHE, President
Web address: www.methodistsouthlake.com/
Control: Partnership, Investor–owned (for–profit) **Service:** General medical and
surgical

Staffed Beds: 54 **Admissions:** 134 **Census:** 3 **Outpatient Visits:** 1794
Births: 0 **Total Expense ($000):** 18087 **Payroll Expense ($000):** 4334
Personnel: 158

☐ **TEXAS HEALTH HARRIS METHODIST HOSPITAL SOUTHLAKE (450888)**,
1545 East Southlake Boulevard, Zip 76092-6422; tel. 817/748-8700 **A**1 10 **F**3
29 30 40 64 74 79 81 85 107 111 113 114 119 130 **P**2
Primary Contact: Traci Bernard, R.N., President, Chief Executive Officer and Chief
Operating Officer
CFO: Mitchell Mulvehill, Group Financial Officer
CMO: David Taunton M.D., Chief of Staff
CHR: Tasha Sledge, Director Human Resources
CNO: Debra Ennis R.N., Vice President and Chief Nursing Officer
Web address: www.texashealthsouthlake.com
Control: Corporation, Investor–owned (for–profit) **Service:** Surgical

Staffed Beds: 23 **Admissions:** 1004 **Census:** 7 **Outpatient Visits:** 12943
Births: 0 **Total Expense ($000):** 51145 **Payroll Expense ($000):** 10972
Personnel: 144

SPEARMAN—Hansford County

★ **HANSFORD HOSPITAL (451344)**, 707 South Roland Street, Zip 79081-3441;
tel. 806/659-2535 **A**10 18 **F**3 11 32 34 35 40 43 56 57 59 62 63 64 65 68 69
77 78 93 107 114 127 130 133 148 **P**6
Primary Contact: Jonathan D. Bailey, Chief Executive Officer and Administrator
CFO: Scott Beedy, Chief Financial Officer
CMO: Mark Garnett M.D., Chief of Staff
CHR: Jackie Nelson, Director Human Resources
Web address: www.hchd.net
Control: Hospital district or authority, Government, Nonfederal **Service:** General
medical and surgical

Staffed Beds: 14 **Admissions:** 125 **Census:** 2 **Outpatient Visits:** 31093
Births: 0 **Total Expense ($000):** 11738 **Payroll Expense ($000):** 4527
Personnel: 99

STAFFORD—Fort Bend County

ATRIUM MEDICAL CENTER (452114), 11929 West Airport Boulevard,
Zip 77477-2451; tel. 281/207-8200 **A**10 22 **F**1 3 18 26 28 29 45 46 56 59 60
64 65 68 70 74 77 82 83 85 90 91 107 114 119 130 148
Primary Contact: Ahmad Zaid, Chief Executive Officer
CFO: Ana Urbina, Chief Financial Officer
CMO: Shatish Patel M.D., Chief Medical Officer
CNO: Ava Hearing, Chief Nursing Officer
Web address: www.atriummedicalcenter.com
Control: Partnership, Investor–owned (for–profit) **Service:** Acute long–term care
hospital

Staffed Beds: 68 **Admissions:** 365 **Census:** 27 **Outpatient Visits:** 594
Births: 0 **Total Expense ($000):** 13818 **Payroll Expense ($000):** 5885
Personnel: 122

STAMFORD—Jones County

STAMFORD MEMORIAL HOSPITAL (450306), 1601 Columbia Street,
Zip 79553-6863, Mailing Address: P.O.Box 911, 79553-0911; tel. 325/773-
2725 **A**10 **F**10 11 28 30 34 35 36 40 41 53 57 59 64 65 81 89 93 107 114
119 127 128 133 144 146 148 **P**6
Primary Contact: Richard G. DeFoore, FACHE, Chief Executive Officer
CFO: Elizabeth Miller CPA, Chief Financial Officer
CMO: Douglas Kruckner M.D., Medical Director
CHR: Cheryl Hertel, Coordinator Human Resources
CNO: Rickie Young, Chief Nursing Officer
Web address: www.stamfordhosp.com/
Control: Other not–for–profit (including NFP Corporation) **Service:** General
medical and surgical

Staffed Beds: 11 **Admissions:** 110 **Census:** 1 **Outpatient Visits:** 15140
Births: 0 **Total Expense ($000):** 23903 **Payroll Expense ($000):** 4349
Personnel: 166

STANTON—Martin County

MARTIN COUNTY HOSPITAL DISTRICT (451333), 600 Interstate 20E,
Zip 79782, Mailing Address: P.O.Box 640, 79782-0640; tel. 432/607-3200 **A**10
18 **F**3 7 29 34 35 39 40 45 57 59 64 65 75 81 87 93 107 114 119 127 133
P6
Primary Contact: Rance Ramsey, Chief Executive Officer
CFO: Michele Cathey, Interim Chief Financial officer
CIO: Freddy Oliveras, Chief Information Officer
CHR: Paula Dority, Director Human Resources
CNO: Brandi Avila, Chief Nursing Officer
Web address: www.martincountyhospital.org/
Control: Hospital district or authority, Government, Nonfederal **Service:** General
medical and surgical

Staffed Beds: 18 **Admissions:** 174 **Census:** 4 **Outpatient Visits:** 9180
Births: 1 **Total Expense ($000):** 17174 **Payroll Expense ($000):** 6187
Personnel: 152

STEPHENVILLE—Erath County

⊞ **TEXAS HEALTH HARRIS METHODIST HOSPITAL STEPHENVILLE (450351)**,
411 North Belknap Street, Zip 76401-3415; tel. 254/965-1500 **A**1 10 20 **F**3 13
15 29 30 34 35 39 40 41 43 45 50 51 57 59 64 65 68 70 75 76 77 79 81 85
86 89 107 108 111 114 118 119 129 130 146 147 148 149 **P**6 **S** Texas Health
Resources, Arlington, TX
Primary Contact: Christopher Leu, President
CMO: Marilyn Brister M.D., Chief of Staff
CHR: Kimberly Leondar, Director Human Resources
CNO: Cynthia L McCarthy MS, R.N., Chief Nursing Officer
Web address: www.texashealth.org/landing.cfm?id=108
Control: Other not–for–profit (including NFP Corporation) **Service:** General
medical and surgical

Staffed Beds: 54 **Admissions:** 2162 **Census:** 18 **Outpatient Visits:** 29558
Births: 419 **Total Expense ($000):** 43894 **Payroll Expense ($000):** 16644
Personnel: 209

Many Facility Codes have changed. Please refer to the AHA Guide Code Chart. © 2017 AHA Guide

SUGAR LAND—Fort Bend County

⇑ **EMERUS HOSPITAL – SUGAR LAND (670058)**, 16000 Southwest Freeway, Suite 100, Zip 77479–2674; tel. 281/277–0911 **A**10 21 **F**3 40 75 107 114 119 149 **P**5 **S** Emerus, The Woodlands, TX
Primary Contact: Mike Kohler, Chief Executive Officer
Web address: www.emerus.com
Control: Corporation, Investor–owned (for–profit) **Service:** General medical and surgical

Staffed Beds: 7 **Admissions:** 88 **Census:** 1 **Outpatient Visits:** 5189 **Births:** 0 **Total Expense ($000):** 5333 **Payroll Expense ($000):** 1738 **Personnel:** 26

⊠ **HEALTHSOUTH SUGAR LAND REHABILITATION HOSPITAL (673042)**, 1325 Highway 6, Zip 77478–4906; tel. 281/276–7574 **A**1 10 **F**3 29 34 75 87 90 95 96 130 132 146 148 **S** HEALTHSOUTH Corporation, Birmingham, AL
Primary Contact: Nicholas Hardin, FACHE, Chief Executive Officer
CFO: Carol Neilson CPA, Controller
CNO: Steve Midgett R.N., Chief Nursing Officer
Web address: www.healthsouthsugarland.com
Control: Corporation, Investor–owned (for–profit) **Service:** Rehabilitation

Staffed Beds: 50 **Admissions:** 1409 **Census:** 46 **Outpatient Visits:** 0 **Births:** 0 **Total Expense ($000):** 19263 **Payroll Expense ($000):** 9855 **Personnel:** 184

★ ⇑ **HOUSTON METHODIST SUGAR LAND HOSPITAL (450820)**, 16655 SW Freeway, Zip 77479–2329; tel. 281/274–7000 **A**2 3 10 21 **F**3 12 13 15 18 20 22 24 26 29 30 31 33 35 36 37 38 39 40 41 42 44 45 46 47 49 50 51 53 54 58 59 60 61 64 65 68 70 73 74 75 76 77 78 79 81 82 84 85 86 87 91 92 93 94 96 100 102 107 108 110 111 114 115 118 119 120 121 123 124 126 130 131 132 135 145 146 147 148 149 150 **P**6 **S** Houston Methodist, Houston, TX
Primary Contact: Christopher Siebenaler, Chief Executive Officer
CFO: Lowell Stanton, Chief Financial Officer
CMO: Jeffrey Jackson M.D., Medical Director
CHR: Luis Mario Garcia Jr, Director Human Resources
Web address: www.methodisthealth.com
Control: Other not–for–profit (including NFP Corporation) **Service:** General medical and surgical

Staffed Beds: 305 **Admissions:** 17032 **Census:** 209 **Outpatient Visits:** 201446 **Births:** 3727 **Total Expense ($000):** 370450 **Payroll Expense ($000):** 128612 **Personnel:** 2067

⊠ **KINDRED HOSPITAL SUGAR LAND (452080)**, 1550 First Colony Boulevard, Zip 77479–4000; tel. 281/275–6000, (Includes KINDRED HOSPITAL TOWN AND COUNTRY, 1120 Business Center Drive, Houston, Texas, Zip 77043, tel. 713/932–2700) **A**1 10 **F**1 3 29 31 35 45 57 64 65 75 77 85 87 91 107 130 148 149 **S** Kindred Healthcare, Louisville, KY
Primary Contact: John D. Cross, Chief Executive Officer
CFO: Sara Rodriguez, Chief Financial Officer
CMO: Subodh Bhuchar M.D., Chief of Staff
CIO: Feisal Ndomea, Director Case Management
CHR: Lupe Delgado, Coordinator Human Resources
CNO: Hala Alameddine, Chief Nursing Executive
Web address: www.kindred.com
Control: Corporation, Investor–owned (for–profit) **Service:** Acute long–term care hospital

Staffed Beds: 171 **Admissions:** 1564 **Census:** 108 **Outpatient Visits:** 56 **Births:** 0 **Total Expense ($000):** 61257 **Payroll Expense ($000):** 22105 **Personnel:** 349

⊠ **MEMORIAL HERMANN SUGAR LAND HOSPITAL (450848)**, 17500 West Grand Parkway South, Zip 77479–2562; tel. 281/725–5000 **A**1 3 5 10 **F**3 8 11 13 15 18 20 22 29 30 34 35 36 37 40 41 42 43 44 45 46 47 48 49 50 51 55 56 57 59 60 64 68 70 72 74 75 76 77 78 79 81 82 85 86 87 91 92 93 97 107 108 109 110 111 112 114 117 119 126 129 130 135 146 147 148 **P**5 6 **S** Memorial Hermann Health System, Houston, TX
Primary Contact: Gregory Haralson, FACHE, Chief Executive Officer
CFO: Lisa Kendler, Chief Financial Officer
CMO: William Riley M.D., Jr, Chief of Staff
CHR: Robert Blake, Chief Human Resources Officer Southwest Market
Web address: www.memorialhermann.org
Control: Other not–for–profit (including NFP Corporation) **Service:** General medical and surgical

Staffed Beds: 87 **Admissions:** 5889 **Census:** 56 **Outpatient Visits:** 93628 **Births:** 1543 **Total Expense ($000):** 136525 **Payroll Expense ($000):** 45015 **Personnel:** 481

⇑ **METHODIST SUGAR LAND HOSPITAL** See Houston Methodist Sugar Land Hospital

★ ⇑ **ST. LUKE'S SUGAR LAND HOSPITAL (670053)**, 1317 Lake Pointe Parkway, Zip 77478–3997; tel. 281/637–7000 **A**10 21 **F**3 15 18 20 22 26 29 30 34 35 37 39 40 41 44 45 46 49 50 57 60 64 68 70 72 74 75 76 79 81 82 85 107 108 110 111 115 119 126 130 146 147 148 **S** Catholic Health Initiatives, Englewood, CO
Primary Contact: Robert A. Heifner, FACHE, Chief Executive Officer
CFO: Bill Beauchamp, Chief Financial Officer
CNO: Wes Garrison
Web address: www.stlukessugarland.com
Control: Church operated, Nongovernment, not–for–profit **Service:** General medical and surgical

Staffed Beds: 96 **Admissions:** 3719 **Census:** 50 **Outpatient Visits:** 23919 **Births:** 288 **Total Expense ($000):** 86171 **Payroll Expense ($000):** 31071 **Personnel:** 352

SUGAR LAND REHABILITATION HOSPITAL See Healthsouth Sugar Land Rehabilitation Hospital

TRIUMPH HOSPITAL SOUTHWEST See Kindred Hospital Sugar Land

SULPHUR SPRINGS—Hopkins County

★ **CHRISTUS MOTHER FRANCES HOSPITAL – SULPHUR SPRINGS (450236)**, 115 Airport Road, Zip 75482–2105; tel. 903/885–7671, (Data for 285 days) **A**3 10 **F**1 7 11 13 15 28 29 34 35 40 43 45 57 59 70 73 76 79 80 81 93 96 107 110 111 115 119 127 130 144 146 **P**6 **S** CHRISTUS Health, Irving, TX
Primary Contact: Paul Harvery, President and Chief Executive Officer
COO: Donna Geiken Wallace, Chief Operating Officer and Chief Financial Officer
CFO: Donna Geiken Wallace, Chief Operating Officer and Chief Financial Officer
CMO: Chris Gallagher M.D., Chief Medical Officer
CHR: Donna Rudzik, Director Human Resources
CNO: Terri Bunch R.N., MSN, Chief Nursing Officer
Web address: www.tmfhc.org/maps-and-locations/locations-profile/?id=72&searchId=8bcb329f-a152-e611-b37f-2c768a4e1b84&sort=11&page=1&pageSize=10
Control: Hospital district or authority, Government, Nonfederal **Service:** General medical and surgical

Staffed Beds: 50 **Admissions:** 2109 **Census:** 28 **Outpatient Visits:** 53058 **Births:** 547 **Total Expense ($000):** 42746 **Payroll Expense ($000):** 16132 **Personnel:** 459

SUNNYVALE—Dallas County

⊠ **BAYLOR SCOTT & WHITE MEDICAL CENTER – SUNNYVALE (670060)**, 231 South Collins Road, Zip 75182–4624; tel. 972/892–3000 **A**1 10 **F**3 13 15 18 20 22 24 29 34 35 40 45 49 57 59 64 70 74 75 76 77 79 80 81 82 85 87 90 93 107 108 110 111 114 115 119 130 135 146 147 148 149 **P**2 **S** TENET Healthcare Corporation, Dallas, TX
Primary Contact: Collin LeMaistre, Chief Executive Officer
COO: Josiah De La Garza, Chief Operating Officer
CFO: Mike Davis, Chief Financial Officer
CMO: William G. Jones M.D., Chief Medical Officer
CHR: David Olmstead, Chief Human Resource Officer
CNO: Deborah A Moeller R.N., MS, Interim Chief Nursing Officer
Web address: www.BaylorScottandWhite.com/Sunnyvale
Control: Partnership, Investor–owned (for–profit) **Service:** General medical and surgical

Staffed Beds: 70 **Admissions:** 4130 **Census:** 46 **Outpatient Visits:** 49466 **Births:** 597 **Total Expense ($000):** 71862 **Payroll Expense ($000):** 28115 **Personnel:** 302

SWEENY—Brazoria County

★ **SWEENY COMMUNITY HOSPITAL (451311)**, 305 North McKinney Street, Zip 77480–2895; tel. 979/548–1500 **A**10 18 **F**3 7 10 11 15 29 34 35 40 43 45 53 56 57 59 65 69 70 75 81 85 93 103 104 107 110 114 119 130 132 133 143 145 148 149
Primary Contact: Scott Briner, Chief Executive Officer
CFO: Hong Wade, Chief Financial Officer
CMO: Enrique A Leal M.D., III, Chief of Staff
CIO: Stuart Butler, Director Information Technology
CHR: Rebecca McKay, Director Human Resources
CNO: Sherri Pierce R.N., Chief Nursing Officer
Web address: www.sweenyhospital.org
Control: Hospital district or authority, Government, Nonfederal **Service:** General medical and surgical

Staffed Beds: 14 **Admissions:** 194 **Census:** 2 **Outpatient Visits:** 15438 **Births:** 0 **Total Expense ($000):** 46194 **Payroll Expense ($000):** 7540 **Personnel:** 181

TX

Hospital, Medicare Provider Number, Address, Telephone, Approval, Facility, and Physician Codes, Health Care System

★ American Hospital Association (AHA) membership
□ The Joint Commission accreditation
○ Healthcare Facilities Accreditation Program
◇ DNV Healthcare Inc. accreditation
⇑ Center for Improvement in Healthcare Quality Accreditation
△ Commission on Accreditation of Rehabilitation Facilities (CARF) accreditation

SWEETWATER—Nolan County

★ ⇧ **ROLLING PLAINS MEMORIAL HOSPITAL (450055)**, 200 East Arizona Street, Zip 79556–7199, Mailing Address: P.O.Box 690, 79556–0690; tel. 325/235–1701 **A**10 20 21 **F**3 11 13 15 28 29 34 40 43 45 53 57 59 62 70 76 77 79 81 85 89 91 93 107 108 114 119 127 130 133 135 146 148
Primary Contact: Donna Boatright, MSN, Chief Executive Officer
COO: Rhonda Guelker, Senior Director Finance
CFO: Rhonda Guelker, Senior Director Finance
CMO: Ronnie Dennis, Chief of Staff
CIO: Rhonda Guelker, Senior Director Finance
CHR: Ame Monroe, Director Human Resources
CNO: Rosa Best, Chief Nursing Officer
Web address: www.rpmh.net
Control: Hospital district or authority, Government, Nonfederal **Service**: General medical and surgical

Staffed Beds: 53 **Admissions:** 1103 **Census:** 12 **Outpatient Visits:** 59483 **Births:** 265 **Total Expense ($000):** 33050 **Payroll Expense ($000):** 15288 **Personnel:** 287

TAHOKA—Lynn County

★ **LYNN COUNTY HOSPITAL DISTRICT (451351)**, 2600 Lockwood, Zip 79373–4118; tel. 806/998–4533 **A**10 18 **F**3 7 10 13 29 32 34 35 40 43 44 53 54 56 57 59 64 65 66 75 86 93 97 107 133 147 148 149 **P**5
Primary Contact: Randy L. Lindauer, Ph.D., FACHE, President and Chief Executive Officer
CFO: Steve Brock, Chief Financial Officer
CMO: Donald Freitag M.D., Chief Medical Officer
CIO: Jim Brown, Director Information Technology
CHR: Jill Stone, Manager Human Resources
CNO: Angie Jalomo, Chief Nursing Officer
Web address: www.lchdhealthcare.org
Control: Hospital district or authority, Government, Nonfederal **Service**: General medical and surgical

Staffed Beds: 16 **Admissions:** 203 **Census:** 7 **Outpatient Visits:** 7843 **Births:** 0 **Total Expense ($000):** 11933 **Payroll Expense ($000):** 4854 **Personnel:** 100

TAYLOR—Williamson County

⊞ **BAYLOR SCOTT & WHITE MEDICAL CENTER – TAYLOR (451374)**, 305 Mallard Lane, Zip 76574–1208; tel. 512/352–7611 **A**1 10 18 **F**3 18 29 34 35 40 45 50 56 57 59 62 64 65 68 75 77 81 82 85 87 91 92 93 97 107 108 111 119 127 129 130 132 133 135 146 148 149 **S** Baylor Scott & White Health, Dallas, TX
Primary Contact: Tim Tarbell, Director Operations
CIO: Tim Tarbell, Director Operations
Web address: www.swtaylor.org
Control: Other not–for–profit (including NFP Corporation) **Service**: General medical and surgical

Staffed Beds: 25 **Admissions:** 434 **Census:** 7 **Outpatient Visits:** 56522 **Births:** 0 **Total Expense ($000):** 21151 **Payroll Expense ($000):** 10864 **Personnel:** 124

JOHNS COMMUNITY HOSPITAL See Baylor Scott & White Medical Center – Taylor

TEMPLE—Bell County

★ **BAYLOR SCOTT AND WHITE CONTINUING CARE HOSPITAL (452105)**, 546 North Kegley Road, Zip 76502–4069; tel. 254/215–0900 **A**10 **F**1 3 29 30 31 60 68 85 107 119 130 **S** Baylor Scott & White Health, Dallas, TX
Primary Contact: Kimberly K. Langston, R.N., Chief Executive Officer
CMO: David P Ciceri M.D., Chief Medical Officer
CNO: Robert Pisicotta, Chief Nursing Officer
Web address: www.sw.org/location/temple–cch
Control: Other not–for–profit (including NFP Corporation) **Service**: Acute long–term care hospital

Staffed Beds: 50 **Admissions:** 372 **Census:** 30 **Outpatient Visits:** 0 **Births:** 0 **Total Expense ($000):** 19572 **Payroll Expense ($000):** 8187 **Personnel:** 102

CENTRAL TEXAS VETERANS AFFAIRS HEALTH CARE SYSTEM, OLIN E. TEAGUE VETERANS MEDICAL CENTER See Central Texas Veterans Health Care System

⊞ △ **CENTRAL TEXAS VETERANS HEALTH CARE SYSTEM**, 1901 Veterans Memorial Drive, Zip 76504–7493; tel. 254/778–4811, (Nonreporting) (Includes CENTRAL TEXAS VETERANS AFFAIRS HEALTH CARE SYSTEM, OLIN E. TEAGUE VETERANS MEDICAL CENTER, 1901 Veterans Memorial Drive, Temple, Texas, Zip 76504, tel. 254/778–4811; Christopher R. Sandles, FACHE, Director; CENTRAL TEXAS VETERANS HEALTH CARE SYSTEM, DORIS MILLER VETERANS MEDICAL CENTER, 4800 Memorial Drive, Waco, Texas, Zip 76711–1397, tel. 254/752–6581; Christopher R. Sandles, FACHE, Director) **A**1 3 5 7 8 **S** Department of Veterans Affairs, Washington, DC
Primary Contact: Christopher R. Sandles, FACHE, Director
COO: Andrew T. Garcia, Acting Associate Director
CFO: Rosey Anzures, Acting Chief Financial Officer
CMO: Olawale Fashina M.D., Chief of Staff
CIO: Victor Vitolas, Acting Chief Information Technology Services
CHR: Mary P. Doerfler, Chief Human Resources Officer
CNO: Bryan W. Sisk, Associate Director Patient and Nursing Services
Web address: www.centraltexas.va.gov/
Control: Veterans Affairs, Government, federal **Service**: General medical and surgical

Staffed Beds: 1532

MCLANE CHILDREN'S HOSPITAL SCOTT & WHITE See Scott & White Medical Center – Temple

⊞ **SCOTT & WHITE MEDICAL CENTER – TEMPLE (450054)**, 2401 South 31st Street, Zip 76508–0002; tel. 254/724–2111, (Includes MCLANE CHILDREN'S HOSPITAL SCOTT & WHITE, 1901 SW H K Dodgen Loop, Temple, Texas, Zip 76502–1896, tel. 254/771–8600; John Boyd III, M.D., Chief Executive Officer; MCLANE CHILDREN'S HOSPITAL SCOTT & WHITE, 2401 South 31st Street, Temple, Texas, Zip 76508–0001, tel. 877/724–5437; John Boyd III, M.D., Chief Executive Officer and Chief Medical Officer) (Total facility includes 29 beds in nursing home–type unit) **A**1 2 3 5 8 10 **F**3 5 7 8 9 11 12 13 14 15 17 18 19 20 22 24 25 26 27 28 29 30 31 32 33 34 35 36 37 38 39 40 41 43 45 46 47 48 49 50 51 52 54 55 56 57 58 59 60 61 62 63 64 65 66 67 68 70 71 72 73 74 75 76 77 78 79 81 82 83 84 85 86 87 88 89 92 93 94 97 98 99 100 101 102 104 107 108 109 110 111 113 114 115 116 117 119 120 121 122 123 124 126 128 129 130 131 132 134 135 137 138 141 142 143 144 145 146 147 148 149 **S** Baylor Scott & White Health, Dallas, TX
Primary Contact: Shahin Motakef, FACHE, Chief Executive Officer
CFO: Alita Prosser, Chief Financial Officer
CMO: Stephen Sibbitt M.D., Chief Medical Officer
CIO: Matthew Chambers, Chief Information Officer
CHR: Pat Balz, Vice President Operations Human Resources
CNO: Gerald W Bryant R.N., Chief Nursing Officer
Web address: www.sw.org/location/temple–hospital
Control: Other not–for–profit (including NFP Corporation) **Service**: General medical and surgical

Staffed Beds: 642 **Admissions:** 34681 **Census:** 467 **Outpatient Visits:** 1729488 **Births:** 2838 **Total Expense ($000):** 921729 **Payroll Expense ($000):** 283593 **Personnel:** 5355

TERRELL—Kaufman County

☐ **TERRELL STATE HOSPITAL (454006)**, 1200 East Brin Street, Zip 75160–2938, Mailing Address: P.O.Box 70, 75160–9000; tel. 972/524–6452 **A**1 3 10 **F**30 34 39 57 68 75 86 87 98 99 100 101 103 130 132 135 146 **P**6 **S** Texas Department of State Health Services, Austin, TX
Primary Contact: Dorothy Floyd, Ph.D., Superintendent
CFO: David R. Teel, Financial Officer
CMO: Mark Messer D.O., Clinical Director
CIO: Sims Anderson, Manager Facility Automation
CNO: Kathryn Griffin, Chief Nurse Executive
Web address: www.dshs.state.tx.us/mhhospitals/terrellsh
Control: State, Government, Nonfederal **Service**: Psychiatric

Staffed Beds: 288 **Admissions:** 1613 **Census:** 244 **Outpatient Visits:** 0 **Births:** 0 **Total Expense ($000):** 85662 **Payroll Expense ($000):** 37068 **Personnel:** 867

TEXARKANA—Bowie County

✙ **CHRISTUS ST. MICHAEL HEALTH SYSTEM (450801)**, 2600 St Michael Drive, Zip 75503–5220; tel. 903/614–1000, (Includes CHRISTUS ST. MICHAEL HOSPITAL–ATLANTA, 1007 South William Street, Atlanta, Texas, Zip 75551–3245, tel. 903/799–3000; Thomas McKinney, Administrator) **A**1 2 10 **F**3 11 13 15 17 18 20 22 24 26 28 29 30 31 34 35 40 41 43 45 48 49 51 53 55 56 57 59 60 64 65 68 70 71 72 73 74 75 76 77 78 79 80 81 82 84 85 86 87 89 92 97 107 108 109 110 111 114 115 118 119 120 121 122 123 124 126 129 130 131 132 135 143 144 146 147 148 149 **P**8 **S** CHRISTUS Health, Irving, TX
Primary Contact: Chris Karam, FACHE, President and Chief Executive Officer
COO: Jason Rounds, Chief Operating Officer and Administrator
CFO: Glen Boles, Vice President and Chief Financial Officer
CMO: Mike Finley M.D., Chief Medical Officer
CIO: Alana Higgins, Regional Information Management Executive
CHR: Jennifer Wright, Vice President Regional Human Resources
CNO: Louise Thornell, Chief Nursing Officer
Web address: www.christusstmichael.org
Control: Church operated, Nongovernment, not–for–profit **Service:** General medical and surgical

Staffed Beds: 354 **Admissions:** 13160 **Census:** 156 **Outpatient Visits:** 154132 **Births:** 1620 **Total Expense ($000):** 226776 **Payroll Expense ($000):** 72105 **Personnel:** 1649

✙ △ **CHRISTUS ST. MICHAEL REHABILITATION HOSPITAL (453065)**, 2400 St Michael Drive, Zip 75503–2374; tel. 903/614–4000 **A**1 7 10 **F**3 11 18 28 29 30 34 35 57 59 65 68 75 77 79 82 87 90 93 96 132 135 143 148 149 **S** CHRISTUS Health, Irving, TX
Primary Contact: Patrick Flannery, Administrator
CFO: Glen Boles, Vice President and Chief Financial Officer
CMO: Richard Sharp M.D., Medical Director
CIO: Alana Higgins, Regional Information Management Executive
CHR: Jennifer Wright, Vice President Human Resources
CNO: Stacey Breedlove, Chief Nursing Officer
Web address: www.christusstmichael.org/rehab
Control: Church operated, Nongovernment, not–for–profit **Service:** Rehabilitation

Staffed Beds: 50 **Admissions:** 1136 **Census:** 33 **Outpatient Visits:** 10730 **Births:** 0 **Total Expense ($000):** 22613 **Payroll Expense ($000):** 10723 **Personnel:** 197

✙ **HEALTHSOUTH REHABILITATION HOSPITAL OF TEXARKANA (453053)**, 515 West 12th Street, Zip 75501–4416; tel. 903/735–5000 **A**1 10 **F**3 28 29 42 64 74 77 79 90 91 93 95 96 130 131 132 143 148 **P**5 **S** HEALTHSOUTH Corporation, Birmingham, AL
Primary Contact: Harlo McCall, Chief Executive Officer
CFO: Phylis Buck, Controller
CMO: Mark A Wren M.D., Medical Director
CHR: Ann R Clapp, Director Human Resources
CNO: Lorri Oglesby, Chief Nursing Officer
Web address: www.healthsouthtexarkana.com
Control: Corporation, Investor–owned (for–profit) **Service:** Rehabilitation

Staffed Beds: 60 **Admissions:** 1250 **Census:** 42 **Outpatient Visits:** 8494 **Births:** 0 **Total Expense ($000):** 16728 **Payroll Expense ($000):** 9051 **Personnel:** 160

✙ **POST ACUTE MEDICAL SPECIALTY HOSPITAL OF TEXARKANA – NORTH (452061)**, 2400 St Michael Drive, 2nd Floor, Zip 75503–2372; tel. 903/614–7600 **A**1 10 **F**1 3 29 130 148 **S** Post Acute Medical, LLC, Enola, PA
Primary Contact: Lorraine Murray, Chief Executive Officer
Web address: www.postacutemedical.com
Control: Corporation, Investor–owned (for–profit) **Service:** Acute long–term care hospital

Staffed Beds: 49 **Admissions:** 588 **Census:** 36 **Outpatient Visits:** 0 **Births:** 0 **Total Expense ($000):** 16966 **Payroll Expense ($000):** 6292 **Personnel:** 99

☐ **WADLEY REGIONAL MEDICAL CENTER (450200)**, 1000 Pine Street, Zip 75501–5170; tel. 903/798–8000 **A**1 3 10 **F**3 11 13 15 18 20 22 24 28 29 30 31 34 35 40 43 45 49 50 56 57 59 60 64 65 70 71 73 74 75 76 77 78 79 81 85 86 87 89 98 103 107 108 110 111 114 115 119 126 130 146 147 148 149 **S** IASIS Healthcare, Franklin, TN
Primary Contact: Thomas D. Gilbert, FACHE, Chief Executive Officer
CFO: Bonny Sorensen, Chief Financial Officer
CIO: Matt Kesterson, Director Information Services
CHR: Debby Butler, Director Human Resources
CNO: Shelly Strayhorn R.N., Chief Nursing Officer
Web address: www.wadleyhealth.com
Control: Corporation, Investor–owned (for–profit) **Service:** General medical and surgical

Staffed Beds: 179 **Admissions:** 6884 **Census:** 83 **Outpatient Visits:** 87368 **Births:** 1260 **Total Expense ($000):** 92677 **Payroll Expense ($000):** 40381 **Personnel:** 640

THE WOODLANDS—Montgomery County

★ ⇑ **CHI ST. LUKE'S HEALTH–THE WOODLANDS HOSPITAL (450862)**, 17200 St. Luke's Way, Zip 77384–8007; tel. 936/266–2000 **A**10 21 **F**3 11 12 13 15 18 20 22 24 26 28 29 30 34 35 38 40 41 45 49 50 57 58 59 64 68 70 72 74 75 76 78 79 81 82 85 86 87 89 90 93 107 108 109 110 111 114 118 119 124 126 129 130 131 135 145 146 147 148 **P**5 **S** Catholic Health Initiatives, Englewood, CO
Primary Contact: David Argueta, Chief Executive Officer
CMO: Charles Sims M.D., Chief of Staff
Web address: www.stlukeswoodlands.com
Control: Church operated, Nongovernment, not–for–profit **Service:** General medical and surgical

Staffed Beds: 207 **Admissions:** 10650 **Census:** 123 **Outpatient Visits:** 76788 **Births:** 2012 **Total Expense ($000):** 188003 **Payroll Expense ($000):** 71215 **Personnel:** 918

★ **HOUSTON METHODIST THE WOODLANDS HOSPITAL**, 17201 Interstate 45 South, Zip 77385; tel. 713/790–3333 (Nonreporting) **S** Houston Methodist, Houston, TX
Primary Contact: Debra F. Sukin, Regional Vice President and Chief Executive Officer
CNO: Kerrie Guerrero R.N., MSN, Vice President and Chief Nursing Officer
Web address: www.houstonmethodist.org/locations/the–woodlands/
Control: Other not–for–profit (including NFP Corporation) **Service:** General medical and surgical

Staffed Beds: 187

MEMORIAL HERMANN THE WOODLANDS HOSPITAL See Memorial Hermann Greater Heights Hospital, Houston

NEXUS SPECIALTY HOSPITAL THE WOODLANDS (452057), 9182 Six Pines Drive, Zip 77380–3670; tel. 281/364–0317 (Nonreporting) **A**10
Primary Contact: Mikael Simpson, Chief Executive Officer
CFO: David Strickler, Chief Financial Officer
CMO: Ather Siddiqi M.D., Medical Director
CIO: Noe Salinas, Vice President Information Technology
CHR: Kevin McAndrews, Vice President, Human Resources
CNO: Rhena Anderson, Chief Nursing Officer
Web address: www.nexusspecialty.com
Control: Partnership, Investor–owned (for–profit) **Service:** Acute long–term care hospital

Staffed Beds: 21

★ ⇑ **ST. LUKE'S LAKESIDE HOSPITAL (670059)**, 17400 St. Luke's Way, Zip 77384–8036; tel. 936/266–9000 **A**10 21 **F**3 18 20 22 26 29 30 34 35 40 50 57 59 64 68 75 79 81 87 94 107 111 115 119 130 131 135 **P**5 **S** Catholic Health Initiatives, Englewood, CO
Primary Contact: David Argueta, Chief Executive Officer
CMO: Bruce Lachterman M.D., Chief of Medical Staff
CIO: Paul Solverson, Chief Information Officer
CHR: Debra Roberts, Director of Human Resources
CNO: Diane Freeman R.N., Assistant Vice President and Chief Nursing Officer
Web address: www.stlukeslakeside.com/
Control: Corporation, Investor–owned (for–profit) **Service:** Surgical

Staffed Beds: 30 **Admissions:** 816 **Census:** 5 **Outpatient Visits:** 16382 **Births:** 0 **Total Expense ($000):** 39137 **Payroll Expense ($000):** 8081 **Personnel:** 122

★ **WOODLANDS SPECIALTY HOSPITAL**, 9182 Six Pines Drive, Zip 77380–3670, Mailing Address: 25540 I–45 North, Suite 100, Spring, 77380–3670; tel. 281/602–8160 **F**3 18 20 22 24 26 29 40 45 46 47 48 49 75 77 79 81 82 87 107 108 109 111 112 113 115 118 119 149
Primary Contact: Don Vickers, Chief Executive Officer
CFO: Virginia de Bond, Chief Financial Officer
Web address: www.woodlandsspecialtyhospital.com/
Control: Individual, Investor–owned (for–profit) **Service:** General medical and surgical

Staffed Beds: 6 **Admissions:** 475 **Census:** 2 **Outpatient Visits:** 3400 **Births:** 0 **Personnel:** 177

TX

Hospital, Medicare Provider Number, Address, Telephone, Approval, Facility, and Physician Codes, Health Care System

★ American Hospital Association (AHA) membership
☐ The Joint Commission accreditation
○ Healthcare Facilities Accreditation Program
◇ DNV Healthcare Inc. accreditation
⇑ Center for Improvement in Healthcare Quality Accreditation
△ Commission on Accreditation of Rehabilitation Facilities (CARF) accreditation

THROCKMORTON—Throckmorton County

THROCKMORTON COUNTY MEMORIAL HOSPITAL (451339), 802 North Minter Street, Zip 76483–5357, Mailing Address: P.O.Box 729, 76483–0729; tel. 940/849–2151 **A**10 18 **F**1 4 7 40 41 43 44 50 59 61 64 65 67 68 79 87 97 127 128 130 133 148 **P**5 6
Primary Contact: Kirby Gober, Chief Executive Officer
CFO: Cindy Parker, Chief Financial Officer and Director Human Resources
CMO: Ruth Ebangit M.D., Chief of Staff and Medical Officer
CIO: Amber Myer, Director Medical Technology
CHR: Cindy Parker, Chief Financial Officer and Director Human Resources
CNO: Pam Stamm, Chief Nursing Officer
Web address: www.throckmortonhospital.com/index.html
Control: County, Government, Nonfederal **Service**: General medical and surgical

Staffed Beds: 14 **Admissions**: 70 **Census**: 1 **Outpatient Visits**: 7585 **Births**: 0 **Total Expense ($000)**: 4013 **Payroll Expense ($000)**: 1614 **Personnel**: 48

TOMBALL—Harris County

⇑ **EMERUS COMMUNITY HOSPITAL (670095)**, 24429 State Highway 249, Zip 77375–8214; tel. 281/516–0911 **A**21 **F**3 40 75 107 114 119 149 **P**5 **S** Emerus, The Woodlands, TX
Primary Contact: Paula Gonzales, Administrator
Web address: www.emerus.com/tomball/
Control: Corporation, Investor–owned (for–profit) **Service**: General medical and surgical

Staffed Beds: 8 **Admissions**: 75 **Census**: 1 **Outpatient Visits**: 5474 **Births**: 0 **Total Expense ($000)**: 5994 **Payroll Expense ($000)**: 1813 **Personnel**: 31

⊞ **KINDRED HOSPITAL TOMBALL (452074)**, 505 Graham Drive, Zip 77375–3368; tel. 281/255–5600, (Includes KINDRED HOSPITAL SPRING, 205 Hollow Tree Lane, Houston, Texas, Zip 77090, tel. 832/249–2700; Tracy Kohler, Chief Executive Officer) **A**1 10 **F**1 3 18 29 30 31 42 49 64 70 74 75 78 79 84 85 86 87 93 94 107 119 130 **S** Kindred Healthcare, Louisville, KY
Primary Contact: Tracy Kohler, Chief Executive Officer
Web address: www.khtomball.com/
Control: Partnership, Investor–owned (for–profit) **Service**: Acute long–term care hospital

Staffed Beds: 258 **Admissions**: 2056 **Census**: 145 **Outpatient Visits**: 3407 **Births**: 0 **Total Expense ($000)**: 85842 **Payroll Expense ($000)**: 31276 **Personnel**: 441

⊞ **TOMBALL REGIONAL MEDICAL CENTER (450670)**, 605 Holderrieth Street, Zip 77375–6445; tel. 281/401–7500, (Includes KINDRED HOSPITAL THE HEIGHTS, 1800 West 26th Street, Houston, Texas, Zip 77008–1450, tel. 832/673–4200; William Elsesser, Chief Executive Officer) **A**1 10 **F**3 8 12 13 15 18 20 22 24 26 28 29 30 34 40 42 44 45 46 47 48 49 50 51 53 54 57 59 60 64 70 72 74 75 76 79 80 81 82 85 86 87 90 91 94 96 98 102 103 107 108 110 111 114 115 116 117 119 124 126 129 130 131 132 146 148 149 **P**6 **S** HCA Healthcare, Nashville, TN
Primary Contact: Brett Kinman, Interim Chief Executive Officer
COO: Brett Kinman, Chief Operating Officer
CFO: Richard Ervin, Chief Financial Officer
CMO: Ian Glass M.D., Chief Medical Officer
CIO: Marisa Smith, Director
CHR: Vanessa Anyaso, Chief Human Resources
Web address: www.tomballregionalmedicalcenter.com
Control: Corporation, Investor–owned (for–profit) **Service**: General medical and surgical

Staffed Beds: 191 **Admissions**: 9229 **Census**: 130 **Outpatient Visits**: 66884 **Births**: 1107 **Total Expense ($000)**: 178215 **Payroll Expense ($000)**: 61413 **Personnel**: 880

TROPHY CLUB—Denton County

☐ **BAYLOR MEDICAL CENTER AT TROPHY CLUB (450883)**, 2850 East State Highway 114, Zip 76262–5302; tel. 817/837–4600 **A**1 10 **F**3 29 40 64 70 75 79 81 85 87 107 108 111 114 118 121 123 141
Primary Contact: Melanie Chick, Chief Executive Officer
CFO: Jonathan Saunders, Chief Financial Officer
CMO: Mike Stanton D.O., Medical Director
CIO: Scot Bradford, Chief Information Officer
CHR: Donna Irvin, Director Human Resources
CNO: Tina Huddleston R.N., Chief Nursing Officer
Web address: www.baylortrophyclub.com
Control: Partnership, Investor–owned (for–profit) **Service**: General medical and surgical

Staffed Beds: 22 **Admissions**: 948 **Census**: 6 **Outpatient Visits**: 8962 **Births**: 0 **Total Expense ($000)**: 63472 **Payroll Expense ($000)**: 10938 **Personnel**: 190

TULIA—Swisher County

★ **SWISHER MEMORIAL HOSPITAL DISTRICT (451349)**, 539 Southeast Second, Zip 79088–2400, Mailing Address: P.O.Box 808, 79088–0808; tel. 806/995–3581 **A**10 18 **F**3 7 10 11 29 34 35 40 43 50 53 57 59 64 65 68 77 93 107 114 127 129 130 133 **P**4
Primary Contact: Ryan Barnard, FACHE, Chief Executive Officer
CFO: Connie Wilhelm, Chief Financial Officer
CIO: Brad Roberts, Network Administrator
Web address: www.swisherhospital.com
Control: Other not–for–profit (including NFP Corporation) **Service**: General medical and surgical

Staffed Beds: 20 **Admissions**: 208 **Census**: 2 **Outpatient Visits**: 22305 **Births**: 0 **Total Expense ($000)**: 11054 **Payroll Expense ($000)**: 4260 **Personnel**: 81

TYLER—Smith County

⊞ **CHRISTUS MOTHER FRANCES HOSPITAL – TYLER (450102)**, 800 East Dawson Street, Zip 75701–2036; tel. 903/593–8441, (Includes LOUIS & PEACHES OWEN HEART HOSPITAL, 703 South Fleishel Avenue, Tyler, Texas, Zip 75701–2015, tel. 903/606–3000; John McGreevy, FACHE, Chief Executive Officer) **A**1 2 3 10 **F**3 7 8 11 12 13 15 17 18 19 20 22 24 26 28 29 30 31 32 34 37 40 43 45 46 47 48 49 50 51 53 54 55 59 60 64 66 68 70 72 73 74 75 76 77 78 79 80 81 82 83 84 85 86 87 89 93 107 108 110 111 114 115 118 119 124 126 127 129 130 131 132 134 144 146 147 148 **P**5 6 7 8 **S** CHRISTUS Health, Irving, TX
Primary Contact: Jason J. Proctor, Chief Operating Officer
CFO: Joyce Hester CPA, Senior Vice President and Chief Financial Officer
CMO: Fadi Nasrallah M.D., Vice President Medical Affairs
CIO: Jeff Pearson, Vice President and Chief Information Officer
CHR: Thomas Wilken, Senior Vice President and Chief Human Resources Officer
CNO: Robert Rose R.N., MS, Senior Vice President and System Chief Nursing Officer
Web address: www.tmfhc.org
Control: Other not–for–profit (including NFP Corporation) **Service**: General medical and surgical

Staffed Beds: 458 **Admissions**: 24012 **Census**: 307 **Outpatient Visits**: 595093 **Births**: 2704 **Total Expense ($000)**: 548163 **Payroll Expense ($000)**: 169659 **Personnel**: 3398

⊞ **CHRISTUS TRINITY MOTHER FRANCES REHABILITATION HOSPITAL (453056)**, 3131 Troup Highway, Zip 75701–8352; tel. 903/510–7000 **A**1 10 **F**3 9 28 29 56 60 74 75 77 79 82 87 90 91 95 96 130 131 132 143 148 **S** HEALTHSOUTH Corporation, Birmingham, AL
Primary Contact: Sharla Anderson, Chief Executive Officer
CFO: Michael G Treadway, Controller
CMO: Bradley Merritt M.D., Medical Director
Web address: www.tmfrehabhospital.com
Control: Partnership, Investor–owned (for–profit) **Service**: Rehabilitation

Staffed Beds: 74 **Admissions**: 1784 **Census**: 63 **Outpatient Visits**: 278 **Births**: 0 **Total Expense ($000)**: 19286 **Payroll Expense ($000)**: 10575 **Personnel**: 145

⊞ **EAST TEXAS MEDICAL CENTER REHABILITATION HOSPITAL (453072)**, 701 Olympic Plaza Circle, Zip 75701–1950, Mailing Address: P.O.Box 7530, 75711–7530; tel. 903/596–3000 **A**1 10 **F**3 28 29 30 34 53 57 75 86 90 91 93 96 130 131 132 148 149 **S** East Texas Medical Center Regional Healthcare System, Tyler, TX
Primary Contact: Eddie L. Howard, Vice President and Chief Operating Officer
COO: Eddie L Howard, Chief Operating Officer
CFO: James Blanton, Chief Financial Officer
CMO: Jerry Schwarzbach M.D., Medical Director
CIO: Paula Anthony, Vice President Information Services
CHR: David L Langston, Corporate Vice President Human Resources
CNO: Laurie Lehnhof-Watts, Assistant Administrator Patient Services
Web address: www.etmc.org
Control: Other not–for–profit (including NFP Corporation) **Service**: Rehabilitation

Staffed Beds: 49 **Admissions**: 974 **Census**: 33 **Outpatient Visits**: 86791 **Births**: 0 **Total Expense ($000)**: 27167 **Payroll Expense ($000)**: 12728 **Personnel**: 180

TX

Many Facility Codes have changed. Please refer to the AHA Guide Code Chart. © 2017 AHA Guide

☒ **EAST TEXAS MEDICAL CENTER SPECIALTY HOSPITAL (452051)**, 1000 South Beckham, 5th Floor, Zip 75701–1908, Mailing Address: P.O.Box 7018, 75711–7018; tel. 903/596–3600 **A**1 10 **F**1 3 29 30 75 84 130 148 149 **S** East Texas Medical Center Regional Healthcare System, Tyler, TX
Primary Contact: Eddie L. Howard, Vice President and Chief Operating Officer
CFO: James Blanton, Chief Financial Officer
CMO: J David Johnson M.D., Chief of Staff
CIO: Paula Anthony, Vice President Information Services
CHR: David L Langston, Corporate Vice President Human Resources
CNO: Laurie Lehnhof–Watts, Assistant Administrator Risk Management Performance Improvement and Education
Web address: www.etmc.org
Control: Other not–for–profit (including NFP Corporation) **Service**: Acute long–term care hospital

Staffed Beds: 36 **Admissions**: 315 **Census**: 26 **Outpatient Visits**: 0 **Births**: 0 **Total Expense ($000)**: 14372 **Payroll Expense ($000)**: 4642 **Personnel**: 68

☒ **EAST TEXAS MEDICAL CENTER TYLER (450083)**, 1000 South Beckham Street, Zip 75701–1908, Mailing Address: Box 6400, 75711–6400; tel. 903/597–0351, (Includes EAST TEXAS MEDICAL CENTER BEHAVIORAL HEALTH CENTER, 4101 University Boulevard, Tyler, Texas, Zip 75701–6600, tel. 903/566–8668; Jerry W Echols, Administrator and Chief Executive Officer) **A**1 2 3 5 10 **F**3 5 8 11 12 13 15 17 18 20 22 24 26 28 29 30 31 34 35 37 38 40 42 43 44 45 46 47 48 49 51 56 58 59 60 61 64 65 68 70 71 73 74 75 76 78 79 80 81 82 84 85 86 87 89 93 98 99 100 101 102 103 104 105 107 110 111 115 117 118 119 120 121 123 124 126 129 130 132 138 141 145 146 147 148 149 150 **S** East Texas Medical Center Regional Healthcare System, Tyler, TX
Primary Contact: Robert B. Evans, FACHE, Administrator and Chief Executive Officer
CFO: Byron Hale, Chief Financial Officer
CMO: John Andrews M.D., Chief of Staff
CIO: Paula Anthony, Vice President Information Services
CHR: Mike Gray, Corporate Vice President Human Resources
CNO: Mariarose Kulma R.N., Vice President Patient Services
Web address: www.etmc.org
Control: Other not–for–profit (including NFP Corporation) **Service**: General medical and surgical

Staffed Beds: 399 **Admissions**: 20680 **Census**: 274 **Outpatient Visits**: 110956 **Births**: 709 **Total Expense ($000)**: 406937 **Payroll Expense ($000)**: 126206 **Personnel**: 2177

☒ **TEXAS SPINE & JOINT HOSPITAL (450864)**, 1814 Roseland Boulevard, Suite 100, Zip 75701–4262; tel. 903/525–3300 **A**1 3 10 **F**8 29 39 40 77 79 81 82 85 107 111 114 119 144
Primary Contact: Tony Wahl, Chief Executive Officer
CFO: Greg Cummings, Chief Financial Officer
CMO: Kim Foreman M.D., Chief of Staff
CNO: Aaron Fleet R.N., Chief Nursing Officer
Web address: www.tsjh.org
Control: Partnership, Investor–owned (for–profit) **Service**: Orthopedic

Staffed Beds: 18 **Admissions**: 2279 **Census**: 15 **Outpatient Visits**: 44627 **Births**: 0 **Total Expense ($000)**: 82499 **Payroll Expense ($000)**: 18513 **Personnel**: 318

★ **TYLER CONTINUECARE HOSPITAL (452091)**, 800 East Dawson, 4th Floor, Zip 75701–2036; tel. 903/531–4080 **A**10 **F**1 3 29 34 40 57 59 85 86 130 148 **P**4 **S** Community Hospital Corporation, Plano, TX
Primary Contact: Stephanie Hyde, R.N., MSN, Chief Executive Officer
Web address: www.continuecare.org
Control: Other not–for–profit (including NFP Corporation) **Service**: Acute long–term care hospital

Staffed Beds: 51 **Admissions**: 530 **Census**: 41 **Outpatient Visits**: 0 **Births**: 0 **Total Expense ($000)**: 23130 **Payroll Expense ($000)**: 8455 **Personnel**: 112

☒ **UNIVERSITY OF TEXAS HEALTH NORTHEAST (450690)**, 11937 Highway 271, Zip 75708–3154; tel. 903/877–7777 **A**1 2 8 10 **F**3 8 11 15 18 20 22 24 26 28 29 30 31 32 34 35 40 45 46 47 49 50 53 54 55 56 57 58 59 64 65 68 70 71 75 77 78 79 81 84 85 86 87 93 94 97 98 99 101 102 103 104 105 106 107 108 110 111 114 115 116 117 118 119 120 121 123 124 129 130 132 135 143 146 147 148 **P**6 **S** University of Texas System, Austin, TX
Primary Contact: Kirk A. Calhoun, M.D., President
COO: Joe Woelkers, Executive Vice President and Chief Staff
CFO: Vernon Moore, Senior Vice President Chief Business and Finance
CMO: Steven Cox M.D., Chief Medical Officer
CIO: Vernon Moore, Senior Vice President Chief Business and Finance
CHR: Jesse Gomez, Vice President Human Resources
CNO: Don Hunt M.D., Vice President Patient Centered Care and Chief Nursing Officer
Web address: www.uthct.edu
Control: State, Government, Nonfederal **Service**: General medical and surgical

Staffed Beds: 130 **Admissions**: 1986 **Census**: 35 **Outpatient Visits**: 306875 **Births**: 0 **Total Expense ($000)**: 198224 **Payroll Expense ($000)**: 70187 **Personnel**: 1374

UVALDE—Uvalde County

☒ **UVALDE MEMORIAL HOSPITAL (450177)**, 1025 Garner Field Road, Zip 78801–4809; tel. 830/278–6251 **A**1 10 20 **F**3 11 13 15 18 29 30 34 39 40 43 45 50 57 59 63 64 68 70 76 79 81 84 85 86 87 93 104 107 108 110 111 115 118 119 130 132 133 146 147 148 149 **P**3
Primary Contact: Thomas Nordwick, FACHE, Chief Executive Officer
CFO: Valerie Lopez CPA, Chief Financial Officer
CMO: Jared Reading M.D., Chief of Staff
CIO: Blake Eaker, Interim Director Information Services
CHR: Charla Carter, Human Resource Officer
CNO: Adam Apolinar, Chief Nursing Officer
Web address: www.umhtx.org
Control: Hospital district or authority, Government, Nonfederal **Service**: General medical and surgical

Staffed Beds: 44 **Admissions**: 1524 **Census**: 12 **Outpatient Visits**: 68943 **Births**: 424 **Total Expense ($000)**: 54611 **Payroll Expense ($000)**: 22291 **Personnel**: 429

VAN HORN—Culberson County

CULBERSON HOSPITAL (451338), Eisenhower–Farm Market Road 2185, Zip 79855, Mailing Address: P.O.Box 609, 79855–0609; tel. 432/283–2760 **A**10 18 **F**3 7 34 40 43 57 59 65 66 68 93 107 114 119 127 133 148 149 **P**6 **S** Preferred Management Corporation, Shawnee, OK
Primary Contact: Jonathon Voelkel, Administrator
CMO: John A. Thomas M.D., Chief Medical Staff
Web address: www.culbersonhospital.org
Control: Corporation, Investor–owned (for–profit) **Service**: General medical and surgical

Staffed Beds: 14 **Admissions**: 123 **Census**: 2 **Outpatient Visits**: 9664 **Births**: 0 **Total Expense ($000)**: 6247 **Payroll Expense ($000)**: 2846 **Personnel**: 63

VERNON—Wilbarger County

NORTH TEXAS STATE HOSPITAL, Highway 70 Northwest, Zip 76384, Mailing Address: P.O.Box 2231, 76385–2231; tel. 940/552–9901 **F**30 50 56 57 68 87 96 97 98 99 100 101 103 130 132 135 143 146 149**P**6 **S** Texas Department of State Health Services, Austin, TX
Primary Contact: James E. Smith, Superintendent
CFO: Robin Moreno, Financial Officer
CIO: Chad Hughes, Information Officer
Web address: www.online.dshs.state.tx.us/northtexassh/default.htm
Control: State, Government, Nonfederal **Service**: Psychiatric

Staffed Beds: 640 **Admissions**: 1866 **Census**: 567 **Outpatient Visits**: 0 **Births**: 0 **Personnel**: 2029

TX

WILBARGER GENERAL HOSPITAL (450584), 920 Hillcrest Drive, Zip 76384–3196; tel. 940/552-9351 **A**10 20 **F**3 11 15 28 29 34 35 40 43 45 54 56 57 60 62 75 77 81 85 86 87 93 103 107 108 110 111 115 119 124 130 132 133 146 148 **P**6
Primary Contact: Claudia A. Eisenmann, FACHE, Chief Executive Officer
CFO: Richard W Stokes CPA, Jr, Chief Financial Officer
CMO: Travis Lehman M.D., Medical Director
CIO: Ken Mikos, Director Information Technology
CHR: Alisha Nix, Director Human Resources
CNO: Kim Pierson R.N., Chief Nursing Officer
Web address: www.wghospital.com
Control: Hospital district or authority, Government, Nonfederal **Service**: General medical and surgical

Staffed Beds: 27 **Admissions**: 446 **Census**: 6 **Outpatient Visits**: 12895
Births: 0 **Total Expense ($000)**: 17163 **Payroll Expense ($000)**: 6921
Personnel: 144

VICTORIA—Victoria County

★ ⇑ **CITIZENS MEDICAL CENTER (450023)**, 2701 Hospital Drive, Zip 77901–5749; tel. 361/573-9181, (Total facility includes 20 beds in nursing home–type unit) **A**2 10 21 **F**3 11 12 13 15 18 20 22 24 28 29 30 31 34 35 40 41 43 45 46 49 50 51 53 54 56 57 59 62 64 65 70 72 74 75 76 77 78 79 81 82 85 86 87 89 93 97 107 108 109 110 111 113 114 115 116 117 118 119 120 121 123 126 128 129 130 131 132 135 146 147 148 149 **P**4
Primary Contact: Michael R. Olson, Chief Executive Officer
CFO: Carolyn Zafereo, Chief Accounting Officer
CMO: Daniel Cano M.D., Chief Medical Officer
CIO: Russell Witte, Director Information Technology
CHR: Kathleen C Mosmeyer, Director Human Resources
Web address: www.citizensmedicalcenter.org
Control: County, Government, Nonfederal **Service**: General medical and surgical

Staffed Beds: 265 **Admissions**: 7357 **Census**: 108 **Outpatient Visits**: 121636 **Births**: 796 **Total Expense ($000)**: 163977 **Payroll Expense ($000)**: 71708 **Personnel**: 1106

DETAR HEALTHCARE SYSTEM (450147), 506 East San Antonio Street, Zip 77901–6060, Mailing Address: P.O.Box 2089, 77902–2089; tel. 361/575-7441, (Includes DETAR HOSPITAL NORTH, 101 Medical Drive, Victoria, Texas, Zip 77904–3198, tel. 361/573–6100; William R Blanchard, Chief Executive Officer) **A**1 3 10 **F**3 12 13 15 18 20 22 24 26 28 29 30 31 34 39 40 41 43 45 47 49 50 51 53 56 64 70 72 74 75 76 77 78 79 81 82 85 86 87 89 90 91 93 98 103 104 107 108 110 111 114 118 119 126 130 132 146 147 148 **P**3 5 **S** Community Health Systems, Inc., Franklin, TN
Primary Contact: William R. Blanchard, Chief Executive Officer
COO: George N Parsley, Chief Operating Officer
CFO: Donald E Hagan, Chief Financial Officer
CMO: Conde Nevin Anderson M.D., Chief of Staff
CIO: Kim Tompkins, Director Information Services
CHR: Dwight Linton, Director Human Resources
CNO: Sammie Drehr, Chief Nursing Officer
Web address: www.detar.com
Control: Corporation, Investor–owned (for–profit) **Service**: General medical and surgical

Staffed Beds: 245 **Admissions**: 9376 **Census**: 115 **Outpatient Visits**: 99016 **Births**: 1328 **Total Expense ($000)**: 149330 **Payroll Expense ($000)**: 57281 **Personnel**: 936

★ **PAM REHABILITATION HOSPITAL OF VICTORIA (673056)**, 101 James Coleman Drive, Zip 77904–3147; (Nonreporting) **S** Post Acute Medical, LLC, Enola, PA
Primary Contact: Shawn Todd, Chief Executive Officer
Web address: www.warmsprings.org/our-facilities/outpatient-rehabilitation/warm-springs-rehabilitation-center-victoria/
Control: Partnership, Investor–owned (for–profit) **Service**: Rehabilitation

Staffed Beds: 26

PAM SPECIALTY HOSPITAL OF VICTORIA NORTH (452094), 102 Medical Drive, Zip 77904–3101; tel. 361/576-6200 **A**1 10 **F**1 3 29 64 75 77 85 93 94 96 148 **S** Post Acute Medical, LLC, Enola, PA
Primary Contact: Christina Adrean, Chief Executive Officer
CMO: Adam Burick M.D., Chief Medical Officer
CHR: Waynea Finley, Corporate Director Human Resources
CNO: Chris Reed, Director of Nursing
Web address: www.warmsprings.org
Control: Partnership, Investor–owned (for–profit) **Service**: Acute long–term care hospital

Staffed Beds: 26 **Admissions**: 589 **Census**: 25 **Outpatient Visits**: 9380
Births: 0 **Total Expense ($000)**: 13810 **Payroll Expense ($000)**: 5538
Personnel: 113

PAM SPECIALTY HOSPITAL OF VICTORIA SOUTH (452056), 506 East San Antonio Street, 3rd Floor, Zip 77901–6060; tel. 361/575-1445 **A**1 10 **F**1 3 29 30 31 82 85 86 87 97 130 148 **S** Post Acute Medical, LLC, Enola, PA
Primary Contact: Christina Adrean, Chief Executive Officer
CMO: Adam Burick M.D., Chief Medical Officer
CHR: Waynea Finley, Manager Human Resources
CNO: Pamella Barrett, Director of Nursing
Web address: www.khvictoria.com
Control: Partnership, Investor–owned (for–profit) **Service**: Acute long–term care hospital

Staffed Beds: 23 **Admissions**: 333 **Census**: 22 **Outpatient Visits**: 0 **Births**: 0
Total Expense ($000): 11087 **Payroll Expense ($000)**: 4489 **Personnel**: 76

WACO—Mclennan County

BAYLOR SCOTT & WHITE MEDICAL CENTER – HILLCREST (450101), 100 Hillcrest Medical Boulevard, Zip 76712–8897; tel. 254/202-2000, (Total facility includes 20 beds in nursing home–type unit) **A**1 2 10 **F**3 8 11 13 15 18 20 22 24 26 28 29 30 31 34 40 43 46 49 50 51 53 54 56 57 59 60 63 64 70 72 74 75 76 78 79 81 82 84 85 86 87 89 90 93 96 107 108 110 111 115 118 119 120 121 123 128 129 130 131 132 135 145 146 148 149 **S** Baylor Scott & White Health, Dallas, TX
Primary Contact: Glenn A. Robinson, FACHE, President
COO: David Blackwell, Vice President Operations
CFO: Richard Perkins, Chief Financial Officer
CMO: J. E. Morrison M.D., M.P.H., Chief Medical Officer
CNO: Rebecca K Hardie, Chief Nursing Officer
Web address: www.sw.org/hillcrest-medical-center
Control: Other not–for–profit (including NFP Corporation) **Service**: General medical and surgical

Staffed Beds: 275 **Admissions**: 13352 **Census**: 170 **Outpatient Visits**: 156128 **Births**: 2828 **Total Expense ($000)**: 242021 **Payroll Expense ($000)**: 76771 **Personnel**: 1227

CENTRAL TEXAS VETERANS HEALTH CARE SYSTEM, DORIS MILLER VETERANS MEDICAL CENTER See Central Texas Veterans Health Care System, Temple

PROVIDENCE HEALTHCARE NETWORK (450042), 6901 Medical Parkway, Zip 76712–7998, Mailing Address: P.O.Box 2589, 76702–2589; tel. 254/751-4000, (Nonreporting) (Includes DEPAUL CENTER, 301 Londonderry Drive, Waco, Texas, Zip 76712, tel. 254/776–5970; Vicky Campbell, Vice President Mental Health and Support Services) **A**1 2 3 10 **S** Ascension Healthcare, Saint Louis, MO
Primary Contact: Steven Province, Interim President and Chief Executive Officer
COO: Steven Province, Senior Vice President and Chief Operating Officer
CFO: Karen K. Richardson, Senior Vice President and Chief Financial Officer
CMO: T Marc Barrett M.D., Senior Vice President and Chief Medical Officer
CIO: Jay Scherler, Vice President Finance and Chief Information Officer
CNO: Christine Courtney R.N., Vice President and Chief Nursing Officer
Web address: www.providence.net
Control: Church operated, Nongovernment, not–for–profit **Service**: General medical and surgical

Staffed Beds: 284

WAXAHACHIE—Ellis County

BAYLOR SCOTT & WHITE MEDICAL CENTER AT WAXAHACHIE (450372), 2400 North I–35E, Zip 75165; tel. 469/843-4000 **A**1 2 3 10 **F**3 11 12 13 15 28 29 30 31 34 35 37 39 40 41 45 47 49 50 51 54 57 58 59 60 64 68 70 74 75 76 78 79 80 81 82 84 85 86 87 100 102 107 108 109 110 111 114 115 117 118 119 120 121 124 129 130 131 132 135 145 146 147 148 149 **S** Baylor Scott & White Health, Dallas, TX
Primary Contact: Christopher York, FACHE, President
COO: Cindy Murray R.N., Chief Nursing Officer and Chief Operating Officer
CFO: Cheryl McMullan, Chief Financial Officer
CMO: Thomas Glenn Ledbetter M.D., Chief Medical Officer
CNO: Cindy Murray R.N., Chief Nursing Officer and Chief Operating Officer
Web address: www.baylorhealth.com/PhysiciansLocations/Waxahachie/Pages/Default.aspx
Control: Other not–for–profit (including NFP Corporation) **Service**: General medical and surgical

Staffed Beds: 104 **Admissions**: 5723 **Census**: 56 **Outpatient Visits**: 89749
Births: 725 **Total Expense ($000)**: 122042 **Payroll Expense ($000)**: 42821
Personnel: 479

WEATHERFORD—Parker County

WEATHERFORD REGIONAL MEDICAL CENTER (450203), 713 East Anderson Street, Zip 76086–5705; tel. 682/582–1000 **A**1 10 12 13 **F**3 8 13 15 17 18 20 22 28 29 34 35 40 43 48 49 51 57 59 60 68 70 74 75 76 77 79 81 82 85 93 98 103 107 110 111 114 115 119 130 131 132 133 135 146 148 149 **S** Community Health Systems, Inc., Franklin, TN
Primary Contact: David Orcutt, Chief Executive Officer
CFO: Nancy Cooke, Chief Financial Officer
CMO: Sanjeeb Shrestha M.D., Chief Medical Staff
CIO: Brett Cates, Director Information Services
CNO: Donna Boone MS, R.N., Chief Nursing Officer
Web address: www.weatherfordregional.com
Control: Corporation, Investor–owned (for–profit) **Service:** General medical and surgical

Staffed Beds: 92 **Admissions:** 5593 **Census:** 58 **Outpatient Visits:** 85792 **Births:** 874 **Total Expense ($000):** 101313 **Payroll Expense ($000):** 29050 **Personnel:** 496

WEATHERFORD REHABILITATION HOSPITAL (673062), 703 Eureka Street, Zip 76086–6547; tel. 682/803–0100 **F**3 28 29 30 34 35 50 56 57 59 68 74 75 82 86 87 90 91 96 130 131 148
Primary Contact: Cole E. Hatcher, Chief Executive Officer
Web address: www.weatherfordrehab.com
Control: Corporation, Investor–owned (for–profit) **Service:** Rehabilitation

Staffed Beds: 26 **Admissions:** 407 **Census:** 12 **Outpatient Visits:** 0 **Births:** 0 **Total Expense ($000):** 5914 **Payroll Expense ($000):** 2631 **Personnel:** 77

WEBSTER—Harris County

BAY AREA REGIONAL MEDICAL CENTER (670096), 200 Blossom Street, Zip 77598–4204; tel. 281/525–7000 **A**1 **F**3 12 15 17 18 20 22 24 26 29 30 34 35 40 45 47 49 50 57 59 64 70 74 75 77 78 79 80 81 82 84 85 87 91 107 108 110 111 115 119 130 135 149 **P**4
Primary Contact: Stephen K. Jones Jr, FACHE, Chief Executive Officer
COO: Benjamin Casmer FACHE, Chief Operating Officer
CFO: Paul Hanson, Chief Financial Officer
CMO: Michael Lyons, Chief Medical Officer
CIO: Mark Albright, Chief Information Officer
CHR: Brad Horst, Vice President, Human Resources
CNO: Susan White R.N., Chief Nursing Officer
Web address: www.barmc.us/
Control: Corporation, Investor–owned (for–profit) **Service:** General medical and surgical

Staffed Beds: 96 **Admissions:** 5303 **Census:** 54 **Outpatient Visits:** 36986 **Births:** 0 **Total Expense ($000):** 176511 **Payroll Expense ($000):** 38403 **Personnel:** 605

CLEAR LAKE REGIONAL MEDICAL CENTER (450617), 500 Medical Center Boulevard, Zip 77598–4220; tel. 281/332–2511, (Includes ALVIN DIAGNOSTIC AND URGENT CARE CENTER, 301 Medic Lane, Alvin, Texas, Zip 77511–5597, tel. 281/331–6141; MAINLAND MEDICAL CENTER, 6801 'E' 'F' Lowry Expressway, Texas City, Texas, Zip 77591, tel. 409/938–5000; Tripp Montalbo, Chief Executive Officer) **A**1 2 3 5 10 **F**3 11 12 13 15 17 18 19 20 22 24 26 28 29 31 34 35 40 41 43 44 45 46 47 49 50 51 56 57 59 60 64 70 72 74 75 76 78 79 80 81 85 86 87 88 89 90 91 93 94 96 98 100 101 103 104 105 107 108 110 111 114 115 119 124 126 130 132 135 146 147 148 149 **S** HCA Healthcare, Nashville, TN
Primary Contact: Todd Caliva, FACHE, Chief Executive Officer
CFO: Jeff Sliwinski, Chief Financial Officer
CMO: Richard Marietta M.D., Medical Director
CIO: Ley Samson, Director Management Information Systems
CHR: Brad Horst, Director Human Resources
Web address: www.clearlakermc.com
Control: Partnership, Investor–owned (for–profit) **Service:** General medical and surgical

Staffed Beds: 632 **Admissions:** 30520 **Census:** 451 **Outpatient Visits:** 183581 **Births:** 3970 **Total Expense ($000):** 424612 **Payroll Expense ($000):** 182251 **Personnel:** 2335

CLEAR LAKE REHABILITATION HOSPITAL See Kindred Rehabilitation Hospital Clear Lake

CORNERSTONE HOSPITAL OF HOUSTON AT CLEARLAKE (452032), 709 Medical Center Boulevard, Zip 77598; tel. 281/332–3322, (Includes CORNERSTONE HOSPITAL OF HOUSTON – BELLAIRE, 5314 Dashwood, Houston, Texas, Zip 77081–4603, tel. 713/295–5300; Colin O'Sullivan, Interim Chief Executive Officer) **A**1 10 **F**1 3 29 30 44 50 56 75 82 85 86 87 130 148 149 **S** Cornerstone Healthcare Group, Dallas, TX
Primary Contact: Amy Stasney, R.N., Chief Executive Officer
COO: Brenda Lucero, Chief Clinical Officer
CFO: A Shane Wells, Chief Financial Officer
CMO: Mark Barlow M.D., Chief Medical Officer and President Medical Staff
CIO: Jerald Harris, Chief Information Officer
CHR: Yolanda Jacobs, Coordinator Human Resources
Web address: www.cornerstonehealthcaregroup.com
Control: Partnership, Investor–owned (for–profit) **Service:** Acute long–term care hospital

Staffed Beds: 148 **Admissions:** 1148 **Census:** 79 **Outpatient Visits:** 0 **Births:** 0 **Total Expense ($000):** 35388 **Payroll Expense ($000):** 17201 **Personnel:** 218

HOUSTON PHYSICIANS HOSPITAL (670008), 333 North Texas Avenue, Suite 100, Zip 77598–4966; tel. 281/557–5620 **A**10 21 **F**3 29 37 40 51 64 74 79 81 82 85 86 91 93 107 111 114 141 149
Primary Contact: Nicholas Crafts, Chief Executive Officer
Web address: www.houstonphysicianshospital.com
Control: Corporation, Investor–owned (for–profit) **Service:** Surgical

Staffed Beds: 21 **Admissions:** 669 **Census:** 3 **Outpatient Visits:** 47159 **Births:** 0 **Total Expense ($000):** 43640 **Payroll Expense ($000):** 9610 **Personnel:** 197

KINDRED HOSPITAL CLEAR LAKE (452075), 350 Blossom Street, Zip 77598; tel. 281/316–7800 **A**1 **F**1 3 29 45 57 60 64 75 77 85 91 93 96 107 130 148 **S** Kindred Healthcare, Louisville, KY
Primary Contact: Mary Harbeson, R.N., Chief Executive Officer
Web address: www.khclearlake.com
Control: Corporation, Investor–owned (for–profit) **Service:** Acute long–term care hospital

Staffed Beds: 110 **Admissions:** 1207 **Census:** 83 **Outpatient Visits:** 3475 **Births:** 0 **Total Expense ($000):** 45291 **Payroll Expense ($000):** 17741 **Personnel:** 234

KINDRED REHABILITATION HOSPITAL CLEAR LAKE (453052), 655 East Medical Center Boulevard, Zip 77598–4328; tel. 281/286–1500 **A**1 10 **F**3 29 64 74 75 79 90 93 95 130 131 132 143 146 148
Primary Contact: Sandra Hegland, Chief Executive Officer
CFO: Michael McFall, Chief Financial Officer
CMO: Michael Rosenblatt M.D., Medical Director
CHR: Monica Little, Coordinator Human Resources
CNO: Kathy Hutchins–Otero, Chief Clinical Officer
Web address: www.khrehabclearlake.com/
Control: Corporation, Investor–owned (for–profit) **Service:** Rehabilitation

Staffed Beds: 60 **Admissions:** 930 **Census:** 34 **Outpatient Visits:** 6943 **Births:** 0 **Total Expense ($000):** 14949 **Payroll Expense ($000):** 7871 **Personnel:** 154

WELLINGTON—Collingsworth County

COLLINGSWORTH GENERAL HOSPITAL (451355), 1013 15th Street, Zip 79095–3703, Mailing Address: P.O.Box 1112, 79095–1112; tel. 806/447–2521 **A**10 18 **F**3 40 43 57 59 64 65 66 68 93 97 107 114 127 130 133 **S** Preferred Management Corporation, Shawnee, OK
Primary Contact: Candy Powell, Administrator
CFO: Larry Stephens, Chief Financial Officer
CMO: Wesley Nickens M.D., Chief of Staff
CIO: Thomas T. Ng, Chief Information Officer
CHR: April Wright, Human Resources Officer
CNO: Vikki Barton R.N., Chief Nursing Officer
Web address: www.collingsworthgeneral.net
Control: Corporation, Investor–owned (for–profit) **Service:** General medical and surgical

Staffed Beds: 13 **Admissions:** 198 **Census:** 4 **Outpatient Visits:** 8620 **Births:** 0 **Total Expense ($000):** 6691 **Payroll Expense ($000):** 2823 **Personnel:** 64

Hospital, Medicare Provider Number, Address, Telephone, Approval, Facility, and Physician Codes, Health Care System

★ American Hospital Association (AHA) membership
□ The Joint Commission accreditation
○ Healthcare Facilities Accreditation Program
◇ DNV Healthcare Inc. accreditation
⇑ Center for Improvement in Healthcare Quality Accreditation
△ Commission on Accreditation of Rehabilitation Facilities (CARF) accreditation

WESLACO—Hidalgo County

☒ **KNAPP MEDICAL CENTER (450128)**, 1401 East Eighth Street, Zip 78596–6640, Mailing Address: P.O.Box 1110, 78599–1110; tel. 956/968–8567 **A**1 3 5 10 **F**3 8 11 12 13 15 20 22 29 30 31 34 35 39 40 43 44 46 49 50 51 56 57 59 60 63 64 70 73 74 75 76 77 78 79 81 82 84 85 86 87 89 93 107 108 110 111 114 115 119 130 131 132 134 135 143 146 147 148 **P**8 **S** Prime Healthcare, Ontario, CA
Primary Contact: Rene Lopez, Chief Executive Officer
CFO: Dinah L. Gonzalez, Chief Financial Officer
CIO: Teri Garza, Director Health Information Services
CHR: Emmett Craig, Chief Human Resources Officer
CNO: Anna Hinojosa MSN, R.N., Interim Chief Nursing Officer
Web address: www.knappmed.org
Control: Other not–for–profit (including NFP Corporation) **Service:** General medical and surgical

Staffed Beds: 195 **Admissions:** 8533 **Census:** 94 **Outpatient Visits:** 84745 **Births:** 1586 **Total Expense ($000):** 115202 **Payroll Expense ($000):** 46710 **Personnel:** 712

WESLACO REGIONAL REHABILITATION HOSPITAL (453091), 906 South James Street, Zip 78596–9840; tel. 956/969–2222 **A**10 **F**3 29 34 75 77 86 87 90 94 96 130 132 148 149 **P**6
Primary Contact: Jessie Smedley, Chief Executive Officer
COO: Corina Humphreys, Chief Operating Officer
CFO: Ernest Nash, Chief Financial Officer
CMO: Daisy Arce, President Medical Staff
CHR: Debbie Pemelton, Director Human Resources
CNO: Rita Mata–Guerrero, Director of Nursing
Web address: www.wrrh.ernesthealth.com
Control: Partnership, Investor–owned (for–profit) **Service:** Rehabilitation

Staffed Beds: 32 **Admissions:** 596 **Census:** 21 **Outpatient Visits:** 0 **Births:** 0 **Total Expense ($000):** 10065 **Payroll Expense ($000):** 4705 **Personnel:** 91

WHEELER—Wheeler County

PARKVIEW HOSPITAL (451334), 901 Sweetwater Street, Zip 79096–2421, Mailing Address: P.O.Box 1030, 79096–1030; tel. 806/826–5581 **A**10 18 **F**3 7 10 40 43 59 62 64 65 68 91 93 107 114 127 128 130 133 148
Primary Contact: Monica Kidd, R.N., MSN, Administrator
CFO: Jace Henderson, Chief Financial Officer
CMO: John P. Lavelle M.D., Chief Medical Officer
CNO: Melisa Scales, Director of Nursing
Web address: www.parkviewhosp.org
Control: Hospital district or authority, Government, Nonfederal **Service:** General medical and surgical

Staffed Beds: 15 **Admissions:** 133 **Census:** 2 **Outpatient Visits:** 3790 **Births:** 1 **Total Expense ($000):** 7636 **Payroll Expense ($000):** 3549 **Personnel:** 104

WICHITA FALLS—Wichita County

☒ **HEALTHSOUTH REHABILITATION HOSPITAL–WICHITA FALLS (453054)**, 3901 Armory Road, Zip 76302–2204; tel. 940/720–5700 **A**1 10 **F**3 28 29 64 68 74 75 77 79 86 87 90 91 93 94 95 96 130 132 **S** HEALTHSOUTH Corporation, Birmingham, AL
Primary Contact: Robbi Hudson, Chief Executive Officer
CFO: Tom Box CPA, Chief Financial Officer
CMO: Virgil Frardo M.D., Medical Director
CIO: Mary Walker, Manager Information Technology
CHR: Kathleen Pirtle, Director Human Resources
CNO: Karla Dwyer R.N., MSN, Chief Nursing Officer
Web address: www.healthsouthwichitafalls.com
Control: Partnership, Investor–owned (for–profit) **Service:** Rehabilitation

Staffed Beds: 63 **Admissions:** 1437 **Census:** 51 **Outpatient Visits:** 6487 **Births:** 0 **Total Expense ($000):** 15739 **Payroll Expense ($000):** 9614 **Personnel:** 175

☐ **KELL WEST REGIONAL HOSPITAL (450827)**, 5420 Kell West Boulevard, Zip 76310–1610; tel. 940/692–5888 **A**1 10 **F**3 39 40 49 51 54 59 65 74 75 78 79 81 85 91 107 108 114 119 126 129 130 135
Primary Contact: Jerry Myers, M.D., Chief Executive Officer and Medical Director
CFO: Fran Lindemann, Director Finance
Web address: www.kellwest.com
Control: Partnership, Investor–owned (for–profit) **Service:** General medical and surgical

Staffed Beds: 41 **Admissions:** 1171 **Census:** 10 **Outpatient Visits:** 25418 **Births:** 0 **Total Expense ($000):** 31719 **Payroll Expense ($000):** 10331 **Personnel:** 265

☐ **NORTH TEXAS STATE HOSPITAL, WICHITA FALLS CAMPUS (454008)**, 6515 Lake Road, Zip 76308–5419, Mailing Address: Box 300, 76307–0300; tel. 940/692–1220, (Nonreporting) **A**1 10
Primary Contact: James E. Smith, Superintendent
CFO: Robin Moreno, Chief Financial Officer
CMO: Eulon Ross Taylor, Clinical Director
CIO: Chad Hughes, Chief Information Officer
Web address: www.online.dshs.state.tx.us/northtexassh/default.htm
Control: State, Government, Nonfederal **Service:** Psychiatric

Staffed Beds: 381

☐ **PROMISE HOSPITAL OF WICHITA FALLS (452068)**, 1103 Grace Street, Zip 76301–4414; tel. 940/720–6633 **A**1 10 **F**1 3 29 30 31 56 75 77 82 85 86 87 91 100 130 143 148 **P**8 **S** Promise Healthcare, Boca Raton, FL
Primary Contact: Michael L. McEachern, Chief Executive Officer
CFO: Debbie Herder, Controller
CMO: Robert McBroom M.D., Medical Director
CIO: Gail McIlroy, Director Medical Records
CNO: Deanna Dowling R.N., Chief Nursing Officer
Web address: www.promise–wichitafalls.com
Control: Corporation, Investor–owned (for–profit) **Service:** Acute long–term care hospital

Staffed Beds: 31 **Admissions:** 295 **Census:** 22 **Outpatient Visits:** 0 **Births:** 0 **Total Expense ($000):** 10747 **Payroll Expense ($000):** 4709 **Personnel:** 75

☐ **RED RIVER HOSPITAL, LLC (454018)**, 1505 Eighth Street, Zip 76301–3106; tel. 940/322–3171 **A**1 10 **F**4 5 29 38 50 86 87 98 99 100 101 102 103 104 105 106 130 135 143 **P**5 **S** Acadia Healthcare Company, Inc., Franklin, TN
Primary Contact: James Wilfer, Chief Executive Officer
CFO: Bruce Porter, Chief Financial Officer
CMO: Harvey C Martin M.D., Medical Director
CIO: Fay Helton, Director Medical Records
CHR: Kimberley Pellegrin, Director, Human Resources
CNO: Glenda Lawrence R.N., Chief Nursing Officer
Web address: www.redriverhospital.com
Control: Corporation, Investor–owned (for–profit) **Service:** Psychiatric

Staffed Beds: 96 **Admissions:** 2298 **Census:** 74 **Outpatient Visits:** 4496 **Births:** 0 **Total Expense ($000):** 11443 **Payroll Expense ($000):** 6460 **Personnel:** 199

☒ **UNITED REGIONAL HEALTH CARE SYSTEM (450010)**, 1600 11th Street, Zip 76301–4300; tel. 940/764–7000, (Includes UNITED REGIONAL HEALTH CARE SYSTEM–ELEVENTH STREET CAMPUS, 1600 11th Street, Wichita Falls, Texas, Zip 76301–9988, tel. 940/764–7000) **A**1 3 10 20 **F**3 11 12 13 15 17 18 20 21 22 24 26 28 29 30 31 32 34 35 37 39 40 43 44 45 46 47 48 49 50 51 53 57 59 60 61 64 65 68 70 73 74 75 76 77 78 79 80 81 82 84 85 86 87 89 92 93 102 107 110 111 114 115 116 117 118 119 126 130 131 132 134 146 147 148 149 **P**3
Primary Contact: Phyllis A. Cowling, CPA, President and Chief Executive Officer
COO: Nancy Townley R.N., Senior Vice President Operations
CFO: Robert M Pert, Vice President Finance and Chief Financial Officer
CMO: Lee Rodgers M.D., Vice President Quality
CIO: Jerry Marshall, Director Information Services, Information Technology Security Officer
CHR: Kristi Faulkner, Vice President Organizational Growth
CNO: Jane Ritter R.N., Vice President, Patient Care and Clinical Services
Web address: www.unitedregional.org
Control: Other not–for–profit (including NFP Corporation) **Service:** General medical and surgical

Staffed Beds: 286 **Admissions:** 14624 **Census:** 167 **Outpatient Visits:** 126093 **Births:** 2093 **Total Expense ($000):** 281962 **Payroll Expense ($000):** 110951 **Personnel:** 1819

WINNIE—Chambers County

RICELAND MEDICAL CENTER (451328), 538 Broadway, Zip 77665–7600; tel. 409/296–6000 **A**10 18 **F**3 29 34 40 59 65 81 105 107 119 127 133 146
Primary Contact: Daniel Yancy, Chief Executive Officer
CFO: Julie Harris, Chief Financial Officer
CMO: Leonidas Andres M.D., Chief of Staff
CHR: Anha Simon, Director Human Resources
Web address: www.energis.in/index.html
Control: Partnership, Investor–owned (for–profit) **Service:** General medical and surgical

Staffed Beds: 25 **Admissions:** 307 **Census:** 3 **Outpatient Visits:** 53065 **Births:** 0 **Total Expense ($000):** 22563 **Payroll Expense ($000):** 7920 **Personnel:** 196

TX

WINNSBORO—Wood County

⊠ **CHRISTUS MOTHER FRANCES HOSPITAL – WINNSBORO (451381)**, 719 West Coke Road, Zip 75494–3011; tel. 903/342–5227 **A**1 10 18 **F**3 18 29 30 34 35 40 43 45 57 59 64 68 70 75 79 81 82 85 87 93 102 107 108 111 115 119 127 129 130 131 132 133 146 148 **P**5 6 7 8 **S** CHRISTUS Health, Irving, TX
Primary Contact: Shelly Johnson, Chief Executive Officer
CFO: Glenn Peltier, Chief Financial Officer
CNO: Kevin Jablonski, Chief Nursing Officer
Web address: www.tmfhs.org
Control: Other not–for–profit (including NFP Corporation) **Service**: General medical and surgical

Staffed Beds: 25 **Admissions**: 434 **Census**: 7 **Outpatient Visits**: 22907 **Births**: 0 **Total Expense ($000)**: 16729 **Payroll Expense ($000)**: 5188 **Personnel**: 97

TEXAS HEALTH PRESBYTERIAN HOSPITAL WINNSBORO See Christus Mother Frances Hospital – Winnsboro

WINTERS—Runnels County

★ **NORTH RUNNELS HOSPITAL (451315)**, 7821 State Highway 153, Zip 79567–7345, Mailing Address: P.O.Box 185, 79567–0185; tel. 325/754–1317 **A**10 18 **F**7 11 40 57 59 62 65 66 68 97 107 119 127 133 **P**5
Primary Contact: Richard C. Mathis, Chief Executive Officer
CMO: Mark McKinnon M.D., Chief of Staff
CNO: Bobbie Collom, Nursing Director
Control: Hospital district or authority, Government, Nonfederal **Service**: General medical and surgical

Staffed Beds: 21 **Admissions**: 141 **Census**: 1 **Outpatient Visits**: 5140 **Births**: 0 **Total Expense ($000)**: 5331 **Payroll Expense ($000)**: 2510 **Personnel**: 54

WOODVILLE—Tyler County

★ **TYLER COUNTY HOSPITAL (450460)**, 1100 West Bluff Street, Zip 75979–4799, Mailing Address: P.O.Box 549, 75979–0549; tel. 409/283–8141 **A**10 20 **F**3 11 30 35 40 43 57 59 64 75 107 114 119 127 146
Primary Contact: Sandra Gayle. Wright, Chief Executive Officer
CFO: Scott Elton McCluskey, Chief Financial Officer
CMO: Paula Lajean Denson M.D., President
CIO: Rachel Joy Haygood, Director Information Technology
CHR: Kenneth Lynn Jobe, Director Human Resources
CNO: Sondra Dianne Wilson RN, MSN,CEN R.N., MSN, Assistant Administrator and Chief Nursing Officer
Web address: www.tchospital.us
Control: Hospital district or authority, Government, Nonfederal **Service**: General medical and surgical

Staffed Beds: 25 **Admissions**: 471 **Census**: 4 **Outpatient Visits**: 25555 **Births**: 1 **Total Expense ($000)**: 11867 **Payroll Expense ($000)**: 4780 **Personnel**: 113

YOAKUM—Lavaca County

★ **YOAKUM COMMUNITY HOSPITAL (451346)**, 1200 Carl Ramert Drive, Zip 77995–4868; tel. 361/293–2321 **A**10 18 **F**3 11 13 15 29 34 35 40 43 56 57 59 64 70 76 79 81 85 86 93 107 108 111 114 119 129 132 133 134 146 148 **S** Community Hospital Corporation, Plano, TX
Primary Contact: Karen Barber, R.N., Chief Executive Officer
CFO: Robert Foret, Chief Financial Officer
CMO: Timothy Wagner M.D., Chief Medical Staff
CIO: Barbara Vasek, Director Information Technology
CHR: Karen Roznovsky, Director Human Resources
CNO: Jennifer Franklin R.N., Chief Clinical Officer
Web address: www.yoakumhospital.org
Control: Other not–for–profit (including NFP Corporation) **Service**: General medical and surgical

Staffed Beds: 25 **Admissions**: 938 **Census**: 12 **Outpatient Visits**: 21845 **Births**: 53 **Total Expense ($000)**: 18719 **Payroll Expense ($000)**: 7610 **Personnel**: 104

TX

Hospital, Medicare Provider Number, Address, Telephone, Approval, Facility, and Physician Codes, Health Care System

★ American Hospital Association (AHA) membership ○ Healthcare Facilities Accreditation Program ⇑ Center for Improvement in Healthcare Quality Accreditation
□ The Joint Commission accreditation ◇ DNV Healthcare Inc. accreditation △ Commission on Accreditation of Rehabilitation Facilities (CARF) accreditation

© 2017 AHA Guide *Many Facility Codes have changed. Please refer to the AHA Guide Code Chart.* Hospitals **A655**

UTAH

AMERICAN FORK—Utah County

✠ **AMERICAN FORK HOSPITAL (460023)**, 170 North 1100 East, Zip 84003–2096; tel. 801/855–3300 **A**1 3 10 **F**3 13 15 18 26 29 30 31 34 38 39 40 45 46 49 50 53 57 59 60 64 68 70 73 76 78 79 81 82 85 86 87 89 92 93 107 108 109 110 111 114 115 119 121 123 129 130 132 146 148 149 **P**6 **S** Intermountain Healthcare, Inc., Salt Lake City, UT
Primary Contact: Jason Wilson, Administrator and Chief Executive Officer
CMO: Paul H Robinson M.D., Medical Director
CIO: Mary Gathers, Manager Information Systems
CHR: Luke P Morris, Assistant Vice President Talent
CNO: Terri Lynn Hunter R.N., Nurse Administrator
Web address: www.intermountainhealthcare.org
Control: Other not–for–profit (including NFP Corporation) **Service**: General medical and surgical

Staffed Beds: 89 **Admissions:** 6230 **Census:** 42 **Outpatient Visits:** 333308 **Births:** 3075 **Total Expense ($000):** 118151 **Payroll Expense ($000):** 38396 **Personnel:** 695

BEAVER—Beaver County

BEAVER VALLEY HOSPITAL (460035), 1109 North 100 West, Zip 84713, Mailing Address: P.O.Box 1670, 84713–1670; tel. 435/438–7100, (Nonreporting) **A**10 18 20
Primary Contact: Scott Langford, Administrator
Web address: www.bvhospital.com/
Control: City, Government, Nonfederal **Service**: General medical and surgical

Staffed Beds: 49

BLANDING—San Juan County

✠ **BLUE MOUNTAIN HOSPITAL (461310)**, 802 South 200 West, Suite A, Zip 84511–3910; tel. 435/678–3993 **A**1 10 18 **F**3 8 13 15 40 45 50 60 65 68 75 81 107 110 111 119 133 146
Primary Contact: Jeremy Lyman, Chief Executive Officer
CFO: Jimmy Johnson, Chief Financial Officer
CMO: Mahana Fisher M.D., Medical Director
CIO: Anthony Torres, Manager Information Technology
CHR: Gail M. Northern, Director Human Resources
CNO: Derrill Kent Turek R.N., Chief Nursing Officer
Web address: www.bmhutah.org/
Control: Other not–for–profit (including NFP Corporation) **Service**: General medical and surgical

Staffed Beds: 11 **Admissions:** 341 **Census:** 3

BOUNTIFUL—Davis County

✠ **LAKEVIEW HOSPITAL (460042)**, 630 East Medical Drive, Zip 84010–4908; tel. 801/299–2200, (Nonreporting) **A**1 10 13 **S** HCA Healthcare, Nashville, TN
Primary Contact: Troy Wood, Chief Executive Officer
CFO: Wayne Dalton, Chief Financial Officer
CMO: Michael Hess M.D., Chief Medical Officer
CIO: Mark Ellis, Director Information Technology
CHR: Julie Isom, Director Human Resources
CNO: Marilyn Mariani R.N., Chief Nursing Officer
Web address: www.lakeviewhospital.com
Control: Corporation, Investor–owned (for–profit) **Service**: General medical and surgical

Staffed Beds: 119

SOUTH DAVIS COMMUNITY HOSPITAL (462003), 401 South 400 East, Zip 84010–4933; tel. 801/295–2361 (Nonreporting) **A**10
Primary Contact: David Bland, Chief Executive Officer
CMO: Scott Southworth M.D., Medical Director
CHR: Jamey Sulser, Director Human Resources
Web address: www.sdch.com
Control: Other not–for–profit (including NFP Corporation) **Service**: Acute long–term care hospital

Staffed Beds: 176

BRIGHAM CITY—Box Elder County

✠ **BRIGHAM CITY COMMUNITY HOSPITAL (460017)**, 950 South Medical Drive, Zip 84302–4724; tel. 435/734–9471, (Nonreporting) **A**1 10 **S** HCA Healthcare, Nashville, TN
Primary Contact: Richard Spuhler, Chief Executive Officer
CMO: Joel Gardner D.O., Chief Medical Officer
CIO: Steve Reichard, Manager Information Systems
CHR: Tracie Greene, Director Human Resources
CNO: Jerry Bushman, Chief Nursing Officer
Web address: www.brighamcityhospital.com
Control: Corporation, Investor–owned (for–profit) **Service**: General medical and surgical

Staffed Beds: 39

CEDAR CITY—Iron County

✠ **CEDAR CITY HOSPITAL (460007)**, 1303 North Main Street, Zip 84721–9746; tel. 435/868–5000 **A**1 10 20 **F**3 13 15 28 29 31 34 35 40 45 46 57 59 64 70 75 76 77 78 79 81 85 86 87 97 107 110 111 114 119 130 146 147 148 **P**5 **S** Intermountain Healthcare, Inc., Salt Lake City, UT
Primary Contact: Eric Packer, Chief Executive Officer
CFO: Reed Sargent, Assistant Administrator Finance
Web address: www.intermountainhealthcare.org/locations/cedar–city–hospital/
Control: Other not–for–profit (including NFP Corporation) **Service**: General medical and surgical

Staffed Beds: 48 **Admissions:** 3591 **Census:** 17 **Births:** 859 **Total Expense ($000):** 71231 **Payroll Expense ($000):** 20775 **Personnel:** 354

DELTA—Millard County

★ **DELTA COMMUNITY MEDICAL CENTER (461300)**, 126 South White Sage Avenue, Zip 84624–8937; tel. 435/864–5591 **A**10 18 **F**3 8 11 13 15 29 31 34 38 40 41 42 43 45 54 57 59 64 68 71 75 76 81 82 86 87 89 102 107 111 119 128 133 144 145 146 149 **P**5 8 **S** Intermountain Healthcare, Inc., Salt Lake City, UT
Primary Contact: Lenny Lyons, Administrator
CFO: Chris Thompson, Chief Financial Officer
Web address: www.ihc.com
Control: Other not–for–profit (including NFP Corporation) **Service**: General medical and surgical

Staffed Beds: 18 **Admissions:** 241 **Census:** 2 **Outpatient Visits:** 21348 **Births:** 107 **Total Expense ($000):** 9581 **Payroll Expense ($000):** 3417 **Personnel:** 49

DRAPER—Salt Lake County

✠ **LONE PEAK HOSPITAL (460060)**, 1925 South State Street, Zip 84020; tel. 801/545–8000 (Nonreporting) **A**1 10 **S** HCA Healthcare, Nashville, TN
Primary Contact: Mark Meadows, Chief Executive Officer
Web address: www.lonepeakhospital.com
Control: Corporation, Investor–owned (for–profit) **Service**: General medical and surgical

Staffed Beds: 32

FILLMORE—Millard County

★ **FILLMORE COMMUNITY HOSPITAL (461301)**, 674 South Highway 99, Zip 84631–5013; tel. 435/743–5591 **A**10 18 **F**3 8 11 13 15 29 31 34 38 40 41 43 50 56 57 59 62 63 64 67 68 75 81 82 86 87 93 107 110 119 128 133 145 146 147 148 149 **S** Intermountain Healthcare, Inc., Salt Lake City, UT
Primary Contact: Lenny Lyons, Administrator
CFO: Chris Thompson, Chief Financial Officer
Web address: www.ihc.com
Control: Other not–for–profit (including NFP Corporation) **Service**: General medical and surgical

Staffed Beds: 19 **Admissions:** 184 **Census:** 10 **Outpatient Visits:** 7142 **Births:** 37 **Total Expense ($000):** 9153 **Payroll Expense ($000):** 3223 **Personnel:** 49

GUNNISON—Sanpete County

★ **GUNNISON VALLEY HOSPITAL (461306)**, 64 East 100 North, Zip 84634, Mailing Address: P.O.Box 759, 84634–0759; tel. 435/528–7246, (Total facility includes 99 beds in nursing home–type unit) **A**10 18 **F**7 11 13 15 18 34 35 39 40 45 56 57 59 62 63 64 65 79 81 82 85 97 100 102 107 115 119 129 130 132 135 146 147 148 149 **P**6
Primary Contact: Mark F. Dalley, Administrator
CFO: Brian Murray, Chief Financial Officer
CIO: Mike Ryan, Director of Information Services
CHR: Liz Brown, Manager Human Resources
CNO: Brenda Bartholomew, Chief Nursing Officer
Web address: www.gvhospital.org
Control: County, Government, Nonfederal **Service**: General medical and surgical

Staffed Beds: 124 **Admissions:** 884 **Census:** 79 **Outpatient Visits:** 29013 **Births:** 159 **Total Expense ($000):** 21985 **Payroll Expense ($000):** 6045 **Personnel:** 157

UT

Many Facility Codes have changed. Please refer to the AHA Guide Code Chart. © 2017 AHA Guide

HEBER CITY—Wasatch County

★ **HEBER VALLEY MEDICAL CENTER (461307)**, 1485 South Highway 40, Zip 84032–3522; tel. 435/654–2500 **A**10 18 **F**13 15 29 32 34 35 40 43 45 46 50 57 59 60 62 65 68 75 76 77 79 81 82 84 86 87 93 97 102 107 109 110 111 112 114 115 119 129 130 131 133 146 147 149 **S** Intermountain Healthcare, Inc., Salt Lake City, UT
Primary Contact: Shawn Morrow, Administrator
CFO: Craig Mills, Chief Financial Officer
CMO: Stanton B McDonald M.D., Medical Director
CHR: Bruce Dent, Human Resources Director
CNO: Gayle Sturgis R.N., Nurse Administrator
Web address: www.intermountainhealthcare.org
Control: Other not–for–profit (including NFP Corporation) **Service:** General medical and surgical

Staffed Beds: 19 Admissions: 613 Census: 4

KANAB—Kane County

KANE COUNTY HOSPITAL (461309), 355 North Main Street, Zip 84741–3260; tel. 435/644–5811, (Nonreporting) **A**10 18
Primary Contact: Sherrie Pandya, Administrator
CFO: Stephen Howells, Chief Financial Officer
CMO: Darin Ott D.O., Chief of Staff
CHR: Laurali Noteman, Director Human Resources
CNO: Charlene Kelly, Chief Nursing Officer
Web address: www.kanecountyhospital.net
Control: Hospital district or authority, Government, Nonfederal **Service:** General medical and surgical

Staffed Beds: 25

LAYTON—Davis County

★ ⇑ **DAVIS HOSPITAL AND MEDICAL CENTER (460041)**, 1600 West Antelope Drive, Zip 84041–1142; tel. 801/807–1000 **A**3 10 21 **F**3 8 11 12 13 15 17 18 20 22 26 28 29 31 34 35 38 40 42 43 45 46 47 48 49 55 57 59 64 65 68 70 72 73 74 75 76 77 78 79 81 82 85 86 87 89 90 93 94 98 102 105 107 108 109 110 111 114 115 116 117 119 120 126 129 130 146 147 148 149 **S** IASIS Healthcare, Franklin, TN
Primary Contact: Michael Jensen, Chief Executive Officer
COO: Jared Spackman, Chief Operating Officer
CFO: Jared Spackman, Chief Financial Officer
CMO: Les Greenwood M.D., President, Medical Staff
CIO: Shane Williams, Director Information Systems
CHR: Tara Figgins, Director Human Resources
CNO: Chris Johnson R.N., MSN, Chief Nursing Officer
Web address: www.davishospital.com
Control: Corporation, Investor–owned (for–profit) **Service:** General medical and surgical

Staffed Beds: 221 Admissions: 5915 Census: 62 Outpatient Visits: 176568 Births: 1587 Personnel: 724

LOGAN—Cache County

⊞ **LOGAN REGIONAL HOSPITAL (460015)**, 1400 North 500 East, Zip 84341–2455; tel. 435/716–1000, (Total facility includes 11 beds in nursing home–type unit) **A**1 10 **F**3 8 11 13 14 15 18 20 22 28 29 31 32 34 35 36 37 38 40 43 44 45 46 49 50 51 57 59 60 64 68 70 73 74 75 76 77 78 79 81 82 85 86 87 89 91 93 96 97 98 99 100 101 102 103 104 105 107 108 109 110 111 114 115 118 119 120 121 123 126 128 129 130 131 132 135 146 147 148 149 **P**6 **S** Intermountain Healthcare, Inc., Salt Lake City, UT
Primary Contact: Kyle A. Hansen, Chief Executive Officer
COO: Brandon McBride, Operations Officer
CFO: Alan Robinson, Chief Financial Officer
CMO: Todd A Brown M.D., Medical Director
CIO: Dave Felts, Chief Information Systems
CHR: Jolene Clonts, Director Human Resources
CNO: Neil C Perkes, Operations Officer
Web address: www.loganregionalhospital.org
Control: Other not–for–profit (including NFP Corporation) **Service:** General medical and surgical

Staffed Beds: 139 Admissions: 6852 Census: 55 Outpatient Visits: 307064 Births: 2521 Total Expense ($000): 152286 Payroll Expense ($000): 47843 Personnel: 895

MIDVALE—Salt Lake County

☐ **HIGHLAND RIDGE HOSPITAL (464015)**, 7309 South 180 West, Zip 84047–3769; tel. 801/569–2153 (Nonreporting) **A**1 **S** Acadia Healthcare Company, Inc., Franklin, TN
Primary Contact: Matt Wilburn, Chief Executive Officer
COO: Robert Beatty, Chief Operating Officer
CFO: Sheri Sorenson, Manager Business Office
CHR: Carol Cunningham, Administrative Assistant
Web address: www.highlandridgehospital.com
Control: Corporation, Investor–owned (for–profit) **Service:** Psychiatric

Staffed Beds: 83

MILFORD—Beaver County

★ **MILFORD VALLEY MEMORIAL HOSPITAL (461305)**, 850 North Main Street, Zip 84751–0640, Mailing Address: P.O.Box 640, 84751–0640; tel. 435/387–2411, (Nonreporting) **A**10 18
Primary Contact: Scott Langford, Administrator
COO: Michelle Barton, Chief Operating Officer
CFO: Tyler Moss, Chief Financial Officer
CNO: Amy Contreras Esq, Chief Nursing Officer
Web address: www.milfordmemorialhospital.org
Control: Hospital district or authority, Government, Nonfederal **Service:** General medical and surgical

Staffed Beds: 25

MOAB—Grand County

★ **MOAB REGIONAL HOSPITAL (461302)**, 450 West Williams Way, Zip 84532–2065, Mailing Address: P.O.Box 998, 84532–0998; tel. 435/719–3500 **A**10 18 **F**3 4 5 11 13 15 29 30 31 34 35 40 43 45 57 59 63 64 65 66 67 68 73 75 76 79 81 82 85 86 89 90 97 107 110 111 114 115 119 128 130 131 132 133 144 148 **P**6
Primary Contact: Jennifer Sadoff, Chief Executive Officer
COO: Vicki Gigliotti, Chief Clinical Officer
CFO: Craig M Daniels, Chief Financial Officer
CMO: Steven V. Rouzer M.D., Chief Medical Officer
CIO: Mike Foster, Manager Information Systems
CHR: Katherine Sullivan, Director, Human Resources
Web address: www.mrhmoab.org
Control: Other not–for–profit (including NFP Corporation) **Service:** General medical and surgical

Staffed Beds: 17 Admissions: 545 Census: 5 Outpatient Visits: 14467 Births: 73

MONTICELLO—San Juan County

SAN JUAN HEALTH SERVICE DISTRICT (461308), 380 West 100 North, Zip 84535, Mailing Address: P.O.Box 308, 84535–0308; tel. 435/587–2116 **A**10 18 **F**3 13 15 29 31 32 34 35 38 39 40 41 44 45 47 50 56 57 59 64 65 66 68 76 79 80 81 82 87 107 110 114 119 127 128 133 145 148 **P**6
Primary Contact: Clayton Holt, Chief Executive Officer
CFO: Lyman Duncan, Chief Financial Officer
CMO: Kelly Jeppesen, Chief Medical Officer
CIO: Julie Bingham, IT Supervisor
CHR: Deana Dalton, Human Resources
CNO: Laurie Schafer, Chief Nursing Officer
Web address: www.sanjuanhealthservices.org/
Control: Hospital district or authority, Government, Nonfederal **Service:** General medical and surgical

Staffed Beds: 25 Admissions: 244 Census: 2 Outpatient Visits: 4343 Births: 44 Total Expense ($000): 14490 Payroll Expense ($000): 5807 Personnel: 98

MOUNT PLEASANT—Sanpete County

★ **SANPETE VALLEY HOSPITAL (461303)**, 1100 South Medical Drive, Zip 84647–2222; tel. 435/462–2441, (Nonreporting) **A**10 18 **S** Intermountain Healthcare, Inc., Salt Lake City, UT
Primary Contact: Aaron C. Wood, Chief Executive Officer and Administrator
COO: Kristina Skinner, Director Quality
CFO: Chris Thompson, Chief Financial Officer
CMO: David Krzymowski M.D., Chief of Staff
CIO: Michael Ence, Computer Specialist
CHR: Brett Gray, Director Human Resource
CNO: Ryan Robison, Chief Nursing Officer
Web address: www.intermountainhealthcare.com
Control: Other not–for–profit (including NFP Corporation) **Service:** General medical and surgical

Staffed Beds: 18

UT

MURRAY—Salt Lake County

☐ △ **INTERMOUNTAIN MEDICAL CENTER (460010)**, 5121 South Cottonwood Street, Zip 84107–5701; tel. 801/507–7000 **A**1 2 5 7 10 **F**3 7 8 11 12 13 15 17 18 20 22 24 26 28 29 30 31 34 35 37 38 39 40 41 43 44 45 46 47 48 49 50 51 52 53 54 55 56 57 58 59 60 61 63 64 66 68 70 71 72 74 75 76 77 78 79 81 82 84 85 86 87 90 91 92 93 94 96 97 99 100 102 103 107 108 109 110 111 114 115 116 117 118 119 120 121 123 124 126 129 130 131 132 135 137 138 139 141 142 143 146 147 148 149 **S** Intermountain Healthcare, Inc., Salt Lake City, UT
Primary Contact: Joseph Mott, Chief Executive Officer
COO: Kelly L Duffin, Operations Officer
CFO: Royce Stephens, Director Finance
CMO: Mark Ott M.D., Regional Chief Medical Director
CIO: David Baird, Director of Information Systems
CHR: Tiffiny J Lipscomb, Manager Human Resources
CNO: Suzanne P. Anderson, Nurse Administrator
Web address: www.intermountainhealthcare.org
Control: Other not-for-profit (including NFP Corporation) **Service:** General medical and surgical

Staffed Beds: 502 **Admissions:** 26544 **Census:** 328 **Outpatient Visits:** 1160840 **Births:** 4880 **Total Expense ($000):** 784742 **Payroll Expense ($000):** 240053 **Personnel:** 3983

LANDMARK HOSPITAL OF SALT LAKE CITY (462006), 4252 South Birkhill Boulevard, Zip 84107–5715; tel. 801/268–5400 (Nonreporting) **A**10 22 **S** Landmark Hospitals, Cape Girardeau, MO
Primary Contact: Ted Paarlberg, Chief Executive Officer
Web address: www.landmarkhospitals.com/utah.aspx
Control: Partnership, Investor-owned (for-profit) **Service:** Acute long-term care hospital

Staffed Beds: 38

☒ **THE ORTHOPEDIC SPECIALTY HOSPITAL (460049)**, 5848 South 300 East, Zip 84107–6121; tel. 801/314–4100 **A**1 10 **F**3 9 29 32 34 35 37 44 50 53 57 58 59 64 68 74 75 77 79 81 82 85 86 87 91 92 93 94 100 107 111 114 115 119 130 131 132 134 135 146 149 **S** Intermountain Healthcare, Inc., Salt Lake City, UT
Primary Contact: Lisa Bagley, Nurse Administrator
CFO: Sherlyn Lewis, Manager Finance
CMO: Jon Sundin M.D., Medical Director
CIO: David Baird, Chief Information Officer
CHR: Tina Tasso, Manager Human Resources
Web address: www.intermountainhealthcare.org
Control: Other not-for-profit (including NFP Corporation) **Service:** Orthopedic

Staffed Beds: 40 **Admissions:** 1991 **Census:** 11 **Outpatient Visits:** 224774 **Births:** 0 **Total Expense ($000):** 70078 **Payroll Expense ($000):** 19440 **Personnel:** 347

NEPHI—Juab County

★ **CENTRAL VALLEY MEDICAL CENTER (461304)**, 48 West 1500 North, Zip 84648–8900; tel. 435/623–3000, (Nonreporting) **A**10 18 **S** Rural Health Group, Nephi, UT
Primary Contact: Mark R. Stoddard, Chief Executive Officer
COO: Randy Cuff, Chief Operating Officer
CFO: Brent Davis, Chief Financial Officer
CMO: Mark Oveson M.D., Chief Medical Staff
CIO: Ken Richens, Chief Information Officer
CHR: Brian Allsop, Director Human Resources
CNO: Randy Allinson R.N., Chief Nursing Officer
Web address: www.cvmed.net
Control: Other not-for-profit (including NFP Corporation) **Service:** General medical and surgical

Staffed Beds: 27

NORTH LOGAN—Cache County

☒ **CACHE VALLEY HOSPITAL (460054)**, 2380 North 400 East, Zip 84341–6000; tel. 435/713–9700, (Nonreporting) **A**1 10 **S** HCA Healthcare, Nashville, TN
Primary Contact: John C. Worley III, Chief Executive Officer
CFO: David S Geary, Chief Financial Officer
CMO: Matt Welter, Chief Medical Officer
Web address: www.cachevalleyhospital.com/
Control: Corporation, Investor-owned (for-profit) **Service:** General medical and surgical

Staffed Beds: 22

OGDEN—Weber County

☒ **MCKAY–DEE HOSPITAL (460004)**, 4401 Harrison Boulevard, Zip 84403–3195; tel. 801/387–2800 **A**1 2 3 10 **F**3 8 11 12 13 15 17 18 20 22 24 26 28 29 30 31 34 35 38 40 43 44 45 46 49 50 51 53 54 55 57 58 59 60 61 64 65 66 67 68 70 72 74 75 76 77 78 79 81 82 84 85 86 87 89 90 91 93 97 98 99 100 101 102 104 105 107 108 110 111 114 115 116 117 118 119 120 121 123 126 129 130 131 132 134 135 146 147 148 149 **P**6 **S** Intermountain Healthcare, Inc., Salt Lake City, UT
Primary Contact: Michael A. Clark, Administrator
COO: Michael A Clark, Chief Operating Officer
CFO: Doug Smith, Chief Financial Officer
CMO: Christine Nefcy M.D., Chief Medical Officer
CIO: Mary Gathers, Director Information Systems
CHR: Lee Lorimer IV, Regional Director Human Resources
CNO: Bonnie Jacklin R.N., MSN, Chief Nursing Officer
Web address: www.mckay-dee.org
Control: Other not-for-profit (including NFP Corporation) **Service:** General medical and surgical

Staffed Beds: 312 **Admissions:** 18619 **Census:** 192 **Outpatient Visits:** 238564 **Births:** 3972 **Total Expense ($000):** 404516 **Payroll Expense ($000):** 129228 **Personnel:** 1908

☒ **OGDEN REGIONAL MEDICAL CENTER (460005)**, 5475 South 500 East, Zip 84405–6905; tel. 801/479–2111, (Nonreporting) **A**1 10 13 **S** HCA Healthcare, Nashville, TN
Primary Contact: Mark B. Adams, Chief Executive Officer
COO: Brian Lines, Chief Operating Officer
CFO: Judd Taylor, Chief Financial Officer
CMO: Jeffrey Abel M.D., Chief Medical Officer
CIO: Eric Peterson, Director
CHR: Chris Bissenden, Director Human Resources
CNO: Elizabeth B. Later R.N., Chief Nursing Officer
Web address: www.ogdenregional.com
Control: Corporation, Investor-owned (for-profit) **Service:** General medical and surgical

Staffed Beds: 167

OREM—Utah County

☒ **OREM COMMUNITY HOSPITAL (460043)**, 331 North 400 West, Zip 84057–1999; tel. 801/224–4080 **A**1 10 **F**3 11 13 15 29 32 35 38 40 43 54 59 64 75 76 81 82 86 87 93 97 107 111 119 132 135 146 **S** Intermountain Healthcare, Inc., Salt Lake City, UT
Primary Contact: J. Francis. Gibson, Administrator and Chief Executive Officer
CMO: Neil Whitaker M.D., Chief Medical Director
CIO: Diane Rindlisbacher, Manager Information Systems
CHR: Pamela S Niece, Director Human Resources
Web address: www.intermountainhealthcare.org
Control: Other not-for-profit (including NFP Corporation) **Service:** General medical and surgical

Staffed Beds: 18 **Admissions:** 1155 **Census:** 6 **Outpatient Visits:** 9890 **Births:** 1061 **Total Expense ($000):** 26821 **Payroll Expense ($000):** 10194 **Personnel:** 155

☐ **PROVO CANYON BEHAVIORAL HOSPITAL (464014)**, 1350 East 750 North, Zip 84097–4345; tel. 801/852–2273 (Nonreporting) **A**1 10 **S** Universal Health Services, Inc., King of Prussia, PA
Primary Contact: Jeremy Cottle, Ph.D., Chief Executive Officer
CFO: Emmy Adams, Chief Financial Officer
CHR: Diann Decker, Chief Human Resource Officer
Web address: www.pcbh.com
Control: Corporation, Investor-owned (for-profit) **Service:** Psychiatric

Staffed Beds: 80

☒ **TIMPANOGOS REGIONAL HOSPITAL (460052)**, 750 West 800 North, Zip 84057–3660; tel. 801/714–6000, (Nonreporting) **A**1 10 **S** HCA Healthcare, Nashville, TN
Primary Contact: Kimball S. Anderson, FACHE, Chief Executive Officer
COO: Austin Lane Manning, Chief Operating Officer
CFO: Jody S Dial, Chief Financial Officer
CMO: Randle L Likes M.D., Chief Medical Officer
CIO: Richard Neilson, Director of Information Services
CHR: Tim Black, Director Human Resources
CNO: Sandy Ewell, Chief Nursing Officer
Web address: www.timpanogosregionalhospital.com
Control: Corporation, Investor-owned (for-profit) **Service:** General medical and surgical

Staffed Beds: 105

UT

PANGUITCH—Garfield County

★ **GARFIELD MEMORIAL HOSPITAL (460033)**, 200 North 400 East, Zip 84759, Mailing Address: P.O.Box 389, 84759–0389; tel. 435/676–8811, (Total facility includes 21 beds in nursing home–type unit) **A**10 20 **F**2 13 15 28 29 32 34 35 40 45 56 57 59 64 65 75 76 81 82 87 97 107 110 119 127 128 130 133 148 149 **P**6 **S** Intermountain Healthcare, Inc., Salt Lake City, UT
Primary Contact: Alberto Vasquez, Administrator
CFO: Reed Sargent, Assistant Administrator Finance
Web address: www.ihc.com/hospitals/garfield
Control: Other not–for–profit (including NFP Corporation) **Service:** General medical and surgical

Staffed Beds: 36 **Admissions:** 614 **Census:** 23 **Outpatient Visits:** 9898 **Births:** 32 **Total Expense ($000):** 12624 **Payroll Expense ($000):** 6227 **Personnel:** 112

PARK CITY—Summit County

✠ **PARK CITY HOSPITAL (460057)**, 900 Round Valley Drive, Zip 84060–7552; tel. 435/658–7000 **A**1 10 **F**3 12 13 15 18 29 34 35 36 37 39 40 43 45 49 50 51 53 57 59 64 68 70 75 76 79 81 82 86 87 93 107 108 110 111 115 119 129 130 131 146 147 148 149 **S** Intermountain Healthcare, Inc., Salt Lake City, UT
Primary Contact: Si William. Hutt, Administrator
CFO: Lori Nielson, Regional Finance Director
CMO: Wain Allen M.D., Medical Director
CHR: Christopher Saling, Manager Human Resources
CNO: Dan Davis, MSN R.N., Nurse Administrator
Web address: www.intermountainhealthcare.org
Control: Other not–for–profit (including NFP Corporation) **Service:** General medical and surgical

Staffed Beds: 37 **Admissions:** 1818 **Census:** 11 **Outpatient Visits:** 109149 **Births:** 364 **Total Expense ($000):** 78831 **Payroll Expense ($000):** 25419 **Personnel:** 335

PAYSON—Utah County

✠ **MOUNTAIN VIEW HOSPITAL (460013)**, 1000 East 100 North, Zip 84651–1600; tel. 801/465–7000, (Nonreporting) **A**1 10 **S** HCA Healthcare, Nashville, TN
Primary Contact: Kevin Johnson, Chief Executive Officer
COO: Ric Johnson, Associate Administrator
CFO: Steven R Schramm, Chief Financial Officer
CMO: Jeffrey Wallentine, Chief of Staff
CIO: Cindy Mecham, Health Information Director
CHR: Wally Trotter, Director Human Resources
CNO: Lisa Taylor, Director of Nursing
Web address: www.mvhpayson.com
Control: Corporation, Investor–owned (for–profit) **Service:** General medical and surgical

Staffed Beds: 114

PRICE—Carbon County

✠ **CASTLEVIEW HOSPITAL (460011)**, 300 North Hospital Drive, Zip 84501–4200; tel. 435/637–4800 **A**1 10 20 **F**3 8 11 12 13 15 29 31 34 39 40 41 45 47 48 50 51 57 59 68 70 75 76 77 78 79 81 82 85 86 87 89 93 107 108 110 111 115 119 127 129 130 131 133 146 147 148 **S** LifePoint Health, Brentwood, TN
Primary Contact: Mark Holyoak, Chief Executive Officer
CFO: Greg Cook, Chief Financial Officer
CMO: Glen T. Etzel M.D., Chief of Staff
CIO: Fiore Wilson, Director Information Systems
CHR: Misty Birch, Director Human Resources
CNO: Grant Barraclough R.N., Chief Nursing Officer
Web address: www.castleviewhospital.net
Control: Corporation, Investor–owned (for–profit) **Service:** General medical and surgical

Staffed Beds: 49 **Admissions:** 1644 **Census:** 13 **Outpatient Visits:** 58068 **Births:** 274 **Total Expense ($000):** 37784 **Payroll Expense ($000):** 13998 **Personnel:** 357

PROVO—Utah County

☐ **UTAH STATE HOSPITAL (464001)**, 1300 East Center Street, Zip 84606–3554, Mailing Address: P.O.Box 270, 84603–0270; tel. 801/344–4400 **A**1 3 10 **F**30 34 56 75 77 86 87 91 98 99 100 101 103 130 135 143 146 149 150 **P**6
Primary Contact: Dallas Earnshaw, Superintendent
COO: Dallas Earnshaw, Superintendent
CFO: Robert Burton, Manager Finance
CMO: Madhu Gundlapalli M.D., Clinical Director
CIO: Jill Hill, Director Information Technology
CHR: Devin Patrick, Manager Human Resources
CNO: Chris Metcalf, Director of Nursing
Web address: www.ush.utah.gov
Control: State, Government, Nonfederal **Service:** Psychiatric

Staffed Beds: 329 **Admissions:** 322 **Census:** 298 **Outpatient Visits:** 0 **Births:** 0 **Total Expense ($000):** 58830 **Payroll Expense ($000):** 34165 **Personnel:** 745

✠ △ **UTAH VALLEY HOSPITAL (460001)**, 1034 North 500 West, Zip 84604–3337; tel. 801/357–7850 **A**1 2 3 7 10 **F**3 13 15 17 18 20 21 22 23 24 25 26 28 29 30 31 34 35 38 39 40 43 44 45 48 49 50 51 53 57 59 60 61 64 68 70 72 73 74 75 76 77 78 79 81 82 84 85 86 87 89 90 91 92 93 94 96 97 98 99 100 101 102 103 107 108 110 111 114 115 116 117 118 119 121 123 126 129 130 131 132 146 148 149 **S** Intermountain Healthcare, Inc., Salt Lake City, UT
Primary Contact: Steve Smoot, Administrator
CFO: Rod Lisonbee, Chief Financial Officer
CIO: Mary Gathers, Director Information Systems
CHR: Luke P Morris, Assistant Vice President Talent
CNO: Lisa A. Paletta R.N., FACHE, Chief Nursing Officer
Web address: www.utahvalleyregional.org
Control: Other not–for–profit (including NFP Corporation) **Service:** General medical and surgical

Staffed Beds: 344 **Admissions:** 18932 **Census:** 185 **Outpatient Visits:** 716351 **Births:** 3749 **Total Expense ($000):** 467719 **Payroll Expense ($000):** 156039 **Personnel:** 3075

☐ **UTAH VALLEY SPECIALTY HOSPITAL (462005)**, 306 River Bend Lane, Zip 84604–5625; tel. 801/226–8880 (Nonreporting) **A**1 10 **S** Ernest Health, Inc., Albuquerque, NM
Primary Contact: Ezra Segura, Chief Executive Officer
Web address: www.uvsh.ernesthealth.com
Control: Corporation, Investor–owned (for–profit) **Service:** Acute long–term care hospital

Staffed Beds: 40

RICHFIELD—Sevier County

✠ **SEVIER VALLEY HOSPITAL (460026)**, 1000 North Main Street, Zip 84701–1857; tel. 435/893–4100 **A**1 10 20 **F**3 13 15 29 31 34 40 41 43 59 62 63 65 68 75 76 78 79 81 89 107 108 110 111 115 119 129 146 147 148 149 **P**6 **S** Intermountain Healthcare, Inc., Salt Lake City, UT
Primary Contact: Gary E. Beck, Administrator
CFO: Chris Thompson, Chief Financial Officer
CMO: Justin Abbott M.D., Medical Director
CHR: Katey Nelson, Director Human Resources
CNO: Cami Blackham R.N., Nurse Administrator
Web address: www.sevierhospital.org
Control: Other not–for–profit (including NFP Corporation) **Service:** General medical and surgical

Staffed Beds: 29 **Admissions:** 816 **Census:** 6 **Outpatient Visits:** 66917 **Births:** 204 **Total Expense ($000):** 31872 **Payroll Expense ($000):** 8358 **Personnel:** 159

RIVERTON—Salt Lake County

✠ **RIVERTON HOSPITAL (460058)**, 3741 West 12600 South, Zip 84065–7215; tel. 801/285–4000 **A**1 3 10 **F**3 13 15 29 30 31 34 35 39 40 41 44 45 46 47 48 49 50 51 57 59 64 68 70 73 75 76 77 78 79 81 85 86 87 89 91 93 94 97 107 108 110 111 114 115 118 119 129 130 131 146 147 148 149 **S** Intermountain Healthcare, Inc., Salt Lake City, UT
Primary Contact: Blair Kent, Administrator
CFO: Royce Stephens, Chief Financial Officer
CMO: David Haselton, Chief Medical Officer
CIO: Susan Hanks, Chief Information Officer
Web address: www.intermountainhealthcare.org/
Control: Other not–for–profit (including NFP Corporation) **Service:** General medical and surgical

Staffed Beds: 88 **Admissions:** 5713 **Census:** 36 **Outpatient Visits:** 326113 **Births:** 2614 **Total Expense ($000):** 111998 **Payroll Expense ($000):** 30437 **Personnel:** 551

UT

Hospital, Medicare Provider Number, Address, Telephone, Approval, Facility, and Physician Codes, Health Care System

★ American Hospital Association (AHA) membership
☐ The Joint Commission accreditation
○ Healthcare Facilities Accreditation Program
◇ DNV Healthcare Inc. accreditation
⇑ Center for Improvement in Healthcare Quality Accreditation
△ Commission on Accreditation of Rehabilitation Facilities (CARF) accreditation

ROOSEVELT—Duchesne County

★ **UINTAH BASIN MEDICAL CENTER (460019)**, 250 West 300 North, 75–2, Zip 84066–2336; tel. 435/722–6163, (Total facility includes 75 beds in nursing home–type unit) **A**10 20 **F**6 7 11 13 15 17 35 40 43 45 50 52 53 54 57 59 60 62 63 70 73 76 77 79 81 82 84 85 87 89 93 107 108 110 111 115 119 127 128 129 130 131 132 135 146 147 148 **P**3
Primary Contact: James I. Marshall, President and Chief Executive Officer
CFO: Brent Hales, Chief Financial Officer
CMO: Gary B White M.D., Chief Medical Staff
CHR: Randall Bennett, Assistant Administrator
Web address: www.ubmc.org
Control: Other not–for–profit (including NFP Corporation) **Service:** General medical and surgical

Staffed Beds: 124 **Admissions:** 1904 **Census:** 79 **Outpatient Visits:** 66934 **Births:** 596 **Total Expense ($000):** 77524 **Payroll Expense ($000):** 24459 **Personnel:** 593

SAINT GEORGE—Washington County

⊞ △ **DIXIE REGIONAL MEDICAL CENTER (460021)**, 1380 East Medical Center Drive, Zip 84790–2123; tel. 435/251–1000, (Includes DIXIE REGIONAL MEDICAL CENTER, 544 South 400 East, St George, Utah, Zip 84770, tel. 940/764–7000) **A**1 7 10 **F**3 11 12 13 15 18 19 20 22 23 24 26 28 29 30 31 34 35 38 40 43 44 45 46 49 50 51 53 54 55 56 57 58 59 64 65 68 70 72 74 75 76 77 78 79 80 81 82 84 85 86 87 89 90 92 93 96 98 100 102 105 107 108 110 111 114 115 116 117 119 120 121 123 129 130 131 132 146 147 148 149 **P**6 **S** Intermountain Healthcare, Inc., Salt Lake City, UT
Primary Contact: Terri Kane, Chief Executive Officer
CFO: Steven Vance, Chief Financial Officer
CMO: Steven Van Norman M.D., Medical Director
CIO: Lance Bedingfield, Director Information Services
CHR: Vicki Wilson, Human Resources Director
CNO: Gary Cunningham, Chief Nursing Officer
Web address: www.intermountainhealthcare.org
Control: Other not–for–profit (including NFP Corporation) **Service:** General medical and surgical

Staffed Beds: 261 **Admissions:** 16549 **Census:** 167 **Outpatient Visits:** 527869 **Births:** 2422 **Total Expense ($000):** 444789 **Payroll Expense ($000):** 134141 **Personnel:** 2267

SALT LAKE CITY—Salt Lake County

⊞ **LDS HOSPITAL (460006)**, Eighth Avenue and 'C' Street, Zip 84143–0001; tel. 801/408–1100 **A**1 2 3 5 10 **F**3 4 5 7 8 12 13 15 18 28 29 30 31 34 35 36 37 38 39 40 44 45 46 48 49 50 51 52 53 54 55 56 57 58 59 60 61 63 64 65 66 68 70 73 74 75 76 77 78 79 81 82 85 86 87 91 92 93 94 96 98 100 101 102 103 104 105 107 108 109 110 111 114 115 119 120 121 123 124 126 129 130 131 132 135 136 146 147 148 **S** Intermountain Healthcare, Inc., Salt Lake City, UT
Primary Contact: Jim Sheets, Chief Executive Officer and Administrator
CFO: Dan Brady, Chief Financial Officer
CMO: Kerry Fisher M.D., Medical Director
CIO: David Baird, Chief Information Officer
CHR: Mollee Lamb, Manager Human Resources
CNO: Brandon Vonk, Nurse Administrator
Web address: www.intermountainhealthcare.org
Control: Other not–for–profit (including NFP Corporation) **Service:** General medical and surgical

Staffed Beds: 260 **Admissions:** 10822 **Census:** 121 **Outpatient Visits:** 207392 **Births:** 2232 **Total Expense ($000):** 236750 **Payroll Expense ($000):** 68105 **Personnel:** 1188

⊞ **MARIAN CENTER (464012)**, 451 East Bishop Federal Lane, Zip 84115–2357; tel. 801/487–7557 **A**1 10 **F**29 34 98 100 101 103 104 130
Primary Contact: Brent Wilson, Chief Executive Officer
Web address: www.stjosephvilla.com
Control: Corporation, Investor–owned (for–profit) **Service:** Psychiatric

Staffed Beds: 14 **Admissions:** 181 **Census:** 8 **Outpatient Visits:** 2432 **Births:** 0 **Total Expense ($000):** 2522 **Payroll Expense ($000):** 1343 **Personnel:** 31

☐ **PRIMARY CHILDREN'S HOSPITAL (463301)**, 100 North Mario Capecchi Drive, Zip 84113–1100; tel. 801/662–1000 **A**1 3 5 10 **F**3 4 5 11 16 17 19 21 23 25 27 29 30 31 32 34 35 36 37 38 39 40 41 43 44 45 46 49 50 53 54 55 57 58 59 60 61 63 64 65 68 72 73 74 75 77 78 79 80 81 82 84 85 86 87 88 89 90 92 93 96 98 99 100 101 102 104 105 106 107 108 111 113 114 115 116 117 118 119 124 129 130 131 133 134 136 137 138 139 141 142 146 148 149 **S** Intermountain Healthcare, Inc., Salt Lake City, UT
Primary Contact: Katy Welkie MBA, R.N., Chief Executive Officer
CFO: Jeremiah Radandt, Chief Financial Officer
CMO: Ed Clark M.D., Chief Medical Officer
CIO: Joe Hales, Chief Information Officer
CHR: Albert Bennett Buckworth, Human Resources Administrative Director
CNO: Judy Geiger R.N., Chief Nursing Officer
Web address: www.intermountainhealthcare.org
Control: Other not–for–profit (including NFP Corporation) **Service:** Children's general medical and surgical

Staffed Beds: 289 **Admissions:** 13499 **Census:** 195 **Outpatient Visits:** 282813 **Births:** 0 **Total Expense ($000):** 474110 **Payroll Expense ($000):** 165245 **Personnel:** 2762

PROMISE HOSPITAL OF SALT LAKE (462004), 8 Avenue, C Street, Zip 84143; tel. 801/408–7110 **A**10 **F**1 3 29 65 75 77 85 130 148 **P**8 **S** Promise Healthcare, Boca Raton, FL
Primary Contact: Wayne Kinsey, Chief Executive Officer
CMO: Geoff Harding, Chief Clinical Officer
Web address: www.promise–saltlake.com
Control: Corporation, Investor–owned (for–profit) **Service:** Acute long–term care hospital

Staffed Beds: 41 **Admissions:** 438 **Census:** 34 **Outpatient Visits:** 0 **Births:** 0 **Personnel:** 143

☐ **SALT LAKE BEHAVIORAL HEALTH (464013)**, 3802 South 700 East, Zip 84106–1182; tel. 801/264–6000 (Nonreporting) **A**1 10 **S** Universal Health Services, Inc., King of Prussia, PA
Primary Contact: Kreg Gillman, Chief Executive Officer
COO: Jim Hess, Chief Operations Officer
CFO: Daren Woolstenhulme, Chief Financial Officer
CMO: Monica Polk M.D., Chief Medical Officer
CHR: Robyn Holsten, Human Resources Director
CNO: Suzanne Nelson R.N., Director of Nursing
Web address: www.saltlakebehavioralhealth.com
Control: Corporation, Investor–owned (for–profit) **Service:** Psychiatric

Staffed Beds: 118

★ ⇑ **SALT LAKE REGIONAL MEDICAL CENTER (460003)**, 1050 East South Temple, Zip 84102–1507; tel. 801/350–4111, (Nonreporting) **A**3 5 10 21 **S** IASIS Healthcare, Franklin, TN
Primary Contact: Dale Johns, FACHE, Chief Executive Officer
COO: Scot Stevens, Assistant Administrator
CFO: Brian Ebright, Chief Financial Officer
CMO: Blake Johnson M.D., Chief of Staff
CIO: Mark Runyan, Director Information Services
CHR: Carolyn Livingston, Director Human Resources
CNO: Terron Arbon R.N., Chief Nursing Officer
Web address: www.saltlakeregional.com
Control: Corporation, Investor–owned (for–profit) **Service:** General medical and surgical

Staffed Beds: 132

☐ **SHRINERS HOSPITALS FOR CHILDREN–SALT LAKE CITY (463302)**, 1275 East Fairfax Road, Zip 84103–4399; tel. 801/536–3500, (Nonreporting) **A**1 3 5 10 **S** Shriners Hospitals for Children, Tampa, FL
Primary Contact: Kevin Martin, M.P.H., R.N., FACHE, Administrator
CFO: Heath Braby, Director Fiscal Services
CMO: Kristen Carroll M.D., Chief of Staff
CIO: Mike Allen, Director Information Technology
CHR: Kris Goldman, Director Human Resources
CNO: Gail McGuill R.N., MSN, Chief Nursing Officer and Administrative Director of Patient Care Services
Web address: www.shrinershospitalsforchildren.org/Hospitals/Locations/SaltLakeCity.aspx
Control: Other not–for–profit (including NFP Corporation) **Service:** Children's orthopedic

Staffed Beds: 18

⊞ **ST. MARK'S HOSPITAL (460047)**, 1200 East 3900 South, Zip 84124–1390; tel. 801/268–7111, (Nonreporting) **A**1 3 10 **S** HCA Healthcare, Nashville, TN
Primary Contact: Steven B. Bateman, Chief Executive Officer
CFO: Bryan McKinley, Chief Financial Officer
CMO: J Eric Vanderhooft M.D., President Medical Staff
CIO: Jesse Trujillo, Chief Information Officer
CHR: Robyn Opheikens, Assistant Administrator Human Resources
Web address: www.stmarkshospital.com
Control: Corporation, Investor–owned (for–profit) **Service:** General medical and surgical

Staffed Beds: 277

★ △ ⇑ **UNIVERSITY OF UTAH HEALTH (460009)**, 50 North Medical Drive, Zip 84132–0002; tel. 801/587–3572 **A**3 5 7 8 10 21 **F**3 5 6 7 8 9 11 12 13 15 16 17 18 20 22 24 26 28 29 30 31 34 35 36 37 38 39 40 42 43 44 45 46 47 48 49 50 51 52 53 54 55 57 58 59 60 61 64 65 68 70 71 72 73 74 75 76 77 78 79 80 81 82 83 84 85 86 87 90 91 92 93 94 95 96 97 98 100 101 102 103 104 105 106 107 108 109 110 111 112 113 114 115 116 117 118 119 120 121 123 124 126 129 130 131 132 134 135 136 137 138 139 140 141 142 143 144 146 147 148 149 **P**1
Primary Contact: Gordon Crabtree, Interim Chief Executive Officer
CFO: Gordon Crabtree, Chief Financial Officer
CMO: Thomas Miller M.D., Medical Director
CIO: James Turnbull, Chief Information Officer
CHR: Dale A Spartz, Chief Human Resources Officer
CNO: Margaret Pearce R.N., Ph.D., Chief Nursing Officer
Web address: www.uuhsc.utah.edu
Control: State, Government, Nonfederal **Service:** General medical and surgical

Staffed Beds: 585 **Admissions:** 26700 **Census:** 426 **Outpatient Visits:** 1992312 **Births:** 4075 **Total Expense ($000):** 1356855 **Payroll Expense ($000):** 456581 **Personnel:** 10095

⇑ **UNIVERSITY OF UTAH NEUROPSYCHIATRIC INSTITUTE (464009)**, 501 South Chipeta Way, Zip 84108–1222; tel. 801/583–2500 **A**3 5 10 21 **F**4 5 34 35 38 57 58 98 99 100 101 102 103 104 105 106 130
Primary Contact: Ross Van Vranken, Executive Director
CFO: Becky Schaefer, Chief Financial Officer
CMO: James Ashworth M.D., Medical Director
Web address: www.med.utah.edu/uni
Control: State, Government, Nonfederal **Service:** Psychiatric

> **Staffed Beds:** 157 **Admissions:** 4803 **Census:** 115 **Outpatient Visits:** 34495 **Births:** 0 **Total Expense ($000):** 86325 **Payroll Expense ($000):** 31580 **Personnel:** 736

⊞ △ **VETERANS AFFAIRS SALT LAKE CITY HEALTH CARE SYSTEM**, 500 Foothill Drive, Zip 84148–0002; tel. 801/582–1565 **A**1 3 5 7 **F**3 4 5 8 12 18 20 22 24 28 29 30 34 35 36 38 39 40 44 45 46 47 48 49 50 53 54 55 56 57 58 59 60 61 62 63 64 65 70 71 74 75 77 78 79 81 82 83 84 85 86 87 90 92 93 94 96 97 98 100 101 102 103 104 105 106 107 108 109 111 114 115 116 117 118 119 126 127 129 130 132 133 135 137 143 144 146 147 148 149 **P**6 **S** Department of Veterans Affairs, Washington, DC
Primary Contact: Shella D. Stovall, R.N., Acting Director
CFO: Val Martin, Director Financial Management Services Center
CMO: Ronald J Gebhart M.D., Chief of Staff
CIO: Lisa Leonelis, Chief Information Officer
CHR: Lisa Porter, Director Human Resources, Leadership and Education
Web address: www.saltlakecity.va.gov/
Control: Veterans Affairs, Government, federal **Service:** General medical and surgical

> **Staffed Beds:** 130 **Admissions:** 4554 **Census:** 94 **Outpatient Visits:** 685269 **Births:** 0 **Personnel:** 2304

SANDY—Salt Lake County

⊞ **ALTA VIEW HOSPITAL (460044)**, 9660 South 1300 East, Zip 84094–3793; tel. 801/501–2600 **A**1 2 10 **F**3 8 12 13 15 29 30 31 34 35 38 39 40 44 45 46 47 48 49 50 51 53 54 56 57 59 64 68 70 75 76 77 78 79 81 85 86 87 92 93 102 107 108 110 111 115 119 129 130 131 132 135 146 147 **S** Intermountain Healthcare, Inc., Salt Lake City, UT
Primary Contact: Blair Kent, Administrator
CFO: Chris Hargis, Manager Finance
CHR: Leslie Bates, Manager Human Resources
Web address: www.intermountainhealthcare.org
Control: Other not–for–profit (including NFP Corporation) **Service:** General medical and surgical

> **Staffed Beds:** 69 **Admissions:** 3150 **Census:** 21 **Outpatient Visits:** 264143 **Births:** 1055 **Total Expense ($000):** 94076 **Payroll Expense ($000):** 26517 **Personnel:** 464

⊞ **HEALTHSOUTH REHABILITATION HOSPITAL OF UTAH (463025)**, 8074 South 1300 East, Zip 84094–0743; tel. 801/561–3400, (Nonreporting) **A**1 10 **S** HEALTHSOUTH Corporation, Birmingham, AL
Primary Contact: Jeff Frandsen, Chief Executive Officer
CMO: Joseph VickRoy M.D., Medical Director
CHR: Troy Jensen, Director Human Resources
Web address: www.healthsouthutah.com
Control: Corporation, Investor–owned (for–profit) **Service:** Rehabilitation

> **Staffed Beds:** 105

SOUTH OGDEN—Weber County

NORTHERN UTAH REHABILITATION HOSPITAL (463027), 5825 Harrison Boulevard, Zip 84403–4316; tel. 801/475–5254 **F**34 90 93 96 **P**4 5 **S** Ernest Health, Inc., Albuquerque, NM
Primary Contact: Ryan Keele, Chief Executive Officer
COO: Reuben Jessop, Chief Operating Officer
CFO: Daniel J Foster, Chief Financial Officer
CNO: Terina Chapman, Director of Nursing
Web address: www.ernesthealth.com/gallery-item/northern–utah–rehabilitation-hospital/
Control: Corporation, Investor–owned (for–profit) **Service:** Rehabilitation

> **Staffed Beds:** 20 **Admissions:** 446 **Census:** 18 **Outpatient Visits:** 1169 **Total Expense ($000):** 11350 **Payroll Expense ($000):** 4449 **Personnel:** 96

TOOELE—Tooele County

⊞ **MOUNTAIN WEST MEDICAL CENTER (460014)**, 2055 North Main Street, Zip 84074–9819; tel. 435/843–3600 **A**1 10 **F**3 7 13 15 18 29 30 34 40 49 50 51 57 64 67 68 70 74 75 76 77 79 81 85 87 89 93 97 102 107 110 111 114 115 118 119 126 130 132 135 146 147 148 **S** Quorum Health, Brentwood, TN
Primary Contact: Philip Eaton, Interim Chief Executive Officer
CMO: James Antinori M.D., Chief of Staff
CIO: Marc Taylor, IS Director
CHR: Matthew Flygare, Director Human Resources
CNO: Yvonne Nielson, Chief Nursing Officer, Director Quality Management and Regulatory Compliance
Web address: www.mountainwestmc.com
Control: Corporation, Investor–owned (for–profit) **Service:** General medical and surgical

> **Staffed Beds:** 44 **Admissions:** 1674 **Census:** 11 **Outpatient Visits:** 83177 **Births:** 435 **Total Expense ($000):** 35124 **Payroll Expense ($000):** 13404 **Personnel:** 245

TREMONTON—Box Elder County

★ **BEAR RIVER VALLEY HOSPITAL (460039)**, 905 North 1000 West, Zip 84337–2497; tel. 435/207–4500 **A**10 **F**3 13 15 28 29 34 35 37 38 40 45 46 48 50 51 57 59 62 64 68 69 71 76 77 79 81 82 84 85 87 89 90 93 97 99 100 101 102 103 104 107 108 109 110 111 115 119 129 130 132 134 146 147 148 **P**6 **S** Intermountain Healthcare, Inc., Salt Lake City, UT
Primary Contact: James Montgomery, Interim Chief Executive Officer
CHR: Joy Sadler, Director Human Resources
CNO: Penny Marshall, Chief Nursing Officer
Web address: www.intermountainhealthcare.org/locations/bear-river-valley-hospital/
Control: Other not–for–profit (including NFP Corporation) **Service:** General medical and surgical

> **Staffed Beds:** 14 **Admissions:** 402 **Census:** 2 **Outpatient Visits:** 41268 **Births:** 114 **Total Expense ($000):** 21423 **Payroll Expense ($000):** 7621 **Personnel:** 112

VERNAL—Uintah County

⊞ **ASHLEY REGIONAL MEDICAL CENTER (460030)**, 150 West 100 North, Zip 84078–2036; tel. 435/789–3342, (Nonreporting) **A**1 10 20 **S** LifePoint Health, Brentwood, TN
Primary Contact: Ben Cluff, Chief Executive Officer
CFO: Chad Labrum, Chief Financial Officer
CMO: Dennis Lewis M.D., Chief of Staff
CIO: Cameron Winn, Director Information Services
CHR: Deena Mansfield, Director Human Resources
CNO: Greg Gardiner, Chief Clinical Officer
Web address: www.ashleyregional.com
Control: Corporation, Investor–owned (for–profit) **Service:** General medical and surgical

> **Staffed Beds:** 39

WEST JORDAN—Salt Lake County

★ ⇑ **JORDAN VALLEY MEDICAL CENTER (460051)**, 3580 West 9000 South, Zip 84088–8812; tel. 801/561–8888, (Nonreporting) (Includes MOUNTAIN POINT MEDICAL CENTER, 3000 North Triumph Boulevard, Lehii, Utah, Zip 84043, Lehi, tel. 385/345–3000) **A**10 21 **S** IASIS Healthcare, Franklin, TN
Primary Contact: Steven Anderson, Chief Executive Officer
COO: Jon Butterfield, Chief Operating Officer
CFO: Kurt Shipley, Chief Financial Officer
CMO: B Dee Allred M.D., President Medical Staff
Web address: www.jordanvalleymc.com
Control: Partnership, Investor–owned (for–profit) **Service:** General medical and surgical

> **Staffed Beds:** 183

WEST VALLEY CITY—Salt Lake County

★ **JORDAN VALLEY MEDICAL CENTER WEST VALLEY CAMPUS**, 3460 South Pioneer Parkway, Zip 84120–2049; tel. 801/561–8888, (Nonreporting) **S** IASIS Healthcare, Franklin, TN
Primary Contact: Steven Anderson, Chief Executive Officer
COO: Jon Butterfield, Administrator and Chief Operating Officer
CFO: Steven Payne, Chief Financial Officer
CMO: Justin Parkinson M.D., President Medical Staff
CIO: Mark Runyan, Director Information Systems
CHR: Rob Burnett, Director Human Resources
Web address: www.pioneervalleyhospital.com
Control: Corporation, Investor–owned (for–profit) **Service:** General medical and surgical

> **Staffed Beds:** 101

UT

Hospital, Medicare Provider Number, Address, Telephone, Approval, Facility, and Physician Codes, Health Care System

★ American Hospital Association (AHA) membership
□ The Joint Commission accreditation
○ Healthcare Facilities Accreditation Program
◇ DNV Healthcare Inc. accreditation
⇑ Center for Improvement in Healthcare Quality Accreditation
△ Commission on Accreditation of Rehabilitation Facilities (CARF) accreditation

VERMONT

BENNINGTON—Bennington County

☒ **SOUTHWESTERN VERMONT MEDICAL CENTER (470012)**, 100 Hospital Drive, Zip 05201–5004; tel. 802/442–6361, (Nonreporting) **A**1 2 10
Primary Contact: Thomas A. Dee, President and Chief Executive Officer
CFO: Stephen D Majetich CPA, Chief Financial Officer
CMO: Trey Dobson M.D., Chief Medical Officer
CIO: Richard Ogilvie, Chief Information Officer
CHR: Rudolph D Weaver, Vice President Human Resources
CNO: Carol Conroy R.N., Chief Nursing Officer
Web address: www.svhealthcare.org
Control: Other not–for–profit (including NFP Corporation) **Service**: General medical and surgical

Staffed Beds: 77

BERLIN—Washington County

☒ **THE UNIVERSITY OF VERMONT HEALTH NETWORK CENTRAL VERMONT MEDICAL CENTER (470001)**, 130 Fisher Road, Zip 05602–9516, Mailing Address: P.O.Box 547, Barre, 05641–0547; tel. 802/371–4100, (Total facility includes 153 beds in nursing home–type unit) **A**1 2 3 10 **F**3 5 11 13 15 18 28 29 30 31 34 35 36 40 44 45 48 49 50 51 53 54 59 63 64 65 68 70 74 75 76 77 78 79 81 82 84 85 86 87 92 93 94 96 97 98 99 100 102 103 104 107 108 110 111 114 118 119 120 121 123 128 130 131 132 135 141 143 146 147 148 149 **P**6
Primary Contact: Anna Noonan, President and Chief Operating Officer
COO: Nancy Lothian, Chief Operating Officer and Chief Information Officer
CFO: Cheyenne Holland, Chief Financial Officer
CMO: Philip Brown D.O., Vice President Medical Affairs
CHR: Robert Patterson, Vice President Human Resources and Rehabilitation Services
CNO: Matthew Choate, Chief Nursing Officer
Web address: www.cvmc.org/
Control: Other not–for–profit (including NFP Corporation) **Service**: General medical and surgical

Staffed Beds: 245 **Admissions**: 4539 **Census**: 169 **Outpatient Visits**: 424134 **Births**: 310 **Total Expense ($000)**: 141218 **Payroll Expense ($000)**: 70682 **Personnel**: 1381

VERMONT PSYCHIATRIC CARE HOSPITAL (474004), 350 Fisher Road, Zip 5602; tel. 802/828–3300
Primary Contact: Melissa Bailey, Commissioner, Department of Mental Health
Web address: www.mentalhealth.vermont.gov/Vermont–psychiatric–care–hospital
Control: State, Government, Nonfederal **Service**: Psychiatric

Staffed Beds: 25

BRATTLEBORO—Windham County

★ **BRATTLEBORO MEMORIAL HOSPITAL (470011)**, 17 Belmont Avenue, Zip 05301–3498; tel. 802/257–0341 **A**10 **F**3 11 13 15 18 28 29 30 31 34 35 39 40 45 49 50 51 53 55 57 59 64 68 70 74 75 76 77 79 81 85 87 93 107 108 110 111 115 118 119 130 131 132 135 146 147 148
Primary Contact: Steven R. Gordon, President and Chief Executive Officer
CFO: Michael Rogers, Vice President Fiscal Services
CMO: Kathleen McGraw M.D., Chief Medical Officer
CIO: Jonathan Farina, Chief Information Officer
CHR: William Norwood, Vice President, Human Resources
CNO: Mary Urquhart R.N., Vice President Patient Care
Web address: www.bmhvt.org
Control: Other not–for–profit (including NFP Corporation) **Service**: General medical and surgical

Staffed Beds: 42 **Admissions**: 1611 **Census**: 14 **Outpatient Visits**: 160898 **Births**: 302 **Total Expense ($000)**: 76429 **Payroll Expense ($000)**: 33060 **Personnel**: 409

☒ **BRATTLEBORO RETREAT (474001)**, Anna Marsh Lane, Zip 5301, Mailing Address: P.O.Box 803, 05302–0803; tel. 802/257–7785 **A**1 5 10 **F**29 34 35 50 68 98 99 100 101 102 103 104 105 106 135 149 **P**6
Primary Contact: Louis Josephson, Ph.D., President and Chief Executive Officer
COO: Gerri Cote, Chief Operating Officer
CFO: Steven Monette, Chief Financial Officer
CMO: Frederick Engstrom M.D., Chief Medical Officer
CHR: Jeffrey T. Corrigan, Vice President Human Resources
CNO: Linda J. Nagy MSN, R.N., Chief Nursing Officer
Web address: www.brattlebororetreat.org
Control: Other not–for–profit (including NFP Corporation) **Service**: Psychiatric

Staffed Beds: 118 **Admissions**: 3805 **Census**: 105 **Outpatient Visits**: 34371 **Births**: 0 **Total Expense ($000)**: 68554 **Payroll Expense ($000)**: 42777 **Personnel**: 546

BURLINGTON—Chittenden County

☒ **UNIVERSITY OF VERMONT MEDICAL CENTER (470003)**, 111 Colchester Avenue, Zip 05401–1473; tel. 802/847–0000, (Includes FANNY ALLEN CAMPUS, 101 College Parkway, Colchester, Vermont, Zip 05446–3035, tel. 802/655–1234; MEDICAL CENTER HOSPITAL CAMPUS, Colchester Avenue, Burlington, Vermont, Zip 5401, tel. 802/847–2345; VERMONT CHILDREN'S HOSPITAL, 111 Colchester Avenue, Burlington, Vermont, Zip 05401–1473, tel. 802/847–0000) **A**1 2 3 5 6 7 9 11 12 13 15 17 18 19 20 21 22 23 24 25 26 28 29 30 31 32 34 35 36 37 39 40 43 44 45 46 47 48 49 50 51 52 54 55 56 57 58 59 60 61 63 64 65 66 68 70 72 73 74 75 76 77 78 79 81 82 84 85 86 87 88 89 90 91 92 93 94 96 97 98 99 100 101 102 103 104 105 107 108 110 111 114 115 116 117 118 119 120 121 123 124 126 128 129 130 131 132 135 136 138 141 142 143 144 145 146 147 148 **P**6
Primary Contact: Eileen Whalen, R.N., President and Chief Operating Officer
CFO: Todd Keating, Chief Financial Officer
CMO: Stephen Leffler, Chief Medical Officer
CHR: Jerald Novak, Chief People Officer
Web address: www.uvmhealth.org/medcenter/Pages/default.aspx
Control: Other not–for–profit (including NFP Corporation) **Service**: General medical and surgical

Staffed Beds: 460 **Admissions**: 19880 **Census**: 315 **Outpatient Visits**: 1088180 **Births**: 2346 **Total Expense ($000)**: 1107671 **Payroll Expense ($000)**: 537996 **Personnel**: 6798

MIDDLEBURY—Addison County

★ **PORTER MEDICAL CENTER (471307)**, 115 Porter Drive, Zip 05753–8423; tel. 802/388–4701, (Nonreporting) **A**10 18
Primary Contact: Fred Kniffin, M.D., Chief Executive Officer
CFO: Steve Ciampa, Vice President Finance
CMO: Fred Kniffin M.D., Chief Medical Officer
CIO: Rebecca Woods, Chief Information Officer
CHR: David Fuller, Director Human Resources
CNO: Lorraina Smith–Zuba R.N., MSN, Chief Nursing Officer
Web address: www.portermedical.org
Control: Other not–for–profit (including NFP Corporation) **Service**: General medical and surgical

Staffed Beds: 25

MORRISVILLE—Lamoille County

★ **COPLEY HOSPITAL (471305)**, 528 Washington Highway, Zip 05661–8973; tel. 802/888–8888 **A**10 18 **F**1 3 4 8 11 13 15 18 28 29 30 31 34 35 38 39 40 44 45 57 58 59 64 65 67 70 74 75 76 77 78 79 81 82 86 87 89 93 98 107 108 110 111 114 118 119 128 129 130 131 133 135 146 147 148
Primary Contact: Arthur Mathisen, FACHE, President and Chief Executive Officer
COO: Greg Ward, Vice President Support and Ancillary Services
CFO: Rassoul Rangaviz, Chief Financial Officer
CMO: Joel Silverstein M.D., Chief Medical Officer
CIO: Randy Chesley, Director Information Technology
CHR: Amy Fitzgerald, Human Resources Manager
CNO: Lori Profota R.N., Chief Nursing Officer
Web address: www.copleyvt.org
Control: Other not–for–profit (including NFP Corporation) **Service**: General medical and surgical

Staffed Beds: 25 **Admissions**: 1782 **Census**: 14 **Outpatient Visits**: 84293 **Births**: 212 **Total Expense ($000)**: 64312 **Payroll Expense ($000)**: 28975 **Personnel**: 346

NEWPORT—Orleans County

★ **NORTH COUNTRY HOSPITAL AND HEALTH CENTER (471304)**, 189 Prouty Drive, Zip 05855–9326; tel. 802/334–7331 **A**10 18 **F**11 13 15 28 29 30 31 34 35 40 43 45 53 70 74 75 76 77 78 79 81 82 84 85 89 93 107 108 110 111 114 118 119 127 129 130 131 133 135 146 148 149
Primary Contact: Claudio D. Fort, President and Chief Executive Officer
COO: Thomas Frank, Chief Operating Officer
CFO: Andre Bissonnette, Chief Financial Officer
CHR: William Perket, Vice President Human Resources
CNO: Avril Cochran R.N., Vice President Patient Care Services
Web address: www.nchsi.org
Control: Other not–for–profit (including NFP Corporation) **Service**: General medical and surgical

Staffed Beds: 25 **Admissions**: 1396 **Census**: 15 **Outpatient Visits**: 67973 **Births**: 178 **Total Expense ($000)**: 84100 **Payroll Expense ($000)**: 37831 **Personnel**: 515

VT

Many Facility Codes have changed. Please refer to the AHA Guide Code Chart. © 2017 AHA Guide

RANDOLPH—Orange County

★ **GIFFORD MEDICAL CENTER (471301)**, 44 South Main Street, Zip 05060–1381, Mailing Address: P.O.Box 2000, 05060–2000; tel. 802/728–7000, (Nonreporting) **A**2 10 18
Primary Contact: Dan Bennett, President and Chief Executive Officer
CFO: Jeff Hebert, Interim Vice President Finance
CMO: Joshua Plavin M.D., Medical Director Medicine Division
CIO: Sean Patrick, Director Information Systems
CHR: Janice Davis, Interim Director Human Resources
CNO: Linda Minsinger, Vice President Hospital Division
Web address: www.giffordmed.org
Control: Other not–for–profit (including NFP Corporation) **Service:** General medical and surgical

Staffed Beds: 52

RUTLAND—Rutland County

⊞ **RUTLAND REGIONAL MEDICAL CENTER (470005)**, 160 Allen Street, Zip 05701–4595; tel. 802/775–7111 **A**1 2 10 **F**3 13 15 18 28 29 31 34 36 37 38 40 45 47 48 50 55 57 59 61 64 65 70 74 76 78 79 81 82 83 84 85 87 89 92 93 98 100 101 102 103 104 107 108 109 110 111 115 117 118 119 120 121 123 124 129 130 133 135 146 147 148 149 150
Primary Contact: Thomas W. Huebner, President
CFO: Ed Ogorzalek, Chief Financial Officer
CMO: Baxter C Holland M.D., Chief Medical Officer
CNO: Carol Egan R.N., MSN, Chief Nursing Officer
Web address: www.rrmc.org
Control: Other not–for–profit (including NFP Corporation) **Service:** General medical and surgical

Staffed Beds: 121 **Admissions:** 5691 **Census:** 84 **Outpatient Visits:** 244330 **Births:** 361 **Total Expense ($000):** 243643 **Payroll Expense ($000):** 117772 **Personnel:** 1346

SAINT ALBANS—Franklin County

⊞ **NORTHWESTERN MEDICAL CENTER (470024)**, 133 Fairfield Street, Zip 05478–1726; tel. 802/524–5911 **A**1 2 10 20 **F**3 5 11 13 15 28 29 30 32 34 35 36 37 38 40 43 44 45 50 51 57 58 59 63 64 65 69 70 75 76 77 78 79 81 82 84 85 86 87 89 93 96 97 107 108 110 111 114 119 130 131 132 133 134 135 143 144 146 147 148 **P**6 **S** QHR, Brentwood, TN
Primary Contact: Jill Berry. Bowen, Chief Executive Officer
COO: Jane Catton R.N., Chief Operating Officer and Chief Nursing Officer
CFO: Christopher Hickey, Chief Financial Officer
CMO: Lowery Sullivan M.D., Chief Medical Officer
CIO: Joel Benware, Vice President Information Technology and Compliance
CHR: Thomas C Conley, Vice President, Human Resources and Organizational Development
CNO: Jane Catton R.N., Chief Operating Officer and Chief Nursing Officer
Web address: www.northwesternmedicalcenter.org
Control: Other not–for–profit (including NFP Corporation) **Service:** General medical and surgical

Staffed Beds: 55 **Admissions:** 2610 **Census:** 22 **Outpatient Visits:** 94081 **Births:** 369 **Total Expense ($000):** 100754 **Payroll Expense ($000):** 48000 **Personnel:** 633

SAINT JOHNSBURY—Caledonia County

★ **NORTHEASTERN VERMONT REGIONAL HOSPITAL (471303)**, 1315 Hospital Drive, Zip 05819–9210, Mailing Address: PO Box 905, 05819–0905; tel. 802/748–8141, (Nonreporting) **A**10 18
Primary Contact: Paul R. Bengtson, Chief Executive Officer
CFO: Robert Hersey, Chief Financial Officer
CMO: Michael Rousse M.D., Vice President of Medical Affairs
CIO: Shawn Burroughs, Director of Information Services
CHR: Elizabeth Gwatkin, Vice President Human Resources
CNO: Seleem Choudhury R.N., MSN, Chief Nursing Officer
Web address: www.nvrh.org
Control: Other not–for–profit (including NFP Corporation) **Service:** General medical and surgical

Staffed Beds: 25

SPRINGFIELD—Windsor County

★ **SPRINGFIELD HOSPITAL (471306)**, 25 Ridgewood Road, Zip 05156–3050, Mailing Address: 25 Ridgewood Rd, 05156–3050; tel. 802/885–2151, (Nonreporting) **A**10 18
Primary Contact: Timothy R. Ford, President and Chief Executive Officer
CFO: Scott Whittemore, Chief Financial Officer and Chief of Ancillary Services
CMO: Richard Marasa M.D., President Medical Staff
CIO: Kyle Peoples, Director Technology Management Services
CHR: Janet Lyle, Chief Human Resources and Allied Health Services
CNO: Janet Sherer, Chief of Patient Care Services
Web address: www.springfieldmed.org
Control: Other not–for–profit (including NFP Corporation) **Service:** General medical and surgical

Staffed Beds: 35

TOWNSHEND—Windham County

★ **GRACE COTTAGE HOSPITAL (471300)**, 185 Grafton Road, Zip 05353–0216, Mailing Address: P.O.Box 216, 05353–0216; tel. 802/365–7357 **A**10 18 **F**3 18 29 30 34 35 40 50 57 59 64 65 66 68 83 85 93 96 97 104 107 119 127 130 132 133 135 146 147
Primary Contact: Roger Allbee, Chief Executive Officer and Administrator
COO: Jeanne M Fortier R.N., Chief Nursing Officer and Interim Chief Operating Officer
CFO: Stephen A Brown, Chief Financial Officer
CMO: Timothy Shafer M.D., Medical Director
CIO: Tony Marques, Director Information Systems
CHR: Christopher J Lackney, Director Human Resources
CNO: Jeanne M Fortier R.N., Chief Nursing Officer and Interim Chief Operating Officer
Web address: www.gracecottage.org
Control: Other not–for–profit (including NFP Corporation) **Service:** General medical and surgical

Staffed Beds: 19 **Admissions:** 363 **Census:** 11 **Outpatient Visits:** 20822 **Births:** 0 **Total Expense ($000):** 23901 **Payroll Expense ($000):** 11110 **Personnel:** 144

WHITE RIVER JUNCTION—Windsor County

⊞ **WHITE RIVER JUNCTION VETERANS AFFAIRS MEDICAL CENTER**, 215 North Main Street, Zip 05009–0001; tel. 802/295–9363 **A**1 3 5 8 **F**3 4 5 12 18 29 30 31 33 35 36 38 39 40 45 46 47 48 49 50 53 56 58 59 60 61 63 64 65 70 74 75 77 78 79 81 82 84 85 86 87 89 92 93 97 98 100 101 102 103 104 106 107 108 111 114 115 116 117 118 119 127 130 132 135 141 143 146 147 148 149 **P**6 **S** Department of Veterans Affairs, Washington, DC
Primary Contact: Matthew Mulcahy, Acting Director
CFO: Joan Wilmot, Chief Finance Officer
CMO: M. Ganga Hematillake M.D., Chief of Staff
CIO: Matthew Rafus, Chief Information Officer
CHR: Barbara Nadeau, Chief Human Resources Management Service
Web address: www.whiteriver.va.gov/
Control: Veterans Affairs, Government, federal **Service:** General medical and surgical

Staffed Beds: 74 **Admissions:** 1191 **Census:** 29 **Outpatient Visits:** 260612 **Births:** 0 **Total Expense ($000):** 204343 **Payroll Expense ($000):** 102484 **Personnel:** 1014

WINDSOR—Windsor County

★ △ **MT. ASCUTNEY HOSPITAL AND HEALTH CENTER (471302)**, 289 County Road, Zip 05089–9000; tel. 802/674–6711 **A**7 10 18 **F**3 8 10 11 15 28 29 30 31 32 34 35 36 40 41 44 45 49 50 54 56 57 59 63 64 65 66 68 69 70 71 75 77 78 81 82 85 86 87 90 91 92 93 94 95 96 97 99 100 103 104 107 110 111 114 119 125 129 130 132 133 134 135 143 146 148 149 **P**6
Primary Contact: Joseph L. Perras, Chief Executive Officer
COO: Paul Calandrella, Chief Operating Officer
CFO: David Sanville, Chief Financial Officer
CHR: Jean Martaniuk, Director Human Resources
CNO: Deanna Orfanidis MS, R.N., Interim Chief Nursing Officer
Web address: www.mtascutneyhospital.org
Control: Other not–for–profit (including NFP Corporation) **Service:** General medical and surgical

Staffed Beds: 35 **Admissions:** 977 **Census:** 27 **Outpatient Visits:** 79686 **Births:** 0 **Total Expense ($000):** 49568 **Payroll Expense ($000):** 23456 **Personnel:** 365

VT

VIRGINIA

ABINGDON—Washington County

☒ **JOHNSTON MEMORIAL HOSPITAL (490053)**, 16000 Johnston Memorial Drive, Zip 24211–7659; tel. 276/258–1000 **A**1 2 10 13 **F**3 8 11 13 15 18 20 22 26 28 29 30 31 34 35 39 40 44 45 46 47 48 49 50 51 54 57 59 60 63 64 68 70 74 75 76 77 78 79 81 82 84 85 87 93 97 100 107 110 111 114 115 118 119 120 121 123 129 130 132 135 143 144 145 146 147 148 **S** Mountain States Health Alliance, Johnson City, TN
Primary Contact: Stan Hickson, FACHE, President and Chief Executive Officer
COO: Bryan Mullins, Chief Operating Officer
CFO: John Jeter, Assistant Administrator and Chief Financial Officer
CMO: Brian Condit M.D., Chief Medical Officer
CIO: Jackson Dale, Director Management Information Services
CHR: Jackie G Phipps, Director Human Resources
CNO: Nikki VanBuren, Chief Nursing Officer
Web address: www.jmh.org
Control: Other not–for–profit (including NFP Corporation) **Service**: General medical and surgical

Staffed Beds: 116 **Admissions**: 8409 **Census**: 81 **Outpatient Visits**: 157331 **Births**: 701 **Total Expense ($000)**: 131446 **Payroll Expense ($000)**: 39332 **Personnel**: 640

ALDIE—Loudoun County

☒ **HEALTHSOUTH REHABILITATION HOSPITAL OF NORTHERN VIRGINIA (493033)**, 24430 Millstream Drive, Zip 20105–3098; tel. 703/957–2000 **A**1 10 **F**29 90 **P**5 **S** HEALTHSOUTH Corporation, Birmingham, AL
Primary Contact: Alfred Santos, Chief Executive Officer
Web address: www.healthsouthnorthernvirginia.com
Control: Individual, Investor–owned (for–profit) **Service**: Rehabilitation

Staffed Beds: 60 **Admissions**: 1550 **Census**: 49 **Outpatient Visits**: 0 **Births**: 0 **Personnel**: 128

ALEXANDRIA—Alexandria City County

☒ **INOVA ALEXANDRIA HOSPITAL (490040)**, 4320 Seminary Road, Zip 22304–1535; tel. 703/504–3167 **A**1 2 5 10 **F**3 11 13 14 15 17 18 20 22 24 26 28 29 30 31 34 35 38 39 40 42 44 45 46 48 49 50 51 54 55 56 57 58 59 60 61 63 64 65 66 68 70 72 74 75 76 77 78 79 80 81 82 84 85 86 87 91 92 93 100 101 102 107 108 110 111 114 115 118 119 120 121 123 124 129 130 131 132 135 145 146 147 148 149 **P**6 **S** Inova Health System, Falls Church, VA
Primary Contact: Susan Carroll, Regional Executive Officer–Eastern Region
CFO: Todd Lockcuff, Chief Financial Officer
CMO: William L Jackson, Chief Medical Officer
CHR: Hugo Aguas, Vice President Human Resources
Web address: www.inova.org
Control: Other not–for–profit (including NFP Corporation) **Service**: General medical and surgical

Staffed Beds: 334 **Admissions**: 16498 **Census**: 193 **Outpatient Visits**: 178252 **Births**: 3446 **Total Expense ($000)**: 301406 **Payroll Expense ($000)**: 105719 **Personnel**: 1312

ALEXANDRIA—Fairfax County

☒ **INOVA MOUNT VERNON HOSPITAL (490122)**, 2501 Parker's Lane, Zip 22306–3209; tel. 703/664–7000 **A**1 2 3 5 10 **F**3 5 11 14 15 18 26 28 29 30 31 34 35 37 38 39 40 42 44 45 48 49 50 51 53 54 55 57 58 59 60 61 63 64 65 68 70 74 75 77 78 79 81 82 84 85 86 87 90 91 92 93 94 95 96 98 100 101 102 103 104 105 107 108 110 111 114 115 118 119 130 131 132 135 145 146 147 148 149 **P**6 **S** Inova Health System, Falls Church, VA
Primary Contact: Donald Brideau, M.D., Interim Chief Executive Officer
CFO: Tammy Razmic, Associate Administrator Finance and Chief Financial Officer
CMO: Donald Brideau M.D., Chief Medical Officer
CHR: Bev Sugar, Associate Administrator and Director Human Resources
Web address: www.inova.org
Control: Other not–for–profit (including NFP Corporation) **Service**: General medical and surgical

Staffed Beds: 237 **Admissions**: 9222 **Census**: 148 **Outpatient Visits**: 96808 **Births**: 0 **Total Expense ($000)**: 186614 **Payroll Expense ($000)**: 68298 **Personnel**: 890

ARLINGTON—Arlington County

CAPITAL HOSPICE (490129), 4715 15th Street North, Zip 22205–2640; tel. 703/538–2065, (Nonreporting) **A**3 10
Primary Contact: Malene S. Davis, R.N., President and Chief Executive Officer
CFO: David Schwind, Chief Financial Officer
CIO: Diane Rigsby, Chief Information Officer
Web address: www.capitalhospice.org
Control: Other not–for–profit (including NFP Corporation) **Service**: Other specialty treatment

Staffed Beds: 15

☒ △ **VIRGINIA HOSPITAL CENTER – ARLINGTON (490050)**, 1701 North George Mason Drive, Zip 22205–3698; tel. 703/558–5000 **A**1 2 3 5 7 10 **F**3 4 5 8 11 12 13 15 17 18 20 22 24 26 28 29 30 31 34 35 37 38 40 45 46 47 48 49 50 51 53 54 56 57 58 59 60 61 64 65 66 68 70 72 73 74 75 76 77 78 79 81 82 84 85 86 87 89 90 91 92 93 94 95 96 97 98 100 102 103 104 105 107 108 110 111 114 115 116 117 118 119 120 121 123 124 126 129 130 132 135 144 145 146 147 148 149 **P**6
Primary Contact: James B. Cole, Chief Executive Officer
COO: Carl Bahnlein, Executive Vice President and Chief Operating Officer
CFO: Robin Norman, Senior Vice President and Chief Financial Officer
CMO: Jeffrey P DiLisi, Vice President and Chief Medical Officer
CIO: Russ McWey M.D., Vice President and Chief Information Officer
CHR: Michael Malone, Vice President and Chief Human Resources Officer
CNO: Darlene Vrotsos R.N., Senior Vice President and Chief Nursing Officer
Web address: www.virginiahospitalcenter.com
Control: Other not–for–profit (including NFP Corporation) **Service**: General medical and surgical

Staffed Beds: 357 **Admissions**: 22135 **Census**: 281 **Outpatient Visits**: 353831 **Births**: 4911 **Total Expense ($000)**: 384757 **Payroll Expense ($000)**: 164502 **Personnel**: 2925

BEDFORD—Bedford City County

☒ **BEDFORD MEMORIAL HOSPITAL (490088)**, 1613 Oakwood Street, Zip 24523–1213, Mailing Address: P.O.Box 688, 24523–0688; tel. 540/586–2441, (Total facility includes 111 beds in nursing home–type unit) **A**1 10 **F**2 3 11 15 28 29 30 34 35 40 42 46 53 57 59 63 67 70 81 84 85 86 87 97 107 110 119 128 129 130 143 146 148 **P**6 **S** Centra Health, Inc., Lynchburg, VA
Primary Contact: Patti Jurkus, Chief Executive Officer
CFO: Donald E Lorton, Executive Vice President
CMO: E Allen Joslyn M.D., Chief Medical Officer
Web address: www.bmhva.com
Control: Other not–for–profit (including NFP Corporation) **Service**: General medical and surgical

Staffed Beds: 145 **Admissions**: 1829 **Census**: 111 **Outpatient Visits**: 59335 **Births**: 0 **Total Expense ($000)**: 41434 **Payroll Expense ($000)**: 20070 **Personnel**: 326

BIG STONE GAP—Wise County

☒ **WELLMONT LONESOME PINE HOSPITAL (490114)**, 1990 Holton Avenue East, Zip 24219–3350; tel. 276/523–3111 **A**1 10 13 **F**3 11 15 29 30 31 34 40 45 49 50 57 59 70 76 77 78 79 81 82 85 87 89 93 107 108 110 111 118 119 120 121 129 130 135 146 148 **S** Wellmont Health System, Kingsport, TN
Primary Contact: Dale Clark, President
CFO: Regina Day, Executive Vice President of Finance
CMO: Michael Ketcham, President, Medical Staff
CHR: Bobby Collins, Director Human Resources
CNO: Cindy Stidham, Executive Director of Patient Care Services
Web address: www.wellmont.org
Control: Other not–for–profit (including NFP Corporation) **Service**: General medical and surgical

Staffed Beds: 32 **Admissions**: 1175 **Census**: 8 **Outpatient Visits**: 41773 **Births**: 286 **Total Expense ($000)**: 47585 **Payroll Expense ($000)**: 8457 **Personnel**: 184

VA

Many Facility Codes have changed. Please refer to the AHA Guide Code Chart.
© 2017 AHA Guide

BLACKSBURG—Montgomery County

⊠ **LEWISGALE HOSPITAL MONTGOMERY (490110)**, 3700 South Main Street, Zip 24060–7081, Mailing Address: P.O.Box 90004, 24062–9004; tel. 540/951–1111, (Nonreporting) **A**1 10 12 13 **S** HCA Healthcare, Nashville, TN
Primary Contact: Alan J. Fabian, Chief Executive Officer
COO: Matt Mathias, Chief Operating Officer
CFO: Timothy W Haasken, Chief Financial Officer
CIO: Diron Lane, Director Information Systems
CNO: Ellen Y Linkenhoker, Chief Nursing Officer
Web address: www.lewisgale.com
Control: Corporation, Investor–owned (for–profit) **Service**: General medical and surgical

Staffed Beds: 89

BRISTOL—Bristol City County

⊠ **REHABILITATION HOSPITAL OF SOUTHWEST VIRGINIA (493034)**, 103 North Street, Zip 24201–3201; tel. 276/642–7900, (Nonreporting) **A**1 10 **S** HEALTHSOUTH Corporation, Birmingham, AL
Primary Contact: Georgeanne Cole, Chief Executive Officer
Web address: www.rehabilitationhospitalswvirginia.com
Control: Corporation, Investor–owned (for–profit) **Service**: Rehabilitation

Staffed Beds: 25

BURKEVILLE—Nottoway County

PIEDMONT GERIATRIC HOSPITAL (490134), 5001 East Patrick Henry Hwy, Zip 23922–3460, Mailing Address: P.O.Box 427, 23922–0427; tel. 434/767–4401, (Nonreporting) **S** Virginia Department of Mental Health, Richmond, VA
Primary Contact: Hilton McDaniel, President
CFO: James G Ayers, Chief Financial Officer
CMO: Hugo Falcon M.D., Director Medical Services
CHR: Michael Wimsatt, Director Human Resources
Web address: www.pgh.dmhmrsas.virginia.gov
Control: State, Government, Nonfederal **Service**: Other specialty treatment

Staffed Beds: 150

CATAWBA—Roanoke County

☐ **CATAWBA HOSPITAL (490135)**, 5525 Catawba Hospital Drive, Zip 24070–2115, Mailing Address: P.O.Box 200, 24070–0200; tel. 540/375–4200 **A**1 3 10 **F**29 30 35 38 39 44 50 68 75 77 98 103 130 146 149 **P**6 **S** Virginia Department of Mental Health, Richmond, VA
Primary Contact: Walton F. Mitchell III, Director
COO: Charles Law Ph.D., Chief Operating Officer
CFO: Cecil Hardin CPA, Chief Financial Officer
CMO: Yad Jabbarpour M.D., Chief of Staff
CIO: Charles Law Ph.D., Chief Operating Officer
CHR: Patricia Ebbett, Chief Human Resources Officer
CNO: Vicky Fisher Ph.D., R.N., Chief Nurse Executive
Web address: www.catawba.dbhds.virginia.gov
Control: State, Government, Nonfederal **Service**: Psychiatric

Staffed Beds: 110 Admissions: 456 Census: 102 Outpatient Visits: 0 Births: 0 Total Expense ($000): 23534 Payroll Expense ($000): 12546 Personnel: 257

CHARLOTTESVILLE—Charlottesville City County

★ ⇧ **MARTHA JEFFERSON HOSPITAL (490077)**, 500 Martha Jefferson Drive, Zip 22911–4668; tel. 434/654–7000 **A**2 5 10 21 **F**3 8 11 12 13 15 18 20 22 26 28 29 30 31 34 35 36 40 41 42 44 45 46 47 49 50 51 52 55 56 57 58 59 61 64 65 66 68 70 74 75 76 77 78 79 81 82 84 85 86 87 91 92 93 94 97 107 108 110 111 114 115 116 117 118 119 120 121 123 124 129 130 131 132 134 135 141 145 146 147 149 **P**1 **S** Sentara Healthcare, Norfolk, VA
Primary Contact: Jonathan S. Davis, FACHE, President
COO: Amy Black R.N., MSN, Chief Operating Officer
CFO: J Michael Burris, Vice President Corporate Services and Chief Financial Officer
CMO: F Michael Ashby M.D., Vice President and Medical Director
CIO: Marijo Lecker, Vice President
CHR: Debbie Desmond, Director Human Resources
Web address: www.marthajefferson.org
Control: Other not–for–profit (including NFP Corporation) **Service**: General medical and surgical

Staffed Beds: 144 Admissions: 9234 Census: 93 Outpatient Visits: 294806 Births: 1576 Total Expense ($000): 280349 Payroll Expense ($000): 120725 Personnel: 1554

⊠ △ **UNIVERSITY OF VIRGINIA MEDICAL CENTER (490009)**, 1215 Lee Street, Zip 22908–0001, Mailing Address: P.O.Box 800809, 22908–0809; tel. 434/924–0211, (Includes UNIVERSITY OF VIRGINIA CHILDREN'S HOSPITAL, 1215 Lee Street, Charlottesville, Virginia, Zip 22908, PO Box 800566, 22908, tel. 434/243–5500) **A**1 2 3 5 7 8 10 **F**3 4 5 6 7 8 9 11 12 13 15 16 17 18 19 20 21 22 23 24 25 26 27 28 29 30 31 32 34 35 36 37 38 39 40 41 43 44 45 46 47 48 49 50 51 52 54 55 56 57 58 59 60 61 62 63 64 65 66 68 69 70 71 72 73 74 75 76 77 78 79 80 81 82 83 84 85 86 87 88 89 90 91 92 93 94 97 98 99 100 101 102 103 104 107 108 110 111 112 114 115 116 117 118 119 120 121 123 124 126 129 130 131 132 134 135 136 137 138 139 140 141 142 143 145 146 147 148 149 **P**3 4 **S** UVA Health System, Charlottesville, VA
Primary Contact: Pamela Sutton–Wallace, Chief Executive Officer
COO: William T. Fulkerson, Chief Operating Officer
CFO: Nick Mendyka, Chief Financial Officer
CMO: Chris A. Ghaemmaghami M.D., Chief Medical Officer
CIO: Richard Skinner, Chief Information Technology Officer
CHR: John Boswell, Chief Human Resources Officer
CNO: Mary E. Dixon, Interim Chief Nursing Officer
Web address: www.healthsystem.virginia.edu
Control: State, Government, Nonfederal **Service**: General medical and surgical

Staffed Beds: 593 Admissions: 27800 Census: 462 Outpatient Visits: 1980961 Births: 1671 Total Expense ($000): 1424342 Payroll Expense ($000): 500027 Personnel: 7520

CHARLOTTESVILLE—Albemarle County

⊠ **UVA TRANSITIONAL CARE HOSPITAL (492011)**, 2965 Ivy Rd (250 West), Zip 22903–9330; tel. 434/924–8245 **A**1 10 **F**1 3 29 30 60 77 85 94 114 129 130 146 148 149 **P**3 4 **S** UVA Health System, Charlottesville, VA
Primary Contact: Christine K. Matt, Associate Chief
Web address: www.uvahealth.com/services/transitional–care–hospital
Control: State, Government, Nonfederal **Service**: Acute long–term care hospital

Staffed Beds: 40 Admissions: 383 Census: 31 Outpatient Visits: 0 Births: 0 Total Expense ($000): 20862 Payroll Expense ($000): 8456 Personnel: 133

⊠ **UVA–HEALTHSOUTH REHABILITATION HOSPITAL (493029)**, 515 Ray C Hunt Drive, Zip 22903–2981; tel. 434/244–2000 **A**1 3 5 10 **F**3 28 29 30 34 54 57 59 60 64 68 74 75 77 90 91 93 94 96 131 132 143 148 **P**5 **S** HEALTHSOUTH Corporation, Birmingham, AL
CFO: Dianna Gomez, Controller
CMO: Alan Alfano, Medical Director
CIO: Michael Vanhoy, Director of Quality
CHR: Tonya Loving, Director of Human Resources
CNO: Sherry Herring, Chief Nursing Officer
Web address: www.uvahealthsouth.com
Control: Corporation, Investor–owned (for–profit) **Service**: Rehabilitation

Staffed Beds: 50 Admissions: 1190 Census: 42 Outpatient Visits: 28815 Births: 0 Total Expense ($000): 21892 Payroll Expense ($000): 13582 Personnel: 225

CHESAPEAKE—Chesapeake City County

★ ◯ **CHESAPEAKE REGIONAL HEALTHCARE (490120)**, 736 Battlefield Boulevard North, Zip 23320–4941, Mailing Address: P.O.Box 2028, 23327–2028; tel. 757/312–8121 **A**2 3 10 11 **F**3 6 10 11 12 13 15 18 20 22 26 28 29 30 31 34 35 37 40 44 45 46 49 50 53 54 57 58 59 61 62 63 64 65 66 68 69 70 71 73 74 75 76 77 78 79 81 83 84 85 86 87 89 91 93 100 101 102 103 107 108 110 111 114 115 118 119 120 121 123 126 129 130 132 135 141 142 143 146 147 148 149 **P**6 8
Primary Contact: Reese Jackson, Chief Executive Officer
COO: Kenneth R. Deans Jr, Vice President and Interim Chief Operating Officer
CMO: Paul Brainstein M.D., Interim Chief Medical Officer
CHR: Deborah L Rosenburg, Vice President Human Resources
CNO: Elaine Griffiths R.N., Chief Nursing Officer
Web address: www.chesapeakeregional.com
Control: Hospital district or authority, Government, Nonfederal **Service**: General medical and surgical

Staffed Beds: 310 Admissions: 15499 Census: 177 Outpatient Visits: 189785 Births: 2445 Total Expense ($000): 273123 Payroll Expense ($000): 101644 Personnel: 1775

VA

Hospital, Medicare Provider Number, Address, Telephone, Approval, Facility, and Physician Codes, Health Care System
★ American Hospital Association (AHA) membership ◯ Healthcare Facilities Accreditation Program ⇧ Center for Improvement in Healthcare Quality Accreditation
☐ The Joint Commission accreditation ◇ DNV Healthcare Inc. accreditation △ Commission on Accreditation of Rehabilitation Facilities (CARF) accreditation

CHRISTIANSBURG—Montgomery County

⊞ **CARILION NEW RIVER VALLEY MEDICAL CENTER (490042)**, 2900 Lamb Circle, Zip 24073–6344, Mailing Address: P.O.Box 5, Radford, 24143–0005; tel. 540/731–2000, (Includes CARILION CLINIC SAINT ALBANS HOSPITAL, 2900 Lamb Circle, Christiansburg, Virginia, Zip 24073–6344, tel. 540/731–2000) **A**1 10 13 19 **F**3 5 12 13 15 18 20 22 26 28 29 30 31 34 35 36 40 43 45 47 48 49 50 51 53 57 59 60 62 63 64 65 68 70 74 75 76 77 79 81 82 84 85 86 87 89 91 92 93 96 98 99 102 103 104 105 107 108 110 111 114 115 118 119 126 129 130 131 135 146 147 148 149 **P**6 **S** Carilion Clinic, Roanoke, VA
Primary Contact: William Flattery, Vice President and Administrator Western Division
CFO: Rob Vaughan, Chief Financial Officer
CMO: Dennis Means M.D., Vice President Medical Affairs
CIO: Daniel Borchi, Chief Information Officer
CHR: Patti Jurkus, Director Human Resources
Web address: www.carilionclinic.org/Carilion/cnrv
Control: Other not–for–profit (including NFP Corporation) **Service:** General medical and surgical

Staffed Beds: 85 **Admissions:** 8547 **Census:** 90 **Outpatient Visits:** 101232 **Births:** 1204 **Total Expense ($000):** 163903 **Payroll Expense ($000):** 58683 **Personnel:** 946

CLINTWOOD—Dickenson County

DICKENSON COMMUNITY HOSPITAL (491303), 312 Hospital Drive, Zip 24228, Mailing Address: P.O.Box 1440, 24228–1440; tel. 276/926–0300 **A**10 18 **F**3 29 40 44 64 97 98 104 107 111 119 130 148 **S** Mountain States Health Alliance, Johnson City, TN
Primary Contact: Mark T. Leonard, Chief Executive Officer
CFO: Kevin Morrison, Chief Financial Officer
CMO: Erin Mullins D.O., Chief Medical Staff
CHR: Valeri J Colyer, Director Human Resources
CNO: Terri Roop, Director Patient Care Services
Web address: www.msha.com/dch
Control: Other not–for–profit (including NFP Corporation) **Service:** General medical and surgical

Staffed Beds: 7 **Admissions:** 114 **Census:** 2 **Outpatient Visits:** 28003 **Births:** 0 **Total Expense ($000):** 8011 **Payroll Expense ($000):** 3152 **Personnel:** 49

CULPEPER—Culpeper County

⊞ **NOVANT HEALTH UVA HEALTH SYSTEM CULPEPER MEDICAL CENTER (490019)**, 501 Sunset Lane, Zip 22701–3917, Mailing Address: P.O.Box 592, 22701–0500; tel. 540/829–4100, (Nonreporting) **A**1 3 5 10 **S** UVA Health System, Charlottesville, VA
Primary Contact: Greg Napps, Chief Executive Officer
COO: Greg Napps, Chief Executive Officer
CFO: David J Plaviak, Interim Chief Financial Officer
CMO: Morton Chiles M.D., Chief Medical Officer
CIO: Steven Speelman, Director Information Systems
CHR: Susan Edwards, Vice President Human Resources
Web address: www.culpeperhealth.org
Control: Other not–for–profit (including NFP Corporation) **Service:** General medical and surgical

Staffed Beds: 68

DANVILLE—Danville City County

☐ **SOUTHERN VIRGINIA MENTAL HEALTH INSTITUTE (494017)**, 382 Taylor Drive, Zip 24541–4023; tel. 434/799–6220, (Nonreporting) **A**1 10 **S** Virginia Department of Mental Health, Richmond, VA
Primary Contact: William Cook, Director
CFO: Wayne Peters, Administrator
CMO: Pravin Patel M.D., Acting President and Chief Executive Officer
CIO: Larry Hays, Director Information Technology
CHR: Stephanie Haywood, Director Human Resources
CNO: Kathy M Dodd, Director of Nursing
Web address: www.svmhi.dbhds.virginia.gov
Control: State, Government, Nonfederal **Service:** Psychiatric

Staffed Beds: 72

⊞ **SOVAH HEALTH–DANVILLE (490075)**, 142 South Main Street, Zip 24541–2922; tel. 434/799–2100, (Nonreporting) **A**1 2 10 12 13 **S** LifePoint Health, Brentwood, TN
Primary Contact: Alan Larson, Chief Executive Officer
CFO: Mark T Anderson, Chief Financial Officer
CMO: James F Starling M.D., Chief Medical Officer
CIO: David Cartwright, Director Management Information Systems
CNO: Aundrea Mills, Chief Nursing Officer
Web address: www.danvilleregional.com/
Control: Other not–for–profit (including NFP Corporation) **Service:** General medical and surgical

Staffed Beds: 250

DULLES—Loudoun County

★ **STONESPRINGS HOSPITAL CENTER (490145)**, 24440 Stone Spring Boulevard, Zip 20166–2247; tel. 571/349–4000 (Nonreporting) **S** HCA Healthcare, Nashville, TN
Primary Contact: Lance Jones, Chief Executive Officer
COO: Benjamin Brown, Chief Operating Officer
CFO: Candi Christopher CPA, Chief Financial Officer
CMO: Walter R Zolkiwsky M.D., Chief Medical Officer
CHR: Tiffani Smith, Chief Human Resources Officer
CNO: Michelle L. Epps MSN, R.N., Chief Nursing Officer
Web address: www.stonespringshospital.com
Control: Investor–owned (for–profit) **Service:** General medical and surgical

Staffed Beds: 124

EMPORIA—Emporia City County

⊞ **SOUTHERN VIRGINIA REGIONAL MEDICAL CENTER (490097)**, 727 North Main Street, Zip 23847–1274; tel. 434/348–4400 **A**1 10 **F**3 11 15 26 28 29 30 31 40 45 49 50 57 59 62 64 70 77 78 79 81 85 93 98 103 107 115 119 124 129 130 133 146 148 **S** Community Health Systems, Inc., Franklin, TN
Primary Contact: Matt Tavenner, Chief Executive Officer
CFO: Jim Porter, Chief Financial Officer
CMO: Fitzgerald Marcelin M.D., Chief of Staff
CIO: Larry Gold, Vice President, Information Services
CHR: Becky Parrish, Director Human Resources
CNO: Linda Burnette R.N., Chief Nursing Officer
Web address: www.svrmc.com
Control: Corporation, Investor–owned (for–profit) **Service:** General medical and surgical

Staffed Beds: 80 **Admissions:** 1433 **Census:** 17 **Outpatient Visits:** 22748 **Births:** 0 **Total Expense ($000):** 31190 **Payroll Expense ($000):** 10155 **Personnel:** 186

FAIRFAX—Fairfax County

⊞ **INOVA FAIR OAKS HOSPITAL (490101)**, 3600 Joseph Siewick Drive, Zip 22033–1798; tel. 703/391–3600 **A**1 2 3 5 10 **F**3 11 12 13 14 15 18 29 30 31 34 35 37 38 39 40 44 45 47 48 49 50 51 55 57 58 59 60 61 64 65 68 69 70 72 74 75 76 77 78 79 80 81 82 84 85 86 87 89 91 92 93 100 101 102 107 108 110 111 114 115 118 119 120 121 123 126 129 130 131 132 135 145 146 147 148 149 **P**6 **S** Inova Health System, Falls Church, VA
Primary Contact: John L. Fitzgerald, Chief Executive Officer
CFO: Jerry Seager, Assistant Vice President and Chief Financial Officer
CMO: G Michael Lynch M.D., Chief Medical Officer
CIO: Marshall Ruffin, Chief Information Officer
CHR: Jeanne Robinson, Director Human Resources
Web address: www.inova.org
Control: Other not–for–profit (including NFP Corporation) **Service:** General medical and surgical

Staffed Beds: 201 **Admissions:** 12655 **Census:** 115 **Outpatient Visits:** 103437 **Births:** 3385 **Total Expense ($000):** 235348 **Payroll Expense ($000):** 71590 **Personnel:** 981

FALLS CHURCH—Fairfax County

⊞ **DOMINION HOSPITAL (494023)**, 2960 Sleepy Hollow Road, Zip 22044–2030; tel. 703/536–2000, (Nonreporting) **A**1 10 **S** HCA Healthcare, Nashville, TN
Primary Contact: Lee Higginbotham, Chief Executive Officer
CFO: Edward R Stojakovich, Chief Financial Officer
CMO: Gary Litovitz M.D., Medical Director
CIO: Leslie Gilliam, Director Health Information Management
CHR: Lesley Channell, Vice President Human Resources
Web address: www.dominionhospital.com
Control: Corporation, Investor–owned (for–profit) **Service:** Psychiatric

Staffed Beds: 100

⊞ **INOVA FAIRFAX HOSPITAL (490063)**, 3300 Gallows Road, Zip 22042–3300; tel. 703/776–4001, (Includes INOVA FAIRFAX HOSPITAL FOR CHILDREN, 3300 Gallows Road, Falls Church, Virginia, Zip 22042–3307, tel. 703/776–4002) **A**1 2 3 5 8 10 **F**3 4 5 6 8 9 11 12 13 14 15 17 18 19 20 21 22 23 24 25 26 27 28 29 30 31 32 34 35 36 37 38 39 40 41 42 43 44 45 46 47 48 49 50 51 53 54 55 56 57 58 59 60 61 63 64 65 66 68 70 71 72 74 75 76 77 78 79 80 81 82 83 84 85 86 87 88 89 91 92 93 94 96 97 98 99 100 101 102 103 104 105 107 108 109 110 111 114 115 116 117 118 119 120 121 123 124 126 129 130 131 132 134 135 136 137 138 140 141 142 145 146 147 148 149 150 **P**6 **S** Inova Health System, Falls Church, VA
Primary Contact: Patrick Christiansen, Ph.D., Chief Executive Officer
CFO: Ronald Ewald, Chief Financial Officer
CMO: Joseph Hallal M.D., Chief Medical Officer
CIO: Geoffrey Brown, Vice President Information Systems
CHR: Ken Hull, Director Human Resources
Web address: www.inova.org
Control: Other not–for–profit (including NFP Corporation) **Service:** General medical and surgical

Staffed Beds: 1002 **Admissions:** 49799 **Census:** 720 **Outpatient Visits:** 407358 **Births:** 10282 **Total Expense ($000):** 1287301 **Payroll Expense ($000):** 406393 **Personnel:** 6058

VA

Many Facility Codes have changed. Please refer to the AHA Guide Code Chart. © 2017 AHA Guide

☐ **NORTHERN VIRGINIA MENTAL HEALTH INSTITUTE (494010)**, 3302 Gallows Road, Zip 22042–3398; tel. 703/207–7100 **A**1 3 5 10 **F**29 30 44 50 59 68 75 77 87 97 98 101 106 130 132 **S** Virginia Department of Mental Health, Richmond, VA
Primary Contact: Tammy Peacock, Ph.D., Facility Director
CFO: John Poffenbarger, Director Fiscal Services
CMO: R Maximilien del Rio M.D., Medical Director
CHR: Cynthia Lott, Director Human Resources
Web address: www.nvmhi.dbhds.virginia.gov
Control: State, Government, Nonfederal **Service:** Psychiatric

> **Staffed Beds:** 134 **Admissions:** 1060 **Census:** 122 **Outpatient Visits:** 0
> **Births:** 0 **Total Expense ($000):** 31518 **Payroll Expense ($000):** 18098
> **Personnel:** 306

FARMVILLE—Prince Edward County

⊞ **CENTRA SOUTHSIDE COMMUNITY HOSPITAL (490090)**, 800 Oak Street, Zip 23901–1199; tel. 434/392–8811 **A**1 5 10 20 **F**3 11 13 15 22 28 29 30 34 35 40 44 45 49 50 57 59 62 63 64 70 74 75 76 77 79 81 82 85 86 87 89 93 107 108 110 111 115 118 119 129 130 132 133 146 147 148 **P**6 **S** Centra Health, Inc., Lynchburg, VA
Primary Contact: Thomas Angelo, Chief Executive Officer
Web address: www.sch.centrahealth.com/
Control: Other not-for-profit (including NFP Corporation) **Service:** General medical and surgical

> **Staffed Beds:** 86 **Admissions:** 3905 **Census:** 33 **Outpatient Visits:** 157219
> **Births:** 362 **Total Expense ($000):** 80840 **Payroll Expense ($000):** 38018
> **Personnel:** 508

SOUTHSIDE COMMUNITY HOSPITAL See Centra Southside Community Hospital

FISHERSVILLE—Augusta County

⊞ **AUGUSTA HEALTH (490018)**, 78 Medical Center Drive, Zip 22939–2332, Mailing Address: P.O.Box 1000, 22939–1000; tel. 540/932–4000 **A**1 2 3 10 **F**3 5 7 11 13 15 18 20 22 26 28 29 30 31 32 34 35 38 40 41 45 46 47 48 49 50 51 53 54 56 57 58 59 61 62 63 64 65 66 68 70 71 74 75 76 77 78 79 81 82 84 85 86 87 89 90 91 93 96 97 98 100 102 103 104 106 107 108 110 111 112 114 115 118 119 120 121 126 128 129 130 131 132 135 144 146 147 148 **P**8
Primary Contact: Mary N. Mannix, FACHE, President and Chief Executive Officer
CMO: Richard Embrey M.D., Chief Medical Officer
CIO: Michael Canfield, Chief Information Officer
CHR: Sue Krzastek, Vice President Human Resources
Web address: www.augustahealth.com
Control: Other not-for-profit (including NFP Corporation) **Service:** General medical and surgical

> **Staffed Beds:** 211 **Admissions:** 10992 **Census:** 115 **Outpatient Visits:** 747617 **Births:** 1175 **Total Expense ($000):** 293188 **Payroll Expense ($000):** 121748 **Personnel:** 1862

WOODROW WILSON REHABILITATION CENTER, 243 Woodrow Wilson Avenue, Zip 22939, Mailing Address: P.O.Box 1500, 22939–1500; tel. 540/332–7000, (Nonreporting)
Primary Contact: Richard Luck, Ed.D., Facility Director
COO: Richard Luck Ed.D., Facility Director
CFO: Ernie Steidle, Chief Operating Officer
CMO: Mammen Mathew M.D., Chief Rehabilitation Medicine
CIO: Keith Burt, Director Marketing
CHR: Debbie Mitchell, Director Human Resources
Web address: www.wwrc.net
Control: State, Government, Nonfederal **Service:** Rehabilitation

> **Staffed Beds:** 30

FORT BELVOIR—Fairfax County

⊞ **FORT BELVOIR COMMUNITY HOSPITAL**, 9300 Dewitt Loop, Zip 22060–5285; tel. 571/231–3224, (Nonreporting) **A**1 3 5 **S** Department of the Army, Office of the Surgeon General, Falls Church, VA
Primary Contact: Colonel Jason S. Wieman, Director
CMO: Lieutenant ColonelMark D Harris, Deputy Commander Clinical Services
CIO: Terrance Branch, Chief Information Management
Web address: www.fbch.capmed.mil/SitePages/Home.aspx
Control: Army, Government, federal **Service:** General medical and surgical

> **Staffed Beds:** 46

FRANKLIN—Franklin City County

⊞ **SOUTHAMPTON MEMORIAL HOSPITAL (490092)**, 100 Fairview Drive, Zip 23851–1238, Mailing Address: P.O.Box 817, 23851–0817; tel. 757/569–6100, (Nonreporting) **A**1 10 20 **S** Community Health Systems, Inc., Franklin, TN
Primary Contact: Kimberly W. Marks, Chief Executive Officer
CFO: Steve Ramey, Chief Financial Officer
CMO: Donald Bowling M.D., Chief Medical Staff
CIO: Kristie Howell, System Information Technology Director
CHR: Loretha Ricks, Human Resources Supervisor
CNO: Laurie Ross, Chief Nursing Officer
Web address: www.smhfranklin.com
Control: Corporation, Investor-owned (for-profit) **Service:** General medical and surgical

> **Staffed Beds:** 72

FREDERICKSBURG—Fredericksburg City County

⊞ **HEALTHSOUTH REHABILITATION HOSPITAL OF FREDERICKSBURG (493032)**, 300 Park Hill Drive, Zip 22401–3387; tel. 540/368–7300, (Nonreporting) **A**1 10 **S** HEALTHSOUTH Corporation, Birmingham, AL
Primary Contact: Gary J. Herbek, Chief Executive Officer
Web address: www.fredericksburgrehabhospital.com
Control: Corporation, Investor-owned (for-profit) **Service:** Rehabilitation

> **Staffed Beds:** 40

⊞ **MARY WASHINGTON HOSPITAL (490022)**, 1001 Sam Perry Boulevard, Zip 22401–3354; tel. 540/741–1100 **A**1 2 3 5 10 **F**3 5 13 15 18 20 22 24 26 28 29 30 31 34 35 36 40 42 43 44 45 46 47 48 49 50 54 55 57 58 59 62 64 70 72 74 75 76 77 78 79 81 83 84 85 86 87 89 92 93 96 98 99 100 101 102 104 105 107 108 111 114 115 118 119 120 121 124 126 129 130 131 132 135 146 147 148 149 **S** Mary Washington Healthcare, Fredericksburg, VA
Primary Contact: Michael P. McDermott, M.D., President and Chief Executive Officer
COO: Thomas Gettinger, Executive Vice President and Chief Operating Officer
CFO: Sean Barden, Executive Vice President and Chief Financial Officer
CMO: Rebecca Bigoney, Executive Vice President and Chief Medical Officer
CIO: Justin K. Box, Senior Vice President & Chief Information Officer
CHR: Kathryn S Wall, Executive Vice President, Human Resources and Organizational Development
CNO: Eileen L Dohmann R.N., Senior Vice President and Chief Nursing Officer
Web address: www.marywashingtonhealthcare.com
Control: Other not-for-profit (including NFP Corporation) **Service:** General medical and surgical

> **Staffed Beds:** 451 **Admissions:** 21790 **Census:** 271 **Outpatient Visits:** 335253 **Births:** 2753 **Total Expense ($000):** 395400 **Payroll Expense ($000):** 122172 **Personnel:** 1691

SNOWDEN AT FREDERICKSBURG, 1200 Sam Perry Boulevard, Zip 22401–4456; tel. 540/741–3900 (Nonreporting)
Primary Contact: Charles Scercy, Corporate Director
Web address: www.marywashingtonhealthcare.com/locations/snowden-at-fredericksburg
Control: Other not-for-profit (including NFP Corporation) **Service:** Psychiatric

> **Staffed Beds:** 30

FREDERICKSBURG—Spotsylvania County

⊞ **SPOTSYLVANIA REGIONAL MEDICAL CENTER (490141)**, 4600 Spotsylvania Parkway, Zip 22408–7762; tel. 540/498–4000, (Nonreporting) **A**1 10 **S** HCA Healthcare, Nashville, TN
Primary Contact: Michael Clark, Chief Executive Officer
COO: Roberta Tinch, Chief Operations Officer
CFO: David McKnight CPA, Chief Financial Officer
Web address: www.spotsrmc.com
Control: Corporation, Investor-owned (for-profit) **Service:** General medical and surgical

> **Staffed Beds:** 100

VA

Hospital, Medicare Provider Number, Address, Telephone, Approval, Facility, and Physician Codes, Health Care System

★ American Hospital Association (AHA) membership
☐ The Joint Commission accreditation
○ Healthcare Facilities Accreditation Program
◇ DNV Healthcare Inc. accreditation
⇑ Center for Improvement in Healthcare Quality Accreditation
△ Commission on Accreditation of Rehabilitation Facilities (CARF) accreditation

FRONT ROYAL—Warren County

⊠ **WARREN MEMORIAL HOSPITAL (490033)**, 1000 North Shenandoah Avenue, Zip 22630–3598; tel. 540/636–0300, (Total facility includes 120 beds in nursing home–type unit) **A**1 3 10 13 **F**3 11 13 15 28 29 30 34 35 36 40 50 53 54 56 57 59 64 65 67 70 75 76 77 79 81 82 85 86 87 93 96 107 108 111 114 118 119 128 130 132 135 144 146 147 148 **P**6 **S** Valley Health System, Winchester, VA
Primary Contact: Floyd Heater, President and Chief Executive Officer
CFO: Phillip Graybeal CPA, Chief Financial Officer
CMO: Robert Meltvedt M.D., Jr, Vice President Medical Affairs
CNO: Terri Wright, Vice President and Chief Nursing Officer
Web address: www.valleyhealthlink.com/WMH
Control: Other not–for–profit (including NFP Corporation) **Service**: General medical and surgical

Staffed Beds: 180 **Admissions:** 2619 **Census:** 135 **Outpatient Visits:** 59004 **Births:** 367 **Total Expense ($000):** 68103 **Payroll Expense ($000):** 26496 **Personnel:** 409

GALAX—Galax City County

⊠ **TWIN COUNTY REGIONAL HEALTHCARE (490115)**, 200 Hospital Drive, Zip 24333–2227; tel. 276/236–8181, (Nonreporting) **A**1 10 20 **S** Duke LifePoint Healthcare, Brentwood, TN
Primary Contact: Dale Alward, Chief Executive Officer
CFO: Marita Caldwell, Chief Financial Officer
CHR: Kristal Herrington, Senior Director, Human Resources
CNO: Agnes A Smith MSN, R.N., Chief Nursing Officer
Web address: www.tcrh.org
Control: Other not–for–profit (including NFP Corporation) **Service**: General medical and surgical

Staffed Beds: 141

GLOUCESTER—Gloucester County

⇧ **RIVERSIDE WALTER REED HOSPITAL (490130)**, 7519 Hospital Drive, Zip 23061–4178, Mailing Address: P.O.Box 1130, 23061–1130; tel. 804/693–8800 **A**2 10 21 **F**3 15 28 29 34 35 40 44 45 50 51 57 59 60 64 70 71 75 77 78 79 81 85 86 87 92 93 96 107 108 110 111 114 115 116 118 119 120 121 123 130 132 146 147 148 149 **P**6 **S** Riverside Health System, Newport News, VA
Primary Contact: Megan Kleckner, Vice President and Administrator
CHR: Tabetha Holt, Director of Human Resources
Web address: www.riversideonline.com
Control: Other not–for–profit (including NFP Corporation) **Service**: General medical and surgical

Staffed Beds: 29 **Admissions:** 2685 **Census:** 28 **Outpatient Visits:** 85131 **Births:** 0 **Total Expense ($000):** 63038 **Payroll Expense ($000):** 18737 **Personnel:** 315

GRUNDY—Buchanan County

⊠ **BUCHANAN GENERAL HOSPITAL (490127)**, 1535 Slate Creek Road, Zip 24614–6974; tel. 276/935–1000 **A**1 10 20 **F**3 15 18 28 29 30 34 35 40 41 45 57 59 62 64 70 81 85 87 89 93 107 108 110 132 135 146 148
Primary Contact: Robert D. Ruchti, Chief Executive Officer
COO: Scott M Pittman, Chief Operating Officer
CFO: Kim Boyd, Chief Financial Officer
CIO: Rita Ramey, Director Information Systems
CHR: Wanda B Stiltner, Director Human Resources
CNO: Patty Dorton, Director of Nursing
Web address: www.bgh.org
Control: Other not–for–profit (including NFP Corporation) **Service**: General medical and surgical

Staffed Beds: 49 **Admissions:** 1245 **Census:** 15 **Outpatient Visits:** 46304 **Births:** 0 **Total Expense ($000):** 23010 **Payroll Expense ($000):** 9131 **Personnel:** 221

HAMPTON—Hampton City County

⊠ **HAMPTON VETERANS AFFAIRS MEDICAL CENTER**, 100 Emancipation Drive, Zip 23667–0001; tel. 757/722–9961, (Total facility includes 112 beds in nursing home–type unit) **A**1 3 5 **F**3 4 5 8 15 30 31 34 35 39 46 48 49 53 54 56 57 58 59 60 61 62 63 64 65 68 70 74 75 77 78 79 80 81 82 83 84 85 86 87 91 92 93 94 96 97 98 100 101 103 104 106 107 108 109 110 111 114 115 119 128 129 130 132 135 143 144 146 147 148 149 **S** Department of Veterans Affairs, Washington, DC
Primary Contact: J. Ronald. Johnson, Medical Center Director
COO: Lorraine B Price, Associate Director
CFO: Terry Grew, Chief Business Office
CMO: Val Gibberman M.D., Acting Chief of Staff
CIO: Cary Parks, Chief Information Resource Management
Web address: www.hampton.va.gov/
Control: Veterans Affairs, Government, federal **Service**: General medical and surgical

Staffed Beds: 451 **Admissions:** 1390 **Census:** 122 **Outpatient Visits:** 278415 **Births:** 0 **Personnel:** 1686

★ ⇧ **SENTARA CAREPLEX HOSPITAL (490093)**, 3000 Coliseum Drive, Zip 23666–5963; tel. 757/736–1000 **A**2 3 5 10 21 **F**3 8 11 12 15 18 20 22 26 28 29 30 31 34 35 36 37 38 39 40 41 42 44 45 46 47 48 49 50 54 55 56 57 58 59 60 61 62 63 64 65 68 70 74 75 77 78 79 80 81 82 84 85 86 87 91 92 93 94 96 97 100 102 103 107 108 110 111 114 118 119 120 121 123 126 129 130 131 132 135 141 144 145 146 147 148 149 **P**6 **S** Sentara Healthcare, Norfolk, VA
Primary Contact: Debra A. Flores, R.N., MS, President and Administrator
COO: Chet Hart, Vice President Operations
CFO: Cheryl Larner, Chief Financial Officer
CMO: Arthur Greene M.D., Vice President Medical Affairs
CIO: Thomas Ewing, Director Information Technology
CHR: David Kidd, Manager Human Resources
Web address: www.sentara.com
Control: Other not–for–profit (including NFP Corporation) **Service**: General medical and surgical

Staffed Beds: 162 **Admissions:** 8430 **Census:** 108 **Outpatient Visits:** 423738 **Births:** 0 **Total Expense ($000):** 207197 **Payroll Expense ($000):** 85334 **Personnel:** 1296

⊠ **U. S. AIR FORCE HOSPITAL**, 77 Nealy Avenue, Zip 23665–2040; tel. 757/764–6969, (Nonreporting) **A**1 3 **S** Department of the Air Force, Washington, DC
Primary Contact: Colonel Susan Pietrykowski, Commander
COO: ColonelMichael Dietz, Administrator
CFO: MajorSteven Dadd, Flight Commander Resource Management
CMO: ColonelPaul Gourley M.D., Chief Hospital Services
CIO: MajorMerlinda Vergonio, Chief Information Management and Technology
CHR: MajorSteven Dadd, Flight Commander Resource Management
CNO: ColonelMarlene Kerchenski, Chief Nurse
Web address: www.jble.af.mil
Control: Air Force, Government, federal **Service**: General medical and surgical

Staffed Beds: 65

HARRISONBURG—Harrisonburg City County

★ ⇧ **SENTARA RMH MEDICAL CENTER (490004)**, 2010 Health Campus Drive, Zip 22801–3293; tel. 540/689–1000 **A**2 5 10 21 **F**3 5 8 11 12 13 15 17 18 20 22 24 26 28 29 30 31 32 34 35 36 40 41 44 45 46 47 48 49 50 53 54 55 56 57 59 63 64 65 66 68 70 71 73 74 76 77 78 79 81 82 84 85 86 87 89 93 97 98 100 102 104 105 107 108 110 111 114 115 116 117 118 119 120 121 129 130 131 132 135 141 144 145 146 147 148 149 **P**6 8 **S** Sentara Healthcare, Norfolk, VA
Primary Contact: Douglas J. Moyer, President
COO: Richard L Haushalter, Senior Vice President Operations and Chief Operating Officer
CFO: J Michael Burris, Chief Financial Officer
CMO: Susan McDonald, Vice President, Medical Affairs
CNO: Donna S Hahn R.N., Vice President Acute Care and Chief Nurse Executive
Web address: www.rmhonline.com
Control: Other not–for–profit (including NFP Corporation) **Service**: General medical and surgical

Staffed Beds: 244 **Admissions:** 13585 **Census:** 139 **Outpatient Visits:** 409045 **Births:** 1761 **Total Expense ($000):** 389681 **Payroll Expense ($000):** 159606 **Personnel:** 2404

HAYMARKET—Prince William County

⊠ **NOVANT HEALTH UVA HEALTH SYSTEM HAYMARKET MEDICAL CENTER (490144)**, 15225 Heathcote Boulevard, Zip 20155–4023, Mailing Address: 14535 John Marshall Hwy, Gainesville, 20155–4023; tel. 571/284–1000 **A**1 10 **F**3 8 11 12 13 15 18 29 30 34 35 37 40 44 45 46 47 49 50 56 57 58 59 60 63 64 65 70 74 75 76 78 79 81 84 85 87 91 92 100 102 107 108 110 111 114 119 130 131 132 135 141 146 147 149 **S** Novant Health, Winston Salem, NC
Primary Contact: Margaret Gill, Senior Vice President and Chief Executive Officer
CFO: Charles Coder, Vice President
CMO: Doug Wall M.D., Vice President of Medical Affairs
CIO: David B Garrett, Senior Vice President and Chief Information Officer
CHR: Tracy Bowers, Vice President Human Resources and Administrative Services
CNO: Maggie C Conklin M.P.H., Interim Chief Nursing Officer
Web address: www.novanthealth.org
Control: Other not–for–profit (including NFP Corporation) **Service**: General medical and surgical

Staffed Beds: 18 **Admissions:** 2398 **Census:** 19 **Outpatient Visits:** 127859 **Births:** 610 **Total Expense ($000):** 58994 **Payroll Expense ($000):** 19012 **Personnel:** 244

HOPEWELL—Hopewell City County

⊠ **JOHN RANDOLPH MEDICAL CENTER (490020)**, 411 West Randolph Road, Zip 23860–2938; tel. 804/541–1600, (Nonreporting) **A**1 2 10 **S** HCA Healthcare, Nashville, TN
Primary Contact: Joseph Mazzo, Chief Executive Officer
CFO: Jennifer Honaker, Chief Financial Officer
CHR: MaDena DuChemin, Assistant Administrator Human Resources
Web address: www.johnrandolphmed.com
Control: Corporation, Investor–owned (for–profit) **Service**: General medical and surgical

Staffed Beds: 112

Many Facility Codes have changed. Please refer to the AHA Guide Code Chart. © 2017 AHA Guide

HOT SPRINGS—Bath County

✠ **BATH COMMUNITY HOSPITAL (491300)**, 83 Park Drive, Zip 24445–2788, Mailing Address: P.O.Box Z, 24445–0750; tel. 540/839–7000 **A**1 10 18 **F**3 5 7 15 28 29 30 34 35 40 44 45 50 53 56 57 59 74 75 77 81 85 87 90 93 97 99 100 102 104 107 114 115 119 127 129 130 132 133 135 143 146 147 148 **P**6
Primary Contact: Kathy Landreth, Interim Chief Executive Officer
COO: Mitzi Grey, Chief Operating Officer
CMO: James Redington M.D., Chief of Staff
CIO: Tracy Bartley, Manager Information Technology
CHR: Patricia Foutz, Director Human Resources
CNO: Kyna Moore R.N., Director of Nursing
Web address: www.bcchospital.org
Control: Other not–for–profit (including NFP Corporation) **Service**: General medical and surgical

Staffed Beds: 25 **Admissions:** 335 **Census:** 6 **Outpatient Visits:** 15224
Births: 0 **Total Expense ($000):** 19952 **Payroll Expense ($000):** 8756
Personnel: 152

KILMARNOCK—Lancaster County

✠ **RAPPAHANNOCK GENERAL HOSPITAL (490123)**, 101 Harris Drive, Zip 22482–3880, Mailing Address: P.O.Box 1449, 22482–1449; tel. 804/435–8000 **A**1 10 18 **F**11 15 18 20 22 24 26 28 29 30 31 34 35 38 40 41 44 45 46 50 57 59 60 64 68 74 75 78 81 84 85 86 87 98 100 103 104 105 107 108 111 115 118 119 130 146 148 149 150 **S** Bon Secours Health System, Inc., Marriottsville, MD
Primary Contact: Mark M. Gordon, Chief Executive Officer
Web address: www.rgh–hospital.com
Control: Other not–for–profit (including NFP Corporation) **Service**: General medical and surgical

Staffed Beds: 35 **Admissions:** 1523 **Census:** 19 **Outpatient Visits:** 17399
Births: 0 **Total Expense ($000):** 31582 **Payroll Expense ($000):** 14639
Personnel: 317

LEBANON—Russell County

☐ **RUSSELL COUNTY MEDICAL CENTER (490002)**, 58 Carroll Street, Zip 24266, Mailing Address: P.O.Box 3600, 24266–0200; tel. 276/883–8000 **A**1 10 **F**3 11 15 29 30 34 35 40 44 45 50 56 57 59 62 63 64 68 70 75 78 81 85 93 97 98 99 100 101 102 103 104 107 108 110 111 114 118 119 127 129 130 133 146 147 148 **S** Mountain States Health Alliance, Johnson City, TN
Primary Contact: Stephen K. Givens, Assistant Vice President and Administrator
CFO: John Jeter, Chief Financial Officer
CMO: Brian Condit M.D., Vice President Chief Medical Officer, Virginia Operations Medical Staff Services
CHR: Beth Hill, Director Human Resources
CNO: Greta M. Morrison, Assistant Chief Nursing Officer
Web address: www.mountainstateshealth.com/rcmc
Control: Other not–for–profit (including NFP Corporation) **Service**: General medical and surgical

Staffed Beds: 78 **Admissions:** 2013 **Census:** 25 **Outpatient Visits:** 25712
Births: 0 **Total Expense ($000):** 23253 **Payroll Expense ($000):** 8454
Personnel: 129

LEESBURG—Loudoun County

✠ **INOVA LOUDOUN HOSPITAL (490043)**, 44045 Riverside Parkway, Zip 20176–5101, Mailing Address: P.O.Box 6000, 20177–0600; tel. 703/858–6000, (Total facility includes 100 beds in nursing home–type unit) **A**1 2 5 10 **F**3 5 11 13 14 15 18 20 22 26 28 29 30 31 34 35 37 38 39 40 41 42 44 45 48 49 50 54 55 57 58 59 60 61 63 64 65 66 67 68 70 71 72 74 75 76 77 78 79 80 81 82 84 85 86 87 89 91 92 93 96 98 100 101 102 103 104 105 107 108 110 111 114 115 118 119 120 121 123 126 128 130 131 132 135 145 146 147 148 149 **P**6 **S** Inova Health System, Falls Church, VA
Primary Contact: Deborah Addo, Chief Executive Officer
CFO: William Bane, Chief Financial Officer
CMO: Christopher Chiantella M.D., Chief Medical Officer
CHR: Sarah Pavik, Director Human Resources and Guest Services
CNO: Elizabeth Dugan Ph.D., R.N., MSN, Chief Nursing Officer
Web address: www.inova.org
Control: Other not–for–profit (including NFP Corporation) **Service**: General medical and surgical

Staffed Beds: 286 **Admissions:** 14022 **Census:** 232 **Outpatient Visits:** 146105 **Births:** 2831 **Total Expense ($000):** 263918 **Payroll Expense ($000):** 92130 **Personnel:** 1275

LEXINGTON—Lexington City County

✠ **CARILION STONEWALL JACKSON HOSPITAL (491304)**, 1 Health Circle, Zip 24450–2492; tel. 540/458–3300 **A**1 10 18 **F**3 8 11 15 18 19 28 29 30 34 35 40 45 50 53 56 57 59 65 68 70 75 77 79 81 85 87 91 93 97 107 108 110 111 115 119 127 129 130 131 132 133 135 146 148 149 **P**6 **S** Carilion Clinic, Roanoke, VA
Primary Contact: Charles E. Carr, Vice President and Administrator
CMO: Lyle McClung M.D., Chief of Staff
Web address: www.carilionclinic.org/Carilion/csjh
Control: Other not–for–profit (including NFP Corporation) **Service**: General medical and surgical

Staffed Beds: 10 **Admissions:** 1250 **Census:** 14 **Outpatient Visits:** 29809
Births: 0 **Total Expense ($000):** 31579 **Payroll Expense ($000):** 11449
Personnel: 201

LOW MOOR—Alleghany County

✠ **LEWISGALE HOSPITAL ALLEGHANY (490126)**, One ARH Lane, Zip 24457, Mailing Address: P.O.Box 7, 24457–0007; tel. 540/862–6011, (Nonreporting) **A**1 10 20 **S** HCA Healthcare, Nashville, TN
Primary Contact: William Windham, Chief Executive Officer
CMO: Michele Ballou M.D., Chief Medical Staff
CIO: Jeffrey Steelman, Director Information Systems
CHR: Bernard M Campbell, Administrator Human Resources
CNO: Robin Broughman R.N., Ph.D., Chief Nursing Officer
Web address: www.alleghanyregional.com
Control: Corporation, Investor–owned (for–profit) **Service**: General medical and surgical

Staffed Beds: 146

LURAY—Page County

✠ **PAGE MEMORIAL HOSPITAL (491307)**, 200 Memorial Drive, Zip 22835–1005; tel. 540/743–4561 **A**1 10 18 **F**3 7 8 11 15 28 29 30 34 35 40 53 56 57 59 60 64 66 68 69 74 75 77 79 81 85 90 93 107 108 110 111 114 119 127 128 129 130 133 135 143 146 148 **P**2 **S** Valley Health System, Winchester, VA
Primary Contact: N Travis. Clark, President
CFO: Phillip Graybeal CPA, Chief Financial Officer
Web address: www.valleyhealthlink.com/page
Control: Other not–for–profit (including NFP Corporation) **Service**: General medical and surgical

Staffed Beds: 25 **Admissions:** 690 **Census:** 11 **Outpatient Visits:** 79080
Births: 0 **Total Expense ($000):** 30207 **Payroll Expense ($000):** 14199
Personnel: 184

LYNCHBURG—Lynchburg City County

CENTRA HEALTH See Centra Lynchburg General Hospital

✠ **CENTRA LYNCHBURG GENERAL HOSPITAL (490021)**, 1920 Atherholt Road, Zip 24501–1104; tel. 434/200–4700, (Includes CENTRA VIRGINIA BAPTIST HOSPITAL, 3300 Rivermont Avenue, Lynchburg, Virginia, Zip 24503–2053, tel. 434/200–4000; LYNCHBURG GENERAL HOSPITAL, 1901 Tate Springs Road, Lynchburg, Virginia, Zip 24501–1167, tel. 434/200–3000) (Total facility includes 433 beds in nursing home–type unit) **A**1 2 3 5 10 20 **F**2 3 4 5 7 10 11 12 13 15 17 18 19 20 22 24 26 28 29 30 31 34 35 37 38 40 42 43 44 45 46 47 48 49 50 53 54 55 56 57 59 60 61 62 63 64 67 68 70 71 72 73 74 75 76 77 78 79 80 81 82 84 85 86 87 89 90 91 92 93 94 96 98 99 100 101 102 103 104 105 106 107 108 110 111 114 115 119 120 121 123 124 125 126 127 128 129 130 131 132 133 135 143 144 146 147 148 **P**7 **S** Centra Health, Inc., Lynchburg, VA
Primary Contact: E W. Tibbs, President and Chief Executive Officer
CFO: Lewis C Addison, Senior Vice President and Chief Financial Officer
CMO: Chalmers Nunn M.D., Chief Medical Officer and Senior Vice President
CIO: Ben Clark, Vice President and Chief Information Officer
CHR: Jan Walker, Director Human Resources
Web address: www.centrahealth.com
Control: Other not–for–profit (including NFP Corporation) **Service**: General medical and surgical

Staffed Beds: 1054 **Admissions:** 29497 **Census:** 768 **Outpatient Visits:** 614584 **Births:** 2641 **Total Expense ($000):** 788375 **Payroll Expense ($000):** 342169 **Personnel:** 5369

CENTRA SPECIALTY HOSPITAL (492010), 3300 Rivermont Avenue, Zip 24503–2030; tel. 434/200–1799 (Nonreporting) **A**10
Primary Contact: Kay Bowling, Chief Executive Officer
Control: Partnership, Investor–owned (for–profit) **Service**: Acute long–term care hospital

Staffed Beds: 36

VA

MADISON HEIGHTS—Amherst County

☒ **CENTRAL VIRGINIA TRAINING CENTER (490108)**, 210 East Colony Road, Zip 24572–2005, Mailing Address: P.O.Box 1098, Lynchburg, 24505–1098; tel. 434/947–6326, (Nonreporting) **A**10 **S** Virginia Department of Mental Health, Richmond, VA
Primary Contact: David Cole, Assistant Director of Administration, Chief Financial Officer, Department of Behavioral Health and D
CFO: Charles Felmlee, Assistant Director Fiscal Services
CMO: Balraj Bawa M.D., Assistant Director Medical Services
CHR: Burchkhard Blob, Manager Human Resources
Web address: www.cvtc.dmhmrsas.virginia.gov/
Control: State, Government, Nonfederal **Service**: Intellectual disabilities

Staffed Beds: 1112

MANASSAS—Manassas City County

☒ **NOVANT HEALTH UVA HEALTH SYSTEM PRINCE WILLIAM MEDICAL CENTER (490045)**, 8700 Sudley Road, Zip 20110–4418, Mailing Address: P.O.Box 2610, 20108–0867; tel. 703/369–8000 **A**1 2 3 10 **F**3 5 8 10 11 13 15 18 19 20 22 26 28 29 30 31 32 34 35 36 37 38 39 40 44 45 46 47 48 49 50 53 54 57 59 64 65 70 71 72 75 76 77 78 79 81 82 84 85 86 87 89 93 97 98 100 101 102 103 104 107 108 110 111 114 115 116 117 118 119 120 121 123 126 129 130 131 132 134 135 141 146 147 148 149 **S** Novant Health, Winston Salem, NC
Primary Contact: Margaret Gill, Senior Vice President and Chief Executive Officer
CFO: Charles Coder, Vice President
CMO: Doug Wall M.D., Vice President Medical Affairs
CIO: David B Garrett, Senior Vice President and Chief Information Officer
CHR: Tracy Bowers, Vice President Human Resources and Administrative Services
CNO: Maggie C Conklin M.P.H., Interim Chief Nurse Officer
Web address: www.pwhs.org
Control: Other not–for–profit (including NFP Corporation) **Service**: General medical and surgical

Staffed Beds: 87 **Admissions**: 7445 **Census**: 87 **Outpatient Visits**: 233637 **Births**: 1472 **Total Expense ($000)**: 161886 **Payroll Expense ($000)**: 59971 **Personnel**: 852

MARION—Smyth County

☐ **SMYTH COUNTY COMMUNITY HOSPITAL (490038)**, 245 Medical Park Drive, Zip 24354, Mailing Address: P.O.Box 880, 24354–0880; tel. 276/378–1000, (Total facility includes 109 beds in nursing home–type unit) **A**1 10 **F**3 11 15 18 28 29 30 31 34 35 40 45 50 51 54 57 59 62 64 67 68 70 75 77 78 79 81 85 87 90 93 97 107 110 111 115 118 119 127 128 129 131 132 133 135 144 146 147 148 **S** Mountain States Health Alliance, Johnson City, TN
Primary Contact: Stan Hickson, FACHE, President and Chief Executive Officer
CFO: John Jeter, Assistant Vice President and Chief Financial Officer
CHR: Sue Henderson, Human Resource Manager
Web address: www.msha.com/scch
Control: Other not–for–profit (including NFP Corporation) **Service**: General medical and surgical

Staffed Beds: 153 **Admissions**: 1560 **Census**: 113 **Outpatient Visits**: 62098 **Births**: 0 **Total Expense ($000)**: 40049 **Payroll Expense ($000)**: 13277 **Personnel**: 262

☐ **SOUTHWESTERN VIRGINIA MENTAL HEALTH INSTITUTE (490105)**, 340 Bagley Circle, Zip 24354–3390; tel. 276/783–1200, (Nonreporting) **A**1 10 **S** Virginia Department of Mental Health, Richmond, VA
Primary Contact: Cynthia McClaskey, Ph.D., Director
CIO: Kim Ratliff, Director Health Information Management
Web address: www.swmhi.dmhmrsas.virginia.gov/
Control: State, Government, Nonfederal **Service**: Psychiatric

Staffed Beds: 166

MARTINSVILLE—Martinsville City County

☒ **SOVAH HEALTH–MARTINSVILLE (490079)**, 320 Hospital Drive, Zip 24112–1981, Mailing Address: P.O.Box 4788, 24115–4788; tel. 276/666–7200, (Nonreporting) **A**1 2 10 19 **S** LifePoint Health, Brentwood, TN
Primary Contact: Michael Ehrat, Chief Executive Officer
CFO: Brandy Hanners, Chief Financial Officer
CIO: Jeff Butker, Chief Information Officer
CHR: Sherry Schofield, Director Human Resources
CNO: Michael Pittman, Chief Nursing Officer
Web address: www.martinsvillehospital.com
Control: Corporation, Investor–owned (for–profit) **Service**: General medical and surgical

Staffed Beds: 220

MECHANICSVILLE—Hanover County

☒ **BON SECOURS MEMORIAL REGIONAL MEDICAL CENTER (490069)**, 8260 Atlee Road, Zip 23116–1844; tel. 804/764–6000 **A**1 2 3 5 10 **F**11 15 18 20 22 24 26 28 29 30 31 34 35 38 40 44 45 46 50 57 59 60 64 68 74 75 78 81 84 85 86 87 100 103 104 105 107 108 111 115 118 119 130 145 146 148 149 150 **S** Bon Secours Health System, Inc., Marriottsville, MD
Primary Contact: Mark M. Gordon, Chief Executive Officer
COO: Gary A. Welch, Assistant to the Chief Executive Officer and Administrative Director Support Systems
CFO: Stephan F Quiriconi, Vice President Finance
CMO: Sunil K. Sinha M.D., FACHE, Chief Medical Officer
CIO: Gwen Harding, Site Manager Information Systems
CHR: Rebecca Kamguia, Administrative Director Human Resources
CNO: Jill M Kennedy R.N., Vice President, Ambulatory Patient Care Services
Web address: www.bonsecours.com
Control: Other not–for–profit (including NFP Corporation) **Service**: General medical and surgical

Staffed Beds: 225 **Admissions**: 13482 **Census**: 171 **Outpatient Visits**: 80694 **Births**: 1485 **Total Expense ($000)**: 329590 **Payroll Expense ($000)**: 103696 **Personnel**: 1735

☒ **SHELTERING ARMS REHABILITATION HOSPITAL (493025)**, 8254 Atlee Road, Zip 23116–1844; tel. 804/764–1000 **A**1 3 10 **F**3 29 30 34 35 50 53 54 57 58 59 64 68 74 75 77 79 82 86 87 90 91 92 93 94 95 96 130 131 132 146 148 **P**6
Primary Contact: Mary A. Zweifel, MS, President and Chief Executive Officer
COO: Amy J Showalter R.N., Chief Operating Officer
CFO: James Litsinger CPA, Vice President and Chief Financial Officer
CMO: Hillary Hawkins M.D., Medical Director
CIO: Chris Sorenson, Chief Information Officer
CHR: Ellen B Vance, Chief Human Resource Officer
CNO: Sandra Eyler MS, Chief Nursing Officer
Web address: www.shelteringarms.com
Control: Other not–for–profit (including NFP Corporation) **Service**: Rehabilitation

Staffed Beds: 40 **Admissions**: 861 **Census**: 35 **Outpatient Visits**: 82833 **Births**: 0 **Total Expense ($000)**: 39464 **Payroll Expense ($000)**: 21362 **Personnel**: 138

MIDLOTHIAN—Chesterfield County

☒ **BON SECOURS ST. FRANCIS MEDICAL CENTER (490136)**, 13710 St Francis Boulevard, Zip 23114–3267; tel. 804/594–7300 **A**1 2 3 5 10 **F**3 8 11 13 15 17 18 20 22 26 28 29 30 31 34 35 40 42 45 46 50 54 55 57 59 60 61 64 65 68 70 72 74 75 76 78 79 81 84 85 86 87 94 107 108 109 111 115 117 118 119 120 121 123 126 130 135 146 147 148 **S** Bon Secours Health System, Inc., Marriottsville, MD
Primary Contact: Chris Accashian, Chief Executive Officer
COO: Toni R Ardabell, Chief Executive Officer, Bon Secours Virginia
CFO: Stephan F Quiriconi, Vice President, Finance
CMO: John McCurley M.D., Chief Medical Officer
CIO: Terri Spence, Vice President and Regional Chief Information Officer
CHR: James C Godwin Jr, Vice President, Human Resources
CNO: Barbara L. Gesme MSN, Vice President Patient Care Services & Chief Nurse Executive
Web address: www.bonsecours.com/sfmc/default.asp
Control: Other not–for–profit (including NFP Corporation) **Service**: General medical and surgical

Staffed Beds: 135 **Admissions**: 9525 **Census**: 99 **Outpatient Visits**: 89888 **Births**: 2218 **Total Expense ($000)**: 242677 **Payroll Expense ($000)**: 159090 **Personnel**: 1388

☐ **SHELTERING ARMS HOSPITAL SOUTH (493030)**, 13700 St. Francis Boulevard, Suite 400, Zip 23114–3222; tel. 804/764–1000 **A**1 5 10 **F**3 29 30 34 35 50 53 54 57 58 59 64 68 74 75 77 79 82 86 87 90 91 92 93 94 95 96 130 131 132 146 148 **P**6
Primary Contact: Mary A. Zweifel, MS, President and Chief Executive Officer
COO: Amy J Showalter R.N., Chief Operating Officer
CFO: James Litsinger CPA, Chief Operating Officer
CMO: Timothy Silver M.D., Medical Director, SAH–S
CIO: Chris Sorenson, Chief Health Information Officer
CHR: Ellen B Vance, Chief Human Resources Officer
CNO: Sandra Eyler MS, Chief Nursing Officer
Web address: www.shelteringarms.com
Control: Other not–for–profit (including NFP Corporation) **Service**: Rehabilitation

Staffed Beds: 28 **Admissions**: 653 **Census**: 21 **Outpatient Visits**: 7138 **Births**: 0 **Total Expense ($000)**: 11568 **Payroll Expense ($000)**: 5522 **Personnel**: 78

VA

NEW KENT—New Kent County

☐ **CUMBERLAND HOSPITAL (493300)**, 9407 Cumberland Road, Zip 23124–2029; tel. 804/966–2242 **A1** 10 **F**12 28 29 32 35 38 44 50 53 57 59 68 74 75 77 86 87 91 96 98 99 100 101 106 130 132 143 148 **P**6 **S** Universal Health Services, Inc., King of Prussia, PA
Primary Contact: Patrice Gay. Brooks, Chief Executive Officer
CFO: Joanne Rial, Chief Financial Officer
CMO: Daniel N Davidow M.D., Medical Director
CIO: Leslie Bowery, Director of Standards and Compliance
CHR: Kim Ivey, Director of Human Resources
CNO: Paula Roberts, Chief Nursing Officer
Web address: www.cumberlandhospital.com
Control: Corporation, Investor–owned (for–profit) **Service:** Children's general medical and surgical

Staffed Beds: 118 **Admissions:** 279 **Census:** 103 **Outpatient Visits:** 0 **Births:** 0 **Total Expense ($000):** 19400 **Payroll Expense ($000):** 11747 **Personnel:** 241

NEWPORT NEWS—Newport News City County

⇧ **HAMPTON ROADS SPECIALTY HOSPITAL (492008)**, 245 Chesapeake Avenue, Zip 23607–6038; tel. 757/534–5000 (Nonreporting) **A**10 21 **S** Riverside Health System, Newport News, VA
Primary Contact: Courtney Detwiler, R.N., Administrator
Web address: www.hamptonroadsspecialtyhospital.com
Control: Other not–for–profit (including NFP Corporation) **Service:** Acute long–term care hospital

Staffed Beds: 25

KEYSTONE NEWPORT NEWS, 17579 Warwick Boulevard, Zip 23603–1343; tel. 757/888–0400 **F**29 30 32 50 75 98 99 106 132 143 149
Primary Contact: Paul Kirkham, Chief Executive Officer
COO: Paul Kirkham, Chief Executive Officer
CFO: Joe Brooks, Chief Financial Officer
CMO: Avtar Dhillon M.D., Medical Director
CIO: Terry Rethamel, Director of Support Services
CHR: Shawn Marston, Director Human Resources
CNO: Karen Bruce, Director of Nursing
Web address: www.newportnewsbhc.com/
Control: Corporation, Investor–owned (for–profit) **Service:** Children's hospital psychiatric

Staffed Beds: 132 **Admissions:** 626 **Census:** 109 **Outpatient Visits:** 0 **Births:** 0

⊞ **MARY IMMACULATE HOSPITAL (490041)**, 2 Bernardine Drive, Zip 23602–4499; tel. 757/886–6000, (Total facility includes 115 beds in nursing home–type unit) **A**1 10 **F**3 5 11 12 13 15 18 20 22 24 26 28 29 30 31 32 34 35 36 37 38 40 44 45 46 50 51 57 59 61 63 64 67 68 70 71 73 74 75 76 77 78 79 81 82 84 85 86 87 91 93 102 107 108 111 114 118 119 130 131 132 143 145 146 147 148 149 **P**6 **S** Bon Secours Health System, Inc., Marriottsville, MD
Primary Contact: Darlene Stephenson, Chief Executive Officer
COO: Darlene Stephenson, Vice President Operations
CIO: Terri Spence, Vice President Information Services
CHR: Vickie Witcher Humphries, Vice President Human Resources
Web address: www.bonsecourshamptonroads.com
Control: Other not–for–profit (including NFP Corporation) **Service:** General medical and surgical

Staffed Beds: 238 **Admissions:** 8743 **Census:** 165 **Outpatient Visits:** 108496 **Births:** 1563 **Total Expense ($000):** 167341 **Payroll Expense ($000):** 48186 **Personnel:** 930

⇧ **RIVERSIDE REGIONAL MEDICAL CENTER (490052)**, 500 J Clyde Morris Boulevard, Zip 23601–1929; tel. 757/594–2000, (Includes RIVERSIDE BEHAVIORAL HEALTH CENTER, 2244 Executive Drive, Hampton, Virginia, Zip 23666–2430, tel. 757/827–1001; Debra Campbell, R.N., Administrator) **A**2 3 5 10 13 21 **F**3 4 8 13 15 18 20 22 24 26 29 30 31 32 34 35 36 40 43 44 45 49 50 51 54 56 58 60 64 70 72 74 75 76 77 78 79 81 82 84 85 86 87 91 93 94 96 98 99 102 103 106 107 108 110 111 114 115 116 117 118 119 120 121 123 124 126 129 130 131 132 141 143 146 148 149 **P**6 **S** Riverside Health System, Newport News, VA
Primary Contact: Michael J. Doucette, Senior Vice President and Administrator
COO: William B Downey, Chief Operating Officer
CFO: Wade Broughman, Executive Vice President and Chief Financial Officer
CMO: Barry L Gross M.D., Executive Vice President and Chief Medical Officer
CIO: Dennis Loftis, Senior Vice President and Chief Information Officer
CHR: Sally Hartman, Senior Vice President
CNO: Candice R. Carroll, Nurse Executive
Web address: www.riversideonline.com/rrmc/index.cfm
Control: Other not–for–profit (including NFP Corporation) **Service:** General medical and surgical

Staffed Beds: 307 **Admissions:** 20502 **Census:** 306 **Outpatient Visits:** 606200 **Births:** 2656 **Total Expense ($000):** 735463 **Payroll Expense ($000):** 199615 **Personnel:** 2022

⊞ **RIVERSIDE REHABILITATION INSTITUTE (493027)**, 245 Chesapeake Avenue, Zip 23607–6038; tel. 757/928–8000 **A**1 3 5 10 **F**29 30 57 64 77 82 87 90 91 93 94 96 130 132 146 **P**6 **S** Riverside Health System, Newport News, VA
Primary Contact: Daniel Ballin, Administrator
COO: William B Downey, President and Chief Executive Officer
CFO: Bill Austin, Senior Vice President of Finance
CMO: C Renee Moss M.D., Chief Medical Officer
CIO: Dennis Loftis, Senior Vice President of Information Systems
CHR: Rob Cuthrell, Director of Human Resources
CNO: Debbie Outlaw R.N., Director Patient Care Services
Web address: www.riversideonline.com/rri/index.cfm
Control: Other not–for–profit (including NFP Corporation) **Service:** Rehabilitation

Staffed Beds: 30 **Admissions:** 737 **Census:** 29 **Outpatient Visits:** 15305 **Births:** 0 **Total Expense ($000):** 15664 **Payroll Expense ($000):** 7994 **Personnel:** 148

NORFOLK—Norfolk City County

⊞ ⇧ **BON SECOURS–DEPAUL MEDICAL CENTER (490011)**, 150 Kingsley Lane, Zip 23505–6038; tel. 757/889–5000, (Total facility includes 24 beds in nursing home–type unit) **A**1 2 3 5 10 21 **F**3 11 13 15 18 20 22 29 30 31 34 35 40 44 45 46 50 51 56 57 59 61 64 68 70 71 74 75 76 78 79 81 82 84 85 86 87 93 97 102 107 108 110 111 114 115 118 119 120 121 128 129 130 131 132 143 145 146 147 148 149 **P**6 **S** Bon Secours Health System, Inc., Marriottsville, MD
Primary Contact: John E. Barrett III, Chief Executive Officer
CFO: Charmaine Rochester, Vice President Finance
CMO: Raymond McCue M.D., Chief Medical Officer
CIO: Lynne Zultanky, Director Corporate Communications and Media Relations
CHR: Vickie Witcher Humphries, Vice President Human Resources
CNO: Michael J. Bratton R.N., Chief Nurse Executive and Vice President Patient Care Services
Web address: www.bonsecourshamptonroads.com
Control: Other not–for–profit (including NFP Corporation) **Service:** General medical and surgical

Staffed Beds: 204 **Admissions:** 6703 **Census:** 89 **Outpatient Visits:** 345320 **Births:** 1413 **Total Expense ($000):** 211487 **Payroll Expense ($000):** 69072 **Personnel:** 1096

☐ **CHILDREN'S HOSPITAL OF THE KING'S DAUGHTERS (493301)**, 601 Children's Lane, Zip 23507–1910; tel. 757/668–7000 **A**1 3 5 10 **F**3 7 8 9 12 16 17 19 21 23 25 27 29 30 31 32 34 35 39 40 41 44 45 48 49 50 54 55 57 58 59 60 61 64 65 66 68 72 73 74 75 77 78 79 80 81 84 85 86 87 88 89 90 91 92 93 97 99 100 102 107 111 115 118 119 129 130 131 132 134 138 144 145 146 148 149 **P**8
Primary Contact: James D. Dahling, President and Chief Executive Officer
COO: John P Harding, Chief Operating Officer
CFO: Dennis Ryan, Senior Vice President and Chief Financial Officer
CMO: Chris Foley, Chief of Medicine
CIO: Deborah Barnes, Vice President and Chief Information Officer
CHR: Paul J Morlock FACHE, Vice President Human Resources and Occupational Health
CNO: Karen Mitchell, Vice President Patient Care Services
Web address: www.chkd.org
Control: Other not–for–profit (including NFP Corporation) **Service:** Children's general medical and surgical

Staffed Beds: 206 **Admissions:** 5476 **Census:** 138 **Outpatient Visits:** 263898 **Births:** 0 **Total Expense ($000):** 327304 **Payroll Expense ($000):** 136494 **Personnel:** 2318

HOSPITAL FOR EXTENDED RECOVERY (492007), 600 Gresham Drive, Suite 700, Zip 23507–1904; tel. 757/388–1700 (Nonreporting) **A**10
Primary Contact: Aimee Vergara, Chief Executive Officer
Control: Other not–for–profit (including NFP Corporation) **Service:** Acute long–term care hospital

Staffed Beds: 35

☐ **KEMPSVILLE CENTER FOR BEHAVIORAL HEALTH**, 860 Kempsville Road, Zip 23502–3980; tel. 757/461–4565, (Nonreporting) **A**1
Primary Contact: Jaime Fernandez, Chief Executive Officer
Control: Corporation, Investor–owned (for–profit) **Service:** Psychiatric

Staffed Beds: 77

VA

Hospital, Medicare Provider Number, Address, Telephone, Approval, Facility, and Physician Codes, Health Care System

★ American Hospital Association (AHA) membership   ○ Healthcare Facilities Accreditation Program   ⇧ Center for Improvement in Healthcare Quality Accreditation
☐ The Joint Commission accreditation   ◇ DNV Healthcare Inc. accreditation   △ Commission on Accreditation of Rehabilitation Facilities (CARF) accreditation

LAKE TAYLOR TRANSITIONAL CARE HOSPITAL (492001), 1309 Kempsville Road, Zip 23502–2286; tel. 757/461–5001, (Nonreporting) **A**3 5 10
Primary Contact: Thomas J. Orsini, President and Chief Executive Officer
CFO: Robert W Fogg, Director Finance
CMO: Kevin Murray M.D., Director Medical Services
CIO: Mark Davis, Director Information Systems
CHR: LeeAnn Lowman, Director Human Resources
Web address: www.laketaylor.org
Control: Hospital district or authority, Government, Nonfederal **Service**: Acute long–term care hospital

Staffed Beds: 293

★ ⇑ **SENTARA LEIGH HOSPITAL (490046)**, 830 Kempsville Road, Zip 23502–3920; tel. 757/261–6000 **A**2 3 5 10 21 **F**3 8 9 13 15 18 20 22 26 28 29 30 31 34 35 36 37 38 39 40 41 42 44 45 46 47 48 49 50 51 53 54 55 56 57 58 59 60 61 63 64 65 68 70 71 74 75 76 77 78 79 81 82 84 85 86 87 91 92 93 94 96 97 100 102 107 108 110 111 114 119 126 130 131 132 135 141 144 145 146 147 148 149 **P**6 **S** Sentara Healthcare, Norfolk, VA
Primary Contact: Joanne Inman, Administrator
COO: Howard P Kern, President and Chief Operating Officer
CFO: Robert Broermann, Senior Vice President and Chief Financial Officer
CMO: Terry Gilliland M.D., Chief Medical Officer
CIO: Bert Reese, Chief Information Officer
CHR: Michael V Taylor, Senior Vice President Human Resources
CNO: Genemarie McGee R.N., MS, Chief Nursing Officer
Web address: www.sentara.com
Control: Other not–for–profit (including NFP Corporation) **Service**: General medical and surgical

Staffed Beds: 250 Admissions: 15586 Census: 176 Outpatient Visits: 469262 Births: 2096 Total Expense ($000): 265343 Payroll Expense ($000): 106802 Personnel: 1682

★ ⇑ **SENTARA NORFOLK GENERAL HOSPITAL (490007)**, 600 Gresham Drive, Zip 23507–1904; tel. 757/388–3000 **A**2 3 5 8 10 21 **F**3 7 11 12 13 15 16 17 18 20 22 24 26 28 29 30 31 34 35 36 37 38 39 40 41 43 44 45 46 47 48 49 50 51 52 53 54 56 57 58 59 60 61 63 64 65 66 68 70 71 74 75 76 77 78 79 81 82 84 85 86 87 90 91 92 93 94 96 97 98 100 101 102 103 107 108 109 110 111 114 115 116 117 118 119 120 121 123 124 126 129 130 131 132 135 136 137 138 141 142 144 145 146 147 148 149 **P**6 **S** Sentara Healthcare, Norfolk, VA
Primary Contact: Kurt T. Hofelich, President
CFO: Robert Broermann, Senior Vice President and Chief Financial Officer
CIO: Bert Reese, Chief Information Officer
Web address: www.sentara.com
Control: Other not–for–profit (including NFP Corporation) **Service**: General medical and surgical

Staffed Beds: 495 Admissions: 25675 Census: 421 Outpatient Visits: 1148159 Births: 2856 Total Expense ($000): 742729 Payroll Expense ($000): 256317 Personnel: 3955

NORTON—Norton City County

★ **MOUNTAIN VIEW REGIONAL MEDICAL CENTER (490027)**, 310 Third Street NE, Zip 24273–1137; tel. 276/679–9100, (Total facility includes 44 beds in nursing home–type unit) **F**3 11 15 28 29 34 40 45 48 49 50 57 59 70 75 77 81 85 87 89 93 107 108 111 115 118 119 128 130 135 146 **S** Wellmont Health System, Kingsport, TN
Primary Contact: Dale Clark, President
CFO: Regina Day, Executive Director Finance
CMO: Michael Ketcham, Chief Medical Officer
CHR: Bobby Collins, Director Human Resources
CNO: Cindy Stidham, Executive Director of Patient Care
Web address: www.wellmont.org
Control: Other not–for–profit (including NFP Corporation) **Service**: General medical and surgical

Staffed Beds: 70 Admissions: 1264 Census: 42 Outpatient Visits: 33658 Births: 0 Total Expense ($000): 24595 Payroll Expense ($000): 6371 Personnel: 174

○ **NORTON COMMUNITY HOSPITAL (490001)**, 100 15th Street NW, Zip 24273–1616; tel. 276/679–9600 **A**10 11 13 **F**3 11 13 15 18 28 29 30 34 35 40 44 45 51 53 57 62 63 64 68 70 75 76 77 79 81 82 87 90 91 93 107 108 110 111 115 116 117 118 119 129 130 131 133 135 146 147 148 **S** Mountain States Health Alliance, Johnson City, TN
Primary Contact: Mark T. Leonard, Chief Executive Officer
CFO: Stephen Sawyer, Chief Financial Officer
CMO: Allen Mullens M.D., Chief Medical Staff
CIO: Judy Lawson, Director Information Services
CHR: Valeri J Colyer, Director Human Resources
Web address: www.msha.com/nch
Control: Other not–for–profit (including NFP Corporation) **Service**: General medical and surgical

Staffed Beds: 57 Admissions: 3380 Census: 33 Outpatient Visits: 74787 Births: 252 Total Expense ($000): 49188 Payroll Expense ($000): 19740 Personnel: 326

ONANCOKE—Accomack County

★ ⇑ **RIVERSIDE SHORE MEMORIAL HOSPITAL (490037)**, 204800 Market Street, Zip 23417, Mailing Address: P.O.Box 17, Nassawadox, 23413–0017; tel. 757/302–2100 **A**2 3 10 20 21 **F**3 11 13 15 18 28 29 30 31 34 40 45 49 50 59 64 70 74 75 76 77 78 79 81 85 93 107 110 111 114 118 119 121 129 130 132 146 **P**6 **S** Riverside Health System, Newport News, VA
Primary Contact: John Peterman, Vice President and Administrator
CFO: W William Austin Jr, Senior Vice President Finance
CMO: David Jones, Service Chief
CHR: Nicole Miller, Director Human Resources
Web address: www.riversideonline.com
Control: Other not–for–profit (including NFP Corporation) **Service**: General medical and surgical

Staffed Beds: 26 Admissions: 2611 Census: 25 Outpatient Visits: 84260 Births: 345 Total Expense ($000): 66268 Payroll Expense ($000): 19433 Personnel: 314

⇑ **SHORE MEMORIAL HOSPITAL** See Riverside Shore Memorial Hospital

PEARISBURG—Giles County

⊞ **CARILION GILES COMMUNITY HOSPITAL (491302)**, 159 Hartley Way, Zip 24134–2471; tel. 540/921–6000 **A**1 10 18 **F**3 11 15 18 28 29 34 35 36 40 45 50 53 57 59 64 65 68 70 75 77 79 81 85 86 87 91 93 96 107 108 110 111 115 118 119 127 130 133 135 146 147 148 149 **P**6 **S** Carilion Clinic, Roanoke, VA
Primary Contact: William Flattery, Vice President and Administrator Western Division
CMO: John Tamminen M.D., President Medical Staff
CHR: Carrie Boggess, Human Resource Generalist
CNO: Veronica Stump, Director of Nursing
Web address: www.carilionclinic.org/Carilion/cgch
Control: Other not–for–profit (including NFP Corporation) **Service**: General medical and surgical

Staffed Beds: 14 Admissions: 1091 Census: 16 Outpatient Visits: 26505 Births: 0 Total Expense ($000): 31563 Payroll Expense ($000): 11927 Personnel: 199

PETERSBURG—Petersburg City County

☐ **CENTRAL STATE HOSPITAL**, 26317 West Washington Street, Zip 23803–2727, Mailing Address: P.O.Box 4030, 23803–0030; tel. 804/524–7000 **A**1 **F**30 65 75 77 87 98 101 130 149 **S** Virginia Department of Mental Health, Richmond, VA
Primary Contact: Rebecca Vauter, PsyD, Facility Director
COO: Ann Bailey, Assistant Director Administration
CFO: Robert Kaufman, Director Financial Services
CMO: Ronald O Forbes M.D., Medical Director
CIO: Jonathan Baber, Director Information Technology
CHR: Tracy Salisbury, Regional Manager Human Resources
CNO: Eva Parham R.N., Chief Nurse Executive
Web address: www.csh.dbhds.virginia.gov
Control: State, Government, Nonfederal **Service**: Psychiatric

Staffed Beds: 277 Admissions: 800 Census: 231 Outpatient Visits: 0 Births: 0 Total Expense ($000): 70535 Payroll Expense ($000): 42005 Personnel: 892

⊞ **HEALTHSOUTH REHABILITATION HOSPITAL OF PETERSBURG (493031)**, 95 Medical Park Boulevard, Zip 23805–9233; tel. 804/504–8100, (Nonreporting) **A**1 10 **S** HEALTHSOUTH Corporation, Birmingham, AL
Primary Contact: Tracy Penn. Turman, Chief Executive Officer
Web address: www.healthsouthpetersburg.com
Control: Corporation, Investor–owned (for–profit) **Service**: Rehabilitation

Staffed Beds: 64

☐ **HIRAM W. DAVIS MEDICAL CENTER (490104)**, 26317 West Washington Street, Zip 23803–2727, Mailing Address: P.O.Box 4030, 23803–0030; tel. 804/524–7344 (Nonreporting) **A**1 10 **S** Virginia Department of Mental Health, Richmond, VA
Primary Contact: Brenda Buenvenida, Director
CFO: Robert Kaufman, Fiscal Officer
CHR: Tracy Salisbury, Director Human Resources
Control: State, Government, Nonfederal **Service**: Other specialty treatment

Staffed Beds: 10

VA

✠ **POPLAR SPRINGS HOSPITAL (494022)**, 350 Poplar Drive, Zip 23805–9367; tel. 804/733–6874, (Nonreporting) **A**1 10 **S** Universal Health Services, Inc., King of Prussia, PA
Primary Contact: Stephen Reider, Chief Operating Officer and Interim Chief Executive Officer
COO: Rachel Beal, Chief Operating Officer
CFO: Michael Felice, Chief Financial Officer
CMO: Thresa Simon M.D., Medical Director
CHR: Morris Mitchell, Director Human Resources
Web address: www.poplarsprings.com
Control: Corporation, Investor–owned (for–profit) **Service**: Psychiatric

Staffed Beds: 180

✠ **SOUTHSIDE REGIONAL MEDICAL CENTER (490067)**, 200 Medical Park Boulevard, Zip 23805–9274; tel. 804/765–5000 **A**1 2 3 10 **F**3 12 13 15 17 18 20 22 24 26 28 29 30 31 34 35 40 43 45 46 47 48 49 50 54 56 57 59 60 64 70 72 74 75 76 77 78 79 81 82 85 86 87 89 91 92 93 96 97 98 101 102 105 107 108 110 111 112 114 115 116 117 119 120 121 122 124 130 131 132 135 146 147 148 **P**6 **S** Community Health Systems, Inc., Franklin, TN
Primary Contact: Trent Nobles, Chief Executive Officer
COO: Jerad Hanlon, Chief Operating Officer
CMO: Boyd Wickizer M.D., Jr, Chief Medical Officer
CIO: Eric Synnestvedt, Director Information Technology
CHR: Irene Buskey, Director Human Resources
CNO: Beverly Bzdek Smith, Chief Nursing Officer
Web address: www.srmconline.com
Control: Corporation, Investor–owned (for–profit) **Service**: General medical and surgical

Staffed Beds: 300 Admissions: 13013 Census: 168 Outpatient Visits: 112079 Births: 1054 Total Expense ($000): 179931 Payroll Expense ($000): 67943 Personnel: 1181

PORTSMOUTH—Portsmouth City County

✠ **BON SECOURS MARYVIEW MEDICAL CENTER (490017)**, 3636 High Street, Zip 23707–3270; tel. 757/398–2200, (Total facility includes 120 beds in nursing home–type unit) **A**1 2 3 5 10 **F**3 4 5 11 12 13 15 17 18 20 22 24 26 28 29 30 31 34 35 36 37 38 40 42 44 45 46 50 51 54 57 59 61 62 63 64 66 67 68 70 71 73 74 75 76 77 78 79 81 82 84 85 86 87 90 91 93 96 97 98 99 100 101 102 103 104 105 106 107 108 110 111 114 115 118 119 121 126 128 129 130 131 132 134 135 143 145 146 147 149 **P**6 **S** Bon Secours Health System, Inc., Marriottsville, MD
Primary Contact: Joseph M. Oddis, Chief Executive Officer
CFO: Ernest C Padden, Chief Financial Officer
CMO: Warren Austin M.D., Vice President Medical Affairs
CIO: Terri Spence, Chief Information Officer
CHR: Vickie Witcher Humphries, Director Human Resources
CNO: Leana Fox MSN, Interim Chief Nurse Executive
Web address: www.bonsecourshamptonroads.com
Control: Other not–for–profit (including NFP Corporation) **Service**: General medical and surgical

Staffed Beds: 466 Admissions: 12076 Census: 259 Outpatient Visits: 607254 Births: 886 Total Expense ($000): 350273 Payroll Expense ($000): 131857 Personnel: 2040

✠ **NAVAL MEDICAL CENTER**, 620 John Paul Jones Circle, Zip 23708–2197; tel. 757/953–1980, (Nonreporting) **A**1 2 3 5 **S** Bureau of Medicine and Surgery, Department of the Navy, Falls Church, VA
Primary Contact: Captain Matthew Case, MSC, USN, Executive Officer
CMO: CaptainCynthia J Gantt, Chief of Staff
CIO: Lieutenant ColonelKaren Albany, Chief Information Officer
Web address: www.nmcphc.med.navy.mil/
Control: Navy, Government, federal **Service**: General medical and surgical

Staffed Beds: 274

PULASKI—Pulaski County

✠ **LEWISGALE HOSPITAL PULASKI (490116)**, 2400 Lee Highway, Zip 24301–2326, Mailing Address: P.O.Box 759, 24301–0759; tel. 540/994–8100, (Nonreporting) **A**1 2 10 **S** HCA Healthcare, Nashville, TN
Primary Contact: Derek Vance, Chief Executive Officer
CFO: Jeff Kurcab, Chief Financial Officer
CMO: Karanita Ojomo M.D., Chief of Staff
CIO: Diron Lane, Director Information Systems
CHR: Jana Beckner, Director Human Resources
CNO: Linda M. Shepherd, Chief Nursing Officer
Web address: www.lewisgale.com/
Control: Corporation, Investor–owned (for–profit) **Service**: General medical and surgical

Staffed Beds: 54

RESTON—Fairfax County

✠ **RESTON HOSPITAL CENTER (490107)**, 1850 Town Center Parkway, Zip 20190–3219; tel. 703/689–9000 **A**1 2 10 **F**3 8 12 13 14 15 18 20 22 26 29 30 34 35 37 39 40 41 43 44 45 46 47 48 49 50 51 53 54 55 57 58 59 60 63 64 65 68 69 70 72 74 75 76 77 78 79 81 82 84 85 87 89 91 93 94 96 97 107 108 110 111 114 115 117 118 119 120 121 123 124 126 127 130 131 132 135 145 146 147 148 **S** HCA Healthcare, Nashville, TN
Primary Contact: John A. Deardorff, President and Chief Executive, Northern Virginia Market
COO: Jane Raymond, Vice President and Chief Operating Officer
CFO: Edward R Stojakovich, Chief Financial Officer
CMO: Walter R Zolkiwsky M.D., Chief Medical Officer
CIO: Paresh Shah, Director Information Systems
CHR: Lesley Channell, Vice President Human Resources
CNO: Cynthia Glover R.N., Vice President and Chief Nursing Officer
Web address: www.restonhospital.com
Control: Corporation, Investor–owned (for–profit) **Service**: General medical and surgical

Staffed Beds: 199 Admissions: 12979 Census: 138 Births: 3576

RICHLANDS—Tazewell County

✠ **CLINCH VALLEY MEDICAL CENTER (490060)**, 6801 Governor G C Peery Highway, Zip 24641–2194; tel. 276/596–6000, (Total facility includes 14 beds in nursing home–type unit) **A**1 10 **F**3 12 13 14 15 17 18 20 22 28 29 30 31 34 35 39 40 41 45 49 50 55 56 57 59 64 70 75 76 77 78 79 81 85 86 87 89 90 93 94 97 107 108 110 111 114 115 118 119 120 121 128 129 130 132 134 135 143 144 146 147 148 149 150 **S** LifePoint Health, Brentwood, TN
Primary Contact: Peter Mulkey, Chief Executive Officer
COO: Jennifer Coello, Chief Operating Officer
CFO: Jason Schmiedt, Chief Financial Officer
CMO: George Farrell M.D., Chief Medical Officer
CIO: Chris Perkins, Director Information Services
CHR: John Knowles, Director Human Resources
CNO: Clint Kendall R.N., Chief Nursing Officer
Web address: www.clinchvalleymedicalcenter.com
Control: Corporation, Investor–owned (for–profit) **Service**: General medical and surgical

Staffed Beds: 111 Admissions: 3768 Census: 42 Outpatient Visits: 92445 Births: 303 Personnel: 458

RICHMOND—Chesterfield County

JOHNSTON–WILLIS HOSPITAL See Chippenham Hospital

RICHMOND—Henrico County

✠ **BON SECOURS ST. MARY'S HOSPITAL (490059)**, 5801 Bremo Road, Zip 23226–1907; tel. 804/285–2011, (Includes BON SECOURS ST. MARY'S CHILDREN'S SERVICES, 5801 Bremo Road, Richmond, Virginia, Zip 23226–1907, tel. 804/285–2011) **A**1 2 3 5 10 **F**3 7 8 11 12 13 15 17 18 20 22 24 26 28 29 30 31 34 35 36 39 40 41 45 46 47 49 50 56 57 59 61 63 64 70 72 73 74 75 76 78 79 80 81 82 84 85 87 88 89 98 100 101 102 103 104 105 107 108 110 111 114 115 116 117 118 119 120 121 123 124 126 129 130 132 135 143 146 147 148 149 150 **P**6 **S** Bon Secours Health System, Inc., Marriottsville, MD
Primary Contact: Francine Barr, R.N., MS, Chief Executive Officer
COO: Francine Barr R.N., MS, Vice President and Chief Operating Officer
CFO: Stephan F Quiriconi, Chief Financial Officer
CMO: Khiet Trinh M.D., Chief Medical Officer
CIO: Terri Spence, Chief Information Officer
CHR: Kristin Crandall, Director Human Resources
Web address: www.bonsecours.com
Control: Church operated, Nongovernment, not–for–profit **Service**: General medical and surgical

Staffed Beds: 391 Admissions: 19523 Census: 265 Outpatient Visits: 164436 Births: 2129 Total Expense ($000): 502016 Payroll Expense ($000): 171128 Personnel: 2646

✠ **HEALTHSOUTH REHABILITATION HOSPITAL OF VIRGINIA (493028)**, 5700 Fitzhugh Avenue, Zip 23226–1800; tel. 804/288–5700, (Nonreporting) **A**1 10 **S** HEALTHSOUTH Corporation, Birmingham, AL
Primary Contact: David Cashwell, Chief Executive Officer
CMO: Roger Giordano M.D., Medical Director
CIO: Faye Encke, Director Information Management
CHR: Tonya Ferguson, Director Human Resources
CNO: Michelle Anthony, Chief Nursing Officer
Web address: www.healthsouthrichmond.com
Control: Corporation, Investor–owned (for–profit) **Service**: Rehabilitation

Staffed Beds: 40

VA

✠ **HENRICO DOCTORS' HOSPITAL (490118)**, 1602 Skipwith Road, Zip 23229–5205; tel. 804/289–4500, (Nonreporting) (Includes HENRICO DOCTORS' HOSPITAL – FOREST, 1602 Skipwith Road, Richmond, Virginia, Zip 23229–5298, tel. 804/289–4500; HENRICO DOCTORS' HOSPITAL – PARHAM, 7700 East Parham Road, Richmond, Virginia, Zip 23294–4301, tel. 804/747–5600; David Donaldson, Chief Executive Officer; HENRICO DOCTORS' HOSPITAL – RETREAT CAMPUS, 2621 Grove Avenue, Richmond, Virginia, Zip 23220–4308, tel. 804/254–5100; William Wagnon, Chief Executive Officer) **A**1 2 10 **S** HCA Healthcare, Nashville, TN
Primary Contact: William Wagnon, Chief Executive Officer
COO: Lisa R Valentine, Chief Operating Officer
CFO: Christopher Denton, Chief Financial Officer
CIO: Daniel Patton, Director Information Systems
CHR: Steven Burgess, Administrator Human Resources
Web address: www.henricodoctorshospital.com
Control: Corporation, Investor–owned (for–profit) **Service**: General medical and surgical

Staffed Beds: 559

KINDRED HOSPITAL RICHMOND See Vibra Hospital Of Richmond

✠ **VIBRA HOSPITAL OF RICHMOND (492009)**, 2220 Edward Holland Drive, Zip 23230–2519; tel. 804/678–7000 **A**1 10 **F**1 28 29 30 44 60 74 75 82 83 84 85 87 100 **S** Vibra Healthcare, Mechanicsburg, PA
Primary Contact: Linda Tiemens, Chief Executive Officer
CMO: Gerard Weeden, Chief Medical Officer
CHR: Jonnitra Peeples, Chief Human Resource Officer
CNO: Crystal Richardson, Chief Nursing Officer
Web address: www.vhrichmond.com
Control: Corporation, Investor–owned (for–profit) **Service**: Acute long–term care hospital

Staffed Beds: 60 Admissions: 532 Census: 45 Outpatient Visits: 0 Births: 0 Total Expense ($000): 23486 Payroll Expense ($000): 14414

RICHMOND—Goochland County

HALLMARK YOUTHCARE – RICHMOND, 12800 West Creek Parkway, Zip 23238–1116; tel. 804/784–2200, (Nonreporting)
Primary Contact: Di Hayes, Chief Executive Officer
Web address: www.hallmarkyouthcare.org
Control: State, Government, Nonfederal **Service**: Children's hospital psychiatric

Staffed Beds: 84

RICHMOND—Richmond City County

✠ **BON SECOURS–RICHMOND COMMUNITY HOSPITAL (490094)**, 1500 North 28th Street, Zip 23223–5396, Mailing Address: P.O.Box 27184, 23261–7184; tel. 804/225–1700 **A**1 3 10 **F**3 11 14 15 18 23 24 30 31 33 34 35 36 37 38 40 41 44 45 46 50 57 59 60 64 68 70 74 75 78 81 84 85 86 87 98 100 103 104 105 107 108 111 115 118 119 130 132 145 146 147 148 149 150 **P**6 8 **S** Bon Secours Health System, Inc., Marriottsville, MD
Primary Contact: Mark M. Gordon, Chief Executive Officer
CIO: Jeff Burke, Chief Information Officer
CHR: Shelia White, Director Human Resources
Web address: www.bonsecours.com
Control: Other not–for–profit (including NFP Corporation) **Service**: General medical and surgical

Staffed Beds: 85 Admissions: 2033 Census: 28 Outpatient Visits: 35218 Births: 0 Total Expense ($000): 77654 Payroll Expense ($000): 19697 Personnel: 376

★ **CHILDREN'S HOSPITAL OF RICHMOND AT VCU–BROOK ROAD CAMPUS (493302)**, 2924 Brook Road, Zip 23220–1298; tel. 804/321–7474, (Nonreporting) **A**3 5 10 **S** VCU Health System, Richmond, VA
Primary Contact: Jeniece S. Roane, MS, R.N., Interim Vice President, Children's Services
CFO: James A Deyarmin, Controller
CMO: Eugene A Monasterio M.D., Medical Director
CIO: Tim Gibbs, Director of Information Technology, Information Security Officer
CNO: Sharon Darby R.N., FACHE, Vice President, Clinical Operations
Web address: www.chrichmond.org
Control: Other not–for–profit (including NFP Corporation) **Service**: Children's rehabilitation

Staffed Beds: 36

✠ ⇑ **CHIPPENHAM HOSPITAL (490112)**, 7101 Jahnke Road, Zip 23225–4044; tel. 804/320–3911, (Includes CHIPPENHAM MEDICAL CENTER, 7101 Jahnke Road, Richmond, Virginia, Zip 23225, tel. 804/320–3911; JOHNSTON–WILLIS HOSPITAL, 1401 Johnston–Willis Drive, Richmond, Virginia, Zip 23235, tel. 804/330–2000; Zachary McCluskey, Chief Executive Officer) **A**1 2 3 5 10 21 **F**3 4 8 13 15 17 18 19 20 22 24 26 28 29 30 31 34 35 37 38 40 41 42 43 45 46 47 49 50 55 57 58 59 60 61 64 68 70 72 73 74 75 76 77 78 79 80 81 84 85 86 87 88 89 90 96 98 99 100 101 102 103 104 105 107 108 109 110 111 115 118 119 120 121 123 124 126 130 131 135 146 147 148 149 **S** HCA Healthcare, Nashville, TN
Primary Contact: Greg Lowe, Chief Executive Officer
COO: Jeremy Gray, Chief Operating Officer
CFO: Lynn Strader, Chief Financial Officer
CMO: Georgean DeBlois M.D., Chairman Medical Staff
CIO: Tracy Hechler, Healthcare Director Information Services
CHR: Kris Lukish, Human Resources Officer
Web address: www.cjwmedical.com
Control: Corporation, Investor–owned (for–profit) **Service**: General medical and surgical

Staffed Beds: 765 Admissions: 35209 Census: 512 Outpatient Visits: 308904 Births: 2834 Personnel: 2738

✠ △ **HUNTER HOLMES MCGUIRE VETERANS AFFAIRS MEDICAL CENTER-RICHMOND**, 1201 Broad Rock Boulevard, Zip 23249–0002; tel. 804/675–5000, (Total facility includes 98 beds in nursing home–type unit) **A**1 3 5 7 8 **F**3 4 5 8 9 12 15 17 18 20 22 24 26 28 29 30 31 34 35 36 38 39 40 44 45 46 47 48 49 50 51 53 54 56 57 58 59 60 61 62 63 64 65 66 70 71 74 75 77 78 79 81 82 83 84 85 86 87 90 91 92 93 94 95 96 97 98 100 102 103 104 106 107 108 110 111 115 117 118 119 120 121 124 126 127 128 129 130 131 132 135 137 141 143 144 145 146 147 148 149 **P**6 **S** Department of Veterans Affairs, Washington, DC
Primary Contact: John A. Brandecker, M.P.H., Director
COO: Alan Lombardo, Associate Director
CFO: Tanza Westry, Chief Financial Officer
CMO: Julie Beales M.D., Chief of Staff
CIO: David Dahlstrand, Chief, OI&T
CHR: Adriana H Hamilton, Chief Human Resources Officer
CNO: Marjorie Lyne, Associate Director for Patient Care Services
Web address: www.richmond.va.gov/
Control: Veterans Affairs, Government, federal **Service**: General medical and surgical

Staffed Beds: 381 Admissions: 7641 Census: 229 Outpatient Visits: 705982 Births: 0 Total Expense ($000): 645813 Payroll Expense ($000): 398656 Personnel: 3450

✠ **VCU MEDICAL CENTER (490032)**, 1250 East Marshall Street, Zip 23298–5051, Mailing Address: P.O.Box 980510, 23298–0510; tel. 804/828–9000, (Includes CHILDREN'S HOSPITAL OF RICHMOND AT VCU, 1000 East Broad Street, Richmond, Virginia, Zip 23219–1918, PO Box 980646, 23298–0646, tel. 804/828–2467) **A**1 5 8 10 **F**2 3 5 6 8 9 11 12 13 15 16 17 18 19 20 21 22 23 24 25 26 27 28 29 30 31 32 34 35 36 37 38 39 40 41 43 44 45 46 47 48 49 50 51 52 54 55 56 57 58 59 60 61 62 64 65 66 68 70 72 73 74 75 76 78 79 80 81 82 83 84 85 86 87 88 89 90 91 92 93 95 96 97 98 99 100 101 102 103 104 107 108 109 110 111 114 115 116 117 118 119 120 121 123 124 126 129 130 131 132 134 135 138 139 141 142 143 145 146 147 148 149 150 **P**6 **S** VCU Health System, Richmond, VA
Primary Contact: Deborah W. Davis, Chief Executive Officer and Vice President Clinical Services
COO: Paul J Wesolowski, Chief Operating Officer
CFO: Melinda Hancock, Chief Financial Officer
CMO: Ron Clark M.D., Vice President Clinical Activities and Chief Medical Officer
CIO: Susan Steagall, Vice President Information Services
CHR: Maria Curran, Vice President Human Resources
CNO: Deb Zimmermann R.N., Chief Nursing Officer and Vice President Patient Care Services
Web address: www.vcuhealth.org
Control: Hospital district or authority, Government, Nonfederal **Service**: General medical and surgical

Staffed Beds: 786 Admissions: 33327 Census: 613 Outpatient Visits: 754528 Births: 2509 Total Expense ($000): 1282293 Payroll Expense ($000): 446638 Personnel: 7999

VA

ROANOKE—Roanoke County

✠ **CARILION ROANOKE MEMORIAL HOSPITAL (490024)**, Belleview at Jefferson Street, Zip 24014, Mailing Address: P.O.Box 13367, 24033–3367; tel. 540/981–7000, (Includes CARILION CLINIC CHILDREN'S HOSPITAL, 1906 Belleview Avenue, SE, Roanoke, Virginia, Zip 24014–1838, tel. 540/981–7000; CARILION ROANOKE COMMUNITY HOSPITAL, 101 Elm Avenue SE, Roanoke, Virginia, Zip 24013–2230, P O Box 12946, 24029–2946, tel. 540/985–8000; ROANOKE MEMORIAL REHABILITATION CENTER, South Jefferson and McClanahan Streets, Roanoke, Virginia, Zip 24014, P O Box 13367, 24033, tel. 703/342–4541) **A**1 2 3 5 8 10 13 **F**3 5 7 8 9 11 12 13 15 17 18 19 20 22 24 26 28 29 30 31 32 33 34 35 36 37 38 39 40 41 43 44 45 46 47 48 49 50 51 52 53 54 55 56 57 58 59 60 61 62 63 64 65 66 68 70 71 72 73 74 75 76 77 78 79 81 82 83 84 85 86 87 88 89 90 91 92 93 96 97 98 99 100 101 102 103 104 106 107 108 110 111 113 114 115 116 117 118 119 120 121 123 124 126 129 130 131 132 134 135 143 144 146 147 148 149 **P**6 **S** Carilion Clinic, Roanoke, VA
Primary Contact: Steven C. Arner, President
COO: Steven C. Arner, President
CFO: Donald B Halliwill, Executive Vice President and Chief Financial Officer
CHR: Heather S Shepardson, Vice President Human Resources
CNO: Margaret M. Scheaffel, Chief Nursing Officer
Web address: www.carilionclinic.org
Control: Other not–for–profit (including NFP Corporation) **Service:** General medical and surgical

Staffed Beds: 634 **Admissions:** 37795 **Census:** 559 **Outpatient Visits:** 258707 **Births:** 3262 **Total Expense ($000):** 1111230 **Payroll Expense ($000):** 488605 **Personnel:** 6447

ROCKY MOUNT—Franklin County

✠ **CARILION FRANKLIN MEMORIAL HOSPITAL (490089)**, 180 Floyd Avenue, Zip 24151–1389; tel. 540/483–5277 **A**1 3 10 **F**3 11 15 18 28 29 30 34 35 40 45 50 53 57 59 62 63 65 68 70 75 81 84 85 91 93 96 107 110 115 119 130 132 135 146 149 **P**6 **S** Carilion Clinic, Roanoke, VA
Primary Contact: William D. Jacobsen, FACHE, Administrator and Hospital Vice President
COO: Steven C. Arner, Executive Vice President of Administration
CFO: Donald B Halliwill, Chief Financial Officer
CMO: Patrice M Weiss, Executive Vice President, Administration
CIO: Robert Keith Perry, Senior Vice President, Chief Information Officer
CHR: Paul C. Hudgins, Senior Vice President
CNO: Margaret M. Scheaffel, Chief Nursing Officer
Web address: www.carilionclinic.org/CFMH
Control: Other not–for–profit (including NFP Corporation) **Service:** General medical and surgical

Staffed Beds: 12 **Admissions:** 1398 **Census:** 13 **Outpatient Visits:** 39945 **Births:** 0 **Total Expense ($000):** 36662 **Payroll Expense ($000):** 14544 **Personnel:** 251

SALEM—Salem City County

✠ **LEWIS–GALE MEDICAL CENTER (490048)**, 1900 Electric Road, Zip 24153–7494; tel. 540/776–4000, (Nonreporting) (Includes LEWIS–GALE PAVILION, 1902 Braeburn Drive, Salem, Virginia, Zip 24153–7391, tel. 703/772–2800) **A**1 2 10 **S** HCA Healthcare, Nashville, TN
Primary Contact: Brian Baumgardner, Chief Executive Officer
COO: Michael Abbott, Chief Operating Officer
CFO: Angela D Reynolds, Chief Financial Officer
CMO: Joseph Nelson M.D., President Medical Staff
CIO: Beth Cole, Director Information Services
CHR: Dale Beaudoin, Vice President Human Resources
Web address: www.lewis–gale.com
Control: Corporation, Investor–owned (for–profit) **Service:** General medical and surgical

Staffed Beds: 521

✠ **SALEM VETERANS AFFAIRS MEDICAL CENTER**, 1970 Roanoke Boulevard, Zip 24153–6478; tel. 540/982–2463, (Nonreporting) **A**1 3 5 8 **S** Department of Veterans Affairs, Washington, DC
Primary Contact: Rebecca J. Stackhouse, Medical Center Director
CFO: Codie Walker, Chief Financial Officer
CMO: Anne Hutchins M.D., Chief of Staff
CIO: Sharon Collins, Chief Information Officer
CHR: Brian Zeman, Chief Human Resources
CNO: Teresa England R.N., Ph.D., Nurse Executive
Web address: www.salem.va.gov
Control: Veterans Affairs, Government, federal **Service:** General medical and surgical

Staffed Beds: 200

SOUTH BOSTON—Halifax County

★ ⇑ **SENTARA HALIFAX REGIONAL HOSPITAL (490013)**, 2204 Wilborn Avenue, Zip 24592–1638; tel. 434/517–3100, (Total facility includes 384 beds in nursing home–type unit) **A**10 21 **F**3 11 13 14 15 17 18 20 28 29 30 31 34 35 38 39 40 41 44 45 46 47 48 50 51 56 57 59 60 61 62 63 64 65 68 70 74 75 76 77 78 79 81 82 84 85 86 87 89 92 93 94 96 97 100 101 102 103 104 107 108 110 111 114 115 116 117 118 119 127 128 129 130 131 132 135 145 146 147 148 149 **P**4 7 **S** Sentara Healthcare, Norfolk, VA
Primary Contact: Chris A. Lumsden, Chief Executive Officer
CFO: Stewart R Nelson, Chief Financial Officer
CMO: Said Iskandar M.D., Chief Medical Officer
CIO: William Zirkle, Manager Information Systems
CHR: Catherine Howard, Director Human Resources
CNO: Patricia F Thomas, Chief Nursing Officer
Web address: www.hrhs.org
Control: Other not–for–profit (including NFP Corporation) **Service:** General medical and surgical

Staffed Beds: 456 **Admissions:** 4346 **Census:** 387 **Outpatient Visits:** 97122 **Births:** 427 **Total Expense ($000):** 129786 **Payroll Expense ($000):** 56694 **Personnel:** 558

SOUTH HILL—Mecklenburg County

✠ **VCU HEALTH COMMUNITY MEMORIAL HOSPITAL (490098)**, 125 Buena Vista Circle, Zip 23970–1431, Mailing Address: P.O.Box 90, 23970–0090; tel. 434/447–3151, (Total facility includes 110 beds in nursing home–type unit) **A**1 2 10 20 **F**3 11 15 18 28 29 30 31 34 35 40 45 46 49 50 53 54 56 59 62 63 64 65 70 74 75 77 78 79 81 82 84 85 86 87 93 96 97 107 108 110 111 115 117 118 119 121 123 127 128 130 131 132 133 135 146 147 148 **S** VCU Health System, Richmond, VA
Primary Contact: W Scott. Burnette, Chief Executive Officer
CFO: Kenneth Libby, Vice President Finance
CMO: Manhal Saleeby M.D., Chief of Staff
CIO: Brian Rock, Director of Information Systems
CHR: Maria Stephens, PHR, SHRM–CP, Director Human Resources, Education and Occupational Health and Wellness
CNO: Ursula N Butts FACHE, Vice President of Patient Care Services
Web address: www.cmh–sh.org
Control: Other not–for–profit (including NFP Corporation) **Service:** General medical and surgical

Staffed Beds: 178 **Admissions:** 3030 **Census:** 141 **Outpatient Visits:** 127539 **Births:** 0 **Total Expense ($000):** 90189 **Payroll Expense ($000):** 35849 **Personnel:** 648

STAFFORD—Stafford County

✠ **STAFFORD HOSPITAL (490140)**, 101 Hospital Center Boulevard, Zip 22554–6200; tel. 540/741–9000 **A**1 5 10 **F**3 13 15 18 20 22 26 29 30 31 34 35 36 40 44 45 46 47 48 49 50 54 57 58 59 64 70 73 74 75 76 77 78 79 81 84 85 86 87 92 93 96 102 107 108 110 111 115 118 119 120 122 129 130 131 132 135 146 147 148 149 **S** Mary Washington Healthcare, Fredericksburg, VA
Primary Contact: Michael P. McDermott, M.D., President and Chief Executive Officer
COO: Thomas Gettinger, Executive Vice President and Chief Operating Officer
CFO: Sean Barden, Executive Vice President and Chief Financial Officer
CMO: Rebecca Bigoney, Executive Vice President and Chief Medical Officer
CIO: Justin K. Box, Senior Vice President and Chief Information Officer
CHR: Kathryn S Wall, Executive Vice President Human Resources and Organizational Development
CNO: Eileen L Dohmann R.N., Senior Vice President and Chief Nursing Officer
Web address: www.mwhc.com
Control: Other not–for–profit (including NFP Corporation) **Service:** General medical and surgical

Staffed Beds: 100 **Admissions:** 4616 **Census:** 43 **Outpatient Visits:** 64261 **Births:** 1123 **Total Expense ($000):** 84117 **Payroll Expense ($000):** 25966 **Personnel:** 346

STAUNTON—Staunton City County

COMMONWEALTH CENTER FOR CHILDREN AND ADOLESCENTS, 1355 Richmond Road, Zip 24401–9146, Mailing Address: Box 4000, 24402–4000; tel. 540/332–2100, (Nonreporting) **A**3 5 **S** Virginia Department of Mental Health, Richmond, VA
Primary Contact: Mary Clare. Smith, Acting Facility Director
Web address: www.ccca.dbhds.virginia.gov
Control: State, Government, Nonfederal **Service:** Children's other specialty

Staffed Beds: 60

VA

Hospital, Medicare Provider Number, Address, Telephone, Approval, Facility, and Physician Codes, Health Care System

★ American Hospital Association (AHA) membership ○ Healthcare Facilities Accreditation Program ⇑ Center for Improvement in Healthcare Quality Accreditation
□ The Joint Commission accreditation ◇ DNV Healthcare Inc. accreditation △ Commission on Accreditation of Rehabilitation Facilities (CARF) accreditation

☐ **WESTERN STATE HOSPITAL (494021)**, 103 Valley Center Drive, Zip 24401–9146, Mailing Address: P.O.Box 2500, 24402–2500; tel. 540/332–8000, (Nonreporting) **A**1 3 5 10 **S** Virginia Department of Mental Health, Richmond, VA
Primary Contact: Mary Clare. Smith, Director
CFO: Jon Chapman, Fiscal Officer
CMO: Jonathan Anderson, Medical Director
CIO: Sharon Johnson, Director Health Information Management
CHR: Kimberly Harman, Regional Manager Human Resources
CNO: Diane Pavalonis, Chief Nurse Executive
Web address: www.dbhds.virginia.gov
Control: State, Government, Nonfederal **Service**: Psychiatric

Staffed Beds: 260

STUART—Patrick County

★ ⇑ **PIONEER COMMUNITY HOSPITAL OF PATRICK (491306)**, 18688 Jeb Stuart Highway, Zip 24171–1559; tel. 276/694–3151 **A**10 18 21 **F**3 29 34 40 50 59 75 81 85 86 87 90 107 119 127 130 133 146 148 149 **P**5 **S** Pioneer Health Services, Magee, MS
Primary Contact: Jeanette Filpi, Chief Executive Officer
CFO: Julie Gieger, Chief Financial Officer
CMO: Richard C Cole, Chief of Staff
CIO: Jack York, Chief Information Officer
CHR: Paul Trussell, Vice President Human Resources
CNO: Gerald Grass, Chief Nursing Officer
Web address: www.pchpatrick.com
Control: Corporation, Investor–owned (for–profit) **Service**: General medical and surgical

Staffed Beds: 15 Admissions: 575 Census: 12 Outpatient Visits: 19589 Births: 2

SUFFOLK—Suffolk City County

★ ⇑ **SENTARA OBICI HOSPITAL (490044)**, 2800 Godwin Boulevard, Zip 23434–8038; tel. 757/934–4000 **A**2 3 5 10 21 **F**3 8 11 13 15 18 20 22 28 29 30 31 34 35 36 37 38 39 40 41 42 44 45 47 49 50 54 56 57 58 59 60 61 63 64 65 68 70 71 73 74 75 76 77 78 79 81 82 84 85 86 87 91 92 93 96 97 98 100 107 108 110 111 114 115 118 119 120 121 126 128 129 130 131 132 135 141 142 144 145 146 147 148 149 **P**6 **S** Sentara Healthcare, Norfolk, VA
Primary Contact: Steve Julian, M.D., President
CFO: Mike Mounie, Director Finance
CMO: Steve Julian M.D., Vice President Medical Affairs
CIO: Alice Oxton, Director Information Technology
CHR: Deborah Ferguson, Human Resources Consultant
Web address: www.sentara.com
Control: Other not–for–profit (including NFP Corporation) **Service**: General medical and surgical

Staffed Beds: 176 Admissions: 9421 Census: 106 Outpatient Visits: 335973 Births: 1433 Total Expense ($000): 177332 Payroll Expense ($000): 74910 Personnel: 1148

TAPPAHANNOCK—Essex County

⇑ **RIVERSIDE TAPPAHANNOCK HOSPITAL (490084)**, 618 Hospital Road, Zip 22560–5000; tel. 804/443–3311 **A**10 20 21 **F**3 11 15 18 26 29 30 31 34 35 36 37 38 40 44 45 49 50 51 55 56 57 59 60 62 63 64 70 74 75 77 78 79 81 82 84 85 86 87 91 92 93 97 100 102 103 107 108 110 111 115 116 117 118 119 129 130 131 132 133 135 144 146 147 148 **P**6 **S** Riverside Health System, Newport News, VA
Primary Contact: Esther Muscari. Desimini, Administrator
CFO: Jeri Sibley, Director Revenue Cycle
CMO: Richard Dunn M.D., Chief Medical Officer
CHR: Lindsey Custer, Director Human Resources
CNO: Judith Matthews, Nurse Executive
Web address: www.riverside–online.com
Control: Other not–for–profit (including NFP Corporation) **Service**: General medical and surgical

Staffed Beds: 16 Admissions: 1717 Census: 15 Outpatient Visits: 59272 Births: 0 Total Expense ($000): 58251 Payroll Expense ($000): 15188 Personnel: 211

TAZEWELL—Tazewell County

⊞ **CARILION TAZEWELL COMMUNITY HOSPITAL (490117)**, 141 Ben Bolt Avenue, Zip 24651–9700, Mailing Address: 388 Ben Bolt Avenue, 24651; tel. 276/988–8700 **A**1 10 **F**3 11 15 29 30 34 40 44 45 50 57 59 62 64 65 68 75 77 81 85 87 91 93 107 111 114 119 133 135 146 149 **P**6 **S** Carilion Clinic, Roanoke, VA
Primary Contact: Kathren Dowdy, MSN, Regional Hospital Senior Director
CMO: Kevin Combs, Chief of Staff
CHR: Carrie Boggess, Human Resources Generalist
CNO: Kathren Dowdy MSN, Senior Director, Chief Executive Officer and Chief Nursing Officer
Web address: www.carilionclinic.org
Control: Other not–for–profit (including NFP Corporation) **Service**: General medical and surgical

Staffed Beds: 6 Admissions: 595 Census: 6 Outpatient Visits: 14816 Births: 0 Total Expense ($000): 13917 Payroll Expense ($000): 5452 Personnel: 94

VIRGINIA BEACH—Virginia Beach City County

★ ⇑ **SENTARA PRINCESS ANNE HOSPITAL (490119)**, 2025 Glenn Mitchell Drive, Zip 23456–0178; tel. 757/507–1000 **A**2 3 5 10 21 **F**3 8 11 13 15 18 20 22 26 28 29 30 31 34 35 36 37 38 39 40 41 44 45 46 47 49 50 53 54 55 56 57 58 59 60 61 63 64 65 68 70 71 72 73 74 75 76 77 78 79 81 82 84 85 86 87 91 92 93 94 96 97 100 102 107 108 110 111 114 115 118 119 126 129 130 131 132 135 141 144 145 146 147 148 149 **P**6 **S** Sentara Healthcare, Norfolk, VA
Primary Contact: Thomas B. Thames, M.D., President
COO: Howard P Kern, Chief Operating Officer
CFO: Robert Broermann, Senior Vice President and Chief Financial Officer
CMO: Terry Gilliland M.D., Senior Vice President and Chief Medical Officer
CIO: Bert Reese, Chief Information Officer
CHR: Michael V Taylor, Vice President Human Resources
CNO: Grace Myers MSN, Vice President, Nurse Executive
Web address: www.sentara.com
Control: Other not–for–profit (including NFP Corporation) **Service**: General medical and surgical

Staffed Beds: 160 Admissions: 11733 Census: 135 Outpatient Visits: 368710 Births: 2546 Total Expense ($000): 207537 Payroll Expense ($000): 69344 Personnel: 1415

★ ⇑ **SENTARA VIRGINIA BEACH GENERAL HOSPITAL (490057)**, 1060 First Colonial Road, Zip 23454–3002; tel. 757/395–8000 **A**2 3 5 10 21 **F**3 5 11 15 17 18 20 22 24 26 28 29 30 31 34 36 37 38 39 40 41 42 43 44 45 46 47 48 49 50 51 53 54 55 56 57 58 59 60 61 63 64 65 68 70 71 74 75 77 78 79 81 82 84 85 86 87 90 92 93 94 96 97 98 100 101 102 103 107 108 109 110 111 114 115 118 119 120 121 123 126 129 130 131 132 135 141 142 144 145 146 147 148 149 **P**6 **S** Sentara Healthcare, Norfolk, VA
Primary Contact: Elwood Bernard. Boone III, FACHE, President
CFO: Marley Nacey, Director Finance
CHR: Michelle Meekins, Manager Human Resources
CNO: Peggy Braun R.N., Vice President Patient Care Services and Chief Nurse Executive
Web address: www.sentara.com
Control: Other not–for–profit (including NFP Corporation) **Service**: General medical and surgical

Staffed Beds: 259 Admissions: 13783 Census: 196 Outpatient Visits: 439767 Births: 0 Total Expense ($000): 254505 Payroll Expense ($000): 110896 Personnel: 1717

☐ **VIRGINIA BEACH PSYCHIATRIC CENTER (494025)**, 1100 First Colonial Road, Zip 23454–2403; tel. 757/496–6000 (Nonreporting) **A**1 10 **S** Universal Health Services, Inc., King of Prussia, PA
Primary Contact: Dustin Davis, Chief Executive Officer
Web address: www.vbpcweb.com
Control: Corporation, Investor–owned (for–profit) **Service**: Psychiatric

Staffed Beds: 100

WARRENTON—Fauquier County

⊞ △ **FAUQUIER HOSPITAL (490023)**, 500 Hospital Drive, Zip 20186–3099; tel. 540/316–5000, (Nonreporting) **A**1 2 5 7 10 **S** LifePoint Health, Brentwood, TN
Primary Contact: Chad Melton, Chief Executive Officer
CFO: Lionel J Phillips, Vice President Financial Services
CMO: Anhtai H Nguyen M.D., FACS, Vice President Medical Affairs and Chief Medical Officer
CIO: Donna Staton, Chief Information Officer
CHR: Katy Reeves, Vice President Human Resources
CNO: Linda Sharkey R.N., MSN, Vice President Patient Care Services and Chief Nurse Executive
Web address: www.fauquierhospital.org
Control: Other not–for–profit (including NFP Corporation) **Service**: General medical and surgical

Staffed Beds: 86

VA

WILLIAMSBURG—James City County

☐ **EASTERN STATE HOSPITAL (490109)**, 4601 Ironbound Road, Zip 23188–2652; tel. 757/253–5161, (Nonreporting) **A**1 3 5 10 **S** Virginia Department of Mental Health, Richmond, VA
Primary Contact: John M. Favret, Director
CFO: E Clifford Love, Director Fiscal Services
CMO: Guillermo Schrader M.D., Acting Medical Director
CIO: Barbara Lambert, Director Healthcare Compliance
CHR: Edie Rogan, Manager Human Resources
Web address: www.esh.dmhmrsas.virginia.gov/
Control: State, Government, Nonfederal **Service**: Psychiatric

Staffed Beds: 334

☐ ⇑ **RIVERSIDE DOCTORS' HOSPITAL (490143)**, 1500 Commonwealth Avenue, Zip 23185–5229; tel. 757/585–2200 **A**1 10 21 **F**3 11 28 29 34 35 40 44 45 50 57 59 64 70 74 75 77 79 81 82 85 86 87 91 92 107 108 115 118 119 120 121 123 130 132 146 148 149 **P**6 **S** Riverside Health System, Newport News, VA
Primary Contact: Adria Vanhoozier, Administrator
CNO: Arlene Messina R.N., MSN, Director of Nursing
Web address: www.riversideonline.com/rdhw
Control: Other not–for–profit (including NFP Corporation) **Service**: General medical and surgical

Staffed Beds: 13 **Admissions**: 1511 **Census**: 13 **Outpatient Visits**: 27485 **Births**: 0 **Total Expense ($000)**: 42349 **Payroll Expense ($000)**: 11731 **Personnel**: 222

WILLIAMSBURG—York County

★ ⇑ **SENTARA WILLIAMSBURG REGIONAL MEDICAL CENTER (490066)**, 100 Sentara Circle, Zip 23188–5713; tel. 757/984–6000 **A**2 10 21 **F**3 8 11 13 15 18 20 22 28 29 30 31 34 35 36 37 39 40 41 43 44 45 46 47 48 49 50 51 54 55 56 57 58 59 60 61 63 64 65 68 70 74 75 76 77 78 79 81 82 84 85 86 87 89 90 91 92 93 94 96 97 100 102 103 107 108 110 111 114 115 116 117 118 119 129 130 131 132 135 141 144 145 146 147 148 149 **P**6 **S** Sentara Healthcare, Norfolk, VA
Primary Contact: David J. Masterson, President
CFO: Andreas Roehrle, Director Finance
CMO: Joe Robbins M.D., Vice President Medical Affairs
CIO: Mike Freeman, Director Information Technology
CHR: Lois B Demerich, Director Human Resources
CNO: Donna Wilmoth, Vice President Patient Care Services and Chief Nursing Officer
Web address: www.sentara.com
Control: Other not–for–profit (including NFP Corporation) **Service**: General medical and surgical

Staffed Beds: 145 **Admissions**: 7318 **Census**: 76 **Outpatient Visits**: 299204 **Births**: 965 **Total Expense ($000)**: 149600 **Payroll Expense ($000)**: 61587 **Personnel**: 911

☐ **THE PAVILION AT WILLIAMSBURG PLACE (494032)**, 5483 Mooretown Road, Zip 23188–2108; tel. 757/565–0106 (Nonreporting) **A**1 10
Primary Contact: Shirley Repta, Chief Executive Officer
CMO: Avtar Dhilion, Medical Director
CNO: Shedale Tindall, Chief Nursing Officer
Web address: www.pavilionwp.com
Control: Corporation, Investor–owned (for–profit) **Service**: Psychiatric

Staffed Beds: 57

WINCHESTER—Winchester City County

✠ **WINCHESTER MEDICAL CENTER (490005)**, 1840 Amherst Street, Zip 22601–2808, Mailing Address: P.O.Box 3340, 22604–2540; tel. 540/536–8000 **A**1 2 3 5 10 **F**3 5 11 12 13 15 17 18 20 22 24 26 28 29 30 31 32 34 35 38 39 40 41 43 44 45 46 47 49 50 51 54 55 56 57 58 59 61 62 64 65 66 68 70 71 72 74 75 76 77 78 79 80 81 82 84 85 86 87 89 90 91 92 93 97 98 100 101 102 103 104 107 108 110 111 114 115 116 117 118 119 120 121 123 124 126 129 130 131 132 135 136 146 147 148 **P**5 **S** Valley Health System, Winchester, VA
Primary Contact: Grady W. Philips III, President
CFO: Robert Amos, Vice President and Chief Financial Officer
CMO: Nicolas Restrepo M.D., Vice President Medical Affairs
CIO: Joan Roscoe, Chief Information Officer
CHR: Elizabeth Savage, Vice President and Human Resources Officer
CNO: Anne Whiteside, Vice President Nursing
Web address: www.valleyhealthlink.com/WMC
Control: Other not–for–profit (including NFP Corporation) **Service**: General medical and surgical

Staffed Beds: 485 **Admissions**: 22428 **Census**: 311 **Outpatient Visits**: 368572 **Births**: 2207 **Total Expense ($000)**: 532010 **Payroll Expense ($000)**: 170926 **Personnel**: 2422

WOODBRIDGE—Prince William County

★ ⇑ **SENTARA NORTHERN VIRGINIA MEDICAL CENTER (490113)**, 2300 Opitz Boulevard, Zip 22191–3399; tel. 703/523–1000 **A**2 10 21 **F**3 7 8 11 12 13 15 18 20 22 28 29 30 31 34 35 40 41 42 44 45 49 50 54 55 56 57 59 60 61 62 63 64 65 66 68 70 71 72 74 75 76 77 78 79 81 82 85 86 87 91 92 93 94 96 99 100 102 107 108 110 111 114 115 118 119 121 126 130 131 132 135 141 143 145 146 147 148 149 **P**6 **S** Sentara Healthcare, Norfolk, VA
Primary Contact: Katherine Johnson, Ph.D., President
CMO: David M Schwartz D.O., Vice President, Medical Affairs
CIO: Thomas Ewing, Director Information Technology
CHR: Brett Willsie, Vice President Human Resources
CNO: Valerie E Keane FACHE, Chief Nursing Executive
Web address: www.sentara.com/northernvirginia
Control: Other not–for–profit (including NFP Corporation) **Service**: General medical and surgical

Staffed Beds: 181 **Admissions**: 9997 **Census**: 106 **Outpatient Visits**: 328785 **Births**: 1746 **Total Expense ($000)**: 221815 **Payroll Expense ($000)**: 76023 **Personnel**: 1134

WOODSTOCK—Shenandoah County

✠ **SHENANDOAH MEMORIAL HOSPITAL (491305)**, 759 South Main Street, Zip 22664–1127; tel. 540/459–1100 **A**1 10 18 **F**3 11 15 28 29 30 35 40 45 50 53 57 59 64 65 68 69 70 75 77 79 81 82 87 92 93 97 107 108 110 114 118 119 130 132 133 135 146 148 **S** Valley Health System, Winchester, VA
Primary Contact: N Travis. Clark, President
CFO: Phillip Graybeal CPA, Vice President, Finance
CMO: Greg Byrd, Vice President Medical Affairs
CIO: James Burton, Vice President and Chief Information Officer, Valley Health
CHR: Abbey Rembold, Manager, Human Resource Business Partnerships
CNO: Lisa Heishman R.N., Vice President
Web address: www.valleyhealthlink.com/shenandoah
Control: Other not–for–profit (including NFP Corporation) **Service**: General medical and surgical

Staffed Beds: 25 **Admissions**: 1521 **Census**: 15 **Outpatient Visits**: 66361 **Births**: 0 **Total Expense ($000)**: 51545 **Payroll Expense ($000)**: 19727 **Personnel**: 248

WYTHEVILLE—Wythe County

✠ **WYTHE COUNTY COMMUNITY HOSPITAL (490111)**, 600 West Ridge Road, Zip 24382–1099; tel. 276/228–0200 **A**1 10 20 **F**3 13 15 18 26 28 29 32 34 35 37 40 45 50 51 55 57 59 62 63 64 65 68 70 75 76 77 79 81 82 84 85 86 87 91 92 93 107 110 111 114 119 128 129 131 132 133 135 146 147 148 **S** LifePoint Health, Brentwood, TN
Primary Contact: Adam Martin, Chief Operating Officer and Interim Chief Executive Officer
COO: Adam Martin, Chief Operating Officer
CFO: John D White, Chief Financial Officer
CMO: George Farrell M.D., Chief of Staff
CIO: Andrea Harless, Director Information Services
CHR: Kristie Walker, Director of Human Resources
CNO: Theresa Dix R.N., Chief Nursing Officer
Web address: www.wcchcares.com
Control: Corporation, Investor–owned (for–profit) **Service**: General medical and surgical

Staffed Beds: 70 **Admissions**: 2296 **Census**: 23 **Outpatient Visits**: 63180 **Births**: 326 **Total Expense ($000)**: 38550 **Payroll Expense ($000)**: 15274 **Personnel**: 265

VA

Hospital, Medicare Provider Number, Address, Telephone, Approval, Facility, and Physician Codes, Health Care System

★ American Hospital Association (AHA) membership
☐ The Joint Commission accreditation
○ Healthcare Facilities Accreditation Program
◇ DNV Healthcare Inc. accreditation
⇑ Center for Improvement in Healthcare Quality Accreditation
△ Commission on Accreditation of Rehabilitation Facilities (CARF) accreditation

WASHINGTON

ABERDEEN—Grays Harbor County

☐ **GRAYS HARBOR COMMUNITY HOSPITAL (500031)**, 915 Anderson Drive, Zip 98520–1097; tel. 360/532–8330 **A**1 10 20 **F**1 3 15 32 34 35 40 43 50 54 59 64 65 67 75 82 86 90 97 107 110 119 127 128 130 146
Primary Contact: Tom Jensen, Chief Executive Officer
COO: Larry Kahl R.N., Chief Operating Officer
CFO: Joe Vessey, Chief Financial Officer
CMO: Anne Marie Wong M.D., Chief Medical Officer
CIO: Brad Wallace, Director Information Services
CHR: Julie Feller, Executive Director Human Resources
Web address: www.ghcares.org
Control: Other not–for–profit (including NFP Corporation) **Service**: General medical and surgical

> **Staffed Beds**: 105 **Admissions**: 2878 **Census**: 28 **Births**: 461 **Total Expense ($000)**: 104081 **Payroll Expense ($000)**: 40994

ANACORTES—Skagit County

★ ⇑ **ISLAND HOSPITAL (500007)**, 1211 24th Street, Zip 98221–2562; tel. 360/299–1300 **A**2 10 21 **F**3 8 11 13 15 28 29 30 31 34 35 40 43 45 50 53 57 59 62 64 70 75 76 77 78 79 81 82 85 86 89 93 96 97 99 100 104 107 108 110 111 114 115 116 119 127 129 130 132 134 135 144 146 147 148 149 **P**6
Primary Contact: Vincent Oliver, FACHE, Administrator
CFO: Elise Cutter, Chief Financial Officer
CIO: Tom Bluhm, Director Information Systems
CNO: Lois Pate R.N., Chief Nursing Officer
Web address: www.islandhospital.org
Control: Hospital district or authority, Government, Nonfederal **Service**: General medical and surgical

> **Staffed Beds**: 43 **Admissions**: 3037 **Census**: 26 **Outpatient Visits**: 218139 **Births**: 435 **Total Expense ($000)**: 98362 **Payroll Expense ($000)**: 41550 **Personnel**: 611

ARLINGTON—Snohomish County

⇑ **CASCADE VALLEY HOSPITAL AND CLINICS (500060)**, 330 South Stillaguamish Avenue, Zip 98223–1642; tel. 360/435–2133, (Nonreporting) **A**10 21 **S** Skagit Regional Health, Mount Vernon, WA
Primary Contact: Michael Liepman, Chief Executive Officer
CFO: Thomas Litaker, Regional Vice President and Chief Financial Officer
CMO: Peter Wolff M.D., President Medical Staff
CIO: John Dwight, Regional Vice President and Chief Information Officer
CHR: Deborah Martin, Regional Vice President Human Resources
CNO: Michelle Sand R.N., MSN, Vice President and Chief Nursing Officer
Web address: www.cascadevalley.org
Control: Hospital district or authority, Government, Nonfederal **Service**: General medical and surgical

> **Staffed Beds**: 48

AUBURN—King County

☐ △ **MULTICARE AUBURN MEDICAL CENTER (500015)**, 202 North Division, Plaza One, Zip 98001–4908; tel. 253/833–7711 **A**1 7 10 **F**3 13 18 20 22 28 29 30 34 35 40 41 43 45 49 51 57 64 65 68 70 73 74 75 76 77 79 81 84 85 87 93 96 98 102 103 107 108 111 114 115 119 126 129 130 132 135 146 148 **S** MultiCare Health System, Tacoma, WA
Primary Contact: Mark Smith, President and Chief Operating Officer
CFO: Anna Loomis, Senior Vice President Chief Financial Officer
CMO: Chad Krilich M.D., Chief Med Officer–AMC/CMC
CHR: Kevin B Dull, Senior Vice President Human Potential
CNO: Roseanna Bell, Chief Nurse Executive
Web address: www.multicare.org/auburn–medical–center/
Control: Other not–for–profit (including NFP Corporation) **Service**: General medical and surgical

> **Staffed Beds**: 153 **Admissions**: 6693 **Census**: 103 **Outpatient Visits**: 66193 **Births**: 1203 **Total Expense ($000)**: 176309 **Payroll Expense ($000)**: 70725 **Personnel**: 781

BELLEVUE—King County

⊞ **OVERLAKE MEDICAL CENTER (500051)**, 1035 116th Avenue NE, Zip 98004–4604; tel. 425/688–5000 **A**1 2 10 **F**3 11 12 13 15 17 18 20 22 24 26 29 30 31 34 35 36 37 38 39 40 41 43 44 45 46 47 48 49 54 55 56 57 58 59 61 64 65 68 70 72 73 74 75 76 77 78 79 81 82 84 85 86 87 92 93 97 98 100 101 102 103 104 105 107 108 110 111 114 115 116 117 118 119 120 121 123 124 126 130 131 132 134 135 144 145 146 147 148 149 **P**6
Primary Contact: J. Michael. Marsh, President and Chief Executive Officer
COO: Thomas DeBord, Chief Operating Officer
CFO: Andrew Tokar, Interim Chief Financial Officer
CMO: David Knoepfler M.D., Chief Medical Officer
CHR: Lisa M Brock, Chief Human Resource Officer
CNO: Julie Clayton, Chief Nursing Officer and Vice President Patient Care Services
Web address: www.overlakehospital.org
Control: Other not–for–profit (including NFP Corporation) **Service**: General medical and surgical

> **Staffed Beds**: 282 **Admissions**: 18115 **Census**: 178 **Outpatient Visits**: 239162 **Births**: 3944 **Total Expense ($000)**: 496268 **Payroll Expense ($000)**: 208473 **Personnel**: 2192

BELLINGHAM—Whatcom County

★ △ ⇑ **PEACEHEALTH ST. JOSEPH MEDICAL CENTER (500030)**, 2901 Squalicum Parkway, Zip 98225–1851; tel. 360/734–5400 **A**2 5 7 10 20 21 **F**2 3 13 17 18 20 22 24 26 28 29 30 31 34 35 40 41 43 45 46 47 48 49 50 51 56 57 58 59 63 64 65 70 74 75 76 77 78 79 81 84 85 86 87 89 90 92 93 94 96 97 98 106 107 108 109 114 115 118 119 120 121 123 129 130 131 132 135 141 146 148 **S** PeaceHealth, Vancouver, WA
Primary Contact: Dale Zender, President Hospital Services NW
COO: Stephen R Omta, Chief Operating Officer
CFO: Carolyn Foster, Interim Executive Director and Chief Financial Officer
CMO: Chris Sprowl M.D., Vice President
CIO: Kelly Lundy, Chief Information Officer
CHR: Cindy C Klein, Vice President Human Resources
Web address: www.peacehealth.org
Control: Church operated, Nongovernment, not–for–profit **Service**: General medical and surgical

> **Staffed Beds**: 253 **Admissions**: 15102 **Census**: 179 **Births**: 1878 **Total Expense ($000)**: 493283 **Payroll Expense ($000)**: 183310

⇑ **ST. JOSEPH HOSPITAL** See Peacehealth St. Joseph Medical Center

BREMERTON—Kitsap County

⊞ **HARRISON MEDICAL CENTER (500039)**, 2520 Cherry Avenue, Zip 98310–4229; tel. 360/744–3911 **A**1 2 10 **F**3 11 12 13 15 18 20 22 24 26 28 29 30 31 34 35 38 40 43 44 45 46 47 49 54 57 59 64 70 73 74 75 76 77 78 79 80 81 82 84 85 86 87 93 94 96 107 108 110 111 114 115 117 119 120 121 124 126 129 130 132 135 144 146 147 148 149 **S** Catholic Health Initiatives, Englewood, CO
Primary Contact: David W. Schultz, FACHE, Market President, Peninsula Region
CFO: Mike Fitzgerald, Chief Financial Officer
CIO: Rand Strobel, Regional Chief Information Officer, Information Technology Services
CHR: Marie LaMarche, Executive Director, Human Resources, Organizational Development, Employee Health
CNO: Jeanell Rasmussen R.N., Vice President Patient Care Services and Chief Nursing Officer
Web address: www.harrisonmedical.org
Control: Church operated, Nongovernment, not–for–profit **Service**: General medical and surgical

> **Staffed Beds**: 260 **Admissions**: 12892 **Census**: 149 **Outpatient Visits**: 297003 **Births**: 1924

⊞ **NAVAL HOSPITAL BREMERTON**, One Boone Road, Zip 98312–1898; tel. 360/475–4000, (Nonreporting) **A**1 3 5 **S** Bureau of Medicine and Surgery, Department of the Navy, Falls Church, VA
Primary Contact: Commander David Weiss, Commanding Officer
CFO: Judith Hogan, Comptroller and Director Resources and Logistics
CIO: Patrick Flaherty, Director Management Information
Web address: www.med.navy.mil/sites/nhbrem/Pages/default.aspx
Control: Navy, Government, federal **Service**: General medical and surgical

> **Staffed Beds**: 30

Many Facility Codes have changed. Please refer to the AHA Guide Code Chart. © 2017 AHA Guide

BREWSTER—Okanogan County

THREE RIVERS HOSPITAL (501324), 507 Hospital Way, Zip 98812–0577, Mailing Address: P.O.Box 577, 98812–0577; tel. 509/689–2517, (Nonreporting) **A**10 18
Primary Contact: Scott Graham, Chief Executive Officer
CFO: Jennifer Munson, Chief Financial Officer
CMO: Gordon Tagge M.D., President Medical Staff
CIO: Edgar Alejandro Arellano, Chief Information Technologist
CHR: Anita Fisk, Director Human Resources
CNO: Gretchen Aguilar, Director Patient Care and Chief Nursing Officer
Web address: www.threerivershospital.net
Control: Hospital district or authority, Government, Nonfederal **Service:** General medical and surgical

Staffed Beds: 20

BURIEN—King County

☒ △ **HIGHLINE MEDICAL CENTER (500011)**, 16251 Sylvester Road SW, Zip 98166–3052; tel. 206/244–9970 **A**1 2 7 10 **F**3 8 11 13 15 18 29 30 34 35 38 40 43 44 45 49 50 51 57 59 70 72 74 75 76 79 80 81 85 86 87 92 93 107 108 110 111 114 115 117 119 130 132 135 146 147 149 **S** Catholic Health Initiatives, Englewood, CO
Primary Contact: Anthony McLean, President
CMO: Dennis De Leon M.D., Associate Chief Medical Officer and Vice President Medical Affairs
CHR: Grace M Henley, Assistant Administrator Human Resources
CNO: Kim Baisch R.N., Associate Vice President Patient Care Services
Web address: www.hchnet.org
Control: Church operated, Nongovernment, not–for–profit **Service:** General medical and surgical

Staffed Beds: 128 **Admissions:** 7193 **Census:** 86 **Outpatient Visits:** 110289 **Births:** 867

☒ **REGIONAL HOSPITAL FOR RESPIRATORY AND COMPLEX CARE (502001)**, 16251 Sylvester Road SW, Zip 98166–3017; tel. 206/248–4548 **A**1 10 **F**1 29 30 44 50 75 85 87 130 135 148 149 **S** Catholic Health Initiatives, Englewood, CO
Primary Contact: Anne McBride, Chief Executive Officer
CMO: Embra Roper, Chief Medical Officer
CHR: Valerie Albano, Director, Human Resources
CNO: Christi Sifri, Chief Nursing Executive
Web address: www.regionalhospital.org
Control: Church operated, Nongovernment, not–for–profit **Service:** Acute long–term care hospital

Staffed Beds: 26 **Admissions:** 187 **Census:** 20 **Outpatient Visits:** 0 **Births:** 0

CENTRALIA—Lewis County

☒ **PROVIDENCE CENTRALIA HOSPITAL (500019)**, 914 South Scheuber Road, Zip 98531–9027; tel. 360/736–2803 **A**1 3 10 20 **F**3 8 11 13 15 29 30 31 34 35 40 43 50 51 57 58 59 64 68 70 75 76 77 78 79 80 81 82 84 85 86 87 93 107 108 110 111 114 115 116 117 118 119 120 121 123 124 130 132 146 148 149 150 **S** Providence St. Joseph Health, Renton, WA
Primary Contact: Medrice Coluccio, R.N., Southwest Region Chief Executive
CFO: Denise Marroni, Chief Financial Officer
CMO: Kevin Caserta M.D., Chief Medical Officer
CIO: Kerry Miles, Site Director
CHR: Susan Meenk, Vice President Service Area
CNO: Michelle James, Regional Chief Nursing Officer
Web address: www.providence.org
Control: Church operated, Nongovernment, not–for–profit **Service:** General medical and surgical

Staffed Beds: 91 **Admissions:** 5340 **Census:** 50 **Outpatient Visits:** 301560 **Births:** 717 **Personnel:** 650

CHELAN—Chelan County

★ **LAKE CHELAN COMMUNITY HOSPITAL AND CLINICS (501334)**, 503 East Highland Avenue, Zip 98816–8631, Mailing Address: P.O.Box 908, 98816–0908; tel. 509/682–3300 **A**10 18 **F**5 7 8 11 13 15 29 30 32 34 35 36 38 40 41 43 44 45 50 56 57 59 63 64 65 66 68 71 74 75 76 77 79 80 81 84 85 86 87 91 92 93 94 97 99 100 101 104 106 107 108 110 111 119 127 130 131 132 133 134 135 143 144 146 147 149 **P**6
Primary Contact: Kevin Abel, Chief Executive Officer
COO: Brad Hankins, Chief Operating Quality Officer
CFO: Vickie Bodle, Chief Financial Officer
CMO: Ty Witt M.D., Chief Medical Officer
CIO: Ross Hurd, Chief Information Officer
CHR: DeLynn K Barnett, Director Human Resources
Web address: www.lakechelancommunityhospital.com
Control: Hospital district or authority, Government, Nonfederal **Service:** General medical and surgical

Staffed Beds: 25 **Admissions:** 740 **Census:** 16 **Outpatient Visits:** 27795 **Births:** 114 **Total Expense ($000):** 27118 **Payroll Expense ($000):** 16023 **Personnel:** 232

CHEWELAH—Stevens County

☒ **PROVIDENCE ST. JOSEPH'S HOSPITAL (501309)**, 500 East Webster Street, Zip 99109–9523; tel. 509/935–8211, (Total facility includes 40 beds in nursing home–type unit) **A**1 10 18 **F**3 8 10 11 15 29 30 34 35 40 43 44 45 57 59 65 75 79 81 82 84 87 91 93 107 114 119 128 133 146 148 **P**6 **S** Providence St. Joseph Health, Renton, WA
Primary Contact: Ronald G. Rehn, Chief Executive Officer
CFO: Helen Andrus, Chief Financial Officer
CMO: Jeff Collins, Chief Medical Officer
CNO: Deborah Watson R.N., Chief Nursing Officer
Web address: www.washington.providence.org/hospitals/st–josephs–hospital/
Control: Church operated, Nongovernment, not–for–profit **Service:** General medical and surgical

Staffed Beds: 55 **Admissions:** 523 **Census:** 47 **Outpatient Visits:** 26082 **Births:** 0 **Total Expense ($000):** 15572 **Payroll Expense ($000):** 9326 **Personnel:** 153

CLARKSTON—Asotin County

★ ⇑ **TRI–STATE MEMORIAL HOSPITAL (501332)**, 1221 Highland Avenue, Zip 99403–2829, Mailing Address: P.O.Box 189, 99403–0189; tel. 509/758–5511 **A**10 18 21 **F**3 8 11 15 34 40 43 45 57 59 60 65 70 75 79 81 82 85 107 110 111 119 129 130 132 133 135 144 146 147 148 **P**6
Primary Contact: Donald Wee, Chief Executive Officer
CFO: Alex Town, Vice President Finance
CMO: Don Greggain M.D., Physician Network Director
CIO: Joleen Carper, Vice President Quality and Risk
CHR: Regana Davis, Vice President Human Resources
CNO: Rhonda Mason, Vice President of Patient Care Services
Web address: www.tsmh.org
Control: Other not–for–profit (including NFP Corporation) **Service:** General medical and surgical

Staffed Beds: 25 **Admissions:** 1210 **Census:** 11

COLFAX—Whitman County

★ **WHITMAN HOSPITAL AND MEDICAL CENTER (501327)**, 1200 West Fairview Street, Zip 99111–9579; tel. 509/397–3435 **A**10 18 **F**3 13 15 29 34 35 40 43 45 50 53 64 68 75 76 79 81 84 85 87 89 93 107 110 111 114 119 130 133 149 **P**6 **S** Providence St. Joseph Health, Renton, WA
Primary Contact: Hank Hanigan, MS, R.N., Chief Executive Officer
CFO: Hank Hanigan MS, R.N., Interim Chief Financial Officer
CMO: Jeffrey Jones, Chief of Staff
CHR: Michelle Ellis, Director Human Resources
CNO: Sandy Fitzmaurice MS, R.N., Interim Chief Nursing Officer
Web address: www.whitmanhospital.org
Control: Hospital district or authority, Government, Nonfederal **Service:** General medical and surgical

Staffed Beds: 25 **Admissions:** 497 **Census:** 5 **Outpatient Visits:** 14759 **Births:** 41

COLVILLE—Stevens County

☒ **PROVIDENCE MOUNT CARMEL HOSPITAL (501326)**, 982 East Columbia Avenue, Zip 99114–3352; tel. 509/685–5100 **A**1 3 10 18 **F**3 11 13 15 29 30 34 40 43 44 45 57 59 64 70 75 76 77 79 81 82 84 85 86 87 93 107 108 115 118 119 123 129 131 132 133 135 146 148 **P**6 **S** Providence St. Joseph Health, Renton, WA
Primary Contact: Ronald G. Rehn, Chief Executive Officer
CFO: Helen Andrus, Chief Financial Officer
CNO: Deborah Watson R.N., Chief Nursing Officer
Web address: www.mtcarmelhospital.org
Control: Church operated, Nongovernment, not–for–profit **Service:** General medical and surgical

Staffed Beds: 25 **Admissions:** 1145 **Census:** 14 **Outpatient Visits:** 72119 **Births:** 228 **Total Expense ($000):** 31101 **Payroll Expense ($000):** 15324 **Personnel:** 238

COUPEVILLE—Island County

★ **WHIDBEYHEALTH (501339)**, 101 North Main Street, Zip 98239–3413; tel. 360/678–5151, (Nonreporting) **A**2 10 18
Primary Contact: Geri Forbes, Chief Executive Officer
CMO: Gabe Barrio M.D., Chief of Staff
CNO: Linda Stephens Gipson MSN, Ph.D., Chief Nursing Officer
Web address: www.whidbeygen.org
Control: Hospital district or authority, Government, Nonfederal **Service:** General medical and surgical

Staffed Beds: 25

WA

Hospital, Medicare Provider Number, Address, Telephone, Approval, Facility, and Physician Codes, Health Care System

★ American Hospital Association (AHA) membership
□ The Joint Commission accreditation
○ Healthcare Facilities Accreditation Program
◇ DNV Healthcare Inc. accreditation
⇑ Center for Improvement in Healthcare Quality Accreditation
△ Commission on Accreditation of Rehabilitation Facilities (CARF) accreditation

DAVENPORT—Lincoln County

★ **LINCOLN HOSPITAL (501305)**, 10 Nicholls Street, Zip 99122–9729;
tel. 509/725–7101, (Nonreporting) **A**10 18
Primary Contact: Tyson Lacy, Chief Executive Officer and Superintendent
CFO: Tim O'Connell, Chief Financial Officer
CMO: Fred Reed M.D., Chief of Staff
CIO: Elliott Donson, Chief Information Specialist
CHR: Becky Bailey, Director Human Resources
CNO: Jennifer Larmer R.N., Chief Clinical Officer
Web address: www.lincolnhospital.org
Control: Hospital district or authority, Government, Nonfederal **Service:** General
medical and surgical

Staffed Beds: 60

DAYTON—Columbia County

COLUMBIA COUNTY HEALTH SYSTEM (501302), 1012 South Third Street,
Zip 99328–1696; tel. 509/382–2531 **A**10 18 **F**3 11 34 35 40 43 50 57 59 64
65 68 75 77 85 87 93 97 107 111 127 130 132 133 135 143 146 148 **P**6
Primary Contact: Shane McGuire, Chief Executive Officer
CFO: Lee H Holter, Chief Financial Officer
CHR: Steven J Stahl, Director Human Resources
CNO: Stephanie Carpenter, Director of Nursing Services
Web address: www.cchd–wa.org
Control: Hospital district or authority, Government, Nonfederal **Service:** General
medical and surgical

Staffed Beds: 44 Admissions: 209 Census: 34

EDMONDS—Snohomish County

⇑ **STEVENS HEALTHCARE** See Swedish/Edmonds

★ ⇑ **SWEDISH/EDMONDS (500026)**, 21601 76th Avenue West, Zip 98026–
7506; tel. 425/640–4000 **A**2 10 21 **F**2 3 11 13 15 18 20 22 26 28 29 30 31
34 35 38 40 41 43 45 49 56 59 60 61 64 65 68 70 73 74 75 76 77 78 79
81 82 84 85 87 91 92 93 96 98 100 101 102 104 105 107 108 111 114 115
116 119 124 126 129 130 131 132 135 141 146 147 148 149 **P**6 **S** Swedish
Health Services, Seattle, WA
Primary Contact: Sarah Zabel, Vice President, Operations
CMO: Sandeep Sachdeva M.D., Vice President Medical Affairs
CNO: Jean Doerge R.N., MSN, Nurse Executive
Web address: www.swedish.org
Control: Other not–for–profit (including NFP Corporation) **Service:** General
medical and surgical

Staffed Beds: 164 Admissions: 10517 Census: 123 Outpatient Visits: 153262 Births: 1230 Total Expense ($000): 259118 Payroll Expense ($000): 93834 Personnel: 1062

ELLENSBURG—Kittitas County

★ **KITTITAS VALLEY HEALTHCARE (501333)**, 603 South Chestnut Street,
Zip 98926–3875; tel. 509/962–7302, (Nonreporting) **A**3 10 18
Primary Contact: Julie Petersen, Chief Executive Officer
COO: Catherine Bambrick, Chief Operating Officer
CFO: Libby Allgood, Chief Financial Officer
CMO: Don Solberg M.D., Chief Medical Officer
CNO: Rhonda C Holden R.N., MSN, Chief Nursing Officer
Web address: www.kvhealthcare.org
Control: Hospital district or authority, Government, Nonfederal **Service:** General
medical and surgical

Staffed Beds: 25

ELMA—Grays Harbor County

SUMMIT PACIFIC MEDICAL CENTER (501304), 600 East Main Street,
Zip 98541–9560; tel. 360/346–2222, (Nonreporting) **A**10 18
Primary Contact: Josh Martin, Chief Executive Officer
COO: Josh Martin, Chief Operating Officer
CFO: William Callicoat, Chief Financial Officer
CMO: William Hurley M.D., Chief Medical Officer
CIO: Jeff Painter, Manager Information Technology
CHR: Mindy Portchy, Manager Human Resources
CNO: Brenda West R.N., MSN, Chief Nursing Officer
Web address: www.markreed.org
Control: Corporation, Investor–owned (for–profit) **Service:** General medical and
surgical

Staffed Beds: 6

ENUMCLAW—King County

★ **ST. ELIZABETH HOSPITAL (501335)**, 1455 Battersby Avenue, Zip 98022–3634,
Mailing Address: P.O.Box 218, 98022–0218; tel. 360/802–8800 **A**10 18 **F**3 13
15 18 29 30 34 35 38 40 44 45 50 57 64 70 74 75 76 79 81 85 87 107 108
110 111 115 119 130 135 146 149 **S** Catholic Health Initiatives, Englewood, CO
Primary Contact: Syd Bersante, R.N., Market President
COO: Joseph Wilczek, Chief Executive Officer
CFO: Philip Hjembo, Chief Financial Officer
CHR: Jerilyn Ray, Manager Human Resources
Web address: www.fhshealth.org
Control: Church operated, Nongovernment, not–for–profit **Service:** General
medical and surgical

Staffed Beds: 25 Admissions: 1600 Census: 13 Outpatient Visits: 38165 Births: 343

EPHRATA—Grant County

★ **COLUMBIA BASIN HOSPITAL (501317)**, 200 Nat Washington Way, Zip 98823–
1982; tel. 509/754–4631, (Nonreporting) **A**10 18
Primary Contact: Rosalinda Kibby, Superintendent and Administrator
CFO: Rhonda Handley, Chief Financial Officer
CMO: Lowell C Allred M.D., Chief of Staff
CHR: Suzanne Little, Human Resources Specialist
Web address: www.columbiabasinhospital.org
Control: Hospital district or authority, Government, Nonfederal **Service:** General
medical and surgical

Staffed Beds: 25

EVERETT—Snohomish County

⊞ △ **PROVIDENCE REGIONAL MEDICAL CENTER EVERETT (500014)**, 1321
Colby Avenue, Zip 98201–1665, Mailing Address: P.O.Box 1147, 98206–1147;
tel. 425/261–2000, (Includes PROVIDENCE EVERETT MEDICAL CENTER – COLBY
CAMPUS, 1321 Colby Avenue, Everett, Washington, Zip 98206, P O Box 1147,
98206, tel. 425/261–2000; PROVIDENCE EVERETT MEDICAL CENTER – PACIFIC
CAMPUS, Pacific and Nassau Streets, Everett, Washington, Zip 98201, P O Box
1067, 98206–1067, tel. 206/258–7123) **A**1 2 3 5 7 10 **F**3 4 5 11 12 13 15 17
18 20 22 24 26 28 29 30 31 32 34 35 36 37 38 40 43 44 45 46 47 48 49 50
54 55 56 57 58 59 61 64 65 66 68 70 72 73 74 75 76 77 78 79 80 81 84 85
86 87 89 90 93 94 96 100 107 108 109 110 111 114 115 116 117 118 119
120 121 123 124 126 129 130 131 132 135 144 145 146 147 148 149 **P**6 **S**
Providence St. Joseph Health, Renton, WA
Primary Contact: Kim Williams, R.N., MS, Chief Administrative Officer
CFO: Sheri Feeney, Chief Financial Officer
CMO: Frank Andersen, Interim Chief Medical Officer
CIO: Matt Wonser, Director, Information Services
CHR: Lori A Vocca, Vice President Human Resources
CNO: Barbara M Hyland–Hill R.N., Chief Nursing Officer
Web address: www.providence.org
Control: Church operated, Nongovernment, not–for–profit **Service:** General
medical and surgical

Staffed Beds: 501 Admissions: 31247 Census: 399 Outpatient Visits: 482868 Births: 4749 Total Expense ($000): 544963 Payroll Expense ($000): 242065 Personnel: 3060

FEDERAL WAY—King County

⊞ **ST. FRANCIS HOSPITAL (500141)**, 34515 Ninth Avenue South, Zip 98003–
6799; tel. 253/944–8100 **A**1 2 10 **F**3 8 11 12 13 15 18 20 22 29 30 34 35 38
40 43 44 45 49 50 51 57 59 64 70 73 74 75 76 77 78 79 80 81 85 86 87 92
93 107 108 110 111 114 117 119 126 129 130 132 135 146 147 **S** Catholic
Health Initiatives, Englewood, CO
Primary Contact: Anthony McLean, Market President
CFO: Mike Fitzgerald, Chief Financial Officer
CIO: Rand Strobel, Regional Chief Information Officer
CHR: Les Soltis, Director – Human Resources
Web address: www.fhshealth.org
Control: Church operated, Nongovernment, not–for–profit **Service:** General
medical and surgical

Staffed Beds: 118 Admissions: 8542 Census: 91 Births: 1320 Total Expense ($000): 196937 Payroll Expense ($000): 63161

FORKS—Clallam County

⇑ **FORKS COMMUNITY HOSPITAL (501325)**, 530 Bogachiel Way, Zip 98331–
9120; tel. 360/374–6271, (Total facility includes 20 beds in nursing home–type
unit) **A**10 18 21 **F**40 45 81 91 107 110 127 129 130 133
Primary Contact: Tim Cournyer, Administrator
CFO: Joe Bradick, Chief Financial Officer
CIO: Andrea Perkins–Peppers, Chief Information Officer
CHR: Cindy Paget, Chief Human Resources Officer
CNO: Laura Kripinski, Chief Nursing Officer
Web address: www.forkshospital.org
Control: Hospital district or authority, Government, Nonfederal **Service:** General
medical and surgical

Staffed Beds: 45 Admissions: 421 Census: 23 Births: 72 Total Expense ($000): 27811 Payroll Expense ($000): 12801

WA

Many Facility Codes have changed. Please refer to the AHA Guide Code Chart. © 2017 AHA Guide

FRIDAY HARBOR—San Juan County

★ ⇑ **PEACEHEALTH PEACE ISLAND MEDICAL CENTER (501340)**, 1117 Spring Street, Zip 98250–9782; tel. 360/378–2141 **A**5 10 18 21 **F**3 11 15 29 30 31 34 35 40 44 45 46 47 48 49 50 57 59 64 65 68 77 78 81 84 87 97 102 107 108 110 115 119 130 135 146 148 **S** PeaceHealth, Vancouver, WA
Primary Contact: Merry Ann Keane, Chief Administrative Officer
CFO: Carolyn Foster, Chief Financial Officer
CMO: Michael Sullivan M.D., Medical Director Emergency Services
CHR: Lorraine Allison, Human Resource Partner
CNO: Sheryl Murphy, Chief Nursing Officer and Director of Clinical Services
Web address: www.peacehealth.org
Control: Other not–for–profit (including NFP Corporation) **Service**: General medical and surgical

Staffed Beds: 10 **Admissions**: 108 **Census**: 1 **Outpatient Visits**: 13768 **Births**: 0 **Total Expense ($000)**: 12369 **Payroll Expense ($000)**: 4931 **Personnel**: 42

GIG HARBOR—Pierce County

✠ **ST. ANTHONY HOSPITAL (500151)**, 11567 Canterwood Boulevard NW, Zip 98332–5812; tel. 253/530–2000 **A**1 10 **F**3 11 12 15 18 20 29 30 31 34 38 40 44 45 49 50 51 57 59 60 64 70 74 75 78 79 81 85 87 92 93 107 108 110 111 114 115 119 129 130 132 135 146 147 **S** Catholic Health Initiatives, Englewood, CO
Primary Contact: David W. Schultz, FACHE, President, Penisula Region
Web address: www.fhshealth.org/
Control: Church operated, Nongovernment, not–for–profit **Service**: General medical and surgical

Staffed Beds: 80 **Admissions**: 5695 **Census**: 62 **Total Expense ($000)**: 122869 **Payroll Expense ($000)**: 38101

GOLDENDALE—Klickitat County

KLICKITAT VALLEY HEALTH (501316), 310 South Roosevelt Avenue, Zip 98620–9201; tel. 509/773–4022 **A**3 10 18 **F**3 8 15 18 29 30 34 35 40 43 45 57 59 62 63 64 65 68 75 77 81 83 84 85 97 98 107 119 127 128 130 133 135 146 148 149
Primary Contact: Leslie Hiebert, Chief Executive Officer
CFO: Jamie Eldred, Controller
CMO: Rod Krehbiel M.D., Chief of Staff
CIO: Jonathan Hatfield, Supervisor Information Technology
CHR: Herbert Hill, Director Human Resources
CNO: Gwen Cox, Director Nursing Services
Web address: www.kvhealth.net
Control: Hospital district or authority, Government, Nonfederal **Service**: General medical and surgical

Staffed Beds: 17 **Admissions**: 310 **Census**: 4 **Outpatient Visits**: 5222 **Births**: 0 **Total Expense ($000)**: 21471 **Payroll Expense ($000)**: 10697

GRAND COULEE—Grant County

COULEE COMMUNITY HOSPITAL See Coulee Medical Center

COULEE MEDICAL CENTER (501308), 411 Fortuyn Road, Zip 99133–8718; tel. 509/633–1753, (Total facility includes 20 beds in nursing home–type unit) **A**10 18 **F**35 40 46 59 65 76 79 81 85 87 97 107 110 119 128 130 133 147 148
Primary Contact: Ramona Hicks, Interim Chief Executive Officer
CFO: Paul Babcock, Chief Financial Officer
CMO: Andrew Castrodale M.D., Chief Medical Officer
CHR: Heather McCleary, Director Human Resources
Web address: www.cmccares.org
Control: Hospital district or authority, Government, Nonfederal **Service**: General medical and surgical

Staffed Beds: 45 **Admissions**: 460 **Census**: 16 **Births**: 92

ILWACO—Pacific County

★ **OCEAN BEACH HOSPITAL (501314)**, 174 First Avenue North, Zip 98624–9137, Mailing Address: P.O.Box H, 98624–0258; tel. 360/642–3181 **A**10 18 **F**3 11 15 18 28 29 30 31 34 35 40 43 45 56 57 59 68 75 77 78 79 81 85 86 87 93 97 102 107 111 114 119 127 128 130 132 133 135 149 **P**6
Primary Contact: Larry Cohen, Chief Executive Officer
CFO: Kathy Hubbard, Controller
CMO: Patty Malone M.D., Chief Medical Officer
CIO: Julie P Oakes R.N., Manager Risk and Quality
CHR: Beth Whitton, Director Human Resources
CNO: Linda Kaino, Chief Nursing Officer
Web address: www.oceanbeachhospital.com
Control: Hospital district or authority, Government, Nonfederal **Service**: General medical and surgical

Staffed Beds: 15 **Admissions**: 339 **Census**: 4 **Outpatient Visits**: 33656 **Births**: 0 **Total Expense ($000)**: 21594 **Payroll Expense ($000)**: 9669 **Personnel**: 142

ISSAQUAH—King County

★ ⇑ **SWEDISH/ISSAQUAH (500152)**, 751 NE Blakely Drive, Zip 98029–6201; tel. 425/313–4000 **A**3 10 21 **F**3 12 13 15 18 20 22 29 30 31 34 35 37 38 40 41 45 48 49 50 56 57 58 59 60 61 64 65 68 70 73 74 75 76 77 78 79 81 82 85 86 87 89 92 93 96 97 102 107 108 110 111 114 115 119 126 129 130 131 132 134 135 141 143 146 147 148 149 **S** Swedish Health Services, Seattle, WA
Primary Contact: Guy Hudson, Chief Executive Officer
COO: Jeffery Robert, Chief Operating Officer
Web address: www.swedish.org/issaquah
Control: Other not–for–profit (including NFP Corporation) **Service**: General medical and surgical

Staffed Beds: 134 **Admissions**: 7703 **Census**: 59 **Outpatient Visits**: 114451 **Births**: 1564 **Total Expense ($000)**: 235041 **Payroll Expense ($000)**: 61946 **Personnel**: 708

KENNEWICK—Benton County

☐ **TRIOS HEALTH (500053)**, 900 South Auburn Street, Zip 99336–5621, Mailing Address: P.O.Box 6128, 99336–0128; tel. 509/586–6111 **A**1 2 10 13 **F**2 8 11 13 15 18 20 28 29 30 31 34 35 40 45 49 50 54 56 57 59 62 64 70 73 74 75 76 77 78 79 80 81 85 86 87 89 93 97 107 108 110 111 114 119 129 130 144 146 147
Primary Contact: Craig R. Cudworth, FACHE, Interim Chief Executive Officer
CFO: Tony Sudduth, Chief Financial Officer
CIO: Michael Cloutier, Director Information Services
CHR: Russ Keefer, Chief Human Resources Officer
Web address: www.trioshealth.org
Control: Hospital district or authority, Government, Nonfederal **Service**: General medical and surgical

Staffed Beds: 111 **Admissions**: 6356 **Census**: 52 **Births**: 1601 **Total Expense ($000)**: 204680 **Payroll Expense ($000)**: 85057

KIRKLAND—King County

EVERGREEN HEALTHCARE See Evergreenhealth, Monroe

✠ **EVERGREENHEALTH (500124)**, 12040 NE 128th Street, Zip 98034–3013; tel. 425/899–1000 **A**1 2 3 5 10 **F**3 8 11 12 13 15 18 20 22 28 29 30 34 35 37 38 40 42 43 44 45 46 49 50 51 54 55 56 58 59 61 62 63 64 65 68 70 71 72 73 74 75 76 78 79 80 81 82 84 85 86 87 90 91 92 93 94 95 96 97 100 102 103 107 108 110 111 114 115 119 120 121 123 124 126 129 130 131 132 134 135 144 146 147 148 149 **P**4 6
Primary Contact: Robert H. Malte, Chief Executive Officer
COO: Neil Johnson, Chief Operating Officer
CFO: Chrissy Yamada CPA, Chief Financial Officer
CMO: Jeff Tomlin M.D., Chief Medical and Quality Officer
CIO: Tom Martin, Chief Strategy and Information Officer
CHR: Bob Sampson, Vice President, Human Resources
CNO: Nancee Hofmeister R.N., Chief Nursing Officer
Web address: www.evergreenhealth.com
Control: Hospital district or authority, Government, Nonfederal **Service**: General medical and surgical

Staffed Beds: 278 **Admissions**: 15672 **Census**: 170 **Outpatient Visits**: 776739 **Births**: 4713 **Total Expense ($000)**: 641745 **Payroll Expense ($000)**: 330231 **Personnel**: 3699

✠ **FAIRFAX BEHAVIORAL HEALTH (504002)**, 10200 NE 132nd Street, Zip 98034–2899; tel. 425/821–2000, (Nonreporting) (Includes FAIRFAX BEHAVIORAL HEALTH EVERETT, 916 Pacific Avenue, Everett, Washington, Zip 98201–4147, tel. 425/821–2000) **A**1 10 **S** Universal Health Services, Inc., King of Prussia, PA
Primary Contact: Ron Escarda, Chief Executive Officer
COO: Todd Thama, Chief Operating Officer
CFO: Pam Rhoads, Chief Financial Officer
CMO: Samir Aziz M.D., Medical Director
CHR: Anne Schreiber, Manager Human Resources
Web address: www.fairfaxhospital.com
Control: Corporation, Investor–owned (for–profit) **Service**: Psychiatric

Staffed Beds: 103

WA

Hospital, Medicare Provider Number, Address, Telephone, Approval, Facility, and Physician Codes, Health Care System

★ American Hospital Association (AHA) membership	○ Healthcare Facilities Accreditation Program	⇑ Center for Improvement in Healthcare Quality Accreditation
☐ The Joint Commission accreditation	◇ DNV Healthcare Inc. accreditation	△ Commission on Accreditation of Rehabilitation Facilities (CARF) accreditation

LAKEWOOD—Pierce County

⊠ △ **ST. CLARE HOSPITAL (500021)**, 11315 Bridgeport Way SW, Zip 98499–3004; tel. 253/985–1711 **A**1 2 3 7 10 **F**3 8 18 29 30 31 34 35 38 40 44 45 49 50 51 57 59 64 70 74 75 77 78 79 80 81 82 85 86 87 92 93 107 108 111 114 119 129 130 132 135 146 149 **S** Catholic Health Initiatives, Englewood, CO
Primary Contact: Syd Bersante, R.N., President
CFO: Mike Fitzgerald, Chief Financial Officer
CIO: Bruce Elkington, Regional Chief Information Officer
CHR: David C. Lawson, Senior Vice President Human Resources
Web address: www.fhshealth.org
Control: Church operated, Nongovernment, not–for–profit **Service:** General medical and surgical

Staffed Beds: 103 **Admissions:** 6136 **Census:** 82 **Outpatient Visits:** 104434 **Births:** 0

LEAVENWORTH—Chelan County

★ **CASCADE MEDICAL CENTER (501313)**, 817 Commercial Street, Zip 98826–1316; tel. 509/548–5815 **A**5 10 18 **F**3 7 15 34 40 41 45 50 59 64 65 68 77 87 91 93 94 97 104 107 110 114 127 128 130 131 133 148 **P**6
Primary Contact: Diane Blake, Chief Executive Officer
COO: Amy Webb, Chief Operating Officer
CFO: Jim Hopkins, Chief Financial Officer
CMO: Karl Kranz M.D., Chief of Staff
CIO: Charles Amstutz, Director of Information Technology
CHR: Reyne Boik, Director Human Resources
Web address: www.cascademedical.org
Control: Hospital district or authority, Government, Nonfederal **Service:** General medical and surgical

Staffed Beds: 9 **Admissions:** 153 **Census:** 4 **Outpatient Visits:** 32193 **Births:** 0 **Total Expense ($000):** 15777 **Payroll Expense ($000):** 8347 **Personnel:** 119

LONGVIEW—Cowlitz County

⊠ ⇑ **PEACEHEALTH ST. JOHN MEDICAL CENTER (500041)**, 1615 Delaware Street, Zip 98632–2367, Mailing Address: P.O.Box 3002, 98632–0302; tel. 360/414–2000 **A**1 2 10 19 21 **F**5 11 13 15 18 20 22 26 28 29 30 31 32 33 34 35 38 40 43 45 46 49 50 51 56 57 59 60 61 63 64 65 68 70 71 74 75 76 77 78 79 80 81 82 84 85 93 94 96 97 98 99 100 101 102 104 107 108 109 111 114 115 117 119 120 121 129 130 144 145 146 147 148 **S** PeaceHealth, Vancouver, WA
Primary Contact: Renato V. Baciarelli, Interim Chief Administrative Officer
CFO: Ronald K Benfield, Chief Financial Officer
CMO: Eleen Kirman M.D., Chief Medical Officer
CHR: Kelley Frengle, Director, Human Resources
Web address: www.peacehealth.org
Control: Hospital district or authority, Government, Nonfederal **Service:** General medical and surgical

Staffed Beds: 180 **Admissions:** 7234 **Census:** 82 **Births:** 857 **Total Expense ($000):** 263899 **Payroll Expense ($000):** 111451

MEDICAL LAKE—Spokane County

☐ **EASTERN STATE HOSPITAL (504004)**, Maple Street, Zip 99022–0045, Mailing Address: P.O.Box 800, 99022–0800; tel. 509/565–4705, (Nonreporting) **A**1 3 10
Primary Contact: Dorothy Sawyer, Chief Executive Officer
COO: Ronda Kenney, Chief Operating Officer
CMO: Kamal Floura M.D., Medical Director
CNO: Chet Roshetko, Chief Nursing Officer
Web address: www.dshs.wa.gov/mhsystems/esh.shtml
Control: State, Government, Nonfederal **Service:** Psychiatric

Staffed Beds: 287

MONROE—Snohomish County

★ ⇑ **EVERGREENHEALTH MONROE (500084)**, 14701 179th SE, Zip 98272–1108, Mailing Address: P.O.Box 646, 98272–0646; tel. 360/794–7497, (Nonreporting) **A**10 21
Primary Contact: Renee K. Jensen, Senior Vice President and Chief Administrative Officer
CFO: Scott Olander, Chief Financial Officer
CMO: Jack Handley M.D., Chief Medical Officer
CIO: John Gepford, Director Information Systems
CHR: Kathryn Rothberg, Director Human Resources
CNO: Debbie T Brown R.N., Chief Nursing Officer
Web address: www.evergreenhealthmonroe.com
Control: Hospital district or authority, Government, Nonfederal **Service:** General medical and surgical

Staffed Beds: 68

MORTON—Lewis County

★ **MORTON GENERAL HOSPITAL (501319)**, 521 Adams Avenue, Zip 98356–9323, Mailing Address: P.O.Box 1138, 98356–0019; tel. 360/496–5112 **A**10 18 **F**3 34 35 40 45 59 68 77 81 93 97 107 119 127 129 130 132 133 135 146 148 149 **P**6
Primary Contact: Leianne Everett, Chief Executive Officer
CFO: Geoff Hamilton, Interim Chief Financial Officer
CIO: Randy Nielsen, Director Information Technology
CHR: Shannon Kelly, Director Human Resources
CNO: Heidi Anderson, Chief Nursing Officer
Web address: www.mortongeneral.org
Control: Hospital district or authority, Government, Nonfederal **Service:** General medical and surgical

Staffed Beds: 25 **Admissions:** 262 **Census:** 2 **Outpatient Visits:** 19429 **Births:** 0 **Total Expense ($000):** 23761 **Payroll Expense ($000):** 11605 **Personnel:** 159

MOSES LAKE—Grant County

★ **SAMARITAN HEALTHCARE (500033)**, 801 East Wheeler Road, Zip 98837–1899; tel. 509/765–5606 **A**10 20 **F**3 8 13 15 28 29 30 34 35 40 43 45 50 57 59 64 65 68 70 75 76 79 80 81 85 86 87 89 97 107 108 110 111 115 118 119 127 130 132 135 144 146 147
Primary Contact: Theresa Sullivan, Chief Executive Officer
COO: Becky DeMers R.N., Chief Operating Officer
CFO: Paul Ishizuka, Chief Financial Officer and Chief Operating Officer
CMO: Thomas Tuszynski M.D., Chief of Staff
CHR: Lisa A McDaniel, Chief Human Resources Officer
CNO: Kathryn E Trumbull R.N., Chief Nursing Officer and Vice President Patient Care Services
Web address: www.samaritanhealthcare.com
Control: Hospital district or authority, Government, Nonfederal **Service:** General medical and surgical

Staffed Beds: 50 **Admissions:** 2906 **Census:** 23 **Outpatient Visits:** 49814 **Births:** 1006 **Total Expense ($000):** 71744 **Payroll Expense ($000):** 32871 **Personnel:** 454

MOUNT VERNON—Skagit County

★ ⇑ **SKAGIT REGIONAL HEALTH (500003)**, 1415 East Kincaid, Zip 98274–4126, Mailing Address: P.O.Box 1376, 98273–1376; tel. 360/424–4111 **A**2 5 10 13 19 21 **F**3 11 13 18 20 26 28 29 30 31 32 34 35 36 40 41 43 44 45 46 47 48 49 50 51 53 57 58 59 60 65 66 68 70 74 76 77 78 79 80 81 82 84 85 86 89 90 93 96 97 98 107 108 109 111 115 116 117 118 119 120 121 122 123 124 127 129 130 131 132 144 146 147 148 **P**6 **S** Skagit Regional Health, Mount Vernon, WA
Primary Contact: , R.N.
COO: Jim Geist, Executive Vice President and Chief Operating Officer
CFO: Thomas Litaker, Regional Vice President and Chief Financial Officer
CMO: Jeffrey S. Gibbs M.D., Regional Vice President Medical Affairs
CIO: John Dwight, Regional Vice President and Chief Information Officer
CHR: Deborah Martin, Regional Vice President Human Resources
CNO: Roxanne Olason R.N., FACHE, Vice President and Chief Nursing Officer
Web address: www.skagitregionalhealth.org
Control: Hospital district or authority, Government, Nonfederal **Service:** General medical and surgical

Staffed Beds: 173 **Admissions:** 7622 **Census:** 91 **Outpatient Visits:** 570375 **Births:** 1203 **Total Expense ($000):** 354651 **Payroll Expense ($000):** 149269 **Personnel:** 2029

NEWPORT—Pend Oreille County

NEWPORT HOSPITAL AND HEALTH SERVICES (501310), 714 West Pine Street, Zip 99156–9046; tel. 509/447–2441, (Total facility includes 50 beds in nursing home–type unit) **A**10 18 **F**8 10 11 13 15 32 34 40 41 50 57 59 64 75 76 77 79 81 82 87 89 93 97 107 111 114 119 127 128 130 133 146 147 148
Primary Contact: Thomas W. Wilbur, Chief Executive Officer and Superintendent
COO: Shelley Froehlich R.N., Director Nursing Services
CMO: Clay Kersting M.D., Chief Medical Staff
CIO: Walter Price, Director Information Technology
CHR: Joseph Clouse, Chief Administrative Officer
Web address: www.newporthospitalandhealth.org
Control: Hospital district or authority, Government, Nonfederal **Service:** General medical and surgical

Staffed Beds: 74 **Admissions:** 699 **Census:** 47 **Births:** 67 **Total Expense ($000):** 28666 **Payroll Expense ($000):** 15616

Many Facility Codes have changed. Please refer to the AHA Guide Code Chart.   © 2017 AHA Guide

OAK HARBOR—Island County

✠ **NAVAL HOSPITAL OAK HARBOR**, 3475 North Saratoga Street, Zip 98278–8800; tel. 360/257–9500, (Nonreporting) **A**1 **S** Bureau of Medicine and Surgery, Department of the Navy, Falls Church, VA
Primary Contact: Commander Frederick Joseph. McDonald, Commanding Officer
COO: LieutenantMichael Bowers, Interim Director for Administration
CFO: LieutenantMatthew Martin, Director Resource Management
CMO: Lieutenant CommanderCatherine Borja M.D., Chairman Executive Committee Medical Staff
CIO: Gregory Carruth, Head Information Management
CHR: LieutenantMichael Bowers, Head Human Resources
CNO: CaptainKaren Pruett–Baer, Senior Nurse Executive
Web address: www.med.navy.mil/sites/nhoh/Pages/default.aspx
Control: Navy, Government, federal **Service:** General medical and surgical

Staffed Beds: 29

ODESSA—Lincoln County

★ **ODESSA MEMORIAL HEALTHCARE CENTER (501307)**, 502 East Amende Drive, Zip 99159–7003, Mailing Address: P.O.Box 368, 99159–0368; tel. 509/982–2611, (Nonreporting) **A**10 18
Primary Contact: Mo P. Sheldon, FACHE, Chief Executive Officer and Administrator
CFO: Annette Edwards, Chief Financial Officer
CMO: Linda J Powel M.D., Medical Director
CHR: Jodi J Bailey, Human Resources Director
CNO: Megan Shepard, Director Clinical Services
Web address: www.omhc.org
Control: Hospital district or authority, Government, Nonfederal **Service:** General medical and surgical

Staffed Beds: 25

OLYMPIA—Thurston County

☐ **CAPITAL MEDICAL CENTER (500139)**, 3900 Capital Mall Drive SW, Zip 98502–5026, Mailing Address: P.O.Box 19002, 98507–0013; tel. 360/754–5858 **A**1 10 **F**3 8 11 12 13 15 22 28 29 30 31 35 37 40 43 59 64 68 72 76 77 78 79 81 82 85 86 87 93 107 108 111 114 118 119 132 146 147 148 **S** RCCH HealthCare Partners, Brentwood, TN
Primary Contact: Mark Turner, Chief Executive Officer
CFO: Brian Anderson, Chief Financial Officer
CMO: Rojesh Sharangpani M.D., Chief of Staff
CIO: Renee Crotty, Coordinator Marketing and Public Relations
CHR: Dana Vandewege, Director Human Resources
Web address: www.capitalmedical.com
Control: Partnership, Investor–owned (for–profit) **Service:** General medical and surgical

Staffed Beds: 52 Admissions: 4352 Census: 37 Births: 669

✠ △ **PROVIDENCE ST. PETER HOSPITAL (500024)**, 413 Lilly Road NE, Zip 98506–5166; tel. 360/491–9480 **A**1 3 7 10 **F**3 5 8 11 13 15 17 18 20 22 24 26 28 29 30 31 34 35 38 40 43 44 45 46 47 48 49 51 53 56 57 58 59 64 68 70 73 74 75 76 77 78 79 80 81 82 84 85 86 87 89 90 92 93 96 98 99 100 101 102 104 105 107 108 110 111 114 115 116 117 118 119 124 126 129 130 132 135 145 146 148 149 150 **S** Providence St. Joseph Health, Renton, WA
Primary Contact: Medrice Coluccio, R.N., Chief Executive Officer
COO: Paul G Wilkinson, Chief Operating Officer
CFO: Denise Marroni, Chief Financial Officer
CMO: Kevin Caserta M.D., Chief Medical Officer
CIO: Kerry Miles, Chief Information Officer
CHR: Susan Meenk, Vice President Human Resources
CNO: Michelle James, Chief Nursing Officer
Web address: www.providence.org/swsa/facilities/st_peter_hospital
Control: Church operated, Nongovernment, not–for–profit **Service:** General medical and surgical

Staffed Beds: 350 Admissions: 15382 Census: 258 Outpatient Visits: 353771 Births: 2238 Total Expense ($000): 330431 Payroll Expense ($000): 164847 Personnel: 2133

OMAK—Okanogan County

MID–VALLEY HOSPITAL (501328), 810 Jasmine, Zip 98841–9578, Mailing Address: P.O.Box 793, 98841–0793; tel. 509/826–1760 **A**5 10 18 **F**11 13 15 29 34 40 43 45 57 59 64 65 68 70 76 81 82 87 89 93 107 115 119 127 133 135
Primary Contact: Alan Fisher, Chief Executive Officer
CFO: Scott Attridge, Chief Financial Officer
CMO: Jennifer Thill, Chief of Staff
CIO: Ethan Harris, Manager Information Systems
CHR: Randy Coffell, Manager Human Resources
CNO: Rebecca Christoph, Director Nursing and Patient Care Services
Web address: www.mvhealth.org
Control: Hospital district or authority, Government, Nonfederal **Service:** General medical and surgical

Staffed Beds: 30 Admissions: 776 Census: 6 Total Expense ($000): 30373 Payroll Expense ($000): 14564

OTHELLO—Adams County

★ **OTHELLO COMMUNITY HOSPITAL (501318)**, 315 North 14th Avenue, Zip 99344–1297; tel. 509/488–2636, (Nonreporting) **A**10 18
Primary Contact: Connie Agenbroad, Chief Executive Officer
CFO: Mark Bunch, Director Finance
CHR: Mindy Gonzales, Chief Human Resources Officer
CNO: Tina Bernsen, Chief Nursing Officer
Web address: www.othellocommunityhospital.org
Control: Hospital district or authority, Government, Nonfederal **Service:** General medical and surgical

Staffed Beds: 25

PASCO—Franklin County

✠ △ **LOURDES MEDICAL CENTER (501337)**, 520 North Fourth Avenue, Zip 99301–5257; tel. 509/547–7704 **A**1 7 10 18 **F**8 13 15 18 29 30 34 35 37 40 41 42 45 46 50 52 56 57 59 68 70 74 75 76 77 79 80 81 84 90 91 96 97 107 108 110 111 114 118 126 129 130 131 143 144 145 146 147 **S** Ascension Healthcare, Saint Louis, MO
Primary Contact: John Serle, FACHE, President and Chief Executive Officer
CFO: Frank Becker, Chief Financial Officer
CMO: Venkataraman Sambasivan M.D., Chief Medical Officer
CIO: Deb Carpenter, Director Information Technology
CHR: Barbara Blood, Executive Director Human Resources
CNO: Denise Clapp, Chief Nursing Officer
Web address: www.lourdeshealth.net
Control: Church operated, Nongovernment, not–for–profit **Service:** General medical and surgical

Staffed Beds: 53 Admissions: 2037 Census: 21 Total Expense ($000): 99302 Payroll Expense ($000): 32564

POMEROY—Garfield County

★ **GARFIELD COUNTY PUBLIC HOSPITAL DISTRICT (501301)**, 66 North 6th Street, Zip 99347–9705; tel. 509/843–1591, (Nonreporting) **A**10 18
Primary Contact: Brenda Parnell, Chief Executive Officer
CMO: Glenn Jefferson, Chief Medical Officer
CHR: Alicia Scharnhorst, Human Resources and Administrative Assistant
CNO: Barbara DeHerrera, Chief Nursing Officer
Web address: www.pomeroymd.com
Control: Hospital district or authority, Government, Nonfederal **Service:** General medical and surgical

Staffed Beds: 25

PORT ANGELES—Clallam County

★ ⇑ **OLYMPIC MEDICAL CENTER (500072)**, 939 Caroline Street, Zip 98362–3997; tel. 360/417–7000 **A**2 5 10 21 **F**3 13 15 18 28 29 31 34 40 45 54 57 59 62 64 70 74 75 76 77 78 79 81 82 85 87 89 91 93 97 107 108 110 111 114 119 121 123 127 129 131 132 144 146 147 148
Primary Contact: Eric Lewis, Chief Executive Officer
CFO: Darryl Wolfe, Chief Financial Officer
CMO: R Scott Kennedy M.D., Chief Medical Officer and Hospital Chief Operating Officer
CHR: Richard Newman, Chief Human Resources Officer
CNO: Lorraine Wall, Chief Nursing Officer
Web address: www.olympicmedical.org
Control: Hospital district or authority, Government, Nonfederal **Service:** General medical and surgical

Staffed Beds: 67 Admissions: 4373 Census: 40 Births: 448 Total Expense ($000): 163087 Payroll Expense ($000): 78197

WA

Hospital, Medicare Provider Number, Address, Telephone, Approval, Facility, and Physician Codes, Health Care System

★ American Hospital Association (AHA) membership
☐ The Joint Commission accreditation
○ Healthcare Facilities Accreditation Program
◇ DNV Healthcare Inc. accreditation
⇑ Center for Improvement in Healthcare Quality Accreditation
△ Commission on Accreditation of Rehabilitation Facilities (CARF) accreditation

PORT TOWNSEND—Jefferson County

★ ⇑ **JEFFERSON HEALTHCARE (501323)**, 834 Sheridan Street, Zip 98368–2443; tel. 360/385–2200 **A**10 18 21 **F**13 15 18 28 29 31 34 35 40 45 46 50 62 63 65 70 76 81 87 93 107 110 111 114 119 127 129 130 135 146 148
Primary Contact: Mike Glenn, Chief Executive Officer
COO: Paula Dowdle, Chief Operating Officer
CFO: Hilary Whittington, Chief Financial Officer
CMO: Joe Mattern M.D., Chief Medical Officer
CHR: Heather Bailey, Chief Human Resources Officer
CNO: Joyce Cardinal, Chief Nursing Executive
Web address: www.jeffersonhealthcare.org
Control: Hospital district or authority, Government, Nonfederal **Service**: General medical and surgical

Staffed Beds: 25 **Admissions**: 1237 **Census**: 12 **Births**: 100 **Total Expense ($000)**: 85968 **Payroll Expense ($000)**: 42217

PROSSER—Benton County

★ **PMH MEDICAL CENTER (501312)**, 723 Memorial Street, Zip 99350–1524; tel. 509/786–2222 **A**10 18 **F**3 7 11 12 13 15 29 34 35 37 40 41 43 44 45 50 52 53 54 57 59 65 68 75 76 77 79 81 82 85 87 89 91 93 97 107 108 110 119 127 128 130 131 132 133 135 143 146 148 **P**8
Primary Contact: Craig J. Marks, FACHE, Chief Executive Officer
CFO: Tim Cooper, Chief Financial Officer
CIO: Jim Zoesch, Information Technology Director
CNO: Marla Davis, Interim Chief Nursing Officer
Web address: www.pmhmedicalcenter.com/
Control: Hospital district or authority, Government, Nonfederal **Service**: General medical and surgical

Staffed Beds: 25 **Admissions**: 1029 **Census**: 11 **Total Expense ($000)**: 44282 **Payroll Expense ($000)**: 19636

PULLMAN—Whitman County

⇑ **PULLMAN REGIONAL HOSPITAL (501331)**, 835 SE Bishop Boulevard, Zip 99163–5512; tel. 509/332–2541 **A**10 18 21 **F**3 13 15 28 29 30 34 35 36 37 38 40 43 44 45 47 50 51 53 55 57 59 64 68 70 74 75 76 77 78 79 81 86 87 89 93 98 101 102 104 105 107 108 110 111 114 118 119 126 129 130 131 132 133 144 146 **P**5 6 7
Primary Contact: Scott K. Adams, FACHE, Chief Executive Officer
CFO: Steven Febus, Chief Financial Officer
CMO: Gerald L Early M.D., Chief Medical Officer
CHR: Bernadette Berney, Director Human Resources
Web address: www.pullmanhospital.org
Control: Hospital district or authority, Government, Nonfederal **Service**: General medical and surgical

Staffed Beds: 25 **Admissions**: 1330 **Census**: 10 **Outpatient Visits**: 77911 **Births**: 434

PUYALLUP—Pierce County

GOOD SAMARITAN COMMUNITY HEALTHCARE See Multicare Good Samaritan Hospital

☐ △ **MULTICARE GOOD SAMARITAN HOSPITAL (500079)**, 401 15th Avenue SE, Zip 98372–3770, Mailing Address: P.O.Box 1247, 98371–0192; tel. 253/697–4000 **A**1 2 3 7 10 13 **F**3 11 13 15 18 20 22 24 28 29 30 31 34 35 38 40 41 43 45 47 48 50 51 55 56 57 58 59 61 64 65 66 68 70 73 74 75 76 78 79 80 81 82 84 85 87 89 90 91 93 96 97 102 106 107 108 111 114 115 117 118 119 126 129 130 132 146 147 148 149 **S** MultiCare Health System, Tacoma, WA
Primary Contact: Christopher Bredeson, President and Chief Operating Officer
COO: Christopher Bredeson, President and Chief Operating Officer
CFO: Anna Loomis, Senior Vice President Chief Financial Officer
CMO: Walter Fink, Chief Medical Officer
CHR: Kevin B Dull, Senior Vice President Human Potential
CNO: Lucy Norris, Administrator Interim Chief Nursing Officer
Web address: www.multicare.org/good–samaritan–hospital/
Control: Other not–for–profit (including NFP Corporation) **Service**: General medical and surgical

Staffed Beds: 287 **Admissions**: 17002 **Census**: 225 **Outpatient Visits**: 135987 **Births**: 2396 **Total Expense ($000)**: 409450 **Payroll Expense ($000)**: 158768 **Personnel**: 1379

QUINCY—Grant County

★ **QUINCY VALLEY MEDICAL CENTER (501320)**, 908 10th Avenue SW, Zip 98848–1376; tel. 509/787–3531, (Nonreporting) **A**10 18
Primary Contact: Glenda Bishop, Interim Chief Executive Officer
CFO: Dean Taplett, Controller
CMO: Mark Vance M.D., Chief Medical Officer
CIO: Ruth Vance, Director Information Systems
CHR: Alene Walker, Director Human Resources
Web address: www.quincyhospital.org
Control: County, Government, Nonfederal **Service**: General medical and surgical

Staffed Beds: 25

RENTON—King County

⊠ **UW MEDICINE/VALLEY MEDICAL CENTER (500088)**, 400 South 43rd Street, Zip 98055–5714, Mailing Address: P.O.Box 50010, 98058–5010; tel. 425/228–3450 **A**1 2 3 5 10 **F**3 8 11 13 15 18 19 20 22 26 28 29 30 31 32 34 35 36 37 38 40 43 44 45 48 49 50 51 53 54 55 57 58 59 60 64 65 66 68 70 72 74 75 76 77 78 79 81 82 83 84 85 86 87 89 91 92 93 94 96 97 100 101 102 104 107 110 111 114 115 118 119 120 121 123 124 126 129 130 131 132 135 144 146 147 148 149 **P**6 **S** UW Medicine, Seattle, WA
Primary Contact: Richard D. Roodman, Chief Executive Officer
CFO: Larry Smith, Senior Vice President and Chief Financial Officer
CMO: Kathryn Beattie M.D., Senior Vice President and Chief Medical Officer
CHR: Barbara Mitchell, Senior Vice President Marketing and Human Resources
CNO: Scott Alleman, Senior Vice President Patient Care Services and Chief Nursing Officer
Web address: www.valleymed.org
Control: Hospital district or authority, Government, Nonfederal **Service**: General medical and surgical

Staffed Beds: 282 **Admissions**: 17518 **Census**: 192 **Outpatient Visits**: 591504 **Births**: 3809 **Total Expense ($000)**: 571184 **Payroll Expense ($000)**: 260139 **Personnel**: 2641

REPUBLIC—Ferry County

★ **FERRY COUNTY MEMORIAL HOSPITAL (501322)**, 36 Klondike Road, Zip 99166–9701; tel. 509/775–3333, (Nonreporting) **A**10 18
Primary Contact: Aaron Edwards, Chief Executive Officer
CFO: Kelly Leslie, Chief Financial Officer
CMO: Farhad H Alrashedy M.D., Chief Medical Officer
CIO: James Davidson, Director of Information Services
CHR: Michelle Loftis, Human Resources Officer
CNO: Thomas Durham, Chief Nursing Officer
Web address: www.fcphd.org
Control: Hospital district or authority, Government, Nonfederal **Service**: General medical and surgical

Staffed Beds: 25

RICHLAND—Benton County

⊠ △ **KADLEC REGIONAL MEDICAL CENTER (500058)**, 888 Swift Boulevard, Zip 99352–3514; tel. 509/946–4611 **A**1 2 3 7 10 **F**3 8 11 13 15 17 18 20 22 24 26 28 29 30 31 32 34 35 36 38 40 42 45 46 47 48 49 50 51 52 54 55 56 57 58 59 64 65 68 70 72 73 74 75 76 78 79 81 82 83 84 85 86 87 89 90 91 93 96 97 100 111 114 115 116 117 118 119 126 127 130 132 144 146 147 148 149 **S** Providence St. Joseph Health, Renton, WA
Primary Contact: Lane A. Savitch, Regional Chief Executive
CFO: Spencer Harris, Senior Director Finance
CMO: Dale Hoekema M.D., Vice President Medical Affairs and Chief Medical Officer
CIO: David Roach, Vice President Information Systems
CHR: Jeffrey A Clark, Vice President Human Resources
CNO: Kirk Harper R.N., Vice President, Nursing
Web address: www.kadlecmed.org
Control: Other not–for–profit (including NFP Corporation) **Service**: General medical and surgical

Staffed Beds: 260 **Admissions**: 14489 **Census**: 176 **Outpatient Visits**: 283290 **Births**: 2793 **Total Expense ($000)**: 479476 **Payroll Expense ($000)**: 233004 **Personnel**: 2739

★ **LOURDES COUNSELING CENTER (504008)**, 1175 Carondelet Drive, Zip 99354–3300; tel. 509/943–9104 **A**10 **F**3 29 30 38 50 64 98 99 100 101 103 104 106 **S** Ascension Healthcare, Saint Louis, MO
Primary Contact: John Serle, President and Chief Executive Officer
CFO: Frank Becker, Chief Financial Officer
CIO: Jared Fleming, Director, Information Services
CHR: Barbara Blood, Director Human Resources
CNO: Denise Clapp, Chief Nursing Officer
Web address: www.lourdeshealth.net
Control: Church operated, Nongovernment, not–for–profit **Service**: Psychiatric

Staffed Beds: 20 **Admissions**: 542 **Census**: 16 **Births**: 0 **Total Expense ($000)**: 18969

RITZVILLE—Adams County

★ **EAST ADAMS RURAL HEALTHCARE (501311)**, 903 South Adams Street, Zip 99169–2298; tel. 509/659–1200, (Nonreporting) **A**10 18
Primary Contact: Gary Bostrom, Chief Executive Officer and Chief Financial Officer
COO: Dina McBride, Chief Operating Officer and Director Human Resources
CFO: Gary Bostrom, Chief Executive Officer and Chief Financial Officer
CMO: Charles Sackmann M.D., Chief of Staff
CIO: Kellie Ottmar, Manager Information Services
CHR: Dina McBride, Chief Operating Officer and Director Human Resources
CNO: Brenda Herr, Chief Nursing Officer
Web address: www.earh.com
Control: Hospital district or authority, Government, Nonfederal **Service**: General medical and surgical

Staffed Beds: 8

WA

Many Facility Codes have changed. Please refer to the AHA Guide Code Chart. © 2017 AHA Guide

SEATTLE—King County

⇑ **KAISER PERMANENTE CAPITOL HILL CAMPUS (500052)**, 201 16th Avenue East, Zip 98112–5226; tel. 206/326–3000, (Nonreporting) **A**3 5 10 21
Primary Contact: Carol M. Taylor, R.N., Regional Director Clinical Operations
Web address: www.ghc.org/html/public/locations/capitol-hill
Control: Corporation, Investor–owned (for–profit) **Service:** General medical and surgical

Staffed Beds: 306

⊠ **KINDRED HOSPITAL SEATTLE–NORTHGATE (502002)**, 10631 8th Avenue NE, Zip 98125–7213; tel. 206/364–2050, (Includes KINDRED HOSPITAL SEATTLE–FIRST HILL, 1334 Terry Avenue, Seattle, Washington, Zip 98101–2747, tel. 206/682–2661; Doug McCoy, Interim Chief Executive Officer) **A**1 10 **F**1 29 30 50 60 70 75 77 85 96 107 119 148 **S** Kindred Healthcare, Louisville, KY
Primary Contact: Jean Clark, Administrator
CFO: David Stob, Chief Financial Officer
Web address: www.kindredhospitalseattle.com/
Control: Corporation, Investor–owned (for–profit) **Service:** General medical and surgical

Staffed Beds: 80 **Admissions:** 617 **Census:** 64 **Births:** 0

☐ **NAVOS (504009)**, 2600 SW Holden Street, Zip 98126–3505; tel. 206/933–7299 **A**1 10 **F**29 65 98 99 100 101 102 103 104
Primary Contact: David Johnson, Chief Executive Officer
COO: Cassie Undlin, Chief Operating Officer
CIO: Mary Sellers, Chief Information Officer
CHR: Karen White, Interim Vice President of Human Resources
CNO: Terry McInerney, Director of Nursing, Inpatient
Web address: www.navos.org
Control: Other not–for–profit (including NFP Corporation) **Service:** Psychiatric

Staffed Beds: 40 **Admissions:** 624 **Census:** 39 **Births:** 0

★ **SCHICK SHADEL HOSPITAL**, 12101 Ambaum Boulevard SW, Zip 98146–2651, Mailing Address: P.O.Box 48149, 98148–0149; tel. 206/244–8100 **F**4 130 132
Primary Contact: Philip Herink, Administrator
CFO: Troy Cherry, Chief Financial Officer
CMO: Kayyan Danbdala M.D., Medical Director
CIO: Peter Vermulen, Director Information Technology
CHR: Elaine Oksendahl, Director Human Resources and Risk Management
Web address: www.schickshadel.com
Control: Corporation, Investor–owned (for–profit) **Service:** Alcoholism and other chemical dependency

Staffed Beds: 55 **Admissions:** 1080 **Census:** 31 **Outpatient Visits:** 0 **Births:** 0 **Total Expense ($000):** 10846 **Payroll Expense ($000):** 5344 **Personnel:** 88

⊠ **SEATTLE CANCER CARE ALLIANCE (500138)**, 825 Eastlake Avenue East, Zip 98109–4405, Mailing Address: P.O.Box 19023, 98109–1023; tel. 206/288–1400 **A**1 2 10 **F**3 15 29 30 31 34 35 39 50 55 57 59 64 68 75 78 80 82 84 86 87 93 100 107 108 110 111 114 115 116 117 119 120 121 123 124 130 132 135 136 142 143 146 147 148 149 **P**1
Primary Contact: Norm Hubbard, Executive Vice President
CFO: Jonathan Tingstad, Vice President and Chief Financial Officer
CMO: Marc Stewart M.D., Vice President and Medical Director
CIO: David Ackerson, Chief Information Officer
CHR: Han Nachtrieb, Vice President Human Resources
Web address: www.seattlecca.org
Control: Other not–for–profit (including NFP Corporation) **Service:** Cancer

Staffed Beds: 20 **Admissions:** 529 **Census:** 17 **Outpatient Visits:** 80546 **Births:** 0 **Total Expense ($000):** 473691 **Payroll Expense ($000):** 93916 **Personnel:** 1149

☐ △ ⇑ **SEATTLE CHILDREN'S HOSPITAL (503300)**, 4800 Sand Point Way NE, Zip 98105–3901, Mailing Address: P.O.Box 5371, 98145–5005; tel. 206/987–2000 **A**1 2 3 5 7 10 21 **F**3 7 8 9 19 21 23 25 27 29 30 31 32 34 35 36 38 39 40 41 43 46 48 49 50 53 54 55 57 58 60 62 64 65 66 68 71 72 74 75 77 78 79 80 81 82 84 85 86 87 88 89 90 93 94 98 99 100 102 104 105 107 108 111 115 116 118 119 126 129 130 131 132 134 136 137 138 139 141 142 143 144 146 148
Primary Contact: Jeff Sperring, M.D., Chief Executive Officer
COO: Cindy Gazecki, Senior Vice President, Hospital Operations
CFO: Kelly Wallace, Senior Vice President and Chief Financial Officer
CMO: David Fisher M.D., Senior Vice President and Chief Medical Officer
CIO: Wes Wright, Senior Vice President and Chief Information Officer
CHR: Steven Hurwitz, Senior Vice President Shared Services
CNO: Susan Heath R.N., Senior Vice President and Chief Nursing Officer
Web address: www.seattlechildrens.org
Control: Other not–for–profit (including NFP Corporation) **Service:** Children's general medical and surgical

Staffed Beds: 316 **Admissions:** 15834 **Census:** 246 **Births:** 0

⊠ △ ⇑ **SWEDISH MEDICAL CENTER–CHERRY HILL CAMPUS (500025)**, 500 17th Avenue, Zip 98122–5711; tel. 206/320–2000 **A**1 2 3 5 7 10 21 **F**3 8 11 17 18 20 21 22 23 24 26 27 28 29 30 31 34 35 37 38 40 45 46 53 57 58 59 61 64 65 68 74 75 77 78 79 80 81 82 83 84 85 87 90 91 92 93 97 100 101 102 107 108 109 111 118 119 124 126 129 130 131 132 135 141 143 146 148 149 **P**6 **S** Swedish Health Services, Seattle, WA
Primary Contact: June Altaras, R.N., Chief Executive Officer
CFO: Jeffrey Veilleux, Senior Vice President and Chief Financial Officer
CIO: Janice Newell, Chief Information Officer
Web address: www.swedish.org
Control: Other not–for–profit (including NFP Corporation) **Service:** General medical and surgical

Staffed Beds: 227 **Admissions:** 10567 **Census:** 154 **Outpatient Visits:** 166992 **Births:** 0 **Total Expense ($000):** 510268 **Payroll Expense ($000):** 134738 **Personnel:** 1482

⊠ ⇑ **SWEDISH MEDICAL CENTER–FIRST HILL (500027)**, 747 Broadway, Zip 98122–4307; tel. 206/386–6000, (Includes SWEDISH MEDICAL CENTER–BALLARD, 5300 Tallman Avenue NW, Seattle, Washington, Zip 98107–3932, tel. 206/782–2700; Jennifer Graves, R.N., MS, Chief Executive) **A**1 2 3 5 10 21 **F**3 4 5 7 8 11 12 13 15 18 19 20 21 22 23 25 26 29 30 31 32 34 35 36 37 38 39 40 41 42 45 46 47 48 49 52 54 55 56 57 58 59 60 61 64 65 66 68 70 71 72 73 74 75 76 77 78 79 80 81 82 83 84 85 86 87 88 89 91 92 93 96 97 98 100 101 102 104 105 107 108 109 110 111 114 115 116 117 118 119 120 121 123 126 127 130 131 132 134 135 136 138 139 141 142 144 146 147 148 149 **P**6 **S** Swedish Health Services, Seattle, WA
Primary Contact: June Altaras, R.N., Chief Executive Officer
CFO: Jeffrey Veilleux, Executive Vice President and Chief Financial Officer
CIO: Janice Newell, Chief Information Officer
Web address: www.swedish.org
Control: Other not–for–profit (including NFP Corporation) **Service:** General medical and surgical

Staffed Beds: 659 **Admissions:** 40139 **Census:** 473 **Outpatient Visits:** 579857 **Births:** 8836 **Total Expense ($000):** 1363844 **Payroll Expense ($000):** 411881 **Personnel:** 4352

⊠ △ **UNIVERSITY OF WASHINGTON MEDICAL CENTER (500008)**, 1959 NE Pacific Street, Zip 98195–6151; tel. 206/598–3300 **A**1 2 3 5 7 8 10 **F**3 9 11 12 13 15 17 18 20 22 24 26 29 30 31 32 34 35 36 40 44 45 46 47 48 49 50 52 54 55 56 57 58 59 60 61 64 65 68 70 72 74 75 76 77 78 79 81 82 84 85 86 87 90 91 92 93 94 95 97 98 100 101 102 103 104 107 110 111 114 115 116 117 118 119 120 121 123 124 126 130 131 132 136 137 138 139 140 141 142 144 145 146 147 148 149 **S** UW Medicine, Seattle, WA
Primary Contact: Geoff Austin, Executive Director
CFO: Lori J Mitchell, Chief Financial Officer
CMO: Tom Staiger M.D., Medical Director
CHR: Jennifer J Petritz, Director Human Resources
CNO: Cindy Sayre Ph.D., R.N., Chief Nursing Officer
Web address: www.uwmedicine.org/uw–medical–center
Control: State, Government, Nonfederal **Service:** General medical and surgical

Staffed Beds: 450 **Admissions:** 18362 **Census:** 362 **Outpatient Visits:** 356079 **Births:** 1921 **Total Expense ($000):** 1186945 **Payroll Expense ($000):** 359300 **Personnel:** 6202

⊠ △ **UW MEDICINE/HARBORVIEW MEDICAL CENTER (500064)**, 325 Ninth Avenue, Zip 98104–2499, Mailing Address: P.O.Box 359717, 98195–9717; tel. 206/744–3000 **A**1 3 5 7 8 10 **F**3 6 10 **F**3 6 11 17 18 20 22 24 29 30 31 32 34 35 36 37 38 40 41 43 45 46 47 48 49 50 56 58 59 60 61 64 65 66 68 70 72 73 74 75 77 78 79 80 81 82 84 85 86 87 88 89 90 91 92 93 94 96 97 98 100 101 102 103 104 105 107 108 111 114 115 118 119 124 129 130 131 132 135 146 147 148 149 150 **P**6 **S** UW Medicine, Seattle, WA
Primary Contact: Paul Hayes, R.N., Executive Director
CFO: Kera Dennis, Assistant Administrator, Finance
CMO: J. Richard Goss M.D., Medical Director
CIO: James Fine M.D., Chief Information Officer
CHR: Nicki McCraw, Assistant Vice President Human Resources
CNO: Darcy Jaffe R.N., Chief Nursing Officer
Web address: www.uwmedicine.org/Patient–Care/Locations/HMC/Pages/default.aspx
Control: County, Government, Nonfederal **Service:** General medical and surgical

Staffed Beds: 413 **Admissions:** 16969 **Census:** 394 **Outpatient Visits:** 383503 **Births:** 0 **Total Expense ($000):** 951799 **Payroll Expense ($000):** 368333 **Personnel:** 5481

WA

✠ **UW MEDICINE/NORTHWEST HOSPITAL & MEDICAL CENTER (500001)**, 1550 North 115th Street, Zip 98133–8401; tel. 206/364–0500 **A**1 2 3 5 10 **F**3 9 11 13 18 20 22 24 26 28 29 30 31 34 35 40 41 43 44 45 46 47 49 50 51 53 54 56 57 58 59 61 64 68 70 73 74 76 77 78 79 80 81 84 85 86 87 96 97 98 100 102 103 104 105 107 108 110 111 114 115 119 126 130 131 132 146 148 **P**6 **S** UW Medicine, Seattle, WA
Primary Contact: Cindy Hecker, Executive Director
CFO: Ketty Hsieh, Senior Director Finance
CMO: Greg Schroedl M.D., Vice President, Medical and Chief Medical Officer
CIO: Eric Neil, Interim Chief Information Officer
CHR: Linda Olmstead, Director, Human Resources
CNO: Susan Manfredi R.N., Vice President and Chief Nursing Officer
Web address: www.uwmedicine.org/Patient–Care/Locations/nwh/Pages/default.aspx
Control: Other not–for–profit (including NFP Corporation) **Service**: General medical and surgical

Staffed Beds: 192 **Admissions**: 10060 **Census**: 133 **Outpatient Visits**: 314085 **Births**: 1233 **Total Expense ($000)**: 380003 **Payroll Expense ($000)**: 159497 **Personnel**: 1881

✠ △ **VETERANS AFFAIRS PUGET SOUND HEALTH CARE SYSTEM**, 1660 South Columbian Way, Zip 98108–1597; tel. 206/762–1010, (Nonreporting) (Includes VETERANS AFFAIRS PUGET SOUND HEALTH CARE SYSTEM–AMERICAN LAKE DIVISION, 9600 Veterans Drive, Tacoma, Washington, Zip 98493–0003, tel. 253/582–8440) **A**1 2 3 5 7 8 **S** Department of Veterans Affairs, Washington, DC
Primary Contact: Michael Tadych, Director
CFO: Kenneth J Hudson, Chief Financial Officer
CMO: Gordon Starkebaum M.D., Chief of Staff
CIO: Glenn Zwinger, Manager Information Systems Services
Web address: www.pugetsound.va.gov/
Control: Veterans Affairs, Government, federal **Service**: General medical and surgical

Staffed Beds: 358

✠ △ **VIRGINIA MASON MEDICAL CENTER (500005)**, 1100 Ninth Avenue, Zip 98101–2756, Mailing Address: P.O.Box 900, 98111–0900; tel. 206/223–6600, (Total facility includes 35 beds in nursing home–type unit) **A**1 2 3 5 7 10 **F**2 3 8 11 12 15 17 18 20 22 24 26 28 29 30 31 34 36 40 44 45 46 47 48 49 50 51 55 56 57 58 59 60 61 63 64 65 68 70 74 75 77 78 79 80 81 82 83 84 85 86 87 91 92 93 94 96 97 98 100 101 102 103 104 107 108 110 111 114 115 117 118 119 120 121 123 126 128 129 130 131 132 135 138 141 142 144 145 146 148 **P**6 **S** Virginia Mason Health System, Seattle, WA
Primary Contact: Gary Kaplan, M.D., FACHE, Chairman and Chief Executive Officer
CFO: Craig Goodrich, Chief Financial Officer
CMO: Michael Glenn M.D., Chief Medical Officer
CIO: Bill Poppy, Chief Information Officer
CHR: Kathy J. Shingleton Ed.D., Vice President, Human Resources
CNO: Charleen Tachibana R.N., Senior Vice President and Chief Nursing Officer
Web address: www.VirginiaMason.org
Control: Other not–for–profit (including NFP Corporation) **Service**: General medical and surgical

Staffed Beds: 223 **Admissions**: 10940 **Census**: 184 **Outpatient Visits**: 893763 **Births**: 0 **Total Expense ($000)**: 978996 **Payroll Expense ($000)**: 469686 **Personnel**: 4594

★ ⇑ **PEACEHEALTH UNITED GENERAL MEDICAL CENTER (501329)**, 2000 Hospital Drive, Zip 98284–4327; tel. 360/856–6021 **A**2 10 18 21 **F**3 11 15 29 30 31 34 35 40 43 45 50 57 59 64 68 70 75 77 78 79 81 85 89 92 93 107 108 110 114 115 118 119 120 121 123 129 130 132 133 143 146 148 149 **P**6 **S** PeaceHealth, Vancouver, WA
Primary Contact: Christopher Johnston, Chief Administrative Officer
CFO: Carolyn Haupt, Chief Financial Officer
CHR: Tracie Skrinde, Senior Human Resources Partner
Web address: www.peacehealth.org/united–general
Control: Church operated, Nongovernment, not–for–profit **Service**: General medical and surgical

Staffed Beds: 25 **Admissions**: 672 **Census**: 7 **Outpatient Visits**: 39759 **Births**: 0 **Total Expense ($000)**: 43782 **Payroll Expense ($000)**: 14652 **Personnel**: 218

✠ **MASON GENERAL HOSPITAL (501336)**, 901 Mountain View Drive, Zip 98584–4401, Mailing Address: P.O.Box 1668, 98584–5001; tel. 360/426–1611 **A**1 10 18 **F**11 13 15 29 30 40 57 68 70 75 79 81 83 85 107 110 130 132 147
Primary Contact: Eric Moll, Chief Executive Officer
COO: Eileen Branscome, Chief Operating Officer
CFO: Merle Brandt, Chief Financial Officer
CMO: Dean Gushee M.D., Medical Director
CIO: Tom Hornburg, Director Information Systems
CHR: Claudia Hawley, Director Human Resources
Web address: www.masongeneral.com
Control: Hospital district or authority, Government, Nonfederal **Service**: General medical and surgical

Staffed Beds: 25 **Admissions**: 1461 **Census**: 12 **Births**: 303

SNOQUALMIE VALLEY HOSPITAL DISTRICT (501338), 9801 Frontier Avenue SE, Zip 98065–9577; tel. 425/831–2300 (Nonreporting) **A**10 18
Primary Contact: Thomas Parker, Chief Executive Officer
CHR: Kimberly D Washburn, Director Human Resources
Web address: www.snoqualmiehospital.org/
Control: Hospital district or authority, Government, Nonfederal **Service**: General medical and surgical

Staffed Beds: 18

WILLAPA HARBOR HOSPITAL (501303), 800 Alder Street, Zip 98586–4900, Mailing Address: P.O.Box 438, 98586–0438; tel. 360/875–5526 **A**10 18 **F**3 8 11 15 34 35 40 41 45 46 50 81 85 87 92 97 107 110 113 119 127 133 145
Primary Contact: Carole Halsan, R.N., Chief Executive Officer
CFO: Terry Stone, Chief Financial Officer and Chief Information Officer
CIO: Terry Stone, Chief Financial Officer and Chief Information Officer
CHR: Krisy L Funkhouser, Manager Human Resources
Web address: www.willapaharborhospital.com
Control: Hospital district or authority, Government, Nonfederal **Service**: General medical and surgical

Staffed Beds: 10 **Admissions**: 302 **Census**: 2 **Total Expense ($000)**: 19537 **Payroll Expense ($000)**: 10625

✠ **MANN–GRANDSTAFF VETERANS AFFAIRS MEDICAL CENTER**, 4815 North Assembly Street, Zip 99205–6197; tel. 509/434–7000, (Total facility includes 34 beds in nursing home–type unit) **A**1 3 5 **F**3 70 90 98 128 **S** Department of Veterans Affairs, Washington, DC
Primary Contact: Tracye B. Davis, Interim Medical Center Director
COO: Perry Klein, Chief Engineering
CFO: Michael Stuhlmiller, Chief Financial Officer
CIO: Rob Fortenberry, Chief Information Officer
CHR: Jacqueline Ross, Chief Human Resources Officer
CNO: Nancy Benton, Assistant Director Patient Care Services
Web address: www.spokane.va.gov/
Control: Veterans Affairs, Government, federal **Service**: General medical and surgical

Staffed Beds: 68 **Admissions**: 1964 **Census**: 51 **Outpatient Visits**: 345932 **Births**: 0 **Total Expense ($000)**: 221523 **Payroll Expense ($000)**: 84608 **Personnel**: 1124

✠ **MULTICARE DEACONESS HOSPITAL (500044)**, 800 West Fifth Avenue, Zip 99204–2803, Mailing Address: P.O.Box 248, 99210–0248; tel. 509/458–5800 **A**1 3 10 **F**3 11 12 13 15 17 18 20 22 24 26 28 29 31 40 43 45 46 47 48 49 50 51 56 60 64 68 70 72 73 74 75 78 79 81 82 85 86 87 91 92 107 108 110 111 113 114 115 119 124 126 129 130 132 146 147 148 **S** MultiCare Health System, Tacoma, WA
Primary Contact: Laureen Driscoll, President
CFO: Rodney Higgins, Chief Financial Officer
CIO: Richard DeRoche, Manager Information Technology
CHR: Melinda Moore, Director Human Resources
CNO: Jennifer Petrik, Interim Chief Nursing Officer
CMO: David Chen, MD, Chief Medical Officer
Web address: www.deaconessspokane.com/Deaconess–Hospital/home.aspx
Control: Corporation, Investor–owned (for–profit) **Service**: General medical and surgical

Staffed Beds: 352 **Admissions**: 11165 **Census**: 157 **Outpatient Visits**: 104066 **Births**: 1465 **Total Expense ($000)**: 239596 **Payroll Expense ($000)**: 91393

WA

PROVIDENCE HOLY FAMILY HOSPITAL (500077), 5633 North Lidgerwood Street, Zip 99208–1224; tel. 509/482–0111 **A**1 2 5 7 10 **F**3 8 11 12 13 15 18 20 22 29 30 31 34 35 37 38 39 40 41 43 45 46 47 48 49 50 53 56 57 58 59 60 61 64 68 70 73 74 75 76 77 78 79 80 81 82 84 85 86 87 89 92 100 107 108 129 130 131 132 135 143 145 146 147 148 149 **P**6 **S** Providence St. Joseph Health, Renton, WA
Primary Contact: Peggy M. Currie, R.N., Chief Operating Officer
COO: Cathy J Simchuk, Chief Operating Officer
CFO: Shelby Stokoe, Chief Financial Officer
CMO: Dean Martz, Chief Medical Officer
CIO: Mark Vogelsang, Director Information Services
CHR: Mark Smith, Director Human Resources
CNO: Sharon Hershman R.N., Chief Nursing Officer
Web address: www.providence.org
Control: Church operated, Nongovernment, not–for–profit **Service:** General medical and surgical

Staffed Beds: 191 **Admissions:** 9042 **Census:** 98 **Outpatient Visits:** 194974 **Births:** 1289 **Total Expense ($000):** 200025 **Payroll Expense ($000):** 56440 **Personnel:** 860

PROVIDENCE SACRED HEART MEDICAL CENTER & CHILDREN'S HOSPITAL (500054), 101 West Eighth Avenue, Zip 99204–2364, Mailing Address: P.O.Box 2555, 99220–2555; tel. 509/474–3131, (Includes SACRED HEART CHILDREN'S HOSPITAL, 101 West Eight Avenue, Spokane, Washington, Zip 99204–2307, PO Box 2555, 99220–2555, tel. 509/474–4841; Keith Georgeson, M.D., Chief Executive) **A**1 2 3 5 10 **F**3 8 13 17 18 19 20 21 22 23 24 25 26 27 29 30 31 35 36 37 40 41 43 45 46 47 48 49 56 68 70 72 73 74 75 76 78 79 81 82 83 84 85 86 87 88 89 92 98 99 100 101 102 103 104 105 106 107 108 109 110 111 112 114 115 118 119 120 121 123 124 126 130 131 132 137 138 142 145 146 147 148 149 **P**6 **S** Providence St. Joseph Health, Renton, WA
Primary Contact: Peggy M. Currie, R.N., Chief Operating Officer
CFO: Shelby Stokoe, Senior Director Finance
CMO: Dean Martz, Chief Medical Officer
CHR: Mark Smith, Director Human Resources
CNO: Susan Stacey, Chief Nursing Officer
Web address: www.shmc.org
Control: Church operated, Nongovernment, not–for–profit **Service:** General medical and surgical

Staffed Beds: 672 **Admissions:** 29048 **Census:** 451 **Outpatient Visits:** 465277 **Births:** 3306 **Total Expense ($000):** 910516 **Payroll Expense ($000):** 292867 **Personnel:** 3600

SHRINERS HOSPITALS FOR CHILDREN–SPOKANE (503302), 911 West Fifth Avenue, Zip 99204–2901, Mailing Address: P.O.Box 2472, 99210–2472; tel. 509/455–7844, (Nonreporting) **A**1 3 10 **S** Shriners Hospitals for Children, Tampa, FL
Primary Contact: Peter G. Brewer, Administrator
CFO: Monica Hickman, Director Fiscal Services
CMO: Glen Baird M.D., Chief of Staff
CIO: Mike Allen, Director Information Services
CHR: Karen Mattern, Director of Human Resources
CNO: Lynda Vilanova, Director Patient Care Services
Web address: www.shrinershospitalsforchildren.org/Hospitals/Locations/Spokane.aspx
Control: Other not–for–profit (including NFP Corporation) **Service:** Children's orthopedic

Staffed Beds: 30

ST. LUKE'S REHABILITATION INSTITUTE (503025), 711 South Cowley Street, Zip 99202–1388; tel. 509/473–6000 **A**1 7 10 **F**28 29 30 36 38 43 50 53 58 64 68 74 75 77 79 82 86 87 90 91 92 93 95 96 130 131 132 135 146 148 149 **P**6 **S** Providence St. Joseph Health, Renton, WA
Primary Contact: Nancy Webster, Administrator and Chief Operating Officer
CFO: Helen Andrus, Chief Financial Officer
CMO: Gregory Carter M.D., Chief Medical Officer
CIO: Fred Galusha, Chief Information Officer
CHR: Staci Franz, Director Human Resources
CNO: Kimberly J Ward, Chief Nurse Officer
Web address: www.st-lukes.org
Control: Other not–for–profit (including NFP Corporation) **Service:** Rehabilitation

Staffed Beds: 72 **Admissions:** 1453 **Census:** 55 **Outpatient Visits:** 75416 **Births:** 0 **Total Expense ($000):** 45301 **Payroll Expense ($000):** 29100 **Personnel:** 499

VETERANS AFFAIRS MEDICAL CENTER See Mann–Grandstaff Veterans Affairs Medical Center

SPOKANE VALLEY—Spokane County

MULTICARE VALLEY HOSPITAL (500119), 12606 East Mission Avenue, Zip 99216–1090; tel. 509/924–6650 **A**1 3 10 **F**3 8 13 20 22 24 29 30 31 35 40 41 43 44 45 46 48 49 50 59 64 68 70 74 76 78 79 81 82 84 85 87 107 108 111 114 119 130 131 143 146 147 **S** MultiCare Health System, Tacoma, WA
Primary Contact: Gregory George. Repetti III, FACHE, Chief Executive Officer
COO: David Martin, Assistant Administrator
CFO: Justin Voelker, Chief Financial Officer
CIO: Brain Jones, Director of Information Technology
CHR: Jamie Caine, Director of Human Resources
CNO: Shannon S Holland R.N., MSN, Chief Nursing Officer
Web address: www.valleyhospital.org
Control: Corporation, Investor–owned (for–profit) **Service:** General medical and surgical

Staffed Beds: 92 **Admissions:** 5568 **Census:** 54 **Outpatient Visits:** 55874 **Births:** 736 **Total Expense ($000):** 90116 **Payroll Expense ($000):** 42953

SUNNYSIDE—Yakima County

★ **SUNNYSIDE COMMUNITY HOSPITAL AND CLINICS (501330)**, 1016 Tacoma Avenue, Zip 98944–2263, Mailing Address: P.O.Box 719, 98944–0719; tel. 509/837–1500 **A**10 18 **F**8 11 13 15 18 20 22 29 30 31 32 34 35 40 41 45 46 50 51 59 60 64 65 68 70 74 76 77 78 79 81 82 87 89 93 107 108 110 111 115 116 117 119 126 127 129 130 131 132 133 144 **S** HealthTech Management Services, Brentwood, TN
Primary Contact: John Gallagher, Chief Executive Officer
CFO: Cary Rowan, Chief Financial Officer
CIO: John Andersen, Manager Information Systems
CHR: Elaina Wagner, Director Human Resources
CNO: Mary Beth Tubbs, Chief Nursing Officer
Web address: www.sunnysidehospital.com
Control: Other not–for–profit (including NFP Corporation) **Service:** General medical and surgical

Staffed Beds: 25 **Admissions:** 1893 **Census:** 18 **Outpatient Visits:** 78345 **Births:** 531 **Total Expense ($000):** 82602 **Payroll Expense ($000):** 31708 **Personnel:** 460

TACOMA—Pierce County

ALLENMORE HOSPITAL See Multicare Tacoma General Hospital

MADIGAN ARMY MEDICAL CENTER, Fitzsimmons Drive, Building 9040, Zip 98431–1100; tel. 253/968–1110 **A**1 2 3 5 **F**3 4 5 7 8 9 11 12 13 14 15 18 19 20 22 29 30 31 32 33 34 35 36 37 38 39 40 41 43 44 45 46 47 48 49 50 51 52 53 54 55 56 57 58 59 60 61 64 65 68 70 72 74 75 76 77 78 79 80 81 82 83 84 85 86 87 88 89 92 93 94 96 97 98 99 100 101 102 103 104 105 106 107 110 111 114 115 116 117 118 119 120 121 122 123 124 126 129 130 131 132 134 135 136 144 145 146 147 148 149 **S** Department of the Army, Office of the Surgeon General, Falls Church, VA
Primary Contact: Colonel Michael Place, M.D., Commander
COO: ColonelR Neal David, Administrator and Chief of Staff
CFO: Lieutenant ColonelBryan Longmuir, Chief Resource Management
CIO: Lieutenant ColonelAndrew Smith, Chief Information Management
CHR: David Aiken, Chief Human Resources Officer
Web address: www.mamc.amedd.army.mil
Control: Army, Government, federal **Service:** General medical and surgical

Staffed Beds: 200 **Admissions:** 11063 **Census:** 101 **Outpatient Visits:** 787388 **Births:** 858 **Total Expense ($000):** 574432 **Payroll Expense ($000):** 254144 **Personnel:** 5013

MULTICARE MARY BRIDGE CHILDREN'S HOSPITAL AND HEALTH CENTER (503301), 317 Martin Luther King Jr Way, Zip 98405–4234, Mailing Address: P.O.Box 5299, 98415–0299; tel. 253/403–1400 **A**1 5 10 **F**3 8 19 21 23 25 27 29 30 31 32 34 35 36 38 39 40 41 43 45 47 48 49 56 57 58 59 60 61 62 63 64 65 66 68 71 74 75 78 79 81 82 84 85 86 87 88 89 91 92 93 94 96 97 99 100 102 104 107 108 111 114 115 116 117 118 119 120 121 123 124 126 129 130 131 132 143 144 146 148 149 150 **S** MultiCare Health System, Tacoma, WA
Primary Contact: Linda Chen, President and Market Leader
COO: Jennifer Hamilton, COO – Mary Bridge
CFO: Anna Loomis, Senior Vice President Chief Financial Officer
CMO: Iain Asplin, Chief Medical Officer
CHR: Kevin B Dull, Senior Vice President Human Potential
CNO: Diana Brovold, Chief Nurse Executive
Web address: www.multicare.org/marybridge
Control: Other not–for–profit (including NFP Corporation) **Service:** Children's general medical and surgical

Staffed Beds: 75 **Admissions:** 3783 **Census:** 40 **Outpatient Visits:** 141975 **Births:** 0 **Total Expense ($000):** 207695 **Payroll Expense ($000):** 79120

WA

Hospital, Medicare Provider Number, Address, Telephone, Approval, Facility, and Physician Codes, Health Care System

★ American Hospital Association (AHA) membership   ○ Healthcare Facilities Accreditation Program   ⇑ Center for Improvement in Healthcare Quality Accreditation
□ The Joint Commission accreditation   ◇ DNV Healthcare Inc. accreditation   △ Commission on Accreditation of Rehabilitation Facilities (CARF) accreditation

⊞ **MULTICARE TACOMA GENERAL HOSPITAL (500129)**, 315 Martin Luther King Jr Way, Zip 98405–4234, Mailing Address: P.O.Box 5299, 98415–0299; tel. 253/403–1000, (Includes ALLENMORE HOSPITAL, 1901 South Union Avenue, Tacoma, Washington, Zip 98405, P O Box 11414, 98411–0414, tel. 253/459–6633; Shelly Mullin, R.N., President Market Leader) **A**1 2 3 10 **F**3 8 13 17 18 20 22 24 26 28 29 30 31 34 35 36 40 42 43 45 46 47 48 49 50 51 53 54 55 57 58 59 64 70 71 72 73 74 75 76 78 79 80 81 82 84 85 87 93 98 99 102 107 108 109 111 114 115 116 117 119 120 121 123 124 126 129 130 131 132 135 146 147 148 149 **S** MultiCare Health System, Tacoma, WA
Primary Contact: Julia Truman, President and Chief Operating Officer
COO: Julia Truman, Chief Operating Officer
CFO: Anna Loomis, Senior Vice President Chief Financial Officer
CHR: Kevin B Dull, Senior Vice President Human Potential
CNO: Anita Wolfe, Chief Nurse Executive
Web address: www.multicare.org
Control: Other not–for–profit (including NFP Corporation) **Service**: General medical and surgical

> **Staffed Beds:** 420 **Admissions:** 18533 **Census:** 276 **Outpatient Visits:** 201932 **Births:** 3115 **Total Expense ($000):** 690409 **Payroll Expense ($000):** 268969 **Personnel:** 2604

⊞ △ **ST. JOSEPH MEDICAL CENTER (500108)**, 1717 South 'J' Street, Zip 98405–3004, Mailing Address: P.O.Box 2197, 98401–2197; tel. 253/426–4101 **A**1 2 3 7 10 **F**3 8 11 12 13 17 18 20 29 30 31 34 35 38 40 43 44 45 46 47 48 49 50 51 55 57 58 59 60 63 64 65 70 72 73 74 75 76 77 78 79 81 82 84 85 86 87 90 92 93 98 102 107 108 111 114 115 119 124 126 130 131 132 135 145 146 148 149 **S** Catholic Health Initiatives, Englewood, CO
Primary Contact: Syd Bersante, President
CFO: Mike Fitzgerald, Chief Financial Officer
CIO: Rand Strobel, Vice President Information Technology and Compliance
CNO: Ruth Flint, Chief Nursing Officer
Web address: www.chifranciscan.org
Control: Church operated, Nongovernment, not–for–profit **Service**: General medical and surgical

> **Staffed Beds:** 366 **Admissions:** 21710 **Census:** 303 **Outpatient Visits:** 289173 **Births:** 4266

VETERANS AFFAIRS PUGET SOUND HEALTH CARE SYSTEM–AMERICAN LAKE DIVISION See Veterans Affairs Puget Sound Health Care System, Seattle

☐ **WESTERN STATE HOSPITAL (504003)**, 9601 Steilacoom Boulevard SW, Zip 98498–7213; tel. 253/582–8900, (Nonreporting) **A**1 5 10
Primary Contact: Cheryl Strange, Interim Chief Executive Officer
COO: David Holt, Chief Operating Officer
CFO: Sue Breen, Chief Financial Officer
CMO: James A Polo M.D., Chief Medical Officer
CHR: Lori Manning, Administrator Human Resources
CNO: Rae Simpson R.N., Chief Nursing Officer
Web address: www.dshs.wa.gov/bhsia/division–state–hospitals/western–state–hospital
Control: State, Government, Nonfederal **Service**: Psychiatric

> **Staffed Beds:** 867

TONASKET—Okanogan County

★ **NORTH VALLEY HOSPITAL (501321)**, 203 South Western Avenue, Zip 98855–8803; tel. 509/486–2151, (Total facility includes 42 beds in nursing home–type unit) **A**10 18 **F**3 13 15 26 29 34 35 40 43 45 50 59 64 75 77 81 82 85 87 93 94 96 97 107 110 111 114 119 128 130 131 132 133 135 148
Primary Contact: Helen Verhasselt, Interim Chief Executive Officer
CFO: Helen Verhasselt, Chief Financial Officer
CMO: Paul Lacey M.D., Chief Medical Staff
CIO: Kelly Cariker, Chief Information Officer
CHR: Jan Gonzales, Director Human Resources
Web address: www.nvhospital.org
Control: Hospital district or authority, Government, Nonfederal **Service**: General medical and surgical

> **Staffed Beds:** 67 **Admissions:** 434 **Census:** 40 **Births:** 85

TOPPENISH—Yakima County

⊞ **TOPPENISH COMMUNITY HOSPITAL (500037)**, 502 West Fourth Avenue, Zip 98948–1616, Mailing Address: P.O.Box 672, 98948–0672; tel. 509/865–3105 **A**1 3 5 10 **F**3 13 15 18 20 28 29 30 34 35 40 43 45 46 50 57 59 68 70 76 79 81 89 107 111 114 119 133 135 **S** Community Health Systems, Inc., Franklin, TN
Primary Contact: Grant Magness, Interim Chief Executive Officer
CFO: Curtis Herrin, Chief Financial Officer
CHR: Rosa Solorzano, Interim Director Human Resources
Web address: www.toppenishhospital.com
Control: Corporation, Investor–owned (for–profit) **Service**: General medical and surgical

> **Staffed Beds:** 48 **Admissions:** 1308 **Census:** 8 **Births:** 435

TUKWILA—King County

⊞ **CASCADE BEHAVIORAL HOSPITAL (504011)**, 12844 Military Road South, Zip 98168–3045; tel. 206/244–0180 (Nonreporting) **A**1 3 10 **S** Acadia Healthcare Company, Inc., Franklin, TN
Primary Contact: Michael Uradnik, Chief Executive Officer
CFO: Gregg Terreson, Chief Financial Officer
CHR: Sherry Cochran, Manager Human Resources
Web address: www.cascadebh.com
Control: Corporation, Investor–owned (for–profit) **Service**: Psychiatric

> **Staffed Beds:** 63

VANCOUVER—Clark County

LEGACY SALMON CREEK HOSPITAL See Legacy Salmon Creek Medical Center

⊞ **LEGACY SALMON CREEK MEDICAL CENTER (500150)**, 2211 NE 139th Street, Zip 98686–2742; tel. 360/487–1000 **A**1 2 5 10 **F**3 11 13 15 18 20 26 28 29 30 31 32 34 35 37 38 39 40 41 44 45 46 47 49 50 51 55 57 59 60 65 68 70 72 74 75 76 77 78 79 80 81 82 84 85 87 93 96 97 107 108 110 111 114 115 116 117 118 119 120 121 129 130 132 146 147 148 **P**6 **S** Legacy Health, Portland, OR
Primary Contact: Bryce R. Helgerson, Chief Administrative Officer
COO: Michael Newcomb D.O., Senior Vice President and Chief Operating Officer
CMO: Lewis Low M.D., Senior Vice President and Chief Medical Officer
CHR: Sonja Steves, Senior Vice President Human Resources
CNO: Carol Bradley MSN, R.N., Senior Vice President and Chief Nursing Officer
Web address: www.legacyhealth.org
Control: Other not–for–profit (including NFP Corporation) **Service**: General medical and surgical

> **Staffed Beds:** 215 **Admissions:** 14856 **Census:** 151 **Outpatient Visits:** 287488 **Births:** 3349 **Total Expense ($000):** 272547 **Payroll Expense ($000):** 143690 **Personnel:** 1637

★ △ ⇑ **PEACEHEALTH SOUTHWEST MEDICAL CENTER (500050)**, 400 NE Mother Joseph Place, Zip 98664–3200, Mailing Address: P.O.Box 1600, 98668–1600; tel. 360/256–2000, (Includes VANCOUVER MEMORIAL CAMPUS, 3400 Main Street, Vancouver, Washington, Zip 98663, tel. 360/514–2000; Sean Gregory, Chief Executive, Columbia Network) **A**2 3 5 7 10 21 **F**3 11 12 13 15 17 18 20 24 26 28 29 30 31 34 35 40 43 44 45 46 49 50 51 54 57 58 59 60 61 62 63 64 65 68 70 72 74 75 76 77 78 79 81 82 84 85 86 87 89 90 92 93 96 97 98 100 101 102 103 104 105 107 108 109 110 111 113 114 115 116 119 120 121 122 124 126 129 130 131 132 135 144 145 146 147 148 **S** PeaceHealth, Vancouver, WA
Primary Contact: Sean Gregory, Chief Executive
COO: Wade Hunt, Chief Operating Officer
CFO: Ronald K Benfield, Chief Financial Officer
CMO: Lawrence Neville, Chief Medical Officer
CIO: Donn McMillan, Senior Director, IST Client Liaison
CHR: Kelley Frengle, Senior Director, Human Resources
CNO: Helen Vos R.N., Interim Chief Nursing Officer
Web address: www.peacehealth.org
Control: Other not–for–profit (including NFP Corporation) **Service**: General medical and surgical

> **Staffed Beds:** 362 **Admissions:** 19665 **Census:** 248 **Births:** 2084 **Total Expense ($000):** 566164 **Payroll Expense ($000):** 191864

⇑ **SOUTHWEST WASHINGTON MEDICAL CENTER** See Peacehealth Southwest Medical Center

WALLA WALLA—Walla Walla County

⊞ △ **PROVIDENCE ST. MARY MEDICAL CENTER (500002)**, 401 West Poplar Street, Zip 99362–2846, Mailing Address: P.O.Box 1477, 99362–0312; tel. 509/897–3320 **A**1 2 7 10 19 **F**3 13 15 18 20 22 28 29 30 31 34 35 40 43 45 46 49 59 60 62 64 70 74 75 76 77 78 79 81 84 85 89 90 92 93 96 97 107 108 110 111 114 115 119 120 121 123 124 129 130 132 135 144 146 147 148 **P**6 **S** Providence St. Joseph Health, Renton, WA
Primary Contact: Susan Blackburn, Chief Administrative Officer
COO: Susan Blackburn, Chief Operating Officer
CMO: Tim Davidson M.D., Chief Executive Physician Services
CIO: Martin Manny, Director, I.S.
CNO: Yvonne M Strader, Chief Nursing Officer
Web address: www.washington.providence.org/hospitals/st–mary/
Control: Church operated, Nongovernment, not–for–profit **Service**: General medical and surgical

> **Staffed Beds:** 85 **Admissions:** 5012 **Census:** 49 **Outpatient Visits:** 182025 **Births:** 648 **Total Expense ($000):** 166119 **Payroll Expense ($000):** 87460 **Personnel:** 863

WA

Many Facility Codes have changed. Please refer to the AHA Guide Code Chart. © 2017 AHA Guide

STATE PENITENTIARY HOSPITAL, 1313 North 13th Street, Zip 99362–8817; tel. 509/525–3610, (Nonreporting)
Primary Contact: Karen Forest, Health Care Manager
Control: State, Government, Nonfederal **Service**: Hospital unit of an institution (prison hospital, college infirmary, etc.)

Staffed Beds: 36

WENATCHEE—Chelan County

★ ⇑ **CONFLUENCE HEALTH/CENTRAL WASHINGTON HOSPITAL (500016)**, 1201 South Miller Street, Zip 98801–3201, Mailing Address: P.O.Box 1887, 98807–1887; tel. 509/662–1511, (Total facility includes 22 beds in nursing home–type unit) **A**2 10 19 21 **F**3 13 17 18 20 22 24 26 28 29 30 31 34 35 40 43 45 46 47 49 50 62 63 64 68 69 70 73 74 75 76 78 79 81 84 85 86 89 91 93 94 95 107 111 114 115 119 127 128 130 146 148
Primary Contact: Peter Rutherford, M.D., Chief Executive Officer
COO: Vikki Noyes, Executive Vice President and Chief Operating Officer
CFO: John Doyle, Chief Financial Officer
CMO: Stuart Freed M.D., Chief Medical Officer
CIO: Robert Pageler, Chief Information Officer
CHR: Jim Wood, Chief Administrative Officer
CNO: Tracey A Kasnic, Senior Vice President Inpatient and Chief Nursing Officer
Web address: www.cwhs.com
Control: Other not–for–profit (including NFP Corporation) **Service**: General medical and surgical

Staffed Beds: 198 **Admissions**: 10878 **Census**: 123 **Outpatient Visits**: 153104 **Births**: 1687 **Total Expense ($000)**: 328096 **Payroll Expense ($000)**: 91328

△ **CONFLUENCE HEALTH/WENATCHEE VALLEY HOSPITAL (500148)**, 820 North Chelan Avenue, Zip 98801–2028; tel. 509/663–8711 (Nonreporting) **A**2 7 10
Primary Contact: Peter Rutherford, M.D., Chief Executive Officer
COO: Kevin Gilbert R.N., Vice President
CFO: John Doyle, Chief Financial Officer
CMO: Stuart Freed M.D., Medical Director
CIO: Robert Pageler, Chief Information Officer
CHR: Jim Wood, Chief Human Resources Officer
CNO: Tracey A Kasnic, Chief Nursing Officer
Web address: www.wvmedical.com
Control: Partnership, Investor–owned (for–profit) **Service**: General medical and surgical

Staffed Beds: 20

WHITE SALMON—Klickitat County

SKYLINE HOSPITAL (501315), 211 Skyline Drive, Zip 98672–1918, Mailing Address: P.O.Box 99, 98672–0099; tel. 509/493–1101 **A**10 18 **F**3 15 18 34 35 40 43 45 57 59 64 74 81 82 87 93 107 115 119 131 133 146 149 **P**6
Primary Contact: Robert P. Kimmes, Chief Executive Officer
CFO: Brenda Schneider, Chief Financial Officer
CMO: Christopher Samuels, Chief of Staff
CIO: Steve Opbroek, Manager Information Technology
CHR: Jessie Ramos, Manager Human Resources
CNO: Stefanie Boen, Chief Nursing Officer
Web address: www.skylinehospital.org
Control: Hospital district or authority, Government, Nonfederal **Service**: General medical and surgical

Staffed Beds: 16 **Admissions**: 239 **Census**: 2 **Outpatient Visits**: 15206 **Births**: 0 **Total Expense ($000)**: 18237 **Payroll Expense ($000)**: 9022 **Personnel**: 138

YAKIMA—Yakima County

✠ **VIRGINIA MASON MEMORIAL (500036)**, 2811 Tieton Drive, Zip 98902–3761; tel. 509/575–8000 **A**1 2 3 5 10 **F**3 8 9 11 13 15 17 18 20 22 26 28 29 30 31 32 34 35 36 40 41 42 43 44 45 46 47 49 50 51 54 55 57 59 60 62 63 64 68 70 72 74 75 76 77 78 79 81 82 84 85 86 87 89 91 92 93 96 98 100 102 104 107 108 110 111 114 116 117 119 120 121 123 124 129 130 131 132 135 144 146 147 148 **P**4 6 7 **S** Virginia Mason Health System, Seattle, WA
Primary Contact: Russ Myers, Chief Executive Officer
COO: James Aberle, Vice President, Chief Operations Officer
CFO: Tim Reed, Vice President and Chief Financial Officer
CMO: Marty Brueggemann, Chief Medical Officer
CIO: Jeff Yamada, Vice President
CHR: Jolene R Seda, Vice President People and Culture
CNO: Diane Patterson, Vice President, Chief Nursing Officer
Web address: www.yakimamemorial.org
Control: Other not–for–profit (including NFP Corporation) **Service**: General medical and surgical

Staffed Beds: 226 **Admissions**: 11751 **Census**: 122 **Outpatient Visits**: 502503 **Births**: 2759 **Total Expense ($000)**: 414353 **Payroll Expense ($000)**: 178279 **Personnel**: 2383

✠ △ **YAKIMA REGIONAL MEDICAL AND CARDIAC CENTER (500012)**, 110 South Ninth Avenue, Zip 98902–3315; tel. 509/575–5000 **A**1 7 10 **F**3 15 17 18 19 20 22 24 26 28 29 30 34 35 37 40 41 43 45 46 49 50 57 58 59 60 62 63 64 65 67 68 70 74 77 78 79 81 82 85 87 89 90 93 96 102 107 108 110 111 115 119 126 130 132 144 145 146 **S** Community Health Systems, Inc., Franklin, TN
Primary Contact: Bryan Braegger, Interim Chief Executive Officer
CMO: Dave Atteberry M.D., Chief of Staff
CHR: Ralph L Lundberg, Director Human Resources
Web address: www.yakimaregional.net
Control: Corporation, Investor–owned (for–profit) **Service**: General medical and surgical

Staffed Beds: 167 **Admissions**: 3961 **Census**: 51 **Total Expense ($000)**: 106645 **Payroll Expense ($000)**: 36908

WA

WEST VIRGINIA

BECKLEY—Raleigh County

☐ **BECKLEY ARH HOSPITAL (510062)**, 306 Stanaford Road, Zip 25801–3142; tel. 304/255–3000 **A**1 10 **F**3 6 11 15 17 18 20 28 29 30 31 34 35 39 40 43 44 45 46 47 48 49 50 51 54 56 57 59 60 61 64 65 70 74 75 77 78 79 81 82 84 85 86 87 89 92 93 97 98 99 100 101 102 103 105 107 108 109 110 111 114 115 116 118 119 129 130 132 146 148 **P**6 **S** Appalachian Regional Healthcare, Inc., Lexington, KY
Primary Contact: Rocco K. Massey, Community Chief Executive Officer
CMO: Ahmad Khiami, Chief of Staff
CHR: Sue Thomas, Manager Human Resources
CNO: Angela Rivera, Chief Nursing Officer
Web address: www.arh.org
Control: Other not–for–profit (including NFP Corporation) **Service**: General medical and surgical

Staffed Beds: 170 **Admissions**: 6846 **Census**: 106 **Outpatient Visits**: 88964 **Births**: 0 **Total Expense ($000)**: 96337 **Payroll Expense ($000)**: 25530 **Personnel**: 549

✚ **BECKLEY VETERANS AFFAIRS MEDICAL CENTER**, 200 Veterans Avenue, Zip 25801–6499; tel. 304/255–2121, (Nonreporting) **A**1 **S** Department of Veterans Affairs, Washington, DC
Primary Contact: Stacy J. Vasquez, Director
CFO: Terry Massey, Chief Fiscal Services
CMO: John David Berryman M.D., Chief of Staff
CIO: Sherry Gregg, Chief Information Technology Officer
CNO: Debra Lynn Legg, Associate Director Patient Care Services and Nurse Executive
Web address: www.beckley.va.gov/
Control: Veterans Affairs, Government, federal **Service**: General medical and surgical

Staffed Beds: 40

✚ **RALEIGH GENERAL HOSPITAL (510070)**, 1710 Harper Road, Zip 25801–3397; tel. 304/256–4100 **A**1 10 19 **F**3 13 15 17 18 20 22 29 30 31 34 35 40 43 45 49 50 57 59 60 64 70 74 75 76 78 79 81 85 87 89 107 108 110 111 114 115 117 119 126 130 132 146 147 149 **S** LifePoint Health, Brentwood, TN
Primary Contact: Matthew S. Roberts, Chief Executive Officer
CFO: Randy Harrison, Chief Financial Officer
CMO: Syed Siddiqi M.D., President Medical Staff
CIO: Kevin Sexton, Director Information Systems
CHR: Chris T Beebe, Director Human Resources
CNO: Alene Lewis R.N., Chief Nursing Officer
Web address: www.raleighgeneral.com
Control: Corporation, Investor–owned (for–profit) **Service**: General medical and surgical

Staffed Beds: 229 **Admissions**: 9947 **Census**: 121 **Outpatient Visits**: 93542 **Births**: 1020 **Total Expense ($000)**: 133937 **Payroll Expense ($000)**: 43401 **Personnel**: 784

BERKELEY SPRINGS—Morgan County

★ **WAR MEMORIAL HOSPITAL (511309)**, One Healthy Way, Zip 25411–7463; tel. 304/258–1234, (Total facility includes 16 beds in nursing home–type unit) **A**10 18 **F**3 11 15 28 29 30 34 35 40 45 50 53 54 57 59 64 65 77 79 81 85 86 93 97 107 119 129 130 133 **P**6 **S** Valley Health System, Winchester, VA
Primary Contact: Thomas S. Kluge, President
CFO: Kathryn Morales, Director of Finance
CMO: Gerald Bechamps M.D., Vice President Medical Affairs
CHR: Abbey Rembold, Human Resources Senior Generalist
CNO: Heather Sigel, Director of Clinical Services
Web address: www.valleyhealthlink.com/war
Control: Other not–for–profit (including NFP Corporation) **Service**: General medical and surgical

Staffed Beds: 41 **Admissions**: 369 **Census**: 24 **Outpatient Visits**: 38573 **Births**: 0 **Total Expense ($000)**: 22130 **Payroll Expense ($000)**: 9170 **Personnel**: 142

BLUEFIELD—Mercer County

✚ **BLUEFIELD REGIONAL MEDICAL CENTER (510071)**, 500 Cherry Street, Zip 24701–3390; tel. 304/327–1100 **A**1 10 12 13 19 **F**3 8 13 15 18 20 22 28 29 31 34 40 43 45 46 47 49 50 56 57 59 60 64 68 70 74 75 76 78 79 81 86 89 96 107 108 110 111 115 118 119 121 124 126 127 129 130 132 144 146 147 **P**8 **S** Community Health Systems, Inc., Franklin, TN
Primary Contact: Derek W. Cimala, Interim Chief Executive Officer
COO: Michael Makosky, Chief Operating Officer
CMO: Joel Shor M.D., Chief of Staff
CIO: Rose Lasker, Director Information Services
CHR: Sandee Cheynet, Vice President Administrative Services
Web address: www.bluefield.org
Control: Corporation, Investor–owned (for–profit) **Service**: General medical and surgical

Staffed Beds: 92 **Admissions**: 3450 **Census**: 36 **Outpatient Visits**: 76401 **Births**: 493 **Total Expense ($000)**: 82808 **Payroll Expense ($000)**: 22383 **Personnel**: 413

BRIDGEPORT—Harrison County

✚ **UNITED HOSPITAL CENTER (510006)**, 327 Medical Park Drive, Zip 26330–9006; tel. 681/342–1000 **A**1 2 3 5 10 12 13 **F**3 5 11 13 15 17 18 20 22 28 29 30 31 34 37 38 40 45 46 47 48 49 51 54 57 58 59 60 62 63 64 68 70 74 75 76 77 78 79 81 84 85 86 87 89 92 93 97 98 99 100 101 102 103 104 107 108 110 111 114 115 117 118 119 120 121 123 126 128 129 130 131 132 146 147 148 **P**1 6 7 **S** West Virginia University Health System, Morgantown, WV
Primary Contact: Michael C. Tillman, President and Chief Executive Officer
COO: John Fernandez, Chief Operating Officer
CFO: Jim Rutkowski, Chief Financial Officer
CMO: Eric Radcliffe, Medical Director
CIO: Brian Cottrill, Chief Information Officer
CHR: Timothy M Allen, Vice President Human Resources
CNO: Stephanie Smart, Chief Nursing Officer
Web address: www.thenewuhc.com
Control: Other not–for–profit (including NFP Corporation) **Service**: General medical and surgical

Staffed Beds: 264 **Admissions**: 12453 **Census**: 172 **Outpatient Visits**: 594503 **Births**: 1081 **Total Expense ($000)**: 294126 **Payroll Expense ($000)**: 115567 **Personnel**: 2014

BUCKEYE—Pocahontas County

★ **POCAHONTAS MEMORIAL HOSPITAL (511314)**, 150 Duncan Road, Zip 24924; tel. 304/799–7400 **A**10 18 **F**3 7 11 29 30 34 35 40 43 50 56 57 59 64 65 68 75 77 86 93 97 107 119 127 130 132 133 135 149
Primary Contact: Barbara Lay, Chief Executive Officer
COO: Terry Wagner R.N., Chief Operating Officer
CFO: Jon Boyette, Chief Financial Officer
CMO: Jeffrey Pilney, Chief Medical Officer
CIO: Samuel Walker, Director of IT
CHR: Katie Brown, Coordinator Human Resources
CNO: Kyna Moore R.N., Chief Nursing Officer
Web address: www.pmhwv.org/
Control: County, Government, Nonfederal **Service**: General medical and surgical

Staffed Beds: 24 **Admissions**: 213 **Census**: 3 **Outpatient Visits**: 23072 **Births**: 1 **Total Expense ($000)**: 13484 **Payroll Expense ($000)**: 8109 **Personnel**: 134

BUCKHANNON—Upshur County

✚ **ST. JOSEPH'S HOSPITAL OF BUCKHANNON (511321)**, 1 Amalia Drive, Zip 26201–2276; tel. 304/473–2000, (Total facility includes 20 beds in nursing home–type unit) **A**1 10 18 **F**3 11 13 15 18 28 29 30 31 34 35 40 43 44 45 50 57 59 64 65 70 75 76 79 81 83 84 85 87 89 107 110 115 119 128 129 130 132 133 135 144 146 147 **P**6 **S** West Virginia University Health System, Morgantown, WV
Primary Contact: Skip Gjolberg, FACHE, Administrator
CFO: Russell J. Plywaczynski CPA, Director of Finance
CMO: Bartley Brown D.O., Chief of Staff
CIO: Brian Williams, Web Services and Information Technology Manager
CHR: Anissa J Hite Davis, Vice President Human Resources
CNO: Annamarie Chidester R.N., Vice President, Patient Care Services
Web address: www.stj.net
Control: Other not–for–profit (including NFP Corporation) **Service**: General medical and surgical

Staffed Beds: 51 **Admissions**: 935 **Census**: 16 **Outpatient Visits**: 97517 **Births**: 326 **Total Expense ($000)**: 42173 **Payroll Expense ($000)**: 19105 **Personnel**: 380

CHARLESTON—Kanawha County

CAMC MEMORIAL HOSPITAL See Charleston Area Medical Center

CAMC WOMEN AND CHILDREN'S HOSPITAL See Charleston Area Medical Center

★ △ ⇑ **CHARLESTON AREA MEDICAL CENTER (510022)**, 501 Morris Street, Zip 25301–1300, Mailing Address: P.O.Box 1547, 25326–1547; tel. 304/388–5432, (Includes CAMC MEMORIAL HOSPITAL, 3200 MacCorkle Avenue SE, Charleston, West Virginia, Zip 25304, tel. 304/388–5973; Jeffrey L. Oskin, Vice President and Administrator; CAMC TEAYS VALLEY HOSPITAL, 1400 Hospital Drive, Hurricane, West Virginia, Zip 25526–9202, tel. 304/757–1700; Randall H Hodges, FACHE, Vice President and Administrator; CAMC WOMEN AND CHILDREN'S HOSPITAL, 800 Pennsylvania Avenue, Charleston, West Virginia, Zip 25302, P O Box 6669, 25362, tel. 304/388–5432; Andrew Weber, Vice President and Administrator; GENERAL HOSPITAL, 501 Morris Street, Charleston, West Virginia, Zip 25301, Box 1393, 25325, tel. 304/388–5432; Michael D Williams, Vice President and Administrator) **A**2 3 5 7 8 10 12 13 21 **F**3 8 11 12 13 15 17 18 19 20 22 24 26 28 29 30 31 32 34 35 38 39 40 41 43 44 45 46 47 48 49 50 51 52 54 55 56 57 59 60 61 64 65 68 70 72 74 75 76 77 78 79 81 82 84 85 86 88 89 90 91 92 93 94 96 97 98 99 100 101 102 103 104 107 108 110 111 114 115 116 117 118 119 120 121 123 124 126 129 130 131 132 134 135 138 141 143 144 145 146 147 148 149 150 **P**6
Primary Contact: David L. Ramsey, President and Chief Executive Officer
COO: Glenn Crotty M.D., Jr, Executive Vice President and Chief Operating Officer
CFO: Larry C Hudson, Executive Vice President and Chief Financial Officer
CMO: T Pinckney McIlwain M.D., Vice President and Chief Medical Officer
CIO: Eileen Clark, Vice President Information Services
CHR: Kristi Snyder, Vice President Human Resources
CNO: Ronald E Moore R.N., MSN, Vice President Professional Practice and Chief Nursing Officer
Web address: www.camc.org
Control: Other not–for–profit (including NFP Corporation) **Service**: General medical and surgical

Staffed Beds: 846 **Admissions:** 34912 **Census:** 514 **Outpatient Visits:** 804120 **Births:** 2489 **Total Expense ($000):** 1034655 **Payroll Expense ($000):** 398309 **Personnel:** 6290

☐ **CHARLESTON SURGICAL HOSPITAL (510091)**, 1306 Kanawha Boulevard East, Zip 25301–3001, Mailing Address: P.O.Box 2271, 25328–2271; tel. 304/343–4371 **A**1 10 **F**3 45 57 59 75 79 81 111 119 126 141
Primary Contact: Christina Arvon, Administrator and Chief Executive Officer
CMO: James W Candill M.D., President Medical Staff
Web address: www.eyeandearclinicwv.org
Control: Corporation, Investor–owned (for–profit) **Service**: General medical and surgical

Staffed Beds: 6 **Admissions:** 228 **Census:** 1 **Outpatient Visits:** 15558 **Births:** 0 **Total Expense ($000):** 17778 **Payroll Expense ($000):** 4959 **Personnel:** 121

GENERAL HOSPITAL See Charleston Area Medical Center

✠ **HIGHLAND HOSPITAL (514001)**, 300 56th Street SE, Zip 25304–2361, Mailing Address: P.O.Box 4107, 25364–4107; tel. 304/926–1600 **A**1 10 **F**3 29 34 35 38 50 57 59 86 87 98 99 101 103 106 130 135 149
Primary Contact: Cynthia A. Persily, Ph.D., R.N., President and Chief Executive Officer
COO: Rick Rucker, Chief Operating Officer
CFO: Chris K. Miller, Chief Financial Officer
CMO: Kiran S. Devaraj, Chief Medical Officer and Chief Clinical Officer
CIO: Damon Carradine, Director Information Technology
CNO: Leigh Dalton, Director of Nursing and Patient Care Services
Web address: www.highlandhosp.com
Control: Other not–for–profit (including NFP Corporation) **Service**: Psychiatric

Staffed Beds: 104 **Admissions:** 2310 **Census:** 62 **Outpatient Visits:** 0 **Births:** 0 **Total Expense ($000):** 21401 **Payroll Expense ($000):** 11126 **Personnel:** 357

✠ **SAINT FRANCIS HOSPITAL (510031)**, 333 Laidley Street, Zip 25301–1628, Mailing Address: P.O.Box 471, 25322–0471; tel. 304/347–6500, (Total facility includes 25 beds in nursing home–type unit) **A**1 10 **F**3 11 15 18 20 22 29 30 34 37 45 48 49 51 57 58 59 60 64 68 69 70 74 75 77 79 81 82 84 86 87 93 107 108 110 111 115 119 128 130 131 146 147 148 **S** Thomas Health System, Inc., South Charleston, WV
Primary Contact: Daniel Lauffer, FACHE, President and Chief Executive Officer
COO: Brian Ulery, Senior Vice President and Chief Operating Officer
CFO: Renee Cross, Senior Vice President and Chief Financial Officer
CMO: Matthew Upton, Chief Medical Officer and Chief Medical Information Officer
CIO: Jeremy Taylor, Director Information Services
CHR: Pete Rawlings, Chief Human Resource Officer
CNO: Rebecca Brannon R.N., Senior Vice President and Chief Nursing Officer
Web address: www.stfrancishospital.com
Control: Other not–for–profit (including NFP Corporation) **Service**: General medical and surgical

Staffed Beds: 65 **Admissions:** 1777 **Census:** 25 **Outpatient Visits:** 90487 **Births:** 0 **Total Expense ($000):** 84584 **Payroll Expense ($000):** 27736 **Personnel:** 471

✠ **SELECT SPECIALTY HOSPITAL–CHARLESTON (512002)**, 333 Laidley Street, 3rd Floor East, Zip 25301–1614; tel. 304/720–7234 **A**1 10 **F**1 29 74 75 79 85 130 148 149 **S** Select Medical Corporation, Mechanicsburg, PA
Primary Contact: Frank Weber, Chief Executive Officer
CHR: Sabrina White, Coordinator Human Resources
Web address: www.selectspecialtyhospitals.com/company/locations/charleston.aspx
Control: Corporation, Investor–owned (for–profit) **Service**: Acute long–term care hospital

Staffed Beds: 32 **Admissions:** 429 **Census:** 29 **Outpatient Visits:** 0 **Births:** 0 **Total Expense ($000):** 16564 **Payroll Expense ($000):** 6329 **Personnel:** 100

CLARKSBURG—Harrison County

☐ **HIGHLAND–CLARKSBURG HOSPITAL (514011)**, 3 Hospital Plaza, Zip 26301–9316; tel. 304/969–3100 (Nonreporting) **A**1 10
Primary Contact: Michael Casdorph, Chief Executive Officer
CFO: Shelly Giaguinto, Chief Financial Officer
CMO: Christi Cooper–Lehki, Chief Clinical Officer
CIO: Kimberly Samuelson, Director of Information Management
CHR: Robert L Boyles, Director of Human Resources
CNO: Melissa Hitt, Director of Nursing
Web address: www.highlandhosp.com
Control: Other not–for–profit (including NFP Corporation) **Service**: Psychiatric

Staffed Beds: 116

✠ **LOUIS A. JOHNSON VETERANS AFFAIRS MEDICAL CENTER**, 1 Medical Center Drive, Zip 26301–4199; tel. 304/623–3461, (Nonreporting) **A**1 2 3 5 **S** Department of Veterans Affairs, Washington, DC
Primary Contact: Glenn R. Snider, M.D., Interim Director
CMO: Glenn R Snider M.D., Chief of Staff
CIO: Michael Matthey, Facility Chief Information Officer
CHR: Ian Jacobs, Chief, Human Resource Management Service
Web address: www.clarksburg.va.gov
Control: Veterans Affairs, Government, federal **Service**: General medical and surgical

Staffed Beds: 71

ELKINS—Randolph County

✠ **DAVIS MEDICAL CENTER (510030)**, Gorman Avenue and Reed Street, Zip 26241, Mailing Address: P.O.Box 1484, 26241–1484; tel. 304/636–3300 **A**1 2 10 20 **F**11 13 15 28 29 30 31 32 34 35 40 49 50 51 54 57 59 64 68 69 70 71 75 76 78 79 81 82 84 85 86 87 89 92 94 97 107 108 109 110 111 115 116 117 118 119 121 123 129 130 132 135 146 147 148 **P**3 8 **S** Davis Health System, Elkins, WV
Primary Contact: Vance Jackson, FACHE, Chief Executive Officer
COO: Greg Johnson, Vice President of Operations
CFO: Rebecca J Hammer, Chief Financial Officer
CMO: Anne Banfield, Chief, Medical Staff
CIO: Steve Crowl, Director of Information Services
CHR: Jon Steen, Director Human Resources
CNO: Pamela Smithson R.N., Vice President Nursing
Web address: www.davishealthsystem.com
Control: Other not–for–profit (including NFP Corporation) **Service**: General medical and surgical

Staffed Beds: 80 **Admissions:** 2902 **Census:** 27 **Outpatient Visits:** 150741 **Births:** 304 **Total Expense ($000):** 92604 **Payroll Expense ($000):** 41681 **Personnel:** 674

WV

Hospital, Medicare Provider Number, Address, Telephone, Approval, Facility, and Physician Codes, Health Care System

★ American Hospital Association (AHA) membership
☐ The Joint Commission accreditation
○ Healthcare Facilities Accreditation Program
◇ DNV Healthcare Inc. accreditation
⇑ Center for Improvement in Healthcare Quality Accreditation
△ Commission on Accreditation of Rehabilitation Facilities (CARF) accreditation

FAIRMONT—Marion County

✠ **FAIRMONT REGIONAL MEDICAL CENTER (510047)**, 1325 Locust Avenue, Zip 26554–1435; tel. 304/367–7100, (Nonreporting) **A**1 2 10 **S** Alecto Healthcare, Irvine, CA
Primary Contact: Robert S. Adcock, Chief Executive Officer
CFO: Daniel Honerbrink, Vice President Finance and Chief Financial Officer
CMO: Wes Steele M.D., Chief of Staff
CIO: Mike Wooddell, Director Information Services
CHR: Jim Harris, Vice President Human Resources
CNO: Michelle L Luffey MSN, R.N., Chief Nursing Officer
Web address: www.frmcwv.com
Control: Other not–for–profit (including NFP Corporation) **Service:** General medical and surgical

Staffed Beds: 140

GASSAWAY—Braxton County

BRAXTON COUNTY MEMORIAL HOSPITAL (511308), 100 Hoylman DR, Zip 26624–9318, Mailing Address: 100 Hoylman Drive, 26624–9318; tel. 304/364–5156 **A**10 18 **F**3 8 11 15 30 32 34 35 40 43 45 57 59 62 64 75 81 97 107 108 114 127 130 133 146 147 149 **P**6
Primary Contact: Ben Vincent, FACHE, Chief Executive Officer
CFO: Kimber Knight, Chief Financial Officer
CMO: Russell L Stewart D.O., Medical Director
CNO: Julia Rose R.N., Director of Nursing
Web address: www.braxtonmemorial.org
Control: Other not–for–profit (including NFP Corporation) **Service:** General medical and surgical

Staffed Beds: 25 Admissions: 252 Census: 2 Outpatient Visits: 44407 Births: 0 Total Expense ($000): 16985 Payroll Expense ($000): 7398 Personnel: 152

GLEN DALE—Marshall County

✠ **REYNOLDS MEMORIAL HOSPITAL (510013)**, 800 Wheeling Avenue, Zip 26038–1697; tel. 304/845–3211, (Nonreporting) **A**1 10 **S** West Virginia University Health System, Morgantown, WV
Primary Contact: David F. Hess, M.D., Chief Executive Officer
COO: Kevin Britt, Chief Operating Officer
CFO: William Robert Hunt, Chief Financial Officer
CMO: David F Hess M.D., President Medical Staff
CIO: Warren Kelley, Chief Information Officer
CHR: R. Craig Madden, Director Employee Relations
CNO: Carol R Miller R.N., Chief Nursing Officer
Web address: www.reynoldsmemorial.com
Control: Other not–for–profit (including NFP Corporation) **Service:** General medical and surgical

Staffed Beds: 99

GRAFTON—Taylor County

GRAFTON CITY HOSPITAL (511307), 1 Hospital Plaza, Zip 26354–1283; tel. 304/265–0400, (Total facility includes 76 beds in nursing home–type unit) **A**10 18 **F**11 15 29 30 32 34 35 38 39 40 45 50 53 54 56 57 59 61 64 65 67 75 81 84 85 86 87 91 92 93 94 97 100 101 103 104 107 108 110 114 119 127 128 129 130 131 132 133 135 146 147 **P**6
Primary Contact: Patrick D. Shaw, Chief Executive Officer
CFO: Regina Pickens, Chief Financial Officer
CMO: David B Bender M.D., Chief Medical Staff
CIO: Jim Harris, Director Information Technology
CHR: Missey Kimbrew, Director Human Resources
CNO: Violet Shaw R.N., Director of Nursing
Web address: www.graftonhospital.com
Control: City, Government, Nonfederal **Service:** General medical and surgical

Staffed Beds: 101 Admissions: 555 Census: 74 Outpatient Visits: 33925 Births: 0 Total Expense ($000): 18579 Payroll Expense ($000): 10279 Personnel: 244

GRANTSVILLE—Calhoun County

★ **MINNIE HAMILTON HEALTHCARE CENTER (511303)**, 186 Hospital Drive, Zip 26147–7100; tel. 304/354–9244, (Total facility includes 24 beds in nursing home–type unit) **A**10 18 **F**3 7 11 15 28 29 30 32 34 35 36 39 40 41 43 44 50 53 56 57 59 61 64 65 66 68 75 82 84 86 87 93 97 99 101 107 108 119 127 130 132 133 134 135 143 144 146 147 148 149 150 **P**6
Primary Contact: Steve Whited, Chief Executive Officer
CMO: Suresh Balasubramony M.D., Chief Medical Officer
CIO: Brent Barr, Chief Information Officer
CHR: Sheila Gherke, Director Human Resources
CNO: Kim Houchin, Chief Nursing Officer
Web address: www.mhhcc.com
Control: Other not–for–profit (including NFP Corporation) **Service:** General medical and surgical

Staffed Beds: 42 Admissions: 174 Census: 29 Births: 0 Personnel: 226

HINTON—Summers County

☐ **SUMMERS COUNTY ARH HOSPITAL (511310)**, Terrace Street, Zip 25951–2407, Mailing Address: Drawer 940, 25951–0940; tel. 304/466–1000 **A**1 10 18 **F**11 15 29 30 32 34 35 40 44 50 54 57 59 62 64 65 71 77 81 82 85 86 87 93 97 107 110 114 119 127 130 133 146 147 148 **P**6 **S** Appalachian Regional Healthcare, Inc., Lexington, KY
Primary Contact: Wesley Dangerfield, Community Chief Executive Officer
CMO: Waheed Khan M.D., President Medical Staff
CIO: Brent Styer, Chief Information Officer
CHR: Beth Elswick, Administrative Assistant
CNO: Sharon Milburn, Chief Nursing Officer
Web address: www.arh.org
Control: Other not–for–profit (including NFP Corporation) **Service:** General medical and surgical

Staffed Beds: 25 Admissions: 504 Census: 8 Outpatient Visits: 28669 Births: 0 Total Expense ($000): 13653 Payroll Expense ($000): 4792 Personnel: 110

HUNTINGTON—Cabell County

✠ **CABELL HUNTINGTON HOSPITAL (510055)**, 1340 Hal Greer Boulevard, Zip 25701–0195; tel. 304/526–2000, (Includes HOOPS FAMILY CHILDREN'S HOSPITAL, 1340 Hal Greer Boulevard, Huntington, West Virginia, Zip 25701–3800, tel. 304/526–2000) (Total facility includes 15 beds in nursing home–type unit) **A**1 2 3 5 8 10 **F**3 5 7 9 11 12 13 15 16 18 19 20 22 26 28 29 30 31 32 34 35 37 38 39 40 41 43 44 45 46 47 48 49 50 51 52 54 55 56 57 58 59 61 62 64 65 70 72 73 74 75 76 77 78 79 81 82 84 85 87 88 89 92 93 94 96 97 104 107 108 110 111 112 114 115 117 118 119 120 121 123 124 126 128 129 130 131 132 134 144 145 146 147 148 149 150
Primary Contact: Kevin N. Fowler, President and Chief Executive Officer
CFO: David M Ward, Chief Financial Officer and Chief Acquisition Officer
CMO: Hoyt J Burdick M.D., Vice President Medical Affairs
CIO: Dennis Lee, Vice President and Chief Information Officer
CHR: Barry Tourigny, Vice President Human Resources and Organizational Development
CNO: Joy S Pelfrey R.N., MSN, Vice President and Chief Nursing Officer
Web address: www.cabellhuntington.org
Control: Other not–for–profit (including NFP Corporation) **Service:** General medical and surgical

Staffed Beds: 303 Admissions: 27637 Census: 276 Outpatient Visits: 593672 Births: 2676 Total Expense ($000): 477599 Payroll Expense ($000): 167043 Personnel: 2475

☐ **CORNERSTONE HOSPITAL OF HUNTINGTON (512003)**, 2900 First Avenue, Two East, Zip 25702–1241; tel. 304/399–2600 **A**1 10 **F**1 29 148 **S** Cornerstone Healthcare Group, Dallas, TX
Primary Contact: Cynthia Isaacs, Chief Executive Officer
CFO: Frank Carter, Chief Financial Officer
CMO: William Beam M.D., Chief of Staff
Web address: www.chghospitals.com
Control: Corporation, Investor–owned (for–profit) **Service:** Acute long–term care hospital

Staffed Beds: 28 Admissions: 358 Census: 25 Outpatient Visits: 0 Total Expense ($000): 10533 Payroll Expense ($000): 4656 Personnel: 64

✠ **HEALTHSOUTH HUNTINGTON REHABILITATION HOSPITAL (513028)**, 6900 West Country Club Drive, Zip 25705–2000; tel. 304/733–1060 **A**1 10 **F**29 34 59 90 95 96 148 149 **S** HEALTHSOUTH Corporation, Birmingham, AL
Primary Contact: Michael E. Zuliani, Chief Executive Officer
CHR: Jenny Overcash, Director Human Resources
CNO: Ann Evans, Chief Nursing Officer
Web address: www.healthsouthhuntington.com
Control: Corporation, Investor–owned (for–profit) **Service:** Rehabilitation

Staffed Beds: 62 Admissions: 1360 Census: 46 Outpatient Visits: 0 Births: 0 Total Expense ($000): 10740 Payroll Expense ($000): 7836 Personnel: 155

☐ **MILDRED MITCHELL–BATEMAN HOSPITAL (514009)**, 1530 Norway Avenue, Zip 25705–1358, Mailing Address: P.O.Box 448, 25709–0448; tel. 304/525–7801 **A**1 3 10 **F**3 4 11 30 86 87 97 98 103 106 130 135 143 146 149 150 **P**6
Primary Contact: Craig A. Richards, Chief Executive Officer
CFO: Lucille Gedies, Chief Financial Officer
CMO: Shahid Masood M.D., Clinical Director
CIO: Elias Majdalani, Director Management Information Systems
CHR: Kieth Anne Worden, Director Human Resources
CNO: Patricia Hamilton R.N., Director of Nursing
Web address: www.batemanhospital.org
Control: State, Government, Nonfederal **Service:** Psychiatric

Staffed Beds: 110 Admissions: 546 Census: 110 Outpatient Visits: 0 Births: 0 Total Expense ($000): 47119 Payroll Expense ($000): 15257 Personnel: 411

WV

Many Facility Codes have changed. Please refer to the AHA Guide Code Chart. © 2017 AHA Guide

□ **RIVER PARK HOSPITAL (514008)**, 1230 Sixth Avenue, Zip 25701–2312,
Mailing Address: P.O.Box 1875, 25719–1875; tel. 304/526–9111 **A**1 3 10 **F**29
34 35 38 98 99 100 101 102 103 106 130 143 149 **P**4 5 6 **S** Universal Health
Services, Inc., King of Prussia, PA
Primary Contact: Terry A. Stephens, Chief Executive Officer
CFO: Steve Kuhn, Chief Financial Officer
CMO: Mark A. Hughes M.D., Medical Director
CIO: James Martin, Chief Information Officer
CHR: Mary Stratton, Director Human Resources
CNO: Michelle Gilliland, Director of Nursing
Web address: www.riverparkhospital.net
Control: Corporation, Investor–owned (for–profit) **Service:** Psychiatric

> **Staffed Beds:** 175 **Admissions:** 1224 **Census:** 147 **Outpatient Visits:** 0
> **Births:** 0 **Total Expense ($000):** 23692 **Payroll Expense ($000):** 12759
> **Personnel:** 293

⊞ **ST. MARY'S MEDICAL CENTER (510007)**, 2900 First Avenue, Zip 25702–
1272; tel. 304/526–1234, (Total facility includes 19 beds in nursing home–type
unit) **A**1 2 3 10 **F**3 11 13 15 17 18 20 22 24 26 28 29 30 31 32 34 35 36
39 40 42 43 44 45 46 47 48 49 50 53 54 55 57 58 59 60 61 62 64 65 66
67 68 70 74 75 76 77 78 79 81 82 84 85 86 87 89 90 92 93 96 97 98 100
101 102 103 107 108 110 111 114 115 118 119 120 121 123 124 126 128
129 130 132 135 144 145 146 147 148 149 **P**8 **S** Pallottine Health Services,
Huntington, WV
Primary Contact: Michael G. Sellards, President and Chief Executive Officer
COO: Todd Campbell, Senior Vice President and Chief Operating Officer
CFO: Angela Swearingen, Vice President Finance
CMO: Ernest Lee Taylor M.D., Vice President Medical Affairs
CIO: David Wendell, Manager, Information Systems
CHR: Susan Beth Robinson, Vice President Human Resources
CNO: Elizabeth Bosley, Vice President Patient Services and Chief Nursing Officer
Web address: www.st-marys.org
Control: Church operated, Nongovernment, not–for–profit **Service:** General
medical and surgical

> **Staffed Beds:** 393 **Admissions:** 15563 **Census:** 251 **Outpatient Visits:**
> 254309 **Births:** 381 **Total Expense ($000):** 401224 **Payroll Expense
> ($000):** 125256 **Personnel:** 2476

HUNTINGTON—Wayne County

⊞ **HUNTINGTON VETERANS AFFAIRS MEDICAL CENTER**, 1540 Spring Valley
Drive, Zip 25704–9300; tel. 304/429–6741, (Nonreporting) **A**1 3 5 **S** Department
of Veterans Affairs, Washington, DC
Primary Contact: Brian Nimmo, Director
CIO: Gary Henderson, Chief Information Resources Management Services
Web address: www.huntington.va.gov/
Control: Veterans Affairs, Government, federal **Service:** General medical and
surgical

> **Staffed Beds:** 80

KEYSER—Mineral County

⊞ **POTOMAC VALLEY HOSPITAL (511315)**, 100 Pin Oak Lane, Zip 26726–5908;
tel. 304/597–3500 **A**1 10 18 **F**3 15 18 28 29 30 34 35 40 44 45 50 57 59 63
64 68 70 71 75 79 81 85 86 87 93 107 108 110 111 114 119 127 130 132
133 135 146 148 149 **S** West Virginia University Health System, Morgantown, WV
Primary Contact: Linda K. Shroyer, Administrator
CFO: Marian Cardwell, Chief Financial Officer
CMO: Charles Bess M.D., Medical Director
CIO: Micah Reel, Director of Bio–Med
CHR: Dianne Smith, Director Personnel and Human Resources
CNO: Mary Ann Billings, Director of Nursing
Web address: www.potomacvalleyhospital.com
Control: Other not–for–profit (including NFP Corporation) **Service:** General
medical and surgical

> **Staffed Beds:** 25 **Admissions:** 991 **Census:** 8 **Outpatient Visits:** 43486
> **Births:** 0 **Total Expense ($000):** 20494 **Payroll Expense ($000):** 9005
> **Personnel:** 186

KINGWOOD—Preston County

★ **PRESTON MEMORIAL HOSPITAL (511312)**, 150 Memorial Drive, Zip 26537–
1495; tel. 304/329–1400 **A**10 18 **F**3 12 15 18 28 29 30 34 35 40 43 45 47
48 50 53 57 59 64 65 70 74 75 76 77 81 92 93 97 107 108 110 111 114
119 129 132 133 135 144 146 147 148 **P**6 **S** Monongalia Health System,
Morgantown, WV
Primary Contact: Melissa Lockwood, Chief Executive Officer
CFO: Robert W Milvet Jr, Chief Financial Officer
CIO: Beth Horne, System Administrator Information Technology
CHR: Michele Batiste, Director Human Resources
Web address: www.prestonmemorial.org
Control: Other not–for–profit (including NFP Corporation) **Service:** General
medical and surgical

> **Staffed Beds:** 25 **Admissions:** 870 **Census:** 7 **Outpatient Visits:** 65003
> **Births:** 1 **Total Expense ($000):** 35098 **Payroll Expense ($000):** 16064
> **Personnel:** 308

LOGAN—Logan County

⊞ **LOGAN REGIONAL MEDICAL CENTER (510048)**, 20 Hospital Drive,
Zip 25601–3452; tel. 304/831–1101 **A**1 10 20 **F**3 11 13 15 18 20 28 29 31 34
35 40 43 45 49 51 54 57 59 64 65 70 74 75 76 77 78 79 81 82 86 87 89 90
92 93 97 107 108 110 111 114 115 117 118 119 129 130 133 135 146 147
P6 **S** LifePoint Health, Brentwood, TN
Primary Contact: Kevin Zachary, Chief Executive Officer
COO: Simon Ratliff, Chief Operating Officer
CFO: Tim Matney, Chief Financial Officer
CMO: Kathy Harvey D.O., Chief Medical Officer
CIO: Barry Hensley, Director Information Systems
CHR: Jessica Martin, Director Human Resources
CNO: Karen Barnes, Interim Chief Nursing Officer
Web address: www.loganregionalmedicalcenter.com
Control: Corporation, Investor–owned (for–profit) **Service:** General medical and
surgical

> **Staffed Beds:** 129 **Admissions:** 4518 **Census:** 63 **Outpatient Visits:**
> 100225 **Births:** 230 **Total Expense ($000):** 75276 **Payroll Expense ($000):**
> 27306 **Personnel:** 603

MADISON—Boone County

⊞ **BOONE MEMORIAL HOSPITAL (511313)**, 701 Madison Avenue, Zip 25130–
1699; tel. 304/369–1230, (Nonreporting) **A**1 10 18
Primary Contact: Virgil Underwood, Chief Executive Officer
CFO: Randy Foxx, Chief Financial Officer
CMO: Ziad Chanaa M.D., Chief of Staff
CIO: Susan Shreve, Executive Director Information Technology
CHR: Sheliah Cook, Director Human Resources
CNO: Teresa Meade R.N., Chief Nursing Officer
Web address: www.bmh.org
Control: Other not–for–profit (including NFP Corporation) **Service:** General
medical and surgical

> **Staffed Beds:** 25

MARTINSBURG—Berkeley County

⊞ **BERKELEY MEDICAL CENTER (510008)**, 2500 Hospital Drive, Zip 25401–
3402; tel. 304/264–1000 **A**1 2 3 5 10 **F**3 11 12 13 15 17 18 20 22 28 29 30
31 34 35 38 40 43 44 45 47 49 51 53 57 59 62 64 70 72 74 75 77 78 79 81
82 84 85 86 87 92 93 98 102 103 104 107 108 110 111 115 118 119 124
129 130 131 132 135 143 144 145 146 147 148 **S** West Virginia University
Health System, Morgantown, WV
Primary Contact: Anthony Zelenka, President and Chief Operating Officer
CFO: Kathleen Quinones, Interim Vice President Finance
CIO: Mark Combs, Interim Director System Information Technology
CHR: Michelle Thomas, Vice President Human Resources
CNO: Donna Clews Ph.D., R.N., Vice President Patient Care Services
Web address: www.cityhospital.org
Control: Other not–for–profit (including NFP Corporation) **Service:** General
medical and surgical

> **Staffed Beds:** 195 **Admissions:** 8787 **Census:** 104 **Outpatient Visits:**
> 259882 **Births:** 1044 **Total Expense ($000):** 178831 **Payroll Expense
> ($000):** 60547 **Personnel:** 1185

WV

Hospital, Medicare Provider Number, Address, Telephone, Approval, Facility, and Physician Codes, Health Care System

★ American Hospital Association (AHA) membership ○ Healthcare Facilities Accreditation Program ⇑ Center for Improvement in Healthcare Quality Accreditation
□ The Joint Commission accreditation ◇ DNV Healthcare Inc. accreditation △ Commission on Accreditation of Rehabilitation Facilities (CARF) accreditation

✠ **MARTINSBURG VETERANS AFFAIRS MEDICAL CENTER**, 510 Butler Avenue, Zip 25405–9990; tel. 304/263–0811, (Total facility includes 178 beds in nursing home–type unit) **A**1 3 5 **F**3 4 5 7 10 15 18 22 24 26 29 30 31 33 34 35 38 39 40 45 46 47 48 49 50 53 55 56 58 59 61 62 63 64 65 66 68 70 74 75 77 78 79 81 82 83 84 85 87 91 92 93 94 97 98 101 102 103 104 105 106 107 108 111 114 115 118 119 127 128 129 130 132 133 135 141 142 143 146 147 148 149 150 **S** Department of Veterans Affairs, Washington, DC
Primary Contact: Timothy J. Cooke, Medical Center Director and Chief Executive Officer
COO: Timothy J Cooke, Medical Center Director and Chief Executive Officer
CMO: Jonathan Fierer M.D., Chief of Staff
CIO: Mary Ann Creel, Chief Information Resource Management
CHR: Brenda Byrd–Pelaez, Chief Human Resources Management Office
CNO: Susan George R.N., M.P.H., Associate Director Patient Care Services
Web address: www.martinsburg.va.gov/
Control: Veterans Affairs, Government, federal **Service**: General medical and surgical

Staffed Beds: 487 **Admissions**: 3787 **Census**: 406 **Outpatient Visits**: 515032 **Births**: 0 **Total Expense ($000)**: 300593 **Payroll Expense ($000)**: 138612 **Personnel**: 1993

MONTGOMERY—Fayette County

✠ **MONTGOMERY GENERAL HOSPITAL (511318)**, 401 Sixth Avenue, Zip 25136–2116, Mailing Address: P.O.Box 270, 25136–0270; tel. 304/442–5151, (Total facility includes 44 beds in nursing home–type unit) **A**1 10 18 **F**3 11 15 29 30 34 35 40 45 49 50 53 57 59 64 67 68 77 81 87 93 97 107 110 111 114 119 128 129 130 131 133 135 146 147 **P**6 8
Primary Contact: Vickie Gay, Chief Executive Officer
CFO: Sherri Murray, Chief Financial Officer
CMO: Traci Acklin M.D., Chief of Staff
CIO: Denzil Blevins, Director Information Systems
CHR: Kelly D Frye, Director Human Resources
Web address: www.mghwv.com
Control: Other not–for–profit (including NFP Corporation) **Service**: General medical and surgical

Staffed Beds: 69 **Admissions**: 392 **Census**: 45 **Outpatient Visits**: 66972 **Births**: 0 **Total Expense ($000)**: 21721 **Payroll Expense ($000)**: 10516 **Personnel**: 219

MORGANTOWN—Monongalia County

CHESTNUT RIDGE HOSPITAL See West Virginia University Hospitals

✠ **HEALTHSOUTH MOUNTAINVIEW REGIONAL REHABILITATION HOSPITAL (513030)**, 1160 Van Voorhis Road, Zip 26505–3437; tel. 304/598–1100 **A**1 5 10 **F**3 29 34 57 59 64 74 75 79 86 87 90 91 93 94 96 107 130 132 148 **S** HEALTHSOUTH Corporation, Birmingham, AL
Primary Contact: Tracy Vinciguerra, Chief Executive Officer
CFO: Jason Gizzi, Controller
CMO: Govind Patel M.D., Medical Director
CIO: Robin Wherry, Risk Manager and Director Quality Assurance and Health Information Management
CHR: Shannon Hyde, Director Human Resources
CNO: Stacy Jones, Chief Nursing Officer
Web address: www.healthsouthmountainview.com
Control: Corporation, Investor–owned (for–profit) **Service**: Rehabilitation

Staffed Beds: 96 **Admissions**: 2135 **Census**: 70 **Outpatient Visits**: 8722 **Births**: 0 **Total Expense ($000)**: 26099 **Payroll Expense ($000)**: 13422 **Personnel**: 252

✠ **MON HEALTH MEDICAL CENTER (510024)**, 1200 J D Anderson Drive, Zip 26505–3486; tel. 304/598–1200 **A**1 2 3 10 19 **F**3 15 17 18 20 22 24 26 28 29 30 31 32 34 35 40 43 45 46 49 50 51 54 55 57 59 60 64 65 68 70 74 75 76 77 78 79 81 82 84 85 86 87 89 97 107 108 110 111 114 115 116 118 119 126 127 129 130 132 135 145 146 147 148 149 **P**6 8 **S** Monongalia Health System, Morgantown, WV
Primary Contact: Darryl L. Duncan, President and Chief Executive Officer
COO: Linda Neu Ollis FACHE, Chief Operating Officer
CFO: Daris Rosencrance, Chief Financial Officer
CMO: Matthew P Darmelio, Chief of Staff
CIO: Steve Carter, Chief Information Officer
CHR: Melissa Shreves Shahnam, Director Human Resources
Web address: www.mongeneral.com
Control: Other not–for–profit (including NFP Corporation) **Service**: General medical and surgical

Staffed Beds: 185 **Admissions**: 8003 **Census**: 95 **Outpatient Visits**: 312824 **Births**: 1136 **Total Expense ($000)**: 251116 **Payroll Expense ($000)**: 92771 **Personnel**: 1365

✠ **WEST VIRGINIA UNIVERSITY HOSPITALS (510001)**, 1 Medical Center Drive, Zip 26506–4749; tel. 304/598–4000, (Includes CHESTNUT RIDGE HOSPITAL, 930 Chestnut Ridge Road, Morgantown, West Virginia, Zip 26505–2854, tel. 304/293–4000; WEST VIRGINIA UNIVERSITY CHILDREN'S HOSPITAL, Medical Center Drive, Department 8200, Morgantown, West Virginia, Zip 26506–8111, tel. 800/982–6277) **A**1 3 5 8 10 19 **F**3 4 5 8 11 12 13 15 17 18 19 20 21 22 23 24 25 26 27 28 29 30 31 32 34 35 36 37 38 39 40 41 43 44 45 46 47 48 49 50 51 52 53 54 55 56 57 58 59 60 61 64 65 68 70 71 72 74 75 76 77 78 79 80 81 82 83 84 85 86 87 88 89 91 92 93 97 98 99 100 101 102 103 104 105 106 107 108 109 110 111 114 115 116 117 118 119 120 121 123 124 126 127 129 130 131 132 135 136 141 144 145 146 147 148 149 **P**1 **S** West Virginia University Health System, Morgantown, WV
Primary Contact: Albert L. Wright Jr, PharmD, President and Chief Executive Officer
COO: Ron Pellegrino, Chief Operating Officer
CFO: Melissa McCoy, Vice President and Chief Financial Officer
CMO: Judie Charlton M.D., Chief Medical Officer
CIO: James Venturella, Vice President Information Technology
CHR: Leeann Cerimele, Vice President Human Resources
CNO: Douglas W Mitchell, Vice President and Chief Nursing Officer
Web address: www.health.wvu.edu
Control: Other not–for–profit (including NFP Corporation) **Service**: General medical and surgical

Staffed Beds: 555 **Admissions**: 29137 **Census**: 450 **Outpatient Visits**: 769101 **Births**: 1549 **Total Expense ($000)**: 895613 **Payroll Expense ($000)**: 284806 **Personnel**: 5569

NEW MARTINSVILLE—Wetzel County

✠ **WETZEL COUNTY HOSPITAL (510072)**, 3 East Benjamin Drive, Zip 26155–2758; tel. 304/455–8000 **A**1 10 20 **F**3 8 15 28 30 31 34 40 43 45 57 59 64 65 70 75 77 81 85 90 93 94 107 108 114 118 119 127 130 132 133 135 146 148 **P**6
Primary Contact: Brian K. Felici, Chief Executive Officer
CFO: Edwin Szewczyk, Chief Financial Officer
CMO: Donald A. Blum M.D., Chief of Staff
CIO: Amy Frazier, Supervisor Management Information Systems
CHR: Sarah Boley, Director Human Resources
Web address: www.wetzelcountyhospital.com
Control: County, Government, Nonfederal **Service**: General medical and surgical

Staffed Beds: 44 **Admissions**: 507 **Census**: 7 **Outpatient Visits**: 86417 **Births**: 0 **Total Expense ($000)**: 20837 **Payroll Expense ($000)**: 9159 **Personnel**: 200

OAK HILL—Fayette County

✠ **PLATEAU MEDICAL CENTER (511317)**, 430 Main Street, Zip 25901–3455; tel. 304/469–8600 **A**1 10 18 **F**3 15 18 29 30 34 35 40 45 46 50 57 59 64 68 70 75 77 81 85 87 91 93 97 107 108 110 111 115 119 126 127 129 133 146 **S** Community Health Systems, Inc., Franklin, TN
Primary Contact: Derek W. Cimala, Interim Chief Executive Officer
COO: Michael Makosky, Chief Operating Officer
CFO: Heather Hylton, Chief Financial Officer
CMO: Jacob McNeel D.O., Chief of Staff
CIO: Nick Stover, Director Information Systems
CHR: Tammie Chinn, Director Marketing and Public Relations
CNO: Randell Thompson, Chief Nursing Officer
Web address: www.plateaumedicalcenter.com
Control: Corporation, Investor–owned (for–profit) **Service**: General medical and surgical

Staffed Beds: 25 **Admissions**: 1113 **Census**: 9 **Outpatient Visits**: 53613 **Births**: 0 **Total Expense ($000)**: 31616 **Payroll Expense ($000)**: 12486 **Personnel**: 197

PARKERSBURG—Wood County

✠ **CAMDEN CLARK MEDICAL CENTER (510058)**, 800 Garfield Avenue, Zip 26101–5378, Mailing Address: P.O.Box 718, 26102–0718; tel. 304/424–2111 **A**1 10 13 **F**3 7 8 11 12 13 15 17 18 20 22 24 28 29 30 31 34 35 40 43 45 50 51 53 54 57 58 59 64 65 66 68 70 74 75 76 78 79 81 84 85 86 87 89 92 97 98 100 101 102 107 108 110 111 114 115 116 117 118 119 120 121 123 124 129 130 132 135 146 147 148 **P**6 8 **S** West Virginia University Health System, Morgantown, WV
Primary Contact: David K. McClure, President and Chief Executive Officer
CFO: Carolyn Allen, Vice President and Chief Financial Officer
CMO: David Gnegy M.D., Vice President of Medical Affairs
CIO: Josh Woods, Director Information Systems
CHR: Tom Heller, Vice President Operations and Human Resources
CNO: Tom L Mars R.N., MSN, Vice President Patient Care Services and Chief Nursing Officer
Web address: www.camdenclark.org
Control: Other not–for–profit (including NFP Corporation) **Service**: General medical and surgical

Staffed Beds: 245 **Admissions**: 11487 **Census**: 131 **Outpatient Visits**: 288097 **Births**: 1372 **Total Expense ($000)**: 218036 **Payroll Expense ($000)**: 67554 **Personnel**: 1640

Many Facility Codes have changed. Please refer to the AHA Guide Code Chart. © 2017 AHA Guide

✠ **HEALTHSOUTH WESTERN HILLS REGIONAL REHABILITATION HOSPITAL (513027)**, 3 Western Hills Drive, Zip 26105–8122; tel. 304/420–1300 **A1** 10 **F**29 64 90 93 94 96 130 148 149 **S** HEALTHSOUTH Corporation, Birmingham, AL
Primary Contact: Alvin R. Lawson, FACHE, JD, Chief Executive Officer
CFO: Jessica Gum, Controller
CMO: Kalapala Rao M.D., Medical Director
CHR: Julie Swanson, Coordinator Human Resources
CNO: Tonda Hockenberry, Chief Nursing Officer
Web address: www.healthsouthwesternhills.com
Control: Corporation, Investor–owned (for–profit) **Service:** Rehabilitation

Staffed Beds: 40 **Admissions:** 1096 **Census:** 36 **Outpatient Visits:** 5710 **Births:** 0 **Total Expense ($000):** 14641 **Payroll Expense ($000):** 6364 **Personnel:** 129

PETERSBURG—Grant County

★ **GRANT MEMORIAL HOSPITAL (511316)**, 117 Hospital Drive, Zip 26847–9566, Mailing Address: P.O.Box 1019, 26847–1019; tel. 304/257–1026, (Total facility includes 20 beds in nursing home–type unit) **A**10 18 **F**3 11 13 15 18 28 29 30 34 35 40 45 50 57 59 64 65 67 68 70 75 76 77 79 81 84 85 86 87 93 102 107 108 110 114 118 119 128 130 131 132 133 135 146 147 148 149 **P**6
Primary Contact: Mary Beth. Barr, R.N., Chief Executive Officer
CMO: Bruce W Leslie M.D., Chief of Staff
CIO: Derek Nesselrodt, Director Information Systems
CHR: Ronnie Arbaugh, Director Human Resources
CNO: Kimberly Linville, Chief Nursing Officer
Web address: www.grantmemorial.com
Control: County, Government, Nonfederal **Service:** General medical and surgical

Staffed Beds: 45 **Admissions:** 1729 **Census:** 33 **Outpatient Visits:** 44568 **Births:** 253 **Total Expense ($000):** 35360 **Payroll Expense ($000):** 14237 **Personnel:** 317

PHILIPPI—Barbour County

★ **BROADDUS HOSPITAL (511300)**, 1 Healthcare Drive, Zip 26416–9405, Mailing Address: P.O.Box 930, 26416–0930; tel. 304/457–1760, (Total facility includes 60 beds in nursing home–type unit) **A**10 18 **F**3 15 29 30 34 35 40 50 57 59 64 75 85 87 107 110 115 119 128 130 132 133 135 143 146 **P**8 **S** Davis Health System, Elkins, WV
Primary Contact: Dana L. Gould, Chief Executive Officer
CFO: Cathy Kalar, Chief Financial Officer
CHR: Penny D Brown, Director of Human Resources
Web address: www.davishealthsystem.org/
Control: Other not–for–profit (including NFP Corporation) **Service:** General medical and surgical

Staffed Beds: 72 **Admissions:** 198 **Census:** 59 **Outpatient Visits:** 23262 **Births:** 0 **Total Expense ($000):** 16489 **Payroll Expense ($000):** 6975 **Personnel:** 139

POINT PLEASANT—Mason County

✠ **PLEASANT VALLEY HOSPITAL (510012)**, 2520 Valley Drive, Zip 25550–2031; tel. 304/675–4340, (Total facility includes 100 beds in nursing home–type unit) **A**1 10 **F**3 11 13 15 17 18 24 26 28 29 30 31 34 35 40 43 45 46 47 48 50 53 56 57 59 62 63 64 65 70 74 75 76 77 78 79 81 85 86 87 89 93 107 108 110 111 114 115 118 119 128 129 130 131 132 143 144 146 147 148 **P**6
Primary Contact: Glen A. Washington, Chief Executive Officer
COO: William A Barker Jr, Vice President Administration
CFO: Richard Hogan, Chief Financial Officer
CMO: Agnes Enrico–Simon M.D., President Medical Staff
CIO: Paula Brooker, Director Information Services
CHR: David A Brown, Director Human Resources and Corporate Compliance
CNO: Amber Findley, Senior Director Nursing Services and NRC Administrator
Web address: www.pvalley.org
Control: Other not–for–profit (including NFP Corporation) **Service:** General medical and surgical

Staffed Beds: 201 **Admissions:** 2142 **Census:** 115 **Outpatient Visits:** 204281 **Births:** 123 **Total Expense ($000):** 67197 **Payroll Expense ($000):** 24986 **Personnel:** 565

PRINCETON—Mercer County

✠ **HEALTHSOUTH SOUTHERN HILLS REHABILITATION HOSPITAL (513026)**, 120 Twelfth Street, Zip 24740–2352; tel. 304/487–8000 **A1** 10 **F**29 56 57 59 60 74 75 77 79 87 90 94 130 132 148 **S** HEALTHSOUTH Corporation, Birmingham, AL
Primary Contact: Robert Williams, Chief Executive Officer
CFO: Melinda Fanning, Chief Financial Officer and Controller
CMO: Robert Walker M.D., Medical Director
CIO: Brian Bales, Director Plant Operations
CHR: Jan Thibodeau, Director Human Resources
CNO: Lisa Lester, Chief Nursing Officer
Web address: www.healthsouthsouthernhills.com
Control: Corporation, Investor–owned (for–profit) **Service:** Rehabilitation

Staffed Beds: 45 **Admissions:** 1009 **Census:** 33 **Outpatient Visits:** 0 **Births:** 0 **Personnel:** 123

✠ **PRINCETON COMMUNITY HOSPITAL (510046)**, 122 12th Street, Zip 24740–2352, Mailing Address: P.O.Box 1369, 24740–1369; tel. 304/487–7000 **A**1 2 10 19 **F**3 11 12 13 15 17 29 30 31 32 34 35 39 40 44 45 46 48 49 50 51 53 57 59 64 65 70 74 75 76 77 78 79 81 85 86 87 89 93 98 100 101 102 103 104 107 108 110 111 114 115 118 119 127 129 130 131 132 135 141 142 144 146 147 149 **P**1
Primary Contact: Jeffrey Lilley, CPA, Chief Executive Officer
CFO: Frank J Sinicrope Jr, Vice President Financial Services
CMO: Wesley Asbury M.D., President Medical Staff
CIO: Stephen A Curry, Director Information Services
CHR: Heather Poff, Director Human Resources
CNO: Rose Morgan MS, R.N., Vice President Patient Care Services
Web address: www.pchonline.org
Control: City, Government, Nonfederal **Service:** General medical and surgical

Staffed Beds: 210 **Admissions:** 8217 **Census:** 119 **Outpatient Visits:** 239289 **Births:** 684 **Total Expense ($000):** 133854 **Payroll Expense ($000):** 50309 **Personnel:** 1043

RANSON—Jefferson County

✠ **JEFFERSON MEDICAL CENTER (511319)**, 300 South Preston Street, Zip 25438–1631; tel. 304/728–1600 **A**1 3 5 10 18 **F**3 11 13 15 29 30 34 35 38 40 43 44 45 57 59 64 70 74 75 76 77 79 81 82 85 86 87 92 93 100 102 107 108 110 111 115 118 119 129 130 132 133 135 146 148 **S** West Virginia University Health System, Morgantown, WV
Primary Contact: Neil R. McLaughlin, R.N., Administrator and Vice President, Operations
CFO: Kathleen Quinones, Interim Vice President Finance
CMO: David A. Baltierra M.D., President Medical Staff
CIO: Mark Combs, Chief Information Security Officer
CNO: Linda Blanc R.N., Administrative Director of Nursing
Web address: www.wvuniversityhealthcare.com/locations/Jefferson–Medical–Center.aspx
Control: Other not–for–profit (including NFP Corporation) **Service:** General medical and surgical

Staffed Beds: 25 **Admissions:** 1270 **Census:** 10 **Outpatient Visits:** 68156 **Births:** 247 **Total Expense ($000):** 43187 **Payroll Expense ($000):** 15825 **Personnel:** 332

RIPLEY—Jackson County

☐ **JACKSON GENERAL HOSPITAL (511320)**, 122 Pinnell Street, Zip 25271–9101, Mailing Address: P.O.Box 720, 25271–0720; tel. 304/372–2731 **A**1 10 18 **F**3 11 15 29 30 34 35 40 43 45 50 51 57 59 64 68 75 79 81 85 87 93 107 108 110 114 119 127 132 133 **P**6
Primary Contact: Stephanie McCoy, President and Chief Executive Officer
CFO: Angela Frame, Chief Financial Officer
CMO: James G Gaal M.D., Chief of Medical Staff
CIO: John Manley, Director Information Systems
CHR: Jeffrey Tabor, Director Human Resources
Web address: www.jacksongeneral.com
Control: Other not–for–profit (including NFP Corporation) **Service:** General medical and surgical

Staffed Beds: 25 **Admissions:** 620 **Census:** 7 **Outpatient Visits:** 43044 **Births:** 0 **Total Expense ($000):** 23671 **Payroll Expense ($000):** 9732 **Personnel:** 241

WV

ROMNEY—Hampshire County

✠ **HAMPSHIRE MEMORIAL HOSPITAL (511311)**, 363 Sunrise Boulevard, Zip 26757–4607; tel. 304/822–4561, (Total facility includes 30 beds in nursing home–type unit) **A**1 10 18 **F**3 15 29 30 40 45 50 54 59 64 65 71 77 79 81 85 86 93 97 107 119 127 128 129 130 133 148 **P**6 **S** Valley Health System, Winchester, VA
Primary Contact: Thomas S. Kluge, President
CFO: Kathryn Morales, Director of Finance
CMO: Gerald Bechamps M.D., Vice President of Medical Affairs
CHR: Abbey Rembold, Human Resources Senior Generalist
CNO: Mary Sas, Director of Clinical Services
Web address: www.valleyhealthlink.com/hampshire
Control: Other not–for–profit (including NFP Corporation) **Service:** General medical and surgical

Staffed Beds: 44 **Admissions:** 460 **Census:** 37 **Outpatient Visits:** 47480 **Births:** 0 **Total Expense ($000):** 24870 **Payroll Expense ($000):** 9341 **Personnel:** 152	

RONCEVERTE—Greenbrier County

★ ○ **GREENBRIER VALLEY MEDICAL CENTER (510002)**, 202 Maplewood Avenue, Zip 24970–1334, Mailing Address: P.O.Box 497, 24970–0497; tel. 304/647–4411 **A**10 11 12 13 **F**13 15 18 20 29 34 40 45 49 51 57 59 60 68 70 75 79 81 86 87 107 108 110 111 114 116 119 120 129 133 146 **P**6 **S** Community Health Systems, Inc., Franklin, TN
Primary Contact: Tom Neal, Chief Executive Officer
CFO: Paige Adkins, Chief Financial Officer
CMO: John Johnson M.D., Chief of Staff
CIO: Matt Turley, Interim Director Information Systems
CHR: Melissa Wickline, Director Marketing
CNO: Charlene Warren R.N., Chief Nursing Officer
Web address: www.gvmc.com
Control: Corporation, Investor–owned (for–profit) **Service:** General medical and surgical

Staffed Beds: 113 **Admissions:** 3132 **Census:** 34 **Outpatient Visits:** 58503 **Births:** 463 **Total Expense ($000):** 54578 **Payroll Expense ($000):** 18865 **Personnel:** 472	

SISTERSVILLE—Tyler County

★ **SISTERSVILLE GENERAL HOSPITAL (511304)**, 314 South Wells Street, Zip 26175–1098; tel. 304/652–2611, (Nonreporting) **A**10 18
Primary Contact: Brandon Chadock, Interim Chief Executive Officer
COO: Brandon Chadock, Director of Operations
CMO: Amanda Nichols M.D., Chief of Staff
CIO: Casey Tuttle, Director Information Technology
CNO: Stephen Todd Strickler, Director of Nursing
Web address: www.sistersvillehospital.com
Control: City, Government, Nonfederal **Service:** General medical and surgical

Staffed Beds: 12	

SOUTH CHARLESTON—Kanawha County

✠ **THOMAS MEMORIAL HOSPITAL (510029)**, 4605 MacCorkle Avenue SW, Zip 25309–1398; tel. 304/766–3600 **A**1 3 5 10 **F**3 4 5 11 13 15 17 18 20 22 29 30 31 32 34 35 38 40 43 45 46 47 48 49 50 53 54 57 59 60 64 65 68 69 70 72 74 75 76 77 78 79 81 84 85 86 87 89 92 93 98 100 101 102 103 104 105 107 108 110 111 114 115 118 119 120 121 123 124 126 129 130 131 132 143 144 146 147 **S** Thomas Health System, Inc., South Charleston, WV
Primary Contact: Daniel Lauffer, FACHE, President and Chief Executive Officer
COO: Brian Ulery, Chief Operating Officer
CFO: Timothy Skeldon, Chief Financial Officer
CMO: Matthew Upton, Chief Medical Information Officer
CHR: Patrick Rawlings, Human Resources Director
CNO: Rebecca Brannon R.N., Chief Nursing Officer
Web address: www.thomashealth.org
Control: Other not–for–profit (including NFP Corporation) **Service:** General medical and surgical

Staffed Beds: 211 **Admissions:** 7457 **Census:** 97 **Outpatient Visits:** 232373 **Births:** 1060 **Total Expense ($000):** 174466 **Payroll Expense ($000):** 53420 **Personnel:** 1122	

SPENCER—Roane County

✠ **ROANE GENERAL HOSPITAL (511306)**, 200 Hospital Drive, Zip 25276–1050; tel. 304/927–4444, (Total facility includes 35 beds in nursing home–type unit) **A**1 10 18 **F**1 3 11 15 28 29 34 35 40 43 45 53 57 59 64 65 67 81 82 85 89 90 93 97 107 108 110 114 119 127 128 130 132 133 148 **P**6
Primary Contact: Douglas E. Bentz, Chief Executive Officer
CFO: Kyle A. Pierson, Chief Financial Officer
CMO: Hong–Kin Ng M.D., Chief Medical Officer
CIO: Tony Keaton, Director Information Systems
CHR: Jeffery B Hunt, Vice President, Business Development and Support Services
CNO: Julie R. Carr, Chief Nursing Officer
Web address: www.roanegeneralhospital.com
Control: Other not–for–profit (including NFP Corporation) **Service:** General medical and surgical

Staffed Beds: 60 **Admissions:** 234 **Census:** 36 **Outpatient Visits:** 41819 **Births:** 0 **Total Expense ($000):** 30311 **Payroll Expense ($000):** 13669 **Personnel:** 279	

SUMMERSVILLE—Nicholas County

✠ **SUMMERSVILLE REGIONAL MEDICAL CENTER (510082)**, 400 Fairview Heights Road, Zip 26651–9308; tel. 304/872–2891, (Nonreporting) **A**1 10 20 **S** QHR, Brentwood, TN
Primary Contact: Karen A. Fiducia, FACHE, President and Chief Executive Officer
CFO: Brian Kelbaugh, Chief Financial Officer
CMO: Bandy Mullins M.D., Chief of Staff
CIO: Mike Ellison, Information Systems Lead
CHR: David M Henderson, Director Human Resources
CNO: Jennifer McCue, Director Patient Care
Web address: www.summersvilleregional.org/
Control: City, Government, Nonfederal **Service:** General medical and surgical

Staffed Beds: 105	

WEBSTER SPRINGS—Webster County

★ **WEBSTER COUNTY MEMORIAL HOSPITAL (511301)**, 324 Miller Mountain Drive, Zip 26288–1087, Mailing Address: P.O.Box 312, 26288–0312; tel. 304/847–5682, (Nonreporting) **A**10 18
Primary Contact: Jeffrey A. Powelson, Interim Chief Executive Officer
CIO: Jeannie Fisher, Coordinator Information Technology
CHR: Michelle Holcomb, Human Resources
Web address: www.wcmhwv.org
Control: Other not–for–profit (including NFP Corporation) **Service:** General medical and surgical

Staffed Beds: 15	

WEIRTON—Brooke County

✠ **WEIRTON MEDICAL CENTER (510023)**, 601 Colliers Way, Zip 26062–5091; tel. 304/797–6000, (Total facility includes 33 beds in nursing home–type unit) **A**1 10 **F**3 5 9 11 13 15 17 18 20 22 28 29 30 32 34 35 37 39 40 41 43 45 46 47 48 49 50 51 53 54 56 57 59 60 61 62 64 68 70 74 75 76 77 78 79 81 82 85 86 89 90 92 93 96 97 99 100 101 102 103 104 107 108 110 111 114 115 116 118 119 124 126 128 129 130 131 132 135 143 145 146 147 148 149
Primary Contact: John C. Frankovitch, President and Chief Executive Officer
COO: David S Artman, Chief Operating Officer
CFO: Gene Trout, Chief Financial Officer
CMO: Atul Shetty, Chief of Staff
CIO: Cristen Nopwaskey, Chief Information Officer
CHR: Gabe D'Ortenzio, Director of Human Resources
CNO: Denise P Westwood, Chief Nursing Officer
Web address: www.weirtonmedical.com
Control: Other not–for–profit (including NFP Corporation) **Service:** General medical and surgical

Staffed Beds: 167 **Admissions:** 6254 **Census:** 91 **Outpatient Visits:** 409211 **Births:** 384 **Total Expense ($000):** 162679 **Payroll Expense ($000):** 71186 **Personnel:** 1102	

WELCH—Mcdowell County

WELCH COMMUNITY HOSPITAL (510086), 454 McDowell Street, Zip 24801–2097; tel. 304/436–8461, (Total facility includes 59 beds in nursing home–type unit) **A**10 20 **F**3 13 15 29 35 40 45 50 57 59 64 65 66 67 68 70 75 76 81 86 87 97 107 110 114 119 127 130 135 146 147 148 **P**6
Primary Contact: Walter J. Garrett, Chief Executive Officer
COO: Heather Smith, Chief Operating Officer
CFO: Johnny Brant, Chief Financial Officer
CMO: Chandra Sharma M.D., Chief of Staff
CHR: Diana Blankenship, Director Human Resources
CNO: Mark Simpson, Director of Nursing
Control: State, Government, Nonfederal **Service:** General medical and surgical

Staffed Beds: 108 **Admissions:** 797 **Census:** 44 **Outpatient Visits:** 23930 **Births:** 41 **Total Expense ($000):** 30738 **Payroll Expense ($000):** 9586 **Personnel:** 296	

WV

Many Facility Codes have changed. Please refer to the AHA Guide Code Chart. © 2017 AHA Guide

WESTON—Lewis County

☒ **STONEWALL JACKSON MEMORIAL HOSPITAL (510038)**, 230 Hospital Plaza, Zip 26452–8558; tel. 304/269–8000 **A**1 10 **F**3 11 13 15 28 29 30 31 35 40 43 45 48 50 56 57 59 62 64 68 70 75 76 78 79 81 85 86 87 93 94 97 107 108 111 114 118 119 129 130 131 132 135 145 146 147 148 **P**6
Primary Contact: Avah Stalnaker, Chief Executive Officer
COO: Kevin P Stalnaker CPA, Assistant Chief Executive Officer
CFO: Joe Barnes, Chief Financial Officer
CMO: Joseph Snead, Chief of Medical Staff
CIO: Kay Butcher, Director Health Information Management
CHR: Rhonda M Hager, Director Human Resources
CNO: Carole Norton, Chief Nursing Officer
Web address: www.stonewallhospital.com
Control: Other not–for–profit (including NFP Corporation) **Service**: General medical and surgical

Staffed Beds: 70 **Admissions**: 1739 **Census**: 18 **Outpatient Visits**: 90210 **Births**: 192 **Total Expense ($000)**: 47593 **Payroll Expense ($000)**: 24144 **Personnel**: 414

☐ **WILLIAM R. SHARPE, JR. HOSPITAL (514010)**, 936 Sharpe Hospital Road, Zip 26452–8550; tel. 304/269–1210 **A**1 3 5 10 **F**11 30 53 56 75 86 87 98 100 101 103 130 132 143 146 **P**6
Primary Contact: Parker Haddix, Chief Executive Officer
COO: Terry L. Small, Assistant Chief Executive Officer
CFO: Robert J. Kimble, Chief Financial Officer
CIO: Pam Lewis, Chief Compliance Officer
CNO: Cheryl France M.D., Chief Medical Officer
Web address: www.wvdhhr.org/sharpe
Control: State, Government, Nonfederal **Service**: Psychiatric

Staffed Beds: 150 **Admissions**: 517 **Census**: 142 **Outpatient Visits**: 0 **Births**: 0 **Total Expense ($000)**: 62606 **Payroll Expense ($000)**: 13731 **Personnel**: 466

WHEELING—Ohio County

☐ ○ **OHIO VALLEY MEDICAL CENTER (510039)**, 2000 Eoff Street, Zip 26003–3870; tel. 304/234–0123 **A**1 2 3 10 11 12 13 **F**3 5 9 11 13 15 18 20 28 29 30 31 34 35 38 40 43 44 48 49 50 51 53 55 56 57 58 59 60 61 64 65 68 70 74 75 76 77 78 79 81 82 84 85 86 87 89 93 97 98 99 100 101 102 103 104 105 107 108 110 111 114 115 116 117 119 121 123 129 130 131 132 134 135 146 147 148 149 150 **P**6 **S** Alecto Healthcare, Irvine, CA
Primary Contact: Lex Reddy, President and Chief Executive Officer
COO: Kelly Bettem, Vice President, Ambulatory Services
CFO: Lisa M. Simon, Senior Vice President and Chief Financial Officer
CIO: Michael Martz, Chief Information Officer
CHR: Robert Wright, Senior Human Resource Advisor
CNO: Patsy George R.N., Vice President and Chief Nursing Officer
Web address: www.ovmc–eorh.com
Control: Other not–for–profit (including NFP Corporation) **Service**: General medical and surgical

Staffed Beds: 169 **Admissions**: 5614 **Census**: 80 **Outpatient Visits**: 139132 **Births**: 398 **Total Expense ($000)**: 114090 **Payroll Expense ($000)**: 45381 **Personnel**: 931

★ **PETERSON HEALTHCARE AND REHABILITATION HOSPITAL (513025)**, Homestead Avenue, Zip 26003; tel. 304/234–0500, (Total facility includes 150 beds in nursing home–type unit) **A**10 **F**29 34 50 56 57 59 75 77 86 87 90 93 96 128 130 131 132 143 148
Primary Contact: Diane Miller, Administrator
CFO: Tammy Bortz, Director of Finance
CMO: William Mercer M.D., Director
CIO: Hope Miller, Director of Medical Records
CHR: Spencer McIlvain, Director of Human Resources
CNO: Charlene Jones, Chief Nursing Officer
Web address: www.petersonrehabilitationhospital.com
Control: Corporation, Investor–owned (for–profit) **Service**: Rehabilitation

Staffed Beds: 172 **Admissions**: 751 **Census**: 147 **Outpatient Visits**: 2959 **Births**: 0 **Total Expense ($000)**: 19430 **Payroll Expense ($000)**: 5640 **Personnel**: 129

☐ **WHEELING HOSPITAL (510050)**, 1 Medical Park, Zip 26003–6379; tel. 304/243–3000 **A**1 2 3 10 13 **F**3 9 11 13 15 17 18 20 22 24 26 28 29 30 31 32 34 35 36 40 43 44 45 46 47 49 50 51 53 54 57 58 59 61 62 64 65 66 67 68 70 73 74 75 76 77 78 79 81 82 84 85 86 87 89 90 92 93 96 97 98 99 100 107 108 110 111 114 115 118 119 120 121 123 124 126 128 129 130 131 132 135 143 146 147 148 149 150 **P**5
Primary Contact: Ronald L. Violi, Chief Executive Officer
CMO: Angelo Georges M.D., President Medical and Dental Staff
CIO: David Rapp, Chief Information Officer
CHR: Kareen Simon, Vice President of Operations
CNO: Kathy Stahl, Chief Nursing Officer
Web address: www.wheelinghospital.org
Control: Other not–for–profit (including NFP Corporation) **Service**: General medical and surgical

Staffed Beds: 223 **Admissions**: 10508 **Census**: 118 **Outpatient Visits**: 609229 **Births**: 1274 **Total Expense ($000)**: 294247 **Payroll Expense ($000)**: 129580 **Personnel**: 2023

WILLIAMSON—Mingo County

☒ **WILLIAMSON MEMORIAL HOSPITAL (510077)**, 859 Alderson Street, Zip 25661–3215, Mailing Address: P.O.Box 1980, 25661–1980; tel. 304/235–2500 **A**1 10 **F**3 15 18 26 28 29 30 34 40 49 50 51 57 59 65 70 74 75 77 79 81 87 91 93 107 108 114 119 130 131 135 149 **P**6 **S** Community Health Systems, Inc., Franklin, TN
Primary Contact: Cindy Segar–Miller, Chief Executive Officer
CFO: Robert Haralson, Chief Financial Officer
CMO: C. Donovan Beckett, Chief Medical Officer
CHR: Tammie Chinn, Chief Human Resource Officer
CNO: Stacey Markus, Chief Nursing Officer
Web address: www.williamsonmemorial.net
Control: Corporation, Investor–owned (for–profit) **Service**: General medical and surgical

Staffed Beds: 76 **Admissions**: 905 **Census**: 8 **Outpatient Visits**: 29105 **Births**: 0 **Total Expense ($000)**: 17749 **Payroll Expense ($000)**: 6064 **Personnel**: 127

WV

Hospital, Medicare Provider Number, Address, Telephone, Approval, Facility, and Physician Codes, Health Care System

★ American Hospital Association (AHA) membership
☐ The Joint Commission accreditation
○ Healthcare Facilities Accreditation Program
◇ DNV Healthcare Inc. accreditation
⇑ Center for Improvement in Healthcare Quality Accreditation
△ Commission on Accreditation of Rehabilitation Facilities (CARF) accreditation

© 2017 AHA Guide   *Many Facility Codes have changed. Please refer to the AHA Guide Code Chart.*   Hospitals **A697**

WISCONSIN

AMERY—Polk County

★ **AMERY HOSPITAL AND CLINIC (521308)**, 265 Griffin Street East, Zip 54001–1439; tel. 715/268–8000 **A**3 10 18 **F**3 6 11 13 15 18 19 28 29 31 34 35 36 38 40 44 45 50 53 54 56 57 59 64 65 68 74 75 76 77 78 81 82 85 86 87 89 92 93 96 97 98 99 100 103 104 107 108 110 111 115 119 127 130 131 132 133 135 143 144 145 146 148 **P**6 **S** HealthPartners, Bloomington, MN
Primary Contact: Debra Rudquist, FACHE, President and Chief Executive Officer
CMO: James Quenan M.D., Chief Medical Officer
CIO: Patrice P Wolff, Director Management Information Systems
CHR: Joanne Jackson, Administrator Human Resources, Community Relations and Quality Improvement
Web address: www.amerymedicalcenter.org
Control: Other not–for–profit (including NFP Corporation) **Service:** General medical and surgical

Staffed Beds: 11 **Admissions:** 967 **Census:** 11 **Outpatient Visits:** 114403 **Births:** 126 **Total Expense ($000):** 54449 **Payroll Expense ($000):** 31770 **Personnel:** 281		

ANTIGO—Langlade County

✠ **ASPIRUS LANGLADE HOSPITAL (521350)**, 112 East Fifth Avenue, Zip 54409–2796; tel. 715/623–2331 **A**1 10 18 **F**2 3 6 10 11 12 13 15 29 30 31 34 35 36 40 43 50 53 54 56 57 59 60 63 64 65 68 69 70 75 76 77 78 79 81 82 84 85 86 87 89 92 93 96 97 99 100 101 103 104 107 108 110 111 115 118 119 121 127 129 130 131 132 133 144 146 147 148 **S** Aspirus, Inc., Wausau, WI
Primary Contact: Andrew J. Barth, Chief Executive Officer
CFO: Pat Tincher, Director Finance
CHR: Janelle K. Markgraf, Director Human Resources and Off Campus Services
CNO: Sherry Bunten, Director Patient Care Services
Web address: www.aspirus.org
Control: Church operated, Nongovernment, not–for–profit **Service:** General medical and surgical

Staffed Beds: 21 **Admissions:** 1208 **Census:** 10 **Outpatient Visits:** 116658 **Births:** 243 **Total Expense ($000):** 91711 **Payroll Expense ($000):** 33592 **Personnel:** 372		

APPLETON—Outagamie County

✠ **ST. ELIZABETH HOSPITAL (520009)**, 1506 South Oneida Street, Zip 54915–1305; tel. 920/738–2000 **A**1 2 3 5 10 **F**3 4 5 6 8 9 11 13 15 17 18 20 22 24 26 28 29 30 31 32 36 37 40 41 43 44 45 46 47 48 49 56 65 68 69 70 72 74 75 76 77 78 79 80 81 82 83 84 85 86 87 89 91 92 93 94 96 97 98 99 100 102 103 104 105 106 107 108 109 110 111 112 113 114 115 116 117 118 119 120 121 122 123 124 126 129 130 131 144 145 146 147 148 149 **S** Ascension Healthcare, Saint Louis, MO
Primary Contact: Monica Hilt, President
CFO: Jeff Badger, Chief Financial Officer
CMO: Lawrence Donatelle M.D., Vice President Medical Affairs
CIO: Will Weider, Chief Information Officer
CHR: Vince Gallucci, Senior Vice President Human Resources
Web address: www.affinityhealth.org
Control: Church operated, Nongovernment, not–for–profit **Service:** General medical and surgical

Staffed Beds: 190 **Admissions:** 8353 **Census:** 97 **Outpatient Visits:** 219604 **Births:** 1193 **Total Expense ($000):** 166069 **Payroll Expense ($000):** 64156 **Personnel:** 854		

☐ **THEDACARE REGIONAL MEDICAL CENTER–APPLETON (520160)**, 1818 North Meade Street, Zip 54911–3496; tel. 920/731–4101, (Nonreporting) **A**1 2 3 5 10 **S** ThedaCare, Inc., Appleton, WI
Primary Contact: Brian Burmeister, Senior Vice President
CFO: Tim Olson, Senior Vice President Finance
CMO: Gregory L Long M.D., Chief Medical Officer
CIO: Keith Livingston, Senior Vice President and Chief Information Officer
CHR: Maureen Pistone, Senior Vice President Talent Development and Human Resources
Web address: www.thedacare.org
Control: Other not–for–profit (including NFP Corporation) **Service:** General medical and surgical

Staffed Beds: 149		

ASHLAND—Ashland County

✠ **MEMORIAL MEDICAL CENTER – ASHLAND (521359)**, 1615 Maple Lane, Zip 54806–3689; tel. 715/685–5500 **A**1 10 18 **F**3 5 13 15 28 30 31 34 40 43 45 48 49 57 59 64 65 68 75 76 79 80 81 82 85 86 87 89 90 93 94 96 98 99 100 101 102 103 104 105 107 108 110 111 115 118 119 120 121 123 126 129 130 132 135 144 148 149
Primary Contact: Jason T. Douglas, Chief Executive Officer
COO: Karen Hansen, Vice President and Chief Operating Officer
CFO: Kent Dumonseau, Vice President Finance and Information Services
CIO: Todd Reynolds, Chief Information Officer
CHR: Diane Lulich, Director Human Resources
CNO: Kathryn Tuttle R.N., Director of Nursing
Web address: www.ashlandmmc.com
Control: Other not–for–profit (including NFP Corporation) **Service:** General medical and surgical

Staffed Beds: 35 **Admissions:** 2006 **Census:** 19 **Outpatient Visits:** 17752 **Births:** 205 **Total Expense ($000):** 58113 **Payroll Expense ($000):** 23836 **Personnel:** 409		

BALDWIN—St. Croix County

★ **WESTERN WISCONSIN HEALTH (521347)**, 1100 Bergslien Street, Zip 54002–2600; tel. 715/684–3311 **A**10 18 **F**3 11 13 15 17 28 29 31 32 34 35 36 40 41 43 45 48 50 53 55 57 59 64 65 68 70 75 76 77 78 79 80 81 84 85 86 87 89 90 93 96 97 104 107 108 110 111 115 119 127 129 130 131 132 133 143 144 146 147 148 149 150
Primary Contact: Alison Page, Chief Executive Officer
CFO: Brian A Lovdahl, Chief Financial Officer
CMO: Clint Semrau, Chief of Staff
CIO: Kendra Shaw, Chief Information Officer
CHR: Chris Riba, Director Human Resources
Web address: www.wwhealth.org
Control: Other not–for–profit (including NFP Corporation) **Service:** General medical and surgical

Staffed Beds: 15 **Admissions:** 467 **Census:** 4 **Outpatient Visits:** 58772 **Births:** 106 **Total Expense ($000):** 36715 **Payroll Expense ($000):** 17517 **Personnel:** 235		

BARABOO—Sauk County

✠ **ST. CLARE HOSPITAL (520057)**, 707 14th Street, Zip 53913–1597; tel. 608/356–1400 **A**1 3 5 10 **F**5 11 12 13 15 28 29 34 36 40 56 64 69 70 75 76 77 78 80 81 82 86 89 93 107 108 116 118 119 130 131 144 **S** SSM Health, Saint Louis, MO
Primary Contact: Laura Jelle, President
CFO: Troy Walker, Director Finance
CMO: Maureen Murphy M.D., Director of Medical Affairs
CIO: Heather Stephens, Director of Information Health Technology
CHR: Jason Stelzer, Director Human Resources
CNO: Ginger Selle, Vice President Patient Care Services
Web address: www.stclare.com
Control: Church operated, Nongovernment, not–for–profit **Service:** General medical and surgical

Staffed Beds: 60 **Admissions:** 1899 **Census:** 17 **Outpatient Visits:** 102840 **Births:** 244 **Total Expense ($000):** 50926 **Payroll Expense ($000):** 20724 **Personnel:** 295		

BARRON—Barron County

☐ **MAYO CLINIC HEALTH SYSTEM – NORTHLAND IN BARRON (521315)**, 1222 East Woodland Avenue, Zip 54812–1798; tel. 715/537–3186 **A**1 10 18 **F**3 6 8 13 15 18 28 29 30 31 32 34 35 36 40 43 44 45 53 54 56 57 59 60 64 65 69 75 76 77 78 79 80 81 82 84 85 86 87 89 90 93 97 100 104 107 110 115 118 130 131 132 133 135 144 145 146 147 148 149 **P**6 **S** Mayo Clinic, Rochester, MN
Primary Contact: Maurita Sullivan, Vice President
COO: Karolyn Bartlett, Assistant Administrator
CFO: Paul Bammel, Vice President
CMO: Richard Nagler M.D., Chief of Staff
CIO: Todd Muden, Section Head Information Management
CHR: Blythe Rinaldi, Vice President
CNO: Patricia Keller MSN, R.N., Nurse Administrator
Web address: www.luthermidelfortnorthland.org
Control: Other not–for–profit (including NFP Corporation) **Service:** General medical and surgical

Staffed Beds: 23 **Admissions:** 1017 **Census:** 14 **Outpatient Visits:** 63501 **Births:** 136 **Total Expense ($000):** 57575 **Payroll Expense ($000):** 25362 **Personnel:** 313		

Many Facility Codes have changed. Please refer to the AHA Guide Code Chart. © 2017 AHA Guide

BEAVER DAM—Dodge County

☒ **BEAVER DAM COMMUNITY HOSPITALS (520076)**, 707 South University Avenue, Zip 53916–3089; tel. 920/887–7181, (Total facility includes 115 beds in nursing home–type unit) **A**1 10 19 **F**3 6 8 10 11 13 15 17 28 29 30 31 34 36 37 40 41 43 44 45 47 51 53 56 57 59 62 63 64 65 69 70 74 75 76 77 78 79 80 81 82 85 86 87 89 93 96 97 107 108 110 111 114 115 118 119 128 129 130 131 132 135 143 144 146 147 148 149 150 **P**6
Primary Contact: Kimberly J. Miller, FACHE, President and Chief Executive Officer
COO: David Corso, Chief Operating Officer
CMO: Jason Smith, Chief Medical Officer
CHR: Melanie Bruins, Chief Talent Officer
CNO: Carolyn Catton, Interim Chief Patient Care Officer
Web address: www.bdch.com
Control: Other not–for–profit (including NFP Corporation) **Service:** General medical and surgical

Staffed Beds: 163 Admissions: 1875 Census: 107 Outpatient Visits: 98442 Births: 333 Total Expense ($000): 88936 Payroll Expense ($000): 32109 Personnel: 554

BELOIT—Rock County

☐ **BELOIT HEALTH SYSTEM (520100)**, 1969 West Hart Road, Zip 53511–2299; tel. 608/364–5011 **A**1 3 10 **F**5 6 9 10 11 12 13 15 17 20 22 24 28 29 36 40 43 51 53 54 56 60 62 70 75 76 77 78 80 81 82 86 87 89 93 99 100 101 102 103 104 108 111 116 118 119 130 131 144 147
Primary Contact: Timothy M. McKevett, President
CFO: William E Groeper, Vice President Finance
CMO: Kenneth Klein M.D., Vice President Medical Affairs
CHR: Thomas J McCawley, Vice President
CNO: Doris Mulder, Vice President Nursing
Web address: www.beloithealthsystem.org
Control: Other not–for–profit (including NFP Corporation) **Service:** General medical and surgical

Staffed Beds: 103 Admissions: 4075 Census: 47 Outpatient Visits: 354893 Births: 514 Total Expense ($000): 213376 Payroll Expense ($000): 96076 Personnel: 1275

BERLIN—Green Lake County

☐ **THEDACARE REGIONAL MEDICAL CENTER–BERLIN (521355)**, 225 Memorial Drive, Zip 54923–1295; tel. 920/361–1313, (Total facility includes 37 beds in nursing home–type unit) **A**1 10 18 **F**11 13 15 17 28 29 34 40 43 51 53 56 69 70 75 76 78 80 81 82 86 87 88 89 90 93 107 108 111 116 119 128 130 131 144 147 **S** ThedaCare, Inc., Appleton, WI
Primary Contact: John Feeney, President and Chief Executive Officer
CFO: Thomas P Krystowiak, Chief Financial Officer
Web address: www.chnwi.org
Control: Other not–for–profit (including NFP Corporation) **Service:** General medical and surgical

Staffed Beds: 62 Admissions: 1461 Census: 42 Outpatient Visits: 45538 Births: 101 Total Expense ($000): 41370 Payroll Expense ($000): 17556 Personnel: 344

BLACK RIVER FALLS—Jackson County

☐ **BLACK RIVER MEMORIAL HOSPITAL (521333)**, 711 West Adams Street, Zip 54615–9113; tel. 715/284–5361 **A**1 10 18 **F**3 11 13 29 34 35 40 41 44 45 50 53 56 57 59 62 63 65 69 75 76 77 81 84 85 86 89 93 107 111 115 116 118 119 130 131 132 133 134 135 144 146 148
Primary Contact: Mary Beth White–Jacobs, FACHE, R.N., President and Chief Executive Officer
COO: Holly Winn FACHE, Chief Operating Officer
CFO: Robert Daley CPA, Chief Financial Officer
CMO: Esteban Miller, Chief Medical Officer
CIO: Robert Daley CPA, Vice President Fiscal and Information Technology Services
CNO: Melissa Bergerson R.N., Chief Nursing Officer
Web address: www.brmh.net
Control: Other not–for–profit (including NFP Corporation) **Service:** General medical and surgical

Staffed Beds: 25 Admissions: 1083 Census: 8 Outpatient Visits: 11836 Births: 137 Total Expense ($000): 44959 Payroll Expense ($000): 21089 Personnel: 297

BLOOMER—Chippewa County

☐ **MAYO CLINIC HEALTH SYSTEM – CHIPPEWA VALLEY IN BLOOMER (521314)**, 1501 Thompson Street, Zip 54724–1299; tel. 715/568–2000 **A**1 10 18 **F**3 8 15 18 28 29 30 32 34 35 40 43 44 45 53 54 56 57 59 64 65 75 77 78 80 81 84 85 86 87 90 93 96 97 107 110 115 119 130 132 133 135 144 146 147 148 149 **P**6 **S** Mayo Clinic, Rochester, MN
Primary Contact: Maurita Sullivan, Vice President
Web address: www.bloomermedicalcenter.org
Control: Other not–for–profit (including NFP Corporation) **Service:** General medical and surgical

Staffed Beds: 19 Admissions: 440 Census: 13 Outpatient Visits: 47991 Births: 0 Total Expense ($000): 32667 Payroll Expense ($000): 15938 Personnel: 198

BOSCOBEL—Grant County

GUNDERSEN BOSCOBEL AREA HOSPITAL AND CLINICS (521344), 205 Parker Street, Zip 53805–1698; tel. 608/375–4112 **A**10 18 **F**3 8 11 15 28 29 31 34 37 38 40 43 53 56 57 59 62 64 70 75 78 79 81 82 85 86 87 93 94 97 107 108 110 118 119 127 130 131 133 135 144 147 148 **P**2 6
Primary Contact: David Hartberg, Chief Executive Officer
CFO: Melissa Uselman, Chief Financial Officer
CMO: Marilu Bintz M.D., Chief of Staff
CIO: Tonia Midtlien, Information Systems Support Specialist
CHR: Jennifer Dax, Director Human Resources
CNO: Theresa Lynn Braudt, Chief Nursing Officer
Web address: www.gundersenhealth.org/boscobel
Control: Other not–for–profit (including NFP Corporation) **Service:** General medical and surgical

Staffed Beds: 8 Admissions: 193 Census: 2 Outpatient Visits: 7918 Births: 0 Total Expense ($000): 16208 Payroll Expense ($000): 5391 Personnel: 108

BROOKFIELD—Waukesha County

★ **WHEATON FRANCISCAN HEALTHCARE – ELMBROOK MEMORIAL (520170)**, 19333 West North Avenue, Zip 53045–4198; tel. 262/785–2000 **F**3 4 8 11 12 13 15 17 18 20 22 24 26 28 29 30 31 34 35 36 40 43 45 46 47 49 50 54 56 59 64 65 68 70 72 74 75 76 77 78 79 80 81 82 83 84 85 86 87 89 90 91 92 93 97 99 100 107 108 109 110 111 112 114 115 117 118 119 120 121 122 123 124 126 130 131 132 135 143 145 146 148 149 **S** Ascension Healthcare, Saint Louis, MO
Primary Contact: Timothy Richman, Chief Executive Officer
CFO: Michael Petitt, Director of Finance
CMO: Rita Hanson M.D., Vice President Medical Affairs
CIO: Andrew Donovan, Director Information Technology
CHR: Christopher Morris, Director Human Resources
Web address: www.wfhealthcare.org
Control: Church operated, Nongovernment, not–for–profit **Service:** General medical and surgical

Staffed Beds: 122 Admissions: 4346 Census: 49 Outpatient Visits: 70986 Births: 522 Total Expense ($000): 111362 Payroll Expense ($000): 36775 Personnel: 529

BURLINGTON—Racine County

☒ **AURORA MEMORIAL HOSPITAL OF BURLINGTON (520059)**, 252 McHenry Street, Zip 53105–1828; tel. 262/767–6000 **A**1 2 10 **F**3 8 11 15 17 18 20 26 28 29 30 34 35 36 40 43 44 45 46 47 48 50 51 53 56 57 59 60 68 70 74 75 79 80 81 82 84 85 86 87 89 93 94 96 107 108 109 110 111 115 116 118 119 130 131 132 134 135 146 148 149 **P**6 **S** Aurora Health Care, Milwaukee, WI
Primary Contact: Lisa Just, President
CFO: Stuart Arnett, Vice President Finance and Chief Financial Officer
CIO: Jean Chase, Regional Manager Information Services
CHR: Gene Krauklis, Regional Vice President Human Resources
Web address: www.aurorahealthcare.org
Control: Other not–for–profit (including NFP Corporation) **Service:** General medical and surgical

Staffed Beds: 55 Admissions: 2194 Census: 19 Outpatient Visits: 79865 Births: 0 Total Expense ($000): 70323 Payroll Expense ($000): 22153 Personnel: 378

WI

CHILTON—Calumet County

✠ **CALUMET MEDICAL CENTER (521317)**, 614 Memorial Drive, Zip 53014–1597; tel. 920/849–2386 **A**1 10 18 **F**3 7 11 15 28 29 34 35 40 42 43 45 54 56 57 59 64 65 75 78 79 80 81 82 85 86 87 89 92 93 97 107 110 115 119 129 130 131 132 133 144 145 146 148 **P**7 **S** Ascension Healthcare, Saint Louis, MO
Primary Contact: Jennifer Derks, Chief Administrative Officer
CFO: Jeff Badger, Chief Financial Officer
CMO: Mark W Kehrberg M.D., Chief Medical Officer
CIO: Will Weider, Chief Information Officer
CHR: Beth O'laire, Manager Human Resources
Web address: www.affinityhealth.org
Control: Other not–for–profit (including NFP Corporation) **Service:** General medical and surgical

Staffed Beds: 15 **Admissions:** 417 **Census:** 5 **Outpatient Visits:** 47091 **Births:** 0 **Total Expense ($000):** 23168 **Payroll Expense ($000):** 8368 **Personnel:** 104

CHIPPEWA FALLS—Chippewa County

✠ **HSHS ST. JOSEPH'S HOSPITAL (520017)**, 2661 County Highway I, Zip 54729–5407; tel. 715/723–1811 **A**1 10 **F**3 4 5 11 13 15 17 28 29 30 34 38 40 43 54 56 59 62 63 64 69 70 75 76 79 80 81 82 84 85 86 87 88 89 93 100 101 102 104 105 107 110 111 115 119 129 130 132 144 145 146 147 148 149 **P**6 7 **S** HSHS Hospital Sisters Health System, Springfield, IL
Primary Contact: Julie Manas, Interim Chief Executive Officer
CFO: David Nelson FACHE, Divisional Chief Financial Officer
CIO: Kevin Groskreutz, Division Chief Information Officer, Ancillary Systems
CHR: Rick Tolson, Divisional Chief People Officer
CNO: Stella Clark MSN, R.N., Chief Nursing Officer
Web address: www.stjoeschipfalls.com
Control: Church operated, Nongovernment, not–for–profit **Service:** General medical and surgical

Staffed Beds: 102 **Admissions:** 3174 **Census:** 38 **Outpatient Visits:** 83213 **Births:** 410 **Total Expense ($000):** 64684 **Payroll Expense ($000):** 27495 **Personnel:** 317

COLUMBUS—Columbia County

✠ **COLUMBUS COMMUNITY HOSPITAL, INC. (521338)**, 1515 Park Avenue, Zip 53925–2402; tel. 920/623–2200 **A**1 10 18 **F**3 8 13 15 16 17 18 28 29 34 40 45 47 50 51 54 56 57 64 70 75 76 77 78 79 80 81 85 86 88 91 93 96 97 110 114 115 118 119 129 130 132 133 135 144 146 147 149 150
Primary Contact: John D. Russell, President and Chief Executive Officer
CFO: Phillip G Roberts, Vice President Finance and Chief Financial Officer
CMO: Gary Galvin, Chief of the Medical Staff
CIO: Phillip G Roberts, Vice President Finance and Chief Financial Officer
CHR: Ann Roundy, Vice President Employee Services
CNO: Jamie Hendrix, Vice President Patient Care Services
Web address: www.cch–inc.com
Control: Other not–for–profit (including NFP Corporation) **Service:** General medical and surgical

Staffed Beds: 25 **Admissions:** 945 **Census:** 9 **Outpatient Visits:** 45101 **Births:** 65 **Total Expense ($000):** 38176 **Payroll Expense ($000):** 15550 **Personnel:** 214

CUBA CITY—Grant County

SOUTHWEST HEALTH CENTER NURSING HOME See Southwest Health

CUDAHY—Milwaukee County

AURORA ST. LUKE'S SOUTH SHORE See Aurora St. Luke's Medical Center, Milwaukee

CUMBERLAND—Barron County

✠ **CUMBERLAND MEMORIAL HOSPITAL (521353)**, 1110 Seventh Avenue, Zip 54829–9138; tel. 715/822–2741, (Total facility includes 46 beds in nursing home–type unit) **A**1 10 18 **F**11 13 15 28 29 34 40 43 53 55 56 75 76 77 78 81 82 86 87 89 93 107 125 128 130 131 144 **P**8
Primary Contact: Michael Gutsch, Chief Executive Officer
COO: Bob Lindberg, Chief Operating Officer
CFO: Angela Martens, Chief Financial Officer
CMO: Tom Lingen M.D., Chief of Staff
CIO: Jason Morse, Director Information Technology
CHR: Hilary Butzler, Director Human Resources
Web address: www.cumberlandhealthcare.com
Control: Other not–for–profit (including NFP Corporation) **Service:** General medical and surgical

Staffed Beds: 71 **Admissions:** 578 **Census:** 51 **Outpatient Visits:** 13516 **Births:** 43 **Total Expense ($000):** 24380 **Payroll Expense ($000):** 11413 **Personnel:** 171

DARLINGTON—Lafayette County

MEMORIAL HOSPITAL OF LAFAYETTE COUNTY (521312), 800 Clay Street, Zip 53530–1228, Mailing Address: P.O.Box 70, 53530–0070; tel. 608/776–4466 **A**10 18 **F**1 11 15 28 29 34 40 43 54 56 64 75 76 80 81 82 86 89 90 93 102 105 107 111 116 119 130 131 144
Primary Contact: Julie Chikowski, Administrator
CFO: Marie Wamsley, Chief Financial Officer
Web address: www.memorialhospitaloflafayettecounty.org
Control: County, Government, Nonfederal **Service:** General medical and surgical

Staffed Beds: 25 **Admissions:** 224 **Census:** 4 **Outpatient Visits:** 20001 **Births:** 0 **Total Expense ($000):** 14178 **Payroll Expense ($000):** 3966 **Personnel:** 129

DODGEVILLE—Iowa County

✠ **UPLAND HILLS HEALTH (521352)**, 800 Compassion Way, Zip 53533–1956, Mailing Address: P.O.Box 800, 53533–0800; tel. 608/930–8000, (Total facility includes 44 beds in nursing home–type unit) **A**1 10 18 **F**3 8 11 13 15 17 28 29 34 36 40 41 43 44 45 50 53 54 56 57 59 62 63 64 65 67 68 70 75 76 77 78 79 80 81 82 83 84 85 86 87 88 89 90 93 97 107 110 111 114 115 119 127 128 129 130 131 133 144 146 147 148 **P**6
Primary Contact: Lisa W. Schnedler, FACHE, President and Chief Executive Officer
CFO: Karl Pustina, Vice President Finance
CIO: Karen Thuli, Coordinator Information Systems
CHR: Troy Marx, Director Human Resources
CNO: Lynn Hebgen, Vice President Nursing
Web address: www.uplandhillshealth.org
Control: Other not–for–profit (including NFP Corporation) **Service:** General medical and surgical

Staffed Beds: 69 **Admissions:** 1218 **Census:** 49 **Outpatient Visits:** 59433 **Births:** 275 **Total Expense ($000):** 42786 **Payroll Expense ($000):** 18714 **Personnel:** 276

DURAND—Pepin County

★ **CHIPPEWA VALLEY HOSPITAL AND OAKVIEW CARE CENTER (521307)**, 1220 Third Avenue West, Zip 54736–1600, Mailing Address: P.O.Box 224, 54736–0224; tel. 715/672–4211 **A**10 18 **F**3 8 15 18 28 29 30 34 35 40 43 56 57 59 75 81 84 86 87 96 97 107 110 114 130 133 **S** Adventist Health System Sunbelt Health Care Corporation, Altamonte Springs, FL
Primary Contact: Douglas R. Peterson, President and Chief Executive Officer
Web address: www.chippewavalleyhospital.com/
Control: Church operated, Nongovernment, not–for–profit **Service:** General medical and surgical

Staffed Beds: 25 **Admissions:** 333 **Census:** 5 **Outpatient Visits:** 14610 **Births:** 0 **Total Expense ($000):** 12981 **Payroll Expense ($000):** 5606 **Personnel:** 89

EAGLE RIVER—Vilas County

★ **MINISTRY EAGLE RIVER MEMORIAL HOSPITAL (521300)**, 201 Hospital Road, Zip 54521–8835; tel. 715/479–7411 **A**10 18 **F**3 11 15 28 29 30 35 40 45 47 50 57 59 64 68 75 80 81 82 84 85 86 87 89 93 107 110 111 115 119 130 133 146 148 149 **S** Ascension Healthcare, Saint Louis, MO
Primary Contact: Sandra L. Anderson, President and Chief Executive Officer
COO: Laurie Oungst, Vice President, Operations
CFO: Jamon Lamers, Director Finance
CMO: Elmer Linboom M.D., Medical Staff President
CIO: Howard Dobizl, Director Information Technology Services
CHR: Michelle Cornelius, Director Human Resources for Northern Region
CNO: Deborah Karow R.N., Vice President Patient Care Services
Web address: www.ministryhealth.org
Control: Church operated, Nongovernment, not–for–profit **Service:** General medical and surgical

Staffed Beds: 13 **Admissions:** 397 **Census:** 4 **Outpatient Visits:** 19243 **Births:** 0 **Total Expense ($000):** 14545 **Payroll Expense ($000):** 7350 **Personnel:** 86

WI

Many Facility Codes have changed. Please refer to the AHA Guide Code Chart. © 2017 AHA Guide

EAU CLAIRE—Eau Claire County

☐ **MAYO CLINIC HEALTH SYSTEM IN EAU CLAIRE (520070)**, 1221 Whipple Street, Zip 54703–5270, Mailing Address: P.O.Box 4105, 54702–4105; tel. 715/838–3311 **A**1 2 3 5 10 19 **F**3 4 5 6 8 12 13 15 17 18 20 22 24 26 28 29 30 31 32 34 35 36 37 40 43 44 45 46 48 49 53 55 56 57 58 59 60 64 65 70 71 72 74 75 76 78 79 80 81 82 83 84 85 86 87 89 90 92 93 96 97 98 99 100 101 102 103 104 105 107 108 110 111 115 118 119 120 121 124 126 129 130 132 135 144 145 146 147 148 149 **P**6 **S** Mayo Clinic, Rochester, MN
Primary Contact: Richard Helmer, M.D., Chief Executive Officer
COO: John M Dickey, Chief Administrative Officer
CFO: Denise Mattison, Director Finance and Accounting Services
CMO: Robert C Peck M.D., Chief Medical Officer
CHR: Kenneth Lee, Division Chair, Human Resource Advisory
CNO: Pamela K. White R.N., MSN, Chief Nursing Officer and Vice President
Web address: www.mhs.mayo.edu
Control: Other not–for–profit (including NFP Corporation) **Service**: General medical and surgical

Staffed Beds: 185 **Admissions**: 10122 **Census**: 121 **Outpatient Visits**: 199185 **Births**: 1100 **Total Expense ($000)**: 254989 **Payroll Expense ($000)**: 101175 **Personnel**: 1528

☐ **OAKLEAF SURGICAL HOSPITAL (520196)**, 3802 West Oakwood Mall Drive, Zip 54701–3016; tel. 715/831–8130 **A**1 10 **F**3 37 45 47 48 51 64 75 79 80 81 82 85 107 111 114 119 130 **S** National Surgical Healthcare, Chicago, IL
Primary Contact: Anne Hargrave–Thomas, Chief Executive Officer
COO: Erma Radke, Director of Operations
CFO: Denise Freid–Scheppke, Chief Accounting Officer
CHR: Dorothy Conroy, Director Human Resources
CNO: Jacquelyn Maki, Chief Nursing Officer
Web address: www.oakleafmedical.com
Control: Corporation, Investor–owned (for–profit) **Service**: Surgical

Staffed Beds: 13 **Admissions**: 720 **Census**: 4 **Outpatient Visits**: 10275 **Births**: 0 **Total Expense ($000)**: 49667 **Payroll Expense ($000)**: 12748 **Personnel**: 228

⊞ △ **SACRED HEART HOSPITAL (520013)**, 900 West Clairemont Avenue, Zip 54701–6122; tel. 715/717–4121 **A**1 2 3 5 7 10 19 **F**3 6 11 12 13 15 17 18 20 22 24 28 29 30 31 32 34 35 38 40 41 43 45 46 47 48 49 50 51 53 56 57 58 59 60 64 69 70 72 74 75 76 78 79 80 81 82 84 85 86 87 88 89 90 91 92 93 94 96 97 98 99 100 101 102 103 104 107 108 110 111 112 114 115 116 117 118 119 120 121 123 124 126 129 130 132 135 141 144 145 146 147 149 150 **P**6 7 **S** HSHS Hospital Sisters Health System, Springfield, IL
Primary Contact: Julie Manas, President and Chief Executive Officer
CFO: David Nelson FACHE, Chief Financial Officer
CMO: Humayun Khan M.D., Chief Medical Officer
CIO: Kevin Groskreutz, Chief Information Officer
CHR: Craig Brenholt, Division Director People Services
CNO: Amy L. Dwyer R.N., MSN, Chief Nursing Officer
Web address: www.sacredhearteauclaire.org
Control: Church operated, Nongovernment, not–for–profit **Service**: General medical and surgical

Staffed Beds: 205 **Admissions**: 9588 **Census**: 126 **Outpatient Visits**: 114578 **Births**: 885 **Total Expense ($000)**: 218493 **Payroll Expense ($000)**: 73514 **Personnel**: 1048

EDGERTON—Rock County

⊞ **EDGERTON HOSPITAL AND HEALTH SERVICES (521319)**, 11101 North Sherman Road, Zip 53534–9002; tel. 608/884–3441 **A**1 10 18 **F**3 8 11 15 18 28 34 40 41 43 44 45 48 49 59 64 65 75 77 81 85 90 92 93 97 107 108 110 111 115 119 129 130 132 133 134 135 144 146 148
Primary Contact: Jim Schultz, Chief Executive Officer
CFO: Charles Roader, Vice President Finance
CMO: Brian Stubitsch M.D., Chief Medical Officer
CIO: JT Johrendt, Information Technology Network Specialist
CHR: Mark Kindschi, Director Human Resources
CNO: Sue Alwin–Popp, Chief Clinical Officer
Web address: www.edgertonhospital.com
Control: Other not–for–profit (including NFP Corporation) **Service**: General medical and surgical

Staffed Beds: 18 **Admissions**: 401 **Census**: 9 **Outpatient Visits**: 15240 **Births**: 0 **Total Expense ($000)**: 20987 **Payroll Expense ($000)**: 9524 **Personnel**: 128

ELKHORN—Walworth County

⊞ △ **AURORA LAKELAND MEDICAL CENTER (520102)**, W3985 County Road NN, Zip 53121–4389; tel. 262/741–2000 **A**1 2 7 10 **F**3 11 13 17 18 29 30 34 35 36 40 43 44 45 47 48 49 50 51 56 57 59 60 68 70 74 75 76 79 80 81 84 85 86 87 89 90 93 94 96 100 107 108 111 115 118 119 129 130 131 132 135 146 148 149 **P**6 **S** Aurora Health Care, Milwaukee, WI
Primary Contact: Lisa Just, President
CFO: Stuart Arnett, Regional Vice President Finance
CMO: Greg Gerber M.D., Chief Medical Officer
CIO: Jean Chase, Regional Manager Information Services
CHR: Gene Krauklis, Regional Vice President Human Resources
Web address: www.aurorahealthcare.org
Control: Other not–for–profit (including NFP Corporation) **Service**: General medical and surgical

Staffed Beds: 67 **Admissions**: 2671 **Census**: 25 **Outpatient Visits**: 74101 **Births**: 715 **Total Expense ($000)**: 64179 **Payroll Expense ($000)**: 20023 **Personnel**: 363

FOND DU LAC—Fond Du Lac County

FOND DU LAC COUNTY MENTAL HEALTH CENTER (524025), 459 East First Street, Zip 54935–4599; tel. 920/929–3502 **A**10 **F**4 38 98 99 102 103 130 **P**6
Primary Contact: J.R. Musunuru, M.D., Executive Director
Web address: www.fdlco.wi.gov
Control: County, Government, Nonfederal **Service**: Psychiatric

Staffed Beds: 25 **Admissions**: 970 **Census**: 14 **Outpatient Visits**: 681 **Births**: 0 **Total Expense ($000)**: 3687 **Payroll Expense ($000)**: 2409 **Personnel**: 48

⊞ △ **ST. AGNES HOSPITAL (520088)**, 430 East Division Street, Zip 54935–4560, Mailing Address: P.O.Box 385, 54936–0385; tel. 920/929–2300 **A**1 2 7 10 20 **F**2 3 5 6 8 11 13 15 18 20 22 24 28 29 30 31 33 34 40 43 44 45 46 47 48 49 50 51 53 54 55 56 57 59 62 63 64 66 67 68 69 74 75 76 77 78 79 80 81 82 84 85 86 87 90 92 93 96 97 98 99 100 101 102 103 104 105 107 108 109 110 111 115 118 119 120 121 123 124 126 129 130 131 132 134 135 143 144 146 147 148 149 150 **P**3 6
Primary Contact: Steven N. Little, President and Chief Executive Officer
COO: Katherine Vergos, Chief Operating Officer and Chief Nursing Officer
CFO: Bonnie Schmitz, Vice President and Chief Financial Officer
CMO: Derek Colmenares M.D., Chief Medical Officer
CIO: Nancy Birschbach, Vice President and Chief Information Officer
CHR: Sue Edminster, Vice President Human Resources
CNO: Katherine Vergos, Chief Operating Officer and Chief Nursing Officer
Web address: www.agnesian.com
Control: Church operated, Nongovernment, not–for–profit **Service**: General medical and surgical

Staffed Beds: 160 **Admissions**: 6882 **Census**: 75 **Outpatient Visits**: 762856 **Births**: 792 **Total Expense ($000)**: 341172 **Payroll Expense ($000)**: 127033 **Personnel**: 1951

FORT ATKINSON—Jefferson County

⊞ **FORT HEALTHCARE (520071)**, 611 East Sherman Avenue, Zip 53538–1998; tel. 920/568–5000 **A**1 10 **F**3 11 12 13 15 28 29 34 35 40 47 48 50 53 55 56 57 59 68 75 76 77 79 80 81 85 86 87 89 90 93 94 96 107 108 110 111 115 118 119 124 130 132 135 144 145 146 147 149 150 **P**1 5
Primary Contact: Michael S. Wallace, President and Chief Executive Officer
CFO: James J Nelson, Senior Vice President Finance and Strategic Planning
CMO: Thomas Nordland, Chief Medical Officer
CIO: Christopher Manakas, Chief Information Officer
CHR: Nancy Alstad, Director Human Resources
Web address: www.forthealthcare.com
Control: Other not–for–profit (including NFP Corporation) **Service**: General medical and surgical

Staffed Beds: 72 **Admissions**: 1995 **Census**: 15 **Outpatient Visits**: 280286 **Births**: 430 **Total Expense ($000)**: 116534 **Payroll Expense ($000)**: 38880 **Personnel**: 495

WI

Hospital, Medicare Provider Number, Address, Telephone, Approval, Facility, and Physician Codes, Health Care System

★ American Hospital Association (AHA) membership
☐ The Joint Commission accreditation
○ Healthcare Facilities Accreditation Program
◇ DNV Healthcare Inc. accreditation
⇧ Center for Improvement in Healthcare Quality Accreditation
△ Commission on Accreditation of Rehabilitation Facilities (CARF) accreditation

FRANKLIN—Milwaukee County

☒ **MIDWEST ORTHOPEDIC SPECIALTY HOSPITAL (520205)**, 10101 South 27th Street, 2nd Floor, Zip 53132–7209; tel. 414/817–5800 **A**1 3 5 10 **F**29 34 80 81 82 86 130 131 **S** Ascension Healthcare, Saint Louis, MO
Primary Contact: Sheila Gansemer, R.N., Vice President of Patient Care Services
CFO: Aaron Bridgeland, Director Finance
CMO: Daniel Guehlstorf M.D., Chief of Staff
CIO: Gregory Smith, Senior Vice President and Chief Information Officer
CHR: Robert Bauer, Vice President Human Resources
CNO: Sheila Gansemer R.N., Vice President Patient Care Services and Chief Nursing Officer
Web address: www.mymosh.com/
Control: Partnership, Investor–owned (for–profit) **Service**: General medical and surgical

Staffed Beds: 16 **Admissions**: 1473 **Census**: 9 **Outpatient Visits**: 6011 **Births**: 0 **Total Expense ($000)**: 42163 **Payroll Expense ($000)**: 6750 **Personnel**: 113

☒ **WHEATON FRANCISCAN HEALTHCARE – FRANKLIN (520204)**, 10101 South 27th Street, Zip 53132–7209; tel. 414/325–4700 **A**1 10 **F**3 15 18 20 22 26 29 30 34 35 40 43 44 45 48 49 50 57 59 64 65 68 70 74 75 77 79 81 82 85 86 87 91 92 93 96 97 107 108 110 111 115 119 126 130 131 135 144 146 **S** Ascension Healthcare, Saint Louis, MO
Primary Contact: Sheila Gansemer, R.N., Vice President Patient Care Services and Chief Nursing Officer
CFO: Aaron Bridgeland, Director Finance
CMO: Michelle Graham M.D., Vice President Medical Affairs
CIO: Gregory Smith, Senior Vice President and Chief Information Officer
CHR: Robert Bauer, Vice President Human Resources
CNO: Sheila Gansemer R.N., Vice President Patient Care Services and Chief Nursing Officer
Web address: www.mywheaton.org/
Control: Church operated, Nongovernment, not–for–profit **Service**: General medical and surgical

Staffed Beds: 44 **Admissions**: 2333 **Census**: 27 **Outpatient Visits**: 89609 **Births**: 0 **Total Expense ($000)**: 75057 **Payroll Expense ($000)**: 26563 **Personnel**: 407

FRIENDSHIP—Adams County

MOUNDVIEW MEMORIAL HOSPITAL & CLINICS (521309), 402 West Lake Street, Zip 53934–9699, Mailing Address: P.O.Box 40, 53934–0040; tel. 608/339–3331 **A**10 18 **F**6 11 15 28 29 34 36 40 53 56 64 77 81 82 86 87 93 107 108 111 119 130 131 **P**2 6
Primary Contact: Don Heinz, Chief Executive Officer
Web address: www.moundview.org
Control: Other not–for–profit (including NFP Corporation) **Service**: General medical and surgical

Staffed Beds: 25 **Admissions**: 175 **Census**: 2 **Outpatient Visits**: 39697 **Births**: 0 **Total Expense ($000)**: 16665 **Payroll Expense ($000)**: 7223 **Personnel**: 106

GLENDALE—Milwaukee County

ORTHOPAEDIC HOSPITAL OF WISCONSIN – GLENDALE (520194), 475 West River Woods Parkway, Zip 53212–1081; tel. 414/961–6800 **A**10 **F**29 34 38 53 64 80 81 82 86 93 107 111 119 130 131
Primary Contact: Brian J. Cramer, Chief Executive Officer
CFO: Tom Swiderski, Chief Financial Officer
CMO: Rory Wright M.D., President Medical Staff
CIO: Todd Heikkinen, Manager Sports Medicine and Rehabilitation Services
CNO: Nanette Johnson, Chief Nursing Officer
Web address: www.ohow.org
Control: Partnership, Investor–owned (for–profit) **Service**: Orthopedic

Staffed Beds: 30 **Admissions**: 1310 **Census**: 8 **Outpatient Visits**: 28954 **Births**: 0 **Total Expense ($000)**: 36463 **Payroll Expense ($000)**: 12356 **Personnel**: 195

GRAFTON—Ozaukee County

☒ **AURORA MEDICAL CENTER GRAFTON (520207)**, 975 Port Washington Road, Zip 53024–9201; tel. 262/329–1000 **A**1 2 3 5 10 **F**3 8 13 15 17 18 20 22 24 26 28 29 30 31 34 35 36 37 40 43 44 45 46 47 48 49 50 51 53 54 60 64 65 68 70 72 74 75 76 79 80 81 82 85 86 87 89 90 92 93 94 96 107 108 110 111 114 115 116 117 118 119 120 121 126 130 131 135 146 147 148 149 **P**6 **S** Aurora Health Care, Milwaukee, WI
Primary Contact: David Graebner, Interim President
CMO: Doug McManus, Chief Medical Officer
CNO: Terry Kabitzke–Groth R.N., Vice President Nursing
Web address: www.aurorahealthcare.org
Control: Other not–for–profit (including NFP Corporation) **Service**: General medical and surgical

Staffed Beds: 127 **Admissions**: 7588 **Census**: 73 **Outpatient Visits**: 119288 **Births**: 938 **Total Expense ($000)**: 180428 **Payroll Expense ($000)**: 51222 **Personnel**: 890

GRANTSBURG—Burnett County

★ **BURNETT MEDICAL CENTER (521331)**, 257 West St George Avenue, Zip 54840–7827; tel. 715/463–5353, (Total facility includes 50 beds in nursing home–type unit) **A**10 18 **F**2 3 13 15 28 29 30 31 34 35 40 43 45 56 57 59 64 68 75 76 77 78 80 81 84 86 87 89 90 93 97 107 115 127 128 130 131 132 133 135 144 148 **P**6
Primary Contact: Gordon Lewis, Chief Executive Officer
CFO: Charles J Faught, Chief Financial Officer
CMO: Hans Rechsteiner M.D., Chief of Staff
CIO: Andy Douglas, Manager Information Technology
CHR: Sandy Hinrichs, Director Human Resources
Web address: www.burnettmedicalcenter.com
Control: Other not–for–profit (including NFP Corporation) **Service**: General medical and surgical

Staffed Beds: 67 **Admissions**: 382 **Census**: 51 **Outpatient Visits**: 33925 **Births**: 39 **Total Expense ($000)**: 14965 **Payroll Expense ($000)**: 6903 **Personnel**: 135

GREEN BAY—Brown County

☒ △ **AURORA BAYCARE MEDICAL CENTER (520193)**, 2845 Greenbrier Road, Zip 54311–6519, Mailing Address: P.O.Box 8900, 54308–8900; tel. 920/288–8000 **A**1 2 7 10 **F**3 8 12 13 15 17 18 19 20 22 24 26 28 29 30 31 32 33 34 35 36 40 43 44 45 46 47 48 49 50 53 54 57 58 59 64 65 70 72 74 75 76 78 79 80 81 82 85 86 87 89 90 93 94 96 107 108 109 110 111 114 115 116 118 119 120 121 123 124 126 129 130 131 132 135 144 146 147 148 149 **P**6 **S** Aurora Health Care, Milwaukee, WI
Primary Contact: Daniel T. Meyer, President
COO: Daniel T Meyer, President
CFO: Gwen Christensen, Vice President, Finance
CMO: Brian Johnson M.D., Chief Medical Officer
CIO: Chuck Geurts, Manager Information Technology Client Services
CHR: Elizabeth A Kirby, Senior Director Human Resources
CNO: Heather Schroeder R.N., Vice President Nursing
Web address: www.aurorabaycare.com
Control: Partnership, Investor–owned (for–profit) **Service**: General medical and surgical

Staffed Beds: 167 **Admissions**: 8806 **Census**: 101 **Outpatient Visits**: 319511 **Births**: 1402 **Total Expense ($000)**: 298121 **Payroll Expense ($000)**: 92493 **Personnel**: 1342

★ ⇑ **BELLIN MEMORIAL HOSPITAL (520049)**, 744 South Webster Avenue, Zip 54301–3581, Mailing Address: P.O.Box 23400, 54305–3400; tel. 920/433–3500 **A**2 10 21 **F**3 12 13 15 17 18 20 22 24 26 28 29 30 31 35 36 37 40 41 42 43 44 45 46 47 48 49 51 53 54 59 62 64 71 74 75 76 77 78 79 80 81 82 83 84 85 86 87 89 90 91 92 96 97 106 107 108 110 111 115 116 118 119 121 123 124 126 127 129 130 131 132 133 144 145 146 148 149 **P**2 6
Primary Contact: George Kerwin, President and Chief Executive Officer
CFO: Jim Dietsche, Chief Financial Officer
CMO: Ed Millermaier M.D., Chief Medical Officer
CIO: John Rocheleau, Vice President Business Support and Information Technology
CHR: Troy L Koebke, Director Human Resources Management
CNO: Laura Hieb R.N., Chief Nursing Officer
Web address: www.bellin.org
Control: Church operated, Nongovernment, not–for–profit **Service**: General medical and surgical

Staffed Beds: 167 **Admissions**: 8657 **Census**: 82 **Outpatient Visits**: 993057 **Births**: 1433 **Total Expense ($000)**: 428813 **Payroll Expense ($000)**: 198365 **Personnel**: 2586

WI

⇧ **BELLIN PSYCHIATRIC CENTER (524038)**, 301 East St Joseph Street,
Zip 54301, Mailing Address: P.O.Box 23725, 54305–3725; tel. 920/433–3630
A3 10 21 **F**4 5 6 29 34 36 38 53 54 56 64 75 86 87 98 99 100 101 102 103
104 105 130 **P**2 6
Primary Contact: Sharla Baenen, MSN, R.N., President
COO: Chris Woleske, Chief Operating Officer
CFO: Kevin McGurk, Controller
CIO: Troy Schiesl, Director Information Services
CHR: Troy L Koebke, Director Human Resources
CNO: Crystal Malakar, Team Leader Inpatient Nursing
Web address: www.bellin.org
Control: Church operated, Nongovernment, not–for–profit **Service**: Psychiatric

Staffed Beds: 53 **Admissions:** 1590 **Census:** 20 **Outpatient Visits:** 67960 **Births:** 0 **Total Expense ($000):** 19999 **Payroll Expense ($000):** 12774 **Personnel:** 139		

BROWN COUNTY COMMUNITY TREATMENT CENTER (524014), 3150
Gershwin Drive, Zip 54311–5899; tel. 920/391–4700 **A**10 **F**98 102 106 130
135 143 146 148 149
Primary Contact: Roberta Morschauser, Administrator
CFO: Margaret Hoff, Account Manager
CMO: Yogesh Pareek M.D., Clinical Director
CIO: Dawn LaPlant, Manager Health Information Management
CHR: Brent R Miller, Manager Human Resources
Web address: www.co.brown.wi.us/
Control: County, Government, Nonfederal **Service**: Psychiatric

Staffed Beds: 16 **Admissions:** 837 **Census:** 12 **Outpatient Visits:** 0 **Births:** 0 **Total Expense ($000):** 3908 **Payroll Expense ($000):** 2603 **Personnel:** 65	

BROWN COUNTY HUMAN SERVICES MENTAL HEALTH CENTER See Brown
County Community Treatment Center

✠ **HSHS ST. MARY'S HOSPITAL MEDICAL CENTER (520097)**, 1726 Shawano
Avenue, Zip 54303–3282; tel. 920/498–4200 **A**1 2 10 **F**3 13 15 17 18 20 22
26 28 29 30 31 34 35 40 43 44 45 46 47 48 49 50 51 53 55 57 59 64 65 68
69 70 74 75 76 77 78 79 80 81 82 84 85 86 87 92 94 96 102 107 108 110
111 114 115 116 117 118 119 130 132 143 145 146 147 148 149 150 **P**2 **S**
HSHS Hospital Sisters Health System, Springfield, IL
Primary Contact: Therese B. Pandl, President and Chief Executive Officer
COO: Lawrence J Connors, Chief Operating Officer
CFO: Greg Simia, Chief Financial Officer
CMO: Ken Johnson, Chief Physician Executive
CIO: Shane Miller, Chief Information Officer
CHR: Christine Jensema, Chief People Officer
CNO: Paula Hafeman R.N., MSN, FACHE, Chief Nursing Officer
Web address: www.stmgb.org
Control: Church operated, Nongovernment, not–for–profit **Service**: General
medical and surgical

Staffed Beds: 83 **Admissions:** 3976 **Census:** 35 **Outpatient Visits:** 105967 **Births:** 559 **Total Expense ($000):** 134357 **Payroll Expense ($000):** 36501 **Personnel:** 416	

✠ **HSHS ST. VINCENT HOSPITAL (520075)**, 835 South Van Buren Street,
Zip 54301–3526, Mailing Address: P.O.Box 13508, 54307–3508; tel. 920/433–
0111 **A**1 2 10 **F**3 5 9 11 12 13 15 17 18 20 22 24 29 30 31 32 34 35 36 40
43 44 45 49 50 51 56 57 58 59 60 62 64 65 68 70 72 74 75 76 77 78 79 80
81 83 84 85 86 87 88 89 90 91 92 94 96 107 108 110 111 114 115 116 117
118 119 120 121 123 124 126 129 130 132 135 143 144 146 147 148 149
150 **P**2 **S** HSHS Hospital Sisters Health System, Springfield, IL
Primary Contact: Therese B. Pandl, President and Chief Executive Officer
COO: Lawrence J Connors, Chief Operating Officer
CFO: Greg Simia, Chief Financial Officer
CMO: Ken Johnson, Chief Physician Executive
CIO: Shane Miller, Chief Information Officer
CHR: Christine Jensema, Chief People Officer
CNO: Paula Hafeman R.N., MSN, FACHE, Chief Nurse Executive
Web address: www.stvincenthospital.org
Control: Church operated, Nongovernment, not–for–profit **Service**: General
medical and surgical

Staffed Beds: 255 **Admissions:** 10364 **Census:** 135 **Outpatient Visits:** 160507 **Births:** 1103 **Total Expense ($000):** 339577 **Payroll Expense ($000):** 88703 **Personnel:** 1397	

GREENFIELD—Milwaukee County

KINDRED HOSPITAL–MILWAUKEE See Post Acute Medical Specialty Hospital Of
Milwaukee

✠ **POST ACUTE MEDICAL SPECIALTY HOSPITAL OF MILWAUKEE (522004)**,
5017 South 110Th Street, Zip 53228–3131; tel. 414/427–8282 **A**1 10 **F**1 3 29
83 84 85 100 106 130 143 148 **P**5 **S** Post Acute Medical, LLC, Enola, PA
Primary Contact: Carin Croker, Chief Executive Officer
CMO: Alok Goyal M.D., Medical Director
CNO: Dorie Petitt, Chief Nursing Officer
Web address: www.postacutemedical.com/
Control: Corporation, Investor–owned (for–profit) **Service**: Acute long–term care
hospital

Staffed Beds: 56 **Admissions:** 464 **Census:** 31 **Outpatient Visits:** 0 **Births:** 0 **Total Expense ($000):** 17928 **Payroll Expense ($000):** 7864 **Personnel:** 153	

HARTFORD—Washington County

✠ **AURORA MEDICAL CENTER IN WASHINGTON COUNTY (520038)**, 1032 East
Sumner Street, Zip 53027–1698; tel. 262/673–2300, (Nonreporting) **A**1 2 10 **S**
Aurora Health Care, Milwaukee, WI
Primary Contact: David Graebner, President
CIO: John Sipek, Supervisor Client Services
CNO: Terry Kabitzke–Groth R.N., Chief Nursing Officer
Web address: www.aurorahealthcare.org
Control: Other not–for–profit (including NFP Corporation) **Service**: General
medical and surgical

Staffed Beds: 34	

HAYWARD—Sawyer County

★ **HAYWARD AREA MEMORIAL HOSPITAL AND WATER'S EDGE (521336)**,
11040 North State Road 77, Zip 54843–6391; tel. 715/934–4321, (Total facility
includes 70 beds in nursing home–type unit) **A**10 18 **F**3 10 11 13 15 30 31 34
35 40 41 43 45 51 57 59 64 68 75 76 77 78 79 81 82 85 86 93 96 107 110
111 115 119 124 128 129 130 132 133 134 135 145 146 148
Primary Contact: Timothy M. Gullingsrud, Chief Executive Officer
COO: Brad Zeller, Vice President Operations
CFO: Kent Dumonseau, Vice President Finance and Information Services
CHR: Rose Gates, Director Human Resources
Web address: www.hamhnh.com
Control: Other not–for–profit (including NFP Corporation) **Service**: General
medical and surgical

Staffed Beds: 75 **Admissions:** 841 **Census:** 75 **Outpatient Visits:** 15904 **Births:** 160 **Total Expense ($000):** 33914 **Payroll Expense ($000):** 13661 **Personnel:** 189	

HILLSBORO—Vernon County

★ **GUNDERSEN ST. JOSEPH'S HOSPITAL AND CLINICS (521304)**, 400
Water Avenue, Zip 54634–9054, Mailing Address: P.O.Box 527, 54634–0527;
tel. 608/489–8000 **A**10 18 **F**3 15 18 29 30 34 40 41 43 44 45 50 53 54 56 57
59 64 69 75 77 79 80 81 82 85 86 87 89 90 93 97 99 100 101 103 104 107
108 110 114 127 130 131 133 144 145 146 147 148
Primary Contact: Danielle Gearhart, Chief Executive Officer
CFO: Robin Nelson, Chief Financial Officer
CMO: William Cooke M.D., Chief of Staff
CIO: Danial Phetteplace, Director Information Technology
CHR: Kristie McCoic, Clinic Operations Officer and Director Human Resources
Web address: www.gundersenhealth.org/st–josephs
Control: Other not–for–profit (including NFP Corporation) **Service**: General
medical and surgical

Staffed Beds: 13 **Admissions:** 266 **Census:** 3 **Outpatient Visits:** 33313 **Births:** 0 **Total Expense ($000):** 18728 **Payroll Expense ($000):** 7488 **Personnel:** 155	

WI

Hospital, Medicare Provider Number, Address, Telephone, Approval, Facility, and Physician Codes, Health Care System		
★ American Hospital Association (AHA) membership	◯ Healthcare Facilities Accreditation Program	⇧ Center for Improvement in Healthcare Quality Accreditation
☐ The Joint Commission accreditation	◇ DNV Healthcare Inc. accreditation	△ Commission on Accreditation of Rehabilitation Facilities (CARF) accreditation

HUDSON—St. Croix County

☐ **HUDSON HOSPITAL AND CLINIC (521335)**, 405 Stageline Road, Zip 54016–7848; tel. 715/531–6000 **A**1 3 10 18 **F**3 5 8 13 15 18 26 28 29 30 31 32 34 35 36 38 40 43 44 45 46 50 53 55 56 57 59 64 68 74 75 76 77 78 79 80 81 85 86 87 89 93 94 96 107 110 111 115 117 119 129 130 132 133 135 143 146 148 149 **S** HealthPartners, Bloomington, MN
Primary Contact: Marian M. Furlong, R.N., FACHE, President and Chief Executive Officer
CFO: Douglas E Johnson, Interim Vice President Operations and Chief Financial Officer
CMO: Paul Scott M.D., Chief of Staff
CHR: Scott J Allen, Director Human Resources
Web address: www.hudsonhospital.org
Control: Other not–for–profit (including NFP Corporation) **Service**: General medical and surgical

Staffed Beds: 24 **Admissions**: 1331 **Census**: 9 **Outpatient Visits**: 34881 **Births**: 564 **Total Expense ($000)**: 51533 **Payroll Expense ($000)**: 19000 **Personnel**: 233

JANESVILLE—Rock County

✠ **MERCYHEALTH HOSPITAL AND TRAUMA CENTER – JANESVILLE (520066)**, 1000 Mineral Point Avenue, Zip 53548–2982, Mailing Address: P.O.Box 5003, 53547–5003; tel. 608/756–6000, (Nonreporting) **A**1 2 10 **S** Mercy Health System, Janesville, WI
Primary Contact: Javon R. Bea, President and Chief Executive Officer
CFO: John Cook, Vice President and Chief Financial Officer
CMO: Mark L. Goelzer M.D., Director Medical Affairs
CHR: Kathy Harris, Vice President
CNO: Sue Ripsch, Vice President and Chief Nursing Officer
Web address: www.mercyhealthsystem.org
Control: Other not–for–profit (including NFP Corporation) **Service**: General medical and surgical

Staffed Beds: 132

✠ **ST. MARY'S JANESVILLE HOSPITAL (520208)**, 3400 East Racine Steeet, Zip 53546–2344; tel. 608/373–8000 **A**1 10 **F**11 13 28 29 34 38 40 70 75 76 77 80 81 82 86 87 89 90 93 107 108 111 118 119 130 **S** SSM Health, Saint Louis, MO
Primary Contact: Michael E. Zilm, Interim President
Web address: www.stmarysjanesville.com
Control: Church operated, Nongovernment, not–for–profit **Service**: General medical and surgical

Staffed Beds: 50 **Admissions**: 2766 **Census**: 24 **Outpatient Visits**: 34072 **Births**: 476 **Total Expense ($000)**: 61211 **Payroll Expense ($000)**: 20940 **Personnel**: 302

KENOSHA—Kenosha County

✠ **AURORA MEDICAL CENTER (520189)**, 10400 75th Street, Zip 53142–7884; tel. 262/948–5600 **A**1 2 10 **F**3 8 11 13 15 17 18 19 20 22 26 28 29 30 31 34 35 36 40 43 44 45 46 47 48 49 50 51 54 57 59 60 64 68 70 72 74 75 76 79 80 81 82 84 85 86 87 89 93 94 96 100 107 108 110 111 114 115 116 117 118 119 120 121 123 126 129 130 131 132 135 146 148 149 **P**6 **S** Aurora Health Care, Milwaukee, WI
Primary Contact: Douglas E. Koch, Market President
COO: Linda A. Gump, Chief Clinical Services Officer
CFO: Laurie B. Yake, Vice President Finance
CMO: James Santarelli M.D., President Medical Staff
CIO: Debora R. Chapdelaine, Manager Information Technology
CHR: Kellie Nelson, Director Human Resources
CNO: Donna F. Jamieson Ph.D., R.N., Chief Nursing Officer
Web address: www.aurorahealthcare.org
Control: Other not–for–profit (including NFP Corporation) **Service**: General medical and surgical

Staffed Beds: 79 **Admissions**: 5313 **Census**: 49 **Outpatient Visits**: 184779 **Births**: 706 **Total Expense ($000)**: 138488 **Payroll Expense ($000)**: 41675 **Personnel**: 715

☐ **UNITED HOSPITAL SYSTEM–KENOSHA CAMPUS (520021)**, 6308 Eighth Avenue, Zip 53143–5082; tel. 262/656–2011, (Nonreporting) **A**1 2 10
Primary Contact: Richard O. Schmidt Jr, President and Chief Executive Officer
Web address: www.unitedhospitalsystem.org/
Control: Other not–for–profit (including NFP Corporation) **Service**: General medical and surgical

Staffed Beds: 247

LA CROSSE—La Crosse County

✠ △ **GUNDERSEN HEALTH SYSTEM (520087)**, 1900 South Avenue, Zip 54601–5467; tel. 608/782–7300 **A**1 2 3 5 7 8 10 **F**3 4 5 6 9 11 13 15 18 19 20 22 24 28 29 30 31 32 34 35 36 38 40 43 45 46 47 48 49 50 51 52 54 55 56 59 61 64 68 72 74 75 76 77 78 79 80 81 82 83 85 86 87 88 89 90 91 92 93 94 96 97 98 99 100 101 102 103 104 105 106 107 108 109 110 111 114 115 116 117 118 119 120 121 123 124 126 129 130 131 134 144 145 146 147 148 149 150
Primary Contact: Scott W. Rathgaber, M.D., Chief Executive Officer and Board Chair
COO: Kathy Klock R.N., Senior Vice President Clinical Operations and Human Resources
CFO: Dara Bartels, Chief Financial Officer
CMO: Greg Thompson, Chief Medical Officer
CIO: Deb Rislow, Chief Information Officer
CHR: Kathy Klock R.N., Senior Vice President Clinical Operations and Human Resources
Web address: www.gundluth.org
Control: Other not–for–profit (including NFP Corporation) **Service**: General medical and surgical

Staffed Beds: 269 **Admissions**: 14678 **Census**: 183 **Outpatient Visits**: 646659 **Births**: 1533 **Total Expense ($000)**: 808040 **Payroll Expense ($000)**: 294394 **Personnel**: 2666

✠ **MAYO CLINIC HEALTH SYSTEM – FRANCISCAN HEALTHCARE IN LA CROSSE (520004)**, 700 West Avenue South, Zip 54601–4783; tel. 608/785–0940 **A**1 2 3 5 10 **F**1 2 3 4 5 6 8 9 11 13 14 15 16 17 18 19 20 21 22 23 25 26 27 28 29 30 31 32 34 35 36 40 43 44 45 50 52 53 54 55 56 57 58 59 61 64 65 66 68 69 70 71 72 74 75 76 77 78 79 80 81 82 84 85 86 87 88 89 90 93 94 97 98 99 100 101 102 103 104 105 107 108 109 110 111 112 114 115 117 118 119 120 121 123 124 127 129 130 131 132 134 135 143 144 145 146 147 148 149 150 **S** Mayo Clinic, Rochester, MN
Primary Contact: Timothy Johnson, M.D., President and Chief Executive Officer
COO: Joseph J Kruse, Executive Vice President
CFO: Tom Tiggelaar, Vice President Finance
CMO: David Rushlow, Vice President Medical Affairs
CIO: Neal Sanger, Vice President Information Services
Web address: www.franciscanskemp.org
Control: Church operated, Nongovernment, not–for–profit **Service**: General medical and surgical

Staffed Beds: 81 **Admissions**: 6066 **Census**: 60 **Outpatient Visits**: 98259 **Births**: 821 **Total Expense ($000)**: 357485 **Payroll Expense ($000)**: 177350 **Personnel**: 1890

LADYSMITH—Rusk County

★ **RUSK COUNTY MEMORIAL HOSPITAL (521328)**, 900 College Avenue West, Zip 54848–2116; tel. 715/532–5561 **A**10 18 **F**3 11 15 28 29 34 36 40 43 44 45 50 51 53 56 57 59 64 68 70 77 81 85 86 87 89 93 97 107 110 111 115 116 117 118 119 127 132 133 144 146 147 148 **P**6
Primary Contact: Charisse S. Oland, FACHE, Chief Executive Officer
CFO: David Kuehn, Chief Financial Officer
CMO: Ganesh Pawar M.D., Chief of Staff
CHR: Rita Telitz, Chief Administrative Officer
CNO: Debra Frenn FACHE, Chief Patient Care Officer
Web address: www.ruskhospital.org
Control: County, Government, Nonfederal **Service**: General medical and surgical

Staffed Beds: 25 **Admissions**: 500 **Census**: 6 **Outpatient Visits**: 32836 **Births**: 0 **Total Expense ($000)**: 22719 **Payroll Expense ($000)**: 9722 **Personnel**: 147

LAKE GENEVA—Walworth County

MERCYHEALTH HOSPITAL AND MEDICAL CENTER – WALWORTH (521357), N2950 State Road 67, Zip 53147–2655; tel. 262/245–0535 **A**10 18 **F**3 5 9 11 13 15 18 26 29 31 34 35 38 40 44 45 50 57 59 65 70 74 75 76 77 78 79 81 82 85 87 89 92 93 94 96 97 100 101 103 104 107 108 110 111 114 118 119 129 130 131 132 133 135 144 146 147 148 149 **P**6 **S** Mercy Health System, Janesville, WI
Primary Contact: Javon R. Bea, President and Chief Executive Officer
COO: Jennifer Hallatt, Vice President
CNO: Caryn Lynn Oleston MSN, R.N., FACHE, Chief Nursing Officer
Web address: www.mercyhealthsystem.org
Control: Other not–for–profit (including NFP Corporation) **Service**: General medical and surgical

Staffed Beds: 18 **Admissions**: 1180 **Census**: 10 **Outpatient Visits**: 150729 **Births**: 164 **Total Expense ($000)**: 69224 **Payroll Expense ($000)**: 17655 **Personnel**: 318

WI

Many Facility Codes have changed. Please refer to the AHA Guide Code Chart. © 2017 AHA Guide

LANCASTER—Grant County

⊞ **GRANT REGIONAL HEALTH CENTER (521322)**, 507 South Monroe Street, Zip 53813–2054; tel. 608/723–2143 **A**1 10 18 **F**3 8 11 13 15 28 29 34 35 36 40 43 44 52 53 55 56 57 59 64 65 68 69 75 76 77 79 80 81 82 84 85 86 87 89 90 93 97 107 110 115 119 127 129 130 131 132 133 135 144 146 148 **P**6 **S** HealthTech Management Services, Brentwood, TN
Primary Contact: Nicole Clapp, R.N., MSN, FACHE, President and Chief Executive Officer
CFO: Dawn Bandy, Chief Financial Officer
CMO: Jessica Varnam, Chief of Staff
CIO: Ken Kaiser, Coordinator Information Systems
CHR: Stacy L Martin, Director Human Resources
CNO: Jennifer Rutkowski R.N., MSN, Vice President Professional Services
Web address: www.grantregional.com
Control: Other not–for–profit (including NFP Corporation) **Service**: General medical and surgical

Staffed Beds: 8 **Admissions:** 668 **Census:** 5 **Outpatient Visits:** 28285 **Births:** 171 **Total Expense ($000):** 25353 **Payroll Expense ($000):** 12995 **Personnel:** 175	

MADISON—Dane County

☐ **MENDOTA MENTAL HEALTH INSTITUTE (524008)**, 301 Troy Drive, Zip 53704–1599; tel. 608/301–1000 **A**1 3 5 10 **F**6 29 30 34 35 38 50 56 57 58 59 65 66 68 75 82 86 87 98 100 101 103 104 105 106 130 132 135 143 146 148 149 150
Primary Contact: Greg Van Rybroek, Chief Executive Officer
CFO: Stacie Schiereck, Director Management Services
CMO: Molli Martha Rolli M.D., Medical Director
CNO: Jane Walters, Director of Nursing
Web address: www.dhfs.state.wi.us
Control: State, Government, Nonfederal **Service**: Psychiatric

Staffed Beds: 274 **Admissions:** 499 **Census:** 271 **Outpatient Visits:** 0 **Births:** 0 **Total Expense ($000):** 65645 **Payroll Expense ($000):** 38154 **Personnel:** 732	

⊞ **SELECT SPECIALTY HOSPITAL–MADISON (522008)**, 801 Braxton Place, Zip 53715–1415; tel. 608/260–2700 **A**1 10 **F**1 3 29 30 35 60 75 85 86 119 130 148 **P**8 **S** Select Medical Corporation, Mechanicsburg, PA
Primary Contact: David Ross, Chief Executive Officer
CHR: Mallary Stramowski, Chief Human Resources Officer
CNO: Dana McKinney, Chief Nursing Officer
Web address: www.madison.selectspecialtyhospitals.com
Control: Corporation, Investor–owned (for–profit) **Service**: Acute long–term care hospital

Staffed Beds: 52 **Admissions:** 467 **Census:** 39 **Outpatient Visits:** 0 **Births:** 0 **Total Expense ($000):** 26993 **Payroll Expense ($000):** 10927 **Personnel:** 169	

⊞ **ST. MARY'S HOSPITAL (520083)**, 700 South Park Street, Zip 53715–1830; tel. 608/251–6100 **A**1 3 10 **F**2 9 11 13 15 17 20 22 24 28 29 34 40 43 53 56 64 70 72 75 76 78 80 81 82 86 89 90 98 100 101 102 103 107 108 118 119 130 141 **S** SSM Health, Saint Louis, MO
Primary Contact: Jon Rozenfeld, President
COO: Kristin McManmon, Chief Operating Officer
CFO: Steve Caldwell, Vice President Finance and Chief Financial Officer
CHR: Linda Taplin Statz, System Vice President – Employee Experience
CNO: Ginger Malone MSN, RN–B, Chief Nursing Officer
Web address: www.stmarysmadison.com
Control: Church operated, Nongovernment, not–for–profit **Service**: General medical and surgical

Staffed Beds: 355 **Admissions:** 20514 **Census:** 253 **Outpatient Visits:** 107457 **Births:** 3100 **Total Expense ($000):** 380639 **Payroll Expense ($000):** 133587 **Personnel:** 1832	

⊞ **UNITYPOINT HEALTH MERITER (520089)**, 202 South Park Street, Zip 53715–1507; tel. 608/417–6000 **A**1 3 5 10 **F**3 4 5 9 11 12 13 15 17 18 20 22 24 26 28 29 30 31 32 34 35 36 37 40 41 43 45 46 48 49 50 53 56 57 58 59 64 65 66 68 70 71 72 74 75 76 78 79 80 81 84 85 86 87 90 92 93 96 97 98 99 100 101 102 103 104 105 106 107 108 110 111 115 118 119 126 130 132 135 145 146 147 148 149 **P**6 **S** UnityPoint Health, West Des Moines, IA
Primary Contact: Arthur Nizza, President and Chief Executive Officer
CFO: Beth Erdman, Chief Financial Officer
CMO: Geoff Priest M.D., Chief Medical Officer
CIO: Denise Gomez, Assistant Vice President Information Systems
CHR: James Arnett, Vice President Human Resources
CNO: Pat Grunwald MSN, Chief Nursing Officer
Web address: www.meriter.com
Control: Other not–for–profit (including NFP Corporation) **Service**: General medical and surgical

Staffed Beds: 308 **Admissions:** 14970 **Census:** 177 **Outpatient Visits:** 207045 **Births:** 4153 **Total Expense ($000):** 425744 **Payroll Expense ($000):** 141333 **Personnel:** 2071	

⊞ **UNIVERSITY OF WISCONSIN HOSPITALS AND CLINICS AUTHORITY (520098)**, 600 Highland Avenue, Zip 53792–0002; tel. 608/263–6400, (Includes AMERICAN FAMILY CHILDREN'S HOSPITAL, 1675 Highland Avenue, Madison, Wisconsin, Zip 53705, tel. 608/890–5437; Jeffrey S Poltawsky, Senior Vice President) **A**1 2 3 5 8 10 13 **F**3 5 6 8 9 12 15 16 17 18 19 20 21 22 23 24 25 26 27 28 29 30 31 32 34 35 36 37 40 41 43 44 45 46 47 48 49 50 51 52 53 54 55 56 57 58 59 60 61 62 64 68 70 72 74 77 78 79 80 81 82 83 84 85 86 87 88 89 90 92 93 94 95 97 98 100 102 103 107 108 110 111 112 114 115 116 117 118 119 120 121 123 124 126 129 130 131 132 134 135 136 137 138 139 140 141 142 145 146 147 148 **S** UW Health System, Madison, WI
Primary Contact: Alan Kaplan, M.D., Chief Executive Officer
COO: Ron Sliwinski, Chief of Hospital Division
CFO: Robert Flannery, Chief Financial Officer
CMO: Peter Newcomer M.D., Chief Medical Officer
CIO: Jocelyn DeWitt Ph.D., Vice President and Chief Information Officer
CHR: Elizabeth T Bolt, Chief Human Resources Officer
CNO: Beth Houlahan R.N., Senior Vice President and Chief Nursing Officer
Web address: www.uwhealth.org
Control: Other not–for–profit (including NFP Corporation) **Service**: General medical and surgical

Staffed Beds: 598 **Admissions:** 32380 **Census:** 440 **Outpatient Visits:** 920233 **Births:** 0 **Total Expense ($000):** 1548771 **Payroll Expense ($000):** 525766 **Personnel:** 9712	

⊞ **UW HEALTH REHABILITATION HOSPITAL (523028)**, 5115 North Biltmore Lane, Zip 53718–2161; tel. 608/592–8100 **F**3 29 31 34 35 60 68 90 94 96 132 148 **P**3 **S** UW Health System, Madison, WI
Primary Contact: Gregory A. Banaszynski, Chief Executive Officer
CFO: Karen Bindl CPA, Controller
Web address: www.uwhealth.org
Control: Corporation, Investor–owned (for–profit) **Service**: Rehabilitation

Staffed Beds: 35 **Admissions:** 815 **Census:** 28 **Outpatient Visits:** 0 **Births:** 0 **Total Expense ($000):** 15384 **Payroll Expense ($000):** 4627 **Personnel:** 133	

⊞ **WILLIAM S. MIDDLETON MEMORIAL VETERANS HOSPITAL**, 2500 Overlook Terrace, Zip 53705–2286; tel. 608/256–1901, (Nonreporting) **A**1 3 5 **S** Department of Veterans Affairs, Washington, DC
Primary Contact: John J. Rohrer, Director
CFO: Evarista Mikell, Assistant Finance Officer
CMO: Alan J Bridges M.D., Chief of Staff
CIO: Randall Margenau, Chief Information Officer
CHR: Stuart Souders, Chief, Human Resources
CNO: Rebecca Kordahl R.N., Associate Director, Patient Care Services
Web address: www.madison.va.gov
Control: Veterans Affairs, Government, federal **Service**: General medical and surgical

Staffed Beds: 87	

WI

MANITOWOC—Manitowoc County

✠ **HOLY FAMILY MEMORIAL (520107)**, 2300 Western Avenue, Zip 54220–3712, Mailing Address: P.O.Box 1450, 54221–1450; tel. 920/320–2011 **A**1 2 10 **F**3 5 8 11 13 15 17 20 22 26 28 29 30 31 34 36 40 43 45 46 47 48 49 50 51 53 54 56 57 58 59 62 63 64 65 68 70 75 76 77 78 79 80 81 82 85 86 89 93 97 104 107 108 110 111 115 118 119 121 130 132 135 146 148 149 **P**6 **S** Franciscan Sisters of Christian Charity Sponsored Ministries, Inc., Manitowoc, WI
Primary Contact: Mark P. Herzog, President and Chief Executive Officer
COO: Jane Curran–Meuli, Chief Operating Officer
CFO: Patricia Huettl, Vice President Finance and Chief Financial Officer
CMO: Steve Driggers M.D., Chief Medical Officer
CIO: Theron Pappas, Director Management Information Systems
CHR: Laura M Fielding, Administrative Director Organizational Development
CNO: Bonny Range MSN, Chief Nursing Officer
Web address: www.hfmhealth.org
Control: Church operated, Nongovernment, not–for–profit **Service:** General medical and surgical

Staffed Beds: 60 **Admissions:** 2500 **Census:** 23 **Outpatient Visits:** 223707 **Births:** 209 **Total Expense ($000):** 122657 **Payroll Expense ($000):** 62871 **Personnel:** 685

MARINETTE—Marinette County

✠ **BAY AREA MEDICAL CENTER (520113)**, 3100 Shore Drive, Zip 54143–4242; tel. 715/735–6621 **A**1 10 20 **F**3 7 11 13 15 17 18 20 22 28 29 30 31 34 40 43 44 45 48 50 51 54 57 59 70 74 75 76 77 78 79 80 81 82 85 86 87 89 93 96 107 108 110 111 114 115 119 121 124 130 131 143 146 147 148 **P**8
Primary Contact: Edward A. Harding, FACHE, President and Chief Executive Officer
COO: Bernie VanCourt, Chief Operating Officer
CFO: Matt Huff, Chief Financial Officer
CMO: Richard Stein M.D., Chief Medical Officer
CIO: Pete Eisenzoph, Director Information Technology
CHR: Ken Joyner, Vice President of Employee Services
CNO: Bernie VanCourt, Interim Chief Nursing Officer
Web address: www.bamc.org
Control: Other not–for–profit (including NFP Corporation) **Service:** General medical and surgical

Staffed Beds: 55 **Admissions:** 2934 **Census:** 27 **Outpatient Visits:** 125674 **Births:** 271 **Total Expense ($000):** 109277 **Payroll Expense ($000):** 45401 **Personnel:** 511

MARSHFIELD—Wood County

✠ △ **MARSHFIELD MEDICAL CENTER (520037)**, 611 St Joseph Avenue, Zip 54449–1898; tel. 715/387–1713, (Includes MARSHFIELD CHILDEN'S HOSPITAL, 611 Saint Joseph Avenue, Marshfield, Wisconsin, Zip 54449–1832, tel. 715/387–1713) **A**1 2 3 5 7 10 20 **F**3 5 6 7 9 11 12 13 16 17 18 19 20 22 24 26 27 28 29 30 31 34 35 36 38 40 41 43 44 49 50 52 55 61 64 68 69 70 72 74 75 76 77 78 79 80 81 82 83 84 85 86 87 88 89 90 93 96 98 100 101 102 103 108 111 116 117 118 119 120 121 123 124 126 127 130 132 135 136 144 146 147 148 149 **S** Marshfield Clinic Health System, Marshfield, WI
Primary Contact: Edward H. Wolf, Chief Administrative Officer
CFO: William J Hinner, Vice President Financial Analysis and Planning Ministry Health Care
CMO: Peter Stamas M.D., Vice President Medical Affairs
CIO: Will Weider, Chief Information Officer
CHR: Cheryl F Zima, Vice President Human Resources Ministry Health Care
CNO: Robin Kretschman MSN, R.N., Vice President Patient Care Services
Web address: www.stjosephs–marshfield.org
Control: Church operated, Nongovernment, not–for–profit **Service:** General medical and surgical

Staffed Beds: 200 **Admissions:** 11964 **Census:** 179 **Outpatient Visits:** 52081 **Births:** 1100 **Total Expense ($000):** 277928 **Payroll Expense ($000):** 91931 **Personnel:** 1076

NORWOOD HEALTH CENTER (524019), 1600 North Chestnut Avenue, Zip 54449–1499; tel. 715/384–2188, (Total facility includes 24 beds in nursing home–type unit) **A**10 **F**3 4 30 69 75 98 99 100 101 102 103 104 106 128 130 143 146 148 **P**6
Primary Contact: Jordan Bruce, Administrator
CFO: Jo Timmerman, Manager Accounting
CHR: Larry Shear, Administrative Assistant
Web address: www.co.wood.wi.us/norwood/index.htm
Control: County, Government, Nonfederal **Service:** Psychiatric

Staffed Beds: 40 **Admissions:** 629 **Census:** 31 **Outpatient Visits:** 0 **Births:** 0 **Total Expense ($000):** 3952 **Payroll Expense ($000):** 1456 **Personnel:** 37

MAUSTON—Juneau County

☐ **MILE BLUFF MEDICAL CENTER (520109)**, 1050 Division Street, Zip 53948–1997; tel. 608/847–6161, (Total facility includes 105 beds in nursing home–type unit) **A**1 10 20 **F**3 10 11 13 15 18 28 29 30 31 34 35 36 40 43 44 45 46 50 56 57 59 60 62 65 66 68 69 71 75 76 77 78 79 80 81 82 85 86 87 89 92 93 94 96 97 107 108 110 111 112 114 115 117 118 119 125 127 128 129 130 131 132 135 143 144 145 146
Primary Contact: James M. O'Keefe, President and Chief Executive Officer
Web address: www.milebluff.com
Control: Other not–for–profit (including NFP Corporation) **Service:** General medical and surgical

Staffed Beds: 113 **Admissions:** 1324 **Census:** 113 **Outpatient Visits:** 170950 **Births:** 162 **Total Expense ($000):** 74013 **Payroll Expense ($000):** 38864 **Personnel:** 496

MEDFORD—Taylor County

✠ **ASPIRUS MEDFORD HOSPITAL & CLINICS, INC. (521324)**, 135 South Gibson Street, Zip 54451–1696; tel. 715/748–8100, (Total facility includes 109 beds in nursing home–type unit) **A**1 10 18 **F**1 3 8 10 11 13 15 18 28 29 32 34 36 40 41 43 50 53 55 56 57 58 59 60 64 65 68 75 76 77 78 81 82 85 86 87 89 90 93 97 107 110 111 115 116 118 119 125 127 128 129 130 131 132 133 135 144 146 147 148 **S** Aspirus, Inc., Wausau, WI
Primary Contact: Rick L. Nevers, Interim Chief Executive Officer
CFO: Greg Shaw, Vice President, Finance
CMO: Erik Branstetter M.D., Chief Medical Officer
CIO: Todd Richardson, Chief Information Officer
CHR: Angela C. Hupf, Vice President Human Resources and Community Relations
CNO: Barb Lato, Chief Nursing Officer
Web address: www.aspirus.org
Control: Other not–for–profit (including NFP Corporation) **Service:** General medical and surgical

Staffed Beds: 124 **Admissions:** 973 **Census:** 78 **Outpatient Visits:** 79487 **Births:** 285 **Total Expense ($000):** 58974 **Payroll Expense ($000):** 24655 **Personnel:** 328

MENOMONEE FALLS—Waukesha County

✠ △ **COMMUNITY MEMORIAL HOSPITAL (520103)**, W180 N8085 Town Hall Road, Zip 53051–3518, Mailing Address: P.O.Box 408, 53052–0408; tel. 262/251–1000 **A**1 2 3 7 10 **F**3 5 9 11 13 15 18 20 22 24 26 28 29 30 31 34 35 36 38 40 42 44 45 46 47 49 50 51 56 57 59 60 64 65 66 68 72 74 75 76 77 78 79 80 81 82 84 85 86 87 90 93 96 97 98 100 101 102 103 104 107 108 110 111 114 115 116 117 118 119 120 121 123 126 129 130 131 132 135 145 146 147 148 149 150
Primary Contact: Teri Lux, President
COO: Allen Ericson, Chief Operating Officer, Community Hospital Division and President, St. Joseph's Hospital
CFO: Scott Hawig, Senior Vice President of Finance, Chief Financial Officer and Treasurer
CMO: David Goldberg M.D., Vice President Medical Affairs and Chief Medical Officer
CIO: William Showalter, Senior Vice President Information Systems, Chief Information Officer
CHR: Keith Allen, Senior Vice President and Chief Human Resources Officer
Web address: www.communitymemorial.com
Control: Other not–for–profit (including NFP Corporation) **Service:** General medical and surgical

Staffed Beds: 198 **Admissions:** 7990 **Census:** 93 **Outpatient Visits:** 89551 **Births:** 907 **Total Expense ($000):** 190095 **Payroll Expense ($000):** 65748 **Personnel:** 1074

MENOMONIE—Dunn County

☐ **MAYO CLINIC HEALTH SYSTEM – RED CEDAR IN MENOMONIE (521340)**, 2321 Stout Road, Zip 54751–2397; tel. 715/235–5531 **A**1 10 18 **F**3 8 11 13 15 17 18 28 29 30 31 32 34 35 36 40 43 44 45 53 54 55 56 57 59 60 64 65 70 75 76 77 78 79 80 81 82 84 85 86 87 89 90 93 97 99 100 101 102 103 104 107 108 110 111 115 119 127 129 130 131 132 133 135 144 146 147 148 149 **P**6 **S** Mayo Clinic, Rochester, MN
Primary Contact: Steven Lindberg, Chief Administrative Officer
CFO: Jeanie Lubinsky, Chief Financial Officer
CMO: Mark Deyo Svendsen M.D., Medical Director
CIO: Frank Wrogg, Director Information Technology
CHR: Leann Wurtzel, Director Human Resources
Web address: www.rcmc–mhs.org
Control: Other not–for–profit (including NFP Corporation) **Service:** General medical and surgical

Staffed Beds: 25 **Admissions:** 1241 **Census:** 12 **Outpatient Visits:** 110067 **Births:** 303 **Total Expense ($000):** 76361 **Payroll Expense ($000):** 37605 **Personnel:** 416

WI

Many Facility Codes have changed. Please refer to the AHA Guide Code Chart. © 2017 AHA Guide

RED CEDAR MEDICAL CENTER–MAYO HEALTH SYSTEM See Mayo Clinic Health System – Red Cedar In Menomonie

MEQUON—Ozaukee County

COLUMBIA CENTER BIRTH HOSPITAL (520195), 13125 North Port Washington Road, Zip 53097–2416; tel. 262/243–7408 **A**10 **F**3 13 30 34 64 76 81 85 86 87 104 132
Primary Contact: Candy J. Casey, R.N., MS, President and Chief Executive Officer
CMO: Daniel Hagerman M.D., President Medical Staff
Web address: www.columbiacenter.org
Control: Other not–for–profit (including NFP Corporation) **Service:** General medical and surgical

Staffed Beds: 6 **Admissions:** 563 **Census:** 4 **Outpatient Visits:** 358 **Births:** 559 **Total Expense ($000):** 6502 **Payroll Expense ($000):** 3040 **Personnel:** 49	

COLUMBIA ST. MARY'S OZAUKEE HOSPITAL (520027), 13111 North Port Washington Road, Zip 53097–2416; tel. 262/243–7300 **A**1 2 10 **F**4 5 9 15 17 20 22 24 28 29 34 36 38 40 43 51 53 54 56 64 70 75 77 78 80 81 86 89 90 93 98 100 102 103 107 108 111 116 118 119 130 144 147 **P**6 **S** Ascension Healthcare, Saint Louis, MO
Primary Contact: Bev Weber, Interim President
CFO: Rhonda Anderson, Executive Vice President Finance and Chief Financial Officer
CMO: David Shapiro M.D., Vice President Medical Affairs and Chief Medical Officer
CIO: Mary Paul, Chief Information Officer
CHR: Cheryl Hill, Vice President Human Resources
Web address: www.columbia-stmarys.org
Control: Church operated, Nongovernment, not–for–profit **Service:** General medical and surgical

Staffed Beds: 115 **Admissions:** 5053 **Census:** 61 **Outpatient Visits:** 291565 **Births:** 0 **Total Expense ($000):** 145956 **Payroll Expense ($000):** 54165 **Personnel:** 755	

MERRILL—Lincoln County

GOOD SAMARITAN HEALTH CENTER OF MERRILL See Ministry Good Samaritan Health Center

MINISTRY GOOD SAMARITAN HEALTH CENTER (521339), 601 South Center Avenue, Zip 54452–3404; tel. 715/536–5511 **A**1 10 18 **F**3 15 28 29 30 31 34 35 40 41 43 44 45 50 56 57 64 68 74 75 78 80 81 82 85 86 87 93 97 107 108 110 111 115 118 119 130 132 133 135 144 146 147 149 **P**2 **S** Ascension Healthcare, Saint Louis, MO
Primary Contact: Dawn Gapko, Chief Administrative Officer
CFO: David Jirovec, Director Finance
CHR: Nancy Kwiesielewicz, Human Resources Manager
CNO: Kristine McGarigle R.N., Vice President Patient Care
Web address: www.ministryhealth.org
Control: Church operated, Nongovernment, not–for–profit **Service:** General medical and surgical

Staffed Beds: 10 **Admissions:** 456 **Census:** 3 **Outpatient Visits:** 18034 **Births:** 0 **Total Expense ($000):** 22837 **Payroll Expense ($000):** 10574 **Personnel:** 82	

MILWAUKEE—Milwaukee County

★ △ **AURORA SINAI MEDICAL CENTER (520064)**, 945 North 12th Street, Zip 53233–1337, Mailing Address: P.O.Box 342, 53201–0342; tel. 414/219–2000 **A**2 3 5 7 8 **F**3 6 11 12 13 15 18 20 22 26 29 30 31 32 34 35 36 37 38 40 44 45 46 47 49 50 51 54 56 57 59 60 62 64 65 66 72 74 75 76 77 78 79 80 81 82 84 85 86 87 89 90 91 92 93 94 96 102 103 107 108 110 111 114 119 123 126 129 130 131 132 135 144 146 147 148 149 **P**6 **S** Aurora Health Care, Milwaukee, WI
Primary Contact: Jessica Bauer, Chief Executive Officer
CHR: Heidi Grow, Director Human Resources
CNO: Ania Horner R.N., Vice President and Chief Nurse Executive
Web address: www.aurorahealthcare.org
Control: Other not–for–profit (including NFP Corporation) **Service:** General medical and surgical

Staffed Beds: 202 **Admissions:** 7891 **Census:** 107 **Outpatient Visits:** 255441 **Births:** 2090 **Total Expense ($000):** 189183 **Payroll Expense ($000):** 66168 **Personnel:** 1066	

⊞ △ **AURORA ST. LUKE'S MEDICAL CENTER (520138)**, 2900 West Oklahoma Avenue, Zip 53215–4330, Mailing Address: P.O.Box 2901, 53201–2901; tel. 414/649–6000, (Includes AURORA ST. LUKE'S SOUTH SHORE, 5900 South Lake Drive, Cudahy, Wisconsin, Zip 53110–8903, tel. 414/769–9000) **A**1 2 3 5 7 8 10 **F**1 3 4 5 11 12 15 17 18 19 20 22 24 26 28 29 30 31 34 35 36 37 38 40 41 43 44 45 46 47 49 50 51 54 56 57 58 59 60 64 65 66 68 70 74 75 78 79 80 81 82 84 85 86 87 89 90 91 92 93 94 96 98 100 101 102 103 104 105 107 108 110 111 114 115 116 117 118 119 120 121 123 124 126 129 130 131 132 134 135 136 137 138 139 140 142 143 144 145 146 147 148 149 **P**6 **S** Aurora Health Care, Milwaukee, WI
Primary Contact: Marie Golanowski, R.N., MS, President
CFO: Nan Nelson, Senior Vice President Finance
CMO: Jeffrey A. Smith M.D., Senior Vice President and Chief Medical Officer
CIO: Philip Loftus Ph.D., Vice President and Chief Information Officer
CHR: Thomas C Ter Horst, Vice President Human Resources
CNO: Faye Zwieg, Vice President and Chief Nursing Officer
Web address: www.aurorahealthcare.org
Control: Other not–for–profit (including NFP Corporation) **Service:** General medical and surgical

Staffed Beds: 723 **Admissions:** 35739 **Census:** 569 **Outpatient Visits:** 573750 **Births:** 0 **Total Expense ($000):** 1066759 **Payroll Expense ($000):** 307853 **Personnel:** 5061	

⊞ **CHILDREN'S HOSPITAL OF WISCONSIN (523300)**, 9000 West Wisconsin Avenue, Zip 53226–4810, Mailing Address: P.O.Box 1997, 53201–1997; tel. 414/266–2000 **A**1 3 5 10 **F**12 20 22 24 28 29 34 36 38 40 43 51 54 60 61 64 72 75 77 78 81 82 86 87 88 89 93 99 100 104 107 108 111 118 119 130 131 136 137 138 140 141 **P**2 **S** Children's Hospital and Health System, Milwaukee, WI
Primary Contact: Peggy N. Troy, President and Chief Executive Officer
CFO: Marc Cadieux, Corporate Vice President and Chief Financial Officer
CMO: Michael Gutzeit M.D., Chief Medical Officer
CIO: Michael B Nauman, Chief Information Officer
CHR: Thomas Shanahan, Vice President, Human Resources
CNO: Nancy K Korom, Chief Nursing Officer and Vice President
Web address: www.chw.org
Control: Other not–for–profit (including NFP Corporation) **Service:** Children's general medical and surgical

Staffed Beds: 176 **Admissions:** 8425 **Census:** 176 **Outpatient Visits:** 355761 **Births:** 0 **Total Expense ($000):** 546350 **Payroll Expense ($000):** 168525 **Personnel:** 2473	

⊞ △ **CLEMENT J. ZABLOCKI VETERANS AFFAIRS MEDICAL CENTER**, 5000 West National Avenue, Zip 53295–0001; tel. 414/384–2000, (Nonreporting) **A**1 2 3 5 7 **S** Department of Veterans Affairs, Washington, DC
Primary Contact: Daniel Zomchek, Ph.D., Executive Director
COO: James McClain, Deputy Director
CFO: John Lasota, Assistant Finance Officer
CMO: Michael Erdmann M.D., Chief of Staff
CIO: Bryan Vail, Chief Information Officer
CHR: Kay Schwieger, Chief Human Resources Officer
CNO: Mary E. Brunn R.N., Acting Associate Director Nursing
Web address: www.milwaukee.va.gov/
Control: Veterans Affairs, Government, federal **Service:** General medical and surgical

Staffed Beds: 637	

⊞ **COLUMBIA ST. MARY'S HOSPITAL MILWAUKEE (520051)**, 2301 North Lake Drive, Zip 53211–4508; tel. 414/291–1000, (Includes COLUMBIA ST. MARY'S COLUMBIA HOSPITAL, 2025 East Newport Avenue, Milwaukee, Wisconsin, Zip 53211–2990, tel. 414/961–3300; COLUMBIA ST. MARY'S MILWAUKEE HOSPITAL, 2323 North Lake Drive, Milwaukee, Wisconsin, Zip 53211–9682, P O Box 503, 53201–0503, tel. 414/291–1000) **A**1 2 3 5 10 **F** 3 4 5 12 13 20 24 29 36 38 39 40 43 51 53 54 75 77 78 102 103 104 108 111 116 118 119 130 144 147 **S** Ascension Healthcare, Saint Louis, MO
Primary Contact: Kelly Elkins, President
CFO: Rhonda Anderson, Executive Vice President Finance and Chief Financial Officer
CMO: David Shapiro M.D., Vice President Medical Affairs and Chief Medical Officer
CIO: Mary Paul, Chief Information Officer
CHR: Cheryl Hill, Vice President Human Resources
Web address: www.columbia–stmarys.org
Control: Church operated, Nongovernment, not–for–profit **Service:** General medical and surgical

Staffed Beds: 244 **Admissions:** 12004 **Census:** 160 **Outpatient Visits:** 747636 **Births:** 2750 **Total Expense ($000):** 471136 **Payroll Expense ($000):** 176509 **Personnel:** 2173	

WI

Hospital, Medicare Provider Number, Address, Telephone, Approval, Facility, and Physician Codes, Health Care System

★ American Hospital Association (AHA) membership
□ The Joint Commission accreditation
○ Healthcare Facilities Accreditation Program
◇ DNV Healthcare Inc. accreditation
⇑ Center for Improvement in Healthcare Quality Accreditation
△ Commission on Accreditation of Rehabilitation Facilities (CARF) accreditation

✠ △ **FROEDTERT MEMORIAL LUTHERAN HOSPITAL (520177)**, 9200 West Wisconsin Avenue, Zip 53226–3596, Mailing Address: P.O.Box 26099, 53226–0099; tel. 414/805–3000 **A**1 2 3 5 7 8 10 **F**3 6 9 12 13 15 17 18 20 22 24 26 29 30 31 34 35 37 38 40 43 44 45 46 47 48 49 50 51 52 54 55 56 57 58 59 60 61 64 68 70 74 75 76 77 78 79 80 81 84 85 86 87 90 91 92 93 94 95 96 97 100 107 108 110 111 113 114 115 116 117 118 119 120 121 123 124 126 129 130 131 132 134 135 136 137 138 139 140 141 142 145 146 147 148 149 150
Primary Contact: Catherine Buck, President
CFO: Scott Hawig, Senior Vice President Finance, Chief Financial Officer and Treasurer
CMO: Lee Biblo M.D., Chief Medical Officer
CIO: William Showalter, Senior Vice President and Chief Information Officer
CHR: Keith Allen, Senior Vice President and Chief Human Resources Officer
CNO: Kathleen Bechtel MSN, R.N., Vice President Patient Care Services and Chief Nursing Officer
Web address: www.froedtert.com
Control: Other not–for–profit (including NFP Corporation) **Service**: General medical and surgical

Staffed Beds: 536 **Admissions**: 26534 **Census**: 407 **Outpatient Visits**: 723228 **Births**: 2316 **Total Expense ($000)**: 1282213 **Payroll Expense ($000)**: 312556 **Personnel**: 5113

★ **MILWAUKEE COUNTY BEHAVIORAL HEALTH DIVISION (524001)**, 9455 Watertown Plank Road, Zip 53226–3559; tel. 414/257–6995 **A**3 5 10 **F**35 50 98 99 100 101 102 104 105 106 146 149 **P**6
Primary Contact: Alicia Modjeska, Interim Administrator
COO: Jennifer Bergersen, Interim Chief Operating Officer
CFO: Randy Oleszak, Director Fiscal Services
CMO: John Schneider M.D., Medical Director
CIO: Chris Lindberg, Chief Information Officer
CHR: Ara Garcia, Manager Human Resources
CNO: Nancy Ann Marigomen R.N., Director of Nursing
Web address: www.milwaukeecounty.org
Control: County, Government, Nonfederal **Service**: Psychiatric

Staffed Beds: 60 **Admissions**: 1300 **Census**: 49 **Outpatient Visits**: 9085 **Births**: 0 **Total Expense ($000)**: 181468 **Payroll Expense ($000)**: 30214 **Personnel**: 436

✠ △ **SACRED HEART REHABILITATION INSTITUTE (523025)**, 2323 North Lake Drive, Zip 53211–4508; tel. 414/585–1000 **A**1 7 10 **F**9 29 34 54 56 64 75 77 86 90 93 98 100 102 103 130 131 **P**6 **S** Ascension Healthcare, Saint Louis, MO
Primary Contact: Kelly Elkins, President and Chief Executive Officer
CFO: Rhonda Anderson, Executive Vice President Finance and Chief Financial Officer
CMO: David Shapiro M.D., Vice President Medical Affairs and Chief Medical Officer
CIO: Mary Paul, Vice President and Chief Information Officer
CHR: Cheryl Hill, Vice President Human Resources
Web address: www.columbia–stmarys.org/SHRI
Control: Church operated, Nongovernment, not–for–profit **Service**: Rehabilitation

Staffed Beds: 16 **Admissions**: 260 **Census**: 12 **Outpatient Visits**: 10383 **Births**: 0 **Total Expense ($000)**: 10783 **Payroll Expense ($000)**: 4578 **Personnel**: 73

✠ **SELECT SPECIALTY HOSPITAL–MILWAUKEE (522006)**, 8901 West Lincoln Avenue, 2nd Floor, Zip 53227–2409, Mailing Address: West Allis, tel. 414/328–7700 **A**1 10 **F**1 3 4 29 60 76 78 80 85 89 90 98 100 130 148 **P**2 **S** Select Medical Corporation, Mechanicsburg, PA
Primary Contact: Mary Kay. Diderrich, R.N., Chief Executive Officer
CMO: Matt Mathai M.D., Medical Director
CHR: Chris Froh, Senior Coordinator Human Resources
CNO: Jane Cerra, Market Nurse Executive and Chief Nursing Officer
Web address: www.selectspecialtyhospitals.com/company/locations/milwaukee.aspx
Control: Corporation, Investor–owned (for–profit) **Service**: Acute long–term care hospital

Staffed Beds: 34 **Admissions**: 505 **Census**: 49 **Outpatient Visits**: 0 **Births**: 0 **Total Expense ($000)**: 30617 **Payroll Expense ($000)**: 11041 **Personnel**: 185

✠ **WHEATON FRANCISCAN HEALTHCARE – ST. FRANCIS (520078)**, 3237 South 16th Street, Zip 53215; tel. 414/647–5000 **A**1 2 10 **F**3 9 13 15 18 20 22 24 26 28 29 30 31 38 40 45 46 47 48 49 50 54 56 64 68 72 74 75 76 77 78 79 80 81 82 85 86 87 92 93 97 98 100 101 102 103 104 107 108 109 110 111 114 115 117 118 121 122 123 124 129 130 131 132 144 145 146 147 148 149 **S** Ascension Healthcare, Saint Louis, MO
Primary Contact: Coreen Dicus–Johnson, President
CFO: Aaron Bridgeland, Director Finance
CMO: Michelle Graham M.D., Vice President Medical Affairs
CIO: Gregory Smith, Senior Vice President and Chief Information Officer
Web address: www.mywheaton.org/stfrancis
Control: Church operated, Nongovernment, not–for–profit **Service**: General medical and surgical

Staffed Beds: 167 **Admissions**: 7483 **Census**: 98 **Outpatient Visits**: 167359 **Births**: 747 **Total Expense ($000)**: 186609 **Payroll Expense ($000)**: 68200 **Personnel**: 1016

✠ **WHEATON FRANCISCAN HEALTHCARE – ST. JOSEPH'S (520136)**, 5000 West Chambers Street, Zip 53210–1650; tel. 414/447–2000 **A**1 3 5 10 **F**3 6 8 11 13 15 17 18 20 22 24 26 28 29 30 31 34 35 37 40 41 43 45 46 48 49 50 53 54 56 58 59 64 65 68 70 72 74 75 76 77 79 80 81 82 84 85 87 89 90 91 92 93 96 97 107 108 109 110 111 112 113 114 115 117 118 119 129 130 131 135 143 144 145 146 147 148 149 **S** Ascension Healthcare, Saint Louis, MO
Primary Contact: Debra K. Standridge, President
CFO: Michael Petitt, Director of Finance
CMO: Rita Hanson M.D., Vice President Medical Affairs
CIO: Andrew Donovan, Regional Director Information Services
CHR: Christopher Morris, Senior Director, Human Resources
Web address: www.mywheaton.org/stjoseph
Control: Church operated, Nongovernment, not–for–profit **Service**: General medical and surgical

Staffed Beds: 217 **Admissions**: 8274 **Census**: 115 **Outpatient Visits**: 309712 **Births**: 2604 **Total Expense ($000)**: 242828 **Payroll Expense ($000)**: 89115 **Personnel**: 1457

MONROE—Green County

☐ **MONROE CLINIC (520028)**, 515 22nd Avenue, Zip 53566–1598; tel. 608/324–2000 **A**1 3 10 13 **F**3 5 6 8 9 13 15 17 18 20 22 26 28 29 30 31 32 34 35 37 38 40 43 44 45 46 49 50 55 56 57 59 62 63 65 68 70 74 75 76 77 79 80 81 82 84 85 86 90 93 97 99 100 101 102 103 104 107 108 110 111 112 115 117 119 126 129 130 131 132 135 144 145 146 147 148 **P**6
Primary Contact: Michael B. Sanders, President and Chief Executive Officer
CFO: Jim Nemeth, Chief Financial Officer
CMO: Mark Thompson M.D., Chief Medical Officer
CIO: Carrie Blum, Chief Information Officer
CHR: Jane Monahan, Vice President Ministry, Spiritual Care and Human Resources
CNO: Paula Elmer R.N., MSN, Vice President and Chief Nursing Officer
Web address: www.monroeclinic.org
Control: Other not–for–profit (including NFP Corporation) **Service**: General medical and surgical

Staffed Beds: 58 **Admissions**: 2576 **Census**: 22 **Outpatient Visits**: 270403 **Births**: 479 **Total Expense ($000)**: 166824 **Payroll Expense ($000)**: 80888 **Personnel**: 959

NEENAH—Winnebago County

☐ **CHILDREN'S HOSPITAL OF WISCONSIN–FOX VALLEY (523302)**, 130 Second Street, Zip 54956–2883; tel. 920/969–7900 **A**1 10 **F**29 34 38 72 75 86 89 93 130 **S** Children's Hospital and Health System, Milwaukee, WI
Primary Contact: Peggy N. Troy, President and Chief Executive Officer
COO: Debra Franckowiak, Executive Director
CFO: Marc Cadieux, Corporate Vice President and Chief Financial Officer
CMO: Paul Myers M.D., Neonatologist and Chief Medical Officer
CIO: Michael B Nauman, Chief Information Officer and Corporate Vice President
CHR: Thomas Shanahan, Vice President, Human Resources
CNO: Nancy K Korom, Chief Nursing Officer and Vice President
Web address: www.chw.org
Control: Other not–for–profit (including NFP Corporation) **Service**: Children's general medical and surgical

Staffed Beds: 12 **Admissions**: 519 **Census**: 12 **Outpatient Visits**: 12954 **Births**: 0 **Total Expense ($000)**: 26456 **Payroll Expense ($000)**: 10073 **Personnel**: 129

WI

Many Facility Codes have changed. Please refer to the AHA Guide Code Chart. © 2017 AHA Guide

☐ **THEDACARE REGIONAL MEDICAL CENTER–NEENAH (520045)**, 130 Second Street, Zip 54956–2883, Mailing Address: P.O.Box 2021, 54957–2021; tel. 920/729–3100 **A**1 2 3 10 **F**4 5 7 9 11 12 13 15 17 20 22 28 29 34 36 40 43 51 53 55 56 60 64 69 70 75 76 78 80 82 86 87 88 90 93 98 99 101 102 103 104 105 107 108 111 118 119 130 144 147 **S** ThedaCare, Inc., Appleton, WI
Primary Contact: Brian Burmeister, Senior Vice President, ThedaCare Hospitals
CFO: Tim Olson, Senior Vice President Finance
CMO: Gregory L Long M.D., Chief Medical Officer
CIO: Keith Livingston, Senior Vice President and Chief Information Officer
CHR: Maureen Pistone, Senior Vice President Human Resources
Web address: www.thedacare.org
Control: Other not–for–profit (including NFP Corporation) **Service:** General medical and surgical

Staffed Beds: 151 **Admissions:** 7367 **Census:** 81 **Outpatient Visits:** 91415 **Births:** 1365 **Total Expense ($000):** 162745 **Payroll Expense ($000):** 63381 **Personnel:** 878

NEILLSVILLE—Clark County

★ **MEMORIAL MEDICAL CENTER – NEILLSVILLE (521323)**, 216 Sunset Place, Zip 54456–1799; tel. 715/743–3101 **A**10 18 **F**3 6 10 11 15 28 29 30 34 40 41 43 45 50 55 56 59 66 75 77 79 80 81 85 86 87 89 90 93 96 97 107 108 110 111 115 119 127 130 131 132 133 144 146 147 **P**6
Primary Contact: Ryan T. Neville, FACHE, President and Chief Executive Officer
CMO: Timothy Meyer M.D., Chief of Staff
CIO: Derrick Longdo, Director Information Systems
CHR: Tamie Zarak, Director Human Resources
Web address: www.memorialmedcenter.org
Control: Other not–for–profit (including NFP Corporation) **Service:** General medical and surgical

Staffed Beds: 29 **Admissions:** 318 **Census:** 15 **Outpatient Visits:** 22915 **Births:** 0 **Total Expense ($000):** 25284 **Payroll Expense ($000):** 12790 **Personnel:** 192

NEW LONDON—Outagamie County

☐ **THEDACARE MEDICAL CENTER–NEW LONDON (521326)**, 1405 Mill Street, Zip 54961–0307, Mailing Address: P.O.Box 307, 54961–0307; tel. 920/531–2000 **A**1 10 18 **F**7 11 13 15 28 29 34 40 43 56 64 75 76 80 81 82 86 87 89 90 93 107 108 111 119 131 141 **S** ThedaCare, Inc., Appleton, WI
Primary Contact: William Schmidt, President and Chief Executive Officer
CFO: Betty Gehring, Finance Director, Operations
CMO: Paul Hoell M.D., President Medical Staff
CNO: Peggy School, Director of Nursing
Web address: www.thedacare.org
Control: Other not–for–profit (including NFP Corporation) **Service:** General medical and surgical

Staffed Beds: 25 **Admissions:** 612 **Census:** 8 **Outpatient Visits:** 29121 **Births:** 97 **Total Expense ($000):** 23797 **Payroll Expense ($000):** 11014 **Personnel:** 141

NEW RICHMOND—St. Croix County

★ **WESTFIELDS HOSPITAL (521345)**, 535 Hospital Road, Zip 54017–1449; tel. 715/243–2600 **A**3 10 18 **F**1 3 13 15 28 29 30 31 32 34 35 38 40 43 44 45 47 50 56 57 59 64 68 70 74 75 76 77 78 79 80 81 82 84 86 87 89 90 93 94 97 104 107 109 110 111 115 117 119 129 130 131 132 133 143 145 146 148 149 **P**8 **S** HealthPartners, Bloomington, MN
Primary Contact: Steven Massey, President and Chief Executive Officer
CFO: Jason J. Luhrs, Vice President Fiscal Services
CMO: David O DeGear M.D., Vice President Medical Affairs
CIO: Patrice P Wolff, Director Information Services
CHR: Chad P Engstrom, Director Human Resources
Web address: www.westfieldshospital.com
Control: Other not–for–profit (including NFP Corporation) **Service:** General medical and surgical

Staffed Beds: 25 **Admissions:** 811 **Census:** 7 **Outpatient Visits:** 86325 **Births:** 132 **Total Expense ($000):** 51350 **Payroll Expense ($000):** 17561 **Personnel:** 271

OCONOMOWOC—Waukesha County

⊞ **OCONOMOWOC MEMORIAL HOSPITAL (520062)**, 791 Summit Avenue, Zip 53066–3896; tel. 262/569–9400 **A**1 2 10 **F**3 11 13 15 20 22 26 28 29 30 31 35 37 40 45 46 47 48 49 64 74 75 76 78 79 80 81 82 83 87 89 92 93 107 108 110 111 114 115 118 119 120 121 126 130 132 135 146 147 148 149 **S** ProHealth Care, Inc., Waukesha, WI
Primary Contact: Susan A. Edwards, Chief Executive Officer
COO: Mary Jo O'Malley R.N., MS, Vice President Diagnostics and Support Services
CMO: Brian Lipman M.D., Medical Director and Medical Staff Services
CIO: Christine Bessler, Vice President Information Services
CHR: Edward Malindzak, Chief Human Resources Officer
CNO: Catherine Rapp R.N., MS, Vice President Nursing
Web address: www.prohealthcare.org/locations/locations-v2-detail/?id=1123
Control: Other not–for–profit (including NFP Corporation) **Service:** General medical and surgical

Staffed Beds: 58 **Admissions:** 2996 **Census:** 23 **Outpatient Visits:** 69192 **Births:** 398 **Total Expense ($000):** 92324 **Payroll Expense ($000):** 21231 **Personnel:** 308

⊞ **ROGERS MEMORIAL HOSPITAL (524018)**, 34700 Valley Road, Zip 53066–4599; tel. 262/646–4411, (Includes ROGERS MEMORIAL HOSPITAL–BROWN DEER, 4600 West Schroeder Drive, Brown Deer, Wisconsin, Zip 53223, tel. 414/865–2500; Jim Kubicek, Vice President, Operations; ROGERS MEMORIAL HOSPITAL–WEST ALLIS, 11101 West Lincoln Avenue, West Allis, Wisconsin, Zip 53227, tel. 414/327–3000; T Orvin Fillman, Dr.PH, Vice President, Operations) **A**1 3 10 **F**5 29 34 38 75 86 87 98 99 100 101 102 103 104 105 130
Primary Contact: Paul A. Mueller, Chief Executive Officer
CFO: Gerald A Noll, Chief Financial Officer
CMO: Peter M Lake M.D., Chief Medical Officer
CIO: Wayne Mattson, Management Information Systems Specialist
CHR: Renee A. Patterson, Vice President Employment and Training Services
CNO: Teresa L Schultz R.N., Vice President of Patient Care
Web address: www.rogershospital.org
Control: Other not–for–profit (including NFP Corporation) **Service:** Psychiatric

Staffed Beds: 208 **Admissions:** 8692 **Census:** 147 **Outpatient Visits:** 113977 **Births:** 0 **Total Expense ($000):** 117329 **Payroll Expense ($000):** 75403

OCONTO—Oconto County

⇑ **BELLIN HEALTH OCONTO HOSPITAL (521356)**, 820 Arbutus Avenue, Zip 54153–2004, Mailing Address: P.O.Box 357, 54153–0357; tel. 920/835–1100 **A**10 18 21 **F**15 29 40 43 51 62 64 78 80 81 90 99 100 101 104 107 111 119 130 147 **P**8
Primary Contact: Laura Cormier, Director
CHR: Troy L Koebke, Human Resource Director
Web address: www.bellin.org/facilities_amenities/oconto_hospital_medical_center/
Control: Other not–for–profit (including NFP Corporation) **Service:** General medical and surgical

Staffed Beds: 10 **Admissions:** 151 **Census:** 1 **Outpatient Visits:** 16701 **Births:** 0 **Total Expense ($000):** 13697 **Payroll Expense ($000):** 5263 **Personnel:** 75

OCONTO FALLS—Oconto County

★ **HSHS ST. CLARE MEMORIAL HOSPITAL (521310)**, 855 South Main Street, Zip 54154–1296; tel. 920/846–3444 **A**10 18 **F**3 11 15 28 29 30 31 34 35 40 43 44 50 56 57 59 64 65 68 75 77 79 80 81 85 86 87 89 90 94 96 107 108 110 111 114 119 127 129 130 132 133 144 146 147 148 **P**2 5 **S** HSHS Hospital Sisters Health System, Springfield, IL
Primary Contact: Therese B. Pandl, President and Chief Executive Officer
COO: Daniel DeGroot, Chief Operating Officer
CFO: Greg Simia, Chief Financial Officer
CMO: Ken Johnson, Chief Physician Executive
CIO: Shane Miller, Chief Information Officer
CHR: Christine Jensema, Chief People Officer
CNO: Kay Baranczyk R.N., Chief Nursing Officer
Web address: www.cmhospital.org/index.html
Control: Church operated, Nongovernment, not–for–profit **Service:** General medical and surgical

Staffed Beds: 8 **Admissions:** 643 **Census:** 7 **Outpatient Visits:** 22882 **Births:** 0 **Total Expense ($000):** 32960 **Payroll Expense ($000):** 9319 **Personnel:** 117

WI

OSCEOLA—Polk County

★ **OSCEOLA MEDICAL CENTER (521318)**, 2600 65th Avenue, Zip 54020–4370, Mailing Address: P.O.Box 218, 54020–0218; tel. 715/294–2111 **A**10 18 **F**3 8 11 13 15 28 29 31 32 34 35 40 41 43 45 50 53 56 57 59 64 65 66 70 75 76 77 78 81 85 86 87 89 93 96 97 107 110 111 115 119 127 129 133 135 144 145 146 148 149 150 **P**6
Primary Contact: Tom G. Geskermann, Chief Executive Officer
CMO: Rene Milner, Chief Medical Officer
CIO: Shawn Kammerud, Manager Information Services
CHR: Margie Evenson, Manager Human Resources
Web address: www.osceolamedicalcenter.com
Control: Other not–for–profit (including NFP Corporation) **Service**: General medical and surgical

Staffed Beds: 18 **Admissions**: 486 **Census**: 5 **Outpatient Visits**: 16315 **Births**: 82 **Total Expense ($000)**: 33058 **Payroll Expense ($000)**: 11928 **Personnel**: 220

OSHKOSH—Winnebago County

✠ **AURORA MEDICAL CENTER OF OSHKOSH (520198)**, 855 North Westhaven Drive, Zip 54904–7668; tel. 920/456–6000 **A**1 2 10 **F**3 8 11 12 13 15 17 18 20 22 26 29 30 34 37 40 43 47 49 53 54 56 60 64 68 70 71 74 75 76 78 79 80 81 82 85 86 87 89 92 93 94 107 108 109 110 111 114 115 117 118 119 120 121 123 129 130 131 145 146 147 148 149 **P**6 **S** Aurora Health Care, Milwaukee, WI
Primary Contact: Jeffrey Bard, President
CFO: Sandra Ewald, Vice President Finance
CMO: Bruce L Van Cleave M.D., Senior Vice President and Chief Medical Officer
CIO: Philip Loftus Ph.D., Vice President and Chief Information Officer
CHR: Linda Mingus, Director Human Resources
CNO: Mary Beth Kingston R.N., MSN, Executive Vice President and Chief Nursing Officer
Web address: www.aurorahealthcare.com
Control: Other not–for–profit (including NFP Corporation) **Service**: General medical and surgical

Staffed Beds: 61 **Admissions**: 3312 **Census**: 29 **Outpatient Visits**: 137531 **Births**: 631 **Total Expense ($000)**: 103934 **Payroll Expense ($000)**: 30926 **Personnel**: 539

✠ △ **MERCY MEDICAL CENTER (520048)**, 500 South Oakwood Road, Zip 54904–7944; tel. 920/223–2000 **A**1 2 7 10 **F**3 4 5 11 13 15 16 17 18 20 22 26 28 29 30 31 34 35 38 40 43 44 46 47 48 49 50 51 53 56 57 59 64 65 68 70 75 76 78 79 80 81 82 84 85 86 87 88 90 92 93 96 98 103 104 107 108 110 111 112 114 117 119 120 121 122 123 126 129 130 131 132 134 144 146 147 148 149 **S** Ascension Healthcare, Saint Louis, MO
Primary Contact: Denise Parrish, Interim Chief Administrative Officer
CFO: Jeff Badger, Chief Financial Officer
CMO: Mark W Kehrberg M.D., Senior Vice President and Chief Medical Officer
CIO: Will Weider, Chief Information Officer
CHR: Vince Gallucci, Senior Vice President Human Resources
Web address: www.affinityhealth.org
Control: Church operated, Nongovernment, not–for–profit **Service**: General medical and surgical

Staffed Beds: 120 **Admissions**: 4536 **Census**: 47 **Outpatient Visits**: 133153 **Births**: 596 **Total Expense ($000)**: 99128 **Payroll Expense ($000)**: 36514 **Personnel**: 432

OSSEO—Trempealeau County

☐ **MAYO CLINIC HEALTH SYSTEM – OAKRIDGE IN OSSEO (521302)**, 13025 Eighth Street, Zip 54758–7634, Mailing Address: P.O.Box 70, 54758–0070; tel. 715/597–3121 **A**1 10 18 **F**3 15 18 28 29 30 32 34 35 40 43 44 45 53 54 56 57 59 64 65 75 77 80 84 85 86 87 90 93 97 107 110 115 130 132 133 135 143 144 146 148 149 **P**6 **S** Mayo Clinic, Rochester, MN
Primary Contact: Dean Eide, Vice President
Web address: www.mayoclinichealthsystem.org/locations/osseo
Control: Other not–for–profit (including NFP Corporation) **Service**: General medical and surgical

Staffed Beds: 18 **Admissions**: 354 **Census**: 12 **Outpatient Visits**: 26468 **Births**: 0 **Total Expense ($000)**: 22494 **Payroll Expense ($000)**: 11111 **Personnel**: 162

PARK FALLS—Price County

★ **FLAMBEAU HOSPITAL (521325)**, 98 Sherry Avenue, Zip 54552–1467, Mailing Address: P.O.Box 310, 54552–0310; tel. 715/762–2484 **A**10 18 **F**11 15 28 29 34 40 53 56 62 63 64 69 75 77 80 81 82 86 87 89 90 93 107 108 119 130 131 **S** Marshfield Clinic Health System, Marshfield, WI
Primary Contact: James R. Braun, Chief Administrative Officer and Chief Financial Officer
CMO: Yusuf Kasirye M.D., Chief of Staff
CHR: Elizabeth Harrop, Director, Human Resources
CNO: Elizabeth Schreiber R.N., Director Patient Care Services
Web address: www.flambeauhospital.org
Control: Other not–for–profit (including NFP Corporation) **Service**: General medical and surgical

Staffed Beds: 25 **Admissions**: 622 **Census**: 5 **Outpatient Visits**: 27314 **Births**: 0 **Total Expense ($000)**: 20958 **Payroll Expense ($000)**: 8869 **Personnel**: 177

PEWAUKEE—Waukesha County

✠ **LIFECARE HOSPITALS OF WISCONSIN (522007)**, 2400 Golf Road, Zip 53072–5590; tel. 262/524–2600 **A**1 10 **F**1 29 34 77 86 90 107 130 **S** LifeCare Management Services, Plano, TX
Primary Contact: David Chaudier, Chief Executive Officer
CMO: John Daniels M.D., Medical Director
CHR: Stephanie Matter, Manager Human Resources
CNO: Angela Osowski, Chief Nursing Officer
Web address: www.lifecare–hospitals.com
Control: Corporation, Investor–owned (for–profit) **Service**: Acute long–term care hospital

Staffed Beds: 24 **Admissions**: 429 **Census**: 24 **Outpatient Visits**: 0 **Births**: 0 **Total Expense ($000)**: 18735 **Payroll Expense ($000)**: 9219 **Personnel**: 148

PLATTEVILLE—Grant County

✠ **SOUTHWEST HEALTH (521354)**, 1400 Eastside Road, Zip 53818–9800; tel. 608/348–2331, (Includes SOUTHWEST HEALTH CENTER NURSING HOME, 808 South Washington Street, Cuba City, Wisconsin, Zip 53807, tel. 608/744–2161) (Total facility includes 78 beds in nursing home–type unit) **A**1 10 18 **F**2 3 6 7 8 13 15 28 29 34 40 43 45 46 47 48 49 50 56 57 58 59 64 65 74 75 76 77 79 80 81 82 83 84 85 86 87 93 96 97 98 100 101 102 103 104 105 106 107 110 111 112 115 119 127 128 129 130 131 132 133 143 144 146 147 148 149
Primary Contact: Dan D. Rohrbach, President and Chief Executive Officer
CFO: Matthew Streeter, Chief Financial Officer
CMO: Andrew Klann D.O., Chief of Staff
CIO: Todd Lull, Director Information Technology
CHR: Holly Beehn, Director Human Resources
CNO: Suzi Okey, Director of Nursing
Web address: www.southwesthealth.org
Control: Other not–for–profit (including NFP Corporation) **Service**: General medical and surgical

Staffed Beds: 113 **Admissions**: 961 **Census**: 86 **Outpatient Visits**: 51541 **Births**: 198 **Total Expense ($000)**: 24278 **Payroll Expense ($000)**: 12753 **Personnel**: 297

PLEASANT PRAIRIE—Kenosha County

★ **UNITED HOSPITAL SYSTEM, ST. CATHERINE'S MEDICAL CENTER CAMPUS**, 9555 76th Street, Zip 53158–1984; tel. 262/656–2011, (Nonreporting) **S** Ascension Healthcare, Saint Louis, MO
Primary Contact: Richard O. Schmidt Jr, President and Chief Executive Officer
Web address: www.uhsi.org
Control: Other not–for–profit (including NFP Corporation) **Service**: General medical and surgical

Staffed Beds: 202

PORTAGE—Columbia County

☐ **DIVINE SAVIOR HEALTHCARE (520041)**, 2817 New Pinery Road, Zip 53901–9240, Mailing Address: P.O.Box 387, 53901–0387; tel. 608/742–4131, (Total facility includes 123 beds in nursing home–type unit) **A**1 3 10 **F**3 4 7 8 11 12 13 15 28 30 31 34 35 36 40 43 54 55 57 58 59 60 62 64 65 69 70 75 76 77 78 79 80 81 82 85 86 87 90 92 93 96 97 107 108 110 111 114 115 118 119 128 129 130 131 132 133 144 145 146 147 **P**6
Primary Contact: Michael Decker, President and Chief Executive Officer
CFO: Marlin Pete Nelson, Vice President Fiscal Services
CMO: Elizabeth Strabel M.D., Chief Medical Staff
CHR: Carol J Bank, Vice President Human Resources
Web address: www.dshealthcare.com
Control: Church operated, Nongovernment, not–for–profit **Service**: General medical and surgical

Staffed Beds: 133 **Admissions**: 2079 **Census**: 114 **Outpatient Visits**: 168837 **Births**: 223 **Total Expense ($000)**: 78139 **Payroll Expense ($000)**: 41658 **Personnel**: 672

WI

Many Facility Codes have changed. Please refer to the AHA Guide Code Chart. © 2017 AHA Guide

PRAIRIE DU CHIEN—Crawford County

CROSSING RIVERS HEALTH MEDICAL CENTER (521330), 37868 US Highway 18, Zip 53821–8416; tel. 608/357–2000 **A**1 10 18 **F**10 11 13 15 28 29 30 31 34 35 36 40 41 50 53 56 57 59 62 63 64 65 68 75 76 77 81 82 83 84 86 87 93 97 104 107 110 111 115 117 119 129 130 131 132 133 135 144 146 147 148
Primary Contact: William P. Sexton, Chief Executive Officer
CFO: Dave Breitbach, Chief Financial Officer
CMO: Steven Bush, Chief Medical Officer
CIO: John Daane, Information Systems Officer
CHR: Samantha Donahue, Director Human Resources
Web address: www.crossingrivers.org
Control: Other not–for–profit (including NFP Corporation) **Service:** General medical and surgical

Staffed Beds: 18 **Admissions:** 1009 **Census:** 10 **Outpatient Visits:** 8775 **Births:** 130 **Total Expense ($000):** 45815 **Payroll Expense ($000):** 20631 **Personnel:** 312

PRAIRIE DU SAC—Sauk County

SAUK PRAIRIE HEALTHCARE (520095), 260 26th Street, Zip 53578–1599; tel. 608/643–3311 **A**3 10 11 **F**3 4 8 11 13 15 29 36 38 40 43 47 48 53 54 55 56 69 75 76 77 79 80 81 82 85 86 89 90 97 102 107 108 110 111 115 118 119 127 129 130 131 132 133 135 144 146 147 **P**7
Primary Contact: Shawn Lerch, Chief Executive Officer
CFO: James Dregney, Vice President Finance and Operations, Chief Financial Officer
CMO: John McAuliffe M.D., Medical Director
CHR: Robbi E Bos, Vice President Human Resources
CNO: Denise Marie Cole–Ouzounian MSN, R.N., Vice President Patient Services
Web address: www.saukprairiehealthcare.org/
Control: Other not–for–profit (including NFP Corporation) **Service:** General medical and surgical

Staffed Beds: 36 **Admissions:** 1850 **Census:** 11 **Outpatient Visits:** 112379 **Births:** 332 **Total Expense ($000):** 84803 **Payroll Expense ($000):** 37998 **Personnel:** 476

RACINE—Racine County

WHEATON FRANCISCAN HEALTHCARE – ALL SAINTS (520096), 3801 Spring Street, Zip 53405–1690; tel. 262/687–4011, (Total facility includes 50 beds in nursing home–type unit) **A**1 2 7 10 **F**3 4 5 6 13 15 17 18 20 22 24 26 28 29 30 31 33 34 35 38 40 44 45 46 48 49 50 51 53 55 56 57 58 59 64 65 68 70 71 72 74 75 76 77 78 79 80 81 82 85 86 87 89 90 91 92 93 96 97 98 99 100 101 102 103 104 105 107 108 110 111 112 115 118 119 120 121 123 124 126 128 129 130 131 132 134 135 146 147 148 **P**6 **S** Ascension Healthcare, Saint Louis, MO
Primary Contact: Susan Boland, R.N., MSN, President and Chief Executive Officer
CFO: Jeanne Gramza, Director Finance
CMO: Jerry Hardacre M.D., Chief of Staff
CIO: Joanne Bisterfeldt, Chief Information Officer
CHR: Mary Jo Wodicka, Vice President Human Resources
CNO: Mary Elizabeth Ouimet MSN, R.N., Senior Vice President and Chief Nursing Officer
Web address: www.allsaintshealth.com
Control: Church operated, Nongovernment, not–for–profit **Service:** General medical and surgical

Staffed Beds: 350 **Admissions:** 12978 **Census:** 202 **Outpatient Visits:** 605075 **Births:** 1683 **Total Expense ($000):** 338273 **Payroll Expense ($000):** 122039 **Personnel:** 2703

REEDSBURG—Sauk County

REEDSBURG AREA MEDICAL CENTER (521351), 2000 North Dewey Street, Zip 53959–1097; tel. 608/524–6487 **A**1 10 18 **F**11 13 15 17 28 29 34 40 43 53 54 64 70 75 76 77 78 80 81 82 86 87 88 89 93 107 111 130 131 144 147
Primary Contact: Robert Van Meeteren, President and Chief Executive Officer
COO: Dale Turner, Chief Operating Officer
CFO: Barry Borchert, Vice President Finance
Web address: www.ramchealth.com
Control: Other not–for–profit (including NFP Corporation) **Service:** General medical and surgical

Staffed Beds: 25 **Admissions:** 1359 **Census:** 11 **Outpatient Visits:** 61424 **Births:** 278 **Total Expense ($000):** 66600 **Payroll Expense ($000):** 27219 **Personnel:** 451

RHINELANDER—Oneida County

MINISTRY SAINT MARY'S HOSPITALS (520019), 2251 North Shore Drive, Zip 54501–6710; tel. 715/361–2000, (Includes ST. MARY'S HOSPITAL, 1044 Kabel Avenue, Rhinelander, Wisconsin, Zip 54501, tel. 715/369–6600) **A**1 3 10 20 **F**3 4 5 13 15 18 28 29 30 31 34 35 40 44 45 49 50 54 57 59 64 65 68 74 75 76 77 78 79 80 81 82 84 85 86 87 89 91 92 93 94 96 98 99 100 101 103 104 107 108 110 111 115 116 117 119 120 121 123 130 131 132 144 146 148 149 **S** Ascension Healthcare, Saint Louis, MO
Primary Contact: Sandra L. Anderson, President and Chief Executive Officer
COO: Laurie Oungst, Vice President and Chief Operating Officer
CFO: Jamon Lamers, Director Finance
CMO: Dean Pollnow M.D., President Medical Staff
CIO: Howard Dobizl, Director Information Services for the Northern Region
CHR: Michelle Cornelius, Director Human Resources for the Northern Region
CNO: Ann Zenk, Vice President Patient Care Services
Web address: www.ministryhealth.org
Control: Church operated, Nongovernment, not–for–profit **Service:** General medical and surgical

Staffed Beds: 56 **Admissions:** 2949 **Census:** 28 **Outpatient Visits:** 113381 **Births:** 330 **Total Expense ($000):** 120744 **Payroll Expense ($000):** 60292 **Personnel:** 355

RICE LAKE—Barron County

LAKEVIEW MEDICAL CENTER (520011), 1700 West Stout Street, Zip 54868–5000; tel. 715/234–1515 **A**1 10 20 **F**3 7 11 13 15 22 26 28 29 31 34 40 41 43 44 45 50 51 53 56 57 59 60 62 63 64 65 68 70 75 76 77 78 80 81 82 85 86 89 93 107 110 111 115 119 130 132 135 146 147 **P**5 **S** Marshfield Clinic Health System, Marshfield, WI
Primary Contact: John L. Olson, M.D., Interim President and Chief Administrative Officer
COO: Cindy Arts–Strenke R.N., Chief Operating Officer and Chief Nursing Officer
CFO: Jacqueline Klein, Chief Financial Officer
CMO: John L. Olson M.D., Medical Director
CIO: Brad Gerrits, Director Information Systems
CHR: Kathy Mitchell, Director Human Resources
Web address: www.lakeviewmedical.com
Control: Other not–for–profit (including NFP Corporation) **Service:** General medical and surgical

Staffed Beds: 40 **Admissions:** 2282 **Census:** 17 **Outpatient Visits:** 114002 **Births:** 465 **Total Expense ($000):** 67892 **Payroll Expense ($000):** 23450 **Personnel:** 399

RICHLAND CENTER—Richland County

RICHLAND HOSPITAL (521341), 333 East Second Street, Zip 53581–1914; tel. 608/647–6321 **A**1 10 18 **F**3 12 13 15 28 31 34 35 37 40 43 49 50 56 57 59 64 65 68 70 75 76 78 79 80 81 85 86 89 92 93 97 107 110 115 119 127 129 130 131 132 133 135 143 146 148 149
Primary Contact: Bruce E. Roesler, FACHE, Chief Executive Officer
CFO: Karen Traynor, Chief Financial Officer
CMO: David May, Chief of Staff
CIO: Jerry Cooper, Manager Data Processing
CHR: Rhonda Sutton, Director Human Resources
CNO: Cindy Hanold, Chief Nursing Officer
Web address: www.richlandhospital.com
Control: Other not–for–profit (including NFP Corporation) **Service:** General medical and surgical

Staffed Beds: 25 **Admissions:** 1091 **Census:** 10 **Outpatient Visits:** 39931 **Births:** 158 **Total Expense ($000):** 36571 **Payroll Expense ($000):** 16000 **Personnel:** 255

WI

RIPON—Fond Du Lac County

☐ **RIPON MEDICAL CENTER (521321)**, 845 Parkside Street, Zip 54971–8505, Mailing Address: P.O.Box 390, 54971–0390; tel. 920/748–3101 **A**1 10 18 **F**3 11 13 15 17 18 28 29 30 31 32 34 35 40 43 44 45 50 51 53 57 59 66 68 69 70 75 76 77 79 80 81 82 85 86 87 88 89 93 96 97 107 108 109 110 111 114 118 119 130 131 132 133 134 135 143 144 146 147 148 149 150 **P**2 6
Primary Contact: Tami Schattschneider, Chief Operating Officer and Chief Nursing Officer
COO: Tami Schattschneider, Chief Operating Officer and Chief Nursing Officer
CFO: Bonnie Schmitz, Chief Financial Officer
CIO: Nancy Birschbach, Vice President and Chief Information Officer
CHR: Sue Edminster, Vice President Human Resources
CNO: Tami Schattschneider, Chief Operating Officer and Chief Nursing Officer
Web address: www.agnesian.com
Control: Church operated, Nongovernment, not–for–profit **Service**: General medical and surgical

Staffed Beds: 18 **Admissions**: 505 **Census**: 5 **Outpatient Visits**: 30661
Births: 47 **Total Expense ($000)**: 27236 **Payroll Expense ($000)**: 10700
Personnel: 123

RIVER FALLS—St. Croix County

☒ **RIVER FALLS AREA HOSPITAL (521349)**, 1629 East Division Street, Zip 54022–1571; tel. 715/425–6155 **A**1 2 10 18 **F**3 11 13 15 28 29 30 31 34 35 40 43 45 50 51 53 64 75 76 78 79 80 81 82 84 86 87 89 90 93 107 111 129 130 131 133 146 147 148 149 **S** Allina Health, Minneapolis, MN
Primary Contact: David R. Miller, President
COO: William Frommelt, Director Operations and Finance
CFO: William Frommelt, Director Operations and Finance
CHR: Kristen Novak, Manager Human Resources
Web address: www.allina.com
Control: Other not–for–profit (including NFP Corporation) **Service**: General medical and surgical

Staffed Beds: 12 **Admissions**: 843 **Census**: 7 **Outpatient Visits**: 22068
Births: 134 **Total Expense ($000)**: 36589 **Payroll Expense ($000)**: 13313
Personnel: 144

SHAWANO—Shawano County

☒ **THEDACARE MEDICAL CENTER–SHAWANO (521346)**, 100 County Road B, Zip 54166–2127; tel. 715/526–2111 **A**1 10 18 **F**11 13 15 28 29 34 40 53 64 75 76 77 78 80 81 82 86 87 90 102 107 108 111 119 130 131 147 **S** ThedaCare, Inc., Appleton, WI
Primary Contact: William Schmidt, Chief Executive Officer
CFO: Kerry Lee Blanke, Chief Financial Officer
CMO: Mindy Frimodig D.O., President Medical Staff ThedaCare Physicians Shawano
CIO: Jennifer Quinn, Quality and Safety Coordinator
CNO: Patricia A Angelucci MS, R.N., Director Patient Care Services
Web address: www.shawanomed.org
Control: Other not–for–profit (including NFP Corporation) **Service**: General medical and surgical

Staffed Beds: 22 **Admissions**: 1437 **Census**: 12 **Outpatient Visits**: 50161
Births: 260 **Total Expense ($000)**: 38699 **Payroll Expense ($000)**: 16954
Personnel: 232

SHEBOYGAN—Sheboygan County

☒ **AURORA SHEBOYGAN MEMORIAL MEDICAL CENTER (520035)**, 2629 North Seventh Street, Zip 53083–4998; tel. 920/451–5000 **A**1 2 10 **F**3 4 8 13 17 18 20 22 26 28 29 30 31 32 34 35 36 40 41 43 44 45 49 50 53 54 56 57 59 60 64 65 68 70 72 74 75 76 78 79 80 81 82 85 86 87 89 90 93 94 96 98 99 100 102 103 104 105 107 108 111 114 115 118 119 120 121 123 129 130 131 132 135 146 147 148 149 **P**6 **S** Aurora Health Care, Milwaukee, WI
Primary Contact: David Graebner, President
CFO: Pamela Ott, Vice President Finance
CMO: Andrea Gavin M.D., Chief Medical officer
CIO: Steve Serketich, Manager Information Services
CHR: Stacie A Schneider, Director Human Resources
CNO: Lori Knitt, Chief Nursing Officer
Web address: www.aurorahealthcare.org
Control: Other not–for–profit (including NFP Corporation) **Service**: General medical and surgical

Staffed Beds: 136 **Admissions**: 5534 **Census**: 52 **Outpatient Visits**: 95459
Births: 848 **Total Expense ($000)**: 124112 **Payroll Expense ($000)**: 37357
Personnel: 621

☒ **HSHS ST. NICHOLAS HOSPITAL (520044)**, 3100 Superior Avenue, Zip 53081–1948; tel. 920/459–8300 **A**1 2 10 **F**3 8 11 13 15 17 18 20 22 28 29 30 31 34 35 36 38 40 43 44 45 47 49 50 53 57 59 60 62 63 64 65 70 71 74 75 76 79 80 81 84 85 86 87 89 90 92 93 107 108 110 111 115 116 117 118 119 120 121 123 129 130 132 146 148 **P**2 **S** HSHS Hospital Sisters Health System, Springfield, IL
Primary Contact: Andrew Bagnall, President and Chief Executive Officer
CFO: Greg Simia, Chief Financial Officer
CMO: Ken Johnson, Chief Physician Executive
CIO: Shane Miller, Chief Information Officer
CHR: Christine Jensema, Chief People Officer
CNO: Mary Martin MSN, R.N., Chief Nursing Officer
Web address: www.stnicholashospital.org
Control: Church operated, Nongovernment, not–for–profit **Service**: General medical and surgical

Staffed Beds: 46 **Admissions**: 2467 **Census**: 22 **Outpatient Visits**: 76704
Births: 257 **Total Expense ($000)**: 84177 **Payroll Expense ($000)**: 23037
Personnel: 327

SHELL LAKE—Washburn County

☐ **INDIANHEAD MEDICAL CENTER (521342)**, 113 Fourth Avenue, Zip 54871–4457, Mailing Address: P.O.Box 300, 54871–0300; tel. 715/468–7833 **A**1 10 18 **F**3 15 17 28 34 40 43 45 50 56 57 62 64 68 70 79 80 81 83 84 85 86 89 93 94 97 107 110 114 119 127 129 130 132 133 144 148 149 150 **P**5
Primary Contact: Paul Naglosky, Administrator
CFO: Michael Elliott, Controller
CMO: Allan Haesemeyer M.D., Chief of Staff
CHR: Gwen Nielsen, Manager Human Resources
Web address: www.indianheadmedicalcenter.com
Control: Corporation, Investor–owned (for–profit) **Service**: General medical and surgical

Staffed Beds: 16 **Admissions**: 286 **Census**: 4 **Outpatient Visits**: 9461
Births: 0 **Total Expense ($000)**: 7188 **Payroll Expense ($000)**: 3011
Personnel: 70

SPARTA—Monroe County

MAYO CLINIC HEALTH SYSTEM – FRANCISCAN HEALTHCARE IN SPARTA (521305), 310 West Main Street, Zip 54656–2171; tel. 608/269–2132 **A**10 18 **F**1 5 6 11 14 15 28 29 30 34 35 40 43 53 56 57 59 64 65 66 68 75 77 80 81 85 86 87 89 90 93 97 107 108 119 127 130 132 133 143 144 146 149 150 **S** Mayo Clinic, Rochester, MN
Primary Contact: Kimberly Hawthorne, Administrator
COO: Joseph J Kruse, Chief Administrative Officer
CFO: Tom Tiggelaar, Vice President Finance ad Chief Financial Officer
CMO: Tracy Warsing M.D., Site Leader Chief of Staff
CHR: Mike J Hesch, Regional Administrator Human Resources
Web address: www.mayoclinichealthsystem.org
Control: Church operated, Nongovernment, not–for–profit **Service**: General medical and surgical

Staffed Beds: 11 **Admissions**: 360 **Census**: 11 **Outpatient Visits**: 24724
Births: 0 **Total Expense ($000)**: 19867 **Payroll Expense ($000)**: 9045
Personnel: 133

SPOONER—Washburn County

★ **SPOONER HEALTH (521332)**, 1280 Chandler Drive, Zip 54801–1299; tel. 715/635–2111 **A**10 18 **F**3 11 13 15 29 31 34 35 40 43 45 50 56 57 59 62 64 65 68 76 78 80 81 85 86 87 89 90 93 103 107 111 119 130 132 133 135 146 148 **S** HealthTech Management Services, Brentwood, TN
Primary Contact: Michael Schafer, Chief Executive Officer and Administrator
CFO: Rebecca Busch, Chief Financial Officer
CMO: Mark Van Etten M.D., Chief of Staff
CHR: Cindy Rouzer, Director Human Resources
CNO: Clint Miller, Chief Nursing Officer
Web address: www.spoonerhealth.com
Control: Other not–for–profit (including NFP Corporation) **Service**: General medical and surgical

Staffed Beds: 25 **Admissions**: 382 **Census**: 6 **Outpatient Visits**: 20770
Births: 3 **Total Expense ($000)**: 17296 **Payroll Expense ($000)**: 6886
Personnel: 108

WI

ST CROIX FALLS—Polk County

★ **ST. CROIX REGIONAL MEDICAL CENTER (521337)**, 235 State Street, Zip 54024–4117; tel. 715/483–3261 **A**10 18 **F**3 6 8 9 11 13 15 18 26 28 29 30 31 32 34 35 36 40 41 43 45 48 50 51 55 56 57 59 64 65 66 70 74 75 76 77 78 79 80 81 82 85 86 87 92 93 94 97 99 100 101 104 107 108 110 111 115 116 117 118 119 126 127 129 130 131 132 133 135 144 146 147 148 **P**5 6
Primary Contact: Dave Dobosenski, Chief Executive Officer
CFO: Sally Bajak, Chief Financial Officer
CMO: Jeffrey Hall DPM, Chief Medical Officer
CIO: Brent McCurdy, Director Management Information
CHR: Lee Ann Vitalis, Executive Director Human Resources
CNO: Laura J. Jensen, Vice President Patient Care Services
Web address: www.scrmc.org
Control: Other not–for–profit (including NFP Corporation) **Service:** General medical and surgical

> **Staffed Beds:** 25 **Admissions:** 1554 **Census:** 14 **Outpatient Visits:** 195586
> **Births:** 299 **Total Expense ($000):** 73662 **Payroll Expense ($000):** 28905
> **Personnel:** 422

STANLEY—Chippewa County

★ **MINISTRY OUR LADY OF VICTORY HOSPITAL (521311)**, 1120 Pine Street, Zip 54768–1297; tel. 715/644–5571 **A**10 18 **F**3 15 29 30 34 35 40 41 43 45 50 56 59 65 75 77 80 81 85 86 87 89 90 93 94 96 97 107 109 110 114 127 130 131 133 144 146 148 149 **P**2 **S** Ascension Healthcare, Saint Louis, MO
Primary Contact: Vanessa Freitag, President
CFO: Terri Lewandowski, Director Financial Services
Web address: www.ministryhealth.org
Control: Other not–for–profit (including NFP Corporation) **Service:** General medical and surgical

> **Staffed Beds:** 5 **Admissions:** 244 **Census:** 4 **Outpatient Visits:** 26172
> **Births:** 0 **Total Expense ($000):** 17366 **Payroll Expense ($000):** 7748
> **Personnel:** 79

STEVENS POINT—Portage County

✚ **MINISTRY SAINT MICHAEL'S HOSPITAL (520002)**, 900 Illinois Avenue, Zip 54481–3196; tel. 715/346–5000 **A**1 3 10 19 **F**3 5 12 13 15 17 28 29 30 34 35 40 43 44 45 47 48 50 51 56 57 59 64 65 68 70 72 74 75 76 77 79 80 81 84 85 86 87 89 90 93 94 98 99 100 101 102 103 104 105 106 107 108 110 111 115 118 119 120 121 129 130 131 132 135 144 146 147 148 149 **S** Ascension Healthcare, Saint Louis, MO
Primary Contact: Jeremy Normington–Slay, FACHE, President, North Central Region
CFO: William J Hinner, Vice President Financial Analysis and Planning
CMO: Ryan Andrews M.D., Chief Medical Officer
CIO: Will Weider, Chief Information Officer
CHR: Celia Shaunessy, Vice President Human Resources
CNO: Tom Veeser, Chief Nursing Officer
Web address: www.ministryhealth.org/SMH/home.nws
Control: Church operated, Nongovernment, not–for–profit **Service:** General medical and surgical

> **Staffed Beds:** 50 **Admissions:** 4455 **Census:** 37 **Outpatient Visits:** 402065
> **Births:** 486 **Total Expense ($000):** 176145 **Payroll Expense ($000):** 93769
> **Personnel:** 523

SAINT MICHAEL'S HOSPITAL See Ministry Saint Michael's Hospital

STOUGHTON—Dane County

☐ **STOUGHTON HOSPITAL ASSOCIATION (521343)**, 900 Ridge Street, Zip 53589–1864; tel. 608/873–6611 **A**1 10 18 **F**3 4 6 8 14 15 26 28 29 34 35 36 40 41 43 45 50 53 54 56 57 59 62 64 65 68 70 71 75 77 79 80 81 85 86 87 89 90 91 93 98 100 103 106 107 115 127 129 130 131 132 133 135 144 146 147 148 149
Primary Contact: Terrence Brenny, President and Chief Executive Officer
CFO: Karen Myers, Vice President Financial Services
CMO: Guirish Agni M.D., Chief of Staff
CIO: Karen Myers, Vice President Financial Services
CHR: Christopher Schmitz, Associate Vice President, Director Human Resources
CNO: Teresa Feidt, Chief Nursing Officer and Vice President, Patient Services
Web address: www.stoughtonhospital.com
Control: Other not–for–profit (including NFP Corporation) **Service:** General medical and surgical

> **Staffed Beds:** 32 **Admissions:** 858 **Census:** 16 **Outpatient Visits:** 54236
> **Births:** 0 **Total Expense ($000):** 38543 **Payroll Expense ($000):** 16162
> **Personnel:** 269

STURGEON BAY—Door County

★ **DOOR COUNTY MEDICAL CENTER (521358)**, 323 South 18th Avenue, Zip 54235–1495; tel. 920/743–5566, (Total facility includes 30 beds in nursing home–type unit) **A**10 18 **F**2 3 11 13 15 17 28 29 30 31 32 34 35 36 40 43 55 56 57 59 61 64 65 66 68 70 75 76 77 78 79 80 81 82 84 85 86 87 89 90 93 107 108 110 111 115 118 119 127 128 129 130 132 133 135 144 145 147 148 149 **P**1 **S** HSHS Hospital Sisters Health System, Springfield, IL
Primary Contact: Gerald M. Worrick, President and Chief Executive Officer
CFO: Brian Stephens, Chief Financial Officer
CMO: James Heise, Chief Medical Officer
CIO: Mary Lopas, Chief Information Officer
CHR: Kelli Bowling, Chief Culture Officer
CNO: Jody Boes, Vice President Patient Care Services
Web address: www.ministryhealth.org
Control: Church operated, Nongovernment, not–for–profit **Service:** General medical and surgical

> **Staffed Beds:** 55 **Admissions:** 1471 **Census:** 36 **Outpatient Visits:** 104005
> **Births:** 146 **Total Expense ($000):** 72969 **Payroll Expense ($000):** 38734
> **Personnel:** 501

DOOR COUNTY MEMORIAL HOSPITAL See Door County Medical Center

SUMMIT—Waukesha County

✚ **AURORA MEDICAL CENTER SUMMIT (520206)**, 36500 Aurora Drive, Zip 53066–4899; tel. 262/434–1000 **A**1 2 10 **F**3 8 11 12 13 15 17 18 19 20 22 24 26 28 29 30 31 34 35 36 40 41 45 47 48 49 50 53 54 57 59 60 64 68 70 72 74 75 76 79 80 81 82 84 85 86 87 89 90 93 94 96 107 108 110 111 114 115 116 117 118 119 120 121 123 126 129 130 131 132 135 146 147 148 149 **P**6 **S** Aurora Health Care, Milwaukee, WI
Primary Contact: Michael Bergmann, President
Web address: www.aurorahealthcare.org
Control: Other not–for–profit (including NFP Corporation) **Service:** General medical and surgical

> **Staffed Beds:** 99 **Admissions:** 3652 **Census:** 35 **Outpatient Visits:** 97764
> **Births:** 456 **Total Expense ($000):** 107246 **Payroll Expense ($000):** 32325
> **Personnel:** 572

SUPERIOR—Douglas County

✚ **ESSENTIA HEALTH ST. MARY'S HOSPITAL OF SUPERIOR (521329)**, 3500 Tower Avenue, Zip 54880–5395; tel. 715/817–7000 **A**1 10 18 **F**11 15 28 29 34 40 56 75 77 78 80 81 82 86 87 90 93 107 119 130 **S** Essentia Health, Duluth, MN
Primary Contact: Terry Jacobson, Administrator and Chief Executive Officer
Web address: www.essentiahealth.org/EssentiaHealthStMarysHospitalofSuperiorFoundation/overview.aspx
Control: Other not–for–profit (including NFP Corporation) **Service:** General medical and surgical

> **Staffed Beds:** 25 **Admissions:** 503 **Census:** 7 **Outpatient Visits:** 52428
> **Births:** 0 **Total Expense ($000):** 35835 **Payroll Expense ($000):** 18533
> **Personnel:** 190

TOMAH—Monroe County

✚ **TOMAH MEMORIAL HOSPITAL (521320)**, 321 Butts Avenue, Zip 54660–1412; tel. 608/372–2181 **A**1 10 18 **F**3 8 11 12 13 18 28 30 31 34 35 40 43 44 56 57 59 63 64 68 76 77 79 80 81 82 83 84 85 86 87 89 90 93 107 111 115 119 129 130 132 133 135 144 146 148 **P**5 6 **S** HealthTech Management Services, Brentwood, TN
Primary Contact: Philip J. Stuart, Administrator and Chief Executive Officer
CFO: Joseph Zeps, Vice President Finance
CIO: LaVonne Smith, Director Health Information Technology
CHR: Brenda Reinert, Director Human Resources
CNO: Tracy Myhre R.N., MSN, Chief Nursing Officer
Web address: www.tomahhospital.org
Control: Other not–for–profit (including NFP Corporation) **Service:** General medical and surgical

> **Staffed Beds:** 25 **Admissions:** 963 **Census:** 8 **Outpatient Visits:** 38467
> **Births:** 307 **Total Expense ($000):** 41796 **Payroll Expense ($000):** 18102
> **Personnel:** 239

WI

Hospital, Medicare Provider Number, Address, Telephone, Approval, Facility, and Physician Codes, Health Care System

★ American Hospital Association (AHA) membership
☐ The Joint Commission accreditation
○ Healthcare Facilities Accreditation Program
◇ DNV Healthcare Inc. accreditation
⇑ Center for Improvement in Healthcare Quality Accreditation
△ Commission on Accreditation of Rehabilitation Facilities (CARF) accreditation

✠ **TOMAH VETERANS AFFAIRS MEDICAL CENTER**, 500 East Veterans Street, Zip 54660–3105; tel. 608/372–3971, (Nonreporting) **A**1 3 **S** Department of Veterans Affairs, Washington, DC
Primary Contact: Victoria Brahm, R.N., MSN, Acting Director
CFO: Jane Mashak–Ekern, Fiscal Officer
CMO: David Houlihan M.D., Chief of Staff
CIO: Edward Hensel, Chief Information Officer
CHR: David Dechant, Chief Human Resources Officer
Web address: www.tomah.va.gov
Control: Veterans Affairs, Government, federal **Service:** General medical and surgical

> **Staffed Beds:** 71

TOMAHAWK—Lincoln County

★ **MINISTRY SACRED HEART HOSPITAL (521313)**, 401 West Mohawk Drive, Zip 54487–2274; tel. 715/453–7700 **A**10 18 **F**3 5 15 28 29 30 34 35 40 45 49 50 57 59 65 68 75 77 80 81 84 86 87 89 91 92 93 96 99 100 101 104 107 109 115 119 130 131 133 146 149 **S** Ascension Healthcare, Saint Louis, MO
Primary Contact: Sandra L. Anderson, President and Chief Executive Officer
COO: Laurie Oungst, Vice President, Operations
CFO: Jamon Lamers, Director Finance
CMO: Russ Sudbury M.D., President Medical Staff
CIO: Howard Dobizl, Director Information Technology Services
CHR: Michelle Cornelius, Director Human Resources
CNO: Ann Zenk, Vice President Patient Care
Web address: www.ministryhealth.org
Control: Church operated, Nongovernment, not–for–profit **Service:** General medical and surgical

> **Staffed Beds:** 12 **Admissions:** 312 **Census:** 3 **Outpatient Visits:** 21007
> **Births:** 0 **Total Expense ($000):** 14549 **Payroll Expense ($000):** 8856
> **Personnel:** 69

TWO RIVERS—Manitowoc County

✠ **AURORA MEDICAL CENTER – MANITOWOC COUNTY (520034)**, 5000 Memorial Drive, Zip 54241–3900; tel. 920/794–5000 **A**1 2 10 **F**3 8 11 13 28 29 30 31 32 34 35 36 37 40 43 44 45 47 48 49 50 56 57 59 64 69 74 75 76 78 79 80 81 82 84 85 86 87 89 93 94 107 108 110 111 114 119 121 123 129 130 131 132 143 145 146 147 148 149 **P**6 **S** Aurora Health Care, Milwaukee, WI
Primary Contact: Cathie A. Kocourek, President
COO: Carrie L Penovich, Chief Clinical Services Officer
CFO: Sandra Ewald, President (Green Bay/Manitowoc Market)
CMO: Paul Mihalakakos M.D., Chief of Staff
CIO: Preston Simons, Chief Information Officer
CHR: Elizabeth A Kirby, Senior Director Human Resources
CNO: Betsy Benz R.N., MS, Chief Nursing Officer
Web address: www.aurorahealthcare.org
Control: Other not–for–profit (including NFP Corporation) **Service:** General medical and surgical

> **Staffed Beds:** 63 **Admissions:** 2193 **Census:** 15 **Outpatient Visits:** 83876
> **Births:** 387 **Total Expense ($000):** 56399 **Payroll Expense ($000):** 18321
> **Personnel:** 321

VIROQUA—Vernon County

VERNON MEMORIAL HEALTHCARE (521348), 507 South Main Street, Zip 54665–2096; tel. 608/637–2101 **A**10 18 **F**3 5 13 15 18 26 28 29 31 34 35 36 37 43 44 53 56 57 59 62 63 64 65 68 75 76 77 79 80 81 82 85 86 87 89 93 97 99 100 103 104 107 110 115 127 129 130 131 132 133 135 144 146 148 149 **P**6
Primary Contact: Kyle Bakkum, Chief Executive Officer and Administrator
COO: Kristy Wiltrout R.N., Chief Operating Officer
CFO: Mary Koenig, Chief Financial Officer
CIO: Scott Adkins, Manager Information Technology
CHR: Kay Starr, Manager Human Resources
Web address: www.vmh.org
Control: Other not–for–profit (including NFP Corporation) **Service:** General medical and surgical

> **Staffed Beds:** 25 **Admissions:** 1231 **Census:** 8 **Outpatient Visits:** 110749
> **Births:** 156 **Total Expense ($000):** 70581 **Payroll Expense ($000):** 28779
> **Personnel:** 362

WATERFORD—Racine County

☐ **LAKEVIEW SPECIALTY HOSPITAL AND REHABILITATION CENTER (522005)**, 1701 Sharp Road, Zip 53185–5214; tel. 262/534–7297 **A**1 10 **F**1 12 29 34 38 53 60 64 75 86 87 90 93 130 **P**6
Primary Contact: Jerry Amato, President and Chief Operating Officer
Web address: www.lakeviewsystem.com
Control: Corporation, Investor–owned (for–profit) **Service:** Acute long–term care hospital

> **Staffed Beds:** 39 **Admissions:** 186 **Census:** 23 **Outpatient Visits:** 5722
> **Births:** 0 **Total Expense ($000):** 18753 **Payroll Expense ($000):** 9036
> **Personnel:** 124

WATERTOWN—Dodge County

✠ **WATERTOWN REGIONAL MEDICAL CENTER (520116)**, 125 Hospital Drive, Zip 53098–3303; tel. 920/261–4210 **A**1 10 **F**3 8 10 11 13 15 18 20 22 26 27 28 29 34 35 36 40 41 44 45 46 47 48 50 53 54 56 57 59 64 65 66 68 69 74 75 76 77 78 79 80 81 82 83 85 86 87 89 90 93 94 96 97 104 107 108 110 111 115 118 119 125 129 130 131 132 133 135 144 146 147 149 **P**8 **S** LifePoint Health, Brentwood, TN
Primary Contact: Richard Keddington, Chief Executive Officer
COO: John P Kosanovich, President
CFO: John Graf, Senior Vice President
CIO: Jennifer Laughlin, Chief Information Officer
CHR: Duane Floyd, Vice President Human Resources and Professional Services
CNO: Mary Kay Diderrich R.N., Vice President Patient Services
Web address: www.watertownregional.com/Main/Home.aspx
Control: Corporation, Investor–owned (for–profit) **Service:** General medical and surgical

> **Staffed Beds:** 56 **Admissions:** 2013 **Census:** 17 **Outpatient Visits:** 170348
> **Births:** 227 **Total Expense ($000):** 92979 **Payroll Expense ($000):** 41176
> **Personnel:** 613

WAUKESHA—Waukesha County

☐ **REHABILITATION HOSPITAL OF WISCONSIN (523027)**, 1625 Coldwater Creek Drive, Zip 53188–8028; tel. 262/521–8800 **A**1 10 **F**3 29 34 35 57 64 65 74 75 79 86 90 91 93 96 97 130 148 149 **S** Kindred Healthcare, Louisville, KY
Primary Contact: Linda Newberry–Ferguson, Chief Executive Officer
CMO: Tim McAvoy M.D., Medical Director
CHR: Jenny Franke, Director Human Resources
CNO: Sharon Behrens R.N., MSN, Chief Clinical Officer
Web address: www.rehabhospitalwi.com
Control: Partnership, Investor–owned (for–profit) **Service:** Rehabilitation

> **Staffed Beds:** 40 **Admissions:** 866 **Census:** 33 **Outpatient Visits:** 5694
> **Births:** 0 **Total Expense ($000):** 13465 **Payroll Expense ($000):** 7029
> **Personnel:** 137

WAUKESHA COUNTY MENTAL HEALTH CENTER (524026), 2501 Airport Road, Zip 53188; tel. 262/548–7950 **A**10 **F**4 44 50 59 98 130 135
Primary Contact: Jeff Lewis, Administrator
CFO: Randy R Setzer, Financial Services Manager
Web address: www.waukeshacounty.gov/
Control: County, Government, Nonfederal **Service:** Psychiatric

> **Staffed Beds:** 28 **Admissions:** 661 **Census:** 18 **Outpatient Visits:** 0 **Births:** 0
> **Total Expense ($000):** 6760 **Payroll Expense ($000):** 3684 **Personnel:** 63

✠ **WAUKESHA MEMORIAL HOSPITAL (520008)**, 725 American Avenue, Zip 53188–5099; tel. 262/928–1000 **A**1 2 3 5 10 **F**3 4 5 6 11 12 13 15 18 20 22 24 26 28 29 30 31 34 35 37 40 42 44 45 46 47 49 50 56 57 58 59 64 68 72 74 75 76 78 79 80 81 82 83 84 85 87 89 92 93 97 98 100 101 102 103 105 107 108 110 111 114 115 116 117 118 119 120 121 123 124 126 129 130 132 135 146 147 148 149 **S** ProHealth Care, Inc., Waukesha, WI
Primary Contact: Susan A. Edwards, Chief Executive Officer
CMO: James D Gardner M.D., Vice President and Chief Medical Officer
CIO: Rodney Dykehouse, Senior Vice President Information Services
CHR: Nadine T Guirl, Senior Vice President Human Resources
Web address: www.prohealthcare.org/locations/locations–v2–detail/?id=1119
Control: Other not–for–profit (including NFP Corporation) **Service:** General medical and surgical

> **Staffed Beds:** 274 **Admissions:** 13038 **Census:** 138 **Outpatient Visits:** 330676 **Births:** 1749 **Total Expense ($000):** 419414 **Payroll Expense ($000):** 112416 **Personnel:** 1795

WI

WAUPACA—Waupaca County

☐ **THEDACARE MEDICAL CENTER–WAUPACA (521334)**, 800 Riverside Drive, Zip 54981–1999; tel. 715/258–1000 **A**1 10 18 **F**11 13 17 28 29 34 40 64 70 75 76 78 80 81 82 86 87 88 89 90 107 111 119 130 144 147 **S** ThedaCare, Inc., Appleton, WI
Primary Contact: Craig A. Kantos, Chief Executive Officer
CFO: Kerry Lee Blanke, Director Financial Services
CMO: James Williams M.D., Chief of Staff
CHR: Kevin Gossens, Director Human Resources
Web address: www.riversidemedical.org
Control: Other not–for–profit (including NFP Corporation) **Service**: General medical and surgical

Staffed Beds: 25 **Admissions**: 930 **Census**: 9 **Outpatient Visits**: 37681
Births: 130 **Total Expense ($000)**: 28563 **Payroll Expense ($000)**: 14825
Personnel: 190

WAUPUN—Dodge County

☐ ⇑ **WAUPUN MEMORIAL HOSPITAL (521327)**, 620 West Brown Street, Zip 53963–1799; tel. 920/324–5581 **A**1 10 18 21 **F**3 11 13 15 18 28 29 30 31 34 35 40 43 44 45 50 51 57 59 60 66 68 69 70 75 76 77 79 81 82 85 86 87 93 96 97 107 108 109 110 114 118 119 124 130 131 132 133 134 135 143 144 146 147 148 149 150 **P**6
Primary Contact: DeAnn Thurmer, Chief Operating Officer
COO: DeAnn Thurmer, Chief Operating Officer
CFO: Bonnie Schmitz, Chief Financial Officer
CMO: Derek Colmenares M.D., Chief Medical Officer
CIO: Nancy Birschbach, Vice President and Chief Information Officer
CHR: Sue Edminster, Vice President Human Resources
CNO: DeAnn Thurmer, Chief Nursing Officer
Web address: www.agnesian.com
Control: Church operated, Nongovernment, not–for–profit **Service**: General medical and surgical

Staffed Beds: 25 **Admissions**: 909 **Census**: 8 **Outpatient Visits**: 57261
Births: 123 **Total Expense ($000)**: 34493 **Payroll Expense ($000)**: 15026
Personnel: 185

WAUSAU—Marathon County

☒ △ **ASPIRUS WAUSAU HOSPITAL, INC. (520030)**, 333 Pine Ridge Boulevard, Zip 54401–4187; tel. 715/847–2121 **A**1 2 3 5 7 10 **F**3 6 7 8 11 12 13 15 17 18 20 22 24 26 28 29 30 31 34 35 36 40 43 44 45 46 47 49 50 51 54 55 56 57 58 59 60 64 65 68 69 70 71 72 74 75 76 78 79 80 81 82 83 84 85 86 87 89 90 92 93 96 97 100 102 103 107 108 110 111 114 115 116 117 118 119 120 121 123 124 126 129 130 132 135 143 144 145 146 147 148 149 150 **P**8 **S** Aspirus, Inc., Wausau, WI
Primary Contact: Darrell Lentz, President
CFO: Sidney C Sczygelski, Senior Vice President Finance and Chief Financial Officer
CMO: William Wessels M.D., Chief Medical Officer
CNO: Jeannine Burnat Nosko, Vice President Patient Care
Web address: www.aspirus.org
Control: Other not–for–profit (including NFP Corporation) **Service**: General medical and surgical

Staffed Beds: 236 **Admissions**: 13141 **Census**: 150 **Outpatient Visits**: 118753
Births: 1171 **Total Expense ($000)**: 403382 **Payroll Expense ($000)**: 140670
Personnel: 2952

★ **NORTH CENTRAL HEALTH CARE (524017)**, 1100 Lake View Drive, Zip 54403–6785; tel. 715/848–4600, (Total facility includes 181 beds in nursing home–type unit) **A**3 10 **F**4 5 29 38 54 75 77 80 87 98 99 102 103 104 105 128 130
Primary Contact: Michael Loy, Interim Chief Executive Officer
CFO: Brenda Glodowski, Chief Financial Officer
CHR: Sue Matis, Director Human Resources
Web address: www.norcen.org
Control: County, Government, Nonfederal **Service**: Psychiatric

Staffed Beds: 197 **Admissions**: 1155 **Census**: 197 **Outpatient Visits**: 130750 **Births**: 0 **Total Expense ($000)**: 36561 **Payroll Expense ($000)**: 16492 **Personnel**: 359

NORTH CENTRAL HEALTH CARE FACILITIES See North Central Health Care

WAUWATOSA—Milwaukee County

☒ **AURORA PSYCHIATRIC HOSPITAL (524000)**, 1220 Dewey Avenue, Zip 53213–2598; tel. 414/454–6600 **A**1 3 5 10 **F**4 5 29 30 32 34 35 38 44 50 54 57 59 64 68 75 86 87 98 99 100 101 102 103 104 105 106 130 132 134 135 149 **P**6 **S** Aurora Health Care, Milwaukee, WI
Primary Contact: Peter Carlson, President, Behavioral Health Services
CFO: Susan Dwyer, Vice President Finance
CMO: Anthony Meyer M.D., Medical Director
CIO: Philip Loftus Ph.D., Vice President and Chief Information Officer
CHR: Pamela Gamb, Manager Human Resources
CNO: Jamie Lewiston R.N., MSN, Chief Nursing Officer
Web address: www.aurorahealthcare.org
Control: Other not–for–profit (including NFP Corporation) **Service**: Psychiatric

Staffed Beds: 91 **Admissions**: 4291 **Census**: 54 **Outpatient Visits**: 68911
Births: 0 **Total Expense ($000)**: 29711 **Payroll Expense ($000)**: 16706
Personnel: 302

WEST ALLIS—Milwaukee County

☒ **AURORA WEST ALLIS MEDICAL CENTER (520139)**, 8901 West Lincoln Avenue, Zip 53227–2409, Mailing Address: P.O.Box 27901, 53227–0901; tel. 414/328–6000 **A**1 2 3 10 **F**3 11 12 13 15 29 30 31 32 34 35 37 38 40 43 44 45 46 49 50 52 54 55 56 57 59 64 65 68 70 72 74 75 76 78 79 80 81 82 84 85 86 87 91 93 94 96 97 107 108 110 111 114 115 116 117 118 119 120 121 123 126 130 132 134 135 146 147 148 149 **P**6 **S** Aurora Health Care, Milwaukee, WI
Primary Contact: Richard A. Kellar, President
COO: Gerard Colman, Chief Operating Officer
CFO: Chris Hemmer, Director Finance
CMO: Andrew McDonagh M.D., Chief Medical Officer
CIO: Philip Loftus Ph.D., Chief Information Officer
CHR: Shannon Christenson, Director Human Resources
CNO: Kathy Becker Ph.D., R.N., Vice President and Chief Nursing Officer
Web address: www.aurorahealthcare.org
Control: Other not–for–profit (including NFP Corporation) **Service**: General medical and surgical

Staffed Beds: 218 **Admissions**: 12593 **Census**: 143 **Outpatient Visits**: 150142
Births: 3333 **Total Expense ($000)**: 206312 **Payroll Expense ($000)**: 66191
Personnel: 1131

WEST BEND—Washington County

☒ **ST. JOSEPH'S HOSPITAL (520063)**, 3200 Pleasant Valley Road, Zip 53095–9274; tel. 262/334–5533 **A**1 2 3 5 10 **F**3 8 13 15 26 28 29 30 31 34 35 40 44 45 46 47 48 49 50 56 57 59 60 63 64 68 75 76 77 78 79 80 81 84 85 86 87 100 101 107 108 110 111 114 115 116 117 118 119 120 121 123 129 130 132 135 145 146 147 148 149 150
Primary Contact: Allen Ericson, Chief Operating Officer, Community Hospital Division and President, St. Joseph's Hospital
COO: Allen Ericson, Chief Operating Officer, Community Hospital Division and President, St. Joseph's Hospital
CFO: Scott Hawig, Senior Vice President of Finance, Chief Financial Officer and Treasurer
CMO: Patrick Gardner M.D., Associate Vice President, Medical Affairs, St. Joseph's Hospital
CIO: William Showalter, Senior Vice President, Chief Information Officer
CHR: Keith Allen, Senior Vice President Human Resources
Web address: www.froedtert.com
Control: Other not–for–profit (including NFP Corporation) **Service**: General medical and surgical

Staffed Beds: 78 **Admissions**: 3897 **Census**: 44 **Outpatient Visits**: 87214
Births: 699 **Total Expense ($000)**: 112549 **Payroll Expense ($000)**: 33964
Personnel: 490

WESTON—Marathon County

☒ **MINISTRY SAINT CLARE'S HOSPITAL (520202)**, 3400 Ministry Parkway, Zip 54476–5220; tel. 715/393–3000 **A**1 10 19 **F**3 11 13 17 18 20 22 24 26 29 30 31 34 35 37 40 43 44 45 46 47 48 49 50 51 57 59 64 68 70 72 74 75 76 78 79 80 81 82 84 85 86 87 89 126 130 132 135 146 147 148 149 150 **P**2 **S** Ascension Healthcare, Saint Louis, MO
Primary Contact: Jeremy Normington-Slay, FACHE, President, North Central Region
CFO: Charlotte Esselman, Director Finance
CMO: Ryan Andrews M.D., Chief Medical Officer
CIO: Tammy Hawkey, Manager Information Technology Client Services
CHR: Nancy Kwiesielewicz, Human Resources Manager
CNO: Sally E. Zillman, Interim Vice President, Patient Care Services
Web address: www.ministryhealth.org
Control: Church operated, Nongovernment, not–for–profit **Service**: General medical and surgical

Staffed Beds: 86 **Admissions**: 6048 **Census**: 56 **Outpatient Visits**: 19811
Births: 521 **Total Expense ($000)**: 101697 **Payroll Expense ($000)**: 34555
Personnel: 324

WI

Hospital, Medicare Provider Number, Address, Telephone, Approval, Facility, and Physician Codes, Health Care System

★ American Hospital Association (AHA) membership   ○ Healthcare Facilities Accreditation Program   ⇑ Center for Improvement in Healthcare Quality Accreditation
☐ The Joint Commission accreditation   ◇ DNV Healthcare Inc. accreditation   △ Commission on Accreditation of Rehabilitation Facilities (CARF) accreditation

WHITEHALL—Trempealeau County

★ **GUNDERSEN TRI–COUNTY HOSPITAL AND CLINICS (521316)**, 18601 Lincoln Street, Zip 54773–8605; tel. 715/538–4361, (Total facility includes 47 beds in nursing home–type unit) **A**10 18 **F**3 7 10 11 14 15 18 28 31 32 34 35 40 43 45 50 53 54 56 57 59 64 65 68 69 71 75 78 79 81 82 85 86 89 90 93 97 99 100 101 104 107 108 127 128 129 130 132 133 135 143 144 146 148
Primary Contact: Joni Olson, Chief Executive Officer
CFO: Roxane K Schliech, Chief Financial Officer
CMO: Kim B Breidenbach, Medical Director
CIO: John Waldera, Director Information Technology
CHR: Jill Wesener Dieck, Director Human Resources
CNO: Kelsey N Underwood, Director of Nursing
Web address: www.gundersenhealth.org/tri–county
Control: Other not–for–profit (including NFP Corporation) **Service**: General medical and surgical

Staffed Beds: 50 **Admissions**: 307 **Census**: 51 **Outpatient Visits**: 32840
Births: 0 **Total Expense ($000)**: 17009 **Payroll Expense ($000)**: 7161
Personnel: 163

WILD ROSE—Waushara County

THEDA CARE MEDICAL CENTER – WILD ROSE (521303), 601 Grove Avenue, Zip 54984–6903, Mailing Address: P.O.Box 243, 54984–0243; tel. 920/622–3257 **A**10 18 **F**11 15 28 29 34 40 43 56 64 75 77 80 81 86 87 89 90 93 99 100 101 102 103 104 107 111 119 131 144 147 **S** ThedaCare, Inc., Appleton, WI
Primary Contact: Craig A. Kantos, Chief Executive Officer
CFO: Thomas P Krystowiak, Vice President Finance
CMO: Michael Staudinger M.D., Chief of Staff
Web address: www.wildrosehospital.org
Control: Other not–for–profit (including NFP Corporation) **Service**: General medical and surgical

Staffed Beds: 25 **Admissions**: 251 **Census**: 5 **Outpatient Visits**: 12872
Births: 0 **Total Expense ($000)**: 9836 **Payroll Expense ($000)**: 5968
Personnel: 106

WINNEBAGO—Winnebago County

☐ **WINNEBAGO MENTAL HEALTH INSTITUTE (524002)**, 1300 South Drive, Zip 54985, Mailing Address: Box 9, 54985–0009; tel. 920/235–4910 **A**1 3 5 10 **F**3 4 5 29 30 57 59 65 75 82 87 98 99 103 130 132 135 143 146 **P**7
Primary Contact: Thomas Speech, Ph.D., Director
COO: Chris Craggs, Deputy Director
CFO: Lisa Spanbauer, Financial Program Supervisor
CMO: Randy Kerswill M.D., Medical Director
CIO: Terrance J. Sweet, Director Information Technology
CHR: Mary Howard, Director Human Resources
CNO: Lori Monroe, Director of Nursing
Web address: www.dhfs.state.wi.us/mh_winnebago
Control: State, Government, Nonfederal **Service**: Psychiatric

Staffed Beds: 184 **Admissions**: 3228 **Census**: 184 **Outpatient Visits**: 0
Births: 0 **Total Expense ($000)**: 55448 **Payroll Expense ($000)**: 35790
Personnel: 598

WISCONSIN RAPIDS—Wood County

⊞ **ASPIRUS RIVERVIEW HOSPITAL AND CLINICS, INC. (520033)**, 410 Dewey Street, Zip 54494–4715, Mailing Address: P.O.Box 8080, 54495–8080; tel. 715/423–6060 **A**1 2 10 **F**3 4 13 15 17 28 30 31 32 34 35 40 43 45 50 56 57 59 64 65 68 69 70 74 75 76 77 78 79 80 81 84 85 86 88 89 90 93 97 98 107 108 110 111 115 117 118 119 120 121 124 129 130 131 132 135 146 148 **S** Aspirus, Inc., Wausau, WI
Primary Contact: Todd Burch, Chief Executive Officer
CFO: Nancy Roth–Mallek, Vice President of Finance
CMO: Thomas Voelker M.D., Chief Medical Officer
CIO: Marjorie Tell, Vice President Information Technology
CHR: Jessica Fox, Director of Human Resources
CNO: Peggy Ose FACHE, MSN, R.N., Chief Nursing Officer
Web address: www.aspirus.org
Control: Other not–for–profit (including NFP Corporation) **Service**: General medical and surgical

Staffed Beds: 75 **Admissions**: 2708 **Census**: 21 **Outpatient Visits**: 50024
Births: 437 **Total Expense ($000)**: 94173 **Payroll Expense ($000)**: 33724
Personnel: 412

WOODRUFF—Oneida County

⊞ **HOWARD YOUNG MEDICAL CENTER (520091)**, 240 Maple Street, Zip 54568–9190, Mailing Address: P.O.Box 470, 54568–0470; tel. 715/356–8000 **A**1 5 10 20 **F**3 8 11 13 15 28 29 30 35 40 43 45 47 48 49 50 57 59 64 68 75 76 77 80 81 82 84 85 86 87 88 89 93 96 107 110 111 115 119 126 129 130 133 146 148 149 **P**6 **S** Ascension Healthcare, Saint Louis, MO
Primary Contact: Sandra L. Anderson, President and Chief Executive Officer
COO: Laurie Oungst, Vice President, Operations
CFO: Jamon Lamers, Director Finance
CMO: John Crump M.D., Medical Staff President
CIO: Howard Dobizl, Director Information Technology Services
CHR: Michelle Cornelius, Director Human Resources
CNO: Deborah Karow R.N., Vice President Patient Care Services
Web address: www.ministryhealth.org
Control: Church operated, Nongovernment, not–for–profit **Service**: General medical and surgical

Staffed Beds: 37 **Admissions**: 2400 **Census**: 24 **Outpatient Visits**: 38029
Births: 249 **Total Expense ($000)**: 48189 **Payroll Expense ($000)**: 22305
Personnel: 237

WI

WYOMING

AFTON—Lincoln County

★ **STAR VALLEY MEDICAL CENTER (531313)**, 901 Adams Street, Zip 83110–9621, Mailing Address: P.O.Box 579, 83110–0579; tel. 307/885–5800, (Nonreporting) **A**10 18
Primary Contact: Mike Hunsaker, Interim President and Chief Executive Officer
COO: Mike Hunsaker, Chief Operating Officer
CFO: Chad Turner, Chief Financial Officer
CMO: Donald Kirk M.D., Chief of Staff
CIO: Amy R Johnson R.N., Quality Improvement Safety Officer
CHR: Trevor Merritt, Director Human Resources
CNO: Derek Greenwald, Chief Nursing Officer
Web address: www.svmcwy.org
Control: Hospital district or authority, Government, Nonfederal **Service**: General medical and surgical

Staffed Beds: 44

BASIN—Big Horn County

SOUTH BIG HORN COUNTY HOSPITAL (531301), 388 South U S Highway 20, Zip 82410–8902; tel. 307/568–3311 (Nonreporting) **A**10 18
Primary Contact: John Adlesich, Chief Executive Officer
Web address: www.midwayclinic.com
Control: Hospital district or authority, Government, Nonfederal **Service**: General medical and surgical

Staffed Beds: 43

BUFFALO—Johnson County

★ **JOHNSON COUNTY HEALTHCARE CENTER (531308)**, 497 West Lott Street, Zip 82834–1691; tel. 307/684–5521, (Total facility includes 44 beds in nursing home–type unit) **A**10 18 **F**11 13 15 28 40 57 62 63 67 70 76 77 79 81 89 93 107 119 130 133
Primary Contact: Nicole Hobbs, Administrator
CMO: Blaine Ruby M.D., Chief of Staff
CIO: Laurie Hansen, Director Administrative Services
CHR: Karen Ferguson, Director Human Resources
CNO: Mary Whaley, Director of Acute Care
Web address: www.jchealthcare.com
Control: Hospital district or authority, Government, Nonfederal **Service**: General medical and surgical

Staffed Beds: 59 **Admissions**: 426 **Census**: 49 **Outpatient Visits**: 17653 **Births**: 54 **Total Expense ($000)**: 21466 **Payroll Expense ($000)**: 11283 **Personnel**: 180

CASPER—Natrona County

☐ **ELKHORN VALLEY REHABILITATION HOSPITAL (533027)**, 5715 East 2nd Street, Zip 82609–4322; tel. 307/265–0005 **A**1 10 **F**3 29 34 35 44 50 68 90 91 92 93 94 96 119 130 132 143 **S** Ernest Health, Inc., Albuquerque, NM
Primary Contact: Michael Phillips, Chief Executive Officer
Web address: www.evrh.ernesthealth.com/
Control: Corporation, Investor–owned (for–profit) **Service**: Rehabilitation

Staffed Beds: 41 **Admissions**: 735 **Census**: 31 **Outpatient Visits**: 3343 **Births**: 0 **Personnel**: 119

○ **MOUNTAIN VIEW REGIONAL HOSPITAL (530033)**, 6550 East Second Street, Zip 82609–4321, Mailing Address: P.O.Box 51888, 82605–1888; tel. 307/995–8100 **A**10 11 **F**18 29 30 35 40 45 46 64 68 70 75 77 79 81 82 84 85 87 93 97 107 111 115 117 118 119 127 130 131 149 **P**2 6 **S** National Surgical Healthcare, Chicago, IL
Primary Contact: Thomas Kopitnik, Acting Chief Executive Officer
Web address: www.mountainviewregionalhospital.com
Control: Corporation, Investor–owned (for–profit) **Service**: Surgical

Staffed Beds: 23 **Admissions**: 950 **Census**: 6 **Outpatient Visits**: 9207 **Births**: 0 **Total Expense ($000)**: 44207 **Payroll Expense ($000)**: 10898 **Personnel**: 243

⇑ **SUMMIT MEDICAL CENTER (530034)**, 6350 East 2nd Street, Zip 82609–4264; tel. 307/232–6600 (Nonreporting) **A**21 **F**3 7 11 12 13 18 20 22 24 28 29 30 31 34 35 40 41 43 45 46 48 49 50 51 53 57 59 60 61 68 70 74 76 79 81 82 85 86 87 89 97 102 107 108 114 118 119 120 121 123 124 126 129 130 132 135 144 146 147 148
Primary Contact: Dennis D. Jack, FACHE, Chief Executive Officer
CFO: Calvin Carey, Chief Financial Officer
CMO: Joseph Vigneri M.D., Chief Medical Officer
CNO: Vanessa Sorensen, Chief Nursing Officer
Web address: www.summitmedicalcasper.com/
Control: Corporation, Investor–owned (for–profit) **Service**: General medical and surgical

Staffed Beds: 16

☐ **WYOMING BEHAVIORAL INSTITUTE (534004)**, 2521 East 15th Street, Zip 82609–4126; tel. 307/237–7444, (Nonreporting) **A**1 10 **S** Universal Health Services, Inc., King of Prussia, PA
Primary Contact: Joseph Gallagher, Chief Executive Officer
CFO: Carmel Bickford, Chief Financial Officer
CMO: Steven Brown M.D., Medical Director
CHR: Jon Barra, Director Human Resources
Web address: www.wbihelp.com
Control: Corporation, Investor–owned (for–profit) **Service**: Psychiatric

Staffed Beds: 129

⊞ **WYOMING MEDICAL CENTER (530012)**, 1233 East Second Street, Zip 82601–2988; tel. 307/577–7201 **A**1 3 10 **P**6
Primary Contact: Michele Chulick, President and Chief Executive Officer
COO: Chad Pew, Chief Operating Officer and Senior Vice President
CFO: Yvonne Wigington, Vice President, Chief Financial Officer
CMO: Carol M Solie M.D., Chief Medical Officer
CIO: Rob Pettigrew, Director Information Technology
CNO: Jan Nixon MS, Senior Vice President Patient Care Services and Chief Nursing Officer
Web address: www.wyomingmedicalcenter.org/
Control: Other not–for–profit (including NFP Corporation) **Service**: General medical and surgical

Staffed Beds: 217 **Admissions**: 8578 **Census**: 93 **Outpatient Visits**: 84116 **Births**: 1132 **Total Expense ($000)**: 211236 **Payroll Expense ($000)**: 75914 **Personnel**: 1033

CHEYENNE—Laramie County

⊞ △ **CHEYENNE REGIONAL MEDICAL CENTER (530014)**, 214 East 23rd Street, Zip 82001–3790; tel. 307/634–2273 **A**1 2 3 5 7 10 20 **F**3 5 8 13 15 17 18 20 22 24 26 28 29 30 31 32 34 35 37 38 40 43 44 45 46 47 48 49 50 51 56 57 59 60 61 62 63 64 65 68 70 73 74 76 77 78 79 81 82 83 84 85 86 87 89 90 91 92 93 96 97 98 99 100 101 102 103 104 105 106 107 108 111 115 116 117 118 119 120 121 122 123 124 126 128 130 131 135 143 146 147 148 149
Primary Contact: Patrick Madigan, Interim Chief Executive Officer
COO: Robin Roling FACHE, MS, R.N., Chief Operating Officer
CFO: Neil W Bertrand, Interim Chief Financial Officer
CMO: Jeffrey Chapman M.D., Chief Medical Officer
CIO: Craig Luzinski FACHE, MSN, R.N., Vice President Performance Optimization
CHR: Craig Luzinski FACHE, MSN, R.N., Vice President Performance Optimization
CNO: Tracy Garcia MS, Chief Nursing Officer
Web address: www.cheyenneregional.org/
Control: County, Government, Nonfederal **Service**: General medical and surgical

Staffed Beds: 138 **Admissions**: 10287 **Census**: 136 **Outpatient Visits**: 182737 **Births**: 1262 **Total Expense ($000)**: 282989 **Payroll Expense ($000)**: 114064 **Personnel**: 2127

Hospital, Medicare Provider Number, Address, Telephone, Approval, Facility, and Physician Codes, Health Care System

★ American Hospital Association (AHA) membership
☐ The Joint Commission accreditation
○ Healthcare Facilities Accreditation Program
◇ DNV Healthcare Inc. accreditation
⇑ Center for Improvement in Healthcare Quality Accreditation
△ Commission on Accreditation of Rehabilitation Facilities (CARF) accreditation

WY

✠ **CHEYENNE VETERANS AFFAIRS MEDICAL CENTER**, 2360 East Pershing Boulevard, Zip 82001–5392; tel. 307/778–7550, (Nonreporting) **A**1 3 **S** Department of Veterans Affairs, Washington, DC
Primary Contact: Paul L. Roberts, Director
CFO: Melvin Cranford, Chief Fiscal Services
CMO: Roger Johnson M.D., Chief of Staff
CIO: Liz McCulloch, Chief Information Resource Management Systems
CHR: Ron Lester, Chief Human Resources
Web address: www.cheyenne.va.gov/
Control: Veterans Affairs, Government, federal **Service**: General medical and surgical

Staffed Beds: 61

CODY—Park County

★ **WEST PARK HOSPITAL (531312)**, 707 Sheridan Avenue, Zip 82414–3409; tel. 307/527–7501, (Total facility includes 87 beds in nursing home–type unit) **A**10 18 **F**3 4 5 6 7 11 13 15 18 24 26 28 29 30 31 34 35 36 37 38 40 43 45 46 50 55 56 57 59 62 63 64 65 68 70 74 75 76 77 78 79 81 84 85 86 87 93 97 99 100 102 103 104 105 107 108 110 111 115 119 120 124 128 130 131 132 133 135 143 144 145 146 147 148 149 **P**6 **S** QHR, Brentwood, TN
Primary Contact: Douglas A. McMillan, Administrator and Chief Executive Officer
CFO: Patrick G McConnell, Chief Financial Officer
CMO: Gary Hart M.D., Chief Medical Officer
CHR: Dick Smith, Director Human Resources
Web address: www.westparkhospital.org
Control: Hospital district or authority, Government, Nonfederal **Service**: General medical and surgical

Staffed Beds: 112 Admissions: 1752 Census: 93 Outpatient Visits: 82048 Births: 227 Total Expense ($000): 89606 Payroll Expense ($000): 34682 Personnel: 535

DOUGLAS—Converse County

★ **MEMORIAL HOSPITAL OF CONVERSE COUNTY (531302)**, 111 South Fifth Street, Zip 82633–2434, Mailing Address: P.O.Box 1450, 82633–1450; tel. 307/358–2122 **A**10 18 **F**3 7 8 13 15 28 29 30 32 34 35 40 43 45 46 50 57 59 64 65 70 74 75 76 79 81 82 85 86 87 89 94 107 109 110 111 115 119 126 127 128 129 130 131 133 135 144 146 147 148 149 **P**6
Primary Contact: Ryan K. Smith, Chief Executive Officer
COO: Karl Edward Hertz, Assistant Administrator
CFO: Curtis R. Dugger, Chief Financial Officer
CMO: James Morgan M.D., Chief Medical Officer
CIO: Dave Patterson, Chief Information Officer
CHR: Linda York, Director Human Resource
CNO: Cristy Dicklich–Cobb, Chief Nursing Officer
Web address: www.conversehospital.com
Control: County, Government, Nonfederal **Service**: General medical and surgical

Staffed Beds: 25 Admissions: 848 Census: 8 Outpatient Visits: 37234 Births: 163 Total Expense ($000): 54170 Payroll Expense ($000): 28258 Personnel: 346

EVANSTON—Uinta County

✠ **EVANSTON REGIONAL HOSPITAL (530032)**, 190 Arrowhead Drive, Zip 82930–9266; tel. 307/789–3636 **A**1 10 20 **F**3 11 13 15 29 34 35 40 43 45 48 60 65 70 74 75 76 77 79 81 82 85 86 87 89 93 107 108 111 115 119 127 128 129 131 133 134 146 147 149 **P**6 **S** Quorum Health, Brentwood, TN
Primary Contact: Jeremy Davis, Chief Executive Officer
CHR: Joshua Jones, Director Human Resources
CNO: Cheri Willard R.N., Chief Nursing Officer
Web address: www.evanstonregionalhospital.com
Control: Corporation, Investor–owned (for–profit) **Service**: General medical and surgical

Staffed Beds: 42 Admissions: 610 Census: 3 Outpatient Visits: 21559 Births: 173 Total Expense ($000): 24640 Payroll Expense ($000): 10872 Personnel: 152

WYOMING STATE HOSPITAL (534001), 830 Highway 150 South, Zip 82931–5341, Mailing Address: P.O.Box 177, 82931–0177; tel. 307/789–3464, (Nonreporting) **A**10
Primary Contact: Rich Dunkley, Administrator
CFO: Paul Mullenax, Business Manager
CIO: Steve Baldwin, Manager Information Technology
Web address: www.health.wyo.gov/statehospital/index.html
Control: State, Government, Nonfederal **Service**: Psychiatric

Staffed Beds: 103

GILLETTE—Campbell County

★ ⇑ **CAMPBELL COUNTY HEALTH (530002)**, 501 South Burma Avenue, Zip 82716–3426, Mailing Address: P.O.Box 3011, 82717–3011; tel. 307/682–8811, (Total facility includes 125 beds in nursing home–type unit) **A**10 20 21 **F**3 5 6 7 8 11 13 15 18 20 22 26 28 29 30 31 34 35 38 40 43 45 50 51 53 54 56 59 60 62 63 64 65 66 68 70 71 73 74 75 76 77 78 79 81 82 84 85 86 87 91 93 94 96 97 98 99 100 101 102 103 104 105 107 108 109 110 111 114 115 116 118 119 120 121 125 129 130 131 132 133 134 135 143 144 146 147 148 149 **P**6
Primary Contact: Andy Fitzgerald, Chief Executive Officer
CFO: Dalton Huber, Chief Financial Officer
CIO: Chris Harrison, Manager Information Systems
CHR: John A Fitch, Vice President Human Resources
CNO: Deb L Tonn, Vice President Patient Care
Web address: www.ccmh.net
Control: Hospital district or authority, Government, Nonfederal **Service**: General medical and surgical

Staffed Beds: 196 Admissions: 2703 Census: 144 Outpatient Visits: 197471 Births: 861 Total Expense ($000): 178670 Payroll Expense ($000): 85345 Personnel: 948

JACKSON—Teton County

✠ **ST. JOHN'S MEDICAL CENTER AND LIVING CENTER (530015)**, 625 East Broadway Street, Zip 83001–8642, Mailing Address: P.O.Box 428, 83001–0428; tel. 307/733–3636, (Nonreporting) **A**1 5 10 20
Primary Contact: Paul Beaupre', M.D., Chief Executive Officer
COO: Gary Tauner, Chief Operating Officer
CFO: John Kren, Chief Financial Officer
CIO: Lance Spranger, Chief Information Officer
CNO: Lynn Kirman R.N., Chief Nursing Officer
Web address: www.tetonhospital.org
Control: Hospital district or authority, Government, Nonfederal **Service**: General medical and surgical

Staffed Beds: 106

KEMMERER—Lincoln County

★ **SOUTH LINCOLN MEDICAL CENTER (531315)**, 711 Onyx Street, Zip 83101–3214; tel. 307/877–4401, (Nonreporting) **A**10 18
Primary Contact: Kristin Housley, Interim Chief Executive Officer
CFO: Curtis Nielson, Chief Financial Officer
CMO: G Christopher Krell M.D., Chief of Staff
CIO: Kristin Housley, Chief Information Officer
CNO: Kathi Parks, Director of Nursing
Web address: www.southlincolnmedical.com
Control: Hospital district or authority, Government, Nonfederal **Service**: General medical and surgical

Staffed Beds: 38

LARAMIE—Albany County

✠ **IVINSON MEMORIAL HOSPITAL (530025)**, 255 North 30th Street, Zip 82072–5140; tel. 307/742–2141 **A**1 10 20 **F**3 7 11 13 15 29 30 31 35 40 51 60 70 73 75 76 77 78 79 81 87 89 93 94 97 98 99 107 108 110 111 115 119 128 129 130 132 133 146 148 149 **P**6
Primary Contact: Doug Faus, FACHE, Chief Executive Officer
COO: Holly Zajic, Chief Operating Officer
CFO: James G Bands IV, Chief Financial Officer
CMO: John Ullrich M.D., Chief of Staff
CIO: Brandon Lewis, Director of Information Technology
CHR: Kayla Parry, Manager Human Resources
CNO: Nicole Roonery, Chief Nursing Officer
Web address: www.ivinsonhospital.org
Control: Hospital district or authority, Government, Nonfederal **Service**: General medical and surgical

Staffed Beds: 99 Admissions: 2076 Census: 24 Outpatient Visits: 38492 Births: 429 Total Expense ($000): 75336 Payroll Expense ($000): 29129 Personnel: 435

Many Facility Codes have changed. Please refer to the AHA Guide Code Chart. © 2017 AHA Guide

LOVELL—Big Horn County

★ **NORTH BIG HORN HOSPITAL DISTRICT (531309)**, 1115 Lane 12, Zip 82431–
9537; tel. 307/548–5200, (Total facility includes 85 beds in nursing home–type
unit) **A**10 18 **F**3 6 7 10 15 28 29 30 34 35 36 40 41 45 50 56 57 59 64 65 66
68 71 75 79 81 82 85 86 87 93 97 107 110 114 119 127 128 130 131 132
133 135 143 146 147 148 **P**3 8
Primary Contact: Rick Schroeder, Chief Executive Officer
CFO: Lori Smith, Chief Financial Officer
CMO: Richard Jay D.O., Chief of Staff
CIO: Lisa Strom, Director Information Systems
CHR: Barbara Shumway, Director Human Resources
CNO: Tina Toner, Director of Nursing
Web address: www.nbhh.com
Control: Hospital district or authority, Government, Nonfederal **Service:** General
medical and surgical

Staffed Beds: 100 **Admissions:** 265 **Census:** 80 **Outpatient Visits:** 15164
Births: 0 **Total Expense ($000):** 17148 **Payroll Expense ($000):** 6414
Personnel: 206

LUSK—Niobrara County

★ **NIOBRARA HEALTH AND LIFE CENTER (531314)**, 921 Ballencee Avenue,
Zip 82225, Mailing Address: P.O.Box 780, 82225–0780; tel. 307/334–4000
(Nonreporting) **A**10 18
Primary Contact: Michelle Skillings, Interim Chief Executive Officer
Web address: www.niobrarahospital.com
Control: Hospital district or authority, Government, Nonfederal **Service:** General
medical and surgical

Staffed Beds: 24

NEWCASTLE—Weston County

★ **WESTON COUNTY HEALTH SERVICES (531303)**, 1124 Washington Boulevard,
Zip 82701–2972; tel. 307/746–4491, (Total facility includes 54 beds in nursing
home–type unit) **A**10 18 **F**3 28 29 35 40 41 43 50 57 59 62 64 77 93 107 114
119 129 130 135 148 **S** Regional Health, Rapid City, SD
Primary Contact: Maureen K. Cadwell, Chief Executive Officer
CFO: Lynn Moller, Chief Financial Officer
CMO: Chuck Franklin M.D., Chief Medical Staff
CIO: Terri Frye, Information Technology Officer
CHR: Julie A Sindlinger, Director of Human Resources
Web address: www.wchs–wy.org
Control: Hospital district or authority, Government, Nonfederal **Service:** General
medical and surgical

Staffed Beds: 66 **Admissions:** 183 **Census:** 58 **Outpatient Visits:** 12921
Births: 0 **Total Expense ($000):** 16315 **Payroll Expense ($000):** 7533
Personnel: 135

POWELL—Park County

★ **POWELL VALLEY HEALTHCARE (531310)**, 777 Avenue 'H', Zip 82435–2296;
tel. 307/754–2267, (Total facility includes 90 beds in nursing home–type unit) **A**10
18 **F**7 10 13 14 15 18 29 34 35 40 45 56 57 59 65 67 70 79 81 82 85 87 97
107 110 111 115 119 130 131 132 133 135 144 146 147 149 **S** HealthTech
Management Services, Brentwood, TN
Primary Contact: Terry Odom, Chief Executive Officer
CFO: Mike Long, Chief Financial Officer
CMO: Valerie Lengfelder M.D., Chief of Staff
CIO: Joshua Baxter, Director, Information Systems
CHR: Cassie Tinsley, Director, Human Resources
CNO: Arleen Campeau R.N., Vice President of Patient Care Services, Chief Nursing
Officer
Web address: www.pvhc.org
Control: Hospital district or authority, Government, Nonfederal **Service:** General
medical and surgical

Staffed Beds: 125 **Admissions:** 533 **Census:** 91 **Outpatient Visits:** 31916
Births: 167 **Total Expense ($000):** 46549 **Payroll Expense ($000):** 21448
Personnel: 341

RAWLINS—Carbon County

★ **MEMORIAL HOSPITAL OF CARBON COUNTY (531316)**, 2221 West
Elm Street, Zip 82301–5108, Mailing Address: P.O.Box 460, 82301–0460;
tel. 307/324–2221, (Nonreporting) **A**10 18 **S** QHR, Brentwood, TN
Primary Contact: Dana Barnett, Chief Executive Officer
CFO: David Pike, Interim Chief Financial Officer
CMO: David Cesko M.D., Chief of Staff
CIO: Toby Schaef, Director Information Technology
CNO: Amber Green R.N., Chief Clinical Officer
Web address: www.imhcc.com
Control: County, Government, Nonfederal **Service:** General medical and surgical

Staffed Beds: 25

RIVERTON—Fremont County

⊞ **SAGEWEST HEALTH CARE AT RIVERTON (530008)**, 2100 West Sunset
Drive, Zip 82501–2274; tel. 307/856–4161, (Includes SAGEWEST HEALTH CARE
AT LANDER, 1320 Bishop Randall Drive, Lander, Wyoming, Zip 82520–3996,
tel. 307/332–4420; Stephen M Erixon, Chief Executive Officer) **A**1 10 20 **F**3 11
12 13 15 28 29 34 35 39 40 43 45 50 57 59 68 70 74 75 76 77 79 81 82 85
87 90 93 97 98 103 106 107 108 110 111 114 115 119 129 130 131 132
146 147 148 149 **P**7 **S** LifePoint Health, Brentwood, TN
Primary Contact: Robert Alan. Daugherty, Chief Executive Officer
COO: Derrick Brumfield, Chief Operating Officer
CFO: Jennifer Hamilton, Chief Financial Officer
CMO: Cielette Karn M.D., Chief of Staff
CIO: Linda Tice, Director Information Systems
CHR: Dawn Nelson, Director Human Resources
CNO: Vickie Bessey MSN, R.N., Chief Nursing Officer
Web address: www.sagewesthealthcare.com
Control: Corporation, Investor–owned (for–profit) **Service:** General medical and
surgical

Staffed Beds: 71 **Admissions:** 2640 **Census:** 24 **Outpatient Visits:** 51569
Births: 485 **Total Expense ($000):** 46585 **Payroll Expense ($000):** 20519
Personnel: 284

ROCK SPRINGS—Sweetwater County

ASPEN MOUNTAIN MEDICAL CENTER (530035), 4401 College Drive, Zip
82901–3507; tel. 307/352–8900 (Nonreporting)
Primary Contact: Steve Perry, Chief Executive Officer
Web address: www.aspenmountainmc.com
Control: Partnership, Investor–owned (for–profit) **Service:** General medical and
surgical

Staffed Beds: 16

⊞ **MEMORIAL HOSPITAL OF SWEETWATER COUNTY (530011)**, 1200
College Drive, Zip 82901–5868, Mailing Address: P.O.Box 1359, 82902–1359;
tel. 307/362–3711 **A**1 10 20 **F**3 5 11 13 15 28 29 30 31 34 35 40 43 48 57
59 60 64 70 75 76 77 78 79 81 82 87 93 96 97 99 100 101 102 103 104 105
107 110 111 114 115 116 118 119 120 121 122 123 129 130 131 132 135
146 147
Primary Contact: Irene Richardson, Interim Chief Executive Officer
COO: Mandeep Gill, Chief Operating Officer
CFO: Irene Richardson, Chief Financial Officer
CMO: Sigsbee Duck M.D., President, Medical Staff
CHR: Amber Fisk, Director Human Resources
CNO: Kallie Mikkelsen, Vice President Nursing
Web address: www.sweetwatermemorial.com/default.aspx
Control: County, Government, Nonfederal **Service:** General medical and surgical

Staffed Beds: 58 **Admissions:** 2615 **Census:** 18 **Outpatient Visits:** 174143
Births: 564 **Total Expense ($000):** 90027 **Payroll Expense ($000):** 36647
Personnel: 568

SHERIDAN—Sheridan County

⊞ **SHERIDAN MEMORIAL HOSPITAL (530006)**, 1401 West Fifth Street, Zip
82801–2799; tel. 307/672–1000, (Nonreporting) **A**1 10 20
Primary Contact: Michael McCafferty, Chief Executive Officer
CFO: Charlotte Marie Mather R.N., Chief Nursing Officer
CMO: John Addlesperger D.O., Chief Medical Officer
CIO: Nyle Morgan, Chief Information Officer
CHR: Len Gross, Chief Human Resources Officer
Web address: www.sheridanhospital.org
Control: County, Government, Nonfederal **Service:** General medical and surgical

Staffed Beds: 88

Hospital, Medicare Provider Number, Address, Telephone, Approval, Facility, and Physician Codes, Health Care System

★ American Hospital Association (AHA) membership   ○ Healthcare Facilities Accreditation Program   ⇑ Center for Improvement in Healthcare Quality Accreditation
□ The Joint Commission accreditation   ◇ DNV Healthcare Inc. accreditation   △ Commission on Accreditation of Rehabilitation Facilities (CARF) accreditation

WY

⊞ SHERIDAN VETERANS AFFAIRS MEDICAL CENTER, 1898 Fort Road, Zip
82801–8320; tel. 307/672–3473, (Nonreporting) **A**1 **S** Department of Veterans
Affairs, Washington, DC
Primary Contact: Kathy Berger, R.N., Interim Director
COO: Chandra Lake, Associate Director
CFO: Donna Fuerstenberg, Fiscal Chief
CMO: Wendell Robison M.D., Chief of Staff
CIO: Anthony Giljum, Chief Information Officer
CHR: James Hardin, Human Resources Officer
Web address: www.sheridan.va.gov/
Control: Veterans Affairs, Government, federal **Service**: Psychiatric

> **Staffed Beds:** 185

SUNDANCE—Crook County

★ CROOK COUNTY MEDICAL SERVICES DISTRICT (531311), 713 Oak Street,
Zip 82729, Mailing Address: P.O.Box 517, 82729–0517; tel. 307/283–3501 **A**10
18 **F**7 40 41 44 57 59 64 65 68 75 107 127 130 133 143 146 148 149 150 **S**
Regional Health, Rapid City, SD
Primary Contact: Nathan Hough, Chief Executive Officer
CFO: Betty Meyers, Chief Financial Officer
CMO: Jeremi Villano M.D., Chief of Staff
CHR: Patricia Feist, Manager Human Resources
Web address: www.ccmsd.org/
Control: Hospital district or authority, Government, Nonfederal **Service**: General
medical and surgical

> **Staffed Beds:** 16 **Admissions:** 125 **Census:** 2 **Outpatient Visits:** 2000
> **Births:** 0

THERMOPOLIS—Hot Springs County

★ HOT SPRINGS COUNTY MEMORIAL HOSPITAL (531304), 150 East Arapahoe
Street, Zip 82443–2498; tel. 307/864–3121 **A**10 18 **F**3 11 13 15 28 29 31 34
35 40 43 45 57 59 64 68 75 81 85 107 108 110 111 115 119 127 129 130
133 135 145 146 148 **S** HealthTech Management Services, Brentwood, TN
Primary Contact: Margie Molitor, FACHE, R.N., Chief Executive Officer
CFO: Shelly Larson, Chief Financial Officer
CHR: Patti Jeunehomme, Director Human Resources
CNO: Sarah Aliff Ph.D., Chief Nursing Officer
Web address: www.hscmh.org
Control: County, Government, Nonfederal **Service**: General medical and surgical

> **Staffed Beds:** 25 **Admissions:** 409 **Census:** 3 **Outpatient Visits:** 13518
> **Births:** 63 **Total Expense ($000):** 15805 **Payroll Expense ($000):** 5389
> **Personnel:** 86

TORRINGTON—Goshen County

★ COMMUNITY HOSPITAL (531307), 2000 Campbell Drive, Zip 82240–1597;
tel. 307/532–4181 **A**10 18 **F**3 11 13 15 28 29 30 31 34 35 36 40 43 45 57 59
61 64 68 70 75 76 77 79 81 85 86 87 89 93 107 110 115 119 131 133 145
146 147 148 **S** Banner Health, Phoenix, AZ
Primary Contact: Shelby Nelson, Interim Chief Executive Officer
CMO: Bonnie Randolph M.D., Chief of Staff
CIO: Rod Miller, Chief Information Technology
Web address: www.bannerhealth.com/Locations/Wyoming/Community+Hospital/
Control: Other not–for–profit (including NFP Corporation) **Service**: General
medical and surgical

> **Staffed Beds:** 20 **Admissions:** 570 **Census:** 5 **Outpatient Visits:** 16859
> **Births:** 72 **Total Expense ($000):** 19077 **Payroll Expense ($000):** 7395
> **Personnel:** 140

WHEATLAND—Platte County

⊞ PLATTE COUNTY MEMORIAL HOSPITAL (531305), 201 14th Street, Zip
82201–3201, Mailing Address: P.O.Box 848, 82201–0848; tel. 307/322–3636
A1 10 18 **F**3 7 11 13 15 29 30 34 35 40 43 45 59 61 64 68 70 75 76 77
79 81 85 86 87 93 107 110 115 119 131 133 145 147 **S** Banner Health,
Phoenix, AZ
Primary Contact: Shelby Nelson, Chief Executive Officer
CFO: James Cussins, Chief Financial Officer
CMO: Willard Woods M.D., Chief Medical Officer
CIO: Robin May, Director Information Systems
CHR: Sandy Dugger, Chief Human Resources Officer
Web address: www.bannerhealth.com/Locations/Wyoming/
Platte+County+Memorial+Hospital
Control: Other not–for–profit (including NFP Corporation) **Service**: General
medical and surgical

> **Staffed Beds:** 25 **Admissions:** 429 **Census:** 4 **Outpatient Visits:** 13485
> **Births:** 50 **Total Expense ($000):** 18077 **Payroll Expense ($000):** 8191
> **Personnel:** 128

WORLAND—Washakie County

★ WASHAKIE MEDICAL CENTER (531306), 400 South 15th Street, Zip 82401–
3531, Mailing Address: P.O.Box 700, 82401–0700; tel. 307/347–3221 **A**10 18
F3 8 13 26 28 29 31 40 43 45 68 70 76 77 81 85 93 107 110 111 115 119
133 148 149 **S** Banner Health, Phoenix, AZ
Primary Contact: Jay Stallings, Chief Executive Officer
CFO: Jennifer Montgomery, Chief Financial Officer
CMO: Ryan Clifford M.D., Chief of Staff
CHR: Jerry Clipp, Manager Human Resources
Web address: www.washakiemedicalcenter.com
Control: Other not–for–profit (including NFP Corporation) **Service**: General
medical and surgical

> **Staffed Beds:** 18 **Admissions:** 426 **Census:** 4 **Births:** 24 **Total Expense
> ($000):** 20942 **Payroll Expense ($000):** 8083 **Personnel:** 111

WY

Many Facility Codes have changed. Please refer to the AHA Guide Code Chart.   © 2017 AHA Guide

AMERICAN SAMOA

PAGO PAGO—Washakie County

LYNDON B. JOHNSON TROPICAL MEDICAL CENTER (640001), Faga'alu Village, Zip 96799, Mailing Address: P.O.Box LBJ, 96799; tel. 684/633–1222, (Nonreporting) **A**10
Primary Contact: Taufete's John. Faumuina, Chief Executive Officer
Web address: www.asmca.org
Control: State, Government, Nonfederal **Service**: General medical and surgical

Staffed Beds: 125

GUAM

AGANA—Guam County

⊞ **U. S. NAVAL HOSPITAL GUAM**, Building #50 Farenholt Avenue, Zip 96910, Mailing Address: PSC 490, Box 208, FPO, 96540; tel. 671/344–9340, (Nonreporting) **A**1 **S** Bureau of Medicine and Surgery, Department of the Navy, Falls Church, VA
Primary Contact: Captain Daniel Cornwell, Command Officer
Web address: www.med.navy.mil/sites/usnhguam/Pages/default.aspx
Control: Navy, Government, federal **Service**: General medical and surgical

Staffed Beds: 55

DEDEDO—Guam County

★ **GUAM REGIONAL MEDICAL CITY**, 133 Route 3, Zip 96932, Mailing Address: P.O.Box 3830, Hagatna, 96932; tel. 671/645–5500 (Nonreporting)
Primary Contact: Gloria Long, Chief Operating Officer
Web address: www.grmc.gu/
Control: Corporation, Investor–owned (for–profit) **Service**: General medical and surgical

Staffed Beds: 130

TAMUNING—Guam County

☐ **GUAM MEMORIAL HOSPITAL AUTHORITY (650001)**, 850 Governor Carlos G Camacho Road, Zip 96913; tel. 671/647–2108, (Nonreporting) **A**1 10
Primary Contact: Joseph P. Verga, FACHE, Chief Executive Officer
CFO: Alan Ulrich, Chief Financial Officer
CMO: James J Stadler M.D., Associate Administrator Medical Services
CIO: Vince Quichocho, Manager Information Systems
CHR: Elizabeth Claros, Administrator Personnel Services
Web address: www.gmha.org
Control: Hospital district or authority, Government, Nonfederal **Service**: General medical and surgical

Staffed Beds: 104

MARSHALL ISLANDS

KWAJALEIN ISLAND—Guam County

KWAJALEIN HOSPITAL, U S Army Kwajalein Atoll, Zip 96960, Mailing Address: Box 1702, APO, UNIT, 96555–5000; tel. 805/355–2225, (Nonreporting) **S** Department of the Army, Office of the Surgeon General, Falls Church, VA
Primary Contact: Elaine McMahon, Administrator
Control: Army, Government, federal **Service**: General medical and surgical

Staffed Beds: 14

NORTHERN MARIANA ISLANDS

SAIPAN—Guam County

★ **COMMONWEALTH HEALTH CENTER (660001)**, Navy Hill Road, Zip 96950, Mailing Address: P.O.Box 500409, 96950; tel. 670/234–8950 (Nonreporting) **A**10
Primary Contact: Esther L. Muna, Chief Executive Officer
CFO: Priscilla Maratita Iakopo, Chief Financial Officer
CMO: John M Tudela M.D., Director of Medical Affairs
CIO: Anthony Reyes, Information Technology Director
CHR: Clarinda Ngiraisui, Human Resource Manager
CNO: Leslie Camacho R.N., Director of Nursing
Web address: www.chcc.gov.mp
Control: Corporation, Investor–owned (for–profit) **Service**: General medical and surgical

Staffed Beds: 86

PUERTO RICO

AGUADILLA—Aguadilla County

HOSPITAL BUEN SAMARITANO (400079), Carr #2 Km 141–1 Ave Severiano Cuevas, Zip 603, Mailing Address: P.O.Box 4055, 00605–4055; tel. 787/658–0000 **A**1 5 10 **F**3 13 14 15 29 30 34 40 41 45 50 57 59 65 70 74 75 76 77 78 79 81 82 87 89 107 111 114 119 130 146 148 149 **P**8
Primary Contact: Marilyn Morales, Chief Executive Officer
CFO: Edwin Orama Acevedo, Financial Supervisor
CMO: Arturo Cedeno Llorens M.D., Medical Director
CHR: Jose Garcia Rivera, Director Human Resources
CNO: Eneida Alicea Perez, Interim Nursing Director
Web address: www.hbspr.org
Control: Other not–for–profit (including NFP Corporation) **Service**: General medical and surgical

Staffed Beds: 138 **Admissions**: 5837 **Census**: 82 **Outpatient Visits**: 52233 **Births**: 193 **Total Expense ($000)**: 37632 **Payroll Expense ($000)**: 11302

AIBONITO—Aibonito County

CENTRO DE SALUD CONDUCTUAL MENONITA–CIMA (404009), Carretera Estatal 14 Interior, Zip 705, Mailing Address: PO Box 871, 705; tel. 787/714–2462, (Nonreporting) **A**1 5 10
Primary Contact: Pedro Melendez, Chief Executive Officer
Web address: www.menonitacima.org
Control: Other not–for–profit (including NFP Corporation) **Service**: Psychiatric

Staffed Beds: 20

Hospital, Medicare Provider Number, Address, Telephone, Approval, Facility, and Physician Codes, Health Care System

★ American Hospital Association (AHA) membership ○ Healthcare Facilities Accreditation Program ⇑ Center for Improvement in Healthcare Quality Accreditation
☐ The Joint Commission accreditation ◇ DNV Healthcare Inc. accreditation △ Commission on Accreditation of Rehabilitation Facilities (CARF) accreditation

MENNONITE GENERAL HOSPITAL (400018), Calle Jose C Vasquez, Zip 705, Mailing Address: P.O.Box 372800, Cayey, 00737–2800; tel. 787/535–1001, (Nonreporting) **A**1 10
Primary Contact: Pedro Melendez, Chief Executive Officer
COO: Marta R Mercado Suro, Chief Operating Officer
CFO: Jose E Solivan, Chief Financial Officer
CMO: Victor Hernandez Miranda M.D., Chief of Staff
CIO: Daniza Morales, Manager Information System
CHR: Evelyn Padilla Ortiz, Director Human Resources
CNO: Gloria Mercado, Director of Nursing
Web address: www.hospitalmenonita.com
Control: Other not–for–profit (including NFP Corporation) **Service**: General medical and surgical

Staffed Beds: 143

ARECIBO—Arecibo County

HOSPITAL METROPOLITANO DR. SUSONI (400117), Calle Palma #55, Zip 612, Mailing Address: P.O.Box 145200, 614; tel. 787/650–1030 **A**10 **F**15 17 29 40 41 45 46 49 51 64 70 74 75 77 87 89 107 110 111 114 119 130 136 147 148
Primary Contact: Yelitza Lucena, Executive Director
CFO: Francisco Silva, Financial Director
CMO: Ada S Miranda M.D., Medical Director
CIO: Mayra Montano, Director Information Systems
CHR: Janira Hernandez, Coordinator Human Resources
CNO: Damaris Rios, Executive Nursing Director
Web address: www.metropavia.com/DrSusoni.cfm
Control: Corporation, Investor–owned (for–profit) **Service**: General medical and surgical

Staffed Beds: 130 Admissions: 7045 Census: 98 Outpatient Visits: 63452 Births: 0 Total Expense ($000): 43442 Payroll Expense ($000): 14293 Personnel: 554

HOSPITAL PAVIA ARECIBO (400087), 129 San Luis Avenue, Zip 612, Mailing Address: P.O.Box 659, 613; tel. 787/650–7272, (Nonreporting) **A**1 3 10
Primary Contact: Jose Luis Rodriguez Collazo, Executive Director
COO: Jamie Rivera, Chief Financial Officer
CFO: Agustin Gonzalez, Director Finance
CMO: Antoine Pavia M.D., Medical Director
CIO: David Valle, Chief Information Officer
CHR: Yesenia Natal, Coordinator Human Resources
CNO: Iris Toledo, Chief Nursing Officer
Web address: www.cayetano@xsn.net
Control: Corporation, Investor–owned (for–profit) **Service**: General medical and surgical

Staffed Beds: 202

BAYAMON—Bayamon County

DOCTOR'S CENTER OF BAYAMON (400102), Extension Hermanas Davila, Zip 960, Mailing Address: P.O.Box 2957, 960; tel. 787/622–5420, (Nonreporting) **A**10
Primary Contact: Maria Marte, Administrator
Web address: www.tuhospitalfamiliar.com
Control: Corporation, Investor–owned (for–profit) **Service**: General medical and surgical

Staffed Beds: 91

HOSPITAL HERMANOS MELENDEZ (400032), Route 2, KM 11–7, Zip 960, Mailing Address: P.O.Box 306, 960; tel. 787/620–8181, (Nonreporting) (Includes PUERTO RICO CHILDREN'S HOSPITAL, P O Box 1999, Bayamon, Puerto Rico, Zip 960, tel. 787/474–1378; Tania Conde, Administrator) **A**1 3 10
Primary Contact: Richard Machado, M.D., President and Chief Executive Officer
CFO: Luz D Medina, Controller
CMO: Norma Ortiz M.D., Medical Director
CIO: Leticia Santana, Administrator Medical Records
Web address: www.hospitalhermanosmelendez.net
Control: Corporation, Investor–owned (for–profit) **Service**: General medical and surgical

Staffed Beds: 211

HOSPITAL SAN PABLO (400109), Calle Santa Cruz 70, Zip 00961–7020, Mailing Address: P.O.Box 236, 00960–0236; tel. 787/740–4747 **A**1 3 5 10 **F**3 8 13 15 17 18 19 20 21 22 23 24 26 29 30 31 34 40 41 45 46 47 49 51 57 59 64 68 70 72 73 74 75 76 77 78 79 80 81 86 87 88 89 92 93 107 108 110 111 114 115 119 126 130 145 146 147 148 **P**5 8
Primary Contact: Claudia V. Guzman, Chief Executive Officer and Managing Director
Web address: www.sanpablo.com
Control: Corporation, Investor–owned (for–profit) **Service**: General medical and surgical

Staffed Beds: 400 Admissions: 15727 Census: 279 Outpatient Visits: 59972 Births: 1223 Personnel: 1454

HOSPITAL UNIVERSITARIO DR. RAMON RUIZ ARNAU (400105), Avenue Laurel #100, Santa Juanita, Zip 956; tel. 787/787–5151, (Nonreporting) **A**1 3 5 10 **S** Puerto Rico Department of Health, San Juan, PR
Primary Contact: Prudencio A. Laureano, Chief Executive Officer
CFO: Elsie Morales, Chief Financial Officer
CMO: Hector Cintron Principe M.D., Director
CIO: Irma Duprey, Administrator Medical Records
CHR: Aurea De Leon, Chief Human Resources Officer
Web address: www.salud.gov.pr/Dept–de–Salud/Pages/Nuestros–Hospitales.aspx
Control: State, Government, Nonfederal **Service**: General medical and surgical

Staffed Beds: 101

CABO ROJO—Cabo Rojo County

HOSPITAL PSIQUIATRICO METROPOLITANO (404007), 108 Munoz Rivera Street, Zip 00623–4060, Mailing Address: P.O.Box 910, 00623–0910; tel. 787/851–2025 **A**1 10 **F**40 41 98 102 103 104 105
Primary Contact: Marco Reyes, Executive Director
Web address: www.metropavia.com/CaboRojo.cfm
Control: Corporation, Investor–owned (for–profit) **Service**: Psychiatric

Staffed Beds: 43 Admissions: 1208 Census: 19 Outpatient Visits: 29610 Births: 0 Total Expense ($000): 4305 Payroll Expense ($000): 2890 Personnel: 80

CAGUAS—Caguas County

HIMA SAN PABLO CAGUAS (400120), Avenida Munoz Marin, Zip 726, Mailing Address: P.O.Box 4980, 726; tel. 787/653–3434 **A**1 2 3 5 10 **F**3 8 13 15 16 20 22 26 29 30 31 34 40 41 42 43 45 46 49 50 57 58 68 70 72 74 75 76 78 79 80 81 87 88 89 93 107 108 111 114 115 116 117 118 119 124 126 130 135 136 141 142 145 146 147 148 **P**8
Primary Contact: Maria E. Jacobo Moreno, Administrator
CFO: Luis A Arroyo, Chief Financial Officer
CMO: Ivan E Del Toro M.D., Medical Director
CIO: Giovanni Piereschi, Vice President Enterprise Information and Chief Information Officer
CHR: Elena Robinson, Chief Human Resources Officer
CNO: Elenia Berrios, Chief Nursing Officer
Web address: www.himasanpablo.com
Control: Corporation, Investor–owned (for–profit) **Service**: General medical and surgical

Staffed Beds: 415 Admissions: 16717 Census: 301 Outpatient Visits: 83220 Births: 1695

HOSPITAL MENONITA DE CAGUAS (400104), P.O. Box 6660, Zip 00726–6660; tel. 787/653–0550 (Nonreporting) **A**1 5 10
Primary Contact: Eric Grafals, JD, Administrator
Web address: www.sistemamenonita.com
Control: Other not–for–profit (including NFP Corporation) **Service**: General medical and surgical

Staffed Beds: 25

CAROLINA—Carolina County

HOSPITAL DE LA UNIVERSIDAD DE PUERTO RICO/DR. FEDERICO TRILLA (400112), 65th Infanteria, KM 8 3, Zip 984, Mailing Address: P.O.Box 6021, 984; tel. 787/757–1800, (Nonreporting) **A**1 3 5 10
Primary Contact: Diraida Maldonado, Chief Executive Officer
COO: Diraida Maldonado, Chief Executive Officer
CFO: Yolanda Quinonez, Chief Financial Officer
CMO: Marina Roman M.D., Medical Director
CIO: Francisco Perez, Manager Management Information Systems
CHR: Betzaida Jimenez, Director Human Resources
Web address: www.hospitalupr.org
Control: Corporation, Investor–owned (for–profit) **Service**: General medical and surgical

Staffed Beds: 250

Many Facility Codes have changed. Please refer to the AHA Guide Code Chart. © 2017 AHA Guide

CASTANER—Lares County

CASTANER GENERAL HOSPITAL (400010), KM 64-2, Route 135, Zip 631, Mailing Address: P.O.Box 1003, 631; tel. 787/829-5010, (Nonreporting) **A**3 5 10
Primary Contact: Domingo Monroig, Executive Director
COO: Agustin Ponce, Supervisor Maintenance
CFO: Guillermo Jimenez, Director Finance
CMO: Jose O Rodriguez M.D., Medical Director
CIO: Domingo Monroig, Executive Director
CHR: Nydimar Salcedo, Chief Human Resources Officer
CNO: Margarita Rentas R.N., Nursing Director
Web address: www.hospitalcastaner.com
Control: Other not-for-profit (including NFP Corporation) **Service:** General medical and surgical

Staffed Beds: 24

CAYEY—Cayey County

HOSPITAL MENONITA DE CAYEY (400013), 4 H Mendoza Street, Zip 00736-3801, Mailing Address: P.O.Box 373130, 00737-3130; tel. 787/263-1001 **A**1 5 10 **F**1 4 8 12 13 15 16 17 18 20 22 24 26 28 29 30 32 34 40 41 42 45 46 47 48 49 65 67 69 70 71 72 73 74 75 76 78 79 80 81 82 85 88 89 90 94 98 107 109 110 111 112 113 114 115 119 120 128 130 132 135 136 143 145 146
Primary Contact: Pedro Melendez, Chief Executive Director
COO: Leda Marta R Mercado, Chief Operating Officer
CFO: Jose E Solivan, Chief Financial Officer
CMO: Luis J Rodriquez Saenz M.D., Medical Director
CIO: Daniza Morales, Chief Information Officer
CHR: Evelyn Padilla Ortiz, Director Human Resources
Web address: www.hospitalmenonita.com
Control: Other not-for-profit (including NFP Corporation) **Service:** General medical and surgical

Staffed Beds: 242 Admissions: 11089 Census: 159 Outpatient Visits: 92789 Births: 2640 Total Expense ($000): 84837 Payroll Expense ($000): 14077

CIDRA—Cidra County

FIRST HOSPITAL PANAMERICANO (404004), State Road 787 KM 1 5, Zip 739, Mailing Address: P.O.Box 1400, 739; tel. 787/739-5555, (Nonreporting) **A**1 3 5 10 **S** Universal Health Services, Inc., King of Prussia, PA
Primary Contact: Astro Munoz, Executive Director
COO: Tim McCarthy, President Puerto Rico Division
CFO: Arthur Fernandez, Chief Financial Officer
CMO: Arlene Martinez–Nieto M.D., Chief Medical Officer
CIO: Tomas Rodriguez, Chief Information Technology Officer
CHR: Shirley Ayala, Director Human Resources
Web address: www.hospitalpanamericano.com
Control: Corporation, Investor-owned (for-profit) **Service:** Psychiatric

Staffed Beds: 153

COTO LAUREL—Ponce County

HOSPITAL SAN CRISTOBAL (400113), 506 Carr Road, Zip 780; tel. 787/848-2100, (Nonreporting) **A**3 5 10
Primary Contact: Pedro L. Benetti–Loyola, Administrator
COO: Pedro L Benetti–Loyola, Senior Executive and Vice President
CFO: Marian Collazo, Director Finance
CMO: Ramon Rodriguez Rivas M.D., Medical Director
CIO: Ramon Acevedo, Supervisor Information Systems
CHR: Candie Rodriguez, Director Human Resources
Web address: www.hospitalsancristobal.com
Control: Corporation, Investor-owned (for-profit) **Service:** Other specialty treatment

Staffed Beds: 103

FAJARDO—Fajardo County

CARIBBEAN MEDICAL CENTER (400131), 151 Avenue Osvaldo Molina, Zip 00738-4013, Mailing Address: Call Box 70006, 00738-7006; tel. 787/801-0081, (Nonreporting) **A**10
Primary Contact: Ana Oliveras Laguna, Administrator
CMO: Miguel Rodriguez, Medical Director
Web address: www.caribbeanmedicalcenter.com
Control: Other not-for-profit (including NFP Corporation) **Service:** General medical and surgical

Staffed Beds: 39

HOSPITAL SAN PABLO DEL ESTE (400125), Avenida General Valero, 404, Zip 738, Mailing Address: P.O.Box 1028, 00738-1028; tel. 787/863-0505 **A**1 10 **F**3 7 13 29 30 34 40 57 58 59 60 68 70 72 73 74 75 76 79 81 87 89 93 98 107 110 111 114 115 116 117 118 119 124 126 130 132 143 146 148 149 **P**1
Primary Contact: Venus V. Ramirez, Executive Director
CFO: Luis A Arroyo, Chief Financial Officer
CMO: Manuel Navas M.D., Medical Director
CHR: Vilma Rodriguez, Director Human Resources
Web address: www.sanpablo.com
Control: Corporation, Investor-owned (for-profit) **Service:** General medical and surgical

Staffed Beds: 221 Admissions: 3157 Census: 55 Outpatient Visits: 21025 Births: 261

GUAYAMA—Guayama County

HOSPITAL EPISCOPAL SAN LUCAS GUAYAMA (400048), Avenue Pedro Albizu Campos, Zip 784, Mailing Address: PO Box 10011, 00785-1006; tel. 787/864-4300 **A**1 3 5 10 **F**3 7 13 15 30 40 41 45 46 65 70 73 75 76 81 87 89 91 93 107 111 114 119 130 135 145 148 149
Primary Contact: Elyonel Ponton, Executive Director
COO: Arnaldo Rodriguez Sanchez M.D., Chief Operating Officer
CFO: Rosemary De La Cruz, Chief Financial Officer
CMO: Gerson Jimenez M.D., Medical Director
CHR: Ivette Lacot, Director Human Resources
Web address: www.ssepr.com
Control: Church operated, Nongovernment, not-for-profit **Service:** General medical and surgical

Staffed Beds: 115 Admissions: 5443 Census: 64 Outpatient Visits: 68542 Births: 463 Total Expense ($000): 30222 Payroll Expense ($000): 8936

GUAYNABO—Guaynabo County

PROFESSIONAL HOSPITAL GUAYNABO (400122), Carretera 199 Km 1.2 Avenue, Zip 969, Mailing Address: PO Box 1609, 970; tel. 787/708-6560 (Nonreporting) **A**3 5 10
Primary Contact: Leonardo Valentin, Chief Executive Officer
Web address: www.professionalhospital.com
Control: Other not-for-profit (including NFP Corporation) **Service:** Psychiatric

Staffed Beds: 54

HATO REY—San Juan County

I. GONZALEZ MARTINEZ ONCOLOGIC HOSPITAL (400012), Puerto Rico Medical Center, Zip 935, Mailing Address: P.O.Box 191811, 00919-1811; tel. 787/765-2382, (Nonreporting) **A**1 2 3 5 10
Primary Contact: Jorge De Jesus, Executive Director
COO: Felix Ortiz Baez, Administrator
CFO: Yolanda Quinones, Director Finance
CMO: Carlos Chevere M.D., Medical Director
CHR: Luz Maria Hernandez, Director Human Resources
Control: Other not-for-profit (including NFP Corporation) **Service:** Cancer

Staffed Beds: 57

HUMACAO—Humacao County

HOSPITAL DR. DOMINGUEZ See Hospital Oriente

HOSPITAL HIMA DE HUMACAO (400005), 3 Font Martelo Street, Zip 00791-3342, Mailing Address: P.O.Box 639, 00792-0639; tel. 787/656-2424 **A**1 10 **F**3 15 40 46 70 74 75 76 78 79 81 87 89 93 107 111 119 130 135
Primary Contact: Aixa Irizarry, Executive Director
COO: Carlos M Pineiro, President
CFO: Luis A Arroyo, Chief Financial Officer
CMO: Francisco R. Carballo M.D., Medical Director
CIO: Giovanni Piereschi, Vice President Management Information Systems
CHR: Iris Abreu, Supervisor Human Resources
Web address: www.himasanpablo.com
Control: Corporation, Investor-owned (for-profit) **Service:** General medical and surgical

Staffed Beds: 64 Admissions: 2217 Census: 39 Outpatient Visits: 65158 Births: 67

Hospital, Medicare Provider Number, Address, Telephone, Approval, Facility, and Physician Codes, Health Care System

★ American Hospital Association (AHA) membership
☐ The Joint Commission accreditation
○ Healthcare Facilities Accreditation Program
◇ DNV Healthcare Inc. accreditation
⇑ Center for Improvement in Healthcare Quality Accreditation
△ Commission on Accreditation of Rehabilitation Facilities (CARF) accreditation

HOSPITAL ORIENTE (400011), 300 Font Martelo Street, Zip 00791–3230, Mailing Address: P.O.Box 699, 00792–0699; tel. 787/852–0505, (Nonreporting) **A**10
Primary Contact: Efrain Pinero, Administrator
CFO: Ivonne Rivera, Director Finance
CMO: Carmelo Herrero M.D., Medical Director
CHR: Ivonne Lopez, Director Human Resources
Control: Corporation, Investor–owned (for–profit) **Service**: General medical and surgical

Staffed Beds: 60

RYDER MEMORIAL HOSPITAL (400007), 355 Font Martelo Street, Zip 00791–3249, Mailing Address: P O Box 859, 00792–0859; tel. 787/852–0768, (Total facility includes 62 beds in nursing home–type unit) **A**5 10 **F**3 13 15 18 20 22 26 29 30 31 34 35 39 40 41 42 57 59 61 62 63 64 65 70 71 72 74 75 76 77 78 79 81 87 89 93 94 97 107 110 111 115 118 119 125 128 130 144 146 147
Primary Contact: Jose R. Feliciano, Chief Executive Officer
CFO: Jose O Ortiz, Chief Financial Officer
CMO: Raul Ramos Pereira M.D., Medical Director
CIO: Joseph V Cruz, Chief Information Officer
CHR: Maria Figueroa, Director Human Resources
CNO: Aurelis Burgus, Nursing Director
Web address: www.hryder@prtc.net
Control: Other not–for–profit (including NFP Corporation) **Service**: General medical and surgical

Staffed Beds: 227 Admissions: 6606 Census: 114 Outpatient Visits: 137965 Births: 707 Personnel: 782

MANATI—Manati County

DOCTORS CENTER (400118), KM 47–7, Zip 674, Mailing Address: P.O.Box 30532, 674; tel. 787/854–3322, (Nonreporting) **A**1 10
Primary Contact: Belinda L. Toro Palacios, Executive Director
Web address: www.tuhospitalfamiliar.com
Control: Corporation, Investor–owned (for–profit) **Service**: General medical and surgical

Staffed Beds: 150

HEALTHSOUTH HOSPITAL OF MANATI (403026), Carretera 2, Kilometro 47 7, Zip 674; tel. 787/621–3800, (Nonreporting) **A**10 **S** HEALTHSOUTH Corporation, Birmingham, AL
Primary Contact: Waleska Crespo–Rivera, Chief Executive Officer
CFO: Jesus M Corazon, Controller
CMO: Jamie L Marrero M.D., Medical Director
CHR: Erika Landrau, Director Human Resources
CNO: Evelyn Diaz R.N., Chief Nursing Officer
Web address: www.healthsouth.com
Control: Corporation, Investor–owned (for–profit) **Service**: Rehabilitation

Staffed Beds: 40

HOSPITAL MANATI MEDICAL CENTER (400114), Calle Hernandez, Carrion 668, Zip 674, Mailing Address: P.O.Box 1142, 00674–1142; tel. 787/621–3700, (Nonreporting) **A**1 3 5 10
Primary Contact: Jose S. Rosado, Executive Director
CFO: Noriselle Rivera–Pol, Vice President Finance
CMO: Luis R Rosa–Toledo M.D., Medical Director
CIO: Alberto Medina, Information Technology Senior Consultant
CHR: Nilda Paravisini, Director Human Resources
Web address: www.manatimedical.com
Control: Corporation, Investor–owned (for–profit) **Service**: General medical and surgical

Staffed Beds: 235

MAYAGUEZ—Mayaguez County

BELLA VISTA HOSPITAL (400014), State Road 349, Zip 680, Mailing Address: P.O.Box 1750, 681; tel. 787/834–6000, (Nonreporting) **A**1 3 5 10
Primary Contact: Luis Rivera Maldonado, Executive Director
CFO: Enrique Rivera, Chief Financial Officer
CMO: Miguel Cruz M.D., Medical Director
CHR: Benjamin Astacio, Director Human Resources
Web address: www.bvhpr.org
Control: Church operated, Nongovernment, not–for–profit **Service**: General medical and surgical

Staffed Beds: 157

DR. RAMON E. BETANCES HOSPITAL–MAYAGUEZ MEDICAL CENTER BRANCH (400103), 410 Hostos Avenue, Zip 00680–1501, Mailing Address: P.O.Box 600, 00681–0600; tel. 787/652–9200 **A**1 3 5 10 **F**3 14 17 18 20 22 24 26 28 29 40 41 43 45 47 48 49 51 68 70 75 79 81 89 107 111 114 115 119 130 143 145 148 149
Primary Contact: Idelfonso Vargas, Executive Director
CMO: Milton D Carrero M.D., Medical Director
CHR: Betsmari Medina, Director Human Resources
Web address: www.mayaguezmedical.com
Control: Corporation, Investor–owned (for–profit) **Service**: General medical and surgical

Staffed Beds: 189 Admissions: 9258 Census: 148 Outpatient Visits: 33615 Births: 0

HOSPITAL PEREA (400123), 15 Basora Street, Zip 681, Mailing Address: P.O.Box 170, 681; tel. 787/834–0101, (Nonreporting) **A**3 10 **S** United Medical Corporation, Windermere, FL
Primary Contact: Jorge I. Martinez, Executive Director
CFO: Joannie Garcia CPA, Director Finance
CMO: Humberto Olivencia M.D., Medical Director
Web address: www.paviahealth.com/perea_hospital.htm
Control: Corporation, Investor–owned (for–profit) **Service**: General medical and surgical

Staffed Beds: 103

HOSPITAL SAN ANTONIO (018487), Calle Dr Ramon Emeterio Betances N #18, Zip 680, Mailing Address: PO Box 546, 00681–0546; tel. 787/834–0050 (Nonreporting) **A**3 5
Primary Contact: Francisco Martinez, Executive Director
Web address: www.hsaipr.com/
Control: Other not–for–profit (including NFP Corporation) **Service**: General medical and surgical

Staffed Beds: 25

MOCA—Moca County

HOSPITAL SAN CARLOS BORROMEO (400111), 550 Concepcion Vera Ayala, Zip 676, Mailing Address: PO Box 68, 676; tel. 787/877–8000, (Nonreporting) **A**10
Primary Contact: Rosaida M. Crespo, Executive Director
COO: Rosaida M Crespo, Executive Director
CFO: Irma Cabrera, Finance Director
CMO: Erick Nieves M.D., Medical Director
CIO: Juan Carlos Soto, Director Information Systems
CHR: Migdalia Ortiz, Director Human Resources
CNO: Luz M Velez, Director–Administration of Nursing Services
Web address: www.hscbpr.org
Control: Other not–for–profit (including NFP Corporation) **Service**: General medical and surgical

Staffed Beds: 106

PONCE—Ponce County

DR. PILA'S HOSPITAL (400003), Avenida Las Americas, Zip 731, Mailing Address: P.O.Box 1910, 00733–1910; tel. 787/848–5600, (Nonreporting) **A**1 3 5 10
Primary Contact: Rafael Alvarado, Chief Executive Officer
Web address: www.drpila.com
Control: Other not–for–profit (including NFP Corporation) **Service**: General medical and surgical

Staffed Beds: 143

HOSPITAL DE DAMAS (400022), 2213 Ponce Bypass, Zip 717; tel. 787/840–8686, (Total facility includes 24 beds in nursing home–type unit) **A**1 3 5 10 **F**3 8 13 14 15 17 18 20 22 24 30 31 40 41 45 46 48 49 62 70 72 74 75 77 78 79 81 86 87 92 94 96 107 108 109 110 111 116 117 118 119 120 121 122 128 129 130 143 145 146 148 149
Primary Contact: Maria Mercedes Torres. Bernal, Administrator
CFO: Julio Colon, Financial Director
CMO: Pedro Benitez M.D., Medical Director
CIO: Bienvenido Ortiz, Coordinator Information Systems
CHR: Gilberto Cuevas, Director Human Resources
CNO: Sandra Dominicci, Nursing Director
Web address: www.hospitaldamas.com/
Control: Other not–for–profit (including NFP Corporation) **Service**: General medical and surgical

Staffed Beds: 201 Admissions: 9855 Census: 127 Outpatient Visits: 42574 Births: 957

HOSPITAL DE PSIQUIATRIA FORENSE, Road 14, Zip 731; tel. 787/844–0210 (Nonreporting)
Primary Contact: Nemuel O. Artiles, FACHE, Administrator
Web address: www.bestmentalhealthfacilities.com/hospital-psiquiatria-forenseponce-in-ponce-pr-731/
Control: State, Government, Nonfederal **Service**: Psychiatric

Staffed Beds: 25

INSPIRA PONCE (404008), Calle Guadalupe, #184, Piso2, Zip 730; tel. 787/709–4130 (Nonreporting) **A**10
Primary Contact: Alberto M. Varela, M.D., President
Web address: www.inspirapr.com
Control: Corporation, Investor–owned (for–profit) **Service**: Psychiatric

Staffed Beds: 30

ST. LUKE'S EPISCOPAL HOSPITAL (400044), 917 Tito Castro Avenue, Zip 00731–4717, Mailing Address: P.O.Box 336810, 00733–6810; tel. 787/844–2080, (Nonreporting) **A**1 3 5 10
Primary Contact: Pedro Barez, FACHE, Chief Operating Officer
CFO: Julio Colon, Chief Financial Officer
CMO: Jenaro Scarano M.D., Medical Director
CHR: Juan Salazar, Director Human Resources
Web address: www.sanlucaspr.com
Control: Church operated, Nongovernment, not–for–profit **Service**: General medical and surgical

Staffed Beds: 334

RIO PIEDRAS—San Juan County

UNIVERSITY PEDIATRIC HOSPITAL (403301), Barrio Monacenno, Carretera 22, Zip 935, Mailing Address: P.O.Box 191079, San Juan, 00910–1070; tel. 787/777–3535, (Nonreporting) **A**1 3 5 10 **S** Puerto Rico Department of Health, San Juan, PR
Primary Contact: Gloria Hernandez, Executive Director
CMO: Myrna Quinones Feliciano M.D., Medical Director
Web address: www.md.rcm.upr.edu/pediatrics/university_pediatric_hospital.php
Control: State, Government, Nonfederal **Service**: Children's general medical and surgical

Staffed Beds: 145

SAN GERMAN—San German County

HOSPITAL DE LA CONCEPCION (400021), Carr 2, Km 173, Bo Cain Alto, Zip 00683–3920, Mailing Address: P.O.Box 285, 00683–0285; tel. 787/892–1860 **A**1 3 5 10 **F**8 13 15 18 20 29 30 34 39 40 45 46 57 58 59 70 72 74 75 77 79 81 87 90 91 93 107 110 111 115 119 130 145 146 148 149 150 **P**7
Primary Contact: Felicita Bonilla, Administrator
COO: Gustavo Almodovar, Executive Director
CFO: Lizmari Calderon, Director Finance
CMO: Ivan Acosta M.D., Medical Director
CIO: Daniel Ferreira, Director Management Information Systems
CHR: Ada Bermudez, Director Human Resources
CNO: Amanda Caraballo, Nursing Director
Web address: www.hospitalconcepcion.org
Control: Church operated, Nongovernment, not–for–profit **Service**: General medical and surgical

Staffed Beds: 187 **Admissions**: 7620 **Census**: 118 **Outpatient Visits**: 100237 **Births**: 552 **Total Expense ($000)**: 69846 **Payroll Expense ($000)**: 24705

HOSPITAL METROPOLITANO SAN GERMAN (400126), Calle Javilla Al Costado Parque de Bombas, Zip 683, Mailing Address: PO Box 63, 683; tel. 787/892–5300, (Nonreporting) **A**10
Primary Contact: Luis A. Berdiel, Executive Director
Control: Corporation, Investor–owned (for–profit) **Service**: Other specialty treatment

Staffed Beds: 40

SAN JUAN—San Juan County

ASHFORD PRESBYTERIAN COMMUNITY HOSPITAL (400001), 1451 Avenue Ashford, Zip 00907–1511, Mailing Address: P.O.Box 9020032, 00902–0032; tel. 787/721–2160 **A**1 5 10 **F**3 8 11 13 15 18 28 30 40 41 45 46 49 51 53 59 65 70 72 75 79 81 82 87 91 93 97 107 110 111 114 116 118 119 130 131 135 146 147 148 **P**5
Primary Contact: Pedro J. Gonzalez, FACHE, Chief Executive Officer
COO: Obdulia Medina, Associate Director for Administrative Support, Clinical Management and Ambulatory Care
CFO: Mayra Torres CPA, Chief Financial Officer
CMO: Francisco de Torres M.D., Medical Director
CIO: Sigfredo Irizarry, Information Technology Director
CHR: Irma Carrillo, Director Human Resources
CNO: Itza Soto MSN, Nursing Executive
Web address: www.presbypr.com
Control: Other not–for–profit (including NFP Corporation) **Service**: General medical and surgical

Staffed Beds: 180 **Admissions**: 9230 **Census**: 121 **Outpatient Visits**: 48735 **Births**: 2649 **Total Expense ($000)**: 69995 **Payroll Expense ($000)**: 21819

AUXILIO MUTUO HOSPITAL (400016), Ponce De Leon Avenue, Zip 00918–1000, Mailing Address: P.O.Box 191227, 00919–1227; tel. 787/758–2000, (Nonreporting) **A**1 3 5 10
Primary Contact: Jorge L Matta. Serrano, Administrator
COO: Carmen Martin, Associate Administrator
CFO: Maria L Marti, Director Fiscal Services
CMO: Jose Isado M.D., Medical Director
CIO: Edgardo Rodriguez, Director Management Information Systems
CHR: Maria Vega, Director Human Resources
Web address: www.auxiliomutuo.com
Control: Other not–for–profit (including NFP Corporation) **Service**: General medical and surgical

Staffed Beds: 483

CARDIOVASCULAR CENTER OF PUERTO RICO AND THE CARIBBEAN (400124), Americo Miranda Centro Medico, Zip 936, Mailing Address: P.O.Box 366528, 00936–6528; tel. 787/754–8500 **A**1 3 5 10 **F**3 17 18 19 20 21 22 23 24 25 26 27 29 30 34 40 57 59 67 70 75 87 89 107 108 109 115 119 130 132 135 137 148 149 **S** Puerto Rico Department of Health, San Juan, PR
Primary Contact: Carlos Cabrera, Executive Director
COO: Wilfredo Rabelo Millan, Chief Operating Officer
CFO: Arthur J Fernandez del Valle, Chief Financial Officer
CMO: Jose E Novoa Loyola M.D., Medical Director
CIO: Eugenio Torres Ayala, Director Information Systems
CHR: Myriam T Rodriguez Schmidt, Director Human Resources
CNO: Pedro Laureano Cantre, Chief Nursing Officer
Web address: www.cardiovascular.gobierno.pr
Control: State, Government, Nonfederal **Service**: Heart

Staffed Beds: 139 **Admissions**: 3922 **Census**: 91 **Outpatient Visits**: 12466 **Births**: 0 **Total Expense ($000)**: 80614 **Payroll Expense ($000)**: 23885

DOCTORS' CENTER HOSPITAL SAN JUAN (400006), 1395 San Rafael Street, Zip 00909–2518, Mailing Address: Box 11338, Santurce Station, 00910–3428; tel. 787/999–7620 **A**10 **F**29 40 41 45 46 70 76 77 81 89 107 111 114 115 119 130 148
Primary Contact: Norma Marrero, Executive Administrator
COO: Norma Marrero, Executive Administrator
CFO: Alejandro Santiago, Director Finance
CMO: Ubaldo Santiago M.D., Chairman
CIO: Luis Alicea, Chief Information Officer
CHR: Carmen Perez, Director Human Resources
CNO: Lesbia Lopez, Chief Nursing Officer
Web address: www.tuhospitalfamiliar.com
Control: Corporation, Investor–owned (for–profit) **Service**: General medical and surgical

Staffed Beds: 133 **Admissions**: 5356 **Census**: 90 **Outpatient Visits**: 24162 **Births**: 62 **Total Expense ($000)**: 32659 **Payroll Expense ($000)**: 9884 **Personnel**: 394

Hospital, Medicare Provider Number, Address, Telephone, Approval, Facility, and Physician Codes, Health Care System

★ American Hospital Association (AHA) membership   ○ Healthcare Facilities Accreditation Program   ⇑ Center for Improvement in Healthcare Quality Accreditation
□ The Joint Commission accreditation   ◇ DNV Healthcare Inc. accreditation   △ Commission on Accreditation of Rehabilitation Facilities (CARF) accreditation

HEALTHSOUTH REHABILITATION HOSPITAL OF SAN JUAN (403025), University Hospital, 3rd Floor, Zip 923, Mailing Address: P.O.Box 70344, 923; tel. 787/274–5100, (Nonreporting) **A**3 5 10 **S** HEALTHSOUTH Corporation, Birmingham, AL
Primary Contact: Daniel Del Castillo, Chief Executive Officer
CFO: Jesus M Corazon, Controller
CMO: Eduardo Ramos M.D., Medical Director
CHR: Frances Fuentes, Coordinator Human Resources
CNO: Zamarys Rivera R.N., Chief Nursing Officer
Web address: www.healthsouthsanjuan.com
Control: Corporation, Investor–owned (for–profit) **Service**: Rehabilitation

Staffed Beds: 32

HOSPITAL CUIDADO AGUDO ESPECIALIZADO EN PACIENTES POLITRAUMATIZADOS (400127), Carr. Num. 22 BO. Monacillos, Centro Medico, Zip 00922–2129, Mailing Address: PO Box 2129, 00922–2129; tel. 787/777–3535 (Nonreporting)
Primary Contact: Victor L. Medina Cruz, M.D., Administrator
Web address: www.asempr.org
Control: Other not–for–profit (including NFP Corporation) **Service**: General medical and surgical

Staffed Beds: 25

HOSPITAL DE PSIQUIATRIA (404006), Dr. Ramon Fernandez Marina, P O Box 2100, Zip 936; tel. 787/766–4646 **A**3 5 **F**3 98 102 103 146
Primary Contact: Elizabeth De Santiago, Executive Director
CMO: Brunilda Vazquez, Medical Director
CHR: Idalia Garcia, Chief Human Resources Officer
Control: State, Government, Nonfederal **Service**: Psychiatric

Staffed Beds: 141 **Admissions**: 525 **Census**: 115 **Births**: 0

HOSPITAL DEL MAESTRO (400004), 550 Sergio Cuevas, Zip 00918–3741, Mailing Address: P.O.Box 364708, 00936–4708; tel. 787/758–8383, (Nonreporting) **A**1 10
Primary Contact: Jorge Torres. Otero, Executive Director
CFO: Marisol Vargas, Director Finance
CMO: Jose Montalvo M.D., Medical Director
CIO: Laura Rodriguez, Director Medical Records
CHR: Orlando Santiago, Human Resources Officer
Web address: www.hospitaldelmaestro.org
Control: Corporation, Investor–owned (for–profit) **Service**: General medical and surgical

Staffed Beds: 250

HOSPITAL METROPOLITAN (400106), 1785 Carr 21, Zip 00921–3399, Mailing Address: P.O.Box 11981, 922; tel. 787/782–9999, (Nonreporting) **A**1 10
Primary Contact: Domingo Nevarez, Chief Executive Officer
CFO: Maritza Rodriguez, Chief Financial Officer
CMO: Maria de los Angeles Correa M.D., Medical Director
CIO: Manuel Santiago, Chief Information Officer
Control: Corporation, Investor–owned (for–profit) **Service**: General medical and surgical

Staffed Beds: 127

HOSPITAL PAVIA–HATO REY (400128), 435 Ponce De Leon Avenue, Zip 00917–3428, Mailing Address: PO Box 190828, 00917–3428; tel. 787/641–2323, (Nonreporting) **A**1 3 5 10 **S** United Medical Corporation, Windermere, FL
Primary Contact: Guillermo Pastrana, Executive Director
Web address: www.paviahealth.com
Control: Corporation, Investor–owned (for–profit) **Service**: General medical and surgical

Staffed Beds: 180

HOSPITAL PAVIA–SANTURCE (400019), 1462 Asia Street, Zip 00909–2143, Mailing Address: Box 11137, Santurce Station, 00910–1137; tel. 787/727–6060, (Nonreporting) **A**1 10 **S** United Medical Corporation, Windermere, FL
Primary Contact: Jose Luis. Rodriguez, Chief Executive Officer
CFO: Francisco Espina, Director Finance
Web address: www.paviahealth.com
Control: Corporation, Investor–owned (for–profit) **Service**: General medical and surgical

Staffed Beds: 198

HOSPITAL PSIQUIATRICO CORRECCIONAL, PMB 302 P O Box 70344, Zip 936; tel. 939/225–2400 (Nonreporting)
Primary Contact: Felicita E. Alvarado, Administrator
Web address: www2.pr.gov/Directorios/Pages/InfoAgencia.aspx?PRIFA=220
Control: State, Government, Nonfederal **Service**: General medical and surgical

Staffed Beds: 25

HOSPITAL SAN FRANCISCO (400098), 371 Avenida De Diego, Zip 00923–1711, Mailing Address: P.O.Box 29025, 00929–0025; tel. 787/767–5100 **A**1 10 **F**3 8 15 30 46 65 70 79 81 87 88 89 107 110 111 114 119 130 141 146 149 150 **S** United Medical Corporation, Windermere, FL
Primary Contact: Marcos Aguila, Chief Executive Officer
CFO: Lizzette Rodriguez, Director Finance
CMO: Hector L Cotto M.D., Medical Director
CIO: Deborah Nieves, Director Management Information Systems
CHR: Sugehi Santiago, Director
Web address: www.metropavia.com/SanFrancisco.cfm
Control: Corporation, Investor–owned (for–profit) **Service**: General medical and surgical

Staffed Beds: 133 **Admissions**: 5890 **Census**: 91 **Outpatient Visits**: 23562 **Births**: 0 **Total Expense ($000)**: 47966 **Payroll Expense ($000)**: 14693 **Personnel**: 497

HOSPITAL SAN GERARDO (400121), 138 Avenue Winston Churchill, Zip 00926–6013; tel. 787/761–8383, (Nonreporting) **A**10
Primary Contact: Henry Ruberte, Administrator
Web address: www.hospitales.cybo.com/PR–biz/hospital–san–gerardo_2P
Control: Other not–for–profit (including NFP Corporation) **Service**: Chronic disease

Staffed Beds: 60

INDUSTRIAL HOSPITAL, Puerto Rico Medical Center, Zip 936, Mailing Address: P.O.Box 365028, 936; tel. 787/754–2525, (Nonreporting)
Primary Contact: Jane Vega, Executive Director
CFO: Robert Bernier Casanova, Chief Financial Officer
CMO: Carmen Carrasquillo M.D., Medical Director
CHR: Sonia M Lebron, Human Resources Specialist
Control: State, Government, Nonfederal **Service**: General medical and surgical

Staffed Beds: 108

SAN JORGE CHILDREN'S HOSPITAL, 252 San Jorge Street, Santurce, Zip 00912–3310, Mailing Address: PO Box 6308, 00912–3310; tel. 787/727–1000 **A**1 3 5 **F**8 31 38 40 41 58 65 75 78 79 81 82 86 87 88 89 94 98 99 100 101 102 104 105 107 111 112 114 115 119 129 130 136 146 147 148 **S** United Medical Corporation, Windermere, FL
Primary Contact: Domingo Cruz, Senior Vice President Operations
CFO: Jose Marrero, Director Finance
CMO: Luis Clavell M.D., Medical Director
CIO: Rogelio Caballero, Chief Information Systems
CHR: Odette Burgos, Supervisor Human Resources
CNO: Leticia Fuentes, Nursing Director
Web address: www.sanjorgechildrenshospital.com
Control: Corporation, Investor–owned (for–profit) **Service**: Children's general medical and surgical

Staffed Beds: 167 **Admissions**: 7159 **Census**: 104 **Outpatient Visits**: 39671 **Births**: 0 **Total Expense ($000)**: 43088 **Payroll Expense ($000)**: 15402 **Personnel**: 510

SAN JUAN CAPESTRANO HOSPITAL (404005), Rural Route 2, Box 11, Zip 926; tel. 787/625–2900 **A**1 5 10 **F**4 5 7 29 37 44 59 66 75 86 87 98 99 100 101 102 103 104 105 130 132 149 **S** Acadia Healthcare Company, Inc., Franklin, TN
Primary Contact: Marta Rivera. Plaza, Chief Executive Officer and Managing Director
CFO: Julia Cruz, Chief Financial Officer
CMO: Jose' Alonso M.D., Medical Director
CIO: Ana Morandeira, Director Marketing
CHR: Luis Rivera, Director Human Resources
Web address: www.sjcapestrano.com
Control: Corporation, Investor–owned (for–profit) **Service**: Psychiatric

Staffed Beds: 158 **Admissions**: 6260 **Census**: 119 **Outpatient Visits**: 33025 **Births**: 0 **Total Expense ($000)**: 26779 **Payroll Expense ($000)**: 10111 **Personnel**: 299

SAN JUAN CITY HOSPITAL (400015), Puerto Rico Medical Center, Zip 928, Mailing Address: PMB 79, P O Box 70344, 00936–8344; tel. 787/766–2222, (Nonreporting) **A**1 3 5 10
Primary Contact: James F. Nieves, Executive Director
COO: Norma Marcano, Chief Operating Officer
CFO: Jaime Rodriguez, Chief Financial Officer
CMO: Raul Reyes M.D., Medical Director
CIO: Gustavo Mesa, Chief Information Officer
CHR: Jose Garcia, Chief Human Resources Officer
Web address: www.massalud.com
Control: City, Government, Nonfederal **Service**: General medical and surgical

Staffed Beds: 267

Many Facility Codes have changed. Please refer to the AHA Guide Code Chart. © 2017 AHA Guide

UNIVERSITY HOSPITAL (400061), Nineyas 869 Rio Piedras, Zip 922, Mailing Address: P.O.Box 2116, 922; tel. 787/754–0101, (Nonreporting) **A**3 5 10 **S** Puerto Rico Department of Health, San Juan, PR
Primary Contact: Jorge Matta. Gonzalez, Executive Director
CFO: Janet Baez, Director
CMO: Ricardo Moscoso M.D., Medical Director
CIO: Josue Martinez, Coordinator Information Systems
CHR: Ramomita Navarro, Director Human Resources
Control: State, Government, Nonfederal **Service**: General medical and surgical

Staffed Beds: 262

VETERANS AFFAIRS CARIBBEAN HEALTHCARE SYSTEM, 10 Casia Street, Zip 00921–3201; tel. 787/641–7582, (Total facility includes 85 beds in nursing home–type unit) **A**1 2 3 5 7 8 **F**3 4 5 8 15 17 18 20 22 24 26 28 29 30 31 34 35 36 38 39 40 45 46 47 48 49 50 53 54 56 57 58 59 60 61 62 63 64 65 70 74 75 77 78 79 80 81 82 83 84 85 86 87 90 92 93 94 98 100 101 102 103 104 105 107 108 110 111 115 116 117 118 119 120 121 127 128 129 130 131 132 135 143 144 145 146 147 148 149 **P**6 **S** Department of Veterans Affairs, Washington, DC
Primary Contact: Antonio Sanchez, M.D., Acting Director
CFO: Oscar Rodriguez, Chief Fiscal Officer
CMO: Antonio Sanchez M.D., Chief of Staff
CIO: Manuel Negron, Chief Information Technology Service
CHR: Omar Ahmed, Acting Manager Human Resources
CNO: Kathleen Ruiz M.D., Associate Director Patient Care Services
Web address: www.caribbean.va.gov/
Control: Veterans Affairs, Government, federal **Service**: General medical and surgical

Staffed Beds: 422 Admissions: 10046 Census: 216 Outpatient Visits: 1073293 Births: 0 Total Expense ($000): 724388 Payroll Expense ($000): 289986

UTUADO—San Juan County

METROPOLITANO DE LA MONTANA (400130), Calle Issac Gonzalez Martinez, Zip 641, Mailing Address: P.O.Box 2600, 641; tel. 787/933–1100 (Nonreporting) **A**10
Primary Contact: Yelitza Sanchez. Rodriguez, Executive Director
Web address: www.metropavia.com/DeLaMontana.cfm
Control: Corporation, Investor–owned (for–profit) **Service**: General medical and surgical

Staffed Beds: 25

VEGA BAJA—Vega Alta County

WILMA N. VAZQUEZ MEDICAL CENTER (400115), KM 39 1/2 Road 2, Call Box 7001, Zip 694; tel. 787/858–1580, (Nonreporting) **A**10
Primary Contact: Ramon J. Vilar, Administrator
COO: Jose O Pabon, Director Operations
CFO: Youdie Reynolds–Gossette, Controller
CMO: Jorge Feria M.D., President Medical Staff
CIO: Miguel Aponte, Supervisor Management Information Systems
CHR: Aymette Garcia, Manager Human Resources
Control: Corporation, Investor–owned (for–profit) **Service**: General medical and surgical

Staffed Beds: 150

YAUCO—Yauco County

HOSPITAL PAVIA YAUCO (400110), Carretera 128 KM 1.0, Zip 698, Mailing Address: P.O.Box 5643, 698; tel. 787/856–1000 **A**1 5 10 **F**3 18 29 34 40 45 46 47 48 49 57 64 68 70 75 76 77 81 86 87 89 92 93 98 100 101 102 103 107 110 111 114 119 130 148 149
Primary Contact: Dinorah Hernandez Esq, Executive Director
CFO: Elizabeth Gonzalez CPA, Financial Director
CMO: Juan Pillot M.D., Esq, Medical Director
CIO: Edson Ortiz, Chief Information Officer
Web address: www.metropavia.com/facilities/hospitals/pavia–yauco/?lang=en/
Control: Corporation, Investor–owned (for–profit) **Service**: General medical and surgical

Staffed Beds: 115 Admissions: 5466 Census: 68 Outpatient Visits: 29831 Births: 207 Total Expense ($000): 26804 Payroll Expense ($000): 7916 Personnel: 304

VIRGIN ISLANDS

CHRISTIANSTED—St. Croix County

☐ **GOVERNOR JUAN F. LUIS HOSPITAL (480002)**, 4007 Estate Diamond Ruby, Zip 00820–4421; tel. 340/778–6311, (Nonreporting) **A**1 10
Primary Contact: Darice S. Plaskett, R.N., FACHE, Interim Chief Executive Officer
CFO: Rosalie Javois, Chief Financial Officer
CMO: Robert Centeno M.D., Chief Medical Officer
CIO: Reuben D Molloy, Chief Information Officer
CHR: Joan Jean–Baptiste, Vice President Human Resources
Web address: www.jflusvi.org
Control: State, Government, Nonfederal **Service**: General medical and surgical

Staffed Beds: 165

SAINT THOMAS—St. Thomas County

☐ **SCHNEIDER REGIONAL MEDICAL CENTER (480001)**, 9048 Sugar Estate, Charlotte Amalie, Zip 802; tel. 340/776–8311 **A**1 10 **F**3 8 13 15 18 20 22 26 29 30 31 34 40 41 45 46 49 50 55 56 57 59 60 64 65 68 70 72 74 75 76 77 78 79 81 85 86 87 89 91 92 93 94 97 98 100 101 102 107 108 114 119 121 130 132 148 **P**5
Primary Contact: Bernard Wheatley, FACHE, Chief Executive Officer
CMO: Thelma Ruth Watson M.D., Medical Director
CIO: J C Creque, Director Management Information Systems
CHR: Marlene J Adams, Director Human Resources
Web address: www.rlshospital.org
Control: Hospital district or authority, Government, Nonfederal **Service**: General medical and surgical

Staffed Beds: 86 Admissions: 3713 Census: 63 Outpatient Visits: 26750 Births: 700 Total Expense ($000): 96975 Payroll Expense ($000): 38391 Personnel: 575

Hospital, Medicare Provider Number, Address, Telephone, Approval, Facility, and Physician Codes, Health Care System

★ American Hospital Association (AHA) membership   ○ Healthcare Facilities Accreditation Program   ⇑ Center for Improvement in Healthcare Quality Accreditation
☐ The Joint Commission accreditation   ◇ DNV Healthcare Inc. accreditation   △ Commission on Accreditation of Rehabilitation Facilities (CARF) accreditation

U.S. Government Hospitals
Outside the United States, by Area

GERMANY

Heidelberg: ★ Heidelberg Army Community Hospital, APO, CMR 242, AE 09042

Landstuhl: ★ Landstuhl Army Regional Medical Center, APO, CMR 402, AE 09180

Wuerzburg: ★ Wuerzburg Army Community Hospital, APO, USAMEDDAC Wuerzburg, Ut 26610, AE 09244

ITALY

Naples: ★ U. S. Naval Hospital, FPO, none, AE 09619

JAPAN

Yokosuka: ★ U. S. Naval Hospital, Box 1487, UNIT 96350

SOUTH KOREA

Seoul: ★ Brian Allgood Army Community Hospital, 121st General Hospital, UNIT 96205

Yongsan: Medcom 18th Commander, Facilities Division Eamc L EM, UNIT 96205

SPAIN

Rota: ★ U. S. Naval Hospital, Rota, FPO, PSC 819, Box 18, AE 09645–2500

TAIWAN

Taipei: ★ U. S. Naval Hospital Taipei, No 300 Shin–Pai Road, Sec 2

This section is an index of all hospitals in alphabetical order by hospital name, followed by the city, state, and page reference to the hospital's listing in Section A.

A

ABBEVILLE AREA MEDICAL CENTER, ABBEVILLE, SC, p. A558

ABBEVILLE GENERAL HOSPITAL, ABBEVILLE, LA, p. A269

ABBOTT NORTHWESTERN HOSPITAL, MINNEAPOLIS, MN, p. A343

ABILENE REGIONAL MEDICAL CENTER, ABILENE, TX, p. A591

ABINGTON HOSPITAL, ABINGTON, PA, p. A528

ABINGTON–LANSDALE HOSPITAL JEFFERSON HEALTH, LANSDALE, PA, p. A538

ABRAHAM LINCOLN MEMORIAL HOSPITAL, LINCOLN, IL, p. A192

ABRAZO ARROWHEAD CAMPUS, GLENDALE, AZ, p. A30

ABRAZO CENTRAL CAMPUS, PHOENIX, AZ, p. A32

ABRAZO MARYVALE CAMPUS, PHOENIX, AZ, p. A32

ABRAZO SCOTTSDALE CAMPUS, PHOENIX, AZ, p. A33

ABRAZO WEST CAMPUS, GOODYEAR, AZ, p. A30

ABROM KAPLAN MEMORIAL HOSPITAL, KAPLAN, LA, p. A277

ACADIA GENERAL HOSPITAL, CROWLEY, LA, p. A273

ACADIA OPTIMA HOSPITAL, LAFAYETTE, LA, p. A278

ACADIA–ST. LANDRY HOSPITAL, CHURCH POINT, LA, p. A273

ACADIA VERMILION HOSPITAL, LAFAYETTE, LA, p. A278

ACCEL REHABILITATION HOSPITAL OF PLANO, PLANO, TX, p. A638

ACCESS HOSPITAL DAYTON, DAYTON, OH, p. A489

ACMH HOSPITAL, KITTANNING, PA, p. A537

ACOMA-CANONCITO-LAGUNA HOSPITAL, ACOMA, NM, p. A424

ACUITY HOSPITAL OF SOUTH TEXAS, SAN ANTONIO, TX, p. A641

ACUITY SPECIALTY HOSPITAL OF NEW JERSEY, ATLANTIC CITY, NJ, p. A411

ACUITY SPECIALTY HOSPITAL OF SOUTHERN NEW JERSEY, WILLINGBORO, NJ, p. A423

ACUITY SPECIALTY HOSPITALS OHIO VALLEY, STEUBENVILLE, OH, p. A499

AD HOSPITAL EAST, HOUSTON, TX, p. A619

ADAIR COUNTY HEALTH SYSTEM, GREENFIELD, IA, p. A228

ADAMS COUNTY REGIONAL MEDICAL CENTER, SEAMAN, OH, p. A499

ADAMS MEMORIAL HOSPITAL, DECATUR, IN, p. A206

ADCARE HOSPITAL OF WORCESTER, WORCESTER, MA, p. A313

ADDISON GILBERT HOSPITAL, GLOUCESTER, MA, p. A307

ADENA GREENFIELD MEDICAL CENTER, GREENFIELD, OH, p. A492

ADENA MEDICAL CENTER, CHILLICOTHE, OH, p. A483

ADENA PIKE MEDICAL CENTER, WAVERLY, OH, p. A502

ADIRONDACK HEALTH, SARANAC LAKE, NY, p. A452

ADVANCED CARE HOSPITAL OF MONTANA, BILLINGS, MT, p. A382

ADVANCED CARE HOSPITAL OF SOUTHERN NEW MEXICO, LAS CRUCES, NM, p. A426

ADVANCED CARE HOSPITAL OF WHITE COUNTY, SEARCY, AR, p. A49

ADVANCED DIAGNOSTICS HOSPITAL, HOUSTON, TX, p. A619

ADVANCED SPECIALTY HOSPITAL OF TOLEDO, TOLEDO, OH, p. A500

ADVANCED SURGICAL HOSPITAL, WASHINGTON, PA, p. A552

ADVENTIST BEHAVIORAL HEALTH AND WELLNESS SERVICES, ROCKVILLE, MD, p. A300

ADVENTIST HEALTH GLENDALE, GLENDALE, CA, p. A62

ADVENTIST HEALTH GLENDALE, GLENDALE, CA, p. A62

ADVENTIST HEALTH MEDICAL CENTER – TEHACHAPI VALLEY, TEHACHAPI, CA, p. A93

ADVENTIST HEALTH SONORA, SONORA, CA, p. A92

ADVENTIST HEALTH ST. HELENA, SAINT HELENA, CA, p. A84

ADVENTIST HEALTH ST. HELENA, VALLEJO, CA, p. A95

ADVENTIST HEALTHCARE PHYSICAL HEALTH AND REHABILITATION, ROCKVILLE, MD, p. A300

ADVENTIST HEALTHCARE SHADY GROVE MEDICAL CENTER, ROCKVILLE, MD, p. A300

ADVENTIST HEALTHCARE WASHINGTON ADVENTIST HOSPITAL, TAKOMA PARK, MD, p. A301

ADVENTIST MEDICAL CENTER – HANFORD, HANFORD, CA, p. A62

ADVENTIST MEDICAL CENTER–PORTLAND, PORTLAND, OR, p. A525

ADVENTIST MEDICAL CENTER–REEDLEY, REEDLEY, CA, p. A82

ADVOCATE BETHANY HOSPITAL, CHICAGO, IL, p. A180

ADVOCATE BROMENN MEDICAL CENTER, NORMAL, IL, p. A195

ADVOCATE BROMENN REGIONAL MEDICAL CENTER, NORMAL, IL, p. A195

ADVOCATE CHRIST MEDICAL CENTER, OAK LAWN, IL, p. A196

ADVOCATE CONDELL MEDICAL CENTER, LIBERTYVILLE, IL, p. A192

ADVOCATE EUREKA HOSPITAL, EUREKA, IL, p. A187

ADVOCATE GOOD SAMARITAN HOSPITAL, DOWNERS GROVE, IL, p. A186

ADVOCATE GOOD SHEPHERD HOSPITAL, BARRINGTON, IL, p. A178

ADVOCATE ILLINOIS MASONIC MEDICAL CENTER, CHICAGO, IL, p. A180

ADVOCATE LUTHERAN GENERAL HOSPITAL, PARK RIDGE, IL, p. A197

ADVOCATE SHERMAN HOSPITAL, ELGIN, IL, p. A186

ADVOCATE SOUTH SUBURBAN HOSPITAL, HAZEL CREST, IL, p. A189

ADVOCATE TRINITY HOSPITAL, CHICAGO, IL, p. A180

AFFINITY MEDICAL CENTER, MASSILLON, OH, p. A495

AHMC ANAHEIM REGIONAL MEDICAL CENTER, ANAHEIM, CA, p. A51

AIKEN REGIONAL MEDICAL CENTERS, AIKEN, SC, p. A558

AKRON CHILDREN'S HOSPITAL, AKRON, OH, p. A479

ALAMANCE REGIONAL MEDICAL CENTER, BURLINGTON, NC, p. A458

ALAMEDA HOSPITAL, ALAMEDA, CA, p. A51

ALASKA NATIVE MEDICAL CENTER, ANCHORAGE, AK, p. A25

ALASKA PSYCHIATRIC INSTITUTE, ANCHORAGE, AK, p. A25

ALASKA REGIONAL HOSPITAL, ANCHORAGE, AK, p. A25

ALBANY MEDICAL CENTER, ALBANY, NY, p. A430

ALBANY MEMORIAL HOSPITAL, ALBANY, NY, p. A430

ALBANY STRATTON VETERANS AFFAIRS MEDICAL CENTER, ALBANY, NY, p. A430

ALBERT EINSTEIN MEDICAL CENTER, PHILADELPHIA, PA, p. A543

ALBERT J. SOLNIT PSYCHIATRIC CENTER – SOUTH CAMPUS, MIDDLETOWN, CT, p. A111

ALEDA E. LUTZ VETERANS AFFAIRS MEDICAL CENTER, SAGINAW, MI, p. A329

ALEXANDRIA VETERANS AFFAIRS HEALTH CARE SYSTEM, PINEVILLE, LA, p. A284

ALEXIAN BROTHERS BEHAVIORAL HEALTH HOSPITAL, HOFFMAN ESTATES, IL, p. A190

ALFRED I. DUPONT HOSPITAL FOR CHILDREN, WILMINGTON, DE, p. A116

ALHAMBRA HOSPITAL MEDICAL CENTER, ALHAMBRA, CA, p. A51

ALICE PECK DAY MEMORIAL HOSPITAL, LEBANON, NH, p. A408

ALLEGAN GENERAL HOSPITAL, ALLEGAN, MI, p. A314

ALLEGHANY MEMORIAL HOSPITAL, SPARTA, NC, p. A471

ALLEGHENY GENERAL HOSPITAL, PITTSBURGH, PA, p. A546

ALLEGHENY VALLEY HOSPITAL, NATRONA HEIGHTS, PA, p. A542

ALLEGIANCE BEHAVIORAL HEALTH CENTER OF PLAINVIEW, PLAINVIEW, TX, p. A637

ALLEGIANCE BEHAVIORAL HEALTH CENTERS OF MONROE, WEST MONROE, LA, p. A287

ALLEGIANCE SPECIALTY HOSPITAL OF GREENVILLE, GREENVILLE, MS, p. A355

ALLEGIANCE SPECIALTY HOSPITAL OF KILGORE, KILGORE, TX, p. A626

ALLEGIANCE SPECIALTY HOSPITAL OF LITTLE ROCK, LITTLE ROCK, AR, p. A45

ALLEN COUNTY REGIONAL HOSPITAL, IOLA, KS, p. A243

ALLEN MEMORIAL HOSPITAL, WATERLOO, IA, p. A236

ALLEN PARISH HOSPITAL, KINDER, LA, p. A277

ALLENDALE COUNTY HOSPITAL, FAIRFAX, SC, p. A561

ALLENMORE HOSPITAL, TACOMA, WA, p. A687

ALLIANCE COMMUNITY HOSPITAL, ALLIANCE, OH, p. A479

ALLIANCE HEALTH CENTER, MERIDIAN, MS, p. A359

ALLIANCE HEALTHCARE SYSTEM, HOLLY SPRINGS, MS, p. A356

ALLIANCEHEALTH CLINTON, CLINTON, OK, p. A506

ALLIANCEHEALTH DEACONESS, OKLAHOMA CITY, OK, p. A511

ALLIANCEHEALTH DURANT, DURANT, OK, p. A506

ALLIANCEHEALTH MADILL, MADILL, OK, p. A509

ALLIANCEHEALTH MIDWEST, MIDWEST CITY, OK, p. A510

ALLIANCEHEALTH PONCA CITY, PONCA CITY, OK, p. A514

ALLIANCEHEALTH SEMINOLE, SEMINOLE, OK, p. A515

ALLIANCEHEALTH WOODWARD, WOODWARD, OK, p. A519

ALLIED SERVICES REHABILITATION HOSPITAL, SCRANTON, PA, p. A550

ALTA BATES SUMMIT MEDICAL CENTER – SUMMIT CAMPUS, OAKLAND, CA, p. A77

ALTA BATES SUMMIT MEDICAL CENTER, BERKELEY, CA, p. A53

ALTA VIEW HOSPITAL, SANDY, UT, p. A661

ALTA VISTA REGIONAL HOSPITAL, LAS VEGAS, NM, p. A427

ALTON MEMORIAL HOSPITAL, ALTON, IL, p. A177

ALTON MENTAL HEALTH CENTER, ALTON, IL, p. A177

ALTOONA REGIONAL HEALTH SYSTEM, ALTOONA, PA, p. A528

ALTRU HEALTH SYSTEM, GRAND FORKS, ND, p. A476

ALTUS BAYTOWN HOSPITAL, BAYTOWN, TX, p. A596

ALVARADO HOSPITAL MEDICAL CENTER, SAN DIEGO, CA, p. A85

ALVARADO PARKWAY INSTITUTE BEHAVIORAL HEALTH SYSTEM, LA MESA, CA, p. A64

ALVIN C. YORK CAMPUS, MURFREESBORO, TN, p. A586

ALVIN DIAGNOSTIC AND URGENT CARE CENTER, ALVIN, TX, p. A592

AMARILLO VETERANS AFFAIRS HEALTH CARE SYSTEM, AMARILLO, TX, p. A592

AMERICAN FORK HOSPITAL, AMERICAN FORK, UT, p. A656

AMERY HOSPITAL AND CLINIC, AMERY, WI, p. A698

AMG PHYSICAL REHABILITATION HOSPITAL, COVINGTON, LA, p. A273

AMG SPECIALTY HOSPITAL–ALBUQUERQUE, ALBUQUERQUE, NM, p. A424

AMG SPECIALTY HOSPITAL–DENHAM SPRINGS, DENHAM SPRINGS, LA, p. A274

AMG SPECIALTY HOSPITAL–EDMOND, EDMOND, OK, p. A507

AMG SPECIALTY HOSPITAL–GREENWOOD, GREENWOOD, MS, p. A355

AMG SPECIALTY HOSPITAL–HOUMA, HOUMA, LA, p. A276

AMG SPECIALTY HOSPITAL–LAFAYETTE, LAFAYETTE, LA, p. A278

AMG SPECIALTY HOSPITAL–LAS VEGAS, LAS VEGAS, NV, p. A402

AMG SPECIALTY HOSPITAL–MUNCIE, MUNCIE, IN, p. A216

AMG SPECIALTY HOSPITAL–TULSA, TULSA, OK, p. A517

AMG SPECIALTY HOSPITAL–WICHITA, WICHITA, KS, p. A253

AMG SPECIALTY HOSPITAL–ZACHARY, ZACHARY, LA, p. A288

AMITA HEALTH ADVENTIST MEDICAL CENTER BOLINGBROOK, BOLINGBROOK, IL, p. A179

AMITA HEALTH ADVENTIST MEDICAL CENTER GLENOAKS, GLENDALE HEIGHTS, IL, p. A188

AMITA HEALTH ADVENTIST MEDICAL CENTER – HINSDALE, HINSDALE, IL, p. A190

AMITA HEALTH ADVENTIST MEDICAL CENTER LAGRANGE, LA GRANGE, IL, p. A191

AMITA HEALTH ELK GROVE VILLAGE, ELK GROVE VILLAGE, IL, p. A186

AMITA HEALTH HOFFMAN ESTATES, HOFFMAN ESTATES, IL, p. A190

ANAHEIM GLOBAL MEDICAL CENTER, ANAHEIM, CA, p. A51

ANAHEIM MEDICAL CENTER, ANAHEIM, CA, p. A51

ANCHOR HOSPITAL, ATLANTA, GA, p. A149

ANCORA PSYCHIATRIC HOSPITAL, HAMMONTON, NJ, p. A414

ANDALUSIA HEALTH, ANDALUSIA, AL, p. A13

ANDERSON COUNTY HOSPITAL, GARNETT, KS, p. A241

ANDERSON HOSPITAL, MARYVILLE, IL, p. A192

ANDERSON REGIONAL HEALTH SYSTEM, MERIDIAN, MS, p. A359

ANDERSON REGIONAL HEALTH SYSTEM SOUTH, MERIDIAN, MS, p. A359

ANDREW MCFARLAND MENTAL HEALTH CENTER, SPRINGFIELD, IL, p. A200

ANDROSCOGGIN VALLEY HOSPITAL, BERLIN, NH, p. A407
ANDRUS PAVILION, YONKERS, NY, p. A456
ANGEL MEDICAL CENTER, FRANKLIN, NC, p. A462
ANIMAS SURGICAL HOSPITAL, DURANGO, CO, p. A101
ANMED HEALTH CANNON, PICKENS, SC, p. A565
ANMED HEALTH MEDICAL CENTER, ANDERSON, SC, p. A558
ANMED HEALTH REHABILITATION HOSPITAL, ANDERSON, SC, p. A558
ANN & ROBERT H. LURIE CHILDREN'S HOSPITAL OF CHICAGO, CHICAGO, IL, p. A180
ANNA JAQUES HOSPITAL, NEWBURYPORT, MA, p. A309
ANNE ARUNDEL MEDICAL CENTER, ANNAPOLIS, MD, p. A294
ANNIE JEFFREY MEMORIAL COUNTY HEALTH CENTER, OSCEOLA, NE, p. A398
ANNIE PENN HOSPITAL, REIDSVILLE, NC, p. A469
ANOKA–METROPOLITAN REGIONAL TREATMENT CENTER, ANOKA, MN, p. A335
ANSON GENERAL HOSPITAL, ANSON, TX, p. A593
ANTELOPE MEMORIAL HOSPITAL, NELIGH, NE, p. A396
ANTELOPE VALLEY HOSPITAL, LANCASTER, CA, p. A65
ANTHONY MEDICAL CENTER, ANTHONY, KS, p. A238
APOLLO BEHAVIORAL HEALTH HOSPITAL, BATON ROUGE, LA, p. A270
APPALACHIAN BEHAVIORAL HEALTHCARE, ATHENS, OH, p. A480
APPLETON AREA HEALTH SERVICES, APPLETON, MN, p. A335
APPLING HEALTHCARE SYSTEM, BAXLEY, GA, p. A152
ARBOUR H. R. I. HOSPITAL, BROOKLINE, MA, p. A305
ARBOUR HOSPITAL, BOSTON, MA, p. A302
ARBOUR–FULLER HOSPITAL, ATTLEBORO, MA, p. A302
ARBUCKLE MEMORIAL HOSPITAL, SULPHUR, OK, p. A516
ARCHBOLD HOSPITAL, ARCHBOLD, OH, p. A480
ARIA – JEFFERSON HEALTH, PHILADELPHIA, PA, p. A543
ARISE AUSTIN MEDICAL CENTER, AUSTIN, TX, p. A594
ARIZONA ORTHOPEDIC SURGICAL HOSPITAL, CHANDLER, AZ, p. A28
ARIZONA SPINE AND JOINT HOSPITAL, MESA, AZ, p. A31
ARIZONA STATE HOSPITAL, PHOENIX, AZ, p. A33
ARKANSAS CHILDREN'S HOSPITAL, LITTLE ROCK, AR, p. A45
ARKANSAS HEART HOSPITAL, LITTLE ROCK, AR, p. A45
ARKANSAS METHODIST MEDICAL CENTER, PARAGOULD, AR, p. A48
ARKANSAS STATE HOSPITAL, LITTLE ROCK, AR, p. A45
ARKANSAS SURGICAL HOSPITAL, NORTH LITTLE ROCK, AR, p. A47
ARKANSAS VALLEY REGIONAL MEDICAL CENTER, LA JUNTA, CO, p. A104
ARMS ACRES, CARMEL, NY, p. A433
ARNOLD PALMER CHILDREN'S HOSPITAL, ORLANDO, FL, p. A137
ARNOT OGDEN MEDICAL CENTER, ELMIRA, NY, p. A435
AROOSTOOK HEALTH CENTER, MARS HILL, ME, p. A292
ARROWHEAD BEHAVIORAL HEALTH HOSPITAL, MAUMEE, OH, p. A495
ARROWHEAD REGIONAL MEDICAL CENTER, COLTON, CA, p. A56
ARTESIA GENERAL HOSPITAL, ARTESIA, NM, p. A425
ASANTE ASHLAND COMMUNITY HOSPITAL, ASHLAND, OR, p. A520
ASANTE ROGUE REGIONAL MEDICAL CENTER, MEDFORD, OR, p. A524
ASANTE THREE RIVERS MEDICAL CENTER, GRANTS PASS, OR, p. A522
ASHE MEMORIAL HOSPITAL, JEFFERSON, NC, p. A465
ASHEVILLE SPECIALTY HOSPITAL, ASHEVILLE, NC, p. A457
ASHFORD PRESBYTERIAN COMMUNITY HOSPITAL, SAN JUAN, PUERTO RICO, p. A725
ASHLAND HEALTH CENTER, ASHLAND, KS, p. A238
ASHLEY COUNTY MEDICAL CENTER, CROSSETT, AR, p. A42
ASHLEY MEDICAL CENTER, ASHLEY, ND, p. A474
ASHLEY REGIONAL MEDICAL CENTER, VERNAL, UT, p. A661
ASHTABULA COUNTY MEDICAL CENTER, ASHTABULA, OH, p. A480
ASPEN MOUNTAIN MEDICAL CENTER, ROCK SPRINGS, WY, p. A719
ASPEN VALLEY HOSPITAL, ASPEN, CO, p. A98
ASPIRE HEALTH PARTNERS, ORLANDO, FL, p. A137
ASPIRE HOSPITAL, CONROE, TX, p. A602
ASPIRUS IRON RIVER HOSPITALS & CLINICS, INC., IRON RIVER, MI, p. A323
ASPIRUS IRONWOOD HOSITAL & CLINICS, INC., IRONWOOD, MI, p. A323
ASPIRUS KEWEENAW HOSPITAL, INC., LAURIUM, MI, p. A325
ASPIRUS LANGLADE HOSPITAL, ANTIGO, WI, p. A698
ASPIRUS MEDFORD HOSPITAL & CLINICS, INC., MEDFORD, WI, p. A706
ASPIRUS ONTONAGON HOSPITAL, INC., ONTONAGON, MI, p. A327

ASPIRUS RIVERVIEW HOSPITAL AND CLINICS, INC., WISCONSIN RAPIDS, WI, p. A716
ASPIRUS WAUSAU HOSPITAL, INC., WAUSAU, WI, p. A715
ASSUMPTION COMMUNITY HOSPITAL, NAPOLEONVILLE, LA, p. A282
ATASCADERO STATE HOSPITAL, ATASCADERO, CA, p. A52
ATCHISON HOSPITAL, ATCHISON, KS, p. A238
ATHENS–LIMESTONE HOSPITAL, ATHENS, AL, p. A14
ATHOL HOSPITAL, ATHOL, MA, p. A302
ATLANTA VETERANS AFFAIRS MEDICAL CENTER, DECATUR, GA, p. A156
ATLANTIC GENERAL HOSPITAL, BERLIN, MD, p. A296
ATLANTIC SHORES HOSPITAL, FORT LAUDERDALE, FL, p. A124
ATLANTICARE REGIONAL MEDICAL CENTER, ATLANTIC CITY, NJ, p. A411
ATLANTICARE REGIONAL MEDICAL CENTER-MAINLAND DIVISION, POMONA, NJ, p. A419
ATMORE COMMUNITY HOSPITAL, ATMORE, AL, p. A14
ATOKA COUNTY MEDICAL CENTER, ATOKA, OK, p. A504
ATRIUM MEDICAL CENTER, MIDDLETOWN, OH, p. A496
ATRIUM MEDICAL CENTER, STAFFORD, TX, p. A646
ATRIUM MEDICAL CENTER OF CORINTH, CORINTH, TX, p. A603
AUBURN COMMUNITY HOSPITAL, AUBURN, NY, p. A431
AUDUBON COUNTY MEMORIAL HOSPITAL, AUDUBON, IA, p. A222
AUGUSTA HEALTH, FISHERSVILLE, VA, p. A667
AUGUSTA UNIVERSITY MEDICAL CENTER, AUGUSTA, GA, p. A151
AULTMAN HOSPITAL, CANTON, OH, p. A482
AULTMAN ORRVILLE HOSPITAL, ORRVILLE, OH, p. A497
AULTMAN SPECIALTY HOSPITAL, CANTON, OH, p. A482
AURELIA OSBORN FOX MEMORIAL HOSPITAL, ONEONTA, NY, p. A449
AURORA BAYCARE MEDICAL CENTER, GREEN BAY, WI, p. A702
AURORA BEHAVIORAL HEALTH SYSTEM EAST, TEMPE, AZ, p. A37
AURORA BEHAVIORAL HEALTH SYSTEM WEST, GLENDALE, AZ, p. A30
AURORA BEHAVIORAL HEALTHCARE SAN DIEGO, SAN DIEGO, CA, p. A85
AURORA CHARTER OAK HOSPITAL, COVINA, CA, p. A57
AURORA LAKELAND MEDICAL CENTER, ELKHORN, WI, p. A701
AURORA MEDICAL CENTER – MANITOWOC COUNTY, TWO RIVERS, WI, p. A714
AURORA MEDICAL CENTER, KENOSHA, WI, p. A704
AURORA MEDICAL CENTER GRAFTON, GRAFTON, WI, p. A702
AURORA MEDICAL CENTER IN WASHINGTON COUNTY, HARTFORD, WI, p. A703
AURORA MEDICAL CENTER OF OSHKOSH, OSHKOSH, WI, p. A710
AURORA MEDICAL CENTER SUMMIT, SUMMIT, WI, p. A713
AURORA MEMORIAL HOSPITAL OF BURLINGTON, BURLINGTON, WI, p. A699
AURORA PSYCHIATRIC HOSPITAL, WAUWATOSA, WI, p. A715
AURORA SANTA ROSA HOSPITAL, SANTA ROSA, CA, p. A91
AURORA SHEBOYGAN MEMORIAL MEDICAL CENTER, SHEBOYGAN, WI, p. A712
AURORA SINAI MEDICAL CENTER, MILWAUKEE, WI, p. A707
AURORA ST. LUKE'S MEDICAL CENTER, MILWAUKEE, WI, p. A707
AURORA ST. LUKE'S SOUTH SHORE, CUDAHY, WI, p. A700
AURORA WEST ALLIS MEDICAL CENTER, WEST ALLIS, WI, p. A715
AUSTEN RIGGS CENTER, STOCKBRIDGE, MA, p. A312
AUSTIN LAKES HOSPITAL, AUSTIN, TX, p. A594
AUSTIN OAKS HOSPITAL, AUSTIN, TX, p. A594
AUSTIN STATE HOSPITAL, AUSTIN, TX, p. A594
AUXILIO MUTUO HOSPITAL, SAN JUAN, PUERTO RICO, p. A725
AVENTURA HOSPITAL AND MEDICAL CENTER, AVENTURA, FL, p. A119
AVERA CREIGHTON HOSPITAL, CREIGHTON, NE, p. A392
AVERA DE SMET MEMORIAL HOSPITAL, DE SMET, SD, p. A569
AVERA DELLS AREA HEALTH CENTER, DELL RAPIDS, SD, p. A569
AVERA DELLS AREA HOSPITAL, DELL RAPIDS, SD, p. A569
AVERA FLANDREAU HOSPITAL, FLANDREAU, SD, p. A570
AVERA FLANDREAU MEDICAL CENTER, FLANDREAU, SD, p. A570
AVERA GETTYSBURG HOSPITAL, GETTYSBURG, SD, p. A570
AVERA GREGORY HOSPITAL, GREGORY, SD, p. A570
AVERA HAND COUNTY MEMORIAL HOSPITAL, MILLER, SD, p. A571
AVERA HEART HOSPITAL OF SOUTH DAKOTA, SIOUX FALLS, SD, p. A572

AVERA HOLY FAMILY HOSPITAL, ESTHERVILLE, IA, p. A227
AVERA MARSHALL REGIONAL MEDICAL CENTER, MARSHALL, MN, p. A343
AVERA MCKENNAN HOSPITAL AND UNIVERSITY HEALTH CENTER, SIOUX FALLS, SD, p. A572
AVERA QUEEN OF PEACE HOSPITAL, MITCHELL, SD, p. A571
AVERA SACRED HEART HOSPITAL, YANKTON, SD, p. A574
AVERA ST. ANTHONY'S HOSPITAL, O'NEILL, NE, p. A398
AVERA ST. BENEDICT HEALTH CENTER, PARKSTON, SD, p. A571
AVERA ST. LUKE'S HOSPITAL, ABERDEEN, SD, p. A568
AVERA ST. MARY'S HOSPITAL, PIERRE, SD, p. A571
AVERA TYLER HOSPITAL, TYLER, MN, p. A349
AVERA WESKOTA MEMORIAL HOSPITAL, WESSINGTON SPRINGS, SD, p. A574
AVISTA ADVENTIST HOSPITAL, LOUISVILLE, CO, p. A106
AVITA ONTARIO HOSPITAL, ONTARIO, OH, p. A497
AVOYELLES HOSPITAL, MARKSVILLE, LA, p. A280

B

BACHARACH INSTITUTE FOR REHABILITATION, POMONA, NJ, p. A419
BACON COUNTY HOSPITAL AND HEALTH SYSTEM, ALMA, GA, p. A149
BAILEY MEDICAL CENTER, OWASSO, OK, p. A514
BAKERSFIELD HEART HOSPITAL, BAKERSFIELD, CA, p. A52
BAKERSFIELD MEMORIAL HOSPITAL, BAKERSFIELD, CA, p. A52
BALDPATE HOSPITAL, GEORGETOWN, MA, p. A307
BALDWIN PARK MEDICAL CENTER, BALDWIN PARK, CA, p. A53
BALL MEMORIAL HOSPITAL, MUNCIE, IN, p. A216
BALLARD REHABILITATION HOSPITAL, SAN BERNARDINO, CA, p. A85
BALLINGER MEMORIAL HOSPITAL, BALLINGER, TX, p. A596
BANNER BAYWOOD MEDICAL CENTER, MESA, AZ, p. A31
BANNER BEHAVIORAL HEALTH HOSPITAL – SCOTTSDALE, SCOTTSDALE, AZ, p. A35
BANNER BOSWELL MEDICAL CENTER, SUN CITY, AZ, p. A36
BANNER CASA GRANDE MEDICAL CENTER, CASA GRANDE, AZ, p. A28
BANNER CHILDREN'S HOSPITAL, MESA, AZ, p. A31
BANNER CHURCHILL COMMUNITY HOSPITAL, FALLON, NV, p. A401
BANNER DEL E. WEBB MEDICAL CENTER, SUN CITY WEST, AZ, p. A37
BANNER DESERT MEDICAL CENTER, MESA, AZ, p. A31
BANNER ESTRELLA MEDICAL CENTER, PHOENIX, AZ, p. A33
BANNER FORT COLLINS MEDICAL CENTER, FORT COLLINS, CO, p. A102
BANNER GATEWAY MEDICAL CENTER, GILBERT, AZ, p. A29
BANNER GOLDFIELD MEDICAL CENTER, APACHE JUNCTION, AZ, p. A28
BANNER HEART HOSPITAL, MESA, AZ, p. A31
BANNER IRONWOOD MEDICAL CENTER, SAN TAN VALLEY, AZ, p. A35
BANNER LASSEN MEDICAL CENTER, SUSANVILLE, CA, p. A93
BANNER PAYSON MEDICAL CENTER, PAYSON, AZ, p. A32
BANNER THUNDERBIRD MEDICAL CENTER, GLENDALE, AZ, p. A30
BANNER – UNIVERSITY MEDICAL CENTER PHOENIX, PHOENIX, AZ, p. A33
BANNER – UNIVERSITY MEDICAL CENTER SOUTH, TUCSON, AZ, p. A37
BANNER – UNIVERSITY MEDICAL CENTER TUCSON, TUCSON, AZ, p. A37
BAPTIST EASLEY HOSPITAL, EASLEY, SC, p. A561
BAPTIST EMERGENCY HOSPITAL, SAN ANTONIO, TX, p. A642
BAPTIST HEALTH CORBIN, CORBIN, KY, p. A256
BAPTIST HEALTH EXTENDED CARE HOSPITAL, LITTLE ROCK, AR, p. A46
BAPTIST HEALTH FLOYD, NEW ALBANY, IN, p. A217
BAPTIST HEALTH LA GRANGE, LA GRANGE, KY, p. A260
BAPTIST HEALTH LEXINGTON, LEXINGTON, KY, p. A260
BAPTIST HEALTH LOUISVILLE, LOUISVILLE, KY, p. A262
BAPTIST HEALTH MADISONVILLE, MADISONVILLE, KY, p. A264
BAPTIST HEALTH MEDICAL CENTER–ARKADELPHIA, ARKADELPHIA, AR, p. A40
BAPTIST HEALTH MEDICAL CENTER–CONWAY, CONWAY, AR, p. A41
BAPTIST HEALTH MEDICAL CENTER–HEBER SPRINGS, HEBER SPRINGS, AR, p. A44

BAPTIST HEALTH MEDICAL CENTER–HOT SPRING COUNTY, MALVERN, AR, p. A46
BAPTIST HEALTH MEDICAL CENTER–LITTLE ROCK, LITTLE ROCK, AR, p. A46
BAPTIST HEALTH MEDICAL CENTER–NORTH LITTLE ROCK, NORTH LITTLE ROCK, AR, p. A48
BAPTIST HEALTH MEDICAL CENTER–STUTTGART, STUTTGART, AR, p. A50
BAPTIST HEALTH PADUCAH, PADUCAH, KY, p. A266
BAPTIST HEALTH REHABILITATION INSTITUTE, LITTLE ROCK, AR, p. A46
BAPTIST HEALTH RICHMOND, RICHMOND, KY, p. A267
BAPTIST HEALTH SOUTH FLORIDA, BAPTIST HOSPITAL OF MIAMI, MIAMI, FL, p. A132
BAPTIST HEALTH SOUTH FLORIDA, DOCTORS HOSPITAL, CORAL GABLES, FL, p. A122
BAPTIST HEALTH SOUTH FLORIDA, HOMESTEAD HOSPITAL, HOMESTEAD, FL, p. A127
BAPTIST HEALTH SOUTH FLORIDA, MARINERS HOSPITAL, TAVERNIER, FL, p. A146
BAPTIST HEALTH SOUTH FLORIDA, SOUTH MIAMI HOSPITAL, MIAMI, FL, p. A132
BAPTIST HEALTH SOUTH FLORIDA, WEST KENDALL BAPTIST HOSPITAL, MIAMI, FL, p. A132
BAPTIST HOSPITAL, PENSACOLA, FL, p. A139
BAPTIST HOSPITAL OF COCKE COUNTY, NEWPORT, TN, p. A587
BAPTIST HOSPITALS OF SOUTHEAST TEXAS, BEAUMONT, TX, p. A597
BAPTIST MEDICAL CENTER, SAN ANTONIO, TX, p. A642
BAPTIST MEDICAL CENTER ATTALA, KOSCIUSKO, MS, p. A357
BAPTIST MEDICAL CENTER BEACHES, JACKSONVILLE BEACH, FL, p. A129
BAPTIST MEDICAL CENTER EAST, MONTGOMERY, AL, p. A21
BAPTIST MEDICAL CENTER JACKSONVILLE, JACKSONVILLE, FL, p. A127
BAPTIST MEDICAL CENTER LEAKE, CARTHAGE, MS, p. A353
BAPTIST MEDICAL CENTER NASSAU, FERNANDINA BEACH, FL, p. A124
BAPTIST MEDICAL CENTER SOUTH, MONTGOMERY, AL, p. A21
BAPTIST MEDICAL CENTER YAZOO, YAZOO CITY, MS, p. A363
BAPTIST MEMORIAL HOSPITAL–BOONEVILLE, BOONEVILLE, MS, p. A352
BAPTIST MEMORIAL HOSPITAL–CALHOUN, CALHOUN CITY, MS, p. A353
BAPTIST MEMORIAL HOSPITAL–COLLIERVILLE, COLLIERVILLE, TN, p. A577
BAPTIST MEMORIAL HOSPITAL–DESOTO, SOUTHAVEN, MS, p. A362
BAPTIST MEMORIAL HOSPITAL FOR WOMEN, MEMPHIS, TN, p. A584
BAPTIST MEMORIAL HOSPITAL–GOLDEN TRIANGLE, COLUMBUS, MS, p. A354
BAPTIST MEMORIAL HOSPITAL–HUNTINGDON, HUNTINGDON, TN, p. A580
BAPTIST MEMORIAL HOSPITAL–MEMPHIS, MEMPHIS, TN, p. A584
BAPTIST MEMORIAL HOSPITAL–NORTH MISSISSIPPI, OXFORD, MS, p. A360
BAPTIST MEMORIAL HOSPITAL–TIPTON, COVINGTON, TN, p. A578
BAPTIST MEMORIAL HOSPITAL–UNION CITY, UNION CITY, TN, p. A590
BAPTIST MEMORIAL HOSPITAL–UNION COUNTY, NEW ALBANY, MS, p. A360
BAPTIST MEMORIAL REHABILITATION HOSPITAL, GERMANTOWN, TN, p. A579
BAPTIST MEMORIAL RESTORATIVE CARE HOSPITAL, MEMPHIS, TN, p. A584
BARAGA COUNTY MEMORIAL HOSPITAL, L'ANSE, MI, p. A324
BARBOURVILLE ARH HOSPITAL, BARBOURVILLE, KY, p. A255
BARIX CLINICS OF PENNSYLVANIA, LANGHORNE, PA, p. A538
BARLOW RESPIRATORY HOSPITAL, LOS ANGELES, CA, p. A67
BARNABAS HEALTH BEHAVIORAL HEALTH CENTER, TOMS RIVER, NJ, p. A421
BARNES-JEWISH HOSPITAL, SAINT LOUIS, MO, p. A376
BARNES-JEWISH ST. PETERS HOSPITAL, SAINT PETERS, MO, p. A379
BARNES-JEWISH WEST COUNTY HOSPITAL, SAINT LOUIS, MO, p. A376
BARNES-KASSON COUNTY HOSPITAL, SUSQUEHANNA, PA, p. A551
BARNESVILLE HOSPITAL, BARNESVILLE, OH, p. A480
BARRETT HOSPITAL & HEALTHCARE, DILLON, MT, p. A384
BARSTOW COMMUNITY HOSPITAL, BARSTOW, CA, p. A53
BARTLETT REGIONAL HOSPITAL, JUNEAU, AK, p. A26

BARTON COUNTY MEMORIAL HOSPITAL, LAMAR, MO, p. A372
BARTON MEMORIAL HOSPITAL, SOUTH LAKE TAHOE, CA, p. A92
BARTOW REGIONAL MEDICAL CENTER, BARTOW, FL, p. A119
BASCOM PALMER EYE INSTITUTE–ANNE BATES LEACH EYE HOSPITAL, MIAMI, FL, p. A133
BASSETT ARMY COMMUNITY HOSPITAL, FORT WAINWRIGHT, AK, p. A26
BASSETT MEDICAL CENTER, COOPERSTOWN, NY, p. A434
BASTROP REHABILITATION HOSPITAL, MONROE, LA, p. A281
BATES COUNTY MEMORIAL HOSPITAL, BUTLER, MO, p. A365
BATH COMMUNITY HOSPITAL, HOT SPRINGS, VA, p. A669
BATH VETERANS AFFAIRS MEDICAL CENTER, BATH, NY, p. A431
BATON ROUGE BEHAVIORAL HOSPITAL, BATON ROUGE, LA, p. A270
BATON ROUGE GENERAL MEDICAL CENTER, BATON ROUGE, LA, p. A270
BATON ROUGE REHABILITATION HOSPITAL, BATON ROUGE, LA, p. A270
BATTLE CREEK VETERANS AFFAIRS MEDICAL CENTER, BATTLE CREEK, MI, p. A315
BATTLE MOUNTAIN GENERAL HOSPITAL, BATTLE MOUNTAIN, NV, p. A401
BAUM HARMON MERCY HOSPITAL, PRIMGHAR, IA, p. A233
BAXTER REGIONAL MEDICAL CENTER, MOUNTAIN HOME, AR, p. A47
BAY AREA HOSPITAL, COOS BAY, OR, p. A521
BAY AREA MEDICAL CENTER, MARINETTE, WI, p. A706
BAY AREA REGIONAL MEDICAL CENTER, WEBSTER, TX, p. A653
BAY MEDICAL CENTER SACRED HEART HEALTH SYSTEM, PANAMA CITY, FL, p. A138
BAY PINES VETERANS AFFAIRS HEALTHCARE SYSTEM, BAY PINES, FL, p. A119
BAYCARE ALLIANT HOSPITAL, DUNEDIN, FL, p. A124
BAYFRONT HEALTH BROOKSVILLE, BROOKSVILLE, FL, p. A121
BAYFRONT HEALTH DADE CITY, DADE CITY, FL, p. A123
BAYFRONT HEALTH PORT CHARLOTTE, PORT CHARLOTTE, FL, p. A140
BAYFRONT HEALTH PUNTA GORDA, PUNTA GORDA, FL, p. A140
BAYFRONT HEALTH ST. PETERSBURG, SAINT PETERSBURG, FL, p. A141
BAYHEALTH MEDICAL CENTER, DOVER, DE, p. A115
BAYHEALTH MEDICAL CENTER, MILFORD MEMORIAL HOSPITAL, MILFORD, DE, p. A115
BAYLOR ALL SAINTS MEDICAL CENTER AT FORT WORTH, FORT WORTH, TX, p. A613
BAYLOR EMERGENCY MEDICAL CENTER AT AUBREY, AUBREY, TX, p. A594
BAYLOR EMERGENCY MEDICAL CENTERS – BURLESON, BURLESON, TX, p. A600
BAYLOR EMERGENCY MEDICAL CENTERS – ROCKWALL, ROCKWALL, TX, p. A640
BAYLOR INSTITUTE FOR REHABILITATION, DALLAS, TX, p. A604
BAYLOR INSTITUTE FOR REHABILITATION AT FORT WORTH, FORT WORTH, TX, p. A613
BAYLOR INSTITUTE FOR REHABILITATION AT FRISCO, FRISCO, TX, p. A615
BAYLOR JACK AND JANE HAMILTON HEART AND VASCULAR HOSPITAL, DALLAS, TX, p. A604
BAYLOR MEDICAL CENTER AT FRISCO, FRISCO, TX, p. A615
BAYLOR MEDICAL CENTER AT GARLAND, GARLAND, TX, p. A616
BAYLOR MEDICAL CENTER AT MCKINNEY, MCKINNEY, TX, p. A632
BAYLOR MEDICAL CENTER AT TROPHY CLUB, TROPHY CLUB, TX, p. A650
BAYLOR MEDICAL CENTER AT UPTOWN, DALLAS, TX, p. A604
BAYLOR ORTHOPEDIC AND SPINE HOSPITAL AT ARLINGTON, ARLINGTON, TX, p. A593
BAYLOR REGIONAL MEDICAL CENTER AT GRAPEVINE, GRAPEVINE, TX, p. A617
BAYLOR REGIONAL MEDICAL CENTER AT PLANO, PLANO, TX, p. A638
BAYLOR SCOTT & WHITE EMERGENCY MEDICAL CENTER–CEDAR PARK, CEDAR PARK, TX, p. A601
BAYLOR SCOTT & WHITE MEDICAL CENTER – CARROLLTON, CARROLLTON, TX, p. A600
BAYLOR SCOTT & WHITE MEDICAL CENTER – CENTENNIAL, FRISCO, TX, p. A615
BAYLOR SCOTT & WHITE MEDICAL CENTER – HILLCREST, WACO, TX, p. A652
BAYLOR SCOTT & WHITE MEDICAL CENTER – IRVING, IRVING, TX, p. A624

BAYLOR SCOTT & WHITE MEDICAL CENTER – LAKE POINTE, ROWLETT, TX, p. A641
BAYLOR SCOTT & WHITE MEDICAL CENTER – LLANO, LLANO, TX, p. A629
BAYLOR SCOTT & WHITE MEDICAL CENTER – MARBLE FALLS, MARBLE FALLS, TX, p. A632
BAYLOR SCOTT & WHITE MEDICAL CENTER – ROUND ROCK, ROUND ROCK, TX, p. A640
BAYLOR SCOTT & WHITE MEDICAL CENTER – SUNNYVALE, SUNNYVALE, TX, p. A647
BAYLOR SCOTT & WHITE MEDICAL CENTER – TAYLOR, TAYLOR, TX, p. A648
BAYLOR SCOTT & WHITE MEDICAL CENTER – WHITE ROCK, DALLAS, TX, p. A604
BAYLOR SCOTT & WHITE MEDICAL CENTER AT WAXAHACHIE, WAXAHACHIE, TX, p. A652
BAYLOR SCOTT & WHITE SURGICAL HOSPITAL AT SHERMAN, SHERMAN, TX, p. A645
BAYLOR SCOTT AND WHITE CONTINUING CARE HOSPITAL, TEMPLE, TX, p. A648
BAYLOR ST. LUKE'S MEDICAL CENTER, HOUSTON, TX, p. A619
BAYLOR ST. LUKE'S MEDICAL CENTER MCNAIR CAMPUS, HOUSTON, TX, p. A619
BAYLOR SURGICAL HOSPITAL AT FORT WORTH, FORT WORTH, TX, p. A613
BAYLOR SURGICAL HOSPITAL AT LAS COLINAS, IRVING, TX, p. A625
BAYLOR UNIVERSITY MEDICAL CENTER, DALLAS, TX, p. A605
BAYNE–JONES ARMY COMMUNITY HOSPITAL, FORT POLK, LA, p. A274
BAYPOINTE BEHAVIORAL HEALTH, MOBILE, AL, p. A20
BAYSHORE MEDICAL CENTER, PASADENA, TX, p. A636
BAYSIDE COMMUNITY HOSPITAL, ANAHUAC, TX, p. A592
BAYSTATE FRANKLIN MEDICAL CENTER, GREENFIELD, MA, p. A307
BAYSTATE MEDICAL CENTER, SPRINGFIELD, MA, p. A311
BAYSTATE NOBLE HOSPITAL, WESTFIELD, MA, p. A312
BAYSTATE WING HOSPITAL, PALMER, MA, p. A310
BCA STONECREST HOSPITAL, DETROIT, MI, p. A317
BEACHAM MEMORIAL HOSPITAL, MAGNOLIA, MS, p. A358
BEACON BEHAVIORAL HEALTHCARE, LACOMBE, LA, p. A278
BEACON BEHAVIORAL HOSPITAL, BUNKIE, LA, p. A272
BEACON BEHAVIORAL HOSPITAL, LUTCHER, LA, p. A280
BEACON BEHAVIORAL HOSPITAL – NEW ORLEANS, NEW ORLEANS, LA, p. A282
BEACON CHILDREN'S HOSPITAL, LUVERNE, AL, p. A20
BEAR LAKE MEMORIAL HOSPITAL, MONTPELIER, ID, p. A174
BEAR RIVER VALLEY HOSPITAL, TREMONTON, UT, p. A661
BEAR VALLEY COMMUNITY HOSPITAL, BIG BEAR LAKE, CA, p. A54
BEARTOOTH BILLINGS CLINIC, RED LODGE, MT, p. A387
BEATRICE COMMUNITY HOSPITAL AND HEALTH CENTER, BEATRICE, NE, p. A391
BEAUFORT COUNTY HOSPITAL, WASHINGTON, NC, p. A472
BEAUFORT MEMORIAL HOSPITAL, BEAUFORT, SC, p. A558
BEAUMONT HOSPITAL – DEARBORN, DEARBORN, MI, p. A317
BEAUMONT HOSPITAL – FARMINGTON HILLS, FARMINGTON HILLS, MI, p. A319
BEAUMONT HOSPITAL – GROSSE POINTE, GROSSE POINTE, MI, p. A322
BEAUMONT HOSPITAL – ROYAL OAK, ROYAL OAK, MI, p. A329
BEAUMONT HOSPITAL – TAYLOR, TAYLOR, MI, p. A331
BEAUMONT HOSPITAL – TRENTON, TRENTON, MI, p. A332
BEAUMONT HOSPITAL – TROY, TROY, MI, p. A332
BEAUMONT HOSPITAL – WAYNE, WAYNE, MI, p. A333
BEAUREGARD MEMORIAL HOSPITAL, DE RIDDER, LA, p. A274
BEAVER COUNTY MEMORIAL HOSPITAL, BEAVER, OK, p. A505
BEAVER DAM COMMUNITY HOSPITALS, BEAVER DAM, WI, p. A699
BEAVER VALLEY HOSPITAL, BEAVER, UT, p. A656
BECKETT SPRINGS, WEST CHESTER, OH, p. A502
BECKLEY ARH HOSPITAL, BECKLEY, WV, p. A690
BECKLEY VETERANS AFFAIRS MEDICAL CENTER, BECKLEY, WV, p. A690
BEDFORD MEMORIAL HOSPITAL, BEDFORD, VA, p. A664
BEDFORD REGIONAL MEDICAL CENTER, BEDFORD, IN, p. A204
BEDFORD VETERANS AFFAIRS MEDICAL CENTER, EDITH NOURSE ROGERS MEMORIAL VETERANS HOSPITAL, BEDFORD, MA, p. A302
BEEBE HEALTHCARE, LEWES, DE, p. A115
BEHAVIORAL CENTER OF MICHIGAN, WARREN, MI, p. A332
BEHAVIORAL HEALTHCARE CENTER AT CLARKSVILLE, CLARKSVILLE, TN, p. A577

C

CHOATE MENTAL HEALTH CENTER, ANNA, IL, p. A177
CHOC CHILDREN'S AT MISSION HOSPITAL, MISSION VIEJO, CA, p. A73
CHOCTAW GENERAL HOSPITAL, BUTLER, AL, p. A15
CHOCTAW HEALTH CENTER, PHILADELPHIA, MS, p. A360
CHOCTAW MEMORIAL HOSPITAL, HUGO, OK, p. A509
CHOCTAW NATION HEALTH CARE CENTER, TALIHINA, OK, p. A516
CHOCTAW REGIONAL MEDICAL CENTER, ACKERMAN, MS, p. A352
CHRIST HOSPITAL, CINCINNATI, OH, p. A483
CHRISTIAN HEALTH CARE CENTER, WYCKOFF, NJ, p. A423
CHRISTIAN HOSPITAL, SAINT LOUIS, MO, p. A377
CHRISTIANA CARE HEALTH SYSTEM, NEWARK, DE, p. A115
CHRISTUS COUSHATTA HEALTH CARE CENTER, COUSHATTA, LA, p. A273
CHRISTUS DUBUIS HOSPITAL OF ALEXANDRIA, ALEXANDRIA, LA, p. A269
CHRISTUS DUBUIS HOSPITAL OF BEAUMONT, BEAUMONT, TX, p. A597
CHRISTUS DUBUIS HOSPITAL OF FORT SMITH, FORT SMITH, AR, p. A43
CHRISTUS DUBUIS HOSPITAL OF HOT SPRINGS, HOT SPRINGS NATIONAL PARK, AR, p. A44
CHRISTUS DUBUIS HOSPITAL OF PARIS, PARIS, TX, p. A636
CHRISTUS GOOD SHEPHERD MEDICAL CENTER, LONGVIEW, TX, p. A629
CHRISTUS GOOD SHEPHERD MEDICAL CENTER-MARSHALL, MARSHALL, TX, p. A632
CHRISTUS HEALTH SHREVEPORT-BOSSIER, SHREVEPORT, LA, p. A285
CHRISTUS LAKE AREA HOSPITAL, LAKE CHARLES, LA, p. A279
CHRISTUS MOTHER FRANCES HOSPITAL – JACKSONVILLE, JACKSONVILLE, TX, p. A625
CHRISTUS MOTHER FRANCES HOSPITAL – SULPHUR SPRINGS, SULPHUR SPRINGS, TX, p. A647
CHRISTUS MOTHER FRANCES HOSPITAL – TYLER, TYLER, TX, p. A650
CHRISTUS MOTHER FRANCES HOSPITAL – WINNSBORO, WINNSBORO, TX, p. A655
CHRISTUS SANTA ROSA HEALTH SYSTEM, SAN ANTONIO, TX, p. A642
CHRISTUS SOUTHEAST TEXAS HOSPITAL, BEAUMONT, TX, p. A597
CHRISTUS SOUTHEAST TEXAS JASPER MEMORIAL, JASPER, TX, p. A625
CHRISTUS SOUTHEAST TEXAS ORTHOPEDIC SPECIALTY CENTER, BEAUMONT, TX, p. A597
CHRISTUS SPOHN HOSPITAL ALICE, ALICE, TX, p. A591
CHRISTUS SPOHN HOSPITAL BEEVILLE, BEEVILLE, TX, p. A598
CHRISTUS SPOHN HOSPITAL CORPUS CHRISTI MEMORIAL, CORPUS CHRISTI, TX, p. A603
CHRISTUS SPOHN HOSPITAL KLEBERG, KINGSVILLE, TX, p. A627
CHRISTUS ST. CATHERINE HOSPITAL, KATY, TX, p. A626
CHRISTUS ST. FRANCES CABRINI HOSPITAL, ALEXANDRIA, LA, p. A269
CHRISTUS ST. MICHAEL HEALTH SYSTEM, TEXARKANA, TX, p. A649
CHRISTUS ST. MICHAEL REHABILITATION HOSPITAL, TEXARKANA, TX, p. A649
CHRISTUS ST. PATRICK HOSPITAL OF LAKE CHARLES, LAKE CHARLES, LA, p. A279
CHRISTUS ST. VINCENT REGIONAL MEDICAL CENTER, SANTA FE, NM, p. A428
CHRISTUS TRINITY MOTHER FRANCES REHABILITATION HOSPITAL, TYLER, TX, p. A650
CIBOLA GENERAL HOSPITAL, GRANTS, NM, p. A426
CIMARRON MEMORIAL HOSPITAL, BOISE CITY, OK, p. A505
CINCINNATI CHILDREN'S HOSPITAL MEDICAL CENTER, CINCINNATI, OH, p. A483
CINCINNATI VETERANS AFFAIRS MEDICAL CENTER, CINCINNATI, OH, p. A484
CIRCLES OF CARE, MELBOURNE, FL, p. A132
CITIZENS BAPTIST MEDICAL CENTER, TALLADEGA, AL, p. A23
CITIZENS MEDICAL CENTER, COLBY, KS, p. A239
CITIZENS MEDICAL CENTER, COLUMBIA, LA, p. A273
CITIZENS MEDICAL CENTER, VICTORIA, TX, p. A652
CITIZENS MEMORIAL HOSPITAL, BOLIVAR, MO, p. A364
CITRUS MEMORIAL HEALTH SYSTEM, INVERNESS, FL, p. A127
CITRUS VALLEY MEDICAL CENTER-INTER COMMUNITY CAMPUS, COVINA, CA, p. A57
CITY OF HOPE'S HELFORD CLINICAL RESEARCH HOSPITAL, DUARTE, CA, p. A58
CLAIBORNE COUNTY MEDICAL CENTER, PORT GIBSON, MS, p. A361

CLAIBORNE MEDICAL CENTER, TAZEWELL, TN, p. A589
CLAIBORNE MEMORIAL MEDICAL CENTER, HOMER, LA, p. A276
CLARA BARTON HOSPITAL, HOISINGTON, KS, p. A242
CLARA MAASS MEDICAL CENTER, BELLEVILLE, NJ, p. A411
CLAREMORE INDIAN HOSPITAL, CLAREMORE, OK, p. A506
CLARIAN ARNETT HOSPITAL, LAFAYETTE, IN, p. A214
CLARIAN HEALTH PARTNERS, INDIANAPOLIS, IN, p. A210
CLARIAN NORTH MEDICAL CENTER, CARMEL, IN, p. A205
CLARIAN WEST MEDICAL CENTER, AVON, IN, p. A203
CLARINDA REGIONAL HEALTH CENTER, CLARINDA, IA, p. A224
CLARION HOSPITAL, CLARION, PA, p. A531
CLARION PSYCHIATRIC CENTER, CLARION, PA, p. A531
CLARITY CHILD GUIDANCE CENTER, SAN ANTONIO, TX, p. A642
CLARK FORK VALLEY HOSPITAL, PLAINS, MT, p. A387
CLARK MEMORIAL HOSPITAL, JEFFERSONVILLE, IN, p. A213
CLARK REGIONAL MEDICAL CENTER, WINCHESTER, KY, p. A268
CLARKE COUNTY HOSPITAL, OSCEOLA, IA, p. A233
CLARKS SUMMIT STATE HOSPITAL, CLARKS SUMMIT, PA, p. A531
CLAXTON-HEPBURN MEDICAL CENTER, OGDENSBURG, NY, p. A448
CLAY COUNTY HOSPITAL, ASHLAND, AL, p. A13
CLAY COUNTY HOSPITAL, FLORA, IL, p. A187
CLAY COUNTY MEDICAL CENTER, CLAY CENTER, KS, p. A239
CLAY COUNTY MEMORIAL HOSPITAL, HENRIETTA, TX, p. A619
CLEAR LAKE REGIONAL MEDICAL CENTER, WEBSTER, TX, p. A653
CLEAR LAKE REHABILITATION HOSPITAL, WEBSTER, TX, p. A653
CLEARVIEW REGIONAL MEDICAL CENTER, MONROE, GA, p. A162
CLEARVISTA HEALTH AND WELLNESS, LORAIN, OH, p. A494
CLEARWATER VALLEY HOSPITAL AND CLINICS, OROFINO, ID, p. A175
CLEMENT J. ZABLOCKI VETERANS AFFAIRS MEDICAL CENTER, MILWAUKEE, WI, p. A707
CLEVELAND AREA HOSPITAL, CLEVELAND, OK, p. A506
CLEVELAND CLINIC, CLEVELAND, OH, p. A485
CLEVELAND CLINIC AKRON GENERAL, AKRON, OH, p. A479
CLEVELAND CLINIC AVON HOSPITAL, AVON, OH, p. A480
CLEVELAND CLINIC CHILDREN'S HOSPITAL FOR REHABILITATION, CLEVELAND, OH, p. A485
CLEVELAND CLINIC FAIRVIEW HOSPITAL, CLEVELAND, OH, p. A485
CLEVELAND CLINIC FLORIDA, WESTON, FL, p. A148
CLEVELAND CLINIC REHABILITATION HOSPITAL, AVON, OH, p. A480
CLEVELAND CLINIC, MEDINA HOSPITAL, MEDINA, OH, p. A495
CLEVELAND EMERGENCY HOSPITAL, CLEVELAND, TX, p. A601
CLIFTON-FINE HOSPITAL, STAR LAKE, NY, p. A452
CLIFTON SPRINGS HOSPITAL AND CLINIC, CLIFTON SPRINGS, NY, p. A434
CLIFTON T. PERKINS HOSPITAL CENTER, JESSUP, MD, p. A299
CLINCH MEMORIAL HOSPITAL, HOMERVILLE, GA, p. A159
CLINCH VALLEY MEDICAL CENTER, RICHLANDS, VA, p. A673
CLINTON HOSPITAL, CLINTON, MA, p. A306
CLINTON MEMORIAL HOSPITAL, WILMINGTON, OH, p. A502
CLOUD COUNTY HEALTH CENTER, CONCORDIA, KS, p. A240
CLOVIS COMMUNITY MEDICAL CENTER, CLOVIS, CA, p. A56
COAL COUNTY GENERAL HOSPITAL, COALGATE, OK, p. A506
COALINGA REGIONAL MEDICAL CENTER, COALINGA, CA, p. A56
COAST PLAZA DOCTORS HOSPITAL, NORWALK, CA, p. A76
COAST PLAZA HOSPITAL, NORWALK, CA, p. A76
COASTAL CAROLINA HOSPITAL, HARDEEVILLE, SC, p. A563
COASTAL HARBOR TREATMENT CENTER, SAVANNAH, GA, p. A164
COATESVILLE VETERANS AFFAIRS MEDICAL CENTER, COATESVILLE, PA, p. A532
COBALT REHABILITATION HOSPITAL, SURPRISE, AZ, p. A37
COBLESKILL REGIONAL HOSPITAL, COBLESKILL, NY, p. A434
COBRE VALLEY COMMUNITY HOSPITAL, GLOBE, AZ, p. A30
COBRE VALLEY REGIONAL MEDICAL CENTER, GLOBE, AZ, p. A30
COCHRAN MEMORIAL HOSPITAL, MORTON, TX, p. A634
COFFEE REGIONAL MEDICAL CENTER, DOUGLAS, GA, p. A156
COFFEY COUNTY HOSPITAL, BURLINGTON, KS, p. A239
COFFEYVILLE REGIONAL MEDICAL CENTER, COFFEYVILLE, KS, p. A239

COGDELL MEMORIAL HOSPITAL, SNYDER, TX, p. A646
COLE MEMORIAL, COUDERSPORT, PA, p. A532
COLEMAN COUNTY MEDICAL CENTER, COLEMAN, TX, p. A602
COLER-GOLDWATER SPECIALTY HOSPITAL AND NURSING FACILITY, NEW ROCHELLE, NY, p. A441
COLISEUM MEDICAL CENTERS, MACON, GA, p. A160
COLISEUM NORTHSIDE HOSPITAL, MACON, GA, p. A161
COLLEGE HOSPITAL CERRITOS, CERRITOS, CA, p. A55
COLLEGE HOSPITAL COSTA MESA, COSTA MESA, CA, p. A56
COLLEGE MEDICAL CENTER, LONG BEACH, CA, p. A66
COLLEGE STATION MEDICAL CENTER, COLLEGE STATION, TX, p. A602
COLLETON MEDICAL CENTER, WALTERBORO, SC, p. A567
COLLINGSWORTH GENERAL HOSPITAL, WELLINGTON, TX, p. A653
COLONEL FLORENCE A. BLANCHFIELD ARMY COMMUNITY HOSPITAL, FORT CAMPBELL, KY, p. A258
COLORADO ACUTE LONG TERM HOSPITAL, DENVER, CO, p. A100
COLORADO CANYONS HOSPITAL AND MEDICAL CENTER, FRUITA, CO, p. A103
COLORADO MENTAL HEALTH INSTITUTE AT FORT LOGAN, DENVER, CO, p. A100
COLORADO MENTAL HEALTH INSTITUTE AT PUEBLO, PUEBLO, CO, p. A106
COLORADO PLAINS MEDICAL CENTER, FORT MORGAN, CO, p. A102
COLORADO RIVER MEDICAL CENTER, NEEDLES, CA, p. A76
COLQUITT REGIONAL MEDICAL CENTER, MOULTRIE, GA, p. A162
COLUMBIA BASIN HOSPITAL, EPHRATA, WA, p. A680
COLUMBIA CENTER BIRTH HOSPITAL, MEQUON, WI, p. A707
COLUMBIA COUNTY HEALTH SYSTEM, DAYTON, WA, p. A680
COLUMBIA MEMORIAL HOSPITAL, ASTORIA, OR, p. A520
COLUMBIA MEMORIAL HOSPITAL, HUDSON, NY, p. A437
COLUMBIA ST. MARY'S HOSPITAL MILWAUKEE, MILWAUKEE, WI, p. A707
COLUMBIA ST. MARY'S OZAUKEE HOSPITAL, MEQUON, WI, p. A707
COLUMBUS COMMUNITY HOSPITAL, COLUMBUS, NE, p. A392
COLUMBUS COMMUNITY HOSPITAL, COLUMBUS, TX, p. A602
COLUMBUS COMMUNITY HOSPITAL, INC., COLUMBUS, WI, p. A700
COLUMBUS DUBLIN SPRINGS, DUBLIN, OH, p. A490
COLUMBUS HOSPITAL LTACH, NEWARK, NJ, p. A417
COLUMBUS REGIONAL HEALTHCARE SYSTEM, WHITEVILLE, NC, p. A472
COLUMBUS REGIONAL HOSPITAL, COLUMBUS, IN, p. A205
COLUMBUS SPECIALTY HOSPITAL, COLUMBUS, GA, p. A154
COMANCHE COUNTY HOSPITAL, COLDWATER, KS, p. A239
COMANCHE COUNTY MEDICAL CENTER, COMANCHE, TX, p. A602
COMANCHE COUNTY MEMORIAL HOSPITAL, LAWTON, OK, p. A509
COMER CHILDREN'S HOSPITAL, CHICAGO, IL, p. A180
COMMONWEALTH CENTER FOR CHILDREN AND ADOLESCENTS, STAUNTON, VA, p. A675
COMMONWEALTH HEALTH CENTER, SAIPAN, NORTHERN MARIANA ISLANDS, p. A721
COMMONWEALTH REGIONAL SPECIALTY HOSPITAL, BOWLING GREEN, KY, p. A255
COMMUNITY AND MISSION HOSPITALS OF HUNTINGTON PARK, HUNTINGTON PARK, CA, p. A63
COMMUNITY BEHAVIORAL HEALTH CENTER, FRESNO, CA, p. A60
COMMUNITY BEHAVIORAL HEALTH HOSPITAL – ALEXANDRIA, ALEXANDRIA, MN, p. A335
COMMUNITY BEHAVIORAL HEALTH HOSPITAL – ANNANDALE, ANNANDALE, MN, p. A335
COMMUNITY BEHAVIORAL HEALTH HOSPITAL – BAXTER, BAXTER, MN, p. A336
COMMUNITY BEHAVIORAL HEALTH HOSPITAL – BEMIDJI, BEMIDJI, MN, p. A336
COMMUNITY BEHAVIORAL HEALTH HOSPITAL – FERGUS FALLS, FERGUS FALLS, MN, p. A339
COMMUNITY BEHAVIORAL HEALTH HOSPITAL – ROCHESTER, ROCHESTER, MN, p. A346
COMMUNITY CARE HOSPITAL, NEW ORLEANS, LA, p. A282
COMMUNITY FIRST MEDICAL CENTER, CHICAGO, IL, p. A180
COMMUNITY GENERAL HEALTH CENTER, FORT FAIRFIELD, ME, p. A291
COMMUNITY-GENERAL HOSPITAL OF GREATER SYRACUSE, SYRACUSE, NY, p. A453
COMMUNITY HEALTH CENTER OF BRANCH COUNTY, COLDWATER, MI, p. A317
COMMUNITY HEALTHCARE SYSTEM, ONAGA, KS, p. A248
COMMUNITY HOSPITAL, GRAND JUNCTION, CO, p. A103

COMMUNITY HOSPITAL, MCCOOK, NE, p. A396
COMMUNITY HOSPITAL, MUNSTER, IN, p. A216
COMMUNITY HOSPITAL, OKLAHOMA CITY, OK, p. A511
COMMUNITY HOSPITAL, TALLASSEE, AL, p. A23
COMMUNITY HOSPITAL, TORRINGTON, WY, p. A720
COMMUNITY HOSPITAL, TRINITY, FL, p. A146
COMMUNITY HOSPITAL, WATERVLIET, MI, p. A333
COMMUNITY HOSPITAL ASSOCIATION, FAIRFAX, MO, p. A368
COMMUNITY HOSPITAL EAST, INDIANAPOLIS, IN, p. A210
COMMUNITY HOSPITAL-FAIRFAX, FAIRFAX, MO, p. A368
COMMUNITY HOSPITAL LONG BEACH, LONG BEACH, CA, p. A66
COMMUNITY HOSPITAL NORTH, INDIANAPOLIS, IN, p. A210
COMMUNITY HOSPITAL OF ANACONDA, ANACONDA, MT, p. A382
COMMUNITY HOSPITAL OF ANDERSON & MADISON COUNTY, ANDERSON, IN, p. A203
COMMUNITY HOSPITAL OF BREMEN, BREMEN, IN, p. A205
COMMUNITY HOSPITAL OF HUNTINGTON PARK, HUNTINGTON PARK, CA, p. A63
COMMUNITY HOSPITAL OF SAN BERNARDINO, SAN BERNARDINO, CA, p. A85
COMMUNITY HOSPITAL OF STAUNTON, STAUNTON, IL, p. A201
COMMUNITY HOSPITAL OF THE MONTEREY PENINSULA, MONTEREY, CA, p. A74
COMMUNITY HOSPITAL SOUTH, INDIANAPOLIS, IN, p. A210
COMMUNITY HOSPITALS AND WELLNESS CENTERS, BRYAN, OH, p. A482
COMMUNITY HOSPITALS AND WELLNESS CENTERS-MONTPELIER, MONTPELIER, OH, p. A496
COMMUNITY HOWARD REGIONAL HEALTH, KOKOMO, IN, p. A213
COMMUNITY HOWARD SPECIALTY HOSPITAL, KOKOMO, IN, p. A213
COMMUNITY MEDICAL CENTER, MISSOULA, MT, p. A386
COMMUNITY MEDICAL CENTER, TOMS RIVER, NJ, p. A421
COMMUNITY MEDICAL CENTER HEALTHCARE SYSTEM, SCRANTON, PA, p. A550
COMMUNITY MEDICAL CENTER OF IZARD COUNTY, CALICO ROCK, AR, p. A41
COMMUNITY MEDICAL CENTER, INC., FALLS CITY, NE, p. A392
COMMUNITY MEMORIAL HEALTHCARE, MARYSVILLE, KS, p. A246
COMMUNITY MEMORIAL HOSPITAL, BURKE, SD, p. A568
COMMUNITY MEMORIAL HOSPITAL, CLOQUET, MN, p. A338
COMMUNITY MEMORIAL HOSPITAL, HAMILTON, NY, p. A437
COMMUNITY MEMORIAL HOSPITAL, HICKSVILLE, OH, p. A492
COMMUNITY MEMORIAL HOSPITAL, MENOMONEE FALLS, WI, p. A706
COMMUNITY MEMORIAL HOSPITAL, REDFIELD, SD, p. A572
COMMUNITY MEMORIAL HOSPITAL, SUMNER, IA, p. A235
COMMUNITY MEMORIAL HOSPITAL, SYRACUSE, NE, p. A400
COMMUNITY MEMORIAL HOSPITAL, TURTLE LAKE, ND, p. A478
COMMUNITY MEMORIAL HOSPITAL, VENTURA, CA, p. A95
COMMUNITY MENTAL HEALTH CENTER, LAWRENCEBURG, IN, p. A214
COMMUNITY REGIONAL MEDICAL CENTER, FRESNO, CA, p. A60
COMPASS BEHAVIORAL CENTER OF ALEXANDRIA, ALEXANDRIA, LA, p. A269
COMPASS BEHAVIORAL CENTER OF HOUMA, HOUMA, LA, p. A276
COMPASS BEHAVIORAL CENTER OF LAFAYETTE, LAFAYETTE, LA, p. A278
COMPASS MEMORIAL HEALTHCARE, MARENGO, IA, p. A231
COMPLEX CARE HOSPITAL AT RIDGELAKE, SARASOTA, FL, p. A142
COMPLEX CARE HOSPITAL AT TENAYA, LAS VEGAS, NV, p. A402
CONCHO COUNTY HOSPITAL, EDEN, TX, p. A609
CONCORD HOSPITAL, CONCORD, NH, p. A407
CONCOURSE DIVISION, NEW ROCHELLE, NY, p. A441
CONEMAUGH MEMORIAL MEDICAL CENTER, JOHNSTOWN, PA, p. A537
CONEMAUGH MEYERSDALE MEDICAL CENTER, MEYERSDALE, PA, p. A541
CONEMAUGH MINERS MEDICAL CENTER, HASTINGS, PA, p. A536
CONEMAUGH NASON MEDICAL CENTER, ROARING SPRING, PA, p. A549
CONFLUENCE HEALTH/CENTRAL WASHINGTON HOSPITAL, WENATCHEE, WA, p. A689
CONFLUENCE HEALTH/WENATCHEE VALLEY HOSPITAL, WENATCHEE, WA, p. A689
CONIFER PARK, GLENVILLE, NY, p. A436
CONNALLY MEMORIAL MEDICAL CENTER, FLORESVILLE, TX, p. A612

CONNECTICUT CHILDREN'S MEDICAL CENTER, HARTFORD, CT, p. A110
CONNECTICUT DEPARTMENT OF CORRECTION'S HOSPITAL, SOMERS, CT, p. A113
CONNECTICUT MENTAL HEALTH CENTER, NEW HAVEN, CT, p. A112
CONNECTICUT VALLEY HOSPITAL, MIDDLETOWN, CT, p. A111
CONNECTICUT VETERANS HOME AND HOSPITAL, ROCKY HILL, CT, p. A112
CONROE REGIONAL MEDICAL CENTER, CONROE, TX, p. A602
CONTINUECARE HOSPITAL AT BAPTIST HEALTH CORBIN, CORBIN, KY, p. A257
CONTINUECARE HOSPITAL AT BAPTIST HEALTH PADUCAH, PADUCAH, KY, p. A266
CONTINUECARE HOSPITAL AT HENDRICK MEDICAL CENTER, ABILENE, TX, p. A591
CONTINUECARE HOSPITAL AT MADISONVILLE, MADISONVILLE, KY, p. A264
CONTINUECARE HOSPITAL AT MEDICAL CENTER (ODESSA), ODESSA, TX, p. A635
CONTINUECARE HOSPITAL AT MIDLAND MEMORIAL, MIDLAND, TX, p. A633
CONTINUECARE HOSPITAL AT PALMETTO HEALTH BAPTIST, COLUMBIA, SC, p. A560
CONTINUING CARE HOSPITAL, LEXINGTON, KY, p. A261
CONTINUING CARE HOSPITAL AT ST. LUKE'S, CEDAR RAPIDS, IA, p. A223
CONTINUOUS CARE CENTERS OF TULSA, TULSA, OK, p. A517
CONTRA COSTA REGIONAL MEDICAL CENTER, MARTINEZ, CA, p. A73
CONWAY MEDICAL CENTER, CONWAY, SC, p. A561
CONWAY MEDICAL CENTER, MONROE, LA, p. A281
CONWAY REGIONAL MEDICAL CENTER, CONWAY, AR, p. A41
CONWAY REGIONAL REHABILITATION HOSPITAL, CONWAY, AR, p. A41
COOK CHILDREN'S MEDICAL CENTER, FORT WORTH, TX, p. A613
COOK HOSPITAL AND CONVALESCENT NURSING CARE UNIT, COOK, MN, p. A338
COOK MEDICAL CENTER-A CAMPUS OF TIFT REGIONAL MEDICAL CENTER, ADEL, GA, p. A149
COOKEVILLE REGIONAL MEDICAL CENTER, COOKEVILLE, TN, p. A577
COOLEY DICKINSON HOSPITAL, NORTHAMPTON, MA, p. A309
COON MEMORIAL HOSPITAL, DALHART, TX, p. A604
COOPER COUNTY MEMORIAL HOSPITAL, BOONVILLE, MO, p. A365
COOPER UNIVERSITY HEALTH CARE, CAMDEN, NJ, p. A412
COOPERSTOWN MEDICAL CENTER, COOPERSTOWN, ND, p. A475
COORDINATED HEALTH-BETHLEHEM, BETHLEHEM, PA, p. A529
COOSA VALLEY MEDICAL CENTER, SYLACAUGA, AL, p. A23
COPIAH COUNTY MEDICAL CENTER, HAZLEHURST, MS, p. A356
COPLEY HOSPITAL, MORRISVILLE, VT, p. A662
COPPER BASIN MEDICAL CENTER, COPPERHILL, TN, p. A577
COPPER QUEEN COMMUNITY HOSPITAL, BISBEE, AZ, p. A28
COQUILLE VALLEY HOSPITAL, COQUILLE, OR, p. A521
CORAL GABLES HOSPITAL, CORAL GABLES, FL, p. A122
CORDELL MEMORIAL HOSPITAL, CORDELL, OK, p. A506
CORDOVA COMMUNITY MEDICAL CENTER, CORDOVA, AK, p. A25
CORNERSTONE BEHAVIORAL HEALTH HOSPITAL OF UNION COUNTY, BERKELEY HEIGHTS, NJ, p. A411
CORNERSTONE HOSPITAL OF AUSTIN, AUSTIN, TX, p. A594
CORNERSTONE HOSPITAL OF BOSSIER CITY, BOSSIER CITY, LA, p. A272
CORNERSTONE HOSPITAL OF HOUSTON AT CLEARLAKE, WEBSTER, TX, p. A653
CORNERSTONE HOSPITAL OF HUNTINGTON, HUNTINGTON, WV, p. A692
CORNERSTONE HOSPITAL OF LITTLE ROCK, LITTLE ROCK, AR, p. A46
CORNERSTONE HOSPITAL-MEDICAL CENTER OF HOUSTON, HOUSTON, TX, p. A619
CORNERSTONE HOSPITAL OF OKLAHOMA-MUSKOGEE, MUSKOGEE, OK, p. A510
CORNERSTONE HOSPITAL OF OKLAHOMA-SHAWNEE, SHAWNEE, OK, p. A515
CORNERSTONE HOSPITAL OF SOUTHWEST LOUISIANA, SULPHUR, LA, p. A287
CORNERSTONE HOSPITAL-WEST MONROE, WEST MONROE, LA, p. A287
CORNERSTONE MEDICAL CENTER, FORT OGLETHORPE, GA, p. A158

CORNERSTONE OF MEDICAL ARTS CENTER HOSPITAL, FRESH MEADOWS, NY, p. A436
CORNERSTONE REGIONAL HOSPITAL, EDINBURG, TX, p. A610
CORONA REGIONAL MEDICAL CENTER, CORONA, CA, p. A56
CORPUS CHRISTI MEDICAL CENTER, CORPUS CHRISTI, TX, p. A603
CORRY MEMORIAL HOSPITAL, CORRY, PA, p. A532
CORTLAND REGIONAL MEDICAL CENTER, CORTLAND, NY, p. A434
CORYELL MEMORIAL HOSPITAL, GATESVILLE, TX, p. A616
COSHOCTON REGIONAL MEDICAL CENTER, COSHOCTON, OH, p. A488
COTEAU DES PRAIRIES HOSPITAL, SISSETON, SD, p. A573
COTTAGE HOSPITAL, WOODSVILLE, NH, p. A410
COTTAGE REHABILITATION HOSPITAL, SANTA BARBARA, CA, p. A90
COULEE COMMUNITY HOSPITAL, GRAND COULEE, WA, p. A681
COULEE MEDICAL CENTER, GRAND COULEE, WA, p. A681
COVENANT CHILDREN'S HOSPITAL, LUBBOCK, TX, p. A630
COVENANT HEALTHCARE, SAGINAW, MI, p. A329
COVENANT HOSPITAL PLAINVIEW, PLAINVIEW, TX, p. A637
COVENANT HOSPITAL-LEVELLAND, LEVELLAND, TX, p. A629
COVENANT MEDICAL CENTER, LUBBOCK, TX, p. A630
COVENANT MEDICAL CENTER, WATERLOO, IA, p. A236
COVENANT SPECIALTY HOSPITAL, LUBBOCK, TX, p. A630
COVINGTON BEHAVIOR HEALTH, COVINGTON, LA, p. A273
COVINGTON COUNTY HOSPITAL, COLLINS, MS, p. A354
COX MEDICAL CENTER BRANSON, BRANSON, MO, p. A365
COX MEDICAL CENTERS, SPRINGFIELD, MO, p. A379
COX MONETT HOSPITAL, MONETT, MO, p. A374
COZAD COMMUNITY HEALTH SYSTEM, COZAD, NE, p. A392
CRAIG HOSPITAL, ENGLEWOOD, CO, p. A102
CRANE MEMORIAL HOSPITAL, CRANE, TX, p. A604
CRAWFORD COUNTY MEMORIAL HOSPITAL, DENISON, IA, p. A226
CRAWFORD MEMORIAL HOSPITAL, ROBINSON, IL, p. A198
CREEDMOOR PSYCHIATRIC CENTER, NEW ROCHELLE, NY, p. A441
CREEK NATION COMMUNITY HOSPITAL, OKEMAH, OK, p. A511
CRENSHAW COMMUNITY HOSPITAL, LUVERNE, AL, p. A20
CRESCENT MEDICAL CENTER LANCASTER, LANCASTER, TX, p. A628
CRESTWOOD MEDICAL CENTER, HUNTSVILLE, AL, p. A19
CRESTWYN BEHAVIORAL HEALTH, MEMPHIS, TN, p. A584
CRETE AREA MEDICAL CENTER, CRETE, NE, p. A392
CRISP REGIONAL HOSPITAL, CORDELE, GA, p. A155
CRITTENDEN COUNTY HOSPITAL, MARION, KY, p. A264
CRITTENTON HOSPITAL MEDICAL CENTER, ROCHESTER, MI, p. A329
CROOK COUNTY MEDICAL SERVICES DISTRICT, SUNDANCE, WY, p. A720
CROSBYTON CLINIC HOSPITAL, CROSBYTON, TX, p. A604
CROSS CREEK HOSPITAL, AUSTIN, TX, p. A595
CROSSING RIVERS HEALTH MEDICAL CENTER, PRAIRIE DU CHIEN, WI, p. A711
CROSSRIDGE COMMUNITY HOSPITAL, WYNNE, AR, p. A50
CROSSROADS COMMUNITY HOSPITAL, MOUNT VERNON, IL, p. A194
CROTCHED MOUNTAIN REHABILITATION CENTER, GREENFIELD, NH, p. A408
CROUSE HEALTH, SYRACUSE, NY, p. A453
CROW/NORTHERN CHEYENNE HOSPITAL, CROW AGENCY, MT, p. A383
CROZER-CHESTER MEDICAL CENTER, UPLAND, PA, p. A552
CUBA MEMORIAL HOSPITAL, CUBA, NY, p. A434
CUERO COMMUNITY HOSPITAL, CUERO, TX, p. A604
CULBERSON HOSPITAL, VAN HORN, TX, p. A651
CULLMAN REGIONAL MEDICAL CENTER, CULLMAN, AL, p. A16
CUMBERLAND COUNTY HOSPITAL, BURKESVILLE, KY, p. A256
CUMBERLAND HALL HOSPITAL, HOPKINSVILLE, KY, p. A259
CUMBERLAND HOSPITAL, NEW KENT, VA, p. A671
CUMBERLAND MEDICAL CENTER, CROSSVILLE, TN, p. A578
CUMBERLAND MEMORIAL HOSPITAL, CUMBERLAND, WI, p. A700
CUMBERLAND RIVER HOSPITAL, CELINA, TN, p. A576
CUMBERLAND SURGICAL HOSPITAL, SAN ANTONIO, TX, p. A642
CURAHEALTH BOSTON NORTH SHORE, PEABODY, MA, p. A310
CURAHEALTH HERITAGE VALLEY, BEAVER, PA, p. A529
CURAHEALTH HOSPITAL BOSTON, BRIGHTON, MA, p. A304
CURAHEALTH HOSPITAL OKLAHOMA CITY, OKLAHOMA CITY, OK, p. A512
CURAHEALTH NASHVILLE, NASHVILLE, TN, p. A586
CURAHEALTH NEW ORLEANS, NEW ORLEANS, LA, p. A282

CURAHEALTH PHOENIX, PEORIA, AZ, p. A32
CURAHEALTH PHOENIX, PHOENIX, AZ, p. A33
CURAHEALTH PITTSBURGH, OAKDALE, PA, p. A542
CURAHEALTH STOUGHTON, STOUGHTON, MA, p. A312
CURAHEALTH TUCSON, TUCSON, AZ, p. A37
CURRY GENERAL HOSPITAL, GOLD BEACH, OR, p. A522
CUSTER REGIONAL HOSPITAL, CUSTER, SD, p. A569
CUYAHOGA FALLS GENERAL HOSPITAL, CUYAHOGA FALLS, OH, p. A488
CUYUNA REGIONAL MEDICAL CENTER, CROSBY, MN, p. A338
CYPRESS CREEK HOSPITAL, HOUSTON, TX, p. A620
CYPRESS FAIRBANKS MEDICAL CENTER, HOUSTON, TX, p. A620
CYPRESS POINTE SURGICAL HOSPITAL, HAMMOND, LA, p. A275

D

D. W. MCMILLAN MEMORIAL HOSPITAL, BREWTON, AL, p. A15
DAHL MEMORIAL HEALTHCARE ASSOCIATION, EKALAKA, MT, p. A384
DAKOTA PLAINS SURGICAL CENTER, ABERDEEN, SD, p. A568
DALE MEDICAL CENTER, OZARK, AL, p. A22
DALLAS BEHAVIORAL HEALTHCARE HOSPITAL, DESOTO, TX, p. A609
DALLAS COUNTY HOSPITAL, PERRY, IA, p. A233
DALLAS COUNTY MEDICAL CENTER, FORDYCE, AR, p. A43
DALLAS MEDICAL CENTER, DALLAS, TX, p. A605
DALLAS REGIONAL MEDICAL CENTER, MESQUITE, TX, p. A633
DAMERON HOSPITAL, STOCKTON, CA, p. A92
DANA–FARBER CANCER INSTITUTE, BOSTON, MA, p. A303
DANBURY HOSPITAL, DANBURY, CT, p. A109
DANIEL DRAKE CENTER FOR POST ACUTE CARE, CINCINNATI, OH, p. A484
DANIELS MEMORIAL HEALTHCARE CENTER, SCOBEY, MT, p. A388
DANVILLE STATE HOSPITAL, DANVILLE, PA, p. A532
DARTMOUTH-HITCHCOCK MEDICAL CENTER, LEBANON, NH, p. A409
DAVID GRANT USAF MEDICAL CENTER, TRAVIS AFB, CA, p. A94
DAVIESS COMMUNITY HOSPITAL, WASHINGTON, IN, p. A221
DAVIS COUNTY HOSPITAL, BLOOMFIELD, IA, p. A223
DAVIS HOSPITAL AND MEDICAL CENTER, LAYTON, UT, p. A657
DAVIS MEDICAL CENTER, ELKINS, WV, p. A691
DAVIS REGIONAL MEDICAL CENTER, STATESVILLE, NC, p. A471
DAY KIMBALL HOSPITAL, PUTNAM, CT, p. A112
DAYTON VETERANS AFFAIRS MEDICAL CENTER, DAYTON, OH, p. A489
DCH REGIONAL MEDICAL CENTER, TUSCALOOSA, AL, p. A23
DE GRAFF MEMORIAL HOSPITAL, NORTH TONAWANDA, NY, p. A447
DE QUEEN MEDICAL CENTER, DE QUEEN, AR, p. A42
DE SOTO REGIONAL HEALTH SYSTEM, MANSFIELD, LA, p. A280
DEACONESS HOSPITAL, EVANSVILLE, IN, p. A207
DEARBORN COUNTY HOSPITAL, LAWRENCEBURG, IN, p. A214
DEBORAH HEART AND LUNG CENTER, BROWNS MILLS, NJ, p. A412
DECATUR COUNTY GENERAL HOSPITAL, PARSONS, TN, p. A588
DECATUR COUNTY HOSPITAL, LEON, IA, p. A230
DECATUR COUNTY MEMORIAL HOSPITAL, GREENSBURG, IN, p. A209
DECATUR HEALTH SYSTEMS, OBERLIN, KS, p. A248
DECATUR MEMORIAL HOSPITAL, DECATUR, IL, p. A185
DECATUR MORGAN HOSPITAL, DECATUR, AL, p. A16
DECKERVILLE COMMUNITY HOSPITAL, DECKERVILLE, MI, p. A317
DEER LODGE MEDICAL CENTER, DEER LODGE, MT, p. A384
DEER'S HEAD HOSPITAL CENTER, SALISBURY, MD, p. A300
DEKALB HEALTH, AUBURN, IN, p. A203
DEKALB MEDICAL AT DOWNTOWN DECATUR, DECATUR, GA, p. A156
DEKALB MEDICAL AT HILLANDALE, LITHONIA, GA, p. A160
DEKALB MEDICAL AT NORTH DECATUR, DECATUR, GA, p. A156
DEKALB REGIONAL MEDICAL CENTER, FORT PAYNE, AL, p. A18

DEL AMO HOSPITAL, TORRANCE, CA, p. A93
DELANO REGIONAL MEDICAL CENTER, DELANO, CA, p. A57
DELAWARE COUNTY MEMORIAL HOSPITAL, DREXEL HILL, PA, p. A533
DELAWARE PSYCHIATRIC CENTER, NEW CASTLE, DE, p. A115
DELL CHILDREN'S MEDICAL CENTER OF CENTRAL TEXAS, AUSTIN, TX, p. A595
DELL SETON MEDICAL CENTER AT THE UNIVERSITY OF TEXAS, AUSTIN, TX, p. A595
DELRAY MEDICAL CENTER, DELRAY BEACH, FL, p. A124
DELTA COMMUNITY MEDICAL CENTER, DELTA, UT, p. A656
DELTA COUNTY MEMORIAL HOSPITAL, DELTA, CO, p. A100
DELTA MEDICAL CENTER, MEMPHIS, TN, p. A584
DELTA MEMORIAL HOSPITAL, DUMAS, AR, p. A42
DELTA REGIONAL MEDICAL CENTER, GREENVILLE, MS, p. A355
DENVER HEALTH, DENVER, CO, p. A100
DENVER SPRINGS, ENGLEWOOD, CO, p. A102
DEQUINCY MEMORIAL HOSPITAL, DEQUINCY, LA, p. A274
DES MOINES DIVISION, DES MOINES, IA, p. A226
DES PERES HOSPITAL, SAINT LOUIS, MO, p. A377
DESERT PARKWAY BEHAVIORAL HEALTHCARE HOSPITAL, LAS VEGAS, NV, p. A403
DESERT REGIONAL MEDICAL CENTER, PALM SPRINGS, CA, p. A78
DESERT SPRINGS HOSPITAL MEDICAL CENTER, LAS VEGAS, NV, p. A403
DESERT VALLEY HOSPITAL, VICTORVILLE, CA, p. A96
DESERT VIEW HOSPITAL, PAHRUMP, NV, p. A405
DESERT VIEW REGIONAL MEDICAL CENTER, PAHRUMP, NV, p. A405
DESERT WILLOW TREATMENT CENTER, LAS VEGAS, NV, p. A403
DESOTO MEMORIAL HOSPITAL, ARCADIA, FL, p. A119
DETAR HEALTHCARE SYSTEM, VICTORIA, TX, p. A652
DEVEREUX CHILDREN'S BEHAVIORAL HEALTH CENTER, MALVERN, PA, p. A539
DEVEREUX GEORGIA TREATMENT NETWORK, KENNESAW, GA, p. A160
DEVEREUX HOSPITAL AND CHILDREN'S CENTER OF FLORIDA, MELBOURNE, FL, p. A132
DEVEREUX TEXAS TREATMENT NETWORK, LEAGUE CITY, TX, p. A628
DEWITT HOSPITAL, DEWITT, AR, p. A42
DICKENSON COMMUNITY HOSPITAL, CLINTWOOD, VA, p. A666
DICKINSON COUNTY HEALTHCARE SYSTEM, IRON MOUNTAIN, MI, p. A323
DIGNITY HEALTH ARIZONA GENERAL HOSPITAL, LAVEEN, AZ, p. A31
DILEY RIDGE MEDICAL CENTER, CANAL WINCHESTER, OH, p. A482
DIMMIT REGIONAL HOSPITAL, CARRIZO SPRINGS, TX, p. A600
DISTRICT ONE HOSPITAL, FARIBAULT, MN, p. A339
DIVINE PROVIDENCE HOSPITAL, WILLIAMSPORT, PA, p. A554
DIVINE SAVIOR HEALTHCARE, PORTAGE, WI, p. A710
DIXIE REGIONAL MEDICAL CENTER, SAINT GEORGE, UT, p. A660
DMC – CHILDREN'S HOSPITAL OF MICHIGAN, DETROIT, MI, p. A317
DMC – DETROIT RECEIVING HOSPITAL, DETROIT, MI, p. A317
DMC HARPER UNIVERSITY HOSPITAL, DETROIT, MI, p. A318
DMC HURON VALLEY–SINAI HOSPITAL, COMMERCE TOWNSHIP, MI, p. A317
DMC – REHABILITATION INSTITUTE OF MICHIGAN, DETROIT, MI, p. A317
DMC – SINAI–GRACE HOSPITAL, DETROIT, MI, p. A317
DOCTOR'S CENTER OF BAYAMON, BAYAMON, PUERTO RICO, p. A722
DOCTOR'S HOSPITAL, LEAWOOD, KS, p. A245
DOCTOR'S HOSPITAL AT RENAISSANCE, EDINBURG, TX, p. A610
DOCTOR'S HOSPITAL OF DEER CREEK, LEESVILLE, LA, p. A280
DOCTOR'S MEMORIAL HOSPITAL, PERRY, FL, p. A139
DOCTORS CENTER, MANATI, PUERTO RICO, p. A724
DOCTORS COMMUNITY HOSPITAL, LANHAM, MD, p. A299
DOCTORS HOSPITAL, AUGUSTA, GA, p. A151
DOCTORS HOSPITAL OF LAREDO, LAREDO, TX, p. A628
DOCTORS HOSPITAL OF MANTECA, MANTECA, CA, p. A73
DOCTORS HOSPITAL OF SARASOTA, SARASOTA, FL, p. A142
DOCTORS MEDICAL CENTER OF MODESTO, MODESTO, CA, p. A74
DOCTORS MEMORIAL HOSPITAL, BONIFAY, FL, p. A120
DOCTORS NEUROPSYCHIATRIC HOSPITAL AND RESEARCH INSTITUTE, BREMEN, IN, p. A205
DOCTORS' CENTER HOSPITAL SAN JUAN, SAN JUAN, PUERTO RICO, p. A725

DOCTORS' HOSPITAL OF MICHIGAN, PONTIAC, MI, p. A328
DODGE COUNTY HOSPITAL, EASTMAN, GA, p. A157
DOMINICAN HOSPITAL, SANTA CRUZ, CA, p. A90
DOMINION HOSPITAL, FALLS CHURCH, VA, p. A666
DONALSONVILLE HOSPITAL, DONALSONVILLE, GA, p. A156
DOOR COUNTY MEDICAL CENTER, STURGEON BAY, WI, p. A713
DOOR COUNTY MEMORIAL HOSPITAL, STURGEON BAY, WI, p. A713
DORMINY MEDICAL CENTER, FITZGERALD, GA, p. A158
DOROTHEA DIX PSYCHIATRIC CENTER, BANGOR, ME, p. A289
DOUGLAS COUNTY COMMUNITY MENTAL HEALTH CENTER, OMAHA, NE, p. A397
DOUGLAS COUNTY HOSPITAL, ALEXANDRIA, MN, p. A335
DOUGLAS COUNTY MEMORIAL HOSPITAL, ARMOUR, SD, p. A568
DOVER BEHAVIORAL HEALTH SYSTEM, DOVER, DE, p. A115
DOWN EAST COMMUNITY HOSPITAL, MACHIAS, ME, p. A292
DOYLESTOWN HOSPITAL, DOYLESTOWN, PA, p. A533
DR. DAN C. TRIGG MEMORIAL HOSPITAL, TUCUMCARI, NM, p. A429
DR. J. CORRIGAN MENTAL HEALTH CENTER, FALL RIVER, MA, p. A306
DR. PILA'S HOSPITAL, PONCE, PUERTO RICO, p. A724
DR. RAMON E. BETANCES HOSPITAL–MAYAGUEZ MEDICAL CENTER BRANCH, MAYAGUEZ, PUERTO RICO, p. A724
DR. SOLOMON CARTER FULLER MENTAL HEALTH CENTER, BOSTON, MA, p. A303
DREW MEMORIAL HEALTH SYSTEM, MONTICELLO, AR, p. A47
DRISCOLL CHILDREN'S HOSPITAL, CORPUS CHRISTI, TX, p. A603
DRUMRIGHT REGIONAL HOSPITAL, DRUMRIGHT, OK, p. A506
DUANE L. WATERS HOSPITAL, JACKSON, MI, p. A323
DUBUIS HOSPITAL OF HOUSTON, HOUSTON, TX, p. A620
DUBUIS HOSPITAL OF PORT ARTHUR, PORT ARTHUR, TX, p. A639
DUKE RALEIGH HOSPITAL, RALEIGH, NC, p. A468
DUKE REGIONAL HOSPITAL, DURHAM, NC, p. A461
DUKE UNIVERSITY HOSPITAL, DURHAM, NC, p. A461
DUKES MEMORIAL HOSPITAL, PERU, IN, p. A218
DUNCAN REGIONAL HOSPITAL, DUNCAN, OK, p. A506
DUNDY COUNTY HOSPITAL, BENKELMAN, NE, p. A391
DUNN MEMORIAL HOSPITAL, BEDFORD, IN, p. A204
DUPONT HOSPITAL, FORT WAYNE, IN, p. A208
DURHAM REGIONAL HOSPITAL, DURHAM, NC, p. A461
DURHAM VETERANS AFFAIRS MEDICAL CENTER, DURHAM, NC, p. A461
DWIGHT DAVID EISENHOWER ARMY MEDICAL CENTER, FORT GORDON, GA, p. A158

E

EAGLEVILLE HOSPITAL, EAGLEVILLE, PA, p. A533
EARLE E. MORRIS ALCOHOL AND DRUG TREATMENT CENTER, COLUMBIA, SC, p. A560
EAST ADAMS RURAL HEALTHCARE, RITZVILLE, WA, p. A684
EAST ALABAMA MEDICAL CENTER, OPELIKA, AL, p. A22
EAST CARROLL PARISH HOSPITAL, LAKE PROVIDENCE, LA, p. A279
EAST CENTRAL REGIONAL HOSPITAL, AUGUSTA, GA, p. A151
EAST CENTRAL REGIONAL HOSPITAL, GRACEWOOD, GA, p. A158
EAST COOPER MEDICAL CENTER, MOUNT PLEASANT, SC, p. A564
EAST COOPER REGIONAL MEDICAL CENTER, MOUNT PLEASANT, SC, p. A564
EAST EL PASO PHYSICIANS MEDICAL CENTER, EL PASO, TX, p. A610
EAST GEORGIA REGIONAL MEDICAL CENTER, STATESBORO, GA, p. A165
EAST JEFFERSON GENERAL HOSPITAL, METAIRIE, LA, p. A281
EAST LIVERPOOL CITY HOSPITAL, EAST LIVERPOOL, OH, p. A490
EAST LOS ANGELES DOCTORS HOSPITAL, LOS ANGELES, CA, p. A68
EAST MISSISSIPPI STATE HOSPITAL, MERIDIAN, MS, p. A359
EAST MORGAN COUNTY HOSPITAL, BRUSH, CO, p. A99
EAST MOUNTAIN HOSPITAL, BELLE MEAD, NJ, p. A411
EAST OHIO REGIONAL HOSPITAL, MARTINS FERRY, OH, p. A495
EAST ORANGE GENERAL HOSPITAL, EAST ORANGE, NJ, p. A413

EAST RIDGE HOSPITAL, EAST RIDGE, TN, p. A578
EAST TENNESSEE CHILDREN'S HOSPITAL, KNOXVILLE, TN, p. A581
EAST TEXAS MEDICAL CENTER ATHENS, ATHENS, TX, p. A594
EAST TEXAS MEDICAL CENTER CARTHAGE, CARTHAGE, TX, p. A601
EAST TEXAS MEDICAL CENTER HENDERSON, HENDERSON, TX, p. A618
EAST TEXAS MEDICAL CENTER JACKSONVILLE, JACKSONVILLE, TX, p. A625
EAST TEXAS MEDICAL CENTER PITTSBURG, PITTSBURG, TX, p. A637
EAST TEXAS MEDICAL CENTER–QUITMAN, QUITMAN, TX, p. A639
EAST TEXAS MEDICAL CENTER REHABILITATION HOSPITAL, TYLER, TX, p. A650
EAST TEXAS MEDICAL CENTER SPECIALTY HOSPITAL, TYLER, TX, p. A651
EAST TEXAS MEDICAL CENTER TYLER, TYLER, TX, p. A651
EASTAR HEALTH SYSTEM, EAST CAMPUS, MUSKOGEE, OK, p. A510
EASTERN IDAHO REGIONAL MEDICAL CENTER, IDAHO FALLS, ID, p. A173
EASTERN LONG ISLAND HOSPITAL, GREENPORT, NY, p. A436
EASTERN LOUISIANA MENTAL HEALTH SYSTEM, JACKSON, LA, p. A276
EASTERN MAINE MEDICAL CENTER, BANGOR, ME, p. A289
EASTERN NEW MEXICO MEDICAL CENTER, ROSWELL, NM, p. A428
EASTERN NIAGARA HOSPITAL, LOCKPORT, NY, p. A438
EASTERN OKLAHOMA MEDICAL CENTER, POTEAU, OK, p. A514
EASTERN PLUMAS HEALTH CARE, PORTOLA, CA, p. A80
EASTERN REGIONAL MEDICAL CENTER, PHILADELPHIA, PA, p. A543
EASTERN SHORE HOSPITAL CENTER, CAMBRIDGE, MD, p. A297
EASTERN STATE HOSPITAL, LEXINGTON, KY, p. A261
EASTERN STATE HOSPITAL, MEDICAL LAKE, WA, p. A682
EASTERN STATE HOSPITAL, WILLIAMSBURG, VA, p. A677
EASTLAND MEMORIAL HOSPITAL, EASTLAND, TX, p. A609
EASTON HOSPITAL, EASTON, PA, p. A533
EASTPOINTE HOSPITAL, DAPHNE, AL, p. A16
EASTSIDE MEDICAL CENTER, SNELLVILLE, GA, p. A165
EASTSIDE PSYCHIATRIC HOSPITAL, TALLAHASSEE, FL, p. A144
EATON RAPIDS MEDICAL CENTER, EATON RAPIDS, MI, p. A319
ED FRASER MEMORIAL HOSPITAL AND BAKER COMMUNITY HEALTH CENTER, MACCLENNY, FL, p. A131
EDEN MEDICAL CENTER, CASTRO VALLEY, CA, p. A55
EDGEFIELD COUNTY HOSPITAL, EDGEFIELD, SC, p. A561
EDGERTON HOSPITAL AND HEALTH SERVICES, EDGERTON, WI, p. A701
EDGEWOOD SURGICAL HOSPITAL, TRANSFER, PA, p. A552
EDMOND MEDICAL CENTER, EDMOND, OK, p. A507
EDWARD HINES, JR. VETERANS AFFAIRS HOSPITAL, HINES, IL, p. A190
EDWARD HOSPITAL, NAPERVILLE, IL, p. A195
EDWARDS COUNTY HOSPITAL AND HEALTHCARE CENTER, KINSLEY, KS, p. A244
EDWIN SHAW REHAB, CUYAHOGA FALLS, OH, p. A488
EFFINGHAM HOSPITAL, SPRINGFIELD, GA, p. A165
EINSTEIN MEDICAL CENTER MONTGOMERY, EAST NORRITON, PA, p. A533
EINSTEIN MEDICAL CENTER PHILADELPHIA, PHILADELPHIA, PA, p. A543
EISENHOWER MEDICAL CENTER, RANCHO MIRAGE, CA, p. A81
EL CAMINO HOSPITAL, MOUNTAIN VIEW, CA, p. A75
EL CAMPO MEMORIAL HOSPITAL, EL CAMPO, TX, p. A610
EL CENTRO REGIONAL MEDICAL CENTER, EL CENTRO, CA, p. A58
EL PASO BEHAVIORAL HEALTH SYSTEM, EL PASO, TX, p. A610
EL PASO CHILDREN'S HOSPITAL, EL PASO, TX, p. A610
EL PASO LTAC HOSPITAL, EL PASO, TX, p. A610
EL PASO PSYCHIATRIC CENTER, EL PASO, TX, p. A610
EL PASO SPECIALTY HOSPITAL, EL PASO, TX, p. A611
ELBERT MEMORIAL HOSPITAL, ELBERTON, GA, p. A157
ELEAH MEDICAL CENTER, ELBOW LAKE, MN, p. A339
ELEANOR SLATER HOSPITAL, CRANSTON, RI, p. A556
ELECTRA MEMORIAL HOSPITAL, ELECTRA, TX, p. A612
ELGIN MENTAL HEALTH CENTER, ELGIN, IL, p. A186
ELIZA COFFEE MEMORIAL HOSPITAL, FLORENCE, AL, p. A18
ELKHART GENERAL HOSPITAL, ELKHART, IN, p. A207
ELKHORN VALLEY REHABILITATION HOSPITAL, CASPER, WY, p. A717

ELKVIEW GENERAL HOSPITAL, HOBART, OK, p. A508
ELLENVILLE REGIONAL HOSPITAL, ELLENVILLE, NY, p. A435
ELLETT MEMORIAL HOSPITAL, APPLETON CITY, MO, p. A364
ELLINWOOD DISTRICT HOSPITAL, ELLINWOOD, KS, p. A240
ELLIOT HOSPITAL, MANCHESTER, NH, p. A409
ELLIS FISCHEL CANCER CENTER, COLUMBIA, MO, p. A366
ELLIS HOSPITAL, SCHENECTADY, NY, p. A452
ELLIS HOSPITAL HEALTH CENTER, SCHENECTADY, NY, p. A452
ELLIS HOSPITAL MCCLELLAN CAMPUS, SCHENECTADY, NY, p. A452
ELLSWORTH COUNTY MEDICAL CENTER, ELLSWORTH, KS, p. A240
ELLWOOD CITY HOSPITAL, ELLWOOD CITY, PA, p. A534
ELMHURST HOSPITAL, ELMHURST, IL, p. A187
ELMIRA PSYCHIATRIC CENTER, ELMIRA, NY, p. A435
ELMORE COMMUNITY HOSPITAL, WETUMPKA, AL, p. A24
ELMWOOD HEALTHCARE CENTER AT THE SPRINGS, GREEN SPRINGS, OH, p. A492
ELY–BLOOMENSON COMMUNITY HOSPITAL, ELY, MN, p. A339
EMANUEL MEDICAL CENTER, SWAINSBORO, GA, p. A165
EMANUEL MEDICAL CENTER, TURLOCK, CA, p. A94
EMERALD COAST BEHAVIORAL HOSPITAL, PANAMA CITY, FL, p. A138
EMERSON HOSPITAL, CONCORD, MA, p. A306
EMERUS COMMUNITY HOSPITAL, TOMBALL, TX, p. A650
EMERUS HOSPITAL – SUGAR LAND, SUGAR LAND, TX, p. A647
EMINENT MEDICAL CENTER, RICHARDSON, TX, p. A639
EMMA PENDLETON BRADLEY HOSPITAL, EAST PROVIDENCE, RI, p. A556
EMORY JOHNS CREEK HOSPITAL, JOHNS CREEK, GA, p. A159
EMORY REHABILITATION HOSPITAL, ATLANTA, GA, p. A150
EMORY SAINT JOSEPH'S HOSPITAL OF ATLANTA, ATLANTA, GA, p. A150
EMORY UNIVERSITY HOSPITAL, ATLANTA, GA, p. A150
EMORY UNIVERSITY HOSPITAL MIDTOWN, ATLANTA, GA, p. A150
ENCINO HOSPITAL MEDICAL CENTER, LOS ANGELES, CA, p. A68
ENDLESS MOUNTAIN HEALTH SYSTEMS, MONTROSE, PA, p. A541
ENGLEWOOD COMMUNITY HOSPITAL, ENGLEWOOD, FL, p. A124
ENGLEWOOD HOSPITAL AND MEDICAL CENTER, ENGLEWOOD, NJ, p. A414
ENLOE MEDICAL CENTER, CHICO, CA, p. A55
ENNIS REGIONAL MEDICAL CENTER, ENNIS, TX, p. A612
EPHRAIM MCDOWELL FORT LOGAN HOSPITAL, STANFORD, KY, p. A268
EPHRAIM MCDOWELL REGIONAL MEDICAL CENTER, DANVILLE, KY, p. A257
ERIE COUNTY MEDICAL CENTER, BUFFALO, NY, p. A432
ERIE VETERANS AFFAIRS MEDICAL CENTER, ERIE, PA, p. A534
ERLANGER BLEDSOE HOSPITAL, PIKEVILLE, TN, p. A588
ERLANGER MEDICAL CENTER, CHATTANOOGA, TN, p. A576
ERLANGER WOMEN'S EAST HOSPITAL, CHATTANOOGA, TN, p. A576
ESKENAZI HEALTH, INDIANAPOLIS, IN, p. A211
ESSENTIA HEALTH ADA, ADA, MN, p. A335
ESSENTIA HEALTH–DEER RIVER, DEER RIVER, MN, p. A338
ESSENTIA HEALTH DULUTH, DULUTH, MN, p. A339
ESSENTIA HEALTH FARGO, FARGO, ND, p. A475
ESSENTIA HEALTH FOSSTON, FOSSTON, MN, p. A340
ESSENTIA HEALTH–GRACEVILLE, GRACEVILLE, MN, p. A340
ESSENTIA HEALTH NORTHERN PINES MEDICAL CENTER, AURORA, MN, p. A335
ESSENTIA HEALTH SANDSTONE, SANDSTONE, MN, p. A348
ESSENTIA HEALTH ST. JOSEPH'S MEDICAL CENTER, BRAINERD, MN, p. A337
ESSENTIA HEALTH ST. MARY'S – DETROIT LAKES, DETROIT LAKES, MN, p. A338
ESSENTIA HEALTH ST. MARY'S HOSPITAL OF SUPERIOR, SUPERIOR, WI, p. A713
ESSENTIA HEALTH ST. MARY'S MEDICAL CENTER, DULUTH, MN, p. A339
ESSENTIA HEALTH–VIRGINIA, VIRGINIA, MN, p. A349
ESSEX COUNTY HOSPITAL CENTER, CEDAR GROVE, NJ, p. A412
ESTES PARK MEDICAL CENTER, ESTES PARK, CO, p. A102
ETHICUS HOSPITAL – GRAPEVINE, GRAPEVINE, TX, p. A617
EUCLID HOSPITAL, EUCLID, OH, p. A491
EUREKA COMMUNITY HEALTH SERVICES AVERA, EUREKA, SD, p. A569
EUREKA COMMUNITY HOSPITAL, EUREKA, IL, p. A187
EUREKA SPRINGS HOSPITAL, EUREKA SPRINGS, AR, p. A42
EVANGELICAL COMMUNITY HOSPITAL, LEWISBURG, PA, p. A539

EVANS MEMORIAL HOSPITAL, CLAXTON, GA, p. A154
EVANS U. S. ARMY COMMUNITY HOSPITAL, FORT CARSON, CO, p. A102
EVANSTON REGIONAL HOSPITAL, EVANSTON, WY, p. A718
EVANSVILLE PSYCHIATRIC CHILDREN CENTER, EVANSVILLE, IN, p. A207
EVANSVILLE STATE HOSPITAL, EVANSVILLE, IN, p. A207
EVERETT TOWER, OKLAHOMA CITY, OK, p. A512
EVERGREEN HEALTHCARE, KIRKLAND, WA, p. A681
EVERGREEN MEDICAL CENTER, EVERGREEN, AL, p. A17
EVERGREENHEALTH, KIRKLAND, WA, p. A681
EVERGREENHEALTH MONROE, MONROE, WA, p. A682
EXCELA FRICK HOSPITAL, MOUNT PLEASANT, PA, p. A541
EXCELA HEALTH WESTMORELAND HOSPITAL, GREENSBURG, PA, p. A535
EXCELA LATROBE AREA HOSPITAL, LATROBE, PA, p. A538
EXCELSIOR SPRINGS HOSPITAL, EXCELSIOR SPRINGS, MO, p. A367
EXETER HOSPITAL, EXETER, NH, p. A408
EYE AND EAR HOSPITAL OF PITTSBURGH, PITTSBURGH, PA, p. A546

F

F. F. THOMPSON HOSPITAL, CANANDAIGUA, NY, p. A433
F. W. HUSTON MEDICAL CENTER, WINCHESTER, KS, p. A254
FAIRBANKS, INDIANAPOLIS, IN, p. A211
FAIRBANKS MEMORIAL HOSPITAL, FAIRBANKS, AK, p. A26
FAIRCHILD MEDICAL CENTER, YREKA, CA, p. A97
FAIRFAX BEHAVIORAL HEALTH, KIRKLAND, WA, p. A681
FAIRFAX COMMUNITY HOSPITAL, FAIRFAX, OK, p. A507
FAIRFAX MEMORIAL HOSPITAL, FAIRFAX, OK, p. A507
FAIRFIELD MEDICAL CENTER, LANCASTER, OH, p. A493
FAIRFIELD MEMORIAL HOSPITAL, FAIRFIELD, IL, p. A187
FAIRFIELD MEMORIAL HOSPITAL, WINNSBORO, SC, p. A567
FAIRLAWN REHABILITATION HOSPITAL, WORCESTER, MA, p. A313
FAIRMONT HOSPITAL, SAN LEANDRO, CA, p. A89
FAIRMONT REGIONAL MEDICAL CENTER, FAIRMONT, WV, p. A692
FAIRMOUNT BEHAVIORAL HEALTH SYSTEM, PHILADELPHIA, PA, p. A543
FAIRVIEW DEVELOPMENTAL CENTER, COSTA MESA, CA, p. A57
FAIRVIEW HOSPITAL, GREAT BARRINGTON, MA, p. A307
FAIRVIEW LAKES HEALTH SERVICES, WYOMING, MN, p. A351
FAIRVIEW NORTHLAND MEDICAL CENTER, PRINCETON, MN, p. A346
FAIRVIEW PARK HOSPITAL, DUBLIN, GA, p. A157
FAIRVIEW REGIONAL MEDICAL CENTER, FAIRVIEW, OK, p. A508
FAIRVIEW RIDGES HOSPITAL, BURNSVILLE, MN, p. A337
FAIRVIEW RIVERSIDE HOSPITAL, MINNEAPOLIS, MN, p. A343
FAIRVIEW SOUTHDALE HOSPITAL, EDINA, MN, p. A339
FAIRWAY MEDICAL SURGICAL HOSPITAL, COVINGTON, LA, p. A273
FAITH COMMUNITY HOSPITAL, JACKSBORO, TX, p. A625
FAITH REGIONAL HEALTH SERVICES, NORFOLK, NE, p. A396
FALL RIVER HOSPITAL, HOT SPRINGS, SD, p. A570
FALLON MEDICAL COMPLEX, BAKER, MT, p. A382
FALLS COMMUNITY HOSPITAL AND CLINIC, MARLIN, TX, p. A632
FALMOUTH HOSPITAL, FALMOUTH, MA, p. A306
FANNIN REGIONAL HOSPITAL, BLUE RIDGE, GA, p. A152
FARGO VETERANS AFFAIRS HEALTH CARE SYSTEM, FARGO, ND, p. A475
FAULKTON AREA MEDICAL CENTER, FAULKTON, SD, p. A569
FAUQUIER HOSPITAL, WARRENTON, VA, p. A676
FAWCETT MEMORIAL HOSPITAL, PORT CHARLOTTE, FL, p. A140
FAXTON ST. LUKE'S HEALTHCARE, UTICA, NY, p. A454
FAYETTE COUNTY HOSPITAL, VANDALIA, IL, p. A202
FAYETTE COUNTY MEMORIAL HOSPITAL, WASHINGTON COURT HOUSE, OH, p. A502
FAYETTE MEDICAL CENTER, FAYETTE, AL, p. A17
FAYETTE REGIONAL HEALTH SYSTEM, CONNERSVILLE, IN, p. A206
FAYETTEVILLE VETERANS AFFAIRS MEDICAL CENTER, FAYETTEVILLE, NC, p. A462
FEATHER RIVER HOSPITAL, PARADISE, CA, p. A79
FEDERAL CORRECTIONAL INSTITUTE HOSPITAL, LITTLETON, CO, p. A105
FEDERAL MEDICAL CENTER, LEXINGTON, KY, p. A261
FERRELL HOSPITAL, ELDORADO, IL, p. A186
FERRY COUNTY MEMORIAL HOSPITAL, REPUBLIC, WA, p. A684

G

H

HAHNEMANN UNIVERSITY HOSPITAL, PHILADELPHIA, PA, p. A544
HALE COUNTY HOSPITAL, GREENSBORO, AL, p. A18
HALE HO'OLA HAMAKUA, HONOKAA, HI, p. A168
HALIFAX HEALTH MEDICAL CENTER OF DAYTONA BEACH, DAYTONA BEACH, FL, p. A123
HALIFAX REGIONAL MEDICAL CENTER, ROANOKE RAPIDS, NC, p. A469
HALLMARK HEALTH SYSTEM, MELROSE, MA, p. A308
HALLMARK YOUTHCARE – RICHMOND, RICHMOND, VA, p. A674
HAMILTON CENTER, TERRE HAUTE, IN, p. A220
HAMILTON COUNTY HOSPITAL, SYRACUSE, KS, p. A252
HAMILTON GENERAL HOSPITAL, HAMILTON, TX, p. A618
HAMILTON HOSPITAL, OLNEY, TX, p. A636
HAMILTON HOSPITAL, WEBSTER CITY, IA, p. A236
HAMILTON MEDICAL CENTER, DALTON, GA, p. A156
HAMILTON MEMORIAL HOSPITAL DISTRICT, MCLEANSBORO, IL, p. A193
HAMLIN MEMORIAL HOSPITAL, HAMLIN, TX, p. A618
HAMMOND–HENRY HOSPITAL, GENESEO, IL, p. A188
HAMOT MEDICAL CENTER, ERIE, PA, p. A534
HAMPSHIRE MEMORIAL HOSPITAL, ROMNEY, WV, p. A696
HAMPSTEAD HOSPITAL, HAMPSTEAD, NH, p. A408
HAMPTON BEHAVIORAL HEALTH CENTER, WESTAMPTON, NJ, p. A422
HAMPTON REGIONAL MEDICAL CENTER, VARNVILLE, SC, p. A566
HAMPTON ROADS SPECIALTY HOSPITAL, NEWPORT NEWS, VA, p. A671
HAMPTON VETERANS AFFAIRS MEDICAL CENTER, HAMPTON, VA, p. A668
HANCOCK COUNTY HEALTH SYSTEM, BRITT, IA, p. A223
HANCOCK MEDICAL CENTER, BAY SAINT LOUIS, MS, p. A352
HANCOCK REGIONAL HOSPITAL, GREENFIELD, IN, p. A209
HANNIBAL REGIONAL HOSPITAL, HANNIBAL, MO, p. A368
HANOVER HOSPITAL, HANOVER, KS, p. A242
HANOVER HOSPITAL, HANOVER, PA, p. A535
HANS P. PETERSON MEMORIAL HOSPITAL, PHILIP, SD, p. A571
HANSEN FAMILY HOSPITAL, IOWA FALLS, IA, p. A230
HANSFORD HOSPITAL, SPEARMAN, TX, p. A646
HARBOR BEACH COMMUNITY HOSPITAL, HARBOR BEACH, MI, p. A322
HARBOR HOSPITAL, BALTIMORE, MD, p. A294
HARBOR OAKS HOSPITAL, NEW BALTIMORE, MI, p. A327
HARBOR–UCLA MEDICAL CENTER, TORRANCE, CA, p. A93
HARDEMAN COUNTY MEMORIAL HOSPITAL, QUANAH, TX, p. A639
HARDIN COUNTY GENERAL HOSPITAL, ROSICLARE, IL, p. A199
HARDIN MEDICAL CENTER, SAVANNAH, TN, p. A588
HARDIN MEMORIAL HOSPITAL, ELIZABETHTOWN, KY, p. A257
HARDTNER MEDICAL CENTER, OLLA, LA, p. A284
HARLAN ARH HOSPITAL, HARLAN, KY, p. A259
HARLAN COUNTY HEALTH SYSTEM, ALMA, NE, p. A390
HARLINGEN MEDICAL CENTER, HARLINGEN, TX, p. A618
HARMON MEMORIAL HOSPITAL, HOLLIS, OK, p. A508
HARMON MEDICAL AND REHABILITATION HOSPITAL, LAS VEGAS, NV, p. A403
HARNETT HEALTH SYSTEM, DUNN, NC, p. A461
HARNEY DISTRICT HOSPITAL, BURNS, OR, p. A520
HARPER COUNTY COMMUNITY HOSPITAL, BUFFALO, OK, p. A505
HARPER HOSPITAL DISTRICT FIVE, HARPER, KS, p. A242
HARPER UNIVERSITY HOSPITAL, DETROIT, MI, p. A318
HARRINGTON HOSPITAL, SOUTHBRIDGE, MA, p. A311
HARRIS HEALTH SYSTEM, HOUSTON, TX, p. A620
HARRIS REGIONAL HOSPITAL, SYLVA, NC, p. A471
HARRISBURG MEDICAL CENTER, HARRISBURG, IL, p. A189
HARRISON COMMUNITY HOSPITAL, CADIZ, OH, p. A482
HARRISON COUNTY COMMUNITY HOSPITAL, BETHANY, MO, p. A364
HARRISON COUNTY HOSPITAL, CORYDON, IN, p. A206
HARRISON MEDICAL CENTER, BREMERTON, WA, p. A678
HARRISON MEMORIAL HOSPITAL, CYNTHIANA, KY, p. A257
HARRY S. TRUMAN MEMORIAL VETERANS HOSPITAL, COLUMBIA, MO, p. A367
HARSHA BEHAVIORAL CENTER, TERRE HAUTE, IN, p. A220
HARTFORD HOSPITAL, HARTFORD, CT, p. A110
HARTGROVE HOSPITAL, CHICAGO, IL, p. A181
HASKELL COUNTY COMMUNITY HOSPITAL, STIGLER, OK, p. A516
HASKELL COUNTY HEALTHCARE SYSTEM, STIGLER, OK, p. A516
HASKELL MEMORIAL HOSPITAL, HASKELL, TX, p. A618
HAVASU REGIONAL MEDICAL CENTER, LAKE HAVASU CITY, AZ, p. A31

HAVEN BEHAVIORAL HOSPITAL OF EASTERN PENNSYLVANIA, READING, PA, p. A549
HAVEN BEHAVIORAL HOSPITAL OF FRISCO, FRISCO, TX, p. A615
HAVEN BEHAVIORAL HOSPITAL OF PHILADELPHIA, PHILADELPHIA, PA, p. A544
HAVEN BEHAVIORAL SENIOR CARE OF ALBUQUERQUE, ALBUQUERQUE, NM, p. A424
HAVEN BEHAVIORAL SENIOR CARE OF DAYTON, DAYTON, OH, p. A489
HAVEN SENIOR HORIZONS, PHOENIX, AZ, p. A33
HAVENWYCK HOSPITAL, AUBURN HILLS, MI, p. A314
HAWAII STATE HOSPITAL, KANEOHE, HI, p. A170
HAWARDEN REGIONAL HEALTHCARE, HAWARDEN, IA, p. A229
HAWTHORN CENTER, NORTHVILLE, MI, p. A327
HAWTHORN CHILDREN PSYCHIATRIC HOSPITAL, SAINT LOUIS, MO, p. A377
HAXTUN HOSPITAL DISTRICT, HAXTUN, CO, p. A104
HAYES GREEN BEACH MEMORIAL HOSPITAL, CHARLOTTE, MI, p. A316
HAYS MEDICAL CENTER, HAYS, KS, p. A242
HAYWARD AREA MEMORIAL HOSPITAL AND WATER'S EDGE, HAYWARD, WI, p. A703
HAYWOOD REGIONAL MEDICAL CENTER, CLYDE, NC, p. A460
HAZARD ARH REGIONAL MEDICAL CENTER, HAZARD, KY, p. A259
HAZEL HAWKINS MEMORIAL HOSPITAL, HOLLISTER, CA, p. A63
HEALDSBURG DISTRICT HOSPITAL, HEALDSBURG, CA, p. A63
HEALTH ALLIANCE HOSPITAL - BROADWAY CAMPUS, KINGSTON, NY, p. A438
HEALTH ALLIANCE HOSPITAL - MARY'S AVENUE CAMPUS, KINGSTON, NY, p. A438
HEALTH CENTRAL HOSPITAL, OCOEE, FL, p. A136
HEALTH FIRST CAPE CANAVERAL HOSPITAL, COCOA BEACH, FL, p. A122
HEALTH FIRST HOLMES REGIONAL MEDICAL CENTER, MELBOURNE, FL, p. A132
HEALTH FIRST PALM BAY HOSPITAL, PALM BAY, FL, p. A138
HEALTH FIRST VIERA HOSPITAL, MELBOURNE, FL, p. A132
HEALTHALLIANCE HOSPITALS, LEOMINSTER, MA, p. A308
HEALTHBRIDGE CHILDREN'S HOSPITAL, ORANGE, CA, p. A78
HEALTHBRIDGE CHILDREN'S HOSPITAL OF HOUSTON, HOUSTON, TX, p. A620
HEALTHCENTER NORTHWEST, KALISPELL, MT, p. A386
HEALTHMARK REGIONAL MEDICAL CENTER, DEFUNIAK SPRINGS, FL, p. A123
HEALTHSOURCE SAGINAW, INC., SAGINAW, MI, p. A329
HEALTHSOUTH BAKERSFIELD REHABILITATION HOSPITAL, BAKERSFIELD, CA, p. A52
HEALTHSOUTH BRAINTREE REHABILITATION HOSPITAL, BRAINTREE, MA, p. A304
HEALTHSOUTH CHATTANOOGA REHABILITATION HOSPITAL, CHATTANOOGA, TN, p. A576
HEALTHSOUTH CHESAPEAKE REHABILITATION HOSPITAL, SALISBURY, MD, p. A301
HEALTHSOUTH CITY VIEW REHABILITATION HOSPITAL, FORT WORTH, TX, p. A613
HEALTHSOUTH DEACONESS REHABILITATION HOSPITAL, EVANSVILLE, IN, p. A207
HEALTHSOUTH DESERT CANYON REHABILITATION HOSPITAL, LAS VEGAS, NV, p. A403
HEALTHSOUTH EAST VALLEY REHABILITATION HOSPITAL, MESA, AZ, p. A31
HEALTHSOUTH EMERALD COAST REHABILITATION HOSPITAL, PANAMA CITY, FL, p. A138
HEALTHSOUTH HARMARVILLE REHABILITATION HOSPITAL, PITTSBURGH, PA, p. A546
HEALTHSOUTH HOSPITAL OF MANATI, MANATI, PUERTO RICO, p. A724
HEALTHSOUTH HUNTINGTON REHABILITATION HOSPITAL, HUNTINGTON, WV, p. A692
HEALTHSOUTH LAKESHORE REHABILITATION HOSPITAL, BIRMINGHAM, AL, p. A14
HEALTHSOUTH LAKEVIEW REHABILITATION HOSPITAL, ELIZABETHTOWN, KY, p. A257
HEALTHSOUTH MOUNTAINVIEW REGIONAL REHABILITATION HOSPITAL, MORGANTOWN, WV, p. A694
HEALTHSOUTH NEW ENGLAND REHABILITATION HOSPITAL, WOBURN, MA, p. A313
HEALTHSOUTH NITTANY VALLEY REHABILITATION HOSPITAL, PLEASANT GAP, PA, p. A548
HEALTHSOUTH NORTHERN KENTUCKY REHABILITATION HOSPITAL, EDGEWOOD, KY, p. A257
HEALTHSOUTH PLANO REHABILITATION HOSPITAL, PLANO, TX, p. A638
HEALTHSOUTH READING REHABILITATION HOSPITAL, READING, PA, p. A549

HEALTHSOUTH REGIONAL SPECIALTY HOSPITAL, MECHANICSBURG, PA, p. A540
HEALTHSOUTH REHABILITATION HOSPITAL – ABILENE, ABILENE, TX, p. A591
HEALTHSOUTH REHABILITATION HOSPITAL – AUSTIN, AUSTIN, TX, p. A595
HEALTHSOUTH REHABILITATION HOSPITAL – DALLAS, DALLAS, TX, p. A605
HEALTHSOUTH REHABILITATION HOSPITAL – HENDERSON, HENDERSON, NV, p. A402
HEALTHSOUTH REHABILITATION HOSPITAL – MID–CITIES, BEDFORD, TX, p. A597
HEALTHSOUTH REHABILITATION HOSPITAL, CONCORD, NH, p. A407
HEALTHSOUTH REHABILITATION HOSPITAL, CUTLER BAY, FL, p. A122
HEALTHSOUTH REHABILITATION HOSPITAL, DOTHAN, AL, p. A17
HEALTHSOUTH REHABILITATION HOSPITAL, FAYETTEVILLE, AR, p. A42
HEALTHSOUTH REHABILITATION HOSPITAL, KINGSPORT, TN, p. A581
HEALTHSOUTH REHABILITATION HOSPITAL, LARGO, FL, p. A130
HEALTHSOUTH REHABILITATION HOSPITAL AT DRAKE, CINCINNATI, OH, p. A484
HEALTHSOUTH REHABILITATION HOSPITAL AT MARTIN HEALTH, STUART, FL, p. A143
HEALTHSOUTH REHABILITATION HOSPITAL–LAS VEGAS, LAS VEGAS, NV, p. A403
HEALTHSOUTH REHABILITATION HOSPITAL MEMPHIS–NORTH, MEMPHIS, TN, p. A584
HEALTHSOUTH REHABILITATION HOSPITAL MIDLAND–ODESSA, MIDLAND, TX, p. A633
HEALTHSOUTH REHABILITATION HOSPITAL NORTH TEXAS, RICHARDSON, TX, p. A639
HEALTHSOUTH REHABILITATION HOSPITAL OF ALEXANDRIA, ALEXANDRIA, LA, p. A269
HEALTHSOUTH REHABILITATION HOSPITAL OF ALTAMONTE SPRINGS, ALTAMONTE SPRINGS, FL, p. A119
HEALTHSOUTH REHABILITATION HOSPITAL OF ALTOONA, ALTOONA, PA, p. A528
HEALTHSOUTH REHABILITATION HOSPITAL OF ARLINGTON, ARLINGTON, TX, p. A593
HEALTHSOUTH REHABILITATION HOSPITAL OF AUSTIN, AUSTIN, TX, p. A595
HEALTHSOUTH REHABILITATION HOSPITAL OF BATON ROUGE, BATON ROUGE, LA, p. A270
HEALTHSOUTH REHABILITATION HOSPITAL OF CHARLESTON, CHARLESTON, SC, p. A559
HEALTHSOUTH REHABILITATION HOSPITAL OF COLORADO SPRINGS, COLORADO SPRINGS, CO, p. A99
HEALTHSOUTH REHABILITATION HOSPITAL OF COLUMBIA, COLUMBIA, SC, p. A560
HEALTHSOUTH REHABILITATION HOSPITAL OF CYPRESS, HOUSTON, TX, p. A620
HEALTHSOUTH REHABILITATION HOSPITAL OF DAYTON, DAYTON, OH, p. A489
HEALTHSOUTH REHABILITATION HOSPITAL OF ERIE, ERIE, PA, p. A534
HEALTHSOUTH REHABILITATION HOSPITAL OF FLORENCE, FLORENCE, SC, p. A562
HEALTHSOUTH REHABILITATION HOSPITAL OF FORT SMITH, FORT SMITH, AR, p. A43
HEALTHSOUTH REHABILITATION HOSPITAL OF FORT WORTH, FORT WORTH, TX, p. A613
HEALTHSOUTH REHABILITATION HOSPITAL OF FRANKLIN, FRANKLIN, TN, p. A578
HEALTHSOUTH REHABILITATION HOSPITAL OF FREDERICKSBURG, FREDERICKSBURG, VA, p. A667
HEALTHSOUTH REHABILITATION HOSPITAL OF HUMBLE, LLC, HUMBLE, TX, p. A624
HEALTHSOUTH REHABILITATION HOSPITAL OF JONESBORO, JONESBORO, AR, p. A45
HEALTHSOUTH REHABILITATION HOSPITAL OF LITTLETON, LITTLETON, CO, p. A105
HEALTHSOUTH REHABILITATION HOSPITAL OF MECHANICSBURG, MECHANICSBURG, PA, p. A540
HEALTHSOUTH REHABILITATION HOSPITAL OF MEMPHIS, MEMPHIS, TN, p. A584
HEALTHSOUTH REHABILITATION HOSPITAL OF MIAMI, CUTLER BAY, FL, p. A122
HEALTHSOUTH REHABILITATION HOSPITAL OF MIDDLETOWN, MIDDLETOWN, DE, p. A115
HEALTHSOUTH REHABILITATION HOSPITAL OF MODESTO, MODESTO, CA, p. A74
HEALTHSOUTH REHABILITATION HOSPITAL OF MONTGOMERY, MONTGOMERY, AL, p. A21
HEALTHSOUTH REHABILITATION HOSPITAL OF NEW MEXICO, ALBUQUERQUE, NM, p. A424

J

J. ARTHUR DOSHER MEMORIAL HOSPITAL, SOUTHPORT, NC, p. A471
J. C. BLAIR MEMORIAL HOSPITAL, HUNTINGDON, PA, p. A536
J. D. MCCARTY CENTER FOR CHILDREN WITH DEVELOPMENTAL DISABILITIES, NORMAN, OK, p. A511
JACK C. MONTGOMERY VETERANS AFFAIRS MEDICAL CENTER, MUSKOGEE, OK, p. A510
JACK D WEILER HOSPITAL OF ALBERT EINSTEIN COLLEGE OF MEDICINE, NEW ROCHELLE, NY, p. A441
JACK HUGHSTON MEMORIAL HOSPITAL, PHENIX CITY, AL, p. A22
JACKSON BEHAVIORAL HEALTH HOSPITAL, MIAMI, FL, p. A133
JACKSON COUNTY HOSPITAL DISTRICT, EDNA, TX, p. A610
JACKSON COUNTY MEMORIAL HOSPITAL, ALTUS, OK, p. A504
JACKSON COUNTY REGIONAL HEALTH CENTER, MAQUOKETA, IA, p. A231
JACKSON GENERAL HOSPITAL, RIPLEY, WV, p. A695
JACKSON HEALTH SYSTEM, MIAMI, FL, p. A133
JACKSON HOSPITAL, MARIANNA, FL, p. A131
JACKSON HOSPITAL AND CLINIC, MONTGOMERY, AL, p. A21
JACKSON–MADISON COUNTY GENERAL HOSPITAL, JACKSON, TN, p. A580
JACKSON MEDICAL CENTER, JACKSON, AL, p. A19
JACKSON NORTH MEDICAL CENTER, NORTH MIAMI BEACH, FL, p. A136
JACKSON PARISH HOSPITAL, JONESBORO, LA, p. A277
JACKSON PARK HOSPITAL AND MEDICAL CENTER, CHICAGO, IL, p. A181
JACKSON PURCHASE MEDICAL CENTER, MAYFIELD, KY, p. A264
JACKSON SOUTH COMMUNITY HOSPITAL, MIAMI, FL, p. A133
JACOBSON MEMORIAL HOSPITAL CARE CENTER, ELGIN, ND, p. A475
JAMAICA HOSPITAL MEDICAL CENTER, NEW ROCHELLE, NY, p. A441
JAMES A. HALEY VETERANS' HOSPITAL–TAMPA, TAMPA, FL, p. A144
JAMES B. HAGGIN MEMORIAL HOSPITAL, HARRODSBURG, KY, p. A259
JAMES CANCER HOSPITAL AND SOLOVE RESEARCH INSTITUTE, COLUMBUS, OH, p. A487
JAMES E. VAN ZANDT VETERANS AFFAIRS MEDICAL CENTER, ALTOONA, PA, p. A528
JAMES H. QUILLEN VETERANS AFFAIRS MEDICAL CENTER, MOUNTAIN HOME, TN, p. A586
JAMES J. PETERS VETERANS AFFAIRS MEDICAL CENTER, NEW ROCHELLE, NY, p. A442
JAMESTOWN REGIONAL MEDICAL CENTER, JAMESTOWN, ND, p. A476
JANE PHILLIPS MEDICAL CENTER, BARTLESVILLE, OK, p. A505
JANE PHILLIPS NOWATA HEALTH CENTER, NOWATA, OK, p. A511
JANE TODD CRAWFORD HOSPITAL, GREENSBURG, KY, p. A259
JASPER GENERAL HOSPITAL, BAY SPRINGS, MS, p. A352
JASPER MEMORIAL HOSPITAL, MONTICELLO, GA, p. A162
JAY COUNTY HOSPITAL, PORTLAND, IN, p. A218
JAY HOSPITAL, JAY, FL, p. A129
JEANES HOSPITAL, PHILADELPHIA, PA, p. A544
JEFF DAVIS HOSPITAL, HAZLEHURST, GA, p. A158
JEFFERSON COMMUNITY HEALTH AND LIFE, FAIRBURY, NE, p. A392
JEFFERSON COUNTY HEALTH CENTER, FAIRFIELD, IA, p. A227
JEFFERSON COUNTY HOSPITAL, FAYETTE, MS, p. A354
JEFFERSON COUNTY HOSPITAL, WAURIKA, OK, p. A519
JEFFERSON COUNTY MEMORIAL HOSPITAL, WINCHESTER, KS, p. A254
JEFFERSON DAVIS COMMUNITY HOSPITAL, PRENTISS, MS, p. A361
JEFFERSON HEALTHCARE, PORT TOWNSEND, WA, p. A684
JEFFERSON HOSPITAL, JEFFERSON HILLS, PA, p. A537
JEFFERSON HOSPITAL, LOUISVILLE, GA, p. A160
JEFFERSON MEDICAL CENTER, RANSON, WV, p. A695
JEFFERSON REGIONAL MEDICAL CENTER, PINE BLUFF, AR, p. A48
JELLICO COMMUNITY HOSPITAL, JELLICO, TN, p. A580
JENNERSVILLE REGIONAL HOSPITAL, WEST GROVE, PA, p. A553
JENNIE EDMUNDSON HOSPITAL, COUNCIL BLUFFS, IA, p. A225

JENNIE M. MELHAM MEMORIAL MEDICAL CENTER, BROKEN BOW, NE, p. A391
JENNIE STUART MEDICAL CENTER, HOPKINSVILLE, KY, p. A260
JENNINGS AMERICAN LEGION HOSPITAL, JENNINGS, LA, p. A277
JENNINGS SENIOR CARE HOSPITAL, JENNINGS, LA, p. A277
JEROLD PHELPS COMMUNITY HOSPITAL, GARBERVILLE, CA, p. A61
JEROME GOLDEN CENTER FOR BEHAVIORAL HEALTH, INC., WEST PALM BEACH, FL, p. A147
JERSEY CITY MEDICAL CENTER, JERSEY CITY, NJ, p. A415
JERSEY COMMUNITY HOSPITAL, JERSEYVILLE, IL, p. A191
JERSEY SHORE HOSPITAL, JERSEY SHORE, PA, p. A537
JESSE BROWN VETERANS AFFAIRS MEDICAL CENTER, CHICAGO, IL, p. A181
JEWELL COUNTY HOSPITAL, MANKATO, KS, p. A246
JEWISH HOME OF SAN FRANCISCO, SAN FRANCISCO, CA, p. A87
JEWISH HOSPITAL, LOUISVILLE, KY, p. A262
JEWISH HOSPITAL–SHELBYVILLE, SHELBYVILLE, KY, p. A267
JFK JOHNSON REHABILITATION INSTITUTE, EDISON, NJ, p. A413
JFK MEDICAL CENTER, ATLANTIS, FL, p. A119
JFK MEDICAL CENTER, EDISON, NJ, p. A413
JFK MEDICAL CENTER NORTH CAMPUS, WEST PALM BEACH, FL, p. A147
JIM TALIAFERRO COMMUNITY MENTAL HEALTH, LAWTON, OK, p. A509
JOHN C. FREMONT HEALTHCARE DISTRICT, MARIPOSA, CA, p. A73
JOHN C. STENNIS MEMORIAL HOSPITAL, DE KALB, MS, p. A354
JOHN D. ARCHBOLD MEMORIAL HOSPITAL, THOMASVILLE, GA, p. A166
JOHN D. DINGELL VETERANS AFFAIRS MEDICAL CENTER, DETROIT, MI, p. A318
JOHN F. KENNEDY MEMORIAL HOSPITAL, INDIO, CA, p. A63
JOHN H. STROGER JR. HOSPITAL OF COOK COUNTY, CHICAGO, IL, p. A181
JOHN HEINZ INSTITUTE OF REHABILITATION MEDICINE, WILKES, PA, p. A554
JOHN J. MADDEN MENTAL HEALTH CENTER, HINES, IL, p. A190
JOHN J. PERSHING VETERANS AFFAIRS MEDICAL CENTER, POPLAR BLUFF, MO, p. A375
JOHN MUIR BEHAVIORAL HEALTH CENTER, CONCORD, CA, p. A56
JOHN MUIR MEDICAL CENTER, CONCORD, CONCORD, CA, p. A56
JOHN MUIR MEDICAL CENTER, WALNUT CREEK, WALNUT CREEK, CA, p. A96
JOHN PETER SMITH HOSPITAL, FORT WORTH, TX, p. A613
JOHN RANDOLPH MEDICAL CENTER, HOPEWELL, VA, p. A668
JOHN T. MATHER MEMORIAL HOSPITAL, PORT JEFFERSON, NY, p. A450
JOHNS COMMUNITY HOSPITAL, TAYLOR, TX, p. A648
JOHNS HOPKINS ALL CHILDREN'S HOSPITAL, SAINT PETERSBURG, FL, p. A141
JOHNS HOPKINS BAYVIEW MEDICAL CENTER, BALTIMORE, MD, p. A294
JOHNS HOPKINS HOSPITAL, BALTIMORE, MD, p. A294
JOHNSON CITY MEDICAL CENTER, JOHNSON CITY, TN, p. A581
JOHNSON COUNTY COMMUNITY HOSPITAL, MOUNTAIN CITY, TN, p. A586
JOHNSON COUNTY HEALTHCARE CENTER, BUFFALO, WY, p. A717
JOHNSON COUNTY HOSPITAL, TECUMSEH, NE, p. A400
JOHNSON MEMORIAL HEALTH SERVICES, DAWSON, MN, p. A338
JOHNSON MEMORIAL HOSPITAL, FRANKLIN, IN, p. A209
JOHNSON MEMORIAL MEDICAL CENTER, STAFFORD SPRINGS, CT, p. A113
JOHNSON REGIONAL MEDICAL CENTER, CLARKSVILLE, AR, p. A41
JOHNSTON HEALTH, SMITHFIELD, NC, p. A470
JOHNSTON MEMORIAL HOSPITAL, ABINGDON, VA, p. A664
JOHNSTON MEMORIAL HOSPITAL, TISHOMINGO, OK, p. A517
JOHNSTON R. BOWMAN HEALTH CENTER, CHICAGO, IL, p. A181
JOHNSTON–WILLIS HOSPITAL, RICHMOND, VA, p. A673
JOINT TOWNSHIP DISTRICT MEMORIAL HOSPITAL, SAINT MARYS, OH, p. A498
JONES MEMORIAL HOSPITAL, WELLSVILLE, NY, p. A455
JORDAN VALLEY MEDICAL CENTER, WEST JORDAN, UT, p. A661
JORDAN VALLEY MEDICAL CENTER WEST VALLEY CAMPUS, WEST VALLEY CITY, UT, p. A661

JOYCE EISENBERG–KEEFER MEDICAL CENTER, RESEDA, CA, p. A82
JPS HEALTH NETWORK, FORT WORTH, TX, p. A613
JULIAN F. KEITH ALCOHOL AND DRUG ABUSE TREATMENT CENTER, BLACK MOUNTAIN, NC, p. A458
JUPITER MEDICAL CENTER, JUPITER, FL, p. A129

K

KADLEC REGIONAL MEDICAL CENTER, RICHLAND, WA, p. A684
KAHI MOHALA BEHAVIORAL HEALTH, EWA BEACH, HI, p. A168
KAHUKU MEDICAL CENTER, KAHUKU, HI, p. A169
KAISER FOUNDATION HOSPITAL, MARTINEZ, CA, p. A73
KAISER FOUNDATION HOSPITAL WESTSIDE MEDICAL CENTER, HILLSBORO, OR, p. A522
KAISER FOUNDATION MENTAL HEALTH CENTER, LOS ANGELES, CA, p. A68
KAISER PERMANENTE ANTIOCH MEDICAL CENTER, ANTIOCH, CA, p. A51
KAISER PERMANENTE BALDWIN PARK MEDICAL CENTER, BALDWIN PARK, CA, p. A53
KAISER PERMANENTE CAPITOL HILL CAMPUS, SEATTLE, WA, p. A685
KAISER PERMANENTE DOWNEY MEDICAL CENTER, DOWNEY, CA, p. A57
KAISER PERMANENTE FONTANA MEDICAL CENTER, FONTANA, CA, p. A59
KAISER PERMANENTE FREMONT MEDICAL CENTER, FREMONT, CA, p. A60
KAISER PERMANENTE FRESNO MEDICAL CENTER, FRESNO, CA, p. A61
KAISER PERMANENTE LOS ANGELES MEDICAL CENTER, LOS ANGELES, CA, p. A68
KAISER PERMANENTE MANTECA MEDICAL CENTER, MANTECA, CA, p. A73
KAISER PERMANENTE MEDICAL CENTER, HONOLULU, HI, p. A168
KAISER PERMANENTE MORENO VALLEY MEDICAL CENTER, MORENO VALLEY, CA, p. A75
KAISER PERMANENTE OAKLAND MEDICAL CENTER, OAKLAND, CA, p. A77
KAISER PERMANENTE ORANGE COUNTY ANAHEIM MEDICAL CENTER, ANAHEIM, CA, p. A51
KAISER PERMANENTE PANORAMA CITY MEDICAL CENTER, LOS ANGELES, CA, p. A68
KAISER PERMANENTE REDWOOD CITY MEDICAL CENTER, REDWOOD CITY, CA, p. A82
KAISER PERMANENTE RICHMOND MEDICAL CENTER, RICHMOND, CA, p. A82
KAISER PERMANENTE RIVERSIDE MEDICAL CENTER, RIVERSIDE, CA, p. A82
KAISER PERMANENTE ROSEVILLE MEDICAL CENTER, ROSEVILLE, CA, p. A83
KAISER PERMANENTE SACRAMENTO MEDICAL CENTER, SACRAMENTO, CA, p. A83
KAISER PERMANENTE SAN DIEGO MEDICAL CENTER, SAN DIEGO, CA, p. A85
KAISER PERMANENTE SAN FRANCISCO MEDICAL CENTER, SAN FRANCISCO, CA, p. A87
KAISER PERMANENTE SAN JOSE MEDICAL CENTER, SAN JOSE, CA, p. A88
KAISER PERMANENTE SAN LEANDRO MEDICAL CENTER, SAN LEANDRO, CA, p. A89
KAISER PERMANENTE SAN RAFAEL MEDICAL CENTER, SAN RAFAEL, CA, p. A89
KAISER PERMANENTE SANTA CLARA MEDICAL CENTER, SANTA CLARA, CA, p. A90
KAISER PERMANENTE SANTA ROSA MEDICAL CENTER, SANTA ROSA, CA, p. A91
KAISER PERMANENTE SOUTH BAY MEDICAL CENTER, LOS ANGELES, CA, p. A68
KAISER PERMANENTE SOUTH SACRAMENTO MEDICAL CENTER, SACRAMENTO, CA, p. A83
KAISER PERMANENTE SOUTH SAN FRANCISCO, SOUTH SAN FRANCISCO, CA, p. A92
KAISER PERMANENTE VACAVILLE MEDICAL CENTER, VACAVILLE, CA, p. A95
KAISER PERMANENTE VALLEJO MEDICAL CENTER, VALLEJO, CA, p. A95
KAISER PERMANENTE WALNUT CREEK MEDICAL CENTER, WALNUT CREEK, CA, p. A96
KAISER PERMANENTE WEST LOS ANGELES MEDICAL CENTER, LOS ANGELES, CA, p. A69

L

M

MEMORIAL HOSPITAL PEMBROKE, PEMBROKE PINES, FL, p. A139
MEMORIAL HOSPITAL WEST, PEMBROKE PINES, FL, p. A139
MEMORIAL MEDICAL CENTER – ASHLAND, ASHLAND, WI, p. A698
MEMORIAL MEDICAL CENTER – LEE CAMPUS, JOHNSTOWN, PA, p. A537
MEMORIAL MEDICAL CENTER – NEILLSVILLE, NEILLSVILLE, WI, p. A709
MEMORIAL MEDICAL CENTER, LAS CRUCES, NM, p. A426
MEMORIAL MEDICAL CENTER, MODESTO, CA, p. A74
MEMORIAL MEDICAL CENTER, PORT LAVACA, TX, p. A639
MEMORIAL MEDICAL CENTER, SPRINGFIELD, IL, p. A200
MEMORIAL REGIONAL HEALTH, CRAIG, CO, p. A100
MEMORIAL REGIONAL HOSPITAL, HOLLYWOOD, FL, p. A127
MEMORIAL SATILLA HEALTH, WAYCROSS, GA, p. A167
MEMORIAL SLOAN-KETTERING CANCER CENTER, NEW ROCHELLE, NY, p. A442
MEMORIAL SPECIALTY HOSPITAL, LAKE CHARLES, LA, p. A279
MEMPHIS MENTAL HEALTH INSTITUTE, MEMPHIS, TN, p. A584
MEMPHIS VETERANS AFFAIRS MEDICAL CENTER, MEMPHIS, TN, p. A585
MENA REGIONAL HEALTH SYSTEM, MENA, AR, p. A47
MENDOCINO COAST DISTRICT HOSPITAL, FORT BRAGG, CA, p. A59
MENDOTA MENTAL HEALTH INSTITUTE, MADISON, WI, p. A705
MENIFEE VALLEY MEDICAL CENTER, SUN CITY, CA, p. A93
MENLO PARK SURGICAL HOSPITAL, MENLO PARK, CA, p. A73
MENNINGER CLINIC, HOUSTON, TX, p. A622
MENNONITE GENERAL HOSPITAL, AIBONITO, PUERTO RICO, p. A722
MENORAH MEDICAL CENTER, OVERLAND PARK, KS, p. A249
MENTAL HEALTH INSTITUTE, CHEROKEE, IA, p. A224
MENTAL HEALTH INSTITUTE, INDEPENDENCE, IA, p. A229
MENTAL HEALTH SERVICES FOR CLARK AND MADISON COUNTIES, SPRINGFIELD, OH, p. A499
MERCER HEALTH, COLDWATER, OH, p. A487
MERCY ALLEN HOSPITAL, OBERLIN, OH, p. A497
MERCY FITZGERALD HOSPITAL, DARBY, PA, p. A532
MERCY GENERAL HOSPITAL, SACRAMENTO, CA, p. A83
MERCY GILBERT MEDICAL CENTER, GILBERT, AZ, p. A29
MERCY HEALTH – ANDERSON HOSPITAL, CINCINNATI, OH, p. A484
MERCY HEALTH – CLERMONT HOSPITAL, BATAVIA, OH, p. A480
MERCY HEALTH – FAIRFIELD HOSPITAL, FAIRFIELD, OH, p. A491
MERCY HEALTH – MARCUM AND WALLACE, IRVINE, KY, p. A260
MERCY HEALTH – ST. CHARLES HOSPITAL, OREGON, OH, p. A497
MERCY HEALTH – ST. ELIZABETH BOARDMAN HOSPITAL, BOARDMAN, OH, p. A481
MERCY HEALTH – ST. ELIZABETH YOUNGSTOWN HOSPITAL, YOUNGSTOWN, OH, p. A503
MERCY HEALTH – ST. JOSEPH WARREN HOSPITAL, WARREN, OH, p. A501
MERCY HEALTH – WEST HOSPITAL, CINCINNATI, OH, p. A484
MERCY HEALTH – WILLARD HOSPITAL, WILLARD, OH, p. A502
MERCY HEALTH HACKLEY CAMPUS, MUSKEGON, MI, p. A327
MERCY HEALTH LOVE COUNTY, MARIETTA, OK, p. A510
MERCY HEALTH SAINT MARY'S, GRAND RAPIDS, MI, p. A321
MERCY HEALTH, LAKESHORE CAMPUS, SHELBY, MI, p. A330
MERCY HOSPITAL, BUFFALO, NY, p. A433
MERCY HOSPITAL, COON RAPIDS, MN, p. A338
MERCY HOSPITAL, MOOSE LAKE, MN, p. A344
MERCY HOSPITAL, MOUNDRIDGE, KS, p. A247
MERCY HOSPITAL ADA, ADA, OK, p. A504
MERCY HOSPITAL AND MEDICAL CENTER, CHICAGO, IL, p. A182
MERCY HOSPITAL ARDMORE, ARDMORE, OK, p. A504
MERCY HOSPITAL AURORA, AURORA, MO, p. A364
MERCY HOSPITAL BERRYVILLE, BERRYVILLE, AR, p. A40
MERCY HOSPITAL BOONEVILLE, BOONEVILLE, AR, p. A41
MERCY HOSPITAL CARTHAGE, CARTHAGE, MO, p. A366
MERCY HOSPITAL CASSVILLE, CASSVILLE, MO, p. A366
MERCY HOSPITAL COLUMBUS, COLUMBUS, KS, p. A240
MERCY HOSPITAL EL RENO, EL RENO, OK, p. A507
MERCY HOSPITAL FORT SCOTT, FORT SCOTT, KS, p. A241
MERCY HOSPITAL FORT SMITH, FORT SMITH, AR, p. A43
MERCY HOSPITAL HEALDTON, HEALDTON, OK, p. A508
MERCY HOSPITAL JEFFERSON, CRYSTAL CITY, MO, p. A367
MERCY HOSPITAL JOPLIN, JOPLIN, MO, p. A370
MERCY HOSPITAL KINGFISHER, KINGFISHER, OK, p. A509
MERCY HOSPITAL LEBANON, LEBANON, MO, p. A372

MERCY HOSPITAL LINCOLN, TROY, MO, p. A380
MERCY HOSPITAL LOGAN COUNTY, GUTHRIE, OK, p. A508
MERCY HOSPITAL OF DEFIANCE, DEFIANCE, OH, p. A490
MERCY HOSPITAL OF FOLSOM, FOLSOM, CA, p. A59
MERCY HOSPITAL OF FRANCISCAN SISTERS, OELWEIN, IA, p. A232
MERCY HOSPITAL OF PORTLAND, PORTLAND, ME, p. A292
MERCY HOSPITAL OF SCRANTON, SCRANTON, PA, p. A550
MERCY HOSPITAL OKLAHOMA CITY, OKLAHOMA CITY, OK, p. A512
MERCY HOSPITAL OZARK, OZARK, AR, p. A48
MERCY HOSPITAL PARIS, PARIS, AR, p. A48
MERCY HOSPITAL ROGERS, ROGERS, AR, p. A49
MERCY HOSPITAL SPRINGFIELD, SPRINGFIELD, MO, p. A379
MERCY HOSPITAL ST. LOUIS, SAINT LOUIS, MO, p. A377
MERCY HOSPITAL TISHOMINGO, TISHOMINGO, OK, p. A517
MERCY HOSPITAL WALDRON, WALDRON, AR, p. A50
MERCY HOSPITAL WASHINGTON, WASHINGTON, MO, p. A381
MERCY HOSPITAL WATONGA, WATONGA, OK, p. A519
MERCY HOSPITALS OF BAKERSFIELD, BAKERSFIELD, CA, p. A53
MERCY IOWA CITY, IOWA CITY, IA, p. A229
MERCY MEDICAL CENTER, BALTIMORE, MD, p. A295
MERCY MEDICAL CENTER, CANTON, OH, p. A482
MERCY MEDICAL CENTER, NAMPA, ID, p. A174
MERCY MEDICAL CENTER, OSHKOSH, WI, p. A710
MERCY MEDICAL CENTER, ROCKVILLE CENTRE, NY, p. A451
MERCY MEDICAL CENTER, ROSEBURG, OR, p. A526
MERCY MEDICAL CENTER, SPRINGFIELD, MA, p. A311
MERCY MEDICAL CENTER–CENTERVILLE, CENTERVILLE, IA, p. A224
MERCY MEDICAL CENTER–CLINTON, CLINTON, IA, p. A224
MERCY MEDICAL CENTER–DES MOINES, DES MOINES, IA, p. A226
MERCY MEDICAL CENTER–DUBUQUE, DUBUQUE, IA, p. A227
MERCY MEDICAL CENTER–DYERSVILLE, DYERSVILLE, IA, p. A227
MERCY MEDICAL CENTER MERCED, MERCED, CA, p. A73
MERCY MEDICAL CENTER MOUNT SHASTA, MOUNT SHASTA, CA, p. A75
MERCY MEDICAL CENTER–NEW HAMPTON, NEW HAMPTON, IA, p. A232
MERCY MEDICAL CENTER NORTH, POWELL, TN, p. A588
MERCY MEDICAL CENTER–NORTH IOWA, MASON CITY, IA, p. A231
MERCY MEDICAL CENTER REDDING, REDDING, CA, p. A81
MERCY MEDICAL CENTER–SIOUX CITY, SIOUX CITY, IA, p. A235
MERCY MEDICAL CENTER WEST, KNOXVILLE, TN, p. A581
MERCY MEDICAL CENTER, CEDAR RAPIDS, IOWA, CEDAR RAPIDS, IA, p. A223
MERCY MEMORIAL HOSPITAL, URBANA, OH, p. A501
MERCY PHILADELPHIA HOSPITAL, PHILADELPHIA, PA, p. A544
MERCY REGIONAL MEDICAL CENTER, DURANGO, CO, p. A101
MERCY REGIONAL MEDICAL CENTER, LORAIN, OH, p. A494
MERCY REGIONAL MEDICAL CENTER, VILLE PLATTE, LA, p. A287
MERCY REHABILITATION HOSPITAL OKLAHOMA CITY, OKLAHOMA CITY, OK, p. A512
MERCY REHABILITATION HOSPITAL ST. LOUIS, CHESTERFIELD, MO, p. A366
MERCY REHABILITATION HOSPITAL SPRINGFIELD, SPRINGFIELD, MO, p. A380
MERCY SAN JUAN MEDICAL CENTER, CARMICHAEL, CA, p. A55
MERCY ST. ANNE HOSPITAL, TOLEDO, OH, p. A500
MERCY ST. FRANCIS HOSPITAL, MOUNTAIN VIEW, MO, p. A374
MERCY ST. VINCENT MEDICAL CENTER, TOLEDO, OH, p. A500
MERCY TIFFIN HOSPITAL, TIFFIN, OH, p. A500
MERCYHEALTH HOSPITAL – ROCKTON AVENUE, ROCKFORD, IL, p. A199
MERCYHEALTH HOSPITAL AND MEDICAL CENTER – HARVARD, HARVARD, IL, p. A189
MERCYHEALTH HOSPITAL AND MEDICAL CENTER – WALWORTH, LAKE GENEVA, WI, p. A704
MERCYHEALTH HOSPITAL AND TRAUMA CENTER – JANESVILLE, JANESVILLE, WI, p. A704
MERIDIAN HEALTH SERVICES, MUNCIE, IN, p. A216
MERIT HEALTH BILOXI, BILOXI, MS, p. A352
MERIT HEALTH CENTRAL, JACKSON, MS, p. A356
MERIT HEALTH MADISON, CANTON, MS, p. A353
MERIT HEALTH NATCHEZ, NATCHEZ, MS, p. A359
MERIT HEALTH NORTHWEST MISSISSIPPI, CLARKSDALE, MS, p. A353
MERIT HEALTH RANKIN, BRANDON, MS, p. A353

MERIT HEALTH RIVER OAKS, FLOWOOD, MS, p. A354
MERIT HEALTH RIVER REGION, VICKSBURG, MS, p. A362
MERIT HEALTH WESLEY, HATTIESBURG, MS, p. A356
MERIT HEALTH WOMAN'S HOSPITAL, FLOWOOD, MS, p. A354
MERITCARE MAYVILLE UNION HOSPITAL, MAYVILLE, ND, p. A477
MERITCARE MEDICAL CENTER, FARGO, ND, p. A475
MERITCARE THIEF RIVER FALLS NORTHWEST MEDICAL CENTER, THIEF RIVER FALLS, MN, p. A349
MERITUS MEDICAL CENTER, HAGERSTOWN, MD, p. A299
MERRICK MEDICAL CENTER, CENTRAL CITY, NE, p. A391
MESA HILLS SPECIALTY HOSPITAL, EL PASO, TX, p. A611
MESA SPRINGS, FORT WORTH, TX, p. A614
MESA VIEW REGIONAL HOSPITAL, MESQUITE, NV, p. A404
MESCALERO PUBLIC HEALTH SERVICE INDIAN HOSPITAL, MESCALERO, NM, p. A427
MESILLA VALLEY HOSPITAL, LAS CRUCES, NM, p. A427
MESQUITE REHABILITATION INSTITUTE, MESQUITE, TX, p. A633
MESQUITE SPECIALTY HOSPITAL, MESQUITE, TX, p. A633
METHODIST AMBULATORY SURGERY HOSPITAL – NORTHWEST, SAN ANTONIO, TX, p. A643
METHODIST BEHAVIORAL HOSPITAL OF ARKANSAS, MAUMELLE, AR, p. A47
METHODIST CHARLTON MEDICAL CENTER, DALLAS, TX, p. A606
METHODIST DALLAS MEDICAL CENTER, DALLAS, TX, p. A606
METHODIST HEALTHCARE MEMPHIS HOSPITALS, MEMPHIS, TN, p. A585
METHODIST HOSPITAL, HENDERSON, KY, p. A259
METHODIST HOSPITAL, INDIANAPOLIS, IN, p. A211
METHODIST HOSPITAL, PHILADELPHIA, PA, p. A545
METHODIST HOSPITAL, SAN ANTONIO, TX, p. A643
METHODIST HOSPITAL FOR SURGERY, ADDISON, TX, p. A591
METHODIST HOSPITAL OF CHICAGO, CHICAGO, IL, p. A182
METHODIST HOSPITAL OF SACRAMENTO, SACRAMENTO, CA, p. A83
METHODIST HOSPITAL OF SOUTHERN CALIFORNIA, ARCADIA, CA, p. A52
METHODIST HOSPITAL SOUTH, JOURDANTON, TX, p. A625
METHODIST HOSPITAL UNION COUNTY, MORGANFIELD, KY, p. A265
METHODIST HOSPITALS, GARY, IN, p. A209
METHODIST JENNIE EDMUNDSON HOSPITAL, COUNCIL BLUFFS, IA, p. A225
METHODIST LE BONHEUR GERMANTOWN HOSPITAL, GERMANTOWN, TN, p. A579
METHODIST MANSFIELD MEDICAL CENTER, MANSFIELD, TX, p. A631
METHODIST MCKINNEY HOSPITAL, MCKINNEY, TX, p. A632
METHODIST MEDICAL CENTER OF ILLINOIS, PEORIA, IL, p. A197
METHODIST MEDICAL CENTER OF OAK RIDGE, OAK RIDGE, TN, p. A587
METHODIST OLIVE BRANCH HOSPITAL, OLIVE BRANCH, MS, p. A360
METHODIST REHABILITATION CENTER, JACKSON, MS, p. A357
METHODIST REHABILITATION HOSPITAL, DALLAS, TX, p. A606
METHODIST RICHARDSON MEDICAL CENTER, RICHARDSON, TX, p. A639
METHODIST SOUTHLAKE HOSPITAL, SOUTHLAKE, TX, p. A646
METHODIST STONE OAK HOSPITAL, SAN ANTONIO, TX, p. A643
METHODIST SUGAR LAND HOSPITAL, SUGAR LAND, TX, p. A647
METHODIST WEST HOUSTON HOSPITAL, HOUSTON, TX, p. A622
METHODIST WILLOWBROOK HOSPITAL, HOUSTON, TX, p. A622
METHODIST WOMEN'S HOSPITAL, ELKHORN, NE, p. A392
METRO HEALTH HOSPITAL, WYOMING, MI, p. A333
METROHEALTH MEDICAL CENTER, CLEVELAND, OH, p. A486
METROPLEX ADVENTIST HOSPITAL, KILLEEN, TX, p. A627
METROPOLITAN ST. LOUIS PSYCHIATRIC CENTER, SAINT LOUIS, MO, p. A377
METROPOLITAN STATE HOSPITAL, NORWALK, CA, p. A76
METROPOLITANO DE LA MONTANA, UTUADO, PUERTO RICO, p. A727
METROSOUTH MEDICAL CENTER, BLUE ISLAND, IL, p. A178
METROWEST MEDICAL CENTER, FRAMINGHAM, MA, p. A306
MIAMI COUNTY MEDICAL CENTER, PAOLA, KS, p. A249
MIAMI HEART CAMPUS AT MOUNT SINAI MEDICAL CENTER, MIAMI BEACH, FL, p. A134
MIAMI JEWISH HOME AND HOSPITAL FOR AGED, MIAMI, FL, p. A133
MIAMI VALLEY HOSPITAL, DAYTON, OH, p. A489

NORTH TEXAS MEDICAL CENTER, GAINESVILLE, TX, p. A615
NORTH TEXAS STATE HOSPITAL, VERNON, TX, p. A651
NORTH TEXAS STATE HOSPITAL, WICHITA FALLS CAMPUS, WICHITA FALLS, TX, p. A654
NORTH VALLEY HEALTH CENTER, WARREN, MN, p. A350
NORTH VALLEY HOSPITAL, TONASKET, WA, p. A688
NORTH VALLEY HOSPITAL, WHITEFISH, MT, p. A389
NORTH VISTA HOSPITAL, NORTH LAS VEGAS, NV, p. A404
NORTHBAY MEDICAL CENTER, FAIRFIELD, CA, p. A59
NORTHBAY VACAVALLEY HOSPITAL, VACAVILLE, CA, p. A95
NORTHBROOK BEHAVIORAL HEALTH HOSPITAL, BLACKWOOD, NJ, p. A411
NORTHCOAST BEHAVIORAL HEALTHCARE, NORTHFIELD, OH, p. A497
NORTHCREST MEDICAL CENTER, SPRINGFIELD, TN, p. A589
NORTHEAST GEORGIA MEDICAL CENTER, GAINESVILLE, GA, p. A158
NORTHEAST GEORGIA MEDICAL CENTER BARROW, WINDER, GA, p. A167
NORTHEAST GEORGIA MEDICAL CENTER BRASELTON, BRASELTON, GA, p. A153
NORTHEAST REGIONAL MEDICAL CENTER, KIRKSVILLE, MO, p. A371
NORTHEAST REHABILITATION HOSPITAL, SALEM, NH, p. A410
NORTHEASTERN CENTER, AUBURN, IN, p. A203
NORTHEASTERN HEALTH SYSTEM, TAHLEQUAH, OK, p. A516
NORTHEASTERN HEALTH SYSTEM SEQUOYAH, SALLISAW, OK, p. A515
NORTHEASTERN NEVADA REGIONAL HOSPITAL, ELKO, NV, p. A401
NORTHEASTERN VERMONT REGIONAL HOSPITAL, SAINT JOHNSBURY, VT, p. A663
NORTHERN ARIZONA VETERANS AFFAIRS HEALTH CARE SYSTEM, PRESCOTT, AZ, p. A34
NORTHERN CALIFORNIA REHABILITATION HOSPITAL, REDDING, CA, p. A81
NORTHERN COCHISE COMMUNITY HOSPITAL, WILLCOX, AZ, p. A38
NORTHERN COLORADO LONG TERM ACUTE HOSPITAL, JOHNSTOWN, CO, p. A104
NORTHERN COLORADO REHABILITATION HOSPITAL, JOHNSTOWN, CO, p. A104
NORTHERN DUTCHESS HOSPITAL, RHINEBECK, NY, p. A450
NORTHERN HOSPITAL OF SURRY COUNTY, MOUNT AIRY, NC, p. A467
NORTHERN IDAHO ADVANCED CARE HOSPITAL, POST FALLS, ID, p. A175
NORTHERN INYO HOSPITAL, BISHOP, CA, p. A54
NORTHERN LOUISIANA MEDICAL CENTER, RUSTON, LA, p. A285
NORTHERN MAINE MEDICAL CENTER, FORT KENT, ME, p. A291
NORTHERN MONTANA HEALTH CARE, HAVRE, MT, p. A385
NORTHERN NAVAJO MEDICAL CENTER, SHIPROCK, NM, p. A428
NORTHERN NEVADA ADULT MENTAL HEALTH SERVICES, SPARKS, NV, p. A406
NORTHERN NEVADA MEDICAL CENTER, SPARKS, NV, p. A406
NORTHERN ROCKIES MEDICAL CENTER, CUT BANK, MT, p. A383
NORTHERN UTAH REHABILITATION HOSPITAL, SOUTH OGDEN, UT, p. A661
NORTHERN VIRGINIA MENTAL HEALTH INSTITUTE, FALLS CHURCH, VA, p. A667
NORTHERN WESTCHESTER HOSPITAL, MOUNT KISCO, NY, p. A440
NORTHFIELD HOSPITAL, NORTHFIELD, MN, p. A345
NORTHKEY COMMUNITY CARE, COVINGTON, KY, p. A257
NORTHLAKE BEHAVIORAL HEALTH SYSTEM, MANDEVILLE, LA, p. A280
NORTHLAND LTAC HOSPITAL, KANSAS CITY, MO, p. A370
NORTHPORT VETERANS AFFAIRS MEDICAL CENTER, NORTHPORT, NY, p. A448
NORTHRIDGE HOSPITAL MEDICAL CENTER, LOS ANGELES, CA, p. A70
NORTHRIDGE MEDICAL CENTER, COMMERCE, GA, p. A155
NORTHSHORE GLENBROOK HOSPITAL, GLENVIEW, IL, p. A189
NORTHSHORE HIGHLAND PARK HOSPITAL, HIGHLAND PARK, IL, p. A190
NORTHSHORE REGIONAL MEDICAL CENTER, SLIDELL, LA, p. A286
NORTHSHORE SPECIALTY HOSPITAL, COVINGTON, LA, p. A273
NORTHSHORE UNIVERSITY HEALTH SYSTEM, EVANSTON, IL, p. A187
NORTHSIDE HOSPITAL, ATLANTA, GA, p. A150
NORTHSIDE HOSPITAL, SAINT PETERSBURG, FL, p. A141

NORTHSIDE HOSPITAL–CHEROKEE, CANTON, GA, p. A153
NORTHSIDE HOSPITAL–FORSYTH, CUMMING, GA, p. A155
NORTHSIDE MEDICAL CENTER, COLUMBUS, GA, p. A155
NORTHSIDE MEDICAL CENTER, YOUNGSTOWN, OH, p. A503
NORTHSIDE MEDICAL CENTER, YOUNGSTOWN, OH, p. A503
NORTHWEST CENTER FOR BEHAVIORAL HEALTH, FORT SUPPLY, OK, p. A508
NORTHWEST COMMUNITY HOSPITAL, ARLINGTON HEIGHTS, IL, p. A177
NORTHWEST FLORIDA COMMUNITY HOSPITAL, CHIPLEY, FL, p. A121
NORTHWEST HILLS SURGICAL HOSPITAL, AUSTIN, TX, p. A595
NORTHWEST HOSPITAL, RANDALLSTOWN, MD, p. A300
NORTHWEST MEDICAL CENTER, ALBANY, MO, p. A364
NORTHWEST MEDICAL CENTER, MARGATE, FL, p. A131
NORTHWEST MEDICAL CENTER, TUCSON, AZ, p. A38
NORTHWEST MEDICAL CENTER, WINFIELD, AL, p. A24
NORTHWEST MEDICAL CENTER – SPRINGDALE, SPRINGDALE, AR, p. A49
NORTHWEST MISSOURI PSYCHIATRIC REHABILITATION CENTER, SAINT JOSEPH, MO, p. A376
NORTHWEST OHIO PSYCHIATRIC HOSPITAL, TOLEDO, OH, p. A500
NORTHWEST SPECIALTY HOSPITAL, POST FALLS, ID, p. A175
NORTHWEST SURGICAL HOSPITAL, OKLAHOMA CITY, OK, p. A512
NORTHWEST TEXAS HEALTHCARE SYSTEM, AMARILLO, TX, p. A592
NORTHWESTERN MEDICAL CENTER, SAINT ALBANS, VT, p. A663
NORTHWESTERN MEDICINE CENTRAL DUPAGE HOSPITAL, WINFIELD, IL, p. A202
NORTHWESTERN MEDICINE DELNOR HOSPITAL, GENEVA, IL, p. A188
NORTHWESTERN MEDICINE KISHWAUKEE HOSPITAL, DEKALB, IL, p. A185
NORTHWESTERN MEDICINE LAKE FOREST HOSPITAL, LAKE FOREST, IL, p. A192
NORTHWESTERN MEDICINE VALLEY WEST HOSPITAL, SANDWICH, IL, p. A200
NORTHWESTERN MEMORIAL HOSPITAL, CHICAGO, IL, p. A182
NORTHWOOD DEACONESS HEALTH CENTER, NORTHWOOD, ND, p. A474
NORTON AUDUBON HOSPITAL, LOUISVILLE, KY, p. A263
NORTON BROWNSBORO HOSPITAL, LOUISVILLE, KY, p. A263
NORTON CHILDREN'S HOSPITAL, LOUISVILLE, KY, p. A263
NORTON COMMUNITY HOSPITAL, NORTON, VA, p. A672
NORTON COUNTY HOSPITAL, NORTON, KS, p. A247
NORTON HEALTHCARE PAVILION, LOUISVILLE, KY, p. A263
NORTON HOSPITAL, LOUISVILLE, KY, p. A263
NORTON SOUND REGIONAL HOSPITAL, NOME, AK, p. A26
NORTON WOMEN'S AND CHILDREN'S HOSPITAL, LOUISVILLE, KY, p. A263
NORWALK HOSPITAL, NORWALK, CT, p. A112
NORWEGIAN AMERICAN HOSPITAL, CHICAGO, IL, p. A182
NORWOOD HEALTH CENTER, MARSHFIELD, WI, p. A706
NORWOOD HOSPITAL, NORWOOD, MA, p. A310
NOVANT HEALTH BRUNSWICK MEDICAL CENTER, BOLIVIA, NC, p. A458
NOVANT HEALTH CHARLOTTE ORTHOPAEDIC HOSPITAL, CHARLOTTE, NC, p. A459
NOVANT HEALTH FORSYTH MEDICAL CENTER, WINSTON, NC, p. A473
NOVANT HEALTH HUNTERSVILLE MEDICAL CENTER, HUNTERSVILLE, NC, p. A465
NOVANT HEALTH MATTHEWS MEDICAL CENTER, MATTHEWS, NC, p. A466
NOVANT HEALTH MEDICAL PARK HOSPITAL, WINSTON, NC, p. A473
NOVANT HEALTH PRESBYTERIAN MEDICAL CENTER, CHARLOTTE, NC, p. A460
NOVANT HEALTH ROWAN MEDICAL CENTER, SALISBURY, NC, p. A470
NOVANT HEALTH THOMASVILLE MEDICAL CENTER, THOMASVILLE, NC, p. A471
NOVANT HEALTH UVA HEALTH SYSTEM CULPEPER MEDICAL CENTER, CULPEPER, VA, p. A666
NOVANT HEALTH UVA HEALTH SYSTEM HAYMARKET MEDICAL CENTER, HAYMARKET, VA, p. A668
NOVANT HEALTH UVA HEALTH SYSTEM PRINCE WILLIAM MEDICAL CENTER, MANASSAS, VA, p. A670
NOVATO COMMUNITY HOSPITAL, NOVATO, CA, p. A76
NOXUBEE GENERAL HOSPITAL, MACON, MS, p. A358
NYACK HOSPITAL, NYACK, NY, p. A448
NYC HEALTH + HOSPITALS / BELLEVUE, NEW ROCHELLE, NY, p. A444
NYC HEALTH + HOSPITALS / CARTER, NEW ROCHELLE, NY, p. A444

NYC HEALTH + HOSPITALS / CONEY ISLAND, NEW ROCHELLE, NY, p. A444
NYC HEALTH + HOSPITALS / ELMHURST, NEW ROCHELLE, NY, p. A445
NYC HEALTH + HOSPITALS / HARLEM, NEW ROCHELLE, NY, p. A445
NYC HEALTH + HOSPITALS / JACOBI, NEW ROCHELLE, NY, p. A445
NYC HEALTH + HOSPITALS / KINGS COUNTY, NEW ROCHELLE, NY, p. A445
NYC HEALTH + HOSPITALS / LINCOLN, NEW ROCHELLE, NY, p. A445
NYC HEALTH + HOSPITALS / METROPOLITAN, NEW ROCHELLE, NY, p. A445
NYC HEALTH + HOSPITALS / NORTH CENTRAL BRONX, NEW ROCHELLE, NY, p. A445
NYC HEALTH + HOSPITALS / QUEENS, NEW ROCHELLE, NY, p. A445
NYC HEALTH + HOSPITALS / WOODHULL, NEW ROCHELLE, NY, p. A446
NYU HOSPITAL FOR JOINT DISEASES, NEW ROCHELLE, NY, p. A446
NYU LANGONE HOSPITALS, NEW ROCHELLE, NY, p. A446
NYU WINTHROP HOSPITAL, MINEOLA, NY, p. A439

O

O'BLENESS MEMORIAL HOSPITAL, ATHENS, OH, p. A480
O'CONNOR HOSPITAL, DELHI, NY, p. A435
O'CONNOR HOSPITAL, SAN JOSE, CA, p. A88
OAK HILL HOSPITAL, BROOKSVILLE, FL, p. A121
OAK VALLEY HOSPITAL DISTRICT, OAKDALE, CA, p. A77
OAKBEND MEDICAL CENTER, RICHMOND, TX, p. A640
OAKDALE COMMUNITY HOSPITAL, OAKDALE, LA, p. A284
OAKLAND MEDICAL CENTER, OAKLAND, CA, p. A77
OAKLAND MERCY HOSPITAL, OAKLAND, NE, p. A396
OAKLAND REGIONAL HOSPITAL, SOUTHFIELD, MI, p. A331
OAKLAWN HOSPITAL, MARSHALL, MI, p. A326
OAKLAWN PSYCHIATRIC CENTER, GOSHEN, IN, p. A209
OAKLEAF SURGICAL HOSPITAL, EAU CLAIRE, WI, p. A701
OAKWOOD CORRECTIONAL FACILITY, LIMA, OH, p. A493
OAKWOOD SPRINGS, OKLAHOMA CITY, OK, p. A512
OASIS BEHAVIORAL HEALTH – CHANDLER, CHANDLER, AZ, p. A28
OASIS HOSPITAL, PHOENIX, AZ, p. A34
OCALA REGIONAL MEDICAL CENTER, OCALA, FL, p. A136
OCEAN BEACH HOSPITAL, ILWACO, WA, p. A681
OCEAN SPRINGS HOSPITAL, OCEAN SPRINGS, MS, p. A360
OCEANS BEHAVIORAL HEALTH CENTER PERMIAN BASIN, MIDLAND, TX, p. A633
OCEANS BEHAVIORAL HOSPITAL ABILENE, ABILENE, TX, p. A591
OCEANS BEHAVIORAL HOSPITAL KATY, KATY, TX, p. A626
OCEANS BEHAVIORAL HOSPITAL LONGVIEW, LONGVIEW, TX, p. A630
OCEANS BEHAVIORAL HOSPITAL LUFKIN, LUFKIN, TX, p. A631
OCEANS BEHAVIORAL HOSPITAL OF ALEXANDRIA, ALEXANDRIA, LA, p. A269
OCEANS BEHAVIORAL HOSPITAL OF BATON ROUGE, BATON ROUGE, LA, p. A270
OCEANS BEHAVIORAL HOSPITAL OF BROUSSARD, BROUSSARD, LA, p. A272
OCEANS BEHAVIORAL HOSPITAL OF CROWLEY, RAYNE, LA, p. A284
OCEANS BEHAVIORAL HOSPITAL OF DE RIDDER, DERIDDER, LA, p. A274
OCEANS BEHAVIORAL HOSPITAL OF GREATER NEW ORLEANS, KENNER, LA, p. A277
OCEANS BEHAVIORAL HOSPITAL OF KENTWOOD, KENTWOOD, LA, p. A277
OCEANS BEHAVIORAL HOSPITAL OF LAKE CHARLES, LAKE CHARLES, LA, p. A279
OCEANS BEHAVIORAL HOSPITAL OF OPELOUSAS, OPELOUSAS, LA, p. A284
OCH REGIONAL MEDICAL CENTER, STARKVILLE, MS, p. A362
OCHILTREE GENERAL HOSPITAL, PERRYTON, TX, p. A637
OCHSNER EXTENDED CARE HOSPITAL OF KENNER, KENNER, LA, p. A277
OCHSNER MEDICAL CENTER – KENNER, KENNER, LA, p. A277
OCHSNER MEDICAL CENTER – NORTH SHORE, SLIDELL, LA, p. A286
OCHSNER MEDICAL CENTER–BATON ROUGE, BATON ROUGE, LA, p. A270

P

PARK RIDGE HEALTH, HENDERSONVILLE, NC, p. A464
PARK ROYAL HOSPITAL, FORT MYERS, FL, p. A125
PARKER ADVENTIST HOSPITAL, PARKER, CO, p. A106
PARKLAND HEALTH & HOSPITAL SYSTEM, DALLAS, TX, p. A606
PARKLAND HEALTH CENTER - FARMINGTON COMMUNITY, FARMINGTON, MO, p. A368
PARKLAND HEALTH CENTER-BONNE TERRE, BONNE TERRE, MO, p. A364
PARKLAND MEDICAL CENTER, DERRY, NH, p. A407
PARKRIDGE MEDICAL CENTER, CHATTANOOGA, TN, p. A576
PARKSIDE PSYCHIATRIC HOSPITAL AND CLINIC, TULSA, OK, p. A517
PARKVIEW COMMUNITY HOSPITAL MEDICAL CENTER, RIVERSIDE, CA, p. A82
PARKVIEW HOSPITAL, EL RENO, OK, p. A507
PARKVIEW HOSPITAL, WHEELER, TX, p. A654
PARKVIEW HUNTINGTON HOSPITAL, HUNTINGTON, IN, p. A210
PARKVIEW LAGRANGE HOSPITAL, LAGRANGE, IN, p. A214
PARKVIEW MEDICAL CENTER, PUEBLO, CO, p. A106
PARKVIEW NOBLE HOSPITAL, KENDALLVILLE, IN, p. A213
PARKVIEW ORTHO HOSPITAL, FORT WAYNE, IN, p. A208
PARKVIEW REGIONAL HOSPITAL, MEXIA, TX, p. A633
PARKVIEW REGIONAL MEDICAL CENTER, FORT WAYNE, IN, p. A208
PARKVIEW WABASH COUNTY HOSPITAL, WABASH, IN, p. A221
PARKVIEW WHITLEY HOSPITAL, COLUMBIA CITY, IN, p. A205
PARKWAY MEDICAL CENTER, DECATUR, AL, p. A16
PARKWEST MEDICAL CENTER, KNOXVILLE, TN, p. A582
PARKWOOD BEHAVIORAL HEALTH SYSTEM, OLIVE BRANCH, MS, p. A360
PARMER COUNTY COMMUNITY HOSPITAL, FRIONA, TX, p. A615
PARMER MEDICAL CENTER, FRIONA, TX, p. A615
PARRISH MEDICAL CENTER, TITUSVILLE, FL, p. A146
PARSONS STATE HOSPITAL AND TRAINING CENTER, PARSONS, KS, p. A249
PASSAVANT AREA HOSPITAL, JACKSONVILLE, IL, p. A191
PATEWOOD MEMORIAL HOSPITAL, GREENVILLE, SC, p. A562
PATHWAY REHABILITATION HOSPITAL, BOSSIER CITY, LA, p. A272
PATHWAYS OF TENNESSEE, JACKSON, TN, p. A580
PATIENTS CHOICE MEDICAL CENTER OF SMITH COUNTY, RALEIGH, MS, p. A361
PATIENTS MEDICAL CENTER, PASADENA, TX, p. A637
PATIENTS' HOSPITAL OF REDDING, REDDING, CA, p. A81
PATRICK B. HARRIS PSYCHIATRIC HOSPITAL, ANDERSON, SC, p. A558
PATTON STATE HOSPITAL, PATTON, CA, p. A79
PAUL B. HALL REGIONAL MEDICAL CENTER, PAINTSVILLE, KY, p. A266
PAUL OLIVER MEMORIAL HOSPITAL, FRANKFORT, MI, p. A320
PAULDING COUNTY HOSPITAL, PAULDING, OH, p. A498
PAULS VALLEY GENERAL HOSPITAL, PAULS VALLEY, OK, p. A514
PAWHUSKA HOSPITAL, PAWHUSKA, OK, p. A514
PAWNEE COUNTY MEMORIAL HOSPITAL AND RURAL HEALTH CLINIC, PAWNEE CITY, NE, p. A399
PAWNEE VALLEY COMMUNITY HOSPITAL, LARNED, KS, p. A245
PAYNE WHITNEY PSYCHIATRIC CLINIC, NEW ROCHELLE, NY, p. A446
PEACEHEALTH COTTAGE GROVE COMMUNITY MEDICAL CENTER, COTTAGE GROVE, OR, p. A521
PEACEHEALTH KETCHIKAN MEDICAL CENTER, KETCHIKAN, AK, p. A26
PEACEHEALTH PEACE HARBOR MEDICAL CENTER, FLORENCE, OR, p. A521
PEACEHEALTH PEACE ISLAND MEDICAL CENTER, FRIDAY HARBOR, WA, p. A681
PEACEHEALTH SACRED HEART MEDICAL CENTER AT RIVERBEND, SPRINGFIELD, OR, p. A527
PEACEHEALTH SACRED HEART MEDICAL CENTER UNIVERSITY DISTRICT, EUGENE, OR, p. A521
PEACEHEALTH SOUTHWEST MEDICAL CENTER, VANCOUVER, WA, p. A688
PEACEHEALTH ST. JOHN MEDICAL CENTER, LONGVIEW, WA, p. A682
PEACEHEALTH ST. JOSEPH MEDICAL CENTER, BELLINGHAM, WA, p. A678
PEACEHEALTH UNITED GENERAL MEDICAL CENTER, SEDRO—WOOLLEY, WA, p. A686
PEACHFORD BEHAVIORAL HEALTH SYSTEM, ATLANTA, GA, p. A150
PEAK BEHAVIORAL HEALTH SERVICES, SANTA TERESA, NM, p. A428
PEAK VIEW BEHAVIORAL HEALTH, COLORADO SPRINGS, CO, p. A99

PEARL RIVER COUNTY HOSPITAL, POPLARVILLE, MS, p. A361
PEARLAND MEDICAL CENTER, PEARLAND, TX, p. A637
PECONIC BAY MEDICAL CENTER, RIVERHEAD, NY, p. A450
PECOS COUNTY MEMORIAL HOSPITAL, FORT STOCKTON, TX, p. A613
PEKIN HOSPITAL, PEKIN, IL, p. A197
PELHAM MEDICAL CENTER, GREER, SC, p. A563
PELLA REGIONAL HEALTH CENTER, PELLA, IA, p. A233
PEMBINA COUNTY MEMORIAL HOSPITAL AND WEDGEWOOD MANOR, CAVALIER, ND, p. A474
PEMBROKE HOSPITAL, PEMBROKE, MA, p. A310
PEMISCOT MEMORIAL HEALTH SYSTEM, HAYTI, MO, p. A369
PEN BAY MEDICAL CENTER, ROCKPORT, ME, p. A293
PENDER COMMUNITY HOSPITAL, PENDER, NE, p. A399
PENDER MEMORIAL HOSPITAL, BURGAW, NC, p. A458
PENINSULA HOSPITAL, LOUISVILLE, TN, p. A583
PENINSULA REGIONAL MEDICAL CENTER, SALISBURY, MD, p. A301
PENN HIGHLANDS BROOKVILLE, BROOKVILLE, PA, p. A530
PENN HIGHLANDS CLEARFIELD, CLEARFIELD, PA, p. A531
PENN HIGHLANDS DUBOIS, DUBOIS, PA, p. A533
PENN HIGHLANDS ELK, SAINT MARYS, PA, p. A549
PENN MEDICINE CHESTER COUNTY HOSPITAL, WEST CHESTER, PA, p. A553
PENN PRESBYTERIAN MEDICAL CENTER, PHILADELPHIA, PA, p. A545
PENN STATE HEALTH ST. JOSEPH, READING, PA, p. A549
PENN STATE HERSHEY REHABILITATION HOSPITAL, HUMMELSTOWN, PA, p. A536
PENN STATE MILTON S. HERSHEY MEDICAL CENTER, HERSHEY, PA, p. A536
PENNSYLVANIA HOSPITAL, PHILADELPHIA, PA, p. A545
PENNSYLVANIA PSYCHIATRIC INSTITUTE, HARRISBURG, PA, p. A536
PENOBSCOT BAY MEDICAL CENTER, ROCKPORT, ME, p. A293
PENOBSCOT VALLEY HOSPITAL, LINCOLN, ME, p. A292
PENROSE–ST. FRANCIS HEALTH SERVICES, COLORADO SPRINGS, CO, p. A100
PERHAM HEALTH, PERHAM, MN, p. A346
PERKINS COUNTY HEALTH SERVICES, GRANT, NE, p. A393
PERMIAN REGIONAL MEDICAL CENTER, ANDREWS, TX, p. A592
PERRY COMMUNITY HOSPITAL, LINDEN, TN, p. A583
PERRY COUNTY GENERAL HOSPITAL, RICHTON, MS, p. A361
PERRY COUNTY MEMORIAL HOSPITAL, PERRYVILLE, MO, p. A375
PERRY COUNTY MEMORIAL HOSPITAL, TELL CITY, IN, p. A220
PERRY HOSPITAL, PERRY, GA, p. A163
PERRY MEMORIAL HOSPITAL, PERRY, OK, p. A514
PERRY MEMORIAL HOSPITAL, PRINCETON, IL, p. A198
PERSHING GENERAL HOSPITAL, LOVELOCK, NV, p. A404
PERSON MEMORIAL HOSPITAL, ROXBORO, NC, p. A470
PETALUMA VALLEY HOSPITAL, PETALUMA, CA, p. A79
PETERSBURG MEDICAL CENTER, PETERSBURG, AK, p. A27
PETERSON HEALTHCARE AND REHABILITATION HOSPITAL, WHEELING, WV, p. A697
PETERSON REGIONAL MEDICAL CENTER, KERRVILLE, TX, p. A626
PHELPS COUNTY REGIONAL MEDICAL CENTER, ROLLA, MO, p. A376
PHELPS MEMORIAL HEALTH CENTER, HOLDREGE, NE, p. A394
PHELPS MEMORIAL HOSPITAL CENTER, SLEEPY HOLLOW, NY, p. A452
PHILADELPHIA VETERANS AFFAIRS MEDICAL CENTER, PHILADELPHIA, PA, p. A545
PHILIP HEALTH SERVICES, PHILIP, SD, p. A571
PHILLIPS COUNTY HOSPITAL, MALTA, MT, p. A386
PHILLIPS COUNTY HOSPITAL, PHILLIPSBURG, KS, p. A250
PHILLIPS EYE INSTITUTE, MINNEAPOLIS, MN, p. A344
PHOEBE PUTNEY MEMORIAL HOSPITAL, ALBANY, GA, p. A149
PHOEBE SUMTER MEDICAL CENTER, AMERICUS, GA, p. A149
PHOEBE WORTH MEDICAL CENTER, SYLVESTER, GA, p. A165
PHOENIX CHILDREN'S HOSPITAL, PHOENIX, AZ, p. A34
PHOENIX VETERANS AFFAIRS HEALTH CARE SYSTEM, PHOENIX, AZ, p. A34
PHOENIXVILLE HOSPITAL, PHOENIXVILLE, PA, p. A546
PHS SANTA FE INDIAN HOSPITAL, SANTA FE, NM, p. A428
PHYSICIANS ALLIANCE HOSPITAL OF HOUMA, HOUMA, LA, p. A276
PHYSICIANS BEHAVIORAL HOSPITAL, SHREVEPORT, LA, p. A285
PHYSICIANS CARE SURGICAL HOSPITAL, ROYERSFORD, PA, p. A549

PHYSICIANS' HOSPITAL IN ANADARKO, ANADARKO, OK, p. A504
PHYSICIANS MEDICAL CENTER, HOUMA, LA, p. A276
PHYSICIANS' MEDICAL CENTER, NEW ALBANY, IN, p. A217
PHYSICIANS REGIONAL – PINE RIDGE, NAPLES, FL, p. A135
PHYSICIANS' SPECIALTY HOSPITAL, FAYETTEVILLE, AR, p. A42
PHYSICIANS SURGICAL HOSPITAL – QUAIL CREEK, AMARILLO, TX, p. A592
PICKENS COUNTY MEDICAL CENTER, CARROLLTON, AL, p. A16
PIEDMONT ATHENS REGIONAL MEDICAL CENTER, ATHENS, GA, p. A149
PIEDMONT FAYETTE HOSPITAL, FAYETTEVILLE, GA, p. A157
PIEDMONT GERIATRIC HOSPITAL, BURKEVILLE, VA, p. A665
PIEDMONT HENRY HOSPITAL, STOCKBRIDGE, GA, p. A165
PIEDMONT HOSPITAL, ATLANTA, GA, p. A150
PIEDMONT MEDICAL CENTER, ROCK HILL, SC, p. A565
PIEDMONT MOUNTAINSIDE HOSPITAL, JASPER, GA, p. A159
PIEDMONT NEWNAN HOSPITAL, NEWNAN, GA, p. A162
PIEDMONT NEWTON HOSPITAL, COVINGTON, GA, p. A155
PIGGOTT COMMUNITY HOSPITAL, PIGGOTT, AR, p. A48
PIH HEALTH HOSPITAL–DOWNEY, DOWNEY, CA, p. A58
PIH HEALTH HOSPITAL–WHITTIER, WHITTIER, CA, p. A97
PIKE COUNTY MEMORIAL HOSPITAL, LOUISIANA, MO, p. A372
PIKES PEAK REGIONAL HOSPITAL, WOODLAND PARK, CO, p. A108
PIKEVILLE MEDICAL CENTER, PIKEVILLE, KY, p. A266
PILGRIM PSYCHIATRIC CENTER, BRENTWOOD, NY, p. A432
PINCKNEYVILLE COMMUNITY HOSPITAL, PINCKNEYVILLE, IL, p. A198
PINE CREEK MEDICAL CENTER, DALLAS, TX, p. A606
PINE REST CHRISTIAN MENTAL HEALTH SERVICES, GRAND RAPIDS, MI, p. A321
PINE VALLEY SPECIALTY HOSPITAL, HOUSTON, TX, p. A622
PINEVILLE COMMUNITY HOSPITAL ASSOCIATION, PINEVILLE, KY, p. A266
PINNACLE HOSPITAL, CROWN POINT, IN, p. A206
PINNACLE POINTE HOSPITAL, LITTLE ROCK, AR, p. A46
PINNACLE SPECIALTY HOSPITAL, TULSA, OK, p. A518
PINNACLEHEALTH AT COMMUNITY GENERAL OSTEOPATHIC HOSPITAL, HARRISBURG, PA, p. A536
PINNACLEHEALTH HARRISBURG HOSPITAL, HARRISBURG, PA, p. A536
PIONEER COMMUNITY HOSPITAL OF ABERDEEN, ABERDEEN, MS, p. A352
PIONEER COMMUNITY HOSPITAL OF EARLY, BLAKELY, GA, p. A152
PIONEER COMMUNITY HOSPITAL OF PATRICK, STUART, VA, p. A676
PIONEER MEDICAL CENTER, BIG TIMBER, MT, p. A382
PIONEER MEMORIAL HOSPITAL, HEPPNER, OR, p. A522
PIONEER MEMORIAL HOSPITAL AND HEALTH SERVICES, VIBORG, SD, p. A573
PIONEER SPECIALTY HOSPITAL, PONTIAC, MI, p. A328
PIONEERS MEDICAL CENTER, MEEKER, CO, p. A106
PIONEERS MEMORIAL HEALTHCARE DISTRICT, BRAWLEY, CA, p. A54
PIPESTONE COUNTY MEDICAL CENTER AVERA, PIPESTONE, MN, p. A346
PITT COUNTY MEMORIAL HOSPITAL, GREENVILLE, NC, p. A463
PLACENTIA–LINDA HOSPITAL, PLACENTIA, CA, p. A80
PLAINS MEMORIAL HOSPITAL, DIMMITT, TX, p. A609
PLAINS REGIONAL MEDICAL CENTER, CLOVIS, NM, p. A425
PLAINVIEW HOSPITAL, PLAINVIEW, NY, p. A449
PLANO SPECIALTY HOSPITAL, PLANO, TX, p. A638
PLANO SURGICAL HOSPITAL, PLANO, TX, p. A638
PLANTATION GENERAL HOSPITAL, PLANTATION, FL, p. A140
PLATEAU MEDICAL CENTER, OAK HILL, WV, p. A694
PLATTE COUNTY MEMORIAL HOSPITAL, WHEATLAND, WY, p. A720
PLATTE HEALTH CENTER AVERA, PLATTE, SD, p. A571
PLATTE VALLEY MEDICAL CENTER, BRIGHTON, CO, p. A99
PLAZA SPECIALTY HOSPITAL, HOUSTON, TX, p. A622
PLEASANT VALLEY HOSPITAL, POINT PLEASANT, WV, p. A695
PLUM CREEK SPECIALTY HOSPITAL, AMARILLO, TX, p. A592
PLUMAS DISTRICT HOSPITAL, QUINCY, CA, p. A81
PLYMOUTH MEDICAL CENTER, PLYMOUTH, IN, p. A218
PMH MEDICAL CENTER, PROSSER, WA, p. A684
POCAHONTAS COMMUNITY HOSPITAL, POCAHONTAS, IA, p. A233
POCAHONTAS MEMORIAL HOSPITAL, BUCKEYE, WV, p. A690
POINCIANA MEDICAL CENTER, KISSIMMEE, FL, p. A129
POINTE COUPEE GENERAL HOSPITAL, NEW ROADS, LA, p. A283
POLK MEDICAL CENTER, CEDARTOWN, GA, p. A154
POMERADO HOSPITAL, POWAY, CA, p. A80

POMERENE HOSPITAL, MILLERSBURG, OH, p. A496
POMONA VALLEY HOSPITAL MEDICAL CENTER, POMONA, CA, p. A80
PONDERA MEDICAL CENTER, CONRAD, MT, p. A383
POPLAR BLUFF REGIONAL MEDICAL CENTER, POPLAR BLUFF, MO, p. A375
POPLAR COMMUNITY HOSPITAL, POPLAR, MT, p. A387
POPLAR SPRINGS HOSPITAL, PETERSBURG, VA, p. A673
PORT ST. LUCIE HOSPITAL, PORT ST. LUCIE, FL, p. A140
PORTER ADVENTIST HOSPITAL, DENVER, CO, p. A101
PORTER MEDICAL CENTER, MIDDLEBURY, VT, p. A662
PORTER REGIONAL HOSPITAL, VALPARAISO, IN, p. A220
PORTER–STARKE SERVICES, VALPARAISO, IN, p. A221
PORTERVILLE DEVELOPMENTAL CENTER, PORTERVILLE, CA, p. A80
PORTNEUF MEDICAL CENTER, POCATELLO, ID, p. A175
PORTSMOUTH REGIONAL HOSPITAL, PORTSMOUTH, NH, p. A410
POST ACUTE MEDICAL SPECIALTY HOSPITAL OF CORPUS CHRISTI – NORTH, CORPUS CHRISTI, TX, p. A603
POST ACUTE MEDICAL SPECIALTY HOSPITAL OF CORPUS CHRISTI – SOUTH, CORPUS CHRISTI, TX, p. A603
POST ACUTE MEDICAL SPECIALTY HOSPITAL OF MILWAUKEE, GREENFIELD, WI, p. A703
POST ACUTE MEDICAL SPECIALTY HOSPITAL OF TEXARKANA – NORTH, TEXARKANA, TX, p. A649
POST ACUTE MEDICAL SPECIALTY HOSPITAL OF TULSA, TULSA, OK, p. A518
POST ACUTE/WARM SPRINGS REHABILITATION HOSPITAL OF ALLEN, ALLEN, TX, p. A591
POST ACUTE/WARM SPRINGS SPECIALTY HOSPITAL OF LULING, LULING, TX, p. A631
POST ACUTE/WARM SPRINGS SPECIALTY HOSPITAL OF NEW BRAUNFELS, NEW BRAUNFELS, TX, p. A635
POST ACUTE/WARM SPRINGS SPECIALTY HOSPITAL OF SAN ANTONIO, SAN ANTONIO, TX, p. A643
POTOMAC RIDGE BEHAVIORAL HEALTH, ROCKVILLE, MD, p. A300
POTOMAC VALLEY HOSPITAL, KEYSER, WV, p. A693
POTTSTOWN MEMORIAL MEDICAL CENTER, POTTSTOWN, PA, p. A548
POUDRE VALLEY HOSPITAL, FORT COLLINS, CO, p. A102
POWELL VALLEY HEALTHCARE, POWELL, WY, p. A719
POWER COUNTY HOSPITAL DISTRICT, AMERICAN FALLS, ID, p. A171
PRAGUE COMMUNITY HOSPITAL, PRAGUE, OK, p. A515
PRAIRIE COMMUNITY HEALTH CENTER, TERRY, MT, p. A388
PRAIRIE COMMUNITY HOSPITAL, TERRY, MT, p. A388
PRAIRIE LAKES HEALTHCARE SYSTEM, WATERTOWN, SD, p. A574
PRAIRIE RIDGE HOSPITAL AND HEALTH SERVICES, ELBOW LAKE, MN, p. A339
PRAIRIE ST. JOHN'S, FARGO, ND, p. A475
PRAIRIE VIEW, NEWTON, KS, p. A247
PRAIRIECARE – BROOKLYN PARK, BROOKLYN PARK, MN, p. A337
PRATT REGIONAL MEDICAL CENTER, PRATT, KS, p. A250
PRATTVILLE BAPTIST HOSPITAL, PRATTVILLE, AL, p. A22
PREMIER SURGICAL INSTITUTE, GALENA, KS, p. A241
PRENTICE WOMEN'S HOSPITAL, CHICAGO, IL, p. A182
PRESBYTERIAN ESPANOLA HOSPITAL, ESPANOLA, NM, p. A426
PRESBYTERIAN HOSPITAL, ALBUQUERQUE, NM, p. A425
PRESBYTERIAN HOSPITAL, CHARLOTTE, NC, p. A460
PRESBYTERIAN–ORTHOPAEDIC HOSPITAL, CHARLOTTE, NC, p. A460
PRESBYTERIAN TOWER, OKLAHOMA CITY, OK, p. A513
PRESBYTERIAN–ST. LUKE'S MEDICAL CENTER, DENVER, CO, p. A101
PRESENCE COVENANT MEDICAL CENTER, URBANA, IL, p. A202
PRESENCE HOLY FAMILY MEDICAL CENTER, DES PLAINES, IL, p. A185
PRESENCE MERCY MEDICAL CENTER, AURORA, IL, p. A177
PRESENCE RESURRECTION MEDICAL CENTER, CHICAGO, IL, p. A182
PRESENCE SAINT FRANCIS HOSPITAL, EVANSTON, IL, p. A187
PRESENCE SAINT JOSEPH HOSPITAL, CHICAGO, IL, p. A182
PRESENCE SAINT JOSEPH HOSPITAL, ELGIN, IL, p. A186
PRESENCE SAINT JOSEPH MEDICAL CENTER, JOLIET, IL, p. A191
PRESENCE SAINTS MARY & ELIZABETH MEDICAL CENTER, CHICAGO, IL, p. A183
PRESENCE ST. MARY'S HOSPITAL, KANKAKEE, IL, p. A191
PRESENCE UNITED SAMARITANS MEDICAL CENTER, DANVILLE, IL, p. A185
PRESENTATION MEDICAL CENTER, ROLLA, ND, p. A478
PRESTON MEMORIAL HOSPITAL, KINGWOOD, WV, p. A693
PREVOST MEMORIAL HOSPITAL, DONALDSONVILLE, LA, p. A274

PRIMARY CHILDREN'S HOSPITAL, SALT LAKE CITY, UT, p. A660
PRINCE GEORGE'S HOSPITAL CENTER, CHEVERLY, MD, p. A297
PRINCETON BAPTIST MEDICAL CENTER, BIRMINGHAM, AL, p. A15
PRINCETON COMMUNITY HOSPITAL, PRINCETON, WV, p. A695
PROFESSIONAL HOSPITAL GUAYNABO, GUAYNABO, PUERTO RICO, p. A723
PROGRESS WEST HOSPITAL, O'FALLON, MO, p. A374
PROMEDICA BAY PARK HOSPITAL, OREGON, OH, p. A497
PROMEDICA BIXBY HOSPITAL, ADRIAN, MI, p. A314
PROMEDICA DEFIANCE REGIONAL HOSPITAL, DEFIANCE, OH, p. A490
PROMEDICA FLOWER HOSPITAL, SYLVANIA, OH, p. A500
PROMEDICA FOSTORIA COMMUNITY HOSPITAL, FOSTORIA, OH, p. A491
PROMEDICA HERRICK HOSPITAL, TECUMSEH, MI, p. A332
PROMEDICA MEMORIAL HOSPITAL, FREMONT, OH, p. A491
PROMEDICA MONROE REGIONAL HOSPITAL, MONROE, MI, p. A326
PROMEDICA TOLEDO HOSPITAL, TOLEDO, OH, p. A500
PROMISE HOSPITAL BATON ROUGE – MAIN CAMPUS, BATON ROUGE, LA, p. A271
PROMISE HOSPITAL OF BATON ROUGE – MID–CITY CAMPUS, BATON ROUGE, LA, p. A271
PROMISE HOSPITAL OF BATON ROUGE – OCHSNER CAMPUS, BATON ROUGE, LA, p. A271
PROMISE HOSPITAL OF DALLAS, DALLAS, TX, p. A606
PROMISE HOSPITAL OF EAST LOS ANGELES, LOS ANGELES, CA, p. A70
PROMISE HOSPITAL OF FLORIDA AT THE VILLAGES, OXFORD, FL, p. A137
PROMISE HOSPITAL OF FORT MYERS, FORT MYERS, FL, p. A125
PROMISE HOSPITAL OF LOUISIANA – SHREVEPORT CAMPUS, SHREVEPORT, LA, p. A285
PROMISE HOSPITAL OF MIAMI, MIAMI, FL, p. A133
PROMISE HOSPITAL OF MISS LOU, VIDALIA, LA, p. A287
PROMISE HOSPITAL OF MISS LOU, VIDALIA, LA, p. A287
PROMISE HOSPITAL OF OVERLAND PARK, OVERLAND PARK, KS, p. A249
PROMISE HOSPITAL OF PHOENIX, MESA, AZ, p. A32
PROMISE HOSPITAL OF SALT LAKE, SALT LAKE CITY, UT, p. A660
PROMISE HOSPITAL OF SAN DIEGO, SAN DIEGO, CA, p. A85
PROMISE HOSPITAL OF VICKSBURG, VICKSBURG, MS, p. A362
PROMISE HOSPITAL OF WICHITA FALLS, WICHITA FALLS, TX, p. A654
PROMISE SPECIALTY HOSPITAL OF SHREVEPORT, SHREVEPORT, LA, p. A285
PROVENA MERCY MEDICAL CENTER, AURORA, IL, p. A178
PROVENA SAINT JOSEPH HOSPITAL, ELGIN, IL, p. A186
PROVENA SAINT JOSEPH MEDICAL CENTER, JOLIET, IL, p. A191
PROVENA ST. MARY'S HOSPITAL, KANKAKEE, IL, p. A191
PROVIDENCE ALASKA MEDICAL CENTER, ANCHORAGE, AK, p. A25
PROVIDENCE CENTRALIA HOSPITAL, CENTRALIA, WA, p. A679
PROVIDENCE HEALTHCARE NETWORK, WACO, TX, p. A652
PROVIDENCE HOLY CROSS MEDICAL CENTER, LOS ANGELES, CA, p. A70
PROVIDENCE HOLY FAMILY HOSPITAL, SPOKANE, WA, p. A687
PROVIDENCE HOOD RIVER MEMORIAL HOSPITAL, HOOD RIVER, OR, p. A522
PROVIDENCE HOSPITAL, COLUMBIA, SC, p. A560
PROVIDENCE HOSPITAL, MOBILE, AL, p. A20
PROVIDENCE HOSPITAL, WASHINGTON, DC, p. A118
PROVIDENCE HOSPITAL NORTHEAST, COLUMBIA, SC, p. A560
PROVIDENCE HOSPITAL OF NORTH HOUSTON, HOUSTON, TX, p. A622
PROVIDENCE KODIAK ISLAND MEDICAL CENTER, KODIAK, AK, p. A26
PROVIDENCE LITTLE COMPANY OF MARY MEDICAL CENTER – TORRANCE, TORRANCE, CA, p. A94
PROVIDENCE LITTLE COMPANY OF MARY MEDICAL CENTER SAN PEDRO, LOS ANGELES, CA, p. A70
PROVIDENCE MEDFORD MEDICAL CENTER, MEDFORD, OR, p. A524
PROVIDENCE MEDICAL CENTER, KANSAS CITY, KS, p. A244
PROVIDENCE MEDICAL CENTER, WAYNE, NE, p. A400
PROVIDENCE MILWAUKIE HOSPITAL, MILWAUKIE, OR, p. A524
PROVIDENCE MOUNT CARMEL HOSPITAL, COLVILLE, WA, p. A679

PROVIDENCE NEWBERG MEDICAL CENTER, NEWBERG, OR, p. A524
PROVIDENCE PORTLAND MEDICAL CENTER, PORTLAND, OR, p. A525
PROVIDENCE–PROVIDENCE PARK HOSPITALS, SOUTHFIELD, MI, p. A331
PROVIDENCE–PROVIDENCE PARK HOSPITAL, NOVI CAMPUS, NOVI, MI, p. A327
PROVIDENCE REGIONAL MEDICAL CENTER EVERETT, EVERETT, WA, p. A680
PROVIDENCE SACRED HEART MEDICAL CENTER & CHILDREN'S HOSPITAL, SPOKANE, WA, p. A687
PROVIDENCE SAINT JOHN'S HEALTH CENTER, SANTA MONICA, CA, p. A91
PROVIDENCE SAINT JOSEPH MEDICAL CENTER, BURBANK, CA, p. A54
PROVIDENCE SEASIDE HOSPITAL, SEASIDE, OR, p. A527
PROVIDENCE SEWARD MEDICAL CENTER, SEWARD, AK, p. A27
PROVIDENCE ST. JOSEPH MEDICAL CENTER, POLSON, MT, p. A387
PROVIDENCE ST. JOSEPH'S HOSPITAL, CHEWELAH, WA, p. A679
PROVIDENCE ST. MARY MEDICAL CENTER, WALLA WALLA, WA, p. A688
PROVIDENCE ST. PETER HOSPITAL, OLYMPIA, WA, p. A683
PROVIDENCE ST. VINCENT MEDICAL CENTER, PORTLAND, OR, p. A526
PROVIDENCE TARZANA MEDICAL CENTER, LOS ANGELES, CA, p. A71
PROVIDENCE VALDEZ MEDICAL CENTER, VALDEZ, AK, p. A27
PROVIDENCE VETERANS AFFAIRS MEDICAL CENTER, PROVIDENCE, RI, p. A557
PROVIDENCE WILLAMETTE FALLS MEDICAL CENTER, OREGON CITY, OR, p. A524
PROVIDENT HOSPITAL OF COOK COUNTY, CHICAGO, IL, p. A183
PROVO CANYON BEHAVIORAL HOSPITAL, OREM, UT, p. A658
PROWERS MEDICAL CENTER, LAMAR, CO, p. A105
PSYCHIATRIC INSTITUTE OF WASHINGTON, WASHINGTON, DC, p. A118
PSYCHIATRIC PAVILION NEW ORLEANS, NEW ORLEANS, LA, p. A283
PULASKI MEMORIAL HOSPITAL, WINAMAC, IN, p. A221
PULLMAN REGIONAL HOSPITAL, PULLMAN, WA, p. A684
PUNXSUTAWNEY AREA HOSPITAL, PUNXSUTAWNEY, PA, p. A548
PURCELL MUNICIPAL HOSPITAL, PURCELL, OK, p. A515
PUSHMATAHA HOSPITAL, ANTLERS, OK, p. A504
PUTNAM COMMUNITY MEDICAL CENTER, PALATKA, FL, p. A138
PUTNAM COUNTY HOSPITAL, GREENCASTLE, IN, p. A209
PUTNAM COUNTY MEMORIAL HOSPITAL, UNIONVILLE, MO, p. A380
PUTNAM GENERAL HOSPITAL, EATONTON, GA, p. A157
PUTNAM HOSPITAL CENTER, CARMEL, NY, p. A433

Q

QUAIL RUN BEHAVIORAL HEALTH, PHOENIX, AZ, p. A34
QUEEN OF THE VALLEY MEDICAL CENTER, NAPA, CA, p. A76
QUEENS Children's hospital psychiatric CENTER, NEW ROCHELLE, NY, p. A446
QUILLEN REHABILITATION HOSPITAL, JOHNSON CITY, TN, p. A581
QUINCY VALLEY MEDICAL CENTER, QUINCY, WA, p. A684

R

RADY CHILDREN'S HOSPITAL AND HEALTH CENTER, SAN DIEGO, CA, p. A86
RADY CHILDREN'S HOSPITAL – SAN DIEGO, SAN DIEGO, CA, p. A85
RAINBOW MENTAL HEALTH FACILITY, KANSAS CITY, KS, p. A244
RAINY LAKE MEDICAL CENTER, INTERNATIONAL FALLS, MN, p. A341
RALEIGH GENERAL HOSPITAL, BECKLEY, WV, p. A690
RALPH H. JOHNSON VETERANS AFFAIRS MEDICAL CENTER, CHARLESTON, SC, p. A559

RANCHO LOS AMIGOS NATIONAL REHABILITATION CENTER, DOWNEY, CA, p. A58
RANCHO SPRINGS MEDICAL CENTER, MURRIETA, CA, p. A75
RANDOLPH HOSPITAL, ASHEBORO, NC, p. A457
RANGE REGIONAL HEALTH SERVICES, HIBBING, MN, p. A341
RANGELY DISTRICT HOSPITAL, RANGELY, CO, p. A107
RANKEN JORDAN PEDIATRIC BRIDGE HOSPITAL, MARYLAND HEIGHTS, MO, p. A373
RANKIN COUNTY HOSPITAL DISTRICT, RANKIN, TX, p. A639
RANSOM MEMORIAL HOSPITAL, OTTAWA, KS, p. A248
RAPID CITY REGIONAL HOSPITAL, RAPID CITY, SD, p. A572
RAPIDES REGIONAL MEDICAL CENTER, ALEXANDRIA, LA, p. A269
RAPPAHANNOCK GENERAL HOSPITAL, KILMARNOCK, VA, p. A669
RAULERSON HOSPITAL, OKEECHOBEE, FL, p. A136
RAWLINS COUNTY HEALTH CENTER, ATWOOD, KS, p. A238
RAY COUNTY MEMORIAL HOSPITAL, RICHMOND, MO, p. A375
RC HOSPITAL AND CLINICS, OLIVIA, MN, p. A345
READING HEALTH REHABILITATION HOSPITAL, WYOMISSING, PA, p. A555
READING HOSPITAL, WEST READING, PA, p. A553
REAGAN MEMORIAL HOSPITAL, BIG LAKE, TX, p. A598
REBOUND BEHAVIORAL HEALTH, LANCASTER, SC, p. A564
RECEPTION AND MEDICAL CENTER, LAKE BUTLER, FL, p. A129
RED BAY HOSPITAL, RED BAY, AL, p. A22
RED BUD REGIONAL HOSPITAL, RED BUD, IL, p. A198
RED CEDAR MEDICAL CENTER–MAYO HEALTH SYSTEM, MENOMONIE, WI, p. A707
RED LAKE INDIAN HEALTH SERVICE HOSPITAL, RED LAKE, MN, p. A346
RED RIVER BEHAVIORAL CENTER, BOSSIER CITY, LA, p. A272
RED RIVER BEHAVIORAL HEALTH SYSTEM, GRAND FORKS, ND, p. A476
RED RIVER HOSPITAL, LLC, WICHITA FALLS, TX, p. A654
RED ROCK BEHAVIORAL HOSPITAL, LAS VEGAS, NV, p. A403
REDINGTON–FAIRVIEW GENERAL HOSPITAL, SKOWHEGAN, ME, p. A293
REDLANDS COMMUNITY HOSPITAL, REDLANDS, CA, p. A82
REDMOND REGIONAL MEDICAL CENTER, ROME, GA, p. A163
REDWOOD AREA HOSPITAL, REDWOOD FALLS, MN, p. A346
REDWOOD MEMORIAL HOSPITAL, FORTUNA, CA, p. A59
REEDSBURG AREA MEDICAL CENTER, REEDSBURG, WI, p. A711
REEVES COUNTY HOSPITAL, PECOS, TX, p. A637
REEVES MEMORIAL MEDICAL CENTER, BERNICE, LA, p. A271
REFUGIO COUNTY MEMORIAL HOSPITAL, REFUGIO, TX, p. A639
REGENCY HOSPITAL CLEVELAND EAST, WARRENSVILLE HEIGHTS, OH, p. A501
REGENCY HOSPITAL CLEVELAND EAST, WARRENSVILLE HEIGHTS, OH, p. A501
REGENCY HOSPITAL OF CENTRAL GEORGIA, MACON, GA, p. A161
REGENCY HOSPITAL OF COLUMBUS, COLUMBUS, OH, p. A488
REGENCY HOSPITAL OF FLORENCE, FLORENCE, SC, p. A562
REGENCY HOSPITAL OF GREENVILLE, GREENVILLE, SC, p. A563
REGENCY HOSPITAL OF HATTIESBURG, HATTIESBURG, MS, p. A356
REGENCY HOSPITAL OF MERIDIAN, MERIDIAN, MS, p. A359
REGENCY HOSPITAL OF MINNEAPOLIS, GOLDEN VALLEY, MN, p. A340
REGENCY HOSPITAL OF NORTHWEST ARKANSAS – SPRINGDALE, SPRINGDALE, AR, p. A50
REGENCY HOSPITAL OF NORTHWEST INDIANA, EAST CHICAGO, IN, p. A206
REGENCY HOSPITAL OF SOUTH ATLANTA, EAST POINT, GA, p. A157
REGENCY HOSPITAL OF TOLEDO, SYLVANIA, OH, p. A500
REGINA HOSPITAL, HASTINGS, MN, p. A341
REGIONAL GENERAL HOSPITAL, WILLISTON, FL, p. A148
REGIONAL HEALTH SERVICES OF HOWARD COUNTY, CRESCO, IA, p. A225
REGIONAL HOSPITAL FOR RESPIRATORY AND COMPLEX CARE, BURIEN, WA, p. A679
REGIONAL HOSPITAL OF SCRANTON, SCRANTON, PA, p. A550
REGIONAL MEDICAL CENTER, MANCHESTER, IA, p. A231
REGIONAL MEDICAL CENTER, ORANGEBURG, SC, p. A565
REGIONAL MEDICAL CENTER BAYONET POINT, HUDSON, FL, p. A127
REGIONAL MEDICAL CENTER OF SAN JOSE, SAN JOSE, CA, p. A88
REGIONAL MENTAL HEALTH CENTER, MERRILLVILLE, IN, p. A215

REGIONAL ONE HEALTH, MEMPHIS, TN, p. A585
REGIONAL ONE HEALTH EXTENDED CARE HOSPITAL, MEMPHIS, TN, p. A585
REGIONAL REHABILITATION HOSPITAL, PHENIX CITY, AL, p. A22
REGIONAL WEST GARDEN COUNTY, OSHKOSH, NE, p. A398
REGIONAL WEST MEDICAL CENTER, SCOTTSBLUFF, NE, p. A399
REGIONS HOSPITAL, SAINT PAUL, MN, p. A348
REHABILITATION HOSPITAL OF FORT WAYNE, FORT WAYNE, IN, p. A208
REHABILITATION HOSPITAL OF INDIANA, INDIANAPOLIS, IN, p. A212
REHABILITATION HOSPITAL OF JENNINGS, JENNINGS, LA, p. A277
REHABILITATION HOSPITAL OF NORTHWEST OHIO, TOLEDO, OH, p. A500
REHABILITATION HOSPITAL OF OVERLAND PARK, OVERLAND PARK, KS, p. A249
REHABILITATION HOSPITAL OF RHODE ISLAND, NORTH SMITHFIELD, RI, p. A556
REHABILITATION HOSPITAL OF SAVANNAH, SAVANNAH, GA, p. A164
REHABILITATION HOSPITAL OF SOUTHERN NEW MEXICO, LAS CRUCES, NM, p. A427
REHABILITATION HOSPITAL OF SOUTHWEST VIRGINIA, BRISTOL, VA, p. A665
REHABILITATION HOSPITAL OF THE NORTHWEST, POST FALLS, ID, p. A175
REHABILITATION HOSPITAL OF THE PACIFIC, HONOLULU, HI, p. A169
REHABILITATION HOSPITAL OF WISCONSIN, WAUKESHA, WI, p. A714
REHABILITATION HOSPITAL, NAVICENT HEALTH, MACON, GA, p. A161
REHABILITATION INSTITUTE OF OREGON, PORTLAND, OR, p. A525
REHOBOTH MCKINLEY CHRISTIAN HEALTH CARE SERVICES, GALLUP, NM, p. A426
REID HEALTH, RICHMOND, IN, p. A219
RENAISSANCE SPECIALTY HOSPITAL OF CENTRAL INDIANA, MUNCIE, IN, p. A216
RENOWN REGIONAL MEDICAL CENTER, RENO, NV, p. A405
RENOWN REHABILITATION HOSPITAL, RENO, NV, p. A405
RENOWN SOUTH MEADOWS MEDICAL CENTER, RENO, NV, p. A405
REPUBLIC COUNTY HOSPITAL, BELLEVILLE, KS, p. A238
RESEARCH BELTON HOSPITAL, BELTON, MO, p. A364
RESEARCH MEDICAL CENTER, KANSAS CITY, MO, p. A370
RESOLUTE HEALTH, NEW BRAUNFELS, TX, p. A635
RESTON HOSPITAL CENTER, RESTON, VA, p. A673
RESURRECTION MEDICAL CENTER, CHICAGO, IL, p. A183
REYNOLDS MEMORIAL HOSPITAL, GLEN DALE, WV, p. A692
RHEA MEDICAL CENTER, DAYTON, TN, p. A578
RHODE ISLAND HOSPITAL, PROVIDENCE, RI, p. A557
RICE MEDICAL CENTER, EAGLE LAKE, TX, p. A609
RICE MEMORIAL HOSPITAL, WILLMAR, MN, p. A350
RICELAND MEDICAL CENTER, WINNIE, TX, p. A654
RICHARD H. HUTCHINGS PSYCHIATRIC CENTER, SYRACUSE, NY, p. A453
RICHARD L. ROUDEBUSH VETERANS AFFAIRS MEDICAL CENTER, INDIANAPOLIS, IN, p. A212
RICHARDSON MEDICAL CENTER, RAYVILLE, LA, p. A284
RICHLAND HOSPITAL, RICHLAND CENTER, WI, p. A711
RICHLAND PARISH HOSPITAL, DELHI, LA, p. A274
RICHMOND STATE HOSPITAL, RICHMOND, IN, p. A219
RICHMOND UNIVERSITY MEDICAL CENTER, NEW ROCHELLE, NY, p. A446
RIDDLE HOSPITAL, MEDIA, PA, p. A541
RIDDLE MEMORIAL HOSPITAL, MEDIA, PA, p. A541
RIDEOUT MEMORIAL HOSPITAL, MARYSVILLE, CA, p. A73
RIDGE BEHAVIORAL HEALTH SYSTEM, LEXINGTON, KY, p. A261
RIDGECREST REGIONAL HOSPITAL, RIDGECREST, CA, p. A82
RIDGEVIEW BEHAVIORAL HOSPITAL, MIDDLE POINT, OH, p. A496
RIDGEVIEW INSTITUTE, SMYRNA, GA, p. A165
RIDGEVIEW LE SUEUR MEDICAL CENTER, LE SUEUR, MN, p. A342
RIDGEVIEW MEDICAL CENTER, WACONIA, MN, p. A350
RIDGEVIEW PSYCHIATRIC HOSPITAL AND CENTER, OAK RIDGE, TN, p. A588
RIDGEVIEW SIBLEY MEDICAL CENTER, ARLINGTON, MN, p. A335
RILEY HOSPITAL, MERIDIAN, MS, p. A359
RILEY HOSPITAL FOR CHILDREN, INDIANAPOLIS, IN, p. A212
RILEY HOSPITAL FOR CHILDREN AT INDIANA UNIVERSITY HEALTH, INDIANAPOLIS, IN, p. A212
RINGGOLD COUNTY HOSPITAL, MOUNT AYR, IA, p. A231
RIO GRANDE HOSPITAL, DEL NORTE, CO, p. A100

RIO GRANDE REGIONAL HOSPITAL, MCALLEN, TX, p. A632
RIO GRANDE STATE CENTER/SOUTH TEXAS HEALTH CARE SYSTEM, HARLINGEN, TX, p. A618
RIPON MEDICAL CENTER, RIPON, WI, p. A712
RIVENDELL BEHAVIORAL HEALTH, BOWLING GREEN, KY, p. A256
RIVENDELL BEHAVIORAL HEALTH SERVICES OF ARKANSAS, BENTON, AR, p. A40
RIVER BEND HOSPITAL, WEST LAFAYETTE, IN, p. A221
RIVER CREST HOSPITAL, SAN ANGELO, TX, p. A641
RIVER FALLS AREA HOSPITAL, RIVER FALLS, WI, p. A712
RIVER HOSPITAL, ALEXANDRIA BAY, NY, p. A430
RIVER PARK HOSPITAL, HUNTINGTON, WV, p. A693
RIVER POINT BEHAVIORAL HEALTH, JACKSONVILLE, FL, p. A128
RIVER VALLEY MEDICAL CENTER, DARDANELLE, AR, p. A42
RIVER'S EDGE HOSPITAL AND CLINIC, SAINT PETER, MN, p. A348
RIVERCREST SPECIALTY HOSPITAL, MISHAWAKA, IN, p. A216
RIVEREDGE HOSPITAL, FOREST PARK, IL, p. A188
RIVERLAND MEDICAL CENTER, FERRIDAY, LA, p. A274
RIVERSIDE CENTER FOR BEHAVIORAL MEDICINE, RIVERSIDE, CA, p. A82
RIVERSIDE COMMUNITY HOSPITAL, RIVERSIDE, CA, p. A82
RIVERSIDE DOCTORS' HOSPITAL, WILLIAMSBURG, VA, p. A677
RIVERSIDE HOSPITAL OF LOUISIANA, ALEXANDRIA, LA, p. A269
RIVERSIDE MEDICAL CENTER, FRANKLINTON, LA, p. A275
RIVERSIDE MEDICAL CENTER, KANKAKEE, IL, p. A191
RIVERSIDE MEDICAL CENTER, RIVERSIDE, CA, p. A83
RIVERSIDE REGIONAL MEDICAL CENTER, NEWPORT NEWS, VA, p. A671
RIVERSIDE REHABILITATION INSTITUTE, NEWPORT NEWS, VA, p. A671
RIVERSIDE SHORE MEMORIAL HOSPITAL, ONANCOKE, VA, p. A672
RIVERSIDE TAPPAHANNOCK HOSPITAL, TAPPAHANNOCK, VA, p. A676
RIVERSIDE UNIVERSITY HEALTH SYSTEM–MEDICAL CENTER, MORENO VALLEY, CA, p. A75
RIVERSIDE WALTER REED HOSPITAL, GLOUCESTER, VA, p. A668
RIVERTON HOSPITAL, RIVERTON, UT, p. A659
RIVERVALLEY BEHAVIORAL HEALTH HOSPITAL, OWENSBORO, KY, p. A265
RIVERVIEW BEHAVIORAL HEALTH, TEXARKANA, AR, p. A50
RIVERVIEW HEALTH, CROOKSTON, MN, p. A338
RIVERVIEW HEALTH, NOBLESVILLE, IN, p. A217
RIVERVIEW PSYCHIATRIC CENTER, AUGUSTA, ME, p. A289
RIVERVIEW REGIONAL MEDICAL CENTER, CARTHAGE, TN, p. A575
RIVERVIEW REGIONAL MEDICAL CENTER, GADSDEN, AL, p. A18
RIVERWOOD HEALTHCARE CENTER, AITKIN, MN, p. A335
RMC ANNISTON, ANNISTON, AL, p. A13
RMC JACKSONVILLE, JACKSONVILLE, AL, p. A19
RMC–STRINGFELLOW MEMORIAL HOSPITAL, ANNISTON, AL, p. A13
RML SPECIALTY HOSPITAL, CHICAGO, IL, p. A183
RML SPECIALTY HOSPITAL, HINSDALE, IL, p. A190
ROANE GENERAL HOSPITAL, SPENCER, WV, p. A696
ROANE MEDICAL CENTER, HARRIMAN, TN, p. A579
ROBERT E. BUSH NAVAL HOSPITAL, TWENTYNINE PALMS, CA, p. A95
ROBERT J. DOLE VETERANS AFFAIRS MEDICAL CENTER, WICHITA, KS, p. A253
ROBERT WOOD JOHNSON UNIVERSITY HOSPITAL, NEW BRUNSWICK, NJ, p. A417
ROBERT WOOD JOHNSON UNIVERSITY HOSPITAL AT HAMILTON, HAMILTON, NJ, p. A414
ROBERT WOOD JOHNSON UNIVERSITY HOSPITAL RAHWAY, RAHWAY, NJ, p. A419
ROBERT WOOD JOHNSON UNIVERSITY HOSPITAL SOMERSET, SOMERVILLE, NJ, p. A420
ROBLEY REX VETERANS AFFAIRS MEDICAL CENTER, LOUISVILLE, KY, p. A263
ROCHELLE COMMUNITY HOSPITAL, ROCHELLE, IL, p. A198
ROCHESTER GENERAL HOSPITAL, ROCHESTER, NY, p. A451
ROCHESTER PSYCHIATRIC CENTER, ROCHESTER, NY, p. A451
ROCK COUNTY HOSPITAL, BASSETT, NE, p. A390
ROCK PRAIRIE BEHAVIORAL HEALTH, COLLEGE STATION, TX, p. A602
ROCK SPRINGS, GEORGETOWN, TX, p. A616
ROCKCASTLE REGIONAL HOSPITAL AND RESPIRATORY CARE CENTER, MOUNT VERNON, KY, p. A265
ROCKDALE HOSPITAL, ROCKDALE, TX, p. A640
ROCKDALE MEDICAL CENTER, CONYERS, GA, p. A155

ROCKEFELLER UNIVERSITY HOSPITAL, NEW ROCHELLE, NY, p. A446
ROCKFORD CENTER, NEWARK, DE, p. A115
ROCKLAND Children's hospital psychiatric CENTER, ORANGEBURG, NY, p. A449
ROCKLAND PSYCHIATRIC CENTER, ORANGEBURG, NY, p. A449
ROCKVILLE GENERAL HOSPITAL, VERNON, CT, p. A113
ROGER MILLS MEMORIAL HOSPITAL, CHEYENNE, OK, p. A505
ROGER WILLIAMS MEDICAL CENTER, PROVIDENCE, RI, p. A557
ROGERS MEMORIAL HOSPITAL, OCONOMOWOC, WI, p. A709
ROLLING HILLS HOSPITAL, ADA, OK, p. A504
ROLLING HILLS HOSPITAL, FRANKLIN, TN, p. A579
ROLLING PLAINS MEMORIAL HOSPITAL, SWEETWATER, TX, p. A648
ROLLINS–BROOK COMMUNITY HOSPITAL, LAMPASAS, TX, p. A628
ROME MEMORIAL HOSPITAL, ROME, NY, p. A451
RONALD REAGAN UCLA MEDICAL CENTER, LOS ANGELES, CA, p. A71
ROOKS COUNTY HEALTH CENTER, PLAINVILLE, KS, p. A250
ROOSEVELT GENERAL HOSPITAL, PORTALES, NM, p. A427
ROOSEVELT HOSPITAL, NEW ROCHELLE, NY, p. A446
ROOSEVELT MEDICAL CENTER, CULBERTSON, MT, p. A383
ROOSEVELT WARM SPRINGS REHABILITATION AND SPECIALTY HOSPITALS – LTAC, WARM SPRINGS, GA, p. A167
ROOSEVELT WARM SPRINGS REHABILITATION HOSPITAL – REHAB, WARM SPRINGS, GA, p. A167
ROPER ST. FRANCIS, CHARLESTON, SC, p. A559
ROPER ST. FRANCIS MOUNT PLEASANT HOSPITAL, MOUNT PLEASANT, SC, p. A564
ROSE MEDICAL CENTER, DENVER, CO, p. A101
ROSEBUD HEALTH CARE CENTER, FORSYTH, MT, p. A384
ROSELAND COMMUNITY HOSPITAL, CHICAGO, IL, p. A183
ROSWELL PARK CANCER INSTITUTE, BUFFALO, NY, p. A433
ROTARY REHABILITATION HOSPITAL, MOBILE, AL, p. A20
ROTHMAN SPECIALTY HOSPITAL, BENSALEM, PA, p. A529
ROUNDUP MEMORIAL HEALTHCARE, ROUNDUP, MT, p. A388
ROXBOROUGH MEMORIAL HOSPITAL, PHILADELPHIA, PA, p. A545
ROXBURY TREATMENT CENTER, SHIPPENSBURG, PA, p. A551
ROYAL OAKS HOSPITAL, WINDSOR, MO, p. A381
RUBY VALLEY HOSPITAL, SHERIDAN, MT, p. A388
RUMFORD HOSPITAL, RUMFORD, ME, p. A293
RUNNELLS CENTER FOR REHABILITATION AND HEALTHCARE, BERKELEY HEIGHTS, NJ, p. A411
RUSH–COPLEY MEDICAL CENTER, AURORA, IL, p. A178
RUSH COUNTY MEMORIAL HOSPITAL, LA CROSSE, KS, p. A244
RUSH FOUNDATION HOSPITAL, MERIDIAN, MS, p. A359
RUSH MEMORIAL HOSPITAL, RUSHVILLE, IN, p. A219
RUSH OAK PARK HOSPITAL, OAK PARK, IL, p. A196
RUSH UNIVERSITY MEDICAL CENTER, CHICAGO, IL, p. A183
RUSK COUNTY MEMORIAL HOSPITAL, LADYSMITH, WI, p. A704
RUSK STATE HOSPITAL, RUSK, TX, p. A641
RUSSELL COUNTY HOSPITAL, RUSSELL SPRINGS, KY, p. A267
RUSSELL COUNTY MEDICAL CENTER, LEBANON, VA, p. A669
RUSSELL MEDICAL CENTER, ALEXANDER CITY, AL, p. A13
RUSSELL REGIONAL HOSPITAL, RUSSELL, KS, p. A250
RUSSELLVILLE HOSPITAL, RUSSELLVILLE, AL, p. A23
RUSTON REGIONAL SPECIALTY HOSPITAL, RUSTON, LA, p. A285
RUTHERFORD REGIONAL HEALTH SYSTEM, RUTHERFORDTON, NC, p. A470
RUTLAND REGIONAL MEDICAL CENTER, RUTLAND, VT, p. A663
RYDER MEMORIAL HOSPITAL, HUMACAO, PUERTO RICO, p. A724

S

SABETHA COMMUNITY HOSPITAL, SABETHA, KS, p. A250
SABINE COUNTY HOSPITAL, HEMPHILL, TX, p. A618
SABINE MEDICAL CENTER, MANY, LA, p. A280
SACRED HEART HOSPITAL, ALLENTOWN, PA, p. A528
SACRED HEART HOSPITAL, EAU CLAIRE, WI, p. A701
SACRED HEART HOSPITAL ON THE EMERALD COAST, MIRAMAR BEACH, FL, p. A135

SACRED HEART HOSPITAL ON THE GULF, PORT ST. JOE, FL, p. A140
SACRED HEART HOSPITAL PENSACOLA, PENSACOLA, FL, p. A139
SACRED HEART REHABILITATION INSTITUTE, MILWAUKEE, WI, p. A708
SACRED OAK MEDICAL CENTER, HOUSTON, TX, p. A622
SADDLEBACK MEMORIAL MEDICAL CENTER, LAGUNA HILLS, CA, p. A65
SAFE HAVEN HOSPITAL OF POCATELLO, POCATELLO, ID, p. A175
SAFE HAVEN HOSPITAL OF TREASURE VALLEY, BOISE, ID, p. A171
SAGAMORE Children's hospital psychiatric CENTER, DIX HILLS, NY, p. A435
SAGE MEMORIAL HOSPITAL, GANADO, AZ, p. A29
SAGE REHABILITATION HOSPITAL, BATON ROUGE, LA, p. A271
SAGEWEST HEALTH CARE AT RIVERTON, RIVERTON, WY, p. A719
SAINT AGNES HEALTHCARE, BALTIMORE, MD, p. A295
SAINT AGNES MEDICAL CENTER, FRESNO, CA, p. A61
SAINT ALPHONSUS MEDICAL CENTER – BAKER CITY, BAKER CITY, OR, p. A520
SAINT ALPHONSUS MEDICAL CENTER – NAMPA, NAMPA, ID, p. A174
SAINT ALPHONSUS MEDICAL CENTER – ONTARIO, ONTARIO, OR, p. A524
SAINT ALPHONSUS REGIONAL MEDICAL CENTER, BOISE, ID, p. A172
SAINT ANNE'S HOSPITAL, FALL RIVER, MA, p. A306
SAINT ANTHONY HOSPITAL, CHICAGO, IL, p. A183
SAINT ANTHONY MEMORIAL, MICHIGAN CITY, IN, p. A215
SAINT BARNABAS BEHAVIORAL HEALTH CENTER, TOMS RIVER, NJ, p. A421
SAINT BARNABAS MEDICAL CENTER, LIVINGSTON, NJ, p. A415
SAINT CLARE'S HEALTH CENTER AT SUSSEX, SUSSEX, NJ, p. A421
SAINT CLARE'S HEALTH SYSTEM, DENVILLE, NJ, p. A412
SAINT CLARE'S HOSPITAL/BOONTON TOWNSHIP, BOONTON TOWNSHIP, NJ, p. A412
SAINT CLARE'S HOSPITAL/DENVILLE, DENVILLE, NJ, p. A412
SAINT ELIZABETH'S MEDICAL CENTER, WABASHA, MN, p. A349
SAINT ELIZABETHS HOSPITAL, WASHINGTON, DC, p. A118
SAINT FRANCIS HEART HOSPITAL, TULSA, OK, p. A518
SAINT FRANCIS HOSPITAL, CHARLESTON, WV, p. A691
SAINT FRANCIS HOSPITAL, EVANSTON, IL, p. A187
SAINT FRANCIS HOSPITAL, MEMPHIS, TN, p. A585
SAINT FRANCIS HOSPITAL, TULSA, OK, p. A518
SAINT FRANCIS HOSPITAL AND MEDICAL CENTER, HARTFORD, CT, p. A110
SAINT FRANCIS HOSPITAL–BARTLETT, BARTLETT, TN, p. A575
SAINT FRANCIS HOSPITAL MUSKOGEE, MUSKOGEE, OK, p. A511
SAINT FRANCIS HOSPITAL SOUTH, TULSA, OK, p. A518
SAINT FRANCIS HOSPITAL VINITA, VINITA, OK, p. A519
SAINT FRANCIS MEDICAL CENTER, CAPE GIRARDEAU, MO, p. A365
SAINT FRANCIS MEMORIAL HOSPITAL, SAN FRANCISCO, CA, p. A87
SAINT JOHN HOSPITAL, LEAVENWORTH, KS, p. A245
SAINT JOSEPH – MARTIN, MARTIN, KY, p. A264
SAINT JOSEPH BEREA, BEREA, KY, p. A255
SAINT JOSEPH EAST, LEXINGTON, KY, p. A261
SAINT JOSEPH HOSPITAL, CHICAGO, IL, p. A183
SAINT JOSEPH HOSPITAL, DENVER, CO, p. A101
SAINT JOSEPH HOSPITAL, LEXINGTON, KY, p. A261
SAINT JOSEPH LONDON, LONDON, KY, p. A262
SAINT JOSEPH MOUNT STERLING, MOUNT STERLING, KY, p. A265
SAINT JOSEPH'S HOSPITAL OF ATLANTA, ATLANTA, GA, p. A151
SAINT JOSEPH'S MEDICAL CENTER, YONKERS, NY, p. A456
SAINT LOUISE REGIONAL HOSPITAL, GILROY, CA, p. A61
SAINT LUKE INSTITUTE, SILVER SPRING, MD, p. A301
SAINT LUKE'S CUSHING HOSPITAL, LEAVENWORTH, KS, p. A245
SAINT LUKE'S EAST HOSPITAL, LEE'S SUMMIT, MO, p. A372
SAINT LUKE'S HOSPITAL OF KANSAS CITY, KANSAS CITY, MO, p. A370
SAINT LUKE'S NORTH HOSPITAL - BARRY ROAD, KANSAS CITY, MO, p. A371
SAINT LUKE'S SOUTH HOSPITAL, OVERLAND PARK, KS, p. A249
SAINT MARGARET MERCY HEALTHCARE CENTERS, HAMMOND, IN, p. A210

SAINT MARGARET MERCY HEALTHCARE CENTERS–SOUTH CAMPUS, DYER, IN, p. A206
SAINT MARY'S HOSPITAL, WATERBURY, CT, p. A114
SAINT MARY'S REGIONAL MEDICAL CENTER, RENO, NV, p. A405
SAINT MARY'S REGIONAL MEDICAL CENTER, RUSSELLVILLE, AR, p. A49
SAINT MICHAEL'S HOSPITAL, STEVENS POINT, WI, p. A713
SAINT MICHAEL'S MEDICAL CENTER, NEWARK, NJ, p. A417
SAINT PETER'S UNIVERSITY HOSPITAL, NEW BRUNSWICK, NJ, p. A417
SAINT SIMONS BY–THE–SEA HOSPITAL, SAINT SIMONS ISLAND, GA, p. A164
SAINT THOMAS DEKALB HOSPITAL, SMITHVILLE, TN, p. A589
SAINT THOMAS HICKMAN HOSPITAL, CENTERVILLE, TN, p. A576
SAINT THOMAS HIGHLANDS HOSPITAL, SPARTA, TN, p. A589
SAINT THOMAS HOSPITAL FOR SPINAL SURGERY, NASHVILLE, TN, p. A586
SAINT THOMAS MIDTOWN HOSPITAL, NASHVILLE, TN, p. A586
SAINT THOMAS RIVER PARK HOSPITAL, MC MINNVILLE, TN, p. A583
SAINT THOMAS RUTHERFORD HOSPITAL, MURFREESBORO, TN, p. A586
SAINT THOMAS STONES RIVER HOSPITAL, WOODBURY, TN, p. A590
SAINT THOMAS WEST HOSPITAL, NASHVILLE, TN, p. A586
SAINT VINCENT HOSPITAL, ERIE, PA, p. A534
SAINT VINCENT HOSPITAL, WORCESTER, MA, p. A313
SAINTS MARY & ELIZABETH MEDICAL CENTER, CHICAGO, IL, p. A183
SAINTS MEDICAL CENTER, LOWELL, MA, p. A308
SAKAKAWEA MEDICAL CENTER, HAZEN, ND, p. A476
SALEM HEALTH WEST VALLEY, DALLAS, OR, p. A521
SALEM HOSPITAL, SALEM, MA, p. A311
SALEM HOSPITAL, SALEM, OR, p. A526
SALEM MEMORIAL DISTRICT HOSPITAL, SALEM, MO, p. A379
SALEM REGIONAL MEDICAL CENTER, SALEM, OH, p. A499
SALEM TOWNSHIP HOSPITAL, SALEM, IL, p. A199
SALEM VETERANS AFFAIRS MEDICAL CENTER, SALEM, VA, p. A675
SALINA REGIONAL HEALTH CENTER, SALINA, KS, p. A251
SALINA SURGICAL HOSPITAL, SALINA, KS, p. A251
SALINAS VALLEY MEMORIAL HEALTHCARE SYSTEM, SALINAS, CA, p. A84
SALINE MEMORIAL HOSPITAL, BENTON, AR, p. A40
SALT LAKE BEHAVIORAL HEALTH, SALT LAKE CITY, UT, p. A660
SALT LAKE REGIONAL MEDICAL CENTER, SALT LAKE CITY, UT, p. A660
SAM RAYBURN MEMORIAL VETERANS CENTER, BONHAM, TX, p. A598
SAMARITAN ALBANY GENERAL HOSPITAL, ALBANY, OR, p. A520
SAMARITAN BEHAVIORAL HEALTH CENTER–DESERT SAMARITAN MEDICAL CENTER, MESA, AZ, p. A32
SAMARITAN HEALTHCARE, MOSES LAKE, WA, p. A682
SAMARITAN HOSPITAL, MACON, MO, p. A373
SAMARITAN HOSPITAL, TROY, NY, p. A454
SAMARITAN LEBANON COMMUNITY HOSPITAL, LEBANON, OR, p. A523
SAMARITAN MEDICAL CENTER, WATERTOWN, NY, p. A455
SAMARITAN NORTH LINCOLN HOSPITAL, LINCOLN CITY, OR, p. A523
SAMARITAN PACIFIC COMMUNITIES HOSPITAL, NEWPORT, OR, p. A524
SAME DAY SURGERY CENTER, RAPID CITY, SD, p. A572
SAMPSON REGIONAL MEDICAL CENTER, CLINTON, NC, p. A460
SAMUEL MAHELONA MEMORIAL HOSPITAL, KAPAA, HI, p. A170
SAMUEL SIMMONDS MEMORIAL HOSPITAL, BARROW, AK, p. A25
SAN ANGELO COMMUNITY MEDICAL CENTER, SAN ANGELO, TX, p. A641
SAN ANTONIO BEHAVIORAL HEALTHCARE HOSPITAL, SAN ANTONIO, TX, p. A643
SAN ANTONIO REGIONAL HOSPITAL, UPLAND, CA, p. A95
SAN ANTONIO STATE HOSPITAL, SAN ANTONIO, TX, p. A643
SAN BERNARDINO MOUNTAINS COMMUNITY HOSPITAL DISTRICT, LAKE ARROWHEAD, CA, p. A65
SAN CARLOS APACHE HEALTHCARE CORPORATION, PERIDOT, AZ, p. A32
SAN DIEGO COUNTY PSYCHIATRIC HOSPITAL, SAN DIEGO, CA, p. A86
SAN DIEGO MEDICAL CENTER, SAN DIEGO, CA, p. A86
SAN DIMAS COMMUNITY HOSPITAL, SAN DIMAS, CA, p. A86

SELECT SPECIALTY HOSPITAL–NORTH KNOXVILLE, POWELL, TN, p. A588

SELECT SPECIALTY HOSPITAL-NORTHEAST NEW JERSEY, ROCHELLE PARK, NJ, p. A420

SELECT SPECIALTY HOSPITAL–NORTHERN KENTUCKY, FORT THOMAS, KY, p. A258

SELECT SPECIALTY HOSPITAL–NORTHWEST DETROIT, DETROIT, MI, p. A318

SELECT SPECIALTY HOSPITAL–OKLAHOMA CITY, OKLAHOMA CITY, OK, p. A513

SELECT SPECIALTY HOSPITAL-OMAHA, OMAHA, NE, p. A398

SELECT SPECIALTY HOSPITAL–ORLANDO, ORLANDO, FL, p. A137

SELECT SPECIALTY HOSPITAL–PALM BEACH, LAKE WORTH, FL, p. A130

SELECT SPECIALTY HOSPITAL–PANAMA CITY, PANAMA CITY, FL, p. A138

SELECT SPECIALTY HOSPITAL–PENSACOLA, PENSACOLA, FL, p. A139

SELECT SPECIALTY HOSPITAL–PHOENIX, PHOENIX, AZ, p. A34

SELECT SPECIALTY HOSPITAL–PHOENIX DOWNTOWN, PHOENIX, AZ, p. A34

SELECT SPECIALTY HOSPITAL–PITTSBURGH/UPMC, PITTSBURGH, PA, p. A547

SELECT SPECIALTY HOSPITAL–PONTIAC, PONTIAC, MI, p. A328

SELECT SPECIALTY HOSPITAL–QUAD CITIES, DAVENPORT, IA, p. A225

SELECT SPECIALTY HOSPITAL–SAGINAW, SAGINAW, MI, p. A329

SELECT SPECIALTY HOSPITAL–SAVANNAH, SAVANNAH, GA, p. A164

SELECT SPECIALTY HOSPITAL–SIOUX FALLS, SIOUX FALLS, SD, p. A572

SELECT SPECIALTY HOSPITAL-SPRINGFIELD, SPRINGFIELD, MO, p. A380

SELECT SPECIALTY HOSPITAL-ST. LOUIS, SAINT CHARLES, MO, p. A376

SELECT SPECIALTY HOSPITAL–TALLAHASSEE, TALLAHASSEE, FL, p. A144

SELECT SPECIALTY HOSPITAL–TRI CITIES, BRISTOL, TN, p. A575

SELECT SPECIALTY HOSPITAL–TULSA MIDTOWN, TULSA, OK, p. A518

SELECT SPECIALTY HOSPITAL–WESTERN MICHIGAN, MUSKEGON, MI, p. A327

SELECT SPECIALTY HOSPITAL–WICHITA, WICHITA, KS, p. A253

SELECT SPECIALTY HOSPITAL–YORK, YORK, PA, p. A555

SELECT SPECIALTY HOSPITAL–YOUNGSTOWN, YOUNGSTOWN, OH, p. A503

SELECT SPECIALTY HOSPITAL-WESTERN MISSOURI, KANSAS CITY, MO, p. A371

SELECT SPECIALTY HOSPITAL—WILMINGTON, WILMINGTON, DE, p. A116

SELF REGIONAL HEALTHCARE, GREENWOOD, SC, p. A563

SENECA HEALTHCARE DISTRICT, CHESTER, CA, p. A55

SENTARA ALBEMARLE MEDICAL CENTER, ELIZABETH CITY, NC, p. A462

SENTARA CAREPLEX HOSPITAL, HAMPTON, VA, p. A668

SENTARA HALIFAX REGIONAL HOSPITAL, SOUTH BOSTON, VA, p. A675

SENTARA LEIGH HOSPITAL, NORFOLK, VA, p. A672

SENTARA NORFOLK GENERAL HOSPITAL, NORFOLK, VA, p. A672

SENTARA NORTHERN VIRGINIA MEDICAL CENTER, WOODBRIDGE, VA, p. A677

SENTARA OBICI HOSPITAL, SUFFOLK, VA, p. A676

SENTARA PRINCESS ANNE HOSPITAL, VIRGINIA BEACH, VA, p. A676

SENTARA RMH MEDICAL CENTER, HARRISONBURG, VA, p. A668

SENTARA VIRGINIA BEACH GENERAL HOSPITAL, VIRGINIA BEACH, VA, p. A676

SENTARA WILLIAMSBURG REGIONAL MEDICAL CENTER, WILLIAMSBURG, VA, p. A677

SEQUEL POMEGRANATE HEALTH SYSTEMS, COLUMBUS, OH, p. A488

SEQUOIA HOSPITAL, REDWOOD CITY, CA, p. A82

SERENITY SPRINGS SPECIALTY HOSPITAL, RUSTON, LA, p. A285

SETON EDGAR B. DAVIS HOSPITAL, LULING, TX, p. A631

SETON HIGHLAND LAKES, BURNET, TX, p. A600

SETON MEDICAL CENTER, DALY CITY, CA, p. A57

SETON MEDICAL CENTER AUSTIN, AUSTIN, TX, p. A595

SETON MEDICAL CENTER HARKER HEIGHTS, HARKER HEIGHTS, TX, p. A618

SETON MEDICAL CENTER HAYS, KYLE, TX, p. A627

SETON MEDICAL CENTER WILLIAMSON, ROUND ROCK, TX, p. A641

SETON NORTHWEST HOSPITAL, AUSTIN, TX, p. A595

SETON SHOAL CREEK HOSPITAL, AUSTIN, TX, p. A595

SETON SMITHVILLE REGIONAL HOSPITAL, SMITHVILLE, TX, p. A646

SETON SOUTHWEST HOSPITAL, AUSTIN, TX, p. A595

SEVEN HILLS HOSPITAL, HENDERSON, NV, p. A402

SEVEN RIVERS REGIONAL MEDICAL CENTER, CRYSTAL RIVER, FL, p. A122

SEVIER VALLEY HOSPITAL, RICHFIELD, UT, p. A659

SEWICKLEY VALLEY HOSPITAL, (A DIVISION OF VALLEY MEDICAL FACILITIES), SEWICKLEY, PA, p. A550

SEYMOUR HOSPITAL, SEYMOUR, TX, p. A645

SHADOW MOUNTAIN BEHAVIORAL HEALTH SYSTEM, TULSA, OK, p. A518

SHAMROCK GENERAL HOSPITAL, SHAMROCK, TX, p. A645

SHANDS LAKE SHORE REGIONAL MEDICAL CENTER, LAKE CITY, FL, p. A130

SHANDS LIVE OAK REGIONAL MEDICAL CENTER, LIVE OAK, FL, p. A131

SHANDS STARKE, STARKE, FL, p. A143

SHANDS STARKE REGIONAL MEDICAL CENTER, STARKE, FL, p. A143

SHANNON MEDICAL CENTER, SAN ANGELO, TX, p. A641

SHARE MEDICAL CENTER, ALVA, OK, p. A504

SHARKEY–ISSAQUENA COMMUNITY HOSPITAL, ROLLING FORK, MS, p. A361

SHARON HOSPITAL, SHARON, CT, p. A113

SHARON REGIONAL HEALTH SYSTEM, SHARON, PA, p. A551

SHARP CHULA VISTA MEDICAL CENTER, CHULA VISTA, CA, p. A55

SHARP CORONADO HOSPITAL AND HEALTHCARE CENTER, CORONADO, CA, p. A56

SHARP GROSSMONT HOSPITAL, LA MESA, CA, p. A64

SHARP MEMORIAL HOSPITAL, SAN DIEGO, CA, p. A86

SHARP MESA VISTA HOSPITAL, SAN DIEGO, CA, p. A86

SHASTA REGIONAL MEDICAL CENTER, REDDING, CA, p. A81

SHAWNEE MISSION MEDICAL CENTER, SHAWNEE MISSION, KS, p. A252

SHELBY BAPTIST MEDICAL CENTER, ALABASTER, AL, p. A13

SHELBY MEMORIAL HOSPITAL, SHELBYVILLE, IL, p. A200

SHELTERING ARMS HOSPITAL SOUTH, MIDLOTHIAN, VA, p. A670

SHELTERING ARMS REHABILITATION HOSPITAL, MECHANICSVILLE, VA, p. A670

SHENANDOAH MEDICAL CENTER, SHENANDOAH, IA, p. A234

SHENANDOAH MEMORIAL HOSPITAL, WOODSTOCK, VA, p. A677

SHENANGO VALLEY CAMPUS, FARRELL, PA, p. A535

SHEPHERD CENTER, ATLANTA, GA, p. A151

SHEPPARD PRATT HEALTH SYSTEM, BALTIMORE, MD, p. A295

SHERIDAN COMMUNITY HOSPITAL, SHERIDAN, MI, p. A330

SHERIDAN COUNTY HEALTH COMPLEX, HOXIE, KS, p. A243

SHERIDAN MEMORIAL HOSPITAL, PLENTYWOOD, MT, p. A387

SHERIDAN MEMORIAL HOSPITAL, SHERIDAN, WY, p. A719

SHERIDAN VETERANS AFFAIRS MEDICAL CENTER, SHERIDAN, WY, p. A720

SHERMAN HOSPITAL, ELGIN, IL, p. A186

SHERMAN OAKS HOSPITAL, LOS ANGELES, CA, p. A71

SHIRLEY RYAN ABILITYLAB, CHICAGO, IL, p. A183

SHOALS HOSPITAL, MUSCLE SHOALS, AL, p. A22

SHODAIR CHILDREN'S HOSPITAL, HELENA, MT, p. A385

SHORE MEDICAL CENTER, SOMERS POINT, NJ, p. A420

SHORE MEMORIAL HOSPITAL, ONANCOKE, VA, p. A672

SHOSHONE MEDICAL CENTER, KELLOGG, ID, p. A173

SHRINERS HOSPITALS FOR CHILDREN–BOSTON, BOSTON, MA, p. A304

SHRINERS HOSPITALS FOR CHILDREN–CHICAGO, CHICAGO, IL, p. A184

SHRINERS HOSPITALS FOR CHILDREN–CINCINNATI, CINCINNATI, OH, p. A484

SHRINERS HOSPITALS FOR CHILDREN–GALVESTON, GALVESTON, TX, p. A615

SHRINERS HOSPITALS FOR CHILDREN–GREENVILLE, GREENVILLE, SC, p. A563

SHRINERS HOSPITALS FOR CHILDREN–HONOLULU, HONOLULU, HI, p. A169

SHRINERS HOSPITALS FOR CHILDREN–HOUSTON, HOUSTON, TX, p. A622

SHRINERS HOSPITALS FOR CHILDREN–LEXINGTON, LEXINGTON, KY, p. A261

SHRINERS HOSPITALS FOR CHILDREN–NORTHERN CALIFORNIA, SACRAMENTO, CA, p. A83

SHRINERS HOSPITALS FOR CHILDREN–PHILADELPHIA, PHILADELPHIA, PA, p. A545

SHRINERS HOSPITALS FOR CHILDREN–PORTLAND, PORTLAND, OR, p. A525

SHRINERS HOSPITALS FOR CHILDREN–SALT LAKE CITY, SALT LAKE CITY, UT, p. A660

SHRINERS HOSPITALS FOR CHILDREN–SHREVEPORT, SHREVEPORT, LA, p. A286

SHRINERS HOSPITALS FOR CHILDREN–SPOKANE, SPOKANE, WA, p. A687

SHRINERS HOSPITALS FOR CHILDREN–SPRINGFIELD, SPRINGFIELD, MA, p. A311

SHRINERS HOSPITALS FOR CHILDREN–ST. LOUIS, SAINT LOUIS, MO, p. A377

SHRINERS HOSPITALS FOR CHILDREN–TAMPA, TAMPA, FL, p. A145

SHRINERS HOSPITALS FOR CHILDREN–TWIN CITIES, MINNEAPOLIS, MN, p. A344

SIBLEY MEMORIAL HOSPITAL, WASHINGTON, DC, p. A118

SIDNEY HEALTH CENTER, SIDNEY, MT, p. A388

SIDNEY REGIONAL MEDICAL CENTER, SIDNEY, NE, p. A400

SIERRA NEVADA MEMORIAL HOSPITAL, GRASS VALLEY, CA, p. A62

SIERRA TUCSON, TUCSON, AZ, p. A38

SIERRA VIEW MEDICAL CENTER, PORTERVILLE, CA, p. A80

SIERRA VISTA HOSPITAL, SACRAMENTO, CA, p. A84

SIERRA VISTA HOSPITAL, TRUTH OR CONSEQUENCES, NM, p. A429

SIERRA VISTA REGIONAL MEDICAL CENTER, SAN LUIS OBISPO, CA, p. A89

SIGNATURE HEALTHCARE BROCKTON HOSPITAL, BROCKTON, MA, p. A304

SIGNATURE PSYCHIATRIC HOSPITAL, KANSAS CITY, MO, p. A370

SILOAM SPRINGS REGIONAL HOSPITAL, SILOAM SPRINGS, AR, p. A49

SILVER CROSS HOSPITAL, NEW LENOX, IL, p. A195

SILVER CROSS HOSPITAL, NEW LENOX, IL, p. A195

SILVER HILL HOSPITAL, NEW CANAAN, CT, p. A111

SILVER LAKE MEDICAL CENTER, LOS ANGELES, CA, p. A71

SIMI VALLEY HOSPITAL, SIMI VALLEY, CA, p. A92

SIMPSON GENERAL HOSPITAL, MENDENHALL, MS, p. A358

SINAI HOSPITAL OF BALTIMORE, BALTIMORE, MD, p. A296

SINGING RIVER HEALTH SYSTEM, PASCAGOULA, MS, p. A360

SIOUX CENTER HEALTH, SIOUX CENTER, IA, p. A235

SIOUX FALLS SPECIALTY HOSPITAL, SIOUX FALLS, SD, p. A572

SIOUX FALLS VETERANS AFFAIRS HEALTH CARE SYSTEM, SIOUX FALLS, SD, p. A573

SIOUXLAND SURGERY CENTER, DAKOTA DUNES, SD, p. A569

SISKIN HOSPITAL FOR PHYSICAL REHABILITATION, CHATTANOOGA, TN, p. A576

SISTER EMMANUEL HOSPITAL, MIAMI, FL, p. A134

SISTER KENNY REHABILITATION INSTITUTE, MINNEAPOLIS, MN, p. A344

SISTERS OF CHARITY HOSPITAL OF BUFFALO, BUFFALO, NY, p. A433

SISTERSVILLE GENERAL HOSPITAL, SISTERSVILLE, WV, p. A696

SITKA COMMUNITY HOSPITAL, SITKA, AK, p. A27

SKAGIT REGIONAL HEALTH, MOUNT VERNON, WA, p. A682

SKIFF MEDICAL CENTER, NEWTON, IA, p. A232

SKY LAKES MEDICAL CENTER, KLAMATH FALLS, OR, p. A523

SKY RIDGE MEDICAL CENTER, LONE TREE, CO, p. A105

SKYLINE HOSPITAL, WHITE SALMON, WA, p. A689

SLEEPY EYE MEDICAL CENTER, SLEEPY EYE, MN, p. A348

SLIDELL MEMORIAL HOSPITAL, SLIDELL, LA, p. A286

SMDC MEDICAL CENTER, DULUTH, MN, p. A339

SMITH COUNTY MEMORIAL HOSPITAL, SMITH CENTER, KS, p. A252

SMYTH COUNTY COMMUNITY HOSPITAL, MARION, VA, p. A670

SNOQUALMIE VALLEY HOSPITAL DISTRICT, SNOQUALMIE, WA, p. A686

SNOWDEN AT FREDERICKSBURG, FREDERICKSBURG, VA, p. A667

SOCORRO GENERAL HOSPITAL, SOCORRO, NM, p. A429

SOIN MEDICAL CENTER, BEAVERCREEK, OH, p. A481

SOLARA HOSPITAL HARLINGEN, HARLINGEN, TX, p. A618

SOLARA HOSPITAL MCALLEN, MCALLEN, TX, p. A632

SOLDIERS AND SAILORS MEMORIAL HOSPITAL, WELLSBORO, PA, p. A553

SOLDIERS AND SAILORS MEMORIAL HOSPITAL OF YATES COUNTY, PENN YAN, NY, p. A449

SOMERSET HOSPITAL, SOMERSET, PA, p. A551

SOMERVILLE HOSPITAL, SOMERVILLE, MA, p. A311

SONOMA DEVELOPMENTAL CENTER, ELDRIDGE, CA, p. A58

SONOMA VALLEY HOSPITAL, SONOMA, CA, p. A92

SONOMA WEST MEDICAL CENTER, SEBASTOPOL, CA, p. A91

SONORA BEHAVIORAL HEALTH HOSPITAL, TUCSON, AZ, p. A38

ST. LUKE'S MERIDIAN MEDICAL CENTER, MERIDIAN, ID, p. A174
ST. LUKE'S REGIONAL MEDICAL CENTER, BOISE, ID, p. A172
ST. LUKE'S REHABILITATION HOSPITAL, BOISE, ID, p. A172
ST. LUKE'S REHABILITATION HOSPITAL, CHESTERFIELD, MO, p. A366
ST. LUKE'S REHABILITATION INSTITUTE, SPOKANE, WA, p. A687
ST. LUKE'S SUGAR LAND HOSPITAL, SUGAR LAND, TX, p. A647
ST. LUKE'S UNIVERSITY HOSPITAL – BETHLEHEM CAMPUS, BETHLEHEM, PA, p. A529
ST. LUKE'S WOOD RIVER MEDICAL CENTER, KETCHUM, ID, p. A174
ST. MARGARET'S HOSPITAL, SPRING VALLEY, IL, p. A200
ST. MARK'S HOSPITAL, SALT LAKE CITY, UT, p. A660
ST. MARK'S MEDICAL CENTER, LA GRANGE, TX, p. A627
ST. MARTIN HOSPITAL, BREAUX BRIDGE, LA, p. A272
ST. MARY MEDICAL CENTER, APPLE VALLEY, CA, p. A52
ST. MARY MEDICAL CENTER, HOBART, IN, p. A210
ST. MARY MEDICAL CENTER, LANGHORNE, PA, p. A538
ST. MARY MEDICAL CENTER, LONG BEACH, CA, p. A67
ST. MARY MERCY HOSPITAL, LIVONIA, MI, p. A325
ST. MARY REHABILITATION HOSPITAL, LANGHORNE, PA, p. A538
ST. MARY–CORWIN MEDICAL CENTER, PUEBLO, CO, p. A107
ST. MARY'S GENERAL HOSPITAL, PASSAIC, NJ, p. A418
ST. MARY'S GOOD SAMARITAN HOSPITAL, GREENSBORO, GA, p. A158
ST. MARY'S HEALTH CARE SYSTEM, ATHENS, GA, p. A149
ST. MARY'S HEALTHCARE, AMSTERDAM, NY, p. A430
ST. MARY'S HEALTHCARE, AMSTERDAM, NY, p. A431
ST. MARY'S HOSPITAL, COTTONWOOD, ID, p. A173
ST. MARY'S HOSPITAL, MADISON, WI, p. A705
ST. MARY'S HOSPITAL, TROY, NY, p. A454
ST. MARY'S HOSPITAL AND MEDICAL CENTER, GRAND JUNCTION, CO, p. A103
ST. MARY'S HOSPITAL AND REHABILITATION CENTER, MINNEAPOLIS, MN, p. A344
ST. MARY'S INNOVIS HEALTH, DETROIT LAKES, MN, p. A338
ST. MARY'S JANESVILLE HOSPITAL, JANESVILLE, WI, p. A704
ST. MARY'S JEFFERSON MEMORIAL HOSPITAL, JEFFERSON CITY, TN, p. A580
ST. MARY'S MEDICAL CENTER, BLUE SPRINGS, MO, p. A364
ST. MARY'S MEDICAL CENTER, DULUTH, MN, p. A339
ST. MARY'S MEDICAL CENTER, HUNTINGTON, WV, p. A693
ST. MARY'S MEDICAL CENTER, SAN FRANCISCO, CA, p. A88
ST. MARY'S MEDICAL CENTER, WEST PALM BEACH, FL, p. A147
ST. MARY'S OF MICHIGAN, SAGINAW, MI, p. A330
ST. MARY'S OF MICHIGAN STANDISH HOSPITAL, STANDISH, MI, p. A331
ST. MARY'S REGIONAL MEDICAL CENTER, ENID, OK, p. A507
ST. MARY'S REGIONAL MEDICAL CENTER, LEWISTON, ME, p. A291
ST. MARY'S SACRED HEART HOSPITAL, LAVONIA, GA, p. A160
ST. MICHAEL'S HOSPITAL AVERA, TYNDALL, SD, p. A573
ST. PATRICK HOSPITAL, MISSOULA, MT, p. A387
ST. PETER'S HOSPITAL, ALBANY, NY, p. A430
ST. PETER'S HOSPITAL, HELENA, MT, p. A385
ST. PETERSBURG GENERAL HOSPITAL, SAINT PETERSBURG, FL, p. A142
ST. RITA'S MEDICAL CENTER, LIMA, OH, p. A493
ST. ROSE DOMINICAN HOSPITALS - ROSE DE LIMA CAMPUS, HENDERSON, NV, p. A402
ST. ROSE DOMINICAN HOSPITALS - SAN MARTIN CAMPUS, LAS VEGAS, NV, p. A404
ST. ROSE DOMINICAN HOSPITALS - SIENA CAMPUS, HENDERSON, NV, p. A402
ST. ROSE HOSPITAL, HAYWARD, CA, p. A63
ST. TAMMANY PARISH HOSPITAL, COVINGTON, LA, p. A273
ST. THERESA SPECIALTY HOSPITAL, KENNER, LA, p. A277
ST. THOMAS MORE HOSPITAL, CANON CITY, CO, p. A99
ST. VINCENT ANDERSON REGIONAL HOSPITAL, ANDERSON, IN, p. A203
ST. VINCENT CARMEL HOSPITAL, CARMEL, IN, p. A205
ST. VINCENT CHARITY MEDICAL CENTER, CLEVELAND, OH, p. A486
ST. VINCENT CLAY HOSPITAL, BRAZIL, IN, p. A204
ST. VINCENT DUNN HOSPITAL, BEDFORD, IN, p. A204
ST. VINCENT FISHERS HOSPITAL, FISHERS, IN, p. A207
ST. VINCENT GENERAL HOSPITAL DISTRICT, LEADVILLE, CO, p. A105
ST. VINCENT HEALTHCARE, BILLINGS, MT, p. A382
ST. VINCENT INDIANAPOLIS HOSPITAL, INDIANAPOLIS, IN, p. A212
ST. VINCENT JENNINGS HOSPITAL, NORTH VERNON, IN, p. A218
ST. VINCENT KOKOMO, KOKOMO, IN, p. A213

ST. VINCENT MEDICAL CENTER, LOS ANGELES, CA, p. A71
ST. VINCENT MEDICAL CENTER OF EVANSVILLE, EVANSVILLE, IN, p. A207
ST. VINCENT MERCY HOSPITAL, ELWOOD, IN, p. A207
ST. VINCENT RANDOLPH HOSPITAL, WINCHESTER, IN, p. A221
ST. VINCENT REHABILITATION HOSPITAL, SHERWOOD, AR, p. A49
ST. VINCENT SALEM HOSPITAL, SALEM, IN, p. A219
ST. VINCENT SETON SPECIALTY HOSPITAL, INDIANAPOLIS, IN, p. A212
ST. VINCENT WARRICK HOSPITAL, BOONVILLE, IN, p. A204
ST. VINCENT WILLIAMSPORT HOSPITAL, WILLIAMSPORT, IN, p. A221
ST. VINCENT'S BEHAVIORAL HEALTH, WESTPORT, CT, p. A114
ST. VINCENT'S BIRMINGHAM, BIRMINGHAM, AL, p. A15
ST. VINCENT'S BLOUNT, ONEONTA, AL, p. A22
ST. VINCENT'S CHILTON HOSPITAL, CLANTON, AL, p. A16
ST. VINCENT'S EAST, BIRMINGHAM, AL, p. A15
ST. VINCENT'S MEDICAL CENTER, BRIDGEPORT, CT, p. A109
ST. VINCENT'S MEDICAL CENTER CLAY COUNTY, MIDDLEBURG, FL, p. A134
ST. VINCENT'S MEDICAL CENTER RIVERSIDE, JACKSONVILLE, FL, p. A128
ST. VINCENT'S MEDICAL CENTER SOUTHSIDE, JACKSONVILLE, FL, p. A128
ST. VINCENT'S ST. CLAIR, PELL CITY, AL, p. A22
STAFFORD COUNTY HOSPITAL, STAFFORD, KS, p. A252
STAFFORD HOSPITAL, STAFFORD, VA, p. A675
STAMFORD HOSPITAL, STAMFORD, CT, p. A113
STAMFORD MEMORIAL HOSPITAL, STAMFORD, TX, p. A646
STANDING ROCK SERVICE UNIT, FORT YATES HOSPITAL, INDIAN HEALTH SERVICE, DHHS, FORT YATES, ND, p. A476
STANFORD HEALTH CARE – VALLEYCARE, PLEASANTON, CA, p. A80
STANFORD HEALTH CARE, PALO ALTO, CA, p. A79
STANISLAUS SURGICAL HOSPITAL, MODESTO, CA, p. A74
STANTON COUNTY HOSPITAL, JOHNSON, KS, p. A243
STAR VALLEY MEDICAL CENTER, AFTON, WY, p. A717
STARKE HOSPITAL, KNOX, IN, p. A213
STARKE MEMORIAL HOSPITAL, KNOX, IN, p. A213
STARR COUNTY MEMORIAL HOSPITAL, RIO GRANDE CITY, TX, p. A640
STARR REGIONAL MEDICAL CENTER, ATHENS, TN, p. A575
STATE CORRECTIONAL INSTITUTION AT CAMP HILL, CAMP HILL, PA, p. A531
STATE HOSPITAL NORTH, OROFINO, ID, p. A175
STATE HOSPITAL SOUTH, BLACKFOOT, ID, p. A171
STATE PENITENTIARY HOSPITAL, WALLA WALLA, WA, p. A689
STATEN ISLAND UNIVERSITY HOSPITAL, NEW ROCHELLE, NY, p. A446
STE. GENEVIEVE COUNTY MEMORIAL HOSPITAL, STE GENEVIEVE, MO, p. A380
STEELE MEMORIAL MEDICAL CENTER, SALMON, ID, p. A176
STEPHENS COUNTY HOSPITAL, TOCCOA, GA, p. A166
STEPHENS MEMORIAL HOSPITAL, BRECKENRIDGE, TX, p. A599
STEPHENS MEMORIAL HOSPITAL, NORWAY, ME, p. A292
STERLING REGIONAL MEDCENTER, STERLING, CO, p. A107
STERLING SURGICAL HOSPITAL, SLIDELL, LA, p. A286
STERLINGTON REHABILITATION HOSPITAL, BASTROP, LA, p. A270
STEVEN AND ALEXANDRA COHEN CHILDREN'S MEDICAL CENTER OF NEW YORK, NEW ROCHELLE, NY, p. A446
STEVENS COMMUNITY MEDICAL CENTER, MORRIS, MN, p. A344
STEVENS COUNTY HOSPITAL, HUGOTON, KS, p. A243
STEVENS HEALTHCARE, EDMONDS, WA, p. A680
STEWART & LYNDA RESNICK NEUROPSYCHIATRIC HOSPITAL AT UCLA, LOS ANGELES, CA, p. A71
STEWART MEMORIAL COMMUNITY HOSPITAL, LAKE CITY, IA, p. A230
STILLWATER BILLINGS CLINIC, COLUMBUS, MT, p. A383
STILLWATER MEDICAL CENTER, STILLWATER, OK, p. A516
STILWELL MEMORIAL HOSPITAL, STILWELL, OK, p. A516
STONE COUNTY HOSPITAL, WIGGINS, MS, p. A363
STONE COUNTY MEDICAL CENTER, MOUNTAIN VIEW, AR, p. A47
STONECREST CENTER, DETROIT, MI, p. A318
STONESPRINGS HOSPITAL CENTER, DULLES, VA, p. A666
STONEWALL JACKSON MEMORIAL HOSPITAL, WESTON, WV, p. A697
STONEWALL MEMORIAL HOSPITAL, ASPERMONT, TX, p. A594
STONY BROOK UNIVERSITY HOSPITAL, STONY BROOK, NY, p. A453
STORMONT VAIL HEALTH, TOPEKA, KS, p. A252

STORY COUNTY MEDICAL CENTER, NEVADA, IA, p. A232
STOUGHTON HOSPITAL ASSOCIATION, STOUGHTON, WI, p. A713
STRAITH HOSPITAL FOR SPECIAL SURGERY, SOUTHFIELD, MI, p. A331
STRATEGIC BEHAVIORAL HEALTH – CHARLOTTE, CHARLOTTE, NC, p. A460
STRATEGIC BEHAVIORAL HEALTH – RALEIGH, GARNER, NC, p. A463
STRATEGIC BEHAVIORAL HEALTH – WILMINGTON, LELAND, NC, p. A466
STRAUB MEDICAL CENTER, HONOLULU, HI, p. A169
STREAMWOOD BEHAVIORAL HEALTH CENTER, STREAMWOOD, IL, p. A201
STRONG MEMORIAL HOSPITAL OF THE UNIVERSITY OF ROCHESTER, ROCHESTER, NY, p. A451
STROUD REGIONAL MEDICAL CENTER, STROUD, OK, p. A516
STS. MARY & ELIZABETH HOSPITAL, LOUISVILLE, KY, p. A263
STURDY MEMORIAL HOSPITAL, ATTLEBORO, MA, p. A302
STURGIS HOSPITAL, STURGIS, MI, p. A331
STURGIS REGIONAL HOSPITAL, STURGIS, SD, p. A573
SUBURBAN COMMUNITY HOSPITAL, NORRISTOWN, PA, p. A542
SUBURBAN HOSPITAL, BETHESDA, MD, p. A297
SUGAR LAND REHABILITATION HOSPITAL, SUGAR LAND, TX, p. A647
SULLIVAN COUNTY COMMUNITY HOSPITAL, SULLIVAN, IN, p. A220
SULLIVAN COUNTY MEMORIAL HOSPITAL, MILAN, MO, p. A373
SUMMA AKRON CITY HOSPITAL, AKRON, OH, p. A479
SUMMA HEALTH SYSTEM, AKRON, OH, p. A479
SUMMA HEALTH SYSTEM, AKRON, OH, p. A479
SUMMA REHAB HOSPITAL, AKRON, OH, p. A479
SUMMA SAINT THOMAS HOSPITAL, AKRON, OH, p. A479
SUMMA WESTERN RESERVE HOSPITAL, CUYAHOGA FALLS, OH, p. A489
SUMMERLIN HOSPITAL MEDICAL CENTER, LAS VEGAS, NV, p. A404
SUMMERS COUNTY ARH HOSPITAL, HINTON, WV, p. A692
SUMMERSVILLE REGIONAL MEDICAL CENTER, SUMMERSVILLE, WV, p. A696
SUMMIT BEHAVIORAL HEALTHCARE, CINCINNATI, OH, p. A484
SUMMIT HEALTHCARE REGIONAL MEDICAL CENTER, SHOW LOW, AZ, p. A36
SUMMIT MEDICAL CENTER, CASPER, WY, p. A717
SUMMIT MEDICAL CENTER, EDMOND, OK, p. A507
SUMMIT OAKS HOSPITAL, SUMMIT, NJ, p. A421
SUMMIT PACIFIC MEDICAL CENTER, ELMA, WA, p. A680
SUMMIT SURGICAL, HUTCHINSON, KS, p. A243
SUMMITRIDGE HOSPITAL, LAWRENCEVILLE, GA, p. A160
SUMNER COUNTY HOSPITAL DISTRICT ONE, CALDWELL, KS, p. A239
SUMNER REGIONAL MEDICAL CENTER, GALLATIN, TN, p. A579
SUMNER REGIONAL MEDICAL CENTER, WELLINGTON, KS, p. A253
SUN BEHAVIORAL HOUSTON, HOUSTON, TX, p. A622
SUNBURY COMMUNITY HOSPITAL AND OUTPATIENT CENTER, SUNBURY, PA, p. A551
SUNCOAST BEHAVIORAL HEALTH CENTER, BRADENTON, FL, p. A121
SUNDANCE BEHAVIORAL HEALTHCARE, ARLINGTON, TX, p. A593
SUNNYSIDE COMMUNITY HOSPITAL AND CLINICS, SUNNYSIDE, WA, p. A687
SUNNYVIEW REHABILITATION HOSPITAL, SCHENECTADY, NY, p. A452
SUNRISE CANYON HOSPITAL, LUBBOCK, TX, p. A630
SUNRISE HOSPITAL AND MEDICAL CENTER, LAS VEGAS, NV, p. A404
SUNY DOWNSTATE MEDICAL CENTER UNIVERSITY HOSPITAL, NEW ROCHELLE, NY, p. A447
SURGERY SPECIALTY HOSPITALS OF AMERICA, PASADENA, TX, p. A637
SURGICAL HOSPITAL AT SOUTHWOODS, YOUNGSTOWN, OH, p. A503
SURGICAL HOSPITAL OF OKLAHOMA, OKLAHOMA CITY, OK, p. A513
SURGICAL INSTITUTE OF READING, WYOMISSING, PA, p. A555
SURGICAL SPECIALTY CENTER AT COORDINATED HEALTH, ALLENTOWN, PA, p. A528
SURGICAL SPECIALTY CENTER OF BATON ROUGE, BATON ROUGE, LA, p. A271
SURPRISE VALLEY HEALTH CARE DISTRICT, CEDARVILLE, CA, p. A55

SUSAN B. ALLEN MEMORIAL HOSPITAL, EL DORADO, KS, p. A240
SUTTER AMADOR HOSPITAL, JACKSON, CA, p. A64
SUTTER AUBURN FAITH HOSPITAL, AUBURN, CA, p. A52
SUTTER CENTER FOR PSYCHIATRY, SACRAMENTO, CA, p. A84
SUTTER COAST HOSPITAL, CRESCENT CITY, CA, p. A57
SUTTER DAVIS HOSPITAL, DAVIS, CA, p. A57
SUTTER DELTA MEDICAL CENTER, ANTIOCH, CA, p. A51
SUTTER LAKESIDE HOSPITAL, LAKEPORT, CA, p. A65
SUTTER MATERNITY AND SURGERY CENTER OF SANTA CRUZ, SANTA CRUZ, CA, p. A91
SUTTER MEDICAL CENTER, SACRAMENTO, SACRAMENTO, CA, p. A84
SUTTER ROSEVILLE MEDICAL CENTER, ROSEVILLE, CA, p. A83
SUTTER SANTA ROSA REGIONAL HOSPITAL, SANTA ROSA, CA, p. A91
SUTTER SOLANO MEDICAL CENTER, VALLEJO, CA, p. A95
SUTTER SURGICAL HOSPITAL – NORTH VALLEY, YUBA CITY, CA, p. A97
SUTTER TRACY COMMUNITY HOSPITAL, TRACY, CA, p. A94
SWAIN COMMUNITY HOSPITAL, BRYSON CITY, NC, p. A458
SWEDISH COVENANT HOSPITAL, CHICAGO, IL, p. A184
SWEDISH MEDICAL CENTER, ENGLEWOOD, CO, p. A102
SWEDISH MEDICAL CENTER–CHERRY HILL CAMPUS, SEATTLE, WA, p. A685
SWEDISH MEDICAL CENTER–FIRST HILL, SEATTLE, WA, p. A685
SWEDISH/EDMONDS, EDMONDS, WA, p. A680
SWEDISH/ISSAQUAH, ISSAQUAH, WA, p. A681
SWEDISHAMERICAN – A DIVISION OF UW HEALTH, ROCKFORD, IL, p. A199
SWEENY COMMUNITY HOSPITAL, SWEENY, TX, p. A647
SWEETWATER HOSPITAL, SWEETWATER, TN, p. A589
SWIFT COUNTY – BENSON HEALTH SERVICES, BENSON, MN, p. A336
SWISHER MEMORIAL HOSPITAL DISTRICT, TULIA, TX, p. A650
SYCAMORE MEDICAL CENTER, MIAMISBURG, OH, p. A496
SYCAMORE SHOALS HOSPITAL, ELIZABETHTON, TN, p. A578
SYCAMORE SPRINGS HOSPITAL, LAFAYETTE, IN, p. A214
SYOSSET HOSPITAL, SYOSSET, NY, p. A453
SYRACUSE VETERANS AFFAIRS MEDICAL CENTER, SYRACUSE, NY, p. A453
SYRINGA HOSPITAL AND CLINICS, GRANGEVILLE, ID, p. A173

T

T. C. THOMPSON CHILDREN'S HOSPITAL, CHATTANOOGA, TN, p. A577
T. J. SAMSON COMMUNITY HOSPITAL, GLASGOW, KY, p. A259
T.J. HEALTH COLUMBIA, COLUMBIA, KY, p. A256
TAHOE FOREST HOSPITAL DISTRICT, TRUCKEE, CA, p. A94
TAHOE PACIFIC HOSPITALS, SPARKS, NV, p. A406
TAKOMA REGIONAL HOSPITAL, GREENEVILLE, TN, p. A579
TALLAHASSEE MEMORIAL HEALTHCARE, TALLAHASSEE, FL, p. A144
TALLAHATCHIE GENERAL HOSPITAL, CHARLESTON, MS, p. A353
TAMPA COMMUNITY HOSPITAL, TAMPA, FL, p. A145
TAMPA GENERAL HOSPITAL, TAMPA, FL, p. A145
TANNER HIGGINS GENERAL HOSPITAL, BREMEN, GA, p. A153
TANNER MEDICAL CENTER–CARROLLTON, CARROLLTON, GA, p. A153
TANNER MEDICAL CENTER–VILLA RICA, VILLA RICA, GA, p. A166
TAUNTON STATE HOSPITAL, TAUNTON, MA, p. A312
TAYLOR HARDIN SECURE MEDICAL FACILITY, TUSCALOOSA, AL, p. A24
TAYLOR HOSPITAL, RIDLEY PARK, PA, p. A549
TAYLOR REGIONAL HOSPITAL, CAMPBELLSVILLE, KY, p. A256
TAYLOR REGIONAL HOSPITAL, HAWKINSVILLE, GA, p. A158
TAYLORVILLE MEMORIAL HOSPITAL, TAYLORVILLE, IL, p. A201
TECHE REGIONAL MEDICAL CENTER, MORGAN CITY, LA, p. A282
TELECARE HERITAGE PSYCHIATRIC HEALTH CENTER, OAKLAND, CA, p. A77
TEMECULA VALLEY HOSPITAL, TEMECULA, CA, p. A93
TEMPLE UNIVERSITY HOSPITAL, PHILADELPHIA, PA, p. A546
TEN BROECK DUPONT, LOUISVILLE, KY, p. A263

TEN BROECK TENNESSEE TREATMENT FACILITY, COOKEVILLE, TN, p. A577
TEN LAKES CENTER, DENNISON, OH, p. A490
TENNESSEE VALLEY HEALTHCARE SYSTEM, NASHVILLE, TN, p. A587
TENNOVA HEALTHCARE–CLARKSVILLE, CLARKSVILLE, TN, p. A577
TENNOVA HEALTHCARE – CLEVELAND, CLEVELAND, TN, p. A577
TENNOVA HEALTHCARE DYERSBURG REGIONAL MEDICAL CENTER, DYERSBURG, TN, p. A578
TENNOVA HEALTHCARE–HARTON, TULLAHOMA, TN, p. A589
TENNOVA HEALTHCARE–JAMESTOWN, JAMESTOWN, TN, p. A580
TENNOVA HEALTHCARE–JEFFERSON MEMORIAL HOSPITAL, JEFFERSON CITY, TN, p. A580
TENNOVA HEALTHCARE–LAFOLLETTE MEDICAL CENTER, LA FOLLETTE, TN, p. A582
TENNOVA HEALTHCARE–LEBANON, LEBANON, TN, p. A582
TENNOVA HEALTHCARE REGIONAL HOSPITAL OF JACKSON, JACKSON, TN, p. A580
TENNOVA HEALTHCARE–SHELBYVILLE, SHELBYVILLE, TN, p. A589
TENNOVA HEALTHCARE VOLUNTEER COMMUNITY HOSPITAL, MARTIN, TN, p. A583
TENNOVA NEWPORT MEDICAL CENTER, NEWPORT, TN, p. A587
TENNOVA PHYSICIANS REGIONAL MEDICAL CENTER, KNOXVILLE, TN, p. A582
TERENCE CARDINAL COOKE HEALTH CARE CENTER, NEW ROCHELLE, NY, p. A447
TERRE HAUTE REGIONAL HOSPITAL, TERRE HAUTE, IN, p. A220
TERREBONNE GENERAL MEDICAL CENTER, HOUMA, LA, p. A276
TERRELL STATE HOSPITAL, TERRELL, TX, p. A648
TETON VALLEY HEALTH CARE, DRIGGS, ID, p. A173
TEWKSBURY HOSPITAL, TEWKSBURY, MA, p. A312
TEXAS CENTER FOR INFECTIOUS DISEASE, SAN ANTONIO, TX, p. A644
TEXAS CHILDREN'S HOSPITAL, HOUSTON, TX, p. A623
TEXAS COUNTY MEMORIAL HOSPITAL, HOUSTON, MO, p. A369
TEXAS GENERAL HOSPITAL, GRAND PRAIRIE, TX, p. A617
TEXAS GENERAL HOSPITAL – VAN ZANDT REGIONAL MEDICAL CENTER, GRAND SALINE, TX, p. A617
TEXAS HEALTH ARLINGTON MEMORIAL HOSPITAL, ARLINGTON, TX, p. A593
TEXAS HEALTH CENTER FOR DIAGNOSTIC & SURGERY, PLANO, TX, p. A638
TEXAS HEALTH HARRIS METHODIST HOSPITAL ALLIANCE, FORT WORTH, TX, p. A614
TEXAS HEALTH HARRIS METHODIST HOSPITAL AZLE, AZLE, TX, p. A596
TEXAS HEALTH HARRIS METHODIST HOSPITAL CLEBURNE, CLEBURNE, TX, p. A601
TEXAS HEALTH HARRIS METHODIST HOSPITAL FORT WORTH, FORT WORTH, TX, p. A614
TEXAS HEALTH HARRIS METHODIST HOSPITAL HURST–EULESS–BEDFORD, BEDFORD, TX, p. A597
TEXAS HEALTH HARRIS METHODIST HOSPITAL SOUTHLAKE, SOUTHLAKE, TX, p. A646
TEXAS HEALTH HARRIS METHODIST HOSPITAL SOUTHWEST FORT WORTH, FORT WORTH, TX, p. A614
TEXAS HEALTH HARRIS METHODIST HOSPITAL STEPHENVILLE, STEPHENVILLE, TX, p. A646
TEXAS HEALTH HEART & VASCULAR HOSPITAL ARLINGTON, ARLINGTON, TX, p. A593
TEXAS HEALTH HUGULEY HOSPITAL FORT WORTH SOUTH, BURLESON, TX, p. A600
TEXAS HEALTH PRESBYTERIAN HOSPITAL ALLEN, ALLEN, TX, p. A591
TEXAS HEALTH PRESBYTERIAN HOSPITAL DALLAS, DALLAS, TX, p. A607
TEXAS HEALTH PRESBYTERIAN HOSPITAL DENTON, DENTON, TX, p. A608
TEXAS HEALTH PRESBYTERIAN HOSPITAL FLOWER MOUND, FLOWER MOUND, TX, p. A612
TEXAS HEALTH PRESBYTERIAN HOSPITAL KAUFMAN, KAUFMAN, TX, p. A626
TEXAS HEALTH PRESBYTERIAN HOSPITAL OF ROCKWALL, ROCKWALL, TX, p. A640
TEXAS HEALTH PRESBYTERIAN HOSPITAL PLANO, PLANO, TX, p. A638
TEXAS HEALTH PRESBYTERIAN HOSPITAL WINNSBORO, WINNSBORO, TX, p. A655
TEXAS HEALTH SPECIALTY HOSPITAL, FORT WORTH, TX, p. A614
TEXAS HOSPITAL FOR ADVANCED MEDICINE, DALLAS, TX, p. A607

TEXAS INSTITUTE FOR SURGERY AT TEXAS HEALTH PRESBYTERIAN DALLAS, DALLAS, TX, p. A607
TEXAS NEUROREHAB CENTER, AUSTIN, TX, p. A596
TEXAS ORTHOPEDIC HOSPITAL, HOUSTON, TX, p. A623
TEXAS REHABILITATION HOSPITAL OF ARLINGTON, ARLINGTON, TX, p. A594
TEXAS REHABILITATION HOSPITAL OF FORT WORTH, FORT WORTH, TX, p. A614
TEXAS SCOTTISH RITE HOSPITAL FOR CHILDREN, DALLAS, TX, p. A607
TEXAS SPINE & JOINT HOSPITAL, TYLER, TX, p. A651
TEXAS STAR RECOVERY, AUSTIN, TX, p. A596
TEXOMA MEDICAL CENTER, DENISON, TX, p. A608
THAYER COUNTY HEALTH SERVICES, HEBRON, NE, p. A394
THE ACADIA HOSPITAL, BANGOR, ME, p. A289
THE ALLEN PAVILION, NEW ROCHELLE, NY, p. A447
THE AROOSTOOK MEDICAL CENTER, PRESQUE ISLE, ME, p. A293
THE BRIDGEWAY, NORTH LITTLE ROCK, AR, p. A48
THE BROOK AT DUPONT, LOUISVILLE, KY, p. A263
THE BROOK HOSPITAL – KMI, LOUISVILLE, KY, p. A263
THE CENTERS, OCALA, FL, p. A136
THE CHARLOTTE HUNGERFORD HOSPITAL, TORRINGTON, CT, p. A113
THE CHILDREN'S CENTER REHABILITATION HOSPITAL, BETHANY, OK, p. A505
THE CHILDREN'S HOME OF PITTSBURGH, PITTSBURGH, PA, p. A547
THE CHILDREN'S INSTITUTE OF PITTSBURGH, PITTSBURGH, PA, p. A547
THE CONNECTICUT HOSPICE, BRANFORD, CT, p. A109
THE CORE INSTITUTE SPECIALTY HOSPITAL, PHOENIX, AZ, p. A34
THE HEALTHCENTER, KALISPELL, MT, p. A386
THE HEART HOSPITAL AT DEACONESS GATEWAY, NEWBURGH, IN, p. A217
THE HEART HOSPITAL BAYLOR DENTON, DENTON, TX, p. A608
THE HEART HOSPITAL BAYLOR PLANO, PLANO, TX, p. A638
THE HOSPITAL AT WESTLAKE MEDICAL CENTER, AUSTIN, TX, p. A596
THE HOSPITAL OF CENTRAL CONNECTICUT, NEW BRITAIN, CT, p. A111
THE HOSPITALS OF PROVIDENCE EAST CAMPUS, EL PASO, TX, p. A611
THE HOSPITALS OF PROVIDENCE MEMORIAL CAMPUS, EL PASO, TX, p. A611
THE HOSPITALS OF PROVIDENCE SIERRA CAMPUS, EL PASO, TX, p. A611
THE HOSPITALS OF PROVIDENCE TRANSMOUNTAIN CAMPUS, EL PASO, TX, p. A612
THE HSC PEDIATRIC CENTER, WASHINGTON, DC, p. A118
THE JEWISH HOSPITAL – MERCY HEALTH, CINCINNATI, OH, p. A484
THE MEDICAL CENTER ALBANY, ALBANY, KY, p. A255
THE MEDICAL CENTER AT CAVERNA, HORSE CAVE, KY, p. A260
THE MEDICAL CENTER AT ELIZABETH PLACE, DAYTON, OH, p. A490
THE MEDICAL CENTER OF SOUTHEAST TEXAS, PORT ARTHUR, TX, p. A639
THE METHODIST HOSPITAL, HOUSTON, TX, p. A623
THE MIAMI MEDICAL CENTER, MIAMI, FL, p. A134
THE NEUROMEDICAL CENTER REHABILITATION HOSPITAL, BATON ROUGE, LA, p. A271
THE ORTHOPEDIC SPECIALTY HOSPITAL, MURRAY, UT, p. A658
THE OUTER BANKS HOSPITAL, NAGS HEAD, NC, p. A467
THE PAVILION, CHAMPAIGN, IL, p. A180
THE PAVILION AT WILLIAMSBURG PLACE, WILLIAMSBURG, VA, p. A677
THE PHYSICIANS CENTRE HOSPITAL, BRYAN, TX, p. A600
THE QUEEN'S MEDICAL CENTER, HONOLULU, HI, p. A169
THE REHABILITATION INSTITUTE OF ST. LOUIS, SAINT LOUIS, MO, p. A378
THE UNIVERSITY OF KANSAS HEALTH SYSTEM, KANSAS CITY, KS, p. A244
THE UNIVERSITY OF TOLEDO MEDICAL CENTER, TOLEDO, OH, p. A501
THE UNIVERSITY OF VERMONT HEALTH NETWORK - ALICE HYDE MEDICAL CENTER, MALONE, NY, p. A439
THE UNIVERSITY OF VERMONT HEALTH NETWORK CENTRAL VERMONT MEDICAL CENTER, BERLIN, VT, p. A662
THE UNIVERSITY OF VERMONT HEALTH NETWORK ELIZABETHTOWN COMMUNITY HOSPITAL, ELIZABETHTOWN, NY, p. A435
THE UNIVERSITY OF VERMONT HEALTH NETWORK-CHAMPLAIN VALLEY PHYSICIANS HOSPITAL, PLATTSBURGH, NY, p. A449
THE VILLAGES REGIONAL HOSPITAL, THE VILLAGES, FL, p. A146

U

V

WESTERN PSYCHIATRIC INSTITUTE AND CLINIC, PITTSBURGH, PA, p. A548
WESTERN REGIONAL MEDICAL CENTER, GOODYEAR, AZ, p. A30
WESTERN STATE HOSPITAL, HOPKINSVILLE, KY, p. A260
WESTERN STATE HOSPITAL, STAUNTON, VA, p. A676
WESTERN STATE HOSPITAL, TACOMA, WA, p. A688
WESTERN WISCONSIN HEALTH, BALDWIN, WI, p. A698
WESTFIELD MEMORIAL HOSPITAL, WESTFIELD, NY, p. A456
WESTFIELDS HOSPITAL, NEW RICHMOND, WI, p. A709
WESTLAKE HOSPITAL, MELROSE PARK, IL, p. A193
WESTON COUNTY HEALTH SERVICES, NEWCASTLE, WY, p. A719
WESTPARK SPRINGS, RICHMOND, TX, p. A640
WESTSIDE REGIONAL MEDICAL CENTER, PLANTATION, FL, p. A140
WESTSIDE SURGICAL HOSPITAL, HOUSTON, TX, p. A624
WETZEL COUNTY HOSPITAL, NEW MARTINSVILLE, WV, p. A694
WHEATLAND MEMORIAL HEALTHCARE, HARLOWTON, MT, p. A385
WHEATON FRANCISCAN HEALTHCARE – ALL SAINTS, RACINE, WI, p. A711
WHEATON FRANCISCAN HEALTHCARE – ELMBROOK MEMORIAL, BROOKFIELD, WI, p. A699
WHEATON FRANCISCAN HEALTHCARE – FRANKLIN, FRANKLIN, WI, p. A702
WHEATON FRANCISCAN HEALTHCARE – ST. FRANCIS, MILWAUKEE, WI, p. A708
WHEATON FRANCISCAN HEALTHCARE – ST. JOSEPH'S, MILWAUKEE, WI, p. A708
WHEELING HOSPITAL, WHEELING, WV, p. A697
WHIDBEYHEALTH, COUPEVILLE, WA, p. A679
WHIDDEN MEMORIAL HOSPITAL, EVERETT, MA, p. A306
WHITE COMMUNITY HOSPITAL, AURORA, MN, p. A335
WHITE MEMORIAL MEDICAL CENTER, LOS ANGELES, CA, p. A72
WHITE MOUNTAIN REGIONAL MEDICAL CENTER, SPRINGERVILLE, AZ, p. A36
WHITE PLAINS HOSPITAL CENTER, WHITE PLAINS, NY, p. A456
WHITE RIVER JUNCTION VETERANS AFFAIRS MEDICAL CENTER, WHITE RIVER JUNCTION, VT, p. A663
WHITE RIVER MEDICAL CENTER, BATESVILLE, AR, p. A40
WHITESBURG ARH HOSPITAL, WHITESBURG, KY, p. A268
WHITING FORENSIC DIVISION OF CONNECTICUT VALLEY HOSPITAL, MIDDLETOWN, CT, p. A111
WHITINSVILLE MEDICAL CENTER, WHITINSVILLE, MA, p. A313
WHITMAN HOSPITAL AND MEDICAL CENTER, COLFAX, WA, p. A679
WHITTEN CENTER, CLINTON, SC, p. A560
WHITTIER HOSPITAL MEDICAL CENTER, WHITTIER, CA, p. A97
WHITTIER PAVILION, HAVERHILL, MA, p. A307
WHITTIER REHABILITATION HOSPITAL, BRADFORD, MA, p. A304
WHITTIER REHABILITATION HOSPITAL, WESTBOROUGH, MA, p. A312
WICHITA COUNTY HEALTH CENTER, LEOTI, KS, p. A245
WICHITA SPECIALTY HOSPITAL, WICHITA, KS, p. A254
WICKENBURG COMMUNITY HOSPITAL, WICKENBURG, AZ, p. A38
WILBARGER GENERAL HOSPITAL, VERNON, TX, p. A652
WILCOX MEDICAL CENTER, LIHUE, HI, p. A170
WILKES–BARRE GENERAL HOSPITAL, WILKES, PA, p. A554
WILKES–BARRE VETERANS AFFAIRS MEDICAL CENTER, WILKES, PA, p. A554
WILLAMETTE VALLEY MEDICAL CENTER, MCMINNVILLE, OR, p. A523
WILLAPA HARBOR HOSPITAL, SOUTH BEND, WA, p. A686
WILLIAM BEAUMONT ARMY MEDICAL CENTER, EL PASO, TX, p. A612
WILLIAM BEE RIRIE HOSPITAL, ELY, NV, p. A401
WILLIAM J. MCCORD ADOLESCENT TREATMENT FACILITY, ORANGEBURG, SC, p. A565
WILLIAM NEWTON HOSPITAL, WINFIELD, KS, p. A254
WILLIAM P. CLEMENTS, JR. UNIVERSITY HOSPITAL, DALLAS, TX, p. A607
WILLIAM R. SHARPE, JR. HOSPITAL, WESTON, WV, p. A697

WILLIAM S. HALL PSYCHIATRIC INSTITUTE, COLUMBIA, SC, p. A561
WILLIAM S. MIDDLETON MEMORIAL VETERANS HOSPITAL, MADISON, WI, p. A705
WILLIAMSON MEDICAL CENTER, FRANKLIN, TN, p. A579
WILLIAMSON MEMORIAL HOSPITAL, WILLIAMSON, WV, p. A697
WILLIAMSPORT HOSPITAL AND MEDICAL CENTER, WILLIAMSPORT, PA, p. A554
WILLIAMSPORT REGIONAL MEDICAL CENTER, WILLIAMSPORT, PA, p. A554
WILLINGWAY HOSPITAL, STATESBORO, GA, p. A165
WILLIS–KNIGHTON BOSSIER HEALTH CENTER, BOSSIER CITY, LA, p. A272
WILLIS–KNIGHTON MEDICAL CENTER, SHREVEPORT, LA, p. A286
WILLOW CREST HOSPITAL, MIAMI, OK, p. A510
WILLOW ROCK CENTER, SAN LEANDRO, CA, p. A89
WILLOW SPRINGS CENTER, RENO, NV, p. A405
WILLS MEMORIAL HOSPITAL, WASHINGTON, GA, p. A167
WILMA N. VAZQUEZ MEDICAL CENTER, VEGA BAJA, PUERTO RICO, p. A727
WILMINGTON TREATMENT CENTER, WILMINGTON, NC, p. A472
WILMINGTON VETERANS AFFAIRS MEDICAL CENTER, WILMINGTON, DE, p. A116
WILSON MEDICAL CENTER, NEODESHA, KS, p. A247
WILSON MEDICAL CENTER, WILSON, NC, p. A472
WILSON MEMORIAL HOSPITAL, SIDNEY, OH, p. A499
WILSON MEMORIAL REGIONAL MEDICAL CENTER, JOHNSON CITY, NY, p. A438
WILSON N. JONES MEDICAL CENTER, SHERMAN, TX, p. A645
WILSON N. JONES REGIONAL MEDICAL CENTER, SHERMAN, TX, p. A645
WINCHESTER HOSPITAL, WINCHESTER, MA, p. A313
WINCHESTER MEDICAL CENTER, WINCHESTER, VA, p. A677
WINDHAM COMMUNITY MEMORIAL HOSPITAL, WILLIMANTIC, CT, p. A114
WINDHAM HOSPITAL, WILLIMANTIC, CT, p. A114
WINDHAVEN PSYCHIATRIC HOSPITAL, PRESCOTT VALLEY, AZ, p. A35
WINDMOOR HEALTHCARE OF CLEARWATER, CLEARWATER, FL, p. A122
WINDOM AREA HOSPITAL, WINDOM, MN, p. A350
WINDSOR–LAURELWOOD CENTER FOR BEHAVIORAL MEDICINE, WILLOUGHBY, OH, p. A502
WINKLER COUNTY MEMORIAL HOSPITAL, KERMIT, TX, p. A626
WINN ARMY COMMUNITY HOSPITAL, HINESVILLE, GA, p. A159
WINN PARISH MEDICAL CENTER, WINNFIELD, LA, p. A288
WINNEBAGO MENTAL HEALTH INSTITUTE, WINNEBAGO, WI, p. A716
WINNER REGIONAL HEALTHCARE CENTER, WINNER, SD, p. A574
WINNESHIEK MEDICAL CENTER, DECORAH, IA, p. A226
WINNIE PALMER HOSPITAL FOR WOMEN AND BABIES, ORLANDO, FL, p. A137
WINONA HEALTH, WINONA, MN, p. A350
WINSTON MEDICAL CENTER, LOUISVILLE, MS, p. A358
WINTER HAVEN HOSPITAL, WINTER HAVEN, FL, p. A148
WINTER PARK MEMORIAL HOSPITAL, WINTER PARK, FL, p. A148
WIREGRASS MEDICAL CENTER, GENEVA, AL, p. A18
WISE HEALTH SYSTEM, DECATUR, TX, p. A607
WISHEK COMMUNITY HOSPITAL AND CLINICS, WISHEK, ND, p. A478
WITHAM HEALTH SERVICES, LEBANON, IN, p. A214
WK BOSSIER HEALTH CENTER, BOSSIER CITY, LA, p. A272
WM. JENNINGS BRYAN DORN VETERANS AFFAIRS MEDICAL CENTER, COLUMBIA, SC, p. A561
WOMACK ARMY MEDICAL CENTER, FORT BRAGG, NC, p. A462
WOMAN'S HOSPITAL, BATON ROUGE, LA, p. A271
WOMAN'S HOSPITAL OF TEXAS, HOUSTON, TX, p. A624
WOMEN AND CHILDREN'S HOSPITAL, BUFFALO, NY, p. A433
WOMEN'S AND CHILDREN'S HOSPITAL, LAFAYETTE, LA, p. A279
WOMEN & INFANTS HOSPITAL OF RHODE ISLAND, PROVIDENCE, RI, p. A557
WOOD COUNTY HOSPITAL, BOWLING GREEN, OH, p. A482

WOODLAND HEALTHCARE, WOODLAND, CA, p. A97
WOODLAND HEIGHTS MEDICAL CENTER, LUFKIN, TX, p. A631
WOODLAND HILLS MEDICAL CENTER, LOS ANGELES, CA, p. A72
WOODLANDS SPECIALTY HOSPITAL, THE WOODLANDS, TX, p. A650
WOODLAWN HOSPITAL, ROCHESTER, IN, p. A219
WOODROW WILSON REHABILITATION CENTER, FISHERSVILLE, VA, p. A667
WOODWINDS HEALTH CAMPUS, WOODBURY, MN, p. A351
WOOSTER COMMUNITY HOSPITAL, WOOSTER, OH, p. A503
WORCESTER RECOVERY CENTER AND HOSPITAL, WORCESTER, MA, p. A313
WRANGELL MEDICAL CENTER, WRANGELL, AK, p. A27
WRAY COMMUNITY DISTRICT HOSPITAL, WRAY, CO, p. A108
WRIGHT MEMORIAL HOSPITAL, TRENTON, MO, p. A380
WRIGHT PATTERSON MEDICAL CENTER, WRIGHT, OH, p. A503
WUESTHOFF MEDICAL CENTER – MELBOURNE, MELBOURNE, FL, p. A132
WUESTHOFF MEDICAL CENTER – ROCKLEDGE, ROCKLEDGE, FL, p. A141
WYANDOT MEMORIAL HOSPITAL, UPPER SANDUSKY, OH, p. A501
WYCKOFF HEIGHTS MEDICAL CENTER, NEW ROCHELLE, NY, p. A447
WYOMING BEHAVIORAL INSTITUTE, CASPER, WY, p. A717
WYOMING COUNTY COMMUNITY HOSPITAL, WARSAW, NY, p. A455
WYOMING MEDICAL CENTER, CASPER, WY, p. A717
WYOMING STATE HOSPITAL, EVANSTON, WY, p. A718
WYOMING VALLEY HEALTH CARE SYSTEM, WILKES, PA, p. A554
WYTHE COUNTY COMMUNITY HOSPITAL, WYTHEVILLE, VA, p. A677

Y

YAKIMA REGIONAL MEDICAL AND CARDIAC CENTER, YAKIMA, WA, p. A689
YALE–NEW HAVEN HOSPITAL, NEW HAVEN, CT, p. A112
YALOBUSHA GENERAL HOSPITAL, WATER VALLEY, MS, p. A362
YAMPA VALLEY MEDICAL CENTER, STEAMBOAT SPRINGS, CO, p. A107
YAVAPAI REGIONAL MEDICAL CENTER – EAST, PRESCOTT VALLEY, AZ, p. A35
YAVAPAI REGIONAL MEDICAL CENTER, PRESCOTT, AZ, p. A35
YOAKUM COMMUNITY HOSPITAL, YOAKUM, TX, p. A655
YOAKUM COUNTY HOSPITAL, DENVER CITY, TX, p. A608
YORK GENERAL, YORK, NE, p. A400
YORK HOSPITAL, YORK, ME, p. A293
YOUTH VILLAGES INNER HARBOUR CAMPUS, DOUGLASVILLE, GA, p. A157
YUKON–KUSKOKWIM DELTA REGIONAL HOSPITAL, BETHEL, AK, p. A25
YUMA DISTRICT HOSPITAL, YUMA, CO, p. A108
YUMA REGIONAL MEDICAL CENTER, YUMA, AZ, p. A39
YUMA REHABILITATION HOSPITAL, YUMA, AZ, p. A39

Z

ZEELAND COMMUNITY HOSPITAL, ZEELAND, MI, p. A334
ZUCKER HILLSIDE HOSPITAL, NEW ROCHELLE, NY, p. A447
ZUCKERBERG SAN FRANCISCO GENERAL HOSPITAL AND TRAUMA CENTER, SAN FRANCISCO, CA, p. A88

© 2017 AHA Guide

Index of Hospitals

Index of Health Care Professionals

This section is an index of the key health care professionals for the hospitals and/or health care systems listed in this publication. The index is in alphabetical order, by individual, followed by the title, institutional affiliation, city, state and page reference to the hospital and/or health care system listing in section A and/or B.

A

AAGARD, Kim, Chief Financial Officer, Tri–County Hospital, Wadena, MN, p. A350

AALBORG, Chase, Vice President and Chief Financial Officer, Amita Health Adventist Medical Center Glenoaks, Glendale Heights, IL, p. A188

AASE, Katie, Director of Nursing, Rock County Hospital, Bassett, NE, p. A390

AASVED, Craig E., Chief Executive Officer, Shodair Children's Hospital, Helena, MT, p. A385

ABAIR, Cynthia, Associate Director, Va San Diego Healthcare System, San Diego, CA, p. A86

ABANG, Toni M.D., Medical Director, Healthsouth Lakeview Rehabilitation Hospital, Elizabethtown, KY, p. A257

ABBATE, Anthony, Director of Information Services, San Ramon Regional Medical Center, San Ramon, CA, p. A90

ABBATIELLO, Michael, Chief Financial Officer, Spring Harbor Hospital, Westbrook, ME, p. A293

ABBEY, Kurt, Chief Nursing Officer, Ozarks Medical Center, West Plains, MO, p. A381

ABBOTT, Dana, Market Human Resources Director, Shands Live Oak Regional Medical Center, Live Oak, FL, p. A131

ABBOTT, Jody, Senior Vice President and Chief Operating Officer, North Kansas City Hospital, North Kansas City, MO, p. A374

ABBOTT, Joe, Director Information Systems, North Ottawa Community Hospital, Grand Haven, MI, p. A320

ABBOTT, Justin M.D., Medical Director, Sevier Valley Hospital, Richfield, UT, p. A659

ABBOTT, Michael, Chief Operating Officer, Lewis–Gale Medical Center, Salem, VA, p. A675

ABBOTT, Peggy L., President and Chief Executive Officer, Ouachita County Medical Center, Camden, AR, p. A41

ABDA, William, Chief Human Resources Officer, Clarks Summit State Hospital, Clarks Summit, PA, p. A531

ABDELKARIM, Riad Z. M.D., Vice President and Chief Medical Officer, St. Mary Medical Center, Apple Valley, CA, p. A52

ABDELNASER, Mohammad, Chief Nursing Officer, Centinela Hospital Medical Center, Inglewood, CA, p. A63

ABE, Ann, Administrator and Chief Operating Officer, Orange County Global Medical Center, Inc., Santa Ana, CA, p. A90

ABEL, Danielle, Vice President of Patient Care Services, Chi Lakewood Health, Baudette, MN, p. A336

ABEL, Jeffrey M.D., Chief Medical Officer, Ogden Regional Medical Center, Ogden, UT, p. A658

ABEL, Kevin, Chief Executive Officer, Lake Chelan Community Hospital And Clinics, Chelan, WA, p. A679

ABEL, Stacy L, Director Human Resources, Craig Hospital, Englewood, CO, p. A102

ABELLERA, Roland, Vice President and Chief Operating Officer, St. Bernard Hospital And Health Care Center, Chicago, IL, p. A184

ABELY, Susan Cerrone
Chief Information Officer, St. Joseph Health Services Of Rhode Island, North Providence, RI, p. A556
Vice President and Chief Information Officer, Roger Williams Medical Center, Providence, RI, p. A557

ABERCROMBIE, David E., Chief Executive Officer, Montgomery County Memorial Hospital, Red Oak, IA, p. A234

ABERCROMBIE, David, Controller, Baptist Health South Florida, Homestead Hospital, Homestead, FL, p. A127

ABERCROMBIE, Les S III, Vice President Human Resouces, Northwest Medical Center – Springdale, Springdale, AR, p. A49

ABERCROMBIE, Zach, Chief Financial Officer, Citizens Baptist Medical Center, Talladega, AL, p. A23

ABERLE, James, Vice President, Chief Operations Officer, Virginia Mason Memorial, Yakima, WA, p. A689

ABERNATHY, Clint, President and Chief Operating Officer, Texas Health Harris Methodist Hospital Alliance, Fort Worth, TX, p. A614

ABINSAY, Alvin M.D., Chief Medical Staff, Carolinas Hospital System Marion, Mullins, SC, p. A565

ABLA, Mike, Director of Nursing, Griffin Memorial Hospital, Norman, OK, p. A511

ABNEY, Stuart, Controller, Jasper Memorial Hospital, Monticello, GA, p. A162

ABOUD, Al CPA, Chief Financial Officer, Hackensack Meridian Health Mountainside Medical Center, Montclair, NJ, p. A416

ABRAHAM, Akram M.D., Chief of Staff, Harmon Memorial Hospital, Hollis, OK, p. A508

ABRAHAM, Brian, Chief Executive Officer, Mesquite Rehabilitation Institute, Mesquite, TX, p. A633

ABRAHAM, Brian, Chief Executive Officer, Mesquite Rehabilitation Institute, Mesquite, TX, p. B50

ABRAHAM, JiJi, Chief Financial Officer, Kaiser Permanente Riverside Medical Center, Riverside, CA, p. A82

ABRAHAM, Paul B., FACHE, Chief Executive Officer, Cumberland Surgical Hospital, San Antonio, TX, p. A642

ABRAHAM, Paul B., FACHE, Chief Executive Officer, Cumberland Surgical Hospital, San Antonio, TX, p. B98

ABRAHAMSON–BATY, Sherri, Director Patient Care Services, Cambridge Medical Center, Cambridge, MN, p. A337

ABRAHAMY, Ran M.D., Chief of Staff, University Hospital And Medical Center, Tamarac, FL, p. A144

ABRAMS, Danielle, Manager Human Resources, Marketing and Executive Assistant, St. Vincent Clay Hospital, Brazil, IN, p. A204

ABRAMS, David, Vice President Human Resources, North Memorial Medical Center, Robbinsdale, MN, p. A346

ABREU, Iris, Supervisor Human Resources, Hospital Hima De Humacao, Humacao, PR, p. A723

ABREU, John, Vice President and Chief Financial Officer, Portneuf Medical Center, Pocatello, ID, p. A175

ABRINA, Sofia R.N.
Administrator, Montclair Hospital Medical Center, Montclair, CA, p. A74
Chief Executive Officer, Glendora Community Hospital, Glendora, CA, p. A62

ABROMOVICH, Sari, Chief Executive Officer, Harbor Oaks Hospital, New Baltimore, MI, p. A327

ABRUTZ, Joseph F. Jr, Administrator, Cameron Regional Medical Center, Cameron, MO, p. A365

ABSALON, Jeffrey, M.D.
Chief Physician Officer, St. Charles Bend, Bend, OR, p. A520
Chief Physician Officer, St. Charles Redmond, Redmond, OR, p. A526

ABSHIER, Trey, Chief Executive Officer, North Shore Medical Center, Miami, FL, p. A133

ABUNDO, Manuel M.D., Chief of Staff, Wahiawa General Hospital, Wahiawa, HI, p. A170

ABY, Sherry, Director Information Management, Carlisle Regional Medical Center, Carlisle, PA, p. A531

ACCASHIAN, Chris, Chief Executive Officer, Bon Secours St. Francis Medical Center, Midlothian, VA, p. A670

ACERRA–WILLIAMS, Karen, Acting Director, Bedford Veterans Affairs Medical Center, Edith Nourse Rogers Memorial Veterans Hospital, Bedford, MA, p. A302

ACETO, Anthony, Vice President Human Resources, Norwalk Hospital, Norwalk, CT, p. A112

ACEVEDO, Edwin Orama, Financial Supervisor, Hospital Buen Samaritano, Aguadilla, PR, p. A721

ACEVEDO, Elizabeth, Director Human Resources, Houston Methodist Willowbrook Hospital, Houston, TX, p. A621

ACEVEDO, Jose, M.D.
President and Chief Executive Officer, Geneva General Hospital, Geneva, NY, p. A436
President and Chief Executive Officer, Soldiers And Sailors Memorial Hospital Of Yates County, Penn Yan, NY, p. A449

ACEVEDO, Ramon, Supervisor Information Systems, Hospital San Cristobal, Coto Laurel, PR, p. A723

ACEVEDO, Vanessa, Interim Chief Executive Officer, Chg Hospital Tucson, Llc, Tucson, AZ, p. A37

ACHARYA, Ganesh, Chief Executive Officer, Good Samaritan Hospital–North, Bakersfield, CA, p. A52

ACHEBE, James Bob M.D., President Medical Staff, South Shore Hospital, Chicago, IL, p. A184

ACHTER, Dick, Chief Financial Officer, Barrett Hospital & Healthcare, Dillon, MT, p. A384

ACHURY, Dario, Director of Information Management, St. Anthony's Rehabilitation Hospital, Lauderdale Lakes, FL, p. A130

ACKER, David B., FACHE, President and Chief Executive Officer, Canton–Potsdam Hospital, Potsdam, NY, p. A450

ACKER, Peter W., President and Chief Executive Officer, Carolinas Healthcare System Lincoln, Lincolnton, NC, p. A466

ACKERMAN, F. Kenneth., Hospital Administrator, Mayo Clinic Hospital – Rochester, Rochester, MN, p. A346

ACKERMAN, F. Kenneth, Chair, Hospital Operation, Mayo Clinic Hospital – Rochester, Rochester, MN, p. A346

ACKERMAN, Sigurd H M.D., President and Chief Executive Officer, Silver Hill Hospital, New Canaan, CT, p. A111

ACKERSON, David, Chief Information Officer, Seattle Cancer Care Alliance, Seattle, WA, p. A685

ACKERT, Sara, Associate Director, Sioux Falls Veterans Affairs Health Care System, Sioux Falls, SD, p. A573

ACKLAND, Jeanne, Director of Finance, Fillmore County Hospital, Geneva, NE, p. A393

ACKLEY, Michael
Chief Financial Officer, Kentucky River Medical Center, Jackson, KY, p. A260
Chief Financial Officer, Three Rivers Medical Center, Louisa, KY, p. A262

ACKLIN, Traci M.D., Chief of Staff, Montgomery General Hospital, Montgomery, WV, p. A694

ACKMAN, Jeffrey D. M.D., Chief of Staff, Shriners Hospitals For Children–Chicago, Chicago, IL, p. A184

ACKMAN, Laura, Chief Operating Officer and Administrator, Essentia Health Northern Pines Medical Center, Aurora, MN, p. A335

ACOSTA, Ivan M.D., Medical Director, Hospital De La Concepcion, San German, PR, p. A725

ACOSTA, Louis M.D., Chief of Staff, Silver Lake Medical Center, Los Angeles, CA, p. A71

ACOSTA–CARLSON, Francisca M.D., Chief of Staff, Lexington Regional Health Center, Lexington, NE, p. A394

ACOSTA–CRUZ, Maridel, Chief Executive Officer, First Texas Hospital, Houston, TX, p. A620

ACREE, Charis L, Vice President and Chief Operating Officer, West Georgia Health, Lagrange, GA, p. A160

ADAIR, Dale K M.D., Chief Medical Officer, Wernersville State Hospital, Wernersville, PA, p. A553

ADAIR, Julie, Interim Corporate Chief Human Resources Officer, Fresno Heart And Surgical Hospital, Fresno, CA, p. A60

ADAIR–TRIPLETT, Alonna, Chief Nurse Executive, Claremore Indian Hospital, Claremore, OK, p. A506

ADAM, Sheryl, Chief Financial Officer, Hanover Hospital, Hanover, KS, p. A242

ADAMO, James D. M.D., Medical Director, Harbor Oaks Hospital, New Baltimore, MI, p. A327

ADAMO, Peter J.
Chief Executive Officer, Roxborough Memorial Hospital, Philadelphia, PA, p. A545
Chief Executive Officer, Suburban Community Hospital, Norristown, PA, p. A542
President and Chief Executive Officer, Waterbury Hospital, Waterbury, CT, p. A114

ADAMOLEKUN, Michelle
Chief Human Resource Officer, St. Vincent's Medical Center Riverside, Jacksonville, FL, p. A128
Vice President Human Resource Market Lead Florida/ Alabama Ministry Market, Sacred Heart Hospital Pensacola, Pensacola, FL, p. A139

ADAMS, Alan L., Administrator, Stilwell Memorial Hospital, Stilwell, OK, p. A516

ADAMS, Bob, Director Information Services, Bay Area Hospital, Coos Bay, OR, p. A521

ADAMS, Brian
President and CEO, Florida Hospital Tampa, Tampa, FL, p. A144
President and Chief Executive Officer, Florida Hospital At Connerton Long Term Acute Care, Land O'Lakes, FL, p. A130

ADAMS, Carla, Chief Nursing Officer, Northern Nevada Medical Center, Sparks, NV, p. A406

ADAMS, Cathleen, Chief Nursing Officer, Carepartners Health Services, Asheville, NC, p. A457

ADAMS, Charlotte, Director of Human Resources, Carolina Pines Regional Medical Center, Hartsville, SC, p. A563

ADAMS, Chris, Vice President Patient Care Services, Good Samaritan Regional Health Center, Mount Vernon, IL, p. A194

ADAMS, Cynthia, Vice President Human Resources, Tristar Stonecrest Medical Center, Smyrna, TN, p. A589

ADAMS, Denise, Human Resources Generalist, Wellmont Hancock County Hospital, Sneedville, TN, p. A589

ADAMS, Emmy
Chief Financial Officer, Mayhill Hospital, Denton, TX, p. A608
Chief Financial Officer, Provo Canyon Behavioral Hospital, Orem, UT, p. A658

ADAMS, Essie, Director of Nursing, Kedren Community Mental Health Center, Los Angeles, CA, p. A69

ADAMS, Felicia M MS, Chief Nursing Officer, Mid–Columbia Medical Center, The Dalles, OR, p. A527

ADAMS, Fiona, Interim Administrator, Southern Crescent Hospital For Specialty Care, Riverdale, GA, p. A163

ADAMS, Gini, Director Employee and Public Relations, Yuma District Hospital, Yuma, CO, p. A108

ADAMS, J'Dee, Chief Operating Officer, North Canyon Medical Center, Gooding, ID, p. A173

ADAMS, Jason, M.D.
Medical Staff President, Forest Health Medical Center, Ypsilanti, MI, p. A333
Chief Operating Officer, Christus St. Vincent Regional Medical Center, Santa Fe, NM, p. A428

ADAMS, Jennifer B, Chief Operating Officer and Chief Financial Officer, Lake City Medical Center, Lake City, FL, p. A129

ADAMS, Jo, Director Human Resources, Donalsonville Hospital, Donalsonville, GA, p. A156

ADAMS, Karen, Vice President Human Resources, Baxter Regional Medical Center, Mountain Home, AR, p. A47

ADAMS, Kimberly, Manager Human Resources, Carroll County Memorial Hospital, Carrollton, KY, p. A256

ADAMS, Lana, Chief Financial Officer, Lafayette General Medical Center, Lafayette, LA, p. A278

ADAMS, Laura L, Vice President, Finance, St. Vincent Anderson Regional Hospital, Anderson, IN, p. A203

ADAMS, Leslie, Chief Nursing Executive, Saint Joseph Berea, Berea, KY, p. A255

ADAMS, Mark A., President and Chief Executive Officer, Methodist Rehabilitation Center, Jackson, MS, p. A357

ADAMS, Mark B., Chief Executive Officer, Ogden Regional Medical Center, Ogden, UT, p. A658

ADAMS, Marlene J, Director Human Resources, Schneider Regional Medical Center, Saint Thomas, VI, p. A727

ADAMS, Marsha, Interim Director Human Resources, Texas Health Harris Methodist Hospital Cleburne, Cleburne, TX, p. A601

ADAMS, Martin D. CPA, Vice President Finance and Chief Financial Officer, Paris Community Hospital, Paris, IL, p. A197

ADAMS, Mary Jane R.N., MSN, Senior Vice President and Chief Nursing Officer, University Of Louisville Hospital, Louisville, KY, p. A264

ADAMS, Matthew, Administrator, Oklahoma State University Medical Center, Tulsa, OK, p. A517

ADAMS, Michael, Chief Operating Officer, Scottsdale Liberty Hospital, Scottsdale, AZ, p. A36

ADAMS, Mike M.D., Chief Medical Officer, Gateway Regional Medical Center, Granite City, IL, p. A189

ADAMS, Nancy D. R.N., Senior Vice President and Chief Operating Officer, Western Maryland Regional Medical Center, Cumberland, MD, p. A298

ADAMS, Norma, Director Human Resources, Southern Regional Medical Center, Riverdale, GA, p. A163

ADAMS, Patsy, Vice President Human Resources, Redmond Regional Medical Center, Rome, GA, p. A163

ADAMS, Renee, Director Information Technology, Chan Soon–Shiong Medical Center, Windber, PA, p. A554

ADAMS, Robert H. Jr, President, Hackensack Meridian Health Southern Ocean Medical Center, Manahawkin, NJ, p. A416

ADAMS, Robert H, Vice President Operations, Hackensack Meridian Health Jersey Shore University Medical Center, Neptune, NJ, p. A417

ADAMS, Robin, Director Human Resources, Reeves Memorial Medical Center, Bernice, LA, p. A271

ADAMS, Russell M.D., Chief Medical Officer, Unitypoint Health – Marshalltown, Marshalltown, IA, p. A231

ADAMS, Scott K., FACHE, Chief Executive Officer, Pullman Regional Hospital, Pullman, WA, p. A684

ADAMS, Shannon, Chief Financial Officer, Avera Holy Family Hospital, Estherville, IA, p. A227

ADAMS, Sharon, R.N.
Senior Vice President Patient Care Services and Chief Quality Officer, Mercy Medical Center, Springfield, MA, p. A311

Chief Nursing Officer, Danbury Hospital, Danbury, CT, p. A109

Chief Operating Officer, Danbury Hospital, Danbury, CT, p. A109

ADAMS, Shaun, Chief Financial Officer, Tennova Healthcare–Harton, Tullahoma, TN, p. A589

ADAMS, Shawn, Chief Financial Officer, Christus Southeast Texas Hospital, Beaumont, TX, p. A597

ADAMS, Shelah, Chief Executive Officer, Timberlawn Mental Health System, Dallas, TX, p. A607

ADAMS SULLIVAN, Martha, Chief Executive Officer, Nyc Health + Hospitals / Gouverneur, New York, NY, p. B93

ADAMS, Susan, Chief Nursing Officer and Chief Operating Officer, Specialty Hospital Of Lorain, Amherst, OH, p. A479

ADAMS, T Gard M.D., Chief of Staff, Caro Community Hospital, Caro, MI, p. A316

ADAMS, Tony, President, Barix Clinics Of Pennsylvania, Langhorne, PA, p. A538

ADAMSKI, Joseph, Chief Nursing Officer, Healthsouth Rehabilitation Hospital, Concord, NH, p. A407

ADAMSON, James, Chief Executive Officer, Mountain View Hospital, Idaho Falls, ID, p. A173

ADAMSON, Nancy, Chief Nursing Officer, Banner Del E. Webb Medical Center, Sun City West, AZ, p. A37

ADCOCK, Robert S., Chief Executive Officer, Fairmont Regional Medical Center, Fairmont, WV, p. A692

ADCOCK, William, Chief Financial Officer, Union General Hospital, Farmerville, LA, p. A274

ADDINGTON, Tom, Chief Information Officer, Saint Michael's Medical Center, Newark, NJ, p. A417

ADDISON, Holland M M.D., Medical Director, Select Specialty Hospital – Belhaven, Jackson, MS, p. A357

ADDISON, John Bruce D.O., Chief Medical Officer, Mccamey County Hospital District, Mccamey, TX, p. A632

ADDISON, Lenora, Vice President Patient Care and Nursing, Medstar Harbor Hospital, Baltimore, MD, p. A295

ADDISON, Lewis C, Senior Vice President and Chief Financial Officer, Centra Lynchburg General Hospital, Lynchburg, VA, p. A669

ADDLESPERGER, John D.O., Chief Medical Officer, Sheridan Memorial Hospital, Sheridan, WY, p. A719

ADDO, Deborah, Chief Executive Officer, Inova Loudoun Hospital, Leesburg, VA, p. A669

ADEMA, Carolyn, Vice President, Human Resources, St. Tammany Parish Hospital, Covington, LA, p. A273

ADEN, Susie, Director of IP Services, Pocahontas Community Hospital, Pocahontas, IA, p. A233

ADER, Michael H M.D., Vice President Medical Affairs, Hanover Hospital, Hanover, PA, p. A535

ADERS, Deb MS, R.N., Interim Chief Nursing Officer, Yuma Regional Medical Center, Yuma, AZ, p. A39

ADESSO, Patrick, Director Information Technology and Systems, Specialty Hospital Jacksonville, Jacksonville, FL, p. A128

ADKINS, Gary W., President, Parkview Noble Hospital, Kendallville, IN, p. A213

ADKINS, Gary W, Chief Executive Officer, Parkview Noble Hospital, Kendallville, IN, p. A213

ADKINS, Kedrick D., Chief Financial Officer, Mayo Clinic Hospital – Rochester, Rochester, MN, p. A346

ADKINS, Kevin, Director Human Resources, Medical City Green Oaks Hospital, Dallas, TX, p. A606

ADKINS, Melisa, Chief Executive Officer, Heartland Regional Medical Center, Marion, IL, p. A192

ADKINS, Michael, Chief Operating Officer, Houston Northwest Medical Center, Houston, TX, p. A621

ADKINS, Paige, Chief Financial Officer, Greenbrier Valley Medical Center, Ronceverte, WV, p. A696

ADKINS, Raymond, Chief Information Officer, Peninsula Regional Medical Center, Salisbury, MD, p. A301

ADKINS, Scott, Manager Information Technology, Vernon Memorial Healthcare, Viroqua, WI, p. A714

ADKINS, Tyler, Chief Financial Officer, Vaughan Regional Medical Center, Selma, AL, p. A23

ADLER, Josh M.D., Chief Medical Officer, Ucsf Medical Center, San Francisco, CA, p. A88

ADLER, Kenneth M.D., Medical Director, Arrowhead Behavioral Health Hospital, Maumee, OH, p. A495

ADLER, Maurita, Director Information Services, Gottlieb Memorial Hospital, Melrose Park, IL, p. A193

ADLESICH, John, Chief Executive Officer, South Big Horn County Hospital, Basin, WY, p. A717

ADMA, Vishal M.D., Medical Director, KVC Prairie Ridge Psychiatric Hospital, Kansas City, KS, p. A244

ADORNATO, Sara F., Executive Director, Barnes–Kasson County Hospital, Susquehanna, PA, p. A551

ADORNETTO–GARCIA, Debra MSN, R.N., Chief Nursing Officer, Banner Gateway Medical Center, Gilbert, AZ, p. A29

ADREAN, Christina
Chief Executive Officer, Pam Specialty Hospital Of Victoria North, Victoria, TX, p. A652

Chief Executive Officer, Pam Specialty Hospital Of Victoria South, Victoria, TX, p. A652

ADRIAANSE, Steven W, Vice President and Chief Human Resources Officer, Tallahassee Memorial Healthcare, Tallahassee, FL, p. A144

ADVEY, Linda, Manager Information Systems, Glenbeigh Hospital And Outpatient Centers, Rock Creek, OH, p. A498

AEMMER, Anthony, Director of Nursing, Wellstone Regional Hospital, Jeffersonville, IN, p. A213

AFABLE, Richard, M.D., M.P.H., Interim President and Chief Executive Officer, Mission Hospital, Mission Viejo, CA, p. A74

AFANEH, Bassam M.D., Chief of Staff, Deckerville Community Hospital, Deckerville, MI, p. A317

AFENYA, Kenneth M.D., Chief of Staff, Baptist Memorial Hospital–Tipton, Covington, TN, p. A578

AFIFI, Alaa Y M.D., Chief of Staff, Corona Regional Medical Center, Corona, CA, p. A56

AFLAK, Ziba, Chief Financial Officer, Kindred Hospital–San Francisco Bay Area, San Leandro, CA, p. A89

AFZAL, Muhammed M.D., Chief of Staff, Sutter Medical Center, Sacramento, Sacramento, CA, p. A84

AGANA, Ben M.D., Medical Director, Healthsouth Rehabilitation Hospital The Woodlands, Conroe, TX, p. A603

AGEE, Joan, Vice President Patient Care Services, St. Joseph Regional Medical Center, Lewiston, ID, p. A174

AGEE, Nancy Howell., President and Chief Executive Officer, Carilion Clinic, Roanoke, VA, p. B25

AGENBROAD, Connie, Chief Executive Officer, Othello Community Hospital, Othello, WA, p. A683

AGLOINGA, Roy, Chief Administrative Officer, Norton Sound Regional Hospital, Nome, AK, p. A26

AGNEW, Mary Christine R.N., MS, Vice President and Chief Nursing Officer, Reading Hospital, West Reading, PA, p. A553

AGNI, Guirish M.D., Chief of Staff, Stoughton Hospital Association, Stoughton, WI, p. A713

AGOSTINI, Irene M.D., Chief Medical Officer, University Of New Mexico Hospitals, Albuquerque, NM, p. A425

AGOSTO, Paula M R.N., MSN, Senior Vice President and Chief Nursing Officer, Children's Hospital Of Philadelphia, Philadelphia, PA, p. A543

AGRELA, Ramona, Associate Chancellor & Chief Human Resources Executive, Uc Irvine Medical Center, Orange, CA, p. A78

AGRESTI, Katie R.N., Director Patient Care Services, Lecom Health Millcreek Community Hospital, Erie, PA, p. A534

AGUAS, Hugo, Vice President Human Resources, Inova Alexandria Hospital, Alexandria, VA, p. A664

AGUILA, Marcos, Chief Executive Officer, Hospital San Francisco, San Juan, PR, p. A726

AGUILAR, Gretchen, Director Patient Care and Chief Nursing Officer, Three Rivers Hospital, Brewster, WA, p. A679

AGUILAR, Marisa, Chief Operating Officer, Valley Baptist Medical Center–Brownsville, Brownsville, TX, p. A599

AGUILERA, Louie, Director Information Technology, Foundation Surgical Hospital Of El Paso, El Paso, TX, p. A611

AGUILLARD, Clay, R.N., Administrator, Baton Rouge Behavioral Hospital, Baton Rouge, LA, p. A270

AGUINAGA, Miguel M.D., FACS, Medical Director, Advanced Care Hospital Of White County, Searcy, AR, p. A49

AGUIRRE, Jose M.D., Medical Director, Carson Tahoe Continuing Care Hospital, Carson City, NV, p. A401

AGUIRRE, Kim, Director Finance, Northern Cochise Community Hospital, Willcox, AZ, p. A38

AGWUNOBI, Andrew, M.D., Interim Chief Executive Officer, Uconn, John Dempsey Hospital, Farmington, CT, p. A110

AHAINE, Israel, Chief Nursing Officer, West Oaks Hospital, Houston, TX, p. A624

AHEARN, Patrick
Chief Operating Officer and Senior Vice President, Saint Barnabas Medical Center, Livingston, NJ, p. A415
Chief Operating Officer, Community Medical Center, Toms River, NJ, p. A421

AHL, Dennis, Director Information Technology, Jefferson Community Health And Life, Fairbury, NE, p. A392

AHLERS, Tim, Chief Operating Officer, Unitypoint Health – Finley Hospital, Dubuque, IA, p. A227

AHMAD, Shariq M.D., Chief of Staff, Baptist Hospitals Of Southeast Texas, Beaumont, TX, p. A597

AHMAD, Yousuf, Divisional Senior Vice President and Chief Network Transformation Officer, Mercy Health – Fairfield Hospital, Fairfield, OH, p. A491

AHMED, Ashraf M.D., Senior Vice President Physician and Hospital Services, Alliance Community Hospital, Alliance, OH, p. A479

AHMED, Bilal M.D., Medical Director, Wyoming County Community Hospital, Warsaw, NY, p. A455

ALLA, Vamseedhar M.D., Director Medical Staff, Connecticut Veterans Home And Hospital, Rocky Hill, CT, p. A112

ALLARD, Joan, Director Human Resources, Heart Of Florida Regional Medical Center, Davenport, FL, p. A123

ALLARD, Marie, Finance Manager, Brighton Center For Recovery, Brighton, MI, p. A315

ALLATT, Richard M.D., Medical Director, Healthsouth Nittany Valley Rehabilitation Hospital, Pleasant Gap, PA, p. A548

ALLBEE, Roger, Chief Executive Officer and Administrator, Grace Cottage Hospital, Townshend, VT, p. A663

ALLDREDGE, Kim, Director Human Resources, Lawrence County Memorial Hospital, Lawrenceville, IL, p. A192

ALLEE, Erin R.N., Director of Nursing, Royal Oaks Hospital, Windsor, MO, p. A381

ALLEMAN, Scott, Senior Vice President Patient Care Services and Chief Nursing Officer, Uw Medicine/Valley Medical Center, Renton, WA, p. A684

ALLEN, Audrey, Coordinator Benefits, Dallas County Medical Center, Fordyce, AR, p. A43

ALLEN, Brian M.D., President Medical Staff, Georgetown Community Hospital, Georgetown, KY, p. A258

ALLEN, Candice, Director of Nursing, Rio Grande Hospital, Del Norte, CO, p. A100

ALLEN, Carolyn, Vice President and Chief Financial Officer, Camden Clark Medical Center, Parkersburg, WV, p. A694

ALLEN, David B., Chief Executive Officer, Carle Richland Memorial Hospital, Olney, IL, p. A196

ALLEN, Dawn R.N., Chief Clinical Officer, Redwood Area Hospital, Redwood Falls, MN, p. A346

ALLEN, Devon M.D., Chief of Medical Staff, Samuel Simmonds Memorial Hospital, Barrow, AK, p. A25

ALLEN, Donald, Chief Operating Officer, Unity Medical & Surgical Hospital, Mishawaka, IN, p. A216

ALLEN, Jason
Chief Operating Officer, Brook Lane Health Services, Hagerstown, MD, p. A299
Director Patient Care Services, Brook Lane Health Services, Hagerstown, MD, p. A299

ALLEN, Jennifer, Vice President Human Resources, Plantation General Hospital, Plantation, FL, p. A140

ALLEN, John, Chief Information Officer, Holzer Medical Center, Gallipolis, OH, p. A491

ALLEN, Judy, Human Resource Specialist, Carl Albert Community Mental Health Center, Mcalester, OK, p. A510

ALLEN, Kandice K., R.N., Chief Executive Officer, Share Medical Center, Alva, OK, p. A504

ALLEN, Karen A R.N., Chief Nursing Officer, Butler Health System, Butler, PA, p. A530

ALLEN, Keith
Senior Vice President and Chief Human Resources Officer, Community Memorial Hospital, Menomonee Falls, WI, p. A706
Senior Vice President and Chief Human Resources Officer, Froedtert Memorial Lutheran Hospital, Milwaukee, WI, p. A708
Senior Vice President Human Resources, St. Joseph's Hospital, West Bend, WI, p. A715

ALLEN, Kent, Director Human Resources, West Branch Regional Medical Center, West Branch, MI, p. A333

ALLEN, Linda M, Vice President Human Resources, The Children's Institute Of Pittsburgh, Pittsburgh, PA, p. A547

ALLEN, Lori
Chief Financial Officer and Interim Chief Executive Officer, Anthony Medical Center, Anthony, KS, p. A238
Chief Financial Officer, Anthony Medical Center, Anthony, KS, p. A238

ALLEN, Lucretia, Director Human Resources, Sweetwater Hospital, Sweetwater, TN, p. A589

ALLEN, Mark, Chief Operating Officer, Marian Regional Medical Center, Santa Maria, CA, p. A91

ALLEN, Mary Beth, Vice President Human Resources, Emory University Hospital, Atlanta, GA, p. A150

ALLEN, Mike
Director Information Services, Shawnee Mission Medical Center, Shawnee Mission, KS, p. A252
Director Information Services, Shriners Hospitals For Children–Spokane, Spokane, WA, p. A687
Director Information Technology, Shriners Hospitals For Children–Salt Lake City, Salt Lake City, UT, p. A660

ALLEN, Myrna R.N., MS, Chief Operating and Nursing Officer, Martin Luther King, Jr. Community Hospital, Los Angeles, CA, p. A69

ALLEN, Nancy R.N., MS, Director, Patient Services and Chief Nursing Executive, Advocate Eureka Hospital, Eureka, IL, p. A187

ALLEN, Nikki, Patient Care Executive, Sutter Amador Hospital, Jackson, CA, p. A64

ALLEN, Patty, St. John's Vice President Finance, St. John's Hospital, Springfield, IL, p. A201

ALLEN, R Keith, Senior Vice President Human Resources, University Of Maryland Medical Center, Baltimore, MD, p. A296

ALLEN, Richard
Chief Executive Officer, Palmdale Regional Medical Center, Palmdale, CA, p. A78
Chief Executive Officer, Warren General Hospital, Warren, PA, p. A552

ALLEN, Rob, Chief Executive Officer, Sitka Community Hospital, Sitka, AK, p. A27

ALLEN, Robert
Chief Financial Officer, Keck Hospital Of Usc, Los Angeles, CA, p. A69
Chief Financial Officer, USC Norris Comprehensive Cancer Center, Los Angeles, CA, p. A71
Chief Financial Officer, USC Verdugo Hills Hospital, Glendale, CA, p. A62

ALLEN, Robin, Chief Executive Officer, The Hospital At Westlake Medical Center, Austin, TX, p. A596

ALLEN, Scott J, Director Human Resources, Hudson Hospital And Clinic, Hudson, WI, p. A704

ALLEN, Steve, M.D., Chief Executive Officer, Nationwide Children's Hospital, Columbus, OH, p. A487

ALLEN, Timothy J.
Chief Executive Officer, Leonard J. Chabert Medical Center, Houma, LA, p. A276
Chief Executive Officer, Ochsner St. Anne General Hospital, Raceland, LA, p. A284

ALLEN, Timothy M, Vice President Human Resources, United Hospital Center, Bridgeport, WV, p. A690

ALLEN, Vicki, R.N., MS
Vice President Patient Care Services and Chief Nursing Officer, Harnett Health System, Dunn, NC, p. A461
Chief Financial Officer, Chicot Memorial Medical Center, Lake Village, AR, p. A45

ALLEN, Wain M.D., Medical Director, Park City Hospital, Park City, UT, p. A659

ALLEN, Wayne, Chief Financial Officer, Mendocino Coast District Hospital, Fort Bragg, CA, p. A59

ALLEN, Zac CPA, Chief Financial Officer, Cherokee Medical Center, Centre, AL, p. A16

ALLEN–JOHNSON, Angela, Director Information Services, Ephraim Mcdowell Regional Medical Center, Danville, KY, p. A257

ALLENSWORTH, Ed M.D., Medical Director, Saint Francis Hospital Vinita, Vinita, OK, p. A519

ALLEY, David, Chief Financial Officer, Starr Regional Medical Center, Athens, TN, p. A575

ALLEY, John L., Chief Executive Officer, Woodlawn Hospital, Rochester, IN, p. A219

ALLEY, Jon D.O., President Medical Staff, Cameron Memorial Community Hospital, Angola, IN, p. A203

ALLEY, Steve B M.D., Chief of Staff, Crosbyton Clinic Hospital, Crosbyton, TX, p. A604

ALLGEIER, Patricia R.N., Chief Nursing Officer, Boys Town National Research Hospital, Omaha, NE, p. A397

ALLGOOD, Libby, Chief Financial Officer, Kittitas Valley Healthcare, Ellensburg, WA, p. A680

ALLICON, Keary T, Vice President Finance and Chief Financial Officer, Baystate Wing Hospital, Palmer, MA, p. A310

ALLIES, Karla, Director Human Resources, Rosebud Health Care Center, Forsyth, MT, p. A384

ALLINSON, Randy R.N., Chief Nursing Officer, Central Valley Medical Center, Nephi, UT, p. A658

ALLISON, David G., President and Chief Executive Officer, University Medical Center, Lubbock, TX, p. A631

ALLISON, Lorraine, Human Resource Partner, Peacehealth Peace Island Medical Center, Friday Harbor, WA, p. A681

ALLISON, Steve, Director Human Resources, Logan County Hospital, Oakley, KS, p. A248

ALLMAN, Rex M.D., President Medical Staff, Pulaski Memorial Hospital, Winamac, IN, p. A221

ALLORE, Gary, Chief Financial Officer, Mercy Health Hackley Campus, Muskegon, MI, p. A327

ALLPHIN, Allan M.D., Chief of Staff, Mercy Hospital Springfield, Springfield, MO, p. A379

ALLPORT, Jeff, Vice President, Chief Information Officer, Valley Presbyterian Hospital, Los Angeles, CA, p. A72

ALLRED, Al W, Chief Financial Officer, Florida Hospital New Smyrna, New Smyrna Beach, FL, p. A135

ALLRED, B Dee M.D., President Medical Staff, Jordan Valley Medical Center, West Jordan, UT, p. A661

ALLRED, Lowell C M.D., Chief of Staff, Columbia Basin Hospital, Ephrata, WA, p. A680

ALLRED, William M.D., Vice President Medical Affairs, St. John Medical Center, Tulsa, OK, p. A518

ALLSOP, Brian, Director Human Resources, Central Valley Medical Center, Nephi, UT, p. A658

ALLSTOTT, Patti, Administrative Coordinator Human Resources and Grant Writer, Pioneer Memorial Hospital, Heppner, OR, p. A522

ALLUMS, Allyson, Director Medical Records, North Caddo Medical Center, Vivian, LA, p. A287

ALLUSON, Valerie M.D., Chief Medical Officer, Hackensack Meridian Health Mountainside Medical Center, Montclair, NJ, p. A416

ALMAUHY, Deborah R.N., Chief Nursing Officer, Emory Rehabilitation Hospital, Atlanta, GA, p. A150

ALMEIDA, Sergio, Director Information Systems, West Houston Medical Center, Houston, TX, p. A623

ALMEIDA–SUAREZ, Mario M.D., Chief of Staff, Larkin Community Hospital, South Miami, FL, p. A143

ALMENDINGER, J Todd., President and Chief Executive Officer, Magruder Memorial Hospital, Port Clinton, OH, p. A498

ALMETER, Connie, Director of Nursing, Wyoming County Community Hospital, Warsaw, NY, p. A455

ALMODOVAR, Gustavo, Executive Director, Hospital De La Concepcion, San German, PR, p. A725

ALMOHAMMED, Salah, Chief of Staff, East Texas Medical Center Carthage, Carthage, TX, p. A601

ALO, Kathleen, Chief Nursing Officer, Mammoth Hospital, Mammoth Lakes, CA, p. A72

ALONSO, Gwen, Chief Nursing Officer, Florida Hospital Zephyrhills, Zephyrhills, FL, p. A148

ALONSO, Jose' M.D., Medical Director, San Juan Capestrano Hospital, San Juan, PR, p. A726

ALONZO, Patti, Manager Human Resources, Pacifica Hospital Of The Valley, Los Angeles, CA, p. A70

ALPERT, Jeffrey M.D., Medical Director, Wichita County Health Center, Leoti, KS, p. A245

ALPERT, Len, Director Human Resources, Larkin Behavioral Health Services, Hollywood, FL, p. A127

ALRASHEDY, Farhad H M.D., Chief Medical Officer, Ferry County Memorial Hospital, Republic, WA, p. A684

ALREDGE, William, Administrator and Chief Financial Officer, Genesis Behavioral Hospital, Breaux Bridge, LA, p. A272

ALSADON, Danielle, Clinic/Hospital Manager, Kenmare Community Hospital, Kenmare, ND, p. A477

ALSIP, Bryan M.D., Executive Vice President, Chief Medical Officer, University Health System, San Antonio, TX, p. A644

ALSTAD, Nancy, Director Human Resources, Fort Healthcare, Fort Atkinson, WI, p. A701

ALT, Melinda
Chief Financial Officer, Audubon County Memorial Hospital, Audubon, IA, p. A222
Chief Financial Officer, Guthrie County Hospital, Guthrie Center, IA, p. A228

ALTARAS, June
Chief Executive Officer, Swedish Medical Center–Cherry Hill Campus, Seattle, WA, p. A685
Chief Executive Officer, Swedish Medical Center–First Hill, Seattle, WA, p. A685

ALTEBARMAKIAN, Varouj M.D., Physician in Chief, Kaiser Permanente Fresno Medical Center, Fresno, CA, p. A61

ALTENBURGER, Andy
Chief Information Officer, Delta Regional Medical Center, Greenville, MS, p. A355
Chief Information Officer, Marietta Memorial Hospital, Marietta, OH, p. A494

ALTENDORF, Amanda, Chief Human Resources and Quality Management, Red River Behavioral Health System, Grand Forks, ND, p. A476

ALTHOEN, David, Director Financial Planning and Analysis, Forest Health Medical Center, Ypsilanti, MI, p. A333

ALTHOUSE, Douglas, Chief Medical Staff, Kearney County Health Services, Minden, NE, p. A396

ALTMAN, Alexander B III, Chief Financial Officer, Union County General Hospital, Clayton, NM, p. A425

ALTMAN, Angie, Director Human Resources, Shands Lake Shore Regional Medical Center, Lake City, FL, p. A130

ALTMAN, Brett, Chief Executive Officer, Cass County Memorial Hospital, Atlantic, IA, p. A222

ALTMAN, Deana, Interim Chief Nursing Officer, Harney District Hospital, Burns, OR, p. A520

ALTMAN, Harold M.D., Chief Medical Officer, Acmh Hospital, Kittanning, PA, p. A537

ALTOM, Andy, Chief Executive Officer, Methodist Behavioral Hospital Of Arkansas, Maumelle, AR, p. A47

ALTON, Aaron K., President and Chief Executive Officer, Sisters Of Mary Of The Presentation Health System, Fargo, ND, p. B118

ALTOSE, Murray M.D., Chief of Staff, Louis Stokes Cleveland Veterans Affairs Medical Center, Cleveland, OH, p. A486

ALTSHULER, Keith, President and Chief Administrative Officer, Fort Sanders Regional Medical Center, Knoxville, TN, p. A581

© 2017 AHA Guide

ALUISE, Tony, Chief Executive Officer, Three Gables Surgery Center, Proctorville, OH, p. A498

ALURI, Bapu M.D., Chief Medical Officer, Yuma Rehabilitation Hospital, Yuma, AZ, p. A39

ALVARADO, Felicita E., Administrator, Hospital Psiquiatrico Correccional, San Juan, PR, p. A726

ALVARADO, Rafael, Chief Executive Officer, Dr. Pila's Hospital, Ponce, PR, p. A724

ALVARADO, Ramona, Interim Manager Human Resources, Adventist Medical Center–Reedley, Reedley, CA, p. A82

ALVAREZ, Dena C R.N., COO & Chief Compliance Officer, Brodstone Memorial Hospital, Superior, NE, p. A400

ALVAREZ, Janie, Accounting Director, Cornerstone Regional Hospital, Edinburg, TX, p. A610

ALVAREZ, Jose M.D., Chief Medical Staff, Circles Of Care, Melbourne, FL, p. A132

ALVAREZ, Maria Charlotte M.D., Chief of Staff, Sheridan Community Hospital, Sheridan, MI, p. A330

ALVAREZ, Valerie, Executive Assistant, Adventist Medical Center–Reedley, Reedley, CA, p. A82

ALVERSON, Tammy S M.D., Chief of Staff, Coshocton Regional Medical Center, Coshocton, OH, p. A488

ALVES, Richard, Chief Financial Officer, Kaiser Permanente Fresno Medical Center, Fresno, CA, p. A61

ALVEY, Raymond, Chief Financial Officer, SSM Health Saint Louis University Hospital, Saint Louis, MO, p. A378

ALWARD, Dale, Chief Executive Officer, Twin County Regional Healthcare, Galax, VA, p. A668

ALWIN–POPP, Sue, Chief Clinical Officer, Edgerton Hospital And Health Services, Edgerton, WI, p. A701

ALWINE, Steven, Chief Executive Officer, Healthsouth Rehabilitation Hospital Of York, York, PA, p. A555

ALZEIN, Bashar M.D., President Medical Staff, Illini Community Hospital, Pittsfield, IL, p. A198

AMADO, Mitchell, Senior Vice President Finance and Chief Financial Officer, Glens Falls Hospital, Glens Falls, NY, p. A436

AMANTEA, Paul, Director Finance, University Hospitals Geauga Medical Center, Chardon, OH, p. A483

AMAR, Eugene Jr, Administrator, Kohala Hospital, Kohala, HI, p. A170

AMATO, Jerry, President and Chief Operating Officer, Lakeview Specialty Hospital And Rehabilitation Center, Waterford, WI, p. A714

AMBACHER, Linda, Interim Chief Nursing Officer, Hackettstown Medical Center, Hackettstown, NJ, p. A414

AMBERSON, Rosemarie, Vice President Human Resources, Aventura Hospital And Medical Center, Aventura, FL, p. A119

AMBROSE, Sherie, Chief Nurse Executive, Sequoia Hospital, Redwood City, CA, p. A82

AMBROSIANI, Michael, Chief Financial Officer, Knox Community Hospital, Mount Vernon, OH, p. A496

AMBROSINI, Joseph, Director Human Resources, Olympia Medical Center, Los Angeles, CA, p. A70

AMEEN, David J., Interim Chief Executive Officer, Coquille Valley Hospital, Coquille, OR, p. A521

AMENT, Arlinda K R.N., Interim Chief Nursing Officer, Beatrice Community Hospital And Health Center, Beatrice, NE, p. A391

AMENT, Rick, Chief Executive Officer, Robert J. Dole Veterans Affairs Medical Center, Wichita, KS, p. A253

AMERSON, Jeff, Director Information System, West Florida Hospital, Pensacola, FL, p. A139

AMES, Becky, Chief Executive Officer, Medical Center Of Southeast Texas, Beaumont, TX, p. A597

AMES, Laura, Chief Executive Officer, Healthsouth New England Rehabilitation Hospital, Woburn, MA, p. A313

AMIN, Saad, Medical Director Hospital, Kindred Hospital–Greensboro, Greensboro, NC, p. A463

AMIRNENI, Vamsee M.D., Chief of Staff, Mercy Allen Hospital, Oberlin, OH, p. A497

AMMAZZALORSO, Michael M.D., Chief Medical Officer, NYU Winthrop Hospital, Mineola, NY, p. A439

AMMONS, Eric, President, Mercy Hospital Jefferson, Crystal City, MO, p. A367

AMODO, Mitch, Vice President and Chief Financial Officer, Orange Regional Medical Center, Middletown, NY, p. A439

AMOROSE, Carl, Vice President Finance, Norton Hospital, Louisville, KY, p. A263

AMOROSO, Mitze, Chief Information Officer, Terence Cardinal Cooke Health Care Center, New Rochelle, NY, p. A447

AMOS, John
Chief Executive Officer, Yavapai Regional Medical Center – East, Prescott Valley, AZ, p. A35
President and Chief Executive Officer, Yavapai Regional Medical Center, Prescott, AZ, p. A35

AMOS, Robert, Vice President and Chief Financial Officer, Winchester Medical Center, Winchester, VA, p. A677

AMOX, Mark J., President and Chief Executive Officer, El Paso Children's Hospital, El Paso, TX, p. A610

AMROM, George M.D., Vice President Medical Affairs, Hahnemann University Hospital, Philadelphia, PA, p. A544

AMSBERRY, Shelly, Director of Nursing, Jennie M. Melham Memorial Medical Center, Broken Bow, NE, p. A391

AMSTUTZ, Charles, Director of Information Technology, Cascade Medical Center, Leavenworth, WA, p. A682

AMSTUTZ, Terry, Chief Executive Officer, Anson General Hospital, Anson, TX, p. A593

AMYX, Maleigha, Chief Information Officer, Rockcastle Regional Hospital And Respiratory Care Center, Mount Vernon, KY, p. A265

ANASTASI, Frank, Chief Financial Officer, Pennsylvania Hospital, Philadelphia, PA, p. A545

ANAYA, Sandra J., R.N., Chief Executive Officer, Palo Verde Hospital, Blythe, CA, p. A54

ANCHONDO, Laura, Administrator Human Resources, Kindred Hospital El Paso, El Paso, TX, p. A611

ANDERS, Anna, Vice President and Chief Nursing Officer, Carson Tahoe Health, Carson City, NV, p. A401

ANDERS, James M Jr, Administrator and Chief Operating Officer, Kennedy Krieger Institute, Baltimore, MD, p. A294

ANDERS, Mark, Administrator, Villa Feliciana Medical Complex, Jackson, LA, p. A276

ANDERS, Robert, Chief Financial Officer, Ouachita County Medical Center, Camden, AR, p. A41

ANDERSEN, Connie R.N., MS, Chief Nursing Officer, Sarasota Memorial Health Care System, Sarasota, FL, p. A142

ANDERSEN, Donia L, Director of Nursing, Centennial Peaks Hospital, Louisville, CO, p. A106

ANDERSEN, Frank, Interim Chief Medical Officer, Providence Regional Medical Center Everett, Everett, WA, p. A680

ANDERSEN, Janet
Chief Financial Officer, East Texas Medical Center Pittsburg, Pittsburg, TX, p. A637
Chief Financial Officer, East Texas Medical Center–Quitman, Quitman, TX, p. A639

ANDERSEN, John, Manager Information Systems, Sunnyside Community Hospital And Clinics, Sunnyside, WA, p. A687

ANDERSEN, Sue
Chief Financial Officer, French Hospital Medical Center, San Luis Obispo, CA, p. A89
Vice President and Service Area and Chief Financial Officer, Marian Regional Medical Center, Santa Maria, CA, p. A91

ANDERSEN, Toni R.N., Chief Nurse Executive, Kaiser Permanente Fontana Medical Center, Fontana, CA, p. A59

ANDERSEN, Tracy, Chief Information Officer, St. Mary's Regional Medical Center, Enid, OK, p. A507

ANDERSEN, Wendy, Director Human Resources, Eastern Idaho Regional Medical Center, Idaho Falls, ID, p. A173

ANDERSON, Allen
Chief Executive Officer, Avera Tyler Hospital, Tyler, MN, p. A349
Director Human Resources, Madison Healthcare Services, Madison, MN, p. A342

ANDERSON, Allyson, President, Legacy Meridian Park Medical Center, Tualatin, OR, p. A527

ANDERSON, Angela L, Director Human Resources, Newton Medical Center, Newton, KS, p. A247

ANDERSON, Angie, Director Information Technology, Crawford County Memorial Hospital, Denison, IA, p. A226

ANDERSON, Ashley, Manager Human Resources, Winona Health, Winona, MN, p. A350

ANDERSON, Barbara M., President and Chief Executive Officer, Franciscan St. Anthony Health – Crown Point, Crown Point, IN, p. A206

ANDERSON, Benjamin, Chief Executive Officer and Administrator, Kearny County Hospital, Lakin, KS, p. A244

ANDERSON, Brad, Chief Financial Officer, Community Memorial Hospital, Cloquet, MN, p. A338

ANDERSON, Brian
Chief Financial Officer, Capital Medical Center, Olympia, WA, p. A683
Chief Financial Officer, Simi Valley Hospital, Simi Valley, CA, p. A92

ANDERSON, Calandra, Vice President Patient Care and Chief Nursing Officer, Mclaren Oakland, Pontiac, MI, p. A328

ANDERSON, Charles, M.D.
Chief Medical Officer, Desert Regional Medical Center, Palm Springs, CA, p. A78
Market Chief Medical Officer, John F. Kennedy Memorial Hospital, Indio, CA, p. A63

ANDERSON, Cherri, Chief Nursing Officer, Banner Behavioral Health Hospital – Scottsdale, Scottsdale, AZ, p. A35

ANDERSON, Christine, Chief Nursing Officer and Vice President of Patient Care Services, Lincolnhealth, Damariscotta, ME, p. A290

ANDERSON, Conde Nevin M.D., Chief of Staff, Detar Healthcare System, Victoria, TX, p. A652

ANDERSON, Craig, Director Management Information Systems, River Bend Hospital, West Lafayette, IN, p. A221

ANDERSON, Dana, Administrator, Long–Term Acute Care Hospital, Mosaic Life Care At St. Joseph, Saint Joseph, MO, p. A376

ANDERSON, Darla, Chief Financial Officer, Ridgeview Sibley Medical Center, Arlington, MN, p. A335

ANDERSON, Dave FACHE, Vice President Administration, Carolinas Healthcare System Union, Monroe, NC, p. A467

ANDERSON, David, Chief Executive Officer, Jackson Purchase Medical Center, Mayfield, KY, p. A264

ANDERSON, Dawn, Chief Nursing Officer, Select Specialty Hospital–Sioux Falls, Sioux Falls, SD, p. A572

ANDERSON, Dianne J., MS, R.N., President and Chief Executive Officer, Lawrence General Hospital, Lawrence, MA, p. A307

ANDERSON, Donna K R.N., Chief Nursing Officer, Anmed Health Cannon, Pickens, SC, p. A565

ANDERSON, Duke, President and Chief Executive Officer, Hillsdale Hospital, Hillsdale, MI, p. A322

ANDERSON, Edwin M.D., Chief of Staff and Chief Medical Officer, Bigfork Valley Hospital, Bigfork, MN, p. A336

ANDERSON, Gaynell M.D., Medical Director, St. Anthony Shawnee Hospital, Shawnee, OK, p. A516

ANDERSON, Gina, Human Resources Officer, Riverview Regional Medical Center, Carthage, TN, p. A575

ANDERSON, Heidi, Chief Nursing Officer, Morton General Hospital, Morton, WA, p. A682

ANDERSON, Holly, Supervisor Human Resources, Sanford Rock Rapids Medical Center, Rock Rapids, IA, p. A234

ANDERSON, Jason, Chief Financial Officer, Mackinac Straits Health System, Inc., Saint Ignace, MI, p. A330

ANDERSON, Jay
President, Northwestern Medicine Kishwaukee Hospital, Dekalb, IL, p. A185
President, Northwestern Medicine Valley West Hospital, Sandwich, IL, p. A200

ANDERSON, Jimmy, Director of Information Systems, Tennova Healthcare Regional Hospital Of Jackson, Jackson, TN, p. A580

ANDERSON, Joann, President and Chief Executive Officer, Southeastern Health, Lumberton, NC, p. A466

ANDERSON, Jodie, Director Human Resources, Mitchell County Regional Health Center, Osage, IA, p. A233

ANDERSON, John D., FACHE, Administrator, Marshall Medical Center South, Boaz, AL, p. A15

ANDERSON, John G., FACHE
President and Chief Executive Officer, Anderson Regional Health System South, Meridian, MS, p. A359
President and Chief Executive Officer, Anderson Regional Health System, Meridian, MS, p. A359

ANDERSON, Jonathan, Medical Director, Western State Hospital, Staunton, VA, p. A676

ANDERSON, Kathleen, Director, Acute Clinical Systems, Greenville Health System – Laurens County Memorial Hospital, Clinton, SC, p. A560

ANDERSON, Kenneth M.D., Vice President and Chief Medical Officer, Baptist Health Louisville, Louisville, KY, p. A262

ANDERSON, Kimball S., FACHE, Chief Executive Officer, Timpanogos Regional Hospital, Orem, UT, p. A658

ANDERSON, Kristin, Director, Human Resources, California Hospital Medical Center, Los Angeles, CA, p. A67

ANDERSON, Libby, Chief Financial Officer, Satanta District Hospital And Long Term Care, Satanta, KS, p. A251

ANDERSON, Louis, Chief Financial Officer, Mcleod Health Cheraw, Cheraw, SC, p. A559

ANDERSON, Lucia E, Senior Vice President Operations and Chief Nurse Executive, Lake Region Healthcare, Fergus Falls, MN, p. A340

ANDERSON, Lynne, Chief Executive Officer, Stephens County Hospital, Toccoa, GA, p. A166

ANDERSON, Mark T, Chief Financial Officer, Sovah Health–Danville, Danville, VA, p. A666

ANDERSON, Mark, Chief Financial Officer, Lane Regional Medical Center, Zachary, LA, p. A288

ANDERSON, Michael Bruce Ph.D., Chief Operating Officer, Metropolitan St. Louis Psychiatric Center, Saint Louis, MO, p. A377

ANDERSON, Michael, M.D., President, Ucsf Medical Center, San Francisco, CA, p. A88

ANDERSON, Mickey M.D., Vice President Medical Affairs, Flaget Memorial Hospital, Bardstown, KY, p. A255

ANDERSON, Patricia, Chief Nursing Officer, Riverview Regional Medical Center, Carthage, TN, p. A575

ANDERSON, Patrick
Chief Information Officer and Senior Vice President, Hoag Memorial Hospital Presbyterian, Newport Beach, CA, p. A76
Chief Information Officer, Memorial Medical Center, Modesto, CA, p. A74

ANDERSON, Paula, Administrative Director Human Resources, Endless Mountain Health Systems, Montrose, PA, p. A541

ANDERSON, Randy, Chief Executive Officer, Canyon Vista Medical Center, Sierra Vista, AZ, p. A36

ANDERSON, Rhena
Chief Nursing Officer, Nexus Specialty Hospital The Woodlands, The Woodlands, TX, p. A649
Chief Nursing Officer, Nexus Specialty Hospital, Shenandoah, TX, p. A645

ANDERSON, Rhonda
Executive Vice President Finance and Chief Financial Officer, Columbia St. Mary's Hospital Milwaukee, Milwaukee, WI, p. A707
Executive Vice President Finance and Chief Financial Officer, Columbia St. Mary's Ozaukee Hospital, Mequon, WI, p. A707
Executive Vice President Finance and Chief Financial Officer, Sacred Heart Rehabilitation Institute, Milwaukee, WI, p. A708

ANDERSON, Rick M.D., Senior Vice President and Chief Medical Officer, TMC Healthcare, Tucson, AZ, p. A38

ANDERSON, Richard A., President and Chief Executive Officer, St. Luke'S University Health Network, Bethlehem, PA, p. B121

ANDERSON, Robert C, Interim Chief Financial Officer, Alameda Hospital, Alameda, CA, p. A51

ANDERSON, Robert G Jr, Executive Vice President and Chief Operating Officer, OSF Saint Francis Medical Center, Peoria, IL, p. A197

ANDERSON, Rohan, Chief Information Officer, Doctors Memorial Hospital, Bonifay, FL, p. A120

ANDERSON, Rosemary, Administrator, CCC At Pineview Hospital, Lakeside, AZ, p. A31

ANDERSON, Sandra L.
President and Chief Executive Officer, Howard Young Medical Center, Woodruff, WI, p. A716
President and Chief Executive Officer, Ministry Eagle River Memorial Hospital, Eagle River, WI, p. A700
President and Chief Executive Officer, Ministry Sacred Heart Hospital, Tomahawk, WI, p. A714
President and Chief Executive Officer, Ministry Saint Mary's Hospitals, Rhinelander, WI, p. A711

ANDERSON, Scott, Chief Medical Officer, Banner Del E. Webb Medical Center, Sun City West, AZ, p. A37

ANDERSON, Sharla, Chief Executive Officer, Christus Trinity Mother Frances Rehabilitation Hospital, Tyler, TX, p. A650

ANDERSON, Shawn, Chief Operating Officer, Cary Medical Center, Caribou, ME, p. A290

ANDERSON, Sims, Manager Facility Automation, Terrell State Hospital, Terrell, TX, p. A648

ANDERSON, Stephanie, Executive Vice President and Chief Operating Officer, Woman's Hospital, Baton Rouge, LA, p. A271

ANDERSON, Stephen, M.D.
Chief Medical Officer, Mishawaka Medical Center, Mishawaka, IN, p. A216
Chief Medical Officer, Plymouth Medical Center, Plymouth, IN, p. A218

ANDERSON, Steven
Chief Executive Officer, Jordan Valley Medical Center West Valley Campus, West Valley City, UT, p. A661
Chief Executive Officer, Jordan Valley Medical Center, West Jordan, UT, p. A661

ANDERSON, Susan, Director Information Systems, Texas Health Presbyterian Hospital Plano, Plano, TX, p. A638

ANDERSON, Suzanne P., Nurse Administrator, Intermountain Medical Center, Murray, UT, p. A658

ANDERSON, Terry R.N., Director of Nursing Services, Chippewa County–Montevideo Hospital, Montevideo, MN, p. A344

ANDERSON, Thomas, M.D.
Vice President Medical Affairs, Chambersburg Hospital, Chambersburg, PA, p. A531
Vice President Medical Affairs, Waynesboro Hospital, Waynesboro, PA, p. A553

ANDERSON, Thomas, Vice President Medical Affairs, Lakeview Hospital, Stillwater, MN, p. A349

ANDERSON, Tim, Controller, Van Matre Healthsouth Rehabilitation Hospital, Rockford, IL, p. A199

ANDERSON, Timothy Craig Jr, Chief Nursing Officer, Wellmont Bristol Regional Medical Center, Bristol, TN, p. A575

ANDERSON, Traci, Chief Financial Officer, Memorial Hospital, Seminole, TX, p. A645

ANDERSON, Valerie, Chief Nursing Officer, Select Specialty Hospital–Tri Cities, Bristol, TN, p. A575

ANDERSON, William M.D., Medical Director, Rosebud Health Care Center, Forsyth, MT, p. A384

ANDERT, Nancy, Director Human Resources, Murray County Medical Center, Slayton, MN, p. A348

ANDERT, Vicki, Chief Nursing Officer, Eureka Springs Hospital, Eureka Springs, AR, p. A42

ANDRADA, Sally, Chief Information Officer, Los Alamitos Medical Center, Los Alamitos, CA, p. A67

ANDRADE, Marise, Controller, Southern Inyo Healthcare District, Lone Pine, CA, p. A66

ANDRAE, Andrea, Chief Financial Officer, Blue Mountain Hospital, Lehighton, PA, p. A539

ANDRE, Katelyn, Human Resource Coordinator, Select Specialty Hospital–Macomb County, Mount Clemens, MI, p. A326

ANDRABI, Imran A., M.D., President and Chief Executive Officer, Thedacare, Inc., Appleton, WI, p. A552

ANDREAS, Ginger, Coordinator Personnel and Credentialing, El Campo Memorial Hospital, El Campo, TX, p. A610

ANDREAS, Lori
Chief Operating Officer, Johnson Memorial Health Services, Dawson, MN, p. A338
Director Patient Care Services, Johnson Memorial Health Services, Dawson, MN, p. A338

ANDREASEN, Raymond M.D., Chief Medical Officer–Inpatient, California Medical Facility, Vacaville, CA, p. A95

ANDRES, Chad, Chief Information Officer, Desert View Hospital, Pahrump, NV, p. A405

ANDRES, Elizabeth, Director Human Resources, Atascadero State Hospital, Atascadero, CA, p. A52

ANDRES, Leonidas M.D., Chief of Staff, Riceland Medical Center, Winnie, TX, p. A654

ANDRESEN, Daniel, Chief information Officer, Mercy Medical Center Merced, Merced, CA, p. A73

ANDREWS, Callie
Chief Operating Officer and Facility Compliance Officer, Wellstar Cobb Hospital, Austell, GA, p. A152
Chief Operating Officer, Eastside Medical Center, Snellville, GA, p. A165

ANDREWS, Carolle, Vice President, Interim Human Resources Officer, Uconn, John Dempsey Hospital, Farmington, CT, p. A110

ANDREWS, Charles, Director Information Technology, West Springs Hospital, Grand Junction, CO, p. A103

ANDREWS, David, Manager Information Systems, Chicot Memorial Medical Center, Lake Village, AR, p. A45

ANDREWS, Jim, Chief Financial Officer, North Okaloosa Medical Center, Crestview, FL, p. A122

ANDREWS, John M.D., Chief of Staff, East Texas Medical Center Tyler, Tyler, TX, p. A651

ANDREWS, Lisa, Director Human Resources, Lancaster Rehabilitation Hospital, Lancaster, PA, p. A538

ANDREWS, Maria R., MS, Director, Charlie Norwood Veterans Affairs Medical Center, Augusta, GA, p. A151

ANDREWS, Michael, Coordinator Information Systems, Harlan County Health System, Alma, NE, p. A390

ANDREWS, Michele, Chief Clinical Officer, Integrity Transitional Hospital, Denton, TX, p. A608

ANDREWS, Mike
Associate Administrator and Chief Operating Officer, OCH Regional Medical Center, Starkville, MS, p. A362
Associate Administrator and Chief Operating Officer, OCH Regional Medical Center, Starkville, MS, p. A362

ANDREWS, Paul
Chief Executive Officer, The Brook At Dupont, Louisville, KY, p. A263
Chief Executive Officer, The Brook Hospital – Kmi, Louisville, KY, p. A263

ANDREWS, Rebecca, Chief Financial Officer, Vibra Hospital Of Northern California, Redding, CA, p. A81

ANDREWS, Ryan, M.D.
Chief Medical Officer, Ministry Saint Clare's Hospital, Weston, WI, p. A715
Chief Medical Officer, Ministry Saint Michael's Hospital, Stevens Point, WI, p. A713

ANDREWS, Steve, Chief Financial Officer, Three Rivers Health, Three Rivers, MI, p. A332

ANDREWS, Sue E., Chief Financial Officer, O'Connor Hospital, Delhi, NY, p. A435

ANDREWS, Susan E., Chief Executive Officer, Touro Infirmary, New Orleans, LA, p. A283

ANDREWS, Terri, Director Information Technology, Alamance Regional Medical Center, Burlington, NC, p. A458

ANDRITSCH, Scott, Chief Financial Officer, Sullivan County Community Hospital, Sullivan, IN, p. A220

ANDRO, Ronald J., President and Chief Executive Officer, West Penn Hospital, Pittsburgh, PA, p. A548

ANDRUS, Helen
Chief Financial Officer, Providence Mount Carmel Hospital, Colville, WA, p. A679
Chief Financial Officer, Providence St. Joseph's Hospital, Chewelah, WA, p. A679
Chief Financial Officer, St. Luke's Rehabilitation Institute, Spokane, WA, p. A687

ANDRUS, Jonathon, Chief Executive Officer, Fairchild Medical Center, Yreka, CA, p. A97

ANDRUS, Terry W., President, East Alabama Medical Center, Opelika, AL, p. A22

ANDURSKY, John, Chief Financial Officer, Highlands Hospital, Connellsville, PA, p. A532

ANFINSON, Julie, Director Human Resources, Mercy Medical Center–Sioux City, Sioux City, IA, p. A235

ANGELI, Maribeth, Chief Nursing Officer, Tyler Memorial Hospital, Tunkhannock, PA, p. A552

ANGELL, Deborah, Chief Financial Officer, Syracuse Veterans Affairs Medical Center, Syracuse, NY, p. A453

ANGELL, Nancy, Associate Administrator Personnel, Sagamore Children's Hospital Psychiatric Center, Dix Hills, NY, p. A435

ANGELO, Gregory, Chief Fiscal Program, James J. Peters Veterans Affairs Medical Center, New Rochelle, NY, p. A442

ANGELO, Thomas, Chief Executive Officer, Centra Southside Community Hospital, Farmville, VA, p. A667

ANGELUCCI, Patricia A MS, R.N., Director Patient Care Services, Thedacare Medical Center–Shawano, Shawano, WI, p. A712

ANGERAMI, Deborah
Chief Operating Officer, Health First Community Hospitals, Health First Cape Canaveral Hospital, Cocoa Beach, FL, p. A122
Chief Operating Officer, Health First Community Hospitals, Health First Palm Bay Hospital, Palm Bay, FL, p. A138
Chief Operating Officer, Health First Viera Hospital, Melbourne, FL, p. A132

ANGERMEIER, Elizabeth, Director of Nursing, Evansville Psychiatric Children Center, Evansville, IN, p. A207

ANGLE, Mary Ann R.N., FACHE, Chief Nursing Officer, Tristar Summit Medical Center, Hermitage, TN, p. A580

ANGLIN, Jason, Chief Executive Officer, Memorial Medical Center, Port Lavaca, TX, p. A639

ANGUS, Jolyn M R.N., Chief Nursing Officer, Miami Valley Hospital, Dayton, OH, p. A489

ANISKO RYAN, Karen, Director Business Development and Communications, Uc San Diego Health, San Diego, CA, p. A86

ANKIN, Michael G M.D., Vice President Medical Affairs & Chief Medical Officer, Northwestern Medicine Lake Forest Hospital, Lake Forest, IL, p. A192

ANMUTH, Craig M.D., Medical Director, Bacharach Institute For Rehabilitation, Pomona, NJ, p. A419

ANNARINO, Phillip, Vice President Human Resources, Fisher–Titus Medical Center, Norwalk, OH, p. A497

ANNARUMO, Beverly, R.N., MSN, President, Ellwood City Hospital, Ellwood City, PA, p. A534

ANNECHARICO, Mary Alice
System Vice President and Chief Information Officer, Henry Ford Hospital, Detroit, MI, p. A318
System Vice President and Chief Information Officer, Henry Ford West Bloomfield Hospital, West Bloomfield, MI, p. A333
System Vice President and Chief Information Officer, Henry Ford Wyandotte Hospital, Wyandotte, MI, p. A333

ANNESSER, Sue, Director Information Systems, Freeman Neosho Hospital, Neosho, MO, p. A374

ANOLIK, Adam, Chief Financial Officer, Highland Hospital, Rochester, NY, p. A450

ANSALDO, Luanne, Chief Operating Officer, Aventura Hospital And Medical Center, Aventura, FL, p. A119

ANSELL, David A M.D., Senior Vice President Clinical Affairs and Chief Medical Officer, Rush University Medical Center, Chicago, IL, p. A183

ANSELMA, M, Chief Operating Officer, OSF Saint Anthony's Health Center, Alton, IL, p. A177

ANSHUTZ, Margie, Chief Development Officer, Hamilton Center, Terre Haute, IN, p. A220

ANSI, Azena, Manager Health Information Management, Horizon Specialty Hospital, Las Vegas, NV, p. A403

ANSLEY, Pamela, Director Finance, Sutter Center For Psychiatry, Sacramento, CA, p. A84

ANTCZAK, Kenneth, Vice President Human Resources, St. Mary Mercy Hospital, Livonia, MI, p. A325

ANTES, John, President, Missouri Baptist Medical Center, Saint Louis, MO, p. A377

ANTHONY, Ashley, R.N., Chief Executive Officer, Delta Memorial Hospital, Dumas, AR, p. A42

ANTHONY, Jean, R.N., President and Chief Executive Officer, Hills & Dales General Hospital, Cass City, MI, p. A316

ANTHONY, Kim, Director Human Resources, Burke Medical Center, Waynesboro, GA, p. A167

ANTHONY, Mark, Executive Vice President and Chief Operating Officer, Borgess Medical Center, Kalamazoo, MI, p. A324

ANTHONY, Michelle, Chief Nursing Officer, Healthsouth Rehabilitation Hospital Of Virginia, Richmond, VA, p. A673

ANTHONY, Paula
Vice President Information Services, East Texas Medical Center Pittsburg, Pittsburg, TX, p. A637
Vice President Information Services, East Texas Medical Center Rehabilitation Hospital, Tyler, TX, p. A650
Vice President Information Services, East Texas Medical Center Specialty Hospital, Tyler, TX, p. A651
Vice President Information Services, East Texas Medical Center Tyler, Tyler, TX, p. A651

ANTHONY, Sharon
Chief Executive Officer, Select Specialty Hospital–Phoenix, Phoenix, AZ, p. A34
Market Administrator, Select Specialty Hospital–Phoenix Downtown, Phoenix, AZ, p. A34

ANTINELLI, Mark, Manager Human Resources, Syracuse Veterans Affairs Medical Center, Syracuse, NY, p. A453

ANTINORI, James M.D., Chief of Staff, Mountain West Medical Center, Tooele, UT, p. A661

ANTLE, Sue, Director of Nursing, Casey County Hospital, Liberty, KY, p. A262

ANTOINE, Greg M.D., Chief of Staff, Fayetteville Veterans Affairs Medical Center, Fayetteville, NC, p. A462

ANTON, Lourdes, Director Human Resources, Palm Springs General Hospital, Hialeah, FL, p. A126

ANTONACCI, Amy MSN, R.N., Vice President Nursing Services, Alliance Community Hospital, Alliance, OH, p. A479

ANTONECCHIA, Paul M.D., Vice President Medical Affairs and Chief Medical Officer, St. John's Riverside Hospital, Yonkers, NY, p. A456

ANTONSON, Pete, Chief Executive Officer, Northwood Deaconess Health Center, Northwood, ND, p. A477

ANTONUCCI, Lawrence, M.D.
Chief Operating Officer, Lee Memorial Hospital, Fort Myers, FL, p. A125
Chief Executive Officer, Cape Coral Hospital, Cape Coral, FL, p. A121
President and Chief Executive Officer, Gulf Coast Medical Center, Fort Myers, FL, p. A125

ANTRUM, Sheila R.N., President, Ucsf Medical Center, San Francisco, CA, p. A88

ANTRUM, Vi–Anne, Chief Nursing Officer, Olean General Hospital, Olean, NY, p. A448

ANUSZKIEWICZ, Dawn, Chief Executive Officer, Psychiatric Pavilion New Orleans, New OrleansOchsner Medical Center, New Orleans, LA, p. A283

ANWAR, Muhammad M.D., Chief Medical Officer, Encino Hospital Medical Center, Los Angeles, CA, p. A68

ANYASO, Vanessa, Chief Human Resources, Tomball Regional Medical Center, Tomball, TX, p. A650

ANZURES, Rosey, Acting Chief Financial Officer, Central Texas Veterans Health Care System, Temple, TX, p. A648

APIKI, Zessica L, Accountant, Molokai General Hospital, Kaunakakai, HI, p. A170

APLAND, Wendy, Interim Chief Financial Officer, Peacehealth Sacred Heart Medical Center University District, Eugene, OR, p. A521

APOLINAR, Adam, Chief Nursing Officer, Uvalde Memorial Hospital, Uvalde, TX, p. A651

APOLIONA, Nicole M.D., Medical Director, Kula Hospital, Kula, HI, p. A170

APONTE, Miguel, Supervisor Management Information Systems, Wilma N. Vazquez Medical Center, Vega Baja, PR, p. A727

APPEL, Sheril, Chief Executive Officer, Healthsouth Rehabilitation Hospital Of Arlington, Arlington, TX, p. A593

APPENHEIMER, A. Timothy M.D., Vice President and Chief Medical Officer, Katherine Shaw Bethea Hospital, Dixon, IL, p. A185

APPLEBAUM, Jon D., President and Chief Operating Officer, Novant Health Thomasville Medical Center, Thomasville, NC, p. A471

APPLEGATE, MaryJane, Chief Clinical Officer, Knoxville Hospital & Clinics, Knoxville, IA, p. A230

APPLEGEET, Carol MSN, R.N., Vice President and Chief Nursing Officer, Fort Hamilton Hospital, Hamilton, OH, p. A492

APPLETON, Joe M.D., Chief of Surgery, Milan General Hospital, Milan, TN, p. A585

APRILE, Patricia, Chief Operating Officer, Southern Maine Health Care – Biddeford Medical Center, Biddeford, ME, p. A290

AQUILINA, Anthony, D.O.
Chief Medical Officer, Geisinger–Community Medical Center, Scranton, PA, p. A550
Regional President, Geisinger Wyoming Valley Medical Center, Wilkes Barre, PA, p. A554
Regional President, Geisinger–Community Medical Center, Scranton, PA, p. A550

AQUILINA, Anthony , D.O.

AQUILINA, Joanne, Vice President Finance and Chief Financial Officer, Bethesda Hospital East, Boynton Beach, FL, p. A120

AQUILINA, Salvatore, Chief Executive Officer, Pam Specialty Hospital Of Wilkes–Barre, Wilkes Barre, PA, p. A554

ARABIT, Aleen D.
Chief Executive Officer, Kindred Hospital–Houston Northwest, Houston, TX, p. A621
Executive Director, Kindred Hospital–Houston Northwest, Houston, TX, p. A621

ARAD, Lana
Chief Financial Officer, Good Samaritan Hospital, San Jose, CA, p. A88
Chief Financial Officer, Mountainview Hospital, Las Vegas, NV, p. A403

ARAGON, Juliette, Finance Director, Turquoise Lodge Hospital, Albuquerque, NM, p. A425

ARAKELIAN, Armen
Chief Information Officer, Fulton County Medical Center, Mc Connellsburg, PA, p. A540
Chief Information Officer, J. C. Blair Memorial Hospital, Huntingdon, PA, p. A536

ARAMBULA, Frank, Chief Financial Officer, Arrowhead Regional Medical Center, Colton, CA, p. A56

ARANDA, Heather R R.N., MSN, Chief Nursing Officer, F. W. Huston Medical Center, Winchester, KS, p. A254

ARANIO, Lani, Regional Director Human Resources, Samuel Mahelona Memorial Hospital, Kapaa, HI, p. A170

ARATOW, Michael M.D., Chief Information Officer, San Mateo Medical Center, San Mateo, CA, p. A89

ARAUJO, Marianne D R.N., Ph.D., FACHE, Vice President Nursing and Chief Nurse Executive, Advocate Good Shepherd Hospital, Barrington, IL, p. A178

ARAUJO, Markeeta, Chief Nursing Officer, Desert View Hospital, Pahrump, NV, p. A405

ARBAUGH, Ronnie, Director Human Resources, Grant Memorial Hospital, Petersburg, WV, p. A695

ARBON, Don, Vice President Finance, Mid–Columbia Medical Center, The Dalles, OR, p. A527

ARBON, Terron R.N., Chief Nursing Officer, Salt Lake Regional Medical Center, Salt Lake City, UT, p. A660

ARMADA, Anthony A., Chief Executive Officer, Swedish/Issaquah, Issaquah, WA, p. B104

ARMAND, Sandra, Director, Lafayette General Medical Center, Lafayette, LA, p. A278

ARMATO, Carl S., President and Chief Executive Officer, Novant Health, Winston Salem, NC, p. B92

ARMBRUSTER, Kent A W M.D., Vice President Medical Affairs, Little Company Of Mary Hospital And Health Care Centers, Evergreen Park, IL, p. A187

ARMBRUSTER, Rebecca M.D., Chief Medical Officer, Jeanes Hospital, Philadelphia, PA, p. A544

ARMFIELD, Ben
Associate Administrator, Fresno Heart And Surgical Hospital, Fresno, CA, p. A60
Chief Financial Officer, Fresno Heart And Surgical Hospital, Fresno, CA, p. A60

ARMISTEAD, Russell, Chief Executive Officer, Uf Health Jacksonville, Jacksonville, FL, p. A128

ARMOUR, John, Chief Financial Officer, Bayshore Medical Center, Pasadena, TX, p. A636

ARMOUR, Meri, President, Methodist Healthcare Memphis Hospitals, Memphis, TN, p. A585

ARMSTRONG, Alan M.D., Chief Medical Officer, Pine Rest Christian Mental Health Services, Grand Rapids, MI, p. A321

ARMSTRONG, Deborah, Chief Executive Officer, Piedmont Henry Hospital, Stockbridge, GA, p. A165

ARMSTRONG, Evelyn, Chief Nursing Officer, Healthsouth Rehabilitation Hospital Of Erie, Erie, PA, p. A534

ARMSTRONG, Gary, Executive Vice President, Methodist Rehabilitation Center, Jackson, MS, p. A357

ARMSTRONG, James, Manager Information Technology, UHS Delaware Valley Hospital, Walton, NY, p. A454

ARMSTRONG, Jeffery CPA, Chief Financial Officer, Granville Health System, Oxford, NC, p. A468

ARMSTRONG, Jeremy, FACHE, Chief Executive Officer, Mitchell County Hospital Health Systems, Beloit, KS, p. A239

ARMSTRONG, Kim, Chief Financial Officer, Windom Area Hospital, Windom, MN, p. A350

ARMSTRONG, Kyle, President, Baylor Medical Center At Mckinney, Mckinney, TX, p. A632

ARMSTRONG, Lori R.N., MSN, Chief Nursing Officer, Kaiser Permanente Santa Clara Medical Center, Santa Clara, CA, p. A90

ARMSTRONG, Mark M.D., Medical Director, Baylor Medical Center At Uptown, Dallas, TX, p. A604

ARMSTRONG, Neil G FACHE, Vice President and Chief Operating Officer, Divine Providence Hospital, Williamsport, PA, p. A554

ARMSTRONG, Robert, Senior Vice President and Chief Operating Officer, Lima Memorial Health System, Lima, OH, p. A493

ARMSTRONG, Roger
Interim Chief Financial Officer, Pioneers Memorial Healthcare District, Brawley, CA, p. A54
Vice President Finance and Chief Financial Officer, Unitypoint Health – Proctor, Peoria, IL, p. A197

ARMSTRONG, William C
Senior Vice President and Chief Financial Officer, Mercy Medical Center, Rockville Centre, NY, p. A451
Vice President and Chief Financial Officer, St. Francis Hospital, The Heart Center, Roslyn, NY, p. A451

ARMSTRONG–HUFF, Glenda, Assistant Superintendent, Texas Center For Infectious Disease, San Antonio, TX, p. A644

ARNAU, Barbara R.N., Chief Nursing Officer, Chestatee Regional Hospital, Dahlonega, GA, p. A156

ARNDELL, Scott, Chief Financial Officer, Twin Lakes Regional Medical Center, Leitchfield, KY, p. A260

ARNER, Steven C.
Executive Vice President of Administration, Carilion Franklin Memorial Hospital, Rocky Mount, VA, p. A675
President, Carilion Roanoke Memorial Hospital, Roanoke, VA, p. A675
President, Carilion Roanoke Memorial Hospital, Roanoke, VA, p. A675

ARNESON, Brenda, Administrative Assistant, St. Andrew's Health Center, Bottineau, ND, p. A474

ARNESON, Garrett FACHE, R.N., Chief Operating Officer, Acuity Specialty Hospital Of Southern New Jersey, Willingboro, NJ, p. A423

ARNETT, Charlene, Chief Executive Officer, Montevista Hospital, Las Vegas, NV, p. A403

ARNETT, Jacob, Chief Information Technology Officer, Lakeside Behavioral Health System, Memphis, TN, p. A584

ARNETT, James, Vice President Human Resources, Unitypoint Health Meriter, Madison, WI, p. A705

ARNETT, Randal M., President and Chief Executive Officer, Southern Ohio Medical Center, Portsmouth, OH, p. A498

ARNETT, Sallie, Vice President Information Systems, Licking Memorial Hospital, Newark, OH, p. A497

ARNETT, Stuart
Regional Vice President Finance, Aurora Lakeland Medical Center, Elkhorn, WI, p. A701
Vice President Finance and Chief Financial Officer, Aurora Memorial Hospital Of Burlington, Burlington, WI, p. A699

ARNHART, Carol, Vice President Finance and Chief Financial Officer, Siskin Hospital For Physical Rehabilitation, Chattanooga, TN, p. A576

ARNOLD, Ann M.D., Medical Director, Medical City Plano, Plano, TX, p. A638

ARNOLD, Bill, President and Chief Executive Officer, Monmouth Medical Center, Long Branch Campus, Long Branch, NJ, p. A415

ARNOLD, Dustin D.O., Chief Medical Officer, Unitypoint Health – St. Luke's Hospital, Cedar Rapids, IA, p. A223

ARNOLD, Jeffrey M.D., Chief Medical Officer, Santa Clara Valley Medical Center, San Jose, CA, p. A89

ARNOLD, Kimberly N R.N., Chief Nursing Officer and Interim Chief Quality Officer, Alliancehealth Woodward, Woodward, OK, p. A519

ARNOLD, Leslie, Chief Executive Officer and Administrator, Chi St. Vincent Morrilton, Morrilton, AR, p. A47

ARNOLD, Scott, Senior Vice President Information Systems, Tampa General Hospital, Tampa, FL, p. A145

ARNOW, Debra R.N., VP Patient Care & Chief Nursing Officer, Children's Hospital And Medical Center, Omaha, NE, p. A397

ARNTZ, Mary, Manager Business Office and Executive Assistant, Physicians' Medical Center, New Albany, IN, p. A217

AROCHA, Joe, Chief of Staff, Alleghany Memorial Hospital, Sparta, NC, p. A471

AROCHO, Jacqueline, Administrator, Baycare Alliant Hospital, Dunedin, FL, p. A124

AROLA, Denise, Chief Financial Officer, Memorial Regional Health, Craig, CO, p. A100

ARORA, Gaurau M.D., Chief Medical Officer, Indiana University Health Tipton Hospital, Tipton, IN, p. A220

ARORA, Pamela
Senior Vice President and Chief Information Officer, Children's Medical Center Plano, Plano, TX, p. A638
Senior Vice President Information Systems, Children's Health System Of Texas, Dallas, TX, p. A605

ARORA, Sat M.D., President Medical and Dental Staff, Crozer–Chester Medical Center, Upland, PA, p. A552

ARRANTS, Diane, Chief Information Officer, Kershawhealth, Camden, SC, p. A558

ARROGANTE, Revelyn M.D., Medical Director, Northern Colorado Rehabilitation Hospital, Johnstown, CO, p. A104

ARROWOOD, Al, Interim President, Washington County Hospital, Plymouth, NC, p. A468

ARROWOOD, Melina, Interim President and Chief Nursing Officer, Transylvania Regional Hospital, Brevard, NC, p. A458

ARROYO, Luis A
  Chief Financial Officer, Hima San Pablo Caguas, Caguas, PR, p. A722
  Chief Financial Officer, Hospital Hima De Humacao, Humacao, PR, p. A723
  Chief Financial Officer, Hospital San Pablo Del Este, Fajardo, PR, p. A723

ARSENAULT, Lisa, Vice President Human Resources and Compliance, Millinocket Regional Hospital, Millinocket, ME, p. A292

ARSLANPAY, Robin F, Director Human Resources, Lifecare Hospitals Of Pittsburgh, Pittsburgh, PA, p. A546

ARSURA, Edward M.D., Chief Medical Officer, Richmond University Medical Center, New Rochelle, NY, p. A446

ARTENSTEIN, Andrew M.D., Chief Physician Executive, Chief Academic Officer and President, Baystate Medical Practices, Baystate Medical Center, Springfield, MA, p. A311

ARTERBURN, Catherine T R.N., Vice President Human Resources, Sidney Regional Medical Center, Sidney, NE, p. A400

ARTHUR, John
  Chief Financial Officer, St. Vincent Mercy Hospital, Elwood, IN, p. A207
  Chief Financial Officer, St. Vincent Randolph Hospital, Winchester, IN, p. A221

ARTHUR, Lawrence J., President, Rural Community Hospitals Of America, Kansas City, MO, p. B109

ARTHUR, Rita K, Director Human Resources, Littleton Adventist Hospital, Littleton, CO, p. A105

ARTILES, Nemuel O., FACHE, Administrator, Hospital De Psiquiatria Forense, Ponce, PR, p. A725

ARTIS, Cornelius M.D., Chief Medical Officer, Our Community Hospital, Scotland Neck, NC, p. A470

ARTMAN, David S, Chief Operating Officer, Weirton Medical Center, Weirton, WV, p. A696

ARTS–STRENKE, Cindy R.N., Chief Operating Officer and Chief Nursing Officer, Lakeview Medical Center, Rice Lake, WI, p. A711

ARUNAMATA, Peti, Interim Area Director Information Technology, Kaiser Permanente San Francisco Medical Center, San Francisco, CA, p. A87

ARVIDSON, Betty, Chief Financial Officer, Riverview Health, Crookston, MN, p. A338

ARVIN, Douglas, Vice President Finance and Chief Financial Officer, Wellstar Kennestone Hospital, Marietta, GA, p. A161

ARVIN, Jon A M.D., Chief Medical Officer, Rockcastle Regional Hospital And Respiratory Care Center, Mount Vernon, KY, p. A265

ARVON, Christina, Administrator and Chief Executive Officer, Charleston Surgical Hospital, Charleston, WV, p. A691

ARZE, Steven M.D., Chief Medical Officer and Vice President Medical Affairs, Baylor Medical Center At Garland, Garland, TX, p. A616

ASADA, Bonnie, Chief Nursing Officer, Alvarado Parkway Institute Behavioral Health System, La Mesa, CA, p. A64

ASAFTEI, Laura, Administrative Director, Florida Hospital Zephyrhills, Zephyrhills, FL, p. A148

ASAOKA, Danny
  Executive Director Information Systems, Long Beach Memorial Medical Center, Long Beach, CA, p. A66
  Executive Director Information Systems, Miller Children's & Women's Hospital Long Beach, Long Beach, CA, p. A67

ASBERRY, James, Chief Executive Officer, Post Acute/Warm Springs Specialty Hospital Of San Antonio, San Antonio, TX, p. A643

ASBURY, Wesley M.D., President Medical Staff, Princeton Community Hospital, Princeton, WV, p. A695

ASCHOFF, Jodi, Chief Financial Officer, Osmond General Hospital, Osmond, NE, p. A398

ASH, Michael A, Chief Transformation Officer, Nebraska Medicine – Nebraska Medical Center, Omaha, NE, p. A397

ASH, Richard M., Chief Executive Officer, United Hospital District, Blue Earth, MN, p. A336

ASHBY, F Michael M.D., Vice President and Medical Director, Martha Jefferson Hospital, Charlottesville, VA, p. A665

ASHBY, Fred, Director Information Technology, Fort Washington Medical Center, Oxen Hill, MD, p. A300

ASHBY, Kim, Vice President of Finance, Baptist Health Madisonville, Madisonville, KY, p. A264

ASHBY, Pamela, Vice President Human Resources, Medstar National Rehabilitation Hospital, Washington, DC, p. A117

ASHCOM, Thomas L., M.D., Ph.D., Chief Executive Officer, Kansas Heart Hospital, Wichita, KS, p. A253

ASHENFELTER, Kathy, Chief Financial Officer, Swedish Medical Center, Englewood, CO, p. A102

ASHLEY, Ada, HIM Director, Lifebrite Community Hospital Of Stokes, Danbury, NC, p. A460

ASHLEY, Dennis H
  Vice President Human Resources, Montefiore Mount Vernon, Mount Vernon, NY, p. A440
  Vice President Human Resources, Montefiore New Rochelle, New Rochelle, NY, p. A440

ASHLEY, Kent, Chief Financial Officer, Mesa Springs, Fort Worth, TX, p. A614

ASHLEY, Sharon MSN, Chief Nursing Officer, Adams County Regional Medical Center, Seaman, OH, p. A499

ASHLEY, Stanley M.D., Senior Vice President Medical Affairs and Chief Medical Officer, Brigham And Women's Hospital, Boston, MA, p. A303

ASHRAF, Mirza M.D., Medical Director, Carthage Area Hospital, Carthage, NY, p. A434

ASHTON, Michael, Administrator, Bayhealth Medical Center, Dover, DE, p. A115

ASHWORTH, Fred, Chief Financial Officer, Regional Medical Center Of San Jose, San Jose, CA, p. A88

ASHWORTH, James M.D., Medical Director, University Of Utah Neuropsychiatric Institute, Salt Lake City, UT, p. A661

ASIC, Jason, Chief Operating Officer, Mercy Health – West Hospital, Cincinnati, OH, p. A484

ASKEW, Pam R.N., Vice President Patient Care Services, Unitypoint Health – Trinity Muscatine, Muscatine, IA, p. A232

ASKINAZI, Murray, Senior Vice President and Chief Financial Officer, New York–Presbyterian/Lawrence Hospital, Bronxville, NY, p. A432

ASKINS, Stephen M.D., Chief of Staff, Lake City Community Hospital, Lake City, SC, p. A564

ASLIN, Judy MSN, R.N., Vice President and Chief Nursing Officer, Southeast Hospital, Cape Girardeau, MO, p. A366

ASNEN, Mark, Chief Executive Officer, Trihealth Rehabilitation Hospital, Cincinnati, OH, p. A485

ASPEL, Tracy, Chief Nursing Officer, Northern Inyo Hospital, Bishop, CA, p. A54

ASPLIN, Iain, Chief Medical Officer, Multicare Mary Bridge Children's Hospital And Health Center, Tacoma, WA, p. A687

ASPLUND, David, Chief Operating Officer, Motion Picture And Television Fund Hospital And Residential Services, Los Angeles, CA, p. A70

ASSAAD, Haney, Vice President Medical Affairs, North Ottawa Community Hospital, Grand Haven, MI, p. A320

ASSAVAPISITKUL, Colleen, Chief Nursing Officer, St. Helena Hospital Clear Lake, Clearlake, CA, p. A56

ASTACIO, Benjamin, Director Human Resources, Bella Vista Hospital, Mayaguez, PR, p. A724

ASTLEFORD, Daniel, Vice President Operations, Lafayette Regional Health Center, Lexington, MO, p. A372

ATADERO, Robyn R.N., Chief Nursing Officer, Pioneers Memorial Healthcare District, Brawley, CA, p. A54

ATCHISON, Garfield, Chief Executive Officer, Frye Regional Medical Center, Hickory, NC, p. A464

ATCHISON, Marcie
  Vice President Human Resources, Community Hospital Long Beach, Long Beach, CA, p. A66
  Vice President Human Resources, Long Beach Memorial Medical Center, Long Beach, CA, p. A66
  Vice President Human Resources, Miller Children's & Women's Hospital Long Beach, Long Beach, CA, p. A67

ATCHLEY, Mark, Vice President and Chief Financial Officer, Medical City Dallas, Dallas, TX, p. A606

ATHERTON, Dorie, Manager Human Resources, University Behavioral Health Of Denton, Denton, TX, p. A608

ATHEY, Alycia, Director of Nursing, Prairie Ridge Hospital And Health Services, Elbow Lake, MN, p. A339

ATKIN, Suzanne M.D., Chief Medical Officer, University Hospital, Newark, NJ, p. A418

ATKINS, Christa, Administrator, Commonwealth Regional Specialty Hospital, Bowling Green, KY, p. A255

ATKINS, James PharmD, Chief Operating Officer, Piedmont Henry Hospital, Stockbridge, GA, p. A165

ATKINS, Jim, Director Employee Services, St. Luke's Rehabilitation Hospital, Boise, ID, p. A172

ATKINS, Jodi, Human Resources Specialist, Baptist Medical Center Nassau, Fernandina Beach, FL, p. A124

ATKINS, Melissa, CPA, Chief Executive Officer, Graham County Hospital, Hill City, KS, p. A242

ATKINS, Tracy, Chief Operating and Nursing Officer, Orchard Hospital, Gridley, CA, p. A62

ATKINS–GUIDRY, Stephanie, Administrator and Chief Nursing Officer, Usmd Hospital At Fort Worth, Fort Worth, TX, p. A614

ATKINSON, James M.D., Medical Director, Ucla Medical Center–Santa Monica, Santa Monica, CA, p. A91

ATKINSON, Jodi, President and Chief Executive Officer, St. Andrew's Health Center, Bottineau, ND, p. A474

ATKINSON, Johnie M, Chief Human Resources Officer, Saint Vincent Hospital, Erie, PA, p. A534

ATTEBERRY, Dave M.D., Chief of Staff, Yakima Regional Medical And Cardiac Center, Yakima, WA, p. A689

ATTEBERY, Tim, Chief Executive Officer, Wellmont Holston Valley Medical Center, Kingsport, TN, p. A581

ATTEBURY, Mary, Chief Operating Officer, Northwest Missouri Psychiatric Rehabilitation Center, Saint Joseph, MO, p. A376

ATTERBERG, Linda, Chief Information Officer, Unitypoint Health–Keokuk, Keokuk, IA, p. A230

ATTLESEY–PRIES, Jacqueline M MS, R.N., Chief Nursing Officer, Vice President, Boulder Community Health, Boulder, CO, p. A98

ATTRIDGE, Scott
  Chief Financial Officer, Chi St. Anthony Hospital, Pendleton, OR, p. A524
  Chief Financial Officer, Mid–Valley Hospital, Omak, WA, p. A683

ATTY, James, Chief Executive Officer, Waverly Health Center, Waverly, IA, p. A236

ATWAL, Money, Chief Information Officer, Hilo Medical Center, Hilo, HI, p. A168

ATWOOD, Julie, Director Human Resources, San Bernardino Mountains Community Hospital District, Lake Arrowhead, CA, p. A65

ATWOOD, Linda, Chief Nursing Officer, Merit Health Woman's Hospital, Flowood, MS, p. A354

AUBEL, Eugenia, President, Mercy Health – St. Elizabeth Boardman Hospital, Boardman, OH, p. A481

AUBEL, James, Chief Financial Officer, Upmc Jameson Hospital, New Castle, PA, p. A542

AUBIN, Michael D, President, Baptist Medical Center Jacksonville, Jacksonville, FL, p. A127

AUBRY, Michael, Director Information Systems, Adventist Medical Center – Hanford, Hanford, CA, p. A62

AUBUCHON, Christy, Director Personnel, Washington County Memorial Hospital, Potosi, MO, p. A375

AUCKER, Kendra A.
  President and Chief Executive Officer, Evangelical Community Hospital, Lewisburg, PA, p. A539
  Vice President Operations, Evangelical Community Hospital, Lewisburg, PA, p. A539

AUCKERMAN, Graydon Todd, Chief Nursing Officer, Ohiohealth Rehabilitation Hospital, Columbus, OH, p. A488

AUDETT, John R M.D., Medical Director Clinical Affairs, Overlook Medical Center, Summit, NJ, p. A421

AUDIRSCH, Lanell, Administrative Assistant, North Caddo Medical Center, Vivian, LA, p. A287

AUERBACH, Bruce S., M.D., President and Chief Executive Officer, Sturdy Memorial Hospital, Attleboro, MA, p. A302

AUERBACH, Jeffrey D.O., Medical Director, Bon Secours Community Hospital, Port Jervis, NY, p. A450

AUERBACH, Lorraine P., FACHE, President and Chief Executive Officer, Dameron Hospital, Stockton, CA, p. A92

AUGSBURGER, Marc, R.N., President and Chief Executive Officer, Caro Community Hospital, Caro, MI, p. A316

AUGSBURGER, Tod
  President and Chief Executive Officer, Lexington Medical Center, West Columbia, SC, p. A567
  Senior Vice President and Chief Operating Officer, Lexington Medical Center, West Columbia, SC, p. A567

AUGUST, Brad, Director Information Systems, Fairfield Memorial Hospital, Fairfield, IL, p. A187

AUGUST, Prudence, Chief Information Officer, Palomar Medical Center, Escondido, CA, p. A58

AUGUSTIN, Robert, Director Human Resources, Southern Tennessee Regional Health System–Lawrenceburg, Lawrenceburg, TN, p. A582

AUGUSTIN, W Walter CPA, III, Vice President Financial Services and Chief Financial Officer, University Of Maryland Rehabilitation & Orthopaedic Institute, Baltimore, MD, p. A296

AUGUSTINE, David, Chief Executive Officer, Trego County–Lemke Memorial Hospital, Wakeeney, KS, p. A253

AUGUSTUS, Richard M.D., Chief Medical Officer, West Valley Medical Center, Caldwell, ID, p. A172

AUGUSTYNIAK, Becky, Director Human Resources, Northside Medical Center, Columbus, GA, p. A155

AUKES, Amy
  Human Resources Analyst, Avera Flandreau Hospital, Flandreau, SD, p. A570
  Regional Manager of Human Resources, Avera Dells Area Hospital, Dell Rapids, SD, p. A569

AULWES, Linda, Human Resources Coordinator, Guttenberg Municipal Hospital, Guttenberg, IA, p. A228

AUNAN, Milton E CPA, II, Senior Vice President and Chief Financial Officer, Unitypoint Health – St. Luke's Hospital, Cedar Rapids, IA, p. A223

AURAND, Brendan, Director, Human Resources, Fairmount Behavioral Health System, Philadelphia, PA, p. A543

AURILIO, Lisa R.N., MSN, Chief Operating Officer, Akron Children's Hospital, Akron, OH, p. A479

AUSMAN, Dan F., President and Chief Executive Officer, Methodist Hospital Of Southern California, Arcadia, CA, p. A52

AUSTIN, Aaron
  Market Vice President Human Resources, Chi St. Vincent Hot Springs, Hot Springs, AR, p. A44
  Market Vice President Human Resources, Chi St. Vincent Infirmary Medical Center, Little Rock, AR, p. A46
  Market Vice President Human Resources, Chi St. Vincent Morrilton, Morrilton, AR, p. A47

AUSTIN, Bill, Senior Vice President of Finance, Riverside Rehabilitation Institute, Newport News, VA, p. A671

AUSTIN, Dan
  Director Information Technology, Arkansas Methodist Medical Center, Paragould, AR, p. A48
  Manager Data Processing, Ashley County Medical Center, Crossett, AR, p. A42

AUSTIN, Debbie W MSN, R.N., Vice President Patient Care Services, P & S Surgical Hospital, Monroe, LA, p. A281

AUSTIN, Donnica, Vice President, Operations, Holy Cross Hospital, Chicago, IL, p. A181

AUSTIN, Geoff, Executive Director, University Of Washington Medical Center, Seattle, WA, p. A685

AUSTIN, Joe, Executive Vice President and Chief Operating Officer, Phoebe Putney Memorial Hospital, Albany, GA, p. A149

AUSTIN, Judy, Director Human Resources, Campbellton Graceville Hospital, Graceville, FL, p. A126

AUSTIN, Laura, Vice President Finance and Chief Financial Officer, Community Hospital Of Anaconda, Anaconda, MT, p. A382

AUSTIN, Sherri MSN, R.N., Chief Nursing Officer, Wrangell Medical Center, Wrangell, AK, p. A27

AUSTIN, W William Jr, Senior Vice President Finance, Riverside Shore Memorial Hospital, Onancoke, VA, p. A672

AUSTIN, Warren M.D., Vice President Medical Affairs, Bon Secours Maryview Medical Center, Portsmouth, VA, p. A673

AUSTIN–MOORE, Gale, Director Area Technology, Kaiser Permanente Vallejo Medical Center, Vallejo, CA, p. A95

AUSTRIA, Ramon R.N., Chief Nursing Officer, Vibra Rehabilitation Hospital Lake Travis, Lakeway, TX, p. A628

AUTELLI, Oscar, Chief Information Officer, Lac+Usc Medical Center, Los Angeles, CA, p. A69

AUTREY, Pamela Spencer R.N., Ph.D., MSN, Chief Nursing Officer, Medical West, Bessemer, AL, p. A14

AVANT, Andre, Facility Automation Manager, Texas Center For Infectious Disease, San Antonio, TX, p. A644

AVATO, Rich, Director, St. Mary's Medical Center, West Palm Beach, FL, p. A147

AVELINO, Joseph, Chief Executive Officer, College Medical Center, Long Beach, CA, p. A66

AVERETT, Elaine, Chief Financial Officer, Grove Hill Memorial Hospital, Grove Hill, AL, p. A19

AVERILL, Clark, Director Information Technology, St. Luke's Hospital, Duluth, MN, p. A339

AVERNA, Russell
  Vice President Human Resources, Spaulding Rehabilitation Hospital, Charlestown, MA, p. A305
  Vice President of Human Resources, Spaulding Rehabilitation Hospital Cape Cod, East Sandwich, MA, p. A306

AVERY, Danny, Chief Financial Officer and Chief Operating Officer, Mangum Regional Medical Center, Mangum, OK, p. A509

AVERY, Donald R., FACHE, President and Chief Executive Officer, Fairview Park Hospital, Dublin, GA, p. A157

AVERY, John B. III, Administrator, Perry Community Hospital, Linden, TN, p. A583

AVERY, Jonathan, Chief Administrative Officer, Legacy Good Samaritan Medical Center, Portland, OR, p. A525

AVIADO, Gail, Chief Nursing Officer, Montclair Hospital Medical Center, Montclair, CA, p. A74

AVIGDOR, Lauren, Director Human Resources, Advanced Specialty Hospital Of Toledo, Toledo, OH, p. A500

AVILA, Brandi, Chief Nursing Officer, Martin County Hospital District, Stanton, TX, p. A646

AVILA, Patrick, Chief Operating Officer, Belton Regional Medical Center, Belton, MO, p. A364

AVVISATO, Michael, Senior Vice President and Chief Financial Officer, Allied Services Rehabilitation Hospital, Scranton, PA, p. A550

AVVISATO, Mike, Vice President and Chief Financial Officer, John Heinz Institute Of Rehabilitation Medicine, Wilkes, PA, p. A554

AWALD, Tamara, Chief Nursing Officer and Chief Operating Officer, Plymouth Medical Center, Plymouth, IN, p. A218

AWALT, Scott, Chief Financial Officer, Sanford Hillsboro Medical Center, Hillsboro, ND, p. A476

AWAN, Naveed, FACHE, Chief Executive Officer, St. Helena Parish Hospital, Greensburg, LA, p. A275

AWOLOWO, Yinusa, Business Officer, Kingsboro Psychiatric Center, New Rochelle, NY, p. A442

AWWAD, Emad, Director Care Delivery Sites Information Systems and Technology, Lakeview Hospital, Stillwater, MN, p. A349

AXTELL, Vicki, Director Human Resources, Livingston Healthcare, Livingston, MT, p. A386

AYALA, Jose L M.D., Chief Medical Officer, Valley Baptist Medical Center–Brownsville, Brownsville, TX, p. A599

AYALA, Lisa R.N., Director Human Resources, Specialty Hospital Jacksonville, Jacksonville, FL, p. A128

AYALA, Shirley, Director Human Resources, First Hospital Panamericano, Cidra, PR, p. A723

AYCOCK, Mark, Chief Operating Officer, Spartanburg Medical Center, Spartanburg, SC, p. A566

AYERS, James G, Chief Financial Officer, Piedmont Geriatric Hospital, Burkeville, VA, p. A665

AYERS, Jessi, Chief Financial Officer, Person Memorial Hospital, Roxboro, NC, p. A470

AYERS, Matthew, Chief Administrative Officer, Norton Hospital, Louisville, KY, p. A263

AYKUL, Nikki, Manager Business Office, Lifecare Hospitals Of Pittsburgh, Pittsburgh, PA, p. A546

AYOUB, John J., FACHE, Chief Executive Officer, Mobridge Regional Hospital, Mobridge, SD, p. A571

AYRES, Robert, Director Information Systems, Firelands Regional Health System, Sandusky, OH, p. A499

AYRES, Shane, Chief Financial Officer, Sanford Wheaton Medical Center, Wheaton, MN, p. A350

AZAR, Jennifer, Director Human Resources, Turning Point Hospital, Moultrie, GA, p. A162

AZCONA, Alain
  Chief Executive Officer, Aurora Behavioral Healthcare San Diego, San Diego, CA, p. A85
  Director Business Development, Aurora Behavioral Healthcare San Diego, San Diego, CA, p. A85

AZCUY, Karla, Acting Chief Human Resources Officer, Va Portland Healthcare System, Portland, OR, p. A525

AZEVEDO, Michael M.D., Medical Director, San Joaquin Valley Rehabilitation Hospital, Fresno, CA, p. A61

AZIZ, Samir M.D., Medical Director, Fairfax Behavioral Health, Kirkland, WA, p. A681

AZIZKHAN, Richard G., M.D., President and Chief Executive Officer, Children's Hospital And Medical Center, Omaha, NE, p. A397

AZURE, Vernon, Clinical Director, Indian Health Service – Quentin N. Burdick Memorial Health Care Facility, Belcourt, ND, p. A474

B

BAAS, Daniel R.N., Chief Nursing Officer, Baylor Emergency Medical Center At Aubrey, Aubrey, TX, p. A594

BAAS, Dina, Director Financial Services, Orange City Area Health System, Orange City, IA, p. A232

BABAKANIAN, Ed, Chief Information Officer, Uc San Diego Health, San Diego, CA, p. A86

BABB, A. Mitch, Vice President, Operations, Duke Regional Hospital, Durham, NC, p. A461

BABB, Cindy, Executive Director Human Resources and Organizational Effectiveness, St. Vincent Kokomo, Kokomo, IN, p. A213

BABB, Dan, Chief Financial Officer, DMC – Rehabilitation Institute Of Michigan, Detroit, MI, p. A317

BABB, Donald J., Chief Executive Officer, Citizens Memorial Hospital, Bolivar, MO, p. A364

BABB, Kathy, Manager Human Resources, Clifton Springs Hospital And Clinic, Clifton Springs, NY, p. A434

BABCOCK, Daniel, Chief Executive Officer, Marlette Regional Hospital, Marlette, MI, p. A325

BABCOCK, Kimberly, Administrative Director of Operations, Kalkaska Memorial Health Center, Kalkaska, MI, p. A324

BABCOCK, Paul, Chief Financial Officer, Coulee Medical Center, Grand Coulee, WA, p. A681

BABCOCK, Robert, M.D.
  Chief of Staff, Canandaigua Veterans Affairs Medical Center, Canandaigua, NY, p. A433
  Interim Chief of Staff, Bath Veterans Affairs Medical Center, Bath, NY, p. A431

BABER, Jonathan, Director Information Technology, Central State Hospital, Petersburg, VA, p. A672

BABICH, Eli, Chief Nursing Officer, Select Specialty Hospital–Pittsburgh/Upmc, Pittsburgh, PA, p. A547

BABINEAU, Timothy J., M.D., President and Chief Executive Officer, Lifespan Corporation, Providence, RI, p. B78

BABUSCIO, Cathy, Director Human Resources, Mat–Su Regional Medical Center, Palmer, AK, p. A27

BACA, Modesto, Chief Information Officer, Amarillo Veterans Affairs Health Care System, Amarillo, TX, p. A592

BACH, Dawn M MS, Chief Clinical Officer, Buena Vista Regional Medical Center, Storm Lake, IA, p. A235

BACHA, Fadi M.D., Chief Medical Officer, Select Specialty Hospital–Lexington, Lexington, KY, p. A261

BACHELDOR, H Lee D.O., Chief Medical Officer, St. John River District Hospital, East China, MI, p. A319

BACHER, Beth, Chief Executive Officer, Healthsouth Valley Of The Sun Rehabilitation Hospital, Glendale, AZ, p. A30

BACHMAN, John Page, Corporate Vice President, St. John Medical Center, Tulsa, OK, p. A518

BACHMAN, Judith Lynn
  Chief Operating Officer, Fox Chase Cancer Center–American Oncologic Hospital, Philadelphia, PA, p. A543
  Chief Operating Officer, Jeanes Hospital, Philadelphia, PA, p. A544

BACHMAN, Roberta, Director Human Resources, Riverview Behavioral Health, Texarkana, AR, p. A50

BACHMEIER, Susan T. MSN, R.N., Chief Nursing Officer, Wake Forest Baptist Health–Davie Medical Center, Bermuda Run, NC, p. A457

BACIARELLI, Renato V., Interim Chief Administrative Officer, Peacehealth St. John Medical Center, Longview, WA, p. A682

BACK, Barbara, Manager Human Resources, Encino Hospital Medical Center, Los Angeles, CA, p. A68

BACKER, Jacqueline Ann, Vice President of Human Resources, Providence Medical Center, Wayne, NE, p. A400

BACON, Jeff D.O., Chief Medical Officer, Sterling Regional Medcenter, Sterling, CO, p. A107

BACON, Ken J., President and Chief Executive Officer, Shawnee Mission Medical Center, Shawnee Mission, KS, p. A252

BADEN, Robert M, Chief Financial Officer, Lompoc Valley Medical Center, Lompoc, CA, p. A66

BADEN, Thomas Jr, Chief Information Officer, Community Behavioral Health Hospital – Rochester, Rochester, MN, p. A346

BADGER, Jeff
  Chief Financial Officer, Calumet Medical Center, Chilton, WI, p. A700
  Chief Financial Officer, Mercy Medical Center, Oshkosh, WI, p. A710
  Chief Financial Officer, St. Elizabeth Hospital, Appleton, WI, p. A698

BADILLO, Linda, M.D., Chief of Medical Staff, Medical Center Of Trinity, Trinity, FL, p. A146

BADINGER, Sandy, Chief Financial Officer, Slidell Memorial Hospital, Slidell, LA, p. A286

BAECHLE, Christopher, Chief Executive Officer, St. Luke's Rehabilitation Hospital, Chesterfield, MO, p. A366

BAEHSER, Deborah, Vice President Patient Care Services, Cape Regional Medical Center, Cape May Court House, NJ, p. A412

BAENEN, Sharla, MSN, R.N., President, Bellin Psychiatric Center, Green Bay, WI, p. A703

BAER, Douglas M., Chief Executive Officer, Brooks Rehabilitation Hospital, Jacksonville, FL, p. A128

BAEZ, Janet, Director, University Hospital, San Juan, PR, p. A727

BAEZ, Juan M.D., President Medical Staff, Robert Wood Johnson University Hospital Rahway, Rahway, NJ, p. A419

BAGGERLY, Karen, Chief Nursing Officer and Vice President, Covenant Medical Center, Lubbock, TX, p. A630

BAGGETT, Al M.D., Interim Chief of Staff, Taylor Regional Hospital, Hawkinsville, GA, p. A158

BAGGETT, Margarita, MSN, R.N.
  Chief Nursing Officer, Uc San Diego Health, San Diego, CA, p. A86
  Interim Chief Operating Officer, Uc San Diego Health, San Diego, CA, p. A86

BAGLEY, Brenda, Director Human Resources, TMC Bonham Hospital, Bonham, TX, p. A598

BAGLEY, Lisa, Nurse Administrator, The Orthopedic Specialty Hospital, Murray, UT, p. A658

BAGNALL, Andrew, President and Chief Executive Officer, Hshs St. Nicholas Hospital, Sheboygan, WI, p. A712

BAGNELL, Kelly M.D., Chief of Staff, Providence St. Joseph Medical Center, Polson, MT, p. A387

BAHL, Barry I, Director, St. Cloud Veterans Affairs Health Care System, Saint Cloud, MN, p. A347

BAHLS, Fredrick M.D., Chief of Staff, Veterans Affairs Central Iowa Health Care System, Des Moines, IA, p. A226

BAHNLEIN, Carl, Executive Vice President and Chief Operating Officer, Virginia Hospital Center – Arlington, Arlington, VA, p. A664

BAIDA–FRAGOSO, Nicolas M.D., Clinical Director, El Paso Psychiatric Center, El Paso, TX, p. A610

BAIER, Roger, Chief Executive Officer, Sanford Mayville Medical Center, Mayville, ND, p. A477

BAIG, Mirza, M.D., Medical Director, Uh Rehabilitation Hospital, Beachwood, OH, p. A480

BAILEY, Ann, Assistant Director Administration, Central State Hospital, Petersburg, VA, p. A672

BAILEY, Becky, R.N.
Director Nursing, Kansas Surgery And Recovery Center, Wichita, KS, p. A253
Director Human Resources, Lincoln Hospital, Davenport, WA, p. A680

BAILEY, Brenda, Assistant Administrator, Windsor–Laurelwood Center For Behavioral Medicine, Willoughby, OH, p. A502

BAILEY, Bruce P.
Chief Executive Officer, Tidelands Georgetown Memorial Hospital, Georgetown, SC, p. A562
Chief Executive Officer, Tidelands Waccamaw Community Hospital, Murrells Inlet, SC, p. A565

BAILEY, Cheryl R.N., Chief Nursing Officer Vice President Patient Care Services, Cullman Regional Medical Center, Cullman, AL, p. A16

BAILEY, Cori, Accountant, Tyler Holmes Memorial Hospital, Winona, MS, p. A363

BAILEY, Craig, MS, Chief Executive Officer and Administrator, Colorado Acute Long Term Hospital, Denver, CO, p. A100

BAILEY, Dan, Director Information Systems, Norton Sound Regional Hospital, Nome, AK, p. A26

BAILEY, David, FACHE, Chief Executive Officer, Community Hospital Of Bremen, Bremen, IN, p. A205

BAILEY, David J., M.D., President and Chief Executive Officer, Nemours, Jacksonville, FL, p. B89

BAILEY, Dawn A R.N., Vice President Nursing and Chief Nursing Officer, Euclid Hospital, Euclid, OH, p. A491

BAILEY, Dianne, Chief Information Officer, Pana Community Hospital, Pana, IL, p. A196

BAILEY, Heather, Chief Human Resources Officer, Jefferson Healthcare, Port Townsend, WA, p. A684

BAILEY, Jodi J, Human Resources Director, Odessa Memorial Healthcare Center, Odessa, WA, p. A683

BAILEY, John E., Chief Financial Officer, Moore County Hospital District, Dumas, TX, p. A609

BAILEY, Jonathan D., Chief Executive Officer and Administrator, Hansford Hospital, Spearman, TX, p. A646

BAILEY, Joy, Director Information Technology, Sutter Amador Hospital, Jackson, CA, p. A64

BAILEY, Joyce, Vice President Patient Care, Chi St. Anthony Hospital, Pendleton, OR, p. A524

BAILEY, Kathy C., Ph.D., FACHE, President and Chief Executive Officer, Carolinas Healthcare System Blue Ridge, Morganton, NC, p. A467

BAILEY, Kelly, Chief Executive Officer and Administrator, Kindred Hospital–White Rock, Dallas, TX, p. A605

BAILEY, Larry, Chief Executive Officer, Indiana University Health Paoli Hospital, Paoli, IN, p. A218

BAILEY, Leisa M.D., Chief of Staff, Doctors Memorial Hospital, Bonifay, FL, p. A120

BAILEY, Lori R.N., Vice President and Chief Nursing Officer, Ottumwa Regional Health Center, Ottumwa, IA, p. A233

BAILEY, Marquita, Chief Nursing Officer, Dekalb Regional Medical Center, Fort Payne, AL, p. A18

BAILEY, Matthew D., FACHE, President, Indiana University Health Bloomington Hospital, Bloomington, IN, p. A204

BAILEY, Melissa, Commissioner, Department of Mental Health, Vermont Psychiatric Care Hospital, Berlin, VT, p. A662

BAILEY, Mikeana, Director Human Resources, Brownwood Regional Medical Center, Brownwood, TX, p. A599

BAILEY, Owen, FACHE, Chief Executive Officer and Senior Associate Vice President for Medical Affairs, University Of South Alabama Hospitals, Mobile, AL, p. B140

BAILEY, Robert W, Chief Information Officer, Hawthorn Center, Northville, MI, p. A327

BAILEY, Ron, Chief Financial Officer, Franklin Foundation Hospital, Franklin, LA, p. A275

BAILEY, Russell, Chief Executive Officer, Texas Rehabilitation Hospital Of Fort Worth, Fort Worth, TX, p. A614

BAILEY, Scott
Chief Financial Officer, Saint Francis Hospital Muskogee, Muskogee, OK, p. A511
Chief Operating Officer, Saint Mary's Regional Medical Center, Russellville, AR, p. A49

BAILEY, Thomas, Chief Operating Officer, Bothwell Regional Health Center, Sedalia, MO, p. A379

BAILEY, Travis A, Vice President Administration, St. Claire Healthcare, Morehead, KY, p. A265

BAILEY–NEWELL, Susan, Vice President Human Resources, Baylor St. Luke's Medical Center, Houston, TX, p. A619

BAILEY–OETKER, Jessica, Director Quality and Medical Staff, Providence Willamette Falls Medical Center, Oregon City, OR, p. A524

BAIN, Joel, Director Information Services, Tristar Summit Medical Center, Hermitage, TN, p. A580

BAIN, Mark, Chief Human Resources, Veterans Affairs Connecticut Healthcare System, West Haven, CT, p. A114

BAIN, Pat, Chief Nursing Officer, Lower Bucks Hospital, Bristol, PA, p. A530

BAIO, Katie, Human Resource Director, Amita Health Adventist Medical Center Bolingbrook, Bolingbrook, IL, p. A179

BAIR, Ada, Chief Executive Officer, Memorial Hospital, Carthage, IL, p. A179

BAIR, Connie, Human Resources Assistant, Pike County Memorial Hospital, Louisiana, MO, p. A372

BAIRD, David
Chief Information Officer, LDS Hospital, Salt Lake City, UT, p. A660
Chief Information Officer, The Orthopedic Specialty Hospital, Murray, UT, p. A658
Director of Information Systems, Intermountain Medical Center, Murray, UT, p. A658

BAIRD, Donna, Vice President Corporate Services, Bay Medical Center Sacred Heart Health System, Panama City, FL, p. A138

BAIRD, Glen M.D., Chief of Staff, Shriners Hospitals For Children–Spokane, Spokane, WA, p. A687

BAIRD, John D., Chief Executive Officer, Metrosouth Medical Center, Blue Island, IL, p. A178

BAISCH, Kim R.N., Associate Vice President Patient Care Services, Highline Medical Center, Burien, WA, p. A679

BAISDEN, Monica, Director Human Resources, Memorial Hermann Northeast, Humble, TX, p. A624

BAJAK, Sally, Chief Financial Officer, St. Croix Regional Medical Center, St Croix Falls, WI, p. A713

BAJARI, Pamela R R.N., Nurse Executive MHSATS, Community Behavioral Health Hospital – Rochester, Rochester, MN, p. A346

BAKAR, Anne L.
President and Chief Executive Officer, Telecare Heritage Psychiatric Health Center, Oakland, CA, p. A77
President and Chief Executive Officer, Willow Rock Center, San Leandro, CA, p. A89

BAKER, Alison M.D., Chief of Staff, Missouri Baptist Sullivan Hospital, Sullivan, MO, p. A380

BAKER, Annessa, Site Executive and Chief Nursing Officer, Jewish Hospital–Shelbyville, Shelbyville, KY, p. A267

BAKER, Bonnie, M.D.
Chief Medical Services, Veterans Health Care System Of The Ozarks, Fayetteville, AR, p. A43
Vice President Finance and Chief Financial Officer, Butler Hospital, Providence, RI, p. A556

BAKER, Brenda, Chief Financial Officer, Riverview Health, Noblesville, IN, p. A217

BAKER, Damon D.O., Chief Medical Officer, Oklahoma State University Medical Center, Tulsa, OK, p. A517

BAKER, Deborah
Chief Nursing Officer, Helen Newberry Joy Hospital, Newberry, MI, p. A327
Vice President, Nursing, Johns Hopkins Hospital, Baltimore, MD, p. A294
Vice President, Patient Care Services, Mount Auburn Hospital, Cambridge, MA, p. A305

BAKER, Denis, Chief Information Officer, Sarasota Memorial Health Care System, Sarasota, FL, p. A142

BAKER, Donald CPA, Chief Financial Officer, Hillcrest Medical Center, Tulsa, OK, p. A517

BAKER, Erin, Chief Executive Officer, Eminent Medical Center, Richardson, TX, p. A639

BAKER, Frank, Chief Information Officer, Mary Breckinridge Arh Hospital, Hyden, KY, p. A260

BAKER, Gary E., Senior Vice President and Chief Executive Officer, Honorhealth Scottsdale Shea Medical Center, Scottsdale, AZ, p. A36

BAKER, Harlan T, Department Leader Information Systems, Mcdonough District Hospital, Macomb, IL, p. A192

BAKER, J Matthew M.D., President Medical Staff, Bertrand Chaffee Hospital, Springville, NY, p. A452

BAKER, Joann, Administrator, Doctors Memorial Hospital, Bonifay, FL, p. A120

BAKER, Joel D.O., Chief Medical Officer, Wayne County Hospital, Corydon, IA, p. A225

BAKER, John, Chief Executive Officer, Red River Behavioral Health System, Grand Forks, ND, p. A476

BAKER, Jon, Chief Financial Officer, Tristar Hendersonville Medical Center, Hendersonville, TN, p. A580

BAKER, Judy, Chief Financial Officer, Kindred Hospital–Mansfield, Mansfield, TX, p. A631

BAKER, Kristie, Chief Nursing Officer, Two Rivers Behavioral Health System, Kansas City, MO, p. A371

BAKER, Maia MSN, Chief Nurse Executive, Rio Grande State Center/South Texas Health Care System, Harlingen, TX, p. A618

BAKER, Mark A., Chief Executive Officer, Jack Hughston Memorial Hospital, Phenix City, AL, p. A22

BAKER, Melissa
Director, Human Resources, Providence Little Company Of Mary Medical Center – Torrance, Torrance, CA, p. A94
Director, Human Resources, Providence Little Company Of Mary Medical Center San Pedro, Los Angeles, CA, p. A70

BAKER, Michael D.O., Chief of Staff, Daviess Community Hospital, Washington, IN, p. A221

BAKER, Michelle, Director Information Systems, Indiana University Health White Memorial Hospital, Monticello, IN, p. A216

BAKER, Nichelle A, Chair Human Resources, Mayo Clinic Hospital, Phoenix, AZ, p. A33

BAKER, Paige MSN, R.N., Chief Nursing Officer, Lee's Summit Medical Center, Lee's Summit, MO, p. A372

BAKER, Patrick R.N., Vice President, Chief Nursing Officer, West Chester Hospital, West Chester, OH, p. A502

BAKER, Paula F, President and Chief Executive Officer, Freeman Health System, Joplin, MO, p. A369

BAKER, Phillip, Vice President and Chief Financial Officer, Fawcett Memorial Hospital, Port Charlotte, FL, p. A140

BAKER, R Hal M.D., Vice President and Chief Information Officer, Wellspan York Hospital, York, PA, p. A555

BAKER, Reese, Director Information Systems, Crittenden County Hospital, Marion, KY, p. A264

BAKER, Reta K., President, Mercy Hospital Fort Scott, Fort Scott, KS, p. A241

BAKER, Ron, FACHE, Chief Executive Officer, Saint Luke's East Hospital, Lee's Summit, MO, p. A372

BAKER, Roni, Director of Nursing, Herington Municipal Hospital, Herington, KS, p. A242

BAKER, Sharon, Director Support Services, Fairbanks, Indianapolis, IN, p. A211

BAKER, Steve, Vice President and Chief Technology and Information Officer, Columbus Regional Hospital, Columbus, IN, p. A205

BAKER, Vanya, Director, Wake Forest Baptist Health – Wilkes Medical Center, North Wilkesboro, NC, p. A468

BAKER, W Douglas., Director, Julian F. Keith Alcohol And Drug Abuse Treatment Center, Black Mountain, NC, p. A458

BAKER, Wendell H. Jr, President, Vidant Edgecombe Hospital, Tarboro, NC, p. A471

BAKER–WITT, Francine, R.N., Interim Chief Executive Officer, Effingham Hospital, Springfield, GA, p. A165

BAKEWELL, Nancy, Administrator, Monroe Hospital, Bloomfield, IN, p. A204

BAKHTIER, Hasan M.D., Medical Director, Community Mental Health Center, Lawrenceburg, IN, p. A214

BAKICH, Sandy, Director Information Management, Delano Regional Medical Center, Delano, CA, p. A57

BAKKEN, Mary, Executive Vice President and Chief Operating Officer, Silver Cross Hospital, New Lenox, IL, p. A195

BAKKUM, Kyle, Chief Executive Officer and Administrator, Vernon Memorial Healthcare, Viroqua, WI, p. A714

BAKOS, Marty, Chief Financial Officer, Mountain Vista Medical Center, Mesa, AZ, p. A31

BALASIA, Tim, Chief Financial Officer, Johnson Memorial Hospital, Franklin, IN, p. A209

BALASUBRAMONY, Suresh M.D., Chief Medical Officer, Minnie Hamilton Healthcare Center, Grantsville, WV, p. A692

BALASUNDARAM, Anusuya M.D., Medical Director, Hampton Behavioral Health Center, Westampton, NJ, p. A422

BALAZY, Thomas E M.D., Medical Director, Craig Hospital, Englewood, CO, p. A102

BALCAVAGE, Thomas, Vice President Chief Patient Safety and Quality Officer, Kennedy Health System, Stratford, NJ, p. A420

BALCEZAK, Thomas M.D., Senior Vice President Medical Affairs and Chief Medical Officer, Yale–New Haven Hospital, New Haven, CT, p. A112

BALDAUF, Robb, Coordinator Information Systems, Lodi Community Hospital, Lodi, OH, p. A493

BALDERRAMA, Jose, Vice President Human Resources, Valley Hospital, Ridgewood, NJ, p. A420

BALDOSARO, Thomas
Chief Financial Officer, Inspira Medical Center–Elmer, Elmer, NJ, p. A413
Chief Financial Officer, Inspira Medical Center–Vineland, Vineland, NJ, p. A422

BALDRIDGE, Dava R.N., Chief Nursing Officer, Hillcrest Hospital – South, Tulsa, OK, p. A517

BALDWIN, Barbara, Chief Information Officer, Anne Arundel Medical Center, Annapolis, MD, p. A294

BALDWIN, Bruce A., Chief Executive Officer, Newberry County Memorial Hospital, Newberry, SC, p. A565

BALDWIN, Ellen R.N., Chief Nursing Officer, Texas Health Center For Diagnostic & Surgery, Plano, TX, p. A638

BALDWIN, Erin M.P.H., Chief Operating Officer, Mahaska Health Partnership, Oskaloosa, IA, p. A233

BALDWIN, Nathan M.D., President Medical Staff, Baptist Memorial Hospital–Booneville, Booneville, MS, p. A352

BALDWIN, Steve
Manager Information Technology, Wyoming State Hospital, Evanston, WY, p. A718
Vice President Finance, The Willough At Naples, Naples, FL, p. A135

BALDWIN, William, Chief Information Officer, Ashe Memorial Hospital, Jefferson, NC, p. A465

BALES, Brian, Director Plant Operations, Healthsouth Southern Hills Rehabilitation Hospital, Princeton, WV, p. A695

BALES, Correen, Executive Director Human Resources, UNM Sandoval Regional Medical Center, Inc., Rio Rancho, NM, p. A428

BALES, Glenn, Chief Financial Officer, Providence Saint Joseph Medical Center, Burbank, CA, p. A54

BALES–CHUBB, Denyse, President and Chief Executive Officer, Florida Hospital Wesley Chapel, Wesley Chapel, FL, p. A147

BALFOUR, Ann M., R.N., President, St. Joseph Health System, Tawas City, MI, p. A331

BALKO, Tom, Manager Information Systems, Redwood Area Hospital, Redwood Falls, MN, p. A346

BALL, Cassie, Chief Financial Officer, Hilton Head Hospital, Hilton Head Island, SC, p. A564

BALL, Charlie, Chief Operating Officer, Specialty Rehabilitation Hospital Of Coushatta, Coushatta, LA, p. A273

BALL, Connie, Chief Financial Officer, Specialty Rehabilitation Hospital Of Coushatta, Coushatta, LA, p. A273

BALL, Craig, Chief Executive Officer, Specialty Rehabilitation Hospital Of Coushatta, Coushatta, LA, p. A273

BALL, James, Chief Operating Officer, Executive, St. Anthony's Rehabilitation Hospital, Lauderdale Lakes, FL, p. A130

BALL, Jim, Chief Operating Officer, St. Catherine's Rehabilitation Hospital, North Miami, FL, p. A136

BALL, Johnny Percy III, Assistant Administrator Human Resources, South Georgia Medical Center, Valdosta, GA, p. A166

BALL, Rodney, Vice President Finance, Carolinas Healthcare System Northeast, Concord, NC, p. A460

BALLA, Matt, Chief Executive Officer, St. Vincent Dunn Hospital, Bedford, IN, p. A204

BALLANCE, Amy, Interim Chief Executive Officer, Hshs St. Joseph's Hospital, Breese, IL, p. A179

BALLANCE, William, Chief of Medical Staff, Vidant Bertie Hospital, Windsor, NC, p. A473

BALLARD, Christine
President and Chief Executive Officer, Muncy Valley Hospital, Muncy, PA, p. A542
Vice President Human Resources, Soldiers And Sailors Memorial Hospital, Wellsboro, PA, p. A553
Vice President Human Resources, Williamsport Regional Medical Center, Williamsport, PA, p. A554

BALLARD, Jerry, Director Information Systems, Central Florida Regional Hospital, Sanford, FL, p. A142

BALLARD, John, Ph.D., Chief Executive Officer, Kentucky River Medical Center, Jackson, KY, p. A260

BALLARD, Lorraine L, Director Human Resources, St. Helena Parish Hospital, Greensburg, LA, p. A275

BALLARD, Marsha, Human Resources, Christus Mother Frances Hospital – Jacksonville, Jacksonville, TX, p. A625

BALLARD, Richard R., Chief Executive Officer and Administrator, University Of Miami Hospital And Clinics, Miami, FL, p. A134

BALLARD, Terri, Chief Nursing Officer, Healthsouth Northern Kentucky Rehabilitation Hospital, Edgewood, KY, p. A257

BALLESTERO, Susan, Vice President and Chief Human Resources Officer, Saint Peter's University Hospital, New Brunswick, NJ, p. A417

BALLIETT, Matt, Chief Information Officer, Coal County General Hospital, Coalgate, OK, p. A506

BALLIN, Daniel, Administrator, Riverside Rehabilitation Institute, Newport News, VA, p. A671

BALLINGHOFF, James R MSN, R.N., Chief Nursing Officer and Associate Executive Director, Penn Presbyterian Medical Center, Philadelphia, PA, p. A545

BALLMAN, Patricia, Director, Westfield Memorial Hospital, Westfield, NY, p. A456

BALLOU, Michele M.D., Chief Medical Staff, Lewisgale Hospital Alleghany, Low Moor, VA, p. A669

BALOGA–ALTIERI, Bonnie Ph.D., R.N., Vice President Patient Care Services and Chief Nursing Officer, Children's Specialized Hospital, New Brunswick, NJ, p. A417

BALSANO, Tony, Vice President Finance, Saint Francis Medical Center, Cape Girardeau, MO, p. A365

BALSAR, Jeffrey R., President and Chief Executive Officer Vanderbilt Medical Center and Dean, Vanderbilt University Scho, Vanderbilt University Medical Center, Nashville, TN, p. A587

BALT, David D.O., Chief Medical Officer, Avera Queen Of Peace Hospital, Mitchell, SD, p. A571

BALTIERRA, David A. M.D., President Medical Staff, Jefferson Medical Center, Ranson, WV, p. A695

BALUKOFF, Sam, Interim Administrator, Geisinger Medical Center, Danville, PA, p. A532

BALUNTANSKI, Brian, Chief Financial Officer, Mclaren Macomb, Mount Clemens, MI, p. A326

BALZ, Pat, Vice President Operations Human Resources, Scott & White Medical Center – Temple, Temple, TX, p. A648

BALZANO, Janice, President and Chief Executive Officer, St. Petersburg General Hospital, Saint Petersburg, FL, p. A142

BAMAN, Raj D.O., President Medical Staff, Samaritan North Lincoln Hospital, Lincoln City, OR, p. A523

BAMBERGER, Josh, Administrator, Runnells Center For Rehabilitation And Healthcare, Berkeley Heights, NJ, p. A411

BAMBRICK, Catherine, Chief Operating Officer, Kittitas Valley Healthcare, Ellensburg, WA, p. A680

BAME, Jeremiah R.N., Chief Nursing Officer, Piedmont Newton Hospital, Covington, GA, p. A155

BAMMEL, Paul, Vice President, Mayo Clinic Health System – Northland In Barron, Barron, WI, p. A698

BANASZYNSKI, Gregory A., Chief Executive Officer, Uw Health Rehabilitation Hospital, Madison, WI, p. A705

BANBURY, Brian, Director Site Information Systems, Advocate Christ Medical Center, Oak Lawn, IL, p. A196

BANCO, Leonard M.D., Senior Vice President and Chief Medical Officer, Bristol Hospital, Bristol, CT, p. A109

BANDA, Venkat M.D., President Medical Staff, Promise Hospital Of Baton Rouge – Ochsner Campus, Baton Rouge, LA, p. A271

BANDFIELD–KEOUGH, Kathryn, Vice President Patient Care Services, Munson Healthcare Cadillac Hospital, Cadillac, MI, p. A315

BANDLA, H. M.D., Chief Clinical Affairs, Walter P. Reuther Psychiatric Hospital, Westland, MI, p. A333

BANDS, James G IV, Chief Financial Officer, Ivinson Memorial Hospital, Laramie, WY, p. A718

BANDY, Dawn, Chief Financial Officer, Grant Regional Health Center, Lancaster, WI, p. A705

BANDY, Don, Director Information Technology, Alliancehealth Deaconess, Oklahoma City, OK, p. A511

BANDY, Jennifer, Human Resource Business Partner, Wake Forest Baptist Health–Davie Medical Center, Bermuda Run, NC, p. A457

BANDY, P Ross M.D., Chief Medical Officer and Chief of Staff, Levi Hospital, Hot Springs National Park, AR, p. A44

BANE, William, Chief Financial Officer, Inova Loudoun Hospital, Leesburg, VA, p. A669

BANFIELD, Anne, Chief, Medical Staff, Davis Medical Center, Elkins, WV, p. A691

BANG, W J M.D., Chief of Staff, Reeves County Hospital, Pecos, TX, p. A637

BANGA, Alok M.D., Medical Director, Sierra Vista Hospital, Sacramento, CA, p. A84

BANIEWICZ, John M.D., Chief Medical Officer, Lake Health, Concord Township, OH, p. A488

BANK, Carol J, Vice President Human Resources, Divine Savior Healthcare, Portage, WI, p. A710

BANKER, Julie G R.N., MSN, Chief Nursing Officer, Lehigh Regional Medical Center, Lehigh Acres, FL, p. A131

BANKERS, Diane, Senior Vice President, Nursing Services, Firstlight Health System, Mora, MN, p. A344

BANKS, Chester, Director Human Resources, East Orange General Hospital, East Orange, NJ, p. A413

BANKS, Elizabeth, Chief Executive Officer, Summit Behavioral Healthcare, Cincinnati, OH, p. A484

BANKS, Matthew, Chief Executive Officer, Davis Regional Medical Center, Statesville, NC, p. A471

BANKS, Maureen
Chief Operating Officer, Spaulding Rehabilitation Hospital, Charlestown, MA, p. A305
President, Spaulding Hospital For Continuing Medical Care Cambridge, Cambridge, MA, p. A305
President, Spaulding Rehabilitation Hospital Cape Cod, East Sandwich, MA, p. A306

BANKS, Robbi, Vice President, Human Resources, Medical Center Health System, Odessa, TX, p. A635

BANKS, Shane M.D., Chief of Staff, Ogallala Community Hospital, Ogallala, NE, p. A396

BANKS, Walter, Director Human Resources, Baptist Memorial Hospital–Desoto, Southaven, MS, p. A362

BANKSTON, Doug, Director Technical Services, North Oaks Medical Center, Hammond, LA, p. A275

BANKTSON, Julie, Manager Human Resources, Paul Oliver Memorial Hospital, Frankfort, MI, p. A320

BANNER, Fred, Chief Information Officer, Shore Medical Center, Somers Point, NJ, p. A420

BANOS, Edward, Interim Chief Executive Officer, University Health System, San Antonio, TX, p. A644

BANUEDOS, Jorge, Director Human Resources, Metropolitan State Hospital, Norwalk, CA, p. A76

BAPTISTE, Ernest, Executive Director, NYC Health + Hospitals / Kings County, New Rochelle, NY, p. A445

BAQUET, Shawn, Chief of Staff, Iberia Medical Center, New Iberia, LA, p. A282

BARANCZYK, Kay R.N., Chief Nursing Officer, Hshs St. Clare Memorial Hospital, Oconto Falls, WI, p. A709

BARANSKI, David J, Vice President Human Resources, Phoebe Putney Memorial Hospital, Albany, GA, p. A149

BARANSKI, Kenneth, Chief Financial Officer, Hills & Dales General Hospital, Cass City, MI, p. A316

BARBA, James J., President and Chief Executive Officer, Albany Medical Center, Albany, NY, p. A430

BARBADIAN, John, Vice President Human Resources, Tulare Regional Medical Center, Tulare, CA, p. A94

BARBAREE, Jerry, Director Human Resources, Baptist Memorial Hospital – Memphis, Memphis, TN, p. A584

BARBARIN, LaSharndra, Chief Executive Officer, Medical City Lewisville, Lewisville, TX, p. A629

BARBAROTTA, Ann Marie., Executive Director, Creedmoor Psychiatric Center, New Rochelle, NY, p. A441

BARBEE, Daniel, Chief Executive Officer, The University Of Toledo Medical Center, Toledo, OH, p. A501

BARBEE, Ovell, Senior Vice President, Human Resources, Spectrum Health – Butterworth Hospital, Grand Rapids, MI, p. A321

BARBER, Chris B., FACHE, President and Chief Executive Officer, St. Bernards Medical Center, Jonesboro, AR, p. A45

BARBER, Eric A., President and Chief Executive Officer, Mary Lanning Healthcare, Hastings, NE, p. A394

BARBER, Karen, R.N., Chief Executive Officer, Yoakum Community Hospital, Yoakum, TX, p. A655

BARBER, Keith, CPA, Chief Executive Officer, Houston Methodist Willowbrook Hospital, Houston, TX, p. A621

BARBER, Michael, Chief Operating Officer, Penn Medicine Chester County Hospital, West Chester, PA, p. A553

BARBER, Richard M.D., Chief Medical Officer, Wake Forest Baptist Health – Wilkes Medical Center, North Wilkesboro, NC, p. A468

BARBER, Roxann E, Regional Ambulatory Care and Ancillary Services Officer, Presence Mercy Medical Center, Aurora, IL, p. A177

BARBER, Scott
Chief Executive Officer, Decatur County General Hospital, Parsons, TN, p. A588
Vice President, Camden General Hospital, Camden, TN, p. A575

BARBER, Wendi, Vice President Finance and Chief Financial Officer, Park Ridge Health, Hendersonville, NC, p. A464

BARBINI, Gerald J., President and Chief Executive Officer, Allegan General Hospital, Allegan, MI, p. A314

BARBO, Steve, R.N., Administrator, Citizens Medical Center, Columbia, LA, p. A273

BARBOUR, Alexis, Director Finance, Columbus Dublin Springs, Dublin, OH, p. A490

BARBOUR, Michael B, Chief Nursing Officer, Emerald Coast Behavioral Hospital, Panama City, FL, p. A138

BARBUAT, James P, Chief Financial Officer, Gunnison Valley Hospital, Gunnison, CO, p. A103

BARCELLONA, Nicholas J., Chief Financial Officer, Children's Hospital Of Pittsburgh Of Upmc, Pittsburgh, PA, p. A546

BARCHI, Daniel, Senior Vice President, Technical Services and Chief Information Officer, Bridgeport Hospital, Bridgeport, CT, p. A109

BARCLAY, Bonnie, Chief Nursing Officer, Lifecare Hospitals Of Chester County, West Chester, PA, p. A553

BARCLAY, Duane D.O., Chief Medical Officer, Dekalb Medical At Hillandale, Lithonia, GA, p. A160

BARCLAY, Emily, Vice President Human Resources, Dana–Farber Cancer Institute, Boston, MA, p. A303

BARCLAY, Jeremy, Chief Executive Officer, St. David's Round Rock Medical Center, Round Rock, TX, p. A641

BARCLAY, Rick, Vice President Support Services, Mercy Hospital Rogers, Rogers, AR, p. A49

BARCUS, Krista, Human Resources Leader, SSM Health St. Francis Hospital – Maryville, Maryville, MO, p. A373

BARD, Jeffrey, President, Aurora Medical Center Of Oshkosh, Oshkosh, WI, p. A710

BARDEN, Sean
  Executive Vice President and Chief Financial Officer, Mary Washington Hospital, Fredericksburg, VA, p. A667
  Executive Vice President and Chief Financial Officer, Stafford Hospital, Stafford, VA, p. A675

BARDIER, Catherine, Vice President, Human Resources, Elliot Hospital, Manchester, NH, p. A409

BARDWELL, Carol A R.N., MSN, Chief Nurse Executive, Martha's Vineyard Hospital, Oak Bluffs, MA, p. A310

BARDWELL, Jean, Vice President and Chief Financial Officer, Ranken Jordan Pediatric Bridge Hospital, Maryland Heights, MO, p. A373

BARDWELL, Sheila, Director Information Systems, Baptist Memorial Hospital–Golden Triangle, Columbus, MS, p. A354

BAREFOOT, Denise, Director of Information Technology, Carolina Pines Regional Medical Center, Hartsville, SC, p. A563

BAREIS, Charles M.D., Medical Director, Macneal Hospital, Berwyn, IL, p. A178

BARELA, Barbara, Director Human Resources, Gila Regional Medical Center, Silver City, NM, p. A429

BAREZ, Pedro, FACHE, Chief Operating Officer, St. Luke's Episcopal Hospital, Ponce, PR, p. A725

BARFIELD, Donna, Chief Nursing Officer, Tennova Healthcare Volunteer Community Hospital, Martin, TN, p. A583

BARHAM, Ed M.D., Chief of Staff, Merit Health Woman's Hospital, Flowood, MS, p. A354

BARIOLA, Christopher L., Chief Executive Officer, Baptist Memorial Rehabilitation Hospital, Germantown, TN, p. A579

BARKER, Alanna, Director Human Resources, Metrosouth Medical Center, Blue Island, IL, p. A178

BARKER, James, Chief Executive Officer, Munson Healthcare Manistee Hospital, Manistee, MI, p. A325

BARKER, Karen, Vice President and Chief Information Officer, Sinai Hospital Of Baltimore, Baltimore, MD, p. A296

BARKER, Kathryn L, Chief Human Resources Management, Veterans Health Care System Of The Ozarks, Fayetteville, AR, p. A43

BARKER, Louise, R.N., Chief Executive Officer, Central Louisiana Surgical Hospital, Alexandria, LA, p. A269

BARKER, Richard, Administrator and Chief Executive Officer, Mercy Health Love County, Marietta, OK, p. A510

BARKER, Russell, Community Chief Executive Officer, Mcdowell Arh Hospital, Mcdowell, KY, p. A264

BARKER, Russell, Information Officer, U. S. Public Health Service Indian Hospital–Whiteriver, Whiteriver, AZ, p. A38

BARKER, William A Jr, Vice President Administration, Pleasant Valley Hospital, Point Pleasant, WV, p. A695

BARKHYMER, Mary C R.N., MSN, Vice President Patient Care Services and Chief Nursing Officer, Upmc St. Margaret, Pittsburgh, PA, p. A548

BARKMAN, Joseph, Vice President Financial Services, Oaklawn Psychiatric Center, Goshen, IN, p. A209

BARKSDALE, Mary, Director Human Resources, Person Memorial Hospital, Roxboro, NC, p. A470

BARKSDALE, Vickie, Manager Human Resources, North Oak Regional Medical Center, Senatobia, MS, p. A361

BARLAGE, Seth, Associate Medical Center Director, John J. Pershing Veterans Affairs Medical Center, Poplar Bluff, MO, p. A375

BARLEY, Leonard M.D., Chief Medical Officer, Windsor–Laurelwood Center For Behavioral Medicine, Willoughby, OH, p. A502

BARLEY, Tammy, Director, Human Resources, Healthsouth Rehabilitation Hospital Of Jonesboro, Jonesboro, AR, p. A45

BARLIS, Ellen, Chief Financial Officer, NYC Health + Hospitals / Jacobi, New Rochelle, NY, p. A445

BARLOW, Mark M.D., Chief Medical Officer and President Medical Staff, Cornerstone Hospital Of Houston At Clearlake, Webster, TX, p. A653

BARLOW, Roddex, Chief Operating Officer, The Hospitals Of Providence Memorial Campus, El Paso, TX, p. A611

BARMECHA, Jitendra M.D., M.P.H., Senior Vice President and Chief Information Officer, St. Barnabas Hospital, New Rochelle, NY, p. A446

BARNARD, Jeanna, FACHE, Chief Executive Officer, Bayshore Medical Center, Pasadena, TX, p. A636

BARNARD, Kerri, Director Human Resources, Larned State Hospital, Larned, KS, p. A245

BARNARD, Lawrence, President and Chief Executive Officer, St. Rose Dominican Hospitals – San Martin Campus, Las Vegas, NV, p. A404

BARNARD, Ryan, FACHE, Chief Executive Officer, Swisher Memorial Hospital District, Tulia, TX, p. A650

BARNCORD, Sharon, Human Resource Business Partner, Kaiser Permanente South San Francisco, South San Francisco, CA, p. A92

BARNELL, Phil, Chief Medical Officer, Hshs St. Mary's Hospital, Decatur, IL, p. A185

BARNES, Alan, Chief Financial Officer, North Star Behavioral Health System, Anchorage, AK, p. A25

BARNES, Becky, Chief Operating Officer, Rapides Regional Medical Center, Alexandria, LA, p. A269

BARNES, Bridget, Vice President and Chief Information Officer, Ohsu Hospital, Portland, OR, p. A525

BARNES, Deborah, Vice President and Chief Information Officer, Children's Hospital Of The King's Daughters, Norfolk, VA, p. A671

BARNES, Donald K, Chief Human Resources Officer, Duke Raleigh Hospital, Raleigh, NC, p. A468

BARNES, Douglas A M.D., Chief of Staff, Shriners Hospitals For Children–Houston, Houston, TX, p. A622

BARNES, Gary, Senior Vice President, Chief Information Officer, Medical Center Health System, Odessa, TX, p. A635

BARNES, Gloria V. MSN, Assistant Vice President Patient Care Services, Southeastern Regional Medical Center, Newnan, GA, p. A162

BARNES, Jacqueline, Manager Health Information, Select Specialty Hospital–Jackson, Jackson, MS, p. A357

BARNES, Jeff, Director Information Technology, Girard Medical Center, Girard, KS, p. A241

BARNES, Joe, Chief Financial Officer, Stonewall Jackson Memorial Hospital, Weston, WV, p. A697

BARNES, John, Administrative Director Human Resources, Beverly Hospital, Montebello, CA, p. A74

BARNES, Karen, Interim Chief Nursing Officer, Logan Regional Medical Center, Logan, WV, p. A693

BARNES, Larry, Vice President Information Technology, Salina Regional Health Center, Salina, KS, p. A251

BARNES, Laura P MSN, Vice President Patient Care Services and Chief Nursing Officer, East Tennessee Children's Hospital, Knoxville, TN, p. A581

BARNES, Leslie, Chief Financial Officer, Parkview Medical Center, Pueblo, CO, p. A106

BARNES, Marla, Director of Nursing, Pushmataha Hospital, Antlers, OK, p. A504

BARNES, Michael, Chief Information Officer, North Valley Hospital, Whitefish, MT, p. A389

BARNES, P. Marie, Director, Human Resources, North Mississippi Medical Center–Pontotoc, Pontotoc, MS, p. A360

BARNES, Sherry, Director Health Information and Quality Management, Rolling Hills Hospital, Ada, OK, p. A504

BARNES, William, Administrator, Kimble Hospital, Junction, TX, p. A625

BARNETT, Barbara M.D., Medical Director, Glen Cove Hospital, Glen Cove, NY, p. A436

BARNETT, Dana, Chief Executive Officer, Memorial Hospital Of Carbon County, Rawlins, WY, p. A719

BARNETT, DeLynn K, Director Human Resources, Lake Chelan Community Hospital And Clinics, Chelan, WA, p. A679

BARNETT, Frederick M.D., Chief of Staff, Metroplex Adventist Hospital, Killeen, TX, p. A627

BARNETT, Julia, Chief Nursing Officer, Union General Hospital, Blairsville, GA, p. A152

BARNETT, Kelly, Human Resource Officer, Brownfield Regional Medical Center, Brownfield, TX, p. A599

BARNETT, Laura, Executive Director, Human Resources, Brigham And Women's Faulkner Hospital, Boston, MA, p. A303

BARNETT, Lori R.N., MSN, Chief Nursing Officer, Troy Community Hospital, Troy, PA, p. A552

BARNETT, Pam R.N., Director of Nursing, Highland District Hospital, Hillsboro, OH, p. A492

BARNETT, Shawn, Chief Operating Officer, Chi St. Luke's Health Memorial Livingston, Livingston, TX, p. A629

BARNETT, Steve, President and Chief Executive Officer, Mckenzie Health System, Sandusky, MI, p. A330

BARNETT, Tom, Chief Information Officer, Highland Hospital, Rochester, NY, p. A450

BARNETTE, Brian, Chief Information Officer, Shepherd Center, Atlanta, GA, p. A151

BARNHARDT, Bonnie, Executive Director Human Resources, Ridgeview Le Sueur Medical Center, Le Sueur, MN, p. A342

BARNHART, Ann, Chief Executive Officer, Heart Of Florida Regional Medical Center, Davenport, FL, p. A123

BARNHART, Cody, Chief Executive Officer, St. Luke's Medical Center, Crosby, ND, p. A475

BARNHART, David, Director Information Systems, Wuesthoff Medical Center – Rockledge, Rockledge, FL, p. A141

BARNHART, J. T., Chief Executive Officer, Dallas Medical Center, Dallas, TX, p. A605

BARNHART, Jeff, Chief Executive Officer, Hereford Regional Medical Center, Hereford, TX, p. A619

BARNHART, Linda, Vice President and Chief Nursing Officer, Bethesda Hospital, Saint Paul, MN, p. A347

BARNO, Jill M.D., Chief Medical Officer, Berger Health System, Circleville, OH, p. A485

BARONE, Richard M.D., Medical Director, Montefiore New Rochelle, New Rochelle, NY, p. A440

BARONOFF, Peter R.

BARR, Andrew M., Commanding Officer, Tripler Army Medical Center, Honolulu, HI, p. A169

BARR, Ann
  Chief Information Officer – Bay Area, California Pacific Medical Center–St. Luke's Campus, San Francisco, CA, p. A87
  Chief Information Officer – Bay Area, California Pacific Medical Center, San Francisco, CA, p. A87
  Chief Information Officer, Sutter Health Bay Area, Sutter Maternity And Surgery Center Of Santa Cruz, Santa Cruz, CA, p. A91

BARR, Brent, Chief Information Officer, Minnie Hamilton Healthcare Center, Grantsville, WV, p. A692

BARR, Bret A., Executive Vice President and Chief Financial Officer, Conway Medical Center, Conway, SC, p. A561

BARR, Catherine
  President, East Region, Woodwinds Health Campus, Woodbury, MN, p. A351
  Senior Vice President and Chief Operating Officer, Bethesda Hospital, Saint Paul, MN, p. A347
  Senior Vice President and Chief Operating Officer, St. John's Hospital, Maplewood, MN, p. A343
  Senior Vice President and Chief Operating Officer, St. Joseph's Hospital, Saint Paul, MN, p. A348

BARR, Francine, R.N., MS
  Vice President and Chief Operating Officer, Bon Secours St. Mary's Hospital, Richmond, VA, p. A673
  Chief Executive Officer, Bon Secours St. Mary's Hospital, Richmond, VA, p. A673

BARR, Kristine, Vice President Communication Services, O'Bleness Memorial Hospital, Athens, OH, p. A480

BARR, Kyle J
  Senior Vice President, Chief Team Resources Officer, Mease Dunedin Hospital, Dunedin, FL, p. A124
  Senior Vice President, Chief Team Resources Officer, Morton Plant North Bay Hospital, New Port Richey, FL, p. A135

BARR, Kyle, Senior Vice President, Chief Team Resources Officer, Mease Countryside Hospital, Safety Harbor, FL, p. A141

BARR, Laurie C
  Vice President Human Resources, Salem Health West Valley, Dallas, OR, p. A521
  Vice President Human Resources, Salem Hospital, Salem, OR, p. A526

BARR, Mary Beth., R.N., Chief Executive Officer, Grant Memorial Hospital, Petersburg, WV, p. A695

BARR, Vivian C, Director Human Resources, Tanner Medical Center–Carrollton, Carrollton, GA, p. A153

BARRA, Jon, Director Human Resources, Wyoming Behavioral Institute, Casper, WY, p. A717

BARRY, Anne, Deputy Commissioner, Minnesota Department Of Human Services, Saint Paul, MN, p. B85

BARRACLOUGH, Grant R.N., Chief Nursing Officer, Castleview Hospital, Price, UT, p. A659

BARRALL, Audrey, Director Human Resources, St. Helena Hospital Clear Lake, Clearlake, CA, p. A56

BARRAMEDA, Maricar, Chief Information Officer, NYC Health + Hospitals / Lincoln, New Rochelle, NY, p. A445

BARRERA, Edward, Director Communications, Encino Hospital Medical Center, Los Angeles, CA, p. A68

BARRERA, Liflor, Manager Human Resources, Wahiawa General Hospital, Wahiawa, HI, p. A170

BARRERE, Davie Ann, Coordinator Information Technology, Dahl Memorial Healthcare Association, Ekalaka, MT, p. A384

BARRETT, Anne J, Associate Executive Director Human Resources, Southside Hospital, Bay Shore, NY, p. A431

BARRETT, Bill, Manager Human Resources, Wilson N. Jones Regional Medical Center, Sherman, TX, p. A645

BARRETT, Cindy, Administrative Assistant, Patton State Hospital, Patton, CA, p. A79

BARRETT, James W. Jr, Chief Executive Officer, Richardson Medical Center, Rayville, LA, p. A284

BARRETT, Jason P., Chief Executive Officer, Flagler Hospital, Saint Augustine, FL, p. A141

BARRETT, John E. III, Chief Executive Officer, Bon Secours–Depaul Medical Center, Norfolk, VA, p. A671

BARRETT, John, Regional Director Human Resources, Franciscan St. Anthony Health – Michigan City, Michigan City, IN, p. A215

BARRETT, Kerry Flynn, Vice President Human Resources, Northern Westchester Hospital, Mount Kisco, NY, p. A440

BARRETT, Linda, Vice President of Information Services, Community Hospital Of Bremen, Bremen, IN, p. A205

BARRETT, Lynn, Chief Nursing Officer, Centerpoint Medical Center, Independence, MO, p. A369

BARRETT, Pam, Human Resources Director, Colorado River Medical Center, Needles, CA, p. A76

BARRETT, Pamella, Director of Nursing, Pam Specialty Hospital Of Victoria South, Victoria, TX, p. A652

BARRETT, T Marc M.D., Senior Vice President and Chief Medical Officer, Providence Healthcare Network, Waco, TX, p. A652

BARRICK, Lisa, Controller, Healthsouth Scottsdale Rehabilitation Hospital, Scottsdale, AZ, p. A35

BARRILLEAUX, Scott G., FACHE, Chief Executive Officer, Drew Memorial Health System, Monticello, AR, p. A47

BARRIO, Gabe M.D., Chief of Staff, Whidbeyhealth, Coupeville, WA, p. A679

BARROCAS, Albert M.D., Chief Medical Officer, Wellstar Atlanta Medical Center, Atlanta, GA, p. A151

BARRON, Kathleen, Executive Director, Temple University Hospital, Philadelphia, PA, p. A546

BARRON, Steven, Interim Chief Executive Officer, San Gorgonio Memorial Hospital, Banning, CA, p. A53

BARROW, Robert, Chief Executive Officer, Doctors' Hospital Of Michigan, Pontiac, MI, p. A328

BARROW, William F. II, Chief Executive Officer, Beauregard Memorial Hospital, De Ridder, LA, p. A274

BARROWS, Cheryl, Vice President Human Resources, Sturdy Memorial Hospital, Attleboro, MA, p. A302

BARRY, Rick, Director Information Systems, Baylor Medical Center At Frisco, Frisco, TX, p. A615

BARRY, Thomas, Chief Executive Officer, Pulaski Memorial Hospital, Winamac, IN, p. A221

BARSOM, Michael, M.D., Executive Director, Metropolitan State Hospital, Norwalk, CA, p. A76

BARSOUM, Wael, M.D., President, Cleveland Clinic Florida, Weston, FL, p. A148

BARSTAD, Stacy
Chief Executive Officer, Sanford Tracy Medical Center, Tracy, MN, p. A349
Chief Executive Officer, Sanford Westbrook Medical Center, Westbrook, MN, p. A350

BARTAL, Ely, M.D.
Chief Executive Officer and Medical Director, Kansas Surgery And Recovery Center, Wichita, KS, p. A253
Chief Executive Officer, Kansas Surgery And Recovery Center, Wichita, KS, p. A253

BARTELL, Michael, Chief Executive Officer, Regional Rehabilitation Hospital, Phenix City, AL, p. A22

BARTELS, Bruce J., Interim Chief Executive Officer, Lafayette Physical Rehabilitation Hospital, Lafayette, LA, p. A278

BARTELS, Dara, Chief Financial Officer, Gundersen Health System, La Crosse, WI, p. A704

BARTELS, Jennifer, Director Human Resources, Pawnee County Memorial Hospital And Rural Health Clinic, Pawnee City, NE, p. A399

BARTH, Andrew J., Chief Executive Officer, Aspirus Langlade Hospital, Antigo, WI, p. A698

BARTH, Marci, Chief Nursing Officer, Fayette County Hospital, Vandalia, IL, p. A202

BARTH, Tara, Chief Nursing Officer, Western Arizona Regional Medical Center, Bullhead City, AZ, p. A28

BARTHEL, Gayle, Coordinator Human Resources, Select Specialty Hospital–Flint, Flint, MI, p. A319

BARTHOLOMEW, Brenda, Chief Nursing Officer, Gunnison Valley Hospital, Gunnison, UT, p. A656

BARTHOLOMEW, K A M.D., Medical Director, Faulkton Area Medical Center, Faulkton, SD, p. A569

BARTHOLOMEW, Shelley, Director Human Resources, Decatur County General Hospital, Parsons, TN, p. A588

BARTILSON, Jim, Manager Information Systems, South Peninsula Hospital, Homer, AK, p. A26

BARTINGALE, Robert, Administrator, Mayo Clinic Health System In Fairmont, Fairmont, MN, p. A339

BARTLETT, Beth MSN, R.N., Vice President Nursing, Chi Health Saint Francis, Grand Island, NE, p. A393

BARTLETT, Freda, Director of Nursing, Crosbyton Clinic Hospital, Crosbyton, TX, p. A604

BARTLETT, Karolyn, Assistant Administrator, Mayo Clinic Health System – Northland In Barron, Barron, WI, p. A698

BARTLETT, Regina, Chief Executive Officer, Tristar Hendersonville Medical Center, Hendersonville, TN, p. A580

BARTLETT, Richard M.D., Chief Medical Officer, Odessa Regional Medical Center South Campus, Odessa, TX, p. A636

BARTLETT, Ronald E, Chief Financial Officer, Boston Medical Center, Boston, MA, p. A303

BARTLETT, Thomas G. III, Administrator, Laird Hospital, Union, MS, p. A362

BARTLETT, Wayne, Director Information Systems, Alvarado Hospital Medical Center, San Diego, CA, p. A85

BARTLEY, Tracy, Manager Information Technology, Bath Community Hospital, Hot Springs, VA, p. A669

BARTOLETTI, Freddy M.D., Chief of Staff, Community Hospital Of Anaconda, Anaconda, MT, p. A382

BARTOLOTTA, Carmen J, Chief Nursing Officer, Missouri Baptist Sullivan Hospital, Sullivan, MO, p. A380

BARTON, Cheryl Lynne., R.N., Chief Executive Officer, Southeast Health Center Of Ripley County, Doniphan, MO, p. A367

BARTON, Michelle, Chief Operating Officer, Milford Valley Memorial Hospital, Milford, UT, p. A657

BARTON, Thomas M.D., Medical Director, Tops Surgical Specialty Hospital, Houston, TX, p. A623

BARTON, Vikki R.N., Chief Nursing Officer, Collingsworth General Hospital, Wellington, TX, p. A653

BARTOS, John M., Chief Executive Officer, Marcus Daly Memorial Hospital, Hamilton, MT, p. A385

BARWICK, Kim, Vice President Human Resources, Anthony Medical Center, Anthony, KS, p. A238

BARWIS, Kurt A., FACHE, President and Chief Executive Officer, Bristol Hospital, Bristol, CT, p. A109

BASA, Rhea, Director Human Resources, Morrill County Community Hospital, Bridgeport, NE, p. A391

BASA–REYES, Fiona, Chief Executive Officer, Kindred Hospital–Baldwin Park, Baldwin Park, CA, p. A53

BASCH, Jim, Chief Financial Officer, Coquille Valley Hospital, Coquille, OR, p. A521

BASCOM, Steven M.D., Chief Medical Officer, Guthrie County Hospital, Guthrie Center, IA, p. A228

BASELGA, Jose M.D., Physician–in–Chief, Memorial Sloan–Kettering Cancer Center, New Rochelle, NY, p. A442

BASEY, Marjorie, Chief Financial Officer, Rehabilitation Hospital Of Indiana, Indianapolis, IN, p. A212

BASH, Camille, Chief Financial Officer, Doctors Community Hospital, Lanham, MD, p. A299

BASHIR, Chowdry M.D., Chief of Staff, Richard L. Roudebush Veterans Affairs Medical Center, Indianapolis, IN, p. A212

BASIL, Christine M., MSN, RN, Chief Operating Officer and Chief Nursing Officer, Holy Family Hospital, Methuen, MA, p. A308

BASILE, Michele S., Chief Executive Officer, Kindred Hospital South Philadelphia, Philadelphia, PA, p. A544

BASLER, Cyndi, Chief Operating Officer, Iron County Medical Center, Pilot Knob, MO, p. A375

BASQUE, Tonya, Chief Nursing Officer, Freestone Medical Center, Fairfield, TX, p. A612

BASQUILL, Debra, Director Human Resources, Jennersville Regional Hospital, West Grove, PA, p. A553

BASRIA, Deborah, Human Resources Payroll Administrator, Kindred Hospital Bay Area–Tampa, Tampa, FL, p. A145

BASS, Andrew C. M.D., Medical Director, Shands Live Oak Regional Medical Center, Live Oak, FL, p. A131

BASS, Darren, President, Cox Monett Hospital, Monett, MO, p. A374

BASS, Louis A., Chief Executive Officer, RMC Anniston, Anniston, AL, p. A13

BASS, Michael, Chief Executive Officer, Kindred Hospital–Philadelphia, Philadelphia, PA, p. A544

BASS, Sonya MS, Chief Nursing Officer, Colorado Plains Medical Center, Fort Morgan, CO, p. A102

BASSETT, Eugene, President and Chief Executive Officer, St. Rose Dominican Hospitals – Siena Campus, Henderson, NV, p. A402

BASSETT, Kimberly S., R.N., President, Norwood Hospital, Norwood, MA, p. A310

BASSO, Marty
Chief Financial Officer, Sibley Memorial Hospital, Washington, DC, p. A118
Senior Vice President Finance, Suburban Hospital, Bethesda, MD, p. A297

BASTIANELLO, Carol, Director Human Resources, Aspirus Iron River Hospitals & Clinics, Inc., Iron River, MI, p. A323

BASTIEN, Samuel A. IV, Ph.D., Chief Executive Officer, Four Winds Hospital, Saratoga Springs, NY, p. A452

BASTING, Gregory, M.D.

Vice President Medical Affairs, Allied Services Rehabilitation Hospital, Scranton, PA, p. A550
Vice President Medical Affairs, John Heinz Institute Of Rehabilitation Medicine, Wilkes, PA, p. A554

BATA, Katie
Vice President Human Resources, Advocate Illinois Masonic Medical Center, Chicago, IL, p. A180
Vice President Human Resources, Advocate Lutheran General Hospital, Park Ridge, IL, p. A197

BATAL, Lucille M., Administrator, Baldpate Hospital, Georgetown, MA, p. A307

BATCHELOR, Dale M.D., Chief Medical Officer, Saint Thomas West Hospital, Nashville, TN, p. A586

BATCHELOR, Daniela, Director Human Resources, Springhill Memorial Hospital, Mobile, AL, p. A20

BATCHLOR, Elaine, M.D., M.P.H., Chief Executive Officer, Martin Luther King, Jr. Community Hospital, Los Angeles, CA, p. A69

BATEMAN, Bryan S., Chief Executive Officer, Christus Lake Area Hospital, Lake Charles, LA, p. A279

BATEMAN, Jana R.N., Chief Nursing Officer, East Texas Medical Center Jacksonville, Jacksonville, TX, p. A625

BATEMAN, Kenneth, CPA, President and Chief Executive Officer, Southeast Hospital, Cape Girardeau, MO, p. A366

BATEMAN, Mark T, Interim Chief Operating Officer, Saint Agnes Medical Center, Fresno, CA, p. A61

BATEMAN, Steven B., Chief Executive Officer, St. Mark's Hospital, Salt Lake City, UT, p. A660

BATES, Christine, Chief Nursing Officer, Shodair Children's Hospital, Helena, MT, p. A385

BATES, Don, Chief Executive Officer, Golden Plains Community Hospital, Borger, TX, p. A598

BATES, Earl, Director Information Technology, Western Mental Health Institute, Bolivar, TN, p. A575

BATES, Joe M.D., Clinical Director, Rusk State Hospital, Rusk, TX, p. A641

BATES, Leslie, Manager Human Resources, Alta View Hospital, Sandy, UT, p. A661

BATES, Margaret, Chief of Staff, Good Samaritan Hospital, Los Angeles, CA, p. A68

BATES, Ondrea, Senior Vice President, Operations and Continuum of Care, Henry Ford Allegiance Health, Jackson, MI, p. A323

BATES, Richard, Vice President of Medical Affairs, Midmichigan Medical Center – Alpena, Alpena, MI, p. A314

BATES, Robert A., Executive Director Finance and Chief Financial Officer, St. Vincent Carmel Hospital, Carmel, IN, p. A205

BATES, Victoria A., Director Human Resources, Memorial Hospital Of Salem County, Salem, NJ, p. A420

BATH, Harneet M.D., Vice President, Chief Medicine Officer, OSF Saint Anthony Medical Center, Rockford, IL, p. A199

BATISTE, Michele, Director Human Resources, Preston Memorial Hospital, Kingwood, WV, p. A693

BATORY, Robert J, Vice President Human Resources, Wellspan York Hospital, York, PA, p. A555

BATRASH, Ahmad, Chief of Staff, Kansas City Veterans Affairs Medical Center, Kansas City, MO, p. A370

BATSHAW, Mark L M.D., Physician–in–Chief, Executive Vice President and Chief Academic Officer, Children's National Health System, Washington, DC, p. A117

BATTEY, Patrick M., M.D., Chief Executive Officer, Piedmont Hospital, Atlanta, GA, p. A150

BATTISTA, Edward
Vice President Human Resources, California Pacific Medical Center–St. Luke's Campus, San Francisco, CA, p. A87
Vice President Human Resources, California Pacific Medical Center, San Francisco, CA, p. A87
Vice President Human Resources, Good Samaritan Hospital, San Jose, CA, p. A88

BATTLE, Joe, Director, James A. Haley Veterans' Hospital–Tampa, Tampa, FL, p. A144

BATTLES, Lindsay, Director Human Resources, Healthsouth Rehabilitation Hospital – Dallas, Dallas, TX, p. A605

BATTS, Kayla, Manager Human Resources, Baptist Health La Grange, La Grange, KY, p. A260

BATTY, Jill I, Chief Financial Officer, Cambridge Health Alliance, Cambridge, MA, p. A305

BATTY, Mark, Chief Executive Officer, Rochelle Community Hospital, Rochelle, IL, p. A198

BATULIS, Scott, President and Chief Executive Officer, Orange Regional Medical Center, Middletown, NY, p. A439

BATY, Krista R.N., Chief Nursing Officer, Cedar Park Regional Medical Center, Cedar Park, TX, p. A601

BATZEL, Linnean M.D., Senior Vice President Quality and Medical Affairs and Chief Medical Officer, Upmc Altoona, Altoona, PA, p. A528

BAUER, Jessica, Chief Executive Officer, Aurora Sinai Medical Center, Milwaukee, WI, p. A707

BAUER, John, Chief Operating Officer, Pam Specialty Hospital Of Covington, Covington, LA, p. A273

BAUER, Jonathan, Director Information Systems, Somerset Hospital, Somerset, PA, p. A551

BAUER, K Robert. Jr, Interim Chief Executive Officer, Northside Medical Center, Youngstown, OH, p. A503

BAUER, Kyle, Chief Executive Officer and Chief Financial Officer, Cuyuna Regional Medical Center, Crosby, MN, p. A338

BAUER, Robert
Director Human Resources, Borgess–Lee Memorial Hospital, Dowagiac, MI, p. A318
Vice President Human Resources, Midwest Orthopedic Specialty Hospital, Franklin, WI, p. A702
Vice President Human Resources, Wheaton Franciscan Healthcare – Franklin, Franklin, WI, p. A702

BAUER, Roberta M.D., Acting Chair Medical Staff, Cleveland Clinic Children's Hospital For Rehabilitation, Cleveland, OH, p. A485

BAUER, Sandra A, Director Human Resources, Jefferson Community Health And Life, Fairbury, NE, p. A392

BAUER, Shar, Executive Secretary, Wishek Community Hospital And Clinics, Wishek, ND, p. A478

BAUER, Tracy, Chief Executive Officer, Midwest Medical Center, Galena, IL, p. A188

BAUER, William, M.D.
Medical Director, Montevista Hospital, Las Vegas, NV, p. A403
Vice President Finance and Chief Financial Officer, Lehigh Valley Hospital – Hazleton, Hazleton, PA, p. A536

BAUM, David M.D., Senior Vice President Medical Services, F. F. Thompson Hospital, Canandaigua, NY, p. A433

BAUM, Judy, Chief Executive Officer, Mountain Valley Regional Rehabilitation Hospital, Prescott Valley, AZ, p. A35

BAUMAN, Chris, Director of Nursing, Ballard Rehabilitation Hospital, San Bernardino, CA, p. A85

BAUMAN, Jonathan M.D., Chief Medical Officer, Four Winds Hospital, Katonah, NY, p. A438

BAUMAN, Stephen R., Medical Center Director, Veterans Affairs Central California Health Care System, Fresno, CA, p. A61

BAUMAN, Tracie R.N., Chief Nursing Officer, Great Lakes Specialty Hospital–Grand Rapids, Grand Rapids, MI, p. A321

BAUMBERGER, David M.D., Chief Medical Officer, Decatur Memorial Hospital, Decatur, IL, p. A185

BAUMERT, Steven P., President and Chief Executive Officer, Methodist Jennie Edmundson Hospital, Council Bluffs, IA, p. A225

BAUMGARDNER, Brian, Chief Executive Officer, Lewis–Gale Medical Center, Salem, VA, p. A675

BAUMGARDNER, David, Director Information Management, Union Hospital, Dover, OH, p. A490

BAUMGARTNER, Jennifer, Chief Information Officer, Perkins County Health Services, Grant, NE, p. A393

BAUMGARTNER, Michael A., President, SSM Health St. Francis Hospital – Maryville, Maryville, MO, p. A373

BAUNCHALK, James M, Deputy Chief Clinical Services, Dwight David Eisenhower Army Medical Center, Fort Gordon, GA, p. A158

BAUR, Heidi R.N., MS, Chief Nursing Officer, St. Christopher's Hospital For Children, Philadelphia, PA, p. A545

BAUSCHKA, Martha F. R.N., Vice President and Chief Nursing Officer, Southwest General Health Center, Middleburg Heights, OH, p. A496

BAUTE, Corey
Vice President Human Resources, Franciscan St. Francis Health – Indianapolis, Indianapolis, IN, p. A211
Vice President of Human Resource, Franciscan St. Francis Health–Carmel, Carmel, IN, p. A205

BAVA, Michele, Director Human Resources, Doctors Medical Center Of Modesto, Modesto, CA, p. A74

BAVERSO, Lou, Vice President Operations, Magee–Womens Hospital Of Upmc, Pittsburgh, PA, p. A547

BAW, Joseph, Director Human Resources, Riveredge Hospital, Forest Park, IL, p. A188

BAWA, Balraj M.D., Assistant Director Medical Services, Central Virginia Training Center, Madison Heights, VA, p. A670

BAXA, Erin M.D., Chief Medical Officer, Osborne County Memorial Hospital, Osborne, KS, p. A248

BAXLEY, Edmond Russell. III, President and Chief Executive Officer, Beaufort Memorial Hospital, Beaufort, SC, p. A558

BAXTER, Greg M.D., Senior Vice President Medical Affairs and Chief Medical Officer, Elliot Hospital, Manchester, NH, p. A409

BAXTER, Joshua, Director, Information Systems, Powell Valley Healthcare, Powell, WY, p. A719

BAXTER, Michael T., President and Chief Executive Officer, Parkview Medical Center, Pueblo, CO, p. A106

BAXTER, Robert O., Regional Chief Executive Officer, Lima, St. Rita's Medical Center, Lima, OH, p. A493

BAYARDO, Fernando M.D., Chief Medical Officer, Presbyterian Espanola Hospital, Espanola, NM, p. A426

BAYER, Brian, Information Technology Site Leader, Kalamazoo Psychiatric Hospital, Kalamazoo, MI, p. A324

BAYLESS, Victoria, President and Chief Executive Officer, Anne Arundel Medical Center, Annapolis, MD, p. A294

BAYOUMY, Sam, Chief Executive Officer, Cleveland Clinic Rehabilitation Hospital, Avon, OH, p. A480

BAYTOS, David G., Chief Executive Officer, Methodist Olive Branch Hospital, Olive Branch, MS, p. A360

BAYTOS, David G, Interim President, Methodist Healthcare Memphis Hospitals, Memphis, TN, p. A585

BAYUS, Robin, Chief Financial Officer, Rancho Los Amigos National Rehabilitation Center, Downey, CA, p. A58

BAZELEY, Stephen M.D., Vice President Medical Affairs, St. Luke's Hospital, Maumee, OH, p. A495

BAZEMORE, Webster Carl M.D., Interim Chief of Staff, Charles George Veterans Affairs Medical Center, Asheville, NC, p. A457

BEA, Javon R.
Chief Executive Officer, Mercyhealth Hospital And Medical Center – Harvard, Harvard, IL, p. A189
President and Chief Executive Officer, Mercyhealth Hospital – Rockton Avenue, Rockford, IL, p. A199
President and Chief Executive Officer, Mercyhealth Hospital And Medical Center – Walworth, Lake Geneva, WI, p. A704
President and Chief Executive Officer, Mercyhealth Hospital And Trauma Center – Janesville, Janesville, WI, p. A704

BEACH, Karrie, Vice President Finance, Community Memorial Hospital, Syracuse, NE, p. A400

BEACH, Sarah, Director of Nursing, Jerold Phelps Community Hospital, Garberville, CA, p. A61

BEACHMAN, Michelle, Chief Financial Officer, Twin Rivers Regional Medical Center, Kennett, MO, p. A371

BEADMAN, Cindi, Director Medical Records, Harper Hospital District Five, Harper, KS, p. A242

BEAL, Christopher M.D., Chief of Staff, Sparrow Clinton Hospital, Saint Johns, MI, p. A330

BEAL, Dwight, Chief Fiscal Services, Jack C. Montgomery Veterans Affairs Medical Center, Muskogee, OK, p. A510

BEAL, Rachel, Chief Operating Officer, Poplar Springs Hospital, Petersburg, VA, p. A673

BEAL, Walter Edwin., Chief Executive Officer, Central Regional Hospital, Butner, NC, p. A458

BEALES, Julie M.D., Chief of Staff, Hunter Holmes Mcguire Veterans Affairs Medical Center–Richmond, Richmond, VA, p. A674

BEAM, William M.D., Chief of Staff, Cornerstone Hospital Of Huntington, Huntington, WV, p. A692

BEAMAN, Charles D. Jr, Chief Executive Officer, Palmetto Health, Columbia, SC, p. B96

BEAMAN, Frank, Chief Executive Officer, Faith Community Hospital, Jacksboro, TX, p. A625

BEAMES, Bo, Interim Chief Executive Officer, Miners' Colfax Medical Center, Raton, NM, p. A427

BEAN, Howard M.D., Chief Medical Officer, Mary Black Health System–Spartanburg, Spartanburg, SC, p. A566

BEAN, Roberta R.N., Associate Chief Nursing Officer, Banner Fort Collins Medical Center, Fort Collins, CO, p. A102

BEAN, Todd, Chief Medical Officer, Cass County Memorial Hospital, Atlantic, IA, p. A222

BEAR, John, Hospital Administrator Officer and Supervisor Human Resources, Lawton Indian Hospital, Lawton, OK, p. A509

BEARD, Angie, R.N.
Houston County Community Hospital, Erin, TN, p. A578
Chief Nursing Officer, Northcrest Medical Center, Springfield, TN, p. A589

BEARD, Bert, Chief Executive Officer, Maria Parham Medical Center, Henderson, NC, p. A464

BEARD, Bradley, Regional President, Fairview Southdale Hospital, Edina, MN, p. A339

BEARD, Chris, Chief Nursing Officer, Brownfield Regional Medical Center, Brownfield, TX, p. A599

BEARD, Edward L, R.N., Chief Operating Officer and Chief Nursing Officer, Catawba Valley Medical Center, Hickory, NC, p. A464

BEARD, Gerald C, Chief Operating Officer, Healthmark Regional Medical Center, Defuniak Springs, FL, p. A123

BEARD, Joan, Chief Nursing Officer, Northwest Florida Community Hospital, Chipley, FL, p. A121

BEARD, Rhonda
Director Human Resources, Palestine Regional Medical Center–East, Palestine, TX, p. A636
Director Human Resources, Palestine Regional Medical Center, Palestine, TX, p. A636

BEARD, Robert, Chief Clinical Officer, Vibra Hospital Of Northwestern Indiana, Crown Point, IN, p. A206

BEARD, Tim
Chief Executive Officer, Cimarron Memorial Hospital, Boise City, OK, p. A505
Director, Information Technology, Cimarron Memorial Hospital, Boise City, OK, p. A505

BEARDEN, Amy R.N., MSN, Vice President Patient Care Services and Chief Nursing Officer, St. Luke's Magic Valley Medical Center, Twin Falls, ID, p. A176

BEASLEY, Carla, Director of Nursing, Mitchell County Hospital, Camilla, GA, p. A153

BEASLEY, Jared R.N., Vice President Patient Care, Parkview Lagrange Hospital, Lagrange, IN, p. A214

BEASLEY, Ruth, Director Human Resources, Vanderbilt Stallworth Rehabilitation Hospital, Nashville, TN, p. A587

BEATTIE, Kathryn M.D., Senior Vice President and Chief Medical Officer, Uw Medicine/Valley Medical Center, Renton, WA, p. A684

BEATTIE, Mac, Computer Network Specialist, Deer's Head Hospital Center, Salisbury, MD, p. A300

BEATTY, Alan L, Vice President Human Resources, Shore Medical Center, Somers Point, NJ, p. A420

BEATTY, Ann, Director Human Resources, Cleveland Clinic Fairview Hospital, Cleveland, OH, p. A485

BEATTY, Dale E MSN, R.N., Chief Nursing Officer, University Of Illinois Hospital & Health Sciences System, Chicago, IL, p. A184

BEATTY, Jim, Chief Operating Officer, Overland Park Regional Medical Center, Overland Park, KS, p. A249

BEATTY, John, Vice President Human Resources, Barnes–Jewish Hospital, Saint Louis, MO, p. A376

BEATTY, Robert, Chief Operating Officer, Highland Ridge Hospital, Midvale, UT, p. A657

BEATTY, Talia, Director Human Resources, Sunbury Community Hospital And Outpatient Center, Sunbury, PA, p. A551

BEATY, Holly, Chief Financial Officer, South Central Kansas Medical Center, Arkansas City, KS, p. A238

BEAUBIEN, Troy, Director Information Services, Manatee Memorial Hospital, Bradenton, FL, p. A120

BEAUCHAMP, Bill, Chief Financial Officer, St. Luke's Sugar Land Hospital, Sugar Land, TX, p. A647

BEAUCHANE, Nichole, Director Information Technology, Riverview Health, Crookston, MN, p. A338

BEAUDOIN, Dale, Vice President Human Resources, Lewis–Gale Medical Center, Salem, VA, p. A675

BEAUDOIN, Paul, Chief Financial Officer, Day Kimball Hospital, Putnam, CT, p. A112

BEAULAC, Gary, Chief Operating Officer, Henry Ford Macomb Hospitals, Clinton Township, MI, p. A316

BEAULIEU, Jennifer, Director of Nursing, Intermountain Hospital, Boise, ID, p. A171

BEAULIEU, Lynn R.N., Chief Nursing Officer, Healthsouth Walton Rehabilitation Hospital, Augusta, GA, p. A151

BEAULIEU, Michael Gregory M.D., Chief Medical Officer, Helen Newberry Joy Hospital, Newberry, MI, p. A327

BEAUPRE', Paul, M.D., Chief Executive Officer, St. John's Medical Center And Living Center, Jackson, WY, p. A718

BEAUREGARD, Paige, Chief Executive Officer, Regency Hospital Of Greenville, Greenville, SC, p. A563

BEAVEN, Stacey R.N., Chief Nursing Officer, Saint Thomas Rutherford Hospital, Murfreesboro, TN, p. A586

BEAVER, Michael D, Chief Executive Officer, Methodist Hospital, San Antonio, TX, p. A643

BEAVER, Patrick MSN, R.N., Chief Nursing Officer, East Cooper Medical Center, Mount Pleasant, SC, p. A564

BEAVER, Randy, Chief Information Officer, Palo Alto County Health System, Emmetsburg, IA, p. A227

BEAVER, Rhonda, Chief Operating Officer, Creek Nation Community Hospital, Okemah, OK, p. A511

BEBOW, Gary, FACHE, Administrator and Chief Executive Officer, White River Medical Center, Batesville, AR, p. A40

BECHAMPS, Gerald, M.D.
Vice President Medical Affairs, War Memorial Hospital, Berkeley Springs, WV, p. A690
Vice President of Medical Affairs, Hampshire Memorial Hospital, Romney, WV, p. A696

BECHTEL, Kathleen MSN, R.N., Vice President Patient Care Services and Chief Nursing Officer, Froedtert Memorial Lutheran Hospital, Milwaukee, WI, p. A708

BECK, Allan, Chief Executive Officer, Baylor Orthopedic And Spine Hospital At Arlington, Arlington, TX, p. A593

BECK, Ann
Vice President and Chief Financial Officer, Carson Tahoe Continuing Care Hospital, Carson City, NV, p. A401
Vice President Finance, Carson Tahoe Health, Carson City, NV, p. A401

BECK, David, Chief Operating Officer, Lane Regional Medical Center, Zachary, LA, p. A288

BECK, Debbie, Manager Human Resource and Payroll, Ochiltree General Hospital, Perryton, TX, p. A637

BECK, Gary E., Administrator, Sevier Valley Hospital, Richfield, UT, p. A659

BECK, Howard M.D., Chief of Staff, Grace Medical Center, Lubbock, TX, p. A630

BECK, J Christopher D.O., President Medical Staff, Aspen Valley Hospital, Aspen, CO, p. A98

BECK, Pamela, Interim Chief Executive Officer, Tennova Physicians Regional Medical Center, Knoxville, TN, p. A582

BECK, Rebecca
President, Wellmont Hancock County Hospital, Sneedville, TN, p. A589
President, Wellmont Hawkins County Memorial Hospital, Rogersville, TN, p. A588

BECK, Brian, PHR,MHROD, Vice President Human Resources, Oak Valley Hospital District, Oakdale, CA, p. A77

BECK, Steve MS, Director Human Resources, Kearney Regional Medical Center, Kearney, NE, p. A394

BECKER, Cindy, Vice President and Chief Operating Officer, Highland Hospital, Rochester, NY, p. A450

BECKER, Eric
Chief Executive Officer, Texas Orthopedic Hospital, Houston, TX, p. A623
Chief Operating Officer, Research Medical Center, Kansas City, MO, p. A370

BECKER, Frank
Chief Financial Officer, Lourdes Counseling Center, Richland, WA, p. A684
Chief Financial Officer, Lourdes Medical Center, Pasco, WA, p. A683

BECKER, Kathleen R., M.P.H., JD, President, SSM Health Saint Louis University Hospital, Saint Louis, MO, p. A378

BECKER, Kathy Ph.D., R.N., Vice President and Chief Nursing Officer, Aurora West Allis Medical Center, West Allis, WI, p. A715

BECKER, Kelly, Administrative Coordinator Human Resources, Kindred Hospital Indianapolis North, Indianapolis, IN, p. A211

BECKER, Preston, Chief Executive Officer, Carson Valley Medical Center, Gardnerville, NV, p. A402

BECKER, Ralph W, Vice President, Chief Financial Officer, Saint Mary's Hospital, Waterbury, CT, p. A114

BECKES, Hap, Director Information Systems, Sullivan County Community Hospital, Sullivan, IN, p. A220

BECKETT, C. Donovan, Chief Medical Officer, Williamson Memorial Hospital, Williamson, WV, p. A697

BECKHAM, Steve, Director Human Resources, Magee General Hospital, Magee, MS, p. A358

BECKMAN, Beth P R.N., Ph.D., Chief Nursing Officer, Baylor Regional Medical Center At Grapevine, Grapevine, TX, p. A617

BECKMANN, Gregory, Chief Executive Officer, Chi Health Plainview, Plainview, NE, p. A399

BECKNER, Jana, Director Human Resources, Lewisgale Hospital Pulaski, Pulaski, VA, p. A673

BECKSVOORT, Jennifer F, Senior Human Resource Business Partner, Spectrum Health Zeeland Community Hospital, Zeeland, MI, p. A334

BECKWITH, Jami, Director Human Resources, Choctaw Nation Health Care Center, Talihina, OK, p. A516

BEDARD, Lori, Interim Chief Executive Officer, Healthsouth Rehabilitation Hospital Of Altamonte Springs, Altamonte Springs, FL, p. A119

BEDELL, Mikael M.D., Medical Director, Cascade Medical Center, Cascade, ID, p. A172

BEDFORD, Tim, Chief Executive Officer, Emerald Coast Behavioral Hospital, Panama City, FL, p. A138

BEDGER, Kathy, Chief Nursing Officer, Penn Highlands Clearfield, Clearfield, PA, p. A531

BEDI, Andrew, Chief Operating Officer, Tristar Greenview Regional Hospital, Bowling Green, KY, p. A256

BEDICK, Jennifer L., Deputy Commander Nursing, Tripler Army Medical Center, Honolulu, HI, p. A169

BEDINGFIELD, Lance, Director Information Services, Dixie Regional Medical Center, Saint George, UT, p. A660

BEDSOLE, Jessica, Director, Human Resources, Wellstar Paulding Hospital, Hiram, GA, p. A159

BEDZYK, J. Paul, Deputy Director Administration, Elmira Psychiatric Center, Elmira, NY, p. A435

BEEBE, Chris T, Director Human Resources, Raleigh General Hospital, Beckley, WV, p. A690

BEEBY, Lori, Director Information Systems, Community Hospital, Mccook, NE, p. A396

BEECHLER, Jane, Director Healthcare Information Systems, Wyoming County Community Hospital, Warsaw, NY, p. A455

BEECHY, Andrew, Manager Information Technology Systems, Lee's Summit Medical Center, Lee's Summit, MO, p. A372

BEED, Donna E, Chief Information Management Division, Tripler Army Medical Center, Honolulu, HI, p. A169

BEEDLE, Chester
Chief Financial Officer, Kern Valley Healthcare District, Lake Isabella, CA, p. A65
Interim Chief Financial Officer, Adventist Health Medical Center – Tehachapi Valley, Tehachapi, CA, p. A93

BEEDY, Scott, Chief Financial Officer, Hansford Hospital, Spearman, TX, p. A646

BEEG, Gregg M FACHE, Chief Financial Officer, Oaklawn Hospital, Marshall, MI, p. A326

BEEG, Gregg, Chief Financial Officer, Mclaren Central Michigan, Mount Pleasant, MI, p. A326

BEEHLER, Darryl D.O., Chief of Staff, Chi St. Joseph's Health, Park Rapids, MN, p. A345

BEEHN, Holly, Director Human Resources, Southwest Health, Platteville, WI, p. A710

BEELER, Janelle E, Human Resource Manager, Baraga County Memorial Hospital, L'Anse, MI, p. A324

BEERS, Nathaniel, M.D., President and Chief Executive Officer, The Hsc Pediatric Center, Washington, DC, p. A118

BEESON, John C M.D., Chief Medical Officer, Christus St. Vincent Regional Medical Center, Santa Fe, NM, p. A428

BEGALSKE, Kathy, Chief Nursing Officer, Gundersen Palmer Lutheran Hospital And Clinics, West Union, IA, p. A236

BEGAN, Victoria D., R.N., MS, President and Chief Executive Officer, San Carlos Apache Healthcare Corporation, Peridot, AZ, p. A32

BEGAY, Trudy, Human Resources Specialist, Hopi Health Care Center, Keams Canyon, AZ, p. A30

BEGAYE, Lorraine, Supervisory Human Resource Specialist, Chinle Comprehensive Health Care Facility, Chinle, AZ, p. A28

BEGGANE, Thomas, Manager Human Resources, Lac–Olive View–Ucla Medical Center, Los Angeles, CA, p. A69

BEGLEY, Robyn R.N., Chief Nursing Officer, Atlanticare Regional Medical Center, Atlantic City, NJ, p. A411

BEHAN, Lawrence
Vice President Administration and Finance, Chief Financial Officer, Walden Behavioral Care, Waltham, MA, p. A312
Vice President Administration and Finance, Chief Financial Officer, Walden Behavioral Care, Waltham, MA, p. A312

BEHAR, Robert, M.D., Chief Executive Officer, North Cypress Medical Center, Cypress, TX, p. A604

BEHM, Anthony D.O., Chief of Staff, Erie Veterans Affairs Medical Center, Erie, PA, p. A534

BEHNE, Carl P., Chief Executive Officer, Greene County Medical Center, Jefferson, IA, p. A230

BEHNER, Bruce M, Chief Operating Officer, Knox Community Hospital, Mount Vernon, OH, p. A496

BEHNKEN, Nick, Supervisor Information Technology, Red Bud Regional Hospital, Red Bud, IL, p. A198

BEHRENDT, Darcy R.N., Vice President, Patient Care Services, Chi Health Missouri Valley, Missouri Valley, IA, p. A231

BEHRENDTSEN, Ole, M.D.
Medical Director, Santa Barbara County Psychiatric Health Facility, Santa Barbara, CA, p. A90
Interim Director, Santa Barbara County Psychiatric Health Facility, Santa Barbara, CA, p. A90

BEHRENS, Colleen, Director Information Technology, Community Memorial Healthcare, Marysville, KS, p. A246

BEHRENS, Karen, Director Technology Services, Perry Memorial Hospital, Princeton, IL, p. A198

BEHRENS, Sharon R.N., MSN, Chief Clinical Officer, Rehabilitation Hospital Of Wisconsin, Waukesha, WI, p. A714

BEHZAD, John, Chief Executive Officer, California Rehabilitation Institute, Los Angeles, CA, p. A67

BEIDELSCHIES, Sandra MSN, R.N., Vice President Patient Services, Wood County Hospital, Bowling Green, OH, p. A482

BEIERMAN, Jennifer, Director Human Resources, Boone County Health Center, Albion, NE, p. A390

BEIGHLE, John, Flight Chief Medical Information Systems, Wright Patterson Medical Center, Wright, OH, p. A503

BEIKMAN, Sara, Director of Nursing, Clay County Medical Center, Clay Center, KS, p. A239

BEILER, Jeffrey, Associate Director, Philadelphia Veterans Affairs Medical Center, Philadelphia, PA, p. A545

BEINDIT, Dawn, Labor Relations Partner, St. John River District Hospital, East China, MI, p. A319

BEISWENGER, Joel, Chief Executive Officer, Tri–County Hospital, Wadena, MN, p. A350

BEITCHER, Bob, Chief Executive Officer, Motion Picture And Television Fund Hospital And Residential Services, Los Angeles, CA, p. A70

BEITER, Amy, M.D., President and Chief Executive Officer, Carondelet St. Mary's Hospital, Tucson, AZ, p. A37

BEITING, Mark, Vice President Human Resources, Alta Bates Summit Medical Center – Summit Campus, Oakland, CA, p. A77

BEITZEL, Mark, Director Information Systems, Advocate Lutheran General Hospital, Park Ridge, IL, p. A197

BEJNAR, Darla M.D., Chief Medical Officer, Socorro General Hospital, Socorro, NM, p. A429

BELAIR, Norman, Senior Vice President and Chief Financial Officer, Southern Maine Health Care – Biddeford Medical Center, Biddeford, ME, p. A290

BELANGER, Robert, Chief Executive Officer, Sanford Bagley Medical Center, Bagley, MN, p. A336

BELCHER, Debbie, Director Human Resource, Vibra Rehabilitation Hospital Lake Travis, Lakeway, TX, p. A628

BELCHER, Laura, Administrator, The Medical Center Albany, Albany, KY, p. A255

BELDECOS, Athena M.D., Medical Director, Vibra Hospital Of Charleston, Mt. Pleasant, SC, p. A564

BELGARDE, Donna, Human Resources Specialist, Indian Health Service – Quentin N. Burdick Memorial Health Care Facility, Belcourt, ND, p. A474

BELHASEN, F K M.D., Medical Director, Paul B. Hall Regional Medical Center, Paintsville, KY, p. A266

BELJIN, Dawn R.N., Chief Nursing Officer, Dallas Medical Center, Dallas, TX, p. A605

BELKOSKI, Dave, Chief Financial Officer, University Hospital Mcduffie, Thomson, GA, p. A166

BELKOSKI, David, Senior Vice President and Chief Financial Officer, University Hospital, Augusta, GA, p. A152

BELL, Billie, Chief Nursing Officer, Medina Regional Hospital, Hondo, TX, p. A619

BELL, Brian, Associate Administrator and Chief Operating Officer, National Park Medical Center, Hot Springs, AR, p. A44

BELL, Cindy, Director Finance, Willow Crest Hospital, Miami, OK, p. A510

BELL, Gary C., LFACHE, Chief Executive Officer, Lehigh Regional Medical Center, Lehigh Acres, FL, p. A131

BELL, Gordon M.D., Chief of Staff, Frances Mahon Deaconess Hospital, Glasgow, MT, p. A384

BELL, Heath, Vice President, Chief Information Officer, Northwestern Medicine Valley West Hospital, Sandwich, IL, p. A200

BELL, Hollis M.D., Medical Director, Mercy Rehabilitation Hospital Springfield, Springfield, MO, p. A380

BELL, Julie
Chief Nursing Officer, Covenant Specialty Hospital, Lubbock, TX, p. A630
Interim Chief Executive Officer and Chief Nursing Officer, Covenant Specialty Hospital, Lubbock, TX, p. A630

BELL, Kae, Chief Financial Officer, Brentwood Hospital, Shreveport, LA, p. A285

BELL, Kenneth, Chief Executive Officer, Healthsouth Scottsdale Rehabilitation Hospital, Scottsdale, AZ, p. A35

BELL, Madeline, President and Chief Executive Officer, Children's Hospital Of Philadelphia, Philadelphia, PA, p. A543

BELL, Michael, Chief Operating Officer, Sierra Vista Regional Medical Center, San Luis Obispo, CA, p. A89

BELL, Pam, Vice President Patient Care Services and Chief Nursing Officer, Presence Resurrection Medical Center, Chicago, IL, p. A182

BELL, Randall C M.D., Medical Director, Lifecare Hospitals Of San Antonio, San Antonio, TX, p. A643

BELL, Roderick, Chief Financial Officer, College Hospital Cerritos, Cerritos, CA, p. A55

BELL, Rodric M.D., Medical Director, Healthsouth Tustin Rehabilitation Hospital, Tustin, CA, p. A94

BELL, Roseanna, Chief Nurse Executive, Multicare Auburn Medical Center, Auburn, WA, p. A678

BELL, Sammie Jr, Chief Financial Officer, Tallahatchie General Hospital, Charleston, MS, p. A353

BELL, Scot, Chief Medical Officer, Anderson Regional Health System, Meridian, MS, p. A359

BELL, Sonja, Coordinator Human Resources, Sedgwick County Health Center, Julesburg, CO, p. A104

BELL, Stuart M.D., Vice President, Medical Affairs, Medstar Union Memorial Hospital, Baltimore, MD, p. A295

BELL, Talana, Chief Financial Officer, Flowers Hospital, Dothan, AL, p. A16

BELL, Tammie
Director Human Resources, Mckenzie Regional Hospital, Mckenzie, TN, p. A584
Director Human Resources, Tennova Healthcare Volunteer Community Hospital, Martin, TN, p. A583

BELL, W Scot M.D., Chief Medical Officer, Rush Foundation Hospital, Meridian, MS, p. A359

BELLAMY, David, Chief Financial Officer, Mclaren Northern Michigan, Petoskey, MI, p. A328

BELLAND, Patrick, President, Fairview Ridges Hospital, Burnsville, MN, p. A337

BELLATTY, Christine, Acting Director of Nursing, Dorothea Dix Psychiatric Center, Bangor, ME, p. A289

BELLEAU, Christopher M.D., Medical Director, Sage Rehabilitation Hospital, Baton Rouge, LA, p. A271

BELLEAU, Donella, Director Human Resources, Graham County Hospital, Hill City, KS, p. A242

BELLINGER, Sean, Chief Executive Officer, Cedar Crest Hospital And Residential Treatment Center, Belton, TX, p. A598

BELLO, Stephen, Executive Director, Long Island Jewish Medical Center, New Rochelle, NY, p. A442

BELLUCCI, Alessandro, M.D., Executive Director, North Shore University Hospital, Manhasset, NY, p. A439

BELLUCY, Regina, Vice President Human Resources, Bethesda Hospital East, Boynton Beach, FL, p. A120

BELMONT, Angela R.N., Interim Chief Nursing Officer, Faxton St. Luke's Healthcare, Utica, NY, p. A454

BELMONT, Chris, Chief Information Officer and Vice President, University Of Texas M.D. Anderson Cancer Center, Houston, TX, p. A623

BELMONT, James, Associate Director, Northern Arizona Veterans Affairs Health Care System, Prescott, AZ, p. A34

BELT, Katrina, Chief Financial Officer, Baptist Medical Center East, Montgomery, AL, p. A21

BELTRAN, Grace, Director Human Resources, Foundation Surgical Hospital of El Paso, El Paso, TX, p. A611

BELTZ, John, Chief Financial Officer, Hendry Regional Medical Center, Clewiston, FL, p. A122

BELZER, Leslie, Director Human Resources, Howard County Medical Center, Saint Paul, NE, p. A399

BEMENT, Douglas J, Chief Financial Officer, Kosciusko Community Hospital, Warsaw, IN, p. A221

BEN, Sabrina, Director Human Resources, North Star Behavioral Health System, Anchorage, AK, p. A25

BENAQUISTA, Kathleen, Executive Vice President and Chief Financial Officer, Maricopa Integrated Health System, Phoenix, AZ, p. A33

BENAVIDES, Christina, Director Employee Services, Otto Kaiser Memorial Hospital, Kenedy, TX, p. A626

BENCITO ACA–AC, Norie Lee Reyes R.N., MS, Director of Nursing, Loma Linda University Behavioral Medicine Center, Redlands, CA, p. A81

BENCOMO, Dionisio, Chief Executive Officer, Select Specialty Hospital–Miami, Miami, FL, p. A133

BENDER, Brad M.D., Chief of Staff, North Florida/South Georgia Veteran's Health System, Gainesville, FL, p. A126

BENDER, Daniel, Chief Operating Officer, South Bay Hospital, Sun City Center, FL, p. A143

BENDER, David B M.D., Chief Medical Staff, Grafton City Hospital, Grafton, WV, p. A692

BENDER, David, Chief Executive Officer, Gouverneur Hospital, Gouverneur, NY, p. A436

BENDER, Robert, Chief Financial Officer, Banner Casa Grande Medical Center, Casa Grande, AZ, p. A28

BENDER, Steve, Chief Financial Officer, Wuesthoff Medical Center – Melbourne, Melbourne, FL, p. A132

BENDINELLI, Emily, Director of Nurses, Ashley County Medical Center, Crossett, AR, p. A42

BENDYNA, Peter J, Director Human Resources, Wyoming County Community Hospital, Warsaw, NY, p. A455

BENEDICT, Brian, Director of Information Technology, Murray–Calloway County Hospital, Murray, KY, p. A265

BENEDICT, Eva, R.N., President and Chief Executive Officer, Jones Memorial Hospital, Wellsville, NY, p. A455

BENEDICT, Joy M, Director Human Resources, Baptist Health Richmond, Richmond, KY, p. A267

BENEFIELD, Justin, President, Ghs Hillcrest Memorial Hospital, Simpsonville, SC, p. B55

BENEFIELD, Marlene, Director Human Resources, Cherokee Medical Center, Centre, AL, p. A16

BENEPAL, Jaspreet, Chief Nursing Officer, Contra Costa Regional Medical Center, Martinez, CA, p. A73

BENETTI–LOYOLA, Pedro L., Administrator, Hospital San Cristobal, Coto Laurel, PR, p. A723

BENETTI–LOYOLA, Pedro L, Senior Executive and Vice President, Hospital San Cristobal, Coto Laurel, PR, p. A723

BENFIELD, Angie, Human Resources Generalist, Union Medical Center, Union, SC, p. A566

BENFIELD, Justin
Southern Region Chief Operating Officer, Greenville Health System – Laurens County Memorial Hospital, Clinton, SC, p. A560
Southern Region Chief Operating Officer, Greenville Health System – Laurens County Memorial Hospital, Clinton, SC, p. A560

BENFIELD, Ronald K
Chief Financial Officer, Peacehealth Southwest Medical Center, Vancouver, WA, p. A688

Chief Financial Officer, Peacehealth St. John Medical Center, Longview, WA, p. A682

BENGSTON, Jennifer M.D., Chief Medical Officer, Valley County Health System, Ord, NE, p. A398

BENGTSON, Paul R., Chief Executive Officer, Northeastern Vermont Regional Hospital, Saint Johnsbury, VT, p. A663

BENGYAK, Daniel, Vice President, Human Resources, St. Luke's Cornwall Hospital, Newburgh, NY, p. A447

BENHAM, D'Linda, Director of Nursing, Fisher County Hospital District, Rotan, TX, p. A640

BENINK, Eric M.D., Chief Medical Officer, Medical City Arlington, Arlington, TX, p. A593

BENITEZ, Pedro M.D., Medical Director, Hospital De Damas, Ponce, PR, p. A724

BENJAMIN, Christian, USAF, MC, Commander, Mike O'Callaghan Federal Hospital, Nellis Afb, NV, p. A404

BENNER, Brenda, Director Human Resources, Healthsouth Rehabilitation Hospital Of Sarasota, Sarasota, FL, p. A142

BENNETT, Anthony M.D., Chief Clinical Affairs, Baptist Health Medical Center–Little Rock, Little Rock, AR, p. A46

BENNETT, Bart
Chief Financial Officer, Springbrook Behavioral Health System, Travelers Rest, SC, p. A566
Chief Information Technology Officer, Springbrook Behavioral Health System, Travelers Rest, SC, p. A566

BENNETT, Courtney, Human Resource Manager, Alleghany Memorial Hospital, Sparta, NC, p. A471

BENNETT, Dan, President and Chief Executive Officer, Gifford Medical Center, Randolph, VT, p. A663

BENNETT, Darnell, Director Finance, Horizon Specialty Hospital, Las Vegas, NV, p. A403

BENNETT, E Kyle., President and Chief Executive Officer, Memorial Hospital And Health Care Center, Jasper, IN, p. A212

BENNETT, Edwin, Controller, Turning Point Hospital, Moultrie, GA, p. A162

BENNETT, Elizabeth, Interim Chief Executive Officer, Tri Parish Rehabilitation Hospital, Leesville, LA, p. A280

BENNETT, Fay, Vice President Employee Services, Guadalupe Regional Medical Center, Seguin, TX, p. A644

BENNETT, Gary M.D., Chief of Medical Staff, Chapman Global Medical Center, Orange, CA, p. A77

BENNETT, James, Chief Executive Officer, Surgical Institute Of Reading, Wyomissing, PA, p. A555

BENNETT, Kay R
System Director Human Resources, Baptist Medical Center South, Montgomery, AL, p. A21
Vice President Human Resources, Baptist Medical Center East, Montgomery, AL, p. A21

BENNETT, Kimberly R.N., Director Patient Care, Christus Dubuis Hospital Of Alexandria, Alexandria, LA, p. A269

BENNETT, Laurie, Director Human Resources, Sarasota Memorial Health Care System, Sarasota, FL, p. A142

BENNETT, Lee W
Chief Financial Officer, Sitka Community Hospital, Sitka, AK, p. A27
Interim Chief Financial Officer, Cordova Community Medical Center, Cordova, AK, p. A25

BENNETT, Leo M.D., Deputy Commander Clinical Services, Bassett Army Community Hospital, Fort Wainwright, AK, p. A26

BENNETT, Lisa, Chief Financial Officer, Waverly Health Center, Waverly, IA, p. A236

BENNETT, Mary Ann, R.N., Chief Operating Officer and Chief Nursing Officer, Springbrook Behavioral Health System, Travelers Rest, SC, p. A566
Chief Nursing Officer, Glendora Community Hospital, Glendora, CA, p. A62

BENNETT, Melissa, Chief Nursing Officer, Trumbull Memorial Hospital, Warren, OH, p. A501

BENNETT, Nathan M.D., Chief Medical Officer, Mercy Hospital Waldron, Waldron, AR, p. A50

BENNETT, Patti, Chief Nursing Officer and Senior Vice President, Christus Good Shepherd Medical Center, Longview, TX, p. A629

BENNETT, Randall, Assistant Administrator, Uintah Basin Medical Center, Roosevelt, UT, p. A660

BENNETT, Richard G., M.D., President, Johns Hopkins Bayview Medical Center, Baltimore, MD, p. A294

BENNETT, Richard I, Senior Vice President and Chief Financial Officer, Delaware County Memorial Hospital, Drexel Hill, PA, p. A533

BENNETT, Robert M.D., Medical Director, Millwood Hospital, Arlington, TX, p. A593

BENNETT, Ron, Chief Financial Officer, Abilene Regional Medical Center, Abilene, TX, p. A591

BENNETT, Sharon, Manager Information Systems, Cobre Valley Regional Medical Center, Globe, AZ, p. A30

BENNETT, Sheila R.N., Vice President & Chief Nursing Officer, Floyd Medical Center, Rome, GA, p. A163

BENNETT, Tony N., Chief Executive Officer, Healthsouth Emerald Coast Rehabilitation Hospital, Panama City, FL, p. A138

BENNETT, Wayne, Chief Financial Officer, Franklin Memorial Hospital, Farmington, ME, p. A291

BENNETT, W Bradley., President and Chief Executive Officer, Fundamental Long Term Care Holdings, Llc, Sparks Glencoe, MD, p. B53

BENOIT, Paul, Associate Administrator, Central Louisiana State Hospital, Pineville, LA, p. A284

BENOIT, Rebecca R.N., Chief Nursing Officer, Lafayette General Medical Center, Lafayette, LA, p. A278

BENSEMA, David, Chief Information Officer, Baptist Health La Grange, La Grange, KY, p. A260

BENSEN, Carol MSN, R.N., Chief Nursing Officer, St. Patrick Hospital, Missoula, MT, p. A387

BENSON, Cheryl, Chief Operating Officer, Wernersville State Hospital, Wernersville, PA, p. A553

BENSON, Chris, Chief Financial Officer, Dekalb Regional Medical Center, Fort Payne, AL, p. A18

BENSON, Eric, Vice President Human Resources & Wellness, Sarah Bush Lincoln Health Center, Mattoon, IL, p. A193

BENSON, Kathryn, Human Resources Partner, Avera St. Anthony's Hospital, O'Neill, NE, p. A398

BENSON, Kevin, Chief Financial Officer, Ortonville Area Health Services, Ortonville, MN, p. A345

BENTLEY, Scott, Chief Financial Officer, Woman's Hospital Of Texas, Houston, TX, p. A624

BENTON, Dennis C., Senior Vice President and Area Manager, Kaiser Permanente Woodland Hills Medical Center, Los Angeles, CA, p. A69

BENTON, Edred, Chief Executive Officer and Chief Operating Officer, Cleveland Area Hospital, Cleveland, OK, p. A506

BENTON, Nancy, Assistant Director Patient Care Services, Mann–Grandstaff Veterans Affairs Medical Center, Spokane, WA, p. A686

BENTON, Tony, Chief Operating Officer, Johnson City Medical Center, Johnson City, TN, p. A581

BENTOUNSI, Karima, Interim Chief Executive Officer, DMC Huron Valley–Sinai Hospital, Commerce Township, MI, p. A317

BENTZ, Douglas E., Chief Executive Officer, Roane General Hospital, Spencer, WV, p. A696

BENVENUTTI, Cathy, Human Resource Director, Hancock Medical Center, Bay Saint Louis, MS, p. A352

BENWARE, Joel, Vice President Information Technology and Compliance, Northwestern Medical Center, Saint Albans, VT, p. A663

BENZ, Betsy R.N., MS, Chief Nursing Officer, Aurora Medical Center – Manitowoc County, Two Rivers, WI, p. A714

BENZ, Mark A., President and Chief Executive Officer, Carondelet St. Joseph's Hospital, Tucson, AZ, p. A37

BENZ, Robert M.D., Chief Medical Officer, Lankenau Medical Center, Wynnewood, PA, p. A555

BENZEL, Cindy, Manager Human Resources, Sanford Vermillion Medical Center, Vermillion, SD, p. A573

BEPLER, Gerold, M.D., Ph.D., President and Chief Executive Officer, Karmanos Cancer Center, Detroit, MI, p. A318

BERARDI, Paula, Manager Human Resources, Bournewood Health Systems, Brookline, MA, p. A305

BERCHER, Richard M.D., Chief Medical Officer, Paris Regional Medical Center, Paris, TX, p. A636

BERCI, Haya, Executive Director of Nursing, Joyce Eisenberg–Keefer Medical Center, Reseda, CA, p. A82

BERDAN, Barclay E., FACHE, Chief Executive Officer, Texas Health Harris Methodist Hospital Southwest Fort Worth, Fort Worth, TX, p. A614

BERDIEL, Luis A., Executive Director, Hospital Metropolitano San German, San German, PR, p. A725

BERENS, Jeff MS, Chief Nursing Officer, Sanford Vermillion Medical Center, Vermillion, SD, p. A573

BERENTES, Amy R.N., MSN, Vice President Patient Care Services, Mercy Medical Center–Clinton, Clinton, IA, p. A224

BERETTA, Dante M.D., Chief of Staff, Centracare Health–Melrose, Melrose, MN, p. A343

BERG, Gary L D.O., Chief Medical Officer, St. John Macomb–Oakland Hospital, Warren, MI, p. A332

BERG, James, FACHE, President, Texas Health Presbyterian Hospital Dallas, Dallas, TX, p. A607

BERG, Jon M.D., Chief of Staff, Northwood Deaconess Health Center, Northwood, ND, p. A477

BERG, Tony L. M.D., Chief of Staff, Winner Regional Healthcare Center, Winner, SD, p. A574

BERG, William, Chief Information Officer, Naval Hospital Pensacola, Pensacola, FL, p. A139

BERGE, Ron, Executive Vice President and Chief Operating Officer, National Jewish Health, Denver, CO, p. A101

BERGEAUX, Scott M.D., Chief Medical Staff, Abrom Kaplan Memorial Hospital, Kaplan, LA, p. A277

BERGEMANN, John, Director Human Resources, Crouse Health, Syracuse, NY, p. A453

BERGENFELD, Joel M., Chief Executive Officer, Physicians For Healthy Hospitals, Hemet, CA, p. B98

BERGEN, Jan L., President and Chief Executive Officer, Lancaster General Hospital, Lancaster, PA, p. A538

BERGER, George, Controller, Healthsouth Rehabilitation Hospital Of Altoona, Altoona, PA, p. A528

BERGER, Kathy
Director, Veterans Affairs Montana Health Care System, Fort Harrison, MT, p. A384
Interim Director, Sheridan Veterans Affairs Medical Center, Sheridan, WY, p. A720

BERGERON, Johnny, Manager Information Technology, Avoyelles Hospital, Marksville, LA, p. A280

BERGERON, Pierre, Information Services Director, Wellington Regional Medical Center, Wellington, FL, p. A147

BERGERON, Timothy, Deputy Commander, Administration, Bassett Army Community Hospital, Fort Wainwright, AK, p. A26

BERGERSEN, Jennifer, Interim Chief Operating Officer, Milwaukee County Behavioral Health Division, Milwaukee, WI, p. A708

BERGERSON, Melissa R.N., Chief Nursing Officer, Black River Memorial Hospital, Black River Falls, WI, p. A699

BERGES, Iris, Chief Executive Officer, Larkin Behavioral Health Services, Hollywood, FL, p. A127

BERGFORT, Joe, Chief Information Officer, Ucsf Medical Center, San Francisco, CA, p. A88

BERGHOLM, Brenda MSN, R.N., Chief Nursing Officer, Caribou Memorial Hospital And Living Center, Soda Springs, ID, p. A176

BERGLING, Richard Q., Chief Executive Officer, Morton County Health System, Elkhart, KS, p. A240

BERGMAN, Angela, Director of Quality, Risk and Health Information Management, Van Matre Healthsouth Rehabilitation Hospital, Rockford, IL, p. A199

BERGMAN, Chris, Chief Financial Officer, Children's Medical Center, Dayton, OH, p. A489

BERGMAN, Jim, Director Human Resources, Northeast Regional Medical Center, Kirksville, MO, p. A371

BERGMAN–EVANS, Brenda
Chief Nursing Officer, Chi Health Lakeside, Omaha, NE, p. A397
Chief Nursing Officer, Chi Health Midlands, Papillion, NE, p. A399
Interim Chief Nursing Officer, Chi Health Mercy Council Bluffs, Council Bluffs, IA, p. A225

BERGMANN, Michael, President, Aurora Medical Center Summit, Summit, WI, p. A713

BERGMANN, Peter U., President, University Hospitals Parma Medical Center, Parma, OH, p. A498

BERGQUIST, Susan, Human Resources Generalist, Kindred Hospital–La Mirada, La Mirada, CA, p. A64

BERGSENG, John H D.O., Vice President Medical Affairs, Glencoe Regional Health Services, Glencoe, MN, p. A340

BERGSTEDT, Sharon, Director of Nursing, Alaska Psychiatric Institute, Anchorage, AK, p. A25

BERGSTROM, Jenny, Project Manager Information Technology, Cloud County Health Center, Concordia, KS, p. A240

BERKOWITZ, David J, Vice President and Chief Operating Officer, Hackensack Meridian Health Palisades Medical Center, North Bergen, NJ, p. A418

BERKRAM, Treasure, Chief Financial Officer, Northern Rockies Medical Center, Cut Bank, MT, p. A383

BERLINGHOFF, Kathleen, Director Human Resources, Sharon Hospital, Sharon, CT, p. A113

BERLOT, Alvin M.D., Medical Director, Bucktail Medical Center, Renovo, PA, p. A549

BERLOWITZ, Dan M.D., M.P.H., Acting Chief of Staff, Bedford Veterans Affairs Medical Center, Edith Nourse Rogers Memorial Veterans Hospital, Bedford, MA, p. A302

BERLUCCHI, Scott A., FACHE, President and Chief Executive Officer, Auburn Community Hospital, Auburn, NY, p. A431

BERLYN, Maria, Assistant Vice President Nursing Services, John Heinz Institute Of Rehabilitation Medicine, Wilkes, PA, p. A554

BERMAN, Alan S. M.D., Medical Director, Mountain Valley Regional Rehabilitation Hospital, Prescott Valley, AZ, p. A35

BERMAN, Manuel S, FACHE
President and Chief Executive Officer, Tuality Healthcare, Hillsboro, OR, p. A522

BERMUDEZ, Ada, Director Human Resources, Hospital De La Concepcion, San German, PR, p. A725

BERMUDEZ, Armand M.D., Medical Director, Select Specialty Hospital Of Southeast Ohio, Newark, OH, p. A497

BERMUDEZ, Yuri M.D., Chief of Staff, South Texas Health System, Edinburg, TX, p. A610

BERNAL, Hector, Chief Executive Officer, Post Acute Medical Specialty Hospital Of Corpus Christi – North, Corpus Christi, TX, p. A603

BERNAL, Maria Mercedes Torres., Administrator, Hospital De Damas, Ponce, PR, p. A724

BERNARD, David P., FACHE, Chief Executive Officer, Houston Methodist San Jacinto Hospital, Baytown, TX, p. A597

BERNARD, Donald P
Chief Financial Officer, Kaiser Permanente Fontana Medical Center, Fontana, CA, p. A59
Chief Financial Officer, St. John's Pleasant Valley Hospital, Camarillo, CA, p. A54
Chief Financial Officer, St. John's Regional Medical Center, Oxnard, CA, p. A78

BERNARD, Doug M.D., Chief Medical Officer, White River Medical Center, Batesville, AR, p. A40

BERNARD, Mark L., Chief Executive Officer, Resolute Health, New Braunfels, TX, p. A635

BERNARD, Robert M.D., Chief of Staff, Alexandria Veterans Affairs Health Care System, Pineville, LA, p. A284

BERNARD, Traci, R.N., President, Chief Executive Officer and Chief Operating Officer, Texas Health Harris Methodist Hospital Southlake, Southlake, TX, p. A646

BERNARDI, Barbara R.N., Nurse Executive, Upmc Jameson Hospital, New Castle, PA, p. A542

BERNARDO, Maria M.D., Chief of Staff, Bullock County Hospital, Union Springs, AL, p. A24

BERNASEK, Robert M.D., Vice President and Chief Medical Officer, Southeast Georgia Health System Brunswick Campus, Brunswick, GA, p. A153

BERNATIS, Terry D., Director Human Resources, Community Healthcare System, Onaga, KS, p. A248

BERND, Jason, Vice President, Novant Health Charlotte Orthopaedic Hospital, Charlotte, NC, p. A459

BERNERT–YAP, Kellie, Director Human Resources, Vibra Specialty Hospital Of Portland, Portland, OR, p. A525

BERNEY, Bernadette, Director Human Resources, Pullman Regional Hospital, Pullman, WA, p. A684

BERNHARDT–KADLEC, Peggy, Chief Human Resources Officer, Searhc Mt. Edgecumbe Hospital, Sitka, AK, p. A27

BERNICK, Michael, Executive Vice President and Chief Financial Officer, Clarity Child Guidance Center, San Antonio, TX, p. A642

BERNIER, Justin R.N., Director of Nursing, Seaside Behavioral Center, New OrleansRiver Oaks Hospital, New Orleans, LA, p. A283

BERNS, Erin, Director Human Resources, Veterans Memorial Hospital, Waukon, IA, p. A236

BERNSEN, Tina, Chief Nursing Officer, Othello Community Hospital, Othello, WA, p. A683

BERNSTEIN, Lee
Regional Executive Vice President and Chief Operating Officer, SSM Health St. Clare Hospital – Fenton, Fenton, MO, p. A368
Regional Executive Vice President and Chief Operating Officer, SSM Health St. Joseph – St. Charles, Saint Charles, MO, p. A376
Regional Executive Vice President of Hospital and Chief Operating Officer, SSM Health St. Joseph Hospital – Lake Saint Louis, Lake Saint Louis, MO, p. A372

BERNSTEIN, Les, Chief Information Officer, Cookeville Regional Medical Center, Cookeville, TN, p. A577

BERNSTEIN, Michael, Chief Financial Officer, Tulare Regional Medical Center, Tulare, CA, p. A94

BERNSTEIN, Paul E M.D., Area Medical Director, Kaiser Permanente San Diego Medical Center, San Diego, CA, p. A85

BERRIOS, Elenia, Chief Nursing Officer, Hima San Pablo Caguas, Caguas, PR, p. A722

BERRY, C. Ross., Chief Executive Officer, South Georgia Medical Center, Valdosta, GA, p. A166

BERRY, Carlos E. M.D., Acting Chief of Staff, Tuscaloosa Veterans Affairs Medical Center, Tuscaloosa, AL, p. A24

BERRY, Cheryl Furdge, Chief Nursing Officer, Baptist Memorial Hospital–Tipton, Covington, TN, p. A578

BERRY, David T.
President, Children's Health Clinical Operations, Children's Medical Center Plano, Plano, TX, p. A638
President, Children's Health Clinical Operations, Our Children's House, Dallas, TX, p. A606
President, System Clinical Operations, Children's Health System Of Texas, Dallas, TX, p. A605

BERRY, Deborah, Director of Operations, Greene County Hospital, Leakesville, MS, p. A358

BERRY, Dennis, Chief Executive Officer, Tennessee Health Management, Parsons, TN, p. B126

BERRY, Greg, Chief Financial Officer, Doctors Medical Center Of Modesto, Modesto, CA, p. A74

BERRY, James T., FACHE, Executive Vice President and Administrator, Northeastern Health System, Tahlequah, OK, p. A516

BERRY, Julie, Chief Information Officer, Saint Anne's Hospital, Fall River, MA, p. A306

BERRY, Linda, Vice President Human Resources, Guthrie Towanda Memorial Hospital, Towanda, PA, p. A551

BERRY, Rebecca
Senior Director Human Resources, St. Charles Prineville, Prineville, OR, p. A526
Vice President Human Resources, St. Charles Bend, Bend, OR, p. A520
Vice President Human Resources, St. Charles Redmond, Redmond, OR, p. A526

BERRY–BARBOSA, Lisa, Vice President Human Resources, Beth Israel Deaconess Hospital Plymouth, Plymouth, MA, p. A310

BERRYMAN, John David M.D., Chief of Staff, Beckley Veterans Affairs Medical Center, Beckley, WV, p. A690

BERRYMAN, William R M.D., Chief of Staff, Grand Junction Veterans Health Care System, Grand Junction, CO, p. A103

BERSANTE, Syd, R.N.
President, St. Joseph Medical Center, Tacoma, WA, p. A688
Market President, St. Elizabeth Hospital, Enumclaw, WA, p. A680
President, St. Clare Hospital, Lakewood, WA, p. A682

BERSHAD, Joshua M M.D., Senior Vice President Medical Affairs and Chief Medical Officer, Robert Wood Johnson University Hospital, New Brunswick, NJ, p. A417

BERSINGER, David M.D., Chief of Staff, Mcleod Health Cheraw, Cheraw, SC, p. A559

BERT, Alisa
Chief Financial Officer, Aventura Hospital And Medical Center, Aventura, FL, p. A119
Interim Chief Executive Officer, Aventura Hospital And Medical Center, Aventura, FL, p. A119

BERTHIL, Emmanuel, Chief Clinical Officer, Vibra Hospital Of Southeastern Massachusetts, New Bedford, MA, p. A309

BERTKE, Bradley J., President and Chief Operating Officer, Mercy St. Anne Hospital, Toledo, OH, p. A500

BERTRAND, Joan L., Vice President Human Resources, Adcare Hospital Of Worcester, Worcester, MA, p. A313

BERTRAND, Neil W, Interim Chief Financial Officer, Cheyenne Regional Medical Center, Cheyenne, WY, p. A717

BERTSCH, Darrold, Chief Executive Officer, Sakakawea Medical Center, Hazen, ND, p. A476

BERTSCH, John M.D., Chief of Staff, Euclid Hospital, Euclid, OH, p. A491

BERUBE, Cathy, Chief Financial Officer, I–70 Community Hospital, Sweet Springs, MO, p. A380

BERWALD, Margaret R.N., MSN, Senior Vice President Patient Services, Torrance Memorial Medical Center, Torrance, CA, p. A94

BERZ, Derek, Chief Operating Officer, Kaiser Permanente Los Angeles Medical Center, Los Angeles, CA, p. A68

BESCOE, Bradley, Chief Financial Officer, Straith Hospital For Special Surgery, Southfield, MI, p. A331

BESHEL, Michael R.N., Vice President Patient Care and Chief Nursing Officer, Nazareth Hospital, Philadelphia, PA, p. A545

BESIO, Adam, Chief Information Officer, Memorial Medical Center, Port Lavaca, TX, p. A639

BESPALEC, Jason M.D., Chief of Staff, Fillmore County Hospital, Geneva, NE, p. A393

BESS, Amy, Chief Financial Officer, Mizell Memorial Hospital, Opp, AL, p. A22

BESS, Charles M.D., Medical Director, Potomac Valley Hospital, Keyser, WV, p. A693

BESS, Timothy A., Chief Executive Officer, Lake Cumberland Regional Hospital, Somerset, KY, p. A267

BESSE, Kim
Senior Vice President and Chief Human Resource Officer, Children's Health System Of Texas, Dallas, TX, p. A605
Senior Vice President and Chief Human Resource Officer, Children's Medical Center Plano, Plano, TX, p. A638

BESSEY, Kerry, Senior Vice President and Chief Human Resources Officer, Memorial Sloan–Kettering Cancer Center, New Rochelle, NY, p. A442

BESSEY, Vickie MSN, R.N., Chief Nursing Officer, Sagewest Health Care At Riverton, Riverton, WY, p. A719

BESSLER, Christine, Vice President Information Services, Oconomowoc Memorial Hospital, Oconomowoc, WI, p. A709

BESSLER, September, Director, Human Resources, Brookings Health System, Brookings, SD, p. A568

BESSON, Kathleen, Executive Vice President and Chief Operating Officer, Caromont Regional Medical Center, Gastonia, NC, p. A463

BESST, Kara, President and Chief Executive Officer, Gritman Medical Center, Moscow, ID, p. A174

BEST, Rosa, Chief Nursing Officer, Rolling Plains Memorial Hospital, Sweetwater, TX, p. A648

BESTEN, Robert, Chief Financial Officer, Mary Breckinridge Arh Hospital, Hyden, KY, p. A260

BESTGEN, Pat, Manager Human Resources, Cameron Regional Medical Center, Cameron, MO, p. A365

BESWICK, Elizabeth, Vice President Human Resources and Public Relations, Carteret Health Care, Morehead City, NC, p. A467

BETANCOURT, Erika, Coordinator Human Resources, Cornerstone Regional Hospital, Edinburg, TX, p. A610

BETTCHER, Sue R.N., Vice President of Nursing Services, Community Hospital Of Bremen, Bremen, IN, p. A205

BETTEM, Kelly, Vice President, Ambulatory Services, Ohio Valley Medical Center, Wheeling, WV, p. A697

BETTINELLI, Stephanie M, Vice President of Human Resources, Winchester Hospital, Winchester, MA, p. A313

BETTS, Brooks, Director Information Systems and Chief Information Officer, Pen Bay Medical Center, Rockport, ME, p. A293

BETTS, Crystal
  Chief Financial Officer, Incline Village Community Hospital, Incline Village, NV, p. A402
  Chief Financial Officer, Tahoe Forest Hospital District, Truckee, CA, p. A94

BETTS, Kristen A, Director Team Resources, St. Anthony's Hospital, Saint Petersburg, FL, p. A142

BETTS, Tracy, Chief Financial Officer, Hardeman County Memorial Hospital, Quanah, TX, p. A639

BETZ, Paul FACHE, Chief Operating Officer and Senior Vice President, Maury Regional Hospital, Columbia, TN, p. A577

BEUCLER, MSN, RN, BS–NE, FACHE, Lori A R.N., Vice President and Chief Nursing Officer, Williamsport Regional Medical Center, Williamsport, PA, p. A554

BEUS, Lance, Administrator, Christus Southeast Texas Jasper Memorial, Jasper, TX, p. A625

BEUTIN, Brian, MS, Chief Executive Officer, Banner Behavioral Health Hospital – Scottsdale, Scottsdale, AZ, p. A35

BEUTKE, Kenneth, President, OSF Saint Elizabeth Medical Center, Ottawa, IL, p. A196

BEVARD, Julie, Director Human Resources, Perkins County Health Services, Grant, NE, p. A393

BEVEL, John, Manager Information Systems, Shriners Hospitals For Children–Northern California, Sacramento, CA, p. A83

BEVERLY, Douglas H., Chief Executive Officer, Healthsouth Rehabilitation Hospital Of North Alabama, Huntsville, AL, p. A19

BEVERLY, Esther, Vice President Human Resources, Tri–City Medical Center, Oceanside, CA, p. A77

BEVERS, Donald, Chief Financial Officer, Memorial Hospital Of Salem County, Salem, NJ, p. A420

BEYER, Jim, Administrative Director Human Resources, Norman Regional Health System, Norman, OK, p. A511

BEYER, Laurie, Senior Vice President and Chief Financial Officer, Union Hospital, Elkton, MD, p. A298

BEYER, Teri, Chief Information Officer, Quality, Rice Memorial Hospital, Willmar, MN, p. A350

BEZARD, Herve M.D., Chief of Staff, Boulder City Hospital, Boulder City, NV, p. A401

BHAGAT, Sarah, Chief Operating Officer and Vice President of Organizational Effectiveness, Lakeland Regional Health, Lakeland, FL, p. A130

BHAMBI, Brijesh M.D., Chief Medical Officer, Bakersfield Heart Hospital, Bakersfield, CA, p. A52

BHAMBRA, Jody, Chief Nursing Officer, Hartgrove Hospital, Chicago, IL, p. A181

BHANDARI, Raj M.D., Physician–in–Chief, Kaiser Permanente San Jose Medical Center, San Jose, CA, p. A88

BHARUCHA, Bomi, Chief Financial Officer, Reeves County Hospital, Pecos, TX, p. A637

BHATEJA, Renu M.D., President Medical Staff, Ridgeview Psychiatric Hospital And Center, Oak Ridge, TN, p. A588

BHATIA, Sanjay, Chief Medical Officer, Lower Bucks Hospital, Bristol, PA, p. A530

BHAYANI, Sam B M.D., Chief Medical Officer, Barnes–Jewish West County Hospital, Saint Louis, MO, p. A376

BHOORASINGH, Merlene , Administrator, Kindred Hospital Ocala, Ocala, FL, p. B72

BHOORASINGH, Merlene, Administrator, Kindred Hospital Ocala, Ocala, FL, p. A136

BHUCHAR, Subodh M.D., Chief of Staff, Kindred Hospital Sugar Land, Sugar Land, TX, p. A647

BIAGIONI, Donna K R.N., MSN, Director of Nursing, Maniilaq Health Center, Kotzebue, AK, p. A26

BIALORUCKI, Tom, Chief Information Officer, Adena Pike Medical Center, Waverly, OH, p. A502

BIANCHI, Patty, Chief Executive Officer, Pershing General Hospital, Lovelock, NV, p. A404

BIAS, Richard R, Chief Operating Officer, Lahey Hospital & Medical Center, Burlington, Burlington, MA, p. A305

BIBAL, Antoinette, Director Human Resources, Kindred Hospital–Baldwin Park, Baldwin Park, CA, p. A53

BIBB, Jeff, Chief Operating Officer, Oklahoma Center For Orthopedic And Multi–Specialty Surgery, Oklahoma City, OK, p. A512

BIBB, Lisa, Director Human Resources, San Angelo Community Medical Center, San Angelo, TX, p. A641

BIBBY, John, Vice President Human Resources, Los Robles Hospital And Medical Center, Thousand Oaks, CA, p. A93

BIBEAU, Roland R., President and Chief Operating Officer, Novant Health Matthews Medical Center, Matthews, NC, p. A466

BIBER, Carl, Chief Financial Officer, Columbus Regional Healthcare System, Whiteville, NC, p. A472

BIBLO, Lee M.D., Chief Medical Officer, Froedtert Memorial Lutheran Hospital, Milwaukee, WI, p. A708

BIBY, Thom, Chief Financial Officer, Tulsa Spine And Specialty Hospital, Tulsa, OK, p. A518

BICHIMER, Michael, Acting Vice President of Finance, Ohiohealth Medcentral Mansfield Hospital, Mansfield, OH, p. A494

BICKEL, George, Director, Information Systems, Merit Health Biloxi, Biloxi, MS, p. A352

BICKEL, Jim, Chief Executive Officer, Columbus Regional Hospital, Columbus, IN, p. A205

BICKFORD, Carmel, Chief Financial Officer, Wyoming Behavioral Institute, Casper, WY, p. A717

BICKFORD, David, Chief Information Officer, Melissa Memorial Hospital, Holyoke, CO, p. A104

BIDDLE, Kenneth, Controller, Kensington Hospital, Philadelphia, PA, p. A544

BIDES, Adrienne, Assistant Chief Financial Officer and Budget Analyst, Big Spring State Hospital, Big Spring, TX, p. A598

BIDLEMAN, Angie, Chief Nursing Officer, Jane Phillips Medical Center, Bartlesville, OK, p. A505

BIE, Gary E CPA, Chief Financial Officer, Stony Brook University Hospital, Stony Brook, NY, p. A453

BIEBER, Courtney, Director Information Systems, Mercy Regional Medical Center, Ville Platte, LA, p. A287

BIEBER, Eric, M.D., President and Chief Executive Officer, Rochester Regional Health , Rochester, NY, p. B109

BIEBER, Judi, Senior Vice President Human Resources, Beth Israel Deaconess Medical Center, Boston, MA, p. A302

BIEDIGER, Daniel F, Vice President Human Resources, Firsthealth Moore Regional Hospital, Pinehurst, NC, p. A468

BIEDRON, Janet, R.N., Chief Executive Officer, Lifecare Hospitals Of Chester County, West Chester, PA, p. A553

BIEGERT, Dara, Vice President Human Resources, Medical City Lewisville, Lewisville, TX, p. A629

BIEGLER, Elizabeth Anne, R.N.
  Chief Nursing Officer, Ohiohealth Dublin Methodist Hospital, Dublin, OH, p. A490
  Chief Nursing Officer, Ohiohealth Grady Memorial Hospital, Delaware, OH, p. A490

BIEHL, Albert M.D., Vice President Medical Affairs, Bethesda Hospital East, Boynton Beach, FL, p. A120

BIEKER, Jeff, Director Human Resource, Trego County–Lemke Memorial Hospital, Wakeeney, KS, p. A253

BIEL, Christopher, Chief Information Officer, Goodland Regional Medical Center, Goodland, KS, p. A241

BIELECKI, Thomas A, Chief Financial Officer, Geisinger Wyoming Valley Medical Center, Wilkes Barre, PA, p. A554

BIEN, John, Vice President Finance, United Hospital, Saint Paul, MN, p. A348

BIENIEK, Sherrie, M.D.
  Medical Director, Atlantic Shores Hospital, Fort Lauderdale, FL, p. A124
  Medical Director, Fort Lauderdale Hospital, Fort Lauderdale, FL, p. A124

BIER, Alan M.D., Executive Vice President and Chief Medical Officer, Gwinnett Hospital System, Lawrenceville, GA, p. A160

BIERI, Bryan, Manager Finance, Kansas City Veterans Affairs Medical Center, Kansas City, MO, p. A370

BIERLE, Dennis, Chief Operating Officer, Nebraska Medicine – Nebraska Medical Center, Omaha, NE, p. A397

BIERMAN, Debra, Associate Executive Director Human Resources, North Shore University Hospital, Manhasset, NY, p. A439

BIERMAN, Joan, Vice President Finance, Cherokee Regional Medical Center, Cherokee, IA, p. A224

BIERMAN, Marcia M.D., Chief of Staff, North Shore Medical Center, Miami, FL, p. A133

BIERMAN, Ronald L., Chief Executive Officer, Trumbull Memorial Hospital, Warren, OH, p. A501

BIERSCHENK, Cindy
  Director Financial Services, Optim Medical Center – Screven, Sylvania, GA, p. A165
  Director of Financial Services, Optim Medical Center – Jenkins, Millen, GA, p. A162

BIERSCHENK, Kevin, Chief Executive Officer, Dodge County Hospital, Eastman, GA, p. A157

BIERUT, Barbara, Chief Financial Officer, Healthsouth Rehabilitation Hospital Of Sarasota, Sarasota, FL, p. A142

BIGELOW, Barbara, Administrator, Providence Kodiak Island Medical Center, Kodiak, AK, p. A26

BIGELOW, Timothy, Director Human Resources, Butler Hospital, Providence, RI, p. A556

BIGGAR, Carrie, Chief Financial Officer, Osceola Regional Medical Center, Kissimmee, FL, p. A129

BIGGERSTAFF, David, Chief Operating Officer, Children's Hospital Colorado, Aurora, CO, p. A98

BIGGINS, Lillie RN, R.N., President, Texas Health Harris Methodist Hospital Fort Worth, Fort Worth, TX, p. A614

BIGGS, Daniel, Director Human Resources, Valley View Hospital, Glenwood Springs, CO, p. A103

BIGGS, Jeremy, Chief Executive Officer, Methodist Medical Center Of Oak Ridge, Oak Ridge, TN, p. A587

BIGGS, Kelly M.D., Chief Medical Officer, Tyrone Hospital, Tyrone, PA, p. A552

BIGGS, R. Lee M.D., Chief Medical Officer, Eastern Idaho Regional Medical Center, Idaho Falls, ID, p. A173

BIGHAM, Laurie S R.N., FACHE, Chief Nursing Officer, Lovelace Medical Center, Albuquerque, NM, p. A424

BIGLER, Pamela MSN, R.N., Senior Vice President, Chief Nursing Officer, Carle Foundation Hospital, Urbana, IL, p. A201

BIGLEY, John M.D., Medical Director, Kaiser Permanente Baldwin Park Medical Center, Baldwin Park, CA, p. A53

BIGNAULT, Jon M.D., Chief of Staff, Athens–Limestone Hospital, Athens, AL, p. A14

BIGONEY, Rebecca
  Executive Vice President and Chief Medical Officer, Mary Washington Hospital, Fredericksburg, VA, p. A667
  Executive Vice President and Chief Medical Officer, Stafford Hospital, Stafford, VA, p. A675

BIGOS, Ardelle R.N., MSN, Chief Nursing Officer and Vice President Patient Care Services, Maine Coast Memorial Hospital, Ellsworth, ME, p. A291

BIHUNIAK, Peter, Vice President Finance, Robert Wood Johnson University Hospital Rahway, Rahway, NJ, p. A419

BIITTNER, Sallie, Vice President Human Resources, St. Joseph's Hospital Health Center, Syracuse, NY, p. A453

BILL, Charles E., Chief Executive Officer, Bartlett Regional Hospital, Juneau, AK, p. A26

BILLECI, Theresa, Executive Director, Porterville Developmental Center, Porterville, CA, p. A80

BILLIG, Samantha, Chief Executive Officer, Healthsouth Rehabilitation Hospital – Henderson, Henderson, NV, p. A402

BILLINGS, Mark, Chief Operating Officer, Halifax Health Medical Center Of Daytona Beach, Daytona Beach, FL, p. A123

BILLINGS, Mary Ann, Director of Nursing, Potomac Valley Hospital, Keyser, WV, p. A693

BILLINGS, Robert E, Chief Financial Officer, Largo Medical Center, Largo, FL, p. A130

BILLINGSLEA, Anidra, Health Insurance Management, Healthsouth Rehabilitation Hospital Of Montgomery, Montgomery, AL, p. A21

BILLINGSLEY, Margaret R.N., MSN, Chief Nursing Officer, T. J. Samson Community Hospital, Glasgow, KY, p. A259

BILLINGTON, Carole R.N., MSN, Vice President Operations, Chief Nursing Officer, Saint Anne's Hospital, Fall River, MA, p. A306

BILLMEYER, Joe, Director, Information Services, Mercy Medical Center–Dubuque, Dubuque, IA, p. A227

BILLS, James, Chief Executive Officer, Logan Memorial Hospital, Russellville, KY, p. A267

BILLY, Frank, Chief Financial Officer, Kindred Hospital Bay Area–Tampa, Tampa, FL, p. A145

BILUNKA, Dianne C, Director Human Resources, Clarion Psychiatric Center, Clarion, PA, p. A531

BINDERMAN, Judi, Chief Information Technology Officer and Chief Medical Informatics Officer, St. Francis Medical Center, Lynwood, CA, p. A72

BINDERMAN, Warren S., Chief Financial Officer, Lifebrite Community Hospital Of Stokes, Danbury, NC, p. A460

BINDL, Karen CPA, Controller, Uw Health Rehabilitation Hospital, Madison, WI, p. A705

BINGHAM, Julie, IT Supervisor, San Juan Health Service District, Monticello, UT, p. A657

BINGHAM, Leslie, Senior Vice President and Chief Executive Officer, Valley Baptist Medical Center–Brownsville, Brownsville, TX, p. A599

BINGHAM, Paulette, Director Nursing Services, Ohio Valley Hospital, Mckees Rocks, PA, p. A540

BINGHAM, Ronald T, Chief Operating Officer, Antelope Valley Hospital, Lancaster, CA, p. A65

BINGMAN, Ryan, Director Operations, Grundy County Memorial Hospital, Grundy Center, IA, p. A228

BINKLEY, Sharon, Director Human Resources, Fairfax Community Hospital, Fairfax, OK, p. A507

BINTZ, Marilu M.D., Chief of Staff, Gundersen Boscobel Area Hospital And Clinics, Boscobel, WI, p. A699

BIRCH, Misty, Director Human Resources, Castleview Hospital, Price, UT, p. A659

BIRCHMEIER, Kevin, Director Human Resources, Covenant Healthcare, Saginaw, MI, p. A329

BIRD, Jace M.D., Chief Medical Officer, Missouri River Medical Center, Fort Benton, MT, p. A384

BIRD, Jeffrey C, M.D., Chief Operating Officer and Chief Medical Officer, Indiana University Health Ball Memorial Hospital, Muncie, IN, p. A216

BIRD, Lindsay, Director Finance, South Pointe Hospital, Warrensville Heights, OH, p. A501

BIRD, Michele
    Chief Human Resources Officer, Hemet Valley Medical Center, Hemet, CA, p. A63
    Chief Human Resources Officer, Menifee Valley Medical Center, Sun City, CA, p. A93

BIRDSONG, Brady, Chief Information Officer, Saint Elizabeths Hospital, Washington, DC, p. A118

BIREN, David, Chief Financial Officer, Mayo Clinic Health System In Lake City, Lake City, MN, p. A341

BIRENBERG, Allan, Vice President Medical Affairs, Medstar Harbor Hospital, Baltimore, MD, p. A295

BIRI, Abel, Chief Executive Officer, Florida Hospital Waterman, Tavares, FL, p. A145

BIRKEL, Sue M R.N., Director of Nursing, Butler County Health Care Center, David City, NE, p. A392

BIRKENSTOCK, Timothy L, Chief Financial Officer, Nicklaus Children's Hospital, Miami, FL, p. A133

BIRKHOFER, Colleen, Chief Nursing Officer, Trenton Psychiatric Hospital, Trenton, NJ, p. A422

BIRMINGHAM, Karen, Director Human Resources, West Springs Hospital, Grand Junction, CO, p. A103

BIRSCHBACH, Nancy
    Vice President and Chief Information Officer, Ripon Medical Center, Ripon, WI, p. A712
    Vice President and Chief Information Officer, St. Agnes Hospital, Fond Du Lac, WI, p. A701
    Vice President and Chief Information Officer, Waupun Memorial Hospital, Waupun, WI, p. A715

BISCONE, Mark A., President and Chief Executive Officer, Pen Bay Medical Center, Rockport, ME, p. A293

BISDORF, Jonathan, Director Information Technology, Ohio Valley Surgical Hospital, Springfield, OH, p. A499

BISH, Carol, Human Resources Coordinator, North Greenville Hospital, Travelers Rest, SC, p. A566

BISHARA, Reemon M.D., Medical Director, Coastal Harbor Treatment Center, Savannah, GA, p. A164

BISHOP, Abby, Chief Information Officer, Mclaren Port Huron, Port Huron, MI, p. A328

BISHOP, Amy Leigh, Director Human Resources, Red Bay Hospital, Red Bay, AL, p. A22

BISHOP, Bill, Chief Information Officer, Colquitt Regional Medical Center, Moultrie, GA, p. A162

BISHOP, Bryan, Chief Financial Officer, Heartland Behavioral Health Services, Nevada, MO, p. A374

BISHOP, Elizabeth, Business Office Manager, Salina Surgical Hospital, Salina, KS, p. A251

BISHOP, Glenda, Interim Chief Executive Officer, Quincy Valley Medical Center, Quincy, WA, p. A684

BISHOP, Janice E R.N., Chief Nursing Officer, Tewksbury Hospital, Tewksbury, MA, p. A312

BISHOP, John
    Chief Executive Officer, Community Hospital Long Beach, Long Beach, CA, p. A66
    Chief Executive Officer, Long Beach Memorial Medical Center, Long Beach, CA, p. A66
    Chief Executive Officer, Miller Children's & Women's Hospital Long Beach, Long Beach, CA, p. A67
    President, St. Charles Madras, Madras, OR, p. A523
    President, St. Charles Prineville, Prineville, OR, p. A526

BISHOP, Steve, Chief Financial Officer, Up Health System– Portage, Hancock, MI, p. A322

BISIGNANI, Thomas, Chief Financial Officer, Moses Taylor Hospital, Scranton, PA, p. A550

BISSENDEN, Chris, Director Human Resources, Ogden Regional Medical Center, Ogden, UT, p. A658

BISSONETTE, Christine R.N., Service Line Director for Acute Services, Kalkaska Memorial Health Center, Kalkaska, MI, p. A324

BISSONNETTE, Andre, Chief Financial Officer, North Country Hospital And Health Center, Newport, VT, p. A662

BISTERFELDT, Joanne, Chief Information Officer, Wheaton Franciscan Healthcare – All Saints, Racine, WI, p. A711

BITAR, Adib M.D., Medical Director, Aurora Charter Oak Hospital, Covina, CA, p. A57

BITAR, Ali M.D., Vice President Medical Affairs, DMC – Rehabilitation Institute Of Michigan, Detroit, MI, p. A317

BITHER, Dean, Chief Financial Officer, Inland Hospital, Waterville, ME, p. A293

BITNER, Janet, Chief Operating Officer, Texas Neurorehab Center, Austin, TX, p. A596

BITSILLY, Christina, Human Resource Specialist, U. S. Public Health Service Indian Hospital, Crownpoint, NM, p. A425

BITSOLI, Deborah, CPA, President, Morton Hospital And Medical Center, Taunton, MA, p. A312

BITTNER, Augustine, Chief Information Officer, Robley Rex Veterans Affairs Medical Center, Louisville, KY, p. A263

BITTNER, David, Chief Financial Officer, Mount Sinai Rehabilitation Hospital, Hartford, CT, p. A110

BITZ, Joan, Chief Nursing Officer, Meeker Memorial Hospital, Litchfield, MN, p. A342

BIUSO, Joseph M.D., Vice President and Chief of Medical Affairs, Floyd Medical Center, Rome, GA, p. A163

BIXLER, David, Chief Executive Officer, Rhea Medical Center, Dayton, TN, p. A578

BJARNASON, Dana Ph.D., R.N., Vice President and Chief Nursing Officer, Ohsu Hospital, Portland, OR, p. A525

BJELLA, Karmon T., President, Midmichigan Medical Center – Alpena, Alpena, MI, p. A314

BJERKE, Carolyn, Director Human Resources, Mercy Hospital Kingfisher, Kingfisher, OK, p. A509

BJERKE, Erik, Chief Executive Officer, Madison Healthcare Services, Madison, MN, p. A342

BJERKNES, Dan
    Director Human Resources, Chi St. Alexius Health – Williston Medical Center, Williston, ND, p. A478
    Market Leader, Chi St. Alexius Health – Williston Medical Center, Williston, ND, p. A478

BJORDAHL, Kevin M.D., Chief Medical Officer, Milbank Area Hospital Avera, Milbank, SD, p. A570

BJORNSTAD, Brad M.D., Vice President and Chief Medical Officer, Florida Hospital Tampa, Tampa, FL, p. A144

BLABER, Reginald, M.D., FACC, President, Our Lady Of Lourdes Medical Center, Camden, NJ, p. A412

BLACK, Amy, R.N., MSN
    Chief Operating Officer, Martha Jefferson Hospital, Charlottesville, VA, p. A665
    Risk Manager/PI Director, Brynn Marr Hospital, Jacksonville, NC, p. A465

BLACK, Charles Jr, Chief Financial Officer, Rockcastle Regional Hospital And Respiratory Care Center, Mount Vernon, KY, p. A265

BLACK, Gary E., President and Chief Executive Officer, UNC Lenoir Healthcare, Kinston, NC, p. A465

BLACK, Jason, Vice President and Chief Nurse Executive, Adventist Health Glendale, Glendale, CA, p. A62

BLACK, Jessica, Chief Executive Officer, Brentwood Meadows, Newburgh, IN, p. A217

BLACK, Marcey, Chief Financial Officer, Northwest Florida Community Hospital, Chipley, FL, p. A121

BLACK, Marilynn
    Chief Information Officer, Northern Arizona Healthcare, Flagstaff Medical Center, Flagstaff, AZ, p. A29
    Chief Information Officer, Northern Arizona Healthcare, Verde Valley Medical Center, Cottonwood, AZ, p. A28

BLACK, Michael, Director Human Resources, East Georgia Regional Medical Center, Statesboro, GA, p. A165

BLACK, Paul S
    Interim Administrator, Winston Medical Center, Louisville, MS, p. A358
    Chief Financial Officer, Scott Regional Hospital, Morton, MS, p. A359
    Controller, H. C. Watkins Memorial Hospital, Quitman, MS, p. A361

BLACK, Robert O., Chief Executive Officer, Linton Hospital, Linton, ND, p. A477

BLACK, Ronald M.D., Chief Medical Officer, Clark Fork Valley Hospital, Plains, MT, p. A387

BLACK, Stephen, MS, Health Care System Director, St. Cloud Veterans Affairs Health Care System, Saint Cloud, MN, p. A347

BLACK, Terri, Network Manager, Lucas County Health Center, Chariton, IA, p. A224

BLACK, Tim, Director Human Resources, Timpanogos Regional Hospital, Orem, UT, p. A658

BLACKADAR, Sam M.D., Medical Director, Cordova Community Medical Center, Cordova, AK, p. A25

BLACKBEAR, Annabelle, Human Resources Specialist, U. S. Public Health Service Indian Hospital, Pine Ridge, SD, p. A571

BLACKBURN, Christy R.N., Chief Nursing Officer, Candler County Hospital, Metter, GA, p. A161

BLACKBURN, Lisa R, Director Human Resources, St. Margaret's Hospital, Spring Valley, IL, p. A200

BLACKBURN, Mary, Vice President Operations and Chief Practice Officer, Hugh Chatham Memorial Hospital, Elkin, NC, p. A462

BLACKBURN, Susan
    Chief Administrative Officer, Providence St. Mary Medical Center, Walla Walla, WA, p. A688
    Chief Operating Officer, Providence St. Mary Medical Center, Walla Walla, WA, p. A688

BLACKFORD, Nate, Chief Operating Officer, Northwest Medical Center, Albany, MO, p. A364

BLACKHAM, Cami R.N., Nurse Administrator, Sevier Valley Hospital, Richfield, UT, p. A659

BLACKHURST, Kristi, Interim Vice President Operations, Asante Rogue Regional Medical Center, Medford, OR, p. A524

BLACKMON, Jenean
    Assistant Vice President and Chief Information Officer, Mcleod Medical Center Dillon, Dillon, SC, p. A561
    Associate Vice President and Chief Information Officer, Mcleod Regional Medical Center, Florence, SC, p. A562

BLACKWELL, David, Vice President Operations, Baylor Scott & White Medical Center – Hillcrest, Waco, TX, p. A652

BLACKWELL, Jack, Chief Financial Officer, Highlands Regional Medical Center, Prestonsburg, KY, p. A266

BLACKWELL, James, President and Chief Executive Officer, Clara Barton Hospital, Hoisington, KS, p. A242

BLACKWELL, Lenore, Director Human Resources, Tennova Healthcare–Harton, Tullahoma, TN, p. A589

BLACKWELL, Timothy, Manager Human Resources, Rolling Hills Hospital, Ada, OK, p. A504

BLACKWOOD, Jim, Chief Executive Officer, Tallahatchie General Hospital, Charleston, MS, p. A353

BLACKWOOD, Mark M.D., Chief of Staff, Bolivar Medical Center, Cleveland, MS, p. A353

BLAD, Nathan
    Chief Executive Officer, Rc Hospital And Clinics, Olivia, MN, p. A345
    Chief Financial Officer, Rc Hospital And Clinics, Olivia, MN, p. A345

BLADEN, Anthony M., Vice President Human Resources, Calvert Memorial Hospital, Prince Frederick, MD, p. A300

BLAHA, Bill, Manager Information Technology, Tri–County Hospital, Wadena, MN, p. A350

BLAHNIK, David, Chief Operating Officer, Twin Valley Behavioral Healthcare, Columbus, OH, p. A488

BLAIR, Brenda, Vice President Human Resources, Alice Peck Day Memorial Hospital, Lebanon, NH, p. A408

BLAIR, Diane, Human Resources and Admissions, Chi Health Plainview, Plainview, NE, p. A399

BLAIR, Heidi L, Vice President Administration, Centerstone Hospital, Bradenton, FL, p. A120

BLAIR, Jan, Director Human Resources, Clinton Memorial Hospital, Wilmington, OH, p. A502

BLAIR, Judy, Senior Vice President Clinical Services and Chief Nursing Officer, Adventist Health Glendale, Glendale, CA, p. A62

BLAIR, Mark M.D., Medical Director, Columbus Dublin Springs, Dublin, OH, p. A490

BLAIR, Mendy MSN, Vice President and Chief Nursing Officer, Baptist Health Richmond, Richmond, KY, p. A267

BLAIR, Raymond W M.D., Jr, Chief of Staff, Ennis Regional Medical Center, Ennis, TX, p. A612

BLAIR, Robert D., Chief Executive Officer, Spine Hospital Of Louisiana (Formally The Neuromedical Center Surgical Hospital), Baton Rouge, LA, p. A271

BLAKE, Alan M.D., President Medical Staff, Samaritan Lebanon Community Hospital, Lebanon, OR, p. A523

BLAKE, Daphne R.N., MSN, Chief Nursing Officer, Guadalupe Regional Medical Center, Seguin, TX, p. A644

BLAKE, Diane, Chief Executive Officer, Cascade Medical Center, Leavenworth, WA, p. A682

BLAKE, Jean, Chief Nursing Officer, University Hospitals Cleveland Medical Center, Cleveland, OH, p. A486

BLAKE, Kelly, Chief Executive Officer, Select Specialty Hospital–Johnstown, Johnstown, PA, p. A537

BLAKE, Robert, Chief Human Resources Officer Southwest Market, Memorial Hermann Sugar Land Hospital, Sugar Land, TX, p. A647

BLAKE, Sheryl Lewis., FACHE, President, Spectrum Health Pennock, Hastings, MI, p. A322

BLAKE, Skylier R.N., Chief Nursing Officer, El Paso Ltac Hospital, El Paso, TX, p. A610

BLAKE, Steven, Corporate Chief Financial Officer, East Los Angeles Doctors Hospital, Los Angeles, CA, p. A68

BLAKELEY, Scott, Chief Executive Officer, Sundance Behavioral Healthcare, Arlington, TX, p. A593

BLAKELY, Michelle, Associate Director, Jesse Brown Veterans Affairs Medical Center, Chicago, IL, p. A181

BLAKEMORE, Chris, Interim Chief Information Officer, Christus Good Shepherd Medical Center, Longview, TX, p. A629

BLAKENEY, Dell, Vice President and Chief Information Officer, South Central Regional Medical Center, Laurel, MS, p. A358

BLAKEY GORMAN, Mary, Director Human Resources, Northwest Missouri Psychiatric Rehabilitation Center, Saint Joseph, MO, p. A376

BLALOCK, Anthony P. M.D., Chief Medical Officer, Our Lady Of Lourdes Regional Medical Center, Lafayette, LA, p. A279

BLALOCK, Tracey MSN, R.N., Chief Nurse Executive, Medical Center, Navicent Health, Macon, GA, p. A161

BLANC, Linda R.N., Administrative Director of Nursing, Jefferson Medical Center, Ranson, WV, p. A695

BLANCHARD, Charmaine, Chief Nursing Officer, Healthsouth Rehabilitation Hospital At Martin Health, Stuart, FL, p. A143

BLANCHARD, Timothy D, Chief Financial Officer, Kingman Regional Medical Center, Kingman, AZ, p. A30

BLANCHARD, William R., Chief Executive Officer, Detar Healthcare System, Victoria, TX, p. A652

BLANCHARD, William R, Chief Executive Officer, Detar Healthcare System, Victoria, TX, p. A652

BLANCHAT, Tim, Chief Information Officer, Catawba Valley Medical Center, Hickory, NC, p. A464

BLANCHETTE, Edward A., M.D., Director, Connecticut Department Of Correction's Hospital, Somers, CT, p. A113

BLANCO, Andres, Director Management Information Systems, Westside Regional Medical Center, Plantation, FL, p. A140

BLAND, Casey, Director of Nursing, Rush Foundation Hospital, Meridian, MS, p. A359

BLAND, David, Chief Executive Officer, South Davis Community Hospital, Bountiful, UT, p. A656

BLAND, Douglas, Manager Information Services, Spring View Hospital, Lebanon, KY, p. A260

BLANEY, Gerard, Vice President Finance and Interim Chief Financial Officer, Einstein Medical Center Philadelphia, Philadelphia, PA, p. A543

BLANK, Arthur J., President and Chief Executive Officer, Mount Desert Island Hospital, Bar Harbor, ME, p. A289

BLANK, Kim, Director Human Resources, Lake Region Healthcare, Fergus Falls, MN, p. A340

BLANKE, Kerry Lee
Chief Financial Officer, Thedacare Medical Center–Shawano, Shawano, WI, p. A712
Director Financial Services, Thedacare Medical Center–Waupaca, Waupaca, WI, p. A715

BLANKENSHIP, Diana, Director Human Resources, Welch Community Hospital, Welch, WV, p. A696

BLANKENSHIP, Jeff, CPA
Chief Financial Officer, Pathways Of Tennessee, Jackson, TN, p. A580
Vice President and Chief Financial Officer, Jackson–Madison County General Hospital, Jackson, TN, p. A580

BLANKENSHIP, Stacy, Chief Nursing Officer, Mercy Hospital Washington, Washington, MO, p. A381

BLANSKY, Richard M.D., Chief Medical Officer, Our Lady Of Lourdes Memorial Hospital, Inc., Binghamton, NY, p. A432

BLANTON, Christina, Administrative Assistant and Human Resources Coordinator, Select Specialty Hospital–Knoxville, Knoxville, TN, p. A582

BLANTON, Forest
Administrator Process Engineering, Memorial Regional Hospital, Hollywood, FL, p. A127
Chief Information Officer, Memorial Hospital Pembroke, Pembroke Pines, FL, p. A139
Chief Information Officer, Memorial Hospital West, Pembroke Pines, FL, p. A139
Senior VP and Chief Information Officer, Memorial Hospital Miramar, Miramar, FL, p. A135

BLANTON, James
Chief Financial Officer, East Texas Medical Center Rehabilitation Hospital, Tyler, TX, p. A650
Chief Financial Officer, East Texas Medical Center Specialty Hospital, Tyler, TX, p. A651

BLANTON, Kevin D.O., Chief of Staff, Goodall–Witcher Hospital Authority, Clifton, TX, p. A601

BLANTON, Ron, Chief Fiscal Services, Boise Veterans Affairs Medical Center, Boise, ID, p. A171

BLAS, Phil, Chief Information Officer, John C. Fremont Healthcare District, Mariposa, CA, p. A73

BLASER, Karla, Director Human Resources, Unitypoint Health – Trinity Muscatine, Muscatine, IA, p. A232

BLASING, Amy, Chief Executive Officer, Lovelace Westside Hospital, Albuquerque, NM, p. A424

BLASINGAME, Billy, Chief Executive Officer, Continuecare Hospital At Hendrick Medical Center, Abilene, TX, p. A591

BLASIUS, Rita, Assistant Administrator and Chief Financial Officer, Avera St. Benedict Health Center, Parkston, SD, p. A571

BLASKO, Edward, Chief of Staff, Carolinas Healthcare System Anson, Wadesboro, NC, p. A472

BLASY, Christopher M.D., Chief of Staff, Carl Vinson Veterans Affairs Medical Center, Dublin, GA, p. A157

BLAUER, Michael, Administrator, St. Luke's Elmore, Mountain Home, ID, p. A174

BLAUSTEIN, Ron, Chief Financial Officer, Ann & Robert H. Lurie Children's Hospital Of Chicago, Chicago, IL, p. A180

BLAUWET, Judy, M.P.H., R.N.
Senior Vice President of Hospital Operations and Chief Nursing Officer, Avera Mckennan Hospital And University Health Center, Sioux Falls, SD, p. A572
Senior Vice President Operations and Chief Nursing Officer, Avera Mckennan Hospital And University Health Center, Sioux Falls, SD, p. A572

BLAYLOCK, Darrell, Chief Executive Officer, Tennova Healthcare Volunteer Community Hospital, Martin, TN, p. A583

BLAYLOCK, Kevin, Chief Executive Officer, Oklahoma Spine Hospital, Oklahoma City, OK, p. A513

BLAYLOCK, L Dwayne.
Chief Executive Officer, Merit Health Rankin, Brandon, MS, p. A353
Chief Executive Officer, Merit Health River Oaks, Flowood, MS, p. A354

BLAZAKIS, Shelly, Director Human Resources Services, Scripps Memorial Hospital–La Jolla, La Jolla, CA, p. A64

BLAZEK, Dennis, Chief Information Officer, Clarke County Hospital, Osceola, IA, p. A233

BLAZEK, Robert, System Director, Human Resources Business Partners, Elmhurst Hospital, Elmhurst, IL, p. A187

BLAZIER, Patty, Chief Nursing Officer, Hamilton Memorial Hospital District, Mcleansboro, IL, p. A193

BLEAK, Jason, Administrator and Chief Executive Officer, Grover C. Dils Medical Center, Caliente, NV, p. A401

BLECHA, Timothy M.D., Medical Director, Brodstone Memorial Hospital, Superior, NE, p. A400

BLEDSOE, Bill, Administrator, North Metro Medical Center, Jacksonville, AR, p. A45

BLEDSOE, Dana, MS, R.N., Chief Executive Officer, Nemours Children's Hospital, Orlando, FL, p. A137

BLEDSOE, Richard, Director Information Systems, Mary Black Health System – Gaffney, Gaffney, SC, p. A562

BLENDERMAN, Robert, Senior Vice President and Chief Operating Officer, New York–Presbyterian Queens, New Rochelle, NY, p. A444

BLESI, Michael, Director Information Technology, Rainy Lake Medical Center, International Falls, MN, p. A341

BLESSING, Brian, Chief Financial Officer, Texas Health Harris Methodist Hospital Azle, Azle, TX, p. A596

BLEVINS, Bonnie R.N., Chief Financial Officer, Faith Community Hospital, Jacksboro, TX, p. A625

BLEVINS, Denzil, Director Information Systems, Montgomery General Hospital, Montgomery, WV, p. A694

BLEVINS, Matthew H., Chief Executive Officer, Barstow Community Hospital, Barstow, CA, p. A53

BLEVINS, Pam, R.N.
Director Information Technology Member Hospitals Mission, Mcdowell Hospital, Marion, NC, p. A466
Director, Clinical Informatics, Blue Ridge Regional Hospital, Spruce Pine, NC, p. A471

BLIGHTON, Gordon, Director Resource Management, Naval Hospital Camp Pendleton, Camp Pendleton, CA, p. A54

BLINCO, Lynne, Chief Executive Officer, Healthsouth Rehabilitation Hospital Of Dayton, Dayton, OH, p. A489

BLISS, Howard, Director of Information Systems, Helen Newberry Joy Hospital, Newberry, MI, p. A327

BLIVEN, Donna, Vice President Patient Care Services and Chief Nursing Officer, Jones Memorial Hospital, Wellsville, NY, p. A455

BLOB, Burchkhard, Manager Human Resources, Central Virginia Training Center, Madison Heights, VA, p. A670

BLOCHLINGER, Pamela, Acting Vice President Finance, Cloud County Health Center, Concordia, KS, p. A240

BLOCK, Annie, Director Human Resources, Poplar Community Hospital, Poplar, MT, p. A387

BLOCK, Deborah, Vice President Nursing and Chief Nursing Officer, Oconee Regional Medical Center, Milledgeville, GA, p. A161

BLOCK, Linn R.N., Chief Nursing Officer, Manning Regional Healthcare Center, Manning, IA, p. A231

BLODGETT, Debbie, Director Fiscal Services, Ochiltree General Hospital, Perryton, TX, p. A637

BLOEMER, Brad, Vice President Finance and Chief Financial Officer, Arkansas Methodist Medical Center, Paragould, AR, p. A48

BLOEMKER, Jeff, Chief Executive Officer, I–70 Community Hospital, Sweet Springs, MO, p. A380

BLOM, David P., President and Chief Executive Officer, Ohiohealth, Columbus, OH, p. B94

BLOMQUIST, David, Director Information Technology, Mckenzie–Willamette Medical Center, Springfield, OR, p. A527

BLOMSTEDT, Jason, Chief of Staff, Community Hospital, Mccook, NE, p. A396

BLOOD, Barbara
Director Human Resources, Lourdes Counseling Center, Richland, WA, p. A684
Executive Director Human Resources, Lourdes Medical Center, Pasco, WA, p. A683

BLOOM, Laura, Director Human Resources, Coffee Regional Medical Center, Douglas, GA, p. A156

BLOOM, Rob, Chief Financial Officer, Carthage Area Hospital, Carthage, NY, p. A434

BLOOMQUIST, Aaron
Chief Financial Officer, Maple Grove Hospital, Maple Grove, MN, p. A343
Chief Financial Officer, North Memorial Medical Center, Robbinsdale, MN, p. A346

BLOUGH, Daniel D. Jr, Chief Executive Officer, Punxsutawney Area Hospital, Punxsutawney, PA, p. A548

BLUE, Gaea, R.N., Administrator and Chief Executive Officer, Avera Weskota Memorial Hospital, Wessington Springs, SD, p. A574

BLUE, Jan L, Vice President Human Resources, Hoag Memorial Hospital Presbyterian, Newport Beach, CA, p. A76

BLUE, Lee Ann MSN, R.N., Chief Nursing Officer and Executive Vice President Patient Care Services, Eskenazi Health, Indianapolis, IN, p. A211

BLUHM, Tom, Director Information Systems, Island Hospital, Anacortes, WA, p. A678

BLUM, Carrie, Chief Information Officer, Monroe Clinic, Monroe, WI, p. A708

BLUM, Daniel, President, Phelps Memorial Hospital Center, Sleepy Hollow, NY, p. A452

BLUM, Donald A. M.D., Chief of Staff, Wetzel County Hospital, New Martinsville, WV, p. A694

BLUM, Walter B M.D., Chief of Staff, Mcleod Medical Center Dillon, Dillon, SC, p. A561

BLUNK, Jim D.O., Chief Medical Officer, Sumner County Hospital District One, Caldwell, KS, p. A239

BLURTON, Cheri
Director Human Resources, HIPAA Privacy Officer, Great River Medical Center, Blytheville, AR, p. A40
Director Human Resources, South Mississippi County Regional Medical Center, Osceola, AR, p. A48

BLYE, Colleen M, Executive Vice President and Chief Financial Officer, Montefiore Medical Center, New Rochelle, NY, p. A443

BLYTHE, Thomas W, System Vice President Human Resources, Good Samaritan Regional Health Center, Mount Vernon, IL, p. A194

BOAL, Jeremy, M.D., President, Mount Sinai Beth Israel, New Rochelle, NY, p. A443

BOARD, Patricia, Vice President Human Resources, Community Hospital Of Bremen, Bremen, IN, p. A205

BOARDMAN, Debra K., FACHE, President and Chief Executive Officer, Range Regional Health Services, Hibbing, MN, p. A341

BOAS, Erik, Chief Financial Officer, University Of Maryland Charles Regional Medical Center, La Plata, MD, p. A299

BOATMAN, Robert, Director Information Technology, Richmond State Hospital, Richmond, IN, p. A219

BOATRIGHT, Donna, MSN, Chief Executive Officer, Rolling Plains Memorial Hospital, Sweetwater, TX, p. A648

BOATTENHAMER, Greg, Chief Executive Officer, Decatur County Hospital, Leon, IA, p. A230

BOBBITT, James, Vice President Human Resources, Group Ministry Market, Saint Agnes Healthcare, Baltimore, MD, p. A295

BOBBS, Kathy J., FACHE, President and Chief Executive Officer, Women's And Children's Hospital, Lafayette, LA, p. A279

BOBEK, Bruce, President Professional Staff, Columbia Memorial Hospital, Astoria, OR, p. A520

BOBO, Matt, Chief Information Officer, Meade District Hospital, Meade, KS, p. A247

BOBSEINE, Shannon, Manager Human Resources, TLC Health Network – Lake Shore Hospital, Irving, NY, p. A437

BOCCELLATO, Judy R.N., MSN, Chief Nursing Officer, Specialty Hospital Of Central Jersey, Lakewood, NJ, p. A415

BOCHATON, Philippe, President, Baylor Scott & White Medical Center – Round Rock, Round Rock, TX, p. A640

BOCKENEK, William M.D., Chief Medical Officer, Carolinas Rehabilitation, Charlotte, NC, p. A459

BODENHAM, Steve, Senior Manager Clinical Engineering, Indiana University Health North Hospital, Carmel, IN, p. A205

BODENNER, Nancy, Director Human Resources, St. Joseph Health System, Tawas City, MI, p. A331

BODENSTEINER, Kim, Chief Financial Officer, Essentia Health Fosston, Fosston, MN, p. A340

BODIN, Donna L, Vice President, Woman's Hospital, Baton Rouge, LA, p. A271

BODINE, Maureen, Chief Clinical Officer, Kindred Hospital–San Diego, San Diego, CA, p. A85

BODKINS, Melissa R.N., Chief Clinical Officer, Tri Valley Health System, Cambridge, NE, p. A391

BODLE, Vickie, Chief Financial Officer, Lake Chelan Community Hospital And Clinics, Chelan, WA, p. A679

BODLOVIC, Kirk
Vice President and Chief Financial Officer, Providence St. Joseph Medical Center, Polson, MT, p. A387
WMSA Chief Financial Officer, St. Patrick Hospital, Missoula, MT, p. A387

BODNAR, Darrell, Director Information, Weeks Medical Center, Lancaster, NH, p. A408

BODWELL, Amy, Vice President Finance, Methodist Richardson Medical Center, Richardson, TX, p. A639

BODY, Daniel J., Chief Executive Officer, Psychiatric Institute Of Washington, Washington, DC, p. A118

BOECKMANN, Patricia R.N., Chief Operating Officer and Chief Nursing Officer, Straub Medical Center, Honolulu, HI, p. A169

BOEHLER, Richard, M.D., President and Chief Executive Officer, St. Joseph Hospital, Nashua, NH, p. A409

BOEHM, Scott D, Executive Vice President Human Resources and Facilities, Sanford Bismarck, Bismarck, ND, p. A474

BOEHMER, Bernard M.D., Medical Director, Cassia Regional Medical Center, Burley, ID, p. A172

BOEHNKE, Winnie, Director Human Resources, Timberlawn Mental Health System, Dallas, TX, p. A607

BOEMER, Sally Mason
Chief Financial Officer, North Shore Medical Center, Salem, MA, p. A311
Senior Vice President Finance, Massachusetts General Hospital, Boston, MA, p. A303

BOEMMEL, Michael, Vice President and Chief Financial Officer, Medstar National Rehabilitation Hospital, Washington, DC, p. A117

BOEN, Stefanie, Chief Nursing Officer, Skyline Hospital, White Salmon, WA, p. A689

BOER, Jeff, Director Information Technology, Pulaski Memorial Hospital, Winamac, IN, p. A221

BOERGER, Judy MSN, Chief Nursing Executive, Parkview Regional Medical Center, Fort Wayne, IN, p. A208

BOERGER, Kathy, Director Human Resources, Upper Valley Medical Center, Troy, OH, p. A501

BOERSCHEL, Viva, Director of Nursing, Floyd County Medical Center, Charles City, IA, p. A224

BOERSMA, Wendy R.N., Vice President and Chief Nursing Officer, Henry Ford Allegiance Health, Jackson, MI, p. A323

BOES, Jody, Vice President Patient Care Services, Door County Medical Center, Sturgeon Bay, WI, p. A713

BOESE, Chris, Vice President and Chief Nursing Officer, Regions Hospital, Saint Paul, MN, p. A348

BOETTGER, Denise, Vice President Nursing and Chief Nursing Officer, OSF Saint Anthony's Health Center, Alton, IL, p. A177

BOGARD, Tim, Manager Information Technology, Highland District Hospital, Hillsboro, OH, p. A492

BOGARDUS, Tim, Chief Executive Officer, Oasis Hospital, Phoenix, AZ, p. A34

BOGEN, Mark A., Senior Vice President and Chief Financial Officer, South Nassau Communities Hospital, Oceanside, NY, p. A448

BOGERS, Christina, Chief Clinical Officer, North Valley Hospital, Whitefish, MT, p. A389

BOGGESS, Carrie
Human Resource Generalist, Carilion Giles Community Hospital, Pearisburg, VA, p. A672
Human Resources Generalist, Carilion Tazewell Community Hospital, Tazewell, VA, p. A676

BOGGESS, Jack, Chief Executive Officer, Healthsouth Rehabilitation Hospital Round Rock, Round Rock, TX, p. A640

BOGGUS, Bradley, Chief Financial Officer, Clinton Memorial Hospital, Wilmington, OH, p. A502

BOGLE, Bryan, Chief Executive Officer, Winn Parish Medical Center, Winnfield, LA, p. A288

BOGLE, William J, Director Information Systems, North Arkansas Regional Medical Center, Harrison, AR, p. A44

BOGOLIN, Loretta MSN, R.N., Chief Nursing Officer and Vice President Care Services, Vassar Brothers Medical Center, Poughkeepsie, NY, p. A450

BOHACH, Christopher DPM, Chief of Staff, Mercy Health – Willard Hospital, Willard, OH, p. A502

BOHALL, Karen, Director Human Resources, Upmc Chautauqua Wca, Jamestown, NY, p. A437

BOHATY, Richard, Director Information Technology, Chi Health St Elizabeth, Lincoln, NE, p. A395

BOHLIN, Sarah, Human Resources Director, North Carolina Specialty Hospital, Durham, NC, p. A461

BOHN, Terry, Director, Human Resources, Orange County Global Medical Center, Inc., Santa Ana, CA, p. A90

BOHNEN, Christa N, Director Human Resources, Ellsworth County Medical Center, Ellsworth, KS, p. A240

BOHNENKAMP, Russ, Chief Financial Officer, Chadron Community Hospital And Health Services, Chadron, NE, p. A392

BOICE, Sheila, Director Human Resources, Barton County Memorial Hospital, Lamar, MO, p. A372

BOIK, Reyne, Director Human Resources, Cascade Medical Center, Leavenworth, WA, p. A682

BOIKE, Darlene, Chief Financial Officer, Chippewa County–Montevideo Hospital, Montevideo, MN, p. A344

BOILEAU, Michel M.D., Chief Clinical Officer, St. Charles Prineville, Prineville, OR, p. A526

BOILY, Cindy, MSN, R.N.
Senior Vice President and Chief Nursing Officer, Wakemed Cary Hospital, Cary, NC, p. A458
Senior Vice President and Chief Nursing Officer, Wakemed Raleigh Campus, Raleigh, NC, p. A469

BOIS, Alain R.N., Director of Nursing, Northern Maine Medical Center, Fort Kent, ME, p. A291

BOISVERT, Gerald J, Vice President and Chief Financial Officer, Connecticut Children's Medical Center, Hartford, CT, p. A110

BOJO, Rolland, R.N.
Chief Nursing Officer, Administrator Patient Care and Services, Catskill Regional Medical Center, Harris, NY, p. A437
Administrator, Grover M. Hermann Hospital, Callicoon, NY, p. A433

BOKA, Darin, Chief Information Officer, Mclaren Oakland, Pontiac, MI, p. A328

BOKON, Mark, Chief Information Officer, Northwest Medical Center – Springdale, Springdale, AR, p. A49

BOLAND, E. Kay R.N., MS, Vice President and Chief Nursing Officer, United Health Services Hospitals–Binghamton, Binghamton, NY, p. A432

BOLAND, Susan, R.N., MSN, President and Chief Executive Officer, Wheaton Franciscan Healthcare – All Saints, Racine, WI, p. A711

BOLANDER, Patrick C
Chief Financial Officer, East Cooper Medical Center, Mount Pleasant, SC, p. A564
Chief Financial Officer, Georgetown Community Hospital, Georgetown, KY, p. A258

BOLANO, Odette, R.N., President, Saint Alphonsus Regional Medical Center, Boise, ID, p. A172

BOLCAVAGE, Ted, Vice President Division Controller, Inpatient, Ohiohealth Rehabilitation Hospital, Columbus, OH, p. A488

BOLDA, Craig, Chief Operating Officer, St. Catherine Hospital, East Chicago, IN, p. A206

BOLDING, Kay R.N., MS, Vice President Patient Care Services and Chief Nursing Officer, Jackson County Memorial Hospital, Altus, OK, p. A504

BOLDUC, Tiana, Chief Information Officer, Mercy Hospital Ozark, Ozark, AR, p. A48

BOLEN, David, Vice President and Chief Financial Officer, Passavant Area Hospital, Jacksonville, IL, p. A191

BOLEN, Shannon, Director Human Resources, Baptist Memorial Hospital–Booneville, Booneville, MS, p. A352

BOLES, Bonnie M.D.
Administrator, Tanner Higgins General Hospital, Bremen, GA, p. A153
Administrator, Tanner Medical Center–Villa Rica, Villa Rica, GA, p. A166

BOLES, Glen
Vice President and Chief Financial Officer, Christus St. Michael Health System, Texarkana, TX, p. A649
Vice President and Chief Financial Officer, Christus St. Michael Rehabilitation Hospital, Texarkana, TX, p. A649

BOLES, Lee, Assistant Administrator and Chief Financial Officer, Hunt Regional Medical Center, Greenville, TX, p. A617

BOLEWARE, Mike, Administrator, Franklin County Memorial Hospital, Meadville, MS, p. A358

BOLEY, Jason M.D., Medical Director, Rock Prairie Behavioral Health, College Station, TX, p. A602

BOLEY, Sarah, Director Human Resources, Wetzel County Hospital, New Martinsville, WV, p. A694

BOLIN, Cris, Chief Financial Officer, Grand River Hospital District, Rifle, CO, p. A107

BOLIN, Kari, Chief Nursing Officer, Putnam Community Medical Center, Palatka, FL, p. A138

BOLIN, Paul, Vice President Human Resources, The Acadia Hospital, Bangor, ME, p. A289

BOLINGER, John M.D., Vice President Medical Affairs, Union Hospital, Terre Haute, IN, p. A220

BOLLARD, Robert, Chief Financial Officer, Healthsouth Rehabilitation Hospital – Henderson, Henderson, NV, p. A402

BOLLICH, Mary, Director of Nurses, AMG Specialty Hospital–Lafayette, Lafayette, LA, p. A278

BOLLIER, Sheila A., Chief Executive Officer, Healthsouth Rehabilitation Hospital Of Cypress, Houston, TX, p. A620

BOLLINGER, Bill, Chief Information Officer, Carroll County Memorial Hospital, Carrollton, MO, p. A366

BOLLINGER, Bruce M.D., Medical Director, Baylor Surgical Hospital At Fort Worth, Fort Worth, TX, p. A613

BOLLINGER, Candace, Director of Nursing, Mercy Hospital Booneville, Booneville, AR, p. A41

BOLLMANN, Brett, Administrator, Memorial Hospital, Chester, IL, p. A180

BOLLU, Prabhu, Director Information Technology, Wilson N. Jones Regional Medical Center, Sherman, TX, p. A645

BOLOGNA, Monica R.N., Chief Nursing Officer, West Jefferson Medical Center, Marrero, LA, p. A281

BOLOGNANI, Laurie, Human Resources Officer, Speare Memorial Hospital, Plymouth, NH, p. A410

BOLOR, Erlinda R.N., Chief Nursing Officer, San Joaquin General Hospital, French Camp, CA, p. A60

BOLT, Elizabeth T, Chief Human Resources Officer, University Of Wisconsin Hospitals And Clinics Authority, Madison, WI, p. A705

BOLTER, Cindy, Chief Nursing and Operations Officer, John Muir Behavioral Health Center, Concord, CA, p. A56

BOLTON, Jeffrey W, Chief Administrative Officer, Mayo Clinic Hospital – Rochester, Rochester, MN, p. A346

BOMAR, Jacob, Director Information Technology, Hardin Medical Center, Savannah, TN, p. A588

BOMBA, Douglas, Chief Financial Officer, Cameron Memorial Community Hospital, Angola, IN, p. A203

BOMER, Starsky, Chief Executive Officer, Sacred Oak Medical Center, Houston, TX, p. A622

BOMGAARS, Scott M.D., Vice President Medical Affairs, Methodist Jennie Edmundson Hospital, Council Bluffs, IA, p. A225

BOMSTAD, Heather MSN, R.N., Vice President Patient Care Services and Chief Nursing Officer, OSF Saint Paul Medical Center, Mendota, IL, p. A193

BONACORSO, Donna, Interim Chief Nursing Officer, Community Medical Center, Toms River, NJ, p. A421

BONACQUISTI, Gary M.D., Chief Medical Officer, Texas Health Presbyterian Hospital Of Rockwall, Rockwall, TX, p. A640

BONAR, Carrie, Chief Information Officer, Southern California Hospital At Culver City, Culver City, CA, p. A57

BONAR, Lynette, FACHE, R.N., Chief Executive Officer, Tuba City Regional Health Care Corporation, Tuba City, AZ, p. A37

BONAR, Robert, Jr, Chief Executive Officer, Children's Hospitals And Clinics Of Minnesota, Minneapolis, MN, p. A343

BONASORD, Cheryl, MSN, RN, Vice President and Chief Nursing Officer, Nashoba Valley Medical Center, Ayer, MA, p. A302

BONAZZOLA, Michael M.D., Interim Chief Medical Officer, Ohsu Hospital, Portland, OR, p. A525

BONCZEK, Mary Ellen R.N., Chief Nursing Executive, New Hanover Regional Medical Center, Wilmington, NC, p. A472

BOND, Lee, Chief Operating Officer, Singing River Health System, Pascagoula, MS, p. A360

BOND, Rodney, Director of Information Technology, Northern Hospital Of Surry County, Mount Airy, NC, p. A467

BOND, Sharon, Director Human Resources, College Station Medical Center, College Station, TX, p. A602

BONDEROFF, Scott, President, O'Connor Hospital, Delhi, NY, p. A435

BONDI, Blaise, Chief Financial Officer, Baylor Scott & White Medical Center – Centennial, Frisco, TX, p. A615

BONDURANT, Barry, Administrator and Chief Executive Officer, Baptist Memorial Hospital–Union City, Union City, TN, p. A590

BONDURANT, Charles, Chief Information Officer, Meadows Regional Medical Center, Vidalia, GA, p. A166

BONEY, Rebecca R.N., Chief Nursing Officer, Healthsouth Rehabilitation Hospital Of Middletown, Middletown, DE, p. A115

BONFILIO, Nicholas M.D., Chief of Staff, Great Halls Hospital, Great Falls, MT, p. A385

BONI, Shirley M, Administrative Officer, San Carlos Apache Healthcare Corporation, Peridot, AZ, p. A32

BONILLA, Felicita, Administrator, Hospital De La Concepcion, San German, PR, p. A725

BONILLA, Tony, Chief Executive Officer, Icon Hospital, Humble, TX, p. A624

BONIN, Stephanie, Chief Executive Officer, Acadia Vermilion Hospital, Lafayette, LA, p. A278

BONK, Daniel J., Chief Executive Officer, Nix Health Care System, San Antonio, TX, p. A643

BONNAR, David, Chief Information Officer, Kaiser Permanente Fresno Medical Center, Fresno, CA, p. A61

BONNER, Brad L., Executive Director, Human Resources and General Counsel, Crawford County Memorial Hospital, Denison, IA, p. A226

BONNER, Gwen, Chief Operating Officer, Saint Francis Hospital–Bartlett, Bartlett, TN, p. A575

BONNER, Lenne
President, Clearwater Valley Hospital And Clinics, Orofino, ID, p. A175
President, St. Mary's Hospital, Cottonwood, ID, p. A173

BONNER, Robert
Chief Financial Officer, Glendora Community Hospital, Glendora, CA, p. A62
Chief Financial Officer, Montclair Hospital Medical Center, Montclair, CA, p. A74
Chief Financial Officer, San Dimas Community Hospital, San Dimas, CA, p. A86

BONO, Anthony Jr, Chief Nursing Officer, Grove City Medical Center, Grove City, PA, p. A535

BONOMO, Carrie M.D., Chief of Staff, Riverland Medical Center, Ferriday, LA, p. A274

BONTRAGER, Mandy, Director Nursing, Holton Community Hospital, Holton, KS, p. A242

BONZO, Kelly, Director, Baptist Health Richmond, Richmond, KY, p. A267

BOO, Thomas M.D., Chief of Staff, Northern Inyo Hospital, Bishop, CA, p. A54

BOOHER, Terresa O., Vice President of Patient Care Services, Highlands Regional Medical Center, Prestonsburg, KY, p. A266

BOOKER, Angela, Director of Nursing Services, Teton Valley Health Care, Driggs, ID, p. A173

BOOM, Marc L., M.D., Chief Executive Officer, Houston Methodist, Houston, TX, p. B66

BOONE, Donna MS, R.N., Chief Nursing Officer, Weatherford Regional Medical Center, Weatherford, TX, p. A653

BOONE, Elwood Bernard. III, FACHE, President, Sentara Virginia Beach General Hospital, Virginia Beach, VA, p. A676

BOONE, Margie, Registered Health Information Technician, Cumberland River Hospital, Celina, TN, p. A576

BOONE, Richard, Chief Financial Officer, Johnson City Medical Center, Johnson City, TN, p. A581

BOORAS, Laura, Vice President Human Resources, Coliseum Medical Centers, Macon, GA, p. A160

BOORE, Chad, President, OSF St. Joseph Medical Center, Bloomington, IL, p. A178

BOORNAZIAN, John M.D., Chief Medical Officer, Huggins Hospital, Wolfeboro, NH, p. A410

BOOSALIS, Mary H., President, Premier Health, Dayton, OH, p. B99

BOOTH, Christy, Chief Human Resources Officer, Doctors Memorial Hospital, Bonifay, FL, p. A120

BOOTH, Daniel
Vice President Operations and Chief Human Resources Officer, Inland Hospital, Waterville, ME, p. A293
Vice President Operations, Inland Hospital, Waterville, ME, p. A293

BOOTH, Patrick M., FACHE, President and Chief Executive Officer, Fremont Health, Fremont, NE, p. A393

BORCHERS, Jonathan M.D., Chief Medical Officer, Washington County Memorial Hospital, Potosi, MO, p. A375

BORCHERT, Barry, Vice President Finance, Reedsburg Area Medical Center, Reedsburg, WI, p. A711

BORCHI, Daniel, Chief Information Officer, Carilion New River Valley Medical Center, Christiansburg, VA, p. A666

BORDELON, Rock, President and Chief Executive Officer, Allegiance Health Management, Shreveport, LA, p. B8

BORDEN, Eric, Chief Operating Officer and Chief Financial Officer, Jewell County Hospital, Mankato, KS, p. A246

BORDEN, Sandy, Chief Financial Officer, Brodstone Memorial Hospital, Superior, NE, p. A400

BORDENKIRCHER, Kimberly Hupp., Chief Executive Officer, Henry County Hospital, Napoleon, OH, p. A496

BORDERS, James M.D., Chief Medical Officer, Baptist Health Lexington, Lexington, KY, p. A260

BORDO, David, M.D.
Chief Medical Officer, Presence Holy Family Medical Center, Des Plaines, IL, p. A185
Chief Medical Officer, Presence Resurrection Medical Center, Chicago, IL, p. A182
Vice President and Chief Medical Officer, Community First Medical Center, Chicago, IL, p. A180

BOREL, Patricia, Chief Financial Officer, Central Community Hospital, Elkader, IA, p. A227

BOREN, Kevin
Chief Financial Officer, Essentia Health Duluth, Duluth, MN, p. A339
Chief Financial Officer, Essentia Health Northern Pines Medical Center, Aurora, MN, p. A335

BORENGASSER, Connie, Chief Executive Officer, Vantage Point Of Northwest Arkansas, Fayetteville, AR, p. A43

BORENS, Dwan, Chief Nursing Officer, St. John Broken Arrow, Broken Arrow, OK, p. A505

BORER, Tom, Vice President Operations, Promedica Fostoria Community Hospital, Fostoria, OH, p. A491

BORG, David E., Chief of Medical Staff, Community Medical Center, Inc., Falls City, NE, p. A392

BORGERSON, Carol, Business Office Manager and Chief Financial Officer, Madison Healthcare Services, Madison, MN, p. A342

BORGSTROM, Marna P., Chief Executive Officer, Yale–New Haven Hospital, New Haven, CT, p. A112

BORING, Ron , Senior Vice President and Chief Operating Officer, Mcleod Regional Medical Center, Florence, SC, p. A562

BORIS, Diane
Chief Financial Officer, Lehigh Valley Hospital – Schuylkill South Jackson Street, Pottsville, PA, p. A548
Vice President and Chief Financial Officer, Lehigh Valley Hospital – Schuylkill East Norwegian Street, Pottsville, PA, p. A548

BORIS, Jamie M.D., President Medical Staff, Washington Health System Greene, Waynesburg, PA, p. A553

BORJA, Catherine M.D., Chairman Executive Committee Medical Staff, Naval Hospital Oak Harbor, Oak Harbor, WA, p. A683

BORMANN, Jim, Director Human Resources, Passavant Area Hospital, Jacksonville, IL, p. A191

BORN, Michael, M.D., President and Chief Executive Officer, Swedishamerican – A Division Of Uw Health, Rockford, IL, p. A199

BORNICK, Brian, Chief Information Officer, Minneapolis Veterans Affairs Health Care System, Minneapolis, MN, p. A344

BORNMANN, Debra, Chief Executive Officer, Warm Springs Rehabilitation Hospital Of San Antonio, San Antonio, TX, p. A644

BOROS, Dean B., Medical Center Director, James H. Quillen Veterans Affairs Medical Center, Mountain Home, TN, p. A586

BOROWSKI, Thomas
Administrator, Mayo Clinic Health System In Waseca, Waseca, MN, p. A350
Chief Information Officer, Mayo Clinic Health System In Saint James, Saint James, MN, p. A347

BORRENPOHL, James, Market Site Director, Community Hospital Of San Bernardino, San Bernardino, CA, p. A85

BORTEL, Karol, Vice President Financial Services, Wood County Hospital, Bowling Green, OH, p. A482

BORTKE, Todd, Director Information Systems, Chi St. Alexius Health, Bismarck, ND, p. A474

BORTZ, Tammy, Director of Finance, Peterson Healthcare And Rehabilitation Hospital, Wheeling, WV, p. A697

BORYSZAK, Martin, President and Chief Executive Officer, Sisters Of Charity Hospital Of Buffalo, Buffalo, NY, p. A433

BORZON, Eve R.N., Chief Operating Officer, NYC Health + Hospitals / Woodhull, New Rochelle, NY, p. A446

BOS, Robbi E, Vice President Human Resources, Sauk Prairie Healthcare, Prairie Du Sac, WI, p. A711

BOSCIA, Michael, Chief Financial Officer, Bartow Regional Medical Center, Bartow, FL, p. A119

BOSCO, John, Senior Vice President and Chief Information Officer, Long Island Jewish Medical Center, New Rochelle, NY, p. A442

BOSCO, Maureen, Executive Director, Central New York Psychiatric Center, Marcy, NY, p. A439

BOSER, Andrew, Chief Executive Officer, Cuba Memorial Hospital, Cuba, NY, p. A434

BOSHUT, Sami, Chief Information Officer, Jamaica Hospital Medical Center, New Rochelle, NY, p. A441

BOSLEY, Elizabeth, Vice President Patient Services and Chief Nursing Officer, St. Mary's Medical Center, Huntington, WV, p. A693

BOSO, William, Executive Director, Administrator, Southern Indiana Rehabilitation Hospital, New Albany, IN, p. A217

BOSS, Craig M.D., Chief Medical Officer, Munson Healthcare Charlevoix Hospital, Charlevoix, MI, p. A316

BOST, Cecelia, Chief Operating Officer, Alliance Healthcare System, Holly Springs, MS, p. A356

BOST, Marcus, Director Information Services and Chief Information Officer, Adena Greenfield Medical Center, Greenfield, OH, p. A492

BOSTER, Brian M.D., Medical Director, Select Specialty Hospital–Cincinnati, Cincinnati, OH, p. A484

BOSTIC, Deborah R.N., Chief Nursing Officer, Texas Health Presbyterian Hospital Denton, Denton, TX, p. A608

BOSTIC, William, Administrative Assistant Human Resources, Surprise Valley Health Care District, Cedarville, CA, p. A55

BOSTON, Barbara, Interim Chief Operating Officer, Hahnemann University Hospital, Philadelphia, PA, p. A544

BOSTON–LEARY, Katie, Senior Vice President Patient Care Services, Union Hospital, Elkton, MD, p. A298

BOSTROM, Brenda, Director of Nursing, Coteau Des Prairies Hospital, Sisseton, SD, p. A573

BOSTROM, Gary, Chief Executive Officer and Chief Financial Officer, East Adams Rural Healthcare, Ritzville, WA, p. A684

BOSTROM, Stuart M.D., Director Medical Affairs, Sutter Roseville Medical Center, Roseville, CA, p. A83

BOSTWICK, John, Interim Chief Financial Officer, Henderson County Community Hospital, Lexington, TN, p. A583

BOSTWICK, Monte J., Market Chief Executive Officer, Chi St. Luke's Health Memorial Lufkin, Lufkin, TX, p. A631

BOSTWICK, Shari, Director Human Resources, New London Hospital, New London, NH, p. A410

BOSWELL, Debbie, Chief Operating Officer and Chief Nursing Officer, Mercy Medical Center, Roseburg, OR, p. A526

BOSWELL, Diane, Director Human Resources and Marketing, Salem Township Hospital, Salem, IL, p. A199

BOSWELL, John, Chief Human Resources Officer, University Of Virginia Medical Center, Charlottesville, VA, p. A665

BOSWELL, William D. M.D., Jr, Chief Medical Officer, City Of Hope's Helford Clinical Research Hospital, Duarte, CA, p. A58

BOSWINKEL, Jan M.D., Vice President Medical Operations and Chief Safety Officer, Children's Hospital Of Philadelphia, Philadelphia, PA, p. A543

BOSWORTH, Dawn, Director Human Resources, Arrowhead Behavioral Health Hospital, Maumee, OH, p. A495

BOTHE, Albert M.D., Jr, Chief Medical Officer, Geisinger Medical Center, Danville, PA, p. A532

BOTHNER, Joan M.D., Chief Medical Officer, Children's Hospital Colorado, Aurora, CO, p. A98

BOTHUN, Crystal, Chief Financial Officer, Johnson Memorial Health Services, Dawson, MN, p. A338

BOTINE, Gary, Vice President, Chief Financial Officer, Mary Greeley Medical Center, Ames, IA, p. A222

BOTLER, Joel M.D., Chief Medical Officer, Maine Medical Center, Portland, ME, p. A292

BOTNEY, Mitchell M.D., Vice President Medical Affairs and Chief Medical Officer, Missouri Baptist Medical Center, Saint Louis, MO, p. A377

BOTTENFIELD, Dana, Vice President Human Resources, St. Jude Children's Research Hospital, Memphis, TN, p. A585

BOTTGER, Barry, Chief Financial Officer, Republic County Hospital, Belleville, KS, p. A238

BOTTOM, Paige, Director Operations, Wilmington Treatment Center, Wilmington, NC, p. A472

BOUCK, Nancy, Director Human Resources, Huron Medical Center, Bad Axe, MI, p. A314

BOUCOT, Mark G., FACHE, President and Chief Executive Officer, Garrett Regional Medical Center, Oakland, MD, p. A300

BOUDREAUX, Angela, Director Information Technology, St. Charles Parish Hospital, Luling, LA, p. A280

BOUDREAUX, Scott, Chief Executive Officer, Fairway Medical Surgical Hospital, Covington, LA, p. A273

BOUFFARD, Rodney, Superintendent, Riverview Psychiatric Center, Augusta, ME, p. A289

BOUGHAL, Ginni, Director Health Information and Information Technology, Peacehealth Peace Harbor Medical Center, Florence, OR, p. A521

BOUHAROUN, Khalil, Chief Information Officer, The Hsc Pediatric Center, Washington, DC, p. A118

BOULA, Rodney, Chief Executive Officer, Calais Regional Hospital, Calais, ME, p. A290

BOULENGER, Albert, Chief Executive Officer, Baptist Health South Florida, Baptist Hospital Of Miami, Miami, FL, p. A132

BOULLION, Leona, Chief Operating Officer, Women's And Children's Hospital, Lafayette, LA, p. A279

BOUQUET, Sheena
Vice President, Lafayette General Medical Center, Lafayette, LA, p. A278
Vice President, Lafayette General Surgical Hospital, Lafayette, LA, p. A278

BOUQUIO, George, Director Human Resources, South Beach Psychiatric Center, New Rochelle, NY, p. A446

BOUR, Eric, M.D., FACS
  Chief Executive Officer, Piedmont Newton Hospital, Covington, GA, p. A155
  President, GHS Hillcrest Memorial Hospital, Simpsonville, SC, p. A566
BOURGEOIS, Jeff A., President and Chief Executive Officer, San Juan Regional Medical Center, Farmington, NM, p. A426
BOURLAND, Don, Vice President Human Resources, Peacehealth Peace Harbor Medical Center, Florence, OR, p. A521
BOURLAND, Renee, Human Resources Specialist, San Antonio State Hospital, San Antonio, TX, p. A643
BOURN, Jennifer, Director, Health Information Services and Medical Staff Services, Centerpointe Hospital, Saint Charles, MO, p. A376
BOURNE, Kara R.N., MSN, Chief Nursing Officer and Chief Operating Officer, Foothill Regional Medical Center, Tustin, CA, p. A94
BOURNE, Kimberly L., Chief Executive Officer, Taylorville Memorial Hospital, Taylorville, IL, p. A201
BOURQUE, Teresa, Sr. Administrator for Nursing/Chief Nurse, Hurley Medical Center, Flint, MI, p. A319
BOUTROS, Akram, M.D., FACHE, President and Chief Executive Officer, Metrohealth Medical Center, Cleveland, OH, p. A486
BOUTROS, Nashaat M.D., Clinical Director, Center For Behavioral Medicine, Kansas City, MO, p. A370
BOUTWELL, Wayne, Chief Executive Officer, Regency Hospital Of Central Georgia, Macon, GA, p. A161
BOUYEA, Lawanda Janine, Director Human Resources, Natividad Medical Center, Salinas, CA, p. A84
BOVA, Sheila, Chief Financial Officer, Kindred Hospital–Albuquerque, Albuquerque, NM, p. A424
BOVIO, Ernest L. Jr, Chief Executive Officer, High Point Regional Health System, High Point, NC, p. A464
BOWCUTT, Marilyn A R.N., MSN, President and Chief Operating Officer, University Hospital, Augusta, GA, p. A152
BOWE, Christopher M.D., Chief Medical Officer, Medical Affairs, St. Mary's Regional Medical Center, Lewiston, ME, p. A291
BOWEN, Aaron, Chief Executive Officer, Arizona State Hospital, Phoenix, AZ, p. A33
BOWEN, Christine R.N., Chief Nursing Officer, DMC Harper University Hospital, Detroit, MI, p. A318
BOWEN, Jill Berry., Chief Executive Officer, Northwestern Medical Center, Saint Albans, VT, p. A663
BOWEN, Julie, Executive Director of Information Technology, Gibson Area Hospital And Health Services, Gibson City, IL, p. A188
BOWEN, Mary Beth R.N., Vice President Nursing and Chief Nursing Officer, United Memorial Medical Center, Batavia, NY, p. A431
BOWEN, Rodger W M.P.H., Chief Financial Officer, Scenic Mountain Medical Center, Big Spring, TX, p. A598
BOWEN, Stephen, Administrator, Lavaca Medical Center, Hallettsville, TX, p. A617
BOWEN, Tim, Administrator, Baptist Health Medical Center – Conway, Conway, AR, p. A41
BOWER, David M.D., Chief of Staff, Atlanta Veterans Affairs Medical Center, Decatur, GA, p. A156
BOWER, James M.D., Chief Medical Officer, Research Medical Center, Kansas City, MO, p. A370
BOWER, Kay, Associate Director for Patient Care Services, Battle Creek Veterans Affairs Medical Center, Battle Creek, MI, p. A315
BOWERMAN, Joeann, Director of Nursing, Chambers Memorial Hospital, Danville, AR, p. A42
BOWERMAN, Stephen, Senior Vice President, Chief Financial Officer, Midland Memorial Hospital, Midland, TX, p. A633
BOWERS, Daniel, Chief Operating Officer, Riverside Community Hospital, Riverside, CA, p. A82
BOWERS, David N M.D., Medical Director, Siskin Hospital For Physical Rehabilitation, Chattanooga, TN, p. A576
BOWERS, Melodee, Director Human Resources, Carle Hoopeston Regional Health Center, Hoopeston, IL, p. A190
BOWERS, Michael E., President, SSM Health St. Joseph – St. Charles, Saint Charles, MO, p. A376
BOWERS, Michael
  Head Human Resources, Naval Hospital Oak Harbor, Oak Harbor, WA, p. A683
  Interim Director for Administration, Naval Hospital Oak Harbor, Oak Harbor, WA, p. A683
BOWERS, Sharon R.N., Manager of Community, Public and Employee Relations, Sheridan Community Hospital, Sheridan, MI, p. A330
BOWERS, Shelby, Director Marketing and Public Relations, Peninsula Hospital, Louisville, TN, p. A583

BOWERS, Tracy
  Vice President Human Resources and Administrative Services, Novant Health Uva Health System Haymarket Medical Center, Haymarket, VA, p. A668
  Vice President Human Resources and Administrative Services, Novant Health Uva Health System Prince William Medical Center, Manassas, VA, p. A670
BOWERY, Leslie, Director of Standards and Compliance, Cumberland Hospital, New Kent, VA, p. A671
BOWES, Arthur, Senior Vice President Human Resources, North Shore Medical Center, Salem, MA, p. A311
BOWES, Matthew M.D., Chief of Staff, Mackinac Straits Health System, Inc., Saint Ignace, MI, p. A330
BOWES, William, Chief Financial Officer, Uams Medical Center, Little Rock, AR, p. A46
BOWLEG, Teresa R.N., Chief Nursing Officer, Murphy Medical Center, Murphy, NC, p. A467
BOWLES, Patrica R.N., Chief Nursing Officer, Franklin County Medical Center, Preston, ID, p. A175
BOWLES, Tara, Employee Relations Director, Rawlins County Health Center, Atwood, KS, p. A238
BOWLING, Donald M.D., Chief Medical Staff, Southampton Memorial Hospital, Franklin, VA, p. A667
BOWLING, Karen, Chief Information Officer, St. Mary's Regional Medical Center, Lewiston, ME, p. A291
BOWLING, Kay, Chief Executive Officer, Centra Specialty Hospital, Lynchburg, VA, p. A669
BOWLING, Kelli, Chief Culture Officer, Door County Medical Center, Sturgeon Bay, WI, p. A713
BOWLING, Nancy, Director Human Resources, Shoals Hospital, Muscle Shoals, AL, p. A22
BOWMAN, Dyan, Director Human Resources, Newberry County Memorial Hospital, Newberry, SC, p. A565
BOWMAN, Joe, Chief Financial Officer, Tristar Ashland City Medical Center, Ashland City, TN, p. A575
BOWMAN, Joseph E, Chief Financial Officer, Tristar Stonecrest Medical Center, Smyrna, TN, p. A589
BOWMAN, Julie, Senior Vice President, Patient Care and Chief Nursing Officer, Phoenix Children's Hospital, Phoenix, AZ, p. A34
BOWMAN, Ken, Chief Executive Officer, Van Matre Healthsouth Rehabilitation Hospital, Rockford, IL, p. A199
BOWMAN, Mark M.D., President Medical Staff, Tillamook Regional Medical Center, Tillamook, OR, p. A527
BOWMAN, Maureen, Vice President and Chief Nursing Officer, Beaumont Hospital – Royal Oak, Royal Oak, MI, p. A329
BOWMAN, Scott, Administrator, Sweetwater Hospital, Sweetwater, TN, p. A589
BOWMAN, William M.D., Vice President Medical Affairs, Moses H. Cone Memorial Hospital, Greensboro, NC, p. A463
BOWMER, Carolyn, , Lawrence Memorial Hospital, Lawrence, KS, p. A245
BOWSER, John, Vice President, Chief Financial Officer, OSF Saint Luke Medical Center, Kewanee, IL, p. A191
BOX, Darrel, Chief Executive Officer, Lafayette Regional Health Center, Lexington, MO, p. A372
BOX, Justin K.
  Senior Vice President & Chief Information Officer, Mary Washington Hospital, Fredericksburg, VA, p. A667
  Senior Vice President and Chief Information Officer, Stafford Hospital, Stafford, VA, p. A675
BOX, Tom CPA, Chief Financial Officer, Healthsouth Rehabilitation Hospital–Wichita Falls, Wichita Falls, TX, p. A654
BOXELL, Shelley, R.N.
  Chief Nursing Officer, Rehabilitation Hospital Of Fort Wayne, Fort Wayne, IN, p. A208
  Interim Chief Operating Officer, Rehabilitation Hospital Of Fort Wayne, Fort Wayne, IN, p. A208
  Chief Nursing Officer and Interim Chief Operating Officer, Rehabilitation Hospital Of Fort Wayne, Fort Wayne, IN, p. A208
BOYCE, Charlotte, Chief Nursing Officer, Healthsouth Rehabilitation Hospital Memphis–North, Memphis, TN, p. A584
BOYD, Aaron M.D., Chief Medical Officer, Norman Regional Health System, Norman, OK, p. A511
BOYD, Andre Sr, Executive Vice President, Hospital Division, New Hanover Regional Medical Center, Wilmington, NC, p. A472
BOYD, Cathy, Chief Nursing Officer, Select Specialty Hospital–Pontiac, Pontiac, MI, p. A328
BOYD, Christopher L., Senior Vice President and Area Manager, Kaiser Permanente Santa Clara Medical Center, Santa Clara, CA, p. A90
BOYD, Dennis, Chief Financial Officer, St. Mark's Medical Center, La Grange, TX, p. A627
BOYD, Diana, Vice President Nursing, Union Hospital, Dover, OH, p. A490

BOYD, Ellen, Director Human Resources, Emanuel Medical Center, Swainsboro, GA, p. A165
BOYD, Jason E, Chief Operating Officer, Tristar Skyline Medical Center, Nashville, TN, p. A587
BOYD, John W., PsyD, Chief Executive Officer, Sutter Center For Psychiatry, Sacramento, CA, p. A84
BOYD, John, III, M.D.
  Chief Executive Officer and Chief Medical Officer, Scott & White Medical Center – Temple, Temple, TX, p. A648
  Chief Executive Officer, Scott & White Medical Center – Temple, Temple, TX, p. A648
BOYD, Kenneth Jr, President and Chief Executive Officer, Mcdonough District Hospital, Macomb, IL, p. A192
BOYD, Kim, Chief Financial Officer, Buchanan General Hospital, Grundy, VA, p. A668
BOYD, Steven R.N., Nurse Executive, Levi Hospital, Hot Springs National Park, AR, p. A44
BOYD, Travis, Manager, Information Technology, Mercy Hospital Lincoln, Troy, MO, p. A380
BOYER, Aurelia, Senior Vice President and Chief Information Officer, New York–Presbyterian Hospital, New Rochelle, NY, p. A444
BOYER, Charlene, Chief Nursing Officer, Kaiser Permanente Oakland Medical Center, Oakland, CA, p. A77
BOYER, Cheryl T
  Vice President Human Resources, Levindale Hebrew Geriatric Center And Hospital, Baltimore, MD, p. A294
  Vice President Human Resources, Sinai Hospital Of Baltimore, Baltimore, MD, p. A296
BOYER, Craig, Vice President Finance, Sanford Bemidji Medical Center, Bemidji, MN, p. A336
BOYER, Jim, Vice President Information Technology and Chief Information Officer, Rush Memorial Hospital, Rushville, IN, p. A219
BOYER, Roderick M.D., Medical Director, Select Specialty Hospital–Downriver, Wyandotte, MI, p. A333
BOYER, Steve M.D., Chief Medical Officer, Regional West Garden County, Oshkosh, NE, p. A398
BOYER, William, Chief Financial Officer, Community Memorial Hospital, Redfield, SD, p. A572
BOYETTE, Jon, Chief Financial Officer, Pocahontas Memorial Hospital, Buckeye, WV, p. A690
BOYKIN, Arthur M.D., Chief of Staff, Gadsden Regional Medical Center, Gadsden, AL, p. A18
BOYKIN, Doyle, R.N., MSN
  Administrator, Presbyterian Hospital, Albuquerque, NM, p. A425
  President, Presbyterian Hospital, Albuquerque, NM, p. A425
BOYKIN, George G., Chief Executive Officer, Strategic Behavioral Health – Charlotte, Charlotte, NC, p. A460
BOYLAN, Eugene, Chief Executive Officer, First Hospital Wyoming Valley, Kingston, PA, p. A537
BOYLE, Donna, Director, JFK Medical Center North Campus, West Palm Beach, FL, p. A147
BOYLE, James W M.D., Chief Medical Officer, Upmc Passavant, Pittsburgh, PA, p. A547
BOYLE, Kathy R.N., Ph.D., Chief Nursing Officer, Denver Health, Denver, CO, p. A100
BOYLE, Linda Lake., R.N., MSN, Director, Central Alabama Veterans Health Care System, Montgomery, AL, p. A21
BOYLE, Linda Lake, R.N., MSN, Director, Central Alabama Veterans Health Care System, Montgomery, AL, p. B42
BOYLE, Lisa M.D., Vice President Medical Affairs and Medical Director, Medstar Georgetown University Hospital, Washington, DC, p. A117
BOYLE, Patrick R
  Vice President Human Resources, Geneva General Hospital, Geneva, NY, p. A436
  Vice President Human Resources, Soldiers And Sailors Memorial Hospital Of Yates County, Penn Yan, NY, p. A449
BOYLE, Thomas W, Chief Financial Officer, St. Lawrence Rehabilitation Center, Lawrenceville, NJ, p. A415
BOYLES, Clay
  Director Human Resources, Peachford Behavioral Health System, Atlanta, GA, p. A150
  Executive Director, Human Resources, Piedmont Newnan Hospital, Newnan, GA, p. A162
BOYLES, George, Senior Vice President of Finance and Chief Financial Officer, Mercer Health, Coldwater, OH, p. A487
BOYLES, Lee, President, Chi St. Gabriel's Health, Little Falls, MN, p. A342
BOYLES, Mary Gen, Chief Nursing Officer, Healthsouth Rehabilitation Hospital Of Altoona, Altoona, PA, p. A528
BOYLES, Robert L, Director of Human Resources, Highland–Clarksburg Hospital, Clarksburg, WV, p. A691
BOYNE, Barbara, Executive Director, Operations, Bethesda North Hospital, Cincinnati, OH, p. A483

BOYNTON, James P Jr, Chief Financial Officer, Carolina Center For Behavioral Health, Greer, SC, p. A563

BOYNTON, Kimberly, President and Chief Executive Officer, Crouse Health, Syracuse, NY, p. A453

BOYNTON, Stephanie, Administrator, Erlanger Bledsoe Hospital, Pikeville, TN, p. A588

BOYO, Tosan O., Chief Operating Officer, Zuckerberg San Francisco General Hospital And Trauma Center, San Francisco, CA, p. A88

BOYSEN, Doug, Chief Legal Counsel and Vice President Human Resources, Good Samaritan Regional Medical Center, Corvallis, OR, p. A521

BOYSEN, James M.D., Executive Medical Director, Texas Neurorehab Center, Austin, TX, p. A596

BOZELL, Jerry, Vice President, Human Resources, Jay County Hospital, Portland, IN, p. A218

BOZZUTO, Elizabeth R.N., Chief Nursing Officer and Vice President, Saint Mary's Hospital, Waterbury, CT, p. A114

BRAASCH, David A., President, Alton Memorial Hospital, Alton, IL, p. A177

BRABAND, Jon D., FACHE, President and Chief Executive Officer, Glencoe Regional Health Services, Glencoe, MN, p. A340

BRABY, Heath, Director Fiscal Services, Shriners Hospitals For Children–Salt Lake City, Salt Lake City, UT, p. A660

BRACEY, Donny, Director Information Services, Marion General Hospital, Columbia, MS, p. A354

BRACK, Nancy R, Vice President Human Resources, Community Memorial Hospital, Syracuse, NE, p. A400

BRACKEEN, Steven W R.N., Chief Nursing Officer, Merit Health Northwest Mississippi, Clarksdale, MS, p. A353

BRACKEN, Thomas H M.D., Vice President Medical Affairs, Mille Lacs Health System, Onamia, MN, p. A345

BRACKETT, Lori, Director Human Resources, Healthsouth Bakersfield Rehabilitation Hospital, Bakersfield, CA, p. A52

BRACKLEY, Donna R.N., MSN, Senior Vice President Patient Care Services, John Muir Medical Center, Concord, Concord, CA, p. A56

BRACKS, Adam, Chief Executive Officer, Alliancehealth Seminole, Seminole, OK, p. A515

BRACY, Dale, Chief Financial Officer, College Hospital Costa Mesa, Costa Mesa, CA, p. A56

BRADBURY, Monica, Chief Executive Officer, Clarks Summit State Hospital, Clarks Summit, PA, p. A531

BRADDOCK, Mary B, Director Human Resources, Palo Pinto General Hospital, Mineral Wells, TX, p. A633

BRADEN, Pamela, Administrator, Cambridge Behavioral Hospital, Cambridge, OH, p. A482

BRADFORD, Beth, Director Human Resources, Floyd Medical Center, Rome, GA, p. A163

BRADFORD, Cora, Chief Financial Officer, Jackson Parish Hospital, Jonesboro, LA, p. A277

BRADFORD, Randy L., Chief Executive Officer, Eastern Shore Hospital Center, Cambridge, MD, p. A297

BRADFORD, Scot, Chief Information Officer, Baylor Medical Center At Trophy Club, Trophy Club, TX, p. A650

BRADFORD, Susan, Director Nursing, Kansas Heart Hospital, Wichita, KS, p. A253

BRADICK, Joe, Chief Financial Officer, Forks Community Hospital, Forks, WA, p. A680

BRADLEY, Betsy, Coordinator Performance Improvement, Central State Hospital, Milledgeville, GA, p. A161

BRADLEY, Carol, MSN, R.N.
Senior Vice President and Chief Nursing Officer, Legacy Meridian Park Medical Center, Tualatin, OR, p. A527
Senior Vice President and Chief Nursing Officer, Legacy Salmon Creek Medical Center, Vancouver, WA, p. A688

BRADLEY, Cindy, Interim CEO, Montrose Memorial Hospital, Montrose, CO, p. A106

BRADLEY, Connie, R.N., MSN, FACHE
Chief Nursing Officer, Health First Cape Canaveral Hospital, Cocoa Beach, FL, p. A122
Chief Nursing Officer, Health First Palm Bay Hospital, Palm Bay, FL, p. A138
Senior Vice President and Chief Nursing Officer, Health First Viera Hospital, Melbourne, FL, p. A132

BRADLEY, Deidre, Vice President Human Resources, Clark Regional Medical Center, Winchester, KY, p. A268

BRADLEY, Douglas M.D., Chief Medical Officer, Belton Regional Medical Center, Belton, MO, p. A364

BRADLEY, Eric, Director Computer Information Services, Summit Behavioral Healthcare, Cincinnati, OH, p. A484

BRADLEY, Ken, Administrator, Florida Hospital, Orlando, FL, p. A137

BRADLEY, Linda, Chief Executive Officer, Centinela Hospital Medical Center, Inglewood, CA, p. A63

BRADLEY, Lisa CPA, Chief Financial Officer, Glenwood Regional Medical Center, West Monroe, LA, p. A288

BRADLEY, Louis P. Jr, Chief Executive Officer, Promise Hospital Of Dallas, Dallas, TX, p. A606

BRADLEY, Louis, Chief Executive Officer, Mesquite Specialty Hospital, Mesquite, TX, p. A633

BRADLEY, Lucinda A., Interim Chief Executive Officer, Crawford Memorial Hospital, Robinson, IL, p. A198

BRADLEY, Melody, Chief Nursing Officer, Miracle Mile Medical Center, Los Angeles, CA, p. A70

BRADLEY, Michelle, Director Health Information Management, AMG Specialty Hospital–Wichita, Wichita, KS, p. A253

BRADLEY, Sara, Chief Financial Officer, Oklahoma State University Medical Center, Tulsa, OK, p. A517

BRADLEY, Stacye R.N., Chief Nursing Officer, Union County General Hospital, Clayton, NM, p. A425

BRADLEY, Terri CPA, Vice President Financial Services and Chief Financial Officer, Western Missouri Medical Center, Warrensburg, MO, p. A380

BRADSHAW, Benjamin M.D., President Medical Staff, Texas Health Presbyterian Hospital Kaufman, Kaufman, TX, p. A626

BRADSHAW, David
Chief Information Officer, Memorial Hermann – Texas Medical Center, Houston, TX, p. A621
Chief Information Officer, Memorial Hermann Greater Heights Hospital, Houston, TX, p. A621
Chief Information Officer, Memorial Hermann Rehabilitation Hospital – Katy, Katy, TX, p. A626

BRADSHAW, Jeremy, Chief Executive Officer, Mountainview Hospital, Las Vegas, NV, p. A403

BRADSHAW, Justin, Chief Executive Officer, Banner Desert Medical Center, Mesa, AZ, p. A31

BRADSHAW, Pamela, Chief Nursing Officer, Shannon Medical Center, San Angelo, TX, p. A641

BRADSHAW, Rita, Director Human Resources, Chatuge Regional Hospital And Nursing Home, Hiawassee, GA, p. A159

BRADSHAW, Thomas A, Vice President Operations, Wayne Memorial Hospital, Goldsboro, NC, p. A463

BRADTMILLER, Theresa MSN, R.N., Chief Nursing Officer, Adams Memorial Hospital, Decatur, IN, p. A206

BRADY, Dan, Chief Financial Officer, LDS Hospital, Salt Lake City, UT, p. A660

BRADY, James, Area Information Officer, Kaiser Permanente Orange County Anaheim Medical Center, Anaheim, CA, p. A51

BRADY, Jeff
Chief Information Officer, Tug Valley Arh Regional Medical Center, South Williamson, KY, p. A267
Director Information Systems, Hazard Arh Regional Medical Center, Hazard, KY, p. A259
Director Information Systems, Mcdowell Arh Hospital, Mcdowell, KY, p. A264
Director Information Systems, Morgan County Arh Hospital, West Liberty, KY, p. A268

BRADY, John, Vice President Physician Services and Organizational Planning, Marianjoy Rehabilitation Hospital, Wheaton, IL, p. A202

BRADY, Karen, Vice President, Chief Nursing Officer, Legacy Silverton Medical Center, Silverton, OR, p. A527

BRADY, Kit, Vice President Human Resources, Education and Guest Experience, Gillette Children's Specialty Healthcare, Saint Paul, MN, p. A347

BRADY, Linda, M.D., President and Chief Executive Officer, Kingsbrook Jewish Medical Center, New Rochelle, NY, p. A442

BRADY, Lisa, Senior Vice President and Chief Operating Officer, St. Joseph's Healthcare System, Paterson, NJ, p. A418

BRADY, Mike, Director Information Technology, Up Health System–Bell, Ishpeming, MI, p. A323

BRADY, Patrick R., Chief Executive Officer, Sutter Roseville Medical Center, Roseville, CA, p. A83

BRADY, Tim, Director Information Systems, Mt. Washington Pediatric Hospital, Baltimore, MD, p. A295

BRAEGGER, Bryan, Interim Chief Executive Officer, Yakima Regional Medical And Cardiac Center, Yakima, WA, p. A689

BRAGDON, Carol, Director Human Resources, Saint Thomas Rutherford Hospital, Murfreesboro, TN, p. A586

BRAGG, Craig, Chief Executive Officer, Trustpoint Rehabilitation Hospital Of Lubbock, Lubbock, TX, p. A630

BRAGG, Deborah L, Senior Vice President, Finance, Decatur Memorial Hospital, Decatur, IL, p. A185

BRAGG, Lisa, Vice President Human Resources, Knox Community Hospital, Mount Vernon, OH, p. A496

BRAHM, Victoria, R.N., MSN, Acting Director, Tomah Veterans Affairs Medical Center, Tomah, WI, p. A714

BRAIN, David, Interim Vice President Finance, St. James Healthcare, Butte, MT, p. A383

BRAINSTEIN, Paul M.D., Interim Chief Medical Officer, Chesapeake Regional Healthcare, Chesapeake, VA, p. A665

BRAITHWAITE, Robert, President and Chief Executive Officer, Hoag Memorial Hospital Presbyterian, Newport Beach, CA, p. A76

BRAKENHOFF, Jason, Director Information Services, Presbyterian–St. Luke's Medical Center, Denver, CO, p. A101

BRALY, Cindy Ridge MAAL, R.N., Chief Nursing Officer, Surgical Hospital Of Oklahoma, Oklahoma City, OK, p. A513

BRANAN, Annette, Chief Nursing Officer and Vice President Patient Care Services, Select Specialty Hospital – Northeast Atlanta, Atlanta, GA, p. A151

BRANCH, Terrance, Chief Information Management, Fort Belvoir Community Hospital, Fort Belvoir, VA, p. A667

BRANCHICK, James, R.N., MS, Senior Vice President and Area Manager, Kaiser Permanente Downey Medical Center, Downey, CA, p. A57

BRANCO, Patrick J., Chief Executive Officer, Heart Of America Medical Center, Rugby, ND, p. A478

BRANDECKER, John A., M.P.H., Director, Hunter Holmes Mcguire Veterans Affairs Medical Center–Richmond, Richmond, VA, p. A674

BRANDENBURG, Valerie, Director Human Resources, Northwest Hospital, Randallstown, MD, p. A300

BRANDIS, Destin, Chief Information Officer, William Bee Ririe Hospital, Ely, NV, p. A401

BRANDNER, Nicholas R., Chief Executive Officer, Freeman Regional Health Services, Freeman, SD, p. A570

BRANDON, David R., President and Chief Executive Officer, Unitypoint Health – Finley Hospital, Dubuque, IA, p. A227

BRANDON, Deborah, Director Total Quality Management, Eastern Louisiana Mental Health System, Jackson, LA, p. A276

BRANDON, Heather, Vice President of Finance, Grant, Ohiohealth Grant Medical Center, Columbus, OH, p. A487

BRANDON, Wendy H., Chief Executive Officer, Central Florida Regional Hospital, Sanford, FL, p. A142

BRANDOS, Orla MSN, R.N., Vice President of Patient Care Services and Chief Nursing Officer, Newport Hospital, Newport, RI, p. A556

BRANDSTATER, Ronda, Vice President Patient Care, Grandview Medical Center, Dayton, OH, p. A489

BRANDT, Debbie, Director Human Resources, Community Hospital, Munster, IN, p. A216

BRANDT, Lauren, Chief Clinical Officer, Central Texas Rehabilitation Hospital, Austin, TX, p. A594

BRANDT, Matthew, Chief Financial Officer, St. Alexius Hospital – Broadway Campus, Saint Louis, MO, p. A378

BRANDT, Merle, Chief Financial Officer, Mason General Hospital, Shelton, WA, p. A686

BRANDT, Rob, Chief Executive Officer, Mountainview Medical Center, White Sulphur Springs, MT, p. A389

BRANDT, Steve M.D., Chief of Staff, Dale Medical Center, Ozark, AL, p. A22

BRANN, Terry, Chief Financial Officer, Mainegeneral Medical Center, Augusta, ME, p. A289

BRANNAN, Debbie
Chief Financial Officer, George Regional Hospital, Lucedale, MS, p. A358
Chief Financial Officer, Greene County Hospital, Leakesville, MS, p. A358

BRANNEN, Charles C, Senior Vice President and Chief Operating Officer, Southeast Alabama Medical Center, Dothan, AL, p. A17

BRANNIGAN, Timothy, Director Information Services, Platte Valley Medical Center, Brighton, CO, p. A99

BRANNON, Jeffrey M., Chief Executive Officer, Wiregrass Medical Center, Geneva, AL, p. A18

BRANNON, Jim, Vice President Human Resources, Atlantic General Hospital, Berlin, MD, p. A296

BRANNON, Linda, Vice President Human Resources, Circles Of Care, Melbourne, FL, p. A132

BRANNON, Rebecca, R.N.
Chief Nursing Officer, Thomas Memorial Hospital, South Charleston, WV, p. A696
Senior Vice President and Chief Nursing Officer, Saint Francis Hospital, Charleston, WV, p. A691

BRANSCOME, Eileen, Chief Operating Officer, Mason General Hospital, Shelton, WA, p. A686

BRANSCUM, Suzette, Director of Nursing, Vantage Point Of Northwest Arkansas, Fayetteville, AR, p. A43

BRANSON, Jason, Chief Executive Officer, Pam Specialty Hospital Of Lafayette, Lafayette, LA, p. A279

BRANSTETTER, Erik M.D., Chief Medical Officer, Aspirus Medford Hospital & Clinics, Inc., Medford, WI, p. A706

BRANT, Johnny, Chief Financial Officer, Welch Community Hospital, Welch, WV, p. A696

BRANT, Mick, FACHE, Chief Executive Officer, Gothenburg Health, Gothenburg, NE, p. A393

BRANT–LUCICH, Kim, Director, Information Systems, Providence Little Company Of Mary Medical Center San Pedro, Los Angeles, CA, p. A70

BRANTZ, Jerry, Chief Executive Officer and Chief Financial Officer, Shoshone Medical Center, Kellogg, ID, p. A173

BRASEL, James, Chief Financial Officer, Jane Phillips Medical Center, Bartlesville, OK, p. A505

BRASSINGER, Cindy, Chief Operating Officer, Vibra Hospital Of Southeastern Michigan, Llc, Lincoln Park, MI, p. A325

BRATCHER, Tammy
Director Information Technology, South Mississippi County Regional Medical Center, Osceola, AR, p. A48
Director System Information Technology, Great River Medical Center, Blytheville, AR, p. A40

BRATKO, Eddie, Chief Operating Officer, Mercy Hospital, Buffalo, NY, p. A433

BRATTON, Michael J. R.N., Chief Nurse Executive and Vice President Patient Care Services, Bon Secours–Depaul Medical Center, Norfolk, VA, p. A671

BRATTVET, William W., Chief Executive Officer, Haven Behavioral Hospital Of Frisco, Frisco, TX, p. A615

BRAUDT, Theresa Lynn, Chief Nursing Officer, Gundersen Boscobel Area Hospital And Clinics, Boscobel, WI, p. A699

BRAUGHTON, David, Chief Operating Officer, Lifestream Behavioral Center, Leesburg, FL, p. A131

BRAUN, James R., Chief Administrative Officer and Chief Financial Officer, Flambeau Hospital, Park Falls, WI, p. A710

BRAUN, Matthew, Chief Information Officer, UNM Sandoval Regional Medical Center, Inc., Rio Rancho, NM, p. A428

BRAUN, Peggy R.N., Vice President Patient Care Services and Chief Nurse Executive, Sentara Virginia Beach General Hospital, Virginia Beach, VA, p. A676

BRAUN, Richard G, CPA, Jr
Senior Vice President and Chief Financial Officer, Bradford Regional Medical Center, Bradford, PA, p. A530
Senior Vice President and Chief Financial Officer, Olean General Hospital, Olean, NY, p. A448

BRAUN, Tim, Assistant Administrator, Carroll County Memorial Hospital, Carrollton, MO, p. A366

BRAUNSCHEIDEL, Joseph, Administrator, St. Joseph's Hospital, Elmira, NY, p. A435

BRAVERMAN, Kelly, President, Indiana University Health Frankfort, Frankfort, IN, p. A208

BRAVERMAN, Steven E., M.D., Director, Edward Hines, Jr. Veterans Affairs Hospital, Hines, IL, p. A190

BRAVO, Arturo M.D., Chief of Staff, Cypress Fairbanks Medical Center, Houston, TX, p. A620

BRAVO, Stacey, Vice President Human Resources, Medical City Denton, Denton, TX, p. A608

BRAWLEY, Carrie, Administrator, Behavioral Healthcare Center At Martin, Martin, TN, p. A583

BRAXTON, Edwin R, Director Human Resources, Lompoc Valley Medical Center, Lompoc, CA, p. A66

BRAY, Jason, Chief Information Officer, Mcalester Regional Health Center, Mcalester, OK, p. A510

BRAY, John M.D., Medical Director, Select Specialty Hospital–Pensacola, Pensacola, FL, p. A139

BRAY, Karen A R.N., MSN, Vice President Patient Care Services, Washington Hospital, Washington, PA, p. A552

BRAY, Pam, Director of Nursing and Director Inpatient Services, Upmc Kane, Kane, PA, p. A537

BRAYFORD, Amy, Chief Human Resources Officer, Geisinger Medical Center, Danville, PA, p. A532

BRAYTON, Jackie, Vice President Human Resources, Portsmouth Regional Hospital, Portsmouth, NH, p. A410

BRAYTON, Ranee C., FACHE, R.N., MSN
Chief Executive Officer, Moberly Regional Medical Center, Moberly, MO, p. A373
Chief Executive Officer, Northeast Regional Medical Center, Kirksville, MO, p. A371

BRAZ, Marcus, Chief Executive Officer, Healthsouth Rehabilitation Hospital Of Sarasota, Sarasota, FL, p. A142

BRAZEL, Gary M.D., Chief Medical Officer, St. Vincent Mercy Hospital, Elwood, IN, p. A207

BRAZEL, Gary M.D., Chief Medical Officer, St. Vincent Randolph Hospital, Winchester, IN, p. A221

BRAZIL, Wendy, Chief Operating Officer, Neosho Memorial Regional Medical Center, Chanute, KS, p. A239

BREA, Christie, Manager Human Resources, Promise Hospital Of Phoenix, Mesa, AZ, p. A32

BREADY, Sharon, R.N.
Chief Executive Officer, Careone At Hacksensack University Medical Center At Pascack Valley, Westwood, NJ, p. A422
Chief Executive Officer, Careone At Raritan Bay Medical Center, Perth Amboy, NJ, p. A419
Chief Executive Officer, Careone At Trinitas Regional Medical Center, Elizabeth, NJ, p. A413

BREAKWELL, Michael R.N., Nurse Executive, Twin Valley Behavioral Healthcare, Columbus, OH, p. A488

BREAZEALE, Scott, Chief Nursing Officer, Neshoba County General Hospital, Philadelphia, MS, p. A360

BREDEHOEFT, Tina, Human Resources, I–70 Community Hospital, Sweet Springs, MO, p. A380

BREDESON, Christopher, President and Chief Operating Officer, Multicare Good Samaritan Hospital, Puyallup, WA, p. A684

BREDTHAUER, Vicki R.N., Director of Nursing, Valley County Health System, Ord, NE, p. A398

BREEDEN, Patricia M.D., Chief of Staff, Lexington Veterans Affairs Medical Center, Lexington, KY, p. A261

BREEDEN, Susan M., Administrator and Chief Executive Officer, Baptist Memorial Hospital–Huntingdon, Huntingdon, TN, p. A580

BREEDLOVE, Jean Ann
Chief Information Officer, Children's Mercy Hospital Kansas City, Kansas City, MO, p. A370
Chief Information Officer, Children's Mercy South, Overland Park, KS, p. A249

BREEDLOVE, Stacey, Chief Nursing Officer, Christus St. Michael Rehabilitation Hospital, Texarkana, TX, p. A649

BREEDVELD, Stacey R.N., MSN, Associate Director for Patient Care, Veterans Affairs Ann Arbor Healthcare System, Ann Arbor, MI, p. A314

BREEN, Charles J M.D., Medical Director, Sanford Hillsboro Medical Center, Hillsboro, ND, p. A476

BREEN, Donna M.D., Chief of Staff, Avoyelles Hospital, Marksville, LA, p. A280

BREEN, Sue, Chief Financial Officer, Western State Hospital, Tacoma, WA, p. A688

BREEN, Thomas, Vice President and Chief Financial Officer, South County Hospital, Wakefield, RI, p. A557

BREHMER, Jennifer, Director of Patient Care, New ULM Medical Center, New Ulm, MN, p. A345

BREIDENBACH, Kim B, Medical Director, Gundersen Tri–County Hospital And Clinics, Whitehall, WI, p. A716

BREIDSTER, Cara, Chief Financial Officer, Indiana University Health Arnett Hospital, Lafayette, IN, p. A214

BREITBACH, Dave, Chief Financial Officer, Crossing Rivers Health Medical Center, Prairie Du Chien, WI, p. A711

BREITENBACH, Ray M.D., Chief of Staff, Doctors' Hospital Of Michigan, Pontiac, MI, p. A328

BREITFELDER, Michelle
Chief Nursing Officer, Piedmont Mountainside Hospital, Jasper, GA, p. A159
Chief Operating Officer, Northside Medical Center, Columbus, GA, p. A155

BREITLING, Bryan
Administrator, Avera Hand County Memorial Hospital, Miller, SD, p. A571
Interim Administrator and Chief Executive Officer, Avera De Smet Memorial Hospital, De Smet, SD, p. A569

BREKKE, Erin, Director Human Resources, Burgess Health Center, Onawa, IA, p. A232

BRELAND, Kelly R CPA, Director Support Services, Mississippi State Hospital, Whitfield, MS, p. A363

BREMER, David D.O., Chief of Staff, Midmichigan Medical Center–Clare, Clare, MI, p. A316

BRENAN, Kevin, Chief Financial Officer, Emory Saint Joseph's Hospital Of Atlanta, Atlanta, GA, p. A150

BRENDEN, Stephanie D, Vice President Finance, Columbia Memorial Hospital, Astoria, OR, p. A520

BRENDLE, Judi, Vice President Clinical Support and Chief Nursing Officer, Bassett Medical Center, Cooperstown, NY, p. A434

BRENDLER, Stephen, Director Information Systems, Hilton Head Hospital, Hilton Head Island, SC, p. A564

BRENHOLT, Craig, Division Director People Services, Sacred Heart Hospital, Eau Claire, WI, p. A701

BRENKLE, George, Chief Information Officer, Umass Memorial Medical Center, Worcester, MA, p. A313

BRENN, Andrea R.N., Chief Nursing Officer, Texoma Medical Center, Denison, TX, p. A608

BRENNAN, Angela M.D., Chief of Staff, Howard County Medical Center, Saint Paul, NE, p. A399

BRENNAN, Kevin F CPA, Executive Vice President and Chief Financial Officer, Geisinger Medical Center, Danville, PA, p. A532

BRENNAN, Lina, Site Administrator, Soldiers And Sailors Memorial Hospital Of Yates County, Penn Yan, NY, p. A449

BRENNAN, Noreen, Chief Nursing Officer, NYC Health + Hospitals / Metropolitan, New Rochelle, NY, p. A445

BRENNAN, Patrick J M.D., Senior Vice President and Chief Medical Officer, Hospital Of The University Of Pennsylvania, Philadelphia, PA, p. A544

BRENNAN, Patrick, Director Information System Technology, SSM Health Saint Louis University Hospital, Saint Louis, MO, p. A378

BRENNAN, Theresa M.D., Chief Medical Officer, University Of Iowa Hospitals And Clinics, Iowa City, IA, p. A230

BRENNER, Lawrence M.D., Chief of Staff, Corpus Christi Medical Center, Corpus Christi, TX, p. A603

BRENNER, Pattie R.N., Chief Nursing Officer, Healthsouth Rehabilitation Hospital, Largo, FL, p. A130

BRENNER, William
Chief Financial Officer, Kindred Hospital Indianapolis South, Greenwood, IN, p. A209
Chief Financial Officer, Kindred Hospital–Indianapolis, Indianapolis, IN, p. A211

BRENNY, Terrence, President and Chief Executive Officer, Stoughton Hospital Association, Stoughton, WI, p. A713

BREON, Richard C., President and Chief Executive Officer, Spectrum Health, Grand Rapids, MI, p. B120

BRES, Thomas, Senior Vice President and Chief Administrative Officer, Sparrow Hospital, Lansing, MI, p. A324

BRESCIA, Michael J M.D., Executive Medical Director, Calvary Hospital, New Rochelle, NY, p. A441

BRESLIN, Susan R.N., MSN, Vice President Patient Care Services and Chief Nursing Officer, Dekalb Medical At North Decatur, Decatur, GA, p. A156

BRESNAHAN, Jacky, Director Human Resources, Mahaska Health Partnership, Oskaloosa, IA, p. A233

BRESNAHAN, Patti, Director Human Resources, Mercy Medical Center, Canton, OH, p. A482

BRETTNER, Eric, Vice President and Chief Financial Officer, St. Mary's Medical Center, San Francisco, CA, p. A88

BREUDER, Andrew M.D., Chief of Staff, Manchester Veterans Affairs Medical Center, Manchester, NH, p. A409

BREUER, Jason, President and Chief Executive Officer, Stevens Community Medical Center, Morris, MN, p. A344

BREUER, Rick, Chief Executive Officer and Administrator, Community Memorial Hospital, Cloquet, MN, p. A338

BREUM, Linda G R.N., MSN, Chief Nursing Officer, Florida Hospital New Smyrna, New Smyrna Beach, FL, p. A135

BREVING, Robert M.D., Chief of Staff, National Park Medical Center, Hot Springs, AR, p. A44

BREWER, Anna, Interim Chief Financial Officer, Henry Mayo Newhall Hospital, Valencia, CA, p. A95

BREWER, Becca, Chief Operations Officer, Falls Community Hospital And Clinic, Marlin, TX, p. A632

BREWER, David, Chief Financial Officer, Promedica Memorial Hospital, Fremont, OH, p. A491

BREWER, Douglas, Chief Executive Officer, Citizens Baptist Medical Center, Talladega, AL, p. A23

BREWER, Gary L., Chief Executive Officer, Valley View Hospital, Glenwood Springs, CO, p. A103

BREWER, Jennifer Lynn., Chief Executive Officer, Healthsouth Plano Rehabilitation Hospital, Plano, TX, p. A638

BREWER, Jim M.P.H., Chief Financial Officer, Healthmark Regional Medical Center, Defuniak Springs, FL, p. A123

BREWER, Kaye, Vice President Human Resources, Maury Regional Hospital, Columbia, TN, p. A577

BREWER, Kelley, R.N., MSN, President, Lakeside Women's Hospital, Oklahoma City, OK, p. A512

BREWER, Peter G., Administrator, Shriners Hospitals For Children–Spokane, Spokane, WA, p. A687

BREWER, Rebecca, FACHE, Chief Executive Officer, Lake Wales Medical Center, Lake Wales, FL, p. A130

BREWER, Ruby RN, Senior Vice President, Chief Nursing and Quality Officer, East Jefferson General Hospital, Metairie, LA, p. A281

BREWER, Traci, Chief Clinical Officer, Kindred Hospital Dallas Central, Dallas, TX, p. A605

BREXLER, James L., President and Chief Executive Officer, Doylestown Hospital, Doylestown, PA, p. A533

BREYFOGLE, Cynthia, FACHE, Director, Charles George Veterans Affairs Medical Center, Asheville, NC, p. A457

BREZA, Lisa R.N., Vice President and Chief Nursing Officer, Robert Wood Johnson University Hospital At Hamilton, Hamilton, NJ, p. A414

BREZENOFF, Stanley, Interim President and Chief Executive Officer, Nyc Health + Hospitals, New York, NY, p. B93

BREZNY, Angie, Director Human Resources, Prague Community Hospital, Prague, OK, p. A515

BRIAN, David
Chief Information Officer, Shriners Hospitals For Children–Cincinnati, Cincinnati, OH, p. A484
Director Information Services, Shriners Hospitals For Children–Lexington, Lexington, KY, p. A261

BRICHER, Joan, Senior Vice President Finance and Chief Financial Officer, Santa Barbara Cottage Hospital, Santa Barbara, CA, p. A90

BRICKHOUSE, Jeremiah
Chief Information Officer, St. Charles Bend, Bend, OR, p. A520
Chief Information Officer, St. Charles Redmond, Redmond, OR, p. A526

BRICKMAN, Jeffrey L., FACHE, Interim Chief Executive Officer, Central Maine Medical Center, Lewiston, ME, p. A291

BRICKNER, Derek, President Medical Staff, Jamestown Regional Medical Center, Jamestown, ND, p. A476

BRICKNER, Greg, Vice President and Director, Business Development, Wellstar Atlanta Medical Center, Atlanta, GA, p. A151

BRIDEAU, Donald
Chief Medical Officer, Inova Mount Vernon Hospital, Alexandria, VA, p. A664
Interim Chief Executive Officer, Inova Mount Vernon Hospital, Alexandria, VA, p. A664

BRIDEN, David, Chief Information Officer, Exeter Hospital, Exeter, NH, p. A408

BRIDGE, Lauren M R.N., Chief Nursing Officer, Kaiser Sunnyside Medical Center, Clackamas, OR, p. A520

BRIDGELAND, Aaron
Director Finance, Midwest Orthopedic Specialty Hospital, Franklin, WI, p. A702
Director Finance, Wheaton Franciscan Healthcare – Franklin, Franklin, WI, p. A702
Director Finance, Wheaton Franciscan Healthcare – St. Francis, Milwaukee, WI, p. A708

BRIDGES, Alan J M.D., Chief of Staff, William S. Middleton Memorial Veterans Hospital, Madison, WI, p. A705

BRIDGES, Carol M.D., Medical Director, Broadwater Health Center, Townsend, MT, p. A389

BRIDGES, James M, Executive Vice President and Chief Operating Officer, Palmetto Health Baptist, Columbia, SC, p. A560

BRIDGES, Jane Ann, Chief Financial Officer, Nacogdoches Memorial Hospital, Nacogdoches, TX, p. A634

BRIDGES, Mary, Director Human Resources, Ouachita County Medical Center, Camden, AR, p. A41

BRIDGES, Richard M.D., Chief of Staff, Hood Memorial Hospital, Amite, LA, p. A270

BRIDGES, Stephanie, Chief Executive Officer, Healthsouth Rehabilitation Hospital Of Memphis, Memphis, TN, p. A584

BRIDGEWATER, Melinda, Director, Information Services, Montana State Hospital, Warm Springs, MT, p. A389

BRIESEMEISTER, Eric, Chief Executive Officer, Unitypoint Health – Jones Regional Medical Center, Anamosa, IA, p. A222

BRIETE, Mark M.D., Vice President Medical Affairs, Mercy Hospital Jefferson, Crystal City, MO, p. A367

BRIGGS, Deborah, Vice President Human Resources, Marketing, Volunteer Services and Community Relations, Ellenville Regional Hospital, Ellenville, NY, p. A435

BRIGGS, Gary, Vice President Human Resources, Tristar Southern Hills Medical Center, Nashville, TN, p. A587

BRIGGS, Michael M.D., Chief Medical Officer, Essentia Health Fargo, Fargo, ND, p. A475

BRIGGS, Paul, Executive Vice President and Chief Operating Officer, Presbyterian Hospital, Albuquerque, NM, p. A425

BRIGGS, Sharlet, Ph.D.
Chief Operating Officer, San Joaquin Community Hospital, Bakersfield, CA, p. A53
Market Chief Executive Officer and President, San Joaquin Community Hospital, Bakersfield, CA, p. A53

BRIGGS, Thomas, Chief Financial Officer, Alliancehealth Madill, Madill, OK, p. A509

BRIGGS, Vicki R., President and Chief Executive Officer, St. Vincent's Medical Center, Bridgeport, CT, p. A109

BRIGHAM, Randy, Chief Human Resource Officer, Estes Park Medical Center, Estes Park, CO, p. A102

BRIGHT, Cheryl, Executive Director, Fairview Developmental Center, Costa Mesa, CA, p. A57

BRIGHT, Janet L, Vice President, Chief Nursing Officer, Novant Health Forsyth Medical Center, Winston, NC, p. A473

BRIGHT, Kim M.D., Clinical Director, Springfield Hospital Center, Sykesville, MD, p. A301

BRILEY, Jay, President, Vidant Duplin Hospital, Kenansville, NC, p. A465

BRILL, Beth K., Senior Director Human Resources, Barnesville Hospital, Barnesville, OH, p. A480

BRILL, Elizabeth M.D., Chief Operating Officer, Ohiohealth Riverside Methodist Hospital, Columbus, OH, p. A488

BRILL, Karen R.N., Chief Nursing Officer, Vice President Care, Gillette Children's Specialty Healthcare, Saint Paul, MN, p. A347

BRILLI, Richard M.D., Chief Medical Officer, Nationwide Children's Hospital, Columbus, OH, p. A487

BRILLIANT, Lawrence M.D., Vice President and Chief Medical Officer, St. Mary Medical Center, Langhorne, PA, p. A538

BRILLIANT, Patrick D., President and Chief Executive Officer, Riverside Community Hospital, Riverside, CA, p. A82

BRILLIANT, Steven M.D., Chief of Staff, Veterans Affairs Sierra Nevada Health Care System, Reno, NV, p. A405

BRIM, Celena
Chief Financial Officer, Palestine Regional Medical Center–East, Palestine, TX, p. A636
Chief Financial Officer, Palestine Regional Medical Center, Palestine, TX, p. A636

BRINDLE, Charles B M.D., Chief Medical Staff, Iowa Specialty Hospital–Belmond, Belmond, IA, p. A222

BRINER, Junior, Chief Operating Officer, Lawrence Memorial Hospital, Walnut Ridge, AR, p. A50

BRINER, Scott, Chief Executive Officer, Sweeny Community Hospital, Sweeny, TX, p. A647

BRINKERHOFF, Douglas M.D., Clinical Director, San Carlos Apache Healthcare Corporation, Peridot, AZ, p. A32

BRINKHAUS, Theresa, Chief Financial Officer, St. Helena Parish Hospital, Greensburg, LA, p. A275

BRINKLEY, Charles III, Chief Financial Officer, Merit Health Biloxi, Biloxi, MS, p. A352

BRINKMAN, Dan, R.N., Chief Executive Officer, Hilo Medical Center, Hilo, HI, p. A168

BRINKMAN, Janet, Director Human Resources, Colorado Plains Medical Center, Fort Morgan, CO, p. A102

BRINSON, David, Director Information Technology, Parkview Wabash County Hospital, Wabash, IN, p. A221

BRINSON, Pam, Nurse Executive, South Mississippi State Hospital, Purvis, MS, p. A361

BRIONES, Melba M.D., Medical Director, Evansville State Hospital, Evansville, IN, p. A207

BRISBOE, Mark
VP and Chief Financial Officer, Sparrow Clinton Hospital, Saint Johns, MI, p. A330
VP and Chief Financial Officer, Sparrow Ionia Hospital, Ionia, MI, p. A323

BRISCOE, Charles G
Chief Operating Officer, Houston Medical Center, Warner Robins, GA, p. A167
Chief Operating Officer, Perry Hospital, Perry, GA, p. A163

BRISCOE, Janell
Chief Executive Officer, Healthsouth City View Rehabilitation Hospital, Fort Worth, TX, p. A613
Chief Executive Officer, Healthsouth Rehabilitation Hospital Of Fort Worth, Fort Worth, TX, p. A613

BRISCOE, Mary Beth, Chief Financial Officer, University Of Alabama Hospital, Birmingham, AL, p. A15

BRISENDINE, Chad
Chief Information Officer, St. Luke's Hospital – Quakertown Campus, Quakertown, PA, p. A549
Chief Information Officer, St. Luke's University Hospital – Bethlehem Campus, Bethlehem, PA, p. A529
Vice President and Chief Information Officer, St. Luke's Hospital – Miners Campus, Coaldale, PA, p. A531

BRISSE, Thomas M., President and Chief Executive Officer, Mclaren Macomb, Mount Clemens, MI, p. A326

BRISTER, Kim, Director Human Resources, Wellspan Gettysburg Hospital, Gettysburg, PA, p. A535

BRISTER, Marilyn M.D., Chief of Staff, Texas Health Harris Methodist Hospital Stephenville, Stephenville, TX, p. A646

BRISTOL, Michelle, Director of Nursing, Clifton–Fine Hospital, Star Lake, NY, p. A452

BRISTOW, Clyde A. MSN, R.N., III, Senior Director Nursing and Clinical Services, Chief Nursing Officer, Wake Forest Baptist Health–Lexington Medical Center, Lexington, NC, p. A466

BRITO, Manuela, Chief Financial Officer Post Acute Care, NYC Health + Hospitals / Carter, New Rochelle, NY, p. A444

BRITT, Kevin, Chief Operating Officer, Reynolds Memorial Hospital, Glen Dale, WV, p. A692

BRITT, Key, Associate Director, Greenwood Leflore Hospital, Greenwood, MS, p. A355

BRITT, Linda, Director Information Systems, Baptist Memorial Hospital–North Mississippi, Oxford, MS, p. A360

BRITT, Suzanne, Director Human Resources, Samaritan Hospital, Macon, MO, p. A373

BRITT, Tommy, Vice President of Human Resources, West Georgia Health, Lagrange, GA, p. A160

BRITTAIN, Libby, Director Human Resources, Steele Memorial Medical Center, Salmon, ID, p. A176

BRITTON, David, Interim Chief Financial Officer, Medina Memorial Hospital, Medina, NY, p. A439

BRITTON, Lynn, President and Chief Executive Officer, Mercy, Chesterfield, MO, p. B83

BRITTON, John, Vice President Information Services, Fisher–Titus Medical Center, Norwalk, OH, p. A497

BRITTON, Natalie, Director Human Resources, Legacy Silverton Medical Center, Silverton, OR, p. A527

BRITTON, William N, Associate Administrator Finance, Alfred I. Dupont Hospital For Children, Wilmington, DE, p. A116

BRIX, Hsiu–chin R.N., Director of Nursing, St. Lawrence Rehabilitation Center, Lawrenceville, NJ, p. A415

BROADBENT, Sherri D.O., Chief of Staff, Madison County Health Care System, Winterset, IA, p. A237

BROADWATER, Gary W, Chief Financial Officer, Mccready Health, Crisfield, MD, p. A298

BROADWAY, Chris, Manager Information Technology, Mayers Memorial Hospital District, Fall River Mills, CA, p. A59

BROBST, Mary R.N., MSN, Senior Vice President Patient Care Services and Chief Nursing Officer, Mercy Medical Center, Cedar Rapids, Iowa, Cedar Rapids, IA, p. A223

BROCK, B. J., Nursing Director, Tanner Higgins General Hospital, Bremen, GA, p. A153

BROCK, Jamie, Director Human Resources, Chan Soon–Shiong Medical Center, Windber, PA, p. A554

BROCK, Kyle, Vice President Human Resources, Glens Falls Hospital, Glens Falls, NY, p. A436

BROCK, Lisa M, Chief Human Resource Officer, Overlake Medical Center, Bellevue, WA, p. A678

BROCK, Melinda, Director Human Resources, Alliancehealth Woodward, Woodward, OK, p. A519

BROCK, Nancy, Chief Financial Officer, Houston Methodist St. Catherine Hospital, Katy, TX, p. A626

BROCK, Paul, Administrator, East Central Regional Hospital, Augusta, GA, p. A151

BROCK, Robert
Chief Financial Officer and Vice President, Rollins–Brook Community Hospital, Lampasas, TX, p. A628
Vice President Finance, Saint Joseph – Martin, Martin, KY, p. A264

BROCK, Shea C., Chief Financial Officer, Navarro Regional Hospital, Corsicana, TX, p. A603

BROCK, Steve, Chief Financial Officer, Lynn County Hospital District, Tahoka, TX, p. A648

BROCK, Theresa, Vice President Nursing, Good Shepherd Health Care System, Hermiston, OR, p. A522

BROCK, William, Chief Information Officer, Atlanta Veterans Affairs Medical Center, Decatur, GA, p. A156

BROCKERT, Nicholas, President, Saint Luke's Cushing Hospital, Leavenworth, KS, p. A245

BROCKETTE, Darby, Chief Executive Officer, Rehabilitation Hospital Of The Northwest, Post Falls, ID, p. A175

BROCKHAUS, Jennifer, Chief Information Officer, Sidney Regional Medical Center, Sidney, NE, p. A400

BROCKHOUSE, Dena M, Director Human Resources, Mercy Iowa City, Iowa City, IA, p. A229

BROCKMAN, Vicki R.N., Chief Nursing Officer, Texas Health Harris Methodist Hospital Cleburne, Cleburne, TX, p. A601

BROCKMEYER, Heather, Human Resource Administrative Officer, Nevada Regional Medical Center, Nevada, MO, p. A374

BROCKMEYER, JoEllyn, Director Human Resources, Indiana University Health White Memorial Hospital, Monticello, IN, p. A216

BROCKUS, Harry, Chief Executive Officer, Carle Hoopeston Regional Health Center, Hoopeston, IL, p. A190

BROCKWELL, Linda, Chief Nursing Officer, Wickenburg Community Hospital, Wickenburg, AZ, p. A38

BRODBECK, Kathleen MSN, RN–B, Chief Nursing Officer, St. James Mercy Hospital, Hornell, NY, p. A437

BRODBECK, Lisa, Chief Financial Officer, Medical City Lewisville, Lewisville, TX, p. A629

BRODHEAD, Richard Ross, Director Human Resources, St. Vincent Randolph Hospital, Winchester, IN, p. A221

BRODHEAD, Ross
Executive Director, Human Resources, St. Vincent Anderson Regional Hospital, Anderson, IN, p. A203
Manager Human Resources, St. Vincent Mercy Hospital, Elwood, IN, p. A207

BRODIAN, Craig R, Vice President Human Resources, Johns Hopkins Bayview Medical Center, Baltimore, MD, p. A294

BRODRICK, Theresa M R.N., MSN, Ph.D., Chief Nursing Officer, Alamance Regional Medical Center, Burlington, NC, p. A458

BRODY, Anne Marie, Director Information Systems Customer Service, Providence Saint Joseph Medical Center, Burbank, CA, p. A54

BROEKHUIS, Arlyn
Chief Information Officer, Sanford Medical Center Fargo, Fargo, ND, p. A475
Vice President and Chief Information Officer, Sanford Usd Medical Center, Sioux Falls, SD, p. A572

BROERMANN, Robert
Senior Vice President and Chief Financial Officer, Sentara Leigh Hospital, Norfolk, VA, p. A672
Senior Vice President and Chief Financial Officer, Sentara Norfolk General Hospital, Norfolk, VA, p. A672
Senior Vice President and Chief Financial Officer, Sentara Princess Anne Hospital, Virginia Beach, VA, p. A676

BROGAN, Gerard Jr, M.D., Executive Director, Huntington Hospital, Huntington, NY, p. A437

BROGGER, Portlyn, Divisional President, Rehabilitation Hospital Of Overland Park, Overland Park, KS, p. A249

BROHAWN, Bill, Chief of Staff, Trace Regional Hospital, Houston, MS, p. A356

BROKAW, Sara, Vice President Patient Care Services, Bellevue Hospital, Bellevue, OH, p. A481

BROKENSHIRE, Shelia Kay, Vice President of Nursing, Van Wert County Hospital, Van Wert, OH, p. A501

BROMAN, Craig J., FACHE, President, St. Cloud Hospital, Saint Cloud, MN, p. A347

BROMLEY, Trudy, Vice President Human Resources, JFK Medical Center, Atlantis, FL, p. A119

BRONER, Eloise, President and Chief Executive Officer, Good Samaritan Hospital, Dayton, OH, p. A489

BRONHARD, John, Chief Financial Officer, Healthalliance Hospitals, Leominster, MA, p. A308

BROOCKS, Kelli C, Director Human Resources, Public Relations and Physician Recruitment, Beauregard Memorial Hospital, De Ridder, LA, p. A274

BROOKE, William R M.D., President Medical Staff, Pickens County Medical Center, Carrollton, AL, p. A16

BROOKER, Brian, Chief Executive Officer, Cypress Creek Hospital, Houston, TX, p. A620

BROOKER, Doug A., Chief Financial Officer, Bryan W. Whitfield Memorial Hospital, Demopolis, AL, p. A16

BROOKER, Paula, Director Information Services, Pleasant Valley Hospital, Point Pleasant, WV, p. A695

BROOKER, Susan E R.N., Chief Clinical Officer, Vibra Specialty Hospital Of Portland, Portland, OR, p. A525

BROOKES, Jeffrey, M.D.
Chief Medical Officer, Parkview Lagrange Hospital, Lagrange, IN, p. A214
Medical Director, Parkview Whitley Hospital, Columbia City, IN, p. A205

BROOKMAN, Mark
Chief Information Officer, Medical Center At Bowling Green, Bowling Green, KY, p. A256
Chief Information Officer, Medical Center At Scottsville, Scottsville, KY, p. A267
Chief Information Officer, The Medical Center Albany, Albany, KY, p. A255
Vice President and Chief Information Officer, Medical Center At Franklin, Franklin, KY, p. A258
Vice President, Chief Information Officer, The Medical Center At Caverna, Horse Cave, KY, p. A260

BROOKS, Albert M.D., Chief Medical Staff Services, Washington Hospital Healthcare System, Fremont, CA, p. A60

BROOKS, Anthony, Chief Information Officer, Miami Veterans Affairs Healthcare System, Miami, FL, p. A133

BROOKS, April, Chief Nursing Officer, Healthsouth Rehabilitation Hospital Of Columbia, Columbia, SC, p. A560

BROOKS, Brian, Information Manager, Dewitt Hospital, Dewitt, AR, p. A42

BROOKS, Colin B., Chief Financial Officer, Southwest General Hospital, San Antonio, TX, p. A644

BROOKS, David, M.D.
Chief Medical Officer, Valley View Hospital, Glenwood Springs, CO, p. A103
President, St. Joseph Mercy Ann Arbor, Ypsilanti, MI, p. A334

BROOKS, Harris W., Chief Executive Officer, Palo Pinto General Hospital, Mineral Wells, TX, p. A633

BROOKS, Jeffrey M.D., Chief Medical Officer, Parkview Huntington Hospital, Huntington, IN, p. A210

BROOKS, Jerome M, Chief Operating Officer, South Texas Health System, Edinburg, TX, p. A610

BROOKS, Joe, Chief Financial Officer, Keystone Newport News, Newport News, VA, p. A671

BROOKS, Lisa
Chief Financial Officer, Comanche County Hospital, Coldwater, KS, p. A239
Chief Financial Officer, Comanche County Hospital, Coldwater, KS, p. A239

BROOKS, Lori, Director Human Resources, Red Bud Regional Hospital, Red Bud, IL, p. A198

BROOKS, Nick, Director of Information Systems, Citrus Memorial Health System, Inverness, FL, p. A127

BROOKS, Patrice Gay., Chief Executive Officer, Cumberland Hospital, New Kent, VA, p. A671

BROOKS, Robert M. FACHE, Executive Vice President, Chief Operating Officer, Erlanger Medical Center, Chattanooga, TN, p. A576

BROOKS, Steven Michael, Vice President Human Resources, Southeastern Ohio Regional Medical Center, Cambridge, OH, p. A482

BROOKS, Troy, Assistant Administrator Fiscal Services, Piedmont Newton Hospital, Covington, GA, p. A155

BROOKS–WILLIAMS, Denise, President and Chief Executive Officer, Henry Ford Wyandotte Hospital, Wyandotte, MI, p. A333

BROOKSHIRE, Tim, FACHE, Interim Chief Operating Officer, Patewood Memorial Hospital, Greenville, SC, p. A562

BROOKSHIRE–HEAVIN, Keri S., Chief Nurse Executive, Phelps County Regional Medical Center, Rolla, MO, p. A376

BROPHY, Beth, Interim VP for Human Resources, Hurley Medical Center, Flint, MI, p. A319

BROSIUS, William, Vice President and Chief Financial Officer, Baylor St. Luke's Medical Center, Houston, TX, p. A619

BROSKEY, Steven, Associate Director, Veterans Affairs Roseburg Healthcare System, Roseburg, OR, p. A526

BROSNAHAN, Jan, Chief Financial Officer, Winona Health, Winona, MN, p. A350

BROSNAN, Kimberly, Director Human Resources, Norwood Hospital, Norwood, MA, p. A310

BROSS, James B., President, St. Luke's Hospital, Columbus, NC, p. A460

BROST, Wade, Executive Director, Anoka–Metropolitan Regional Treatment Center, Anoka, MN, p. A335

BROTEN, Kurt
Chief Financial Officer, Palmdale Regional Medical Center, Palmdale, CA, p. A78
Chief Financial Officer, Palmdale Regional Medical Center, Palmdale, CA, p. A79
Chief Financial Officer, Vista Del Mar Hospital, Ventura, CA, p. A96

BROTHMAN, Joe, Assistant Vice President, Information Systems, Medstar Washington Hospital Center, Washington, DC, p. A118

BROUGHMAN, Robin R.N., Ph.D., Chief Nursing Officer, Lewisgale Hospital Alleghany, Low Moor, VA, p. A669

BROUGHMAN, Wade
Chief Financial Officer, Southcoast Hospitals Group, Fall River, MA, p. A306
Executive Vice President and Chief Financial Officer, Riverside Regional Medical Center, Newport News, VA, p. A671

BROUSSARD, Clifford M., FACHE, Administrator, Wk Bossier Health Center, Bossier City, LA, p. A272

BROUSSARD, Heidi, Chief Nursing Officer, Abbeville General Hospital, Abbeville, LA, p. A269

BROUSSARD, Kari, Chief Nursing Officer, Oakdale Community Hospital, Oakdale, LA, p. A284

BROUSSARD, Terry J, Interim Chief Nursing Officer, Our Lady Of Lourdes Regional Medical Center, Lafayette, LA, p. A279

BROUWER, Heath, Administrator, Douglas County Memorial Hospital, Armour, SD, p. A568

BROVOLD, Diana, Chief Nurse Executive, Multicare Mary Bridge Children's Hospital And Health Center, Tacoma, WA, p. A687

BROWDER, Renate R.N., Director of Nursing, Lake City Community Hospital, Lake City, SC, p. A564

BROWER, Laura E R.N., MSN, Chief Nursing Officer, Augusta University Medical Center, Augusta, GA, p. A151

BROWN, Alisa, Administrative Assistant, Dewitt Hospital, Dewitt, AR, p. A42

BROWN, Angel, Director Human Resources, Morton Plant Hospital, Clearwater, FL, p. A121

BROWN, Ann R., M.D., Director, Va Greater Los Angeles Healthcare System, Los Angeles, CA, p. A72

BROWN, Austin, Chief Executive Officer, Seven Rivers Regional Medical Center, Crystal River, FL, p. A122

BROWN, B Blaine, Vice President and General Counsel, Prattville Baptist Hospital, Prattville, AL, p. A21

BROWN, Bartley D.O., Chief of Staff, St. Joseph's Hospital Of Buckhannon, Buckhannon, WV, p. A690

BROWN, Benjamin, Chief Operating Officer, Stonesprings Hospital Center, Dulles, VA, p. A666

BROWN, Bryan, Executive Director, Mercy Hospital Fort Smith, Fort Smith, AR, p. A43

BROWN, Chad J., M.P.H., President, Wake Forest Baptist Health–Davie Medical Center, Bermuda Run, NC, p. A457

BROWN, Cheryl, Chief Executive Officer, Henderson Health Care Services, Henderson, NE, p. A394

BROWN, Chistiane, Assistant Vice President, Medstar Montgomery Medical Center, Olney, MD, p. A300

BROWN, Christi, Director Human Resources, Our Lady Of The Angels Hospital, Bogalusa, LA, p. A272

BROWN, Chuck, Administrator, Bethesda North Hospital, Cincinnati, OH, p. A483

BROWN, Crystal M.D., Medical Director, Medical Center Of Peach County, Navicent Health, Bryon, GA, p. A153

BROWN, Cynthia, Director of Nursing, Hill Hospital Of Sumter County, York, AL, p. A24

BROWN, Damon, Interim Chief Executive Officer, Tennova Healthcare Regional Hospital Of Jackson, Jackson, TN, p. A580

BROWN, Darin, Vice President Finance, Henry County Hospital, New Castle, IN, p. A217

BROWN, David A, Director Human Resources and Corporate Compliance, Pleasant Valley Hospital, Point Pleasant, WV, p. A695

BROWN, Deana, Director Administrative Services, Franciscan Health Rensselear, Rensselaer, IN, p. A218

BROWN, Debbie T R.N., Chief Nursing Officer, Evergreenhealth Monroe, Monroe, WA, p. A682

BROWN, Deborah, Chief Nursing Officer, Logan Memorial Hospital, Russellville, KY, p. A267

BROWN, Debra L, Area Financial Officer, Kaiser Permanente Manteca Medical Center, Manteca, CA, p. A73

BROWN, Denise, Vice President Human Resources, Presence Saint Joseph Hospital, Chicago, IL, p. A182

BROWN, Derek, Chief Information Officer, Jellico Community Hospital, Jellico, TN, p. A580

BROWN, Doris, Chief Executive Officer and Administrator, Carnegie Tri–County Municipal Hospital, Carnegie, OK, p. A505

BROWN, Ed
Chief Financial Officer, Cibola General Hospital, Grants, NM, p. A426
Chief Information Officer, Medical Center, Navicent Health, Macon, GA, p. A161

BROWN, Eric M.D., Physician Executive, Palmetto Health Richland, Columbia, SC, p. A560

BROWN, Geoffrey
Chief Information Officer, Piedmont Fayette Hospital, Fayetteville, GA, p. A157
Chief Information Officer, Piedmont Mountainside Hospital, Jasper, GA, p. A159
Vice President Information Systems, Inova Fairfax Hospital, Falls Church, VA, p. A666

BROWN, George J., M.D., President and Chief Executive Officer, Legacy Health, Portland, OR, p. B75

BROWN, Greg, Administrator, St. Vincent's Blount, Oneonta, AL, p. A22

BROWN, Howard, Chief Financial Officer, North Shore Medical Center, Miami, FL, p. A133

BROWN, Hugh, Chief Executive Officer, St. David's Medical Center, Austin, TX, p. A596

BROWN, James H, Chief Financial Officer, Centerpoint Medical Center, Independence, MO, p. A369

BROWN, Janice, Chief Financial Officer, Coosa Valley Medical Center, Sylacauga, AL, p. A23

BROWN, Jason, M.D.
Chief Medical Officer, Banner Goldfield Medical Center, Apache Junction, AZ, p. A28
Director Information Systems, Sanford Sheldon Medical Center, Sheldon, IA, p. A234
Director, Sycamore Medical Center, Miamisburg, OH, p. A496

BROWN, Jay
Senior Vice President, Chief Information Officer, West Chester Hospital, West Chester, OH, p. A502
Vice President and Chief Information Officer, University Of Cincinnati Medical Center, Cincinnati, OH, p. A485

BROWN, Jayma, Director of Nursing, Oakland Mercy Hospital, Oakland, NE, p. A396

BROWN, Jeffrey P M.D., Chief Medical Officer, Indiana University Health Arnett Hospital, Lafayette, IN, p. A214

BROWN, Jenny, Director of Human Resources, Vidant Beaufort Hospital, Washington, NC, p. A472

BROWN, Jill, Chief Financial Officer, Miller County Hospital, Colquitt, GA, p. A154

BROWN, Jim, Director Information Technology, Lynn County Hospital District, Tahoka, TX, p. A648

BROWN, Joe, Vice President Operations, Baylor Scott & White Medical Center – Round Rock, Round Rock, TX, p. A640

BROWN, John D, Director Information Systems, Pacific Alliance Medical Center, Los Angeles, CA, p. A70

BROWN, Jon, Chief Information Officer, Mission Hospital, Asheville, NC, p. A457

BROWN, Joni, Director Human Resources, Rehabilitation Hospital Of Indiana, Indianapolis, IN, p. A212

BROWN, Joseph, Vice President Operations, Baylor Regional Medical Center At Plano, Plano, TX, p. A638

BROWN, Judy, Executive Vice President and Chief Operating Officer, East Jefferson General Hospital, Metairie, LA, p. A281

BROWN, Karen C, Vice President Chief Operating Officer, OSF Saint Anthony Medical Center, Rockford, IL, p. A199

BROWN, Karen
Manager Information Technology, Guthrie Towanda Memorial Hospital, Towanda, PA, p. A551
Senior Director of Human Resources, Bridgepoint Hospital Capitol Hill, Washington, DC, p. A117

BROWN, Katie, Coordinator Human Resources, Pocahontas Memorial Hospital, Buckeye, WV, p. A690

BROWN, Ken, Vice President and Chief Human Resource Officer, Pratt Regional Medical Center, Pratt, KS, p. A250

BROWN, Kendra, Job Requisition Coordinator, Rusk State Hospital, Rusk, TX, p. A641

BROWN, Kendrick, Interim Director, Veterans Affairs North Texas Health Care System, Dallas, TX, p. A607

BROWN, Kevin, Chief Executive Officer, La Paz Regional Hospital, Parker, AZ, p. A32

BROWN, Kris, Associate Director, Bay Pines Veterans Affairs Healthcare System, Bay Pines, FL, p. A119

BROWN, LaRay, President and Chief Executive Officer, Interfaith Medical Center, New Rochelle, NY, p. A441

BROWN, Lewis, Director Information Technology, BSA Hospital, Llc, Amarillo, TX, p. A592

BROWN, Lisa, Director of Nursing, Pearl River County Hospital, Poplarville, MS, p. A361

BROWN, Liz, Manager Human Resources, Gunnison Valley Hospital, Gunnison, UT, p. A656

BROWN, Lorenzo, Chief Executive Officer, Florida Hospital Deland, Deland, FL, p. A123

BROWN, Lori J R.N., FACHE, Vice President and Chief Nursing Executive, Borgess Medical Center, Kalamazoo, MI, p. A324

BROWN, Lori, Chief Nursing Officer, Baptist Memorial Hospital–Union City, Union City, TN, p. A590

BROWN, Margaret, Director Medical Records, Vantage Point Of Northwest Arkansas, Fayetteville, AR, p. A43

BROWN, Mark, BSN, MSN, Chief Nursing Officer, Seton Medical Center, Daly City, CA, p. A57

BROWN, Markham M.D., Chief Medical Staff, Mike O'Callaghan Federal Hospital, Nellis Afb, NV, p. A404

BROWN, Marlon, Human Resources, Essex County Hospital Center, Cedar Grove, NJ, p. A412

BROWN, Martin, Vice President Information Services and Chief Information Officer, Nathan Littauer Hospital And Nursing Home, Gloversville, NY, p. A436

BROWN, Mary Beth, Director Human Resources, Bertrand Chaffee Hospital, Springville, NY, p. A452

BROWN, Mary J. MSN, R.N., Vice President and Chief Nursing Officer, Mercy Medical Center–Des Moines, Des Moines, IA, p. A226

BROWN, Mary W, Senior Vice President Operations, St. Joseph's Hospital Health Center, Syracuse, NY, p. A453

BROWN, Michael L.
Regional President and Chief Executive Officer, Presence Mercy Medical Center, Aurora, IL, p. A177
Regional President and Chief Executive Officer, Presence Saint Joseph Hospital, Elgin, IL, p. A186

BROWN, Michael D.O., Chief of Staff, TMC Bonham Hospital, Bonham, TX, p. A598

BROWN, Mike, Chief Financial Officer, Carlinville Area Hospital, Carlinville, IL, p. A179

BROWN, Molly B., Chief Operating Officer, University Of Mississippi Medical Center Grenada, Grenada, MS, p. A355

BROWN, Natalie, Chief Human Resources Management Services, Memphis Veterans Affairs Medical Center, Memphis, TN, p. A585

BROWN, Pam, Human Resources Manager, Behavioral Healthcare Center At Columbia, Columbia, TN, p. A577

BROWN, Pat R.N., Chief Nursing Officer, San Gorgonio Memorial Hospital, Banning, CA, p. A53

BROWN, Patsy, Site Coordinator Human Resources, Erlanger Bledsoe Hospital, Pikeville, TN, p. A588

BROWN, Patti M.D., Medical Director, Healthsouth Reading Rehabilitation Hospital, Reading, PA, p. A549

BROWN, Penny D, Director of Human Resources, Broaddus Hospital, Philippi, WV, p. A695

BROWN, Philip D.O., Vice President Medical Affairs, The University Of Vermont Health Network Central Vermont Medical Center, Berlin, VT, p. A662

BROWN, Phyllis, Chief Executive Officer, Marshall Medical Center, Lewisburg, TN, p. A582

BROWN, Randal M.D., Chief of Medical Staff, Guadalupe County Hospital, Santa Rosa, NM, p. A428

BROWN, Regenia, Vice President Human Resources, Magnolia Regional Health Center, Corinth, MS, p. A354

BROWN, Rex H., President and Chief Executive Officer, Hillsboro Area Hospital, Hillsboro, IL, p. A190

BROWN, Rickie F, Chief Financial Officer, Monroe County Medical Center, Tompkinsville, KY, p. A268

BROWN, Rita, Director Human Resources, Richardson Medical Center, Rayville, LA, p. A284

BROWN, Robert, M.D.
Chief Medical Officer, Park Plaza Hospital, Houston, TX, p. A622
Chief Operating Officer, Parkview Community Hospital Medical Center, Riverside, CA, p. A82

BROWN, Roberta, Chief Nursing Officer, Community Hospital Of Staunton, Staunton, IL, p. A201

BROWN, Robin
Chief Executive, Senior Vice President, Scripps Green Hospital, La Jolla, CA, p. A64
Chief Information Officer and Compliance Officer, St. Joseph Medical Center, Houston, TX, p. A622

BROWN, Rodger, Vice President Human Resources, North Mississippi Medical Center – Tupelo, Tupelo, MS, p. A362

BROWN, Scott, Chief Financial Officer, Valir Rehabilitation Hospital, Oklahoma City, OK, p. A514

BROWN, Shane, Vice President and Chief Human Resources Officer, CGH Medical Center, Sterling, IL, p. A201

BROWN, Shannon, Chief Executive Officer, Huntsville Memorial Hospital, Huntsville, TX, p. A624

BROWN, Sharon, R.N., MSN
Vice President Patient Care and Chief Nursing Officer, St. Mary Medical Center, Langhorne, PA, p. A538
Deputy Commander Nursing, Winn Army Community Hospital, Hinesville, GA, p. A159
Vice President Human Resources, Sierra View Medical Center, Porterville, CA, p. A80

BROWN, Sherry, Director Human Resources, Cleveland Area Hospital, Cleveland, OK, p. A506

BROWN, Stephen A, Chief Financial Officer, Grace Cottage Hospital, Townshend, VT, p. A663

BROWN, Steve
Chief Quality Officer, Saint Alphonsus Regional Medical Center, Boise, ID, p. A172
Chief Information Officer, Wellstar Sylvan Grove Hospital, Jackson, GA, p. A159
Director Information Systems, Wellstar Spalding Regional Hospital, Griffin, GA, p. A158
Health Services Director, U. S. Penitentiary Infirmary, Lewisburg, PA, p. A539

BROWN, Steven, M.D.
Medical Director, Wyoming Behavioral Institute, Casper, WY, p. A717
Vice President Finance, Anderson Regional Health System South, Meridian, MS, p. A359
Vice President Finance, Anderson Regional Health System, Meridian, MS, p. A359
Vice President Fiscal Affairs, Mary Rutan Hospital, Bellefontaine, OH, p. A481

BROWN, Susan
Chief Human Resources Officer, Wellstar North Fulton Hospital, Roswell, GA, p. A164
Chief Nursing Officer, El Paso Behavioral Health System, El Paso, TX, p. A610

BROWN, Terry L, Chief Financial Officer, Raulerson Hospital, Okeechobee, FL, p. A136

BROWN, Theodore
Chief Operating Officer, Community Howard Regional Health, Kokomo, IN, p. A213
Vice President Financial Services, Community Howard Regional Health, Kokomo, IN, p. A213

BROWN, Todd A M.D., Medical Director, Logan Regional Hospital, Logan, UT, p. A657

BROWN, Tom M.D., President Medical Staff, Wayne Healthcare, Greenville, OH, p. A492

BROWN, Traci, Human Resources Generalist, Medical Arts Hospital, Lamesa, TX, p. A628

BROWN, Vance, M.D., President and Chief Executive Officer, Bassett Medical Center, Cooperstown, NY, p. A434

BROWN, Wendy W M.D., M.P.H., Chief of Staff, Jesse Brown Veterans Affairs Medical Center, Chicago, IL, p. A181

BROWN, William A., FACHE, President and CEO, Baptist Health Paducah, Paducah, KY, p. A266

BROWN, Willie, Director Administration, Naval Hospital Beaufort, Beaufort, SC, p. A558

BROWN, Winfield S., FACHE
President and Chief Executive Officer, Athol Hospital, Athol, MA, p. A302
President and Chief Executive Officer, Heywood Hospital, Gardner, MA, p. A307

BROWN–ROBERTS, Bonita, Director Information Systems, Advocate Trinity Hospital, Chicago, IL, p. A180

BROWN–SMITH, Clarissa, Director Fiscal Services, Shriners Hospitals For Children–Shreveport, Shreveport, LA, p. A286

BROWN–TEZERA, Belina MSN, Associate Director Patient Care Services, John D. Dingell Veterans Affairs Medical Center, Detroit, MI, p. A318

BROWNE, John
Assistant Administrator Finance, Kindred Hospital–Brea, Brea, CA, p. A54
Senior Chief Financial Officer, Kindred Hospital Riverside, Perris, CA, p. A79

BROWNE, Mark, M.D.
Chief Medical Officer, Roane Medical Center, Harriman, TN, p. A579

Covenant Health, Senior Vice President and Chief Medical Officer, Methodist Medical Center Of Oak Ridge, Oak Ridge, TN, p. A587

BROWNER, Warren S., M.D., M.P.H.
Chief Executive Officer, California Pacific Medical Center–St. Luke's Campus, San Francisco, CA, p. A87
Chief Executive Officer, California Pacific Medical Center, San Francisco, CA, p. A87

BROWNEWELL, Victoria, Chief Nursing Officer, Houston Methodist West Hospital, Houston, TX, p. A621

BROWNFIELD, Mona M.D., Chief Medical Staff, Cooper County Memorial Hospital, Boonville, MO, p. A365

BROWNING, Douglas
Chief Financial Officer, Porter Regional Hospital, Valparaiso, IN, p. A220
Chief Financial Officer, Texas Health Center For Diagnostic & Surgery, Plano, TX, p. A638

BROWNING, Michael
Chief Financial Officer, Madison Health, London, OH, p. A494
Chief Financial Officer, Promedica Flower Hospital, Sylvania, OH, p. A500

BROWNING, Susan, Executive Director, Long Island Jewish Medical Center, New Rochelle, NY, p. A442

BROWNLEE, Tamarah, Vice President, Human Resources, Indiana University Health West Hospital, Avon, IN, p. A203

BROWNSWORTH, Ray, Chief Executive Officer, Van Buren County Hospital, Keosauqua, IA, p. A230

BROYHILL, David, Chief Information Management, Brooke Army Medical Center, Fort Sam Houston, TX, p. A613

BROYLES, Susan, Director Human Resources and Safety, Unicoi County Memorial Hospital, Erwin, TN, p. A578

BRUBAKER, Kathy M. R.N., MSN, Vice President and Chief Nursing Officer, St. Joseph Mercy Chelsea, Chelsea, MI, p. A316

BRUBAKER, Margaret M, Senior Vice President Human Resources, Brookdale Hospital Medical Center, New Rochelle, NY, p. A441

BRUCE, Bill, FACHE, Chief Executive Officer, Crawford County Memorial Hospital, Denison, IA, p. A226

BRUCE, Caleigh, Vice President Human Resources, Ferrell Hospital, Eldorado, IL, p. A186

BRUCE, Jordan, Administrator, Norwood Health Center, Marshfield, WI, p. A706

BRUCE, Karen, Director of Nursing, Keystone Newport News, Newport News, VA, p. A671

BRUCE, Michael D., Chief Executive Officer, Lake Martin Community Hospital, Dadeville, AL, p. A16

BRUCE, Mike, Chief Financial Officer, Elmore Community Hospital, Wetumpka, AL, p. A24

BRUCE, Scott, Vice President Operations, St. Mary's Healthcare, Amsterdam, NY, p. A430

BRUCKNER, Alison, Chief Operating Officer, Cass County Memorial Hospital, Atlantic, IA, p. A222

BRUDNICKI, Gary F, Senior Executive Vice President, Chief Operating Officer and Chief Financial Officer, Westchester Medical Center, Valhalla, NY, p. A454

BRUEGGEMANN, Marty, Chief Medical Officer, Virginia Mason Memorial, Yakima, WA, p. A689

BRUENS, Dennis, Vice President Operations, St. Thomas More Hospital, Canon City, CO, p. A99

BRUFF, Edward, President and Chief Executive Officer, Covenant Healthcare, Saginaw, MI, p. A329

BRUGGEMAN, Chris, Chief Operating Officer, Riverview Health, Crookston, MN, p. A338

BRUHL, Lisa G, Chief Operating Officer, Lallie Kemp Medical Center, Independence, LA, p. A276

BRUHL, Steven, Chief Medical Officer, Mercy Tiffin Hospital, Tiffin, OH, p. A500

BRUHN, Charles E., Interim Chief Executive Officer, Chippewa County–Montevideo Hospital, Montevideo, MN, p. A344

BRUHN, Julie R.N., MS, Associate Director Patient Care and Nurse Executive, Fargo Veterans Affairs Health Care System, Fargo, ND, p. A475

BRUI, Thomas M, Director Resource Management, Naval Hospital Lemoore, Lemoore, CA, p. A65

BRUINS, Melanie, Chief Talent Officer, Beaver Dam Community Hospitals, Beaver Dam, WI, p. A699

BRUMFIELD, Derrick, Chief Operating Officer, Sagewest Health Care At Riverton, Riverton, WY, p. A719

BRUMFIELD, Rita R.N., MSN, Chief Nursing Officer, Ste. Genevieve County Memorial Hospital, Ste Genevieve, MO, p. A380

BRUMMER, Amy R.N., MSN, Chief Nursing Officer, Saint Luke's North Hospital – Barry Road, Kansas City, MO, p. A371

BRUMMETT, Vince, Director Administrative Services, Panola Medical Center, Batesville, MS, p. A352

BRUNDAGE, Kelsey B., Director Human Resources, Arkansas Valley Regional Medical Center, La Junta, CO, p. A104

BRUNDISE, Cynthia, Vice President Human Resources, St. Anthony Hospital, Oklahoma City, OK, p. A513

BRUNELLE, Diane MSN, R.N., Director Patient Care Services and Chief Nursing Officer, Shriners Hospitals For Children–Springfield, Springfield, MA, p. A311

BRUNER, Deborah, Chief Executive Officer and Administrator, Minneola District Hospital, Minneola, KS, p. A247

BRUNING, Troy, Director Information Technology, Meeker Memorial Hospital, Litchfield, MN, p. A342

BRUNKE, Renea, Vice President Human Resources, Chandler Regional Medical Center, Chandler, AZ, p. A28

BRUNN, Mary E. R.N., Acting Associate Director Nursing, Clement J. Zablocki Veterans Affairs Medical Center, Milwaukee, WI, p. A707

BRUNO, Catherine FACHE, Chief Information Officer, Eastern Maine Medical Center, Bangor, ME, p. A289

BRUNO, John P, Vice President Human Resources, St. Joseph's Healthcare System, Paterson, NJ, p. A418

BRUNO, Judy, Chief Nursing Officer, Vidant Roanoke–Chowan Hospital, Ahoskie, NC, p. A457

BRUNS, Susan, Chief Nursing Officer, Phoebe Sumter Medical Center, Americus, GA, p. A149

BRUNSON, Pam, Director Human Resources, South Baldwin Regional Medical Center, Foley, AL, p. A18

BRUNT, C Hal M.D., Medical Director, Lakeside Behavioral Health System, Memphis, TN, p. A584

BRUNTON, Hope, Chief Manpower Branch, Irwin Army Community Hospital, Junction City, KS, p. A243

BRUNTZ, Troy, President and Chief Executive Officer, Community Hospital, Mccook, NE, p. A396

BRUS, Sarah, Director Human Resources, Doctor's Memorial Hospital, Perry, FL, p. A139

BRUSCO, Louis M.D., Chief Medical Officer, Morristown Medical Center, Morristown, NJ, p. A416

BRUSVEN, Jessica, Chief Executive Officer, Marias Medical Center, Shelby, MT, p. A388

BRUTON, Jeff, Director Human Resources, Fairview Park Hospital, Dublin, GA, p. A157

BRUUN, Edward, President and Chief Executive Officer, Sparrow Clinton Hospital, Saint Johns, MI, p. A330

BRVENIK, Richard A., President, Carteret Health Care, Morehead City, NC, p. A467

BRYAN, Darlene, R.N.
Chief Nursing Officer, Humboldt General Hospital, Winnemucca, NV, p. A406
Interim Chief Executive Officer and Administrator, Humboldt General Hospital, Winnemucca, NV, p. A406

BRYAN, Douglas, President, Medical Staff, Mercyhealth Hospital And Medical Center – Harvard, Harvard, IL, p. A189

BRYAN, Jason, Director Human Resources, Middle Park Medical Center–Kremmling, Kremmling, CO, p. A104

BRYAN, Jay, President and Chief Executive Officer, Mercy Health, Lakeshore Campus, Shelby, MI, p. A330

BRYAN, Kenneth E FACHE, President and Chief Executive Officer, Harnett Health System, Dunn, NC, p. A461

BRYAN, Linda, Vice President Human Resources, Fawcett Memorial Hospital, Port Charlotte, FL, p. A140

BRYAN, Lynda, Vice President Human Resources, Northwest Medical Center, Margate, FL, p. A131

BRYAN, Margaret, Administrator, Shriners Hospitals For Children–Northern California, Sacramento, CA, p. A83

BRYAN, Mark, Chief Executive Officer, Delray Medical Center, Delray Beach, FL, p. A124

BRYAN, Sarah, Manager Human Resources, The Heart Hospital At Deaconess Gateway, Newburgh, IN, p. A217

BRYAN–SMITH, Lissa, Chief Administrative Officer, Geisinger–Bloomsburg Hospital, Bloomsburg, PA, p. A530

BRYANT, Amy, Chief Financial Officer, Cornerstone Hospital Of Southwest Louisiana, Sulphur, LA, p. A287

BRYANT, Dawn, Vice President Human Resources, North Kansas City Hospital, North Kansas City, MO, p. A374

BRYANT, Gary
Chief Financial Officer, Carepoint Health Bayonne Medical Center, Bayonne, NJ, p. A411
Executive Vice President and Chief Financial Officer, Carepoint Health Christ Hospital, Jersey City, NJ, p. A415

BRYANT, Gayla, R.N., Interim Administrator and Vice President Rehabilitation Operations, Sage Rehabilitation Hospital, Baton Rouge, LA, p. A271

BRYANT, Gerald W R.N., Chief Nursing Officer, Scott & White Medical Center – Temple, Temple, TX, p. A648

BRYANT, Karen, Chief Support Services Officer, Prowers Medical Center, Lamar, CO, p. A105

BRYANT, Kay, Executive Director Human Resources, Saint Clare's Health System, Denville, NJ, p. A412

BRYANT, Lidia, Director Human Resources, Ottumwa Regional Health Center, Ottumwa, IA, p. A233

BRYANT, Lisa G, Director Human Resources, Anmed Health Cannon, Pickens, SC, p. A565

BRYANT, Marcia R.N., Vice President, Clinical Operations, The Outer Banks Hospital, Nags Head, NC, p. A467

BRYANT, Maureen A., FACHE, President, Northwestern Medicine Delnor Hospital, Geneva, IL, p. A188

BRYANT, Pam, Director Human Resources, Helen Keller Hospital, Sheffield, AL, p. A23

BRYANT, Ronald, President, Baystate Noble Hospital, Westfield, MA, p. A312

BRYANT, Rusty, Director Information Technology, Drew Memorial Health System, Monticello, AR, p. A47

BRYANT, Valerie, Chief Financial Officer, Deckerville Community Hospital, Deckerville, MI, p. A317

BRYANT, William, Chief Executive Officer, Lifecare Hospital Of Dayton, Miamisburg, OH, p. A495

BRYANT–MOBLEY, Phyllis M.D., Director Medical Services, William S. Hall Psychiatric Institute, Columbia, SC, p. A561

BRYCE, Keith, Vice President Finance and Chief Financial Officer, Mt. Graham Regional Medical Center, Safford, AZ, p. A35

BRYER, Alex, Director Information Management, Los Robles Hospital And Medical Center, Thousand Oaks, CA, p. A93

BRYNER, Jennifer, Director Nursing, Petersburg Medical Center, Petersburg, AK, p. A27

BRYSON, Kellie, Director Human Resources, The Hospital At Westlake Medical Center, Austin, TX, p. A596

BUCCI, Annette, Senior Administrator Human Resources, Burke Rehabilitation Hospital, White Plains, NY, p. A456

BUCCIARELLI, Brant, Chief Information Officer, Riverview Health, Noblesville, IN, p. A217

BUCCOLO, Martin A., Ph.D., Chief Executive Officer, Four Winds Hospital, Katonah, NY, p. A438

BUCH, Naishadh, Chief Operating Officer, Lompoc Valley Medical Center, Lompoc, CA, p. A66

BUCHANAN, Dennis, Vice President Human Resources, New York–Presbyterian Brooklyn Methodist Hospital, New Rochelle, NY, p. A444

BUCHANAN, Donald E., Chief Executive Officer, Haskell County Community Hospital, Stigler, OK, p. A516

BUCHANAN, Donna, Director Nursing, Stroud Regional Medical Center, Stroud, OK, p. A516

BUCHANAN, Ian B., Interim Chief Executive Officer, Nash Health Care Systems, Rocky Mount, NC, p. A469

BUCHANAN, Jean, Director Human Resources, Broughton Hospital, Morganton, NC, p. A467

BUCHANAN, Robert, Chief Information Officer, Anna Jaques Hospital, Newburyport, MA, p. A309

BUCHANAN, Toni, Chief Financial Officer, Unicoi County Memorial Hospital, Erwin, TN, p. A578

BUCHANAN, Tracy, Chief Executive Officer and President, Carepartners Health Services, Asheville, NC, p. A457

BUCHART, Phyllis, Chief Operating Officer, Marina Del Rey Hospital, Marina Del Rey, CA, p. A73

BUCHE, Karen, Chief Human Resource Officer, Douglas County Community Mental Health Center, Omaha, NE, p. A397

BUCHELE, Paula, Chief Human Resources, Bay Pines Veterans Affairs Healthcare System, Bay Pines, FL, p. A119

BUCHER, Ben, Chief Executive Officer, Towner County Medical Center, Cando, ND, p. A474

BUCHHEIT, Anne, Coordinator Mental Health Local Information Systems, Buffalo Psychiatric Center, Buffalo, NY, p. A432

BUCHHEIT, Joe, Chief Financial Officer, Our Lady Of Bellefonte Hospital, Ashland, KY, p. A255

BUCHHOLZ, Kari, Director Health Information Management, Wishek Community Hospital And Clinics, Wishek, ND, p. A478

BUCHNESS, Michael P. M.D., Director Medical, Deer's Head Hospital Center, Salisbury, MD, p. A300

BUCIENSKI, Jennifer C, Vice President Human Resources, Hayes Green Beach Memorial Hospital, Charlotte, MI, p. A316

BUCK, Catherine, President, Froedtert Memorial Lutheran Hospital, Milwaukee, WI, p. A708

BUCK, Linda K, Vice President Human Resources, Unitypoint Health – Proctor, Peoria, IL, p. A197

BUCK, Nathan R.N., Nursing Manager, Mountain River Birthing And Surgery Center, Blackfoot, ID, p. A171

BUCK, Phylis, Controller, Healthsouth Rehabilitation Hospital Of Texarkana, Texarkana, TX, p. A649

BUCK, Shelly, Chief Nursing Executive and Chief Operating Officer, Bon Secours Baltimore Health System, Baltimore, MD, p. A294

BUCK, Tavia, Chief Nursing Officer, Roper St. Francis Mount Pleasant Hospital, Mount Pleasant, SC, p. A564

BUCK, William, Chief of Staff, Horton Community Hospital, Horton, KS, p. A243

BUCKHOY, Sandra, Chief Clinical Officer, Kindred Hospital Chicago–Northlake, Northlake, IL, p. A195

BUCKLEY, David, Acting Chief Information Management Services, Oklahoma City Veterans Affairs Medical Center, Oklahoma City, OK, p. A513

BUCKLEY, Dawne, Interim Chief Executive Officer, Mayhill Hospital, Denton, TX, p. A608

BUCKLEY, John M.D., President Medical Staff, Vibra Hospital Of Denver, Thornton, CO, p. A107

BUCKLEY, Kalvin, Director Information Systems, Woodland Heights Medical Center, Lufkin, TX, p. A631

BUCKLEY, Karen L R.N., Chief Nursing Officer, Community Behavioral Health Center, Fresno, CA, p. A60

BUCKLEY, Martha, Chief Medical Informatics Officer, Fairfield Medical Center, Lancaster, OH, p. A493

BUCKLEY, Patrick, Vice President Human Resources, St. Elizabeth Medical Center, Utica, NY, p. A454

BUCKLEY, Peter, M.D., Interim Chief Executive Officer, Augusta University Medical Center, Augusta, GA, p. A151

BUCKLEY, William M.D., Chief of Staff, Elkhart General Hospital, Elkhart, IN, p. A207

BUCKMINSTER, Joe, Manager Information Technology, Community Medical Center, Inc., Falls City, NE, p. A392

BUCKNER, Marlys, Chief Nursing Officer, Barton County Memorial Hospital, Lamar, MO, p. A372

BUCKNER, Twila R.N., Chief Nursing Officer, Cass Regional Medical Center, Harrisonville, MO, p. A368

BUCKWORTH, Albert Bennett, Human Resources Administrative Director, Primary Children's Hospital, Salt Lake City, UT, p. A660

BUDA, Jeff, Chief Information Officer, Floyd Medical Center, Rome, GA, p. A163

BUDD, Edward, President and Chief Executive Officer, Thorek Memorial Hospital, Chicago, IL, p. A184

BUDDE, Rex P., President and Chief Executive Officer, Southern Illinois Healthcare, Carbondale, IL, p. B119

BUDZINSKY, Chris
Vice President Nursing and Chief Nursing Officer Alexian Brothers Acute Care Ministries, Amita Health Hoffman Estates, Hoffman Estates, IL, p. A190
Vice President, Nursing and Chief Nursing Officer, Amita Health Elk Grove Village, Elk Grove Village, IL, p. A186

BUE, Cheryl, Health Information Transcriptionist, Faulkton Area Medical Center, Faulkton, SD, p. A569

BUEHLER, Bonnie, Chief Information Officer, St. Mary Medical Center, Langhorne, PA, p. A538

BUEHRLE, Jeff, Chief Financial Officer, Banner – University Medical Center South, Tucson, AZ, p. A37

BUELL, Jack, Director Information Services, Sutter Lakeside Hospital, Lakeport, CA, p. A65

BUENVENIDA, Brenda, Director, Hiram W. Davis Medical Center, Petersburg, VA, p. A672

BUER, Shane, Vice President, Human Resources, Mercy Medical Center–Clinton, Clinton, IA, p. A224

BUFFENBARGER, Andrew, Chief Compliance Officer, Kirby Medical Center, Monticello, IL, p. A194

BUFFINGTON, John, Chief Operating Officer, San Juan Regional Medical Center, Farmington, NM, p. A426

BUFFINGTON, Mike, Manager Information Technology, Kansas Medical Center, Andover, KS, p. A238

BUFKIN, Ben, Human Resource Director, Bolivar Medical Center, Cleveland, MS, p. A353

BUGALLO–MUROS, Mariana, Vice President Chief Human Resources Officer, H. Lee Moffitt Cancer Center And Research Institute, Tampa, FL, p. A144

BUGAYONG, Carol, Human Resources Director, Healthsouth Rehabilitation Hospital Of Tallahassee, Tallahassee, FL, p. A144

BUGG, Robert
Acting Chief Executive Officer, Broward Health North, Deerfield Beach, FL, p. A123
Chief Financial Officer, Broward Health North, Deerfield Beach, FL, p. A123

BUGNA, Eric M.D., Chief of Staff, Eastern Plumas Health Care, Portola, CA, p. A80

BUHLKE, Brian M.D., Medical Director, Genoa Medical Facilities, Genoa, NE, p. A393

BUI, Steven M.D., Chief of Staff, Orange County Global Medical Center, Inc., Santa Ana, CA, p. A90

BUIT, Timothy, Executive Vice President and Chief Financial Officer, Bellevue Hospital, Bellevue, OH, p. A481

BUKOSKY, Mike, President, Hospital Division, Usmd Health System, Irving, TX, p. B142

BULAU, Chris, Manager Information Technology, Ridgeview Sibley Medical Center, Arlington, MN, p. A335

BULEN, Susan R M.D., Medical Director, Healthsouth Rehabilitation Hospital Of Southern Arizona, Tucson, AZ, p. A38

BULFIN, Joey R.N., Interim Chief Executive Officer, St. Mary's Medical Center, West Palm Beach, FL, p. A147

BURKS, Matt, Director Information Technology, Unity Medical Center, Manchester, TN, p. A583

BURKS, Melvin, Chief Executive Officer, Hamilton Center, Terre Haute, IN, p. A220

BURKS, Tami, Chief Fiscal Services, Iraan General Hospital, Iraan, TX, p. A624

BURKS, Tami, Comptroller, Rankin County Hospital District, Rankin, TX, p. A639

BURLESON, Linda, Administrative Secretary, Clay County Memorial Hospital, Henrietta, TX, p. A619

BURLESON, Stan M.D., Chief Medical Staff, Dewitt Hospital, Dewitt, AR, p. A42

BURLING, Chris M.D., Chief of Staff, Titus Regional Medical Center, Mount Pleasant, TX, p. A634

BURLINGAME DEAL, Penney, FACHE, R.N., Chief Executive Officer, Onslow Memorial Hospital, Jacksonville, NC, p. A465

BURMAN, Don
Director, Veterans Affairs Nebraska–Western Iowa Health Care System – Lincoln, Lincoln, NE, p. A395
Director, Veterans Affairs Nebraska–Western Iowa Health Care System, Omaha, NE, p. A398

BURMEISTER, Brian
Senior Vice President, ThedaCare Hospitals, Thedacare Regional Medical Center–Neenah, Neenah, WI, p. A709
Senior Vice President, Thedacare Regional Medical Center– Appleton, Appleton, WI, p. A698

BURMESTER, Mark A, Vice President Strategy and Communications, Kaiser Sunnyside Medical Center, Clackamas, OR, p. A520

BURNAM, Gregg, Chief Information Officer and Manager Business Office, Mangum Regional Medical Center, Mangum, OK, p. A509

BURNELL, Lori R.N., Ph.D., Senior Vice President and Chief Nursing Officer, Valley Presbyterian Hospital, Los Angeles, CA, p. A72

BURNES BOLTON, Linda R.N., Vice President and Chief Nursing Officer, Cedars–Sinai Medical Center, Los Angeles, CA, p. A67

BURNETT, Anthony M.D., Medical Director, Julian F. Keith Alcohol And Drug Abuse Treatment Center, Black Mountain, NC, p. A458

BURNETT, Brad, Chief Financial Officer, Heart Of Texas Memorial Hospital, Brady, TX, p. A599

BURNETT, Brenda, Vice President Patient Care Services and Chief Nursing Officer, Titusville Area Hospital, Titusville, PA, p. A551

BURNETT, Cindi, Chief Human Resources Officer, Madison County Memorial Hospital, Madison, FL, p. A131

BURNETT, Mark, President and Chief Executive Officer, Scott County Hospital, Scott City, KS, p. A251

BURNETT, Michael, Chief Executive Officer, Piedmont Fayette Hospital, Fayetteville, GA, p. A157

BURNETT, Rob, Director Human Resources, Jordan Valley Medical Center West Valley Campus, West Valley City, UT, p. A661

BURNETT, Tasha, Director of Nursing, Falls Community Hospital And Clinic, Marlin, TX, p. A632

BURNETTE, Linda R.N., Chief Nursing Officer, Southern Virginia Regional Medical Center, Emporia, VA, p. A666

BURNETTE, Peg, Chief Financial Officer, Denver Health, Denver, CO, p. A100

BURNETTE, Sheri, R.N., Chief Executive Officer and Administrator, Cornerstone Hospital Of Bossier City, Bossier City, LA, p. A272

BURNETTE, W Scott., Chief Executive Officer, VCU Health Community Memorial Hospital, South Hill, VA, p. A675

BURNEY, Sibte M.D., Senior Vice President Medical Affairs and Chief Medical Officer, Kingsbrook Jewish Medical Center, New Rochelle, NY, p. A442

BURNHAM, Sharon, Director of Nursing, Simpson General Hospital, Mendenhall, MS, p. A358

BURNS, Barry, Vice President, Methodist Ambulatory Surgery Hospital – Northwest, San Antonio, TX, p. A643

BURNS, Becky L, Manager Health Information Management, Ellinwood District Hospital, Ellinwood, KS, p. A240

BURNS, Bruce R., Chief Financial Officer, Concord Hospital, Concord, NH, p. A407

BURNS, Christal R.N., Chief Nursing Officer, Care Regional Medical Center, Aransas Pass, TX, p. A593

BURNS, Helen K, Ph.D., R.N.
Senior Vice President and Chief Nursing Officer, Excela Frick Hospital, Mount Pleasant, PA, p. A541
Senior Vice President and Chief Nursing Officer, Excela Health Westmoreland Hospital, Greensburg, PA, p. A535
Senior Vice President and Chief Nursing Officer, Excela Latrobe Area Hospital, Latrobe, PA, p. A538

BURNS, Helene M MSN, R.N., Chief Nursing Executive, Kennedy Health System, Stratford, NJ, p. A420

BURNS, Jeff, Manager of Information Technology, Mary Free Bed Rehabilitation Hospital, Grand Rapids, MI, p. A321

BURNS, Jon P
Chief Information Officer, University Of Maryland Medical Center, Baltimore, MD, p. A296
Senior Vice President and Chief Information Officer, University Of Maryland Baltimore Washington Medical Center, Glen Burnie, MD, p. A298
Senior Vice President and Chief Information Officer, University Of Maryland Medical Center Midtown Campus, Baltimore, MD, p. A296

BURNS, Katherine, Vice President Human Resources, High Point Regional Health System, High Point, NC, p. A464

BURNS, Kathryn I. R.N., Director of Nursing, Medicine Lodge Memorial Hospital, Medicine Lodge, KS, p. A247

BURNS, Larry P Jr, Chief Operating Officer, Yavapai Regional Medical Center, Prescott, AZ, p. A35

BURNS, Patricia, Chief Executive Officer, JFK Medical Center North Campus, West Palm Beach, FL, p. A147

BURNS, Patrick, Vice President Finance, Acmh Hospital, Kittanning, PA, p. A537

BURNS, Rhonda, Director Human Resources, Caldwell Medical Center, Princeton, KY, p. A266

BURNS, Sonda, Chief Executive Officer, Select Specialty Hospital–Akron, Akron, OH, p. A479

BURNS, Steve, Chief Operating Officer, Cumberland County Hospital, Burkesville, KY, p. A256

BURNS, Steven, Director Fiscal Services, Summit Behavioral Healthcare, Cincinnati, OH, p. A484

BURNS, Terry M, Chief Financial Officer, Sycamore Medical Center, Miamisburg, OH, p. A496

BURNS, Tom M.D., Chief of Staff, The Hospital At Westlake Medical Center, Austin, TX, p. A596

BURNS–TISDALE, Susan, Senior Vice President Clinical Operations, Interim CNO, Exeter Hospital, Exeter, NH, p. A408

BURPEE, Scott, President, Safe Haven Health Care, Pocatello, ID, p. B110

BURRAGE, Chris, Manager Information Technology, Coalinga Regional Medical Center, Coalinga, CA, p. A56

BURRELL, Carol H.
Chief Executive Officer, Northeast Georgia Medical Center Braselton, Braselton, GA, p. A153
Chief Executive Officer, Northeast Georgia Medical Center, Gainesville, GA, p. A158

BURRESS, Lori, Vice President Patient Services and Chief Nursing Officer, Mt. Graham Regional Medical Center, Safford, AZ, p. A35

BURRIS, Bradley D., Chief Executive Officer, Pipestone County Medical Center Avera, Pipestone, MN, p. A346

BURRIS, Don, Chief Executive Officer, Foundation Surgical Hospital Of El Paso, El Paso, TX, p. A611

BURRIS, J Michael
Chief Financial Officer, Sentara Rmh Medical Center, Harrisonburg, VA, p. A668
Vice President Corporate Services and Chief Financial Officer, Martha Jefferson Hospital, Charlottesville, VA, p. A665

BURRIS, Lisa
Director Human Resources, Southern Indiana Rehabilitation Hospital, New Albany, IN, p. A217
Manager Human Resources, Frazier Rehab Institute, Louisville, KY, p. A262

BURRISS, Jessica, Chief Financial Officer, Healthsouth Rehabilitation Hospital Of Columbia, Columbia, SC, p. A560

BURRISS, Stephen W., President, UNC Rex Health Care, Raleigh, NC, p. A469

BURROUGHS, Shawn, Director of Information Services, Northeastern Vermont Regional Hospital, Saint Johnsbury, VT, p. A663

BURROUGHS, Steven, Chief Financial Officer, Palms West Hospital, Loxahatchee, FL, p. A131

BURROUGHS, Susan R FACHE, Chief Operating Officer, Kershawhealth, Camden, SC, p. A558

BURROUGHS, Valentine M.D., Chief Medical Officer, East Orange General Hospital, East Orange, NJ, p. A413

BURROW, Debbie R.N., Chief Nursing Officer, Saline Memorial Hospital, Benton, AR, p. A40

BURROWS, Susan M, Vice President Human Resources, Martin Luther King, Jr. Community Hospital, Los Angeles, CA, p. A69

BURRUS, Gary, Director Information Technology, Winner Regional Healthcare Center, Winner, SD, p. A574

BURT, Alan, Director Information Services, Sunrise Hospital And Medical Center, Las Vegas, NV, p. A404

BURT, Keith, Director Marketing, Woodrow Wilson Rehabilitation Center, Fishersville, VA, p. A667

BURT, Linda K, Corporate Vice President Finance, Nebraska Methodist Hospital, Omaha, NE, p. A398

BURT, Noel F Ph.D., Chief Human Resources Officer, Moses H. Cone Memorial Hospital, Greensboro, NC, p. A463

BURT, Suzanne M, Director Human Resources, Covenant Medical Center, Waterloo, IA, p. A236

BURTCH, Gloria, Director Human Resources, Cornerstone Of Medical Arts Center Hospital, Fresh Meadows, NY, p. A436

BURTCHELL, Scott, Director Information Systems, Maine Coast Memorial Hospital, Ellsworth, ME, p. A291

BURTHAY, Darcy, MSN, R.N., President and Chief Executive Officer, Providence Hospital, Washington, DC, p. A118

BURTON, Angela, Privacy Officer, Wayne County Hospital, Monticello, KY, p. A265

BURTON, Becky, R.N., Chief Executive Officer and Market Chief Executive Officer, Vibra Hospital Of Amarillo, Amarillo, TX, p. A592

BURTON, Carmella, Chief Nursing Officer, Anmed Health Rehabilitation Hospital, Anderson, SC, p. A558

BURTON, Charles, Chief Human Resources, Carl R. Darnall Army Medical Center, Fort Hood, TX, p. A613

BURTON, Cynthia R.N., Chief Nursing Officer, Rockcastle Regional Hospital And Respiratory Care Center, Mount Vernon, KY, p. A265

BURTON, James, Vice President and Chief Information Officer, Valley Health, Shenandoah Memorial Hospital, Woodstock, VA, p. A677

BURTON, Luanne, Director Human Resources, Healthsouth Rehabilitation Hospital Of Columbia, Columbia, SC, p. A560

BURTON, Robert, Manager Finance, Utah State Hospital, Provo, UT, p. A659

BURTON, Stacey R., Director Human Resources, Muscogee Creek Nation Medical Center, Okmulgee, OK, p. A514

BURY, Peter, Vice President Finance, Ohiohealth Riverside Methodist Hospital, Columbus, OH, p. A488

BURZYNSKI, Cheryl A., MSN, President, Mclaren Bay Special Care, Bay City, MI, p. A315

BUSBEE, Cathy L, Chief Nursing Officer, Woodland Heights Medical Center, Lufkin, TX, p. A631

BUSBY, Jay M.D., President Medical Staff, Franklin Medical Center, Winnsboro, LA, p. A288

BUSBY, Kathy, Medical Record Technician, Chillicothe Hospital District, Chillicothe, TX, p. A601

BUSCH, Michael D.

BUSCH, Michael D
Executive Vice President and Chief Operating Officer, Excela Frick Hospital, Mount Pleasant, PA, p. A541
Executive Vice President and Chief Operating Officer, Excela Health Westmoreland Hospital, Greensburg, PA, p. A535
Executive Vice President and Chief Operating Officer, Excela Latrobe Area Hospital, Latrobe, PA, p. A538

BUSCH, Rebecca, Chief Financial Officer, Spooner Health, Spooner, WI, p. A712

BUSCH, Steve, Chief Operating Officer, Midwest Medical Center, Galena, IL, p. A188

BUSH, Amy, Vice President Operations, Upmc Mckeesport, Mckeesport, PA, p. A540

BUSH, Bruce A M.D., Senior Vice President Medical Affairs, Indiana Regional Medical Center, Indiana, PA, p. A537

BUSH, Michael M.D., Chief Medical Officer, Holy Rosary Healthcare, Miles City, MT, p. A386

BUSH, Stephen, Chief Financial Officer, TMC Healthcare, Tucson, AZ, p. A38

BUSH, Steven, Chief Medical Officer, Crossing Rivers Health Medical Center, Prairie Du Chien, WI, p. A711

BUSH, Wayne M.D., Chief of Staff, Tristar Greenview Regional Hospital, Bowling Green, KY, p. A256

BUSHART, Phyllis R.N., Chief Operating Officer, Providence Tarzana Medical Center, Los Angeles, CA, p. A71

BUSHART, Stephanie, Chief Financial Officer, Ochsner Medical Center–Baton Rouge, Baton Rouge, LA, p. A270

BUSHELL, Michael, President, Saint Anne's Hospital, Fall River, MA, p. A306

BUSHEY, Dale, Chief Financial Officer, OSS Orthopaedic Hospital, York, PA, p. A555

BUSHMAN, Jerry, Chief Nursing Officer, Brigham City Community Hospital, Brigham City, UT, p. A656

BUSHNELL, Kim MSN, R.N., Vice President, Patient Care Services, Mercy Medical Center, Baltimore, MD, p. A295

BUSINELLE, Denise, Chief Financial Officer, Fairway Medical Surgical Hospital, Covington, LA, p. A273

BUSKEY, Irene, Director Human Resources, Southside Regional Medical Center, Petersburg, VA, p. A673

BUSS, Georganna, Chief Executive Officer, Harper County Community Hospital, Buffalo, OK, p. A505

BUSS, Theresa L, Regional Vice President Human Resources, Windham Hospital, Willimantic, CT, p. A114

BUSSELL, Walter
Chief Financial Officer, Memorial Hospital West, Pembroke Pines, FL, p. A139
Chief Financial Officer, Memorial Regional Hospital, Hollywood, FL, p. A127

BUSSIERE, Mark, Administrator Human Resources, New Hampshire Hospital, Concord, NH, p. A407

BUSSLER, David, Chief Information Officer, Sheridan Community Hospital, Sheridan, MI, p. A330

BUSTLE, John P., M.D., Interim Chief Executive Officer, Bates County Memorial Hospital, Butler, MO, p. A365

BUTCHER, Gina, Chief Financial Officer, Garden City Hospital, Garden City, MI, p. A320

BUTCHER, Kay, Director Health Information Management, Stonewall Jackson Memorial Hospital, Weston, WV, p. A697

BUTE, Phil, Manager Information Technology, Clay County Hospital, Flora, IL, p. A187

BUTERBAUGH, Roger W, Chief Human Resources Officer, Charlie Norwood Veterans Affairs Medical Center, Augusta, GA, p. A151

BUTERBAUGH, William, Director Support Services, Fulton County Medical Center, Mc Connellsburg, PA, p. A540

BUTKER, Jeff, Chief Information Officer, Sovah Health–Martinsville, Martinsville, VA, p. A670

BUTLER, Anita M., Chief Executive Officer, Spartanburg Hospital For Restorative Care, Spartanburg, SC, p. A566

BUTLER, Brad, Network Administrator, Barton County Memorial Hospital, Lamar, MO, p. A372

BUTLER, Carol A R.N., MSN, VP Patient Care Services & Operations, St. Anthony North Health Campus, Westminster, CO, p. A108

BUTLER, Catherine M.D., Chief Medical Staff, Hancock County Health System, Britt, IA, p. A223

BUTLER, Chris, Chief Information Officer, Monmouth Medical Center, Long Branch Campus, Long Branch, NJ, p. A415

BUTLER, Dana M.D., Medical Director, Sunrise Canyon Hospital, Lubbock, TX, p. A630

BUTLER, David, President and Chief Executive Officer, Tillamook Regional Medical Center, Tillamook, OR, p. A527

BUTLER, Debby
Director Human Resources, Wadley Regional Medical Center At Hope, Hope, AR, p. A44
Director Human Resources, Wadley Regional Medical Center, Texarkana, TX, p. A649

BUTLER, Linda H. M.D., Chief Medical Officer, UNC Rex Health Care, Raleigh, NC, p. A469

BUTLER, Margaret E, Vice President Chief Operating Officer, Seton Northwest Hospital, Seton Northwest Hospital, Austin, TX, p. A595

BUTLER, Margaret, Vice President Human Resources, Abbott Northwestern Hospital, Minneapolis, MN, p. A343

BUTLER, Monique, Chief Operating Officer, DMC – Children's Hospital Of Michigan, Detroit, MI, p. A317

BUTLER, Randy
Chief Financial Officer, West Florida Hospital, Pensacola, FL, p. A139
Interim Chief Executive Officer, Southwestern Medical Center, Lawton, OK, p. A509

BUTLER, Rosemary M R.N., MSN, Chief Nurse Executive, Kaiser Permanente Riverside Medical Center, Riverside, CA, p. A82

BUTLER, Scott A., Chief Executive Officer, Select Specialty Hospital–Evansville, Evansville, IN, p. A207

BUTLER, Stuart, Director Information Technology, Sweeny Community Hospital, Sweeny, TX, p. A647

BUTT, Zaahra, Chief Executive Officer, Select Specialty Hospital–Grosse Pointe, Grosse Pointe, MI, p. A322

BUTTELL, Phil, Chief Operating Officer, Centerpoint Medical Center, Independence, MO, p. A369

BUTTER, Hazel, Manager Human Resources, Hammond–Henry Hospital, Geneseo, IL, p. A188

BUTTERFIELD, Cindy, Director, Fiscal and Administrative Services, Connecticut Valley Hospital, Middletown, CT, p. A111

BUTTERFIELD, Jon
Administrator and Chief Operating Officer, Jordan Valley Medical Center West Valley Campus, West Valley City, UT, p. A661
Chief Operating Officer, Jordan Valley Medical Center, West Jordan, UT, p. A661

BUTTERFIELD, Scott, Chief Executive Officer, Select Specialty Hospital – Lincoln, Lincoln, NE, p. A395

BUTTERMORE, Bruce
Director Human Resources, Parkview Lagrange Hospital, Lagrange, IN, p. A214
Manager Human Resources, Parkview Noble Hospital, Kendallville, IN, p. A213

BUTTON, Charlie A., Chief Executive Officer, Regional Medical Center, Manchester, IA, p. A231

BUTTS, Kim, System Nurse Executive, Anchor Hospital, Atlanta, GA, p. A149

BUTTS, Paula Yvonne
Chief Nursing Officer, Piedmont Henry Hospital, Stockbridge, GA, p. A165

Chief Nursing Officer, Wellstar Atlanta Medical Center, Atlanta, GA, p. A151

BUTTS, Ursula N FACHE, Vice President of Patient Care Services, VCU Health Community Memorial Hospital, South Hill, VA, p. A675

BUTZINE, Bart, Director Information Technology, Community Hospital, Grand Junction, CO, p. A103

BUTZLER, Hilary, Director Human Resources, Cumberland Memorial Hospital, Cumberland, WI, p. A700

BUUCK, Brian, Chief Executive Officer, Ridgeview Psychiatric Hospital And Center, Oak Ridge, TN, p. A588

BUURMAN, Rita K., Interim Chief Executive Officer, Morris County Hospital, Council Grove, KS, p. A240

BUZACHERO, Victor, Corporate Senior Vice President for Innovation, Human Resources and Performance Management, Scripps Green Hospital, La Jolla, CA, p. A64

BYARS, Stephanie, Chief Nursing Officer, Unity Medical Center, Manchester, TN, p. A583

BYDA, Jeff, Vice President Information Technology, Mercy Fitzgerald Hospital, Darby, PA, p. A532

BYERS, John M.D., Medical Director, Select Specialty Hospital–Tri Cities, Bristol, TN, p. A575

BYERS, Suzann, Director of Nursing, Southern Indiana Rehabilitation Hospital, New Albany, IN, p. A217

BYERS, Tracy, Chief Executive Officer, Drumright Regional Hospital, Drumright, OK, p. A506

BYERS, William J., Chief Information Officer, Western Maryland Regional Medical Center, Cumberland, MD, p. A298

BYLER, Karen, Information Technology Generalist, Warren State Hospital, Warren, PA, p. A552

BYNUM, Justin
Chief Financial Officer, Saint Anthony Hospital, Chicago, IL, p. A183
Chief Operating Officer, Norwegian American Hospital, Chicago, IL, p. A182

BYRD, Catherine, Vice President Patient Services, Parkview Noble Hospital, Kendallville, IN, p. A213

BYRD, David, Chief Financial Officer, The Hospitals Of Providence Transmountain Campus, El Paso, TX, p. A612

BYRD, Greg, Vice President Medical Affairs, Shenandoah Memorial Hospital, Woodstock, VA, p. A677

BYRD, Lu R.N., MSN, Vice President Hospital Operations and Chief Nursing Officer, Billings Clinic, Billings, MT, p. A382

BYRD, O Wayne M.D., Chief of Staff, H. C. Watkins Memorial Hospital, Quitman, MS, p. A361

BYRD, Rebecca, President Medical Staff, Grandview Medical Center, Birmingham, AL, p. A14

BYRD–PELAEZ, Brenda, Chief Human Resources Management Office, Martinsburg Veterans Affairs Medical Center, Martinsburg, WV, p. A694

BYRNE, Frank J, Vice President Finance, Newport Hospital, Newport, RI, p. A556

BYRNES, Matthew C M.D., Chief Medical Officer, St. Catherine Hospital, Garden City, KS, p. A241

BYRNS, David, Chief Executive Officer, Putnam County Memorial Hospital, Unionville, MO, p. A380

BYROM, David, Chief Executive Officer, Coryell Memorial Hospital, Gatesville, TX, p. A616

C

CAAMANO, Tero, Director Information Technology, Saint Clare's Health System, Denville, NJ, p. A412

CABALLERO, Rogelio, Chief Information Systems, San Jorge Children's Hospital, San Juan, PR, p. A726

CABIBBO, Tiffany, Vice President of Nursing, Baptist Health Madisonville, Madisonville, KY, p. A264

CABIGAO, Edwin, Chief Nursing Officer, Jewish Home Of San Francisco, San Francisco, CA, p. A87

CABRERA, Carlos, Executive Director, Cardiovascular Center Of Puerto Rico And The Caribbean, San Juan, PR, p. A725

CABRERA, Irma, Finance Director, Hospital San Carlos Borromeo, Moca, PR, p. A724

CABRERA, Sheelah, Chief Information Officer, La Rabida Children's Hospital, Chicago, IL, p. A181

CABUNOC, Brenda, Chief Human Resources, Va Greater Los Angeles Healthcare System, Los Angeles, CA, p. A72

CACCIAMANI, John D. ., M.D., Chief Executive Officer, Chestnut Hill Hospital, Philadelphia, PA, p. B35

CACCIAMANI, John D., M.D., Chief Executive Officer, Chestnut Hill Hospital, Philadelphia, PA, p. A543

CADE, Paul, Administrator and Chief Executive Officer, Baptist Memorial Hospital–Golden Triangle, Columbus, MS, p. A354

CADIEUX, Marc
Corporate Vice President and Chief Financial Officer, Children's Hospital Of Wisconsin–Fox Valley, Neenah, WI, p. A708
Corporate Vice President and Chief Financial Officer, Children's Hospital Of Wisconsin, Milwaukee, WI, p. A707

CADIGAN, Elizabeth R.N., MSN, Senior Vice President Patient Care Services and Chief Nursing Officer, Cambridge Health Alliance, Cambridge, MA, p. A305

CADOGAN, David, Chief Medical Officer, Alaska Regional Hospital, Anchorage, AK, p. A25

CADORETTE, Brenda E, Chief Nursing Officer, Berkshire Medical Center, Pittsfield, MA, p. A310

CADWELL, Carrie M.D., Chief Clinical Officer, Four County Counseling Center, Logansport, IN, p. A215

CADWELL, Jason, Chief Financial Officer, Four County Counseling Center, Logansport, IN, p. A215

CADWELL, Maureen K., Chief Executive Officer, Weston County Health Services, Newcastle, WY, p. A719

CADY, Kathy, Coordinator Human Resources, Accounts Payable and Payroll, Safe Haven Hospital Of Treasure Valley, Boise, ID, p. A171

CADY, Thomas, Vice President Human Resources, Heywood Hospital, Gardner, MA, p. A307

CADY, Tina, Controller, The Women's Hospital, Newburgh, IN, p. A217

CAFASSO, Michael, Vice President Operations, St. Mary–Corwin Medical Center, Pueblo, CO, p. A107

CAGLE, Jennifer, Director of Nursing, North Mississippi Medical Center–Hamilton, Hamilton, AL, p. A19

CAGLE, Karen, Chief Nursing Officer, Select Specialty Hospital–Nashville, Nashville, TN, p. A587

CAGNA, Ralph A
Director Information Technology Operations, Cleveland Clinic Health System South Market, Marymount Hospital, Garfield Heights, OH, p. A492
Director Information Technology, South Pointe Hospital, Warrensville Heights, OH, p. A501

CAHALAN, Jay P., Chief Executive Officer, Columbia Memorial Hospital, Hudson, NY, p. A437

CAHILL, Donna, Vice President Human Resources, Hackensack Meridian Health Palisades Medical Center, North Bergen, NJ, p. A418

CAHILL, Joseph, Executive Vice President and Chief Operating Officer, South Shore Hospital, South Weymouth, MA, p. A311

CAHILL, Kathleen, Chief Executive Officer, Mesa Hills Specialty Hospital, El Paso, TX, p. A611

CAHILL, Marty, Chief Executive Officer, Samaritan Lebanon Community Hospital, Lebanon, OR, p. A523

CAHILL, Patricia R.N., Vice President, Patient Care Services and Chief Nursing Officer, Bronx–Lebanon Hospital Center Health Care System, New Rochelle, NY, p. A440

CAHO–MOONEY, Linda, Chief Financial Officer, Claiborne County Medical Center, Port Gibson, MS, p. A361

CAHOJ, Lindsey, Chief Nursing Officer, Select Specialty Hospital–Wichita, Wichita, KS, p. A253

CAIN, Amy, District Director Human Resources, Kindred Hospital South Philadelphia, Philadelphia, PA, p. A544

CAIN, Donna, Director Information Systems Department, Cypress Fairbanks Medical Center, Houston, TX, p. A620

CAIN, Mark, Chief Executive Officer, Tennova Healthcare–Lafollette Medical Center, La Follette, TN, p. A582

CAIN, Roxie, Chief Financial Officer, Big Horn County Memorial Hospital, Hardin, MT, p. A385

CAIN, William, Controller, Penn Highlands Clearfield, Clearfield, PA, p. A531

CAINE, Jamie, Director of Human Resources, Multicare Valley Hospital, Spokane Valley, WA, p. A687

CAIRNS, Craig M.D., Vice President Medical Affairs, Licking Memorial Hospital, Newark, OH, p. A497

CALAIS, C Matthew, Senior Vice President and Chief Information Officer, Legacy Good Samaritan Medical Center, Portland, OR, p. A525

CALAIS, Daniel Jr, Superintendent, Bridgewater State Hospital, Bridgewater, MA, p. A304

CALAMARI, Frank A., President and Chief Executive Officer, Calvary Hospital, New Rochelle, NY, p. A441

CALAMARI, Jacquelyn MSN, MS, Chief Nursing Officer and Vice President, Patient Care Services, Middlesex Hospital, Middletown, CT, p. A111

CALANDRELLA, Paul, Chief Operating Officer, Mt. Ascutney Hospital And Health Center, Windsor, VT, p. A663

CALANDRIELLO, John, Vice President and Chief Financial Officer, Hackensack Meridian Health Palisades Medical Center, North Bergen, NJ, p. A418

CALARCO, Marge, Chief Nursing Executive, Michigan Medicine, Ann Arbor, MI, p. A314

CALAWAY, Shearmaine, Director Human Resources, East Mississippi State Hospital, Meridian, MS, p. A359

CALBONE, Angelo G., President and Chief Executive Officer, Saratoga Hospital, Saratoga Springs, NY, p. A452

CALBY, Elizabeth, Vice President Human Resources, Advocate Good Samaritan Hospital, Downers Grove, IL, p. A186

CALDARI, Patricia, Vice President, Richmond University Medical Center, New Rochelle, NY, p. A446

CALDAS, Robert D.O., Chief Medical Officer, Southcoast Hospitals Group, Fall River, MA, p. A306

CALDEIRA, Amy, Director Information Technology and Systems, Fort Walton Beach Medical Center, Fort Walton Beach, FL, p. A125

CALDERA, Ken, Director Human Resources, Kessler Institute For Rehabilitation, West Orange, NJ, p. A422

CALDERON, Lizmari, Director Finance, Hospital De La Concepcion, San German, PR, p. A725

CALDWELL, Charles M.D., Chief of Staff, Byrd Regional Hospital, Leesville, LA, p. A280

CALDWELL, Dan, Chief Executive Officer, South Texas Health System, Edinburg, TX, p. A610

CALDWELL, Dari, R.N., Ph.D., FACHE, President and Chief Operating Officer, Novant Health Rowan Medical Center, Salisbury, NC, p. A470

CALDWELL, Darren, Vice President and Administrator, Unity Health White County Medical Center, Searcy, AR, p. A49

CALDWELL, Eric, Director Finance, Northside Hospital–Forsyth, Cumming, GA, p. A155

CALDWELL, Marita, Chief Financial Officer, Twin County Regional Healthcare, Galax, VA, p. A668

CALDWELL, Matthew T.
President and Chief Executive Officer, Mercy Memorial Hospital, Urbana, OH, p. A501
President and Chief Executive Officer, Springfield Regional Medical Center, Springfield, OH, p. A499

CALDWELL, Nesa, Chief Nursing Officer, Solara Hospital Harlingen, Harlingen, TX, p. A618

CALDWELL, Paul, Facility Coordinator Information Technology Customer Relations, Page Hospital, Page, AZ, p. A32

CALDWELL, Steve, Vice President Finance and Chief Financial Officer, St. Mary's Hospital, Madison, WI, p. A705

CALDWELL, William E. Jr, Chief Executive Officer, Wilson Medical Center, Wilson, NC, p. A472

CALEY, Carl
Chief Financial Officer, Spring Valley Hospital Medical Center, Las Vegas, NV, p. A404
Chief Financial Officer, St. Cloud Regional Medical Center, Saint Cloud, FL, p. A141

CALHOUN, Cathy, Director Human Resources, River Point Behavioral Health, Jacksonville, FL, p. A128

CALHOUN, Joshua M.D., Medical Director, Hawthorn Children Psychiatric Hospital, Saint Louis, MO, p. A377

CALHOUN, Kevin P., Chief Executive Officer, Munising Memorial Hospital, Munising, MI, p. A326

CALHOUN, Kirk A., M.D., President, University Of Texas Health Northeast, Tyler, TX, p. A651

CALHOUN, Robert, Chief Executive Officer, Merit Health Biloxi, Biloxi, MS, p. A352

CALHOUN, Timothy
Vice President Finance and Chief Financial Officer, Lakeland Medical Center, St. Joseph, Saint Joseph, MI, p. A330
Vice President Finance, Chief Financial Officer, Lakeland Hospital, Watervliet, Watervliet, MI, p. A333

CALIA, Christopher, Vice President Human Resources, Chi St. Luke's Health Brazosport, Lake Jackson, TX, p. A628

CALIFORNIA, Randy, Chief Operating Officer, Warren General Hospital, Warren, PA, p. A552

CALIGIURI, Michael, M.D., Chief Executive Officer, James Cancer Hospital And Solove Research Institute, Columbus, OH, p. A487

CALIME, Erica, Director Human Resources, Baylor Scott & White Medical Center – Carrollton, Carrollton, TX, p. A600

CALIVA, Todd, FACHE, Chief Executive Officer, Clear Lake Regional Medical Center, Webster, TX, p. A653

CALKIN, Steven D.O., Vice President Medical Affairs, Mclaren Oakland, Pontiac, MI, p. A328

CALKINS, Paul M.D., Chief Medical Officer, Indiana University Health North Hospital, Carmel, IN, p. A205

CALL, Carie, Computer Support, Cassia Regional Medical Center, Burley, ID, p. A172

CALL, Stacie, R.N.
Vice President Patient Care and Chief Nursing Officer, East Liverpool City Hospital, East Liverpool, OH, p. A490
Chief Nursing Officer, Mercy Health – St. Elizabeth Boardman Hospital, Boardman, OH, p. A481

CALLAGHAN, Barbara, Interim Chief Executive Officer, Atrium Medical Center Of Corinth, Corinth, TX, p. A603

CALLAGHAN, James III, M.D., President and Chief Executive Officer, Franciscan St. Francis Health – Indianapolis, Indianapolis, IN, p. A211

CALLAGHAN, Peter, President and Chief Operating Officer, Columbus Hospital Ltach, Newark, NJ, p. A417

CALLAHAN, Ame, Acting Manager Resource Management Service, Northern Arizona Veterans Affairs Health Care System, Prescott, AZ, p. A34

CALLAHAN, Charles D Ph.D., Executive Vice President and Chief Operating Officer, Memorial Medical Center, Springfield, IL, p. A200

CALLAHAN, Christopher M, Vice President Human Resources, Exeter Hospital, Exeter, NH, p. A408

CALLAHAN, Kelly, Public Information Officer, Elgin Mental Health Center, Elgin, IL, p. A186

CALLAHAN, Kevin J., President and Chief Executive Officer, Exeter Hospital, Exeter, NH, p. A408

CALLAHAN, Larry A., Senior Vice President Human Resources, Grady Memorial Hospital, Atlanta, GA, p. A150

CALLAHAN, Mark, Chief Operating Officer, Mary Lanning Healthcare, Hastings, NE, p. A394

CALLAHAN, Mary Beth, Chief Financial Officer, Mclaren Lapeer Region, Lapeer, MI, p. A325

CALLAHAN, Neil, Chief Executive Officer, Brooke Glen Behavioral Hospital, Fort Washington, PA, p. A535

CALLAHAN, Robert W. Jr, Interim Director, Wilmington Veterans Affairs Medical Center, Wilmington, DE, p. A116

CALLAHAN, Shannon, Director Human Resources, Sitka Community Hospital, Sitka, AK, p. A27

CALLAHAN, Teresa, R.N., MSN, Chief Executive Officer, Iraan General Hospital, Iraan, TX, p. A624

CALLAHAN, William, Chief Information Management Division, Bayne–Jones Army Community Hospital, Fort Polk, LA, p. A274

CALLAN, Michael, Executive Vice President and Chief Financial Officer, Kidspeace Children's Hospital, Orefield, PA, p. A542

CALLANAN, Patrick, Vice President Patient Care Services, Mercy Hospital Fort Scott, Fort Scott, KS, p. A241

CALLAS, Robin B R.N., Vice President Human Resources, Rutherford Regional Health System, Rutherfordton, NC, p. A470

CALLAWAY, Blair, Chief Financial Officer, Texas Orthopedic Hospital, Houston, TX, p. A623

CALLECOD, David L., President and Chief Executive Officer, Lafayette General Health, Lafayette, LA, p. B74

CALLENS, Don M.D., Chief Medical Officer, Liberty Dayton Regional Medical Center, Liberty, TX, p. A629

CALLENS, Paul A., Ph.D., Director, North Mississippi State Hospital, Tupelo, MS, p. A362

CALLICOAT, William, Chief Financial Officer, Summit Pacific Medical Center, Elma, WA, p. A680

CALLISTE, Gregory, Ph.D., FACHE, Chief Executive Officer, NYC Health + Hospitals / Woodhull, New Rochelle, NY, p. A446

CALLISTER, T Brian M.D., Chief Medical Officer, Tahoe Pacific Hospitals, Sparks, NV, p. A406

CALLMAN, Mark M.D., Chief Medical Officer, Fawcett Memorial Hospital, Port Charlotte, FL, p. A140

CALLOWAY, Maria R.N., MSN, Chief Nursing Officer, Central Florida Regional Hospital, Sanford, FL, p. A142

CALMAN, Kurt, Chief Information Officer, United Memorial Medical Center, Batavia, NY, p. A431

CALUBAQUIB, Evelyn, Chief Nursing Officer, Greater El Monte Community Hospital, South El Monte, CA, p. A92

CALVARUSO, Gaspare, President, Capital Region Medical Center, Jefferson City, MO, p. A369

CALVERT, Mandy, Director Information Systems, Southern Coos Hospital And Health Center, Bandon, OR, p. A520

CALVERT, Sarah, Chief Nursing Officer, Mcgehee–Desha County Hospital, Mcgehee, AR, p. A47

CALVIN, Harley D.O., Chief Medical Officer, Rush County Memorial Hospital, La Crosse, KS, p. A244

CALVIN, Irene, Vice President Human Resources, South Oaks Hospital, Amityville, NY, p. A430

CALVIN, Jeff, Chief Financial Officer, Michiana Behavioral Health Center, Plymouth, IN, p. A218

CAMA, Joseph M.D., President Medical Staff, Guthrie Towanda Memorial Hospital, Towanda, PA, p. A551

CAMACHO, Leslie R.N., Director of Nursing, Commonwealth Health Center, Saipan, MP, p. A721

CAMARDELLO, Heidi, Vice President Patient Care Services and Chief Nursing Officer, Little Falls Hospital, Little Falls, NY, p. A438

CAMERON, Carl, Director Information Systems, Holyoke Medical Center, Holyoke, MA, p. A307

CAMERON, Don, Chief Operating Officer, Allegiance Behavioral Health Center Of Plainview, Plainview, TX, p. A637

CAMERON, Kim, Manager Health Information Services, Patients' Hospital Of Redding, Redding, CA, p. A81

CAMMACK, Geri R.N., Director of Nursing, Lost Rivers Medical Center, Arco, ID, p. A171

CAMMENGA, Randall M.D., Vice President Medical Affairs, Goshen Hospital, Goshen, IN, p. A209

CAMP, Claude E Chip III, FACHE, Chief Executive Officer, Brownwood Regional Medical Center, Brownwood, TX, p. A599

CAMP, Claude E Chip'". III, FACHE, Chief Executive Officer, Brownwood Regional Medical Center, Brownwood, TX, p. B36

CAMP, David, Director Human Resources, St. Mary's Regional Medical Center, Enid, OK, p. A507

CAMP, Lea Ann R.N., Chief Nursing Officer, Greene County General Hospital, Linton, IN, p. A215

CAMPA, Melissa, Controller, Kindred Hospital El Paso, El Paso, TX, p. A611

CAMPANA, Thomas M.D., Chief of Staff, Spectrum Health Reed City Hospital, Reed City, MI, p. A329

CAMPANELLA, Alfred, Chief Information Officer, Virtua Voorhees, Voorhees, NJ, p. A422

CAMPAS, Janice, Chief Financial Officer, Wichita County Health Center, Leoti, KS, p. A245

CAMPBELL, Al, Senior Vice President and Chief Operating Officer, Fort Washington Medical Center, Oxen Hill, MD, p. A300

CAMPBELL, Amy, Chief Financial Officer, Community Hospital North, Indianapolis, IN, p. A210

CAMPBELL, Andrew, Associate Executive Director, NYC Health + Hospitals / Coney Island, New Rochelle, NY, p. A444

CAMPBELL, April, Director Human Resources, Broadwater Health Center, Townsend, MT, p. A389

CAMPBELL, Bernard M, Administrator Human Resources, Lewisgale Hospital Alleghany, Low Moor, VA, p. A669

CAMPBELL, Brian, Director Professional Services, U. S. Public Health Service Indian Hospital–Whiteriver, Whiteriver, AZ, p. A38

CAMPBELL, C Scott, Market Chief Executive Officer, Physicians Regional – Pine Ridge, Naples, FL, p. A135

CAMPBELL, Carla R.N., Chief Nurse Officer, Mercy Hospital And Medical Center, Chicago, IL, p. A182

CAMPBELL, Chad, Chief Executive Officer, Mckenzie–Willamette Medical Center, Springfield, OR, p. A527

CAMPBELL, Christine, Controller, Vanderbilt Stallworth Rehabilitation Hospital, Nashville, TN, p. A587

CAMPBELL, Cinthia, Chief Nursing Officer, Healthsouth Chattanooga Rehabilitation Hospital, Chattanooga, TN, p. A576

CAMPBELL, David, Administrator, Perry Hospital, Perry, GA, p. A163

CAMPBELL, Dean, Vice President Information Services and Chief Information Officer, Good Samaritan Hospital, Los Angeles, CA, p. A68

CAMPBELL, Deborah, Administrator, Thomas H. Boyd Memorial Hospital, Carrollton, IL, p. A179

CAMPBELL, Debra, R.N., Administrator, Riverside Regional Medical Center, Newport News, VA, p. A671

CAMPBELL, Emily, Senior Director Human Resources, The University Of Vermont Health Network – Alice Hyde Medical Center, Malone, NY, p. A439

CAMPBELL, Eric, Chief Financial Officer, Oswego Hospital, Oswego, NY, p. A449

CAMPBELL, Gary, Chief Executive Officer, St. Vincent General Hospital District, Leadville, CO, p. A105

CAMPBELL, Ivy, Director of Nursing, Community Medical Center, Inc., Falls City, NE, p. A392

CAMPBELL, John
Chief Information Officer, Spaulding Hospital For Continuing Medical Care Cambridge, Cambridge, MA, p. A305
Chief Information Officer, Spaulding Rehabilitation Hospital Cape Cod, East Sandwich, MA, p. A306
Chief Information Officer, Spaulding Rehabilitation Hospital, Charlestown, MA, p. A305

CAMPBELL, Kathy, Interim Chief Nursing Officer, Wellmont Holston Valley Medical Center, Kingsport, TN, p. A581

CAMPBELL, Matthew J., Chief Executive Officer, Select Specialty Hospital–Saginaw, Saginaw, MI, p. A329

CAMPBELL, Melissa, Controller, Mercy Rehabilition Hospital Springfield, Springfield, MO, p. A380

CAMPBELL, Melvin M.D., Medical Staff Chairman, Brown County Hospital, Ainsworth, NE, p. A390

CAMPBELL, Pamela M.D., Medical Director, Lincoln Prairie Behavioral Health Center, Springfield, IL, p. A200

CAMPBELL, Sandra M. R.N., Chief Nursing Officer, Dodge County Hospital, Eastman, GA, p. A157

CAMPBELL, Scott, Market Chief Executive Officer, Providence Hospital, Columbia, SC, p. A560

CAMPBELL, Shari, Chief Operating Officer, Kearny County Hospital, Lakin, KS, p. A244

CAMPBELL, Sharon J, Director, Human Resources, Park Ridge Health, Hendersonville, NC, p. A464

CAMPBELL, Sherry May, Director of Human Resources, Medical Records, Seaside Behavioral Center, New OrleansRiver Oaks Hospital, New Orleans, LA, p. A283

CAMPBELL, Stephen J, Chief Operating Officer, Pioneers Memorial Healthcare District, Brawley, CA, p. A54

CAMPBELL, Susie, Chief Executive Officer, Community Hospital Of Staunton, Staunton, IL, p. A201

CAMPBELL, Suzannah, Administrator, St. Vincent's Chilton Hospital, Clanton, AL, p. A16

CAMPBELL, Suzanne, Director Patient Services, Spearfish Regional Hospital, Spearfish, SD, p. A573

CAMPBELL, Teresa R.N., Chief Nursing Executive, Sutter Lakeside Hospital, Lakeport, CA, p. A65

CAMPBELL, Todd, Senior Vice President and Chief Operating Officer, St. Mary's Medical Center, Huntington, WV, p. A693

CAMPBELL, Vicky, Vice President Mental Health and Support Services, Providence Healthcare Network, Waco, TX, p. A652

CAMPEAU, Arleen R.N., Vice President of Patient Care Services, Chief Nursing Officer, Powell Valley Healthcare, Powell, WY, p. A719

CAMPO, Mary Beth MS, R.N., Director of Nursing, Eastern Niagara Hospital, Lockport, NY, p. A438

CAMPOS, Christina, Administrator, Guadalupe County Hospital, Santa Rosa, NM, p. A428

CAMPOS, Emilio, Deparment Head Information Technology, Guadalupe County Hospital, Santa Rosa, NM, p. A428

CAMPOVERDE, Jacqueline, Business Manager, Essex County Hospital Center, Cedar Grove, NJ, p. A412

CAMPS, Lourdes R.N., Chief Nursing Officer, Hialeah Hospital, Hialeah, FL, p. A126

CANADY, Carolyn, Chief Financial Officer, Sierra Nevada Memorial Hospital, Grass Valley, CA, p. A62

CANADY, Michael, M.D.
Interim Chief Executive Officer, Holzer Medical Center – Jackson, Jackson, OH, p. A492
Interim Chief Executive Officer, Holzer Medical Center, Gallipolis, OH, p. A491

CANALE, Joseph, Business Manager, Trenton Psychiatric Hospital, Trenton, NJ, p. A422

CANALEJO, Donald, Director Human Resources, Lower Keys Medical Center, Key West, FL, p. A129

CANALES, Joe
Director Human Resources, Seton Edgar B. Davis Hospital, Luling, TX, p. A631
Director Human Resources, Seton Shoal Creek Hospital, Austin, TX, p. A595
Vice President Human Resources, Ministry Market Texas, Dell Seton Medical Center At The University Of Texas, Austin, TX, p. A595
Vice President Human Resources, Seton Medical Center Austin, Austin, TX, p. A595
Vice President, Ascension and Human Resources Officer, Texas Market, Seton Northwest Hospital, Austin, TX, p. A595

CANARD, Robert Shannon., Chief Executive Officer, Select Specialty Hospital – Belhaven, Jackson, MS, p. A357

CANCEL, Diana, Director Human Resources, Glendora Community Hospital, Glendora, CA, p. A62

CANDELA, Chris, President and Chief Executive Officer, Mclaren Lapeer Region, Lapeer, MI, p. A325

CANDIA, Gary R., Ph.D., FACHE, Chief Administrative Officer, Abington–Lansdale Hospital Jefferson Health, Lansdale, PA, p. A538

CANDILL, James W M.D., President Medical Staff, Charleston Surgical Hospital, Charleston, WV, p. A691

CANDIO, Christine M., R.N., FACHE, President and Chief Executive Officer, St. Luke's Hospital, Chesterfield, MO, p. A366

CANDULLO, Carl, Chief Information Officer, Munroe Regional Medical Center, Ocala, FL, p. A136

CANEDO, Jim, Chief Financial Officer, College Medical Center, Long Beach, CA, p. A66

CANFIELD, Brian, Chief Operating Officer, Firsthealth Moore Regional Hospital, Pinehurst, NC, p. A468

CANFIELD, Michael, Chief Information Officer, Augusta Health, Fishersville, VA, p. A667

CANIZARO, Tom, Vice President and Chief Financial Officer, South Central Regional Medical Center, Laurel, MS, p. A358

CANLAS, Emma, Chief Financial Officer, Valley View Medical Center, Fort Mohave, AZ, p. A29

CANNARA, Christopher, Chief Executive Officer, Kindred Hospital–New Jersey Morris County, Dover, NJ, p. A413

CANNIFF, Christopher, Executive Director, Human Resources, Harrington Hospital, Southbridge, MA, p. A311

CANNING, John, Chief Financial Officer, Blythedale Children's Hospital, Valhalla, NY, p. A454

CANNINGTON, H D, Interim Chief Financial Officer, Fishermen's Hospital, Marathon, FL, p. A131

CANNON, Brenda R.N., Director of Nursing, Laughlin Memorial Hospital, Greeneville, TN, p. A579

CANNON, Gayle, Director Human Resources, Childress Regional Medical Center, Childress, TX, p. A601

CANNON, Linda, Chief Medical Records Services, San Diego County Psychiatric Hospital, San Diego, CA, p. A86

CANNON, Robert W., President, Barnes–Jewish Hospital, Saint Louis, MO, p. A376

CANO, Daniel M.D., Chief Medical Officer, Citizens Medical Center, Victoria, TX, p. A652

CANTLEY, J Scott., President and Chief Executive Officer, Marietta Memorial Hospital, Marietta, OH, p. A494

CANTRE, Pedro Laureano, Chief Nursing Officer, Cardiovascular Center Of Puerto Rico And The Caribbean, San Juan, PR, p. A725

CANTRELL, David CPA, Vice President and Chief Financial Officer, West Hills Hospital And Medical Center, Los Angeles, CA, p. A72

CANTRELL, Dedra
Chief Information Officer, Emory Saint Joseph's Hospital Of Atlanta, Atlanta, GA, p. A150
Chief Information Officer, Emory University Hospital Midtown, Atlanta, GA, p. A150

CANTU, Andrew, Chief Financial Officer, Kern Medical Center, Bakersfield, CA, p. A53

CANTU, Janie, Director Human Resources, Crosbyton Clinic Hospital, Crosbyton, TX, p. A604

CAPASSO, Beverly, Interim President and Chief Executive Officer, Broward Health, Fort Lauderdale, FL, p. B23

CAPECE, Vincent G. Jr, President and Chief Executive Officer, Middlesex Hospital, Middletown, CT, p. A111

CAPERS, Travis, FACHE, President, SSM Health St. Mary's Hospital – St. Louis, Saint Louis, MO, p. A378

CAPILI, Anthony M.D., Chief of Staff, Bayside Community Hospital, Anahuac, TX, p. A592

CAPIOLA, Richard M.D., Chief Medical Officer, Baton Rouge Behavioral Hospital, Baton Rouge, LA, p. A270

CAPITELLI, Robert M.D., Senior Vice President and Chief Medical Officer, St. Tammany Parish Hospital, Covington, LA, p. A273

CAPITULO, Kathleen Ph.D., R.N., Chief Nurse Executive, James J. Peters Veterans Affairs Medical Center, New Rochelle, NY, p. A442

CAPLAN, Margaret B., Director, Veterans Affairs Hudson Valley Health Care System, Montrose, NY, p. A440

CAPLE, Jocelyn M.D., Chief Medical Officer, Frisbie Memorial Hospital, Rochester, NH, p. A410

CAPLES, Greg, Chief Operating Officer, Tristar Summit Medical Center, Hermitage, TN, p. A580

CAPO, Ann Marie R.N., Chief Nursing Officer, Uconn, John Dempsey Hospital, Farmington, CT, p. A110

CAPOTE, Henry, Interim Chief Financial Officer, Coral Gables Hospital, Coral Gables, FL, p. A122

CAPPEL, Blaine, Director Information Systems, Memorial Health System, Abilene, KS, p. A238

CAPPLEMAN, Troy M.D., Chief of Staff, Tippah County Hospital, Ripley, MS, p. A361

CAPPS, Anita R.N., Chief Nursing Executive, Community Hospital South, Indianapolis, IN, p. A210

CAPPS, Kim, Chief Financial Officer, Hayes Green Beach Memorial Hospital, Charlotte, MI, p. A316

CAPPS, Melissa, Site Leader Information Technology, St. Luke's Magic Valley Medical Center, Twin Falls, ID, p. A176

CAPPS, Rick, Chief Financial Officer, Cumberland County Hospital, Burkesville, KY, p. A256

CAPRICO, Rick, Chief Financial Officer, Catskill Regional Medical Center, Harris, NY, p. A437

CAPSHAW, Marcia, Chief Operating Officer, West Central Georgia Regional Hospital, Columbus, GA, p. A155

CAPUANO, Terry Ann, R.N., MSN, FACHE
Executive Vice President and Chief Operating Officer, Lehigh Valley Hospital–Muhlenberg, Bethlehem, PA, p. A529
Executive Vice President and Chief Operating Officer, Lehigh Valley Hospital, Allentown, PA, p. A528

CAPUANO, Tony, Chief Operating Officer, Saint Francis Hospital Muskogee, Muskogee, OK, p. A511

CAPUTO, Louis, Chief Executive Officer, Tristar Stonecrest Medical Center, Smyrna, TN, p. A589

CAPUTO, Michael, Chief Information Officer, Musc Medical Center Of Medical University Of South Carolina, Charleston, SC, p. A559

CARABALLO, Amanda, Nursing Director, Hospital De La Concepcion, San German, PR, p. A725

CARACCIOLO, Kevin, Chief Human Resources Officer, Palm Beach Gardens Medical Center, Palm Beach Gardens, FL, p. A138

CARACCIOLO, Mary Jo, Human Resource Director, Wellington Regional Medical Center, Wellington, FL, p. A147

CARALIS, George P, Interim Chief Executive Officer, Suny Downstate Medical Center University Hospital, New Rochelle, NY, p. A447

CARBALLO, Francisco R. M.D., Medical Director, Hospital Hima De Humacao, Humacao, PR, p. A723

CARBONE, Davide M., FACHE, Chief Executive Officer, Osceola Regional Medical Center, Kissimmee, FL, p. A129

CARBONE, Dominick M.D., Chief of Staff, Hugh Chatham Memorial Hospital, Elkin, NC, p. A462

CARD, Dean
Chief Financial Officer, Kindred Hospital South Florida–Fort Lauderdale, Fort Lauderdale, FL, p. A125
Chief Financial Officer, Kindred Hospital The Palm Beaches, Riviera Beach, FL, p. A140

CARD, Edwin, President Medical Staff, Mcdonough District Hospital, Macomb, IL, p. A192

CARD, Mike, Chief Information Officer, Audubon County Memorial Hospital, Audubon, IA, p. A222

CARDA, Greg, Vice President Finance, Missouri Delta Medical Center, Sikeston, MO, p. A379

CARDALI, Paul M.D., Chief of Staff, Lakeway Regional Hospital, Morristown, TN, p. A585

CARDELL, Melinda H.
Interim Chief Information Officer, Roper St. Francis Mount Pleasant Hospital, Mount Pleasant, SC, p. A564
Interim Vice President and Chief Information Officer, Roper St. Francis, Charleston, SC, p. A559

CARDENAS, Carlos, M.D., Chief Administrative Officer, Doctor's Hospital At Renaissance, Edinburg, TX, p. A610

CARDENAS, Lydia, Director Human Resources, River Crest Hospital, San Angelo, TX, p. A641

CARDENAS, Mark, Director Plant Operations, Vibra Hospital Of Northern California, Redding, CA, p. A81

CARDENAS, Mitzi
Chief Information Officer, Truman Medical Center–Hospital Hill, Kansas City, MO, p. A371
Chief Information Officer, Truman Medical Center–Lakewood, Kansas City, MO, p. A371

CARDIFF, Michael, Systems Supervisor, Abrom Kaplan Memorial Hospital, Kaplan, LA, p. A277

CARDINAL, Joyce, Chief Nursing Executive, Jefferson Healthcare, Port Townsend, WA, p. A684

CARDLE, Lori, Senior Vice President, Chief Operating Officer, Valley Presbyterian Hospital, Los Angeles, CA, p. A72

CARDWELL, Marian, Chief Financial Officer, Potomac Valley Hospital, Keyser, WV, p. A693

CAREY, Ann
Chief Information Officer, St. Vincent's Medical Center Southside, Jacksonville, FL, p. A128
Vice President and Chief Information Officer, St. Vincent's Medical Center Riverside, Jacksonville, FL, p. A128

CAREY, Calvin, Chief Financial Officer, Summit Medical Center, Casper, WY, p. A717

CAREY, Eric R, Vice President Information Systems and Chief Information Officer, Valley Hospital, Ridgewood, NJ, p. A420

CAREY, Jeannie R.N., Director Patient Care, Perry Memorial Hospital, Perry, OK, p. A514

CAREY, Robin, Director of Nursing, Jasper Memorial Hospital, Monticello, GA, p. A162

CARGONARA, Douglas Ph.D., Chief Information Officer, Pilgrim Psychiatric Center, Brentwood, NY, p. A432

CARIGSON, John, Chief Financial Officer, Covenant Specialty Hospital, Lubbock, TX, p. A630

CARIKER, Kelly, Chief Information Officer, North Valley Hospital, Tonasket, WA, p. A688

CARLE, Chris, Senior Vice President and Chief Operating Officer, St. Elizabeth Florence, Florence, KY, p. A258

CARLETON, David
Chief Information Officer, Heritage Valley Health System, Beaver, PA, p. A529
Chief Information Officer, Sewickley Valley Hospital, (A Division Of Valley Medical Facilities), Sewickley, PA, p. A550

CARLINO, Tracy R.N., Chief Nursing Officer, Virtua Marlton, Marlton, NJ, p. A416

CARLISLE, Charles, Director, East Mississippi State Hospital, Meridian, MS, p. A359

CARLISLE, Sandy, Manager Human Resources, Holzer Medical Center – Jackson, Jackson, OH, p. A492

CARLOCK, Carey, Chief Executive Officer, Riveredge Hospital, Forest Park, IL, p. A188

CARLOS, Ilona M.D., President Medical Staff, Thorek Memorial Hospital, Chicago, IL, p. A184

CARLSON, Bev, Chief Financial Officer, Delta County Memorial Hospital, Delta, CO, p. A100

CARLSON, Brian J., FACHE
Chief Executive Officer, Sanford Medical Center Thief River Falls, Thief River Falls, MN, p. A349

CARSON, Carole, Director of Nursing Operations, Rehabilitation Hospital Of Southern New Mexico, Las Cruces, NM, p. A427

CARSON, Debbie, Director Human Resources, Promise Hospital Of Vicksburg, Vicksburg, MS, p. A362

CARSON, Joe, Director Human Resources, Glen Oaks Hospital, Greenville, TX, p. A617

CARSON, Kara Jo, Chief Financial Officer, Pinckneyville Community Hospital, Pinckneyville, IL, p. A198

CARSON, Mitchell C., President and Chief Executive Officer, Longmont United Hospital, Longmont, CO, p. A105

CARSTENS, Cynthia L., R.N., President and Chief Executive Officer, Stewart Memorial Community Hospital, Lake City, IA, p. A230

CARSTENSEN, Karla, Director Patient Care, Avera Dells Area Hospital, Dell Rapids, SD, p. A569

CARTAGENA, Maria M.D., Chief Medical Officer, Brylin Hospitals, Buffalo, NY, p. A432

CARTER, Barbara, Chief Nursing Officer, Cimarron Memorial Hospital, Boise City, OK, p. A505

CARTER, Billie, Chief Operating Officer and Assistant Administrator, Stonewall Memorial Hospital, Aspermont, TX, p. A594

CARTER, Charla, Human Resource Officer, Uvalde Memorial Hospital, Uvalde, TX, p. A651

CARTER, Christen, Director Public Relations, Roosevelt Warm Springs Rehabilitation Hospital – Rehab, Warm Springs, GA, p. A167

CARTER, D. Montez., President, St. Mary's Good Samaritan Hospital, Greensboro, GA, p. A158

CARTER, Dennis M.D., Chief of Staff, Eastern Oklahoma Medical Center, Poteau, OK, p. A514

CARTER, Donna MSN, R.N., Chief Nursing Officer, Minden Medical Center, Minden, LA, p. A281

CARTER, Douglas S M.D., Vice President and Chief Medical Officer, Major Hospital, Shelbyville, IN, p. A219

CARTER, Frank, Chief Financial Officer, Cornerstone Hospital Of Huntington, Huntington, WV, p. A692

CARTER, Gary L M.D., Vice President and Chief Medical Officer, North Kansas City Hospital, North Kansas City, MO, p. A374

CARTER, Gregory M.D., Chief Medical Officer, St. Luke's Rehabilitation Institute, Spokane, WA, p. A687

CARTER, Jessica Y, Chief Financial Officer, Crisp Regional Hospital, Cordele, GA, p. A155

CARTER, Jim, Chief Operating Officer, Grady General Hospital, Cairo, GA, p. A153

CARTER, Josh, Chief Executive Officer, Memphis Mental Health Institute, Memphis, TN, p. A584

CARTER, Leonard M, Chief Human Resources Officer, FHN Memorial Hospital, Freeport, IL, p. A188

CARTER, Leonard, Campus Administrator, South Georgia Medical Center, Valdosta, GA, p. A166

CARTER, Leslia, Administrator, North Mississippi Medical Center–Pontotoc, Pontotoc, MS, p. A360

CARTER, Lisa, Chief Executive Officer, Johnson City Medical Center, Johnson City, TN, p. A581

CARTER, Malinda Yvonne, Vice President Human Resources, Saint Anthony Hospital, Chicago, IL, p. A183

CARTER, Marcia, Director Human Resources, Bluegrass Community Hospital, Versailles, KY, p. A268

CARTER, Michael, M.D.
Chief Medical Officer, Houston County Community Hospital, Erin, TN, p. A578
Administrator Information Technology, Northwest Ohio Psychiatric Hospital, Toledo, OH, p. A500

CARTER, Misty, Vice President Human Resources and Ancillary Services, Great Plains Regional Medical Center, Elk City, OK, p. A507

CARTER, Priscilla, Chief Financial Officer, Mesa Hills Specialty Hospital, El Paso, TX, p. A611

CARTER, Rebecca W., MSN, R.N., FACHE, Chief Executive Officer and Chief Nursing Officer, Blue Ridge Regional Hospital, Spruce Pine, NC, p. A471

CARTER, Rebecca W MSN, R.N., FACHE, Chief Executive Officer and Chief Nursing Officer, Blue Ridge Regional Hospital, Spruce Pine, NC, p. A471

CARTER, Richard, M.D.
Chief Medical Director, Hamilton County Hospital, Syracuse, KS, p. A252
Chief of Staff, Tennova Healthcare–Jefferson Memorial Hospital, Jefferson City, TN, p. A580
District Chief Executive Officer, Hunt Regional Medical Center, Greenville, TX, p. A617

CARTER, Shanti, Chief Executive Officer, Kingwood Pines Hospital, Kingwood, TX, p. A627

CARTER, Steve, Chief Information Officer, Mon Health Medical Center, Morgantown, WV, p. A694

CARTER, Teresa, Vice President Patient Care Services, Onecore Health, Oklahoma City, OK, p. A513

CARTER, Theodora, Administrative Director Human Resources, Hackensack Meridian Health Pascack Valley Medical Center, Westwood, NJ, p. A423

CARTER, Vickie, Information Systems Director, Sumner Regional Medical Center, Gallatin, TN, p. A579

CARTWRIGHT, Bryan, Chief Information Technology Officer, Missouri River Medical Center, Fort Benton, MT, p. A384

CARTWRIGHT, David A, Vice President Finance and Support Services, Advocate Condell Medical Center, Libertyville, IL, p. A192

CARTWRIGHT, David, Director Management Information Systems, Sovah Health–Danville, Danville, VA, p. A666

CARTWRIGHT, Debra
Chief Financial Officer, St. Francis Health, Topeka, KS, p. A252
Chief Financial Officer, St. Joseph Medical Center, Kansas City, MO, p. A371

CARUCCI, Dean, Chief Executive Officer, Portsmouth Regional Hospital, Portsmouth, NH, p. A410

CARUGATI, Diane, Chief Operating Officer, Friends Hospital, Philadelphia, PA, p. A544

CARUSO, Diane M MSN, Chief Nursing Officer, Healthsouth Scottsdale Rehabilitation Hospital, Scottsdale, AZ, p. A35

CARUSO, DonM.D.
Chief Medical Officer, Cheshire Medical Center, Keene, NH, p. A408
Chief Executive Officer and President, Cheshire Medical Center, Keene, NH, p. A408

CARUSO, Maria, Chief Financial Officer, Venice Regional Bayfront Health, Venice, FL, p. A146

CARVER, Carol MSN, R.N., Vice President Patient Services, Clarity Child Guidance Center, San Antonio, TX, p. A642

CARVER, Christy, R.N., Chief Executive Officer, Lifecare Hospitals Of Dallas, Dallas, TX, p. A605

CARVER, Deborah, Chief Nursing Officer, Providence Tarzana Medical Center, Los Angeles, CA, p. A71

CARVETH, Barbara, Chief Financial Officer, University Of Colorado Hospital, Aurora, CO, p. A98

CARVOLTH, Richard M.D., Chief Medical Officer, Santa Rosa Memorial Hospital, Santa Rosa, CA, p. A91

CARYER, Steve, Chief Financial Officer, Community Memorial Hospital, Hicksville, OH, p. A492

CARYNSKI, Paula A., MS, R.N., President, OSF Saint Anthony Medical Center, Rockford, IL, p. A199

CASABONA, Nicholas, Chief Information Officer, NYU Winthrop Hospital, Mineola, NY, p. A439

CASANO, Jayleen Ph.D., FACHE, Chief Operations and Nursing Officer, Abrazo Central Campus, Phoenix, AZ, p. A32

CASANOVA, Robert Bernier, Chief Financial Officer, Industrial Hospital, San Juan, PR, p. A726

CASAREZ, Margaret, Chief Financial Officer, San Joaquin Valley Rehabilitation Hospital, Fresno, CA, p. A61

CASAREZ, Teresa, Director Human Resources, New Mexico Rehabilitation Center, Roswell, NM, p. A428

CASDORPH, Michael, Chief Executive Officer, Highland–Clarksburg Hospital, Clarksburg, WV, p. A691

CASE, Cliff, Chief Financial Officer, Mineral Community Hospital, Superior, MT, p. A388

CASE, Ed, Executive Vice President and Chief Financial Officer, Shirley Ryan Abilitylab, Chicago, IL, p. A183

CASE, Harvey, President, Vidant Beaufort Hospital, Washington, NC, p. A472

CASE, Linda, Administrator, Hillside Rehabilitation Hospital, Warren, OH, p. A501

CASE, Matthew, MSC, USN, Executive Officer, Naval Medical Center, Portsmouth, VA, p. A673

CASERTA, Kevin, M.D.
Chief Medical Officer, Providence Centralia Hospital, Centralia, WA, p. A679
Chief Medical Officer, Providence St. Peter Hospital, Olympia, WA, p. A683

CASEY, Candy J., R.N., MS, President and Chief Executive Officer, Columbia Center Birth Hospital, Mequon, WI, p. A707

CASEY, Dina, Human Resources Officer, Lane County Hospital, Dighton, KS, p. A240

CASEY, Joseph, Chief Financial Officer, Sturdy Memorial Hospital, Attleboro, MA, p. A302

CASEY, Kevin M.D., Chief Clinical Officer, St. Rita's Medical Center, Lima, OH, p. A493

CASEY, Rick D.O., Chief Medical Staff, Cedar County Memorial Hospital, El Dorado Springs, MO, p. A367

CASH, Jeff, Senior Vice President and Chief Information Officer, Mercy Medical Center, Cedar Rapids, Iowa, Cedar Rapids, IA, p. A223

CASH, Jordan , President, Integris Southwest Medical Center, Oklahoma City, OK, p. B69

CASH, Jordan, President, Integris Southwest Medical Center, Oklahoma City, OK, p. A512

CASHEN CHACON, Chanda, Executive Vice President and Chief Operating Officer, Arkansas Children's Hospital, Little Rock, AR, p. A45

CASHMAN, Tim, Chief Financial Officer, Estes Park Medical Center, Estes Park, CO, p. A102

CASHWELL, David, Chief Executive Officer, Healthsouth Rehabilitation Hospital Of Virginia, Richmond, VA, p. A673

CASIANO, Manuel M.D., Senior Vice President Medical Affairs, Frederick Regional Health System, Frederick, MD, p. A298

CASILLAS, Rosalind C, Chief Nursing Officer, Lawrence Memorial Hospital, Walnut Ridge, AR, p. A50

CASMER, Benjamin FACHE, Chief Operating Officer, Bay Area Regional Medical Center, Webster, TX, p. A653

CASNER, Trina, President and Chief Executive Officer, Pana Community Hospital, Pana, IL, p. A196

CASOLA, Frances, Senior Vice President Operations, Saint Joseph's Medical Center, Yonkers, NY, p. A456

CASON, Amy MSN, Chief Nursing Officer, Tristar Stonecrest Medical Center, Smyrna, TN, p. A589

CASON, Cathy, Chief Financial Officer, Jeff Davis Hospital, Hazlehurst, GA, p. A158

CASON, Diane, Chief Information Officer, Controller and Director Human Resources, Lake Butler Hospital Hand Surgery Center, Lake Butler, FL, p. A129

CASON, Randall R., FACHE, Senior Administrator, Via Christi Hospital Pittsburg, Pittsburg, KS, p. A250

CASON, Will, Vice President Human Resources, St. Rita's Medical Center, Lima, OH, p. A493

CASPER, Rylee R.N., Chief Nursing Officer, Newman Memorial Hospital, Shattuck, OK, p. A515

CASPERSON, William M.D., Vice President Medical Affairs, Memorial Hospital, Belleville, IL, p. A178

CASS, Julene J R.N., Director of Nursing, Community Memorial Hospital, Redfield, SD, p. A572

CASS, Paul D.O., Chief Medical & Clinical Integration Officer, Wentworth–Douglass Hospital, Dover, NH, p. A407

CASSADY, Perry M.D., Medical Director, Physicians' Medical Center, New Albany, IN, p. A217

CASSAGNE, Nancy R., FACHE, Chief Executive Officer, West Jefferson Medical Center, Marrero, LA, p. A281

CASSEDY, Ryan, Chief Executive Officer, Vibra Hospital Of Fort Wayne, Fort Wayne, IN, p. A208

CASSEL, Asenath, Chief Nursing Officer, Wellington Regional Medical Center, Wellington, FL, p. A147

CASSEL, Kari
Senior Vice President and Chief Information Officer, Uf Health Jacksonville, Jacksonville, FL, p. A128
Senior Vice President and Chief Information Officer, Uf Health Shands Hospital, Gainesville, FL, p. A126

CASSELL, Sally, Manager Human Resources, Ozark Health Medical Center, Clinton, AR, p. A41

CASSELS, William H., Administrator, Dch Regional Medical Center, Tuscaloosa, AL, p. A23

CASSIDAY, Cheryl R.N., Director of Nursing, Chadron Community Hospital And Health Services, Chadron, NE, p. A392

CASSIDY, Donna, Chief Nursing Executive, Bronson South Haven Hospital, South Haven, MI, p. A331

CASSIDY, Doris B, Associate Director, Veterans Health Care System Of The Ozarks, Fayetteville, AR, p. A43

CASSIDY, John W., M.D., President, Chief Executive Officer and Chief Medical Officer, Nexus Health Systems, Houston, TX, p. B90

CASSIDY, Joseph J, Vice President, Holy Redeemer Hospital, Meadowbrook, PA, p. A540

CASSLE, Susie R.N., MSN, Vice President Nursing Services, Hendrick Health System, Abilene, TX, p. A591

CASTALDO, Jennifer R.N., Vice President, Patient Care and Chief Nursing Officer, Henry Mayo Newhall Hospital, Valencia, CA, p. A95

CASTANEDA, Edmundo
President, Mercy General Hospital, Sacramento, CA, p. A83
President, Mercy Hospital Of Folsom, Folsom, CA, p. A59

CASTANEDA, Marissa, Chief Operating Officer and Director Marketing, Doctor's Hospital At Renaissance, Edinburg, TX, p. A610

CASTANEDA, Trevor, Chief Executive Officer, Tennova Newport Medical Center, Newport, TN, p. A587

CASTEEL, Brian, Information Technology Technician, Hardin County General Hospital, Rosiclare, IL, p. A199

CASTEEL, Karen, Director Human Resources, Palms Of Pasadena Hospital, Saint Petersburg, FL, p. A141

CASTEEL, Lisa, Assistant Administrator and Chief Financial Officer, Henry County Medical Center, Paris, TN, p. A588

CASTEEL, Rick
Vice President Management Information Systems and Chief Information Officer, University Of Maryland Harford Memorial Hospital, Havre De Grace, MD, p. A299

Vice President Management Information Systems and Chief Information Officer, University Of Maryland Upper Chesapeake Medical Center, Bel Air, MD, p. A296

CASTILLO, Carol, Medical Director, Sonoma Developmental Center, Eldridge, CA, p. A58

CASTILLO, Dan A., FACHE, Chief Executive Officer, Lac+Usc Medical Center, Los Angeles, CA, p. A69

CASTILLO, Edgar, Chief Financial Officer, Larkin Community Hospital, South Miami, FL, p. A143

CASTILLO, Paul, Chief Financial Officer, Michigan Medicine, Ann Arbor, MI, p. A314

CASTILLO, Ralph A., CPA, Chief Executive Officer, Morgan Memorial Hospital, Madison, GA, p. A161

CASTILLO, Randall, Vice President, Operations, Mercy Hospital Of Folsom, Folsom, CA, p. A59

CASTILLO, Renee, Chief Nursing Officer, Plains Memorial Hospital, Dimmitt, TX, p. A609

CASTILLO, Rita S R.N., Chief Quality Officer and Risk Management, Methodist Hospital South, Jourdanton, TX, p. A625

CASTLE, Bill, Chief Financial Officer, Huron Medical Center, Bad Axe, MI, p. A314

CASTLE, Dorothy, Director Human Resources, North Mississippi Medical Center–Eupora, Eupora, MS, p. A354

CASTLE, Eric, Director Information Services, Lawnwood Regional Medical Center & Heart Institute, Fort Pierce, FL, p. A125

CASTLE, Samantha, Chief Executive Officer, University Behavioral Health Of Denton, Denton, TX, p. A608

CASTLEBERRY, Ginger, Corporate Risk Manager, Quality and Patient Safety, Valir Rehabilitation Hospital, Oklahoma City, OK, p. A514

CASTLEMAN, Pam MSN, Chief Nursing Officer, Regional One Health, Memphis, TN, p. A585

CASTON, David, Chief Executive Officer, Reeves Memorial Medical Center, Bernice, LA, p. A271

CASTOR, Susan, Chief Nursing Officer, Healthsouth Rehabilitation Hospital Of Toms River, Toms River, NJ, p. A421

CASTRO, Ana, Director Information Technology, Gerald Champion Regional Medical Center, Alamogordo, NM, p. A424

CASTRO, Craig
Chief Executive Officer, Clovis Community Medical Center, Clovis, CA, p. A56
Chief Information Officer, Community Regional Medical Center, Fresno, CA, p. A60

CASTRO, Jill M.D., Medical Director, Healthsouth Rehabilitation Hospital Of Littleton, Littleton, CO, p. A105

CASTRO, Pete D.O., Chief of Staff, Heart Of Texas Memorial Hospital, Brady, TX, p. A599

CASTRO, Richard
Chief Executive Officer, Ahmc Anaheim Regional Medical Center, Anaheim, CA, p. A51
Chief Executive Officer, Whittier Hospital Medical Center, Whittier, CA, p. A97

CASTRODALE, Andrew M.D., Chief Medical Officer, Coulee Medical Center, Grand Coulee, WA, p. A681

CASTRONUEVO, Joseph, Director Information Management, St. Lawrence Rehabilitation Center, Lawrenceville, NJ, p. A415

CASWELL, Lori, Director Information Technology, Good Samaritan Medical Center, Brockton, MA, p. A304

CASWELL, Penny, Director of Nursing, Bloomington Meadows Hospital, Bloomington, IN, p. A204

CATALA, Lucy, Vice President Finance, Baylor All Saints Medical Center At Fort Worth, Fort Worth, TX, p. A613

CATALDO, Linda, Human Resources Secretary, Prevost Memorial Hospital, Donaldsonville, LA, p. A274

CATALDO, Vincent A., Administrator, Prevost Memorial Hospital, Donaldsonville, LA, p. A274

CATALIOTTI, Palmira, Senior Vice President, Chief Financial Officer and Treasurer, NYU Winthrop Hospital, Mineola, NY, p. A439

CATANIA, Joseph M., Chief Executive Officer, St. Anthony's Rehabilitation Hospital, Lauderdale Lakes, FL, p. A130

CATAUDELLA, Mary, Corporate Director Human Resources, Jersey City Medical Center, Jersey City, NJ, p. A415

CATENA, Cornelio R., President and Chief Executive Officer, Wilkes–Barre General Hospital, Wilkes, PA, p. A554

CATES, Brett, Director Information Services, Weatherford Regional Medical Center, Weatherford, TX, p. A653

CATES, Jessica, Fiscal Manager, Western State Hospital, Hopkinsville, KY, p. A260

CATES, Rodney, Senior Vice President Human Resources, Covenant Children's Hospital, Lubbock, TX, p. A630

CATHEY, Michele, Interim Chief Financial officer, Martin County Hospital District, Stanton, TX, p. A646

CATHEY, Walt, Chief Executive Officer, Covenant Medical Center, Lubbock, TX, p. A630

CATINO, Anne MS, R.N., Vice President and Chief Nursing Officer, Holy Redeemer Hospital, Meadowbrook, PA, p. A540

CATTALANI, Mark M.D., Clinical Director, Richard H. Hutchings Psychiatric Center, Syracuse, NY, p. A453

CATTELL, JoAnne, Chief Nursing Officer, St. Petersburg General Hospital, Saint Petersburg, FL, p. A142

CATTELL, Nancy E, Vice President Human Resources, Liberty Hospital, Liberty, MO, p. A372

CATTON, Carolyn, Interim Chief Patient Care Officer, Beaver Dam Community Hospitals, Beaver Dam, WI, p. A699

CATTON, Jane, R.N.
Chief Operating Officer and Chief Nursing Officer, Northwestern Medical Center, Saint Albans, VT, p. A663
Chief Operating Officer and Chief Nursing Officer, Northwestern Medical Center, Saint Albans, VT, p. A663

CAUDILL, Allan M.D., Chief of Staff, Bronson South Haven Hospital, South Haven, MI, p. A331

CAUDILL, David, Administrator, Grisell Memorial Hospital District One, Ransom, KS, p. A250

CAUGHELL, David M.D., Chief of Staff, Jane Phillips Nowata Health Center, Nowata, OK, p. A511

CAUGHEY, Michelle M.D., Physician In Chief, Kaiser Permanente South San Francisco, South San Francisco, CA, p. A92

CAUGHMAN, Katie
Chief Financial Officer, St. John Broken Arrow, Broken Arrow, OK, p. A505
Chief Financial Officer, St. John Owasso, Owasso, OK, p. A514

CAUSEY, Cynthia, Associate Administrator Human and Mission Services, Mcleod Medical Center Dillon, Dillon, SC, p. A561

CAUSEY, Jack M., Chief Executive Officer, Leesville Rehabilitation Hospital, Leesville, LA, p. A280

CAUSEY, Jennifer, Chief Executive Officer, Select Specialty Hospital–Nashville, Nashville, TN, p. A587

CAUWENBERG, Jude M.D., Chief of Staff, Ashtabula County Medical Center, Ashtabula, OH, p. A480

CAVA, Anthony V., President, Robert Wood Johnson University Hospital Somerset, Somerset, NJ, p. A420

CAVANAUGH, Cheryl, Senior Director Human Resources, Valley Regional Hospital, Claremont, NH, p. A407

CAVANAUGH, Paul, Director Human Resources, Friends Hospital, Philadelphia, PA, p. A544

CAVAZOS, David–Paul, Chief Executive Officer, Republic County Hospital, Belleville, KS, p. A238

CAVE, Chuck CPA, Chief Financial Officer, Wilson N. Jones Regional Medical Center, Sherman, TX, p. A645

CAVE, Rogelio M.D., Medical Director, Roseland Community Hospital, Chicago, IL, p. A183

CAVELL, Richard M.D., Medical Director, University Health Conway, Monroe, LA, p. A281

CAVEN, Tom M.D., Vice President, Medical Director, Dell Seton Medical Center At The University Of Texas, Austin, TX, p. A595

CAVENEY, Timothy, President, South Shore Hospital, Chicago, IL, p. A184

CAVERNO, John
Chief Human Resources Officer, Excela Frick Hospital, Mount Pleasant, PA, p. A541
Chief Human Resources Officer, Excela Health Westmoreland Hospital, Greensburg, PA, p. A535

CAWLEY, Karen, Chief Executive Officer, Curahealth Phoenix, Phoenix, AZ, p. A33

CAWLEY, Patrick J., M.D., Chief Executive Officer, MUSC Health and Vice President for Health Affairs, University, Musc Medical Center Of Medical University Of South Carolina, Charleston, SC, p. A559

CAWLEY, Patrick J, M.D., Chief Executive Officer, MUSC Health and Vice President for Health Affairs, University, Musc Medical Center Of Medical University Of South Carolina, Charleston, SC, p. A559

CAWOOD, Marina, Administrative Assistant, Middlesboro Arh Hospital, Middlesboro, KY, p. A264

CAYER, Gerald, Chief Executive Officer, Lewis County General Hospital, Lowville, NY, p. A438

CAYTON, Mical, Area Information Officer, Kaiser Permanente Antioch Medical Center, Antioch, CA, p. A51

CAZARES, Erik, Chief Nursing Officer, The Hospitals Of Providence Sierra Campus, El Paso, TX, p. A611

CAZAYOUX, John, Chief Financial Officer, Pointe Coupee General Hospital, New Roads, LA, p. A283

CAZES, Anna Leah, Senior Vice President, Chief Operating Officer, Lake Charles Memorial Hospital, Lake Charles, LA, p. A279

CECAVA, Eric
Chief Operating Officer, Adena Medical Center, Chillicothe, OH, p. A483
Chief Operating Officer, Adena Pike Medical Center, Waverly, OH, p. A502

CECH, Bob, Regional Finance Officer, Presence Saints Mary & Elizabeth Medical Center, Chicago, IL, p. A183

CECIL, Bruce, Clinical Financial Officer, Fresno Surgical Hospital, Fresno, CA, p. A60

CECIL, Janell R.N., MSN, Senior Vice President and Chief Nursing Officer, University Of Tennessee Medical Center, Knoxville, TN, p. A582

CECIL, Jason, Vice President, Information, Capital Region Medical Center, Jefferson City, MO, p. A369

CECIL, Jon C
Chief Human Resource Officer, Cape Coral Hospital, Cape Coral, FL, p. A121
Chief Human Resource Officer, Gulf Coast Medical Center, Fort Myers, FL, p. A125
Chief Human Resource Officer, Lee Memorial Hospital, Fort Myers, FL, p. A125

CEDENO LLORENS, Arturo M.D., Medical Director, Hospital Buen Samaritano, Aguadilla, PR, p. A721

CEDOTAL, Kiley P., FACHE
Chief Executive Officer, Promise Hospital Baton Rouge – Main Campus, Baton Rouge, LA, p. A271
Chief Executive Officer, Promise Hospital Of Baton Rouge – Mid–City Campus, Baton Rouge, LA, p. A271
Chief Executive Officer, Promise Hospital Of Baton Rouge – Ochsner Campus, Baton Rouge, LA, p. A271

CEHELYK, Bohdan M.D., Chief Medical Officer, East Mountain Hospital, Belle Mead, NJ, p. A411

CELLA, Ann S R.N., Senior Vice President, Patient Care Services, St. Francis Hospital, The Heart Center, Roslyn, NY, p. A451

CELLA, Robert, M.D.
Chief Medical Officer, Albany Memorial Hospital, Albany, NY, p. A430
Chief Medical Officer, St. Peter's Hospital, Albany, NY, p. A430

CELSOR, Reba, Chief Executive Officer, Tennova Healthcare Dyersburg Regional Medical Center, Dyersburg, TN, p. A578

CELUCH, Paul
Chief Human Resource Officer, East Los Angeles Doctors Hospital, Los Angeles, CA, p. A68
Corporate Human Resources Director, Community Hospital Of Huntington Park, Huntington Park, CA, p. A63

CEMATE, David D FACHE, Senior Vice President and Chief Operating Officer, Mercy Medical Center, Canton, OH, p. A482

CEMENO, Michael J, Chief Information Officer, Waterbury Hospital, Waterbury, CT, p. A114

CENTENO, Robert M.D., Chief Medical Officer, Governor Juan F. Luis Hospital, Christiansted, VI, p. A727

CEPEDA, Aaron, Director Nursing Operations, South Texas Rehabilitation Hospital, Brownsville, TX, p. A599

CERALDI, Christopher M.D., Chief of Staff, Abbeville Area Medical Center, Abbeville, SC, p. A558

CERCEO, Richard, Executive Vice President and Chief Operating Officer, Mercy Hospital And Medical Center, Chicago, IL, p. A182

CERIMELE, Joseph D.O., Medical Director, Hillside Rehabilitation Hospital, Warren, OH, p. A501

CERIMELE, Leeann, Vice President Human Resources, West Virginia University Hospitals, Morgantown, WV, p. A694

CERISE, Fred, M.D., Chief Executive Officer, Parkland Health & Hospital System, Dallas, TX, p. A606

CERNAVA, Joanne, Director Human Resources, Kessler Marlton Rehabilitation, Marlton, NJ, p. A416

CERNOCH, Desiree, Director of Nurses, El Campo Memorial Hospital, El Campo, TX, p. A610

CERONE, Shane, Interim President and Chief Executive Officer, Mercy Iowa City, Iowa City, IA, p. A229

CERRA, Jane, Market Nurse Executive and Chief Nursing Officer, Select Specialty Hospital–Milwaukee, Milwaukee, WI, p. A708

CERULLO, Timothy J., Chief Executive Officer, Bayfront Health Port Charlotte, Port Charlotte, FL, p. A140

CERVANTES, Jason
Chief Information Officer, East Los Angeles Doctors Hospital, Los Angeles, CA, p. A68
Corporate Chief Information Officer, Community Hospital Of Huntington Park, Huntington Park, CA, p. A63

CERVINO, Noel A., President and Chief Executive Officer, University Of Maryland Charles Regional Medical Center, La Plata, MD, p. A299

CESAREZ, Margaret, Chief Financial Officer, Gateway Rehabilitation Hospital, Florence, KY, p. A258

CESCA, Ken, Vice President Human Resources, Midstate Medical Center, Meriden, CT, p. A111

CESKO, David M.D., Chief of Staff, Memorial Hospital Of Carbon County, Rawlins, WY, p. A719

CHA BRIDIER, Vicky, Chief Operating Officer, College Station Medical Center, College Station, TX, p. A602

CHABALOWSKI, Edward, Chief Financial Officer, Geisinger–Community Medical Center, Scranton, PA, p. A550

CHABOT, Judy, Chief Nursing Officer, Los Alamitos Medical Center, Los Alamitos, CA, p. A67

CHACKO, Benson, Chief Operating Officer, The Hospitals Of Providence Sierra Campus, El Paso, TX, p. A611

CHACON, Barbara, Chief Financial Officer, The Core Institute Specialty Hospital, Phoenix, AZ, p. A34

CHADEK, Richard M.D., Clinical Director, Lawton Indian Hospital, Lawton, OK, p. A509

CHADHA, Beenu, Chief Financial Officer, San Ramon Regional Medical Center, San Ramon, CA, p. A90

CHADOCK, Brandon
Director of Operations, Sistersville General Hospital, Sistersville, WV, p. A696
Interim Chief Executive Officer, Sistersville General Hospital, Sistersville, WV, p. A696

CHADWICK, Maureen C R.N., Chief Nursing Officer, Saint Vincent Hospital, Erie, PA, p. A534

CHADWICK, Sharon M, Director Human Resources, Abrazo Arrowhead Campus, Glendale, AZ, p. A30

CHAFFIN, Linda, Director Medical Review, Baptist Memorial Hospital–Booneville, Booneville, MS, p. A352

CHAHANOVICH, Jen, President and Chief Executive Officer, Wilcox Medical Center, Lihue, HI, p. A170

CHALFANT, Cathie, Director Human Resources, Harrison County Community Hospital, Bethany, MO, p. A364

CHALIAN, Christopher M.D., Medical Director, Casa Colina Hospital And Health Systems, Pomona, CA, p. A80

CHALK, Jackie, Director Human Resources, Healthsouth Rehabilitation Hospital, Largo, FL, p. A130

CHALKE, Dennis, Senior Vice President, Chief Financial Officer and Treasurer, Baystate Medical Center, Springfield, MA, p. A311

CHALONER, Robert S, Chief Administrative Officer, Stony Brook University Hospital, Stony Brook, NY, p. A453

CHALPHANT, Steve, Director Information Management Service Line, Wm. Jennings Bryan Dorn Veterans Affairs Medical Center, Columbia, SC, p. A561

CHALTRY, Richard M.D., Director Medical Staff, Aspirus Ontonagon Hospital, Inc., Ontonagon, MI, p. A327

CHALTRY, William, Chief Nursing Officer, New Mexico Rehabilitation Center, Roswell, NM, p. A428

CHALUPA, Rebecca MSN, R.N., Chief Nursing Officer, Houston Methodist San Jacinto Hospital, Baytown, TX, p. A597

CHAMBERLIN, Kim, Vice President Patient Services and Chief Nursing Officer, Mercy Medical Center–North Iowa, Mason City, IA, p. A231

CHAMBERS, Bradley
President and Senior Vice President, MedStar Health, Medstar Good Samaritan Hospital, Baltimore, MD, p. A295
President, Medstar Union Memorial Hospital, Baltimore, MD, p. A295

CHAMBERS, Gwen, Executive Director Human Resources, Methodist Hospital Of Southern California, Arcadia, CA, p. A52

CHAMBERS, Matthew
Chief Information Officer, Baylor Scott & White Medical Center – Round Rock, Round Rock, TX, p. A640
Chief Information Officer, Scott & White Medical Center – Temple, Temple, TX, p. A648

CHAMBERS, Regina, Vice President Human Resource, Rome Memorial Hospital, Rome, NY, p. A451

CHAMBLEE, Jane, Manager Human Resources, North Mississippi Medical Center–Iuka, Iuka, MS, p. A356

CHAMBLESS, Lesley
Assistant Vice President Human Resources, Carolinas Healthcare System Lincoln, Lincolnton, NC, p. A466
Assistant Vice President Workforce Relations, Carolinas Healthcare System Northeast, Concord, NC, p. A460

CHAMBLISS, James W, Chief of Staff, Magnolia Regional Medical Center, Magnolia, AR, p. A46

CHAMPAGNE, Charles D., Chief Financial Officer, Northeast Rehabilitation Hospital, Salem, NH, p. A410

CHAMPAGNE, Laurie, Controller, Curahealth New Orleans, New Orleans, LA, p. A282

CHAMPAVANNARATH, Vilakon, Director Information Systems, Bartow Regional Medical Center, Bartow, FL, p. A119

CHAMPION, Joshua I, Director, Florida Hospital–Flagler, Palm Coast, FL, p. A138

CHAN, Eric, M.D., Chief Executive Officer, Surgery Specialty Hospitals Of America, Pasadena, TX, p. A637

CHAN, Fred, Chief Financial Officer, Intracare North Hospital, Houston, TX, p. A621

CHAN, Joyce, Chief Human Resources Officer, Centracare Health–Melrose, Melrose, MN, p. A343

CHAN, Thomas T, Chief Financial Officer, Meritus Medical Center, Hagerstown, MD, p. A299

CHANAA, Ziad M.D., Chief of Staff, Boone Memorial Hospital, Madison, WV, p. A693

CHANAGA, Luis, Chief Financial Officer, Grandview Medical Center, Dayton, OH, p. A489

CHANCE, Tammara D.O., Chief of Staff, Boone County Hospital, Boone, IA, p. A223

CHANCELLOR, Jayme, Chief Operating Officer, Northside Hospital, Saint Petersburg, FL, p. A141

CHAND, Parveen, Chief Operating Officer, Eskenazi Health, Indianapolis, IN, p. A211

CHANDLER, Aileen, Chief Nursing Officer, Ogallala Community Hospital, Ogallala, NE, p. A396

CHANDLER, Carla, Vice President and Chief Financial Officer, Emory University Hospital, Atlanta, GA, p. A150

CHANDLER, Christopher, Chief Executive Officer, Pioneer Community Hospital Of Aberdeen, Aberdeen, MS, p. A352

CHANDLER, Laurie
Chairman, Prairie Community Hospital, Terry, MT, p. A388
Financial Officer, Prairie Community Hospital, Terry, MT, p. A388

CHANDLER, Loren, President, Mount Sinai Hospital, Chicago, IL, p. A182

CHANDLER, Ryan
Chief Executive Officer, Midtown Medical Center West, Columbus, GA, p. A154
Interim Chief Executive Officer, Northside Medical Center, Columbus, GA, p. A155

CHANDLER, Ryan, President and Chief Executive Officer, Midtown Medical Center, Columbus, GA, p. A154

CHANDLER, Vincent, Director Information Services, Porterville Developmental Center, Porterville, CA, p. A80

CHANDLER, Wendy
Assistant Administrator Human Resources, Christus St. Patrick Hospital Of Lake Charles, Lake Charles, LA, p. A279
Regional Vice President Human Resources, Christus St. Frances Cabrini Hospital, Alexandria, LA, p. A269
Vice President Human Resources, Christus Health Shreveport–Bossier, Shreveport, LA, p. A285

CHANDRAN, Kutty M.D., Regional Medical Officer, Broward Health Coral Springs, Coral Springs, FL, p. A122

CHANDRASENA, Anita M.D., Vice President Medical Affairs, Sequoia Hospital, Redwood City, CA, p. A82

CHANDY, Joseph, Administrator, Methodist Hospital Of Chicago, Chicago, IL, p. A182

CHANEZ, Adolfo, Vice President Finance and Chief Financial Officer, Saddleback Memorial Medical Center, Laguna Hills, CA, p. A65

CHANG, Alex, Chief Operating Officer, Englewood Community Hospital, Englewood, FL, p. A124

CHANG, Jason, M.D.
Chief Medical Director, Rehabilitation Hospital Of The Pacific, Honolulu, HI, p. A169
Executive Vice President and Chief Operating Officer, The Queen's Medical Center, Honolulu, HI, p. A169

CHANG, Myrna, Chief Nursing Executive, Sutter Davis Hospital, Davis, CA, p. A57

CHANG, Sang–ick M.D., M.P.H., Chief Medical Officer, Highland Hospital, Oakland, CA, p. A77

CHANNELL, Lesley
Vice President Human Resources, Reston Hospital Center, Reston, VA, p. A673
Vice President Human Resources, Dominion Hospital, Falls Church, VA, p. A666

CHAPDELAINE, Debora R., Manager Information Technology, Aurora Medical Center, Kenosha, WI, p. A704

CHAPITAL, Alyssa B M.D., Medical Director, Mayo Clinic Hospital, Mayo Clinic Hospital, Phoenix, AZ, p. A33

CHAPLIN, Steven M.D., Medical Director, Kahi Mohala Behavioral Health, Ewa Beach, HI, p. A168

CHAPMAN, Bradley, President, Penn Highlands Elk, Saint Marys, PA, p. A549

CHAPMAN, Cully, Chief Financial Officer, Lutheran Hospital Of Indiana, Fort Wayne, IN, p. A208

CHAPMAN, Emily, Chief Medical Officer, Children's Hospitals And Clinics Of Minnesota, Minneapolis, MN, p. A343

CHAPMAN, Jeffrey M.D., Chief Medical Officer, Cheyenne Regional Medical Center, Cheyenne, WY, p. A717

CHAPMAN, Jon, Fiscal Officer, Western State Hospital, Staunton, VA, p. A676

CHAPMAN, Judy, Interim Director Information Systems, Lock Haven Hospital, Lock Haven, PA, p. A539

CHAPMAN, Karen, Director Human Resources, Chester Regional Medical Center, Chester, SC, p. A559

CHAPMAN, Kathleen Esq, Deputy Director, Patient Care Services, Va Portland Healthcare System, Portland, OR, p. A525

CHAPMAN, Kathy R.N., Chief Clinical Officer and Vice President of Patient Services, Allegan General Hospital, Allegan, MI, p. A314

CHAPMAN, Patrick
Assistant Vice President Operations, JFK Medical Center North Campus, West Palm Beach, FL, p. A147
Chief Executive Officer, Tippah County Hospital, Ripley, MS, p. A361

CHAPMAN, Rachel, Nurse Manager, Noland Hospital Birmingham, Birmingham, AL, p. A15

CHAPMAN, Rick, Chief Information Officer, Kindred Hospital North Florida, Green Cove Springs, FL, p. A126

CHAPMAN, Roland, Chief Information Officer, Northern Navajo Medical Center, Shiprock, NM, p. A428

CHAPMAN, Scott, Administrator, Manhattan Surgical, Manhattan, KS, p. A246

CHAPMAN, Teresa, Vice President Human Resources, Marianjoy Rehabilitation Hospital, Wheaton, IL, p. A202

CHAPMAN, Terina, Director of Nursing, Northern Utah Rehabilitation Hospital, South Ogden, UT, p. A661

CHAPPELL, Brandee, Director of Nursing, Lifecare Hospitals Of North Carolina, Rocky Mount, NC, p. A469

CHAPPELL, Robert M.D., Chief Medical Officer and Chief Quality Officer, Huntsville Hospital, Huntsville, AL, p. A19

CHAPPELL, Teresa, Chief Information Officer, Johnston Health, Smithfield, NC, p. A470

CHAPPLE, Albert J. R.N., Chief Clinical Officer, Kindred Rehabilitation Hospital Northeast Houston, Humble, TX, p. A624

CHAPPLE, Scott, Chief Operating Officer, Oroville Hospital, Oroville, CA, p. A78

CHARARA, Kassem, Chief Medical Officer, Beaumont Hospital – Taylor, Taylor, MI, p. A331

CHARDAVOYNE, Alan
Chief Financial Officer, Moses Ludington Hospital, Ticonderoga, NY, p. A454
Chief Financial Officer, The University Of Vermont Health Network Elizabethtown Community Hospital, Elizabethtown, NY, p. A435

CHARETTE, Deborah, Director of Nursing, East Mountain Hospital, Belle Mead, NJ, p. A411

CHARLAT, Richard A, Chief of Staff, Iowa City Veterans Affairs Health Care System, Iowa City, IA, p. A229

CHARLES, Charlotte, Director Acute Patient Services, Madison Community Hospital, Madison, SD, p. A570

CHARLES, Sally, Coordinator Human Resources, Grace Medical Center, Lubbock, TX, p. A630

CHARLES, Timothy L., President and Chief Executive Officer, Mercy Medical Center, Cedar Rapids, Iowa, Cedar Rapids, IA, p. A223

CHARLTON, Beth, Vice President Patient Services and Chief Nursing Officer, Covenant Healthcare, Saginaw, MI, p. A329

CHARLTON, Francis M.D., Jr, Chief Medical Staff, St. Mary's Medical Center, San Francisco, CA, p. A88

CHARLTON, Judie M.D., Chief Medical Officer, West Virginia University Hospitals, Morgantown, WV, p. A694

CHARMEL, Patrick, President and Chief Executive Officer, Griffin Hospital, Derby, CT, p. A110

CHARTIER, Bridgett, Director of Nursing, Beartooth Billings Clinic, Red Lodge, MT, p. A387

CHARTIER, Terry
Director, Information Systems, Mercy Medical Center–New Hampton, New Hampton, IA, p. A232
Director, Information Systems, Mercy Medical Center–North Iowa, Mason City, IA, p. A231

CHARVAT, Peter, Chief Medical Officer, Johnston Health, Smithfield, NC, p. A470

CHASE, Brenda, Chief Operating Officer, Mercy Hospital Rogers, Rogers, AR, p. A49

CHASE, Jean
Regional Manager Information Services, Aurora Lakeland Medical Center, Elkhorn, WI, p. A701
Regional Manager Information Services, Aurora Memorial Hospital Of Burlington, Burlington, WI, p. A699

CHASE, Kyle, Chief Financial Officer, Glacial Ridge Health System, Glenwood, MN, p. A340

CHASE, Layla, Interim Chief Financial Officer, Bunkie General Hospital, Bunkie, LA, p. A272

CHASE, Pansy, Director Human Resources, Vidant Duplin Hospital, Kenansville, NC, p. A465

CHASE, Robert, M.D.
Chief Medical Officer, Westlake Hospital, Melrose Park, IL, p. A193
Physician Advisor, West Suburban Medical Center, Oak Park, IL, p. A196

CHASE, Susan, Vice President, Carolinas Rehabilitation, Charlotte, NC, p. A459

CHASIN, Marc M.D., Chief Information Officer, St. Luke's Regional Medical Center, Boise, ID, p. A172

CHASSE, Floyd, Vice President Human Resources, Erlanger Medical Center, Chattanooga, TN, p. A576

CHASTAIN, James G., FACHE, Director, Mississippi State Hospital, Whitfield, MS, p. A363

© 2017 AHA Guide

CHASTAIN, Katherine L R.N., Chief Nursing Officer, Sacred Heart Hospital On The Gulf, Port St. Joe, FL, p. A140

CHASTAIN, Stephen L M.D., Chief Medical Officer, Healthsouth Rehabilitation Hospital At Martin Health, Stuart, FL, p. A143

CHASTANG, Mark J., M.P.H., Chief Executive Officer, Saint Elizabeths Hospital, Washington, DC, p. A118

CHASTANT, Lee, Chief Executive Officer, West Feliciana Parish Hospital, Saint Francisville, LA, p. A285

CHATANI, Kumar
Chief Information Officer, Mount Sinai Health System, Mount Sinai West, New Rochelle, NY, p. A443
Chief Information Officer, Mount Sinai Health System, New York Eye And Ear Infirmary Of Mount Sinai, New Rochelle, NY, p. A443
Senior Vice President and Chief Information Officer Mount Sinai Health System, Mount Sinai Beth Israel, New Rochelle, NY, p. A443
Senior Vice President and Chief Information Officer Mount Sinai Health System, Mount Sinai Hospital, New Rochelle, NY, p. A443

CHATELAIN, Alicia, Director Human Resource, Hood Memorial Hospital, Amite, LA, p. A270

CHATELAIN, Vincent, Director Business Development, Seaside Behavioral Center, New OrleansRiver Oaks Hospital, New Orleans, LA, p. A283

CHATLEY, Alice M R.N., MSN, Vice President Acute Care Services, SSM Health St. Mary's Hospital – Jefferson City, Jefferson City, MO, p. A369

CHATMAN, Hubert, Chief Civilian Personnel, Wright Patterson Medical Center, Wright, OH, p. A503

CHATMAN, Jim, Chief Financial Officer, Maria Parham Medical Center, Henderson, NC, p. A464

CHATMAN, Mary Ph.D., Senior Vice President, Chief Operating Officer and Chief Nursing Officer, Memorial Health, Savannah, GA, p. A164

CHATTERJEE, Kanan M.D., Chief of Staff, Lebanon Veterans Affairs Medical Center, Lebanon, PA, p. A538

CHATTERTON, Bryan, Chief Executive Officer, Kindred Hospital–Indianapolis, Indianapolis, IN, p. A211

CHAUDHARY, Shahid M.D., Chief Medical Officer, Avera St. Luke's Hospital, Aberdeen, SD, p. A568

CHAUDHRY, Riaz M.D., Chief Medical Officer, Mercy Health – St. Charles Hospital, Oregon, OH, p. A497

CHAUDIER, David, Chief Executive Officer, Lifecare Hospitals Of Wisconsin, Pewaukee, WI, p. A710

CHAUHAN, Varun, Chief Executive Officer, Select Specialty Hospital – Boardman, Boardman, OH, p. A481

CHAUSSARD, David, Chief Executive Officer, Hillcrest Hospital Claremore, Claremore, OK, p. A506

CHAVEZ, Irene, Senior Vice President and Area Manager, Kaiser Permanente San Jose Medical Center, San Jose, CA, p. A88

CHAVEZ, Kevin, Chief Executive Officer, Bridgepoint Hospital National Harbor, Washington, DC, p. A117

CHAVEZ, Shari, Chief Nursing Officer, Swedish Medical Center, Englewood, CO, p. A102

CHAVEZ, Steven, Vice President Finance and Operations, Kettering Medical Center, Kettering, OH, p. A493

CHAVEZ, Virgil, Director Information Technology, Tsehootsooi Medical Center, Fort Defiance, AZ, p. A29

CHAVEZ STUMP, Tammie U., R.N., Chief Executive Officer, Union County General Hospital, Clayton, NM, p. A425

CHAVIS, Anthony D M.D., Vice President Enterprise Medical Officer, Community Hospital Foundation, Community Hospital Of The Monterey Peninsula, Monterey, CA, p. A74

CHAWLA, Nikki M.D., Medical Director, Alliancehealth Seminole, Seminole, OK, p. A515

CHAYER, Olivia, Director, Human Resources, York Hospital, York, ME, p. A293

CHECK, Arthur M.D., Chief Medical Officer, Story County Medical Center, Nevada, IA, p. A232

CHECKETTS, Lannie
Chief Financial Officer, Saint Alphonsus Medical Center – Nampa, Nampa, ID, p. A174
Chief Financial Officer, Saint Alphonsus Medical Center – Ontario, Ontario, OR, p. A524

CHEEK, Holly, Vice President and Chief Nursing Officer, Columbus Regional Hospital, Columbus, IN, p. A205

CHEEK, Michael, Chief Financial Officer, Christus Good Shepherd Medical Center–Marshall, Marshall, TX, p. A632

CHEEMA, Linde, Vice President Human Resources, Sequoia Hospital, Redwood City, CA, p. A82

CHEESEMAN, Karen, Chief Executive Officer, Mackinac Straits Health System, Inc., Saint Ignace, MI, p. A330

CHEEVER, Liz, Administrator, Miracle Mile Medical Center, Los Angeles, CA, p. A70

CHEKURU, Naidu M.D., Chief Medical Officer, Covenant Specialty Hospital, Lubbock, TX, p. A630

CHELLAPPA, Sheila M.D., Chief of Staff, Coatesville Veterans Affairs Medical Center, Coatesville, PA, p. A532

CHEN, Bonny M.D., Vice President and Chief Medical Officer, Amita Health Adventist Medical Center – Hinsdale, Hinsdale, IL, p. A190

CHEN, David, M.D.
Chief Medical Officer, Bozeman Health Deaconess Hospital, Bozeman, MT, p. A382
Chief Medical Officer, Multicare Deaconess Hospital, Spokane, WA, p. A686

CHEN, Helen M.D., Chief Medical Officer, Hebrew Rehabilitation Center, Roslindale, MA, p. A310

CHEN, Linda, President and Market Leader, Multicare Mary Bridge Children's Hospital And Health Center, Tacoma, WA, p. A687

CHEN, Stephen M.D., Chief Medicare, Alhambra Hospital Medical Center, Alhambra, CA, p. A51

CHEN, Van M.D., Medical Director, Ballard Rehabilitation Hospital, San Bernardino, CA, p. A85

CHENEY, David, Chief Executive Officer, Sutter Medical Center, Sacramento, Sacramento, CA, p. A84

CHENG, Alice, President and Chief Executive Officer, Beverly Hospital, Montebello, CA, p. A74

CHENG, Rebecca
Chief Financial Officer, Adventist Health Glendale, Glendale, CA, p. A62
Chief Financial Officer, California Hospital Medical Center, Los Angeles, CA, p. A67

CHENG, Ringo, Director Information Technology, Surgery Specialty Hospitals Of America, Pasadena, TX, p. A637

CHENNAULT, Paula, Administrator, Behavioral Healthcare Center At Columbia, Columbia, TN, p. A577

CHENOWETH, Don, Chief Information Officer, Prince George's Hospital Center, Cheverly, MD, p. A297

CHENOWETH, Judy, Chief Nursing Officer, Russell County Hospital, Russell Springs, KY, p. A267

CHERAMIE, Bennett, Vice President Information Technology, Baton Rouge General Medical Center, Baton Rouge, LA, p. A270

CHERAY, James M.D., Chief Medical Officer, Menorah Medical Center, Overland Park, KS, p. A249

CHERMSIDE, Paula L., Chief Executive Officer, Aspirus Ironwood Hosital & Clinics, Inc., Ironwood, MI, p. A323

CHERMSIDE, Paula L, Chief Executive Officer, Aspirus Ironwood Hosital & Clinics, Inc., Ironwood, MI, p. A323

CHERNOW, David S., President and Chief Executive Officer, Select Medical Corporation, Mechanicsburg, PA, p. B113

CHERONE, Nancy, Executive Director and Administrator, Nazareth Hospital, Philadelphia, PA, p. A545

CHERRNAY LEVY, Jennifer, Director Human Resources, Texas Institute For Surgery At Texas Health Presbyterian Dallas, Dallas, TX, p. A607

CHERRY, Deano, Chief Information Officer, Upmc Kane, Kane, PA, p. A537

CHERRY, Jean, Executive Vice President, Commonwealth Regional Specialty Hospital, Bowling Green, KY, p. A255

CHERRY, Jonathan M., President and Chief Executive Officer, Lifestream Behavioral Center, Leesburg, FL, p. A131

CHERRY, Kris Ph.D., R.N., Chief Nursing Officer, Saint Francis Hospital–Bartlett, Bartlett, TN, p. A575

CHERRY, Michael, Chief Financial Officer, Tennova Healthcare–Lafollette Medical Center, La Follette, TN, p. A582

CHERRY, Robert M.D., Chief Medical and Quality Officer, Ronald Reagan Ucla Medical Center, Los Angeles, CA, p. A71

CHERRY, Troy, Chief Financial Officer, Schick Shadel Hospital, Seattle, WA, p. A685

CHESLEK, Ingrid R.N., Chief Nursing Officer, Mary Free Bed Rehabilitation Hospital, Grand Rapids, MI, p. A321

CHESLEY, Jeanine, Chief Executive Officer, New England Rehabilitation Hospital Of Portland, Portland, ME, p. A292

CHESLEY, Judy S M.D., Chief of Staff, Sanford Luverne Medical Center, Luverne, MN, p. A342

CHESLEY, Randy, Director Information Technology, Copley Hospital, Morrisville, VT, p. A662

CHESLEY, Walter, Senior Vice President Human Resources, Hennepin County Medical Center, Minneapolis, MN, p. A343

CHESNOS, Richard C, Senior Vice President Finance and Chief Financial Officer, St. Clair Hospital, Pittsburgh, PA, p. A547

CHESSARE, John B., M.D., M.P.H., FACHE, President and Chief Executive Officer, Greater Baltimore Medical Center, Baltimore, MD, p. A294

CHESSIN, Neil A, Vice President, Upmc Jameson Hospital, New Castle, PA, p. A542

CHESSON, Andrew, Chief Medical Officer, Catawba Valley Medical Center, Hickory, NC, p. A464

CHESSUM, George
Senior Vice President and Chief Information Officer, Community First Medical Center, Chicago, IL, p. A180
Senior Vice President Information Systems and Chief Information Officer, Presence Saint Joseph Hospital, Chicago, IL, p. A182
Vice President Information Systems, Presence Saint Francis Hospital, Evanston, IL, p. A187

CHESTER, Julie, Vice President Human Resources, University Hospitals Cleveland Medical Center, Cleveland, OH, p. A486

CHESTER, Linnes L USAF, MSC, Administrator, Mike O'Callaghan Federal Hospital, Nellis Afb, NV, p. A404

CHESTER, William, Manager Human Resources, Grand Junction Veterans Health Care System, Grand Junction, CO, p. A103

CHESTNUT–RAULS, Monica, Vice President Human Resources, Peconic Bay Medical Center, Riverhead, NY, p. A450

CHEUNG, Alan M.D., Vice President Medical Affairs, Castle Medical Center, Kailua, HI, p. A169

CHEUNG, Marilou, Assistant Administrator Finance, Kaiser Permanente Woodland Hills Medical Center, Los Angeles, CA, p. A69

CHEUNG, Raymond M.D., Chief of Staff, San Ramon Regional Medical Center, San Ramon, CA, p. A90

CHEVERE, Carlos M.D., Medical Director, I. Gonzalez Martinez Oncologic Hospital, Hato Rey, PR, p. A723

CHEW, Roy G., Ph.D., President, Kettering Medical Center, Kettering, OH, p. A493

CHEYNET, Sandee, Vice President Administrative Services, Bluefield Regional Medical Center, Bluefield, WV, p. A690

CHHABRA, Ankit, Director Finance, Cleveland Clinic Fairview Hospital, Cleveland, OH, p. A485

CHIACCHIARO, Peter, Vice President Human Resources, St. Joseph Hospital, Bethpage, NY, p. A431

CHIANESE, Charles, Vice President, Chief Operating Officer, Children's Specialized Hospital, New Brunswick, NJ, p. A417

CHIANTELLA, Christopher M.D., Chief Medical Officer, Inova Loudoun Hospital, Leesburg, VA, p. A669

CHIARCHIARO, Martha, Vice President Human Resources, Clinton Hospital, Clinton, MA, p. A306

CHIAVETTA, Robert, Vice President Finance, United Memorial Medical Center, Batavia, NY, p. A431

CHICARELLI, Michael, Interim Chief Executive Officer, University Of New Mexico Hospitals, Albuquerque, NM, p. A425

CHICK, Melanie, Chief Executive Officer, Baylor Medical Center At Trophy Club, Trophy Club, TX, p. A650

CHICKEN, Kurt, Director Support Services, Gundersen Palmer Lutheran Hospital And Clinics, West Union, IA, p. A236

CHIDESTER, Annamarie R.N., Vice President, Patient Care Services, St. Joseph's Hospital Of Buckhannon, Buckhannon, WV, p. A690

CHIEFFO, Ron, Chief Information Officer, Colorado River Medical Center, Needles, CA, p. A76

CHIKOWSKI, Julie, Administrator, Memorial Hospital Of Lafayette County, Darlington, WI, p. A700

CHILCOTT, Stephen, Associate Director Human Resources, University Of California, Davis Medical Center, Sacramento, CA, p. A84

CHILD, Clint L R.N., Chief Nursing Officer, Saint Alphonsus Medical Center – Nampa, Nampa, ID, p. A174

CHILDERS, Bethany, Director Human Resources, Fremont Health, Fremont, NE, p. A393

CHILDERS, Christy, Director Information Technology, P & S Surgical Hospital, Monroe, LA, p. A281

CHILDERS, James R, Vice President and Chief Financial Officer, Gibson General Hospital, Princeton, IN, p. A218

CHILDERS, Linda, Director Human Resources, Wallowa Memorial Hospital, Enterprise, OR, p. A521

CHILDERS, Scott W., Administrator, Mercy Hospital Lebanon, Lebanon, MO, p. A372

CHILDERS, Susan M., CPA, Chief Executive Officer, Mee Memorial Hospital, King City, CA, p. A64

CHILDS, Joe M.D., Vice President Medical Services, East Tennessee Children's Hospital, Knoxville, TN, p. A581

CHILDS, Michelle, Senior Administrative Director Human Resources, Salinas Valley Memorial Healthcare System, Salinas, CA, p. A84

CHILES, Kevin, Vice President Human Resources, Hutchinson Regional Medical Center, Hutchinson, KS, p. A243

CHILES, Morton M.D., Chief Medical Officer, Novant Health Uva Health System Culpeper Medical Center, Culpeper, VA, p. A666

CHILESE, Melody, Chief Nurse Executive, Hawthorn Children Psychiatric Hospital, Saint Louis, MO, p. A377

CHILESKI, Andy, Chief Information Officer and Vice President Facilities, Berger Health System, Circleville, OH, p. A485

CHILL, Martha O'Regan
Interim Chief Information Officer, Wellmont Bristol Regional Medical Center, Bristol, TN, p. A575
Interim Chief Information Officer, Wellmont Hancock County Hospital, Sneedville, TN, p. A589

CHILSON, Terrance, Chief of Staff, Tyler Memorial Hospital, Tunkhannock, PA, p. A552

CHILTON, Bryan, Director Information Systems, Navarro Regional Hospital, Corsicana, TX, p. A603

CHILTON, Hal, Senior Vice President and Chief Operating Officer, Adventist Health St. Helena, Saint Helena, CA, p. A84

CHIN, Ellyn, Vice President Finance, Gottlieb Memorial Hospital, Melrose Park, IL, p. A193

CHINBURG, Paul M.D., Medical Director, Lane County Hospital, Dighton, KS, p. A240

CHING, Angelica, Director Information Systems, Monterey Park Hospital, Monterey Park, CA, p. A75

CHINN, Tammie
Chief Human Resource Officer, Williamson Memorial Hospital, Williamson, WV, p. A697
Director Marketing and Public Relations, Plateau Medical Center, Oak Hill, WV, p. A694

CHINN, Terri, Vice President Finance, St. Mary's Hospital And Medical Center, Grand Junction, CO, p. A103

CHINNOCK, Rachel, Chief Human Resources Officer, Latimer County General Hospital, Wilburton, OK, p. A519

CHIOLO, Denise, Chief Human Resources Officer, Phoenixville Hospital, Phoenixville, PA, p. A546

CHIPMAN, Glen, Chief Financial Officer, Healthsource Saginaw, Inc., Saginaw, MI, p. A329

CHIPMAN, Kim, Chief Clinical Officer, Kindred Hospital–White Rock, Dallas, TX, p. A605

CHIRICHELLA, Joseph, President and Chief Executive Officer, Deborah Heart And Lung Center, Browns Mills, NJ, p. A412

CHISHOLM, Sarah, R.N., Administrator, Oceans Behavioral Hospital Of Kentwood, Kentwood, LA, p. A277

CHISHOLM, Sharon, Entity Human Resource Officer, Texas Health Presbyterian Hospital Allen, Allen, TX, p. A591

CHISSELL, Herbert G M.D., Chief Medical Officer, Torrance State Hospital, Torrance, PA, p. A551

CHISTIANSEN, Lia, Vice President, Hospital Operations, Woodwinds Health Campus, Woodbury, MN, p. A351

CHITCHYAN, Ara M.D., Medical Director, Roosevelt Warm Springs Rehabilitation Hospital – Rehab, Warm Springs, GA, p. A167

CHITTENDEN, Michael D., President, St. Vincent Carmel Hospital, Carmel, IN, p. A205

CHIUMINETTA, Leigh, Interim Chief Information Officer, St. Mary's Healthcare, Amsterdam, NY, p. A430

CHIVERS, John, Senior Vice President Finance, Sierra View Medical Center, Porterville, CA, p. A80

CHMIELEWSKI, Linda A R.N., Vice President Operations, St. Cloud Hospital, Saint Cloud, MN, p. A347

CHMURA, David, Chief Information Officer, Copper Queen Community Hospital, Bisbee, AZ, p. A28

CHOATE, Charlotte, Director Information Systems, University Hospital Summerville, Augusta, GA, p. A152

CHOATE, Matthew, Chief Nursing Officer, The University Of Vermont Health Network Central Vermont Medical Center, Berlin, VT, p. A662

CHOCKLETT, Wyatt, Chief Operating Officer, Doctors Hospital Of Sarasota, Sarasota, FL, p. A142

CHODKOWSKI, Paul J., President and Chief Executive Officer, St. Anthony Summit Medical Center, Frisco, CO, p. A103

CHOINIERE, Leon, Vice President, Chief Financial Officer, St. Mary Medical Center, Long Beach, CA, p. A67

CHOINKA, Keith A, Vice President Information Systems and Chief Information Officer, St. Joseph Hospital, Nashua, NH, p. A409

CHOKSHI, Sushil M.D., Chief Medical Officer, Faith Community Hospital, Jacksboro, TX, p. A625

CHOLGER, Dave, Chief Financial Officer, Woodlawn Hospital, Rochester, IN, p. A219

CHONG, Johnnette, Chief Financial Officer, Los Angeles Community Hospital At Los Angeles, Los Angeles, CA, p. A69

CHOPIN, Candice, Vice President Human Resources, Women's And Children's Hospital, Lafayette, LA, p. A279

CHOPRA, Praveen, Executive Vice President and Chief Information and Transformative Innovative Environment Officer, Thomas Jefferson University Hospitals, Philadelphia, PA, p. A546

CHORD, Ginger, Coordinator Human Resources, Sturgis Regional Hospital, Sturgis, SD, p. A573

CHOREY, Raymond M., President and Chief Executive Officer, Southeastern Ohio Regional Medical Center, Cambridge, OH, p. A482

CHOU, Rebecca, Director Information Systems, Palestine Regional Medical Center–East, Palestine, TX, p. A636

CHOU, Rebecca, Directory Information Systems, Palestine Regional Medical Center, Palestine, TX, p. A636

CHOUDHURY, Golam, Chief of Staff, Desert Springs Hospital Medical Center, Las Vegas, NV, p. A403

CHOUDHURY, Seleem R.N., MSN, Chief Nursing Officer, Northeastern Vermont Regional Hospital, Saint Johnsbury, VT, p. A663

CHOY, Ann N., Manager Human Resources and Payroll, Kuakini Medical Center, Honolulu, HI, p. A168

CHOZINSKI, Joseph P M.D., Deputy Commander Clinical Services, Brooke Army Medical Center, Fort Sam Houston, TX, p. A613

CHRENCIK, Robert A., President and Chief Executive Officer, University Of Maryland Medical System, Baltimore, MD, p. B139

CHRICEOL, Earlene, Chief Nursing Officer, Richardson Medical Center, Rayville, LA, p. A284

CHRISTENSEN, Carl, Senior Vice President and Chief Information Officer, Northwestern Memorial HealthCare, Northwestern Memorial Hospital, Chicago, IL, p. A182

CHRISTENSEN, Claudia, Director, Human Resources, Mills–Peninsula Health Services, Burlingame, CA, p. A54

CHRISTENSEN, Connie, Chief Financial Officer, Morrill County Community Hospital, Bridgeport, NE, p. A391

CHRISTENSEN, David M.D., Senior Vice President and Chief Medical Officer, Valley Children's Healthcare, Madera, CA, p. A72

CHRISTENSEN, Earlene, Director Human Resources, Fayette County Memorial Hospital, Washington Court House, OH, p. A502

CHRISTENSEN, Elizabeth B, Director Human Resources, Mercy Hospital Of Portland, Portland, ME, p. A292

CHRISTENSEN, G N M.D., Chief Medical Officer, William Bee Ririe Hospital, Ely, NV, p. A401

CHRISTENSEN, Gwen, Vice President, Finance, Aurora Baycare Medical Center, Green Bay, WI, p. A702

CHRISTENSEN, Jay, FACHE, Chief Executive Officer, Mahaska Health Partnership, Oskaloosa, IA, p. A233

CHRISTENSEN, Jeffrey, Chief Executive Officer, Healthsouth Rehabilitation Institute Of Tucson, Tucson, AZ, p. A38

CHRISTENSEN, Kim, Interim Chief Nursing Executive, Sheridan Community Hospital, Sheridan, MI, p. A330

CHRISTENSEN, Mark
Chief Financial Officer, Weiser Memorial Hospital, Weiser, ID, p. A176
Director, Finance, Cassia Regional Medical Center, Burley, ID, p. A172

CHRISTENSEN, Marti, Director of Psychiatric Nursing, Douglas County Community Mental Health Center, Omaha, NE, p. A397

CHRISTENSEN, Scott, Chief Executive Officer, Delta Regional Medical Center, Greenville, MS, p. A355

CHRISTENSEN, Todd
Chief Financial Officer, Kittson Memorial Healthcare Center, Hallock, MN, p. A341
Executive Director Finance, Sanford Thief River Falls Behavioral Health Center, Thief River Falls, MN, p. A349
Executive Director Fiscal Services, Sanford Medical Center Thief River Falls, Thief River Falls, MN, p. A349

CHRISTENSEN, Troy, Chief Financial Officer, Madison Memorial Hospital, Rexburg, ID, p. A175

CHRISTENSEN, W R M.D., Chief of Staff, East Texas Medical Center Pittsburg, Pittsburg, TX, p. A637

CHRISTENSEN–MORES, Donna JD, Director Human Resources, Myrtue Medical Center, Harlan, IA, p. A229

CHRISTENSON, Paul, Chief Financial Officer, Pampa Regional Medical Center, Pampa, TX, p. A636

CHRISTENSON, Ron, Chief Financial Officer, Morris County Hospital, Council Grove, KS, p. A240

CHRISTENSON, Shannon, Director Human Resources, Aurora West Allis Medical Center, West Allis, WI, p. A715

CHRISTIAN, Bruce C., President and Chief Executive Officer, Amita Health Adventist Medical Center Glenoaks, Glendale Heights, IL, p. A188

CHRISTIAN, Bruce, President and Chief Executive Officer, Amita Health Adventist Medical Center Bolingbrook, Bolingbrook, IL, p. A179

CHRISTIAN, Glenn, Administrator, Mayo Clinic Health System In Cannon Falls, Cannon Falls, MN, p. A337

CHRISTIAN, Greg, Executive Director, Kaiser Permanente Fontana Medical Center, Fontana, CA, p. A59

CHRISTIAN, Karolyne, Director Human Resources, Byrd Regional Hospital, Leesville, LA, p. A280

CHRISTIAN, Lynn R.N., MSN, Division Director, Acute Care Nursing, Centracare Health–Monticello, Monticello, MN, p. A344

CHRISTIANO, Barbara, Vice President, Patient Care Services and Chief Nursing Officer, University Medical Center Of Princeton At Plainsboro, Plainsboro, NJ, p. A419

CHRISTIANSEN, Anne, Chief Financial Officer, Pioneer Memorial Hospital And Health Services, Viborg, SD, p. A573

CHRISTIANSEN, Hilary, Chief Financial Officer, George C Grape Community Hospital, Hamburg, IA, p. A228

CHRISTIANSEN, Keith, Chief Nursing Officer, Select Specialty Hospital–Erie, Erie, PA, p. A534

CHRISTIANSEN, Patrick, Ph.D., Chief Executive Officer, Inova Fairfax Hospital, Falls Church, VA, p. A666

CHRISTIANSEN, Sara, Interim Director Human Resources, Ridgeview Sibley Medical Center, Arlington, MN, p. A335

CHRISTIANSON, Chad, Chief Executive Officer, Ocala Regional Medical Center, Ocala, FL, p. A136

CHRISTIANSON, Clinton J., FACHE, President, Mercy Medical Center–Centerville, Centerville, IA, p. A224

CHRISTIANSON, Delano, Administrator, Centracare Health–Sauk Centre, Sauk Centre, MN, p. A348

CHRISTIE, Janet L., Senior Vice President Human Resources, Uf Health Shands Hospital, Gainesville, FL, p. A126

CHRISTINE, Gerald, Chief Financial Officer, Lakewood Ranch Medical Center, Bradenton, FL, p. A120

CHRISTION, Lydia, Director Human Resources, Healthsouth Rehabilitation Hospital, Dothan, AL, p. A17

CHRISTISON, George M.D., Medical Director, Patton State Hospital, Patton, CA, p. A79

CHRISTMAN, Lawrence, Chief Financial Officer and Chief Operating Officer, Riverview Health, Noblesville, IN, p. A217

CHRISTMAN, Thomas C, Director Plant Operations, Kindred Hospital–St. Louis, Saint Louis, MO, p. A377

CHRISTMANN, Linda M.D., Chief of Staff, Manatee Memorial Hospital, Bradenton, FL, p. A120

CHRISTOPH, Rebecca, Director Nursing and Patient Care Services, Mid–Valley Hospital, Omak, WA, p. A683

CHRISTOPHEL, Randal, President and Chief Executive Officer, Goshen Hospital, Goshen, IN, p. A209

CHRISTOPHER, Candi CPA, Chief Financial Officer, Stonesprings Hospital Center, Dulles, VA, p. A666

CHRISTOPHER, Sue, Vice President, Human Resources, Baptist Health Floyd, New Albany, IN, p. A217

CHRISTY, Rose, Executive Director of Medical Services, Hamilton Center, Terre Haute, IN, p. A220

CHROBAK, Jeffrey, Vice President Finance and Chief Financial Officer, Sharon Regional Health System, Sharon, PA, p. A551

CHU, Betty M.D., Chief Medical Officer and Vice President of Medical Affairs, Henry Ford West Bloomfield Hospital, West Bloomfield, MI, p. A333

CHU, Edward, Chief Financial Officer, Leahi Hospital, Honolulu, HI, p. A168

CHUA, Jesus M.D., Chief of Staff, Franklin Foundation Hospital, Franklin, LA, p. A275

CHUE, Bevins M.D., Medical Director, Healthsouth Desert Canyon Rehabilitation Hospital, Las Vegas, NV, p. A403

CHUGDEN, Robert M.D., Chief Medical Officer, West Jefferson Medical Center, Marrero, LA, p. A281

CHUKWUMA, Lilian, Chief Financial Officer, United Medical Center, Washington, DC, p. A118

CHULICK, Michele, President and Chief Executive Officer, Wyoming Medical Center, Casper, WY, p. A717

CHUN, Ryan, Information Resources Management, San Francisco Va Medical Center, San Francisco, CA, p. A87

CHUNG, Esther, Chief Operating Officer, St. David's Medical Center, Austin, TX, p. A596

CHUNG, Maria CPA, Director Fiscal Services, Shriners Hospitals For Children–Boston, Boston, MA, p. A304

CHUNG, Michael
Chief Financial Officer, Ahmc Anaheim Regional Medical Center, Anaheim, CA, p. A51
Chief Financial Officer, Greater El Monte Community Hospital, South El Monte, CA, p. A92

CHUNG, William M.D., Chief of Staff, Chinese Hospital, San Francisco, CA, p. A87

CHUNN, Ashley, Director of Nursing, Atmore Community Hospital, Atmore, AL, p. A14

CHURCH, Brian, Senior Vice President and Chief Financial Officer, Phoebe Putney Memorial Hospital, Albany, GA, p. A149

CHURCH, Kim
Manager Human Resources, G. Werber Bryan Psychiatric Hospital, Columbia, SC, p. A560
Manager Human Resources, William S. Hall Psychiatric Institute, Columbia, SC, p. A561

CHURCH, Rhonda, Director Human Resources, Bastrop Rehabilitation Hospital, Monroe, LA, p. A281

CHURCHILL, Brigitte, Director of Human Resources, Memorial Satilla Health, Waycross, GA, p. A167

CHURCHILL, Larry, Director Information Services, Alliancehealth Woodward, Woodward, OK, p. A519

CHURCHILL, Sandi, Vice President Business Development and Operations, Professional Services, Advocate Good Samaritan Hospital, Downers Grove, IL, p. A186

CHURCHILL, Timothy A.
Interim Chief Executive Officer, Franklin Memorial Hospital, Farmington, ME, p. A291

President, Stephens Memorial Hospital, Norway, ME, p. A292

CHURCHWELL, Kevin B M.D., Chief Operating Officer and Executive Vice President Health Affairs, Boston Children's Hospital, Boston, MA, p. A302

CIAMPA, Amy, Chief Financial Officer, Park Royal Hospital, Fort Myers, FL, p. A125

CIAMPA, Steve, Vice President Finance, Porter Medical Center, Middlebury, VT, p. A662

CIANCIOLO, Kirk D.O., Chief Medical Officer, Blake Medical Center, Bradenton, FL, p. A120

CIANCIOTTO CROYLE, Allison, Vice President of Human Resources, Mercy Medical Center, Rockville Centre, NY, p. A451

CIANFLONE, Laura, Director Human Resources, Kenmore Mercy Hospital, Kenmore, NY, p. A438

CIANFRANI, Michelle, Director Information Technology, Gilbert Hospital, Gilbert, AZ, p. A29

CIAREFELLA, Donna, Director Human Resources, Vibra Hospital Of Western Massachusetts, Springfield, MA, p. A312

CICCARELLI, John, Director Information Technology, Parkview Community Hospital Medical Center, Riverside, CA, p. A82

CICCARELLI, Thomas, Chief Information Officer, East Orange General Hospital, East Orange, NJ, p. A413

CICCONE, Josie, Director, Human Resources, Garden City Hospital, Garden City, MI, p. A320

CICE, Donna, Vice President Human Resources, Huntington Hospital, Huntington, NY, p. A437

CICERI, David P M.D., Chief Medical Officer, Baylor Scott And White Continuing Care Hospital, Temple, TX, p. A648

CICIRETTI, Mary Louise, Director Human Resources, Riddle Hospital, Media, PA, p. A541

CIENCEWICKI, Michael M.D., Vice President Medical Affairs, Hackensack Meridian Health Raritan Bay Medical Center, Perth Amboy, NJ, p. A419

CIHA, Clayton, President and Chief Executive Officer, Alexian Brothers Behavioral Health Hospital, Hoffman Estates, IL, p. A190

CIHAK, Scott A., President and Chief Executive Officer, Tristar Centennial Medical Center, Nashville, TN, p. A587

CIMALA, Derek W.
Interim Chief Executive Officer, Bluefield Regional Medical Center, Bluefield, WV, p. A690
Interim Chief Executive Officer, Plateau Medical Center, Oak Hill, WV, p. A694

CIMINO, Michael A. Jr, Chief Financial Officer, Banner Behavioral Health Hospital – Scottsdale, Scottsdale, AZ, p. A35

CIMMINO, Denise MSN, R.N., Assistant Vice President, Nursing and Patient Care Services, Carepoint Health Christ Hospital, Jersey City, NJ, p. A415

CINICOLA, John, M.D.
Chief Medical Officer, Heritage Valley Health System, Beaver, PA, p. A529
Chief Medical Officer, Sewickley Valley Hospital, (A Division Of Valley Medical Facilities), Sewickley, PA, p. A550

CINTRON, Jacob, FACHE, President and Chief Executive Officer, University Medical Center Of El Paso, El Paso, TX, p. A612

CIOFFI, Cheryl R.N., Senior Vice President Patient Care Services and Chief Nursing Officer, Frederick Regional Health System, Frederick, MD, p. A298

CIOTA, Mark, M.D.
Chief Executive Officer, Mayo Clinic Health System In Albert Lea, Albert Lea, MN, p. A335
Chief Executive Officer, Mayo Clinic Health System–Albert Lea And Austin, Austin, MN, p. A336

CIRALDO, Lou, Information Services Representative, University Hospitals Geauga Medical Center, Chardon, OH, p. A483

CIRBA, Michael, Chief Information Officer, Good Shepherd Specialty Hospital, Bethlehem, PA, p. A529

CIRO, Maria, Director Human Resources, Acuity Specialty Hospital Of New Jersey, Atlantic City, NJ, p. A411

CIROCCO, Anthony, Chief Financial Officer, Dignity Health Arizona General Hospital, Laveen, AZ, p. A31

CIRONE, Laura, Manager Human Resources, Rochelle Community Hospital, Rochelle, IL, p. A198

CIRPILI, Avni, Senior Vice President, Chief Nursing Officer, Menninger Clinic, Houston, TX, p. A622

CITA, Bob, Chief Information Officer, Searhc Mt. Edgecumbe Hospital, Sitka, AK, p. A27

CITAK, Michael M.D., Chief Medical Officer, Lake Cumberland Regional Hospital, Somerset, KY, p. A267

CITRO, Tina R.N., Chief Nursing Officer, Vice President, Patient Services, Wellspan Ephrata Community Hospital, Ephrata, PA, p. A534

CIUFO, Donna R.N., Vice President and Chief Nurse Executive, Hackensack Meridian Health Southern Ocean Medical Center, Manahawkin, NJ, p. A416

CIVAN, Dino, Chief Information Officer, NYC Health + Hospitals / Kings County, New Rochelle, NY, p. A445

CIVIC, Dave M.D., Associate Director Clinical Services, U.S. Public Health Service Phoenix Indian Medical Center, Phoenix, AZ, p. A34

CIVITELLO, Dean
Vice President Human Resources, Saint Joseph's Medical Center, Yonkers, NY, p. A456
Vice President, Human Resources, Public Relations and Development, The University Of Vermont Health Network–Champlain Valley Physicians Hospital, Plattsburgh, NY, p. A449

CLAASSENS, Nicolise, Nurse Executive, West Central Georgia Regional Hospital, Columbus, GA, p. A155

CLABAUGH, John, Director Human Resources, Saint Luke's East Hospital, Lee's Summit, MO, p. A372

CLABUESCH, Paul, President and Chief Executive Officer, Harbor Beach Community Hospital, Harbor Beach, MI, p. A322

CLACK, Deborah, Chief Nursing Officer, Hunt Regional Medical Center, Greenville, TX, p. A617

CLAIR OLIVER, Delores, Chief Clinical Officer and Chief Operating Officer, Bridgepoint Hospital Capitol Hill, Washington, DC, p. A117

CLANCY, Mikki, Chief Operating Officer, Miami Valley Hospital, Dayton, OH, p. A489

CLANCY, Patricia M.D., Director Medical Services, Maniilaq Health Center, Kotzebue, AK, p. A26

CLAPP, Ann R, Director Human Resources, Healthsouth Rehabilitation Hospital Of Texarkana, Texarkana, TX, p. A649

CLAPP, Denise
Chief Nursing Officer, Lourdes Counseling Center, Richland, WA, p. A684
Chief Nursing Officer, Lourdes Medical Center, Pasco, WA, p. A683

CLAPP, Nicole, R.N., MSN, FACHE, President and Chief Executive Officer, Grant Regional Health Center, Lancaster, WI, p. A705

CLAPP, Steve, President and Chief Executive Officer, Curae Health, Clinton, TN, p. B40

CLAPP, William M.D., Chief of Medical Staff, Methodist Hospital Union County, Morganfield, KY, p. A265

CLARK, Allan W M.D., Medical Director, Southwood Psychiatric Hospital, Pittsburgh, PA, p. A547

CLARK, Anna, Chief Operating Officer, Copper Basin Medical Center, Copperhill, TN, p. A577

CLARK, Ashley, Coordinator Human Resources, Noland Hospital Birmingham, Birmingham, AL, p. A15

CLARK, Ben, Vice President and Chief Information Officer, Centra Lynchburg General Hospital, Lynchburg, VA, p. A669

CLARK, Christopher, D.O.
President and Chief Executive Officer, Saint Vincent Hospital, Erie, PA, p. A534
President and Chief Executive Officer, Westfield Memorial Hospital, Westfield, NY, p. A456

CLARK, Dale, President, Mountain View Regional Medical Center, Norton, VA, p. A672

CLARK, Dale
President, Wellmont Lonesome Pine Hospital, Big Stone Gap, VA, p. A664
Interim Chief Executive Officer, Hardeman County Memorial Hospital, Quanah, TX, p. A639

CLARK, David, Interim Chief Executive Officer, W. J. Mangold Memorial Hospital, Lockney, TX, p. A629

CLARK, Debra, Chief Nursing Officer, Bayfront Health Port Charlotte, Port Charlotte, FL, p. A140

CLARK, Denise, Chief Nursing Officer, Holy Cross Hospital, Taos, NM, p. A429

CLARK, Ed M.D., Chief Medical Officer, Primary Children's Hospital, Salt Lake City, UT, p. A660

CLARK, Eileen, Vice President Information Services, Charleston Area Medical Center, Charleston, WV, p. A691

CLARK, Heather, Chief Executive Officer, Caldwell Memorial Hospital, Columbia, LA, p. A273

CLARK, Janice, Manager Human Resources, Garfield Park Hospital, Chicago, IL, p. A181

CLARK, Jason, Director Quality Improvement, Risk Management and Information System, Greenwood County Hospital, Eureka, KS, p. A241

CLARK, Jean, Administrator, Kindred Hospital Seattle–Northgate, Seattle, WA, p. A685

CLARK, Jeff, Director Information Systems, Graham Regional Medical Center, Graham, TX, p. A617

CLARK, Jeffrey A, Vice President Human Resources, Kadlec Regional Medical Center, Richland, WA, p. A684

CLARK, Jeremy L., Market Chief Executive Officer, Hilton Head Hospital, Hilton Head Island, SC, p. A564

CLARK, John, Chief Financial Officer, Childrens Care Hospital And School, Sioux Falls, SD, p. A572

CLARK, Judith, Chief Financial Officer, Takoma Regional Hospital, Greeneville, TN, p. A579

CLARK, Karen
Vice President Operations, Advocate South Suburban Hospital, Hazel Crest, IL, p. A189
Director Administrative Services, Sonoma Developmental Center, Eldridge, CA, p. A58
Vice President Patient Care Services, St. Mary's Regional Medical Center, Lewiston, ME, p. A291

CLARK, Kent M.D., Chief Medical Affairs and Quality, Waldo County General Hospital, Belfast, ME, p. A290

CLARK, Lisa, Director Human Resources, Willamette Valley Medical Center, Mcminnville, OR, p. A523

CLARK, Mark A
Vice President Operations, Good Samaritan Regional Health Center, Mount Vernon, IL, p. A194
Vice President Operations, SSM Health St. Mary's Hospital Centralia, Centralia, IL, p. A179

CLARK, Mark
Chief Information Officer, Yampa Valley Medical Center, Steamboat Springs, CO, p. A107
Human Resources Liaison, U.S. Air Force Regional Hospital, Elmendorf Afb, AK, p. A26

CLARK, Megan, Coordinator Human Resources, Genesis Medical Center–Aledo, Aledo, IL, p. A177

CLARK, Michael A
Administrator, Mckay-Dee Hospital, Ogden, UT, p. A658
Chief Operating Officer, Mckay-Dee Hospital, Ogden, UT, p. A658

CLARK, Michael
Chief Executive Officer, Spotsylvania Regional Medical Center, Fredericksburg, VA, p. A667
Executive Vice President and Chief Financial Officer, FHN Memorial Hospital, Freeport, IL, p. A188
Fiscal Administrative Manager, Connecticut Veterans Home And Hospital, Rocky Hill, CT, p. A112

CLARK, N Travis
President, Page Memorial Hospital, Luray, VA, p. A669
President, Shenandoah Memorial Hospital, Woodstock, VA, p. A677

CLARK, N Travis.
President, Page Memorial Hospital, Luray, VA, p. B142
President, Shenandoah Memorial Hospital, Woodstock, VA, p. B142

CLARK, Nancy, Vice President Human Resources, Regional Medical Center Of San Jose, San Jose, CA, p. A88

CLARK, Patrick, Manager Information Technology, Sunnyview Rehabilitation Hospital, Schenectady, NY, p. A452

CLARK, Ralph H. Jr, FACHE, Chief Executive Officer, Medical Center Barbour, Eufaula, AL, p. A17

CLARK, Randal, Vice President Finance, Sebasticook Valley Health, Pittsfield, ME, p. A292

CLARK, Renee, Senior Vice President and Chief Operating Officer, Southcoast Hospitals Group, Fall River, MA, p. A306

CLARK, Rhonda, Interim Chief Nursing Officer, Alta Vista Regional Hospital, Las Vegas, NM, p. A427

CLARK, Robert J., President and Chief Executive Officer, Bristol Bay Area Health Corporation, Dillingham, AK, p. A26

CLARK, Robin, Chief Nursing Officer, Select Specialty Hospital–Greensboro, Greensboro, NC, p. A463

CLARK, Rodney, Chief Operating Officer, North Sunflower Medical Center, Ruleville, MS, p. A361

CLARK, Ron M.D., Vice President Clinical Activities and Chief Medical Officer, VCU Medical Center, Richmond, VA, p. A674

CLARK, Sharon, Director Human Resources, Hillsboro Area Hospital, Hillsboro, IL, p. A190

CLARK, Shawn, Director Information Systems, The Physicians Centre Hospital, Bryan, TX, p. A600

CLARK, Stella MSN, R.N., Chief Nursing Officer, Hshs St. Joseph's Hospital, Chippewa Falls, WI, p. A700

CLARK, Steven, Chief Financial Officer, Easton Hospital, Easton, PA, p. A533

CLARK, Teresa J R.N., MS, Chief Nursing Officer, Cook Children's Medical Center, Fort Worth, TX, p. A613

CLARK, Teresa, Chief Executive Officer and Administrator, Wichita County Health Center, Leoti, KS, p. A245

CLARK, Theo, Director Financial Services, Promise Hospital Of Phoenix, Mesa, AZ, p. A32

CLARK, Thomas A., Regional President and Chief Executive Officer, Avera Queen Of Peace Hospital, Mitchell, SD, p. A571

CLARK, Timothy L., Interim Chief Executive Officer, Promise Hospital Of San Diego, San Diego, CA, p. A85

CLARK, Troy
Chief Executive Officer, Healthsouth Rehabilitation Hospital, Kingsport, TN, p. A581
Interim Administrator, Dr. Dan C. Trigg Memorial Hospital, Tucumcari, NM, p. A429
Interim Administrator, Plains Regional Medical Center, Clovis, NM, p. A425
CLARK, William H, Chief Financial Officer, Caldwell Memorial Hospital, Columbia, LA, p. A273
CLARK, William M.D., Chief Clinical Affairs, Caro Center, Caro, MI, p. A316
CLARKE, Clifton, Vice President Medical Management, Advocate Illinois Masonic Medical Center, Chicago, IL, p. A180
CLARKE, James M.D., Vice President Medical Affairs and Clinical Effectiveness, Hackensack Meridian Health Ocean Medical Center, Brick Township, NJ, p. A412
CLAROS, Elizabeth, Administrator Personnel Services, Guam Memorial Hospital Authority, Tamuning, GU, p. A721
CLARY, Brandon
Chief Executive Officer, Anmed Health Cannon, Pickens, SC, p. A565
Chief Executive Officer, Elbert Memorial Hospital, Elberton, GA, p. A157
CLARY, Elizabeth P., R.N., Vice President Behavioral Health, Peninsula Hospital, Louisville, TN, p. A583
CLATANOFF, Kris, Director Human Resources, St. Joseph Medical Center, Houston, TX, p. A622
CLAUDY, Frank M.D., Vice President Medical Staff Affairs, Genesis Medical Center–Davenport–West Central Park, Davenport, IA, p. A225
CLAUNCH, Jeremy, Chief Financial Officer, Power County Hospital District, American Falls, ID, p. A171
CLAUSEN, Patricia J R.N., Chief Nurse Executive, Kaiser Permanente Downey Medical Center, Downey, CA, p. A57
CLAUSSEN, Denise R.N., MSN, Chief Nursing Officer, Texas Health Presbyterian Hospital Kaufman, Kaufman, TX, p. A626
CLAUSSEN, Tammy, Chief Human Resource Officer, Tri Valley Health System, Cambridge, NE, p. A391
CLAVELL, Luis M.D., Medical Director, San Jorge Children's Hospital, San Juan, PR, p. A726
CLAWSON, Tonya, Manager Human Resources, Mercy Medical Center–Centerville, Centerville, IA, p. A224
CLAXTON, Tracey
Chief Financial Officer, Chester Regional Medical Center, Chester, SC, p. A559
Chief Financial Officer, Jennersville Regional Hospital, West Grove, PA, p. A553
CLAY, David, Chief Executive Officer, Lower Keys Medical Center, Key West, FL, p. A129
CLAY, Elysia, Chief Nursing Officer, Healthsouth Rehabilitation Hospital – Dallas, Dallas, TX, p. A605
CLAYMORE, Krystal, Chief Financial Officer, Great Plains Health, North Platte, NE, p. A396
CLAYPOOL, Blain, Interim Chief Executive Officer, St. Joseph Regional Medical Center, Lewiston, ID, p. A174
CLAYTON, Donald, M.D., President, Indiana University Health Arnett Hospital, Lafayette, IN, p. A214
CLAYTON, Edward, Chief Executive Officer, Phelps County Regional Medical Center, Rolla, MO, p. A376
CLAYTON, Julie, Chief Nursing Officer and Vice President Patient Care Services, Overlake Medical Center, Bellevue, WA, p. A678
CLAYTON, Kent G., Chief Executive Officer, Los Alamitos Medical Center, Los Alamitos, CA, p. A67
CLAYTON, Melissa S. CPA, Chief Financial Officer, Northlake Behavioral Health System, Mandeville, LA, p. A280
CLAYTON, Philip A., President and Chief Executive Officer, Conway Medical Center, Conway, SC, p. A561
CLEARY, Gerard M. M.D., Senior Vice President, Chief of Staff and Chief Medical Officer, Abington Hospital, Abington, PA, p. A528
CLEARY, Mary Elizabeth., Chief Executive Officer, Macneal Hospital, Berwyn, IL, p. A178
CLEARY, Steven R, Chief Financial Officer, Overland Park Regional Medical Center, Overland Park, KS, p. A249
CLEAVER, Chuck, Vice President and Chief Financial Officer, Martin Health System, Stuart, FL, p. A143
CLECKLER, Jason, Chief Executive Officer, Delta County Memorial Hospital, Delta, CO, p. A100
CLEGG, Travis, Vice President, Operations, Castle Medical Center, Kailua, HI, p. A169
CLELAND, Dub, Chief Financial Officer, Oklahoma Surgical Hospital, Tulsa, OK, p. A517
CLELAND, Richard C., FACHE, Administrator, Ira Davenport Memorial Hospital, Bath, NY, p. A431
CLELAND, William H M.D., Chief Medical Officer, University Of Mississippi Medical Center, Jackson, MS, p. A357

CLEMEN, Linda R.N., MS, Vice President and Chief Nursing Officer, Katherine Shaw Bethea Hospital, Dixon, IL, p. A185
CLEMENT, Bernie, Chief Information Officer, Thibodaux Regional Medical Center, Thibodaux, LA, p. A287
CLEMENT, Bruce, Chief Operating Officer, Slidell Memorial Hospital, Slidell, LA, p. A286
CLEMENT, Charles, Chief Executive Officer, Searhc Mt. Edgecumbe Hospital, Sitka, AK, p. A27
CLEMENT, Clayton L., Interim Administrator, Community Howard Specialty Hospital, Kokomo, IN, p. A213
CLEMENT, Kevin J., Chief Executive Officer, Landmark Hospital Of Joplin, Joplin, MO, p. A369
CLEMENT, Michelle, Executive Assistant/Human Resources Director, Roundup Memorial Healthcare, Roundup, MT, p. A388
CLEMENTS, James, Chief Executive Officer, Cullman Regional Medical Center, Cullman, AL, p. A16
CLEMENTS, John R, Chief Financial Officer, Mccullough–Hyde Memorial Hospital/Trihealth, Oxford, OH, p. A498
CLEMMENSEN, Scott
Vice President Human Resources and Leadership Enhancement, Capital Health Medical Center–Hopewell, Pennington, NJ, p. A418
Vice President Human Resources and Leadership Enhancement, Capital Health Regional Medical Center, Trenton, NJ, p. A421
CLEMMER, Deb, Vice President Human Resources, Bothwell Regional Health Center, Sedalia, MO, p. A379
CLEMONS, Deneace, Chief Operating Officer, Twin Lakes Regional Medical Center, Leitchfield, KY, p. A260
CLER, Leslie M.D., Chief Medical Officer, Methodist Dallas Medical Center, Dallas, TX, p. A606
CLERE, Trevor, Director Information Technology, Mercy Medical Center, Canton, OH, p. A482
CLEVELAND, Austin, Chief Executive Officer, Solara Hospital Mcallen, Mcallen, TX, p. A632
CLEVELAND, Cynthia Ph.D., R.N., Associate Director for Patient Care Services and Nurse Executive, Birmingham Veterans Affairs Medical Center, Birmingham, AL, p. A14
CLEVENGER, Erin R, Chief Nursing Officer and Director of Quality, Memorial Medical Center, Port Lavaca, TX, p. A639
CLEWS, Donna Ph.D., R.N., Vice President Patient Care Services, Berkeley Medical Center, Martinsburg, WV, p. A693
CLIFFE, Peggy, Chief Executive Officer, Select Specialty Hospital–Wichita, Wichita, KS, p. A253
CLIFFORD, James, Administrator, Farren Care Center, Turners Falls, MA, p. B129
CLIFFORD, Michael J, Director Finance, Wayne Memorial Hospital, Honesdale, PA, p. A536
CLIFFORD, Ryan M.D., Chief of Staff, Washakie Medical Center, Worland, WY, p. A720
CLINE, Richard D.O., Chief of Staff, Lincoln County Health System, Fayetteville, TN, p. A578
CLINE, Vickie, Director Human Resources, Northwest Medical Center, Albany, MO, p. A364
CLINGENPEEL, Jeremy, Administrator, Satanta District Hospital And Long Term Care, Satanta, KS, p. A251
CLINGER, Dallas, Administrator, Power County Hospital District, American Falls, ID, p. A171
CLINITE, Ed D.O., Chief of Staff, Adventist Health Sonora, Sonora, CA, p. A92
CLINTON, Lee, FACHE, Chief Executive Officer, Titusville Area Hospital, Titusville, PA, p. A551
CLINTON, Lori, Chief Nursing Officer, Sparta Community Hospital, Sparta, IL, p. A200
CLIPP, Jerry, Manager Human Resources, Washakie Medical Center, Worland, WY, p. A720
CLISTER, Martha L, Director Human Resources, Canonsburg Hospital, Canonsburg, PA, p. A531
CLOHSEY, Maria, Director of Nursing, Hackensack Meridian Health Shore Rehabilitation Institute, Brick, NJ, p. A412
CLONCH, Les, Chief Information Officer, Texas Scottish Rite Hospital For Children, Dallas, TX, p. A607
CLONTS, Jolene, Director Human Resources, Logan Regional Hospital, Logan, UT, p. A657
CLOONAN, Shawn, Executive Vice President and Chief Operating Officer, Memorial Hermann – Texas Medical Center, Houston, TX, p. A621
CLOSE, Debra, Chief Executive Officer, Dukes Memorial Hospital, Peru, IN, p. A218
CLOUD, Avery, Vice President and Chief Information Officer, New Hanover Regional Medical Center, Wilmington, NC, p. A472
CLOUD, Sylvia, Director Human Resources, Silver Lake Medical Center, Los Angeles, CA, p. A71
CLOUGH, Jeanette G., President and Chief Executive Officer, Mount Auburn Hospital, Cambridge, MA, p. A305
CLOUGH, Sheila, Chief Executive Officer, Asante Ashland Community Hospital, Ashland, OR, p. A520

CLOUGH–BERRY, Cherie, Vice President, Finance, Hampstead Hospital, Hampstead, NH, p. A408
CLOUSE, Joseph, Chief Administrative Officer, Newport Hospital And Health Services, Newport, WA, p. A682
CLOUSE DAY, Sherry, Vice President Finance, Mercy Hospital Berryville, Berryville, AR, p. A40
CLOUTIER, Jonathan, Manager, Information Services, Buffalo Hospital, Buffalo, MN, p. A337
CLOUTIER, Mary, Director Human Resources, Adventist Behavioral Health And Wellness Services, Rockville, MD, p. A300
CLOUTIER, Michael, Director Information Services, Trios Health, Kennewick, WA, p. A681
CLOVER, Robert
Interim Superintendent, Larue D. Carter Memorial Hospital, Indianapolis, IN, p. A211
Superintendent and Chief Executive Officer, Logansport State Hospital, Logansport, IN, p. A215
CLOWES, Jennifer, Chief Financial Officer, Broadwater Health Center, Townsend, MT, p. A389
CLOYD, Elizabeth R.N., Chief Nurse Executive and Executive Vice President, Harris Health System, Houston, TX, p. A620
CLUCK, Robert N M.D., Vice President and Medical Director, Texas Health Arlington Memorial Hospital, Arlington, TX, p. A593
CLUFF, Ben, Chief Executive Officer, Ashley Regional Medical Center, Vernal, UT, p. A661
CLUNN, Amy M.D., Medical Director, Healthsouth Rehabilitation Hospital Of Ocala, Ocala, FL, p. A136
CLUTE, Gerald B.
Chief Executive Officer, Hollywood Presbyterian Medical Center, Los Angeles, CA, p. A68
Chief Executive Officer, Southern California Hospital At Culver City, Culver City, CA, p. A57
CLUTE, Gerald, Chief Executive Officer, East Los Angeles Doctors Hospital, Los Angeles, CA, p. A68
CLUTTS, Kathaleen, Chief Human Resources Officer, Des Peres Hospital, Saint Louis, MO, p. A377
CLYNE, Mary Ellen, MSN, Ph.D., R.N., President and Chief Executive Officer, Clara Maass Medical Center, Belleville, NJ, p. A411
CMIEL, Peggy R.N., Chief Nursing Officer, Chinese Hospital, San Francisco, CA, p. A87
COATES, Jennifer, Coordinator Information Technology, Purcell Municipal Hospital, Purcell, OK, p. A515
COATES, Robert M.D., Vice President, Medical Affairs, Hunterdon Medical Center, Flemington, NJ, p. A414
COATS, Daniel J, Vice President Operations, Mercy Hospital Ada, Ada, OK, p. A504
COATS, John M.D., Chief Medical Staff, Morehouse General Hospital, Bastrop, LA, p. A270
COATS, Kevin
Chief Financial Officer, Baylor Medical Center At Frisco, Frisco, TX, p. A615
Chief Operating Officer and Chief Financial Officer, Baylor Medical Center At Frisco, Frisco, TX, p. A615
COBARRUBIAS, Samuel M.D., Chief of Staff, Clinch Memorial Hospital, Homerville, GA, p. A159
COBB, April, Chief Nursing Officer, Healthsouth Lakeshore Rehabilitation Hospital, Birmingham, AL, p. A14
COBB, Heidi R.N., Chief Nursing Officer, Medical Arts Hospital, Lamesa, TX, p. A628
COBB, Janice M R.N., Chief Nursing Officer, Tennessee Valley Healthcare System, Nashville, TN, p. A587
COBB, Jason E., FACHE, Chief Executive Officer, Rapides Regional Medical Center, Alexandria, LA, p. A269
COBB, Jeff, Information Technologist, Guthrie County Hospital, Guthrie Center, IA, p. A228
COBB, Lindsay, Director Human Resources, Liberty Healthcare Systems, Bastrop, LA, p. A270
COBB, Stephen M.D., Chief Medical Officer, Presbyterian–St. Luke's Medical Center, Denver, CO, p. A101
COBBLE, Emlyn, Vice President and Chief Support Officer, Parkwest Medical Center, Knoxville, TN, p. A582
COBBS, Wendy, Director of Human Resources, Promise Hospital Of Baton Rouge – Ochsner Campus, Baton Rouge, LA, p. A271
COBURN, Meridith
Vice President Information Services, Saint Francis Hospital, Tulsa, OK, p. A518
Vice President, Information Systems, Saint Francis Hospital South, Tulsa, OK, p. A518
COBURN, Paul, Chief Financial Officer, Liberty Healthcare Systems, Bastrop, LA, p. A270
COBURN, Thomas C. M.D., Chief Medical Officer, Middle Park Medical Center–Kremmling, Kremmling, CO, p. A104
COCCA, Lisa, Chief Executive Officer, Belmont Pines Hospital, Youngstown, OH, p. A503

COLLAZO, Marian, Director Finance, Hospital San Cristobal, Coto Laurel, PR, p. A723

COLLETT, John, Vice President and Chief Financial Officer, Cayuga Medical Center At Ithaca, Ithaca, NY, p. A437

COLLETT, Josh, Director Human Resources, Pineville Community Hospital Association, Pineville, KY, p. A266

COLLETTI, Teresa, Director Patient Services, South Florida Baptist Hospital, Plant City, FL, p. A140

COLLEY, Sarah, Senior Vice President Human Resources, Regional One Health, Memphis, TN, p. A585

COLLIER, Betty, Chief Human Resources Officer, Johnson Regional Medical Center, Clarksville, AR, p. A41

COLLIER, Brad, Director, Piedmont Newton Hospital, Covington, GA, p. A155

COLLIER, Jack M.D., Chief of Staff, Mountainview Hospital, Las Vegas, NV, p. A403

COLLIER, Russell J., FACHE, President and Chief Executive Officer, Christus Good Shepherd Medical Center–Marshall, Marshall, TX, p. A632

COLLIER, Shari, Chief Financial Officer, Presbyterian–St. Luke's Medical Center, Denver, CO, p. A101

COLLINI, M. Patrick M.D., President Medical Staff, Usmd Hospital At Arlington, Arlington, TX, p. A594

COLLINS, Alesha Danielle MSN, R.N., Chief Nursing Officer, Howard Memorial Hospital, Nashville, AR, p. A47

COLLINS, Annasue, Chief Nursing Officer, Ten Broeck Tennessee Treatment Facility, Cookeville, TN, p. A577

COLLINS, Bobby
   Director Human Resources, Mountain View Regional Medical Center, Norton, VA, p. A672
   Director Human Resources, Wellmont Lonesome Pine Hospital, Big Stone Gap, VA, p. A664

COLLINS, Chauncey, Chief Operating Officer and Chief Financial Officer, Austen Riggs Center, Stockbridge, MA, p. A312

COLLINS, Daniel M.D., Clinical Director, New Mexico Behavioral Health Institute At Las Vegas, Las Vegas, NM, p. A427

COLLINS, Dennis, Chief Financial Officer, The Brook Hospital – Kmi, Louisville, KY, p. A263

COLLINS, Edmund, Chief Information Officer, Martin Health System, Stuart, FL, p. A143

COLLINS, Frances, Director of Nursing, Andrew Mcfarland Mental Health Center, Springfield, IL, p. A200

COLLINS, Harold E JD, Chief Financial Officer, Franciscan Healthcare – Munster, Munster, IN, p. A217

COLLINS, James M., President and Chief Executive Officer, St. Clair Hospital, Pittsburgh, PA, p. A547

COLLINS, Jeff, Chief Medical Officer, Providence St. Joseph's Hospital, Chewelah, WA, p. A679

COLLINS, Jeffrey A., M.D., Senior Vice President and Area Manager, Kaiser Permanente Roseville Medical Center, Roseville, CA, p. A83

COLLINS, John F., President and Chief Executive Officer, NYU Winthrop Hospital, Mineola, NY, p. A439

COLLINS, John P., FACHE, Medical Center Director, Veterans Affairs Central Western Massachusetts Healthcare System, Leeds, MA, p. A308

COLLINS, John R, Chief Financial Officer, Hemet Valley Medical Center, Hemet, CA, p. A63

COLLINS, John, Corporate Chief Financial Officer, Chapman Global Medical Center, Orange, CA, p. A77

COLLINS, John
   Chief Financial Officer, Anaheim Global Medical Center, Anaheim, CA, p. A51
   Chief Financial Officer, Orange County Global Medical Center, Inc., Santa Ana, CA, p. A90
   Chief Financial Officer, South Coast Global Medical Center, Santa Ana, CA, p. A90

COLLINS, Karen S., R.N., Chief Executive Officer, Lady Of The Sea General Hospital, Cut Off, LA, p. A274

COLLINS, Kevin J. M.D., Medical Director, St. Vincent Rehabilitation Hospital, Sherwood, AR, p. A49

COLLINS, Kimberly M.D., Chief of Staff, Saint Thomas Dekalb Hospital, Smithville, TN, p. A589

COLLINS, Leonora, Chief Nursing Officer, Nashville General Hospital, Nashville, TN, p. A586

COLLINS, Pam, Director Human Resources, Fairway Medical Surgical Hospital, Covington, LA, p. A273

COLLINS, Pamela, Vice President Chief Patient Services Officer, Mccullough–Hyde Memorial Hospital/Trihealth, Oxford, OH, p. A498

COLLINS, Richard F M.D., Executive Vice President and Chief Medical Officer, Jefferson Hospital, Jefferson Hills, PA, p. A537

COLLINS, Ricky M M.D., Chief of Staff, Whitesburg Arh Hospital, Whitesburg, KY, p. A268

COLLINS, Ron, Interim Chief Financial Officer, Mission Regional Medical Center, Mission, TX, p. A633

COLLINS, Sandra, Chief Clinical Officer, Kindred Hospital–Philadelphia, Philadelphia, PA, p. A544

COLLINS, Sharon
   Chief Information Officer, Salem Veterans Affairs Medical Center, Salem, VA, p. A675
   Director Human Resources and Chief Operating Officer, Russell Regional Hospital, Russell, KS, p. A250
   Interim Chief Executive Officer, Russell Regional Hospital, Russell, KS, p. A250

COLLINS, Sherry, Chief Nursing Officer, South Bay Hospital, Sun City Center, FL, p. A143

COLLINS, Teresa L R.N., Chief Nursing Officer, Overland Park Regional Medical Center, Overland Park, KS, p. A249

COLLINS, Thomas M., President, Chairman and Chief Executive Officer, Medical City Green Oaks Hospital, Dallas, TX, p. A606

COLLIPP, Dan M.D., Chief of Staff, Wayne Memorial Hospital, Jesup, GA, p. A159

COLLISON, June, President, Community Hospital Of San Bernardino, San Bernardino, CA, p. A85

COLLOM, Bobbie, Nursing Director, North Runnels Hospital, Winters, TX, p. A655

COLMAN, Gerard, Chief Operating Officer, Aurora West Allis Medical Center, West Allis, WI, p. A715

COLMENARES, Derek
   Chief Medical Officer, St. Agnes Hospital, Fond Du Lac, WI, p. A701
   Chief Medical Officer, Waupun Memorial Hospital, Waupun, WI, p. A715

COLOMBO, Armando, Chief Operating Officer, Sheppard Pratt Health System, Baltimore, MD, p. A295

COLOMBO, Lisa R.N., Senior Vice President Patient Care Services and Chief Nursing Officer, Umass Memorial Medical Center, Worcester, MA, p. A313

COLON, Julio
   Chief Financial Officer, St. Luke's Episcopal Hospital, Ponce, PR, p. A725
   Financial Director, Hospital De Damas, Ponce, PR, p. A724

COLON, Omar M.D., Medical Director, Healthsouth Plano Rehabilitation Hospital, Plano, TX, p. A638

COLONES, Robert L., President and Chief Executive Officer, Mcleod Regional Medical Center, Florence, SC, p. A562

COLONNELLI, Kim, Chief Nursing Officer, Corona Regional Medical Center, Corona, CA, p. A56

COLORADO, Judy R.N., Chief Nursing Officer, Monmouth Medical Center, Southern Campus, Lakewood, NJ, p. A415

COLPITTS, Robert, Chief Human Resource Service, Bedford Veterans Affairs Medical Center, Edith Nourse Rogers Memorial Veterans Hospital, Bedford, MA, p. A302

COLSDEN, Kristen, Director of Nursing, Osmond General Hospital, Osmond, NE, p. A398

COLSON, Wayne, Chief Financial Officer, Southwestern Medical Center, Lawton, OK, p. A509

COLTHARP, Missy, Director, Baptist Memorial Hospital–Union County, New Albany, MS, p. A360

COLTON, Jan M.D., Acting Clinical Director, U. S. Public Health Service Indian Hospital, Pine Ridge, SD, p. A571

COLUCCI, Eugene, Vice President Finance, Greenwich Hospital, Greenwich, CT, p. A110

COLUCCIO, Medrice, R.N.
   Chief Executive Officer, Providence St. Peter Hospital, Olympia, WA, p. A683
   Southwest Region Chief Executive, Providence Centralia Hospital, Centralia, WA, p. A679

COLVARD, Dusty, Manager Information Technology, Adventist Health Medical Center – Tehachapi Valley, Tehachapi, CA, p. A93

COLVERT, Richard, Chief Information Officer, Royal Oaks Hospital, Windsor, MO, p. A381

COLVIN, Garren
   Chief Executive Officer, St. Elizabeth Edgewood, Edgewood, KY, p. A257
   Chief Executive Officer, St. Elizabeth Florence, Florence, KY, p. A258
   Chief Executive Officer, St. Elizabeth Fort Thomas, Fort Thomas, KY, p. A258
   Chief Executive Officer, St. Elizabeth Grant, Williamstown, KY, p. A268

COLVIN, William, Human Resources Officer, Claiborne Memorial Medical Center, Homer, LA, p. A276

COLWELL, Dean D.O., Vice President Medical Affairs, Ohiohealth Doctors Hospital, Columbus, OH, p. A487

COLWELL, Melodie, Chief Financial Officer, Drew Memorial Health System, Monticello, AR, p. A47

COLYER, Valeri J
   Director Human Resources, Dickenson Community Hospital, Clintwood, VA, p. A666
   Director Human Resources, Norton Community Hospital, Norton, VA, p. A672

COMAIANNI, Sheri, Vice President Human Resources, Bakersfield Memorial Hospital, Bakersfield, CA, p. A52

COMBEST, Felton M.D., Vice President Medical Affairs, Magnolia Regional Health Center, Corinth, MS, p. A354

COMBETTA, Jeffery M.D., Medical Director, Bastrop Rehabilitation Hospital, Monroe, LA, p. A281

COMBS, Kevin, Chief of Staff, Carilion Tazewell Community Hospital, Tazewell, VA, p. A676

COMBS, Mark
   Chief Information Security Officer, Jefferson Medical Center, Ranson, WV, p. A695
   Interim Director System Information Technology, Berkeley Medical Center, Martinsburg, WV, p. A693

COMBS, Meri R.N., Vice President and Chief Nursing Officer, Madera Community Hospital, Madera, CA, p. A72

COMBS, Mike, Manager Information Technology, Holdenville General Hospital, Holdenville, OK, p. A508

COMBS, Will, Director Information Technology, Harrison Community Hospital, Cadiz, OH, p. A482

COMER, Fannessa, Chief Executive Officer, Northern Navajo Medical Center, Shiprock, NM, p. A428

COMER, Jennifer M.D., Medical Director, Valle Vista Hospital, Greenwood, IN, p. A209

COMER, Randy
   Chief Financial Officer, Athens–Limestone Hospital, Athens, AL, p. A14
   Chief Operating Officer, Athens–Limestone Hospital, Athens, AL, p. A14

COMER, Scott M, Vice President Human Resources, Marshall Medical Center, Placerville, CA, p. A80

COMERFORD, Jennifer, Manager Information Services, Midstate Medical Center, Meriden, CT, p. A111

COMITTO, Judy, Vice President Information Services and Chief Information Officer, Trinitas Regional Medical Center, Elizabeth, NJ, p. A413

COMP, Susan, Senior Vice President and Chief Nursing Officer, Pinnaclehealth Harrisburg Hospital, Harrisburg, PA, p. A536

COMPTON, Brenda, Manager Information Technology, Plumas District Hospital, Quincy, CA, p. A81

COMPTON, Mark, Chief Financial Officer, Laughlin Memorial Hospital, Greeneville, TN, p. A579

COMPTON, Randy, Information Technology and System Director, Logan Memorial Hospital, Russellville, KY, p. A267

COMPTON, Ty, Chief Nursing Officer, Horton Community Hospital, Horton, KS, p. A243

COMPTON–OGLE, Carri, Administrative Officer, Heartland Behavioral Health Services, Nevada, MO, p. A374

CONANT, Cathy, Chief Human Resources and Personnel, Eastern Plumas Health Care, Portola, CA, p. A80

CONANT, Merrill M.D., Chief of Staff, Western Plains Medical Complex, Dodge City, KS, p. A240

CONANT, Sonya, Senior Director Human Resources, Alaska Native Medical Center, Anchorage, AK, p. A25

CONAWAY, E Edwin M.D., Vice President Medical Affairs and Chief Medical Officer, Southeastern Ohio Regional Medical Center, Cambridge, OH, p. A482

CONCANNON, Laura M.D., Regional Chief Medical Officer, Presence Saints Mary & Elizabeth Medical Center, Chicago, IL, p. A183

CONCEPCION, Walter, Chief Executive Officer, West Gables Rehabilitation Hospital, Miami, FL, p. A134

CONCORDIA, Elizabeth B., President and Chief Executive Officer, University Of Colorado Health, Fort Collins, CO, p. B139

CONDE, Tania, Administrator, Hospital Hermanos Melendez, Bayamon, PR, p. A722

CONDIT, Brian, M.D.
   Chief Medical Officer, Johnston Memorial Hospital, Abingdon, VA, p. A664
   Vice President Chief Medical Officer, Virginia Operations Medical Staff Services, Russell County Medical Center, Lebanon, VA, p. A669

CONDIT, Edward, President and Chief Executive Officer, St. Mary's General Hospital, Passaic, NJ, p. A418

CONDOLUCI, David M.D., Senior Vice President and Chief Medical Officer, Kennedy Health System, Stratford, NJ, p. A420

CONDON, Joseph
   Director Human Resources, Texas Health Specialty Hospital, Fort Worth, TX, p. A614
   Entity Human Resources Officer, Texas Health Harris Methodist Hospital Fort Worth, Fort Worth, TX, p. A614

CONDRY, Donna, Director Human Resources, Unitypoint Health – Jones Regional Medical Center, Anamosa, IA, p. A222

CONE, Maryann, Chief Operating Officer, Sharp Grossmont Hospital, La Mesa, CA, p. A64

CONEJO, David, Chief Executive Officer, Rehoboth Mckinley Christian Health Care Services, Gallup, NM, p. A426

CONFALONE, Daniel, Chief Financial Officer and Vice President Finance, St. Mary Medical Center, Langhorne, PA, p. A538

CONFER, James, Manager Information Systems, Clarion Hospital, Clarion, PA, p. A531

CONGDON, James B M.D., Medical Director, Horsham Clinic, Ambler, PA, p. A529

CONGER, Sue, Chief Operating Officer, Eastside Psychiatric Hospital, Tallahassee, FL, p. A144

CONKLIN, Maggie C, M.P.H.
  Interim Chief Nurse Officer, Novant Health Uva Health System Prince William Medical Center, Manassas, VA, p. A670
  Interim Chief Nursing Officer, Novant Health Uva Health System Haymarket Medical Center, Haymarket, VA, p. A668

CONKLIN, Michael E Jr, Chief Financial Officer, St. Joseph Health Services Of Rhode Island, North Providence, RI, p. A556

CONKLIN, Robin R.N., Chief Nursing Officer, Carondelet St. Joseph's Hospital, Tucson, AZ, p. A37

CONKLING, Victoria, Vice President Patient Care Services and Chief Nursing Officer, Uhs Delaware Valley Hospital, Walton, NY, p. A454

CONLEY, Carol, Chief Nursing Officer, Landmark Medical Center, Woonsocket, RI, p. A557

CONLEY, Christopher M.D., President of the Medical Staff, Tristar Skyline Medical Center, Nashville, TN, p. A587

CONLEY, Joanna J., FACHE, Chief Executive Officer, Tristar Southern Hills Medical Center, Nashville, TN, p. A587

CONLEY, Kenneth, Chief Financial Officer, Baptist Memorial Hospital – Calhoun, Calhoun City, MS, p. A353

CONLEY, Melissa, Director Human Resources, Midwest Medical Center, Galena, IL, p. A188

CONLEY, Michelle E R.N., Chief Nursing Officer, Aria – Jefferson Health, Philadelphia, PA, p. A543

CONLEY, Teressa
  President and Chief Executive Officer, St. Rose Dominican Hospitals – Rose De Lima Campus, Henderson, NV, p. A402
  Vice President and Chief Operating Officer, St. Rose Dominican Hospitals – Rose De Lima Campus, Henderson, NV, p. A402
  Manager Human Resources, Cherokee Regional Medical Center, Cherokee, IA, p. A224

CONLEY, Thomas C, Vice President, Human Resources and Organizational Development, Northwestern Medical Center, Saint Albans, VT, p. A663

CONLON, John M.D., Chief Medical Officer, Saint Anne's Hospital, Fall River, MA, p. A306

CONN, Stephanie, Administrator and Chief Nursing Officer, Coshocton Regional Medical Center, Coshocton, OH, p. A488

CONNAWAY, Jessica, Director Human Resources, Crossroads Community Hospital, Mount Vernon, IL, p. A194

CONNEL, Lorene, Chief Human Resources Management Service, Veterans Affairs Eastern Colorado Health Care System, Denver, CO, p. A101

CONNELL, Faith, Director of Nursing, Turning Point Hospital, Moultrie, GA, p. A162

CONNELL, Pam, Manager Human Resources, Windsor–Laurelwood Center For Behavioral Medicine, Willoughby, OH, p. A502

CONNELLEY, Bertha Mary, Director Human Resources, Austen Riggs Center, Stockbridge, MA, p. A312

CONNELLY, Jac, Chief Financial Officer, Rose Medical Center, Denver, CO, p. A101

CONNELLY, Kathryn, Manager Information Technology, Connecticut Valley Hospital, Middletown, CT, p. A111

CONNELLY, Steven M.D., President and Chief Medical Officer, Park Nicollet Methodist Hospital, Saint Louis Park, MN, p. A347

CONNER, Chad, Administrator, Northern Louisiana Medical Center, Ruston, LA, p. A285

CONNER, Jeff M.D., Chief Medical Staff, Loma Linda University Medical Center–Murrieta, Murrieta, CA, p. A75

CONNER, June, R.N., Chief Operating Officer, Emory University Hospital, Atlanta, GA, p. A150

CONNER, Laurie A., FACHE, Interim Chief Executive Officer, Skiff Medical Center, Newton, IA, p. A232

CONNER, Stacey, Director Personnel, Ed Fraser Memorial Hospital And Baker Community Health Center, Macclenny, FL, p. A131

CONNERS, Stephanie, Senior Executive Vice President Chief Operating Officer and Chief Nursing Officer, Cooper University Health Care, Camden, NJ, p. A412

CONNERTON, Kathryn, President and Chief Executive Officer, Our Lady Of Lourdes Memorial Hospital, Inc., Binghamton, NY, p. A432

CONNOLLY, Christine M.D., Chief of Staff, Keefe Memorial Hospital, Cheyenne Wells, CO, p. A99

CONNOLLY, Seam, Commissioner, Connecticut Veterans Home And Hospital, Rocky Hill, CT, p. A112

CONNOLLY, Teresa R.N., Chief Nursing Officer, Mayo Clinic Hospital, Phoenix, AZ, p. A33

CONNOLLY ROBBINS, Danielle, Chief Nursing Officer, Select Specialty Hospital–Knoxville, Knoxville, TN, p. A582

CONNOR, Brian, President, Christus Spohn Hospital Corpus Christi Memorial, Corpus Christi, TX, p. A603

CONNOR, Della, Director Human Resource, Firsthealth Moore Regional Hospital – Hamlet, Hamlet, NC, p. A464

CONNOR, Paul J. III, President and Chief Executive Officer, Eastern Long Island Hospital, Greenport, NY, p. A436

CONNOR, Starr, Chief Nursing Officer, Fairfield Memorial Hospital, Winnsboro, SC, p. A567

CONNOR, William
  Assistant Administrator and Director Human Resources, River Hospital, Alexandria Bay, NY, p. A430
  Assistant Administrator and Director Human Resources, River Hospital, Alexandria Bay, NY, p. A430

CONNORS, Alfred M.D., Executive Vice President and Chief Quality Officer and Interim Chief Medical Officer, Metrohealth Medical Center, Cleveland, OH, p. A486

CONNORS, Dennis, Executive Director, Lenox Hill Hospital, New Rochelle, NY, p. A442

CONNORS, Lawrence J
  Chief Operating Officer, Hshs St. Mary's Hospital Medical Center, Green Bay, WI, p. A703
  Chief Operating Officer, Hshs St. Vincent Hospital, Green Bay, WI, p. A703

CONNORS, Michael
  Senior Vice President and Chief Financial Officer, Cape Cod Hospital, Hyannis, MA, p. A307
  Senior Vice President and Chief Financial Officer, Falmouth Hospital, Falmouth, MA, p. A306

CONNORS, Robert, M.D., President, Spectrum Health – Butterworth Hospital, Grand Rapids, MI, p. A321

CONNOVICH, Ron D
  Chief Financial Officer and Chief Operating Officer, Soin Medical Center, Beavercreek, OH, p. A481
  Chief Financial Officer, Greene Memorial Hospital, Xenia, OH, p. A503

CONNY, Sophia, Deputy Administrative Officer, U. S. Public Health Service Indian Hospital, Pine Ridge, SD, p. A571

CONOVER, Candy, Administrator, Saint Clare Home, Peoria Heights, IL, p. B95

CONOVER, Jevne, Chief Executive Officer, Great Lakes Specialty Hospital–Grand Rapids, Grand Rapids, MI, p. A321

CONRAD, Daniel S., M.D., President, Phillips Eye Institute, Minneapolis, MN, p. A344

CONRAD, Elizabeth P., Senior Vice President and Chief Human Resource Officer, Lahey Hospital & Medical Center, Burlington, Burlington, MA, p. A305

CONRAD, Heidi, Vice President and Chief Financial Officer, Regions Hospital, Saint Paul, MN, p. A348

CONRATH, Mark, Chief Financial Officer, Drumright Regional Hospital, Drumright, OK, p. A506

CONROW–VERVERIS, Stacy, Director Human Resources, Mineral Community Hospital, Superior, MT, p. A388

CONROY, Carol R.N., Chief Nursing Officer, Southwestern Vermont Medical Center, Bennington, VT, p. A662

CONROY, Dorothy, Director Human Resources, Oakleaf Surgical Hospital, Eau Claire, WI, p. A701

CONROY, Joanne M., M.D., President and Chief Executive Officer, Dartmouth–Hitchcock Medical Center, Lebanon, NH, p. A409

CONROY, Michael, Chief Financial Officer, Pine Creek Medical Center, Dallas, TX, p. A606

CONROY, Mike, Chief Financial Officer, Methodist Mckinney Hospital, Mckinney, TX, p. A632

CONROY, Tracy, Chief Executive Officer, Daviess Community Hospital, Washington, IN, p. A221

CONSBRUCK, Todd
  Chief Executive Officer, Avera Creighton Hospital, Creighton, NE, p. A392
  President and Chief Executive Officer, Avera St. Anthony's Hospital, O'Neill, NE, p. A398

CONSIDINE, William H., President, Akron Children's Hospital, Akron, OH, p. A479

CONSIGLIO, Gayle, Chief Information Officer, Mclaren Lapeer Region, Lapeer, MI, p. A325

CONSIGNEY, Ginger, Vice President Human Resources, Lake Charles Memorial Hospital, Lake Charles, LA, p. A279

CONSOLVER, Roberta, Chief Information Officer, Healthbridge Children's Hospital, Orange, CA, p. A78

CONSTANT, Jean–Charles, Administrator, Dover Behavioral Health System, Dover, DE, p. A115

CONSTANTINE, Candida MSN, R.N., Chief Nursing Officer, South Texas Health System, Edinburg, TX, p. A610

CONTE, John, Director Facility Services and Real Estate, Wayne Memorial Hospital, Honesdale, PA, p. A536

CONTI, John, Director Finance, Shriners Hospitals For Children–Greenville, Greenville, SC, p. A563

CONTRERAS, Amy Esq, Chief Nursing Officer, Milford Valley Memorial Hospital, Milford, UT, p. A657

CONTRERAS, Marta, Chief Nursing Officer and Chief Operating Officer, Foundation Surgical Hospital Of El Paso, El Paso, TX, p. A611

CONVERY, Luanne, Vice President Patient Care Services, Putnam Hospital Center, Carmel, NY, p. A433

CONWAY, Jimmy M.D., President Medical Staff, Northwest Surgical Hospital, Oklahoma City, OK, p. A512

CONWAY, Kevin, Chief Information Officer, Upmc Mercy, Pittsburgh, PA, p. A547

CONWILL, Michael, Director Human Resources, Corpus Christi Medical Center, Corpus Christi, TX, p. A603

CONYERS, Robin, Administrator, Chi Health Creighton University Medical Center – Bergan Mercy, Omaha, NE, p. A397

COOGAN, Ben, Chief Operating Officer, Medical City Arlington, Arlington, TX, p. A593

COOK, Aaron, Director Information Services, Christus Lake Area Hospital, Lake Charles, LA, p. A279

COOK, Alan, Chief Medical Officer, Central Regional Hospital, Butner, NC, p. A458

COOK, Brenda, Chief Nursing Officer, Monroe Hospital, Bloomfield, IN, p. A204

COOK, Brian, FACHE, President and Chief Executive Officer, North Florida Regional Medical Center, Gainesville, FL, p. A125

COOK, Brooke, Director of Nursing, Strategic Behavioral Health – Wilmington, Leland, NC, p. A466

COOK, Carla, Director of Nursing, Scotland County Hospital, Memphis, MO, p. A373

COOK, Darrin, Chief Executive Officer and Administrator, Horizon Specialty Hospital, Las Vegas, NV, p. A403

COOK, David A, Vice President and Chief Financial Officer, University Hospitals Elyria Medical Center, Elyria, OH, p. A491

COOK, David, Manager Information Systems, Christus Dubuis Hospital Of Hot Springs, Hot Springs National Park, AR, p. A44

COOK, Elizabeth, Chief Information Officer, Mizell Memorial Hospital, Opp, AL, p. A22

COOK, G. Anthony M.D., Medical Director, Hemphill County Hospital, Canadian, TX, p. A600

COOK, Greg, Chief Financial Officer, Castleview Hospital, Price, UT, p. A659

COOK, Heidi, Chief Nursing Officer, Warner Hospital And Health Services, Clinton, IL, p. A184

COOK, Janie, Director Information Systems, Passavant Area Hospital, Jacksonville, IL, p. A191

COOK, John
  Interim Chief Information Officer, University Of California, Davis Medical Center, Sacramento, CA, p. A84
  Senior Vice President & Chief Financial Officer, Mercyhealth Hospital – Rockton Avenue, Rockford, IL, p. A199

COOK, John, Vice President and Chief Financial Officer, Mercyhealth Hospital And Trauma Center – Janesville, Janesville, WI, p. A704

COOK, Katheryn R.N., Nurse Executive, Cincinnati Veterans Affairs Medical Center, Cincinnati, OH, p. A484

COOK, Kathy, FACHE, MSN, President, Mercy Health – St. Joseph Warren Hospital, Warren, OH, p. A501

COOK, Kevin S., Chief Executive Officer, University Of Mississippi Medical Center, Jackson, MS, p. A357

COOK, Kim, Interim Clinical Applications Services Manager, Tri–City Medical Center, Oceanside, CA, p. A77

COOK, LaMont, Administrator, F. W. Huston Medical Center, Winchester, KS, p. A254

COOK, Linda, Vice President Human Resources, St. Joseph Hospital, Eureka, CA, p. A58

COOK, Lottie, Superintendent, Evansville Psychiatric Children Center, Evansville, IN, p. A207

COOK, Marcia, Director Information Technology, Bates County Memorial Hospital, Butler, MO, p. A365

COOK, Mary Ann R.N., Director of Nursing, Red Lake Indian Health Service Hospital, Red Lake, MN, p. A346

COOK, Natalie
  Administrative Director of Human Resources, Manchester Memorial Hospital, Manchester, CT, p. A110
  Administrative Director, Human Resources, Rockville General Hospital, Vernon, CT, p. A113

COOK, Pamela W, Chief Financial Officer, Trace Regional Hospital, Houston, MS, p. A356

COOK, Patrick, Vice President Support Services, Morgan Memorial Hospital, Madison, GA, p. A161

CORNELIUS, Teresa R.N., Interim Chief Nursing Officer, Hshs St. Joseph's Hospital, Highland, IL, p. A190
CORNELL, John, Vice President Finance, Meadows Regional Medical Center, Vidalia, GA, p. A166
CORNES, Robert S., Commander, Ireland Army Community Hospital, Fort Knox, KY, p. A258
CORNET, Trina JD, Vice President Human Resources, Jamaica Hospital Medical Center, New Rochelle, NY, p. A441
CORNETT, Sheila, Manager Human Resources, Hazard Arh Regional Medical Center, Hazard, KY, p. A259
CORNETT, Suzanne, Director Human Resources, Southern Kentucky Rehabilitation Hospital, Bowling Green, KY, p. A256
CORNICELLI, Kari
   Chief Financial Officer, Sharp Grossmont Hospital, La Mesa, CA, p. A64
   Chief Financial Officer, Sharp Memorial Hospital, San Diego, CA, p. A86
   Chief Financial Officer, Sharp Mesa Vista Hospital, San Diego, CA, p. A86
CORNWALL, Thomas M.D., Medical Director, Holly Hill Hospital, Raleigh, NC, p. A469
CORNWELL, Cheryl J, Chief Financial Officer, Lake District Hospital, Lakeview, OR, p. A523
CORNWELL, Cheryl, Chief Financial Officer, Great Falls Hospital, Great Falls, MT, p. A385
CORNWELL, Daniel, Command Officer, U. S. Naval Hospital Guam, Agana, GU, p. A721
CORNWELL, Richard, Chief Executive Officer, Surprise Valley Health Care District, Cedarville, CA, p. A55
CORONEL, Jorge, Chief Information Officer, Regional Hospital Of Scranton, Scranton, PA, p. A550
CORPORA, Don, Executive Vice President and Chief Human Resources Officer, Cleveland Clinic Akron General, Akron, OH, p. A479
CORRADO, Bob, Chief Information Officer, Canandaigua Veterans Affairs Medical Center, Canandaigua, NY, p. A433
CORRADO, Theresa, Director Finance, St. Luke's Hospital – Quakertown Campus, Quakertown, PA, p. A549
CORREA, Elizabeth, Director Information Management, Big Spring State Hospital, Big Spring, TX, p. A598
CORREA, Leo, Chief Executive Officer and Administrator, St. Catherine Hospital, East Chicago, IN, p. A206
CORREA, Maria de los Angeles M.D., Medical Director, Hospital Metropolitan, San Juan, PR, p. A726
CORREA, Omar, Chief Financial Officer, Texas Neurorehab Center, Austin, TX, p. A596
CORREA, Sharon, Vice President and Chief Information Officer, Adventist Health Glendale, Glendale, CA, p. A62
CORREIA, Antonio, Chief Financial Officer, Holyoke Medical Center, Holyoke, MA, p. A307
CORRELL, Anne, Chief Clinical Officer, Kindred Hospital– Greensboro, Greensboro, NC, p. A463
CORRIDON, Fran, Vice President Human Resources and Shared Services, Hackensack Meridian Health Mountainside Medical Center, Montclair, NJ, p. A416
CORRIGAN, Heidi, Manager Human Resources, Trinity Hospital, Weaverville, CA, p. A96
CORRIGAN, Jeffrey T.
   Interim Director Human Resources, Day Kimball Hospital, Putnam, CT, p. A112
   Vice President Human Resources, Brattleboro Retreat, Brattleboro, VT, p. A662
CORRIGAN, Paula, Vice President and Chief Financial Officer, OSF Saint James – John W. Albrecht Medical Center, Pontiac, IL, p. A198
CORRIGAN, Thomas L, Senior Vice President Finance, Managed Care and Chief Financial Officer, Christiana Care Health System, Newark, DE, p. A115
CORS, William K M.D., Vice President and Chief Medical Quality Officer, Lehigh Valley Hospital – Pocono, East Stroudsburg, PA, p. A533
CORSO, David, Chief Operating Officer, Beaver Dam Community Hospitals, Beaver Dam, WI, p. A699
CORTI, Ronald J., President and Chief Executive Officer, St. John's Riverside Hospital, Yonkers, NY, p. A456
CORUM, Sharon, Chief Financial Officer, Kingwood Pines Hospital, Kingwood, TX, p. A627
CORWIN, Florence
   Director Administration, Pilgrim Psychiatric Center, Brentwood, NY, p. A432
   Director for Administration, Pilgrim Psychiatric Center, Brentwood, NY, p. A432
CORWIN, Nancy
   Chief Nursing Officer, Summit Surgical, Hutchinson, KS, p. A243
   Chief Operating Officer, Summit Surgical, Hutchinson, KS, p. A243

CORWIN, Steven J., M.D., President and Chief Executive Officer, New York–Presbyterian Hospital, New Rochelle, NY, p. A444
CORZINE, Judy, Administrative Director and Chief Information Officer, Stormont Vail Health, Topeka, KS, p. A252
COSBY, Christopher, Chief Executive Officer, Poinciana Medical Center, Kissimmee, FL, p. A129
COSBY, Dwan, Manager Human Resources, Mclaren Oakland, Pontiac, MI, p. A328
COSBY, Ernestine Y., Vice President Clinical Services and Chief Nursing Officer, Sheppard Pratt Health System, Baltimore, MD, p. A295
COSGROVE, Delos, M.D., President and Chief Executive Officer, Cleveland Clinic, Cleveland, OH, p. A485
COSLETT, John R.N., Chief Nursing Officer, Kansas Spine And Specialty Hospital, Wichita, KS, p. A253
COSTA, Christopher P. M.D., Chief of Staff, Gordon Memorial Health Services, Gordon, NE, p. A393
COSTA, Joe
   Acting Chief Fiscal Officer, Veterans Affairs Boston Healthcare System Brockton Division, Brockton, MA, p. A305
   Chief Financial Officer, Veterans Affairs Boston Healthcare System, West Roxbury, MA, p. A312
COSTA, Mark E., Executive Director, Kaiser Permanente Orange County Anaheim Medical Center, Anaheim, CA, p. A51
COSTA, Michael G, Vice President Human Resources, Chi St. Joseph Regional Health Center, Bryan, TX, p. A600
COSTAKIS, Angie, Chief Information Officer, Claiborne Memorial Medical Center, Homer, LA, p. A276
COSTANTINO, Vincent
   Interim President and Chief Administrative Officer, St. Francis Medical Center, Trenton, NJ, p. A422
   Vice President Operations and Human Resources, Hackensack Meridian Health Raritan Bay Medical Center, Perth Amboy, NJ, p. A419
COSTANZO, Kristin L., Direct–In–Market Lead Human Relations Partner, St. Vincent's Blount, Oneonta, AL, p. A22
COSTELLA, Jeane L, Vice President, New York–Presbyterian/ Hudson Valley Hospital, Cortlandt Manor, NY, p. A434
COSTELLO, Jeff
   Chief Financial Officer, Elkhart General Hospital, Elkhart, IN, p. A207
   Chief Financial Officer, Memorial Hospital Of South Bend, South Bend, IN, p. A220
COSTELLO, Jodi, Chief Executive Officer, Select Specialty Hospital–Youngstown, Youngstown, OH, p. A503
COSTELLO, Susan, Chief Nursing Officer, Lucile Salter Packard Children's Hospital Stanford, Palo Alto, CA, p. A79
COSTIC, Andrew
   Regional Chief Financial Officer, Abraham Lincoln Memorial Hospital, Lincoln, IL, p. A192
   Regional Chief Financial Officer, Taylorville Memorial Hospital, Taylorville, IL, p. A201
COSTIE, Glenn A., FACHE, Director, Dayton Veterans Affairs Medical Center, Dayton, OH, p. A489
COSTNER, Marc, Chief Financial Officer, Chestnut Hill Hospital, Philadelphia, PA, p. A543
COTA, Scott M.D., Director Medical Services, Naval Hospital Lemoore, Lemoore, CA, p. A65
COTE, Gerri, Chief Operating Officer, Brattleboro Retreat, Brattleboro, VT, p. A662
COTE, Mary, Director Human Resources, New England Rehabilitation Hospital Of Portland, Portland, ME, p. A292
COTT, Gary M.D., Executive Vice President Medical and Clinical Services, National Jewish Health, Denver, CO, p. A101
COTTEN, Brandon, Chief Financial Officer, Dewitt Hospital, Dewitt, AR, p. A42
COTTER, Bonny, Chief Nursing Officer, Baraga County Memorial Hospital, L'Anse, MI, p. A324
COTTER, Carole
   Senior Vice President and Chief Information Officer, Emma Pendleton Bradley Hospital, East Providence, RI, p. A556
   Senior Vice President and Chief Information Officer, Rhode Island Hospital, Providence, RI, p. A557
   Vice President and Chief Information Officer, Miriam Hospital, Providence, RI, p. A556
COTTERMAN, Rob, Chief Executive Officer, Middle Tennessee Mental Health Institute, Nashville, TN, p. A586
COTTINGHAM, Jerod, Director Information Systems, Carlinville Area Hospital, Carlinville, IL, p. A179
COTTLE, Jeremy, Ph.D., Chief Executive Officer, Provo Canyon Behavioral Hospital, Orem, UT, p. A658
COTTLE, Mike, Chief Information Officer, Newton Medical Center, Newton, KS, p. A247
COTTO, Hector L M.D., Medical Director, Hospital San Francisco, San Juan, PR, p. A726

COTTON, C Gerald, Interim Chief Operating Officer, Baptist Medical Center Leake, Carthage, MS, p. A353
COTTON, Michael, Chief Financial Officer, Gadsden Regional Medical Center, Gadsden, AL, p. A18
COTTRELL, Leslie R.N., MSN, Nurse Lead, Iroquois Memorial Hospital And Resident Home, Watseka, IL, p. A202
COTTRILL, Brian, Chief Information Officer, United Hospital Center, Bridgeport, WV, p. A690
COUCH, Beulah, Director Human Resources, Mary Breckinridge Arh Hospital, Hyden, KY, p. A260
COUCH, Bill, Chief Financial Officer, Ashley County Medical Center, Crossett, AR, p. A42
COUCH, Chad, Chief Medical Officer, Wellmont Bristol Regional Medical Center, Bristol, TN, p. A575
COUCHMAN, Diane, Vice President Patient Care Services and Chief Nursing Executive, Calvert Memorial Hospital, Prince Frederick, MD, p. A300
COUGHLIN, Ann, Director Human Resources, Boundary Community Hospital, Bonners Ferry, ID, p. A172
COUGHLIN, Cynthia MS, R.N., Chief Nursing Officer, Cheshire Medical Center, Keene, NH, p. A408
COUGHLIN, Kevin B., Chief Executive Officer, Beth Israel Deaconess Hospital Plymouth, Plymouth, MA, p. A310
COUGHLIN, Michael, Chief Executive Officer, Crotched Mountain Rehabilitation Center, Greenfield, NH, p. A408
COULTER, Barbara
   Director Information Systems, Franciscan St. Francis Health – Indianapolis, Indianapolis, IN, p. A211
   Director Information Systems, Franciscan St. Francis Health – Mooresville, Mooresville, IN, p. A216
COUNTS, Virginia, Manager Human Resources, Scott & White Hospital – Brenham, Brenham, TX, p. A599
COUNTY–TEEMER, Vickie, Coordinator Human Resources, Mitchell County Hospital, Camilla, GA, p. A153
COURIS, John D., Chief Executive Officer, Tampa General Hospital, Tampa, FL, p. A145
COURNYER, Tim, Administrator, Forks Community Hospital, Forks, WA, p. A680
COURREGE, Gary, Chief Information Officer, Jennings American Legion Hospital, Jennings, LA, p. A277
COURTNEY, Christine R.N., Vice President and Chief Nursing Officer, Providence Healthcare Network, Waco, TX, p. A652
COURTOIS, Harold, Chief Executive Officer, Memorial Health System, Abilene, KS, p. A238
COURTOIS, Robert, Vice President Finance, Otsego Memorial Hospital, Gaylord, MI, p. A320
COURY, Justin, Chief Operating Officer, Tristar Centennial Medical Center, Nashville, TN, p. A587
COURY, Tiffany, Chief Operating Officer, Northern Nevada Medical Center, Sparks, NV, p. A406
COUSAR, Myra, Director Human Resources, Baptist Memorial Hospital–Tipton, Covington, TN, p. A578
COUSINEAU, Cathy, Director Human Resources, Kaiser Permanente Woodland Hills Medical Center, Los Angeles, CA, p. A69
COUTURE, Maureen, Chief Nursing Officer and Vice President Nursing, Cardinal Hill Rehabilitation Hospital, Lexington, KY, p. A261
COUVILLON, Larry M.D., Chief Medical Officer, Memorial Hospital At Gulfport, Gulfport, MS, p. A355
COVA, Charles J., Senior Vice President, Operations, Marian Regional Medical Center, Santa Maria, CA, p. A91
COVAULT, Julie, Vice President Finance, Wilson Memorial Hospital, Sidney, OH, p. A499
COVAULT, Myra, Associate Vice President of Human Resources, Hardin Memorial Hospital, Elizabethtown, KY, p. A257
COVELL, Nancy, Director Human Resources, Cameron Memorial Community Hospital, Angola, IN, p. A203
COVELLI, Margaret R.N., Chief Nursing Officer, Spring Valley Hospital Medical Center, Las Vegas, NV, p. A404
COVER, Barry M.D., Medical Director, Magruder Memorial Hospital, Port Clinton, OH, p. A498
COVERT, Kathy MSN, Vice President Human Resources, Schneck Medical Center, Seymour, IN, p. A219
COVERT, Michael H., FACHE, Chief Executive Officer, Baylor St. Luke's Medical Center Mcnair Campus, Houston, TX, p. A619
COVERT, Terri, Vice President Human Resources, Mission Hospital, Mission Viejo, CA, p. A74
COVEY, Staci, R.N., MS
   President, Guthrie Towanda Memorial Hospital, Towanda, PA, p. A551
   President, Troy Community Hospital, Troy, PA, p. A552
COVINGTON, Casey M.D., President Elect, Medical Staff, Jennie Stuart Medical Center, Hopkinsville, KY, p. A260
COVINGTON, Celia MSN, R.N., Director of Nursing, St. Mary's Good Samaritan Hospital, Greensboro, GA, p. A158

COVINGTON, Jerome M.D., Chief Medical Officer, Lower Keys Medical Center, Key West, FL, p. A129

COVONE, Ann Marie, Senior Vice President and Chief Financial Officer, Terence Cardinal Cooke Health Care Center, New Rochelle, NY, p. A447

COWAN, Christopher, Senior Vice President and Chief Human Resources Officer, Christiana Care Health System, Newark, DE, p. A115

COWAN, J W., Administrator, Choctaw General Hospital, Butler, AL, p. A15

COWAN, Leslie R.N., Chief Nursing Officer, Henry County Hospital, New Castle, IN, p. A217

COWAN, Ronald M, Vice President Information Systems, Geisinger–Lewistown Hospital, Lewistown, PA, p. A539

COWART, Mark, Chief Information Officer, Carl Vinson Veterans Affairs Medical Center, Dublin, GA, p. A157

COWART, Timothy, Chief Executive Officer, The Centers, Ocala, FL, p. A136

COWLES, John, Chief Financial Officer, Silver Lake Medical Center, Los Angeles, CA, p. A71

COWLING, Phyllis A., CPA, President and Chief Executive Officer, United Regional Health Care System, Wichita Falls, TX, p. A654

COX, Amber, Director Human Resources, East Texas Medical Center Carthage, Carthage, TX, p. A601

COX, Brian, Director Information Systems, Baptist Health Floyd, New Albany, IN, p. A217

COX, Carla C., Chief Nursing Officer, Indiana University Health Ball Memorial Hospital, Muncie, IN, p. A216

COX, Chandler, Director Human Resources, Mena Regional Health System, Mena, AR, p. A47

COX, David W, Chief Financial Officer, Marin General Hospital, Greenbrae, CA, p. A62

COX, Debbie D, Administrative Director Human Resources, Central Texas Medical Center, San Marcos, TX, p. A644

COX, Denida A., Chief Nursing Officer, South Georgia Medical Center, Valdosta, GA, p. A166

COX, Dianne E, Vice President of Human Resources, Kaweah Delta Medical Center, Visalia, CA, p. A96

COX, Dina, Director Human Resources, Kansas Rehabilitation Hospital, Topeka, KS, p. A252

COX, Dorothy, Manager Information Systems, Hackettstown Medical Center, Hackettstown, NJ, p. A414

COX, Gwen, Director Nursing Services, Klickitat Valley Health, Goldendale, WA, p. A681

COX, Jeffrey
   Chief Information Officer, Glendora Community Hospital, Glendora, CA, p. A62
   Director Information Technology, San Dimas Community Hospital, San Dimas, CA, p. A86

COX, Keith, Chief Executive Officer and Administrator, Lifecare Hospitals Of Shreveport, Shreveport, LA, p. A285

COX, Kenneth, M.D.
   Chief Medical Officer, Lucile Salter Packard Children's Hospital Stanford, Palo Alto, CA, p. A79
   Interim Chief Financial Officer, Mckenzie County Healthcare System, Watford City, ND, p. A478

COX, Leigh, Chief Information Officer, Wellstar Windy Hill Hospital, Marietta, GA, p. A161

COX, Lisa D. R.N., MSN, Chief Nursing Officer, Cypress Fairbanks Medical Center, Houston, TX, p. A620

COX, Lynna B, Director Health Information Services, Anson General Hospital, Anson, TX, p. A593

COX, Matthew, Chief Financial Officer, St. Joseph's Hospital And Medical Center, Phoenix, AZ, p. A34

COX, Randy, Chief Information Officer, St. Vincent Indianapolis Hospital, IndianapolisSt. Vincent Heart Center, Indianapolis, IN, p. A212

COX, Raymond L. M.D., Chief Medical Officer, Providence Hospital, Washington, DC, p. A118

COX, Russell, President and Chief Executive Officer, Norton Healthcare, Louisville, KY, p. B92

COX, Sandra, Controller, Permian Regional Medical Center, Andrews, TX, p. A592

COX, Sharon K., FACHE, Chief Executive Officer, Rawlins County Health Center, Atwood, KS, p. A238

COX, Sheila, Director Human Resources, Cibola General Hospital, Grants, NM, p. A426

COX, Steven M.D., Chief Medical Officer, University Of Texas Health Northeast, Tyler, TX, p. A651

COX–HENLEY, Michelle R.N., MSN, Associate Director for Patient and Nursing Services, Charlie Norwood Veterans Affairs Medical Center, Augusta, GA, p. A151

COY, Nelson, Director Human Resources, Tahoe Pacific Hospitals, Sparks, NV, p. A406

COYE, Ed
   Director Information Technology Mission Health System Hospitals, Angel Medical Center, Franklin, NC, p. A462
   Director Information Technology, Transylvania Regional Hospital, Brevard, NC, p. A458

COYLE, Michael F., Chief Executive Officer, Coteau Des Prairies Hospital, Sisseton, SD, p. A573

COYNE, Margarita Frances MS, R.N., Interim Chief Nursing Officer, Roswell Park Cancer Institute, Buffalo, NY, p. A433

COYNE, Rose, Interim CFO, Haywood Regional Medical Center, Clyde, NC, p. A460

COZART, Adrienne, Vice President Human Resources, University Medical Center, Lubbock, TX, p. A631

CRABB, David W M.D., Chief Medical Officer, Eskenazi Health, Indianapolis, IN, p. A211

CRABB, Ian M.D., Chief Medical Officer, Orthonebraska Hospital, Omaha, NE, p. A398

CRABBE, Amy J
   Senior Vice President Human Resources, Watauga Medical Center, Boone, NC, p. A458
   Vice President People Services, Charles A. Cannon Memorial Hospital, Newland, NC, p. A468

CRABDREE, Nathan, Chief Financial Officer, Mountainview Regional Medical Center, Las Cruces, NM, p. A427

CRABTREE, Douglas, Chief Executive Officer, Eastern Idaho Regional Medical Center, Idaho Falls, ID, p. A173

CRABTREE, Gordon
   Chief Financial Officer, University Of Utah Health, Salt Lake City, UT, p. A660
   Interim Chief Executive Officer, University Of Utah Health, Salt Lake City, UT, p. A660

CRABTREE, John D M.D., Chief of Staff, Tennova Healthcare–Harton, Tullahoma, TN, p. A589

CRABTREE, Robert M.D., Chief of Staff and Medical Director, Physicians Surgical Hospital – Quail Creek, Amarillo, TX, p. A592

CRABTREE, Susan, Director Human Resources, Simi Valley Hospital, Simi Valley, CA, p. A92

CRACOLICI, Frank J., President and Chief Executive Officer, St. Vincent Medical Center, Los Angeles, CA, p. A71

CRACROFT, Davis M.D., Senior Director Medical Affairs, Scripps Mercy Hospital, San Diego, CA, p. A86

CRAFT, Brian, Group Finance Officer, Texas Health Presbyterian Hospital Dallas, Dallas, TX, p. A607

CRAFT, Christina, Director Information Systems, Washington County Hospital, Plymouth, NC, p. A468

CRAFT, Kirby, Chief Information Officer, Magee General Hospital, Magee, MS, p. A358

CRAFTS, Nicholas, Chief Executive Officer, Houston Physicians Hospital, Webster, TX, p. A653

CRAGGS, Chris, Deputy Director, Winnebago Mental Health Institute, Winnebago, WI, p. A716

CRAIG, Alan M.D., Physician Advisor, Princeton Baptist Medical Center, Birmingham, AL, p. A15

CRAIG, Celine H, Director Human Resources, King's Daughters Medical Center, Brookhaven, MS, p. A353

CRAIG, Cheniere, Director Human Resources, P & S Surgical Hospital, Monroe, LA, p. A281

CRAIG, Donnette, Director Human Resources, Christus Coushatta Health Care Center, Coushatta, LA, p. A273

CRAIG, Elizabeth J MSN, Chief Nursing Officer and Vice President Patient Services, Temple University Hospital, Philadelphia, PA, p. A546

CRAIG, Emmett
   Chief Human Resources Officer, Knapp Medical Center, Weslaco, TX, p. A654
   Director Human Resources, Harlingen Medical Center, Harlingen, TX, p. A618

CRAIG, Jeff, Chief Human Resource Management, Veterans Affairs Maryland Health Care System–Baltimore Division, Baltimore, MD, p. A296

CRAIG, Julian R, Chief Medical Officer, United Medical Center, Washington, DC, p. A118

CRAIG, Mike
   Chief Financial Officer, Indiana University Health Bloomington Hospital, Bloomington, IN, p. A204
   Vice President, Chief Financial Officer, Indiana University Health Bedford Hospital, Bedford, IN, p. A204

CRAIG, Pamela R.N., Chief Nursing Officer, Seton Medical Center Harker Heights, Harker Heights, TX, p. A618

CRAIG, Patrice, Manager Human Resources, Southern Arizona Veterans Affairs Health Care System, Tucson, AZ, p. A38

CRAIG, Rebecca W, Vice President and Chief Financial Officer, Wayne Memorial Hospital, Goldsboro, NC, p. A463

CRAIG, Scott M.D., Medical Director, Healthsouth Rehabilitation Hospital Of Franklin, Franklin, TN, p. A578

CRAIG, Sherry, Director Human Resources, Trace Regional Hospital, Houston, MS, p. A356

CRAIG, William J CPA, Chief Financial Officer, Howard Memorial Hospital, Nashville, AR, p. A47

CRAIGER, Lisa, Vice President, Chief Nursing Officer, Jay County Hospital, Portland, IN, p. A218

CRAIGIE, James N M.D., Vice President Medical Affairs, Mcleod Loris Seacoast Hospital, Loris, SC, p. A564

CRAIGIN, Jane, Chief Executive Officer, St. Vincent Williamsport Hospital, Williamsport, IN, p. A221

CRAIN, Doris
   Vice President and Chief Information Officer, Broward Health North, Deerfield Beach, FL, p. A123
   Vice President Information Services, Broward Health Medical Center, Fort Lauderdale, FL, p. A124

CRAIN, Greg, FACHE, Vice President and Administrator, Baptist Health Medical Center–Little Rock, Little Rock, AR, p. A46

CRAIN, Michelle B., R.N., MSN, Administrator and Chief Operating Officer, Heart Hospital Of Lafayette, Lafayette, LA, p. A278

CRAMBES, Terry, Manager Finance, Warren State Hospital, Warren, PA, p. A552

CRAMER, Brian J., Chief Executive Officer, Orthopaedic Hospital Of Wisconsin – Glendale, Glendale, WI, p. A702

CRAMER, James R
   Vice President and Chief Information Officer, Honorhealth Scottsdale Osborn Medical Center, Scottsdale, AZ, p. A36
   Vice President and Chief Information Officer, Honorhealth Scottsdale Shea Medical Center, Scottsdale, AZ, p. A36

CRAMER, Lonnie, Chief Operating Officer, Penrose–St. Francis Health Services, Colorado Springs, CO, p. A100

CRANDALL, Kristin, Director Human Resources, Bon Secours St. Mary's Hospital, Richmond, VA, p. A673

CRANDELL, Kristy M.D., Medical Staff President, Red Bay Hospital, Red Bay, AL, p. A22

CRANE, David, Chief Executive Officer, National Surgical Healthcare, Chicago, IL, p. B88

CRANFORD, Melvin, Chief Fiscal Services, Cheyenne Veterans Affairs Medical Center, Cheyenne, WY, p. A718

CRATON, Deborah W M.D., Chief Medical Officer, St. Vincent Dunn Hospital, Bedford, IN, p. A204

CRAVEN, Brian, Senior Vice President Finance, Magnolia Regional Health Center, Corinth, MS, p. A354

CRAVEN, Darcy, President, Kaleida Health, Buffalo, NY, p. A432

CRAVEN, Denise, Director Information Systems Relationship Management, Springfield Regional Medical Center, Springfield, OH, p. A499

CRAVENS, Marc
   Chief Financial Officer, Pinnacle Specialty Hospital, Tulsa, OK, p. A518
   Interim Chief Executive Officer, Pinnacle Specialty Hospital, Tulsa, OK, p. A518

CRAW, David, Coordinator Information Technology, Dundy County Hospital, Benkelman, NE, p. A391

CRAWFORD, Allen, Chief Nursing Officer, Jeff Davis Hospital, Hazlehurst, GA, p. A158

CRAWFORD, Angie, R.N., Chief Executive Officer, Riverview Behavioral Health, Texarkana, AR, p. A50

CRAWFORD, Arnita, Director Human Resources, Woman's Hospital Of Texas, Houston, TX, p. A624

CRAWFORD, Jeff
   Chief Executive Officer, Healthsouth Rehabilitation Hospital The Vintage, Houston, TX, p. A620
   Chief Executive Officer, Healthsouth Rehabilitation Hospital The Woodlands, Conroe, TX, p. A603
   Chief Executive Officer, Healthsouth Rehabilitation Hospital Vision Park, Shenandoah, TX, p. A645

CRAWFORD, Jim, Chief Financial Officer, Lawrence Medical Center, Moulton, AL, p. A21

CRAWFORD, John W
   Chief Financial Officer, Muscogee Creek Nation Medical Center, Okmulgee, OK, p. A514
   Chief Financial Officer, St. John Sapulpa, Sapulpa, OK, p. A515

CRAWFORD, Linda R.N., MSN, Chief Nursing Officer, Cookeville Regional Medical Center, Cookeville, TN, p. A577

CRAWFORD, Lucinda
   Vice President Financial Services, Vidant Duplin Hospital, Kenansville, NC, p. A465
   Vice President of Patient Care Services, Vidant Beaufort Hospital, Washington, NC, p. A472

CRAWFORD, Mark W., Chief Executive Officer, Northwest Texas Healthcare System, Amarillo, TX, p. A592

CRAWFORD, Mark W, Chief Executive Officer, Northwest Texas Healthcare System, Amarillo, TX, p. A592

CRAWFORD, Pam R.N., Ph.D., Vice President of Nursing and Chief Nursing Officer, Ohiohealth Medcentral Mansfield Hospital, Mansfield, OH, p. A494

CRAWFORD, Ryan, Director Talent, Southwestern Regional Medical Center, Tulsa, OK, p. A518

CRAWFORD, Susan, Manager Human Resources, Fayette County Hospital, Vandalia, IL, p. A202

CRUMP, John M.D., Medical Staff President, Howard Young Medical Center, Woodruff, WI, p. A716

CRUMP, Rick, Chief Financial Officer, Lakeland Behavioral Health System, Springfield, MO, p. A379

CRUMPTON, Patsy Sue R.N., Chief Nursing Officer, National Park Medical Center, Hot Springs, AR, p. A44

CRUNK, Frances H, Vice President and Chief Financial Officer, Florida Hospital Waterman, Tavares, FL, p. A145

CRUSE, Ray, Chief Executive Officer, Lakeland Hospital, Watervliet, Watervliet, MI, p. A333

CRUSON, Jim, Chief Information Officer, Riverview Behavioral Health, Texarkana, AR, p. A50

CRUTCHFIELD, David, Vice President, Information Services & Chief Information Officer, Conway Medical Center, Conway, SC, p. A561

CRUTHIRDS, Richard, Director Information Systems, Peterson Regional Medical Center, Kerrville, TX, p. A626

CRUZ, Arlene, Director, Rush Oak Park Hospital, Oak Park, IL, p. A196

CRUZ, Dimitri, Vice President Information Technology, Englewood Hospital And Medical Center, Englewood, NJ, p. A414

CRUZ, Domingo, Senior Vice President Operations, San Jorge Children's Hospital, San Juan, PR, p. A726

CRUZ, Joseph V, Chief Information Officer, Ryder Memorial Hospital, Humacao, PR, p. A724

CRUZ, Julia, Chief Financial Officer, San Juan Capestrano Hospital, San Juan, PR, p. A726

CRUZ, Michael A., M.D., President, OSF Saint Francis Medical Center, Peoria, IL, p. A197

CRUZ, Michael, Senior Vice President Operations, BSA Hospital, Llc, Amarillo, TX, p. A592

CRUZ, Miguel
   Medical Director, Bella Vista Hospital, Mayaguez, PR, p. A724
   Medical Staff Credentialing Coordinator, Healthsouth Rehabilitation Hospital Of Miami, Cutler Bay, FL, p. A122

CRUZ, Obed, Vice President and Chief Nursing Officer, Amita Health Adventist Medical Center Bolingbrook, Bolingbrook, IL, p. A179

CRYER, Betty R.N., Administrator/Chief Nursing Officer, Anderson Regional Health System South, Meridian, MS, p. A359

CRYER, Selena, Director Human Resources, Ennis Regional Medical Center, Ennis, TX, p. A612

CSEPKE, Cheryl, Controller, Kindred Rehabilitation Hospital Northeast Houston, Humble, TX, p. A624

CUDWORTH, Craig R., FACHE, Interim Chief Executive Officer, Trios Health, Kennewick, WA, p. A681

CUELLAR, Eddie, Vice President Information Systems, Methodist Hospital, San Antonio, TX, p. A643

CUELLAR, Jacob, M.D., Chief Executive Officer, Laurel Ridge Treatment Center, San Antonio, TX, p. A642

CUENCA, Derrick, Chief Executive Officer, Lake Granbury Medical Center, Granbury, TX, p. A617

CUEVAS, Gilberto, Director Human Resources, Hospital De Damas, Ponce, PR, p. A724

CUEVAS, Jacki, Director Health Information Services, Regional Rehabilitation Hospital, Phenix City, AL, p. A22

CUFF, Randy, Chief Operating Officer, Central Valley Medical Center, Nephi, UT, p. A658

CULBERSON, David K., Chief Executive Officer, San Joaquin General Hospital, French Camp, CA, p. A60

CULBERT, Devon, Controller, The Hospital At Westlake Medical Center, Austin, TX, p. A596

CULLEN, Barry, Chief Executive Officer, Southeast Michigan Surgical Hospital, Warren, MI, p. A332

CULLEN, James T. III, Director Finance, Wyoming County Community Hospital, Warsaw, NY, p. A455

CULLEN, John, M.D.
   Chief of Staff and Medical Director Long Term Care, Providence Valdez Medical Center, Valdez, AK, p. A27
   Chief Executive Officer, Thomas B. Finan Center, Cumberland, MD, p. A298

CULLEN, Kelly

CULLEN, Kelly R.N., Director of Operations, Mease Countryside Hospital, Safety Harbor, FL, p. A141

CULLEN, Kelly R.N., Director of Operations, Mease Dunedin Hospital, Dunedin, FL, p. A124

CULLEN, Michael, Senior Vice President and Chief Financial Officer, South Shore Hospital, South Weymouth, MA, p. A311

CULLEN, Neil, Director Human Resources, Healthsouth Rehabilitation Hospital Of Southern Arizona, Tucson, AZ, p. A38

CULLEN, Paul T M.D., Vice President Medical Affairs, Washington Hospital, Washington, PA, p. A552

CULLEN, Scott, Chief Executive Officer, Northwest Hills Surgical Hospital, Austin, TX, p. A595

CULLITON, Gerald F., Medical Center Director, Veterans Affairs Connecticut Healthcare System, West Haven, CT, p. A114

CULP, Judy, Chief Financial Officer, Hill Regional Hospital, Hillsboro, TX, p. A619

CULPEPPER, Michelle, Director Human Resources, Chicago Lakeshore Hospital, Chicago, IL, p. A180

CULVER, Douglas, Chief Financial Officer, Mercy Hospital Carthage, Carthage, MO, p. A366

CULVER, Shawna, Director Information Systems, Western Plains Medical Complex, Dodge City, KS, p. A240

CUMBEE, Lib, Director Information Systems, Providence Hospital, Columbia, SC, p. A560

CUMBIE, Dan L, Chief Nursing Officer, Flowers Hospital, Dothan, AL, p. A16

CUMBO, Adam, Chief Financial Officer, Dukes Memorial Hospital, Peru, IN, p. A218

CUMING, Ric, Chief Nurse Executive, Christiana Care Health System, Newark, DE, p. A115

CUMMINGS, Allana, Chief Information Officer, Children's Healthcare Of Atlanta, Atlanta, GA, p. A150

CUMMINGS, Brooke, Chief Financial Officer, Our Lady Of The Angels Hospital, Bogalusa, LA, p. A272

CUMMINGS, Greg, Chief Financial Officer, Texas Spine & Joint Hospital, Tyler, TX, p. A651

CUMMINGS, Jerry, Chief Operating Officer, Putnam County Memorial Hospital, Unionville, MO, p. A380

CUMMINGS, Kelly, Chief Nursing Officer, Abington–Lansdale Hospital Jefferson Health, Lansdale, PA, p. A538

CUMMINGS, Steve M.D., Chief of Medical Staff, Stillwater Medical Center, Stillwater, OK, p. A516

CUMMINGS, Steven, Chief Operating Officer and Chief Information Officer, Baystate Noble Hospital, Westfield, MA, p. A312

CUMMINS, Frank L, Vice President Human Resources, Honorhealth Deer Valley Medical Center, Phoenix, AZ, p. A33

CUMMINS, Thomas H., M.D.
   Chief Medical Officer, Chi St. Vincent Hot Springs, Hot Springs, AR, p. A44
   Chief Medical Officer, Chi St. Vincent Infirmary Medical Center, Little Rock, AR, p. A46
   Chief Medical Officer, Chi St. Vincent Morrilton, Morrilton, AR, p. A47
   Senior Vice President and Chief Medical Officer, Chi St. Vincent Medical Center–North, Sherwood, AR, p. A49

CUNNINGHAM, James D.O., Chief of Staff, Audubon County Memorial Hospital, Audubon, IA, p. A222

CUNNINGHAM, Becky, Controller, Salem Memorial District Hospital, Salem, MO, p. A379

CUNNINGHAM, Brian, Chief Executive Officer, Wahiawa General Hospital, Wahiawa, HI, p. A170

CUNNINGHAM, Carol, Administrative Assistant, Highland Ridge Hospital, Midvale, UT, p. A657

CUNNINGHAM, Connie, Chief Information Officer, Ellwood City Hospital, Ellwood City, PA, p. A534

CUNNINGHAM, Debbie, R.N.
   President, Moses H. Cone Memorial Hospital, Greensboro, NC, p. A463
   Senior Vice President, Cone Health and President, Maternal, Child and Behavioral Health Services, Moses H. Cone Memorial Hospital, Greensboro, NC, p. A463

CUNNINGHAM, Dennis J. M.D., Chief Medical Officer, Mclaren Macomb, Mount Clemens, MI, p. A326

CUNNINGHAM, Gail, Interim Chief Medical Officer, University Of Maryland St. Joseph Medical Center, Towson, MD, p. A301

CUNNINGHAM, Gary, Chief Nursing Officer, Dixie Regional Medical Center, Saint George, UT, p. A660

CUNNINGHAM, James C M.D., Chief Medical Officer, Cook Children's Medical Center, Fort Worth, TX, p. A613

CUNNINGHAM, Julie, Associate Administrator and Chief Human Resources Officer, Pioneers Memorial Healthcare District, Brawley, CA, p. A54

CUNNINGHAM, Keith W M.D., Medical Director, Healthsouth Scottsdale Rehabilitation Hospital, Scottsdale, AZ, p. A35

CUNNINGHAM, M Edward., Chief Executive Officer, Gateway Regional Medical Center, Granite City, IL, p. A189

CUNNINGHAM, Michelle P., Chief Executive Officer, Highlands Hospital, Connellsville, PA, p. A532

CUNNINGHAM, Peggy, Chief Executive Officer, Peak Behavioral Health Services, Santa Teresa, NM, p. A428

CUNNINGHAM, Regina, Ph.D., R.N., Chief Executive Officer, Hospital Of The University Of Pennsylvania, Philadelphia, PA, p. A544

CUPPS, Cheryl, Director Finance, Griffin Memorial Hospital, Norman, OK, p. A511

CURD, R Blake., M.D., Chief Executive Officer, Sioux Falls Specialty Hospital, Sioux Falls, SD, p. A572

CURLEE, Robbin, Controller, RMC Jacksonville, Jacksonville, AL, p. A19

CURLING, Susan M.D., Chief Medical Officer, Memorial Hermann Northeast, Humble, TX, p. A624

CURNEL, Robin, Chief Operating Officer and Chief Nursing Officer, Crittenden County Hospital, Marion, KY, p. A264

CURPHY, Rona, President and Chief Executive Officer, Banner Casa Grande Medical Center, Casa Grande, AZ, p. A28

CURRAN, Dezerae, Director Human Resources, Osawatomie State Hospital, Osawatomie, KS, p. A248

CURRAN, Maria, Vice President Human Resources, VCU Medical Center, Richmond, VA, p. A674

CURRAN, Michael, President, Crozer–Chester Medical Center, Upland, PA, p. A552

CURRAN, Todd A. M.D., President Medical Staff, OSS Orthopaedic Hospital, York, PA, p. A555

CURRAN–MEULI, Jane, Chief Operating Officer, Holy Family Memorial, Manitowoc, WI, p. A706

CURRANS, Sheila, Chief Executive Officer, Harrison Memorial Hospital, Cynthiana, KY, p. A257

CURREN, Robert
   Director Information Technology, Center For Behavioral Medicine, Kansas City, MO, p. A370
   Western Region Chief Information Technology Officer, Northwest Missouri Psychiatric Rehabilitation Center, Saint Joseph, MO, p. A376

CURRIE, Michelle, Chief Financial Officer, Red River Behavioral Health System, Grand Forks, ND, p. A476

CURRIE, Peggy M., R.N.
   Chief Operating Officer, Providence Holy Family Hospital, Spokane, WA, p. A687
   Chief Operating Officer, Providence Sacred Heart Medical Center & Children's Hospital, Spokane, WA, p. A687

CURRIE, Scott D, Vice President and Chief Financial Officer, Midmichigan Medical Center–Midland, Midland, MI, p. A326

CURRIE, Stuart, Chief Medical Officer, Tuality Healthcare, Hillsboro, OR, p. A522

CURRIN, Randy, Chief Operating Officer, Bay Medical Center Sacred Heart Health System, Panama City, FL, p. A138

CURRY, Cheryl, Chief Financial Officer, Littleton Adventist Hospital, Littleton, CO, p. A105

CURRY, Christopher, Chief Executive Officer, Kindred Hospital Peoria, Peoria, IL, p. A197

CURRY, Jeffrey T
   Executive Vice President and Chief Financial Officer, Excela Frick Hospital, Mount Pleasant, PA, p. A541
   Executive Vice President and Chief Financial Officer, Excela Health Westmoreland Hospital, Greensburg, PA, p. A535

CURRY, Robert H
   President and Chief Executive Officer, Citrus Valley Medical Center–Inter Community Campus, Covina, CA, p. A57
   President and Chief Executive Officer, Foothill Presbyterian Hospital, Glendora, CA, p. A62

CURRY, Robert H.
   President and Chief Executive Officer, Citrus Valley Health Partners, Covina, CA, p. B31
   President and Chief Executive Officer, Citrus Valley Medical Center-Inter Community Campus, Covina, CA, p. B31
   President and Chief Executive Officer, Foothill Presbyterian Hospital, Glendora, CA, p. B31

CURRY, Stephen A, Director Information Services, Princeton Community Hospital, Princeton, WV, p. A695

CURRY, Steve, Regional Director Human Resources, Four County Counseling Center, Logansport, IN, p. A215

CURRY–PELYAK, Mary Jane R.N., Vice President and Chief Clinical Officer, The Villages Regional Hospital, The Villages, FL, p. A146

CURTI, Tate, Senior Vice President and Chief Operating Officer, Southern New Hampshire Medical Center, Nashua, NH, p. A409

CURTIN, Sean, Chief Financial Officer, The University Of Vermont Health Network – Alice Hyde Medical Center, Malone, NY, p. A439

CURTIS, Bryan, Chief Information Officer, Memorial Regional Health, Craig, CO, p. A100

CURTIS, Edgar J., FACHE, President and Chief Executive Officer, Memorial Medical Center, Springfield, IL, p. A200

CURTIS, George, Chief Information Officer, Houston Medical Center, Warner Robins, GA, p. A167

CURTIS, Janis, Interim Director Information Technology, Duke Raleigh Hospital, Raleigh, NC, p. A468

CURTIS, Joy U, Senior Vice President Human Resources, Cambridge Health Alliance, Cambridge, MA, p. A305

CURTIS, Lorna, Chief Financial Officer, John F. Kennedy Memorial Hospital, Indio, CA, p. A63

CURTIS, Michael, Chief Administrative Officer, Mckenzie County Healthcare System, Watford City, ND, p. A478

CURTIS, Scott A., Administrator and Chief Executive Officer, Kossuth Regional Health Center, Algona, IA, p. A222

CURTIS, Tracie, Business Partner Human Resources, Cleveland Clinic, Medina Hospital, Medina, OH, p. A495

CURTRIGHT, Jonathan W., Chief Executive Officer and Chief Operating Officer, University Of Missouri Health Care, Columbia, MO, p. A367

CURVIN, Thomas J M.D., Chief of Staff, Rankin County Hospital District, Rankin, TX, p. A639

CUSA, Philip L., Hospital Director, Eastpointe Hospital, Daphne, AL, p. A16

CUSACK, Susan, Executive Director, Mercy Fitzgerald Hospital, Darby, PA, p. A532

CUSACK–MCGUIRK, Joan, Interim President and Chief Executive Officer, St. Luke's Cornwall Hospital, Newburgh, NY, p. A447

CUSANO, Susan, Director Human Resources, Four Winds Hospital, Katonah, NY, p. A438

CUSENZ, Bruce J M.D., Medical Director, Eastern Niagara Hospital, Lockport, NY, p. A438

CUSHING, Ginger, Chief Executive Officer, Pioneer Community Hospital Of Early, Blakely, GA, p. A152

CUSHING, Heidi, Director Finance, Gordon Memorial Health Services, Gordon, NE, p. A393

CUSHING, Herbert M.D., Chief Medical Officer, Temple University Hospital, Philadelphia, PA, p. A546

CUSHMAN, Bonnie, Chief Financial Officer, Northern Colorado Rehabilitation Hospital, Johnstown, CO, p. A104

CUSSINS, James, Chief Financial Officer, Platte County Memorial Hospital, Wheatland, WY, p. A720

CUSTER, Joshua, Director Finance, St. Luke's Magic Valley Medical Center, Twin Falls, ID, p. A176

CUSTER, Lindsey, Director Human Resources, Riverside Tappahannock Hospital, Tappahannock, VA, p. A676

CUSTER–MITCHELL, Marilyn J., President, Parkview Wabash County Hospital, Wabash, IN, p. A221

CUSTIN, Melinda, Chief Information Officer, Jps Health Network, Fort Worth, TX, p. A613

CUSTODIO, David, M.D., President Summa Health System Akron, Summa Health System, Akron, OH, p. A479

CUSUMANO, Margaret M R.N., MSN, Vice President Patient Care Services and Chief Nursing Officer, Saint Joseph's Medical Center, Yonkers, NY, p. A456

CUTHRELL, Rob, Director of Human Resources, Riverside Rehabilitation Institute, Newport News, VA, p. A671

CUTLIFF, Bryan, Chief Executive Officer, Select Specialty Hospital–Ann Arbor, Ypsilanti, MI, p. A334

CUTOLO, Edward M.D., Jr, Chief of Staff, James A. Haley Veterans' Hospital–Tampa, Tampa, FL, p. A144

CUTRELL, Carrie, Chief Nursing Officer, Arkansas Valley Regional Medical Center, La Junta, CO, p. A104

CUTRIGHT, Bruce E MS, Vice President Human Resources, Mary Lanning Healthcare, Hastings, NE, p. A394

CUTSFORTH, Shawn, Information Systems Officer, Pioneer Memorial Hospital, Heppner, OR, p. A522

CUTSINGER, David, Chief Information Officer, Hamilton Memorial Hospital District, Mcleansboro, IL, p. A193

CUTTER, Elise, Chief Financial Officer, Island Hospital, Anacortes, WA, p. A678

CUZZOLA, Anthony, Vice President and Administrator, JFK Johnson Rehabilitation Institute, Edison, NJ, p. A413

CYBORON, Abigail, Chief Financial Officer, Chase County Community Hospital, Imperial, NE, p. A394

CYTLAK, David
Chief Financial Officer, Blanchard Valley Hospital, Findlay, OH, p. A491
Vice President Finance, Bluffton Hospital, Bluffton, OH, p. A481

CZAHOR, John, IT Site Executive, University Of Maryland Charles Regional Medical Center, La Plata, MD, p. A299

CZAJKA, Paul M., Interim Chief Executive Officer, St. Mary Medical Center, Long Beach, CA, p. A67

CZAJKA , Paul M., Interim Chief Executive Officer, St. Mary Medical Center, Long Beach, CA, p. B47

CZAJKA, Paul M, Vice President Chief Operating Officer, St. Mary Medical Center, Long Beach, CA, p. A67

CZAJKOWSKI, Cheryl, Associate Director Patient and Nursing Services, Syracuse Veterans Affairs Medical Center, Syracuse, NY, p. A453

CZEREW, Jane, Vice President Clinical Services and Quality, Spectrum Health Zeeland Community Hospital, Zeeland, MI, p. A334

CZINCILA, Robert D.O., Medical Staff President, Einstein Medical Center Montgomery, East Norriton, PA, p. A533

CZYMBOR, Mary, Chief Medical Officer, Milford Regional Medical Center, Milford, MA, p. A309

CZYZ, AnneMarie R.N., MS, Ed.D., Senior Vice President Operations, Chief Operating Officer and Chief Nursing Officer, St. Joseph's Hospital Health Center, Syracuse, NY, p. A453

D

D'ACCURZIO, Albert M.D., Medical Director, St. Elizabeth Medical Center, Utica, NY, p. A454

D'AGNES, Michael R., FACHE, President and Chief Executive Officer, Hackensack Meridian Health Raritan Bay Medical Center, Perth Amboy, NJ, p. A419

D'AMBROSIO, Matthew MSN, R.N., Chief Nursing Officer, Healthsouth Rehabilitation Institute Of San Antonio (Riosa), San Antonio, TX, p. A642

D'AMBROSIO, Paul, Chief Operating Officer, Complex Care Hospital At Tenaya, Las Vegas, NV, p. A402

D'AMICO, David, Chief Financial Officer, St. Anthony's Rehabilitation Hospital, Lauderdale Lakes, FL, p. A130

D'AMICO, Ken, Chief Executive Officer, AMG Specialty Hospital–Albuquerque, Albuquerque, NM, p. A424

D'AMICO, Paul M.D., Chief of Staff, Carolinas Healthcare System Stanly, Albemarle, NC, p. A457

D'AMORE, Seanna, Director Human Resources, Penn Highlands Elk, Saint Marys, PA, p. A549

D'ANGELO, Jennifer, Vice President Information Services, Christian Health Care Center, Wyckoff, NJ, p. A423

D'ANGINA, Joseph, Area Finance Officer, Kaiser Permanente Vallejo Medical Center, Vallejo, CA, p. A95

D'APOLLO, Julie R.N., Director of Nursing, Hampstead Hospital, Hampstead, NH, p. A408

D'AQUILA, Richard, President, Yale–New Haven Hospital, New Haven, CT, p. A112

D'AURIA, Joseph, Director Finance, Morristown Medical Center, Morristown, NJ, p. A416

D'AVINO , Mary Lou, Chief Executive Officer, Fairlawn Rehabilitation Hospital, Worcester, MA, p. B63

D'AVINO, Mary Lou, Chief Executive Officer, Fairlawn Rehabilitation Hospital, Worcester, MA, p. A313

D'ELIA, Peter, Chief Financial Officer, Saint Vincent Hospital, Worcester, MA, p. A313

D'ERAMO, John, Chief Operating Officer, Connecticut Valley Hospital, Middletown, CT, p. A111

D'ETTORRE, Joseph A., Chief Executive Officer, Wyandot Memorial Hospital, Upper Sandusky, OH, p. A501

D'ORTENZIO, Gabe, Director of Human Resources, Weirton Medical Center, Weirton, WV, p. A696

D'sOUZA, Carol, Chief Human Resources Officer, Banner Casa Grande Medical Center, Casa Grande, AZ, p. A28

D'sOUZA, Gladys, Chief Nursing Officer, Barlow Respiratory Hospital, Los Angeles, CA, p. A67

DAANE, John, Information Systems Officer, Crossing Rivers Health Medical Center, Prairie Du Chien, WI, p. A711

DABNEY, Ann, Manager Human Resources, Spring View Hospital, Lebanon, KY, p. A260

DACE, Linda, Vice President Finance, Mcdonough District Hospital, Macomb, IL, p. A192

DACEY, Michael J., M.D.
President and Chief Operating Officer, Kent County Memorial Hospital, Warwick, RI, p. A557
President, Memorial Hospital Of Rhode Island, Pawtucket, RI, p. A556

DADD, Steven, Flight Commander Resource Management, U. S. Air Force Hospital, Hampton, VA, p. A668

DADO, Joe
Chief Information Officer, Conemaugh Memorial Medical Center, Johnstown, PA, p. A537
Chief Information Officer, Conemaugh Miners Medical Center, Hastings, PA, p. A536

DAEGER, Brian, Vice President Financial Services, Margaret Mary Health, Batesville, IN, p. A203

DAFFRON, Eric Allen, Division Director, Information Systems, Southeast Alabama Medical Center, Dothan, AL, p. A17

DAGENBACH, Pete, Chief Financial Officer, Adams County Regional Medical Center, Seaman, OH, p. A499

DAGLIO, Michael, President, Norwalk Hospital, Norwalk, CT, p. A112

DAHDUL, Adnan M.D., Medical Director, Healthsouth Rehabilitation Hospital Of Western Massachusetts, Ludlow, MA, p. A308

DAHL, Robert, President and Chief Executive Officer, Presence Resurrection Medical Center, Chicago, IL, p. A182

DAHLBERG, Connie, Director Business and Employee, Sleepy Eye Medical Center, Sleepy Eye, MN, p. A348

DAHLHAUSEN, Daniel J M.D., President of Medical Staff/Chief Medical Officer, Anmed Health Cannon, Pickens, SC, p. A565

DAHLING, James D., President and Chief Executive Officer, Children's Hospital Of The King's Daughters, Norfolk, VA, p. A671

DAHLSTRAND, David, Chief, OI&T, Hunter Holmes Mcguire Veterans Affairs Medical Center–Richmond, Richmond, VA, p. A674

DAHLSTROM, Sheri R.N., Chief Nursing Officer, Banner Estrella Medical Center, Phoenix, AZ, p. A33

DAIGLE, Charles D
Chief Operating Officer, Wk Bossier Health Center, Bossier City, LA, p. A272
Senior Vice President and Chief Operating Officer, Willis–Knighton Medical Center, Shreveport, LA, p. A286

DAIGLE, Cindy, Chief Financial Officer, Northern Maine Medical Center, Fort Kent, ME, p. A291

DAIGLE, Jennifer R.N., Director of Nursing and Utilization Review, Carolina Center For Behavioral Health, Greer, SC, p. A563

DAIGLE, Richard
Chief Information Officer, Manchester Memorial Hospital, Manchester, CT, p. A110
Chief Information Officer, Rockville General Hospital, Vernon, CT, p. A113

DAIKER, David, Chief Information Resource Management, Veterans Affairs Nebraska–Western Iowa Health Care System – Lincoln, Lincoln, NE, p. A395

DAILEY, Gina, Chief Financial Officer, Pinnacle Pointe Hospital, Little Rock, AR, p. A46

DAILEY, Jacqueline, Chief Information Officer, West Penn Hospital, Pittsburgh, PA, p. A548

DAILEY, Richard R D.O., President Medical Staff, Ellett Memorial Hospital, Appleton City, MO, p. A364

DAISLEY, Samuel D.O., Vice President Medical Affairs, Upmc Horizon, Farrell, PA, p. A535

DAJCZAK, Stanislaw M.D., Chief of Staff, Promedica Defiance Regional Hospital, Defiance, OH, p. A490

DALBY, William, Director Fiscal Services, Shriners Hospitals For Children–Northern California, Sacramento, CA, p. A83

DALE, Jackson
Director Management Information Services, Johnston Memorial Hospital, Abingdon, VA, p. A664
Site Manager Information Systems, Indian Path Medical Center, Kingsport, TN, p. A581

DALE, Jae, Chief Executive Officer, Oro Valley Hospital, Oro Valley, AZ, p. A32

DALEBOUT, Kenneth, Site Administrator, Marian Regional Medical Center, Santa Maria, CA, p. A91

DALEY, Robert
Chief Financial Officer, Black River Memorial Hospital, Black River Falls, WI, p. A699
Vice President Fiscal and Information Technology Services, Black River Memorial Hospital, Black River Falls, WI, p. A699

DALGAI, Netrisha, Director of Operations, Sage Memorial Hospital, Ganado, AZ, p. A29

DALL, Jamie, Chief Financial Officer, New Hampshire Hospital, Concord, NH, p. A407

DALLER, Sue R.N., Assistant Administrator Nursing, Hermann Area District Hospital, Hermann, MO, p. A369

DALLEY, Mark F., Administrator, Gunnison Valley Hospital, Gunnison, UT, p. A656

DALLIS, Donna R.N., Vice President Patient Care, Northeastern Health System, Tahlequah, OK, p. A516

DALPOAS, Dolan, President and Chief Executive Officer, Abraham Lincoln Memorial Hospital, Lincoln, IL, p. A192

DALTON, Deana, Human Resources, San Juan Health Service District, Monticello, UT, p. A657

DALTON, Eric
Chief Financial Officer, Memorial Medical Center, Modesto, CA, p. A74
Chief Financial Officer, Sutter Tracy Community Hospital, Tracy, CA, p. A94

DALTON, John, President and Chief Executive Officer, Inland Hospital, Waterville, ME, p. A293

DALTON, Leigh, Director of Nursing and Patient Care Services, Highland Hospital, Charleston, WV, p. A691

DALTON, Nissi, Manager Human Resources, Baylor Institute For Rehabilitation At Fort Worth, Fort Worth, TX, p. A613

DALTON, Valerie, R.N., Administrator, Oceans Behavioral Hospital Of Baton Rouge, Baton Rouge, LA, p. A270

DALTON, Wayne, Chief Financial Officer, Lakeview Hospital, Bountiful, UT, p. A656

DALY, Cindy R.N., Director of Nursing, Syringa Hospital And Clinics, Grangeville, ID, p. A173

DALY, Derek, Chief Executive Officer, Blue Mountain Hospital, John Day, OR, p. A523

DALY, Linda, Vice President Human Resources, Auburn Community Hospital, Auburn, NY, p. A431

DALY, Thomas M CPA, Chief Financial Officer, University Hospital, Newark, NJ, p. A418

DALY, William, Chief Executive Officer, Pennsylvania Psychiatric Institute, Harrisburg, PA, p. A536

DAMA, Sunil M.D., Medical Director, Select Specialty Hospital – Cincinnati North, Cincinnati, OH, p. A484

DAMBOISE, Robin, Director Human Resources, Northern Maine Medical Center, Fort Kent, ME, p. A291

DAMIANO, Louis, Acting President, Holy Cross Health, Silver Spring, MD, p. A301

DAMICO, Donna, Director Human Resources, Carolinas Hospital System, Florence, SC, p. A561

DAMM, Julie, Chief Financial Officer, Hancock County Health System, Britt, IA, p. A223

DAMMEYER, Matt Ph.D., Chief Operating Officer, Central Peninsula Hospital, Soldotna, AK, p. A27

DAMODARAN, A N M.D., President Medical Staff, Starke Hospital, Knox, IN, p. A213

DAMON, Chad, Contractor, St. Vincent Dunn Hospital, Bedford, IN, p. A204

DAMON, Kerry, Director Human Resources, Baystate Franklin Medical Center, Greenfield, MA, p. A307

DAMRON, Greg, Vice President Finance and Chief Financial Officer, Augusta University Medical Center, Augusta, GA, p. A151

DAMRON, Paul, Chief Financial Officer, Highlands Regional Medical Center, Sebring, FL, p. A143

DAMRON, Tony, Vice President Information Services, Pikeville Medical Center, Pikeville, KY, p. A266

DAMSCHRODER, Robin, Chief Operating Officer, St. Joseph Mercy Livingston Hospital, Howell, MI, p. A322

DANBDALA, Kayyan M.D., Medical Director, Schick Shadel Hospital, Seattle, WA, p. A685

DANCER, Stephanie, Manager Human Resources, Pauls Valley General Hospital, Pauls Valley, OK, p. A514

DANCH, Stephen M, Chief Financial Officer, Upmc Hamot, Erie, PA, p. A534

DANCY, Peter C. Jr, Director, Alexandria Veterans Affairs Health Care System, Pineville, LA, p. A284

DANDORPH, Michael J, President and Chief Operating Officer, Rush University Medical Center, Chicago, IL, p. A183

DANDRIDGE, Thomas, Interim Chief Executive Officer, Sierra Vista Hospital, Truth Or Consequences, NM, p. A429

DANE, Brenda, Director, Human Resources, Highlands Regional Medical Center, Sebring, FL, p. A143

DANE, Jeff, Executive Vice President and Chief Financial Officer, University Medical Center, Lubbock, TX, p. A631

DANELLO, Sherry, MSN, R.N.
Vice President and Chief Nursing Officer, Candler Hospital, Savannah, GA, p. A164
Vice President and Chief Nursing Officer, St. Joseph's Hospital, Savannah, GA, p. A165

DANESHMAND, Alex D.O., Chief Patient Safety Officer, Lee Memorial Hospital, Fort Myers, FL, p. A125

DANG, Cynthia, Vice President Human Resources, Medical City North Hills, North Richland Hills, TX, p. A635

DANGERFIELD, Wesley, Community Chief Executive Officer, Summers County Arh Hospital, Hinton, WV, p. A692

DANIEL, Christopher W., Administrator, Sterling Surgical Hospital, Slidell, LA, p. A286

DANIEL, Dena, Director Information Systems, Jackson County Memorial Hospital, Altus, OK, p. A504

DANIEL, Joyce, Chief Executive Officer and Chief Nursing Officer, Blackwell Regional Hospital, Blackwell, OK, p. A505

DANIEL, Karen
Chief Executive Officer, Warm Springs Medical Center, Warm Springs, GA, p. A167
Director Human Resources, Bibb Medical Center, Centreville, AL, p. A16

DANIEL, Ron, Manager Information Systems, Matheny Medical And Educational Center, Peapack, NJ, p. A418

DANIEL, S. M.D., Chief Medical Officer, Spring Valley Hospital Medical Center, Las Vegas, NV, p. A404

DANIELS, Alex, Chief Nurse Executive, U. S. Public Health Service Indian Hospital, Crownpoint, NM, p. A425

DANIELS, Andrew J., Chief Executive Officer, Memorial Regional Health, Craig, CO, p. A100

DANIELS, Andy
Chief Operating Officer, Bucyrus Community Hospital, Bucyrus, OH, p. A482
Vice President Non–Clinical Operations and Information Systems, Galion Community Hospital, Galion, OH, p. A491

DANIELS, Anita
Director, Bronx Psychiatric Center, New Rochelle, NY, p. A440
Executive Director, New York City Children's Center, New Rochelle, NY, p. A443

DANIELS, Betty M.D., Chief of Staff, St. Bernardine Medical Center, San Bernardino, CA, p. A85

DANIELS, Buddy, Chief Operating Officer, Poplar Bluff Regional Medical Center, Poplar Bluff, MO, p. A375

DANIELS, Craig M, Chief Financial Officer, Moab Regional Hospital, Moab, UT, p. A657

DANIELS, D. Jeffery.
Chief Executive Officer, Bingham Memorial Hospital, Blackfoot, ID, p. A171
Chief Executive Officer, Mountain River Birthing And Surgery Center, Blackfoot, ID, p. A171

DANIELS, Don, M.D.
Chief Medical Officer, Rollins–Brook Community Hospital, Lampasas, TX, p. A628
Executive Vice President and Chief Operating Officer, Swedishamerican – A Division Of Uw Health, Rockford, IL, p. A199

DANIELS, John M.D., Medical Director, Lifecare Hospitals Of Wisconsin, Pewaukee, WI, p. A710

DANIELS, Judy, Vice President Human Resources, Our Lady Of Bellefonte Hospital, Ashland, KY, p. A255

DANIELS, Karen MSN, R.N., Chief Nursing Officer, Halifax Regional Medical Center, Roanoke Rapids, NC, p. A469

DANIELS, Kristin, Manager Human Resources, Sutter Center For Psychiatry, Sacramento, CA, p. A84

DANIELS, Mark M.D., Vice President Physician Enterprise, Northwestern Medicine Delnor Hospital, Geneva, IL, p. A188

DANIELS, S Janette, Director Human Resources, Healthsouth Rehabilitation Hospital Of Fort Smith, Fort Smith, AR, p. A43

DANIELS, Sarah, Vice President, Information Technology, Mayo Clinic Health System In Mankato, Mankato, MN, p. A342

DANIELS, Susan, Chief Financial Officer, Pawnee County Memorial Hospital And Rural Health Clinic, Pawnee City, NE, p. A399

DANIELS, Todd M.D., Medical Director, Healthsouth Rehabilitation Hospital Of Arlington, Arlington, TX, p. A593

DANIELS, Troy P, Chief Human Resources Officer, Forrest General Hospital, Hattiesburg, MS, p. A355

DANIELSON, Carol R.N., Senior Vice President and Chief Nursing Officer, Gwinnett Hospital System, Lawrenceville, GA, p. A160

DANIELYAN, Arman M.D., Chief of Staff, John Muir Behavioral Health Center, Concord, CA, p. A56

DANKERT, Sheri
Chief Financial Officer, Mayo Clinic Health System In Albert Lea, Albert Lea, MN, p. A335
Vice President Finance, Mayo Clinic Health System–Albert Lea And Austin, Austin, MN, p. A336

DANN, Doreen R.N., Chief Operating Officer, Victor Valley Global Medical Center, Victorville, CA, p. A96

DANNA, Denise Esq, Chief Nursing Officer, University Medical Center, New Orleans, LA, p. A283

DANOWSKI, Dale G R.N., Senior Vice President, Chief Nursing Officer, St. Vincent's Medical Center, Bridgeport, CT, p. A109

DANSBY, Tommy, Chief Medical Officer, Liberty Healthcare Systems, Bastrop, LA, p. A270

DANUSER, James, Chief Information Officer, Veterans Affairs Central Iowa Health Care System, Des Moines, IA, p. A226

DAOUD, Joudat M.D., Chief of Staff, Community Health Center Of Branch County, Coldwater, MI, p. A317

DAQUIOAG, Francis, Controller, Kahuku Medical Center, Kahuku, HI, p. A169

DARBONNE, Tina, Chief Financial Officer, Central Louisiana State Hospital, Pineville, LA, p. A284

DARBY, Kristin, Chief Information Officer, Eastern Regional Medical Center, Philadelphia, PA, p. A543

DARBY, Sharon R.N., FACHE, Vice President, Clinical Operations, Children's Hospital Of Richmond At Vcu–Brook Road Campus, Richmond, VA, p. A674

DARCY, Deborah, Human Resources, Chg Hospital Tucson, Llc, Tucson, AZ, p. A37

DARDANO, Anthony M.D., Chief Medical Officer, Delray Medical Center, Delray Beach, FL, p. A124

DARDEAU, Sean T., FACHE, Chief Executive Officer, Mary Black Health System–Spartanburg, Spartanburg, SC, p. A566

DAREY, Roland M.D., Medical Director, Wamego Health Center, Wamego, KS, p. A253

DARLING, Cory, Chief Operating Officer, Tristar Hendersonville Medical Center, Hendersonville, TN, p. A580

DARLING, Rudy, Chief Operating Officer, Baxter Regional Medical Center, Mountain Home, AR, p. A47

DARMELIO, Matthew P, Chief of Staff, Mon Health Medical Center, Morgantown, WV, p. A694

DARNAUER, Kristina M.D., Chief of Staff, Hospital District No 1 Of Rice County, Lyons, KS, p. A246

DARNELL, Linda, Director Management Information Systems, King's Daughters' Health, Madison, IN, p. A215

DARRINGTON, Gilbert, Director Human Resources, Jackson Hospital And Clinic, Montgomery, AL, p. A21

DARVIN, Ken M.D., Chief of Staff, Stroud Regional Medical Center, Stroud, OK, p. A516

DASARO, Lynda, Director Human Resources, Sutter Roseville Medical Center, Roseville, CA, p. A83

DASCANI, Jimmy, Chief Executive Officer, Landmark Hospital Of Southwest Florida, Naples, FL, p. A135

DASCENZO, Douglas R MSN, R.N., Chief Nursing Officer, St. Joseph Mercy Oakland, Pontiac, MI, p. A328

DASCHER, Norman E., Jr
Chief Executive Officer, Samaritan Hospital, Troy, NY, p. A454
Chief Executive Officer, St. Mary's Hospital, Troy, NY, p. A454

DASHIELD, Luanne G, Personnel Administrator, Deer's Head Hospital Center, Salisbury, MD, p. A300

DASKALAKIS, Tom G., Chief Administrative Officer, West Chester Hospital, West Chester, OH, p. A502

DASKALAKIS, Tom G, Chief Administrative Officer, West Chester Hospital, West Chester, OH, p. A502

DASS, Karla, Director Human Resources, Regional General Hospital, Williston, FL, p. A148

DASSENKO, Dennis, Chief Information Officer, Essentia Health Duluth, Duluth, MN, p. A339

DAUBERT, Stephanie
Chief Financial Officer, Nebraska Medicine – Bellevue, Bellevue, NE, p. A391
Chief Financial Officer, Nebraska Medicine – Nebraska Medical Center, Omaha, NE, p. A397

DAUBY, Randall W., CPA, Chief Executive Officer, Pinckneyville Community Hospital, Pinckneyville, IL, p. A198

DAUGHDRILL, Diane, Director Human Resources, Jefferson Davis Community Hospital, Prentiss, MS, p. A361

DAUGHDRILL, Richard, R.N., Chief Executive Officer, Curahealth New Orleans, New Orleans, LA, p. A282

DAUGHERTY, Beth Ann R.N., M.P.H., Vice President Care Services and Chief Nursing Executive, Sparrow Clinton Hospital, Saint Johns, MI, p. A330

DAUGHERTY, Don, Director Information Systems, Fleming County Hospital, Flemingsburg, KY, p. A258

DAUGHERTY, Marney, Worklife Services Consultant, Brighton Center For Recovery, Brighton, MI, p. A315

DAUGHERTY, Robert Alan., Chief Executive Officer, Sagewest Health Care At Riverton, Riverton, WY, p. A719

DAUGHERTY, Stephen J.
Chief Executive Officer, Coliseum Northside Hospital, Macon, GA, p. A161
Interim Chief Executive Officer, Coliseum Medical Centers, Macon, GA, p. A160

DAUM, Karen R.N., MS, Vice President and Chief Nursing Officer, Passavant Area Hospital, Jacksonville, IL, p. A191

DAUTERIVE, F Ralph M.D., Vice President Medical Affairs, Ochsner Medical Center–Baton Rouge, Baton Rouge, LA, p. A270

DAVACHI, Khosrow, Chief Medical Officer, Bridgepoint Hospital National Harbor, Washington, DC, p. A117

DAVE, Bhasker J., M.D., Superintendent, Mental Health Institute, Independence, IA, p. A229

DAVE', Rajesh J M.D., Executive Vice President and Chief Medical Officer, United Health Services Hospitals–Binghamton, Binghamton, NY, p. A432

DAVENPORT, David, Director Human Resources, Washington County Hospital, Nashville, IL, p. A195

DAVENPORT, Doug, Interim Chief Financial Officer, Mercy Iowa City, Iowa City, IA, p. A229

DAVENPORT, Douglas, Chief Financial Officer, Bethesda Hospital, Saint Paul, MN, p. A347

DAVENPORT, Ginger, Director Human Resources, Promise Hospital Of Dallas, Dallas, TX, p. A606

DAVENPORT, Paula, Chief Nursing Officer, Princeton Baptist Medical Center, Birmingham, AL, p. A15

DAVENPORT, Polly J., FACHE, R.N.
President, Chi St. Vincent Infirmary Medical Center, Little Rock, AR, p. A46
Senior Vice President, Chief Operating Officer, President CHI St. Vincent Infirmary Medical Center a, Chi St. Vincent Medical Center–North, Sherwood, AR, p. A49

DAVENPORT, Sally M., R.N., MS
Chief Executive Officer, Ephraim Mcdowell Health, Danville, KY, p. B49
Chief Executive Officer, Ephraim Mcdowell Regional Medical Center, Danville, KY, p. B50
President and Chief Executive Officer, Ephraim Mcdowell Fort Logan Hospital, Stanford, KY, p. B50

DAVENPORT, Sally M, R.N., MS
Chief Executive Officer, Ephraim Mcdowell Regional Medical Center, Danville, KY, p. A257
President and Chief Executive Officer, Ephraim Mcdowell Fort Logan Hospital, Stanford, KY, p. A268
Chief Nursing Officer and Chief Operating Officer, Ephraim Mcdowell Regional Medical Center, Danville, KY, p. A257

DAVES, Ronnie, Chief Executive Officer, North Okaloosa Medical Center, Crestview, FL, p. A122

DAVID, Biff, R.N., Administrator, St. Landry Extended Care Hospital, Opelousas, LA, p. A284

DAVID, Michelle, Chief Executive Officer, Valley Hospital Phoenix, Phoenix, AZ, p. A34

DAVID, R Neal, Administrator and Chief of Staff, Madigan Army Medical Center, Tacoma, WA, p. A687

DAVID, Robert G., President, St. John Medical Center, Westlake, OH, p. A502

DAVIDOFF, Ravin M.D., Chief Medical Officer, Boston Medical Center, Boston, MA, p. A303

DAVIDOW, Daniel N M.D., Medical Director, Cumberland Hospital, New Kent, VA, p. A671

DAVIDSON, Brian, M.D., President and Chief Medical Officer, St. Mary's Hospital And Medical Center, Grand Junction, CO, p. A103

DAVIDSON, Camille, Director Human Resources, Stanton County Hospital, Johnson, KS, p. A243

DAVIDSON, Diane, Senior Vice President Human Resources, Essentia Health Duluth, Duluth, MN, p. A339

DAVIDSON, Dianne, Chief Operating Officer, Union General Hospital, Farmerville, LA, p. A274

DAVIDSON, Elizabeth R.N., MSN, Vice President, Patient Care Services, OSF Saint James – John W. Albrecht Medical Center, Pontiac, IL, p. A198

DAVIDSON, Gary, M.D.
Medical Director, Select Specialty Hospital–Johnstown, Johnstown, PA, p. A537
Senior Vice President and Chief Information Officer, Lancaster General Hospital, Lancaster, PA, p. A538

DAVIDSON, Gordon L, Chief Financial Officer, Bozeman Health Deaconess Hospital, Bozeman, MT, p. A382

DAVIDSON, Gregg Agustin., FACHE, President and Chief Executive Officer, Skagit Regional Health, Mount Vernon, WA, p. B118

DAVIDSON, James N., Troop Commander, Tripler Army Medical Center, Honolulu, HI, p. A169

DAVIDSON, James
Chief Executive Officer, Saint Mary's Regional Medical Center, Russellville, AR, p. A49
Director of Information Services, Ferry County Memorial Hospital, Republic, WA, p. A684

DAVIDSON, John, Vice President Human Resources, Sharon Regional Health System, Sharon, PA, p. A551

DAVIDSON, Nancy, Senior Vice President and Chief Financial Officer, Jackson County Memorial Hospital, Altus, OK, p. A504

DAVIDSON, Paulette
Chief Operating Officer, Rapid City Regional Hospital, Rapid City, SD, p. A572
Chief Operating Officer and Interim President, Rapid City Regional Hospital, Rapid City, SD, p. A572

DAVIDSON, Rocky, Chief Financial Officer, Larkin Behavioral Health Services, Hollywood, FL, p. A127

DAVIDSON, Rowena, Manager Business Office, AMG Specialty Hospital–Edmond, Edmond, OK, p. A507

DAVIDSON, Stephen, Director Human Resources, Lafayette Regional Health Center, Lexington, MO, p. A372

DAVIDSON, Stuart, President Medical Staff, Mount Desert Island Hospital, Bar Harbor, ME, p. A289

DAVIDSON, Tim M.D., Chief Executive Physician Services, Providence St. Mary Medical Center, Walla Walla, WA, p. A688

DAVIDSON, Tori R.N., Chief Nursing Officer, Tsehootsooi Medical Center, Fort Defiance, AZ, p. A29

DAVILA, Susan, Chief Executive Officer, Desert View Hospital, Pahrump, NV, p. A405

DAVIN, Joni, Director Information and Business Management Service Line, Veterans Affairs Eastern Kansas Health Care System, Topeka, KS, p. A252

DAVINI, John, Vice President, St. Rose Hospital, Hayward, CA, p. A63

DAVIS, Adam
Chief Information Officer, Cornerstone Hospital–West Monroe, West Monroe, LA, p. A287
Director Information Technology, Chg Hospital Tucson, Llc, Tucson, AZ, p. A37

DAVIS, Amelia, Director of Nursing, Crossridge Community Hospital, Wynne, AR, p. A50

DAVIS, Andrea, Chief Executive Officer, Healthsouth Desert Canyon Rehabilitation Hospital, Las Vegas, NV, p. A403

DAVIS, Andrew L Jr, Chief Operating Officer, Erie County Medical Center, Buffalo, NY, p. A432

DAVIS, Andy, Chief Operating Officer, St. Vincent's Birmingham, Birmingham, AL, p. A15

DAVIS, Anne, Director Human Resources, Mason District Hospital, Havana, IL, p. A189

DAVIS, Astrid R.N., Chief Nursing Officer, Wellspan York Hospital, York, PA, p. A555

DAVIS, Autherine, Director Human Resources, D. W. Mcmillan Memorial Hospital, Brewton, AL, p. A15

DAVIS, Barry L., FACHE, President and Chief Executive Officer, Arkansas Methodist Medical Center, Paragould, AR, p. A48

DAVIS, Ben, Interim Chief Executive Officer, Osceola Community Hospital, Sibley, IA, p. A234

DAVIS, Betty, Director Administrative Services, Porterville Developmental Center, Porterville, CA, p. A80

DAVIS, Brenda, Vice President Patient Services, Indiana University Health Bedford Hospital, Bedford, IN, p. A204

DAVIS, Brent
Chief Financial Officer, Central Valley Medical Center, Nephi, UT, p. A658
Human Resources Team Leader, Arkansas Heart Hospital, Little Rock, AR, p. A45
Interim Chief Executive Officer, Avista Adventist Hospital, Louisville, CO, p. A106

DAVIS, C.J., Chief Executive Officer/ Executive Director, Four County Counseling Center, Logansport, IN, p. A215

DAVIS, Cathy J
Director Human Resources, Promedica Bixby Hospital, Adrian, MI, p. A314
Director Human Resources, Promedica Herrick Hospital, Tecumseh, MI, p. A332

DAVIS, Charissa, Chief Nursing Officer and Director of Nursing, Oasis Behavioral Health – Chandler, Chandler, AZ, p. A28

DAVIS, Charlotte C, Director Human Resources, Lincoln Trail Behavioral Health System, Radcliff, KY, p. A266

DAVIS, Cheryl M.D., Chief Medical Officer, Scotland Health Care System, Laurinburg, NC, p. A466

DAVIS, Dan, Managing Director and Chief Financial Officer, Integris Southwest Medical Center, Oklahoma City, OK, p. A512

DAVIS, Daniel E, Chief Financial Officer, Kingwood Medical Center, Kingwood, TX, p. A627

DAVIS, Darcy, Chief Financial Officer, Lakeside Medical Center, Belle Glade, FL, p. A119

DAVIS, David, Chief Operating Officer, Western Maryland Hospital Center, Hagerstown, MD, p. A299

DAVIS, Deborah W., Chief Executive Officer and Vice President Clinical Services, VCU Medical Center, Richmond, VA, p. A674

DAVIS, Debra K., Director of Operations, Winner Regional Healthcare Center, Winner, SD, p. A574

DAVIS, Deland, Chief Financial Officer, Indian Health Service – Quentin N. Burdick Memorial Health Care Facility, Belcourt, ND, p. A474

DAVIS, Dell, Director Information Systems, United Memorial Medical Care, Houston, TX, p. A623

DAVIS, Dustin, Chief Executive Officer, Virginia Beach Psychiatric Center, Virginia Beach, VA, p. A676

DAVIS, Elaine, Chief Nursing Officer and Vice President Patient Services, RMC Anniston, Anniston, AL, p. A13

DAVIS, Ellen, Service Unit Director, U. S. Public Health Service Indian Hospital, Pine Ridge, SD, p. A571

DAVIS, Evan, Director Technology and Environmental Services, Barbourville Arh Hospital, Barbourville, KY, p. A255

DAVIS, Gannon, Director Human Resources, Medical West, Bessemer, AL, p. A14

DAVIS, Gary
Director Information Systems, Great River Medical Center, West Burlington, IA, p. A236
Vice President Information Systems, Baptist Medical Center, San Antonio, TX, p. A642

DAVIS, Heather, M.D.
Chief of Staff, Pender Memorial Hospital, Burgaw, NC, p. A458
Administrator, Scott Regional Hospital, Morton, MS, p. A359

DAVIS, Howard Z M.D., Chief Medical Officer, Providence Tarzana Medical Center, Los Angeles, CA, p. A71

DAVIS, Jack, Vice President Human Resources, Faxton St. Luke's Healthcare, Utica, NY, p. A454

DAVIS, James R.
Chief Executive Officer, University Hospital Summerville, Augusta, GA, p. A152
Chief Executive Officer, University Hospital, Augusta, GA, p. A152

DAVIS, Janet R.N., MS, Senior Vice President and Chief Nursing Officer, Tampa General Hospital, Tampa, FL, p. A145

DAVIS, Janice, Interim Director Human Resources, Gifford Medical Center, Randolph, VT, p. A663

DAVIS, Jeff
Chief Financial Officer, Harrison County Hospital, Corydon, IN, p. A206
Senior Vice President Human Resources, Massachusetts General Hospital, Boston, MA, p. A303

DAVIS, Jeffrey D.O., Chief Medical Officer, St. Mary's Medical Center, West Palm Beach, FL, p. A147

DAVIS, Jeremy, Chief Executive Officer, Evanston Regional Hospital, Evanston, WY, p. A718

DAVIS, John William Bill
Chief Executive Officer, Ochsner Medical Center – North Shore, Slidell, LA, p. A286
Chief Executive Officer, Slidell Memorial Hospital, Slidell, LA, p. A286

DAVIS, John, Chief Human Resources Officer, Bristol Bay Area Health Corporation, Dillingham, AK, p. A26

DAVIS, Johnnie, Director Human Resources, Medicine Lodge Memorial Hospital, Medicine Lodge, KS, p. A247

DAVIS, Jon, Chief Financial Officer, Community Hospital–Fairfax, Fairfax, MO, p. A368

DAVIS, Jonathan S., FACHE, President, Martha Jefferson Hospital, Charlottesville, VA, p. A665

DAVIS, Justin
Chief Executive Officer, Moses Taylor Hospital, Scranton, PA, p. A550
Chief Executive Officer, Regional Hospital Of Scranton, Scranton, PA, p. A550

DAVIS, Karen, Chief Nursing Officer and Vice President, Nursing, Howard County General Hospital, Columbia, MD, p. A298

DAVIS, Kassi, Director Patient Care Services, Willow Crest Hospital, Miami, OK, p. A510

DAVIS, Kenneth L., M.D., President and Chief Executive, Mount Sinai Health System, New York, NY, p. B87

DAVIS, Kenneth, M.D.
Chief Medical Officer, Christus Santa Rosa Health System, San Antonio, TX, p. A642
Assistant Vice President Information Systems, Kennedy Krieger Institute, Baltimore, MD, p. A294

DAVIS, LaKeitha, Director Human Resources, Medical Center Of South Arkansas, El Dorado, AR, p. A42

DAVIS, Lance PharmD, Associate Director, Miami Veterans Affairs Healthcare System, Miami, FL, p. A133

DAVIS, Leslie C., President, Magee–Womens Hospital Of Upmc, Pittsburgh, PA, p. A547

DAVIS, Lisa, Vice President Finance, Saint Thomas West Hospital, Nashville, TN, p. A586

DAVIS, Lora, FACHE, Chief Executive Officer, Select Specialty Hospital–Tallahassee, Tallahassee, FL, p. A144

DAVIS, Lorraine, Vice President Human Resources, Horn Memorial Hospital, Ida Grove, IA, p. A229

DAVIS, Lyle E., Administrator, Cozad Community Health System, Cozad, NE, p. A392

DAVIS, Malene S., R.N., President and Chief Executive Officer, Capital Hospice, Arlington, VA, p. A664

DAVIS, Margaret, Interim Chief Executive Officer, Pecos County Memorial Hospital, Fort Stockton, TX, p. A613

DAVIS, Mark, M.D.
Chief of Staff, Newberry County Memorial Hospital, Newberry, SC, p. A565
Director Information Systems, Lake Taylor Transitional Care Hospital, Norfolk, VA, p. A672

DAVIS, Marla, Interim Chief Nursing Officer, Pmh Medical Center, Prosser, WA, p. A684

DAVIS, Matt, FACHE, Chief Executive Officer, Conroe Regional Medical Center, Conroe, TX, p. A602

DAVIS, Maureen, Administrator, Southern Nevada Medical And Rehabilitation Center, Las Vegas, NV, p. B53

DAVIS, Melissa
Chief Clinical Officer, Andalusia Health, Andalusia, AL, p. A13
Chief Operating Officer, Andalusia Health, Andalusia, AL, p. A13

DAVIS, Mike, Chief Financial Officer, Baylor Scott & White Medical Center – Sunnyvale, Sunnyvale, TX, p. A647

DAVIS, Myra, Senior Vice President and Chief Information Officer, Texas Children's Hospital, Houston, TX, p. A623

DAVIS, Myrna, Manager Human Resources, Palo Verde Hospital, Blythe, CA, p. A54

DAVIS, Natalie R.N., Interim Chief Nursing Officer, Mcleod Health Clarendon, Manning, SC, p. A564

DAVIS, Pam, Chief Nursing Officer, Galesburg Cottage Hospital, Galesburg, IL, p. A188

DAVIS, Patricia, Chief Nursing Officer, South Central Kansas Medical Center, Arkansas City, KS, p. A238

DAVIS, Paula M, Chief Human Resources Officer, Sonoma Valley Hospital, Sonoma, CA, p. A92

DAVIS, Rachel, Director, Sharp Coronado Hospital And Healthcare Center, Coronado, CA, p. A56

DAVIS, Randy
Chief Executive Officer, Northcrest Medical Center, Springfield, TN, p. A589
Vice President and Chief Information Officer, CGH Medical Center, Sterling, IL, p. A201

DAVIS, Ray
Administrative Director Information Systems, The Hospitals Of Providence Sierra Campus, El Paso, TX, p. A611
Administrative Director, The Hospitals Of Providence Memorial Campus, El Paso, TX, p. A611
Chief Information Officer, The Hospitals Of Providence Transmountain Campus, El Paso, TX, p. A612

DEBOER, K C., President and Chief Executive Officer, Jamestown Regional Medical Center, Jamestown, ND, p. A476

DEBOLT, Larry W, Chief Financial Officer, Bluffton Regional Medical Center, Bluffton, IN, p. A204

DEBONA, Paul, Chief Executive Officer, Baylor Surgical Hospital At Fort Worth, Fort Worth, TX, p. A613

DEBOOY, Ann R.N., Chief Nursing Officer, Memorial Medical Center, Las Cruces, NM, p. A426

DEBORD, Thomas, Chief Operating Officer, Overlake Medical Center, Bellevue, WA, p. A678

DEBRUYCKER, Allison, Administrator, Magnolia Behavioral Hospital Of East Texas, Longview, TX, p. A630

DECELIS, Lori, Director Human Resources, Hampton Behavioral Health Center, Westampton, NJ, p. A422

DECELL, Daniela, Chief Executive Officer, Medical City Las Colinas, Irving, TX, p. A625

DECHABERT, Rebecca, Acting Director Personnel, New York State Psychiatric Institute, New Rochelle, NY, p. A444

DECHAIRO–MARINO, Ann R.N., Ph.D., Chief Nursing Officer, Providence Holy Cross Medical Center, Los Angeles, CA, p. A70

DECHANT, David, Chief Human Resources Officer, Tomah Veterans Affairs Medical Center, Tomah, WI, p. A714

DECKARD, Rick, Chief Fiscal Service, Chillicothe Veterans Affairs Medical Center, Chillicothe, OH, p. A483

DECKARD, Steven D, Vice President Human Resources, Indiana University Health Bloomington Hospital, Bloomington, IN, p. A204

DECKER, Diann, Chief Human Resource Officer, Provo Canyon Behavioral Hospital, Orem, UT, p. A658

DECKER, Janet, Assistant Vice President, Information Systems, Medstar Union Memorial Hospital, Baltimore, MD, p. A295

DECKER, Jeanine, Manager Human Resources, Arizona State Hospital, Phoenix, AZ, p. A33

DECKER, Kevin, Chief Executive Officer, Forrest City Medical Center, Forrest City, AR, p. A43

DECKER, Michael, President and Chief Executive Officer, Divine Savior Healthcare, Portage, WI, p. A710

DECKER, Wyatt, Chief Executive Officer, Mayo Clinic in Arizona, Mayo Clinic Hospital, Phoenix, AZ, p. A33

DECORTE, Raymond P M.D., Chief Medical Officer, East Jefferson General Hospital, Metairie, LA, p. A281

DECREMER, Dean, Information Systems Manager, Dickinson County Healthcare System, Iron Mountain, MI, p. A323

DEE, Thomas A., President and Chief Executive Officer, Southwestern Vermont Medical Center, Bennington, VT, p. A662

DEEN, Cecelia Esq, Chief Nursing Officer, Southeast Colorado Hospital District, Springfield, CO, p. A107

DEERING, Linda, MSN, R.N., President, Advocate Sherman Hospital, Elgin, IL, p. A186

DEERING, Lisa, Administrator, Heatherhill Care Communities, Chardon, OH, p. A483

DEES, Edith, Vice President Information Services and Chief Information Officer, Geisinger Holy Spirit, Camp Hill, PA, p. A530

DEFIGUIEREDO, Kathy, Director, Information Technology, Chi St. Luke's Health Memorial Livingston, Livingston, TX, p. A629

DEFOE, Mike, Chief Financial Officer, Perry Memorial Hospital, Princeton, IL, p. A198

DEFOORE, Richard G., FACHE, Chief Executive Officer, Stamford Memorial Hospital, Stamford, TX, p. A646

DEFORD, Drexel, Chief Information Officer, Scripps Mercy Hospital, San Diego, CA, p. A86

DEFRANCESCO, Anthony, Associate Director, Va Long Beach Healthcare System, Long Beach, CA, p. A67

DEFURIO, Ken, President and Chief Executive Officer, Butler Health System, Butler, PA, p. A530

DEGEAR, David O M.D., Vice President Medical Affairs, Westfields Hospital, New Richmond, WI, p. A709

DEGENNARO, Vincent M.D., Chief of Staff, Miami Veterans Affairs Healthcare System, Miami, FL, p. A133

DEGINA, Anthony M, President and Chief Executive Officer, Largo Medical Center, Largo, FL, p. A130

DEGNAN, William, Vice President Finance, Aria – Jefferson Health, Philadelphia, PA, p. A543

DEGRAVELLE, Eric, Director Human Resources, Thibodaux Regional Medical Center, Thibodaux, LA, p. A287

DEGROOT, Daniel, Chief Operating Officer, Hshs St. Clare Memorial Hospital, Oconto Falls, WI, p. A709

DEGROOT, Randy, President and Chief Executive Officer, Community Health Center Of Branch County, Coldwater, MI, p. A317

DEHART, Kristen, Chief Executive Officer, Excelsior Springs Hospital, Excelsior Springs, MO, p. A367

DEHAVEN, Bryce, Chief Financial Officer, Medical Center Of Aurora, Aurora, CO, p. A98

DEHERRERA, Barbara, Chief Nursing Officer, Garfield County Public Hospital District, Pomeroy, WA, p. A683

DEHNING, Cielo M.D., Medical Director, Mid–America Rehabilitation Hospital, Shawnee Mission, KS, p. A251

DEIBEL, Justin, Senior Vice President and Chief Financial Officer, Mercy Medical Center, Baltimore, MD, p. A295

DEININGER, Robert, Chief Executive Officer, Florida Hospital Fish Memorial, Orange City, FL, p. A136

DEIS, Terrence G., CPA, FACHE, President, Saint Joseph London, London, KY, p. A262

DEITRICK, Diana, Director Information Services, Devereux Hospital And Children's Center Of Florida, Melbourne, FL, p. A132

DEJACO, Lynn S, Chief Financial Officer, Firsthealth Moore Regional Hospital, Pinehurst, NC, p. A468

DEJESUS, David, Senior Vice President Human Resources, Southcoast Hospitals Group, Fall River, MA, p. A306

DEJONG, Tyler
Director of Operational Finance, Chi Health Midlands, Papillion, NE, p. A399
Director, Operational Finance, Chi Health Lakeside, Omaha, NE, p. A397

DEKEYZER, Ron, Regional Director Information Systems, Christus St. Vincent Regional Medical Center, Santa Fe, NM, p. A428

DEKOK, Joni, Chief Nursing Officer, Sanford Sheldon Medical Center, Sheldon, IA, p. A234

DEKONING, Bernard L. M.D., Chief of Staff, Wm. Jennings Bryan Dorn Veterans Affairs Medical Center, Columbia, SC, p. A561

DEKREY, Dale MS, Associate Director Operations and Resources, Fargo Veterans Affairs Health Care System, Fargo, ND, p. A475

DEKREY, Daniel M.D., Chief of Staff, Sanford Bemidji Medical Center, Bemidji, MN, p. A336

DEKRUSE, Jet L., Administrator, Humboldt County Mental Health, Eureka, CA, p. A58

DEL CASTILLO, Daniel, Chief Executive Officer, Healthsouth Rehabilitation Hospital Of San Juan, San Juan, PR, p. A726

DEL GAUDIO, Frank J., Director and Chief Executive Officer, Essex County Hospital Center, Cedar Grove, NJ, p. A412

DEL GUIDICE, Mary Margaret R.N., Chief Nursing Officer, Pennsylvania Hospital, Philadelphia, PA, p. A545

DEL RIO, R Maxilimien M.D., Medical Director, Northern Virginia Mental Health Institute, Falls Church, VA, p. A667

DEL TORO, Gustavo M.D., Chief Medical Officer, Wyckoff Heights Medical Center, New Rochelle, NY, p. A447

DEL TORO, Ivan E M.D., Medical Director, Hima San Pablo Caguas, Caguas, PR, p. A722

DELA TORRE, Victor, Command Legal Officer, Naval Hospital Lemoore, Lemoore, CA, p. A65

DELAGARDELLE, Pamela K., President and Chief Executive Officer, Unitypoint Health – Waterloo, Waterloo, IA, p. A236

DELAHANTY, Paula
Regional Chief Nursing Officer, Pen Bay Medical Center, Rockport, ME, p. A293
Regional Chief Nursing Officer, Waldo County General Hospital, Belfast, ME, p. A290

DELANCEY, Darlene, Interim Director, Albany Stratton Veterans Affairs Medical Center, Albany, NY, p. A430

DELANEY, Bryan, Director Information Technology, Crossroads Community Hospital, Mount Vernon, IL, p. A194

DELANEY, Kristi, Director, Human Resources, Siskin Hospital For Physical Rehabilitation, Chattanooga, TN, p. A576

DELANEY, Patrick, Administrative Director, Operations, Robert Wood Johnson University Hospital Somerset, Somerville, NJ, p. A420

DELATTE, Sandra, Director Human Resources, Villa Feliciana Medical Complex, Jackson, LA, p. A276

DELAVAN, Karen, Interim Director Human Resources, Comanche County Medical Center, Comanche, TX, p. A602

DELEON, Arsenio V M.D., Chief Medical Officer, Select Specialty Hospital–Macomb County, Mount Clemens, MI, p. A326

DELEON, Joseph, President, Texas Health Harris Methodist Hospital Southwest Fort Worth, Fort Worth, TX, p. A614

DELEON, Marcos
Vice President Community Engagement, Truman Medical Center–Hospital Hill, Kansas City, MO, p. A371
Vice President Community Engagement, Truman Medical Center–Lakewood, Kansas City, MO, p. A371

DELFS, Michael, Chief Executive Officer, Mercy Hospital, Moose Lake, MN, p. A344

DELGADO, Eric, Chief Financial Officer, Lakewood Regional Medical Center, Lakewood, CA, p. A65

DELGADO, Lupe, Coordinator Human Resources, Kindred Hospital Sugar Land, Sugar Land, TX, p. A647

DELGADO, Pete, President and Chief Executive Officer, Salinas Valley Memorial Healthcare System, Salinas, CA, p. A84

DELGRECO, Trish, Director of Nursing, Ohiohealth Medcentral Shelby Hospital, Shelby, OH, p. A499

DELIEN, Rudie, Director Human Resources, Devereux Georgia Treatment Network, Kennesaw, GA, p. A160

DELISE, Donna, Associate Director Patient Care Services, Oklahoma City Veterans Affairs Medical Center, Oklahoma City, OK, p. A513

DELLASEGA, Dave, President and Chief Executive Officer, Great Plains Health Alliance, Inc., Wichita, KS, p. B54

DELLA FLORA, Thomas, Vice President and Chief Information Officer, Catholic Medical Center, Manchester, NH, p. A409

DELLA LANA, David M.D., Chief of Staff, Fairchild Medical Center, Yreka, CA, p. A97

DELLEA, Eugene A., President, Fairview Hospital, Great Barrington, MA, p. A307

DELLER, Jerry, Chief Executive Officer, Landmark Hospital Of Columbia, Columbia, MO, p. A367

DELLICK, Charles, Director Information Technology, Magruder Memorial Hospital, Port Clinton, OH, p. A498

DELLICKER, Sandra, Director of Human Resources, Saint Anne's Hospital, Fall River, MA, p. A306

DELLOCONO, John, Senior Vice President and Chief Financial Officer, Centrastate Healthcare System, Freehold, NJ, p. A414

DELLSPERGER, Kevin M.D., Chief Medical Officer, Augusta University Medical Center, Augusta, GA, p. A151

DELONG, Patricia, Chief Nursing Officer, Essentia Health St. Joseph's Medical Center, Brainerd, MN, p. A337

DELORENZO, David, Senior Director Human Resources, Sisters Of Charity Hospital Of Buffalo, Buffalo, NY, p. A433

DELORME, Robert, Vice President Medical Affairs, Community Memorial Hospital, Hamilton, NY, p. A437

DELPHIN-RITTMON, Miriam, Ph.D., Commissioner, Connecticut Department Of Mental Health And Addiction Services, Hartford, CT, p. B38

DELPLEACHE, Michael, Specialist Information Technology, Anchor Hospital, Atlanta, GA, p. A149

DELVEAUX, Joe, Manager Information Services, St. Francis Regional Medical Center, Shakopee, MN, p. A348

DEMAIO, Joan, Vice President Nursing, Milford Hospital, Milford, CT, p. A111

DEMARCO, Victor, Chief Financial Officer, Bronx–Lebanon Hospital Center Health Care System, New Rochelle, NY, p. A440

DEMAREST, Pamela MSN, R.N., Chief Nursing Officer, UNM Sandoval Regional Medical Center, Inc., Rio Rancho, NM, p. A428

DEMASIE, Dennis, Vice President Information Systems and Chief Information Officer, Rush–Copley Medical Center, Aurora, IL, p. A178

DEMATTEO, Kathleen, Chief Information Officer, Danbury Hospital, Danbury, CT, p. A109

DEMBLA, Preeti, Chief Medical Officer and Medical Director, Rehabilitation Hospital Of Fort Wayne, Fort Wayne, IN, p. A208

DEMERICH, Lois B, Director Human Resources, Sentara Williamsburg Regional Medical Center, Williamsburg, VA, p. A677

DEMERS, Becky R.N., Chief Operating Officer, Samaritan Healthcare, Moses Lake, WA, p. A682

DEMERS, Vickie, Chief Executive Officer, Healthsouth Lakeshore Rehabilitation Hospital, Birmingham, AL, p. A14

DEMETRIADES, James, Vice President, Operations, University Medical Center Of Princeton At Plainsboro, Plainsboro, NJ, p. A419

DEMING, Mark, Administrator, Finance and Support, Beaumont Hospital – Taylor, Taylor, MI, p. A331

DEMING, Peggy, Executive Vice President and Chief Financial Officer, University Health System, San Antonio, TX, p. A644

DEMING, Terra, Director Human Resources, Otsego Memorial Hospital, Gaylord, MI, p. A320

DEMLAKIAN, Vahan, Director of Human Resources, Gateways Hospital And Mental Health Center, Los Angeles, CA, p. A68

DEMMEL, Ruth M.D., Chief Medical Officer, Perkins County Health Services, Grant, NE, p. A393

DEMOE, Sara, Chief Financial Officer, North Canyon Medical Center, Gooding, ID, p. A173

DEMORLIS, John M.D., Chief Medical Staff, Salem Memorial District Hospital, Salem, MO, p. A379

DEMORROW, Dawn P, Chief Human Resources Service, Wilkes–Barre Veterans Affairs Medical Center, Wilkes, PA, p. A554

DEMPSEY, Jeffrey, President and Chief Executive Officer, Mercy Health – St. Charles Hospital, Oregon, OH, p. A497

DEMPSEY, Jeffrey
President and Chief Operating Officer, Mercy Health – St. Charles Hospital, Oregon, OH, p. A497
President, Mercy St. Vincent Medical Center, Toledo, OH, p. A500

DEMPSEY, John J., Chief Executive Officer, Little Colorado Medical Center, Winslow, AZ, p. A39

DEMURO, Rob M.D., Chief Medical Officer, The University Of Vermont Health Network Elizabethtown Community Hospital, Elizabethtown, NY, p. A435

DENCKLAU, Larry D.O., Chief of Staff, Baylor Scott & White Medical Center – Lake Pointe, Rowlett, TX, p. A641

DENEFF, Randall, Vice President Finance, Mary Free Bed Rehabilitation Hospital, Grand Rapids, MI, p. A321

DENEGRI, David, Chief Financial Officer, Parkwood Behavioral Health System, Olive Branch, MS, p. A360

DENEN, Bruce, Manager Data Processing, Fayette County Memorial Hospital, Washington Court House, OH, p. A502

DENG, Mei, Chief Financial Officer, T. J. Samson Community Hospital, Glasgow, KY, p. A259

DENHAM, Stephanie, Chief Financial Officer and Human Resources Officer, Phillips County Hospital, Malta, MT, p. A386

DENICOLA, Joseph, Chief Executive Officer and Managing Director, Arrowhead Behavioral Health Hospital, Maumee, OH, p. A495

DENIGRIS, Deborah, Chief Nursing Officer, Kingsboro Psychiatric Center, New Rochelle, NY, p. A442

DENIKE, Michael D.O., Vice President, Medical Affairs, Blanchard Valley Hospital, Findlay, OH, p. A491

DENIO, Arthur E, Vice President and Chief Financial Officer, Northbay Medical Center, Fairfield, CA, p. A59

DENISIENKO, Mary, Vice President Human Resources, Palos Health, Palos Heights, IL, p. A196

DENISON, Rita, Director of Information Systems, Sturgis Hospital, Sturgis, MI, p. A331

DENKER, Jill, Executive Director Human Resources, Lexington Regional Health Center, Lexington, NE, p. A394

DENKINGER, Marshall M.D., Chief Medical Officer, St. Anthony Summit Medical Center, Frisco, CO, p. A103

DENMARK, Donald
Chief Medical Officer, Carondelet St. Joseph's Hospital, Tucson, AZ, p. A37
Chief Medical Officer, Carondelet St. Mary's Hospital, Tucson, AZ, p. A37

DENNETT, Bryan M.D., Chief of Staff, William Newton Hospital, Winfield, KS, p. A254

DENNEY, Jeff
Chief Executive Officer, Select Specialty Hospital–Springfield, Springfield, MO, p. A380
Chief Executive Officer, Select Specialty Hospital–St. Louis, Saint Charles, MO, p. A376

DENNIS, Kera, Assistant Administrator, Finance, Uw Medicine/Harborview Medical Center, Seattle, WA, p. A685

DENNIS, Michael, Director, William J. Mccord Adolescent Treatment Facility, Orangeburg, SC, p. A565

DENNIS, Ronnie, Chief of Staff, Rolling Plains Memorial Hospital, Sweetwater, TX, p. A648

DENNISON, Cynthia, Assistant Chief Financial Officer 3, Mercy Tiffin Hospital, Tiffin, OH, p. A500

DENNY, Donald M.D., Senior Vice President, Medical Affairs, University Medical Center Of Princeton At Plainsboro, Plainsboro, NJ, p. A419

DENO, Mark S, Chief Operating Officer, Medical Center Of Aurora, Aurora, CO, p. A98

DENSON, Anna, Human Resources Specialist, Choctaw Health Center, Philadelphia, MS, p. A360

DENSON, Paula Lajean M.D., President, Tyler County Hospital, Woodville, TX, p. A655

DENT, Bob R.N., Senior Vice President, Chief Operating Officer and Chief Nursing Officer, Midland Memorial Hospital, Midland, TX, p. A633

DENT, Bruce, Human Resources Director, Heber Valley Medical Center, Heber City, UT, p. A657

DENTEN, Jane MSN, R.N., Chief Nurse Executive, Advocate Lutheran General Hospital, Park Ridge, IL, p. A197

DENTON, Brian, Administrator, Mercy Hospital Kingfisher, Kingfisher, OK, p. A509

DENTON, Christopher, Chief Financial Officer, Henrico Doctors' Hospital, Richmond, VA, p. A674

DENTON, Genise, Manager Human Resources, John J. Pershing Veterans Affairs Medical Center, Poplar Bluff, MO, p. A375

DENTON, Joe, Executive Vice President and Chief Financial Officer, Mobile Infirmary Medical Center, Mobile, AL, p. A20

DENTON, Renee, Chief Operating Officer, Freeman Neosho Hospital, Neosho, MO, p. A374

DENTON, Roy M.D., Chief Medical Officer, Conway Regional Rehabilitation Hospital, Conway, AR, p. A41

DENTON, Tony JD, Senior Vice President and Chief Operating Officer, Michigan Medicine, Ann Arbor, MI, p. A314

DENTONI, Terry, Chief Nursing Officer, Zuckerberg San Francisco General Hospital And Trauma Center, San Francisco, CA, p. A88

DENUCCI, Alex, Chief Financial Officer, Franciscan Children's, Brighton, MA, p. A304

DEPASQUALE, Joseph M.D., Interim Chief Medical Officer, Saint Michael's Medical Center, Newark, NJ, p. A417

DEPAULIS, Hugh, Interim Vice President and Chief Financial Officer, Mercy Medical Center–Sioux City, Sioux City, IA, p. A235

DEPKO, Mike, Director Information Technology, Brown County Hospital, Ainsworth, NE, p. A390

DEPLONTY, Sandy, Senior Director Clinical Services, War Memorial Hospital, Sault Sainte Marie, MI, p. A330

DEPOMPEI, Patricia, President, University Hospitals Cleveland Medical Center, Cleveland, OH, p. A486

DEPOOTER, Stephen, Chief Information Officer, Norwegian American Hospital, Chicago, IL, p. A182

DEPPERMAN, Kristi, Chief Financial Officer, Memphis Veterans Affairs Medical Center, Memphis, TN, p. A585

DEPRATO, Jeremy, Director Information Technology, Spine Hospital Of Louisiana (Formally The Neuromedical Center Surgical Hospital), Baton Rouge, LA, p. A271

DERAMUS, Brenda, Manager Human Resources, Sutter Lakeside Hospital, Lakeport, CA, p. A65

DERBY, Richard P, Vice President Finance, Barton Memorial Hospital, South Lake Tahoe, CA, p. A92

DERFLINGER, Terri, Site Administrator, Mercy Hospital Of Franciscan Sisters, Oelwein, IA, p. A232

DERK, Tammy L., Chief Executive Officer, Lancaster Rehabilitation Hospital, Lancaster, PA, p. A538

DERKS, Jennifer, Chief Administrative Officer, Calumet Medical Center, Chilton, WI, p. A700

DERMAN, Nancy, Director Human Resources, Southwest Connecticut Mental Health System, Bridgeport, CT, p. A109

DEROCHE, Glynis R., Administrator, Acadia Optima Hospital, Lafayette, LA, p. A278

DEROCHE, Richard, Manager Information Technology, Multicare Deaconess Hospital, Spokane, WA, p. A686

DERONCEREY, Josiane, Director Human Resources, Carepoint Health Christ Hospital, Jersey City, NJ, p. A415

DEROSSITT, James M.D., Chief of Staff, Forrest City Medical Center, Forrest City, AR, p. A43

DEROUEN, Jason, Director Management Information Systems, Grace Medical Center, Lubbock, TX, p. A630

DERRICO, Patricia FACHE, R.N., Chief Nursing Officer, Coliseum Northside Hospital, Macon, GA, p. A161

DERSCH, Stephen M.D., President Medical Staff, Regency Hospital Of Florence, Florence, SC, p. A562

DERUS, Charles M.D., Vice President Medical Management, Advocate Good Samaritan Hospital, Downers Grove, IL, p. A186

DERUYTER, David N. M.D., President Medical Staff, Select Specialty Hospital Midtown Atlanta, Atlanta, GA, p. A151

DERYNCK, Dodie, Chief Nursing Officer, Avera Marshall Regional Medical Center, Marshall, MN, p. A343

DESAI, Ankur, Interim Chief Medical officer, Rome Memorial Hospital, Rome, NY, p. A451

DESAI, Nimesh M.D., Medical Director, Massena Memorial Hospital, Massena, NY, p. A439

DESAI, Shailesh M.D., Chief of Staff, Baum Harmon Mercy Hospital, Primghar, IA, p. A233

DESALVO, Susan, Manager Human Resources, Bath Veterans Affairs Medical Center, Bath, NY, p. A431

DESANTIS, Vincent, Vice President Finance, Phelps Memorial Hospital Center, Sleepy Hollow, NY, p. A452

DESART, Amy, Vice President, Chief Financial Officer, Missouri Baptist Medical Center, Saint Louis, MO, p. A377

DESCHAMBEAU, Wayne G., President and Chief Executive Officer, Wayne Healthcare, Greenville, OH, p. A492

DESCHENE, Normand E., FACHE, Chief Executive Officer, Lowell General Hospital, Lowell, MA, p. A308

DESCHRYVER, Joseph, Chief Executive Officer, Good Samaritan Hospital, San Jose, CA, p. A88

DESEI, Nitin M.D., Medical Director, Regional Rehabilitation Hospital, Phenix City, AL, p. A22

DESIMINI, Esther Muscari., Administrator, Riverside Tappahannock Hospital, Tappahannock, VA, p. A676

DESIMONE, Maureen, Chief Operating Officer, Blythedale Children's Hospital, Valhalla, NY, p. A454

DESIMONE, Shane M.D., Chief of Staff, Jane Todd Crawford Hospital, Greensburg, KY, p. A259

DESJEUNES, Carol, Vice President and Chief Operating Officer, Psychiatric Institute Of Washington, Washington, DC, p. A118

DESKINS, Juanita, Chief Operating Officer, Pikeville Medical Center, Pikeville, KY, p. A266

DESMARTEAU, Lisa Jo, Chief Financial Officer, Miami Jewish Home And Hospital For Aged, Miami, FL, p. A133

DESMOND, Debbie, Director Human Resources, Martha Jefferson Hospital, Charlottesville, VA, p. A665

DESMOND, Heather, Chief Financial Officer, Bibb Medical Center, Centreville, AL, p. A16

DESMOND, Jeffrey M.D., Chief Medical Officer, Michigan Medicine, Ann Arbor, MI, p. A314

DESMOND, P Craig., Chief Executive Officer, Southwest General Hospital, San Antonio, TX, p. A644

DESOTO, James, M.D.
Vice President Medical Affairs, Mercy Medical Center Redding, Redding, CA, p. A81
Vice President Medical Affairs, St. Elizabeth Community Hospital, Red Bluff, CA, p. A81
Interim President, Mercy Medical Center Redding, Redding, CA, p. A81

DESOUZA, Jacqueline, Chief Executive Officer, Research Medical Center, Kansas City, MO, p. A370

DESPRES, Paul J., Chief Executive Officer, Eleanor Slater Hospital, Cranston, RI, p. A556

DESROCHES, Jeff, Manager Information Systems, Ahmc Anaheim Regional Medical Center, Anaheim, CA, p. A51

DESTEFANO, Geraldine R.N., MS, Chief Nursing Officer, JFK Medical Center North Campus, West Palm Beach, FL, p. A147

DESTEFANO, Stephen, Chief Financial Officer, Magee Rehabilitation Hospital, Philadelphia, PA, p. A544

DETANO, Teresa R., M.P.H., Chief Executive Officer, Select Specialty Hospital–Northern Kentucky, Fort Thomas, KY, p. A258

DETTERMAN, B Lynn.
President and Chief Executive Officer, Mercy Health – Willard Hospital, Willard, OH, p. A502
President and Chief Executive Officer, Mercy Hospital Of Defiance, Defiance, OH, p. A490
President and Chief Executive Officer, Mercy Tiffin Hospital, Tiffin, OH, p. A500

DETTMER, Brantley, Administrator and Chief Operating Officer, Kaiser Foundation Hospital Westside Medical Center, Hillsboro, OR, p. A522

DETWILER, Courtney, R.N., Administrator, Hampton Roads Specialty Hospital, Newport News, VA, p. A671

DETWILER, Eric, Director Information Technology, Barnes–Kasson County Hospital, Susquehanna, PA, p. A551

DEUEL, Teresa L., Chief Executive Officer, Hodgeman County Health Center, Jetmore, KS, p. A243

DEURMIER, Carol, Chief Executive Officer, St. Michael's Hospital Avera, Tyndall, SD, p. A573

DEUTSCH, Stephen, Vice President Operations and Support, Spencer Hospital, Spencer, IA, p. A235

DEVANATHAN, Raja M.D., Chief Medical Officer, Vibra Hospital Of Northwestern Indiana, Crown Point, IN, p. A206

DEVANEY, Catherine, Chief Executive Officer, Healthsouth Rehabilitation Hospital, Concord, NH, p. A407

DEVARAJ, Kiran S., Chief Medical Officer and Chief Clinical Officer, Highland Hospital, Charleston, WV, p. A691

DEVARAJAN, Vadakkipalayam N., Chief Medical Staff, St. Charles Parish Hospital, Luling, LA, p. A280

DEVAULT, Jennifer, Vice President Associate Services, F. F. Thompson Hospital, Canandaigua, NY, p. A433

DEVAULT, Rosanne, Chief Financial Officer, Mckenzie–Willamette Medical Center, Springfield, OR, p. A527

DEVAULT, Roseann M, Chief Financial Officer, Tennova Healthcare–Jefferson Memorial Hospital, Jefferson City, TN, p. A580

DEVAUX, Sheri, Information Technology Manager, Connecticut Veterans Home And Hospital, Rocky Hill, CT, p. A112

DEVENUTO, Joseph, Vice President and Chief Information Officer, Norton Women's And Children's Hospital, Louisville, KY, p. A263

DEVENY, T. Clifford, M.D., Interim Chief Executive Officer, Summa Health , Akron, OH, p. B122

DEVERA, Rozelle, Director of Information Systems, Gateways Hospital And Mental Health Center, Los Angeles, CA, p. A68

DEVEREUX, Chris, Human Resources Director, Business Partner, Edward Hospital, Naperville, IL, p. A195

DEVILLE, Linda F., Chief Executive Officer, Bunkie General Hospital, Bunkie, LA, p. A272

DEVIN, Brian V., Chief Executive Officer, Pappas Rehabilitation Hospital For Children, Canton, MA, p. A305

DEVIN, Joseph, Chief Financial Officer, Boone County Hospital, Boone, IA, p. A223

DEVINE, Joseph W., FACHE, President and Chief Executive Officer, Kennedy Health System, Stratford, NJ, p. A420

DEVINE, Kathryn, Vice President Human Resources, Upmc Presbyterian Shadyside, Pittsburgh, PA, p. A547

DEVITA, James M.D., Chief Medical Officer, Tewksbury Hospital, Tewksbury, MA, p. A312

DEVITO, Joseph M, Vice President Finance and Chief Operating Officer, Geisinger–Bloomsburg Hospital, Bloomsburg, PA, p. A530

DEVLIN, James, Director Information Systems, St. Cloud Regional Medical Center, Saint Cloud, FL, p. A141

DEVOCELLE, Frank H., President and Chief Executive Officer, Olathe Medical Center, Olathe, KS, p. A248

DEVORE, Druery, Chief of Medical Staff, Northern Hospital Of Surry County, Mount Airy, NC, p. A467

DEVORE, Kathy, Administrator, Continuecare Hospital At Madisonville, Madisonville, KY, p. A264

DEVORE, Paul A M.D., Medical Director, Gladys Spellman Specialty Hospital And Nursing Center, Cheverly, MD, p. A297

DEVORSETZ, Marc, Chief Executive Officer, Baylor Scott & White Surgical Hospital At Sherman, Sherman, TX, p. A645

DEW, Douglas M.D., President Medical Staff, Flagler Hospital, Saint Augustine, FL, p. A141

DEWAN, Vijay M.D., Clinical Director, Lincoln Regional Center, Lincoln, NE, p. A395

DEWANE, Patti, Vice President Finance and Treasurer, Swedishamerican – A Division Of Uw Health, Rockford, IL, p. A199

DEWAR, William M.D., Chief of Staff, Wayne Memorial Hospital, Honesdale, PA, p. A536

DEWBERRY, Robbie, Chief Executive Officer, Mitchell County Hospital, Colorado City, TX, p. A602

DEWERFF, Mike, President and Chief Executive Officer, Unitypoint Health – Trinity Regional Medical Center, Fort Dodge, IA, p. A227

DEWISPELARE, Cheryl M, Chief Human Resources Officer, Veterans Affairs Nebraska–Western Iowa Health Care System, Omaha, NE, p. A398

DEWITT, Alan Neil, Chief Medical Officer, Summit Healthcare Regional Medical Center, Show Low, AZ, p. A36

DEWITT, Jocelyn Ph.D., Vice President and Chief Information Officer, University Of Wisconsin Hospitals And Clinics Authority, Madison, WI, p. A705

DEWORTH, Gerald M, Associate Director, Carl Vinson Veterans Affairs Medical Center, Dublin, GA, p. A157

DEXTER, Heather, Chief Executive Officer, Emory Saint Joseph's Hospital Of Atlanta, Atlanta, GA, p. A150

DEXTER, Sue, Administrative Department Leader Human Resources, Mcdonough District Hospital, Macomb, IL, p. A192

DEYARMIN, James A, Controller, Children's Hospital Of Richmond At Vcu–Brook Road Campus, Richmond, VA, p. A674

DEYO–ALLERS, Margaret, Vice President, Chief Nursing Officer, St. Luke's Cornwall Hospital, Newburgh, NY, p. A447

DEYOUNG, Keith M.D., Chief Medical Staff, Wallowa Memorial Hospital, Enterprise, OR, p. A521

DHAWAN, Ajay M.D., Chief of Staff, Veterans Affairs Northern Indiana Health Care System, Fort Wayne, IN, p. A208

DHAWAN, Rahul M.D., Chief Medical Officer, St. Francis Medical Center, Lynwood, CA, p. A72

DHILION, Avtar, Medical Director, The Pavilion At Williamsburg Place, Williamsburg, VA, p. A677

DHILLON, Avtar M.D., Medical Director, Keystone Newport News, Newport News, VA, p. A671

DHINGRA, Ashok M.D., Executive Medical Director, Healthsouth Deaconess Rehabilitation Hospital, Evansville, IN, p. A207

DHULIPALA, Vasudeva M.D., Medical Director, Healthsouth Rehabilitation Hospital Of Alexandria, Alexandria, LA, p. A269

DHUPER, Aman, President and Chief Executive Officer, St. Rose Hospital, Hayward, CA, p. A63

DI BACCO, David J, Chief Operating Officer, Eastern Niagara Hospital, Lockport, NY, p. A438

DI BERNARDO, Deborah, Chief Information Officer, Saint Joseph's Medical Center, Yonkers, NY, p. A456

DIAL, Jody S, Chief Financial Officer, Timpanogos Regional Hospital, Orem, UT, p. A658

DIAL, Ray D., Director of Nursing, Nebraska Medicine – Bellevue, Bellevue, NE, p. A391

DIALTO, Margaret, Regional Chief Human Resource Officer, Staten Island University Hospital, New Rochelle, NY, p. A446

DIAMOND, Anne, President and Chief Executive Officer, Day Kimball Hospital, Putnam, CT, p. A112

DIAMOND, Kevin M. M.D., Chief Medical Officer, Lawrence Memorial Hospital, Walnut Ridge, AR, p. A50

DIAMOND, Lester K., President, St. Dominic–Jackson Memorial Hospital, Jackson, MS, p. A357

DIAMOND, Timothy, Chief Information Officer, Methodist Hospitals, Gary, IN, p. A209

DIANDA–MARTIN, Barb, Chief Nursing Officer, Mercy St. Anne Hospital, Toledo, OH, p. A500

DIANGELO, John A.
President and Chief Executive Officer, Inspira Medical Center–Elmer, Elmer, NJ, p. A413
President and Chief Executive Officer, Inspira Medical Center–Vineland, Vineland, NJ, p. A422
President and Chief Executive Officer, Inspira Medical Center–Woodbury, Woodbury, NJ, p. A423

DIASIO, Anthony J, Chief Financial Officer, Fox Chase Cancer Center–American Oncologic Hospital, Philadelphia, PA, p. A543

DIAZ, Al, M.D., Chief Executive Officer, Kindred Hospital Rome, Rome, GA, p. A163

DIAZ, Evelyn R.N., Chief Nursing Officer, Healthsouth Hospital Of Manati, Manati, PR, p. A724

DIAZ, Georgina
Chief Executive Officer, Jackson Health System, Miami, FL, p. A133
Chief Operating Officer, Palmetto General Hospital, Hialeah, FL, p. A126

DIAZ, Janine, Human Resources Manager, Emory Rehabilitation Hospital, Atlanta, GA, p. A150

DIAZ, Jesse, Chief Information Officer, Phoebe Putney Memorial Hospital, Albany, GA, p. A149

DIAZ, Jimmy, Director Information Technology, Odessa Regional Medical Center, Odessa, TX, p. A635

DIAZ, Jose, Director Information Systems, St. Vincent Medical Center Of Evansville, Evansville, IN, p. A207

DIAZ, Joseph M.D., Chief Medical Officer, Memorial Hospital Of Rhode Island, Pawtucket, RI, p. A556

DIAZ, Ron, Manager Operations, Albany Stratton Veterans Affairs Medical Center, Albany, NY, p. A430

DIAZ, Steve M.D., Chief Medical Officer, Mainegeneral Medical Center, Augusta, ME, p. A289

DIBBLE, Lynn, Vice President Patient Care Services, Guthrie Towanda Memorial Hospital, Towanda, PA, p. A551

DIBNER, David A, Senior Vice President Hospital Operations and Musculoskeletel Strategic Areas, NYU Langone Hospitals, New Rochelle, NY, p. A446

DICESARE, Gayle, President and Chief Executive Officer, Rivervalley Behavioral Health Hospital, Owensboro, KY, p. A265

DICESARE, Jan, Vice President Financial Operations, St. Vincent's East, Birmingham, AL, p. A15

DICICCO, Marilyn, Director Human Resources, Chestnut Hill Hospital, Philadelphia, PA, p. A543

DICK, Andy, Director Information Services, Saline Memorial Hospital, Benton, AR, p. A40

DICK, David, Chief Executive Officer, Huron Regional Medical Center, Huron, SD, p. A570

DICK, Frances, Chief Executive Officer, Oceans Behavioral Hospital Lufkin, Lufkin, TX, p. A631

DICK, Lynette, Director of Support Services, Ellsworth County Medical Center, Ellsworth, KS, p. A240

DICK, Mollie, Coordinator Human Resources, Wayne County Hospital, Monticello, KY, p. A265

DICK, Myra, Manager Business Office, AMG Specialty Hospital–Wichita, Wichita, KS, p. A253

DICKENS, Betty, Director Human Resources, Sierra Tucson, Tucson, AZ, p. A38

DICKENS, Shelby, Director, Patient Care Services, Fort Madison Community Hospital, Fort Madison, IA, p. A228

DICKERSON, Gene M.D., Vice President Medical Affairs, Palmetto Health Tuomey, Sumter, SC, p. A566

DICKERSON, Kathy, Chief Financial Officer, Healthsouth Rehabilitation Hospital Of Arlington, Arlington, TX, p. A593

DICKERSON, Melody Ford, Chief Nursing Officer, Memorial Hermann Greater Heights Hospital, Houston, TX, p. A621

DICKERSON, Michelle, Chief Nursing Officer, Frye Regional Medical Center, Hickory, NC, p. A464

DICKERSON, Sandra, Chief Executive Officer, Greenwood County Hospital, Eureka, KS, p. A241

DICKERSON, Taylor, Chief Information Officer, Lake City Medical Center, Lake City, FL, p. A129

DICKERSON, Toby, Chief Information Resources Management Services, Durham Veterans Affairs Medical Center, Durham, NC, p. A461

DICKEY, Ashley, Director Human Resources, Benson Hospital, Benson, AZ, p. A28

DICKEY, John M, Chief Administrative Officer, Mayo Clinic Health System In Eau Claire, Eau Claire, WI, p. A701

DICKEY, Mark, Director Business Development, Valir Rehabilitation Hospital, Oklahoma City, OK, p. A514

DICKEY, Sarah J., Director Human Resources, Marshall Browning Hospital, Du Quoin, IL, p. A186

DICKINSON, Ashley, Chief Executive Officer, La Porte Hospital, La Porte, IN, p. A214

DICKINSON, Cathy C, Vice President Human Resources, Baptist Health Medical Center – North Little Rock, North Little Rock, AR, p. A48

DICKINSON, Galen, Chief Financial Officer, Cary Medical Center, Caribou, ME, p. A290

DICKINSON, Lani, Interim Chief Nursing Officer, San Ramon Regional Medical Center, San Ramon, CA, p. A90

DICKLICH–COBB, Cristy, Chief Nursing Officer, Memorial Hospital Of Converse County, Douglas, WY, p. A718

DICKMAN, Kathy, Director Information Technology, Mccullough–Hyde Memorial Hospital/Trihealth, Oxford, OH, p. A498

DICKREITER, Adrian, Vice President Technology, Nix Health Care System, San Antonio, TX, p. A643

DICKS, Mandy, Director of Nursing, Lake Butler Hospital Hand Surgery Center, Lake Butler, FL, p. A129

DICKSON, Anita, Director Human Resources, Five Rivers Medical Center, Pocahontas, AR, p. A48

DICKSON, Eric, M.D., President and Chief Executive Officer, Umass Memorial Health Care, Inc., Worcester, MA, p. B131

DICKSON, James J., Administrator and Chief Executive Officer, Copper Queen Community Hospital, Bisbee, AZ, p. A28

DICKSON, Scott, Director Information Technology, Reeves Memorial Medical Center, Bernice, LA, p. A271

DICKSON, Thomas C.
Chief Executive Officer, Banner – University Medical Center South, Tucson, AZ, p. A37
Chief Executive Officer, Banner – University Medical Center Tucson, Tucson, AZ, p. A37

DICKSON, William, Executive Director, Capital District Psychiatric Center, Albany, NY, p. A430

DICUS–JOHNSON, Coreen, President, Wheaton Franciscan Healthcare – St. Francis, Milwaukee, WI, p. A708

DIDDLE, Derrick, Chief Information Officer, Colorado Canyons Hospital And Medical Center, Fruita, CO, p. A103

DIDENKO, Dima, Chief Financial Officer, Florida Hospital Tampa, Tampa, FL, p. A144

DIDERRICH, Mary Kay., R.N., Chief Executive Officer, Select Specialty Hospital–Milwaukee, Milwaukee, WI, p. A708

DIDERRICH, Mary Kay R.N., Vice President Patient Services, Watertown Regional Medical Center, Watertown, WI, p. A714

DIEBLING, Tara, Chief Executive Officer, The Rehabilitation Institute Of St. Louis, Saint Louis, MO, p. A378

DIEDERICH, John A, Senior Vice President Operations and Chief Operating Officer, Rush–Copley Medical Center, Aurora, IL, p. A178

DIEFFENBACH, Todd, Chief Financial Officer, Tyrone Hospital, Tyrone, PA, p. A552

DIEGEL, James A., Chief Executive Officer, Howard University Hospital, Washington, DC, p. A117

DIEHL, Robert, President, Mark Twain Medical Center, San Andreas, CA, p. A84

DIEITZ, Zach, Chief Executive Officer, Seton Medical Center Harker Heights, Harker Heights, TX, p. A618

DIENER, D Michael., Chief Executive Officer, Fayette County Memorial Hospital, Washington Court House, OH, p. A502

DIERKENS, Janelle, Chief Administration Officer, New York State Psychiatric Institute, New Rochelle, NY, p. A444

DIERKER, Anne, Vice President Hospital Services, Pekin Hospital, Pekin, IL, p. A197

DIERS, Suzanne R.N., Director Patient Care Services, Shriners Hospitals For Children–Portland, Portland, OR, p. A525

DIESTEL, Peter, Senior Vice President and Chief Operating Officer, Valley Hospital, Ridgewood, NJ, p. A420

DIETER, Brian, President and Chief Executive Officer, Mary Greeley Medical Center, Ames, IA, p. A222

DIETERICH, Kevin, Director Information Services, Inland Hospital, Waterville, ME, p. A293

DIETLIN, Steve, Chief Executive Officer, Tri–City Medical Center, Oceanside, CA, p. A77

DIETRICH, Brenda, Chief Human Resources Officer, Banner Boswell Medical Center, Sun City, AZ, p. A36

DIETRICK, Brian, Director Information Systems, Wilson Medical Center, Wilson, NC, p. A472

DIETSCH, Barry, Chief Financial Officer, Virginia Gay Hospital, Vinton, IA, p. A235

DIETSCHE, Jim, Chief Financial Officer, Bellin Memorial Hospital, Green Bay, WI, p. A702

DIETZ, Michael, Administrator, U. S. Air Force Hospital, Hampton, VA, p. A668

DIGEROLAMO, Anthony, R.N., MSN, Chief Executive Officer, Psychiatric Pavilion New Orleans, New OrleansOchsner Medical Center, New Orleans, LA, p. A283

DIGUILIO, Jason, Controller, Uh Avon Rehabilitation Hospital, Avon, OH, p. A480

DIIESO, Nicholas T R.N., Chief Operating Officer, Mount Auburn Hospital, Cambridge, MA, p. A305

DIIORIO, Emil, M.D., Chief Executive Officer, Surgical Specialty Center At Coordinated Health, Allentown, PA, p. A528

DIKE, Charles M.D., Chief of Staff, Sanford Worthington Medical Center, Worthington, MN, p. A351

DIKOS, Julie A., MSN, R.N., President and Chief Executive Officer, Asheville Specialty Hospital, Asheville, NC, p. A457

DILALLO, Kevin, Chief Executive Officer, Manatee Memorial Hospital, Bradenton, FL, p. A120

DILISI, Jeffrey P, Vice President and Chief Medical Officer, Virginia Hospital Center – Arlington, Arlington, VA, p. A664

DILL, Stephen M.D., Chief of Staff, Leconte Medical Center, Sevierville, TN, p. A588

DILLARD, Evan S., M.P.H., FACHE, President and Chief Executive Officer, Forrest General Hospital, Hattiesburg, MS, p. A355

DILLARD, Sharon, Chief Nursing Officer, Poinciana Medical Center, Kissimmee, FL, p. A129

DILLEHUNT, David B
 Chief Information Officer, Firsthealth Montgomery Memorial Hospital, Troy, NC, p. A472
 Chief Information Officer, Firsthealth Moore Regional Hospital, Pinehurst, NC, p. A468

DILLION, Tim, Vice President of Human Resources, Devereux Hospital And Children's Center Of Florida, Melbourne, FL, p. A132

DILLON, Jim, Chief Financial Officer, Rangely District Hospital, Rangely, CO, p. A107

DILLON, Lorie, Chief Executive Officer, Geisinger Healthsouth Rehabilitation Hospital, Danville, PA, p. A532

DILLON, Mary E MS, R.N., Vice President Patient Care Services, Sisters Of Charity Hospital Of Buffalo, Buffalo, NY, p. A433

DILORENZO, Randolph M.D., Medical Director, Syosset Hospital, Syosset, NY, p. A453

DILORETO, David M.D., Executive Vice President and Chief Medical Officer, Presence Saint Francis Hospital, Evanston, IL, p. A187

DIMAMBRO, Christina, Chief Financial Officer, Havasu Regional Medical Center, Lake Havasu City, AZ, p. A31

DIMARCO, Lisa R.N., FACHE, Vice President Patient Care Service and Chief Nursing Officer, Little Company Of Mary Hospital And Health Care Centers, Evergreen Park, IL, p. A187

DIMARE, John M.D., Medical Director, Foothill Presbyterian Hospital, Glendora, CA, p. A62

DIMEK, Carolyn, Acting Superintendent, Dorothea Dix Psychiatric Center, Bangor, ME, p. A289

DIMICHELE, Maria, Administrative Assistant, Kensington Hospital, Philadelphia, PA, p. A544

DIMITROVA, Gergana M.D., Medical Director, Carolina Center For Behavioral Health, Greer, SC, p. A563

DIMM, Adam, Chief Executive Officer, J. C. Blair Memorial Hospital, Huntingdon, PA, p. A536

DIMMICK, Scott, Senior Vice President and Chief Human Resources Officer, Lakeland Regional Health, Lakeland, FL, p. A130

DIMOND, Margaret, Ph.D., President and Chief Executive Officer, Crittenton Hospital Medical Center, Rochester, MI, p. A329

DIMURIA, Asja, Chief Financial Officer, Abrazo West Campus, Goodyear, AZ, p. A30

DINARDO, Mark, Chief Nursing Officer, Healthsouth Rehabilitation Hospital Of Modesto, Modesto, CA, p. A74

DINGER, Bradley, Financial Representative, Upmc Northwest, Seneca, PA, p. A550

DINGILIAN, John M.D., Chief Medical Officer, Simi Valley Hospital, Simi Valley, CA, p. A92

DINGLE, Steve M.D., Chief Medical Officer, Arizona State Hospital, Phoenix, AZ, p. A33

DINGLEDINE, Jon, Senior Director Human Resources and Support Services, Mercer Health, Coldwater, OH, p. A487

DINGLER, Chance M.D., Chief Medical Officer, Nocona General Hospital, Nocona, TX, p. A635

DINHAM, Vilma L R.N., Chief Nursing Officer, Encino Hospital Medical Center, Los Angeles, CA, p. A68

DINKHA, Duncan M.D., Chief of Staff, Morrison Community Hospital, Morrison, IL, p. A194

DINKINS, Vicki, Director Human Resources, South Georgia Medical Center Lanier Campus, Lakeland, GA, p. A160

DINON, Nancy, Vice President Human Resources, Health Central Hospital, Ocoee, FL, p. A136

DINSLAGE, Dennis, Vice President Finance and Chief Financial Officer, St. Francis Memorial Hospital, West Point, NE, p. A400

DINSMORE, Brad
 Chief Executive Officer, Healthsouth Rehabilitation Hospital – Austin, Austin, TX, p. A595
 Chief Executive Officer, Healthsouth Rehabilitation Hospital Of Austin, Austin, TX, p. A595

DION, Jeffrey P.
 Vice President Finance and Chief Financial Officer, Newton–Wellesley Hospital, Newton Lower Falls, MA, p. A309
 Vice President Finance, St. Elizabeth's Medical Center, Brighton, MA, p. A304

DIONISOPOULOS, Peter, Chief Medical Officer, Chi Health Nebraska Heart, Lincoln, NE, p. A395

DIPALMA, Maureen, Chief Financial Officer, Tewksbury Hospital, Tewksbury, MA, p. A312

DIPAOLO, Joseph
 President, Sussex and Warren Region, Hackettstown Medical Center, Hackettstown, NJ, p. A414
 President, Sussex and Warren Region, Newton Medical Center, Newton, NJ, p. A418

DIPIETRO, Sandra P, Chief Financial Officer, St. Tammany Parish Hospital, Covington, LA, p. A273

DIPILLA, Victor, Vice President and Chief Business Development Officer, Christ Hospital, Cincinnati, OH, p. A483

DISANTE, Ginger, Chief Nursing Executive, Christus Health Shreveport–Bossier, Shreveport, LA, p. A285

DISANZO, Frank, Vice President and Chief Information Officer and Chief Strategy Officer, Saint Peter's University Hospital, New Brunswick, NJ, p. A417

DISESA, Verdi, M.D., President and Chief Executive Officer, Temple University Hospital, Philadelphia, PA, p. A546

DISLER, Jordi K., President, Parkview Lagrange Hospital, Lagrange, IN, p. A214

DISPOTO, Martha R.N., I, Chief Nurse Executive, Anaheim Medical Center, Kaiser Permanente Orange County Anaheim Medical Center, Anaheim, CA, p. A51

DISWOOD, Lavenia R.N., Chief Nurse Executive, Northern Navajo Medical Center, Shiprock, NM, p. A428

DITMANSON, Paul M.D., Clinical Director, Red Lake Indian Health Service Hospital, Red Lake, MN, p. A346

DITORO, Michael
 Chief Operating Officer, Westlake Hospital, Melrose Park, IL, p. A193
 Interim Chief Executive Officer, Westlake Hospital, Melrose Park, IL, p. A193

DITTBENNER, Beth, Regional Director, Human Resources, Mayo Clinic Health System In Mankato, Mankato, MN, p. A342

DITTMANN, Gerald P, Vice President Human Resources, Mount Nittany Medical Center, State College, PA, p. A551

DITTO, Debbie CPA, Controller, Lincoln Trail Behavioral Health System, Radcliff, KY, p. A266

DITURO, Beth, Divisional Chief Information Officer, Lenox Hill Hospital, New Rochelle, NY, p. A442

DITZLER, Andru, Chief Information Officer, Lebanon Veterans Affairs Medical Center, Lebanon, PA, p. A538

DIVERSI, Sarah, Chief Financial Officer, Our Community Hospital, Scotland Neck, NC, p. A470

DIVINS, Brooke, Manager Human Resources, Clarion Hospital, Clarion, PA, p. A531

DIVITO, Frank, Manager Information Systems, Upmc Jameson Hospital, New Castle, PA, p. A542

DIX, Roger J, Vice President Finance, Hannibal Regional Hospital, Hannibal, MO, p. A368

DIX, Theresa R.N., Chief Nursing Officer, Wythe County Community Hospital, Wytheville, VA, p. A677

DIXON, Christy, Chief Human Resources Officer, Healthsouth Rehabilitation Hospital Of Humble, Llc, Humble, TX, p. A624

DIXON, Debbie, Director Human Resources, Pampa Regional Medical Center, Pampa, TX, p. A636

DIXON, Del, Chief Information Officer, South Shore Hospital, South Weymouth, MA, p. A311

DIXON, Florine, Chief Operating Officer, Memorial Hospital, Carthage, IL, p. A179

DIXON, Gregg
 Chief Financial Officer, Asheville Specialty Hospital, Asheville, NC, p. A457
 Chief Financial Officer, Carepartners Health Services, Asheville, NC, p. A457

DIXON, John, Chief Medical Officer, Mobile Infirmary Medical Center, Mobile, AL, p. A20

DIXON, Lisa, Business Partner and Human Resource Director, Linden Oaks Hospital, Naperville, IL, p. A195

DIXON, Mary E., Interim Chief Nursing Officer, University Of Virginia Medical Center, Charlottesville, VA, p. A665

DIXON, Michael L, Director, Human Resources, Beaumont Hospital – Royal Oak, Royal Oak, MI, p. A329

DIXON, Michael, Director Human Resources, Self Regional Healthcare, Greenwood, SC, p. A563

DIXON, Sally J., Chief Executive Officer, Memorial Hospital, York, PA, p. A555

DIXON, Shannon
 Manager Business Office, Weisbrod Memorial County Hospital, Eads, CO, p. A102
 Manager Business Office, Weisbrod Memorial County Hospital, Eads, CO, p. A102

DIXON, Todd, R.N.
 Chief Operating Officer, Coliseum Medical Centers, Macon, GA, p. A160
 Chief Operating Officer, Coliseum Northside Hospital, Macon, GA, p. A161

DIZNEY, Donald R., Chairman and Chief Executive Officer, United Medical Corporation, Windermere, FL, p. B132

DOAK, Scott
 System Vice President, Human Resources, University Of North Carolina Hospitals, Chapel Hill, NC, p. A459
 Vice President, Human Resources, UNC Rex Health Care, Raleigh, NC, p. A469

DOAN, Angela, Chief Financial Officer, Scott Memorial Hospital, Scottsburg, IN, p. A219

DOANE, Peter, M.D.
 Chief Medical Officer, Franklin Regional Hospital, Franklin, NH, p. A408
 Chief Medical Officer, Lakes Region General Hospital, Laconia, NH, p. A408

DOBBING, Eileen R.N., Senior Vice President for Patient Care Services, Memorial Hospital Of Rhode Island, Pawtucket, RI, p. A556

DOBBINS, Jim, Vice President Human Resources, UNC Lenoir Healthcare, Kinston, NC, p. A465

DOBBS, Jacee, Chief Information Officer, Citizens Medical Center, Colby, KS, p. A239

DOBBS, Stephanie, Chief Nursing Officer, Sanford Clear Lake Medical Center, Clear Lake, SD, p. A569

DOBIE, Linda R.N., JD, Vice President, Legal Affairs, Torrance Memorial Medical Center, Torrance, CA, p. A94

DOBIN, Jennifer, Executive Vice President Human Resources, Carepoint Health Bayonne Medical Center, Bayonne, NJ, p. A411

DOBIZL, Howard
 Director Information Services for the Northern Region, Ministry Saint Mary's Hospitals, Rhinelander, WI, p. A711
 Director Information Technology Services, Howard Young Medical Center, Woodruff, WI, p. A716
 Director Information Technology Services, Ministry Eagle River Memorial Hospital, Eagle River, WI, p. A700
 Director Information Technology Services, Ministry Sacred Heart Hospital, Tomahawk, WI, p. A714

DOBKIN, Eric D M.D., Vice President Medical Affairs, Suburban Hospital, Bethesda, MD, p. A297

DOBOSENSKI, Dave, Chief Executive Officer, St. Croix Regional Medical Center, St Croix Falls, WI, p. A713

DOBOSH, Joseph J Jr, Vice President and Chief Financial Officer, Children's Specialized Hospital, New Brunswick, NJ, p. A417

DOBRAWA, Stanley
 Area Technology Director, Kaiser Permanente San Rafael Medical Center, San Rafael, CA, p. A89
 Area Technology Director, Kaiser Permanente Santa Rosa Medical Center, Santa Rosa, CA, p. A91

DOBRINSKI, Sandra, Director of Nursing, Comanche County Hospital, Coldwater, KS, p. A239

DOBROVICH, Michael M.D., Chief Medical Officer, St. John Medical Center, Westlake, OH, p. A502

DOBSON, Glenda, Chief Executive Officer, Cypress Pointe Surgical Hospital, Hammond, LA, p. A275

DOBSON, Glenn E, Vice President, Finance and Chief Financial Officer, Aspirus Iron River Hospitals & Clinics, Inc., Iron River, MI, p. A323

DOBSON, Trey M.D., Chief Medical Officer, Southwestern Vermont Medical Center, Bennington, VT, p. A662

DOCIMO, Anne M.D., Executive Vice President and Chief Medical Officer, Jefferson Health, Thomas Jefferson University Hospitals, Philadelphia, PA, p. A546

DODD, Jeff M.D., Chief of Staff, Tahoe Forest Hospital District, Truckee, CA, p. A94

DODD, John, Vice President Human Resources, Central Peninsula Hospital, Soldotna, AK, p. A247

DODD, Kathy M, Director of Nursing, Southern Virginia Mental Health Institute, Danville, VA, p. A666

DODD, Pam, Chief Operating Officer, Harper County Community Hospital, Buffalo, OK, p. A505

DODDS, George M.D., Medical Director, Gouverneur Hospital, Gouverneur, NY, p. A436

DODDS, Rick A.
 President, Greene Memorial Hospital, Xenia, OH, p. A503
 President, Soin Medical Center, Beavercreek, OH, p. A481

DODDS, Sheryl, Chief Clinical Officer, Florida Hospital, Orlando, FL, p. A137

DODERER, Marcella, FACHE, President and Chief Executive Officer, Arkansas Children's Hospital, Little Rock, AR, p. A45

DODGE, Cynthia J., Director Human Resources, Vibra Hospital Of Springfield, Springfield, IL, p. A201

DODGE, Terry M.D., Chief of Staff, Chester Regional Medical Center, Chester, SC, p. A559

DODSON, Louise, R.N.
 Chief Nursing Officer, Wagoner Community Hospital, Wagoner, OK, p. A519
 Chief Operating Officer and Chief Nursing Officer, Wagoner Community Hospital, Wagoner, OK, p. A519

DODSON, Paige M.D., M.P.H., Chief Medical Officer, Susan B. Allen Memorial Hospital, El Dorado, KS, p. A240

DODSON, Thomas, Executive Director, Buffalo Psychiatric Center, Buffalo, NY, p. A432
DODSWORTH, Richard, Chief Human Resource Officer, Macneal Hospital, Berwyn, IL, p. A178
DOEHRING, Christopher, M.D.
  Vice President Medical Affairs, Franciscan St. Francis Health – Indianapolis, Indianapolis, IN, p. A211
  Vice President of Medical Affairs, Franciscan St. Francis Health–Carmel, Carmel, IN, p. A205
DOELING, Mariann, R.N., President, Chi St Alexius Health Carrington Medical Center, Carrington, ND, p. A474
DOELLING, James, Chief Nurse Executive, Va Greater Los Angeles Healthcare System, Los Angeles, CA, p. A72
DOERFLER, Mary P., Chief Human Resources Officer, Central Texas Veterans Health Care System, Temple, TX, p. A648
DOERGE, Jean B MS, R.N., Chief Nursing Executive, Unitypoint Health – Trinity Bettendorf, Bettendorf, IA, p. A222
DOERGE, Jean R.N., MSN, Nurse Executive, Swedish/Edmonds, Edmonds, WA, p. A680
DOERING, Dean, Chief Executive Officer, Central Prison Hospital, Raleigh, NC, p. A468
DOERR, Brian, Chief Information Officer, Continuecare Hospital At Baptist Health Corbin, Corbin, KY, p. A257
DOGGETT, Geri, Director Business, East Mississippi State Hospital, Meridian, MS, p. A359
DOGGETT, Sherri L, Vice President Patient Services, Mercy Medical Center–Centerville, Centerville, IA, p. A224
DOHERTY, Allison, Chief Financial Officer, Spine Hospital Of Louisiana (Formally The Neuromedical Center Surgical Hospital), Baton Rouge, LA, p. A271
DOHERTY, Bryan, Management Information Technology Services I, Sagamore Children's Hospital Psychiatric Center, Dix Hills, NY, p. A435
DOHERTY, Dan, Vice President, Operations, Advocate Trinity Hospital, Chicago, IL, p. A180
DOHERTY, Donna R.N., Vice President of Nursing and Chief Nursing Officer, Beth Israel Deaconess Hospital Plymouth, Plymouth, MA, p. A310
DOHERTY, Donnie, Director Information Systems, Fairfield Memorial Hospital, Winnsboro, SC, p. A567
DOHERTY, John, Vice President Finance, University Of Minnesota Medical Center, Fairview, Minneapolis, MN, p. A344
DOHERTY, Randy, CPA, Chief Executive Officer, Healthsouth Braintree Rehabilitation Hospital, Braintree, MA, p. A304
DOHERTY, Ray, Director Information Technology, Clinton Memorial Hospital, Wilmington, OH, p. A502
DOHERTY, William J. M.D., Executive Vice President and Chief Operating Officer, Hallmark Health System, Melrose, MA, p. A308
DOHMANN, Eileen L, R.N.
  Senior Vice President and Chief Nursing Officer, Mary Washington Hospital, Fredericksburg, VA, p. A667
  Senior Vice President and Chief Nursing Officer, Stafford Hospital, Stafford, VA, p. A675
DOI, Kathy, Executive Director Human Resources, Ahmc Anaheim Regional Medical Center, Anaheim, CA, p. A51
DOIDGE, John C, Vice President Finance, Glencoe Regional Health Services, Glencoe, MN, p. A340
DOKKEN, Susan, Chief Human Resources, St. Joseph Regional Medical Center, Lewiston, ID, p. A174
DOKSUM, Kathryn, Director Finance, Samaritan North Lincoln Hospital, Lincoln City, OR, p. A523
DOLAN, Lisa, Interim Chief Executive Officer, Dupont Hospital, Fort Wayne, IN, p. A208
DOLAN, Mary, Regional Director Information Services and HIPAA Security Official, Shriners Hospitals For Children–Boston, Boston, MA, p. A304
DOLAN, Patricia R R.N., MS, Vice President/ Chief Nursing Officer, Florida Hospital Waterman, Tavares, FL, p. A145
DOLAN, Steve, Chief Information Officer, Eastpointe Hospital, Daphne, AL, p. A16
DOLBEE, Hilary, Chief Financial Officer, Monroe Hospital, Bloomfield, IN, p. A204
DOLE, Patricia, Vice President Patient Care Services, TLC Health Network – Lake Shore Hospital, Irving, NY, p. A437
DOLEN, Cassie, Vice President Finance and Chief Financial Officer, Hutchinson Regional Medical Center, Hutchinson, KS, p. A243
DOLLINS, Gary, Director Management Information Systems, Poplar Bluff Regional Medical Center, Poplar Bluff, MO, p. A375
DOLOHANTY-JOHNSON, Bridget MSN, R.N., Vice President Patient Care Services, Parkview Whitley Hospital, Columbia City, IN, p. A205
DOLORESCO, Laureen R.N., Associate Director for Patient Care and Nursing Services, James A. Haley Veterans' Hospital–Tampa, Tampa, FL, p. A144

DOMALESKI, Vareen O'Keefe MS, R.N., Vice Patient Care Services and Chief Nursing Officer, Emma Pendleton Bradley Hospital, East Providence, RI, p. A556
DOMANICO, Lee, Chief Executive Officer, Marin General Hospital, Greenbrae, CA, p. A62
DOMANN, Debbie, Director of Operations, Fillmore County Hospital, Geneva, NE, p. A393
DOMANSKY, John, Vice President Operations, Rutherford Regional Health System, Rutherfordton, NC, p. A470
DOMAYER, Cory, Chief Financial Officer, Florida Hospital–Flagler, Palm Coast, FL, p. A138
DOMBROUSKI, Joyce, R.N., Chief Executive Officer, St. Patrick Hospital, Missoula, MT, p. A387
DOMEIER, Sandy, Director Patient Care Services, Ridgeview Sibley Medical Center, Arlington, MN, p. A335
DOMINGO, Connie M.D., Medical Director, Weisman Children's Rehabilitation Hospital, Marlton, NJ, p. A416
DOMINGUE, Buffy, Chief Executive Officer, Lafayette Surgical Specialty Hospital, Lafayette, LA, p. A278
DOMINGUEZ, Brenda, Director Human Resources, Cypress Creek Hospital, Houston, TX, p. A620
DOMINGUEZ, Ed, President Medical Staff, Vibra Specialty Hospital At Desoto, Desoto, TX, p. A609
DOMINGUEZ, Marie, Commander, Martin Army Community Hospital, Fort Benning, GA, p. A158
DOMINICCI, Sandra, Nursing Director, Hospital De Damas, Ponce, PR, p. A724
DOMINIQUE, Ravon, Chief Nursing Officer, Brentwood Hospital, Shreveport, LA, p. A285
DOMINO, Laura R.N., Vice President Patient Care Services, Hammond–Henry Hospital, Geneseo, IL, p. A188
DOMINSKI, Paul, Vice President Human Resources, Park Nicollet Methodist Hospital, Saint Louis Park, MN, p. A347
DOMMER, Matthew M.D., Chief Medical Officer, Bronson Lakeview Hospital, Paw Paw, MI, p. A327
DOMON, Steven, M.D.
  Medical Director, Arkansas State Hospital, Little Rock, AR, p. A45
  Interim Chief Executive Officer, Arkansas State Hospital, Little Rock, AR, p. A45
DONAHEY, Kenneth C., Chief Executive Officer, Oviedo Medical Center, Oviedo, FL, p. A137
DONAHOE, Lauren, Chief Executive Officer, Select Specialty Hospital–Laurel Highlands, Latrobe, PA, p. A538
DONAHUE, Edward M.D., Chief Medical Officer, St. Joseph's Hospital And Medical Center, Phoenix, AZ, p. A34
DONAHUE, Kristine Marie, Administrator, Clinical Operations, Beaumont Hospital – Taylor, Taylor, MI, p. A331
DONAHUE, Michael M.D., Medical Director, Select Specialty Hospital–Pittsburgh/Upmc, Pittsburgh, PA, p. A547
DONAHUE, Ruth R.N., Chief Nursing Officer, Harrison County Hospital, Corydon, IN, p. A206
DONAHUE, Samantha, Director Human Resources, Crossing Rivers Health Medical Center, Prairie Du Chien, WI, p. A711
DONALD, Steve M.D., Chief of Staff, Washington County Hospital, Chatom, AL, p. A16
DONALDSON, Brooke G, Assistant Administrator Human Resources, Jackson Hospital, Marianna, FL, p. A131
DONALDSON, David, Chief Executive Officer, Henrico Doctors' Hospital, Richmond, VA, p. A674
DONALDSON, Jill, Vice President Operations, Medstar Harbor Hospital, Baltimore, MD, p. A295
DONALDSON, Les R.N., Chief of Staff, Roosevelt General Hospital, Portales, NM, p. A427
DONALDSON, Lori, Chief Financial Officer, Uc San Diego Health, San Diego, CA, p. A86
DONALDSON, Nesha, Chief Financial Officer, Cullman Regional Medical Center, Cullman, AL, p. A16
DONALDSON, Shirley, Chief Financial Officer, New Mexico Rehabilitation Center, Roswell, NM, p. A428
DONALDSON, Tammy, Director of Nursing, Highlands Hospital, Connellsville, PA, p. A532
DONATELLE, Lawrence M.D., Vice President Medical Affairs, St. Elizabeth Hospital, Appleton, WI, p. A698
DONATO, Cyndy, Vice President, Human Resources, Missouri Baptist Medical Center, Saint Louis, MO, p. A377
DONAWAY, Duane, Director Information Technology, Hendrick Health System, Abilene, TX, p. A591
DONELAN, Matthias B M.D., Chief of Staff, Shriners Hospitals For Children–Boston, Boston, MA, p. A304
DONENWIRTH, Karl, Vice President Information Services, Northcoast Behavioral Healthcare, Northfield, OH, p. A497
DONGILLI, Paul, Jr, Ph.D., FACHE
  President and Chief Executive Officer, Madonna Rehabilitation Hospital, Lincoln, NE, p. A395
  President and Chief Executive Officer, Madonna Rehabilitation Specialty Hospital, Bellevue, NE, p. A391
DONHAM, Guyle M.D., Chief of Staff, Comanche County Medical Center, Comanche, TX, p. A602

DONICA, Joanna, Director Human Resource, Pam Rehabilitation Hospital Of Beaumont, Beaumont, TX, p. A597
DONLEY, Linda, Vice President Operations, Ira Davenport Memorial Hospital, Bath, NY, p. A431
DONLIN, Bruce, Director Information Services, Mount Desert Island Hospital, Bar Harbor, ME, p. A289
DONLIN, John
  Director Human Resources, Shriners Hospitals For Children–Springfield, Springfield, MA, p. A311
  Regional Director Human Resources – Boston, Erie, and Springfield, Shriners Hospitals For Children–Boston, Boston, MA, p. A304
DONLIN, Michael T., FACHE, Administrator, Floyd Valley Healthcare, Le Mars, IA, p. A230
DONNELLY, Gloria, Director Human Resources, Euclid Hospital, Euclid, OH, p. A491
DONNELLY, James E, Chief Nursing Officer and Vice President Patient Care Services, Upmc Hamot, Erie, PA, p. A534
DONNELLY, Lane M.D., Chief Medical Officer, Nemours Children's Hospital, Orlando, FL, p. A137
DONNELLY, Sheryl, Human Resources Specialist, State Hospital South, Blackfoot, ID, p. A171
DONNELY, Lisa, Controller II, Central Texas Rehabilitation Hospital, Austin, TX, p. A594
DONOGHUE, Alicia, Director Human Resources, Eastpointe Hospital, Daphne, AL, p. A16
DONOHUE, Carolyn Viall MSN, R.N., Vice President Nursing, Roper St. Francis, Charleston, SC, p. A559
DONOHUE, Mary Ann T Ph.D., R.N., Chief Patient Care Services Officer, Stony Brook University Hospital, Stony Brook, NY, p. A453
DONOHUE–RYAN, MaryAnn, Vice President Patient Care Services, Englewood Hospital And Medical Center, Englewood, NJ, p. A414
DONOVAN, Andrew
  Director Information Technology, Wheaton Franciscan Healthcare – Elmbrook Memorial, Brookfield, WI, p. A699
  Regional Director Information Services, Wheaton Franciscan Healthcare – St. Joseph's, Milwaukee, WI, p. A708
DONOVAN, James W., President and Chief Executive Officer, Lincolnhealth, Damariscotta, ME, p. A290
DONOVAN, Jenny, Director Human Resources, Wright Memorial Hospital, Trenton, MO, p. A380
DONOVAN, Kevin
  Chief Executive Officer, Lakes Region General Hospital, Laconia, NH, p. A408
  President and CEO, Franklin Regional Hospital, Franklin, NH, p. A408
DONOVAN, Mary, Controller, Healthsouth Rehabilitation Institute Of Tucson, Tucson, AZ, p. A38
DONOVAN, Mike, Chief Financial Officer, Lemuel Shattuck Hospital, Jamaica Plain, MA, p. A307
DONOVAN, Patrick M.D., Director Medical Staff, Healthsouth Rehabilitation Hospital Of Fort Worth, Fort Worth, TX, p. A613
DONSON, Elliott, Chief Information Specialist, Lincoln Hospital, Davenport, WA, p. A680
DONZE, Richard D D.O., Senior Vice President Medical Affairs, Penn Medicine Chester County Hospital, West Chester, PA, p. A553
DOODY, Kris A., R.N., Chief Executive Officer, Cary Medical Center, Caribou, ME, p. A290
DOOKEERAM, David, Chief Operating Officer, Porter Adventist Hospital, Denver, CO, p. A101
DOOLEY, Jerry, Interim Chief Executive Officer, Teche Regional Medical Center, Morgan City, LA, p. A282
DOOLEY, Kimberly H., Administrator, Lafayette General Surgical Hospital, Lafayette, LA, p. A278
DOOLEY, Lisa, Health Information Officer, Middlesboro Arh Hospital, Middlesboro, KY, p. A264
DOOLEY, Mark J., Chief Executive Officer, Wilson Memorial Hospital, Sidney, OH, p. A499
DOOLING, Edward, Vice President, Human Resources, Masonicare Health Center, Wallingford, CT, p. A113
DOOLITTLE, Jon D., Regional President, Northwest Medical Center, Albany, MO, p. A364
DOORENBOS, Pamela, Medical Director, Medical Affairs, Maple Grove Hospital, Maple Grove, MN, p. A343
DOORN, Douglas, Chief Executive Officer, Lewis And Clark Specialty Hospital, Yankton, SD, p. A574
DOPERAK, Martin, Commander, Weed Army Community Hospital, Fort Irwin, CA, p. A59
DORAK, John, Chief Information Officer, Nicholas H. Noyes Memorial Hospital, Dansville, NY, p. A434
DORAN, Judy R.N., Vice President of Hospital Services and Chief Nurse Executive, Carolinas Healthcare System Stanly, Albemarle, NC, p. A457

Index of Health Care Professionals / Doran

DORAN, Ken, Interim Chief Executive Officer, Carson Tahoe Health, Carson City, NV, p. A401

DORAN, T M.D., Chief of Staff, Perry Memorial Hospital, Princeton, IL, p. A198

DORIA, Thomas
Vice President and Patient Services – West, Morton Plant North Bay Hospital, New Port Richey, FL, p. A135
Vice President and Patient Services West, St. Anthony's Hospital, Saint Petersburg, FL, p. A142
Vice President Patient Services – West, Morton Plant Hospital, Clearwater, FL, p. A121
Vice President, Patient Services and Chief Nursing Officer, Mease Countryside Hospital, Safety Harbor, FL, p. A141
Vice President, Patient Services and Chief Nursing Officer, Mease Dunedin Hospital, Dunedin, FL, p. A124

DORION, Heath, Physician Administrator, Mercy Health – St. Elizabeth Boardman Hospital, Boardman, OH, p. A481

DORITY, Paula, Director Human Resources, Martin County Hospital District, Stanton, TX, p. A646

DORMAN, Christopher, Senior Vice President/Chief Operating Officer, Tift Regional Medical Center, Tifton, GA, p. A166

DORMAN, Doug, Vice President Human Resources, GHS Greenville Memorial Hospital, Greenville, SC, p. A562

DORMAN, Julie, Human Resources Director, Parkwood Behavioral Health System, Olive Branch, MS, p. A360

DORMAN, Stephen M.D., Chief Medical Officer, New Mexico Rehabilitation Center, Roswell, NM, p. A428

DORNOFF, Edward G., Associate Director, Battle Creek Veterans Affairs Medical Center, Battle Creek, MI, p. A315

DOROGY, Sharon, Chief Information Officer, The Children's Institute Of Pittsburgh, Pittsburgh, PA, p. A547

DOROTHY, Jonnie, Senior Director Human Resources, Massena Memorial Hospital, Massena, NY, p. A439

DORR, Amy
Vice President Human Resources, Mclaren Greater Lansing, Lansing, MI, p. A324
Vice President Human Resources, Mclaren Lapeer Region, Lapeer, MI, p. A325

DORRIS, Ronald E., Chief Executive Officer, Carrus Hospitals, Sherman, TX, p. B26

DORRIS, Steve, Chief Financial Officer, Poplar Bluff Regional Medical Center, Poplar Bluff, MO, p. A375

DORSCH, Anthony, Chief Financial Officer, Providence Alaska Medical Center, Anchorage, AK, p. A25

DORSEY, Bob, Human Resources Coordinator, Select Specialty Hospital – Lincoln, Lincoln, NE, p. A395

DORSEY, John T M.D., Vice President Physician Services and Chief Medical Officer, Mercyhealth Hospital – Rockton Avenue, Rockford, IL, p. A199

DORSEY, Michael A., FACHE, Chief Executive Officer, Johnson Regional Medical Center, Clarksville, AR, p. A41

DORSEY, William, M.D., Board Chairman and Chief Executive Officer, Jackson Park Hospital And Medical Center, Chicago, IL, p. A181

DORST, Jake, Chief Information Officer, Tahoe Forest Hospital District, Truckee, CA, p. A94

DORTON, Patty, Director of Nursing, Buchanan General Hospital, Grundy, VA, p. A668

DOSCHER, Suzanne C., Chief Executive Officer, Fairfield Memorial Hospital, Winnsboro, SC, p. A567

DOSHI, Nikunj D.O., Chief Medical Officer, Banner Gateway Medical Center, Gilbert, AZ, p. A29

DOSI, Abhishek, Chief Executive Officer, Sutter Solano Medical Center, Vallejo, CA, p. A95

DOSS, Delilah, Director, Human Resources, Mountainview Regional Medical Center, Las Cruces, NM, p. A427

DOSS, Mounir F, Executive Vice President and Chief Financial Officer, Jamaica Hospital Medical Center, New Rochelle, NY, p. A441

DOSSETT, Jeffrey, Chief Operating Officer, Abrazo West Campus, Goodyear, AZ, p. A30

DOSSETT, Phyllis, Director of Clinical Services, Wellmont Hancock County Hospital, Sneedville, TN, p. A589

DOSTAL, Drew H., R.N., FACHE, Chief Executive Officer, Ogallala Community Hospital, Ogallala, NE, p. A396

DOTEN, Charles, Chief Executive Officer, Promise Hospital Of Miami, Miami, FL, p. A133

DOTTS–MCCOOL, Michelle, Chief Nursing Officer, St. Vincent Dunn Hospital, Bedford, IN, p. A204

DOTY, Lisa, Manager Human Resources, Desert View Hospital, Pahrump, NV, p. A405

DOUBLE, Ron
Chief Information Officer, Parkview Huntington Hospital, Huntington, IN, p. A210
Chief Information Officer, Parkview Noble Hospital, Kendallville, IN, p. A213
Chief Information Technology Officer, Parkview Lagrange Hospital, Lagrange, IN, p. A214

DOUCETTE, Diane, R.N., President, Mount Carmel New Albany Surgical Hospital, New Albany, OH, p. A496

DOUCETTE, Elmer H, Chief Financial Officer, Redington–Fairview General Hospital, Skowhegan, ME, p. A293

DOUCETTE, Michael J., Senior Vice President and Administrator, Riverside Regional Medical Center, Newport News, VA, p. A671

DOUD, Tony
Controller, St. Joseph Health System, Tawas City, MI, p. A331
Controller, St. Mary's Of Michigan Standish Hospital, Standish, MI, p. A331

DOUGHERTY, Chuck, Chief Information Officer, Shenandoah Medical Center, Shenandoah, IA, p. A234

DOUGHERTY, David, Chief Information Management Officer, Irwin Army Community Hospital, Junction City, KS, p. A243

DOUGHERTY, James, Commander, U.S. Air Force Medical Center Keesler, Keesler Afb, MS, p. A357

DOUGHERTY, Terry, Director Human Resources, Bryn Mawr Hospital, Bryn Mawr, PA, p. A530

DOUGHTY, Cathy, Vice President Human Resources, Sheppard Pratt Health System, Baltimore, MD, p. A295

DOUGHTY, Linda, Chief Nursing Officer, Alaska Regional Hospital, Anchorage, AK, p. A25

DOUGHTY, Stephanie
Chief Financial Officer, Medical Center Of The Rockies, Loveland, CO, p. A106
Chief Financial Officer, Poudre Valley Hospital, Fort Collins, CO, p. A102

DOUGLAS, Andy, Manager Information Technology, Burnett Medical Center, Grantsburg, WI, p. A702

DOUGLAS, Bill, Senior Vice President and Chief Financial Officer, Riverside Medical Center, Kankakee, IL, p. A191

DOUGLAS, Debbie, Director Human Resources, Putnam County Memorial Hospital, Unionville, MO, p. A380

DOUGLAS, Doug, Interim Vice President Human Resources, Beaufort Memorial Hospital, Beaufort, SC, p. A558

DOUGLAS, Errol, Director Human Resources, University Of Miami Hospital, Miami, FL, p. A134

DOUGLAS, Jason T., Chief Executive Officer, Memorial Medical Center – Ashland, Ashland, WI, p. A698

DOUGLAS, Johnna, Human Resources Manager, Massac Memorial Hospital, Metropolis, IL, p. A194

DOUGLAS, Pam, Chief Nursing Officer, Putnam General Hospital, Eatonton, GA, p. A157

DOUGLAS, Paul, Vice President Human Resources, Baton Rouge General Medical Center, Baton Rouge, LA, p. A270

DOUGLAS, Phillip B, Chairman and Chief Executive Officer, Lifecare Hospitals Of Dallas, Dallas, TX, p. A605

DOUGLAS–WALSH, Marlene, Chief Executive Officer, Kirkbride Center, Philadelphia, PA, p. A544

DOVEL, Melissa, Manager Human Resources, Atrium Medical Center Of Corinth, Corinth, TX, p. A603

DOVER, Jerry, Chief Executive Officer, Sullivan County Memorial Hospital, Milan, MO, p. A373

DOVNARSKY, James M.D., Director Pulmonary Medical, Kindred Hospital South Philadelphia, Philadelphia, PA, p. A544

DOW, Janet R.N., Chief Nursing Officer, Santiam Hospital, Stayton, OR, p. A527

DOW, Laura, Chief Financial Officer, Memorial Health, Savannah, GA, p. A164

DOWDLE, Paula, Chief Operating Officer, Jefferson Healthcare, Port Townsend, WA, p. A684

DOWDY, Kathren
Senior Director, Chief Executive Officer and Chief Nursing Officer, Carilion Tazewell Community Hospital, Tazewell, VA, p. A676
Regional Hospital Senior Director, Carilion Tazewell Community Hospital, Tazewell, VA, p. A676

DOWDY, Michael, Chief Executive Officer, Central Montana Medical Center, Lewistown, MT, p. A386

DOWELL, James, Administrator and Chief Executive Officer, Little River Memorial Hospital, Ashdown, AR, p. A40

DOWELL, Kim, R.N., Chief Executive Officer, Jellico Community Hospital, Jellico, TN, p. A580

DOWERS, Cindy, Chief Nursing Officer, Harsha Behavioral Center, Terre Haute, IN, p. A220

DOWGUN, Richard, Chief Information Officer, St. Francis Medical Center, Trenton, NJ, p. A422

DOWIS, Jeff, M.D., Interim Chief Executive Officer, Mountain Lakes Medical Center, Clayton, GA, p. A154

DOWLING, Deanna R.N., Chief Nursing Officer, Promise Hospital Of Wichita Falls, Wichita Falls, TX, p. A654

DOWLING, Lisa, Manager Finance, Mercy Hospital Tishomingo, Tishomingo, OK, p. A517

DOWLING, Michael J., President and Chief Executive Officer, Northwell Health, New Hyde Park, NY, p. B91

DOWN, Melanie Falls, Site Manager, Crow/Northern Cheyenne Hospital, Crow Agency, MT, p. A383

DOWN, Philip B., Chief Executive Officer, Doctors Community Hospital, Lanham, MD, p. A299

DOWNARD, Diane, Chief Financial Officer, Coal County General Hospital, Coalgate, OK, p. A506

DOWNES, Patrick, Chief Executive Officer, East Cooper Medical Center, Mount Pleasant, SC, p. A564

DOWNES, Thomas M.D., Chief Medical Officer, Poudre Valley Hospital, Fort Collins, CO, p. A102

DOWNEY, Daniel, Chief Fiscal Service, Veterans Affairs New York Harbor Healthcare System, New Rochelle, NY, p. A447

DOWNEY, Susan, R.N., MS, Chief Executive Officer, Curahealth Hospital Boston, Brighton, MA, p. A304

DOWNEY, William B
Chief Operating Officer, Riverside Regional Medical Center, Newport News, VA, p. A671
President and Chief Executive Officer, Riverside Rehabilitation Institute, Newport News, VA, p. A671

DOWNEY, William B., President and Chief Executive Officer, Riverside Health System, Newport News, VA, p. B108

DOWNIE, Beth, Chief Information Officer, Newton–Wellesley Hospital, Newton Lower Falls, MA, p. A309

DOWNING, James R., M.D., Chief Executive Officer, St. Jude Children's Research Hospital, Memphis, TN, p. A585

DOWNING, Jeff R.N., MS, Chief Nursing Officer, National Jewish Health, Denver, CO, p. A101

DOWNS, Bryan, Director Information Systems, Central Peninsula Hospital, Soldotna, AK, p. A27

DOWNS, Lisa M R.N., Chief Nursing Officer, Sarah D. Culbertson Memorial Hospital, Rushville, IL, p. A199

DOWNS, Patricia, Director Human Resources, Northern Nevada Medical Center, Sparks, NV, p. A406

DOWNS, Ray, Senior Staff Accountant, Healthmark Regional Medical Center, Defuniak Springs, FL, p. A123

DOYLE, Ben R.N., Director of Nursing, Jefferson Hospital, Louisville, GA, p. A160

DOYLE, Christopher, Chief Executive Officer, Physicians Care Surgical Hospital, Royersford, PA, p. A549

DOYLE, Craig, Director and Chief Information Officer, St. Tammany Parish Hospital, Covington, LA, p. A273

DOYLE, Jay, President and Chief Executive Officer, St. James Healthcare, Butte, MT, p. A383

DOYLE, John
Chief Financial Officer, Confluence Health/Central Washington Hospital, Wenatchee, WA, p. A689
Chief Financial Officer, Confluence Health/Wenatchee Valley Hospital, Wenatchee, WA, p. A689
Vice President Finance, Paoli Hospital, Paoli, PA, p. A542

DOYLE, Kelly, Chief Executive Officer, Rothman Specialty Hospital, Bensalem, PA, p. A529

DOYLE, Mark, Administrator and Chief Executive Officer, Memorial Hospital Pembroke, Pembroke Pines, FL, p. A139

DOYLE, Matt, Chief Executive Officer, Strategic Behavioral Health – Raleigh, Garner, NC, p. A463

DOYLE, Matthew, Chief Financial Officer, Methodist Hospitals, Gary, IN, p. A209

DOYLE, Michael M.D., Vice President Medical Affairs, Vassar Brothers Medical Center, Poughkeepsie, NY, p. A450

DOZIER, Carol
Chief Financial Officer, Lifestream Behavioral Center, Leesburg, FL, p. A131
President and Chief Executive Officer, King's Daughters' Health, Madison, IN, p. A215

DOZIER, Michael, Vice President, Chief Information Officer, Lafayette General Medical Center, Lafayette, LA, p. A278

DOZIER, Mike, Chief Information Officer, Southeast Hospital, Cape Girardeau, MO, p. A366

DRABANT, Leah, Director of Finance, Complex Care Hospital At Ridgelake, Sarasota, FL, p. A142

DRAEGER, Anne, Chief Nursing Officer, Owatonna Hospital, Owatonna, MN, p. A345

DRAEGER, Trish, Chief Nursing Officer, Healthsouth Deaconess Rehabilitation Hospital, Evansville, IN, p. A207

DRAIME, D. Eric, Vice President and Chief Financial Officer, Avita Ontario Hospital, Ontario, OH, p. A497

DRAKE, Carolyn, Director of Nursing, Milan General Hospital, Milan, TN, p. A585

DRAKE, Derek Scott, Chief Nursing Officer, St. Francis Medical Center, Lynwood, CA, p. A72

DRAKE, Frank A., Director, Southern Oregon-White City Veterans Affairs Rehabilitation Center And Clinics, White City, OR, p. B44

DRAKE, Marian, Chief Financial Officer, Greenwood County Hospital, Eureka, KS, p. A241

DRAPER, Jason, Chief Financial Officer, Tennova Healthcare Volunteer Community Hospital, Martin, TN, p. A583

DRAPER, Vivian, Chief Financial Officer, U.S. Public Health Service Indian Hospital–Sells, Sells, AZ, p. A36

DREGNEY, James, Vice President Finance and Operations, Chief Financial Officer, Sauk Prairie Healthcare, Prairie Du Sac, WI, p. A711

DREHER, Craig, Chief Information Officer, Mercy Hospital Of Portland, Portland, ME, p. A292

DREHER, Ronald, Finance Officer, Robert J. Dole Veterans Affairs Medical Center, Wichita, KS, p. A253

DREHR, Sammie, Chief Nursing Officer, Detar Healthcare System, Victoria, TX, p. A652

DRENTH, Nancy E R.N., Director Ancillary Services, Sanford Luverne Medical Center, Luverne, MN, p. A342

DRESSER, Carol Ann, Vice President Information Services and Chief Information Officer, Hallmark Health System, Melrose, MA, p. A308

DRESSLER, Kaeli R.N., MSN, Chief Nursing Officer, Peterson Regional Medical Center, Kerrville, TX, p. A626

DREW, Jeff, Fiscal Officer, Aleda E. Lutz Veterans Affairs Medical Center, Saginaw, MI, p. A329

DREW, Jim, Chief Information Officer, Saint Thomas Midtown Hospital, Nashville, TN, p. A586

DREWS, Manty, Chief Information Officer, Adventist Health Sonora, Sonora, CA, p. A92

DREXLER, Diane, R.N.
Chief Nursing Officer, Yavapai Regional Medical Center – East, Prescott Valley, AZ, p. A35
Chief Nursing Officer, Yavapai Regional Medical Center, Prescott, AZ, p. A35

DRIGGERS, Steve M.D., Chief Medical Officer, Holy Family Memorial, Manitowoc, WI, p. A706

DRIGGS, Christi, Chief Financial Officer, Phillips County Hospital, Phillipsburg, KS, p. A250

DRINKWATER, Jinia R.N., Director Patient Care Services, Healthsouth Braintree Rehabilitation Hospital, Braintree, MA, p. A304

DRINKWATER, Linda, Chief Financial Officer, Waldo County General Hospital, Belfast, ME, p. A290

DRINKWITZ, Jeremy, Chief Operating Officer, Sparks Regional Medical Center, Fort Smith, AR, p. A44

DRISCOLL, Laureen, President, Multicare Deaconess Hospital, Spokane, WA, p. A686

DRISCOLL, Nancy, Chief Nursing Officer, Longmont United Hospital, Longmont, CO, p. A105

DRISCOLL, Philip J Jr, Chief Executive Officer, Kessler Institute For Rehabilitation, West Orange, NJ, p. A422

DRIVER, Ramona, Director Human Resources, De Queen Medical Center, De Queen, AR, p. A42

DRONE, Marilyn R.N., MSN, Vice President, CNO, St. Mary Medical Center, Apple Valley, CA, p. A52

DROZD, Carol, Chief Operating Officer, St. Mark's Medical Center, La Grange, TX, p. A627

DRUMMOND, Michael, Chief Financial Officer, Runnells Center For Rehabilitation And Healthcare, Berkeley Heights, NJ, p. A411

DRURY, Dennis, Director Information Technology, Northern Cochise Community Hospital, Willcox, AZ, p. A38

DRVARIC, David M M.D., Chief of Staff, Shriners Hospitals For Children–Springfield, Springfield, MA, p. A311

DRY, Laurence
Chief Operating Officer, Acute Care Hospitals Northern Region, Amita Health Elk Grove Village, Elk Grove Village, IL, p. A186
Chief Operating Officer, Acute Care Hospitals Northern Region, Amita Health Hoffman Estates, Hoffman Estates, IL, p. A190

DRYMON, Lisa, Manager, Fairfax Community Hospital, Fairfax, OK, p. A507

DRZEWIECKI–BURGER, Mary Jo, Administrative Manager, Caro Center, Caro, MI, p. A316

DU PONT, Karen, Chief Human Resource Officer, Casa Colina Hospital And Health Systems, Pomona, CA, p. A80

DUANE, Paul K, Chief Financial Officer and Office of Health Reform, Palmetto Health Richland, Columbia, SC, p. A560

DUARTE, Ray, Director, Information Technology and Services, Monmouth Medical Center, Southern Campus, Lakewood, NJ, p. A415

DUBE, Cynthia M.D., Medical Director, Mayo Clinic Health System–Albert Lea And Austin, Austin, MN, p. A336

DUBE, Sheri, Chief Operating Officer, St. David's North Austin Medical Center, Austin, TX, p. A596

DUBICKI, Robert, Executive Vice President and Chief Operating Officer, Kingsbrook Jewish Medical Center, New Rochelle, NY, p. A442

DUBROW, Melissa
Chief Operating Officer, Waynesboro Hospital, Waynesboro, PA, p. A553
Vice President and Chief Operating Officer, Waynesboro Hospital, Waynesboro, PA, p. A553

DUBRUYNE, Sharon, Director Human Resources, College Hospital Costa Mesa, Costa Mesa, CA, p. A56

DUCEY, Ann, Chief Information Officer, Boys Town National Research Hospital, Omaha, NE, p. A397

DUCHARME, Adele
Interim Chief Executive Officer, Saint Luke's North Hospital – Barry Road, Kansas City, MO, p. A371
Chief Executive Officer, Saint Luke's Cushing Hospital, Leavenworth, KS, p. A245

DUCHARME, Maria R.N., Senior Vice President Patient Care Services and Chief Nursing Officer, Miriam Hospital, Providence, RI, p. A556

DUCHAUSSEE, Michel, Chief Financial Officer, Atlantic Shores Hospital, Fort Lauderdale, FL, p. A124

DUCHEMIN, MaDena, Assistant Administrator Human Resources, John Randolph Medical Center, Hopewell, VA, p. A668

DUCHENE, Pam R.N., Vice President Patient Care Services, St. Joseph Hospital, Nashua, NH, p. A409

DUCHESNEAU, Angy, Senior Director Human Resources, Lakeview Hospital, Stillwater, MN, p. A349

DUCK, Sigsbee M.D., President, Medical Staff, Memorial Hospital Of Sweetwater County, Rock Springs, WY, p. A719

DUCKER, Thomas M.D., Chief of Staff, Peterson Regional Medical Center, Kerrville, TX, p. A626

DUCKERT, Jon, FACHE, Chief Executive Officer, Baylor Medical Center At Uptown, Dallas, TX, p. A604

DUCKWORTH, Allison G. R.N., FACHE, Chief Operating Officer and Chief Nursing Officer, Firsthealth Richmond Memorial Hospital, Rockingham, NC, p. A469

DUCKWORTH, Bob, Director Information Systems, Medical West, Bessemer, AL, p. A14

DUDLEY, Edward L III, Executive Vice President and Chief Financial Officer, Catholic Medical Center, Manchester, NH, p. A409

DUDLEY, Heather, Director Administrative Services, Brookhaven Hospital, Tulsa, OK, p. A517

DUDLEY, W. Steve CPA, Chief Financial Officer, Ed Fraser Memorial Hospital And Baker Community Health Center, Macclenny, FL, p. A131

DUET, Kendrick, Chief Operating Officer, Leonard J. Chabert Medical Center, Houma, LA, p. A276

DUFF, James M.D., Chief Medical Officer, Cox Medical Center Branson, Branson, MO, p. A365

DUFF, Jim, Chief Financial Officer, Colorado Mental Health Institute At Pueblo, Pueblo, CO, p. A106

DUFF, Mary Claire CPA, Chief Financial Officer, Ridgeview Psychiatric Hospital And Center, Oak Ridge, TN, p. A588

DUFFEE, Patrick, Director Medical Information Systems, Delta Medical Center, Memphis, TN, p. A584

DUFFEY, Pam MSN, R.N., Chief Nursing Officer, Texas Health Specialty Hospital, Fort Worth, TX, p. A614

DUFFIN, Kelly L, Operations Officer, Intermountain Medical Center, Murray, UT, p. A658

DUFFORD, Shawn M.D., Vice President Medical Affairs and Chief Medical Officer, Saint Joseph Hospital, Denver, CO, p. A101

DUFFY, Beth, Chief Operating Officer, Einstein Medical Center Montgomery, East Norriton, PA, p. A533

DUFFY, Daniel D.O., Chief Medical Director, Healthsource Saginaw, Inc., Saginaw, MI, p. A329

DUFFY, Delilah, Interim Chief Nurse Officer, Central Montana Medical Center, Lewistown, MT, p. A386

DUFFY, Kenneth M.D., Medical Director, Seiling Municipal Hospital, Seiling, OK, p. A515

DUFFY, Marie Theresa, Chief Operating Officer, Carepoint Health Christ Hospital, Jersey City, NJ, p. A415

DUFFY, Pamela
Vice President Operations and Chief Nursing Officer, Northwestern Medicine Kishwaukee Hospital, Dekalb, IL, p. A185
Vice President Operations and Chief Nursing Officer, Northwestern Medicine Valley West Hospital, Sandwich, IL, p. A200

DUFFY, Timothy W, General Director, Albany Medical Center, Albany, NY, p. A430

DUFT, Ryan R.N., Chief Nursing Officer, Fredonia Regional Hospital, Fredonia, KS, p. A241

DUGAN, Elizabeth Ph.D., R.N., MSN, Chief Nursing Officer, Inova Loudoun Hospital, Leesburg, VA, p. A669

DUGAN, Gary M.D., Vice President Medical Affairs, Penn Highlands Dubois, Dubois, PA, p. A533

DUGAR, Edward, R.N., Chief Executive Officer, Hood Memorial Hospital, Amite, LA, p. A270

DUGAS, Sheri, Director Health Information Management, Oakdale Community Hospital, Oakdale, LA, p. A284

DUGGAL, Harpreet M.D., Medical Director, Department of Health and Human Services, Humboldt County Mental Health, Eureka, CA, p. A58

DUGGAN, Allison A.N. FACS, Chief Operating Officer, Oswego Hospital, Oswego, NY, p. A449

DUGGAN, Daniel, Chief Operating Officer, Bon Secours St. Francis Health System, Greenville, SC, p. A562

DUGGAN, James E, Director Human Resources, Western Massachusetts Hospital, Westfield, MA, p. A313

DUGGAN, Margaret M. M.D., Chief Medical Officer, Brigham And Women's Faulkner Hospital, Boston, MA, p. A303

DUGGAN, Tonya, Director Human Resources, Northern Louisiana Medical Center, Ruston, LA, p. A285

DUGGAR, Susan R.N., MSN, Vice President Nursing, Spartanburg Medical Center, Spartanburg, SC, p. A566

DUGGER, Curtis R., Chief Financial Officer, Memorial Hospital Of Converse County, Douglas, WY, p. A718

DUGGER, Sandy, Chief Human Resources Officer, Platte County Memorial Hospital, Wheatland, WY, p. A720

DUHAIME, Robert A R.N., Senior Vice President Clinical Operations and Chief Nursing Officer, Catholic Medical Center, Manchester, NH, p. A409

DUHE, Louis, Senior Director Information Technology, George Washington University Hospital, Washington, DC, p. A117

DUHON, Thomas, Director Human Resources, Heart Hospital Of Lafayette, Lafayette, LA, p. A278

DUKE, Ezekiel M.D., Chief of Staff, Knox County Hospital, Knox City, TX, p. A627

DUKE, Kelly, Chief Executive Officer, Mimbres Memorial Hospital, Deming, NM, p. A426

DUKE, Lee M M.D., II, Senior Vice President and Chief Physician Executive, Lancaster General Hospital, Lancaster, PA, p. A538

DUKES, Brenda, Director Human Resources, Sonoma Developmental Center, Eldridge, CA, p. A58

DUKOFF, Ruth M.D., Medical Director, North Star Behavioral Health System, Anchorage, AK, p. A25

DULANEY, Paul M.D., Chief of Staff, Troy Regional Medical Center, Troy, AL, p. A23

DULL, David M.D., Chief Medical Officer, Penrose–St. Francis Health Services, Colorado Springs, CO, p. A100

DULL, Kevin B
Senior Vice President Human Potential, Multicare Auburn Medical Center, Auburn, WA, p. A678
Senior Vice President Human Potential, Multicare Good Samaritan Hospital, Puyallup, WA, p. A684
Senior Vice President Human Potential, Multicare Mary Bridge Children's Hospital And Health Center, Tacoma, WA, p. A687
Senior Vice President Human Potential, Multicare Tacoma General Hospital, Tacoma, WA, p. A688

DULNY, David
Chief Financial Officer, Providence Medical Center, Kansas City, KS, p. A244
Chief Financial Officer, Saint John Hospital, Leavenworth, KS, p. A245

DUMAL, Jennifer R.N., Chief Operating Officer of Clinical and Chief Nursing Officer, Memorial Hospital At Gulfport, Gulfport, MS, p. A355

DUMKE, Steve FACHE, Executive Vice President and Chief Operating Officer, Christian Health Care Center, Wyckoff, NJ, p. A423

DUMONSEAU, Kent
Vice President Finance and Information Services, Hayward Area Memorial Hospital And Water's Edge, Hayward, WI, p. A703
Vice President Finance and Information Services, Memorial Medical Center – Ashland, Ashland, WI, p. A698

DUMONT, Amy R.N., MSN, Chief Nursing Officer, Concord Hospital, Concord, NH, p. A407

DUMONT, Frank, Assistant Vice President Human Resources and Corporate Compliance, Eastern Long Island Hospital, Greenport, NY, p. A436

DUNAVAN, Chad R.N., Vice President, Chief Nursing Officer, Medical Center Health System, Odessa, TX, p. A635

DUNCAN, Allison, Chief Financial Officer, Arrowhead Behavioral Health Hospital, Maumee, OH, p. A495

DUNCAN, Barbara, Chief Financial Officer, Habersham Medical Center, Demorest, GA, p. A156

DUNCAN, Charles M.D., Medical Director, Kindred Hospital–San Antonio, San Antonio, TX, p. A642

DUNCAN, Cindy
Director Human Resources, Roosevelt General Hospital, Portales, NM, p. A427
Manager Human Resources, Plains Regional Medical Center, Clovis, NM, p. A425

DUNCAN, Cynthia, Chief Executive Officer, Roger Mills Memorial Hospital, Cheyenne, OK, p. A505

DUNCAN, Darryl L., President and Chief Executive Officer, Mon Health Medical Center, Morgantown, WV, p. A694

DUNCAN, Jeremy, Director Information Systems, Lawrence Medical Center, Moulton, AL, p. A21

DUNCAN, Jimmy, Vice President Human Resources, Wellstar Kennestone Hospital, Marietta, GA, p. A161

DUNCAN, Joani, Chief Human Resource Officer, Ann & Robert H. Lurie Children's Hospital Of Chicago, Chicago, IL, p. A180

DUNCAN, Leeann, Director Patient Care Services, Harbor Oaks Hospital, New Baltimore, MI, p. A327

DUNCAN, Linda, Director Human Resources, Lee's Summit Medical Center, Lee's Summit, MO, p. A372

DUNCAN, Lyman, Chief Financial Officer, San Juan Health Service District, Monticello, UT, p. A657

DUNCAN, Michael J., President and Chief Executive Officer, Penn Medicine Chester County Hospital, West Chester, PA, p. A553

DUNCAN, Nathan, Chief Executive Officer, Lakeland Behavioral Health System, Springfield, MO, p. A379

DUNCAN, Thomas M, Executive Vice President and Chief Financial Officer, Miami Valley Hospital, Dayton, OH, p. A489

DUNCAN, Traci A, Vice President, Chief Nursing Officer, Northbay Medical Center, Fairfield, CA, p. A59

DUNFORD, Bill, Manager, Northside Hospital–Cherokee, Canton, GA, p. A153

DUNGAN, Janice L, Senior Vice President Clinical Services, Lake Regional Health System, Osage Beach, MO, p. A374

DUNHAM, Cathy, Vice President Human Resources, Mcpherson Hospital, Mcpherson, KS, p. A246

DUNHAM, Shelly, Chief Executive Officer, Okeene Municipal Hospital, Okeene, OK, p. A511

DUNIO, Gina, Chief Human Resources, James E. Van Zandt Veterans Affairs Medical Center, Altoona, PA, p. A528

DUNKER, Karla, Director Finance, Sedgwick County Health Center, Julesburg, CO, p. A104

DUNKIEL, Barbara, Director Human Resources, Healthsouth Sunrise Rehabilitation Hospital, Sunrise, FL, p. A143

DUNKIN, Jackie J., Director Human Resources, Platte Valley Medical Center, Brighton, CO, p. A99

DUNKIN, Jennifer, Chief Nursing Officer, Moberly Regional Medical Center, Moberly, MO, p. A373

DUNKIN, John, Executive Director, Amita Health Elk Grove Village, Elk Grove Village, IL, p. A186

DUNKLE, David, Vice President Medical Affairs, Johnson Memorial Hospital, Franklin, IN, p. A209

DUNKLEY, Rich, Administrator, Wyoming State Hospital, Evanston, WY, p. A718

DUNLAY, Sherry, R.N., MSN
Vice President Patient Care Services and Chief Nursing Officer, SSM Health St. Mary's Hospital Centralia, Centralia, IL, p. A179
Vice President Chief Nursing Officer, Integris Bass Pavilion, Enid, OK, p. A507

DUNLEAVY, Christopher, Senior Vice President Finance and Chief Financial Officer, Brigham And Women's Hospital, Boston, MA, p. A303

DUNLEY, Pamela L., MS, R.N., Chief Executive Officer, Elmhurst Hospital, Elmhurst, IL, p. A187

DUNLOP, James H, CPA, Jr
Chief Financial Officer, Sisters Of Charity Hospital Of Buffalo, Buffalo, NY, p. A433
Executive Vice President and Chief Financial Officer, Kenmore Mercy Hospital, Kenmore, NY, p. A438
Senior Vice President Finance and Chief Financial Officer, Mercy Hospital, Buffalo, NY, p. A433

DUNMYER, Daniel C., Chief Executive Officer, Vibra Hospital Of Charleston, Mt. Pleasant, SC, p. A564

DUNN, Daniel N, Vice President Operations, Wentworth–Douglass Hospital, Dover, NH, p. A407

DUNN, E D, Vice President Human Resources, Virtua Memorial, Mount Holly, NJ, p. A416

DUNN, Edna, Chief Nursing Officer, Western Plains Medical Complex, Dodge City, KS, p. A240

DUNN, Hope, Chief Nursing Officer, Healthsouth East Valley Rehabilitation Hospital, Mesa, AZ, p. A31

DUNN, Jack M.D., Chief of Staff, La Paz Regional Hospital, Parker, AZ, p. A32

DUNN, Janice
Chief Financial Officer, Plymouth Medical Center, Plymouth, IN, p. A218
Vice President and Chief Financial Officer, Southeast Georgia Health System Brunswick Campus, Brunswick, GA, p. A153

DUNN, Leonard M.D., Chief Medical Officer, Baycare Alliant Hospital, Dunedin, FL, p. A124

DUNN, Marcy
Vice President Information Services and Chief Information Officer, Good Samaritan Hospital Medical Center, West Islip, NY, p. A455
Vice President Information Services and Chief Information Officer, Mercy Medical Center, Rockville Centre, NY, p. A451
Vice President Information Services and Chief Information Officer, St. Francis Hospital, The Heart Center, Roslyn, NY, p. A451

DUNN, Margie, Director Human Resources, Middle Tennessee Mental Health Institute, Nashville, TN, p. A586

DUNN, Nicholas, Director Information Systems, Mena Regional Health System, Mena, AR, p. A47

DUNN, Patrick A R.N., Chief Nursing Officer, Lea Regional Medical Center, Hobbs, NM, p. A426

DUNN, Richard M.D., Chief Medical Officer, Riverside Tappahannock Hospital, Tappahannock, VA, p. A676

DUNN, Rosemary R.N., Chief Nursing Officer, Hahnemann University Hospital, Philadelphia, PA, p. A544

DUNN, Sheila, Assistant Administrator Human Resources, Dale Medical Center, Ozark, AL, p. A22

DUNN, Tandra, Director of Nursing, San Luis Valley Health Conejos County Hospital, La Jara, CO, p. A104

DUNN, Terry, Director Information Technology, Battle Mountain General Hospital, Battle Mountain, NV, p. A401

DUNNAM, Lorie, Superintendent, Big Spring State Hospital, Big Spring, TX, p. A598

DUNNE, Elizabeth, President and Chief Executive Officer, Peacehealth, Vancouver, WA, p. B97

DUNPHY–ALEXANDER, Shannon, Director, Mercyhealth Hospital And Medical Center – Harvard, Harvard, IL, p. A189

DUNWOODY, Robert, Chief Financial Officer, Lawnwood Regional Medical Center & Heart Institute, Fort Pierce, FL, p. A125

DUPPER, Harold, Chief Financial Officer, Platte Valley Medical Center, Brighton, CO, p. A99

DUPRE, Charlotte W., Chief Executive Officer, Southern Regional Medical Center, Riverdale, GA, p. A163

DUPREE, Lucy G, Director Human Resources, Columbia Memorial Hospital, Astoria, OR, p. A520

DUPREY, Irma, Administrator Medical Records, Hospital Universitario Dr. Ramon Ruiz Arnau, Bayamon, PR, p. A722

DUPUIS, Pamela M R.N., Senior Vice President Patient Care Services, Montefiore New Rochelle, New Rochelle, NY, p. A440

DUQUETTE, Connie, Director Human Resources, Sharp Memorial Hospital, San Diego, CA, p. A86

DUQUETTE, William M., Chief Executive Officer, Baptist Health South Florida, Homestead Hospital, Homestead, FL, p. A127

DURALL, Aaron, Chief Executive Officer, Chestatee Regional Hospital, Dahlonega, GA, p. A156

DURAN, Aurelio, Chief of Staff, Orlando Regional Medical Center, Orlando, FL, p. A137

DURAN, Jody, Manager Information Systems, Livingston Healthcare, Livingston, MT, p. A386

DURAND, Crista F., President, Newport Hospital, Newport, RI, p. A556

DURAND, Mark, Assistant Administrator Operations, Christus Southeast Texas Jasper Memorial, Jasper, TX, p. A625

DURANT, Charles E. Jr, FACHE, Chief Executive Officer, Calhoun–Liberty Hospital, Blountstown, FL, p. A120

DURBAK, Ivan, Chief Information Officer, Bronx–Lebanon Hospital Center Health Care System, New Rochelle, NY, p. A440

DURBIN, Melissa R.N., Chief Nursing Officer, Boca Raton Regional Hospital, Boca Raton, FL, p. A120

DURDEN, Rhonda, Chief Financial Officer, Emanuel Medical Center, Swainsboro, GA, p. A165

DURFLINGER, Kathy R.N., Vice President and Chief Nursing Officer, Avita Ontario Hospital, Ontario, OH, p. A497

DURGIN, Manal, Network Medical Director, Devereux Hospital And Children's Center Of Florida, Melbourne, FL, p. A132

DURHAM, Karla, Director of Information Systems, Baptist Health Madisonville, Madisonville, KY, p. A264

DURHAM, Laurie Lea, Chief Executive Officer, Prairie Community Hospital, Terry, MT, p. A388

DURHAM, Linda, Director Human Resources, Henderson County Community Hospital, Lexington, TN, p. A583

DURHAM, Thomas, Chief Nursing Officer, Ferry County Memorial Hospital, Republic, WA, p. A684

DURIS, Deb, Director of Nursing, Northwest Ohio Psychiatric Hospital, Toledo, OH, p. A500

DURNEY, Gerry, Chief Operating Officer, Good Samaritan Regional Medical Center, Suffern, NY, p. A453

DURNIAT–SUSHRSTEDT, Karen, Nurse Executive, Appalachian Behavioral Healthcare, Athens, OH, p. A480

DURNIOK, Brian
President, Upmc Northwest, Seneca, PA, p. A550
Vice President Human Resources, Upmc Northwest, Seneca, PA, p. A550
Vice President Operations, Upmc Northwest, Seneca, PA, p. A550

DURON, Kety, Vice President Human Resources, Stanford Health Care, Palo Alto, CA, p. A79

DUROVICH, Christopher J., President and Chief Executive Officer, Children's Health System Of Texas, Dallas, TX, p. A605

DURR, Amber, Human Resources Executive, Community Hospital–Fairfax, Fairfax, MO, p. A368

DURR, Durinda, Vice President Clinical Services and Chief Nursing Officer, Rome Memorial Hospital, Rome, NY, p. A451

DURST, Geoff, Vice President Finance, Avera St. Luke's Hospital, Aberdeen, SD, p. A568

DURST, Sue R.N., MS, Vice President Plant Operations, Mclaren Macomb, Mount Clemens, MI, p. A326

DURSTELER, Courtney, Chief Human Resources Officer, Franklin County Medical Center, Preston, ID, p. A175

DURYEE, Edward E, Director Information Systems, Saint Francis Medical Center, Cape Girardeau, MO, p. A365

DUSANG, Nina, Vice President Finance and Chief Financial Officer, Dch Regional Medical Center, Tuscaloosa, AL, p. A23

DUSENBERY, Jack
President and Chief Executive Officer, Covenant Medical Center, Waterloo, IA, p. A236
President and Chief Executive Officer, Covenant Medical Center, Waterloo, IA, p. A236

DUTCHER, Phillip C, Chief Operating Officer, Nch Downtown Naples Hospital, Naples, FL, p. A135

DUTHE, Robert J, Director Information Systems and Chief Information Officer, Cortland Regional Medical Center, Cortland, NY, p. A434

DUTLA, Nimal M.D., Chief Medical Staff, Holzer Medical Center – Jackson, Jackson, OH, p. A492

DUTMERS, David, Manager Technology Information System, Spectrum Health United Hospital, Greenville, MI, p. A322

DUTTON, Angela, Chief Human Resources Management Service, Robley Rex Veterans Affairs Medical Center, Louisville, KY, p. A263

DUTTON, Rebecca, Director Human Resources, Larue D. Carter Memorial Hospital, Indianapolis, IN, p. A211

DUTTON, Teresa R.N., Chief Nursing Officer, Baylor Scott & White Surgical Hospital At Sherman, Sherman, TX, p. A645

DUVAL, Rob, Chief Human Resources Officer, Emma Pendleton Bradley Hospital, East Providence, RI, p. A556

DUVALL, Richard, Chief Executive Officer, Carthage Area Hospital, Carthage, NY, p. A434

DUVALL, Wendy, Chief Executive Officer, Barton County Memorial Hospital, Lamar, MO, p. A372

DUVVURI, Vikas M.D., Medical Director, Fremont Hospital, Fremont, CA, p. A60

DWIGHT, John
Regional Vice President and Chief Information Officer, Cascade Valley Hospital And Clinics, Arlington, WA, p. A678
Regional Vice President and Chief Information Officer, Skagit Regional Health, Mount Vernon, WA, p. A682

DWORAK, Paige, Interim Chief Executive Officer, East Orange General Hospital, East Orange, NJ, p. A413

DWORKIN, Darren, Senior Vice President Enterprise Information Systems and Chief Information Officer, Cedars–Sinai Medical Center, Los Angeles, CA, p. A67

DWORKIN, Jack H M.D., Vice President Medical Affairs and Chief Medical Officer, Centrastate Healthcare System, Freehold, NJ, p. A414

DWORKIN, Paul M.D., Physician–in–Chief, Connecticut Children's Medical Center, Hartford, CT, p. A110

DWYER, Amy L. R.N., MSN, Chief Nursing Officer, Sacred Heart Hospital, Eau Claire, WI, p. A701

DWYER, Cathy, Senior Administrator Information Systems, Burke Rehabilitation Hospital, White Plains, NY, p. A456

DWYER, James P, D.O.
Executive Vice President and Chief Medical Officer, Virtua Memorial, Mount Holly, NJ, p. A416
Executive Vice President and Chief Medical Officer, Virtua Voorhees, Voorhees, NJ, p. A422

DWYER, Karla R.N., MSN, Chief Nursing Officer, Healthsouth Rehabilitation Hospital–Wichita Falls, Wichita Falls, TX, p. A654

DWYER, Susan, Vice President Finance, Aurora Psychiatric Hospital, Wauwatosa, WI, p. A715

DWYER, William, Vice President and Chief Human Resources Officer, Children's Specialized Hospital, New Brunswick, NJ, p. A417

DYBAAL, Landon, Chief Executive Officer, Garfield County Health Center, Jordan, MT, p. A386

DYCHE, Ginny, Director Community Relations, Aspen Valley Hospital, Aspen, CO, p. A98

DYCUS, Steve, Director Marketing and Public Relations, Williamson Medical Center, Franklin, TN, p. A579

DYE, Blake A., President, St. Vincent Indianapolis Hospital, IndianapolisSt. Vincent Heart Center, Indianapolis, IN, p. A212

DYE, Chris, Director Information Systems, Saint Joseph – Martin, Martin, KY, p. A264

DYE, Dana, R.N., Vice President, Administrator and Chief Executive Officer, Baptist Memorial Hospital – Memphis, Memphis, TN, p. A584

DYE, David Bryan M.D., Chief Medical Officer, Purcell Municipal Hospital, Purcell, OK, p. A515

DYE, Emily, Vice President Human Resources, Tristar Summit Medical Center, Hermitage, TN, p. A580

DYE, Kathy
Chief Nursing Officer, Adena Pike Medical Center, Waverly, OH, p. A502
Interim Administrator, Adena Greenfield Medical Center, Greenfield, OH, p. A492

DYE, Leslie, Chief Executive Officer, Phs Santa Fe Indian Hospital, Santa Fe, NM, p. A428

DYER, Ed, Chief Executive Officer, Stroud Regional Medical Center, Stroud, OK, p. A516

DYER, Edward L, Chief Executive Officer, Cornerstone Hospital Of Austin, Austin, TX, p. A594

DYER, Kathleen, Vice President and Chief Information Officer, Adventist Behavioral Health And Wellness Services, Rockville, MD, p. A300

DYKEHOUSE, Rod, Chief Information Officer, Penn State Milton S. Hershey Medical Center, Hershey, PA, p. A536

DYKEHOUSE, Rodney, Senior Vice President Information Services, Waukesha Memorial Hospital, Waukesha, WI, p. A714

DYKES, Bradford W., President and Chief Executive Officer, Indiana University Health Bedford Hospital, Bedford, IN, p. A204

DYKES, Nichole, Chief Financial Officer, Healthsouth Rehabilitation Hospital North Texas, Richardson, TX, p. A639

DYKSTERHOUSE, Trevor J., President, Forest Health Medical Center, Ypsilanti, MI, p. A333

DYKSTRA, Lisa, Senior Vice President and Chief Information Officer, Ann & Robert H. Lurie Children's Hospital Of Chicago, Chicago, IL, p. A180

DYLE, Amanda, Chief Financial Officer, Walker Baptist Medical Center, Jasper, AL, p. A20

DYRKACZ, Anna, Chief Financial Officer, Vibra Hospital Of Western Massachusetts, Springfield, MA, p. A312

DYSART–CREDEUR, Amy, Administrator, Oceans Behavioral Hospital Of Broussard, Broussard, LA, p. A272

DZIEDZICKI, Ron R.N., Chief Operating Officer, University Hospitals Cleveland Medical Center, Cleveland, OH, p. A486

DZIESINSKI, Ray R, Vice President and Chief Financial Officer, Sheppard Pratt Health System, Baltimore, MD, p. A295

E

EADS, Barry, Chief Nursing Officer, Healthsouth Rehabilitation Of Gadsden, Gadsden, AL, p. A18

EADY, Bruce, Chief Executive Officer, Mercy Rehabilitation Hospital Springfield, Springfield, MO, p. A380

EAGAR, Troy, Director Human Resources, Mountain Valley Regional Rehabilitation Hospital, Prescott Valley, AZ, p. A35

EAGEN, Mary K R.N., MS, Executive Vice President, Chief Nursing Officer, Parkland Health & Hospital System, Dallas, TX, p. A606

EAGERTON, Gregory S Ph.D., R.N., Nurse Executive, Durham Veterans Affairs Medical Center, Durham, NC, p. A461

EAKER, Blake, Interim Director Information Services, Uvalde Memorial Hospital, Uvalde, TX, p. A651

EAKS, Alan, Chief Executive Officer and Managing Director, Spring Mountain Sahara, Las Vegas, NV, p. A403

EAKS, C Alan., Chief Executive Officer and Managing Director, Spring Mountain Treatment Center, Las Vegas, NV, p. A404

EAMRANOND, Pracha M.D., Senior Vice President Population Health and Medical Affairs, Lawrence General Hospital, Lawrence, MA, p. A307

EARDLEY, Robert K, Senior Vice President and Chief Information Officer, Houston Methodist Hospital, Houston, TX, p. A620

EARL, Mindy, Health Information Manager, Power County Hospital District, American Falls, ID, p. A171

EARLE, Audra, FACHE, Chief Executive Officer, Watsonville Community Hospital, Watsonville, CA, p. A96

EARLES, Greg, Chief Executive Officer, Coliseum Northside Hospital, Macon, GA, p. B58

EARLEY, Robert, President and Chief Executive Officer, Jps Health Network, Fort Worth, TX, p. A613

EARLEY, Tom, Chief Financial Officer, Alliancehealth Woodward, Woodward, OK, p. A519

EARLS, Sandra, Chief Financial Officer, Coalinga Regional Medical Center, Coalinga, CA, p. A56

EARLY, Elfie, Manager Data Services, Georgia Regional Hospital At Atlanta, Decatur, GA, p. A156

EARLY, Gerald L M.D., Chief Medical Officer, Pullman Regional Hospital, Pullman, WA, p. A684

EARNSHAW, Dallas, Superintendent, Utah State Hospital, Provo, UT, p. A659

EASLEY, Evan M.D., Chief Medical Officer, Carson Valley Medical Center, Gardnerville, NV, p. A402

EASLEY, Mike, Vice President and Chief Operating Officer, Sabine County Hospital, Hemphill, TX, p. A618

EASSON, Jacob, Chief Financial Officer, Blackwell Regional Hospital, Blackwell, OK, p. A505

EAST, Becky CPA, Senior Vice President, Chief Financial Officer, Bronson Lakeview Hospital, Paw Paw, MI, p. A327

EASTBURG, Mark C., Ph.D., President and Chief Executive Officer, Pine Rest Christian Mental Health Services, Grand Rapids, MI, p. A321

EASTER, Susan, Chief Nursing Officer, Palacios Community Medical Center, Palacios, TX, p. A636

EASTERLING, Jamie, Executive Director, Operations, Good Samaritan Hospital, Cincinnati, OH, p. A484

EASTERWOOD, Diane J, Human Resources Business Partner, Kaiser Permanente San Francisco Medical Center, San Francisco, CA, p. A87

EASTHOPE, Kerry, Area Finance Officer, Kaiser Permanente Antioch Medical Center, Antioch, CA, p. A51

EASTMAN, David, Site Director, Ukiah Valley Medical Center, Ukiah, CA, p. A95

EASTON, Laura J., President and Chief Executive Officer, Caldwell Unc Health Care, Lenoir, NC, p. A466

EASTON, Laura J, President and Chief Executive Officer, Caldwell Unc Health Care, Lenoir, NC, p. A466

EATHERLY, Theresa, Chief Financial Officer, United Memorial Medical Care, Houston, TX, p. A623

EATON, Jim, Chief Financial Officer, Wise Health System, Decatur, TX, p. A607

EATON, Philip, Interim Chief Executive Officer, Mountain West Medical Center, Tooele, UT, p. A661

EAVENSON, Paul, Chief Executive Officer, First Baptist Medical Center, Dallas, TX, p. A605

EAVENSON, Steve, Vice President Finance, Mercy Health Saint Mary's, Grand Rapids, MI, p. A321

EAVES, Clinton, Administrator, Jasper General Hospital, Bay Springs, MS, p. A352

EAVES, Dan, Chief Executive Officer, Marshall Browning Hospital, Du Quoin, IL, p. A186

EBANGIT, Ruth M.D., Chief of Staff and Medical Officer, Throckmorton County Memorial Hospital, Throckmorton, TX, p. A650

EBBETT, Patricia, Chief Human Resources Officer, Catawba Hospital, Catawba, VA, p. A665

EBELING, April, Chief Executive Officer, AMG Specialty Hospital–Zachary, Zachary, LA, p. A288

EBERHARDT, Lisa, Chief Nursing Officer, Clark Fork Valley Hospital, Plains, MT, p. A387

EBERSOLE, Nathan, Controller, Calhoun–Liberty Hospital, Blountstown, FL, p. A120

EBERT, Michael M.D., Chief of Staff, Veterans Affairs Connecticut Healthcare System, West Haven, CT, p. A114

EBERT–LOOMIS, Cynthia R.N., Chief Nursing Officer, Summit Healthcare Regional Medical Center, Show Low, AZ, p. A36

EBERTH, Denise A, Chief Human Resources Officer, Allegan General Hospital, Allegan, MI, p. A314

EBLIN, Steven E., Chief Executive Officer / President, Randolph Hospital, Asheboro, NC, p. A457

EBNER, Joseph M.D., Chief Medical Officer, Speare Memorial Hospital, Plymouth, NH, p. A410

EBRI, Patrick D Ph.D., FACHE, Vice President Human Resources, Southeast Georgia Health System Camden Campus, Saint Marys, GA, p. A164

EBRIGHT, Brian, Chief Financial Officer, Salt Lake Regional Medical Center, Salt Lake City, UT, p. A660

ECHOLS, Jerry W, Administrator and Chief Executive Officer, East Texas Medical Center Tyler, Tyler, TX, p. A651

ECKELS, Dan, Chief Financial Officer, Washington Regional Medical Center, Fayetteville, AR, p. A43

ECKENFELS, Susan, Chief Financial Officer, Ste. Genevieve County Memorial Hospital, Ste Genevieve, MO, p. A380

ECKERT, Mark, Vice President Finance, Ochsner Medical Center – Kenner, Kenner, LA, p. A277

ECKERT, Mary L., President and Chief Executive Officer, Lecom Health Millcreek Community Hospital, Erie, PA, p. A534

ECKERT, Susan E. R.N., MSN, Senior Vice President and Chief Nursing Officer, Medstar Washington Hospital Center, Washington, DC, p. A118

ECKFORD, Marjorie, Chief Nursing Officer, Menlo Park Surgical Hospital, Menlo Park, CA, p. A73

ECKLAND, Christopher M.D., Chief Medical Officer, Miami County Medical Center, Paola, KS, p. A249

ECKSTEIN, Melissa, Chief Executive Officer, Palo Verde Behavioral Health, Tucson, AZ, p. A38

ECKSTEIN, William, Chief Executive Officer and Chief Financial Officer, Columbus Specialty Hospital, Columbus, GA, p. A154

EDALATI, David M.D., Medical Director, Meadowbrook Rehabilitation Hospital, Gardner, KS, p. A241

EDDEY, Gary E M.D., Medical Director, Matheny Medical And Educational Center, Peapack, NJ, p. A418

EDDINGTON, Tonya, Coordinator Human Resources, Select Specialty Hospital–Springfield, Springfield, MO, p. A380

EDDLEMAN, Patricia, Fiscal Officer, Heartland Behavioral Healthcare, Massillon, OH, p. A495

EDDY, Lee Anne, Senior Vice President and Chief Nursing Officer, Arkansas Children's Hospital, Little Rock, AR, p. A45

EDELMAN, Marc D, Vice President Operations, Bristol Hospital, Bristol, CT, p. A109

EDEN, Tina M, Director of Nursing, Virginia Gay Hospital, Vinton, IA, p. A235

EDENFIELD, Janet, Director Financial Services, Georgia Regional Hospital At Savannah, Savannah, GA, p. A164

EDGAR, Joseph H, Senior Vice President Operations, Wellspan Gettysburg Hospital, Gettysburg, PA, p. A535

EDGAR, Nancy, Vice President Human Resources, Methodist Hospital, San Antonio, TX, p. A643

EDGAR, Steven, FACHE, President and Chief Executive Officer, Medical City Denton, Denton, TX, p. A608

EDIN, Scott D, Vice President, Finance and Chief Financial Officer, Northfield Hospital, Northfield, MN, p. A345

EDLER, Susie R.N., Chief Nursing Officer, Dallas Behavioral Healthcare Hospital, Desoto, TX, p. A609

EDMINSTER, Sue
Vice President Human Resources, Ripon Medical Center, Ripon, WI, p. A712
Vice President Human Resources, St. Agnes Hospital, Fond Du Lac, WI, p. A701
Vice President Human Resources, Waupun Memorial Hospital, Waupun, WI, p. A715

EDMONDS, Kelly, Chief Financial Officer, Western Maryland Hospital Center, Hagerstown, MD, p. A299

EDMONDSON, Bobby, Controller, Regional Rehabilitation Hospital, Phenix City, AL, p. A22

EDMONDSON, James H., Chief Executive Officer, Southern Tennessee Regional Health System–Pulaski, Pulaski, TN, p. A588

EDMONSON, Cole R.N., MS, FACHE, Vice President and Chief Nursing Officer, Texas Health Presbyterian Hospital Dallas, Dallas, TX, p. A607

EDMUNDS, Liza, Director Human Resources, Tennova Healthcare–Clarksville, Clarksville, TN, p. A577

EDNEY, Daniel M.D., Chief of Staff, Promise Hospital Of Vicksburg, Vicksburg, MS, p. A362

EDRINGTON, Katherine R.N., Administrator, Mercy Health – Anderson Hospital, Cincinnati, OH, p. A484

EDWARD, Adolphe, Chief Executive Officer, El Centro Regional Medical Center, El Centro, CA, p. A58

EDWARDS, Aaron, Chief Executive Officer, Ferry County Memorial Hospital, Republic, WA, p. A684

EDWARDS, Angela Imelda R.N., Chief Nurse Executive, NYC Health + Hospitals / Woodhull, New Rochelle, NY, p. A446

EDWARDS, Annette, Chief Financial Officer, Odessa Memorial Healthcare Center, Odessa, WA, p. A683

EDWARDS, Becky, Manager Human Resources, Irwin County Hospital, Ocilla, GA, p. A163

EDWARDS, Bob S. Jr, FACHE, Chief Executive Officer, Mendocino Coast District Hospital, Fort Bragg, CA, p. A59

EDWARDS, Bruce
Vice President Human Resources, Heritage Valley Health System, Beaver, PA, p. A529
Vice President Human Resources, Sewickley Valley Hospital, (A Division Of Valley Medical Facilities), Sewickley, PA, p. A550

EDWARDS, Chris M.D., Chief Medical Officer, Maury Regional Hospital, Columbia, TN, p. A577

EDWARDS, Dana, Chief Financial Officer, Healthsouth Sea Pines Rehabilitation Hospital, Melbourne, FL, p. A132

EDWARDS, Dennis M.D., Vice President Medical Affairs, Chi Health Good Samaritan, Kearney, NE, p. A394

EDWARDS, Gregg
Chief People Officer, Asante Rogue Regional Medical Center, Medford, OR, p. A524
Chief People Officer, Asante Three Rivers Medical Center, Grants Pass, OR, p. A522
Vice President Human Resources, Asante Ashland Community Hospital, Ashland, OR, p. A520

EDWARDS, Jeff, Manager Information Services, Mendocino Coast District Hospital, Fort Bragg, CA, p. A59

EDWARDS, John R., Administrator and Chief Executive Officer, Pacific Alliance Medical Center, Los Angeles, CA, p. A70

EDWARDS, Kathleen, Manager Information Systems Operation, Healthsouth Rehabilitation Hospital Of Altoona, Altoona, PA, p. A528

EDWARDS, Kristy M.D., Chief Medical Officer, Lillian M. Hudspeth Memorial Hospital, Sonora, TX, p. A646

EDWARDS, Marti, MSN, R.N.
Chief Nursing Officer, Rml Specialty Hospital, Chicago, IL, p. A183
Chief Nursing Officer, Rml Specialty Hospital, Hinsdale, IL, p. A190

EDWARDS, Matt, Vice President Nursing Services and Chief Nursing Officer, Anderson Regional Health System, Meridian, MS, p. A359

EDWARDS, Michelle, Executive Vice President Information Technology, Palmetto Health Baptist, Columbia, SC, p. A560

EDWARDS, Nicki E Ph.D., R.N., Interim Chief Nursing Officer, Sierra Vista Regional Medical Center, San Luis Obispo, CA, p. A89

EDWARDS, Rebecca
Chief Human Resources Officer, Penn Highlands Brookville, Brookville, PA, p. A530
Chief Nursing Officer, Greenwood Leflore Hospital, Greenwood, MS, p. A355
Director Human Resources, Martin General Hospital, Williamston, NC, p. A472

EDWARDS, Rick, Vice President and Chief Financial Officer, Hancock Regional Hospital, Greenfield, IN, p. A209

EDWARDS, Samuel M.D., Chief of Staff, Florida Hospital Deland, Deland, FL, p. A123

EDWARDS, Steven D., President and Chief Executive Officer, Cox Medical Centers, Springfield, MO, p. A379

EDWARDS, Susan A.
Chief Executive Officer, Oconomowoc Memorial Hospital, Oconomowoc, WI, p. A709
Chief Executive Officer, Waukesha Memorial Hospital, Waukesha, WI, p. A714

EDWARDS, Susan, Vice President Human Resources, Novant Health Uva Health System Culpeper Medical Center, Culpeper, VA, p. A666

EDWARDS, Terry, Controller, Carolinas Healthcare System Kings Mountain, Kings Mountain, NC, p. A465

EDWARDS, Todd, Director Information Management Systems, Chi St. Luke's Health Brazosport, Lake Jackson, TX, p. A628

EDWARDS, William, Information Technology Generalist, Wernersville State Hospital, Wernersville, PA, p. A553

EESLEY, Michael S.
Chief Executive Officer, Centegra Hospital – Mchenry, Mchenry, IL, p. A193
Chief Executive Officer, Centegra Hospital – Woodstock, Woodstock, IL, p. A202

EGAN, Carol R.N., MSN, Chief Nursing Officer, Rutland Regional Medical Center, Rutland, VT, p. A663

EGAN, Kim, Executive Director Human Resources, Regions Hospital, Saint Paul, MN, p. A348

EGAN, Timothy, President and Chief Executive Officer, Roseland Community Hospital, Chicago, IL, p. A183

EGBERT, James, Chief of Staff, Vidant Beaufort Hospital, Washington, NC, p. A472

EGERTON, W Eugene M.D., Chief Medical Officer, University Of Maryland Medical Center Midtown Campus, Baltimore, MD, p. A296

EGGEN, Caity, Chief Human Resource Officer, Cuyuna Regional Medical Center, Crosby, MN, p. A338

EGGERS, Judy, Manager Human Resources, Alliance Healthcare System, Holly Springs, MS, p. A356

EGGLESTON, Brett, Chief Financial Officer, Callaway District Hospital, Callaway, NE, p. A391

EGGLESTON, Kirk W., Commanding Officer, Winn Army Community Hospital, Hinesville, GA, p. A159

EGGLESTON, Lara
Finance Manager, University Hospitals Conneaut Medical Center, Conneaut, OH, p. A488
Finance Manager, University Hospitals Geneva Medical Center, Geneva, OH, p. A492

EGGLESTON, Ryan, Chief Financial Officer, Desert View Hospital, Pahrump, NV, p. A405

EGYUD, Amber R.N., Vice President Chief Nursing Officer, Forbes Hospital, Monroeville, PA, p. A541

EHASZ, James, Chief Financial Officer, Copper Queen Community Hospital, Bisbee, AZ, p. A28

EHLER, Phyllis, Director Human Resources, Avera St. Benedict Health Center, Parkston, SD, p. A571

EHLERS, Jeffrey, Chief Financial Officer, Memorial Health, Marysville, OH, p. A495

EHLINGER, Forrest, System Chief Financial Officer, Benefis Health System, Great Falls, MT, p. A385

EHLKE, Ranae, Administrative Secretary and Coordinator Risk Management and Human Resources, Kenmare Community Hospital, Kenmare, ND, p. A477

EHLY, Ronda S R.N., Chief Nursing Officer, Mary Lanning Healthcare, Hastings, NE, p. A394

EHN, Jerry, Chief Operating Officer, Northfield Hospital, Northfield, MN, p. A345

EHN, Nicole M.D., Chief of Staff, Van Diest Medical Center, Webster City, IA, p. A236

EHRAT, Michael, Chief Executive Officer, Sovah Health–Martinsville, Martinsville, VA, p. A670

EHRENBERGER, David M.D., Chief Medical Officer, Avista Adventist Hospital, Louisville, CO, p. A106

EHRICH, Laurie, Chief Communications Officer, Wayne County Hospital, Corydon, IA, p. A225

EHRLICH, Frank, M.D.
Chief Medical Officer, Health Alliance Hospital – Broadway Campus, Kingston, NY, p. A438
Chief Medical Officer, Health Alliance Hospital – Mary's Avenue Campus, Kingston, NY, p. A438

EHRLICH, Susan P., M.D., Chief Executive Officer, Zuckerberg San Francisco General Hospital And Trauma Center, San Francisco, CA, p. A88

EHTISHAM, Saad, R.N., FACHE
Vice President and Chief Operating Officer, Leesburg Regional Medical Center, Leesburg, FL, p. A130
Vice President and Chief Operating Officer, The Villages Regional Hospital, The Villages, FL, p. A146

EICHENAUER, Donald T., Chief Executive Officer, Wyoming County Community Hospital, Warsaw, NY, p. A455

EICHENBERGER, Daniel J., M.D., President and Chief Executive Officer, Baptist Health Floyd, New Albany, IN, p. A217

EICHNER, John, Vice President Finance, TLC Health Network – Lake Shore Hospital, Irving, NY, p. A437

EIDAM, JoEllen, FACHE, Chief Executive Officer, Adams Memorial Hospital, Decatur, IN, p. A206

EIDE, Dean, Vice President, Mayo Clinic Health System – Oakridge In Osseo, Osseo, WI, p. A710

EIDE, Tom, Chief Financial Officer, Prairie St. John's, Fargo, ND, p. A475

EIFFERT, Sarah, Director Human Resources, Mercy Rehabilitation Hospital Springfield, Springfield, MO, p. A380

EIG, Blair M.D., Senior Vice President Medical Affairs, Holy Cross Health, Silver Spring, MD, p. A301

EIKE, Gail, Chief Financial Officer, Sanford Jackson Medical Center, Jackson, MN, p. A341

EILBRACHT, Hans, Chief Information Officer, Hamilton Center, Terre Haute, IN, p. A220

EILER, John M, Ph.D., President, Barnes–Jewish Hospital, Saint Louis, MO, p. A376

EIMERS, Katy, Human Resources Officer, Syringa Hospital And Clinics, Grangeville, ID, p. A173

EIPE, Joseph M.D., Chief Medical Officer, Pacifica Hospital Of The Valley, Los Angeles, CA, p. A70

EISCHENS, Shelby, Chief Medical Officer, Brookings Health System, Brookings, SD, p. A568

EISEL, Tom, Chief Financial Officer, Poinciana Medical Center, Kissimmee, FL, p. A129

EISELE, Karla M.D., Clinical Director, State Hospital North, Orofino, ID, p. A175

EISEMANN, Bradley, Administrator, Beacon Children's Hospital, Luverne, AL, p. A20

EISEN, Robert A, Vice President Human Resources, Northern California Region, Queen Of The Valley Medical Center, Napa, CA, p. A76

EISENMAN, Edward, Chief Executive Officer, Sunnyview Rehabilitation Hospital, Schenectady, NY, p. A452

EISENMANN, Claudia A., FACHE, Chief Executive Officer, Wilbarger General Hospital, Vernon, TX, p. A652

EISENTRAGER, Steve, President, Ohio Valley Surgical Hospital, Springfield, OH, p. A499

EISENZOPH, Pete, Director Information Technology, Bay Area Medical Center, Marinette, WI, p. A706

EISMAN, Michael M.D., Medical Director, Schuyler Hospital, Montour Falls, NY, p. A439

EISNER, Nina W., Chief Executive Officer and Managing Director, Ridge Behavioral Health System, Lexington, KY, p. A261

EITZEN, Tamara, Chief Nursing Officer, Fairview Regional Medical Center, Fairview, OK, p. A508

EIXENBERGER, Timothy D., Chief Nursing Officer, Southcoast Hospitals Group, Fall River, MA, p. A306

EKENGREN, Francie H M.D., Chief Medical Officer, Wesley Medical Center, Wichita, KS, p. A254

EKEREN, Douglas R., Regional President and Chief Executive Officer, Avera Sacred Heart Hospital, Yankton, SD, p. A574

EKPO, Felix, Manager, Information Systems, Arrowhead Regional Medical Center, Colton, CA, p. A56

EL KHALILI, Nizar M.D., Medical Director, Sycamore Springs Hospital, Lafayette, IN, p. A214

EL–DALATI, Sam M.D., Chief Medical Officer, Mercy Regional Medical Center, Lorain, OH, p. A494

EL–MELIGI, Christi J., R.N., Chief Executive Officer, Sage Memorial Hospital, Ganado, AZ, p. A29

EL–SOLH, Ali M.D., Interim Chief of Staff, Veterans Affairs Western New York Healthcare System–Buffalo Division, Buffalo, NY, p. A433

ELAM, Lora R.N., Chief Nursing Officer, Wayne County Hospital, Monticello, KY, p. A265

ELAM, Moses D M.D., Physician–in–Chief, Kaiser Permanente Manteca Medical Center, Manteca, CA, p. A73

ELARBEE, Vernon, Director of Human Resources, Florida Hospital North Pinellas, Tarpon Springs, FL, p. A145

ELBERT, Darlene M R.N., MS, Assistant Administrator and Chief Nursing Officer, Kossuth Regional Health Center, Algona, IA, p. A222

ELDER, Deborah, Director Human Resources, Scenic Mountain Medical Center, Big Spring, TX, p. A598

ELDIDY, Rene M.D., Chief of Staff, Centracare Health–Long Prairie, Long Prairie, MN, p. A342

ELDRED, Jamie, Controller, Klickitat Valley Health, Goldendale, WA, p. A681

ELDRIDGE, Janet, Director Human Resources and Personnel, Brooks County Hospital, Quitman, GA, p. A163

ELDRIDGE, Jim, Area Financial Officer, Kaiser Permanente Sacramento Medical Center, Sacramento, CA, p. A83

ELDRIDGE, Laurie, Chief Financial Officer, Marshall Medical Center, Placerville, CA, p. A80

ELDRIDGE, Lisa, Human Resources Officer, Thomas H. Boyd Memorial Hospital, Carrollton, IL, p. A179

ELEGANT, Bruce M., FACHE, President and Chief Executive Officer, Rush Oak Park Hospital, Oak Park, IL, p. A196

ELENBAAS, Jerry, Chief Executive Officer and Division President, Pam Rehabilitation Hospital Of Tulsa, Tulsa, OK, p. A517

ELFERT, Mike, Director Information Services, Lourdes Medical Center Of Burlington County, Willingboro, NJ, p. A423

ELFORD, Dorothy J., Chief Executive Officer, Acuity Hospital Of South Texas, San Antonio, TX, p. A641

ELGARICO, David, Chief Operating Officer, Touro Infirmary, New Orleans, LA, p. A283

ELI, Bev, Chief Nursing Officer, Cox Monett Hospital, Monett, MO, p. A374

ELIAS, Jose, Director Information Technology, Fort Duncan Regional Medical Center, Eagle Pass, TX, p. A609

ELICH, Elizabeth, Vice President Human Resources, Piedmont Medical Center, Rock Hill, SC, p. A565

ELIE, Charlene, Vice President Patient Care Services, Clinton Hospital, Clinton, MA, p. A306

ELIOT, Jason L, Vice President Human Resources, Integris Baptist Medical Center, Oklahoma City, OK, p. A512

ELKINGTON, Bruce, Regional Chief Information Officer, St. Clare Hospital, Lakewood, WA, p. A682

ELKINGTON, Mark M.D., Chief Medical Officer, Willow Crest Hospital, Miami, OK, p. A510

ELKINS, Carl, Director Information Technology, Rollins–Brook Community Hospital, Lampasas, TX, p. A628

ELKINS, James N., FACHE, Director, Texas Center For Infectious Disease, San Antonio, TX, p. A644

ELKINS, Kelly
President and Chief Executive Officer, Sacred Heart Rehabilitation Institute, Milwaukee, WI, p. A708
President, Columbia St. Mary's Hospital Milwaukee, Milwaukee, WI, p. A707

ELKINS, Wendy, Director Operations, Dundy County Hospital, Benkelman, NE, p. A391

ELLEDGE, David
Controller, Select Specialty Hospital–Knoxville, Knoxville, TN, p. A582
Controller, Select Specialty Hospital–North Knoxville, Powell, TN, p. A588

ELLEN, Jonathan D M.D., Medical Director, Healthsouth Rehabilitation Hospital Of Memphis, Memphis, TN, p. A584

ELLEN, Jonathan M., M.D., President, Johns Hopkins All Children's Hospital, Saint Petersburg, FL, p. A141

ELLENBURG, Cynthia, Director Health Information Services, Baptist Easley Hospital, Easley, SC, p. A561

ELLER, Bill, Director Information Technology, El Campo Memorial Hospital, El Campo, TX, p. A610

ELLER, Steven M
Chief Human Resources Officer, Beacon Health System, Memorial Hospital Of South Bend, South Bend, IN, p. A220
Vice President Human Resources, Elkhart General Hospital, Elkhart, IN, p. A207

ELLERSON, Thomas, Chief Information Officer, Our Lady Of Lourdes Memorial Hospital, Inc., Binghamton, NY, p. A432

ELLEY, Michael, Chief Information Officer, Owensboro Health Regional Hospital, Owensboro, KY, p. A265

ELLINGTON, Christopher, Executive Vice President and Chief Financial Officer, University Of North Carolina Hospitals, Chapel Hill, NC, p. A459

ELLIOTT, Amy M.D., Director Medical Affairs, District One Hospital, Faribault, MN, p. A339

ELLIOTT, Barb
  Chief Financial Officer, Fairbanks, Indianapolis, IN, p. A211
  Interim President and Chief Executive Officer, Fairbanks, Indianapolis, IN, p. A211

ELLIOTT, Charles W. Jr, Chief Executive Officer, Johnston Health, Smithfield, NC, p. A470

ELLIOTT, Jennifer, Chief Nursing Officer, Saint Thomas West Hospital, Nashville, TN, p. A586

ELLIOTT, Jim
  Director Human Resources, Bryce Hospital, Tuscaloosa, AL, p. A23
  Director Human Resources, Mary S Harper Geriatric Psychiatry Center, Tuscaloosa, AL, p. A24

ELLIOTT, Laura, Director Human Resources, Northeastern Nevada Regional Hospital, Elko, NV, p. A401

ELLIOTT, Lee Ann R.N., Director of Nursing, Select Rehabilitation Hospital Of Denton, Denton, TX, p. A608

ELLIOTT, Marye, Chief Nursing Officer, Brookwood Baptist Medical Center, Birmingham, AL, p. A14

ELLIOTT, Michael, M.D.
  Chief Medical Officer and Senior Vice President of Medical Affairs, Avera Mckennan Hospital And University Health Center, Sioux Falls, SD, p. A572
  Controller, Indianhead Medical Center, Shell Lake, WI, p. A712

ELLIOTT, Peyton, Vice President Operations, Houston Methodist West Hospital, Houston, TX, p. A621

ELLIOTT, R James, Vice President Human Resources, The Charlotte Hungerford Hospital, Torrington, CT, p. A113

ELLIOTT, Rhonda M., Director Information Technology and Meaningful Use, Person Memorial Hospital, Roxboro, NC, p. A470

ELLIOTT, Robin, Personnel Officer, Community Memorial Hospital, Sumner, IA, p. A235

ELLIOTT, Shane, Associate Director Administration, Veterans Affairs Loma Linda Healthcare System, Loma Linda, CA, p. A66

ELLIOTT MSN, Randi, Chief Nursing Officer, Baylor Medical Center At Frisco, Frisco, TX, p. A615

ELLIS, Amanda, Chief Financial Officer, Barbourville Arh Hospital, Barbourville, KY, p. A255

ELLIS, Angela R.N., Chief Nursing Officer, Terre Haute Regional Hospital, Terre Haute, IN, p. A220

ELLIS, Bob, Director of Nursing, D. W. Mcmillan Memorial Hospital, Brewton, AL, p. A15

ELLIS, Deb, Director Human Resources, Perry Memorial Hospital, Perry, OK, p. A514

ELLIS, Elmer G., FACHE, President and Chief Executive Officer, East Texas Medical Center Regional Healthcare System, Tyler, TX, p. B48

ELLIS, Kristin, Controller, Munson Healthcare Cadillac Hospital, Cadillac, MI, p. A315

ELLIS, Lisa, Chief Operating Officer, Alliancehealth Midwest, Midwest City, OK, p. A510

ELLIS, Mark, Director Information Technology, Lakeview Hospital, Bountiful, UT, p. A656

ELLIS, Michael J., FACHE, Chief Executive Officer, Hill Regional Hospital, Hillsboro, TX, p. A619

ELLIS, Michelle, Director Human Resources, Whitman Hospital And Medical Center, Colfax, WA, p. A679

ELLIS, Mike, Chief Financial Officer, Carson Valley Medical Center, Gardnerville, NV, p. A402

ELLIS, Paula, Administrator, Saint John Hospital, Leavenworth, KS, p. A245

ELLIS, Richard, Chief Executive Officer, Tennova Healthcare–Harton, Tullahoma, TN, p. A589

ELLIS, Scott D.O., Chief Medical Officer, Memorial Regional Health, Craig, CO, p. A100

ELLIS, Susan Renee' R.N., MSN, Vice President of Human Resources, Highlands Regional Medical Center, Prestonsburg, KY, p. A266

ELLIS, Tammy FACHE, R.N., Vice President Patient Services, Texas Health Huguley Hospital Fort Worth South, Burleson, TX, p. A600

ELLIS, Thomas J, Vice President Human Resources, Mt. Washington Pediatric Hospital, Baltimore, MD, p. A295

ELLIS, Wendel D.O., Chief Medical Staff, Greeley County Health Services, Tribune, KS, p. A252

ELLISH, Patti M., FACHE, President and Chief Executive Officer, St. Tammany Parish Hospital, Covington, LA, p. A273

ELLISON, Darcy R.N., MSN, Senior Vice President, Chief Nursing Officer and Inpatient Flow, St. Vincent Medical Center Of Evansville, Evansville, IN, p. A207

ELLISON, Keith, Chief Nursing Officer, Big Bend Regional Medical Center, Alpine, TX, p. A592

ELLISON, Laura, Chief Financial Officer, Bon Secours Baltimore Health System, Baltimore, MD, p. A294

ELLISON, Mike, Information Systems Lead, Summersville Regional Medical Center, Summersville, WV, p. A696

ELLISON, Patricia, Chief Financial Officer, Streamwood Behavioral Health Center, Streamwood, IL, p. A201

ELLSWORTH, Anthon, Director Information Technology, Mt. Graham Regional Medical Center, Safford, AZ, p. A35

ELLWANGER, Dina R.N., Chief Nursing Officer, Saint Alphonsus Medical Center – Ontario, Ontario, OR, p. A524

ELLZEY, Bob S., FACHE, President, Texas Health Harris Methodist Hospital Azle, Azle, TX, p. A596

ELMER, Paula R.N., MSN, Vice President and Chief Nursing Officer, Monroe Clinic, Monroe, WI, p. A708

ELMORE, Kevin, Chief Information Officer, Covenant Hospital–Levelland, Levelland, TX, p. A629

ELMORE, Nadine, Chief Executive Officer, Dahl Memorial Healthcare Association, Ekalaka, MT, p. A384

ELMORE, Trent, Director Human Resources, Springs Memorial Hospital, Lancaster, SC, p. A564

ELROD, Emily R.N., Director of Nursing, Saint Thomas Stones River Hospital, Woodbury, TN, p. A590

ELROD, James K., FACHE, Chief Executive Officer, Willis-Knighton Medical Center, Shreveport, LA, p. A286

ELROD, Keri, Administrator, Willis–Knighton Medical Center, Shreveport, LA, p. A286

ELROD, Sonya, Chief Nursing Officer, Elbert Memorial Hospital, Elberton, GA, p. A157

ELS, Veronica, Chief Nursing Officer, Lafayette General Surgical Hospital, Lafayette, LA, p. A278

ELSBERRY, Kevin, Senior Vice President Human Resources, Mercy Medical Center–Des Moines, Des Moines, IA, p. A226

ELSBREE, Heidi, Vice President People and Culture, Mercyhealth Hospital – Rockton Avenue, Rockford, IL, p. A199

ELSE, Ryan M.D., Vice President Medical Affairs, Mercy Hospital, Coon Rapids, MN, p. A338

ELSESSER, William, Chief Executive Officer, Tomball Regional Medical Center, Tomball, TX, p. A650

ELSWICK, Beth, Administrative Assistant, Summers County Arh Hospital, Hinton, WV, p. A692

ELWELL, Richard, Senior Vice President and Chief Financial Officer, Elliot Hospital, Manchester, NH, p. A448

ELWELL, Russell M.D., Medical Director, Westfield Memorial Hospital, Westfield, NY, p. A456

ELY, Thomas L D.O., Chief Medical Officer, Tennova Healthcare–Clarksville, Clarksville, TN, p. A577

EMAMGHORAISHI, Anna, Human Resources, Midwest City Specialty Hospital, Midwest City, OK, p. A510

EMANUEL, Kate, Director Human Resources, Clarke County Hospital, Osceola, IA, p. A233

EMBREE, Steve, Chief Financial Officer, Up Health System–Marquette, Marquette, MI, p. A326

EMBREY, Jeffrey M.D., Chief Medical Officer, Baylor Scott & White Medical Center–Irving, Irving, TX, p. A624

EMBREY, Richard M.D., Chief Medical Officer, Augusta Health, Fishersville, VA, p. A667

EMBURY, Stuart M.D., Chief Medical Officer, Phelps Memorial Health Center, Holdrege, NE, p. A394

EMDUR, Larry, D.O.
  Chief Medical Officer, Alvarado Hospital Medical Center, San Diego, CA, p. A85
  Chief of Staff, Promise Hospital Of San Diego, San Diego, CA, p. A85

EMEOTT, Sandra R.N., Chief Nursing Officer, Northwest Medical Center, Margate, FL, p. A131

EMERICK, Ron M.D., Chief of Staff, Doctor's Memorial Hospital, Perry, FL, p. A139

EMERSON, Leah, Director of Nursing, St. Luke Community Healthcare, Ronan, MT, p. A387

EMERSON, Sherri Leigh, Chief Operating Officer, Texas Health Heart & Vascular Hospital Arlington, Arlington, TX, p. A593

EMERY, Andrew, Chief Executive Officer, Bayfront Health Punta Gorda, Punta Gorda, FL, p. A140

EMGE, Joann, Chief Executive Officer, Sparta Community Hospital, Sparta, IL, p. A200

EMIG, Laura, Director Marketing Operations, Healthsouth Rehabilitation Hospital Of York, York, PA, p. A555

EMMINGER, Dianne, Vice President Information Services, Acmh Hospital, Kittanning, PA, p. A537

EMMONS, Michelle, Associate Executive Director, NYC Health + Hospitals / Kings County, New Rochelle, NY, p. A445

EMON, Dee R.N., Chief Information Officer, Wake Forest Baptist Health–Lexington Medical Center, Lexington, NC, p. A466

EMPEDRAD, Globert, Chief Clinical Officer, Curahealth Tucson, Tucson, AZ, p. A37

EMPEY, Dennis
  Chief Financial Officer, Kenmare Community Hospital, Kenmare, ND, p. A477
  Chief Financial Officer, Trinity Health, Minot, ND, p. A477

ENCAPERA, Kimberly M.D., Medical Director, Rehabilitation Hospital Of Southern New Mexico, Las Cruces, NM, p. A427

ENCE, Michael, Computer Specialist, Sanpete Valley Hospital, Mount Pleasant, UT, p. A657

ENCKE, Faye, Director Information Management, Healthsouth Rehabilitation Hospital Of Virginia, Richmond, VA, p. A673

ENDEN, Jay M.D., Medical Director, Southside Hospital, Bay Shore, NY, p. A431

ENDERS, Robert A. Jr, President, Chatham Hospital, Siler City, NC, p. A470

ENDOM, Beth W R.N., MSN, Vice President and Chief Nursing Officer, South Central Regional Medical Center, Laurel, MS, p. A358

ENDRES, Jack A., FACHE, JD, Administrator, East Texas Medical Center Athens, Athens, TX, p. A594

ENG, Bland, Chief Executive Officer, Brandon Regional Hospital, Brandon, FL, p. A121

ENG, Jeffrey M.D., Medical Director, Healthsouth Rehabilitation Hospital Of Montgomery, Montgomery, AL, p. A21

ENGBRECHT, Chad, Chief Financial Officer, Alvarado Parkway Institute Behavioral Health System, La Mesa, CA, p. A64

ENGEL, David, Chief Executive Officer and Administrator, Southeast Colorado Hospital District, Springfield, CO, p. A107

ENGEL, Dawn M, Chief Nursing Officer, Geary Community Hospital, Junction City, KS, p. A243

ENGELKE, Brian, Chief Financial Officer, Community Hospital Of Staunton, Staunton, IL, p. A201

ENGESSER, Edward, Chief Financial Officer and Chief Information Officer, Barlow Respiratory Hospital, Los Angeles, CA, p. A67

ENGFEHR, Tricia A, Chief Human Resources, Selby General Hospital, Marietta, OH, p. A494

ENGLAND, Dave, Director Human Resources, Lakeland Behavioral Health System, Springfield, MO, p. A379

ENGLAND, Donna, Director Medical Records, Healthsouth Rehabilitation Hospital Of Fort Smith, Fort Smith, AR, p. A43

ENGLAND, Leslie, Chief of Staff, Merit Health Natchez, Natchez, MS, p. A359

ENGLAND, Mary Ann, Chief Nurse Executive, Wilcox Medical Center, Lihue, HI, p. A170

ENGLAND, Richard N, Chief Financial Officer, Palo Verde Behavioral Health, Tucson, AZ, p. A38

ENGLAND, Stacy, Community Chief Nursing Officer, Middlesboro Arh Hospital, Middlesboro, KY, p. A264

ENGLAND, Teresa R.N., Ph.D., Nurse Executive, Salem Veterans Affairs Medical Center, Salem, VA, p. A675

ENGLE, Dan, Chief Information Officer, Thayer County Health Services, Hebron, NE, p. A394

ENGLE, Dana E., Chief Executive Officer, Madison Health, London, OH, p. A494

ENGLE, Lisa, Director Information Technology, Texoma Medical Center, Denison, TX, p. A608

ENGLE, Sharon, Director Clinical Services, Noland Hospital Birmingham, Birmingham, AL, p. A15

ENGLE–RAMIREZ, Jeanette, Chief Executive Officer, Menlo Park Surgical Hospital, Menlo Park, CA, p. A73

ENGLEHART, Jay M.D., Medical Director, Southeast Missouri Mental Health Center, Farmington, MO, p. A368

ENGLEHART, Michael, President and Chief Executive Officer, Presence Health, Chicago, IL, p. B100

ENGLERT, William, Chief Executive Officer, Allegheny Valley Hospital, Natrona Heights, PA, p. A542

ENGLERTH, LaDonna, Administrator, East Carroll Parish Hospital, Lake Providence, LA, p. A279

ENGLISH, Anne L, Director Human Resources, Uhs Chenango Memorial Hospital, Norwich, NY, p. A448

ENGLISH, Brett, Chief Financial Officer, Mary Black Health System–Spartanburg, Spartanburg, SC, p. A566

ENGLISH, Dennis M.D., Vice President Medical Affairs, Magee–Womens Hospital Of Upmc, Pittsburgh, PA, p. A547

ENGLISH, Jeff
  Interim Chief Executive Officer, St. Mary's Sacred Heart Hospital, Lavonia, GA, p. A160
  Vice President Human Resources, St. Mary's Health Care System, Athens, GA, p. A149

ENGLISH, Julene, Director Human Resources, Kentfield Rehabilitation And Specialty Hospital, Kentfield, CA, p. A64

ENGLISH, Kathy L R.N., MSN, Executive Vice President and Chief Operating Officer, Children's Hospital And Medical Center, Omaha, NE, p. A397

ENGLISH, Laurie, Senior Vice President and Chief Human Resource Officer, Excela Latrobe Area Hospital, Latrobe, PA, p. A538

ENGSTROM, Chad P, Director Human Resources, Westfields Hospital, New Richmond, WI, p. A709

ENGSTROM, Frederick M.D., Chief Medical Officer, Brattleboro Retreat, Brattleboro, VT, p. A662

ENICKS, Charles, Chief Information Officer, Augusta University Medical Center, Augusta, GA, p. A151

ENJADY, Rainey, Administrative Officer, Mescalero Public Health Service Indian Hospital, Mescalero, NM, p. A427

ENNEN, Philip L.
President and Chief Executive Officer, Community Hospitals And Wellness Centers–Montpelier, Montpelier, OH, p. A496
Vice President and Chief Executive Officer, Community Hospitals And Wellness Centers, Bryan, OH, p. A482

ENNIS, Debra R.N., Vice President and Chief Nursing Officer, Texas Health Harris Methodist Hospital Southlake, Southlake, TX, p. A646

ENNIS, Virgil, Chief Information Officer, Helen Hayes Hospital, West Haverstraw, NY, p. A455

ENOCHS, Darren, Director Human Resources, Promise Hospital Of Overland Park, Overland Park, KS, p. A249

ENOKA, Christina, Director Human Resources and Risk Management, Kahi Mohala Behavioral Health, Ewa Beach, HI, p. A168

ENRICO–SIMON, Agnes M.D., President Medical Staff, Pleasant Valley Hospital, Point Pleasant, WV, p. A695

ENRIQUEZ, Kelly, Chief Executive Officer, Sebastian River Medical Center, Sebastian, FL, p. A142

ENSEY, Jeremy, Chief Executive Officer, St. Luke Hospital And Living Center, Marion, KS, p. A246

ENSLEY, Terrasina, Director Human Resources, Fannin Regional Hospital, Blue Ridge, GA, p. A152

ENSMINGER, Jennifer, Chief Operating Officer, College Medical Center, Long Beach, CA, p. A66

ENSRUDE, Layne, Chief Financial Officer, First Care Health Center, Park River, ND, p. A478

ENTIN, Ari, Chief Information Officer, Natividad Medical Center, Salinas, CA, p. A84

ENTLER, Paul D.O., Medical Director, Sparrow Specialty Hospital, Lansing, MI, p. A324

ENTWISTLE, David, President and Chief Executive Officer, Stanford Health Care, Palo Alto, CA, p. A79

ENTZMINGER, Julie, Manager Human Resources, Chi Oakes Hospital, Oakes, ND, p. A477

EOLOFF, Eric J., President, Mercy Hospital Washington, Washington, MO, p. A381

EPPERSON, Edward L., Chief Executive Officer, Carson Tahoe Health, Carson City, NV, p. A401

EPPERSON, Elysia, Director Human Resources, East Texas Medical Center Jacksonville, Jacksonville, TX, p. A625

EPPERSON, James, Interim Chief Nursing Officer, Grandview Medical Center, Birmingham, AL, p. A14

EPPERSON, Jeff, Chief Financial Officer, Millwood Hospital, Arlington, TX, p. A593

EPPLER, Todd, FACHE, Chief Executive Officer, De Soto Regional Health System, Mansfield, LA, p. A280

EPPLEY, Doug, Director of Nursing, Bridgewell Hospital Of Cincinnati, Cincinnati, OH, p. A483

EPPS, Donna
Vice President and Chief Human Resources Officer, Lawrence + Memorial Hospital, New London, CT, p. A112
Vice President, Chief Human Resource Officer, Westerly Hospital, Westerly, RI, p. A557

EPPS, Jerry M.D., Senior Vice President and Chief Medical Officer, University Of Tennessee Medical Center, Knoxville, TN, p. A582

EPPS, Michelle L. MSN, R.N., Chief Nursing Officer, Stonesprings Hospital Center, Dulles, VA, p. A666

EPSTEIN, Michael M.D., Senior Vice President Medical Affairs, Johns Hopkins All Children's Hospital, Saint Petersburg, FL, p. A141

ERDMAN, Beth, Chief Financial Officer, Unitypoint Health Meriter, Madison, WI, p. A705

ERDMAN, Donja, Chief Financial Officer, Marcus Daly Memorial Hospital, Hamilton, MT, p. A385

ERDMAN, John M.D., Chief of Staff, Cornerstone Medical Center, Fort Oglethorpe, GA, p. A158

ERDMANN, Michael M.D., Chief of Staff, Clement J. Zablocki Veterans Affairs Medical Center, Milwaukee, WI, p. A707

ERDOS, Joseph M.D., Chief Information Officer, Veterans Affairs Connecticut Healthcare System, West Haven, CT, p. A114

ERDRICH, Louis P., Acting Chief Executive Officer, U.S. Public Health Service Indian Hospital, Cass Lake, MN, p. A338

EREMAN, Melissa R.N., Chief Nursing Officer, Coleman County Medical Center, Coleman, TX, p. A602

ERGLE, Jeanine, Chief Financial Officer, Bay Pines Veterans Affairs Healthcare System, Bay Pines, FL, p. A119

ERICKSON, Ashley M., Chief Executive Officer, Sanford Aberdeen Medical Center, Aberdeen, SD, p. A568

ERICKSON, Bonnie, Chief Executive Officer, Rainy Lake Medical Center, International Falls, MN, p. A341

ERICKSON, Brent J., Administrator, Wright Patterson Medical Center, Wright, OH, p. A503

ERICKSON, Brent J, Administrator, Wright Patterson Medical Center, Wright, OH, p. A503

ERICKSON, Doug, Chief Financial Officer, Prague Community Hospital, Prague, OK, p. A515

ERICKSON, Jake, Chief Operating Officer, Bingham Memorial Hospital, Blackfoot, ID, p. A171

ERICKSON, Karyn, Director Human Resources, Delta Medical Center, Memphis, TN, p. A584

ERICKSON, Kerrie, Vice President of Finance, Stevens Community Medical Center, Morris, MN, p. A344

ERICKSON, Laura R.N., Chief Nursing Officer, Pondera Medical Center, Conrad, MT, p. A383

ERICKSON, Nancy
Administrator Information Systems, Kossuth Regional Health Center, Algona, IA, p. A222
Human Resource Director, Southern Inyo Healthcare District, Lone Pine, CA, p. A66

ERICKSON, Robert J., President, Presence Saint Joseph Medical Center, Joliet, IL, p. A191

ERICKSON, Vonnie, Human Resource Manager, Chippewa County–Montevideo Hospital, Montevideo, MN, p. A344

ERICSON, Allen
Chief Operating Officer, Community Hospital Division and President, St. Joseph's Hospital, Community Memorial Hospital, Menomonee Falls, WI, p. A706
Chief Operating Officer, Community Hospital Division and President, St. Joseph's Hospital, St. Joseph's Hospital, West Bend, WI, p. A715

ERICSON, Bob, Chief Financial Officer, Hemphill County Hospital, Canadian, TX, p. A600

ERICSON, Kim
Vice President Finance, Fairview Lakes Health Services, Wyoming, MN, p. A351
Vice President Finance, Fairview Northland Medical Center, Princeton, MN, p. A346

ERIXON, Stephen M, Chief Executive Officer, Sagewest Health Care At Riverton, Riverton, WY, p. A719

ERKEN, Carole L, Human Resources Leader, Kaiser Permanente Panorama City Medical Center, Los Angeles, CA, p. A68

ERLBACHER, David M.D., Chief of Staff, Myrtue Medical Center, Harlan, IA, p. A229

ERLING, Brian, Group Chief Medical Officer, St. Anthony Hospital, Lakewood, CO, p. A105

ERMANN, William, President and Chief Executive Officer, Southwest Medical Center, Liberal, KS, p. A246

ERTEL, David, Chief Financial Officer, Einstein Medical Center Montgomery, East Norriton, PA, p. A533

ERTEL, Matthew, Chief Financial Officer, Gibson Area Hospital And Health Services, Gibson City, IL, p. A188

ERUKHIMOU, Jeffrey M.D., Medical Director, Curahealth Heritage Valley, Beaver, PA, p. A529

ERVIN, Fulton
Chief Financial Officer, Mcleod Regional Medical Center, Florence, SC, p. A562
Senior Vice President and Chief Financial Officer, Mcleod Medical Center Dillon, Dillon, SC, p. A561

ERVIN, Joan, Administrator, Mcleod Medical Center Dillon, Dillon, SC, p. A561

ERVIN, Paul D, Chief Financial Officer, Valley Behavioral Health System, Barling, AR, p. A40

ERVIN, Richard, Chief Financial Officer, Tomball Regional Medical Center, Tomball, TX, p. A650

ERVING–MENGEL, Tammi R.N., MSN, Vice President, Chief Nursing Officer, High Point Regional Health System, High Point, NC, p. A464

ERWAY, Robert, Director for Administration, Bronx Psychiatric Center, New Rochelle, NY, p. A440

ERWIN, Connie, Manager, Samaritan Lebanon Community Hospital, Lebanon, OR, p. A523

ESCARDA, Ron, Chief Executive Officer, Fairfax Behavioral Health, Kirkland, WA, p. A681

ESCHENBRENNER, Wade, Chief Financial Officer, Lexington Regional Health Center, Lexington, NE, p. A394

ESHLEMAN, James D.O., President Medical Staff, Stephens Memorial Hospital, Norway, ME, p. A292

ESKER, Jerry, President and Chief Executive Officer, Sarah Bush Lincoln Health Center, Mattoon, IL, p. A193

ESLAVA, Lee, Chief Medical Officer, South Baldwin Regional Medical Center, Foley, AL, p. A18

ESLINGER, Jennifer, President, Mobile Infirmary Medical Center, Mobile, AL, p. A20

ESPARZA, Becky, Human Resources, Crane Memorial Hospital, Crane, TX, p. A604

ESPARZA, Caroline
Senior Vice President, Chief Operating Officer and Chief Nurse Officer, Simi Valley Hospital, Simi Valley, CA, p. A92
Sr. VP, COO & CNO, Simi Valley Hospital, Simi Valley, CA, p. A92

ESPELAND, Darryl, D.O.
Chief Medical Staff, Fallon Medical Complex, Baker, MT, p. A382
Medical Director, Dahl Memorial Healthcare Association, Ekalaka, MT, p. A384

ESPELAND, David, Chief Executive Officer, Fallon Medical Complex, Baker, MT, p. A382

ESPINA, Francisco, Director Finance, Hospital Pavia–Santurce, San Juan, PR, p. A726

ESPINOZA, John, Chief Human Resources Officer, University Medical Center, Las Vegas, NV, p. A404

ESPINOZA, Judy, Chief Human Resources Officer, Via Christi Hospital On St. Francis, Wichita, KS, p. A254

ESPINOZA, Richard, Chief Administrative Officer, Highland Hospital, Oakland, CA, p. A77

ESPIRITU, DoreeAnn V., M.D., Interim Chair, Behavioral Health Services, Henry Ford Kingswood Hospital, Ferndale, MI, p. A319

ESPOSITO, Mary H, Assistant Executive Director, Devereux Georgia Treatment Network, Kennesaw, GA, p. A160

ESPOSITO, Pamela, Director Administration, Buffalo Psychiatric Center, Buffalo, NY, p. A432

ESPY, Christine, Division Director, Mid–Columbia Medical Center, The Dalles, OR, p. A527

ESROCK, Brett A., FACHE, Chief Executive Officer, Health First Holmes Regional Medical Center, Melbourne, FL, p. A132

ESSELMAN, Charlotte, Director Finance, Ministry Saint Clare's Hospital, Weston, WI, p. A715

ESSENPREIS, Helen MSN, R.N., Chief Nursing Officer, Hshs St. Joseph's Hospital, Breese, IL, p. A179

ESSEX, Jeshahnton, Vice President of Administration, Riddle Hospital, Media, PA, p. A541

ESSMYER, Dale M.D., Chief of Staff, Sullivan County Memorial Hospital, Milan, MO, p. A373

ESTAY, Mike, Chief Financial Officer, Hood Memorial Hospital, Amite, LA, p. A270

ESTES, Barbara M.D., Chief of Staff, Calvert Memorial Hospital, Prince Frederick, MD, p. A300

ESTES, Benton D, Materials Management, Baptist Medical Center Yazoo, Yazoo City, MS, p. A363

ESTES, Melinda, M.D., President and Chief Executive Officer, Saint Luke'S Health System, Kansas City, MO, p. B111

ESTES, Michael, Director Human Resources, University Of Mississippi Medical Center, Jackson, MS, p. A357

ESTES, Stephen A., Chief Executive Officer, Rockcastle Regional Hospital And Respiratory Care Center, Mount Vernon, KY, p. A265

ESTEVEZ, Aurora M.D., Chief Medical Officer, Texas Health Presbyterian Hospital Dallas, Dallas, TX, p. A607

ESTEVEZ, Mercy, Administrator, Port St. Lucie Hospital, Port St. Lucie, FL, p. A140

ESTRADA, Luis, Director Multifacility Information Systems, North Shore Medical Center, Miami, FL, p. A133

ESTRADA, Marina, Director Human Resources, El Paso Children's Hospital, El Paso, TX, p. A610

ESTRELLA, Mario B, Chief Nursing Officer, Nacogdoches Medical Center, Nacogdoches, TX, p. A634

ETCHASON, Barbara, HR Manager, West Gables Rehabilitation Hospital, Miami, FL, p. A134

ETCITTY, Ronnye, Director Human Resources, Rehoboth Mckinley Christian Health Care Services, Gallup, NM, p. A426

ETHERIDGE, Darold, Vice President and Chief Financial Officer, Wellstar Cobb Hospital, Austell, GA, p. A152

ETHERINGTON, Betty, Chief Financial Officer, Humboldt County Memorial Hospital, Humboldt, IA, p. A229

ETHERINGTON, Rosalie, Superintendent and Chief Executive Officer, North Dakota State Hospital, Jamestown, ND, p. A477

ETHRIDGE, Sandy, Interim Chief Operating Officer, Baptist Medical Center, San Antonio, TX, p. A642

ETTER, Carl J., Chief Executive and Senior Vice President, Scripps Memorial Hospital–Encinitas, Encinitas, CA, p. A58

ETTESTAD, Donita R.N., MS, Chief Nursing Officer, Rainy Lake Medical Center, International Falls, MN, p. A341

ETZEL, Glen T. M.D., Chief of Staff, Castleview Hospital, Price, UT, p. A659

EUBANKS, Bill, Senior Vice President and Chief Information Officer, University Medical Center, Lubbock, TX, p. A631

EUBANKS, Susan, Chief Nursing Officer, Page Hospital, Page, AZ, p. A32

EULER, Barbara, Director Human Resources, Tennova Healthcare Regional Hospital Of Jackson, Jackson, TN, p. A580

EULIARTE, Mary Ann, R.N.
Chief Nursing Officer, Memorial Hermann Rehabilitation Hospital – Katy, Katy, TX, p. A626
Chief Operating Officer and Chief Nursing Officer, Tirr Memorial Hermann, Houston, TX, p. A623
Chief Operating Officer, Memorial Hermann Rehabilitation Hospital – Katy, Katy, TX, p. A626

EURE, Thomas, Vice President Administration, Carolinas Healthcare System Blue Ridge, Morganton, NC, p. A467

EUSEBIO, Barbara R.N., JD, Vice President, Chief Nurse Executive, St. Mary's Medical Center, San Francisco, CA, p. A88

EUSTACE, Scott, Director Health Information Technology, Trenton Psychiatric Hospital, Trenton, NJ, p. A422

EVANCHO, Timothy R., Chief Financial Officer, Southeastern Ohio Regional Medical Center, Cambridge, OH, p. A482

EVANDER, Justin N.
Administrator and Chief Operating Officer, Kaiser Sunnyside Medical Center, Clackamas, OR, p. A520
Chief Financial Officer, Kaiser Sunnyside Medical Center, Clackamas, OR, p. A520

EVANOFF, John M.D., Vice President Medical Affairs, Promedica Flower Hospital, Sylvania, OH, p. A500

EVANS, Ann, Chief Nursing Officer, Healthsouth Huntington Rehabilitation Hospital, Huntington, WV, p. A692

EVANS, Arthur D., Chief Executive Officer and Administrator, Bryan W. Whitfield Memorial Hospital, Demopolis, AL, p. A16

EVANS, Bonnie, Chief Executive Officer, Kessler Institute For Rehabilitation, West Orange, NJ, p. A422

EVANS, Brian G., FACHE, Chief Executive Officer, Clarke County Hospital, Osceola, IA, p. A233

EVANS, Brian
Chief of Medicine, Sierra Nevada Memorial Hospital, Grass Valley, CA, p. A62
Chief Information Officer, Milford Hospital, Milford, CT, p. A111

EVANS, Chris, Vice President Operations, Chi Health Creighton University Medical Center – Bergan Mercy, Omaha, NE, p. A397

EVANS, Cindy R.N., MS, Chief Nursing Officer, Legacy Good Samaritan Medical Center, Portland, OR, p. A525

EVANS, Dave, Chief Financial Officer, Community Hospital Of San Bernardino, San Bernardino, CA, p. A85

EVANS, Dawn, Manager Information Technology, SSM Health St. Mary's Hospital – Audrain, Mexico, MO, p. A373

EVANS, Dwight M.D., Chief of Staff, Veterans Affairs Loma Linda Healthcare System, Loma Linda, CA, p. A66

EVANS, Eric, Chief Executive Officer, Bayshore Medical Center, Pasadena, TX, p. A636

EVANS, George, Vice President and Chief Information Officer, Candler Hospital, Savannah, GA, p. A164

EVANS, Janice, Chief Financial Officer, John J. Madden Mental Health Center, Hines, IL, p. A190

EVANS, Jeff W., Vice President Information and Technology, Hannibal Regional Hospital, Hannibal, MO, p. A368

EVANS, Jeremy, Vice President Operations, Kootenai Health, Coeur D'Alene, ID, p. A173

EVANS, Kelley, Chief Administrative Officer, Beartooth Billings Clinic, Red Lodge, MT, p. A387

EVANS, Kirstie, Chief Financial Officer, Covington County Hospital, Collins, MS, p. A354

EVANS, Lola, Director of Nursing, Oakland Regional Hospital, Southfield, MI, p. A331

EVANS, Lorrie, Director Human Resources, Laurel Oaks Behavioral Health Center, Dothan, AL, p. A17

EVANS, Manuel J, Senior Vice President Finance and Chief Financial Officer, Geisinger Holy Spirit, Camp Hill, PA, p. A530

EVANS, Melinda S
Vice President Finance, Saint Joseph East, Lexington, KY, p. A261
Vice President Finance, Saint Joseph Hospital, Lexington, KY, p. A261

EVANS, Michael C., Chief Executive Officer and Deputy Director of Finance and Administration, Santa Barbara County Psychiatric Health Facility, Santa Barbara, CA, p. A90

EVANS, Robert B., FACHE, Administrator and Chief Executive Officer, East Texas Medical Center Tyler, Tyler, TX, p. A651

EVANS, Rod, Chief Information Officer, Community Healthcare System, Onaga, KS, p. A248

FVANS, Ronald A. M.D., Chief Medical Officer, Citizens Memorial Hospital, Bolivar, MO, p. A364

EVANS, S Lagina, R.N.
Assistant Chief Nursing Officer, Optim Medical Center – Jenkins, Millen, GA, p. A162
Assistant Chief Nursing Officer, Optim Medical Center – Screven, Sylvania, GA, p. A165

EVANS, Sam, Chief Human Resources Management, G.V. (Sonny) Montgomery Veterans Affairs Medical Center, Jackson, MS, p. A356

EVANS, Scott, PharmD, FACHE, Senior Vice President and Chief Executive Officer, Sharp Grossmont Hospital, La Mesa, CA, p. A64

EVANS, Susan, Chief Nursing Officer, Old Vineyard Behavioral Health Services, Winston, NC, p. A473

EVANS, Tim, Assistant Financial Director, Devereux Children's Behavioral Health Center, Malvern, PA, p. A539

EVANS, Timothy, Vice President and Chief Financial Officer, Self Regional Healthcare, Greenwood, SC, p. A563

EVANS–HARRISON, Martina R.N., MSN, Chief Nurse Executive, Methodist Hospital Of Sacramento, Sacramento, CA, p. A83

EVE, John, Vice President Human Resources and Education, Wilson Memorial Hospital, Sidney, OH, p. A499

EVELIUS, Karen, Director Human Resources, Medstar Harbor Hospital, Baltimore, MD, p. A295

EVELYN, David M M.D., Vice President Medical Affairs, Cayuga Medical Center At Ithaca, Ithaca, NY, p. A437

EVENS, James, Executive Director, Human Resources and General Services, Cole Memorial, Coudersport, PA, p. A532

EVENS, Richard R., Chief Executive Officer, Healthsouth Northern Kentucky Rehabilitation Hospital, Edgewood, KY, p. A257

EVENS, Tamara, Director Human Resources, Moses Ludington Hospital, Ticonderoga, NY, p. A454

EVENSON, Margie, Manager Human Resources, Osceola Medical Center, Osceola, WI, p. A710

EVERDING, Dawn, Chief Financial Officer, Community Memorial Hospital, Sumner, IA, p. A235

EVERETT, John, Chief Financial Officer, Cogdell Memorial Hospital, Snyder, TX, p. A646

EVERETT, Leianne, Chief Executive Officer, Morton General Hospital, Morton, WA, p. A682

EVERETT, Michael, Chief Executive Officer, Scott Memorial Hospital, Scottsburg, IN, p. A219

EVERETT, Neil, Vice President Human Resources, Uh Portage Medical Center, Ravenna, OH, p. A498

EVERHART, Martin S, Senior Vice President Human Resources, Robert Wood Johnson University Hospital, New Brunswick, NJ, p. A417

EVERLY, Nanette, Manager Human Resources and Administrative Assistant, Jefferson County Health Center, Fairfield, IA, p. A227

EVERS, Andrea, Director Information Technology, Haxtun Hospital District, Haxtun, CO, p. A104

EVERS, Anthony, Chief Financial Officer, Katherine Shaw Bethea Hospital, Dixon, IL, p. A185

EVERS–MANLY, Shirley, Chief Nursing Officer, Howard University Hospital, Washington, DC, p. A117

EVERSOLE, Matt, Regional Vice President Information Services, Mercy Health – Anderson Hospital, Cincinnati, OH, p. A484

EVERT, Barbara, M.D.
Vice President Medical Affairs, Ohiohealth Dublin Methodist Hospital, Dublin, OH, p. A490
Vice President Medical Affairs, Ohiohealth Grady Memorial Hospital, Delaware, OH, p. A490

EVINS, Starling C M.D., Chief of Staff, Williamson Medical Center, Franklin, TN, p. A579

EVISCHI, Deland
Chief Financial Officer, SSM Health St. Mary's Hospital Centralia, Centralia, IL, p. A179
Regional Chief Financial Officer, Southern Illinois, Good Samaritan Regional Health Center, Mount Vernon, IL, p. A194

EVOLGA, Nancy K, Director Human Resources, Florida Hospital New Smyrna, New Smyrna Beach, FL, p. A135

EWALD, Luanne T., Interim Chief Executive Officer, DMC – Children's Hospital Of Michigan, Detroit, MI, p. A317

EWALD, Ronald, Chief Financial Officer, Inova Fairfax Hospital, Falls Church, VA, p. A666

EWALD, Sandra
President (Green Bay/Manitowoc Market), Aurora Medical Center – Manitowoc County, Two Rivers, WI, p. A714
Vice President Finance, Aurora Medical Center Of Oshkosh, Oshkosh, WI, p. A710

EWELL, Dorene L, Director Human Resources and Education, Harrisburg Medical Center, Harrisburg, IL, p. A189

EWELL, Sandy, Chief Nursing Officer, Timpanogos Regional Hospital, Orem, UT, p. A658

EWING, Brenda, Chief Nursing Officer, Firsthealth Moore Regional Hospital – Hamlet, Hamlet, NC, p. A464

EWING, Catherine M.D., Chief Nursing Officer, Baylor Institute For Rehabilitation At Fort Worth, Fort Worth, TX, p. A613

EWING, Chandler, Chief Executive Officer, Select Specialty Hospital–Jackson, Jackson, MS, p. A357

EWING, Corey, Chief Executive Officer, Gadsden Regional Medical Center, Gadsden, AL, p. A18

EWING, Steven, Interim Chief Executive Officer, San Angelo Community Medical Center, San Angelo, TX, p. B36

EWING, Thomas
Director Information Technology, Sentara Careplex Hospital, Hampton, VA, p. A668
Director Information Technology, Sentara Northern Virginia Medical Center, Woodbridge, VA, p. A677

EXLINE, Michael
Chief Financial Officer, Carrus Rehabilitation Hospital, Sherman, TX, p. A645
Chief Financial Officer, Carrus Specialty Hospital, Sherman, TX, p. A645

EYE, Jeffrey L R.N., Vice President Patient Care Services, Murray–Calloway County Hospital, Murray, KY, p. A265

EYLER, Sandra, MS
Chief Nursing Officer, Sheltering Arms Hospital South, Midlothian, VA, p. A670
Chief Nursing Officer, Sheltering Arms Rehabilitation Hospital, Mechanicsville, VA, p. A670

EZZIE, Michael, Director of Medical Education and Interim Vice President of Medical Affairs, Ohiohealth Grant Medical Center, Columbus, OH, p. A487

F

FAAS, Michael D., President and Chief Executive Officer, Metro Health Hospital, Wyoming, MI, p. A333

FABER, Chris, Human Resources Analyst, Stanford Health Care – Valleycare, Pleasanton, CA, p. A80

FABER, Tammy, Director Human Resources, Hegg Memorial Health Center Avera, Rock Valley, IA, p. A234

FABIAN, Alan J., Chief Executive Officer, Lewisgale Hospital Montgomery, Blacksburg, VA, p. A665

FABIAN, Roxanne, Director of Nursing–Acute Care, Lifecare Medical Center, Roseau, MN, p. A347

FABIANO, Tom, Director Human Resources, Mount Auburn Hospital, Cambridge, MA, p. A305

FABIN, Peggy, Director Human Resources, Phillips County Hospital, Phillipsburg, KS, p. A250

FABRICK, Peter, Vice President Clinical Operations, Mountain View Hospital, Idaho Falls, ID, p. A173

FABRY, Joseph D.O., Chief of Staff, Sutter Maternity And Surgery Center Of Santa Cruz, Santa Cruz, CA, p. A91

FACKRELL, Sherlyn, Finance Controller, Grover C. Dils Medical Center, Caliente, NV, p. A401

FACTEAU, Patrick M, Chief Financial Officer, Massena Memorial Hospital, Massena, NY, p. A439

FADALE, Sean, President and Chief Executive Officer, Community Memorial Hospital, Hamilton, NY, p. A437

FADLER, Jeannie R.N., Vice President Patient Care Services, Saint Francis Medical Center, Cape Girardeau, MO, p. A365

FAGAN, Erin, Manager Human Resources, George Washington University Hospital, Washington, DC, p. A117

FAGAN, Mary MSN, R.N., Chief Nursing Officer, Rady Children's Hospital – San Diego, San Diego, CA, p. A85

FAGAN, Michael
Chief Financial Officer, Huntington Hospital, Huntington, NY, p. A437
Senior Vice President Finance, New York–Presbyterian Brooklyn Methodist Hospital, New Rochelle, NY, p. A444

FAGBONGBE, Eniola M.D., Chief Medical Staff, Grove Hill Memorial Hospital, Grove Hill, AL, p. A19

FAGERBERG, Lesley, Vice President Fiscal Services, Heart Of The Rockies Regional Medical Center, Salida, CO, p. A107

FAGERSTROM, Joel, Executive Vice President and Chief Operating Officer, St. Luke's Hospital – Miners Campus, Coaldale, PA, p. A531

FAGG, Cindy, Fiscal Officer, Battle Mountain General Hospital, Battle Mountain, NV, p. A401

FAHERTY, Jay W., Chief Executive Officer, Tallahassee Memorial Healthcare, Tallahassee, FL, p. A144

FAHEY, Dana, Manager Management Information Systems, Santa Barbara County Psychiatric Health Facility, Santa Barbara, CA, p. A90

FAHEY, Linda L R.N., Chief Nurse Executive, Decatur Memorial Hospital, Decatur, IL, p. A185

FAHEY, Patrick, M.D.
Chief Medical Director, Rml Specialty Hospital, Chicago, IL, p. A183
Chief Medical Officer, Rml Specialty Hospital, Hinsdale, IL, p. A190

FAHEY, Stephen P., Executive Director, Sierra Tucson, Tucson, AZ, p. A38

FAHEY, Stephen P, Executive Director, Sierra Tucson, Tucson, AZ, p. A38

FAHEY, Walter, Chief Information Officer, Maimonides Medical Center, New Rochelle, NY, p. A442

FAILE, J Gene., Chief Executive Officer and President, Wake Forest Baptist Health – Wilkes Medical Center, North Wilkesboro, NC, p. A468

FAILLA, Richard, Chief Executive Officer, Red Rock Behavioral Hospital, Las Vegas, NV, p. A403

FAIN, Marilyn R.N., MSN, Chief Operating Officer, Banner Fort Collins Medical Center, Fort Collins, CO, p. A102

FAIN, Nona Ph.D., R.N., Director of Nursing, Belmont Behavioral Hospital, Philadelphia, PA, p. A543

FAIRBANKS, Bruce, Vice President and Chief Financial Officer, Southeast Hospital, Cape Girardeau, MO, p. A366

FAIRBANKS, Trish R.N., Associate Vice President and Chief Nursing Officer, Linden Oaks Hospital, Naperville, IL, p. A195

FAIRCHILD, David M.D., Chief Medical Officer, Tufts Medical Center, Boston, MA, p. A304

FAIRCHILDS, Constance R.N., Vice President Patient Care Services, Emanuel Medical Center, Turlock, CA, p. A94

FAIRCLOTH, Karen, Chief Financial Officer, Memorial Hospital And Manor, Bainbridge, GA, p. A152

FAIRFAX, Tom, Director Information Systems, Bothwell Regional Health Center, Sedalia, MO, p. A379

FAIRFAX, Walter M.D., Chief Medical Officer, Kootenai Health, Coeur D'Alene, ID, p. A173

FAIRLEY, Dawn Ann M.D., Chief of Staff, Putnam County Memorial Hospital, Unionville, MO, p. A380

FAIRLEY, Susan, Chief Nursing Officer, Barton Memorial Hospital, South Lake Tahoe, CA, p. A92

FAISAL, Mohammad, President Medical Staff, Shands Lake Shore Regional Medical Center, Lake City, FL, p. A130

FALCON, Hugo M.D., Director Medical Services, Piedmont Geriatric Hospital, Burkeville, VA, p. A665

FALCONE, Lynn, Chief Executive Officer, Cuero Community Hospital, Cuero, TX, p. A604

FALGOUT, Charlene, Chief Nursing Officer, St. Francis Hospital, Columbus, GA, p. A155

FALIVENA, Richard D.O., M.P.H., Vice President and Chief Medical Officer, Saratoga Hospital, Saratoga Springs, NY, p. A452

FALK, Chelsie, Chief Nursing Officer, Sanford Wheaton Medical Center, Wheaton, MN, p. A350

FALKENBERRY, Jody, Director Information Systems, Monroe County Hospital, Monroeville, AL, p. A21

FALL, J Mark., Chief Executive Officer, Carelink Of Jackson, Jackson, MI, p. A323

FALLEN, Barbara, FACHE, Director, Veterans Affairs Loma Linda Healthcare System, Loma Linda, CA, p. A66

FALLIS, Susan, Chief Nursing Officer, Buffalo Psychiatric Center, Buffalo, NY, p. A432

FALLON, Angela, Acting Chief Executive Officer, U.S. Public Health Service Indian Hospital–Sells, Sells, AZ, p. A36

FALLON, Jeanne M.
Chief Information Officer, Falmouth Hospital, Falmouth, MA, p. A306
Senior Vice President and Chief Information Officer, Cape Cod Hospital, Hyannis, MA, p. A307

FALLON, L J JD, Executive Vice President, Chief Legal and Human Resources Officer, Carle Foundation Hospital, Urbana, IL, p. A201

FALSETTI, Domonic F M.D., Chief of Staff and Medical Director, Mount St. Mary's Hospital And Health Center, Lewiston, NY, p. A438

FALTERMAN, James B M.D., Jr, Medical Director, University Hospital And Clinics, Lafayette, LA, p. A283

FAMMARTINO, Gary, Administrator, St. Vincent Fishers Hospital, Fishers, IN, p. A207

FANALE, Linda, Chief Financial Officer, Conemaugh Miners Medical Center, Hastings, PA, p. A536

FANNIN, Allyson, Human Resources Officer, Lasalle General Hospital, Jena, LA, p. A276

FANNIN, Pam, Coordinator Human Resources, Lifecare Hospital Of Dayton, Miamisburg, OH, p. A495

FANNING, Melinda, Chief Financial Officer and Controller, Healthsouth Southern Hills Rehabilitation Hospital, Princeton, WV, p. A695

FANNING, Teresa E, Director of Patient Care, Avera Hand County Memorial Hospital, Miller, SD, p. A571

FANNON, Susan, Chief Nursing Officer, Indian Path Medical Center, Kingsport, TN, p. A581

FANSLER, Janet R.N., Executive Vice President and Chief Nurse Executive, Lakeland Regional Health, Lakeland, FL, p. A130

FANTANO, Gene, Chief Financial Officer, Aurora Behavioral Healthcare San Diego, San Diego, CA, p. A85

FARAH, Tony M.D., President Medical Staff, Allegheny General Hospital, Pittsburgh, PA, p. A546

FARBER, Bobbi M.D., Chief Medical Officer, St. Francis Hospital, Columbus, GA, p. A155

FARBER, Nancy D., Chief Executive Officer, Washington Hospital Healthcare System, Fremont, CA, p. A60

FARBER, Niceta, Chief Executive Officer, Sheridan County Health Complex, Hoxie, KS, p. A243

FARBER, Stephen D., Chief Financial Officer, Kindred Hospital–New Jersey Morris County, Dover, NJ, p. A413

FARELL, Clay, Chief Operation Officer, Los Alamitos Medical Center, Los Alamitos, CA, p. A67

FARGASON, Crayton A M.D., Medical Director, Children's Of Alabama, Birmingham, AL, p. A14

FARGUSON, Jack, Director Information Technology, TMC Bonham Hospital, Bonham, TX, p. A598

FARIA, Mary, FACHE, Ph.D., Vice President and Chief Operating Officer, Seton Southwest Hospital, Austin, TX, p. A595

FARINA, Albert M
Chief Financial Officer, Montefiore Mount Vernon, Mount Vernon, NY, p. A440
Senior Vice President and Chief Financial Officer, Montefiore New Rochelle, New Rochelle, NY, p. A440

FARINA, Jonathan, Chief Information Officer, Brattleboro Memorial Hospital, Brattleboro, VT, p. A662

FARISH, Audra, Vice President Human Resources, Emory Saint Joseph's Hospital Of Atlanta, Atlanta, GA, p. A150

FARKAS, Laura, Director Human Resources, Fairview Hospital, Great Barrington, MA, p. A307

FARLEY, Chris, Interim Chief Executive Officer and Managing Director, Willow Springs Center, Reno, NV, p. A405

FARMER, Carlos R.N., Director Clinical Operations, RMC Jacksonville, Jacksonville, AL, p. A19

FARMER, Kathleen, Assistant Administrator Finance and Chief Financial Officer, El Centro Regional Medical Center, El Centro, CA, p. A58

FARMER, Pat, Coordinator Human Resources and Safety Officer, Institute For Orthopaedic Surgery, Lima, OH, p. A493

FARMER, William M.D., Chief of Staff, Evergreen Medical Center, Evergreen, AL, p. A17

FARNHAM, Diane, Acting Director Human Resources, Lallie Kemp Medical Center, Independence, LA, p. A276

FARNHAM, Krista, Chief Operating Officer, Providence Portland Medical Center, Portland, OR, p. A525

FARO, Joan M.D., Chief Medical Officer, John T. Mather Memorial Hospital, Port Jefferson, NY, p. A450

FARR, Lorraine, Manager Human Resources, Georgia Regional Hospital At Atlanta, Decatur, GA, p. A156

FARR, Ronald, Chief Financial Officer, Jewish Hospital, Louisville, KY, p. A262

FARR, William L M.D., Chief Medical Officer, University Hospital, Augusta, GA, p. A152

FARRAGE, Jim M.D., Medical Director, Southern Kentucky Rehabilitation Hospital, Bowling Green, KY, p. A256

FARRAND, Cynthia B, President, Moses H. Cone Memorial Hospital, Greensboro, NC, p. A463

FARRAUTO, Joseph, Director Human Resources, Eastern Niagara Hospital, Lockport, NY, p. A438

FARRELL, America S., FACHE, Chief Executive Officer, College Station Medical Center, College Station, TX, p. A602

FARRELL, Brenda, Vice President Finance, Brookhaven Memorial Hospital Medical Center, Patchogue, NY, p. A449

FARRELL, Coleen M, Vice President Human Resources, Mid Coast Hospital, Brunswick, ME, p. A290

FARRELL, Darin, Administrator, Arbuckle Memorial Hospital, Sulphur, OK, p. A516

FARRELL, George, M.D.
Chief Medical Officer, Clinch Valley Medical Center, Richlands, VA, p. A673
Chief of Staff, Wythe County Community Hospital, Wytheville, VA, p. A677

FARRELL, Katie, Chief Operating Officer, Abington–Lansdale Hospital Jefferson Health, Lansdale, PA, p. A538

FARRELL, Roy M.D., Chief Medical Officer, Carondelet Holy Cross Hospital, Nogales, AZ, p. A32

FARRELL, Steven E M.D., Chief Medical Officer, Forrest General Hospital, Hattiesburg, MS, p. A355

FARRELL, Terence, Vice President and Administrator, Herrin Hospital, Herrin, IL, p. A189

FARRELL, Teresa, Chief Human Resources Officer, Nacogdoches Medical Center, Nacogdoches, TX, p. A634

FARRELL, Timothy, Executive Director, St. Lawrence Psychiatric Center, Ogdensburg, NY, p. A448

FARRELLY, Irene, Vice President and Chief Information Officer, Brooklyn Hospital Center, New Rochelle, NY, p. A441

FARRINGTON, Robyn, Chief Nursing Officer, Broward Health Medical Center, Fort Lauderdale, FL, p. A124

FARRIS, James R. FACHE, Chief Executive Officer, Union County Hospital, Anna, IL, p. A177

FARRIS, Jason, Chief Nursing Officer, Midwest City Specialty Hospital, Midwest City, OK, p. A510

FARRISH, John, Health Information Director, University Of Mississippi Medical Center Grenada, Grenada, MS, p. A355

FARROW, Diane, Manager Information Technology and Systems, Willamette Valley Medical Center, Mcminnville, OR, p. A523

FARRUGIA, Gianrico, M.D., Vice President and Chief Executive Officer, Mayo Clinic Jacksonville, Jacksonville, FL, p. A128

FARSHAO, Nosratian M.D., Chief Medical Staff, Memorial Hospital Of Gardena, Gardena, CA, p. A61

FARUGIA, Celeste R.N., MSN, Chief Nurse Executive, Kaiser Permanente Panorama City Medical Center, Los Angeles, CA, p. A68

FARWELL, Brenda
Director Human Resources, Providence Medical Center, Kansas City, KS, p. A244
Director Human Resources, Saint John Hospital, Leavenworth, KS, p. A245

FASANO, Philip, Chief Information Officer, Kaiser Permanente Sacramento Medical Center, Sacramento, CA, p. A83

FASELIS, Charles, M.D., Acting Medical Center Director, Washington Dc Veterans Affairs Medical Center, Washington, DC, p. A118

FASHINA, Olawale M.D., Chief of Staff, Central Texas Veterans Health Care System, Temple, TX, p. A648

FAST, Gary M.D., Medical Director, Prairie View, Newton, KS, p. A247

FASTHORSE, Lena, Supervisor Human Resource, U. S. Public Health Service Indian Hospital–Whiteriver, Whiteriver, AZ, p. A38

FATCH, Casey, Chief Operating Officer, Tri–City Medical Center, Oceanside, CA, p. A77

FATTIG, Marty, Chief Executive Officer, Nemaha County Hospital, Auburn, NE, p. A390

FATULA, Suzette
Chief Financial Officer, Oakdale Community Hospital, Oakdale, LA, p. A284
Chief Financial Officer, Winn Parish Medical Center, Winnfield, LA, p. A288

FAUBION, Matthew M.D., Clinical Director, Kerrville State Hospital, Kerrville, TX, p. A626

FAUCETT, Michael, Chief Operating Officer, Lake City Community Hospital, Lake City, SC, p. A564

FAUCHER, Kimberly M.D., Chief Medical Officer, Frank R. Howard Memorial Hospital, Willits, CA, p. A97

FAUCHEUX, Lisa, Director Human Resources, St. James Parish Hospital, Lutcher, LA, p. A280

FAUGHT, Charles J, Chief Financial Officer, Burnett Medical Center, Grantsburg, WI, p. A702

FAUL, Jennifer, Chief Operating Officer, Prairie St. John's, Fargo, ND, p. A475

FAULIS, Karen, Chief Executive Officer, Hi–Desert Medical Center, Yucca Valley, CA, p. A97

FAULKNER, Cheryl, Director of Nursing, Mckenzie County Healthcare System, Watford City, ND, p. A478

FAULKNER, Cynthia R.N., Chief Nursing Executive, Pender Memorial Hospital, Burgaw, NC, p. A458

FAULKNER, Kristi, Vice President Organizational Growth, United Regional Health Care System, Wichita Falls, TX, p. A654

FAULKNER, Laura, Chief Human Resource Management Service, Lexington Veterans Affairs Medical Center, Lexington, KY, p. A261

FAULKNER, Mark T., President, Baptist Health Care Corporation, Pensacola, FL, p. B19

FAULKNER, Sharon, Chief Nursing Officer, AMG Specialty Hospital–Denham Springs, Denham Springs, LA, p. A274

FAUMUINA, Taufete's John., Chief Executive Officer, Lyndon B. Johnson Tropical Medical Center, Pago Pago, AS, p. A721

FAUS, Doug, FACHE, Chief Executive Officer, Ivinson Memorial Hospital, Laramie, WY, p. A718

FAUST, Bill D., Administrator, Floyd County Medical Center, Charles City, IA, p. A224

FAUST, Cheryl, Chief Nursing Officer, Edgefield County Hospital, Edgefield, SC, p. A561

FAUTHEREE, Greg M.D., Medical Director, Spine Hospital Of Louisiana (Formally The Neuromedical Center Surgical Hospital), Baton Rouge, LA, p. A271

FAVATA, Valerie R.N., MS, Chief Nursing Officer, Oswego Hospital, Oswego, NY, p. A449

FAVRET, John M., Director, Eastern State Hospital, Williamsburg, VA, p. A677

FAY, Brian, Director Information Systems, Sidney Health Center, Sidney, MT, p. A388

FAYEN, Edward J, Associate Administrator Operations and Support, Washington Hospital Healthcare System, Fremont, CA, p. A60

FAYRE, Gail M.D., Medical Director, Anna Jaques Hospital, Newburyport, MA, p. A309

FAZIO, Charles, Chief Health Officer and Medical Director Health Plan, Regions Hospital, Saint Paul, MN, p. A348

FEAGIN, Bridgett
Chief Financial Officer, DMC – Detroit Receiving Hospital, Detroit, MI, p. A317
Chief Financial Officer, DMC Harper University Hospital, Detroit, MI, p. A318

FEASEL, Jeff, Chief Executive Officer, Halifax Health Medical Center Of Daytona Beach, Daytona Beach, FL, p. A123

FEATHER, Leroy P, Vice President Finance, Community Hospitals And Wellness Centers, Bryan, OH, p. A482

FEAZELL, Kayla, Chief Executive Officer, Healthsouth Rehabilitation Of Gadsden, Gadsden, AL, p. A18

FEBRY, Ricardo M.D., Medical Director, St. Theresa Specialty Hospital, Kenner, LA, p. A277

FEBUS, Steven, Chief Financial Officer, Pullman Regional Hospital, Pullman, WA, p. A684

FEDELE, Jerry J., President and Chief Executive Officer, Boca Raton Regional Hospital, Boca Raton, FL, p. A120

FEDER, Diane, R.N., FACHE, Senior Vice President and Chief Operating Officer, Witham Health Services, Lebanon, IN, p. A214

FEDERICO, Skip, Director Information Systems, Fairway Medical Surgical Hospital, Covington, LA, p. A273

FEDERINKO, David, Chief Information Officer, Allegan General Hospital, Allegan, MI, p. A314

FEDEROFF, Howard, M.D., Vice Chancellor, Health Affairs & Chief Executive Officer, UC Irvine Health, Uc Irvine Medical Center, Orange, CA, p. A78

FEDIE, Corey J., Chief Operating Officer, Kit Carson County Health Service District, Burlington, CO, p. A99

FEDIE, Corey J, Chief Operating Officer, Kit Carson County Health Service District, Burlington, CO, p. A99

FEDORA, Deborah, Director Human Resources, Paoli Hospital, Paoli, PA, p. A542

FEELEY, Daniel, Interim Chief Financial Officer, Medstar Southern Maryland Hospital Center, Clinton, MD, p. A297

FEEMAN, Kimberly, Senior Vice President and Chief Operating Officer, Wellspan Good Samaritan Hospital, Lebanon, PA, p. A539

FEEN, Jim, Senior Vice President and Chief Information Officer, Southcoast Hospitals Group, Fall River, MA, p. A306

FEENEY, Daniel M.D., Medical Director, Brentwood Hospital, Shreveport, LA, p. A285

FEENEY, John, President and Chief Executive Officer, Thedacare Regional Medical Center–Berlin, Berlin, WI, p. A699

FEENEY, Sheri, Chief Financial Officer, Providence Regional Medical Center Everett, Everett, WA, p. A680

FEESS, David, President and Chief Executive Officer, Liberty Hospital, Liberty, MO, p. A372

FEGAN, Claudia M.D., Chief Medical Officer, John H. Stroger Jr. Hospital Of Cook County, Chicago, IL, p. A181

FEGAN, Theresa R.N., Chief Clinical Officer, Tahoe Pacific Hospitals, Sparks, NV, p. A406

FEGHALI, Georges, M.D.
Senior Vice President Quality and Chief Medical Officer, Bethesda North Hospital, Cincinnati, OH, p. A483
Senior Vice President Quality and Chief Medical Officer, Good Samaritan Hospital, Cincinnati, OH, p. A484

FEH, Godwin, Interim Administrator, Pawhuska Hospital, Pawhuska, OK, p. A514

FEHRING, Marcia
Chief Financial Officer and Interim Chief Executive Officer, Horn Memorial Hospital, Ida Grove, IA, p. A229
Chief Financial Officer, Horn Memorial Hospital, Ida Grove, IA, p. A229

FEICKERT, Brent, Chief Financial Officer, Unitypoint Health – Trinity Regional Medical Center, Fort Dodge, IA, p. A227

FEIDT, Leslie, Chief Information Officer, Erie County Medical Center, Buffalo, NY, p. A432

FEIDT, Teresa, Chief Nursing Officer and Vice President, Patient Services, Stoughton Hospital Association, Stoughton, WI, p. A713

FEIKE, Jeffrey, President and Chief Administrative Officer, Fort Loudoun Medical Center, Lenoir City, TN, p. A582

FEILER, Kenneth H., Chief Medical Officer and Chief Executive Officer, Rose Medical Center, Denver, CO, p. A101

FEILMEIER, Patricia A., Interim Chief Nursing Officer, Coastal Carolina Hospital, Hardeeville, SC, p. A563

FEILNER, Margaret, Director Information Services, SSM Health St. Joseph – St. Charles, Saint Charles, MO, p. A376

FEINBERG, Daniel M.D., Chief Medical Officer, Pennsylvania Hospital, Philadelphia, PA, p. A545

FEINBERG, David T., M.D., President and Chief Executive Officer, Geisinger Health, Danville, PA, p. B53

FEINBERG, Jason, M.D.
Vice President Medical Affairs and Chief Medical Officer, Geneva General Hospital, Geneva, NY, p. A436
Vice President Medical Affairs and Chief Medical Officer, Soldiers And Sailors Memorial Hospital Of Yates County, Penn Yan, NY, p. A449

FEINER, David M.D., Chief Staff, Calais Regional Hospital, Calais, ME, p. A290

FEIRN, Greg, CPA, President and Chief Executive Officer, Lcmc Health, New Orleans, LA, p. B75

FEISAL, J Philip., President and Chief Executive Officer, Spartanburg Medical Center, Spartanburg, SC, p. A566

FEIST, Patricia, Manager Human Resources, Crook County Medical Services District, Sundance, WY, p. A720

FEISTRITZER, Nancye R., Chief Nursing Officer, Emory University Hospital, Atlanta, GA, p. A150

FELDER, Debra A, Director Human Resources, Shriners Hospitals For Children–Cincinnati, Cincinnati, OH, p. A484

FELDMAN, David L.
President and Chief Executive Officer, Circles Of Care, Melbourne, FL, p. A132
Executive Vice President and Treasurer, Circles Of Care, Melbourne, FL, p. A132

FELDMAN, Deborah A., President and Chief Executive Officer, Children's Medical Center, Dayton, OH, p. A489

FELDMAN, Joel
Regional President, St. Vincent Indianapolis Hospital, IndianapolisSt. Vincent Heart Center, Indianapolis, IN, p. A212
Regional President, St. Vincent Seton Specialty Hospital, Indianapolis, IN, p. A212

FELDMAN, Mitchell S., Chief Executive Officer, West Boca Medical Center, Boca Raton, FL, p. A120

FELDMANN, Scott, Director Information Technology, SSM Health Depaul Hospital – St. Louis, Bridgeton, MO, p. A365

FELDSTEIN, Charles S M.D., Vice President Medical Affairs, St. Rose Hospital, Hayward, CA, p. A63

FELEGE, Lester, Controller, Healthsouth New England Rehabilitation Hospital, Woburn, MA, p. A313

FELICE, Michael, Chief Financial Officer, Poplar Springs Hospital, Petersburg, VA, p. A673

FELICETTI, Jacqueline, Chief Human Resource Officer, Penn Medicine Chester County Hospital, West Chester, PA, p. A553

FELICI, Brian K., Chief Executive Officer, Wetzel County Hospital, New Martinsville, WV, p. A694

FELICIANO, Jose R., Chief Executive Officer, Ryder Memorial Hospital, Humacao, PR, p. A724

FELICIANO, Myrna Quinones M.D., Medical Director, University Pediatric Hospital, Rio Piedras, PR, p. A725

FELICIANO, Pablo, Manager Human Resources, Veterans Affairs Central Western Massachusetts Healthcare System, Leeds, MA, p. A308

FELIZ, Miriam M.D., Medical Director, St. Catherine's Rehabilitation Hospital, North Miami, FL, p. A136

FELKNER, Joseph G
Chief Financial Officer, Health First Viera Hospital, Melbourne, FL, p. A132
Executive Vice President and Chief Financial Officer, Health First Palm Bay Hospital, Palm Bay, FL, p. A138
Executive Vice President, Finance and Chief Financial Officer, Health First Holmes Regional Medical Center, Melbourne, FL, p. A132
Senior Vice President Finance and Chief Financial Officer, Health First Cape Canaveral Hospital, Cocoa Beach, FL, p. A122

FELL, David M.D., Chief Medical Officer, Tulsa Spine And Specialty Hospital, Tulsa, OK, p. A518

FELLER, Alicia, Chief Executive Officer, Southwest Connecticut Mental Health System, Bridgeport, CT, p. A109

FELLER, Julie, Executive Director Human Resources, Grays Harbor Community Hospital, Aberdeen, WA, p. A678

FELLOWS, Rhonda R.N., Chief Nursing Officer, Van Buren County Hospital, Keosauqua, IA, p. A230

FELLOWS, Steven A
Executive Vice President and Chief Operating Officer, Goleta Valley Cottage Hospital, Santa Barbara, CA, p. A90
Executive Vice President and Chief Operating Officer, Santa Barbara Cottage Hospital, Santa Barbara, CA, p. A90
Executive Vice President and Chief Operating Officer, Santa Ynez Valley Cottage Hospital, Solvang, CA, p. A92

FELMLEE, Charles, Assistant Director Fiscal Services, Central Virginia Training Center, Madison Heights, VA, p. A670

FELTMAN, Steven CPA, Chief Financial Officer, Essentia Health–Virginia, Virginia, MN, p. A349

FELTON, David
Manager Information Systems, Waldo County General Hospital, Belfast, ME, p. A290
Regional Chief Information Officer, Lincolnhealth, Damariscotta, ME, p. A290

FELTS, Dave, Chief Information Systems, Logan Regional Hospital, Logan, UT, p. A657

FENDER, Tamra, Chief Nursing Officer, Marias Medical Center, Shelby, MT, p. A388

FENDT, Phil, Chief Financial Officer, Memorial Community Health, Aurora, NE, p. A390

FENELLO, Michael A., Administrator and West Region Chief Executive Officer, St. Luke's Magic Valley Medical Center, Twin Falls, ID, p. A176

FENER, Michael
Executive Director, Plainview Hospital, Plainview, NY, p. A449
Executive Director, Syosset Hospital, Syosset, NY, p. A453

FENN, Jeffrey R.
Chief Executive Officer, Select Specialty Hospital – Northeast Atlanta, Atlanta, GA, p. A151
Chief Executive Officer, Select Specialty Hospital Midtown Atlanta, Atlanta, GA, p. A151

FENN, Mark, Director Human Resources, Pulaski Memorial Hospital, Winamac, IN, p. A221

FENNELL, Charles, Vice President Information Management, St. Joseph's Hospital Health Center, Syracuse, NY, p. A453

FENNELL, Colin M.D., Chief Medical Officer, Riverview Health, Crookston, MN, p. A338

FENNELL, David M.D., Acting Medical Director, Atascadero State Hospital, Atascadero, CA, p. A52

FENSKE, Bill, Chief Financial Officer, Rice Memorial Hospital, Willmar, MN, p. A350

FENSKE, Candace, Chief Executive Officer, Madelia Community Hospital, Madelia, MN, p. A342

FENSKE, Mary, Human Resource Business Partner, Spectrum Health United Hospital, Greenville, MI, p. A322

FENSTERLE, Chris, Chief Operating Officer, Frye Regional Medical Center, Hickory, NC, p. A464

FENWICK, Sandra L., M.P.H., President and Chief Executive Officer, Boston Children's Hospital, Boston, MA, p. A302

FEOLA, Ferd, Chief Information Officer, Lehigh Valley Hospital – Pocono, East Stroudsburg, PA, p. A533

FERBER, Robert M.D., Chief Clinical Innovation Officer, Nanticoke Memorial Hospital, Seaford, DE, p. A116

FERCH, Wayne
President and Chief Executive Officer, Adventist Medical Center – Hanford, Hanford, CA, p. A62
President and Chief Executive Officer, Adventist Medical Center–Reedley, Reedley, CA, p. A82
President and Chief Executive Officer, Central Valley General Hospital, Hanford, CA, p. A63

FERDOUS, Riza, Health Services Director, Ossining Correctional Facilities Hospital, Ossining, NY, p. A449

FERGUS, Janie
Director and Chief Information Officer, Saint Joseph East, Lexington, KY, p. A261
Director and Chief Information Officer, Saint Joseph Hospital, Lexington, KY, p. A261

FERGUS, Linda, Manager Information Technology, Allegheny Valley Hospital, Natrona Heights, PA, p. A542

FERGUSON, Allison, Director Human Resources, Avoyelles Hospital, Marksville, LA, p. A280

FERGUSON, Cathy R.N., MSN, Vice President and Chief Nursing Officer, Hamilton Medical Center, Dalton, GA, p. A156

FERGUSON, Cheryl L, Associate Administrator, Sanford Canby Medical Center, Canby, MN, p. A337

FERGUSON, Clifford, Director Information Technology and Systems, Bayshore Medical Center, Pasadena, TX, p. A636

FERGUSON, Daniel, Chief of Staff, Grove City Medical Center, Grove City, PA, p. A535

FERGUSON, Deborah
Director, Human Resources, Sentara Albemarle Medical Center, Elizabeth City, NC, p. A462
Human Resources Consultant, Sentara Obici Hospital, Suffolk, VA, p. A676

FERGUSON, Denise, Chief Nursing Officer, Baptist Memorial Hospital–Collierville, Collierville, TN, p. A577

FERGUSON, G Thomas, Senior Vice President and Chief Human Resources Officer, New York–Presbyterian Hospital, New Rochelle, NY, p. A444

FERGUSON, Gordon B., President and Chief Executive Officer, Saint Thomas Rutherford Hospital, Murfreesboro, TN, p. A586

FERGUSON, Karen, Director Human Resources, Johnson County Healthcare Center, Buffalo, WY, p. A717

FERGUSON, Marla J., Commanding Officer, Bayne–Jones Army Community Hospital, Fort Polk, LA, p. A274

FERGUSON, Michael, Chief Financial Officer, Harbor Oaks Hospital, New Baltimore, MI, p. A327

FERGUSON, Nina L, Director Human Resources, Little Colorado Medical Center, Winslow, AZ, p. A39

FERGUSON, Randy, Chief Information Officer, Ridgecrest Regional Hospital, Ridgecrest, CA, p. A82

FERGUSON, Rick, Chief Executive Officer, Oklahoma Surgical Hospital, Tulsa, OK, p. A517

FERGUSON, Susan, Administrator, Good Shepherd Specialty Hospital, Bethlehem, PA, p. A529

FERGUSON, Tonya, Director Human Resources, Healthsouth Rehabilitation Hospital Of Virginia, Richmond, VA, p. A673

FERGUSON, Zeta, Chief Human Resources, Atlanta Veterans Affairs Medical Center, Decatur, GA, p. A156

FERIA, Jorge M.D., President Medical Staff, Wilma N. Vazquez Medical Center, Vega Baja, PR, p. A727

FERNALD, Catherine Shull., MSN, Chief Operating Officer, Carepoint Health Bayonne Medical Center, Bayonne, NJ, p. A411

FERNALD, Catherine Shull MSN, Chief Operating Officer – Bayonne Medical Center, Carepoint Health Bayonne Medical Center, Bayonne, NJ, p. A411

FERNANDES, Roxanne R.N., Chief Nursing Officer, Children's Hospitals And Clinics Of Minnesota, Minneapolis, MN, p. A343

FERNANDEZ, Alexander, Chief Financial Officer, Broward Health Medical Center, Fort Lauderdale, FL, p. A124

FERNANDEZ, Arthur, Chief Financial Officer, First Hospital Panamericano, Cidra, PR, p. A723

FERNANDEZ, Aurelio, Chief Executive Officer, Memorial Healthcare System, Hollywood, FL, p. B82

FERNANDEZ, Benigno J M.D., Executive Medical Director, Laurel Ridge Treatment Center, San Antonio, TX, p. A642

FERNANDEZ, Darlene, Chief Financial Officer, UNM Sandoval Regional Medical Center, Inc., Rio Rancho, NM, p. A428

FERNANDEZ, Jaime, Chief Executive Officer, Kempsville Center For Behavioral Health, Norfolk, VA, p. A671

FERNANDEZ, Jean, Chief Information Officer, Beth Israel Deaconess Hospital–Milton, Milton, MA, p. A309

FERNANDEZ, John R., President and Chief Executive Officer, Massachusetts Eye And Ear Infirmary, Boston, MA, p. A303

FERNANDEZ, John, Chief Operating Officer, United Hospital Center, Bridgeport, WV, p. A690

FERNANDEZ, Mark M.D., Chief of Staff and President Medical Staff, Illinois Valley Community Hospital, Peru, IL, p. A197

FERNANDEZ, Richard W., President and Chief Executive Officer, Beth Israel Deaconess Hospital–Milton, Milton, MA, p. A309

FERNANDEZ, Ruben D R.N., Vice President and Chief Nursing Officer, Hackensack Meridian Health Palisades Medical Center, North Bergen, NJ, p. A418

FERNANDEZ, Tracey, Chief Financial Officer, St. Mary Medical Center, Apple Valley, CA, p. A52

FERNANDEZ DEL VALLE, Arthur J, Chief Financial Officer, Cardiovascular Center Of Puerto Rico And The Caribbean, San Juan, PR, p. A725

FERNANDEZ–BRAVO, Grisel, R.N., Administrator and Chief Executive Officer, Memorial Hospital Miramar, Miramar, FL, p. A135

FERNYAK, Susan M.D., Interim Chief Medical Officer & Chief Quality Officer, San Mateo Medical Center, San Mateo, CA, p. A89

FERRACANE, Tony, Vice President Human Resources, St. Mary Medical Center, Hobart, IN, p. A210

FERRANTI, Jeffrey M.D., Chief Information Officer, Duke University Hospital, Durham, NC, p. A461

FERRARO, Claudio J., Senior Administrator, Via Christi Hospital On St. Teresa, Wichita, KS, p. A254

FERRARO, Claudio J, President, Via Christi Hospital On St. Francis, Wichita, KS, p. A254

FERRAROTTI, Gianna, Director Human Resources North Region, Ohiohealth Marion General Hospital, Marion, OH, p. A494

FERREIRA, Daniel, Director Management Information Systems, Hospital De La Concepcion, San German, PR, p. A725

FERRELL, Angie
Director Human Resources, Mercy Health – Anderson Hospital, Cincinnati, OH, p. A484
Director Human Resources, Mercy Health – Clermont Hospital, Batavia, OH, p. A480

FERRELL, Eileen Brennan MS, R.N., Vice President and Chief Nursing Officer, Medstar Georgetown University Hospital, Washington, DC, p. A117

FERRELL, Jennifer, Chief Nursing Officer, Healthsouth Rehabilitation Hospital Of Memphis, Memphis, TN, p. A584

FERRELL, Marc C., President and Chief Executive Officer, Bridgepoint Healthcare, Portsmouth, NH, p. B22

FERRELL, Ronald, Chief Information Officer, New Mexico Veterans Affairs Health Care System – Raymond G. Murphy Medical Center, Albuquerque, NM, p. A424

FERRELLI, John, Chief Executive Officer, Seton Medical Center, Daly City, CA, p. A57

FERREN, Alison, Vice President Information Technology and Chief Information Officer, Abington–Lansdale Hospital Jefferson Health, Lansdale, PA, p. A538

FERRERO, Marcia L MS, Chief Nursing Officer, Heritage Valley Health System, Beaver, PA, p. A529

FERRETTI, Andrea, Interim Chief Nursing Officer, Vice President and Associate Chief Nursing Officer Network of Care, Children's Hospital Colorado, Aurora, CO, p. A98

FERNIANY, William, Ph.D., Chief Executive Officer, Uab Health System, Birmingham, AL, p. B131

FERRIS, David, Chief Nursing Officer and Vice President Patient Care Services, Claxton–Hepburn Medical Center, Ogdensburg, NY, p. A448

FERRIS, Joseph, Chief Financial Officer, Veterans Affairs Black Hills Health Care System, Fort Meade, SD, p. A570

FERRIS, Mark M.D., Medical Director, Kindred Hospital–White Rock, Dallas, TX, p. A605

FERRIS, Michael M.D., Chief Medical Officer, Chi Health St Elizabeth, Lincoln, NE, p. A395

FERRONI, Karen M.D., Medical Director, Holyoke Medical Center, Holyoke, MA, p. A307

FERRY, Jane M.D., Vice President Medical Affairs, Grand View Health, Sellersville, PA, p. A550

FERRY, Thomas, Business Administrator, Oakwood Correctional Facility, Lima, OH, p. A493

FERTIG, Ashley
Chief Nursing Officer, University Hospitals Conneaut Medical Center, Conneaut, OH, p. A488
Chief Nursing Officer, University Hospitals Geneva Medical Center, Geneva, OH, p. A492

FESKO, Donald P., President and Chief Executive Officer, Community Healthcare System, Hammond, IN, p. B36

FESSER, James, Chief Nursing Officer, Palo Pinto General Hospital, Mineral Wells, TX, p. A633

FETTER, Trevor, President and Chief Executive Officer, Tenet Healthcare Corporation, Dallas, TX, p. B124

FETTEROLF, Kim R.N., Chief Clinical Officer, Acuity Specialty Hospital Of Southern New Jersey, Willingboro, NJ, p. A423

FETTERS, Valerie, Chief Financial Officer, Hillsdale Hospital, Hillsdale, MI, p. A322

FEUCHT, Jason, Chief Financial Officer, Kossuth Regional Health Center, Algona, IA, p. A222

FEUER, Tammy, Chief Executive Officer, Healthsouth Rehabilitation Hospital Of Vineland, Vineland, NJ, p. A422

FEUNNING, Charles M.D., President Medical Staff, Summa Western Reserve Hospital, Cuyahoga Falls, OH, p. A489

FIBIYI, Abayomi, Chief Human Resources Officer, North Vista Hospital, North Las Vegas, NV, p. A404

FICCHI, Adrienne, Vice President Information Management, Philadelphia Veterans Affairs Medical Center, Philadelphia, PA, p. A545

FICICCHY, Teri R.N., MSN, Chief Nursing Officer, Bon Secours St. Francis Health System, Greenville, SC, p. A562

FIDLER, Soniya MS, Chief Human Resources and Compliance Officer, Yampa Valley Medical Center, Steamboat Springs, CO, p. A107

FIDUCIA, Karen A., FACHE, President and Chief Executive Officer, Summersville Regional Medical Center, Summersville, WV, p. A696

FIELD, Clifford M.D., Medical Director, Kau Hospital, Pahala, HI, p. A170

FIELD, Edward, Administrator, Loma Linda University Behavioral Medicine Center, Redlands, CA, p. A81

FIELD, Kori, Director of Nursing, Brodstone Memorial Hospital, Superior, NE, p. A400

FIELD, Laurie, Director Human Resources, Eaton Rapids Medical Center, Eaton Rapids, MI, p. A319

FIELDER, Barb, Vice President Finance, St. Joseph Mercy Chelsea, Chelsea, MI, p. A316

FIELDER, Jaf, Vice President and Administrator, Willis–Knighton Medical Center, Shreveport, LA, p. A286

FIELDING, Colene, Manager Business Office, Baylor Medical Center At Uptown, Dallas, TX, p. A604

FIELDING, Laura M, Administrative Director Organizational Development, Holy Family Memorial, Manitowoc, WI, p. A706

FIELDS, Donald R., Community Chief Executive Officer, Harlan Arh Hospital, Harlan, KY, p. A259

FIELDS, Greg, Director Information Technology, Elbert Memorial Hospital, Elberton, GA, p. A157

FIELDS, Laurie, Director Human Resources, Continuecare Hospital At Hendrick Medical Center, Abilene, TX, p. A591

FIERER, Jonathan M.D., Chief of Staff, Martinsburg Veterans Affairs Medical Center, Martinsburg, WV, p. A694

FIERRO, Barbara, Director, Human Resources, St. Francis Hospital, The Heart Center, Roslyn, NY, p. A451

FIETEK, Denise, Information Technology, Rio Grande Hospital, Del Norte, CO, p. A100

FIFE, Stephen, Chief Financial Officer, Cape Fear Valley – Bladen County Hospital, Elizabethtown, NC, p. A462

FIFIELD, Michael, Vice President Human Resources, Oneida Healthcare, Oneida, NY, p. A448

FIGGINS, Tara, Director Human Resources, Davis Hospital And Medical Center, Layton, UT, p. A657

FIGUEROA, Maria, Director Human Resources, Ryder Memorial Hospital, Humacao, PR, p. A724

FIGUEROA, Roseann, Director Human Resources, Doctors Hospital Of Laredo, Laredo, TX, p. A628

FIKE, Ruthita J, Chief Executive Officer, Loma Linda University Behavioral Medicine Center, Redlands, CA, p. A81

FILADORA, Victor A M.D., MS, II, Chief Clinical Services, Roswell Park Cancer Institute, Buffalo, NY, p. A433

FILER, Christine, Director Human Resources, Healthsouth Rehabilitation Hospital Of Altoona, Altoona, PA, p. A528

FILES, Ashley S, Director Human Resources and Public Relations and Marketing, Winn Parish Medical Center, Winnfield, LA, p. A288

FILES, Carol, Chief Financial Officer, Advanced Diagnostics Hospital, Houston, TX, p. A619

FILIPINI, Alfred, Manager Human Resources, Ancora Psychiatric Hospital, Hammonton, NJ, p. A414

FILIPOWICZ, Thomas M.D., Medical Director, St. Luke's Hospital – Quakertown Campus, Quakertown, PA, p. A549

FILLER, Richard
Chief Financial Officer, Berger Health System, Circleville, OH, p. A485
Chief Human Resource Officer, Berger Health System, Circleville, OH, p. A485

FILLER, Scott, Chief Executive Officer, Healthsouth Rehabilitation Hospital Of Altoona, Altoona, PA, p. A528

FILLINGIM, Jed, Acting Chief Operating Officer and Associate Director, G.V. (Sonny) Montgomery Veterans Affairs Medical Center, Jackson, MS, p. A356

FILLIPO, Brian M.D., Chief Medical Officer, Guthrie Robert Packer Hospital, Sayre, PA, p. A549

FILLMAN, T Orvin, Dr.PH, Vice President, Operations, Rogers Memorial Hospital, Oconomowoc, WI, p. A709

FILOSA, Frank, Fiscal Manager, Washington Dc Veterans Affairs Medical Center, Washington, DC, p. A118

FILOSA, Shannon M., Executive Director Women's and Children, Saint Francis Hospital, Tulsa, OK, p. A518

FILPI, Jeanette, Chief Executive Officer, Pioneer Community Hospital Of Patrick, Stuart, VA, p. A676

FILSON, Debbie, Chief Financial Officer, Ashland Health Center, Ashland, KS, p. A238

FINAN, John J. Jr, FACHE, President and Chief Executive Officer, Franciscan Missionaries Of Our Lady Health System, Inc., Baton Rouge, LA, p. B53

FINAN, Timothy J.
President and Chief Executive Officer, Bradford Regional Medical Center, Bradford, PA, p. A530
President and Chief Executive Officer, Olean General Hospital, Olean, NY, p. A448

FINCH, John
Chief Information and Community Officer, Health Alliance Hospital – Mary's Avenue Campus, Kingston, NY, p. A438
Vice President Information Services, Health Alliance Hospital – Broadway Campus, Kingston, NY, p. A438

FINCH, Kenneth A., President and Chief Executive Officer, Texas Health Huguley Hospital Fort Worth South, Burleson, TX, p. A600

FINCH, Kim, Chief Nursing Officer, Kosciusko Community Hospital, Warsaw, IN, p. A221

FINCH, Robert D., Vice President Human Resources, Piedmont Athens Regional Medical Center, Athens, GA, p. A149

FINCH, Roy
Chief Executive Officer, Palestine Regional Medical Center–East, Palestine, TX, p. A636
Chief Executive Officer, Palestine Regional Medical Center, Palestine, TX, p. A636
Chief Operating Officer, Longview Regional Medical Center, Longview, TX, p. A630

FINCH, Steve, Chief Financial Officer, Guidance Center, Flagstaff, AZ, p. A29

FINCH, Teresa, Chief Financial Officer, Trident Medical Center, Charleston, SC, p. A559

FINCHER, Jodi
Administrator, St. Joseph Medical Center, Kansas City, MO, p. A371

Vice President Patient Care Services, Saint John Hospital, Leavenworth, KS, p. A245

FINDLAY, Andrew L., Deputy Commander Clinical Services, Tripler Army Medical Center, Honolulu, HI, p. A169

FINDLAY, Kelly, Director of Nurses, Pawnee County Memorial Hospital And Rural Health Clinic, Pawnee City, NE, p. A399

FINDLEY, Amber, Senior Director Nursing Services and NRC Administrator, Pleasant Valley Hospital, Point Pleasant, WV, p. A695

FINDLEY, John T
Chief Medical Officer, Beatrice Community Hospital And Health Center, Beatrice, NE, p. A391
Chief Medical Officer and Interim Chief Executive Officer, Beatrice Community Hospital And Health Center, Beatrice, NE, p. A391

FINE, Allan, Chief Operating Officer, New York Eye And Ear Infirmary Of Mount Sinai, New Rochelle, NY, p. A443

FINE, James M.D., Chief Information Officer, Uw Medicine/Harborview Medical Center, Seattle, WA, p. A685

FINE, Mathew N. M.D., Chief Medical Officer, Oroville Hospital, Oroville, CA, p. A78

FINE, Peter S., FACHE, President and Chief Executive Officer, Banner Health, Phoenix, AZ, p. B17

FINELLI, Frederick M.D., Vice President Medical Affairs, Medstar Montgomery Medical Center, Olney, MD, p. A300

FINELLI, Peter, Chief Financial Officer, Banner Payson Medical Center, Payson, AZ, p. A32

FINESTEIN, Brian, Chief Executive Officer, Saint Clare's Health System, Denville, NJ, p. A412

FINETTI, Yoany R.N., Chief Nursing Officer, Barnes–Jewish West County Hospital, Saint Louis, MO, p. A376

FINK, Renee CPA, Chief Financial Officer, Dundy County Hospital, Benkelman, NE, p. A391

FINK, Tom, Vice President Regional Finance Officer, Range Regional Health Services, Hibbing, MN, p. A341

FINK, Walter, Chief Medical Officer, Multicare Good Samaritan Hospital, Puyallup, WA, p. A684

FINKEL, Naomi, Nurse Executive, Montgomery County Emergency Service, Norristown, PA, p. A542

FINKENBINER, Joy, Vice President, Operations, Genesys Regional Medical Center, Grand Blanc, MI, p. A320

FINLAYSON, Susan D MSN, R.N., Senior Vice President of MMC Operations, Mercy Medical Center, Baltimore, MD, p. A295

FINLEY, Alan, Chief Operating Officer, Conway Regional Medical Center, Conway, AR, p. A41

FINLEY, Cindy, Chief Nursing Officer, Iron County Medical Center, Pilot Knob, MO, p. A375

FINLEY, Delvecchio, Chief Executive Officer, Highland Hospital, Oakland, CA, p. A77

FINLEY, Jane
Senior Vice President & Area Manager, Kaiser Permanente San Diego Medical Center, San Diego, CA, p. A85
Senior Vice President and Area Manager, Kaiser Permanente San Diego Medical Center, San Diego, CA, p. A85

FINLEY, Kevan, Chief Executive Officer, Oklahoma Forensic Center, Vinita, OK, p. A519

FINLEY, Mike M.D., Chief Medical Officer, Christus St. Michael Health System, Texarkana, TX, p. A649

FINLEY, Tommy, Chief Information Officer, Rutherford Regional Health System, Rutherfordton, NC, p. A470

FINLEY, Waynea
Corporate Director Human Resources, Pam Specialty Hospital Of Victoria North, Victoria, TX, p. A652
Manager Human Resources, Pam Specialty Hospital Of Victoria South, Victoria, TX, p. A652
Senior Vice President Human Resources, Pam Specialty Hospital Of Covington, Covington, LA, p. A273
System Director Human Resources, Warm Springs Rehabilitation Hospital Of San Antonio, San Antonio, TX, p. A644

FINLEY–HAZLE, Gabrielle, Chief Executive Officer, St. Mary's Medical Center, West Palm Beach, FL, p. A147

FINN, Barry C., President and Chief Executive Officer, Rush–Copley Medical Center, Aurora, IL, p. A178

FINN, Patti, Chief Executive Officer, Fulton County Health Center, Wauseon, OH, p. A502

FINNEGAN, Jay, Chief Executive Officer, St. Lucie Medical Center, Port St. Lucie, FL, p. A140

FINNEGAN, Mary Jane, Chief Nursing Officer, St. Catherine Of Siena Medical Center, Smithtown, NY, p. A452

FINNERTY, Kimberley MSN, R.N., Chief Nursing Officer, Jefferson Hospital, Jefferson Hills, PA, p. A537

FINNEY, David R.N., Vice President Nursing, Uhs Chenango Memorial Hospital, Norwich, NY, p. A448

FINNEY, Michele, Chief Executive Officer, Desert Regional Medical Center, Palm Springs, CA, p. A78

FINSTAD, Gary A M.D., Chief of Staff, Kern Valley Healthcare District, Lake Isabella, CA, p. A65

FIORE–LOPEZ, Nicolette R.N., Chief Nursing Officer, St. Charles Hospital, Port Jefferson, NY, p. A450

FIORET, Phil M.D., Vice President Medical Affairs, King's Daughters Medical Center, Ashland, KY, p. A255

FIRES, Wiley M., Administrator, Shamrock General Hospital, Shamrock, TX, p. A645

FIRES, Wiley M, Administrator, Shamrock General Hospital, Shamrock, TX, p. A645

FIRMAN, Julie, R.N.
Chief Nursing Officer, St. Joseph Memorial Hospital, Murphysboro, IL, p. A194
Vice President and Chief Nursing Officer, Memorial Hospital Of Carbondale, Carbondale, IL, p. A179

FIRMIN, Kelli, Interim Chief Nursing Officer, Pre–Op and PACU Manager, Surgical Specialty Center Of Baton Rouge, Baton Rouge, LA, p. A271

FIRMINGER, Barbara, Chief Administrative Officer, Verde Valley Medical Center, Cottonwood, AZ, p. A28

FIRTCH, William M.D., Physician In Chief, Kaiser Permanente Redwood City Medical Center, Redwood City, CA, p. A82

FISCHBACH, John, Vice President of Finance, Chief Financial Officer, Lima Memorial Health System, Lima, OH, p. A493

FISCHELS, Diane, Senior Vice President and Chief Operating Officer, Mercy Medical Center–North Iowa, Mason City, IA, p. A231

FISCHER, Angie, Chief Financial Officer, Loring Hospital, Sac City, IA, p. A234

FISCHER, Jason
Chief Information Officer, Pih Health Hospital – Downey, Downey, CA, p. A58
Chief Information Officer, Pih Health Hospital–Whittier, Whittier, CA, p. A97

FISCHER, JC, Director Human Resources, Mercy Regional Medical Center, Lorain, OH, p. A494

FISCHER, Linda, Director Information Services, Huntington Hospital, Huntington, NY, p. A437

FISCHER, Lisa, Director Human Resources, Brown County Hospital, Ainsworth, NE, p. A390

FISCHER, Racheal Z., Chief Executive Officer, Select Specialty Hospital–Augusta, Augusta, GA, p. A152

FISCHER, Robert M.D., Medical Director, Methodist Hospital For Surgery, Addison, TX, p. A591

FISCHER, Sandra, Director Human Resources, W. G. (Bill) Heffner Veterans Affairs Medical Center, Salisbury, NC, p. A470

FISCHER, Steven P, Chief Financial Officer, Beth Israel Deaconess Medical Center, Boston, MA, p. A302

FISCHER, Tamara, Chief Nursing Officer, Okeene Municipal Hospital, Okeene, OK, p. A511

FISER, David, Vice President and Chief Information Officer, Cleveland Clinic Akron General, Akron, OH, p. A479

FISH, Carolyn, Director Human Resources, Mission Community Hospital, Los Angeles, CA, p. A70

FISH, Elizabeth
Chief Information Officer, University Of Maryland Shore Medical Center At Dorchester, Cambridge, MD, p. A297
Chief Information Officer, University Of Maryland Shore Medical Center At Easton, Easton, MD, p. A298
Senior Director Site Executive and Information Technology, University Of Maryland Shore Medical Center At Chestertown, Chestertown, MD, p. A297

FISHBAUGHER, David, Chief Medical Information, Mercy Iowa City, Iowa City, IA, p. A229

FISHEL, Stephanie, Vice President Patient Care Services and Chief Nursing Officer, Nathan Littauer Hospital And Nursing Home, Gloversville, NY, p. A436

FISHER, Alan, Chief Executive Officer, Mid–Valley Hospital, Omak, WA, p. A683

FISHER, Charles, Chief Executive Officer, U. S. Public Health Service Indian Hospital, Eagle Butte, SD, p. A569

FISHER, David, M.D.
Senior Vice President and Chief Medical Officer, Seattle Children's Hospital, Seattle, WA, p. A685
Director Information Systems, Heart Of Lancaster Regional Medical Center, Lititz, PA, p. A539
Vice President Human Resources, Signature Healthcare Brockton Hospital, Brockton, MA, p. A304

FISHER, Diane R.N., VP, Patient Care Services, Otsego Memorial Hospital, Gaylord, MI, p. A320

FISHER, Irv, Director, Information Services, Hahnemann University Hospital, Philadelphia, PA, p. A544

FISHER, J. Matthew, Chief Financial Officer, Russell Medical Center, Alexander City, AL, p. A13

FISHER, Jacob, Chief Executive Officer, Tampa Community Hospital, Tampa, FL, p. A145

FISHER, Jan E., Executive Vice President, Chief Operating Officer and Chief Administrative Officer, Williamsport Regional Medical Center, Williamsport, PA, p. A554

FISHER, Jan E, Executive Vice President, Chief Operating Officer and Chief Administrative Officer, Williamsport Regional Medical Center, Williamsport, PA, p. A554

FISHER, Jeannie, Coordinator Information Technology, Webster County Memorial Hospital, Webster Springs, WV, p. A696

FISHER, Jennifer A, Manager Human Resources, Henry County Hospital, Napoleon, OH, p. A496

FISHER, John M.D., Chief Medical Officer, Martin Luther King, Jr. Community Hospital, Los Angeles, CA, p. A69

FISHER, Kenneth, Associate Vice President Finance and Chief Financial Officer, University Of Iowa Hospitals And Clinics, Iowa City, IA, p. A230

FISHER, Kerry M.D., Medical Director, LDS Hospital, Salt Lake City, UT, p. A660

FISHER, Lynn M.D., Chief of Staff, Rooks County Health Center, Plainville, KS, p. A250

FISHER, Mahana M.D., Medical Director, Blue Mountain Hospital, Blanding, UT, p. A656

FISHER, Mathew M.D., Medical Director, Springbrook Behavioral Health System, Travelers Rest, SC, p. A566

FISHER, Michael W., Director, Va Portland Healthcare System, Portland, OR, p. A525

FISHER, Michael, President and Chief Executive Officer, Cincinnati Children's Hospital Medical Center, Cincinnati, OH, p. A483

FISHER, Richard, M.D., President and Chief Executive Officer, Fox Chase Cancer Center–American Oncologic Hospital, Philadelphia, PA, p. A543

FISHER, Ryan
Director Human Resources, Bluffton Hospital, Bluffton, OH, p. A481
Director of Human Resources, Blanchard Valley Hospital, Findlay, OH, p. A491

FISHER, Sharon M.D., Chief of Staff, Bartlett Regional Hospital, Juneau, AK, p. A26

FISHER, Sharon R.N., Chief Nursing Officer, Tyrone Hospital, Tyrone, PA, p. A552

FISHER, Teresa, R.N.
Chief Nursing Officer, Fort Loudoun Medical Center, Lenoir City, TN, p. A582
Chief Nursing Officer, Lakewood Health System, Staples, MN, p. A349

FISHER, Thomas, Senior Vice President and Chief Financial Officer, University Of Tennessee Medical Center, Knoxville, TN, p. A582

FISHER, Vicky Ph.D., R.N., Chief Nurse Executive, Catawba Hospital, Catawba, VA, p. A665

FISHER–FORD, Karen, Director of Health Information Management, West Central Georgia Regional Hospital, Columbus, GA, p. A155

FISHKIN, Edward M.D., Medical Director, NYC Health + Hospitals / Woodhull, New Rochelle, NY, p. A446

FISK, Amber, Director Human Resources, Memorial Hospital Of Sweetwater County, Rock Springs, WY, p. A719

FISK, Anita, Director Human Resources, Three Rivers Hospital, Brewster, WA, p. A679

FISK, Kathryn M, Chief Human Resources Officer, El Camino Hospital, Mountain View, CA, p. A75

FISK, Kellee J, Chief People Officer, Altru Health System, Grand Forks, ND, p. A476

FISLER, Eileen, Chief Financial Officer, Pacifica Hospital Of The Valley, Los Angeles, CA, p. A70

FITCH, Andrew, Chief Financial Officer, St. Elias Specialty Hospital, Anchorage, AK, p. A25

FITCH, James A, Director Human Resources, Houston Methodist St. Catherine Hospital, Katy, TX, p. A626

FITCH, John A, Vice President Human Resources, Campbell County Health, Gillette, WY, p. A718

FITE, David, Director Information Technology, Towner County Medical Center, Cando, ND, p. A474

FITE, Theresa R.N., Chief Financial Officer, Fleming County Hospital, Flemingsburg, KY, p. A258

FITTS, Barry
Chief Information Officer, Hillside Rehabilitation Hospital, Warren, OH, p. A501
Chief Information Officer, Trumbull Memorial Hospital, Warren, OH, p. A501

FITZGERALD, Amy, Human Resources Manager, Copley Hospital, Morrisville, VT, p. A662

FITZGERALD, Andy, Chief Executive Officer, Campbell County Health, Gillette, WY, p. A718

FITZGERALD, George, Regional Director Information Systems, Lifecare Hospitals Of Pittsburgh, Pittsburgh, PA, p. A546

FITZGERALD, John L., Chief Executive Officer, Inova Fair Oaks Hospital, Fairfax, VA, p. A666

FITZGERALD, Mike
  Chief Financial Officer, Harrison Medical Center, Bremerton, WA, p. A678
  Chief Financial Officer, St. Clare Hospital, Lakewood, WA, p. A682
  Chief Financial Officer, St. Francis Hospital, Federal Way, WA, p. A680
  Chief Financial Officer, St. Joseph Medical Center, Tacoma, WA, p. A688

FITZGERALD, Patty, Staff Services, Munson Healthcare Charlevoix Hospital, Charlevoix, MI, p. A316

FITZGERALD, Philip, Chief Operating Officer, John F. Kennedy Memorial Hospital, Indio, CA, p. A63

FITZGERALD, Thomas J. III, Interim Director, Va Palo Alto Health Care System, Palo Alto, CA, p. A79

FITZMAURICE, Dennis
  Interim Chief Executive Officer, Community First Medical Center, Chicago, IL, p. A180
  Vice President, Professional Services, Community First Medical Center, Chicago, IL, p. A180

FITZMAURICE, Sandy MS, R.N., Interim Chief Nursing Officer, Whitman Hospital And Medical Center, Colfax, WA, p. A679

FITZPATRICK, Anna, Director Human Resources, St. Anthony Regional Hospital, Carroll, IA, p. A223

FITZPATRICK, Daniel, Director Human Resources, Whitesburg Arh Hospital, Whitesburg, KY, p. A268

FITZPATRICK, James G., FACHE, Chief Executive Officer, Mercy Medical Center–Sioux City, Sioux City, IA, p. A235

FITZPATRICK, James M.D., Vice President Medical Affairs, Kenmore Mercy Hospital, Kenmore, NY, p. A438

FITZPATRICK, Leigh Ann, Superintendent, Kerrville State Hospital, Kerrville, TX, p. A626

FITZSIMMONS, Shaun, Director Information Technology Services, Community Medical Center, Toms River, NJ, p. A421

FITZSIMONS, Patricia Sue R.N., Ph.D., Senior Vice President Patient Services, Yale–New Haven Hospital, New Haven, CT, p. A112

FIX, Judith A R.N., MSN, Senior Vice President and Chief Nursing Officer, Long Beach Memorial Medical Center, Long Beach, CA, p. A66

FLACH, Shannan, Chief Executive Officer, Kingman Community Hospital, Kingman, KS, p. A244

FLACK, Charles, Interim Chief Information Officer, Orange County Global Medical Center, Inc., Santa Ana, CA, p. A90

FLAHERTY, Daniel M.D., Chief Medical Staff, Prairie Lakes Healthcare System, Watertown, SD, p. A574

FLAHERTY, John
  Chief Financial Officer, Healthsouth Rehabilitation Hospital Of Western Massachusetts, Ludlow, MA, p. A308
  Controller, Fairlawn Rehabilitation Hospital, Worcester, MA, p. A313

FLAHERTY, Linda R.N., Senior Vice President, Patient Care Services, Mclean Hospital, Belmont, MA, p. A302

FLAHERTY, Patrick, Director Management Information, Naval Hospital Bremerton, Bremerton, WA, p. A678

FLAHERTY, Steve, Chief Executive Officer, Warm Springs Rehabilitation Hospital Of San Antonio, San Antonio, TX, p. A644

FLAHERTY, Tom, Assistant Administrator, Los Angeles County Central Jail Hospital, Los Angeles, CA, p. A69

FLAKE, Robert, Chief Executive Officer, Middle Park Medical Center–Kremmling, Kremmling, CO, p. A104

FLAMING, Patrick R.N., Director Inpatient Operations, Prairie View, Newton, KS, p. A247

FLAMM, Cindy, Manager Quality, Choate Mental Health Center, Anna, IL, p. A177

FLANAGAN, Carl J., Chief Financial Officer, La Paz Regional Hospital, Parker, AZ, p. A32

FLANAGAN, Michael J, Senior Vice President and Chief Operating Officer, St. Clair Hospital, Pittsburgh, PA, p. A547

FLANAGAN, Thomas M.D., Medical Director, Aurora Behavioral Healthcare San Diego, San Diego, CA, p. A85

FLANARY, Tresha R.N., Chief Clinical Services Officer, Wamego Health Center, Wamego, KS, p. A253

FLANDERS, David, Chief Operating Officer, Candler County Hospital, Metter, GA, p. A161

FLANIGAN, Erin, Vice President Human Resources, Wentworth–Douglass Hospital, Dover, NH, p. A407

FLANIGAN, Kevin, M.D., Chief Executive Officer, Northern Inyo Hospital, Bishop, CA, p. A54

FLANNERY, Donna M., Chief Executive Officer, Mercy Rehabilitation Hospital St. Louis, Chesterfield, MO, p. A366

FLANNERY, Lindsay R.N., Vice President Patient Care Services, Avera Sacred Heart Hospital, Yankton, SD, p. A574

FLANNERY, Maureen, Vice President Clinic Operations, Straub Medical Center, Honolulu, HI, p. A169

FLANNERY, Patrick, Administrator, Christus St. Michael Rehabilitation Hospital, Texarkana, TX, p. A649

FLANNERY, Robert, Chief Financial Officer, University Of Wisconsin Hospitals And Clinics Authority, Madison, WI, p. A705

FLANZ, Bruce J., President and Chief Executive Officer, Jamaica Hospital Medical Center, New Rochelle, NY, p. A441

FLASCHENRIEM, Julie, Chief Information Officer, Park Nicollet Methodist Hospital, Saint Louis Park, MN, p. A347

FLASHER, Sara, Chief Nurse Executive, Warren State Hospital, Warren, PA, p. A552

FLATOW, Evan, M.D., President, Mount Sinai West, New Rochelle, NY, p. A443

FLATT, G Wayne D.O., Chief Medical Director, Pushmataha Hospital, Antlers, OK, p. A504

FLATTERY, William
  Vice President and Administrator Western Division, Carilion Giles Community Hospital, Pearisburg, VA, p. A672
  Vice President and Administrator Western Division, Carilion New River Valley Medical Center, Christiansburg, VA, p. A666

FLAVIO, Chuck, Chief Executive Officer, Saint Simons By–The–Sea Hospital, Saint Simons Island, GA, p. A164

FLECHSIG, Randolph K., Administrator, Sheridan Community Hospital, Sheridan, MI, p. A330

FLECK, Julie, Chief Operating Officer, Parkview Ortho Hospital, Fort Wayne, IN, p. A208

FLEEGEL, Monica, Director Human Resources, Mayo Clinic Health System In Albert Lea, Albert Lea, MN, p. A335

FLEENOR, Dennis, R.N., Administrator, Muleshoe Area Medical Center, Muleshoe, TX, p. A634

FLEET, Aaron R.N., Chief Nursing Officer, Texas Spine & Joint Hospital, Tyler, TX, p. A651

FLEISCHMANN, Craig, Vice President Finance, University Of Maryland Medical Center Midtown Campus, Baltimore, MD, p. A296

FLEISCHMANN, Tim, Chief Financial Officer, Tuality Healthcare, Hillsboro, OR, p. A522

FLEISHMAN, Samuel A M.D., Chief Medical Officer, Cape Fear Valley Medical Center, Fayetteville, NC, p. A462

FLEITES, Fernando, Senior Vice President Human Resources, Bon Secours St. Francis Health System, Greenville, SC, p. A562

FLEMER, Andrew, Chief Operating Officer, South Georgia Medical Center, Valdosta, GA, p. A166

FLEMING, Harry, Chief Executive Officer, Nobilis Health Corporation, Houston, TX, p. B90

FLEMING, Jared, Director, Information Services, Lourdes Counseling Center, Richland, WA, p. A684

FLEMING, Joshua, Vice President Chief Clinical Officer, Leesburg Regional Medical Center, Leesburg, FL, p. A130

FLEMING, Michael, Chief People Officer, Banner – University Medical Center Phoenix, Phoenix, AZ, p. A33

FLEMING, Shane
  Chief Financial Officer, Capital Health Medical Center–Hopewell, Pennington, NJ, p. A418
  Chief Financial Officer, Capital Health Regional Medical Center, Trenton, NJ, p. A421

FLEMING, Valarie MSN, Chief Nursing Executive, California Hospital Medical Center, Los Angeles, CA, p. A67

FLEMING, William P, Chief Operating Officer, Norwood Hospital, Norwood, MA, p. A310

FLEMMING, Libby, Controller and Chief Information Officer, South Georgia Medical Center Lanier Campus, Lakeland, GA, p. A160

FLEMMING, Michael, Administrator, Cornerstone Behavioral Health Hospital Of Union County, Berkeley Heights, NJ, p. A411

FLESNER, Lynn, Director of Nursing, Glacial Ridge Health System, Glenwood, MN, p. A340

FLETCHALL, Terry L., President and Chief Executive Officer, Santiam Hospital, Stayton, OR, p. A527

FLETCHER, Audrey, Chief Operating Officer, Madison Memorial Hospital, Rexburg, ID, p. A175

FLETCHER, Bill, Director Information Technology, Cooper County Memorial Hospital, Boonville, MO, p. A365

FLETCHER, Chris, Director of Human Resources, Fishermen's Hospital, Marathon, FL, p. A131

FLETCHER, Jennifer, Chief of Staff, Decatur County Memorial Hospital, Greensburg, IN, p. A209

FLETCHER, John R., President, Lehigh Valley Hospital – Hazleton, Hazleton, PA, p. A536

FLETCHER, John, Chief Executive Officer, Patrick B. Harris Psychiatric Hospital, Anderson, SC, p. A558

FLETCHER, Josie, Interim Chief Nursing Officer, Iberia Medical Center, New Iberia, LA, p. A282

FLETCHER, Kathy R.N., MSN, Interim Chief Nursing Officer, Val Verde Regional Medical Center, Del Rio, TX, p. A608

FLETCHER, Kevin, Director Information Systems, Medical City Mckinney, Mckinney, TX, p. A632

FLETCHER, Melissa, Chief Executive Officer, Ellett Memorial Hospital, Appleton City, MO, p. A364

FLETCHER, Michael M.D., Vice President and Chief Medical Officer, Hancock Regional Hospital, Greenfield, IN, p. A209

FLETCHER, Richard, PharmD, Chief Executive Officer, Shasta Regional Medical Center, Redding, CA, p. A81

FLETCHER, Stephanie L CPA, Chief Financial Officer, Union General Hospital, Blairsville, GA, p. A152

FLETT, Will, Vice President Finance and Chief Financial Officer, Avera Queen Of Peace Hospital, Mitchell, SD, p. A571

FLICEK, David, President and Chief Executive Officer, Avera Mckennan Hospital And University Health Center, Sioux Falls, SD, p. A572

FLICKEMA, James, Vice President Market Development, Otsego Memorial Hospital, Gaylord, MI, p. A320

FLICKINGER, Kenneth E, Chief Financial Officer, Penn Medicine Chester County Hospital, West Chester, PA, p. A553

FLINCHBAUGH, Robert D.O., Chief Medical Officer, Winneshiek Medical Center, Decorah, IA, p. A226

FLINN, Charles, Vice President, Chief Operating Officer, Saint Mary's Hospital, Waterbury, CT, p. A114

FLINN, James, JD, FACHE, Chief Executive Officer, St. Luke's Medical Center, Phoenix, AZ, p. A34

FLINT, Jennifer, Chief Financial Officer, Laird Hospital, Union, MS, p. A362

FLINT, Ruth, Chief Nursing Officer, St. Joseph Medical Center, Tacoma, WA, p. A688

FLIPPO, Mary Elizabeth R.N., MSN, Vice President and Chief Nursing Officer, Martin Health System, Stuart, FL, p. A143

FLIS, James D, Chief Financial Officer, Livengrin Foundation, Bensalem, PA, p. A529

FLODEN, Scott, Chief Executive Officer, Promise Hospital Of Phoenix, Mesa, AZ, p. A32

FLOOD, James, Director Information Systems, Claxton–Hepburn Medical Center, Ogdensburg, NY, p. A448

FLOOD, Rebecca L R.N., MS, Senior Vice President Nursing, New York–Presbyterian Brooklyn Methodist Hospital, New Rochelle, NY, p. A444

FLOREN, Joshua, President, Texas Health Presbyterian Hospital Plano, Plano, TX, p. A638

FLORENTINE, Erich
  Chief People Officer, Inspira Medical Center–Elmer, Elmer, NJ, p. A413
  Chief People Officer, Inspira Medical Center–Vineland, Vineland, NJ, p. A422

FLORES, Andrea, Director, Information Systems, Providence Little Company Of Mary Medical Center – Torrance, Torrance, CA, p. A94

FLORES, Debbie
  Chief Executive Officer, Banner Del E. Webb Medical Center, Sun City West, AZ, p. A37
  Interim Chief Executive Officer, Banner Boswell Medical Center, Sun City, AZ, p. A36

FLORES, Debra A., R.N., MS, President and Administrator, Sentara Careplex Hospital, Hampton, VA, p. A668

FLORES, Ernest Jr, Chief Executive Officer, Dimmit Regional Hospital, Carrizo Springs, TX, p. A600

FLORES, Jacob, Chief Information Officer, Frio Regional Hospital, Pearsall, TX, p. A637

FLORES, Jeanne, Consultant to the President, Cedars–Sinai Medical Center, Los Angeles, CA, p. A67

FLORES, Jerome, Chief Financial Officer, Sunrise Canyon Hospital, Lubbock, TX, p. A630

FLORES, Linda R.N., MSN, Vice President Nursing Services, Parkview Medical Center, Pueblo, CO, p. A106

FLORIT, Mary, Interim Chief Nursing Officer, Central Carolina Hospital, Sanford, NC, p. A470

FLORKOWSKI, Doug, Chief Executive Officer, Lawrence County Memorial Hospital, Lawrenceville, IL, p. A192

FLOURA, Kamal M.D., Medical Director, Eastern State Hospital, Medical Lake, WA, p. A682

FLOWE, Kenneth M.D., Chief Medical Officer, Rice Memorial Hospital, Willmar, MN, p. A350

FLOWERS, Deborah, Director Human Resources, Monroe County Hospital, Forsyth, GA, p. A158

FLOWERS, Frank M. M.D., Area Medical Director, Kaiser Permanente Riverside Medical Center, Riverside, CA, p. A82

FLOWERS, Michael, Director Information Management, Calhoun–Liberty Hospital, Blountstown, FL, p. A120

FLOWERS, Scott, Vice President Professional Services, Thibodaux Regional Medical Center, Thibodaux, LA, p. A287

FLOWERS, Susan S MSN, R.N., Chief Nursing Officer, Cumberland County Hospital, Burkesville, KY, p. A256

FLOWERS, Taylor, Senior Vice President Human Resources, Onslow Memorial Hospital, Jacksonville, NC, p. A465

FLOYD, Dorothy, Ph.D., Superintendent, Terrell State Hospital, Terrell, TX, p. A648

FLOYD, Duane, Vice President Human Resources and Professional Services, Watertown Regional Medical Center, Watertown, WI, p. A714

FLOYD, Jacqueline, Chief Nursing Officer, Healthsouth Rehabilitation Hospital Of Fort Smith, Fort Smith, AR, p. A43

FLOYD, Kiley, Chief Executive Officer, Nemaha Valley Community Hospital, Seneca, KS, p. A251

FLOYD, Miranda R.N., Chief Nursing Officer, Northwest Medical Center, Albany, MO, p. A364

FLOYD, Robert D.O., Chief Medical Staff, Davis County Hospital, Bloomfield, IA, p. A223

FLOYD, Terri, Chief Financial Officer, Bates County Memorial Hospital, Butler, MO, p. A365

FLOYD, William Brian., President, Vidant Medical Center, Greenville, NC, p. A463

FLUGUM, Aaron, Chief Executive Officer, Mercy Medical Center–New Hampton, New Hampton, IA, p. A232

FLUKE, Cinda, R.N.
Chief Nursing Officer, Saint Joseph Mount Sterling, Mount Sterling, KY, p. A265
Interim Site Executive, Saint Joseph Mount Sterling, Mount Sterling, KY, p. A265

FLUTY, Lisa, Director Information Services, Baptist Health Lexington, Lexington, KY, p. A260

FLYGARE, Matthew, Director Human Resources, Mountain West Medical Center, Tooele, UT, p. A661

FLYNN, Brian, Chief Human Resources Officer, Veterans Affairs Northern Indiana Health Care System, Fort Wayne, IN, p. A208

FLYNN, Chanda R.N., MSN, Chief Nursing Officer, Mary Black Health System–Spartanburg, Spartanburg, SC, p. A566

FLYNN, Cheryl, Senior Vice President Chief Human Resources Officer, Methodist Charlton Medical Center, Dallas, TX, p. A606

FLYNN, James, Chief Executive Officer, Galesburg Cottage Hospital, Galesburg, IL, p. A188

FLYNN, Julianne M.D., Chief of Staff, South Texas Veterans Health Care System, San Antonio, TX, p. A644

FLYNN, Kristin, Chief Human Resources Officer, Sierra Vista Regional Medical Center, San Luis Obispo, CA, p. A89

FLYNN, Matthew J, Senior Vice President and Chief Financial Officer, Northwestern Medicine Lake Forest Hospital, Lake Forest, IL, p. A192

FLYNN, Patrick, Chief Financial Officer, Warm Springs Medical Center, Warm Springs, GA, p. A167

FOARD, Mesa, Director Information technology, William S. Hall Psychiatric Institute, Columbia, SC, p. A561

FOELSCH, Paul, Vice President and Chief Information Technology Officer, North Kansas City Hospital, North Kansas City, MO, p. A374

FOELSKE, Loren
Vice President Finance, Northwestern Medicine Kishwaukee Hospital, Dekalb, IL, p. A185
Vice President Finance, Northwestern Medicine Valley West Hospital, Sandwich, IL, p. A200

FOGARTY, John M., President and Chief Executive Officer, Beth Israel Deaconess Hospital–Needham Campus, Needham, MA, p. A309

FOGARTY, Kathleen R., MS, Director, Kansas City Veterans Affairs Medical Center, Kansas City, MO, p. A370

FOGELSON, Julia, R.N., Chief Operating Officer and Chief Nursing Executive, French Hospital Medical Center, San Luis Obispo, CA, p. A89

FOGG, Robert W, Director Finance, Lake Taylor Transitional Care Hospital, Norfolk, VA, p. A672

FOGLE, Dennis, Vice President of Human Resources, Rush Memorial Hospital, Rushville, IN, p. A219

FOJTASEK, Georgia R., R.N., President and Chief Executive Officer, Henry Ford Allegiance Health, Jackson, MI, p. A323

FOLEY, Chris, Chief of Medicine, Children's Hospital Of The King's Daughters, Norfolk, VA, p. A671

FOLEY, Crystal, Director Human Resources, Rockdale Hospital, Rockdale, TX, p. A640

FOLEY, James T CPA, Vice President and Chief Financial Officer, Shore Medical Center, Somers Point, NJ, p. A420

FOLEY, Jay
Chief Operating Officer, Southwestern Regional Medical Center, Tulsa, OK, p. A518
Interim President and Chief Executive Officer, Southwestern Regional Medical Center, Tulsa, OK, p. A518

FOLEY, John, Chief Information Officer, Allegheny General Hospital, Pittsburgh, PA, p. A546

FOLEY, Michael M.D., Chief Medical Officer, North Okaloosa Medical Center, Crestview, FL, p. A122

FOLEY, Regina R.N., FACHE, Vice President Nursing and Operations, Hackensack Meridian Health Ocean Medical Center, Brick Township, NJ, p. A412

FOLK, Jeffrey R M.D., Vice President Medical Affairs and Chief Medical Officer, Piedmont Newnan Hospital, Newnan, GA, p. A162

FOLKENBERG, Todd, Chief Executive Officer, Castle Rock Adventist Hospital, Castle Rock, CO, p. A99

FOLL, Gary R, Chief Financial Officer, Atchison Hospital, Atchison, KS, p. A238

FOLLETT, Mike, Interim Chief Executive Officer, Stillwater Billings Clinic, Columbus, MT, p. A383

FOLLETT, Traci, Director Clinical Infomatics, Sierra View Medical Center, Porterville, CA, p. A80

FOLLOWELL, Rob, Chief Executive Officer, Southern Tennessee Regional Health System–Winchester, Winchester, TN, p. A590

FOLSKE, Lance, Chief Executive Officer, Carrollton Springs, Carrollton, TX, p. A601

FOLSOM, Lori S, Assistant Vice President Human Resources, Tift Regional Medical Center, Tifton, GA, p. A166

FOLTZ, JoAnn M., R.N., Chief Executive Officer, Sanford Wheaton Medical Center, Wheaton, MN, p. A350

FONDA, Joan, Chief Nursing Officer, Twin Cities Community Hospital, Templeton, CA, p. A93

FONDESSY, Terrence M.D., Vice President Medical Affairs, Promedica Fostoria Community Hospital, Fostoria, OH, p. A491

FONDREN, Shay, Administrator, Hale County Hospital, Greensboro, AL, p. A18

FONG, Joseph, Administrator, Providence Seward Medical Center, Seward, AK, p. A27

FONKEN, Paul M.D., Chief of Staff, Estes Park Medical Center, Estes Park, CO, p. A102

FONTAINE–WESTHART, Mark, Associate Director, Bedford Veterans Affairs Medical Center, Edith Nourse Rogers Memorial Veterans Hospital, Bedford, MA, p. A302

FONTENAULT, Richard, Director Information Systems, Medical City Green Oaks Hospital, Dallas, TX, p. A606

FONTENELLE, Mary, Executive Nurse Director, Eastern Louisiana Mental Health System, Jackson, LA, p. A276

FONTENOT, Jude, Administrator, Lafayette General Medical Center, Lafayette, LA, p. A278

FONTENOT, Teri G., FACHE, President and Chief Executive Officer, Woman's Hospital, Baton Rouge, LA, p. A271

FONTENOT, Terrie, Chief Nursing Officer, Sacred Heart Hospital Pensacola, Pensacola, FL, p. A139

FONTENOT, Theresa
Administrator, Oceans Behavioral Hospital Of Crowley, Rayne, LA, p. A284
Executive Director, Oceans Behavioral Hospital Of Opelousas, Opelousas, LA, p. A284

FONZIE, Juril, Director Human Resources, Helena Regional Medical Center, Helena, AR, p. A44

FOOTE, Donald E, Fiscal Officer, Wilkes–Barre Veterans Affairs Medical Center, Wilkes, PA, p. A554

FOOTE, John, Chief Information Officer, Manchester Veterans Affairs Medical Center, Manchester, NH, p. A409

FOOTE, Mark, Chief Financial Officer, Madera Community Hospital, Madera, CA, p. A72

FORAND, Angela, Director, William S. Hall Psychiatric Institute, Columbia, SC, p. A561

FORBES, Brenda, Controller, Healthsouth Rehabilitation Hospital Of Fort Smith, Fort Smith, AR, p. A43

FORBES, Dan, Vice President Human Resources, Ohsu Hospital, Portland, OR, p. A525

FORBES, Geri, Chief Executive Officer, Whidbeyhealth, Coupeville, WA, p. A679

FORBES, Jonathan, Director Human Resources, Ashtabula County Medical Center, Ashtabula, OH, p. A480

FORBES, Ronald O M.D., Medical Director, Central State Hospital, Petersburg, VA, p. A672

FORBES, Vidette J R.N., Chief Nursing Officer and Chief Operating Officer, Healthsouth Rehabilitation Hospital – Austin, Austin, TX, p. A595

FORBORT, Gordy, Chief Financial Officer, Firstlight Health System, Mora, MN, p. A344

FORD, Alisa, Vice President Human Resources, The University Of Kansas Health System, Kansas City, KS, p. A244

FORD, Angelique, Administrator Human Resources, Spring Valley Hospital Medical Center, Las Vegas, NV, p. A404

FORD, Cindy R.N., Chief Nursing Officer, Harrisburg Medical Center, Harrisburg, IL, p. A189

FORD, Cora, Vice President Human Resources, Our Lady Of The Lake Regional Medical Center, Baton Rouge, LA, p. A271

FORD, Donald, M.D., Interim President, Hillcrest Hospital, Cleveland, OH, p. A486

FORD, James, Director Human Resources, Sparks Medical Center – Van Buren, Van Buren, AR, p. A50

FORD, Jarvis, Chief Executive Officer, Healthsouth Rehabilitation Hospital Of Mechanicsburg, Mechanicsburg, PA, p. A540

FORD, Karen, Chief Nursing Officer, Sabine Medical Center, Many, LA, p. A280

FORD, LeeAnn, Director Human Resources and Imaging, The Physicians Centre Hospital, Bryan, TX, p. A600

FORD, Marcia F, Chief Operating Officer, Hawthorn Children Psychiatric Hospital, Saint Louis, MO, p. A377

FORD, Michael, Vice President Patient Services, Wood County Hospital, Bowling Green, OH, p. A482

FORD, Timothy R., President and Chief Executive Officer, Springfield Hospital, Springfield, VT, p. A663

FORDE, Steve, Chief Financial Officer, Nelson County Health System, Mcville, ND, p. A477

FORDE, Terry, President and Chief Executive Officer, Adventist Healthcare, Gaithersburg, MD, p. B7

FORDYCE, Brian, Director Information Technology, Roosevelt Medical Center, Culbertson, MT, p. A383

FORDYCE, Carol, Director Patient Care Services, Sullivan County Memorial Hospital, Milan, MO, p. A373

FORDYCE, Michael L., President and Chief Executive Officer, Craig Hospital, Englewood, CO, p. A102

FOREMAN, Christopher, Director Human Resources, Santa Rosa Medical Center, Milton, FL, p. A134

FOREMAN, Kim M.D., Chief of Staff, Texas Spine & Joint Hospital, Tyler, TX, p. A651

FOREMAN, Lee Ann
Vice President Human Resources, Mississippi Baptist Medical Center, Jackson, MS, p. A357
Vice President Human Resources, Select Specialty Hospital – Belhaven, Jackson, MS, p. A357

FOREMAN, Nena, Chief Nursing Officer, Palo Verde Hospital, Blythe, CA, p. A54

FORESE, Laura M.D., M.P.H., Executive Vice President and Chief Medical Officer, New York–Presbyterian Hospital, New Rochelle, NY, p. A444

FOREST, Karen, Health Care Manager, State Penitentiary Hospital, Walla Walla, WA, p. A689

FORET, Chris M.D., Chief of Staff, Riverside Medical Center, Franklinton, LA, p. A275

FORET, Robert, Chief Financial Officer, Yoakum Community Hospital, Yoakum, TX, p. A655

FORGE, Brenda J, Vice President, Human Resources, Regional West Medical Center, Scottsbluff, NE, p. A399

FORGEY, Warren, CPA, FACHE, President and Chief Executive Officer, Schneck Medical Center, Seymour, IN, p. A219

FORKEL, Todd
Interim Chief Executive Officer, Avera St. Mary's Hospital, Pierre, SD, p. A571
President and Chief Executive Officer, Avera St. Luke's Hospital, Aberdeen, SD, p. A568

FORKNER, Christine, Executive Vice President and Chief Financial Officer, National Jewish Health, Denver, CO, p. A101

FORNIER–JOHNSON, Michelle, Group Vice President Human Resources, St. Anthony Hospital, Lakewood, CO, p. A105

FORREST, Brian, Vice President Human Resources, Cayuga Medical Center At Ithaca, Ithaca, NY, p. A437

FORREST, Mary Helen R.N., Chief Nursing Officer, Uams Medical Center, Little Rock, AR, p. A46

FORREST, Molly, President and Chief Executive Officer, Joyce Eisenberg–Keefer Medical Center, Reseda, CA, p. A82

FORRESTER, John M, Director Information Services, Hamilton Medical Center, Dalton, GA, p. A156

FORSCH, Randall T M.D., M.P.H., Chief Medical Officer, St. Joseph Mercy Chelsea, Chelsea, MI, p. A316

FORSTER, Tracy B R.N., Senior Director of Nursing, Novant Health Matthews Medical Center, Matthews, NC, p. A466

FORSTNER, Jim, Chief Operating Officer, Dekalb Medical At North Decatur, Decatur, GA, p. A156

FORSYTH, Beth, Chief Operating Officer, Good Samaritan Medical Center, Lafayette, CO, p. A104

FORSYTH, Larry, Director Information Services, Ou Medical Center, Oklahoma City, OK, p. A513

FORT, Claudio D., President and Chief Executive Officer, North Country Hospital And Health Center, Newport, VT, p. A662

FORT, Glenn, Chief Medical Officer, Landmark Medical Center, Woonsocket, RI, p. A557

FORTENBERRY, Denise, Chief Nursing Officer and Chief Compliance Officer, Cypress Pointe Surgical Hospital, Hammond, LA, p. A275

FORTENBERRY, Doris, Coordinator Human Resources, Delta Memorial Hospital, Dumas, AR, p. A42

FORTENBERRY, Rob, Chief Information Officer, Mann–Grandstaff Veterans Affairs Medical Center, Spokane, WA, p. A686

FORTIER, Jeanne M, R.N., Chief Nursing Officer and Interim Chief Operating Officer, Grace Cottage Hospital, Townshend, VT, p. A663

FORTIN, Amanda, Manager Finance, Decatur Health Systems, Oberlin, KS, p. A248

FORTIN, Laura R.N., Chief Operating Officer, St. Joseph Medical Center, Houston, TX, p. A622

FORTNEY, John
Chief Medical Officer, Adena Pike Medical Center, Waverly, OH, p. A502
Senior System Medical Advisor, Adena Medical Center, Chillicothe, OH, p. A483

FORTUNATO-HABIB, Mary, Chief Nursing Officer, Healthalliance Hospitals, Leominster, MA, p. A308

FOSBERG, Renee, Chief Information Officer, Emerson Hospital, Concord, MA, p. A306

FOSINA, Michael, M.P.H., FACHE, President, New York–Presbyterian/Lawrence Hospital, Bronxville, NY, p. A432

FOSNESS, Nick, Chief Executive Officer, Marshall County Healthcare Center Avera, Britton, SD, p. A568

FOSNOCHT, Kevin M.D., Chief Medical Officer and Associate Executive Director, Penn Presbyterian Medical Center, Philadelphia, PA, p. A545

FOSS, David, Chief Information Officer, New London Hospital, New London, NH, p. A410

FOSS, R Coleman., Chief Executive Officer, Tennova Healthcare – Cleveland, Cleveland, TN, p. A577

FOSS, R Coleman, Chief Executive Officer, Tennova Healthcare – Cleveland, Cleveland, TN, p. A577

FOSSUM, John, Chief Executive Officer, Ely–Bloomenson Community Hospital, Ely, MN, p. A339

FOSTER, Barbara A, Regional Human Resources Director, Select Specialty Hospital—Wilmington, Wilmington, DE, p. A116

FOSTER, Becky
Employee Relations Specialist, Sanford Tracy Medical Center, Tracy, MN, p. A349
Employee Relations Specialist, Sanford Westbrook Medical Center, Westbrook, MN, p. A350

FOSTER, Beverly, Chief Executive Officer, Kindred Hospital Chicago–Northlake, Northlake, IL, p. A195

FOSTER, Bob, Chief Information Officer, South Georgia Medical Center, Valdosta, GA, p. A166

FOSTER, Brian, Chief Information Officer, Vail Valley Health Hospital, Vail, CO, p. A108

FOSTER, Carolyn
Chief Financial Officer, Peacehealth Peace Island Medical Center, Friday Harbor, WA, p. A681
Interim Executive Director and Chief Financial Officer, Peacehealth St. Joseph Medical Center, Bellingham, WA, p. A678

FOSTER, Charles, Regional Director Human Resources, Christus Southeast Texas Hospital, Beaumont, TX, p. A597

FOSTER, Chris, Director Health Information Management, Deer Lodge Medical Center, Deer Lodge, MT, p. A384

FOSTER, Daniel J, Chief Financial Officer, Northern Utah Rehabilitation Hospital, South Ogden, UT, p. A661

FOSTER, Gary, R.N.
Associate Administrator, Banner Estrella Medical Center, Phoenix, AZ, p. A33
Vice President and Chief Financial Officer, Saratoga Hospital, Saratoga Springs, NY, p. A452

FOSTER, Kennetha, Chief Nursing Officer, Mission Regional Medical Center, Mission, TX, p. A633

FOSTER, Larry, R.N., MSN, Chief Executive Officer, Kindred Chicago–Central Hospital, Chicago, IL, p. A181

FOSTER, Michael, Director Information Systems, East Cooper Medical Center, Mount Pleasant, SC, p. A564

FOSTER, Mickey, President, Moses H. Cone Memorial Hospital, Greensboro, NC, p. A463

FOSTER, Mike, Manager Information Systems, Moab Regional Hospital, Moab, UT, p. A657

FOSTER, Mitzi, Director Information Services, Southern Tennessee Regional Health System–Pulaski, Pulaski, TN, p. A588

FOSTER, Rebecca MSN, R.N., Chief Nursing Officer, Cumberland Medical Center, Crossville, TN, p. A578

FOSTER, Robert, Director Human Resources, L. V. Stabler Memorial Hospital, Greenville, AL, p. A18

FOSTER, Stephanie MSN, R.N., Chief Nursing Officer, Longview Regional Medical Center, Longview, TX, p. A630

FOSTER, Steven, Chief Executive Officer, Chi St. Luke's Health – Patients Medical Center, Pasadena, TX, p. A637

FOSTER, Terri, Hospital Finance Officer, Baylor Regional Medical Center At Grapevine, Grapevine, TX, p. A617

FOSTER, Timothy, Acting Chief Medical Officer, Newton–Wellesley Hospital, Newton Lower Falls, MA, p. A309

FOSTER, Wanda R.N., MS, FACHE, MSN, Vice President Nursing, Mcdonough District Hospital, Macomb, IL, p. A192

FOTIADIS, George M.D., Chief of Staff, Clarke County Hospital, Osceola, IA, p. A233

FOTTER, Robert L, Chief Financial Officer, Littleton Regional Healthcare, Littleton, NH, p. A409

FOTTER, Robert, Chief Financial Officer, Pennsylvania Psychiatric Institute, Harrisburg, PA, p. A536

FOUGHT, Scott, Vice President Finance, Promedica Bay Park Hospital, Oregon, OH, p. A497

FOULKE, Elvia, Executive Vice President and Chief Operating Officer, Foothill Presbyterian Hospital, Glendora, CA, p. A62

FOUNTAIN, Aaron, Chief Information Officer, Brandon Regional Hospital, Brandon, FL, p. A121

FOUNTAIN, Wesley D, Chief Financial Officer, St. David's South Austin Medical Center, Austin, TX, p. A596

FOUREZ, Yvonne, Chief Financial Officer, Washington County Memorial Hospital, Potosi, MO, p. A375

FOURNIER, Joseph, Chief Human Resources Officer, Michigan Medicine, Ann Arbor, MI, p. A314

FOURRE, Mark
Chief Executive Officer, Waldo County General Hospital, Belfast, ME, p. A290
Senior Vice President and Chief Medical Officer, Lincolnhealth, Damariscotta, ME, p. A290

FOUSE, Carla, Chief Nursing Officer, St. Vincent Randolph Hospital, Winchester, IN, p. A221

FOUSE, Sarah, Associate Director of Patient Services, Captain James A. Lovell Federal Health Care Center, North Chicago, IL, p. A195

FOUST, Lisa
Senior Vice President Human Resources, John Muir Behavioral Health Center, Concord, CA, p. A56
Senior Vice President Human Resources, John Muir Medical Center, Concord, Concord, CA, p. A56
Senior Vice President, Human Resources, John Muir Medical Center, Walnut Creek, Walnut Creek, CA, p. A96

FOUST–COFIELD, Misti R.N., Vice President and Chief Nursing Officer, Reid Health, Richmond, IN, p. A219

FOUTS, Phillip, Chief Financial Officer, Fannin Regional Hospital, Blue Ridge, GA, p. A152

FOUTZ, Patricia, Director Human Resources, Bath Community Hospital, Hot Springs, VA, p. A669

FOWLER, Andrew, Vice President Information Services, Atlantic General Hospital, Berlin, MD, p. A296

FOWLER, Barry, Director Human and System Resources, Clark Fork Valley Hospital, Plains, MT, p. A387

FOWLER, Brian, Information Technology Director, Jeff Davis Hospital, Hazlehurst, GA, p. A158

FOWLER, Kate, Chief Financial Officer, West Valley Medical Center, Caldwell, ID, p. A172

FOWLER, Kevin N., President and Chief Executive Officer, Cabell Huntington Hospital, Huntington, WV, p. A692

FOWLER, Kevin, Director Finance, Putnam County Hospital, Greencastle, IN, p. A209

FOWLER, Marcia, Chief Executive Officer, Bournewood Health Systems, Brookline, MA, p. A305

FOWLER, Maureen, Director Human Resources, Conifer Park, Glenville, NY, p. A436

FOWLER, Ruth, Senior Vice President and Chief Financial Officer, Children's Healthcare Of Atlanta, Atlanta, GA, p. A150

FOWLER, Ryan, Chief Administrative Officer, Lower Umpqua Hospital District, Reedsport, OR, p. A526

FOWLER, Steven M.D., President Medical Staff, Genesis Medical Center, Dewitt, De Witt, IA, p. A225

FOX, Alan, Chief Financial Officer, Saint Francis Memorial Hospital, San Francisco, CA, p. A87

FOX, Carol J. M.D., Senior Vice President and Chief Medical Officer, Excela Latrobe Area Hospital, Latrobe, PA, p. A538

FOX, David, President, Advocate Good Samaritan Hospital, Downers Grove, IL, p. A186

FOX, Debra, Chief Nursing Officer, University Medical Center, Las Vegas, NV, p. A404

FOX, E. Kay, Director of Nursing, Black River Medical Center, Poplar Bluff, MO, p. A375

FOX, Jay, President, Baylor Scott & White Medical Center – Round Rock, Round Rock, TX, p. A640

FOX, Jerry Jr, Chief Information Officer, Alton Memorial Hospital, Alton, IL, p. A177

FOX, Jessica, Director of Human Resources, Aspirus Riverview Hospital And Clinics, Inc., Wisconsin Rapids, WI, p. A716

FOX, John A. M.D., Chief of Staff, Shriners Hospitals For Children–Shreveport, Shreveport, LA, p. A286

FOX, John M.D., Medical Director, Vibra Hospital Of San Diego, San Diego, CA, p. A86

FOX, John T., President and Chief Executive Officer, Beaumont Health, Southfield, MI, p. B21

FOX, Leana MSN, Interim Chief Nurse Executive, Bon Secours Maryview Medical Center, Portsmouth, VA, p. A673

FOX, Randy, Director Performance Improvement and Risk Management, Lakeland Behavioral Health System, Springfield, MO, p. A379

FOX, Starla, Director of Nursing, Bristol Bay Area Health Corporation, Dillingham, AK, p. A26

FOX, Susan, President and Chief Executive Officer, White Plains Hospital Center, White Plains, NY, p. A456

FOX, William, Chief Executive Officer, AMG Specialty Hospital – Las Vegas, Las Vegas, NV, p. A402

FOXX, Randy, Chief Financial Officer, Boone Memorial Hospital, Madison, WV, p. A693

FOY, Gregory S., Human Resources System Leader, Scheurer Hospital, Pigeon, MI, p. A328

FRACHISEUR, Kenny, Chief Information Officer, Ouachita County Medical Center, Camden, AR, p. A41

FRACICA, Phil M.D., Vice President and Chief Medical Officer, Mercy Gilbert Medical Center, Gilbert, AZ, p. A29

FRACK, Darla R.N., RN, Vice President, Patient Services, St. Luke's Hospital – Anderson Campus, Easton, PA, p. A534

FRACK, Gina, Interim Chief Executive Officer, Norton County Hospital, Norton, KS, p. A247

FRAHER, Francis D, Vice President and Chief Financial Officer, Northwestern Memorial Hospital, Northwestern Memorial Hospital, Chicago, IL, p. A182

FRAIOLA, Anthony, Associate Administrator Administrative and Support Services, Hawaii State Hospital, Kaneohe, HI, p. A170

FRAKER, Steve, Chief Financial Officer, Banner Churchill Community Hospital, Fallon, NV, p. A401

FRALICKER, Tammy MS, R.N., Chief Nursing Officer, Crawford Memorial Hospital, Robinson, IL, p. A198

FRAME, Angela, Chief Financial Officer, Jackson General Hospital, Ripley, WV, p. A695

FRAME, Ken, Chief Nursing Officer, Ashtabula County Medical Center, Ashtabula, OH, p. A480

FRANCE, Cheryl M.D., Chief Medical Officer, William R. Sharpe, Jr. Hospital, Weston, WV, p. A697

FRANCE, James M.D., Chief of Staff, Conway Regional Medical Center, Conway, AR, p. A41

FRANCETICH, Kane, Chief Information Officer, Gritman Medical Center, Moscow, ID, p. A174

FRANCIK, Tamara, Human Resources Generalist, Thayer County Health Services, Hebron, NE, p. A394

FRANCIOLI, Carl H, Vice President Finance, Johns Hopkins Bayview Medical Center, Baltimore, MD, p. A294

FRANCIS, Carolyn R.N., MSN, Director of Nursing, Lasalle General Hospital, Jena, LA, p. A276

FRANCIS, Christy, Chief Executive Officer, Hemphill County Hospital, Canadian, TX, p. A600

FRANCIS, Jeffrey, Vice President Finance and Chief Financial Officer, Methodist Jennie Edmundson Hospital, Council Bluffs, IA, p. A225

FRANCIS, Lana B., Chief Executive Officer, Lasalle General Hospital, Jena, LA, p. A276

FRANCIS, Mark J., President and Chief Executive Officer, Colorado Canyons Hospital And Medical Center, Fruita, CO, p. A103

FRANCIS, Mark J, President and Chief Executive Officer, Colorado Canyons Hospital And Medical Center, Fruita, CO, p. A103

FRANCIS, Perry, Supervisory Information Technology Specialist, Chinle Comprehensive Health Care Facility, Chinle, AZ, p. A28

FRANCIS, Rebekah, JD
Chief Financial Officer, Aurora Behavioral Health System East, Tempe, AZ, p. A37
Chief Financial Officer, Aurora Behavioral Health System West, Glendale, AZ, p. A30

FRANCISCO, Gerard E M.D., Chief Medical Officer, Tirr Memorial Hermann, Houston, TX, p. A623

FRANCKOWIAK, Debra, Executive Director, Children's Hospital Of Wisconsin–Fox Valley, Neenah, WI, p. A708

FRANCO, Glenda, Director, Human Resources, Vibra Hospital Of Sacramento, Folsom, CA, p. A59

FRANCO, Luis M.D., Medical Director, United Medical Rehabilitation Hospital, Hammond, LA, p. A276

FRANCO, Richard, Chief Financial Officer, Community First Medical Center, Chicago, IL, p. A180

FRANCO, Roger, Director Human Resources, St. John's Episcopal Hospital–South Shore, New Rochelle, NY, p. A446

FRANCO, Rosemary, Chief Nursing Officer, Cochran Memorial Hospital, Morton, TX, p. A634

FRANCOIS, Fritz M.D., Chief Medical Officer, NYU Langone Hospitals, New Rochelle, NY, p. A446

FRANCOIS, Gregory La, President, The Aroostook Medical Center, Presque Isle, ME, p. A293

FRANDSEN, Jeff, Chief Executive Officer, Healthsouth Rehabilitation Hospital Of Utah, Sandy, UT, p. A661

FRANK, Barbara, Human Resource Specialist, Caro Center, Caro, MI, p. A316

FRANK, Daniel, Chief Financial Officer, Longmont United Hospital, Longmont, CO, p. A105

FRANK, Debra, Chief Financial Officer, Ness County Hospital District No 2, Ness City, KS, p. A247

FRANK, James, CPA, Chief Executive Officer, Providence Medical Center, Wayne, NE, p. A400

FRANK, Kevin, Administrator, Louisiana Extended Care Hospital Of Lafayette, Lafayette, LA, p. A278

FRANK, Kim, Chief Human Resources Officer, Virginia Gay Hospital, Vinton, IA, p. A235

FRANK, Mitchell, Chief Financial Officer, Tennova Healthcare–Shelbyville, Shelbyville, TN, p. A589

FRANK, Patricia, Chief Nursing Officer, Henry County Hospital, Napoleon, OH, p. A496

FRANK, Robert A
  Senior Vice President of Operations, University Of Maryland Shore Medical Center At Chestertown, Chestertown, MD, p. A297
  Senior Vice President of Operations, University Of Maryland Shore Medical Center At Easton, Easton, MD, p. A298
  Senior Vice President Operations, University Of Maryland Shore Medical Center At Dorchester, Cambridge, MD, p. A297

FRANK, Rondel, Administrator, United Medical Rehabilitation Hospital, Gretna, LA, p. A275

FRANK, Stanley , Chief Executive Officer, Ohio Hospital For Psychiatry, Columbus, OH, p. B4

FRANK, Stanley, Chief Executive Officer, Ohio Hospital For Psychiatry, Columbus, OH, p. A487

FRANK, Thomas, Chief Operating Officer, North Country Hospital And Health Center, Newport, VT, p. A662

FRANK–LIGHTFOOT, Loraine R.N., Vice President, Patient Care Services and Chief Nursing Officer, Munson Medical Center, Traverse City, MI, p. A332

FRANKE, Jenny, Director Human Resources, Rehabilitation Hospital Of Wisconsin, Waukesha, WI, p. A714

FRANKE, John, Chief Financial Officer, Baptist Health Lexington, Lexington, KY, p. A260

FRANKE, Paul M.D., Chief Medical Officer, Alaska Native Medical Center, Anchorage, AK, p. A25

FRANKEL, Harris M.D., Interim Chief Medical Officer, Nebraska Medicine – Nebraska Medical Center, Omaha, NE, p. A397

FRANKEL, Michele, Associate Executive Director Finance, Glen Cove Hospital, Glen Cove, NY, p. A436

FRANKEN, Stephanie, Vice President Operational Finance, Chi St. Alexius Health – Dickinson Medical Center, Dickinson, ND, p. A475

FRANKENSTEIN, Richard M.D., Vice President and Chief Medical Officer, Henry Mayo Newhall Hospital, Valencia, CA, p. A95

FRANKL, Angie, Director Human Resources, Adair County Health System, Greenfield, IA, p. A228

FRANKLIN, Chuck M.D., Chief Medical Staff, Weston County Health Services, Newcastle, WY, p. A719

FRANKLIN, Clay, Chief Executive Officer, Alliancehealth Midwest, Midwest City, OK, p. A510

FRANKLIN, Ed, Chief Human Resources Officer, Page Hospital, Page, AZ, p. A32

FRANKLIN, James P., Administrator, Baptist Memorial Hospital – Calhoun, Calhoun City, MS, p. A353

FRANKLIN, Jennifer R.N., Chief Clinical Officer, Yoakum Community Hospital, Yoakum, TX, p. A655

FRANKLIN, Matthew, Director Human Resources, Warren General Hospital, Warren, PA, p. A552

FRANKLIN, Michael A., FACHE, President and Chief Executive Officer, Atlantic General Hospital, Berlin, MD, p. A296

FRANKLIN, Tammy, Manager Personnel and Marketing, Covenant Hospital–Levelland, Levelland, TX, p. A629

FRANKO, Stephen
  Senior Vice President and Chief Financial Officer, St. Vincent's Medical Center, Bridgeport, CT, p. A109
  Vice President Finance and Chief Financial Officer, Mount St. Mary's Hospital And Health Center, Lewiston, NY, p. A438
  Vice President Finance and Chief Financial Officer, Regional Hospital Of Scranton, Scranton, PA, p. A550

FRANKOVITCH, John C., President and Chief Executive Officer, Weirton Medical Center, Weirton, WV, p. A696

FRANKS, Cathy RN, Chief Operating Officer, Community Medical Center Of Izard County, Calico Rock, AR, p. A41

FRANKS, Charles, Chief Human Resources, Louis Stokes Cleveland Veterans Affairs Medical Center, Cleveland, OH, p. A486

FRANKS, Dennis
  Interim Chief Financial Officer, Doctors' Hospital Of Michigan, Pontiac, MI, p. A328

Vice President Operations, Doctors' Hospital Of Michigan, Pontiac, MI, p. A328
  Chief Executive Officer, Neosho Memorial Regional Medical Center, Chanute, KS, p. A239

FRANSEN, Mitchell, Chief Financial Officer, Mesa View Regional Hospital, Mesquite, NV, p. A404

FRANSON, John K M.D., Chief Medical Staff, Caribou Memorial Hospital And Living Center, Soda Springs, ID, p. A176

FRANTZ, Steven, Chief Financial Officer, Saint Francis Hospital, Memphis, TN, p. A585

FRANTZ, Vincent M.D., Chief of Staff, Plumas District Hospital, Quincy, CA, p. A81

FRANTZ, Zoe, Chief Executive Officer, Sycamore Springs Hospital, Lafayette, IN, p. A214

FRANZ, Eric, Vice President, Finance and Chief Financial Officer, Graham Hospital Association, Canton, IL, p. A179

FRANZ, Staci, Director Human Resources, St. Luke's Rehabilitation Institute, Spokane, WA, p. A687

FRANZ, Thomas M.D., Medical Director, Healthsouth Harmarville Rehabilitation Hospital, Pittsburgh, PA, p. A546

FRANZEL, Carrie, Chief Nursing Officer, Huron Medical Center, Bad Axe, MI, p. A314

FRANZELLA, Susan, Human Resource Business Partner, Kaiser Permanente San Jose Medical Center, San Jose, CA, p. A88

FRARDO, Virgil M.D., Medical Director, Healthsouth Rehabilitation Hospital–Wichita Falls, Wichita Falls, TX, p. A654

FRASCA, Edith, Controller and Chief Financial Officer, The Pavilion, Champaign, IL, p. A180

FRASCH, Sara, Chief Human Resource Officer, University Of New Mexico Hospitals, Albuquerque, NM, p. A425

FRASER, Cathryn, Chief Human Resources Officer, Mayo Clinic Hospital – Rochester, Rochester, MN, p. A346

FRASER, James, Administrator Finance, Via Christi Hospital Manhattan, Inc., Manhattan, KS, p. A246

FRASER, John M., FACHE, President and Chief Executive Officer, Nebraska Methodist Health System, Inc., Omaha, NE, p. B88

FRASIER, Nora R.N., FACHE, Chief Nursing Officer, Methodist Mansfield Medical Center, Mansfield, TX, p. A631

FRATZKE, Mark, R.N., Senior Vice President and Area Manager, Kaiser Permanente Oakland Medical Center, Oakland, CA, p. A77

FRAUENHOFER, Chris, Chief Financial Officer, Maine Coast Memorial Hospital, Ellsworth, ME, p. A291

FRAZEE, Kim R.N., Vice President Physician and Business Development, Hackensack Meridian Health Southern Ocean Medical Center, Manahawkin, NJ, p. A416

FRAZIER, Amy, Supervisor Management Information Systems, Wetzel County Hospital, New Martinsville, WV, p. A694

FRAZIER, Brandon, Chief Financial Officer, Seaside Behavioral Center, New OrleansRiver Oaks Hospital, New Orleans, LA, p. A283

FRAZIER, Derrick A., FACHE, Chief Executive Officer, Morehouse General Hospital, Bastrop, LA, p. A270

FRAZIER, Joel L M.D., Medical Director, Onecore Health, Oklahoma City, OK, p. A513

FRAZIER, Kimberly R.N., Chief Nursing Officer, East Los Angeles Doctors Hospital, Los Angeles, CA, p. A68

FRAZIER, Shane, Chief Executive Officer, Pinnacle Pointe Hospital, Little Rock, AR, p. A46

FREAS, Mary Ann, Senior Vice President and Chief Financial Officer, Southwest General Health Center, Middleburg Heights, OH, p. A496

FRED, Mark R.N., Chief Operating Officer, Kirby Medical Center, Monticello, IL, p. A194

FREDEBOELLING, Elizabeth E., MSN, R.N., Chief Executive Officer, Healthbridge Children's Hospital Of Houston, Houston, TX, p. A620

FREDERICK, Brenda, Director Human Resources, Laurel Ridge Treatment Center, San Antonio, TX, p. A642

FREDERICK, Dessa, Manager Human Resources, St. James Behavioral Health Hospital, Gonzales, LA, p. A275

FREDERICK, Gretchen A R.N., Director Patient Care Services, Buffalo Hospital, Buffalo, MN, p. A337

FREDERICK, John, Chief Financial Officer, West Central Georgia Regional Hospital, Columbus, GA, p. A155

FREDERICK, Ryannon, Chief Nursing Officer, Mayo Clinic Jacksonville, Jacksonville, FL, p. A128

FREDERICKS, Raymond F., President and CEO, JFK Medical Center, Edison, NJ, p. A413

FREDERICKSON, Kathy, Information Systems Site Lead, Sutter Delta Medical Center, Antioch, CA, p. A51

FREDETTE, Beth, Chief Information Officer, Children's Medical Center, Dayton, OH, p. A489

FREDRICH, Nancy R.N., Chief Clinical Officer, Cooper County Memorial Hospital, Boonville, MO, p. A365

FREDRICK, Joyce, Associate Director, Veterans Affairs Central Western Massachusetts Healthcare System, Leeds, MA, p. A308

FREDRICK, Rick, Director Information Technology, Cottage Hospital, Woodsville, NH, p. A410

FREDRICKSON, Kelley, Director Information Services, Medical City Fort Worth, Fort Worth, TX, p. A614

FREDRICKSON, Mark A M.D., Medical Director, Healthsouth Rehabilitation Hospital Midland–Odessa, Midland, TX, p. A633

FREEBERN, Joseph, Executive Director, Mid–Hudson Forensic Psychiatric Center, New Hampton, NY, p. A440

FREEBORN, Fawn, Human Resources Generalist, Schoolcraft Memorial Hospital, Manistique, MI, p. A325

FREEBURG, Rick
  Chief Executive Officer, Baptist Health South Florida, Mariners Hospital, Tavernier, FL, p. A146
  Chief Executive Officer, Fishermen's Hospital, Marathon, FL, p. A131

FREEBURN, Mark, Chief Executive Officer, Helen M. Simpson Rehabilitation Hospital, Harrisburg, PA, p. A535

FREED, Nancy, Chief Financial Officer, Seiling Municipal Hospital, Seiling, OK, p. A515

FREED, Stuart, M.D.
  Chief Medical Officer, Confluence Health/Central Washington Hospital, Wenatchee, WA, p. A689
  Medical Director, Confluence Health/Wenatchee Valley Hospital, Wenatchee, WA, p. A689

FREED–SIGURDSSON, Anna M.D., Medical Director, Healthsouth Rehabilitation Hospital – Dallas, Dallas, TX, p. A605

FREEDMAN, Barry R., President and Chief Executive Officer, Einstein Medical Center Philadelphia, Philadelphia, PA, p. A543

FREEDMAN, Kenneth M.D., Chief Medical Officer, Lemuel Shattuck Hospital, Jamaica Plain, MA, p. A307

FREEDMAN, Rick, Commanding Officer, Naval Hospital Camp Lejeune, Camp Lejeune, NC, p. A458

FREEHILL, Sarah, Chief Nursing Officer, Arbuckle Memorial Hospital, Sulphur, OK, p. A516

FREEHOF, Leonard, Chief Executive Officer and Managing Director, Spring Valley Hospital Medical Center, Las Vegas, NV, p. A404

FREELAND, R Alan M.D., Chief Clinical Officer, Twin Valley Behavioral Healthcare, Columbus, OH, p. A488

FREEMAN, Brian, President, Carolinas Healthcare System Stanly, Albemarle, NC, p. A457

FREEMAN, Diane R.N., Assistant Vice President and Chief Nursing Officer, St. Luke's Lakeside Hospital, The Woodlands, TX, p. A649

FREEMAN, Donald, President and Chief Executive Officer, Preferred Management Corporation, Shawnee, OK, p. B99

FREEMAN, Gail, Chief Nursing Officer, San Gabriel Valley Medical Center, San Gabriel, CA, p. A88

FREEMAN, Jerry, Chief, Human Resources Management Services, Durham Veterans Affairs Medical Center, Durham, NC, p. A461

FREEMAN, Kimberlee R.N., MSN, Vice President Patient Care Services and Chief Nursing Officer, Wayne Healthcare, Greenville, OH, p. A492

FREEMAN, Marianne, Vice President Human Resources, Rockdale Medical Center, Conyers, GA, p. A155

FREEMAN, Michael
  Director Human Resources, Alta Vista Regional Hospital, Las Vegas, NM, p. A427
  Director Human Resources, Huhukam Memorial Hospital, Sacaton, AZ, p. A35

FREEMAN, Mike, Director Information Technology, Sentara Williamsburg Regional Medical Center, Williamsburg, VA, p. A677

FREEMAN, Peggy, Chief Physicians Services Officer, Dickinson County Healthcare System, Iron Mountain, MI, p. A323

FREEMAN, Richard
  Chief Medical Officer, St. Vincent Indianapolis Hospital, IndianapolisSt. Vincent Heart Center, Indianapolis, IN, p. A212
  President and Chief Executive Officer, Robert Wood Johnson University Hospital At Hamilton, Hamilton, NJ, p. A414

FREEMAN, Robert, Director Human Resources, Sparks Regional Medical Center, Fort Smith, AR, p. A44

FREESE DECKER, Christina, FACHE, President, Spectrum Health Hospital Group, Spectrum Health – Butterworth Hospital, Grand Rapids, MI, p. A321

FREID–SCHEPPKE, Denise, Chief Accounting Officer, Oakleaf Surgical Hospital, Eau Claire, WI, p. A701

FREIER, Toby, President, New Ulm Medical Center, New Ulm, MN, p. A345

FREIJ, Walid M.D., Chief of Staff, Vaughan Regional Medical Center, Selma, AL, p. A23

FREILICH, Josh, Vice President and Chief Nurse Executive, Mercy Hospital Of Folsom, Folsom, CA, p. A59

FREIMARK, Jeffrey P., Chief Executive Officer, Miami Jewish Home And Hospital For Aged, Miami, FL, p. A133

FREISCHLAG, Julie Ann
FREISCHLAG, Julie Ann., M.D., Chief Executive Officer, Wake Forest Baptist Medical Center, Winston, NC, p. A473

FREITAG, Donald M.D., Chief Medical Officer, Lynn County Hospital District, Tahoka, TX, p. A648

FREITAG, Vanessa, President, Ministry Our Lady Of Victory Hospital, Stanley, WI, p. A713

FRELING, Eric M.D., Director Medical Staff Affairs, Memorial Hospital West, Pembroke Pines, FL, p. A139

FRENCH, Dean O M.D., Chief of Staff, Faith Regional Health Services, Norfolk, NE, p. A396

FRENCH, Dean, M.D., Chief Executive Officer, Community Medical Center, Missoula, MT, p. A386

FRENCH, Holly, Chief Financial Officer, Newman Regional Health, Emporia, KS, p. A240

FRENCH, Tracy
  Chief Financial Officer, Banner Goldfield Medical Center, Apache Junction, AZ, p. A28
  Chief Financial Officer, Banner Ironwood Medical Center, San Tan Valley, AZ, p. A35

FRENGLE, Kelley
  Director, Human Resources, Peacehealth St. John Medical Center, Longview, WA, p. A682
  Senior Director, Human Resources, Peacehealth Southwest Medical Center, Vancouver, WA, p. A688

FRENIER, Karen, President, Orlando Regional Medical Center, Orlando, FL, p. A137

FRENN, Debra FACHE, Chief Patient Care Officer, Rusk County Memorial Hospital, Ladysmith, WI, p. A704

FRERER, Mary
  Chief Human Resources Officer, Freeman Health System, Joplin, MO, p. A369
  Chief Human Resources Officer, Freeman Neosho Hospital, Neosho, MO, p. A374

FRERICHS, Craig, Chief Information Technology Service, Grand Junction Veterans Health Care System, Grand Junction, CO, p. A103

FRESHOUR, David, Chief Financial Officer, Comanche County Medical Center, Comanche, TX, p. A602

FREUDENBERG, Liz, Chief Financial Officer, Healthsouth Rehabilitation Hospital Of Littleton, Littleton, CO, p. A105

FREUDENBERGER, Joe, Chief Executive Officer, Oakbend Medical Center, Richmond, TX, p. A640

FREY, Jack, Acting Business Manager, Greystone Park Psychiatric Hospital, Morris Plains, NJ, p. A416

FREY, James Jr, Acting Manager Human Resources, Greystone Park Psychiatric Hospital, Morris Plains, NJ, p. A416

FREY, Jeff, Business Administrator, Andrew Mcfarland Mental Health Center, Springfield, IL, p. A200

FREY, Paul, Director Information Technology Applications, Indiana Orthopaedic Hospital, Indianapolis, IN, p. A211

FREY, Rachel, Director Human Resources, Athens–Limestone Hospital, Athens, AL, p. A14

FREYER, Mary, Chief Operating Officer, Little Company Of Mary Hospital And Health Care Centers, Evergreen Park, IL, p. A187

FREYER, Sharon R.N., Chief Nursing Officer, Baptist Health Paducah, Paducah, KY, p. A266

FREYMULLER, Robert S., Chief Executive Officer, Summerlin Hospital Medical Center, Las Vegas, NV, p. A404

FREYSINGER, Edward E., Chief Administrative Officer, Peacehealth Ketchikan Medical Center, Ketchikan, AK, p. A26

FREYTAG, Peter, Senior Vice President Finance and Chief Financial Officer, Bristol Hospital, Bristol, CT, p. A109

FRIARTE, Pedro, Director of Physician Services, Coral Gables Hospital, Coral Gables, FL, p. A122

FRICK, Mark P, Senior Vice President Human Resources, Somerset Hospital, Somerset, PA, p. A551

FRICK, Mary Jo, Director Finance, St. Catherine's Rehabilitation Hospital, North Miami, FL, p. A136

FRICKE, Rhett D., Chief Executive Officer, Ballinger Memorial Hospital, Ballinger, TX, p. A596

FRIDAY, Jason M.D., Medical Director, Aurora Behavioral Health System East, Tempe, AZ, p. A37

FRIDAY, Lisa, Director Human Resources, Christus Lake Area Hospital, Lake Charles, LA, p. A279

FRIDKIN, Marjorie M.D., Chief Medical Officer, Garrett Regional Medical Center, Oakland, MD, p. A300

FRIED, Guy M.D., Chief Medical Officer, Magee Rehabilitation Hospital, Philadelphia, PA, p. A544

FRIED, Jeffrey M., FACHE, President and Chief Executive Officer, Beebe Healthcare, Lewes, DE, p. A115

FRIED, Tera, Manager Human Resources, West River Regional Medical Center, Hettinger, ND, p. A476

FRIEDBERG, Robert, President and Chief Executive Officer, Health Quest Systems, Inc., LaGrangeville, NY, p. B61

FRIEDEN, Robert
  Vice President Information Systems, Genesis Medical Center–Aledo, Aledo, IL, p. A177
  Vice President Information Systems, Genesis Medical Center–Davenport–West Central Park, Davenport, IA, p. A225
  Vice President Information Systems, Genesis Medical Center, Silvis, Silvis, IL, p. A200

FRIEDENBACH, Daryl, Director Fiscal Services, Floyd Valley Healthcare, Le Mars, IA, p. A230

FRIEDLINE, Jennifer R.N., Director of Nursing, Mercy Rehabilitation Hospital Springfield, Springfield, MO, p. A380

FRIEDLY, Jennifer, Chief Operating Officer and Vice President, Unitypoint Health – Waterloo, Waterloo, IA, p. A236

FRIEDMAN, Jonathan, Public Affairs Officer, Captain James A. Lovell Federal Health Care Center, North Chicago, IL, p. A195

FRIEDMAN, Lloyd M.D., Vice President Medical Affairs and Chief Operating Officer, Milford Hospital, Milford, CT, p. A111

FRIEDRICH, Daniel J. III, Chief Executive Officer, Blake Medical Center, Bradenton, FL, p. A120

FRIEL, Donald F., Executive Vice President, Holy Redeemer Hospital, Meadowbrook, PA, p. A540

FRIEL, John P., Chief Executive Officer, Bear Valley Community Hospital, Big Bear Lake, CA, p. A54

FRIELING, Jeff
  Chief Information Officer, Pathways Of Tennessee, Jackson, TN, p. A580
  Vice President and Chief Information Officer, Jackson–Madison County General Hospital, Jackson, TN, p. A580
  Vice President Information Systems, Camden General Hospital, Camden, TN, p. A575

FRIEND, Lori, Human Resources Director, Alliancehealth Seminole, Seminole, OK, p. A515

FRIERSON, Cathy, Chief Human Resource Officer, Danbury Hospital, Danbury, CT, p. A109

FRIES, Richard W, Vice President Finance, Allegheny General Hospital, Pittsburgh, PA, p. A546

FRIESEN, Dale L, Chief Financial Officer, Carelink Of Jackson, Jackson, MI, p. A323

FRIESEN, Lynette, Manager Human Resources, Henderson Health Care Services, Henderson, NE, p. A394

FRIGEN, Karen, Director Human Resources, Shriners Hospitals For Children–Twin Cities, Minneapolis, MN, p. A344

FRIGO, Dave
  Vice President Financial Planning and Treasury, Cleveland Clinic Akron General, Akron, OH, p. A479
  Chief Financial Officer, Edwin Shaw Rehab, Cuyahoga Falls, OH, p. A488
  Director Finance and Controller, Lodi Community Hospital, Lodi, OH, p. A493

FRIGON, Shelby, Chief Financial Officer, Saint Luke's South Hospital, Overland Park, KS, p. A249

FRIGY, Alan M.D., President Medical Staff, Pana Community Hospital, Pana, IL, p. A196

FRIMODIG, Mindy D.O., President Medical Staff ThedaCare Physicians Shawano, Thedacare Medical Center–Shawano, Shawano, WI, p. A712

FRISBEE, Kent, Director Human Resources, Saint Thomas Highlands Hospital, Sparta, TN, p. A589

FRISINA, Marcy, Chief Nursing Officer, Fawcett Memorial Hospital, Port Charlotte, FL, p. A140

FRITSCH, William M.D., Medical Director, Landmark Hospital Of Cape Girardeau, Cape Girardeau, MO, p. A365

FRITTON, Amy, Controller, Sierra Tucson, Tucson, AZ, p. A38

FRITTS, Doris, R.N., Executive Director, Same Day Surgery Center, Rapid City, SD, p. A572

FRITTS, Robert G, Chief Financial Officer and Senior Vice President, Carolinas Healthcare System Blue Ridge, Morganton, NC, p. A467

FRITZ, Robert, Chief Information Officer, Brook Lane Health Services, Hagerstown, MD, p. A299

FROCHTZWAJG, Stanley M.D., Chief Medical Officer, Community Memorial Hospital, Ventura, CA, p. A95

FROEHLICH, Shelley R.N., Director Nursing Services, Newport Hospital And Health Services, Newport, WA, p. A682

FROEMKE, Janet, Human Resources Officer, Chi Lisbon Health, Lisbon, ND, p. A477

FROESE, Kristi
  Chief Nursing Officer, Chi St. Luke's Health Memorial Livingston, Livingston, TX, p. A629
  Vice President Clinical Operations, Chi St. Luke's Health Memorial Livingston, Livingston, TX, p. A629

FROH, Chris, Senior Coordinator Human Resources, Select Specialty Hospital–Milwaukee, Milwaukee, WI, p. A708

FROHNHOFER, Erin J
  Director Human Resources, Southwood Psychiatric Hospital, Pittsburgh, PA, p. A547
  Vice President Human Resources, Ohio Valley Hospital, Mckees Rocks, PA, p. A540

FROISLAND, Jeffrey R, Chief Financial Officer, Mayo Clinic Hospital, Phoenix, AZ, p. A33

FROMHOLD, John A., FACHE, Chief Executive Officer, Hackensack Meridian Health Mountainside Medical Center, Montclair, NJ, p. A416

FROMM, Dan, Chief Financial Officer, Woodwinds Health Campus, Woodbury, MN, p. A351

FROMME, Richard, Chief Financial Officer, Cavalier County Memorial Hospital And Clinics, Langdon, ND, p. A477

FROMMELT, William, Director Operations and Finance, River Falls Area Hospital, River Falls, WI, p. A712

FRONZA, Sarah, President, Legacy Silverton Medical Center, Silverton, OR, p. A527

FROSCH, Kevin, Chief Financial Officer, Medina Regional Hospital, Hondo, TX, p. A619

FROST, Eric, Associate Vice President Human Resources, Upstate University Hospital, Syracuse, NY, p. A453

FROST, Joan R.N., Chief Operating Officer, Mercy Hospital Washington, Washington, MO, p. A381

FROST, Mark I, M.D.
  Senior Vice President Medical Affairs, Saint Francis Health System, Saint Francis Hospital, Tulsa, OK, p. A518
  Senior Vice President Medical Affairs, Laureate Psychiatric Clinic And Hospital, Tulsa, OK, p. A517
  Senior Vice President Medical Affairs, Saint Francis Hospital South, Tulsa, OK, p. A518

FROST, Sarah
  Administrator and Chief Operating Officer, Banner – University Medical Center South, Tucson, AZ, p. A37
  Chief Operating Officer and Administrator, University of Arizona Medical Center – South Campus, Banner – University Medical Center Tucson, Tucson, AZ, p. A37

FROWNFELTER, Penny, Chief Nursing Officer, Healthsouth Nittany Valley Rehabilitation Hospital, Pleasant Gap, PA, p. A548

FRUGE, Janie, R.N., MSN, FACHE, Chief Executive Officer, West Calcasieu Cameron Hospital, Sulphur, LA, p. A287

FRUM, Judy R.N., Chief Nursing Officer, Memorial Hospital Pembroke, Pembroke Pines, FL, p. A139

FRUM, R David.
  President, Bridgton Hospital, Bridgton, ME, p. A290
  President, Rumford Hospital, Rumford, ME, p. A293

FRY, Kenneth, Chief Financial Officer, Saint Alphonsus Regional Medical Center, Boise, ID, p. A172

FRY, Robin CPA, Market Controller, Kindred Hospital Dallas Central, Dallas, TX, p. A605

FRY, Terry R.N., Chief Nursing Officer, Upper Valley Medical Center, Troy, OH, p. A501

FRYE, Kelly D, Director Human Resources, Montgomery General Hospital, Montgomery, WV, p. A694

FRYE, Terri, Information Technology Officer, Weston County Health Services, Newcastle, WY, p. A719

FRYER, Ramona D, Chief Financial Officer, Wk Bossier Health Center, Bossier City, LA, p. A272

FRYFOGLE, Anthoney, Chief Information Officer, George Regional Hospital, Lucedale, MS, p. A358

FUCCI, Thomas, FACHE, Chief Executive Officer, Select Specialty Hospital–Erie, Erie, PA, p. A534

FUCHS, Mary Ann R.N., Vice President Patient Care and System Chief Nurse Executive, Duke University Hospital, Durham, NC, p. A461

FUEHRER, Susan, Director, Louis Stokes Cleveland Veterans Affairs Medical Center, Cleveland, OH, p. A486

FUENTES, Frances, Coordinator Human Resources, Healthsouth Rehabilitation Hospital Of San Juan, San Juan, PR, p. A726

FUENTES, Leticia, Nursing Director, San Jorge Children's Hospital, San Juan, PR, p. A726

FUENTES, Miguel A, President and Chief Executive Officer, Bronx–Lebanon Hospital Center Health Care System, New Rochelle, NY, p. A440

FUERSTENBERG, Donna, Fiscal Chief, Sheridan Veterans Affairs Medical Center, Sheridan, WY, p. A720

FUGATTE, Cheryl MSN, Vice President and Chief Nursing Officer, Jewish Hospital, Louisville, KY, p. A262

FUGITT, Jacki L., Director Employee Relations, OSF Saint Francis Medical Center, Peoria, IL, p. A197

FUGLER, Shawna R.N., Chief Nursing Officer, Memorial Hermann Surgical Hospital Kingwood, Kingwood, TX, p. A627

FUHRMAN, Bradley M.D., Physician in Chief, El Paso Children's Hospital, El Paso, TX, p. A610

FUHRMAN, Dennis, Vice President Finance, Essentia Health Fargo, Fargo, ND, p. A475

FUHRMAN, L Wesley., President and Chief Executive Officer, Warwick Manor Behavioral Health, East New Market, MD, p. A298

FUHRO, Mary, Chief Nursing Officer, Newark Beth Israel Medical Center, Newark, NJ, p. A417

FUHS, Veronica, Chief Executive Officer, Monroe County Hospital And Clinics, Albia, IA, p. A222

FUJINAKA, Jason, Manager Information System, Wahiawa General Hospital, Wahiawa, HI, p. A170

FULCHER, Cathe, Superintendent, Evansville State Hospital, Evansville, IN, p. A207

FULCHER, Kimberly, Chief Human Resources Officer, Halifax Health Medical Center Of Daytona Beach, Daytona Beach, FL, p. A123

FULCHER, Martha MSN, Chief Nursing Officer, Och Regional Medical Center, Starkville, MS, p. A362

FULKERSON, Judy, Director Human Resources, Tristar Greenview Regional Hospital, Bowling Green, KY, p. A256

FULKERSON, Kimberly, Chief Nursing Officer, Dupont Hospital, Fort Wayne, IN, p. A208

FULKERSON, Richard, Director Fiscal Services, Shriners Hospitals For Children–Springfield, Springfield, MA, p. A311

FULKERSON, William T., Chief Operating Officer, University Of Virginia Medical Center, Charlottesville, VA, p. A665

FULKS, Chris, Vice President Finance, Lake Huron Medical Center, Port Huron, MI, p. A328

FULKS, Gerald N., President, West Georgia Health, Lagrange, GA, p. A160

FULLBRIGHT, Gary D, Comptroller, Citizens Memorial Hospital, Bolivar, MO, p. A364

FULLER, Cara
 Vice President Human Resources, Unitypoint Health – Trinity Bettendorf, Bettendorf, IA, p. A222
 Vice President Human Resources, Unitypoint Health – Trinity Rock Island, Rock Island, IL, p. A199

FULLER, Cheryl, Director Information Resources, Kansas Neurological Institute, Topeka, KS, p. A252

FULLER, Dale, Vice President and Chief Information Officer, Upmc Altoona, Altoona, PA, p. A528

FULLER, David
 Director Human Resources, Porter Medical Center, Middlebury, VT, p. A662
 Interim Chief Executive Officer, Northern Louisiana Medical Center, Ruston, LA, p. A285

FULLER, Debbie, Director Health Information Systems and Chief Information Officer, Doctors Medical Center Of Modesto, Modesto, CA, p. A74

FULLER, Jami, Manager Information Technology, Catalina Island Medical Center, Avalon, CA, p. A52

FULLER, Jane, Vice President Human Resources, North Florida Regional Medical Center, Gainesville, FL, p. A125

FULLER, Jeremy, Director Information Systems, Conroe Regional Medical Center, Conroe, TX, p. A602

FULLER, Jill, R.N., President and Chief Executive Officer, Prairie Lakes Healthcare System, Watertown, SD, p. A574

FULLER, Marion, Chief of Staff, Munson Healthcare Manistee Hospital, Manistee, MI, p. A325

FULLER–WILLIAMS, Vonetta, Director Human Resources Strategic and Business Services, Baylor Scott & White Medical Center–Irving, Irving, TX, p. A624

FULLMER, John, Chief Financial Officer, Bingham Memorial Hospital, Blackfoot, ID, p. A171

FULLUM, Jane, Vice President Patient Care Services, East Alabama Medical Center, Opelika, AL, p. A22

FULTON, Lorna, Director Human Resources, Vibra Hospital Of Denver, Thornton, CO, p. A107

FULTON, Lynn, President, OSF Saint Luke Medical Center, Kewanee, IL, p. A191

FUNDERBURG, Michelle, Director Human Resources, Stephens Memorial Hospital, Breckenridge, TX, p. A599

FUNDERBURK, Mark, Executive Vice President and Administrator, University Medical Center, Lubbock, TX, p. A631

FUNG, Adrian, Director Information Systems, Tennova Healthcare–Lebanon, Lebanon, TN, p. A582

FUNK, Luann A, Administrative Assistant and Manager Human Resources, Pana Community Hospital, Pana, IL, p. A196

FUNKHOUSER, Krisy L, Manager Human Resources, Willapa Harbor Hospital, South Bend, WA, p. A686

FUQUA, David G., Chief Executive Officer, Marshall County Hospital, Benton, KY, p. A255

FUQUA, David, Director Human Resources Management, University Health Shreveport, Shreveport, LA, p. A286

FUQUA, Leon, Chief Operating Officer, Wise Health System, Decatur, TX, p. A607

FURER, Darnell F, MS, R.N.
 Vice President of Patient Care Services, Lehigh Valley Hospital – Schuylkill East Norwegian Street, Pottsville, PA, p. A548
 Vice President Patient Care Services and Chief Nursing Officer, Lehigh Valley Hospital – Schuylkill South Jackson Street, Pottsville, PA, p. A548

FURGURSON, Carol, Chief Operating Officer, Saint Louise Regional Hospital, Gilroy, CA, p. A61

FURLONG, Marian M., R.N., FACHE, President and Chief Executive Officer, Hudson Hospital And Clinic, Hudson, WI, p. A704

FURLOW, Pete, Director Information Technology Services, RMC Anniston, Anniston, AL, p. A13

FURMAN, Keith, Chief Executive Officer, Rock Springs, Georgetown, TX, p. A616

FURNAS, David, Chief Information Officer, Gila Regional Medical Center, Silver City, NM, p. A429

FURNEY, June R.N., Director of Nursing, Brooks County Hospital, Quitman, GA, p. A163

FURNISS, Scott, Vice President and Chief Financial Officer, Saint Agnes Healthcare, Baltimore, MD, p. A295

FURR, Robert, Director Information Services, Anmed Health Cannon, Pickens, SC, p. A565

FUSCHILLO, Ronald
 Chief Information Officer, Renown Rehabilitation Hospital, Reno, NV, p. A405
 Chief Information Officer, Renown South Meadows Medical Center, Reno, NV, p. A405

FUSCO, Gina, Chief Executive Officer, Foundations Behavioral Health, Doylestown, PA, p. A533

FUSCO, Kevin, Corporate Chief Operating Officer, Broward Health North, Deerfield Beach, FL, p. A123

FUSELIER, Gerald, Chief Operating Officer, Savoy Medical Center, Mamou, LA, p. A280

FUSELIER, Michael FACHE, CPA, R.N., Chief Financial Officer, Central Louisiana Surgical Hospital, Alexandria, LA, p. A269

FUSILERO, Jane, Vice President Chief Nursing Officer, H. Lee Moffitt Cancer Center And Research Institute, Tampa, FL, p. A144

FUSON, Kimberly J., Interim Regional Administrator, Kula Hospital, Kula, HI, p. B71

FUSTON, Kathie, Director Human Resources, Moore County Hospital District, Dumas, TX, p. A609

FUTCH, Margaret A., Chief Executive Officer, Healthsouth Rehabilitation Hospital, Dothan, AL, p. A17

FUTRAL, Cindy, Director Human Resources, Elmore Community Hospital, Wetumpka, AL, p. A24

FUTRELL, Cynthia MSN, R.N., Chief Nursing Officer, Marion General Hospital, Marion, IN, p. A215

FYBEL, Gary G., FACHE, Chief Executive, Senior Vice President, Scripps Memorial Hospital–La Jolla, La Jolla, CA, p. A64

G

GAAL, James G M.D., Chief of Medical Staff, Jackson General Hospital, Ripley, WV, p. A695

GAASCH, Andrew
 Chief Financial Officer, Parker Adventist Hospital, Parker, CO, pp. A106
 Chief Financial Officer, Porter Adventist Hospital, Denver, CO, p. A101

GABALDON, Karen, Chief Management Information Systems, West Palm Beach Veterans Affairs Medical Center, West Palm Beach, FL, p. A147

GABEL, Christopher, Chief Operating Officer, Larkin Behavioral Health Services, Hollywood, FL, p. A127

GABEL, Kelly, Chief of Staff, Citizens Medical Center, Colby, KS, p. A239

GABEL, Marcia, Chief Financial Officer, Lane County Hospital, Dighton, KS, p. A240

GABLE, Beth, Administrative Assistant, Jasper General Hospital, Bay Springs, MS, p. A352

GABLENZ, Gordon, Vice President Finance, Ridgeview Medical Center, Waconia, MN, p. A350

GABORIAULT, Randall, Chief Information Officer, Christiana Care Health System, Newark, DE, p. A115

GABRIEL, Joel M.D., Medical Director, Memorial Health Care Systems, Seward, NE, p. A399

GABRIEL, Scott F., President, Parkview Whitley Hospital, Columbia City, IN, p. A205

GABRIEL, Shirley, Vice President and Chief Information Officer, University Hospital, Augusta, GA, p. A152

GABRIELE, Joan, Deputy Executive Director, NYC Health + Hospitals / Queens, New Rochelle, NY, p. A445

GABRYEL, Timothy M.D., Vice President Medical Affairs and Medical Director, Mercy Hospital, Buffalo, NY, p. A433

GABUAT, Jesse, Interim Chief Nursing Officer, Aventura Hospital And Medical Center, Aventura, FL, p. A119

GAC, Deborah, Vice President Human Resources, Valley Presbyterian Hospital, Los Angeles, CA, p. A72

GADALLAH, Yousri M.D., Chief Medical Officer, Pershing General Hospital, Lovelock, NV, p. A404

GADDAM, Sumalatha, Senior Vice President and Chief Information Officer, Kent County Memorial Hospital, Warwick, RI, p. A557

GADDAM, Summa, Chief Information Officer, Butler Hospital, Providence, RI, p. A556

GADDIS, Cathryn H, Director Human Resources, Rivervalley Behavioral Health Hospital, Owensboro, KY, p. A265

GADDY, Pam, Director, Patient Care Services and Chief Nursing Officer, Firsthealth Montgomery Memorial Hospital, Troy, NC, p. A472

GADDY, Roger A Jr, Chief Medical Officer, Fairfield Memorial Hospital, Winnsboro, SC, p. A567

GADE, Swami P M.D., Medical Director, Tioga Medical Center, Tioga, ND, p. A478

GADEN, Paul, Chief Executive Officer, Providence Portland Medical Center, Portland, OR, p. A525

GAEDE, John, Director Information Systems, El Centro Regional Medical Center, El Centro, CA, p. A58

GAFFOLI, Jill, Director Human Resources, Physicians Regional – Pine Ridge, Naples, FL, p. A135

GAFFORD, Deborah, Chief Financial Officer, Menorah Medical Center, Overland Park, KS, p. A249

GAFFORD, Grady Paul, Chief Financial Officer, Brownfield Regional Medical Center, Brownfield, TX, p. A599

GAGE, Bobby, Director Information Technology, Wabash General Hospital, Mount Carmel, IL, p. A194

GAGE, Eileen, R.N.
 Vice President Nursing, Geneva General Hospital, Geneva, NY, p. A436
 Vice President Nursing, Soldiers And Sailors Memorial Hospital Of Yates County, Penn Yan, NY, p. A449

GAGE, Kevin, Chief Financial Officer, Stamford Hospital, Stamford, CT, p. A113

GAGE, Mark D.O., Medical Director, Brookhaven Hospital, Tulsa, OK, p. A517

GAGE, Susan, Financial Manager, Veterans Affairs Western New York Healthcare System–Buffalo Division, Buffalo, NY, p. A433

GAGER, Brian
 Vice President Operations, Acute Care Hospitals, St. John's Hospital, Maplewood, MN, p. A343
 Vice President, Acute Care Operations, St. Joseph's Hospital, Saint Paul, MN, p. A348

GAGLIARDI, Teresa, R.N.
 Chief Nursing Officer, Trinity Hospital Twin City, Dennison, OH, p. A490
 Chief Nursing Officer and Interim Chief Executive Officer, Trinity Hospital Twin City, Dennison, OH, p. A490

GAGLIO, Tony CPA, Senior Vice President and Chief Financial Officer, Menninger Clinic, Houston, TX, p. A622

GAGNE, Cheryl I, Vice President Patient Care Services and Chief Nursing Officer, Southern New Hampshire Medical Center, Nashua, NH, p. A409

GAGNON, Andy, Manager Information Technology, Via Christi Hospital Manhattan, Inc., Manhattan, KS, p. A246

GAINER, Rolf B., Ph.D., Chief Executive Officer, Brookhaven Hospital, Tulsa, OK, p. A517

GAINEY, Rachel T., , Mcleod Health Clarendon, Manning, SC, p. A564

GAINEY, Shari W
 Chief Human Resource Officer, Tanner Medical Center–Villa Rica, Villa Rica, GA, p. A166
 Human Resource Director, Tanner Higgins General Hospital, Bremen, GA, p. A153

GAJ, Steve, Facility Chief Information Officer, Louis Stokes Cleveland Veterans Affairs Medical Center, Cleveland, OH, p. A486

GAJEWSKI, Christie, Director Human Resources, Pinckneyville Community Hospital, Pinckneyville, IL, p. A198

GALANDA, Chris, Chief Information Officer, Wilkes–Barre General Hospital, Wilkes, PA, p. A554

GALANG, Michael, M.D.
 Chief Information Officer, Mercy Hospital, Buffalo, NY, p. A433
 Chief Information Officer, Sisters Of Charity Hospital Of Buffalo, Buffalo, NY, p. A433

GALARNEAU, Ciprian, Director Information Systems, Tri Valley Health System, Cambridge, NE, p. A391

GALARNEAU, Gerard M.D., Regional Chief Medical Officer, Catskill Regional Medical Center, Harris, NY, p. A437

GALATI, John P., Chief Executive Officer, TLC Health Network – Lake Shore Hospital, Irving, NY, p. A437

GALAVIZ, Veronica, Chief Financial Officer, Lovelace Regional Hospital – Roswell, Roswell, NM, p. A428

GALBRAITH, Kathleen B., FACHE, President, Duke Regional Hospital, Durham, NC, p. A461

GALDIERI, Lou, R.N.
President, Mease Countryside Hospital, Safety Harbor, FL, p. A141
President, Mease Dunedin Hospital, Dunedin, FL, p. A124

GALE, Gabrielle, Chief Financial Officer, Lighthouse Care Center Of Conway, Conway, SC, p. A561

GALE, Melissa, Chief Executive Officer, Landmann–Jungman Memorial Hospital Avera, Scotland, SD, p. A572

GALE, Michael, Chief Financial Officer, Bournewood Health Systems, Brookline, MA, p. A305

GALEY, John P M.D., Chief Medical Officer, Schoolcraft Memorial Hospital, Manistique, MI, p. A325

GALIPEAU, Michelle, Director Human Resources, St. Vincent's Birmingham, Birmingham, AL, p. A15

GALKOWSKI, James, Associate Director for Operations, Fayetteville Veterans Affairs Medical Center, Fayetteville, NC, p. A462

GALLAGHER, Chris M.D., Chief Medical Officer, Christus Mother Frances Hospital – Sulphur Springs, Sulphur Springs, TX, p. A647

GALLAGHER, Deborah, Manager Human Resources, Ojai Valley Community Hospital, Ojai, CA, p. A77

GALLAGHER, Doug, Director Human Resources, Carolinas Continuecare Hospital At Pineville, Charlotte, NC, p. A459

GALLAGHER, J. P., Chief Operating Officer, Northshore University Health System, Evanston, IL, p. A187

GALLAGHER, James, Chief Executive Officer, Oasis Behavioral Health – Chandler, Chandler, AZ, p. A28

GALLAGHER, Jeannie
Chief Human Resource Officer, North Colorado Medical Center, Greeley, CO, p. A103
jeanie.gallagher@bannerhealth.com, Mckee Medical Center, Loveland, CO, p. A106

GALLAGHER, John, Chief Executive Officer, Sunnyside Community Hospital And Clinics, Sunnyside, WA, p. A687

GALLAGHER, Joseph, Chief Executive Officer, Wyoming Behavioral Institute, Casper, WY, p. A717

GALLAGHER, Karen, Vice President Human Resources and Learning, Brooks Rehabilitation Hospital, Jacksonville, FL, p. A128

GALLAGHER, Pamela, Chief Financial Officer, Providence Hospital, Columbia, SC, p. A560

GALLAGHER, Regen D.O., Chief Medical Officer, Cary Medical Center, Caribou, ME, p. A290

GALLAGHER, Sherry, Director Nursing, Department of Health and Human Services, Humboldt County Mental Health, Eureka, CA, p. A58

GALLAHOM, Gerty, Director Human Resources, Maniilaq Health Center, Kotzebue, AK, p. A26

GALLARDO, Kathleen, Chief Nursing Officer, Select Specialty Hospital–Flint, Flint, MI, p. A319

GALLARDO, Ysidro, Associate Administrator Human Resources, Hazel Hawkins Memorial Hospital, Hollister, CA, p. A63

GALLATI, Todd, FACHE, President and Chief Executive Officer, Trident Medical Center, Charleston, SC, p. A559

GALLAY, Emily, Vice President and Chief Information Officer, Lakeland Medical Center, St. Joseph, Saint Joseph, MI, p. A330

GALLEGOS, Colleen, Director Human Resources, Guadalupe County Hospital, Santa Rosa, NM, p. A428

GALLEGOS, Enrique, Chief Executive Officer, Laredo Medical Center, Laredo, TX, p. A628

GALLEGOS, Kelly, Administrator, San Luis Valley Health Conejos County Hospital, La Jara, CO, p. A104

GALLEGOS, Ken, Director Support Services and Information Technology, Medina Regional Hospital, Hondo, TX, p. A619

GALLI, Jodi B. R.N., Chief Nursing Officer, Kaiser Permanente Redwood City Medical Center, Redwood City, CA, p. A82

GALLIART, Mark, Chief Executive Officer, Mcbride Orthopedic Hospital, Oklahoma City, OK, p. A512

GALLIK, Becky, Information Systems Manager, Firstlight Health System, Mora, MN, p. A344

GALLIN, John I., M.D., Director, National Institutes Of Health Clinical Center, Bethesda, MD, p. A297

GALLO, Ronald, Director Human Resources, Blythedale Children's Hospital, Valhalla, NY, p. A454

GALLOGLY–SIMON, Catherine A R.N., MS, Chief Nursing Officer, Wyckoff Heights Medical Center, New Rochelle, NY, p. A447

GALLUCCI, Vince
Senior Vice President Human Resources, Mercy Medical Center, Oshkosh, WI, p. A710

Senior Vice President Human Resources, St. Elizabeth Hospital, Appleton, WI, p. A698

GALONSKY, Ronald J.
Chief Executive Officer, Chapman Global Medical Center, Orange, CA, p. A77
Chief Executive Officer, South Coast Global Medical Center, Santa Ana, CA, p. A90

GALT, Nick
Chief Financial Officer, Medical City Las Colinas, Irving, TX, p. A625
Chief Financial Officer, Medical City North Hills, North Richland Hills, TX, p. A635

GALUSHA, Fred, Chief Information Officer, St. Luke's Rehabilitation Institute, Spokane, WA, p. A687

GALVIN, Gary, Chief of the Medical Staff, Columbus Community Hospital, Inc., Columbus, WI, p. A700

GALYON, Darlene, Director Human Resources, Choctaw Memorial Hospital, Hugo, OK, p. A509

GAMACHE, Cynde R.N., Vice President and Chief Nursing Officer, Baptist Hospital, Pensacola, FL, p. A139

GAMB, Pamela, Manager Human Resources, Aurora Psychiatric Hospital, Wauwatosa, WI, p. A715

GAMBLA, Kurt D.O., Chief Medical Officer, Beaufort Memorial Hospital, Beaufort, SC, p. A558

GAMBLE, Brian, Chief Financial Officer, Karmanos Cancer Center, Detroit, MI, p. A318

GAMBLE, Kathleen, Fiscal Officer, Patton State Hospital, Patton, CA, p. A79

GAMBLE, Robert M.D., Chief of Staff, Terrebonne General Medical Center, Houma, LA, p. A276

GAMBOA, Eileen, Director Human Resources, Oakbend Medical Center, Richmond, TX, p. A640

GAMET, Nicki, R.N.
Chief Nursing Officer, Mercy Hospital Cassville, Cassville, MO, p. A366
Vice President and Chief Nursing Officer, Mercy Hospital Aurora, Aurora, MO, p. A364

GAMEZ, Kriss, Director Human Resources, Baylor Regional Medical Center At Plano, Plano, TX, p. A638

GAMINO, Randall, Director Perot Site, St. Joseph's Medical Center, Stockton, CA, p. A93

GAMMIERE, Thomas A., Chief Executive, Senior Vice President, Scripps Mercy Hospital, San Diego, CA, p. A86

GANDHI, Tejas Ph.D., Chief Operating Officer, Baystate Medical Center, Springfield, MA, p. A311

GANDY, Galina, Vice President Information Technology, Columbia Memorial Hospital, Astoria, OR, p. A520

GANDY, Patrick W. Jr, CPA, Executive Vice President and Chief Executive Officer, Lafayette General Medical Center, Lafayette, LA, p. A278

GANGULY, Devabrata M.D., Medical Director, Christus Dubuis Hospital Of Paris, Paris, TX, p. A636

GANGULY, Indranil, Vice President and Chief Information Officer, JFK Medical Center, Edison, NJ, p. A413

GANGULY, Neal, Chief Information Officer, JFK Johnson Rehabilitation Institute, Edison, NJ, p. A413

GANLEY, Evan, Manager Human Resources, Lifecare Hospitals Of Chester County, West Chester, PA, p. A553

GANN, Lisa R.N., Chief Nursing Officer, Tristar Hendersonville Medical Center, Hendersonville, TN, p. A580

GANN, Michele, Vice President Patient Services, Mercy Hospital Berryville, Berryville, AR, p. A40

GANNON, Ronnie, Director Information Services, Tristar Southern Hills Medical Center, Nashville, TN, p. A587

GANNOTTA, Richard J., Chief Operating Officer, Uc Irvine Medical Center, Orange, CA, p. A78

GANS, Bruce M M.D., Executive Vice President and Chief Medical Officer, Kessler Institute For Rehabilitation, West Orange, NJ, p. A422

GANSEMER, Sheila, R.N.
Vice President Patient Care Services and Chief Nursing Officer, Midwest Orthopedic Specialty Hospital, Franklin, WI, p. A702
Vice President Patient Care Services and Chief Nursing Officer, Wheaton Franciscan Healthcare – Franklin, Franklin, WI, p. A702
Vice President of Patient Care Services, Midwest Orthopedic Specialty Hospital, Franklin, WI, p. A702
Vice President Patient Care Services and Chief Nursing Officer, Wheaton Franciscan Healthcare – Franklin, Franklin, WI, p. A702

GANSKE, Jary, Chief Financial Officer, Methodist Mansfield Medical Center, Mansfield, TX, p. A631

GANTNER, John, President and Chief Executive Officer, Robert Wood Johnson University Hospital, New Brunswick, NJ, p. A417

GANTT, Cynthia J, Chief of Staff, Naval Medical Center, Portsmouth, VA, p. A673

GANTZER, Ann M Ph.D., R.N., Vice President Patient Services and Chief Nursing Officer, Swedishamerican – A Division Of Uw Health, Rockford, IL, p. A199

GAPKO, Dawn, Chief Administrative Officer, Ministry Good Samaritan Health Center, Merrill, WI, p. A707

GAPSTUR, Roxanna L., Ph.D., R.N., President, Park Nicollet Methodist Hospital, Saint Louis Park, MN, p. A347

GARAY, Kenneth M.D., Chief Medical Officer, Jersey City Medical Center, Jersey City, NJ, p. A415

GARBANZOS, Del, Director Human Resources, Delano Regional Medical Center, Delano, CA, p. A57

GARBARINO, James, Chief Financial Officer, Clay County Medical Center, Clay Center, KS, p. A239

GARBER, Mary, Vice President Finance, Mercy Hospital Ada, Ada, OK, p. A504

GARCIA, Andrew T., Acting Associate Director, Central Texas Veterans Health Care System, Temple, TX, p. A648

GARCIA, Antonio M., Chief Nursing Officer, Doctors Hospital Of Manteca, Manteca, CA, p. A73

GARCIA, Ara, Manager Human Resources, Milwaukee County Behavioral Health Division, Milwaukee, WI, p. A708

GARCIA, Aymette, Manager Human Resources, Wilma N. Vazquez Medical Center, Vega Baja, PR, p. A727

GARCIA, Danette, Director Human Resources, Healthsouth Valley Of The Sun Rehabilitation Hospital, Glendale, AZ, p. A30

GARCIA, Estevan M.D., Chief Medical Officer, Brookdale Hospital Medical Center, New Rochelle, NY, p. A441

GARCIA, Evangeline M.D., Clinical Director, Eastern Shore Hospital Center, Cambridge, MD, p. A297

GARCIA, Georgina R., R.N., Executive Director, Kaiser Permanente West Los Angeles Medical Center, Los Angeles, CA, p. A69

GARCIA, Gerard, Chief Human Resource Officer, University Hospital, Newark, NJ, p. A418

GARCIA, Idalia, Chief Human Resources Officer, Hospital De Psiquiatria, San Juan, PR, p. A726

GARCIA, Iris, Director, Information Services, Jerome Golden Center For Behavioral Health, Inc., West Palm Beach, FL, p. A147

GARCIA, Irma, Job Coordinator, Rio Grande State Center/ South Texas Health Care System, Harlingen, TX, p. A618

GARCIA, Jacob, Chief Information Officer, Little Colorado Medical Center, Winslow, AZ, p. A39

GARCIA, Jannina, Director of Human Resources, Florida Hospital Fish Memorial, Orange City, FL, p. A136

GARCIA, Joanne, Chief Operating Officer, Kindred Chicago–Central Hospital, Chicago, IL, p. A181

GARCIA, Joannie CPA, Director Finance, Hospital Perea, Mayaguez, PR, p. A724

GARCIA, Jose, M.D.
Chief Medical Staff, Dundy County Hospital, Benkelman, NE, p. A391
Chief Human Resources Officer, San Juan City Hospital, San Juan, PR, p. A726

GARCIA, Kathleen, Controller, St. John's Episcopal Hospital–South Shore, New Rochelle, NY, p. A446

GARCIA, Luis Mario Jr, Director Human Resources, Houston Methodist Sugar Land Hospital, Sugar Land, TX, p. A647

GARCIA, Margaret, Manager Human Resources, Baylor Medical Center At Frisco, Frisco, TX, p. A615

GARCIA, Michael A, Vice President and Chief Information Officer, Jackson Health System, Miami, FL, p. A133

GARCIA, Orlando M.D., Chief Medical Officer, Hialeah Hospital, Hialeah, FL, p. A126

GARCIA, Robert W M.D., Chief Medical Officer, Iraan General Hospital, Iraan, TX, p. A624

GARCIA, Roland
Senior Vice President and Chief Information Officer, Baptist Medical Center Beaches, Jacksonville Beach, FL, p. A129
Senior Vice President and Chief Information Officer, Baptist Medical Center Jacksonville, Jacksonville, FL, p. A127

GARCIA, Rudy, Chief Executive Officer, Westchester General Hospital, Miami, FL, p. A134

GARCIA, Sharon, Human Resources Representative, Medina Regional Hospital, Hondo, TX, p. A619

GARCIA, Shawn, Manager Human Resources, Memorial Hospital Los Banos, Los Banos, CA, p. A72

GARCIA, Sylvia, Chief Accounting Officer, South Texas Spine And Surgical Hospital, San Antonio, TX, p. A643

GARCIA, Tracy MS, Chief Nursing Officer, Cheyenne Regional Medical Center, Cheyenne, WY, p. A717

GARD, Emily, Chief Clinical Officer, Kindred Hospital–San Francisco Bay Area, San Leandro, CA, p. A89

GARDINER, Greg, Chief Clinical Officer, Ashley Regional Medical Center, Vernal, UT, p. A661

GARDINER, Karen, Human Resources Director, Bayfront Health Port Charlotte, Port Charlotte, FL, p. A140

GAUL, Mike, Director Information Technology, Golden Valley Memorial Healthcare, Clinton, MO, p. A366

GAULKE, Becky, Chief Nursing Officer, Ely–Bloomenson Community Hospital, Ely, MN, p. A339

GAULT, Cindy L., Chief Financial Officer, Union Medical Center, Union, SC, p. A566

GAURON, Patricia, Director Human Resources, Holy Family Hospital, Methuen, MA, p. A308

GAUTHIER, Paul, Chief Information Resources Management, Veterans Affairs Montana Health Care System, Fort Harrison, MT, p. A384

GAUTNEY, Steven, Chief Executive Officer, Crisp Regional Hospital, Cordele, GA, p. A155

GAVALCHIK, Stephen M., FACHE, Community Chief Executive Officer, Morgan County Arh Hospital, West Liberty, KY, p. A268

GAVENS, Mark R, Executive Vice President Health System Hospital Operations and Chief Operating Officer of Cedars–Sinai Medical Center, Cedars–Sinai Medical Center, Los Angeles, CA, p. A67

GAVIN, Andrea M.D., Chief Medical officer, Aurora Sheboygan Memorial Medical Center, Sheboygan, WI, p. A712

GAVIN, Donald, Chief Financial Officer, Southern Tennessee Regional Health System–Pulaski, Pulaski, TN, p. A588

GAVIN, Todd, Chief Medical Officer, Madelia Community Hospital, Madelia, MN, p. A342

GAVINO, Rey M.D., Chief of Staff, RMC Jacksonville, Jacksonville, AL, p. A19

GAVORA, George, Director Program Evaluation, Kingsboro Psychiatric Center, New Rochelle, NY, p. A442

GAVULIC, Melany
President & Chief Executive Officer, Hurley Medical Center, Flint, MI, p. A319
Senior Vice President Operations & COO, Hurley Medical Center, Flint, MI, p. A319

GAW, Kris, Executive Vice President and Chief Operating Officer, Maricopa Integrated Health System, Phoenix, AZ, p. A33

GAWALUCK, David
Vice President and Chief Information Officer, Excela Frick Hospital, Mount Pleasant, PA, p. A541
Vice President and Chief Information Officer, Excela Health Westmoreland Hospital, Greensburg, PA, p. A535
Vice President and Chief Information Officer, Excela Latrobe Area Hospital, Latrobe, PA, p. A538

GAWITH, Marlene, Director of Nursing, Ottawa County Health Center, Minneapolis, KS, p. A247

GAWLER, William, Chief Information Officer, Chillicothe Veterans Affairs Medical Center, Chillicothe, OH, p. A483

GAWNE, Bernard B M.D., Vice President and Chief Medical Officer, Christ Hospital, Cincinnati, OH, p. A483

GAY, Christophe M.D., Chief of Staff, Chi St. Joseph Health Bellville Hospital, Bellville, TX, p. A598

GAY, Don, Director Human Resources, West Hills Hospital, Reno, NV, p. A405

GAY, Kent E. M.D., Chief of Medical Staff, Arkansas Valley Regional Medical Center, La Junta, CO, p. A104

GAY, Kristi
Chief Financial Officer, Chi St. Luke's Health Memorial Lufkin, Lufkin, TX, p. A631
Chief Financial Officer, Chi St. Luke's Health Memorial San Augustine, San Augustine, TX, p. A644

GAY, Michael, Chief Operating Officer, Habersham Medical Center, Demorest, GA, p. A156

GAY, Perry, President and Chief Executive Officer, Logansport Memorial Hospital, Logansport, IN, p. A215

GAY, Vickie, Chief Executive Officer, Montgomery General Hospital, Montgomery, WV, p. A694

GAYNE, William, Chief Financial Officer, Medstar Washington Hospital Center, Washington, DC, p. A118

GAYNOR, Sheila, Director Human Resources, Perry County Memorial Hospital, Tell City, IN, p. A220

GAYTKO, Caren, Chief Nursing Officer, Regency Hospital Of Minneapolis, Golden Valley, MN, p. A340

GAZAWAY, William, Information Technology Security Officer, Alliancehealth Ponca City, Ponca City, OK, p. A514

GAZECKI, Cindy, Senior Vice President, Hospital Operations, Seattle Children's Hospital, Seattle, WA, p. A685

GEARHARD, Cynthia, Chief Nursing Officer, St. Luke's Regional Medical Center, Boise, ID, p. A172

GEARHART, Danielle, Chief Executive Officer, Gundersen St. Joseph's Hospital And Clinics, Hillsboro, WI, p. A703

GEARHART, Heidi, Director Information Systems, Arkansas Valley Regional Medical Center, La Junta, CO, p. A104

GEARY, David S, Chief Financial Officer, Cache Valley Hospital, North Logan, UT, p. A658

GEARY, Herb J
Chief Nursing Officer, Santa Ynez Valley Cottage Hospital, Solvang, CA, p. A92
Vice President Patient Care Services and Chief Nursing Officer, Santa Barbara Cottage Hospital, Santa Barbara, CA, p. A90

GEBHARD, Scott
Chief Operating Officer, JFK Johnson Rehabilitation Institute, Edison, NJ, p. A413
Executive VP and Chief Operating Officer, JFK Medical Center, Edison, NJ, p. A413

GEBHART, Cheryl
Chief Human Resources Officer, Tuality Healthcare, Hillsboro, OR, p. A522
Director Human Resources Providence Health Plan and Providence Medical Group, Providence Newberg Medical Center, Newberg, OR, p. A524

GEBHART, Jim Jr, FACHE, President, Mercy Hospital Oklahoma City, Oklahoma City, OK, p. A512

GEBHART, Ronald J M.D., Chief of Staff, Veterans Affairs Salt Lake City Health Care System, Salt Lake City, UT, p. A661

GEDDINGS, Toni, Director Human Resources, Cullman Regional Medical Center, Cullman, AL, p. A16

GEDIES, Lucille, Chief Financial Officer, Mildred Mitchell–Bateman Hospital, Huntington, WV, p. A692

GEE, Kyle
Chief Financial Officer, Beartooth Billings Clinic, Red Lodge, MT, p. A387
Chief Financial Officer, Pioneer Medical Center, Big Timber, MT, p. A382
Regional Vice President Financial Operations, Roundup Memorial Healthcare, Roundup, MT, p. A388

GEE, Thomas H., Administrator, Henry County Medical Center, Paris, TN, p. A588

GEER, Nicholas, Chief Financial Officer, Dallas Medical Center, Dallas, TX, p. A605

GEERTS, Jodi, Chief Nursing Officer, Henry County Health Center, Mount Pleasant, IA, p. A232

GEESEY, Wanda, Director Human Resources, Pennsylvania Psychiatric Institute, Harrisburg, PA, p. A536

GEHLAUF, Dee Ann, Senior Vice President Business and Organization Development, Marietta Memorial Hospital, Marietta, OH, p. A494

GEHLHAUSEN, Sherri, Assistant Chief Financial Officer, Logansport Memorial Hospital, Logansport, IN, p. A215

GEHRIG, Ryan
President, Mercy Hospital Fort Smith, Fort Smith, AR, p. A43
President, Mercy Hospital Fort Smith, Fort Smith, AR, p. A43

GEHRING, Betty, Finance Director, Operations, Thedacare Medical Center–New London, New London, WI, p. A709

GEHRING, Jay, Director Information Systems, Kingman Community Hospital, Kingman, KS, p. A244

GEHRING, Mikaela, Chief Operating Officer, Compass Memorial Healthcare, Marengo, IA, p. A231

GEHRING, Samuel M.D., Chief of Staff, Fleming County Hospital, Flemingsburg, KY, p. A258

GEHRING, Terri
Interim Chief Executive Officer, Mcpherson Hospital, Mcpherson, KS, p. A246
Vice President Operations, Mcpherson Hospital, Mcpherson, KS, p. A246

GEIER, Joyce, Director Nursing, Girard Medical Center, Girard, KS, p. A241

GEIER, Kathy, Director of Nursing, Chase County Community Hospital, Imperial, NE, p. A394

GEIGER, Deb, Executive Director of Acute Care, Harbor Beach Community Hospital, Harbor Beach, MI, p. A322

GEIGER, Judy R.N., Chief Nursing Officer, Primary Children's Hospital, Salt Lake City, UT, p. A660

GEIGER, Ralph M.D., Chief of Staff, Sebastian River Medical Center, Sebastian, FL, p. A142

GEIGLE, Joseph, Director Human Resources, Fort Hamilton Hospital, Hamilton, OH, p. A492

GEIL, Kristie A, VP, Chief Nursing Officer, CGH Medical Center, Sterling, IL, p. A201

GEISLER, Linda W R.N., FACHE, Vice President Patient Services, Centrastate Healthcare System, Freehold, NJ, p. A414

GEIST, Jim, Executive Vice President and Chief Operating Officer, Skagit Regional Health, Mount Vernon, WA, p. A682

GEITZ, Cheri, Director Human Resources, Hansen Family Hospital, Iowa Falls, IA, p. A230

GEITZ, James M.D., Chief of Staff, Newman Regional Health, Emporia, KS, p. A240

GEIVER, Betsy, Chief Human Resources Officer, Sioux Falls Veterans Affairs Health Care System, Sioux Falls, SD, p. A573

GELDERS, Albert M.D., Chief of Staff, Oak Valley Hospital District, Oakdale, CA, p. A77

GELDHOF, Jay
Director Information Systems, Greater El Monte Community Hospital, South El Monte, CA, p. A92

Director Information Systems, Whittier Hospital Medical Center, Whittier, CA, p. A97

GELFAND, Andrew M.D., Medical Director, Our Children's House, Dallas, TX, p. A606

GELL, Michael, Director Human Resources, Boys Town National Research Hospital, Omaha, NE, p. A397

GELLER, Harold S., Chief Executive Officer, Chi St. Anthony Hospital, Pendleton, OR, p. A524

GELLER, Mark, M.D., President and Chief Executive Officer, Nyack Hospital, Nyack, NY, p. A448

GELLER, Robert D M.D., Vice President Medical Affairs, FHN Memorial Hospital, Freeport, IL, p. A188

GELLER, Warren, President and Chief Executive Officer, Englewood Hospital And Medical Center, Englewood, NJ, p. A414

GEMBOL, Leslie MSN, R.N., Chief Nursing Officer, Baylor Scott & White Medical Center – Round Rock, Round Rock, TX, p. A640

GEMME, Donna T R.N., Chief Nursing Officer Vice President Patient Care Services, Metrowest Medical Center, Framingham, MA, p. A306

GENESIO, Sabina, Finance Officer for Institutes, Colorado Mental Health Institute At Fort Logan, Denver, CO, p. A100

GENEVRO, Thomas A, Vice President Human Resources, Butler Health System, Butler, PA, p. A530

GENGLER, Laraine, Chief Financial Officer, Lindsborg Community Hospital, Lindsborg, KS, p. A246

GENNA, Nick, Administrator, Treasure Valley Hospital, Boise, ID, p. A172

GENNARO, John, FACHE, Director, Erie Veterans Affairs Medical Center, Erie, PA, p. A534

GENOVESE, Vincent P M.D., President Medical Staff, Owensboro Health Muhlenberg Community Hospital, Greenville, KY, p. A259

GENSERT, Kurt G FACHE, R.N., Vice President Operations, Platte Valley Medical Center, Brighton, CO, p. A99

GENTILE, John, M.D.
Vice President Medical Affairs, Alta Bates Summit Medical Center – Summit Campus, Oakland, CA, p. A77
Vice President Medical Affairs, Alta Bates Summit Medical Center, Berkeley, CA, p. A53

GENTILE, Serge, Director Human Resources, Belmont Community Hospital, Bellaire, OH, p. A481

GENTNER, Rocky, Chief Financial Officer, Newport Bay Hospital, Newport Beach, CA, p. A76

GENTRY, Cheryl G., Interim Chief Executive Officer, Select Specialty Hospital – Cleveland Gateway, Cleveland, OH, p. A486

GENTRY, Jeanine, Chief Executive Officer, Steele Memorial Medical Center, Salmon, ID, p. A176

GENTRY, Jennifer R.N., Chief Nursing Officer, Christus Spohn Hospital Corpus Christi Memorial, Corpus Christi, TX, p. A603

GENTRY, Kristen, Chief Operating Officer, Venice Regional Bayfront Health, Venice, FL, p. A146

GENTRY, Lee, FACHE, Vice President and Administrator, Baptist Health Extended Care Hospital, Little Rock, AR, p. A46

GENTRY, Margie, Controller, T. J. Samson Community Hospital, Glasgow, KY, p. A259

GEOGHEGAN, Jeffrey, Chief Financial Officer, Uconn, John Dempsey Hospital, Farmington, CT, p. A110

GEORGE, Alan E., Chief Executive Officer, Rockdale Medical Center, Conyers, GA, p. A155

GEORGE, Brad, Director Information Systems, Parkland Medical Center, Derry, NH, p. A407

GEORGE, Dana, Chief Human Resources Officer, Abrazo Central Campus, Phoenix, AZ, p. A32

GEORGE, Daniel M, Executive Vice President, Operations, Covenant Healthcare, Saginaw, MI, p. A329

GEORGE, Denise, R.N., President, Northern Dutchess Hospital, Rhinebeck, NY, p. A450

GEORGE, Gary, Senior Vice President Human Resources, Mercy St. Vincent Medical Center, Toledo, OH, p. A500

GEORGE, P A M.D., Chief of Staff, Madison Medical Center, Fredericktown, MO, p. A368

GEORGE, Patsy R.N., Vice President and Chief Nursing Officer, Ohio Valley Medical Center, Wheeling, WV, p. A697

GEORGE, Saju, Chief Executive Officer, Garden City Hospital, Garden City, MI, p. A320

GEORGE, Shayne, Chief Executive Officer, Regional Medical Center Bayonet Point, Hudson, FL, p. A127

GEORGE, Susan R.N., M.P.H., Associate Director Patient Care Services, Martinsburg Veterans Affairs Medical Center, Martinsburg, WV, p. A694

GEORGE, Tracy L, Chief Financial Officer, St. James Parish Hospital, Lutcher, LA, p. A280

GEORGE, William M.D., Chief of Staff, Beartooth Billings Clinic, Red Lodge, MT, p. A387

GEORGES, Angelo M.D., President Medical and Dental Staff, Wheeling Hospital, Wheeling, WV, p. A697

GEORGESON, Keith, M.D., Chief Executive, Providence Sacred Heart Medical Center & Children's Hospital, Spokane, WA, p. A687

GEPFORD, John, Director Information Systems, Evergreenhealth Monroe, Monroe, WA, p. A682

GERBER, Allen M.D., Chief of Staff, Baptist Health Medical Center–Hot Spring County, Malvern, AR, p. A46

GERBER, Andrew, M.D., Ph.D., Medical Director and Chief Executive Officer, Austen Riggs Center, Stockbridge, MA, p. A312

GERBER, Greg M.D., Chief Medical Officer, Aurora Lakeland Medical Center, Elkhorn, WI, p. A701

GERDES, Isaac, Chief Executive Officer, Sanford Webster Medical Center, Webster, SD, p. A574

GERDTS, Elizabeth, Chief Nursing Officer, NYC Health + Hospitals / North Central Bronx, New Rochelle, NY, p. A445

GERE, Zsaber, Chief Human Resource Officer, Banner Behavioral Health Hospital – Scottsdale, Scottsdale, AZ, p. A35

GERETY, Meghan M.D., Chief of Staff, New Mexico Veterans Affairs Health Care System – Raymond G. Murphy Medical Center, Albuquerque, NM, p. A424

GERHART, Paul, Chief Financial Officer, Sanford Canton–Inwood Medical Center, Canton, SD, p. A568

GERIG, Stacey L., Chief Executive Officer, Odessa Regional Medical Center, Odessa, TX, p. A635

GERIG, Stacey, Chief Executive Officer, Odessa Regional Medical Center South Campus, Odessa, TX, p. A636

GERING, Paul M.D., Vice President Medical Affairs, Saint Alphonsus Medical Center – Ontario, Ontario, OR, p. A524

GERKE, Daniel, Chief Nursing Officer, Wright Patterson Medical Center, Wright, OH, p. A503

GERKE, Sarah, Manager Human Resources, Warner Hospital And Health Services, Clinton, IL, p. A184

GERLACH, Carl, Chief Financial Officer, Curry General Hospital, Gold Beach, OR, p. A522

GERLACH, Judith LeAnn, Chief Nursing Officer, Helena Regional Medical Center, Helena, AR, p. A44

GERLACH, Matthew S
  Chief Operating Officer, Children's Hospital Of Orange County, Orange, CA, p. A78
  Chief Operating Officer, Choc Children's At Mission Hospital, Mission Viejo, CA, p. A73

GERMANY, Alan
  Chief Executive Officer and Chief Restructuring Officer, Southern Inyo Healthcare District, Lone Pine, CA, p. A66
  Chief Operating Officer, Tulare Regional Medical Center, Tulare, CA, p. A94
  Interim Chief Executive Officer, Tulare Regional Medical Center, Tulare, CA, p. A94

GERMUSKA, Natalie, R.N., MSN, Market Chief Executive Officer, Kindred Hospital–San Diego, San Diego, CA, p. A85

GERNDT, Angie, Human Resources Manager, Central Community Hospital, Elkader, IA, p. A227

GERNHART, Diana, Senior Vice President and Hospital Chief Financial Officer, Ohsu Hospital, Portland, OR, p. A525

GERRIOR, Marilyn R.N., MSN, Chief Nursing Executive, Saint Louise Regional Hospital, Gilroy, CA, p. A61

GERRITS, Brad, Director Information Systems, Lakeview Medical Center, Rice Lake, WI, p. A711

GERSON, Elaine, Chief Clinical Officer and General Counsel, Aspen Valley Hospital, Aspen, CO, p. A98

GERSTENBERGER, Linda
  Vice President Human Resources, St. Rose Dominican Hospitals – San Martin Campus, Las Vegas, NV, p. A404
  Vice President Human Resources, St. Rose Dominican Hospitals – Siena Campus, Henderson, NV, p. A402

GERSTNER, Nancy, Manager Human Resources, Robert J. Dole Veterans Affairs Medical Center, Wichita, KS, p. A253

GERVELER, Patrick M, Vice President Finance and Chief Financial Officer, Blessing Hospital, Quincy, IL, p. A198

GESKERMANN, Tom G., Chief Executive Officer, Osceola Medical Center, Osceola, WI, p. A710

GESME, Barbara L. MSN, Vice President Patient Care Services & Chief Nurse Executive, Bon Secours St. Francis Medical Center, Midlothian, VA, p. A670

GESSLING, Heather M.D., Chief Medical Officer, Moberly Regional Medical Center, Moberly, MO, p. A373

GESSNER, Christopher A., President, Children's Hospital Of Pittsburgh Of Upmc, Pittsburgh, PA, p. A546

GETCHIUS, Joseph, Director Information Technology, Benewah Community Hospital, Saint Maries, ID, p. A175

GETMAN, Sylvia, President and Chief Executive Officer, Adirondack Health, Saranac Lake, NY, p. A452

GETSAY, Timothy, Chief Information Officer, Vice President of Performance & Information Mgmt, Gillette Children's Specialty Healthcare, Saint Paul, MN, p. A347

GETTINGER, Thomas
  Executive Vice President and Chief Operating Officer, Mary Washington Hospital, Fredericksburg, VA, p. A667
  Executive Vice President and Chief Operating Officer, Stafford Hospital, Stafford, VA, p. A675

GETTINGS, Scott M.D., Senior Vice President and Chief Medical Officer, Health First Viera Hospital, Melbourne, FL, p. A132

GETTYS, Sky, Chief Financial Officer, Fairfield Medical Center, Lancaster, OH, p. A493

GETZ, Liz, Chief Information Officer, Aultman Hospital, Canton, OH, p. A482

GEUDER, Denise, Vice President Patient Care Service and Chief Nursing Officer, Southwestern Regional Medical Center, Tulsa, OK, p. A518

GEURTS, Chuck, Manager Information Technology Client Services, Aurora Baycare Medical Center, Green Bay, WI, p. A702

GEWECKE, Tyler, Information Technology Technician, Fillmore County Hospital, Geneva, NE, p. A393

GFELLER, Michael, Director Information Systems, Medical City Plano, Plano, TX, p. A638

GHAEMMAGHAMI, Chris A. M.D., Chief Medical Officer, University Of Virginia Medical Center, Charlottesville, VA, p. A665

GHAFFARI, Bahram, President, Delano Regional Medical Center, Delano, CA, p. A57

GHALI, Sara, Chief Financial Officer, Green Valley Hospital, Green Valley, AZ, p. A30

GHERINGHELLI, Thomas, Senior Vice President, Chief Financial Officer, New England Baptist Hospital, Boston, MA, p. A303

GHERKE, Sheila, Director Human Resources, Minnie Hamilton Healthcare Center, Grantsville, WV, p. A692

GHIDOTTI, Craig J, Vice President Human Resources, Lake Health, Concord Township, OH, p. A488

GHION, Christopher, Vice President and Chief Information Officer, Adventist Healthcare Shady Grove Medical Center, Rockville, MD, p. A300

GHOSH, Avijit, M.D., Chief Executive Officer, University Of Illinois Hospital & Health Sciences System, Chicago, IL, p. A184

GHOSH, Tarun, Chief Information Officer, Rideout Memorial Hospital, Marysville, CA, p. A73

GHULUM, Evelyn, Chief Financial Officer, Jellico Community Hospital, Jellico, TN, p. A580

GIAGUINTO, Shelly, Chief Financial Officer, Highland–Clarksburg Hospital, Clarksburg, WV, p. A691

GIAMPA, Patricia L, Chief Nursing Officer, Searhc Mt. Edgecumbe Hospital, Sitka, AK, p. A27

GIAMPEITRO, Vincent, Chief Executive Officer, Arthur Brisbane Children Treatment Center, Farmingdale, NJ, p. B47

GIANCOLA, Louis R., President and Chief Executive Officer, South County Hospital, Wakefield, RI, p. A557

GIANELLI, Arthur A., M.P.H., President, Mount Sinai West, New Rochelle, NY, p. A443

GIANG, Vernon
  Chief Medical Executive, California Pacific Medical Center–St. Luke's Campus, San Francisco, CA, p. A87
  Chief Medical Executive, California Pacific Medical Center, San Francisco, CA, p. A87

GIANGARDELLA, Mike, Vice President Finance and Administration, Salem Regional Medical Center, Salem, OH, p. A499

GIANNONE, John M.D., Chief Medical Officer, Uhs Delaware Valley Hospital, Walton, NY, p. A454

GIANNOSA, Amy, Director Human Resources, Havenwyck Hospital, Auburn Hills, MI, p. A314

GIANNUZZI, Donna R.N., Chief Nursing Officer, Lee Memorial Hospital, Fort Myers, FL, p. A125

GIANSANTE, Joseph, Vice President Human Resources, Ellis Hospital, Schenectady, NY, p. A452

GIARDINA, Deborah, Director Human Resources and Medical Staff Services, Rehabilitation Hospital Of Fort Wayne, Fort Wayne, IN, p. A208

GIBB, Matthew M.D., Executive Vice President and System Chief Medical Officer, Carle Foundation Hospital, Urbana, IL, p. A201

GIBB, Randall K., M.D., Chief Executive Officer, Billings Clinic, Billings, MT, p. A382

GIBBENS, Lori, Controller, Healthsouth Rehabilitation Hospital Of Erie, Erie, PA, p. A534

GIBBERMAN, Val M.D., Acting Chief of Staff, Hampton Veterans Affairs Medical Center, Hampton, VA, p. A668

GIBBES, Gregg, Chief Executive Officer, Covington County Hospital, Collins, MS, p. A354

GIBBONE, Brian, Chief Executive Officer, Sunnyside Community Hospital And Clinics, Sunnyside, WA, p. B65

GIBBONS, Barbara, Vice President Patient Care Services, St. Joseph Hospital, Bethpage, NY, p. A431

GIBBONS, David, President, Upmc Hamot, Erie, PA, p. A534

GIBBONS, Jason, Chief Financial Officer, Minidoka Memorial Hospital, Rupert, ID, p. A175

GIBBS, Christopher Michael, Director Information Management Systems, Taylor Regional Hospital, Campbellsville, KY, p. A256

GIBBS, Jeffrey S. M.D., Regional Vice President Medical Affairs, Skagit Regional Health, Mount Vernon, WA, p. A682

GIBBS, Kenneth, President and Chief Executive Officer, Maimonides Medical Center, New Rochelle, NY, p. A442

GIBBS, Michael, President, Avera Heart Hospital Of South Dakota, Sioux Falls, SD, p. A572

GIBBS, Parker M.D., Chief Medical Officer, Uf Health Shands Hospital, Gainesville, FL, p. A126

GIBBS, Tim, Director of Information Technology, Information Security Officer, Children's Hospital Of Richmond At Vcu–Brook Road Campus, Richmond, VA, p. A674

GIBBS, Vickie, Director Nursing, Phillips County Hospital, Phillipsburg, KS, p. A250

GIBBS–MCELVY, Shelana M.D., Medical Director, Healthsouth Rehabilitation Hospital Of Sewickley, Sewickley, PA, p. A550

GIBNEY, Thomas, Senior Vice President and Chief Financial Officer, St. Luke's Cornwall Hospital, Newburgh, NY, p. A447

GIBSON, Armetria, Human Resources Generalist, Select Specialty Hospital Midtown Atlanta, Atlanta, GA, p. A151

GIBSON, Belinda D R.N., Senior Vice President Patient Services, BSA Hospital, Llc, Amarillo, TX, p. A592

GIBSON, Connie R.N., Director Human Resources, Mary Black Health System – Gaffney, Gaffney, SC, p. A562

GIBSON, David R. – Chief Executive Officer, Carl R. Darnall Army Medical Center, Fort Hood, TX, p. A613

GIBSON, Elizabeth, Director Human Resources, Mid–America Rehabilitation Hospital, Shawnee Mission, KS, p. A251

GIBSON, J. Francis., Administrator and Chief Executive Officer, Orem Community Hospital, Orem, UT, p. A658

GIBSON, Jack, Administrator, Noland Hospital Tuscaloosa, Tuscaloosa, AL, p. A24

GIBSON, Joel, Vice President Human Resources, Henry Ford Macomb Hospitals, Clinton Township, MI, p. A316

GIBSON, Mary Helen, Director Human Resources, Floyd Valley Healthcare, Le Mars, IA, p. A230

GIBSON, Megan, Nurse Manager, River Bend Hospital, West Lafayette, IN, p. A221

GIBSON, Robert L, Director Employee Relations, OSF Saint Elizabeth Medical Center, Ottawa, IL, p. A196

GIBSON, Todd, Chief Financial Officer, Medical City Denton, Denton, TX, p. A608

GIBSON, William R., Chief Executive Officer, Lincoln Regional Center, Lincoln, NE, p. A395

GICCA, Ron, Chief Executive Officer, Wuesthoff Medical Center – Melbourne, Melbourne, FL, p. A132

GICZI, Mary Beth, Director Human Resources, Healthsouth Scottsdale Rehabilitation Hospital, Scottsdale, AZ, p. A35

GIDDINGS, Carleen, Information Technology System Leader, Scheurer Hospital, Pigeon, MI, p. A328

GIDDINGS, Claudia R.N., Chief Nursing Officer, Our Community Hospital, Scotland Neck, NC, p. A470

GIDEON, Daniel L., FACHE, President, Methodist Hospital For Surgery, Addison, TX, p. A591

GIEGER, Julie
  Chief Financial Officer, Lackey Memorial Hospital, Forest, MS, p. A354
  Chief Financial Officer, Pioneer Community Hospital Of Aberdeen, Aberdeen, MS, p. A352
  Chief Financial Officer, Pioneer Community Hospital Of Patrick, Stuart, VA, p. A676

GIER, Jennifer, Director Human Resources, Brynn Marr Hospital, Jacksonville, NC, p. A465

GIERTUGA, Garry, Site Manager Human Resources, Amita Health Adventist Medical Center Lagrange, La Grange, IL, p. A191

GIESE, Angela, Chief Human Resource Officer, Abrazo Maryvale Campus, Phoenix, AZ, p. A32

GIESE, Kristine A, Chief Operating Officer, Providence Medical Center, Wayne, NE, p. A400

GIETTER, Marci, Interim Executive Director, Hackensack Meridian Health Shore Rehabilitation Institute, Brick, NJ, p. A412

GIFFORD, Ellen, Director Human Resources, Alliancehealth Deaconess, Oklahoma City, OK, p. A511

GIGLIO, Aimee M., Chief Human Resources Officer, Dartmouth–Hitchcock Medical Center, Lebanon, NH, p. A409

GIGLIOTTI, Vicki, Chief Clinical Officer, Moab Regional Hospital, Moab, UT, p. A657

GIL, Julio, Manager Information Services, Hazel Hawkins Memorial Hospital, Hollister, CA, p. A63

GILBERT, Andrea F., FACHE, President, Bryn Mawr Hospital, Bryn Mawr, PA, p. A530

GILBERT, Cameron R., Ph.D., President and Chief Executive Officer, Neuropsychiatric Hospitals, Mishawaka, IN, p. B89

GILBERT, Carla, Director Finance, Cedar County Memorial Hospital, El Dorado Springs, MO, p. A367

GILBERT, Christy
  Chief Executive Officer, Rivercrest Specialty Hospital, Mishawaka, IN, p. A216
  Interim Chief Executive Officer, Doctors Neuropsychiatric Hospital And Research Institute, Bremen, IN, p. A205

GILBERT, Jack, Vice President Finance and Facilities, Advocate Illinois Masonic Medical Center, Chicago, IL, p. A180

GILBERT, James B., Chief Financial Officer, Palms Of Pasadena Hospital, Saint Petersburg, FL, p. A141

GILBERT, Kevin R.N., Vice President, Confluence Health/Wenatchee Valley Hospital, Wenatchee, WA, p. A689

GILBERT, Kim R.N., Chief Nursing Officer, Electra Memorial Hospital, Electra, TX, p. A612

GILBERT, Thomas D., FACHE, Chief Executive Officer, Wadley Regional Medical Center At Hope, Hope, AR, p. A44

GILBERT, Thomas D., FACHE, Chief Executive Officer, Wadley Regional Medical Center, Texarkana, TX, p. A649

GILBERT, Thomas, Director Information Technology Services, Lake Cumberland Regional Hospital, Somerset, KY, p. A267

GILBERT, Valarie R.N., Chief Nursing Officer, Texas Health Harris Methodist Hospital Azle, Azle, TX, p. A596

GILBERT, William L., Hospital Director, Arrowhead Regional Medical Center, Colton, CA, p. A56

GILBERTSON, Gerry, Administrator, Centracare Health–Melrose, Melrose, MN, p. A343

GILCHRIST, Doug, Chief Operating Officer, Summit Healthcare Regional Medical Center, Show Low, AZ, p. A36

GILDON, Lisa
  Group Financial Officer, Texas Health Presbyterian Hospital Allen, Allen, TX, p. A591
  Vice President and Chief Financial Officer, Texas Health Presbyterian Hospital Plano, Plano, TX, p. A638

GILES, Charles M.D., President Medical Staff, T.J. Health Columbia, Columbia, KY, p. A256

GILES, Jared, Chief Operating Officer, Rancho Springs Medical Center, Murrieta, CA, p. A75

GILES, Kent, Interim Chief Executive Officer, Livingston Hospital And Healthcare Services, Salem, KY, p. A267

GILES, Lori, Interim Chief Nursing Officer, Piedmont Athens Regional Medical Center, Athens, GA, p. A149

GILES, Steve, Chief Information Officer, Hollywood Presbyterian Medical Center, Los Angeles, CA, p. A68

GILES, William, Chief Executive Officer, Regional West Garden County, Oshkosh, NE, p. A398

GILG, Ronald, Assistant Vice President Talent, Eastern Regional Medical Center, Philadelphia, PA, p. A543

GILGEN, Steve, Chief Financial Officer, Murphy Medical Center, Murphy, NC, p. A467

GILJUM, Anthony, Chief Information Officer, Sheridan Veterans Affairs Medical Center, Sheridan, WY, p. A720

GILKEY, Edward M.D., Vice President Medical Affairs, St. Luke's Hospital – Warren Campus, Phillipsburg, NJ, p. A419

GILL, Mandeep, Chief Operating Officer, Memorial Hospital Of Sweetwater County, Rock Springs, WY, p. A719

GILL, Margaret
  Senior Vice President and Chief Executive Officer, Novant Health Uva Health System Haymarket Medical Center, Haymarket, VA, p. A668
  Senior Vice President and Chief Executive Officer, Novant Health Uva Health System Prince William Medical Center, Manassas, VA, p. A670

GILL, Mark, Vice President Finance and Chief Financial Officer, Cape Regional Medical Center, Cape May Court House, NJ, p. A412

GILLAM, Sally A R.N., Chief Nursing Officer, St. David's South Austin Medical Center, Austin, TX, p. A596

GILLARD, Austin M., Chief Executive Officer, Clay County Medical Center, Clay Center, KS, p. A239

GILLEN, Mark T
  Director Finance and Operations, Owatonna Hospital, Owatonna, MN, p. A345
  Director of Operations, Owatonna Hospital, Owatonna, MN, p. A345

GILLES, Ken
  Associate Chief Information Officer, Essentia Health St. Mary's – Detroit Lakes, Detroit Lakes, MN, p. A338

  Chief Information Officer, Essentia Health Fargo, Fargo, ND, p. A475

GILLESPIE, Anne R.N., Associate Director Patient Care and Nursing Services, Veterans Affairs Loma Linda Healthcare System, Loma Linda, CA, p. A66

GILLESPIE, Bob
  Chief Information Technology Officer, Connally Memorial Medical Center, Floresville, TX, p. A612
  Chief Operating Officer, Connally Memorial Medical Center, Floresville, TX, p. A612

GILLESPIE, Curt, Chief Executive Officer, Mental Health Services For Clark And Madison Counties, Springfield, OH, p. A499

GILLESPIE, Karen, Director Human Resources, Anderson County Hospital, Garnett, KS, p. A241

GILLESPIE, Lisa M.D., Chief Medical Officer, Rockdale Medical Center, Conyers, GA, p. A155

GILLESPIE, Richard, Chief Executive Officer, Jefferson County Hospital, Waurika, OK, p. A519

GILLESPIE, Thomas, Chief Information Officer, Fulton State Hospital, Fulton, MO, p. A368

GILLESPIE, Tim, Manager Information Systems, Carle Richland Memorial Hospital, Olney, IL, p. A196

GILLESPIE, Tina, Chief Executive Officer, Harrison County Community Hospital, Bethany, MO, p. A364

GILLETTE, Karen, Associate Director Patient Care Services, Memphis Veterans Affairs Medical Center, Memphis, TN, p. A585

GILLETTE, Nicole R.N., Chief Nursing Officer, West Branch Regional Medical Center, West Branch, MI, p. A333

GILLETTE, Robert, Chief Information Officer, St. Elizabeth Medical Center, Utica, NY, p. A454

GILLETTE, Tom, Senior Vice President and Chief Information Officer, Mount Sinai Medical Center, Miami Beach, FL, p. A134

GILFILLAN, Richard J., M.D., Chief Executive Officer, Trinity Health, Livonia, MI, p. B128

GILLIAM, David M.D., Medical Director, Bloomington Meadows Hospital, Bloomington, IN, p. A204

GILLIAM, Eric
  President, Saint Joseph Berea, Berea, KY, p. A255
  President, Saint Joseph East, Lexington, KY, p. A261

GILLIAM, Leslie, Director Health Information Management, Dominion Hospital, Falls Church, VA, p. A666

GILLIAN, Tom, Chief Operating Officer, River Bend Hospital, West Lafayette, IN, p. A221

GILLIAND, Michael M.D., Chief of Staff, Chi St. Luke's Health Brazosport, Lake Jackson, TX, p. A628

GILLIANO, Patti, Chief Nursing Officer, Baylor Scott & White Medical Center – Lake Pointe, Rowlett, TX, p. A641

GILLILAND, Michelle, Director of Nursing, River Park Hospital, Huntington, WV, p. A693

GILLILAND, Sharon, Chief of Staff, Baraga County Memorial Hospital, L'Anse, MI, p. A324

GILLILAND, Terry, M.D.
  Chief Medical Officer, Sentara Leigh Hospital, Norfolk, VA, p. A672
  Senior Vice President and Chief Medical Officer, Sentara Princess Anne Hospital, Virginia Beach, VA, p. A676

GILLIS, Anne, Chief Financial Officer, Holy Cross Health, Silver Spring, MD, p. A301

GILLMAN, Kreg, Chief Executive Officer, Salt Lake Behavioral Health, Salt Lake City, UT, p. A660

GILLY, Mike, Chief Information Officer, Our Lady Of The Angels Hospital, Bogalusa, LA, p. A272

GILMAN, Howard M.D., Medical Executive, Christian Health Care Center, Wyckoff, NJ, p. A423

GILMAN, Kim
  Chief Executive Officer and Chief Nursing Officer, Southwest Georgia Regional Medical Center, Cuthbert, GA, p. A156
  Chief Executive Officer and Chief Nursing Officer, Southwest Georgia Regional Medical Center, Cuthbert, GA, p. A156
  Chief Executive Officer, Phoebe Worth Medical Center, Sylvester, GA, p. A165
  Chief Nursing Officer, Phoebe Worth Medical Center, Sylvester, GA, p. A165

GILMORE, Hugh V M.D., Vice President Medical Affairs, Seton Medical Center Williamson, Round Rock, TX, p. A641

GILMORE, Joshua, Chief Executive Officer, Iron County Medical Center, Pilot Knob, MO, p. A375

GILMORE, Linda, Chief Nursing Officer/Chief Administrative Officer, Littleton Regional Healthcare, Littleton, NH, p. A409

GILMORE, Phillip K., FACHE, Chief Executive Officer, Ashley County Medical Center, Crossett, AR, p. A42

GILMORE, Stephen
  Chief Financial Officer, Piedmont Medical Center, Rock Hill, SC, p. A565

  Interim Chief Executive Officer, Piedmont Medical Center, Rock Hill, SC, p. A565

GILPIN, Michael W., Vice President Human Resources, Sampson Regional Medical Center, Clinton, NC, p. A460

GILSON, Sheila R.N., Chief Operating Officer, Kaiser Permanente Redwood City Medical Center, Redwood City, CA, p. A82

GILTNER, Michelle, Interim Chief Nursing Officer, Uh Regional Hospitals, Cleveland, OH, p. A486

GIN, Nancy M.D., Area Associate Medical Director, Kaiser Permanente Orange County Anaheim Medical Center, Anaheim, CA, p. A51

GINGERICH, Jim, Chief Executive Officer, Prairie Ridge Hospital And Health Services, Elbow Lake, MN, p. A339

GINGRAS, Sean CPA, Chief Financial Officer, Centerstone Hospital, Bradenton, FL, p. A120

GINGRICH, Joye, Director Patient Care Services and Chief Nursing Officer, J. C. Blair Memorial Hospital, Huntingdon, PA, p. A536

GINGRICH, Mary, Director Health Care Services, Kansas Neurological Institute, Topeka, KS, p. A252

GINN, Bobby, Chief Operating Officer, Crestwood Medical Center, Huntsville, AL, p. A19

GINN, Doug, Executive Vice President Operations, Peak Behavioral Health Services, Santa Teresa, NM, p. A428

GINNATY, Rayn, Vice President Nursing, Benefis Health System, Great Falls, MT, p. A385

GINSBERG, Jo–Ann M., R.N., MSN, Director, Marion Veterans Affairs Medical Center, Marion, IL, p. A192

GINSBERG, Ronald L M.D., Vice President Medical Affairs, Northwest Hospital, Randallstown, MD, p. A300

GINSBURG, J Lawrence M.D., Vice President Medical Affairs, Evangelical Community Hospital, Lewisburg, PA, p. A539

GINTER, Gary, System Vice President and Chief Information Officer, Miami Valley Hospital, Dayton, OH, p. A489

GINTOLI, Eric, Administrator, Seaside Health System, Baton Rouge, LA, p. A271

GINTZIG, Donald R.
  President and Chief Executive Officer, Wakemed Cary Hospital, Cary, NC, p. A458
  President and Chief Executive Officer, Wakemed Raleigh Campus, Raleigh, NC, p. A469

GIOIA, Anthony, Chief Financial Officer, Indiana Orthopaedic Hospital, Indianapolis, IN, p. A211

GIORDANO, Paul D, Vice President Human Resources, South Nassau Communities Hospital, Oceanside, NY, p. A448

GIORDANO, Peter, Senior Director Human Resources, Harrison Community Hospital, Cadiz, OH, p. A482

GIORDANO, Roger M.D., Medical Director, Healthsouth Rehabilitation Hospital Of Virginia, Richmond, VA, p. A673

GIORDANO, Susan R.N., Chief Nursing Officer, Hackensack Meridian Health Pascack Valley Medical Center, Westwood, NJ, p. A423

GIPP, Jana, Chief Executive Officer, Standing Rock Service Unit, Fort Yates Hospital, Indian Health Service, Dhhs, Fort Yates, ND, p. A476

GIPSON, Linda Stephens MSN, Ph.D., Chief Nursing Officer, Whidbeyhealth, Coupeville, WA, p. A679

GIRALT, Juana
  Chief Financial Officer, River Crest Hospital, San Angelo, TX, p. A641
  Interim Chief Executive Officer, River Crest Hospital, San Angelo, TX, p. A641

GIRARD, Thomas R
  Vice President Human Resources, Lincolnhealth, Damariscotta, ME, p. A290
  Vice President Human Resources, Pen Bay Medical Center, Rockport, ME, p. A293

GIRARDEAU, Brian, Director Information System, East Georgia Regional Medical Center, Statesboro, GA, p. A165

GIRARDIER, Cheryl, Director Information Technology, Lecom Health Millcreek Community Hospital, Erie, PA, p. A534

GIRARDY, James M.D., Vice President, Chief Surgical Officer, OSF Saint Anthony Medical Center, Rockford, IL, p. A199

GIRTEN, David M, Corporate Director Financial Services, St. Vincent Seton Specialty Hospital, Indianapolis, IN, p. A212

GIRTY, Tara, Director Human Resources, Kiowa District Hospital And Manor, Kiowa, KS, p. A244

GISH, Kevin, Administrator and Vice President, Essentia Health Fosston, Fosston, MN, p. A340

GISLER, Greg, Chief Financial Officer, Mcbride Orthopedic Hospital, Oklahoma City, OK, p. A512

GISLESON, Joni, Director Finance, Gundersen Palmer Lutheran Hospital And Clinics, West Union, IA, p. A236

GITMAN, Michael M.D., Medical Director, North Shore University Hospital, Manhasset, NY, p. A439

GITTELMAN, Michael B.
  Administrator, Bascom Palmer Eye Institute–Anne Bates Leach Eye Hospital, Miami, FL, p. A133

GOFF, Gary E. M.D., Medical Director, Promise Hospital Of Dallas, Dallas, TX, p. A606

GOFF, Vivian, R.N., Chief Executive Officer, Landmark Hospital Of Athens, Athens, GA, p. A149

GOGGIN, Daniel
Senior Vice President and Chief Financial Officer, Chi St. Joseph Health Burleson Hospital, Caldwell, TX, p. A600
Senior Vice President and Chief Financial Officer, Chi St. Joseph Health Grimes Hospital, Navasota, TX, p. A634

GOGGIN, Kathy, Director Administrative Services, Devereux Georgia Treatment Network, Kennesaw, GA, p. A160

GOGUEN, Craig, Chief Executive Officer, Emerus, The Woodlands, TX, p. B49

GOINS, Rick, Chief Executive Officer, Massac Memorial Hospital, Metropolis, IL, p. A194

GOLAN, Marc
Chief Financial Officer, Franciscan Health Hammond, Hammond, IN, p. A210
Chief Financial Officer, Franciscan St. Anthony Health – Crown Point, Crown Point, IN, p. A206
Regional Chief Financial Officer, Franciscan St. Anthony Health – Michigan City, Michigan City, IN, p. A215

GOLANOWSKI, Marie, R.N., MS, President, Aurora St. Luke's Medical Center, Milwaukee, WI, p. A707

GOLBIN, Jason M.D., Chief Medical Officer, St. Catherine Of Siena Medical Center, Smithtown, NY, p. A452

GOLD, Barbara M.D., Chief Medical Officer, University Of Minnesota Medical Center, Fairview, Minneapolis, MN, p. A344

GOLD, Joseph M.D., Chief Medical Officer, Mclean Hospital, Belmont, MA, p. A302

GOLD, Larry, Vice President, Information Services, Southern Virginia Regional Medical Center, Emporia, VA, p. A666

GOLDAMMER, Kyle, Chief Financial Officer, Sioux Falls Specialty Hospital, Sioux Falls, SD, p. A572

GOLDBERG, Andrew S, Associate Executive Director, Syosset Hospital, Syosset, NY, p. A453

GOLDBERG, David M.D., Vice President Medical Affairs and Chief Medical Officer, Community Memorial Hospital, Menomonee Falls, WI, p. A706

GOLDBERG, Frederick M.D., Vice President Medical Affairs and Chief Medical Officer, Nathan Littauer Hospital And Nursing Home, Gloversville, NY, p. A436

GOLDBERG, Gary M.D., Chief Medical Officer, North Hawaii Community Hospital, Kamuela, HI, p. A169

GOLDBERG, Jonathan, Senior Vice President and Chief Information Officer, Arkansas Children's Hospital, Little Rock, AR, p. A45

GOLDBERG, Michael, Executive Director, Long Island Jewish Medical Center, New Rochelle, NY, p. A442

GOLDBERG, Paul R, Chief Financial Officer, Jersey City Medical Center, Jersey City, NJ, p. A415

GOLDBERG, Stephanie J MSN, R.N., Senior Vice President and Chief Nursing Officer, Hospital For Special Surgery, New Rochelle, NY, p. A441

GOLDBERGER, Joseph, M.D.
Chief Medical Officer, Yavapai Regional Medical Center – East, Prescott Valley, AZ, p. A35
Chief Medical Officer, Yavapai Regional Medical Center, Prescott, AZ, p. A35

GOLDEN, Joy, Chief Executive Officer, Lakeside Behavioral Health System, Memphis, TN, p. A584

GOLDEN, Virginia L.
Chief Executive Officer, Albany Memorial Hospital, Albany, NY, p. A430
Chief Executive Officer, St. Peter's Hospital, Albany, NY, p. A430

GOLDEN, William M.D., Chief Medical Officer, East Alabama Medical Center, Opelika, AL, p. A22

GOLDENBERG, Dianne, Chief Executive Officer, Palm Beach Gardens Medical Center, Palm Beach Gardens, FL, p. A138

GOLDENSTEIN, Rachel R.N., Chief Nursing Officer, Buchanan County Health Center, Independence, IA, p. A229

GOLDFARB, I William, Chief Medical Officer, West Penn Hospital, Pittsburgh, PA, p. A548

GOLDFARB, Timothy, Interim Chief Executive Officer, Ohsu Hospital, Portland, OR, p. A525

GOLDFRACH, Andrew, Chief Executive Officer, Uh Avon Rehabilitation Hospital, Avon, OH, p. A480

GOLDHAGEN, Michele M.D., Chief of Staff, Russell Medical Center, Alexander City, AL, p. A13

GOLDIS, Glenn, Chief Medical Officer, Kern Medical Center, Bakersfield, CA, p. A53

GOLDMAN, David M.D., Vice President Medical Affairs and Education, Prince George's Hospital Center, Cheverly, MD, p. A297

GOLDMAN, Eric, Chief Executive Officer, Palms West Hospital, Loxahatchee, FL, p. A131

GOLDMAN, Kris, Director Human Resources, Shriners Hospitals For Children–Salt Lake City, Salt Lake City, UT, p. A660

GOLDSCHMIDT, Pascal J., M.D., Chief Executive Officer, University Of Miami Health System, Miami, FL, p. B140

GOLDSMITH, Cheri L
Director Financial Services, Parkland Health Center – Farmington Community, Farmington, MO, p. A368
Director Financial Services, Parkland Health Center–Bonne Terre, Bonne Terre, MO, p. A364

GOLDSMITH, Dana L M.D., Vice President Medical Affairs, Pen Bay Medical Center, Rockport, ME, p. A293

GOLDSTEIN, Allan M.D., Medical Director and Chief of Staff, Select Specialty Hospital–Birmingham, Birmingham, AL, p. A15

GOLDSTEIN, David M.D., Chief Medical Officer, Contra Costa Regional Medical Center, Martinez, CA, p. A73

GOLDSTEIN, Gary W., M.D., President and Chief Executive Officer, Kennedy Krieger Institute, Baltimore, MD, p. A294

GOLDSTEIN, Gerald M.D., Senior Vice President and Chief Medical Officer, Western Maryland Regional Medical Center, Cumberland, MD, p. A298

GOLDSTEIN, Lawrence M.D., Chief Medical Officer, Vibra Hospital Of Mahoning Valley, Boardman, OH, p. A481

GOLDSTEIN, Lisa, Executive Vice President and Chief Operating Officer, Hospital For Special Surgery, New Rochelle, NY, p. A441

GOLDSTEIN, Mark L., President and Chief Executive Officer, Anna Jaques Hospital, Newburyport, MA, p. A309

GOLDSTEIN, Sandy R.N., Chief Nursing Officer, Banner Lassen Medical Center, Susanville, CA, p. A93

GOLDSTEIN, Steven I.
President and Chief Executive Officer, Highland Hospital, Rochester, NY, p. A450
President and Chief Executive Officer, Strong Memorial Hospital Of The University Of Rochester, Rochester, NY, p. A451

GOLDSZER, Robert M.D., Senior Vice President and Chief Medical Officer, Mount Sinai Medical Center, Miami Beach, FL, p. A134

GOLICH, Jacob, Chief Executive Officer, Mountain Vista Medical Center, Mesa, AZ, p. A31

GOLIGHTLY, Beverly, Director Information Technology, St. Vincent's East, Birmingham, AL, p. A15

GOLKE, Rynae, Director Human Resources, Jacobson Memorial Hospital Care Center, Elgin, ND, p. A475

GOLL, Cheri MSN, R.N., Chief Nursing Executive, Advocate Sherman Hospital, Elgin, IL, p. A186

GOLLAHER, Jeffrey, Chief Executive Officer, Hendricks Community Hospital Association, Hendricks, MN, p. A341

GOLLINGER, Mary A MS, R.N., Director of Nursing, Schwab Rehabilitation Hospital, Chicago, IL, p. A183

GOLOLOBOV, Alexey, Chief Financial Officer, Columbus Hospital Ltach, Newark, NJ, p. A417

GOLOVAN, Ronald M.D., Vice President Medical Operations, Lutheran Hospital, Cleveland, OH, p. A486

GOMBAR, Greg A
Chief Financial Officer, Carolinas Healthcare System University, Charlotte, NC, p. A459
Chief Financial Officer, Carolinas Medical Center, Charlotte, NC, p. A459

GOMBERG, Sandra, Chief Operating Officer, Aria – Jefferson Health, Philadelphia, PA, p. A543

GOMBERT, Laurie H., Administrator, Coordinated Health–Bethlehem, Bethlehem, PA, p. A529

GOMES, Carol FACHE, Chief Operating Officer, Stony Brook University Hospital, Stony Brook, NY, p. A453

GOMEZ, Carmen, Director Human Resources, North Shore Medical Center, Miami, FL, p. A133

GOMEZ, Denise, Assistant Vice President Information Systems, Unitypoint Health Meriter, Madison, WI, p. A705

GOMEZ, Dianna, Controller, Uva–Healthsouth Rehabilitation Hospital, Charlottesville, VA, p. A665

GOMEZ, Dolores S. R.N., Chief Operating Officer, Mills–Peninsula Health Services, Burlingame, CA, p. A54

GOMEZ, Gloria M.D., Medical Director, East Mississippi State Hospital, Meridian, MS, p. A359

GOMEZ, Jay Michael, Chief Financial Officer, Memorial Hermann Surgical Hospital Kingwood, Kingwood, TX, p. A627

GOMEZ, Jesse, Vice President Human Resources, University Of Texas Health Northeast, Tyler, TX, p. A651

GOMEZ, Mike, Site Manager Medical Information Systems, Our Lady Of Bellefonte Hospital, Ashland, KY, p. A255

GOMEZ, Omar M.D., Chief of Staff, Cornerstone Regional Hospital, Edinburg, TX, p. A610

GOMEZ, Richard, Assistant Vice President Information Technology Division, Hillcrest Medical Center, Tulsa, OK, p. A517

GOMEZ, Robin, R.N., MSN, Administrator, Alvarado Hospital Medical Center, San Diego, CA, p. A85

GOMEZ–LUNA, Sandra, Medical Director, Southwest Connecticut Mental Health System, Bridgeport, CT, p. A109

GOMPF, Shelly, Director Human Resources, Douglas County Hospital, Alexandria, MN, p. A335

GONCZ, Gray, Vice President of Medical Affairs, Trinity Health System, Steubenville, OH, p. A500

GONDER, Christie, Chief Nursing Officer, Salinas Valley Memorial Healthcare System, Salinas, CA, p. A84

GONG, Christopher M.D., Chief Staff, Huron Medical Center, Bad Axe, MI, p. A314

GONGAWARE, Robert, Senior Vice President Finance, Indiana Regional Medical Center, Indiana, PA, p. A537

GONYEA, Sonja, Director Human Resources, United Memorial Medical Center, Batavia, NY, p. A431

GONZALES, Amy, Director of Human Resources, Mckenzie County Healthcare System, Watford City, ND, p. A478

GONZALES, Angela, Manager Human Resources, San Mateo Medical Center, San Mateo, CA, p. A89

GONZALES, Ed
Vice President Human Resources, Marian Regional Medical Center, Santa Maria, CA, p. A91
Vice President Human Resources, St. John's Pleasant Valley Hospital, Camarillo, CA, p. A54
Vice President Human Resources, St. John's Regional Medical Center, Oxnard, CA, p. A78

GONZALES, Jan, Director Human Resources, North Valley Hospital, Tonasket, WA, p. A688

GONZALES, Mike, Chief Financial Officer, Vibra Hospital Of San Diego, San Diego, CA, p. A86

GONZALES, Mindy, Chief Human Resources Officer, Othello Community Hospital, Othello, WA, p. A683

GONZALES, Paula, Administrator, Emerus Community Hospital, Tomball, TX, p. A650

GONZALES, Rachel Ann., Chief Executive Officer, Madison Memorial Hospital, Rexburg, ID, p. A175

GONZALEZ, Agustin, Director Finance, Hospital Pavia Arecibo, Arecibo, PR, p. A722

GONZALEZ, Alan, Chief Operating Officer, Fort Duncan Regional Medical Center, Eagle Pass, TX, p. A609

GONZALEZ, Aurelio, Chief Financial Officer, University Hospital And Medical Center, Tamarac, FL, p. A144

GONZALEZ, David, M.D.
Medical Director, Brook Lane Health Services, Hagerstown, MD, p. A299
Chief Clinical Officer, Advanced Diagnostics Hospital, Houston, TX, p. A619

GONZALEZ, Dinah L., Chief Financial Officer, Knapp Medical Center, Weslaco, TX, p. A654

GONZALEZ, Elizabeth CPA, Financial Director, Hospital Pavia Yauco, Yauco, PR, p. A727

GONZALEZ, Hugo M.D., Chief Medical Officer, Sister Emmanuel Hospital, Miami, FL, p. A134

GONZALEZ, Jacqueline, Senior Vice President and Chief Nursing Officer, Nicklaus Children's Hospital, Miami, FL, p. A133

GONZALEZ, Jaime, Administrator, St. Catherine's Rehabilitation Hospital, North Miami, FL, p. A136

GONZALEZ, Jerry, Interim Chief Nursing Officer, Las Palmas Medical Center, El Paso, TX, p. A611

GONZALEZ, Jorge F, M.D.
Chief Medical Officer, Florida Hospital Heartland Medical Center, Sebring, FL, p. A142
Vice President and Chief Nursing Officer, Florida Hospital Wauchula, Wauchula, FL, p. A147

GONZALEZ, Jorge Matta., Executive Director, University Hospital, San Juan, PR, p. A727

GONZALEZ, Laura, Interim Chief Nurse Executive, South Shore Hospital, Chicago, IL, p. A184

GONZALEZ, Pedro J., FACHE, Chief Executive Officer, Ashford Presbyterian Community Hospital, San Juan, PR, p. A725

GONZALEZ, Rainier, Chairman and Chief Executive Officer, Pacer Health Corporation, Miami Lakes, FL, p. B96

GONZALEZ, Richard, Chief Executive Officer, The Medical Center Of Southeast Texas, Port Arthur, TX, p. A639

GONZALEZ, Roberto, Executive Director Human Resources, Carepoint Health Hoboken University Medical Center, Hoboken, NJ, p. A414

GONZALEZ, Susan, Director of Clinical Services, Stanislaus Surgical Hospital, Modesto, CA, p. A74

GONZALEZ, Victoria, Chief Financial Officer, The Hospitals Of Providence Sierra Campus, El Paso, TX, p. A611

GONZALEZ–FAJARDO, Ana, Human Resources Director, Palmetto General Hospital, Hialeah, FL, p. A126

GOOCH, Mathew, Chief Executive Officer, Healthsouth Rehabilitation Hospital Of Middletown, Middletown, DE, p. A115

GOOD, Jo, Director of Nursing, Palmetto Lowcountry Behavioral Health, Charleston, SC, p. A559
GOOD, Vance A M.D., Chief Medical Staff, Troy Community Hospital, Troy, PA, p. A552
GOODALL, David M.D., Chief Medical Staff, Essentia Health–Deer River, Deer River, MN, p. A338
GOODBALIAN, Terry
  Regional Chief Financial Officer, Henry Ford West Bloomfield Hospital, West Bloomfield, MI, p. A333
  Vice President Finance and Chief Financial Officer, Henry Ford Macomb Hospitals, Clinton Township, MI, p. A316
  Vice President, Finance and Chief Financial Officer, Henry Ford Wyandotte Hospital, Wyandotte, MI, p. A333
GOODE, Jennifer, Director Human Resources, Russell County Hospital, Russell Springs, KY, p. A267
GOODE, Lori, Director Human Resources, Baptist Memorial Hospital–Union County, New Albany, MS, p. A360
GOODE, Richard P., Executive Vice President and Chief Financial Officer, Children's Health System Of Texas, Dallas, TX, p. A605
GOODE, Shayne, Administrator, Post Acute/Warm Springs Specialty Hospital Of New Braunfels, New Braunfels, TX, p. A635
GOODE, Vicky, Director Human Resources, Lifecare Hospitals Of North Carolina, Rocky Mount, NC, p. A469
GOODIN, Antonia M., Chief Executive Officer and Chief Financial Officer, Claiborne Memorial Medical Center, Homer, LA, p. A276
GOODIN, Scott, Interim Chief Financial Officer, Chinese Hospital, San Francisco, CA, p. A87
GOODING, Lari, Chief Executive Officer, Allendale County Hospital, Fairfax, SC, p. A561
GOODISON, Sharon A R.N., MS, Chief Nursing Officer, Jackson Hospital And Clinic, Montgomery, AL, p. A21
GOODLETT, Lisa, Senior Vice President and Chief Financial Officer, Laurel Regional Hospital, Laurel, MD, p. A299
GOODMAN, Brenda, Chief Nursing Officer, Medical Center Of Peach County, Navicent Health, Bryon, GA, p. A153
GOODMAN, Charlene, Director Human Resources, Rush County Memorial Hospital, La Crosse, KS, p. A244
GOODMAN, David M Ph.D., Chief Information Officer, Veterans Affairs Boston Healthcare System, West Roxbury, MA, p. A312
GOODMAN, Doug, Vice President Human Resources, Brandon Regional Hospital, Brandon, FL, p. A121
GOODMAN, Larry J., M.D., Chief Executive Officer, Rush University Medical Center, Chicago, IL, p. A183
GOODMAN, Louis, Senior Vice President Human Resources, Monongahela Valley Hospital, Monongahela, PA, p. A541
GOODMAN, Mary Jo, Chief Operating Officer, Park Plaza Hospital, Houston, TX, p. A622
GOODMAN, Shane, Chief Nursing Officer, De Soto Regional Health System, Mansfield, LA, p. A280
GOODMAN, Steven, Chief Operating Officer, Willow Crest Hospital, Miami, OK, p. A510
GOODMAN, William H., Vice President Medical Affairs, Chief Medical Officer, Catholic Medical Center, Manchester, NH, p. A409
GOODNOW, John H., Chief Executive Officer, Benefis Health System, Great Falls, MT, p. A385
GOODPASTER, Amber, Chief Financial Officer, Clark Regional Medical Center, Winchester, KY, p. A268
GOODRICH, C Harlan, Vice President and Chief Information Officer, Midmichigan Medical Center–Midland, Midland, MI, p. A326
GOODRICH, Craig, Chief Financial Officer, Virginia Mason Medical Center, Seattle, WA, p. A686
GOODRICH, Zane, Vice President Finance, East Tennessee Children's Hospital, Knoxville, TN, p. A581
GOODROW, Darrin
  Chief Information Officer, Moses Ludington Hospital, Ticonderoga, NY, p. A454
  Chief Information Officer, The University Of Vermont Health Network – Alice Hyde Medical Center, Malone, NY, p. A439
  Chief Information Officer, The University Of Vermont Health Network Elizabethtown Community Hospital, Elizabethtown, NY, p. A435
GOODSON, David, Chief Executive Officer, Select Specialty Hospital–Pensacola, Pensacola, FL, p. A139
GOODSPEED, Darwin, Director, Sioux Falls Veterans Affairs Health Care System, Sioux Falls, SD, p. A573
GOODSTEIN, Ruth, Controller, Healthsouth Sunrise Rehabilitation Hospital, Sunrise, FL, p. A143
GOODWIN, Jeremy M.D., President, Medical Staff, Monroe County Hospital, Forsyth, GA, p. A158
GOODWIN, Jeronica, Senior Director Human Resources, Howard University Hospital, Washington, DC, p. A117
GOODWIN, Keith D., President and Chief Executive Officer, East Tennessee Children's Hospital, Knoxville, TN, p. A581

COODWIN, Linda, Group Chief Nursing Officer, St. Anthony Hospital, Lakewood, CO, p. A105
GOODWIN, W Jarrad M.D., Director, University Of Miami Hospital And Clinics, Miami, FL, p. A134
GOOLSBY, Elizabeth, Director, Fayetteville Veterans Affairs Medical Center, Fayetteville, NC, p. A462
GOPALAM, Gopinath, Chief Executive Officer, Apollo Behavioral Health Hospital, Baton Rouge, LA, p. A270
GOPINATH, Anil FACHE, M.D., Regional Chief Medical Officer, Presence Mercy Medical Center, Aurora, IL, p. A177
GORANSON, Ken, Chief Financial Officer, Benson Hospital, Benson, AZ, p. A28
GORBY, Cherie, Chief Operations Officer, Uchealth Memorial, Colorado Springs, CO, p. A100
GORBY, Karen S., R.N., MSN, FACHE, President and Chief Nursing Officer, Angel Medical Center, Franklin, NC, p. A462
GORCZYCA, Julie A R.N., Chief Nursing Officer, Genesys Regional Medical Center, Grand Blanc, MI, p. A320
GORDIAN, Michael, Chief Financial Officer, Western Plains Medical Complex, Dodge City, KS, p. A240
GORDNER, Barbie, Director Human Resources, Acuity Hospital Of South Texas, San Antonio, TX, p. A641
GORDON, Cyndy, Chief Operating Officer, Rideout Memorial Hospital, Marysville, CA, p. A73
GORDON, Dan, Chief Financial Officer, Feather River Hospital, Paradise, CA, p. A79
GORDON, Kevin M.D., Chief of Staff, Alliancehealth Durant, Durant, OK, p. A506
GORDON, Mandy, Human Resource Coordinator, Phoebe Worth Medical Center, Sylvester, GA, p. A165
GORDON, Mark M.
  Chief Executive Officer, Bon Secours Memorial Regional Medical Center, Mechanicsville, VA, p. A670
  Chief Executive Officer, Bon Secours–Richmond Community Hospital, Richmond, VA, p. A674
  Chief Executive Officer, Rappahannock General Hospital, Kilmarnock, VA, p. A669
GORDON, Mark, Chief Nursing Officer, Kern Valley Healthcare District, Lake Isabella, CA, p. A65
GORDON, Nancy Gail R.N., MSN, Chief Nursing Officer and Vice President of Nursing, Baptist Health South Florida, Homestead Hospital, Homestead, FL, p. A127
GORDON, Robert, Manager Information Systems, Halifax Regional Medical Center, Roanoke Rapids, NC, p. A469
GORDON, Steve, Director Human Resources, Lake City Medical Center, Lake City, FL, p. A129
GORDON, Steven R., President and Chief Executive Officer, Brattleboro Memorial Hospital, Brattleboro, VT, p. A662
GORDON, Susan R.N., Chief Nursing Officer, Memorial Hospital, York, PA, p. A555
GORDON, Thomas, Chief Information Officer, Virtua Marlton, Marlton, NJ, p. A416
GORDON, Wayne
  Chief Financial Officer, Memorial Hermann Rehabilitation Hospital – Katy, Katy, TX, p. A626
  Chief Financial Officer, Tirr Memorial Hermann, Houston, TX, p. A623
GORE, Carol MSN, R.N., Chief Nursing Officer, Saint Mary's Regional Medical Center, Russellville, AR, p. A49
GORE, Gary R., Chief Executive Officer, Marshall Health System, Guntersville, AL, p. B79
GORE, Tim, Chief Financial Officer, Rivendell Behavioral Health, Bowling Green, KY, p. A256
GOREAU, Judy R.N., Director of Nursing, Eastside Psychiatric Hospital, Tallahassee, FL, p. A144
GOREY, Peter, Administrative Coordinator, Rockland Children's Hospital Psychiatric Center, Orangeburg, NY, p. A449
GORLEWSKI, Todd, Senior Vice President and Chief Financial Officer, St. Barnabas Hospital, New Rochelle, NY, p. A446
GORMAN, Brandon, Chief Financial Officer, Bradley County Medical Center, Warren, AR, p. A50
GORMAN, Jodie, Director Human Resources, Salem Memorial District Hospital, Salem, MO, p. A379
GORMAN, Kathleen MSN, R.N., Executive Vice President Patient Care Services and Chief Operating Officer, Children's National Health System, Washington, DC, p. A117
GORMAN, Matt, Administrator, Polk Medical Center, Cedartown, GA, p. A154
GORMLEY, Ann H, Senior Vice President Human Resources, Pinnaclehealth Harrisburg Hospital, Harrisburg, PA, p. A536
GORMLEY, Maureen E R.N., M.P.H., Chief Operating Officer, National Institutes Of Health Clinical Center, Bethesda, MD, p. A297
GORMSEN, David D.O., Vice President and Chief Medical Officer, Mercy Medical Center, Canton, OH, p. A482
GORN, Angela, Vice President, Norton Sound Regional Hospital, Nome, AK, p. A26

GORSUCH, Penelope Franklin, Associate Director Patient Care Services, Dayton Veterans Affairs Medical Center, Dayton, OH, p. A489
GOSCH, Shawn, Chief Financial Officer, Burgess Health Center, Onawa, IA, p. A232
GOSEY, J M.D., Medical Director, Southern Surgical Hospital, Slidell, LA, p. A286
GOSHE, Nick, Chief Executive Officer, Rangely District Hospital, Rangely, CO, p. A107
GOSHIA, Rob, Chief Financial Officer, Paulding County Hospital, Paulding, OH, p. A498
GOSLEE, Belle, Chief Nursing Officer, Healthsouth Chesapeake Rehabilitation Hospital, Salisbury, MD, p. A301
GOSNEY, Brett, Chief Executive Officer, Animas Surgical Hospital, Durango, CO, p. A101
GOSS, J. Richard M.D., Medical Director, Uw Medicine/Harborview Medical Center, Seattle, WA, p. A685
GOSS, Norma R.N., Chief Nursing Officer, Flaget Memorial Hospital, Bardstown, KY, p. A255
GOSS, Roger, Director, Information Services, North Sunflower Medical Center, Ruleville, MS, p. A361
GOSSELIN, Gail
  Director Human Resources, Landmark Medical Center, Woonsocket, RI, p. A557
  Director Human Resources, Rehabilitation Hospital Of Rhode Island, North Smithfield, RI, p. A556
GOSSENS, Kevin, Director Human Resources, Thedacare Medical Center–Waupaca, Waupaca, WI, p. A715
GOSSETT, Lisa MSN, R.N., Chief Nursing Officer, Ohiohealth Riverside Methodist Hospital, Columbus, OH, p. A488
GOTSOULIAS, Kostas, Interim Chief Executive Officer, Aspire Hospital, Conroe, TX, p. A602
GOTTI, Sreekant, Director Information Systems, Desert Valley Hospital, Victorville, CA, p. A96
GOTTLIEB, Jonathan M.D., Senior Vice President and Chief Medical Officer, University Of Maryland Medical Center, Baltimore, MD, p. A296
GOTTSCHALK, Amy M.D., Chief Medical Officer, Verde Valley Medical Center; Vice President Quality, Northern Arizona Healthcare, Verde Valley Medical Center, Cottonwood, AZ, p. A28
GOTTSCHALL, Dan, Senior Vice President and Chief Clinical Officer, St. Vincent's Medical Center, Bridgeport, CT, p. A109
GOUGEON, Michele L, Executive Vice President and Chief Operating Officer, Mclean Hospital, Belmont, MA, p. A302
GOUGH, Galal S M.D., Chief of Staff, Coast Plaza Hospital, Norwalk, CA, p. A76
GOUGH, Michelle MSN, RN–B, Chief Nursing Officer, Southwest Mississippi Regional Medical Center, Mccomb, MS, p. A358
GOULD, Christine, Director Human Resources, Martha's Vineyard Hospital, Oak Bluffs, MA, p. A310
GOULD, Dana L., Chief Executive Officer, Broaddus Hospital, Philippi, WV, p. A695
GOULD, Jacquelyn M MS, R.N., Vice President Patient Care Services and Chief Nursing Officer, Wellspan Good Samaritan Hospital, Lebanon, PA, p. A539
GOULD, Tamara R.N., Vice President Clinical Services and Chief Nursing Officer, Wabash General Hospital, Mount Carmel, IL, p. A194
GOULD, William R, Vice President Human Resources, Saint Joseph Hospital, Denver, CO, p. A101
GOULET, James P, Vice President Operations, Columbus Community Hospital, Columbus, NE, p. A392
GOULSON, Dan M.D., Chief Medical Officer, Our Lady Of Bellefonte Hospital, Ashland, KY, p. A255
GOURLEY, Paul M.D., Chief Hospital Services, U. S. Air Force Hospital, Hampton, VA, p. A668
GOVE, Cynthia A, Chief Operating Officer, Hampstead Hospital, Hampstead, NH, p. A408
GOVINDAIAH, Rajesh G M.D., Chief Medical Officer, Memorial Medical Center, Springfield, IL, p. A200
GOVORCHIN, Pete, Senior Vice President Operations, Midwestern Regional Medical Center, Zion, IL, p. A202
GOWEN, Tina, System Controller, Westfield Memorial Hospital, Westfield, NY, p. A456
GOWDER, Mike, Chief Executive Officer, Union General Hospital, Inc., Blairsville, GA, p. B132
GOWER, Gary, Chief Information Officer, Appling Healthcare System, Baxley, GA, p. A152
GOYAL, Alok M.D., Medical Director, Post Acute Medical Specialty Hospital Of Milwaukee, Greenfield, WI, p. A703
GOYAL, Deepak M.D., Chief of Staff, Jacobson Memorial Hospital Care Center, Elgin, ND, p. A475
GOYKOVICH, Stephen D.O., Chief Medical Officer, Jersey Shore Hospital, Jersey Shore, PA, p. A537
GOYTIA–LEOS, Dina M.D., Chief of Staff, Nix Health Care System, San Antonio, TX, p. A643

GRAY, Terry, Vice President Human Resources, Emanuel Medical Center, Turlock, CA, p. A94

GRAY, Thomas M.D., Medical Director, Montana State Hospital, Warm Springs, MT, p. A389

GRAY, Tracy
Chief Information Officer, Grady General Hospital, Cairo, GA, p. A153
Chief Information Officer, Mitchell County Hospital, Camilla, GA, p. A153
Senior Vice President Information Services, John D. Archbold Memorial Hospital, Thomasville, GA, p. A166

GRAYBEAL, Phillip, CPA
Chief Financial Officer, Page Memorial Hospital, Luray, VA, p. A669
Chief Financial Officer, Warren Memorial Hospital, Front Royal, VA, p. A668
Vice President, Finance, Shenandoah Memorial Hospital, Woodstock, VA, p. A677

GRAYBILL, Matthew P, Vice President, Human Resources and Chief Administrative Officer, Children's Medical Center, Dayton, OH, p. A489

GRAYSON, Barbara, Vice President Human Resources, Mercy Hospital Washington, Washington, MO, p. A381

GREAKER, Mark, Chief Information Officer, New York–Presbyterian Queens, New Rochelle, NY, p. A444

GREAR, Esther, Director Hospital Social Work and Assistant Hospital Administrator, Windhaven Psychiatric Hospital, Prescott Valley, AZ, p. A35

GREASON, Linda, Vice President Human Resources, Milford Regional Medical Center, Milford, MA, p. A309

GREBOSKY, Jamie M.D., Vice President of Medical Affairs, Asante Rogue Regional Medical Center, Medford, OR, p. A524

GRECCO, Jamie
Chief Human Resource Executive, NYC Health + Hospitals / Jacobi, New Rochelle, NY, p. A445
Director Human Resources Post Acute, NYC Health + Hospitals / Carter, New Rochelle, NY, p. A444

GRECO, Andrew, Chief Financial Officer, Calvary Hospital, New Rochelle, NY, p. A441

GRECO, Margaret, Chief Human Resources, Keller Army Community Hospital, West Point, NY, p. A455

GREELEY, Donna, Director Human Resources, Spalding Rehabilitation Hospital, Aurora, CO, p. A98

GREELEY, Gerald, Chief Information Officer, Signature Healthcare Brockton Hospital, Brockton, MA, p. A304

GREEN, Amber R.N., Chief Clinical Officer, Memorial Hospital Of Carbon County, Rawlins, WY, p. A719

GREEN, Arnold, Senior Vice President and Chief Operating Officer, Mcleod Loris Seacoast Hospital, Loris, SC, p. A564

GREEN, Barbara, Director Human Resources, O'Connor Hospital, Delhi, NY, p. A435

GREEN, Brenda, Director of Nursing, Ruby Valley Hospital, Sheridan, MT, p. A388

GREEN, Calvin, Chief Executive Officer, Sabine Medical Center, Many, LA, p. A280

GREEN, Christi R.N., MS, Vice President, Human Resources, Frisbie Memorial Hospital, Rochester, NH, p. A410

GREEN, Christopher, Chief Financial Officer, Carolinas Hospital System Marion, Mullins, SC, p. A565

GREEN, Dante, Assistant Vice President Operations, New Orleans East Hospital, New Orleans, LA, p. A282

GREEN, Darryl, Director Administration, Naval Hospital Jacksonville, Jacksonville, FL, p. A128

GREEN, David F. M.D., Chief Medical Officer, Concord Hospital, Concord, NH, p. A407

GREEN, David, Chief Human Resources, West Palm Beach Veterans Affairs Medical Center, West Palm Beach, FL, p. A147

GREEN, Debra Jane R.N., Director of Nursing, Turquoise Lodge Hospital, Albuquerque, NM, p. A425

GREEN, Dona, Chief Operating Officer, NYC Health + Hospitals / Queens, New Rochelle, NY, p. A445

GREEN, Elizabeth, Chief Human Resources Officer, Cooper University Health Care, Camden, NJ, p. A412

GREEN, Garry Kim., FACHE, Administrator, Shriners Hospitals For Children–Shreveport, Shreveport, LA, p. A286

GREEN, Gayle, Director of Nursing, Hale Ho'Ola Hamakua, Honokaa, HI, p. A168

GREEN, Gene E., M.D., Chief Executive Officer, South Shore Hospital, South Weymouth, MA, p. A311

GREEN, Jack W., Administrator, Antelope Memorial Hospital, Neligh, NE, p. A396

GREEN, John, Vice President Finance, St. Peter's Hospital, Helena, MT, p. A385

GREEN, Julie, Vice President Human Resources, Cheshire Medical Center, Keene, NH, p. A408

GREEN, Karen, Chief Information Officer, Brooks Rehabilitation Hospital, Jacksonville, FL, p. A128

GREEN, Kaye, FACHE, Director, W. G. (Bill) Heffner Veterans Affairs Medical Center, Salisbury, NC, p. A470

GREEN, Ladonna, Director Human Resources, Glen Rose Medical Center, Glen Rose, TX, p. A616

GREEN, Larry D. Jr, Chief Executive Officer, Windhaven Psychiatric Hospital, Prescott Valley, AZ, p. A35

GREEN, Marsha, Chief Executive Officer, Essentia Health–Deer River, Deer River, MN, p. A338

GREEN, Meredith, Chief Nursing Officer, Washington Regional Medical Center, Fayetteville, AR, p. A43

GREEN, Patrick
President and Chief Executive Officer, Lawrence + Memorial Hospital, New London, CT, p. A112
President and Chief Executive Officer, Westerly Hospital, Westerly, RI, p. A557

GREEN, Paul, Chief Clinical Officer, Kindred Hospital–Aurora, Aurora, CO, p. A98

GREEN, Rhonda G., Administrator, Lallie Kemp Medical Center, Independence, LA, p. A276

GREEN, Ricky, Senior Human Resources Business Partner, Spectrum Health Big Rapids Hospital, Big Rapids, MI, p. A315

GREEN, Rose Marie, Director Human Resources, Humboldt General Hospital, Winnemucca, NV, p. A406

GREEN, Steve, Comptroller, Jasper General Hospital, Bay Springs, MS, p. A352

GREEN, Susan, Senior Vice President Finance, Chief Financial Officer, Lowell General Hospital, Lowell, MA, p. A308

GREEN, Tracy V., Chief Financial Officer, NYC Health + Hospitals / Metropolitan, New Rochelle, NY, p. A445

GREEN, Vince
Chief Operating Officer, St. Joseph Hospital, Fort Wayne, IN, p. A208
Interim Chief Administrative Officer, St. Joseph Hospital, Fort Wayne, IN, p. A208

GREEN, Vincent, Medical Director, Greenville Health System – Laurens County Memorial Hospital, Clinton, SC, p. A560

GREENBERG, Mark, M.D.
Chief Medical Officer, Cape Coral Hospital, Cape Coral, FL, p. A121
Medical Director, Gulf Coast Medical Center, Fort Myers, FL, p. A125

GREENBERG, Raymond, M.D., Executive Vice Chancellor, University Of Texas System, Austin, TX, p. B141

GREENBLATT, James M.D., Chief Medical Officer, Vice President Medical Clinical Services, Walden Behavioral Care, Waltham, MA, p. A312

GREENE, Arthur M.D., Vice President Medical Affairs, Sentara Careplex Hospital, Hampton, VA, p. A668

GREENE, Beth, Chief Operating Officer, Cherokee Indian Hospital, Cherokee, NC, p. A460

GREENE, Bradley, Chief Financial Officer, Wellstar Douglas Hospital, Douglasville, GA, p. A157

GREENE, Cora, Senior Director, Chief Nursing Officer, Novant Health Rowan Medical Center, Salisbury, NC, p. A470

GREENE, Dustin, Chief Executive Officer, Tristar Horizon Medical Center, Dickson, TN, p. A578

GREENE, Erin, Coordinator Human Resources, Kindred Hospital–San Francisco Bay Area, San Leandro, CA, p. A89

GREENE, Hugh, President and Chief Executive Officer, Baptist Health, Jacksonville, FL, p. B18

GREENE, Kathleen, Director Human Resources, Promise Hospital Of San Diego, San Diego, CA, p. A85

GREENE, Melodi R.N., MS, Chief Nursing Officer, Community Howard Regional Health, Kokomo, IN, p. A213

GREENE, Palmer R.N., Chief Nursing Officer, Sierra Vista Hospital, Truth Or Consequences, NM, p. A429

GREENE, Robert, Director Information Technology, Promise Hospital Of Miss Lou, Vidalia, LA, p. A287

GREENE, Scott, Chief Information Officer, Tennova Healthcare–Clarksville, Clarksville, TN, p. A577

GREENE, Todd, Chief Executive Officer, Arizona Spine And Joint Hospital, Mesa, AZ, p. A31

GREENE, Tracie, Director Human Resources, Brigham City Community Hospital, Brigham City, UT, p. A656

GREENFIELD, Tadd, Executive Vice President and Chief Operating Officer, Regional West Medical Center, Scottsbluff, NE, p. A399

GREENLEE, Kathryn M, R.N.
Vice President, Clinical Services/CNO, Promedica Bixby Hospital, Adrian, MI, p. A314
Vice President, Clinical Services/CNO, Promedica Herrick Hospital, Tecumseh, MI, p. A332

GREENMAN, Jennifer, Vice President Chief Information Officer, H. Lee Moffitt Cancer Center And Research Institute, Tampa, FL, p. A144

GREENMAN, Sharon, Director Human Resources, Melissa Memorial Hospital, Holyoke, CO, p. A104

GREENWALD, Derek, Chief Nursing Officer, Star Valley Medical Center, Afton, WY, p. A717

GREENWOOD, Annette June, Chief Nursing Officer, Riverside Community Hospital, Riverside, CA, p. A82

GREENWOOD, Les M.D., President, Medical Staff, Davis Hospital And Medical Center, Layton, UT, p. A657

GREENWOOD, Sherri, Chief Nursing Officer, St. John's Hospital, Springfield, IL, p. A201

GREENWOOD, Susan R.N., Vice President and Chief Nursing Officer, St. Bernards Medical Center, Jonesboro, AR, p. A45

GREER, Troy, Chief Executive Officer, Lovelace Medical Center, Albuquerque, NM, p. A424

GREGERSON, Scott, President and Chief Executive Officer, Stanford Health Care – Valleycare, Pleasanton, CA, p. A80

GREGG, Richard M.D., Medical Director, Lifecare Hospital Of Dayton, Miamisburg, OH, p. A495

GREGG, Shawna, Director Human Resources, Porterville Developmental Center, Porterville, CA, p. A80

GREGG, Sherry, Chief Information Technology Officer, Beckley Veterans Affairs Medical Center, Beckley, WV, p. A690

GREGG, Tom, Vice President Human Resources, Chi St. Alexius Health, Bismarck, ND, p. A474

GREGG, Travis, Director Support Services, Kearney Regional Medical Center, Kearney, NE, p. A394

GREGGAIN, Don M.D., Physician Network Director, Tri–State Memorial Hospital, Clarkston, WA, p. A679

GREGONIS, Michael, Comptroller, Naval Hospital Jacksonville, Jacksonville, FL, p. A128

GREGOR, Brian, Manager Information Technology Operations, Adventist Health Glendale, Glendale, CA, p. A62

GREGORIAN, Myra, Vice President and Chief Human Resources Officer, Children's Hospital Los Angeles, Los Angeles, CA, p. A68

GREGORICH, Miki, Director Human Resources, Pioneer Medical Center, Big Timber, MT, p. A382

GREGORY, Adina
Chief Nursing Officer, Great Bend Regional Hospital, Great Bend, KS, p. A241
Chief Operating Officer, Great Bend Regional Hospital, Great Bend, KS, p. A241

GREGORY, Audrey, R.N., MSN, Chief Executive Officer, Saint Francis Hospital, Memphis, TN, p. A585

GREGORY, Ben, Chief Executive Officer, Walter B. Jones Alcohol And Drug Abuse Treatment Center, Greenville, NC, p. A464

GREGORY, Jan, Chief of Human Resources, Crittenden County Hospital, Marion, KY, p. A264

GREGORY, Jay M.D., Chief Medical Officer, Saint Francis Hospital Muskogee, Muskogee, OK, p. A511

GREGORY, Jim, Controller, Methodist Hospital Of Chicago, Chicago, IL, p. A182

GREGORY, Luke, Chief Executive Officer, Vanderbilt University Medical Center, Nashville, TN, p. A587

GREGORY, Phyllis, Registered Health Information Administrator, Southern Inyo Healthcare District, Lone Pine, CA, p. A66

GREGORY, Sean
Chief Executive, Columbia Network, Peacehealth Southwest Medical Center, Vancouver, WA, p. A688
Chief Executive, Peacehealth Southwest Medical Center, Vancouver, WA, p. A688

GREGORY, Shawn, Chief Financial Officer, St. Petersburg General Hospital, Saint Petersburg, FL, p. A142

GREGORY, Trip, Senior Vice President Human Resources, Palmetto Health Baptist, Columbia, SC, p. A560

GREGOS, Ruth, Director Finance, Shriners Hospitals For Children–Tampa, Tampa, FL, p. A145

GREIMAN, Alan W., Chief Executive Officer and President, Royal Oaks Hospital, Windsor, MO, p. A381

GREINER, Walter, Chief Financial Officer, Atlanticare Regional Medical Center, Atlantic City, NJ, p. A411

GREINER, William M.D., Chief of Staff, F. W. Huston Medical Center, Winchester, KS, p. A254

GRENALDO, Paul, Executive Vice President and Chief Operating Officer, Doctors Community Hospital, Lanham, MD, p. A299

GRENDON, M Todd M.D., President Medical Staff, Presence Saint Joseph Hospital, Chicago, IL, p. A182

GRENIER, Raymond, Chief Financial Officer, Memorial Medical Center, Las Cruces, NM, p. A426

GRENNAN, M. Joseph M.D., Jr, Senior Vice President and Chief Medical Officer, Reading Hospital, West Reading, PA, p. A553

GRESSLE, Charles, Chief Executive Officer, Medical City Plano, Plano, TX, p. A638

GREW, Kate MSN, R.N., Vice President/Chief Nurse Executive, Carolinas Healthcare System Northeast, Concord, NC, p. A460

GREW, Terry, Chief Business Office, Hampton Veterans Affairs Medical Center, Hampton, VA, p. A668

GREY, Michael M.D., Interim Chief Medical Officer, Saint Francis Hospital And Medical Center, Hartford, CT, p. A110

GREY, Mitzi, Chief Operating Officer, Bath Community Hospital, Hot Springs, VA, p. A669

GRIBBIN, John, FACHE, President and Chief Executive Officer, Centrastate Healthcare System, Freehold, NJ, p. A414

GRICE, William N., Executive Director, Kaiser Permanente Los Angeles Medical Center, Los Angeles, CA, p. A68

GRICUS, Peggy, R.N., Vice President, Patient Care Services and Chief Nursing Officer, Silver Cross Hospital, New Lenox, IL, p. A195

GRIDLEY, Mark, FACHE, President and Chief Executive Officer, FHN Memorial Hospital, Freeport, IL, p. A188

GRIEB, Paula, R.N.
Chief Nursing Officer, Promedica Fostoria Community Hospital, Fostoria, OH, p. A491
Vice President Patient Care Service and Chief Nursing Officer, Promedica Bay Park Hospital, Oregon, OH, p. A497

GRIEP, John M.D., Chief Medical Director, St. Catherine Hospital, East Chicago, IN, p. A206

GRIESHEIM, Glen, Chief Executive Officer, Select Specialty Hospital–Des Moines, Des Moines, IA, p. A226

GRIESHEIM, Glen, Chief Executive Officer, Select Specialty Hospital-Des Moines, Des Moines, IA, p. B114

GRIEST, Mary, Vice President Finance and Chief Financial Officer, University Hospitals Samaritan Medical Center, Ashland, OH, p. A480

GRIFFES, Carol, Administrator, Duane L. Waters Hospital, Jackson, MI, p. A323

GRIFFIN, Amy, Vice President Patient Care Services, John D. Archbold Memorial Hospital, Thomasville, GA, p. A166

GRIFFIN, Barbara J MSN, R.N., Chief Nursing Officer, Rapides Regional Medical Center, Alexandria, LA, p. A269

GRIFFIN, Betty, Interim Chief Nursing Officer, Chester Regional Medical Center, Chester, SC, p. A559

GRIFFIN, Brad, Chief Executive Officer, Gulf Coast Medical Center, Panama City, FL, p. A138

GRIFFIN, Brian, Director Information Services, Springhill Medical Center, Springhill, LA, p. A286

GRIFFIN, Charles, Director of Nursing, Clay County Hospital, Ashland, AL, p. A13

GRIFFIN, Christopher B., Chief Executive Officer, D. W. Mcmillan Memorial Hospital, Brewton, AL, p. A15

GRIFFIN, Cindy
Chief Nursing Officer, Liberty Dayton Regional Medical Center, Liberty, TX, p. A629
Director Human Resources, Medical Center Barbour, Eufaula, AL, p. A17

GRIFFIN, Dean A., Chief Executive Officer, Lawrence Medical Center, Moulton, AL, p. A21

GRIFFIN, Douglas M.D., Vice President Medical Officer, Sanford Medical Center Fargo, Fargo, ND, p. A475

GRIFFIN, Holly R.N., Chief Nursing Officer, Lady Of The Sea General Hospital, Cut Off, LA, p. A274

GRIFFIN, James, Manager Information Systems, Martin General Hospital, Williamston, NC, p. A472

GRIFFIN, Jeannine M.D., Chief of Staff, Memorial Medical Center, Port Lavaca, TX, p. A639

GRIFFIN, Jeff, Assistant Vice President Finance, Carolinas Healthcare System Anson, Wadesboro, NC, p. A472

GRIFFIN, Joe, Controller, Healthsouth Rehabilitation Hospital Round Rock, Round Rock, TX, p. A640

GRIFFIN, Kathryn, Chief Nurse Executive, Terrell State Hospital, Terrell, TX, p. A648

GRIFFIN, Margaret Elizabeth., Chief Executive Officer, Honorhealth John C. Lincoln Medical Center, Phoenix, AZ, p. A33

GRIFFIN, Matthew M.D., Vice President Medical Affairs, DMC – Sinai–Grace Hospital, Detroit, MI, p. A317

GRIFFIN, Paulette, Director Human Resources, DMC – Sinai–Grace Hospital, Detroit, MI, p. A317

GRIFFIN, Philip, Director of Operations, Rochester Psychiatric Center, Rochester, NY, p. A451

GRIFFIN–JONES, Christie R.N., Chief Nursing Officer, Healthsouth Rehabilitation Hospital Of Humble, Llc, Humble, TX, p. A624

GRIFFIN–MAHON, Selena, Assistant Vice President Human Resources, Bronx–Lebanon Hospital Center Health Care System, New Rochelle, NY, p. A440

GRIFFIS, Daniel M.D., Chief Medical Officer, Syringa Hospital And Clinics, Grangeville, ID, p. A173

GRIFFITH, Barbara, M.D.
Chief Medical Officer, Duke Regional Hospital, Durham, NC, p. A461
Vice President Human Resources, St. Anthony's Rehabilitation Hospital, Lauderdale Lakes, FL, p. A130

GRIFFITH, David M.D., Medical Director, Texas Center For Infectious Disease, San Antonio, TX, p. A644

GRIFFITH, H. Wes, Chief Financial Officer, Tennova Healthcare – Cleveland, Cleveland, TN, p. A577

GRIFFITH, James D
Chief Operating Officer, Tanner Medical Center–Carrollton, Carrollton, GA, p. A153
Chief Operating Officer, Tanner Higgins General Hospital, Bremen, GA, p. A153

GRIFFITH, James D., Chief Operating Officer, Tanner Medical Center-Carrollton, Carrollton, GA, p. B124

GRIFFITH, Jeanne, Chief Nursing Officer, Coryell Memorial Hospital, Gatesville, TX, p. A616

GRIFFITH, John H., Ph.D., President & Chief Executive Officer, Kedren Community Mental Health Center, Los Angeles, CA, p. A69

GRIFFITH, Joshua, Manager Human Resources, Presbyterian Espanola Hospital, Espanola, NM, p. A426

GRIFFITH, Leah, Chief Executive Officer, Big Sandy Medical Center, Big Sandy, MT, p. A382

GRIFFITH, Patti R.N., MS, Chief Nursing Officer, Methodist Hospital For Surgery, Addison, TX, p. A591

GRIFFITH, Susan M, Chief Operations Officer, Eastern State Hospital, Lexington, KY, p. A261

GRIFFITHS, Elaine R.N., Chief Nursing Officer, Chesapeake Regional Healthcare, Chesapeake, VA, p. A665

GRIFFITHS, Mark, Director Management Information Systems, Incline Village Community Hospital, Incline Village, NV, p. A402

GRIGG, Dan, Chief Executive Officer, Harney District Hospital, Burns, OR, p. A520

GRIGG, William E., Senior Vice President and Chief Financial Officer, Methodist Hospital Of Southern California, Arcadia, CA, p. A52

GRIGGS, Shannon, Interim Chief Executive Officer, Research Medical Center, Kansas City, MO, p. A370

GRIGGS, Stacie, MIS Analyst, North Mississippi Medical Center–West Point, West Point, MS, p. A363

GRIGSBY, Jan, Vice President and Chief Financial Officer, Springhill Memorial Hospital, Mobile, AL, p. A20

GRIGSON, John A, Vice President and Chief Financial Officer, Covenant Medical Center, Lubbock, TX, p. A630

GRILL, Laura D R.N., Executive Vice President and Administrator, East Alabama Medical Center, Opelika, AL, p. A22

GRILLO, Jorge C, Chief Information Officer, Canton–Potsdam Hospital, Potsdam, NY, p. A450

GRIM, Andrew, Chief Financial Officer, San Gabriel Valley Medical Center, San Gabriel, CA, p. A88

GRIMALDI, Richard, President Medical Staff, Highlands Hospital, Connellsville, PA, p. A532

GRIMES, Pam, Director Human Resources, AMG Specialty Hospital–Edmond, Edmond, OK, p. A507

GRIMES, Paula R.N., MSN, Chief Nursing Officer, Nea Baptist Memorial Hospital, Jonesboro, AR, p. A45

GRIMES, Teresa G., Chief Executive Officer, Washington County Hospital, Chatom, AL, p. A16

GRIMES, Walter, Director Information Technology, Christus Good Shepherd Medical Center–Marshall, Marshall, TX, p. A632

GRIMLEY, Karen A, Chief Nursing Executive, Ronald Reagan Ucla Medical Center, Los Angeles, CA, p. A71

GRIMM, Tamara R.N., Chief Clinical Officer and Chief Nursing Officer, Cornerstone Hospital Of Bossier City, Bossier City, LA, p. A272

GRIMM, William, Chief Information Officer, Henry County Hospital, Napoleon, OH, p. A496

GRIMMER, Michael, Chief Operating Officer, Athol Hospital, Athol, MA, p. A302

GRIMMETT, Teresa, Chief Executive Officer, Wayne Medical Center, Waynesboro, TN, p. A590

GRIMSHAW, Bruce P., FACHE, Chief Executive Officer, Southern California Hospital At Hollywood, Los Angeles, CA, p. A71

GRIMSHAW, Matthew, Market Chief Executive Officer, Trinity Health System, Steubenville, OH, p. A500

GRIMSLEY, Denise, R.N., Vice President and Administrator, Florida Hospital Wauchula, Wauchula, FL, p. A147

GRINER, Alisa R, Director, Human Resources, Memorial Health, Savannah, GA, p. A164

GRINER, Ginny, Director Human Resources, George E. Weems Memorial Hospital, Apalachicola, FL, p. A119

GRIPPI, Michael M.D., Chief Medical Officer, Good Shepherd Penn Partners Specialty Hospital At Rittenhouse, Philadelphia, PA, p. A544

GRISH, John, Chief Financial Officer, Johnson Memorial Medical Center, Stafford Springs, CT, p. A113

GRISHOW, Cathy, Director Human Resources, Ellett Memorial Hospital, Appleton City, MO, p. A364

GRISIER, Douglas D.O., Medical Director, Healthsouth Rehabilitation Hospital Of Erie, Erie, PA, p. A534

GRISMER, Margaret, Chief Executive Officer, Kiowa District Hospital And Manor, Kiowa, KS, p. A244

GRISNAK, Karen R.N., Chief Operating Officer and Assistant Administrator Quality Services, Kaiser Permanente Vallejo Medical Center, Vallejo, CA, p. A95

GRISPINO, Frank, Vice President Operations, SSM Health St. Francis Hospital – Maryville, Maryville, MO, p. A373

GRISSLER, Brian G., President and Chief Executive Officer, Stamford Hospital, Stamford, CT, p. A113

GRISSOM, Robyn, Director Employee Relations, OSF Saint Anthony's Health Center, Alton, IL, p. A177

GRISSOM, Tina, Chief Information Technology Officer, Arkansas State Hospital, Little Rock, AR, p. A45

GROCE, Vicky, Chief Nursing Officer, Lincoln County Health System, Fayetteville, TN, p. A578

GROCHALA, Eugene
Vice President Information Systems, Capital Health Medical Center–Hopewell, Pennington, NJ, p. A418
Vice President Information Systems, Capital Health Regional Medical Center, Trenton, NJ, p. A421

GROCHOLSKI, James F., FACHE, Chief Executive Officer, Wesley Rehabilitation Hospital, Wichita, KS, p. A254

GROENEWEG, Jennifer R.N., Director of Nursing, Spectrum Health Special Care Hospital, Grand Rapids, MI, p. A321

GROENIG, Matt, Vice President Finance, St. Luke's Mccall, Mccall, ID, p. A174

GROEPER, William E, Vice President Finance, Beloit Health System, Beloit, WI, p. A699

GROEPPER, Ronald
Senior Vice President and Area Manager, Kaiser Permanente San Francisco Medical Center, San Francisco, CA, p. A87
Senior Vice President and Area Manager, Kaiser Permanente South San Francisco, South San Francisco, CA, p. A92

GROESBECK, John
Area Finance Officer, Kaiser Permanente San Rafael Medical Center, San Rafael, CA, p. A89
Area Finance Officer, Kaiser Permanente Santa Rosa Medical Center, Santa Rosa, CA, p. A91

GROGAN, Ed, Vice President Information Services and Chief Information Officer, Calvert Memorial Hospital, Prince Frederick, MD, p. A300

GRONERT, Thomas, Chief Information Officer, University Of Maryland St. Joseph Medical Center, Towson, MD, p. A301

GRONEWOLD, Russell, Chief Financial Officer, Bryan Medical Center, Lincoln, NE, p. A395

GRONOW, Thomas, Chief Operating Officer, University Of Colorado Hospital, Aurora, CO, p. A98

GROOM, Scott C, Vice President Information Services and Chief Information Officer, Bassett Medical Center, Cooperstown, NY, p. A434

GROOMS, Kim, Administrator, King's Daughters Medical Center Ohio, Portsmouth, OH, p. A498

GROOMS, Richard Walter Jr, Chief Human Resources Officer, Anmed Health Medical Center, Anderson, SC, p. A558

GROS, Albert M.D., Chief Medical Officer, St. David's South Austin Medical Center, Austin, TX, p. A596

GROS, Mark, Director Human Resources, United Medical Rehabilitation Hospital, Hammond, LA, p. A276

GROSE, Jana, Chief Information Officer, Massena Memorial Hospital, Massena, NY, p. A439

GROSECLOSE, Cathy, Vice President Patient Care Services, Grady Memorial Hospital, Chickasha, OK, p. A505

GROSKREUTZ, Kevin
Chief Information Officer, Sacred Heart Hospital, Eau Claire, WI, p. A701
Division Chief Information Officer, Ancillary Systems, Hshs St. Joseph's Hospital, Chippewa Falls, WI, p. A700

GROSS, Barry L M.D., Executive Vice President and Chief Medical Officer, Riverside Regional Medical Center, Newport News, VA, p. A671

GROSS, Cathy, Director Health Information Management Systems, Wrangell Medical Center, Wrangell, AK, p. A27

GROSS, Cindy, Director of Finance, Barnes–Jewish St. Peters Hospital, Saint Peters, MO, p. A379

GROSS, Denton, Director Information Services, Larue D. Carter Memorial Hospital, Indianapolis, IN, p. A211

GROSS, Kevin J., FACHE, Chief Executive Officer, Hillcrest Medical Center, Tulsa, OK, p. A517

GROSS, Kristin, Director Information Technology Center, Avera Mckennan Hospital And University Health Center, Sioux Falls, SD, p. A572

GROSS, Len, Chief Human Resources Officer, Sheridan Memorial Hospital, Sheridan, WY, p. A719

GROSS, Mark
Executive Vice President and Chief Financial Officer, Bronson South Haven Hospital, South Haven, MI, p. A331

Senior Business Director Finance, Mercy Health, Lakeshore Campus, Shelby, MI, p. A330

GROSS, Paul, Human Services and Finance Officer, Larry B. Zieverink, Sr. Alcoholism Treatment Center, Raleigh, NC, p. A469

GROSS, Peter A M.D., Senior Vice President and Chief Medical Officer, Hackensack Meridian Health Hackensack University Medical Center, Hackensack, NJ, p. A414

GROSS, Randy, Chief Operating Officer, Kendall Regional Medical Center, Miami, FL, p. A133

GROSS, Tina MSN, R.N., Chief Nursing Officer, Sparrow Specialty Hospital, Lansing, MI, p. A324

GROSSMAN, Drew, Chief Executive Officer, Broward Health Coral Springs, Coral Springs, FL, p. A122

GROSSMAN, Hannah M.D., Chief Medical Officer, Los Robles Hospital And Medical Center, Thousand Oaks, CA, p. A93

GROSSMAN, Joseph, President and Chief Executive Officer, Appalachian Regional Healthcare, Inc., Lexington, KY, p. B10

GROSSMAN, Martin, Chief of Staff, Aventura Hospital And Medical Center, Aventura, FL, p. A119

GROSSMAN, Robert I., M.D., Chief Executive Officer, NYU Langone Hospitals, New Rochelle, NY, p. A446

GROSSO, Michael M.D., Senior Vice President Medical Affairs, Huntington Hospital, Huntington, NY, p. A437

GROTELUSCHEN, Ronald J., Chief Financial Officer, Coastal Carolina Hospital, Hardeeville, SC, p. A563

GROTH, McGarrett, Chief of Staff, Atchison Hospital, Atchison, KS, p. A238

GROVE, Julia, Chief Nursing Officer, Jackson Purchase Medical Center, Mayfield, KY, p. A264

GROVER, James, Manager Data Processing, Atascadero State Hospital, Atascadero, CA, p. A52

GROVES, Ned, Executive Vice President and Administrator, Memorial Sloan–Kettering Cancer Center, New Rochelle, NY, p. A442

GROVES, Tandy, Coordinator Human Resources, Bailey Medical Center, Owasso, OK, p. A514

GROW, Heidi, Director Human Resources, Aurora Sinai Medical Center, Milwaukee, WI, p. A707

GROW, Julie E, Chief Financial Officer, Hocking Valley Community Hospital, Logan, OH, p. A494

GROWSE, Michael M.D., Clinical Director, Federal Medical Center, Lexington, KY, p. A261

GRUBB, Michael
Chief Financial Officer, Bridgepoint Hospital Capitol Hill, Washington, DC, p. A117
Chief Financial Officer, Bridgepoint Hospital National Harbor, Washington, DC, p. A117

GRUBB, Nora, Chief Financial Officer, Big Sandy Medical Center, Big Sandy, MT, p. A382

GRUBBS, Stephen, Chief Executive Officer, Bay Medical Center Sacred Heart Health System, Panama City, FL, p. A138

GRUBER, Kreg, Chief Operating Officer, Memorial Hospital Of South Bend, South Bend, IN, p. A220

GRUBER, Norman F., President and Chief Executive Officer, Salem Health, Salem, OR, p. B111

GRUBER, Scott M.D., Chief of Staff, John D. Dingell Veterans Affairs Medical Center, Detroit, MI, p. A318

GRUEBER, Cynthia M, Senior Vice President and Chief Operating Officer, Ohsu Hospital, Portland, OR, p. A525

GRUEN, Jeremy, Director Information Systems, Pike County Memorial Hospital, Louisiana, MO, p. A372

GRUHONJIC, Osman, Chief Financial Officer, Lehigh Regional Medical Center, Lehigh Acres, FL, p. A131

GRUN, Joseph, Chief Information Officer, New York State Psychiatric Institute, New Rochelle, NY, p. A444

GRUNDSTROM, Jason
Chief Executive Officer, Kindred Hospital Northland, Kansas City, MO, p. A370
Interim Chief Executive Officer, Kindred Hospital Kansas City, Kansas City, MO, p. A370

GRUNHOVD, April, Chief Nursing Officer, Riverview Health, Crookston, MN, p. A338

GRUNWALD, Pat MSN, Chief Nursing Officer, Unitypoint Health Meriter, Madison, WI, p. A705

GRUVER, Laquita, Fiscal Officer, Grand Junction Veterans Health Care System, Grand Junction, CO, p. A103

GRUZENSKY, Denton, Director Human Resources, Feather River Hospital, Paradise, CA, p. A79

GRZYBOWSKI, John M.D., Medical Director, Mayo Clinic Health System In Albert Lea, Albert Lea, MN, p. A335

GUACCIO, Anthony, President and Chief Executive Officer, Swedish Covenant Hospital, Chicago, IL, p. A184

GUADAGNOLI, Donald M.D., Chief Medical Officer, Cape Cod Hospital, Hyannis, MA, p. A307

GUAJARDO, Carlos, Chief Financial Officer, South Texas Health System, Edinburg, TX, p. A610

GUAJARDO, Michael, Director Finance, Christus Spohn Hospital Alice, Alice, TX, p. A591

GUARINO, Celia R.N., MSN, Vice President and Chief Nursing Officer, Holy Cross Health, Silver Spring, MD, p. A301

GUARINO, Rick M.D., Vice President Medical Affairs, Wilson Medical Center, Wilson, NC, p. A472

GUARNESCHELLI, Philip
Interim Chief Executive Officer, Pinnaclehealth Harrisburg Hospital, Harrisburg, PA, p. A536
Senior Vice President and Chief Operating Officer, Pinnaclehealth Harrisburg Hospital, Harrisburg, PA, p. A536

GUARNI, Andrew, Chief Financial Officer, Hoag Memorial Hospital Presbyterian, Newport Beach, CA, p. A76

GUARNIERI, Candace
Chief Financial Officer, Phoebe Worth Medical Center, Sylvester, GA, p. A165
Chief Financial Officer, Southwest Georgia Regional Medical Center, Cuthbert, GA, p. A156

GUARRACINO, Joseph, Senior Vice President and Chief Financial Officer, White Plains Hospital Center, White Plains, NY, p. A456

GUARRERA, Frank, Executive Vice President and Chief Financial Officer, Motion Picture And Television Fund Hospital And Residential Services, Los Angeles, CA, p. A70

GUBERMAN, Wayne, Director Finance, Matheny Medical And Educational Center, Peapack, NJ, p. A418

GUDAHL, Shanna, Manager Human Resources, United Hospital District, Blue Earth, MN, p. A336

GUEHLSTORF, Daniel M.D., Chief of Staff, Midwest Orthopedic Specialty Hospital, Franklin, WI, p. A702

GUELKER, Rhonda, Senior Director Finance, Rolling Plains Memorial Hospital, Sweetwater, TX, p. A648

GUERCI, Alan D., M.D., President and Chief Executive Officer, Catholic Health Services Of Long Island, Rockville Centre, NY, p. B28

GUERIN, Stephanie, Chief Nursing Officer, Healthsouth Rehabilitation Hospital Round Rock, Round Rock, TX, p. A640

GUERMONPREZ, D. Scott., FACHE, Director, Northport Veterans Affairs Medical Center, Northport, NY, p. A448

GUERRANT, Eric M.D., President Medical Staff, Ephraim Mcdowell Regional Medical Center, Danville, KY, p. A257

GUERRERO, Bonnie, Director Human Resources, Valley View Medical Center, Fort Mohave, AZ, p. A29

GUERRERO, Kerrie R.N., MSN, Vice President and Chief Nursing Officer, Houston Methodist The Woodlands Hospital, The Woodlands, TX, p. A649

GUERRERO, Marisa, Director Human Resources, Laredo Specialty Hospital, Laredo, TX, p. A628

GUERRIERO, John A., Chief of Staff, Berwick Hospital Center, Berwick, PA, p. A529

GUERRIERO, Marianne, Nurse Executive, Christian Health Care Center, Wyckoff, NJ, p. A423

GUESMAN, Kim R.N., Chief Nursing Officer, Beaumont Hospital – Farmington Hills, Farmington Hills, MI, p. A319

GUEST, William M.D., Senior Vice President and Chief Medical Officer, Tift Regional Medical Center, Tifton, GA, p. A166

GUEVARA, Al Jr, FACHE, President, Chi St. Luke's Health Brazosport, Lake Jackson, TX, p. A628

GUFFEY, Dale, Chief Financial Officer, Lower Keys Medical Center, Key West, FL, p. A129

GUFFEY, Jay, Senior Vice President and Chief Operating Officer, Mercy Hospital Springfield, Springfield, MO, p. A379

GUGEL, Paul, Manager Information Technology, Marlette Regional Hospital, Marlette, MI, p. A325

GUGLIELMO, Elaine, Vice President Human Resources and Organizational Development, Stamford Hospital, Stamford, CT, p. A113

GUIDERA, Kenneth M.D., Chief of Staff, Shriners Hospitals For Children–Twin Cities, Minneapolis, MN, p. A344

GUIDO–ALLEN, Debra, Vice President and Chief Nursing Officer, Beaumont Hospital – Troy, Troy, MI, p. A332

GUIDRY, Charles W, Chief Operating Officer, Abbeville General Hospital, Abbeville, LA, p. A269

GUIDRY, Linda, Human Resources Generalist, Abrom Kaplan Memorial Hospital, Kaplan, LA, p. A277

GUIDRY, Lloyd, Chief Operating Officer, Lady Of The Sea General Hospital, Cut Off, LA, p. A274

GUIDRY, Ruth, Chief Nursing Officer, Lafayette Surgical Specialty Hospital, Lafayette, LA, p. A278

GUIDRY, Stephanie, Chief Executive Officer, Franklin Foundation Hospital, Franklin, LA, p. A275

GUIDRY, Trisha, Administrator, Baton Rouge Rehabilitation Hospital, Baton Rouge, LA, p. A270

GUIGNIER, Liz, Vice President Human Resources, Eisenhower Medical Center, Rancho Mirage, CA, p. A81

GUILD, Anthony, Chief Executive Officer, Rolling Hills Hospital, Ada, OK, p. A504

GUILFOIL, Thomas, Director Human Resources, Baystate Wing Hospital, Palmer, MA, p. A310

GUILLORY, Larry, Chief Human Resources Officer, Baylor Emergency Medical Center At Aubrey, Aubrey, TX, p. A594

GUILLORY, Nicholas D., MSN, Interim Administrator, Oceans Behavioral Hospital Of Alexandria, Alexandria, LA, p. A269

GUIMARAES, Antonio M.D., Clinical Director, U.S. Public Health Service Indian Hospital, Cass Lake, MN, p. A338

GUINA, Michelle, Manager Human Resources, Sutter Surgical Hospital – North Valley, Yuba City, CA, p. A97

GUINN, Judy, Chief Human Resources Officer, Graham Regional Medical Center, Graham, TX, p. A617

GUIRL, Nadine T, Senior Vice President Human Resources, Waukesha Memorial Hospital, Waukesha, WI, p. A714

GULARTE, Steven, Chief Executive Officer, Bayside Community Hospital, Anahuac, TX, p. A592

GULL, Joann Bernadette, Chief Nursing Officer, NYC Health + Hospitals / Elmhurst, New Rochelle, NY, p. A445

GULLINGSRUD, Timothy M., Chief Executive Officer, Hayward Area Memorial Hospital And Water's Edge, Hayward, WI, p. A703

GULRICH, Erica, Chief Executive Officer, Northwest Medical Center, Margate, FL, p. A131

GUM, Jessica, Controller, Healthsouth Western Hills Regional Rehabilitation Hospital, Parkersburg, WV, p. A695

GUMATO, Sixta M.D., Chief Medical Officer, Crane Memorial Hospital, Crane, TX, p. A604

GUMBINER, Carl H M.D., Senior Vice President Medical Affairs and Chief Medical Officer, Children's Hospital And Medical Center, Omaha, NE, p. A397

GUMBS, Milton A M.D., Vice President and Medical Director, Bronx–Lebanon Hospital Center Health Care System, New Rochelle, NY, p. A440

GUMMADI, Subhaker, M.D.
Chief Medical Staff, Promise Hospital Baton Rouge – Main Campus, Baton Rouge, LA, p. A271
President Medical Staff, Promise Hospital Of Baton Rouge – Mid–City Campus, Baton Rouge, LA, p. A271

GUMP, Linda A., Chief Clinical Services Officer, Aurora Medical Center, Kenosha, WI, p. A704

GUNABALAN, Ryan, Chief Executive Officer, Behavioral Center Of Michigan, Warren, MI, p. A332

GUNDERSEN, Robert A., Market Chief Executive Officer, Curahealth Stoughton, Stoughton, MA, p. A312

GUNDLAPALLI, Madhu M.D., Clinical Director, Utah State Hospital, Provo, UT, p. A659

GUNDT, Kristin, Chief Nursing Officer, Community Hospital, Grand Junction, CO, p. A103

GUNKEL, Jeff, Chief Information Officer, Jamestown Regional Medical Center, Jamestown, ND, p. A476

GUNN, Deborah, Chief Information Officer, W. G. (Bill) Heffner Veterans Affairs Medical Center, Salisbury, NC, p. A470

GUNN, Terry, FACHE, Chief Executive Officer, Kershawhealth, Camden, SC, p. A558

GUNNELL, Nancy
Chief Human Resource Officer, West Suburban Medical Center, Oak Park, IL, p. A196
Chief Human Resource Officer, Westlake Hospital, Melrose Park, IL, p. A193

GUNNERSEN, Nils, Administrator, Bertrand Chaffee Hospital, Springville, NY, p. A452

GUNTHER, DNP, Anne R.N., MSN, Chief Nursing Officer, Aultman Hospital, Canton, OH, p. A482

GUNTLOW, Ann Marie, Chief Nursing Officer, Ellenville Regional Hospital, Ellenville, NY, p. A435

GUNUKULA, Srinivas M.D., Chief of Staff, Dallas Regional Medical Center, Mesquite, TX, p. A633

GUOYAVATIN, Kora
Chief Financial Officer, Garden Grove Hospital And Medical Center, Garden Grove, CA, p. A61
Chief Financial Officer, West Anaheim Medical Center, Anaheim, CA, p. A51

GUPTA, Anil M.D., Chief of Staff, Kindred Hospital–Baldwin Park, Baldwin Park, CA, p. A53

GUPTA, Arun M.D., Vice President Medical Affairs, South Pointe Hospital, Warrensville Heights, OH, p. A501

GUPTA, Ashok K M.D., Chief of Staff, Eaton Rapids Medical Center, Eaton Rapids, MI, p. A319

GUPTA, John, Executive Vice President and Chief Operating Officer, Brooklyn Hospital Center, New Rochelle, NY, p. A441

GUPTA, Saurabh, Chief Medical Officer, Rockford Center, Newark, DE, p. A115

GUPTA, Vijay D M.D., President and Chief Executive Officer, Franciscan Healthcare – Munster, Munster, IN, p. A217

GURR, Lory, Chief Human Resources Division, Evans U. S. Army Community Hospital, Fort Carson, CO, p. A102

GURRAD, Trece, Vice President Patient Care Services, Columbia Memorial Hospital, Astoria, OR, p. A520

GURROLA, Jose, Administrator, New Mexico Rehabilitation Center, Roswell, NM, p. A428

GURULE, Eric, Chief Information Officer, Turquoise Lodge Hospital, Albuquerque, NM, p. A425

GURUNG, Anju M.D., Chief Medical Officer, Mahnomen Health Center, Mahnomen, MN, p. A342

GUSHEE, Dean M.D., Medical Director, Mason General Hospital, Shelton, WA, p. A686

GUSHO, Michael, Chief Financial Officer, St. Joseph Mercy Oakland, Pontiac, MI, p. A328

GUSTAFSON, Brian, Chief Financial Officer, Veterans Affairs Montana Health Care System, Fort Harrison, MT, p. A384

GUSTAFSON, Connie, Director of Nursing, Jacobson Memorial Hospital Care Center, Elgin, ND, p. A475

GUSTAFSON, Michael, M.D., President, Brigham And Women's Faulkner Hospital, Boston, MA, p. A303

GUSTAFSON, Sarah S, Vice President of Finance, Grand Itasca Clinic And Hospital, Grand Rapids, MN, p. A340

GUSTER, Cherie M R.N., MSN, Senior Vice President and Chief Nursing Officer, Cleveland Clinic Akron General, Akron, OH, p. A479

GUSTILO, Maria, M.D.
  Medical Director, Osawatomie State Hospital, Osawatomie, KS, p. A248
  Medical Director, Rainbow Mental Health Facility, Kansas City, KS, p. A244

GUSTIN, Michael, Information Technology, John J. Pershing Veterans Affairs Medical Center, Poplar Bluff, MO, p. A375

GUTHMILLER, Martin W., Chief Executive Officer, Orange City Area Health System, Orange City, IA, p. A232

GUTHRIE, Pamela A, Chief Human Resources Officer, Hillcrest Hospital Pryor, Pryor, OK, p. A515

GUTHRIE, Todd, Chief of Staff, Mercy Medical Center Mount Shasta, Mount Shasta, CA, p. A75

GUTIERREZ, Lori, Chief Financial Officer, Rochelle Community Hospital, Rochelle, IL, p. A198

GUTIERREZ, Michelle, Executive Director Human Resources, Orange Coast Memorial Medical Center, Fountain Valley, CA, p. A60

GUTIERREZ, Noe, Chief Financial Officer, Lake Granbury Medical Center, Granbury, TX, p. A617

GUTIERREZ, Santiago M.D., Chief Medical Officer, Doctors Hospital Of Laredo, Laredo, TX, p. A628

GUTIERREZ, Vickie, Director of Patient Care, Dr. Dan C. Trigg Memorial Hospital, Tucumcari, NM, p. A429

GUTIERREZ, Victor A M.D., Medical Director, Allegiance Behavioral Health Center Of Plainview, Plainview, TX, p. A637

GUTJAHR, Susan, Reimbursement Specialist, Sparta Community Hospital, Sparta, IL, p. A200

GUTMAN, Luisa, Senior Vice President and Chief Operating Officer, Holy Cross Hospital, Fort Lauderdale, FL, p. A125

GUTNICK, Michael, Executive Vice President and Chief Financial Officer, Memorial Sloan-Kettering Cancer Center, New Rochelle, NY, p. A442

GUTOW, Andrew M.D., Medical Director, Menlo Park Surgical Hospital, Menlo Park, CA, p. A73

GUTOWSKI, Jennifer S.
  Acting Director, Southern Arizona Veterans Affairs Health Care System, Tucson, AZ, p. A38
  Director, Veterans Affairs Pacific Islands Health Care System, Honolulu, HI, p. A169

GUTSCH, Michael, Chief Executive Officer, Cumberland Memorial Hospital, Cumberland, WI, p. A700

GUTSCHENRITTER, John, Chief Financial Officer, Wilson Medical Center, Neodesha, KS, p. A247

GUTTENBERG, Ellen, Chief Operating Officer, Frances Mahon Deaconess Hospital, Glasgow, MT, p. A384

GUTTIN, Enrique M.D., FACS, Chief of Staff, Wilmington Veterans Affairs Medical Center, Wilmington, DE, p. A116

GUTTMACHER, Laurence M.D., Clinical Director, Rochester Psychiatric Center, Rochester, NY, p. A451

GUTZEIT, Michael M.D., Chief Medical Officer, Children's Hospital Of Wisconsin, Milwaukee, WI, p. A707

GUY, Glenda, Director, Health Information Management, Ten Broeck Tennessee Treatment Facility, Cookeville, TN, p. A577

GUY, Kimberly, President, St. Joseph's Hospital, Tampa, FL, p. A145

GUYETTE, William M.D., President Medical Staff, Livingston Hospital And Healthcare Services, Salem, KY, p. A267

GUZ, Andrew, Chief Executive Officer, Lakewood Ranch Medical Center, Bradenton, FL, p. A120

GUZAK, Jason, Chief Financial Officer, Rock Springs, Georgetown, TX, p. A616

GUZMAN, Claudia V., Chief Executive Officer and Managing Director, Hospital San Pablo, Bayamon, PR, p. A722

GUZMAN, Lisa, Human Resource Vice President, Redlands Community Hospital, Redlands, CA, p. A82

GWATKIN, Elizabeth, Vice President Human Resources, Northeastern Vermont Regional Hospital, Saint Johnsbury, VT, p. A663

GWYN, Andrea, Chief Operating Officer, Terre Haute Regional Hospital, Terre Haute, IN, p. A220

GWYN, Brian
  President and Chief Executive Officer, Carolinas Healthcare System Cleveland, Shelby, NC, p. A470
  President and Chief Executive Officer, Carolinas Healthcare System Kings Mountain, Kings Mountain, NC, p. A465

GYIMAH, Ed, Chief Financial Officer, Howard University Hospital, Washington, DC, p. A117

GYNTHER, Tracy R.N., Vice President and Chief Nursing Officer, West Georgia Health, Lagrange, GA, p. A160

GYROS, Guy, Chief Financial Officer, Huntsville Memorial Hospital, Huntsville, TX, p. A624

H

HAACK, Wanda MSN, R.N., Chief Nursing Officer, Genesis Medical Center, Dewitt, De Witt, IA, p. A225

HAAG, Adam, Manager Information Technology, Coffey County Hospital, Burlington, KS, p. A239

HAAGENSON, Deb R.N., Vice President of Patient Care, Chi St. Joseph's Health, Park Rapids, MN, p. A345

HAAK, Karen S. R.N., MSN, Chief Nursing Officer, Good Samaritan Hospital, Vincennes, IN, p. A221

HAAR, Clare A., Chief Executive Officer, Eastern Niagara Hospital, Lockport, NY, p. A438

HAAS, Christine, Chief Information Officer, Jersey Shore Hospital, Jersey Shore, PA, p. A537

HAAS, Robert M.D., Chief Medical Officer, Liberty Hospital, Liberty, MO, p. A372

HAAS, Scott A M.D., Chief Medical Officer, Eastern State Hospital, Lexington, KY, p. A261

HAAS, Steven J
  Chief Financial Officer, Health Alliance Hospital – Broadway Campus, Kingston, NY, p. A438
  Chief Financial Officer, Health Alliance Hospital – Mary's Avenue Campus, Kingston, NY, p. A438

HAAS, Susan, Director Human Resources, Aurora Behavioral Healthcare San Diego, San Diego, CA, p. A85

HAASE, Patricia, Director Information Technology and Communications, Marian Regional Medical Center, Santa Maria, CA, p. A91

HAASE, Ronald
  Chief Human Resources Officer, Northern Arizona Healthcare, Flagstaff Medical Center, Flagstaff, AZ, p. A29
  Chief Human Resources Officer, Northern Arizona Healthcare, Verde Valley Medical Center, Cottonwood, AZ, p. A28

HAASKEN, Timothy W, Chief Financial Officer, Lewisgale Hospital Montgomery, Blacksburg, VA, p. A665

HABIB, Noel M.D., Chief Medical Officer, Huhukam Memorial Hospital, Sacaton, AZ, p. A35

HABIS, Saba M.D., Chief Medical Officer, Freeman Health System, Joplin, MO, p. A369

HABOWSKI, Michael J., President and Chief Executive Officer, Ashtabula County Medical Center, Ashtabula, OH, p. A480

HACHEY, Michael
  Senior Vice President and Chief Financial Officer, Emerson Hospital, Concord, MA, p. A306
  Senior Vice President and Chief Financial Officer, Mercy Hospital Of Portland, Portland, ME, p. A292

HACKBARTH, John CPA, Senior Vice President Finance and Chief Financial Officer, Owensboro Health Regional Hospital, Owensboro, KY, p. A265

HACKER, Leanne, Chief Financial Officer, Eastern New Mexico Medical Center, Roswell, NM, p. A428

HACKER, Mary Dee R.N., Vice President, Patient Care Services and Chief Nursing Officer, Children's Hospital Los Angeles, Los Angeles, CA, p. A68

HACKER, Phillip
  Chief Financial Officer, Stone County Medical Center, Mountain View, AR, p. A47
  Chief Financial Officer, White River Medical Center, Batesville, AR, p. A40

HACKETT, Leslie, Chief Nursing Officer, Covenant Hospital Plainview, Plainview, TX, p. A637

HACKSTEDDE, Anita, M.D.
  Vice President Medical Affairs, Salem Regional Medical Center, Salem, OH, p. A499
  President and Chief Executive Officer, Salem Regional Medical Center, Salem, OH, p. A499

HADAWAY, Krystal, Director Human Resources, Healthsource Saginaw, Inc., Saginaw, MI, p. A329

HADDAD, Housam M.D., Chief of Staff, Casey County Hospital, Liberty, KY, p. A262

HADDADIN, Maen M.D., President Medical Staff, Chi Health Mercy Corning, Corning, IA, p. A224

HADDICAN, James, Chief Financial Officer, Vice President Finance, Gillette Children's Specialty Healthcare, Saint Paul, MN, p. A347

HADDIX, Parker, Chief Executive Officer, William R. Sharpe, Jr. Hospital, Weston, WV, p. A697

HADDOX, Melissa, Controller, Healthsouth Rehabilitation Hospital Of Cypress, Houston, TX, p. A620

HADLEY, David R, Managing Director and Chief Financial Officer, Integris Baptist Medical Center, Oklahoma City, OK, p. A512

HADLEY, Gerard, Vice President Finance for Brigham & Women's Faulkner Hospital and Vice President Finance and Controller, Brigham And Women's Faulkner Hospital, Boston, MA, p. A303

HADLEY, H Roger M.D., Vice President, Medical Affairs, Loma Linda University Medical Center, Loma Linda, CA, p. A66

HADLEY, Steven N, Chief Financial Officer, Kansas Medical Center, Andover, KS, p. A238

HADLEY, Susan R.N., MS, Chief Nursing Officer, Dickinson County Healthcare System, Iron Mountain, MI, p. A323

HADZEGA, Angela, Chief Financial Officer, Upmc Kane, Kane, PA, p. A537

HAEFELE, John M.D., Chief Medical Officer, Community Memorial Healthcare, Marysville, KS, p. A246

HAEHN, Debra, Chief Financial Officer, Clay County Memorial Hospital, Henrietta, TX, p. A619

HAENELT, Michael, Chief Information Management, Weed Army Community Hospital, Fort Irwin, CA, p. A59

HAESEMEYER, Allan M.D., Chief of Staff, Indianhead Medical Center, Shell Lake, WI, p. A712

HAESEMEYER, Christa, Chief Nursing Officer, Lincoln County Hospital, Lincoln, KS, p. A246

HAFEMAN, Paula, R.N., MSN, FACHE
  Chief Nurse Executive, Hshs St. Vincent Hospital, Green Bay, WI, p. A703
  Chief Nursing Officer, Hshs St. Mary's Hospital Medical Center, Green Bay, WI, p. A703

HAFFEY, Robert, R.N., President, Delaware County Memorial Hospital, Drexel Hill, PA, p. A533

HAFFORD, Juliet, Director Human Resources, Beaumont Hospital – Trenton, Trenton, MI, p. A332

HAFIZ, Irfan
  Vice President Medical Affairs, Centegra Hospital – Mchenry, Mchenry, IL, p. A193
  Vice President Medical Affairs, Centegra Hospital – Woodstock, Woodstock, IL, p. A202

HAGAN, Donald E, Chief Financial Officer, Detar Healthcare System, Victoria, TX, p. A652

HAGAN, Eric, R.N., Executive Vice President and Administrator, Medical Center At Scottsville, Scottsville, KY, p. A267

HAGAN, Frank, Senior Vice President Finance, Saint Joseph's Medical Center, Yonkers, NY, p. A456

HAGEL, Bonnie, Chief Financial Officer, Logan County Hospital, Oakley, KS, p. A248

HAGELBERG, Robbi, Vice President Nursing Services and Chief Nursing Officer, Lakeview Hospital, Stillwater, MN, p. A349

HAGELTHORN, Diane, Human Resources Generalist, Modoc Medical Center, Alturas, CA, p. A51

HAGEN, Bruce P., President, Ohiohealth Marion General Hospital, Marion, OH, p. A494

HAGEN, Lynne D, Human Resources Officer, Avera Mckennan Hospital And University Health Center, Sioux Falls, SD, p. A572

HAGEN, Mary R.N., MSN, VP and Chief Nursing Officer, Unitypoint Health – Waterloo, Waterloo, IA, p. A236

HAGEN, Paulette, Human Resources and Administrative Services Director, Centracare Health–Paynesville, Paynesville, MN, p. A345

HAGENS, Gary, Chief Operating Officer and Chief Medical Officer, Springfield Regional Medical Center, Springfield, OH, p. A499

HAGENS, Paul, Vice President Human Resources, Doctors Community Hospital, Lanham, MD, p. A299

HAGER, Rhonda M, Director Human Resources, Stonewall Jackson Memorial Hospital, Weston, WV, p. A697

HAGERMAN, Daniel M.D., President Medical Staff, Columbia Center Birth Hospital, Mequon, WI, p. A707

HAGERSTROM, Paige A, System Director of Talent Management, St. Joseph Hospital, Bangor, ME, p. A289

HAGERTY, Cindy, Assistant Chief Nurse Officer and Administrator of Operations, Via Christi Rehabilitation Hospital, Wichita, KS, p. A254

HAGGARD, Tommy, Chief Executive Officer, Bluegrass Community Hospital, Versailles, KY, p. A268

HAGGART, Sandra, Chief Nursing Officer, St. Vincent Clay Hospital, Brazil, IN, p. A204

HAGGERTY, Cheryl Kay, Chief Nursing Officer, Assistant Chief Executive Officer, Mercy Medical Center–New Hampton, New Hampton, IA, p. A232

HAGLER, Dan M.D., Vice President and Chief Medical Officer, Carolinas Healthcare System Northeast, Concord, NC, p. A460

HAGLUND, Nicole, Vice President of Nursing Services, Providence Medical Center, Wayne, NE, p. A400

HAGOOD, Teena, Chief Nursing Officer, Kimble Hospital, Junction, TX, p. A625

HAGY, Kelly, Director Human Resources, Cumberland Hall Hospital, Hopkinsville, KY, p. A259

HAGY, Michelle, Chief Financial Officer, Pikeville Medical Center, Pikeville, KY, p. A266

HAHEY, Joanne A
Senior Vice President and Chief Financial Officer, University Of Maryland Shore Medical Center At Dorchester, Cambridge, MD, p. A297
Senior Vice President and Chief Financial Officer, University Of Maryland Shore Medical Center At Easton, Easton, MD, p. A298
Vice President Finance and Chief Financial Officer, University Of Maryland Shore Medical Center At Chestertown, Chestertown, MD, p. A297

HAHN, Donna S R.N., Vice President Acute Care and Chief Nurse Executive, Sentara Rmh Medical Center, Harrisonburg, VA, p. A668

HAHN, Jen, Finance Manager, Uh Portage Medical Center, Ravenna, OH, p. A498

HAHN, Joseph M.D., Chief of Staff, Cleveland Clinic, Cleveland, OH, p. A485

HAHN, Kurt M.D., Acting Clinical Director, Elmira Psychiatric Center, Elmira, NY, p. A435

HAHN, Lori, Vice President Nursing Services, Chi St. Alexius Health – Williston Medical Center, Williston, ND, p. A478

HAHN, Ray, Hospital Administrator, Kaiser Permanente Medical Center, Honolulu, HI, p. A168

HAHN, Stephen, Deputy to the President and Chief Operating Officer, University Of Texas M.D. Anderson Cancer Center, Houston, TX, p. A623

HAHS, Seth, Chief of Staff, Salem Township Hospital, Salem, IL, p. A199

HAIGH, Sara, Associate Director, Durham Veterans Affairs Medical Center, Durham, NC, p. A461

HAIGLER, Tonda V., Chief Operating Officer, Merit Health Biloxi, Biloxi, MS, p. A352

HAIL, Brian, Chief Executive Officer, Cherokee Nation W.W. Hastings Indian Hospital, Tahlequah, OK, p. A516

HAIN, Jim, Chief Operating Officer, Lexington Regional Health Center, Lexington, NE, p. A394

HAINES, Christopher D.O., Vice President and Chief Medical Officer, Children's Specialized Hospital, New Brunswick, NJ, p. A417

HAIR, Denise J., Vice President of Nursing Services and Chief Nursing Officer, Dameron Hospital, Stockton, CA, p. A92

HAIR, Kelly, Director Information Systems and Data Analytics, Abbeville General Hospital, Abbeville, LA, p. A269

HAIR, Troy, Chief Financial Officer, Abbeville General Hospital, Abbeville, LA, p. A269

HAISLIP, Heidi M.D., Chief of Staff, Alliancehealth Madill, Madill, OK, p. A509

HAIZLIP, Thomas M M.D., Jr, Chief of Staff, Charles A. Cannon Memorial Hospital, Newland, NC, p. A468

HAJEK, Julie, Director Human Resources, St. David's Medical Center, Austin, TX, p. A596

HAKENSON, Diana, Director of Patient Care Services, Newport Bay Hospital, Newport Beach, CA, p. A76

HALAMA, George, Vice President Finance, Mcpherson Hospital, Mcpherson, KS, p. A246

HALAMKA, John M.D., Chief Information Officer, Beth Israel Deaconess Medical Center, Boston, MA, p. A302

HALDEMAN, Larry M.D., Executive Vice President and Chief Medical Officer, Wellstar Windy Hill Hospital, Marietta, GA, p. A161

HALDER, Ranjay M.D., Chief Medical Director, Centerstone Hospital, Bradenton, FL, p. A120

HALE, Becky, Director Human Resources, Hill Regional Hospital, Hillsboro, TX, p. A619

HALE, Byron, Chief Financial Officer, East Texas Medical Center Tyler, Tyler, TX, p. A651

HALE, Danny, Director Human Resources, Southwestern Medical Center, Lawton, OK, p. A509

HALE, Donna, Director of Nursing, Baptist Memorial Rehabilitation Hospital, Germantown, TN, p. A579

HALE, Kirsten
Coordinator Health Information Services, University Hospitals Conneaut Medical Center, Conneaut, OH, p. A488
Coordinator Health Informations Systems and Coding, University Hospitals Geneva Medical Center, Geneva, OH, p. A492

HALE, Margie, R.N., MSN, Chief Executive Officer, Baraga County Memorial Hospital, L'Anse, MI, p. A324

HALE, Renae, Chief Nursing Officer, Lincoln Prairie Behavioral Health Center, Springfield, IL, p. A200

HALE, Ron, Superintendent, Colorado Mental Health Institute At Pueblo, Pueblo, CO, p. A106

HALE, Steven D., FACHE, Chief Executive Officer, Weiser Memorial Hospital, Weiser, ID, p. A171

HALE, Tonia, Chief Nursing Officer, Tennova Newport Medical Center, Newport, TN, p. A587

HALEN, Catherine, Vice President Human Resources, Beebe Healthcare, Lewes, DE, p. A115

HALES, Brent, Chief Financial Officer, Uintah Basin Medical Center, Roosevelt, UT, p. A660

HALES, Joe, Chief Information Officer, Primary Children's Hospital, Salt Lake City, UT, p. A660

HALEY, Bob J., Chief Executive Officer, Pekin Hospital, Pekin, IL, p. A197

HALEY, James M.D., Senior Vice President and Chief Medical Officer, Unity Hospital, Rochester, NY, p. A451

HALEY, Michael E., President, Indiana University Health Ball Memorial Hospital, Muncie, IN, p. A216

HALEY, Thomas
Information Technology Services Site Director, Chi Health Mercy Council Bluffs, Council Bluffs, IA, p. A225
Information Technology Systems Site Director, Chi Health Lakeside, Omaha, NE, p. A397
Information Technology Systems Site Director, Chi Health Midlands, Papillion, NE, p. A399

HALFEN, John M.D., Medical Director, Lakewood Health System, Staples, MN, p. A349

HALFHILL, Patrick, Chief Financial Officer, Madison County Memorial Hospital, Madison, FL, p. A131

HALFORD, Dianne, Chief Financial Officer, Saint Clare's Health System, Denville, NJ, p. A412

HALIMI, Hamid M.D., Medical Director, Select Specialty Hospital–Ann Arbor, Ypsilanti, MI, p. A334

HALL, Becky R.N., Director Nursing, Rumford Hospital, Rumford, ME, p. A293

HALL, Catherine, Manager Human Resources, Jefferson Hospital, Louisville, GA, p. A160

HALL, Dan R.N., Chief Operating Officer, St. John Owasso, Owasso, OK, p. A514

HALL, David
Chief Information Officer, Pineville Community Hospital Association, Pineville, KY, p. A266
Senior Vice President and Chief Operating Officer, University Of Tennessee Medical Center, Knoxville, TN, p. A582

HALL, Gary, Vice President of Information Technology, Estes Park Medical Center, Estes Park, CO, p. A102

HALL, Geoffrey, Chief Executive Officer, Edwin Shaw Rehab, Cuyahoga Falls, OH, p. A488

HALL, George, M.D.
Vice President Medical Affairs, St. Elizabeth Florence, Florence, KY, p. A258
Vice President Medical Affairs, St. Elizabeth Fort Thomas, Fort Thomas, KY, p. A258

HALL, Jeanne, Director Information Systems, Shriners Hospitals For Children–St. Louis, Saint Louis, MO, p. A377

HALL, Jeffrey DPM, Chief Medical Officer, St. Croix Regional Medical Center, St Croix Falls, WI, p. A713

HALL, Jeremy, Assistant Administrator and Chief Financial Officer, Middlesboro Arh Hospital, Middlesboro, KY, p. A264

HALL, Jim, Acting Chief Information Officer, Central Arkansas Veterans Healthcare System, Little Rock, AR, p. A46

HALL, Kathy J., Administrator, St. Vincent Warrick Hospital, Boonville, IN, p. A204

HALL, Kenneth C R.N., Chief Nursing Officer, Mishawaka Medical Center, Mishawaka, IN, p. A216

HALL, Kent M.D., Vice President and Chief Medical Officer, The University Of Vermont Health Network–Champlain Valley Physicians Hospital, Plattsburgh, NY, p. A449

HALL, Linda, Administrator and Chief Executive Officer, Chillicothe Hospital District, Chillicothe, TX, p. A601

HALL, Margaret M.D., Chief Medical Officer, Lakeside Women's Hospital, Oklahoma City, OK, p. A512

HALL, Mark, Interim Chief Executive Officer, Lubbock Heart & Surgical Hospital, Lubbock, TX, p. A630

HALL, Mary A, Chief Medical Staff, Mcdowell Arh Hospital, Mcdowell, KY, p. A264

HALL, Melissa
Chief Nursing Officer, Coffey County Hospital, Burlington, KS, p. A239
Human Resources, Munising Memorial Hospital, Munising, MI, p. A326

HALL, Morrison, Chief Financial Officer, Pender Memorial Hospital, Burgaw, NC, p. A458

HALL, Richard, Chief Executive Officer, Samuel Simmonds Memorial Hospital, Barrow, AK, p. A25

HALL, Roger L.
President, Sacred Heart Hospital On The Emerald Coast, Miramar Beach, FL, p. A135
President, Sacred Heart Hospital On The Gulf, Port St. Joe, FL, p. A140

HALL, Ryan, Vice President, Providence Hospital, Columbia, SC, p. A560

HALL, Sally, Manager Human Resources, South Texas Spine And Surgical Hospital, San Antonio, TX, p. A643

HALL, Stephanie
Chief Medical Officer, Keck Hospital Of Usc, Los Angeles, CA, p. A69
Chief Medical Officer, Usc Verdugo Hills Hospital, Glendale, CA, p. A62
Medical Director, Usc Norris Comprehensive Cancer Center, Los Angeles, CA, p. A71

HALL, Steve, Chief Financial Officer, Pekin Hospital, Pekin, IL, p. A197

HALL, Terry E., Chief of Staff, Harrison County Community Hospital, Bethany, MO, p. A364

HALL, Trudy M.D., Vice President Medical Affairs, Laurel Regional Hospital, Laurel, MD, p. A299

HALL, Trudy, M.D., Vice President Medical Affairs and Interim Chief Executive Officer, Laurel Regional Hospital, Laurel, MD, p. A299

HALL, Veronica R.N., Chief Operating Officer, Henry Ford Hospital, Detroit, MI, p. A318

HALL, Wyatt M.D., Chief Medical Officer, Longmont United Hospital, Longmont, CO, p. A105

HALLADAY, Mark, Director Information Services, F. F. Thompson Hospital, Canandaigua, NY, p. A433

HALLAL, Joseph M.D., Chief Medical Officer, Inova Fairfax Hospital, Falls Church, VA, p. A666

HALLATT, Jennifer
Chief Operating Officer, Mercyhealth Hospital And Medical Center – Harvard, Harvard, IL, p. A189
Vice President, Mercyhealth Hospital And Medical Center – Walworth, Lake Geneva, WI, p. A704

HALLEY, Andrea, Director Human Resources, Hopedale Medical Complex, Hopedale, IL, p. A190

HALLEY, Lisa B, Vice President Human Resources, Holzer Medical Center, Gallipolis, OH, p. A491

HALLICK, Susan M R.N., Executive Vice President and Chief Nursing Officer, Geisinger Medical Center, Danville, PA, p. A532

HALLIDAY, Lisa, Director Accounting Services, Taylor Regional Hospital, Hawkinsville, GA, p. A158

HALLIWILL, Donald B
Chief Financial Officer, Carilion Franklin Memorial Hospital, Rocky Mount, VA, p. A675
Executive Vice President and Chief Financial Officer, Carilion Roanoke Memorial Hospital, Roanoke, VA, p. A675

HALLMARK, Todd, Chief Operating Officer, Choctaw Nation Health Care Center, Talihina, OK, p. A516

HALLOCK, Mirya, Administrator, Webster County Community Hospital, Red Cloud, NE, p. A399

HALPIN, Jean
President, Ohiohealth Medcentral Mansfield Hospital, Mansfield, OH, p. A494
President, Ohiohealth Medcentral Shelby Hospital, Shelby, OH, p. A499

HALPIN, Kim, Director Human Resources, Arms Acres, Carmel, NY, p. A433

HALSAN, Carole, R.N., Chief Executive Officer, Willapa Harbor Hospital, South Bend, WA, p. A686

HALSELL, David, Senior Vice President and Chief Financial Officer, Lake Regional Health System, Osage Beach, MO, p. A374

HALSTEAD, Lisa, Chief Nursing Officer, Integris Miami Hospital, Miami, OK, p. A510

HALTER, Bev, Director Human Resources and Payroll, Liberty Medical Center, Chester, MT, p. A383

HALTER, Kevin, Chief Executive Officer, Our Lady Of Bellefonte Hospital, Ashland, KY, p. A255

HALTER, Michael P., Chief Executive Officer, Hahnemann University Hospital, Philadelphia, PA, p. A544

HALTOM, Shannon, Vice President, Patient Care Services, Chi St. Luke's Health Brazosport, Lake Jackson, TX, p. A628

HALVORSEN, Lisa, Chief Nurse Executive, Providence Milwaukie Hospital, Milwaukie, OR, p. A524

HALVORSON, Marla, Director Human Resources, St. Luke's Hospital, Duluth, MN, p. A339

HAM, Michael, Chief Executive Officer, Park Royal Hospital, Fort Myers, FL, p. A125

HAMAM, Hisham M.D., Chief of Staff, Northern Cochise Community Hospital, Willcox, AZ, p. A38

HAMAN, Timothy M.D., Vice President Medical Affairs, Christus St. Patrick Hospital Of Lake Charles, Lake Charles, LA, p. A279

HAMATY, Edward G. D.O., Chief Medical Officer, Acuity Specialty Hospital Of Southern New Jersey, Willingboro, NJ, p. A423

HAMB, Aaron M.D., Chief Medical Officer, Provident Hospital Of Cook County, Chicago, IL, p. A183

HAMBLIN, Garth, Chief Financial Officer, Bear Valley Community Hospital, Big Bear Lake, CA, p. A54

HAMBLIN, James, Chief Financial Officer, White Mountain Regional Medical Center, Springerville, AZ, p. A36

HAMBLIN, Scott M.D., President Medical Staff, White Mountain Regional Medical Center, Springerville, AZ, p. A36

HAMBRIDGE, Mark, Director Information Systems, Livingston Regional Hospital, Livingston, TN, p. A583

HAMBY, Kelley, Vice President Patient Care, Baptist Health Medical Center – North Little Rock, North Little Rock, AR, p. A48

HAMEL, Cathleen, Chief Nurse Executive, St. Rose Dominican Hospitals – Siena Campus, Henderson, NV, p. A402

HAMEL, Loren, M.D., President and Chief Executive Officer, Lakeland Medical Center, St. Joseph, Saint Joseph, MI, p. A330

HAMEL, Susan, Chief Nursing Officer, St. Luke's Hospital, Duluth, MN, p. A339

HAMILL, Dave H., President and Chief Executive Officer, Hampton Regional Medical Center, Varnville, SC, p. A566

HAMILTON, Adriana H, Chief Human Resources Officer, Hunter Holmes Mcguire Veterans Affairs Medical Center– Richmond, Richmond, VA, p. A674

HAMILTON, Aggie, Chief Human Resources, Veterans Affairs Montana Health Care System, Fort Harrison, MT, p. A384

HAMILTON, Brandy, Chief Executive Officer, Suncoast Behavioral Health Center, Bradenton, FL, p. A121

HAMILTON, Catherine, Chief Nursing Officer, Hedrick Medical Center, Chillicothe, MO, p. A366

HAMILTON, Chanda, Chief Information Officer, Clifton T. Perkins Hospital Center, Jessup, MD, p. A299

HAMILTON, Dan, Chief Operating Officer, Nor–Lea Hospital District, Lovington, NM, p. A427

HAMILTON, Gary, Interim Chief Executive Officer, Pioneer Medical Center, Big Timber, MT, p. A382

HAMILTON, Geoff, Interim Chief Financial Officer, Morton General Hospital, Morton, WA, p. A682

HAMILTON, Jennifer
    Chief Financial Officer, Sagewest Health Care At Riverton, Riverton, WY, p. A719
    COO – Mary Bridge, Multicare Mary Bridge Children's Hospital And Health Center, Tacoma, WA, p. A687

HAMILTON, Marci, Chief Nursing Officer, Orthopaedic Hospital Of Lutheran Health Network, Fort Wayne, IN, p. A208

HAMILTON, Marilyn, Director Human Resources, Promise Hospital Baton Rouge – Main Campus, Baton Rouge, LA, p. A271

HAMILTON, Nancy, Chief Human and Learning Resources, Veterans Affairs New Jersey Health Care System, East Orange, NJ, p. A413

HAMILTON, Patricia, R.N.
    Director of Nursing, Mildred Mitchell–Bateman Hospital, Huntington, WV, p. A692
    Chief Executive Officer, Rebound Behavioral Health, Lancaster, SC, p. A564

HAMILTON, Peggy, Chief Financial Officer, Bayside Community Hospital, Anahuac, TX, p. A592

HAMILTON, Phil, R.N., Chief Executive Officer, General John J. Pershing Memorial Hospital, Brookfield, MO, p. A365

HAMILTON, Randal S., Chief Executive Officer, Select Specialty Hospital–Panama City, Panama City, FL, p. A138

HAMILTON, Scott
    Chief Financial Officer, Peninsula Hospital, Louisville, TN, p. A583
    Vice President and Chief Financial Officer, Parkwest Medical Center, Knoxville, TN, p. A582

HAMILTON, Sharon, Chief Nursing Officer, Healthsouth Emerald Coast Rehabilitation Hospital, Panama City, FL, p. A138

HAMILTON, Terry, President, St. John Macomb–Oakland Hospital, Warren, MI, p. A332

HAMILTON, Thomas D.O., Chief Medical Officer, St. Francis Health, Topeka, KS, p. A252

HAMILTON, Tom M.D., Chief of Staff, Decatur County General Hospital, Parsons, TN, p. A588

HAMILTON–BEYER, Maggie, Chief Financial Officer, Knoxville Hospital & Clinics, Knoxville, IA, p. A230

HAMLIN, Faye, Manager Human Resources, Julian F. Keith Alcohol And Drug Abuse Treatment Center, Black Mountain, NC, p. A458

HAMM, Jay, R.N., FACHE, Chief Operating Officer, Palmetto Health Richland, Columbia, SC, p. A560

HAMM, Sonja, Vice President Human and Foundation Resources, Lakes Regional Healthcare, Spirit Lake, IA, p. A235

HAMMAKER, Barry M.D., Chief Medical Officer and Chief Clinical Officer, Vail Valley Health Hospital, Vail, CO, p. A108

HAMMAN, Baron L M.D., Chief Medical Officer, Texas Health Heart & Vascular Hospital Arlington, Arlington, TX, p. A593

HAMMEL, Leah, Acting Administrator, Chester Mental Health Center, Chester, IL, p. A180

HAMMER, Kristine, Director of Finance, Centracare Health– Monticello, Monticello, MN, p. A344

HAMMER, Rebecca J, Chief Financial Officer, Davis Medical Center, Elkins, WV, p. A691

HAMMERAN, Kevin R., Chief Executive Officer and Administrator, Baptist Memorial Hospital For Women, Memphis, TN, p. A584

HAMMES, Chris, Interim President, Integris Grove Hospital, Grove, OK, p. A508

HAMMES, Paul, Chief Executive Officer, Hugh Chatham Memorial Hospital, Elkin, NC, p. A462

HAMMETT, Doran, Chief Financial Officer, Petersburg Medical Center, Petersburg, AK, p. A27

HAMMETT, George, Director Human Resources, Carolina Center For Behavioral Health, Greer, SC, p. A563

HAMMETT, Richard A., President and Chief Executive Officer, Swedish Medical Center, Englewood, CO, p. A102

HAMMETT, Troy
    Chief Financial Officer, Chi Memorial, Chattanooga, TN, p. A576
    Vice President and Chief Financial Officer, Ohiohealth Doctors Hospital, Columbus, OH, p. A487

HAMMOCK, Preston W., President, Alamance Regional Medical Center, Burlington, NC, p. A458

HAMMON, Selene Q., Chief Executive Officer, Dallas Behavioral Healthcare Hospital, Desoto, TX, p. A609

HAMMOND, Flora M.D., Chief Medical Affairs, Rehabilitation Hospital of Indiana, Indianapolis, IN, p. A212

HAMMOND, Michael
    Chief Financial Officer, Lourdes Medical Center Of Burlington County, Willingboro, NJ, p. A423
    Chief Financial Officer, Our Lady Of Lourdes Medical Center, Camden, NJ, p. A412

HAMMOND, Nancy M.D., Vice President, Chief Medical Officer, Saint Agnes Healthcare, Baltimore, MD, p. A295

HAMMOND, Patti, Chief Operating Officer, Adirondack Health, Saranac Lake, NY, p. A452

HAMMOND, Reed, Chief Operating Officer, Conroe Regional Medical Center, Conroe, TX, p. A602

HAMMONDS, Janie, Human Resources Officer, Columbus Community Hospital, Columbus, TX, p. A602

HAMMONDS, Laura, Assistant Administrator, Jasper Memorial Hospital, Monticello, GA, p. A162

HAMNER, Candy, Vice President and Chief Nursing Officer, Levindale Hebrew Geriatric Center And Hospital, Baltimore, MD, p. A294

HAMON, Beta, Chief Medical Officer, Sanford Rock Rapids Medical Center, Rock Rapids, IA, p. A234

HAMON, Eric, Executive Vice President and Chief Financial Officer, Driscoll Children's Hospital, Corpus Christi, TX, p. A603

HAMPF, Carl M.D., Chief Medical Officer, Saint Thomas Hospital For Spinal Surgery, Nashville, TN, p. A586

HAMPTON, Angie, Director Human Resources, Porter Regional Hospital, Valparaiso, IN, p. A220

HAMPTON, Connie, Nurse Executive, Carl Vinson Veterans Affairs Medical Center, Dublin, GA, p. A157

HAMPTON, David M.D., Chief Medical Staff, Pampa Regional Medical Center, Pampa, TX, p. A636

HAMPTON, Jeff, Director Information Systems, Lehigh Regional Medical Center, Lehigh Acres, FL, p. A131

HAMPTON, Mary Ann R.N., MSN, Chief Nursing Officer, Des Peres Hospital, Saint Louis, MO, p. A377

HAMRICK, Jan, Chief Financial Officer, Dodge County Hospital, Eastman, GA, p. A157

HAMSTRA, Nancy, Chief Operating Officer, University Hospital, Newark, NJ, p. A418

HAMULA, Michelle, Director of Nursing and Quality, Chan Soon–Shiong Medical Center, Windber, PA, p. A554

HAN, Kevin, Vice President and Chief Financial Officer, Stormont Vail Health, Topeka, KS, p. A252

HANCOCK, Brian, M.D., Director, Richard L. Roudebush Veterans Affairs Medical Center, Indianapolis, IN, p. A212

HANCOCK, J Brian M.D., Chief of Staff, Fargo Veterans Affairs Health Care System, Fargo, ND, p. A475

HANCOCK, Katherine R.N., Executive Chief Nursing Officer, Cleveland Clinic, Cleveland, OH, p. A485

HANCOCK, Kerry, Director Human Resources, Bacon County Hospital And Health System, Alma, GA, p. A149

HANCOCK, Lori, Chief Business Officer, West Palm Beach Veterans Affairs Medical Center, West Palm Beach, FL, p. A147

HANCOCK, Melinda, Chief Financial Officer, VCU Medical Center, Richmond, VA, p. A674

HANCOCK, Myrna, Director Financial Services, Choctaw Health Center, Philadelphia, MS, p. A360

HANCOCK, Paul M.D., Chief Medical Officer, Swedish Medical Center, Englewood, CO, p. A102

HANCOCK, Sharon, Chief Human Resources Officer, Mccullough–Hyde Memorial Hospital/Trihealth, Oxford, OH, p. A498

HANCOCK, Stacey J, Vice President, Human Resources, Wellstar Atlanta Medical Center, Atlanta, GA, p. A151

HANCOCK, Todd, President and Chief Executive Officer, Christus Good Shepherd Medical Center, Longview, TX, p. A629

HANDEL, Daniel M.D., Chief Medical Officer, Musc Medical Center Of Medical University Of South Carolina, Charleston, SC, p. A559

HANDLER, Michael M.D., Vice President Medical Affairs and Chief Medical Officer, SSM Health St. Joseph Hospital – Lake Saint Louis, Lake Saint Louis, MO, p. A372

HANDLEY, Charles
    Chief Financial Officer, Plaza Specialty Hospital, Houston, TX, p. A622
    Chief Financial Officer, The Hospitals Of Providence Memorial Campus, El Paso, TX, p. A611

HANDLEY, Jack M.D., Chief Medical Officer, Evergreenhealth Monroe, Monroe, WA, p. A682

HANDLEY, Rhonda, Chief Financial Officer, Columbia Basin Hospital, Ephrata, WA, p. A680

HANDOL, Nelson M.D., Medical Director, Laurel Oaks Behavioral Health Center, Dothan, AL, p. A17

HANDWERK, Ashley, Director, Human Resources, Medstar Union Memorial Hospital, Baltimore, MD, p. A295

HANDY, Steven P., CPA, Chief Executive Officer, Uniontown Hospital, Uniontown, PA, p. A552

HANEFELD, Darlene, Chief Human Resources Officer, Banner Churchill Community Hospital, Fallon, NV, p. A401

HANENBURG, Thomas S., Senior Vice President and Area Manager, Kaiser Permanente San Leandro Medical Center, San Leandro, CA, p. A89

HANEY, Judy, Chief Nursing Officer, Twin Rivers Regional Medical Center, Kennett, MO, p. A371

HANEY, Kathryn, Controller, Healthsouth Valley Of The Sun Rehabilitation Hospital, Glendale, AZ, p. A30

HANEY, Lisa, Chief Executive Officer, St. Mary Rehabilitation Hospital, Langhorne, PA, p. A538

HANEY, Mark, President, Wellstar Paulding Hospital, Hiram, GA, p. A159

HANGER, Kelvin, Chief Executive Officer, Trihealth Evendale Hospital, Cincinnati, OH, p. A485

HANIGAN, Hank, MS, R.N.
    Interim Chief Financial Officer, Whitman Hospital And Medical Center, Colfax, WA, p. A679
    Chief Executive Officer, Whitman Hospital And Medical Center, Colfax, WA, p. A679

HANISCH, Denise M.D., Chief of Staff, Avera St. Mary's Hospital, Pierre, SD, p. A571

HANKINS, Brad, Chief Operating Quality Officer, Lake Chelan Community Hospital And Clinics, Chelan, WA, p. A679

HANKS, John, Director Information Systems, East Tennessee Children's Hospital, Knoxville, TN, p. A581

HANKS, Susan, Chief Information Officer, Riverton Hospital, Riverton, UT, p. A659

HANLEY, Bob, Chief Human Resources Officer, University Of Chicago Medical Center, Chicago, IL, p. A184

HANLEY, Darlene S., R.N., FACHE, President and Chief Executive Officer, St. Lawrence Rehabilitation Center, Lawrenceville, NJ, p. A415

HANLEY, Matthew, Chief Financial Officer, OSF Saint Anthony's Health Center, Alton, IL, p. A177

HANLON, Jerad, Chief Operating Officer, Southside Regional Medical Center, Petersburg, VA, p. A673

HANNA, Casey M.D., Chief of Staff, Wagoner Community Hospital, Wagoner, OK, p. A519

HANNA, Mitchell J.
    Chief Executive Officer, Sutter Auburn Faith Hospital, Auburn, CA, p. A52
    Chief Executive Officer, Sutter Coast Hospital, Crescent City, CA, p. A57

HANNA, Philip S., Chief Executive Officer, Dewitt Hospital, Dewitt, AR, p. A42

HANNA, Robb, Executive Director Information Technology, Lexington Regional Health Center, Lexington, NE, p. A394

HANNAH, Jill, Director Human Resources, James Cancer Hospital And Solove Research Institute, Columbus, OH, p. A487

HANNAPEL, Andrew, Chief Medical Officer, Chatham Hospital, Siler City, NC, p. A470

HANNERS, Brandy, Chief Financial Officer, Sovah Health–Martinsville, Martinsville, VA, p. A670

HANNERS, Rodney B.
  Chief Executive Officer, Keck Hospital Of Usc, Los Angeles, CA, p. A69
  Chief Executive Officer, Usc Norris Comprehensive Cancer Center, Los Angeles, CA, p. A71

HANNON, Barbara A R.N., Interim Chief Nursing Officer and Chief Clinical Officer, Curry General Hospital, Gold Beach, OR, p. A522

HANNON, Edward J., FACHE, President, Chi Health Saint Francis, Grand Island, NE, p. A393

HANNON, Jennifer, Director Human Resources, Madison County Health Care System, Winterset, IA, p. A237

HANNON, Kay, Director Information Systems, Des Peres Hospital, Saint Louis, MO, p. A377

HANNON, Patricia, Chief Nursing Officer, Vaughan Regional Medical Center, Selma, AL, p. A23

HANNON, Trish, FACHE, R.N., President and Chief Executive Officer, New England Baptist Hospital, Boston, MA, p. A303

HANOLD, Cindy, Chief Nursing Officer, Richland Hospital, Richland Center, WI, p. A711

HANS, Christopher, Chief Financial Officer, Riverside University Health System–Medical Center, Moreno Valley, CA, p. A75

HANSCOM, Kristine, Chief Financial Officer, Tufts Medical Center, Boston, MA, p. A304

HANSCOME, Joyce, Chief Information Officer, Doctors Community Hospital, Lanham, MD, p. A299

HANSEL, Jimmie W., Ph.D., Chief Executive Officer, Edwards County Hospital And Healthcare Center, Kinsley, KS, p. A244

HANSEN, Carolyn, Chief Nursing Officer, Bingham Memorial Hospital, Blackfoot, ID, p. A171

HANSEN, Chris, Senior Vice President Ambulatory Services and Chief Information Officer, The University Of Kansas Health System, Kansas City, KS, p. A244

HANSEN, Gayle B, R.N.
  Chief Integration Officer, Mayo Clinic Health System In Saint James, Saint James, MN, p. A347
  Chief Operating Officer, Mayo Clinic Health System In Fairmont, Fairmont, MN, p. A339

HANSEN, Jay, Director Information Services, Oconee Memorial Hospital, Seneca, SC, p. A566

HANSEN, Karen, Vice President and Chief Operating Officer, Memorial Medical Center – Ashland, Ashland, WI, p. A698

HANSEN, Kristy CPA, Chief Financial Officer, Myrtue Medical Center, Harlan, IA, p. A229

HANSEN, Kyle A., Chief Executive Officer, Logan Regional Hospital, Logan, UT, p. A657

HANSEN, Kyle, Corporate Director Information Systems, Riverside Medical Center, Kankakee, IL, p. A191

HANSEN, Laurie
  Director Administrative Services, Johnson County Healthcare Center, Buffalo, WY, p. A717
  Vice President of Operations, Emory Johns Creek Hospital, Johns Creek, GA, p. A159

HANSEN, Linda, Director Human Resources, Bakersfield Heart Hospital, Bakersfield, CA, p. A52

HANSEN, Michael T., FACHE, President and Chief Executive Officer, Columbus Community Hospital, Columbus, NE, p. A392

HANSEN, Michelle, Director, Chi Health Good Samaritan, Kearney, NE, p. A394

HANSEN, Misty, Chief Financial Officer, Banner – University Medical Center Tucson, Tucson, AZ, p. A37

HANSEN, Paul, Administrator, Maniilaq Health Center, Kotzebue, AK, p. A26

HANSEN, Steven, Director Information Technology, Healdsburg District Hospital, Healdsburg, CA, p. A63

HANSEN, Tim, Interim Chief Human Resource Officer, Denver Health, Denver, CO, p. A100

HANSERT, Benjamin K., Administrator, North Baldwin Infirmary, Bay Minette, AL, p. A14

HANSON, Brent, Chief Executive Officer, Pine Valley Specialty Hospital, Houston, TX, p. A622

HANSON, Denise, Information Technology Specialist, St. Cloud Veterans Affairs Health Care System, Saint Cloud, MN, p. A347

HANSON, Emily M.D., President, Medical Staff, St. Joseph Memorial Hospital, Murphysboro, IL, p. A194

HANSON, Gregory S., M.D., Chief Executive Officer, Clark Fork Valley Hospital, Plains, MT, p. A387

HANSON, Jane E, R.N.
  Interim Chief Executive Officer, Chandler Regional Medical Center, Chandler, AZ, p. A28
  Interim President and Chief Executive Officer, Mercy Gilbert Medical Center, Gilbert, AZ, p. A29
  Chief Operating Officer, Chandler Regional Medical Center, Chandler, AZ, p. A28
  Chief Operating Officer, Mercy Gilbert Medical Center, Gilbert, AZ, p. A29

HANSON, Jane E., R.N.
  Interim Chief Executive Officer, Chandler Regional Medical Center, Chandler, AZ, p. B46
  Interim President and Chief Executive Officer, Mercy Gilbert Medical Center, Gilbert, AZ, p. B46

HANSON, Jesica, Vice President and Chief Financial Officer, Bakersfield Memorial Hospital, Bakersfield, CA, p. A52

HANSON, Jim, Director Information Systems, Avera Queen Of Peace Hospital, Mitchell, SD, p. A571

HANSON, Lesley, Director Human Resources, Lake District Hospital, Lakeview, OR, p. A523

HANSON, Mary Ann, Director Personnel, Mental Health Institute, Cherokee, IA, p. A224

HANSON, Paul A., FACHE, President, Sanford Usd Medical Center, Sioux Falls, SD, p. A572

HANSON, Paul, Chief Financial Officer, Bay Area Regional Medical Center, Webster, TX, p. A653

HANSON, Rhonda, Director Human Resources, Huron Regional Medical Center, Huron, SD, p. A570

HANSON, Rita, M.D.
  Vice President Medical Affairs, Wheaton Franciscan Healthcare – Elmbrook Memorial, Brookfield, WI, p. A699
  Vice President Medical Affairs, Wheaton Franciscan Healthcare – St. Joseph's, Milwaukee, WI, p. A708

HANSON, Samantha, Chief Human Resources Officer, Children's Hospitals And Clinics Of Minnesota, Minneapolis, MN, p. A343

HANSON, Tamra, Human Resource Manager, Dorothea Dix Psychiatric Center, Bangor, ME, p. A289

HANYAK, Diana C., Chief Executive Officer, Healthsouth Tustin Rehabilitation Hospital, Tustin, CA, p. A94

HANZLIK, Debra Dawn R.N., Director of Nursing, Niobrara Valley Hospital, Lynch, NE, p. A395

HAPNEY, Sherry, Chief Financial Officer, Healthsouth Rehabilitation Hospital Of Fort Worth, Fort Worth, TX, p. A613

HAPPEL, Terry J M.D., Vice President and Chief Medical Officer, Chandler Regional Medical Center, Chandler, AZ, p. A28

HAQQANI, Rahim M.D., Medical Director, Dallas Behavioral Healthcare Hospital, Desoto, TX, p. A609

HAQUE, Haroon M.D., Medical Director, Chg Hospital Tucson, Llc, Tucson, AZ, p. A37

HARA, Karen, Personnel Management Specialist, Hawaii State Hospital, Kaneohe, HI, p. A170

HARALDSON, Richard, Chief Executive Officer, Sidney Health Center, Sidney, MT, p. A388

HARALSON, Gregory
  Chief Operating Officer, Medical City Fort Worth, Fort Worth, TX, p. A614
  Chief Executive Officer, Memorial Hermann Greater Heights Hospital, Houston, TX, p. A621
  Chief Executive Officer, Memorial Hermann Sugar Land Hospital, Sugar Land, TX, p. A647

HARALSON, Robert, Chief Financial Officer, Williamson Memorial Hospital, Williamson, WV, p. A697

HARARI, Jack L M.D., Chief Medical Officer, West Boca Medical Center, Boca Raton, FL, p. A120

HARBAUGH, Charles, Director Human Resources, Mountain Lakes Medical Center, Clayton, GA, p. A154

HARBAUGH, Ken, Vice President and Chief Financial Officer, OSF Saint Francis Medical Center, Peoria, IL, p. A197

HARBERT, Jim, Chief Technology Officer, Anthony Medical Center, Anthony, KS, p. A238

HARBERTS, Jerry, Information Technologist, Madison Healthcare Services, Madison, MN, p. A342

HARBESON, Mary, R.N., Chief Executive Officer, Kindred Hospital Clear Lake, Webster, TX, p. A653

HARBIN, Cathy
  Chief Nursing Officer, Roosevelt Warm Springs Rehabilitation And Specialty Hospitals – Ltac, Warm Springs, GA, p. A167
  Chief Nursing Officer, Roosevelt Warm Springs Rehabilitation Hospital – Rehab, Warm Springs, GA, p. A167

HARBIN, Jason, Director of Nursing, Ward Memorial Hospital, Monahans, TX, p. A634

HARBISON, Linda, Chief Nursing Officer, Red Bud Regional Hospital, Red Bud, IL, p. A198

HARBOR, Mike, Chief Financial Officer, Nevada Regional Medical Center, Nevada, MO, p. A374

HARCHENKO, Vern M.D., Chief of Staff, Chi St. Alexius Health Garrison, Garrison, ND, p. A476

HARCLERODE, Timothy
  Chief Executive Officer, Conemaugh Miners Medical Center, Hastings, PA, p. A536
  Chief Executive Officer, Conemaugh Nason Medical Center, Roaring Spring, PA, p. A549

HARCUP, Craig M.D., Hospital Medical Director, Complex Care Hospital At Ridgelake, Sarasota, FL, p. A142

HARDACRE, Jerry M.D., Chief of Staff, Wheaton Franciscan Healthcare – All Saints, Racine, WI, p. A711

HARDAGE, Tony, Assistant Vice President and Administrator, Baptist Health Medical Center–Arkadelphia, Arkadelphia, AR, p. A40

HARDAN, Terry, Director Human Resources, Longview Regional Medical Center, Longview, TX, p. A630

HARDCASTLE, Brad, Chief Financial Officer, South Baldwin Regional Medical Center, Foley, AL, p. A18

HARDCASTLE, Kathy, Director Human Resources, Texas Health Presbyterian Hospital Denton, Denton, TX, p. A608

HARDEE, Gary R M.D., Medical Director, Plains Memorial Hospital, Dimmitt, TX, p. A609

HARDEMAN, Diane, Director Personnel, Stephens County Hospital, Toccoa, GA, p. A166

HARDEN, Diane P
  Chief Financial Officer, Leesburg Regional Medical Center, Leesburg, FL, p. A130
  Senior Vice President and Chief Financial Officer, The Villages Regional Hospital, The Villages, FL, p. A146

HARDESTY, Keith, Chief Financial Officer, Springfield Hospital Center, Sykesville, MD, p. A301

HARDIE, Rebecca K, Chief Nursing Officer, Baylor Scott & White Medical Center – Hillcrest, Waco, TX, p. A652

HARDIN, Cecil CPA, Chief Financial Officer, Catawba Hospital, Catawba, VA, p. A665

HARDIN, Ellen L, Chief Human Resources Officer, Mendocino Coast District Hospital, Fort Bragg, CA, p. A59

HARDIN, James, Human Resources Officer, Sheridan Veterans Affairs Medical Center, Sheridan, WY, p. A720

HARDIN, Leslie, Chief Executive Officer and Chief Financial Officer, Seymour Hospital, Seymour, TX, p. A645

HARDIN, Marci, Manager Information Technology, Nevada Regional Medical Center, Nevada, MO, p. A374

HARDIN, Mark M.D., Medical Director, Ed Fraser Memorial Hospital And Baker Community Health Center, Macclenny, FL, p. A131

HARDIN, Nicholas, FACHE, Chief Executive Officer, Healthsouth Sugar Land Rehabilitation Hospital, Sugar Land, TX, p. A647

HARDING, Barry, Interim Chief Executive Officer and Chief Financial Officer, Sumner Regional Medical Center, Wellington, KS, p. A253

HARDING, Cathy, Chief Clinical Officer, Vibra Hospital Of Springfield, Springfield, IL, p. A201

HARDING, Christina, Vice President Finance, Mount Desert Island Hospital, Bar Harbor, ME, p. A289

HARDING, Denise, Director Human Resources, Plumas District Hospital, Quincy, CA, p. A81

HARDING, Edward A., FACHE, President and Chief Executive Officer, Bay Area Medical Center, Marinette, WI, p. A706

HARDING, Geoff, Chief Clinical Officer, Promise Hospital Of Salt Lake, Salt Lake City, UT, p. A660

HARDING, Gwen, Site Manager Information Systems, Bon Secours Memorial Regional Medical Center, Mechanicsville, VA, p. A670

HARDING, Helen, Chief Nursing Officer, Fairfield Medical Center, Lancaster, OH, p. A493

HARDING, John P, Chief Operating Officer, Children's Hospital Of The King's Daughters, Norfolk, VA, p. A671

HARDING, Rick, Chief Executive Officer, Sun Behavioral Houston, Houston, TX, p. A622

HARDISON, Randall M.D., Chief Medical Officer, Arizona Orthopedic Surgical Hospital, Chandler, AZ, p. A28

HARDOBY, Greg, Director Personnel, Runnells Center For Rehabilitation And Healthcare, Berkeley Heights, NJ, p. A411

HARDWICK, Garry R.N., Chief Operating Officer, Newport Bay Hospital, Newport Beach, CA, p. A76

HARDY, Bob, Chief Operating Officer, Opelousas General Health System, Opelousas, LA, p. A289

HARDY, James D.O., Chief of Staff, Dayton Veterans Affairs Medical Center, Dayton, OH, p. A489

HARDY, Janice, Chief Human Resource Management Service, Central Alabama Veterans Health Care System, Montgomery, AL, p. A21

HARDY, Kevin, Chief Financial Officer, Healthsouth Treasure Coast Rehabilitation Hospital, Vero Beach, FL, p. A146

HARDY, LaBon, Chief Information Officer, Ralph H. Johnson Veterans Affairs Medical Center, Charleston, SC, p. A559

HARDY, Margaret, R.N., MS, Vice President, St. Vincent's Medical Center, Bridgeport, CT, p. A109

HARDY, Melanie D.O., Chief of Staff, Marias Medical Center, Shelby, MT, p. A388

HARDY, Valonia, Chief Healthy Living Officer, Tsehootsooi Medical Center, Fort Defiance, AZ, p. A29

HARGENS, Scott James.
  Administrator and Chief Executive Officer, Avera Dells Area Hospital, Dell Rapids, SD, p. A569
  Administrator and Chief Executive Officer, Avera Flandreau Hospital, Flandreau, SD, p. A570

HARGENS, Scott James, Administrator and Chief Executive Officer, Avera Dells Area Hospital, Dell Rapids, SD, p. B16

HARGER, Anita
  Chief Human Resource Officer, Kingman Regional Medical Center, Kingman, AZ, p. A30
  Director Human Resources, Mercy Gilbert Medical Center, Gilbert, AZ, p. A29

HARGETT, Fred M
  Executive Vice President and Chief Financial Officer, Novant Health Brunswick Medical Center, Bolivia, NC, p. A458
  Executive Vice President and Chief Financial Officer, Novant Health Charlotte Orthopaedic Hospital, Charlotte, NC, p. A459
  Executive Vice President and Chief Financial Officer, Novant Health Forsyth Medical Center, Winston, NC, p. A473
  Executive Vice President and Chief Financial Officer, Novant Health Huntersville Medical Center, Huntersville, NC, p. A465
  Executive Vice President and Chief Financial Officer, Novant Health Matthews Medical Center, Matthews, NC, p. A466
  Executive Vice President and Chief Financial Officer, Novant Health Medical Park Hospital, Winston, NC, p. A473
  Executive Vice President and Chief Financial Officer, Novant Health Presbyterian Medical Center, Charlotte, NC, p. A460
  Executive Vice President and Chief Financial Officer, Novant Health Rowan Medical Center, Salisbury, NC, p. A470
  Executive Vice President and Chief Financial Officer, Novant Health Thomasville Medical Center, Thomasville, NC, p. A471

HARGETT, Stephen A, Senior Vice President and Chief Financial Officer, Marina Del Rey Hospital, Marina Del Rey, CA, p. A73

HARGETT, Stephen, Administrator Finance and Support Services, Musc Medical Center Of Medical University Of South Carolina, Charleston, SC, p. A559

HARGIS, Bryan J.
  Chief Executive Officer, Florence Hospital At Anthem, Florence, AZ, p. A29
  Chief Executive Officer, Gilbert Hospital, Gilbert, AZ, p. A29

HARGIS, Chris, Manager Finance, Alta View Hospital, Sandy, UT, p. A661

HARGRAVE, Dallas, Human Resources Director, Bartlett Regional Hospital, Juneau, AK, p. A26

HARGRAVE, David, Chief Information Officer, Ward Memorial Hospital, Monahans, TX, p. A634

HARGRAVE–THOMAS, Anne, Chief Executive Officer, Oakleaf Surgical Hospital, Eau Claire, WI, p. A701

HARGRODER, Ty M.D., Chief of Staff, Acadia–St. Landry Hospital, Church Point, LA, p. A273

HARGROVE, Ben, Human Resources Director, Lifestream Behavioral Center, Leesburg, FL, p. A131

HARGROVE, Jeno R.N., Director of Nursing, Columbus Community Hospital, Columbus, TX, p. A602

HARGROVE, Tressa B, Director Human Resources, Jackson Purchase Medical Center, Mayfield, KY, p. A264

HARIHARAN, Parma M.D., Chief of Staff, Mercy Health – Clermont Hospital, Batavia, OH, p. A480

HARKER, Jodie, Director Human Resources, Van Diest Medical Center, Webster City, IA, p. A236

HARKEY, FACHE, Shirley S R.N., Vice President, Patient Services, Wayne Memorial Hospital, Goldsboro, NC, p. A463

HARKINS, Shelly M.D., Chief Medical Officer, Hshs St. Elizabeth's Hospital, Belleville, IL, p. A178

HARKLEROAD, Rod, R.N., Chief Executive Officer, Haywood Regional Medical Center, Clyde, NC, p. A460

HARKNESS, Charles D.O., Vice President Medical Affairs, Southeast Alabama Medical Center, Dothan, AL, p. A17

HARLAN, Kevin W., President, Joint Township District Memorial Hospital, Saint Marys, OH, p. A498

HARLAN, Thomas P., Chief Executive Officer, Continuecare Hospital At Palmetto Health Baptist, Columbia, SC, p. A560

HARLE, Connie, Chief Nursing Officer, Range Regional Health Services, Hibbing, MN, p. A341

HARLESS, Andrea, Director Information Services, Wythe County Community Hospital, Wytheville, VA, p. A677

HARLESS, Cheryl, Chief Nursing Officer, Doctors Medical Center Of Modesto, Modesto, CA, p. A74

HARLIN, Tim M.D., Chief Operations Officer, Denver Health, Denver, CO, p. A100

HARLING, Roxanne, Chief Nursing Officer, Abraham Lincoln Memorial Hospital, Lincoln, IL, p. A192

HARLOVIC, Michael, R.N., President and Chief Executive Officer, Oswego Hospital, Oswego, NY, p. A449

HARLOW, Donald, Director of Information Services, Mountainview Regional Medical Center, Las Cruces, NM, p. A427

HARLOW, Tammy
  Chief Nurse Executive, Riverview Regional Medical Center, Gadsden, AL, p. A18
  Director of Nursing, Grady General Hospital, Cairo, GA, p. A153

HARLOW, Thomas R., FACHE, President, Wellspan Good Samaritan Hospital, Lebanon, PA, p. A539

HARLOWE, Michael, President and Chief Executive Officer, Indiana University Health Tipton Hospital, Tipton, IN, p. A220

HARMAN, Kenneth, Chief Executive Officer, Pioneers Medical Center, Meeker, CO, p. A106

HARMAN, Kimberly, Regional Manager Human Resources, Western State Hospital, Staunton, VA, p. A676

HARMON, Amy, Chief Financial Officer, Elkview General Hospital, Hobart, OK, p. A508

HARMON, Clifford K., Chief Executive Officer, Harrison Community Hospital, Cadiz, OH, p. A482

HARMON, Connie, Director of Nursing, Lakeland Hospital, Watervliet, Watervliet, MI, p. A333

HARMON, David D.O., Vice President Medical Services, Rivervalley Behavioral Health Hospital, Owensboro, KY, p. A265

HARMON, James
  Information Technology, Cypress Creek Hospital, Houston, TX, p. A620
  Network Administrator, West Oaks Hospital, Houston, TX, p. A624

HARMON, Jennifer, Director of Human Resources, St. Cloud Regional Medical Center, Saint Cloud, FL, p. A141

HARMON, Thomas M.D., Vice President Medical Affairs, Ohiohealth Riverside Methodist Hospital, Columbus, OH, p. A488

HARMOND, Joshua, Assistant Chief Financial Officer, Physicians' Specialty Hospital, Fayetteville, AR, p. A42

HARMS, Arlene, Chief Executive Officer, Rio Grande Hospital, Del Norte, CO, p. A100

HARMS, George
  Chief Financial Officer, Hays Medical Center, Hays, KS, p. A242
  Chief Financial Officer, Pawnee Valley Community Hospital, Larned, KS, p. A245

HARNED, Barbara R.N., MSN, Chief Nursing Officer, Monroe County Hospital, Monroeville, AL, p. A21

HARNESS, Phil, Chief Executive Officer, Doctor's Hospital, Leawood, KS, p. A245

HARNEY, Geraldine, Chief Financial Officer, U.S. Public Health Service Phoenix Indian Medical Center, Phoenix, AZ, p. A34

HARNING, Richard, Vice President Finance and Chief Financial Officer, Allegan General Hospital, Allegan, MI, p. A314

HARPE, Michael, Vice President Human Resources, Community Hospital Of Anderson & Madison County, Anderson, IN, p. A203

HARPER, Cindy, Manager Patient Data, Westfield Memorial Hospital, Westfield, NY, p. A456

HARPER, Corwin N
  Senior Vice President and Area Manager, Kaiser Permanente Manteca Medical Center, Manteca, CA, p. A73
  Senior Vice President and Area Manager, Kaiser Permanente Vallejo Medical Center, Vallejo, CA, p. A95
  Administrator, Kaiser Permanente Manteca Medical Center, Manteca, CA, p. A73
  Senior Vice President and Area Manager, Kaiser Permanente Manteca Medical Center, Manteca, CA, p. A73

HARPER, Corwin N.
  Senior Vice President and Area Manager, Kaiser Permanente Manteca Medical Center, Manteca, CA, p. B71
  Senior Vice President and Area Manager, Kaiser Permanente Vallejo Medical Center, Vallejo, CA, p. B71

HARPER, David
  Chief Information Officer, Wills Memorial Hospital, Washington, GA, p. A167
  Director, Site Information Systems, Advocate Eureka Hospital, Eureka, IL, p. A187

HARPER, Eric, Chief Information Officer, Southeastern Health, Lumberton, NC, p. A466

HARPER, Heather L., FACHE, Chief Executive Officer, Lovelace Regional Hospital – Roswell, Roswell, NM, p. A428

HARPER, James F, Senior Vice President and Chief Human Resources Officer, Tidelands Georgetown Memorial Hospital, Georgetown, SC, p. A562

HARPER, Kirk R.N., Vice President, Nursing, Kadlec Regional Medical Center, Richland, WA, p. A684

HARPER, R Andrew M.D., Medical Director, University Of Texas Harris County Psychiatric Center, Houston, TX, p. A623

HARPER, Wally G, Vice President Human Resources, Gaylord Hospital, Wallingford, CT, p. A113

HARPER, William F M.D., Chief of Staff, Birmingham Veterans Affairs Medical Center, Birmingham, AL, p. A14

HARPER–O'CONNOR, Paul
  Interim Administrator, Lanai Community Hospital, Lanai City, HI, p. A170
  Interim Regional Administrator, Kula Hospital, Kula, HI, p. A170

HARR, Donald, Controller, Ray County Memorial Hospital, Richmond, MO, p. A375

HARREL, Mark, Chief Executive Officer, Phelps Memorial Health Center, Holdrege, NE, p. A394

HARRELL, Aaron, Director, Grove Hill Memorial Hospital, Grove Hill, AL, p. A19

HARRELL, Joy R.N., Chief Nursing Officer, Mimbres Memorial Hospital, Deming, NM, p. A426

HARRELL, Michael
  Chief Executive Officer, Promise Hospital Of Miss Lou, Vidalia, LA, p. A287
  Chief Executive Officer, Promise Hospital Of Vicksburg, Vicksburg, MS, p. A362

HARRELL, Paula, Chief Nursing Officer, Regional One Health Extended Care Hospital, Memphis, TN, p. A585

HARRELL, Steven W FACHE, Chief Operating Officer, Florida Hospital New Smyrna, New Smyrna Beach, FL, p. A135

HARRELL, Thomas, M.D., Commander, U.S. Air Force Medical Center Keesler, Keesler Afb, MS, p. A357

HARRELSON, Rick M.D., President Medical Staff, Medical Center Enterprise, Enterprise, AL, p. A17

HARRIER, Margie MSN, R.N., Medical Center Chief Operations Officer, Kaiser Permanente Orange County Anaheim Medical Center, Anaheim, CA, p. A51

HARRIGER, Richard, Director of Emergency Services, Kimball Health Services, Kimball, NE, p. A394

HARRILSON, Annette, Chief Clinical Officer, Select Specialty Hospital Midtown Atlanta, Atlanta, GA, p. A151

HARRINGTON, Dawn, Chief Information Officer, University Of New Mexico Hospitals, Albuquerque, NM, p. A425

HARRINGTON, Hal, Vice President Human Resources, Merit Health River Region, Vicksburg, MS, p. A362

HARRINGTON, Jason, FACHE, President and Chief Executive Officer, Lakes Regional Healthcare, Spirit Lake, IA, p. A235

HARRINGTON, Jeff, Chief Financial Officer, Children's Hospital Colorado, Aurora, CO, p. A98

HARRINGTON, Kathleen, Vice President Human Resources, Beth Israel Deaconess Hospital–Milton, Milton, MA, p. A309

HARRIS, Alicia, Director Fiscal Services, Mississippi State Hospital, Whitfield, MS, p. A363

HARRIS, Allen M.D., Clinical Director, South Mississippi State Hospital, Purvis, MS, p. A361

HARRIS, Andrew E., Chief Executive Officer, Blue Mountain Hospital, Lehighton, PA, p. A539

HARRIS, Andrew E, Chief Executive Officer, Blue Mountain Hospital, Lehighton, PA, p. A539

HARRIS, Betty J, Director Human Resources, Southern California Hospital At Culver City, Culver City, CA, p. A57

HARRIS, Burt
  Acting Chief Executive Officer, Canyon Ridge Hospital, Chino, CA, p. A55
  Chief Financial Officer, Canyon Ridge Hospital, Chino, CA, p. A55

HARRIS, C Martin, M.D.
  Chief Information Officer, Cleveland Clinic Children's Hospital For Rehabilitation, Cleveland, OH, p. A485
  Chief Information Officer, Cleveland Clinic Fairview Hospital, Cleveland, OH, p. A485
  Chief Information Officer, Cleveland Clinic, Cleveland, OH, p. A485
  Chief Information Officer, Lutheran Hospital, Cleveland, OH, p. A486

HARRIS, David, Director Information Systems, De Queen Medical Center, De Queen, AR, p. A42

HARRIS, Denise H. R.N., MSN, Chief Nursing Officer, Baptist Health South Florida, West Kendall Baptist Hospital, Miami, FL, p. A132

HARVERY, Paul, President and Chief Executive Officer, Christus Mother Frances Hospital – Sulphur Springs, Sulphur Springs, TX, p. A647

HARVEY, Alice, Director of Nursing, Heatherhill Care Communities, Chardon, OH, p. A483

HARVEY, Anne MSN, Chief Nursing Officer, El Paso Specialty Hospital, El Paso, TX, p. A611

HARVEY, Jennifer, Director Human Resources, Golden Plains Community Hospital, Borger, TX, p. A598

HARVEY, John
Chief Executive Officer, Oklahoma Heart Hospital, Oklahoma City, OK, p. A513
Chief Executive Officer, Oklahoma Heart Hospital South Campus, Oklahoma City, OK, p. A513

HARVEY, John, M.D., Chief Executive Officer, Oklahoma Heart Hospital, Oklahoma City, OK, p. A513

HARVEY, Kathy D.O., Chief Medical Officer, Logan Regional Medical Center, Logan, WV, p. A693

HARVEY, Kevin, Chief Financial Officer, Mckenzie Regional Hospital, Mckenzie, TN, p. A584

HARVEY, Linda, Chief Financial Officer, West Feliciana Parish Hospital, Saint Francisville, LA, p. A285

HARVEY, Michael, FACHE, President and Chief Executive Officer, Community Memorial Hospital, Syracuse, NE, p. A400

HARVILL, Brian
Vice President Financial Services, Vidant Bertie Hospital, Windsor, NC, p. A473
Vice President Financial Services, Vidant Chowan Hospital, Edenton, NC, p. A462

HARVIN, Schley, Information Technology Technician, Hood Memorial Hospital, Amite, LA, p. A270

HASBROUCK, Matthew Steven, Chief Operating Officer, Fairview Park Hospital, Dublin, GA, p. A157

HASELTON, David, Chief Medical Officer, Riverton Hospital, Riverton, UT, p. A659

HASHMI, Faraz, Chief Executive Officer, Texas General Hospital – Van Zandt Regional Medical Center, Grand Saline, TX, p. A617

HASHMI, Mubashir, Chief Information Officer, Pacifica Hospital Of The Valley, Los Angeles, CA, p. A70

HASHMI, Suleman, President and Chief Executive Officer, Texas General Hospital, Grand Prairie, TX, p. A617

HASKELL, Jeffrey M.D., Chief Medical Staff, Lost Rivers Medical Center, Arco, ID, p. A171

HASKINS, Don, Administrative Director Human Resources, Southwest Mississippi Regional Medical Center, Mccomb, MS, p. A358

HASLETT, Tom, Interim Chief Information Officer, Macneal Hospital, Berwyn, IL, p. A178

HASNI, Kamran M.D., Chief of Medical Staff, Barbourville Arh Hospital, Barbourville, KY, p. A255

HASS, Roxanne, Director of Nursing, Chi St. Joseph Health Madison Hospital, Madisonville, TX, p. A631

HASSAN, Tariq M.D., Associate Director of Patient Care, Captain James A. Lovell Federal Health Care Center, North Chicago, IL, p. A195

HASSANI, Dahlia, Vice President of Medical Affairs, Baylor All Saints Medical Center At Fort Worth, Fort Worth, TX, p. A613

HASSELBRACK, Jeni, Director Human Resources, Gordon Hospital, Calhoun, GA, p. A153

HAST, Anne S., R.N., Chief Executive Officer, Advanced Surgical Hospital, Washington, PA, p. A552

HAST, Anne S R.N., Director of Nursing, Advanced Surgical Hospital, Washington, PA, p. A552

HASTIN, Kathy, Administrative Assistant Human Resources, River Valley Medical Center, Dardanelle, AR, p. A42

HASTINGS, Clare R.N., Ph.D., Chief Nurse Officer, National Institutes Of Health Clinical Center, Bethesda, MD, p. A297

HASTINGS, Sarah M, Executive Director, Ridgeview Medical Center, Waconia, MN, p. A350

HASTINGS–SMITH, Julie, Associate Chief Financial Officer, Abrazo Maryvale Campus, Phoenix, AZ, p. A32

HATCH, Brooke, Director Human Resource, Bradley County Medical Center, Warren, AR, p. A50

HATCH, Tammy, Manager, Sebasticook Valley Health, Pittsfield, ME, p. A292

HATCHER, Amy, Chief Financial Officer, Children's Hospital And Medical Center, Omaha, NE, p. A397

HATCHER, Cole E., Chief Executive Officer, Weatherford Rehabilitation Hospital, Weatherford, TX, p. A653

HATCHER, Julie, Vice President Human Resources, O'Connor Hospital, San Jose, CA, p. A88

HATCHES, Ann
Director, Human Resources, Holy Cross Hospital, Chicago, IL, p. A181
Interim Director Human Resources, Mount Sinai Hospital, Chicago, IL, p. A182

HATFIELD, Chad, Chief Executive Officer, Northeast Georgia Medical Center Barrow, Winder, GA, p. A167

HATFIELD, Jonathan, Supervisor Information Technology, Klickitat Valley Health, Goldendale, WA, p. A681

HATFIELD, Timothy A., Community Chief Executive Officer, Tug Valley Arh Regional Medical Center, South Williamson, KY, p. A267

HATHAWAY, William M.D., Chief Medical Officer, Mission Hospital, Asheville, NC, p. A457

HATHCOCK, Claudette
Administrative Director Human Resources, University Of Mississippi Medical Center Grenada, Grenada, MS, p. A355
Human Resources Director, University Of Mississippi Medical Center Holmes County, Lexington, MS, p. A358

HATIRAS, Spiros, FACHE, President and Chief Executive Officer, Holyoke Medical Center, Holyoke, MA, p. A307

HATLESTAD, Jill, Vice President Human Resources and Marketing, Glencoe Regional Health Services, Glencoe, MN, p. A340

HATTERER–HOAG, Dawn, Director Human Resources, Psychiatric Institute Of Washington, Washington, DC, p. A118

HATTON, Tad
Chief Operating Officer, St. David's Round Rock Medical Center, Round Rock, TX, p. A641
Vice President Chief Operating Officer, Seton Medical Center Austin, Austin, TX, p. A595

HAUBL, Eileen, Senior Vice President and Chief Financial Officer, Mission Hospital, Mission Viejo, CA, p. A74

HAUG, Darin L., President and Chief Executive Officer, Fitzgibbon Hospital, Marshall, MO, p. A373

HAUGE, Meri R.N., MSN, Associate Director of Patient Care Services and Nurse Executive, St. Cloud Veterans Affairs Health Care System, Saint Cloud, MN, p. A347

HAUGER, Clint, Chief Executive Officer, Palmetto Lowcountry Behavioral Health, Charleston, SC, p. A559

HAUGH, William, Administrator, Georgetown Community Hospital, Georgetown, KY, p. A258

HAUGHEY, Tracie
Chief Executive Officer and Chief Financial Officer, Wills Memorial Hospital, Washington, GA, p. A167
Chief Executive Officer and Chief Financial Officer, Wills Memorial Hospital, Washington, GA, p. A167

HAULER, Jennifer, D.O.
Chief Medical Officer, Good Samaritan Hospital, Dayton, OH, p. A489
Chief Medical Officer, Upper Valley Medical Center, Troy, OH, p. A501

HAUN, Richard, Chief Financial Officer, Wuesthoff Medical Center – Rockledge, Rockledge, FL, p. A141

HAUPERT, John M., FACHE, Chief Executive Officer, Grady Memorial Hospital, Atlanta, GA, p. A150

HAUPT, Carolyn, Chief Financial Officer, Peacehealth United General Medical Center, Sedro——Woolley, WA, p. A686

HAUPT, William, Administrator, Florida Hospital, Orlando, FL, p. A137

HAUSAUER, Patricia K, Director Finance, Baptist Medical Center Nassau, Fernandina Beach, FL, p. A124

HAUSE, Eileen, Chief Executive Officer, Kensington Hospital, Philadelphia, PA, p. A544

HAUSER, Mark J M.D., Chief Medical Officer, Baptist Health South Florida, Baptist Hospital Of Miami, Miami, FL, p. A132

HAUSER, Megan, Director Human Resources, Shriners Hospitals For Children–Philadelphia, Philadelphia, PA, p. A545

HAUSHALTER, Brandon, Chief Executive Officer, Kendall Regional Medical Center, Miami, FL, p. A133

HAUSHALTER, Richard L, Senior Vice President Operations and Chief Operating Officer, Sentara Rmh Medical Center, Harrisonburg, VA, p. A668

HAUSMANN, Jena, President and Chief Executive Officer, Children's Hospital Colorado, Aurora, CO, p. A98

HAUSMANN, Sherry
President, Via Christi Hospital On St. Francis, Wichita, KS, p. A254
President, Via Christi Rehabilitation Hospital, Wichita, KS, p. A254

HAUSWIRTH, Michael
Chief Executive Officer, Aspirus Keweenaw Hospital, Inc., Laurium, MI, p. A325
Chief Executive Officer, Aspirus Ontonagon Hospital, Inc., Ontonagon, MI, p. A327

HAUSWIRTH, Renay, Chief Financial Officer, Palo Alto County Health System, Emmetsburg, IA, p. A227

HAVARD, Greg, Chief Executive Officer, George Regional Hospital, Lucedale, MS, p. A358

HAVEN, Adrian C, Site Manager, Gallup Indian Medical Center, Gallup, NM, p. A426

HAVENS, Jennifer, Chief Executive Officer and Director of Nursing Operations, Grundy County Memorial Hospital, Grundy Center, IA, p. A228

HAVERSTOCK, Loren, Manager Human Resources, Harrison County Hospital, Corydon, IN, p. A206

HAVRILLA, David A, Chief Financial Officer, Medstar Montgomery Medical Center, Olney, MD, p. A300

HAWIG, Scott
Senior Vice President Finance, Chief Financial Officer and Treasurer, Froedtert Memorial Lutheran Hospital, Milwaukee, WI, p. A708
Senior Vice President of Finance, Chief Financial Officer and Treasurer, Community Memorial Hospital, Menomonee Falls, WI, p. A706
Senior Vice President of Finance, Chief Financial Officer and Treasurer, St. Joseph's Hospital, West Bend, WI, p. A715

HAWK, Kevin, Chief Executive Officer, Hillcrest Hospital Cushing, Cushing, OK, p. A506

HAWKEY, Tammy, Manager Information Technology Client Services, Ministry Saint Clare's Hospital, Weston, WI, p. A715

HAWKINS, Bryan, Controller, Firsthealth Montgomery Memorial Hospital, Troy, NC, p. A472

HAWKINS, Ellis, President, SSM Health St. Clare Hospital – Fenton, Fenton, MO, p. A368

HAWKINS, Hillary M.D., Medical Director, Sheltering Arms Rehabilitation Hospital, Mechanicsville, VA, p. A670

HAWKINS, Jason F., President and Chief Executive Officer, Fulton County Medical Center, Mc Connellsburg, PA, p. A540

HAWKINS, Kidada, Chief Executive Officer, Shoals Hospital, Muscle Shoals, AL, p. A22

HAWKINS, Sheri, Chief Nursing Officer, Shawnee Mission Medical Center, Shawnee Mission, KS, p. A252

HAWKINS, Tami R.N., MSN, Vice President Patient Care and Chief Nursing Officer, Texas Health Presbyterian Hospital Of Rockwall, Rockwall, TX, p. A640

HAWKINSON, Curtis R., Chief Executive Officer, Community Memorial Healthcare, Marysville, KS, p. A246

HAWLEY, Claudia, Director Human Resources, Mason General Hospital, Shelton, WA, p. A686

HAWLEY, Jason, Manager Information Services, Yuma District Hospital, Yuma, CO, p. A108

HAWLEY, William, President and Chief Executive Officer, Fawcett Memorial Hospital, Port Charlotte, FL, p. A140

HAWLIK, Teresa MSN, Chief Nurse Executive, Nebraska Spine Hospital, Omaha, NE, p. A398

HAWTHORNE, Kimberly, Administrator, Mayo Clinic Health System – Franciscan Healthcare In Sparta, Sparta, WI, p. A712

HAWTOF, Jeffrey M.D., Vice President Medical Operations and Informatics, Beebe Healthcare, Lewes, DE, p. A115

HAYDEN, Crystal MSN, R.N., Senior Vice President and Chief Nursing Officer, Nash Health Care Systems, Rocky Mount, NC, p. A469

HAYDEN, James M.D., Chief Medical Officer, J. C. Blair Memorial Hospital, Huntingdon, PA, p. A536

HAYDEN, Jamie, Chief Financial Officer, Eastland Memorial Hospital, Eastland, TX, p. A609

HAYDEN, John
Senior Vice President and Chief Human Resources Officer, Bronson Lakeview Hospital, Paw Paw, MI, p. A327
Senior Vice President and Human Resources Officer, Bronson Battle Creek, Battle Creek, MI, p. A315
Vice President and Chief Human Resources Officer, Bronson Methodist Hospital, Kalamazoo, MI, p. A324

HAYDEN, Karen, Director Health Information Services, Performance Improvement and Risk Management, Valle Vista Hospital, Greenwood, IN, p. A209

HAYDEN–PUGH, Beverly P. R.N., Senior Vice President and Chief Nursing Officer, Valley Children's Healthcare, Madera, CA, p. A72

HAYEK, Anthony D.O., Medical Director, Edwin Shaw Rehab, Cuyahoga Falls, OH, p. A488

HAYES, Audimarie R.N., Chief Nursing Officer, North Texas Medical Center, Gainesville, TX, p. A615

HAYES, Cheryl, Vice President Patient Care Services, Kenmore Mercy Hospital, Kenmore, NY, p. A438

HAYES, David R, Chief Financial Officer, T.J. Health Columbia, Columbia, KY, p. A256

HAYES, Deborah Marie R.N., MS, Chief Hospital Officer and Chief Nursing Officer, Christ Hospital, Cincinnati, OH, p. A483

HAYES, Di, Chief Executive Officer, Hallmark Youthcare – Richmond, Richmond, VA, p. A674

HAYES, Donna, Controller, Decatur County General Hospital, Parsons, TN, p. A588

HAYES, Elaine, Controller, Sts. Mary & Elizabeth Hospital, Louisville, KY, p. A263

HAYES, Elizabeth, R.N., Interim Administrator, Blowing Rock Rehabilitation & Davant Extended Care Center, Blowing Rock, NC, p. B10

HAYES, Farrell, Chief Financial Officer, Cornerstone Medical Center, Fort Oglethorpe, GA, p. A158

HAYES, James L, Director Human Resources, Western State Hospital, Hopkinsville, KY, p. A260

HAYES, Jo, Chief Nursing Officer, Horn Memorial Hospital, Ida Grove, IA, p. A229

HAYES, June, Chief Financial Officer, Harrisburg Medical Center, Harrisburg, IL, p. A189

HAYES, Kathe, Executive Director, Western New York Children's Hospital Psychiatric Center, West Seneca, NY, p. A455

HAYES, Kelly, Chief Financial Officer, Methodist Hospital For Surgery, Addison, TX, p. A591

HAYES, Kevin M.D., Chief of Staff, Pioneer Community Hospital Of Aberdeen, Aberdeen, MS, p. A352

HAYES, Lisa G., Chief Clinical Officer, AMG Specialty Hospital – Muncie, Muncie, IN, p. A216

HAYES, Paul, R.N., Executive Director, Uw Medicine/ Harborview Medical Center, Seattle, WA, p. A685

HAYES, Sharon, Chief Executive Officer, Palms Of Pasadena Hospital, Saint Petersburg, FL, p. A141

HAYES, Stacy R.N., Chief Nursing Officer, Arizona Spine And Joint Hospital, Mesa, AZ, p. A31

HAYES, Susan, Director Human Resources, Southeastern Health, Lumberton, NC, p. A466

HAYES, Tammy A. R.N., MS, Chief Nurse Executive and Long Term Care Administrator, Northfield Hospital, Northfield, MN, p. A345

HAYES, Thomas P., Chief Executive Officer, Eastern Plumas Health Care, Portola, CA, p. A80

HAYES, Warren, Chief of Staff, Montgomery County Memorial Hospital, Red Oak, IA, p. A234

HAYES, William M., Chief Executive Officer, Northside Hospital–Cherokee, Canton, GA, p. A153

HAYGOOD, Rachel Joy, Director Information Technology, Tyler County Hospital, Woodville, TX, p. A655

HAYHURST, Leslie, Director Information Systems, Washington Health System Greene, Waynesburg, PA, p. A553

HAYMAN, Judy A., Ph.D., Interim Director, Syracuse Veterans Affairs Medical Center, Syracuse, NY, p. A453

HAYMON, Beverly, Chief Financial Officer, Princeton Baptist Medical Center, Birmingham, AL, p. A15

HAYN, Jed, Chief Information Officer, Walter B. Jones Alcohol And Drug Abuse Treatment Center, Greenville, NC, p. A464

HAYNES, Apryl, R.N., Vice President, Chief Operating Officer, Administrator, Seton Edgar B. Davis Hospital, Luling, TX, p. A631

HAYNES, Deatosha D., Interim Associates Director for Patient, Veterans Affairs Gulf Coast Veterans Health Care System, Biloxi, MS, p. A352

HAYNES, Elaine S R.N., MSN, Vice President Patient Services and Chief Nursing Executive, Carolinas Healthcare System Lincoln, Lincolnton, NC, p. A466

HAYNES, Jamil, Regional Director Human Resources, Integris Miami Hospital, Miami, OK, p. A510

HAYNES, Jill, Financial Coach, Bath Veterans Affairs Medical Center, Bath, NY, p. A431

HAYNES, John H M.D., Jr, Chief of Medical Staff, North Caddo Medical Center, Vivian, LA, p. A287

HAYNES, Laurie, Chief Financial Officer, Gulf Coast Medical Center, Panama City, FL, p. A138

HAYNES, Mark M.D., Chief of Staff, Claiborne Memorial Medical Center, Homer, LA, p. A276

HAYNES, Robert Gerard., FACHE, Chief Executive Officer, Guadalupe Regional Medical Center, Seguin, TX, p. A644

HAYNES, William, Director Information Technology, Central Louisiana State Hospital, Pineville, LA, p. A284

HAYS, Cheryl M., FACHE, Administrator and Chief Operating Officer, Marshall Medical Center North, Guntersville, AL, p. A19

HAYS, Cheryl M FACHE, Administrator and Chief Operating Officer, Marshall Medical Center North, Guntersville, AL, p. A19

HAYS, Chuck, President and Chief Executive Officer, Mainegeneral Medical Center, Augusta, ME, p. A289

HAYS, Harry, Chief Executive Officer, Carroll County Memorial Hospital, Carrollton, KY, p. A256

HAYS, Larry, Director Information Technology, Southern Virginia Mental Health Institute, Danville, VA, p. A666

HAYS, Richard O, Chief Fiscal Service, Veterans Affairs Southern Nevada Healthcare System, North Las Vegas, NV, p. A405

HAYS, Richard M.D., Chief Medical Officer, Wellington Regional Medical Center, Wellington, FL, p. A147

HAYS, Timothy A, Vice President Human Resources, Johnston Health, Smithfield, NC, p. A470

HAYTAIAN, Mike, Head Director Information Resources Management, Naval Hospital Jacksonville, Jacksonville, FL, p. A128

HAYWARD, Ernest M.D., Chief of Staff, Saddleback Memorial Medical Center, Laguna Hills, CA, p. A65

HAYWOOD, Nancy
Chief Financial Officer, Genesys Regional Medical Center, Grand Blanc, MI, p. A320
Chief Financial Officer, St. Mary's Of Michigan, Saginaw, MI, p. A330

HAYWOOD, Stephanie, Director Human Resources, Southern Virginia Mental Health Institute, Danville, VA, p. A666

HAZELBAKER, Matthew M.D., President Medical Staff, Memorial Health, Marysville, OH, p. A495

HEAD, David M.D., Chief Medical Staff, Norton Sound Regional Hospital, Nome, AK, p. A26

HEAD, Susan, Director Nursing Services, U.S. Public Health Service Blackfeet Community Hospital, Saint Mary, MT, p. A388

HEADLAND, Mark, Chief Information Officer, Choc Children's At Mission Hospital, Mission Viejo, CA, p. A73

HEADLEY, Kim R.N., Chief Nursing Officer, Healthsouth Rehabilitation Hospital Of Montgomery, Montgomery, AL, p. A21

HEALY, John, Manager Information Technology, Friends Hospital, Philadelphia, PA, p. A544

HEALY–COLLIER, Kathy, Chief Operating Officer, Brookwood Baptist Medical Center, Birmingham, AL, p. A14

HEARD, Alex M.D., Chief Medical Officer, Falmouth Hospital, Falmouth, MA, p. A306

HEARD, Heather, Director Human Resources, Holdenville General Hospital, Holdenville, OK, p. A508

HEARD, John E., Chief Executive Officer, Mcgehee–Desha County Hospital, Mcgehee, AR, p. A47

HEARD, M Denise, Director Business Services, North Mississippi Medical Center–Pontotoc, Pontotoc, MS, p. A360

HEARING, Ava, Chief Nursing Officer, Atrium Medical Center, Stafford, TX, p. A646

HEARING, Tim, Associate Information Technology Director, Raulerson Hospital, Okeechobee, FL, p. A136

HEARNE, Diane, Director Human Resources, Arizona Spine And Joint Hospital, Mesa, AZ, p. A31

HEARNSBERGER, John M.D., Chief of Staff, Howard Memorial Hospital, Nashville, AR, p. A47

HEATER, Floyd, President and Chief Executive Officer, Warren Memorial Hospital, Front Royal, VA, p. A668

HEATH, Ed, FACHE, Chief Executive Officer, Owensboro Health Muhlenberg Community Hospital, Greenville, KY, p. A259

HEATH, Lisa M.D., President Medical Staff, Saint Luke's South Hospital, Overland Park, KS, p. A249

HEATH, Megan, Chief Nursing Officer, Gordon Memorial Health Services, Gordon, NE, p. A393

HEATH, Merry, Chief Nursing Officer, Piedmont Fayette Hospital, Fayetteville, GA, p. A157

HEATH, Susan R.N., Senior Vice President and Chief Nursing Officer, Seattle Children's Hospital, Seattle, WA, p. A685

HEATH, William, Chief Executive Officer, Regency Hospital Of Hattiesburg, Hattiesburg, MS, p. A356

HEATHERLY, John, Assistant Administrator Support Services, Hunt Regional Medical Center, Greenville, TX, p. A617

HEATHERLY, Neil, Chief Executive Officer, Parkwest Medical Center, Knoxville, TN, p. A582

HEATHERLY, Steve
Chief Executive Officer, Harris Regional Hospital, Sylva, NC, p. A471
Chief Executive Officer, Swain Community Hospital, Bryson City, NC, p. A458

HEATHERLY–LLOYD, Sara, Chief Operating Officer, Tennova Healthcare–Lafollette Medical Center, La Follette, TN, p. A582

HEATON, Crystal, Director of Finance, St. Vincent Warrick Hospital, Boonville, IN, p. A204

HEATON, John M.D., Senior Vice President and Medical Director, Children's Hospital, New Orleans, LA, p. A282

HEBBERD, Hilda R.N., MSN, Senior Director Clinical Services, Marlette Regional Hospital, Marlette, MI, p. A325

HEBEL, Barbara, Vice President Human Resources, Doylestown Hospital, Doylestown, PA, p. A533

HEBERT, Bryan, Director Information Systems, The Medical Center Of Southeast Texas, Port Arthur, TX, p. A639

HEBERT, Carol, Director Human Resources, The Medical Center Of Southeast Texas, Port Arthur, TX, p. A639

HEBERT, Gerard, Chief Financial Officer, Texoma Medical Center, Denison, TX, p. A608

HEBERT, Jeff, Interim Vice President Finance, Gifford Medical Center, Randolph, VT, p. A663

HEBERT, Katherine D., Chief Executive Officer, University Hospital And Clinics, Lafayette, LA, p. A279

HEBERT, Rachel, Chief Financial Officer, Heart Hospital Of Lafayette, Lafayette, LA, p. A278

HEBERT, Timothy, Director Human Resources, Teche Regional Medical Center, Morgan City, LA, p. A282

HEBGEN, Lynn, Vice President Nursing, Upland Hills Health, Dodgeville, WI, p. A700

HEBL, James, Regional Vice President, Mayo Clinic Health System In Mankato, Mankato, MN, p. A342

HECHLER, Tracy, Healthcare Director Information Services, Chippenham Hospital, Richmond, VA, p. A674

HECHT, David M.D., Chief of Staff, James H. Quillen Veterans Affairs Medical Center, Mountain Home, TN, p. A586

HECKATHORNE, Daniel R, Chief Financial Officer, Memorial Hospital Of Gardena, Gardena, CA, p. A61

HECKER, Cindy, Executive Director, Uw Medicine/Northwest Hospital & Medical Center, Seattle, WA, p. A686

HECKER, Julie, Vice President, Operations, Upmc Mercy, Pittsburgh, PA, p. A547

HECKER, Lisa, Director Human Resources, Hedrick Medical Center, Chillicothe, MO, p. A366

HECKERMAN, Ray, Chief Executive Officer and Managing Director, Coastal Harbor Treatment Center, Savannah, GA, p. A164

HECKERT, Robert J. Jr, Chief Executive Officer, Gerald Champion Regional Medical Center, Alamogordo, NM, p. A424

HEDBERG, Beth R.N., Director Nursing, Lindsborg Community Hospital, Lindsborg, KS, p. A246

HEDDE, Charles C M.D., Chief Medical Officer, Good Samaritan Hospital, Vincennes, IN, p. A221

HEDDERMAN, Michael, Senior Vice President Finance and Chief Financial Officer, Marianjoy Rehabilitation Hospital, Wheaton, IL, p. A202

HEDGES, David, Chief Financial Officer, Southwestern Regional Medical Center, Tulsa, OK, p. A518

HEDLUND, Chris, Director Information Systems, Community Hospital–Fairfax, Fairfax, MO, p. A368

HEDRIX, Michael D., Administrator and President, Essentia Health Sandstone, Sandstone, MN, p. A348

HEEGAARD, William M.D., Chief Medical Officer, Hennepin County Medical Center, Minneapolis, MN, p. A343

HEEMANN, John, Vice President and Chief Information Officer, Aspire Hospital, Conroe, TX, p. A602

HEFFERNAN, Paul F, Vice President Human Resources, Women & Infants Hospital Of Rhode Island, Providence, RI, p. A557

HEFFERNAN, Rebecca, Director Human Resources, Metrowest Medical Center, Framingham, MA, p. A306

HEFFERS, Margaret, Assistant Vice President Human Resources, Geisinger Wyoming Valley Medical Center, Wilkes Barre, PA, p. A554

HEFFLINGER, Larry, Director Information Systems, Fulton County Health Center, Wauseon, OH, p. A502

HEFLIN, Clyde M.D., Chief Medical Officer, Curahealth Nashville, Nashville, TN, p. A586

HEFNER, Donna J., R.N., President and Chief Executive Officer, Sierra View Medical Center, Porterville, CA, p. A80

HEFNER, Kathy, Chief Nursing Officer, Mcdowell Hospital, Marion, NC, p. A466

HEGGEM, Mark M.D., Chief Medical Officer, Riverwood Healthcare Center, Aitkin, MN, p. A335

HEGGEN, Karra R.N., Vice President Nursing, Elkhart General Hospital, Elkhart, IN, p. A207

HEGGEN, Steve, Administrative Director Human Resources, St. Joseph Hospital, Fort Wayne, IN, p. A208

HEGGER, John, Director Information Systems, Union County Hospital, Anna, IL, p. A177

HEGLAND, Sandra, Chief Executive Officer, Kindred Rehabilitation Hospital Clear Lake, Webster, TX, p. A653

HEGSTROM, Michael T M.D., Chief Medical Officer, Geisinger–Lewistown Hospital, Lewistown, PA, p. A539

HEICHERT, Susan
Chief Information Officer, Mercy Hospital, Coon Rapids, MN, p. A338
Senior Vice President and Chief Information Officer, Abbott Northwestern Hospital, Minneapolis, MN, p. A343
Senior Vice President, United Hospital, Saint Paul, MN, p. A348

HEIDT, Robert, Director Information Systems, Pembina County Memorial Hospital And Wedgewood Manor, Cavalier, ND, p. A474

HEIFNER, Bruce, Chief Financial Officer, Pella Regional Health Center, Pella, IA, p. A233

HEIFNER, Robert A., FACHE, Chief Executive Officer, St. Luke's Sugar Land Hospital, Sugar Land, TX, p. A647

HEIKKINEN, Todd, Manager Sports Medicine and Rehabilitation Services, Orthopaedic Hospital Of Wisconsin – Glendale, Glendale, WI, p. A702

HEILMAN, Brooke, Chief Financial Officer, Bowdle Hospital, Bowdle, SD, p. A568

HEIM, Chad, Management Information System Director, Lifestream Behavioral Center, Leesburg, FL, p. A131

HEIM, Nicole, Chief Information Officer, Milford Regional Medical Center, Milford, MA, p. A309

HEIM, Richard, President, Advocate South Suburban Hospital, Hazel Crest, IL, p. A189

HEIM, Tonya R.N., MSN, Vice President Patient Services and Chief Nursing Officer, Memorial Hospital And Health Care Center, Jasper, IN, p. A212

HEIMALL, Michael S., Director, Walter Reed National Military Medical Center, Bethesda, MD, p. A297

HEIMAN, Thomas, Vice President Information Services and Chief Information Officer, John T. Mather Memorial Hospital, Port Jefferson, NY, p. A450

HEIN, Jodi R.N., Vice President Chief Nurse Executive, St. Mary Medical Center, Long Beach, CA, p. A67

HEINE, Ann, Chief Executive Officer, Surgical Specialty Center Of Baton Rouge, Baton Rouge, LA, p. A271

HEINECK, Susan M.D., President Professional Staff, Providence Seaside Hospital, Seaside, OR, p. A527

HEINEMANN, Don, Administrator and Chief Executive Officer, Blount Memorial Hospital, Maryville, TN, p. A583

HEINEMEIER, Robert, Interim Chief Financial Officer, Sonoma West Medical Center, Sebastopol, CA, p. A91

HEINISCH, Sheri, Compliance Officer, Chi Lisbon Health, Lisbon, ND, p. A477

HEINRICH, Bill, Chief Financial Officer, Florida Hospital Zephyrhills, Zephyrhills, FL, p. A148

HEINRICH, Kerry
  Chief Executive Officer, Loma Linda University Children's Hospital, Loma Linda, CA, p. A66
  Chief Executive Officer, Loma Linda University Medical Center, Loma Linda, CA, p. A66

HEINRICHS, Alice CPA, Chief Financial Officer, Van Diest Medical Center, Webster City, IA, p. A236

HEINS, Patrick, President, Vidant Roanoke–Chowan Hospital, Ahoskie, NC, p. A457

HEINSOHN, Carmel M.D., Medical Director, Bournewood Health Systems, Brookline, MA, p. A305

HEINTZ, Shirley R.N., MS, Vice President Patient Care, Liberty Hospital, Liberty, MO, p. A372

HEINTZELMAN, Gayle R.N., Site Administrator and Chief Nursing Officer, Mercy Health – Clermont Hospital, Batavia, OH, p. A480

HEINZ, Don, Chief Executive Officer, Moundview Memorial Hospital & Clinics, Friendship, WI, p. A702

HEINZE, Kyle, Coordinator Information Technology, Riveredge Hospital, Forest Park, IL, p. A188

HEINZMAN, Jerry, Senior Vice President and Chief Financial Officer, Sampson Regional Medical Center, Clinton, NC, p. A460

HEINZMANN, Bill, Director Human Resources, Texoma Medical Center, Denison, TX, p. A608

HEISE, James, Chief Medical Officer, Door County Medical Center, Sturgeon Bay, WI, p. A713

HEISE, Teresa, Coordinator Management Information Systems, Pender Community Hospital, Pender, NE, p. A399

HEISEL, Diane, Acting Director, Center For Forensic Psychiatry, Saline, MI, p. A330

HEISER, Eric, Chief Information Resource Management, Sioux Falls Veterans Affairs Health Care System, Sioux Falls, SD, p. A573

HEISHMAN, Lisa R.N., Vice President, Shenandoah Memorial Hospital, Woodstock, VA, p. A677

HEISMEYER, Joyce, Chief Operating Officer, Kansas Heart Hospital, Wichita, KS, p. A253

HEISSER, Randy M.D., Medical Director, Kindred Hospital–Chattanooga, Chattanooga, TN, p. A576

HEIT, Ryan, Chief Financial Officer, Northern Nevada Medical Center, Sparks, NV, p. A406

HEITMAN, Susan, Chief Nursing Officer, Winneshiek Medical Center, Decorah, IA, p. A226

HEITMEYER, Paulette, Administrator and Chief Operating Officer, Marina Del Rey Hospital, Marina Del Rey, CA, p. A73

HEITZMAN, Cynthia R.N., Chief Nursing Officer, Seven Rivers Regional Medical Center, Crystal River, FL, p. A122

HELDRETH, Karen, Director Data Processing, Mercy Hospital El Reno, El Reno, OK, p. A507

HELDT, Katie, Chief Nursing Officer, Greene County Medical Center, Jefferson, IA, p. A230

HELFER, Cassandra, Chief Financial Officer, Ralph H. Johnson Veterans Affairs Medical Center, Charleston, SC, p. A559

HELFER, David, FACHE, President, Texas Institute For Surgery At Texas Health Presbyterian Dallas, Dallas, TX, p. A607

HELGERSON, Bryce R., Chief Administrative Officer, Legacy Salmon Creek Medical Center, Vancouver, WA, p. A688

HELGESEN, Roald, Chief Executive Officer, Alaska Native Medical Center, Anchorage, AK, p. A25

HELGESON, Heidi E M.D., Chief Medical Officer, Rio Grande Hospital, Del Norte, CO, p. A100

HELGET, Peggy R.N., MSN, Vice President Patient Services and Chief Nursing Officer, Methodist Jennie Edmundson Hospital, Council Bluffs, IA, p. A225

HELLA, Timothy, Chief Information Officer, Otsego Memorial Hospital, Gaylord, MI, p. A320

HELLAND, Don M.D., Chief Medical Officer, Roosevelt Medical Center, Culbertson, MT, p. A383

HELLE, Dan, Human Resources Officer, Iowa City Veterans Affairs Health Care System, Iowa City, IA, p. A229

HELLELAND, Brian, Chief Executive Officer, St. Jude Medical Center, Fullerton, CA, p. A61

HELLER, Michael, Chief Financial Officer, Corry Memorial Hospital, Corry, PA, p. A532

HELLER, Tom, Vice President Operations and Human Resources, Camden Clark Medical Center, Parkersburg, WV, p. A694

HELLINGER, Jeffrey, Interim Chief Financial Officer, Lewis County General Hospital, Lowville, NY, p. A438

HELLYER, Nancy R., R.N., FACHE, Chief Executive Officer, Christus St. Frances Cabrini Hospital, Alexandria, LA, p. A269

HELM, Carrie, Chief Executive Officer, Arkansas Surgical Hospital, North Little Rock, AR, p. A47

HELM, Pamela E., Executive Director, Devereux Texas Treatment Network, League City, TX, p. A628

HELMER, Richard, M.D., Chief Executive Officer, Mayo Clinic Health System In Eau Claire, Eau Claire, WI, p. A701

HELMS, Candace, Director Information Services, Good Samaritan Medical Center, West Palm Beach, FL, p. A147

HELMS, Ella Raye., Chief Executive Officer, Cogdell Memorial Hospital, Snyder, TX, p. A646

HELMS, James, Vice President Finance, Jones Memorial Hospital, Wellsville, NY, p. A455

HELMS, Joseph, Director Information Systems, Dekalb Regional Medical Center, Fort Payne, AL, p. A18

HELPER, Mark A, Vice President, Chief Financial Officer, Munson Medical Center, Traverse City, MI, p. A332

HELSEL, David S., M.D., Chief Executive Officer, Spring Grove Hospital Center, Baltimore, MD, p. A296

HELSEL, Elizabeth, Chief Executive Officer, U.S. Public Health Service Indian Hospital, Parker, AZ, p. A32

HELSPER, Richard S, Chief Operating Officer, Genesis Healthcare System, Zanesville, OH, p. A503

HELSTROM, James, Chief Medical Officer, Fox Chase Cancer Center–American Oncologic Hospital, Philadelphia, PA, p. A543

HELTON, Deirdre, Director Human Resources, Lakeway Regional Hospital, Morristown, TN, p. A585

HELTON, Fay, Director Medical Records, Red River Hospital, Llc, Wichita Falls, TX, p. A654

HELTON, R.J D.O., Chief of Staff, Coal County General Hospital, Coalgate, OK, p. A506

HELTON, Stephanie, Chief Financial Officer, Weatherford Regional Hospital, Weatherford, OK, p. A519

HELVEY, John, Chief Information Officer, Orchard Hospital, Gridley, CA, p. A62

HELWIG, Kent R., Chief Executive Officer, Select Specialty Hospital – Dallas Garland, Garland, TX, p. A616

HEMATILLAKE, M. Ganga M.D., Chief of Staff, White River Junction Veterans Affairs Medical Center, White River Junction, VT, p. A663

HEMBREE, Greg, Senior Vice President and Chief Financial Officer, St. Francis Hospital, Columbus, GA, p. A155

HEMKER, Debbie, Senior Vice President and Area Manager, Kaiser Permanente Fresno Medical Center, Fresno, CA, p. A61

HEMKER, Robert, President and Chief Executive Officer, Palomar Health, Escondido, CA, p. B96

HEMMER, Chris, Director Finance, Aurora West Allis Medical Center, West Allis, WI, p. A715

HEMMING, Stuart, Chief Operating Officer, Portsmouth Regional Hospital, Portsmouth, NH, p. A410

HEMPEL, Stephen M.D., President Medical Staff, Lakeland Medical Center, St. Joseph, Saint Joseph, MI, p. A330

HEMPHILL, Dana, Manager Human Resources, Shoshone Medical Center, Kellogg, ID, p. A173

HEMPHILL, Robyn, Chief Executive Officer and Chief Nursing Officer, Monroe Surgical Hospital, Monroe, LA, p. A281

HEMPLER, Shannan, Director Human Resources, Norton County Hospital, Norton, KS, p. A247

HEMSATH, Randolph M.D., Medical Director, Suncoast Behavioral Health Center, Bradenton, FL, p. A121

HENDEE, Daniel, Director, Philadelphia Veterans Affairs Medical Center, Philadelphia, PA, p. A545

HENDEL, Dawna R.N., Chief Nursing Officer and Vice President Patient Care Services, Providence Saint John's Health Center, Santa Monica, CA, p. A91

HENDERSHOT, Richard
  Chief Financial Officer, Casey County Hospital, Liberty, KY, p. A262
  Chief Financial Officer, Jane Todd Crawford Hospital, Greensburg, KY, p. A259

HENDERSON, Claudia, Chief Human Resources, St. Elizabeth's Medical Center, Brighton, MA, p. A304

HENDERSON, David K M.D., Deputy Director Clinical Care, National Institutes Of Health Clinical Center, Bethesda, MD, p. A297

HENDERSON, David M, Director Human Resources, Summersville Regional Medical Center, Summersville, WV, p. A696

HENDERSON, Deborah, Acting Chief Financial Officer, Harry S. Truman Memorial Veterans Hospital, Columbia, MO, p. A367

HENDERSON, Donald G.
  President and Chief Executive Officer, Leesburg Regional Medical Center, Leesburg, FL, p. A130
  President and Chief Executive Officer, The Villages Regional Hospital, The Villages, FL, p. A146

HENDERSON, Gary A., Administrator, Carolinas Healthcare System Anson, Wadesboro, NC, p. A472

HENDERSON, Gary, Chief Information Resources Management Services, Huntington Veterans Affairs Medical Center, Huntington, WV, p. A693

HENDERSON, Greg, Interim Administrator, Loma Linda University Medical Center–Murrieta, Murrieta, CA, p. A75

HENDERSON, Jace, Chief Financial Officer, Parkview Hospital, Wheeler, TX, p. A654

HENDERSON, Jessica, Employee Relations Specialist, Fitzgibbon Hospital, Marshall, MO, p. A373

HENDERSON, John, M.D.
  Chief Medical Officer, Unity Health White County Medical Center, Searcy, AR, p. A49
  Chief Executive Officer, Childress Regional Medical Center, Childress, TX, p. A601

HENDERSON, John, Chief Human Resources Management, James H. Quillen Veterans Affairs Medical Center, Mountain Home, TN, p. A586

HENDERSON, John, Vice President and Chief Information Officer, Children's Hospital Of Orange County, Orange, CA, p. A78

HENDERSON, Katherine, President, Seton Medical Center Austin, Austin, TX, p. A595

HENDERSON, Kathy, Director Human Resources, Willow Crest Hospital, Miami, OK, p. A510

HENDERSON, Larry M.D., Medical Director, Greene County Hospital, Leakesville, MS, p. A358

HENDERSON, Lisa, Chief Operations Officer, Palacios Community Medical Center, Palacios, TX, p. A636

HENDERSON, Lori, Chief Nursing Officer, Vice President Clinical, Colorado Canyons Hospital And Medical Center, Fruita, CO, p. A103

HENDERSON, Lorrie, Ph.D., Chief Executive Officer, Huhukam Memorial Hospital, Sacaton, AZ, p. A35

HENDERSON, Melody Ph.D., R.N., Chief Operating Officer and Chief Nursing Officer, Golden Plains Community Hospital, Borger, TX, p. A598

HENDERSON, Mike, Director Human Resources, Forest View Psychiatric Hospital, Grand Rapids, MI, p. A320

HENDERSON, Pamela S, Vice President Human Resources, Memorial Hospital Of Carbondale, Carbondale, IL, p. A179

HENDERSON, Patricia R.N., Vice President Nursing and Clinical Services, Glencoe Regional Health Services, Glencoe, MN, p. A340

HENDERSON, Paula
  Vice President Human Resources, University Of Maryland Medical Center Midtown Campus, Baltimore, MD, p. A296
  Vice President Human Resources, University Of Maryland Rehabilitation & Orthopaedic Institute, Baltimore, MD, p. A296

HENDERSON, Peggy, Director Health Information, Rmc–Stringfellow Memorial Hospital, Anniston, AL, p. A13

HENDERSON, Rex M.D., Chief of Staff, Mcdowell Hospital, Marion, NC, p. A466

HENDERSON, Sue, Human Resource Manager, Smyth County Community Hospital, Marion, VA, p. A670

HENDERSON, Travis M.D., Chief of Staff, Mobridge Regional Hospital, Mobridge, SD, p. A571

HENDERSON, Vickie M.D., Chief Medical Officer, Saint Mary's Regional Medical Center, Russellville, AR, p. A49

HENDERSON, Volante, Director Human Resources, Healthsouth Walton Rehabilitation Hospital, Augusta, GA, p. A151

HENDLER, Robert S M.D., Regional Chief Medical Officer, Baylor Scott & White Medical Center – Centennial, Frisco, TX, p. A615

HENDREN, Karen, Vice President of Finance and Operations, Mercy Hospital Ardmore, Ardmore, OK, p. A504

HENDRICK, Kirk, Director Information Systems, Northside Hospital, Saint Petersburg, FL, p. A141

HENDRICKS, Marcia, R.N., FACHE

HENDRICKSEN, Sherry R.N., MSN, Chief Nursing Officer, Continuecare Hospital At Hendrick Medical Center, Abilene, TX, p. A591

HENDRICKSON, Leslie, Director Human Resources, Coteau Des Prairies Hospital, Sisseton, SD, p. A573

HENDRICKSON, Roman M.D., Medical Director, Ruby Valley Hospital, Sheridan, MT, p. A388

HENDRIX, Angie, Director of Nursing, Evergreen Medical Center, Evergreen, AL, p. A17

HENDRIX, Billie R.N., Director of Nursing, W. J. Mangold Memorial Hospital, Lockney, TX, p. A629

HENDRIX, Jamie, Vice President Patient Care Services, Columbus Community Hospital, Inc., Columbus, WI, p. A700

HENDRIX, Michael A. Jr, Chief Financial Officer, St. Joseph Hospital, Bangor, ME, p. A289

HENDRIX, Michael, Chief Financial Officer, St. Mary's Regional Medical Center, Lewiston, ME, p. A291

HENDRIXSON, Mark M.D., Chief Medical Officer, Tennova Healthcare–Jamestown, Jamestown, TN, p. A580

HENDRY, Christopher M.D., Chief Medical Officer, Medical Center, Navicent Health, Macon, GA, p. A161

HENDRYX, Joel M.D., Chief Medical Officer, University Medical Center Of El Paso, El Paso, TX, p. A612

HENES, Jean M R.N., MSN, RN–B, Director of Nursing, Avera Creighton Hospital, Creighton, NE, p. A392

HENESSEE, Nolan, Vice President and Chief Information Officer, St. Joseph's Hospital, Savannah, GA, p. A165

HENINGER, Bev, Director of Nursing, Kenmare Community Hospital, Kenmare, ND, p. A477

HENKE, Georgia, Operational Account Manager, OSF Saint Anthony's Health Center, Alton, IL, p. A17

HENKE, Mark, Chief Financial Officer, Mena Regional Health System, Mena, AR, p. A47

HENKENIUS, Jim, Chief Financial Officer, Stewart Memorial Community Hospital, Lake City, IA, p. A230

HENLEY, Donald, Vice President Human Resources, Grove City Medical Center, Grove City, PA, p. A535

HENLEY, Grace M, Assistant Administrator Human Resources, Highline Medical Center, Burien, WA, p. A679

HENNEBOLD, Julie R.N., Interim Chief Nursing Officer, Winner Regional Healthcare Center, Winner, SD, p. A574

HENNEMAN, Diane, Chief Executive Officer, Havenwyck Hospital, Auburn Hills, MI, p. A314

HENNENBERG, Shayla, Director Human Resources, Essentia Health Ada, Ada, MN, p. A335

HENNESSEY, Ruth, Executive Vice President and Chief Administrative Officer, St. Francis Hospital, The Heart Center, Roslyn, NY, p. A451

HENNESSY, John, Chief Financial Officer, Bonner General Hospital, Sandpoint, ID, p. A176

HENNIGAN, Michael M.D., Medical Director, Healthsouth Emerald Coast Rehabilitation Hospital, Panama City, FL, p. A138

HENNIKA, Billi Jo, Vice President Operations, Mckenzie Health System, Sandusky, MI, p. A330

HENNING, Cindy R.N., Chief Nursing Officer, Houston Northwest Medical Center, Houston, TX, p. A621

HENNING, William C., Administrator and Chief Executive Officer, Baptist Memorial Hospital–North Mississippi, Oxford, MS, p. A360

HENNIS, Michelle, Administrative Director Financial Services, Grace Hospital, Cleveland, OH, p. A485

HENRICH, Christy, Controller, Kindred Hospital Of Northern Indiana, Mishawaka, IN, p. A216

HENRICI, Michael, Associate Administrator, Roxborough Memorial Hospital, Philadelphia, PA, p. A545

HENRICKS, William Ph.D., Vice President and Chief Operating Officer, Seton Shoal Creek Hospital, Austin, TX, p. A595

HENRY, Aden R.N., Vice President, Patient Care, La Rabida Children's Hospital, Chicago, IL, p. A181

HENRY, Andrea, Director of Nursing, Sweetwater Hospital, Sweetwater, TN, p. A589

HENRY, Anna, Chief Information Officer, Kimble Hospital, Junction, TX, p. A625

HENRY, Chris, Associate Administrator and Chief Financial Officer, Washington Hospital Healthcare System, Fremont, CA, p. A60

HENRY, Dane W., Chief Executive Officer, Lake Regional Health System, Osage Beach, MO, p. A374

HENRY, David, President and Chief Executive Officer, Northern Montana Health Care, Havre, MT, p. A385

HENRY, Donna, Vice President of Nursing Services, Four County Counseling Center, Logansport, IN, p. A215

HENRY, Edwina J, Assistant Chief Nursing Officer, Parkview Regional Hospital, Mexia, TX, p. A633

HENRY, Hannah, Interim Vice President of Human Resources, Emory Johns Creek Hospital, Johns Creek, GA, p. A159

HENRY, Heather, Manager Information Systems, Hammond–Henry Hospital, Geneseo, IL, p. A188

HENRY, Jake Jr, Chief Executive Officer and President, Saint Francis Health System, Saint Francis Hospital, Tulsa, OK, p. A518

HENRY, James L, Director Human Resources, Healthsouth Sea Pines Rehabilitation Hospital, Melbourne, FL, p. A132

HENRY, Joy R.N., Director Nurses, Faith Community Hospital, Jacksboro, TX, p. A625

HENRY, Joyce, Controller, Healthsouth Rehabilitation Hospital Of York, York, PA, p. A555

HENRY, Peter M.D., Chief Medical Officer, Essentia Health St. Joseph's Medical Center, Brainerd, MN, p. A337

HENRY, Roshonda, Chief Nursing Officer, Healthsouth Rehabilitation Hospital Of Cypress, Houston, TX, p. A620

HENRY, Tim, Accountant, Chatuge Regional Hospital And Nursing Home, Hiawassee, GA, p. A159

HENRY, William
Director Human Resources, East Texas Medical Center Henderson, Henderson, TX, p. A618
Director Human Resources, East Texas Medical Center–Quitman, Quitman, TX, p. A639

HENSEL, David, Director Financial Operations, Ohiohealth Grady Memorial Hospital, Delaware, OH, p. A490

HENSEL, Edward, Chief Information Officer, Tomah Veterans Affairs Medical Center, Tomah, WI, p. A714

HENSLEIGH, David, Director Medical Staff, Clay County Hospital, Ashland, AL, p. A13

HENSLEY, Angela, Director of Nursing, Pathways Of Tennessee, Jackson, TN, p. A580

HENSLEY, Anna
Chief Operating Officer, Ohiohealth Dublin Methodist Hospital, Dublin, OH, p. A490
Chief Operating Officer, Ohiohealth Grady Memorial Hospital, Delaware, OH, p. A490

HENSLEY, Barry, Director Information Systems, Logan Regional Medical Center, Logan, WV, p. A693

HENSLEY, Kristy, Director Human Resources, Indiana Orthopaedic Hospital, Indianapolis, IN, p. A211

HENSON, Judith, Vice President Patient Care Services, Southeast Georgia Health System Brunswick Campus, Brunswick, GA, p. A153

HENSON, Lily M.D., Chief Medical Officer, Piedmont Henry Hospital, Stockbridge, GA, p. A165

HENSON, Maureen, Vice President Human Resources, Rapid City Regional Hospital, Rapid City, SD, p. A572

HENSON, Pam, Executive Director, Pathways Of Tennessee, Jackson, TN, p. A580

HENSON, Steve, Chief Executive Officer, Bradley County Medical Center, Warren, AR, p. A50

HENTHORN, Cheryl, Chief Executive Officer, Summa Rehab Hospital, Akron, OH, p. A479

HENTON, Thomas, Chief Executive Officer, Sumner County Hospital District One, Caldwell, KS, p. A239

HENTZEN PAGE, Ann
Medical Director, Summit Surgical, Hutchinson, KS, p. A243
Chief Executive Officer, Summit Surgical, Hutchinson, KS, p. A243

HENZE, Rick, Chief Financial Officer, St. Mary's Healthcare, Amsterdam, NY, p. A430

HEPNER, Tim M.D., Chief Medical Officer, St. John Owasso, Owasso, OK, p. A514

HERALD, Kathleen R, Vice President and Chief Information Officer, Lexington Medical Center, West Columbia, SC, p. A567

HERB, Beth, Administrator, State Correctional Institution At Camp Hill, Camp Hill, PA, p. A531

HERBECK, Marilyn, Coordinator Human Resources, Community Hospital Of Staunton, Staunton, IL, p. A201

HERBEK, Gary J., Chief Executive Officer, Healthsouth Rehabilitation Hospital Of Fredericksburg, Fredericksburg, VA, p. A667

HERBEL, Aaron, Administrator, Mercy Hospital, Moundridge, KS, p. A247

HERBER, Steven
President and Chief Executive Officer, Adventist Health St. Helena, Saint Helena, CA, p. A84
President and Chief Executive Officer, Adventist Health St. Helena, Vallejo, CA, p. A95

HERBERGER, Eva, Administrator Human Resources, Usc Verdugo Hills Hospital, Glendale, CA, p. A62

HERBERT, Daniel M.D., Medical Administrative Officer, Millinocket Regional Hospital, Millinocket, ME, p. A292

HERBERT, Laurie, Vice President Operations, Three Rivers Health, Three Rivers, MI, p. A332

HERBOLD, Charlotte, Manager Business Officer, Garfield County Health Center, Jordan, MT, p. A386

HERBST, Garay, Chief Executive Officer, Kaweah Delta Medical Center, Visalia, CA, p. A96

HERBST, Gary, Senior Vice President and Chief Financial Officer, Kaweah Delta Medical Center, Visalia, CA, p. A96

HERDER, Debbie, Controller, Promise Hospital Of Wichita Falls, Wichita Falls, TX, p. A654

HEREFORD, James, President and Chief Executive Officer, Fairview Health Services, Minneapolis, MN, p. B51

HERFORT, Oliver M.D., Chief Medical Officer, Valley Regional Hospital, Claremont, NH, p. A407

HERGET, Jordan
Chief Operating Officer, Good Samaritan Hospital, San Jose, CA, p. A88
President and Chief Executive Officer, O'Connor Hospital, San Jose, CA, p. A88
President and Chief Executive Officer, Saint Louise Regional Hospital, Gilroy, CA, p. A61

HERING, John M.D., Chief Medical Officer, Centracare Health–Monticello, Monticello, MN, p. A344

HERING, Kristine R.N., Chief Nursing Officer, Speare Memorial Hospital, Plymouth, NH, p. A410

HERINGER, Mark, Interim Director Information Systems, Adventist Health St. Helena, Saint Helena, CA, p. A84

HERINK, Philip, Administrator, Schick Shadel Hospital, Seattle, WA, p. A685

HERLONG, John, Medical Staff President, UNC Lenoir Healthcare, Kinston, NC, p. A465

HERMAN, David C., M.D., Chief Executive Officer, Essentia Health, Duluth, MN, p. B50

HERMAN, Jeff, Chief Executive Officer, Prairie St. John's, Fargo, ND, p. A475

HERMAN, John W.
President, Fairview Lakes Health Services, Wyoming, MN, p. A351
President, Fairview Northland Medical Center, Princeton, MN, p. A346

HERMAN, Michael
Chief Executive Officer, Riverview Regional Medical Center, Carthage, TN, p. A575
Chief Executive Officer, Trousdale Medical Center, Hartsville, TN, p. A579

HERMANN, Terri R.N., Chief Nursing Officer, Franklin Hospital District, Benton, IL, p. A178

HERMES, Dina, Chief Financial Officer, Golden Plains Community Hospital, Borger, TX, p. A598

HERMOSA, Mercy, Director of Information System, Coral Gables Hospital, Coral Gables, FL, p. A122

HERNANDEZ, Ashley, Chief Information Technology Officer, Pender Memorial Hospital, Burgaw, NC, p. A458

HERNANDEZ, Debra T., Vice President, Chief Operation Officer and Chief Nursing Officer, Dell Seton Medical Center At The University Of Texas, Austin, TX, p. A595

HERNANDEZ, Dinorah Esq, Executive Director, Hospital Pavia Yauco, Yauco, PR, p. A727

HERNANDEZ, George B. Jr, President and Chief Executive Officer, University Health System, San Antonio, TX, p. A644

HERNANDEZ, Gloria, Executive Director, University Pediatric Hospital, Rio Piedras, PR, p. A725

HERNANDEZ, Janira, Coordinator Human Resources, Hospital Metropolitano Dr. Susoni, Arecibo, PR, p. A722

HERNANDEZ, Kim, Chief Human Resources Officer, AMG Specialty Hospital–Denham Springs, Denham Springs, LA, p. A274

HERNANDEZ, Kristen, Director Human Resources, Healthsouth Rehabilitation Hospital Of New Mexico, Albuquerque, NM, p. A424

HERNANDEZ, Leonard, Chief Executive Officer, Coffey County Hospital, Burlington, KS, p. A239

HERNANDEZ, Lisa J. R.N., Vice President, Patient Care Continuum and Chief Nursing Officer, Sarah Bush Lincoln Health Center, Mattoon, IL, p. A193

HERNANDEZ, Luis A., Chief Executive Officer, United Medical Center, Washington, DC, p. A118

HERNANDEZ, Luz Maria, Director Human Resources, I. Gonzalez Martinez Oncologic Hospital, Hato Rey, PR, p. A723

HERNANDEZ, Matt, Director of Information Technology and System, Kendall Regional Medical Center, Miami, FL, p. A133

HERNANDEZ, Reyna, Chief Financial Officer, Healthsouth Rehabilitation Hospital Of Miami, Cutler Bay, FL, p. A122

HERNANDEZ, Sandi, Controller, Lafayette General Surgical Hospital, Lafayette, LA, p. A278

HERNANDEZ, Susan
Chief Nurse Executive, University Of Texas Southwestern Medical Center, Dallas, TX, p. A607
Chief Nursing Officer, Rice Medical Center, Eagle Lake, TX, p. A609

HERNANDEZ–KEEBLE, Sonia, Superintendent, Rio Grande State Center/South Texas Health Care System, Harlingen, TX, p. A618

HERNANDEZ–LICHTL, Javier, Chief Executive Officer, Baptist Health South Florida, West Kendall Baptist Hospital, Miami, FL, p. A132

HERNDON, Amy, Chief Finance Officer, Morristown–Hamblen Healthcare System, Morristown, TN, p. A586

HERNDON, David N M.D., Chief of Staff, Shriners Hospitals For Children–Galveston, Galveston, TX, p. A615

HERNDON, Lori, R.N., President and Chief Executive Officer, Atlanticare Regional Medical Center, Atlantic City, NJ, p. A411

HERNDON, Robert Scott
  Chief Financial Officer, Seton Shoal Creek Hospital, Austin, TX, p. A595
  Vice President Chief Financial Officer, Seton Medical Center Austin, Austin, TX, p. A595

HERNDON, Scott
  Chief Financial Officer, Ministry Market Texas, Dell Seton Medical Center At The University Of Texas, Austin, TX, p. A595
  Chief Financial Officer, Texas Market, Seton Northwest Hospital, Austin, TX, p. A595
  Chief Financial Officer, Kendall Regional Medical Center, Miami, FL, p. A133

HERNE, Mose, Chief Executive Officer, Hopi Health Care Center, Keams Canyon, AZ, p. A30

HEROLD, Mary, Director Human Resources, Share Medical Center, Alva, OK, p. A504

HERPFER, Caroline, Chief Nursing Officer, Arizona Orthopedic Surgical Hospital, Chandler, AZ, p. A28

HERR, Brenda, Chief Nursing Officer, East Adams Rural Healthcare, Ritzville, WA, p. A684

HERR, Michael, Chief Operating Officer, Starr Regional Medical Center, Athens, TN, p. A575

HERRARA, Espie, Chief Financial Officer, Peak Behavioral Health Services, Santa Teresa, NM, p. A428

HERRERA, Jocelyn A.
  Director Human Resources, Kaiser Permanente Orange County Anaheim Medical Center, Anaheim, CA, p. A51
  Human Resources Director, Kaiser Permanente San Diego Medical Center, San Diego, CA, p. A85

HERRERA, Veronica, Director Human Resources, Las Encinas Hospital, Pasadena, CA, p. A79

HERRERA, Yamila, Director Human Resources, Hialeah Hospital, Hialeah, FL, p. A126

HERRERO, Carmelo M.D., Medical Director, Hospital Oriente, Humacao, PR, p. A724

HERRIN, Curtis, Chief Financial Officer, Toppenish Community Hospital, Toppenish, WA, p. A688

HERRING, Davey M.D., Chief Medical Officer, Dorminy Medical Center, Fitzgerald, GA, p. A158

HERRING, Donnette, Chief Information Officer, Vidant Medical Center, Greenville, NC, p. A463

HERRING, Randy M.D., Chief of Staff, Coon Memorial Hospital, Dalhart, TX, p. A604

HERRING, Sherry, Chief Nursing Officer, Uva–Healthsouth Rehabilitation Hospital, Charlottesville, VA, p. A665

HERRINGTON, Bruce M.D., Chief Medical Officer, South Georgia Medical Center Lanier Campus, Lakeland, GA, p. A160

HERRINGTON, Kristal, Senior Director, Human Resources, Twin County Regional Healthcare, Galax, VA, p. A668

HERRIOTT, Sue A. R.N., Executive Director Support Services, OSF St. Joseph Medical Center, Bloomington, IL, p. A178

HERRMAN, Edward, R.N., FACHE
  President, Integris Bass Baptist Health Center, Enid, OK, p. A507
  President, Integris Bass Pavilion, Enid, OK, p. A507

HERRMANN, Deborah M.D., Chief of Staff, I–70 Community Hospital, Sweet Springs, MO, p. A380

HERRMANN, Lee, Chief Healthcare Technology Officer, Santa Clara Valley Medical Center, San Jose, CA, p. A89

HERRMANN, Tim, R.N., Administrator, Peacehealth Cottage Grove Community Medical Center, Cottage Grove, OR, p. A521

HERRON, Katherine, Director Human Resources, Richard H. Hutchings Psychiatric Center, Syracuse, NY, p. A453

HERRON, Mary Beth, Director of Human Resources, Illinois Valley Community Hospital, Peru, IL, p. A197

HERSEY, Robert, Chief Financial Officer, Northeastern Vermont Regional Hospital, Saint Johnsbury, VT, p. A663

HERSHBERGER, Brandy, Chief Nursing Officer, Palms Of Pasadena Hospital, Saint Petersburg, FL, p. A141

HERSHBERGER, Scott, Acting Chief Information Management Services, Battle Creek Veterans Affairs Medical Center, Battle Creek, MI, p. A315

HERSHMAN, Sharon R.N., Chief Nursing Officer, Providence Holy Family Hospital, Spokane, WA, p. A687

HERTEL, Cheryl, Coordinator Human Resources, Stamford Memorial Hospital, Stamford, TX, p. A646

HERTEL, Holly, Director Nursing, Larned State Hospital, Larned, KS, p. A245

HERTZ, Karl Edward, Assistant Administrator, Memorial Hospital Of Converse County, Douglas, WY, p. A718

HERWIG, Brian J., Chief Executive Officer, Perry County Memorial Hospital, Tell City, IN, p. A220

HERZBERG, Deborah L., R.N., MS, FACHE, Chief Executive Officer, Tri Valley Health System, Cambridge, NE, p. A391

HERZL–BETZ, Kenneth
  Chief Medical Officer and Senior Vice President Medical Affairs, St. Joseph's Hospital, Elmira, NY, p. A435
  Chief Medical Officer, Arnot Ogden Medical Center, Elmira, NY, p. A435

HERZOG, Dean, Chief Financial Officer, Kona Community Hospital, Kealakekua, HI, p. A170

HERZOG, Mark P., President and Chief Executive Officer, Holy Family Memorial, Manitowoc, WI, p. A706

HERZOG, Vernail, Chief Executive Officer, Allegiance Specialty Hospital Of Greenville, Greenville, MS, p. A355

HESCH, Dennis, Executive Vice President Finance, System Chief Financial Officer, Carle Foundation Hospital, Urbana, IL, p. A201

HESCH, Mike J, Regional Administrator Human Resources, Mayo Clinic Health System – Franciscan Healthcare In Sparta, Sparta, WI, p. A712

HESS, David F., M.D., Chief Executive Officer, Reynolds Memorial Hospital, Glen Dale, WV, p. A692

HESS, David F M.D., President Medical Staff, Reynolds Memorial Hospital, Glen Dale, WV, p. A692

HESS, Heidi, Chief Nursing Officer, Genesis Medical Center–Aledo, Aledo, IL, p. A177

HESS, Jim, Chief Operations Officer, Salt Lake Behavioral Health, Salt Lake City, UT, p. A660

HESS, Michael M.D., Chief Medical Officer, Lakeview Hospital, Bountiful, UT, p. A656

HESS, Pamela
  Chief Financial Officer, St. Joseph Hospital, Fort Wayne, IN, p. A208
  Chief Financial Officer, St. Vincent's Medical Center Riverside, Jacksonville, FL, p. A128
  Chief Financial Officer, St. Vincent's Medical Center Southside, Jacksonville, FL, p. A128

HESS, Phil, Chief Executive Officer, Wellspan Philhaven, Mount Gretna, PA, p. A541

HESS, Steve
  Vice President & Chief Information Officer, Medical Center Of The Rockies, Loveland, CO, p. A106
  Vice President Information Services and Chief Information Officer, University Of Colorado Hospital, Aurora, CO, p. A98

HESS, Susan, Director Human Resources, J. C. Blair Memorial Hospital, Huntingdon, PA, p. A536

HESSE, Fred M.D., Medical Director, Arms Acres, Carmel, NY, p. A433

HESSE, Nancy, MSN, R.N., President and Chief Executive Officer, Eastern Regional Medical Center, Philadelphia, PA, p. A543

HESSE, Nancy, MSN, R.N., President and Chief Executive Officer, Eastern Regional Medical Center, Philadelphia, PA, p. B24

HESSELRODE, Renee, Director Health Information Management, Landmark Hospital Of Cape Girardeau, Cape Girardeau, MO, p. A365

HESSHEIMER, Susan, Director Human Resources, Johnson County Hospital, Tecumseh, NE, p. A400

HESSING, Jeffrey M.D., Medical Director, Treasure Valley Hospital, Boise, ID, p. A172

HESSMAN, Mary Pat, Chief Fiscal, Northport Veterans Affairs Medical Center, Northport, NY, p. A448

HESTER, Amber, Chief Executive Officer, Curahealth Boston North Shore, Peabody, MA, p. A310

HESTER, Charles H. CPA, Jr, Chief Financial Officer, Merit Health Northwest Mississippi, Clarksdale, MS, p. A353

HESTER, Josh, Chief Operating Officer, Gadsden Regional Medical Center, Gadsden, AL, p. A18

HESTER, Joyce CPA, Senior Vice President and Chief Financial Officer, Christus Mother Frances Hospital – Tyler, Tyler, TX, p. A650

HESTER, Kathy, Chief Nursing Officer, Orange Park Medical Center, Orange Park, FL, p. A136

HESTER, Michael, Chief Executive Officer, Liberty Regional Medical Center, Hinesville, GA, p. A159

HESTER, Steven M.D., Vice President Medical Affairs, Norton Women's And Children's Hospital, Louisville, KY, p. A263

HESTON, Cathy, Chief Nursing Officer, Three Rivers Medical Center, Louisa, KY, p. A262

HETHERINGTON, Ray, Network Administrator, Wheatland Memorial Healthcare, Harlowton, MT, p. A385

HETLETVED, Beth, Director of Nurses, Chi St. Alexius Health Garrison, Garrison, ND, p. A476

HETT, Samantha, Manager Human Resources, Satanta District Hospital And Long Term Care, Satanta, KS, p. A251

HETTICH, E Paul, Chief Financial Officer, Brylin Hospitals, Buffalo, NY, p. A432

HETTINGER, JoAnn R.N., Director of Patient Care Services, Avera Weskota Memorial Hospital, Wessington Springs, SD, p. A574

HETTINGER, MaryLou, Director Quality Management, Devereux Children's Behavioral Health Center, Malvern, PA, p. A539

HETTINGER, Tiffany Erin, Associate Chief Nursing Officer, North Colorado Medical Center, Greeley, CO, p. A103

HETU, Maureen, Chief Information Officer, Our Lady Of Lourdes Medical Center, Camden, NJ, p. A412

HETZ, Mark
  Chief Information Officer, Asante Ashland Community Hospital, Ashland, OR, p. A520
  Chief Information Officer, Asante Rogue Regional Medical Center, Medford, OR, p. A524
  Chief Information Officer, Asante Three Rivers Medical Center, Grants Pass, OR, p. A522

HEURING, Ron, Director Information Systems, Perry County Memorial Hospital, Perryville, MO, p. A375

HEURTIN, John, Chief Financial Officer, Lee's Summit Medical Center, Lee's Summit, MO, p. A372

HEUSER, Keith E., President, Chi Mercy Health, Valley City, ND, p. A478

HEUSTON, Melanie M, Chief Nursing Office, Meritus Medical Center, Hagerstown, MD, p. A299

HEVER, Susan C, Director Human Resources, Brookhaven Memorial Hospital Medical Center, Patchogue, NY, p. A449

HEWSTON, MaryAnn R.N., Chief Nurse Executive, Meadville Medical Center, Meadville, PA, p. A540

HEYDON, Larry, President and Chief Executive Officer, Johnson Memorial Hospital, Franklin, IN, p. A209

HEYN, Matthew M., Chief Executive Officer, Ransom Memorial Hospital, Ottawa, KS, p. A248

HEYWOOD, Matthew, Chief Executive Officer, Aspirus, Inc., Wausau, WI, p. B14

HIATT, Tim, Chief Information Officer, Brodstone Memorial Hospital, Superior, NE, p. A400

HIBBARD, Carrie, Human Resource Business Partner, Adventist Healthcare Physical Health And Rehabilitation, Rockville, MD, p. A300

HIBBS, Cathy, Chief Executive Officer, Carlsbad Medical Center, Carlsbad, NM, p. A425

HIBEN, Daniel, Chief Executive Officer, Oswego Community Hospital, Oswego, KS, p. A248

HIBSCHMAN, Kimberly, Chief Financial Officer, Riverview Behavioral Health, Texarkana, AR, p. A50

HICKEY, Beth, Vice President, Finance, Advocate Lutheran General Hospital, Park Ridge, IL, p. A197

HICKEY, Christopher, Chief Financial Officer, Northwestern Medical Center, Saint Albans, VT, p. A663

HICKEY, Conner, Chief Operating Officer, Woodland Heights Medical Center, Lufkin, TX, p. A631

HICKEY, Marcia H, Senior Vice President Operations, Hebrew Center For Health Rehabilitation, West Hartford, CT, p. A114

HICKEY–BOYNTON, Meg, Director Human Resources and Marketing, Community Hospital Of Anaconda, Anaconda, MT, p. A382

HICKLING, Andrea, Vice President of Finance and Chief Financial Officer, Northern Hospital Of Surry County, Mount Airy, NC, p. A467

HICKLING, Karen
  Director Human Resources, Palmdale Regional Medical Center, Palmdale, CA, p. A78
  Director Human Resources, Palmdale Regional Medical Center, Palmdale, CA, p. A79

HICKMAN, George, Executive Vice President and Chief Information Officer, Albany Medical Center, Albany, NY, p. A430

HICKMAN, Louise R.N., Vice President of Patient Care Services, Jefferson Regional Medical Center, Pine Bluff, AR, p. A48

HICKMAN, Monica, Director Fiscal Services, Shriners Hospitals For Children–Spokane, Spokane, WA, p. A687

HICKMAN, Troy, Director Human Resources, Harper Hospital District Five, Harper, KS, p. A242

HICKS, Christia, Vice President Human Resources, Eskenazi Health, Indianapolis, IN, p. A211

HICKS, Crystal R.N., Chief Nursing Officer, Harrison County Community Hospital, Bethany, MO, p. A364

HICKS, Dana, Director of Nursing, Community Medical Center Of Izard County, Calico Rock, AR, p. A41

HICKS, Janelle R.N., Vice President Patient Services, Hocking Valley Community Hospital, Logan, OH, p. A494

HICKS, Joan, Chief Information Officer, University Of Alabama Hospital, Birmingham, AL, p. A15

HICKS, John R., President and Chief Executive Officer, Platte Valley Medical Center, Brighton, CO, p. A99

HICKS, Kevin J., President and CEO, Overland Park Regional Medical Center, Overland Park, KS, p. A249

HICKS, Marshall, M.D., Interim President, University Of Texas M.D. Anderson Cancer Center, Houston, TX, p. A623

HICKS, Michael L, Senior Vice President and Chief Operating Officer, Ingalls Memorial Hospital, Harvey, IL, p. A189

HICKS, Ramona, Interim Chief Executive Officer, Coulee Medical Center, Grand Coulee, WA, p. A681

HICKS, Scott, Vice President, Clark Memorial Hospital, Jeffersonville, IN, p. A213

HICKS, Susan, Chief Executive Officer, Sky Ridge Medical Center, Lone Tree, CO, p. A105

HICKS, Terri, Chief Operating Officer and Chief Financial Officer, P & S Surgical Hospital, Monroe, LA, p. A281

HICKS, William, Chief Executive Officer, NYC Health + Hospitals / Bellevue, New Rochelle, NY, p. A444

HICKSON, Stan
President and Chief Executive Officer, Johnston Memorial Hospital, Abingdon, VA, p. A664
President and Chief Executive Officer, Smyth County Community Hospital, Marion, VA, p. A670

HIDAY, Holly, Director Human Resources, Kalamazoo Psychiatric Hospital, Kalamazoo, MI, p. A324

HIEB, Dorothy, Director Human Resources, Sanford Chamberlain Medical Center, Chamberlain, SD, p. A568

HIEB, Laura R.N., Chief Nursing Officer, Bellin Memorial Hospital, Green Bay, WI, p. A702

HIEBERT, Leslie, Chief Executive Officer, Klickitat Valley Health, Goldendale, WA, p. A681

HIGA, Russel JD, Regional Director Human Resources, Leahi Hospital, Honolulu, HI, p. A168

HIGDON, Kevin J, Chief Financial Officer, Mishawaka Medical Center, Mishawaka, IN, p. A216

HIGDON, Ricky, Chief Executive Officer, AMG Specialty Hospital–Edmond, Edmond, OK, p. A507

HIGGINBOTHAM, G Douglas, President and Chief Executive Officer, South Central Regional Medical Center, Laurel, MS, p. A358

HIGGINBOTHAM, Lee, Chief Executive Officer, Dominion Hospital, Falls Church, VA, p. A666

HIGGINBOTHAM, Michael, Chief Executive Officer, Cornerstone Hospital–Medical Center Of Houston, Houston, TX, p. A619

HIGGINS, Alana
Regional Information Management Executive, Christus St. Michael Health System, Texarkana, TX, p. A649
Regional Information Management Executive, Christus St. Michael Rehabilitation Hospital, Texarkana, TX, p. A649

HIGGINS, John, Vice President and Chief Financial Officer, Good Samaritan Medical Center, Lafayette, CO, p. A104

HIGGINS, Kevin A, Chief Financial Officer, Olmsted Medical Center, Rochester, MN, p. A347

HIGGINS, Larisa, Administrator and Chief Operating Officer, Laredo Rehabilitation Hospital, Laredo, TX, p. A628

HIGGINS, Larry, Vice President Human Resources, King's Daughters Medical Center, Ashland, KY, p. A255

HIGGINS, Michael, Commander, David Grant Usaf Medical Center, Travis Afb, CA, p. A94

HIGGINS, Rodney, Chief Financial Officer, Multicare Deaconess Hospital, Spokane, WA, p. A686

HIGGINS, Thomas M.D., Chief Medical Officer, Baystate Franklin Medical Center, Greenfield, MA, p. A307

HIGGINS, William M.D., Vice President Medical Affairs, New York–Presbyterian/Hudson Valley Hospital, Cortlandt Manor, NY, p. A434

HIGGINS BOWERS, Shirley, Senior Vice President Human Resources, JFK Medical Center, Edison, NJ, p. A413

HIGGINSON, David, Executive Vice President and Chief Administrative Officer, Phoenix Children's Hospital, Phoenix, AZ, p. A34

HIGH, Kim, Chief Financial Officer, Baptist Memorial Hospital–Union County, New Albany, MS, p. A360

HIGHTOWER, Bernita, Chief Human Resources, Martin Army Community Hospital, Fort Benning, GA, p. A158

HIGHTOWER, Skip
Chief Financial Officer, Brooks County Hospital, Quitman, GA, p. A163
Chief Financial Officer, Grady General Hospital, Cairo, GA, p. A153
Senior Vice President and Chief Financial Officer, John D. Archbold Memorial Hospital, Thomasville, GA, p. A166
Senior Vice President and Chief Financial Officer, Mitchell County Hospital, Camilla, GA, p. A153

HIJECK, Thomas W. R.N., MS, Vice President Nursing Services and Chief Nursing Officer, Harrington Hospital, Southbridge, MA, p. A311

HILBERS, Cassie R.N., Chief Nursing Officer, Gothenburg Health, Gothenburg, NE, p. A393

HILDEBRAND, Randall M.D., Chief Medical Officer, Great Bend Regional Hospital, Great Bend, KS, p. A241

HILDEBRANDT, James D.O., Vice President Medical Affairs, Sarah Bush Lincoln Health Center, Mattoon, IL, p. A193

HILDRETH, Beth, Vice President Human Resources, Ohiohealth Medcentral Mansfield Hospital, Mansfield, OH, p. A494

HILDRETH, Joe, Director Information Technology, Three Rivers Hospital, Waverly, TN, p. A590

HILDWEIN, Robin, Chief Information Officer, Boca Raton Regional Hospital, Boca Raton, FL, p. A120

HILFIGER, Janie, Chief Administrative Officer, Soldiers And Sailors Memorial Hospital, Wellsboro, PA, p. A553

HILL, Beth, Director Human Resources, Russell County Medical Center, Lebanon, VA, p. A669

HILL, Cheryl
Vice President Human Resources, Columbia St. Mary's Hospital Milwaukee, Milwaukee, WI, p. A707
Vice President Human Resources, Columbia St. Mary's Ozaukee Hospital, Mequon, WI, p. A707
Vice President Human Resources, Sacred Heart Rehabilitation Institute, Milwaukee, WI, p. A708

HILL, Herbert, Director Human Resources, Klickitat Valley Health, Goldendale, WA, p. A681

HILL, Jack
Chief Operating Officer and Administrator, The Jewish Hospital – Mercy Health, Cincinnati, OH, p. A484
Vice President and Chief Operating Officer, Union Hospital Clinton, Clinton, IN, p. A205

HILL, James P, Senior Vice President Administrative Services, Medstar Washington Hospital Center, Washington, DC, p. A118

HILL, Janice, R.N., Administrator, Baptist Memorial Restorative Care Hospital, Memphis, TN, p. A584

HILL, Jason M.D., Chief Medical Officer, Choctaw Nation Health Care Center, Talihina, OK, p. A516

HILL, Jill, Director Information Technology, Utah State Hospital, Provo, UT, p. A659

HILL, Joe B Jr, Vice President Human Resources, Trident Medical Center, Charleston, SC, p. A559

HILL, John, President and Chief Executive Officer, Bozeman Health Deaconess Hospital, Bozeman, MT, p. A382

HILL, Karen S R.N., FACHE, Chief Operating Officer and Chief Nursing Officer, Baptist Health Lexington, Lexington, KY, p. A260

HILL, Karen
Departmental Personnel Officer, Zuckerberg San Francisco General Hospital And Trauma Center, San Francisco, CA, p. A88
Director Human Resources, Baylor Institute For Rehabilitation, Dallas, TX, p. A604

HILL, Kerry
Chief Financial Officer, Vista Medical Center East, Waukegan, IL, p. A202
Chief Financial Officer, Vista Medical Center West, Waukegan, IL, p. A202

HILL, Leo, Chief Information Officer, Massachusetts Eye And Ear Infirmary, Boston, MA, p. A303

HILL, Nancy L R.N., MSN, Chief Operating Officer, Medical City North Hills, North Richland Hills, TX, p. A635

HILL, Nancy R.N., Chief Nursing Officer, Johnson Regional Medical Center, Clarksville, AR, p. A41

HILL, Ned, President and Chief Executive Officer, Northern Hospital Of Surry County, Mount Airy, NC, p. A467

HILL, Robert
Chief Medical Officer, Borgess–Lee Memorial Hospital, Dowagiac, MI, p. A318
Vice President Medical Staff Affairs, Borgess Medical Center, Kalamazoo, MI, p. A324

HILL, Scott, Chief Executive Officer, Columbus Regional Healthcare System, Columbus, GA, p. B32

HILL, Stephen, Vice President and Chief Nursing Officer, Valley Baptist Medical Center–Harlingen, Harlingen, TX, p. A618

HILL, Stuart, Vice President and Treasurer, Unity Health White County Medical Center, Searcy, AR, p. A49

HILL, Terri L., Vice President and Administrator, Union Hospital Clinton, Clinton, IN, p. A205

HILL, Timothy, Chief Operating Officer, Uams Medical Center, Little Rock, AR, p. A46

HILL–DAVIS, Nancy L, Vice President Human Resources, Mercy Hospital And Medical Center, Chicago, IL, p. A182

HILLARD, Mary R.N., MSN, Vice President Patient Care Services and Clinical Operations, Chief Nursing Executive, Advocate Condell Medical Center, Libertyville, IL, p. A192

HILLARY, Maureen, Chief Nursing Officer, Hayes Green Beach Memorial Hospital, Charlotte, MI, p. A316

HILLEGASS, Bonnie Essex., Chief Executive Officer, Harmon Medical And Rehabilitation Hospital, Las Vegas, NV, p. A403

HILLEMEIER, A. Craig., M.D., Chief Executive Officer, Penn State Milton S. Hershey Medical Center, Hershey, PA, p. A536

HILLESTAD, Tammy, Chief Nursing Officer, Brookings Health System, Brookings, SD, p. A568

HILLIARD, David J D.O., Chief of Staff, Barnesville Hospital, Barnesville, OH, p. A480

HILLIS, David W., Chairman and Chief Executive Officer, Adcare Hospital Of Worcester, Worcester, MA, p. A313

HILLIS, Jeffrey W, Chief Operating Officer, Adcare Hospital Of Worcester, Worcester, MA, p. A313

HILLMAN, Annette, Director Human Resources, Doctor's Hospital Of Deer Creek, Leesville, LA, p. A280

HILLMAN, Brandon, Interim Administrator, Director of Hospital Services, Christus Coushatta Health Care Center, Coushatta, LA, p. A273

HILLS, Cindi, Director Human Resources, Riverwood Healthcare Center, Aitkin, MN, p. A335

HILLYER, Lisa L, Human Resources Manager, Box Butte General Hospital, Alliance, NE, p. A390

HILT, Monica, President, St. Elizabeth Hospital, Appleton, WI, p. A698

HILTON, Craig, Chief Executive Officer and Managing Director, Hampton Behavioral Health Center, Westampton, NJ, p. A422

HILTON, Daniel M.D., Chief of Staff, Fountain Valley Regional Hospital And Medical Center, Fountain Valley, CA, p. A60

HILTON, Lois, Director Human Resources, Desoto Memorial Hospital, Arcadia, FL, p. A119

HILTON, Richard G., Administrator and Chief Executive Officer, Och Regional Medical Center, Starkville, MS, p. A362

HILTON–SIEBERT, Stephanie, MSN, President and Chief Executive Officer, Marion General Hospital, Marion, IN, p. A215

HILTUNEN, Theresa, Entity Information Officer, Penn Presbyterian Medical Center, Philadelphia, PA, p. A545

HILTZ, Paul C., FACHE, Interim Chief Executive Officer, Mercy Medical Center, Canton, OH, p. A482

HIMES, Judy N. MSN, R.N., Chief Nursing Officer, Penn State Milton S. Hershey Medical Center, Hershey, PA, p. A536

HINCHEY, Paul P.
President and Chief Executive Officer, Candler Hospital, Savannah, GA, p. A164
President and Chief Executive Officer, St. Joseph's Hospital, Savannah, GA, p. A165

HINCKLEY, Fran X., Chief Information Officer, North Shore Medical Center, Salem, MA, p. A311

HINDMAN, Robbie, Vice President Patient Care Services and Chief Nursing Officer, Walker Baptist Medical Center, Jasper, AL, p. A20

HINDS, Bob, Executive Director, Bradford Health Services At Huntsville, Madison, AL, p. A20

HINDS, Nigel, Chief Financial Officer, Florida Hospital Deland, Deland, FL, p. A123

HINE, Kristy, Associate Vice President Finance, Geisinger–Lewistown Hospital, Lewistown, PA, p. A539

HINE, Rhonda R.N., Interim Chief Nursing Executive, Mason District Hospital, Havana, IL, p. A189

HINEMAN, Elizabeth M.D., Chief Medical Staff, Scott County Hospital, Scott City, KS, p. A251

HINER, Jill, Vice President and Chief Financial Officer, Summa Western Reserve Hospital, Cuyahoga Falls, OH, p. A489

HINER, Peggy, Director Human Resources, Wheatland Memorial Healthcare, Harlowton, MT, p. A385

HINES, Andrew, Administrator, St. James Behavioral Health Hospital, Gonzales, LA, p. A275

HINES, Darlene, Chief Operating Officer, Fairfield Memorial Hospital, Winnsboro, SC, p. A567

HINES, Frederick W., President and Chief Executive Officer, Clarity Child Guidance Center, San Antonio, TX, p. A642

HINES, JeDonne, Chief Financial Officer, Intermountain Hospital, Boise, ID, p. A171

HINES, Linda, Vice President Information Technology and Information Systems, University Of Maryland Rehabilitation & Orthopaedic Institute, Baltimore, MD, p. A296

HINES, Lisa, Director Nursing, Eastern Shore Hospital Center, Cambridge, MD, p. A297

HINES, Mary Beth D.O., Chief Medical Officer, Up Health System–Portage, Hancock, MI, p. A322

HINES, Randall G., Ph.D., Chief Executive Officer, Anchor Hospital, Atlanta, GA, p. A149

HINESLEY, Jay, FACHE, Chief Executive Officer, Tennova Healthcare–Lebanon, Lebanon, TN, p. A582

HINKLE, Stacey, Director Information Technology, Banner Desert Medical Center, Mesa, AZ, p. A31

HINNER, William J
Vice President Financial Analysis and Planning Ministry Health Care, Marshfield Medical Center, Marshfield, WI, p. A706
Vice President Financial Analysis and Planning, Ministry Saint Michael's Hospital, Stevens Point, WI, p. A713
HINOJOSA, Anna MSN, R.N., Interim Chief Nursing Officer, Knapp Medical Center, Weslaco, TX, p. A654
HINRICHS, Becky Kay, Vice President Human Resources, Riverside Medical Center, Kankakee, IL, p. A191
HINRICHS, Sandy, Director Human Resources, Burnett Medical Center, Grantsburg, WI, p. A702
HINSHAW, Bruce, Director Human Resources, Artesia General Hospital, Artesia, NM, p. A425
HINTON, James H., President and Chief Executive Officer, Baylor Scott & White Health, Dallas, TX, p. B20
HINTZ, Lori, Coordinator Information Systems, Rochester Psychiatric Center, Rochester, NY, p. A451
HINTZE, Hart, Chief Nursing Officer, Banner Payson Medical Center, Payson, AZ, p. A32
HINTZE, Paul M.D., Vice President Medical Affairs, Mercy Hospital St. Louis, Saint Louis, MO, p. A377
HIOTT, Jimmy O.
Chief Executive Officer, Colleton Medical Center, Walterboro, SC, p. A567
Chief Financial Officer, Colleton Medical Center, Walterboro, SC, p. A567
HIPKISS, Tom, Vice President Finance, Forbes Hospital, Monroeville, PA, p. A541
HIRKALER, Kim, Director Human Resources, Bon Secours Community Hospital, Port Jervis, NY, p. A450
HIROMOTO, Brenda, Director of Nursing, Rehabilitation Hospital Of The Pacific, Honolulu, HI, p. A169
HIROSE, Mivic, Executive Administrator, Laguna Honda Hospital And Rehabilitation Center, San Francisco, CA, p. A87
HIRSCH, Edward M.D., Vice President Chief Medical and Quality Officer, Kaweah Delta Medical Center, Visalia, CA, p. A96
HIRSCH, Leslie D., FACHE, Interim Chief Executive Officer and President, Saint Peter's University Hospital, New Brunswick, NJ, p. A417
HIRSCH, Ted W, Senior Executive Director, Kalispell Regional Healthcare, Kalispell, MT, p. A386
HIRSCHBERG, Paula R.N., Director of Nursing, Timberlawn Mental Health System, Dallas, TX, p. A607
HIRSHBERG, Mark, Interim Chief Executive Officer, Cooper County Memorial Hospital, Boonville, MO, p. A365
HIRST, Barb, Vice President Human Resources and Chief Nursing Officer, Salem Regional Medical Center, Salem, OH, p. A499
HISE, Landon, Chief Executive Officer, Cordell Memorial Hospital, Cordell, OK, p. A506
HISEY, Commie D.O., Chief of Staff, Memorial Hospital, Gonzales, TX, p. A616
HITE DAVIS, Anissa J, Vice President Human Resources, St. Joseph's Hospital Of Buckhannon, Buckhannon, WV, p. A690
HITT, John M.D., Executive Vice President and Chief Medical Officer, Maricopa Integrated Health System, Phoenix, AZ, p. A33
HITT, Melissa, Director of Nursing, Highland–Clarksburg Hospital, Clarksburg, WV, p. A691
HITT, Patricia A, Associate Director, Grand Junction Veterans Health Care System, Grand Junction, CO, p. A103
HIXENBAUGH, Cynthia, Director Human Resources, Pershing General Hospital, Lovelock, NV, p. A404
HIXSON, Kim, Vice President of Financial Officer and Chief Financial Officer, Providence Medical Center, Wayne, NE, p. A400
HJEMBO, Philip, Chief Financial Officer, St. Elizabeth Hospital, Enumclaw, WA, p. A680
HLAHOL, Jan, Manager Human Resources, Cleveland Clinic Children's Hospital For Rehabilitation, Cleveland, OH, p. A485
HLUCHY, Nicholas, Business Analyst, Support Services Manager, Baton Rouge Rehabilitation Hospital, Baton Rouge, LA, p. A270
HO–SHING, Viodelda, Deputy Director Administration, Creedmoor Psychiatric Center, New Rochelle, NY, p. A441
HOAG, Abby, Director, Human Resources, Uh Avon Rehabilitation Hospital, Avon, OH, p. A480
HOAGBIN, Joseph, M.D.
Chief Medical Officer, Chi Health Immanuel, Omaha, NE, p. A397
Chief Quality Officer, Chi Health Mercy Council Bluffs, Council Bluffs, IA, p. A225
HOAR, Brad, Director Information and Technology, Cedar Park Regional Medical Center, Cedar Park, TX, p. A601

HOARD, Kaylee S, Chief Financial Officer, Cook Hospital And Convalescent Nursing Care Unit, Cook, MN, p. A338
HOBACK, Kim, Supervisor Information Systems, Athens–Limestone Hospital, Athens, AL, p. A14
HOBAN, Donna M.D., Senior Vice President and Chief Medical Officer, Beaumont Hospital – Grosse Pointe, Grosse Pointe, MI, p. A322
HOBAN, Douglas M, Vice President and Chief Financial Officer, Mercy Hospital Lebanon, Lebanon, MO, p. A372
HOBAN, Robert E., President, St. John Hospital And Medical Center, Detroit, MI, p. A318
HOBART, Robert, Director Management Information Systems, Heartland Behavioral Healthcare, Massillon, OH, p. A495
HOBBS, Donna, Nurse Executive, U.S. Public Health Service Indian Hospital–Sells, Sells, AZ, p. A36
HOBBS, Ed, Director Information Services, Dekalb Health, Auburn, IN, p. A203
HOBBS, Emilie, Director Human Resources, Woodland Heights Medical Center, Lufkin, TX, p. A631
HOBBS, Keith, Chief Executive Officer, Usc Verdugo Hills Hospital, Glendale, CA, p. A62
HOBBS, Mike, Chief Financial Officer, Clay County Hospital, Flora, IL, p. A187
HOBBS, Nicole, Administrator, Johnson County Healthcare Center, Buffalo, WY, p. A717
HOBBS, Steve E.
Chief Financial Officer, Eliza Coffee Memorial Hospital, Florence, AL, p. A18
Chief Financial Officer, Shoals Hospital, Muscle Shoals, AL, p. A22
HOBBS, Tommy, Chief Executive Officer, Illinois Valley Community Hospital, Peru, IL, p. A197
HOBGOOD, Lisa, Chief Information Officer, The Heart Hospital At Deaconess Gateway, Newburgh, IN, p. A217
HOBGOOD, Marcus, Director Information Services, University Health Shreveport, Shreveport, LA, p. A286
HOBSON, Christopher Brian, Chief Operating Officer, Wellmont Bristol Regional Medical Center, Bristol, TN, p. A575
HOCATE, Crispin P, Professional and Support Services Officer, Texas Health Presbyterian Hospital Allen, Allen, TX, p. A591
HOCE, N. Kristopher., President, Morton Plant Hospital, Clearwater, FL, p. A121
HOCHENBERG, Paul S, Executive Director, Westchester Medical Center, Valhalla, NY, p. A454
HOCHMAN, Rodney F., M.D., President and Chief Executive Officer, Providence St. Joseph Health, Renton, WA, p. B103
HOCHSTETLER, Amy, Chief Financial Officer, Orthopaedic Hospital Of Lutheran Health Network, Fort Wayne, IN, p. A208
HOCK, Douglas G, Executive Vice President and Chief Operating Officer, Children's Hospital Of Philadelphia, Philadelphia, PA, p. A543
HOCKADAY, Christina, FACHE, Chief Executive Officer, Assumption Community Hospital, Napoleonville, LA, p. A282
HOCKENBERRY, Michael A, Senior Vice President and Chief Operating Officer, Hanover Hospital, Hanover, PA, p. A535
HOCKENBERRY, Tonda, Chief Nursing Officer, Healthsouth Western Hills Regional Rehabilitation Hospital, Parkersburg, WV, p. A695
HOCKENBURY, Debbie, Assistant Administrator and Chief Financial Officer, William Newton Hospital, Winfield, KS, p. A254
HOCKERSMITH, Lisa K., Vice President Human Resources, Kern Medical Center, Bakersfield, CA, p. A53
HOCKERT, Steve, Chief Executive Officer, Onecore Health, Oklahoma City, OK, p. A513
HOCKING, Dale E, Chief Financial Officer, Jupiter Medical Center, Jupiter, FL, p. A129
HOCKING, Patrick
Chief Financial Officer, Asante Ashland Community Hospital, Ashland, OR, p. A520
Chief Financial Officer, Asante Rogue Regional Medical Center, Medford, OR, p. A524
Chief Financial Officer, Asante Three Rivers Medical Center, Grants Pass, OR, p. A522
HOCUM, Timothy, Chief Financial Officer, Providence Kodiak Island Medical Center, Kodiak, AK, p. A26
HODGE, Ian, Chief Executive Officer, Yuma Rehabilitation Hospital, Yuma, AZ, p. A39
HODGE, Lisa, Manager, Human Resources, Rolling Hills Hospital, Franklin, TN, p. A579
HODGE, Montie, Vice President Information Technology and Chief Information Officer, Regional West Medical Center, Scottsbluff, NE, p. A399
HODGE, Pamela R.N., Chief Nursing Officer and Coordinator Performance Improvement, Jellico Community Hospital, Jellico, TN, p. A580

HODGES, Alan, Chief Executive Officer, Hancock Medical Center, Bay Saint Louis, MS, p. A352
HODGES, Calvin, Director Human Resources, Alliancehealth Ponca City, Ponca City, OK, p. A514
HODGES, Craig, Director Information Services, Hancock Medical Center, Bay Saint Louis, MS, p. A352
HODGES, Dawn, Director Human Resources, Grand River Hospital District, Rifle, CO, p. A107
HODGES, Jay, Chief Financial Officer, TMC Bonham Hospital, Bonham, TX, p. A598
HODGES, Leisha, Human Resources Officer, Eastland Memorial Hospital, Eastland, TX, p. A609
HODGES, Randall H, FACHE, Vice President and Administrator, Charleston Area Medical Center, Charleston, WV, p. A691
HODGIN, Robin R.N., Vice President of Patient Services and Chief Nursing Officer, Northern Hospital Of Surry County, Mount Airy, NC, p. A467
HODGSON, Judith Ann, Chief Nursing Officer, Cheyenne County Hospital, Saint Francis, KS, p. A251
HODNETT, Laura, Interim Chief Nursing Officer, Glen Rose Medical Center, Glen Rose, TX, p. A616
HODSON, Don M.D., Chief Medical Officer, St. Luke Hospital And Living Center, Marion, KS, p. A246
HOEFER, Bill, Chief Operating Officer, St. Anthony's Medical Center, Saint Louis, MO, p. A378
HOEFER, Robert William FACHE, Chief Operating Officer, SSM Health Saint Louis University Hospital, Saint Louis, MO, p. A378
HOEFLING, Tracy, Chief Financial Officer, The Heart Hospital At Deaconess Gateway, Newburgh, IN, p. A217
HOEFS, Dennis, Manager Information Technology, New Mexico Rehabilitation Center, Roswell, NM, p. A428
HOEHN, Charles, President, Medical Staff, Van Wert County Hospital, Van Wert, OH, p. A501
HOEHNS, Brent M.D., Chief of Medical Staff, Knoxville Hospital & Clinics, Knoxville, IA, p. A230
HOEKEMA, Dale M.D., Vice President Medical Affairs and Chief Medical Officer, Kadlec Regional Medical Center, Richland, WA, p. A684
HOELL, Paul M.D., President Medical Staff, Thedacare Medical Center–New London, New London, WI, p. A709
HOELSCHER, Steven C, Chief Operating Officer, Valley Regional Medical Center, Brownsville, TX, p. A599
HOERTZ, Joanne, Vice President of Nursing, Brooks Rehabilitation Hospital, Jacksonville, FL, p. A128
HOESCH, Marty, Director Information Systems, North Suburban Medical Center, Thornton, CO, p. A107
HOEY, Amy J R.N., MS, Executive Vice President and Chief Operating Officer, Lowell General Hospital, Lowell, MA, p. A308
HOFELICH, Kurt T., President, Sentara Norfolk General Hospital, Norfolk, VA, p. A672
HOFER, Maggie, Human Resources Representative, Hawarden Regional Healthcare, Hawarden, IA, p. A229
HOFF, David L., Chief Executive Officer, Wayne Memorial Hospital, Honesdale, PA, p. A536
HOFF, Deanna R.N., Director of Nursing, Bacon County Hospital And Health System, Alma, GA, p. A149
HOFF, Linda, Senior Vice President and Chief Financial Officer, Legacy Mount Hood Medical Center, Gresham, OR, p. A522
HOFF, Margaret, Account Manager, Brown County Community Treatment Center, Green Bay, WI, p. A703
HOFFBERGER, Darren D.O., Chief of Staff, Broward Health North, Deerfield Beach, FL, p. A123
HOFFER, Nolan, Senior Director, St. Luke's Rehabilitation Hospital, Boise, ID, p. A172
HOFFMAN, Barbara M.D., Chief Medical Officer, St. Christopher's Hospital For Children, Philadelphia, PA, p. A545
HOFFMAN, Brad, Administrative Director Human Resources, Shawnee Mission Medical Center, Shawnee Mission, KS, p. A252
HOFFMAN, Brian
Chief Medical Services, Veterans Affairs Boston Healthcare System, West Roxbury, MA, p. A312
Director Human Resources, Lancaster Regional Medical Centers, Lancaster, PA, p. A538
HOFFMAN, Carole, Vice President, Parkridge Medical Center, Chattanooga, TN, p. A576
HOFFMAN, Chris, Chief Operating Officer, Highlands Regional Medical Center, Prestonsburg, KY, p. A266
HOFFMAN, Daniel M.D., Administrative Medical Director, Good Samaritan Regional Health Center, Mount Vernon, IL, p. A194
HOFFMAN, Debbie, Vice President Patient Services, SSM Health St. Francis Hospital – Maryville, Maryville, MO, p. A373

HOFFMAN, Debra, Manager Human Resources, Kern Valley Healthcare District, Lake Isabella, CA, p. A65
HOFFMAN, Howard M.D., Medical Director, Psychiatric Institute Of Washington, Washington, DC, p. A118
HOFFMAN, Jerry, Chief Financial Officer, Platte Health Center Avera, Platte, SD, p. A571
HOFFMAN, Joseph E
  Executive Vice President and Chief Financial Officer, University Of Maryland Harford Memorial Hospital, Havre De Grace, MD, p. A299
  Executive Vice President and Chief Financial Officer, University Of Maryland Upper Chesapeake Medical Center, Bel Air, MD, p. A296
HOFFMAN, Marcus, Area Chief Financial Officer, Kaiser Permanente Orange County Anaheim Medical Center, Anaheim, CA, p. A51
HOFFMAN, Pamela S, Director of Human Resources, Monroe Hospital, Bloomfield, IN, p. A204
HOFFMAN, Robert P, Vice President and Director Patient Care Services, Wilkes–Barre General Hospital, Wilkes, PA, p. A554
HOFFMAN, Ron, Chief Operating Officer, St. John Sapulpa, Sapulpa, OK, p. A515
HOFFMAN, Tom, Manager Information Systems, Wayne Memorial Hospital, Honesdale, PA, p. A536
HOFFMAN, Trudy, Executive Director, Northwest Center For Behavioral Health, Fort Supply, OK, p. A508
HOFFMAN, Val, Chief Financial Officer, Granite Falls Municipal Hospital And Manor, Granite Falls, MN, p. A340
HOFFMANN, Wanda, Director Human Resources, Seaside Behavioral Center, New OrleansRiver Oaks Hospital, New Orleans, LA, p. A283
HOFIUS, Chuck, Chief Executive Officer, Perham Health, Perham, MN, p. A346
HOFLER, Linda D Ph.D., R.N., FACHE, Senior Vice President, Nurse Executive, Vidant Medical Center, Greenville, NC, p. A463
HOFMAN, William, Manager Information Technology, Wake Forest Baptist Health – Wilkes Medical Center, North Wilkesboro, NC, p. A468
HOFMEISTER, Nancee R.N., Chief Nursing Officer, Evergreenhealth, Kirkland, WA, p. A681
HOFSTETTER, Peter A., Chief Executive Officer, Willamette Valley Medical Center, Mcminnville, OR, p. A523
HOGAN, Dan, Chief Financial Officer, Desoto Memorial Hospital, Arcadia, FL, p. A119
HOGAN, Judith, Comptroller and Director Resources and Logistics, Naval Hospital Bremerton, Bremerton, WA, p. A678
HOGAN, Michael, Chief Resource Management, General Leonard Wood Army Community Hospital, Fort Leonard Wood, MO, p. A368
HOGAN, Richard H CPA, Chief Financial Officer, Landmark Hospital Of Cape Girardeau, Cape Girardeau, MO, p. A365
HOGAN, Richard, Chief Financial Officer, Pleasant Valley Hospital, Point Pleasant, WV, p. A695
HOGAN, Sean, FACHE, President, SSM Health Depaul Hospital – St. Louis, Bridgeton, MO, p. A365
HOGAN, Timothy J.
  Regional President, Hackensack Meridian Health Bayshore Community Hospital, Holmdel, NJ, p. A415
  Regional President, Hackensack Meridian Health Riverview Medical Center, Red Bank, NJ, p. A420
HOGDSON, Judy R.N., Chief Nursing Officer, Hospital District No 1 Of Rice County, Lyons, KS, p. A246
HOGG, Donna, Supervisor Medical Records, Monroe County Hospital, Forsyth, GA, p. A158
HOGGARD GREEN, Jill, President, Mission Hospital, Asheville, NC, p. A457
HOGUE, Vicky R.N., Vice President Patient Services and Chief Nursing Officer, Wellstar Paulding Hospital, Hiram, GA, p. A159
HOHENBERGER, Joseph, Chief Financial Officer, Ferrell Hospital, Eldorado, IL, p. A186
HOHENSHELL, Valerie, Director of Clinical Services, Memorial Hospital, Gonzales, TX, p. A616
HOLBERT, Brandon, Director, Information Services, Ocala Regional Medical Center, Ocala, FL, p. A136
HOLBROOK, Chip M.D., Chief of Staff, Simpson General Hospital, Mendenhall, MS, p. A358
HOLBROOK, Curtis M.D., Chief Medical Officer, Baylor Scott & White Surgical Hospital At Sherman, Sherman, TX, p. A645
HOLCOMB, Holly, Chief Operating Officer, Childress Regional Medical Center, Childress, TX, p. A601
HOLCOMB, Michelle, Human Resources, Webster County Memorial Hospital, Webster Springs, WV, p. A696
HOLDEMAN, Royce, Chief Financial Officer, Mercy Hospital, Moundridge, KS, p. A247

HOLDEN, Patricia, Chief Executive Officer, Mesa View Regional Hospital, Mesquite, NV, p. A404
HOLDEN, Peter J., Interim President, St. Mary's Regional Medical Center, Lewiston, ME, p. A291
HOLDEN, Rhonda C R.N., MSN, Chief Nursing Officer, Kittitas Valley Healthcare, Ellensburg, WA, p. A680
HOLDEN, Teal A., Chief Executive Officer, Memorial Hermann Surgical Hospital Kingwood, Kingwood, TX, p. A627
HOLDER, Hal
  Director Finance, SSM Health Depaul Hospital – St. Louis, Bridgeton, MO, p. A365
  Regional Chief Financial Officer–Hospital Operations, SSM Health St. Clare Hospital – Fenton, Fenton, MO, p. A368
  Regional Chief Financial Officer, SSM Health St. Joseph Hospital – Lake Saint Louis, Lake Saint Louis, MO, p. A372
HOLDER, Jennifer, Chief Nursing Officer, Trousdale Medical Center, Hartsville, TN, p. A579
HOLDER, Kasey M.D., Vice President Medical Affairs, St. Bernards Medical Center, Jonesboro, AR, p. A45
HOLDER, Michelle, Nurse Executive, Straith Hospital For Special Surgery, Southfield, MI, p. A331
HOLDER, Spencer, Chief Financial Officer, Riverland Medical Center, Ferriday, LA, p. A274
HOLDER–HOOPER, Donna, Chief Human Resource Officer, Healthsouth Rehabilitation Hospital At Martin Health, Stuart, FL, p. A143
HOLEKAMP, Nicholas M.D., Chief Medical Officer, Ranken Jordan Pediatric Bridge Hospital, Maryland Heights, MO, p. A373
HOLGUIN, Brenda, Manager Human Resources, El Paso Behavioral Health System, El Paso, TX, p. A610
HOLGUIN, Mindee, Manager Human Resources, Sierra Vista Hospital, Truth Or Consequences, NM, p. A429
HOLIFIELD, Tracy, Director Information Systems, Merit Health Central, Jackson, MS, p. A356
HOLINER, Joel M.D., Executive Medical Director, Medical City Green Oaks Hospital, Dallas, TX, p. A606
HOLIVER, John J., Chief Executive Officer, St. Joseph Health Services Of Rhode Island, North Providence, RI, p. A556
HOLLAND, Baxter C M.D., Chief Medical Officer, Rutland Regional Medical Center, Rutland, VT, p. A663
HOLLAND, Brad D., Chief Executive Officer, Cedar Park Regional Medical Center, Cedar Park, TX, p. A601
HOLLAND, Charles, President and Chief Executive Officer, St. Bernard Hospital And Health Care Center, Chicago, IL, p. A184
HOLLAND, Cheyenne, Chief Financial Officer, The University Of Vermont Health Network Central Vermont Medical Center, Berlin, VT, p. A662
HOLLAND, David
  Chief Information Officer, Herrin Hospital, Herrin, IL, p. A189
  Vice President Chief Innovation Officer, Memorial Hospital Of Carbondale, Carbondale, IL, p. A179
  Vice President Information Services, St. Joseph Memorial Hospital, Murphysboro, IL, p. A194
HOLLAND, Gabrielle, Chief Financial Officer, Baylor Surgical Hospital At Las Colinas, Irving, TX, p. A625
HOLLAND, Kevin, Chief Executive Officer, Singing River Health System, Pascagoula, MS, p. A360
HOLLAND, Kwi, Vice President Information Services, Knox Community Hospital, Mount Vernon, OH, p. A496
HOLLAND, Michael, M.D., Chief Executive Officer, Rehabilitation Hospital Of Jennings, Jennings, LA, p. A277
HOLLAND, Penny, Associate Director for Patient Care Services, Aleda E. Lutz Veterans Affairs Medical Center, Saginaw, MI, p. A329
HOLLAND, Shannon S R.N., MSN, Chief Nursing Officer, Multicare Valley Hospital, Spokane Valley, WA, p. A687
HOLLAND, Sharron, Chief Financial Officer, Baptist Memorial Hospital–Huntingdon, Huntingdon, TN, p. A580
HOLLAND, Stace D., Chief Executive Officer, Freestone Medical Center, Fairfield, TX, p. A612
HOLLAND, Stephen M.D., Vice President Chief Medical Officer and Medical Director, Gaylord Hospital, Wallingford, CT, p. A113
HOLLEMAN, Ivan, Chief Financial Officer, Baxter Regional Medical Center, Mountain Home, AR, p. A47
HOLLEMAN, James M.D., Chief of Staff, St. Luke's Hospital, Columbus, NC, p. A460
HOLLEMAN, Stephen B, Chief Financial Officer, Shepherd Center, Atlanta, GA, p. A151
HOLLIDAY, Jonathan, Manager Information Technology, Central Community Hospital, Elkader, IA, p. A227
HOLLIDAY, Michael T, Vice President Fiscal and Administrative Services, Van Wert County Hospital, Van Wert, OH, p. A501
HOLLIMAN, Emily L., FACHE, Chief Executive Officer, Hackensack Meridian Health Pascack Valley Medical Center, Westwood, NJ, p. A423

HOLLIN, Sheara, Chief Operating Officer, Hospital Of The University Of Pennsylvania, Philadelphia, PA, p. A544
HOLLINGER, Brad, Chairman and Chief Executive Officer, Vibra Healthcare, Mechanicsburg, PA, p. B143
HOLLINGER, Lori, Manager Human Resources, Fulton State Hospital, Fulton, MO, p. A368
HOLLINGSWORTH, Carl, Chief Financial Officer, Artesia General Hospital, Artesia, NM, p. A425
HOLLINGSWORTH, Christine, Chief Financial Officer, Phoenix Veterans Affairs Health Care System, Phoenix, AZ, p. A34
HOLLINGSWORTH, Nancy, R.N., MSN, President and Chief Executive Officer, Saint Agnes Medical Center, Fresno, CA, p. A61
HOLLINGSWORTH, Sherri
  Chief Human Resources Officer, Pih Health Hospital – Downey, Downey, CA, p. A58
  Chief Human Resources Officer, Pih Health Hospital–Whittier, Whittier, CA, p. A97
HOLLIS, Carla, President and Chief Executive Officer, Columbus Regional Healthcare System, Whiteville, NC, p. A472
HOLLIS, Clara, Administrator, Oceans Behavioral Hospital San Marcos, San Marcos, TX, p. B94
HOLLIS, Gary W, Comptroller, Arkansas State Hospital, Little Rock, AR, p. A45
HOLLIS, Roy, Chief Executive Officer, Houston Behavioral Healthcare Hospital, Houston, TX, p. A620
HOLLISTER, Jerry, Chief Executive Officer, Northeastern Center, Auburn, IN, p. A203
HOLLISTER, Richard, President of Medical Staff, Exeter Hospital, Exeter, NH, p. A408
HOLLON, Kim Norton., FACHE, President and Chief Executive Officer, Signature Healthcare Brockton Hospital, Brockton, MA, p. A304
HOLLOWAY, Kristina, Chief Human Resources Officer, Healdsburg District Hospital, Healdsburg, CA, p. A63
HOLLOWAY, Myra, Director Human Resources Management, Central State Hospital, Milledgeville, GA, p. A161
HOLLOWAY, Walter R, Chief Medical Officer, Ozarks Medical Center, West Plains, MO, p. A381
HOLLOWAY, Whitney, Chief Financial Officer, Berwick Hospital Center, Berwick, PA, p. A529
HOLM, Mary Ann, Office Clerk, Tioga Medical Center, Tioga, ND, p. A478
HOLM, Stan
  Chief Executive Officer, Abrazo Maryvale Campus, Phoenix, AZ, p. A32
  Chief Executive Officer, Abrazo West Campus, Goodyear, AZ, p. A30
HOLMAN, Steve M., Chief Executive Officer, Union Hospital, Terre Haute, IN, p. A220
HOLMBERG, Daniel M.D., Director of Medical Affairs, New Ulm Medical Center, New Ulm, MN, p. A345
HOLMEN, Kenneth D., M.D., President and Chief Executive Officer, Centracare Health, Saint Cloud, MN, p. B30
HOLMES, Dawne, Chief Financial Officer, Greenwood Leflore Hospital, Greenwood, MS, p. A355
HOLMES, Diana, Chief Nursing Officer, Central Regional Hospital, Butner, NC, p. A458
HOLMES, Ginnie, Chief Financial Officer, Electra Memorial Hospital, Electra, TX, p. A612
HOLMES, Heather, Director Health Information Systems, Merit Health Rankin, Brandon, MS, p. A353
HOLMES, Heidi, Chief Information Officer, Oklahoma State University Medical Center, Tulsa, OK, p. A517
HOLMES, James R., President and Chief Executive Officer, Redlands Community Hospital, Redlands, CA, p. A82
HOLMES, John, Business Manager, Ancora Psychiatric Hospital, Hammonton, NJ, p. A414
HOLMES, Phillip Walter M.D., Chief of Staff, Prairie Ridge Hospital And Health Services, Elbow Lake, MN, p. A339
HOLMES, Terry R M.D., Clinical Director, Moccasin Bend Mental Health Institute, Chattanooga, TN, p. A576
HOLMES, Troy, Director Finance, Advanced Specialty Hospital Of Toledo, Toledo, OH, p. A500
HOLMSTROM, Tallulah
  Chief Medical Officer, Carolina Pines Regional Medical Center, Hartsville, SC, p. A563
  Chief Medical Officer, Kershawhealth, Camden, SC, p. A558
HOLOM, Randall G., Chief Executive Officer, Frances Mahon Deaconess Hospital, Glasgow, MT, p. A384
HOLSAPPLE, Kim, Human Resource Specialist, Chester Mental Health Center, Chester, IL, p. A180
HOLSCHBACH, Dennis, Chief Financial Officer, Ruby Valley Hospital, Sheridan, MT, p. A388
HOLSON, Debbie C R.N., MSN, Chief Operating Officer, The Hsc Pediatric Center, Washington, DC, p. A118
HOLSTEN, Robyn, Human Resources Director, Salt Lake Behavioral Health, Salt Lake City, UT, p. A660

HOLT, Clayton, Chief Executive Officer, San Juan Health Service District, Monticello, UT, p. A657

HOLT, David, Chief Operating Officer, Western State Hospital, Tacoma, WA, p. A688

HOLT, Kory
Assistant Vice President for Financial Integration, Avera Flandreau Hospital, Flandreau, SD, p. A570
Division Controller Network Operations, Avera Dells Area Hospital, Dell Rapids, SD, p. A569

HOLT, Peter M.D., Director Medical Affairs, Saint Luke's Hospital Of Kansas City, Kansas City, MO, p. A370

HOLT, Richard R.N., Associate Director Patient Care Services, Veterans Affairs St. Louis Health Care System, Saint Louis, MO, p. A379

HOLT, Sherry, Director Human Resources, Unity Medical Center, Manchester, TN, p. A583

HOLT, Stephen R., M.D., Director, Captain James A. Lovell Federal Health Care Center, North Chicago, IL, p. A195

HOLT, Tabetha, Director of Human Resources, Riverside Walter Reed Hospital, Gloucester, VA, p. A668

HOLT, Thomas A, Chief Financial Officer, Conroe Regional Medical Center, Conroe, TX, p. A602

HOLT, Will, Director Information Technology, Harrison County Community Hospital, Bethany, MO, p. A364

HOLTER, Lee H, Chief Financial Officer, Columbia County Health System, Dayton, WA, p. A680

HOLTHAUS, Julie K, Director Human Resources, Sabetha Community Hospital, Sabetha, KS, p. A250

HOLTHAUS, Monica, Chief Financial Officer, Community Healthcare System, Onaga, KS, p. A248

HOLSTIEN, Bruce, President and Chief Executive Officer, Spartanburg Regional Healthcare System, Spartanburg, SC, p. B119

HOLTZ, George, Director Human Resources, Sharp Grossmont Hospital, La Mesa, CA, p. A64

HOLTZ, Jennifer, Director Finance, Centracare Health–Paynesville, Paynesville, MN, p. A345

HOLTZ, Noel M.D., Chief Medical Officer, Wellstar Douglas Hospital, Douglasville, GA, p. A157

HOLTZMAN, Michael M.D., Medical Director, Kindred Hospital–St. Louis, Saint Louis, MO, p. A377

HOLUBEK, William M.D., Chief Medical Officer, Carepoint Health Christ Hospital, Jersey City, NJ, p. A415

HOLYFIELD, Linda S., R.N., MSN, President and Chief Executive Officer, P & S Surgical Hospital, Monroe, LA, p. A281

HOLYOAK, Mark, Chief Executive Officer, Castleview Hospital, Price, UT, p. A659

HOLZER, Traci, Chief Human Resources Officer, Doctors Hospital Of Manteca, Manteca, CA, p. A73

HOMA, Jim, Chief Executive Officer, Heatherhill Care Communities, Chardon, OH, p. A483

HOMER, Kenneth M.D., Chief Medical Officer, Holy Cross Hospital, Fort Lauderdale, FL, p. A125

HOMYK, Linda, Chief Nursing Officer, Sewickley Valley Hospital, (A Division Of Valley Medical Facilities), Sewickley, PA, p. A550

HONAKER, Jennifer, Chief Financial Officer, John Randolph Medical Center, Hopewell, VA, p. A668

HONEA, Bert, M.D.
Associate Chief Medical Officer Northern Colorado, Banner Fort Collins Medical Center, Fort Collins, CO, p. A102
Medical Director, Mckee Medical Center, Loveland, CO, p. A106

HONEA, Bruce, Director Information Services, Christus Coushatta Health Care Center, Coushatta, LA, p. A273

HONEA, Michael, Chief Financial Officer, Glen Rose Medical Center, Glen Rose, TX, p. A616

HONERBRINK, Daniel, Vice President Finance and Chief Financial Officer, Fairmont Regional Medical Center, Fairmont, WV, p. A692

HONEYCUTT, Cynthia, Director Human Resources, Moccasin Bend Mental Health Institute, Chattanooga, TN, p. A576

HONEYCUTT, Robert C., Chief Executive Officer, Dignity Health Arizona General Hospital, Laveen, AZ, p. A31

HONSINGER, Melissa, Chief Operating Officer, St. Luke's Rehabilitation Hospital, Boise, ID, p. A172

HONTS, Gary, Chief Executive Officer, John F. Kennedy Memorial Hospital, Indio, CA, p. A63

HOOD, Brenda, Chief Executive Officer, Curahealth Hospital Oklahoma City, Oklahoma City, OK, p. A512

HOOD, Cliff, Chief Operating Officer, Central Regional Hospital, Butner, NC, p. A458

HOOD, Kathy, Administrative Assistant Human Resources, Union General Hospital, Blairsville, GA, p. A152

HOOD, M. Michelle., FACHE, President and Chief Executive Officer, Eastern Maine Healthcare Systems, Brewer, ME, p. B48

HOOD, Ron M.D., Chief of Staff, Sutter Amador Hospital, Jackson, CA, p. A64

HOOD, Sam, Director Human Resources, Heartland Regional Medical Center, Marion, IL, p. A192

HOOD, Tom, Chief Operating Officer, King's Daughters Medical Center, Brookhaven, MS, p. A353

HOOK, Diane, Chief Financial Officer, Wayne County Hospital, Corydon, IA, p. A225

HOOKER, Melvin, Chief Human Resources, New Mexico Veterans Affairs Health Care System – Raymond G. Murphy Medical Center, Albuquerque, NM, p. A424

HOOKER, Rita, Administrative Director Information Services, Bon Secours St. Francis Health System, Greenville, SC, p. A562

HOOLAHAN, Susan E R.N., MSN, Vice President Patient Care Services and Chief Nursing Officer, Upmc Passavant, Pittsburgh, PA, p. A547

HOOP, Heather, Human Resources Generalist, Adams County Regional Medical Center, Seaman, OH, p. A499

HOOPER, Grady A., Chief Executive Officer, Hamilton General Hospital, Hamilton, TX, p. A618

HOOPER, Jason R., President and Chief Executive Officer, Kvc Prairie Ridge Psychiatric Hospital, Kansas City, KS, p. A244

HOOPER, Joseph, President and Chief Executive Officer, Community Howard Regional Health, Kokomo, IN, p. A213

HOOPER, Robert A, Director Human Resources, Tristar Skyline Medical Center, Nashville, TN, p. A587

HOOPINGARNER, Darrick, Chief Operating Officer, Dupont Hospital, Fort Wayne, IN, p. A208

HOOPINGARNER, Traci R.N., Chief Nursing Officer, Lawrence Memorial Hospital, Lawrence, KS, p. A245

HOOVER, Alvin, FACHE, Chief Executive Officer, King's Daughters Medical Center, Brookhaven, MS, p. A353

HOOVER, Craig A, Administrator, Kindred Hospital South Florida–Fort Lauderdale, Fort Lauderdale, FL, p. A125

HOOVER, Garrett W., FACHE, President, Guthrie Corning Hospital, Corning, NY, p. A434

HOOVER, Jeremy Steven, Chief Information Officer, Kiowa County Memorial Hospital, Greensburg, KS, p. A242

HOOVER, Leon, Director Information Systems, Hendry Regional Medical Center, Clewiston, FL, p. A122

HOPE, Lisa R, Director Human Resources, Owensboro Health Muhlenberg Community Hospital, Greenville, KY, p. A259

HOPE, Steve, Vice President Corporate Services, Methodist Rehabilitation Center, Jackson, MS, p. A357

HOPE, William IV, Chief of Medical Staff, Vidant Chowan Hospital, Edenton, NC, p. A462

HOPKINS, Frances F, Chief Financial Officer, Sabine Medical Center, Many, LA, p. A280

HOPKINS, Jason, Director, Human Resources, Hamilton Medical Center, Dalton, GA, p. A156

HOPKINS, Jim, Chief Financial Officer, Cascade Medical Center, Leavenworth, WA, p. A682

HOPKINS, Joy, Vice President Patient Care Services, OSF St. Francis Hospital And Medical Group, Escanaba, MI, p. A319

HOPKINS, Kelli, Director Human Resources, Baptist Health Medical Center–Hot Spring County, Malvern, AR, p. A46

HOPKINS, Ken, Vice President Finance and Chief Financial Officer, Norman Regional Health System, Norman, OK, p. A511

HOPKINS, Kevin, Vice President of Operations, Cornerstone Medical Center, Fort Oglethorpe, GA, p. A158

HOPKINS, Ronald D.O., Chief of Staff, Nor–Lea Hospital District, Lovington, NM, p. A427

HOPKINS, William, Director Finance, Carolinas Rehabilitation, Charlotte, NC, p. A459

HOPP, Eva, Chief Nurse Executive, Pinckneyville Community Hospital, Pinckneyville, IL, p. A198

HOPPEN, Claudine N MSN, Interim Chief Nursing Officer, DMC – Children's Hospital Of Michigan, Detroit, MI, p. A317

HOPPER, Tasha, Chief Operating Officer, The Hospitals Of Providence Transmountain Campus, El Paso, TX, p. A612

HOPPS, Deborah, R.N., FACHE, Chief Executive Officer, Vibra Rehabilitation Hospital Lake Travis, Lakeway, TX, p. A628

HOPSON, W Briggs M.D., Clinical Medical Director, Merit Health River Region, Vicksburg, MS, p. A362

HOPSTAD, Kyle, Chief Executive Officer, Broadwater Health Center, Townsend, MT, p. A389

HOPWOOD, James, Chief Financial Officer, Promise Hospital Of Miss Lou, Vidalia, LA, p. A287

HOPWOOD, Jennifer, Vice President, Chief Nursing Officer, OSF Saint Francis Medical Center, Peoria, IL, p. A197

HORAN, Gary S, FACHE, President and Chief Executive Officer, Trinitas Regional Medical Center, Elizabeth, NJ, p. A413

HORATH, Kevin, Vice President Human Resources, Decatur Memorial Hospital, Decatur, IL, p. A185

HORCH, David, Chief Executive, California Medical Facility, Vacaville, CA, p. A95

HORECKA, Richard, Chief Medical Officer, Swift County – Benson Health Services, Benson, MN, p. A336

HORINEK, ReChelle, Chief Financial Officer, Trego County–Lemke Memorial Hospital, Wakeeney, KS, p. A253

HORN, Debbie, Controller, Texas Rehabilitation Hospital Of Arlington, Arlington, TX, p. A594

HORN, Jeff, Vice President, Information and Support Services, Jay County Hospital, Portland, IN, p. A218

HORN, Jon M.D., Chief of Staff, Northeast Georgia Medical Center Barrow, Winder, GA, p. A167

HORN, LeeAnn, Chief Nurse Executive, Providence Kodiak Island Medical Center, Kodiak, AK, p. A26

HORN, Sarah
Chief Nursing Officer, Salem Health West Valley, Dallas, OR, p. A521
Chief Nursing Officer, Salem Hospital, Salem, OR, p. A526

HORN, Syndi, Director Information Systems, Memorial Hospital, Carthage, IL, p. A179

HORNBURG, Tom, Director Information Systems, Mason General Hospital, Shelton, WA, p. A686

HORNE, Beth, System Administrator Information Technology, Preston Memorial Hospital, Kingwood, WV, p. A693

HORNE, Eilene, Manager Human Resources, Mountain View Hospital, Idaho Falls, ID, p. A173

HORNE, Harry D.O., Chief of Staff, Cumberland River Hospital, Celina, TN, p. A576

HORNE, J Mark, Senior Vice President, Ambulatory Services and Chief Operating Officer, Grand View Health, Sellersville, PA, p. A550

HORNE, Perry, Chief Nursing Officer, St. Cloud Regional Medical Center, Saint Cloud, FL, p. A141

HORNE, NEA–BC, Theresa MS, MSN, Vice President Patient Care Services, St. Dominic–Jackson Memorial Hospital, Jackson, MS, p. A357

HORNER, Ania R.N., Vice President and Chief Nurse Executive, Aurora Sinai Medical Center, Milwaukee, WI, p. A707

HORNER, Bryan, President and Chief Executive Officer, Shannon Medical Center, San Angelo, TX, p. A641

HORNER, Cheryl, Supervisor Data Processing, Community Hospital Of Staunton, Staunton, IL, p. A201

HORNER, Eva, Assistant Executive Director Operations, Devereux Hospital And Children's Center Of Florida, Melbourne, FL, p. A132

HORNER, John M., President and Chief Executive Officer, Major Hospital, Shelbyville, IN, p. A219

HORNICK, Gregory MSN, Chief Nursing Officer, Martin General Hospital, Williamston, NC, p. A472

HORNSBY, Donny, Director Fiscal Services, Memphis Mental Health Institute, Memphis, TN, p. A584

HORNUNG, Dona, Director Information and Technology Services, Doctors Hospital, Augusta, GA, p. A151

HORNUNG, Kurt, Director, Medical Center Of Trinity, Trinity, FL, p. A146
Director, Medical Center Of Trinity, Trinity, FL, p. A146

HORRIGAN, Timothy M.D., Chief Quality Officer, Unitypoint Health – Waterloo, Waterloo, IA, p. A236

HORSLEY, Steve, Vice President and Chief Information Officer, Moses H. Cone Memorial Hospital, Greensboro, NC, p. A463

HORSMAN, Sandra, Director, Veterans Affairs Black Hills Health Care System, Fort Meade, SD, p. A570

HORST, Brad
Director Human Resources, Clear Lake Regional Medical Center, Webster, TX, p. A653
Vice President, Human Resources, Bay Area Regional Medical Center, Webster, TX, p. A653

HORSTMAN, Jennifer M R.N., Chief Nursing Officer and Chief Information Officer, Fairbanks, Indianapolis, IN, p. A211

HORTILLOSA, Maria M.D., Chief of Staff, Middlesboro Arh Hospital, Middlesboro, KY, p. A264

HORTON, Alan, Administrator, Putnam General Hospital, Eatonton, GA, p. A157

HORTON, Greg, Director Support Services, State Hospital South, Blackfoot, ID, p. A171

HORTON, Jerrilyn R.N., Chief Nursing Officer, Dewitt Hospital, Dewitt, AR, p. A42

HORTON, Jim, Chief Executive Officer, Rankin County Hospital District, Rankin, TX, p. A639

HORTON, Kenny, Director Information Systems, Walker Baptist Medical Center, Jasper, AL, p. A20

HORTON, Kimberly, R.N., MSN, Chief Executive Officer, Vibra Hospital Of Sacramento, Folsom, CA, p. A59

HORTON, Landon, Director of Nursing, Valley Behavioral Health System, Barling, AR, p. A40

HORTON, Marie, Director Associate Relations, Bartow Regional Medical Center, Bartow, FL, p. A119

HORTON, Sammy, Chief of Staff, Brownwood Regional Medical Center, Brownwood, TX, p. A599

HORTON, Warren, Information Technologist, Baptist Health Medical Center–Stuttgart, Stuttgart, AR, p. A50

HORVAT, Kami, Chief Financial Officer, West Covina Medical Center, West Covina, CA, p. A96
HORVATH, Alex
    Vice President and Chief Human Resources Officer, TMC Healthcare, Tucson, AZ, p. A38
    Vice President Human Resources, Methodist Hospitals, Gary, IN, p. A209
HORVATH, Holly, Director of Nursing, Jerome Golden Center For Behavioral Health, Inc., West Palm Beach, FL, p. A147
HOSKINS, Mary, Chief Executive Officer, Kindred Hospital Detroit, Detroit, MI, p. A318
HOSKINS, Pearly Graham M.D., President Medical Staff, Cape Fear Valley – Bladen County Hospital, Elizabethtown, NC, p. A462
HOSKINS, Shirley, Chief Operating Officer, Meadows Regional Medical Center, Vidalia, GA, p. A166
HOSS, Laurna, Human Resource Coordinator, Select Specialty Hospital–Omaha, Omaha, NE, p. A398
HOSTEENEZ, Vivie, Chief Financial Officer, San Carlos Apache Healthcare Corporation, Peridot, AZ, p. A32
HOSTETTER, Lynne, Vice President Human Resources, The Hsc Pediatric Center, Washington, DC, p. A118
HOTA, Bala, Interim Chief Information Officer, John H. Stroger Jr. Hospital Of Cook County, Chicago, IL, p. A181
HOTALING, Andrew, Chief Executive Officer, Forest View Psychiatric Hospital, Grand Rapids, MI, p. A320
HOTCHKISS, Jason
    Chief Financial Officer / Chief Operating Officer, Ottumwa Regional Health Center, Ottumwa, IA, p. A233
    Chief Financial Officer, Ottumwa Regional Health Center, Ottumwa, IA, p. A233
HOTCHKISS, Kaleigh, Controller, Healthsouth Rehabilitation Hospital Of Southern Arizona, Tucson, AZ, p. A38
HOTES, Lawrence S M.D., Chief Medical Officer, New England Sinai Hospital And Rehabilitation Center, Stoughton, MA, p. A312
HOUCHIN, Kim, Chief Nursing Officer, Minnie Hamilton Healthcare Center, Grantsville, WV, p. A692
HOUGH, Nathan, Chief Executive Officer, Crook County Medical Services District, Sundance, WY, p. A720
HOUGHTON, Roxan, Director Human Resources, Promise Hospital Of Miss Lou, Vidalia, LA, p. A287
HOULAHAN, Beth R.N., Senior Vice President and Chief Nursing Officer, University Of Wisconsin Hospitals And Clinics Authority, Madison, WI, p. A705
HOULE, David, Executive Vice President and Chief Financial Officer, Hebrew Center For Health Rehabilitation, West Hartford, CT, p. A114
HOULIHAN, David M.D., Chief of Staff, Tomah Veterans Affairs Medical Center, Tomah, WI, p. A714
HOUMANN, Lars D, President, Florida Hospital, Orlando, FL, p. A137
HOURANY, Joseph, Chief Medical Officer, Montclair Hospital Medical Center, Montclair, CA, p. A74
HOUSAND, Jill, Director Human Resources, Mesa Springs, Fort Worth, TX, p. A614
HOUSE, David
    Vice President and Chief Information Officer, Baptist Health Medical Center – North Little Rock, North Little Rock, AR, p. A48
    Vice President and Chief Information Officer, Baptist Health Medical Center–Arkadelphia, Arkadelphia, AR, p. A40
    Vice President and Chief Information Officer, Baptist Health Medical Center–Little Rock, Little Rock, AR, p. A46
    Vice President and Chief Information Officer, Baptist Health Rehabilitation Institute, Little Rock, AR, p. A46
    Vice President, Baptist Health Extended Care Hospital, Little Rock, AR, p. A46
HOUSE, John M.D., Chief of Staff, Eureka Springs Hospital, Eureka Springs, AR, p. A42
HOUSER, David M.D., Vice President Medical Affairs, Rapid City Regional Hospital, Rapid City, SD, p. A572
HOUSER, Kurt, Chief Operating Officer, University Medical Center, Las Vegas, NV, p. A404
HOUSER, Robert, FACHE, Chief Executive Officer, Pioneer Memorial Hospital, Heppner, OR, p. A522
HOUSER, Sara, Chief Nursing Officer, Ashe Memorial Hospital, Jefferson, NC, p. A465
HOUSER–HANFELDER, Sallie, FACHE, Director, Veterans Affairs Eastern Colorado Health Care System, Denver, CO, p. A101
HOUSER-HANFELDER, Sallie, FACHE, Director, Veterans Affairs Eastern Colorado Health Care System, Denver, CO, p. B42
HOUSH, Joe, District Director Human Resources, Kindred Hospital–Indianapolis, Indianapolis, IN, p. A211
HOUSLEY, Kristin
    Chief Information Officer, South Lincoln Medical Center, Kemmerer, WY, p. A718

HOUSLEY, Kristin, Interim Chief Executive Officer, South Lincoln Medical Center, Kemmerer, WY, p. A718
HOUSMAN, Bradley W. M.D., Chief Medical Officer, Baptist Health Paducah, Paducah, KY, p. A266
HOUSTON, Anthony, FACHE, President, Chi St. Vincent Hot Springs, Hot Springs, AR, p. A44
HOUSTON, Jerry, Director Information Systems, Jennie Stuart Medical Center, Hopkinsville, KY, p. A260
HOUSTON, Sally M.D., Executive Vice President and Chief Medical Officer, Tampa General Hospital, Tampa, FL, p. A145
HOVAN, Keith A, R.N., President and Chief Executive Officer, Southcoast Hospitals Group, Fall River, MA, p. A306
HOVDENES, Jodi Lynn, Vice President of Patient Care, Chi St Alexius Health Carrington Medical Center, Carrington, ND, p. A474
HOVE, Barton A., President and Chief-Executive Officer, Wellmont Health System, Kingsport, TN, p. B145
HOVENS, Michael R. M.D., Chief Medical Officer, Panola Medical Center, Batesville, MS, p. A352
HOWARD, Catherine, Director Human Resources, Sentara Halifax Regional Hospital, South Boston, VA, p. A675
HOWARD, Cindy, Director Financial Services, Nell J. Redfield Memorial Hospital, Malad City, ID, p. A174
HOWARD, Dan, Director, Information Services, San Gorgonio Memorial Hospital, Banning, CA, p. A53
HOWARD, Daniel, Chief Financial Officer, Maine Veterans Affairs Medical Center, Augusta, ME, p. A289
HOWARD, Darcy, Chief Financial Officer, Citizens Medical Center, Colby, KS, p. A239
HOWARD, Eddie L.
    Vice President and Chief Operating Officer, East Texas Medical Center Rehabilitation Hospital, Tyler, TX, p. A650
    Vice President and Chief Operating Officer, East Texas Medical Center Specialty Hospital, Tyler, TX, p. A651
    Chief Operating Officer, East Texas Medical Center Rehabilitation Hospital, Tyler, TX, p. A650
HOWARD, Gary L, Senior Vice President and Chief Financial Officer, Hamilton Medical Center, Dalton, GA, p. A156
HOWARD, Greg M
    Director Human Resource, Health Alliance Hospital – Broadway Campus, Kingston, NY, p. A438
    Vice President Human Resources, Health Alliance Hospital – Mary's Avenue Campus, Kingston, NY, p. A438
HOWARD, Gwenyth, Vice President Finance, St. Thomas More Hospital, Canon City, CO, p. A99
HOWARD, Kari, Interim Director of Nursing, Pauls Valley General Hospital, Pauls Valley, OK, p. A514
HOWARD, Lisa M., Director, Veterans Affairs Sierra Nevada Health Care System, Reno, NV, p. A405
HOWARD, Lisa M, Associate Director, Veterans Affairs Sierra Nevada Health Care System, Reno, NV, p. A405
HOWARD, Loy M., President and Chief Executive Officer, Tanner Health System, Carrollton, GA, p. B124
HOWARD, Mary, Director Human Resources, Winnebago Mental Health Institute, Winnebago, WI, p. A716
HOWARD, Melissa, Chief Nurse Executive, ICH & FPH, Citrus Valley Medical Center–Inter Community Campus, Covina, CA, p. A57
HOWARD, Michele, Vice President Nursing Services, Perry County Memorial Hospital, Tell City, IN, p. A220
HOWARD, Mike, Chief Operating Officer, Eliza Coffee Memorial Hospital, Florence, AL, p. A18
HOWARD, Opal R, Executive Director Human Resources, Florida Hospital Memorial Medical Center, Daytona Beach, FL, p. A123
HOWARD, Pamela B., R.N., Chief Executive Officer, Administrator and Risk Manager, Lake Butler Hospital Hand Surgery Center, Lake Butler, FL, p. A129
HOWARD, Ron, Chief Financial Officer, Holly Hill Hospital, Raleigh, NC, p. A469
HOWARD, Sabra, Manager Human Resources, Harlan Arh Hospital, Harlan, KY, p. A259
HOWARD, Teresa, Manager Human Resources, Yoakum County Hospital, Denver City, TX, p. A608
HOWARD, Tim, Chief Human Resources Officer, Fountain Valley Regional Hospital And Medical Center, Fountain Valley, CA, p. A60
HOWARD, Timothy W., Chief Executive Officer, Amg Integrated Healthcare Management, Lafayette, LA, p. B9
HOWARD, Tom, Chief Financial Officer, Texas Health Presbyterian Hospital Flower Mound, Flower Mound, TX, p. A612
HOWARD, Win, Chief Executive Officer, Asante Three Rivers Medical Center, Grants Pass, OR, p. A522
HOWARD–CROW, Dallis, Chief Human Resources Officer, Emory University Hospital Midtown, Atlanta, GA, p. A150
HOWAT, Greg, Vice President Human Resources, Eastern Maine Medical Center, Bangor, ME, p. A289

HOWDEN, William, Vice President Nursing, Good Samaritan Regional Medical Center, Corvallis, OR, p. A521
HOWE, Debbie, Chief Executive Officer, Weatherford Regional Hospital, Weatherford, OK, p. A519
HOWE, James L, Director Human Resources, Pinnacle Pointe Hospital, Little Rock, AR, p. A46
HOWE, Judson, Chief Financial Officer, Frank R. Howard Memorial Hospital, Willits, CA, p. A97
HOWE, Kenneth M.D., Chief Medical Officer, Southern New Hampshire Medical Center, Nashua, NH, p. A409
HOWE, Mary Lenzini, Vice President Human Resources, Geisinger–Bloomsburg Hospital, Bloomsburg, PA, p. A530
HOWE, Vicki, Health Information Management, Ness County Hospital District No 2, Ness City, KS, p. A247
HOWELL, Amy M, Director Human Resources, St. Luke's Behavioral Health Center, Phoenix, AZ, p. A34
HOWELL, Bradley, Chief Executive Officer, Roundup Memorial Healthcare, Roundup, MT, p. A388
HOWELL, Carrie, Chief Financial Officer, Barstow Community Hospital, Barstow, CA, p. A53
HOWELL, Diana, Director Human Resources, Conroe Regional Medical Center, Conroe, TX, p. A602
HOWELL, Jerry, Administrator, Sabine County Hospital, Hemphill, TX, p. A618
HOWELL, Jill, Chief Nursing Officer, St. Luke's Jerome, Jerome, ID, p. A173
HOWELL, Kathy A, Vice President Human Resources, Lexington Medical Center, West Columbia, SC, p. A567
HOWELL, Kristie, System Information Technology Director, Southampton Memorial Hospital, Franklin, VA, p. A667
HOWELL, Nathan, President and Chief Executive Officer, Claxton–Hepburn Medical Center, Ogdensburg, NY, p. A448
HOWELL, Pat, Chief Nursing Officer, Community Memorial Hospital, Syracuse, NE, p. A400
HOWELL, Ronene, Director Health Information Management, Bryce Hospital, Tuscaloosa, AL, p. A23
HOWELL, Sheri, Deputy Commander Nursing, Brooke Army Medical Center, Fort Sam Houston, TX, p. A613
HOWELL, Timothy W. R.N., Senior Vice President and Chief Nursing Officer, University Medical Center, Lubbock, TX, p. A631
HOWELLS, Stephen, Chief Financial Officer, Kane County Hospital, Kanab, UT, p. A657
HOWERTER, Mark M.D., President Medical Staff, Columbus Community Hospital, Columbus, NE, p. A392
HOWERTON, Russell M M.D., Chief Medical Officer, Wake Forest Baptist Medical Center, Winston, NC, p. A473
HOWERTON, Shawn, M.D., Chief Executive Officer and President, Medical Staff, Sampson Regional Medical Center, Clinton, NC, p. A460
HOWLAND, Sheryl R.N., Executive Director, Patient Care Services, Community Hospital Long Beach, Long Beach, CA, p. A66
HOY, Jonathan B, Chief Financial Officer, Duke Regional Hospital, Durham, NC, p. A461
HOYER, Sara, Director Administrative Services, Kansas Neurological Institute, Topeka, KS, p. A252
HOYES, Garry W., Chief Executive Officer, Columbus Dublin Springs, Dublin, OH, p. A490
HOYOS, Kent, Chief Information Officer, Pomona Valley Hospital Medical Center, Pomona, CA, p. A80
HOYT, Nancy R.N., Vice President Operations/Clinical and Chief Nursing Officer, Mercy Regional Medical Center, Durango, CO, p. A101
HRIT, Barbara, Controller, Beaumont Hospital – Farmington Hills, Farmington Hills, MI, p. A319
HRITZ, Diane, Chief Financial Officer, Advanced Surgical Hospital, Washington, PA, p. A552
HRON, Janine, Chief Executive Officer, Saint Luke's Hospital Of Kansas City, Kansas City, MO, p. A370
HRUBIAK, Dan, Associate Computer Program Analyst, Western New York Children's Hospital Psychiatric Center, West Seneca, NY, p. A455
HRUBY, Deidre, Director of Patient Care, Madelia Community Hospital, Madelia, MN, p. A342
HSIEH, Ketty, Senior Director Finance, Uw Medicine/ Northwest Hospital & Medical Center, Seattle, WA, p. A686
HSING, Shirley
    Chief Financial Officer, North Oaks Medical Center, Hammond, LA, p. A275
    Senior Vice President, Chief Financial Officer, North Oaks Health System, North Oaks Rehabilitation Hospital, Hammond, LA, p. A275
HSU, Wah Chung, Senior Vice President Finance, San Antonio Regional Hospital, Upland, CA, p. A95
HUANG, Joseph M.D., Chief Medical and Quality Officer, Legacy Silverton Medical Center, Silverton, OR, p. A527
HUBBARD, Bill, Vice President, Operations, Carolinas Healthcare System Northeast, Concord, NC, p. A460

HUBBARD, Blake W., FACHE, Chief Executive Officer, Foundation Surgical Hospital Of San Antonio, San Antonio, TX, p. A642

HUBBARD, Brent
Chief Operating Officer, Mercy Hospital Ozark, Ozark, AR, p. A48
Chief Operating Officer, Mercy Hospital Paris, Paris, AR, p. A48
Chief Operating Officer, Mercy Hospital Waldron, Waldron, AR, p. A50

HUBBARD, Daniel, Chief Financial Officer, Sioux Falls Veterans Affairs Health Care System, Sioux Falls, SD, p. A573

HUBBARD, Gwen, Chief Nursing Officer, Sierra Vista Hospital, Sacramento, CA, p. A84

HUBBARD, Kathy
Controller, Ocean Beach Hospital, Ilwaco, WA, p. A681
Manager Human Resources, Nell J. Redfield Memorial Hospital, Malad City, ID, p. A174

HUBBARD, Lisa, Vice President and Chief Nursing Executive, Mercy Medical Center Mount Shasta, Mount Shasta, CA, p. A75

HUBBARD, Mark, Vice President Risk Management, Loma Linda University Behavioral Medicine Center, Redlands, CA, p. A81

HUBBARD, Norm, Executive Vice President, Seattle Cancer Care Alliance, Seattle, WA, p. A685

HUBBARD, Tyson, Director Human Resources, Stanislaus Surgical Hospital, Modesto, CA, p. A74

HUBBS, Olas A. III, FACHE, President and Chief Executive Officer, Memorial Health, Marysville, OH, p. A495

HUBEL, Ed, President, Baptist Medical Center Nassau, Fernandina Beach, FL, p. A124

HUBER, Dalton, Chief Financial Officer, Campbell County Health, Gillette, WY, p. A718

HUBER, Joseph M, Chief Financial Officer, Hospital Of The University Of Pennsylvania, Philadelphia, PA, p. A544

HUBER, Vicki Lynn R.N., MSN, Chief Nursing Officer, Abrazo Scottsdale Campus, Phoenix, AZ, p. A33

HUBL, Bryan M.D., Chief of Staff, Thayer County Health Services, Hebron, NE, p. A394

HUBLEY, Grover M.D., President Medical Staff, Chi St. Joseph Health Madison Hospital, Madisonville, TX, p. A631

HUBSCHMAN, Gary
Administrative Director Finance, Sutter Auburn Faith Hospital, Auburn, CA, p. A52
Administrative Director Finance, Sutter Roseville Medical Center, Roseville, CA, p. A83

HUCK, Karma, Chief Operating Officer, Scott County Hospital, Scott City, KS, p. A251

HUCKABEE, Mike, Network Administrator, Coryell Memorial Hospital, Gatesville, TX, p. A616

HUCKABY, Don, Chief Information Management Service, Veterans Affairs Eastern Colorado Health Care System, Denver, CO, p. A101

HUDA, Edith, Director Human Resources, Daniels Memorial Healthcare Center, Scobey, MT, p. A388

HUDAK, Corey, Director Human Resources, Memorial Hospital, York, PA, p. A555

HUDDLESTON, Tina R.N., Chief Nursing Officer, Baylor Medical Center At Trophy Club, Trophy Club, TX, p. A650

HUDGENS, Roselyn, Director Human Resources, Ballinger Memorial Hospital, Ballinger, TX, p. A596

HUDGINS, Paul C., Senior Vice President, Carilion Franklin Memorial Hospital, Rocky Mount, VA, p. A675

HUDNELL, Sharon R.N., Chief Nursing Officer, Wk Bossier Health Center, Bossier City, LA, p. A272

HUDSON, Beth, Chief Nursing Officer, Baylor Institute For Rehabilitation, Dallas, TX, p. A604

HUDSON, Gary Mikeal., Administrator, East Texas Medical Center Carthage, Carthage, TX, p. A601

HUDSON, Gary Mikeal, Administrator, East Texas Medical Center Carthage, Carthage, TX, p. B122

HUDSON, Guy, Chief Executive Officer, Swedish/Issaquah, Issaquah, WA, p. A681

HUDSON, Janell, Chief Clinical Officer, Sanford Medical Center Thief River Falls, Thief River Falls, MN, p. A349

HUDSON, Kayce H, Executive Director Human Resources, Saddleback Memorial Medical Center, Laguna Hills, CA, p. A65

HUDSON, Kenneth J, Chief Financial Officer, Veterans Affairs Puget Sound Health Care System, Seattle, WA, p. A686

HUDSON, Kent, Chief Financial Officer, Kingman Community Hospital, Kingman, KS, p. A244

HUDSON, Larry C, Executive Vice President and Chief Financial Officer, Charleston Area Medical Center, Charleston, WV, p. A691

HUDSON, Lowell K, Chief Financial Officer, Glen Oaks Hospital, Greenville, TX, p. A617

HUDSON, Maggie, Chief Financial and Operations Officer, Santiam Hospital, Stayton, OR, p. A527

HUDSON, MeKinzie, Chief Financial Officer, Stafford County Hospital, Stafford, KS, p. A252

HUDSON, Mike, Administrator, Federal Correctional Institute Hospital, Littleton, CO, p. A105

HUDSON, Pamela, M.D., Chief Executive Officer, Crestwood Medical Center, Huntsville, AL, p. A19

HUDSON, R. Guy., Chief Executive Officer, Swedish Health Services, Seattle, WA, p. B124

HUDSON, Robbi, Chief Executive Officer, Healthsouth Rehabilitation Hospital–Wichita Falls, Wichita Falls, TX, p. A654

HUDSON–JINKS, Therese M. R.N., MSN, Chief Nursing Officer, Tufts Medical Center, Boston, MA, p. A304

HUEBNER, Thomas W., President, Rutland Regional Medical Center, Rutland, VT, p. A663

HUELSKAMP, Donald, Interim Chief Financial Officer, Harrison Community Hospital, Cadiz, OH, p. A482

HUENERGARDT, Sam D., Chief Executive Officer, Parker Adventist Hospital, Parker, CO, p. A106

HUERTA, Brad, Chief Executive Officer and Administrator, Lost Rivers Medical Center, Arco, ID, p. A171

HUERTA, Guillermo M.D., Chief Medical Officer, Select Specialty Hospital–Omaha, Omaha, NE, p. A398

HUERTA, Jose, Chief Executive Officer, El Paso Ltac Hospital, El Paso, TX, p. A610

HUERTER, Holly
Vice President Human Resources, Methodist Jennie Edmundson Hospital, Council Bluffs, IA, p. A225
Vice President Human Resources, Nebraska Methodist Hospital, Omaha, NE, p. A398

HUESMAN, Carol, Chief Information Officer, Major Hospital, Shelbyville, IN, p. A219

HUETTL, Patricia, Vice President Finance and Chief Financial Officer, Holy Family Memorial, Manitowoc, WI, p. A706

HUFF, Donnie M.D., Chief Medical Officer, Livingston Regional Hospital, Livingston, TN, p. A583

HUFF, Jeff, Assistant Administrator Finance, Fayette Medical Center, Fayette, AL, p. A17

HUFF, Matt, Chief Financial Officer, Bay Area Medical Center, Marinette, WI, p. A706

HUFF, Michael H., Chief Executive Officer, Hamilton Hospital, Olney, TX, p. A636

HUFF, Shelly E, Manager Human Resources, Indiana University Health Tipton Hospital, Tipton, IN, p. A220

HUFFMAN, David, Vice President and Controller, Select Specialty Hospital—Wilmington, Wilmington, DE, p. A116

HUFFMAN, James, Chief Executive Officer and Administrator, Baptist Memorial Hospital–Desoto, Southaven, MS, p. A362

HUFFMAN, Joshua M.D., Chief Medical Staff, Saint Joseph Berea, Berea, KY, p. A255

HUFFMAN, Sherry, Administrator Human Resources, Beaumont Hospital–Dearborn, Dearborn, MI, p. A317

HUFFMAN, Steve, Chief Information Officer, Elkhart General Hospital, Elkhart, IN, p. A207

HUFFMAN, Tim, Western Region Director, Information Systems Business Relationships, Baylor Scott & White Medical Center–Irving, Irving, TX, p. A624

HUFFNER, William, M.D.
Chief Medical Officer, University Of Maryland Shore Medical Center At Chestertown, Chestertown, MD, p. A297
Chief Medical Officer, University Of Maryland Shore Medical Center At Easton, Easton, MD, p. A298
Vice President Medical Affairs, University Of Maryland Shore Medical Center At Dorchester, Cambridge, MD, p. A297

HUFFSTUTLER, Brandon, Chief Information Officer, Electra Memorial Hospital, Electra, TX, p. A612

HUFNAGEL, Keith, Director Human Resources, Stillwater Medical Center, Stillwater, OK, p. A516

HUGAR, Joseph, MD, President, Sharon Regional Health System, Sharon, PA, p. B122

HUGAR, Joseph G., President, Sharon Regional Health System, Sharon, PA, p. A551

HUGGINS, Lois, Chief Human Resources Officer and Senior Vice President Human Resources, Shirley Ryan Abilitylab, Chicago, IL, p. A183

HUGGINS, Michael C, Administrator Network System, Eastern Oklahoma Medical Center, Poteau, OK, p. A514

HUGHES, April, Chief Financial Officer, Peachford Behavioral Health System, Atlanta, GA, p. A150

HUGHES, Bill, Chief Nursing Officer, Granville Health System, Oxford, NC, p. A468

HUGHES, Brandon, Director Human Resources, Hermann Area District Hospital, Hermann, MO, p. A369

HUGHES, Chad
Chief Information Officer, North Texas State Hospital, Wichita Falls Campus, Wichita Falls, TX, p. A654
Information Officer, North Texas State Hospital, Vernon, TX, p. A651

HUGHES, Constance, Director of Nursing, West Gables Rehabilitation Hospital, Miami, FL, p. A134

HUGHES, David S, Chief Financial Officer, Vidant Medical Center, Greenville, NC, p. A463

HUGHES, Dustan M.D., Vice President Medical Affairs, Saint Alphonsus Medical Center – Nampa, Nampa, ID, p. A174

HUGHES, Elisabeth, Director Human Resources and Community Relations, Fairview Regional Medical Center, Fairview, OK, p. A508

HUGHES, James, Director Human Resources, Lake Cumberland Regional Hospital, Somerset, KY, p. A267

HUGHES, Jessica, Director Finance, Hawarden Regional Healthcare, Hawarden, IA, p. A229

HUGHES, Lee R.N., Chief Nursing Officer, Flint River Community Hospital, Montezuma, GA, p. A162

HUGHES, Leigh Ann, Chief Financial Officer, Hardin Medical Center, Savannah, TN, p. A588

HUGHES, Lori, R.N., MSN
Chief Nursing Officer, Vice President Operations & Patient Care Services, Cottage Hospital, Woodsville, NH, p. A410
Chief Nursing Officer, Vice President Operations and Patient Care Services, Cottage Hospital, Woodsville, NH, p. A410

HUGHES, Mark A. M.D., Medical Director, River Park Hospital, Huntington, WV, p. A693

HUGHES, Michael, M.D., President, Summa Health System Barberton, Summa Health System, Akron, OH, p. A479

HUGHES, Robert K., Chief Executive Officer, NYC Health + Hospitals / Carter, New Rochelle, NY, p. A444

HUGHES, Sandra, Chief Financial Officer, Clinch Memorial Hospital, Homerville, GA, p. A159

HUGHES, Susan, Interim Director Human Resources, Winner Regional Healthcare Center, Winner, SD, p. A574

HUGHES, Terry, Director Information Systems, Nantucket Cottage Hospital, Nantucket, MA, p. A309

HUGHES, Thomas, President, St. Joseph Health Services Of Rhode Island, North Providence, RI, p. A556

HUGHES, Veronica, Chief Nursing Officer, Mesilla Valley Hospital, Las Cruces, NM, p. A427

HUGHES–MICKEL, Leann, Chief Information Officer, Touro Infirmary, New Orleans, LA, p. A283

HUGHS, Mary, Chief Human Resources Officer, Our Lady Of Lourdes Memorial Hospital, Inc., Binghamton, NY, p. A432

HUGHSON, John R., Vice President Operations, Scott & White Hospital – Brenham, Brenham, TX, p. A599

HULBERT, Kim R.N., Chief Clinical Officer, Madison County Health Care System, Winterset, IA, p. A237

HULETT, Rachelle, Vice President Human Resources, Mclaren Flint, Flint, MI, p. A319

HULETT, Wendi, Chief Nursing Officer, Artesia General Hospital, Artesia, NM, p. A425

HULL, Brad, Chief Financial Officer, Dale Medical Center, Ozark, AL, p. A22

HULL, Debbie, Chief Financial Officer, Fisher County Hospital District, Rotan, TX, p. A640

HULL, Kathy, President and Chief Executive Officer, Illini Community Hospital, Pittsfield, IL, p. A198

HULL, Ken, Director Human Resources, Inova Fairfax Hospital, Falls Church, VA, p. A666

HULLINGER, Angela, Chief Executive Officer, Meadowbrook Rehabilitation Hospital, Gardner, KS, p. A241

HULSEY, Cathy, Manager of Human Resources, Cornerstone Medical Center, Fort Oglethorpe, GA, p. A158

HULSEY, Grant, Director Information Technology, Baylor Scott & White Surgical Hospital At Sherman, Sherman, TX, p. A645

HULSEY, Kelly, Chief Nursing Officer, Piedmont Hospital, Atlanta, GA, p. A150

HUMBERT, Gilbert Glenn Jr, Interim Chief Nursing Officer, Eliza Coffee Memorial Hospital, Florence, AL, p. A18

HUMBLE, Kathryn G., Chief Human Resources Officer, Beatrice Community Hospital And Health Center, Beatrice, NE, p. A391

HUMBLE, Linnea, Director of Finance, Sutter Lakeside Hospital, Lakeport, CA, p. A65

HUME, Diana, Manager Human Resources, Methodist Mckinney Hospital, Mckinney, TX, p. A632

HUMES, Karen, Chief Information Officer, Titusville Area Hospital, Titusville, PA, p. A551

HUMES, Ronny, Chief Executive Officer, Magnolia Regional Health Center, Corinth, MS, p. A354

HUMME, Sarah, MSN, R.N.
Chief Nursing Officer, Southwest General Hospital, San Antonio, TX, p. A644
Chief Operating Officer, Southwest General Hospital, San Antonio, TX, p. A644

HUMMEL, Angela, Vice President Human Resources, Evangelical Community Hospital, Lewisburg, PA, p. A539

HUMMELKE, Arlita, Manager Human Resources, Mercy Hospital Tishomingo, Tishomingo, OK, p. A517

HUMMER, Christopher R., President, Carolinas Healthcare System Pineville, Charlotte, NC, p. A459

HUMMER, Denise R.N., Vice President Administrative Services, Community Memorial Hospital, Hamilton, NY, p. A437

HUMPHREY, Dale, Chief Executive Officer, Saint Thomas River Park Hospital, Mc Minnville, TN, p. A583

HUMPHREY, James, Vice President Talent Resources and Human Resources for South Side Operating Group, Penrose–St. Francis Health Services, Colorado Springs, CO, p. A100

HUMPHREY, Randy, Chief Financial Officer, Merit Health Wesley, Hattiesburg, MS, p. A356

HUMPHREY, Richard, Executive Vice President and Chief Financial Officer, Parkland Health & Hospital System, Dallas, TX, p. A606

HUMPHREYS, Corina, Chief Operating Officer, Weslaco Regional Rehabilitation Hospital, Weslaco, TX, p. A654

HUMPHREYS, Lynn, Director Human Resources, Henry County Health Center, Mount Pleasant, IA, p. A232

HUMPHRIES, Vickie Witcher
Director Human Resources, Bon Secours Maryview Medical Center, Portsmouth, VA, p. A673
Vice President Human Resources, Bon Secours–Depaul Medical Center, Norfolk, VA, p. A671
Vice President Human Resources, Mary Immaculate Hospital, Newport News, VA, p. A671

HUNDAL, Ranjit M.D., Chief Medical Executive, Mills–Peninsula Health Services, Burlingame, CA, p. A54

HUNDORFEAN, Cynthia, President and Chief Executive Officer, Allegheny Health Network, Pittsburgh, PA, p. B8

HUNGER, Bryan, Chief Executive Officer, Jefferson County Health Center, Fairfield, IA, p. A227

HUNGER, Dennis, Chief Executive Officer, Washington County Hospital And Clinics, Washington, IA, p. A236

HUNSAKER, Mike
Chief Operating Officer, Star Valley Medical Center, Afton, WY, p. A717
Interim President and Chief Executive Officer, Star Valley Medical Center, Afton, WY, p. A717

HUNSBERGER, Tom, Director Human Resources, Olmsted Medical Center, Rochester, MN, p. A347

HUNSICKER, Elizabeth, Chief Executive Officer, West Valley Medical Center, Caldwell, ID, p. A172

HUNT, Amy, Director Human Resources, Menorah Medical Center, Overland Park, KS, p. A249

HUNT, Cheri R.N., Vice President Patient Care Services and Chief Nursing Officer, Children's Mercy Hospital Kansas City, Kansas City, MO, p. A370

HUNT, Cheryl Esq, Vice President Chief Nursing Officer, St. Peter's Hospital, Helena, MT, p. A385

HUNT, Chris, President, Clay County Hospital, Flora, IL, p. A187

HUNT, Christopher, Director, Information Technologies, FISO, Helena Regional Medical Center, Helena, AR, p. A44

HUNT, D Deann, Director Human Resources, Gibson General Hospital, Princeton, IN, p. A218

HUNT, Deloris, Corporate Vice President Human Resources, DMC Harper University Hospital, Detroit, MI, p. A318

HUNT, Don M.D., Vice President Patient Centered Care and Chief Nursing Officer, University Of Texas Health Northeast, Tyler, TX, p. A651

HUNT, Jeffery B, Vice President, Business Development and Support Services, Roane General Hospital, Spencer, WV, p. A696

HUNT, John R., Chief Executive Officer, Healthsouth Rehabilitation Hospital Of Western Massachusetts, Ludlow, MA, p. A308

HUNT, Julie R.N., MS, Chief Nursing Officer, Oro Valley Hospital, Oro Valley, AZ, p. A32

HUNT, Karen, Executive Director, Harsha Behavioral Center, Terre Haute, IN, p. A220

HUNT, Kathy, Chief Executive Officer, Elmwood Healthcare Center At The Springs, Green Springs, OH, p. A492

HUNT, Lynelle, Director of Nursing, Indian Health Service – Quentin N. Burdick Memorial Health Care Facility, Belcourt, ND, p. A474

HUNT, Mary Miles., Chief Executive Officer, Ballard Rehabilitation Hospital, San Bernardino, CA, p. A85

HUNT, Nick, Interim Director of Nursing, Mercy Hospital Waldron, Waldron, AR, p. A50

HUNT, Reta, Director of Nursing, Baylor Scott & White Medical Center – Llano, Llano, TX, p. A629

HUNT, Richard M.D., Chief Operating Officer, Kaiser Sunnyside Medical Center, Clackamas, OR, p. A520

HUNT, W. Jeffrey., Chief Executive Officer, Brandywine Hospital, Coatesville, PA, p. A532

HUNT, Wade, Chief Operating Officer, Peacehealth Southwest Medical Center, Vancouver, WA, p. A688

HUNT, William Robert, Chief Financial Officer, Reynolds Memorial Hospital, Glen Dale, WV, p. A692

HUNTER, Bridgette, Chief Operating Officer, Southwest Idaho Advanced Care Hospital, Boise, ID, p. A172

HUNTER, Byron, Vice President Human Resources, Cape Regional Medical Center, Cape May Court House, NJ, p. A412

HUNTER, Diana, Director of Nursing, Fort Belknap Service Unit, Harlem, MT, p. A385

HUNTER, Fred, R.N., Chief Executive Officer, Desert Valley Hospital, Victorville, CA, p. A96

HUNTER, George, Interim Chief Human Resources Officer, Tuba City Regional Health Care Corporation, Tuba City, AZ, p. A37

HUNTER, Jerry, Vice President, Information Technology, Crotched Mountain Rehabilitation Center, Greenfield, NH, p. A408

HUNTER, Ken, R.N., Chief Executive Officer, Kimball Health Services, Kimball, NE, p. A394

HUNTER, Linda, Chief Nursing Officer, Spring View Hospital, Lebanon, KY, p. A260

HUNTER, Mary Ann, Director Nursing Services, Baptist Easley Hospital, Easley, SC, p. A561

HUNTER, Shelly
Chief Financial Officer, Mercy Hospital Fort Scott, Fort Scott, KS, p. A241
Chief Financial Officer, Mercy Hospital Joplin, Joplin, MO, p. A370

HUNTER, Stephanie, Chief Human Resources Officer, Veterans Affairs Ann Arbor Healthcare System, Ann Arbor, MI, p. A314

HUNTER, Terri Lynn R.N., Nurse Administrator, American Fork Hospital, American Fork, UT, p. A656

HUNTER, Tracy, Chief Human Resources Officer, East Cooper Medical Center, Mount Pleasant, SC, p. A564

HUNTLEY, Adrienne
Chief Human Resources Officer, Saint Francis Hospital–Bartlett, Bartlett, TN, p. A575
Director Human Resources, Healthsouth Rehabilitation Hospital Memphis–North, Memphis, TN, p. A584

HUNTLEY, Devin, Vice President Operations, Community Medical Center, Missoula, MT, p. A386

HUNTON, David M.D., Chief Medical Officer, Mercy Hospital Fort Smith, Fort Smith, AR, p. A43

HUNTSINGER, Kelli, Chief Operating Officer, Northern Inyo Hospital, Bishop, CA, p. A54

HUPF, Angela C., Vice President Human Resources and Community Relations, Aspirus Medford Hospital & Clinics, Inc., Medford, WI, p. A706

HUPP, Diane R.N., Vice President Support Services and Patient Care Services, Children's Hospital Of Pittsburgh Of Upmc, Pittsburgh, PA, p. A546

HURD, Debra J, R.N., MS
Vice President and Chief Nursing Officer, Woodwinds Health Campus, Woodbury, MN, p. A351
Vice President Nursing Acute Care, St. John's Hospital, Maplewood, MN, p. A343
Vice President Nursing, St. Joseph's Hospital, Saint Paul, MN, p. A348

HURD, Ross, Chief Information Officer, Lake Chelan Community Hospital And Clinics, Chelan, WA, p. A679

HURFORD, Bill, Chief Medical Officer, University Of Cincinnati Medical Center, Cincinnati, OH, p. A485

HURLBUT, Marty M.D., Medical Director, Healthsouth Rehabilitation Hospital, Fayetteville, AR, p. A42

HURLEY, Al, Clinic Chief Operating Officer, Sanford Bismarck, Bismarck, ND, p. A474

HURLEY, Jeff, Vice President Human Resources, Flagler Hospital, Saint Augustine, FL, p. A141

HURLEY, Sandra MS, R.N., Chief Nursing Officer, Valley View Hospital, Glenwood Springs, CO, p. A103

HURLEY, William M.D., Chief Medical Officer, Summit Pacific Medical Center, Elma, WA, p. A680

HUROWITZ, Marc P., D.O., President and Chief Executive Officer, Jeanes Hospital, Philadelphia, PA, p. A544

HURSH, John, Vice President Human Resources, Cox Medical Centers, Springfield, MO, p. A379

HURSHE, Joseph R., President, Providence–Providence Park Hospitals, Southfield, MI, p. A331

HURSHE, Joseph R, President, Providence–Providence Park Hospitals, Southfield, MI, p. A331

HURST, Paul M.D., Chief Medical Officer, Banner Heart Hospital, Mesa, AZ, p. A31

HURST, Steve, Information Technology Specialist, Haskell County Community Hospital, Stigler, OK, p. A516

HURT, Carol Anne, Chief Nursing Officer, Tippah County Hospital, Ripley, MS, p. A361

HURT, Christie M.D., Chief of Staff and Medical Director, Mercy Hospital Aurora, Aurora, MO, p. A364

HURT, Kelly, Chief Human Resources Officer Northern Colorado and Western Region, Banner Fort Collins Medical Center, Fort Collins, CO, p. A102

HURT, Todd, Administrator, State Hospital North, Orofino, ID, p. A175

HURT–DEITCH, Sally A., Market Chief Executive Officer, The Hospitals Of Providence Memorial Campus, El Paso, TX, p. A611

HURTADO, Xochy, FACHE, Chief Executive Officer, Val Verde Regional Medical Center, Del Rio, TX, p. A608

HURWITZ, Steven, Senior Vice President Shared Services, Seattle Children's Hospital, Seattle, WA, p. A685

HURZELER, Rosemary Johnson., President and Chief Executive Officer, The Connecticut Hospice, Branford, CT, p. A109

HUSAIN, Syed Arshad M.D., Executive Vice President and Chief Medical Officer, Royal Oaks Hospital, Windsor, MO, p. A381

HUSEBY, Custer, Chief Executive Officer, Vibra Hospital Of Fargo, Fargo, ND, p. A476

HUSHER, Phil, Chief Financial Officer, Winner Regional Healthcare Center, Winner, SD, p. A574

HUSHING–KLINE, Bob, Hospital Administrator, Atascadero State Hospital, Atascadero, CA, p. A52

HUSKEY, Jeff, Chief Executive Officer and Administrator, Clay County Memorial Hospital, Henrietta, TX, p. A619

HUSS, Cathy, Chief Financial Officer, Lifecare Medical Center, Roseau, MN, p. A347

HUSSAIN, Hamid M.D., Medical Director, Our Lady Of The Angels Hospital, Bogalusa, LA, p. A272

HUSSAIN, Iftikhar, Chief Financial Officer, El Camino Hospital, Mountain View, CA, p. A75

HUSSEY, Jamie, Chief Information Officer, Jackson Hospital, Marianna, FL, p. A131

HUSSEY, Stephen M.D., Chief of Staff, Lake District Hospital, Lakeview, OR, p. A523

HUSSON, Charles, Regional Chief Medical Officer, Genesys Regional Medical Center, Grand Blanc, MI, p. A320

HUSTEDT, Dale, Chief Executive Officer, Avera Holy Family Hospital, Estherville, IA, p. A227

HUSTON, Jennifer, Chief Nursing Officer, Lake Wales Medical Center, Lake Wales, FL, p. A130

HUSTON, William R, Senior Vice President and Chief Financial Officer, Texas Scottish Rite Hospital For Children, Dallas, TX, p. A607

HUTCHENRIDER, E. Kenneth. Jr, FACHE, President, Methodist Richardson Medical Center, Richardson, TX, p. A639

HUTCHENS, Zachary M.D., Chief Medical Officer, Saint Thomas Hickman Hospital, Centerville, TN, p. A576

HUTCHES, Trampas, Chief Executive Officer, Melissa Memorial Hospital, Holyoke, CO, p. A104

HUTCHESON, Lorie, Vice President of Human Resources, Shepherd Center, Atlanta, GA, p. A151

HUTCHESON, Lou Ellen M.D., Chief of Staff, Bacon County Hospital And Health System, Alma, GA, p. A149

HUTCHINS, Anne M.D., Chief of Staff, Salem Veterans Affairs Medical Center, Salem, VA, p. A675

HUTCHINS, Michael T., Administrator, Jay Hospital, Jay, FL, p. A129

HUTCHINS–OTERO, Kathy, Chief Clinical Officer, Kindred Rehabilitation Hospital Clear Lake, Webster, TX, p. A653

HUTCHINSON, James CPA, Chief Financial Officer, Affinity Medical Center, Massillon, OH, p. A495

HUTCHISON, Barbra, Director Medical Records, Richland Parish Hospital, Delhi, LA, p. A274

HUTCHISON, Florence N. M.D., Chief of Staff, Ralph H. Johnson Veterans Affairs Medical Center, Charleston, SC, p. A559

HUTCHISON, Harry, Vice President Fiscal Services, St. Bernards Medical Center, Jonesboro, AR, p. A45

HUTCHISON, Lewis, Vice President Operations and Quality, Ashtabula County Medical Center, Ashtabula, OH, p. A480

HUTCHSIN, Joel M.D., Chief Medical Staff, Holton Community Hospital, Holton, KS, p. A242

HUTH, Michael, Chief Financial Officer, Sycamore Springs Hospital, Lafayette, IN, p. A214

HUTH, Richard
Administrator, South Georgia Medical Center Berrien Campus, Nashville, GA, p. A162
Administrator, South Georgia Medical Center Lanier Campus, Lakeland, GA, p. A160

HUTH, Thomas M.D., Vice President Medical Affairs, Reid Health, Richmond, IN, p. A219

HUTSELL, Dick, Vice President Information Technology Services, Saint Louise Regional Hospital, Gilroy, CA, p. A61

HUTSELL, Richard, Vice President and Chief Information Officer, Daughters of Charity Health System, O'Connor Hospital, San Jose, CA, p. A88

HUTSON, Donald
Chief Executive Officer, University Of Mississippi Medical Center Grenada, Grenada, MS, p. A355
Chief Executive Officer, University Of Mississippi Medical Center Holmes County, Lexington, MS, p. A358
HUTSON, Joy M, Director Human Resources, Merit Health Rankin, Brandon, MS, p. A353
HUTSON, Mark S, Chief Information Officer, Greenwood Leflore Hospital, Greenwood, MS, p. A355
HUTSON, Marty, Chief Financial Officer, St. Mary's Health Care System, Athens, GA, p. A149
HUTSON, Vivian T., Director, Cincinnati Veterans Affairs Medical Center, Cincinnati, OH, p. A484
HUTSON, Wayne
Chief Financial Officer, Union Hospital Clinton, Clinton, IN, p. A205
Executive Vice President and Chief Financial Officer, Union Hospital, Terre Haute, IN, p. A220
HUTT, Si William., Administrator, Park City Hospital, Park City, UT, p. A659
HUTTER, Elizabeth, Chief Executive Officer, Cedar Hills Hospital, Portland, OR, p. A526
HUTTER, George, M.D.
Chief Medical Officer, St. Petersburg General Hospital, Saint Petersburg, FL, p. A142
Chief of Staff, Palms Of Pasadena Hospital, Saint Petersburg, FL, p. A141
HUVAL, Shadelle, Director Finance, St. Martin Hospital, Breaux Bridge, LA, p. A272
HUYCKE, Mark M.D., Chief of Staff, Oklahoma City Veterans Affairs Medical Center, Oklahoma City, OK, p. A513
HUYNH, Thai M.D., Chief of Medical Staff, El Campo Memorial Hospital, El Campo, TX, p. A610
HYATT, Charlotte, MSN, R.N., Chief Operating Officer and Chief Nursing Officer, Carelink Of Jackson, Jackson, MI, p. A323
HYATT, David W., Chief Executive Officer, Jay County Hospital, Portland, IN, p. A218
HYATT, Robert M.D., Senior Vice President Medical Affairs, Lake Regional Health System, Osage Beach, MO, p. A374
HYATT, Ronnie, Senior Vice President Finance and Chief Financial Officer, Bon Secours St. Francis Health System, Greenville, SC, p. A562
HYBERGER, Trey, Director Information Technology, Hardin Memorial Hospital, Elizabethtown, KY, p. A257
HYDE, Devon, Chief Executive Officer, Alliancehealth Deaconess, Oklahoma City, OK, p. A511
HYDE, Jane E., President, Wellspan Gettysburg Hospital, Gettysburg, PA, p. A535
HYDE, Keith, Chief Executive, Providence Milwaukie Hospital, Milwaukie, OR, p. A524
HYDE, Robert, Human Resources Business Partner, Kaiser Permanente Santa Clara Medical Center, Santa Clara, CA, p. A90
HYDE, Shannon, Director Human Resources, Healthsouth Mountainview Regional Rehabilitation Hospital, Morgantown, WV, p. A694
HYDE, Stephanie, R.N., MSN, Chief Executive Officer, Tyler Continuecare Hospital, Tyler, TX, p. A651
HYDE, Steve, Chief Executive Officer, Paris Regional Medical Center, Paris, TX, p. A636
HYDER, LouAnn, Director Information Integrity Management, Cardinal Hill Rehabilitation Hospital, Lexington, KY, p. A261
HYDER, Shiraz M.D., Director Medical Affairs, Chi St. Alexius Health, Bismarck, ND, p. A474
HYLAND, Donna W., President and Chief Executive Officer, Children's Healthcare Of Atlanta, Atlanta, GA, p. A150
HYLAND-HILL, Barbara M R.N., Chief Nursing Officer, Providence Regional Medical Center Everett, Everett, WA, p. A680
HYLTON, Heather, Chief Financial Officer, Plateau Medical Center, Oak Hill, WV, p. A694
HYMAN, Bruce M.D., Vice President Clinical Performance, Advocate Sherman Hospital, Elgin, IL, p. A186
HYMBAUGH, Mitzi, Chief Personnel, Ringgold County Hospital, Mount Ayr, IA, p. A231
HYMEL, Paul, Chief Financial Officer, Abrazo Central Campus, Phoenix, AZ, p. A32
HYMER, DNP, RN, CENP, Regina J MSN, R.N., Vice President Patient Care Services and Chief Nursing Officer, Norton Brownsboro Hospital, Louisville, KY, p. A263
HYNES, Kristi, Director Human Resources, Georgetown Behavioral Health Institute, Georgetown, TX, p. A616
HYNES, Mary, Manager Information Services, United Hospital District, Blue Earth, MN, p. A336
HYNOSKI, Michael, Chief Information Resource Management, James E. Van Zandt Veterans Affairs Medical Center, Altoona, PA, p. A528

I

IACOBACCI, Margaret, Vice President Patient Care, Lankenau Medical Center, Wynnewood, PA, p. A555
IACUONE, Karen
Chief Nursing Officer and Chief Operating Officer, Pioneers Medical Center, Meeker, CO, p. A106
Chief Nursing Officer, Pioneers Medical Center, Meeker, CO, p. A106
IAKOPO, Priscilla Maratita, Chief Financial Officer, Commonwealth Health Center, Saipan, MP, p. A721
IANNACCONE, Robert C., Chief Executive Officer, Saint Michael's Medical Center, Newark, NJ, p. A417
IBARRA, Daniel, Chief Financial Officer, Crane Memorial Hospital, Crane, TX, p. A604
IBARRA, Kyle, Director Information Systems, Geary Community Hospital, Junction City, KS, p. A243
IBRAHIM, Tajudeen, Interim Business Administrator, Elgin Mental Health Center, Elgin, IL, p. A186
IBRAHIM, Tommy M.D., Chief Physician Officer, Mercy Medical Center–Des Moines, Des Moines, IA, p. A226
ICENHOWER, Jeremy, Administrator and Chief Executive Officer, De Queen Medical Center, De Queen, AR, p. A42
ICKOWSKI, Michael F, Vice President and Chief Financial Officer, Regional West Medical Center, Scottsbluff, NE, p. A399
IDBEIS, Badr, M.D., Chief Executive Officer, Kansas Medical Center, Andover, KS, p. A238
IDSTEIN, Mary, Chief Financial Officer, Porter–Starke Services, Valparaiso, IN, p. A221
IERARDI, Joseph P., Chief Executive Officer, Wayne Memorial Hospital, Jesup, GA, p. A159
IERO, Tony, Director Management Information Systems, North Philadelphia Health System, Philadelphia, PA, p. A545
IFTINIUK, Alan, Chief Executive Officer, French Hospital Medical Center, San Luis Obispo, CA, p. A89
IGNAS, Ann R.N., MSN, Chief Nurse Executive, Fairfield Memorial Hospital, Fairfield, IL, p. A187
IGO, Angela MSN, R.N., Chief Nursing Officer, Fitzgibbon Hospital, Marshall, MO, p. A373
IMBIMBO, Richard, Chief Financial Officer, Hahnemann University Hospital, Philadelphia, PA, p. A544
IMHOFF, Sarah, Business Administrator, Chester Mental Health Center, Chester, IL, p. A180
IMLAY, Ralph M.D., Chief of Staff, Harper Hospital District Five, Harper, KS, p. A242
IMLER, Jim
Director Human Resources, Gothenburg Health, Gothenburg, NE, p. A393
Director Human Resources, Kimball Health Services, Kimball, NE, p. A394
IMMITI, Vincent F., FACHE, Director, Veterans Affairs New Jersey Health Care System, East Orange, NJ, p. A413
IMSEIS, Mikhail M.D., Chief of Staff, Ness County Hospital District No 2, Ness City, KS, p. A247
IN, Henry, Director Human Resources, Dallas Behavioral Healthcare Hospital, Desoto, TX, p. A609
INCARNATI, Philip A., President and Chief Executive Officer, Mclaren Health Care Corporation, Flint, MI, p. B81
INGE, Laura, Chief Clinical Officer, Kindred Hospital Northland, Kansas City, MO, p. A370
INGE, Ray, Vice President Human Resources, Pomona Valley Hospital Medical Center, Pomona, CA, p. A80
INGHAM, Raymond V., Ph.D., President and Chief Executive Officer, Witham Health Services, Lebanon, IN, p. A214
INGLIS, Suzanne MSN, FACHE, Senior Vice President Nursing Services, Fisher–Titus Medical Center, Norwalk, OH, p. A497
INGRAM, Karen, Director Human Resources, Baptist Memorial Hospital For Women, Memphis, TN, p. A584
INGRAM, Nathan Daniel., Chief Executive Officer and Owner, Lone Star Behavioral Health, Cypress, TX, p. A604
INGWERSON, Connie, Chief Financial Officer, Nemaha Valley Community Hospital, Seneca, KS, p. A251
INHOFE, Kyle, Chief Human Resources Officer, Oklahoma City Veterans Affairs Medical Center, Oklahoma City, OK, p. A513
INMAN, Debbie, Chief Nursing Officer, Physicians Surgical Hospital – Quail Creek, Amarillo, TX, p. A592
INMAN, Joanne, Administrator, Sentara Leigh Hospital, Norfolk, VA, p. A672
INMAN, Julie, Regional Executive Officer, Southeast Missouri Mental Health Center, Farmington, MO, p. A368
INNOCENTI, John, President and Chief Executive Officer, Upmc Presbyterian Shadyside, Pittsburgh, PA, p. A547

INO, Alan, Chief Financial Officer, Good Samaritan Hospital, Los Angeles, CA, p. A68
INOUYE, Valerie, Chief Financial Officer, Zuckerberg San Francisco General Hospital And Trauma Center, San Francisco, CA, p. A88
INSCHO, Kimberly, Vice President Community Relations and Human Resources, Margaret Mary Health, Batesville, IN, p. A203
INSERRA, Toni A., Interim Administrator, South Lyon Medical Center, Yerington, NV, p. A406
INSKEEP, Johnathan, Chief Information Officer, Caribou Memorial Hospital And Living Center, Soda Springs, ID, p. A176
INZANA, Lou, Senior Vice President and Chief Financial Officer, Maine Medical Center, Portland, ME, p. A292
IPSAN, Charlotte, Chief Administrative Officer, Norton Women's And Children's Hospital, Louisville, KY, p. A263
IQBAL, Nayyar M.D., Director Medical Staff, Western State Hospital, Hopkinsville, KY, p. A260
IRELAND, Amy, Chief Financial Officer, Carroll County Memorial Hospital, Carrollton, MO, p. A366
IRELAND, Daniel P., FACHE, President, United Memorial Medical Center, Batavia, NY, p. A431
IRISH, Kevin
Chief Information Officer, Franklin Regional Hospital, Franklin, NH, p. A408
Chief Information Officer, Lakes Region General Hospital, Laconia, NH, p. A408
IRISH–CLARDY, Katherine M.D., Chief Medical Officer, Sparks Regional Medical Center, Fort Smith, AR, p. A44
IRIZARRI, David, Director Information Technology, Northwest Medical Center, Margate, FL, p. A131
IRIZARRY, Aixa, Executive Director, Hospital Hima De Humacao, Humacao, PR, p. A723
IRIZARRY, Lourdes M.D., Chief of Staff, Albany Stratton Veterans Affairs Medical Center, Albany, NY, p. A430
IRIZARRY, Sigfredo, Information Technology Director, Ashford Presbyterian Community Hospital, San Juan, PR, p. A725
IRVIN, Debbie, Director Health Information Management, Bhc Alhambra Hospital, Rosemead, CA, p. A83
IRVIN, Donna, Director Human Resources, Baylor Medical Center At Trophy Club, Trophy Club, TX, p. A650
IRVIN, Mary R.N., MSN, Senior Vice President and Chief Nursing Officer, Bethesda North Hospital, Cincinnati, OH, p. A483
IRVIN, Miriam, CNO, Healthsouth Rehabilitation Hospital, Fayetteville, AR, p. A42
IRVIN, Thomas M, Administrator Human Resources, Ranken Jordan Pediatric Bridge Hospital, Maryland Heights, MO, p. A373
IRVING, Edith E R.N., MS, FACHE, Chief Nursing Officer, West Valley Medical Center, Caldwell, ID, p. A172
IRVING, Kelly Ann MSN, RN–B, Associate Director for Patient Care Services, Michael E. Debakey Veterans Affairs Medical Center, Houston, TX, p. A622
IRVING, Mark, Manager Management Information Systems, OSF St. Francis Hospital And Medical Group, Escanaba, MI, p. A319
IRWIN, Robert G, Vice President Information Systems, Robert Wood Johnson University Hospital, New Brunswick, NJ, p. A417
IRWIN, Ruth, Associate Director Clinical Operations, Stewart & Lynda Resnick Neuropsychiatric Hospital At Ucla, Los Angeles, CA, p. A71
IRWIN, Vivian, Chief Financial Officer and Controller, Healthsouth Rehabilitation Hospital Midland–Odessa, Midland, TX, p. A633
ISAAC, Lisa, Chief Nursing Officer, Choctaw Nation Health Care Center, Talihina, OK, p. A516
ISAAC, Regina, Director of Nursing, Choctaw Health Center, Philadelphia, MS, p. A360
ISAACKS, David, Director, Harry S. Truman Memorial Veterans Hospital, Columbia, MO, p. A367
ISAACKS, Scott R., FACHE, Director and Chief Executive Officer, Ralph H. Johnson Veterans Affairs Medical Center, Charleston, SC, p. A559
ISAACS, Cynthia, Chief Executive Officer, Cornerstone Hospital Of Huntington, Huntington, WV, p. A692
ISAACS, Diane, Director of Nursing, Ouachita County Medical Center, Camden, AR, p. A41
ISAACS, Michael R
Vice President Human Resources, Vista Medical Center East, Waukegan, IL, p. A202
Vice President Human Resources, Vista Medical Center West, Waukegan, IL, p. A202
ISAACSON, Alan R., Interim Superintendent, Austin State Hospital, Austin, TX, p. A594
ISAACSON, Sara, Chief Nursing Officer, Mad River Community Hospital, Arcata, CA, p. A52

JANSEN, David, Vice President Human Resources, Karmanos Cancer Center, Detroit, MI, p. A318

JANSEN, John, Management Information Specialist, Hawaii State Hospital, Kaneohe, HI, p. A170

JANSSEN, Kathy, Director Medical Records, Mountrail County Medical Center, Stanley, ND, p. A478

JANSSEN, Paul, President and Chief Executive Officer, Henry County Hospital, New Castle, IN, p. A217

JANTZEN, Daniel, Chief Financial Officer, Dartmouth–Hitchcock Medical Center, Lebanon, NH, p. A409

JANTZEN, Tammi, Chief Operating Officer, Okeene Municipal Hospital, Okeene, OK, p. A511

JANUS, Tammy, Senior Vice President Human Resources, Mercy Medical Center, Baltimore, MD, p. A295

JANZEN, Wes, Chief Information Officer, Wamego Health Center, Wamego, KS, p. A253

JAQUEZ, Jason, Director Human Resources, Greater El Monte Community Hospital, South El Monte, CA, p. A92

JARAMILLO, Charles, Chief Operating Officer, New Mexico Behavioral Health Institute At Las Vegas, Las Vegas, NM, p. A427

JARBOE, Joe, Director Human Resources, Kosciusko Community Hospital, Warsaw, IN, p. A221

JARBOE, Lori, Chief Executive Officer, Healthsouth Lakeview Rehabilitation Hospital, Elizabethtown, KY, p. A257

JARMER, Ryan, Chief Information Officer, Naval Medical Center San Diego, San Diego, CA, p. A85

JAROPILLO, Erwin, Director Information Systems, Lake Wales Medical Center, Lake Wales, FL, p. A130

JARREAU, Jeff
Chief Human Resources Officer, North Oaks Medical Center, Hammond, LA, p. A275
Senior Vice President, Human Resources, North Oaks Health System, North Oaks Rehabilitation Hospital, Hammond, LA, p. A275

JARREAU, Valerie Sparks R.N., Chief Nursing Officer, Pointe Coupee General Hospital, New Roads, LA, p. A283

JARRELL, Lindsey, Vice President Information Services, St. Joseph's Hospital, Tampa, FL, p. A145

JARRETT, Adam D M.D., Executive Vice President and Chief Medical Officer, Holy Name Medical Center, Teaneck, NJ, p. A421

JARRY, Jacques, Administrator, Bullock County Hospital, Union Springs, AL, p. A24

JARRY, Patricia, Manager Human Resources, Crenshaw Community Hospital, Luverne, AL, p. A20

JARVIS, Dinah, Director of Nursing, Pineville Community Hospital Association, Pineville, KY, p. A266

JARVIS, Keith, Director Information Systems, Longview Regional Medical Center, Longview, TX, p. A630

JARVIS, Susan, Vice President Operations, Sanford Medical Center Fargo, Fargo, ND, p. A475

JARVIS, Tammy, Vice President Clinical Services and Chief Nursing Officer, Texas Institute For Surgery At Texas Health Presbyterian Dallas, Dallas, TX, p. A607

JASPER, Harry, Chief Financial Officer, Jerold Phelps Community Hospital, Garberville, CA, p. A61

JASPER, Jerry, Chief Executive Officer, Brownfield Regional Medical Center, Brownfield, TX, p. A599

JATCZAK, Tracy E CPA, Chief Financial Officer, Box Butte General Hospital, Alliance, NE, p. A390

JAUERSACK, Dawn, Vice President and Chief Financial Officer, Boca Raton Regional Hospital, Boca Raton, FL, p. A120

JAURON, Jason, Director Human Resources, Orange City Area Health System, Orange City, IA, p. A232

JAVOIS, Laurent D.
Chief Executive Officer, St. Louis Psychiatric Rehabilitation Center, Saint Louis, MO, p. A378
Regional Executive Officer, Hawthorn Children Psychiatric Hospital, Saint Louis, MO, p. A377
Regional Executive Officer, Metropolitan St. Louis Psychiatric Center, Saint Louis, MO, p. A377

JAVOIS, Rosalie, Chief Financial Officer, Governor Juan F. Luis Hospital, Christiansted, VI, p. A727

JAY, Richard D.O., Chief of Staff, North Big Horn Hospital District, Lovell, WY, p. A719

JEAN–BAPTISTE, Joan, Vice President Human Resources, Governor Juan F. Luis Hospital, Christiansted, VI, p. A727

JEAN–LOUIS, Marie S R.N., Chief Nursing Officer, Creedmoor Psychiatric Center, New Rochelle, NY, p. A441

JEANS, Joe CPA, Chief Financial Officer, Johnson Regional Medical Center, Clarksville, AR, p. A41

JEANSONNE, Corey, Chief Nursing Officer, Bunkie General Hospital, Bunkie, LA, p. A272

JEDLICKA, Colleen R.N., JD, Chief Nursing Officer, Comanche County Medical Center, Comanche, TX, p. A602

JEFFERSON, Glenn, Chief Medical Officer, Garfield County Public Hospital District, Pomeroy, WA, p. A683

JEFFERSON, Kelly, Vice President, Operations, OSF St. Francis Hospital And Medical Group, Escanaba, MI, p. A319

JEFFRAS, Charles, Executive Director Human Resources, St. Vincent Carmel Hospital, Carmel, IN, p. A205

JEFFRESS, Chuck, Vice President Fiscal Services, Chi St. Luke's Health Brazosport, Lake Jackson, TX, p. A628

JEFFREY, Paul A, President, Moses H. Cone Memorial Hospital, Greensboro, NC, p. A463

JEFFREY, Roberta, Chief Executive Officer, Holdenville General Hospital, Holdenville, OK, p. A508

JEFFRIES, John, Director Finance, Hshs St. Joseph's Hospital, Breese, IL, p. A179

JEHAN, Sayed M.D., Interim Medical Director, Larned State Hospital, Larned, KS, p. A245

JELALIAN, Christine M.D., Medical Director, St. Luke's Cornwall Hospital, Newburgh, NY, p. A447

JELDEN, Dennis M.D., Chief of Staff, Melissa Memorial Hospital, Holyoke, CO, p. A104

JELKS, Kim, Fiscal Officer, Villa Feliciana Medical Complex, Jackson, LA, p. A276

JELLE, Laura, President, St. Clare Hospital, Baraboo, WI, p. A698

JEMJEMIAN, Norair, Senior Vice President and Area Manager, Kaiser Permanente Vacaville Medical Center, Vacaville, CA, p. A95

JENE, Suzanne L., Chief Operating Officer, Tennessee Valley Healthcare System, Nashville, TN, p. A587

JENKINS, Bonnie, Chief Financial Officer, Methodist Hospital Of Sacramento, Sacramento, CA, p. A83

JENKINS, Brian, Director Human Resources, Arbour–Fuller Hospital, Attleboro, MA, p. A302

JENKINS, Debbie, Chief Human Resources Management Service, Veterans Affairs Sierra Nevada Health Care System, Reno, NV, p. A405

JENKINS, Denise, Chief Clinical Officer, Kindred Hospital–Brea, Brea, CA, p. A54

JENKINS, Jimmy M.D., Chief Medical Officer, Geary Community Hospital, Junction City, KS, p. A243

JENKINS, Keith, Director, Human Resources, Grandview Medical Center, Dayton, OH, p. A489

JENKINS, Kevin, President and Chief Executive Officer, St. Anthony North Health Campus, Westminster, CO, p. A108

JENKINS, Linda R.N., Vice President Patient Care Services, St. Jude Medical Center, Fullerton, CA, p. A61

JENKINS, Maynard, Regional Vice President Human Resources, Sutter Maternity And Surgery Center Of Santa Cruz, Santa Cruz, CA, p. A91

JENKINS, Michelle M.D., President Medical Staff, Herrin Hospital, Herrin, IL, p. A189

JENKINS, Rebecca, Director Human Resources Management, Harrison Memorial Hospital, Cynthiana, KY, p. A257

JENKINS, Roger T., Chief Executive Officer, Ethicus Hospital – Grapevine, Grapevine, TX, p. A617

JENKINS, Ruth, Chief Financial Officer, Ridgeview Institute, Smyrna, GA, p. A165

JENNER, Jody J., President and Chief Executive Officer, Broadlawns Medical Center, Des Moines, IA, p. A226

JENNETTE, Brian, Chief Financial Officer, Northside Hospital–Cherokee, Canton, GA, p. A153

JENNINGS, Jason, FACHE, Chief Executive Officer, Scott & White Hospital – College Station, College Station, TX, p. A602

JENNINGS, Keith, Chief Information Officer, Massachusetts General Hospital, Boston, MA, p. A303

JENNINGS, Marilyn, Director Human Resources, Arise Austin Medical Center, Austin, TX, p. A594

JENNINGS, Mark, Chief Information Officer, Saint Anthony Hospital, Chicago, IL, p. A183

JENNINGS, Peter M.D., Chief Medical Officer, Sacred Heart Hospital Pensacola, Pensacola, FL, p. A139

JENNINGS, Shayla, Human Resources Director, Montgomery County Memorial Hospital, Red Oak, IA, p. A234

JENNINGS, William M., President and Chief Executive Officer, Bridgeport Hospital, Bridgeport, CT, p. A109

JENSEMA, Christine
Chief People Officer, Hshs St. Clare Memorial Hospital, Oconto Falls, WI, p. A709
Chief People Officer, Hshs St. Mary's Hospital Medical Center, Green Bay, WI, p. A703
Chief People Officer, Hshs St. Nicholas Hospital, Sheboygan, WI, p. A712
Chief People Officer, Hshs St. Vincent Hospital, Green Bay, WI, p. A703

JENSEN, Amy, Director Human Resources, Community Health Center Of Branch County, Coldwater, MI, p. A317

JENSEN, Annelise, Chief Nursing Officer, Methodist Olive Branch Hospital, Olive Branch, MS, p. A360

JENSEN, Beth, Director Clinic Operations, Mobridge Regional Hospital, Mobridge, SD, p. A571

JENSEN, Camille R.N., Chief Nursing Officer, Mclaren Greater Lansing, Lansing, MI, p. A324

JENSEN, Christopher, Chief Financial Officer, Three Rivers Behavioral Health, West Columbia, SC, p. A567

JENSEN, Dave, Director Human Resources, Performance Improvement and Risk Management, Mountain View Hospital, Gadsden, AL, p. A18

JENSEN, Janette, Manager Human Resources, Avera Holy Family Hospital, Estherville, IA, p. A227

JENSEN, Jeff
Vice President, Medical Affairs, Morton Plant Hospital, Clearwater, FL, p. A121
Vice President, Medical Affairs, Morton Plant North Bay Hospital, New Port Richey, FL, p. A135

JENSEN, Laura J., Vice President Patient Care Services, St. Croix Regional Medical Center, St Croix Falls, WI, p. A713

JENSEN, Leanna, Vice President Finance and Chief Financial Officer, Cobleskill Regional Hospital, Cobleskill, NY, p. A434

JENSEN, Mary, Controller, Mountain View Hospital, Gadsden, AL, p. A18

JENSEN, Michael, Chief Executive Officer, Davis Hospital And Medical Center, Layton, UT, p. A657

JENSEN, Neal, Chief Executive Officer, Cobre Valley Regional Medical Center, Globe, AZ, p. A30

JENSEN, Pamela
President, Promedica Fostoria Community Hospital, Fostoria, OH, p. A491
President, Promedica Memorial Hospital, Fremont, OH, p. A491

JENSEN, Paul M.D., Chief of Staff, Regional Health Services Of Howard County, Cresco, IA, p. A225

JENSEN, Renee K., Senior Vice President and Chief Administrative Officer, Evergreenhealth Monroe, Monroe, WA, p. A682

JENSEN, Ron D.O., Chief Medical Officer and Vice President, Baylor Regional Medical Center At Grapevine, Grapevine, TX, p. A617

JENSEN, Ryan, Chief Executive Officer, Desert Springs Hospital Medical Center, Las Vegas, NV, p. A403

JENSEN, Sherry, Chief Financial Officer, Halifax Regional Medical Center, Roanoke Rapids, NC, p. A469

JENSEN, Tom, Chief Executive Officer, Grays Harbor Community Hospital, Aberdeen, WA, p. A678

JENSEN, Troy, Director Human Resources, Healthsouth Rehabilitation Hospital Of Utah, Sandy, UT, p. A661

JENSEN, Twyla, Director Human Resources, Pioneers Medical Center, Meeker, CO, p. A106

JENTZ, Amy M.D., Chief of Staff, Sparrow Ionia Hospital, Ionia, MI, p. A323

JEPPESEN, Kelly, Chief Medical Officer, San Juan Health Service District, Monticello, UT, p. A657

JEPSON, Brian, President, Ohiohealth Riverside Methodist Hospital, Columbus, OH, p. A488

JEPSON, Jeanne, Director Human Resources, Hackettstown Medical Center, Hackettstown, NJ, p. A414

JEPSON, Mark, Vice President, Silver Cross Hospital , New Lenox, IL, p. A195

JERGER, Greg, Chief Financial Officer, Memorial Health Care Systems, Seward, NE, p. A399

JERINA, Anthony T., Chief Nursing Officer, Hereford Regional Medical Center, Hereford, TX, p. A619

JERNIGAN, Pam, Chief Financial Officer, Unity Medical Center, Manchester, TN, p. A583

JESCH, Doug, Director Human Resources, Starke Hospital, Knox, IN, p. A213

JESIOLOWSKI, Craig A., FACHE, President, Holy Family Hospital, Methuen, MA, p. A308

JESIOLOWSKI, Craig A, FACHE, President, Holy Family Hospital, Methuen, MA, p. A308

JESSOP, Reuben, Chief Operating Officer, Northern Utah Rehabilitation Hospital, South Ogden, UT, p. A661

JESSUP, Dan, Chief Financial Officer, Wallowa Memorial Hospital, Enterprise, OR, p. A521

JESSUP, Daniel, Chief Financial Officer, Legacy Silverton Medical Center, Silverton, OR, p. A527

JESTER, Denise, Chief Financial Officer, Nanticoke Memorial Hospital, Seaford, DE, p. A116

JESTILA–PELTOLA, Gail, Chief Financial Officer, Baraga County Memorial Hospital, L'Anse, MI, p. A324

JESURASA, Jebashini, Vice President, Chief Information Technology Officer, Wyckoff Heights Medical Center, New Rochelle, NY, p. A447

JETER, John H., M.D., President and Chief Executive Officer, Hays Medical Center, Hays, KS, p. A242

JETER, John
Assistant Administrator and Chief Financial Officer, Johnston Memorial Hospital, Abingdon, VA, p. A664
Assistant Vice President and Chief Financial Officer, Smyth County Community Hospital, Marion, VA, p. A670

JOHNSTON, Mike, Director Facilities Operations, Union General Hospital, Blairsville, GA, p. A152
JOHNSTON, Monte, Manager Human Resources, Coquille Valley Hospital, Coquille, OR, p. A521
JOHNSTON, Patricia, Vice President Information Services, Texas Health Harris Methodist Hospital Azle, Azle, TX, p. A596
JOHNSTON, Phyllis M, Vice President, Catawba Valley Medical Center, Hickory, NC, p. A464
JOHNSTON, Scott, Chief of Staff, Onslow Memorial Hospital, Jacksonville, NC, p. A465
JOHNSTON, Susan, Vice President Human Resources, East Alabama Medical Center, Opelika, AL, p. A22
JOHNSTON, Susanne, Manager Human Resources, Lincoln County Medical Center, Ruidoso, NM, p. A428
JOHNSTON, Word, Medical Director, Covington County Hospital, Collins, MS, p. A354
JOHNSTONE, Jennifer, Chief Clinical Officer, Kindred Hospital Rome, Rome, GA, p. A163
JOHRENDT, JT, Information Technology Network Specialist, Edgerton Hospital And Health Services, Edgerton, WI, p. A701
JOICE, Jason M.D., Chief Medical Staff, Hillcrest Hospital Pryor, Pryor, OK, p. A515
JOLLEY, Colby D.O., Acting Chief of Staff, Haxtun Hospital District, Haxtun, CO, p. A104
JOLLEY, Sherry, Director of Operations and Nursing, Red Bay Hospital, Red Bay, AL, p. A22
JOLLY, Gaye, FACHE, Acting President and Chief Administrative Officer, Leconte Medical Center, Sevierville, TN, p. A588
JONAS, Stanley W., Chief Executive Officer, Alliance Community Hospital, Alliance, OH, p. A479
JONASON, Anna Ph.D., R.N., Chief Nursing Officer, Colleton Medical Center, Walterboro, SC, p. A567
JONES, Adrienne, Director Human Resources, Creedmoor Psychiatric Center, New Rochelle, NY, p. A441
JONES, Alesia, Chief Human Resources Officer, University Of Alabama Hospital, Birmingham, AL, p. A15
JONES, Allan, Controller, Healthsouth Rehabilitation Hospital Of Jonesboro, Jonesboro, AR, p. A45
JONES, Amelia
  Chief Operating Officer and Acting Chief Executive Officer, Oakland Regional Hospital, Southfield, MI, p. A331
  Chief Operating Officer, Oakland Regional Hospital, Southfield, MI, p. A331
JONES, America, R.N., Chief Executive Officer, Kindred Hospital El Paso, El Paso, TX, p. A611
JONES, Anetra, R.N.
  Chief Nursing Officer, La Porte Hospital, La Porte, IN, p. A214
  Chief Nursing Officer, Starke Hospital, Knox, IN, p. A213
JONES, Austin CPA, Chief Financial Officer, Physicians Surgical Hospital – Quail Creek, Amarillo, TX, p. A592
JONES, B. Konard., Chief Executive Officer, Northbay Medical Center, Fairfield, CA, p. A59
JONES, B. Konard, Chief Executive Officer, Northbay Medical Center, Fairfield, CA, p. A59
JONES, Beth
  Chief Operating Officer, Reeves Memorial Medical Center, Bernice, LA, p. A271
  Director of Nursing, Reeves Memorial Medical Center, Bernice, LA, p. A271
JONES, Bill, Chief Executive Officer, Jackson County Hospital District, Edna, TX, p. A610
JONES, Brain, Director of Information Technology, Multicare Valley Hospital, Spokane Valley, WA, p. A687
JONES, Carol S. MSN, R.N., Interim Chief Nursing Officer, Morristown Medical Center, Morristown, NJ, p. A416
JONES, Carol, Controller and Manager Business Office, Coryell Memorial Hospital, Gatesville, TX, p. A616
JONES, Carolyn R.N., MSN, Chief Nursing Officer, Box Butte General Hospital, Alliance, NE, p. A390
JONES, Catherine, Chief Nursing Officer, Ancora Psychiatric Hospital, Hammonton, NJ, p. A414
JONES, Charlene, Chief Nursing Officer, Peterson Healthcare And Rehabilitation Hospital, Wheeling, WV, p. A697
JONES, Cheryl L, Vice President Human Resources and Organizational Development, BSA Hospital, Llc, Amarillo, TX, p. A592
JONES, Chris, Chief Executive Officer, Vibra Hospital Of Northern California, Redding, CA, p. A81
JONES, Christian, Chief Executive Officer, Twin Rivers Regional Medical Center, Kennett, MO, p. A371
JONES, Connie, Director Human Resources, Community Behavioral Health Hospital – Rochester, Rochester, MN, p. A346
JONES, Dale, Administrator, Noland Hospital Montgomery, Montgomery, AL, p. A21

JONES, Dana R.N., Chief Nursing Officer, Springhill Medical Center, Springhill, LA, p. A286
JONES, Danny L. Jr FACHE, Chief Executive Officer, St. Francis Hospital, Columbus, GA, p. A155
JONES, Darrell, Interim Chief Executive Officer, Select Specialty Hospital–Omaha, Omaha, NE, p. A398
JONES, David C., Administrator, North Caddo Medical Center, Vivian, LA, p. A287
JONES, David, M.D.
  Chief Medical Officer, Beauregard Memorial Hospital, De Ridder, LA, p. A274
  Chief Financial Officer, Alexian Brothers Behavioral Health Hospital, Hoffman Estates, IL, p. A190
  Chief Nursing Officer, Healthsouth Rehabilitation Hospital Of Arlington, Arlington, TX, p. A593
  Service Chief, Riverside Shore Memorial Hospital, Onancoke, VA, p. A672
JONES, Debbie, Director of Nursing, Brookhaven Hospital, Tulsa, OK, p. A517
JONES, Deborah
  Controller, Sca Houston Hospital For Specialized Surgery, Houston, TX, p. A622
  Interim Chief Nursing Officer, Norwegian American Hospital, Chicago, IL, p. A182
JONES, Derrick, Chief Executive Officer, Lovelace Rehabilitation Hospital, Albuquerque, NM, p. A424
JONES, Don M.D., Chief Medical Officer, Marshall Medical Center North, Guntersville, AL, p. A19
JONES, Donald J., FACHE, Administrator, Fayette Medical Center, Fayette, AL, p. A17
JONES, Douglas A, Chief Operating Officer, Forrest General Hospital, Hattiesburg, MS, p. A355
JONES, Elaine M.D., President Medical Staff, Roger Williams Medical Center, Providence, RI, p. A557
JONES, Evan, Executive Vice President and Chief Financial Officer, Lakeland Regional Health, Lakeland, FL, p. A130
JONES, Evelyn R.N., Vice President Nursing Services, St. Bernard Hospital And Health Care Center, Chicago, IL, p. A184
JONES, Florence, President, Methodist Healthcare Memphis Hospitals, Memphis, TN, p. A585
JONES, Gary, Interim President and Chief Executive Officer, Hebrew Center For Health Rehabilitation, West Hartford, CT, p. A114
JONES, Greg, Chief Financial Officer, Wayne Memorial Hospital, Jesup, GA, p. A159
JONES, Holly A, Administrative Director Nursing Services, Illini Community Hospital, Pittsfield, IL, p. A198
JONES, Janice G, Interim Chief Financial Officer, Controller and Compliance Officer, Mercy Regional Medical Center, Ville Platte, LA, p. A287
JONES, Jason L. R.N., Chief Nursing Officer, Fannin Regional Hospital, Blue Ridge, GA, p. A152
JONES, Jeff, Director Human Resources, Greene Memorial Hospital, Xenia, OH, p. A503
JONES, Jeffrey
  Chief Financial Officer, Moses H. Cone Memorial Hospital, Greensboro, NC, p. A463
  Chief of Staff, Whitman Hospital And Medical Center, Colfax, WA, p. A679
JONES, Jeremy A., Administrator, Mercy Hospital Healdton, Healdton, OK, p. A508
JONES, John H., Chief of Staff, South Sunflower County Hospital, Indianola, MS, p. A356
JONES, Joshua, Director Human Resources, Evanston Regional Hospital, Evanston, WY, p. A718
JONES, Joyce, Director Human Resources, Healthsouth Rehabilitation Hospital, Kingsport, TN, p. A581
JONES, Judy, Chief Clinical Officer, Arkansas Surgical Hospital, North Little Rock, AR, p. A47
JONES, Julie L, Chief Nursing Officer, Community Hospital–Fairfax, Fairfax, MO, p. A368
JONES, Karen, Administrative Director Human Resources, Marion General Hospital, Marion, IN, p. A215
JONES, Karin, Interim Chief Nursing Officer, Healthsouth Rehabilitation Hospital Of New Mexico, Albuquerque, NM, p. A424
JONES, Karol, Chief Nursing Officer, Huntsville Hospital, Huntsville, AL, p. A19
JONES, Kathy, Director Human Resources, Jackson Medical Center, Jackson, AL, p. A19
JONES, Ken M, Chief Operating Officer, Ucsf Medical Center, San Francisco, CA, p. A88
JONES, Kenneth, President, Presence Saint Francis Hospital, Evanston, IL, p. A187
JONES, Kenneth, President, Presence Saint Francis Hospital, Evanston, IL, p. B100
JONES, Kimberly, Director Human Resources, Spine Hospital Of Louisiana (Formally The Neuromedical Center Surgical Hospital), Baton Rouge, LA, p. A271

JONES, Kyle, Controller, Marshall Medical Center, Lewisburg, TN, p. A582
JONES, Lance, Chief Executive Officer, Stonesprings Hospital Center, Dulles, VA, p. A666
JONES, Liston M.D., Medical Director, Springhill Memorial Hospital, Mobile, AL, p. A20
JONES, Lorrie Rickman., Ph.D., Director, Division Of Mental Health, Department Of Human Services, Springfield, IL, p. B47
JONES, Louis, Director Management Information Systems, Heart Of Florida Regional Medical Center, Davenport, FL, p. A123
JONES, M Steven.
  President, Uh Portage Medical Center, Ravenna, OH, p. A498
  President, University Hospitals Conneaut Medical Center, Conneaut, OH, p. A488
  President, University Hospitals Geauga Medical Center, Chardon, OH, p. A483
  President, University Hospitals Geneva Medical Center, Geneva, OH, p. A492
JONES, Mark A., President, Orlando Regional Medical Center, Orlando, FL, p. A137
JONES, Mark, Chief Financial Officer, Hill Country Memorial Hospital, Fredericksburg, TX, p. A615
JONES, Marsha, R.N.
  Director Nursing, Baptist Medical Center Yazoo, Yazoo City, MS, p. A363
  Director of Nursing, Baptist Medical Center Yazoo, Yazoo City, MS, p. A363
JONES, Marshall
  Senior Vice President Human Resources, Maricopa Integrated Health System, Phoenix, AZ, p. A33
  Vice President Human Resources, Yuma Regional Medical Center, Yuma, AZ, p. A39
JONES, Mary Jane R.N., MSN, Vice President Nursing Operations, Northridge Hospital Medical Center, Los Angeles, CA, p. A70
JONES, Matthew, Senior Director Support Services and Facilities, The University Of Vermont Health Network – Alice Hyde Medical Center, Malone, NY, p. A439
JONES, Maud, Manager Medical Records, Tops Surgical Specialty Hospital, Houston, TX, p. A623
JONES, MaxAnne, Director Human Resources, Rock Prairie Behavioral Health, College Station, TX, p. A602
JONES, Melinda R.N., Chief Nursing Officer, Morehouse General Hospital, Bastrop, LA, p. A270
JONES, Mike, Executive Director, Marshall Medical Center, Placerville, CA, p. A80
JONES, Mitchell, Director Information Technology, Little River Memorial Hospital, Ashdown, AR, p. A40
JONES, Pam MSN, R.N., Associate Hospital Director and Chief Nursing Officer, Vanderbilt University Medical Center, Nashville, TN, p. A587
JONES, Pamela K., Executive Director of Finance, Baptist Health Corbin, Corbin, KY, p. A256
JONES, Pat, Director Information Systems, Merit Health River Oaks, Flowood, MS, p. A354
JONES, Patrice I. R.N., MSN, Vice President and Chief Nursing Officer, Uf Health Jacksonville, Jacksonville, FL, p. A128
JONES, Philip L, Chief Financial Officer, Curahealth Nashville, Nashville, TN, p. A586
JONES, Phyllis, Chief Human Resources, Wm. Jennings Bryan Dorn Veterans Affairs Medical Center, Columbia, SC, p. A561
JONES, Rachel, Chief Financial Officer, Watsonville Community Hospital, Watsonville, CA, p. A96
JONES, Ransom, Information Technology Director, Covington County Hospital, Collins, MS, p. A354
JONES, Reginald
  Business Manager, Georgia Regional Hospital At Atlanta, Decatur, GA, p. A156
  Interim President and Chief Executive Officer, Fort Washington Medical Center, Oxen Hill, MD, p. A300
JONES, Rex, Chief Executive Officer, Magnolia Regional Medical Center, Magnolia, AR, p. A46
JONES, Richard W, Chief Financial Officer, Reading Hospital, West Reading, PA, p. A553
JONES, Richard M.D., Medical Director, Healthsouth Rehabilitation Hospital North Texas, Richardson, TX, p. A639
JONES, Rita A., Chief Executive Officer, Dundy County Hospital, Benkelman, NE, p. A391
JONES, Rob, Director of Nursing and Operations, Physicians' Medical Center, New Albany, IN, p. A217
JONES, Robert, Director Management Information Systems, St. Joseph Mercy Oakland, Pontiac, MI, p. A328
JONES, Roger M.D., Interim Chief of Staff, Tennessee Valley Healthcare System, Nashville, TN, p. A587

JUST, Lisa
President, Aurora Lakeland Medical Center, Elkhorn, WI, p. A701
President, Aurora Memorial Hospital Of Burlington, Burlington, WI, p. A699

JUST, Paula
Chief Human Resources Officer, Health First Holmes Regional Medical Center, Melbourne, FL, p. A132
Chief Human Resources Officer, Health First Palm Bay Hospital, Palm Bay, FL, p. A138
Chief Human Resources Officer, Health First Viera Hospital, Melbourne, FL, p. A132
Vice President Human Resources, Health First Cape Canaveral Hospital, Cocoa Beach, FL, p. A122

JUSTICE, Jay D.
Chief Human Resource Officer, Adena Medical Center, Chillicothe, OH, p. A483
Chief Human Resources Officer, Adena Pike Medical Center, Waverly, OH, p. A502

JUSTICE, Kim, Vice President Planning and Operations, Atlantic General Hospital, Berlin, MD, p. A296

JUSTIN, Patrick, Chief Financial Officer, United Hospital District, Blue Earth, MN, p. A336

JUSTIN–TANNER, Karen R.N., Chief Nursing Officer, Fairbanks Memorial Hospital, Fairbanks, AK, p. A26

JUSTUS, Jason, Vice President Finance and Chief Financial Officer, Pomerene Hospital, Millersburg, OH, p. A496

JUTILA, Kathy M.D., Chief of Staff, Wheatland Memorial Healthcare, Harlowton, MT, p. A385

JYRKAS, Wade A, Director Computer Information Systems, Lake Region Healthcare, Fergus Falls, MN, p. A340

K

KA'AKIMAKA, Holly, Director Human Resources, Hilo Medical Center, Hilo, HI, p. A168

KABERLINE, Gene, Chief Financial Officer, Susan B. Allen Memorial Hospital, El Dorado, KS, p. A240

KABITZKE–GROTH, Terry, R.N.
Chief Nursing Officer, Aurora Medical Center In Washington County, Hartford, WI, p. A703
Vice President Nursing, Aurora Medical Center Grafton, Grafton, WI, p. A702

KABLE, Mary Ellen, Chief Executive Officer, Lifecare Hospitals Of Mechanicsburg, Mechanicsburg, PA, p. A540

KACHIGION, Claudia M.D., Medical Director, Alton Mental Health Center, Alton, IL, p. A177

KADDOURI, Sami M.D., Medical Director, Cornerstone Of Medical Arts Center Hospital, Fresh Meadows, NY, p. A436

KADIVAR, Aryan M.D., Chief Medical Officer, Southwestern Medical Center, Lawton, OK, p. A509

KAELIN, Darryl M.D., Medical Director, Frazier Rehab Institute, Louisville, KY, p. A262

KAFKA, Rich M.D., Chief Medical Officer, Avera Gregory Hospital, Gregory, SD, p. A570

KAHL, Larry R.N., Chief Operating Officer, Grays Harbor Community Hospital, Aberdeen, WA, p. A678

KAHL, Vicky, Director Human Resources, Valley Regional Medical Center, Brownsville, TX, p. A599

KAHLE, Russ, Chief Information Officer, Logan County Hospital, Oakley, KS, p. A248

KAHLE, Ty
Assistant Vice President Human Resources, Methodist Hospital Union County, Morganfield, KY, p. A265
Vice President Human Resources, Methodist Hospital, Henderson, KY, p. A259

KAHLER, John G. M.D., Radiologist, Bryan W. Whitfield Memorial Hospital, Demopolis, AL, p. A16

KAHLER, Ralph M.D., Medical Director, Regency Hospital Of Hattiesburg, Hattiesburg, MS, p. A356

KAHLY–MCMAHON, Heidi
Interim Vice President Human Resources, Genesis Medical Center–Davenport–West Central Park, Davenport, IA, p. A225
Vice President Human Resources, Genesis Medical Center, Silvis, Silvis, IL, p. A200

KAHN, Jalil M.D., Chief of Staff, Atrium Medical Center Of Corinth, Corinth, TX, p. A603

KAHN, Maureen A., R.N., President and Chief Executive Officer, Blessing Hospital, Quincy, IL, p. A198

KAHO, Clint, Vice President, Baptist Health Louisville, Louisville, KY, p. A262

KAHRS, Amy, Director of Finance, Franklin County Memorial Hospital, Franklin, NE, p. A392

KAIN, Ruth Ann A. MSN, R.N., Chief Nursing Officer and Vice President Patient Care Services, Indiana University Health North Hospital, Carmel, IN, p. A205

KAINO, Linda, Chief Nursing Officer, Ocean Beach Hospital, Ilwaco, WA, p. A681

KAISER, Brenda, Director Human Resources, Great Bend Regional Hospital, Great Bend, KS, p. A241

KAISER, James, Site Director Information Technology, Upper Valley Medical Center, Troy, OH, p. A501

KAISER, Janet R.N., Chief Nursing Officer, Kansas Medical Center, Andover, KS, p. A238

KAISER, Ken, Coordinator Information Systems, Grant Regional Health Center, Lancaster, WI, p. A705

KAISER, Larry, M.D., President and Chief Executive Officer, Temple University Health System, Philadelphia, PA, p. B124

KAISER, Laura, President and Chief Executive Officer, Ssm Health, Saint Louis, MO, p. B120

KAJIWARA, Gary K., President and Chief Executive Officer, Kuakini Medical Center, Honolulu, HI, p. A168

KAKAVAS, Connie, Chief Human Resources Officer, Summit Healthcare Regional Medical Center, Show Low, AZ, p. A36

KAKI, Karim M.D., Chief Medical Director, Hendry Regional Medical Center, Clewiston, FL, p. A122

KAKUDA, James M.D., Chief of Staff, Pali Momi Medical Center, Aiea, HI, p. A168

KALAJAINEN, Kimberly
Vice President Operations and Chief Information Officer, Lawrence + Memorial Hospital, New London, CT, p. A112
Vice President, Operations and Information Technology, Chief Information Officer, Westerly Hospital, Westerly, RI, p. A557

KALANIHUIA, Janice, President, Molokai General Hospital, Kaunakakai, HI, p. A170

KALAR, Cathy, Chief Financial Officer, Broaddus Hospital, Philippi, WV, p. A695

KALAVAR, Jagadeesh S M.D., Chief of Staff, Michael E. Debakey Veterans Affairs Medical Center, Houston, TX, p. A622

KALCHIK, Kevin, Chief Financial Officer, War Memorial Hospital, Sault Sainte Marie, MI, p. A330

KALE, Debra
Director Human Resources, Carolinas Healthcare System Kings Mountain, Kings Mountain, NC, p. A465
Vice President Human Resources, Carolinas Healthcare System Cleveland, Shelby, NC, p. A470

KALEEL, Reza, Executive Vice President and Chief Operating Officer, St. Mary's Hospital And Medical Center, Grand Junction, CO, p. A103

KALINA, Andrea, Vice President External Affairs and Chief Human Resources Officer, St. Clair Hospital, Pittsburgh, PA, p. A547

KALINSKI, Cami, Director Financial Services, Frances Mahon Deaconess Hospital, Glasgow, MT, p. A384

KALKA, Gina R.N., Chief Nursing Officer, Pecos County Memorial Hospital, Fort Stockton, TX, p. A613

KALKOWSKI, Kelly, Chief Executive Officer, Niobrara Valley Hospital, Lynch, NE, p. A395

KALKUT, Gary M.D., Senior Vice President and Chief Medical Officer, Montefiore Medical Center, New Rochelle, NY, p. A443

KALL, Greg, Chief Information Officer, Summa Health System, Akron, OH, p. A479

KALLAS, Diane, Vice President of Nursing Services, Mclaren Flint, Flint, MI, p. A319

KALLEVIG, Daryl, Chief Information Officer, Riverwood Healthcare Center, Aitkin, MN, p. A335

KALSMAN, Stephen L, Area Finance Officer, Kaiser Permanente San Jose Medical Center, San Jose, CA, p. A88

KALTENBACH, Gretchen R.N., Chief Operating Officer, Genesis Behavioral Hospital, Breaux Bridge, LA, p. A272

KALUA, Patricia, Chief Nurse Executive, Kona Community Hospital, Kealakekua, HI, p. A170

KAMBEROS, Peter N, Chief Operating Officer, Thorek Memorial Hospital, Chicago, IL, p. A184

KAMBEROV, Denis M.D., Chief of Staff, De Soto Regional Health System, Mansfield, LA, p. A280

KAMBIC, Phillip M., President and Chief Executive Officer, Riverside Medical Center, Kankakee, IL, p. A191

KAMBOJ, Pradeep M.D., Chief Medical Staff, Tulare Regional Medical Center, Tulare, CA, p. A94

KAMENS, Eric, Regional Director Information Systems, Shriners Hospitals For Children–Springfield, Springfield, MA, p. A311

KAMERMAYER, Angela K MS, Chief Nursing Officer, Integris Health Edmond, Edmond, OK, p. A507

KAMGUIA, Rebecca, Administrative Director Human Resources, Bon Secours Memorial Regional Medical Center, Mechanicsville, VA, p. A670

KAMIKAWA, Cynthia, R.N., MSN, President, North Hawaii Community Hospital, Kamuela, HI, p. A169

KAMINSKI, Tammy
Vice President Human Resources and Hospitality Services, Mclaren Northern Michigan, Petoskey, MI, p. A328
Director Human Resources, Alaska Regional Hospital, Anchorage, AK, p. A25
Vice President Human Relations, Riverside Community Hospital, Riverside, CA, p. A82
Director Human Resources, Medical Center Enterprise, Enterprise, AL, p. A17

KAMMERER, James M, Vice President Support Services, Great River Medical Center, West Burlington, IA, p. A236

KAMMERUD, Shawn, Manager Information Services, Osceola Medical Center, Osceola, WI, p. A710

KAMOWSKI, David, Vice President and Chief Information Officer, Temple University Hospital, Philadelphia, PA, p. A546

KAMPHUIS, Jan Ph.D., R.N., Executive Vice President and Chief Nurse Executive, Sanford Bismarck, Bismarck, ND, p. A474

KAMPSCHNIEDER, Carol, Vice President Clinical and Regulatory Services, St. Francis Memorial Hospital, West Point, NE, p. A400

KAMPWERTH, Dennis, Director Management Information Systems, Gateway Regional Medical Center, Granite City, IL, p. A189

KAMRAN, Khurram
Vice President Medical Affairs, Promedica Toledo Hospital, Toledo, OH, p. A500
Vice President, Physician Services, Winter Haven Hospital, Winter Haven, FL, p. A148

KANAPARTI, V.R. M.D., Director Medical Services, Kalamazoo Psychiatric Hospital, Kalamazoo, MI, p. A324

KANE, Addy, Chief Financial Officer, Roger Williams Medical Center, Providence, RI, p. A557

KANE, Audrey, Interim Chief Financial Officer, Prowers Medical Center, Lamar, CO, p. A105

KANE, Kelli R, Director of Finance, Barnes–Kasson County Hospital, Susquehanna, PA, p. A551

KANE, Nancy, Assistant Vice President Finance LifeBridge Health, Northwest Hospital, Randallstown, MD, p. A300

KANE, Robert E., Chief Administrative Officer, Divine Providence Hospital, Williamsport, PA, p. A554

KANE, Steve, Director Information Technology, Lower Bucks Hospital, Bristol, PA, p. A530

KANE, Terri, Chief Executive Officer, Dixie Regional Medical Center, Saint George, UT, p. A660

KANE, Thomas R.N., Vice President Patient Services and Chief Nursing Officer, Munson Healthcare Manistee Hospital, Manistee, MI, p. A325

KANIA, Kathy, Chief Information Officer, Staten Island University Hospital, New Rochelle, NY, p. A446

KANNADAY, Colleen, President, Advocate Bromenn Medical Center, Normal, IL, p. A195
President, Advocate Eureka Hospital, Eureka, IL, p. A187

KANTELAS, Sandra Jean, Chief Nursing Officer, University Hospitals Elyria Medical Center, Elyria, OH, p. A491

KANTOS, Craig A.
Chief Executive Officer, Theda Care Medical Center – Wild Rose, Wild Rose, WI, p. A716
Chief Executive Officer, Thedacare Medical Center–Waupaca, Waupaca, WI, p. A715

KANUCH, James A
Vice President Finance, Allegheny Valley Hospital, Natrona Heights, PA, p. A542
Vice President Finance, West Penn Hospital, Pittsburgh, PA, p. A548

KANWAL, Neeraj, M.D., President, Promedica Defiance Regional Hospital, Defiance, OH, p. A490

KAPER, Jonathan, Chief Medical Officer, Beaumont Hospital – Trenton, Trenton, MI, p. A332

KAPLAN, Alan, M.D., Chief Executive Officer, University Of Wisconsin Hospitals And Clinics Authority, Madison, WI, p. A705

KAPLAN, Gary, M.D., FACHE, Chairman and Chief Executive Officer, Virginia Mason Medical Center, Seattle, WA, p. A686

KAPLAN, Ronald, Chief Financial Officer, North Philadelphia Health System, Philadelphia, PA, p. A545

KAPLAN, Tamra PharmD, Chief Operating Officer, Miller Children's & Women's Hospital Long Beach, Long Beach, CA, p. A67

KAPLANIS, Gene, Director Information Technology, Alaska Regional Hospital, Anchorage, AK, p. A25

KAPP, William K. III, M.D., President and Chief Executive Officer, Landmark Hospitals, Cape Girardeau, MO, p. B74

KAPRE, Sheela M.D., Chief Medical Officer, San Joaquin General Hospital, French Camp, CA, p. A60

KAPUR, Karun, Chief Information Officer, Chi Health Creighton University Medical Center – Bergan Mercy, Omaha, NE, p. A397

KARA, Amynah M.D., Chief Medical Officer, Baylor Emergency Medical Center At Aubrey, Aubrey, TX, p. A594

KARAM, Annah, Director Human Resources, San Gorgonio Memorial Hospital, Banning, CA, p. A53

KARAM, Chris, FACHE, President and Chief Executive Officer, Christus St. Michael Health System, Texarkana, TX, p. A649

KARAM, Christopher J, Chief Operating Officer, Mishawaka Medical Center, Mishawaka, IN, p. A216

KARANJAI, Rajohn M.D., Chief Medical Officer, Sidney Health Center, Sidney, MT, p. A388

KARDOW, Vivian
Chief Human Resources Officer, Memorial Hermann – Texas Medical Center, Houston, TX, p. A621
Chief Human Resources Officer, Tirr Memorial Hermann, Houston, TX, p. A623

KAREL, Thomas L, Vice President Organization and Talent Effectiveness, Mercy Health Saint Mary's, Grand Rapids, MI, p. A321

KARG, Gary, Interim Vice President Finance, Christus St. Frances Cabrini Hospital, Alexandria, LA, p. A269

KARIM, Parvez M.D., Chief Medical Officer, Allegiance Specialty Hospital Of Greenville, Greenville, MS, p. A355

KARL, Don
Chief Operating Officer, Las Palmas Medical Center, El Paso, TX, p. A611
Interim Chief Executive Officer, Las Palmas Medical Center, El Paso, TX, p. A611

KARL, Peter J.
President and Chief Executive Officer, Manchester Memorial Hospital, Manchester, CT, p. A110
President and Chief Executive Officer, Rockville General Hospital, Vernon, CT, p. A113

KARL, Thomas P., President, Parkland Health Center – Farmington Community, Farmington, MO, p. A368

KARMACH, Izabela, R.N., Administrator, San Diego County Psychiatric Hospital, San Diego, CA, p. A86

KARN, Cielette M.D., Chief of Staff, Sagewest Health Care At Riverton, Riverton, WY, p. A719

KARNER, Diana M.
Chief Nursing Executive, California Pacific Medical Center–St. Luke's Campus, San Francisco, CA, p. A87
Chief Nursing Officer, California Pacific Medical Center, San Francisco, CA, p. A87

KAROW, Deborah
Vice President Patient Care Services, Howard Young Medical Center, Woodruff, WI, p. A716
Vice President Patient Care Services, Ministry Eagle River Memorial Hospital, Eagle River, WI, p. A700

KARP, Bob M.D., Chief Medical Officer, United Hospital District, Blue Earth, MN, p. A336

KARPF, Michael, Executive Vice President of Health Affairs, University of Kentucky Albert B. Chandler Hospital, Lexington, KY, p. A262

KARSOS, Felicia
Chief Nursing Officer, Meadowlands Hospital Medical Center, Secaucus, NJ, p. A420
President and Chief Executive Officer, Meadowlands Hospital Medical Center, Secaucus, NJ, p. A420

KARSTEN, Margo, Ph.D., MSN, Chief Executive Officer, Banner Fort Collins Medical Center, Fort Collins, CO, p. A102

KARSTEN, Margo
Chief Executive Officer, Mckee Medical Center, Loveland, CO, p. A106
Chief Executive Officer, North Colorado Medical Center, Greeley, CO, p. A103

KARSTEN, Paul H, Vice President Finance and Chief Financial Officer, Pine Rest Christian Mental Health Services, Grand Rapids, MI, p. A321

KARSTETTER, James M. R.N., II, Vice President & Chief Nursing Officer, Western Maryland Regional Medical Center, Cumberland, MD, p. A298

KASIRYE, Yusuf M.D., Chief of Staff, Flambeau Hospital, Park Falls, WI, p. A710

KASITZ, Todd, Vice President Finance, Newton Medical Center, Newton, KS, p. A247

KASNIC, Tracey A
Chief Nursing Officer, Confluence Health/Wenatchee Valley Hospital, Wenatchee, WA, p. A689
Senior Vice President Inpatient and Chief Nursing Officer, Confluence Health/Central Washington Hospital, Wenatchee, WA, p. A689

KASPER, Katie, Chief Clinical Officer, Uh Avon Rehabilitation Hospital, Avon, OH, p. A480

KASPER, Yobi, Chief Information Officer, Advanced Diagnostics Hospital, Houston, TX, p. A619

KASS, Andrew J A M.D., Assistant Superintendent, Albert J. Solnit Psychiatric Center – South Campus, Middletown, CT, p. A111

KASSAB, Jerry, President and Chief Executive Officer, Aspire Health Partners, Orlando, FL, p. A137

KASSAHN, Kristine, Chief Executive Officer, Fresno Surgical Hospital, Fresno, CA, p. A60

KASSER, Michael
Chief Financial Officer, Herrin Hospital, Herrin, IL, p. A189
Vice President Chief Financial Officer and Treasurer, Memorial Hospital Of Carbondale, Carbondale, IL, p. A179

KASSIS, Charles
President, Mercy Medical Center Merced, Merced, CA, p. A73
Chief Medical Staff, Mercy Health – Marcum And Wallace, Irvine, KY, p. A260

KASTANIS, John N., FACHE, President and Chief Executive Officer, University Hospital, Newark, NJ, p. A418

KASTER, Steven M.D., Chief Medical Officer, Medical City Mckinney, Mckinney, TX, p. A632

KATEN–BAHENSKY, Donna, Director, West Palm Beach Veterans Affairs Medical Center, West Palm Beach, FL, p. A147

KATES, Josh, Information Technology Analyst, Andrew Mcfarland Mental Health Center, Springfield, IL, p. A200

KATES, Kenneth P., Chief Executive Officer, University Of Iowa Hospitals And Clinics, Iowa City, IA, p. A230

KATHRINS, Richard J., Ph.D., President and Chief Executive Officer, Bacharach Institute For Rehabilitation, Pomona, NJ, p. A419

KATIGBAK, Michael
Chief Financial Officer, Sage Memorial Hospital, Ganado, AZ, p. A29
Director Computer Services, Sage Memorial Hospital, Ganado, AZ, p. A29

KATNENI, Jitendra P. M.D., Medical Director, Select Specialty Hospital–Flint, Flint, MI, p. A319

KATO, Laura
Vice President Human Resources, St. Francis Medical Center, Lynwood, CA, p. A72
Vice President of Human Resources, San Antonio Regional Hospital, Upland, CA, p. A95

KATSCHKE, R William M.D., Jr, Medical Director, Grover C. Dils Medical Center, Caliente, NV, p. A401

KATZ, Benjamin M.D., Vice President Medical Affairs, Glens Falls Hospital, Glens Falls, NY, p. A436

KATZ, Jeffrey M.D., Chief Medical Officer, Memorial Hermann – Texas Medical Center, Houston, TX, p. A621

KATZ, Michelle, Director Human Resources, Healthsouth Nittany Valley Rehabilitation Hospital, Pleasant Gap, PA, p. A548

KATZ, Mitchell H., M.D., Director, Los Angeles County-Department Of Health Services, Los Angeles, CA, p. B78

KATZ, Richard M.D., Vice President Medical Affairs, Mt. Washington Pediatric Hospital, Baltimore, MD, p. A295

KATZ, Robert M.D., Chief of Staff, Columbus Community Hospital, Columbus, TX, p. A602

KATZ, Yair
Chief Financial Officer, Community Hospital Long Beach, Long Beach, CA, p. A66
Chief Financial Officer, Long Beach Memorial Medical Center, Long Beach, CA, p. A66
Chief Financial Officer, Miller Children's & Women's Hospital Long Beach, Long Beach, CA, p. A67

KAUFMAN, Cheryl
Director Health Information Management, Bayfront Health Dade City, Dade City, FL, p. A123
Information Technology Technician, Coteau Des Prairies Hospital, Sisseton, SD, p. A573

KAUFMAN, Dan, Director Information Services, Paulding County Hospital, Paulding, OH, p. A498

KAUFMAN, Irvin A M.D., Chief Medical Officer, Rady Children's Hospital – San Diego, San Diego, CA, p. A85

KAUFMAN, Mark M.D., Chief of Staff, Northport Veterans Affairs Medical Center, Northport, NY, p. A448

KAUFMAN, Robert
Director Financial Services, Central State Hospital, Petersburg, VA, p. A672
Fiscal Officer, Hiram W. Davis Medical Center, Petersburg, VA, p. A672

KAUFMAN, Ronald L M.D., FACHE, Chief Medical Officer, Lakewood Regional Medical Center, Lakewood, CA, p. A65

KAUFMAN, Samuel, Chief Executive Officer, Henderson Hospital, Henderson, NV, p. A402

KAUPA, Michael, Executive Vice President and Chief Operating Officer, Park Nicollet Methodist Hospital, Saint Louis Park, MN, p. A347

KAUPAS, Bill, Chief Executive Officer, Post Acute/Warm Springs Rehabilitation Hospital Of Allen, Allen, TX, p. A591

KAUTZ, Terri, Manager Human Resources, Weiser Memorial Hospital, Weiser, ID, p. A176

KAUZLARICH, Sidney A. M.D., Medical Director, Douglas County Community Mental Health Center, Omaha, NE, p. A397

KAVALIER, MaryJo, Administrator, Sartori Memorial Hospital, Cedar Falls, IA, p. A223

KAVANAGH, Darina R.N., MSN, Chief Nursing Officer, Good Samaritan Hospital, San Jose, CA, p. A88

KAVANAGH, Sean, Director Information Technology, Pondera Medical Center, Conrad, MT, p. A383

KAVANAUGH, Paul B., President and Chief Executive Officer, Community Care Hospital, New Orleans, LA, p. A282

KAVANAUGH, Samantha, Chief Financial Officer, Riverview Psychiatric Center, Augusta, ME, p. A289

KAVTARADZE, David M.D., Chief of Staff, Crisp Regional Hospital, Cordele, GA, p. A155

KAY, Kirk, Chief Financial Officer, Veterans Affairs Nebraska–Western Iowa Health Care System, Omaha, NE, p. A398

KAY, Robert W, Senior Vice President and Chief Financial Officer, Memorial Medical Center, Springfield, IL, p. A200

KAY–GARCIA, Lisa, Chief Information Officer, Kearny County Hospital, Lakin, KS, p. A244

KAYE, Jessie, Chief Executive Officer, Prairie View, Newton, KS, p. A247

KAYGA, Alicia R. R.N., Chief Nursing Officer, Brownwood Regional Medical Center, Brownwood, TX, p. A599

KAYROUZ, Thomas M.D., Chief Medical Officer, Anmed Health Medical Center, Anderson, SC, p. A558

KAYSER, Sonya J, Human Resources Officer, Avera Marshall Regional Medical Center, Marshall, MN, p. A343

KAZMIERCZAK, Sara Marie R.N., Director of Nursing, North Valley Health Center, Warren, MN, p. A350

KAZMIERCZAK, Stanley, Controller, Presence Saint Joseph Hospital, Chicago, IL, p. A182

KEANE, Dennis M., Vice President Finance and Chief Financial Officer, St. John's Riverside Hospital, Yonkers, NY, p. A456

KEANE, Fran, Vice President Human Resources, Centrastate Healthcare System, Freehold, NJ, p. A414

KEANE, Merry Ann, Chief Administrative Officer, Peacehealth Peace Island Medical Center, Friday Harbor, WA, p. A681

KEANE, Valerie E FACHE, Chief Nursing Executive, Sentara Northern Virginia Medical Center, Woodbridge, VA, p. A677

KEARNEY, Elizabeth R.N., Chief Nursing Officer, Mountain Vista Medical Center, Mesa, AZ, p. A31

KEARNEY, Karen
Vice President Inpatient Rehabilitation Services, Allied Services Rehabilitation Hospital, Scranton, PA, p. A550
Vice President Inpatient Rehabilitation Services, John Heinz Institute Of Rehabilitation Medicine, Wilkes, PA, p. A554

KEARNEY, Lynn, Vice President, Nursing, Robert Wood Johnson University Hospital Somerset, Somerville, NJ, p. A420

KEARNEY, M Clark, Vice President Human Resources, Saint Mary's Hospital, Waterbury, CT, p. A114

KEARNS, Debbie
Chief Executive Officer, Community Hospital, Oklahoma City, OK, p. A511
Chief Executive Officer, Northwest Surgical Hospital, Oklahoma City, OK, p. A512

KEARNS, Donald, M.D., President and Chief Executive Officer, Rady Children's Hospital – San Diego, San Diego, CA, p. A85

KEARNS, Peggy W., MS, FACHE, Executive Director, Veterans Affairs Southern Nevada Healthcare System, North Las Vegas, NV, p. A405

KEATING, Michael, President and Chief Executive Officer, Christ Hospital, Cincinnati, OH, p. A483

KEATING, Todd, Chief Financial Officer, University Of Vermont Medical Center, Burlington, VT, p. A662

KEATON, Tony, Director Information Systems, Roane General Hospital, Spencer, WV, p. A696

KEATON, William A., Chief Executive Officer, Baylor Medical Center At Frisco, Frisco, TX, p. A615

KECK, Paul, M.D., President and Chief Executive Officer, Lindner Center Of Hope, Mason, OH, p. A495

KEDDINGTON, Richard, Chief Executive Officer, Watertown Regional Medical Center, Watertown, WI, p. A714

KEE, Agnes, Financial Manager, Gallup Indian Medical Center, Gallup, NM, p. A426

KEE, Robert, Chief Information Officer, NYC Health + Hospitals / Coney Island, New Rochelle, NY, p. A444

KEEF, Shaun, Chief Executive Officer and Chief Financial Officer, Eastern Oklahoma Medical Center, Poteau, OK, p. A514

KEEFE, Eileen, Chief Nursing Officer, Parkland Medical Center, Derry, NH, p. A407

KEEFER, Russ, Chief Human Resources Officer, Trios Health, Kennewick, WA, p. A681

KEEGAN, Julie, Vice President Finance, Craig Hospital, Englewood, CO, p. A102

KEEGAN, Justin, Director Support Services, Avera Gregory Hospital, Gregory, SD, p. A570

KEEL, Barry L., Administration, North Mississippi Medical Center–West Point, West Point, MS, p. A363

KEEL, Patricia, Senior Vice President and Chief Financial Officer, St. Jude Children's Research Hospital, Memphis, TN, p. A585

KEELAN, John E., Chief Executive Officer, Brodstone Memorial Hospital, Superior, NE, p. A400

KEELE, Denyce, Administrative Assistant and Human Resources Coordinator, Black River Medical Center, Poplar Bluff, MO, p. A375

KEELE, Paula
Manager Information Systems, Presence Covenant Medical Center, Urbana, IL, p. A202
Manager Information Systems, Presence United Samaritans Medical Center, Danville, IL, p. A185

KEELE, Ryan, Chief Executive Officer, Northern Utah Rehabilitation Hospital, South Ogden, UT, p. A661

KEELER, Dave, Chief Financial Officer, Pipestone County Medical Center Avera, Pipestone, MN, p. A346

KEELER, Jason, Executive Vice President and Chief Operating Officer, University Of Chicago Medical Center, Chicago, IL, p. A184

KEELER, Jean M., President and Chief Executive Officer, Grand View Health, Sellersville, PA, p. A550

KEELER, Karl, President, Saint Alphonsus Medical Center – Nampa, Nampa, ID, p. A174

KEELEY, Brian E., President and Chief Executive Officer, Baptist Health South Florida, Coral Gables, FL, p. B19

KEELEY, Katherine M.D., Chief of Staff, Sunrise Hospital And Medical Center, Las Vegas, NV, p. A404

KEELING, Kathy, Director of Nursing, Rehabilitation Hospital Of Rhode Island, North Smithfield, RI, p. A556

KEELING, Kevin, Chief Financial Officer, St. Lucie Medical Center, Port St. Lucie, FL, p. A140

KEELING, Michele A., Senior Vice President and Administrator, Laureate Psychiatric Clinic And Hospital, Tulsa, OK, p. A517

KEELING, Terri, Vice President Information Systems, Upmc Mckeesport, Mckeesport, PA, p. A540

KEEN, Kris, Chief Information Officer, Cameron Memorial Community Hospital, Angola, IN, p. A203

KEEN, Michael, Senior Vice President and Chief Financial Officer, Grand View Health, Sellersville, PA, p. A550

KEEN, Scott R., Chief Executive Officer, Honorhealth Rehabilitation Hospital, Scottsdale, AZ, p. A35

KEENAN, Bob, Chief Medical Officer, H. Lee Moffitt Cancer Center And Research Institute, Tampa, FL, p. A144

KEENAN, Kevin M.D., Physician Advisor, East Cooper Medical Center, Mount Pleasant, SC, p. A564

KEENAN, Nancy C R.N., Senior Vice President and Chief Nursing Officer, Houston Methodist Willowbrook Hospital, Houston, TX, p. A621

KEENAN, Richard, Senior Vice President Finance and Chief Financial Officer, Valley Hospital, Ridgewood, NJ, p. A420

KEENE, Kimberly, Interim Chief Executive Officer, Assistant Vice President Clinical Operations, St. Bernard Parish Hospital, Chalmette, LA, p. A272

KEENER, Vicki, Administrative Assistant and Director Human Resources, Little River Memorial Hospital, Ashdown, AR, p. A40

KEENUM, Patricia, Health Information Management Systems Officer, Merit Health Northwest Mississippi, Clarksdale, MS, p. A353

KEEPSEAGLE, Joelle, Director of Nursing, Standing Rock Service Unit, Fort Yates Hospital, Indian Health Service, Dhhs, Fort Yates, ND, p. A476

KEESBURY, Drew
Chief Financial Officer, La Porte Hospital, La Porte, IN, p. A214
Chief Financial Officer, Starke Hospital, Knox, IN, p. A213

KEEVER, Jerry, Administrator, Sharkey–Issaquena Community Hospital, Rolling Fork, MS, p. A361

KEFALAS, George, Chief Medical Officer, Aultman Specialty Hospital, Canton, OH, p. A482

KEGLEY, Carl J, System Director Information Technology, Fairbanks Memorial Hospital, Fairbanks, AK, p. A26

KEGLEY, Glen, Chief Operating Officer, Hutchinson Health, Hutchinson, MN, p. A341

KEGLEY, Shawn, Director Information Services, Research Medical Center, Kansas City, MO, p. A370

KEHIAYAN, Nancy
Acting Director, Colorado Mental Health Institute At Fort Logan, Denver, CO, p. A100
Director of Nursing, Colorado Mental Health Institute At Fort Logan, Denver, CO, p. A100

KEHRBERG, Mark W, M.D.
Chief Medical Officer, Calumet Medical Center, Chilton, WI, p. A700
Senior Vice President and Chief Medical Officer, Mercy Medical Center, Oshkosh, WI, p. A710

KEHUS, Frank, Associate Director for Operations, Marion Veterans Affairs Medical Center, Marion, IL, p. A192

KEIL, James M.D., Chief Medical Officer, Niobrara Valley Hospital, Lynch, NE, p. A395

KEIM, Thomas, Chief Executive Officer, Ste. Genevieve County Memorial Hospital, Ste Genevieve, MO, p. A380

KEIRNS, Melody, Manager Human Resources, F. W. Huston Medical Center, Winchester, KS, p. A254

KEISER, Trish, Comptroller, Avera Gregory Hospital, Gregory, SD, p. A570

KEISTER, Catharine L, Chief Nursing Officer, Sunbury Community Hospital And Outpatient Center, Sunbury, PA, p. A551

KEITEL, SPHR, Kal, Executive Director Human Resources, Baptist Health Paducah, Paducah, KY, p. A266

KEITH, Bridgette, Director Human Resources, Healthsouth Northern Kentucky Rehabilitation Hospital, Edgewood, KY, p. A257

KEITH, Darlene, Chief Information Systems, Alleghany Memorial Hospital, Sparta, NC, p. A471

KEITH, David N., FACHE, President and Chief Executive Officer, Mcalester Regional Health Center, Mcalester, OK, p. A510

KEITH, Jeannie, Director Patient Care Services and Nurse Executive, Shriners Hospitals For Children–Houston, Houston, TX, p. A622

KEITH, Leesa–Lee R.N., MSN, Chief Nursing Officer, Baystate Franklin Medical Center, Greenfield, MA, p. A307

KEITH, Lorraine
Chief Nursing Officer, St. Vincent's Medical Center Riverside, Jacksonville, FL, p. A128
Chief Nursing Officer, St. Vincent's Medical Center Southside, Jacksonville, FL, p. A128

KELBAUGH, Brian, Chief Financial Officer, Summersville Regional Medical Center, Summersville, WV, p. A696

KELBLY, Kevin, Senior Vice President Finance and Corporate Fiscal Affairs, Carroll Hospital Center, Westminster, MD, p. A301

KELCH, Charles P., Interim Chief Executive Officer, Palo Alto County Health System, Emmetsburg, IA, p. A227

KELL, Douglas B, Chief Financial Officer, Scottsdale Liberty Hospital, Scottsdale, AZ, p. A36

KELLAR, Brian, Chief Executive Officer, Page Hospital, Page, AZ, p. A32

KELLAR, Mark R.N., Interim Chief Nursing Officer, Our Lady Of The Angels Hospital, Bogalusa, LA, p. A272

KELLAR, Richard A., President, Aurora West Allis Medical Center, West Allis, WI, p. A715

KELLEHER, Cynthia, M.P.H., President and Chief Executive Officer, University Of Maryland Rehabilitation & Orthopaedic Institute, Baltimore, MD, p. A296

KELLEHER, John, Vice President Information Technology and Chief Information Officer, Glens Falls Hospital, Glens Falls, NY, p. A436

KELLEHER, Mary Lou R.N., MSN, Vice President, Nursing, Franciscan Children's, Brighton, MA, p. A304

KELLEHER, Mary, Vice President Human Resources, Holyoke Medical Center, Holyoke, MA, p. A307

KELLEHER, Michael, Chief Medical Officer, Ann & Robert H. Lurie Children's Hospital Of Chicago, Chicago, IL, p. A180

KELLEHER, William H, Director, Veterans Affairs Boston Healthcare System Brockton Division, Brockton, MA, p. A305

KELLENBARGER, Lance, Site Director Information Systems, St. Catherine Hospital, Garden City, KS, p. A241

KELLER, Allen, Director Human Resources, Sumner Regional Medical Center, Wellington, KS, p. A253

KELLER, Anita M. R.N., MSN, Chief Nursing Officer, Johnson Memorial Hospital, Franklin, IN, p. A209

KELLER, Ann, Supervisor Health Information Management, Healthsouth Walton Rehabilitation Hospital, Augusta, GA, p. A151

KELLER, Christine, Chief Administrative Officer, Bluffton Hospital, Bluffton, OH, p. A481

KELLER, Diane R., Chief Executive Officer, Memorial Community Health, Aurora, NE, p. A390

KELLER, Gretchen, Director Health Information, Neosho Memorial Regional Medical Center, Chanute, KS, p. A239

KELLER, Jack M., Chief Executive Officer, Saint Thomas Hickman Hospital, Centerville, TN, p. A576

KELLER, James, M.D.
Vice President, Medical Management, Advocate Trinity Hospital, Chicago, IL, p. A180
Chief Information Officer, Borgess–Lee Memorial Hospital, Dowagiac, MI, p. A318

Director Human Resources, Nea Baptist Memorial Hospital, Jonesboro, AR, p. A45

KELLER, Jill R.N., MSN, Vice President for Nursing Services, Quality and Risk Management, Waynesboro Hospital, Waynesboro, PA, p. A553

KELLER, Jim, Site Director Information Services, Mercy Health Saint Mary's, Grand Rapids, MI, p. A321

KELLER, Justin, Chief Information Officer, Murray County Medical Center, Slayton, MN, p. A348

KELLER, Marsha, Director Human Resources, Upmc Kane, Kane, PA, p. A537

KELLER, Maryalice, Vice President Brand and Talent Management, Unity Hospital, Rochester, NY, p. A451

KELLER, Patricia MSN, R.N., Nurse Administrator, Mayo Clinic Health System – Northland In Barron, Barron, WI, p. A698

KELLER, Ruey, Acting Chief Information Officer, Va San Diego Healthcare System, San Diego, CA, p. A86

KELLER, Stewart M.D., Medical Director, Mesa Springs, Fort Worth, TX, p. A614

KELLER, Thomas, President and Chief Executive Officer, Ozarks Medical Center, West Plains, MO, p. A381

KELLER, Wendy, Director Health Information Management, Atrium Medical Center Of Corinth, Corinth, TX, p. A603

KELLERMAN, Laurie MSN, Chief Clinical Officer, Marshall Browning Hospital, Du Quoin, IL, p. A186

KELLERMAN, Scott, Chief Financial Officer, Ely–Bloomenson Community Hospital, Ely, MN, p. A339

KELLEY, Brent, Director Information Technology, Nor–Lea Hospital District, Lovington, NM, p. A427

KELLEY, Danny, Administrative Director, Health Information Technology, Norman Regional Health System, Norman, OK, p. A511

KELLEY, Jalinda, Secretary of Interior Services, Chickasaw Nation Medical Center, Ada, OK, p. A504

KELLEY, Janice, Chief Financial Officer, Marshall County Hospital, Benton, KY, p. A255

KELLEY, Lewis
Chief Operating Officer, Union General Hospital, Blairsville, GA, p. A152
Interim Chief Executive Officer, Union General Hospital, Blairsville, GA, p. A152

KELLEY, Mary, Director Human Resources, The Outer Banks Hospital, Nags Head, NC, p. A467

KELLEY, Meera M.D., Senior Vice President and Chief Medical Officer, Nash Health Care Systems, Rocky Mount, NC, p. A469

KELLEY, Neal, Vice President and Chief Operating Officer, Seton Medical Center Hays, Kyle, TX, p. A627

KELLEY, Randall, FACHE, President, Spectrum Health Ludington Hospital, Ludington, MI, p. A325

KELLEY, Sarah Jo, Director Human Resources, Ste. Genevieve County Memorial Hospital, Ste Genevieve, MO, p. A380

KELLEY, Sharon, Chief Financial Officer, Clifton Springs Hospital And Clinic, Clifton Springs, NY, p. A434

KELLEY, Steven L., President and Chief Executive Officer, Ellenville Regional Hospital, Ellenville, NY, p. A435

KELLEY, Sue, Chief Financial Officer, Cordell Memorial Hospital, Cordell, OK, p. A506

KELLEY, Vicky, Chief Financial Officer, Dequincy Memorial Hospital, Dequincy, LA, p. A274

KELLEY, Warren, Chief Information Officer, Reynolds Memorial Hospital, Glen Dale, WV, p. A692

KELLIHER, Brandon, Chief Information Officer, Great Plains Health, North Platte, NE, p. A396

KELLOGG, Brewster D.O., Chief Medical Officer, Rawlins County Health Center, Atwood, KS, p. A238

KELLOGG, Jason M.D., Chief of Staff, Newport Bay Hospital, Newport Beach, CA, p. A76

KELLOGG, Susan, Administrator Patient Care Services, Carthage Area Hospital, Carthage, NY, p. A434

KELLS, Anne, Interim Chief Financial Officer, Appleton Area Health Services, Appleton, MN, p. A335

KELLUM, Craig, Director Management Information Systems, Cape Fear Valley – Bladen County Hospital, Elizabethtown, NC, p. A462

KELLY, Brian E. M.D., President Medical Staff, Saint Elizabeth's Medical Center, Wabasha, MN, p. A349

KELLY, Brian, M.D.
Vice President Medical Affairs and Medical Director, Sturdy Memorial Hospital, Attleboro, MA, p. A302
Acting Chief Fiscal Service, San Francisco Va Medical Center, San Francisco, CA, p. A87
Vice President Finance, Advocate South Suburban Hospital, Hazel Crest, IL, p. A189

KELLY, Charlene, Chief Nursing Officer, Kane County Hospital, Kanab, UT, p. A657

KELLY, Charles D.O., Vice President Medical Affairs and Chief Medical Officer, Henry Ford Macomb Hospitals, Clinton Township, MI, p. A316

KELLY, Colan, Chief Financial Officer, Pineville Community Hospital Association, Pineville, KY, p. A266

KELLY, Daniel J., President, Chi Health St. Mary's, Nebraska City, NE, p. A396

KELLY, Daniel R., Chief Executive Officer, Mckenzie County Healthcare System, Watford City, ND, p. A478

KELLY, Derek J M.D., Vice President Transformation and Chief Medical Information Officer, Swedish Covenant Hospital, Chicago, IL, p. A184

KELLY, Diane, Chief Operating Officer, Berkshire Medical Center, Pittsfield, MA, p. A310

KELLY, Edward, Chief Executive Officer and President, Milford Regional Medical Center, Milford, MA, p. A309

KELLY, James J. Jr, Senior Vice President and Chief Financial Officer, Uf Health Shands Hospital, Gainesville, FL, p. A126

KELLY, James P., FACHE, Administrator, Community Behavioral Health Hospital – Annandale, Annandale, MN, p. A335

KELLY, Jim, Chief Operating Officer, Nantucket Cottage Hospital, Nantucket, MA, p. A309

KELLY, John, R.N., Chief Nursing Officer and Chief Operating Officer, Umass Memorial–Marlborough Hospital, Marlborough, MA, p. A308

KELLY, Kecia R.N., Chief Nurse Executive, Kaiser Permanente Medical Center, Honolulu, HI, p. A168

KELLY, Laurence E., President and Chief Executive Officer, Nathan Littauer Hospital And Nursing Home, Gloversville, NY, p. A436

KELLY, Leo, Vice President Medical Management, Advocate Lutheran General Hospital, Park Ridge, IL, p. A197

KELLY, Mark
  Administrator, Regional One Health Extended Care Hospital, Memphis, TN, p. A585
  Vice President Finance, St. Francis Medical Center, Trenton, NJ, p. A422

KELLY, Maura, Vice President Fiscal Services, Pen Bay Medical Center, Rockport, ME, p. A293

KELLY, Melissa
  Chief Executive Officer and Chief Financial Officer, Pender Community Hospital, Pender, NE, p. A399

KELLY, Michael
  Vice President Operations, Missouri Baptist Medical Center, Saint Louis, MO, p. A377
  Vice President, Christian Hospital, Saint Louis, MO, p. A377

KELLY, Patrick J., FACHE, Director, Minneapolis Veterans Affairs Health Care System, Minneapolis, MN, p. A344

KELLY, Peter, President, Putnam Hospital Center, Carmel, NY, p. A433

KELLY, Ray R.N., MSN, Vice President Chief Nursing Officer, Texas Health Harris Methodist Hospital Hurst–Euless–Bedford, Bedford, TX, p. A597

KELLY, Robert E, M.D., President, New York–Presbyterian Hospital, New Rochelle, NY, p. A444

KELLY, Scott A., Chief Executive Officer, Asante Rogue Regional Medical Center, Medford, OR, p. A524

KELLY, Shannon, Director Human Resources, Morton General Hospital, Morton, WA, p. A682

KELLY, Stephen M.D., Chief Medical Officer, SSM Health St. Mary's Hospital – St. Louis, Saint Louis, MO, p. A378

KELLY, Steve, Interim Chief Executive Officer, Austin Oaks Hospital, Austin, TX, p. A594

KELLY, Teresa M MSN, R.N., Chief Nursing Officer, Chestnut Hill Hospital, Philadelphia, PA, p. A543

KELLY, Vicky, Chief Financial Officer, De Queen Medical Center, De Queen, AR, p. A42

KELLY, Virginia, Chief Financial Officer, Eastside Psychiatric Hospital, Tallahassee, FL, p. A144

KELMAN, Gregory M.D., Area Medical Director, Kaiser Permanente Woodland Hills Medical Center, Los Angeles, CA, p. A69

KEM, Mark, Vice President Finance and Chief Financial Officer, Chandler Regional Medical Center, Chandler, AZ, p. A28

KEMKA, Joseph, Chief Financial Officer, St. Bernard Parish Hospital, Chalmette, LA, p. A272

KEMKER, S E M.D., President Medical Staff, St. Vincent Salem Hospital, Salem, IN, p. A219

KEMM, Russ M.D., Chief Medical Officer, Nevada Regional Medical Center, Nevada, MO, p. A374

KEMMERER, Jan, Director of Nursing, Mitchell County Hospital Health Systems, Beloit, KS, p. A239

KEMPF, Gary L., R.N., Administrator, Houston Methodist St. Catherine Hospital, Katy, TX, p. A626

KEMPIAK, Matthew, Director Human Resources and Administrative Services, Memorial Hospital Of Gardena, Gardena, CA, p. A61

KEMPINSKI, Paul D, Chief Operating Officer, Alfred I. Dupont Hospital For Children, Wilmington, DE, p. A116

KEMPTON, Matthew, Chief Executive Officer and Administrator, Stephens Memorial Hospital, Breckenridge, TX, p. A599

KENAGY, John Jay
  Senior Vice President and Chief Information Officer, Legacy Meridian Park Medical Center, Tualatin, OR, p. A527
  Senior Vice President and Chief Information Officer, Legacy Mount Hood Medical Center, Gresham, OR, p. A522

KENAGY, Rob M.D., Senior Vice President and Chief Medical Officer, Stormont Vail Health, Topeka, KS, p. A252

KENDALL, Abigail, Chief Nursing Officer, Lake Granbury Medical Center, Granbury, TX, p. A617

KENDALL, Anthony
  Vice President Human Resources, Baptist Health Extended Care Hospital, Little Rock, AR, p. A46
  Vice President Human Resources, Baptist Health Medical Center–Arkadelphia, Arkadelphia, AR, p. A40
  Vice President Human Resources, Baptist Health Medical Center–Little Rock, Little Rock, AR, p. A46
  Vice President Human Resources, Baptist Health Rehabilitation Institute, Little Rock, AR, p. A46

KENDALL, Clint R.N., Chief Nursing Officer, Clinch Valley Medical Center, Richlands, VA, p. A673

KENDALL, Dorothy, Medical Director, William J. Mccord Adolescent Treatment Facility, Orangeburg, SC, p. A565

KENDLE, Melinda
  Director Fiscal Management, Evansville State Hospital, Evansville, IN, p. A207
  Manager Business Office, Evansville Psychiatric Children Center, Evansville, IN, p. A207

KENDLER, Lisa, Chief Financial Officer, Memorial Hermann Sugar Land Hospital, Sugar Land, TX, p. A647

KENDRICK, Donovan M.D., Chief Medical Officer, Baptist Medical Center South, Montgomery, AL, p. A21

KENDRICK, Gary G., FACHE, Interim Chief Executive Officer, Nacogdoches Memorial Hospital, Nacogdoches, TX, p. A634

KENDRICK, Jim R., President and Chief Executive Officer, Community Hospital Corporation, Plano, TX, p. B36

KENDRICK, Ray, Chief Human Resources Officer, Memorial Hospital Miramar, Miramar, FL, p. A135

KENNEDY, Anita J, Vice President Operations, Methodist Hospital Of Sacramento, Sacramento, CA, p. A83

KENNEDY, Brad, Interim Chief Executive Officer, Cardinal Hill Rehabilitation Hospital, Lexington, KY, p. A261

KENNEDY, Carol, Chief Clinical Officer, Barrett Hospital & Healthcare, Dillon, MT, p. A384

KENNEDY, Connie, Director Human Resources, Marlette Regional Hospital, Marlette, MI, p. A325

KENNEDY, Darla, Chief Information Officer, Foothill Regional Medical Center, Tustin, CA, p. A94

KENNEDY, Diana, Director Human Resources, Meadowview Regional Medical Center, Maysville, KY, p. A264

KENNEDY, Eric, Chief Executive Officer, Arbour Hospital, Boston, MA, p. A302

KENNEDY, Jack L R.N., MS, Vice President and Chief Nursing Officer, Pratt Regional Medical Center, Pratt, KS, p. A250

KENNEDY, Jill M R.N., Vice President, Ambulatory Patient Care Services, Bon Secours Memorial Regional Medical Center, Mechanicsville, VA, p. A670

KENNEDY, John M.D., Vice President Medical Affairs, Mercy Health – Fairfield Hospital, Fairfield, OH, p. A491

KENNEDY, Kay, Chief Nurse Executive, Wellstar Cobb Hospital, Austell, GA, p. A152

KENNEDY, Kimberly, Manager Human Resources, OSF Saint Paul Medical Center, Mendota, IL, p. A193

KENNEDY, Larkin, Chief Executive Officer, Rush Foundation Hospital, Meridian, MS, p. A359

KENNEDY, Mary R.N., Chief Nursing Officer, Cleveland Clinic, Medina Hospital, Medina, OH, p. A495

KENNEDY, Nancy A. M.D., Chief Medical Officer, Dearborn County Hospital, Lawrenceburg, IN, p. A214

KENNEDY, Peggy S R.N., MS, FACHE, Vice President and Chief Nurse Executive, Fremont Health, Fremont, NE, p. A393

KENNEDY, R Scott M.D., Chief Medical Officer and Hospital Chief Operating Officer, Olympic Medical Center, Port Angeles, WA, p. A683

KENNEDY, Ryan
  Chief Financial Officer, Holy Name Medical Center, Teaneck, NJ, p. A421
  Chief Operating Officer, Kingman Regional Medical Center, Kingman, AZ, p. A30

KENNEDY, Tiffany, Chief Nursing Officer, Breckinridge Memorial Hospital, Hardinsburg, KY, p. A259

KENNEDY, Timea, Director Human Resources, St. Mary–Corwin Medical Center, Pueblo, CO, p. A107

KENNEDY, Todd S., President and Chief Executive Officer, Providence Hospital, Mobile, AL, p. A20

KENNEMER, Darline, Controller, Methodist Rehabilitation Hospital, Dallas, TX, p. A606

KENNETT, Jerry M.D., Chief Medical Officer, Boone Hospital Center, Columbia, MO, p. A366

KENNEY, Catherine, Chief Nursing Officer, Pampa Regional Medical Center, Pampa, TX, p. A636

KENNEY, Mary Ellen, Chief Human Services, Manchester Veterans Affairs Medical Center, Manchester, NH, p. A409

KENNEY, Ronda, Chief Operating Officer, Eastern State Hospital, Medical Lake, WA, p. A682

KENNINGTON, Lynn, Chief Financial Officer, Alaska Regional Hospital, Anchorage, AK, p. A25

KENNISON, Barbara, Director Clinical Services, Aurora Behavioral Healthcare San Diego, San Diego, CA, p. A85

KENNY, Carolyn, Executive Vice President Clinical Care, Children's Healthcare Of Atlanta, Atlanta, GA, p. A150

KENNY, Virginia, Chief Nursing Officer, Hancock Medical Center, Bay Saint Louis, MS, p. A352

KENSINGER, Brooke, Chief Executive Officer, Central Community Hospital, Elkader, IA, p. A227

KENT, Alan, Chief Executive Officer, Meadows Regional Medical Center, Vidalia, GA, p. A166

KENT, Blair
  Administrator, Alta View Hospital, Sandy, UT, p. A661
  Administrator, Riverton Hospital, Riverton, UT, p. A659

KENT, David
  Chief Medical Officer, Safe Haven Hospital Of Treasure Valley, Boise, ID, p. A171
  Chief Operating Officer, Southeastern Regional Medical Center, Newnan, GA, p. A162

KENT, Robert, D.O., President and Chief Executive Officer, Summa Western Reserve Hospital, Cuyahoga Falls, OH, p. A489

KENTERA, Amy, Chief Information Officer, Conifer Park, Glenville, NY, p. A436

KENTON, Bart, Chief Financial Officer, Holton Community Hospital, Holton, KS, p. A242

KENWOOD, Linda S, R.N., MSN, Chief Nursing Officer and Chief Operating Officer, Shore Medical Center, Somers Point, NJ, p. A420

KEOWN, Janet, Vice President Human Resources, Behavioral Health Network, Natchaug Hospital, Mansfield Center, CT, p. A110

KEPLER, Andrea, Chief Executive Officer, Wernersville State Hospital, Wernersville, PA, p. A553

KEPLINGER, Ron, Chief Information Officer, Western Maryland Hospital Center, Hagerstown, MD, p. A299

KEPNER, Donald L, Chief Financial Officer, Ashtabula County Medical Center, Ashtabula, OH, p. A480

KEPPLE, Jeffrey, M.D., Chief Executive Officer, Plumas District Hospital, Quincy, CA, p. A81

KEPPLER, Edward L. M.D., Chief Medical Officer, Marion General Hospital, Marion, IN, p. A215

KEPPLER, Matthew, Market Chief Executive Officer, Kindred Hospital Indianapolis South, Greenwood, IN, p. A209

KEPSHIRE, Bob, R.N., MS, Administrator and Chief Nursing Officer, University Hospital Mcduffie, Thomson, GA, p. A166

KERBS, Curtis, Regional Chief Information Officer, Memorial Hospital, North Conway, NH, p. A410

KERCHENSKI, Marlene, Chief Nurse, U. S. Air Force Hospital, Hampton, VA, p. A668

KERDEL, Francisco M.D., President Medical Staff, University Of Miami Hospital, Miami, FL, p. A134

KERI, Alison, Director Human Resources, Hiawatha Community Hospital, Hiawatha, KS, p. A242

KERIAN–MASTERS, Carol RN, BSN, Chief Nursing Officer, Regional Health Services Of Howard County, Cresco, IA, p. A225

KERLIN, Kerry, Chief Information Officer, Roswell Park Cancer Institute, Buffalo, NY, p. A433

KERMEN, John D.O., Chief Medical Staff, Mendocino Coast District Hospital, Fort Bragg, CA, p. A59

KERN, Daniel, Chief Executive Officer, Strategic Behavioral Health – Wilmington, Leland, NC, p. A466

KERN, Douglas W., Chief Executive Officer, Northcoast Behavioral Healthcare, Northfield, OH, p. A497

KERN, Gordon M.D., Medical Director, Oswego Community Hospital, Oswego, KS, p. A248

KERN, Howard P
  Chief Operating Officer, Sentara Princess Anne Hospital, Virginia Beach, VA, p. A676
  President and Chief Operating Officer, Sentara Leigh Hospital, Norfolk, VA, p. A672

KERN, Howard P., Chief Executive Officer, Sentara Healthcare, Norfolk, VA, p. B116

KERNAN, Jacqueline D., Vice President, Chief Nursing Officer, OSF Saint Luke Medical Center, Kewanee, IL, p. A191

KERNDL, John, Executive Vice President and Chief Financial Officer, Beaumont Hospital – Royal Oak, Royal Oak, MI, p. A329

KERNELL, Shane, Chief Executive Officer, Graham Regional Medical Center, Graham, TX, p. A617

KERNIVAN, Lorna, Chief Operating Officer, Palms West Hospital, Loxahatchee, FL, p. A131

KERNS, Elizabeth, Senior Vice President and Chief Information Officer, Lakeland Regional Health, Lakeland, FL, p. A130

KEROACK, Mark A., M.D., M.P.H., President and Chief Executive Officer, Baystate Health, Baystate Medical Center, Springfield, MA, p. A311

KERR, Jeff M.D., Chief Medical Officer, Baylor Medical Center At Mckinney, Mckinney, TX, p. A632

KERR, Karen, R.N., President, South Florida Baptist Hospital, Plant City, FL, p. A140

KERR, Mark, Chief Executive Officer, Presentation Medical Center, Rolla, ND, p. A478

KERR, Michael D., Chief Executive Officer, Promise Hospital Of East Los Angeles, Los Angeles, CA, p. A70

KERR, Michael D, Chief Executive Officer, Promise Hospital Of East Los Angeles, Los Angeles, CA, p. A70

KERRINS, David, Vice President Information Services and Chief Information Officer, Dameron Hospital, Stockton, CA, p. A92

KERRWOOD, Patrick, Chief Executive Officer, Siloam Springs Regional Hospital, Siloam Springs, AR, p. A49

KERSCHEN, Susan MS, R.N., Vice President and Chief Nursing Officer, Good Samaritan Medical Center, Lafayette, CO, p. A104

KERSEY, Jerry, Director Employee Relations, Eastern State Hospital, Lexington, KY, p. A261

KERSTETTER, Kathleen R.N., MSN, Chief Clinical Officer, Acuity Specialty Hospital Of New Jersey, Atlantic City, NJ, p. A411

KERSTING, Clay M.D., Chief Medical Staff, Newport Hospital And Health Services, Newport, WA, p. A682

KERSWILL, Randy M.D., Medical Director, Winnebago Mental Health Institute, Winnebago, WI, p. A716

KERTIS, Robert, Vice President Finance, Calvert Memorial Hospital, Prince Frederick, MD, p. A300

KERWIN, George, President and Chief Executive Officer, Bellin Memorial Hospital, Green Bay, WI, p. A702

KERWOOD, Christine, Chief Nursing Officer, East Ohio Regional Hospital, Martins Ferry, OH, p. A495

KERWOOD, Lori A, Director Human Resources, Cooley Dickinson Hospital, Northampton, MA, p. A309

KESSEL, Jennifer, Assistant Vice President, Operations and Human Resources, Aultman Orrville Hospital, Orrville, OH, p. A497

KESSLER, Alexander M.D., Chief of Staff, Northside Hospital–Cherokee, Canton, GA, p. A153

KESSLER, David M.D., Clinical Director, U. S. Public Health Service Indian Hospital, Zuni, NM, p. A429

KESSLER, Dawn
Senior Vice President Human Resources, St. John's Hospital, Maplewood, MN, p. A343
Senior Vice President Human Resources, St. Joseph's Hospital, Saint Paul, MN, p. A348

KESSLER, Jeffrey R, Vice President Information Services, Dana–Farber Cancer Institute, Boston, MA, p. A303

KESSLER, John E., President and Chief Executive Officer, Salem Township Hospital, Salem, IL, p. A199

KESSLER, Joseph, Executive Vice President and Chief Financial Officer, Kaleida Health, Buffalo, NY, p. A432

KESSNER, Jennifer, Financial Director, Roosevelt Medical Center, Culbertson, MT, p. A383

KESTER, Bonnie J R.N., MSN, Vice President Patient Care Services and Chief Nursing Officer, Nantucket Cottage Hospital, Nantucket, MA, p. A309

KESTER, William Thomas
Chief Nursing and Operating Officer, Broward Health Imperial Point, Fort Lauderdale, FL, p. A124
Chief Nursing/Operating Officer, Broward Health Imperial Point, Fort Lauderdale, FL, p. A124

KESTERSON, Matt
Director Information Services, Wadley Regional Medical Center At Hope, Hope, AR, p. A44
Director Information Services, Wadley Regional Medical Center, Texarkana, TX, p. A649

KETCH, Lynn
Human Resources Recruiter Generalist, Integris Canadian Valley Hospital, Yukon, OK, p. A519
Regional Director Integris Southwest Medical Center, Integris Southwest Medical Center, Oklahoma City, OK, p. A512

KETCHAM, Krista, Chief Financial Officer, Buena Vista Regional Medical Center, Storm Lake, IA, p. A235

KETCHAM, Michael
Chief Medical Officer, Mountain View Regional Medical Center, Norton, VA, p. A672

President, Medical Staff, Wellmont Lonesome Pine Hospital, Big Stone Gap, VA, p. A664

KETCHEM, Tami, Human Resource Director, Up Health System–Bell, Ishpeming, MI, p. A323

KETTERHAGEN, James P M.D., Senior Vice President and Chief Medical Officer, Jewish Hospital, Louisville, KY, p. A262

KETTERING, Lisa, Chief Medical Officer, Yampa Valley Medical Center, Steamboat Springs, CO, p. A107

KETTERLING, Kimberly A. R.N., Vice President of Nursing, Chi Oakes Hospital, Oakes, ND, p. A477

KETTERMAN, Patricia P., R.N., President and Chief Administrative Officer, Claiborne Medical Center, Tazewell, TN, p. A589

KEUTER, Mary Beth, Director Patient Care, Continuing Care Hospital At St. Luke's, Cedar Rapids, IA, p. A223

KEY, Lora, Chief Executive Officer, Sabetha Community Hospital, Sabetha, KS, p. A250

KEYONNIE, Christine CPA, Chief Financial Officer, Tuba City Regional Health Care Corporation, Tuba City, AZ, p. A37

KEYS, Janice C. FACHE, Senior Vice President, Chief Nurse Executive, Erlanger Medical Center, Chattanooga, TN, p. A576

KHADE, Kashmira, Coordinator Non–Clinical Services, Behavioral Center Of Michigan, Warren, MI, p. A332

KHALEGHI, Trisha
Chief Executive Officer, Sharp Mesa Vista Hospital, San Diego, CA, p. A86
Senior Vice President and Chief Executive Officer, Sharp Mesa Vista Hospital, San Diego, CA, p. A86

KHALIQUE, Tania, Director Human Resources, Vibra Hospital Of San Diego, San Diego, CA, p. A86

KHAN, Atique M.D., Medical Director, University Behavioral Health Of Denton, Denton, TX, p. A608

KHAN, Dan M.D., Chief Medical Officer, Yoakum County Hospital, Denver City, TX, p. A608

KHAN, Faraz, Chief Financial Officer, Doctors Hospital Of Laredo, Laredo, TX, p. A628

KHAN, Humayun M.D., Chief Medical Officer, Sacred Heart Hospital, Eau Claire, WI, p. A701

KHAN, Sarfraz, Medical Director, Meridian Health Services, Muncie, IN, p. A216

KHAN, Shahbaz M.D., Medical Director, Two Rivers Behavioral Health System, Kansas City, MO, p. A371

KHAN, Waheed M.D., President Medical Staff, Summers County Arh Hospital, Hinton, WV, p. A692

KHANCHANDANI, Ashok, Chief Financial Officer, Oroville Hospital, Oroville, CA, p. A78

KHANDELWAL, Ashish M.D., Medical Director, Healthsouth Rehabilitation Hospital Of Middletown, Middletown, DE, p. A115

KHANNA, Rajive
Chief Executive Officer, Grace Hospital, Cleveland, OH, p. A485
Chief Executive Officer, Specialty Hospital Of Lorain, Amherst, OH, p. A479

KHARONOV, Arthur, Vice President Nursing, Columbus Hospital Ltach, Newark, NJ, p. A417

KHATAMI, Manoochehr M.D., Medical Director, Hickory Trail Hospital, Desoto, TX, p. A609

KHATUA, Sanjeeb M.D., Chief Medical Officer and Vice President, Edward Hospital, Naperville, IL, p. A195

KHDOUR, Adel M.D., Chief Medical Officer, Indiana University Health White Memorial Hospital, Monticello, IN, p. A216

KHEMKA, Hemant, Chief Operating Officer, Surgery Specialty Hospitals Of America, Pasadena, TX, p. A637

KHIAMI, Ahmad, Chief of Staff, Beckley Arh Hospital, Beckley, WV, p. A690

KHIM FUGATE, Guay, Chief Operations Officer, Kindred Hospital Riverside, Perris, CA, p. A79

KHOERL, Thomas, Vice President Finance, Spectrum Health Big Rapids Hospital, Big Rapids, MI, p. A315

KHOO, Alex, Interim Area Finance Officer, Kaiser Permanente San Francisco Medical Center, San Francisco, CA, p. A87

KHOW, Vida J., Chief Executive Officer, Gallup Indian Medical Center, Gallup, NM, p. A426

KIBAR, Nizar M.D., Chief Medical Staff, Kiowa County Memorial Hospital, Greensburg, KS, p. A242

KIBBY, Rosalinda, Superintendent and Administrator, Columbia Basin Hospital, Ephrata, WA, p. A680

KIDA, Sue
Chief Executive Officer, Kessler Institute For Rehabilitation, West Orange, NJ, p. A422
President, Kessler Institute For Rehabilitation, West Orange, NJ, p. A422

KIDD, David, Manager Human Resources, Sentara Careplex Hospital, Hampton, VA, p. A668

KIDD, Monica, R.N., MSN, Administrator, Parkview Hospital, Wheeler, TX, p. A654

KIDD, Sue, Chief Financial Officer, Horton Community Hospital, Horton, KS, p. A243

KIDD, Thomas J., Chief Executive Officer, Macon County General Hospital, Lafayette, TN, p. A582

KIDDER, David M. D.O., Chief Medical Officer, Garfield County Health Center, Jordan, MT, p. A386

KIDDER, Suzanne F, Human Resources Officer, Opelousas General Health System, Opelousas, LA, p. A284

KIEBZAK, Stanley F R.N., Chief Nursing Officer, Healthsouth Rehabilitation Hospital The Vintage, Houston, TX, p. A620

KIEDROWSKI, Brian M.D., Chief Medical Director, Miami Jewish Home And Hospital For Aged, Miami, FL, p. A133

KIEFER, William
Chief Nursing Officer, TMC Bonham Hospital, Bonham, TX, p. A598
Chief Operating Officer, Rehoboth Mckinley Christian Health Care Services, Gallup, NM, p. A426

KIEFFER, Kelley
Chief Nursing Officer, Banner Baywood Medical Center, Mesa, AZ, p. A31
Chief Nursing Officer, Banner Heart Hospital, Mesa, AZ, p. A31

KIEHL, Tiffany, Chief Executive Officer, Mid–America Rehabilitation Hospital, Shawnee Mission, KS, p. A251

KIEHLE, Jessica R.N., Chief Nursing Officer, Abilene Regional Medical Center, Abilene, TX, p. A591

KIELY, Sharon M.D., Senior Vice President Medical Affairs and Chief Medical Officer, Stamford Hospital, Stamford, CT, p. A113

KIERNAN, Richard
Regional Chief Human Resources Officer, Monmouth Medical Center, Southern Campus, Lakewood, NJ, p. A415
Vice President Human Resources, Monmouth Medical Center, Long Branch Campus, Long Branch, NJ, p. A415

KIETZMAN, Jessica
Chief Nursing Officer, St. Vincent Jennings Hospital, North Vernon, IN, p. A218
Interim Administrator, St. Vincent Jennings Hospital, North Vernon, IN, p. A218

KIGER, Tom, Director Information Systems, Trinity Health System, Steubenville, OH, p. A500

KIGHT, Sheila, Director Human Resources, Tristar Horizon Medical Center, Dickson, TN, p. A578

KILARSKI, David J., FACHE, Chief Executive Officer, Firsthealth Moore Regional Hospital, Pinehurst, NC, p. A468

KILBORN, Mark, Director Information Systems, Springhill Memorial Hospital, Mobile, AL, p. A20

KILDAY, Kevin
Chief Financial Officer, Anna Jaques Hospital, Newburyport, MA, p. A309
Vice President Finance, Holy Family Hospital, Methuen, MA, p. A308

KILE, Steven E, Vice President Human Resources, Indiana University Health North Hospital, Carmel, IN, p. A205

KILEY, David, M.D., Interim President, Community Hospital South, Indianapolis, IN, p. A210

KILGORE, Julie, Vice President, Human Resources, Broadlawns Medical Center, Des Moines, IA, p. A226

KILLINGSWORTH, Meri, Chief Operating Officer, Hereford Regional Medical Center, Hereford, TX, p. A619

KILMER, Michael T., Director, Grand Junction Veterans Health Care System, Grand Junction, CO, p. A103

KILPATRICK, Von, Chief Nursing Officer, St. Vincent General Hospital District, Leadville, CO, p. A105

KIM, Donald M.D., Chief Medical Officer, Memorial Regional Hospital, Hollywood, FL, p. A127

KIM, Dong M.D., Chief of Staff, Parkview Community Hospital Medical Center, Riverside, CA, p. A82

KIM, Eric, Chief Information Officer, Las Encinas Hospital, Pasadena, CA, p. A79

KIM, Eugene P. M.D., Chief Medical Officer, St. Jude Medical Center, Fullerton, CA, p. A61

KIM, Hyon Su M.D., Medical Director, Northlake Behavioral Health System, Mandeville, LA, p. A280

KIM, John, Chief Financial Officer, Anchor Hospital, Atlanta, GA, p. A149

KIM, Soon K., M.D., President and Chief Executive Officer, Signature Healthcare Services, Corona, CA, p. B117

KIMBALL, Kevin, Director Information Technology, Brooks Memorial Hospital, Dunkirk, NY, p. A435

KIMBALL, Mark E., Chief Executive Officer, Houston County Community Hospital, Erin, TN, p. A578

KIMBALL, Tim, Chief Nursing Officer, Physicians' Specialty Hospital, Fayetteville, AR, p. A42

KIMBLE, Becky R.N., Chief Nursing Officer, Healthsouth Rehabilitation Hospital Of Jonesboro, Jonesboro, AR, p. A45

KIMBLE, D. Gay, Chief Human Resource Officer, Susan B. Allen Memorial Hospital, El Dorado, KS, p. A240

KIMBLE, Robert J., Chief Financial Officer, William R. Sharpe, Jr. Hospital, Weston, WV, p. A697

KIMBREW, Missey, Director Human Resources, Grafton City Hospital, Grafton, WV, p. A692

KIMBRO, George, Vice President Finance, Angel Medical Center, Franklin, NC, p. A462

KIMBROUGH, Pam M.D., Vice President Medical Affairs, Mercy Hospital Ardmore, Ardmore, OK, p. A504

KIMMEL, Kyle, Chief Financial Officer, Bacon County Hospital And Health System, Alma, GA, p. A149

KIMMEL, Stephen, Chief Financial Officer, Cook Children's Medical Center, Fort Worth, TX, p. A613

KIMMES, Robert P., Chief Executive Officer, Skyline Hospital, White Salmon, WA, p. A689

KIMMET, Jackie, Chief Human Resource Officer, River's Edge Hospital And Clinic, Saint Peter, MN, p. A348

KIMMY, Sharon, Coordinator Human Resources, Corry Memorial Hospital, Corry, PA, p. A532

KIMPLE, Robin, Director Information Services, Wellspan Gettysburg Hospital, Gettysburg, PA, p. A535

KIMZEY, Mike, Chief Executive Officer and Administrator, Oklahoma Center For Orthopedic And Multi-Specialty Surgery, Oklahoma City, OK, p. A512

KINCAID, Kevin, Chief Executive Officer, Knoxville Hospital & Clinics, Knoxville, IA, p. A230

KINDER, Barbara R.N., Chief Clinical Officer, Clark Regional Medical Center, Winchester, KY, p. A268

KINDERED, Deanne, Vice President Finance, Baylor Regional Medical Center At Plano, Plano, TX, p. A638

KINDRED, Bill, Chief Executive Officer, Russell County Hospital, Russell Springs, KY, p. A267

KINDRED, Bryan N., FACHE, President and Chief Executive Officer, Dch Health System, Tuscaloosa, AL, p. B40

KINDSCHI, Mark, Director Human Resources, Edgerton Hospital And Health Services, Edgerton, WI, p. A701

KING, Abner, Chief Operating Officer, Steele Memorial Medical Center, Salmon, ID, p. A176

KING, Beth, Chief Financial Officer, Jersey Community Hospital, Jerseyville, IL, p. A191

KING, Brent R, Chief Medical Officer and Chief Physician, Alfred I. Dupont Hospital For Children, Wilmington, DE, p. A116

KING, Bruce, President and Chief Executive Officer, New London Hospital, New London, NH, p. A410

KING, Chris, Director Information Services, Ohiohealth Marion General Hospital, Marion, OH, p. A494

KING, Christopher, Director Operations and Administrative Services, Matheny Medical And Educational Center, Peapack, NJ, p. A418

KING, Daniel P. MSN, R.N., Chief Nursing Officer, Glenwood Regional Medical Center, West Monroe, LA, p. A288

KING, Don
Chief Executive Officer, Saint Thomas Midtown Hospital, Nashville, TN, p. A586
Chief Executive Officer, Saint Thomas West Hospital, Nashville, TN, p. A586

KING, Donna R.N., FACHE, Vice President Clinical Operations and Chief Nursing Executive, Advocate Illinois Masonic Medical Center, Chicago, IL, p. A180

KING, Doug M.D., Director Clinical Services, Western Mental Health Institute, Bolivar, TN, p. A575

KING, Elizabeth, Director, White Plains Hospital Center, White Plains, NY, p. A456

KING, Glenn, R.N., MSN
Vice President and Chief Nursing Officer, Midmichigan Medical Center–Gladwin, Gladwin, MI, p. A320
Vice President, Chief Nursing Officer, Midmichigan Medical Center–Clare, Clare, MI, p. A316

KING, Grace, Regional Director Human Resources, Broward Health North, Deerfield Beach, FL, p. A123

KING, Heath, Chief Financial Officer, Orange Park Medical Center, Orange Park, FL, p. A136

KING, Janine M.D., Chief of Staff, East Los Angeles Doctors Hospital, Los Angeles, CA, p. A68

KING, Jay, Vice President Human Resources, Mercy Hospitals Of Bakersfield, Bakersfield, CA, p. A53

KING, Jo Nell, Director of Nursing, Northlake Behavioral Health System, Mandeville, LA, p. A280

KING, Joanie, Chief Financial Officer, Carteret Health Care, Morehead City, NC, p. A467

KING, JoAnne, Chief Operating Officer, Florida Hospital–Flagler, Palm Coast, FL, p. A138

KING, Katrina R.N., Senior Director, Nursing, Novant Health Huntersville Medical Center, Huntersville, NC, p. A465

KING, Kim, Director Human Resources and Public Relations, Baptist Memorial Hospital–Huntingdon, Huntingdon, TN, p. A580

KING, Louie
Chief Executive Officer, Benefis Teton Medical Center, Choteau, MT, p. A383
President, Harry Bold Nursing Home Administrator, Missouri River Medical Center, Fort Benton, MT, p. A384

KING, Paul A, Executive Director, Michigan Medicine, Ann Arbor, MI, p. A314

KING, Paul M.D., Medical Director, Parkwood Behavioral Health System, Olive Branch, MS, p. A360

KING, Ray M.D., Senior Vice President and Chief Medical Officer, Henry Ford Allegiance Health, Jackson, MI, p. A323

KING, Sam, Chief Financial Officer, Renown Regional Medical Center, Reno, NV, p. A405

KING, Sammy, Controller, Healthsouth Rehabilitation Hospital Of Ocala, Ocala, FL, p. A136

KING, Sandra, Chief Nursing Officer, Sagamore Children's Hospital Psychiatric Center, Dix Hills, NY, p. A435

KING, Scott M.D., Chief Medical Officer, Shenandoah Medical Center, Shenandoah, IA, p. A234

KING, Tamara R.N., MSN, Chief Nurse Executive, Shepherd Center, Atlanta, GA, p. A151

KING, Val, Chief Information Officer, Val Verde Regional Medical Center, Del Rio, TX, p. A608

KINGHAM, Darrell L CPA, Vice President Finance, Beauregard Memorial Hospital, De Ridder, LA, p. A274

KINGRY, Jennifer, Chief Financial Officer, St. Vincent's Blount, Oneonta, AL, p. A22

KINGSLEY, Christi, Vice President Human Resources, West Calcasieu Cameron Hospital, Sulphur, LA, p. A287

KINGSTON, Eileen M R.N., Nurse Executive, Associate Director Patient Care, Veterans Affairs Nebraska–Western Iowa Health Care System, Omaha, NE, p. A398

KINGSTON, Mary Beth R.N., MSN, Executive Vice President and Chief Nursing Officer, Aurora Medical Center Of Oshkosh, Oshkosh, WI, p. A710

KINGSTON, Mary E.
Chief Executive Officer, South Bay Community, Providence Little Company Of Mary Medical Center – Torrance, Torrance, CA, p. A94
Chief Executive Officer, Providence Little Company Of Mary Medical Center San Pedro, Los Angeles, CA, p. A70

KINGSTON, Peggy, Chief Executive Officer, Select Specialty Hospital–Pontiac, Pontiac, MI, p. A328

KINI, M Narendra., M.D., President and Chief Executive Officer, Nicklaus Children's Hospital, Miami, FL, p. A133

KINKAID, Steve, Director Information Systems, Blue Mountain Hospital, Lehighton, PA, p. A539

KINLEN, Thomas, Superintendent, Larned State Hospital, Larned, KS, p. A245

KINMAN, Amanda, Director of Finance, Saint Joseph Mount Sterling, Mount Sterling, KY, p. A265

KINMAN, Brett
Chief Operating Officer, Tomball Regional Medical Center, Tomball, TX, p. A650
Interim Chief Executive Officer, Tomball Regional Medical Center, Tomball, TX, p. A650

KINNEER, James W, Vice President Organizational Development, Indiana Regional Medical Center, Indiana, PA, p. A537

KINNEMAN, Mary R.N., MSN, Chief Nursing Officer, Vice President Patient Care Services, Norwood Hospital, Norwood, MA, p. A310

KINNEY, Janet, Chief Operating Officer, Northwest Florida Community Hospital, Chipley, FL, p. A121

KINSALA, Edeli, Chief Executive Officer, Sonora Behavioral Health Hospital, Tucson, AZ, p. A38

KINSEL, Mike, Controller, Federal Medical Center, Lexington, KY, p. A261

KINSELLA, Daniel F
Executive Vice President Information Technology, Northwestern Medicine Delnor Hospital, Geneva, IL, p. A188
Vice President and Chief Information Officer, Northwestern Medicine Central Dupage Hospital, Winfield, IL, p. A202

KINSEY, Daniel M.D., Medical Director, Oaklawn Psychiatric Center, Goshen, IN, p. A209

KINSEY, Wayne, Chief Executive Officer, Promise Hospital Of Salt Lake, Salt Lake City, UT, p. A660

KINSLOW, Kathleen, Ed.D., Chief Executive Officer, Aria – Jefferson Health, Philadelphia, PA, p. A543

KINTZ, Ronald J
Chief Financial Officer, Ira Davenport Memorial Hospital, Bath, NY, p. A431
Senior Vice President Finance and Chief Financial Officer, St. Joseph's Hospital, Elmira, NY, p. A435
Vice President and Treasurer, Arnot Ogden Medical Center, Elmira, NY, p. A435

KINYON, Craig C., President, Reid Health, Richmond, IN, p. A219

KINYON, David, Vice President of Operations and Outpatient Services, Asante Three Rivers Medical Center, Grants Pass, OR, p. A522

KINZIC, Elizabeth M.D., Chief of Staff, Share Medical Center, Alva, OK, p. A504

KINZIE, Wesley M.D., Chief of Staff, Stanislaus Surgical Hospital, Modesto, CA, p. A74

KIO, Kenneth, Manager Human Resources, Albany Stratton Veterans Affairs Medical Center, Albany, NY, p. A430

KIPP, Kris M, Executive Director, Patient Services and Chief Nursing Officer, James Cancer Hospital And Solove Research Institute, Columbus, OH, p. A487

KIRACOFE, Darin, Director Information Resource Management, Broughton Hospital, Morganton, NC, p. A467

KIRALY, Denise G, Director, Human Resources and Organization Development, Lima Memorial Health System, Lima, OH, p. A493

KIRBOW, Keith R.N., Vice President and Chief Nursing Officer, Christus Good Shepherd Medical Center–Marshall, Marshall, TX, p. A632

KIRBY, Adrienne, Ph.D., FACHE, President and Chief Executive Officer, Cooper University Health Care, Camden, NJ, p. A412

KIRBY, Brendan M.D., Medical Director, Riverview Psychiatric Center, Augusta, ME, p. A289

KIRBY, Elizabeth A
Senior Director Human Resources, Aurora Baycare Medical Center, Green Bay, WI, p. A702
Senior Director Human Resources, Aurora Medical Center – Manitowoc County, Two Rivers, WI, p. A714

KIRBY, James M. II, President and Chief Executive Officer, Margaret R. Pardee Memorial Hospital, Hendersonville, NC, p. A464

KIRBY, Juliana Kay R.N., MSN, Chief Nursing Officer, Adventist Health Medical Center – Tehachapi Valley, Tehachapi, CA, p. A93

KIRBY, Len, Chief Executive Officer, Garfield Park Hospital, Chicago, IL, p. A181

KIRBY, Penny V MSN, Chief Nursing Officer, Mckenzie Regional Hospital, Mckenzie, TN, p. A584

KIRBY, Ruby, Administrator, Bolivar General Hospital, Bolivar, TN, p. A575

KIRBY, Sarah, R.N., MSN, FACHE, Chief Operating Officer, Palmetto Health Baptist Parkridge, Columbia, SC, p. A560

KIRBY, Tracy
Assistant Vice President Business Relationship Management, Chi St. Vincent Hot Springs, Hot Springs, AR, p. A44
Assistant Vice President Business Relationship Management, Chi St. Vincent Infirmary Medical Center, Little Rock, AR, p. A46
Assistant Vice President Business Relationship Management, Chi St. Vincent Morrilton, Morrilton, AR, p. A47

KIRCH, Cyndi
Vice President Human Resources, Mercy General Hospital, Sacramento, CA, p. A83
Vice President Human Resources, Methodist Hospital Of Sacramento, Sacramento, CA, p. A83

KIRCHER, Janelle, R.N., MSN, Chief Executive Officer, Kindred Hospital–Denver, Denver, CO, p. A101

KIRCHER, Mark, Associate Vice President Finance, Norton Women's And Children's Hospital, Louisville, KY, p. A263

KIRCHNER, Doris, President and Chief Executive Officer, Vail Valley Health Hospital, Vail, CO, p. A108

KIRCHNER, Kent M.D., Chief of Staff, G.V. (Sonny) Montgomery Veterans Affairs Medical Center, Jackson, MS, p. A356

KIRCHNER, Susan M, Director Human Resources, Four Winds Hospital, Saratoga Springs, NY, p. A452

KIRISITS, Christopher, Chief Nursing Officer, Rochester Psychiatric Center, Rochester, NY, p. A451

KIRITANI, Tracy, Vice President and Chief Financial Officer, Clovis Community Medical Center, Clovis, CA, p. A56

KIRK, Darlene, Manager Finance, U. S. Public Health Service Indian Hospital, Crownpoint, NM, p. A425

KIRK, Donald M.D., Chief of Staff, Star Valley Medical Center, Afton, WY, p. A717

KIRK, H Lee. Jr, FACHE, Administrator, Shriners Hospitals For Children–Springfield, Springfield, MA, p. A311

KIRK, J. Douglas M.D., Chief Medical Officer, University Of California, Davis Medical Center, Sacramento, CA, p. A84

KIRK, Jean, Chief Financial Officer, Bennett County Hospital And Nursing Home, Martin, SD, p. A570

KIRK, Linda A., Administrator, Morton Plant Rehabilitation Center, Belleair, FL, p. B87

KIRK, Paul, Vice President, Woman's Hospital, Baton Rouge, LA, p. A271

KIRK, Peggy, Senior Vice President Clinical Operations, Shirley Ryan Abilitylab, Chicago, IL, p. A183

KIRK, Roger L., President and Chief Executive Officer, Bethesda Hospital East, Boynton Beach, FL, p. A120

KIRK, Roger L, President and Chief Executive Officer, Bethesda Hospital East, Boynton Beach, FL, p. A120

KIRK, Vanessa, Director of Nursing, Kiowa County Memorial Hospital, Greensburg, KS, p. A242

KIRK, Warren J., Chief Executive Officer, Doctors Medical Center Of Modesto, Modesto, CA, p. A74

KIRK, Warren, Chief Operating Officer, Doctors Hospital Of Manteca, Manteca, CA, p. A73

KIRKBRIDE, James B., President and Chief Executive Officer, Susan B. Allen Memorial Hospital, El Dorado, KS, p. A240

KIRKER, Donna R.N., MS, Vice President Patient Services and Chief Nursing Officer, Glens Falls Hospital, Glens Falls, NY, p. A436

KIRKER, Lynda I, Chief Financial Officer, Flagler Hospital, Saint Augustine, FL, p. A141

KIRKHAM, Brett, Chief Operating Officer, Alliancehealth Deaconess, Oklahoma City, OK, p. A511

KIRKHAM, Paul, Chief Executive Officer, Keystone Newport News, Newport News, VA, p. A671

KIRKLAND–ROSE, Tina, Coordinator Human Resources, Select Specialty Hospital–Lexington, Lexington, KY, p. A261

KIRKPATRICK, Brett, Executive Director, Mccullough–Hyde Memorial Hospital/Trihealth, Oxford, OH, p. A498

KIRKPATRICK, Kyle
Chief Executive Officer, Baylor Emergency Medical Center At Aubrey, Aubrey, TX, p. A594
Chief Executive Officer, Baylor Emergency Medical Centers – Burleson, Burleson, TX, p. A600
Chief Executive Officer, Baylor Emergency Medical Centers – Rockwall, Rockwall, TX, p. A640
Chief Executive Officer, Baylor Scott & White Emergency Medical Center– Cedar Park, Cedar Park, TX, p. A601

KIRKPATRICK, Lisa, Chief Financial Officer, Ochsner St. Anne General Hospital, Raceland, LA, p. A284

KIRKS, Linda, Vice President and Chief Financial Officer, Christus Santa Rosa Health System, San Antonio, TX, p. A642

KIRMAN, Eleen M.D., Chief Medical Officer, Peacehealth St. John Medical Center, Longview, WA, p. A682

KIRMAN, Lynn R.N., Chief Nursing Officer, St. John's Medical Center And Living Center, Jackson, WY, p. A718

KIRRANE, Sean, Chief Executive Officer, First Physicians Capital Group, Inc., Oklahoma City, OK, p. B52

KIRSHNER, Arthur N, Chief Information Management, Winn Army Community Hospital, Hinesville, GA, p. A159

KIRSHNER, David L., Chief Financial Officer, Strong Memorial Hospital Of The University Of Rochester, Rochester, NY, p. A451

KIRSTEIN, Susan N. R.N., MSN, Chief Nursing Officer, Broadlawns Medical Center, Des Moines, IA, p. A226

KIRTON, Carl Ph.D., Chief Nursing Officer, University Hospital, Newark, NJ, p. A418

KISACKY, Christina A, Vice President, Operations, Uhs Chenango Memorial Hospital, Norwich, NY, p. A448

KISER, Greg, Chief Executive Officer, Three Rivers Medical Center, Louisa, KY, p. A262

KISER, James R. II, Chief Executive Officer, Providence St. Joseph Medical Center, Polson, MT, p. A387

KISER, Pamela R.N., MS, Chief Nursing Executive and Vice President of Nursing, St. John Medical Center, Tulsa, OK, p. A518

KISHNER, Janice, Chief Nursing Officer, St. Bernard Parish Hospital, Chalmette, LA, p. A272

KISKADDON, Robert M.D., Chief Medical Officer, Margaret R. Pardee Memorial Hospital, Hendersonville, NC, p. A464

KISNER, Angela, Director Human Resources and Coordinator Medical Staff, Landmark Hospital Of Cape Girardeau, Cape Girardeau, MO, p. A365

KISS, Meredith, Administrator, Elgin Mental Health Center, Elgin, IL, p. A186

KISSNER, Michael, Chief Executive Officer, Healthsouth Treasure Coast Rehabilitation Hospital, Vero Beach, FL, p. A146

KISTLER, Beckie, Director of Finance, Our Lady Of Peace, Louisville, KY, p. A263

KISTLER, Mike, Chief Executive Officer, Shadow Mountain Behavioral Health System, Tulsa, OK, p. A518

KISTNER, Kasondra, R.N., Chief Executive Officer, Warm Springs Rehabilitation Hospital Of San Antonio, San Antonio, TX, p. A644

KITCHEN, Steven M.D., Chief Medical Officer, Phoebe Putney Memorial Hospital, Albany, GA, p. A149

KITTNER, Bonnie R.N., Chief Nursing Officer, Mendocino Coast District Hospital, Fort Bragg, CA, p. A59

KJERGAARD, Holly, Chief Nursing Officer, Audubon County Memorial Hospital, Audubon, IA, p. A222

KJOSA, Ann Marie R.N., MSN, Chief Nursing Officer, Eastern Idaho Regional Medical Center, Idaho Falls, ID, p. A173

KLANN, Andrew D.O., Chief of Staff, Southwest Health, Platteville, WI, p. A710

KLARNER, Lea Ann H., Chief Executive Officer, Crittenden County Hospital, Marion, KY, p. A264

KLASEK, Chance CPA, Chief Financial Officer, Jefferson Community Health And Life, Fairbury, NE, p. A392

KLASKO, Stephen K, M.D., President and Chief Executive Officer, Thomas Jefferson University Hospitals, Philadelphia, PA, p. A546

KLASKO, Stephen K., M.D., President and Chief Executive Officer, Jefferson Health , Philadelphia, PA, p. B70

KLASS, Cheryl, President, Kaleida Health, Buffalo, NY, p. A432

KLASSEN, Brad, Information Technology Coordinator, Sanford Worthington Medical Center, Worthington, MN, p. A351

KLASSEN, Karen, Controller, Healthsouth Chattanooga Rehabilitation Hospital, Chattanooga, TN, p. A576

KLAUSTERMEIER, Lisa R.N., MSN, Chief Nursing Officer, Anderson Hospital, Maryville, IL, p. A192

KLAWITER, Thomas, Chief Executive Officer, South Texas Spine And Surgical Hospital, San Antonio, TX, p. A643

KLAWITTER, Kyle, Vice President Human Resources, Summa Health System, Akron, OH, p. A479

KLEAM, Douglas V., President, St. Bernardine Medical Center, San Bernardino, CA, p. A85

KLEAS, Tara, Director Human Resources, Healthsouth Rehabilitation Hospital Of Fort Worth, Fort Worth, TX, p. A613

KLEBE, Doug, Vice President Operational Finance, Mercy Medical Center, Roseburg, OR, p. A526

KLECKNER, Megan, Vice President and Administrator, Riverside Walter Reed Hospital, Gloucester, VA, p. A668

KLEEN, Kathy, Chief Nursing Officer, Tri–County Hospital, Wadena, MN, p. A350

KLEFFMAN, Angela, Director of Ancillary Services, Bigfork Valley Hospital, Bigfork, MN, p. A336

KLEHN, Paul, Chief Information Technology Officer, Liberty Hospital, Liberty, MO, p. A372

KLEIN, Aron
Vice President Finance, Advocate Bromenn Medical Center, Normal, IL, p. A195
Vice President of Finance, Advocate Eureka Hospital, Eureka, IL, p. A187

KLEIN, Barbara R.N., Director of Nursing, Arms Acres, Carmel, NY, p. A433

KLEIN, Bernard, M.D., Chief Executive, Providence Holy Cross Medical Center, Los Angeles, CA, p. A70

KLEIN, Cindy C, Vice President Human Resources, Peacehealth St. Joseph Medical Center, Bellingham, WA, p. A678

KLEIN, Cindy, Chief Executive Officer, Lamb Healthcare Center, Littlefield, TX, p. A629

KLEIN, David G., M.D., President, Saint Francis Memorial Hospital, San Francisco, CA, p. A87

KLEIN, David Ph.D., Vice President Operations, Behavioral Health Network, Natchaug Hospital, Mansfield Center, CT, p. A110

KLEIN, Diany, Vice President Human Resources, Community Memorial Hospital, Ventura, CA, p. A95

KLEIN, Edward A, Chief Financial Officer, Johnston Health, Smithfield, NC, p. A470

KLEIN, Jacqueline, Chief Financial Officer, Lakeview Medical Center, Rice Lake, WI, p. A711

KLEIN, Jillyn, Chief Operating Officer, Howard County Medical Center, Saint Paul, NE, p. A399

KLEIN, Julie, Chief Operating Officer, Mckee Medical Center, Loveland, CO, p. A106

KLEIN, Kenneth M.D., Vice President Medical Affairs, Beloit Health System, Beloit, WI, p. A699

KLEIN, Kyle, Assistant Chief Financial Officer, Mercy Health – West Hospital, Cincinnati, OH, p. A484

KLEIN, Perry, Chief Engineering, Mann–Grandstaff Veterans Affairs Medical Center, Spokane, WA, p. A686

KLEIN, Terrence, Vice President and Chief Operating Officer, Franciscan St. Elizabeth Health – Crawfordsville, Crawfordsville, IN, p. A206

KLEINBECK, Seth M. M.D., Chief of Staff, Baptist Health Medical Center–Stuttgart, Stuttgart, AR, p. A50

KLEINE, Doug, IT Director, St. Mary Medical Center, Apple Valley, CA, p. A52

KLEINHANZL, Thomas A., President and Chief Executive Officer, Frederick Regional Health System, Frederick, MD, p. A298

KLEINSASSER, Dustin, Information Technology and BioMed, Fall River Hospital, Hot Springs, SD, p. A570

KLEINSTEUBER, Kathy, Chief Executive Officer, Rehabilitation Hospital Of Savannah, Savannah, GA, p. A164

KLENKE, Lisa R., R.N., Chief Executive Officer, Mercer Health, Coldwater, OH, p. A487

KLENNER, Susan, Chief Nursing Officer and Vice President of Hospital Operations, Olmsted Medical Center, Rochester, MN, p. A347

KLEPIN, Michael R, Administrator, Hunt Regional Medical Center, Greenville, TX, p. A617

KLESS, Adam
Chief Nursing Officer, Highlands Regional Medical Center, Sebring, FL, p. A143
Chief Nursing Officer, Raulerson Hospital, Okeechobee, FL, p. A136

KLESSENS, Thomas
Chief Financial Officer, Landmark Medical Center, Woonsocket, RI, p. A557
Chief Financial Officer, Rehabilitation Hospital Of Rhode Island, North Smithfield, RI, p. A556

KLEVEN, Brian, Chief Financial Officer, St. Rose Dominican Hospitals – Siena Campus, Henderson, NV, p. A402

KLICKSTEIN, Judith S, Chief Information Officer, Cambridge Health Alliance, Cambridge, MA, p. A305

KLIEBERT, Lynn, Chief Financial Officer, Teche Regional Medical Center, Morgan City, LA, p. A282

KLIEWER, Chad, Information Technology Specialist, Mercy Hospital Kingfisher, Kingfisher, OK, p. A509

KLIMEK, David
Chief Human Resources Officer, Miami County Medical Center, Paola, KS, p. A249
Vice President Human Resources, Olathe Medical Center, Olathe, KS, p. A248

KLIMP, Mary J., FACHE, Administrator, Mayo Clinic Health System In New Prague, New Prague, MN, p. A345

KLINE, Brian S, Vice President and Chief Financial Officer, Penn Highlands Dubois, Dubois, PA, p. A533

KLINE, Burke, Chief Executive Officer, Greeley County Health Services, Tribune, KS, p. A252

KLINE, Daniel B, Vice President, Site Administrator, St. Joseph's Healthcare System, Paterson, NJ, p. A418

KLINE, Donald E., President and Chief Executive Officer, Mercy Health – St. Elizabeth Youngstown Hospital, Youngstown, OH, p. A503

KLINE, Jack M.D., Chief of Staff, Mercy Medical Center–New Hampton, New Hampton, IA, p. A232

KLINE, Julie, Senior Vice President Patient Services, Adventist Health Sonora, Sonora, CA, p. A92

KLINE, Mark W M.D., Physician in Chief, Texas Children's Hospital, Houston, TX, p. A623

KLINE, Melissa, Chief Nursing Officer, Metrohealth Medical Center, Cleveland, OH, p. A486

KLINGA, Maria, Director Management Information Systems, Silver Hill Hospital, New Canaan, CT, p. A111

KLINGEMAN, Jennifer, Director of Nursing, Chester Mental Health Center, Chester, IL, p. A180

KLINGENBERG, Pat, Director Human Resources, Towner County Medical Center, Cando, ND, p. A474

KLINGLER, Stacie R.N., Vice President of Patient Services, Franciscan Health Rensselear, Rensselaer, IN, p. A218

KLINGSEIS, Robert, Director Information Systems, Desert Regional Medical Center, Palm Springs, CA, p. A78

KLINK, Sheryl, Chief Financial Officer, Piedmont Hospital, Atlanta, GA, p. A150

KLINKER, Suzanne M., Director, Bay Pines Veterans Affairs Healthcare System, Bay Pines, FL, p. A119

KLINKNER, Donna M, Chief Financial Officer, Madelia Community Hospital, Madelia, MN, p. A342

KLOCK, Kathy, R.N., Senior Vice President Clinical Operations and Human Resources, Gundersen Health System, La Crosse, WI, p. A704

KLOCKMAN, Dena, Chief Financial Officer, Ogallala Community Hospital, Ogallala, NE, p. A396

KLOCKO, Daniel, Vice President Human Resources, Kootenai Health, Coeur D'Alene, ID, p. A173

KLOECKNER, Vicki, Director Human Resources, Hshs Holy Family Hospital In Greenville, Greenville, IL, p. A189

KLOEWER, Ron, Chief Information Officer, Montgomery County Memorial Hospital, Red Oak, IA, p. A234

KLOPFER, Anthony Rudy., FACHE, Director, Veterans Affairs Eastern Kansas Health Care System, Topeka, KS, p. A252

KLOPP, Amanda, Director, Innovation and Clinical Integration, Penn State Health St. Joseph, Reading, PA, p. A549

KLOPPE, William, Chief Financial Officer, Geary Community Hospital, Junction City, KS, p. A243

KLOSTERMAN, Mark D., FACHE, President and Chief Executive Officer, Faith Regional Health Services, Norfolk, NE, p. A396

KLOSTERMEIER, Janice, Senior Vice President and Chief Financial Officer, Valley Presbyterian Hospital, Los Angeles, CA, p. A72

KLUCKHOHN, Christine
President, Continuing Care, Father Baker Manor, Orchard Park, NY, p. B29
President, Continuing Care, Mcauley Residence, Kenmore, NY, p. B29
President, Continuing Care, Mercy Nursing Facility, Buffalo, NY, p. B29

President, Continuing Care, Nazareth Home, Buffalo, NY, p. B29

President, Continuing Care, St. Catherine Laboure, Buffalo, NY, p. B29

President, Continuing Care, St. Elizabeth'S Home, Lancaster, NY, p. B29

President, Continuing Care, St. Francis Of Buffalo, Buffalo, NY, p. B29

President, Continuing Care, St. Francis Of Williamsville, Williamsville, NY, p. B29

KLUGE, Thomas S.
President, Hampshire Memorial Hospital, Romney, WV, p. A696

President, War Memorial Hospital, Berkeley Springs, WV, p. A690

KLUGHERZ, Greg, Vice President Corporate Services and Chief Financial Officer, St. Cloud Hospital, Saint Cloud, MN, p. A347

KLUNE, Peter
Chief Executive Officer, Kauai Veterans Memorial Hospital, Waimea, HI, p. A170

Chief Executive Officer, Samuel Mahelona Memorial Hospital, Kapaa, HI, p. A170

KMETZ, Thomas D., Division President, Norton Children's Hospital, Louisville, KY, p. A263

KNACKSTEDT, Cameron D.O., Chief Medical Staff, Harlan County Health System, Alma, NE, p. A390

KNACKSTEDT, Nathan D.O., Chief of Staff, Clara Barton Hospital, Hoisington, KS, p. A242

KNAK, Roger, Administrator and Chief Executive Officer, Fairview Regional Medical Center, Fairview, OK, p. A508

KNAPHEIDE, Debbie, Site Administrator, Chief Nursing Officer and Chief Operating Officer, Carondelet Holy Cross Hospital, Nogales, AZ, p. A32

KNAPP, Brian A, Vice President Operations, Fairview Ridges Hospital, Burnsville, MN, p. A337

KNE, Tanya M.D., Chief Medical Officer, Banner Desert Medical Center, Mesa, AZ, p. A31

KNECHT, Brian J, Chief Operating Officer, Regional Medical Center Of San Jose, San Jose, CA, p. A88

KNECHT, John, Chief Medical Staff, Linton Hospital, Linton, ND, p. A477

KNEDLER, Marie E., R.N., FACHE, President, Chi Health Mercy Council Bluffs, Council Bluffs, IA, p. A225

KNEELAND, Misty, Chief Medical Staff, Medical Center Of South Arkansas, El Dorado, AR, p. A42

KNEEPPEL, Dennis R.N., Chief Nurse Executive and Chief Operating Officer, Kaiser Permanente San Rafael Medical Center, San Rafael, CA, p. A89

KNEISEL, Kristin, Interim Director, Information Services, Alice Peck Day Memorial Hospital, Lebanon, NH, p. A408

KNEPP, Gary D.O., Chief Medical Officer and Chief Quality Officer, Unitypoint Health – Peoria, Peoria, IL, p. A197

KNEPP, Keith M.D., Executive Vice President and Chief Operating Officer, Unitypoint Health – Peoria, Peoria, IL, p. A197

KNIEVEL, Lon, Chief Executive Officer, Osmond General Hospital, Osmond, NE, p. A398

KNIFFIN, Fred
Chief Medical Officer, Porter Medical Center, Middlebury, VT, p. A662

Chief Executive Officer, Porter Medical Center, Middlebury, VT, p. A662

KNIGHT, Beth, Chief Nursing Officer, Nacogdoches Memorial Hospital, Nacogdoches, TX, p. A634

KNIGHT, Bethany M.D., Chief of Staff, Community Medical Center Of Izard County, Calico Rock, AR, p. A41

KNIGHT, Calvin K., President and Chief Executive Officer, John Muir Health, Walnut Creek, CA, p. B70

KNIGHT, Christopher D., Vice President Finance and Chief Financial Officer, Reid Health, Richmond, IN, p. A219

KNIGHT, Deana, Chief Executive Officer, Select Specialty Hospital–Greensboro, Greensboro, NC, p. A463

KNIGHT, Don, Assistant Administrator and Risk Manager, Teche Regional Medical Center, Morgan City, LA, p. A282

KNIGHT, Jennifer, Manager Human Resources, Waynesboro Hospital, Waynesboro, PA, p. A553

KNIGHT, Kimber, Chief Financial Officer, Braxton County Memorial Hospital, Gassaway, WV, p. A692

KNIGHT, Laura, Chief Nursing Officer, Merit Health Central, Jackson, MS, p. A356

KNIGHT, Mark T, Executive Vice President and Chief Financial Officer, Jackson Health System, Miami, FL, p. A133

KNIGHT, Michael M.D., Medical Director, Hampstead Hospital, Hampstead, NH, p. A408

KNIGHT, Reginald Q., Chief Medical Officer, Aurelia Osborn Fox Memorial Hospital, Oneonta, NY, p. A449

KNIGHT, Ricardo, Interim Medical Director, Van Matre Healthsouth Rehabilitation Hospital, Rockford, IL, p. A199

KNIGHT, Sue CPA, Chief Operating Officer, St. Elizabeth Hospital, Gonzales, LA, p. A275

KNIGHT, Terry, Public Information Officer and Administrative Assistant, California Mens Colony Correctional Treatment Center, San Luis Obispo, CA, p. A89

KNIGHT, Warren, Chief Financial Officer, Baton Rouge Behavioral Hospital, Baton Rouge, LA, p. A270

KNIGHT, Wayne
Chief Financial Officer, Indiana University Health Frankfort, Frankfort, IN, p. A208

Director Finance, St. Vincent Clay Hospital, Brazil, IN, p. A204

KNIPP, Cindi, Director Human Resources, Rooks County Health Center, Plainville, KS, p. A250

KNITT, Lori, Chief Nursing Officer, Aurora Sheboygan Memorial Medical Center, Sheboygan, WI, p. A712

KNITTEL, Monty E., Chief Executive Officer, Feather River Hospital, Paradise, CA, p. A79

KNIZLEY, Andrew, Chief Executive Officer, Memorial Hermann – Texas Medical Center, Houston, TX, p. A621

KNOBLOCH, Stanley
Director Fiscal Services, Sanford Luverne Medical Center, Luverne, MN, p. A342

Director Fiscal Services, Sanford Rock Rapids Medical Center, Rock Rapids, IA, p. A234

KNOCKE, Michael, Chief Information Officer, Kansas Spine And Specialty Hospital, Wichita, KS, p. A253

KNODE, Scott, Chief Financial Officer, Veterans Memorial Hospital, Waukon, IA, p. A236

KNOEPFFLER, Susan R.N., Vice President Nursing, Huntington Hospital, Huntington, NY, p. A437

KNOEPFLER, David M.D., Chief Medical Officer, Overlake Medical Center, Bellevue, WA, p. A678

KNOERL, Thomas, Vice President Finance, Spectrum Health Reed City Hospital, Reed City, MI, p. A329

KNORR, Kelly, Chief Financial Officer, First Hospital Wyoming Valley, Kingston, PA, p. A537

KNOSKE, Thomas, Chief Executive Officer, Regency Hospital Cleveland East, Warrensville Heights, OH, p. A501

KNOUP, Amy, Director Human Resources, Palo Alto County Health System, Emmetsburg, IA, p. A227

KNOUS, Gail, Chief Executive Officer and Chief Compliance Officer, Odessa Regional Medical Center South Campus, Odessa, TX, p. A636

KNOWLES, B K D.O., Chief of Staff, General John J. Pershing Memorial Hospital, Brookfield, MO, p. A365

KNOWLES, Christy, Chief Human Resources Officer, Coosa Valley Medical Center, Sylacauga, AL, p. A23

KNOWLES, John, Director Human Resources, Clinch Valley Medical Center, Richlands, VA, p. A673

KNOWLES, Robert M.D., Chief of Staff, Saint Thomas Highlands Hospital, Sparta, TN, p. A589

KNOWLES–SMITH, Peter M.D., Medical Director, Bennett County Hospital And Nursing Home, Martin, SD, p. A570

KNOWLTON, Robert, Vice President and Chief Financial Officer, Baylor Medical Center At Garland, Garland, TX, p. A616

KNOX, Dennis M., Chief Executive Officer, Mid–Columbia Medical Center, The Dalles, OR, p. A527

KNOX, Jody, Chief Operating Officer, Kindred Hospital Rancho, Rancho Cucamonga, CA, p. A81

KNOX, John E, FACHE, Chief Executive Officer, Baptist Medical Center, San Antonio, TX, p. A642

KNOX, John, Senior Vice President and Chief Information Officer, Carolinas Healthcare System University, Charlotte, NC, p. A459

KNOX, Jud, Chief Executive Officer, York Hospital, York, ME, p. A293

KNOX, Roland, Chief Executive Officer, Northern Cochise Community Hospital, Willcox, AZ, p. A38

KNOX, Stacey A., Administrator, Rock County Hospital, Bassett, NE, p. A390

KNUDSEN, Jessica, Chief Operating Officer and Director Performance Improvement and Risk Management, Holly Hill Hospital, Raleigh, NC, p. A469

KNUDSEN, Mark, Director Fiscal Services, Shriners Hospitals For Children–Portland, Portland, OR, p. A525

KNUDSEN, Mary, Chief Nursing Officer, Northeast Regional Medical Center, Kirksville, MO, p. A371

KNUDSEN, Matthew, Director, Information Systems, Sheppard Pratt Health System, Baltimore, MD, p. A295

KNUDSON, Jenny, Controller, Hiawatha Community Hospital, Hiawatha, KS, p. A242

KNUTH, Kerry, Chief Operating Officer, Mercy Hospital Of Defiance, Defiance, OH, p. A490

KNUTSON, Holly, Manager Information Technology, Kittson Memorial Healthcare Center, Hallock, MN, p. A341

KNUTSON, John P M.D., Chief Medical Staff, Delta County Memorial Hospital, Delta, CO, p. A100

KNUTSON, Larry, Director Finance, Centracare Health–Long Prairie, Long Prairie, MN, p. A342

KO, Tommy M.D., Chief Medical Officer, St. Joseph Medical Center, Kansas City, MO, p. A371

KOBEL, Angela
Chief Financial Officer, Southwest Health System, Cortez, CO, p. A100

Chief Information Officer, Southwest Health System, Cortez, CO, p. A100

KOCH, Carol, Manager Human Resources, Callaway District Hospital, Callaway, NE, p. A391

KOCH, Douglas E., Market President, Aurora Medical Center, Kenosha, WI, p. A704

KOCH, Eric, Chief Nursing Officer, Northern Montana Health Care, Havre, MT, p. A385

KOCH, Holly, Chief Financial Officer, Girard Medical Center, Girard, KS, p. A241

KOCH, Jamie R.N., Director of Nursing, Thayer County Health Services, Hebron, NE, p. A394

KOCH, Joseph G., Chief Executive Officer, Meadowview Regional Medical Center, Maysville, KY, p. A264

KOCHEVAR, Vanessa, Chief Financial Officer, St. Mary–Corwin Medical Center, Pueblo, CO, p. A107

KOCHIE, Daniel A
Chief Financial Officer, Samaritan Hospital, Troy, NY, p. A454

Chief Financial Officer, St. Mary's Hospital, Troy, NY, p. A454

KOCHIS, Mary Ellen MSN, R.N., Administrator Nursing Operations, Beaumont Hospital–Dearborn, Dearborn, MI, p. A317

KOCIOLA, Matthew, Senior Vice President and Chief Financial Officer, Somerset Hospital, Somerset, PA, p. A551

KOCOUREK, Cathie A., President, Aurora Medical Center – Manitowoc County, Two Rivers, WI, p. A714

KOCSIS, Dana, Vice President Nursing and Operations, Lodi Community Hospital, Lodi, OH, p. A493

KOCSIS, Violet, Chief Human Resources Officer, Hunterdon Medical Center, Flemington, NJ, p. A414

KOCZENT, Kurt, Executive Vice President and Chief Operating Officer, F. F. Thompson Hospital, Canandaigua, NY, p. A433

KOEBKE, Troy L
Director Human Resources Management, Bellin Memorial Hospital, Green Bay, WI, p. A702

Director Human Resources, Bellin Psychiatric Center, Green Bay, WI, p. A703

Human Resource Director, Bellin Health Oconto Hospital, Oconto, WI, p. A709

KOEBNICK, Dale, Director Management Information Systems and Patient Access, Metroplex Adventist Hospital, Killeen, TX, p. A627

KOEHLER, Amy, Director Human Resources, Shelby Memorial Hospital, Shelbyville, IL, p. A200

KOEHLER, Maggie, Senior Vice President and Chief Financial Officer, Wilkes–Barre General Hospital, Wilkes, PA, p. A554

KOEHLER, Mike, Interim Chief Information Officer, Piedmont Athens Regional Medical Center, Athens, GA, p. A149

KOELE, Craig, Chief Executive Officer, Cornerstone Hospital Of Oklahoma–Muskogee, Muskogee, OK, p. A510

KOENIG, Donald E.
Chief Operating Officer, Mercy Health – St. Joseph Warren Hospital, Warren, OH, p. A501

Executive Vice President and Regional Chief Operating Officer, President, St. Elizabeth Youngstown Hospital, Mercy Health – St. Elizabeth Youngstown Hospital, Youngstown, OH, p. A503

KOENIG, Harris F., President and Chief Executive Officer, San Antonio Regional Hospital, Upland, CA, p. A95

KOENIG, Mary, Chief Financial Officer, Vernon Memorial Healthcare, Viroqua, WI, p. A714

KOEPKE, Eldon, Chief Financial Officer, Mitchell County Hospital Health Systems, Beloit, KS, p. A239

KOEPKE, Jennifer R.N., Vice President of Patient Care Services and Chief Nursing Officer, Western Missouri Medical Center, Warrensburg, MO, p. A380

KOEPPEL–OLSEN, Carol, Vice President, Patient Care Services, Winter Haven Hospital, Winter Haven, FL, p. A148

KOERNER, Jill, Manager Employee Relations, Weisman Children's Rehabilitation Hospital, Marlton, NJ, p. A416

KOESSL, Brenda R.N., Director of Nursing Services, Frances Mahon Deaconess Hospital, Glasgow, MT, p. A384

KOESTER, Jean, Manager Human Resources, Limestone Medical Center, Groesbeck, TX, p. A617

KOESTERER, Susan, Vice President, Finance, Alton Memorial Hospital, Alton, IL, p. A177

KOETTING, Edward, Chief Financial Officer, Bedford Veterans Affairs Medical Center, Edith Nourse Rogers Memorial Veterans Hospital, Bedford, MA, p. A302

KOZAR, Michael A., Chief Executive Officer, Northwest Florida Community Hospital, Chipley, FL, p. A121

KOZEL, Kenneth D.
President and Chief Executive Officer, University Of Maryland Shore Medical Center At Chestertown, Chestertown, MD, p. A297
President and Chief Executive Officer, University Of Maryland Shore Medical Center At Dorchester, Cambridge, MD, p. A297
President and Chief Executive Officer, University Of Maryland Shore Medical Center At Easton, Easton, MD, p. A298

KOZEL, Mary Ann, Chief Fiscal, Wilmington Veterans Affairs Medical Center, Wilmington, DE, p. A116

KOZIKUSKI, Courtney, Chief Financial Officer, Perry Memorial Hospital, Perry, OK, p. A514

KOZIN, Scott M.D., Chief of Staff, Shriners Hospitals For Children–Philadelphia, Philadelphia, PA, p. A545

KRABBENHOFT, Kelby K., President and Chief Executive Officer, Sanford Health, Sioux Falls, SD, p. B111

KRABILL, Emma, Chief Executive Officer, Scenic Mountain Medical Center, Big Spring, TX, p. A598

KRABLIN, Brett M.D., Chief of Staff, Mercy Hospital Kingfisher, Kingfisher, OK, p. A509

KRAFT, Chris, Director Information Systems, York General, York, NE, p. A400

KRAFVE, Jake Matthew, Chief Financial Officer, Royal Oaks Hospital, Windsor, MO, p. A381

KRAHNERT, John F M.D., Chief Medical Officer, Firsthealth Moore Regional Hospital, Pinehurst, NC, p. A468

KRAJEWSKI, David, Senior Vice President and Chief Financial Officer, Sinai Hospital Of Baltimore, Baltimore, MD, p. A296

KRAMER, Blake, Chief Executive Officer, Franklin Medical Center, Winnsboro, LA, p. A288

KRAMER, Carmen, Chief Executive Officer, Lakeview Behavioral Health, Norcross, GA, p. A162

KRAMER, Danette, Chief Financial Officer, Regional Medical Center, Manchester, IA, p. A231

KRAMER, Janie, Chief Operating Officer, Sharp Memorial Hospital, San Diego, CA, p. A86

KRAMER, Karen R.N., Vice President and System Chief Nursing Officer, Cox Medical Centers, Springfield, MO, p. A379

KRAMER, Kathryn M.D., President Medical Staff, Pekin Hospital, Pekin, IL, p. A197

KRAMER, Kevin, Chief Executive Officer, Modoc Medical Center, Alturas, CA, p. A51

KRAMER, Lynette M.D., Chief Medical Officer, Boone County Health Center, Albion, NE, p. A390

KRAMER, Michael, Chief Executive Officer, Mercy Health – West Hospital, Cincinnati, OH, p. A484

KRAMER, Susan, Director of Human Resources, Levi Hospital, Hot Springs National Park, AR, p. A44

KRAMPITS, Carrie, Director Human Resources, Mckenzie Health System, Sandusky, MI, p. A330

KRANZ, Karl M.D., Chief of Staff, Cascade Medical Center, Leavenworth, WA, p. A682

KRASON, Jane E., R.N., Chief Executive Officer, Appalachian Behavioral Healthcare, Athens, OH, p. A480

KRASS, Todd, Chief Executive Officer, Belton Regional Medical Center, Belton, MO, p. A364

KRAUKLIS, Gene
Regional Vice President Human Resources, Aurora Lakeland Medical Center, Elkhorn, WI, p. A701
Regional Vice President Human Resources, Aurora Memorial Hospital Of Burlington, Burlington, WI, p. A699

KRAUS, Jason, Director Human Resources, Magruder Memorial Hospital, Port Clinton, OH, p. A498

KRAUS, John M.D., Chief Medical Officer, Bryn Mawr Rehabilitation Hospital, Malvern, PA, p. A539

KRAUSE, Donna, Chief Information Officer, Harry S. Truman Memorial Veterans Hospital, Columbia, MO, p. A367

KRAUSE, Jill A., Director, Kalamazoo Psychiatric Hospital, Kalamazoo, MI, p. A324

KRAUSE, Kim, Director Human Resources, Baylor Jack And Jane Hamilton Heart And Vascular Hospital, Dallas, TX, p. A604

KRAUSE, Steven, Manager Information Technology, Franciscan Healthcare – Munster, Munster, IN, p. A217

KRAUSE, Wade M.D., Chief Medical Officer, Connally Memorial Medical Center, Floresville, TX, p. A612

KRAUTSCHEID, Steven P, Ancillary Services Administrator, Tuality Healthcare, Hillsboro, OR, p. A522

KRAVETZ, Michael M.D., Medical Director, Healthsouth Valley Of The Sun Rehabilitation Hospital, Glendale, AZ, p. A30

KRAVETZ, Todd, Chief of Staff, Wickenburg Community Hospital, Wickenburg, AZ, p. A38

KREATSOULAS, Nicholas
Senior Vice President and Chief Medical Officer and Chief Quality Officer, Mercy Health – St. Elizabeth Youngstown Hospital, Youngstown, OH, p. A503
Vice President Medical Affairs, Mercy Health – St. Joseph Warren Hospital, Warren, OH, p. A501

KREBS, Anne, Chief Financial Officer, Butler Health System, Butler, PA, p. A530

KREBS, Cindy, District Director Human Resources, Matagorda Regional Medical Center, Bay City, TX, p. A596

KREBS, George M.D., Chief Medical Officer, Broughton Hospital, Morganton, NC, p. A467

KREBS, Mary Jane, FACHE, President, Spring Harbor Hospital, Westbrook, ME, p. A293

KREBSBACH, Mayla, Chief Executive Officer, Vista Del Mar Hospital, Ventura, CA, p. A96

KREELEY, Chris, Director Nursing, Kessler Marlton Rehabilitation, Marlton, NJ, p. A416

KREHBIEL, Rod M.D., Chief of Staff, Klickitat Valley Health, Goldendale, WA, p. A681

KREIDER, David, Controller, Wellspan Ephrata Community Hospital, Ephrata, PA, p. A534

KREIDER, Robert Q., President and Chief Executive Officer, Devereux, Villanova, PA, p. B46

KREIDLER, Marlene, Executive Director Human Resources, San Joaquin Community Hospital, Bakersfield, CA, p. A53

KREITINGER, Tate J., Chief Executive Officer, The Healthcenter, Kalispell, MT, p. A386

KREITZER, Teri, Director Human Resources, Saint Francis Medical Center, Cape Girardeau, MO, p. A365

KREJCI, Kathy Blair, Chief Nursing Officer, Marshall Medical Center, Placerville, CA, p. A80

KRELL, G Christopher M.D., Chief of Staff, South Lincoln Medical Center, Kemmerer, WY, p. A718

KRELSTEIN, Michael M.D., Medical Director, San Diego County Psychiatric Hospital, San Diego, CA, p. A86

KREN, John, Chief Financial Officer, St. John's Medical Center And Living Center, Jackson, WY, p. A718

KREPPS, John, Senior Vice President Finance, Silver Cross Hospital, New Lenox, IL, p. A195

KRETSCHMAN, Robin MSN, R.N., Vice President Patient Care Services, Marshfield Medical Center, Marshfield, WI, p. A706

KRETSCHMER, Suzanne, Chief Executive Officer, Chg Cornerstone Hospital Conroe, Conroe, TX, p. A602

KRETZ, Blake, FACHE, President, Texas Health Arlington Memorial Hospital, Arlington, TX, p. A593

KRETZINGER, Curt, Chief Operating Officer, Mosaic Life Care At St. Joseph, Saint Joseph, MO, p. A376

KRETZSCHMER, Kendra, Patient Care System Leader, Scheurer Hospital, Pigeon, MI, p. A328

KREUTNER, Ron, Chief Financial Officer, San Joaquin General Hospital, French Camp, CA, p. A60

KREUTZER, Kevin, Chief Financial Officer, Russell Regional Hospital, Russell, KS, p. A250

KREUZ, Betsy, Chief Financial Officer, Upmc Altoona, Altoona, PA, p. A528

KREUZER, Jay E., FACHE, Chief Executive Officer, Kona Community Hospital, Kealakekua, HI, p. A170

KREVANS, Sarah, President and Chief Executive Officer, Sutter Health, Sacramento, CA, p. B123
President, Continuing Care, St. Joseph Manor, Olean, NY, p. B29KREYE, David, Chief Executive Officer, First Surgical Hospital, Bellaire, TX, p. A598

KRHOVSKY, David M.D., Vice President, Medical Affairs, Spectrum Health – Butterworth Hospital, Grand Rapids, MI, p. A321

KRIEGER, Cathy, Human Resources Director, Greene County Medical Center, Jefferson, IA, p. A230

KRIEGER, Mark, Vice President and Chief Financial Officer, Barnes–Jewish Hospital, Saint Louis, MO, p. A368

KRIEGER, Robert M., Chief Executive Officer, Lawnwood Regional Medical Center & Heart Institute, Fort Pierce, FL, p. A125

KRIEGER, Tim, Director Information Systems, Harnett Health System, Dunn, NC, p. A461

KRIER, Jennifer, Vice President Human Resources, Wesley Medical Center, Wichita, KS, p. A254

KRILICH, Chad M.D., Chief Med Officer–AMC/CMC, Multicare Auburn Medical Center, Auburn, WA, p. A678

KRINKE, Susan, Chief Executive Officer, Kindred Hospital Lima, Lima, OH, p. A493

KRIPAKARAN, Kasturi M.D., Medical Director, Andrew Mcfarland Mental Health Center, Springfield, IL, p. A200

KRIPINSKI, Laura, Chief Nursing Officer, Forks Community Hospital, Forks, WA, p. A680

KRISHNAN, Radha M.D., Chief Medical Officer, Antelope Valley Hospital, Lancaster, CA, p. A65

KRISHNAN, Suresh, Vice President and Chief Information Officer, Loretto Hospital, Chicago, IL, p. A181

KRISHNASWAMY, Jaikumar, Chief Executive Officer, Baylor Scott & White Medical Center – Centennial, Frisco, TX, p. A615

KRISTEL, John, President and Chief Executive Officer, Good Shepherd Rehabilitation Hospital, Allentown, PA, p. A528

KRITZ, Howard, Director Human Resources, NYC Health + Hospitals / Bellevue, New Rochelle, NY, p. A444

KRITZER, Tammy, Vice President Clinic Operations, Mayo Clinic Health System–Albert Lea And Austin, Austin, MN, p. A336

KRMPOTIC, Debra J., R.N., Chief Executive Officer, Banner Thunderbird Medical Center, Glendale, AZ, p. A30

KRODEL, Scott, Vice President Information Systems, Johnson Memorial Hospital, Franklin, IN, p. A209

KROESE, Brandi, Director Operations, West Springs Hospital, Grand Junction, CO, p. A103

KROESE, Robert D., FACHE, Chief Executive Officer, Pella Regional Health Center, Pella, IA, p. A233

KROESE, Robert D FACHE, Chief Executive Officer, Pella Regional Health Center, Pella, IA, p. A233

KROLICKI, Karen, Director, Human Resources, Beaumont Hospital – Taylor, Taylor, MI, p. A331

KROLL, Ronald, Chief Financial Officer, Mercy General Hospital, Sacramento, CA, p. A83

KROMER, Harold, Director Site Information Systems, Advocate Condell Medical Center, Libertyville, IL, p. A192

KRONENBERG, Seth M.D., Chief Medical Officer, Crouse Health, Syracuse, NY, p. A453

KROSOFF, Mary June, Chief Human Resources Officer, Highlands Hospital, Connellsville, PA, p. A532

KROUSE, Michael
Chief of Staff, Trinity Hospital, Weaverville, CA, p. A96
Chief Information Officer Information Services, Ohiohealth Grady Memorial Hospital, Delaware, OH, p. A490
Chief Information Officer, Ohiohealth Doctors Hospital, Columbus, OH, p. A487
Chief Information Officer, Ohiohealth Grant Medical Center, Columbus, OH, p. A487
Chief Information Officer, Ohiohealth Riverside Methodist Hospital, Columbus, OH, p. A488
Senior Vice President Chief Information Officer, Ohiohealth Dublin Methodist Hospital, Dublin, OH, p. A490

KROUSE, Stephen W, Chief Human Resource Officer, St. Christopher's Hospital For Children, Philadelphia, PA, p. A545

KRUCKNER, Douglas M.D., Medical Director, Stamford Memorial Hospital, Stamford, TX, p. A646

KRUEGER, Christine M.D., Chief of Staff, Munising Memorial Hospital, Munising, MI, p. A326

KRUEGER, Ellen, Director Human Resources, Chadron Community Hospital And Health Services, Chadron, NE, p. A392

KRUEGER, Eric, Chief Financial Officer, Mercy Hospital And Medical Center, Chicago, IL, p. A182

KRUEGER, James G., M.D., Ph.D., Chief Executive Officer, Rockefeller University Hospital, New Rochelle, NY, p. A446

KRUEGER, Justin, Chief Operating Officer, Mercy Health – Fairfield Hospital, Fairfield, OH, p. A491

KRUG, Robert J., M.D., Chief Executive Officer, Mount Sinai Rehabilitation Hospital, Hartford, CT, p. A110

KRUGEL, Gary M, Chief Financial Officer, Norwegian American Hospital, Chicago, IL, p. A182

KRUGER, Cory, Interim Chief Executive Officer, Nebraska Spine Hospital, Omaha, NE, p. A398

KRUGER, Dale K., Chief Executive Officer, Mahnomen Health Center, Mahnomen, MN, p. A342

KRUGER, George CPA, Chief Financial Officer, Comanche County Memorial Hospital, Lawton, OK, p. A509

KRUMMEL, Dere, Director Information Systems, Ochsner Medical Center – Kenner, Kenner, LA, p. A277

KRUMREY, Arthur J, Chief Information Officer, Loyola University Medical Center, Maywood, IL, p. A193

KRUMWIED, Robert D., President and Chief Executive Officer, Regional Mental Health Center, Merrillville, IN, p. A215

KRUPALA, Judith R.N., Chief Nursing Officer, Cuero Community Hospital, Cuero, TX, p. A604

KRUSE, Joseph J
Chief Administrative Officer, Mayo Clinic Health System – Franciscan Healthcare In Sparta, Sparta, WI, p. A712
Executive Vice President, Mayo Clinic Health System – Franciscan Healthcare In La Crosse, La Crosse, WI, p. A704

KRUSE, Marcia R.N., Director Nursing, Logan County Hospital, Oakley, KS, p. A248

KRUSE, Victoria, Manager Human Resources, Franklin General Hospital, Hampton, IA, p. A228

KRUSIE, Kathleen R., FACHE, President, Community Hospital North, Indianapolis, IN, p. A210

KRUSIE, Kathleen R, FACHE, President, Community Hospital East, Indianapolis, IN, p. A210

KRUYER–COLLINS, Emyle, Chief Human Resources Officer, Unity Medical & Surgical Hospital, Mishawaka, IN, p. A216

KRUZEL, Janet, Business Office Manager, Centracare Health–
Melrose, Melrose, MN, p. A343
KRUZICK, Michael, Acting Chief Financial Officer, Norwalk
Hospital, Norwalk, CT, p. A112
KRUZNER, Melinda, Chief Financial Officer, Lexington Medical
Center, West Columbia, SC, p. A567
KRYSTOWIAK, Thomas P
Chief Financial Officer, Thedacare Regional Medical Center–
Berlin, Berlin, WI, p. A699
Vice President Finance, Theda Care Medical Center – Wild
Rose, Wild Rose, WI, p. A716
KRYZANIAK, Larry, Chief Financial Officer, Hennepin County
Medical Center, Minneapolis, MN, p. A343
KRZASTEK, Sue, Vice President Human Resources, Augusta
Health, Fishersville, VA, p. A667
KRZYMOWSKI, David M.D., Chief of Staff, Sanpete Valley
Hospital, Mount Pleasant, UT, p. A657
KUANGPARICHAT, Manoch M.D., President Medical Staff,
Excelsior Springs Hospital, Excelsior Springs, MO, p. A367
KUBACKI, Clayton, Controller, Kindred Hospital Detroit,
Detroit, MI, p. A318
KUBALA, Joseph
Chief Financial Officer, St. Vincent Jennings Hospital, North
Vernon, IN, p. A218
Director Financial and Support Services, St. Vincent Salem
Hospital, Salem, IN, p. A219
KUBALL, Lana, Director Administrative Services, Lucas
County Health Center, Chariton, IA, p. A224
KUBE, Don M.D., Chief of Staff, Dickinson County Healthcare
System, Iron Mountain, MI, p. A323
KUBIAK, Phillip J., President, Hampstead Hospital,
Hampstead, NH, p. A408
KUBIAK, Richard M.D., Vice President Medical Affairs, Peconic
Bay Medical Center, Riverhead, NY, p. A450
KUBICEK, Jim, Vice President, Operations, Rogers Memorial
Hospital, Oconomowoc, WI, p. A709
KUBOTA, Andrea R.N., MSN, Director Patient Care Services
and Nurse Executive, Shriners Hospitals For Children–
Honolulu, Honolulu, HI, p. A169
KUBOUSHEK, David, Chief, Fiscal Service, Durham Veterans
Affairs Medical Center, Durham, NC, p. A461
KUCERA, Doug, Chief Financial Officer, Crete Area Medical
Center, Crete, NE, p. A392
KUCERA, Kim, Chief Operating Officer, Mille Lacs Health
System, Onamia, MN, p. A345
KUCICH, Vincent
Chief Medical Officer, Presence Covenant Medical Center,
Urbana, IL, p. A202
Chief Medical Officer, Presence United Samaritans Medical
Center, Danville, IL, p. A185
KUCKEWICH, Mike, Director Information Systems, Terre Haute
Regional Hospital, Terre Haute, IN, p. A220
KUCZORA, Paul, Chief Executive Officer, Grant–Blackford
Mental Health Center, Marion, IN, p. A215
KUDER, Merlin, Chief Information Officer, Hamilton County
Hospital, Syracuse, KS, p. A252
KUDLA, Angela MSN, R.N., Chief Nursing Officer, Select
Specialty Hospital–Downriver, Wyandotte, MI, p. A333
KUEHLER, Sheila R.N., Director of Nursing, Knox County
Hospital, Knox City, TX, p. A627
KUEHLER, Stephen A., Administrator, Knox County Hospital,
Knox City, TX, p. A627
KUEHN, David, Chief Financial Officer, Rusk County Memorial
Hospital, Ladysmith, WI, p. A704
KUEHNEMUND, Bonnie, Comptroller, Heart Of America
Medical Center, Rugby, ND, p. A478
KUESTERSTEFFEN, Vicki, Director and Chief Executive
Officer, J. D. Mccarty Center For Children With
Developmental Disabilities, Norman, OK, p. A511
KUGHN, Yvonne, Chief Executive Officer, Select Specialty
Hospital–Pittsburgh/Upmc, Pittsburgh, PA, p. A547
KUHAR, Peggy A R.N., MSN, Chief Nursing Officer, University
Hospitals Geauga Medical Center, Chardon, OH, p. A483
KUHL, Nicholas M.D., Chief of Staff, Spectrum Health Gerber
Memorial, Fremont, MI, p. A320
KUHLMAN, Ian, Manager Information Technology, Shelby
Memorial Hospital, Shelbyville, IL, p. A200
KUHN, Anita, Controller, Texas County Memorial Hospital,
Houston, MO, p. A369
KUHN, Brenda
Chief Nursing Officer, Greene Memorial Hospital, Xenia,
OH, p. A503
Chief Nursing Officer, Kettering Medical Center, Kettering,
OH, p. A493
KUHN, Keith, Chief Executive Officer, Haven Behavioral Senior
Care Of Dayton, Dayton, OH, p. A489
KUHN, Margueritte M.D., Vice President Medical Affairs,
Midmichigan Medical Center–Midland, Midland, MI, p. A326
KUHN, Steve, Chief Financial Officer, River Park Hospital,
Huntington, WV, p. A693

KUHNS, Jay, Vice President Human Resources, Johns Hopkins
All Children's Hospital, Saint Petersburg, FL, p. A141
KUHRT, Sharon, Chief Nursing Officer, New England
Rehabilitation Hospital Of Portland, Portland, ME, p. A292
KUKELHAN, Alison, Manager Human Resources, Adams
Memorial Hospital, Decatur, IN, p. A206
KULHANEK, Linda, Chief Financial Officer, Memorial Hermann
Katy Hospital, Katy, TX, p. A626
KULICK, Daniel M.D., Chief of Staff, Marlette Regional
Hospital, Marlette, MI, p. A325
KULIK, Alec G, Administrator, Cleveland Clinic Children's
Hospital For Rehabilitation, Cleveland, OH, p. A485
KULISZ, Michael
Chief Medical Officer, Northwestern Medicine Kishwaukee
Hospital, Dekalb, IL, p. A185
Chief Medical Officer, Northwestern Medicine Valley West
Hospital, Sandwich, IL, p. A200
KULLMAN, Betsy R.N., MSN, Executive Vice President and
Chief Nursing Officer, Medical Center At Bowling Green,
Bowling Green, KY, p. A256
KULMA, Mariarose R.N., Vice President Patient Services, East
Texas Medical Center Tyler, Tyler, TX, p. A651
KUMAR, Daryn J., Chief Executive Officer, Memorial Medical
Center, Modesto, CA, p. A74
KUMAR, Nanda M.D., Chief of Staff, Vibra Hospital Of
Northern California, Redding, CA, p. A81
KUMMER, Margaret, Chief Human Resource Officer, Citizens
Medical Center, Colby, KS, p. A239
KUNERT, Alicia, MS, Executive Director, Conway Regional
Rehabilitation Hospital, Conway, AR, p. A41
KUNES, Courtney, Director Human Resources, Lock Haven
Hospital, Lock Haven, PA, p. A539
KUNKEL, Elisabeth J., MD, Chief Medical Officer, Pennsylvania
Psychiatric Institute, Harrisburg, PA, p. A536
KUNKEL, Stephanie, Vice President of Human Resources,
Tampa Community Hospital, Tampa, FL, p. A145
KUNNAPPILLY, Chester, M.D., Interim Chief Executive Officer,
San Mateo Medical Center, San Mateo, CA, p. A89
KUNSTLING, Ted M.D., Chief Medical Officer, Duke Raleigh
Hospital, Raleigh, NC, p. A468
KUNTZ, Alicia, Nurse Manager, Lifecare Hospitals Of
Mechanicsburg, Mechanicsburg, PA, p. A540
KUNZ, Donna
System Director Human Resources, Saint Luke's Cushing
Hospital, Leavenworth, KS, p. A245
System Director Human Resources, Saint Luke's North
Hospital – Barry Road, Kansas City, MO, p. A371
System Director Human Resources, Saint Luke's South
Hospital, Overland Park, KS, p. A249
KUNZA, Mary Kay, Manager Human Resources, Mercy
Hospital Lincoln, Troy, MO, p. A380
KUOPUS, Lisa, Chief Nursing Officer, Cumberland Surgical
Hospital, San Antonio, TX, p. A642
KUPER, Kandi, Chief Nursing Officer, Kit Carson County
Health Service District, Burlington, CO, p. A99
KUPFERSTEIN, Ron, Chief Executive Officer, Monrovia
Memorial Hospital, Monrovia, CA, p. A74
KUPLEN, Carol, R.N., MSN, President and Chief Executive
Officer, St. Luke's University Hospital – Bethlehem Campus,
Bethlehem, PA, p. A529
KURAITIS, Kestutis V M.D., Chief of Staff, Pioneers Memorial
Healthcare District, Brawley, CA, p. A54
KURCAB, Jeff, Chief Financial Officer, Lewisgale Hospital
Pulaski, Pulaski, VA, p. A673
KURESKA, Kirk, Chief Executive Officer, San Antonio
Behavioral Healthcare Hospital, San Antonio, TX, p. A643
KURIAN, Santha M.D., Chief of Staff, James E. Van Zandt
Veterans Affairs Medical Center, Altoona, PA, p. A528
KURLE, Janet, Chief Financial Officer, Community Memorial
Hospital, Turtle Lake, ND, p. A478
KUROKI, Helen, Senior Vice President and Chief Medical
Officer, CHI Memorial, Chattanooga, TN, p. A576
KURRA, Shankar M.D., Senior Vice President Medical Affairs,
Fisher–Titus Medical Center, Norwalk, OH, p. A497
KURTIAK, Mary Jo, Chief Executive Officer, Greystone Park
Psychiatric Hospital, Morris Plains, NJ, p. A416
KURTZ, Kris, Controller, Metro Health Hospital, Wyoming,
MI, p. A333
KURTZ, Maria
Director Human Resources, Lutheran Hospital Of Indiana,
Fort Wayne, IN, p. A208
Director Human Resources, Orthopaedic Hospital Of
Lutheran Health Network, Fort Wayne, IN, p. A208
KURTZ, Thomas F Jr, Chief Operating Officer, Georgia
Regional Hospital At Savannah, Savannah, GA, p. A164
KURTZ, Thomas M., President and Chief Executive Officer,
Chan Soon–Shiong Medical Center, Windber, PA, p. A554
KURTZ, Tom, Vice President Information Services and Chief
Information Officer, Memorial Healthcare, Owosso, MI,
p. A327

KURZ, Kenneth R M.D., Chief of Staff, Midstate Medical
Center, Meriden, CT, p. A111
KURZ, Sharon H., Ph.D., Chief Executive Officer, St. Elias
Specialty Hospital, Anchorage, AK, p. A25
KUSHNER, Michael S, Senior Vice President and Chief Talent
Officer, Nicklaus Children's Hospital, Miami, FL, p. A133
KUSLER, Julie, Manager Information Services, Avera St.
Luke's Hospital, Aberdeen, SD, p. A568
KUSNIERZ, William J., Vice President and Chief Financial
Officer, Springfield Regional Medical Center, Springfield,
OH, p. A499
KUTCH, John M., President, Trinity Health, Minot, ND, p. A477
KUTILEK, Richard J, Chief Operating Officer, Calvary Hospital,
New Rochelle, NY, p. A441
KUTNER, Jean M.D., Chief Medical Officer, University Of
Colorado Hospital, Aurora, CO, p. A98
KUVSHINOFF, Boris M.D., II, Chief Medical Officer, Roswell
Park Cancer Institute, Buffalo, NY, p. A433
KUYKENDALL, Jana, Chief Executive Officer, Post Acute/
Warm Springs Specialty Hospital Of Luling, Luling, TX,
p. A631
KUZAS, Betsy, Executive Vice President and Chief Operating
Officer, Phoenix Children's Hospital, Phoenix, AZ, p. A34
KUZEE, Ann, Executive Director Human Resources, Riverview
Health, Noblesville, IN, p. A217
KWIATEK, Susan, R.N., Executive Director, Glen Cove
Hospital, Glen Cove, NY, p. A436
KWIESIELEWICZ, Nancy
Human Resources Manager, Ministry Good Samaritan
Health Center, Merrill, WI, p. A707
Human Resources Manager, Ministry Saint Clare's Hospital,
Weston, WI, p. A715
KYHNELL, Koreen H, Vice President Human Resources,
Indiana University Health Arnett Hospital, Lafayette, IN,
p. A214
KYLER, Yvonne
Director Human Resources, Texas Health Arlington
Memorial Hospital, Arlington, TX, p. A593
Director Human Resources, Texas Health Heart & Vascular
Hospital Arlington, Arlington, TX, p. A593
KYRIACOU, George M., President and Chief Executive Officer,
Gaylord Hospital, Wallingford, CT, p. A113
KYWI, Alberto
Chief Information Officer, Goleta Valley Cottage Hospital,
Santa Barbara, CA, p. A90
Chief Information Officer, Santa Barbara Cottage Hospital,
Santa Barbara, CA, p. A90
KYZAR, Debbie, Chief Financial Officer, Central Carolina
Hospital, Sanford, NC, p. A470

L

L'ITALIEN, Mark, Director Information Services, Salem
Regional Medical Center, Salem, OH, p. A499
LA CAVA, Joseph, Chief Nursing Officer and Director Of
Anesthesia, Desoto Memorial Hospital, Arcadia, FL,
p. A119
LA CROIX, Kent, Chief Information Officer, Schoolcraft
Memorial Hospital, Manistique, MI, p. A325
LABADIE, Wendy, Chief Human Resource Officer, Banner
Estrella Medical Center, Phoenix, AZ, p. A33
LABAGNARA, James M.D., Vice President Medical Affairs, St.
Joseph's Healthcare System, Paterson, NJ, p. A418
LABARGE, Robert J., President and Chief Executive Officer,
Sturgis Hospital, Sturgis, MI, p. A331
LABELLE, Douglas M.D., Chief Medical Officer, Up Health
System–Bell, Ishpeming, MI, p. A323
LABELLE, James, M.D.
Chief Medical Officer, Scripps Green Hospital, La Jolla,
CA, p. A64
Chief Medical Officer, Scripps Memorial Hospital–La Jolla,
La Jolla, CA, p. A64
LABER, Susan R.N., Chief Nursing Officer, Tampa Community
Hospital, Tampa, FL, p. A145
LABIAGA, Kimberly, Human Resources Leader, Kaiser
Permanente Fontana Medical Center, Fontana, CA, p. A59
LABONTE, Karen Y, Chief Nursing Officer, Northwest Medical
Center – Springdale, Springdale, AR, p. A49
LABONTE, Robin, Leader Financial Care, York Hospital, York,
ME, p. A293
LABORANTI, Sarah M, Interim Director Human Resources,
Tennova Physicians Regional Medical Center, Knoxville,
TN, p. A582
LABRIOLA, Suzanne M. D.O., Chief Medical Officer, Allegheny
Valley Hospital, Natrona Heights, PA, p. A542

LABRIOLA, Terri, Human Resources Officer, Sierra Nevada Memorial Hospital, Grass Valley, CA, p. A62

LABRUM, Chad, Chief Financial Officer, Ashley Regional Medical Center, Vernal, UT, p. A661

LACAZE, Todd, Chief Financial Officer, Riverside Community Hospital, Riverside, CA, p. A82

LACEFIELD, Gayla, Director Human Resources, Howard Memorial Hospital, Nashville, AR, p. A47

LACEY, Carmen, MSN, R.N.
President and Director of Patient Care Services, Charles A. Cannon Memorial Hospital, Newland, NC, p. A468
President, Charles A. Cannon Memorial Hospital, Newland, NC, p. A468

LACEY, Paul M.D., Chief Medical Staff, North Valley Hospital, Tonasket, WA, p. A688

LACHANCE, Eric, Chief Financial Officer, Munroe Regional Medical Center, Ocala, FL, p. A136

LACHAPELLE, Diana, Controller, Healthsouth Rehabilitation Hospital, Concord, NH, p. A407

LACHER, Paula A MSN, R.N., Chief Nursing Officer, West Penn Hospital, Pittsburgh, PA, p. A548

LACHINA, Ignazio M.D., Medical Director, Healthsouth Rehabilitation Hospital Of Cypress, Houston, TX, p. A620

LACHNEY, Cheryl
Administrator, Compass Behavioral Center Of Alexandria, Alexandria, LA, p. A269
Director of Nursing, Compass Behavioral Center Of Alexandria, Alexandria, LA, p. A269

LACHOWSKY, John M.D., Chief Medical Officer, Mercy Hospital Ozark, Ozark, AR, p. A48

LACHTERMAN, Bruce M.D., Chief of Medical Staff, St. Luke's Lakeside Hospital, The Woodlands, TX, p. A649

LACKEY, Lori, Chief Financial Officer, Sabetha Community Hospital, Sabetha, KS, p. A250

LACKNEY, Christopher J, Director Human Resources, Grace Cottage Hospital, Townshend, VT, p. A663

LACOT, Ivette, Director Human Resources, Hospital Episcopal San Lucas Guayama, Guayama, PR, p. A723

LACY, Albert, Associate Director of Information Technology, Tampa Community Hospital, Tampa, FL, p. A145

LACY, Angela, Director of Nursing, Bolivar General Hospital, Bolivar, TN, p. A575

LACY, Dwight A., Chief Executive Officer, Millwood Hospital, Arlington, TX, p. A593

LACY, Edward L., FACHE, Vice President and Administrator, Baptist Health Medical Center–Heber Springs, Heber Springs, AR, p. A44

LACY, Tyson, Chief Executive Officer and Superintendent, Lincoln Hospital, Davenport, WA, p. A680

LADAROLA, Sandra, Chief Nursing Officer, Waterbury Hospital, Waterbury, CT, p. A114

LADD, Bill, Director Information Services, Western Missouri Medical Center, Warrensburg, MO, p. A380

LADWIG, Michael M.D., Chief of Staff, Marion Veterans Affairs Medical Center, Marion, IL, p. A192

LADY, Brian, Administrator and Chief Executive Officer, Concho County Hospital, Eden, TX, p. A609

LAFRANCOIS, Gregory, President, The Aroostook Medical Center, Presque Isle, ME, p. B49

LAFERNEY, Jimmy M.D., Vice President Medical Staff Affairs, Baylor Medical Center At Frisco, Frisco, TX, p. A615

LAFFEY, Leah, R.N., Chief Executive Officer, Healthsouth Rehabilitation Hospital Of Sewickley, Sewickley, PA, p. A550

LAFLAMME, Christine R.N., MSN, Chief Nursing Officer, Seton Smithville Regional Hospital, Smithville, TX, p. A646

LAFLEUR, Robert R., Administrator, Memorial Specialty Hospital, Lake Charles, LA, p. A279

LAFRANCOIS, Mary, Vice President Human Resources, Christus Spohn Hospital Corpus Christi Memorial, Corpus Christi, TX, p. A603

LAGASSE, David A, Senior Vice President Fiscal Affairs, Mclean Hospital, Belmont, MA, p. A302

LAGNESE, John M.D., Vice President Medical Affairs, Upmc St. Margaret, Pittsburgh, PA, p. A548

LAGROU, Robert D.O., Medical Director, Henry Ford Kingswood Hospital, Ferndale, MI, p. A319

LAHASKY, Douglas, Chief Financial Officer, Avoyelles Hospital, Marksville, LA, p. A280

LAHAYE, Daniel, Manager, Savoy Medical Center, Mamou, LA, p. A280

LAHOOD, Amy R.N., Director of Nursing, Acadia Vermilion Hospital, Lafayette, LA, p. A278

LAHOUT, Brenda, Chief Nurse Executive, Danville State Hospital, Danville, PA, p. A532

LAHTI, Molly, Director Human Resources, Parkland Medical Center, Derry, NH, p. A407

LAI, Daniel, Controller, Healthsouth Rehabilitation Hospital–Las Vegas, Las Vegas, NV, p. A403

LAI, Iris, Chief Executive Officer, Alhambra Hospital Medical Center, Alhambra, CA, p. A51

LAIBINIS, Walter M.D., Chief Medical Officer, Soldiers And Sailors Memorial Hospital, Wellsboro, PA, p. A553

LAIGN, Michael B., President and Chief Executive Officer, Holy Redeemer Hospital, Meadowbrook, PA, p. A540

LAIL, Steve, Vice President Operations and Chief Operating Officer, Down East Community Hospital, Machias, ME, p. A292

LAIOSA, Sarah M.D., Chief Medical Staff, Harney District Hospital, Burns, OR, p. A520

LAIRD, Alan M.D., Chief Medical Officer, Orange City Area Health System, Orange City, IA, p. A232

LAIRD, Charles, Chief Executive Officer, Menorah Medical Center, Overland Park, KS, p. A249

LAIRD, David, Chief Executive Officer, St. David's Medical Center, Austin, TX, p. A596

LAIRD, Jeff, Controller, Stephens County Hospital, Toccoa, GA, p. A166

LAIRD, Shaw, Chief Information Officer, Chester Regional Medical Center, Chester, SC, p. A559

LAISTER, Judy K, Director, Human Resources, Methodist Mansfield Medical Center, Mansfield, TX, p. A631

LAKE, Chandra, Associate Director, Sheridan Veterans Affairs Medical Center, Sheridan, WY, p. A720

LAKE, Nathan, Vice President Human Resources, Prairie Lakes Healthcare System, Watertown, SD, p. A574

LAKE, Peter M M.D., Chief Medical Officer, Rogers Memorial Hospital, Oconomowoc, WI, p. A709

LAKE, Ryan, Director Medical Imaging and Information Technology, Glencoe Regional Health Services, Glencoe, MN, p. A340

LAKEY, Travis, Chief Financial Officer, Mayers Memorial Hospital District, Fall River Mills, CA, p. A59

LAKINS, Tom, Director Information Systems, Tennova Physicians Regional Medical Center, Knoxville, TN, p. A582

LALIBERTE, John, Chief Information Officer, St. Vincent's Blount, Oneonta, AL, p. A22

LALLY, James M., D.O., President and Chief Medical Officer, Chino Valley Medical Center, Chino, CA, p. A55

LALLY, Robert P Jr, Vice President Finance, Medstar Franklin Square Medical Center, Baltimore, MD, p. A295

LAM, Shiva M.D., Executive Medical Director, Austin Lakes Hospital, Austin, TX, p. A594

LAM, Thomas, Chief Medical Officer, Garfield Medical Center, Monterey Park, CA, p. A75

LAMADELEINE, Joseph, Chief Financial Officer, Veterans Affairs Connecticut Healthcare System, West Haven, CT, p. A114

LAMANTEER, Mike M.D., Senior Vice President Medical Affairs, BSA Hospital, Llc, Amarillo, TX, p. A592

LAMARCHE, Heather, Manager Human Resources, AMG Specialty Hospital–Lafayette, Lafayette, LA, p. A278

LAMARCHE, Marie, Executive Director, Human Resources, Organizational Development, Employee Health, Harrison Medical Center, Bremerton, WA, p. A678

LAMARCHE, Maximo M.D., Chief Medical Officer, AMG Specialty Hospital–Lafayette, Lafayette, LA, p. A278

LAMB, Andrew M.D., Chief of Staff, Alamance Regional Medical Center, Burlington, NC, p. A458

LAMB, Cindy, Director Human Resources, Marias Medical Center, Shelby, MT, p. A388

LAMB, Deanna, Director Human Resources, Central Carolina Hospital, Sanford, NC, p. A470

LAMB, Hope, Manager Human Resources, Kimble Hospital, Junction, TX, p. A625

LAMB, Mollee, Manager Human Resources, LDS Hospital, Salt Lake City, UT, p. A660

LAMB–PAGONE, Jerilynn, Nurse Executive, Connecticut Valley Hospital, Middletown, CT, p. A111

LAMBERT, Amand, Director Human Resources, Allen Parish Hospital, Kinder, LA, p. A277

LAMBERT, Barbara, Director Healthcare Compliance, Eastern State Hospital, Williamsburg, VA, p. A677

LAMBERT, Cheryl, Chief Financial Officer, Acuity Specialty Hospital Of New Jersey, Atlantic City, NJ, p. A411

LAMBERT, Karen A.
President, Advocate Condell Medical Center, Libertyville, IL, p. A192
President, Advocate Good Shepherd Hospital, Barrington, IL, p. A178

LAMBERT, Lynn, Chief Financial Officer, Harnett Health System, Dunn, NC, p. A461

LAMBERT, Paul M.D., Chief of Staff, Boise Veterans Affairs Medical Center, Boise, ID, p. A171

LAMBERT, Robert K., M.D., FACHE, President and Chief Executive Officer, Arnot Health, Elmira, NY, p. B11

LAMBERT, Suzanne R.N., Regional Chief Nursing Officer and Support Services, Presence Saints Mary & Elizabeth Medical Center, Chicago, IL, p. A183

LAMBETH, Laura, Chief Executive Officer, Ashe Memorial Hospital, Jefferson, NC, p. A465

LAMBRECHT, Craig, M.D., President, Sanford Bismarck, Bismarck, ND, p. A474

LAMEBULL, Charlotte, Administrative Officer, Fort Belknap Service Unit, Harlem, MT, p. A385

LAMEN, Drake M., M.D., President, Chief Executive Officer and Chief Medical Officer, Uhs Chenango Memorial Hospital, Norwich, NY, p. A448

LAMERS, Jamon
Director Finance, Howard Young Medical Center, Woodruff, WI, p. A716
Director Finance, Ministry Eagle River Memorial Hospital, Eagle River, WI, p. A700
Director Finance, Ministry Sacred Heart Hospital, Tomahawk, WI, p. A714
Director Finance, Ministry Saint Mary's Hospitals, Rhinelander, WI, p. A711

LAMEY, Mark, Commander, U.S. Air Force Regional Hospital, Elmendorf Afb, AK, p. A26

LAMEY, Rebecca, Vice President Human Resources, Mainegeneral Medical Center, Augusta, ME, p. A289

LAMLE, Sandra, Chief Financial Officer, Okeene Municipal Hospital, Okeene, OK, p. A511

LAMMERS, Sandra, Coordinator Human Resources and Finance, Chi Health Mercy Corning, Corning, IA, p. A224

LAMONT, Jennifer
Chief Financial Officer, West Suburban Medical Center, Oak Park, IL, p. A196
Chief Financial Officer, Westlake Hospital, Melrose Park, IL, p. A193

LAMORELLA, Vincent M, Chief Financial Officer, Clarion Hospital, Clarion, PA, p. A531

LAMOUREUX, John P., Commander, Dwight David Eisenhower Army Medical Center, Fort Gordon, GA, p. A158

LAMOUREUX, Laurie, Director of Finance, Cooley Dickinson Hospital, Northampton, MA, p. A309

LAMPE, Michael M.D., Chief of Staff, Kossuth Regional Health Center, Algona, IA, p. A222

LAMPE, Tammy K, Director Human Resources, Edwards County Hospital And Healthcare Center, Kinsley, KS, p. A244

LAMPLEY, Danny, Chief Operating Officer, Harrisburg Medical Center, Harrisburg, IL, p. A189

LAMPLEY, Joseph D.O., Chief of Staff, Fisher County Hospital District, Rotan, TX, p. A640

LAMPTON, Lucius M.D., Medical Director, Beacham Memorial Hospital, Magnolia, MS, p. A358

LANCASTER, Brian, Executive Director Information Management, Nebraska Medicine – Bellevue, Bellevue, NE, p. A391

LANCASTER, Penny, Controller, Cascade Medical Center, Cascade, ID, p. A172

LANCASTER, Tim, FACHE, President and Chief Executive Officer, Hendrick Health System, Abilene, TX, p. A591

LAND, Steve, Senior Administrator, Wamego Health Center, Wamego, KS, p. A253

LAND, Susann M.D., Chief Medical Officer, Texas Health Harris Methodist Hospital Hurst–Euless–Bedford, Bedford, TX, p. A597

LANDENBERGER, Jason, Director of Nursing, Community Memorial Hospital, Turtle Lake, ND, p. A478

LANDERS, Alice, Administrative Director Operations, Texas Health Harris Methodist Hospital Hurst–Euless–Bedford, Bedford, TX, p. A597

LANDERS, Kimberly A. MS, R.N., Vice President Patient Care Services, Morris Hospital & Healthcare Centers, Morris, IL, p. A194

LANDERS, Lalah R.N., Director of Nursing, Saunders Medical Center, Wahoo, NE, p. A400

LANDINI, Kristin
Vice President Human Resources, Advocate South Suburban Hospital, Hazel Crest, IL, p. A189
Vice President, Human Resources, Advocate Trinity Hospital, Chicago, IL, p. A180

LANDIS, Catherine, R.N., Chief Executive Officer, Healthsouth Rehabilitation Hospital Of Columbia, Columbia, SC, p. A560

LANDIS, Janie, Chief Financial Officer, Russell County Hospital, Russell Springs, KY, p. A267

LANDMAN, Adam M.D., Chief Information Officer, Brigham And Women's Hospital, Boston, MA, p. A303

LANDMAN, Paul, Director Human Resources, Ellwood City Hospital, Ellwood City, PA, p. A534

LANDOLL, Therese, Interim Chief Financial Officer, Community Memorial Healthcare, Marysville, KS, p. A246

LANDRAU, Erika, Director Human Resources, Healthsouth Hospital Of Manati, Manati, PR, p. A724

LANDRENEAU, John Derrick
Director of Nursing and Marketing Manager, Baton Rouge Rehabilitation Hospital, Baton Rouge, LA, p. A270

Director of Nursing, Baton Rouge Rehabilitation Hospital, Baton Rouge, LA, p. A270

LANDRETH, Jonathan, Administrator, United Medical Rehabilitation Hospital, Hammond, LA, p. A276

LANDRETH, Kathy, Interim Chief Executive Officer, Bath Community Hospital, Hot Springs, VA, p. A669

LANDRETH, Sandy, Director Human Resources, Seiling Municipal Hospital, Seiling, OK, p. A515

LANDRETH, Shannan, Information Systems, Livingston Hospital And Healthcare Services, Salem, KY, p. A267

LANDRUM, David, Chief Police Services, Atascadero State Hospital, Atascadero, CA, p. A52

LANDRY, Adam, Director of Information Systems, Northern Maine Medical Center, Fort Kent, ME, p. A291

LANDRY, Candy, Chief Human Resource Officer, Eastside Psychiatric Hospital, Tallahassee, FL, p. A144

LANDRY, Donna F., Chief Operating Officer, Our Lady Of Lourdes Regional Medical Center, Lafayette, LA, p. A279

LANDRY, Lisa G., Human Resources Director, Redington–Fairview General Hospital, Skowhegan, ME, p. A293

LANDRY, Nobie, Chief Financial Officer, Prevost Memorial Hospital, Donaldsonville, LA, p. A274

LANDRY, Ray A., Chief Executive Officer, Abbeville General Hospital, Abbeville, LA, p. A269

LANDRY NUNEZ, Lexis, Chief Executive Officer, St. Catherine Memorial Hospital, New Orleans, LA, p. A283

LANDSMAN, Joseph, President and Chief Executive Officer, University Of Tennessee Medical Center, Knoxville, TN, p. A582

LANDSTROM, John
Director Human Resources, Rml Specialty Hospital, Hinsdale, IL, p. A190
Vice President Human Resources and Operations, Rml Specialty Hospital, Chicago, IL, p. A183

LANE, Charles A., Chief Medical Officer, Anderson Hospital, Maryville, IL, p. A192

LANE, Diron
Director Information Systems, Lewisgale Hospital Montgomery, Blacksburg, VA, p. A665
Director Information Systems, Lewisgale Hospital Pulaski, Pulaski, VA, p. A673

LANE, Kevin, D.O.
Chief of Staff, Hardeman County Memorial Hospital, Quanah, TX, p. A639
Vice President Information Systems, Silver Cross Hospital, New Lenox, IL, p. A195

LANE, Kim, Chief Fiscal Service, Overton Brooks Veterans Affairs Medical Center, Shreveport, LA, p. A285

LANE, Mike, Chief Operating Officer, Twin Cities Community Hospital, Templeton, CA, p. A93

LANE, Richard, Chief Financial Officer, Mid–America Rehabilitation Hospital, Shawnee Mission, KS, p. A251

LANE, Sonia, Interim Chief Nursing Officer, Uc Irvine Medical Center, Orange, CA, p. A78

LANEAUX, Eleanor, Director Information Systems, Placentia–Linda Hospital, Placentia, CA, p. A80

LANER, Richard Jr, Manager Information Systems, Miners' Colfax Medical Center, Raton, NM, p. A427

LANEY, Samuel Mark., M.D., Chief Executive Officer, Mosaic Life Care At St. Joseph, Saint Joseph, MO, p. A376

LANG, Cyndi, Director Information Services, French Hospital Medical Center, San Luis Obispo, CA, p. A89

LANG, Gary M.D., Clinical Director, Claremore Indian Hospital, Claremore, OK, p. A506

LANG, Gordon M.D., Chief of Staff, Trego County–Lemke Memorial Hospital, Wakeeney, KS, p. A253

LANG, Jeff, President, Up Health System–Portage, Hancock, MI, p. A322

LANG, John Christopher., Chief Executive Officer, Cass Regional Medical Center, Harrisonville, MO, p. A368

LANG, Joseph M.D., Chief of Staff, Carolinas Continuecare Hospital At Pineville, Charlotte, NC, p. A459

LANG, Linda, Chief Human Resources Officer, Marin General Hospital, Greenbrae, CA, p. A62

LANG, Nicholas P M.D., Chief Medical Officer, Uams Medical Center, Little Rock, AR, p. A46

LANG, Richard T, Chief Financial Officer, Gouverneur Hospital, Gouverneur, NY, p. A436

LANG, Richard Ed.D., Vice President and Chief Information Officer, Doylestown Hospital, Doylestown, PA, p. A533

LANGAN, Lynn, Chief Nursing Officer, Quillen Rehabilitation Hospital, Johnson City, TN, p. A581

LANGBEHN, Cody, Administrator, St. Luke's Wood River Medical Center, Ketchum, ID, p. A174

LANGBEHN, Jennifer, Medical Director, Mayo Clinic Health System In Saint James, Saint James, MN, p. A347

LANGBERG, Michael L M.D., Senior Vice President Medical Affairs and Chief Medical Officer, Cedars–Sinai Medical Center, Los Angeles, CA, p. A67

LANGDON, Ashlee, Controller, Yalobusha General Hospital, Water Valley, MS, p. A362

LANGDORF, Brad R.N., Vice President Clinical Services and Chief Nursing Officer, Community Hospital, Mccook, NE, p. A396

LANGE, Connie R.N., Vice President Quality, Inpatient and Community Services, Lakes Regional Healthcare, Spirit Lake, IA, p. A235

LANGENBERG, Shannon, Director Human Resources, Jackson County Regional Health Center, Maquoketa, IA, p. A231

LANGENFELD, John, Medical Records Coordinator, Arizona Orthopedic Surgical Hospital, Chandler, AZ, p. A28

LANGFORD, Scott
Administrator, Beaver Valley Hospital, Beaver, UT, p. A656
Administrator, Milford Valley Memorial Hospital, Milford, UT, p. A657

LANGFORD, Terrie, Director Human Resources, Baylor Scott & White Surgical Hospital At Sherman, Sherman, TX, p. A645

LANGHOFF, Erik, M.D., Ph.D., Director, James J. Peters Veterans Affairs Medical Center, New Rochelle, NY, p. A442

LANGLITZ, Sara, Controller, Kindred Hospital Houston Medical Center, Houston, TX, p. A621

LANGMEAD, Paula A., Chief Executive Officer, Springfield Hospital Center, Sykesville, MD, p. A301

LANGSTON, David L
Corporate Vice President Human Resources, East Texas Medical Center Rehabilitation Hospital, Tyler, TX, p. A650
Corporate Vice President Human Resources, East Texas Medical Center Specialty Hospital, Tyler, TX, p. A651

LANGSTON, Kimberly K., R.N., Chief Executive Officer, Baylor Scott And White Continuing Care Hospital, Temple, TX, p. A648

LANIER, Donna R.N., Chief Nursing Officer, Delta Medical Center, Memphis, TN, p. A584

LANIER, Mary, Vice President, Post Acute Services and Site Administrator, California Pacific Medical Center–Davies Campus, San Francisco, CA, p. A87

LANIER, Regina R.N., Senior Vice President and Chief Nursing Officer, Onslow Memorial Hospital, Jacksonville, NC, p. A465

LANKFORD, Deanna, Business Office Manager, Plano Specialty Hospital, Plano, TX, p. A638

LANKOWICZ, Andrew, FACHE, President, Chi St. Alexius Health Devils Lake Hospital, Devils Lake, ND, p. A475

LANNOYE, Craig, Vice President Operations, Wilson Memorial Hospital, Sidney, OH, p. A499

LANOUE, Cheryl, Chief Financial Officer, Ottawa County Health Center, Minneapolis, KS, p. A247

LANS, Sue, Comptroller, Harlan County Health System, Alma, NE, p. A390

LANSDOWNE, Lynn M, Vice President Human Resources, Lehigh Valley Hospital – Pocono, East Stroudsburg, PA, p. A533

LANTOS, Phyllis R, Executive Vice President, Corporate Chief Financial Officer and Treasurer, New York–Presbyterian Hospital, New Rochelle, NY, p. A444

LANTZY, William, Chief Financial Officer, DMC Huron Valley–Sinai Hospital, Commerce Township, MI, p. A317

LANZA, Nicholas, Controller, St. Mary's General Hospital, Passaic, NJ, p. A418

LANZA, Raymond D.O., Medical Director, Runnells Center For Rehabilitation And Healthcare, Berkeley Heights, NJ, p. A411

LAPERLE, Linda M, Vice President Administrative Services, Androscoggin Valley Hospital, Berlin, NH, p. A407

LAPHAM, Lisa, President and Chief Executive Officer, Healthsource Saginaw, Inc., Saginaw, MI, p. A329

LAPLANT, Dawn, Manager Health Information Management, Brown County Community Treatment Center, Green Bay, WI, p. A703

LAPORTE, Todd, Chief Executive Officer, Honorhealth, Scottsdale, AZ, p. B66

LAPOSTA, Mary Jo Ph.D., R.N., Senior Vice President Patient Care and Organizational Excellence, Saratoga Hospital, Saratoga Springs, NY, p. A452

LARA, Anne, Chief Information Officer, Union Hospital, Elkton, MD, p. A298

LARA, Sergio M.D., Chief Medical Officer, Covenant Hospital Plainview, Plainview, TX, p. A637

LARAMIE, Robert, Chief Information Officer, Beverly Hospital, Beverly, MA, p. A302

LARAMIE, Wayne, Vice President Nursing, SSM Health St. Clare Hospital – Fenton, Fenton, MO, p. A368

LARCAS, John M.D., Acting Medical Director, Choate Mental Health Center, Anna, IL, p. A177

LAREAU, Daniel, Executive Director Operations and Information, St. Vincent Carmel Hospital, Carmel, IN, p. A205

LAREAU, Kim, Vice President and Chief Information Officer, Regions Hospital, Saint Paul, MN, p. A348

LARET, Mark R., Chief Executive Officer, Ucsf Medical Center, San Francisco, CA, p. A88

LARIMER, Cynthia M.D., Chief of Staff, Lake Butler Hospital Hand Surgery Center, Lake Butler, FL, p. A129

LARIMORE, Rhonda
Vice President Human Resources, Magee–Womens Hospital Of Upmc, Pittsburgh, PA, p. A547
Vice President, Human Resources, Children's Hospital Of Pittsburgh Of Upmc, Pittsburgh, PA, p. A546

LARISCY, Christopher M.D., Chief of Staff, Davis Regional Medical Center, Statesville, NC, p. A471

LARISCY, Robin Barton M.D., Medical Director, Mary S Harper Geriatric Psychiatry Center, Tuscaloosa, AL, p. A24

LARIVEE, Theresa M., Chief Executive Officer, Pennsylvania Hospital, Philadelphia, PA, p. B140

LARIVEE, Theresa M., Chief Executive Officer, Pennsylvania Hospital, Philadelphia, PA, p. A545

LARIVIERE, Beckye, Controller, Healthsouth Rehabilitation Hospital Of Charleston, Charleston, SC, p. A559

LARKIN, Kevin
Regional Chief Financial Officer, Presence Mercy Medical Center, Aurora, IL, p. A177
Regional Chief Financial Officer, Presence Saint Joseph Hospital, Elgin, IL, p. A186

LARKIN, Kim, Chief Information Officer, Washington County Hospital, Nashville, IL, p. A195

LARKIN–SKINNER, Melissa, Chief Executive Officer, Centerstone Hospital, Bradenton, FL, p. A120

LARMER, Jennifer R.N., Chief Clinical Officer, Lincoln Hospital, Davenport, WA, p. A680

LARNER, Cheryl, Chief Financial Officer, Sentara Careplex Hospital, Hampton, VA, p. A668

LAROSA, Vincent
Director of Information Systems, Landmark Medical Center, Woonsocket, RI, p. A557
Director of Information Technology Services, Rehabilitation Hospital Of Rhode Island, North Smithfield, RI, p. A556

LAROWE, Mary E., FACHE, President and Chief Executive Officer, Brooks Memorial Hospital, Dunkirk, NY, p. A435

LARRISON, Robert G. Jr, President, Carolinas Rehabilitation, Charlotte, NC, p. A459

LARSEN, Bill, Vice President Human Resources, Driscoll Children's Hospital, Corpus Christi, TX, p. A603

LARSEN, Catherine M, Director Marketing, Sutter Tracy Community Hospital, Tracy, CA, p. A94

LARSEN, Donald M.D., Chief Medical Officer, Providence Saint John's Health Center, Santa Monica, CA, p. A91

LARSEN, Kevin, Associate Vice President, Business and Ancillary Services, Uconn, John Dempsey Hospital, Farmington, CT, p. A110

LARSEN, Michael, Director Information Systems, Baylor Medical Center At Garland, Garland, TX, p. A616

LARSEN, Ryan C., FACHE, Administrator, Community Medical Center, Inc., Falls City, NE, p. A392

LARSON, Alan, Chief Executive Officer, Sovah Health–Danville, Danville, VA, p. A666

LARSON, Bill, Vice President Finance and Chief Financial Officer, Torrance Memorial Medical Center, Torrance, CA, p. A94

LARSON, Derek, Information Technology Network, Lakes Regional Healthcare, Spirit Lake, IA, p. A235

LARSON, Eric, Director Human Resources, Healthsouth Harmarville Rehabilitation Hospital, Pittsburgh, PA, p. A546

LARSON, Erick, Vice President and Chief Information Officer, Mid–Columbia Medical Center, The Dalles, OR, p. A527

LARSON, Gordon, Administrator, Pineville Community Hospital Association, Pineville, KY, p. A266

LARSON, Jennifer M.D., Chief of Staff, Blue Ridge Regional Hospital, Spruce Pine, NC, p. A471

LARSON, Jon M.D., Medical Director, Healthsouth Rehabilitation Institute Of Tucson, Tucson, AZ, p. A38

LARSON, Karla, Director Human Resources, Stevens Community Medical Center, Morris, MN, p. A344

LARSON, Kay R.N., Chief Nursing Officer, Essentia Health St. Mary's – Detroit Lakes, Detroit Lakes, MN, p. A338

LARSON, Michael, Vice President Chief Information Officer, Midmichigan Medical Center–Clare, Clare, MI, p. A316

LARSON, Mike, Chief Operating Officer, Essentia Health St. Joseph's Medical Center, Brainerd, MN, p. A337

LARSON, Pamela, Division Director Financial Services, Hutchinson Health, Hutchinson, MN, p. A341

LARSON, Rodney M.D., Medical Director, Fall River Hospital, Hot Springs, SD, p. A570

LARSON, Ronald, Chief Financial Officer, Va San Diego Healthcare System, San Diego, CA, p. A86

LARSON, Scott C., Chief Executive Officer, Sanford Canton–Inwood Medical Center, Canton, SD, p. A568

LARSON, Scott M.D., Vice President Medical Affairs and Chief Medical Officer, Bronson Methodist Hospital, Kalamazoo, MI, p. A324

LARSON, Shelly, Chief Financial Officer, Hot Springs County Memorial Hospital, Thermopolis, WY, p. A720

LARSON, Steve M.D., Director Information Systems, Mercy Medical Center–Sioux City, Sioux City, IA, p. A235

LARSON, Tammy, Chief Financial Officer, Towner County Medical Center, Cando, ND, p. A474

LARSON, Tracy MS, Vice President Patient Care Services and Chief Nursing Officer, Mercy Medical Center–Sioux City, Sioux City, IA, p. A235

LARSON, Walt, Vice President Finance, Tillamook Regional Medical Center, Tillamook, OR, p. A527

LARSON, Wendy, Chief Clinical Officer, Promise Hospital Of Phoenix, Mesa, AZ, p. A32

LASALA, Frank M.D., President Medical Staff, OSF Holy Family Medical Center, Monmouth, IL, p. A194

LASATER, Laci R.N., Chief Nursing Officer, Christus Spohn Hospital Kleberg, Kingsville, TX, p. A627

LASCANO, Terrance, Administrative Officer, U.S. Public Health Service Indian Hospital, Cass Lake, MN, p. A338

LASECKI, Matt, Interim Vice President Human Resources, Providence Hospital, Washington, DC, p. A118

LASHBROOK, Amy, Chief Financial Officer, Community Hospital Of Bremen, Bremen, IN, p. A205

LASHER, Karen, Chief Nursing Officer, Vanderbilt Stallworth Rehabilitation Hospital, Nashville, TN, p. A587

LASHKARI, Haady, Chief Administrative Officer, Ojai Valley Community Hospital, Ojai, CA, p. A77

LASKER, Rose, Director Information Services, Bluefield Regional Medical Center, Bluefield, WV, p. A690

LASKOWSKI, Rose, R.N., Director, Caro Center, Caro, MI, p. A316

LASKY, John Jr, Vice President, Chief Human Resources Officer, Temple University Hospital, Philadelphia, PA, p. A546

LASOTA, John, Assistant Finance Officer, Clement J. Zablocki Veterans Affairs Medical Center, Milwaukee, WI, p. A707

LASSITER, Wright L. III, President and Chief Executive Officer, Henry Ford Health System, Detroit, MI, p. B65

LASTER, Charles, Director Information Management, Wk Bossier Health Center, Bossier City, LA, p. A272

LATER, Elizabeth B. R.N., Chief Nursing Officer, Ogden Regional Medical Center, Ogden, UT, p. A658

LATIBEAUDIERE, Jorge, Chief Financial Officer, Lea Regional Medical Center, Hobbs, NM, p. A426

LATIMER, Kevin, Chief Financial Officer, Childress Regional Medical Center, Childress, TX, p. A601

LATIMER, Timothy, Chief Financial Officer, Great Bend Regional Hospital, Great Bend, KS, p. A241

LATIOLAIS, Ryan J, Director Information Systems, Our Lady Of Lourdes Regional Medical Center, Lafayette, LA, p. A279

LATNEY, Cynthia, Chief Nursing Officer, Penrose–St. Francis Health Services, Colorado Springs, CO, p. A100

LATO, Barb, Chief Nursing Officer, Aspirus Medford Hospital & Clinics, Inc., Medford, WI, p. A706

LATREILLE, William M.D., Chief Medical Officer, The University Of Vermont Health Network – Alice Hyde Medical Center, Malone, NY, p. A439

LATT, Laura, Vice President of Operations, North Memorial Medical Center, Robbinsdale, MN, p. A346

LATTERNER, Renee, Director Human Resources, Lake Wales Medical Center, Lake Wales, FL, p. A130

LATTIMORE, Justin, Chief Financial Officer, Iron County Medical Center, Pilot Knob, MO, p. A375

LATTO, Janet B., Chief Nursing Officer and Disaster Officer, Pacifica Hospital Of The Valley, Los Angeles, CA, p. A70

LATUCHIE, Richard
Chief Information Officer, Spearfish Regional Hospital, Spearfish, SD, p. A573
Vice President Business Development, Rapid City Regional Hospital, Rapid City, SD, p. A572

LATULIPPE, Steve, President Medical Staff, East Liverpool City Hospital, East Liverpool, OH, p. A490

LAU, James M.D., Area Medical Director, Kaiser Permanente Panorama City Medical Center, Los Angeles, CA, p. A68

LAUBENTHAL, Sherrie L R.N., Chief Nursing Officer, Clarinda Regional Health Center, Clarinda, IA, p. A224

LAUDON, Larry A., Administrator, Community Behavioral Health Hospital – Bemidji, Bemidji, MN, p. A336

LAUE, Edward M.D., Chief Medical Officer, Texas Health Huguley Hospital Fort Worth South, Burleson, TX, p. A600

LAUE, Jerry, Administrator, St. Vincent Clay Hospital, Brazil, IN, p. A204

LAUER, Bill, Chief Information Officer, Morris County Hospital, Council Grove, KS, p. A240

LAUF, Michael K.
President and Chief Executive Officer, Cape Cod Hospital, Hyannis, MA, p. A307
President and Chief Executive Officer, Falmouth Hospital, Falmouth, MA, p. A306

LAUFFER, Daniel
President and Chief Executive Officer, Saint Francis Hospital, Charleston, WV, p. A691
President and Chief Executive Officer, Thomas Memorial Hospital, South Charleston, WV, p. A696

LAUFLE, Chuck, Director of Information Services, San Luis Valley Health, Alamosa, CO, p. A98

LAUGHLIN, Jennifer, Chief Information Officer, Watertown Regional Medical Center, Watertown, WI, p. A714

LAUGHLIN, Nancy R.N., Chief Nursing Officer, Orthonebraska Hospital, Omaha, NE, p. A398

LAUGHLIN, Warren, Vice President Human Resources, Longmont United Hospital, Longmont, CO, p. A105

LAUKAITIS, Fran, R.N., FACHE, President, Methodist Charlton Medical Center, Dallas, TX, p. A606

LAUNIUS, Billie, Director Business Finance, Dallas County Medical Center, Fordyce, AR, p. A43

LAUREANO, Prudencio A., Chief Executive Officer, Hospital Universitario Dr. Ramon Ruiz Arnau, Bayamon, PR, p. A722

LAURENTS, W Robert CPA, Chief Financial Officer, Madison Parish Hospital, Tallulah, LA, p. A287

LAURETO, Rose Ann
Chief Information Officer, Promedica Fostoria Community Hospital, Fostoria, OH, p. A491
Chief Information Officer, Promedica Toledo Hospital, Toledo, OH, p. A500
Corporate Vice President Information Resources, Promedica Bay Park Hospital, Oregon, OH, p. A497

LAURIDSEN, Amy, Director Human Resources, Northern Colorado Rehabilitation Hospital, Johnstown, CO, p. A104

LAURIN, George M, Interim Director Human Resources, Crisp Regional Hospital, Cordele, GA, p. A155

LAUTER, Keith A.
Chief Financial Officer, Franciscan St. Francis Health–Carmel, Carmel, IN, p. A205
Regional Chief Financial Officer, Franciscan St. Francis Health – Indianapolis, Indianapolis, IN, p. A211
Vice President Finance, Franciscan St. Elizabeth Health – Crawfordsville, Crawfordsville, IN, p. A206

LAUTEREN, Mark
Chief Information Officer, University Of South Alabama Children's And Women's Hospital, Mobile, AL, p. A20
Chief Information Officer, University Of South Alabama Medical Center, Mobile, AL, p. A21

LAUTNER, Marty, Vice President Finance and Chief Financial Officer, Cardinal Hill Rehabilitation Hospital, Lexington, KY, p. A261

LAUVE, Lisa R. R.N., Regional Chief Nursing Executive and Chief Operating Officer, Christus St. Frances Cabrini Hospital, Alexandria, LA, p. A269

LAUVER, David M.D., Chief Division Hospital Based Care, Central Maine Medical Center, Lewiston, ME, p. A291

LAUZAU, Paul, Controller, Beaumont Hospital – Trenton, Trenton, MI, p. A332

LAVELLE, John P. M.D., Chief Medical Officer, Parkview Hospital, Wheeler, TX, p. A654

LAVELY, Patricia A FACHE, Senior Vice President and Chief Information Officer, Gwinnett Hospital System, Lawrenceville, GA, p. A160

LAVER, Joseph H. M.D., Chief Medical Officer, Stony Brook University Hospital, Stony Brook, NY, p. A453

LAVERY FRASCA, Denise Anne MSN, R.N., Vice President Patient Care Services and Chief Nursing Officer, Jeanes Hospital, Philadelphia, PA, p. A544

LAVIGNETTE, Brooke, Director of Nursing, Sycamore Springs Hospital, Lafayette, IN, p. A214

LAVIOLETTE, Judy, M.D.
Chief Medical Officer, Texas Health Harris Methodist Hospital Azle, Azle, TX, p. A596
Chief Medical Officer, Texas Health Harris Methodist Hospital Cleburne, Cleburne, TX, p. A601

LAVOIE, Brad, Chief Financial Officer, Coastal Harbor Treatment Center, Savannah, GA, p. A164

LAW, Charles, Chief Operating Officer, Catawba Hospital, Catawba, VA, p. A665

LAW, Johnny, Area Information Officer, Kaiser Permanente Oakland Medical Center, Oakland, CA, p. A77

LAWHORN, David M.D., Chief Medical Officer, Shoshone Medical Center, Kellogg, ID, p. A173

LAWHORN, Renee, Director Medical Records, East Texas Medical Center Carthage, Carthage, TX, p. A601

LAWHORNE, Thomas, Chief Financial Officer, Regional Medical Center Bayonet Point, Hudson, FL, p. A127

LAWLER, Anne, Director Human Resources, North Mississippi Medical Center–Hamilton, Hamilton, AL, p. A19

LAWLER, Kay, Business Office Manager, North Mississippi Medical Center–West Point, West Point, MS, p. A363

LAWLER, Patrick, Chief Executive Officer, Youth Villages Inner Harbour Campus, Douglasville, GA, p. A157

LAWLESS, JoBeth, Chief Nursing Officer, Nursing Services and Director Emergency Management Services, Lucas County Health Center, Chariton, IA, p. A224

LAWLESS, Rosalie, Director Human Resources, Fairlawn Rehabilitation Hospital, Worcester, MA, p. A313

LAWONN, Kenneth
Senior Vice President and Chief Information Officer, Chi Health Mercy Corning, Corning, IA, p. A224
Senior Vice President and Chief Information Officer, Chi Health Schuyler, Schuyler, NE, p. A399
Senior Vice President and Chief Information Officer, Sharp Grossmont Hospital, La Mesa, CA, p. A64
Senior Vice President and Chief Information Officer, Sharp Memorial Hospital, San Diego, CA, p. A86
Senior Vice President Information Systems, Sharp Mesa Vista Hospital, San Diego, CA, p. A86

LAWRASON, Jock M.D., Chief Medical Officer, Nantucket Cottage Hospital, Nantucket, MA, p. A309

LAWRENCE, Bruce, President and Chief Executive Officer, Integris Health, Oklahoma City, OK, p. B69

LAWRENCE, Glenda R.N., Chief Nursing Officer, Red River Hospital, Llc, Wichita Falls, TX, p. A654

LAWRENCE, Jeffrey T, Chief Operating Officer, Medical City Denton, Denton, TX, p. A608

LAWRENCE, Jonathan I., System Chief Operating Officer, Arnot Ogden Medical Center, Elmira, NY, p. A435

LAWRENCE, Kelsey, Manager Information Technology, Union County General Hospital, Clayton, NM, p. A425

LAWRENCE, Mark, Director Information Systems, Saint Francis Hospital–Bartlett, Bartlett, TN, p. A575

LAWRENCE, Paige, Assistant Administrator, University Of Mississippi Medical Center Holmes County, Lexington, MS, p. A358

LAWRENCE, Sandra A J
Executive Vice President and Chief Financial Officer, Children's Mercy Hospital Kansas City, Kansas City, MO, p. A370
Executive Vice President and Chief Financial Officer, Children's Mercy South, Overland Park, KS, p. A249

LAWRENCE, Stephanie
Chief Financial Officer, Kentfield Rehabilitation And Specialty Hospital, Kentfield, CA, p. A64
Chief Financial Officer, Vibra Specialty Hospital Of Portland, Portland, OR, p. A525

LAWRENCE, Tiffany, Vice President of Finance, Sanford Medical Center Fargo, Fargo, ND, p. A475

LAWRENCE, William P., President and Chief Executive Officer, Mclaren Central Michigan, Mount Pleasant, MI, p. A326

LAWRENSON, Victoria
Chief Operating Officer, Bullock County Hospital, Union Springs, AL, p. A24
Chief Operating Officer, Crenshaw Community Hospital, Luverne, AL, p. A20

LAWSON, Alvin R., FACHE, JD, Chief Executive Officer, Healthsouth Western Hills Regional Rehabilitation Hospital, Parkersburg, WV, p. A695

LAWSON, Beth, Chief Nursing Officer, Union Medical Center, Union, SC, p. A566

LAWSON, Chad, Chief Information Officer, St. Anthony Regional Hospital, Carroll, IA, p. A223

LAWSON, David C., Senior Vice President Human Resources, St. Clare Hospital, Lakewood, WA, p. A682

LAWSON, Jerry M.D., Chief of Medical Staff, Russell County Hospital, Russell Springs, KY, p. A267

LAWSON, Judy, Director Information Services, Norton Community Hospital, Norton, VA, p. A672

LAWSON, Linda B., Chief Nursing Officer, The Hospitals Of Providence Transmountain Campus, El Paso, TX, p. A612

LAWSON, Michael, President and Chief Operating Officer, Ohiohealth Grant Medical Center, Columbus, OH, p. A487

LAWSON, Penny, Human Resource Director, Quillen Rehabilitation Hospital, Johnson City, TN, p. A581

LAWSON, Ralph E, Executive Vice President and Chief Financial Officer, Baptist Health South Florida, Baptist Hospital Of Miami, Miami, FL, p. A132

LAWSON, Sandra K., Interim Director Fiscal Services, Shriners Hospitals For Children–St. Louis, Saint Louis, MO, p. A377

LAWSON, T. Douglas., Ph.D., FACHE, President, Baylor University Medical Center, Dallas, TX, p. A605

LAWTON, Geoff, Vice President Operations, Littleton Adventist Hospital, Littleton, CO, p. A105

LAY, A K M.D., Jr, Chief Medical Officer, Jasper General Hospital, Bay Springs, MS, p. A352

LAY, Barbara, Chief Executive Officer, Pocahontas Memorial Hospital, Buckeye, WV, p. A690

LAYFIELD, Michael G., Interim Chief Executive Officer, Lauderdale Community Hospital, Ripley, TN, p. A588

LAYNE, Kristine R.N., Chief Nursing Officer, Riverwood Healthcare Center, Aitkin, MN, p. A335

LAYTON, Ann M.D., Chief of Staff, North Metro Medical Center, Jacksonville, AR, p. A45

LAYUGAN, Melvin, Director Human Resources, Horizon Specialty Hospital, Las Vegas, NV, p. A403

LAZARUS, David M.D., Medical Director Clinical Affairs, Newton Medical Center, Newton, NJ, p. A418

LAZO, Nelson, Chief Executive Officer, Baptist Health South Florida, Doctors Hospital, Coral Gables, FL, p. A122

LAZROFF, Gary, Vice President Human Resources, St. John Medical Center, Westlake, OH, p. A502

LAZZARO, Frank A III, Chief Human Resources Officer, Phelps County Regional Medical Center, Rolla, MO, p. A376

LE, Emily, Director Information Technology and Services, Woman's Hospital Of Texas, Houston, TX, p. A624

LE, Jennifer, Chief Financial Officer, Southern Hills Hospital And Medical Center, Las Vegas, NV, p. A403

LE, Tuan, Chief Executive Officer, Christus Dubuis Hospital Of Beaumont, Beaumont, TX, p. A597

LEA, Hampton P S., Acting Chief Executive Officer, Eastern Louisiana Mental Health System, Jackson, LA, p. A276

LEA, Randy M.D., M.P.H., Vice President and Chief Medical Officer, Alice Peck Day Memorial Hospital, Lebanon, NH, p. A408

LEA, Rich, Vice President Operations, Euclid Hospital, Euclid, OH, p. A491

LEACH, Craig, President and Chief Executive Officer, Torrance Memorial Medical Center, Torrance, CA, p. A94

LEACH, Dana, Director Human Resources, Alliancehealth Midwest, Midwest City, OK, p. A510

LEACH, Deonca, Director, Human Resources, Carolinas Rehabilitation, Charlotte, NC, p. A459

LEACH, Mary Anne, Vice President and Chief Information Officer, Children's Hospital Colorado, Aurora, CO, p. A98

LEACH, Ryan, Chief Information Officer, St. John's Hospital, Springfield, IL, p. A201

LEACH, Todd, Vice President and Chief Information Officer, University Of Texas Medical Branch, Galveston, TX, p. A616

LEADBETTER, Dan, Information Technology Systems Site Lead, Chi Lakewood Health, Baudette, MN, p. A336

LEADBETTER, Raymond J.
Interim Chief Executive Officer, Appling Healthcare System, Baxley, GA, p. A152
Revenue Cycle Consultant, Appling Healthcare System, Baxley, GA, p. A152

LEAHY, Kevin D., President and Chief Executive Officer, Franciscan Health, Mishawaka, IN, p. B52

LEAHY, Mary P, Vice President Human Resources, St. Joseph Hospital, Orange, CA, p. A78

LEAHY, Mary, M.D.
Chief Executive Officer, Bon Secours Community Hospital, Port Jervis, NY, p. A450
Chief Executive Officer, Good Samaritan Regional Medical Center, Suffern, NY, p. A453
Chief Executive Officer, St. Anthony Community Hospital, Warwick, NY, p. A455

LEAHY, Rosanne, Vice President Nursing Services, Carolinaeast Health System, New Bern, NC, p. A468

LEAKE, Neta F, Administrative Assistant Human Resources, West Feliciana Parish Hospital, Saint Francisville, LA, p. A285

LEAKE, Sandy MSN, R.N., Associate Director, Nursing and Patient Care Services, Atlanta Veterans Affairs Medical Center, Decatur, GA, p. A156

LEAKEY, Kim R.N., Chief Nursing Officer, Lafayette Regional Health Center, Lexington, MO, p. A372

LEAL, Carlos, Director Information Technology, Valley Regional Medical Center, Brownsville, TX, p. A599

LEAL, Enrique A M.D., III, Chief of Staff, Sweeny Community Hospital, Sweeny, TX, p. A647

LEAL, Joseph M M.D., Jr, Chief of Staff, Glendive Medical Center, Glendive, MT, p. A384

LEAMING, Larry E., Ph.D., FACHE, Chief Executive Officer, Estes Park Medical Center, Estes Park, CO, p. A102

LEAMON, Jim, Chief Financial Officer, JFK Medical Center, Atlantis, FL, p. A119

LEAR, Richard
Director Information Systems, St. David's Medical Center, Austin, TX, p. A596
Director Information Systems, St. David's South Austin Medical Center, Austin, TX, p. A596

LEARSON, Jerome, Manager Information Technology and Chief Security Officer, Palo Verde Hospital, Blythe, CA, p. A54

LEARY, Edward B.
Chief Executive Officer, Vibra Hospital Of Southeastern Massachusetts, New Bedford, MA, p. A309

Interim Chief Executive Officer, Vibra Hospital Of Western Massachusetts, Springfield, MA, p. A312

LEASE, Faye, Director of Nursing, Reeves County Hospital, Pecos, TX, p. A637

LEASE–HOMEYER, Cheryl, Lead Information Technology Business Partner, Mercy Hospital Carthage, Carthage, MO, p. A366

LEASURE, Sandie, Senior Vice President Human Resources, O'Bleness Memorial Hospital, Athens, OH, p. A480

LEATHERS, Cynthia R.N., Chief Nursing Officer, Integris Bass Baptist Health Center, Enid, OK, p. A507

LEAVITT, Jared, Chief Operating Officer, Kern Medical Center, Bakersfield, CA, p. A53

LEAZER, Ronald, Chief Financial Officer, Gateway Regional Medical Center, Granite City, IL, p. A189

LEBEAU, Michelle, Senior Vice President, Chief Operating Officer, Chief Nursing Officer, The University Of Vermont Health Network–Champlain Valley Physicians Hospital, Plattsburgh, NY, p. A449

LEBER, Ian M.D., Chief Medical Officer, Hackensack Meridian Health Bayshore Community Hospital, Holmdel, NJ, p. A415

LEBLANC, Fernis, Chief Operating Officer, Ochsner St. Anne General Hospital, Raceland, LA, p. A284

LEBLANC, Julie, Director of Nursing, Memorial Specialty Hospital, Lake Charles, LA, p. A279

LEBLANC, Karen, Director, Applications, Samaritan Hospital, Troy, NY, p. A454

LEBOWITZ, Howard M.D., Chief Medical Officer, Specialty Hospital Of Central Jersey, Lakewood, NJ, p. A415

LEBRON, Juan M.D., Medical Director, Healthsouth Sea Pines Rehabilitation Hospital, Melbourne, FL, p. A132

LEBRON, Sonia M, Human Resources Specialist, Industrial Hospital, San Juan, PR, p. A726

LEBRUN, James, Chief Executive Officer, Perkins County Health Services, Grant, NE, p. A393

LECATES, William W M.D., Vice President Medical Affairs and Medical Director, Bassett Medical Center, Cooperstown, NY, p. A434

LECHICH, Anthony M.D., Chief Medical Officer, Terence Cardinal Cooke Health Care Center, New Rochelle, NY, p. A447

LECHNER, David M.D., Chief Medical Officer and Vice President Innovation, Community Medical Center, Missoula, MT, p. A386

LECHUGA, Mario, Director Human Resources, Turquoise Lodge Hospital, Albuquerque, NM, p. A425

LECKELT, Mitchell D., Chief Executive Officer, Up Health System–Bell, Ishpeming, MI, p. A323

LECKER, Marijo, Vice President, Martha Jefferson Hospital, Charlottesville, VA, p. A665

LECKEY, Scott
Chief Financial Officer, Banner Desert Medical Center, Mesa, AZ, p. A31
Vice President Finance, Baptist Health Paducah, Paducah, KY, p. A266

LECONTE, Chantal, FACHE, Chief Executive Officer, Memorial Regional Hospital, Hollywood, FL, p. A127

LEDBETTER, Joy, Vice President, Chief Human Resources Officer, Unitypoint Health – Peoria, Peoria, IL, p. A197

LEDBETTER, Thomas Glenn M.D., Chief Medical Officer, Baylor Scott & White Medical Center At Waxahachie, Waxahachie, TX, p. A652

LEDDEN, Edwin L, Assistant Administrator and Director Human Resources, Henry County Medical Center, Paris, TN, p. A588

LEDELL, Michelle
Director Human Resource, Fairview Ridges Hospital, Burnsville, MN, p. A337
Director Human Resources, Fairview Southdale Hospital, Edina, MN, p. A339

LEDERER, Jane R.N., Ed.D., Vice President and Chief Nursing Officer, Kingsbrook Jewish Medical Center, New Rochelle, NY, p. A442

LEDERMAN, Joel, Director Information Systems, Community Health Center Of Branch County, Coldwater, MI, p. A317

LEDERMAN, Mark, Chief Information Officer, Interfaith Medical Center, New Rochelle, NY, p. A441

LEDFORD, Keith M.D., Chief of Staff, Scenic Mountain Medical Center, Big Spring, TX, p. A598

LEDOUX, Roger C., Chief Executive Officer, Byrd Regional Hospital, Leesville, LA, p. A280

LEE, Bill, Chief Executive Officer, Medical City Dallas, Dallas, TX, p. A606

LEE, Brett D., Chief Executive Officer, Baylor Scott & White Medical Center – Lake Pointe, Rowlett, TX, p. A641

LEE, Byong, Chief Information Officer, Limestone Medical Center, Groesbeck, TX, p. A617

LEE, Charles, Director Clinical Operations, Brentwood Hospital, Shreveport, LA, p. A285

LEE, Cheryl D R.N., MSN, Vice President of Patient Care Services and Chief Nursing Officer, University Of Maryland Rehabilitation & Orthopaedic Institute, Baltimore, MD, p. A296

LEE, Cheryl, Human Resources Director, Eliza Coffee Memorial Hospital, Florence, AL, p. A18

LEE. RAYMER, Chris, R.N., MSN, Chief Executive Officer, Mississippi County Hospital System, Blytheville, AR, p. B86

LEE, Darren W.
President and Chief Executive Officer, St. John's Pleasant Valley Hospital, Camarillo, CA, p. A54
President and Chief Executive Officer, St. John's Regional Medical Center, Oxnard, CA, p. A78

LEE, David, Chief Executive Officer, Otto Kaiser Memorial Hospital, Kenedy, TX, p. A626

LEE, Dennis, Vice President and Chief Information Officer, Cabell Huntington Hospital, Huntington, WV, p. A692

LEE, Eric A., President and Chief Executive Officer, Jennie Stuart Medical Center, Hopkinsville, KY, p. A260

LEE, James R M.D., Chief of Staff, Hamilton General Hospital, Hamilton, TX, p. A618

LEE, James Y, Executive Vice President and Chief Operating Officer, New York–Presbyterian/Lawrence Hospital, Bronxville, NY, p. A432

LEE, Jeannie, Director Human Resources, Marshall County Hospital, Benton, KY, p. A255

LEE, Jenny, Human Resources Generalist, Essentia Health–Graceville, Graceville, MN, p. A340

LEE, John Paul M.D., Chief of Staff, Lackey Memorial Hospital, Forest, MS, p. A354

LEE, Joshua M.D., Chief Medical Officer, Loyola University Medical Center, Maywood, IL, p. A193

LEE, Karen
Chief Nursing Officer, Belton Regional Medical Center, Belton, MO, p. A364
Director Human Resources, Gallup Indian Medical Center, Gallup, NM, p. A426

LEE, Kayleen R., Chief Executive Officer, Sioux Center Health, Sioux Center, IA, p. A235

LEE, Kenneth, Division Chair, Human Resource Advisory, Mayo Clinic Health System In Eau Claire, Eau Claire, WI, p. A701

LEE, Kim, Chief Operating Officer, Faith Community Hospital, Jacksboro, TX, p. A625

LEE, Kristina, Director Human Resources, Chi St. Joseph Health Grimes Hospital, Navasota, TX, p. A634

LEE, Kwon, Chief Information Officer, Pennsylvania Hospital, Philadelphia, PA, p. A545

LEE, Lori L, Assistant Vice President Nursing, Nanticoke Memorial Hospital, Seaford, DE, p. A116

LEE, Michael D, Chief Human Resources Officer, Adirondack Health, Saranac Lake, NY, p. A452

LEE, Michael, President, Weeks Medical Center, Lancaster, NH, p. A408

LEE, Mihi, Chief Financial Officer, Coast Plaza Hospital, Norwalk, CA, p. A76

LEE, Mike R.N., Chief Nursing Officer, Matagorda Regional Medical Center, Bay City, TX, p. A596

LEE, Nancy
Vice President Patient Care Services and Chief Nursing Officer, Stanford Health Care, Palo Alto, CA, p. A79
Chief Nursing Officer, Placentia–Linda Hospital, Placentia, CA, p. A80

LEE, Nathan W, Chief Executive Officer, Mary Breckinridge Arh Hospital, Hyden, KY, p. A260

LEE, Pamela R., Chief Operating Officer, Ozarks Medical Center, West Plains, MO, p. A381

LEE, Randall, Vice President and Chief Operating Officer, Baptist Health South Florida, Baptist Hospital Of Miami, Miami, FL, p. A132

LEE, Randy M.D., Senior Vice President Medical Affairs, Community Hospital South, Indianapolis, IN, p. A210

LEE, Robbin, Chief Executive Officer, Wellington Regional Medical Center, Wellington, FL, p. A147

LEE, Ryan, Chief Operating Officer, West Boca Medical Center, Boca Raton, FL, p. A120

LEE, S. Kwon M.D., Chief of Staff, Vibra Hospital Of Sacramento, Folsom, CA, p. A59

LEE, Sherry, Chief Nurse Executive, Fulton State Hospital, Fulton, MO, p. A368

LEE, Stacey, CPA, JD, Chief Executive Officer, Johnson Memorial Health Services, Dawson, MN, p. A338

LEE, Terri
Chief Information Office, Tanner Higgins General Hospital, Bremen, GA, p. A153
Chief Information Officer, Tanner Medical Center–Villa Rica, Villa Rica, GA, p. A166

LEE, Thomas G, Chief Financial Officer, Medicine Lodge Memorial Hospital, Medicine Lodge, KS, p. A247

LEONARD, Chris, Chief Financial Officer, Rolling Hills Hospital, Franklin, TN, p. A579

LEONARD, Donavan, Chief Financial Officer, Baptist Memorial Hospital–Booneville, Booneville, MS, p. A352

LEONARD, Edward F, Executive Vice President and Chief Operating Officer, White Plains Hospital Center, White Plains, NY, p. A456

LEONARD, James C., M.D., President and Chief Executive Officer, Carle Foundation Hospital, Urbana, IL, p. A201

LEONARD, Jayne M.D., Family Medicine, Ashe Memorial Hospital, Jefferson, NC, p. A465

LEONARD, Mark T.
Chief Executive Officer, Dickenson Community Hospital, Clintwood, VA, p. A666
Chief Executive Officer, Norton Community Hospital, Norton, VA, p. A672

LEONARD, Mark, Vice President Finance, Beaumont Hospital – Troy, Troy, MI, p. A332

LEONARD, Robert, Director Information Services, Sierra Vista Regional Medical Center, San Luis Obispo, CA, p. A89

LEONARD, Wes, Chief Executive Officer, Whitten Center, Clinton, SC, p. A560

LEONARD, William H., President, Carolinas Healthcare System University, Charlotte, NC, p. A459

LEONDAR, Kimberly, Director Human Resources, Texas Health Harris Methodist Hospital Stephenville, Stephenville, TX, p. A646

LEONELIS, Lisa, Chief Information Officer, Veterans Affairs Salt Lake City Health Care System, Salt Lake City, UT, p. A661

LEOPARD, Erik, Manager Human Resource, Methodist Hospital For Surgery, Addison, TX, p. A591

LEOPARD, Jimmy, FACHE, Chief Executive Officer, Wagoner Community Hospital, Wagoner, OK, p. A519

LEOPOLD, Michael, Chief Operating Officer, Broward Health Coral Springs, Coral Springs, FL, p. A122

LEPAK, Jason, M.D.
Medical Director, St. John Broken Arrow, Broken Arrow, OK, p. A505
Medical Director, St. John Sapulpa, Sapulpa, OK, p. A515

LEPE, Patti, Chief Financial Officer, Parkview Community Hospital Medical Center, Riverside, CA, p. A82

LEPPER, Dale, Chief Information Officer, Antelope Valley Hospital, Lancaster, CA, p. A65

LEPPKE, Ben, Chief Information Officer, Satanta District Hospital And Long Term Care, Satanta, KS, p. A251

LEQUEUX, Veronica, Vice President Human Resources, Blake Medical Center, Bradenton, FL, p. A120

LERASH, Terrance, President and Chief Executive Officer, Scheurer Hospital, Pigeon, MI, p. A328

LERCH, Gail, R.N.
Executive Vice President Human Resources, Straub Medical Center, Honolulu, HI, p. A169
Vice President Human Resources, Pali Momi Medical Center, Aiea, HI, p. A168
Vice President, Kapiolani Medical Center For Women & Children, Honolulu, HI, p. A168

LERCH, Shawn, Chief Executive Officer, Sauk Prairie Healthcare, Prairie Du Sac, WI, p. A711

LERMA, Robert J., MS, Chief Executive Officer, Austin Lakes Hospital, Austin, TX, p. A594

LERNER, Jerome M.D., Medical Director, Sierra Tucson, Tucson, AZ, p. A38

LEROY, Michael
Senior Vice President and Chief Information Officer, DMC – Detroit Receiving Hospital, Detroit, MI, p. A317
Senior Vice President and Chief Information Officer, DMC Harper University Hospital, Detroit, MI, p. A318

LESCH, Jason, Chief Financial Officer, Auburn Community Hospital, Auburn, NY, p. A431

LESCHER, Mary, Chief Clinical Officer, Doctor's Memorial Hospital, Perry, FL, p. A139

LESHER, Jennifer, Chief Financial Officer, Lock Haven Hospital, Lock Haven, PA, p. A539

LESIAK, Cindy, Vice President Patient Care Services and Director of Nursing, Boone County Health Center, Albion, NE, p. A390

LESINS, Ross, Chief Information Officer, Casa Colina Hospital And Health Systems, Pomona, CA, p. A80

LESKO, Joan, Director Technical Support and Services, Kidspeace Children's Hospital, Orefield, PA, p. A542

LESLIE, Andrea M., MSN, R.N., President, Spectrum Health United Hospital, Greenville, MI, p. A322

LESLIE, Bruce W M.D., Chief of Staff, Grant Memorial Hospital, Petersburg, WV, p. A695

LESLIE, Desdemona, Finance Officer, U. S. Public Health Service Indian Hospital–Whiteriver, Whiteriver, AZ, p. A38

LESLIE, Donald P M.D., Medical Director, Shepherd Center, Atlanta, GA, p. A151

LESLIE, John M.D., Chief Medical Officer, North Arkansas Regional Medical Center, Harrison, AR, p. A44

LESLIE, Kelly, Chief Financial Officer, Ferry County Memorial Hospital, Republic, WA, p. A684

LESLIE, Steve, Chief Financial Officer, Fairbanks Memorial Hospital, Fairbanks, AK, p. A26

LESNIAK, Jacklynn R.N., MS, Vice President Patient Care Services and Chief Nursing Officer, Midwestern Regional Medical Center, Zion, IL, p. A202

LESNICK, Kelly, Resource Manager Flight Commander, Wright Patterson Medical Center, Wright, OH, p. A503

LESNIEWSKI, Amy, Associate Director Patient Care Services, Alexandria Veterans Affairs Health Care System, Pineville, LA, p. A284

LESTER, Lisa, Chief Nursing Officer, Healthsouth Southern Hills Rehabilitation Hospital, Princeton, WV, p. A695

LESTER, Ron, Chief Human Resources, Cheyenne Veterans Affairs Medical Center, Cheyenne, WY, p. A718

LESTER, Wade K, Chief Nursing and Operations Officer, Mid–Jefferson Extended Care Hospital, Nederland, TX, p. A635

LESTER, Wade, Chief Executive Officer, Mid–Jefferson Extended Care Hospital, Nederland, TX, p. A635

LESTER, William M.D., Vice President Medical Affairs, Cardinal Hill Rehabilitation Hospital, Lexington, KY, p. A261

LETCHWORTH, Mike, Manager Information Systems, Cherry Hospital, Goldsboro, NC, p. A463

LETEXIER, Lisa, Interim Chief Executive Officer, Pembina County Memorial Hospital And Wedgewood Manor, Cavalier, ND, p. A474

LETHI, Scott R.N., FACHE, Chief Nursing Officer, Fort Duncan Regional Medical Center, Eagle Pass, TX, p. A609

LETSON, Robert F., FACHE, Chief Executive Officer, South Peninsula Hospital, Homer, AK, p. A26

LETT, Bryan W., Chief Executive Officer, Haven Behavioral Hospital Of Eastern Pennsylvania, Reading, PA, p. A549

LETT, Tammy R.N., Chief Nursing Officer, Hshs Holy Family Hospital In Greenville, Greenville, IL, p. A189

LETTOW, Bonnie, Chief Financial Officer, Franklin General Hospital, Hampton, IA, p. A228

LEU, Christopher, President, Texas Health Harris Methodist Hospital Stephenville, Stephenville, TX, p. A646

LEUBNER, Kristel D.O., Chief of Staff, Chi St. Joseph Health Burleson Hospital, Caldwell, TX, p. A600

LEUDECKE, Amelia, Director Human Resources, Healthsouth Rehabilitation Hospital Round Rock, Round Rock, TX, p. A640

LEUNG, Lawrence M.D., Chief of Staff, Va Palo Alto Health Care System, Palo Alto, CA, p. A79

LEURCK, Trish, Human Resources Director, Amita Health Adventist Medical Center – Hinsdale, Hinsdale, IL, p. A190

LEVANGER, Nathan M.D., Chief of Staff, Teton Valley Health Care, Driggs, ID, p. A173

LEVECK, Dianna, Chief Human Resources Officer, Genesis Healthcare System, Zanesville, OH, p. A503

LEVEILLEE, Mary, Senior Vice President Patient Care Services and Chief Nursing Officer, Butler Hospital, Providence, RI, p. A556

LEVELING, Jim, Director Information Technology, Kansas City Orthopaedic Institute, Leawood, KS, p. A245

LEVER, Roger M.D., President Medical Staff, The Outer Banks Hospital, Nags Head, NC, p. A467

LEVERICH, Karen, Chief Executive Officer, Promise Hospital Of Overland Park, Overland Park, KS, p. A249

LEVERING, Theresa, Director Human Resources, Doctors Hospital Of Sarasota, Sarasota, FL, p. A142

LEVESQUE, David, Director, Information Systems, New Hampshire Hospital, Concord, NH, p. A407

LEVI, John, Director Human Resources, St. Lawrence Rehabilitation Center, Lawrenceville, NJ, p. A415

LEVINE, Alan M., President and Chief Executive Officer, Mountain States Health Alliance, Johnson City, TN, p. B87

LEVIN, Alan M. MSN, R.N., Chief Nursing Officer, New York–Presbyterian Queens, New Rochelle, NY, p. A444

LEVINE, Larry L., President and Chief Executive Officer, Blythedale Children's Hospital, Valhalla, NY, p. A454

LEVINE, Peter H M.D., Executive Medical Director Behavioral Health Services, Adventist Behavioral Health And Wellness Services, Rockville, MD, p. A300

LEVINE, Robert V, Executive Vice President and Chief Operating Officer, Flushing Hospital Medical Center, New Rochelle, NY, p. A441

LEVINE, Stuart M., M.D., President and Chief Medical Officer, Medstar Harbor Hospital, Baltimore, MD, p. A295

LEVINSON, Adam, Associate Director, Information Services, University Behavioral Healthcare, Piscataway, NJ, p. A419

LEVISON, Julie, Director Human Resources, Providence Medford Medical Center, Medford, OR, p. A524

LEVITOW, John, Vice President Patient Care Services and Chief Nursing Officer, Frisbie Memorial Hospital, Rochester, NH, p. A410

LEVITZ, Michele, Director Finance, St. Luke's Hospital – Miners Campus, Coaldale, PA, p. A531

LEVY, Becky, Chief Financial Officer, Paradise Valley Hospital, National City, CA, p. A76

LEVY, Becky
Chief Financial Officer, Shasta Regional Medical Center, Redding, CA, p. A81
Chief Operating Officer, Shasta Regional Medical Center, Redding, CA, p. A81

LEVY, Brian M.D., Medical Director, AMG Specialty Hospital–Edmond, Edmond, OK, p. A507

LEVY, Dana, Chief Nursing Officer, University Of Maryland Charles Regional Medical Center, La Plata, MD, p. A299

LEVY, Scott S M.D., Vice President and Chief Medical Officer, Doylestown Hospital, Doylestown, PA, p. A533

LEVY, Susan M M.D., Vice President Medical Affairs, Levindale Hebrew Geriatric Center And Hospital, Baltimore, MD, p. A294

LEW, Mitchell, M.D., President, Prospect Medical Holdings, Los Angeles, CA, p. B102

LEWANDOWSKI, James, Vice President Human Resources, Perry Memorial Hospital, Princeton, IL, p. A198

LEWANDOWSKI, Jim, Interim Director of Human Resources, Carson Tahoe Health, Carson City, NV, p. A401

LEWANDOWSKI, Terri, Director Financial Services, Ministry Our Lady Of Victory Hospital, Stanley, WI, p. A713

LEWELLEN, Thomas D.O., Chief of Staff, Delta Memorial Hospital, Dumas, AR, p. A42

LEWERKE, Jane, Manager Human Resources, Northern Arizona Veterans Affairs Health Care System, Prescott, AZ, p. A34

LEWGOOD, Tony, Administrator, Shriners Hospitals For Children–Lexington, Lexington, KY, p. A261

LEWIN, Jonathan S., M.D., President, Emory Healthcare, Atlanta, GA, p. B49

LEWIS, Alene R.N., Chief Nursing Officer, Raleigh General Hospital, Beckley, WV, p. A690

LEWIS, Angel
Senior Vice President Administration, Cookeville Regional Medical Center, Cookeville, TN, p. A577
Senior Vice President, Cumberland River Hospital, Celina, TN, p. A576

LEWIS, Barbara, Chief Nursing Officer, Alliancehealth Seminole, Seminole, OK, p. A515

LEWIS, Brandon, Director of Information Technology, Ivinson Memorial Hospital, Laramie, WY, p. A718

LEWIS, Brinsley, FACHE, President, Mount Carmel, Columbus, OH, p. A487

LEWIS, Cameron, Chief Executive Officer, Alliancehealth Clinton, Clinton, OK, p. A506

LEWIS, Carlisle III, Senior Vice President Legal and Human Resources, Sharp Mesa Vista Hospital, San Diego, CA, p. A86

LEWIS, Christine, Controller, Hermann Area District Hospital, Hermann, MO, p. A369

LEWIS, Colleen, Director Human Resources, Texas Neurorehab Center, Austin, TX, p. A596

LEWIS, Courtney, Director Human Resources, Houston Methodist San Jacinto Hospital, Baytown, TX, p. A597

LEWIS, Craig, Chief Financial Officer, Sentara Albemarle Medical Center, Elizabeth City, NC, p. A462

LEWIS, Curtis M.D., Chief of Staff, Grady Memorial Hospital, Atlanta, GA, p. A150

LEWIS, Dana, Director Clinical Services, Southern Kentucky Rehabilitation Hospital, Bowling Green, KY, p. A256

LEWIS, Daniel
Chief Medical Officer, Takoma Regional Hospital, Greeneville, TN, p. A579
Executive Vice President and Chief Operating Officer, Metrohealth Medical Center, Cleveland, OH, p. A486

LEWIS, Darlene, Vice President Human Resources, Canton–Potsdam Hospital, Potsdam, NY, p. A450

LEWIS, Dave, Director Information Services, SSM Health St. Francis Hospital – Maryville, Maryville, MO, p. A373

LEWIS, Dennis M.D., Chief of Staff, Ashley Regional Medical Center, Vernal, UT, p. A661

LEWIS, Donald C Jr, Vice President and Chief Financial Officer, Coffee Regional Medical Center, Douglas, GA, p. A156

LEWIS, Doug
Chief Financial Officer, St. Luke's Rehabilitation Hospital, Boise, ID, p. A172
Chief Financial Officer, Wheatland Memorial Healthcare, Harlowton, MT, p. A385

LEWIS, Douglas, Chief Financial Officer, Boulder City Hospital, Boulder City, NV, p. A401

LEWIS, Eric, Chief Executive Officer, Olympic Medical Center, Port Angeles, WA, p. A683

LEWIS, Gerry
Chief Information Officer, Seton Highland Lakes, Burnet, TX, p. A600

LINDSEY, Hugh M.D., Chief Medical Officer, Hayes Green Beach Memorial Hospital, Charlotte, MI, p. A316

LINDSEY, Jay, Chief Executive Officer, Plano Surgical Hospital, Plano, TX, p. A638

LINDSEY, Kim, Chief Human Resources Officer, Lourdes Hospital, Paducah, KY, p. A266

LINDSEY, Robbie, Chief Information Officer, Twin Lakes Regional Medical Center, Leitchfield, KY, p. A260

LINDSEY, Tony M.D., Chief of Staff, University Of North Carolina Hospitals, Chapel Hill, NC, p. A459

LINDSTROM, David M.D., Vice President Medical Affairs, Promedica Bay Park Hospital, Oregon, OH, p. A497

LINES, Brian, Chief Operating Officer, Ogden Regional Medical Center, Ogden, UT, p. A658

LING, Lori, Information Technician, Windom Area Hospital, Windom, MN, p. A350

LINGEN, Tom M.D., Chief of Staff, Cumberland Memorial Hospital, Cumberland, WI, p. A700

LINGLE, Dan, Chief Nursing Officer, Banner Casa Grande Medical Center, Casa Grande, AZ, p. A28

LINGLE, David, Directors Council Chairman and Chief of Staff, Vidant Roanoke–Chowan Hospital, Ahoskie, NC, p. A457

LINGO, Jessica, Human Resource Generalist, Story County Medical Center, Nevada, IA, p. A232

LINHARES, James, Chief Executive Officer, Bridgepoint Hospital Capitol Hill, Washington, DC, p. A117

LINK, Nate M.D., Medical Director, NYC Health + Hospitals / Bellevue, New Rochelle, NY, p. A444

LINKENHOKER, Ellen Y, Chief Nursing Officer, Lewisgale Hospital Montgomery, Blacksburg, VA, p. A665

LINN, Steven C, M.D.
Chief Medical Officer, Inspira Medical Center–Elmer, Elmer, NJ, p. A413
Chief Medical Officer, Inspira Medical Center–Vineland, Vineland, NJ, p. A422

LINNA, Gina, Manager Human Resources, Aspirus Ontonagon Hospital, Inc., Ontonagon, MI, p. A327

LINNELL, Jon E., Interim Chief Executive Officer, North Valley Health Center, Warren, MN, p. A350

LINNINGTON, Darryl, Chief Financial Officer, Mcalester Regional Health Center, Mcalester, OK, p. A510

LINSCHEID, Carol, Vice President Human Resources, Enloe Medical Center, Chico, CA, p. A55

LINSCOTT, Jason CPA, Chief Financial Officer, Texas Health Presbyterian Hospital Of Rockwall, Rockwall, TX, p. A640

LINSE, Margaret, Administrative Secretary and Director Human Resources, West Holt Medical Services, Atkinson, NE, p. A390

LINSKEY, Chris M.D., Acting Chief Medical Officer, Guidance Center, Flagstaff, AZ, p. A29

LINSTROM, Joseph, Vice President Operations, Suburban Hospital, Bethesda, MD, p. A297

LINTON, Dwight, Director Human Resources, Detar Healthcare System, Victoria, TX, p. A652

LINTZ, Gordon, Chief Administrative Officer, Morristown–Hamblen Healthcare System, Morristown, TN, p. A586

LINVILLE, Kimberly, Chief Nursing Officer, Grant Memorial Hospital, Petersburg, WV, p. A695

LINZMAN, Rob D.O., Chief of Staff, Jefferson County Hospital, Waurika, OK, p. A519

LIPARI, Cheryl, Manager Information Systems, Teche Regional Medical Center, Morgan City, LA, p. A282

LIPE, Curt, Vice President, Chief Financial Officer, OSF St. Mary Medical Center, Galesburg, IL, p. A188

LIPINSKI, Gary, M.D.
Regional Chief Medical Officer, Presence Saint Joseph Medical Center, Joliet, IL, p. A191
Regional Chief Medical Officer, Presence St. Mary's Hospital, Kankakee, IL, p. A191

LIPMAN, Brian M.D., Medical Director and Medical Staff Services, Oconomowoc Memorial Hospital, Oconomowoc, WI, p. A709

LIPMAN, Henry D
Senior Vice President, Financial Strategy and External Relations, Franklin Regional Hospital, Franklin, NH, p. A408
Senior Vice President, Financial Strategy and External Relations, Lakes Region General Hospital, Laconia, NH, p. A408

LIPNER, Zach, Vice President Human Resources, Newark Beth Israel Medical Center, Newark, NJ, p. A417

LIPPERT, Brandt, Vice President Human Resources, Adena Greenfield Medical Center, Greenfield, OH, p. A492

LIPPINCOTT, Ken M.D., Chief of Staff, North Mississippi State Hospital, Tupelo, MS, p. A362

LIPSCOMB, Teresa, Director Human Resources, Springbrook Behavioral Health System, Travelers Rest, SC, p. A566

LIPSCOMB, Tiffiny J, Manager Human Resources, Intermountain Medical Center, Murray, UT, p. A658

LIPSCOMB, Tracy CPA, Vice President Financial Services and Chief Financial Officer, Garrett Regional Medical Center, Oakland, MD, p. A300

LIPSKY, Richard, Chairman and Chief Executive Officer, Columbus Hospital Ltach, Newark, NJ, p. A417

LIPTAK, Valenda M., Chief Executive Officer, Western Massachusetts Hospital, Westfield, MA, p. A313

LIPTON, Pat
Director Team Resources, South Florida Baptist Hospital, Plant City, FL, p. A140
Director Team Resources, St. Joseph's Hospital, Tampa, FL, p. A145

LIPSTEIN, Steven H., Chief Executive Officer, Bjc Healthcare, Saint Louis, MO, p. B21

LIRAKIS, Kathy R.N., Chief Nursing Officer, Blue Hill Memorial Hospital, Blue Hill, ME, p. A290

LIRIO, Ruel R. M.D., Clinical Physician Advisor, Spectrum Health Zeeland Community Hospital, Zeeland, MI, p. A334

LISA, Mark P., FACHE, Chief Executive Officer, Twin Cities Community Hospital, Templeton, CA, p. A93

LISELL, Susan C, Vice President of Clinical Services, Lifecare Medical Center, Roseau, MN, p. A347

LISKA, Lee Ann, Chief Executive Officer, Augusta University Medical Center, Augusta, GA, p. A151

LISKE, Thomas M.D., Chief Medical Officer, Kindred Hospital–Sycamore, Sycamore, IL, p. A201

LISKO, J. Stuart, Regional Director Operations, Critical Access Hospital Operations, Mercy Hospital Booneville, Booneville, AR, p. A41

LISKO, Stuart, Vice President, Chief Financial Officer and Compliance Officer, Levi Hospital, Hot Springs National Park, AR, p. A44

LISKOV, David M.D., Medical Director, First Hospital Wyoming Valley, Kingston, PA, p. A537

LISONBEE, Rod, Chief Financial Officer, Utah Valley Hospital, Provo, UT, p. A659

LISS, Rita, Vice President Fiscal Services and Chief Financial Officer, Boone County Health Center, Albion, NE, p. A390

LIST, Alan F., President and Chief Executive Officer, H. Lee Moffitt Cancer Center And Research Institute, Tampa, FL, p. A144

LISTER, Jack, Director Human Resources, Takoma Regional Hospital, Greeneville, TN, p. A579

LISTI, Daniel, Chief Operating Officer, Valley Baptist Medical Center–Harlingen, Harlingen, TX, p. A618

LISTON, Allison, Director, Human Resources, Cedar Crest Hospital And Residential Treatment Center, Belton, TX, p. A598

LISTON, John, Chief Operating Officer, Mclaren Port Huron, Port Huron, MI, p. A328

LITAKER, Thomas
Regional Vice President and Chief Financial Officer, Cascade Valley Hospital And Clinics, Arlington, WA, p. A678
Regional Vice President and Chief Financial Officer, Skagit Regional Health, Mount Vernon, WA, p. A682

LITKA, Calvin R.N., Director of Nursing, Horsham Clinic, Ambler, PA, p. A529

LITOVITZ, Gary M.D., Medical Director, Dominion Hospital, Falls Church, VA, p. A666

LITSINGER, James
Chief Operating Officer, Sheltering Arms Hospital South, Midlothian, VA, p. A670
Vice President and Chief Financial Officer, Sheltering Arms Rehabilitation Hospital, Mechanicsville, VA, p. A670

LITTERER, Karen, Administrator and Chief Operating Officer, Seton Highland Lakes, Burnet, TX, p. A600

LITTLE, Christopher M, Vice President and Chief Financial Officer, Ellwood City Hospital, Ellwood City, PA, p. A534

LITTLE, Denise, Director Human Resources, St. Elizabeth Community Hospital, Red Bluff, CA, p. A81

LITTLE, Gary M.D., Medical Director, George Washington University Hospital, Washington, DC, p. A117

LITTLE, James P M.D., Medical Director, Healthsouth Rehabilitation Hospital, Kingsport, TN, p. A581

LITTLE, Lou, President and Chief Executive Officer, Sparrow Specialty Hospital, Lansing, MI, p. A324

LITTLE, Monica, Coordinator Human Resources, Kindred Rehabilitation Hospital Clear Lake, Webster, TX, p. A653

LOFGREN, Richard P., M.D., M.P.H., President and CEO, Uc Health, Cincinnati, OH, p. B131

LITTLE, Steven N., President and Chief Executive Officer, St. Agnes Hospital, Fond Du Lac, WI, p. A701

LITTLE, Suzanne, Human Resources Specialist, Columbia Basin Hospital, Ephrata, WA, p. A680

LITTLE, William, Chief Executive Officer, Carolina Pines Regional Medical Center, Hartsville, SC, p. A563

LITTLEDEER, Lenora R.N., Director of Nursing, Lawton Indian Hospital, Lawton, OK, p. A509

LITTLEFIELD, Karen, Director Human Resources, Waldo County General Hospital, Belfast, ME, p. A290

LITTLEJOHN, Edward, Chief Operating Officer, Fountain Valley Regional Hospital And Medical Center, Fountain Valley, CA, p. A60

LITTLEJOHN, Traxler, Human Resources Director, Healthsouth Rehabilitation Hospital Of Charleston, Charleston, SC, p. A559

LITTLEPAGE, Dana, Interim Chief Nursing Officer, St. John's Pleasant Valley Hospital, Camarillo, CA, p. A54

LITTRELL, Angela P., Chief Financial Officer and Chief Operating Officer, Fitzgibbon Hospital, Marshall, MO, p. A373

LITTRELL, Mark, Chief Executive Officer, Lincoln Prairie Behavioral Health Center, Springfield, IL, p. A200

LIU, Marsha, Executive Vice President and Chief Financial Officer, Northwest Community Hospital, Arlington Heights, IL, p. A177

LIUZZA, Jed M, Chief Human Resources Officer, Ou Medical Center, Oklahoma City, OK, p. A513

LIUZZO, Gary, Director Information Systems, Scotland Health Care System, Laurinburg, NC, p. A466

LIVELY, Corey, Chief Executive Officer, Great Plains Regional Medical Center, Elk City, OK, p. A507

LIVELY, David, Chief Nursing Officer, Atoka County Medical Center, Atoka, OK, p. A504

LIVERMAN, Brett, Chief Financial Officer, Alleghany Memorial Hospital, Sparta, NC, p. A471

LIVERSAGE, Lavonne, Director, Fargo Veterans Affairs Health Care System, Fargo, ND, p. A475

LIVESAY, William D.O., Jr, Medical Director, Healthsouth Rehabilitation Hospital Of Charleston, Charleston, SC, p. A559

LIVIN, Lee
Chief Financial Officer, Yavapai Regional Medical Center – East, Prescott Valley, AZ, p. A35
Chief Financial Officer, Yavapai Regional Medical Center, Prescott, AZ, p. A35

LIVINGSTON, Carolyn, Director Human Resources, Salt Lake Regional Medical Center, Salt Lake City, UT, p. A660

LIVINGSTON, Charles
Administrator, Dakota Plains Surgical Center, Aberdeen, SD, p. A568
Chief Executive Officer, Midwest Surgical Hospital, Omaha, NE, p. A397

LIVINGSTON, Denise, Director Human Resources, St. Mary Medical Center, Long Beach, CA, p. A67

LIVINGSTON, Keith
Senior Vice President and Chief Information Officer, Thedacare Regional Medical Center–Appleton, Appleton, WI, p. A698
Senior Vice President and Chief Information Officer, Thedacare Regional Medical Center–Neenah, Neenah, WI, p. A709

LIVINGSTON, Richard M.D., Medical Director, Valley Behavioral Health System, Barling, AR, p. A40

LIVINGSTON, Sam, Information Resource Consultant, G. Werber Bryan Psychiatric Hospital, Columbia, SC, p. A560

LIVSEY, Don, Vice President and Chief Information Officer, Uscf Benioff Children's Hospital Oakland, Oakland, CA, p. A77

LIVVIX, Susan R.N., MSN, Vice President Nursing Services, Paris Community Hospital, Paris, IL, p. A197

LIZZA, Beth, Chief Nursing Officer, Ohio Valley Surgical Hospital, Springfield, OH, p. A499

LJUNGQUIST, Diane, R.N., MS, Chief Executive Officer, Berwick Hospital Center, Berwick, PA, p. A529

LLANO, Manuel R.
Chief Executive Officer, Atlantic Shores Hospital, Fort Lauderdale, FL, p. A124
Chief Executive Officer, Fort Lauderdale Hospital, Fort Lauderdale, FL, p. A124

LLEWELLYN, Michael R, Chief Operating Officer, Laguna Honda Hospital And Rehabilitation Center, San Francisco, CA, p. A87

LLOYD, Donald H. II, Chief Executive Officer, Christus St. Patrick Hospital Of Lake Charles, Lake Charles, LA, p. A279

LLOYD, Richard D.O., Chief of Staff, Harbor Beach Community Hospital, Harbor Beach, MI, p. A322

LLOYD, Russell E., Director, Wilkes–Barre Veterans Affairs Medical Center, Wilkes, PA, p. A554

LO, Eric M.D., Chief Medical Staff, Florida Hospital New Smyrna, New Smyrna Beach, FL, p. A135

LOBBAN, Victoria, Vice President Finance, New England Sinai Hospital And Rehabilitation Center, Stoughton, MA, p. A312

LOBECK, Charles A., Administrator, Shriners Hospitals For Children–Twin Cities, Minneapolis, MN, p. A344

LOCEY, Vicky, Chief Operating and Chief Nursing Officer, Kaiser Permanente Santa Rosa Medical Center, Santa Rosa, CA, p. A91

LOCHALA, Richard, Chief of Staff, Mena Regional Health System, Mena, AR, p. A47

LOCK, Lesa, Chief Nursing Officer, Valley View Medical Center, Fort Mohave, AZ, p. A29

LOCKARD, Dennis, Vice President Fiscal Services and Chief Financial Officer, Wayne Healthcare, Greenville, OH, p. A492

LOCKCUFF, Todd, Chief Financial Officer, Inova Alexandria Hospital, Alexandria, VA, p. A664

LOCKE, Cheryl, Vice President and Chief Human Resource Officer, Wake Forest Baptist Medical Center, Winston, NC, p. A473

LOCKE, Christopher, Chief Executive Officer, Saint Francis Hospital–Bartlett, Bartlett, TN, p. A575

LOCKE, Marianne R.N., MSN, Associate Director Patient Care Services, Edward Hines, Jr. Veterans Affairs Hospital, Hines, IL, p. A190

LOCKE, Stuart, Chief Executive Officer, Southern Kentucky Rehabilitation Hospital, Bowling Green, KY, p. A256

LOCKERD, Marie Paul M.D., Chief Medical Officer, Sanford Jackson Medical Center, Jackson, MN, p. A341

LOCKETT, Kevin, Interim Chief Financial Officer, Mayo Clinic Jacksonville, Jacksonville, FL, p. A128

LOCKHART, Jimmy Wayne M.D., Medical Director, Healthsouth Treasure Coast Rehabilitation Hospital, Vero Beach, FL, p. A146

LOCKLEAR, Ann, Vice President, Human Resources, Scotland Health Care System, Laurinburg, NC, p. A466

LOCKRIDGE, Michael, Chief Financial Officer, Northern Louisiana Medical Center, Ruston, LA, p. A285

LOCKWOOD, Melissa, Chief Executive Officer, Preston Memorial Hospital, Kingwood, WV, p. A693

LOCRICCHIO, Anu, Chief Executive Officer, Pioneer Specialty Hospital, Pontiac, MI, p. A328

LODGE, Dale M., Chief Executive Officer, Winchester Hospital, Winchester, MA, p. A313

LOE, Cindy R.N., Director of Nursing, Essentia Health Northern Pines Medical Center, Aurora, MN, p. A335

LOEFFELHOLZ, Tim, Account Executive Information Technology, Unitypoint Health – Finley Hospital, Dubuque, IA, p. A227

LOELIGER, Eric, Vice President of Medical Affairs, Asante Three Rivers Medical Center, Grants Pass, OR, p. A522

LOEPP, Robert A. Jr, FACHE, Chief Executive Officer, AMG Specialty Hospital–Wichita, Wichita, KS, p. A253

LOERA, Arnold M.D., Clinical Director, Bristol Bay Area Health Corporation, Dillingham, AK, p. A26

LOERINC, Albert M.D., Medical Director, Vibra Hospital Of Southeastern Massachusetts, New Bedford, MA, p. A309

LOESCHER, Cori R.N., Interim Chief Nursing Officer, Brigham And Women's Faulkner Hospital, Boston, MA, p. A303

LOEWENSTEIN, Howard, Chief Information Resource Management Services, Jesse Brown Veterans Affairs Medical Center, Chicago, IL, p. A181

LOFFING, David, Chief Operating Officer, University Of Illinois Hospital & Health Sciences System, Chicago, IL, p. A184

LOFTIS, Dennis
    Senior Vice President and Chief Information Officer, Riverside Regional Medical Center, Newport News, VA, p. A671
    Senior Vice President of Information Systems, Riverside Rehabilitation Institute, Newport News, VA, p. A671

LOFTIS, Michelle, Human Resources Officer, Ferry County Memorial Hospital, Republic, WA, p. A684

LOFTON, Jason M.D., Medical Director, De Queen Medical Center, De Queen, AR, p. A42

LOFTON, Kevin E., FACHE, Chief Executive Officer, Catholic Health Initiatives, Englewood, CO, p. B26

LOFTON, Veronica, Acting Chief Executive Officer, Twin Valley Behavioral Healthcare, Columbus, OH, p. A488

LOFTUS, John M.D., Chief of Staff, Kaiser Permanente Oakland Medical Center, Oakland, CA, p. A77

LOFTUS, Mary Virginia, Chief Nursing Officer, Specialists Hospital – Shreveport, Shreveport, LA, p. A286

LOFTUS, Philip, Ph.D.
    Chief Information Officer, Aurora West Allis Medical Center, West Allis, WI, p. A715
    Vice President and Chief Information Officer, Aurora Medical Center Of Oshkosh, Oshkosh, WI, p. A710
    Vice President and Chief Information Officer, Aurora Psychiatric Hospital, Wauwatosa, WI, p. A715
    Vice President and Chief Information Officer, Aurora St. Luke's Medical Center, Milwaukee, WI, p. A707

LOFTUS, Terry M.D., Chief Medical Officer, Medical City Fort Worth, Fort Worth, TX, p. A614

LOFURNO, Justin A, Director Human Resources, Providence Hospital, Columbia, SC, p. A560

LOGAN, Angela, Chief Nursing Officer, Lutheran Hospital Of Indiana, Fort Wayne, IN, p. A208

LOGAN, Ann P., Chief Operating Officer, Carepoint Health Hoboken University Medical Center, Hoboken, NJ, p. A414

LOGAN, Bradley, Chief Financial Officer, Franklin Woods Community Hospital, Johnson City, TN, p. A581

LOGAN, Denise, Director Human Resources, Specialty Rehabilitation Hospital Of Coushatta, Coushatta, LA, p. A273

LOGAN, John M.D., Chief Medical Officer, Methodist Hospital, Henderson, KY, p. A259

LOGAN, Michael, Chief Financial Officer, Norton Brownsboro Hospital, Louisville, KY, p. A263

LOGAN, Renee, Chief Financial Officer, Murray County Medical Center, Slayton, MN, p. A348

LOGAN–OWENS, Michelle, Chief Operating Officer, Palmetto Health Tuomey, Sumter, SC, p. A566

LOGAR, Michael, Assistant Superintendent, Larue D. Carter Memorial Hospital, Indianapolis, IN, p. A211

LOGDSON, David, Chief Nursing Officer, Twin Lakes Regional Medical Center, Leitchfield, KY, p. A260

LOGOZZO, Vince, Director Information Technology, Aultman Orrville Hospital, Orrville, OH, p. A497

LOGSDON, Terri
    Chief Financial Officer, Covington Behavior Health, Covington, LA, p. A273
    Chief Financial Officer, Hickory Trail Hospital, Desoto, TX, p. A609

LOGUE, Amy Antani Ph.D., Vice President Human Resources, Advocate Condell Medical Center, Libertyville, IL, p. A192

LOH, Marcel C., FACHE, Chief Executive Officer, Providence Saint John's Health Center, Santa Monica, CA, p. A91

LOHMAN, Eric M.D., Chief of Staff, Meadowview Regional Medical Center, Maysville, KY, p. A264

LOHMEIER, Justin M.D., Chief of Staff, Baptist Memorial Hospital–Union County, New Albany, MS, p. A360

LOHN, Eric
    Chief Financial Officer, Lake View Hospital, Two Harbors, MN, p. A349
    Vice President and Chief Financial Officer, St. Luke's Hospital, Duluth, MN, p. A339

LOHR, Daniel E, Regional Vice President Finance, Windham Hospital, Willimantic, CT, p. A114

LOHRMAN, Joseph W., Chief Executive Officer, Annie Jeffrey Memorial County Health Center, Osceola, NE, p. A398

LOHRMAN, Joseph W, Chief Executive Officer, Annie Jeffrey Memorial County Health Center, Osceola, NE, p. A398

LOHSTRETER, Thomas M.D., Chief of Staff, Kittson Memorial Healthcare Center, Hallock, MN, p. A341

LOKKEN, Christine, Director of Finance, Bigfork Valley Hospital, Bigfork, MN, p. A336

LOLLIS, Sylvia, Director Human Resources, Osceola Regional Medical Center, Kissimmee, FL, p. A129

LOLLO, Trisha, President, Barnes–Jewish West County Hospital, Saint Louis, MO, p. A376

LOMAN, Sarah, Director Human Resources, Penobscot Valley Hospital, Lincoln, ME, p. A292

LOMBA, Maria R, Medical Director, New Braunfels Regional Rehabilitation Hospital, New Braunfels, TX, p. A635

LOMBARD, Lisa, Chief Medical Officer, Ohiohealth Rehabilitation Hospital, Columbus, OH, p. A488

LOMBARD, Michael, President, Cornerstone Hospital Of Southwest Louisiana, Sulphur, LA, p. A287

LOMBARDO, Alan, Associate Director, Hunter Holmes Mcguire Veterans Affairs Medical Center–Richmond, Richmond, VA, p. A674

LOMEO, Jody, Chief Executive Officer, Kaleida Health, Buffalo, NY, p. A432

LONERGAN, Araceli, Chief Executive Officer, Community Hospital Of Huntington Park, Huntington Park, CA, p. A63

LONEY, Chris, Director Personnel, Thomas B. Finan Center, Cumberland, MD, p. A298

LONG, Amy, Administrator, Mayo Clinic Health System In Saint James, Saint James, MN, p. A347

LONG, Angela S, Vice President Clinical Services and Chief Nursing Officer, Southeastern Ohio Regional Medical Center, Cambridge, OH, p. A482

LONG, Brian, FACHE, President and Chief Executive Officer, Memorial Healthcare, Owosso, MI, p. A327

LONG, Dennis, Director Human Resources, Western Missouri Medical Center, Warrensburg, MO, p. A380

LONG, Douglas, President and Chief Executive Officer, West Hills Hospital And Medical Center, Los Angeles, CA, p. A72

LONG, Erik
    Controller, Baptist Health South Florida, Mariners Hospital, Tavernier, FL, p. A146
    Controller, Baptist Health South Florida, South Miami Hospital, Miami, FL, p. A132

LONG, Floyd R., Chief Executive Officer, NYC Health + Hospitals / Carter, New Rochelle, NY, p. A444

LONG, Floyd R, Chief Executive Officer, NYC Health + Hospitals / Carter, New Rochelle, NY, p. A444

LONG, Gloria, Chief Operating Officer, Guam Regional Medical City, Dededo, GU, p. A721

LONG, Gregory L
    Chief Medical Officer, Thedacare Regional Medical Center–Appleton, Appleton, WI, p. A698
    Chief Medical Officer, Thedacare Regional Medical Center–Neenah, Neenah, WI, p. A709

LONG, Jeremy, Manager Information Systems, St. Vincent Salem Hospital, Salem, IN, p. A219

LONG, Jessica, Chief Executive Officer, Cornerstone Medical Center, Fort Oglethorpe, GA, p. A158

LONG, Jonathan Ray M.D., Chief of Staff, Weatherford Regional Hospital, Weatherford, OK, p. A519

LONG, Judy M, Chief Nursing Officer and Chief Operating Officer, Appling Healthcare System, Baxley, GA, p. A152

LONG, Karen R.N., FACHE, Vice President Nursing, Bayfront Health St. Petersburg, Saint Petersburg, FL, p. A141

LONG, Michelle
    Human Resources Business Partner, Abraham Lincoln Memorial Hospital, Lincoln, IL, p. A192
    Regional Human Resource Manager, Taylorville Memorial Hospital, Taylorville, IL, p. A201

LONG, Mike, Chief Financial Officer, Powell Valley Healthcare, Powell, WY, p. A719

LONG, Richard M.D., Chief Medical Officer, Upmc Hamot, Erie, PA, p. A534

LONG, Stephanie, President and Chief Executive Officer, River Bend Hospital, West Lafayette, IN, p. A221

LONG, Steven V., FACHE, President and Chief Executive Officer, Hancock Regional Hospital, Greenfield, IN, p. A209

LONG, Terry, Chief Executive Officer, Cherokee Medical Center, Centre, AL, p. A16

LONG, Theresa, Chief Executive Officer, Danville State Hospital, Danville, PA, p. A532

LONGABAUGH, James M.D., Chief Medical Staff, Sabetha Community Hospital, Sabetha, KS, p. A250

LONGACRE, Mark E FACHE, Chief Operating Officer, Orthonebraska Hospital, Omaha, NE, p. A398

LONGBRAKE, Jeffery, President and Chief Executive Officer, Huron Medical Center, Bad Axe, MI, p. A314

LONGDO, Derrick, Director Information Systems, Memorial Medical Center – Neillsville, Neillsville, WI, p. A709

LONGEST, Bruce M.D., President Medical Staff, Baptist Memorial Hospital – Calhoun, Calhoun City, MS, p. A353

LONGEST, Sonya M.D., Chief Medical Officer, Walter B. Jones Alcohol And Drug Abuse Treatment Center, Greenville, NC, p. A464

LONGLEY, Frank, Business Partner Information Technology, Cleveland Clinic, Medina Hospital, Medina, OH, p. A495

LONGMORE, David, Chief Information Officer, Wilkes–Barre Veterans Affairs Medical Center, Wilkes, PA, p. A554

LONGMUIR, Bryan, Chief Resource Management, Madigan Army Medical Center, Tacoma, WA, p. A687

LONGMUIR, Marla M.D., Chief Medical Officer, Mountrail County Medical Center, Stanley, ND, p. A478

LONGNECKER, Stacy, Chief of Staff, Ortonville Area Health Services, Ortonville, MN, p. A345

LONGO, Marybeth, Manager Human Resources, Trenton Psychiatric Hospital, Trenton, NJ, p. A422

LONGPRE, Donald J, Vice President Finance and Chief Financial Officer, North Ottawa Community Hospital, Grand Haven, MI, p. A320

LONGTIN, Brett, Chief Financial Officer, Lake Region Healthcare, Fergus Falls, MN, p. A340

LONIS, Robert
    Chief Financial Officer, Lincoln County Health System, Fayetteville, TN, p. A578
    Interim Chief Financial Officer, Nashville General Hospital, Nashville, TN, p. A586

LOOMIS, Anna
    Senior Vice President Chief Financial Officer, Multicare Auburn Medical Center, Auburn, WA, p. A678
    Senior Vice President Chief Financial Officer, Multicare Good Samaritan Hospital, Puyallup, WA, p. A684
    Senior Vice President Chief Financial Officer, Multicare Mary Bridge Children's Hospital And Health Center, Tacoma, WA, p. A687
    Senior Vice President Chief Financial Officer, Multicare Tacoma General Hospital, Tacoma, WA, p. A688

LOOMIS, Greg
    Interim President and Chief Operating Officer, Mercy Health Hackley Campus, Muskegon, MI, p. A327
    President, Mercy Health Hackley Campus, Muskegon, MI, p. A327
    President, Mercy Health Hackley Campus, Muskegon, MI, p. A327

LOOMIS, Randy, Chief Financial Officer, Dallas County Hospital, Perry, IA, p. A233

LOONEY, Zane, Chief Information Officer, St. Bernard Parish Hospital, Chalmette, LA, p. A272
LOOSBROCK, Tammy
 Chief Executive Officer, Sanford Luverne Medical Center, Luverne, MN, p. A342
 Chief Executive Officer, Sanford Rock Rapids Medical Center, Rock Rapids, IA, p. A234
LOOSEMORE, Tim
 Director, Franciscan St. Anthony Health – Crown Point, Crown Point, IN, p. A206
 Regional Director Information Systems, Franciscan St. Anthony Health – Michigan City, Michigan City, IN, p. A215
LOOSLI, Angela, Assistant Administrator, Operations, State Hospital South, Blackfoot, ID, p. A171
LOPACHIN, Vicki M.D., Chief Medical Officer, Mount Sinai Hospital, New Rochelle, NY, p. A443
LOPAS, Mary, Chief Information Officer, Door County Medical Center, Sturgeon Bay, WI, p. A713
LOPES, Michelle Anne MSN, R.N., Senior Vice President, Patient Care Services & Chief Nursing Officer, John Muir Medical Center, Walnut Creek, Walnut Creek, CA, p. A96
LOPEZ, Augustine, Chief Financial Officer, Salinas Valley Memorial Healthcare System, Salinas, CA, p. A84
LOPEZ, Cesar R.N., Director of Nurses, Chi St. Joseph Health Grimes Hospital, Navasota, TX, p. A634
LOPEZ, David S FACHE, Executive Vice President and Chief Operating Officer, Parkland Health & Hospital System, Dallas, TX, p. A606
LOPEZ, Enrique M.D., Medical Director, Larry B. Zieverink, Sr. Alcoholism Treatment Center, Raleigh, NC, p. A469
LOPEZ, Ericca, Director Human Resources, Canyon Ridge Hospital, Chino, CA, p. A55
LOPEZ, Ivonne, Director Human Resources, Hospital Oriente, Humacao, PR, p. A724
LOPEZ, Leonard H, Chief Operating Officer, Hopi Health Care Center, Keams Canyon, AZ, p. A30
LOPEZ, Leonardo, President Medical Staff, OSF Saint Paul Medical Center, Mendota, IL, p. A193
LOPEZ, Lesbia, Chief Nursing Officer, Doctors' Center Hospital San Juan, San Juan, PR, p. A725
LOPEZ, Lisa M, Director Human Resources, San Joaquin General Hospital, French Camp, CA, p. A60
LOPEZ, Maria Rose R.N., Chief of Nursing, Nix Health Care System, San Antonio, TX, p. A643
LOPEZ, Maritza M.D., Chief of Staff, Sanford Canby Medical Center, Canby, MN, p. A337
LOPEZ, Susan Nordstrom, President, Advocate Illinois Masonic Medical Center, Chicago, IL, p. B7
LOPEZ, Rene, Chief Executive Officer, Knapp Medical Center, Weslaco, TX, p. A654
LOPEZ, Robert, Chief Medical Officer, Highland Community Hospital, Picayune, MS, p. A360
LOPEZ, Rosalio J M.D., Senior Vice President and Chief Medical Officer, Pih Health Hospital–Whittier, Whittier, CA, p. A97
LOPEZ, Steve Kelley., Chief Executive Officer, Colorado River Medical Center, Needles, CA, p. A76
LOPEZ, Steve Kelley, Chief Financial Officer, Colorado River Medical Center, Needles, CA, p. A76
LOPEZ, Steven M.D., Chief Medical Officer, Palmetto Lowcountry Behavioral Health, Charleston, SC, p. A559
LOPEZ, Susan Nordstrom., President, Advocate Illinois Masonic Medical Center, Chicago, IL, p. A180
LOPEZ, Valerie CPA, Chief Financial Officer, Uvalde Memorial Hospital, Uvalde, TX, p. A651
LOPREATO, Elayne
 Chief Clinical Officer, Kindred Hospital The Palm Beaches, Riviera Beach, FL, p. A140
 Chief Executive Officer, Kindred Hospital The Palm Beaches, Riviera Beach, FL, p. A140
LORD, David, President, OSF St. Francis Hospital And Medical Group, Escanaba, MI, p. A319
LORD, Gregory D
 Chief Medical Officer, Leesville Rehabilitation Hospital, Leesville, LA, p. A280
 Medical Director, Doctor's Hospital Of Deer Creek, Leesville, LA, p. A280
LORD, Jeff, Director of Nursing, Connecticut Veterans Home And Hospital, Rocky Hill, CT, p. A112
LORD, Robert L., JD, President and Chief Executive Officer, Martin Health System, Stuart, FL, p. A143
LORENTZ, Derick, Chief Financial Officer, Perkins County Health Services, Grant, NE, p. A393
LORENZ, Paul E., Chief Executive Officer, Santa Clara Valley Medical Center, San Jose, CA, p. A89
LORENZ, Todd, Chief Executive Officer, Pam Rehabilitation Hospital Of Beaumont, Beaumont, TX, p. A597
LORENZEN, Shelli, Chief Human Resources Officer, Manning Regional Healthcare Center, Manning, IA, p. A231
LORENZO, Heather M.D., Vice President and Chief Medical Officer, Meritus Medical Center, Hagerstown, MD, p. A299

LORIMER, Lee IV, Regional Director Human Resources, Mckay–Dee Hospital, Ogden, UT, p. A658
LORMAN, William J Ph.D., Clinical Director, Livengrin Foundation, Bensalem, PA, p. A529
LORMAND, Jared, Vice President Information Technology, Opelousas General Health System, Opelousas, LA, p. A284
LORTON, Donald E, Executive Vice President, Bedford Memorial Hospital, Bedford, VA, p. A664
LOSITO, Glenna R.N., MSN, Chief Nursing Officer, Cibola General Hospital, Grants, NM, p. A426
LOTHE, Eric L FACHE, Senior Vice President and Chief Operating Officer, Unitypoint Health–Iowa Lutheran Hospital, Des Moines, IA, p. A226
LOTHIAN, Nancy, Chief Operating Officer and Chief Information Officer, The University Of Vermont Health Network Central Vermont Medical Center, Berlin, VT, p. A662
LOTT, Benjamin, Chief Executive Officer, Copiah County Medical Center, Hazlehurst, MS, p. A356
LOTT, Cynthia, Director Human Resources, Northern Virginia Mental Health Institute, Falls Church, VA, p. A667
LOTT, Laura, Administrative Director, Eastern Louisiana Mental Health System, Jackson, LA, p. A276
LOTT, Rodney, Director Management Information Systems and Facility Operations, Baylor Scott & White Medical Center – Llano, Llano, TX, p. A629
LOTZE, Eberhard M.D., Chief Medical Officer, Woman's Hospital Of Texas, Houston, TX, p. A624
LOUBERT, Cheryl M.D., Chief Medical Staff, Midmichigan Medical Center–Gladwin, Gladwin, MI, p. A320
LOUDEN CORBETT, Jeanette L, Chief Human Resources Officer, Highland Hospital, Oakland, CA, p. A77
LOUGHERY, Vicki R.N., MS, Chief Nursing Officer, Monadnock Community Hospital, Peterborough, NH, p. A410
LOUGHRAN, Lisa, Chief Nursing Officer, Gunnison Valley Hospital, Gunnison, CO, p. A103
LOUGHRAN, Michael, Vice President Human Resources, Kennedy Krieger Institute, Baltimore, MD, p. A294
LOUGHREY, Barbara, Administrator, Northbrook Behavioral Health Hospital, Blackwood, NJ, p. A411
LOUIS, Alfred M.D., Chief Medical Staff, Pine Valley Specialty Hospital, Houston, TX, p. A622
LOUK, Rodney, Vice President Information Systems, Washington Hospital, Washington, PA, p. A552
LOUKATOS, George M.D., President Medical Staff Affairs, Merit Health Biloxi, Biloxi, MS, p. A352
LOVATO, Anthony, Director Information Technology, Coon Memorial Hospital, Dalhart, TX, p. A604
LOVDAHL, Brian A, Chief Financial Officer, Western Wisconsin Health, Baldwin, WI, p. A698
LOVE, Alex, Acting Manager Human Resources, Alexandria Veterans Affairs Health Care System, Pineville, LA, p. A284
LOVE, Bianca, Assistant Administrator Human Resources, Trinity Hospital Twin City, Dennison, OH, p. A490
LOVE, E Clifford, Director Fiscal Services, Eastern State Hospital, Williamsburg, VA, p. A677
LOVE, Glenn Neil M.D., Medical Director, Hilton Head Hospital, Hilton Head Island, SC, p. A564
LOVE, Tim, Director Information Services, Reid Health, Richmond, IN, p. A219
LOVE, Valerie, Manager Business Office, Heatherhill Care Communities, Chardon, OH, p. A483
LOVE–WATLER, Meylan, Chief Operating Officer, Lower Keys Medical Center, Key West, FL, p. A129
LOVEJOY, David, Chief Operations Officer, Riverview Psychiatric Center, Augusta, ME, p. A289
LOVEJOY, Leslie R.N., Ph.D., Chief Nursing and Quality Officer, Sonoma Valley Hospital, Sonoma, CA, p. A92
LOVEJOY, Rob
 Chief Operating Officer, Sanford Medical Center Thief River Falls, Thief River Falls, MN, p. A349
 Chief Operating Officer, Sanford Thief River Falls Behavioral Health Center, Thief River Falls, MN, p. A349
LOVELACE, Alan, Vice President and Chief Financial Officer, Stillwater Medical Center, Stillwater, OK, p. A516
LOVELACE, Christina, Director Human Resources, Gunnison Valley Hospital, Gunnison, CO, p. A103
LOVELESS, Craig, Chief Executive Officer, Prowers Medical Center, Lamar, CO, p. A105
LOVELESS, Jane Doll, Vice President, Chief Information Officer, Grand View Health, Sellersville, PA, p. A550
LOVELESS, Kurt, Chief Executive Officer, The Core Institute Specialty Hospital, Phoenix, AZ, p. A34
LOVELESS, Steve, President and Chief Executive Officer, St. Vincent Healthcare, Billings, MT, p. A382
LOVELL, Charles D. Jr, FACHE, Chief Executive Officer, Barbourville Arh Hospital, Barbourville, KY, p. A255
LOVELL, Mark, Vice President and Chief Financial Officer, Palmetto Health Tuomey, Sumter, SC, p. A566

LOVELL, Stephanie, Vice President and General Counsel, Boston Medical Center, Boston, MA, p. A303
LOVELL, Terrence, Vice President Human Resources, Union Hospital, Elkton, MD, p. A298
LOVELLETTE, Teresa A, Manager Human Resources, Herrin Hospital, Herrin, IL, p. A189
LOVERA, Carlos, Director Information Systems, Montrose Memorial Hospital, Montrose, CO, p. A106
LOVERING, Keith, Information Technician, Miller County Hospital, Colquitt, GA, p. A154
LOVERING, Richard, Corporate Vice President Human Resources and Organizational Development, Atlanticare Regional Medical Center, Atlantic City, NJ, p. A411
LOVERN, Ed, Chief Operating Officer, Piedmont Hospital, Atlanta, GA, p. A150
LOVERSO, Felice L., Ph.D., President and Chief Executive Officer, Casa Colina Hospital And Health Systems, Pomona, CA, p. A80
LOVETT, Chad, Chief Executive Officer, Kindred Hospital–Greensboro, Greensboro, NC, p. A463
LOVING, David E., Chief Executive Officer, Des Peres Hospital, Saint Louis, MO, p. A377
LOVING, Tonya, Director of Human Resources, Uva–Healthsouth Rehabilitation Hospital, Charlottesville, VA, p. A665
LOVING, William, M.D., Medical Director, Texas Star Recovery, Austin, TX, p. A596
LOVINGOOD, Toni, Chief Operating Officer, Murphy Medical Center, Murphy, NC, p. A467
LOVRICH, John
 Chief Financial Officer, Catalina Island Medical Center, Avalon, CA, p. A52
 Chief Financial Officer, Glenn Medical Center, Willows, CA, p. A97
LOVSHIN, Alex, Chief Operating Officer, Des Peres Hospital, Saint Louis, MO, p. A377
LOW, Kern M.D., Chief Medical Officer, St. Thomas More Hospital, Canon City, CO, p. A99
LOW, Lewis, M.D.
 Chief Medical Officer, Legacy Mount Hood Medical Center, Gresham, OR, p. A522
 Senior Vice President and Chief Medical Officer, Legacy Meridian Park Medical Center, Tualatin, OR, p. A527
 Senior Vice President and Chief Medical Officer, Legacy Salmon Creek Medical Center, Vancouver, WA, p. A688
LOW, Melissa, Chief Clinical Officer, Acuity Hospital Of South Texas, San Antonio, TX, p. A641
LOWE, Bren, Chief Executive Officer, Livingston Healthcare, Livingston, MT, p. A386
LOWE, E. Rick, Chief Executive Officer, Select Specialty Hospital–Augusta, Augusta, GA, p. B114
LOWE, E Rick FACHE, Operations Support Risk Management and Compliance, St. Francis Hospital, Columbus, GA, p. A155
LOWE, Greg, Chief Executive Officer, Chippenham Hospital, Richmond, VA, p. A674
LOWE, Joe, Director Management Information Systems, Cumberland Medical Center, Crossville, TN, p. A578
LOWE, Kristen
 Chief Executive Officer, Kindred Hospital–San Antonio, San Antonio, TX, p. A642
 Interim Chief Executive Officer, Kindred Hospital San Antonio Central, San Antonio, TX, p. A642
LOWE, Lavah Boyers, Chief Nursing Officer, Avista Adventist Hospital, Louisville, CO, p. A106
LOWE, Lavah, Executive Vice President and Chief Operating Officer, Bayfront Health St. Petersburg, Saint Petersburg, FL, p. A141
LOWE, Rob, Director, Healthcare Information Management, Onslow Memorial Hospital, Jacksonville, NC, p. A465
LOWE, Scott
 Director Human Resource, Mcalester Regional Health Center, Mcalester, OK, p. A510
 Interim Market Chief Executive Officer, Physicians Regional – Pine Ridge, Naples, FL, p. A135
LOWELL, David M.D., Chief Medical Officer, Spaulding Rehabilitation Hospital Cape Cod, East Sandwich, MA, p. A306
LOWENTHAL, David M.D., Clinical Director, New York State Psychiatric Institute, New Rochelle, NY, p. A444
LOWENTHAL, Steve B M.D., M.P.H., FACS, Senior Vice President Medical Affairs and Chief Medical Officer, Rush–Copley Medical Center, Aurora, IL, p. A178
LOWERY, Elizabeth, Interim Director, Amarillo Veterans Affairs Health Care System, Amarillo, TX, p. A592
LOWERY, John M.D., Deputy Commander Clinical Services, General Leonard Wood Army Community Hospital, Fort Leonard Wood, MO, p. A368
LOWMAN, LeeAnn, Director Human Resources, Lake Taylor Transitional Care Hospital, Norfolk, VA, p. A672

LOWREY, Linda, Human Resources Officer, Atmore Community Hospital, Atmore, AL, p. A14

LOWRY, Claudia Jean R.N., Director of Nursing, Community Howard Specialty Hospital, Kokomo, IN, p. A213

LOWRY, David M.D., Chief Medical Officer, Caldwell Unc Health Care, Lenoir, NC, p. A466

LOY, Michael, Interim Chief Executive Officer, North Central Health Care, Wausau, WI, p. A715

LOYA, John R, Vice President Human Resources and Organizational Development, Columbus Regional Hospital, Columbus, IN, p. A205

LOYA, Theresa R.N., Chief Nursing Officer, John C. Fremont Healthcare District, Mariposa, CA, p. A73

LOYA, Velma, Administrative Human Resource Coordinator, Rice Medical Center, Eagle Lake, TX, p. A609

LOYD, Chris, Director Human Resources, Methodist Richardson Medical Center, Richardson, TX, p. A639

LOYD, Stephana, Vice President, Chief Nursing Officer, Baptist Health Medical Center – Conway, Conway, AR, p. A41

LOYKE, Christopher, Chief Medical Officer, University Hospitals Parma Medical Center, Parma, OH, p. A498

LOYO–RODRIGUEZ, Raul J, Administrative Analyst III, San Diego County Psychiatric Hospital, San Diego, CA, p. A86

LOZADA, Leonardo J M.D., Chief Physician Executive, Saint Luke's North Hospital – Barry Road, Kansas City, MO, p. A371

LOZANO, Elias B., Executive Officer, Tripler Army Medical Center, Honolulu, HI, p. A169

LOZANO, Melanie, Chief Financial Officer, Concho County Hospital, Eden, TX, p. A609

LOZANO, Michelle, Chief Executive Officer, Lifecare Hospitals Of San Antonio, San Antonio, TX, p. A643

LOZAR, Beverly, Chief Nursing Executive, St. Vincent Charity Medical Center, Cleveland, OH, p. A486

LOZIER, Tim, Director Human Resources, Vibra Specialty Hospital At Desoto, Desoto, TX, p. A609

LUBARSKY, Neil, Senior Vice President, Finance and Chief Financial Officer, Thomas Jefferson University Hospitals, Philadelphia, PA, p. A546

LUBIN, Bertram, M.D., President and Chief Executive Officer, Uscf Benioff Children's Hospital Oakland, Oakland, CA, p. A77

LUBINSKY, Jeanie, Chief Financial Officer, Mayo Clinic Health System – Red Cedar In Menomonie, Menomonie, WI, p. A706

LUBITZ, Robert M.D., Vice President of Medical Affairs, Wellstar Kennestone Hospital, Marietta, GA, p. A161

LUCAS, Benny Lee Jr, Chief Nursing Executive, St. Joseph's Behavioral Health Center, Stockton, CA, p. A92

LUCAS, Bob, Vice President Operations, King's Daughters Medical Center, Ashland, KY, p. A255

LUCAS, Christine, Chief of Staff, Union County Hospital, Anna, IL, p. A177

LUCAS, Denise R.N., MSN, Vice President Clinical Services and Chief Nursing Officer, Margaret R. Pardee Memorial Hospital, Hendersonville, NC, p. A464

LUCAS, Kasey, Chief Executive Officer, Hospital Administrator, Salem Memorial District Hospital, Salem, MO, p. A379

LUCAS, Kelly, Chief Information Officer, Sampson Regional Medical Center, Clinton, NC, p. A460

LUCAS, Marshall M.D., Medical Director, Cypress Creek Hospital, Houston, TX, p. A620

LUCCHESI, Michael M.D., Chief Medical Officer; Chair, Emergency Medicine, Suny Downstate Medical Center University Hospital, New Rochelle, NY, p. A447

LUCE, Glenda, Chief Nursing Officer, Memorial Hospital Of Gardena, Gardena, CA, p. A61

LUCE, Paul W., R.N., MSN, Vice President Operations, Miami County Medical Center, Paola, KS, p. A249

LUCE, Randall R.N., Director of Nursing, Rock Springs, Georgetown, TX, p. A616

LUCENA, Yelitza, Executive Director, Hospital Metropolitano Dr. Susoni, Arecibo, PR, p. A722

LUCERO, Brenda, Chief Clinical Officer, Cornerstone Hospital Of Houston At Clearlake, Webster, TX, p. A653

LUCERO, Lupe, Manager Business Office, Presbyterian Espanola Hospital, Espanola, NM, p. A426

LUCEY, Jeffery M.D., Clinical Director, Kingsboro Psychiatric Center, New Rochelle, NY, p. A442

LUCHSINGER, Catherine MSN, Chief Nursing Officer, Halifax Health Medical Center Of Daytona Beach, Daytona Beach, FL, p. A123

LUCIA, Sandra J, Director Health Information and Corporate Compliance Officer, Hampstead Hospital, Hampstead, NH, p. A408

LUCIANO, Lisa D.O., Medical Director, Hackensack Meridian Health Shore Rehabilitation Institute, Brick, NJ, p. A412

LUCIER, Robbyn, Director Human Resources, Up Health System–Portage, Hancock, MI, p. A322

LUCK, Richard, Facility Director, Woodrow Wilson Rehabilitation Center, Fishersville, VA, p. A667

LUCKE, Kim, Vice President Finance, Northern Montana Health Care, Havre, MT, p. A385

LUCORE, Charles, M.D., President and Chief Executive Officer, St. John's Hospital, Springfield, IL, p. A201

LUDWIG, John A., R.N., President and Chief Operating Officer, Hshs St. Joseph's Hospital, Highland, IL, p. A190

LUDWIG, Walter, Chief Operating Officer, Kenmore Mercy Hospital, Kenmore, NY, p. A438

LUDWIGSEN, Kevin, Chief Information Officer, Southeastern Ohio Regional Medical Center, Cambridge, OH, p. A482

LUEBBERING, Tom, Vice President Finance, Capital Region Medical Center, Jefferson City, MO, p. A369

LUEBCKE, Diane R.N., Director Nursing, Community Memorial Healthcare, Marysville, KS, p. A246

LUECHT, Jackie
Chief Human Resources Officer, Mercy Medical Center–North Iowa, Mason City, IA, p. A231
Director, Human Resources, Mercy Medical Center–New Hampton, New Hampton, IA, p. A232

LUEDDERS, Keith, Chief Operations Officer, Tri Valley Health System, Cambridge, NE, p. A391

LUEDERS, Kathy R.N., Director of Nursing–Acute Care, Saint Elizabeth's Medical Center, Wabasha, MN, p. A349

LUEHRS, Bill, Chief Human Resources Officer, Northshore University Health System, Evanston, IL, p. A187

LUEHRS, Paul R, Chief Operating Officer, Mercy San Juan Medical Center, Carmichael, CA, p. A55

LUFF, Brian, Chief Executive Officer, Quillen Rehabilitation Hospital, Johnson City, TN, p. A581

LUFFEY, Michelle L MSN, R.N., Chief Nursing Officer, Fairmont Regional Medical Center, Fairmont, WV, p. A692

LUFKIN, Kirk M.D., VPMA, Mclaren Northern Michigan, Petoskey, MI, p. A328

LUFKIN, Scott, Director Information Technology, Grundy County Memorial Hospital, Grundy Center, IA, p. A228

LUGER, Gerald M.D., President Medical Staff, Gottlieb Memorial Hospital, Melrose Park, IL, p. A193

LUGO, Cesar, Director Human Resources, Victor Valley Global Medical Center, Victorville, CA, p. A96

LUHRS, Jason J., Vice President Fiscal Services, Westfields Hospital, New Richmond, WI, p. A709

LUKE, Leslie Paul., President and Chief Executive Officer, St. Joseph's Hospital Health Center, Syracuse, NY, p. A453

LUKENS, Tammy, Director Information, Kosciusko Community Hospital, Warsaw, IN, p. A221

LUKER, Patricia A., President, OSF Holy Family Medical Center, Monmouth, IL, p. A194

LUKHARD, Kenneth W., President, Advocate Christ Medical Center, Oak Lawn, IL, p. A196

LUKISH, Kris, Human Resources Officer, Chippenham Hospital, Richmond, VA, p. A674

LULICH, Diane, Director Human Resources, Memorial Medical Center – Ashland, Ashland, WI, p. A698

LULL, Todd, Director Information Technology, Southwest Health, Platteville, WI, p. A710

LULOFF, Lynn, Chief Financial Officer, Winneshiek Medical Center, Decorah, IA, p. A226

LUMPKINS, Deborah MSN, Chief Nursing Officer, Maury Regional Hospital, Columbia, TN, p. A577

LUMPP, Karen, Senior Vice President and Chief Financial Officer, Trinitas Regional Medical Center, Elizabeth, NJ, p. A413

LUMSDEN, Chris A., Chief Executive Officer, Sentara Halifax Regional Hospital, South Boston, VA, p. A675

LUNA, Raul D., Chief Nurse Executive, El Paso Psychiatric Center, El Paso, TX, p. A610

LUNA, Tony M.D., Chief of Staff, Minneola District Hospital, Minneola, KS, p. A247

LUND, Elizabeth M.D., Chief of Staff, Tennova Healthcare Volunteer Community Hospital, Martin, TN, p. A583

LUND, Maggie A., System Vice President Human Resource Market and Labor, Mercy Health – St. Charles Hospital, Oregon, OH, p. A497

LUND, Maggie, Divisional Senior Vice President Human Resources, Mercy Health – Fairfield Hospital, Fairfield, OH, p. A491

LUNDAL, David
Senior Vice President Information Systems and Chief Information Officer, Presence Holy Family Medical Center, Des Plaines, IL, p. A185
System Vice President, Information Systems and Chief Information Officer, Presence Saints Mary & Elizabeth Medical Center, Chicago, IL, p. A183

LUNDBERG, Lanetta, Vice President Culture and People, Peacehealth Ketchikan Medical Center, Ketchikan, AK, p. A26

LUNDBERG, Ralph L, Director Human Resources, Yakima Regional Medical And Cardiac Center, Yakima, WA, p. A689

LUNDE, Susan R.N., Director of Nursing, Fallon Medical Complex, Baker, MT, p. A382

LUNDQUIST, David W., President and Chief Executive Officer, Rome Memorial Hospital, Rome, NY, p. A451

LUNDY, Kelly, Chief Information Officer, Peacehealth St. Joseph Medical Center, Bellingham, WA, p. A678

LUNDY, Marcel, Chief Information Officer, Putnam General Hospital, Eatonton, GA, p. A157

LUNDY, Noah, Director of Human Resources, Maine Coast Memorial Hospital, Ellsworth, ME, p. A291

LUNDY–PAINE, Robert, Director Information Systems, Alameda Hospital, Alameda, CA, p. A51

LUNN, Stephen, Chief Executive Officer, Porter Regional Hospital, Valparaiso, IN, p. A220

LUNN, William, M.D., Chief Executive Officer, Tulane Medical Center, New Orleans, LA, p. A283

LUNNEBORG, Brandi, Chief Executive Officer, Phoebe Sumter Medical Center, Americus, GA, p. A149

LUNNEY, Kathleen MS, R.N., Vice President Patient Care Services and Chief Nursing Officer, Nyack Hospital, Nyack, NY, p. A448

LUNSFORD, Cindy, Executive Vice President and Chief Operating Officer, Peninsula Regional Medical Center, Salisbury, MD, p. A301

LUNSFORD, Kaye W, System Director Human Resources, St. Vincent's Medical Center Southside, Jacksonville, FL, p. A128

LUNT, Kimberly, Controller, Healthsouth Rehabilitation Hospital Of Spring Hill, Brooksville, FL, p. A121

LUNTZ, Adam, Chief Financial Officer, Aultman Orrville Hospital, Orrville, OH, p. A497

LUOMA, Michael M.D., Chief of Staff, Aspirus Keweenaw Hospital, Inc., Laurium, MI, p. A325

LUPINACCI, Michael M.D., Medical Director, Healthsouth Rehabilitation Hospital Of Mechanicsburg, Mechanicsburg, PA, p. A540

LUSSIER, Shirley G, Vice President Human Resources, Northeast Rehabilitation Hospital, Salem, NH, p. A410

LUSTERIO, Efren, Director of Nursing, Behavioral Center Of Michigan, Warren, MI, p. A332

LUTES, Adrianne, Chief Executive Officer, Select Specialty Hospital Daytona Beach, Daytona Beach, FL, p. A123

LUTES, Michael, President, Carolinas Healthcare System Union, Monroe, NC, p. A467

LUTHER, Lori CPA, Chief Financial Officer, Indiana University Health Ball Memorial Hospital, Muncie, IN, p. A216

LUTHER, Tracie, Director Employee and Labor Relations, Brooks Memorial Hospital, Dunkirk, NY, p. A435

LUTHER, Vera M.D., Chief of Staff, Sabine County Hospital, Hemphill, TX, p. A618

LUTKENHAUS, Tiffany, Chief Nursing Officer, Muenster Memorial Hospital, Muenster, TX, p. A634

LUTZ, Barbara, Vice President Human Resources, Heart Of The Rockies Regional Medical Center, Salida, CO, p. A107

LUTZ, Denise, Chief Human Resources Officer, Chi St. Alexius Health – Dickinson Medical Center, Dickinson, ND, p. A475

LUTZ, Don, Director Information Technology, Easton Hospital, Easton, PA, p. A533

LUTZ, Kevin DPM, Chief Operating Officer, Grant, Ohiohealth Grant Medical Center, Columbus, OH, p. A487

LUTZ, Terry, Chief Financial Officer, Scheurer Hospital, Pigeon, MI, p. A328

LUX, Teri, President, Community Memorial Hospital, Menomonee Falls, WI, p. A706

LUZINSKI, Craig, FACHE, MSN, R.N., Vice President Performance Optimization, Cheyenne Regional Medical Center, Cheyenne, WY, p. A717

LYBARGER, Eric, Administrator, Pawnee Valley Community Hospital, Larned, KS, p. A245

LYDICK, Bryan, Chief Executive Officer, Redwood Area Hospital, Redwood Falls, MN, p. A346

LYDON, Jean MS, R.N., System Vice President Operations, Chief Nursing Officer, Elmhurst Hospital, Elmhurst, IL, p. A187

LYLE, Janet, Chief Human Resources and Allied Health Services, Springfield Hospital, Springfield, VT, p. A663

LYLE, Jeff, Chief Operating Officer, Haskell Memorial Hospital, Haskell, TX, p. A618

LYMAN, Jeremy, Chief Executive Officer, Blue Mountain Hospital, Blanding, UT, p. A656

LYNCE, Danialle
Business Partner Human Resources, University Hospitals Conneaut Medical Center, Conneaut, OH, p. A488
Business Partner Human Resources, University Hospitals Geneva Medical Center, Geneva, OH, p. A492
Manager Human Resources, University Hospitals Geauga Medical Center, Chardon, OH, p. A483

LYNCH, Becky, Manager Business Entity Management and Information Systems, OSF St. Mary Medical Center, Galesburg, IL, p. A188

LYNCH, Cecelia R.N., MS, Vice President Patient Care Services and Chief Nursing Officer, Lowell General Hospital, Lowell, MA, p. A308

LYNCH, Danile, Chief Operating Officer, Saint Luke Institute, Silver Spring, MD, p. A301

LYNCH, Elizabeth A, Vice President Human Resources, The Hospital Of Central Connecticut, New Britain, CT, p. A111

LYNCH, Ernest C. III, FACHE, President and Chief Executive Officer, Medical City Mckinney, Mckinney, TX, p. A632

LYNCH, G Michael M.D., Chief Medical Officer, Inova Fair Oaks Hospital, Fairfax, VA, p. A666

LYNCH, James, Senior Vice President and Chief Medical Officer, Beaumont Hospital – Troy, Troy, MI, p. A332

LYNCH, John
  Vice President and Chief Medical Officer, Barnes–Jewish Hospital, Saint Louis, MO, p. A376
  Vice President and Chief Information Officer, Faxton St. Luke's Healthcare, Utica, NY, p. A454

LYNCH, Marc D.O., Chief of Staff, Kindred Hospital–Ontario, Ontario, CA, p. A77

LYNCH, Megan, Manager Human Resources, Johnson Memorial Health Services, Dawson, MN, p. A338

LYNCH, Torie A, Manager Human Resources, Central Montana Medical Center, Lewistown, MT, p. A386

LYNCH, William, Executive Vice President and Chief Operating Officer, Jamaica Hospital Medical Center, New Rochelle, NY, p. A441

LYNCH–KILIC, Cathy, Vice President Human Resources, St. Mary's General Hospital, Passaic, NJ, p. A418

LYND, Samuel, Administrator and Chief Executive Officer, Baptist Memorial Hospital–Tipton, Covington, TN, p. A578

LYNE, Marjorie, Associate Director for Patient Care Services, Hunter Holmes Mcguire Veterans Affairs Medical Center–Richmond, Richmond, VA, p. A674

LYNN, Christina M.D., Medical Director, Three Rivers Behavioral Health, West Columbia, SC, p. A567

LYNN, Jason, Director Finance, St. Vincent's St. Clair, Pell City, AL, p. A22

LYNN, Samuel, Director Human Resources, Northwest Texas Healthcare System, Amarillo, TX, p. A592

LYNSKEY, Jeanne, Vice President and Chief Financial Officer, Milford Regional Medical Center, Milford, MA, p. A309

LYON, Tami, Director Human Resources, Community Memorial Hospital, Burke, SD, p. A568

LYONS, Althea C, Vice President Human Resources and Development, Beverly Hospital, Beverly, MA, p. A302

LYONS, Denise, Chief Nursing Officer, Cumberland Hall Hospital, Hopkinsville, KY, p. A259

LYONS, Jane M., Executive Director, Nyc Health + Hospitals / Sea View, Staten Island, NY, p. B93

LYONS, Jim, Chief Clinic Officer, Hutchinson Health, Hutchinson, MN, p. A341

LYONS, Lenny
  Administrator, Delta Community Medical Center, Delta, UT, p. A656
  Administrator, Fillmore Community Hospital, Fillmore, UT, p. A656

LYONS, Michael
  Chief Medical Officer, Bay Area Regional Medical Center, Webster, TX, p. A653
  Regional Director Information Services, Shriners Hospitals For Children–Galveston, Galveston, TX, p. A615
  Regional Information Systems Director, Shriners Hospitals For Children–Shreveport, Shreveport, LA, p. A286

LYSAGHT, Marcia C R.N., MSN, Associate Director Patient Care Services, Miami Veterans Affairs Healthcare System, Miami, FL, p. A133

LYSAGHT, William, Chief Financial Officer, Kindred Hospital Las Vegas–Sahara, Henderson, NV, p. A402

LYTHGOE, Derek
  Chief Financial Officer, Banner Baywood Medical Center, Mesa, AZ, p. A31
  Chief Financial Officer, Banner Heart Hospital, Mesa, AZ, p. A31

M

MAAS, Vernon M.D., Vice President, Medical Affairs, St. Vincent Medical Center Of Evansville, Evansville, IN, p. A207

MABRY, Jerry D., FACHE, Chief Executive Officer, National Park Medical Center, Hot Springs, AR, p. A44

MACAFEE, Francis M, Vice President Finance and Chief Financial Officer, Guthrie Corning Hospital, Corning, NY, p. A434

MACARONAS, Thomas, Chief Financial Officer, Labette Health, Parsons, KS, p. A249

MACATOL, Matthew M.D., President Medical Staff, Marietta Memorial Hospital, Marietta, OH, p. A494

MACDONALD, Alan G., President and Chief Executive Officer, Hallmark Health System, Melrose, MA, p. A308

MACDONALD, Joan R.N., MSN, Chief Nursing Officer, Aurelia Osborn Fox Memorial Hospital, Oneonta, NY, p. A449

MACDONALD, Laurie, Vice President Finance, Penn Highlands Elk, Saint Marys, PA, p. A549

MACDONALD, Neil, Vice President, Operations, Medstar Union Memorial Hospital, Baltimore, MD, p. A295

MACDOUGALL, David, Chief Financial Officer, United Health Services Hospitals–Binghamton, Binghamton, NY, p. A432

MACE, T. Paul, Chief Medical Officer, Garden Park Medical Center, Gulfport, MS, p. A355

MACEVOY, Bonnie, Chief of Staff, Mad River Community Hospital, Arcata, CA, p. A52

MACFADYEN, James M.D., Medical Director, St. John Vianney Hospital, Downingtown, PA, p. A533

MACH, Robert, Chief Executive Officer, Select Specialty Hospital–Battle Creek, Battle Creek, MI, p. A315

MACHADO, James, President, St. Vincent's Medical Center Clay County, Middleburg, FL, p. A134

MACHADO, Richard, M.D., President and Chief Executive Officer, Hospital Hermanos Melendez, Bayamon, PR, p. A722

MACIAS–HOAG MHA, RN, NEA–BC, Annette, Chief Nursing Officer, University Of Texas Medical Branch, Galveston, TX, p. A616

MACIEL, Maureen M.D., Chief of Staff, Shriners Hospitals For Children–Tampa, Tampa, FL, p. A145

MACIOCE, Gary, President, Penn Highlands Clearfield, Clearfield, PA, p. A531

MACK, Charles, Vice President Finance and Chief Financial Officer, Merit Health Natchez, Natchez, MS, p. A359

MACKAY, Cristal, Chief Operating Officer, Banner Desert Medical Center, Mesa, AZ, p. A31

MACKENROTH, Robin D., Chief Operating Officer, Kaiser Permanente Riverside Medical Center, Riverside, CA, p. A82

MACKENZIE, Susan, Ph.D., Director, Providence Veterans Affairs Medical Center, Providence, RI, p. A557

MACKETT, Charles M.D., Senior Vice President and Chief Medical Officer, Indian River Medical Center, Vero Beach, FL, p. A146

MACKIN, Stephen, President, Mercy Hospital St. Louis, Saint Louis, MO, p. A377

MACKINNON, Paul R.N., Chief Operating Officer, Healthalliance Hospitals, Leominster, MA, p. A308

MACKSOOD, Dan A., Chief Financial Officer, St. Francis Medical Center, Monroe, LA, p. A281

MACKSOOD, Dan, Regional Senior Vice President and Chief Financial Officer, Good Samaritan Hospital Medical Center, West Islip, NY, p. A455

MACLAUGHLIN, Jeremy, Director Human Resources, Citizens Memorial Hospital, Bolivar, MO, p. A364

MACLEAN, Scott, Administrator, Vibra Hospital Of Western Massachusetts, Springfield, MA, p. A312

MACLEOD, Deborah MS, R.N., Vice President Nursing and Patient Care Services, Mid Coast Hospital, Brunswick, ME, p. A290

MACNICOL, Daniel, Chief Executive Officer, Healthsouth Rehabilitation Hospital – Dallas, Dallas, TX, p. A605

MACPHEE, Alan, Chief Executive Officer, John C. Fremont Healthcare District, Mariposa, CA, p. A73

MACRI, Fredrick, Executive Vice President, Rhode Island Hospital, Providence, RI, p. A557

MADAN, Sunil M.D., Chief Medical Officer and Chief Population Health Officer, Doctors Community Hospital, Lanham, MD, p. A299

MADDEN, Ann Marie R.N., Vice President of Patient Care Services and Chief Nursing Officer, Moses H. Cone Memorial Hospital, Greensboro, NC, p. A463

MADDEN, R. Craig, Director Employee Relations, Reynolds Memorial Hospital, Glen Dale, WV, p. A692

MADDOX, Dale, Chief Financial Officer, Medical Center Of South Arkansas, El Dorado, AR, p. A42

MADDOX, Jamie, Chief Nursing Officer, Christus Mother Frances Hospital – Jacksonville, Jacksonville, TX, p. A625

MADER, Elaine M.D., Chief of Staff, Integris Miami Hospital, Miami, OK, p. A510

MADER, Frank, Director Information Services, East Liverpool City Hospital, East Liverpool, OH, p. A490

MADER, Vikki, Director Health Information Services, Pratt Regional Medical Center, Pratt, KS, p. A250

MADIGAN, Catherine, Chief Nursing Officer, University Of North Carolina Hospitals, Chapel Hill, NC, p. A459

MADIGAN, Patrick, Interim Chief Executive Officer, Cheyenne Regional Medical Center, Cheyenne, WY, p. A717

MADISON, Jeffrey, FACHE, Chief Executive Officer, Rockdale Hospital, Rockdale, TX, p. A640

MADKINS, Catrina, Controller and Chief Financial Officer, Healthsouth Plano Rehabilitation Hospital, Plano, TX, p. A638

MADRID, Melissa R.N., Chief Nursing Officer, Harper County Community Hospital, Buffalo, OK, p. A505

MADSEN, Kristin, Chief Nursing Officer, Carson Tahoe Continuing Care Hospital, Carson City, NV, p. A401

MAEKAWA, Steve, Chief Financial Officer, Garfield Medical Center, Monterey Park, CA, p. A75

MAENIUS, Linda, Chief Financial Officer, Laurel Ridge Treatment Center, San Antonio, TX, p. A642

MAERTENS, Mary B., FACHE, President and Chief Executive Officer, Avera Marshall Regional Medical Center, Marshall, MN, p. A343

MAES, Jillian, Director Marketing and Public Relations, St. Thomas More Hospital, Canon City, CO, p. A99

MAES, Stephen, Director Information Systems, Franciscan Health Olympia Fields, Olympia Fields, IL, p. A196

MAESTAS, Sadie, Interim Chief Nursing Officer, Copper Queen Community Hospital, Bisbee, AZ, p. A28

MAGDANGAL, Connie, Executive Vice President and Chief Financial Officer, Bergen Regional Medical Center, Paramus, NJ, p. A418

MAGEE, Becky, Chief Information Officer, Washington Regional Medical Center, Fayetteville, AR, p. A43

MAGEE, James L., Executive Director, Piggott Community Hospital, Piggott, AR, p. A48

MAGEE, Michael J, Chief Financial Officer, Riverside Medical Center, Franklinton, LA, p. A275

MAGEE, Robert A
  Director Human Resources, Shriners Hospitals For Children–Galveston, Galveston, TX, p. A615
  Director Human Resources, Shriners Hospitals For Children–Houston, Houston, TX, p. A622

MAGEE, William F, Chief Financial Officer, Alliance Healthcare System, Holly Springs, MS, p. A356

MAGES, Michael, Chief Executive Officer, Ashland Health Center, Ashland, KS, p. A238

MAGESKI, Denise MSN, R.N., Chief Nurse Executive, Northwestern Medicine Lake Forest Hospital, Lake Forest, IL, p. A192

MAGESTRO, Ben, Chief Operating Officer, North Central Surgical Center, Dallas, TX, p. A606

MAGGARD, Amanda, Chief Executive Officer, Florida Hospital Zephyrhills, Zephyrhills, FL, p. A148

MAGHAZEHE, Al, Ph.D., FACHE
  President and Chief Executive Officer, Capital Health Medical Center–Hopewell, Pennington, NJ, p. A418
  President and Chief Executive Officer, Capital Health Regional Medical Center, Trenton, NJ, p. A421

MAGID, Philip, Director Fiscal Services, Shriners Hospitals For Children–Chicago, Chicago, IL, p. A184

MAGILL, Marc, Director, Jesse Brown Veterans Affairs Medical Center, Chicago, IL, p. A181

MAGNER, Johanna, Interim Chief Nursing Officer, Saint Michael's Medical Center, Newark, NJ, p. A417

MAGNER, Kile, Administrator, Ellinwood District Hospital, Ellinwood, KS, p. A240

MAGNESS, Grant, Interim Chief Executive Officer, Toppenish Community Hospital, Toppenish, WA, p. A688

MAGNUSON, Johna, Director Nursing, Hillsboro Community Hospital, Hillsboro, KS, p. A242

MAGOON, Patrick M., President and Chief Executive Officer, Ann & Robert H. Lurie Children's Hospital Of Chicago, Chicago, IL, p. A180

MAGRUDER, Joan, President, St. Louis Children's Hospital, Saint Louis, MO, p. A378

MAGU, Bharat M.D., Chief Medical Officer, Yuma Regional Medical Center, Yuma, AZ, p. A39

MAGUIRE, David L M.D., Vice President Medical Affairs, Baystate Wing Hospital, Palmer, MA, p. A310

MAGUIRE, Kimberly R.N., Chief Nursing Officer, Mercy Health Hackley Campus, Muskegon, MI, p. A327

MAGUREAN, Vickie, Chief Financial Officer, Seven Rivers Regional Medical Center, Crystal River, FL, p. A122

MAGUTA, Sam, Coordinator Information Systems, Devereux Georgia Treatment Network, Kennesaw, GA, p. A160

MAHAJAN, Naman, Interim Chief Executive Officer, Cypress Fairbanks Medical Center, Houston, TX, p. A620

MAHAJAN, Sumit M.D., Chief Medical Staff, Hi–Desert Medical Center, Yucca Valley, CA, p. A97

MAHAN, Michelle K, Senior Vice President and Chief Financial Officer, Frederick Regional Health System, Frederick, MD, p. A298
MAHAN, Vic
  Chief Information Officer, Chino Valley Medical Center, Chino, CA, p. A55
  Director Information Systems, Garden Grove Hospital And Medical Center, Garden Grove, CA, p. A61
  Director Information Technology, La Palma Intercommunity Hospital, La Palma, CA, p. A65
  Director Information Technology, West Anaheim Medical Center, Anaheim, CA, p. A51
MAHAR, Priscilla, Chief Clinical Officer, Spectrum Health United Hospital, Greenville, MI, p. A322
MAHER, Donna R.N., Chief Operating Officer, Morton Hospital And Medical Center, Taunton, MA, p. A312
MAHER, James M, Senior Vice President and Chief Financial Officer, Robert Wood Johnson University Hospital At Hamilton, Hamilton, NJ, p. A414
MAHER, Jennifer, Chief Executive Officer, Sutter Davis Hospital, Davis, CA, p. A57
MAHER, John P, Executive Vice President and Chief Financial Officer, Nassau University Medical Center, East Meadow, NY, p. A435
MAHER, Sean, Director Human Resources, Devereux Children's Behavioral Health Center, Malvern, PA, p. A539
MAHER, Thomas, Chief Executive Officer and Administrator, Boulder City Hospital, Boulder City, NV, p. A401
MAHERA, Tina M.D., Chief Medical Officer, Garfield Park Hospital, Chicago, IL, p. A181
MAHEUX, Diane, Vice President Finance, Memorial Hospital, North Conway, NH, p. A410
MAHL, Morgan G, Director Human Resources, St. Luke's Hospital – Warren Campus, Phillipsburg, NJ, p. A419
MAHLE, Thomas J., Chief Executive Officer, Las Encinas Hospital, Pasadena, CA, p. A79
MAHMOOD, Ahsan M.D., Chief Medical Officer, Hamilton Center, Terre Haute, IN, p. A220
MAHMOOD, Khalid, M.D., President and Chairman, Crescent Medical Center Lancaster, Lancaster, TX, p. A628
MAHNEKE, Suzette, Associate Vice President of Nursing, Amita Health Adventist Medical Center Glenoaks, Glendale Heights, IL, p. A188
MAHONE, William, President and Chief Executive Officer, Halifax Regional Medical Center, Roanoke Rapids, NC, p. A469
MAHONEY, Bryan, Chief Financial Officer, Columbia Memorial Hospital, Hudson, NY, p. A437
MAHONEY, James, Chief Information Officer, Memorial Hospital, York, PA, p. A555
MAHONEY, Nicole, Chief Financial Officer, Pioneer Memorial Hospital, Heppner, OR, p. A522
MAHONEY, William K., FACHE, President and Chief Executive Officer, Cox Medical Center Branson, Branson, MO, p. A365
MAHONY, Mary A., Commanding Officer, Naval Hospital Lemoore, Lemoore, CA, p. A65
MAHR–CHAN, Lydia, Director of Human Resources, Chinese Hospital, San Francisco, CA, p. A87
MAIDEN, Phillip M.D., Medical Director, Belmont Pines Hospital, Youngstown, OH, p. A503
MAIER, Cindy R.N., Director of Nursing, Ness County Hospital District No 2, Ness City, KS, p. A247
MAIER, Curtis, Administrator, St. Luke's Jerome, Jerome, ID, p. A173
MAIER, Walter M., Chief of Staff, San Bernardino Mountains Community Hospital District, Lake Arrowhead, CA, p. A65
MAIETTA, Carol, Vice President Human Resources and Chief Learning Officer, St. Vincent's East, Birmingham, AL, p. A15
MAIJALA, Jussi, Vice President, Human Resources, Phelps Memorial Hospital Center, Sleepy Hollow, NY, p. A452
MAIN, Cleo, Finance Officer, U.S. Public Health Service Blackfeet Community Hospital, Saint Mary, MT, p. A388
MAINARDI, Carlo M.D., Vice President Medical Affairs and Chief Medical Officer, Park Ridge Health, Hendersonville, NC, p. A464
MAINES, Stephanie, Chief Nursing Officer, Crossroads Community Hospital, Mount Vernon, IL, p. A194
MAINIERI, Kathy, Human Resource Specialist, Sister Emmanuel Hospital, Miami, FL, p. A134
MAIZE, Makyla, Director Information Services, Washington County Hospital And Clinics, Washington, IA, p. A236
MAJAUSKAS, Joel, Chief Information Officer, Clifton Springs Hospital And Clinic, Clifton Springs, NY, p. A434
MAJCHRZAK, John, Chief Financial Officer, Touchette Regional Hospital, Centreville, IL, p. A180
MAJDALANI, Elias, Director Management Information Systems, Mildred Mitchell–Bateman Hospital, Huntington, WV, p. A692

MAJETICH, Stephen D CPA, Chief Financial Officer, Southwestern Vermont Medical Center, Bennington, VT, p. A662
MAJHAIL, Ruby, Chief Financial Officer, St. Luke's Behavioral Health Center, Phoenix, AZ, p. A34
MAJOR, Aprille, Director Human Resources, Foothill Regional Medical Center, Tustin, CA, p. A94
MAJOR, Kerry R.N., MSN, Chief Nursing Officer, Cleveland Clinic Florida, Weston, FL, p. A148
MAJOR, Pattie, Chief Financial Officer, Paul B. Hall Regional Medical Center, Paintsville, KY, p. A266
MAJOR, Shelly, Chief Nursing Officer, Methodist Hospitals, Gary, IN, p. A209
MAJORS, Ed, Chief Executive Officer, Newman Memorial Hospital, Shattuck, OK, p. A515
MAJORS, Valerie, Director Information Services, Western State Hospital, Hopkinsville, KY, p. A260
MAJURE, Thomas K., Administrator, Our Community Hospital, Scotland Neck, NC, p. A470
MAK, David, Chief Financial Officer, El Campo Memorial Hospital, El Campo, TX, p. A610
MAKAROFF, Jason, Chief Operating Officer and Associate Vice President, Adventist Healthcare Physical Health And Rehabilitation, Rockville, MD, p. A300
MAKELA, Taylor, Director Information Technology, Baraga County Memorial Hospital, L'Anse, MI, p. A324
MAKEPEACE, Anne, Director Human Resources, New Ulm Medical Center, New Ulm, MN, p. A345
MAKI, Jacquelyn, Chief Nursing Officer, Oakleaf Surgical Hospital, Eau Claire, WI, p. A701
MAKI, Richard R.N., Vice President Nursing and Chief Nursing Officer, Anna Jaques Hospital, Newburyport, MA, p. A309
MAKORO, Leslie, Director Information management Systems, Merit Health Natchez, Natchez, MS, p. A359
MAKOSKY, Michael
  Chief Operating Officer, Bluefield Regional Medical Center, Bluefield, WV, p. A690
  Chief Operating Officer, Plateau Medical Center, Oak Hill, WV, p. A694
MAKSOUD, Jane, R.N.
  Senior Vice President Human Resources and Labor Relations, Mount Sinai Health System, Mount Sinai Beth Israel, New Rochelle, NY, p. A443
  Senior Vice President Human Resources and Labor Relations, Mount Sinai Health System, Mount Sinai West, New Rochelle, NY, p. A443
  Senior Vice President Human Resources and Labor Relations, Mount Sinai Health System, New York Eye And Ear Infirmary Of Mount Sinai, New Rochelle, NY, p. A443
  Senior Vice President Human Resources and Labor Relations, Mount Sinai Hospital, New Rochelle, NY, p. A443
MAKSYMOW, Michael, Vice President Information Systems, Beebe Healthcare, Lewes, DE, p. A115
MAKUNDA, Beejadi M.D., Chief Medical Officer, Heatherhill Care Communities, Chardon, OH, p. A483
MALAER, Gary, Chief Executive Officer, Carolinas Hospital System, Florence, SC, p. A561
MALAKAR, Crystal, Team Leader Inpatient Nursing, Bellin Psychiatric Center, Green Bay, WI, p. A703
MALAKOFF, Stacey, Executive Vice President and Chief Financial Officer, Hospital For Special Surgery, New Rochelle, NY, p. A441
MALAMED, Michael M.D., Chief of Staff, Sherman Oaks Hospital, Los Angeles, CA, p. A71
MALAN, Glen, Vice President Information Technology and Chief Information Officer, Northwest Community Hospital, Arlington Heights, IL, p. A177
MALANEY, Scott C., FACHE, President and Chief Executive Officer, Blanchard Valley Hospital, Findlay, OH, p. A491
MALCOLM, Dru, Vice President and Chief Nursing Officer, Johnson City Medical Center, Johnson City, TN, p. A581
MALCOLMSON, James F M.D., Chief of Staff, Sierra Vista Hospital, Truth Or Consequences, NM, p. A429
MALDONADO, Diraida, Chief Executive Officer, Hospital De La Universidad De Puerto Rico/Dr. Federico Trilla, Carolina, PR, p. A722
MALENSEK, Frank M.D., Chief Medical Officer, St. Vincent's East, Birmingham, AL, p. A15
MALEY, Shelley, Director Human Resources, St. Luke's Hospital – Quakertown Campus, Quakertown, PA, p. A549
MALIK, Aamir M.D., Chief Medical Officer, Acuity Hospital Of South Texas, San Antonio, TX, p. A641
MALIK, Azfar, M.D.
  Chief Medical Officer, Centerpointe Hospital, Saint Charles, MO, p. A376
  Chief Medical Officer, Signature Psychiatric Hospital, Kansas City, MO, p. A370
MALIK, Chuck
  Director Information Systems, Advocate Good Shepherd Hospital, Barrington, IL, p. A178

Director Information Systems, Advocate Illinois Masonic Medical Center, Chicago, IL, p. A180
MALIK, Tariq F CPA, Chief Financial Officer, Signature Psychiatric Hospital, Kansas City, MO, p. A370
MALIN, Seth M.D., President Medical and Dental Staff, Delaware County Memorial Hospital, Drexel Hill, PA, p. A533
MALINA, Joanne J M.D., Chief of Staff, Veterans Affairs Hudson Valley Health Care System, Montrose, NY, p. A440
MALINDZAK, Edward, Chief Human Resources Officer, Oconomowoc Memorial Hospital, Oconomowoc, WI, p. A709
MALJOVEC, John M.D., Medical Director, Warren General Hospital, Warren, PA, p. A552
MALLETT, Belinda R.N., MS, Vice President, Patient Care and Clinical Services, Soin Medical Center, Beavercreek, OH, p. A481
MALLETT, Conrad Jr., FACHE, Chief Executive Officer, Dmc - Sinai-Grace Hospital, Detroit, MI, p. B126
MALLETT, Teresa, Chief Financial Officer, Madison Community Hospital, Madison, SD, p. A570
MALLETT JR., Conrad, Chief Executive Officer, DMC – Sinai–Grace Hospital, Detroit, MI, p. A317
MALLICOAT, Robert E., Chief Executive Officer, Complex Care Hospital At Ridgelake, Sarasota, FL, p. A142
MALLIK, Subodh M.D., Chief of Staff, Pecos County Memorial Hospital, Fort Stockton, TX, p. A613
MALLING, Timothy M.D., Chief of Staff, Centracare Health–Paynesville, Paynesville, MN, p. A345
MALLONEE, Teresa, Director Human Resources, Angel Medical Center, Franklin, NC, p. A462
MALLORY, Brenda M.D., Medical Director, Penn State Hershey Rehabilitation Hospital, Hummelstown, PA, p. A536
MALLOY, Peter, Chief Information Officer, Cheshire Medical Center, Keene, NH, p. A408
MALM, Brad, Director Human Resources and Education, Lindsborg Community Hospital, Lindsborg, KS, p. A246
MALMSTROM, Ron, Information Research Specialist, Parsons State Hospital And Training Center, Parsons, KS, p. A249
MALONE, Donald A. Jr, President, Lutheran Hospital, Cleveland, OH, p. A486
MALONE, Ginger MSN, RN–B, Chief Nursing Officer, St. Mary's Hospital, Madison, WI, p. A705
MALONE, Meredith, Chief Financial Officer, Tennova Healthcare Dyersburg Regional Medical Center, Dyersburg, TN, p. A578
MALONE, Michael, Vice President and Chief Human Resources Officer, Virginia Hospital Center – Arlington, Arlington, VA, p. A664
MALONE, Patty M.D., Chief Medical Officer, Ocean Beach Hospital, Ilwaco, WA, p. A681
MALONEY, Jay M.D., Chief of Staff, Cabinet Peaks Medical Center, Libby, MT, p. A386
MALONEY, Patrick J.
  Chief Executive Officer, Franciscan Health Dyer, Dyer, IN, p. A206
  Chief Executive Officer, Franciscan Health Hammond, Hammond, IN, p. A210
  Chief Executive Officer, Franciscan Healthcare – Munster, Munster, IN, p. A217
MALONEY, Patrick, Market Chief Executive Officer, Bayfront Health Brooksville, Brooksville, FL, p. A121
MALONEY, Paul V, Vice President Finance, Behavioral Health Network, Natchaug Hospital, Mansfield Center, CT, p. A110
MALOTT, Deanna, Director Human Resources, Henry County Hospital, New Castle, IN, p. A217
MALOTT, Gregg, Chief Financial Officer, Pulaski Memorial Hospital, Winamac, IN, p. A221
MALOTTE, Rebecca
  Executive Director and Chief Nursing Officer, The Heart Hospital At Deaconess Gateway, Newburgh, IN, p. A217
MALSED, Brad, Area Chief Financial Officer, Kaiser Permanente Los Angeles Medical Center, Los Angeles, CA, p. A68
MALSEED, TJ, Vice President and Chief Information Officer, Children's Hospital Los Angeles, Los Angeles, CA, p. A68
MALTE, Robert H., Chief Executive Officer, Evergreenhealth, Kirkland, WA, p. A681
MALYSZEK, Richard M.D., Chief of Staff, Pikes Peak Regional Hospital, Woodland Park, CO, p. A108
MAMANGAKIS, John P., Senior Vice President, Montefiore New Rochelle, New Rochelle, NY, p. A440
MAMBOURG, Rolland M.D., Vice President Medical Affairs, Mercy Health Saint Mary's, Grand Rapids, MI, p. A321
MANAKAS, Christopher, Chief Information Officer, Fort Healthcare, Fort Atkinson, WI, p. A701
MANAS, Julie
  Interim Chief Executive Officer, Hshs St. Joseph's Hospital, Chippewa Falls, WI, p. A700
  President and Chief Executive Officer, Sacred Heart Hospital, Eau Claire, WI, p. A701

MANCHUR, Fred M., Chief Executive Officer, Kettering Health Network, Dayton, OH, p. B72

MANCHUR, Richard, President, Grandview Medical Center, Dayton, OH, p. A489

MANDAL, Alan, Vice President Financial Operations, Scripps Memorial Hospital–La Jolla, La Jolla, CA, p. A64

MANDAL, Konoy M.D., Medical Director, Centennial Peaks Hospital, Louisville, CO, p. A106

MANDANAS, Renato M.D., Chief Medical Officer, Oswego Hospital, Oswego, NY, p. A449

MANDERINO, Michelle, Chief Human Resources, North Florida/South Georgia Veteran's Health System, Gainesville, FL, p. A126

MANDHAN, Narain M.D., Chief Medical Officer, Kirby Medical Center, Monticello, IL, p. A194

MANDI, Deepak M.D., Chief of Staff, West Palm Beach Veterans Affairs Medical Center, West Palm Beach, FL, p. A147

MANDLER, Jeffrey M., Chief Executive Officer, Carepoint Health, Jersey City, NJ, p. B24

MANDRACCHIA, Vincent DPM, Chief Medical Officer, Broadlawns Medical Center, Des Moines, IA, p. A226

MANDSAGER, Richard, M.D., Executive Director, Providence Alaska Medical Center, Anchorage, AK, p. A25

MANESTRINA, Robert, Vice President Human Resources, Inspira Medical Center–Woodbury, Woodbury, NJ, p. A423

MANFREDI, Susan R.N., Vice President and Chief Nursing Officer, Uw Medicine/Northwest Hospital & Medical Center, Seattle, WA, p. A686

MANFREDO, John, Chief Operating Officer, Norman Regional Health System, Norman, OK, p. A511

MANGIN, Paul, Vice President Finance, Mercy Medical Center–Clinton, Clinton, IA, p. A224

MANGIONE, Ellen M.D., Chief of Staff, Veterans Affairs Eastern Colorado Health Care System, Denver, CO, p. A101

MANGONA, John, Vice President, Chief Information Officer and Compliance Officer, Saratoga Hospital, Saratoga Springs, NY, p. A452

MANGRUM, Charlita M.D., Chief of Staff, Firsthealth Moore Regional Hospital – Hamlet, Hamlet, NC, p. A464

MANGUM, Cody, Director Operations, St. Luke's Elmore, Mountain Home, ID, p. A174

MANGUM, Lisa, Chief Nursing Officer, North Canyon Medical Center, Gooding, ID, p. A173

MANGUM, Rozanne, Administrative Assistant and Director Human Resources, Grover C. Dils Medical Center, Caliente, NV, p. A401

MANHEIMER, Dean, Senior Vice President Human Resources, Northwestern Memorial Healthcare, Northwestern Memorial Hospital, Chicago, IL, p. A182

MANIATIS, Theodore M.D., Medical Director, Staten Island University Hospital, New Rochelle, NY, p. A446

MANIGAULT, Merald, Chief Financial Officer, Acuity Hospital Of South Texas, San Antonio, TX, p. A641

MANKER, Marcia
Chief Executive Officer, Orange Coast Memorial Medical Center, Fountain Valley, CA, p. A60
Chief Executive Officer, Saddleback Memorial Medical Center, Laguna Hills, CA, p. A65

MANKINS, Mark L M.D., Chief of Staff, Hamilton Hospital, Olney, TX, p. A636

MANKOSKI, Susan, Vice President Human Resources, SSM Health St. Mary's Hospital – Jefferson City, Jefferson City, MO, p. A369

MANLAGNIT, Maybelle, Senior Accounting Officer, Metropolitan State Hospital, Norwalk, CA, p. A76

MANLEY, Dennis R.N., Chief Nursing Officer, Mercy Hospital Joplin, Joplin, MO, p. A370

MANLEY, John, Director Information Systems, Jackson General Hospital, Ripley, WV, p. A695

MANN, Brian, Chief Executive Officer, Select Specialty Hospital–Danville, Danville, PA, p. A532

MANN, Corey, Director Human Resources, Memorial Health Care Systems, Seward, NE, p. A399

MANN, Erin R.N., Chief Nursing Officer, Mccamey County Hospital District, Mccamey, TX, p. A632

MANN, Julie D, Vice President and Chief Administrative Officer, Katherine Shaw Bethea Hospital, Dixon, IL, p. A185

MANN, Karen R.N., Chief Nursing Officer, Shoshone Medical Center, Kellogg, ID, p. A173

MANN, Lori R.N., MSN, Chief Nursing Officer, Howard A. Rusk Rehabilitation Center, Columbia, MO, p. A367

MANN, Rex M.D., Chief Medical Officer, Ochiltree General Hospital, Perryton, TX, p. A637

MANN, Rhonda, Chief Nursing Officer, Franklin Woods Community Hospital, Johnson City, TN, p. A581

MANN, Todd, Chief Executive Officer, South Texas Health System, Edinburg, TX, p. A610

MANNI, Joseph, Executive Vice President and Chief Operating Officer, Deborah Heart And Lung Center, Browns Mills, NJ, p. A412

MANNICH, Andy, Regional Administrator, Georgia Regional Hospital At Savannah, Savannah, GA, p. A164

MANNING, Angela, Director Health Information Services, Healthsouth Sunrise Rehabilitation Hospital, Sunrise, FL, p. A143

MANNING, Austin Lane, Chief Operating Officer, Timpanogos Regional Hospital, Orem, UT, p. A658

MANNING, Claude, Chief Executive Officer, Palacios Community Medical Center, Palacios, TX, p. A636

MANNING, Donald M.D., Clinical Director, Georgia Regional Hospital At Savannah, Savannah, GA, p. A164

MANNING, James, Administrator, Pathway Rehabilitation Hospital, Bossier City, LA, p. A272

MANNING, JoAnn, Chief Financial Officer, Emory Johns Creek Hospital, Johns Creek, GA, p. A159

MANNING, Kevin, Chief Nursing Officer, Kingwood Medical Center, Kingwood, TX, p. A627

MANNING, Kimberly, Chief Nursing Officer, Washington County Hospital, Plymouth, NC, p. A468

MANNING, Laura, Administrative Director, Guthrie Corning Hospital, Corning, NY, p. A434

MANNING, Lori, Administrator Human Resources, Western State Hospital, Tacoma, WA, p. A688

MANNING, Raymond, Director Information Technology, TLC Health Network – Lake Shore Hospital, Irving, NY, p. A437

MANNION, Stephen, Assistant Vice President Information Systems Customer Service, Medstar Franklin Square Medical Center, Baltimore, MD, p. A295

MANNIX, Mary N., FACHE, President and Chief Executive Officer, Augusta Health, Fishersville, VA, p. A667

MANNS, Bill, President, Mercy Health Saint Mary's, Grand Rapids, MI, p. A321

MANNY, Martin, Director, I.S., Providence St. Mary Medical Center, Walla Walla, WA, p. A688

MANOHARA, Anand, Chief Operating Officer, Good Samaritan Hospital–North, Bakersfield, CA, p. A52

MANSARD, Donna, Chief Executive Officer, Landmark Hospital Of Cape Girardeau, Cape Girardeau, MO, p. A365

MANSEAU, Jani, Vice President Operations and Chief Nursing Officer, Scottsdale Liberty Hospital, Scottsdale, AZ, p. A36

MANSFIELD, Al, Chief Financial Officer, Saint Vincent Hospital, Erie, PA, p. A534

MANSFIELD, David M.D., Chief of Staff, El Paso Specialty Hospital, El Paso, TX, p. A611

MANSFIELD, Deena, Director Human Resources, Ashley Regional Medical Center, Vernal, UT, p. A661

MANSFIELD, Jerry A Ph.D., R.N., Executive Chief Nursing Officer & Chief Patient Experience Officer, Musc Medical Center Of Medical University Of South Carolina, Charleston, SC, p. A559

MANSFIELD, Stephen L., Ph.D., FACHE, President and Chief Executive Officer, Methodist Health System, Dallas, TX, p. B85

MANSKE, Kristin, Chief Executive Officer, Greenwood Regional Rehabilitation Hospital, Greenwood, SC, p. A563

MANSKE, Lou Ann, Director Human Resources, Madonna Rehabilitation Hospital, Lincoln, NE, p. A395

MANSON, David, Manager Human Resources, Santa Clara Valley Medical Center, San Jose, CA, p. A89

MANSON, Kelly, Chief Financial Officer, Veterans Affairs Sierra Nevada Health Care System, Reno, NV, p. A405

MANSON, William T. III, Chief Executive Officer, Anmed Health Medical Center, Anderson, SC, p. A558

MANSON, William T III, Chief Executive Officer, Anmed Health Medical Center, Anderson, SC, p. A558

MANSOOR, Ureej M.D., Chief of Staff, Southeast Health Center Of Ripley County, Doniphan, MO, p. A367

MANSTEDT, Chase, Chief Financial Officer, Saunders Medical Center, Wahoo, NE, p. A400

MANSUKHANI, Martin, Chief Financial Officer, Desert Valley Hospital, Victorville, CA, p. A96

MANSURE, John F., FACHE, President, GHS Greer Memorial Hospital, Greer, SC, p. A563

MANTERNACH, Paul M.D., Senior Vice President Physician Integration, Mercy Medical Center–North Iowa, Mason City, IA, p. A231

MANTOOTH, Charles, President and Chief Executive Officer, Watauga Medical Center, Boone, NC, p. A458

MANTZ, David, Chief Executive Officer, Chicot Memorial Medical Center, Lake Village, AR, p. A45

MANUBENS, Claudio M.D., Chief of Staff, Heart Of Florida Regional Medical Center, Davenport, FL, p. A123

MANUEL, Shasta, Executive Director Finance, St. Anthony Hospital, Oklahoma City, OK, p. A513

MANUEL, Wendy, Vice President and Chief Financial Officer, Rehabilitation Hospital Of The Pacific, Honolulu, HI, p. A169

MANZO, Arnold D, Vice President Human Resources, Saint Barnabas Medical Center, Livingston, NJ, p. A415

MANZO–LUNA, Hilda, Chief Nursing Officer, La Palma Intercommunity Hospital, La Palma, CA, p. A65

MANZOOR, Amir M.D., Medical Director, Select Specialty Hospital–Panama City, Panama City, FL, p. A138

MAPARA, Anupam M.D., Chief of Staff, Sutter Delta Medical Center, Antioch, CA, p. A51

MAPES, Kevin, Director Kansas Division System and Technology Service Center, St. Francis Health, Topeka, KS, p. A252

MAPLES, Michael M.D., Vice President and Chief Medical Officer, Mississippi Baptist Medical Center, Jackson, MS, p. A357

MAPLES, Rickie, Interim Chief Financial Officer, Southeast Health Center Of Ripley County, Doniphan, MO, p. A367

MAPPIN, F Gregory M.D., Vice President Medical Affairs and Chief Medical Officer, Self Regional Healthcare, Greenwood, SC, p. A563

MARAAN, Sheila, Director of Nursing, Brynn Marr Hospital, Jacksonville, NC, p. A465

MARANDI, Hossain, M.D., FACHE, President and Chief Executive Officer, St. Vincent Indianapolis Hospital, IndianapolisSt. Vincent Heart Center, Indianapolis, IN, p. A212

MARANO, Deena, Human Resources Director, Community Hospital Of San Bernardino, San Bernardino, CA, p. A85

MARAS, Greg, Vice President Human Resources, Meadville Medical Center, Meadville, PA, p. A540

MARASA, Richard M.D., President Medical Staff, Springfield Hospital, Springfield, VT, p. A663

MARBLE, Kevin, Director Information Technology, Oklahoma Forensic Center, Vinita, OK, p. A519

MARCANO, Norma, Chief Operating Officer, San Juan City Hospital, San Juan, PR, p. A726

MARCANTEL, Bill, Chief Information Systems, Allen Parish Hospital, Kinder, LA, p. A277

MARCEAUX, Caroline MSN, R.N., Chief Nursing Officer, Acadia General Hospital, Crowley, LA, p. A273

MARCELIN, Fitzgerald M.D., Chief of Staff, Southern Virginia Regional Medical Center, Emporia, VA, p. A666

MARCH, Riley, Manager Information Technology, Southeast Health Center Of Ripley County, Doniphan, MO, p. A367

MARCHAND, Gary G., President and Chief Executive Officer, Memorial Hospital At Gulfport, Gulfport, MS, p. A355

MARCHANT, Joseph, Administrator, Bibb Medical Center, Centreville, AL, p. A16

MARCHETTI, Mark E., President and Chief Executive Officer, Mt. Graham Regional Medical Center, Safford, AZ, p. A35

MARCHIK, Katie A
Interim Chief Financial Officer, Unitypoint Health – Trinity Rock Island, Rock Island, IL, p. A199
Vice President, Consolidated Services, UnityPoint Health and Interim Chief Financial Officer, Trinity Regional Health Sy, Unitypoint Health – Trinity Muscatine, Muscatine, IA, p. A232

MARCIANO, Paolo G M.D., Chief Medical Officer, Beaumont Hospital–Dearborn, Dearborn, MI, p. A317

MARCO, James E Jr, Interim Vice President, Human Resources, Oswego Hospital, Oswego, NY, p. A449

MARCOTTE, Eric M.D., Chief Medical Officer, Riverview Health, Noblesville, IN, p. A217

MARCOTTE, Melissa, Chief Financial Officer, Rainy Lake Medical Center, International Falls, MN, p. A341

MARCOVICI, Mia M.D., Chief Medical Officer, Norristown State Hospital, Norristown, PA, p. A542

MARCOWITZ, David M.D., Chief of Staff, Lucas County Health Center, Chariton, IA, p. A224

MARCRUM, Jennifer, Chief Financial Officer, Sumner County Hospital District One, Caldwell, KS, p. A239

MARCUCCI, John M.D., Vice President Medical Affairs, Baylor Regional Medical Center At Plano, Plano, TX, p. A638

MARCUM, Amie, Human Resources Coordinator, Continuecare Hospital At Baptist Health Corbin, Corbin, KY, p. A257

MARCZEWSKI, Les M.D., Chief Medical Officer, Loring Hospital, Sac City, IA, p. A234

MARDY, Paul, Chief Information Technology Officer, Tennessee Valley Healthcare System, Nashville, TN, p. A587

MAREK, Kyle, Chief Information Officer, Carteret Health Care, Morehead City, NC, p. A467

MAREK, Rick, Vice President Medical Information Systems, Warm Springs Rehabilitation Hospital Of San Antonio, San Antonio, TX, p. A644

MARGENAU, Randall, Chief Information Officer, William S. Middleton Memorial Veterans Hospital, Madison, WI, p. A705

MARGER, Brian, Chief Executive Officer, Tristar Summit Medical Center, Hermitage, TN, p. A580

MARGOLIS, Marilyn, MSN, Chief Executive Officer, Emory Johns Creek Hospital, Johns Creek, GA, p. A159

MARGULIS, Richard T., President and Chief Executive Officer, Brookhaven Memorial Hospital Medical Center, Patchogue, NY, p. A449

MARIANI, Marilyn R.N., Chief Nursing Officer, Lakeview Hospital, Bountiful, UT, p. A656

MARIANI, Meleah, Chief Nursing Officer, Spectrum Health Gerber Memorial, Fremont, MI, p. A320

MARICN, Tanya, Interim Vice President Human Resources, Mercy Hospital Springfield, Springfield, MO, p. A379

MARIETTA, John M.D., Chief Medical Officer, St. David's Medical Center, Austin, TX, p. A596

MARIETTA, Megan, Chief Executive Officer, West Houston Medical Center, Houston, TX, p. A623

MARIETTA, Richard M.D., Medical Director, Clear Lake Regional Medical Center, Webster, TX, p. A653

MARIGOMEN, Nancy Ann R.N., Director of Nursing, Milwaukee County Behavioral Health Division, Milwaukee, WI, p. A708

MARIN, Loyman, Chief Human Resources, Miami Veterans Affairs Healthcare System, Miami, FL, p. A133

MARIN, Octavio, Vice President Long Term Care and Ambulatory Care Services, Bronx-Lebanon Hospital Center Health Care System, New Rochelle, NY, p. A440

MARINARO, Jon M.D., Chief Medical Officer, Kindred Hospital-Albuquerque, Albuquerque, NM, p. A424

MARINI, Frank, Senior Vice President and Chief Information Officer, TMC Healthcare, Tucson, AZ, p. A38

MARINICH, Patsy, Chief Nursing Officer, Cumberland River Hospital, Celina, TN, p. A576

MARINO, A Michael M.D., Senior Vice President Medical Administration, Greenwich Hospital, Greenwich, CT, p. A110

MARINO, Christopher M.D., Chief of Staff, Memphis Veterans Affairs Medical Center, Memphis, TN, p. A585

MARINO, Joseph, Chief Financial Officer, Suburban Community Hospital, Norristown, PA, p. A542

MARINO, Marchita H, Vice President Human Resources, Wuesthoff Medical Center - Rockledge, Rockledge, FL, p. A141

MARINOFF, Peter, President, Paul Oliver Memorial Hospital, Frankfort, MI, p. A320

MARION, Amy, Chief Human Resource Officer, Walter B. Jones Alcohol And Drug Abuse Treatment Center, Greenville, NC, p. A464

MARION, Kristie, Chief Nurse Executive, Memorial Hospital Los Banos, Los Banos, CA, p. A72

MARIOTTI, Denise J., Chief Human Resource Officer, Hospital Of The University Of Pennsylvania, Philadelphia, PA, p. A544

MARKENSON, David M.D., Chief Medical Officer, Sky Ridge Medical Center, Lone Tree, CO, p. A105

MARKER, Jason M.D., Chief Medical Officer, Community Hospital Of Bremen, Bremen, IN, p. A205

MARKER, John, Chief Nursing Officer, Women's And Children's Hospital, Lafayette, LA, p. A279

MARKESINO, Patricia A FACHE, Chief Nurse Executive and Chief Operating Officer, Providence Willamette Falls Medical Center, Oregon City, OR, p. A524

MARKETTI, Dean M
Chief Information Officer, Morris Hospital & Healthcare Centers, Morris, IL, p. A194
Vice President Finance, Morris Hospital & Healthcare Centers, Morris, IL, p. A194

MARKGRAF, Janelle K., Director Human Resources and Off Campus Services, Aspirus Langlade Hospital, Antigo, WI, p. A698

MARKHAM, Barbara, Chief Financial Officer, Glendive Medical Center, Glendive, MT, p. A384

MARKHAM, Kevin, Chief Financial Officer, Eastpointe Hospital, Daphne, AL, p. A16

MARKOS, Dennis R., Chief Executive Officer, Ed Fraser Memorial Hospital And Baker Community Health Center, Macclenny, FL, p. A131

MARKOS, Valerie, Chief Nursing Officer, Ed Fraser Memorial Hospital And Baker Community Health Center, Macclenny, FL, p. A131

MARKOWITZ, Christine, Chief Financial Officer, East Georgia Regional Medical Center, Statesboro, GA, p. A165

MARKOWITZ, Stuart, M.D.
Chief Medical Officer, Hartford Hospital, Hartford, CT, p. A110
President, Hartford Hospital, Hartford, CT, p. A110

MARKOWSKI, Stan, Chief Financial Officer, Palmetto Lowcountry Behavioral Health, Charleston, SC, p. A559

MARKS, Craig J., FACHE, Chief Executive Officer, Pmh Medical Center, Prosser, WA, p. A684

MARKS, Jerry, Vice President Finance, Decatur County Memorial Hospital, Greensburg, IN, p. A209

MARKS, Kimberly W., Chief Executive Officer, Southampton Memorial Hospital, Franklin, VA, p. A667

MARKS, Kindra, Chief Executive Officer, Regency Hospital Of Columbus, Columbus, OH, p. A488

MARKS, Marie, Chief Nursing Officer, Lake Norman Regional Medical Center, Mooresville, NC, p. A467

MARKS, Michael M.D., Chief of Staff, Norwalk Hospital, Norwalk, CT, p. A112

MARKS, Peter, Vice President & Chief Information Officer, Wakemed Raleigh Campus, Raleigh, NC, p. A469

MARKS, Stanley, M.D., FACS
Chief Medical Officer, Memorial Hospital Miramar, Miramar, FL, p. A135
Chief Medical Officer, Memorial Hospital Pembroke, Pembroke Pines, FL, p. A139

MARKSTROM, Susan M.D., Chief of Staff, St. Cloud Veterans Affairs Health Care System, Saint Cloud, MN, p. A347

MARKUS, Stacey, Chief Nursing Officer, Williamson Memorial Hospital, Williamson, WV, p. A697

MARLATT, Pam, Business Systems Director, Essentia Health St. Joseph's Medical Center, Brainerd, MN, p. A337

MARLER, Ruth, Chief Nursing Officer and Chief Operating Officer, Johnston Health, Smithfield, NC, p. A470

MARLER, Steven R., Administrator, Parkland Health Center-Bonne Terre, Bonne Terre, MO, p. A364

MARLER, Steven R, Assistant Administrator, Parkland Health Center - Farmington Community, Farmington, MO, p. A368

MARLEY, Charles D.O., Vice President Medical Affairs, Wellspan Gettysburg Hospital, Gettysburg, PA, p. A535

MARLEY, Kim M.D., Chief Medical Officer, Chan Soon-Shiong Medical Center, Windber, PA, p. A554

MARLEY, Lee, VP/Information Services Chief Application Officer, Presbyterian Hospital, Albuquerque, NM, p. A425

MARLEY, Michael, Chief Information Officer, Veterans Affairs Central Western Massachusetts Healthcare System, Leeds, MA, p. A308

MARLIN, Chris, Director Human Resources, Orange Park Medical Center, Orange Park, FL, p. A136

MARLOW, Gary P, Chief Financial Officer, Beverly Hospital, Beverly, MA, p. A302

MARLOWE, Justin, Information Technology Director, Shands Live Oak Regional Medical Center, Live Oak, FL, p. A131

MARMANDE, Susanne, Administrator, Infirmary Long Term Acute Care Hospital, Mobile, AL, p. A20

MARNEY, Terri A R.N., Director of Nursing, Plains Regional Medical Center, Clovis, NM, p. A425

MARON, Michael, President and Chief Executive Officer, Holy Name Medical Center, Teaneck, NJ, p. A421

MARONEY, Gerry, Chief Information Officer and Security Officer, Gaylord Hospital, Wallingford, CT, p. A113

MAROSTICA, Tony, Chief Compliance and Human Resource Officer, Spanish Peaks Regional Health Center, Walsenburg, CO, p. A108

MAROTTA, Diane, Vice President Human Resources, John T. Mather Memorial Hospital, Port Jefferson, NY, p. A450

MAROUN, Christiane M.D., Chief of Staff, Childrens Care Hospital And School, Sioux Falls, SD, p. A572

MARPLE, Richard M.D., Chief Medical Officer, Baptist Medical Center, San Antonio, TX, p. A642

MARQUES, John, Vice President Human Resources, Banner - University Medical Center Tucson, Tucson, AZ, p. A37

MARQUES, Tony, Director Information Systems, Grace Cottage Hospital, Townshend, VT, p. A663

MARQUSEE, Joanne, President and Chief Executive Officer, Cooley Dickinson Hospital, Northampton, MA, p. A309

MARR, Debbie, Administrative Assistant and Director Human Resources, Fredonia Regional Hospital, Fredonia, KS, p. A241

MARRERO, Jamie L M.D., Medical Director, Healthsouth Hospital Of Manati, Manati, PR, p. A724

MARRERO, Jose, Director Finance, San Jorge Children's Hospital, San Juan, PR, p. A726

MARRERO, Norma, Executive Administrator, Doctors' Center Hospital San Juan, San Juan, PR, p. A725

MARRONI, Denise
Chief Financial Officer, Providence Centralia Hospital, Centralia, WA, p. A679
Chief Financial Officer, Providence St. Peter Hospital, Olympia, WA, p. A683

MARRUFO, Gabriel, Chief Financial Officer, Methodist Stone Oak Hospital, San Antonio, TX, p. A643

MARS, Tom L R.N., MSN, Vice President Patient Care Services and Chief Nursing Officer, Camden Clark Medical Center, Parkersburg, WV, p. A694

MARSEE, DeWayne, Director Information Systems, Mercer Health, Coldwater, OH, p. A487

MARSH, J. Michael., President and Chief Executive Officer, Overlake Medical Center, Bellevue, WA, p. A678

MARSH, Leslie, Chief Executive Officer, Lexington Regional Health Center, Lexington, NE, p. A394

MARSH, Linda, Vice President Financial Services and Chief Financial Officer, Alhambra Hospital Medical Center, Alhambra, CA, p. A51

MARSH, Mark A., President, Health Central Hospital, Ocoee, FL, p. A136

MARSH, Mitch, Interim Executive Director, Terence Cardinal Cooke Health Care Center, New Rochelle, NY, p. A447

MARSH, Rob, Chief Executive Officer, San Jose Behavorial Health, San Jose, CA, p. A88

MARSH, Toby MSN, R.N., Interim Chief Patient Care Services Officer, University Of California, Davis Medical Center, Sacramento, CA, p. A84

MARSHAK, Glenn M.D., Chief of Staff, Mission Community Hospital, Los Angeles, CA, p. A70

MARSHALL, Deborah K, Vice President Public Relations, Good Samaritan Regional Medical Center, Suffern, NY, p. A453

MARSHALL, Erika, Interim Chief Nursing Officer, Calais Regional Hospital, Calais, ME, p. A290

MARSHALL, James I., President and Chief Executive Officer, Uintah Basin Medical Center, Roosevelt, UT, p. A660

MARSHALL, Jerry, Director Information Services, Information Technology Security Officer, United Regional Health Care System, Wichita Falls, TX, p. A654

MARSHALL, Jim, Chief Executive Officer and Administrator, Pemiscot Memorial Health System, Hayti, MO, p. A369

MARSHALL, Judy, Director Human Resources, Holy Cross Hospital, Taos, NM, p. A429

MARSHALL, Julie, Chief Nursing Officer, The University Of Vermont Health Network - Alice Hyde Medical Center, Malone, NY, p. A439

MARSHALL, Ken M.D., Chief Medical Officer, Indiana University Health Bloomington Hospital, Bloomington, IN, p. A204

MARSHALL, Kenneth P., President and Chief Executive Officer, University Of Louisville Hospital, Louisville, KY, p. A264

MARSHALL, Michael, Vice President Finance and Chief Financial Officer, Anderson Hospital, Maryville, IL, p. A192

MARSHALL, Patricia, Assistant Administrator Human Resources, Washington Health System Greene, Waynesburg, PA, p. A553

MARSHALL, Penny, Chief Nursing Officer, Bear River Valley Hospital, Tremonton, UT, p. A661

MARSHALL, Robert L. Jr, FACHE, Chief Executive Officer, Bolivar Medical Center, Cleveland, MS, p. A353

MARSHBURN, Deborah R.N., Chief Nursing Executive, Cape Fear Valley Medical Center, Fayetteville, NC, p. A462

MARSICO, Nick, Vice President and Chief Operating Officer, Magruder Memorial Hospital, Port Clinton, OH, p. A498

MARSO, Paul, Vice President Human Resources, Avera St. Mary's Hospital, Pierre, SD, p. A571

MARSTON, Shawn, Director Human Resources, Keystone Newport News, Newport News, VA, p. A671

MARTANIUK, Jean, Director Human Resources, Mt. Ascutney Hospital And Health Center, Windsor, VT, p. A663

MARTE, Maria, Administrator, Doctor's Center Of Bayamon, Bayamon, PR, p. A722

MARTELL, Gustavo M.D., Chief Medical Officer, The Hospitals Of Providence Transmountain Campus, El Paso, TX, p. A612

MARTENS, Angela, Chief Financial Officer, Cumberland Memorial Hospital, Cumberland, WI, p. A700

MARTENS, Troy, Chief Operating Officer, Unitypoint Health - Trinity Regional Medical Center, Fort Dodge, IA, p. A227

MARTI, Maria L, Director Fiscal Services, Auxilio Mutuo Hospital, San Juan, PR, p. A725

MARTIN, Adam
Chief Operating Officer and Interim Chief Executive Officer, Wythe County Community Hospital, Wytheville, VA, p. A677
Chief Operating Officer, Wythe County Community Hospital, Wytheville, VA, p. A677

MARTIN, Amanda, Manager Human Resources, Ohio Valley Surgical Hospital, Springfield, OH, p. A499

MARTIN, Angelia M.D., Chief of Staff, Northwest Medical Center, Albany, MO, p. A364

MARTIN, Barbara, Chief Nursing Officer, Mercy St. Vincent Medical Center, Toledo, OH, p. A500

MARTIN, Brent, Administrator, Lifecare Hospitals Of Shreveport, Shreveport, LA, p. A285

MARTIN, Brian
Chief Executive Officer, Loring Hospital, Sac City, IA, p. A234
Vice President Medical Affairs, Children's Hospital Of Pittsburgh Of Upmc, Pittsburgh, PA, p. A546

MARTIN, Bruce A, Vice President Human Resources, Carolinaeast Health System, New Bern, NC, p. A468

MARTIN, C Gregory M.D., Chief Medical Officer, Emerson Hospital, Concord, MA, p. A306

MARTIN, Carmen, Associate Administrator, Auxilio Mutuo Hospital, San Juan, PR, p. A725

MARTIN, Cary, Chief Executive Officer, Houston Medical Center, Warner Robins, GA, p. A167

MARTIN, Cheryl
Chief Information Officer, Kingman Regional Medical Center, Kingman, AZ, p. A30
Chief Information Officer, Palmetto Health Tuomey, Sumter, SC, p. A566

MARTIN, Christine M, Vice President and Chief Financial Officer, Carolinas Healthcare System Cleveland, Shelby, NC, p. A470

MARTIN, Connie
Chief Executive Officer and Administrator, Physicians Medical Center, Houma, LA, p. A276
Vice President and Chief Support Officer, Methodist Medical Center Of Oak Ridge, Oak Ridge, TN, p. A587

MARTIN, Corey M.D., Director Medical Affairs, Buffalo Hospital, Buffalo, MN, p. A337

MARTIN, Cyndie, Director, Coal County General Hospital, Coalgate, OK, p. A506

MARTIN, David T., President, Upmc Passavant, Pittsburgh, PA, p. A547

MARTIN, David W M.D., Vice President Chief Medical Officer, Seton Medical Center Austin, Austin, TX, p. A595

MARTIN, David, Assistant Administrator, Multicare Valley Hospital, Spokane Valley, WA, p. A687

MARTIN, Deanna, Chief Executive Officer, Healthsouth Rehabilitation Hospital Of Rock Hill, Rock Hill, SC, p. A565

MARTIN, Deborah
Regional Vice President Human Resources, Cascade Valley Hospital And Clinics, Arlington, WA, p. A678
Regional Vice President Human Resources, Skagit Regional Health, Mount Vernon, WA, p. A682

MARTIN, Debra, Chief Nursing Officer, Hamilton General Hospital, Hamilton, TX, p. A618

MARTIN, Garland M.D., Chief of Staff, Appling Healthcare System, Baxley, GA, p. A152

MARTIN, Garry, Chief Fiscal, Veterans Affairs North Texas Health Care System, Dallas, TX, p. A607

MARTIN, Greg
Administrator, Muscogee Creek Nation Medical Center, Okmulgee, OK, p. A514
Administrator, Muscogee Creek Nation Physical Rehabilitation Center, Okmulgee, OK, p. A514

MARTIN, Gregg, M.D.
Chief Information Officer, Arnot Ogden Medical Center, Elmira, NY, p. A435
Chief Information Officer, Ira Davenport Memorial Hospital, Bath, NY, p. A431
Chief Information Officer, St. Joseph's Hospital, Elmira, NY, p. A435
Medical Director, Red River Hospital, Llc, Wichita Falls, TX, p. A654

MARTIN, Holly
Director Human Resource, Iowa Specialty Hospital–Belmond, Belmond, IA, p. A222
Human Resources Leader, Iowa Specialty Hospital–Clarion, Clarion, IA, p. A224

MARTIN, James D
Chief Financial Officer, Hawthorn Children Psychiatric Hospital, Saint Louis, MO, p. A377
Chief Financial Officer, Metropolitan St. Louis Psychiatric Center, Saint Louis, MO, p. A377
Chief Financial Officer, St. Louis Psychiatric Rehabilitation Center, Saint Louis, MO, p. A378

MARTIN, James, Chief Information Officer, River Park Hospital, Huntington, WV, p. A693

MARTIN, Janice S R.N., Chief Nursing Officer, Davis Regional Medical Center, Statesville, NC, p. A471

MARTIN, Jason M.D., Medical Director, Seton Northwest Hospital, Austin, TX, p. A595

MARTIN, Jeanene R, M.P.H.
Senior Vice President Human Resources and Chief People Officer, Wakemed Cary Hospital, Cary, NC, p. A458
Senior Vice President Human Resources, Wakemed Raleigh Campus, Raleigh, NC, p. A469

MARTIN, Jeffrey H, M.D., Chief of Staff, Murphy Medical Center, Murphy, NC, p. A467

MARTIN, Jeremy, Chief Support Services Officer, St. James Parish Hospital, Lutcher, LA, p. A280

MARTIN, Jessica, Director Human Resources, Logan Regional Medical Center, Logan, WV, p. A693

MARTIN, Josh
Chief Executive Officer, Summit Pacific Medical Center, Elma, WA, p. A680
Chief Operating Officer, Summit Pacific Medical Center, Elma, WA, p. A680

MARTIN, Karen, R.N., MSN
Chief Nursing Officer, Marshall Medical Center, Lewisburg, TN, p. A582

Chief Nursing Officer, Springs Memorial Hospital, Lancaster, SC, p. A564

MARTIN, Keith M.D., Vice President and Medical Director, CGH Medical Center, Sterling, IL, p. A201

MARTIN, Kelly K, Human Resource Officer, Texas Health Presbyterian Hospital Plano, Plano, TX, p. A638

MARTIN, Kelly, Chief Financial Officer, Fairchild Medical Center, Yreka, CA, p. A97

MARTIN, Kenneth A M.D., Chief of Staff, Arkansas Surgical Hospital, North Little Rock, AR, p. A47

MARTIN, Kevin P. M.D., Chief Medical Officer, Four Winds Hospital, Saratoga Springs, NY, p. A452

MARTIN, Kevin, M.P.H., R.N., FACHE, Administrator, Shriners Hospitals For Children–Salt Lake City, Salt Lake City, UT, p. A660

MARTIN, Konnie, Chief Executive Officer, San Luis Valley Health, Alamosa, CO, p. A98

MARTIN, Kory Lann M.D., Chief of Staff, Seymour Hospital, Seymour, TX, p. A645

MARTIN, Kristina, Chief Information Officer, Curry General Hospital, Gold Beach, OR, p. A522

MARTIN, Leslee, Manager Information Technology, Hshs St. Elizabeth's Hospital, Belleville, IL, p. A178

MARTIN, Marlana, Director Human Resources, Benewah Community Hospital, Saint Maries, ID, p. A175

MARTIN, Mary MSN, R.N., Chief Nursing Officer, Hshs St. Nicholas Hospital, Sheboygan, WI, p. A712

MARTIN, Matthew, Director Resource Management, Naval Hospital Oak Harbor, Oak Harbor, WA, p. A683

MARTIN, Nick, Chief Information Officer, Minidoka Memorial Hospital, Rupert, ID, p. A175

MARTIN, Nikki, Chief Financial Officer, Christus Southeast Texas Jasper Memorial, Jasper, TX, p. A625

MARTIN, Pamela, Chief Executive Officer, Kalispell Regional Healthcare, Kalispell, MT, p. A386

MARTIN, Patrick, M.D.
Medical Director, Wilmington Treatment Center, Wilmington, NC, p. A472
Director Information Systems, Calvary Hospital, New Rochelle, NY, p. A441

MARTIN, Patsy, Manager Human Resources, Select Rehabilitation Hospital Of Denton, Denton, TX, p. A608

MARTIN, Paul J, Director Human Resources, Kaiser Permanente Los Angeles Medical Center, Los Angeles, CA, p. A68

MARTIN, Paul, Chief Medical Officer, Grandview Medical Center, Dayton, OH, p. A489

MARTIN, Ric, Information Specialist, Madison State Hospital, Madison, IN, p. A215

MARTIN, Richard A MSN, R.N., Senior Vice President and Chief Nursing Officer, Hoag Memorial Hospital Presbyterian, Newport Beach, CA, p. A76

MARTIN, Sabrina, Chief Executive Officer, Rehabilitation Hospital Of Southern New Mexico, Las Cruces, NM, p. A427

MARTIN, Sharon E M.D., Ph.D., President Medical Staff, Fulton County Medical Center, Mc Connellsburg, PA, p. A540

MARTIN, Sheila, Chief Nursing Officer, Clinton Memorial Hospital, Wilmington, OH, p. A502

MARTIN, Sherri M.D., President Medical Staff, Shawnee Mission Medical Center, Shawnee Mission, KS, p. A252

MARTIN, Stacy L, Director Human Resources, Grant Regional Health Center, Lancaster, WI, p. A705

MARTIN, Susan, Vice President Finance, Middlesex Hospital, Middletown, CT, p. A111

MARTIN, Teresa, Chief Financial Officer, Two Rivers Behavioral Health System, Kansas City, MO, p. A371

MARTIN, Tom, Chief Strategy and Information Officer, Evergreenhealth, Kirkland, WA, p. A681

MARTIN, Tracie M.D., Chief Medical Officer, Oakland Mercy Hospital, Oakland, NE, p. A396

MARTIN, Val, Director Financial Management Services Center, Veterans Affairs Salt Lake City Health Care System, Salt Lake City, UT, p. A661

MARTIN, W. Carl, Chief Operating Officer, Providence Hospital, Columbia, SC, p. A560

MARTIN, Wendy, Chief Financial Officer, Shands Starke Regional Medical Center, Starke, FL, p. A143

MARTIN–PRATT, Diane, Director Information Systems, Niagara Falls Memorial Medical Center, Niagara Falls, NY, p. A447

MARTINEAU, Loraine, Controller, Prairie Ridge Hospital And Health Services, Elbow Lake, MN, p. A339

MARTINEZ, Albino, Director Budget and Finance, Miners' Colfax Medical Center, Raton, NM, p. A427

MARTINEZ, Angel R.N., RN, BSN,, Director Patient Care Services, Shriners Hospitals For Children–Galveston, Galveston, TX, p. A615

MARTINEZ, Darlene, Director Finance, New Mexico Behavioral Health Institute At Las Vegas, Las Vegas, NM, p. A427

MARTINEZ, Eddie, Chief Financial Officer, El Paso Ltac Hospital, El Paso, TX, p. A610

MARTINEZ, Edward, Chief Information Officer, Nicklaus Children's Hospital, Miami, FL, p. A133

MARTINEZ, Eleanor, Chief Nursing Officer, Alhambra Hospital Medical Center, Alhambra, CA, p. A51

MARTINEZ, Fernando, Senior Vice President and Chief Information Officer, Parkland Health & Hospital System, Dallas, TX, p. A606

MARTINEZ, Francisco, Executive Director, Hospital San Antonio, Mayaguez, PR, p. A724

MARTINEZ, Frank, Senior Vice President Human Resources, East Jefferson General Hospital, Metairie, LA, p. A281

MARTINEZ, Jason, Director Information Technology, West Valley Medical Center, Caldwell, ID, p. A172

MARTINEZ, Jeanine, Director Human Resources, Putnam General Hospital, Eatonton, GA, p. A157

MARTINEZ, Jorge I., Executive Director, Hospital Perea, Mayaguez, PR, p. A724

MARTINEZ, Jose M.D., Chief Medical Officer, Northwest Medical Center, Margate, FL, p. A131

MARTINEZ, Josue, Coordinator Information Systems, University Hospital, San Juan, PR, p. A727

MARTINEZ, Katherine, Chief Nursing Officer, North Central Surgical Center, Dallas, TX, p. A606

MARTINEZ, Kathryn J, Chief Nursing Officer, FHN Memorial Hospital, Freeport, IL, p. A188

MARTINEZ, Leanne, Chief Executive Officer and Administrator, Fisher County Hospital District, Rotan, TX, p. A640

MARTINEZ, Lee, Chief Information Officer, Cooley Dickinson Hospital, Northampton, MA, p. A309

MARTINEZ, Louisa, Director of Nursing, Frio Regional Hospital, Pearsall, TX, p. A637

MARTINEZ, Maria, Chief Nursing Officer, La Paz Regional Hospital, Parker, AZ, p. A32

MARTINEZ, Michelle
Chief Executive Officer, U. S. Public Health Service Indian Hospital–Whiteriver, Whiteriver, AZ, p. A38
Controller, Healthsouth Rehabilitation Hospital Of New Mexico, Albuquerque, NM, p. A424

MARTINEZ, Ozalina R.N., Director of Nursing, Northeastern Health System Sequoyah, Sallisaw, OK, p. A515

MARTINEZ, Regina M, Director Human Resources, La Paz Regional Hospital, Parker, AZ, p. A32

MARTINEZ, Rosette, Acting Chief Executive Officer, Lemuel Shattuck Hospital, Jamaica Plain, MA, p. A307

MARTINEZ, Suzanne, Director Human Resources, Centennial Peaks Hospital, Louisville, CO, p. A106

MARTINEZ, Terri, Chief Financial Officer, Plains Memorial Hospital, Dimmitt, TX, p. A609

MARTINEZ, Tina, Director Human Resources, J. D. Mccarty Center For Children With Developmental Disabilities, Norman, OK, p. A511

MARTINEZ, Virginia, Director Human Resources, Copper Queen Community Hospital, Bisbee, AZ, p. A28

MARTINEZ, Yolanda, Chief Fiscal Services, Edward Hines, Jr. Veterans Affairs Hospital, Hines, IL, p. A190

MARTINEZ, Yvette, Director Human Resources, Sutter Auburn Faith Hospital, Auburn, CA, p. A52

MARTINEZ–NIETO, Arlene M.D., Chief Medical Officer, First Hospital Panamericano, Cidra, PR, p. A723

MARTING, Bill, Senior Vice President and Chief Financial Officer, The University Of Kansas Health System, Kansas City, KS, p. A244

MARTINSON, Erling M.D., Medical Director, Nelson County Health System, Mcville, ND, p. A477

MARTINSON, Tiffany, Director Human Resources, Norton Sound Regional Hospital, Nome, AK, p. A26

MARTOCCIO, Debora R.N., Chief Operating Officer, Florida Hospital At Connerton Long Term Acute Care, Land O'Lakes, FL, p. A130

MARTORANO, Ann, Chief Operating Officer, Halifax Health Medical Center Of Daytona Beach, Daytona Beach, FL, p. A123

MARTUCCI, Kathleen, Chief Operating Officer, Helen Hayes Hospital, West Haverstraw, NY, p. A455

MARTZ, Dean
Chief Medical Officer, Providence Holy Family Hospital, Spokane, WA, p. A687
Chief Medical Officer, Providence Sacred Heart Medical Center & Children's Hospital, Spokane, WA, p. A687

MARTZ, Michael, Chief Information Officer, Ohio Valley Medical Center, Wheeling, WV, p. A697

MARVIN, Ryan, Support Services Director, Rawlins County Health Center, Atwood, KS, p. A238

MARYLAND, Patricia A., Dr.PH, President and Chief Executive Officer, Ascension Healthcare, Saint Louis, MO, p. B12

MARX, Troy, Director Human Resources, Upland Hills Health, Dodgeville, WI, p. A700

MARZINZIK, John A., President and Chief Executive Officer, Frisbie Memorial Hospital, Rochester, NH, p. A410

MARZOLF, Steve R.N., Chief Nursing Officer, Spectrum Health Pennock, Hastings, MI, p. A322

MASHAK–EKERN, Jane, Fiscal Officer, Tomah Veterans Affairs Medical Center, Tomah, WI, p. A714

MASI, George V., Chief Executive Officer, Harris Health System, Houston, TX, p. A620

MASIELLO, Matthew M.D., Chief Medical Officer, The Children's Institute Of Pittsburgh, Pittsburgh, PA, p. A547

MASKELL, Denise, Chief Information Officer, Springfield Hospital Center, Sykesville, MD, p. A301

MASLYN, Jay T, Chief Financial Officer, Nicholas H. Noyes Memorial Hospital, Dansville, NY, p. A434

MASON, Bill A., Chief Executive Officer, Meadow Wood Behavioral Health System, New Castle, DE, p. A115

MASON, Drew
    Chief Operating Officer, Grandview Medical Center, Birmingham, AL, p. A14
    President and Chief Executive Officer, Grandview Medical Center, Birmingham, AL, p. A14

MASON, Jeffrey, Chief Executive Officer, The Miami Medical Center, Miami, FL, p. A134

MASON, Jill K MS, R.N., Chief Nursing Officer, Blessing Hospital, Quincy, IL, p. A198

MASON, John, Chief Information Officer, Hill Country Memorial Hospital, Fredericksburg, TX, p. A615

MASON, Kathy, R.N., MSN
    Chief Nursing Officer, Lifecare Hospitals Of Dallas, Dallas, TX, p. A605
    Chief Operating Officer, Atrium Medical Center Of Corinth, Corinth, TX, p. A603

MASON, Kay, Chief Financial Officer, Texas Health Heart & Vascular Hospital Arlington, Arlington, TX, p. A593

MASON, Keith, Chief Executive Officer, Bailey Medical Center, Owasso, OK, p. A514

MASON, Phyllis M.D., Chief Medical Officer, Natchitoches Regional Medical Center, Natchitoches, LA, p. A282

MASON, Rhonda, Vice President of Patient Care Services, Tri–State Memorial Hospital, Clarkston, WA, p. A679

MASON, Sandra MSN, R.N., Director Nursing Services and Senior Nurse Executive, Robert E. Bush Naval Hospital, Twentynine Palms, CA, p. A95

MASON, Stacie, Vice President and Chief Financial Officer, Integris Grove Hospital, Grove, OK, p. A508

MASON, William R, Chief Operating Officer, Brooke Glen Behavioral Hospital, Fort Washington, PA, p. A535

MASON–JONES, Taryn, Chief Nurse Executive, Norristown State Hospital, Norristown, PA, p. A542

MASON–WILLIAMS, Lois, Director of Human Resources, Northwest Ohio Psychiatric Hospital, Toledo, OH, p. A500

MASOOD, Shahid M.D., Clinical Director, Mildred Mitchell–Bateman Hospital, Huntington, WV, p. A692

MASSA, Rhonda, Director of Nursing, Clarion Psychiatric Center, Clarion, PA, p. A531

MASSAAD, Aziz M.D., Medical Staff President, Down East Community Hospital, Machias, ME, p. A292

MASSE, Roger A., FACHE, Chief Executive Officer, Ellsworth County Medical Center, Ellsworth, KS, p. A240

MASSELLA, Joan, Administrative Vice President and Chief Nursing Officer, St. Clair Hospital, Pittsburgh, PA, p. A547

MASSENGALE, David
    Chief Financial Officer, Methodist Hospital Union County, Morganfield, KY, p. A265
    Vice President and Chief Financial Officer, Methodist Hospital, Henderson, KY, p. A259

MASSENGILL, Leigh, Chief Executive Officer, Medical Center Of Trinity, Trinity, FL, p. A146

MASSEY, Gina, Vice President Human Resources, Clarity Child Guidance Center, San Antonio, TX, p. A642

MASSEY, Rocco K., Community Chief Executive Officer, Beckley Arh Hospital, Beckley, WV, p. A690

MASSEY, Steven, President and Chief Executive Officer, Westfields Hospital, New Richmond, WI, p. A709

MASSEY, Terry, Chief Fiscal Services, Beckley Veterans Affairs Medical Center, Beckley, WV, p. A690

MASSIELLO, Martin, Executive Vice President and Chief Operating Officer, Eisenhower Medical Center, Rancho Mirage, CA, p. A81

MASSIET, Jill R.N., Vice President Patient Care, Baptist Health Medical Center–Little Rock, Little Rock, AR, p. A46

MASSIMILLA, John P FACHE, Vice President and Chief Operating Officer, Chambersburg Hospital, Chambersburg, PA, p. A531

MASSINI, Stephen M.
    Chief Financial Officer, Penn State Milton S. Hershey Medical Center, Hershey, PA, p. A536
    Chief Operating Officer, Penn State Milton S. Hershey Medical Center, Hershey, PA, p. A536

MASSMAN, Patty, Director of Nursing, Granite Falls Municipal Hospital And Manor, Granite Falls, MN, p. A340

MAST, Delvin R.N., Director of Nursing, Weatherford Regional Hospital, Weatherford, OK, p. A519

MAST, Duane M.D., Medical Director, Hocking Valley Community Hospital, Logan, OH, p. A494

MAST, Joelle Ph.D., M.D., Chief Medical Officer, Blythedale Children's Hospital, Valhalla, NY, p. A454

MAST, Nathan, Chief Executive Officer, Vibra Hospital Of Mahoning Valley, Boardman, OH, p. A481

MASTER, Moiz M.D., Medical Director of Quality, Piedmont Mountainside Hospital, Jasper, GA, p. A159

MASTERS, Emily, Director Human Resources and Marketing, Windom Area Hospital, Windom, MN, p. A350

MASTERS, Ken, Director Information Technology, Chambers Memorial Hospital, Danville, AR, p. A42

MASTERS, Kim M.D., Medical Director, Saint Simons By–The–Sea Hospital, Saint Simons Island, GA, p. A164

MASTERS, Regina R.N., MSN, Director of Nursing, Continuing Care Hospital, Lexington, KY, p. A261

MASTERSON, David J., President, Sentara Williamsburg Regional Medical Center, Williamsburg, VA, p. A677

MASTERSON, Paul, Chief Financial Officer, Genesis Healthcare System, Zanesville, OH, p. A503

MASTERSON, Sammie, Director Human Resources, Harney District Hospital, Burns, OR, p. A520

MASTERTON, William J., President and Chief Executive Officer, University Medical Center, New Orleans, LA, p. A283

MASTIN, Michelle, Chief Clinical Officer, Curahealth Boston North Shore, Peabody, MA, p. A310

MASTROIANNI, Anthony, Regional Vice President Finance, The William W. Backus Hospital, Norwich, CT, p. A112

MASTROIANNI, Thomas, Administrative Director of Human Resources, Halifax Regional Medical Center, Roanoke Rapids, NC, p. A469

MASTROIANNI, Tom, Vice President Human Resources, New York–Presbyterian/Lawrence Hospital, Bronxville, NY, p. A432

MASTROMANNO, Christopher
    Chief Operating Officer, NYC Health + Hospitals / Jacobi, New Rochelle, NY, p. A445
    Interim Chief Executive Officer, NYC Health + Hospitals / Jacobi, New Rochelle, NY, p. A445

MASTRO, Mary Lou, FACHE, MS, R.N., System Chief Executive Officer, Edward-Elmhurst Healthcare, Naperville, IL, p. B49

MASTROPIETRO, N. A. M.D., Medical Director, Lancaster Regional Medical Centers, Lancaster, PA, p. A538

MATA, Maribel, Director Information Services, Doctors Hospital Of Laredo, Laredo, TX, p. A628

MATA–GUERRERO, Rita, Director of Nursing, Weslaco Regional Rehabilitation Hospital, Weslaco, TX, p. A654

MATAMOROS, Mary L., R.N., Chief Executive Officer, Seaside Behavioral Center, New OrleansRiver Oaks Hospital, New Orleans, LA, p. A283

MATEJICKA, Anthony D.O., M.P.H., Vice President, Chief Medical Officer, Nyack Hospital, Nyack, NY, p. A448

MATEJKA, Cheryl
    Chief Financial Officer, Mercy Hospital St. Louis, Saint Louis, MO, p. A377
    Chief Financial Officer, Mercy Hospital Washington, Washington, MO, p. A381

MATENAER, Thomas M, Chief Financial Officer, Banner Gateway Medical Center, Gilbert, AZ, p. A29

MATHAI, George M.D., Chief of Staff, Three Rivers Hospital, Waverly, TN, p. A590

MATHAI, Matt M.D., Medical Director, Select Specialty Hospital–Milwaukee, Milwaukee, WI, p. A708

MATHEIS, Tracey
    Chief Financial Officer, Moberly Regional Medical Center, Moberly, MO, p. A373
    Chief Operating Officer, Moberly Regional Medical Center, Moberly, MO, p. A373

MATHER, Charlotte Marie R.N., Chief Nursing Officer, Sheridan Memorial Hospital, Sheridan, WY, p. A719

MATHER, Kelly, Chief Executive Officer, Sonoma Valley Hospital, Sonoma, CA, p. A92

MATHER, Martha S, Chief Operating Officer and Vice President, Our Lady Of Peace, Louisville, KY, p. A263

MATHERS, Larry M.D., Chief of Staff, Tennova Newport Medical Center, Newport, TN, p. A587

MATHES, Lisa L, Human Resources Director, Southwest Medical Center, Liberal, KS, p. A246

MATHESON, John A., Interim Chief Executive Officer, Dequincy Memorial Hospital, Dequincy, LA, p. A274

MATHEW, Finny, Chief Executive Officer, Crossroads Community Hospital, Mount Vernon, IL, p. A194

MATHEW, Mammen M.D., Chief Rehabilitation Medicine, Woodrow Wilson Rehabilitation Center, Fishersville, VA, p. A667

MATHEWS, Arun M.D., Chief Medical Officer (Acute), Medical Center Health System, Odessa, TX, p. A635

MATHEWS, Christine W R.N., MSN, Vice President Nursing Services, Geisinger–Lewistown Hospital, Lewistown, PA, p. A539

MATHEWS, Gary M.D., Medical Doctor, Beaver County Memorial Hospital, Beaver, OK, p. A505

MATHEWS, Nimmy, Acting Director Quality Management, San Carlos Apache Healthcare Corporation, Peridot, AZ, p. A32

MATHEWS, Paul G., CPA, Administrator, Hardtner Medical Center, Olla, LA, p. A284

MATHEWSON, Patricia, Chief Nursing Officer, Tulare Regional Medical Center, Tulare, CA, p. A94

MATHIAS, Matt, Chief Operating Officer, Lewisgale Hospital Montgomery, Blacksburg, VA, p. A665

MATHIEU, Angie, System Director Information Technology and Regional Chief Information Officer, The William W. Backus Hospital, Norwich, CT, p. A112

MATHIS, Alison, Chief Nursing Officer, Copiah County Medical Center, Hazlehurst, MS, p. A356

MATHIS, Ashley, Privacy Officer, Columbus Community Hospital, Columbus, TX, p. A602

MATHIS, Jane, Chief Financial Officer, Baylor Surgical Hospital At Fort Worth, Fort Worth, TX, p. A613

MATHIS, Patricia, Associate Director Patient Care Service, Richard L. Roudebush Veterans Affairs Medical Center, Indianapolis, IN, p. A212

MATHIS, Rebecca
    Chief Financial Officer, Amita Health Adventist Medical Center Bolingbrook, Bolingbrook, IL, p. A179
    Chief Financial Officer, Amita Health Adventist Medical Center Lagrange, La Grange, IL, p. A191
    Vice President and Chief Financial Officer, Amita Health Adventist Medical Center – Hinsdale, Hinsdale, IL, p. A190

MATHIS, Richard C., Chief Executive Officer, North Runnels Hospital, Winters, TX, p. A655

MATHIS, Robin, Director of Human Resources, Methodist Olive Branch Hospital, Olive Branch, MS, p. A360

MATHIS, Susan, MSN, R.N., Chief Executive Officer, Centerpointe Hospital, Saint Charles, MO, p. A376

MATHISEN, Arthur, FACHE, President and Chief Executive Officer, Copley Hospital, Morrisville, VT, p. A662

MATHUR, Ashish M.D., Chief of Staff, Siloam Springs Regional Hospital, Siloam Springs, AR, p. A49

MATHURIN, Emile M.D., Jr, Medical Director, Healthsouth Rehabilitation Hospital Of Humble, Llc, Humble, TX, p. A624

MATHURIN, Venra, Vice President Human Resources, Interfaith Medical Center, New Rochelle, NY, p. A441

MATIS, Sue, Director Human Resources, North Central Health Care, Wausau, WI, p. A715

MATLACK, Victoria L.
    Director and Human Resources Business Partner, Ohiohealth Dublin Methodist Hospital, Dublin, OH, p. A490
    Director and Human Resources Business Partner, Ohiohealth Grady Memorial Hospital, Delaware, OH, p. A490

MATNEY, James L., President and Chief Executive Officer, Colquitt Regional Medical Center, Moultrie, GA, p. A162

MATNEY, Patty, Human Resources Consultant, Saint Thomas Hickman Hospital, Centerville, TN, p. A576

MATNEY, Tim, Chief Financial Officer, Logan Regional Medical Center, Logan, WV, p. A693

MATOS, Patricia, Chief Nursing Officer, Stewart & Lynda Resnick Neuropsychiatric Hospital At Ucla, Los Angeles, CA, p. A71

MATSINGER, John D.O., Chief Medical Officer, Virtua Marlton, Marlton, NJ, p. A416

MATT, Christine K., Associate Chief, Uva Transitional Care Hospital, Charlottesville, VA, p. A665

MATT, Robert Lawrence, Vice President and Chief Operating Officer, Hancock Regional Hospital, Greenfield, IN, p. A209

MATTER, Stephanie, Manager Human Resources, Lifecare Hospitals Of Wisconsin, Pewaukee, WI, p. A710

MATTERN, Bonnie, Director Human Resources, Chi St. Alexius Health Devils Lake Hospital, Devils Lake, ND, p. A475

MATTERN, Joe M.D., Chief Medical Officer, Jefferson Healthcare, Port Townsend, WA, p. A684

MATTERN, Karen, Director of Human Resources, Shriners Hospitals For Children–Spokane, Spokane, WA, p. A687

MATTES, Bryan, Associate Administrator, Crossridge Community Hospital, Wynne, AR, p. A50

MATTES, James A., President and Chief Executive Officer, Grande Ronde Hospital, La Grande, OR, p. A523

MATTES, Mark David R.N., MS, Assistant Administrator/ Patient Care Services, Golden Valley Memorial Healthcare, Clinton, MO, p. A366

MATTEUCCI, Dolly, Executive Director, Napa State Hospital, Napa, CA, p. A76

MATTHEI, Ruth R.N., MS, Chief Nursing Officer, Westlake Hospital, Melrose Park, IL, p. A193

MATTHEW, Mathew M.D., Chief Medical Officer, Nazareth Hospital, Philadelphia, PA, p. A545

MATTHEWS, Adora M.D., Medical Director, Healthsouth Rehabilitation Hospital Of Florence, Florence, SC, p. A562

MATTHEWS, Bryan C., Director, Veterans Health Care System Of The Ozarks, Fayetteville, AR, p. A43

MATTHEWS, Carol, Director Human Resources, Saline Memorial Hospital, Benton, AR, p. A40

MATTHEWS, Clinton
President and Chief Executive Officer, Reading Health Rehabilitation Hospital, Wyomissing, PA, p. A555
President and Chief Executive Officer, Reading Hospital, West Reading, PA, p. A553

MATTHEWS, Deborah, Senior Vice President, Tanner Medical Center–Villa Rica, Villa Rica, GA, p. A166

MATTHEWS, Gwen, R.N., MSN, Chief Executive Officer, Ukiah Valley Medical Center, Ukiah, CA, p. A95

MATTHEWS, Judith, Nurse Executive, Riverside Tappahannock Hospital, Tappahannock, VA, p. A676

MATTHEWS, Lori
Vice President Information Technology System, Banner Baywood Medical Center, Mesa, AZ, p. A31
Vice President, Information Technology System, Banner Heart Hospital, Mesa, AZ, p. A31

MATTHEWS, Melissa, Director Human Resources, Dahl Memorial Healthcare Association, Ekalaka, MT, p. A384

MATTHEWS, Michael, Vice President Human Resources, Holland Hospital, Holland, MI, p. A322

MATTHEWS, Oliver M.D., Chief Medical Officer, Eliza Coffee Memorial Hospital, Florence, AL, p. A18

MATTHEWS, Paul M.D., President of Medical Staff, Palo Alto County Health System, Emmetsburg, IA, p. A227

MATTHEWS, Ted, Chief Executive Officer, Eastland Memorial Hospital, Eastland, TX, p. A609

MATTHEY, Michael, Facility Chief Information Officer, Louis A. Johnson Veterans Affairs Medical Center, Clarksburg, WV, p. A691

MATTHIAS, Mark M.D., Vice President of Medical Affairs, St. Cloud Hospital, Saint Cloud, MN, p. A347

MATTHIESSEN, Matthew, Chief Financial Officer, John C. Fremont Healthcare District, Mariposa, CA, p. A73

MATTICE, Gloria R.N., Director Patient Care, George C Grape Community Hospital, Hamburg, IA, p. A228

MATTINGLY, Marty, Chief Human Resources Officer, St. Vincent Medical Center Of Evansville, Evansville, IN, p. A207

MATTISON, Denise, Director Finance and Accounting Services, Mayo Clinic Health System In Eau Claire, Eau Claire, WI, p. A701

MATTISON, Kenneth R., Chief Executive Officer, Florida Hospital New Smyrna, New Smyrna Beach, FL, p. A135

MATTLY, Sheila, Chief Nursing Officer, Wayne County Hospital, Corydon, IA, p. A225

MATTNER, Matthew, Chief Operating Officer, Lutheran Hospital, Cleveland, OH, p. A486

MATTSON, Jodi, Director of Nursing, Cedar Springs Hospital, Colorado Springs, CO, p. A99

MATTSON, Wayne, Management Information Systems Specialist, Rogers Memorial Hospital, Oconomowoc, WI, p. A709

MATUS, Jose M.D., Director Medical, Carrus Rehabilitation Hospital, Sherman, TX, p. A645

MATUSKA, John E., Chief Executive Officer, Green Valley Hospital, Green Valley, AZ, p. A30

MATUSZKIEWICZ, Marcin M.D., Chief of Staff and Medical Director, Jerold Phelps Community Hospital, Garberville, CA, p. A61

MATZENBACHER, Elaine, Chief Financial Officer, Washington County Hospital, Nashville, IL, p. A195

MATZIGKEIT, Linda, Senior Vice President Human Resources, Children's Healthcare Of Atlanta, Atlanta, GA, p. A150

MAUCK, Lynn, R.N., Chief Operating Officer and Chief Nursing Officer, Fishermen's Hospital, Marathon, FL, p. A131

MAURER, Gregory L., Chief Executive Officer, Sheridan Memorial Hospital, Plentywood, MT, p. A387

MAURER, Jackie, Fiscal Officer, Julian F. Keith Alcohol And Drug Abuse Treatment Center, Black Mountain, NC, p. A458

MAURER, Linda, Vice President Patient Care Services, Wilson Memorial Hospital, Sidney, OH, p. A499

MAURER, Marsha L. R.N., MS, Chief Nursing Officer Patient Care Services, Beth Israel Deaconess Medical Center, Boston, MA, p. A302

MAURICE, Timothy, Chief Financial Officer, University Of California, Davis Medical Center, Sacramento, CA, p. A84

MAURIN, Michael J, Chief Financial Officer, Southern Surgical Hospital, Slidell, LA, p. A286

MAURO, Phyllis, Chief Executive Officer, Louisiana Continuing Care Hospital, Marrero, LA, p. A281

MAUST, Richard, Chief Information Officer, RMC Jacksonville, Jacksonville, AL, p. A19

MAVROMATIS, Lou, Vice President Information Technology, Medstar Southern Maryland Hospital Center, Clinton, MD, p. A297

MAX, Cindy, Chief Nursing Officer, Shriners Hospitals For Children–Philadelphia, Philadelphia, PA, p. A545

MAXIE, Bryan K.
Administrator, Marion General Hospital, Columbia, MS, p. A354
Administrator, Walthall County General Hospital, Tylertown, MS, p. A362

MAXSON, Diana, Director Human Resources, University Hospital Summerville, Augusta, GA, p. A152

MAXWELL, Dale, Executive Vice President and Chief Financial Officer, Presbyterian Hospital, Albuquerque, NM, p. A425

MAXWELL, Jody, Manager Business Office, Smith County Memorial Hospital, Smith Center, KS, p. A252

MAXWELL, John, Chief Executive Officer, Central Carolina Hospital, Sanford, NC, p. A470

MAXWELL, Ronnie, Director Information Systems, Glenwood Regional Medical Center, West Monroe, LA, p. A288

MAY, Bill, President and Chief Executive Officer, Adams County Regional Medical Center, Seaman, OH, p. A499

MAY, David, Chief of Staff, Richland Hospital, Richland Center, WI, p. A711

MAY, Frank, Chief Executive Officer, Yampa Valley Medical Center, Steamboat Springs, CO, p. A107

MAY, Kevin B
Chief Financial Officer, Watauga Medical Center, Boone, NC, p. A458
System Director Finance, Charles A. Cannon Memorial Hospital, Newland, NC, p. A468

MAY, Robin, Director Information Systems, Platte County Memorial Hospital, Wheatland, WY, p. A720

MAY, Ronald B, M.D., Vice President Medical Affairs, Carolinaeast Health System, New Bern, NC, p. A468

MAY, Scott, Area Director Technology, Kaiser Permanente Santa Clara Medical Center, Santa Clara, CA, p. A90

MAY, Sonja, Director Human Resources, Morton County Health System, Elkhart, KS, p. A240

MAY, Todd M.D., Chief Medical Officer, Zuckerberg San Francisco General Hospital And Trauma Center, San Francisco, CA, p. A88

MAY, Troy, Chief Information Officer, University Of Louisville Hospital, Louisville, KY, p. A264

MAY, Walter E., President and Chief Executive Officer, Pikeville Medical Center, Pikeville, KY, p. A266

MAY, William J., Administrator, Hawaii State Hospital, Kaneohe, HI, p. A170

MAYBEN, Casey, Chief Nursing Officer, East Texas Medical Center Pittsburg, Pittsburg, TX, p. A637

MAYER, David, Chief of Staff, Wayne County Hospital, Monticello, KY, p. A265

MAYER, Karen M R.N., FACHE, Senior Vice President Patient Care Services, Rush Oak Park Hospital, Oak Park, IL, p. A196

MAYER, Peter, Director Information Systems, Bakersfield Heart Hospital, Bakersfield, CA, p. A52

MAYER, William M.D., Vice President Medical Staff Services, St. Mary's Healthcare, Amsterdam, NY, p. A430

MAYEUX, Tiffany, Interim Chief Financial Officer and Financial Analyst, Lafayette Surgical Specialty Hospital, Lafayette, LA, p. A278

MAYEWSKI, Raymond, M.D.
Chief Medical Officer, Highland Hospital, Rochester, NY, p. A450
Chief Medical Officer, Strong Memorial Hospital Of The University Of Rochester, Rochester, NY, p. A451

MAYFIELD, Michael Bradley M.D., Chief of Staff, Chicot Memorial Medical Center, Lake Village, AR, p. A45

MAYFIELD, William M.D., Chief of Staff, Tristar Stonecrest Medical Center, Smyrna, TN, p. A589

MAYHLE, Douglas M.D., Medical Director, Nicholas H. Noyes Memorial Hospital, Dansville, NY, p. A434

MAYLE, Connie, Vice President Administrative Services, Upmc Horizon, Farrell, PA, p. A535

MAYNARD, Bob, Chief Information Officer, Fairview Regional Medical Center, Fairview, OK, p. A508

MAYNARD, Rhonda, Chief Financial Officer, Tennova Physicians Regional Medical Center, Knoxville, TN, p. A582

MAYO, Andrew, Ph.D., Chief Executive Officer and Managing Director, North Star Behavioral Health System, Anchorage, AK, p. A25

MAYO, Cindy, R.N., FACHE, Chief Executive, Providence Medford Medical Center, Medford, OR, p. A524

MAYO, Elena, Manager, Human Resources, San Dimas Community Hospital, San Dimas, CA, p. A86

MAYO, Hal, Chief Financial Officer, Liberty Dayton Regional Medical Center, Liberty, TX, p. A629

MAYO, Jim M.D., Clinical Director, Cherry Hospital, Goldsboro, NC, p. A463

MAYO, Michael A., FACHE, President, Baptist Medical Center Jacksonville, Jacksonville, FL, p. A127

MAYO, Randy, Director Information Technology, William Newton Hospital, Winfield, KS, p. A254

MAYO, Robert, M.D.
Chief Medical Officer, Rochester General Hospital, Rochester, NY, p. A451
Executive Vice President, Chief Medical Officer, Rochester Regional Health, Newark–Wayne Community Hospital, Newark, NY, p. A447

MAYO, Sarah, Vice President Financial Services, UNC Lenoir Healthcare, Kinston, NC, p. A465

MAYORGA, Oliver, M.D.
Chief Medical Officer, Lawrence + Memorial Hospital, New London, CT, p. A112
Chief Medical Officer, Westerly Hospital, Westerly, RI, p. A557

MAYS, Christine, R.N., MSN
Chief Operating Officer and Chief Nurse Executive, Saint Joseph East, Lexington, KY, p. A261
Chief Operating Officer and Chief Nurse Executive, Saint Joseph Hospital, Lexington, KY, p. A261

MAYS, Dawn, Chief Nursing Officer, Scott Memorial Hospital, Scottsburg, IN, p. A219

MAYS, Raymond M.D., Medical Director, River Crest Hospital, San Angelo, TX, p. A641

MAYS, Sherrie MSN R.N., Vice President and Chief Nursing Officer, Baptist Health Corbin, Corbin, KY, p. A256

MAYSENT, Patty, Interim Chief Executive Officer, Uc San Diego Health, San Diego, CA, p. A86

MAYSILLES, Nancy, R.N., Chief Nursing Officer, Medical Center Of Trinity, Trinity, FL, p. A146

MAYSON, Mark J M.D., Medical Director, Palmetto Health Baptist, Columbia, SC, p. A560

MAZANEC, Lori
Chief Operating Officer, Box Butte General Hospital, Alliance, NE, p. A390
Interim Chief Executive Officer, Box Butte General Hospital, Alliance, NE, p. A390

MAZOUR, Linda M.D., President, Franklin County Memorial Hospital, Franklin, NE, p. A392

MAZUREK, Michele A, Interim Vice President Patient Care Services and Chief Nursing Officer, Mount Sinai Hospital, Chicago, IL, p. A182

MAZZA, Mary, Director Human Resources, Healthsouth Rehabilitation Hospital Of Western Massachusetts, Ludlow, MA, p. A308

MAZZAFERRI, Mary Anthony., Administrator, St. Anthony'S Continuing Care Center, Rock Island, IL, p. B95

MAZZARELLA, Frank M.D., Chief Medical Officer, Clara Maass Medical Center, Belleville, NJ, p. A411

MAZZARELLI, Anthony J JD, M.D., Senior Executive Vice President Chief Physician Executive, Cooper University Health Care, Camden, NJ, p. A412

MAZZO, Joseph, Chief Executive Officer, John Randolph Medical Center, Hopewell, VA, p. A668

MAZZOLA, Joe D.O., Senior Vice President Medical Affairs and Chief Medical Officer, Carolinas Healthcare System Blue Ridge, Morganton, NC, p. A467

MAZZONI, Dean, President and Chief Executive Officer, Franciscan St. Anthony Health – Michigan City, Michigan City, IN, p. A215

MAZZUCA, Darryl, Director Management Information Systems, Little Company Of Mary Hospital And Health Care Centers, Evergreen Park, IL, p. A187

MBENGA, Saul, Manager Information Technology, Alliance Healthcare System, Holly Springs, MS, p. A356

MC BRIDE, Brian, Chief Financial Officer, Rice Medical Center, Eagle Lake, TX, p. A609

MC KELLAR, Grey, Chief Operating Officer and Director of Performance Improvement and Risk, Kingwood Pines Hospital, Kingwood, TX, p. A627

MCADAMS, David, Chief Financial Officer, Lindner Center Of Hope, Mason, OH, p. A495

MCADOO, Jackie, Chief Financial Officer, Grady Memorial Hospital, Chickasha, OK, p. A505

MCAFEE, Thomas J., President, North Market, Northwestern Medicine Lake Forest Hospital, Lake Forest, IL, p. A192

MCALISTER, Julene, Administrator, Mmo Rehabilitation And Wellness Center, Plaquemine, LA, p. A284

MCALISTER, Stephanie, Controller, Tippah County Hospital, Ripley, MS, p. A361

MCALLISTER, Guy, Vice President and Chief Information Officer, Tift Regional Medical Center, Tifton, GA, p. A166

MCALLISTER, Ric, Chief Executive Officer, Windsor–Laurelwood Center For Behavioral Medicine, Willoughby, OH, p. A502

MCALLISTER, Yvonne, Senior Director Human Resources, Southern Maine Health Care – Biddeford Medical Center, Biddeford, ME, p. A290

MCALOON, Richard, Vice President Human Resources, Hartford Hospital, Hartford, CT, p. A110

MCANDREWS, Kevin
Vice President Human Resources, Nexus Specialty Hospital, Shenandoah, TX, p. A645
Vice President, Human Resources, Nexus Specialty Hospital The Woodlands, The Woodlands, TX, p. A649

MCARTHUR, Ronald L., Chief Executive Officer, Summit Healthcare Regional Medical Center, Show Low, AZ, p. A36

MCARTOR, Dana R.N., Director of Nursing, Perkins County Health Services, Grant, NE, p. A393

MCAULIFFE, Gregory, M.D.
Chief Medical Officer, San Luis Valley Health Conejos County Hospital, La Jara, CO, p. A104
Chief Medical Officer, San Luis Valley Health, Alamosa, CO, p. A98

MCAULIFFE, John M.D., Medical Director, Sauk Prairie Healthcare, Prairie Du Sac, WI, p. A711

MCAVOY, Tim M.D., Medical Director, Rehabilitation Hospital Of Wisconsin, Waukesha, WI, p. A714

MCBEE, Jeff, Administrator, Presbyterian Hospital, Albuquerque, NM, p. A425

MCBEE, John, Chief of Staff, Chi St. Anthony Hospital, Pendleton, OR, p. A524

MCBREARTY, Michael M.D., Vice President Medical Affairs, Thomas Hospital, Fairhope, AL, p. A17

MCBRIDE, Anne, Chief Executive Officer, Regional Hospital For Respiratory And Complex Care, Burien, WA, p. A679

MCBRIDE, Brandon, Operations Officer, Logan Regional Hospital, Logan, UT, p. A657

MCBRIDE, Dina, Chief Operating Officer and Director Human Resources, East Adams Rural Healthcare, Ritzville, WA, p. A684

MCBRIDE, Grace, Regional Chief Nursing Officer, Presence Mercy Medical Center, Aurora, IL, p. A177

MCBRIDE, Lamar, Chief Executive Officer, Northern Colorado Long Term Acute Hospital, Johnstown, CO, p. A104

MCBRIDE, Thomas Y III, Executive Vice President and Chief Financial Officer, Gwinnett Hospital System, Lawrenceville, GA, p. A160

MCBROOM, Robert M.D., Medical Director, Promise Hospital Of Wichita Falls, Wichita Falls, TX, p. A654

MCBRYDE, Robin, Chief Information Officer, Alexandria Veterans Affairs Health Care System, Pineville, LA, p. A284

MCCAA, Karen R.N., Vice President Patient Care Services and Chief Nursing Officer, Baptist Medical Center South, Montgomery, AL, p. A21

MCCABE, John P., Executive Vice President, Shriners Hospitals For Children, Tampa, FL, p. B117

MCCABE, Mary, Chief Financial Officer, North Colorado Medical Center, Greeley, CO, p. A103

MCCABE, Patrick G. Jr, FACHE, President and Chief Executive Officer, Levi Hospital, Hot Springs National Park, AR, p. A44

MCCABE, Patrick, Senior Vice President Finance and Chief Financial Officer, Bridgeport Hospital, Bridgeport, CT, p. A109

MCCABE, Steve, Chief Executive Officer, Hill Crest Behavioral Health Services, Birmingham, AL, p. A14

MCCAFFERTY, Michael, Chief Executive Officer, Sheridan Memorial Hospital, Sheridan, WY, p. A719

MCCAFFREY, Roberta A R.N., Vice President and Chief Nursing Officer, Methodist Hospital Of Southern California, Arcadia, CA, p. A52

MCCAHILL, Connie, R.N., President and Chief Executive Officer, Cameron Memorial Community Hospital, Angola, IN, p. A203

MCCAHILL, Mary, Chief Nursing Officer, Thorek Memorial Hospital, Chicago, IL, p. A184

MCCAIN, Rebecca J., Chief Executive Officer, Electra Memorial Hospital, Electra, TX, p. A612

MCCALL, Brad D., JD, Chief Executive Officer, Physicians Surgical Hospital – Quail Creek, Amarillo, TX, p. A592

MCCALL, Debbie, Director Human Resources, Wk Bossier Health Center, Bossier City, LA, p. A272

MCCALL, Harlo, Chief Executive Officer, Healthsouth Rehabilitation Hospital Of Texarkana, Texarkana, TX, p. A649

MCCALL, Lee, Chief Executive Officer, Neshoba County General Hospital, Philadelphia, MS, p. A360

MCCALL, Pam, Director Human Resources, Heatherhill Care Communities, Chardon, OH, p. A483

MCCALLISTER, Bob, Director Human Resources, Baptist Memorial Hospital–Golden Triangle, Columbus, MS, p. A354

MCCALLISTER, Darla, Chief Financial Officer, Lakeside Women's Hospital, Oklahoma City, OK, p. A512

MCCALLISTER, Dianne M.D., Chief Medical Officer, Medical Center Of Aurora, Aurora, CO, p. A98

MCCALLISTER, Sean, Administrator, St. Luke's Mccall, Mccall, ID, p. A174

MCCAMPBELL, Kellie, Coordinator Human Resources, Kindred Hospital–Chattanooga, Chattanooga, TN, p. A576

MCCAMPBELL, Marcia M.D., Chief Medical Officer, Shasta Regional Medical Center, Redding, CA, p. A81

MCCANCE, Dan D.O., Chief of Staff, Hillsdale Hospital, Hillsdale, MI, p. A322

MCCANDLESS, Barbara, Vice President Human Resources, St. Mary's Hospital, Troy, NY, p. A454

MCCANDLESS, David, Vice President Medical Affairs, Upmc Northwest, Seneca, PA, p. A550

MCCANN, Barbara, Director Human Resources, Sunrise Canyon Hospital, Lubbock, TX, p. A630

MCCANN, Kyle, Chief Operating Officer, St. Joseph's Hospital, Savannah, GA, p. A165

MCCANN, Lew, Director Management Information Systems, OSF Holy Family Medical Center, Monmouth, IL, p. A194

MCCARTAN, Mary E, Manager Human Resources, Va Long Beach Healthcare System, Long Beach, CA, p. A67

MCCARTER, Alyssa, Chief Financial Officer, W. J. Mangold Memorial Hospital, Lockney, TX, p. A629

MCCARTER, Scott, Chief Information Officer, Karmanos Cancer Center, Detroit, MI, p. A318

MCCARTHY, Barbara, Chief Executive Officer, Specialty Hospital Jacksonville, Jacksonville, FL, p. A128

MCCARTHY, Brian, Director Information Systems, Memorial Hospital Of Salem County, Salem, NJ, p. A420

MCCARTHY, Cynthia L MS, R.N., Chief Nursing Officer, Texas Health Harris Methodist Hospital Stephenville, Stephenville, TX, p. A646

MCCARTHY, Linda M R.N., VP/ Chief Nursing Officer, Citrus Memorial Health System, Inverness, FL, p. A127

MCCARTHY, Maureen M.D., Chief of Staff, Phoenix Veterans Affairs Health Care System, Phoenix, AZ, p. A34

MCCARTHY, Rick, Chief Information Officer, St. Vincent's Medical Center, Bridgeport, CT, p. A109

MCCARTHY, Sandra Mac
Chief Nursing Officer, Arnot Ogden Medical Center, Elmira, NY, p. A435
Chief Nursing Officer, St. Joseph's Hospital, Elmira, NY, p. A435

MCCARTHY, Tim, President Puerto Rico Division, First Hospital Panamericano, Cidra, PR, p. A723

MCCARTY, Daniel P, Chief Operating Officer, Orange City Area Health System, Orange City, IA, p. A232

MCCARTY, Jacob M., Chief Executive Officer, Kindred Hospital–San Francisco Bay Area, San Leandro, CA, p. A89

MCCARTY, Maryland, Director Information Systems, Wellstar Atlanta Medical Center, Atlanta, GA, p. A151

MCCARTY, Melany R.N., Chief Clinical Officer, Vibra Hospital Of Amarillo, Amarillo, TX, p. A592

MCCARTY, Tim, Chief Information Officer, Oakbend Medical Center, Richmond, TX, p. A640

MCCARTY, Wendy, Director Human Resources, Hillsboro Community Hospital, Hillsboro, KS, p. A242

MCCASLIN, Anna, Chief Financial Officer, Orthonebraska Hospital, Omaha, NE, p. A398

MCCASLIN, Jami, Director Human Resources, Providence Hood River Memorial Hospital, Hood River, OR, p. A522

MCCAUGHEY, James, Chief Strategy Officer, Lucile Salter Packard Children's Hospital Stanford, Palo Alto, CA, p. A79

MCCAULEY, Bryan, Chief Financial Officer, West Jefferson Medical Center, Marrero, LA, p. A281

MCCAULEY, Cynthia, Chief Financial Officer, Good Samaritan Medical Center, West Palm Beach, FL, p. A147

MCCAULEY, Dudley, Controller, Lincoln County Medical Center, Ruidoso, NM, p. A428

MCCAULEY, Jason, Administrator, Jane Phillips Nowata Health Center, Nowata, OK, p. A511

MCCAULEY, Sue E, Director Finance, Baum Harmon Mercy Hospital, Primghar, IA, p. A233

MCCAWLEY, Thomas J, Vice President, Beloit Health System, Beloit, WI, p. A699

MCCHESNEY, Lisa D R.N., Senior Director Information Systems, Upmc Hamot, Erie, PA, p. A534

MCCLAIN, Barbara, Human Resources, Horton Community Hospital, Horton, KS, p. A243

MCCLAIN, James, Deputy Director, Clement J. Zablocki Veterans Affairs Medical Center, Milwaukee, WI, p. A707

MCCLAIN, Richard M.D., Chief Medical Officer, Chickasaw Nation Medical Center, Ada, OK, p. A504

MCCLANAHAN, Gary, Chief Information Officer, Northeastern Health System Sequoyah, Sallisaw, OK, p. A515

MCCLARIGAN, Linda R.N., Chief Nursing Officer, Adirondack Health, Saranac Lake, NY, p. A452

MCCLASKEY, Cynthia, Ph.D., Director, Southwestern Virginia Mental Health Institute, Marion, VA, p. A670

MCCLEARY, Heather, Director Human Resources, Coulee Medical Center, Grand Coulee, WA, p. A681

MCCLEESE, Randy
Chief Information Officer, Methodist Hospital Union County, Morganfield, KY, p. A265
Chief Information Officer, Methodist Hospital, Henderson, KY, p. A259
Vice President Information Services and Chief Information Officer, St. Claire Healthcare, Morehead, KY, p. A265

MCCLELLAN, Ashley, FACHE, Chief Executive Officer, Woman's Hospital Of Texas, Houston, TX, p. A624

MCCLELLAN, Kathryn, Chief Information Officer, Memorial Health, Savannah, GA, p. A164

MCCLELLAND, Michele
Vice President Human Resources, Northwestern Medicine Kishwaukee Hospital, Dekalb, IL, p. A185
Vice President Human Resources, Northwestern Medicine Valley West Hospital, Sandwich, IL, p. A200

MCCLELLAND, Patricia, Director Human Resources, South Texas Health System, Edinburg, TX, p. A610

MCCLINTIC, James M.D., Vice President Medical Affairs, St. Anthony's Hospital, Saint Petersburg, FL, p. A142

MCCLINTICK, Cliff, Chief Information Officer, Lindner Center Of Hope, Mason, OH, p. A495

MCCLOSKEY, Louis, Chief Human Resources, Wilmington Veterans Affairs Medical Center, Wilmington, DE, p. A116

MCCLUNG, James W., Chief Executive Officer, Healthsouth Rehabilitation Hospital Of Alexandria, Alexandria, LA, p. A269

MCCLUNG, Lyle M.D., Chief of Staff, Carilion Stonewall Jackson Hospital, Lexington, VA, p. A669

MCCLURE, David K., President and Chief Executive Officer, Camden Clark Medical Center, Parkersburg, WV, p. A694

MCCLURE, Kenneth M.D., Chief of Staff, Longview Regional Medical Center, Longview, TX, p. A630

MCCLURG, Cathy, Director Human Resources, William Newton Hospital, Winfield, KS, p. A254

MCCLURG, Chris, Vice President Finance and Chief Financial Officer, St. Claire Healthcare, Morehead, KY, p. A265

MCCLURKAN, Mac, Chief Information Officer, Oaklawn Hospital, Marshall, MI, p. A326

MCCLUSKEY, Diane, Chief Human Resources Officer, Placentia–Linda Hospital, Placentia, CA, p. A80

MCCLUSKEY, Scott Elton, Chief Financial Officer, Tyler County Hospital, Woodville, TX, p. A655

MCCLUSKEY, Tabb M.D., Chief Medical Officer, Hendricks Community Hospital Association, Hendricks, MN, p. A341

MCCLUSKEY, Zachary, Chief Executive Officer, Chippenham Hospital, Richmond, VA, p. A674

MCCLUSKY, Derek M.D., Chief of Staff, Northern Louisiana Medical Center, Ruston, LA, p. A285

MCCLYMONT, Troy, Chief Information Technology Officer, Sheridan Memorial Hospital, Plentywood, MT, p. A387

MCCOBB, David, Chief Information Officer, Foothill Presbyterian Hospital, Glendora, CA, p. A62

MCCOIC, Kristie, Clinic Operations Officer and Director Human Resources, Gundersen St. Joseph's Hospital And Clinics, Hillsboro, WI, p. A703

MCCOLLUM, Joann, Chief Nursing Officer, Bolivar Medical Center, Cleveland, MS, p. A353

MCCOLLUM, Kathleen, Senior Vice President, Clinical Integration and Chief Operating Officer, University Of Maryland Baltimore Washington Medical Center, Glen Burnie, MD, p. A298

MCCOLLUM, Ken, Vice President, Human Resources, Northbay Medical Center, Fairfield, CA, p. A59

MCCOLM, Denni, Chief Information Officer, Citizens Memorial Hospital, Bolivar, MO, p. A364

MCCOMAS, Molly, Administrator, Altus Baytown Hospital, Baytown, TX, p. A596

MCCOMB, Canise A, Director Human Resources, Graham Hospital Association, Canton, IL, p. A179

MCCONKEY, Teresa L MSN, R.N., Vice President of Nursing and Chief Nursing Officer, Graham Hospital Association, Canton, IL, p. A179

MCCONLOGUE, Lisa M., MSN, Ph.D., Chief Executive Officer and Managing Director, Fairmount Behavioral Health System, Philadelphia, PA, p. A543

MCCONNACHIE, Angela, Chief Executive Officer and Chief Nursing Officer, Deckerville Community Hospital, Deckerville, MI, p. A317

MCCONNELL, George, Director, Earle E. Morris Alcohol And Drug Treatment Center, Columbia, SC, p. A560

MCCONNELL, Linda M R.N., MSN, FACHE, Associate Medical Center Director Patient Care Services, James H. Quillen Veterans Affairs Medical Center, Mountain Home, TN, p. A586

MCCONNELL, Patrick G, Chief Financial Officer, West Park Hospital, Cody, WY, p. A718

MCCONNELL, Ron, Chief Operating Officer, Upmc Altoona, Altoona, PA, p. A528

MCCONNELL, William, Ph.D., President and Chief Executive Officer, Mercy Regional Medical Center, Durango, CO, p. A101

MCCORD, Sam, Chief Nursing Officer, Willow Springs Center, Reno, NV, p. A405

MCCORMACK, J. David., Chief Executive Officer, Vaughan Regional Medical Center, Selma, AL, p. A23

MCCORMACK, Jane R.N., MSN, Vice President, Chief Nursing Officer and Nursing and Patient Care Services, Unity Hospital, Rochester, NY, p. A451

MCCORMICK, Brad, Chief Financial Officer, Natchitoches Regional Medical Center, Natchitoches, LA, p. A282

MCCORMICK, Daniel M.D., Vice President Medical Staff Affairs, Franciscan St. Anthony Health – Crown Point, Crown Point, IN, p. A206

MCCORMICK, Dee Dawn, Director Personnel and Human Resources, Coon Memorial Hospital, Dalhart, TX, p. A604

MCCORMICK, Jason, Interim Chief Financial Officer, Melissa Memorial Hospital, Holyoke, CO, p. A104

MCCORMICK, Jayne M.D., Chief Medical Officer CDS, Presbyterian Hospital, Albuquerque, NM, p. A425

MCCORMICK, John, President and Chief Executive Officer, Oak Valley Hospital District, Oakdale, CA, p. A77

MCCORMICK, Martha, Chief Executive Officer, Unity Medical Center, Manchester, TN, p. A583

MCCORMICK, Pam, Director Human Resources, Permian Regional Medical Center, Andrews, TX, p. A592

MCCOWN, Fran, Administrator, Haskell Memorial Hospital, Haskell, TX, p. A618

MCCOY, Adriene MS, Corporate Vice President, Baptist Health South Florida, Homestead Hospital, Homestead, FL, p. A127

MCCOY, Andrea C.S. M.D., Chief Medical Officer, Cape Regional Medical Center, Cape May Court House, NJ, p. A412

MCCOY, Craig, Chief Executive Officer, Bon Secours St. Francis Health System, Greenville, SC, p. A562

MCCOY, Doug
Chief Executive Officer, Kindred Hospital Las Vegas–Sahara, Henderson, NV, p. A402
Interim Chief Executive Officer, Kindred Hospital Seattle–Northgate, Seattle, WA, p. A685

MCCOY, Janice M MS, R.N., Chief Clinical Officer, Promise Hospital Of Florida At The Villages, Oxford, FL, p. A137

MCCOY, Jessica, Director Human Resources, Cedar Springs Hospital, Colorado Springs, CO, p. A99

MCCOY, Melissa, Vice President and Chief Financial Officer, West Virginia University Hospitals, Morgantown, WV, p. A694

MCCOY, Mike, Chief Executive Officer, Chambers Memorial Hospital, Danville, AR, p. A42

MCCOY, Shawn W., Chief Executive Officer, Deaconess Hospital, Evansville, IN, p. A207

MCCOY, Stephanie, President and Chief Executive Officer, Jackson General Hospital, Ripley, WV, p. A695

MCCRACKEN, Gail M.D., Medical Director, Baptist Health Extended Care Hospital, Little Rock, AR, p. A46

MCCRACKEN, Mark M.D., Chief of Staff, East Georgia Regional Medical Center, Statesboro, GA, p. A165

MCCRANIE, Robbie, Director Human Resources, Plano Specialty Hospital, Plano, TX, p. A638

MCCRAW, Elizabeth, Vice President, Human Resources, Caromont Regional Medical Center, Gastonia, NC, p. A463

MCCRAW, Nicki, Assistant Vice President Human Resources, Uw Medicine/Harborview Medical Center, Seattle, WA, p. A685

MCCREA, Kim, Chief Human Resources Officer, Ortonville Area Health Services, Ortonville, MN, p. A345

MCCREA, Yvette, Chief Human Resources, Winn Army Community Hospital, Hinesville, GA, p. A159

MCCREARY, Michael, Chief of Services, Mercy Hospital Washington, Washington, MO, p. A381

MCCREARY, William, Vice President and Chief Information Officer, The University Of Toledo Medical Center, Toledo, OH, p. A501

MCCRIMMON, Scott, Manager Information Technology, Northern Arizona Veterans Affairs Health Care System, Prescott, AZ, p. A34

MCCROSKEY, Mark, Vice President Operations, Northeastern Health System, Tahlequah, OK, p. A516

MCCUE, Jennifer, Director Patient Care, Summersville Regional Medical Center, Summersville, WV, p. A696

MCCUE, Raymond M.D., Chief Medical Officer, Bon Secours–Depaul Medical Center, Norfolk, VA, p. A671

MCCUE, Robert N, Vice President Finance, Mid Coast Hospital, Brunswick, ME, p. A290

MCCUE, Steven
Chief Financial Officer, Clinton Hospital, Clinton, MA, p. A306
Chief Financial Officer, Umass Memorial–Marlborough Hospital, Marlborough, MA, p. A308

MCCULLEY, Becky, Chief Operations Officer, University Of Texas Southwestern Medical Center, Dallas, TX, p. A607

MCCULLEY, Larry W., President and Chief Executive Officer, Touchette Regional Hospital, Centreville, IL, p. A180

MCCULLOCH, Greg CPA, Vice President of Finance and Chief Financial Officer, Adventist Health Sonora, Sonora, CA, p. A92

MCCULLOCH, Liz, Chief Information Resource Management Systems, Cheyenne Veterans Affairs Medical Center, Cheyenne, WY, p. A718

MCCULLOUGH, Barbara A, Vice President Human Resources, Washington Hospital, Washington, PA, p. A552

MCCULLOUGH, Bobby
Interim Chief Executive Officer, Memorial Satilla Health, Waycross, GA, p. A167
Chief Operating Officer, Memorial Hospital Jacksonville, Jacksonville, FL, p. A128

MCCULLOUGH, Mary Kelly, Associate Director Patient Care Services, Lexington Veterans Affairs Medical Center, Lexington, KY, p. A261

MCCULLOUGH, Patrick M.D., Chief Medical Services, Summit Behavioral Healthcare, Cincinnati, OH, p. A484

MCCULLOUGH, Wadra, Chief Nursing Officer, Wellstar Spalding Regional Hospital, Griffin, GA, p. A158

MCCULLY, Michael, Chief Operating Officer, Northport Veterans Affairs Medical Center, Northport, NY, p. A448

MCCUNE, Anne, Chief Operating Officer, Lucile Salter Packard Children's Hospital Stanford, Palo Alto, CA, p. A79

MCCUNE, Becky, Director Human Resources, Community Relations and Education, Coffeyville Regional Medical Center, Coffeyville, KS, p. A239

MCCURDY, Brent, Director Management Information, St. Croix Regional Medical Center, St Croix Falls, WI, p. A713

MCCURDY, Judy R.N., Vice President and Chief Nursing Officer, St. Vincent Medical Center, Los Angeles, CA, p. A71

MCCURLEY, John M.D., Chief Medical Officer, Bon Secours St. Francis Medical Center, Midlothian, VA, p. A670

MCCURRY, Michael, President, St. Anthony's Medical Center, Saint Louis, MO, p. A378

MCCUTCHAN, Matt, Chief Financial Officer, Greater Regional Medical Center, Creston, IA, p. A225

MCCUTCHEON, Edna I.
Chief Executive Officer, Norristown State Hospital, Norristown, PA, p. A542
Chief Executive Officer, Torrance State Hospital, Torrance, PA, p. A551

MCDADE, E. R.N., MS, Ph.D., , Walter P. Reuther Psychiatric Hospital, Westland, MI, p. A333

MCDADE, Len, Chief Executive Officer, Continuecare Hospital At Baptist Health Paducah, Paducah, KY, p. A266

MCDANALD, Matt M.D., Chief Medical Officer, Baptist Health La Grange, La Grange, KY, p. A260

MCDANEL, Joyce
Vice President Human Resources and Education, Unitypoint Health – Iowa Methodist Medical Center, Des Moines, IA, p. A226
Vice President Human Resources and Education, Unitypoint Health–Iowa Lutheran Hospital, Des Moines, IA, p. A226

MCDANIEL, Amy, Chief Executive Officer, Iowa Specialty Hospital–Belmond, Belmond, IA, p. A222

MCDANIEL, Donald E III, Chief Financial Officer, Paris Regional Medical Center, Paris, TX, p. A636

MCDANIEL, Graciela, Chief Financial Officer, Philadelphia Veterans Affairs Medical Center, Philadelphia, PA, p. A545

MCDANIEL, Hilton, President, Piedmont Geriatric Hospital, Burkeville, VA, p. A665

MCDANIEL, Kim, Director Human Resources, Healthsouth Rehabilitation Hospital Of Montgomery, Montgomery, AL, p. A21

MCDANIEL, LaDonna, Financial Manager, Prattville Baptist Hospital, Prattville, AL, p. A22

MCDANIEL, Lisa A, Chief Human Resources Officer, Samaritan Healthcare, Moses Lake, WA, p. A682

MCDANIEL, Randy, Information Systems Director, Jackson Purchase Medical Center, Mayfield, KY, p. A264

MCDANIEL, Suzie Q, Chief Human Resource Officer, Bay Area Hospital, Coos Bay, OR, p. A521

MCDANNALD, E.R., Interim Chief Executive Officer, Taylor Regional Hospital, Hawkinsville, GA, p. A158

MCDAVID, Clarence, Vice President Human Resources, Rose Medical Center, Denver, CO, p. A101

MCDERMOTT, James M.D., Chief of Staff, Sedan City Hospital, Sedan, KS, p. A251

MCDERMOTT, Mary MSN, MS, R.N., Senior Vice President Patient Care Services and Chief Nursing Officer, Phelps Memorial Hospital Center, Sleepy Hollow, NY, p. A452

MCDERMOTT, Michael P., M.D.
President and Chief Executive Officer, Mary Washington Hospital, Fredericksburg, VA, p. A667
President and Chief Executive Officer, Stafford Hospital, Stafford, VA, p. A675

MCDERMOTT, Suzan, Director, Human Resources, Gouverneur Hospital, Gouverneur, NY, p. A436

MCDERMOTT–LORD, Sheila, Chief Executive Officer, Haven Behavioral Senior Care Of Albuquerque, Albuquerque, NM, p. A424

MCDEVITT, Robert J M.D., Chief of Staff, Wilson Memorial Hospital, Sidney, OH, p. A499

MCDONAGH, Andrew M.D., Chief Medical Officer, Aurora West Allis Medical Center, West Allis, WI, p. A715

MCDONALD, Amanda MSN, Chief Nurse Executive, Kerrville State Hospital, Kerrville, TX, p. A626

MCDONALD, Carl, Regional Director Human Resources, Broward Health Imperial Point, Fort Lauderdale, FL, p. A124

MCDONALD, Connie, Chief Financial Officer, Marion Veterans Affairs Medical Center, Marion, IL, p. A192

MCDONALD, Edward A, Chief Financial Officer, Adventist Health St. Helena, Vallejo, CA, p. A95

MCDONALD, Elizabeth, Director Human Resources, Wayne Memorial Hospital, Honesdale, PA, p. A536

MCDONALD, Joseph D., FACHE, President and Chief Executive Officer, Catholic Health System, Buffalo, NY, p. B29

MCDONALD, Frederick Joseph., Commanding Officer, Naval Hospital Oak Harbor, Oak Harbor, WA, p. A683

MCDONALD, Gary
Associate Administrator Human Resources, Stone County Medical Center, Mountain View, AR, p. A47
Chief Facilities and Personnel Officer, White River Medical Center, Batesville, AR, p. A40

MCDONALD, Gregory, Vice President Finance and Chief Financial Officer, Roswell Park Cancer Institute, Buffalo, NY, p. A433

MCDONALD, Harold E, Deputy Executive Director and Senior Vice President Administration, Nassau University Medical Center, East Meadow, NY, p. A435

MCDONALD, Holly, Controller, Boundary Community Hospital, Bonners Ferry, ID, p. A172

MCDONALD, Jackie, Chief Nursing Officer, Allegiance Specialty Hospital Of Kilgore, Kilgore, TX, p. A626

MCDONALD, Jeff, Information Technology Manager, Florida Hospital Wauchula, Wauchula, FL, p. A147

MCDONALD, John, M.D.
Chief Medical Officer, Medical City North Hills, North Richland Hills, TX, p. A635
Chief Operating Officer, Northwest Texas Healthcare System, Amarillo, TX, p. A592

MCDONALD, Larry, Director Human Resources, Miami Jewish Home And Hospital For Aged, Miami, FL, p. A133

MCDONALD, Mark, M.D., President and Chief Executive Officer, Institute For Orthopaedic Surgery, Lima, OH, p. A493

MCDONALD, Michael S. Jr, Chief Executive Officer, Friends Hospital, Philadelphia, PA, p. A544

MCDONALD, Shari, Vice President Patient Care Services, Mercy Hospital, Buffalo, NY, p. A433

MCDONALD, Shelly, Chief Human Resources Officer, Ness County Hospital District No 2, Ness City, KS, p. A247

MCDONALD, Stanton B M.D., Medical Director, Heber Valley Medical Center, Heber City, UT, p. A657

MCDONALD, Stuart M.D., President Medical Staff, Kindred Hospital–Fort Worth, Fort Worth, TX, p. A614

MCDONALD, Susan, Vice President, Medical Affairs, Sentara Rmh Medical Center, Harrisonburg, VA, p. A668

MCDONALD, Tedd M.D., Chief Medical Officer, Banner Churchill Community Hospital, Fallon, NV, p. A401

MCDONALD–PINKETT, Shelly, Chief Medical Officer, Howard University Hospital, Washington, DC, p. A117

MCDONNELL, M. Therese M.D., Interim Vice President Patient Safety, Quality and Medical Affairs, Sibley Memorial Hospital, Washington, DC, p. A118

MCDONNELL, Michael M.D., Chief Medical Officer, Mercy Hospital And Medical Center, Chicago, IL, p. A182

MCDONNELL, Nancy, Manager Information Systems, Illinois Valley Community Hospital, Peru, IL, p. A197

MCDOUGLE, Mark, Executive Vice President and Chief Operating Officer, Maimonides Medical Center, New Rochelle, NY, p. A442

MCDOWELL, Arthur V M.D., III, Vice President Clinical Affairs, Middlesex Hospital, Middletown, CT, p. A111

MCDOWELL, Jean, Chief Financial Officer, Kindred Hospital–Dallas, Dallas, TX, p. A605

MCDOWELL, Paul L
Deputy Chief Financial Officer, Mission Hospital, Asheville, NC, p. A457
Vice President Finance and Chief Financial Officer, King's Daughters Medical Center, Ashland, KY, p. A255

MCDOWELL, Richard, M.D.
Medical Director, Kona Community Hospital, Kealakekua, HI, p. A170
Chief Financial Officer, Ridge Behavioral Health System, Lexington, KY, p. A261

MCDOWELL, Wendy R.N., Director of Nursing, Weisbrod Memorial County Hospital, Eads, CO, p. A102

MCDOWN, Missy, Director Information Systems, Via Christi Hospital Pittsburg, Pittsburg, KS, p. A250

MCDRURY, Martha M R.N., Chief Operating Officer and Chief Nursing Officer, Holy Family Hospital, Methuen, MA, p. A308

MCEACHERN, John, Controller, Sebastian River Medical Center, Sebastian, FL, p. A142

MCEACHERN, Michael L., Chief Executive Officer, Promise Hospital Of Wichita Falls, Wichita Falls, TX, p. A654

MCEACHIN, Brenda, Human Resources Director, Jeff Davis Hospital, Hazlehurst, GA, p. A158

MCELDOWNEY, Erin, Manager Human Resources, Haven Senior Horizons, Phoenix, AZ, p. A33

MCELMURRAY, Dodie, Chief Operating Officer, Greenwood Leflore Hospital, Greenwood, MS, p. A355

MCELRATH, Matthew
Chief Human Resources Officer, Keck Hospital Of Usc, Los Angeles, CA, p. A69
Chief Human Resources Officer, Usc Norris Comprehensive Cancer Center, Los Angeles, CA, p. A71

MCELROY, Sherry, Director Health Information Management, Osceola Community Hospital, Sibley, IA, p. A234

MCENTEE, Chris, Network Specialist, Van Buren County Hospital, Keosauqua, IA, p. A230

MCENTEE, Kara, Chief Financial Officer, Van Buren County Hospital, Keosauqua, IA, p. A230

MCENTIRE, Ann MSN, R.N., Chief Nursing Officer, Citizens Baptist Medical Center, Talladega, AL, p. A23

MCEUEN, Jacqueline, Coordinator Human Resources, Chi St. Joseph Health Bellville Hospital, Bellville, TX, p. A598

MCEWAN, Kevin K MSN, R.N., Vice President of Patient Care Service and Chief Nursing Officer, Down East Community Hospital, Machias, ME, p. A292

MCEWEN, Michelle, President and Chief Executive Officer, Speare Memorial Hospital, Plymouth, NH, p. A410

MCFADDEN, Mary T MSN, R.N., Chief Nurse Executive, Providence Portland Medical Center, Portland, OR, p. A525

MCFADYEN, David M., Administrator, St. Luke's Regional Medical Center, Boise, ID, p. A172

MCFALL, Cathy, Human Resources Manager, Kiowa County Memorial Hospital, Greensburg, KS, p. A242

MCFALL, Michael, Chief Financial Officer, Kindred Rehabilitation Hospital Clear Lake, Webster, TX, p. A653

MCFALL, Vicky, Chief Executive Officer, Monroe County Medical Center, Tompkinsville, KY, p. A268

MCFALL–ROBERTS, Ebuni, Director Human Resources, Holly Hill Hospital, Raleigh, NC, p. A469

MCFARLAND, Kenneth D., Chief Executive Officer, Fountain Valley Regional Hospital And Medical Center, Fountain Valley, CA, p. A60

MCFARLAND, Nita, Director of Nursing, Kingman Community Hospital, Kingman, KS, p. A244

MCFARLAND, Rhonda
Director Human Resources, Carolinas Healthcare System Anson, Wadesboro, NC, p. A472
Director Human Resources, Carolinas Healthcare System Union, Monroe, NC, p. A467

MCFARLAND, Rodney M.D., Medical Director, Freeman Neosho Hospital, Neosho, MO, p. A374

MCFARLAND, Tracee, Chief Financial Officer, Claiborne Medical Center, Tazewell, TN, p. A589

MCFARLANE, Kristy S, Director Human Resources, Lifecare Medical Center, Roseau, MN, p. A347

MCFARLANE, Michael
Chief Human Resource Officer, St. Louis Psychiatric Rehabilitation Center, Saint Louis, MO, p. A378
Director Human Resource, Hawthorn Children Psychiatric Hospital, Saint Louis, MO, p. A377
Director Human Resources, Metropolitan St. Louis Psychiatric Center, Saint Louis, MO, p. A377

MCFERRAN, Virginia, Chief Information Officer, Ucla Medical Center–Santa Monica, Santa Monica, CA, p. A91

MCGAHEY, Nikki, Information Officer, Jefferson County Hospital, Waurika, OK, p. A519

MCGANN, Robert M.D., President Medical Staff, Upmc Jameson Hospital, New Castle, PA, p. A542

MCGARIGLE, Kristine R.N., Vice President Patient Care, Ministry Good Samaritan Health Center, Merrill, WI, p. A707

MCGARVEY, Missy, Chief Information Officer, Twin Valley Behavioral Healthcare, Columbus, OH, p. A488

MCGEACHEY, Edward J., President and Chief Executive Officer, Southern Maine Health Care – Biddeford Medical Center, Biddeford, ME, p. A290

MCGEACHEY, Edward J, President and Chief Executive Officer, Southern Maine Health Care – Biddeford Medical Center, Biddeford, ME, p. A290

MCGEE, Angela, Vice President Nursing Services, Aultman Orrville Hospital, Orrville, OH, p. A497

MCGEE, Genemarie R.N., MS, Chief Nursing Officer, Sentara Leigh Hospital, Norfolk, VA, p. A672

MCGEE, Jessica
Chief Financial Officer, AMG Specialty Hospital–Denham Springs, Denham Springs, LA, p. A274
Chief Financial Officer, AMG Specialty Hospital–Lafayette, Lafayette, LA, p. A278

MCGEE, Kevin, Chief Executive Officer, River Point Behavioral Health, Jacksonville, FL, p. A128

MCGEE, Mark F M.D., Chief Clinical Officer, Appalachian Behavioral Healthcare, Athens, OH, p. A480

MCGEE, Terry, Chief Operations Officer, Central State Hospital, Milledgeville, GA, p. A161

MCGEEHAN, Paul M.D., Chief Medical Staff, Corry Memorial Hospital, Corry, PA, p. A532

MCGETTIGAN, Ryan, Chief Information Officer, Coatesville Veterans Affairs Medical Center, Coatesville, PA, p. A532

MCGHEE, Michael M.D., Medical Director, Behavioral Healthcare Center At Clarksville, Clarksville, TN, p. A577

MCGIBBON, Monica, Chief Nursing Officer, Terence Cardinal Cooke Health Care Center, New Rochelle, NY, p. A447

MCGILL, Martha, Executive Vice President and Chief Operating Officer, Nicklaus Children's Hospital, Miami, FL, p. A133

MCGILL, Rusty, System Director Information Technology, Indiana University Health Arnett Hospital, Lafayette, IN, p. A214

MCGILL, Steve, Vice President Finance and Chief Financial Officer, Wabash General Hospital, Mount Carmel, IL, p. A194

MCGILL, Thomas, Chief Information Officer, Butler Health System, Butler, PA, p. A530

MCGILL, Timothy W., Chief Executive Officer, Livingston Regional Hospital, Livingston, TN, p. A583

MCGILVRAY, Greg, Chief Financial Officer, Medical Center Enterprise, Enterprise, AL, p. A17

MCGIMSEY, Erika, Controller, Jewish Hospital–Shelbyville, Shelbyville, KY, p. A267

MCGINTY, Daniel B., President and Chief Executive Officer, Franciscan Sisters Of Christian Charity Sponsored Ministries, Inc., Manitowoc, WI, p. B53

MCGINLEY, Mary Ann Ph.D., Senior Vice President, Patient Services and Chief Nursing Officer, Thomas Jefferson University Hospitals, Philadelphia, PA, p. A546

MCGINNIS, Christina, Director Information Technology, Menorah Medical Center, Overland Park, KS, p. A249

MCGINNIS, Jeff M.D., President Medical Staff, Saint Joseph Mount Sterling, Mount Sterling, KY, p. A265

MCGINNIS, Paula, Chief Executive Officer, St. Joseph's Hospital, Tampa, FL, p. A145

MCGIRL, John, Chief Human Resources Officer, Nch Downtown Naples Hospital, Naples, FL, p. A135

MCGLADE, James, Director Human Resources, United Hospital, Saint Paul, MN, p. A348

MCGLEW, Timothy, Chief Executive Officer, Kern Valley Healthcare District, Lake Isabella, CA, p. A65

MCGLON, Tracy, Director Human Resources, Gulf Coast Medical Center, Panama City, FL, p. A138

MCGLOTHLIN, Wylie M.D., Chief Medical Officer, Henry County Hospital, New Castle, IN, p. A217

MCGLYNN, Mia, Director Management Information Systems, Plantation General Hospital, Plantation, FL, p. A140

MCGOLDRICK, Margaret M., President, Abington Hospital, Abington, PA, p. A528

MCGOVERN, Charles, Chief of Staff, Margaret Mary Health, Batesville, IN, p. A203

MCGOVERN, Joanne MSN, R.N., Chief Nursing Officer, Eastern Regional Medical Center, Philadelphia, PA, p. A543

MCGOVERN, Julia, Vice President Human Resources, Chilton Medical Center, Pompton Plains, NJ, p. A419

MCGOVERN, Julie, Vice President Human Resources, Anne Arundel Medical Center, Annapolis, MD, p. A294

MCGOVERN, Pam, Director Technology, Huggins Hospital, Wolfeboro, NH, p. A410

MCGOVERN, Sandra, Chief Nursing Officer, Up Health System–Bell, Ishpeming, MI, p. A323

MCGOWAN, Donna, Administrator, Lane County Hospital, Dighton, KS, p. A240

MCGOWEN, Bernard A M.D., Medical Director, Kindred Hospital Tarrant County–Arlington, Arlington, TX, p. A593

MCGOWIN, Norman F M.D., III, Chief of Staff, L. V. Stabler Memorial Hospital, Greenville, AL, p. A18

MCGRAIL, David, Vice President Finance, Carney Hospital, Boston, MA, p. A303

MCGRAIL, Karen, District Director Human Resource, Kindred Hospital Detroit, Detroit, MI, p. A318

MCGRAIL, Robert, Chief Executive Officer, West Branch Regional Medical Center, West Branch, MI, p. A333

MCGRATH, Denise B., Chief Executive Officer, Healthsouth Sea Pines Rehabilitation Hospital, Melbourne, FL, p. A132

MCGRATH, Kelly, Chief Medical Officer, Clearwater Valley Hospital And Clinics, Orofino, ID, p. A175

MCGRATH, Lynn M.D., Vice President Medical Affairs, Deborah Heart And Lung Center, Browns Mills, NJ, p. A412

MCGRAW, Belinda
Director Human Resources, Boulder City Hospital, Boulder City, NV, p. A401
Director Human Resources, Complex Care Hospital At Tenaya, Las Vegas, NV, p. A402

MCGRAW, Karin L., MSN, FACHE, Director, Veterans Affairs Pittsburgh Healthcare System, Pittsburgh, PA, p. A548

MCGRAW, Kathleen M.D., Chief Medical Officer, Brattleboro Memorial Hospital, Brattleboro, VT, p. A662

MCGRAW, Scott M.D., Medical Director, Baylor Surgical Hospital At Las Colinas, Irving, TX, p. A625

MCGREAHAM, David S M.D., Vice President Medical Affairs, Munson Medical Center, Traverse City, MI, p. A332

MCGREEVY, John, FACHE
Chief Executive Officer, Christus Mother Frances Hospital – Tyler, Tyler, TX, p. A650
President, Methodist Southlake Hospital, Southlake, TX, p. A646

MCGREGOR, Catherine, Deputy Director Facility and Administrative Services, Capital District Psychiatric Center, Albany, NY, p. A430

MCGREGOR, Julie
Director Human Resources, Sts. Mary & Elizabeth Hospital, Louisville, KY, p. A263
Vice President and Chief People Officer, Jewish Hospital, Louisville, KY, p. A262

MCGREGOR, Robert M.D., Chief Medical Officer, Akron Children's Hospital, Akron, OH, p. A479

MCGREW, David S, Chief Financial Officer, San Mateo Medical Center, San Mateo, CA, p. A89

MCGREW, Deborah A, Vice President and Chief Operating Officer, University Of Texas Medical Branch, Galveston, TX, p. A616

MCGREW, Diane, Chief Nurse Executive, Montgomery County Memorial Hospital, Red Oak, IA, p. A234

MCGRIFF, Marchelle M, Chief Nursing Executive, Sutter Medical Center, Sacramento, Sacramento, CA, p. A84

MCGUCKEN, Holly R.N., Chief Nursing Officer, Fort Walton Beach Medical Center, Fort Walton Beach, FL, p. A125

MCGUE, Lisa, Controller, Healthsouth Northern Kentucky Rehabilitation Hospital, Edgewood, KY, p. A257

MCGUE, Thomas E. M.D., Vice President Medical Affairs and Chief Medical Officer, Newport Hospital, Newport, RI, p. A556

MCGUFFIN, Patty R.N., Chief Nursing Officer, Allen County Regional Hospital, Iola, KS, p. A243

MCGUIGAN, Kevin M.D., Medical Director, St. Lawrence Rehabilitation Center, Lawrenceville, NJ, p. A415

MCGUILL, Gail R.N., MSN, Chief Nursing Officer and Administrative Director of Patient Care Services, Shriners Hospitals For Children–Salt Lake City, Salt Lake City, UT, p. A660

MCGUINNESS, Patrick, Chief Information Management, Keller Army Community Hospital, West Point, NY, p. A455

MCGUIRE, Ann M., Regional Vice President Human Resources, Indiana University Health Ball Memorial Hospital, Muncie, IN, p. A216

MCGUIRE, Cynthia, FACHE, President and Chief Executive Officer, Monadnock Community Hospital, Peterborough, NH, p. A410

MCGUIRE, Matthew, President and Chief Executive Officer, Western Regional Medical Center, Goodyear, AZ, p. A30

MCGUIRE, Patrick, Chief Financial Officer, Michigan Market, St. John Macomb–Oakland Hospital, Warren, MI, p. A332

MCGUIRE, Shane, Chief Executive Officer, Columbia County Health System, Dayton, WA, p. A680

MCGUIRK, Christina Marie R.N., Chief Nursing Officer, Health Central Hospital, Ocoee, FL, p. A136

MCGUIRL, Mary, Director Information Systems, Oneida Healthcare, Oneida, NY, p. A448

MCGURK, Kevin, Controller, Bellin Psychiatric Center, Green Bay, WI, p. A703

MCHARDY, Bryson M.D., President Medical Staff, Hannibal Regional Hospital, Hannibal, MO, p. A368

MCHUGH, Matthew, Director Information Services, Vaughan Regional Medical Center, Selma, AL, p. A23

MCHUGH, Michael J., M.D., Medical Director, Cleveland Clinic Children's Hospital For Rehabilitation, Cleveland, OH, p. A485

MCHUGH, Ryan M.D., Chief of Staff, The Medical Center Of Southeast Texas, Port Arthur, TX, p. A639

MCHUGH, William M.D., Medical Director and Chief Medical Officer, Trinitas Regional Medical Center, Elizabeth, NJ, p. A413

MCILROY, Gail, Director Medical Records, Promise Hospital Of Wichita Falls, Wichita Falls, TX, p. A654

MCILVAIN, Spencer, Director of Human Resources, Peterson Healthcare And Rehabilitation Hospital, Wheeling, WV, p. A697

MCILWAIN, T Pinckney M.D., Vice President and Chief Medical Officer, Charleston Area Medical Center, Charleston, WV, p. A691

MCINERNEY, Terry, Director of Nursing, Inpatient, Navos, Seattle, WA, p. A685

MCINTOSH, Craig, Chief Information Officer, Northwest Specialty Hospital, Post Falls, ID, p. A175

MCINTOSH, Ernasha, Interim Director of Nursing, Sage Memorial Hospital, Ganado, AZ, p. A29

MCINTOSH, Joe, Director Management Information Systems, Logansport State Hospital, Logansport, IN, p. A215

MCINTOSH, Tyler, Chief Financial Officer, Creek Nation Community Hospital, Okemah, OK, p. A511

MCINTYRE, Cindy R.N., Administrative Director Clinical Services, Magee General Hospital, Magee, MS, p. A358

MCINTYRE, Daniel J., President and Chief Executive Officer, The Charlotte Hungerford Hospital, Torrington, CT, p. A113

MCINTYRE, Kathleen, Province Leader, American Province Of Little Company Of Mary Sisters, Evergreen Park, IL, p. B9

MCIWAIN, John, Director Human Resources, Wayne Memorial Hospital, Jesup, GA, p. A159

MCKAIN, Rick, Chief Executive Officer, Anderson County Hospital, Garnett, KS, p. A241

MCKALE, Brigitte MSN, FACHE, Vice President and Chief Nurse Executive, Pali Momi Medical Center, Aiea, HI, p. A168

MCKAY, Amy, Chief Nursing Officer, Mid–America Rehabilitation Hospital, Shawnee Mission, KS, p. A251

MCKAY, Daniel E.
Chief Executive Officer, Sparks Medical Center – Van Buren, Van Buren, AR, p. A50
Chief Executive Officer, Sparks Regional Medical Center, Fort Smith, AR, p. A44

MCKAY, Danny H., Administrator, Noxubee General Hospital, Macon, MS, p. A358

MCKAY, Michael, Chief Information Officer, Wickenburg Community Hospital, Wickenburg, AZ, p. A38

MCKAY, Rebecca, Director Human Resources, Sweeny Community Hospital, Sweeny, TX, p. A647

MCKAY, Ronda R.N., Vice President Patient Care Services, Chief Nursing Officer, Community Hospital, Munster, IN, p. A216

MCKEAN, Kathy M.P.H., R.N., Vice President, Chief Nursing Executive, Hackensack Meridian Health Riverview Medical Center, Red Bank, NJ, p. A420

MCKEE, Debra R.N., Chief Clinical Officer and Chief Nursing Officer, Joint Township District Memorial Hospital, Saint Marys, OH, p. A498

MCKEE, Michele, Vice President and Chief Financial Officer, St. Louis Children's Hospital, Saint Louis, MO, p. A378

MCKEE, Robert J, Vice President Human Resources, Penn Highlands Dubois, Dubois, PA, p. A533

MCKEE, Willis P M.D., Jr, Chief Medical Officer, Frankfort Regional Medical Center, Frankfort, KY, p. A258

MCKEEBY, Ben, Senior Vice President and Chief Information Officer, Grady Memorial Hospital, Atlanta, GA, p. A150

MCKEEBY, Jon W, Chief Information Officer, National Institutes Of Health Clinical Center, Bethesda, MD, p. A297

MCKEEN, Marcia, Director Human Resources, Twin Valley Behavioral Healthcare, Columbus, OH, p. A488

MCKELDIN, Pat, Human Resource Business Partner, Kaiser Permanente Manteca Medical Center, Manteca, CA, p. A73

MCKENNA, Dennis M.D., Interim Vice President Medical Affairs, Albany Medical Center, Albany, NY, p. A430

MCKENNA, Donald, President and Chief Executive Officer, St. Mary's Health Care System, Athens, GA, p. A149

MCKENNA, John F., Chief Executive Officer and Managing Director, Rockford Center, Newark, DE, p. A115

MCKENNA, Quinn, Chief Operating Officer, Stanford Health Care, Palo Alto, CA, p. A79

MCKENNERY, Kay, Interim Chief Executive Officer, Hickory Trail Hospital, Desoto, TX, p. A609

MCKENNEY, Jennifer M.D., Chief Medical Officer, Fredonia Regional Hospital, Fredonia, KS, p. A241

MCKENZIE, Christine, Director Human Resources, Davis Regional Medical Center, Statesville, NC, p. A471

MCKENZIE, Jackie, Director Administrative Services, Beacham Memorial Hospital, Magnolia, MS, p. A358

MCKENZIE, Kimberly, R.N., MSN
Chief Nursing Officer and Chief Operations Officer, Harbor–Ucla Medical Center, Torrance, CA, p. A93
MCKENZIE, Kimberly, R.N., MSN, Interim Chief Executive Officer, Harbor–Ucla Medical Center, Torrance, CA, p. A93

MCKENZIE, Sandra D., Executive Vice President and Chief Operating Officer, Hamilton Medical Center, Dalton, GA, p. A156

MCKENZIE, Troy, Chief information Officer, Faith Community Hospital, Jacksboro, TX, p. A625

MCKENZIE, William G., President, Chief Executive Officer and Chairman, Gilliard Health Services, Montgomery, AL, p. B54

MCKEON, John, Vice President Human Resources, Kingsbrook Jewish Medical Center, New Rochelle, NY, p. A442

MCKEON, Sean, Director, Information Technology, Franciscan Children's, Brighton, MA, p. A304

MCKEOWN, Colleen
Senior Vice President and Area Manager, Kaiser Permanente Antioch Medical Center, Antioch, CA, p. A51
Senior Vice President and Area Manager, Kaiser Permanente Walnut Creek Medical Center, Walnut Creek, CA, p. A96

MCKERNAN, James E., Chief Operating Officer, Bronson Battle Creek, Battle Creek, MI, p. A315

MCKERNAN, Kathleen S., Director Information Systems, Pioneers Memorial Healthcare District, Brawley, CA, p. A54

MCKEVETT, Timothy M., President, Beloit Health System, Beloit, WI, p. A699

MCKIBBEN, Leeanna, R.N., MSN
Vice President Patient Services and Chief Nursing Officer, Upmc Mckeesport, Mckeesport, PA, p. A540
Vice President Patient Services and Chief Nursing Officer, Upmc Mercy, Pittsburgh, PA, p. A547

MCKIBBEN, Sean, President and Chief Operating Officer, Mount Carmel, Columbus, OH, p. A487

MCKIDDY, Paul, Director Information Technology, Monroe County Medical Center, Tompkinsville, KY, p. A268

MCKIE, Kathy, Director Human Resources, Montrose Memorial Hospital, Montrose, CO, p. A106

MCKILLIP, Ed, Director of Finance, Riddle Hospital, Media, PA, p. A541

MCKIMMY, Doyle L., FACHE, Chief Executive Officer, Jewell County Hospital, Mankato, KS, p. A246

MCKINLEY, Bryan, Chief Financial Officer, St. Mark's Hospital, Salt Lake City, UT, p. A660

MCKINLEY, Ernie, Chief Information Officer, University Medical Center, Las Vegas, NV, p. A404

MCKINLEY, Ivy
Director Human Resources, Presence Holy Family Medical Center, Des Plaines, IL, p. A185
Regional Human Resources Officer, Community First Medical Center, Chicago, IL, p. A180
Regional Lead Human Resources, Presence Resurrection Medical Center, Chicago, IL, p. A182

MCKINLEY, John, Director, Information Technology, Community Mental Health Center, Lawrenceburg, IN, p. A214

MCKINLEY, Mike, Information Security Officer, West Texas Veterans Affairs Health Care System, Big Spring, TX, p. A598

MCKINLEY, Ronald Ph.D., Vice President Human Resources and Employee Services, University Of Texas Medical Branch, Galveston, TX, p. A616

MCKINLEY, Rudolph Jr, Vice President Operations and Chief Operating Officer, East Tennessee Children's Hospital, Knoxville, TN, p. A581

MCKINNEY, Brenda, Chief Executive Officer, Reeves County Hospital, Pecos, TX, p. A637

MCKINNEY, Bruce, Business Officer, Administrative Services, Central Prison Hospital, Raleigh, NC, p. A468

MCKINNEY, Dan, Administrator, Hermann Area District Hospital, Hermann, MO, p. A369

MCKINNEY, Dana, Chief Nursing Officer, Select Specialty Hospital–Madison, Madison, WI, p. A705

MCKINNEY, Daniel, Chief Operating Officer, Mary Black Health System–Spartanburg, Spartanburg, SC, p. A566

MCKINNEY, James, Warden, Iowa Medical And Classification Center, Coralville, IA, p. A224

MCKINNEY, Rex, President and Chief Executive Officer, Decatur County Memorial Hospital, Greensburg, IN, p. A209

MCKINNEY, Thomas, Administrator, Christus St. Michael Health System, Texarkana, TX, p. A649

MCKINNON, Mark M.D., Chief of Staff, North Runnels Hospital, Winters, TX, p. A655

MCKINNON, Ron, Chief Information Officer, Ellis Hospital, Schenectady, NY, p. A452

MCKINNON, Scott, President and Chief Executive Officer, Memorial Hospital, North Conway, NH, p. A410

MCKINSTRY, Merissa, Chief Operating Officer, Columbus Dublin Springs, Dublin, OH, p. A490

MCKNIGHT, David CPA, Chief Financial Officer, Spotsylvania Regional Medical Center, Fredericksburg, VA, p. A667

MCKNIGHT, Stephanie, Hospital Nursing Manager, Sanford Bagley Medical Center, Bagley, MN, p. A336

MCKNIGHT, Tim M.D., Chief of Staff, Trinity Hospital Twin City, Dennison, OH, p. A490

MCKOY, Lori, Business Partner, Pender Memorial Hospital, Burgaw, NC, p. A458

MCKULA, Tim, Vice President Information Systems and Chief Information Officer, Shirley Ryan Abilitylab, Chicago, IL, p. A183

MCKUNE, Jeff, Chief Health Informatics Officer, Phelps County Regional Medical Center, Rolla, MO, p. A376

MCLAIN, Allen M.D., Chief of Staff, Grisell Memorial Hospital District One, Ransom, KS, p. A250

MCLAIN, Cindy, Chief Executive Officer, Select Specialty Hospital–Fort Smith, Fort Smith, AR, p. A43

MCLAIN, John R., President and Chief Executive Officer, Bayfront Health St. Petersburg, Saint Petersburg, FL, p. A141

MCLANE, Kerry, Interim Chief Executive Officer, Select Specialty Hospital–Western Missouri, Kansas City, MO, p. A371

MCLARIN, Benita, Chief Operating Officer, Santa Clara Valley Medical Center, San Jose, CA, p. A89

MCLARTY, Walter L
Chief Human Resources Officer, Bethesda North Hospital, Cincinnati, OH, p. A483
Chief Human Resources Officer, Good Samaritan Hospital, Cincinnati, OH, p. A484

MCLAUGHLIN, Amy CPA, Chief Financial Officer, Manning Regional Healthcare Center, Manning, IA, p. A231

MCLAUGHLIN, Cathy R.N., MSN, Chief Nursing Officer, Medical City Arlington, Arlington, TX, p. A593

MCLAUGHLIN, Dan C.
Chief Executive Officer, Menifee Valley Medical Center, Sun City, CA, p. A93
Chief Hospital Executive Officer, Hemet Valley Medical Center, Hemet, CA, p. A63

MCLAUGHLIN, Kathryn, Chief Nursing Officer, Hemet Valley Medical Center, Hemet, CA, p. A63

MCLAUGHLIN, Leslie, Director of Business Development, Michiana Behavioral Health Center, Plymouth, IN, p. A218

MCLAUGHLIN, Maribeth R.N., Vice President Patient Care Services, Magee–Womens Hospital Of Upmc, Pittsburgh, PA, p. A547

MCLAUGHLIN, Neil R., R.N., Administrator and Vice President, Operations, Jefferson Medical Center, Ranson, WV, p. A695

MCLAUGHLIN, Pamela, Chief Financial Officer, Healthsouth Rehabilitation Hospital Of Austin, Austin, TX, p. A595

MCLAUGHLIN, Rebecca, Chief Human Resource Officer, Banner Goldfield Medical Center, Apache Junction, AZ, p. A28

MCLAUGHLIN, Sherry, Director Human Resources, Forrest City Medical Center, Forrest City, AR, p. A43

MCLAURIN, Monty E., Chief Executive Officer, Northwest Market, Indian Path Medical Center, Kingsport, TN, p. A581

MCLAWS, Douglas D.O., Chief Medical Officer, Manning Regional Healthcare Center, Manning, IA, p. A231

MCLEAN, Anthony
Market President, St. Francis Hospital, Federal Way, WA, p. A680
President, Highline Medical Center, Burien, WA, p. A679

MCLEAN, Chris, Chief Administrative Officer, Methodist Healthcare Memphis Hospitals, Memphis, TN, p. A585

MCLEAN, Cindy J R.N., MSN, Director of Nursing, Central Prison Hospital, Raleigh, NC, p. A468

MCLEAN, Georgia, Director Human Resources, Mount Sinai Medical Center, Miami Beach, FL, p. A134

MCLEAN, Robb M.D., Chief Medical Officer, UNM Sandoval Regional Medical Center, Inc., Rio Rancho, NM, p. A428

MCLENDON, Carla
Director Human Resources, Appling Healthcare System, Baxley, GA, p. A152
Director Information Resource Management Services, Charles George Veterans Affairs Medical Center, Asheville, NC, p. A457

MCLENDON, John
Senior Vice President and Chief Information Officer, Amita Health Adventist Medical Center Bolingbrook, Bolingbrook, IL, p. A179

Vice President and Chief Information Officer, Johns Hopkins All Children's Hospital, Saint Petersburg, FL, p. A141

MCLENDON, Tom, Administrator, Evergreen Medical Center, Evergreen, AL, p. A17

MCLEOD, Les, Director of Nursing Services, Blue Mountain Hospital, John Day, OR, p. A523

MCLEOD, Margie, Director Information Technology, North Canyon Medical Center, Gooding, ID, p. A173

MCLEOD, Michael M.D., Chief Medical Officer, Cuero Community Hospital, Cuero, TX, p. A604

MCLEOD, Sheldon, Chief Operating Officer, NYC Health + Hospitals / North Central Bronx, New Rochelle, NY, p. A445

MCLIN, Robert D., President and Chief Executive Officer, Good Samaritan Hospital, Vincennes, IN, p. A221

MCLOONE, Paul, M.D.
Chief Medical Officer, Unitypoint Health – Trinity Bettendorf, Bettendorf, IA, p. A222
Chief Medical Officer, Unitypoint Health – Trinity Rock Island, Rock Island, IL, p. A199

MCMACKIN, Ann, President, Vassar Brothers Medical Center, Poughkeepsie, NY, p. A450

MCMAHAN, Mike, President, St. Francis Regional Medical Center, Shakopee, MN, p. A348

MCMAHAN, Steve M.D., Chief Medical Officer, Glenwood Regional Medical Center, West Monroe, LA, p. A288

MCMAHON, Alisha, Director Human Resources, Mountrail County Medical Center, Stanley, ND, p. A478

MCMAHON, Andrew, Chief Fiscal Officer, Veterans Affairs Central Western Massachusetts Healthcare System, Leeds, MA, p. A308

MCMAHON, Chris, Chief Operating Officer, The Medical Center Of Southeast Texas, Port Arthur, TX, p. A639

MCMAHON, Elaine, Administrator, Kwajalein Hospital, Kwajalein Island, MH, p. A721

MCMAHON, Eugene
Senior Vice President and Chief Medical Officer, Capital Health Medical Center–Hopewell, Pennington, NJ, p. A418
Senior Vice President and Chief Medical Officer, Capital Health Regional Medical Center, Trenton, NJ, p. A421

MCMAHON, Leigh MS, R.N., Senior Vice President Patient Care Services and Chief Nursing Officer, White Plains Hospital Center, White Plains, NY, p. A456

MCMAHON, Nancy, Vice President Human Resources, Miriam Hospital, Providence, RI, p. A556

MCMANMON, Kristin, Chief Operating Officer, St. Mary's Hospital, Madison, WI, p. A705

MCMANUS, Doug, Chief Medical Officer, Aurora Medical Center Grafton, Grafton, WI, p. A702

MCMANUS, Michael T, Chief Operating Officer, Memorial Hospital, Belleville, IL, p. A178

MCMANUS, Ronald, Senior Vice President Clinical Services and Business Entities, Peconic Bay Medical Center, Riverhead, NY, p. A450

MCMASTER, Sandra
Regional Chief Information Officer, Kauai Veterans Memorial Hospital, Waimea, HI, p. A170
Regional Chief Information Officer, Samuel Mahelona Memorial Hospital, Kapaa, HI, p. A170

MCMATH, Mark W
Chief Information Officer, Indiana University Health Bloomington Hospital, Bloomington, IN, p. A204
Chief Information Officer, Methodist Healthcare Memphis Hospitals, Memphis, TN, p. A585

MCMEANS, TJ, Information Technology Technician, Black River Medical Center, Poplar Bluff, MO, p. A375

MCMENAMIN, Anneliese, Senior Vice President Information Technology and Program Services, Kennedy Health System, Stratford, NJ, p. A420

MCMICHEN, Diane, Director Human Resources, Dekalb Regional Medical Center, Fort Payne, AL, p. A18

MCMILLAN, Deborah, Director Human Resources, Glenn Medical Center, Willows, CA, p. A97

MCMILLAN, Donn
Chief Information Officer, Peacehealth Sacred Heart Medical Center University District, Eugene, OR, p. A521
Senior Director, IST Client Liaison, Peacehealth Southwest Medical Center, Vancouver, WA, p. A688

MCMILLAN, Douglas A., Administrator and Chief Executive Officer, West Park Hospital, Cody, WY, p. A718

MCMILLAN, Jon R, Chief Financial Officer, Banner Lassen Medical Center, Susanville, CA, p. A93

MCMILLAN, Sheila, Chief Financial Officer, Park Nicollet Methodist Hospital, Saint Louis Park, MN, p. A347

MCMILLEN, Eric, Chief Executive Officer, Ochsner Medical Center–Baton Rouge, Baton Rouge, LA, p. A270

MCMILLION, Kelley, Chief Nursing Officer, Clay County Memorial Hospital, Henrietta, TX, p. A619

MCMINN, Ken, Director Information Technology, Scotland County Hospital, Memphis, MO, p. A373

MCMINN, Melvin, Director Human Resources, Wernersville State Hospital, Wernersville, PA, p. A553

MCMINOWAY, Kelly R.N., Vice President, Nursing, Baptist Health Floyd, New Albany, IN, p. A217

MCMULLAN, Cheryl, Chief Financial Officer, Baylor Scott & White Medical Center At Waxahachie, Waxahachie, TX, p. A652

MCMULLAN, Heidi R.N., Chief Nursing Officer, Wellspan Philhaven, Mount Gretna, PA, p. A541

MCMULLEN, Thomas A, Chief Financial Officer, Kindred Hospital–Philadelphia, Philadelphia, PA, p. A544

MCMULLIN, John, Chief Financial Officer, Rehoboth Mckinley Christian Health Care Services, Gallup, NM, p. A426

MCMURRAY, Sharon, Director, Human Resources, Rock Springs, Georgetown, TX, p. A616

MCMURREN, Mary Anne, R.N., Chief Administrative Officer, Peacehealth Sacred Heart Medical Center University District, Eugene, OR, p. A521

MCMURREY, Jean Ann R.N., MSN, Chief Nursing Officer, RMC Jacksonville, Jacksonville, AL, p. A19

MCNABB, Dana, Human Resources Manager, Field Memorial Community Hospital, Centreville, MS, p. A353

MCNABB, Teresita R.N., FACHE, Vice President Nursing Services, Terrebonne General Medical Center, Houma, LA, p. A276

MCNAIR, Lisa CPA, Senior Vice President and Chief Financial Officer, Chi St. Joseph Regional Health Center, Bryan, TX, p. A600

MCNAIR, Rebekah, Director Human Resources, Healthsouth Chattanooga Rehabilitation Hospital, Chattanooga, TN, p. A576

MCNAIR, Scott, Chief Financial Officer, Neshoba County General Hospital, Philadelphia, MS, p. A360

MCNALLY, Joseph M.D., Medical Director, Streamwood Behavioral Health Center, Streamwood, IL, p. A201

MCNALLY, Kathy, Chief Nursing Officer, Healthsouth Rehabilitation Hospital At Drake, Cincinnati, OH, p. A484

MCNALLY, Lou–Ann, Executive Director Human Resources and Staff Development, Claxton–Hepburn Medical Center, Ogdensburg, NY, p. A448

MCNALLY, Michael, Vice President Human Resources, United Health Services Hospitals–Binghamton, Binghamton, NY, p. A432

MCNAMARA, John M.D., Senior Vice President, Chief Medical Officer, Torrance Memorial Medical Center, Torrance, CA, p. A94

MCNAMARA, Marilyn M.D., Chief Medical Officer, Southwest General Health Center, Middleburg Heights, OH, p. A496

MCNAMARA, Mike, Chief Information Officer, Mee Memorial Hospital, King City, CA, p. A64

MCNAMARA, Steve, Chief Financial Officer, Orange Coast Memorial Medical Center, Fountain Valley, CA, p. A60

MCNAMARA, Thomas D.O., Vice President Medical Affairs, Wellstar Cobb Hospital, Austell, GA, p. A152

MCNAMARA, Timothy M
Senior Vice President Human Resources, Bradford Regional Medical Center, Bradford, PA, p. A530
Senior Vice President Human Resources, Olean General Hospital, Olean, NY, p. A448

MCNAMEE, Hugar D.O., Chief Medical Officer, Florida Hospital Zephyrhills, Zephyrhills, FL, p. A148

MCNATT, James, Chief Financial Officer, Baylor Scott & White Medical Center – Carrollton, Carrollton, TX, p. A600

MCNAUGHTON, Richard, Chief Information Management Service, Maine Veterans Affairs Medical Center, Augusta, ME, p. A289

MCNEA, Melvin, Chief Executive Officer, Great Plains Health, North Platte, NE, p. A396

MCNEAR, Michael M.D., Chief Medical Officer, Jersey Community Hospital, Jerseyville, IL, p. A191

MCNEECE, Steve, President and Chief Executive Officer, Community Hospital Of Anaconda, Anaconda, MT, p. A382

MCNEEL, Jacob D.O., Chief of Staff, Plateau Medical Center, Oak Hill, WV, p. A694

MCNEEL, Wakelin M.D., Medical Director, Bhc Alhambra Hospital, Rosemead, CA, p. A83

MCNEIL, Ane, Vice President Human Resources, St. Joseph Mercy Oakland, Pontiac, MI, p. A328

MCNEIL, Karen, President, University Hospitals Samaritan Medical Center, Ashland, OH, p. A480

MCNEILL, Michael, Chief Financial Management, New Mexico Veterans Affairs Health Care System – Raymond G. Murphy Medical Center, Albuquerque, NM, p. A424

MCNEY, Jim, Senior Vice President Finance and Chief Financial Officer, North Kansas City Hospital, North Kansas City, MO, p. A374

MCNICHOLS, Janiece
Regional Chief Financial Officer, Hale Ho'Ola Hamakua, Honokaa, HI, p. A168

Regional Chief Financial Officer, Hilo Medical Center, Hilo, HI, p. A168
Regional Chief Financial Officer, Kau Hospital, Pahala, HI, p. A170

MCNULTY, Joseph S. III, President and Chief Executive Officer, Pioneer Health Services, Magee, MS, p. B98

MCNULTY, Stephanie, Chief Operating Officer, St. Petersburg General Hospital, Saint Petersburg, FL, p. A142

MCNULTY, Timothy, Director Human Resources, Spring Harbor Hospital, Westbrook, ME, p. A293

MCNUTT, Elena, Chief Nursing Officer, Desert Springs Hospital Medical Center, Las Vegas, NV, p. A403

MCNUTT, Mike, Assistant Administrator, Covenant Hospital Plainview, Plainview, TX, p. A637

MCNUTT, Pamela
Senior Vice President and Chief Information Officer, Methodist Dallas Medical Center, Dallas, TX, p. A606
Senior Vice President and Chief Information Officer, Methodist Mansfield Medical Center, Mansfield, TX, p. A631
Senior Vice President and Chief Information Officer, Methodist Richardson Medical Center, Richardson, TX, p. A639
Vice President Information Systems, Methodist Charlton Medical Center, Dallas, TX, p. A606

MCPEAK, Sara, Chief Nursing Officer, Carlinville Area Hospital, Carlinville, IL, p. A179

MCPHERSON, Lon M.D., Senior Vice President Medical Affairs and Chief Quality Officer, Munroe Regional Medical Center, Ocala, FL, p. A136

MCPHERSON, Rhonda, Vice President Human Resources, Fayette Regional Health System, Connersville, IN, p. A206

MCQUAID, David P., FACHE, Chief Operating Officer, Ohio State University Wexner Medical Center, Columbus, OH, p. A487

MCQUAID, David P FACHE, Chief Operating Officer, Ohio State University Wexner Medical Center, Columbus, OH, p. A487

MCQUAIDE, Ben M.D., Chief of Staff, Clark Regional Medical Center, Winchester, KY, p. A268

MCQUAIDE, Teresa A., Chief Executive Officer, Trenton Psychiatric Hospital, Trenton, NJ, p. A422

MCQUILLEN, Paul M.D., Chief Medical Officer, Jane Phillips Medical Center, Bartlesville, OK, p. A505

MCQUISTAN, Bob, Vice President Finance, York General, York, NE, p. A400

MCQUISTON, Mike, Administrative Director Human Resources, Wise Health System, Decatur, TX, p. A607

MCRAE, Ashley, Chief Clinical Officer, Kindred Hospital North Florida, Green Cove Springs, FL, p. A126

MCRAE, Colin, Chief Executive Officer, Tennova Healthcare–Jefferson Memorial Hospital, Jefferson City, TN, p. A580

MCRIMMON, Dana
Chief Financial Officer, Mesilla Valley Hospital, Las Cruces, NM, p. A427
Interim Chief Executive Officer, Mesilla Valley Hospital, Las Cruces, NM, p. A427

MCROBERTS, Kevin G FACHE, Senior Vice President of Operations, Lake Regional Health System, Osage Beach, MO, p. A374

MCROBERTS, Susan, R.N., MSN
Chief Nursing Officer, Franciscan St. Francis Health–Carmel, Carmel, IN, p. A205
Vice President and Chief Nursing Officer, Franciscan St. Francis Health – Indianapolis, Indianapolis, IN, p. A211

MCSWAIN, Marilyn, MSN, R.N., Administrator, Lake Charles Memorial Hospital, Lake Charles, LA, p. A279

MCTAGGART, Jac, Chief Executive Officer, Sanford Hillsboro Medical Center, Hillsboro, ND, p. A476

MCTIGRIT, Chris, Manager Information Technology, Delta Memorial Hospital, Dumas, AR, p. A42

MCTIGUE, Mary, Vice President Patient Care Services and Chief Nursing Officer, Trinitas Regional Medical Center, Elizabeth, NJ, p. A413

MCTIGUE, Michael
Chief Information Officer, Clara Maass Medical Center, Belleville, NJ, p. A411
Chief Information Officer, Saint Barnabas Medical Center, Livingston, NJ, p. A415

MCVAY, Tara, Chief Nursing Officer, Logansport Memorial Hospital, Logansport, IN, p. A215

MCVEIGH, Kevin, Chief Human Resources Officer, Banner Desert Medical Center, Mesa, AZ, p. A31

MCVEY, Eric A M.D., Executive Vice President Medical Affairs and Quality, St. Dominic–Jackson Memorial Hospital, Jackson, MS, p. A357

MCVEY, Lynn, Chief Operating Officer, Meadowlands Hospital Medical Center, Secaucus, NJ, p. A420

MCVEY, Marian Lorraine, Chief Nursing Officer, North Greenville Hospital, Travelers Rest, SC, p. A566

MCVEY, Patrick, Chief Executive Officer, Kindred Hospital North Florida, Green Cove Springs, FL, p. A126

MCWAY, Jacob, Senior Vice President and Chief Financial Officer, Cox Medical Centers, Springfield, MO, p. A379

MCWEY, Russ M.D., Vice President and Chief Information Officer, Virginia Hospital Center – Arlington, Arlington, VA, p. A664

MCWHERTER, Joe, Chief Financial Officer, Baptist Memorial Hospital–Desoto, Southaven, MS, p. A362

MCWILLIAMS, Jill, Chief Nursing Officer, Sierra Nevada Memorial Hospital, Grass Valley, CA, p. A62

MEACHAM, Byanka, Director Human Resources, Montgomery County Emergency Service, Norristown, PA, p. A542

MEACHAM, Steve, Vice President Finance, King's Daughters' Health, Madison, IN, p. A215

MEACHEM, Michelle, Director Human Resources, The University Of Vermont Health Network Elizabethtown Community Hospital, Elizabethtown, NY, p. A435

MEAD, Linda, Director Human Resources, Margaretville Hospital, Margaretville, NY, p. A439

MEAD, Richard, Senior Director Human Resources, Saint Francis Memorial Hospital, San Francisco, CA, p. A87

MEAD, Rick, Human Resources Leader, Kaiser Permanente Oakland Medical Center, Oakland, CA, p. A77

MEADE, Andrew, Chief Executive Officer, Select Specialty Hospital–Longview, Longview, TX, p. A630

MEADE, Robert C., Chief Executive Officer, Doctors Hospital Of Sarasota, Sarasota, FL, p. A142

MEADE, Stephanie R.N., MSN, Chief Nursing Officer, Mercy Health – West Hospital, Cincinnati, OH, p. A484

MEADE, Teresa R.N., Chief Nursing Officer, Boone Memorial Hospital, Madison, WV, p. A693

MEADOWS, Barbara, Chief Financial Manager, Captain James A. Lovell Federal Health Care Center, North Chicago, IL, p. A195

MEADOWS, Danny M.D., Medical Director, Logansport State Hospital, Logansport, IN, p. A215

MEADOWS, Hal M.D., Chief Medical Officer, Banner Lassen Medical Center, Susanville, CA, p. A93

MEADOWS, Mark, Chief Executive Officer, Lone Peak Hospital, Draper, UT, p. A656

MEADOWS, Nancy, Chief Financial Officer, Methodist Hospital, San Antonio, TX, p. A643

MEADOWS, Peri, Director Human Resources, Rhea Medical Center, Dayton, TN, p. A578

MEADOWS, Sheila M, Chief Human Resources Officer, Mission Hospital, Asheville, NC, p. A457

MEADOWS, Terri, Chief Nursing Executive, Merit Health Madison, Canton, MS, p. A353

MEADOWS, Theresa, Chief Information Officer, Cook Children's Medical Center, Fort Worth, TX, p. A613

MEANS, Dennis M.D., Vice President Medical Affairs, Carilion New River Valley Medical Center, Christiansburg, VA, p. A666

MEANS, William H. Jr, Administrator, Bastrop Rehabilitation Hospital, Monroe, LA, p. A281

MEARNS, Stephanie, R.N.
Vice President and Chief Nursing Officer, West Hills Hospital And Medical Center, Los Angeles, CA, p. A72
Vice President Patient Care Services and Chief Nurse Executive, Seton Medical Center, Daly City, CA, p. A57

MEARS, Edith, Chief Executive Officer, Regional General Hospital, Williston, FL, p. A148

MEARS, Terry, Director Information Systems, Duke Regional Hospital, Durham, NC, p. A461

MECHAM, Cindy, Health Information Director, Mountain View Hospital, Payson, UT, p. A659

MEDAGLIA, Guy A., President and Chief Executive Officer, Saint Anthony Hospital, Chicago, IL, p. A183

MEDCIROS, Ron, Director Applied Information Technology, Worcester Recovery Center And Hospital, Worcester, MA, p. A313

MEDEIROS, Katherine A., President and Chief Executive Officer, Sierra Nevada Memorial Hospital, Grass Valley, CA, p. A62

MEDEROS, Ana J., Chief Executive Officer, Palmetto General Hospital, Hialeah, FL, p. A126

MEDINA, Alberto, Information Technology Senior Consultant, Hospital Manati Medical Center, Manati, PR, p. A724

MEDINA, Betsmari, Director Human Resources, Dr. Ramon E. Betances Hospital–Mayaguez Medical Center Branch, Mayaguez, PR, p. A724

MEDINA, Ed M.D., Medical Director, Phillips County Hospital, Malta, MT, p. A386

MEDINA, Eleanor M.D., Chief Medical Officer, Behavioral Center Of Michigan, Warren, MI, p. A332

MEDINA, Luz D, Controller, Hospital Hermanos Melendez, Bayamon, PR, p. A722

MEDINA, Marco, Chief Information Officer, Stanton County Hospital, Johnson, KS, p. A243

MEDINA, Obdulia, Associate Director for Administrative Support, Clinical Management and Ambulatory Care, Ashford Presbyterian Community Hospital, San Juan, PR, p. A725

MEDINA, Shelby, Chief Executive Officer, Windom Area Hospital, Windom, MN, p. A350

MEDINA CRUZ, Victor L., M.D., Administrator, Hospital Cuidado Agudo Especializado En Pacientes Politraumatizados, San Juan, PR, p. A726

MEDLAND, Jacqueline, MS, Ph.D., President and Chief Nursing Officer, Highlands–Cashiers Hospital, Highlands, NC, p. A464

MEDLEY, Adron M.D., Chief Medical Staff, Northern Rockies Medical Center, Cut Bank, MT, p. A383

MEDLEY, Barry, Director Information Systems, Cook Medical Center–A Campus Of Tift Regional Medical Center, Adel, GA, p. A149

MEDLEY, Dennis
Chief Executive Officer and Administrator, Physicians' Medical Center, New Albany, IN, p. A217
Chief Executive Officer, Physicians' Medical Center, New Albany, IN, p. A217

MEDLEY, Wathen M.D., Chief Medical Officer, Owensboro Health Regional Hospital, Owensboro, KY, p. A265

MEDLIN, John, Chief Nursing Officer, North Carolina Specialty Hospital, Durham, NC, p. A461

MEDLIN, Marcia, Chief Executive Officer, Select Specialty Hospital–Central Pennsylvania, Camp Hill, PA, p. A530

MEDLIN, Marsha, Senior Vice President of Clinical and Operations, Pam Specialty Hospital Of Covington, Covington, LA, p. A273

MEDLOCK, Darci, Manager Human Resources, St. Vincent Dunn Hospital, Bedford, IN, p. A204

MEDOVICH, Lisa, Chief Financial Officer, Peterson Regional Medical Center, Kerrville, TX, p. A626

MEE, Thomas, R.N., President and Chief Executive Officer, Mclaren Greater Lansing, Lansing, MI, p. A324

MEEKER, Brian D.O., President Medical Staff, Virginia Gay Hospital, Vinton, IA, p. A235

MEEKER, Chris M.D., Chief Medical Officer, Sanford Bismarck, Bismarck, ND, p. A474

MEEKER, Christina, Director Human Resources, Strategic Behavioral Health – Raleigh, Garner, NC, p. A463

MEEKER, Mark D.O., Medical Staff President, OSF St. Mary Medical Center, Galesburg, IL, p. A188

MEEKINS, Lance, Chief Executive Officer, Nocona General Hospital, Nocona, TX, p. A635

MEEKINS, Michelle, Manager Human Resources, Sentara Virginia Beach General Hospital, Virginia Beach, VA, p. A676

MEEKS, Deborah, Chief Nursing Officer, Harlingen Medical Center, Harlingen, TX, p. A618

MEENK, Susan
Vice President Human Resources, Providence St. Peter Hospital, Olympia, WA, p. A683
Vice President Service Area, Providence Centralia Hospital, Centralia, WA, p. A679

MEESE, Larry, Chief Executive Officer, Lane Regional Medical Center, Zachary, LA, p. A288

MEESIG, Deborah M.D., Chief of Staff, Chillicothe Veterans Affairs Medical Center, Chillicothe, OH, p. A483

MEGEHEE, Mark, Vice President and Chief Information Officer, Decatur Morgan Hospital, Decatur, AL, p. A16

MEGGERS, Marla, R.N., MSN
Chief Nursing Officer, Gilbert Hospital, Gilbert, AZ, p. A29
Chief Nursing Officer and Chief Operating Officer, Florence Hospital At Anthem, Florence, AZ, p. A29

MEGLEMRE, Amy J R.N., MSN, Senior Vice President and Chief Nursing Officer, Olathe Medical Center, Olathe, KS, p. A248

MEGLI, Cami, Controller, Morrison Community Hospital, Morrison, IL, p. A194

MEGLIOLA, Donna M, Assistant Vice President, Johnson Memorial Medical Center, Stafford Springs, CT, p. A113

MEGOW, Kimberly M.D., Chief Medical Officer, South Georgia Medical Center, Valdosta, GA, p. A166

MEGUIAR, Ramon V M.D., Chief Medical Officer, Memorial Health, Savannah, GA, p. A164

MEHAFFEY, SHRM–SCP, M. Beth, Senior Vice President Human Resources, Baptist Medical Center Jacksonville, Jacksonville, FL, p. A127

MEHINDRU, Vinay, M.D.
Medical Director, Wuesthoff Medical Center – Rockledge, Rockledge, FL, p. A141
Vice President/Chief Medical Officer, Florida Hospital Waterman, Tavares, FL, p. A145

MEHR, Nicholle, Vice President Operations, Mclaren Oakland, Pontiac, MI, p. A328

MEHTA, Kalpana, Chief Fiscal Services, Jesse Brown Veterans Affairs Medical Center, Chicago, IL, p. A181

MEHTA, Sonia, M.D., Chief Executive Officer and Chief Medical Officer, Loretto Hospital, Chicago, IL, p. A181

MEHTA, Umesh M.D., Interim Chief Medical Officer, Carrier Clinic, Belle Mead, NJ, p. A411

MEIDINGER, Sue, Manager Business Office, Linton Hospital, Linton, ND, p. A477

MEIERGERD, Jean, Chief Information Officer, St. Francis Memorial Hospital, West Point, NE, p. A400

MEIERS, Dawn, Coordinator Medical Staff and Personnel Services, Southeast Michigan Surgical Hospital, Warren, MI, p. A332

MEIGS, Jeffrey L, Chief Financial Officer, Louis A. Weiss Memorial Hospital, Chicago, IL, p. A182

MEIGS, John M.D., Jr, Chief of Staff, Bibb Medical Center, Centreville, AL, p. A16

MEIJER, Carol, Chief Nursing Officer, Southern Coos Hospital And Health Center, Bandon, OR, p. A520

MEINDEL, Nympha R.N., Chief Information Officer, North Shore University Hospital, Manhasset, NY, p. A439

MEINHART, Richard, Manager Information Systems, Daviess Community Hospital, Washington, IN, p. A221

MEINKE, Kenneth, Senior Vice President Administrative Services, Finance and Chief Financial Officer, Spartanburg Medical Center, Spartanburg, SC, p. A566

MEINKE, Victor E, Chief Financial Officer, Jewish Home Of San Francisco, San Francisco, CA, p. A87

MEINKOTH, Jennifer, Chief Information Officer, Memorial Hospital, Belleville, IL, p. A178

MEISINGER, Alan, Chief Financial Officer, Herington Municipal Hospital, Herington, KS, p. A242

MEISNER, Anne, MSN, President and Chief Executive Officer, Southeastern Regional Medical Center, Newnan, GA, p. A162

MEKHAEL, Hani M.D., Chief Staff, Havenwyck Hospital, Auburn Hills, MI, p. A314

MEKO, Christian, Hospital Commander, General Leonard Wood Army Community Hospital, Fort Leonard Wood, MO, p. A368

MELAHN, William L M.D., Vice President Medical Affairs and Chief Medical Officer, St. Claire Healthcare, Morehead, KY, p. A265

MELAN, Kristen, Director Human Resources Administration, Good Shepherd Specialty Hospital, Bethlehem, PA, p. A529

MELANCON, Eric, Chief of Staff, Teche Regional Medical Center, Morgan City, LA, p. A282

MELAND, Jeff M.D., Vice President, Chief Medical Officer, Northfield Hospital, Northfield, MN, p. A345

MELARAGNO, Robert, Vice President Finance, O'Bleness Memorial Hospital, Athens, OH, p. A480

MELBOURNE, John M.D., Medical Director, Conifer Park, Glenville, NY, p. A436

MELBY, Gina, Chief Executive Officer, JFK Medical Center, Atlantis, FL, p. A119

MELBY, Larry, Chief Executive Officer, Select Specialty Hospital–Palm Beach, Lake Worth, FL, p. A130

MELBY, Rachel, Vice President, Chief Financial Officer, Crawford County Memorial Hospital, Denison, IA, p. A226

MELCHER, Nancy, Chief Nursing Officer, Wellstar North Fulton Hospital, Roswell, GA, p. A164

MELCHIOR, Eric L, Executive Vice President and Chief Financial Officer, Greater Baltimore Medical Center, Baltimore, MD, p. A294

MELEAR, Brian, Chief Executive Officer, Raulerson Hospital, Okeechobee, FL, p. A136

MELENDEZ, Alma, Controller, Dimmit Regional Hospital, Carrizo Springs, TX, p. A600

MELENDEZ, Jose M.D., Chief Medical Officer, Uchealth Memorial, Colorado Springs, CO, p. A100

MELENDEZ, Pedro
Chief Executive Director, Hospital Menonita De Cayey, Cayey, PR, p. A723
Chief Executive Officer, Centro De Salud Conductual Menonita–Cima, Aibonito, PR, p. A721
Chief Executive Officer, Mennonite General Hospital, Aibonito, PR, p. A722

MELINE, Brenda, Manager Human Resources, Patients' Hospital Of Redding, Redding, CA, p. A81

MELL, Kevin, Vice President Operations, Medstar Montgomery Medical Center, Olney, MD, p. A300

MELLETT, David, Chief Financial Officer, Harrison Memorial Hospital, Cynthiana, KY, p. A257

MELLGREN, Gustave M.D., Chief of Staff, Glacial Ridge Health System, Glenwood, MN, p. A340

MELLO, Brett, Chief Information Officer, Cayuga Medical Center At Ithaca, Ithaca, NY, p. A437

MELLO, Paul, Manager Data Processing, Metropolitan State Hospital, Norwalk, CA, p. A76

MELLON, Stacy, Manager Human Resource, Hillsdale Hospital, Hillsdale, MI, p. A322

MELLOWS, George, Facility Director, Hawthorn Center, Northville, MI, p. A327

MELNIKOFF, Jean, Vice President Human Resources, Kaiser Permanente Medical Center, Honolulu, HI, p. A168

MELSON, Benjamin B CPA, Senior Vice President and Chief Financial Officer, University Of Texas M.D. Anderson Cancer Center, Houston, TX, p. A623

MELTON, Anne, Chief Nursing Officer, Sumner Regional Medical Center, Gallatin, TN, p. A579

MELTON, Chad, Chief Executive Officer, Fauquier Hospital, Warrenton, VA, p. A676

MELTON, Josh, Chief Information Officer, St. Bernards Medical Center, Jonesboro, AR, p. A45

MELTVEDT, Robert M.D., Jr, Vice President Medical Affairs, Warren Memorial Hospital, Front Royal, VA, p. A668

MELTZER, David B, Chief Financial Officer, Texas Health Presbyterian Hospital Denton, Denton, TX, p. A608

MELTZER, Neil M., President and Chief Executive Officer, Lifebridge Health, Baltimore, MD, p. B76

MELVILLE, Carol, Director Human Resources, West Houston Medical Center, Houston, TX, p. A623

MELVIN, Susan D.O., Chief Medical Officer, Long Beach Memorial Medical Center, Long Beach, CA, p. A66

MENA, Theodore, Chief Executive Officer, Select Specialty Hospital–Orlando, Orlando, FL, p. A137

MENDELOWITZ, Susan, R.N., FACHE
Executive Vice President and Chief Operating Officer, Bergen Regional Medical Center, Paramus, NJ, p. A418
President, Administrator and Chief Operating Officer, Bergen Regional Medical Center, Paramus, NJ, p. A418

MENDEZ, Alex A
Chief Financial Officer, The Miami Medical Center, Miami, FL, p. A134
Executive Vice President of Operations and Chief Financial Officer, Mount Sinai Medical Center, Miami Beach, FL, p. A134

MENDEZ, Bryce H.P., Healthcare Policy Analyst, Bureau Of Medicine And Surgery, Department Of The Navy, Falls Church, VA, p. B23

MENDEZ, James, Chief Executive Officer, Kindred Hospital–Dallas, Dallas, TX, p. A605

MENDEZ, Kim K Ed.D., R.N., Chief Nurse Officer, NYC Health + Hospitals / Bellevue, New Rochelle, NY, p. A444

MENDEZ, Lincoln S., Chief Executive Officer, Baptist Health South Florida, South Miami Hospital, Miami, FL, p. A132

MENDEZ, Nicholas Paul., Chief Executive Officer, Pam Specialty Hospital Of Hammond, Hammond, LA, p. A275

MENDEZ, Samantha, Human Resources, Scottsdale Liberty Hospital, Scottsdale, AZ, p. A36

MENDIOLA–BALDERAS, Rosie L, Director Information Systems, South Texas Health System, Edinburg, TX, p. A610

MENDITTO, Anthony Ph.D., Interim Chief Operating Officer, Fulton State Hospital, Fulton, MO, p. A368

MENDIZABAL, Oscar, Chief Nursing Officer, Highlands Rehabilitation Hospital, El Paso, TX, p. A611

MENDOZA, Aniceta R.N., MSN, Chief Nursing Officer, Valley Baptist Medical Center–Brownsville, Brownsville, TX, p. A599

MENDOZA, Carlos, Controller, Baptist Memorial Rehabilitation Hospital, Germantown, TN, p. A579

MENDOZA, Christopher, Chief Executive Officer, Alliancehealth Ponca City, Ponca City, OK, p. A514

MENDOZA, Dana, Chief Information Officer, Maui Memorial Medical Center, Wailuku, HI, p. A170

MENDOZA, Jackie, Chief Nursing Officer, Chi Health Nebraska Heart, Lincoln, NE, p. A395

MENDOZA, Joseph, M.D.
Medical Director, Porterville Developmental Center, Porterville, CA, p. A80
Chief Financial Officer, Hillcrest Hospital Cushing, Cushing, OK, p. A506
Chief Financial Officer, Hillcrest Hospital Henryetta, Henryetta, OK, p. A508

MENDOZA, Yolanda, Director Human Resources, Rehabilitation Hospital Of Southern New Mexico, Las Cruces, NM, p. A427

MENDYKA, Nick, Chief Financial Officer, University Of Virginia Medical Center, Charlottesville, VA, p. A665

MENEFEE, Jason J, Chief Financial Officer, Mccamey County Hospital District, Mccamey, TX, p. A632

MENGLE, Scott, Vice President Human Resources, Penn State Health St. Joseph, Reading, PA, p. A549

MENKES, Jeffrey, President and Chief Executive Officer, Burke Rehabilitation Hospital, White Plains, NY, p. A456

MENNONNA, Guy, Senior Vice President Human Resources, Bergen Regional Medical Center, Paramus, NJ, p. A418

MENON, Rema M.D., Clinical Director, Parsons State Hospital And Training Center, Parsons, KS, p. A249

MENSCH, Alan M.D., Senior Vice President Medical Affairs, Plainview Hospital, Plainview, NY, p. A449

MENSEN, Amy, Chief Administrative Officer, Regional Medical Center, Manchester, IA, p. A231

MENTGEN, John, FACHE, President and Chief Executive Officer, Regional West Medical Center, Scottsbluff, NE, p. A399

MENTHCOAST, Lynn, Chief Fiscal Service, Tennessee Valley Healthcare System, Nashville, TN, p. A587

MENTINK, Terri, Chief Financial Officer, Oakland Mercy Hospital, Oakland, NE, p. A396

MENTON, Timothy P., Interim Chief Executive Officer, Sierra Vista Regional Medical Center, San Luis Obispo, CA, p. A89

MENTZEL, Bridget, Director Human Resources, Mercy Health – West Hospital, Cincinnati, OH, p. A484

MENTZER, Larry, Chief Human Resources Officer, Veterans Affairs Roseburg Healthcare System, Roseburg, OR, p. A526

MENZEL, Colette Ph.D., Chief Financial Officer, Antelope Valley Hospital, Lancaster, CA, p. A65

MENZIE, Sue R.N., Director Patient Care, Sierra Tucson, Tucson, AZ, p. A38

MERCADO, Felix V., Chief Financial Officer, Lawrence General Hospital, Lawrence, MA, p. A307

MERCADO, Gloria, Director of Nursing, Mennonite General Hospital, Aibonito, PR, p. A722

MERCADO, Leda Marta R, Chief Operating Officer, Hospital Menonita De Cayey, Cayey, PR, p. A723

MERCADO, Rafael Rodriguez., Secretary of Health, Puerto Rico Department Of Health, San Juan, PR, p. B104

MERCER, David, Coordinator Information Systems, Baptist Memorial Hospital–Union City, Union City, TN, p. A590

MERCER, Shawna, Director Human Resources, Kansas Neurological Institute, Topeka, KS, p. A252

MERCER, William M.D., Director, Peterson Healthcare And Rehabilitation Hospital, Wheeling, WV, p. A697

MERCHANT, Deven M.D., Chief Medical Executive, Sutter Davis Hospital, Davis, CA, p. A57

MERCURI, Ralph, Vice President and Chief Financial Officer, Major Hospital, Shelbyville, IN, p. A219

MEREDITH, Katie, Chief Nursing Officer, Select Specialty Hospital–Lexington, Lexington, KY, p. A261

MEREDITH, Keith, Chief Operating Officer, Salem Regional Medical Center, Salem, OH, p. A499

MEREDITH, Linda MSN, MS, Chief Operating Officer, Baylor Scott & White Medical Center – Llano, Llano, TX, p. A629

MEREK, Gloria, Director of Nursing, Springfield Hospital Center, Sykesville, MD, p. A301

MERGEN, Lynn M., Chief Executive Officer, Hillcrest Hospital – South, Tulsa, OK, p. A517

MERIDA, Andy, Director Management Information Systems, Fayette Regional Health System, Connersville, IN, p. A206

MERILLO, Myra, Supervisor Health Information Management, Healthsouth Rehabilitation Hospital Of Spring Hill, Brooksville, FL, p. A121

MERINGOLO, Francis, Vice President Human Resources, Umass Memorial–Marlborough Hospital, Marlborough, MA, p. A308

MERIWETHER, Wayne, Chief Executive Officer, Twin Lakes Regional Medical Center, Leitchfield, KY, p. A260

MERK, Richard
Director Human Resources, Allegiance Behavioral Health Center Of Plainview, Plainview, TX, p. A637
Executive Vice President, Allegiance Behavioral Health Center Of Plainview, Plainview, TX, p. A637

MERKEL, Rebecca, Privacy Officer, Franciscan St. Francis Health–Carmel, Carmel, IN, p. A205

MERKLE, John F., Medical Center Director, Tuscaloosa Veterans Affairs Medical Center, Tuscaloosa, AL, p. A24

MERKLER, Michael, Chief of Staff, Mckenzie Health System, Sandusky, MI, p. A330

MERKLEY, Jason R., Chief Executive Officer, Brookings Health System, Brookings, SD, p. A568

MERKLIN, Paul, Vice President Finance and Chief Financial Officer, Manchester Memorial Hospital, Manchester, KY, p. A264

MERRIFIELD, Matt, Chief Operating Officer, Aiken Regional Medical Centers, Aiken, SC, p. A558

MERRIGAN, Mary C, Manager Public Relations, Sanford Vermillion Medical Center, Vermillion, SD, p. A573

MERRILL, Cheryl Bhima MSN, R.N., Senior Vice President Patient Care Services and Chief Nursing Officer, North Shore Medical Center, Salem, MA, p. A311

MERRILL, Chuck M.D., Vice President Medical Affairs, Marian Regional Medical Center, Santa Maria, CA, p. A91

MERRILL, Mark H., President and Chief Executive Officer, Valley Health System, Winchester, VA, p. B142

MERRILL, Michael M.D., Interim Vice President Medical Affairs, United Memorial Medical Center, Batavia, NY, p. A431

MERRILL, Rick W., System President and Chief Executive Officer, Cook Children's Medical Center, Fort Worth, TX, p. A613

MERRILL, Stacie, Chief Nursing Officer, Baylor Surgical Hospital At Fort Worth, Fort Worth, TX, p. A613

MERRILL, Stephanie, Chief Financial Officer, University Medical Center, Las Vegas, NV, p. A404

MERRITT, Becky A, Director Human Resources, Houston Methodist St. John Hospital, Nassau Bay, TX, p. A634

MERRITT, Belinda M.D., Medical Director, Spire Cane Creek Rehabilitation Hospital, Martin, TN, p. A583

MERRITT, Bradley M.D., Medical Director, Christus Trinity Mother Frances Rehabilitation Hospital, Tyler, TX, p. A650

MERRITT, Janet, Chief Financial Officer, St. Vincent Williamsport Hospital, Williamsport, IN, p. A221

MERRITT, Tim E., Chief Executive Officer, Summitridge Hospital, Lawrenceville, GA, p. A160

MERRITT, Trevor, Director Human Resources, Star Valley Medical Center, Afton, WY, p. A717

MERRY, Duane, Chief Information Officer, Little Falls Hospital, Little Falls, NY, p. A438

MERRYMAN, Angela, Chief Executive Officer, Select Specialty Hospital–Mckeesport, Mckeesport, PA, p. A540

MERRYMAN, Mary, Regional Director Information Management, Christus Health Shreveport–Bossier, Shreveport, LA, p. A285

MERRYMAN, Scott
Chief Financial Officer, Christus Coushatta Health Care Center, Coushatta, LA, p. A273
Chief Financial Officer, Christus Health Shreveport–Bossier, Shreveport, LA, p. A285
Chief Financial Officer, Christus St. Patrick Hospital Of Lake Charles, Lake Charles, LA, p. A279

MERRYWELL, Paul, Chief Information Officer, Sycamore Shoals Hospital, Elizabethton, TN, p. A578

MERSON, John M.D., Chief of Staff, John Muir Medical Center, Concord, Concord, CA, p. A56

MERSON, Wendy, Chief Executive Officer, Windmoor Healthcare Of Clearwater, Clearwater, FL, p. A122

MERTZ, John, Chief Information Officer, South Nassau Communities Hospital, Oceanside, NY, p. A448

MESA, Gustavo, Chief Information Officer, San Juan City Hospital, San Juan, PR, p. A726

MESIC, John M.D., Chief Medical Officer, Sutter Auburn Faith Hospital, Auburn, CA, p. A52

MESICK, Marc, Vice President and Chief Financial Officer, Ellis Hospital, Schenectady, NY, p. A452

MESKAN, Paula R.N., Chief Nursing Officer, River's Edge Hospital And Clinic, Saint Peter, MN, p. A348

MESORAS, Amber, Chief Human Resources Officer, Veterans Affairs Pittsburgh Healthcare System, Pittsburgh, PA, p. A548

MESSA–GILL, Nicole, Manager Human Resources, Northlake Behavioral Health System, Mandeville, LA, p. A280

MESSELT, Mary Jo
Manager Human Resources, Mercy Hospital Watonga, Watonga, OK, p. A519
Senior Human Resources Manager, Mercy Hospital Logan County, Guthrie, OK, p. A508

MESSER, Kelly, Director of Finance, Devereux Hospital And Children's Center Of Florida, Melbourne, FL, p. A132

MESSER, Mark D.O., Clinical Director, Terrell State Hospital, Terrell, TX, p. A648

MESSERSMITH, Scott E, Director Human Resources, Columbus Community Hospital, Columbus, NE, p. A392

MESSINA, Arlene R.N., MSN, Director of Nursing, Riverside Doctors' Hospital, Williamsburg, VA, p. A677

MESSINA, Daniel J., Ph.D., FACHE, President and Chief Executive Officer, Richmond University Medical Center, New Rochelle, NY, p. A446

MESSMAN, Catherine, Chief Financial Officer, Mills–Peninsula Health Services, Burlingame, CA, p. A54

MESTAS, Lisa, Associate Administrator and System Chief Nursing Officer, University Of South Alabama Medical Center, Mobile, AL, p. A21

MESTER, Sulynn R.N., Chief Nursing Officer, Childress Regional Medical Center, Childress, TX, p. A601

MESZLER, Lori A., Chief Financial Officer, Helen Hayes Hospital, West Haverstraw, NY, p. A455

METCALF, Angie L, Vice President and Chief Human Resource Officer, Martin Health System, Stuart, FL, p. A143

METCALF, Chris, Director of Nursing, Utah State Hospital, Provo, UT, p. A659

METCALF, Emma, MSN, R.N., Director, Lexington Veterans Affairs Medical Center, Lexington, KY, p. A261

METCALF, Kathleen, Chief Information Officer, University Hospitals Samaritan Medical Center, Ashland, OH, p. A480

METCALF, Peter M.D., President Medical Staff, Genesis Medical Center, Silvis, Silvis, IL, p. A200

METHE, Joan, Chief Information Officer, Mercy Medical Center, Springfield, MA, p. A311

METHVEN, Jeffrey M, Vice President Ambulatory Services and Chief Human Resources Officer, Saratoga Hospital, Saratoga Springs, NY, p. A452

METHVIN, Jeff, Manager Information Technology, St. Luke Hospital And Living Center, Marion, KS, p. A246

METIKO, Olushola M.D., Medical Director, Central Prison Hospital, Raleigh, NC, p. A468

METINKO, Andrew M.D., Chief Medical Officer, The Hsc Pediatric Center, Washington, DC, p. A118

METIVIER, Roberta, Vice President Human Resources and Administrator, Western Main Nursing Home, Stephens Memorial Hospital, Norway, ME, p. A292

METRO, Michelle, Vice President Nursing, Cloud County Health Center, Concordia, KS, p. A240

METTEAUER, Kenneth, Chief Financial Officer, Redmond Regional Medical Center, Rome, GA, p. A163

METZ, Amy, Chief Executive Officer, Regency Hospital Of Florence, Florence, SC, p. A562

METZ, Bruce Ph.D., Senior Vice President and Chief Information Officer, Lahey Hospital & Medical Center, Burlington, Burlington, MA, p. A305

METZ, Carl
   Vice President Human Resources, Ephraim Mcdowell Regional Medical Center, Danville, KY, p. A257
   Vice President, Ephraim Mcdowell Fort Logan Hospital, Stanford, KY, p. A268

METZGER, Alysha, Director Human Resources, Hill Country Memorial Hospital, Fredericksburg, TX, p. A615

METZGER, Cynthia, Chief Nursing and Operations Officer, Little River Memorial Hospital, Ashdown, AR, p. A40

METZGER, John, Controller, Northkey Community Care, Covington, KY, p. A257

METZGER, Terry, Vice President, Finance, St. Vincent Indianapolis Hospital, IndianapolisSt. Vincent Heart Center, Indianapolis, IN, p. A212

MEUER, Lynn, Interim Chief Nursing Officer, Sibley Memorial Hospital, Washington, DC, p. A118

MEURER, Bryan, Director Information Systems, Mat–Su Regional Medical Center, Palmer, AK, p. A27

MEURER, Lynn MSN, R.N., Interim Chief Nursing Officer, Wellstar Kennestone Hospital, Marietta, GA, p. A161

MEWHIRTER, Michael, President, Fort Hamilton Hospital, Hamilton, OH, p. A492

MEYER, Anthony M.D., Medical Director, Aurora Psychiatric Hospital, Wauwatosa, WI, p. A715

MEYER, Cheryl, MSN
   Director of Nursing, Haven Behavioral Senior Care Of Dayton, Dayton, OH, p. A489
   Director Human Resources, Gundersen Palmer Lutheran Hospital And Clinics, West Union, IA, p. A236

MEYER, Daniel T., President, Aurora Baycare Medical Center, Green Bay, WI, p. A702

MEYER, Daniel T, President, Aurora Baycare Medical Center, Green Bay, WI, p. A702

MEYER, Francis, Vice President Information Systems Technology, Kaleida Health, Buffalo, NY, p. A432

MEYER, Gordon, Director Human Resources, Oakland Regional Hospital, Southfield, MI, p. A331

MEYER, Joe S, Chief Financial Officer, Scott County Hospital, Scott City, KS, p. A251

MEYER, June MSN, R.N., Vice President Chief Nursing Officer, Laurel Regional Hospital, Laurel, MD, p. A299

MEYER, Karen, Vice President Finance and Chief Financial Officer, Rush Memorial Hospital, Rushville, IN, p. A219

MEYER, Kurt A
   Chief Human Resource Officer, Mishawaka Medical Center, Mishawaka, IN, p. A216
   Chief Human Resources Officer, Plymouth Medical Center, Plymouth, IN, p. A218

MEYER, Mark, Chief Financial Officer, Grady Memorial Hospital, Atlanta, GA, p. A150

MEYER, Michele C., Interim Chief Executive Officer, Washington County Memorial Hospital, Potosi, MO, p. A375

MEYER, Michele C, Vice President of Operations, Mercy Hospital Jefferson, Crystal City, MO, p. A367

MEYER, Morgan, Chief Financial Officer, Howard County Medical Center, Saint Paul, NE, p. A399

MEYER, Nate, Director Finance, Douglas County Hospital, Alexandria, MN, p. A335

MEYER, Renae M.D., Chief Medical Officer, St. Francis Memorial Hospital, West Point, NE, p. A400

MEYER, Robert L., President and Chief Executive Officer, Phoenix Children's Hospital, Phoenix, AZ, p. A34

MEYER, Roger M.D., Chief of Staff, Friend Community Healthcare System, Friend, NE, p. A393

MEYER, Timothy M.D., Chief of Staff, Memorial Medical Center – Neillsville, Neillsville, WI, p. A709

MEYER, Traci, Director Human Resources, Canyon Vista Medical Center, Sierra Vista, AZ, p. A36

MEYER, Wessel H. M.D., Chief of Staff, Veterans Affairs Central California Health Care System, Fresno, CA, p. A61

MEYERHOEFER, Todd M.D., Vice President Medical Affairs, Union Hospital, Dover, OH, p. A490

MEYERS, Audrey, FACHE, President and Chief Executive Officer, Valley Hospital, Ridgewood, NJ, p. A420

MEYERS, Betty, Chief Financial Officer, Crook County Medical Services District, Sundance, WY, p. A720

MEYERS, J Cullen., Chief Executive Officer, Pam Specialty Hospital Of Covington, Covington, LA, p. A273

MEYERS, Larry, Chief Information Officer, Wilson Memorial Hospital, Sidney, OH, p. A499

MEYERS, Mark S. M.D., Chief of Staff, Battle Mountain General Hospital, Battle Mountain, NV, p. A401

MEYERS, Russell, FACHE, President and Chief Executive Officer, Midland Memorial Hospital, Midland, TX, p. A633

MEYERS, William, Chief Information Officer, St. Luke's Hospital, Chesterfield, MO, p. A366

MEZA, Eduardo M.D., Medical Director, Prairie St. John's, Fargo, ND, p. A475

MEZA, Lourdes, Coordinator Human Resources, West Covina Medical Center, West Covina, CA, p. A96

MEZOFF, Adam M.D., Vice President and Chief Medical Officer, Children's Medical Center, Dayton, OH, p. A489

MHERABI, Nader, Senior Vice President and Vice Dean, Chief Information Officer, NYU Langone Hospitals, New Rochelle, NY, p. A446

MIANO, Christena, Human Resources Director, Medical Center Of Trinity, Trinity, FL, p. A146

MICAN, Deborah, Chief Nursing Officer and Vice President Nursing, Our Lady Of Lourdes Memorial Hospital, Inc., Binghamton, NY, p. A432

MICCOLI, Vincent
   Executive Director, Kirby Forensic Psychiatric Center, New Rochelle, NY, p. A442
   Executive Director, Manhattan Psychiatric Center–Ward's Island, New Rochelle, NY, p. A442

MICHAUD, Thomas A., Chief Executive Officer, Foundation Surgical Hospital Affiliates, Oklahoma City, OK, p. B52

MICHAEL, Amy J, Chief Operating Officer, Sullivan County Memorial Hospital, Milan, MO, p. A373

MICHAEL, Don, Vice President, Chief Financial Officer, Jay County Hospital, Portland, IN, p. A218

MICHAEL, Elizabeth R.N., MS, Vice President Patient Care Services and Chief Nursing Officer, Stillwater Medical Center, Stillwater, OK, p. A516

MICHAELS, Stephen T. M.D., Chief Operating Officer and Chief Medical Officer, Medstar St. Mary's Hospital, Leonardtown, MD, p. A299

MICHALEK, Debra, Chief Financial Officer, Fayette Regional Health System, Connersville, IN, p. A206

MICHALSKI, Carrie, President and Chief Executive Officer, Riverview Health, Crookston, MN, p. A338

MICHEL, Diane, Senior Vice President, Chief Nursing Officer, Children's Hospital, New Orleans, LA, p. A282

MICHEL, George J, Chief Operating Officer, Larkin Community Hospital, South Miami, FL, p. A143

MICHEL, Randall M.D., Chief of Staff, Lompoc Valley Medical Center, Lompoc, CA, p. A66

MICHEL–OGBORN, Deborah, Chief Information Resource Management, North Florida/South Georgia Veteran's Health System, Gainesville, FL, p. A126

MICHELE, Margorie, Chief Human Resources Officer, Penn Presbyterian Medical Center, Philadelphia, PA, p. A545

MICHELEN, Jeannith
   Associate Executive Director, NYC Health + Hospitals / Elmhurst, New Rochelle, NY, p. A445
   Senior Associate Executive Director, NYC Health + Hospitals / Lincoln, New Rochelle, NY, p. A445
   Senior Associate Executive Director, NYC Health + Hospitals / Queens, New Rochelle, NY, p. A445

MICHELETTI, Susan C., Chief Executive Officer, Emanuel Medical Center, Turlock, CA, p. A94

MICHELL, Pamela W R.N., Vice President, Chief Nursing Officer, Munroe Regional Medical Center, Ocala, FL, p. A136

MICHELSON, Soad M.D., Senior Medical Director, Clarity Child Guidance Center, San Antonio, TX, p. A642

MICHENER, Scott M.D., Chief Medical Officer, Comanche County Memorial Hospital, Lawton, OK, p. A509

MICHL, Michelle, Director Human Resources, Mercy Medical Center Mount Shasta, Mount Shasta, CA, p. A75

MICKAL, Donald M.D., Chief Medical Officer, Women's And Children's Hospital, Lafayette, LA, p. A279

MICKELSON, Brandon, Chief Executive Officer, First Care Health Center, Park River, ND, p. A478

MICKIEWICZ, Nanette, M.D., President, Dominican Hospital, Santa Cruz, CA, p. A90

MIDDENDORF, Bruce M.D., Chief Medical Officer, St. Mary's Health Care System, Athens, GA, p. A149

MIDDLEBROOKS, Mark M.D., Medical Director, Noland Hospital Birmingham, Birmingham, AL, p. A15

MIDDLETON, Jackie, Vice President Human Resources, Methodist Dallas Medical Center, Dallas, TX, p. A606

MIDDLETON, James MSN, R.N., Chief Nursing Officer, Knox Community Hospital, Mount Vernon, OH, p. A496

MIDDLETON, Robert, Chief Nursing Officer, Gerald Champion Regional Medical Center, Alamogordo, NM, p. A424

MIDGETT, Steve R.N., Chief Nursing Officer, Healthsouth Sugar Land Rehabilitation Hospital, Sugar Land, TX, p. A647

MIDKIFF, Stephen L., Chief Executive Officer, Lake Norman Regional Medical Center, Mooresville, NC, p. A467

MIDTLIEN, Tonia, Information Systems Support Specialist, Gundersen Boscobel Area Hospital And Clinics, Boscobel, WI, p. A699

MIEDLER, Michael M.D., Chief Medical Officer, Continuing Care Hospital, Lexington, KY, p. A261

MIESNER, Gail, Chief Financial Officer, Memorial Hospital, Chester, IL, p. A180

MIGOYA, Carlos A., President and Chief Executive Officer, Jackson Health System, Miami, FL, p. A133

MIHALAKAKOS, Paul M.D., Chief of Staff, Aurora Medical Center – Manitowoc County, Two Rivers, WI, p. A714

MIKELL, Evarista, Assistant Finance Officer, William S. Middleton Memorial Veterans Hospital, Madison, WI, p. A705

MIKELL, Jeffrey M.D., Chief Medical Officer, Select Specialty Hospital – Northeast Atlanta, Atlanta, GA, p. A151

MIKHAIL, Ashraf M.D., Medical Director, Brynn Marr Hospital, Jacksonville, NC, p. A465

MIKI, Nobuyuki M.D., Vice President Medical Services and Chief Medical Officer, Kuakini Medical Center, Honolulu, HI, p. A168

MIKITARIAN, George Jr, FACHE, President and Chief Executive Officer, Parrish Medical Center, Titusville, FL, p. A146

MIKITKA, Joseph, Vice President Human Resources, Sacred Heart Hospital, Allentown, PA, p. A528

MIKULA, Joan, Interim Commissioner, Massachusetts Department Of Mental Health, Boston, MA, p. B79

MIKKELSEN, Kallie, Vice President Nursing, Memorial Hospital Of Sweetwater County, Rock Springs, WY, p. A719

MIKKELSON, Tom, M.D.
   Interim Chief Operating Officer, Touchette Regional Hospital, Centreville, IL, p. A180
   Vice President Medical Affairs, Touchette Regional Hospital, Centreville, IL, p. A180

MIKLAVIC, Kirk
   Director Human Resources, Bridgton Hospital, Bridgton, ME, p. A290
   Director, Human Resources, Central Maine Medical Center, Lewiston, ME, p. A291

MIKLOS, Maggie, Director Human Resources, Northside Hospital, Saint Petersburg, FL, p. A141

MIKOS, Kathleen A R.N., Vice President and Chief Nursing Officer, Ingalls Memorial Hospital, Harvey, IL, p. A189

MIKOS, Ken, Director Information Technology, Wilbarger General Hospital, Vernon, TX, p. A652

MIKULIC, Jeannie, Director Human Resources, Providence Portland Medical Center, Portland, OR, p. A525

MILAM, Wendy, Chief Nursing Officer, Healthsouth Rehabilitation Hospital Of Ocala, Ocala, FL, p. A136

MILAN, Isabel R.N., Chief Nursing Officer, Lac+Usc Medical Center, Los Angeles, CA, p. A69

MILAND, Shelly
   Chief Financial Officer, Texas Health Specialty Hospital, Fort Worth, TX, p. A614
   Group Finance Officer, Texas Health Harris Methodist Hospital Cleburne, Cleburne, TX, p. A601
   Group Financial Officer, Texas Health Harris Methodist Hospital Fort Worth, Fort Worth, TX, p. A614

MILANES, Carlos, Chief Executive Officer, Edgefield County Hospital, Edgefield, SC, p. A561

MILANO, Arthur D, Vice President Human Resources, Berkshire Medical Center, Pittsfield, MA, p. A310

MILATOVICH, Natasha, Association Vice President Human Resources, White Memorial Medical Center, Los Angeles, CA, p. A72

MILAZZO, John, Chief Financial Officer, Merit Health River Region, Vicksburg, MS, p. A362

MILBRANDT, David M.D., Vice President Medical Affairs, Fairview Lakes Health Services, Wyoming, MN, p. A351

MILBURN, Sandra, Director Human Resources, Healthsouth Rehabilitation Hospital Of Memphis, Memphis, TN, p. A584

MILBURN, Sharon, Chief Nursing Officer, Summers County Arh Hospital, Hinton, WV, p. A692

MILES, Ben, President, Parkview Regional Medical Center, Fort Wayne, IN, p. A208

MILES, Dana, Chief Nursing Officer and Chief Clinical Officer, Delta Memorial Hospital, Dumas, AR, p. A42

MILES, David K., President and Chief Executive Officer, The Children's Institute Of Pittsburgh, Pittsburgh, PA, p. A547

MILES, John, Chief Financial Officer, Piedmont Newnan Hospital, Newnan, GA, p. A162

MILES, Karen M.D., Medical Director, Strategic Behavioral Health – Raleigh, Garner, NC, p. A463

MILES, Kerry
Chief Information Officer, Providence St. Peter Hospital, Olympia, WA, p. A683
Site Director, Providence Centralia Hospital, Centralia, WA, p. A679

MILES, Lee Ann, Chief Financial Officer, Harrison County Community Hospital, Bethany, MO, p. A364

MILES, Paul V
Chief Operating Officer, Morgan County Arh Hospital, West Liberty, KY, p. A268
Vice President Administration, Whitesburg Arh Hospital, Whitesburg, KY, p. A268

MILETO, Dottie, Chief Nursing Officer, Heart Of Florida Regional Medical Center, Davenport, FL, p. A123

MILIAN, Tony, Chief Financial Officer, Palm Springs General Hospital, Hialeah, FL, p. A126

MILICEVIC, Heather, Director Human Resources, Summa Western Reserve Hospital, Cuyahoga Falls, OH, p. A489

MILIUS, Hank A., Chief Executive Officer, Meridian Health Services, Muncie, IN, p. A216

MILLAN, Wilfredo Rabelo, Chief Operating Officer, Cardiovascular Center Of Puerto Rico And The Caribbean, San Juan, PR, p. A725

MILLARD, James M., President and Chief Executive Officer, Kenmore Mercy Hospital, Kenmore, NY, p. A438

MILLARD, Kathleen, Acting Director Nursing, Kalamazoo Psychiatric Hospital, Kalamazoo, MI, p. A324

MILLEN, Peter S, Chief Medical Officer MHSATS, Community Behavioral Health Hospital – Rochester, Rochester, MN, p. A346

MILLER, Alan B., Chairman and Chief Executive Officer, Universal Health Services, Inc., King of Prussia, PA, p. B134

MILLER, Alan, Administrator, Liberty Healthcare Systems, Bastrop, LA, p. A270

MILLER, Alicia, Director Human Resources, Aspen Valley Hospital, Aspen, CO, p. A98

MILLER, Andy, Chief Financial Officer, Memorial Hospital Jacksonville, Jacksonville, FL, p. A128

MILLER, Barbara, Manager Business Office, Regional General Hospital, Williston, FL, p. A148

MILLER, Ben, Chief Executive Officer, AMG Specialty Hospital–Lafayette, Lafayette, LA, p. A278

MILLER, Brent R, Manager Human Resources, Brown County Community Treatment Center, Green Bay, WI, p. A703

MILLER, Carol R R.N., Chief Nursing Officer, Reynolds Memorial Hospital, Glen Dale, WV, p. A692

MILLER, Carrie, Director Human Resources, Promedica Defiance Regional Hospital, Defiance, OH, p. A490

MILLER, Chad J., President and Chief Executive Officer, Morrow County Hospital, Mount Gilead, OH, p. A496

MILLER, Che' M.D., Chief of Staff, Duncan Regional Hospital, Duncan, OK, p. A506

MILLER, Chris K., Chief Financial Officer, Highland Hospital, Charleston, WV, p. A691

MILLER, Christine
Chief Human Resources Management Services, Maine Veterans Affairs Medical Center, Augusta, ME, p. A289
General Counsel and Vice President Human Resources, Hanover Hospital, Hanover, PA, p. A535

MILLER, Clint, Chief Nursing Officer, Spooner Health, Spooner, WI, p. A712

MILLER, Connie, Vice President Human Resources, Overland Park Regional Medical Center, Overland Park, KS, p. A249

MILLER, Daniel, FACHE
President and Chief Executive Officer, Medical Center Of Aurora, Aurora, CO, p. A98
Human Resources Business Partner, University Hospitals Parma Medical Center, Parma, OH, p. A498
Vice President Human Resources, University Hospitals Elyria Medical Center, Elyria, OH, p. A491
President and Chief Executive Officer, Medical Center Of Aurora, Aurora, CO, p. A98
President and Chief Executive Officer, Spalding Rehabilitation Hospital, Aurora, CO, p. A98
Chief Information Officer, Uams Medical Center, Little Rock, AR, p. A46

MILLER, David R., President, River Falls Area Hospital, River Falls, WI, p. A712

MILLER, Debra, Administrator, Crosbyton Clinic Hospital, Crosbyton, TX, p. A604

MILLER, Derek, Senior Vice President and Chief Financial Officer, Southeast Alabama Medical Center, Dothan, AL, p. A17

MILLER, Diane, Administrator, Peterson Healthcare And Rehabilitation Hospital, Wheeling, WV, p. A697

MILLER, Dionne, Chief Operating Officer, Sutter Roseville Medical Center, Roseville, CA, p. A83

MILLER, Donald L FACHE, Vice President, Operations, St. Luke's Hospital, Chesterfield, MO, p. A366

MILLER, Douglas M.D., Chief of Medical Staff, Clearview Regional Medical Center, Monroe, GA, p. A162

MILLER, Duane
Chief Financial Officer, Chi St. Luke's Health Memorial Livingston, Livingston, TX, p. A629
Chief Financial Officer, Chi St. Luke's Health Memorial Specialty Hospital, Lufkin, TX, p. A631
Chief Financial Officer, Integris Bass Baptist Health Center, Enid, OK, p. A507

MILLER, Dyrek M.D., Chief Medical Staff, Vidant Duplin Hospital, Kenansville, NC, p. A465

MILLER, Elaine G, Director of Nursing, Oaklawn Psychiatric Center, Goshen, IN, p. A209

MILLER, Elizabeth, CPA
Chief Financial Officer, Stamford Memorial Hospital, Stamford, TX, p. A646
Director of Nursing, Harlan County Health System, Alma, NE, p. A390

MILLER, Esteban, Chief Medical Officer, Black River Memorial Hospital, Black River Falls, WI, p. A699

MILLER, Gary L
Regional Director Information Systems, Plymouth Medical Center, Plymouth, IN, p. A218
Senior Director Information Systems, Mishawaka Medical Center, Mishawaka, IN, p. A216

MILLER, Greg, Senior Vice President Operations, Uf Health Jacksonville, Jacksonville, FL, p. A128

MILLER, Hope, Director of Medical Records, Peterson Healthcare And Rehabilitation Hospital, Wheeling, WV, p. A697

MILLER, J D, M.D.
Chief Medical Officer, Hazard Arh Regional Medical Center, Hazard, KY, p. A259
Vice President Medical Affairs, Morgan County Arh Hospital, West Liberty, KY, p. A268
Vice President Medical Affairs, Tug Valley Arh Regional Medical Center, South Williamson, KY, p. A267

MILLER, James L, Chief Financial Officer, Baptist Medical Center Yazoo, Yazoo City, MS, p. A363

MILLER, James, Chief Financial Officer, Women's And Children's Hospital, Lafayette, LA, p. A279

MILLER, Jane E
Director Human Resources, Avera Creighton Hospital, Creighton, NE, p. A392
Human Resources Officer, Avera Sacred Heart Hospital, Yankton, SD, p. A574

MILLER, Jason R., Chief Financial Officer, The Medical Center Of Southeast Texas, Port Arthur, TX, p. A639

MILLER, Jason, M.P.H., Chief Executive Officer, The Bridgeway, North Little Rock, AR, p. A48

MILLER, Jeff, M.D.
Chief of Staff, Parkview Wabash County Hospital, Wabash, IN, p. A221
Chief Operating Officer, Citizens Memorial Hospital, Bolivar, MO, p. A364

MILLER, Jennifer, Chief Executive Officer, Cross Creek Hospital, Austin, TX, p. A595

MILLER, Jeri M.D., President Medical Staff, Fairview Park Hospital, Dublin, GA, p. A157

MILLER, Jon, Director Accounting and Information Services, Hancock Regional Hospital, Greenfield, IN, p. A209

MILLER, Joshua, Director Information Systems, Joint Township District Memorial Hospital, Saint Marys, OH, p. A498

MILLER, Joy, Chief Nursing Officer, Cornerstone Hospital Of Little Rock, Little Rock, AR, p. A46

MILLER, Julie, Chief Operating Officer, Williamson Medical Center, Franklin, TN, p. A579

MILLER, Justin M.D., Chief of Staff, Wabash General Hospital, Mount Carmel, IL, p. A194

MILLER, Karen, Chief Financial Officer, San Juan Regional Medical Center, Farmington, NM, p. A426

MILLER, Kay J R.N., MSN, Chief Nursing Officer, Uchealth Memorial, Colorado Springs, CO, p. A100

MILLER, Ken, Chief Financial Officer, Beaufort Memorial Hospital, Beaufort, SC, p. A558

MILLER, Kevin
President, Chi Health Lakeside, Omaha, NE, p. A397
President, Chi Health Midlands, Papillion, NE, p. A399

MILLER, Kimberly J., FACHE, President and Chief Executive Officer, Beaver Dam Community Hospitals, Beaver Dam, WI, p. A699

MILLER, Kris, Senior Human Resources Business Partner, Spectrum Health Reed City Hospital, Reed City, MI, p. A329

MILLER, Laurie, Administrative Assistant, Sakakawea Medical Center, Hazen, ND, p. A476

MILLER, Leanne R, Director Human Resources, Community Hospital, Mccook, NE, p. A396

MILLER, Lisa, R.N.
Director of Nursing, North Sunflower Medical Center, Ruleville, MS, p. A361
Director Human Resources, Hendry Regional Medical Center, Clewiston, FL, p. A122

MILLER, Maria, Controller, Beaumont Hospital – Grosse Pointe, Grosse Pointe, MI, p. A322

MILLER, Mark, FACHE
Chief Financial Officer, Freeman Regional Health Services, Freeman, SD, p. A570
Director Information Systems, Perry County Memorial Hospital, Tell City, IN, p. A220
Chief Executive Officer, Lake City Medical Center, Lake City, FL, p. A129

MILLER, Mary Beth M.D., Chief of Staff, Cheyenne County Hospital, Saint Francis, KS, p. A251

MILLER, Mary, Vice President Finance and Business Development, Mt. Washington Pediatric Hospital, Baltimore, MD, p. A295

MILLER, Mathew M.D., Vice President and Chief Medical Officer, St. Joseph Hospital, Eureka, CA, p. A58

MILLER, Melissa, Director Human Resources, St. Elizabeth Hospital, Gonzales, LA, p. A275

MILLER, Michael J
Director Human Resources, Barnes–Jewish St. Peters Hospital, Saint Peters, MO, p. A379
Director Human Resources, Progress West Hospital, O'Fallon, MO, p. A374

MILLER, Michele A R.N., MSN, Vice President, Acute and Nursing Services, University Behavioral Healthcare, Piscataway, NJ, p. A419

MILLER, Nancy R.N., Chief Nursing Officer, Van Matre Healthsouth Rehabilitation Hospital, Rockford, IL, p. A199

MILLER, Nicole, Director Human Resources, Riverside Shore Memorial Hospital, Onancoke, VA, p. A672

MILLER, Patrick, Technology Coordinator, San Bernardino Mountains Community Hospital District, Lake Arrowhead, CA, p. A65

MILLER, Paul, Director of Operations, Sanford Chamberlain Medical Center, Chamberlain, SD, p. A568

MILLER, Peter S, Chief Financial Officer, North Vista Hospital, North Las Vegas, NV, p. A404

MILLER, Phil, Chief Information Officer, Unity Health White County Medical Center, Searcy, AR, p. A49

MILLER, Redonda G., M.D., President, Johns Hopkins Hospital, Baltimore, MD, p. A294

MILLER, Richard B. Ph.D., Vice President Hospital Affairs and Chief Financial Officer, Suny Downstate Medical Center University Hospital, New Rochelle, NY, p. A447

MILLER, Richard, Administrator Finance, Banner Thunderbird Medical Center, Glendale, AZ, p. A30

MILLER, Rick
Chief Financial Officer, District One Hospital, Faribault, MN, p. A339
Director, Operations and Finance, District One Hospital, Faribault, MN, p. A339
President and Chief Operating Officer, Nationwide Children's Hospital, Columbus, OH, p. A487

MILLER, Robert R II, Chief Operating Officer, NYC Health + Hospitals / Kings County, New York, NY, p. A445

MILLER, Rod, Chief Information Technology, Community Hospital, Torrington, WY, p. A720

MILLER, Ryan, FACHE, Administrator and Executive Director, Christus Southeast Texas Orthopedic Specialty Center, Beaumont, TX, p. A597

MILLER, Sam, Chief Executive Officer, North Sunflower Medical Center, Ruleville, MS, p. A361

MILLER, Shane
Chief Information Officer, Hshs St. Clare Memorial Hospital, Oconto Falls, WI, p. A709
Chief Information Officer, Hshs St. Mary's Hospital Medical Center, Green Bay, WI, p. A703
Chief Information Officer, Hshs St. Nicholas Hospital, Sheboygan, WI, p. A712
Chief Information Officer, Hshs St. Vincent Hospital, Green Bay, WI, p. A703

MILLER, Stacy, Entity Human Resources Officer, Texas Health Presbyterian Hospital Dallas, Dallas, TX, p. A607

MILLER, Steve, Director Information Systems, Baptist Medical Center South, Montgomery, AL, p. A21

MILLER, Steven, Chief Financial Officer, Florida Hospital North Pinellas, Tarpon Springs, FL, p. A145

MILLER, Susan, Financial Administrator, Faulkton Area Medical Center, Faulkton, SD, p. A569

MILLER, Suzanne R.N., MSN, Senior Director Patient Care Services and Nursing, St. Luke's Wood River Medical Center, Ketchum, ID, p. A174

MILLER, Tamara, R.N., Administrator, Madison Community Hospital, Madison, SD, p. A570

MILLER, Ted, Chief Financial Officer, Baptist Health Floyd, New Albany, IN, p. A217

MILLER, Thomas M.D., Medical Director, University Of Utah Health, Salt Lake City, UT, p. A660

MILLER, Valerie L MSN, R.N., Director of Nursing, Major Hospital, Shelbyville, IN, p. A219

MILLER, Weston M.D., Chief Medical Officer, Abbeville General Hospital, Abbeville, LA, p. A269

MILLER, William, Coordinator Management Information Systems, Livengrin Foundation, Bensalem, PA, p. A529

MILLER–BALFOUR, Pam, Director Human Resources, Socorro General Hospital, Socorro, NM, p. A429

MILLER–COLLETTE, Melody M, Director Human Resources, North Okaloosa Medical Center, Crestview, FL, p. A122

MILLERMAIER, Ed M.D., Chief Medical Officer, Bellin Memorial Hospital, Green Bay, WI, p. A702

MILLICAN, Sharon, Associate Director, Patient Care Services, South Texas Veterans Health Care System, San Antonio, TX, p. A644

MILLIS, David M.D., Clinical Director, Thomas B. Finan Center, Cumberland, MD, p. A298

MILLS, Aundrea, Chief Nursing Officer, Sovah Health–Danville, Danville, VA, p. A666

MILLS, Bryan A., President and Chief Executive Officer, Community Health Network, Indianapolis, IN, p. B32

MILLS, Craig
Chief Financial Officer, Heber Valley Medical Center, Heber City, UT, p. A657
Vice President Human Resources, Peacehealth Sacred Heart Medical Center University District, Eugene, OR, p. A521

MILLS, Dennis, Chief Human Resources Officer, San Ramon Regional Medical Center, San Ramon, CA, p. A90

MILLS, Gene, Director Information Technology, Scenic Mountain Medical Center, Big Spring, TX, p. A598

MILLS, Jerry, Chief Human Resources Management Services, San Francisco Va Medical Center, San Francisco, CA, p. A87

MILLS, Jim, Regional Director Information Technology, Sutter Medical Center, Sacramento, Sacramento, CA, p. A84

MILLS, John E.H., President & Chief Executive Officer, United Medical Rehabilitation Hospitals, Gretna, LA, p. B132

MILLS, John C, Senior Vice President Operations, Cleveland Clinic Fairview Hospital, Cleveland, OH, p. A485

MILLS, Marianne R.N., Chairperson, Stanton County Hospital, Johnson, KS, p. A243

MILLS, Scott M.D., Vice President Medical Staff Administration and Chief Medical Officer, Mid Coast Hospital, Brunswick, ME, p. A290

MILLS, Sean
Chief Financial Officer, Our Lady Of Lourdes Memorial Hospital, Inc., Binghamton, NY, p. A432
Chief Financial Officer, Samaritan Medical Center, Watertown, NY, p. A455

MILLS, Vicki L, Chief Financial Officer, Anderson County Hospital, Garnett, KS, p. A241

MILLS, William, M.D.
Senior Vice President Quality and Professional Affairs, Bradford Regional Medical Center, Bradford, PA, p. A530
Senior Vice President Quality and Professional Affairs, Olean General Hospital, Olean, NY, p. A448

MILLS–MATHEWS, Marcy, Director Human Resources, Palms West Hospital, Loxahatchee, FL, p. A131

MILLSAP, Debra, Director of Nursing, River Crest Hospital, San Angelo, TX, p. A641

MILLSAPS, Janet
Chief Human Resources Officer, Harris Regional Hospital, Sylva, NC, p. A471
Vice President Human Resources, Haywood Regional Medical Center, Clyde, NC, p. A460

MILLSAPS, Jarrett B. Jr, FACHE, Chief Executive Officer, Parkridge Medical Center, Chattanooga, TN, p. A576

MILLSTEAD, Bart, Administrator, Memorial Hospital Of Carbondale, Carbondale, IL, p. A179

MILNE, C Dean D.O., Medical Director, Complex Care Hospital At Tenaya, Las Vegas, NV, p. A402

MILNER, Rene, Chief Medical Officer, Osceola Medical Center, Osceola, WI, p. A710

MILONE, Sheri, Chief Executive Officer and Administrator, Lovelace Women's Hospital, Albuquerque, NM, p. A424

MILOVICH, David, Vice President Human Resources, Saint Mary's Regional Medical Center, Reno, NV, p. A405

MILSTEIN, Marc E., Vice President Information Resources, University Of Texas Southwestern Medical Center, Dallas, TX, p. A607

MILSTIEN, Kim S., Chief Executive Officer, Ventura County Medical Center, Ventura, CA, p. A96

MILTON, Kerry K. R.N., Chief Nursing Officer, St. Tammany Parish Hospital, Covington, LA, p. A273

MILTON, Paul A., Acting President and Chief Executive Officer, Ellis Hospital, Schenectady, NY, p. A452

MILTON, Paul A, Executive Vice President and Chief Operating Officer, Ellis Hospital, Schenectady, NY, p. A452

MILTON, S. Byron M.D., Medical Director, Emory Rehabilitation Hospital, Atlanta, GA, p. A150

MILUS, Lori R.N., MSN, Director of Nursing, Aurora Behavioral Health System West, Glendale, AZ, p. A30

MILVET, Robert W Jr, Chief Financial Officer, Preston Memorial Hospital, Kingwood, WV, p. A693

MIMOSO, Michael, FACHE, President and Chief Executive Officer, Community Medical Center, Toms River, NJ, p. A421

MIMS, Staci, Chief Nursing Officer, Dorminy Medical Center, Fitzgerald, GA, p. A158

MIMS, Tammy, Chief Executive Officer, Jeff Davis Hospital, Hazlehurst, GA, p. A158

MINARD, Keith, Chief Information Officer, Chinese Hospital, San Francisco, CA, p. A87

MINCEY, Wallace D., Chief Executive Officer, Clinch Memorial Hospital, Homerville, GA, p. A159

MINCEY, Wallace D, Chief Executive Officer, Clinch Memorial Hospital, Homerville, GA, p. A159

MINCY, Lowney, Director Information Services, Southside Hospital, Bay Shore, NY, p. A431

MINDEN, Philip, Chief Executive Officer, Bartow Regional Medical Center, Bartow, FL, p. A119

MINEAR, Michael N.
Senior Vice President and Chief Information Officer, Lehigh Valley Hospital–Muhlenberg, Bethlehem, PA, p. A529
Senior Vice President and Chief Information Officer, Lehigh Valley Hospital, Allentown, PA, p. A528

MINEAU, Francine, Chief Nursing Officer, Baton Rouge Behavioral Hospital, Baton Rouge, LA, p. A270

MINER, Bill M.D., Chief of Staff, Huron Regional Medical Center, Huron, SD, p. A570

MINER, Edwina A R.N., Chief Nursing Officer, Ennis Regional Medical Center, Ennis, TX, p. A612

MINER, Greg, Administrator, Siouxland Surgery Center, Dakota Dunes, SD, p. A569

MINER, John, Chief Financial Officer, Kindred Hospital Central Tampa, Tampa, FL, p. A145

MINGLE, Regina, Senior Vice President and Chief Leadership Officer, Lancaster General Hospital, Lancaster, PA, p. A538

MINGS, William M.D., Medical Director, Carl Albert Community Mental Health Center, Mcalester, OK, p. A510

MINGUS, Linda, Director Human Resources, Aurora Medical Center Of Oshkosh, Oshkosh, WI, p. A710

MINIER, Lori, Chief Financial Officer, Benewah Community Hospital, Saint Maries, ID, p. A175

MINIER, Mary, President, Indiana University Health White Memorial Hospital, Monticello, IN, p. A216

MINIOR, Devin M.D., Chief Medical Officer, Banner Casa Grande Medical Center, Casa Grande, AZ, p. A28

MINISSALE, Joseph, President, Methodist Mckinney Hospital, Mckinney, TX, p. A632

MINKS, Michael H.
Chief Information Officer VI, Dell Seton Medical Center At The University Of Texas, Austin, TX, p. A595
Chief Information Officer VI, Seton Medical Center Austin, Austin, TX, p. A595
Chief Information Officer, Seton Edgar B. Davis Hospital, Luling, TX, p. A631
Chief Information Officer, Seton Northwest Hospital, Austin, TX, p. A595
Chief Information Officer, Seton Shoal Creek Hospital, Austin, TX, p. A595

MINNICK, Peggy, R.N., Chief Executive Officer, Bhc Alhambra Hospital, Rosemead, CA, p. A83

MINNIS, Rosanne, Business Officer, Rochester Psychiatric Center, Rochester, NY, p. A451

MINON, Maria, M.D.
Vice President Medical Affairs and Chief Medical Officer, Children's Hospital Of Orange County, Orange, CA, p. A78
Vice President Medical Affairs and Chief Medical Officer, Choc Children's At Mission Hospital, Mission Viejo, CA, p. A73

MINOR, Amy, Chief Nursing Officer, Troy Regional Medical Center, Troy, AL, p. A23

MINOR, Athena, Chief Nursing Officer, Ohio County Hospital, Hartford, KY, p. A259

MINOR, Beverly, Chief Human Resources, Schleicher County Medical Center, Eldorado, TX, p. A612

MINOR, Blaine M.D., Chief of Staff, Murray Medical Center, Chatsworth, GA, p. A154

MINSHEW, Tony L., Vice President, Patient Care Services, Conway Medical Center, Conway, SC, p. A561

MINSINGER, Linda, Vice President Hospital Division, Gifford Medical Center, Randolph, VT, p. A663

MINTEER, Laura, Chief Human Resource Officer, Meritus Medical Center, Hagerstown, MD, p. A299

MINTON, Tamra R.N., MSN, Vice President Patient Care Services and Chief Nursing Officer, Upmc East, Monroeville, PA, p. A541

MINTONYE, Traci, Chief Financial Officer, River Hospital, Alexandria Bay, NY, p. A430

MINTZ, Michael M.D., Chief Medical Officer, South Texas Surgical Hospital, Corpus Christi, TX, p. A603

MIRABELLA, Ilene, Director Human Resources, Vibra Hospital Of Southeastern Massachusetts, New Bedford, MA, p. A309

MIRANDA, Ada S M.D., Medical Director, Hospital Metropolitano Dr. Susoni, Arecibo, PR, p. A722

MIRANDA, Casey D., Executive Vice President and Chief Operating Officer, Jackson County Memorial Hospital, Altus, OK, p. A504

MIRANDA, Ivette, Chief Executive Officer, Healthsouth Rehabilitation Hospital At Martin Health, Stuart, FL, p. A143

MIRANDA, Kim, Chief Financial Officer, St. Elizabeth Community Hospital, Red Bluff, CA, p. A81

MIRANDA, Kimberly
Chief Financial Officer, Mercy Medical Center Mount Shasta, Mount Shasta, CA, p. A75
Regional Vice President Finance and Chief Financial Officer, Mercy Medical Center Redding, Redding, CA, p. A81

MIRANDA, Lisa, Vice President Operations, University Medical Center, New Orleans, LA, p. A283

MIRANDA, Michael, Chief of Staff, Mercy Hospital Booneville, Booneville, AR, p. A41

MIRANDA, Samuel Jr, Chief Nursing Officer, Good Shepherd Specialty Hospital, Bethlehem, PA, p. A529

MIRANDA, Vicki, Vice President Human Resources, Dominican Hospital, Santa Cruz, CA, p. A90

MIRANDA, Victor Hernandez M.D., Chief of Staff, Mennonite General Hospital, Aibonito, PR, p. A722

MIRZA, Irfan, Chief Financial Officer, Plantation General Hospital, Plantation, FL, p. A140

MISHKIND, Steven M.D., Chief of Staff, Desoto Memorial Hospital, Arcadia, FL, p. A119

MISHLER, Sheila, Chief Executive Officer, St. Vincent Indianapolis Hospital, IndianapolisSt. Vincent Heart Center, Indianapolis, IN, p. A212

MISITANO, Anthony F., President and Chief Executive Officer, Post Acute Medical, Llc, Enola, PA, p. B98

MISITI, Joseph M.D., President Medical Staff, Medina Memorial Hospital, Medina, NY, p. A439

MISKIMEN, Theresa M.D., Vice President Medical Services, University Behavioral Healthcare, Piscataway, NJ, p. A419

MISLAN, Tim MS, Vice President and Chief Nurse Executive, Missouri Baptist Medical Center, Saint Louis, MO, p. A377

MISRA, Sahana, Acting Chief of Staff, Va Portland Healthcare System, Portland, OR, p. A525

MISSERITTI, Colomba, Director Human Resources, Rochester Psychiatric Center, Rochester, NY, p. A451

MITCHAM, Debbie, Chief Financial Officer, Northside Hospital, Atlanta, GA, p. A150

MITCHEL, David M., Chief Executive Officer, Avoyelles Hospital, Marksville, LA, p. A280

MITCHELL, Adonna, Director Fiscal Services, North Mississippi Medical Center–Eupora, Eupora, MS, p. A354

MITCHELL, Andrew J., President and Chief Executive Officer, Peconic Bay Medical Center, Riverhead, NY, p. A450

MITCHELL, Barbara
Director Human Resources, Oasis Behavioral Health – Chandler, Chandler, AZ, p. A28
Senior Vice President Marketing and Human Resources, Uw Medicine/Valley Medical Center, Renton, WA, p. A684

MITCHELL, Bridgett, Chief Clinical Officer, Advanced Specialty Hospital Of Toledo, Toledo, OH, p. A500

MITCHELL, Camelia M.D., Medical Director, Texas Rehabilitation Hospital Of Arlington, Arlington, TX, p. A594

MITCHELL, Dave, Manager Information Services, Spectrum Health Gerber Memorial, Fremont, MI, p. A320

MITCHELL, David
Chief Executive Officer, Baptist Emergency Hospital, San Antonio, TX, p. A642
Interim Chief Executive Officer, Baptist Emergency Hospital, San Antonio, TX, p. A642

MITCHELL, Debbie, Director Human Resources, Woodrow Wilson Rehabilitation Center, Fishersville, VA, p. A667

MITCHELL, Douglas W, Vice President and Chief Nursing Officer, West Virginia University Hospitals, Morgantown, WV, p. A694

MITCHELL, Elizabeth C., Chief Executive Officer and Chief Operating Officer, Specialty Hospital Of Meridian, Meridian, MS, p. A359

MITCHELL, Elizabeth C, Chief Operating Officer, Specialty Hospital Of Meridian, Meridian, MS, p. A359

MITCHELL, Errol, Chief Financial Officer, Integris Canadian Valley Hospital, Yukon, OK, p. A519

MITCHELL, Heath, Chief Operating Officer, Memorial Hospital, Seminole, TX, p. A645

MITCHELL, Jack C., FACHE, Chief Executive Officer, Healthsouth Rehabilitation Hospital, Fayetteville, AR, p. A42

MITCHELL, Jenifer R.N., Director of Nursing Services, Mineral Community Hospital, Superior, MT, p. A388

MITCHELL, Jodie, Facility Financial Director, Sturgis Regional Hospital, Sturgis, SD, p. A573

MITCHELL, Joe J., Chief Executive Officer, Acadia General Hospital, Crowley, LA, p. A273

MITCHELL, Karen, Vice President Patient Care Services, Children's Hospital Of The King's Daughters, Norfolk, VA, p. A671

MITCHELL, Kathy, R.N.
Chief Nursing Officer, Doctors Hospital Of Sarasota, Sarasota, FL, p. A142
Chief Nursing Officer, Owensboro Health Muhlenberg Community Hospital, Greenville, KY, p. A259
Director Human Resources, Lakeview Medical Center, Rice Lake, WI, p. A711

MITCHELL, Kenneth W M.D., Medical Director, St. David's North Austin Medical Center, Austin, TX, p. A596

MITCHELL, Kent, Chief Financial Officer, Hamilton Memorial Hospital District, Mcleansboro, IL, p. A193

MITCHELL, Leah R.N., Interim Chief Information Officer, Salem Hospital, Salem, OR, p. A526

MITCHELL, Lori J, Chief Financial Officer, University Of Washington Medical Center, Seattle, WA, p. A685

MITCHELL, Marsha, Director Human Resources, Fleming County Hospital, Flemingsburg, KY, p. A258

MITCHELL, Mary S, Chief Resource Management Services, Birmingham Veterans Affairs Medical Center, Birmingham, AL, p. A14

MITCHELL, Morris, Director Human Resources, Poplar Springs Hospital, Petersburg, VA, p. A673

MITCHELL, Naomi, Director Human Resources, Kentucky River Medical Center, Jackson, KY, p. A260

MITCHELL, Perry M.D., Chief of Staff, Little Colorado Medical Center, Winslow, AZ, p. A39

MITCHELL, Rebekah, Chief Financial Officer, Madison County Health Care System, Winterset, IA, p. A237

MITCHELL, Richard R, Director Information Technology, Eagleville Hospital, Eagleville, PA, p. A533

MITCHELL, Sarah, Director Finance, Mary S Harper Geriatric Psychiatry Center, Tuscaloosa, AL, p. A24

MITCHELL, Scot, FACHE, Chief Executive Officer and Administrator, Cordova Community Medical Center, Cordova, AK, p. A25

MITCHELL, Steve, Chief Operating Officer, Memorial Medical Center, Modesto, CA, p. A74

MITCHELL, Timothy, R.N.
Chief Nursing Officer, Complex Care Hospital At Ridgelake, Sarasota, FL, p. A142
Chief Financial Officer, Fairfield Memorial Hospital, Winnsboro, SC, p. A567

MITCHELL, Walton F. III, Director, Catawba Hospital, Catawba, VA, p. A665

MITCHELL, William, Chief Executive Officer and Administrator, Kindred Hospital Riverside, Perris, CA, p. A79

MITCHELL SANCHEZ, Lexi D.O., Chief of Staff, Clay County Memorial Hospital, Henrietta, TX, p. A619

MITCHUM, Linda, Director of Nursing, William J. Mccord Adolescent Treatment Facility, Orangeburg, SC, p. A565

MITHUN, Robert M.D., Physician in Chief, Kaiser Permanente San Francisco Medical Center, San Francisco, CA, p. A87

MITRICK, Joseph M., FACHE, President, Baptist Medical Center Beaches, Jacksonville Beach, FL, p. A129

MITRY, Norman F.
President and Chief Executive Officer, Heritage Valley Health System, Beaver, PA, p. A529
President and Chief Executive Officer, Sewickley Valley Hospital, (A Division Of Valley Medical Facilities), Sewickley, PA, p. A550

MITTAL, Vikrant M.D., Chief Medical Officer, Danville State Hospital, Danville, PA, p. A532

MIYAMOTO, Faye, Assistant Vice President Human Resources, Rehabilitation Hospital Of The Pacific, Honolulu, HI, p. A169

MIYASAWA, Patricia CPA, Director Fiscal Service, Shriners Hospitals For Children–Honolulu, Honolulu, HI, p. A169

MIYAUCHI, Kimberly R.N., Chief Nursing Officer, Kingman Regional Medical Center, Kingman, AZ, p. A30

MIZE, William D, Chief Operating Officer, Trousdale Medical Center, Hartsville, TN, p. A579

MIZELL, Philip L M.D., Medical Director, The Bridgeway, North Little Rock, AR, p. A48

MIZER, Alison, Chief Financial Officer, St. Anthony North Health Campus, Westminster, CO, p. A108

MIZIA, Robert, Director Information Systems and Chief Information Officer, Inspira Medical Center–Woodbury, Woodbury, NJ, p. A423

MIZONO, Gary M.D., Physician–in–Chief, Kaiser Permanente San Rafael Medical Center, San Rafael, CA, p. A89

MLAWSKY, Karen, Senior Vice President and Chief Operations Officer, TMC Healthcare, Tucson, AZ, p. A38

MMEJE, Ikenna, Chief Operating Officer, Long Beach Memorial Medical Center, Long Beach, CA, p. A66

MO, Lin H, M.P.H., President, Mount Sinai Beth Israel, New Rochelle, NY, p. A443

MOAD, Sharon, Human Resources Director Health Information Management, Elkview General Hospital, Hobart, OK, p. A508

MOAK, Jennifer, Business Office Manager, Lawrence County Hospital, Monticello, MS, p. A359

MOAKLER, Thomas J., Chief Executive Officer, Houlton Regional Hospital, Houlton, ME, p. A291

MOALLEMIAN, Patrick, Chief Executive Officer, Chicago Lakeshore Hospital, Chicago, IL, p. A180

MOATS, Susan K., R.N.
Vice President Patient Care Services and Chief Nursing Officer, The Heart Hospital Baylor Denton, Denton, TX, p. A608
Vice President Patient Care Services and Chief Nursing Officer, The Heart Hospital Baylor Plano, Plano, TX, p. A638

MOAWAD, Gerald, Chief Medical Officer, Bridgepoint Hospital Capitol Hill, Washington, DC, p. A117

MOBLEY, Cheryl, FACHE, President, Texas Health Specialty Hospital, Fort Worth, TX, p. A614

MOBLEY, Dana, Chief Information Officer, Our Community Hospital, Scotland Neck, NC, p. A470

MOCK, Presley M.D., Chief of Staff, Texas Institute For Surgery At Texas Health Presbyterian Dallas, Dallas, TX, p. A607

MODJESKA, Alicia, Interim Administrator, Milwaukee County Behavioral Health Division, Milwaukee, WI, p. A708

MOEEN, Farida, M.D., Chief Executive Officer, United Memorial Medical Care, Houston, TX, p. A623

MOELLER, Deborah A R.N., MS, Interim Chief Nursing Officer, Baylor Scott & White Medical Center – Sunnyvale, Sunnyvale, TX, p. A647

MOEN, Belinda R.N., MSN, Interim Director of Nursing, Mountrail County Medical Center, Stanley, ND, p. A478

MOEN, Daniel, President and Chief Executive Officer, St. Joseph Hospital, Nashua, NH, p. B39

MOEN, Larry, Chief Financial Officer, Coteau Des Prairies Hospital, Sisseton, SD, p. A573

MOFFA, Salvatore M.D., Vice President, Medical Affairs and Chief Medical Officer, Robert Wood Johnson University Hospital Somerset, Somerville, NJ, p. A420

MOFFAT, Jeanne, Manager Information Technology, Keefe Memorial Hospital, Cheyenne Wells, CO, p. A99

MOFFAT, Jennifer, Staff Accountant, Regional West Garden County, Oshkosh, NE, p. A398

MOFFATT, Dan, Chief Information Officer, Sanford Bemidji Medical Center, Bemidji, MN, p. A336

MOFFET, Chris, Director Information Services, Bob Wilson Memorial Grant County Hospital, Ulysses, KS, p. A253

MOFFITT, Brenda L., Chief Nursing Officer, Memorial Health System, Abilene, KS, p. A238

MOFFITT SOD, Rhonda, Chief Nursing Officer, First Hospital Wyoming Valley, Kingston, PA, p. A537

MOGERMAN, Shauna, Chief Executive Officer, Roxbury Treatment Center, Shippensburg, PA, p. A551

MOGG, Cassie, Chief Financial Officer, Covenant Hospital Plainview, Plainview, TX, p. A637

MOHAMED, Antonia, Acting Chief Information Officer, Birmingham Veterans Affairs Medical Center, Birmingham, AL, p. A14

MOHAMMED, Ehtaisham M.D., Chief Medical Officer, Ridgeview Sibley Medical Center, Arlington, MN, p. A335

MOHAN, Amit, President and Chief Executive Officer, Barlow Respiratory Hospital, Los Angeles, CA, p. A67

MOHAN, Rajesh M.D., Chief Medical Officer, Monmouth Medical Center, Southern Campus, Lakewood, NJ, p. A415

MOHANDAS, Arjun M.D., Chief of Staff, Seton Edgar B. Davis Hospital, Luling, TX, p. A631

MOHLER, Brittany, Director Human Resources, Essentia Health–Deer River, Deer River, MN, p. A338

MOHNK, Richard, Vice President Corporate Services, Bayhealth Medical Center, Dover, DE, p. A115

MOHNKERN, Pearl, Vice President and Director Human Resources, Christus St. Vincent Regional Medical Center, Santa Fe, NM, p. A428

MOHR, Amanda, Chief Nursing Officer, Greater Regional Medical Center, Creston, IA, p. A225

MOHR, Amy, Coordinator Human Resources, Forest Health Medical Center, Ypsilanti, MI, p. A333

MOHR, Angela, R.N., MS, Vice President Nursing and Chief Operating Officer, St. Anthony Shawnee Hospital, Shawnee, OK, p. A516

MOHR, Catherine R.N., MSN, Chief Nursing Officer, Guthrie Robert Packer Hospital, Sayre, PA, p. A549

MOHR, Steve
Senior Vice President Finance and Chief Financial Officer, Loma Linda University Behavioral Medicine Center, Redlands, CA, p. A81
Senior Vice President Finance and Chief Financial Officer, Loma Linda University Medical Center, Loma Linda, CA, p. A66

MOISAN, Terrence, M.D., Chief Executive Officer, Palos Health, Palos Heights, IL, p. A196

MOK, Michelle, Chief Financial Officer, Redlands Community Hospital, Redlands, CA, p. A82

MOKDESSI, Margot, Interim Chief Financial Officer, Acadia Vermilion Hospital, Lafayette, LA, p. A278

MOKRY, Deborah, Chief Nurse Executive, St. Louis Psychiatric Rehabilitation Center, Saint Louis, MO, p. A378

MOL, Stacy E CPA, Director Finance, Spencer Hospital, Spencer, IA, p. A235

MOLACEK, Shane, Chief Information Officer, Valley County Health System, Ord, NE, p. A398

MOLELUS, Elena, Manager Human Resources, Santa Barbara County Psychiatric Health Facility, Santa Barbara, CA, p. A90

MOLINA, Isabel M.D., Chief Medical Officer, Lamb Healthcare Center, Littlefield, TX, p. A629

MOLINA, Luis F., Chief Executive Officer and Administrator, Community Hospital, Munster, IN, p. A216

MOLINA, Ricky, Director Marketing and Business Development, Rehabilitation Hospital Of Southern New Mexico, Las Cruces, NM, p. A427

MOLINARO, Frank L. M.D.
Chief Executive Officer, Abrazo Arrowhead Campus, Glendale, AZ, p. A30
Chief Executive Officer, Abrazo Central Campus, Phoenix, AZ, p. A32
Chief Executive Officer, Abrazo Scottsdale Campus, Phoenix, AZ, p. A33

MOLITOR, Margie, FACHE, R.N., Chief Executive Officer, Hot Springs County Memorial Hospital, Thermopolis, WY, p. A720

MOLL, Ben, Assistant Chief Financial Officer, Nashoba Valley Medical Center, Ayer, MA, p. A302

MOLL, Eric, Chief Executive Officer, Mason General Hospital, Shelton, WA, p. A686

MOLL, Gudrun R.N., MSN, Chief Nursing Officer, San Antonio Regional Hospital, Upland, CA, p. A95

MOLL, Jeffrey M.D., Medical Director, Clarion Psychiatric Center, Clarion, PA, p. A531

MOLL, Michael A. M.D., Chief Medical Officer and Chief of Staff, Spanish Peaks Regional Health Center, Walsenburg, CO, p. A108

MOLLER, Dan M.D., Chief Medical Officer, Willis–Knighton Medical Center, Shreveport, LA, p. A286

MOLLER, Lynn, Chief Financial Officer, Weston County Health Services, Newcastle, WY, p. A719

MOLLOHAN, Joan, Vice President Human Resources, Psychiatric Pavilion New Orleans, New OrleansOchsner Medical Center, New Orleans, LA, p. A283

MOLLOY, Kevin
Senior Vice President and Chief Operating Officer, Mount Sinai Beth Israel, New Rochelle, NY, p. A443
Senior Vice President and Chief Operating Officer, Mount Sinai West, New Rochelle, NY, p. A443

MOLLOY, Laurel, Vice President Nursing and Rehab Services, UNC Lenoir Healthcare, Kinston, NC, p. A465

MOLLOY, Reuben D, Chief Information Officer, Governor Juan F. Luis Hospital, Christiansted, VI, p. A727

MOLMEN, David R., M.P.H., Chief Executive Officer, Altru Health System, Grand Forks, ND, p. A476

MOLNAR, Becky, Director of Finance, Cleveland Clinic, Medina Hospital, Medina, OH, p. A495

MOLSBERGER, Shawn, Chief Operating Officer, Tennova Healthcare–Clarksville, Clarksville, TN, p. A577

MOLT, Brianna, Human Resources Director, Genoa Medical Facilities, Genoa, NE, p. A393

MOLYNEUX, Phyllis, Associate Administrator Human Resources and Education, Williamson Medical Center, Franklin, TN, p. A579

MOMEYER, Polly, Manager Human Resources, Lecom Health Millcreek Community Hospital, Erie, PA, p. A534

MONAGHAN, Aimee, Chief Executive Officer, Compass Behavioral Center Of Lafayette, Lafayette, LA, p. A278

MONAHAN, Jane, Vice President Ministry, Spiritual Care and Human Resources, Monroe Clinic, Monroe, WI, p. A708

MONASTERIO, Eugene A M.D., Medical Director, Children's Hospital Of Richmond At Vcu–Brook Road Campus, Richmond, VA, p. A674

MONCHER, Daniel J, Vice President and Chief Financial Officer, Firelands Regional Health System, Sandusky, OH, p. A499

MONCRIEF, William, ORH IT Client Executive, Oakland Regional Hospital, Southfield, MI, p. A331

MONCZEWSKI, Patricia, Chief Operating Officer, Mercy General Hospital, Sacramento, CA, p. A83

MONCZEWSKI, Patti, Chief Operating Officer, Paris Regional Medical Center, Paris, TX, p. A636

MONCZEWSKI, Ted, Vice President Human Resources, St. Vincent Charity Medical Center, Cleveland, OH, p. A486

MONDA, Cam D.O., Medical Director, Greenwood Regional Rehabilitation Hospital, Greenwood, SC, p. A563

MONETTE, Steven, Chief Financial Officer, Brattleboro Retreat, Brattleboro, VT, p. A662

MONGE, Candice R.N., Chief Nurse Executive Officer, Marian Regional Medical Center, Santa Maria, CA, p. A91

MONGELL, Mitchell P., FACHE, Chief Executive Officer, Fort Walton Beach Medical Center, Fort Walton Beach, FL, p. A125

MONGER, Shelton, Director Information Technology, Wayne Healthcare, Greenville, OH, p. A492

MONIACI, Cathy, R.N., MS, Administrator, Shriners Hospitals For Children–Houston, Houston, TX, p. A622

MONJE, Mary Anne, Chief Financial Officer and Chief Operating Officer, Whittier Hospital Medical Center, Whittier, CA, p. A97

MONJESKY, Kimberly, Chief Executive Officer, Pikes Peak Regional Hospital, Woodland Park, CO, p. A108

MONKRES, Paula, Administrative Assistant and Director Human Resources, Nocona General Hospital, Nocona, TX, p. A635

MONROE, Ame, Director Human Resources, Rolling Plains Memorial Hospital, Sweetwater, TX, p. A648

MONROE, Lori, Director of Nursing, Winnebago Mental Health Institute, Winnebago, WI, p. A716

MONROE, Temple, Director Nursing Operations, Wilson Medical Center, Neodesha, KS, p. A247

MONROIG, Domingo, Executive Director, Castaner General Hospital, Castaner, PR, p. A723

MONROY–MILLER, Cherry M.D., Acting Medical Director, Greystone Park Psychiatric Hospital, Morris Plains, NJ, p. A416

MONSANTO, Monte, Chief Information Systems, Russell County Hospital, Russell Springs, KY, p. A267

MONSRUD, Michele, Director Human Resources, Clearview Regional Medical Center, Monroe, GA, p. A162

MONTAGNESE, Robert A., President and Chief Executive Officer, Licking Memorial Hospital, Newark, OH, p. A497

MONTALBO, Tripp, Chief Executive Officer, Clear Lake Regional Medical Center, Webster, TX, p. A653

MONTALVO, Cary L., Chief Executive Officer, Solara Hospital Harlingen, Harlingen, TX, p. A618

MONTALVO, Eladio, Chief Executive Officer, Fort Duncan Regional Medical Center, Eagle Pass, TX, p. A609

MONTALVO, Jose M.D., Medical Director, Hospital Del Maestro, San Juan, PR, p. A726

MONTANA, Jennifer, Manager Human Resources, Community Memorial Hospital, Hamilton, NY, p. A437

MONTANA–RHODES, Lou, Vice President of Patient Care Services, Vidant Beaufort Hospital, Washington, NC, p. A472

MONTANO, Mayra, Director Information Systems, Hospital Metropolitano Dr. Susoni, Arecibo, PR, p. A722

MONTANTE, Carl, Director Information Systems and Information Technology, Shriners Hospitals For Children–Portland, Portland, OR, p. A525

MONTANYE, Richard, Director Information Systems, Hunt Regional Medical Center, Greenville, TX, p. A617

MONTELONGO, Rick J., Chief Executive Officer, St. Mark's Medical Center, La Grange, TX, p. A627

MONTENEGRO, Diana, Director Human Resources, Baptist Health South Florida, South Miami Hospital, Miami, FL, p. A132

MONTER, Brian, MSN, R.N., President, Uh Regional Hospitals, Cleveland, OH, p. A486

MONTGOMERY, Brigett, Director Human Resource, Lawrence Memorial Hospital, Walnut Ridge, AR, p. A50

MONTGOMERY, Daniel, Chief Financial Officer, Specialists Hospital – Shreveport, Shreveport, LA, p. A286

MONTGOMERY, James, Interim Chief Executive Officer, Bear River Valley Hospital, Tremonton, UT, p. A661

MONTGOMERY, Jennifer, R.N., FACHE
  Chief Financial Officer, Washakie Medical Center, Worland, WY, p. A720
  President and Chief Executive Officer, Mclaren Port Huron, Port Huron, MI, p. A328

MONTGOMERY, Lee Anne, R.N., Administrator, Crenshaw Community Hospital, Luverne, AL, p. A20

MONTGOMERY, Margaret, Chief Nursing Officer, Healthsouth Reading Rehabilitation Hospital, Reading, PA, p. A549

MONTGOMERY, Mark M.D., Chief Medical Officer, Texas Health Harris Methodist Hospital Southwest Fort Worth, Fort Worth, TX, p. A614

MONTGOMERY, Mary Jim R.N., MSN, FACHE, Chief Operating Officer, Crisp Regional Hospital, Cordele, GA, p. A155

MONTGOMERY, Peggy, Director Medical Records, Arrowhead Behavioral Health Hospital, Maumee, OH, p. A495

MONTGOMERY, Raymond W. II, FACHE, President and Chief Executive Officer, Unity Health White County Medical Center, Searcy, AR, p. A49

MONTGOMERY, Raymond W II, Chief Executive Officer, Unity Health White County Medical Center, Searcy, AR, p. A49

MONTGOMERY, Robert, Chief Financial Officer, Shriners Hospitals For Children–Lexington, Lexington, KY, p. A261

MONTGOMERY, Roxie, Director of Nursing, Jane Todd Crawford Hospital, Greensburg, KY, p. A259

MONTGOMERY, Susan, Chief Nursing Officer, Asante Ashland Community Hospital, Ashland, OR, p. A520

MONTGOMERY, Tina, Chief Financial Officer, Sidney Health Center, Sidney, MT, p. A388

MONTMENY, Richard, Vice President Professional Services, On–Site Administrator, St. John's Pleasant Valley Hospital, Camarillo, CA, p. A54

MONTOIS, John D., Interim Chief Executive Officer, Highlands Regional Medical Center, Sebring, FL, p. A143

MONTOUR, Vina, Director Information Technology, U.S. Public Health Service Phoenix Indian Medical Center, Phoenix, AZ, p. A34

MONTOYA, Alfred, Director, Manchester Veterans Affairs Medical Center, Manchester, NH, p. A409

MONTOYA, Brooke, Director Human Resources, Lake Granbury Medical Center, Granbury, TX, p. A617

MONTOYA, Lionel J., Chief Financial Officer, Spanish Peaks Regional Health Center, Walsenburg, CO, p. A108

MONZINGO, Ashley, Human Resources, Accounts Payable and Payroll, Tops Surgical Specialty Hospital, Houston, TX, p. A623

MONZON, Rogelio, Chief Financial Officer, Good Samaritan Hospital–North, Bakersfield, CA, p. A52

MOODY, Crystal R, Director Human Resources, Community Medical Center Of Izard County, Calico Rock, AR, p. A41

MOODY, David, Vice President Human Resources, Salina Regional Health Center, Salina, KS, p. A251

MOODY, James, Chief Financial Officer, Donalsonville Hospital, Donalsonville, GA, p. A156

MOODY, Vicky, Director Human Resources, Houlton Regional Hospital, Houlton, ME, p. A291

MOOG, Darlene, Director Human Resources, Healthsouth Deaconess Rehabilitation Hospital, Evansville, IN, p. A207

MOON, Bob, Chief Financial Officer, Christus St. Vincent Regional Medical Center, Santa Fe, NM, p. A428

MOON, David Jr, Director Information Systems, Lake City Community Hospital, Lake City, SC, p. A564

MOON, James, Chief Financial Officer, Pana Community Hospital, Pana, IL, p. A196

MOON, John, Associate Director, Veterans Affairs Eastern Kansas Health Care System, Topeka, KS, p. A252

MOONEY, Robert W M.D., Medical Director, Willingway Hospital, Statesboro, GA, p. A165

MOONEY, Susan E., M.D., MS, President and Chief Executive Officer, Alice Peck Day Memorial Hospital, Lebanon, NH, p. A408

MOORE, Amy, Human Resources, Hamilton Hospital, Olney, TX, p. A636

MOORE, Ben III, President and Chief Executive Officer, River Hospital, Alexandria Bay, NY, p. A430

MOORE, Betty, Business Manager, North Mississippi Medical Center–Iuka, Iuka, MS, p. A356

MOORE, Bill, Chief Human Resources, El Centro Regional Medical Center, El Centro, CA, p. A58

MOORE, Bob, FACHE, Chief Executive Officer, Venice Regional Bayfront Health, Venice, FL, p. A146

MOORE, Brandon, FACHE, Administrator and Chief Executive Officer, Park Place Surgical Hospital, Lafayette, LA, p. A279

MOORE, Brett CPA, Assistant Administrator Finance, Sutter Amador Hospital, Jackson, CA, p. A64

MOORE, Brian, President and Chief Executive Officer, St. Mary–Corwin Medical Center, Pueblo, CO, p. A107

MOORE, C Thomas, Chief Financial Officer, Delta Regional Medical Center, Greenville, MS, p. A355

MOORE, Carrie, Director Human Resources, Meadowbrook Rehabilitation Hospital, Gardner, KS, p. A241

MOORE, Cathy, Chief Nursing Officer, St. Luke's Hospital, Columbus, NC, p. A460

MOORE, Cecelia B CPA, Associate Vice Chancellor Finance, Vanderbilt University Medical Center, Nashville, TN, p. A587

MOORE, Christie, Director Human Resources, Healthsouth Rehabilitation Hospital – Mid–Cities, Bedford, TX, p. A597

MOORE, Courtney, CPA, Chief Executive Officer, Bleckley Memorial Hospital, Cochran, GA, p. A154

MOORE, Dana
  Senior Vice President Information Services, St. Anthony Hospital, Lakewood, CO, p. A105
  Senior Vice President Information Services, St. Anthony North Health Campus, Westminster, CO, p. A108

MOORE, Deborah, Director Human Resources, Walter P. Reuther Psychiatric Hospital, Westland, MI, p. A333

MOORE, Diane C., Chief Executive Officer and Chief Financial Officer, Big Bend Regional Medical Center, Alpine, TX, p. A592

MOORE, Edward H., President and Chief Executive Officer, Harrington Hospital, Southbridge, MA, p. A311

MOORE, Elizabeth, Chief Operating Officer, Silver Hill Hospital, New Canaan, CT, p. A111

MOORE, Emily, Director Human Resources and Information Technology, Haskell Memorial Hospital, Haskell, TX, p. A618

MOORE, Ethel L M.D., Director of Medical Affairs, Fort Belknap Service Unit, Harlem, MT, p. A385

MOORE, Harold, Chief Information Technology Officer, Spartanburg Medical Center, Spartanburg, SC, p. A566

MOORE, James L M.D., Senior Vice President and Chief Medical Officer, Piedmont Athens Regional Medical Center, Athens, GA, p. A149

MOORE, Jason H, Vice President and Chief Operating Officer, Tallahassee Memorial Healthcare, Tallahassee, FL, p. A144

MOORE, Jeffrey Steve, Chief Financial Officer, Fort Walton Beach Medical Center, Fort Walton Beach, FL, p. A125

MOORE, Jody Dewen, District Director Human Resources, Kindred Hospital–San Diego, San Diego, CA, p. A85

MOORE, John G, Vice President and Chief Financial Officer, Carolinas Healthcare System Union, Monroe, NC, p. A467

MOORE, John, M.D.
  Medical Director, Granite County Medical Center, Philipsburg, MT, p. A387
  Vice President Medical Affairs, SSM Health Depaul Hospital – St. Louis, Bridgeton, MO, p. A365
  President, South Lake Hospital, Clermont, FL, p. A122

MOORE, Kandi, Administrator, Specialists Hospital – Shreveport, Shreveport, LA, p. A286

MOORE, Karen O. FACHE, Senior Vice President Operations and Chief Nursing Officer, Lawrence General Hospital, Lawrence, MA, p. A307

MOORE, Karen, Vice President Information Technology and Chief Information Officer, Southern Regional Medical Center, Riverdale, GA, p. A163

MOORE, Keri, Vice President Human Resources and Support Services, Presbyterian–St. Luke's Medical Center, Denver, CO, p. A101

MOORE, Kermit R.N., Chief Operating Officer and Chief Nursing Officer, Nemaha County Hospital, Auburn, NE, p. A390

MOORE, Kyna, R.N.
  Chief Nursing Officer, Pocahontas Memorial Hospital, Buckeye, WV, p. A690
  Director of Nursing, Bath Community Hospital, Hot Springs, VA, p. A669

MOORE, Leigh, Administrative Assistant Human Resources, H. C. Watkins Memorial Hospital, Quitman, MS, p. A361

MOORE, Linda, Manager Human Resources, Seymour Hospital, Seymour, TX, p. A645

MOORE, Margaret, Director Business Office, Sabine County Hospital, Hemphill, TX, p. A618

MOORE, Matthew, Director of Financial Reporting, Effingham Hospital, Springfield, GA, p. A165

MOORE, Melinda, Director Human Resources, Multicare Deaconess Hospital, Spokane, WA, p. A686

MOORE, Michael, Director Information Systems, Troy Regional Medical Center, Troy, AL, p. A23

MOORE, Mike, President and Chief Operating Officer, Jane Phillips Medical Center, Bartlesville, OK, p. A505

MOORE, Neil J., President and Chief Executive Officer, Dimensions Healthcare System, Cheverly, MD, p. B47

MOORE, Nelda, Director Data Processing, Memorial Hospital And Manor, Bainbridge, GA, p. A152

MOORE, Nickie, Chief Financial Officer, North Sunflower Medical Center, Ruleville, MS, p. A361

MOORE, Patricia J, Director Human Resource, Valley Behavioral Health System, Barling, AR, p. A40

MOORE, Paul, Chief Information Officer, Connecticut Mental Health Center, New Haven, CT, p. A112

MOORE, Paula R.N., Chief Clinical Officer, Hugh Chatham Memorial Hospital, Elkin, NC, p. A462

MOORE, Randy, Chief Information Officer, Banner Lassen Medical Center, Susanville, CA, p. A93

MOORE, Rick
  Chief Information Officer, Bethesda North Hospital, Cincinnati, OH, p. A483
  Chief Information Officer, Good Samaritan Hospital, Cincinnati, OH, p. A484

MOORE, Robin A., Vice President Human Resources, Concord Hospital, Concord, NH, p. A407

MOORE, Ronald E R.N., MSN, Vice President Professional Practice and Chief Nursing Officer, Charleston Area Medical Center, Charleston, WV, p. A691

MOORE, Sandee, Chief Operating Officer, Eastern Idaho Regional Medical Center, Idaho Falls, ID, p. A173

MOORE, Saunya, Chief Financial Officer, Parkside Psychiatric Hospital And Clinic, Tulsa, OK, p. A517

MOORE, Shari, Chief Executive Officer, Methodist Rehabilitation Hospital, Dallas, TX, p. A606

MOORE, Steve, Chief Financial Officer, Southern Tennessee Regional Health System–Winchester, Winchester, TN, p. A590

MOORE, Sylvia, Vice President and Chief Operating Officer, Southeast Hospital, Cape Girardeau, MO, p. A366

MOORE, Tim
  Chief Accounting Officer and Vice President Ancillary Services and Finance, Blessing Hospital, Quincy, IL, p. A198
  Vice President Finance, Illini Community Hospital, Pittsfield, IL, p. A198

MOORE, Vernon, Senior Vice President Chief Business and Finance, University Of Texas Health Northeast, Tyler, TX, p. A651

MOORE, Warren E., President and Chief Executive Officer, Children's Specialized Hospital, New Brunswick, NJ, p. A417

MOORE, Wayne, Administrator, Christus Southeast Texas Hospital, Beaumont, TX, p. A597

MOORE, William, Chief Information Officer, Parrish Medical Center, Titusville, FL, p. A146

MOORE–CONNELLY, Marci M.D., Vice President Chief Medical Officer, Memorial Hospital Of Carbondale, Carbondale, IL, p. A179

MOORE–HARDY, Cynthia, FACHE, President and Chief Executive Officer, Lake Health, Concord Township, OH, p. A488

MOORE–JONES, Debra, Chief Executive Officer, Parkside Psychiatric Hospital And Clinic, Tulsa, OK, p. A517

MOOREHOUSE, Brett FACHE, Vice President and Chief Operating Officer, Ranken Jordan Pediatric Bridge Hospital, Maryland Heights, MO, p. A373

MOORER, Thad, Chief Information Officer, Eastside Psychiatric Hospital, Tallahassee, FL, p. A144

MOORHEAD, David M.D., Chief Medical Officer, Florida Hospital, Orlando, FL, p. A137

MOORMAN, Gary L. D.O., Chief Medical Officer and Senior Vice President Medical Affairs, Promedica Monroe Regional Hospital, Monroe, MI, p. A326

MORA, Debbie, Director, Southwest General Hospital, San Antonio, TX, p. A644

MORACA, Lynn, Director Human Resources, Lodi Community Hospital, Lodi, OH, p. A493

MORAHAN, John R., President and Chief Executive Officer, Penn State Health St. Joseph, Reading, PA, p. A549

MORAHAN, John R, President and Chief Executive Officer, Penn State Health St. Joseph, Reading, PA, p. A549

MORAHAN, John, Vice President Finance, St. Joseph Hospital, Bethpage, NY, p. A431

MORALES, Autumn, Chief Medical Staff Officer, Clarinda Regional Health Center, Clarinda, IA, p. A224

MORALES, Daniza
  Chief Information Officer, Hospital Menonita De Cayey, Cayey, PR, p. A723
  Manager Information System, Mennonite General Hospital, Aibonito, PR, p. A722

MORALES, Elsie, Chief Financial Officer, Hospital Universitario Dr. Ramon Ruiz Arnau, Bayamon, PR, p. A722

MORALES, Joel, Chief Financial Officer, Fort Duncan Regional Medical Center, Eagle Pass, TX, p. A609

MORALES, John R, Chief Financial Officer, John H. Stroger Jr. Hospital Of Cook County, Chicago, IL, p. A181

MORALES, Kathryn
  Director of Finance, Hampshire Memorial Hospital, Romney, WV, p. A696

  Director of Finance, War Memorial Hospital, Berkeley Springs, WV, p. A690

MORALES, Kristin, Chief Operating Officer, Harrington Hospital, Southbridge, MA, p. A311

MORALES, Marilyn, Chief Executive Officer, Hospital Buen Samaritano, Aguadilla, PR, p. A721

MORALES, Trish, Director Human Resources, Lakewood Ranch Medical Center, Bradenton, FL, p. A120

MORAN, Alina, Chief Executive Officer, NYC Health + Hospitals / Metropolitan, New Rochelle, NY, p. A445

MORAN, Barbara R.N., Director Patient Care Services and Chief Nursing Officer, Grace Hospital, Cleveland, OH, p. A485

MORAN, Debbie, Executive Director, Carl Albert Community Mental Health Center, Mcalester, OK, p. A510

MORAN, Michael Francis, President and Chief Administrative Officer, Baystate Wing Hospital, Palmer, MA, p. B21

MORAN, Michael Francis., President and Chief Administrative Officer, Baystate Wing Hospital, Palmer, MA, p. A310

MORANDEIRA, Ana, Director Marketing, San Juan Capestrano Hospital, San Juan, PR, p. A726

MORASKO, Jerome
  Chief Executive Officer, Bucyrus Community Hospital, Bucyrus, OH, p. A482
  President and Chief Executive Officer, Avita Ontario Hospital, Ontario, OH, p. A497
  President and Chief Executive Officer, Galion Community Hospital, Galion, OH, p. A491
  Chief Executive Officer, Heart Of The Rockies Regional Medical Center, Salida, CO, p. A107

MORAVICK, Donna, R.N., MSN, Executive Director, Southside Hospital, Bay Shore, NY, p. A431

MORDACH, John P, Senior Vice President and Chief Financial Officer, Rush University Medical Center, Chicago, IL, p. A183

MORDECAI, Steve, Director Human Resources, Griffin Hospital, Derby, CT, p. A110

MOREAU, Steven C., President and Chief Executive Officer, St. Joseph Hospital, Orange, CA, p. A78

MOREFIELD, Terri, Deputy Chief Human Resources Division, Bassett Army Community Hospital, Fort Wainwright, AK, p. A26

MOREIN, Sandy, Chief Nursing Officer, Mercy Regional Medical Center, Ville Platte, LA, p. A287

MORELAND, John M.D., Chief Medical Officer, Marcus Daly Memorial Hospital, Hamilton, MT, p. A385

MORELAND, Tresha, MS
  Regional Vice President Human Resources, Dameron Hospital, Stockton, CA, p. A92
  Vice President Human Resources, Rideout Memorial Hospital, Marysville, CA, p. A73

MORELL, Ixel, Chief Operating Officer, Sierra Vista Hospital, Sacramento, CA, p. A84

MORELLI, Gerald, Director Human Resources, Philadelphia Veterans Affairs Medical Center, Philadelphia, PA, p. A545

MORENO, Debbie R.N., Chief Nursing Officer, Lodi Memorial Hospital, Lodi, CA, p. A66

MORENO, Jorge, Director Information Technology Operations, Canyon Vista Medical Center, Sierra Vista, AZ, p. A36

MORENO, Robin
  Chief Financial Officer, North Texas State Hospital, Wichita Falls Campus, Wichita Falls, TX, p. A654
  Financial Officer, North Texas State Hospital, Vernon, TX, p. A651

MORENO, Sandra, Chief Nursing Officer, Orange County Global Medical Center, Inc., Santa Ana, CA, p. A90

MORENO–COOK, Shannon, Chief Nursing Officer, St. Vincent Rehabilitation Hospital, Sherwood, AR, p. A49

MORETTE, Joseph M, Executive Vice President, Methodist Rehabilitation Center, Jackson, MS, p. A357

MOREY, Scott David
  Chief Nursing Officer, Abrazo Maryvale Campus, Phoenix, AZ, p. A32
  Chief Nursing Officer, Abrazo West Campus, Goodyear, AZ, p. A30

MORGAN, Bradley, Vice President of Operations, The Heart Hospital Baylor Denton, Denton, TX, p. A608

MORGAN, Charlene, Chief Nursing Officer, Henderson County Community Hospital, Lexington, TN, p. A583

MORGAN, David, Vice President and Chief Financial Officer, Bristol Bay Area Health Corporation, Dillingham, AK, p. A26

MORGAN, Dennis P, Chief of Staff, Baptist Memorial Hospital– North Mississippi, Oxford, MS, p. A360

MORGAN, Derek
  Vice President Human Resources, Kettering Medical Center, Kettering, OH, p. A493
  Vice President Human Resources, Sycamore Medical Center, Miamisburg, OH, p. A496

MORGAN, Dirk, Vice President, Murray–Calloway County Hospital, Murray, KY, p. A265

MORGAN, Eric, Chief Executive Officer, Prattville Baptist Hospital, Prattville, AL, p. A22

MORGAN, James M.D., Chief Medical Officer, Memorial Hospital Of Converse County, Douglas, WY, p. A718

MORGAN, Janelle, Interim Director of Nursing, Howard County Medical Center, Saint Paul, NE, p. A399

MORGAN, Jeff, Director Information Systems, Northeastern Nevada Regional Hospital, Elko, NV, p. A401

MORGAN, Jeffrey H., Vice President Finance and Chief Financial Officer, Brooks Memorial Hospital, Dunkirk, NY, p. A435

MORGAN, John, R.N., Chief Executive Officer, Jackson Parish Hospital, Jonesboro, LA, p. A277

MORGAN, Kelly C., President and Chief Executive Officer, Mercy Medical Center, Roseburg, OR, p. A526

MORGAN, Lisa R.N., Vice President Patient Services, King's Daughters' Health, Madison, IN, p. A215

MORGAN, Loretta Y, Director Human Resources, Connally Memorial Medical Center, Floresville, TX, p. A612

MORGAN, Lori, M.D.
  Chief Administrative Officer, Legacy Emanuel Medical Center, Portland, OR, p. A525
  President and Chief Executive Officer, Huntington Memorial Hospital, Pasadena, CA, p. A79

MORGAN, Mace, Director Information Systems, Minden Medical Center, Minden, LA, p. A281

MORGAN, Marguerite J., Administrator, Florida State Hospital, Chattahoochee, FL, p. A121

MORGAN, Mark E., Medical Center Director, Jack C. Montgomery Veterans Affairs Medical Center, Muskogee, OK, p. A510

MORGAN, Matthew, Associate Administrator, Hillcrest Hospital – South, Tulsa, OK, p. A517

MORGAN, Melody, Chief Financial Officer, Fairfield Memorial Hospital, Fairfield, IL, p. A187

MORGAN, Nyle, Chief Information Officer, Sheridan Memorial Hospital, Sheridan, WY, p. A719

MORGAN, Rose MS, R.N., Vice President Patient Care Services, Princeton Community Hospital, Princeton, WV, p. A695

MORGAN, Shawn, Finance Officer, Northern Navajo Medical Center, Shiprock, NM, p. A428

MORGAN, Susan, Director of Nursing Services, Prairie Community Hospital, Terry, MT, p. A388

MORGAN, Teresa
  Assistant Vice President Human Resources, Shannon Medical Center, San Angelo, TX, p. A641
  Chief Financial Officer, Mcgehee–Desha County Hospital, Mcgehee, AR, p. A47

MORGAN, W Hugh M.D., Chief Medical Staff, Edgefield County Hospital, Edgefield, SC, p. A561

MORGAN–FINE, Richard, IT Director, Clarinda Regional Health Center, Clarinda, IA, p. A224

MORGESE, Vincent, M.D., Executive Vice President, Chief Operating Officer and Chief Medical Officer, Queen Of The Valley Medical Center, Napa, CA, p. A76

MORIMOTO, Scott, Director Clinical Informatics, Rehabilitation Hospital Of The Pacific, Honolulu, HI, p. A169

MORIN, Robert J., Vice President Finance and Chief Financial Officer, Sturgis Hospital, Sturgis, MI, p. A331

MORIN–SCRIBNER, Nicole, Director Human Resources, St. Mary's Regional Medical Center, Lewiston, ME, p. A291

MORISCO, Antonietta M.D., Medical Director, Chairman Anesthesiology, Jamaica Hospital Medical Center, New Rochelle, NY, p. A441

MORITZ, Mary, Administrator Human Resources, Humboldt County Memorial Hospital, Humboldt, IA, p. A229

MORK, David L., Jr
  Chief Executive Officer, Roosevelt Warm Springs Rehabilitation And Specialty Hospitals – Ltac, Warm Springs, GA, p. A167
  Chief Executive Officer, Roosevelt Warm Springs Rehabilitation Hospital – Rehab, Warm Springs, GA, p. A167

MORKEL, Derek, Chief Executive Officer, Healthtech Management Services, Brentwood, TN, p. B65

MORKRID, Shirley, Chief Nursing Officer, Liberty Medical Center, Chester, MT, p. A383

MORLOCK, Paul J FACHE, Vice President Human Resources and Occupational Health, Children's Hospital Of The King's Daughters, Norfolk, VA, p. A671

MORON, David M.D., Clinical Director, Rio Grande State Center/South Texas Health Care System, Harlingen, TX, p. A618

MORONY, David, Chief Financial Officer, Casa Colina Hospital And Health Systems, Pomona, CA, p. A80

MORQUECHO, Adam, Director Information Technology, Huntington Beach Hospital, Huntington Beach, CA, p. A63

MORREALE, Daniel
  Chief Information Officer, Hunterdon Medical Center, Flemington, NJ, p. A414
  Vice President and Chief Information Officer, Kingsbrook Jewish Medical Center, New Rochelle, NY, p. A442

MORREALE, Gene, President and Chief Executive Officer, Oneida Healthcare, Oneida, NY, p. A448

MORRELL, Dan, Manager Information Systems, Sierra Vista Hospital, Truth Or Consequences, NM, p. A429

MORRELL, Jeffrey F., Chief Executive Officer, Intermountain Hospital, Boise, ID, p. A171

MORRICAL, Michael, Chief Executive Officer, Mckenzie Regional Hospital, Mckenzie, TN, p. A584

MORRIONE, Thomas, Medical Director, New England Rehabilitation Hospital Of Portland, Portland, ME, p. A292

MORRIS, Alexander, Corporate Director Human Resources, Fort Washington Medical Center, Oxen Hill, MD, p. A300

MORRIS, Barbara R.N., Chief Nursing Officer, Pam Rehabilitation Hospital Of Beaumont, Beaumont, TX, p. A597

MORRIS, Christi, Director of Nursing, Bayside Community Hospital, Anahuac, TX, p. A592

MORRIS, Christopher
    Director Human Resources, Wheaton Franciscan Healthcare – Elmbrook Memorial, Brookfield, WI, p. A699
    Senior Director, Human Resources, Wheaton Franciscan Healthcare – St. Joseph's, Milwaukee, WI, p. A708

MORRIS, Clayton, Medical Director, Griffin Memorial Hospital, Norman, OK, p. A511

MORRIS, David, Chief Executive Officer, Denver Springs, Englewood, CO, p. A102

MORRIS, Debbie M, Director Human Resources, Marcus Daly Memorial Hospital, Hamilton, MT, p. A385

MORRIS, Debra D. R.N., MSN, Chief Nursing Officer, Great Plains Regional Medical Center, Elk City, OK, p. A507

MORRIS, Dennis, Area Finance Officer, Kaiser Permanente Oakland Medical Center, Oakland, CA, p. A77

MORRIS, Donald, Vice President Human Resources, Hillcrest Medical Center, Tulsa, OK, p. A517

MORRIS, Douglas
    Chief Financial Officer, Elmwood Healthcare Center At The Springs, Green Springs, OH, p. A492
    Chief Financial Officer, Vibra Hospital Of Northwestern Indiana, Crown Point, IN, p. A206
    Chief Financial Officer, Vibra Hospital Of Southeastern Michigan, Llc, Lincoln Park, MI, p. A325

MORRIS, Janet, Director Human Resources, Healthsouth Lakeview Rehabilitation Hospital, Elizabethtown, KY, p. A257

MORRIS, Janice, Accountant, Crossridge Community Hospital, Wynne, AR, p. A50

MORRIS, Jarrett L
    Controller and Chief Information Officer, Carolinas Healthcare System Lincoln, Lincolnton, NC, p. A466
    Controller, Carolinas Healthcare System Lincoln, Lincolnton, NC, p. A466

MORRIS, Jerry
    Administrator, Wedowee Hospital, Wedowee, AL, p. A24
    Chief Operating Officer, Tanner Medical Center–Villa Rica, Villa Rica, GA, p. A166

MORRIS, Jim
    Vice President Finance, Baptist Health La Grange, La Grange, KY, p. A260
    Vice President Finance, Baptist Health Louisville, Louisville, KY, p. A262

MORRIS, Jonathan B, M.D.
    Senior Vice President and Chief Information Officer, Wellstar Cobb Hospital, Austell, GA, p. A152
    Senior Vice President and Chief Information Officer, Wellstar Kennestone Hospital, Marietta, GA, p. A161

MORRIS, Lisa, Vice President Human Resources, Swedish Medical Center, Englewood, CO, p. A102

MORRIS, Luke P
    Assistant Vice President Talent, American Fork Hospital, American Fork, UT, p. A656
    Assistant Vice President Talent, Utah Valley Hospital, Provo, UT, p. A659

MORRIS, Marsha, Manager Information Services, Fairview Park Hospital, Dublin, GA, p. A157

MORRIS, Philip, Chief Operating Officer, West Houston Medical Center, Houston, TX, p. A623

MORRIS, R Randall., Administrator, West Carroll Memorial Hospital, Oak Grove, LA, p. A284

MORRIS, Rosanna, Hospital President, Beaumont Hospital – Royal Oak, Royal Oak, MI, p. A329

MORRIS, Tony, Business Manager, Mental Health Institute, Cherokee, IA, p. A224

MORRIS, Will, Director Information Technology, Panola Medical Center, Batesville, MS, p. A352

MORRISON, Christopher, Chief Executive Officer, Ancora Psychiatric Hospital, Hammonton, NJ, p. A414

MORRISON, Deane, Chief Information Officer, Concord Hospital, Concord, NH, p. A407

MORRISON, Dereck, Assistant Administrator, Bryan W. Whitfield Memorial Hospital, Demopolis, AL, p. A16

MORRISON, Devin
    Director Administration, Naval Hospital Pensacola, Pensacola, FL, p. A139
    Director for Administration, Naval Hospital Pensacola, Pensacola, FL, p. A139

MORRISON, Dianne, Director Human Resources, Mizell Memorial Hospital, Opp, AL, p. A22

MORRISON, Greta M., Assistant Chief Nursing Officer, Russell County Medical Center, Lebanon, VA, p. A669

MORRISON, J. E. M.D., M.P.H., Chief Medical Officer, Baylor Scott & White Medical Center – Hillcrest, Waco, TX, p. A652

MORRISON, Kathy E, Executive Director Human Resources, St. Catherine Hospital, Garden City, KS, p. A241

MORRISON, Kevin, Chief Financial Officer, Dickenson Community Hospital, Clintwood, VA, p. A666

MORRISON, Maureen, Vice President, Finance, Advocate Trinity Hospital, Chicago, IL, p. A180

MORRISON, Michael, Chief Financial Officer, Tristar Skyline Medical Center, Nashville, TN, p. A587

MORRISON, Sarah, President and Chief Executive Officer, Shepherd Center, Atlanta, GA, p. A151

MORRISSETT, Barbara, Vice President Human Resources, St. Mary's Medical Center, San Francisco, CA, p. A88

MORRISSETTE, Daniel, Chief Financial Officer, Stanford Health Care, Palo Alto, CA, p. A79

MORRISSEY, Moira, Chief Operating Officer and General Counsel, Four Winds Hospital, Katonah, NY, p. A438

MORRISSEY, Una E, R.N., MSN, Senior Vice President Operations, Chief Operating Officer and Chief Nursing Officer, New York Community Hospital, New Rochelle, NY, p. A443

MORRO, Maryalice, MSN, R.N., Director, Carl Vinson Veterans Affairs Medical Center, Dublin, GA, p. A157

MORROW, Charles M.D., Chief Medical Officer, Spartanburg Medical Center, Spartanburg, SC, p. A566

MORROW, Ginger
    Executive Vice President Human Resources, Christus Good Shepherd Medical Center–Marshall, Marshall, TX, p. A632
    Executive Vice President Human Resources, Christus Good Shepherd Medical Center, Longview, TX, p. A629

MORROW, Jeffrey, Chief Executive Officer, Doctor's Hospital Of Deer Creek, Leesville, LA, p. A280

MORROW, Jennifer, Director Human Resources, San Joaquin Valley Rehabilitation Hospital, Fresno, CA, p. A61

MORROW, Laurie, Executive Director Human Resources, Washington Regional Medical Center, Fayetteville, AR, p. A43

MORROW, Pat, Director Human Resources, Walker Baptist Medical Center, Jasper, AL, p. A20

MORROW, Randy, Vice President and Chief Operating Officer, Boone Hospital Center, Columbia, MO, p. A366

MORROW, Sarah, Vice President Human Resources, Capital Region Medical Center, Jefferson City, MO, p. A369

MORROW, Shawn, Administrator, Heber Valley Medical Center, Heber City, UT, p. A657

MORROW, W. Robert M.D., Executive Vice President and Chief Medical Officer, Children's Health System Of Texas, Dallas, TX, p. A605

MORSCHAUSER, Roberta, Administrator, Brown County Community Treatment Center, Green Bay, WI, p. A703

MORSE, Craig, Chief Financial Officer, Carlsbad Medical Center, Carlsbad, NM, p. A425

MORSE, Elizabeth L, Vice President Nursing and Chief Nursing Officer, Medstar St. Mary's Hospital, Leonardtown, MD, p. A299

MORSE, Jason, Director Information Technology, Cumberland Memorial Hospital, Cumberland, WI, p. A700

MORSTAD, Joan, Director Information Systems, Coliseum Medical Centers, Macon, GA, p. A160

MORTENSEN, Lorrie, R.N., MSN
    Chief Patient Services, Murray County Medical Center, Slayton, MN, p. A348
    Chief Nursing Officer, Catalina Island Medical Center, Avalon, CA, p. A52

MORTENSEN, Shane
    Chief Financial Officer, San Luis Valley Health Conejos County Hospital, La Jara, CO, p. A104
    Chief Financial Officer, San Luis Valley Health, Alamosa, CO, p. A98

MORTENSON, June R.N., Director of Nursing, Power County Hospital District, American Falls, ID, p. A171

MORTHLAND, Tim, Chief of Staff, Franklin Hospital District, Benton, IL, p. A178

MORTINSEN, Roy M.D., Chief of Staff, Sanford Vermillion Medical Center, Vermillion, SD, p. A573

MORTON, David M.D., Clinical Director, West Central Georgia Regional Hospital, Columbus, GA, p. A155

MORTON, Lauren, Chief Operating Officer, The Hospitals Of Providence East Campus, El Paso, TX, p. A611

MORTON, Leslie, Manager Human Resources, Riverview Regional Medical Center, Gadsden, AL, p. A18

MORTON, Robert M.D., Medical Director, Rolling Hills Hospital, Ada, OK, p. A504

MORTON, Stephanie, Chief Information Officer, Providence Alaska Medical Center, Anchorage, AK, p. A25

MORTON, Steve M.D., Chief Medical Officer, Continuecare Hospital At Baptist Health Corbin, Corbin, KY, p. A257

MORTON ROWE, Laura, Director of Human Resources, Providence Saint John's Health Center, Santa Monica, CA, p. A91

MORTOZA, Angela, Chief Executive Officer, Dallas County Hospital, Perry, IA, p. A233

MOSBY, Charmaine T, Area Director Health Information Management, Promise Hospital Baton Rouge – Main Campus, Baton Rouge, LA, p. A271

MOSBY HENRY, Nita, Senior Vice President Human Resources and Chief Inclusion Officer, Children's Hospital Colorado, Aurora, CO, p. A98

MOSCA, Philip M.D., President, Medical Staff, Integris Southwest Medical Center, Oklahoma City, OK, p. A512

MOSCATO, Mary K., FACHE, President, Hebrew Rehabilitation Center, Roslindale, MA, p. A310

MOSCHKAU, Don, Senior Director Human Resources, University Of Minnesota Medical Center, Fairview, Minneapolis, MN, p. A344

MOSCOSO, Ricardo M.D., Medical Director, University Hospital, San Juan, PR, p. A727

MOSEL, Lindy, Director of Nursing, Memorial Community Health, Aurora, NE, p. A390

MOSELY, Chisty, Director Information Management, Saint Simons By–The–Sea Hospital, Saint Simons Island, GA, p. A164

MOSER, Cindy, Director Human Resources, Allegheny Valley Hospital, Natrona Heights, PA, p. A542

MOSER, Joseph M.D., Chief Medical Officer, University Of Maryland Charles Regional Medical Center, La Plata, MD, p. A299

MOSER, Kevin, Vice President of Operations, Baptist Health Madisonville, Madisonville, KY, p. A264

MOSER, Neal M.D., Medical Director, Healthsouth Northern Kentucky Rehabilitation Hospital, Edgewood, KY, p. A257

MOSESIAN, Robert, Controller, Healthsouth Bakersfield Rehabilitation Hospital, Bakersfield, CA, p. A52

MOSHER, Guy W, III
    Manager Information Systems, Geneva General Hospital, Geneva, NY, p. A436
    Manager Information Systems, Soldiers And Sailors Memorial Hospital Of Yates County, Penn Yan, NY, p. A449

MOSHIER, John, Director Human Resources, Clara Barton Hospital, Hoisington, KS, p. A242

MOSHIRPUR, Jasmin, M.D.
    Chief Medical Officer, NYC Health + Hospitals / Queens, New Rochelle, NY, p. A445
    Dean and Medical Director, NYC Health + Hospitals / Elmhurst, New Rochelle, NY, p. A445

MOSHOFSKY, Bill M.D., Chief of Staff, Peacehealth Sacred Heart Medical Center University District, Eugene, OR, p. A521

MOSIER, Dawn, Director Human Resources, Healthsouth Rehabilitation Institute Of Tucson, Tucson, AZ, p. A38

MOSIER, John D.O., Chief of Staff, Herington Municipal Hospital, Herington, KS, p. A242

MOSKOWITZ, Samuel E., President, Medstar Franklin Square Medical Center, Baltimore, MD, p. A295

MOSLEY, Christopher R FACHE, Chief Operating Officer, Grady Memorial Hospital, Atlanta, GA, p. A150

MOSLEY, J. Christopher., Chief Executive Officer, Putnam Community Medical Center, Palatka, FL, p. A138

MOSLEY, J. Christopher, Chief Operating Officer, Orange Park Medical Center, Orange Park, FL, p. A136

MOSLEY, Tonja
    Chief Financial Officer, Heart Of Florida Regional Medical Center, Davenport, FL, p. A123
    Chief Financial Officer, Wellington Regional Medical Center, Wellington, FL, p. A147

MOSMEYER, Kathleen C, Director Human Resources, Citizens Medical Center, Victoria, TX, p. A652

MOSS, Austin, Vice President Human Resources, Jennie Stuart Medical Center, Hopkinsville, KY, p. A260

MOSS, Barry, Chief Executive Officer, Merit Health Central, Jackson, MS, p. A356

MOSS, Bradley, Administrator, Behavioral Healthcare Center At Huntsville, Huntsville, AL, p. A19

MOSS, C Renee M.D., Chief Medical Officer, Riverside Rehabilitation Institute, Newport News, VA, p. A671

MOSS, Jennifer MS, R.N., Chief Clinical Officer, Kirby Medical Center, Monticello, IL, p. A194

MOSS, Keith A, Vice President & Chief Medical Informatics Officers, Riverside Medical Center, Kankakee, IL, p. A191

MOSS, Misty, Director Business Administration, Logansport State Hospital, Logansport, IN, p. A215

MOSS, Ray, Vice President and Chief Information Officer, Henry Mayo Newhall Hospital, Valencia, CA, p. A95

MOSS, Shelby, Human Resource Officer, Sheridan County Health Complex, Hoxie, KS, p. A243

MOSS, Stuart, Chief Financial Officer, Kessler Marlton Rehabilitation, Marlton, NJ, p. A416

MOSS, Tyler, Chief Financial Officer, Milford Valley Memorial Hospital, Milford, UT, p. A657

MOSSER, Kevin H., M.D., President and Chief Executive Officer, Wellspan Health, York, PA, p. B146

MOSSOFF, Alan, Director Finance, Northern Dutchess Hospital, Rhinebeck, NY, p. A450

MOST, Kevin D.O., Vice President Medical Affairs, Northwestern Medicine Central Dupage Hospital, Winfield, IL, p. A202

MOSTOFI, Ann R MSN, R.N., Vice President Patient Care and Chief Nursing Officer, Eisenhower Medical Center, Rancho Mirage, CA, p. A81

MOTAKEF, Shahin, FACHE, Chief Executive Officer, Scott & White Medical Center – Temple, Temple, TX, p. A648

MOTEJZIK, Thomas, Director Information Systems, Carlsbad Medical Center, Carlsbad, NM, p. A425

MOTONAGA, Gregg M.D., Chief of Staff, Central Peninsula Hospital, Soldotna, AK, p. A27

MOTT, Daman MSN, Chief Nursing Officer, Doctors Hospital Of Laredo, Laredo, TX, p. A628

MOTT, Joseph, Chief Executive Officer, Intermountain Medical Center, Murray, UT, p. A658

MOTT, William, Chief Operating Officer, St. John Macomb–Oakland Hospital, Warren, MI, p. A332

MOTTE, Michael J., Chief Executive Officer, St. Alexius Hospital – Broadway Campus, Saint Louis, MO, p. A378

MOUGHAN, Jennifer L, Chief Human Resources Officer, Our Lady Of Lourdes Medical Center, Camden, NJ, p. A412

MOUISSET, Rena B, Director Human Resources and Contract Compliance, St. Martin Hospital, Breaux Bridge, LA, p. A272

MOULTON, Susan, Director Health Information Management, Spring Harbor Hospital, Westbrook, ME, p. A293

MOUNIE, Mike, Director Finance, Sentara Obici Hospital, Suffolk, VA, p. A676

MOUNTAIN, J Michael, Chief Financial Officer, Rivervalley Behavioral Health Hospital, Owensboro, KY, p. A265

MOUSA, Ayman, R.N., Ph.D., Chief Executive Officer, Pacifica Hospital Of The Valley, Los Angeles, CA, p. A70

MOUSA, Cindy, Director Human Resources, Touro Infirmary, New Orleans, LA, p. A283

MOUSTAKAKIS, John, Senior Vice President Information Systems and Chief Information Officer, Westchester Medical Center, Valhalla, NY, p. A454

MOVSESIAN, Gregory M.D., Acting Chief of Staff, Aleda E. Lutz Veterans Affairs Medical Center, Saginaw, MI, p. A329

MOWAN, Chris, Chief Executive Officer, Medical City Dallas, Dallas, TX, p. A606

MOWDER, Kristan, Director Administration and Patient Care Services, Eastern State Hospital, Lexington, KY, p. A261

MOYA, Linda, Director Human Resources, Mesilla Valley Hospital, Las Cruces, NM, p. A427

MOYER, Dale, Vice President Information Systems, Evangelical Community Hospital, Lewisburg, PA, p. A539

MOYER, Debra, R.N.
Chief Nurse Executive, Unitypoint Health–Iowa Lutheran Hospital, Des Moines, IA, p. A226
Chief Nursing Executive and Vice President Nursing Services, Unitypoint Health – Iowa Methodist Medical Center, Des Moines, IA, p. A226

MOYER, Douglas J., President, Sentara Rmh Medical Center, Harrisonburg, VA, p. A668

MOYER, Karen W R.N., Senior Vice President and Chief Nursing Officer, Mount Sinai Medical Center, Miami Beach, FL, p. A134

MOYER, William E., President, St. Luke's Hospital – Miners Campus, Coaldale, PA, p. A531

MRAMOR, Joann, Director Human Resources, Seven Rivers Regional Medical Center, Crystal River, FL, p. A122

MUCARIA, Jaclyn, President, New York–Presbyterian Queens, New Rochelle, NY, p. A444

MUCK, Erin, Vice President, Clinical Nursing, Crawford County Memorial Hospital, Denison, IA, p. A226

MUDEN, Todd, Section Head Information Management, Mayo Clinic Health System – Northland In Barron, Barron, WI, p. A698

MUDRY, Janel, Chief Operating Officer, Washington Health System Greene, Waynesburg, PA, p. A553

MUELLER, Arthur, Director Management Information Systems, Cuero Community Hospital, Cuero, TX, p. A604

MUELLER, Charles M.D., Chief of Staff, Texas County Memorial Hospital, Houston, MO, p. A369

MUELLER, Donald, Vice President and CEO, Erlanger Medical Center, Chattanooga, TN, p. A576

MUELLER, Karen R.N., Chief Nursing Officer, Mount Desert Island Hospital, Bar Harbor, ME, p. A289

MUELLER, Michael E, Chief Financial Officer, Health Central Hospital, Ocoee, FL, p. A136

MUELLER, Paul A., Chief Executive Officer, Rogers Memorial Hospital, Oconomowoc, WI, p. A709

MUELLER, Paul, Chief Financial Officer, Sparta Community Hospital, Sparta, IL, p. A200

MUGGLI, David D., FACHE, Chief Executive Officer, Select Specialty Hospital–Cincinnati, Cincinnati, OH, p. A484

MUHAMMAD, Mark, Manager Human Resources, Michael E. Debakey Veterans Affairs Medical Center, Houston, TX, p. A622

MUHS, David, Chief Financial Officer, Henry County Health Center, Mount Pleasant, IA, p. A232

MUILENBURG, Jeff, Chief of Staff, Memorial Community Health, Aurora, NE, p. A390

MUIR, Brian, Chief of Staff, Minidoka Memorial Hospital, Rupert, ID, p. A175

MULCAHY, Matthew, Acting Director, White River Junction Veterans Affairs Medical Center, White River Junction, VT, p. A663

MULDER, Doris, Vice President Nursing, Beloit Health System, Beloit, WI, p. A699

MULDER, Steven, M.D., President and Chief Executive Officer, Hutchinson Health, Hutchinson, MN, p. A341

MULDERIG, Marsha L. R.N., MSN, Chief Nursing Officer, Crisp Regional Hospital, Cordele, GA, p. A155

MULDOON, Patrick L., FACHE, President, Umass Memorial Medical Center, Worcester, MA, p. A313

MULDOON, Sean R, M.D.
Chief Medical Officer, Kindred Hospital–New Jersey Morris County, Dover, NJ, p. A413
Senior Vice President and Chief Medical Officer–Kindred Healthcare, Hospital Division, Kindred Hospital Northland, Kansas City, MO, p. A370

MULIS, Becky, Director of Health Information Management Systems, Four County Counseling Center, Logansport, IN, p. A215

MULKEY, Peter, Chief Executive Officer, Clinch Valley Medical Center, Richlands, VA, p. A673

MULLEN, Kristin, Chief Operating Officer, Eastern Regional Medical Center, Philadelphia, PA, p. A543

MULLEN, Thomas R., President and Chief Executive Officer, Mercy Medical Center, Baltimore, MD, p. A295

MULLENAX, Paul, Business Manager, Wyoming State Hospital, Evanston, WY, p. A718

MULLENDER, Monica, Director of Nursing, Osborne County Memorial Hospital, Osborne, KS, p. A248

MULLENS, Allen M.D., Chief Medical Staff, Norton Community Hospital, Norton, VA, p. A672

MULLER, Donna L., Interim Chief Financial Officer, Hanover Hospital, Hanover, PA, p. A535

MULLER, Lynn, Chief Financial Officer, North Metro Medical Center, Jacksonville, AR, p. A45

MULLER, Oz, Director Human Resources, Porter Adventist Hospital, Denver, CO, p. A101

MULLER, Ralph W., President and Chief Executive Officer, University Of Pennsylvania Health System, Philadelphia, PA, p. B140

MULLERY, Barbara M, Vice President Administration, Robert Wood Johnson University Hospital Rahway, Rahway, NJ, p. A419

MULLIGAN, Lisa, Commanding Officer, Naval Hospital Camp Pendleton, Camp Pendleton, CA, p. A54

MULLIGAN, Marie R.N., MSN, Vice President Nursing, John T. Mather Memorial Hospital, Port Jefferson, NY, p. A450

MULLIN, Shelly, R.N., President Market Leader, Multicare Tacoma General Hospital, Tacoma, WA, p. A688

MULLINGS, Donna, Director of Nursing, Assumption Community Hospital, Napoleonville, LA, p. A282

MULLINS, Bandy M.D., Chief of Staff, Summersville Regional Medical Center, Summersville, WV, p. A696

MULLINS, Brad, Director Information Technology, Gove County Medical Center, Quinter, KS, p. A250

MULLINS, Bryan, Chief Operating Officer, Johnston Memorial Hospital, Abingdon, VA, p. A664

MULLINS, Cindy, Director Information Technology, Saint Mary's Regional Medical Center, Reno, NV, p. A405

MULLINS, Dustin
Chief Human Resources, Bayne–Jones Army Community Hospital, Fort Polk, LA, p. A274
Chief Resource Management, Bayne–Jones Army Community Hospital, Fort Polk, LA, p. A274

MULLINS, Erin D.O., Chief Medical Staff, Dickenson Community Hospital, Clintwood, VA, p. A666

MULLINS, Larry A., FACHE, President and Chief Executive Officer, Samaritan Health Services, Corvallis, OR, p. B111

MULLINS, Michelle, Chief Information Officer, Oklahoma Heart Hospital, Oklahoma City, OK, p. A513

MULLIS, Jeffrey
Interim Chief Financial Officer, Bayfront Health Port Charlotte, Port Charlotte, FL, p. A140
Interim Chief Financial Officer, Clearview Regional Medical Center, Monroe, GA, p. A162

MULROONEY, JoAnn M R.N., Chief Operating Officer, Trinity Health System, Steubenville, OH, p. A500

MULTACH, Mark M.D., Chief Medical Officer, Mount Sinai Hospital, Chicago, IL, p. A182

MULTACK, Richard D.O., Vice President Medical Management, Advocate South Suburban Hospital, Hazel Crest, IL, p. A189

MULVEHILL, Mitchell, Group Financial Officer, Texas Health Harris Methodist Hospital Southlake, Southlake, TX, p. A646

MULVEY, Lee, Human Resource Officer, Texas Health Harris Methodist Hospital Hurst–Euless–Bedford, Bedford, TX, p. A597

MUMOLIE, Gina
Senior Vice President and Chief Nurse Executive, Inspira Medical Center–Woodbury, Woodbury, NJ, p. A423
Senior Vice President Hospital Administration, Capital Health Regional Medical Center, Trenton, NJ, p. A421

MUMPOWER, Rebecca, Director Marketing, Mesilla Valley Hospital, Las Cruces, NM, p. A427

MUNA, Esther L., Chief Executive Officer, Commonwealth Health Center, Saipan, MP, p. A721

MUNCHEL, Bryan, Senior Vice President and Chief Information Officer, Pam Specialty Hospital Of Covington, Covington, LA, p. A273

MUNDY, Stephens M.
Interim President, The University Of Vermont Health Network – Alice Hyde Medical Center, Malone, NY, p. A439
President and Chief Executive Officer, The University Of Vermont Health Network–Champlain Valley Physicians Hospital, Plattsburgh, NY, p. A449

MUNFORD, Thedosia, Senior Vice President and Chief Nursing Officer, Providence Hospital, Washington, DC, p. A118

MUNGER, Richard, Administrator, Mount Grant General Hospital, Hawthorne, NV, p. A402

MUNGOVAN, Sandy, Chief Information Officer, Harbor–Ucla Medical Center, Torrance, CA, p. A93

MUNHOLLAND, Cleta
Administrator, Louisiana Extended Care Hospital West Monroe, West Monroe, LA, p. A288
Administrator, Specialty Hospital, Monroe, LA, p. A281

MUNIR, Amjad M.D., Medical Director, Healthsouth Chattanooga Rehabilitation Hospital, Chattanooga, TN, p. A576

MUNOZ, Alejandro M.D., Chief Medical Officer, Cedar Crest Hospital And Residential Treatment Center, Belton, TX, p. A598

MUNOZ, Astro, Executive Director, First Hospital Panamericano, Cidra, PR, p. A723

MUNOZ, Thalia H., R.N., MS, Chief Executive Officer, Starr County Memorial Hospital, Rio Grande City, TX, p. A640

MUNSON, Bill, Vice President and Chief Financial Officer, Boulder Community Health, Boulder, CO, p. A98

MUNSON, Jennifer, Chief Financial Officer, Three Rivers Hospital, Brewster, WA, p. A679

MUNSON, Joan, Manager Information Systems, Fairchild Medical Center, Yreka, CA, p. A97

MUNSON, John, Vice President and Chief Financial Officer, St. Anthony Regional Hospital, Carroll, IA, p. A223

MUNSON, Kris, Director Human Resources, Arbour H. R. I. Hospital, Brookline, MA, p. A305

MUNTEFERING, Denise, Vice President Patient Care Services, Avera St. Benedict Health Center, Parkston, SD, p. A571

MUNTZ, Dana M., Chief Executive Officer, St. Vincent Salem Hospital, Salem, IN, p. A219

MUNTZ, Tim, President and Chief Executive Officer, St. Margaret's Hospital, Spring Valley, IL, p. A200

MUNYAN, Lori, Director, Human Resources, Healthsouth Rehabilitation Hospital Of Toms River, Toms River, NJ, p. A421

MURANSKY, Ed, Owner, Surgical Hospital At Southwoods, Youngstown, OH, p. A503

MURCHISON, Sandra, Director Medical Records, Coosa Valley Medical Center, Sylacauga, AL, p. A23

MURDAUGH, Laura, Finance Director, William J. Mccord Adolescent Treatment Facility, Orangeburg, SC, p. A565

MURDOCH, William M.D., Medical Director, Loma Linda University Behavioral Medicine Center, Redlands, CA, p. A81

MURDOCK, Guy, Vice President Human Resources, Healthbridge Children's Hospital Of Houston, Houston, TX, p. A620

MURDOCK, Holly, Human Resources Coordinator, Kindred Hospital Rome, Rome, GA, p. A163

MURDOCK, Mark, FACHE, Director, Veterans Affairs Northern Indiana Health Care System, Fort Wayne, IN, p. A208

MURDOCK–LANGAN, Patricia, M.D.
Chief Medical Officer, Chi Health Lakeside, Omaha, NE, p. A397
Chief Medical Officer, Chi Health Midlands, Papillion, NE, p. A399

MURDY, James B, Chief Financial Officer, Belmont Community Hospital, Bellaire, OH, p. A481

MURILLO, Jeremias M.D., Chief Medical Officer, Newark Beth Israel Medical Center, Newark, NJ, p. A417

MURIN, William J, Chief Human Resources Officer, Uc San Diego Health, San Diego, CA, p. A86

MURPHREE, Shari, Chief Executive Officer, Willow Crest Hospital, Miami, OK, p. A510

MURPHY, Brian, Senior Director Admissions and Referral Services, Hebrew Rehabilitation Center, Roslindale, MA, p. A310

MURPHY, Bruce, M.D., President and Chief Executive Officer, Arkansas Heart Hospital, Little Rock, AR, p. A45

MURPHY, Charles J, Associate Vice President Human Resources, Strong Memorial Hospital Of The University Of Rochester, Rochester, NY, p. A451

MURPHY, Christine MS, Chief Operating Officer, Liberty Healthcare Systems, Bastrop, LA, p. A270

MURPHY, Colleen M.D., Chief of Staff, Clay County Hospital, Flora, IL, p. A187

MURPHY, David, Interim Chief Executive Officer, University Of Minnesota Medical Center, Fairview, Minneapolis, MN, p. A344

MURPHY, Dennis M., President and Chief Executive Officer, Indiana University Health, Indianapolis, IN, p. B68

MURPHY, Elizabeth A R.N., FACHE, Vice President for Patient Care Services, Mercy Health Saint Mary's, Grand Rapids, MI, p. A321

MURPHY, Evelyn R.N., Chief Nursing Officer, St. Mary's Sacred Heart Hospital, Lavonia, GA, p. A160

MURPHY, J Patrick, Chief Financial Officer, North Baldwin Infirmary, Bay Minette, AL, p. A14

MURPHY, James M. M.D., Chief Medical Officer Regional Development and Outpatient Services, New London Hospital, New London, NH, p. A410

MURPHY, James, Chief Executive Officer, South Texas Surgical Hospital, Corpus Christi, TX, p. A603

MURPHY, John B M.D., Vice President Medical Affairs and Chief Medical Officer, Rhode Island Hospital, Providence, RI, p. A557

MURPHY, John M., M.D., President and Chief Executive Officer, Western Connecticut Health Network, Danbury Hospital, Danbury, CT, p. A109

MURPHY, John M, M.D., President and Chief Executive Officer, Western Connecticut Health Network, Danbury Hospital, Danbury, CT, p. A109

MURPHY, Judy, Vice President Human Resources, Southwest General Health Center, Middleburg Heights, OH, p. A496

MURPHY, Julie
Chief Financial Officer, Saint Luke's Cushing Hospital, Leavenworth, KS, p. A245
Chief Financial Officer, Saint Luke's North Hospital – Barry Road, Kansas City, MO, p. A371

MURPHY, Kathy, Site Manager, Mescalero Public Health Service Indian Hospital, Mescalero, NM, p. A427

MURPHY, Kelly, Vice President Human Resources, Colorado Canyons Hospital And Medical Center, Fruita, CO, p. A103

MURPHY, Kevin, Director, Information Technology Services, Bayfront Health St. Petersburg, Saint Petersburg, FL, p. A141

MURPHY, Kyle, Director Information Technology, Mayhill Hospital, Denton, TX, p. A608

MURPHY, Linda, Chief Financial Officer, Osborne County Memorial Hospital, Osborne, KS, p. A248

MURPHY, Lionel
Chief Executive Officer and Administrator, Bethesda Rehabilitation Hospital, Baton Rouge, LA, p. A270
Chief Executive Officer, Southeast Regional Medical Center, Kentwood, LA, p. A277

MURPHY, Margaret M, Chief Executive Officer, Kindred Hospital–Philadelphia, Philadelphia, PA, p. A544

MURPHY, Marie, Director Human Resources, Effingham Hospital, Springfield, GA, p. A165

MURPHY, Mary S, MSN
Regional Chief Nursing Officer, Amita Health Adventist Medical Center Lagrange, La Grange, IL, p. A191
Vice President and Chief Nursing Officer, Amita Health Adventist Medical Center – Hinsdale, Hinsdale, IL, p. A190

MURPHY, Matthew, Chief Financial Officer, Compass Memorial Healthcare, Marengo, IA, p. A231

MURPHY, Maureen M.D., Director of Medical Affairs, St. Clare Hospital, Baraboo, WI, p. A698

MURPHY, Michael D., FACHE, Chief Executive Officer, Abilene Regional Medical Center, Abilene, TX, p. A591

MURPHY, Michael M.D., JD, Chief Medical Officer, Sharp Grossmont Hospital, La Mesa, CA, p. A64

MURPHY, Nancy, Vice President, Human Resources, Franciscan Children's, Brighton, MA, p. A304

MURPHY, Paul, Chief Information Officer, Lane Regional Medical Center, Zachary, LA, p. A288

MURPHY, Peter J., Senior Vice President and Chief Operating Officer, Franciscan St. Francis Health – Mooresville, Mooresville, IN, p. A216

MURPHY, Richard J., President and Chief Executive Officer, South Nassau Communities Hospital, Oceanside, NY, p. A448

MURPHY, Rita, Director Human Resources, Cobre Valley Regional Medical Center, Globe, AZ, p. A30

MURPHY, Sheryl, Chief Nursing Officer and Director of Clinical Services, Peacehealth Peace Island Medical Center, Friday Harbor, WA, p. A681

MURPHY, Steve
Director Information Systems, SSM Health St. Mary's Hospital Centralia, Centralia, IL, p. A179
FM–East Region IS, Good Samaritan Regional Health Center, Mount Vernon, IL, p. A194

MURPHY, Steven, Executive Director, Devereux Hospital And Children's Center Of Florida, Melbourne, FL, p. A132

MURPHY, Terry
Director Information Services, Phoenixville Hospital, Phoenixville, PA, p. A546
President and Chief Executive Officer, Bayhealth Medical Center, Dover, DE, p. A115

MURPHY, Theresa, Chief Nursing Officer, Usc Verdugo Hills Hospital, Glendale, CA, p. A62

MURPHY, Timothy, R.N.
Chief Nursing Officer, Healthsouth Desert Canyon Rehabilitation Hospital, Las Vegas, NV, p. A403
Vice President Human Resources, Mercy Hospital Fort Scott, Fort Scott, KS, p. A241
Vice President Human Resources, Mercy Hospital Joplin, Joplin, MO, p. A370

MURPHY, Tom, Chief Executive Officer, Minidoka Memorial Hospital, Rupert, ID, p. A175

MURPHY–FROBISH, Erin, Vice President Human Resources, Morris Hospital & Healthcare Centers, Morris, IL, p. A194

MURPHY–MIJARES, Monique, Chief Information Officer, Valley View Medical Center, Fort Mohave, AZ, p. A29

MURRAY, Alexander, Interim Associate Director, Veterans Affairs Gulf Coast Veterans Health Care System, Biloxi, MS, p. A352

MURRAY, Beverly, Director of Human Resources, Providence Tarzana Medical Center, Los Angeles, CA, p. A71

MURRAY, Brian, M.D.
Medical Director, Erie County Medical Center, Buffalo, NY, p. A432
Chief Financial Officer, Gunnison Valley Hospital, Gunnison, UT, p. A656

MURRAY, Cindy, R.N., Chief Nursing Officer and Chief Operating Officer, Baylor Scott & White Medical Center At Waxahachie, Waxahachie, TX, p. A652

MURRAY, Dan, PsyD, Chief Executive Officer, Wellspring Foundation, Bethlehem, CT, p. A109

MURRAY, Denise R., Chief Executive Officer, Anmed Health Rehabilitation Hospital, Anderson, SC, p. A558

MURRAY, Diana, Director Information Systems, Grand River Hospital District, Rifle, CO, p. A107

MURRAY, Gerald
President, Upmc Altoona, Altoona, PA, p. A528
President, Upmc Bedford Memorial, Everett, PA, p. A535

MURRAY, James E., Chief Executive Officer, Lifecare Management Services, Plano, TX, p. B76

MURRAY, J. Patrick., FACHE, President and Chief Executive Officer, Peterson Regional Medical Center, Kerrville, TX, p. A626

MURRAY, Julie, Chief Executive Officer, Merrick Medical Center, Central City, NE, p. A391

MURRAY, Kent M.D., Chief of Staff, Robert J. Dole Veterans Affairs Medical Center, Wichita, KS, p. A253

MURRAY, Kevin J, Senior Vice President, John T. Mather Memorial Hospital, Port Jefferson, NY, p. A450

MURRAY, Kevin M.D., Director Medical Services, Lake Taylor Transitional Care Hospital, Norfolk, VA, p. A672

MURRAY, Lorraine, Chief Executive Officer, Post Acute Medical Specialty Hospital Of Texarkana – North, Texarkana, TX, p. A649

MURRAY, Marisa CPA, Director Finance, Hshs St. Francis Hospital, Litchfield, IL, p. A192

MURRAY, Michael, Chief Financial Officer, Christus Dubuis Hospital Of Paris, Paris, TX, p. A636

MURRAY, Sherri, Chief Financial Officer, Montgomery General Hospital, Montgomery, WV, p. A694

MURRAY, Susan, FACHE
Chief Operating Officer, The Queen's Medical Center, Honolulu, HI, p. A169
Director Information Services, Trident Medical Center, Charleston, SC, p. A559

MURRAY, Wesley E., Chief Executive Officer, Texas County Memorial Hospital, Houston, MO, p. A369

MURRELL, Joseph, Chief Executive Officer, Wayne County Hospital, Monticello, KY, p. A265

MURRILL, Michael, MBA, President and Chief Executive Officer, Amita Health Adventist Medical Center Lagrange, La Grange, IL, p. A191

MURROW, Carol, Vice President Business Development, Cox Medical Center Branson, Branson, MO, p. A365

MURRY, Jim, Chief Information Officer, Stony Brook University Hospital, Stony Brook, NY, p. A453

MURT, Mary Lou R.N., Senior Vice President Nursing, Monongahela Valley Hospital, Monongahela, PA, p. A541

MURTHY, Bangalore M.D., Director Medical Staff, Jackson Park Hospital And Medical Center, Chicago, IL, p. A181

MURTHY, Krishna M.D., Chief of Medical Staff, Gibson General Hospital, Princeton, IN, p. A218

MURTOS, Kristen, FACHE, President, Northshore University Health System, Evanston, IL, p. A187

MURZYN, Derek
Chief Executive Officer, Carolinas Continuecare Hospital At Kings Mountain, Kings Mountain, NC, p. A465
Chief Executive Officer, Carolinas Continuecare Hospital At University, Charlotte, NC, p. A459
Market Chief Executive Officer, Carolinas Continuecare Hospital At Pineville, Charlotte, NC, p. A459

MUSACK, Scott, Chief Information Officer, Silver Lake Medical Center, Los Angeles, CA, p. A71

MUSANTE, David M.D., Medical Director, North Carolina Specialty Hospital, Durham, NC, p. A461

MUSGRAVE, Chelsea, Director of Human Resources, Clay County Hospital, Flora, IL, p. A187

MUSICH, Trisha E, R.N., Chief Nursing Officer, Vista Medical Center East, Waukegan, IL, p. A202

MUSOIU, Robert, Director Human Resources, Fairfield Memorial Hospital, Fairfield, IL, p. A187

MUSSI, Natalie, President and Chief Executive Officer, Los Robles Hospital And Medical Center, Thousand Oaks, CA, p. A93

MUSSMAN, Rebekah, Chief Executive Officer, Crete Area Medical Center, Crete, NE, p. A392

MUSSO, Lewis C, Vice President Human Resources, Trinity Health System, Steubenville, OH, p. A500

MUSTACCHIA, Michele, Chief Human Resources Officer, Banner Gateway Medical Center, Gilbert, AZ, p. A29

MUSTARD, Ruth W. R.N., MSN, Associate Director Nursing and Patient Services, Wm. Jennings Bryan Dorn Veterans Affairs Medical Center, Columbia, SC, p. A561

MUSTIAN, J Perry., President and Chief Executive Officer, John D. Archbold Memorial Hospital, Thomasville, GA, p. A166

MUSTIN, Deanna, R.N., Administrator, Bob Wilson Memorial Grant County Hospital, Ulysses, KS, p. A253

MUSUNURU, J.R., M.D., Executive Director, Fond Du Lac County Mental Health Center, Fond Du Lac, WI, p. A701

MUTHU, Karthik, Chief Executive Officer, Healthsouth Rehabilitation Hospital Of Ocala, Ocala, FL, p. A136

MUTTERER, Michael, Senior Vice President and Chief Nursing Officer, Riverside Medical Center, Kankakee, IL, p. A191

MUTZIGER, John M.D., Chief Medical Officer, Laird Hospital, Union, MS, p. A362

MWANIKI, Mary, Chief Financial Officer, Healthsouth Rehabilitation Hospital – Mid–Cities, Bedford, TX, p. A597

MWEBE, David M.D., Chief of Staff, Osmond General Hospital, Osmond, NE, p. A398

MYATT, Kevin A, Senior Vice President Human Resources, Yale–New Haven Hospital, New Haven, CT, p. A112

MYDLER, Todd M.D., Vice President and Chief Medical Officer, Good Samaritan Medical Center, Lafayette, CO, p. A104

MYER, Amber, Director Medical Technology, Throckmorton County Memorial Hospital, Throckmorton, TX, p. A650

MYERS, Becky, Human Resources Specialist, Illini Community Hospital, Pittsfield, IL, p. A198

MYERS, Charles, Chief Nursing Officer, Pam Rehabilitation Hospital Of Tulsa, Tulsa, OK, p. A517

MYERS, Chrissy R.N., Director of Nursing, Behavioral Healthcare Center At Clarksville, Clarksville, TN, p. A577

MYERS, Douglas, Executive Vice President and Chief Financial Officer, Phoenix Children's Hospital, Phoenix, AZ, p. A34

MYERS, Ed, Administrator, Shriners Hospitals For Children–Philadelphia, Philadelphia, PA, p. A545

MYERS, Gabby, Human Resources Director, Advanced Diagnostics Hospital, Houston, TX, p. A619

MYERS, Gary, Chief Executive Officer, Mammoth Hospital, Mammoth Lakes, CA, p. A72

MYERS, Grace MSN, Vice President, Nurse Executive, Sentara Princess Anne Hospital, Virginia Beach, VA, p. A676

MYERS, Jeffrey D., President and Chief Executive Officer, Hamilton Medical Center, Dalton, GA, p. A156

MYERS, Jerry, M.D., Chief Executive Officer and Medical Director, Kell West Regional Hospital, Wichita Falls, TX, p. A654

MYERS, Jessica, Medical Director, Neshoba County General Hospital, Philadelphia, MS, p. A360

MYERS, Julie
Chief Executive Officer, Kindred Hospital–La Mirada, La Mirada, CA, p. A64
Chief Executive Officer, Kindred Hospital–Westminster, Westminster, CA, p. A96

MYERS, Karen, Vice President Financial Services, Stoughton Hospital Association, Stoughton, WI, p. A713

MYERS, Kathy R MS, R.N., Chief Nursing Officer, Tennova Healthcare–Lafollette Medical Center, La Follette, TN, p. A582

MYERS, Keith G., Chairman and Chief Executive Officer, Lhc Group, Lafayette, LA, p. B76

MYERS, Kevin
Director Information Systems, Lake Granbury Medical Center, Granbury, TX, p. A617
Director Information Technology, Wilson Medical Center, Neodesha, KS, p. A247

MYERS, Kimberly, Director Human Resources, Guthrie County Hospital, Guthrie Center, IA, p. A228

MYERS, Lisa, Director Human Resources, Heritage Oaks Hospital, Sacramento, CA, p. A83

MYERS, Loretta MS, R.N., Director, Patient Care, Floyd Valley Healthcare, Le Mars, IA, p. A230

MYERS, Mark M.D., Chief Medical Officer, AMG Specialty Hospital–Tulsa, Tulsa, OK, p. A517

MYERS, Mary R.N., MSN, Chief Nursing Officer, St. Vincent Indianapolis Hospital, IndianapolisSt. Vincent Heart Center, Indianapolis, IN, p. A212

MYERS, Michael D., R.N., Chief Executive Officer, Veterans Memorial Hospital, Waukon, IA, p. A236

MYERS, Michelle F., Director Human Resources, Florida Hospital Wauchula, Wauchula, FL, p. A147

MYERS, Paul M.D., Neonatologist and Chief Medical Officer, Children's Hospital Of Wisconsin–Fox Valley, Neenah, WI, p. A708

MYERS, Philip M.D., Vice President Medical Affairs, University Hospitals Samaritan Medical Center, Ashland, OH, p. A480

MYERS, Randy, Chief Information Officer, Rehoboth Mckinley Christian Health Care Services, Gallup, NM, p. A426

MYERS, Robert T, Chief Operating Officer, Goshen Hospital, Goshen, IN, p. A209

MYERS, Rosemary, Manager, Team Resources, Winter Haven Hospital, Winter Haven, FL, p. A148

MYERS, Russ, Chief Executive Officer, Virginia Mason Memorial, Yakima, WA, p. A689

MYERS, Shane P, Chief Operating Officer, Iberia Medical Center, New Iberia, LA, p. A282

MYERS, Sheri, Vice President Patient Care Services, Mclaren Central Michigan, Mount Pleasant, MI, p. A326

MYERS, Stephen, Chief Executive Officer, Providence Hospital Of North Houston, Houston, TX, p. A622

MYERS, Tara, Director Human Resources, Anmed Health Rehabilitation Hospital, Anderson, SC, p. A558

MYERS, Theresa, Personnel Director, Fallon Medical Complex, Baker, MT, p. A382

MYERS, William, Chief Executive Officer, Montgomery County Emergency Service, Norristown, PA, p. A542

MYHRE, Tracy R.N., MSN, Chief Nursing Officer, Tomah Memorial Hospital, Tomah, WI, p. A713

MYLAVARAPU, Sarada M.D., Chief Medical Officer, Woodland Healthcare, Woodland, CA, p. A97

MYSTER, Jennifer, President, Buffalo Hospital, Buffalo, MN, p. A337

N

NABEL, Elizabeth, M.D., President, Brigham And Women's Hospital, Boston, MA, p. A303

NABORS, Teresa, Director of Nursing, Greenwood Regional Rehabilitation Hospital, Greenwood, SC, p. A563

NACEY, Marley, Director Finance, Sentara Virginia Beach General Hospital, Virginia Beach, VA, p. A676

NACHIMUTHU, Anbu, Chief Financial Officer, Atrium Medical Center Of Corinth, Corinth, TX, p. A603

NACHTIGAL, Amy, Chief Financial Officer, Saint Luke's Hospital Of Kansas City, Kansas City, MO, p. A370

NACHTRIEB, Han, Vice President Human Resources, Seattle Cancer Care Alliance, Seattle, WA, p. A685

NACION, Glenn, Vice President Human Resources, Trinitas Regional Medical Center, Elizabeth, NJ, p. A413

NADEAU, Barbara, Chief Human Resources Management Service, White River Junction Veterans Affairs Medical Center, White River Junction, VT, p. A663

NADEAU, Stephen, Senior Vice President Human Resources, Gwinnett Hospital System, Lawrenceville, GA, p. A160

NADER, Daniel D.O., Chief of Staff, Southwestern Regional Medical Center, Tulsa, OK, p. A518

NADER, Keoni, Director Human Resources, Louis A. Weiss Memorial Hospital, Chicago, IL, p. A182

NADER, Mary, Director Information Technology, Spectrum Health Special Care Hospital, Grand Rapids, MI, p. A321

NADER, Rick Lee, Chief Financial Officer, Haxtun Hospital District, Haxtun, CO, p. A104

NADKARNI, Manasi M.D., Vice President Medical Affairs, Unitypoint Health – Trinity Muscatine, Muscatine, IA, p. A232

NADLE, Patricia A R.N., Chief Nursing Officer, St. Joseph Health Services Of Rhode Island, North Providence, RI, p. A556

NADLER, Tammy R, Chief Financial Officer, Golden Valley Memorial Healthcare, Clinton, MO, p. A366

NADOLNY, Stephanie, Vice President of Hospital Operations, Spaulding Rehabilitation Hospital Cape Cod, East Sandwich, MA, p. A306

NAFZIGER, Laurie N., President and Chief Executive Officer, Oaklawn Psychiatric Center, Goshen, IN, p. A209

NAFZIGER, Steve M.D., Vice President Medical Affairs, Parkview Medical Center, Pueblo, CO, p. A106

NAGARAJ, Alaka M.D., Medical Director, Regency Hospital Of Minneapolis, Golden Valley, MN, p. A340

NAGARAJ, Raghava, Chief Medical Officer, Wake Forest Baptist Health–Lexington Medical Center, Lexington, NC, p. A466

NAGATOSHI, Holly R.N., Chief Nursing Officer, San Dimas Community Hospital, San Dimas, CA, p. A86

NAGEL, Donna, Director Human Resources, AMG Specialty Hospital–Tulsa, Tulsa, OK, p. A517

NAGEL, Melody, Chief Executive Officer, Select Specialty Hospital – Dallas Downtown, Dallas, TX, p. A606

NAGLER, Richard M.D., Chief of Staff, Mayo Clinic Health System – Northland In Barron, Barron, WI, p. A698

NAGLOSKY, Paul, Administrator, Indianhead Medical Center, Shell Lake, WI, p. A712

NAGOWSKI, Michael, Chief Executive Officer, Cape Fear Valley Medical Center, Fayetteville, NC, p. A462

NAGY, Jeff, Chief Financial Officer, River Bend Hospital, West Lafayette, IN, p. A221

NAGY, Kimberly R.N., MS, Executive Vice President, Patient Services and Chief Nursing Officer, Northwest Community Hospital, Arlington Heights, IL, p. A177

NAGY, Linda J. MSN, R.N., Chief Nursing Officer, Brattleboro Retreat, Brattleboro, VT, p. A662

NAGY, Ryan, M.D., Interim President and Chief Medical Officer, Indiana University Health University Hospital, Indianapolis, IN, p. A211

NAHAPETIAN, Arby M.D., Vice President Medical Affairs and Quality, Adventist Health Glendale, Glendale, CA, p. A62

NAHMENSEN, Robert, Chief Financial Officer and Chief Operations Officer, Stanton County Hospital, Johnson, KS, p. A243

NAIBERK, Donald T., Administrator, Butler County Health Care Center, David City, NE, p. A392

NAIL, Cheryl R.N., Chief Nursing Officer, Baylor Scott & White Medical Center – White Rock, Dallas, TX, p. A604

NAIR, Chand M.D., Medical Director, Brooke Glen Behavioral Hospital, Fort Washington, PA, p. A535

NAIR, Vijayachandran M.D., Chief of Staff, John J. Pershing Veterans Affairs Medical Center, Poplar Bluff, MO, p. A375

NAJIEB, LaDonna, Service Area Director Human Resources, Providence Saint Joseph Medical Center, Burbank, CA, p. A54

NAJJAR, Maher M.D., Medical Director, Kindred Hospital Chicago–Northlake, Northlake, IL, p. A195

NAJJAR, Milad, Information Technology, Scottsdale Liberty Hospital, Scottsdale, AZ, p. A36

NAKAMOTO, Kenneth M.D., Vice President Medical Affairs, Pomona Valley Hospital Medical Center, Pomona, CA, p. A80

NAKAMURA, Bridget, Director Information Systems, Simi Valley Hospital, Simi Valley, CA, p. A92

NAKASUJI, Jody, Chief Financial Officer, Harbor–Ucla Medical Center, Torrance, CA, p. A93

NALDI, Robert, Chief Financial Officer, Maimonides Medical Center, New Rochelle, NY, p. A442

NALEPPA, Margaret, Ph.D., President and Chief Executive Officer, Peninsula Regional Medical Center, Salisbury, MD, p. A301

NALL, Brian, President and Chief Operating Officer, Hshs Holy Family Hospital In Greenville, Greenville, IL, p. A189

NALL, Wes
Chief Financial Officer, Monroe County Hospital, Monroeville, AL, p. A21
Interim Chief Executive Officer, Monroe County Hospital, Monroeville, AL, p. A21

NALLE, Tambara, Chief Financial Officer, Eastern State Hospital, Lexington, KY, p. A261

NALLEY, Leanna W, Director Human Resources, Texas Health Harris Methodist Hospital Southwest Fort Worth, Fort Worth, TX, p. A614

NANCE, Christi R.N., MSN, Chief Nursing Officer, Northwest Specialty Hospital, Post Falls, ID, p. A175

NANIA, James A, System Vice President and Chief Financial Officer, Hallmark Health System, Melrose, MA, p. A308

NAPIER, Frank, Interim Chief Financial Officer, Cobre Valley Regional Medical Center, Globe, AZ, p. A30

NAPIER, Michelle, Director of Nursing, Central State Hospital, Louisville, KY, p. A262

NAPIERKOWSKI, Daniel, M.D., President, Euclid Hospital, Euclid, OH, p. A491

NAPOLITANO, Mary Pat, Director Human Resources, Specialty Hospital Of Central Jersey, Lakewood, NJ, p. A415

NAPP, Marc L M.D., Vice President Medical Affairs, Lenox Hill Hospital, New Rochelle, NY, p. A442

NAPPER, Rick D., President and Chief Executive Officer, Chi St. Joseph Regional Health Center, Bryan, TX, p. A600

NAPPS, Greg, Chief Executive Officer, Novant Health Uva Health System Culpeper Medical Center, Culpeper, VA, p. A666

NARAMORE, G Harold M.D., Chief Medical Officer and In house Legal Counsel, Blount Memorial Hospital, Maryville, TN, p. A583

NARANG, Steve, M.D., Chief Executive Officer, Banner – University Medical Center Phoenix, Phoenix, AZ, p. A33

NARANJO, Maria, Director Human Resources, Memorial Hospital West, Pembroke Pines, FL, p. A139

NARBUTAS, Virgis
Chief Executive Officer, La Palma Intercommunity Hospital, La Palma, CA, p. A65
Chief Executive Officer, West Anaheim Medical Center, Anaheim, CA, p. A51

NARROW, Ann, Director of Nursing, River Hospital, Alexandria Bay, NY, p. A430

NARTOWICZ, Lenny, Executive Director, South Oaks Hospital, Amityville, NY, p. A430

NASEM, Charles D., FACHE, Chief Executive Officer, Shands Starke Regional Medical Center, Starke, FL, p. A143

NASER, Bashar, Chief Financial Officer, Gerald Champion Regional Medical Center, Alamogordo, NM, p. A424

NASET–PAYNE, Janet MS, R.N., Chief Nursing Officer, Van Diest Medical Center, Webster City, IA, p. A236

NASH, Daniel J, Chief Information Officer, Citrus Valley Medical Center–Inter Community Campus, Covina, CA, p. A57

NASH, Donna, Director of Nursing, Monroe County Hospital, Forsyth, GA, p. A158

NASH, Ernest
Chief Financial Officer, South Texas Rehabilitation Hospital, Brownsville, TX, p. A599
Chief Financial Officer, Weslaco Regional Rehabilitation Hospital, Weslaco, TX, p. A654

NASH, Gayle R.N., M.P.H., Chief Nursing Officer, Mountainview Regional Medical Center, Las Cruces, NM, p. A427

NASH, Jacqueline, Controller, Beaumont Hospital – Wayne, Wayne, MI, p. A333

NASH, John D., FACHE, President and Chief Executive Officer, Franciscan Children's, Brighton, MA, p. A304

NASH, Mary G Ph.D., R.N., Chief Nursing Officer, Ohio State University Wexner Medical Center, Columbus, OH, p. A487

NASH, Robert M.D., Chief of Staff, Carle Richland Memorial Hospital, Olney, IL, p. A196

NASH, Sandra, Chief Fiscal Service, James H. Quillen Veterans Affairs Medical Center, Mountain Home, TN, p. A586

NASH, Tim M.D., Chief of Staff, Marshall Medical Center, Lewisburg, TN, p. A582

NASHID, Nadia M.D., Chief of Staff, Windham Hospital, Willimantic, CT, p. A114

NASLUND, Kevin, Manager Information Technology, Cherokee Regional Medical Center, Cherokee, IA, p. A224

NASR, Anthony M.D., Chief Medical Staff, Feather River Hospital, Paradise, CA, p. A79

NASRALLAH, Fadi M.D., Vice President Medical Affairs, Christus Mother Frances Hospital – Tyler, Tyler, TX, p. A650

NASSIEF, Raymond, Senior Vice President, Hospital Operations and Support Services, John Muir Medical Center, Walnut Creek, Walnut Creek, CA, p. A96

NASSTROM, Jeff D.O., Chief of Staff, Mitchell County Regional Health Center, Osage, IA, p. A233

NAST, Ed M.D., Chief Medical Officer, Oak Hill Hospital, Brooksville, FL, p. A121

NATAL, Yesenia, Coordinator Human Resources, Hospital Pavia Arecibo, Arecibo, PR, p. A722

NATCHER, Charles, Chief Financial Officer, Kindred Hospital– Los Angeles, Los Angeles, CA, p. A69

NATELSON, Richard M.D., Chief of Staff, Steele Memorial Medical Center, Salmon, ID, p. A176

NATEMAN, Barry, Manager Human Resources, French Hospital Medical Center, San Luis Obispo, CA, p. A89

NATH, Dilip Sc.D., Associate Chief Information Officer, Suny Downstate Medical Center University Hospital, New Rochelle, NY, p. A447

NATH, Pravene, Chief Information Officer, Stanford Health Care, Palo Alto, CA, p. A79

NATHAN, James R.
President and Chief Executive Officer, Lee Memorial Hospital, Fort Myers, FL, p. A125
Chief Executive Officer, Lee Memorial Hospital, Fort Myers, FL, p. A125

NATHANSON, Andrea, Director Finance, Baystate Franklin Medical Center, Greenfield, MA, p. A307

NATHEM, Joanne MSN, R.N., Chief Clinical and Nursing Officer, Waverly Health Center, Waverly, IA, p. A236

NATRAJAN, Sunil M.D., Medical Director, Curahealth Tucson, Tucson, AZ, p. A37

NAU, James, Manager Computer and Applications Support, Delaware Psychiatric Center, New Castle, DE, p. A115

NAUMAN, Michael B
Chief Information Officer and Corporate Vice President, Children's Hospital Of Wisconsin–Fox Valley, Neenah, WI, p. A708
Chief Information Officer, Children's Hospital Of Wisconsin, Milwaukee, WI, p. A707

NAUMOWICH, Sarah, Interim President, Morton Plant North Bay Hospital, New Port Richey, FL, p. A135

NAVA, Madeline, Chief Executive Officer, Plantation General Hospital, Plantation, FL, p. A140

NAVARRO, Israel, Chief Executive Officer, Integrity Transitional Hospital, Denton, TX, p. A608

NAVARRO, Ramomita, Director Human Resources, University Hospital, San Juan, PR, p. A727

NAVARRO, Tess, Chief Financial Officer, Laguna Honda Hospital And Rehabilitation Center, San Francisco, CA, p. A87

NAVAS, Manuel M.D., Medical Director, Hospital San Pablo Del Este, Fajardo, PR, p. A723

NAWROCKI, Bernie
Administrative Director Finance, Promedica Bixby Hospital, Adrian, MI, p. A314
Administrative Director Finance, Promedica Herrick Hospital, Tecumseh, MI, p. A332

NAWROCKI, Edward
President, St. Luke's Hospital – Anderson Campus, Easton, PA, p. A534
President, St. Luke's Hospital – Quakertown Campus, Quakertown, PA, p. A549

NAYAK, Yeshavanth M.D., Interim Chief Medical Officer, Community Medical Center, Toms River, NJ, p. A421

NAZ, Haroon, Chief Executive Officer, Pinnacle Hospital, Crown Point, IN, p. A206

NAZARIAN, Alexander, CPA
Chief Financial Officer, Kirby Medical Center, Monticello, IL, p. A194
Director Information Technology, Kirby Medical Center, Monticello, IL, p. A194

NAZARIO, Uriel M.D., Chief of Medical Staff, Kindred Hospital North Florida, Green Cove Springs, FL, p. A126

NAZE, Jesse, Chief Financial Officer, Fall River Hospital, Hot Springs, SD, p. A570

NAZEER, Imran M.D., Chief of Staff, Woodland Heights Medical Center, Lufkin, TX, p. A631

NDOMEA, Feisal, Director Case Management, Kindred Hospital Sugar Land, Sugar Land, TX, p. A647

NDOW, Emmanuel, Chief Information Officer, Marion General Hospital, Marion, IN, p. A215

NEAL, Bob, Information Technology, Sparrow Ionia Hospital, Ionia, MI, p. A323

NEAL, Greg, FACHE, President, Wellmont Bristol Regional Medical Center, Bristol, TN, p. A575

NEAL, Robert, Manager Information Technology Services, Newman Memorial Hospital, Shattuck, OK, p. A515

NEAL, Roger, Vice President Operations, Duncan Regional Hospital, Duncan, OK, p. A506

NEAL, Terrell, R.N., Chief Operating Officer and Chief Nursing Officer, St. Charles Parish Hospital, Luling, LA, p. A280

NEAL, Tom, Chief Executive Officer, Greenbrier Valley Medical Center, Ronceverte, WV, p. A696

NEALE, Debra R.N., Chief Nursing Officer, O'Connor Hospital, Delhi, NY, p. A435

NEALON, Matthew, Vice President, Chief Financial Officer, University Of Cincinnati Medical Center, Cincinnati, OH, p. A485

NEAPOLITAN, David, Chief Financial Officer, Emanuel Medical Center, Turlock, CA, p. A94

NEAR, Holly, Chief Administrative Officer, Harsha Behavioral Center, Terre Haute, IN, p. A220

NEAT, Gary, Director Information Systems, Ephraim Mcdowell Fort Logan Hospital, Stanford, KY, p. A268

NECAS, Kevin, Chief Financial Officer, University Of Missouri Health Care, Columbia, MO, p. A367

NEEB, Verette R.N., MSN, Chief Nursing Officer, Baylor Medical Center At Uptown, Dallas, TX, p. A604

NEECE, Patrick, Chief Information Officer, Jefferson Regional Medical Center, Pine Bluff, AR, p. A48

NEEDHAM, Kim
Assistant Chief Executive Officer, Vista Medical Center East, Waukegan, IL, p. A202
Assistant Chief Executive Officer, Vista Medical Center West, Waukegan, IL, p. A202

NEEDHAM, Tammy, Chief Nursing Officer, Chatham Hospital, Siler City, NC, p. A470

NEEDLES, Kim, Manager Business Office, Patients' Hospital Of Redding, Redding, CA, p. A81

NEELAGARU, Narasimhulu M.D., Chief of Staff, Northridge Medical Center, Commerce, GA, p. A155

NEELY, Denise R.N., Vice President and Chief Nursing Officer, Bronson Methodist Hospital, Kalamazoo, MI, p. A324

NEELY, Jill, Chief Financial Officer, Titusville Area Hospital, Titusville, PA, p. A551

NEELY, K. Dale, FACHE, Chief Executive Officer, Healthsouth Rehabilitation Hospital Of Tallahassee, Tallahassee, FL, p. A144

NEELY, Kathy E., R.N.
Interim Vice President Patient Care Services, Chi St. Vincent Infirmary Medical Center, Little Rock, AR, p. A46
Interim Vice President Patient Care Services, Chi St. Vincent Morrilton, Morrilton, AR, p. A47

NEELY, Randall
CEO, Simpson General Hospital, Mendenhall, MS, p. A358
Chief Executive Officer, Simpson General Hospital, Mendenhall, MS, p. A358

NEENAN, Sharon R.N., Interim Chief Nursing Officer, Grant, Ohiohealth Grant Medical Center, Columbus, OH, p. A487

NEERGHEEN, Chabilal M.D., Medical Director, Western Massachusetts Hospital, Westfield, MA, p. A313

NEESEN, Cindy, Director of Information Technology, Butler County Health Care Center, David City, NE, p. A392

NEET, Bradley D., FACHE, Chief Executive Officer, Rancho Springs Medical Center, Murrieta, CA, p. A75

NEET, Bradley D, FACHE, Chief Executive Officer, Rancho Springs Medical Center, Murrieta, CA, p. A75

NEFCY, Christine M.D., Chief Medical Officer, Mckay–Dee Hospital, Ogden, UT, p. A658

NEFF, Mark J., FACHE, President and Chief Executive Officer, St. Claire Healthcare, Morehead, KY, p. A265

NEFF, Richard M.D., Interim Chief Medical Officer, Flagstaff Medical Center, Flagstaff, AZ, p. A29

NEFF, William M.D., Chief Medical Officer, Medical Center Of The Rockies, Loveland, CO, p. A106

NEGRON, Manuel, Chief Information Technology Service, Veterans Affairs Caribbean Healthcare System, San Juan, PR, p. A727

NEIDENBACH, John, Vice President and Chief Operating Officer, West Hills Hospital And Medical Center, Los Angeles, CA, p. A72

NEIKIRK, Richard, Chief Executive Officer, Cumberland County Hospital, Burkesville, KY, p. A256

NEIL, Eric, Interim Chief Information Officer, Uw Medicine/ Northwest Hospital & Medical Center, Seattle, WA, p. A686

NEIL, William, Vice President and Chief Information Officer, Indian River Medical Center, Vero Beach, FL, p. A146

NEILSEN SWANSON, Verbelee, Administrator, Florida Hospital, Orlando, FL, p. A137

NEILSON, Carol CPA, Controller, Healthsouth Sugar Land Rehabilitation Hospital, Sugar Land, TX, p. A647

NEILSON, Erinn, Chief Nursing Officer, Minidoka Memorial Hospital, Rupert, ID, p. A175

NEILSON, Karen, Administrator, Safe Haven Hospital Of Pocatello, Pocatello, ID, p. A175

NEILSON, Richard, Director of Information Services, Timpanogos Regional Hospital, Orem, UT, p. A658

NEIMAN, Carla A, Chief Financial Officer, Clark Fork Valley Hospital, Plains, MT, p. A387

NEITZEL, Monte, Chief Executive Officer, Greater Regional Medical Center, Creston, IA, p. A225

NELKIN MCCORMICK, Elizabeth MSN, R.N., Senior Vice President and Chief Nursing Officer, Memorial Sloan– Kettering Cancer Center, New Rochelle, NY, p. A442

NELL, Sergio, Director Information Systems, Watsonville Community Hospital, Watsonville, CA, p. A96

NELLSCH, Verner M.D., Chief of Staff, Chi St. Luke's Health Memorial Livingston, Livingston, TX, p. A629

NELSON, Allison
Chief Financial Officer, Sanford Canby Medical Center, Canby, MN, p. A337
Chief Financial Officer, Sanford Clear Lake Medical Center, Clear Lake, SD, p. A569

NELSON, Barbara J Ph.D., R.N., Chief Nursing Executive, Sutter Roseville Medical Center, Roseville, CA, p. A83

NELSON, Bill, Chief Executive Officer, Mille Lacs Health System, Onamia, MN, p. A345

NELSON, Carol, Director Human Resources, Montevista Hospital, Las Vegas, NV, p. A403

NELSON, Cory, Administrator, Genoa Medical Facilities, Genoa, NE, p. A393

NELSON, David A., President, Chi St. Francis Health, Breckenridge, MN, p. A337

NELSON, David, FACHE, M.D.
Chief Financial Officer, Sacred Heart Hospital, Eau Claire, WI, p. A701
Divisional Chief Financial Officer, Hshs St. Joseph's Hospital, Chippewa Falls, WI, p. A700
Medical Director, Barlow Respiratory Hospital, Los Angeles, CA, p. A67

NELSON, Dawn, Director Human Resources, Sagewest Health Care At Riverton, Riverton, WY, p. A719

NELSON, Deana FACHE, R.N., Executive Vice President and Chief Operating Officer, Tampa General Hospital, Tampa, FL, p. A145

NELSON, Diane R.N., Chief Nursing Officer, Kindred Hospital– Albuquerque, Albuquerque, NM, p. A424

NELSON, Elaine R.N., MSN, Chief Nursing Officer, Texas Health Harris Methodist Hospital Fort Worth, Fort Worth, TX, p. A614

NELSON, Eric, Vice President, Ambulatory Services, Bethesda Hospital, Saint Paul, MN, p. A347

NELSON, Frederick, Administrator, Ochsner Extended Care Hospital Of Kenner, Kenner, LA, p. A277

NELSON, Gina, Chief Financial Officer, Renown South Meadows Medical Center, Reno, NV, p. A405

NELSON, Jack, Vice President Finance and Chief Financial Officer, Ohio Valley Hospital, Mckees Rocks, PA, p. A540

NELSON, Jackie, Director Human Resources, Hansford Hospital, Spearman, TX, p. A646

NELSON, James J, Senior Vice President Finance and Strategic Planning, Fort Healthcare, Fort Atkinson, WI, p. A701

NELSON, Jamie, Vice President and Chief Information Officer, Hospital For Special Surgery, New Rochelle, NY, p. A441

NELSON, Jeri, Chief Financial Officer, Eastern Plumas Health Care, Portola, CA, p. A80

NELSON, Joseph M.D., President Medical Staff, Lewis–Gale Medical Center, Salem, VA, p. A675

NELSON, Julia, Vice President of Human Resources, Northern Hospital Of Surry County, Mount Airy, NC, p. A467

NELSON, Katey, Director Human Resources, Sevier Valley Hospital, Richfield, UT, p. A659

NELSON, Kathy
Chief Financial Officer, Marshall Medical Center North, Guntersville, AL, p. A19
Chief Financial Officer, Marshall Medical Center South, Boaz, AL, p. A15

NELSON, Kellie, Director Human Resources, Aurora Medical Center, Kenosha, WI, p. A704

NELSON, Kerri, Chief Financial Officer, Spectrum Health Ludington Hospital, Ludington, MI, p. A325

NELSON, Lucy, Director Finance, Vice President, Maniilaq Health Center, Kotzebue, AK, p. A26

NELSON, Lynn M., R.N., R.N., Chief Nursing Officer and Chief Operating Officer, St. John's Riverside Hospital, Yonkers, NY, p. A456

NELSON, Marlin Pete, Vice President Fiscal Services, Divine Savior Healthcare, Portage, WI, p. A710

NELSON, Martha
Chief Financial Officer, Antelope Memorial Hospital, Neligh, NE, p. A396
Chief Financial Officer, Niobrara Valley Hospital, Lynch, NE, p. A395

NELSON, Melissa, Assistant Administrator, Baptist Memorial Hospital For Women, Memphis, TN, p. A584

NELSON, Meredith, Chief Financial Officer, Willamette Valley Medical Center, Mcminnville, OR, p. A523

NELSON, Michael E, Chief Financial Officer, Riveredge Hospital, Forest Park, IL, p. A188

NELSON, Michael
Chief Financial Officer, Select Specialty Hospital Midtown Atlanta, Atlanta, GA, p. A151
Executive Vice President and Chief Financial Officer, Pomona Valley Hospital Medical Center, Pomona, CA, p. A80

NELSON, Nan, Senior Vice President Finance, Aurora St. Luke's Medical Center, Milwaukee, WI, p. A707

NELSON, Nancy, Director Human Resources, Intermountain Hospital, Boise, ID, p. A171

NELSON, Nick, Director Support Services, Adams Memorial Hospital, Decatur, IN, p. A206

NELSON, Raymond, Acting Chief Information Resource Management, Fargo Veterans Affairs Health Care System, Fargo, ND, p. A475

NELSON, Richard, Chief of Human Resources Management Services, Central Arkansas Veterans Healthcare System, Little Rock, AR, p. A46

NELSON, RimaAnn O., R.N., Director, Phoenix Veterans Affairs Health Care System, Phoenix, AZ, p. A34

NELSON, Robin, Chief Financial Officer, Gundersen St. Joseph's Hospital And Clinics, Hillsboro, WI, p. A703

NELSON, Selena, Chief Financial Officer, Fallon Medical Complex, Baker, MT, p. A382

NELSON, Shelby
Chief Executive Officer, Platte County Memorial Hospital, Wheatland, WY, p. A720
Interim Chief Executive Officer, Community Hospital, Torrington, WY, p. A720

NELSON, Sherry JD, MS, R.N., Chief Nursing Officer, Springfield Regional Medical Center, Springfield, OH, p. A499

NELSON, Siri, Chief Executive Officer, Renown South Meadows Medical Center, Reno, NV, p. A405

NELSON, Stewart R, Chief Financial Officer, Sentara Halifax Regional Hospital, South Boston, VA, p. A675

NELSON, Suzanne R.N., Director of Nursing, Salt Lake Behavioral Health, Salt Lake City, UT, p. A660

NELSON, Trudy, Chief Human Resource Officer, Niobrara Valley Hospital, Lynch, NE, p. A395

NELSON–JONES, Susan, Director Human Resources, Adventist Health Medical Center – Tehachapi Valley, Tehachapi, CA, p. A93

NEMAZIE, Siamack M.D., Medical Director, Patient Safety Officer, Flushing Hospital Medical Center, New Rochelle, NY, p. A441

NEMECHEK, Victor M.D., Chief of Staff and Chief Medical Officer, Sheridan County Health Complex, Hoxie, KS, p. A243

NEMETH, Jim
Chief Financial Officer, Monroe Clinic, Monroe, WI, p. A708
Senior Vice President of Patient Care Services and Chief Nursing Officer, Memorial Healthcare, Owosso, MI, p. A327

NEMI, Neil, Administrator Facility Information Center, Richard H. Hutchings Psychiatric Center, Syracuse, NY, p. A453

NEONAKIS, Stephanie W, Manager Human Resources, Uh Regional Hospitals, Cleveland, OH, p. A486

NERMOE, Bryan, President, Sanford Bemidji Medical Center, Bemidji, MN, p. A336

NERO, Theresa R R.N., MS, Chief Nursing Officer, Kaiser Permanente San Jose Medical Center, San Jose, CA, p. A88

NESBITT, William, M.D., President, Texas Health Heart & Vascular Hospital Arlington, Arlington, TX, p. A593

NESMITH, Nikki
Chief Executive Officer and Chief Nursing Officer, Evans Memorial Hospital, Claxton, GA, p. A154
Chief Nursing Officer, Evans Memorial Hospital, Claxton, GA, p. A154

NESPOLI, John L., Chief Executive Officer, Sacred Heart Hospital, Allentown, PA, p. A528

NESS, David L, Vice President Operations, Grinnell Regional Medical Center, Grinnell, IA, p. A228

NESS, Edwin, President and Chief Executive Officer, Munson Healthcare, Traverse City, MI, p. B87

NESS, Jon, Chief Executive Officer, Kootenai Health, Coeur D'Alene, ID, p. A173

NESSEL, Mark
Chief Operating Officer, Our Lady Of Lourdes Medical Center, Camden, NJ, p. A412
Executive Vice President and Chief Operating Officer, Lourdes Medical Center Of Burlington County, Willingboro, NJ, p. A423

NESSELRODT, Derek, Director Information Systems, Grant Memorial Hospital, Petersburg, WV, p. A695

NESTER, Brian A., D.O.
President and Chief Executive Officer, Lehigh Valley Hospital–Muhlenberg, Bethlehem, PA, p. A529
President and Chief Executive Officer, Lehigh Valley Hospital, Allentown, PA, p. A528

NESTER, Darlene E.
Chief Human Resources Officer, Hilton Head Hospital, Hilton Head Island, SC, p. A564
Market Chief Human Resources Officer, Coastal Carolina Hospital, Hardeeville, SC, p. A563

NESTER, Michael, Administrator, H. C. Watkins Memorial Hospital, Quitman, MS, p. A361

NESTER WOLFE, Cheryl R., President and Chief Executive Officer, Salem Hospital, Salem, OR, p. A526

NETH, Marvin, Chief Executive Officer, Callaway District Hospital, Callaway, NE, p. A391

NETTERVILLE, Chad, Administrator, Field Memorial Community Hospital, Centreville, MS, p. A353

NETTLES, Angela F, Director Human Resources, Kershawhealth, Camden, SC, p. A558

NETTLES, Robert, Director Human Resources, Mountainview Hospital, Las Vegas, NV, p. A403

NETZER, Craig M.D., President Medical Staff, Wilcox Medical Center, Lihue, HI, p. A170

NEUENDORF, Deborah, Vice President Administration, New York–Presbyterian/Hudson Valley Hospital, Cortlandt Manor, NY, p. A434

NEUENDORF, James M.D., Medical Director, Saint Joseph's Medical Center, Yonkers, NY, p. A456

NEUENDORF, Michael, Chief Executive Officer, Merit Health Wesley, Hattiesburg, MS, p. A356

NEUFELD, Ellis M.D., Chief Medical Officer, St. Jude Children's Research Hospital, Memphis, TN, p. A585

NEUGENT, Kevin, Chief Information Officer, Hayes Green Beach Memorial Hospital, Charlotte, MI, p. A316

NEUHAUS, Joan E
Division Senior Vice President Chief Operating Officer, Chi Health Lakeside, Omaha, NE, p. A397
Division Senior Vice President, Chief Operating Officer, Chi Health Midlands, Papillion, NE, p. A399

NEUJAHR, Elias, President, Christus Santa Rosa Health System, San Antonio, TX, p. A642

NEUMAN, Joe, Chief Executive Officer, Concord Healthcare Group, Lakewood, NJ, p. B37

NEUMAN, Keith A.
Chief Information Officer, Lutheran Hospital Of Indiana, Fort Wayne, IN, p. A208
Chief Information Officer, Orthopaedic Hospital Of Lutheran Health Network, Fort Wayne, IN, p. A208

NEUMAN, Michael J, Vice President Finance, Kennedy Krieger Institute, Baltimore, MD, p. A294

NEUMANN, Jamie, Director Human Resources, Iroquois Memorial Hospital And Resident Home, Watseka, IL, p. A202

NEUMEISTER, Daniel P, Senior Vice President and Chief Operating Officer, Searhc Mt. Edgecumbe Hospital, Sitka, AK, p. A24

NEUNER, Kathy R.N., Chief Nursing Officer, Clark Memorial Hospital, Jeffersonville, IN, p. A213

NEUVIRTH, Stephanie, Chief Human Resource and Diversity Officer, City Of Hope's Helford Clinical Research Hospital, Duarte, CA, p. A58

NEVAREZ, Domingo, Chief Executive Officer, Hospital Metropolitan, San Juan, PR, p. A726

NEVERS, Rick L., Interim Chief Executive Officer, Aspirus Medford Hospital & Clinics, Inc., Medford, WI, p. A706

NEVILL, David S., Chief Executive Officer, Healthsouth Rehabilitation Hospital Of New Mexico, Albuquerque, NM, p. A424

NEVILLE, Bette R.N., MSN, Vice President and Chief Nursing Officer, Mercy Hospital Of Portland, Portland, ME, p. A292

NEVILLE, Lawrence, Chief Medical Officer, Peacehealth Southwest Medical Center, Vancouver, WA, p. A688

NEVILLE, Ryan T., FACHE, President and Chief Executive Officer, Memorial Medical Center – Neillsville, Neillsville, WI, p. A709

NEVIN, James M.D., Vice President Medical Management, Advocate Bromenn Medical Center, Normal, IL, p. A195

NEVIN, Janice E., M.D., M.P.H., Chief Executive Officer, Christiana Care Health System, Newark, DE, p. A115

NEVINS, Norm, Manager Human Resources, Kansas Medical Center, Andover, KS, p. A238

NEWBERRY–FERGUSON, Linda, Chief Executive Officer, Rehabilitation Hospital Of Wisconsin, Waukesha, WI, p. A714

NEWBOLD, Philip A., Chief Executive Officer, Beacon Health System, Memorial Hospital Of South Bend, South Bend, IN, p. A220

NEWBY, Doug, Chief Information Officer, Highlands Medical Center, Scottsboro, AL, p. A23

NEWBY, Glenda, Chief Executive Officer, Dallas Regional Medical Center, Mesquite, TX, p. A633

NEWBY, Nancy M., R.N., Ph.D., FACHE, President and Chief Executive Officer, Washington County Hospital, Nashville, IL, p. A195

NEWCOMB, James, M.D.
Vice President Medical Affairs, Slidell Memorial Hospital, Slidell, LA, p. A286
Vice President Medical, Ochsner Medical Center – North Shore, Slidell, LA, p. A286

NEWCOMB, Michael, D.O.
Senior Vice President and Chief Operating Officer, Legacy Meridian Park Medical Center, Tualatin, OR, p. A527
Senior Vice President and Chief Operating Officer, Legacy Mount Hood Medical Center, Gresham, OR, p. A522
Senior Vice President and Chief Operating Officer, Legacy Salmon Creek Medical Center, Vancouver, WA, p. A688

NEWCOMER, Jeremy, Director Information Services, Elmira Psychiatric Center, Elmira, NY, p. A435

NEWCOMER, Peter M.D., Chief Medical Officer, University Of Wisconsin Hospitals And Clinics Authority, Madison, WI, p. A705

NEWELL, Dan, Chief Financial Officer, Highlands Medical Center, Scottsboro, AL, p. A23

NEWELL, Janice
Chief Information Officer, Swedish Medical Center–Cherry Hill Campus, Seattle, WA, p. A685
Chief Information Officer, Swedish Medical Center–First Hill, Seattle, WA, p. A685

NEWELL, Richard, Chief Executive Officer, Pottstown Memorial Medical Center, Pottstown, PA, p. A548

NEWEY, Mark D.O., Chief of Staff, Mercy Hospital Healdton, Healdton, OK, p. A508

NEWHOUSE, Chuck M.D., Chief of Staff, Boundary Community Hospital, Bonners Ferry, ID, p. A172

NEWHOUSE, Paul R., President, Union Medical Center, Union, SC, p. A566

NEWLAND, Judy, R.N.
Chief Nursing Officer, Tahoe Forest Hospital District, Truckee, CA, p. A94
Chief Operating Officer, Tahoe Forest Hospital District, Truckee, CA, p. A94
Chief Nursing Officer, Incline Village Community Hospital, Incline Village, NV, p. A402

NEWMAN, Billy, Department Head, Naval Hospital Lemoore, Lemoore, CA, p. A65

NEWMAN, Carlotta, Director Human Resources, Northeast Georgia Medical Center Barrow, Winder, GA, p. A167

NEWMAN, Christopher M.D., Vice President Medical Affairs and Chief Medical Officer, Penn State Health St. Joseph, Reading, PA, p. A549

NEWMAN, Cynthia, Manager Human Resources, Petersburg Medical Center, Petersburg, AK, p. A27

NEWMAN, Dan, Chief Executive Officer, Houston Methodist St. John Hospital, Nassau Bay, TX, p. A634

NEWMAN, Diane, FACHE, Administrator, Johnson County Hospital, Tecumseh, NE, p. A400

NEWMAN, Edith, Interim Administrator, John J. Madden Mental Health Center, Hines, IL, p. A190

NEWMAN, Karen Ed.D., MSN, R.N., Vice President and Chief Nursing Officer, Baptist Health Louisville, Louisville, KY, p. A262

NEWMAN, Kurt, M.D., President and Chief Executive Officer, Children's National Health System, Washington, DC, p. A117

NEWMAN, Richard, Chief Human Resources Officer, Olympic Medical Center, Port Angeles, WA, p. A683

NEWMAN, Sonya R.N., Chief Nursing Officer, Blount Memorial Hospital, Maryville, TN, p. A583

NEWMAN, Thomas M
Chief Financial Officer, Upmc Passavant, Pittsburgh, PA, p. A547
Vice President Finance, Upmc St. Margaret, Pittsburgh, PA, p. A548

NEWMILLER, Vicki, Chief Executive Officer, Great Halls Hospital, Great Falls, MT, p. A385

NEWPOWER, Nicole, Coordinator Human Resources, Kindred Hospital–Fort Worth, Fort Worth, TX, p. A614

NEWQUIST, Dennis, Director Information Systems, Abilene Regional Medical Center, Abilene, TX, p. A591

NEWSOM, Cynthia, Chief Executive Officer, Vibra Hospital Of Boise, Meridian, ID, p. A174

NEWSOM, Paul, Chief Operating Officer, Kentuckiana Medical Center, Clarksville, IN, p. A205
NEWSOM, Terri, Vice President of Finance and Chief Financial Officer, GHS Greenville Memorial Hospital, Greenville, SC, p. A562
NEWSOME, Samuel C M.D., Chief of Staff, Lifebrite Community Hospital Of Stokes, Danbury, NC, p. A460
NEWSWANGER, Jeff M.D., Chief Medical Officer, Manchester Memorial Hospital, Manchester, KY, p. A264
NEWTON, Gail R.N., MSN, Vice President Patient Care Services, St. Luke's Hospital – Warren Campus, Phillipsburg, NJ, p. A419
NEWTON, Jennifer R.N., Chief Nursing Officer, Neosho Memorial Regional Medical Center, Chanute, KS, p. A239
NEWTON, Keith, Chief Executive Officer, South Baldwin Regional Medical Center, Foley, AL, p. A18
NEWTON, Steven R., FACHE, President, Baylor Regional Medical Center At Grapevine, Grapevine, TX, p. A617
NEWTON, Susan, Chief Financial Officer, Broward Health Imperial Point, Fort Lauderdale, FL, p. A124
NEWTON, Terri, Chief Nursing Officer, Lakewood Regional Medical Center, Lakewood, CA, p. A65
NEWTON, Wilma, Executive Vice President and Chief Financial Officer, St. Vincent's Birmingham, Birmingham, AL, p. A15
NEZBETH, Jacqueline, Human Resources Officer, Select Specialty Hospital Of Southeast Ohio, Newark, OH, p. A497
NG, Anthony M.D., Vice President and Chief Medical Officer, The Acadia Hospital, Bangor, ME, p. A289
NG, Hong–Kin M.D., Chief Medical Officer, Roane General Hospital, Spencer, WV, p. A696
NG, Thomas T., Chief Information Officer, Collingsworth General Hospital, Wellington, TX, p. A653
NG, Vincent
  Director, Veterans Affairs Boston Healthcare System, West Roxbury, MA, p. A312
  Interim Director, Veterans Affairs Boston Healthcare System Brockton Division, Brockton, MA, p. A305
NGIRAISUI, Clarinda, Human Resource Manager, Commonwealth Health Center, Saipan, MP, p. A721
NGUYEN, Abby R.N., Chief Nursing Officer, Genesis Healthcare System, Zanesville, OH, p. A503
NGUYEN, Anhtai H M.D., FACS, Vice President Medical Affairs and Chief Medical Officer, Fauquier Hospital, Warrenton, VA, p. A676
NGUYEN, Bach, Director Information Systems, Northwest Texas Healthcare System, Amarillo, TX, p. A592
NGUYEN, Dat M.D., Chief of Staff, Stanford Health Care – Valleycare, Pleasanton, CA, p. A80
NGUYEN, Harry, Medical Director, The Woods At Parkside, Gahanna, OH, p. A491
NGUYEN, Nga, Manager Human Resources and Organizational Development, Adventist Health Glendale, Glendale, CA, p. A62
NIBLOCK, Jenny, Chief Clinical Officer, Citizens Medical Center, Colby, KS, p. A239
NICASTRO, Pamela, Director Human Resources, Brylin Hospitals, Buffalo, NY, p. A432
NICAUD, Kent, Chief Operating Officer, Memorial Hospital At Gulfport, Gulfport, MS, p. A355
NICE, Andrew, Chief Operating Officer, Medical City Mckinney, Mckinney, TX, p. A632
NICHELSON, Kathleen, Director Human Resources, Horsham Clinic, Ambler, PA, p. A529
NICHOLAS, Chris, Chief Executive Officer, Renown Rehabilitation Hospital, Reno, NV, p. A405
NICHOLAS, David , Chief Executive Officer, St. John Rehabilitation Hospital, Tulsa, OK, p. B63
NICHOLAS, David, Chief Executive Officer, St. John Rehabilitation Hospital, Tulsa, OK, p. A518
NICHOLS, Amanda M.D., Chief of Staff, Sistersville General Hospital, Sistersville, WV, p. A696
NICHOLS, Barbara, R.N., President and Chief Executive Officer, Corry Memorial Hospital, Corry, PA, p. A532
NICHOLS, Bryan
  Chief Financial Officer, The Heart Hospital Baylor Denton, Denton, TX, p. A608
  Chief Financial Officer, The Heart Hospital Baylor Plano, Plano, TX, p. A638
NICHOLS, Christopher, Chief Executive Officer, Fillmore County Hospital, Geneva, NE, p. A393
NICHOLS, Cynthia, R.N., MSN, Chief Executive Officer, Lakeland Community Hospital, Haleyville, AL, p. A19
NICHOLS, Dia, Chief Executive Officer, Northside Hospital, Saint Petersburg, FL, p. A141
NICHOLS, Donna R.N., Chief Nursing Officer, Goodall–Witcher Hospital Authority, Clifton, TX, p. A601
NICHOLS, Greg, Chief Executive Officer, East Alabama Medical Center, Opelika, AL, p. A22
NICHOLS, Gretchen, R.N., President, Legacy Mount Hood Medical Center, Gresham, OR, p. A522

NICHOLS, Kevin, Controller, Spectrum Health Gerber Memorial, Fremont, MI, p. A320
NICHOLS, Laura L, Director Human Resources, Hancock Regional Hospital, Greenfield, IN, p. A209
NICHOLS, Lisa, R.N., Administrator, St. Vincent's St. Clair, Pell City, AL, p. A22
NICHOLS, Mark, FACHE, Chief Executive Officer, Starr Regional Medical Center, Athens, TN, p. A575
NICHOLS, Michael, Chief Information Officer, Masonicare Health Center, Wallingford, CT, p. A113
NICHOLS, Owen, PsyD, President and Chief Executive Officer, Northkey Community Care, Covington, KY, p. A257
NICHOLS, Randy
  Chief Financial Officer, Great River Medical Center, Blytheville, AR, p. A40
  Chief Financial Officer, South Mississippi County Regional Medical Center, Osceola, AR, p. A48
NICHOLS, Robert R M.D., Vice President Medical Affairs, Mercy Hospital Fort Scott, Fort Scott, KS, p. A241
NICHOLS, Robin
  Chief Financial Officer, Coshocton Regional Medical Center, Coshocton, OH, p. A488
  Interim Chief Financial Officer, Dekalb Medical At North Decatur, Decatur, GA, p. A156
NICHOLS, Suzanne, Director Human Resources, Muleshoe Area Medical Center, Muleshoe, TX, p. A634
NICHOLSON, Britain M.D., Chief Medical Officer, Massachusetts General Hospital, Boston, MA, p. A303
NICHOLSON, Charles, Vice President, Medical Affairs, Sentara Albemarle Medical Center, Elizabeth City, NC, p. A462
NICHOLSON, Chrissy, Vice President Human Resources, Delta Regional Medical Center, Greenville, MS, p. A355
NICHOLSON, Cindy, Director Human Resources, Shelby Baptist Medical Center, Alabaster, AL, p. A13
NICHOLSON, Debra, Manager Finance, Central Alabama Veterans Health Care System, Montgomery, AL, p. A21
NICHOLSON, H. Stacy M.D., M.P.H., Physician in Chief, Phoenix Children's Hospital, Phoenix, AZ, p. A34
NICHOLSON, Jack, Chief Executive Officer, Kindred Hospital–Louisville, Louisville, KY, p. A262
NICHOLSON, Kristin, Coordinator Human Resources, Genesis Medical Center, Dewitt, De Witt, IA, p. A225
NICHOLSON, Molly, MS, R.N.
  Chief Nurse Executive, Presence Covenant Medical Center, Urbana, IL, p. A202
  Vice President of Patient Care/Chief Nurse Executive, Presence United Samaritans Medical Center, Danville, IL, p. A185
NICHOSON, Julia M.D., Chief Medical Officer, Drew Memorial Health System, Monticello, AR, p. A47
NICKEL, Kathleen, Director Communications, Mercy Medical Center, Roseburg, OR, p. A526
NICKELL, Angela, Executive Director, Sequel Pomegranate Health Systems, Columbus, OH, p. A488
NICKELL, Jerry, Vice President Human Resource and Mission, Saint Alphonsus Medical Center – Baker City, Baker City, OR, p. A520
NICKELS, John M.D., President Medical Staff, Grace Hospital, Cleveland, OH, p. A485
NICKENS, Wesley M.D., Chief of Staff, Collingsworth General Hospital, Wellington, TX, p. A653
NICKISCH, Steve, Chief of Staff, Southeast Georgia Health System Camden Campus, Saint Marys, GA, p. A164
NICKRAND, Tami, Director Information Technology, Harbor Beach Community Hospital, Harbor Beach, MI, p. A322
NICKS, Bret M.D., Chief Medical Officer and Chief of Staff, Wake Forest Baptist Health–Davie Medical Center, Bermuda Run, NC, p. A457
NICODEMUS, Lowell, Director Information Systems, Hendricks Regional Health, Danville, IN, p. A206
NICOLAY, Donald M.D., Chief Medical Officer, Community Hospital, Grand Junction, CO, p. A103
NICOLL, C. Diana M.D., Ph.D., Chief of Staff, San Francisco Va Medical Center, San Francisco, CA, p. A87
NICOLSON, Lynne T M.D., Medical Director, Sunnyview Rehabilitation Hospital, Schenectady, NY, p. A452
NICOSIA, Chris, Chief Financial Officer, Corpus Christi Medical Center, Corpus Christi, TX, p. A603
NIECE, Pamela S, Director Human Resources, Orem Community Hospital, Orem, UT, p. A658
NIEDERPRUEM, Mark L., FACHE, Administrator, Shriners Hospitals For Children–Chicago, Chicago, IL, p. A184
NIELSEN, Colleen, Director Operations, Providence St. Joseph Medical Center, Polson, MT, p. A387
NIELSEN, Gregory A., FACHE, Chief Executive Officer, Clinton Memorial Hospital, Wilmington, OH, p. A502
NIELSEN, Gwen, Manager Human Resources, Indianhead Medical Center, Shell Lake, WI, p. A712

NIELSEN, Helen V
  Director Human Resources, Lovelace Medical Center, Albuquerque, NM, p. A424
  Director Human Resources, Lovelace Rehabilitation Hospital, Albuquerque, NM, p. A424
NIELSEN, Kristine, Manager Human Resources, Memorial Community Hospital And Health System, Blair, NE, p. A391
NIELSEN, Randy, Director Information Technology, Morton General Hospital, Morton, WA, p. A682
NIELSEN, Wayne, Director Human Resources, Ocala Regional Medical Center, Ocala, FL, p. A136
NIELSON, Curtis, Chief Financial Officer, South Lincoln Medical Center, Kemmerer, WY, p. A718
NIELSON, Lars M.D., Chief Medical Officer, Weeks Medical Center, Lancaster, NH, p. A408
NIELSON, Lori, Regional Finance Director, Park City Hospital, Park City, UT, p. A659
NIELSON, P Douglas M.D., Chief of Staff, Kahuku Medical Center, Kahuku, HI, p. A169
NIELSON, Yvonne, Chief Nursing Officer, Director Quality Management and Regulatory Compliance, Mountain West Medical Center, Tooele, UT, p. A661
NIEMALA, Amanda, Director of Information Services, Bigfork Valley Hospital, Bigfork, MN, p. A336
NIEMANN, Lynne, Director Nurses and Patient Care, Community Memorial Hospital, Sumner, IA, p. A235
NIEMEIER, Mark, Director Human Resources, Twin Rivers Regional Medical Center, Kennett, MO, p. A371
NIEMUTH, Trisha, Market Chief Executive Officer, Lifecare Hospitals Of Pittsburgh, Pittsburgh, PA, p. A546
NIENHUIS, Jamie, Chief Nursing Officer, Cavalier County Memorial Hospital And Clinics, Langdon, ND, p. A477
NIERMAN, Peter M.D., Chief Medical Officer, Chicago Lakeshore Hospital, Chicago, IL, p. A180
NIERMAN, Stephen A., President, Winter Haven Hospital, Winter Haven, FL, p. A148
NIERMANN, Michelle, Senior Vice President and Chief Operating Officer, Unitypoint Health – St. Luke's Hospital, Cedar Rapids, IA, p. A223
NIERSTEDT, Kelly, President, OSF Saint Francis Medical Center, Peoria, IL, p. A197
NIES, Lynn, Human Resources Officer, Erie Veterans Affairs Medical Center, Erie, PA, p. A534
NIESE, Mel, Chief Fiscal Service, Va Palo Alto Health Care System, Palo Alto, CA, p. A79
NIESSINK, Henry
  Regional Director Information Technology Services, Mercy Medical Center Redding, Redding, CA, p. A81
  Senior Manager Information Technology Systems, St. Elizabeth Community Hospital, Red Bluff, CA, p. A81
NIEVES, Deborah, Director Management Information Systems, Hospital San Francisco, San Juan, PR, p. A726
NIEVES, Erick M.D., Medical Director, Hospital San Carlos Borromeo, Moca, PR, p. A724
NIEVES, James F., Executive Director, San Juan City Hospital, San Juan, PR, p. A726
NIGH, Andrew M.D., Chief of Staff, Indiana University Health West Hospital, Avon, IN, p. A203
NIGHMAN, Mike, Facility Coordinator Information Systems, Shelby Baptist Medical Center, Alabaster, AL, p. A13
NIGHTINGALE, Judi R.N., Dr.PH, Chief Nursing Officer, Riverside University Health System–Medical Center, Moreno Valley, CA, p. A75
NIGRIN, Daniel M.D., Vice President Information Services and Chief Information Officer, Boston Children's Hospital, Boston, MA, p. A302
NIGRO, Lee M.D., Chief Medical Officer, Blue Valley Hospital, Overland Park, KS, p. A248
NIHALANI, Sunil M.D., Chief Medical Staff, Lake Wales Medical Center, Lake Wales, FL, p. A130
NIJOKA, Monica, Chief Nursing Officer, Baton Rouge General Medical Center, Baton Rouge, LA, p. A270
NIKOLIC, Srbo, Chief Financial Officer, Hartgrove Hospital, Chicago, IL, p. A181
NILES, Heather, Director Human Resources Operations, Mercyhealth Hospital And Medical Center – Harvard, Harvard, IL, p. A189
NILSSON, Keith, Chief Financial Officer, Cleveland Clinic Florida, Weston, FL, p. A148
NIMMO, Ben M.D., Medical Director, Pinnacle Pointe Hospital, Little Rock, AR, p. A46
NIMMO, Brian, Director, Huntington Veterans Affairs Medical Center, Huntington, WV, p. A693
NIMS, Carrie, Director of Nursing, Post Acute/Warm Springs Specialty Hospital Of San Antonio, San Antonio, TX, p. A643
NINNEMAN, David, Associate Director, Cincinnati Veterans Affairs Medical Center, Cincinnati, OH, p. A484

NIPPER, Nathan
Chief Operating Officer, Piedmont Fayette Hospital, Fayetteville, GA, p. A157
Vice President and Chief Operating Officer, Piedmont Newnan Hospital, Newnan, GA, p. A162

NIPPERT, Kathi, Acting Chief Human Resources Officer, Kansas City Veterans Affairs Medical Center, Kansas City, MO, p. A370

NISH, Paulette, Chief Nursing Officer, Jersey Shore Hospital, Jersey Shore, PA, p. A537

NISKANEN, Grant M.D., Vice President Medical Affairs, Sky Lakes Medical Center, Klamath Falls, OR, p. A523

NISSEN, Beth, Director Human Resources, Troy Regional Medical Center, Troy, AL, p. A23

NIX, Alisha, Director Human Resources, Wilbarger General Hospital, Vernon, TX, p. A652

NIX, Angela, Administrator, Veterans Affairs North Texas Health Care System, Dallas, TX, p. A607

NIX, Bo, Chief Information Officer, Madison Valley Medical Center, Ennis, MT, p. A384

NIX, D Mark., President and Chief Executive Officer, Infirmary Health System, Mobile, AL, p. B68

NIXDORF, David L, Director Support Services, Frances Mahon Deaconess Hospital, Glasgow, MT, p. A384

NIXON, Jan MS, Senior Vice President Patient Care Services and Chief Nursing Officer, Wyoming Medical Center, Casper, WY, p. A717

NIXON, Myra, Director Human Resources, Healthsouth Rehabilitation Hospital, Concord, NH, p. A407

NIZZA, Arthur, President and Chief Executive Officer, Unitypoint Health Meriter, Madison, WI, p. A705

NNAJI, Felix, Chief Medical Staff, Bolivar General Hospital, Bolivar, TN, p. A575

NOAK, Amy, Director Human Resources, St. David's Round Rock Medical Center, Round Rock, TX, p. A641

NOAKES, Timothy J, Chief Financial Officer, Memorial Hospital Los Banos, Los Banos, CA, p. A72

NOBLE, Angela, Director of Nursing, West Feliciana Parish Hospital, Saint Francisville, LA, p. A285

NOBLE, Damien, Director Information Technology and System, Colleton Medical Center, Walterboro, SC, p. A567

NOBLE, Dave, Director of Nursing, Livingston Healthcare, Livingston, MT, p. A386

NOBLE, James D., Chief Executive Officer, Horton Community Hospital, Horton, KS, p. A243

NOBLE, James S, Chief Financial Officer, Huntington Memorial Hospital, Pasadena, CA, p. A79

NOBLE, Kerry L, Chief Financial Officer, Pemiscot Memorial Health System, Hayti, MO, p. A369

NOBLE, Kerry, Chief Executive Officer, Great Bend Regional Hospital, Great Bend, KS, p. A241

NOBLE, Mallie S., Administrator, Mary Breckinridge Arh Hospital, Hyden, KY, p. A260

NOBLE, Stacy, Administrator, Southeast Rehabilitation Hospital, Lake Village, AR, p. A45

NOBLES, Diane, Nurse Executive, East Mississippi State Hospital, Meridian, MS, p. A359

NOBLES, Sharon, Interim Chief Financial Officer, Baptist Hospital, Pensacola, FL, p. A139

NOBLES, Trent, Chief Executive Officer, Southside Regional Medical Center, Petersburg, VA, p. A673

NOBLIN, Jeff, FACHE, Chief Executive Officer, Southern Tennessee Regional Health System–Lawrenceburg, Lawrenceburg, TN, p. A582

NOCKOWITZ, Richard M.D., Medical Director, Ohio Hospital For Psychiatry, Columbus, OH, p. A487

NOE, Sharon, Chief Executive Officer, Cobalt Rehabilitation Hospital, Surprise, AZ, p. A37

NOEL, Bill, Chief Operating Officer, Grand River Hospital District, Rifle, CO, p. A107

NOEL, Philip J. III, Chief Executive Officer, Ottumwa Regional Health Center, Ottumwa, IA, p. A233

NOEL, Vicki, Vice President Human Resources, Southern Ohio Medical Center, Portsmouth, OH, p. A498

NOESS, Bobbi, Director of Nursing, Bowdle Hospital, Bowdle, SD, p. A568

NOFFSINGER, Sandy, Executive Assistant, Risk Manager and Director Marketing, Dundy County Hospital, Benkelman, NE, p. A391

NOGLER, Wendy, Director Human Resources, Lincoln County Health System, Fayetteville, TN, p. A578

NOKELS, Kevin J., FACHE, Primary, Chi Health Creighton University Medical Center – Bergan Mercy, Omaha, NE, p. A397

NOKES, Gregory, Vice President Human Resources, Middlesex Hospital, Middletown, CT, p. A111

NOLAN, Douglas M.D., Medical Director, Cherokee Nation W.W. Hastings Indian Hospital, Tahlequah, OK, p. A516

NOLAN, Heather, Director Information Services, Northern Louisiana Medical Center, Ruston, LA, p. A285

NOLAN, Jennifer
President and Chief Executive Officer, Flaget Memorial Hospital, Bardstown, KY, p. A255
President, Our Lady Of Peace, Louisville, KY, p. A263
President, Sts. Mary & Elizabeth Hospital, Louisville, KY, p. A263

NOLAN, Joe, Chief Operating Officer, Saint Clare's Health System, Denville, NJ, p. A412

NOLAN, Matthew, Chief Operating Officer, The University Of Vermont Health Network Elizabethtown Community Hospital, Elizabethtown, NY, p. A435

NOLAN, Patrick B, Chief Operating Officer, Inspira Medical Center–Woodbury, Woodbury, NJ, p. A423

NOLAN, Rosemary R.N., MSN, JD, Chief Operating Officer, Temple University Hospital, Philadelphia, PA, p. A546

NOLAN, Roz, Interim Chief Nursing Officer, Community Hospital Of San Bernardino, San Bernardino, CA, p. A85

NOLAND, Pam, Director of Nursing, Northern Cochise Community Hospital, Willcox, AZ, p. A38

NOLASCO, Wanda, Chief Nursing Officer, Fairmount Behavioral Health System, Philadelphia, PA, p. A543

NOLD, Pam, Chief Nurse Executive, Northwest Missouri Psychiatric Rehabilitation Center, Saint Joseph, MO, p. A376

NOLEN, Benny, President and Chief Executive Officer, Methodist Hospital, Henderson, KY, p. A259

NOLES, Coy, Chief Financial Officer Consultant, Hamilton Hospital, Olney, TX, p. A636

NOLL, Gerald A, Chief Financial Officer, Rogers Memorial Hospital, Oconomowoc, WI, p. A709

NOLL, Keith D., President, Wellspan York Hospital, York, PA, p. A555

NOLLETTE, Karen, Chief Financial Officer, West Holt Medical Services, Atkinson, NE, p. A390

NOLLEY, Dexter, Chief Human Resources Officer, Duke Regional Hospital, Durham, NC, p. A461

NOLT, Lori, Director Information Technology, Wellspan Philhaven, Mount Gretna, PA, p. A541

NOLTE, Darlene R, Chief Human Resource Officer, Saint Francis Hospital Vinita, Vinita, OK, p. A519

NONNEMAN, Lisa, Director Information Technology Services, Mary Lanning Healthcare, Hastings, NE, p. A394

NOONAN, Anna, President and Chief Operating Officer, The University Of Vermont Health Network Central Vermont Medical Center, Berlin, VT, p. A662

NOONAN, Kathryn, Director Information Management, Lemuel Shattuck Hospital, Jamaica Plain, MA, p. A307

NOONE, Thomas M.D., Chief Medical Officer, Bayfront Health Port Charlotte, Port Charlotte, FL, p. A140

NOPWASKEY, Cristen, Chief Information Officer, Weirton Medical Center, Weirton, WV, p. A696

NORBURY, Denise
Regional Chief Executive Officer, Center For Behavioral Medicine, Kansas City, MO, p. A370
Regional Executive Officer, Northwest Missouri Psychiatric Rehabilitation Center, Saint Joseph, MO, p. A376

NORBY, Michael, Chief Financial Officer, Harris Health System, Houston, TX, p. A620

NORD, Gay, President, Baylor St. Luke's Medical Center, Houston, TX, p. A619

NORD, Stanley K, Chief Financial Officer, West Houston Medical Center, Houston, TX, p. A623

NORDAHL, Richard E., Chief Executive Officer, Sanford Sheldon Medical Center, Sheldon, IA, p. A234

NORDAHL, Richard E, Chief Financial Officer, Sanford Sheldon Medical Center, Sheldon, IA, p. A234

NORDBERG, Traci, Chief Human Resources Officer, Vanderbilt University Medical Center, Nashville, TN, p. A587

NORDBY, Shawn A, Chief Financial Officer, Mary Lanning Healthcare, Hastings, NE, p. A394

NORDELL, Cindy, Chief Nursing Officer, Healthsouth Rehabilitation Hospital Of Colorado Springs, Colorado Springs, CO, p. A99

NORDING, Rodney, Vice President Organizational Support, Mayo Clinic Health System–Albert Lea And Austin, Austin, MN, p. A336

NORDLAND, Thomas, Chief Medical Officer, Fort Healthcare, Fort Atkinson, WI, p. A701

NORDLUND, Judy R.N., Chief Nursing Officer, Trinity Hospital, Weaverville, CA, p. A96

NORDLUND, Sarah, Director of Nursing, Garfield County Health Center, Jordan, MT, p. A386

NORDSTROM, Janice, Director Human Resources, Landmark Hospital Of Joplin, Joplin, MO, p. A369

NORDSTROM, Katie, Director Human Resources, Beartooth Billings Clinic, Red Lodge, MT, p. A387

NORDWICK, Thomas, FACHE, Chief Executive Officer, Uvalde Memorial Hospital, Uvalde, TX, p. A651

NORDYKE, Charles
Chief Executive Officer, Vibra Hospital Of Northwestern Indiana, Crown Point, IN, p. A206
Chief Executive Officer, Vibra Hospital Of Springfield, Springfield, IL, p. A201

NORDYKE, Melissa, Chief Financial Officer, Seton Smithville Regional Hospital, Smithville, TX, p. A646

NOREEN, James M.D., Chief Medical Officer, Regina Hospital, Hastings, MN, p. A341

NOREEN, Ron, Director, Information Services, Southwest Mississippi Regional Medical Center, Mccomb, MS, p. A358

NORELDIN, Mohsen M.D., President Medical Staff, Athol Hospital, Athol, MA, p. A302

NOREM, Ashley, Chief Information Systems, Starke Hospital, Knox, IN, p. A213

NOREM, Julie MSN, Chief Nursing Officer, Rochelle Community Hospital, Rochelle, IL, p. A198

NOREN, Tom M.D., Chief Medical Officer, Up Health System–Marquette, Marquette, MI, p. A326

NORGAARD, Margaret B.
Chief Executive Officer, Poplar Community Hospital, Poplar, MT, p. A387
Chief Executive Officer, Trinity Hospital, Wolf Point, MT, p. A389

NORICK, Laurence M.D., Clinical Director, U.S. Public Health Service Indian Hospital, Parker, AZ, p. A32

NORIEGA, Donna, Chief Operating Officer, Arizona State Hospital, Phoenix, AZ, p. A33

NORMAN, Daniel, Regional Service Manager, Unitypoint Health – Waterloo, Waterloo, IA, p. A236

NORMAN, Debbie, MSN, R.N.
Chief Nursing Officer, Elkview General Hospital, Hobart, OK, p. A508
Director Human Resources, Central Louisiana Surgical Hospital, Alexandria, LA, p. A269

NORMAN, Jimmy, Chief Financial Officer, Mountain Lakes Medical Center, Clayton, GA, p. A154

NORMAN, Laura, Chief Development and Information Officer, Windhaven Psychiatric Hospital, Prescott Valley, AZ, p. A35

NORMAN, Lori, Chief Financial Officer, Healthsouth Rehabilitation Of Gadsden, Gadsden, AL, p. A18

NORMAN, Mary R.N., Risk and Compliance Officer, Bear Valley Community Hospital, Big Bear Lake, CA, p. A54

NORMAN, Michael L, Executive Vice President and Chief Operating Officer, Landmark Hospital Of Cape Girardeau, Cape Girardeau, MO, p. A365

NORMAN, Michael M.D., Chief Medical Staff, Bear Valley Community Hospital, Big Bear Lake, CA, p. A54

NORMAN, Robin, Senior Vice President and Chief Financial Officer, Virginia Hospital Center – Arlington, Arlington, VA, p. A664

NORMAND, Lorrie, R.N., President, Texas Health Harris Methodist Hospital Cleburne, Cleburne, TX, p. A601

NORMINGTON–SLAY, Jeremy, FACHE
President, North Central Region, Ministry Saint Clare's Hospital, Weston, WI, p. A715
President, North Central Region, Ministry Saint Michael's Hospital, Stevens Point, WI, p. A713

NORQUEST, Cathy, Director Human Resources, York General, York, NE, p. A400

NORRICK, Michael, Director of Campus Operations, Greenville Health System – Laurens County Memorial Hospital, Clinton, SC, p. A560

NORRIS, Charles, Chief Executive Officer, Memorial Hospital, Gonzales, TX, p. A616

NORRIS, David, Chief Medical Staff, Sweetwater Hospital, Sweetwater, TN, p. A589

NORRIS, Kathy, Director Human Resources, Bear Valley Community Hospital, Big Bear Lake, CA, p. A54

NORRIS, Lucy, Administrator Interim Chief Nursing Officer, Multicare Good Samaritan Hospital, Puyallup, WA, p. A684

NORRIS, Robert, Chief Executive Officer, Huntington Creek Recovery Center, Shickshinny, PA, p. A551

NORTH, Ralene, Chief Nurse Executive, Massena Memorial Hospital, Massena, NY, p. A439

NORTHCUTT, Lynn, Chief Information Officer, Carolinas Hospital System, Florence, SC, p. A561

NORTHERN, Gail M., Director Human Resources, Blue Mountain Hospital, Blanding, UT, p. A656

NORTHUP, Carol, R.N., Chief Nursing Officer and Chief Operating Officer, J. Arthur Dosher Memorial Hospital, Southport, NC, p. A471

NORTHUP, Jeffrey D.O., Chief Medical Officer, Knox Community Hospital, Mount Vernon, OH, p. A496

NORTON, Andrew J, M.D.
Chief Medical Officer, Bryn Mawr Hospital, Bryn Mawr, PA, p. A530
Chief Medical Officer, Paoli Hospital, Paoli, PA, p. A542

NORTON, Bill, Chief Nursing Officer, Rehoboth Mckinley Christian Health Care Services, Gallup, NM, p. A426

NORTON, Carole, Chief Nursing Officer, Stonewall Jackson Memorial Hospital, Weston, WV, p. A697

O

OKABE, David
   Executive Vice President, Chief Financial Officer and Treasurer, Pali Momi Medical Center, Aiea, HI, p. A168
   Executive Vice President, Chief Financial Officer and Treasurer, Straub Medical Center, Honolulu, HI, p. A169
   Executive Vice President, Chief Financial Officer and Treasurer, Wilcox Medical Center, Lihue, HI, p. A170
   Senior Vice President, Chief Financial Officer and Treasurer, Kapiolani Medical Center For Women & Children, Honolulu, HI, p. A168
OKECHUKWU, Vitalis C M.D., President Medical Staff, Pam Specialty Hospital Of Lafayette, Lafayette, LA, p. A279
OKEN, Jeffrey, Vice President of Medical Affairs, Marianjoy Rehabilitation Hospital, Wheaton, IL, p. A202
OKERSON, Tara, Director Human Resources, Presentation Medical Center, Rolla, ND, p. A478
OKESON, Keith, President and Chief Executive Officer, Lifecare Medical Center, Roseau, MN, p. A347
OKEY, Suzi, Director of Nursing, Southwest Health, Platteville, WI, p. A710
OKONIEWSKI, Susan M.D., Chief of Staff, Chi St. Gabriel's Health, Little Falls, MN, p. A342
OKSENDAHL, Elaine, Director Human Resources and Risk Management, Schick Shadel Hospital, Seattle, WA, p. A685
OKUHARA, Mary, Chief Human Resource Officer, Lakewood Regional Medical Center, Lakewood, CA, p. A65
OKUNO-JONES, Susan K, Vice President Patient Care Services and Chief Nursing Executive, Advocate Good Samaritan Hospital, Downers Grove, IL, p. A186
OLAND, Charisse S., FACHE, Chief Executive Officer, Rusk County Memorial Hospital, Ladysmith, WI, p. A704
OLANDER, Lisa M., Chief Executive Officer, Haven Behavioral Hospital Of Philadelphia, Philadelphia, PA, p. A544
OLANDER, Scott, Chief Financial Officer, Evergreenhealth Monroe, Monroe, WA, p. A682
OLASON, Roxanne R.N., FACHE, Vice President and Chief Nursing Officer, Skagit Regional Health, Mount Vernon, WA, p. A682
OLDER, Michael M.D., President Medical Staff, Nashoba Valley Medical Center, Ayer, MA, p. A302
OLDHAM, Jennie, Director Human Resources, Goodall–Witcher Hospital Authority, Clifton, TX, p. A601
OLDHAM, Lawrence, Chief Financial Officer, Arise Austin Medical Center, Austin, TX, p. A594
OLDHAM, Marriner M.D., Chief Medical Officer, U.S. Air Force Regional Hospital, Elmendorf Afb, AK, p. A26
OLDS, Debbie D R.N., MSN, Director of Nursing, Willis–Knighton Medical Center, Shreveport, LA, p. A286
OLEJNICZAK, David R, Chief Operating Officer, St. John's Hospital, Springfield, IL, p. A201
OLEKSYK, Mike M.D., Vice President and Chief Medical Officer, Baptist Hospital, Pensacola, FL, p. A139
OLESTON, Caryn Lynn, MSN, R.N., FACHE
   Chief Nursing Officer, Mercyhealth Hospital And Medical Center – Harvard, Harvard, IL, p. A189
   Chief Nursing Officer, Mercyhealth Hospital And Medical Center – Walworth, Lake Geneva, WI, p. A704
OLESZAK, Randy, Director Fiscal Services, Milwaukee County Behavioral Health Division, Milwaukee, WI, p. A708
OLEY, Edwin M., President and Chief Executive Officer, Mercy Regional Medical Center, Lorain, OH, p. A494
OLIGSCHLAEGER, David, Medical Staff President, Shelby Memorial Hospital, Shelbyville, IL, p. A200
OLINDE, Chad E., CPA, Administrator and Chief Executive Officer, Pointe Coupee General Hospital, New Roads, LA, p. A283
OLINGER, Richard P, Chief Financial Officer, Lecom Health Millcreek Community Hospital, Erie, PA, p. A534
OLINSKI, Janis R.N., Vice President Clinical Services, Harrison Community Hospital, Cadiz, OH, p. A482
OLIPHANT, Gerald P, Executive Vice President and Chief Operating Officer, Good Samaritan Hospital, Cincinnati, OH, p. A484
OLIPHANT, Jenny, Executive Vice President and Chief Operating Officer, Bethesda North Hospital, Cincinnati, OH, p. A483
OLIPHANT, Phillip, Chief Information Officer, U.S. Air Force Regional Hospital, Elmendorf Afb, AK, p. A26
OLIVARES, Rafael, Controller, Starr County Memorial Hospital, Rio Grande City, TX, p. A640
OLIVAREZ, Lorenzo, Senior Vice President and Chief Financial Officer, BSA Hospital, Llc, Amarillo, TX, p. A592
OLIVAS, Ray, Chief Fiscal Service, West Texas Veterans Affairs Health Care System, Big Spring, TX, p. A598
OLIVE, Alan C., Chief Executive Officer, Northern Nevada Medical Center, Sparks, NV, p. A406
OLIVENCIA, Humberto M.D., Medical Director, Hospital Perea, Mayaguez, PR, p. A724
OLIVER, David, Director Information Systems, King's Daughters Medical Center, Ashland, KY, p. A255
OLIVER, Diane R.N., MSN, Chief Nursing Officer, Parkwest Medical Center, Knoxville, TN, p. A582

OLIVER, Doug, Chief Financial Officer, Windhaven Psychiatric Hospital, Prescott Valley, AZ, p. A35
OLIVER, Michelle
   Chief Nursing Executive, Shelby Memorial Hospital, Shelbyville, IL, p. A200
   Chief Nursing Officer, Hshs St. Mary's Hospital, Decatur, IL, p. A185
OLIVER, Rick, Information Technology, Hamilton Hospital, Olney, TX, p. A636
OLIVER, Rosalie
   Chief Financial Officer, Florida Hospital Heartland Medical Center, Sebring, FL, p. A142
   Senior Vice President and Chief Financial Officer, Florida Hospital Wauchula, Wauchula, FL, p. A147
OLIVER, Vincent, FACHE, Administrator, Island Hospital, Anacortes, WA, p. A678
OLIVERA, Sue, Vice President, Aultman Hospital, Canton, OH, p. A482
OLIVERAS, Freddy, Chief Information Officer, Martin County Hospital District, Stanton, TX, p. A646
OLIVERAS LAGUNA, Ana, Administrator, Caribbean Medical Center, Fajardo, PR, p. A723
OLIVIER, Athan III, R.N., FACHE, Administrator and Chief Executive Officer, Iberia Rehabilitation Hospital, New Iberia, LA, p. A282
OLIVIER, Edward
   Chief Financial Officer, Charles A. Dean Memorial Hospital, Greenville, ME, p. A291
   Chief Financial Officer, Martha's Vineyard Hospital, Oak Bluffs, MA, p. A310
OLLI, Cindy R.N., Chief Nursing Officer, Schoolcraft Memorial Hospital, Manistique, MI, p. A325
OLLIE, Edwin J, Executive Vice President and Chief Financial Officer, New Hanover Regional Medical Center, Wilmington, NC, p. A472
OLLIS, Linda Neu FACHE, Chief Operating Officer, Mon Health Medical Center, Morgantown, WV, p. A694
OLLSON, Joanne, Vice President Human Resources, Baystate Noble Hospital, Westfield, MA, p. A312
OLM–SHIPMAN, Bobby, Chief Executive Officer, Saint Luke's South Hospital, Overland Park, KS, p. A249
OLMSTEAD, David
   Chief Human Resource Officer – Dallas Market, Baylor Scott & White Medical Center – Lake Pointe, Rowlett, TX, p. A641
   Chief Human Resource Officer, Baylor Scott & White Medical Center – Sunnyvale, Sunnyvale, TX, p. A647
OLMSTEAD, Linda, Director, Human Resources, Uw Medicine/ Northwest Hospital & Medical Center, Seattle, WA, p. A686
OLNEY, Garry M.
   Chief Operating Officer, Providence Little Company Of Mary Medical Center – Torrance, Torrance, CA, p. A94
   Chief Operating Officer, Providence Little Company Of Mary Medical Center San Pedro, Los Angeles, CA, p. A70
OLS, Timothy A., FACHE
   Chief Executive Officer, Baylor Scott & White Medical Center – Llano, Llano, TX, p. A629
   President, Baylor Scott & White Medical Center – Marble Falls, Marble Falls, TX, p. A632
OLSCAMP, Karen E., President and Chief Executive Officer, University Of Maryland Baltimore Washington Medical Center, Glen Burnie, MD, p. A298
OLSEN, Debbie, Human Resource Partner, Sparrow Ionia Hospital, Ionia, MI, p. A323
OLSEN, Jennifer M.D., Chief of Staff, North Canyon Medical Center, Gooding, ID, p. A173
OLSEN, Justin, Chief Operating Officer, Children's Hospital, New Orleans, LA, p. A282
OLSEN, Karen M R.N., Chief Nursing Officer, Mission Hospital, Asheville, NC, p. A457
OLSEN, Ryan, Vice President of Operations, St. Jude Medical Center, Fullerton, CA, p. A61
OLSEN, Sabrina, Chief Financial Officer, Duke University Hospital, Durham, NC, p. A461
OLSON, Brett J M.D., Medical Chief of Staff, Lakes Regional Healthcare, Spirit Lake, IA, p. A235
OLSON, Cheryl, Vice President, Pomerado Hospital, Poway, CA, p. A80
OLSON, Craig, Director Information Technology, Southwestern Regional Medical Center, Tulsa, OK, p. A518
OLSON, Dave, Director of Nursing, Montana State Hospital, Warm Springs, MT, p. A389
OLSON, Diana
   Chief Human Resources Officer, Mercy Health – Willard Hospital, Willard, OH, p. A502
   Director Human Resources, Mercy Tiffin Hospital, Tiffin, OH, p. A500
OLSON, Eric, Chief Financial Officer, Providence Portland Medical Center, Portland, OR, p. A525

OLSON, Erik, Chief Executive Officer, Renown Regional Medical Center, Reno, NV, p. A405
OLSON, Forrest M.D., Chief Medical Officer, Enloe Medical Center, Chico, CA, p. A55
OLSON, John L., M.D.
   Medical Director, Lakeview Medical Center, Rice Lake, WI, p. A711
   Interim President and Chief Administrative Officer, Lakeview Medical Center, Rice Lake, WI, p. A711
OLSON, Joni, Chief Executive Officer, Gundersen Tri–County Hospital And Clinics, Whitehall, WI, p. A716
OLSON, Kevin, Director Information Systems, St. Anthony Hospital, Oklahoma City, OK, p. A513
OLSON, Lacey M.D., Chief Medical Staff, Sanford Chamberlain Medical Center, Chamberlain, SD, p. A568
OLSON, Lynn R, Director Human Resources, Hendricks Community Hospital Association, Hendricks, MN, p. A341
OLSON, Marcia
   Business Office Manager, Webster County Community Hospital, Red Cloud, NE, p. A399
   Business Office Manager, Webster County Community Hospital, Red Cloud, NE, p. A399
   Director Finance and Controller, Spearfish Regional Hospital, Spearfish, SD, p. A573
OLSON, MariBeth R.N., Vice President Patient Care Services, Mercy Hospital, Coon Rapids, MN, p. A338
OLSON, Mark, M.D.
   Chief of Staff, Lincoln Community Hospital And Nursing Home, Hugo, CO, p. A104
   Interim Chief Information Officer, Behavioral Health Network, Natchaug Hospital, Mansfield Center, CT, p. A110
OLSON, Michael R., Chief Executive Officer, Citizens Medical Center, Victoria, TX, p. A652
OLSON, Tim
   Senior Vice President Finance, Thedacare Regional Medical Center–Appleton, Appleton, WI, p. A698
   Senior Vice President Finance, Thedacare Regional Medical Center–Neenah, Neenah, WI, p. A709
OLSON, Tracy L, Human Resource Officer, Avera St. Luke's Hospital, Aberdeen, SD, p. A568
OLSSON, Dave, Director of Marketing, Aspirus Keweenaw Hospital, Inc., Laurium, MI, p. A325
OLSZYK, Mark M.D., Vice President Medical Affairs and Chief Medical Officer, Carroll Hospital Center, Westminster, MD, p. A301
OMAN, Michelle, D.O.
   Chief Medical Officer, Essentia Health Northern Pines Medical Center, Aurora, MN, p. A335
   Chief Medical Officer, Essentia Health–Virginia, Virginia, MN, p. A349
OMAR, Sharif
   Chief Executive Officer, Northwest Medical Center – Springdale, Springdale, AR, p. A49
   Chief Executive Officer, Physicians' Specialty Hospital, Fayetteville, AR, p. A42
OMEL, John, Regional Vice President, Human Resources, Santa Rosa Memorial Hospital, Santa Rosa, CA, p. A91
OMOLARA, Khar M.D., Chief Medical Staff, Jefferson County Hospital, Fayette, MS, p. A354
OMRAN, Yasser M.D., President Medical Staff, Pomerene Hospital, Millersburg, OH, p. A496
OMTA, Stephen R, Chief Operating Officer, Peacehealth St. Joseph Medical Center, Bellingham, WA, p. A678
OMURA, David
   Associate Director, Wm. Jennings Bryan Dorn Veterans Affairs Medical Center, Columbia, SC, p. A561
   Interim Director, Wm. Jennings Bryan Dorn Veterans Affairs Medical Center, Columbia, SC, p. A561
ONEAL, Karen, Chief Financial Officer, Burke Medical Center, Waynesboro, GA, p. A167
ONEILL, John Patrick., Administrator, Shriners Hospitals For Children–Boston, Boston, MA, p. A304
ONEILL, Steve, Chief Information Officer, NYC Health + Hospitals / Carter, New Rochelle, NY, p. A444
ONG, Hannah, Director, Medical Affairs, Saint Elizabeths Hospital, Washington, DC, p. A118
ONG, Richard B, Chief Information Officer, Saint Vincent Hospital, Erie, PA, p. A534
ONI, Buki M.D., Chief Medical Officer, Kenmare Community Hospital, Kenmare, ND, p. A477
ONIFATHER, Jeff, Chief Financial Officer, Cornerstone Of Medical Arts Center Hospital, Fresh Meadows, NY, p. A436
ONO, Craig M.D., Chief of Staff, Shriners Hospitals For Children–Honolulu, Honolulu, HI, p. A169
ONOFRE, Bonnie, Chief Nursing Officer, South Lake Hospital, Clermont, FL, p. A122
OOSTRA, Randall D., FACHE, President and Chief Executive Officer, Promedica Health System, Toledo, OH, p. B101

OPBROEK, Steve, Manager Information Technology, Skyline Hospital, White Salmon, WA, p. A689

OPHAUG, Courtney, FACHE, Chief Executive Officer, Banner Estrella Medical Center, Phoenix, AZ, p. A33

OPHEIKENS, Robyn, Assistant Administrator Human Resources, St. Mark's Hospital, Salt Lake City, UT, p. A660

OPPENHEIMER, Steven, Chief Executive Officer, Del Amo Hospital, Torrance, CA, p. A93

OPPONG, Bernard D.O., Chief of Staff, Madison Health, London, OH, p. A494

OPRANDI, Allison M.D., Chief Medical Officer, Aultman Hospital, Canton, OH, p. A482

OPRISKO, Judy P
Vice President Human Resources, John Heinz Institute Of Rehabilitation Medicine, Wilkes, PA, p. A554
Vice President, Allied Services Rehabilitation Hospital, Scranton, PA, p. A550

OPSETH, Gregory, Chief Nursing Officer, Guthrie County Hospital, Guthrie Center, IA, p. A228

OPSTEDAHL, DeeAnna R.N., Vice President Patient Care Services, Chi St. Alexius Health – Dickinson Medical Center, Dickinson, ND, p. A475

OPSUT, Jennifer, Interim Chief Operating Officer, West Valley Medical Center, Caldwell, ID, p. A172

OQUENDO, Tanja, Chief Human Resources Officer, Flaget Memorial Hospital, Bardstown, KY, p. A255

ORAVEC, Jon, Vice President, Human Resources, Howard County General Hospital, Columbia, MD, p. A298

ORAZINE, Jay, Director Information Services, Baptist Health Paducah, Paducah, KY, p. A266

ORCUTT, David, Chief Executive Officer, Weatherford Regional Medical Center, Weatherford, TX, p. A653

ORDYNA, Daniel, Chief Executive Officer, Portneuf Medical Center, Pocatello, ID, p. A175

ORE, Ruta, Director Human Resources, Pottstown Memorial Medical Center, Pottstown, PA, p. A548

OREAR, Kathy, Director Human Resources, Newman Regional Health, Emporia, KS, p. A240

OREGEL, Omar, Controller, Kindred Hospital–Ontario, Ontario, CA, p. A77

ORELLANA, Feliipe, Chief Medical Officer, Barnes–Jewish St. Peters Hospital, Saint Peters, MO, p. A379

OREMUS, Lisa, Interim Chief Human Resource Officer, Los Alamitos Medical Center, Los Alamitos, CA, p. A67

OREN, Cole R.N., Chief Nursing Officer, Select Specialty Hospital–Durham, Durham, NC, p. A461

OREOL, Harry, Acting Chief Executive Officer, Patton State Hospital, Patton, CA, p. A79

ORFANIDIS, Deanna MS, R.N., Interim Chief Nursing Officer, Mt. Ascutney Hospital And Health Center, Windsor, VT, p. A663

ORIOL, Albert, Vice President Information Management and Chief Information Officer, Rady Children's Hospital – San Diego, San Diego, CA, p. A85

ORLANDI, Mary, Manager Human Resources, Carney Hospital, Boston, MA, p. A303

ORLANDO, Anthony T, Senior Vice President Finance, Englewood Hospital And Medical Center, Englewood, NJ, p. A414

ORLANDO, Charles, Interim Chief Executive Officer, Louis A. Weiss Memorial Hospital, Chicago, IL, p. A182

ORLANDO, Kristin, Director Operations, Mid–Hudson Forensic Psychiatric Center, New Hampton, NY, p. A440

ORLANDO, Lorraine, Vice President Human Resources, New York–Presbyterian Queens, New Rochelle, NY, p. A444

ORMAN, Bernard A. Jr, FACHE, Chief Executive Officer, Samaritan Hospital, Macon, MO, p. A373

ORMOND, Evalyn, Chief Executive Officer, Union General Hospital, Farmerville, LA, p. A274

ORMOND, Jack, Chief Financial Officer, Cuba Memorial Hospital, Cuba, NY, p. A434

ORNELAS, Henry
Chief Operating Officer, Lac+Usc Medical Center, Los Angeles, CA, p. A69
Chief Operating Officer, Salinas Valley Memorial Healthcare System, Salinas, CA, p. A84

OROZCO, Jorge, Chief Executive Officer, Rancho Los Amigos National Rehabilitation Center, Downey, CA, p. A58

ORR, Karen
Administrator and Chief Nursing Officer, Providence Medical Center, Kansas City, KS, p. A244
Chief Nursing Officer, Providence Medical Center, Kansas City, KS, p. A244

ORR, Natassia, Chief Operating Officer, Broward Health Medical Center, Fort Lauderdale, FL, p. A124

ORR, Stephanie, Chief Nursing Officer, Steele Memorial Medical Center, Salmon, ID, p. A176

ORRICK, Charles H., Administrator, Donalsonville Hospital, Donalsonville, GA, p. A156

ORSINI, John
Executive Vice President and Chief Financial Officer, Northwestern Medicine Central Dupage Hospital, Winfield, IL, p. A202
Executive Vice President and Chief Financial Officer, Northwestern Medicine Delnor Hospital, Geneva, IL, p. A188

ORSINI, Thomas J., President and Chief Executive Officer, Lake Taylor Transitional Care Hospital, Norfolk, VA, p. A672

ORT, Linda, Chief Financial Officer, Piggott Community Hospital, Piggott, AR, p. A48

ORTEGA, Becky, Manager Human Resources, Avista Adventist Hospital, Louisville, CO, p. A106

ORTEGA, Cesar M.D., Chief of Staff, United Memorial Medical Care, Houston, TX, p. A623

ORTEGA, Debbie, Chief Human Resource Officer and Vice President Administrative Services, Huntington Memorial Hospital, Pasadena, CA, p. A79

ORTEGA, Jose, Chief Operating Officer, Greater El Monte Community Hospital, South El Monte, CA, p. A92

ORTEGO, Ashley, Director Human Resources and Marketing, Springhill Medical Center, Springhill, LA, p. A286

ORTH, Charam, Director Human Resources, Frances Mahon Deaconess Hospital, Glasgow, MT, p. A384

ORTHAUS, Denis, Director Human Resources, Wellspan Philhaven, Mount Gretna, PA, p. A541

ORTIZ, Anthony, Chief Financial Officer, Pecos County Memorial Hospital, Fort Stockton, TX, p. A613

ORTIZ, Bienvenido, Coordinator Information Systems, Hospital De Damas, Ponce, PR, p. A724

ORTIZ, Blas Jr, Assistant Superintendent and Public Information Officer, Rio Grande State Center/South Texas Health Care System, Harlingen, TX, p. A618

ORTIZ, Edson, Chief Information Officer, Hospital Pavia Yauco, Yauco, PR, p. A727

ORTIZ, Evelyn Padilla
Director Human Resources, Hospital Menonita De Cayey, Cayey, PR, p. A723
Director Human Resources, Mennonite General Hospital, Aibonito, PR, p. A722

ORTIZ, Francisco M.D., Chief of Staff, Jackson County Hospital District, Edna, TX, p. A610

ORTIZ, Jose O, Chief Financial Officer, Ryder Memorial Hospital, Humacao, PR, p. A724

ORTIZ, Migdalia, Director Human Resources, Hospital San Carlos Borromeo, Moca, PR, p. A724

ORTIZ, Nancy, Director Human Resource and Marketing, Frio Regional Hospital, Pearsall, TX, p. A637

ORTIZ, Norma M.D., Medical Director, Hospital Hermanos Melendez, Bayamon, PR, p. A722

ORTIZ BAEZ, Felix, Administrator, I. Gonzalez Martinez Oncologic Hospital, Hato Rey, PR, p. A723

ORTO, Victoria K R.N., Chief Nursing and Patient Care Services Officer, Duke Regional Hospital, Durham, NC, p. A461

ORTOLANI, Philip A, Vice President Operations, Mid Coast Hospital, Brunswick, ME, p. A290

ORTON, Wendy, Chief Nursing Officer, Alleghany Memorial Hospital, Sparta, NC, p. A471

OSANTOSKI, Tina, Director Human Resources, Harbor Beach Community Hospital, Harbor Beach, MI, p. A322

OSARIO, Cesar, Specialist Information Technology, Cedar Crest Hospital And Residential Treatment Center, Belton, TX, p. A598

OSBAHR, Leah, M.P.H., Chief Executive Officer, Helena Regional Medical Center, Helena, AR, p. A44

OSBERG, Art M.D., Chief Medical Officer, Ocala Regional Medical Center, Ocala, FL, p. A136

OSBORN, Kim, Chief Financial Officer, Sequoia Hospital, Redwood City, CA, p. A82

OSBORN, Mary Ann R.N., Senior Vice President and Chief Care Coordinator Officer, Unitypoint Health – St. Luke's Hospital, Cedar Rapids, IA, p. A223

OSBORN, Melodie
Chief Nursing Officer, Renown Rehabilitation Hospital, Reno, NV, p. A405
Chief Nursing Officer, Renown South Meadows Medical Center, Reno, NV, p. A405

OSBORN, Tom D.O., Chief Medical Staff, Holdenville General Hospital, Holdenville, OK, p. A508

OSBORNE, Anna, Chief Human Resources Management Service, West Texas Veterans Affairs Health Care System, Big Spring, TX, p. A598

OSBORNE, Jay M.D., Senior Vice President Medical Affairs, Northside Medical Center, Youngstown, OH, p. A503

OSBORNE, Phil, Director Information Technology, Bourbon Community Hospital, Paris, KY, p. A266

OSBURN, Jerry, Chief Executive Officer, Yoakum County Hospital, Denver City, TX, p. A608

OSBURNF, Theresa, Human Resources Strategic Partners, Providence Seaside Hospital, Seaside, OR, p. A527

OSCADAL, Martin
Senior Vice President Human Resources, St. Elizabeth Florence, Florence, KY, p. A258
Senior Vice President Human Resources, St. Elizabeth Fort Thomas, Fort Thomas, KY, p. A258
Vice President Human Resources, St. Elizabeth Edgewood, Edgewood, KY, p. A257

OSE, Peggy FACHE, MSN, R.N., Chief Nursing Officer, Aspirus Riverview Hospital And Clinics, Inc., Wisconsin Rapids, WI, p. A716

OSEGARD, Jeff, Chief Information Officer, Cass County Memorial Hospital, Atlantic, IA, p. A222

OSEHOBO, Philip M.D., Chief Medical Officer, Wellstar Spalding Regional Hospital, Griffin, GA, p. A158

OSER, William F., M.D.
Chief Medical Officer, JFK Johnson Rehabilitation Institute, Edison, NJ, p. A413
Senior Vice President and Chief Medical Officer, JFK Medical Center, Edison, NJ, p. A413

OSINOWO, Thomas M.D., Chief Clinical Officer, Northwest Ohio Psychiatric Hospital, Toledo, OH, p. A500

OSINSKI, Kathleen, Chief Human Resources Service, John D. Dingell Veterans Affairs Medical Center, Detroit, MI, p. A318

OSKIN, Jeffrey L., Vice President and Administrator, Charleston Area Medical Center, Charleston, WV, p. A691

OSLIN, Dave M.D., Chief of Staff, Philadelphia Veterans Affairs Medical Center, Philadelphia, PA, p. A545

OSOWSKI, Angela, Chief Nursing Officer, Lifecare Hospitals Of Wisconsin, Pewaukee, WI, p. A710

OSSE, John Michael., Interim Chief Executive Officer, Southwest Healthcare Services, Bowman, ND, p. A474

OSSELLO, Susan, Chief Financial Officer, Granite County Medical Center, Philipsburg, MT, p. A387

OSTASZEWSKI, Patricia, MS, Chief Executive Officer, Healthsouth Rehabilitation Hospital Of Toms River, Toms River, NJ, p. A421

OSTBERG, Melissa, Chief Financial Officer, Marias Medical Center, Shelby, MT, p. A388

OSTBLOOM, Jan, Human Resources Consultant, Our Lady Of Peace, Louisville, KY, p. A263

OSTEEN, Tom J, Director Area Technology, Kaiser Permanente Manteca Medical Center, Manteca, CA, p. A73

OSTENSON, Scott, Chief Financial Officer, Jacobson Memorial Hospital Care Center, Elgin, ND, p. A475

OSTER, Kurt, Human Resources Officer, Carl Vinson Veterans Affairs Medical Center, Dublin, GA, p. A157

OSTERBERG, Valerie, Chief Financial Officer, Sanford Vermillion Medical Center, Vermillion, SD, p. A573

OSTERHOUT, David, Assistant Superintendent and Chief Financial Officer, El Paso Psychiatric Center, El Paso, TX, p. A610

OSTERLY, Eric, Chief Financial Officer, Florida Hospital Fish Memorial, Orange City, FL, p. A136

OSTLIG, Jane, Chief Medical Officer, Sanford Mayville Medical Center, Mayville, ND, p. A477

OSTRANDER, Maria DC R.N., MSN, Chief Nurse Executive, San Antonio State Hospital, San Antonio, TX, p. A643

OSTRANDER, Michael, Chief Financial Officer, Nathan Littauer Hospital And Nursing Home, Gloversville, NY, p. A436

OSTROWSKY, Barry, President and Chief Executive Officer, Rwjbarnabas Health, West Orange, NJ, p. B110

OSTROW, Peter M.D., President Medical Staff, Beth Israel Deaconess Hospital–Needham Campus, Needham, MA, p. A309

OSWALD, Kathy, Senior Vice President and Chief Human Resources Officer, Henry Ford Hospital, Detroit, MI, p. A318

OSWALD, Traci L
Vice President Human Resources, Galion Community Hospital, Galion, OH, p. A491
Vice President, Chief Human Resources, Avita Ontario Hospital, Ontario, OH, p. A497

OTERO, Jorge Torres., Executive Director, Hospital Del Maestro, San Juan, PR, p. A726

OTHOLE, Jean, Chief Executive Officer, U. S. Public Health Service Indian Hospital, Zuni, NM, p. A429

OTOTIVO, Brenda, Executive Director, Jim Taliaferro Community Mental Health, Lawton, OK, p. A509

OTOTT, Kelly R.N., Chief Nursing Officer, Washington County Hospital, Washington, KS, p. A253

OTT, Darin D.O., Chief of Staff, Kane County Hospital, Kanab, UT, p. A657

OTT, Eugene J. Jr, Chief Operating Officer, Eagleville Hospital, Eagleville, PA, p. A533

OTT, Laurie, Vice President Human Resources and President University Health Care Foundation, University Hospital, Augusta, GA, p. A152

OTT, Mark M.D., Regional Chief Medical Director, Intermountain Medical Center, Murray, UT, p. A658

OTT, Pamela, Vice President Finance, Aurora Sheboygan Memorial Medical Center, Sheboygan, WI, p. A712

OTT, Ronald H., President, Excela Health Westmoreland Hospital, Greensburg, PA, p. A535

OTTATI, David, Regional Chief Executive Officer, Florida Hospital, Orlando, FL, p. A137

OTTE, Elaine, Chief Operating Officer, Clarinda Regional Health Center, Clarinda, IA, p. A224

OTTEMAN, Diane, Chief Executive Officer, Kindred Chicago–Central Hospital, Chicago, IL, p. A181

OTTEN, Sharon A, Vice President Nursing, Advocate South Suburban Hospital, Hazel Crest, IL, p. A189

OTTENBACHER, John, Chief of Staff, Bowdle Hospital, Bowdle, SD, p. A568

OTTENS, Mark, Chief Nursing Officer, Baptist Memorial Hospital–North Mississippi, Oxford, MS, p. A360

OTTMAR, Kellie, Manager Information Services, East Adams Rural Healthcare, Ritzville, WA, p. A684

OTTO, Sara, Chief Compliance Officer, North Canyon Medical Center, Gooding, ID, p. A173

OTTO, Steve, Chief Executive Officer, Tristar Skyline Medical Center, Nashville, TN, p. A587

OTTOLINO, Joseph
  Chief Operating Officer, West Suburban Medical Center, Oak Park, IL, p. A196
  Interim Chief Executive Officer, West Suburban Medical Center, Oak Park, IL, p. A196

OUBRE, Chris, Information Technology Director, Garden Park Medical Center, Gulfport, MS, p. A355

OUELETTE, Lisa, Director Human Resources, Beaumont Hospital – Troy, Troy, MI, p. A332

OUELLETTE, Demetra
  Chief Operating Officer, Rehabilitation Hospital Of Rhode Island, North Smithfield, RI, p. A556
  President, Roger Williams Medical Center, Providence, RI, p. A557

OUIMET, Mary Elizabeth MSN, R.N., Senior Vice President and Chief Nursing Officer, Wheaton Franciscan Healthcare – All Saints, Racine, WI, p. A711

OUNGST, Laurie
  Vice President and Chief Operating Officer, Ministry Saint Mary's Hospitals, Rhinelander, WI, p. A711
  Vice President, Operations, Howard Young Medical Center, Woodruff, WI, p. A716
  Vice President, Operations, Ministry Eagle River Memorial Hospital, Eagle River, WI, p. A700
  Vice President, Operations, Ministry Sacred Heart Hospital, Tomahawk, WI, p. A714

OURS, Matt, Chief Executive Officer and Managing Director, Rivendell Behavioral Health, Bowling Green, KY, p. A256

OUSEY, Tracy, Director Human Resources, Washington County Hospital And Clinics, Washington, IA, p. A236

OUTHIER, Amy, Director Health Information Management, Weatherford Regional Hospital, Weatherford, OK, p. A519

OUTLAW, Debbie R.N., Director Patient Care Services, Riverside Rehabilitation Institute, Newport News, VA, p. A671

OVANDO, Benjamin, Chief Operations Officer, Rancho Los Amigos National Rehabilitation Center, Downey, CA, p. A58

OVERBEY, William J., Chief Executive Officer, Kansas Rehabilitation Hospital, Topeka, KS, p. A252

OVERBY, Roger, Executive Director Information Systems, Greene County Medical Center, Jefferson, IA, p. A230

OVERCASH, Jenny, Director Human Resources, Healthsouth Huntington Rehabilitation Hospital, Huntington, WV, p. A692

OVERMAN, David S, President and Chief Operating Officer, Children's Hospitals And Clinics Of Minnesota, Minneapolis, MN, p. A343

OVERSTREET, Alyson, Chief Financial Officer, Washington County Hospital, Chatom, AL, p. A16

OVERSTREET, Amy, Director Human Resources, Trousdale Medical Center, Hartsville, TN, p. A579

OVERTON, Camie, Chief Executive Officer, Curahealth Tucson, Tucson, AZ, p. A37

OVERTON, Deana, Director Human Resources, Mitchell County Hospital, Colorado City, TX, p. A602

OVESON, Mark M.D., Chief Medical Staff, Central Valley Medical Center, Nephi, UT, p. A658

OWEN, Christian, Chief Operating Officer, Horsham Clinic, Ambler, PA, p. A529

OWEN, Sabrina, Human Resources Officer, Veterans Affairs Central Iowa Health Care System, Des Moines, IA, p. A226

OWEN, Sandra
  Director Fiscal and Accounting, Harper Hospital District Five, Harper, KS, p. A242
  Interim Chief Executive Officer, Harper Hospital District Five, Harper, KS, p. A242

OWENS, Beverly, Controller, Rehabilitation Hospital, Navicent Health, Macon, GA, p. A161

OWENS, Brian, Chief Operating Officer, Lindner Center Of Hope, Mason, OH, p. A495

OWENS, Craig A., President, Wellstar Douglas Hospital, Douglasville, GA, p. A157

OWENS, Daniel, Chief Executive Officer, Emory University Hospital Midtown, Atlanta, GA, p. A150

OWENS, Diane, Assistant Administrator, St. David's Medical Center, Austin, TX, p. A596

OWENS, Johnathan, Chief Executive Officer, Decatur Health Systems, Oberlin, KS, p. A248

OWENS, Mark M.D., Vice President Medical Affairs, Mercy San Juan Medical Center, Carmichael, CA, p. A55

OWENS, Rick, Chief Financial Officer, D. W. Mcmillan Memorial Hospital, Brewton, AL, p. A15

OWENS, Stephanie, Manager Human Resources, Mcdowell Arh Hospital, Mcdowell, KY, p. A264

OWENSBY, Karen R.N., Chief Clinical Officer, Florida Hospital North Pinellas, Tarpon Springs, FL, p. A145

OWENSBY, Terri R.N., Chief Nursing Executive, Kaiser Permanente South Sacramento Medical Center, Sacramento, CA, p. A83

OWINGS, Karen MSN, Vice President, Patient Care Services, Medstar Union Memorial Hospital, Baltimore, MD, p. A295

OWINGS, Raymond C., Interim Chief Financial Officer, Morehead Memorial Hospital, Eden, NC, p. A461

OWINGS, Thomas, Chief Executive Officer, Wesley Medical Center, Wichita, KS, p. A254

OWREY, Donald R.
  President, Upmc Horizon, Farrell, PA, p. A535
  President, Upmc Jameson Hospital, New Castle, PA, p. A542

OWUSU, Frederick K., Chief Human Resources Officer, Desert Regional Medical Center, Palm Springs, CA, p. A78

OXENDALE, Sharon, Chief Operating Officer, Macneal Hospital, Berwyn, IL, p. A178

OXFORD, Michelle, Chief Operating Officer, Acting Chief Executive Officer, Bakersfield Heart Hospital, Bakersfield, CA, p. A52

OXFORD, Tammy, Director Human Resources, Bob Wilson Memorial Grant County Hospital, Ulysses, KS, p. A253

OXLEY, Dawn R.N., Associate Director Patient Care Services and Nurse Executive, Iowa City Veterans Affairs Health Care System, Iowa City, IA, p. A229

OXLEY, James D.O., Vice President Medical Affairs, Orange Regional Medical Center, Middletown, NY, p. A439

OXLEY, Scott, President, The Acadia Hospital, Bangor, ME, p. A289

OXTON, Alice, Director Information Technology, Sentara Obici Hospital, Suffolk, VA, p. A676

OZBURN, Thomas H., Chief Executive Officer, Parkridge Medical Center, Chattanooga, TN, p. A576

OZEL, A Deniz M.D., Chief Medical Officer, Northeast Rehabilitation Hospital, Salem, NH, p. A410

OZMENT, Mary, Chief Nursing Officer, Hillcrest Hospital Pryor, Pryor, OK, p. A515

OZUAH, Philip O. M.D., Ph.D., Executive Vice President and Chief Operating Officer, Montefiore Medical Center, New Rochelle, NY, p. A443

P

PAARLBERG, Ted, Chief Executive Officer, Landmark Hospital Of Salt Lake City, Murray, UT, p. A658

PAASCH, Michael
  Regional Chief Information Officer, SSM Health St. Mary's Hospital – St. Louis, Saint Louis, MO, p. A378
  Regional Vice President and Chief Information Officer, SSM Cardinal Glennon Children's Hospital, Saint Louis, MO, p. A378
  Vice President, Regional Chief Information Officer, SSM Health St. Clare Hospital – Fenton, Fenton, MO, p. A368

PABLO, Gary M. M.D., Chief Medical Officer, Sacred Heart Hospital On The Emerald Coast, Miramar Beach, FL, p. A135

PABON, Jose O, Director Operations, Wilma N. Vazquez Medical Center, Vega Baja, PR, p. A727

PABON–RAMIREZ, Felix, Chief Information Officer, St. Charles Hospital, Port Jefferson, NY, p. A450

PACCA, Richard M.D., Chief of Staff, Granville Health System, Oxford, NC, p. A468

PACCAPANICCIA, Dominic, Chief Operating Officer, Indiana Regional Medical Center, Indiana, PA, p. A537

PACE, Kathleen MSN, R.N., Chief Nursing Officer, Englewood Community Hospital, Englewood, FL, p. A124

PACE, Kelly, Director Human Resource, Strategic Behavioral Health – Wilmington, Leland, NC, p. A466

PACEK, Thomas
  Vice President Information Systems and Chief Information Officer, Inspira Medical Center–Elmer, Elmer, NJ, p. A413
  Vice President Information Systems and Chief Information Officer, Inspira Medical Center–Vineland, Vineland, NJ, p. A422

PACEY, Amy, Vice President Human Resources, Good Samaritan Medical Center, Lafayette, CO, p. A104

PACHECO, Robert W, Vice President Finance, Women & Infants Hospital Of Rhode Island, Providence, RI, p. A557

PACHUCKI, James J. Jr, Chief Financial Officer, Sunbury Community Hospital And Outpatient Center, Sunbury, PA, p. A551

PACINI, Jenna, Human Resources Specialist, Belmont Behavioral Hospital, Philadelphia, PA, p. A543

PACK, Kathy, Manager Human Resources, Copper Basin Medical Center, Copperhill, TN, p. A577

PACK, Natalie, Chief Financial Officer, St. David's North Austin Medical Center, Austin, TX, p. A596

PACK, William, Chief Financial Officer, Memorial Hermann – Texas Medical Center, Houston, TX, p. A621

PACKER, Eric, Chief Executive Officer, Cedar City Hospital, Cedar City, UT, p. A656

PACKER, Lee, Administrator, South Florida State Hospital, Hollywood, FL, p. A127

PACKER, Steven J., M.D., President and Chief Executive Officer, Community Hospital Of The Monterey Peninsula, Monterey, CA, p. A74

PACKNETT, Michael J., President and Chief Executive Officer, Parkview Health, Fort Wayne, IN, p. B96

PACURA, Lori, MSN, R.N., President, Holy Cross Hospital, Chicago, IL, p. A181

PACYNA, Andrew, FACHE, Acting Director, Veterans Affairs Ann Arbor Healthcare System, Ann Arbor, MI, p. A314

PACZKOWSKI, Rick, Chief Operating Officer, Timberlawn Mental Health System, Dallas, TX, p. A607

PADDEN, Ernest C, Chief Financial Officer, Bon Secours Maryview Medical Center, Portsmouth, VA, p. A673

PADEN, Tawnya, Director Human Resources, Weatherford Regional Hospital, Weatherford, OK, p. A519

PADGETT, Martin, President and Chief Executive Officer, Clark Memorial Hospital, Jeffersonville, IN, p. A213

PADGETT, Shirley, Director Human Resources, Cook Medical Center–A Campus Of Tift Regional Medical Center, Adel, GA, p. A149

PADILLA, Gregory, Administrator, Coast Plaza Hospital, Norwalk, CA, p. A76

PADILLA, Julieta M., Chief Nursing Officer, Hollywood Presbyterian Medical Center, Los Angeles, CA, p. A68

PADILLA, Kathy, Director of Nursing, Marcus Daly Memorial Hospital, Hamilton, MT, p. A385

PADILLA, Rafael R.N., Chief Nursing Officer, Florida Hospital At Connerton Long Term Acute Care, Land O'Lakes, FL, p. A130

PADULA, Judy MSN, R.N., Vice President Patient Care Services and Chief Nursing Officer, St. Joseph's Healthcare System, Paterson, NJ, p. A418

PAFFORD, Roger M.D., Medical Director, Mineral Community Hospital, Superior, MT, p. A388

PAGANA, Charles C M.D., Chief Medical Officer, Sunbury Community Hospital And Outpatient Center, Sunbury, PA, p. A551

PAGANELLI, Deborah, FACHE, President, Texas Health Harris Methodist Hospital Hurst–Euless–Bedford, Bedford, TX, p. A597

PAGE, Alison, Chief Executive Officer, Western Wisconsin Health, Baldwin, WI, p. A698

PAGE, Bob, Chief Executive Officer, The University Of Kansas Health System, Kansas City, KS, p. A244

PAGE, Cynthia FACHE, Chief Operating Officer, OSS Orthopaedic Hospital, York, PA, p. A555

PAGE, Deborah, Chief Human Resources Officer, Duke University Hospital, Durham, NC, p. A461

PAGE, Heather MSN, Director of Nursing, Chi St. Joseph Health Burleson Hospital, Caldwell, TX, p. A600

PAGE, Keith Allen., President and Chief Executive Officer, Anderson Hospital, Maryville, IL, p. A192

PAGE, Nancy E MS, R.N., Interim Chief Nursing Officer, Upstate University Hospital, Syracuse, NY, p. A453

PAGE, Pattie, Director Marketing and Public Relations, Eastside Medical Center, Snellville, GA, p. A165

PARKER, Judy Goforth., Ph.D., Secretary of Health, Chickasaw Nation Medical Center, Ada, OK, p. A504

PARKER, Michael M.D., Chief of Staff, Sharon Hospital, Sharon, CT, p. A113

PARKER, Richard, M.D., President, Marymount Hospital, Garfield Heights, OH, p. A492

PARKER, Robert, Chief Executive Officer and Market President, Clark Regional Medical Center, Winchester, KY, p. A268

PARKER, Sandra K M.D., Chief Medical Officer, Eastpointe Hospital, Daphne, AL, p. A16

PARKER, Theresa M, Regional Finance Director, Transylvania Regional Hospital, Brevard, NC, p. A458

PARKER, Thomas, Chief Executive Officer, Snoqualmie Valley Hospital District, Snoqualmie, WA, p. A686

PARKER, Tina, Director Human Resources, Healthsouth Rehabilitation Hospital Midland–Odessa, Midland, TX, p. A633

PARKER, Travis, Director Human Resources, Southwest Health System, Cortez, CO, p. A100

PARKER, Valerie M.D., Clinical Director, U. S. Public Health Service Indian Hospital, Rosebud, SD, p. A572

PARKEY, Kasey, Coordinator Payroll and Benefits, Post Acute Medical Specialty Hospital Of Corpus Christi – South, Corpus Christi, TX, p. A603

PARKHILL, Cherie, Chief Financial Officer, Crosbyton Clinic Hospital, Crosbyton, TX, p. A604

PARKHURST, James E., President and Chief Executive Officer, Newport Bay Hospital, Newport Beach, CA, p. A76

PARKHURST, Phyllis, Vice President Support Services, Newport Bay Hospital, Newport Beach, CA, p. A76

PARKINSON, Justin M.D., President Medical Staff, Jordan Valley Medical Center West Valley Campus, West Valley City, UT, p. A661

PARKINSON, Michelle A, Director Human Resources, Prairie St. John's, Fargo, ND, p. A475

PARKS, Amanda, Chief Nursing Officer, Lifebrite Community Hospital Of Stokes, Danbury, NC, p. A460

PARKS, Audrey, Senior Administrative Director Information Technology, Salinas Valley Memorial Healthcare System, Salinas, CA, p. A84

PARKS, Cary, Chief Information Resource Management, Hampton Veterans Affairs Medical Center, Hampton, VA, p. A668

PARKS, Dave, Chief Information Officer, Three Rivers Health, Three Rivers, MI, p. A332

PARKS, Ginger, Director Human Resources, Cape Fear Valley – Bladen County Hospital, Elizabethtown, NC, p. A462

PARKS, Jody, Administrator, Ottawa County Health Center, Minneapolis, KS, p. A247

PARKS, Kathi, Director of Nursing, South Lincoln Medical Center, Kemmerer, WY, p. A718

PARKS, Kyle M.D., Chief of Staff, Evans Memorial Hospital, Claxton, GA, p. A154

PARKS, Michelle, Administrator, Rivervalley Behavioral Health Hospital, Owensboro, KY, p. A265

PARKS, Sherry R.N., MS, Chief Nursing Officer, Saint Alphonsus Regional Medical Center, Boise, ID, p. A172

PARKS, Vicki, Chief Financial Officer, Jackson Purchase Medical Center, Mayfield, KY, p. A264

PARKS, Richard H., FACHE, President and Chief Executive Officer, Covenant Health System, Lubbock, TX, p. B39

PARLATO, David, Vice President, Finance, Dearborn County Hospital, Lawrenceburg, IN, p. A214

PARMER, David N., FACHE, Chief Executive Officer, Baptist Hospitals Of Southeast Texas, Beaumont, TX, p. A597

PARMER, David N, FACHE, Chief Executive Officer, Baptist Hospitals Of Southeast Texas, Beaumont, TX, p. A597

PARMER, Michael, Chief Medical Officer, Carepartners Health Services, Asheville, NC, p. A457

PARNEL, George, Chief Financial Officer, Clifton T. Perkins Hospital Center, Jessup, MD, p. A299

PARNELL, Brenda, Chief Executive Officer, Garfield County Public Hospital District, Pomeroy, WA, p. A683

PAROD, Daniel A., Interim President, St. Vincent Medical Center Of Evansville, Evansville, IN, p. A207

PAROD, Daniel A, Chief Operating Officer, St. Vincent Medical Center Of Evansville, Evansville, IN, p. A207

PAROSKI, Margaret M.D., Executive Vice President and Chief Medical Officer, Kaleida Health, Buffalo, NY, p. A432

PARR, James
Chief Financial Officer, Salem Health West Valley, Dallas, OR, p. A521
Chief Financial Officer, Salem Hospital, Salem, OR, p. A526

PARR, Lynnette, Chief Financial Officer, Down East Community Hospital, Machias, ME, p. A292

PARRA, Kristin, Chief Nursing Officer, Yuma Rehabilitation Hospital, Yuma, AZ, p. A39

PARRA, Michelle, Director Human Resources, Kindred Hospital South Bay, Gardena, CA, p. A61

PARRADO, Carlos M.D., Sr., Chief Medical Officer, Roosevelt Warm Springs Rehabilitation And Specialty Hospitals – Ltac, Warm Springs, GA, p. A167

PARRINELLO, Kathleen M Ph.D., Chief Operating Officer, Strong Memorial Hospital Of The University Of Rochester, Rochester, NY, p. A451

PARRISH, Becky, Director Human Resources, Southern Virginia Regional Medical Center, Emporia, VA, p. A666

PARRISH, Carl, Chief Fiscal Service, James E. Van Zandt Veterans Affairs Medical Center, Altoona, PA, p. A528

PARRISH, Denise, Interim Chief Administrative Officer, Mercy Medical Center, Oshkosh, WI, p. A710

PARRISH, James G., FACHE, Chief Executive Officer, Memorial Hospital, Seminole, TX, p. A645

PARRISH, Suann, Chief Financial Officer, Yoakum County Hospital, Denver City, TX, p. A608

PARRISH, Todd M.D., Chief of Staff, East Texas Medical Center Jacksonville, Jacksonville, TX, p. A625

PARROTT, Keith, FACHE, Interim President and Chief Executive Officer, Brookwood Baptist Medical Center, Birmingham, AL, p. A14

PARRY, Kayla, Manager Human Resources, Ivinson Memorial Hospital, Laramie, WY, p. A718

PARRY, Mary, Vice President Operations and Chief Operating Officer, Oneida Healthcare, Oneida, NY, p. A448

PARRY, Timothy R.N., Chief Operating Officer, Highland District Hospital, Hillsboro, OH, p. A492

PARSLEY, George N, Chief Operating Officer, Detar Healthcare System, Victoria, TX, p. A652

PARSON, Charlynne, Nurse Executive, Moccasin Bend Mental Health Institute, Chattanooga, TN, p. A576

PARSONS, Beth, R.N., Administrator, Christus Dubuis Hospital Of Alexandria, Alexandria, LA, p. A269

PARSONS, Brad, FACHE, Administrator and Chief Executive Officer, Nea Baptist Memorial Hospital, Jonesboro, AR, p. A45

PARSONS, Brent, Chief Executive Officer, Bluffton Regional Medical Center, Bluffton, IN, p. A204

PARSONS, Debra, Chief Nursing Officer, Pikeville Medical Center, Pikeville, KY, p. A266

PARSONS, John R.N., Chief Nursing Officer, Trustpoint Rehabilitation Hospital Of Lubbock, Lubbock, TX, p. A630

PARSONS, Terri L., Administrator, Advanced Care Hospital Of White County, Searcy, AR, p. A49

PARTEE, Paris I, Associate Administrator and Director Human Resources, John H. Stroger Jr. Hospital Of Cook County, Chicago, IL, p. A181

PARTENZA, John, Vice President and Treasurer, Northern Westchester Hospital, Mount Kisco, NY, p. A440

PARTHEMORE, Warrenette, Director Human Resources, Promedica Memorial Hospital, Fremont, OH, p. A491

PARTIN, James R M.D., Chief Medical Director, Hill Country Memorial Hospital, Fredericksburg, TX, p. A615

PARTON, Gerald L., FACHE, Chief Executive Officer, East Jefferson General Hospital, Metairie, LA, p. A281

PARTRIDGE, Susan, Director Human Resources, Nantucket Cottage Hospital, Nantucket, MA, p. A309

PARUCH, Randy J, Director, Information Systems, Holland Hospital, Holland, MI, p. A322

PASCASCIO, Dellone, Chief Nursing Officer, Lac–Olive View– Ucla Medical Center, Los Angeles, CA, p. A69

PASCASIO, Robert A., FACHE, Administrator and Chief Executive Officer, Ochiltree General Hospital, Perryton, TX, p. A637

PASCO, Teri, Director Human Resources, East Liverpool City Hospital, East Liverpool, OH, p. A490

PASCOE, John M.D., Executive Medical Director, Timberlawn Mental Health System, Dallas, TX, p. A607

PASCUAL, Bolivar M.D., Medical Director, Essex County Hospital Center, Cedar Grove, NJ, p. A412

PASCUZZI, Robert, Chief Financial Officer, Mercy San Juan Medical Center, Carmichael, CA, p. A55

PASQUALE, Mark
Chief Information Officer, Integris Baptist Medical Center, Oklahoma City, OK, p. A512
Chief Information Officer, Integris Southwest Medical Center, Oklahoma City, OK, p. A512

PASQUIN, Karen MSN, R.N., Chief Nursing Officer, Southwest Health System, Cortez, CO, p. A100

PASS, Christian
Interim Chief Financial Officer, John Muir Medical Center, Concord, Concord, CA, p. A56
Senior Vice President & Chief Financial Officer, John Muir Medical Center, Walnut Creek, Walnut Creek, CA, p. A96
Senior Vice President and Chief Financial Officer, John Muir Behavioral Health Center, Concord, CA, p. A56

PASSANNANTE, Anthony Jr, M.D., Acting President, Hackensack Meridian Health Palisades Medical Center, North Bergen, NJ, p. A418

PASSARELLI, Theresa, Human Resources Generalist, Warm Springs Medical Center, Warm Springs, GA, p. A167

PASSMANN, Frederic K M.D., Chief of Staff, Stonewall Memorial Hospital, Aspermont, TX, p. A594

PASSMORE, Gary, Chief Information Officer, Endless Mountain Health Systems, Montrose, PA, p. A541

PASTERNAK, L. Reuven., M.D., M.P.H., Vice President for Health System and Chief Executive Officer, Stony Brook University Hospital, Stony Brook, NY, p. A453

PASTIAN, Andre R.N., MSN, Chief Nursing Officer, Boulder City Hospital, Boulder City, NV, p. A401

PASTORE, Raymond M.D., Chief Medical Officer, St. John's Episcopal Hospital–South Shore, New Rochelle, NY, p. A446

PASTRANA, Guillermo, Executive Director, Hospital Pavia– Hato Rey, San Juan, PR, p. A726

PASZTOR, Barbara J., R.N.
Vice President Nursing and Patient Care Services, Bluffton Hospital, Bluffton, OH, p. A481
Vice President Patient Care Services and Chief Nursing Officer, Blanchard Valley Hospital, Findlay, OH, p. A491

PATCHELL, Lee, Lead Human Resources Business Partner, Presbyterian Hospital, Albuquerque, NM, p. A425

PATCHIN, J Craig., Administrator, Shriners Hospitals For Children–Portland, Portland, OR, p. A525

PATE, David C., M.D., JD, President and Chief Executive Officer, St. Luke'S Health System, Boise, ID, p. B121

PATE, John M.D., Chief Medical Officer, Tri–County Hospital, Wadena, MN, p. A350

PATE, Lois R.N., Chief Nursing Officer, Island Hospital, Anacortes, WA, p. A678

PATEL, Amita M.D., Medical Director, Haven Behavioral Senior Care Of Dayton, Dayton, OH, p. A489

PATEL, Ashok M.D., Chief of Staff, Sanford Medical Center Thief River Falls, Thief River Falls, MN, p. A349

PATEL, Ben
Chief Information Officer, Holy Cross Hospital, Chicago, IL, p. A181
Chief Information Officer, Mount Sinai Hospital, Chicago, IL, p. A182

PATEL, Bimal
President, Hartford HealthCare East Region, The William W. Backus Hospital, Norwich, CT, p. A112
President, Hartford Healthcare East Region, Windham Hospital, Willimantic, CT, p. A114

PATEL, Binesh M.D., Chief Medical Officer, Mclaren Flint, Flint, MI, p. A319

PATEL, Deepak M.D., Medical Director, Cumberland Hall Hospital, Hopkinsville, KY, p. A259

PATEL, Dilip M.D., Chief of Staff, Greater El Monte Community Hospital, South El Monte, CA, p. A92

PATEL, Fatma M.D., Vice President Medical Affairs, Niagara Falls Memorial Medical Center, Niagara Falls, NY, p. A447

PATEL, Govind M.D., Medical Director, Healthsouth Mountainview Regional Rehabilitation Hospital, Morgantown, WV, p. A694

PATEL, Malini M.D., Medical Director, Elgin Mental Health Center, Elgin, IL, p. A186

PATEL, Natu M M.D., Chief of Staff, Phoebe Worth Medical Center, Sylvester, GA, p. A165

PATEL, Nirav M.D.
Chief of Staff, Los Alamitos Medical Center, Los Alamitos, CA, p. A67
Interim Chief Medical Officer, SSM Health Saint Louis University Hospital, Saint Louis, MO, p. A378

PATEL, Paryus M.D., Chief Medical Officer, Centinela Hospital Medical Center, Inglewood, CA, p. A63

PATEL, Prakash Chandra M.D., Chief of Staff, Kindred Hospital–La Mirada, La Mirada, CA, p. A64

PATEL, Pravin M.D., Acting President and Chief Executive Officer, Southern Virginia Mental Health Institute, Danville, VA, p. A666

PATEL, Pravinchandra M.D., Chief Medical Officer, Barnes– Kasson County Hospital, Susquehanna, PA, p. A551

PATEL, Raj M.D., Medical Director, Lifecare Hospitals Of Chester County, West Chester, PA, p. A553

PATEL, Rajesh M.D., Chief of Staff, Lock Haven Hospital, Lock Haven, PA, p. A539

PATEL, Rakesh D.O., Medical Director, Healthsouth Rehabilitation Hospital Of Altoona, Altoona, PA, p. A528

PATEL, Shalin M.D., Chief Medical Officer, Memorial Hermann Rehabilitation Hospital – Katy, Katy, TX, p. A626

PATEL, Sharad M.D., Medical Director, Florida Hospital At Connerton Long Term Acute Care, Land O'Lakes, FL, p. A130

PATEL, Shatish M.D., Chief Medical Officer, Atrium Medical Center, Stafford, TX, p. A646

PATEL, Suresh M.D., Chief Medical Officer, Cavalier County Memorial Hospital And Clinics, Langdon, ND, p. A477

PATEL, Tanay M. M.D., Chief of Staff, Golden Plains Community Hospital, Borger, TX, p. A598

PATEL, Viraj M.D., Chief Medical Officer, Unity Medical & Surgical Hospital, Mishawaka, IN, p. A216

PATER, Tom
Chief Financial Officer, Rml Specialty Hospital, Hinsdale, IL, p. A190
Vice President Finance and Chief Financial Officer, Rml Specialty Hospital, Chicago, IL, p. A183

PATEY, Jeffrey A M.D., Chief of Staff, Belmont Community Hospital, Bellaire, OH, p. A481

PATHAK, Ajay, President, OSF Saint Anthony's Health Center, Alton, IL, p. A177

PATHAK, Rajiv, Chief of Staff, Marshall Medical Center, Placerville, CA, p. A80

PATIL, Steve, Chief Financial Officer, W. G. (Bill) Heffner Veterans Affairs Medical Center, Salisbury, NC, p. A470

PATILLO, Laura, Manager Human Resources, Fresno Surgical Hospital, Fresno, CA, p. A60

PATINO, Beth, Chief Information Officer, Dekalb Medical At North Decatur, Decatur, GA, p. A156

PATMAS, Michael M.D., Chief Medical Officer, Gritman Medical Center, Moscow, ID, p. A174

PATONAI, Steven D., Interim Chief Executive Officer, Park Plaza Hospital, Houston, TX, p. A622

PATRICIO, Mars Jr, Chief Financial Officer, Seven Hills Hospital, Henderson, NV, p. A402

PATRICK, Ann M, Vice President Human Resources, Northwest Community Hospital, Arlington Heights, IL, p. A177

PATRICK, Barbara, Director Human Resources, Chestatee Regional Hospital, Dahlonega, GA, p. A156

PATRICK, Calvin II, Director Information Services, Florida Hospital New Smyrna, New Smyrna Beach, FL, p. A135

PATRICK, Chad, President and Chief Executive Officer, Orange Park Medical Center, Orange Park, FL, p. A136

PATRICK, Christian C M.D., Chief Medical Officer, Baptist Memorial Hospital – Memphis, Memphis, TN, p. A584

PATRICK, Deborah A.
Senior Vice President Human Resources, Lehigh Valley Hospital–Muhlenberg, Bethlehem, PA, p. A529
Senior Vice President Human Resources, Lehigh Valley Hospital, Allentown, PA, p. A528

PATRICK, Devin, Manager Human Resources, Utah State Hospital, Provo, UT, p. A659

PATRICK, Lisa, Chief Operating Officer, Caldwell Memorial Hospital, Columbia, LA, p. A273

PATRICK, Ronald, Chief Financial Officer, Northwest Medical Center, Tucson, AZ, p. A38

PATRICK, Sandra, Chief Financial Officer, Three Rivers Hospital, Waverly, TN, p. A590

PATRICK, Sean, Director Information Systems, Gifford Medical Center, Randolph, VT, p. A663

PATRIZIO, Gino, Chief Executive Officer, Rideout Memorial Hospital, Marysville, CA, p. A73

PATTEN, William D. Jr, Chief Executive Officer, Holy Cross Hospital, Taos, NM, p. A429

PATTERSON, Anthony, FACHE
Chief Operating Officer, University Of Alabama Hospital, Birmingham, AL, p. A15
Senior Vice President Inpatient Services, University Of Alabama Hospital, Birmingham, AL, p. A15

PATTERSON, Barbara, Chief Financial Officer, Provident Hospital Of Cook County, Chicago, IL, p. A183

PATTERSON, Camie, Chief Operating Officer, Manatee Memorial Hospital, Bradenton, FL, p. A120

PATTERSON, Christina, Chief Financial Officer, Saint Thomas River Park Hospital, Mc Minnville, TN, p. A583

PATTERSON, Dave, Chief Information Officer, Memorial Hospital Of Converse County, Douglas, WY, p. A718

PATTERSON, David, Director Human Resources, Parkside Psychiatric Hospital And Clinic, Tulsa, OK, p. A517

PATTERSON, Debbie, Director Health Information Management, Wesley Rehabilitation Hospital, Wichita, KS, p. A254

PATTERSON, Diane, Vice President, Chief Nursing Officer, Virginia Mason Memorial, Yakima, WA, p. A689

PATTERSON, Elmore, Chief Executive Officer, Greene County Health System, Eutaw, AL, p. A17

PATTERSON, Jan, Chief Nursing Officer, Avera St. Luke's Hospital, Aberdeen, SD, p. A568

PATTERSON, Jeff, Chief Executive Officer, Nacogdoches Medical Center, Nacogdoches, TX, p. A634

PATTERSON, Karen, Deputy Director Operations, Elmira Psychiatric Center, Elmira, NY, p. A435

PATTERSON, Larry R., Deputy Commander Administration, Bayne–Jones Army Community Hospital, Fort Polk, LA, p. A274

PATTERSON, Lisa, Director Human Resources, Pointe Coupee General Hospital, New Roads, LA, p. A283

PATTERSON, Marcia, MSN, R.N.
Chief Nursing Officer, Nor–Lea Hospital District, Lovington, NM, p. A427

Chief Financial Officer, Valley Regional Medical Center, Brownsville, TX, p. A599

PATTERSON, Maria, Manager Health Information Management, Canyon Ridge Hospital, Chino, CA, p. A55

PATTERSON, Mark M.D., Chief Medical Officer, Laughlin Memorial Hospital, Greeneville, TN, p. A579

PATTERSON, Melanie R.N., Vice President Patient Care Services and Chief Nursing Officer, Children's Hospital Of Orange County, Orange, CA, p. A78

PATTERSON, Michael C., Chief Executive Officer, Flint River Community Hospital, Montezuma, GA, p. A162

PATTERSON, Michael N., Chief Executive Officer, Havasu Regional Medical Center, Lake Havasu City, AZ, p. A31

PATTERSON, Mike, Director of Operations, Northside Hospital–Cherokee, Canton, GA, p. A153

PATTERSON, Renee A., Vice President Employment and Training Services, Rogers Memorial Hospital, Oconomowoc, WI, p. A709

PATTERSON, Robert, Vice President Human Resources and Rehabilitation Services, The University Of Vermont Health Network Central Vermont Medical Center, Berlin, VT, p. A662

PATTERSON, Russ
Director Information Technology, St. Rose Dominican Hospitals – Siena Campus, Henderson, NV, p. A402
Site Manager Information Technology, St. Rose Dominican Hospitals – San Martin Campus, Las Vegas, NV, p. A404

PATTERSON, Sam, Chief Financial Officer, Bay Area Hospital, Coos Bay, OR, p. A521

PATTERSON, Steve, Chief Executive Officer, Kindred Hospital–Chattanooga, Chattanooga, TN, p. A576

PATTERSON, Stuart M.D., Chief of Staff, Bartow Regional Medical Center, Bartow, FL, p. A119

PATTERSON, Tony, Chief Financial Officer, James B. Haggin Memorial Hospital, Harrodsburg, KY, p. A259

PATTI, Rosa, Chief Financial Officer, Cameron Regional Medical Center, Cameron, MO, p. A365

PATTON, Christina, Chief Financial Officer, Colorado Plains Medical Center, Fort Morgan, CO, p. A102

PATTON, Daniel, Director Information Systems, Henrico Doctors' Hospital, Richmond, VA, p. A674

PATTON, David J., President, Upmc St. Margaret, Pittsburgh, PA, p. A548

PATTON, Joy, Chief Information Services, Pampa Regional Medical Center, Pampa, TX, p. A636

PATTON, Kevin, Chief Executive Officer, Old Vineyard Behavioral Health Services, Winston, NC, p. A473

PATTON, Meghan
Vice President Human Resources, Abington Hospital, Abington, PA, p. A528
Vice President Human Resources, Abington–Lansdale Hospital Jefferson Health, Lansdale, PA, p. A538

PATTON, Melissa MSN, Director of Nursing, Columbus Dublin Springs, Dublin, OH, p. A490

PATTON, Sally K R.N., MS, Chief Nursing Officer, New London Hospital, New London, NH, p. A410

PATZEK, Dorothy, Vice President Nursing, Blue Mountain Hospital, Lehighton, PA, p. A539

PAUGH, David, Senior Vice President and Chief Financial Officer, Nash Health Care Systems, Rocky Mount, NC, p. A469

PAUL, Adam, Chief Financial Officer, Prairie Lakes Healthcare System, Watertown, SD, p. A574

PAUL, Darrick, Chief People Officer, Musc Medical Center Of Medical University Of South Carolina, Charleston, SC, p. A559

PAUL, Donn, Chief Human Resources, Lackey Memorial Hospital, Forest, MS, p. A354

PAUL, Lise, Vice President Reimbursement and Network Planning, Hebrew Rehabilitation Center, Roslindale, MA, p. A310

PAUL, Mary
Chief Information Officer, Columbia St. Mary's Hospital Milwaukee, Milwaukee, WI, p. A707
Chief Information Officer, Columbia St. Mary's Ozaukee Hospital, Mequon, WI, p. A707
Vice President and Chief Information Officer, Sacred Heart Rehabilitation Institute, Milwaukee, WI, p. A708

PAUL, West M.D., Ph.D.
Senior Vice President and Chief Quality and Medical Staff Officer, Wakemed Raleigh Campus, Raleigh, NC, p. A469
Senior Vice President, Chief Quality and Medical Staff Officer, Wakemed Cary Hospital, Cary, NC, p. A458

PAULEY, Clarence, Senior Vice President and Chief Human Resources Officer, University Of Cincinnati Medical Center, Cincinnati, OH, p. A485

PAULOSKY, David, Chief Financial Officer, Phoenixville Hospital, Phoenixville, PA, p. A546

PAULS, Scott R, Director Information Technology– HealthNet Connect, Guttenberg Municipal Hospital, Guttenberg, IA, p. A228

PAULSEN, Susan, Director Human Resources, Northridge Hospital Medical Center, Los Angeles, CA, p. A70

PAULSON, Adam, Director Finance, Centracare Health–Melrose, Melrose, MN, p. A343

PAULSON, Erik, Director of Finance, J. D. Mccarty Center For Children With Developmental Disabilities, Norman, OK, p. A511

PAULSON, Gordon, Manager Human Resources, Glacial Ridge Health System, Glenwood, MN, p. A340

PAULSON, Sybil K., Administrator, North Oaks Rehabilitation Hospital, Hammond, LA, p. A275

PAULUS, Terresa Ann
Chief Nursing Officer, Banner Goldfield Medical Center, Apache Junction, AZ, p. A28
Chief Nursing Officer, Banner Ironwood Medical Center, San Tan Valley, AZ, p. A35

PAULUS, Ronald A., M.D., President and Chief Executive Officer, Mission Health System, Asheville, NC, p. B85

PAUTLER, J. Stephen FACHE, Chief Operating Officer, Peterson Regional Medical Center, Kerrville, TX, p. A626

PAVALONIS, Diane, Chief Nurse Executive, Western State Hospital, Staunton, VA, p. A676

PAVIA, Antoine M.D., Medical Director, Hospital Pavia Arecibo, Arecibo, PR, p. A722

PAVIK, Sarah, Director Human Resources and Guest Services, Inova Loudoun Hospital, Leesburg, VA, p. A669

PAVILANIS, Charlotte J R.N., Vice President of Clinical Services and Chief Nursing Officer, Sturgis Hospital, Sturgis, MI, p. A331

PAVLATOS, Thales, Medical Director, Ohio Valley Surgical Hospital, Springfield, OH, p. A499

PAWAR, Ganesh M.D., Chief of Staff, Rusk County Memorial Hospital, Ladysmith, WI, p. A704

PAWLAK, Paul, President and Chief Executive Officer, Silver Cross Hospital, New Lenox, IL, p. A195

PAWLEK, Kenny, Chief Operating Officer, Usc Verdugo Hills Hospital, Glendale, CA, p. A62

PAWLOWICZ, James E, Director Human Resources, Shriners Hospitals For Children–Chicago, Chicago, IL, p. A184

PAWLOWSKI, Phil, Chief Financial Officer, Glenbeigh Hospital And Outpatient Centers, Rock Creek, OH, p. A498

PAWOLA, Ken
Chief Operating Officer, Rml Specialty Hospital, Chicago, IL, p. A183
Chief Operating Officer, Rml Specialty Hospital, Hinsdale, IL, p. A190

PAXSON, Gary
Associate Administrator Information Systems, Stone County Medical Center, Mountain View, AR, p. A47
Chief Information Officer, White River Medical Center, Batesville, AR, p. A40

PAXTON, Douglas V., Director, Veterans Affairs Roseburg Healthcare System, Roseburg, OR, p. A526

PAYNE, Angel, Clinical Director, Director of Nursing, Sonora Behavioral Health Hospital, Tucson, AZ, p. A38

PAYNE, James, Director Information Systems, Southern Tennessee Regional Health System–Winchester, Winchester, TN, p. A590

PAYNE, Jason, Executive Vice President and Chief Operating Officer, Rush Foundation Hospital, Meridian, MS, p. A359

PAYNE, Judy H., Chief Executive Officer, Turning Point Hospital, Moultrie, GA, p. A162

PAYNE, Keela, Director Human Resources, Hamilton General Hospital, Hamilton, TX, p. A618

PAYNE, Kenneth G, Chief Financial Officer, Holzer Medical Center, Gallipolis, OH, p. A491

PAYNE, Michael E., Administrator, Girard Medical Center, Girard, KS, p. A241

PAYNE, Michael M.D., Chief of Staff, Dallas County Medical Center, Fordyce, AR, p. A43

PAYNE, Rick, Director Information Systems, Santa Rosa Medical Center, Milton, FL, p. A134

PAYNE, Steven, Chief Financial Officer, Jordan Valley Medical Center West Valley Campus, West Valley City, UT, p. A661

PAYTON, Becky J, Vice President Human Resources, Mercy Hospital Oklahoma City, Oklahoma City, OK, p. A512

PAZDERNIK, Mary, Chief Financial Officer, Mahnomen Health Center, Mahnomen, MN, p. A342

PEA, Richard, Director Human Resources, Memorial Hospital And Health Care Center, Jasper, IN, p. A212

PEABODY, Kim, Chief Operating Officer, The Brook Hospital – Kmi, Louisville, KY, p. A263

PEABODY, Paul, Vice President Information Technology and Chief Information Officer, Bronson Lakeview Hospital, Paw Paw, MI, p. A327

PEACE, Lother E. III, President and Chief Executive Officer, Russell Medical Center, Alexander City, AL, p. A13

PEACH, Larry, Chief Financial Officer, Jefferson County Health Center, Fairfield, IA, p. A227

PEACH, Susan M., R.N., Chief Executive Officer, Sumner Regional Medical Center, Gallatin, TN, p. A579

PEACOCK, Steve, Assistant Vice President, Plaza Specialty Hospital, Houston, TX, p. A622

PEACOCK, Tammy, Ph.D., Facility Director, Northern Virginia Mental Health Institute, Falls Church, VA, p. A667

PEAL, Chip, Chief Executive Officer, Frankfort Regional Medical Center, Frankfort, KY, p. A258

PEARCE, Charles T
Chief Financial and Information Officer, Kalispell Regional Healthcare, Kalispell, MT, p. A386
Chief Financial and Information Officer, The Healthcenter, Kalispell, MT, p. A386

PEARCE, Darren, Administrator and Chief Executive Officer, Medical Center Of Peach County, Navicent Health, Bryon, GA, p. A153

PEARCE, Darren
Executive Director, Rehabilitation Hospital, Navicent Health, Macon, GA, p. A161
Interim Chief Executive Officer, Monroe County Hospital, Forsyth, GA, p. A158

PEARCE, Margaret R.N., Ph.D., Chief Nursing Officer, University Of Utah Health, Salt Lake City, UT, p. A660

PEARCH, William, Chief Information Officer, Yukon–Kuskokwim Delta Regional Hospital, Bethel, AK, p. A25

PEARCY, Joetta J, Director, Human Resources, Glendive Medical Center, Glendive, MT, p. A384

PEARCY, Steve, Director Human Resources, Community Hospital North, Indianapolis, IN, p. A210

PEARLMAN, Helen, Nurse Executive, Minneapolis Veterans Affairs Health Care System, Minneapolis, MN, p. A344

PEARSON, Bruce, Senior Vice President and Chief Operating Officer, Honorhealth Scottsdale Thompson Peak Medical Center, Scottsdale, AZ, p. A36

PEARSON, Christine, Vice President Finance and Chief Financial Officer, Anmed Health Medical Center, Anderson, SC, p. A558

PEARSON, Dawn, Director Human Resources, Healthsouth Rehabilitation Hospital Of Vineland, Vineland, NJ, p. A422

PEARSON, Gregory, Chief Executive Officer, Minden Medical Center, Minden, LA, p. A281

PEARSON, Jeff
Chief Information Officer, Christus Mother Frances Hospital – Jacksonville, Jacksonville, TX, p. A625
Vice President and Chief Information Officer, Christus Mother Frances Hospital – Tyler, Tyler, TX, p. A650

PEARSON, Madelyn R.N., Senior Vice President Patient Care Services and Chief Nursing Officer, Brigham And Women's Hospital, Boston, MA, p. A303

PEARSON, Marshall, Director Management Information Systems, St. David's North Austin Medical Center, Austin, TX, p. A596

PEARSON, Nancy MSN, R.N., Director, Nursing, Novant Health Thomasville Medical Center, Thomasville, NC, p. A471

PEARSON, Susan M.D., Chief Medical Officer, Mayo Clinic Health System In Mankato, Mankato, MN, p. A342

PEART, Carol, Chief Financial Officer, Chicago Lakeshore Hospital, Chicago, IL, p. A180

PEBURN, Eric, Chief Financial Officer, Halifax Health Medical Center Of Daytona Beach, Daytona Beach, FL, p. A123

PECHOUS, Bryan M.D., Vice President Medical Affairs, Unitypoint Health – Finley Hospital, Dubuque, IA, p. A227

PECK, Amy R.N., Chief Nursing Officer, Memorial Regional Health, Craig, CO, p. A100

PECK, Bob, Chief Financial Officer, Wesley Rehabilitation Hospital, Wichita, KS, p. A254

PECK, Charles A., M.D., Interim President and Chief Executive Officer, Piedmont Athens Regional Medical Center, Athens, GA, p. A149

PECK, Darin M.D., Chief of Staff, Charles A. Dean Memorial Hospital, Greenville, ME, p. A291

PECK, Kay E., Ph.D., Chief Executive Officer, Healthsouth Rehabilitation Hospital Of Modesto, Modesto, CA, p. A74

PECK, Michael D, Assistant Administrator, Caribou Memorial Hospital And Living Center, Soda Springs, ID, p. A176

PECK, Robert C M.D., Chief Medical Officer, Mayo Clinic Health System In Eau Claire, Eau Claire, WI, p. A701

PEDANO, Andrea D D.O., Chief Medical Officer, Suburban Community Hospital, Norristown, PA, p. A542

PEDERSEN, Darren, Coordinator Information Technology, Weisman Children's Rehabilitation Hospital, Marlton, NJ, p. A416

PEDERSEN, Paul E M.D., Vice President and Chief Medical Officer, OSF St. Joseph Medical Center, Bloomington, IL, p. A178

PEDERSON, Bryan, Human Resources Manager, Tri–County Hospital, Wadena, MN, p. A350

PEDERSON, Karn, Manager Health Information Management, Mckenzie County Healthcare System, Watford City, ND, p. A478

PEDERSON, Randall K., Chief Executive Officer, Tioga Medical Center, Tioga, ND, p. A478

PEDLEY, Joe CPA, Vice President and Chief Financial Officer, Lawrence Memorial Hospital, Lawrence, KS, p. A245

PEDLOW, Bernadette R, Senior Vice President Business and Chief Operating Officer, Albany Medical Center, Albany, NY, p. A430

PEDRETTI, Jennalee, Vice President Operations, Regional Health Services Of Howard County, Cresco, IA, p. A225

PEDROZA, Fernando, Vice President Information Technology, Poudre Valley Hospital, Fort Collins, CO, p. A102

PEEBLES, Wanda V., Chief Nursing Officer, Jps Health Network, Fort Worth, TX, p. A613

PEEK, Chris, Chief Executive Officer, Caromont Regional Medical Center, Gastonia, NC, p. A463

PEELER, Cindy K R.N., Chief Nursing Officer, Adair County Health System, Greenfield, IA, p. A228

PEELGREN, Jim, Chief Information Officer, Tulare Regional Medical Center, Tulare, CA, p. A94

PEEPLES, John, Senior Vice President Human Resources, Laurel Regional Hospital, Laurel, MD, p. A299

PEEPLES, Jonnitra, Chief Human Resource Officer, Vibra Hospital Of Richmond, Richmond, VA, p. A674

PEER, Julianne, President, Penn Highlands Brookville, Brookville, PA, p. A530

PEERY, Lori, Chief Human Resource Management Services, Va Palo Alto Health Care System, Palo Alto, CA, p. A79

PEET, Fred, Chief Information Officer, Yuma Regional Medical Center, Yuma, AZ, p. A39

PEGE, Diane M.D., Vice President Medical Affairs, Sutter Lakeside Hospital, Lakeport, CA, p. A65

PEHRSON, Jared M.D., Chief of Staff, Saunders Medical Center, Wahoo, NE, p. A400

PEIFFER, Paul, Chief Financial Officer and Vice President, Jackson Hospital And Clinic, Montgomery, AL, p. A21

PEIL, Michael M.D., Chief Medical Director, Kindred Hospital Peoria, Peoria, IL, p. A197

PEIPERT, John R.N., Chief Nursing Officer, Hshs St. Francis Hospital, Litchfield, IL, p. A192

PEKOFSKE, Robert, Vice President Finance, Advocate Christ Medical Center, Oak Lawn, IL, p. A196

PELACCIA, Joseph, President and Chief Executive Officer, Milford Hospital, Milford, CT, p. A111

PELEUSES, John, Interim Chief Executive Officer, Sonoma West Medical Center, Sebastopol, CA, p. A91

PELFREY, Joy S R.N., MSN, Vice President and Chief Nursing Officer, Cabell Huntington Hospital, Huntington, WV, p. A692

PELKOWSKI, Margaret R.N., Vice President Patient Care Services, Calvary Hospital, New Rochelle, NY, p. A441

PELLE, Fred L FACHE, Chief Operating Officer, Wellmont Holston Valley Medical Center, Kingsport, TN, p. A581

PELLEGRIN, Kimberley, Director, Human Resources, Red River Hospital, Llc, Wichita Falls, TX, p. A654

PELLEGRINO, JoAnn, MS, RN, Vice President and Chief Nursing Officer, Niagara Falls Memorial Medical Center, Niagara Falls, NY, p. A447

PELLEGRINO, Ron, Chief Operating Officer, West Virginia University Hospitals, Morgantown, WV, p. A694

PELLERIN, Yvonne, Chief Nursing Officer, St. Elizabeth Hospital, Gonzales, LA, p. A275

PELLICONE, John T M.D., Chief Medical Officer, NYC Health + Hospitals / Metropolitan, New Rochelle, NY, p. A445

PELOT, Jeff, Interim Chief Information Officer, Denver Health, Denver, CO, p. A100

PELTIER, Glenn, Chief Financial Officer, Christus Mother Frances Hospital – Winnsboro, Winnsboro, TX, p. A655

PELTIER, Robert, M.D.
Chief Medical Officer, North Oaks Medical Center, Hammond, LA, p. A275
Senior Vice President, Chief Medical Officer, North Oaks Health System, North Oaks Rehabilitation Hospital, Hammond, LA, p. A275

PELTON, Ed, Chief of Staff, Chadron Community Hospital And Health Services, Chadron, NE, p. A392

PELUSO, Joseph J., Chief Executive Officer, Tyrone Hospital, Tyrone, PA, p. A552

PEMBERTON, Edith, Chief Financial Officer, East Morgan County Hospital, Brush, CO, p. A99

PEMBERTON, Stacy, Chief Nursing Officer, Grand River Hospital District, Rifle, CO, p. A107

PEMELTON, Debbie, Director Human Resources, Weslaco Regional Rehabilitation Hospital, Weslaco, TX, p. A654

PENA, Carolina, Assistant Director Administrator, Larkin Community Hospital, South Miami, FL, p. A143

PENA, Jessica, Manager Finance, Christus Spohn Hospital Kleberg, Kingsville, TX, p. A627

PENA, Julie, Director Finance, Community Howard Specialty Hospital, Kokomo, IN, p. A213

PENA, Terry, Chief Operating Officer and Chief Nursing Officer, San Bernardino Mountains Community Hospital District, Lake Arrowhead, CA, p. A65

PENCO, Kris, Director Information Systems, Coffeyville Regional Medical Center, Coffeyville, KS, p. A239

PENDER, Carol, Assistant Vice President Human Resources, Walden Behavioral Care, Waltham, MA, p. A312

PENDER, Debra MS, R.N., Vice President Nursing, Mercy Hospital Ardmore, Ardmore, OK, p. A504

PENDERGRAFT, Tina, Chief Nursing Officer, Satanta District Hospital And Long Term Care, Satanta, KS, p. A251

PENDLETON, Gretchen, Director Human Resources, Suburban Community Hospital, Norristown, PA, p. A542

PENDLETON, Timothy M.D., President Medical Staff, Penn Highlands Brookville, Brookville, PA, p. A530

PENICK, Lisa R.N., Chief Nursing Officer, Carroll County Memorial Hospital, Carrollton, KY, p. A256

PENLAND, Jennifer
Controller, Kindred Hospital Tarrant County–Arlington, Arlington, TX, p. A593
Controller, Kindred Hospital–White Rock, Dallas, TX, p. A605

PENN, Shelia, Facility Director, Bryce Hospital, Tuscaloosa, AL, p. A23

PENN, Tripp, Chief Executive Officer, Upson Regional Medical Center, Thomaston, GA, p. A166

PENNACCHIO, Suzanne, Chief Nursing Officer, NYC Health + Hospitals / Jacobi, New Rochelle, NY, p. A445

PENNER, Jerome, Chief Executive Officer, Murray–Calloway County Hospital, Murray, KY, p. A265

PENNEY, Cindy L R.N., Vice President Nursing, Mercy Iowa City, Iowa City, IA, p. A229

PENNEY, Jan R.N., Vice President and Chief Nursing Officer, Midmichigan Medical Center–Midland, Midland, MI, p. A326

PENNINGTON, Brian Keith., President and Chief Executive Officer, Medical West, Bessemer, AL, p. A14

PENNINGTON, Kim, Chief Executive Officer, Select Specialty Hospital–Lexington, Lexington, KY, p. A261

PENNINO, Jackie, Director Human Resources, Old Vineyard Behavioral Health Services, Winston, NC, p. A473

PENOVICH, Carrie L, Chief Clinical Services Officer, Aurora Medical Center – Manitowoc County, Two Rivers, WI, p. A714

PENQUE, Sue R.N., Ph.D., Senior Vice President and Chief Nursing Officer, South Nassau Communities Hospital, Oceanside, NY, p. A448

PENROD, Kirt, Chief Financial Officer, Shadow Mountain Behavioral Health System, Tulsa, OK, p. A518

PENTON, Lance, Director, Information Services, Memorial Hospital Jacksonville, Jacksonville, FL, p. A128

PENUEL, Jennifer, Director Human Resources, Madison Medical Center, Fredericktown, MO, p. A368

PEOPLES, Diane, Director Human Resources, Two Rivers Behavioral Health System, Kansas City, MO, p. A371

PEOPLES, Kathleen K R.N., MS, Vice President of Nursing, St. Vincent Kokomo, Kokomo, IN, p. A213

PEOPLES, Kyle, Director Technology Management Services, Springfield Hospital, Springfield, VT, p. A663

PEOPLES, Lynn, Interim Chief Nursing Officer, Person Memorial Hospital, Roxboro, NC, p. A470

PEOPLES, Phyllis L., President and Chief Executive Officer, Terrebonne General Medical Center, Houma, LA, p. A276

PEPE, Joseph, M.D., President and Chief Executive Officer, Catholic Medical Center, Manchester, NH, p. A409

PEPPEL, David
Executive Director, Elmira Psychiatric Center, Elmira, NY, p. A435
Executive Director, Greater Binghamton Health Center, Binghamton, NY, p. A431

PEPPER, L. Douglas M.D., President, Medical Staff, Monongahela Valley Hospital, Monongahela, PA, p. A541

PEPPLER, Lisa, Financial Manager, Parkview Whitley Hospital, Columbia City, IN, p. A205

PERAL, Sherry, Manager Information Systems, Oak Valley Hospital District, Oakdale, CA, p. A77

PERALTA, Pennie R.N., VP, Nursing & Chief Nursing Officer, Bon Secours St. Francis Hospital, Charleston, SC, p. A558

PERCELLO, Thomas, Chief Financial Officer, Community Medical Center, Toms River, NJ, p. A421

PEREACE, Vicki, Manager Human Resources, William Bee Ririe Hospital, Ely, NV, p. A401

PERECKO, Gary L., President, Riddle Hospital, Media, PA, p. A541

PEREIRA, Raul Ramos M.D., Medical Director, Ryder Memorial Hospital, Humacao, PR, p. A724

PEREL, Michael
Regional Chief Financial Officer, Kauai Veterans Memorial Hospital, Waimea, HI, p. A170

Regional Chief Financial Officer, Samuel Mahelona Memorial Hospital, Kapaa, HI, p. A170

PEREZ, Brenda R.N., MSN, Chief Clinical Officer, Kindred Hospital–White Rock, Dallas, TX, p. A605

PEREZ, Carmen, Director Human Resources, Doctors' Center Hospital San Juan, San Juan, PR, p. A725

PEREZ, David, Vice President and Chief Information Officer, Eisenhower Medical Center, Rancho Mirage, CA, p. A81

PEREZ, Edwin, M.D., Chief of Medical Staff, Marshall County Hospital, Benton, KY, p. A255

PEREZ, Francisco, Manager Management Information Systems, Hospital De La Universidad De Puerto Rico/Dr. Federico Trilla, Carolina, PR, p. A722

PEREZ, George, Chief Executive Officer, Campbellton Graceville Hospital, Graceville, FL, p. A126

PEREZ, Joe, Associate Director, South Texas Veterans Health Care System, San Antonio, TX, p. A644

PEREZ, Julie, Chief Financial Officer, St. David's Medical Center, Austin, TX, p. A596

PEREZ, Lisa R.N., Director Nursing, Meadowbrook Rehabilitation Hospital, Gardner, KS, p. A241

PEREZ, Mercedes, Vice President Nursing, Larkin Community Hospital, South Miami, FL, p. A143

PEREZ, Nina R.N., MSN, Chief Nursing Officer, North Okaloosa Medical Center, Crestview, FL, p. A122

PEREZ, Tony M.D., President Medical Staff, Jewish Hospital–Shelbyville, Shelbyville, KY, p. A267

PEREZ, III, Miguel, Chief Information Officer, Driscoll Children's Hospital, Corpus Christi, TX, p. A603

PERI, Gil, President and Chief Operations Officer, Connecticut Children's Medical Center, Hartford, CT, p. A110

PERJON, Cindy, Associate Director, Southwest Connecticut Mental Health System, Bridgeport, CT, p. A109

PERKERSON, Robyn, R.N., Administrator, Lifecare Hospitals Of North Carolina, Rocky Mount, NC, p. A469

PERKES, Neil C, Operations Officer, Logan Regional Hospital, Logan, UT, p. A657

PERKET, William, Vice President Human Resources, North Country Hospital And Health Center, Newport, VT, p. A662

PERKINS, Brett M.D., Chief Medical Staff, Madison County Memorial Hospital, Madison, FL, p. A131

PERKINS, Chris, Director Information Services, Clinch Valley Medical Center, Richlands, VA, p. A673

PERKINS, Dan
Corporate Director Human Resources, Cornerstone Hospital–West Monroe, West Monroe, LA, p. A287
Vice President of Human Resources, Solara Hospital Harlingen, Harlingen, TX, p. A618

PERKINS, Jeanne, Vice President Nursing and Interim Manager Human Resources, Bucyrus Community Hospital, Bucyrus, OH, p. A482

PERKINS, Kathryn, M.D.
Chief Medical Officer, Banner Boswell Medical Center, Sun City, AZ, p. A36
Chief Medical Officer, Banner Thunderbird Medical Center, Glendale, AZ, p. A30

PERKINS, Mike, Vice President and Administrator, Baptist Health Rehabilitation Institute, Little Rock, AR, p. A46

PERKINS, Richard, Chief Financial Officer, Baylor Scott & White Medical Center – Hillcrest, Waco, TX, p. A652

PERKINS, Tom, Chief Information Officer, Shannon Medical Center, San Angelo, TX, p. A641

PERKINS–PEPPERS, Andrea, Chief Information Officer, Forks Community Hospital, Forks, WA, p. A680

PERL, Lawrence M.D., Chief Medical Officer, Columbia Memorial Hospital, Hudson, NY, p. A437

PERLA, Salvatore, President, Nashoba Valley Medical Center, Ayer, MA, p. A302

PERLICH, Gwynn, Vice President of Patient Services and Chief Nursing Officer, St. Vincent Carmel Hospital, Carmel, IN, p. A205

PERLSTEIN, David A., M.D., President and Chief Executive Officer, St. Barnabas Hospital, New Rochelle, NY, p. A446

PERMANN, Darcy, Manager Business Office, Landmann–Jungman Memorial Hospital Avera, Scotland, SD, p. A572

PERMENTER, Ethan
Chief Executive Officer, Parkwood Behavioral Health System, Olive Branch, MS, p. A360
Corporate Vice President, Glen Oaks Hospital, Greenville, TX, p. A617

PERNICE, Paul, Vice President Finance, Beebe Healthcare, Lewes, DE, p. A115

PERRA, Scott H., FACHE
Chief Executive Officer, St. Elizabeth Medical Center, Utica, NY, p. A454
President and Chief Executive Officer, Faxton St. Luke's Healthcare, Utica, NY, p. A454

PERRAS, Joseph L., Chief Executive Officer, Mt. Ascutney Hospital And Health Center, Windsor, VT, p. A663

PERRATTO, Bonnie I MSN, R.N., FACHE, Senior Vice President, Chief Nurse Executive, Bayhealth Medical Center, Dover, DE, p. A115

PERRIGOT, Keri, Manager Human Resources, Cassia Regional Medical Center, Burley, ID, p. A172

PERRIN, Mary R., President and Chief Executive Officer, Children's Hospital, New Orleans, LA, p. A282

PERRINE, Vicki FACHE, Chief Operating Officer, Claxton–Hepburn Medical Center, Ogdensburg, NY, p. A448

PERRITT, Daniel, Chief Financial Officer, Sunrise Hospital And Medical Center, Las Vegas, NV, p. A404

PERRON, Kirk, Administrator and Chief Administrative Officer, Jennings Senior Care Hospital, Jennings, LA, p. A277

PERROTTE, Kenneth, Director Operations, Rockland Children's Hospital Psychiatric Center, Orangeburg, NY, p. A449

PERROTTI, Paul R CPA, Chief Financial Officer, West Georgia Health, Lagrange, GA, p. A160

PERRY, Carol R.N., Vice President and Chief Nursing Officer, Stormont Vail Health, Topeka, KS, p. A252

PERRY, Cheryl
Chief Financial Officer, Vibra Hospital Of Southeastern Massachusetts, New Bedford, MA, p. A309
Executive Director Human Resources, Paris Regional Medical Center, Paris, TX, p. A636

PERRY, Cynthia M.D., Chief of Staff, Stephens Memorial Hospital, Breckenridge, TX, p. A599

PERRY, Darrin Keith, Chief Information Officer and Senior Vice President, St. Jude Children's Research Hospital, Memphis, TN, p. A585

PERRY, Doug M.D., Chief of Staff, Baptist Medical Center Leake, Carthage, MS, p. A353

PERRY, Faye, Chief Nursing Officer, Tennova Healthcare–Clarksville, Clarksville, TN, p. A577

PERRY, Jan R.N., Vice President Patient Care Services, Community Medical Center, Missoula, MT, p. A386

PERRY, Jeff
Director Information Technology, St. John's Pleasant Valley Hospital, Camarillo, CA, p. A54
Director Information Technology, St. John's Regional Medical Center, Oxnard, CA, p. A78

PERRY, Karen, Chief Information Resource Management Services, James H. Quillen Veterans Affairs Medical Center, Mountain Home, TN, p. A586

PERRY, Kathleen, Senior Vice President and Chief Information Officer, Mercy Medical Center, Baltimore, MD, p. A295

PERRY, Matthew J., President and Chief Executive Officer, Genesis Healthcare System, Zanesville, OH, p. A503

PERRY, Matthew, Director Information Systems, Andalusia Health, Andalusia, AL, p. A13

PERRY, Michael, Chief Executive Officer, Michiana Behavioral Health Center, Plymouth, IN, p. A218

PERRY, Nini, Chief Nursing Officer, Georgetown Behavioral Health Institute, Georgetown, TX, p. A616

PERRY, Phil M.D., Regional Chief Medical Officer, Piedmont Medical Center, Rock Hill, SC, p. A565

PERRY, Rhonda S., Chief Financial Officer, Medical Center, Navicent Health, Macon, GA, p. A161

PERRY, Robert Keith, Senior Vice President, Chief Information Officer, Carilion Franklin Memorial Hospital, Rocky Mount, VA, p. A675

PERRY, Sally, Chief Executive Officer, Coastal Harbor Treatment Center, Savannah, GA, p. A164

PERRY, Shaun, Chief Information Officer, Mcgehee–Desha County Hospital, Mcgehee, AR, p. A47

PERRY, Solette, Regional Director Human Resources, Kauai Veterans Memorial Hospital, Waimea, HI, p. A170

PERRY, Stacey, Director, Nursing, Hamilton County Hospital, Syracuse, KS, p. A252

PERRY, Steve, Chief Executive Officer, Aspen Mountain Medical Center, Rock Springs, WY, p. A719

PERRY, Teresa J, Chief Financial Officer, Up Health System–Bell, Ishpeming, MI, p. A323

PERRY, Tim, Executive Director of Human Resources, Baptist Health Corbin, Corbin, KY, p. A256

PERRY, V Mark, Chief Financial Officer, Adventist Medical Center–Portland, Portland, OR, p. A525

PERRYMAN, Mike, Chief Financial Officer, Baptist Memorial Hospital–Union City, Union City, TN, p. A590

PERSE, David F., M.D., President and Chief Executive Officer, St. Vincent Charity Medical Center, Cleveland, OH, p. A486

PERSILY, Cynthia A., Ph.D., R.N., President and Chief Executive Officer, Highland Hospital, Charleston, WV, p. A691

PERSING, Tamara F. MHA, BSN,, Chief Nursing Officer, Evangelical Community Hospital, Lewisburg, PA, p. A539

PERSINGER, Keith D, Senior Vice President Finance and Chief Financial Officer, University Of Maryland Medical Center, Baltimore, MD, p. A296

PERT, Robert M, Vice President Finance and Chief Financial Officer, United Regional Health Care System, Wichita Falls, TX, p. A654

PERUGINO, Tony, Director Finance, Vassar Brothers Medical Center, Poughkeepsie, NY, p. A450

PESCHEL, Colleen, Director Human Resources, Sutter Medical Center, Sacramento, Sacramento, CA, p. A84

PESKIN, Ted M.D., Acute Care Medical Director, Hilo Medical Center, Hilo, HI, p. A168

PESTLE, Janet K. R.N., MSN, Vice President Nursing and Chief Nursing Officer, SSM Health St. Joseph Hospital – Lake Saint Louis, Lake Saint Louis, MO, p. A372

PETER, David, M.D.
Senior Vice President Medical Affairs and Chief Medical Director, Cleveland Clinic Akron General, Akron, OH, p. A479
Senior Vice President Medical Affairs and Chief Medical Officer, Lodi Community Hospital, Lodi, OH, p. A493

PETER, Douglas G M.D., Chief Medical Officer, Gallup Indian Medical Center, Gallup, NM, p. A426

PETER, Jan D, Vice President Fiscal Services and Chief Financial Officer, Good Shepherd Health Care System, Hermiston, OR, p. A522

PETER, John M.D., Vice President Medical Affairs, SSM Cardinal Glennon Children's Hospital, Saint Louis, MO, p. A378

PETERMAN, John, Vice President and Administrator, Riverside Shore Memorial Hospital, Onancoke, VA, p. A672

PETERMAN, Tammy, R.N., MS, Executive Vice President, Chief Operating Officer and Chief Nursing Officer, The University Of Kansas Health System, Kansas City, KS, p. A244

PETERMEIER, Jill, Senior Executive Human Resources, Unitypoint Health – Marshalltown, Marshalltown, IA, p. A231

PETERS, Amy R.N., Chief Nursing Officer, Truman Medical Center–Lakewood, Kansas City, MO, p. A371

PETERS, Bruce
Chief Executive Officer, Mercy Hospitals Of Bakersfield, Bakersfield, CA, p. A53
Vice President and Chief Operating Officer, Bakersfield Memorial Hospital, Bakersfield, CA, p. A52

PETERS, Candace R.N., Director of Nursing, Webster County Community Hospital, Red Cloud, NE, p. A399

PETERS, Connie, R.N., President, Chi Health Schuyler, Schuyler, NE, p. A399

PETERS, Dave, Chief Human Resources Officer, Veterans Affairs Nebraska–Western Iowa Health Care System – Lincoln, Lincoln, NE, p. A395

PETERS, Gerald, Vice President Information Technologies and Chief Information Officer, Lake Health, Concord Township, OH, p. A488

PETERS, Holli, Director Health Information Management, Holton Community Hospital, Holton, KS, p. A242

PETERS, Jan, Vice President Human Resources, Saint Vincent Hospital, Worcester, MA, p. A313

PETERS, Joanna, Director Human Resources, Saunders Medical Center, Wahoo, NE, p. A400

PETERS, Mary
Chief Information Officer, Womack Army Medical Center, Fort Bragg, NC, p. A462
Chief Nursing Officer, Unitypoint Health – Finley Hospital, Dubuque, IA, p. A227

PETERS, Patrick, Chief Executive Officer, Guthrie County Hospital, Guthrie Center, IA, p. A228

PETERS, Suzanne K, Vice President Human Resources, Munson Medical Center, Traverse City, MI, p. A332

PETERS, Violeta, R.N., Chief Executive Officer, Specialty Hospital Of Central Jersey, Lakewood, NJ, p. A415

PETERS, Wayne, Administrator, Southern Virginia Mental Health Institute, Danville, VA, p. A666

PETERSEN, Brenda, Human Resources, Sanford Wheaton Medical Center, Wheaton, MN, p. A350

PETERSEN, Debbie, R.N., Chief Operating Officer and Chief Nursing Officer, Spalding Rehabilitation Hospital, Aurora, CO, p. A98

PETERSEN, Julie, Chief Executive Officer, Kittitas Valley Healthcare, Ellensburg, WA, p. A680

PETERSEN, Richard W., President and Chief Executive Officer, Maine Medical Center, Portland, ME, p. A292

PETERSEN, Richard W, President and Chief Executive Officer, Maine Medical Center, Portland, ME, p. A292

PETERSEN, Susan, Human Resources, Lincoln Community Hospital And Nursing Home, Hugo, CO, p. A104

PETERSEN, Tina, Chief Nursing Officer, Hillcrest Hospital Cushing, Cushing, OK, p. A506

PETERSON, Alison, Vice President Medical Affairs, United Hospital, Saint Paul, MN, p. A348

PETERSON, Anne, Vice President Human Resources and Support Services, Licking Memorial Hospital, Newark, OH, p. A497

PETERSON, Bill, Director Human Resources, Saint Francis Hospital Muskogee, Muskogee, OK, p. A511

PETERSON, Brent A., Administrator, Cherry County Hospital, Valentine, NE, p. A400

PETERSON, Brett, Director of Information Services, Florida Hospital North Pinellas, Tarpon Springs, FL, p. A145

PETERSON, Bruce, Chief Information Officer, Rome Memorial Hospital, Rome, NY, p. A451

PETERSON, Carrie, Director of Nursing, Henderson Health Care Services, Henderson, NE, p. A394

PETERSON, Chad, Chief Information Officer, Northwood Deaconess Health Center, Northwood, ND, p. A477

PETERSON, Cheryl, Business Office Manager, Surgical Institute Of Reading, Wyomissing, PA, p. A555

PETERSON, Dan, Chief Administrative Officer, Sutter Lakeside Hospital, Lakeport, CA, p. A65

PETERSON, David
Chief Information Officer, Laurel Regional Hospital, Laurel, MD, p. A299
Senior Vice President, Chief Technology Officer, Erlanger Medical Center, Chattanooga, TN, p. A576

PETERSON, Denise R.N., FACHE, Vice President, Professional Nursing Practice & Quality, Chief Nursing Officer, Saint Francis Hospital And Medical Center, Hartford, CT, p. A110

PETERSON, Douglas R., President and Chief Executive Officer, Chippewa Valley Hospital And Oakview Care Center, Durand, WI, p. A700

PETERSON, Eric, Director, Ogden Regional Medical Center, Ogden, UT, p. A658

PETERSON, Erica
Chief Executive Officer and Chief Financial Officer, Sanford Chamberlain Medical Center, Chamberlain, SD, p. A568
Chief Executive Officer, Sanford Chamberlain Medical Center, Chamberlain, SD, p. A568

PETERSON, Gary M.D., Vice President Medical Affairs and Chief Medical Officer, St. Luke's Hospital, Duluth, MN, p. A339

PETERSON, James Kevin, Human Resources Leader, Kaiser Permanente South Sacramento Medical Center, Sacramento, CA, p. A83

PETERSON, Jeff M.D., Chief of Staff, Essentia Health Ada, Ada, MN, p. A335

PETERSON, Jeffrey M.D., Medical Director, Cooperstown Medical Center, Cooperstown, ND, p. A475

PETERSON, Jim, Chief Financial Officer, Steele Memorial Medical Center, Salmon, ID, p. A176

PETERSON, Josilyn, Chief Financial Officer, Ballinger Memorial Hospital, Ballinger, TX, p. A596

PETERSON, Judy R.N., Chief Nursing Officer, East Texas Medical Center Carthage, Carthage, TX, p. A601

PETERSON, Julie, Chief Financial Officer, Sutter Delta Medical Center, Antioch, CA, p. A51

PETERSON, Kathy, Director Information Services, OSF Saint Anthony Medical Center, Rockford, IL, p. A199

PETERSON, Katie R.N., Chief Nursing Officer, Pender Community Hospital, Pender, NE, p. A399

PETERSON, Larry, Chief Financial Officer, Allen County Regional Hospital, Iola, KS, p. A243

PETERSON, Linda M.D., Vice President Medical Affairs, Mclaren Greater Lansing, Lansing, MI, p. A324

PETERSON, Mackenzie M.D., Chief of Staff, Anderson County Hospital, Garnett, KS, p. A241

PETERSON, Margaret R., Ph.D., R.N., President, California Hospital Medical Center, Los Angeles, CA, p. A67

PETERSON, Michael, FACHE, M.D.
Chief Operating Officer, Sebasticook Valley Health, Pittsfield, ME, p. A292
Chief of Staff, Pineville Community Hospital Association, Pineville, KY, p. A266
President, Androscoggin Valley Hospital, Berlin, NH, p. A407

PETERSON, Natalie
Director of Human Resources, Optim Medical Center – Jenkins, Millen, GA, p. A162
Human Resources Director, Optim Medical Center – Screven, Sylvania, GA, p. A165

PETERSON, Polly, Information Technology Director, Winona Health, Winona, MN, p. A350

PETERSON, Randall, President and Chief Executive Officer, Stormont Vail Health, Topeka, KS, p. A252

PETERSON, Ronald R., President, Johns Hopkins Health System, Baltimore, MD, p. B70

PETERSON, Robert, I
Chief Executive Officer, Millinocket Regional Hospital, Millinocket, ME, p. A292
Chief Financial Officer, Hackettstown Medical Center, Hackettstown, NJ, p. A414

PETERSON, Ron, FACHE
Chief Information Officer, Pottstown Memorial Medical Center, Pottstown, PA, p. A548
President and Chief Executive Officer, Baxter Regional Medical Center, Mountain Home, AR, p. A47

PETERSON, Scott J., Chief Executive Officer, Healthsouth Rehabilitation Hospital Of Franklin, Franklin, TN, p. A578

PETERSON, Scott, M.D.
President Medical Staff, Avera Flandreau Hospital, Flandreau, SD, p. A570
Vice President of People and Organizational Development, Peninsula Regional Medical Center, Salisbury, MD, p. A301

PETERSON, Seth, Director Information Services, Coshocton Regional Medical Center, Coshocton, OH, p. A488

PETERSON, Shelley R.N., Vice President Patient Services and Chief Nursing Officer, St. Mary's Hospital And Medical Center, Grand Junction, CO, p. A103

PETERSON, Steve M.D., Chief of Staff, Chi Health Plainview, Plainview, NE, p. A399

PETERSON, Steven, Chief Information Officer, Vice President of Operations, Garrett Regional Medical Center, Oakland, MD, p. A300

PETERSON, Tim M.D., Chief of Staff, Meeker Memorial Hospital, Litchfield, MN, p. A342

PETIK, Jason, Chief Executive Officer, Sidney Regional Medical Center, Sidney, NE, p. A400

PETITT, Dorie, Chief Nursing Officer, Post Acute Medical Specialty Hospital Of Milwaukee, Greenfield, WI, p. A703

PETITT, Michael
Director of Finance, Wheaton Franciscan Healthcare – Elmbrook Memorial, Brookfield, WI, p. A699
Director of Finance, Wheaton Franciscan Healthcare – St. Joseph's, Milwaukee, WI, p. A708

PETRE, Patrick A., Chief Executive Officer, Garfield Medical Center, Monterey Park, CA, p. A75

PETRICK, Teresa G, President, Upmc Passavant, Pittsburgh, PA, p. A547

PETRIK, Jennifer, Interim Chief Nursing Officer, Multicare Deaconess Hospital, Spokane, WA, p. A686

PETRILLO, Mary Ann R.N., MSN, Acting Associate Director Nursing and Patient Clinical Services, Bedford Veterans Affairs Medical Center, Edith Nourse Rogers Memorial Veterans Hospital, Bedford, MA, p. A302

PETRILLO, Nancy, Director Human Resources, Matheny Medical And Educational Center, Peapack, NJ, p. A418

PETRINA, Robert, Chief Financial Officer, Alta Bates Summit Medical Center, Berkeley, CA, p. A53

PETRINI, Lindsey, Chief Operating Officer, Wellstar North Fulton Hospital, Roswell, GA, p. A164

PETRITZ, Jennifer J, Director Human Resources, University Of Washington Medical Center, Seattle, WA, p. A685

PETROVICH, Lawrence M.D., Chief Medical Officer, York Hospital, York, ME, p. A293

PETROWER, Stacey, President, New York–Presbyterian/ Hudson Valley Hospital, Cortlandt Manor, NY, p. A434

PETRY, Fernando M.D., Vice President and Chief Medical Officer, Martin Health System, Stuart, FL, p. A143

PETRY, Gary M.D., Chief of Staff, St. Vincent General Hospital District, Leadville, CO, p. A105

PETTEY, Robbie, Chief Financial Officer, National Park Medical Center, Hot Springs, AR, p. A44

PETTIGREW, Dennis
Chief Financial Officer, Saint Michael's Medical Center, Newark, NJ, p. A417
Chief Operating Officer, Saint Michael's Medical Center, Newark, NJ, p. A417

PETTIGREW, Rob, Director Information Technology, Wyoming Medical Center, Casper, WY, p. A717

PETTIJOHN, Kim R.N., MSN, Chief Nursing Officer, Spine Hospital Of Louisiana (Formally The Neuromedical Center Surgical Hospital), Baton Rouge, LA, p. A271

PETTIJOHN, Trent, M.D., Esq
Chief Medical Officer, The Heart Hospital Baylor Denton, Denton, TX, p. A608
Chief Medical Officer, The Heart Hospital Baylor Plano, Plano, TX, p. A638

PETTINATO, Jim, Director Patient Care Services, Wayne Memorial Hospital, Honesdale, PA, p. A536

PETTIT, Amy N., Vice President Nursing Services and Chief Nursing Officer, Schneck Medical Center, Seymour, IN, p. A219

PETTIT, Donny, Chief Financial Officer, Coon Memorial Hospital, Dalhart, TX, p. A604

PETTIT, Harlan M.D., Chief of Medical Staff, Fishermen's Hospital, Marathon, FL, p. A131

PETTITE, Shirley F, Chief Human Resources Officer, Tennessee Valley Healthcare System, Nashville, TN, p. A587

PETTREY, Lisa J., MSN, R.N.

Interim Chief Executive Officer, Regency Hospital Of Columbus, Columbus, OH, p. A488
Chief Executive Officer, Select Specialty Hospital– Columbus, Columbus, OH, p. A488

PETTY, Jane, Director Human Resources, Southern Tennessee Regional Health System–Pulaski, Pulaski, TN, p. A588

PETTY, Russ M.D., Chief of Staff, Towner County Medical Center, Cando, ND, p. A474

PETULA, Ronald J.
Chief Financial Officer, Good Shepherd Rehabilitation Hospital, Allentown, PA, p. A528
Chief Financial Officer, Good Shepherd Specialty Hospital, Bethlehem, PA, p. A529
Vice President Finance, Good Shepherd Penn Partners Specialty Hospital At Rittenhouse, Philadelphia, PA, p. A544

PEW, Chad, Chief Operating Officer and Senior Vice President, Wyoming Medical Center, Casper, WY, p. A717

PFAFF, Joni, Chief Nursing Officer, Grisell Memorial Hospital District One, Ransom, KS, p. A250

PFAFF, Tony, Chief Executive Officer, Deer Lodge Medical Center, Deer Lodge, MT, p. A384

PFALTZGRAFF, George, Chief Medical Officer, Hansen Family Hospital, Iowa Falls, IA, p. A230

PFAU, Ben, Chief Facility and Information Officer, Bay Area Hospital, Coos Bay, OR, p. A521

PFAU, Beth M.D., Chief Medical Officer, Larue D. Carter Memorial Hospital, Indianapolis, IN, p. A211

PFEFFER, Daniel William, Chief Nurse Executive, Weisman Children's Rehabilitation Hospital, Marlton, NJ, p. A416

PFEFFER, Michael, M.D.
Chief Information Officer, Ronald Reagan Ucla Medical Center, Los Angeles, CA, p. A71
Chief Medical Informatics Officer, UCLA Health, Stewart & Lynda Resnick Neuropsychiatric Hospital At Ucla, Los Angeles, CA, p. A71

PFEFFER, Stacey, Senior Vice President Human Resources, NYU Winthrop Hospital, Mineola, NY, p. A439

PFEIFER, Bradley D., FACHE, Chief Executive Officer, West Holt Medical Services, Atkinson, NE, p. A390

PFEIFER, Mark P M.D., Senior Vice President and Chief Medical Officer, University Of Louisville Hospital, Louisville, KY, p. A264

PFEIFFER, James A., FACHE, President and Chief Executive Officer, Self Regional Healthcare, Greenwood, SC, p. A563

PFEIFFER, Margaret R.N., MSN, Vice President Patient Care Services, Good Samaritan Hospital, Los Angeles, CA, p. A68

PFISTER, Joann M, Director Human Resources, Providence Willamette Falls Medical Center, Oregon City, OR, p. A524

PFISTER, Pam, Chief Executive Officer, Morrison Community Hospital, Morrison, IL, p. A194

PFISTER, Scott, Director Finance, Providence St. Vincent Medical Center, Portland, OR, p. A526

PFRANK, Kym, Senior Vice President and Chief Operating Officer, Union Hospital, Terre Haute, IN, p. A220

PHAM, Bong, Chief Medical Officer, Kit Carson County Health Service District, Burlington, CO, p. A99

PHAM, K M.D., Chief of Staff, Winkler County Memorial Hospital, Kermit, TX, p. A626

PHELAN, Cynthia, Vice President Human Resources, Lawrence General Hospital, Lawrence, MA, p. A307

PHELPS, Britton, Chief Executive Officer, Merit Health Madison, Canton, MS, p. A353

PHELPS, Craig M.D., Chief of Staff, Great Plains Regional Medical Center, Elk City, OK, p. A507

PHELPS, David E., President and Chief Executive Officer, Berkshire Medical Center, Pittsfield, MA, p. A310

PHELPS, Gail R.N., Chief Nursing Officer, Haxtun Hospital District, Haxtun, CO, p. A104

PHELPS, Joel, Chief Operating Officer, Salina Regional Health Center, Salina, KS, p. A251

PHELPS, Kathleen, Director Human Resources, Treasure Valley Hospital, Boise, ID, p. A172

PHELPS, Lisa, Senior Vice President, Human Resources, Phoenix Children's Hospital, Phoenix, AZ, p. A34

PHELPS, Michael, President and Chief Executive Officer, Ridgeview Medical Center, Waconia, MN, p. A350

PHETTEPLACE, Danial, Director Information Technology, Gundersen St. Joseph's Hospital And Clinics, Hillsboro, WI, p. A703

PHILIP, Neena S. R.N., Assistant Vice President Nursing, Carepoint Health Hoboken University Medical Center, Hoboken, NJ, p. A414

PHILIPCHUCK, Cynthia R.N., Executive Director of Nursing, Gibson Area Hospital And Health Services, Gibson City, IL, p. A188

PHILIPS, Grady W. III, President, Winchester Medical Center, Winchester, VA, p. A677

PHILLIPS, Alan M, Controller, Healthsouth Nittany Valley Rehabilitation Hospital, Pleasant Gap, PA, p. A548

PHILLIPS, Brent R., President and Chief Executive Officer, Regional Health, Rapid City, SD, p. B108

PHILLIPS, Barry, Executive Director Human Resources, Camden General Hospital, Camden, TN, p. A575

PHILLIPS, Bill, Vice President Information Services, University Health System, San Antonio, TX, p. A644

PHILLIPS, Bobby, Chief Nursing Officer, Medical Center Enterprise, Enterprise, AL, p. A17

PHILLIPS, Courtney, Chief Executive Officer, South Sunflower County Hospital, Indianola, MS, p. A356

PHILLIPS, David D., Chief Executive Officer and Administrator, Barnesville Hospital, Barnesville, OH, p. A480

PHILLIPS, David L.
   Chief Operating Officer, St. John Broken Arrow, Broken Arrow, OK, p. A505
   President and Chief Operating Officer, St. John Owasso, Owasso, OK, p. A514

PHILLIPS, Donna, President, Bryn Mawr Rehabilitation Hospital, Malvern, PA, p. A539

PHILLIPS, Eddie, M.D.
   Chief Medical Affairs, Baptist Health Medical Center – North Little Rock, North Little Rock, AR, p. A48
   Chief Medical Officer, Baptist Health Medical Center–Arkadelphia, Arkadelphia, AR, p. A40

PHILLIPS, Frank M.D., Chief of Staff, Mary Black Health System – Gaffney, Gaffney, SC, p. A562

PHILLIPS, Glenn, Director Information Systems, Gadsden Regional Medical Center, Gadsden, AL, p. A18

PHILLIPS, Heath, Chief Executive Officer, Flowers Hospital, Dothan, AL, p. A16

PHILLIPS, John E., FACHE, President, Methodist Mansfield Medical Center, Mansfield, TX, p. A631

PHILLIPS, John
   Chief of Staff, Great River Medical Center, West Burlington, IA, p. A236
   Vice President Information Services, Chi St. Joseph Regional Health Center, Bryan, TX, p. A600

PHILLIPS, Jonathan, Interim Administrator, University Health Conway, Monroe, LA, p. A281

PHILLIPS, Kelly M.D., M.P.H., Clinical Director and Chief Staff, Spring Grove Hospital Center, Baltimore, MD, p. A296

PHILLIPS, Kimberly A, Chief Financial Officer, The Children's Home Of Pittsburgh, Pittsburgh, PA, p. A547

PHILLIPS, Lionel J, Vice President Financial Services, Fauquier Hospital, Warrenton, VA, p. A676

PHILLIPS, Lori, Vice President and Chief Nursing Officer, Gibson General Hospital, Princeton, IN, p. A218

PHILLIPS, Michael, Chief Executive Officer, Elkhorn Valley Rehabilitation Hospital, Casper, WY, p. A717

PHILLIPS, Monie III, Director Clinical Informatics, Jackson Parish Hospital, Jonesboro, LA, p. A277

PHILLIPS, Paul, Chief Financial Officer, Taylor Regional Hospital, Campbellsville, KY, p. A256

PHILLIPS, Robert A., Chief Executive Officer, Walker Baptist Medical Center, Jasper, AL, p. A20

PHILLIPS, Robert M.D., Ph.D., FACC, Executive Vice President and Chief Medical Officer, Houston Methodist Hospital, Houston, TX, p. A620

PHILLIPS, Sarah, Manager Human Resources, Morgan Memorial Hospital, Madison, GA, p. A161

PHILLIPS, Steve, Information Officer, Greene County General Hospital, Linton, IN, p. A215

PHILLIPS, Tammy, Director, Information Systems, Texas Health Presbyterian Hospital Dallas, Dallas, TX, p. A607

PHILLIPS, Traci, Assistant Superintendent, Big Spring State Hospital, Big Spring, TX, p. A598

PHILPOTT, Jamie R.N., Interim Chief Nursing Officer, Highland Hospital, Rochester, NY, p. A450

PHINNEY, Cody, Administrator, Northern Nevada Adult Mental Health Services, Sparks, NV, p. A406

PHIPPS, Emily, Director Human Resources, Oklahoma Center For Orthopedic And Multi–Specialty Surgery, Oklahoma City, OK, p. A512

PHIPPS, Jackie G, Director Human Resources, Johnston Memorial Hospital, Abingdon, VA, p. A664

PHIPPS ADAMS, Holly, Vice President of Human Resources, Carroll Hospital Center, Westminster, MD, p. A301

PIANALTO, Eric, President, Mercy Hospital Rogers, Rogers, AR, p. A49

PIATKOWSKI, Shannon, Director Information Technology, Blake Medical Center, Bradenton, FL, p. A120

PIATT, Malcolm Keith., M.D., Interim Director, Northern Arizona Veterans Affairs Health Care System, Prescott, AZ, p. A34

PIAZZA, Doreen, Acting Executive Director, South Beach Psychiatric Center, New Rochelle, NY, p. A446

PIAZZA, Kenneth P., Associate Director, Bath Veterans Affairs Medical Center, Bath, NY, p. A431

PIAZZA, Tony, Director Human Resources, Titus Regional Medical Center, Mount Pleasant, TX, p. A634

PICAZA, Jose M.D., Chief of Staff, Unicoi County Memorial Hospital, Erwin, TN, p. A578

PICCIONE, Jennifer, Chief Nursing and Clinical Services Officer, Madison Health, London, OH, p. A494

PICKARD, Bert, Chief Financial Officer, Gilmore Memorial Hospital, Amory, MS, p. A352

PICKEL, Joseph, Director Resource Management, Walter Reed National Military Medical Center, Bethesda, MD, p. A297

PICKENS, Gayle, Chief Nursing Officer, Putnam County Memorial Hospital, Unionville, MO, p. A380

PICKENS, Ramona, Chief Operating Officer, East Cooper Medical Center, Mount Pleasant, SC, p. A564

PICKENS, Regina, Chief Financial Officer, Grafton City Hospital, Grafton, WV, p. A692

PICKER, Josephine MSN, R.N., Director of Nursing, Asheville Specialty Hospital, Asheville, NC, p. A457

PICKERING, David, System Director, Applications, Linden Oaks Hospital, Naperville, IL, p. A195

PICKETT, C. Judson, Chief of Staff, University Hospital Summerville, Augusta, GA, p. A152

PICKETT, Lisa C M.D., Chief Medical Officer, Duke University Hospital, Durham, NC, p. A461

PICKLER, Nancy, Director of Human Resources, Healthsouth East Valley Rehabilitation Hospital, Mesa, AZ, p. A31

PICKUL, David M.D., Chief Medical Officer, Circle Health, Lowell General Hospital, Lowell, MA, p. A308

PICOU, Timothy, Manager Information Technology, Lower Umpqua Hospital District, Reedsport, OR, p. A526

PIEDRAFITE, JoAnn R.N., Chief Nursing Officer, Saint Vincent Hospital, Worcester, MA, p. A313

PIEFFER, Paul
   Chief Operating Officer, Great River Medical Center, Blytheville, AR, p. A40
   Chief Operating Officer, South Mississippi County Regional Medical Center, Osceola, AR, p. A48

PIEH, Samuel
   Chief Operating Officer, DMC Huron Valley–Sinai Hospital, Commerce Township, MI, p. A317
   Chief Operating Officer, Saint Francis Hospital, Memphis, TN, p. A585

PIEPER, Blaine, Chief Executive Officer, Ohio County Hospital, Hartford, KY, p. A259

PIEPHOFF, James, Chief Medical Officer, OSF Saint Anthony's Health Center, Alton, IL, p. A177

PIERCE, Bonnie MSN, R.N., Associate Director for Patient Care Services, Jack C. Montgomery Veterans Affairs Medical Center, Muskogee, OK, p. A510

PIERCE, Christy, Director of Human Resources, Katherine Shaw Bethea Hospital, Dixon, IL, p. A185

PIERCE, Connie, Manager Human Resources, Coalinga Regional Medical Center, Coalinga, CA, p. A56

PIERCE, Felicia, R.N.
   Chief Nursing Officer, Great River Medical Center, Blytheville, AR, p. A40
   Chief Nursing Officer, South Mississippi County Regional Medical Center, Osceola, AR, p. A48

PIERCE, Jeff M
   Manager Human Resources, Marshall Medical Center, Lewisburg, TN, p. A582
   Manager Human Resources, Wayne Medical Center, Waynesboro, TN, p. A590

PIERCE, Jennifer
   Administrative Director of Finance, St. Anthony Shawnee Hospital, Shawnee, OK, p. A516
   Chief Clinical Officer, Kindred Hospital Of Northern Indiana, Mishawaka, IN, p. A216

PIERCE, Kenneth, Chief Financial Officer, Brookhaven Hospital, Tulsa, OK, p. A517

PIERCE, Laura, Director Human Resources, Memorial Medical Center, Las Cruces, NM, p. A426

PIERCE, Margaret H., Executive Director, Kaiser Permanente Baldwin Park Medical Center, Baldwin Park, CA, p. A53

PIERCE, Michael L., Chief Executive Officer, Post Acute Medical Specialty Hospital Of Corpus Christi – South, Corpus Christi, TX, p. A603

PIERCE, Pamela, Deputy Chief Executive Officer, Windhaven Psychiatric Hospital, Prescott Valley, AZ, p. A35

PIERCE, Pat, Director Information Systems, Lakewood Regional Medical Center, Lakewood, CA, p. A65

PIERCE, Reid M.D., Chief Medical Officer, Jefferson Regional Medical Center, Pine Bluff, AR, p. A48

PIERCE, Sherri R.N., Chief Nursing Officer, Sweeny Community Hospital, Sweeny, TX, p. A647

PIERDON, Steven M.D., Executive Vice President and Chief Medical Officer, Geisinger Wyoming Valley Medical Center, Wilkes Barre, PA, p. A554

PIERESCHI, Giovanni
   Vice President Enterprise Information and Chief Information Officer, Hima San Pablo Caguas, Caguas, PR, p. A722

Vice President Management Information Systems, Hospital Hima De Humacao, Humacao, PR, p. A723

PIERLUISI, Guillermo, Vice President of Medical Affairs, Wellstar Paulding Hospital, Hiram, GA, p. A159

PIERRE, Andre, Chief Financial Officer, Forest View Psychiatric Hospital, Grand Rapids, MI, p. A320

PIERRE, Letonia, Coordinator Human Resources, Assumption Community Hospital, Napoleonville, LA, p. A282

PIERSON, Cindy, Interim Chief Nursing Officer, Highlands–Cashiers Hospital, Highlands, NC, p. A464

PIERSON, Jerome, Chief Medical Officer, Mercy Medical Center–Sioux City, Sioux City, IA, p. A235

PIERSON, Kim R.N., Chief Nursing Officer, Wilbarger General Hospital, Vernon, TX, p. A652

PIERSON, Kyle A., Chief Financial Officer, Roane General Hospital, Spencer, WV, p. A696

PIERSON, Lois K., Chief Financial Officer, University Of Texas Harris County Psychiatric Center, Houston, TX, p. A623

PIETRYKOWSKI, Susan, Commander, U. S. Air Force Hospital, Hampton, VA, p. A668

PIETSCH, Al CPA, Senior Vice President and Chief Financial Officer, University Of Maryland Baltimore Washington Medical Center, Glen Burnie, MD, p. A298

PIETZ, Gerald, Vice President Finance, Mercy Hospital, Coon Rapids, MN, p. A338

PIFER, Eric M.D., Chief Medical Officer, El Camino Hospital, Mountain View, CA, p. A75

PIFKO, Duane, Interim Director Financial Services, Daniel Drake Center For Post Acute Care, Cincinnati, OH, p. A484

PIGG, Russell, Chief Executive Officer, Eliza Coffee Memorial Hospital, Florence, AL, p. A18

PIGOTT, John M.D., Chief Medical Officer, Tulane Medical Center, New Orleans, LA, p. A283

PIKE, David, Interim Chief Financial Officer, Memorial Hospital Of Carbon County, Rawlins, WY, p. A719

PIKE, Irving M.D., Senior Vice President and Chief Medical Officer, John Muir Medical Center, Walnut Creek, Walnut Creek, CA, p. A96

PIKE, Pauline, Chief Operating Officer, Beverly Hospital, Beverly, MA, p. A302

PIKE, Randi, Director of Nursing, Pioneer Medical Center, Big Timber, MT, p. A382

PIKE, Ronald F M.D., Medical Director, Adcare Hospital Of Worcester, Worcester, MA, p. A313

PIKE, Tim M.D., Chief Medical Officer, Portsmouth Regional Hospital, Portsmouth, NH, p. A410

PIKER, John F M.D., Medical Director, Villa Feliciana Medical Complex, Jackson, LA, p. A276

PIKULA, Shirley MSN, Associate Director Patient Center Care, San Francisco Va Medical Center, San Francisco, CA, p. A87

PIL, Pieter M.D., Chief Medical Staff, Martha's Vineyard Hospital, Oak Bluffs, MA, p. A310

PILANT, Jason B., Acting President and Chief Administrative Officer, Roane Medical Center, Harriman, TN, p. A579

PILANT, Jason B, Chief Operating Officer, Roane Medical Center, Harriman, TN, p. A579

PILCHER, Shane, Administrative Director Information Systems, Siskin Hospital For Physical Rehabilitation, Chattanooga, TN, p. A576

PILE, Larry, Director Human Resources, Deaconess Hospital, Evansville, IN, p. A207

PILEGGI, Anne, Administrator and Associate Vice President, Christus Mother Frances Hospital – Jacksonville, Jacksonville, TX, p. A625

PILEGGI, Tim, Interim Chief Financial Officer, Christus Good Shepherd Medical Center, Longview, TX, p. A629

PILGRIM, Patti, Chief Financial Officer, Sutter Davis Hospital, Davis, CA, p. A57

PILLION, Scott, Chief Executive Officer, Helen Newberry Joy Hospital, Newberry, MI, p. A327

PILLOT, Juan M.D., Esq, Medical Director, Hospital Pavia Yauco, Yauco, PR, p. A727

PILLSBURY, S Gainer M.D., Associate Chief Medical Officer, Community Hospital Long Beach, Long Beach, CA, p. A66

PILNEY, Jeffrey, Chief Medical Officer, Pocahontas Memorial Hospital, Buckeye, WV, p. A690

PILON, Michele, President and Chief Nursing Officer, Transylvania Regional Hospital, Brevard, NC, p. A458

PILONG, Alfred E. Jr, FACHE, President, Munson Medical Center and Chief Operating Officer, Munson Healthcare, Munson Medical Center, Traverse City, MI, p. A332

PILOT, Dave, Chief Financial Officer, Essentia Health St. Joseph's Medical Center, Brainerd, MN, p. A337

PINA, Julie A., Assistant Vice President Patient Care Services and Chief Nursing Officer, Driscoll Children's Hospital, Corpus Christi, TX, p. A603

PINA, Kate, Director Human Resources, Wickenburg Community Hospital, Wickenburg, AZ, p. A38

PINDERSKI, Christopher M.D., Medical Director of Emergency Room, Black River Medical Center, Poplar Bluff, MO, p. A375

PINE, Richard M., President and Chief Executive Officer, Livengrin Foundation, Bensalem, PA, p. A529

PINEIRO, Carlos M, President, Hospital Hima De Humacao, Humacao, PR, p. A723

PINER, Thomas J., Director for Resources Management, Naval Medical Center San Diego, San Diego, CA, p. A85

PINERO, Efrain, Administrator, Hospital Oriente, Humacao, PR, p. A724

PINETTE, Jameson, Chief Executive Officer, Arbour H. R. I. Hospital, Brookline, MA, p. A305

PINKELMAN, Janet, Director Human Resources, Faith Regional Health Services, Norfolk, NE, p. A396

PINKERTON, Jay, Chief Medical Officer, George Regional Hospital, Lucedale, MS, p. A358

PINKOSKY, Frank
  Executive Vice President, Troy Community Hospital, Troy, PA, p. A552
  Senior Vice President, Guthrie Robert Packer Hospital, Sayre, PA, p. A549

PINO, Elena, Chief Operating Officer and Chief Nursing Officer, Mesa Hills Specialty Hospital, El Paso, TX, p. A611

PINO, Joseph R.
  Chief Operating Officer, Saint Thomas Hospital For Spinal Surgery, Nashville, TN, p. A586
  Chief Operating Officer, Saint Thomas Midtown Hospital, Nashville, TN, p. A586
  Chief Operating Officer, Saint Thomas West Hospital, Nashville, TN, p. A586

PINO, Joseph M.D., Chief Medical Officer, Regional Medical Center Bayonet Point, Hudson, FL, p. A127

PINON, Richard, Chief Medical Officer, Eastern New Mexico Medical Center, Roswell, NM, p. A428

PINSKY, Karen M.D., Chief Medical Information Officer, Penn Medicine Chester County Hospital, West Chester, PA, p. A553

PINTER, Tabatha, Director of Nursing, George Regional Hospital, Lucedale, MS, p. A358

PINTO, Frank, Chief Information Officer, The Hospital Of Central Connecticut, New Britain, CT, p. A111

PINSON, Charles Wright., M.D., Deputy Vice Chancellor for Health Affairs and Chief Executive Officer of Vanderbilt Health System, Vanderbilt Health, Nashville, TN, p. B143

PIPER, Angel, Chief Executive Officer, Valley Behavioral Health System, Barling, AR, p. A40

PIPER, Kevin, Director Information Systems, Florida Hospital Deland, Deland, FL, p. A123

PIPER, Vicky, Vice President Human Resources, Loyola University Medical Center, Maywood, IL, p. A193

PIPGRASS, Michele, Chief Fiscal Service, Oklahoma City Veterans Affairs Medical Center, Oklahoma City, OK, p. A513

PIPKINS, David, Chief Executive Officer and Administrator, Kate Dishman Rehabilitation Hospital, Beaumont, TX, p. A597

PIPPIN, Kim, Chief Nursing Officer, Select Specialty Hospital–Augusta, Augusta, GA, p. A152

PIRKL, Rollie, Chief Financial Officer, Sierra Vista Regional Medical Center, San Luis Obispo, CA, p. A89

PIRO, Michael J, Chief Information Officer, St. John's Episcopal Hospital–South Shore, New Rochelle, NY, p. A446

PIRRI, Christine, Vice President Human Resources, Little Falls Hospital, Little Falls, NY, p. A438

PIRTLE, Kathleen, Director Human Resources, Healthsouth Rehabilitation Hospital–Wichita Falls, Wichita Falls, TX, p. A654

PIRTLE, Randy B, Chief Financial Officer, King's Daughters Medical Center, Brookhaven, MS, p. A353

PISANO, Thomas M.D., Chief Professional Services, Connecticut Valley Hospital, Middletown, CT, p. A111

PISCIOTTA, Michael J., Chief Executive Officer, Southern Surgical Hospital, Slidell, LA, p. A286

PISICOTTA, Robert, Chief Nursing Officer, Baylor Scott And White Continuing Care Hospital, Temple, TX, p. A648

PISPISA, D Patricia, Executive Vice President Patient Care Services, Eastern Long Island Hospital, Greenport, NY, p. A436

PISTONE, Maureen
  Senior Vice President Human Resources, Thedacare Regional Medical Center–Neenah, Neenah, WI, p. A709
  Senior Vice President Talent Development and Human Resources, Thedacare Regional Medical Center–Appleton, Appleton, WI, p. A698

PISZCZATOSKI, Thomas J, Chief Human Resource Officer, St. Mary's Medical Center, West Palm Beach, FL, p. A147

PITCHER, Ellen, Chief Nursing Officer and Chief Operating Officer, El Paso Children's Hospital, El Paso, TX, p. A610

PITCHER, Kerry, Administrator, Hale Ho'Ola Hamakua, Honokaa, HI, p. A168

PITCHFORD, Edward C., President and Chief Executive Officer, Cole Memorial, Coudersport, PA, p. A532

PITCOCK, Nancy, Vice President Nursing and Chief Nursing Officer, St. Vincent Anderson Regional Hospital, Anderson, IN, p. A203

PITMAN, David R, Vice President Finance, Medstar Harbor Hospital, Baltimore, MD, p. A295

PITTMAN, Cyndi, Chief Financial Officer, Baptist Memorial Hospital – Memphis, Memphis, TN, p. A584

PITTMAN, Jennifer, Chief Financial Officer, Shelby Baptist Medical Center, Alabaster, AL, p. A13

PITTMAN, Jeremy, Chief Financial Officer, Castle Rock Adventist Hospital, Castle Rock, CO, p. A99

PITTMAN, Michael, Chief Nursing Officer, Sovah Health–Martinsville, Martinsville, VA, p. A670

PITTMAN, Scott M, Chief Operating Officer, Buchanan General Hospital, Grundy, VA, p. A668

PITTS, Celeste, Chief Financial Officer, Upper Connecticut Valley Hospital, Colebrook, NH, p. A407

PITTS, Lynn, Director Human Resources, Calhoun–Liberty Hospital, Blountstown, FL, p. A120

PITTS, Richard D.O., Ph.D., Medical Director, Arrowhead Regional Medical Center, Colton, CA, p. A56

PITTS, Robert, Executive Director, Wilmington Treatment Center, Wilmington, NC, p. A472

PITTS, Sherry J., Chief Executive Officer, Merit Health Woman's Hospital, Flowood, MS, p. A354

PIVONKA, Mary, Director Quality Management, Rockland Children's Hospital Psychiatric Center, Orangeburg, NY, p. A449

PIZ, Tom, Director Human Resources, Fremont Hospital, Fremont, CA, p. A60

PIZARRO, Hugo A, Vice President Human Resources, Terence Cardinal Cooke Health Care Center, New Rochelle, NY, p. A447

PIZZANO, Michael A., Chief Executive Officer, Kindred Hospital–New Jersey Morris County, Dover, NJ, p. A413

PIZZI, Chris, Chief Operating Officer and Chief Financial Officer, Providence Medford Medical Center, Medford, OR, p. A524

PIZZINO, Mary, Chief Information Officer, Effingham Hospital, Springfield, GA, p. A165

PLACE, Michael, M.D., Commander, Madigan Army Medical Center, Tacoma, WA, p. A687

PLAGGEMEYER, Rikki, Director Acute Care Nursing, Sturgis Regional Hospital, Sturgis, SD, p. A573

PLAISANCE, Stephen, Chief Financial Officer, Meeker Memorial Hospital, Litchfield, MN, p. A342

PLAMONDON, Richard, Vice President Finance and Chief Financial Officer, St. Joseph Hospital, Nashua, NH, p. A409

PLANO, Crystal, Controller, St. Vincent Dunn Hospital, Bedford, IN, p. A204

PLANT, Steven L, Chief Financial Officer, Cottage Hospital, Woodsville, NH, p. A410

PLANTE, Tim, MSN, R.N., President and Chief Executive Officer, Memorial Community Hospital And Health System, Blair, NE, p. A391

PLASKETT, Darice S., R.N., FACHE, Interim Chief Executive Officer, Governor Juan F. Luis Hospital, Christiansted, VI, p. A727

PLASS, Mary Ellen MS, R.N., Senior Vice President and Chief Nursing Officer, Columbia Memorial Hospital, Hudson, NY, p. A437

PLATE, James M.D., Chief of Staff, Kimball Health Services, Kimball, NE, p. A394

PLATER, Queenie C, Vice President Human Resources for JHM Community Division, Sibley Memorial Hospital, Washington, DC, p. A118

PLATOU, Kenneth E S., President, Mercy Medical Center Mount Shasta, Mount Shasta, CA, p. A75

PLATT, Anne, Chief Executive Officer, Sutter Amador Hospital, Jackson, CA, p. A64

PLATT, Dwayne M.D., Chief Medical Officer, Conemaugh Meyersdale Medical Center, Meyersdale, PA, p. A541

PLATT, James, Chief Executive Officer, Jackson Hospital, Marianna, FL, p. A131

PLATZ, Scott, Director Finance, Uh Regional Hospitals, Cleveland, OH, p. A486

PLAUTH, William M.D., Vice President Operations and Chief Medical Officer, Mercy Regional Medical Center, Durango, CO, p. A101

PLAVIAK, David J, Interim Chief Financial Officer, Novant Health Uva Health System Culpeper Medical Center, Culpeper, VA, p. A666

PLAVIN, Joshua M.D., Medical Director Medicine Division, Gifford Medical Center, Randolph, VT, p. A663

PLAZA, Marta Rivera., Chief Executive Officer and Managing Director, San Juan Capestrano Hospital, San Juan, PR, p. A726

PLEDGER, Michelle, Coordinator Human Resources, Grady General Hospital, Cairo, GA, p. A153

PLEMEL, Jeff, Director Health Information, Chippewa County–Montevideo Hospital, Montevideo, MN, p. A344

PLEMMONS, Debra, Chief Nursing Officer, Middle Park Medical Center–Kremmling, Kremmling, CO, p. A104

PLESKOW, Eric D., President and Chief Executive Officer, Brylin Hospitals, Buffalo, NY, p. A432

PLESS, Katy, Director of Human Resources, Carepartners Health Services, Asheville, NC, p. A457

PLETZ, Richard Andrew., Chief Executive Officer, Plaza Specialty Hospital, Houston, TX, p. A622

PLISKO, Rick, Director information Systems, New York–Presbyterian Brooklyn Methodist Hospital, New Rochelle, NY, p. A444

PLOUCK, Tracy, Director, Ohio Department Of Mental Health, Columbus, OH, p. B94

PLOPPER, Michael M.D., Chief Medical Officer, Sharp Mesa Vista Hospital, San Diego, CA, p. A86

PLOSZEK, Judith M., Chief Financial Officer, Tampa General Hospital, Tampa, FL, p. A145

PLOSZEK, Michael, Vice President Physician Strategy and Clinical Operations, Advocate Good Shepherd Hospital, Barrington, IL, p. A178

PLOUSHA–MOORE, Debra, Senior Vice President Human Resources, Carolinas Medical Center, Charlotte, NC, p. A459

PLUARD, Dennis, Vice President Finance and Operations, Sarah Bush Lincoln Health Center, Mattoon, IL, p. A193

PLUMLEE, Steve, Chief Executive Officer, Select Specialty Hospital–North Knoxville, Powell, TN, p. A588

PLUMMER, Debra, Chief Executive Officer, Kindred Hospital Bay Area–Tampa, Tampa, FL, p. A145

PLUMMER, Doug, Chief Operating Officer, Sabine Medical Center, Many, LA, p. A280

PLUNKETT, Alicia, Chief Nurse Executive, Parkwood Behavioral Health System, Olive Branch, MS, p. A360

PLYMELL, Shane
  Chief Executive Officer, Shannon Medical Center, San Angelo, TX, p. A641
  Chief Operating Officer, Shannon Medical Center, San Angelo, TX, p. A641

PLYWACZYNSKI, Russell J. CPA, Director of Finance, St. Joseph's Hospital Of Buckhannon, Buckhannon, WV, p. A690

POBLETE, Ronald M.D., President Medical and Dental Staff, St. Mary's General Hospital, Passaic, NJ, p. A418

POCCHIARI, Michael, Director Human Resources, Garden Park Medical Center, Gulfport, MS, p. A355

POCOCK, Donald, Vice–President Medical Affairs, Carteret Health Care, Morehead City, NC, p. A467

PODE, Maureen, Co–Interim Executive Director, NYC Health + Hospitals / North Central Bronx, New Rochelle, NY, p. A445

PODESTA, Charles H, Chief Information Officer, Uc Irvine Medical Center, Orange, CA, p. A78

PODGES, Christopher J, Chief Information Officer and Vice President Outpatient and Retail Services, Munson Medical Center, Traverse City, MI, p. A332

PODOLSKY, Daniel, M.D.
  President, University Of Texas Southwestern Medical Center, Dallas, TX, p. A607
  President, William P. Clements, Jr. University Hospital, Dallas, TX, p. A607

PODUSKA, Donna D MS, R.N., Chief Nursing Officer, Poudre Valley Hospital, Fort Collins, CO, p. A102

PODZIMEK, Marcia, Chief Human Resources Officer, Wagner Community Memorial Hospital Avera, Wagner, SD, p. A573

POE, Dale
  Vice President and Chief Financial Officer, Hospital Division, Wellmont Bristol Regional Medical Center, Bristol, TN, p. A575
  Vice President and Chief Financial Officer, Wellmont Hawkins County Memorial Hospital, Rogersville, TN, p. A588
  Vice President Finance and Operations, Wellmont Holston Valley Medical Center, Kingsport, TN, p. A581

POE, Terri Lyn, Interim Chief Nursing Officer, University Of Alabama Hospital, Birmingham, AL, p. A15

POEHLER, Kathy, Vice President, Human Resources, University Of Maryland Baltimore Washington Medical Center, Glen Burnie, MD, p. A298

POEST, Scott, Chief Information Officer, Lake Regional Health System, Osage Beach, MO, p. A374

POFAHL, Barnetta, Director Human Resources, Wagoner Community Hospital, Wagoner, OK, p. A519

PORTER, Stephen D., Chief Executive Officer, Bon Secours St. Francis Hospital, Charleston, SC, p. A558

PORTER, T J, Director Human Resources, Bennett County Hospital And Nursing Home, Martin, SD, p. A570

PORTERFIELD, Liza, Chief Financial Officer, Regional Medical Center, Orangeburg, SC, p. A565

PORTMAN, Angela, Chief Executive Officer, Breckinridge Memorial Hospital, Hardinsburg, KY, p. A259

PORTNER, Barry M.D., Chief of Staff, Prowers Medical Center, Lamar, CO, p. A105

PORWOLL, Amy, Vice President of Information Systems, St. Cloud Hospital, Saint Cloud, MN, p. A347

POSCH, Tim B, Business Manager and Director Personnel, Parsons State Hospital And Training Center, Parsons, KS, p. A249

POSECAI, Scott J, Executive Vice President and Chief Financial Officer, Psychiatric Pavilion New Orleans, New OrleansOchsner Medical Center, New Orleans, LA, p. A283

POSEY, Dawn, Chief Operating Officer, Promise Hospital Of Vicksburg, Vicksburg, MS, p. A362

POSEY, Richard B, Director Human Resources, Baptist Easley Hospital, Easley, SC, p. A561

POSMOGA, Paul, Chief Financial Officer, Twin Cities Community Hospital, Templeton, CA, p. A93

POSPISIL, Matt E., Vice President Perioperative Services, Nebraska Medicine – Bellevue, Bellevue, NE, p. A391

POST, Eleanor R.N., Chief Nursing Officer, Rockdale Medical Center, Conyers, GA, p. A155

POST, Gwen R.N., Chief Nursing Officer, Sanford Worthington Medical Center, Worthington, MN, p. A351

POST, John M.D., Medical Director, Morrill County Community Hospital, Bridgeport, NE, p. A391

POST, Kevin D.O., Chief Medical Officer, Hegg Memorial Health Center Avera, Rock Valley, IA, p. A234

POST, Kimberly
Senior Vice President and Chief Clinical Officer, Honorhealth Scottsdale Thompson Peak Medical Center, Scottsdale, AZ, p. A36
Senior Vice President and Chief Executive Officer, Honorhealth Scottsdale Osborn Medical Center, Scottsdale, AZ, p. A36

POST, Michael, Chief Executive Officer, Clarion Psychiatric Center, Clarion, PA, p. A531

POSTERNACK, Charles M.D., Vice President, Boca Raton Regional Hospital, Boca Raton, FL, p. A120

POSTLER-SLATTERY, Diane, Ph.D., President and Chief Executive Officer, Midmichigan Health, Midland, MI, p. B85

POSTLETHWAIT, Betsy, President, Princeton Baptist Medical Center, Birmingham, AL, p. A15

POSTON, Anne, Director of Human Resources/Compliance, Lake City Community Hospital, Lake City, SC, p. A564

POSTULKA, Carol, Administrative Coordinator, Avera Gregory Hospital, Gregory, SD, p. A570

POTEATE, Kathy, Interim Director Human Resources, Hugh Chatham Memorial Hospital, Elkin, NC, p. A462

POTEETE, Robin, Manager Human Resources, Wellmont Hawkins County Memorial Hospital, Rogersville, TN, p. A588

POTITADKUL, Wendy, Chief Information Officer, Sunrise Canyon Hospital, Lubbock, TX, p. A630

POTTENGER, Jay, Administrator, Montana State Hospital, Warm Springs, MT, p. A389

POTTER, Carolyn
Vice President Human Resources, Mclaren Bay Region, Bay City, MI, p. A315
Vice President Human Resources, Mclaren Bay Special Care, Bay City, MI, p. A315
Vice President Human Resources, Mclaren Central Michigan, Mount Pleasant, MI, p. A326

POTTER, Dianne P, Manager Human Resources, Parkview Whitley Hospital, Columbia City, IN, p. A205

POTTER, Val, Director Human Resources, St. Vincent Salem Hospital, Salem, IN, p. A219

POTTORFF, Kelly, Chief Executive Officer, Cheyenne County Hospital, Saint Francis, KS, p. A251

POTTS, Kevin M.D., Medical Director, Kindred Hospital Detroit, Detroit, MI, p. A318

POTTS, Mary Ann, Director Personnel, Community Hospitals And Wellness Centers, Bryan, OH, p. A482

POUGNAUD, Teresa, Vice President Human Resources, Mcleod Loris Seacoast Hospital, Loris, SC, p. A564

POULSON, Rhonda, Chief Nursing Officer and Vice President of Clinical Operations, Chi Memorial, Chattanooga, TN, p. A576

POUND, Steve, Vice President Human Resources, St. Joseph's Hospital, Savannah, GA, p. A165

POUND, Terry, Chief Financial Officer, Hospital District No 1 Of Rice County, Lyons, KS, p. A246

POUND, Veronica, R.N.
Interim Administrator and Director of Patient Care, Socorro General Hospital, Socorro, NM, p. A429

Administrator, Socorro General Hospital, Socorro, NM, p. A429

POVICH, Mark D.O., Medical Director, OSF St. Francis Hospital And Medical Group, Escanaba, MI, p. A319

POWE, Lee, Director Management Information Systems, Hugh Chatham Memorial Hospital, Elkin, NC, p. A462

POWEL, Linda J M.D., Medical Director, Odessa Memorial Healthcare Center, Odessa, WA, p. A683

POWELL, Adam, Program Manager, Marion Veterans Affairs Medical Center, Marion, IL, p. A192

POWELL, Candy, Administrator, Collingsworth General Hospital, Wellington, TX, p. A653

POWELL, Charles, Chief Financial Officer, Arkansas Surgical Hospital, North Little Rock, AR, p. A47

POWELL, D Jerome M.D., Chief Information Officer, Strong Memorial Hospital Of The University Of Rochester, Rochester, NY, p. A451

POWELL, Hannah, Chief Nursing Officer, Mercy Hospital Kingfisher, Kingfisher, OK, p. A509

POWELL, Jackie, Director Human Resources, Pemiscot Memorial Health System, Hayti, MO, p. A369

POWELL, James R, Associate Administrator, Banner Gateway Medical Center, Gilbert, AZ, p. A29

POWELL, Jimmy, Manager Human Resources, Harry S. Truman Memorial Veterans Hospital, Columbia, MO, p. A367

POWELL, Josh, Facility Controller, Cox Monett Hospital, Monett, MO, p. A374

POWELL, Kay, Director Human Resources, Christus Southeast Texas Jasper Memorial, Jasper, TX, p. A625

POWELL, Michelle, Chief Executive Officer, Select Rehabilitation Hospital Of Denton, Denton, TX, p. A608

POWELL, Mike, Chief Executive Officer, Fulton Medical Center, Fulton, MO, p. A368

POWELL, Parker, Chief Executive Officer, Glendive Medical Center, Glendive, MT, p. A384

POWELL, Tammy, FACHE, M.P.H., President, St. Anthony Hospital, Oklahoma City, OK, p. A513

POWELL, Traci, Director Human Resources, Healthsouth Emerald Coast Rehabilitation Hospital, Panama City, FL, p. A138

POWELL, Virginia, Director Finance, Wilmington Treatment Center, Wilmington, NC, p. A472

POWELL–STAFFORD, Valerie L., Chief Executive Officer, Englewood Community Hospital, Englewood, FL, p. A124

POWELSON, Jeffrey A., Interim Chief Executive Officer, Webster County Memorial Hospital, Webster Springs, WV, p. A696

POWER, Bob, Vice President Information Services, Good Samaritan Regional Medical Center, Corvallis, OR, p. A521

POWER, Robert
Associate Executive Director Finance, Southside Hospital, Bay Shore, NY, p. A431
Chief Information Officer, Samaritan Pacific Communities Hospital, Newport, OR, p. A524
Vice President Information Services, Samaritan Lebanon Community Hospital, Lebanon, OR, p. A523

POWERS, Barbara R.N., Chief Nursing Officer, Austin Lakes Hospital, Austin, TX, p. A594

POWERS, Brent M.D., Vice President/Chief Medical Officer, Lexington Medical Center, West Columbia, SC, p. A567

POWERS, Charles M.D., Administrative Medical Director, Wk Bossier Health Center, Bossier City, LA, p. A272

POWERS, Jamekia, Assistant Director Human Resources, Georgia Regional Hospital At Savannah, Savannah, GA, p. A164

POWERS, Judi, Chief Executive Officer, Advanced Care Hospital Of Montana, Billings, MT, p. A382

POWERS, Kelli, Chief Financial Officer, Huntsville Hospital, Huntsville, AL, p. A19

POWERS, Mary, R.N., MSN
Senior Vice President and Chief Nursing Officer, Manchester Memorial Hospital, Manchester, CT, p. A110
Senior Vice President and Chief Nursing Officer, Rockville General Hospital, Vernon, CT, p. A113

POWERS, Ryan J., Vice President Finance, Spectrum Health Zeeland Community Hospital, Zeeland, MI, p. A334

POWERS, Tim, Chief Executive Officer, North Canyon Medical Center, Gooding, ID, p. A173

POWRIE, Raymond M.D., Senior Vice President Quality and Clinical Effectiveness, Women & Infants Hospital Of Rhode Island, Providence, RI, p. A557

POYNTER, Carmen, Director Human Resources, Rockcastle Regional Hospital And Respiratory Care Center, Mount Vernon, KY, p. A265

PRABHU, Asha M.D., Chief Medical Officer, Warren State Hospital, Warren, PA, p. A552

PRACHEIL, Michael, Chief Financial Officer, Gothenburg Health, Gothenburg, NE, p. A393

PRACHT, Matthew, Vice President Finance, Scotland Health Care System, Laurinburg, NC, p. A466

PRADA, Janina
Director Information Services, University Medical Center Of El Paso, El Paso, TX, p. A612
Director Information Technology, El Paso Children's Hospital, El Paso, TX, p. A610

PRAFKA, David Ed.D., Director of Human Resources, Vidant Edgecombe Hospital, Tarboro, NC, p. A471

PRAKASH, Amitabh M.D., Chief Medical Officer, Ahmc Anaheim Regional Medical Center, Anaheim, CA, p. A51

PRAKASH, Vijay, Information Technology Officer, Essex County Hospital Center, Cedar Grove, NJ, p. A412

PRANTE, Melissa, Chief Financial Officer, Kimball Health Services, Kimball, NE, p. A394

PRASAD, Siripurapu, Chief of Staff, Harrison Community Hospital, Cadiz, OH, p. A482

PRATER, Judith, Director of Nursing, Pike County Memorial Hospital, Louisiana, MO, p. A372

PRATER, Marita MS, R.N., Vice President Patient Care Services, Sturdy Memorial Hospital, Attleboro, MA, p. A302

PRATER, Marsha A Ph.D., R.N., Senior Vice President and Chief Nursing Officer, Memorial Medical Center, Springfield, IL, p. A200

PRATER, Robin, Director Human Resources, Howard A. Rusk Rehabilitation Center, Columbia, MO, p. A367

PRATHER, Jean, Director of Human Resources, Greene County General Hospital, Linton, IN, p. A215

PRATHER, Rachael, Chief Nursing Officer, Ferrell Hospital, Eldorado, IL, p. A186

PRATT, Audra, Chief Human Resource Officer, St. Vincent Indianapolis Hospital, IndianapolisSt. Vincent Heart Center, Indianapolis, IN, p. A212

PRATT, Bailey, Chief Financial Officer, Saint Thomas Rutherford Hospital, Murfreesboro, TN, p. A586

PRATT, Dustin M.D., Chief of Staff, Childress Regional Medical Center, Childress, TX, p. A601

PRATT, Lisa D.
Vice President Human Resources, Memorial Hospital Of Rhode Island, Pawtucket, RI, p. A556
Vice President, Human Resources, Mclean Hospital, Belmont, MA, p. A302

PRATT, Mary Ellen., FACHE, Chief Executive Officer, St. James Parish Hospital, Lutcher, LA, p. A280

PRATT, Ramona, Chief Operating Officer, Pih Health Hospital – Downey, Downey, CA, p. A58

PRATT, Timothy J M.D., Vice President Medical Affairs and Chief Medical Officer, SSM Health St. Clare Hospital – Fenton, Fenton, MO, p. A368

PRATT, Troy, Information Technology Site Director, Covenant Medical Center, Lubbock, TX, p. A630

PRAY, Jan, Coordinator Payroll and Benefits, Curahealth Boston North Shore, Peabody, MA, p. A310

PREAU, William M.D., Medical Director, Fairway Medical Surgical Hospital, Covington, LA, p. A273

PREISINGER, Andrea, Director Human Resources, Menninger Clinic, Houston, TX, p. A622

PREMO, Mark, Senior Director HC Intelligence, Providence Portland Medical Center, Portland, OR, p. A525

PRENTISS, Kristin, Chief Financial Officer, Specialty Hospital Of Central Jersey, Lakewood, NJ, p. A415

PRESCOTT, Tina, Vice President, Hospital Services, Jackson–Madison County General Hospital, Jackson, TN, p. A580

PRESNELL, Elizabeth, Assistant Vice President of Finance, St. Luke's Hospital, Columbus, NC, p. A460

PRESS, Robert M.D., Senior Vice President, Vice Dean and Chief Hospital Operations, NYU Langone Hospitals, New Rochelle, NY, p. A446

PRESSER, Jonathan, Vice President Finance and Operations, Norton Audubon Hospital, Louisville, KY, p. A263

PRESSMAN, Eric D.O., Chair Department of Medicine, Englewood Community Hospital, Englewood, FL, p. A124

PRESTEGAARD, Benjamin, Chief Medical Officer, Uh Portage Medical Center, Ravenna, OH, p. A498

PRESTON, Tara
Director Human Resources, Bingham Memorial Hospital, Blackfoot, ID, p. A171
Director Human Resources, Mountain River Birthing And Surgery Center, Blackfoot, ID, p. A171

PRESTON, Troy, Director Human Resources, Schuyler Hospital, Montour Falls, NY, p. A439

PRESTRIDGE, Tim, Interim Chief Financial Officer, Logan Memorial Hospital, Russellville, KY, p. A267

PRETE, Mark M.D., Vice President Medical Affairs, The Charlotte Hungerford Hospital, Torrington, CT, p. A113

PRETTYMAN, Edgar E., PsyD, Chief Executive Officer, Texas Neurorehab Center, Austin, TX, p. A596

PRETZLAFF, Robert, M.D.
Chief Medical Officer, St. Rose Dominican Hospitals – San Martin Campus, Las Vegas, NV, p. A404
Chief Medical Officer, St. Rose Dominican Hospitals – Siena Campus, Henderson, NV, p. A402

PREWITT, Connie F, Chief Financial Officer, Billings Clinic, Billings, MT, p. A382

PREWITT, Margaret Elizabeth, Vice President Patient Services and Chief Nursing Officer, St. Catherine Hospital, Garden City, KS, p. A241

PRIBYL, Stephen J., FACHE, President, District One Hospital, Faribault, MN, p. A339

PRICE, Bernard J, Chief Human Resources Officer, Medical Center, Navicent Health, Macon, GA, p. A161

PRICE, Connie M.D., Chief Medical Officer, Denver Health, Denver, CO, p. A100

PRICE, David
Chief Executive Officer, Honorhealth Deer Valley Medical Center, Phoenix, AZ, p. A33
Chief Executive Officer, Honorhealth Scottsdale Thompson Peak Medical Center, Scottsdale, AZ, p. A36

PRICE, Ed, Chief Nurse Officer, Shelby Baptist Medical Center, Alabaster, AL, p. A13

PRICE, James, Hospital Administrator, State Hospital South, Blackfoot, ID, p. A171

PRICE, John D, Chief Financial Officer, Firsthealth Richmond Memorial Hospital, Rockingham, NC, p. A469

PRICE, John Stephen M.D., Chief of Staff, Fairview Regional Medical Center, Fairview, OK, p. A508

PRICE, Kelley, R.N.
Chief Nursing Officer, Battle Mountain General Hospital, Battle Mountain, NV, p. A401
Interim Chief Executive Officer, Battle Mountain General Hospital, Battle Mountain, NV, p. A401

PRICE, Kevin A
Vice President and Chief Operating Officer, Sparrow Clinton Hospital, Saint Johns, MI, p. A330
Vice President and Chief Operating Officer, Sparrow Ionia Hospital, Ionia, MI, p. A323

PRICE, Kim, Chief Executive Officer, Franklin General Hospital, Hampton, IA, p. A228

PRICE, Kyle, Interim Chief Executive Officer, Memorial Hermann Greater Heights Hospital, Houston, TX, p. A621

PRICE, Larry, Chief Executive Officer, Limestone Medical Center, Groesbeck, TX, p. A617

PRICE, Lawrence, M.D., President and Chief Operating Officer, Butler Hospital, Providence, RI, p. A556

PRICE, Lori, President, Gottlieb Memorial Hospital, Melrose Park, IL, p. A193

PRICE, Lorraine B, Associate Director, Hampton Veterans Affairs Medical Center, Hampton, VA, p. A668

PRICE, Manuel, Director Information Systems, Brookwood Baptist Medical Center, Birmingham, AL, p. A14

PRICE, Meredith, Vice President Fiscal Services and Chief Financial Officer, St. Joseph's Hospital Health Center, Syracuse, NY, p. A453

PRICE, Norman M., FACHE, Chief Executive Officer, Southwest Mississippi Regional Medical Center, Mccomb, MS, p. A358

PRICE, Sam, Executive Vice President Finance/Chief Financial Officer, East Alabama Medical Center, Opelika, AL, p. A22

PRICE, Shari, Director Information Services, Baptist Health Louisville, Louisville, KY, p. A262

PRICE, Shelby, Chief Executive Officer , Louisiana State Hospitals, Baton Rouge, LA, p. B79

PRICE, Terry, Director Information Technology, Great Plains Regional Medical Center, Elk City, OK, p. A507

PRICE, Tonya, Chief Nursing Officer, Wilson N. Jones Regional Medical Center, Sherman, TX, p. A645

PRICE, Walter, Director Information Technology, Newport Hospital And Health Services, Newport, WA, p. A682

PRICE–GHARZEDDINE, Karen, R.N., MS, Chief Executive Officer, San Gabriel Valley Medical Center, San Gabriel, CA, p. A88

PRICE–YONTS, Melody, Chief Executive Officer, Acoma–Canoncito–Laguna Hospital, Acoma, NM, p. A424

PRICKEL, Trisha, Director Information Systems, Margaret Mary Health, Batesville, IN, p. A203

PRIDDY, Ernest C III, Chief Financial Officer, Old Vineyard Behavioral Health Services, Winston, NC, p. A473

PRIDDY, Steven L. M.D., Vice President Physician Affairs and Chief Medical Officer, St. Vincent Carmel Hospital, Carmel, IN, p. A205

PRIDEAUX, Heather, Chief Financial Officer, Rawlins County Health Center, Atwood, KS, p. A238

PRIDGEN, Kim
Chief Financial Officer, Houston County Community Hospital, Erin, TN, p. A578

Chief Financial Officer, Northcrest Medical Center, Springfield, TN, p. A589

PRIDGEN, Parker, Chief Financial Officer, Central Texas Medical Center, San Marcos, TX, p. A644

PRIES, Kathleen M, Director Human Resources, Nazareth Hospital, Philadelphia, PA, p. A545

PRIEST, David, Director Information Systems, Munson Healthcare Charlevoix Hospital, Charlevoix, MI, p. A316

PRIEST, Geoff M.D., Chief Medical Officer, Unitypoint Health Meriter, Madison, WI, p. A705

PRIEST, Mike M.D., Chief of Staff, Pawhuska Hospital, Pawhuska, OK, p. A514

PRIESTLEY, Betty, Manager Business Office, Pine Valley Specialty Hospital, Houston, TX, p. A622

PRIETTO, Carlos, President and Chief Executive Officer, Hoag Orthopedic Institute, Irvine, CA, p. A63

PRIHODA, Matt M.D., Chief of Staff, Washington County Hospital And Clinics, Washington, IA, p. A236

PRILUTSKY, Michael, Chief Operating Officer, Jersey City Medical Center, Jersey City, NJ, p. A415

PRINCE, Clay M.D., Chief Medical Officer, Madison Memorial Hospital, Rexburg, ID, p. A175

PRINCE, Gayle, Director Human Resources, Washington County Regional Medical Center, Sandersville, GA, p. A164

PRINCE, Kem, Manager of Finance, Parkview Noble Hospital, Kendallville, IN, p. A213

PRINCE, Michele, Chief Operating Officer, Lewis County General Hospital, Lowville, NY, p. A438

PRINCE, Sue, Director Information Systems, Northern Westchester Hospital, Mount Kisco, NY, p. A440

PRINCE, Tina R.N., Associate Director Patient Care Services, Chief Nursing Officer, New Mexico Veterans Affairs Health Care System – Raymond G. Murphy Medical Center, Albuquerque, NM, p. A424

PRINCIPE, Hector Cintron M.D., Director, Hospital Universitario Dr. Ramon Ruiz Arnau, Bayamon, PR, p. A722

PRINGLE–MILLER, Letitia, Administrative Director, Palmetto Health Tuomey, Sumter, SC, p. A566

PRINTY, Wayne, Chief Financial Officer and Senior Vice President Finance, Lincolnhealth, Damariscotta, ME, p. A290

PRIORE, Jacqueline, Chief Nursing Officer, Samaritan Hospital, Troy, NY, p. A454

PRISELAC, Thomas M., President and Chief Executive Officer, Cedars–Sinai Medical Center, Los Angeles, CA, p. A67

PRISTER, James R.
President and Chief Executive Officer, Rml Specialty Hospital, Chicago, IL, p. A183
President and Chief Executive Officer, Rml Specialty Hospital, Hinsdale, IL, p. A190

PRITCHARD, Jason, Chief Financial Officer, Hackensack Meridian Health Pascack Valley Medical Center, Westwood, NJ, p. A423

PRITCHARD, Joann, Chief Financial Officer, Erie Veterans Affairs Medical Center, Erie, PA, p. A534

PRITCHETT, Greg, Chief Financial Officer, Cuero Community Hospital, Cuero, TX, p. A604

PRITCHETT, Lynette, Chief Executive Officer, Tennova Healthcare–Jamestown, Jamestown, TN, p. A580

PRITTS, Robert
Chief Executive Officer and Market Executive, SSM Select Rehabilitation Hospital, Richmond Heights, MO, p. A375
Chief Executive Officer, SSM Select Rehabilitation Hospital, Richmond Heights, MO, p. A375

PRIVETT, David, Deputy Director, Western New York Children's Hospital Psychiatric Center, West Seneca, NY, p. A455

PROBASCO, Brent, Chief Financial Officer, Cass Regional Medical Center, Harrisonville, MO, p. A368

PROBST, Keith M.D., Chief of Staff, Avera Holy Family Hospital, Estherville, IA, p. A227

PROBST, Nancy R.N., Chief Nursing Officer, Bigfork Valley Hospital, Bigfork, MN, p. A336

PROBUS, Kimberly, Chief Nursing Officer, Opelousas General Health System, Opelousas, LA, p. A284

PROCHASKA, Jodi, Chief Financial Officer, Butler County Health Care Center, David City, NE, p. A392

PROCHILO, John F. Jr, Chief Executive Officer, Northeast Rehabilitation Hospital, Salem, NH, p. A410

PROCHNOW, Bryan, Chief Financial Officer, Matagorda Regional Medical Center, Bay City, TX, p. A596

PROCTOR, Brandy, Director of Nursing, North Star Behavioral Health System, Anchorage, AK, p. A25

PROCTOR, Jason J., Chief Operating Officer, Christus Mother Frances Hospital – Tyler, Tyler, TX, p. A650

PROCTOR, Quinn, Director Human Resources, Claremore Indian Hospital, Claremore, OK, p. A506

PROCTOR, Sandra R.N., MS, Chief Nurse Executive, Memorial Medical Center, Modesto, CA, p. A74

PROCTOR, Scott, Chief Executive Officer, Safe Haven Hospital Of Treasure Valley, Boise, ID, p. A171

PROCTOR, Stephen, Director of Human Resources/Risk, Russellville Hospital, Russellville, AL, p. A23

PROFOTA, Lori R.N., Chief Nursing Officer, Copley Hospital, Morrisville, VT, p. A662

PROKOPCHAK, Greg, Senior Director Human Resources, Piedmont Hospital, Atlanta, GA, p. A150

PRONGER, Derk F, Chief Operating Officer, Munson Medical Center, Traverse City, MI, p. A332

PRONI, John CPA, Manager Finance and Operations, Baycare Alliant Hospital, Dunedin, FL, p. A124

PROPP, Elizabeth R, Vice President Finance and Chief Financial Officer, Dameron Hospital, Stockton, CA, p. A92

PROSKE, Donna, MS, R.N., Executive Director, Staten Island University Hospital, New Rochelle, NY, p. A446

PROSKOCIL, Danielle, Director Human Resources, Valley County Health System, Ord, NE, p. A398

PROSPER, Charles
Chief Executive Officer, Alta Bates Summit Medical Center – Summit Campus, Oakland, CA, p. A77
Chief Executive Officer, Alta Bates Summit Medical Center, Berkeley, CA, p. A53

PROSSER, Alita, Chief Financial Officer, Scott & White Medical Center – Temple, Temple, TX, p. A648

PROSSER, Edna, Chief Nursing Officer, Ozark Health Medical Center, Clinton, AR, p. A41

PROSSER, Joseph M.D., Chief Medical Officer, Texas Health Harris Methodist Hospital Fort Worth, Fort Worth, TX, p. A614

PROSTKO, Michael M.D., Chief of Staff, Rhea Medical Center, Dayton, TN, p. A578

PROUD, James, Vice President Human Resources and Marketing, Uniontown Hospital, Uniontown, PA, p. A552

PROUJANSKY, Roy, M.D., Chief Executive Officer, Alfred I. Dupont Hospital For Children, Wilmington, DE, p. A116

PROVENZANO, Jeff
Vice President and Chief Financial Officer, Midmichigan Medical Center–Clare, Clare, MI, p. A316
Vice President and Chief Financial Officer, Midmichigan Medical Center–Gladwin, Gladwin, MI, p. A320
Vice President and Chief Financial Officer, Midmichigan Medical Center–Gratiot, Alma, MI, p. A314

PROVENZANO, Stacey, Chief Operating Officer, Greystone Park Psychiatric Hospital, Morris Plains, NJ, p. A416

PROVINCE, Steven
Interim President and Chief Executive Officer, Providence Healthcare Network, Waco, TX, p. A652
Senior Vice President and Chief Operating Officer, Providence Healthcare Network, Waco, TX, p. A652

PRUESS, Mark M.D., Chief Medical Staff, Sparta Community Hospital, Sparta, IL, p. A200

PRUETT–BAER, Karen, Senior Nurse Executive, Naval Hospital Oak Harbor, Oak Harbor, WA, p. A683

PRUITT, Elizabeth Ann, Chief Operating Officer, Affinity Medical Center, Massillon, OH, p. A495

PRUITT, Jeffrey M.D., Chief of Staff, Mercy Hospital Of Defiance, Defiance, OH, p. A490

PRUKOP, Jeff, Director Professional Services, Jackson County Hospital District, Edna, TX, p. A610

PRUNCHUNAS, Edward M, Executive Vice President and Chief Financial Officer, Cedars–Sinai Medical Center, Los Angeles, CA, p. A67

PRUNOSKE, Mark, Chief Financial Officer and Senior Vice President Finance, F. F. Thompson Hospital, Canandaigua, NY, p. A433

PRUSATIS, Michael, Vice President Finance, DMC – Sinai–Grace Hospital, Detroit, MI, p. A317

PRYBYLO, Mary, President and Chief Executive Officer, St. Joseph Hospital, Bangor, ME, p. A289

PRYOR, David, President, Athens–Limestone Hospital, Athens, AL, p. A14

PRYOR, Jon, M.D., Chief Executive Officer, Hennepin County Medical Center, Minneapolis, MN, p. A343

PRYOR, William B, Chief Human Resources Officer, Cape Fear Valley Medical Center, Fayetteville, NC, p. A464

PRZESTRZELSKI, David, Associate Director, Patient Care Services and Chief Nursing Executive, Charles George Veterans Affairs Medical Center, Asheville, NC, p. A457

PRZYBYLSKI, David, Controller, Sparrow Specialty Hospital, Lansing, MI, p. A324

PSAILA, Justin P M.D., Vice President Medical Affairs, St. Luke's Hospital – Anderson Campus, Easton, PA, p. A534

PSCODNA, Susan, Director Human Resources, Mercy Hospital Of Defiance, Defiance, OH, p. A490

PU, Steve D.O., Chief Medical Officer, Poplar Bluff Regional Medical Center, Poplar Bluff, MO, p. A375

PUCHBAUER, Aaron, Interim Chief Executive Officer, Hshs St. Francis Hospital, Litchfield, IL, p. A192

PUCKETT, Clay, Assistant Administrator and Chief Information Officer, Blount Memorial Hospital, Maryville, TN, p. A583

PUCKETT, Doug, President, Indiana University Health West Hospital, Avon, IN, p. A203

PUCKETT, Kristi, Director Human Resources, Grande Ronde Hospital, La Grande, OR, p. A523

PUCLIK, Becky, Division Chief People Officer, St. John's Hospital, Springfield, IL, p. A201

PUENTES, Francisco, Human Resource Officer, San Diego County Psychiatric Hospital, San Diego, CA, p. A86

PUFFENBERGER, James, Vice President and Chief Financial Officer, Mercy Hospital Of Defiance, Defiance, OH, p. A490

PUFFENBERGER, Sheila, Manager Information Technology, Hillsdale Hospital, Hillsdale, MI, p. A322

PUGACH, Judy, Chief Nursing Officer, Pih Health Hospital – Downey, Downey, CA, p. A58

PUGH, Larry, Vice President and Chief Financial Officer, Beverly Hospital, Montebello, CA, p. A74

PUGH, Marcia M.D., Chief Nursing Officer, Bryan W. Whitfield Memorial Hospital, Demopolis, AL, p. A16

PUGH, Marsha, Director Human Resources, Bryan W. Whitfield Memorial Hospital, Demopolis, AL, p. A16

PUGH, Melodee, Director Human Resources, Navarro Regional Hospital, Corsicana, TX, p. A603

PUGH, William H, Senior Vice President Corporate Finance and Chief Financial Officer, Pinnaclehealth Harrisburg Hospital, Harrisburg, PA, p. A536

PUGSLEY, Tim, Chief Information Officer, Orthonebraska Hospital, Omaha, NE, p. A398

PUHL, Cathy A., Vice President Human Resources, Chambersburg Hospital, Chambersburg, PA, p. A531

PUHY, Dorothy E, Executive VP and Chief Operating Officer, Dana–Farber Cancer Institute, Boston, MA, p. A303

PUKALA, Shirley R.N., Assistant Administrator Operations, St. Lawrence Rehabilitation Center, Lawrenceville, NJ, p. A415

PULASKI, Jason, Controller, Healthsouth Reading Rehabilitation Hospital, Reading, PA, p. A549

PULEO, Mark, Vice President and Chief Human Resources Officer, Henry Mayo Newhall Hospital, Valencia, CA, p. A95

PULIDO, Michael, Chief Administrative Officer, Mosaic Life Care At St. Joseph, Saint Joseph, MO, p. A376

PULLARKAT, Sajit, Chief Executive Officer and Managing Director, Centennial Hills Hospital Medical Center, Las Vegas, NV, p. A402

PULLEN, Connie R.N., Chief Nursing Officer, Willamette Valley Medical Center, Mcminnville, OR, p. A523

PULLIAM, Elizabeth, Chief Financial Officer, Christus Mother Frances Hospital – Jacksonville, Jacksonville, TX, p. A625

PULLIN, Dennis W., FACHE, Chief Executive Officer, Virtua Health, Marlton, NJ, p. B145

PULLMAN, Debbie, Director Finance, Avera Hand County Memorial Hospital, Miller, SD, p. A571

PULLMAN, Jayson, Chief Executive Officer, Hawarden Regional Healthcare, Hawarden, IA, p. A229

PULSIPHER, Gary W., President and Chief Executive Officer, Mercy Hospital Joplin, Joplin, MO, p. A370

PULVER, Dayna, Director of Nursing, Friend Community Healthcare System, Friend, NE, p. A393

PUMMEL, Keely, Director, Financial Operations, Ohiohealth Dublin Methodist Hospital, Dublin, OH, p. A490

PUMPHREY, Robbin K, Chief Nursing Officer, Jackson Hospital, Marianna, FL, p. A131

PUNG, Margaret R.N., Chief Nursing Officer, University Of Texas Harris County Psychiatric Center, Houston, TX, p. A623

PUNJABI, Rishab, Chief Financial Officer, Kindred Hospital–La Mirada, La Mirada, CA, p. A64

PUNTEL, Jackie, Senior Director Human Resources, Cleveland Clinic Florida, Weston, FL, p. A148

PUORTO, Charlene, Chief Nursing Officer, Capital District Psychiatric Center, Albany, NY, p. A430

PURCELL, Deborah, Director of Information Technology, Caldwell Unc Health Care, Lenoir, NC, p. A466

PURCELL, Terrance J, Vice President Support Services and Ambulatory Care, Blue Mountain Hospital, Lehighton, PA, p. A539

PURCELL, Terry, Director Information Services, Lea Regional Medical Center, Hobbs, NM, p. A426

PURDY, Bruce M.D., Chief of Staff, Muleshoe Area Medical Center, Muleshoe, TX, p. A634

PURINGTON, Denise, Vice President and Chief Information Officer, Elliot Hospital, Manchester, NH, p. A409

PURINTON, Sandy, Chief Nursing Officer, Trego County–Lemke Memorial Hospital, Wakeeney, KS, p. A253

PURKIS, Sharon, Administrator, Select Specialty Hospital–Muskegon, Muskegon, MI, p. A327

PUROHIT, Divyesh M.D., Chief of Staff, Sullivan County Community Hospital, Sullivan, IN, p. A220

PUROHIT, Kumar, Chief Financial Officer, Rockford Center, Newark, DE, p. A115

PUROHIT, Shamb, Chief Financial Officer, Colquitt Regional Medical Center, Moultrie, GA, p. A162

PURRINGTON, Janice, Coordinator Medical Records, Avera Hand County Memorial Hospital, Miller, SD, p. A571

PURSLEY, Roger, Chief Executive Officer, Western Mental Health Institute, Bolivar, TN, p. A575

PURTLE, Mark, M.D.
Vice President Medical Affairs, Unitypoint Health – Iowa Methodist Medical Center, Des Moines, IA, p. A226
Vice President Medical Affairs, Unitypoint Health–Iowa Lutheran Hospital, Des Moines, IA, p. A226

PURUSHOTHAM, Sanjay, Executive Director Information Systems, Bon Secours Baltimore Health System, Baltimore, MD, p. A294

PURVANCE, Clint, M.D., President and Chief Executive Officer, Barton Memorial Hospital, South Lake Tahoe, CA, p. A92

PURVES, Stephen A., FACHE, President and Chief Executive Officer, Maricopa Integrated Health System, Phoenix, AZ, p. A33

PURVIS, Jay, President and Chief Executive Officer, Wabash General Hospital, Mount Carmel, IL, p. A194

PURVIS, Kevin, Chief Information Officer, Community Howard Regional Health, Kokomo, IN, p. A213

PURVIS, Michael L., Chief Executive Officer, Cook Medical Center–A Campus Of Tift Regional Medical Center, Adel, GA, p. A149

PURVIS, Mike, Chief Administrative Officer, Sutter Santa Rosa Regional Hospital, Santa Rosa, CA, p. A91

PUSHARD, Roland, Director of Nursing, Riverview Psychiatric Center, Augusta, ME, p. A289

PUSTINA, Karl, Vice President Finance, Upland Hills Health, Dodgeville, WI, p. A700

PUSZKARSKA, Lucyna M. M.D., Medical Director, Riveredge Hospital, Forest Park, IL, p. A188

PUTHOFF, Timothy, Chief Executive Officer, Houston Northwest Medical Center, Houston, TX, p. A621

PUTNAM, Mark M.D., Medical Director, Haven Behavioral Hospital Of Eastern Pennsylvania, Reading, PA, p. A549

PUTNAM, Maureen M, Director Human Resources, OSS Orthopaedic Hospital, York, PA, p. A555

PUTNAM, Stewart C, Executive Vice President and Chief Operating Officer, Unity Hospital, Rochester, NY, p. A451

PUTNAM, Timothy L., FACHE, President and Chief Executive Officer, Margaret Mary Health, Batesville, IN, p. A203

PUTZ, Kim R.N., Director, Nursing Hospital, Ridgeview Le Sueur Medical Center, Le Sueur, MN, p. A342

PUVOGEL, LuAnn, R.N., Chief Executive Officer, Salina Surgical Hospital, Salina, KS, p. A251

PUYAU, Susan M.D., Medical Director, Woman's Hospital, Baton Rouge, LA, p. A271

PUZO, Thomas C., President and Chief Executive Officer, Cornerstone Of Medical Arts Center Hospital, Fresh Meadows, NY, p. A436

PUZZUTO, David M.D., Vice President Medical Affairs and Chief Medical Officer, Waterbury Hospital, Waterbury, CT, p. A114

PYGON, Bernard M.D., Chief Medical Officer, University Of Illinois Hospital & Health Sciences System, Chicago, IL, p. A184

PYLE, Diana, Director Human Resources and Executive Assistant to Chief Executive Officer, Cedar County Memorial Hospital, El Dorado Springs, MO, p. A367

PYLE, Julia R.N., Chief Nursing Officer, Newman Regional Health, Emporia, KS, p. A240

PYLE, Rick, Director Information Systems, Harrisburg Medical Center, Harrisburg, IL, p. A189

PYLE FARRELL, Martha, Vice President Human Resources and General Counsel, Massachusetts Eye And Ear Infirmary, Boston, MA, p. A303

PYNE, Mel
Chief Executive Officer, Candler County Hospital, Metter, GA, p. A161
Chief Executive Officer, Emanuel Medical Center, Swainsboro, GA, p. A165
Regional Chief Executive Officer, Dorminy Medical Center, Fitzgerald, GA, p. A158

PYRAH, Scott, Director Information Systems, St. Luke's Rehabilitation Hospital, Boise, ID, p. A172

Q

QUACKENBUSH, Kirk M.D., Chief of Staff, Platte Valley Medical Center, Brighton, CO, p. A99

QUAGLIERI, Mike, Chief Financial Officer, North Central Surgical Center, Dallas, TX, p. A606

QUALIA, Leigh Ann, Director Human Resources, Val Verde Regional Medical Center, Del Rio, TX, p. A608

QUALLS, Brenda, Chief Financial Officer, Oconee Regional Medical Center, Milledgeville, GA, p. A161

QUAM, David M.D., Area Medical Director, Kaiser Permanente Fontana Medical Center, Fontana, CA, p. A59

QUAMMEN, Becky, Chief Information Officer, Howard University Hospital, Washington, DC, p. A117

QUARANTE, Dino CPA, Chief Financial Officer, Oasis Behavioral Health – Chandler, Chandler, AZ, p. A28

QUARLES, Christopher M.D., Director Medical Services, Naval Hospital Jacksonville, Jacksonville, FL, p. A128

QUATE, Becky, Vice President Nursing and Patient Care Services, Iredell Health System, Statesville, NC, p. A471

QUATROCHE, Thomas J. Jr, Chief Executive Officer, Erie County Medical Center, Buffalo, NY, p. A432

QUATTROCCHI, Robert, President and Chief Executive Officer, Northside Hospital, Atlanta, GA, p. A150

QUEBEDEAUX, Jay, Chief Executive Officer, Mena Regional Health System, Mena, AR, p. A47

QUEBODEAUX, Bryce, Chief Executive Officer, Abrom Kaplan Memorial Hospital, Kaplan, LA, p. A277

QUEEN, Sharon H R.N., Chief Nursing Officer, Clearview Regional Medical Center, Monroe, GA, p. A162

QUENAN, James M.D., Chief Medical Officer, Amery Hospital And Clinic, Amery, WI, p. A698

QUESNEL, Brenda R.N., Vice President of Patient Care and Chief Nursing Officer, West Calcasieu Cameron Hospital, Sulphur, LA, p. A287

QUICCI, London, Chief Operating Officer, DMC – Sinai–Grace Hospital, Detroit, MI, p. A317

QUICHOCHO, Vince, Manager Information Systems, Guam Memorial Hospital Authority, Tamuning, GU, p. A721

QUIGLEY, Stephen J., Chief Executive Officer, Southwood Psychiatric Hospital, Pittsburgh, PA, p. A547

QUILLIN, Gayla, Administrator, Parmer Medical Center, Friona, TX, p. A615

QUIN, Robert, Vice President Finance and Chief Financial Officer, Unitypoint Health – Peoria, Peoria, IL, p. A197

QUINLAN, Christine MS, R.N., Chief Nursing Officer, Alexian Brothers Behavioral Health Hospital, Hoffman Estates, IL, p. A190

QUINLAN, Patrick J M.D., Chief Executive Officer, Psychiatric Pavilion New Orleans, New OrleansOchsner Medical Center, New Orleans, LA, p. A283

QUINLIVAN, John, Chief Executive Officer, Redmond Regional Medical Center, Rome, GA, p. A163

QUINLIVAN, Kathy, Director Management Information Systems, Avera Sacred Heart Hospital, Yankton, SD, p. A574

QUINN, Clifton, Chief Executive Officer, Regency Hospital Of Meridian, Meridian, MS, p. A359

QUINN, Donna, Vice President Operations, Driscoll Children's Hospital, Corpus Christi, TX, p. A603

QUINN, Jennifer, Quality and Safety Coordinator, Thedacare Medical Center–Shawano, Shawano, WI, p. A712

QUINN, Judith, Vice President Patient Care Services, Cape Cod Hospital, Hyannis, MA, p. A307

QUINN, Mary Ann
Administrative Assistant, Casey County Hospital, Liberty, KY, p. A262
Administrative Assistant, Jane Todd Crawford Hospital, Greensburg, KY, p. A259

QUINN, Mary Anna, Executive Vice President, Chief Administrative Officer, St. Jude Children's Research Hospital, Memphis, TN, p. A585

QUINN, Paul, Information Systems Manager, Kern Valley Healthcare District, Lake Isabella, CA, p. A65

QUINN, Tim M.D., Executive Vice President and Chief of Clinical Operations and President Mercy Care Management, Mercy Medical Center, Cedar Rapids, Iowa, Cedar Rapids, IA, p. A223

QUINONES, Kathleen
Interim Vice President Finance, Berkeley Medical Center, Martinsburg, WV, p. A693
Interim Vice President Finance, Jefferson Medical Center, Ranson, WV, p. A695

QUINONES, Yolanda, Director Finance, I. Gonzalez Martinez Oncologic Hospital, Hato Rey, PR, p. A723

QUINONEZ, Yolanda, Chief Financial Officer, Hospital De La Universidad De Puerto Rico/Dr. Federico Trilla, Carolina, PR, p. A722

QUINT–BOUZID, Marjorie, Chief Nursing Officer and Vice President Patient Care Services, Fort Washington Medical Center, Oxen Hill, MD, p. A300

QUINTANA, Francisco, Warden, Federal Medical Center, Lexington, KY, p. A261

QUINTANA, Jay, Vice President Operations, Cornerstone Hospital–West Monroe, West Monroe, LA, p. A287

QUINTO, Mike, Chief Information Officer, Watauga Medical Center, Boone, NC, p. A458
QUINTON, Byron, Chief Executive Officer, Clarion Hospital, Clarion, PA, p. A531
QUINTON, J Ben., Administrator, William Newton Hospital, Winfield, KS, p. A254
QUINTYNE, Stephen, Chief Executive Officer, The Vines, Ocala, FL, p. A136
QUIRICONI, Stephan F
  Chief Financial Officer, Bon Secours St. Mary's Hospital, Richmond, VA, p. A673
  Vice President Finance, Bon Secours Memorial Regional Medical Center, Mechanicsville, VA, p. A670
  Vice President, Finance, Bon Secours St. Francis Medical Center, Midlothian, VA, p. A670
QUIRKE, David, Vice President Information Services, Frederick Regional Health System, Frederick, MD, p. A298
QUITO, Arturo L M.D., Chief of Staff, Erlanger Bledsoe Hospital, Pikeville, TN, p. A588
QUO, Justin, Chief of Staff, Chi Lakewood Health, Baudette, MN, p. A336
QVISTGAARD, Guy C, Chief Executive Officer, Highland Hospital, Oakland, CA, p. A77

R

RAAUM, Elizabeth, Manger Business Office, Roosevelt Medical Center, Culbertson, MT, p. A383
RABAGO, Janie, Chief Accountant, San Antonio State Hospital, San Antonio, TX, p. A643
RABEL, Jonas, President, Integris Miami Hospital, Miami, OK, p. A510
RABIDEAU, Ray M.D., Senior Vice President and Chief Medical Officer, Memorial Hospital, North Conway, NH, p. A410
RABIN, Barry M.D., Regional Medical Director, Linden Oaks Hospital, Naperville, IL, p. A195
RABINE, Traci, Vice President Clinic Operations, Prairie Lakes Healthcare System, Watertown, SD, p. A574
RABINOWITZ, Jordy, Senior Vice President Human Resources Operations, Westchester Medical Center, Valhalla, NY, p. A454
RABNER, Barry S., President and Chief Executive Officer, Princeton Healthcare System, University Medical Center Of Princeton At Plainsboro, Plainsboro, NJ, p. A419
RABON, Catherine M.D., Chief Medical Officer, Mcleod Health Clarendon, Manning, SC, p. A564
RABORN, Janelle, Chief Operating Officer, Lovelace Women's Hospital, Albuquerque, NM, p. A424
RACHAL, Paul M.D., Chief Medical Officer, Pointe Coupee General Hospital, New Roads, LA, p. A283
RACHUIG, Sue, Director Information Services, Tulane Medical Center, New Orleans, LA, p. A283
RACKLIFFE, David, Assistant Vice President Information Services, Bristol Hospital, Bristol, CT, p. A163
RACZEK, James M.D., Sr. Vice President of Operations and Chief Medical Officer, Eastern Maine Medical Center, Bangor, ME, p. A289
RADANDT, Jeremiah, Chief Financial Officer, Primary Children's Hospital, Salt Lake City, UT, p. A660
RADCLIFF, Joey, Chief Financial Officer, Five Rivers Medical Center, Pocahontas, AR, p. A48
RADCLIFFE, Eric, Medical Director, United Hospital Center, Bridgeport, WV, p. A690
RADEMACHER, Frank
  Director, Information Systems, St. Joseph Mercy Livingston Hospital, Howell, MI, p. A322
  Senior Director Information Systems, St. Joseph Mercy Ann Arbor, Ypsilanti, MI, p. A334
RADER, Herbert M.D., Advisor for Medical Affairs, New York Community Hospital, New Rochelle, NY, p. A443
RADFORD, Jeffrey, Chief Executive Officer, Select Specialty Hospital–Tri Cities, Bristol, TN, p. A575
RADKE, Erma, Director of Operations, Oakleaf Surgical Hospital, Eau Claire, WI, p. A701
RADNER, Allen M.D., Chief Medical Officer, Salinas Valley Memorial Healthcare System, Salinas, CA, p. A84
RADOTICH, Maureen, Director Human Resources, Providence Valdez Medical Center, Valdez, AK, p. A27
RADTKE, Lisa, Chief Administrative Officer, Winneshiek Medical Center, Decorah, IA, p. A226
RADU, Oana, Chief Executive Officer, Summit Oaks Hospital, Summit, NJ, p. A421
RADUNSKY, Daniel M.D., Medical Staff President, Union County General Hospital, Clayton, NM, p. A425

RADZEVICH, Jason, Vice President Finance, Beth Israel Deaconess Hospital Plymouth, Plymouth, MA, p. A310
RAETHEL, Kathryn A., R.N., M.P.H., President and Chief Executive Officer, Castle Medical Center, Kailua, HI, p. A169
RAETZ, Elizabeth A R.N., MSN, Vice President Nursing and Chief Nursing Officer, Chi Health St Elizabeth, Lincoln, NE, p. A395
RAFALA, Paula, Director, Human Resources, Memorial Medical Center, Modesto, CA, p. A74
RAFFERTY, Diane, Interim Chief Executive Officer, Women & Infants Hospital Of Rhode Island, Providence, RI, p. A557
RAFFERTY, Joyce, Vice President Finance, The University Of Vermont Health Network–Champlain Valley Physicians Hospital, Plattsburgh, NY, p. A449
RAFFERTY, Patrick W, Executive Vice President and Chief Operating Officer, Community Regional Medical Center, Fresno, CA, p. A60
RAFFETY, Leannette, Administrative Generalist, Stroud Regional Medical Center, Stroud, OK, p. A516
RAFFOUL, John, Chief Executive Officer, White Memorial Medical Center, Los Angeles, CA, p. A72
RAFUS, Matthew, Chief Information Officer, White River Junction Veterans Affairs Medical Center, White River Junction, VT, p. A663
RAGAIN, Michael M.D., Chief Medical Officer and Senior Vice President, University Medical Center, Lubbock, TX, p. A631
RAGAN, Donna R.N., Chief Nursing Officer, Shands Live Oak Regional Medical Center, Live Oak, FL, p. A131
RAGAR–THOMAS, Twila, Director Health Information Management and Quality Improvement, Timberlawn Mental Health System, Dallas, TX, p. A607
RAGAS, Rene J., Chief Operating Officer, Our Lady Of The Angels Hospital, Bogalusa, LA, p. A272
RAGER, Claudia R.N., Vice President Patient Care Services, Conemaugh Memorial Medical Center, Johnstown, PA, p. A537
RAGGI, Bob M.D., Chief Medical Officer, Providence Holy Cross Medical Center, Los Angeles, CA, p. A70
RAGGIO, James J., Chief Executive Officer, Lompoc Valley Medical Center, Lompoc, CA, p. A66
RAGGIO, Sharon, President and Chief Executive Officer, West Springs Hospital, Grand Junction, CO, p. A103
RAGLAND, Jane, President Medical Staff, Christus Mother Frances Hospital – Jacksonville, Jacksonville, TX, p. A625
RAGLE, Bertha, Director Personnel, Crossridge Community Hospital, Wynne, AR, p. A50
RAGONA, Robert A, Senior Vice President Finance and Chief Financial Officer, Eastern Long Island Hospital, Greenport, NY, p. A436
RAGONESE–GREEN, Virginia, Chief Nursing Officer, Healthsouth Rehabilitation Hospital Of Southern Arizona, Tucson, AZ, p. A38
RAGSDALE, Sarah R.N., Chief Nursing Officer, Smith County Memorial Hospital, Smith Center, KS, p. A252
RAHDERT, Richard M.D., Medical Director, River Bend Hospital, West Lafayette, IN, p. A221
RAHMAN, Randy
  Chief Information Officer, Miami County Medical Center, Paola, KS, p. A249
  Vice President and Chief Information Officer, Olathe Medical Center, Olathe, KS, p. A248
RAHMAN, Syed M.D., Chief of Staff, Horizon Specialty Hospital, Las Vegas, NV, p. A403
RAHN, Kevin, President Medical Staff, Orthopaedic Hospital Of Lutheran Health Network, Fort Wayne, IN, p. A208
RAINA, Suresh M.D., Vice President Medical Staff and Chief Medical Officer, Hackensack Meridian Health Palisades Medical Center, North Bergen, NJ, p. A418
RAINBOLT, Mike, Chief Financial Officer, Rivendell Behavioral Health Services Of Arkansas, Benton, AR, p. A40
RAINEY, Jackie, Chief Financial Officer, Little River Memorial Hospital, Ashdown, AR, p. A40
RAINEY, Mark J, Director Human Resources, Texas Health Presbyterian Hospital Kaufman, Kaufman, TX, p. A626
RAINS, Celeste D.O., Chief of Staff, Logan County Hospital, Oakley, KS, p. A248
RAINS, Debbie, Coordinator Health Information Management, Erlanger Bledsoe Hospital, Pikeville, TN, p. A588
RAINS, Della, Chief Nursing Officer, Continuecare Hospital At Baptist Health Corbin, Corbin, KY, p. A257
RAINS, Jeff G., Chief Executive Officer, Baptist Medical Center East, Montgomery, AL, p. A21
RAINS, Jon–Michael
  Chief Executive Officer, Carrus Rehabilitation Hospital, Sherman, TX, p. A645
  Chief Executive Officer, Carrus Specialty Hospital, Sherman, TX, p. A645
RAINS, Paul, R.N., MSN, President, St. Joseph's Behavioral Health Center, Stockton, CA, p. A92

RAINS, Ron, Administrator, Texas Health Harris Methodist Hospital Hurst–Euless–Bedford, Bedford, TX, p. A597
RAINS, Steve, Director Information Services, Mckee Medical Center, Loveland, CO, p. A106
RAISNER, Gary, Chief Operating Officer, Norristown State Hospital, Norristown, PA, p. A542
RAJEWSKI, Frank A., Chief Financial Officer and Interim Chief Executive Officer, Rooks County Health Center, Plainville, KS, p. A250
RAJEWSKI, Frank A, Chief Financial Officer, Rooks County Health Center, Plainville, KS, p. A250
RAJKUMAR, Anthony, Chief Executive Officer, NYC Health + Hospitals / Coney Island, New Rochelle, NY, p. A444
RAJPARA, Suresh M.D., Chief Medical Officer, Jerome Golden Center For Behavioral Health, Inc., West Palm Beach, FL, p. A147
RAJU, Vasudeva M.D., Suffix, Chief, Long Term Acute Care Medicine, NYC Health + Hospitals / Carter, New Rochelle, NY, p. A444
RAK, Roger, Director Human Resources, South Shore Hospital, Chicago, IL, p. A184
RAKES, Lori, Chief Operating Officer, Cartersville Medical Center, Cartersville, GA, p. A154
RAKES–STEPHENS, Kim M.D., Chief Medical Staff, Colleton Medical Center, Walterboro, SC, p. A567
RAKOV, Robert M.D., Chief Medical Officer, Cogdell Memorial Hospital, Snyder, TX, p. A646
RALSTIN, Char, Director of Nursing, Haven Senior Horizons, Phoenix, AZ, p. A33
RAMA–BANAAG, Gemma R.N., MSN, Chief Nursing Officer, Paradise Valley Hospital, National City, CA, p. A76
RAMAGE, Gary M.D., Chief Medical Officer, Mckenzie County Healthcare System, Watford City, ND, p. A478
RAMAN, Jayashree, Vice President and Chief Information Officer, Reading Hospital, West Reading, PA, p. A553
RAMAN, Reggie M.D., Medical Director, Peninsula Hospital, Louisville, TN, p. A583
RAMAZANI, Regina
  Chief Financial Officer, Garden Park Medical Center, Gulfport, MS, p. A355
  Chief Financial Officer, Tulane Medical Center, New Orleans, LA, p. A283
  Chief Operating Officer, Garden Park Medical Center, Gulfport, MS, p. A355
RAMEY, Rita, Director Information Systems, Buchanan General Hospital, Grundy, VA, p. A668
RAMEY, Robert L., President, Baptist Health Madisonville, Madisonville, KY, p. A264
RAMEY, Steve, Chief Financial Officer, Southampton Memorial Hospital, Franklin, VA, p. A667
RAMIREZ, Ana, Director of Nursing, Mesa Springs, Fort Worth, TX, p. A614
RAMIREZ, Arthur L., M.D.
  Medical Director, El Paso Behavioral Health System, El Paso, TX, p. A610
  Medical Director, Mesilla Valley Hospital, Las Cruces, NM, p. A427
RAMIREZ, Corazon, M.D., Chief Executive Officer, Pine Creek Medical Center, Dallas, TX, p. A606
RAMIREZ, Eddy, Assistant Vice President Business Development, Ochsner Medical Center – Kenner, Kenner, LA, p. A277
RAMIREZ, Harvey, Chief Information Officer, Coleman County Medical Center, Coleman, TX, p. A602
RAMIREZ, Jaime, Chief Executive Officer, Mccamey County Hospital District, Mccamey, TX, p. A632
RAMIREZ, Karla, Chief Operating Officer, Laurel Ridge Treatment Center, San Antonio, TX, p. A642
RAMIREZ, Omar, Chief Executive Officer, Los Angeles Community Hospital At Los Angeles, Los Angeles, CA, p. A69
RAMIREZ, Ruben M.D., Chief of Staff, Monterey Park Hospital, Monterey Park, CA, p. A75
RAMIREZ, Susan, Chief Nursing Officer, Healthsouth Rehabilitation Hospital–Las Vegas, Las Vegas, NV, p. A403
RAMIREZ, Venus V., Executive Director, Hospital San Pablo Del Este, Fajardo, PR, p. A723
RAMIREZ, Willie, Manager Labor Relations, Laguna Honda Hospital And Rehabilitation Center, San Francisco, CA, p. A87
RAMLO, Ricki, Chief Operating Officer and Human Resources, Jamestown Regional Medical Center, Jamestown, ND, p. A476
RAMM, Crystal, Administrator, Grady General Hospital, Cairo, GA, p. A153
RAMON, Maggie, Chief Financial Officer, Cochran Memorial Hospital, Morton, TX, p. A634
RAMOS, Eduardo M.D., Medical Director, Healthsouth Rehabilitation Hospital Of San Juan, San Juan, PR, p. A726

RAMOS, Eric M.D., Division Chief Medical Officer, Southern Hills Hospital And Medical Center, Las Vegas, NV, p. A403

RAMOS, Holly R.N., Chief Clinical Officer, Kindred Hospital–Ontario, Ontario, CA, p. A77

RAMOS, Jessie, Manager Human Resources, Skyline Hospital, White Salmon, WA, p. A689

RAMOS, Jet, Head Staff Administration, Naval Hospital Camp Pendleton, Camp Pendleton, CA, p. A54

RAMOS, Raymond FACHE, Chief Operating Officer, Doctors Hospital Of Laredo, Laredo, TX, p. A628

RAMOS, Walter J., President, Carney Hospital, Boston, MA, p. A303

RAMPAT, Ananda, Chief Financial Officer, Northwest Medical Center, Margate, FL, p. A131

RAMPP, Randal D M.D., Chief Medical Officer, Saint Thomas River Park Hospital, Mc Minnville, TN, p. A583

RAMSAMY, Dev, Chief Financial Officer, St. Rose Dominican Hospitals – San Martin Campus, Las Vegas, NV, p. A404

RAMSEY, David L., President and Chief Executive Officer, Charleston Area Medical Center, Charleston, WV, p. A691

RAMSEY, Kristin R.N., Senior Vice President and Chief Nursing Executive, Northwestern Memorial Hospital, Northwestern Memorial Hospital, Chicago, IL, p. A182

RAMSEY, Lisa, Chief Financial Officer, Prairie View, Newton, KS, p. A247

RAMSEY, Paul G., M.D., Chief Executive Officer, Uw Medicine, Seattle, WA, p. B142

RAMSEY, Rance, Chief Executive Officer, Martin County Hospital District, Stanton, TX, p. A646

RAMSEY, Rhonda, Controller, Healthsouth Deaconess Rehabilitation Hospital, Evansville, IN, p. A207

RAMSEY, Ross M.D., Chief of Staff, Scheurer Hospital, Pigeon, MI, p. A328

RAMSEY, Roy M., Executive Director, Bradford Health Services At Warrior Lodge, Warrior, AL, p. A24

RAMSEY, Thomas, Chief Financial Officer, Hancock Medical Center, Bay Saint Louis, MS, p. A352

RAMSEY, Tom, Chief Financial Officer, Morehouse General Hospital, Bastrop, LA, p. A270

RAMTHUN, Jane, Chief Financial Officer, Story County Medical Center, Nevada, IA, p. A232

RANA, Chaula M.D., Medical Director, Healthsouth Rehabilitation Institute Of San Antonio (Riosa), San Antonio, TX, p. A642

RANCK, Sonja, MSN, R.N., Chief Operating Officer and Chief Nursing Officer, Skiff Medical Center, Newton, IA, p. A232

RANCOURT, Lindsay, Director of Nursing, Upper Connecticut Valley Hospital, Colebrook, NH, p. A407

RANDALL, Bryan J
   Vice President Finance and Chief Financial Officer, Heritage Valley Health System, Beaver, PA, p. A529
   Vice President Finance and Chief Financial Officer, Sewickley Valley Hospital, (A Division Of Valley Medical Facilities), Sewickley, PA, p. A550

RANDALL, Cherry, Business Officer, Greater Binghamton Health Center, Binghamton, NY, p. A431

RANDLE, Emily, Vice President Operations, Orange Coast Memorial Medical Center, Fountain Valley, CA, p. A60

RANDOLPH, Arianne, Director Human Resources, Pikes Peak Regional Hospital, Woodland Park, CO, p. A108

RANDOLPH, Bonnie M.D., Chief of Staff, Community Hospital, Torrington, WY, p. A720

RANDOLPH, Bruce, Chief Information Technology, Arizona State Hospital, Phoenix, AZ, p. A33

RANDOLPH, Joseph M.D., Chairman Medical Executive Committee, Indiana Orthopaedic Hospital, Indianapolis, IN, p. A211

RANDOLPH, Karsten, Executive Vice President and Chief Financial Officer, Shawnee Mission Medical Center, Shawnee Mission, KS, p. A252

RANDOLPH, Linda, Director Personnel Services, Washington County Hospital, Chatom, AL, p. A16

RANDOLPH, Mark, President, University Health Shreveport, Shreveport, LA, p. A286

RANEY, Hollie, Director of Nursing, Dallas County Medical Center, Fordyce, AR, p. A43

RANEY, Lance C., Commander, Womack Army Medical Center, Fort Bragg, NC, p. A462

RANG, Robert A., R.N., Chief Executive Officer, Wrangell Medical Center, Wrangell, AK, p. A27

RANGAVIZ, Rassoul, Chief Financial Officer, Copley Hospital, Morrisville, VT, p. A662

RANGE, Bonny MSN, Chief Nursing Officer, Holy Family Memorial, Manitowoc, WI, p. A706

RANKIN, Beverley A R.N., Vice President & Chief Nursing Officer, Alice Peck Day Memorial Hospital, Lebanon, NH, p. A408

RANKIN, Cynthia, Chief Nursing Officer, Lovelace Rehabilitation Hospital, Albuquerque, NM, p. A424

RANNEY, Timothy M.D., Chief Medical Officer, Seton Medical Center, Daly City, CA, p. A57

RANSOM, Natalie
   Chief Nursing Officer, Mountainview Hospital, Las Vegas, NV, p. A403
   Chief Nursing Officer, North Florida Regional Medical Center, Gainesville, FL, p. A125

RAO, Gutti, M.D.
   Chief of Staff, Greenwood Leflore Hospital, Greenwood, MS, p. A355
   Medical Director, AMG Specialty Hospital–Greenwood, Greenwood, MS, p. A355

RAO, Kalapala M.D., Medical Director, Healthsouth Western Hills Regional Rehabilitation Hospital, Parkersburg, WV, p. A695

RAPENSKE, Jennifer, Manager Financial Services, Mercy Medical Center–New Hampton, New Hampton, IA, p. A232

RAPP, Catherine R.N., MS, Vice President Nursing, Oconomowoc Memorial Hospital, Oconomowoc, WI, p. A709

RAPP, David, Chief Information Officer, Wheeling Hospital, Wheeling, WV, p. A697

RAPP, Ron, Vice President Finance, Cole Memorial, Coudersport, PA, p. A532

RAPPACH, Shannon, Chief Fiscal Services, Dayton Veterans Affairs Medical Center, Dayton, OH, p. A489

RAPPLEY, Marsha, M.D., Chief Executive Officer and Vice President for Health Sciences, Vcu Health System, Richmond, VA, p. B143

RASCHKE, Judy, Director Human Resources, Pipestone County Medical Center Avera, Pipestone, MN, p. A346

RASHFORD, Jennifer, Manager Human Resources, Lifecare Hospitals Of Mechanicsburg, Mechanicsburg, PA, p. A540

RASH, Martin S., Chief Executive Officer, Rcch Healthcare Partners, Brentwood, TN, p. B107

RASHID, Harun, Vice President and Chief Information Officer, Akron Children's Hospital, Akron, OH, p. A479

RASHILLA, Matt, Chief Information and Application Manager, Monongahela Valley Hospital, Monongahela, PA, p. A541

RASK, Brenda, Vice President Operations, Chi St Alexius Health Carrington Medical Center, Carrington, ND, p. A474

RASKE, Jamie, Information Technology Lead, Avera St. Mary's Hospital, Pierre, SD, p. A571

RASMUSSEN, Cassie M.D., Chief Medical Officer, Adair County Health System, Greenfield, IA, p. A228

RASMUSSEN, Diane, Director Human Resources, Cambridge Medical Center, Cambridge, MN, p. A337

RASMUSSEN, Jeanell R.N., Vice President Patient Care Services and Chief Nursing Officer, Harrison Medical Center, Bremerton, WA, p. A678

RASMUSSEN, John, Vice President for Information Technology, Medstar Georgetown University Hospital, Washington, DC, p. A117

RASMUSSEN, Kyle R., Chief Executive Officer, Meeker Memorial Hospital, Litchfield, MN, p. A342

RASMUSSEN, Rick, Chief Executive Officer, Northwest Specialty Hospital, Post Falls, ID, p. A175

RASMUSSEN, Scott, Director Human Resources, Lincoln Regional Center, Lincoln, NE, p. A395

RASMUSSON, Duane, Vice President Human Resources, St. Cloud Hospital, Saint Cloud, MN, p. A347

RASOOL, Chaudri D.O., Chief of Staff, Gundersen Palmer Lutheran Hospital And Clinics, West Union, IA, p. A236

RASOR, Linda, R.N., Chief Executive Officer, Plains Memorial Hospital, Dimmitt, TX, p. A609

RASTER, Robert M.D., Medical Director, Michiana Behavioral Health Center, Plymouth, IN, p. A218

RATAJ, Marianne R.N., MS, Chief Nursing Officer, Mercy Hospital Fort Smith, Fort Smith, AR, p. A43

RATCLIFF, David M.D., Chief Medical Affairs, Washington Regional Medical Center, Fayetteville, AR, p. A43

RATCLIFF, Paul, Director Information Services, Baylor Scott & White Medical Center – Carrollton, Carrollton, TX, p. A600

RATCLIFFE, Alma M.D., Executive Vice President Medical Staff and Business Development, Saint Clare's Health System, Denville, NJ, p. A412

RATH, Kevin, Vice President and Executive Director, Amita Health Hoffman Estates, Hoffman Estates, IL, p. A190

RATH, Megan, Chief Financial Officer, Wishek Community Hospital And Clinics, Wishek, ND, p. A478

RATHGABER, Scott W., M.D., Chief Executive Officer and Board Chair, Gundersen Health System, La Crosse, WI, p. A704

RATLIFF, Ada
   Chief Executive Officer, Claiborne County Medical Center, Port Gibson, MS, p. A361
   Chief Information Officer, Claiborne County Medical Center, Port Gibson, MS, p. A361

RATLIFF, Bonnie, Chief Information Officer, Columbia Memorial Hospital, Hudson, NY, p. A437

RATLIFF, Kim, Director Health Information Management, Southwestern Virginia Mental Health Institute, Marion, VA, p. A670

RATLIFF, Maggie, Vice President Information Systems, Sarah Bush Lincoln Health Center, Mattoon, IL, p. A193

RATLIFF, Simon, Chief Operating Officer, Logan Regional Medical Center, Logan, WV, p. A693

RATLIFF, Steve, Director Information Technology, Guadalupe Regional Medical Center, Seguin, TX, p. A644

RATNASAMY, Suthanthira M., R.N., FACHE, Chief Executive Officer, Kindred Hospital Bay Area–Tampa, Tampa, FL, p. A145

RATTLE, John, Chief Financial Officer, West Springs Hospital, Grand Junction, CO, p. A103

RATTRAY, Cindy Stewart, Director Human Resources, Jewish Hospital–Shelbyville, Shelbyville, KY, p. A267

RAU, Robin, Chief Executive Officer, Miller County Hospital, Colquitt, GA, p. A154

RAUB, Jessica, Director Health Information Management, Seven Hills Hospital, Henderson, NV, p. A402

RAUCH, Rhonda, Chief Nursing Officer, Lovelace Regional Hospital – Roswell, Roswell, NM, p. A428

RAUCH, Scott C, Vice President Human Resources, Reid Health, Richmond, IN, p. A219

RAUCH, Scott L., M.D., President and Psychiatrist in Chief, Mclean Hospital, Belmont, MA, p. A302

RAUH, Bradley W., Vice President, Chief Operating Officer, Southwest General Health Center, Middleburg Heights, OH, p. A496

RAUH, Cindy R.N., Vice President and Chief Nursing Officer, Duncan Regional Hospital, Duncan, OK, p. A506

RAUNER, Mary Ellen R.N., Chief Nursing Officer, Suburban Community Hospital, Norristown, PA, p. A542

RAUPERS, Deb, MSN, R.N.
   Chief Nursing Officer, Guthrie Corning Hospital, Corning, NY, p. A434
   Vice President Patient Services and Chief Nursing Officer, Cayuga Medical Center At Ithaca, Ithaca, NY, p. A437

RAUTIO, Wendy, Chief Financial Officer, Munising Memorial Hospital, Munising, MI, p. A326

RAVELING, Lynn, Chief Financial Officer, Pocahontas Community Hospital, Pocahontas, IA, p. A233

RAWLEY, Jennifer, PharmD, Chief Executive Officer, Select Specialty Hospital–Durham, Durham, NC, p. A461

RAWLINGS, Linda, Director Human Resources and Personnel, Three Rivers Hospital, Waverly, TN, p. A590

RAWLINGS, Michael, Interim Chief Operating Officer, NYC Health + Hospitals / Bellevue, New Rochelle, NY, p. A444

RAWLINGS, Patrick, Human Resources Director, Thomas Memorial Hospital, South Charleston, WV, p. A696

RAWLINGS, Pete, Chief Human Resource Officer, Saint Francis Hospital, Charleston, WV, p. A691

RAWLINGS, Sheri, Chief Information Officer, San Juan Regional Medical Center, Farmington, NM, p. A426

RAWSON, Richard L, President and Chief Executive Officer, Adventist Medical Center – Hanford, Hanford, CA, p. A62

RAY, Beverly, Director Human Resources, Tennova Healthcare Dyersburg Regional Medical Center, Dyersburg, TN, p. A578

RAY, Brenda, Director Human Resources, Huntsville Memorial Hospital, Huntsville, TX, p. A624

RAY, Denise, Chief Executive Officer, Piedmont Mountainside Hospital, Jasper, GA, p. A159

RAY, Diane R.N., Vice President and Chief Nursing Officer Patient Services, St. Luke's Hospital, Chesterfield, MO, p. A366

RAY, Donald, Vice President Operations, University Of Maryland Medical Center Midtown Campus, Baltimore, MD, p. A296

RAY, Elaine, Administrator, Choate Mental Health Center, Anna, IL, p. A177

RAY, Evan, FACHE, Chief Executive Officer, St. Vincent's Birmingham, Birmingham, AL, p. A15

RAY, Jerilyn, Manager Human Resources, St. Elizabeth Hospital, Enumclaw, WA, p. A680

RAY, Joel MSN, Vice President and Chief Nursing Officer, UNC Rex Health Care, Raleigh, NC, p. A469

RAY, Kirk M., Chief Executive Officer, Kosciusko Community Hospital, Warsaw, IN, p. A221

RAY, Marge, Director Information Systems, Covenant Medical Center, Waterloo, IA, p. A236

RAY, Marilyn MSN, Chief Nursing Officer, Upson Regional Medical Center, Thomaston, GA, p. A166

RAY, Nancy L R.N., Executive Vice President, Chief Nursing Executive, University Health System, San Antonio, TX, p. A644

RAY, Rachel, Chief Financial Officer, Unity Medical Center, Grafton, ND, p. A476

RAY, Roger A M.D., Executive Vice President and Chief Medical Officer, Carolinas Medical Center, Charlotte, NC, p. A459

RAY-SIMONE, Mary Beth, Chief Executive Officer, Select Specialty Hospital–Northeast New Jersey, Rochelle Park, NJ, p. A420

RAYBOURN, Gina, Director Health Information, Ellett Memorial Hospital, Appleton City, MO, p. A364

RAYLS, Kim, Director Human Resources, Twin Lakes Regional Medical Center, Leitchfield, KY, p. A260

RAYMER, Chris Lee., R.N., MSN
Chief Executive Officer, Great River Medical Center, Blytheville, AR, p. A40
Chief Executive Officer, South Mississippi County Regional Medical Center, Osceola, AR, p. A48

RAYMOND, Jane, Vice President and Chief Operating Officer, Reston Hospital Center, Reston, VA, p. A673

RAYMOND, Katherine, Chief Nursing Officer, St. Rose Dominican Hospitals – San Martin Campus, Las Vegas, NV, p. A404

RAYMOND, Mindy, Vice President Human Resources, Boca Raton Regional Hospital, Boca Raton, FL, p. A120

RAYMOND, Scott, Director Information Systems, Orange Coast Memorial Medical Center, Fountain Valley, CA, p. A60

RAYNER, Evan J., Chief Executive Officer, Madera Community Hospital, Madera, CA, p. A72

RAYNER, Thomas J, Senior Vice President and Chief Operating Officer, Kaweah Delta Medical Center, Visalia, CA, p. A96

RAYNES, Anthony M.D., Psychiatrist in Chief, Arbour H. R. I. Hospital, Brookline, MA, p. A305

RAYNES, Scott
President, Baptist Hospital, Pensacola, FL, p. A139
President, Gulf Breeze Hospital, Gulf Breeze, FL, p. A126

RAYNOR, Robert, Human Resources Director, Park Royal Hospital, Fort Myers, FL, p. A125

RAY-SIMONE, Mary Beth., Chief Executive Officer, Select Specialty Hospital-Northeast New Jersey, Rochelle Park, NJ, p. B115

RAYUDU, Subbu M.D., Chief of Staff, Alliance Healthcare System, Holly Springs, MS, p. A356

RAZMIC, Tammy, Associate Administrator Finance and Chief Financial Officer, Inova Mount Vernon Hospital, Alexandria, VA, p. A664

RAZO, Virginia, Chief Executive Officer, Curry General Hospital, Gold Beach, OR, p. A522

REA, Jerry A., Ph.D.
Interim Superintendent, Rainbow Mental Health Facility, Kansas City, KS, p. A244
Superintendent, Osawatomie State Hospital, Osawatomie, KS, p. A248
Superintendent, Parsons State Hospital And Training Center, Parsons, KS, p. A249

READ, Eddie, Interim Chief Financial Officer, Val Verde Regional Medical Center, Del Rio, TX, p. A608

READ, John, Chief Nursing Officer, Allegiance Specialty Hospital Of Greenville, Greenville, MS, p. A355

READ, Paul R.N., MSN, Vice President and Chief Nursing Officer, Springhill Memorial Hospital, Mobile, AL, p. A20

READ, Richard
Chief Financial Officer, Central Florida Regional Hospital, Sanford, FL, p. A142
Chief Financial Officer, Tennova Healthcare Regional Hospital Of Jackson, Jackson, TN, p. A580

READER, G. Whitney M.D., Chief Medical Officer, Kansas Medical Center, Andover, KS, p. A238

READING, Jared M.D., Chief of Staff, Uvalde Memorial Hospital, Uvalde, TX, p. A651

REAGAN, Kevin M.D., Chief Medical Officer, Chi Health Creighton University Medical Center – Bergan Mercy, Omaha, NE, p. A397

REALE, Kelli, Vice President Human Resources, Upmc Mckeesport, Mckeesport, PA, p. A540

REAM, Tom, Regional Chief Information Officer, Sutter Auburn Faith Hospital, Auburn, CA, p. A52

REAMER, Roger J., Chief Executive Officer, Memorial Health Care Systems, Seward, NE, p. A399

REAMES, Jim, Director Human Resources, Bayfront Health St. Petersburg, Saint Petersburg, FL, p. A141

REAMY, Tracy, Administrator, Bozeman Health Big Sky Medical Center, Big Sky, MT, p. A382

REANDEAU, Michael, Chief Information Officer, Mills–Peninsula Health Services, Burlingame, CA, p. A54

REASER, Michelle R.N., Chief Nursing Executive, Lancaster Regional Medical Centers, Lancaster, PA, p. A538

REASONER, Vanessa, Chief Executive Officer, Grace Medical Center, Lubbock, TX, p. A630

REBERRY, Darinda, MSN, R.N., President and Chief Executive Officer, Western Missouri Medical Center, Warrensburg, MO, p. A380

REBLOCK, Kimberly M.D., Chief Operating Officer, The Children's Home Of Pittsburgh, Pittsburgh, PA, p. A547

REBOCK, Michael, Chief Medical Officer, Beaumont Hospital – Farmington Hills, Farmington Hills, MI, p. A319

RECA, Thomas Sr., Deputy Executive Director and Chief Financial Officer, Staten Island University Hospital, New Rochelle, NY, p. A446

RECH, Eunice A MSN, Chief Clinical Officer and Administrator of Quality Services, Tuality Healthcare, Hillsboro, OR, p. A522

RECHNER, Paula M.D., Chief Medical Officer, War Memorial Hospital, Sault Sainte Marie, MI, p. A330

RECHSTEINER, Hans M.D., Chief of Staff, Burnett Medical Center, Grantsburg, WI, p. A702

RECKDENWALD, Jeanine, Vice President Human Resources and Support Services, Bristol Hospital, Bristol, CT, p. A109

RECKERT, Sandy, Director Communications and Public Affairs, Johns Hopkins Bayview Medical Center, Baltimore, MD, p. A294

RECTOR, Fax III, Director Information Technology, Sunbury Community Hospital And Outpatient Center, Sunbury, PA, p. A551

RECTOR, Jeanne, Chief Nursing Officer, Carroll County Memorial Hospital, Carrollton, MO, p. A366

RECUPERO, David, Chief Financial Officer, San Gorgonio Memorial Hospital, Banning, CA, p. A53

REDD, Dakota R.N., Chief Clinical Officer, Kindred Hospital–St. Louis, Saint Louis, MO, p. A377

REDDING, Georgia, Director Human Resources, Forbes Hospital, Monroeville, PA, p. A541

REDDING, Lisa, Manager Human Resources, Morgan County Arh Hospital, West Liberty, KY, p. A268

REDDY, Challa M.D., President Medical Staff, Mayo Regional Hospital, Dover——Foxcroft, ME, p. A291

REDDY, Lex, President and Chief Executive Officer, Ohio Valley Medical Center, Wheeling, WV, p. A697

REDDY, Sridhar M.D., Chief Medical Officer, Lake Huron Medical Center, Port Huron, MI, p. A328

REDDY, Sunil, Chief Executive Officer, Care Regional Medical Center, Aransas Pass, TX, p. A593

REDDY, Prem, M.D., Chairman, President and Chief Executive Officer, Prime Healthcare, Ontario, CA, p. B100

REDHORSE–CHARLEY, Gloria, Director Human Resources, Northern Navajo Medical Center, Shiprock, NM, p. A428

REDING, Janeen K, Director Human Resources, Chi St. Anthony Hospital, Pendleton, OR, p. A524

REDINGTON, James M.D., Chief of Staff, Bath Community Hospital, Hot Springs, VA, p. A669

REDLER, Kathleen A., Director Patient Care Services, Shriners Hospitals For Children–Shreveport, Shreveport, LA, p. A286

REDMON, Gary, Chief Financial Officer, Methodist Hospital South, Jourdanton, TX, p. A625

REDMOND, Michael, Senior Vice President and Chief Operating Officer, Crotched Mountain Rehabilitation Center, Greenfield, NH, p. A408

REDMOND, Paula, Controller, Healthsouth Tustin Rehabilitation Hospital, Tustin, CA, p. A94

REDRICK, Heather, Chief Nursing Officer, Emory Johns Creek Hospital, Johns Creek, GA, p. A159

REECE, Morris A, EVP/COO, Laird Hospital, Union, MS, p. A362

REECER, Jeff, FACHE, Chief Executive Officer, Texas Health Presbyterian Hospital Denton, Denton, TX, p. A608

REED, Alex, Chief Information Officer, Avita Ontario Hospital, Ontario, OH, p. A497

REED, Catherine MSN, R.N., Chief Nursing Officer, Cedar Crest Hospital And Residential Treatment Center, Belton, TX, p. A598

REED, Chris, Director of Nursing, Pam Specialty Hospital Of Victoria North, Victoria, TX, p. A652

REED, Cindy, Director Community Relations, Austin State Hospital, Austin, TX, p. A594

REED, Fred M.D., Chief of Staff, Lincoln Hospital, Davenport, WA, p. A680

REED, Gloria, Leader Human Resources, SSM Health Depaul Hospital – St. Louis, Bridgeton, MO, p. A365

REED, Helen, Director Health Information, North Mississippi Medical Center–Eupora, Eupora, MS, p. A354

REED, Jason, Chief Executive Officer, Beacham Memorial Hospital, Magnolia, MS, p. A358

REED, John E M.D., Medical Director, Baptist Memorial Hospital–Golden Triangle, Columbus, MS, p. A354

REED, Karen, R.N., MSN
Chief Nursing Officer, St. Charles Bend, Bend, OR, p. A520
Chief Nursing Officer, St. Charles Redmond, Redmond, OR, p. A526

REED, Kate, President, St. Joseph's Hospital, Tampa, FL, p. A145

REED, Kathleen, Manager Human Resources, Missouri Baptist Sullivan Hospital, Sullivan, MO, p. A380

REED, Kirby, Director Information Systems, Franciscan Health Rensselear, Rensselaer, IN, p. A218

REED, Leslie, Chief Financial Officer, Wright Memorial Hospital, Trenton, MO, p. A380

REED, Linda
Vice President and Chief Information Officer, St. Joseph's Healthcare System, Paterson, NJ, p. A418
Vice President Information Systems and Chief Information Officer, Newton Medical Center, Newton, NJ, p. A418

REED, Margaret M R.N., Chief Nursing Officer, Altru Health System, Grand Forks, ND, p. A476

REED, Monica, M.D., Administrator, Florida Hospital, Orlando, FL, p. A137

REED, Pamela R., Chief Executive Officer, Kindred Hospital Melbourne, Melbourne, FL, p. A132

REED, Renee
Director Human Resources, Via Christi Hospital Manhattan, Inc., Manhattan, KS, p. A246
Director Human Resources, Wamego Health Center, Wamego, KS, p. A253

REED, Tim, Vice President and Chief Financial Officer, Virginia Mason Memorial, Yakima, WA, p. A689

REED, Tina, Director of Human Resources, Healthsouth Rehabilitation Hospital Of Modesto, Modesto, CA, p. A74

REED, Tracy Collings, Vice President Patient Care Services, Chief Nursing Officer, Siskin Hospital For Physical Rehabilitation, Chattanooga, TN, p. A576

REED, Victoria L., R.N., FACHE, Chief Executive Officer, James B. Haggin Memorial Hospital, Harrodsburg, KY, p. A259

REEDER, Austin, Chief Executive Officer, St. Charles Parish Hospital, Luling, LA, p. A280

REEDER, Carol R.N., Chief Nursing Officer, St. Joseph Hospital, Eureka, CA, p. A58

REEDER, Janet Lee R.N., Chief Nurse Executive, Kaiser Foundation Hospital Westside Medical Center, Hillsboro, OR, p. A522

REEDER, Wendy R.N., Chief Nursing Officer, Harrison Memorial Hospital, Cynthiana, KY, p. A257

REEDY, James Christopher, Chief Nursing Officer, Sutter Delta Medical Center, Antioch, CA, p. A51

REEDY, Janet, Manager Human Resources, St. Thomas More Hospital, Canon City, CO, p. A99

REEFER, John C M.D., Director, Butler Health System, Butler, PA, p. A530

REEL, John, Chief Executive Officer, Texas Rehabilitation Hospital Of Arlington, Arlington, TX, p. A594

REEL, Micah, Director of Bio–Med, Potomac Valley Hospital, Keyser, WV, p. A693

REEL, Stephanie L, Senior Vice President Information Services, Johns Hopkins Hospital, Baltimore, MD, p. A294

REES, Adam, President, Essentia Health St. Joseph's Medical Center, Brainerd, MN, p. A337

REES, Jeff, Director Information Systems, Bacharach Institute For Rehabilitation, Pomona, NJ, p. A419

REES, Matthew, Administrator, Jerold Phelps Community Hospital, Garberville, CA, p. A61

REES, Stephen G. M.D., Vice President Medical Affairs, Lafayette General Medical Center, Lafayette, LA, p. A278

REESE, Bert
Chief Information Officer, Sentara Leigh Hospital, Norfolk, VA, p. A672
Chief Information Officer, Sentara Norfolk General Hospital, Norfolk, VA, p. A672
Chief Information Officer, Sentara Princess Anne Hospital, Virginia Beach, VA, p. A676

REESE, Jeff, Chief Financial Officer, Howard A. Rusk Rehabilitation Center, Columbia, MO, p. A367

REESE, Kathie, R.N., Regional Administrator and Chief Executive Officer, Christus Dubuis Hospital Of Paris, Paris, TX, p. A636

REESE, Maryann, R.N., FACHE, President and Chief Executive Officer, Saint Francis Medical Center, Cape Girardeau, MO, p. A365

REESE, Mike, Chief Financial Officer, Ou Medical Center, Oklahoma City, OK, p. A513

REESE, Todd, Director Human Resources, Castle Medical Center, Kailua, HI, p. A169

REETZ, Brenda, FACHE, Chief Executive Officer, Greene County General Hospital, Linton, IN, p. A215

REETZ, Renee, Director Human Resources, St. Mary's Of Michigan Standish Hospital, Standish, MI, p. A331

REEVE, Jay A., Ph.D., President and Chief Executive Officer, Eastside Psychiatric Hospital, Tallahassee, FL, p. A144

REEVES, Cory, Chief Financial Officer, Gordon Hospital, Calhoun, GA, p. A153

REEVES, Danny, Chief Financial Officer, Penrose–St. Francis Health Services, Colorado Springs, CO, p. A100

REEVES, Katy, Vice President Human Resources, Fauquier Hospital, Warrenton, VA, p. A676
REEVES, Kaylene, Director, Tahoe Pacific Hospitals, Sparks, NV, p. A406
REEVES, Matthew D.O., Esq, Chief Medical Officer, Atrium Medical Center, Middletown, OH, p. A496
REEVES, Mike
 Chief Information Officer, St. John Owasso, Owasso, OK, p. A514
 Vice President, St. John Medical Center, Tulsa, OK, p. A518
REEVES, Pamela J., M.D., Director, John D. Dingell Veterans Affairs Medical Center, Detroit, MI, p. A318
REEVES, Steve M.D., Chief Medical Staff, Greater Regional Medical Center, Creston, IA, p. A225
REEVES, Susan A, Chief Nursing Executive, Dartmouth–Hitchcock Medical Center, Lebanon, NH, p. A409
REEVES, Timothy, Administrator, Bucktail Medical Center, Renovo, PA, p. A549
REEVES, Valerie, Chief Financial Officer, Integris Miami Hospital, Miami, OK, p. A510
REFFNER, Gina, Chief Financial Officer, Little Colorado Medical Center, Winslow, AZ, p. A39
REFNESS, Kristen, Director, Financial Operations, Linden Oaks Hospital, Naperville, IL, p. A195
REGAN, Timothy, M.D., President and Chief Medical Officer, Lakeland Regional Health, Lakeland, FL, p. A130
REGEN, Debbie R.N., Chief Nursing Officer, Hackensack Meridian Health Mountainside Medical Center, Montclair, NJ, p. A416
REGIER, Donald M.D., Chief Medical Officer, Sedgwick County Health Center, Julesburg, CO, p. A104
REGIER, Marion, Chief Executive Officer, Hillsboro Community Hospital, Hillsboro, KS, p. A242
REGIER, Steve, Chief Financial Officer, Kearney Regional Medical Center, Kearney, NE, p. A394
REGISTER, Kellie, Director of Nursing, Clinch Memorial Hospital, Homerville, GA, p. A159
REGISTER, Stephen, Chief Executive Officer, Greenleaf Center, Valdosta, GA, p. A166
REGULA, John
 Chief Information Officer, Allied Services Rehabilitation Hospital, Scranton, PA, p. A550
 Chief Information Officer, John Heinz Institute Of Rehabilitation Medicine, Wilkes, PA, p. A554
REGULA, Terry, Chief Executive Officer, Aultman Specialty Hospital, Canton, OH, p. A482
REHBEIN, Beth, Chief Nursing and Quality Officer, Story County Medical Center, Nevada, IA, p. A232
REHM, Janice, Manager Human Resources, University Of South Alabama Children's And Women's Hospital, Mobile, AL, p. A20
REHM, Micah, Chief Nursing Officer, Forrest General Hospital, Hattiesburg, MS, p. A355
REHMER, Patricia, MSN, FACHE, President, Natchaug Hospital, Mansfield Center, CT, p. A110
REHN, Lindsay, Executive Director of Financial Operations, Wellstar Paulding Hospital, Hiram, GA, p. A159
REHN, Ronald G.
 Chief Executive Officer, Providence Mount Carmel Hospital, Colville, WA, p. A679
 Chief Executive Officer, Providence St. Joseph's Hospital, Chewelah, WA, p. A679
REICH, David L., M.D., President and Chief Operating Officer, Mount Sinai Hospital, New Rochelle, NY, p. A443
REICH, David L M.D., President and Chief Operating Officer, Mount Sinai Hospital, New Rochelle, NY, p. A443
REICH, Joel R, M.D.
 Senior Vice President Medical Affairs, Manchester Memorial Hospital, Manchester, CT, p. A110
 Senior Vice President Medical Affairs, Rockville General Hospital, Vernon, CT, p. A113
REICHARD, Steve, Manager Information Systems, Brigham City Community Hospital, Brigham City, UT, p. A656
REICHERT, Don, Vice President Associate Chief Information Officer, Metrohealth Medical Center, Cleveland, OH, p. A486
REICHERT, James, Chief Medical Officer, Mercer Health, Coldwater, OH, p. A487
REICHFIELD, Michael L., President, Ohiohealth Doctors Hospital, Columbus, OH, p. A487
REICHLE, Paula, Senior Vice President and Chief Operating Officer, Sparrow Hospital, Lansing, MI, p. A324
REICHMAN, Joseph M.D., Vice President Medical Affairs and Clinical Effectiveness, Hackensack Meridian Health Riverview Medical Center, Red Bank, NJ, p. A420
REID, Bernadette, Vice President, Information Technology and Chief Information Officer, Torrance Memorial Medical Center, Torrance, CA, p. A94
REID, Bev, Chief Financial Officer, St. Luke Hospital And Living Center, Marion, KS, p. A246

REID, Jim, Vice President and Chief Information Officer, Covenant Children's Hospital, Lubbock, TX, p. A630
REID, Kelly, Human Resources Director, South Mississippi State Hospital, Purvis, MS, p. A361
REID, Kenneth G., President and Chief Executive Officer, Carlinville Area Hospital, Carlinville, IL, p. A179
REID, Patricia, Director of Nursing, Marion General Hospital, Columbia, MS, p. A354
REID, Richard, Vice President Chief Finance Officer, Sparrow Carson Hospital, Carson City, MI, p. A316
REID, Stephanie R.N., Vice President of Patient Care Services and Chief Nursing Officer, Carroll Hospital Center, Westminster, MD, p. A301
REIDER, Rochelle, Vice President Patient Care, Avera Queen Of Peace Hospital, Mitchell, SD, p. A571
REIDER, Stephen, R.N.
 Director of Nursing, Assistant Vice President Patient Care Services, Walden Behavioral Care, Waltham, MA, p. A312
 Chief Operating Officer and Interim Chief Executive Officer, Poplar Springs Hospital, Petersburg, VA, p. A673
 Administrator, Springbrook Hospital, Brooksville, FL, p. A121
REIDY, Margaret M.D., Vice President Medical Affairs, Upmc Presbyterian Shadyside, Pittsburgh, PA, p. A547
REIFF, Troy T, Corporate Director Operations, St. Vincent Seton Specialty Hospital, Indianapolis, IN, p. A212
REILLY, Brian M, Chief Financial Officer, Robert Wood Johnson University Hospital, New Brunswick, NJ, p. A417
REILLY, Dennis A., President and Chief Executive Officer, Little Company Of Mary Hospital And Health Care Centers, Evergreen Park, IL, p. A187
REILLY, Janelle, Chief Operating Officer, Chi Memorial, Chattanooga, TN, p. A576
REILLY, Joanne, Administrator, Hudson County Meadowview Psychiatric Hospital, Secaucus, NJ, p. A420
REILLY, John M.D., Vice President Medical Affairs and Chief Medical Officer, Mercy Medical Center, Rockville Centre, NY, p. A451
REILLY, Richard, Deputy Executive Director, Syosset Hospital, Syosset, NY, p. A453
REILLY, Robert, Vice President and Chief Financial Officer, Anne Arundel Medical Center, Annapolis, MD, p. A294
REILLY, Theresa MSN, R.N., Senior Vice President Patient Services and Chief Nursing Officer, Abington Hospital, Abington, PA, p. A528
REILLY, Tiffany, Director Human Resources, Childrens Care Hospital And School, Sioux Falls, SD, p. A572
REIMER, Arlo M.D., Chief of Staff, Kearny County Hospital, Lakin, KS, p. A244
REIMER, Randy, Chief Financial Officer, Adventist Behavioral Health And Wellness Services, Rockville, MD, p. A300
REIMER, Ronda R.N., Chief Nursing Officer and Assistant Administrator, Franklin General Hospital, Hampton, IA, p. A228
REIN, Mitchell S M.D., Chief Medical Officer, North Shore Medical Center, Salem, MA, p. A311
REINBOTH, Thomas, Chief Financial Officer, Roxborough Memorial Hospital, Philadelphia, PA, p. A545
REINER, Mark, Chief Medical Office, Executive, St. Anthony's Rehabilitation Hospital, Lauderdale Lakes, FL, p. A130
REINER, Scott, Chief Executive Officer, Adventist Health, Roseville, CA, p. B5
REINERT, Brenda, Director Human Resources, Tomah Memorial Hospital, Tomah, WI, p. A713
REINERT, Chad, Chief Information Officer, Hamilton General Hospital, Hamilton, TX, p. A618
REINHARD, Diane R.N., Vice President of Patient Care Services, Craig Hospital, Englewood, CO, p. A102
REINHARD, Russ, Chief Executive, Providence Willamette Falls Medical Center, Oregon City, OR, p. A524
REINHARD, James S., M.D., Commissioner, Virginia Department Of Mental Health, Richmond, VA, p. B144
REINKE, Bradley M.D., Vice President Medical Affairs and Chief Medical Officer, Dameron Hospital, Stockton, CA, p. A92
REINKE, N Sue, Vice President Human Resources, Geisinger–Lewistown Hospital, Lewistown, PA, p. A539
REINKE, Peggy, R.N., Administrator, Chi Lisbon Health, Lisbon, ND, p. A477
REINKING, Cheryl R.N., MS, Chief Nursing Officer, El Camino Hospital, Mountain View, CA, p. A75
REISELT, Doug
 Vice President and Chief Information Officer, Baptist Memorial Hospital – Memphis, Memphis, TN, p. A584
 Vice President and Chief Information Officer, Baptist Memorial Hospital–Collierville, Collierville, TN, p. A577
REISMAN, Ernestine O, Vice President Human Resources, Down East Community Hospital, Machias, ME, p. A292

REISMAN, Ronald M.D., Chief Medical Director, St. Vincent Seton Specialty Hospital, Indianapolis, IN, p. A212
REISS, Deanna, Hospital Director of Nursing, Devereux Children's Behavioral Health Center, Malvern, PA, p. A539
REISZ, Carol, Chief Financial Officer, North Caddo Medical Center, Vivian, LA, p. A287
REITER, Margaret, Chief Nursing Officer, Capital Health Medical Center–Hopewell, Pennington, NJ, p. A418
REITZ, Brent, President, Adventist Healthcare Physical Health And Rehabilitation, Rockville, MD, p. A300
REITZ, Judy A Sc.D., Executive Vice President and Chief Operating Officer, Johns Hopkins Hospital, Baltimore, MD, p. A294
REITZ, Robert, Ph.D., Chief Executive Officer, Fulton State Hospital, Fulton, MO, p. A368
REITZEL, David, Chief Information Officer, Brookdale Hospital Medical Center, New Rochelle, NY, p. A441
REKOWSKI, Christian
 Information Technology Director, Optim Medical Center – Jenkins, Millen, GA, p. A162
 Information Technology Director, Optim Medical Center – Screven, Sylvania, GA, p. A165
RELPH, Daren, Chief Executive Officer, Wayne County Hospital, Corydon, IA, p. A225
REMALEY, Anne, Vice President Human Resources, Acmh Hospital, Kittanning, PA, p. A537
REMARK, Megan, President and Chief Executive Officer, Regions Hospital, Saint Paul, MN, p. A348
REMBIS, Michael A., FACHE, Corporate Chief Executive Officer, Avanti Hospitals, El Segundo, CA, p. B16
REMBIS, Michael, Chief Executive Officer, Maui Memorial Medical Center, Wailuku, HI, p. A170
REMBOLD, Abbey
 Human Resources Senior Generalist, Hampshire Memorial Hospital, Romney, WV, p. A696
 Human Resources Senior Generalist, War Memorial Hospital, Berkeley Springs, WV, p. A690
 Manager, Human Resource Business Partnerships, Shenandoah Memorial Hospital, Woodstock, VA, p. A677
REMIGIO, Odalys, Assistant Vice President, Finance, Baptist Health South Florida, West Kendall Baptist Hospital, Miami, FL, p. A132
REMILLARD, John R.
 Interim Chief Executive Officer, Moses Ludington Hospital, Ticonderoga, NY, p. A454
 Interim Chief Executive Officer, The University Of Vermont Health Network Elizabethtown Community Hospital, Elizabethtown, NY, p. A435
REMINGTON, Amanda
 Director Human Resources, Wellstar Spalding Regional Hospital, Griffin, GA, p. A158
 Director Human Resources, Wellstar Sylvan Grove Hospital, Jackson, GA, p. A159
REMSPECHER, Mark, Director Human Resources, Southeast Missouri Mental Health Center, Farmington, MO, p. A368
RENDA, Nick, Chief Financial Officer, Merit Health Woman's Hospital, Flowood, MS, p. A354
RENDER–LEACH, Cynthia, Director Human Resources, Highland Community Hospital, Picayune, MS, p. A360
RENEAU, John D., Medical Director, Healthsouth Rehabilitation Hospital–Las Vegas, Las Vegas, NV, p. A403
RENFREE, Mark, Chief Financial Officer, La Rabida Children's Hospital, Chicago, IL, p. A181
RENIER, Hugh, M.D.
 Vice President Medical Affairs, Essentia Health Duluth, Duluth, MN, p. A339
 Vice President Medical Affairs, Essentia Health St. Mary's Medical Center, Duluth, MN, p. A339
RENKIEWICZ, Ginger L, Chief Clinical Officer, Chief Nursing Executive, and Chief Quality Officer, Unitypoint Health – Trinity Rock Island, Rock Island, IL, p. A199
RENN, Amy Katherine, Interim Administrator, Patient Care and Nursing, Via Christi Hospital Pittsburg, Pittsburg, KS, p. A250
RENNEKER, James M MSN, R.N., FACHE, Vice President and Chief Nursing Officer, Loretto Hospital, Chicago, IL, p. A181
RENNER, Dianne, Director Human Resources, Logansport State Hospital, Logansport, IN, p. A215
RENO, Kelly R.N., Chief Nursing Officer, Menorah Medical Center, Overland Park, KS, p. A249
RENO, Mike, Chief Operating Officer, Hill Country Memorial Hospital, Fredericksburg, TX, p. A615
RENO, William M.D., III, President Medical Staff, Merit Health Wesley, Hattiesburg, MS, p. A356
RENSHAW, Dee, Chief Executive Officer, Hillcrest Hospital Henryetta, Henryetta, OK, p. A508
RENTAS, Margarita R.N., Nursing Director, Castaner General Hospital, Castaner, PR, p. A723

© 2017 AHA Guide

RENTFRO, Donald R., Chief Executive Officer, L. V. Stabler Memorial Hospital, Greenville, AL, p. A18

RENTSCH, Richard E, President, Stroud Regional Medical Center, Stroud, OK, p. A516

REOHR, Sara, Regional Controller, West Gables Rehabilitation Hospital, Miami, FL, p. A134

REPAC, Kimberly S, Senior Vice President and Chief Financial Officer, Western Maryland Regional Medical Center, Cumberland, MD, p. A298

REPASS, Lois, Quality Assurance Specialist and Coordinator Performance Improvement, Northern Nevada Adult Mental Health Services, Sparks, NV, p. A406

REPETTI, Gregory George. III, FACHE, Chief Executive Officer, Multicare Valley Hospital, Spokane Valley, WA, p. A687

REPKO, Keith D., Director, Veterans Affairs St. Louis Health Care System, Saint Louis, MO, p. A379

REPPERT, Joseph A, Executive Vice President and Chief Financial Officer, North Mississippi Medical Center – Tupelo, Tupelo, MS, p. A362

REPPY, William
President, Lehigh Valley Hospital – Schuylkill East Norwegian Street, Pottsville, PA, p. A548
President, Lehigh Valley Hospital – Schuylkill South Jackson Street, Pottsville, PA, p. A548

REPTA, Shirley, Chief Executive Officer, The Pavilion At Williamsburg Place, Williamsburg, VA, p. A677

RESENDEZ, James R., Chief Executive Officer, Doctors Hospital Of Laredo, Laredo, TX, p. A628

RESETAR, Gayle L, Vice President and Chief Operating Officer, Tidelands Georgetown Memorial Hospital, Georgetown, SC, p. A562

RESLER, Lori R.N., Chief Nurse, Sullivan County Community Hospital, Sullivan, IN, p. A220

RESSLER, David, Chief Executive Officer, Aspen Valley Hospital, Aspen, CO, p. A98

RESSLER, Dennis, Chief Financial Officer, St. Vincent Kokomo, Kokomo, IN, p. A213

RESTREPO, Macarena, Manager Business Office, Sister Emmanuel Hospital, Miami, FL, p. A134

RESTREPO, Nicolas M.D., Vice President Medical Affairs, Winchester Medical Center, Winchester, VA, p. A677

RESTUCCIA, Michael, Chief Information Officer, Hospital Of The University Of Pennsylvania, Philadelphia, PA, p. A544

RESTUM, William, Chief Executive Officer, DMC – Rehabilitation Institute Of Michigan, Detroit, MI, p. A317

RETALIC, Tammy B. R.N., MS, Chief Nursing Officer, Hebrew Rehabilitation Center, Roslindale, MA, p. A310

RETHAMEL, Terry, Director of Support Services, Keystone Newport News, Newport News, VA, p. A671

RETTGER, Linda M.D., President Medical Staff, Upmc Kane, Kane, PA, p. A537

RETTIG, Jeffrey D.O., Chief of Staff, Limestone Medical Center, Groesbeck, TX, p. A617

RETTIG, Linda, Director Financial Services, Washington County Hospital, Washington, KS, p. A253

REULAND, Charlie Sc.D., Executive Vice President and Chief Operating Officer, Johns Hopkins Bayview Medical Center, Baltimore, MD, p. A294

REUST, Michele, Controller, Memorial Hospital Of Texas County, Guymon, OK, p. A508

REUTTINGER, H. Rex D.O., Chief Medical Officer, Administration, Garden City Hospital, Garden City, MI, p. A320

REVAL, Mary R.N., MSN, Chief Nursing Officer, Gulf Coast Medical Center, Panama City, FL, p. A138

REVELS, Beverly, Director Human Resources, Sutter Amador Hospital, Jackson, CA, p. A64

REVELS, Tonya, Senior Strategic Business Partner, Mcdowell Hospital, Marion, NC, p. A466

REVERMAN, Larry, Director Information Systems, Clark Memorial Hospital, Jeffersonville, IN, p. A213

REVIEL, Jackie, R.N., Chief Executive Officer, Allen Parish Hospital, Kinder, LA, p. A277

REWERTS, Karen
System Vice President Finance, SSM Health St. Joseph – St. Charles, Saint Charles, MO, p. A376
System Vice President of Finance, SSM Cardinal Glennon Children's Hospital, Saint Louis, MO, p. A378
System Vice President of Finance, SSM Health St. Mary's Hospital – St. Louis, Saint Louis, MO, p. A378

REXFORD, Linda, Director Human Resources, Weeks Medical Center, Lancaster, NH, p. A408

REXWINKLE, Lori, Chief Nursing Officer, Coffeyville Regional Medical Center, Coffeyville, KS, p. A239

REYES, Anthony, Information Technology Director, Commonwealth Health Center, Saipan, MP, p. A721

REYES, Glenda, Chief Financial Officer, Northwest Medical Center, Winfield, AL, p. A24

REYES, Marco, Executive Director, Hospital Psiquiatrico Metropolitano, Cabo Rojo, PR, p. A722

REYES, Raul M.D., Medical Director, San Juan City Hospital, San Juan, PR, p. A726

REYES, Roxanne, Director of Nursing, Cornerstone Regional Hospital, Edinburg, TX, p. A610

REYKA, Michael, Ph.D., Chief Executive Officer, Western Maryland Hospital Center, Hagerstown, MD, p. A299

REYMAN, Reed, President, Chi St. Alexius Health – Dickinson Medical Center, Dickinson, ND, p. A475

REYNA, Krista, Chief Nursing Officer, Mcbride Orthopedic Hospital, Oklahoma City, OK, p. A512

REYNGOUDT, Mark, Chief Financial Officer, Carlisle Regional Medical Center, Carlisle, PA, p. A531

REYNOLDS, Angela D, Chief Financial Officer, Lewis–Gale Medical Center, Salem, VA, p. A675

REYNOLDS, Denise, Chief Nursing Officer, Memorial Hospital Miramar, Miramar, FL, p. A135

REYNOLDS, Doug, Area Finance Officer, Kaiser Permanente Redwood City Medical Center, Redwood City, CA, p. A82

REYNOLDS, Hope, Vice President, Human Resources and Service Excellence, Margaret R. Pardee Memorial Hospital, Hendersonville, NC, p. A464

REYNOLDS, Ian, Chief Medical Officer, Advanced Diagnostics Hospital, Houston, TX, p. A619

REYNOLDS, James B M.D., Medical Director, Northwest Missouri Psychiatric Rehabilitation Center, Saint Joseph, MO, p. A376

REYNOLDS, Jay, M.D., Chief Medical Officer and Chief Clinical Officer, The Aroostook Medical Center, Presque Isle, ME, p. A293

REYNOLDS, Katelyn, Manager Human Resources, Greeley County Health Services, Tribune, KS, p. A252

REYNOLDS, Lennetta M, Administrative Supervisor, Community Behavioral Health Hospital – Annandale, Annandale, MN, p. A335

REYNOLDS, Mike
Chief Financial Officer, Delta Medical Center, Memphis, TN, p. A584
Chief Financial Officer, Newberry County Memorial Hospital, Newberry, SC, p. A565

REYNOLDS, Paul M.D., Medical Director, Coleman County Medical Center, Coleman, TX, p. A602

REYNOLDS, Ray, Chief Executive Officer, Glen Rose Medical Center, Glen Rose, TX, p. A616

REYNOLDS, Robert, Director Information Systems, Mary Rutan Hospital, Bellefontaine, OH, p. A481

REYNOLDS, Scott, Vice President Finance, Mercy Hospital Springfield, Springfield, MO, p. A379

REYNOLDS, Teresa
Chief Operating Officer, Haywood Regional Medical Center, Clyde, NC, p. A460
Interim Chief Nursing Officer, Starr Regional Medical Center, Athens, TN, p. A575

REYNOLDS, Todd, Chief Information Officer, Memorial Medical Center – Ashland, Ashland, WI, p. A698

REYNOLDS, Vance V., FACHE, CPA, Chief Executive Officer, Aiken Regional Medical Centers, Aiken, SC, p. A558

REYNOLDS–GOSSETTE, Youdie, Controller, Wilma N. Vazquez Medical Center, Vega Baja, PR, p. A727

REZAC, Julie A R.N., Chief Operating Officer, Saunders Medical Center, Wahoo, NE, p. A400

RHEE, Carolyn F., Chief Executive Officer, Lac–Olive View–Ucla Medical Center, Los Angeles, CA, p. A69

RHEINHEIMER, Rick, Chief Clinical Officer, Kindred Hospital–Chattanooga, Chattanooga, TN, p. A576

RHINE, Kathleen, President and Chief Executive Officer, Mount Nittany Medical Center, State College, PA, p. A551

RHINEHART, Jennie R., Administrator and Chief Executive Officer, Community Hospital, Tallassee, AL, p. A23

RHOADES, Charles E., M.D., Chief Executive Officer, Kansas City Orthopaedic Institute, Leawood, KS, p. A245

RHOADES, Mark, Vice President and Chief Human Resources Officer, Duncan Regional Hospital, Duncan, OK, p. A506

RHOADES, Shelly, Chief Financial Officer, Clarion Psychiatric Center, Clarion, PA, p. A531

RHOADS, Jack M.D., Medical Director, Landmark Hospital Of Joplin, Joplin, MO, p. A369

RHOADS, Pam, Chief Financial Officer, Fairfax Behavioral Health, Kirkland, WA, p. A681

RHODES, David M.D., Senior Vice President Medical Affairs and Chief Medical Officer, Rapides Regional Medical Center, Alexandria, LA, p. A269

RHODES, Helen R.N., Associate Director Operations, Veterans Affairs Northern Indiana Health Care System, Fort Wayne, IN, p. A208

RHODES, Jerome E., Chief Executive Officer, Crc Health Group, Inc., Cupertino, CA, p. B40

RHODES, J Gary., FACHE, Chief Executive Officer, Upmc Kane, Kane, PA, p. A537

RHODES, Pamela R.N., Vice President Patient Care Services and Chief Nursing Officer, Northern Dutchess Hospital, Rhinebeck, NY, p. A450

RHODES, Tracey, Coordinator Human Resources, Evergreen Medical Center, Evergreen, AL, p. A17

RHONE, Steve R.N., MS, Vice President Patient Care Services, Beebe Healthcare, Lewes, DE, p. A115

RHYNALDS, Kayla, Interim Chief Financial Officer, Kearney County Health Services, Minden, NE, p. A396

RHYNE, Craig M.D., FACS, Chief Medical Officer, Covenant Medical Center, Lubbock, TX, p. A630

RHYNE, Dennis M.D., Acting Medical Director, Fairbanks, Indianapolis, IN, p. A211

RHYNE, Tim, Personnel Officer, Ventura County Medical Center, Ventura, CA, p. A96

RIAL, Joanne, Chief Financial Officer, Cumberland Hospital, New Kent, VA, p. A671

RIALS, Joe, Director Fiscal Services, North Mississippi State Hospital, Tupelo, MS, p. A362

RIALS, Loren, Chief Financial Officer, Carolinas Hospital System, Florence, SC, p. A561

RIANO, Omaira D., Chief Nursing Officer, Healthsouth Sunrise Rehabilitation Hospital, Sunrise, FL, p. A143

RIBA, Chris, Director Human Resources, Western Wisconsin Health, Baldwin, WI, p. A698

RICARDO, Jennifer, Director of Human Resources, Westchester General Hospital, Miami, FL, p. A134

RICARTTI, Rebecca R, Interim Director Human Resources, Garfield Medical Center, Monterey Park, CA, p. A75

RICCI, David A., Interim President and Chief Executive Officer, St. Francis Hospital, Wilmington, DE, p. A116

RICCI, Lynn, President and Chief Executive Officer, Hospital For Special Care, New Britain, CT, p. A111

RICCIARDI, Patrice, Director Human Resources, Columbus Hospital Ltach, Newark, NJ, p. A417

RICCIO, Dustin, M.D.
President Eastern Region, Newark–Wayne Community Hospital, Newark, NY, p. A447
President, Clifton Springs Hospital And Clinic, Clifton Springs, NY, p. A434

RICCIO, John A. M.D., Chief Medical Officer, Auburn Community Hospital, Auburn, NY, p. A431

RICCIONI, Michel
Chief Financial Officer, North Hawaii Community Hospital, Kamuela, HI, p. A169
Chief Financial Officer, Petaluma Valley Hospital, Petaluma, CA, p. A79
Chief Financial Officer, Santa Rosa Memorial Hospital, Santa Rosa, CA, p. A91
Chief Financial Officer, St. Joseph Hospital, Eureka, CA, p. A58
Chief Financial Officer, The Queen's Medical Center, Honolulu, HI, p. A169

RICCITELLI, Anthony, Chief Operating Officer, Worcester Recovery Center And Hospital, Worcester, MA, p. A313

RICCITELLI, Anthony, Chief Operating Officer, Worcester Recovery Center And Hospital, Worcester, MA, p. A313

RICCITELLI, Vincent, Vice President Finance, Carepoint Health Hoboken University Medical Center, Hoboken, NJ, p. A414

RICE, Aimee, Human Resources Manager, Riverview Psychiatric Center, Augusta, ME, p. A289

RICE, Amy, Chief Financial Officer, Helena Regional Medical Center, Helena, AR, p. A44

RICE, Ann Madden., Chief Executive Officer, University Of California, Davis Medical Center, Sacramento, CA, p. A84

RICE, Ann Madden, Chief Executive Officer, University Of California, Davis Medical Center, Sacramento, CA, p. A84

RICE, Bernard, Chief Compliance Officer, Rangely District Hospital, Rangely, CO, p. A107

RICE, Carolyn M.D., Director Medical Services, Naval Hospital Pensacola, Pensacola, FL, p. A139

RICE, Craig, Director Information, Schneck Medical Center, Seymour, IN, p. A219

RICE, Devin, Director Information Systems, Clifton–Fine Hospital, Star Lake, NY, p. A452

RICE, James W., Director, Oscar G. Johnson Veterans Affairs Medical Center, Iron Mountain, MI, p. A323

RICE, Mark J., Administrator, Ruston Regional Specialty Hospital, Ruston, LA, p. A285

RICE, Mark CPA, Chief Financial Officer, Jersey Shore Hospital, Jersey Shore, PA, p. A537

RICE, Peter M.D., Medical Director, Peacehealth Ketchikan Medical Center, Ketchikan, AK, p. A26

RICE, Rebecca, FACHE, Chief Executive Officer, Upper Valley Medical Center, Troy, OH, p. A501

RICE, Tim, President and Chief Executive Officer, Lakewood Health System, Staples, MN, p. A349

RICH, Anna, Chief Financial Officer, Complex Care Hospital At Tenaya, Las Vegas, NV, p. A402

RICH, Bill, Chief Executive Officer, Tennova Healthcare–
Shelbyville, Shelbyville, TN, p. A589

RICH, Judy F., MSN, R.N., President and Chief Executive
Officer, TMC Healthcare, Tucson, AZ, p. A38

RICH, Kori, Chief Executive Officer, The Physicians Centre
Hospital, Bryan, TX, p. A600

RICH, Philip M.D., Chief Medical Officer, West Hills Hospital,
Reno, NV, p. A405

RICHAUD, Benjamin, Interim Chief Executive Officer, Merit
Health River Region, Vicksburg, MS, p. B34

RICHARD, Angelique R.N., Ph.D., Vice President Clinical
Nursing, Chief Nursing Officer and Associate Dean for
Practice, College of Nursing, Rush University Medical
Center, Chicago, IL, p. A183

RICHARD, Benjamin, Regional Information Technology
Director, Santa Rosa Memorial Hospital, Santa Rosa, CA,
p. A91

RICHARD, Brandi, Chief Nursing Officer, Michiana Behavioral
Health Center, Plymouth, IN, p. A218

RICHARD, Brent, Administrative Director Information
Systems, Southern Ohio Medical Center, Portsmouth, OH,
p. A498

RICHARD, Christina, Market Chief Executive Officer,
Kindred Hospital Tarrant County–Arlington, Arlington, TX,
p. A593

RICHARD, Marilyn, Director Human Resources, Daviess
Community Hospital, Washington, IN, p. A221

RICHARD, Scott, Vice President Finance and Chief Financial
Officer, St. Elizabeth Hospital, Gonzales, LA, p. A275

RICHARD, Thomas, Director Budget and Revenue Cycle,
Redwood Area Hospital, Redwood Falls, MN, p. A346

RICHARD, Tim, IT Coordinator, Crawford Memorial Hospital,
Robinson, IL, p. A198

RICHARDS, Craig A., Chief Executive Officer, Mildred Mitchell–
Bateman Hospital, Huntington, WV, p. A692

RICHARDS, Frank
Chief Information Officer, Geisinger Medical Center,
Danville, PA, p. A532
Chief Information Officer, Geisinger Wyoming Valley Medical
Center, Wilkes Barre, PA, p. A554

RICHARDS, Jaena, Chief Financial Officer, Deer Lodge Medical
Center, Deer Lodge, MT, p. A384

RICHARDS, Jon, Chief Financial Officer, Tennova Newport
Medical Center, Newport, TN, p. A587

RICHARDS, Jonathan, Chief Financial Officer, David Grant Usaf
Medical Center, Travis Afb, CA, p. A94

RICHARDS, Judith, Director of Nursing, Adcare Hospital Of
Worcester, Worcester, MA, p. A313

RICHARDS, Kelly, MSN
Senior Vice President and Chief Nursing Officer, Covenant
Medical Center, Waterloo, IA, p. A236
Senior Vice President and Chief Nursing Officer, Mercy
Hospital Of Franciscan Sisters, Oelwein, IA, p. A232
Senior Vice President and Chief Nursing Officer, Sartori
Memorial Hospital, Cedar Falls, IA, p. A223

RICHARDS, Kyle, Chief Executive Officer, Lake Region
Healthcare, Fergus Falls, MN, p. A340

RICHARDS, Mandy R.N., MSN, Vice President Patient Care,
United Hospital, Saint Paul, MN, p. A348

RICHARDS, Nate, Director Information Technology, Mitchell
County Hospital Health Systems, Beloit, KS, p. A239

RICHARDS, Sheila K, Human Resources Director, Dallas
Medical Center, Dallas, TX, p. A605

RICHARDS, Stanlee R.N., Chief Nurse Executive, NYC Health
+ Hospitals / Carter, New Rochelle, NY, p. A444

RICHARDS, Suzanne, R.N., M.P.H., FACHE
Chief Executive Officer, Orange County Global Medical
Center, Inc., Santa Ana, CA, p. A90
Chief Executive Officer, Victor Valley Global Medical Center,
Victorville, CA, p. A96

RICHARDS, Thom
Chief Information Technology, Adair County Health System,
Greenfield, IA, p. A228
Director Information Technology, Knoxville Hospital &
Clinics, Knoxville, IA, p. A230

RICHARDSON, Crystal, Chief Nursing Officer, Vibra Hospital
Of Richmond, Richmond, VA, p. A674

RICHARDSON, David M.D., Chief of Staff, Delta Medical
Center, Memphis, TN, p. A584

RICHARDSON, Denise R.N., MSN, Senior Vice President and
Chief Nursing Officer, St. Barnabas Hospital, New Rochelle,
NY, p. A446

RICHARDSON, Dorothy, Director Human Resources, Van
Matre Healthsouth Rehabilitation Hospital, Rockford, IL,
p. A199

RICHARDSON, Dwayne, Chief Operating Officer, Placentia–
Linda Hospital, Placentia, CA, p. A80

RICHARDSON, Greg H, Assistant Administrator Human
Resources, Piedmont Newton Hospital, Covington, GA,
p. A155

RICHARDSON, Irene
Chief Financial Officer, Memorial Hospital Of Sweetwater
County, Rock Springs, WY, p. A719
Interim Chief Executive Officer, Memorial Hospital Of
Sweetwater County, Rock Springs, WY, p. A719

RICHARDSON, James, Chief Medical Officer, Holy Cross
Hospital, Chicago, IL, p. A181

RICHARDSON, Judy M.D., President Medical Staff, Mid–
Columbia Medical Center, The Dalles, OR, p. A527

RICHARDSON, Karen K., Senior Vice President and Chief
Financial Officer, Providence Healthcare Network, Waco,
TX, p. A652

RICHARDSON, Keith, President and Chief Executive Officer,
East Liverpool City Hospital, East Liverpool, OH, p. A490

RICHARDSON, Kevin M.D., Chief of Staff, Southwest
Mississippi Regional Medical Center, Mccomb, MS, p. A358

RICHARDSON, Kirk, R.N., Vice President, Chief Operating
Officer, and Chief Nursing Officer, Bronson Lakeview
Hospital, Paw Paw, MI, p. A327

RICHARDSON, Kristy, Director of Nursing, De Queen Medical
Center, De Queen, AR, p. A42

RICHARDSON, Mark D., President and Chief Executive Officer,
Great River Medical Center, West Burlington, IA, p. A236

RICHARDSON, Nathaniel Jr, President, Decatur Morgan
Hospital, Decatur, AL, p. A16

RICHARDSON, Pamela, Business Manager, Central Regional
Hospital, Butner, NC, p. A458

RICHARDSON, Paul McKinley Jr, Vice President, Medical
Affairs, Conway Medical Center, Conway, SC, p. A561

RICHARDSON, Robert, Information Technology Administrator,
Porter Regional Hospital, Valparaiso, IN, p. A220

RICHARDSON, Rodney, Director of Information Technology,
Baptist Health Corbin, Corbin, KY, p. A256

RICHARDSON, Sarah, Director Information Systems, Belton
Regional Medical Center, Belton, MO, p. A364

RICHARDSON, Stanley, Coordinator Human Resources
and Payroll Benefits, Kindred Hospital–San Antonio, San
Antonio, TX, p. A642

RICHARDSON, Terika, M.P.H., President, Advocate Trinity
Hospital, Chicago, IL, p. A180

RICHARDSON, Terrie, Coordinator Human Resources, Select
Specialty Hospital–Augusta, Augusta, GA, p. A152

RICHARDSON, Timothy J M.D., Chief of Staff, Maine Veterans
Affairs Medical Center, Augusta, ME, p. A289

RICHARDSON, Todd, Chief Information Officer, Aspirus
Medford Hospital & Clinics, Inc., Medford, WI, p. A706

RICHARDSON, William T., President and Chief Executive
Officer, Tift Regional Medical Center, Tifton, GA, p. A166

RICHARDVILLE, Craig D
Chief Information and Analytics Officer, Carolinas
Healthcare System Cleveland, Shelby, NC, p. A470
Chief Information and Analytics Officer, Carolinas
Rehabilitation, Charlotte, NC, p. A459
Senior Vice President and Chief Information and Analytics
Officer, Carolinas Medical Center, Charlotte, NC, p. A459

RICHASON, Amie
Vice President Human Resources, The Villages Regional
Hospital, The Villages, FL, p. A146
Interim Chief Executive Officer, Merit Health River Region,
Vicksburg, MS, p. A362

RICHBOURG, Gail A, Director Human Resources, Mcleod
Health Clarendon, Manning, SC, p. A564

RICHCREEK, Keith, Manager Technical Services, Lafayette
Regional Health Center, Lexington, MO, p. A372

RICHENS, Ken, Chief Information Officer, Central Valley
Medical Center, Nephi, UT, p. A658

RICHERT, Ed M.D., Chief of Staff, Modoc Medical Center,
Alturas, CA, p. A51

RICHERT, Tadd M
Chief Financial Officer, Chi St. Vincent Hot Springs, Hot
Springs, AR, p. A44
Chief Financial Officer, Chi St. Vincent Infirmary Medical
Center, Little Rock, AR, p. A46
Chief Financial Officer, Chi St. Vincent Morrilton, Morrilton,
AR, p. A47
Senior Vice President and Chief Financial Officer, Chi St.
Vincent Medical Center–North, Sherwood, AR, p. A49

RICHETTI, Michael, Chief Financial Officer, Chilton Medical
Center, Pompton Plains, NJ, p. A419

RICHHART, David, Vice President Fiscal Services, Community
Medical Center, Missoula, MT, p. A386

RICHMAN, Craig M.D., Medical Director, Meadows Psychiatric
Center, Centre Hall, PA, p. A531

RICHMAN, Jonathan M.D., Chief of Staff, Chase County
Community Hospital, Imperial, NE, p. A394

RICHMAN, Timothy, Chief Executive Officer, Wheaton
Franciscan Healthcare – Elmbrook Memorial, Brookfield,
WI, p. A699

RICHMOND, Andy, Director Information Technology, Choctaw
Memorial Hospital, Hugo, OK, p. A509

RICHMOND, Craig, Senior Vice President and Chief Financial
Officer, Metrohealth Medical Center, Cleveland, OH,
p. A486

RICHMOND, Fred, Chief Executive Officer, Springwoods
Behavioral Health Hospital, Fayetteville, AR, p. A43

RICHMOND, Ira, Associate Director Patient Care Services,
Veterans Affairs Pittsburgh Healthcare System, Pittsburgh,
PA, p. A548

RICHOUX, Jacquelyn, Chief Financial Officer, Lady Of The Sea
General Hospital, Cut Off, LA, p. A274

RICHTER, Daniel M.D., Chief of Staff, Chi Health Missouri
Valley, Missouri Valley, IA, p. A231

RICHTER, Thomas V., Chief Executive Officer, Pioneer
Memorial Hospital And Health Services, Viborg, SD,
p. A573

RICK, Bob, Vice President Information Technology, Usmd
Hospital At Arlington, Arlington, TX, p. A594

RICKARD, Sheryl, Chief Executive Officer, Bonner General
Hospital, Sandpoint, ID, p. A176

RICKENS, Chris R.N., MS, Senior Vice President and Chief
Nursing Officer, Upmc Altoona, Altoona, PA, p. A528

RICKMAN, Mike, Chief Executive Officer, Shelby Baptist
Medical Center, Alabaster, AL, p. A13

RICKS, Edward, Vice President and Chief Information Officer,
Beaufort Memorial Hospital, Beaufort, SC, p. A558

RICKS, Katie, Interim Chief Executive Officer, Hansen Family
Hospital, Iowa Falls, IA, p. A230

RICKS, Loretha, Human Resources Supervisor, Southampton
Memorial Hospital, Franklin, VA, p. A667

RICKS, Michael, Chief Operating Officer, Hoag Memorial
Hospital Presbyterian, Newport Beach, CA, p. A76

RICO, Carrie, Chief Human Resource Officer, Keefe Memorial
Hospital, Cheyenne Wells, CO, p. A99

RICO, Richard, Vice President and Chief Financial Officer, Sky
Lakes Medical Center, Klamath Falls, OR, p. A523

RIDALL, Jackie, Director Human Resources, Berwick Hospital
Center, Berwick, PA, p. A529

RIDDER, Terri, Director Human Resources, St. Francis
Memorial Hospital, West Point, NE, p. A400

RIDDLE, Kent, Chief Executive Officer, Mary Free Bed
Rehabilitation Hospital, Grand Rapids, MI, p. A321

RIDGE, Frederick R., Chief of Staff, Greene County General
Hospital, Linton, IN, p. A215

RIDGWAY, Diane, President, Methodist Healthcare Memphis
Hospitals, Memphis, TN, p. A585

RIDLEN, Deborah CPA, Vice President Fiscal Services and
Chief Financial Officer, Schneck Medical Center, Seymour,
IN, p. A219

RIDLEY, John, Executive Vice President & Chief Operating
Officer, Decatur Memorial Hospital, Decatur, IL, p. A185

RIDLEY, Pam, Director Information Systems, Henry County
Medical Center, Paris, TN, p. A588

RIDLEY, Zena, Director Human Resources, Harbor Oaks
Hospital, New Baltimore, MI, p. A327

RIDNER, Sheila R.N., Director of Nursing, Behavioral
Healthcare Center At Columbia, Columbia, TN, p. A577

RIEBER, Dan, Chief Financial Officer, Uchealth Memorial,
Colorado Springs, CO, p. A100

RIEBER, Jim, Director Information Systems, Perham Health,
Perham, MN, p. A346

RIECHERS, Thomas M.D., Chief Medical Staff, Mercy Hospital
Washington, Washington, MO, p. A381

RIECK, Amy, Human Resources Officer, Greater Regional
Medical Center, Creston, IA, p. A225

RIEDEL, Sherry, Chief Financial Management Service, John
D. Dingell Veterans Affairs Medical Center, Detroit, MI,
p. A318

RIEDLINGER, Floyd, Director Human Resources, West
Jefferson Medical Center, Marrero, LA, p. A281

RIEDLINGER, Joann, Vice President Nursing and Manager
Information Systems, Bucyrus Community Hospital,
Bucyrus, OH, p. A482

RIEG, Kevin M.D., President Medical Staff, Via Christi
Rehabilitation Hospital, Wichita, KS, p. A254

RIEGE, Michael J., Chief Executive Officer, Virginia Gay
Hospital, Vinton, IA, p. A235

RIEGER, Bill, Chief Information Officer, Flagler Hospital, Saint
Augustine, FL, p. A141

RIEGER, Tim, Chief Financial Officer, St. Rita's Medical Center,
Lima, OH, p. A493

RIEGERT, Patricia, Director Fiscal Services, Danville State
Hospital, Danville, PA, p. A532

RIEKE, Diane, Director Patient Care Services, Patients'
Hospital Of Redding, Redding, CA, p. A81

RIEKS, Katie, Chief Nursing Officer, Hansen Family Hospital,
Iowa Falls, IA, p. A230

RIEMER, Stephanie J., President, Munson Healthcare Grayling
Hospital, Grayling, MI, p. A321

RIER, Kirk, Chief Operating Officer, Iowa Specialty Hospital–
Clarion, Clarion, IA, p. A224

RIES, Heather MSN, R.N., Chief Nursing Officer, Regional Medical Center, Manchester, IA, p. A231

RIESER, Michael M.D., Medical Director, Ridge Behavioral Health System, Lexington, KY, p. A261

RIETMAN, Cheryl, Chief Administrative Officer, Deaconess Hospital, Evansville, IN, p. A207

RIETSEMA, Wouter M.D., Chief Quality and Information Officer, The University Of Vermont Health Network–Champlain Valley Physicians Hospital, Plattsburgh, NY, p. A449

RIFFLE, Virginia, Vice President Patient Care Services, Samaritan North Lincoln Hospital, Lincoln City, OR, p. A523

RIFKIN, Scott, Chief Executive Officer, Anaheim Global Medical Center, Anaheim, CA, p. A51

RIGAS, Warren Alston, Executive Vice President and Chief Operating Officer, Floyd Medical Center, Rome, GA, p. A163

RIGDON, Alice W., Vice President Finance, Saint Joseph Hospital, Denver, CO, p. A101

RIGDON, Edward M.D., Chief Medical Officer, Merit Health Rankin, Brandon, MS, p. A353

RIGDON, Pam, Director Nursing, Laird Hospital, Union, MS, p. A362

RIGGIN, Andrew, Chief Executive Officer, Bennett County Hospital And Nursing Home, Martin, SD, p. A570

RIGGLE, Vikki, Director Human Resources, Eastern Louisiana Mental Health System, Jackson, LA, p. A276

RIGGS, Jennifer R.N., Chief Nurse Officer, Mainegeneral Medical Center, Augusta, ME, p. A289

RIGGS, Jon, Senior Vice President, Chief Financial Officer, Medical Center Health System, Odessa, TX, p. A635

RIGNEY, Alice, Chief Human Resources Officer, Abbeville Area Medical Center, Abbeville, SC, p. A558

RIGSBEE CARROLL, Cristina, Chief Operating Officer, Granville Health System, Oxford, NC, p. A468

RIGSBY, Diane, Chief Information Officer, Capital Hospice, Arlington, VA, p. A664

RILEY, Colleen M.D., Medical Director, Laguna Honda Hospital And Rehabilitation Center, San Francisco, CA, p. A87

RILEY, Jennifer, Vice President Operations, Memorial Regional Health, Craig, CO, p. A100

RILEY, Jim, Director Information Technology, Wagoner Community Hospital, Wagoner, OK, p. A519

RILEY, Joe B., FACHE, President and Chief Executive Officer, Jackson Hospital And Clinic, Montgomery, AL, p. A21

RILEY, Kenneth, Director Information Systems, Baystate Wing Hospital, Palmer, MA, p. A310

RILEY, Linzie, Interim Human Resource Manager, Lifecare Hospitals Of Dallas, Dallas, TX, p. A605

RILEY, Mike, President and Chief Operating Officer, Novant Health Huntersville Medical Center, Huntersville, NC, p. A465

RILEY, Randy
   Chief Financial Officer, Center For Behavioral Medicine, Kansas City, MO, p. A370
   Fiscal and Administrative Manager, Northwest Missouri Psychiatric Rehabilitation Center, Saint Joseph, MO, p. A376

RILEY, Robert, Interim Chief Financial Officer, East Jefferson General Hospital, Metairie, LA, p. A281

RILEY, Susan, Director Human Resources, Healthsouth Rehabilitation Hospital Of Miami, Cutler Bay, FL, p. A122

RILEY, William M.D., Jr, Chief of Staff, Memorial Hermann Sugar Land Hospital, Sugar Land, TX, p. A647

RIMOVSKY, A. Jay., Chief Executive Officer, Central Texas Rehabilitation Hospital, Austin, TX, p. A594

RINALDI, Anthony, Executive Vice President, Fairview Hospital, Great Barrington, MA, p. A307

RINALDI, Blythe, Vice President, Mayo Clinic Health System – Northland In Barron, Barron, WI, p. A698

RINDELS, Doris, Vice President Operations, Grinnell Regional Medical Center, Grinnell, IA, p. A228

RINDFLEISCH, Jody, Manager Human Resources, Redwood Area Hospital, Redwood Falls, MN, p. A346

RINDLISBACHER, Diane, Manager Information Systems, Orem Community Hospital, Orem, UT, p. A658

RINEHART, Linda, Director Human Resources, Healthsouth Treasure Coast Rehabilitation Hospital, Vero Beach, FL, p. A146

RINEHART, Rick, Vice President, Chief Information Officer, Carle Foundation Hospital, Urbana, IL, p. A201

RINEY, Jeremy, Chief Executive Officer, Connally Memorial Medical Center, Floresville, TX, p. A612

RING, Brian K, Chief Operating Officer, Henry County Hospital, New Castle, IN, p. A217

RING, Caroline A, Chief Nursing Officer, Spectrum Health Big Rapids Hospital, Big Rapids, MI, p. A315

RINGE, Kathy, Director Human Resources, Sage Rehabilitation Hospital, Baton Rouge, LA, p. A271

RINGER, Dave M.D., Chief of Staff, St. Mary's Good Samaritan Hospital, Greensboro, GA, p. A158

RINGO, Jonathan, M.D., President and Chief Operating Officer, Sinai Hospital Of Baltimore, Baltimore, MD, p. A296

RINKE, Joseph, Director Human Resources, Streamwood Behavioral Health Center, Streamwood, IL, p. A201

RINKENBERGER, Sean, Chief Financial Officer, St. Andrew's Health Center, Bottineau, ND, p. A474

RINKER, John M., Chief Medical Officer, OSF Saint James – John W. Albrecht Medical Center, Pontiac, IL, p. A198

RINTOUL, Alexander M., Chief Executive Officer, The Medical Center At Elizabeth Place, Dayton, OH, p. A490

RION, Trey, Chief Information Officer, West Calcasieu Cameron Hospital, Sulphur, LA, p. A287

RIOS, Cindy, Chief Financial Officer, Alliancehealth Durant, Durant, OK, p. A506

RIOS, Damaris, Executive Nursing Director, Hospital Metropolitano Dr. Susoni, Arecibo, PR, p. A722

RIOS, Jose C, Director Information Services, Murray Medical Center, Chatsworth, GA, p. A154

RIOS, Margot R.N., Chief Nursing Officer, Christus Spohn Hospital Alice, Alice, TX, p. A591

RIOS, Mary R.N., Interim Director of Nursing, Cordova Community Medical Center, Cordova, AK, p. A25

RIORDAN, Michael C., President and Chief Executive Officer, Greenville Health System, Greenville, SC, p. B55

RIPPE, Diana, Chief Financial Officer, Tri Valley Health System, Cambridge, NE, p. A391

RIPPERGER, Ted, Administrative Director Human Resources, Atrium Medical Center, Middletown, OH, p. A496

RIPPEY, Wesley E M.D., Chief Medical Officer, Adventist Medical Center–Portland, Portland, OR, p. A525

RIPSCH, Sue
   Senior Vice President & Chief Operating Officer, Mercyhealth Hospital – Rockton Avenue, Rockford, IL, p. A199
   Vice President and Chief Nursing Officer, Mercyhealth Hospital And Trauma Center – Janesville, Janesville, WI, p. A704

RISBY, Emile M.D., Clinical Director, Georgia Regional Hospital At Atlanta, Decatur, GA, p. A156

RISHA, Holly, Administrative Director Human Resources, College Hospital Cerritos, Cerritos, CA, p. A55

RISINGER, Jeff, Director Human Resources, Uams Medical Center, Little Rock, AR, p. A46

RISK, Carl W. II, President, Elkhart General Hospital, Elkhart, IN, p. A207

RISKA, Marilouise, Chief Executive Officer, Select Specialty Hospital–Northwest Detroit, Detroit, MI, p. A318

RISLOW, Deb, Chief Information Officer, Gundersen Health System, La Crosse, WI, p. A704

RISOVI, Carol, Human Resources, Chi St Alexius Health Carrington Medical Center, Carrington, ND, p. A474

RISSE, Thomas, Chief Financial Officer and Vice President Business Services, Kaiser Permanente Medical Center, Honolulu, HI, p. A168

RITCHEY, Jim, Director Human Resources, Sky Ridge Medical Center, Lone Tree, CO, p. A105

RITCHIE, Bruce, Vice President of Finance and Chief Financial Officer, Peninsula Regional Medical Center, Salisbury, MD, p. A301

RITCHIE, Eric M.D., Clinical Director, Chinle Comprehensive Health Care Facility, Chinle, AZ, p. A28

RITCHIE, Jill, Director of Nursing, Ellinwood District Hospital, Ellinwood, KS, p. A240

RITCHIE, Jim, Director Management Information Systems, South Shore Hospital, Chicago, IL, p. A184

RITENOUR, Chad W.M. M.D., Chief Medical Officer, Emory University Hospital, Atlanta, GA, p. A150

RITON, John, Director Information Services, Memorial Hospital Of Tampa, Tampa, FL, p. A145

RITTENOUR, Melanie, Director Human Resources, Paulding County Hospital, Paulding, OH, p. A498

RITTER, Jane R.N., Vice President, Patient Care and Clinical Services, United Regional Health Care System, Wichita Falls, TX, p. A654

RITTER, Robert G FACHE, Associate Director, Harry S. Truman Memorial Veterans Hospital, Columbia, MO, p. A367

RITTMAN, Todd, Director of Nursing, Larue D. Carter Memorial Hospital, Indianapolis, IN, p. A211

RITZ, Robert P., President, Mercy Medical Center–Des Moines, Des Moines, IA, p. A226

RITZ, Robert P, President, Mercy Medical Center–Des Moines, Des Moines, IA, p. A226

RITZHS, Michael, Administrator, Elmore Community Hospital, Wetumpka, AL, p. A24

RIVAS, Eloy, Director of Information Systems, Venice Regional Bayfront Health, Venice, FL, p. A146

RIVAS, Jose M.D., Chief of Staff, Community Hospital Of Huntington Park, Huntington Park, CA, p. A63

RIVAS, Ramon Rodriguez M.D., Medical Director, Hospital San Cristobal, Coto Laurel, PR, p. A723

RIVERA, Angela, Chief Nursing Officer, Beckley Arh Hospital, Beckley, WV, p. A690

RIVERA, Anita, Director Human Resources, Peninsula Hospital, Louisville, TN, p. A583

RIVERA, Anthony, Director Human Resources, Hartgrove Hospital, Chicago, IL, p. A181

RIVERA, Ashley, Chief Financial Officer and Chief Executive Officer, Kittson Memorial Healthcare Center, Hallock, MN, p. A341

RIVERA, Christina, Director Human Resources, Southwest General Hospital, San Antonio, TX, p. A644

RIVERA, Cristina, Chief Executive Officer, Rio Grande Regional Hospital, Mcallen, TX, p. A632

RIVERA, Edgar, Chief Information Officer, Brownfield Regional Medical Center, Brownfield, TX, p. A599

RIVERA, Enrique, Chief Financial Officer, Bella Vista Hospital, Mayaguez, PR, p. A724

RIVERA, Ivonne, Director Finance, Hospital Oriente, Humacao, PR, p. A724

RIVERA, Jamie, Chief Financial Officer, Hospital Pavia Arecibo, Arecibo, PR, p. A722

RIVERA, Joe, Chief Information Technology Officer, Laredo Medical Center, Laredo, TX, p. A628

RIVERA, Jose Garcia, Director Human Resources, Hospital Buen Samaritano, Aguadilla, PR, p. A721

RIVERA, Luis, Director Human Resources, San Juan Capestrano Hospital, San Juan, PR, p. A726

RIVERA, Maria, Director Human Resources, Westside Regional Medical Center, Plantation, FL, p. A140

RIVERA, Zamarys R.N., Chief Nursing Officer, Healthsouth Rehabilitation Hospital Of San Juan, San Juan, PR, p. A726

RIVERA MALDONADO, Luis, Executive Director, Bella Vista Hospital, Mayaguez, PR, p. A724

RIVERA–POL, Noriselle, Vice President Finance, Hospital Manati Medical Center, Manati, PR, p. A724

RIVERS, Eric, Chief Information Officer, Mission Community Hospital, Los Angeles, CA, p. A70

RIVERS, Jan, Director Human Resources, Ochsner Medical Center–Baton Rouge, Baton Rouge, LA, p. A270

RIVERS, Nikki R.N., Regional Chief Nursing Officer, South Market, Seton Edgar B. Davis Hospital, Luling, TX, p. A631

RIVOIRE, John, R.N., MSN, Administrator, Louisiana Extended Care Hospital Of Natchitoches, Natchitoches, LA, p. A282

RIZK, Magdy M.D., Chief of Staff, West Houston Medical Center, Houston, TX, p. A623

RIZK, Norman M.D., Chief Medical Officer, Stanford Health Care, Palo Alto, CA, p. A79

RIZK, Rob, Director Information Technology, Good Shepherd Health Care System, Hermiston, OR, p. A522

RIZKALLA, Nasseem M.D., Chief Medical Officer, Aspirus Iron River Hospitals & Clinics, Inc., Iron River, MI, p. A323

RIZZO, Frank, Chief Financial Officer, Central Region, North Shore University Hospital, Manhasset, NY, p. A439

RIZZO, Theresa, Administrator, Franklin County Memorial Hospital, Franklin, NE, p. A392

RIZZUTO, George CPA, Chief Financial Officer, St. Christopher's Hospital For Children, Philadelphia, PA, p. A545

ROACH, Bryan, Chief Financial Officer, Yampa Valley Medical Center, Steamboat Springs, CO, p. A107

ROACH, Crystal, Chief Financial Officer, Trustpoint Rehabilitation Hospital Of Lubbock, Lubbock, TX, p. A630

ROACH, David, Vice President Information Systems, Kadlec Regional Medical Center, Richland, WA, p. A684

ROACH, Dee A M.D., Chief of Staff, Mitchell County Hospital, Colorado City, TX, p. A602

ROACH, Donna
   Chief Information Officer, Sacred Heart Hospital Pensacola, Pensacola, FL, p. A139
   Chief Information Officer, Via Christi Hospital On St. Francis, Wichita, KS, p. A254

ROACH, Geoff, Director Human Resources, Barrett Hospital & Healthcare, Dillon, MT, p. A384

ROACH, Maureen, Senior Chief Financial Officer, Kindred Hospital–St. Louis, Saint Louis, MO, p. A377

ROACH, Renee
   System Vice President, Human Resources, SSM Health St. Clare Hospital – Fenton, Fenton, MO, p. A368
   System Vice President, SSM Health St. Joseph Hospital – Lake Saint Louis, Lake Saint Louis, MO, p. A372

ROACH, Steven P., FACHE, President and Chief Executive Officer, Umass Memorial–Marlborough Hospital, Marlborough, MA, p. A308

ROADER, Charles, Vice President Finance, Edgerton Hospital And Health Services, Edgerton, WI, p. A701

ROAN, Linda Lyn, Chief Nursing Officer, East Morgan County Hospital, Brush, CO, p. A99

ROANE, Jeniece S., MS, R.N., Interim Vice President, Children's Services, Children's Hospital Of Richmond At Vcu–Brook Road Campus, Richmond, VA, p. A674

ROANHORSE, Anslem, Chief Executive Officer, U. S. Public Health Service Indian Hospital, Crownpoint, NM, p. A425

ROARK, Chris, Chief Information Officer, Stillwater Medical Center, Stillwater, OK, p. A516

ROARK, Robert R, Director Human Resources, Laughlin Memorial Hospital, Greeneville, TN, p. A579

ROARTY, Maureen, Executive Vice President Human Resources, Nassau University Medical Center, East Meadow, NY, p. A435

ROAT, David D.O., Medical Director, Ancora Psychiatric Hospital, Hammonton, NJ, p. A414

ROB, Lee, Director Human Resources, Pioneer Community Hospital Of Aberdeen, Aberdeen, MS, p. A352

ROBAN, Michele, Administrator, Arnold Memorial Health Care Center, Adrian, MN, p. B112

ROBB, Joy, Vice President Human Resources, Prairie View, Newton, KS, p. A247

ROBBINS, Dan, Information Technology and Account Executive, St. Vincent Medical Center, Los Angeles, CA, p. A71

ROBBINS, Donald M.D., Jr, Chief Staff, Hills & Dales General Hospital, Cass City, MI, p. A316

ROBBINS, Joe M.D., Vice President Medical Affairs, Sentara Williamsburg Regional Medical Center, Williamsburg, VA, p. A677

ROBBINS, Shannon, Chief Operating Officer, Ohio Hospital For Psychiatry, Columbus, OH, p. A487

ROBEANO, Karen R.N., Chief Nursing Officer and Vice President Patient Care Services, Firsthealth Moore Regional Hospital, Pinehurst, NC, p. A468

ROBERGE, Jeremy

Chief Financial Officer, Huggins Hospital, Wolfeboro, NH, p. A410

Director Reimbursement, Androscoggin Valley Hospital, Berlin, NH, p. A407

President and Chief Executive Officer, Huggins Hospital, Wolfeboro, NH, p. A410

ROBERSON, Ed, Director Information Systems, Houston Northwest Medical Center, Houston, TX, p. A621

ROBERSON, Joe, Chief Executive Officer, Healthsouth Rehabilitation Hospital – Abilene, Abilene, TX, p. A591

ROBERSON, Lynda, Senior Program Director, Rusk State Hospital, Rusk, TX, p. A641

ROBERSON, Meika M.D., Chief Medical Officer, Carepoint Health Hoboken University Medical Center, Hoboken, NJ, p. A414

ROBERSON, Scotty, Assistant Administrator and Chief Nursing Officer, University Of South Alabama Children's And Women's Hospital, Mobile, AL, p. A20

ROBERT, Jeffery, Chief Operating Officer, Swedish/Issaquah, Issaquah, WA, p. A681

ROBERT, Thomas W., Senior Vice President of Finance and Chief Financial Officer, Mercy Medical Center, Springfield, MA, p. A311

ROBERTS, Allyson CPA, Chief Financial Officer, Nor–Lea Hospital District, Lovington, NM, p. A427

ROBERTS, Andrew, Interim Chief Human Resources Officer, Veterans Affairs Gulf Coast Veterans Health Care System, Biloxi, MS, p. A352

ROBERTS, Barbara, Chief Financial Officer, Robley Rex Veterans Affairs Medical Center, Louisville, KY, p. A263

ROBERTS, Bert, Controller, Miracle Mile Medical Center, Los Angeles, CA, p. A70

ROBERTS, Brad, Network Administrator, Swisher Memorial Hospital District, Tulia, TX, p. A650

ROBERTS, Cassidi R.N., Chief Nursing Officer, Medical City Mckinney, Mckinney, TX, p. A632

ROBERTS, Cathy, Vice President Mission Integration and Human Resources, Mercy Regional Medical Center, Durango, CO, p. A101

ROBERTS, Charles, M.D.

Executive Vice President and Executive Medical Director, Children's Mercy Hospital Kansas City, Kansas City, MO, p. A370

Medical Director, Children's Mercy South, Overland Park, KS, p. A249

ROBERTS, Curt L., Chief Executive Officer, Cornerstone Hospital Of Austin, Austin, TX, p. A594

ROBERTS, Cyndi, Director Human Resources, Medical City Fort Worth, Fort Worth, TX, p. A614

ROBERTS, David J., M.D., President, North Shore Medical Center, Salem, MA, p. A311

ROBERTS, David M.D., Chief Medical Officer, Jackson–Madison County General Hospital, Jackson, TN, p. A580

ROBERTS, Deborah R.N., Chief Nursing Officer, The Core Institute Specialty Hospital, Phoenix, AZ, p. A34

ROBERTS, Debra, Director of Human Resources, St. Luke's Lakeside Hospital, The Woodlands, TX, p. A649

ROBERTS, Greg, Superintendent, Oregon State Hospital, Salem, OR, p. A526

ROBERTS, Jason

Director Information System, Carson Valley Medical Center, Gardnerville, NV, p. A402

Director of Information Services, Barton Memorial Hospital, South Lake Tahoe, CA, p. A92

ROBERTS, Jeff, Director Information Technology, Pinckneyville Community Hospital, Pinckneyville, IL, p. A198

ROBERTS, Kathryn, Director Human Resources, Mercy Medical Center–Dubuque, Dubuque, IA, p. A227

ROBERTS, Kenneth D., President, John T. Mather Memorial Hospital, Port Jefferson, NY, p. A450

ROBERTS, Kevin A., FACHE, President and Chief Executive Officer, Adventist Health Glendale, Glendale, CA, p. A62

ROBERTS, Krista, Chief Operating Officer, St. Mary's Regional Medical Center, Enid, OK, p. A507

ROBERTS, Laurel R.N., MSN, Chief Nursing Officer, Rolling Hills Hospital, Franklin, TN, p. A579

ROBERTS, Mark, Chief Operating Officer, Memorial Satilla Health, Waycross, GA, p. A167

ROBERTS, Matthew S., Chief Executive Officer, Raleigh General Hospital, Beckley, WV, p. A690

ROBERTS, Michael, Chief Information Officer, Highlands Regional Medical Center, Prestonsburg, KY, p. A266

ROBERTS, Nancy, Chief Operating Officer, Providence St. Vincent Medical Center, Portland, OR, p. A526

ROBERTS, Pamela W., Chief Executive Officer, Henderson County Community Hospital, Lexington, TN, p. A583

ROBERTS, Paul L., Director, Cheyenne Veterans Affairs Medical Center, Cheyenne, WY, p. A718

ROBERTS, Paula, Chief Nursing Officer, Cumberland Hospital, New Kent, VA, p. A671

ROBERTS, Phillip G, Vice President Finance and Chief Financial Officer, Columbus Community Hospital, Inc., Columbus, WI, p. A700

ROBERTS, Rob, Director Information Technology, Benson Hospital, Benson, AZ, p. A28

ROBERTS, Robert C

Senior Vice President Financial Services, Baptist Health Medical Center – North Little Rock, North Little Rock, AR, p. A48

Senior Vice President Financial Services, Baptist Health Medical Center–Little Rock, Little Rock, AR, p. A46

Senior Vice President, Baptist Health Rehabilitation Institute, Little Rock, AR, p. A46

Vice President and Chief Financial Officer, Baptist Health Medical Center–Arkadelphia, Arkadelphia, AR, p. A40

Vice President, Baptist Health Extended Care Hospital, Little Rock, AR, p. A46

ROBERTS, Robin, Executive Director of Patient Services, Takoma Regional Hospital, Greeneville, TN, p. A579

ROBERTS, Roslyn, Manager, Northside Hospital–Cherokee, Canton, GA, p. A153

ROBERTS, Sally R.N., Director of Nursing, Abrom Kaplan Memorial Hospital, Kaplan, LA, p. A277

ROBERTS, Shayna Brooke, Director Human Resources, Northeastern Health System Sequoyah, Sallisaw, OK, p. A515

ROBERTS, Teresa, Chief Financial Officer, Ringgold County Hospital, Mount Ayr, IA, p. A231

ROBERTS, Todd, Manager Business Operations, Peninsula Hospital, Louisville, TN, p. A583

ROBERTSHAW, Hazel R.N., Ph.D., Chief Nursing Officer, Vice President Patient Services, F. F. Thompson Hospital, Canandaigua, NY, p. A433

ROBERTSON, Carla, Chief Operating Officer and Chief Financial Officer, Saline Memorial Hospital, Benton, AR, p. A40

ROBERTSON, Casey, Chief Executive Officer, Longview Regional Medical Center, Longview, TX, p. A630

ROBERTSON, Darcy, Chief Financial Officer, Page Hospital, Page, AZ, p. A32

ROBERTSON, Elizabeth, Area Controller, Healthsouth Rehabilitation Hospital – Dallas, Dallas, TX, p. A605

ROBERTSON, James A. Jr, President and Chief Executive Officer, Bothwell Regional Health Center, Sedalia, MO, p. A379

ROBERTSON, John L., Administrator, West Central Georgia Regional Hospital, Columbus, GA, p. A155

ROBERTSON, Larry, President, Texas Health Center For Diagnostic & Surgery, Plano, TX, p. A638

ROBERTSON, Laura, R.N., Chief Executive Officer, Banner Desert Medical Center, Mesa, AZ, p. A31

ROBERTSON, Michael, Chief Executive Officer, Piedmont Newnan Hospital, Newnan, GA, p. A162

ROBERTSON, Michelle L., R.N., Chief Operating Officer, Texas Market, Seton Northwest Hospital, Austin, TX, p. A595

ROBERTSON, Misty R.N., Chief Nursing Officer, Bonner General Hospital, Sandpoint, ID, p. A176

ROBERTSON, Patricia Dianne, Chief Financial Officer, Mercy Hospital Watonga, Watonga, OK, p. A519

ROBERTSON, Steve

Executive Vice President and Chief Information Officer, Straub Medical Center, Honolulu, HI, p. A169

Executive Vice President Revenue Cycle Management and Chief Information Officer, Wilcox Medical Center, Lihue, HI, p. A170

Senior Vice President, Pali Momi Medical Center, Aiea, HI, p. A168

Vice President, Kapiolani Medical Center For Women & Children, Honolulu, HI, p. A168

ROBERTSON, William G., President and Chief Executive Officer, Multicare Health System, Tacoma, WA, p. B87

ROBESON, Gail, Vice President Patient Services, Huron Regional Medical Center, Huron, SD, p. A570

ROBICHAUX, Martha, Chief Human Resources Officer, John C. Fremont Healthcare District, Mariposa, CA, p. A73

ROBICHEAUX, James Warren., FACHE, Senior Administrator, East Texas Medical Center Pittsburg, Pittsburg, TX, p. A637

ROBINS, Scott M.D., Chief Medical Officer, Covenant Children's Hospital, Lubbock, TX, p. A630

ROBINSON, Aaron

Chief Executive Officer, Health First Community Hospitals, Health First Cape Canaveral Hospital, Cocoa Beach, FL, p. A122

Chief Executive Officer, Health First Community Hospitals, Health First Palm Bay Hospital, Palm Bay, FL, p. A138

Chief Executive Officer, Health First Community Hospitals, Health First Viera Hospital, Melbourne, FL, p. A132

ROBINSON, Adam M., Director, Veterans Affairs Maryland Health Care System–Baltimore Division, Baltimore, MD, p. A296

ROBINSON, Alan, Chief Financial Officer, Logan Regional Hospital, Logan, UT, p. A657

ROBINSON, Anitra, Human Resources Director, Healthsouth Rehabilitation Hospital Of Middletown, Middletown, DE, p. A115

ROBINSON, Anthony, Manager, Human Resources, Mercy Hospital Of Folsom, Folsom, CA, p. A59

ROBINSON, Bradley, Chief Financial Officer, Evans U. S. Army Community Hospital, Fort Carson, CO, p. A102

ROBINSON, Cliff M.D., Chief of Staff, Central Alabama Veterans Health Care System, Montgomery, AL, p. A21

ROBINSON, David, D.O.

Medical Director, St. Joseph's Behavioral Health Center, Stockton, CA, p. A92

President Medical and Dental Staff, Community Hospital, Munster, IN, p. A216

ROBINSON, Elena, Chief Human Resources Officer, Hima San Pablo Caguas, Caguas, PR, p. A722

ROBINSON, Eric, Chief Executive Officer, Merit Health Natchez, Natchez, MS, p. A359

ROBINSON, Girard M.D., Senior Vice President Medical and Clinical Affairs, Spring Harbor Hospital, Westbrook, ME, p. A293

ROBINSON, Glenn A., FACHE, President, Baylor Scott & White Medical Center – Hillcrest, Waco, TX, p. A652

ROBINSON, Herbert M.D., Vice President, Chief Medical Information Officer, North Oaks Health System, North Oaks Rehabilitation Hospital, Hammond, LA, p. A275

ROBINSON, James L. III, PsyD, President, Presence Saint Joseph Hospital, Chicago, IL, p. A182

ROBINSON, Jeanne, Director Human Resources, Inova Fair Oaks Hospital, Fairfax, VA, p. A666

ROBINSON, Jennifer B, Vice President Human Resources, St. Petersburg General Hospital, Saint Petersburg, FL, p. A142

ROBINSON, Jennifer, Administrator, Behavioral Healthcare Center At Clarksville, Clarksville, TN, p. A577

ROBINSON, Mark, FACHE

Associate Administrator and Chief Financial Officer, Hazel Hawkins Memorial Hospital, Hollister, CA, p. A63

President and Chief Executive Officer, Capital Regional Medical Center, Tallahassee, FL, p. A143

ROBINSON, Mary, Chief Nursing Officer and Vice President Patient Care Services, Texas Health Harris Methodist Hospital Southwest Fort Worth, Fort Worth, TX, p. A614

ROBINSON, Paul H M.D., Medical Director, American Fork Hospital, American Fork, UT, p. A656

ROBINSON, Phil, Chief Financial Officer, Saint Agnes Medical Center, Fresno, CA, p. A61

ROBINSON, Phillip D., President, Lankenau Medical Center, Wynnewood, PA, p. A555

ROBINSON, Raymond, Chief Executive Officer, Pembroke Hospital, Pembroke, MA, p. A310

ROBINSON, Stephen Jr, FACHE, Chief Executive Officer, Ochsner Medical Center – Kenner, Kenner, LA, p. A277

ROBINSON, Susan Beth, Vice President Human Resources, St. Mary's Medical Center, Huntington, WV, p. A693

ROBINSON, Tim, Executive Vice President, Chief Financial and Administrative Officer and Treasurer, Nationwide Children's Hospital, Columbus, OH, p. A487

ROBINSON, Trena, Director, Human Resources, Central Texas Rehabilitation Hospital, Austin, TX, p. A594

ROBINSON, Vance, Chief Information Officer, Iberia Medical Center, New Iberia, LA, p. A282

ROBINSON, William, Director Human Resources, Healthsouth Rehabilitation Hospital Of Erie, Erie, PA, p. A534

ROBISON, Bruce, Vice President and Chief Information Officer, Cox Medical Centers, Springfield, MO, p. A379

ROBISON, John, Chief Executive Officer, Clifton T. Perkins Hospital Center, Jessup, MD, p. A299

ROBISON, Keith, Chief Information Officer, Upmc Chautauqua Wca, Jamestown, NY, p. A437

ROBISON, Neely, Director Human Resources, The Bridgeway, North Little Rock, AR, p. A48

ROBISON, Rob, Director Information Technology, Medical Center Of South Arkansas, El Dorado, AR, p. A42

ROBISON, Ryan, Chief Nursing Officer, Sanpete Valley Hospital, Mount Pleasant, UT, p. A657

ROBISON, Wendell M.D., Chief of Staff, Sheridan Veterans Affairs Medical Center, Sheridan, WY, p. A720

ROBITAILLE, Mark E, FACHE, President and Chief Executive Officer, Martin Health System, Stuart, FL, p. A143

ROBL, Chris, Human Resources, Ellinwood District Hospital, Ellinwood, KS, p. A240

ROBLES, Burt, Vice President Information Services, Guthrie Robert Packer Hospital, Sayre, PA, p. A549

ROCA, Robert M.D., Vice President Medical Affairs, Sheppard Pratt Health System, Baltimore, MD, p. A295

ROCHA, Israel, Chief Executive Officer, NYC Health + Hospitals / Elmhurst, New Rochelle, NY, p. A445

ROCHA, Julie, Vice President Human Resources, Mercy Medical Center Merced, Merced, CA, p. A73

ROCHE, Richard, Administrator, Lakeside Medical Center, Belle Glade, FL, p. A119

ROCHELEAU, John, Vice President Business Support and Information Technology, Bellin Memorial Hospital, Green Bay, WI, p. A702

ROCHER, Leslie, Senior Vice President and Chief Medical Officer, Beaumont Hospital – Royal Oak, Royal Oak, MI, p. A329

ROCHESTER, Charmaine, Vice President Finance, Bon Secours–Depaul Medical Center, Norfolk, VA, p. A671

ROCHIER, Dennis, Chief Medical Officer, Renown South Meadows Medical Center, Reno, NV, p. A405

ROCK, Betty Ann, Vice President Nursing and Chief Nursing Officer, Uniontown Hospital, Uniontown, PA, p. A552

ROCK, Brian, Director of Information Systems, VCU Health Community Memorial Hospital, South Hill, VA, p. A675

ROCK, David, Executive Vice President and Chief Operating Officer, Wyckoff Heights Medical Center, New Rochelle, NY, p. A447

ROCKSMITH, Eugenio M.D., Medical Director, Healthsouth Rehabilitation Hospital Of Vineland, Vineland, NJ, p. A422

ROCKWELL, Jane, Director Support Services, North Metro Medical Center, Jacksonville, AR, p. A45

ROCKWELL, Karla, Director of Nursing, Doctors Memorial Hospital, Bonifay, FL, p. A120

ROCKWELL, Kyle, Chief Executive Officer, Reagan Memorial Hospital, Big Lake, TX, p. A598

ROCKWOOD, John D., President, Medstar National Rehabilitation Hospital, Washington, DC, p. A117

ROCKWOOD, Sylvia, Director Human Resources, Carlisle Regional Medical Center, Carlisle, PA, p. A531

ROCKWOOD, Yvonne, Chief Operating Officer, Poudre Valley Hospital, Fort Collins, CO, p. A102

RODDEN, Celeste, Chief Information Officer, Hillcrest Hospital Claremore, Claremore, OK, p. A506

RODDY, Thomas, Chief Operating Officer, Flowers Hospital, Dothan, AL, p. A16

RODEN, George
   Vice President Human Resources, Mercy Hospital Aurora, Aurora, MO, p. A364
   Vice President Human Resources, Mercy Hospital Cassville, Cassville, MO, p. A366

RODENBAUGH, Cathy, Director Human Resources, Holy Rosary Healthcare, Miles City, MT, p. A386

RODER, Darla, Chief Operating Officer, Cavalier County Memorial Hospital And Clinics, Langdon, ND, p. A477

RODERICK, Travis W., Chief Executive Officer, Premier Surgical Institute, Galena, KS, p. A241

RODERMAN, Nicki, Chief Nursing Officer, Medical City Denton, Denton, TX, p. A608

RODEWALD, Amanda, Interim Chief Financial Officer, Daviess Community Hospital, Washington, IN, p. A221

RODGE, Mark, Director Information Systems, Eaton Rapids Medical Center, Eaton Rapids, MI, p. A319

RODGERS, April, Vice President, Human Resources, Holy Name Medical Center, Teaneck, NJ, p. A421

RODGERS, Bruce C., Chief Administrative Officer, Salem Health West Valley, Dallas, OR, p. A521

RODGERS, Dondie, Interim Chief Nursing Officer, Memorial Hospital Of Texas County, Guymon, OK, p. A508

RODGERS, Jamie, Interim Chief Executive Officer, Choctaw Regional Medical Center, Ackerman, MS, p. A352

RODGERS, Keith, Interim Chief Executive Officer, Continuecare Hospital At Baptist Health Corbin, Corbin, KY, p. A257

RODGERS, Larry, Chief Executive Officer, Poplar Bluff Regional Medical Center, Poplar Bluff, MO, p. A375

RODGERS, Lee M.D., Vice President Quality, United Regional Health Care System, Wichita Falls, TX, p. A654

RODIER, James Barton M.D., Chief Quality Officer, Health Central Hospital, Ocoee, FL, p. A136

RODIS, John F., M.D., President, Saint Francis Hospital And Medical Center, Hartford, CT, p. A110

RODOWICZ, Darlene, Chief Financial Officer, Berkshire Medical Center, Pittsfield, MA, p. A310

RODRIGUES, Pablo M.D., Medical Director, Vibra Hospital Of Amarillo, Amarillo, TX, p. A592

RODRIGUEZ, Alex
   Vice President and Chief Information Officer, St. Elizabeth Edgewood, Edgewood, KY, p. A257
   Vice President and Chief Information Officer, St. Elizabeth Florence, Florence, KY, p. A258
   Vice President and Chief Information Officer, St. Elizabeth Fort Thomas, Fort Thomas, KY, p. A258

RODRIGUEZ, Angie, Human Resource Manager, Carson Tahoe Continuing Care Hospital, Carson City, NV, p. A401

RODRIGUEZ, Ben A., Chief Executive Officer, Hialeah Hospital, Hialeah, FL, p. A126

RODRIGUEZ, Candie, Director Human Resources, Hospital San Cristobal, Coto Laurel, PR, p. A723

RODRIGUEZ, Edgardo, Director Management Information Systems, Auxilio Mutuo Hospital, San Juan, PR, p. A725

RODRIGUEZ, Heather, Chief Nursing Officer, Fresno Heart And Surgical Hospital, Fresno, CA, p. A60

RODRIGUEZ, Jaime, Chief Financial Officer, San Juan City Hospital, San Juan, PR, p. A726

RODRIGUEZ, Joe, Chief Executive Officer, South Texas Health System, Edinburg, TX, p. A610

RODRIGUEZ, Jose Luis., Chief Executive Officer, Hospital Pavia–Santurce, San Juan, PR, p. A726

RODRIGUEZ, Jose O M.D., Medical Director, Castaner General Hospital, Castaner, PR, p. A723

RODRIGUEZ, Joseph R., Chief Executive Officer, Georgetown Behavioral Health Institute, Georgetown, TX, p. A616

RODRIGUEZ, Laura, Director Medical Records, Hospital Del Maestro, San Juan, PR, p. A726

RODRIGUEZ, Lea R.N., Chief Nursing Officer, Vice President Patient Care Services, Clara Maass Medical Center, Belleville, NJ, p. A411

RODRIGUEZ, Leticia, Chief Executive Officer, Ward Memorial Hospital, Monahans, TX, p. A634

RODRIGUEZ, Lizzette, Director Finance, Hospital San Francisco, San Juan, PR, p. A726

RODRIGUEZ, Marco, Chief Financial Officer, Valley Baptist Medical Center–Harlingen, Harlingen, TX, p. A618

RODRIGUEZ, Mario, Chief Executive Officer, Laredo Specialty Hospital, Laredo, TX, p. A628

RODRIGUEZ, Maritza, Chief Financial Officer, Hospital Metropolitan, San Juan, PR, p. A726

RODRIGUEZ, Miguel, Medical Director, Caribbean Medical Center, Fajardo, PR, p. A723

RODRIGUEZ, Onel, Chief Financial Officer, Broward Health Coral Springs, Coral Springs, FL, p. A122

RODRIGUEZ, Oscar, Chief Fiscal Officer, Veterans Affairs Caribbean Healthcare System, San Juan, PR, p. A727

RODRIGUEZ, Patricia M., Senior Vice President and Area Manager, Kaiser Permanente South Sacramento Medical Center, Sacramento, CA, p. A83

RODRIGUEZ, Ramon J., President and Chief Executive Officer, Wyckoff Heights Medical Center, New Rochelle, NY, p. A447

RODRIGUEZ, Rufus M.D., Medical Director, Mayo Clinic Health System In Fairmont, Fairmont, MN, p. A339

RODRIGUEZ, Sara
   Chief Financial Officer, Kindred Hospital Sugar Land, Sugar Land, TX, p. A647
   Human Resources, Seton Smithville Regional Hospital, Smithville, TX, p. A646

RODRIGUEZ, Tammy, Vice President of Patient Care Services, Rollins–Brook Community Hospital, Lampasas, TX, p. A628

RODRIGUEZ, Tomas, Chief Information Technology Officer, First Hospital Panamericano, Cidra, PR, p. A723

RODRIGUEZ, Tony, Director Human Resources, South Texas Rehabilitation Hospital, Brownsville, TX, p. A599

RODRIGUEZ, Vilma, Director Human Resources, Hospital San Pablo Del Este, Fajardo, PR, p. A723

RODRIGUEZ, Wilfredo M.D., Chief of Staff, Battle Creek Veterans Affairs Medical Center, Battle Creek, MI, p. A315

RODRIGUEZ, Yelitza Sanchez., Executive Director, Metropolitano De La Montana, Utuado, PR, p. A727

RODRIGUEZ COLLAZO, Jose Luis, Executive Director, Hospital Pavia Arecibo, Arecibo, PR, p. A722

RODRIGUEZ SCHMIDT, Myriam T, Director Human Resources, Cardiovascular Center Of Puerto Rico And The Caribbean, San Juan, PR, p. A725

RODRIGUEZ, Daisy, Director Human Resources, Fort Duncan Regional Medical Center, Eagle Pass, TX, p. A609

RODRIQUEZ, Monica, Director of Human Resources, Stewart & Lynda Resnick Neuropsychiatric Hospital At Ucla, Los Angeles, CA, p. A71

ROE, Daniel, M.D.
   Chief Medical Officer, Copper Queen Community Hospital, Bisbee, AZ, p. A28
   Chief Operating Officer, Copper Queen Community Hospital, Bisbee, AZ, p. A28

ROE, Timothy J., M.D., President and Chief Executive Officer, Rehabilitation Hospital Of The Pacific, Honolulu, HI, p. A169

ROEBACK, Jason, Chief Operating Officer, Saint Vincent Hospital, Erie, PA, p. A534

ROEBKEN, Curtis M.D., Chief Medical Staff, Kentfield Rehabilitation And Specialty Hospital, Kentfield, CA, p. A64

ROEBUCK, Amanda, Director Patient Care Services, Genoa Medical Facilities, Genoa, NE, p. A393

ROEDER, Donna, Chief Financial Officer, Jackson County Regional Health Center, Maquoketa, IA, p. A231

ROEDER, Werner M.D., Vice President Medical Affairs, New York–Presbyterian/Lawrence Hospital, Bronxville, NY, p. A432

ROEDERER, Chris, Senior Vice President Human Resources, Tampa General Hospital, Tampa, FL, p. A145

ROEHR, Richard
   Chief Operating Officer, Amita Health Adventist Medical Center Bolingbrook, Bolingbrook, IL, p. A179
   Vice President and Chief Operating Officer, Amita Health Adventist Medical Center Glenoaks, Glendale Heights, IL, p. A188

ROEHRLE, Andreas, Director Finance, Sentara Williamsburg Regional Medical Center, Williamsburg, VA, p. A677

ROEMER, Dennis, Executive Vice President and Chief Financial Officer, Lancaster General Hospital, Lancaster, PA, p. A538

ROESER, William, President and Chief Executive Officer, Sparrow Ionia Hospital, Ionia, MI, p. A323

ROESLER, Bruce E., FACHE, Chief Executive Officer, Richland Hospital, Richland Center, WI, p. A711

ROETMAN, James D., President and Chief Executive Officer, Pocahontas Community Hospital, Pocahontas, IA, p. A233

ROEVER, Judy MSN, R.N., Chief Nursing Officer, Scenic Mountain Medical Center, Big Spring, TX, p. A598

ROFFELSEN, Michael S.
   Chief Executive Officer, Healthsouth Sunrise Rehabilitation Hospital, Sunrise, FL, p. A143
   Chief Executive Officer, Kindred Hospital South Florida–Fort Lauderdale, Fort Lauderdale, FL, p. A125

ROGALSKI, Robert, Chief Executive Officer, Excela Health, Greensburg, PA, p. B51

ROGALSKI, Ted, Administrator, Genesis Medical Center–Aledo, Aledo, IL, p. A177

ROGAN, Edie, Manager Human Resources, Eastern State Hospital, Williamsburg, VA, p. A677

ROGERS, Aaron, Chief Executive Officer, Trinity Hospital, Weaverville, CA, p. A96

ROGERS, B. Carter, Chief of Staff, Piedmont Newton Hospital, Covington, GA, p. A155

ROGERS, Carrie, Chief Nursing Officer, Southern Tennessee Regional Health System–Lawrenceburg, Lawrenceburg, TN, p. A582

ROGERS, Cathy M, Manager Human Resources, Greenville Health System – Laurens County Memorial Hospital, Clinton, SC, p. A560

ROGERS, David, Chief Executive Officer, Ortonville Area Health Services, Ortonville, MN, p. A345

ROGERS, Doris, Vice President Human Resources, Saint Luke's Hospital Of Kansas City, Kansas City, MO, p. A370

ROGERS, Eric, Chief Information Officer, Hebrew Rehabilitation Center, Roslindale, MA, p. A310

ROGERS, Gregory H.
   Interim President, Midmichigan Medical Center–Gratiot, Alma, MI, p. A314
   President, Midmichigan Medical Center–Midland, Midland, MI, p. A326

ROGERS, James H., FACHE, Chief Executive Officer, Cornerstone Hospital Of Little Rock, Little Rock, AR, p. A46

ROGERS, Jared, M.D.
President and Chief Executive Officer, Presence Covenant Medical Center, Urbana, IL, p. A202
President and Chief Executive Officer, Presence United Samaritans Medical Center, Danville, IL, p. A185

ROGERS, Joseph J, Vice President and Chief Operating Officer, Redwood Memorial Hospital, Fortuna, CA, p. A59

ROGERS, Kathy, Vice President Marketing, San Luis Valley Health Conejos County Hospital, La Jara, CO, p. A104

ROGERS, Keith
Administrator, Christus Dubuis Hospital Of Fort Smith, Fort Smith, AR, p. A43
Administrator, Christus Dubuis Hospital Of Hot Springs, Hot Springs National Park, AR, p. A44

ROGERS, LaDonna, Director Human Resources, T. J. Samson Community Hospital, Glasgow, KY, p. A259

ROGERS, Lucy, Chief Information Resource Management Systems, Veterans Affairs North Texas Health Care System, Dallas, TX, p. A607

ROGERS, Mark G
Chief Financial Officer, Genesis Medical Center–Aledo, Aledo, IL, p. A177
Interim Vice President Finance and Chief Financial Officer, Genesis Medical Center–Davenport–West Central Park, Davenport, IA, p. A225
Interim Vice President Finance and Chief Financial Officer, Genesis Medical Center, Silvis, Silvis, IL, p. A200

ROGERS, Matt, Chief Financial Officer, Wellspan Philhaven, Mount Gretna, PA, p. A541

ROGERS, Michael, Vice President Fiscal Services, Brattleboro Memorial Hospital, Brattleboro, VT, p. A662

ROGERS, Patricia, Director of Nursing, Dahl Memorial Healthcare Association, Ekalaka, MT, p. A384

ROGERS, Randy, FACHE, Chief Executive Officer, Garden Park Medical Center, Gulfport, MS, p. A355

ROGERS, Rhonda, Chief Financial Officer, Des Peres Hospital, Saint Louis, MO, p. A377

ROGERS, Rich, Vice President Information Services, GHS Greenville Memorial Hospital, Greenville, SC, p. A562

ROGERS, Robert T M.D., II, Medical Director, Canton–Potsdam Hospital, Potsdam, NY, p. A450

ROGERS, Seth, Controller, Healthsouth Rehabilitation Hospital Of Modesto, Modesto, CA, p. A74

ROGERS, Sherry L MS, R.N., Chief Nursing Officer, Redington–Fairview General Hospital, Skowhegan, ME, p. A293

ROGERS, Tammy, Director Human Resources, Mt. San Rafael Hospital, Trinidad, CO, p. A108

ROGERS, Tracy, Chief Executive Officer, North Tampa Behavioral Health, Wesley Chapel, FL, p. A147

ROGERS, Valerie J, Director of Nursing, Cherokee Nation W.W. Hastings Indian Hospital, Tahlequah, OK, p. A516

ROGERS, W Kent., Chief Executive Officer, Southwest Health System, Cortez, CO, p. A100

ROGERS, William, Chief Medical Officer, Gilmore Memorial Hospital, Amory, MS, p. A352

ROGERS, FACHE, SPHR, CHHR, Richard K FACHE, Vice President Human Resources, Wayne Memorial Hospital, Goldsboro, NC, p. A463

ROGNESS, Robin, Vice President and Chief Financial Officer, Mercy Hospital Of Folsom, Folsom, CA, p. A59

ROGOLS, Kevin L., FACHE, Administrator, Kalkaska Memorial Health Center, Kalkaska, MI, p. A324

ROGOZ, Brian, Vice President Finance and Treasurer, The Hospital Of Central Connecticut, New Britain, CT, p. A111

ROHAN, Colleen, Director Human Resources, Little Company Of Mary Hospital And Health Care Centers, Evergreen Park, IL, p. A187

ROHAN, Patrick, Chief Operating Officer, Plantation General Hospital, Plantation, FL, p. A140

ROHLEDER, Scott, Chief Information Officer, Hays Medical Center, Hays, KS, p. A242

ROHMAN, Cindy R.N., MS, Vice President/Chief Nursing Officer, Lexington Medical Center, West Columbia, SC, p. A567

ROHN, Stephen G. M.D., Vice President and Chief Medical Officer, Hamilton Medical Center, Dalton, GA, p. A156

ROHRBACH, Dan D., President and Chief Executive Officer, Southwest Health, Platteville, WI, p. A710

ROHRBACK, Allen, Chief Executive Officer, Madison Valley Medical Center, Ennis, MT, p. A384

ROHRBACK, Jenny, Director Human Resource, Ruby Valley Hospital, Sheridan, MT, p. A388

ROHRER, Harry
Chief Financial Officer, Bascom Palmer Eye Institute–Anne Bates Leach Eye Hospital, Miami, FL, p. A133
Chief Financial Officer, University Of Miami Hospital And Clinics, Miami, FL, p. A134

Chief Financial Officer, University Of Miami Hospital, Miami, FL, p. A134

ROHRER, John J., Director, William S. Middleton Memorial Veterans Hospital, Madison, WI, p. A705

ROHRER, Mark M.D., Chief Medical Officer, Curahealth Hospital Boston, Brighton, MA, p. A304

ROHRICH, George A., FACHE, Chief Executive Officer, River's Edge Hospital And Clinic, Saint Peter, MN, p. A348

ROIZ, JoAnn, Director Human Resources, Healthsouth Tustin Rehabilitation Hospital, Tustin, CA, p. A94

ROJAS, Anna, Chief Executive Officer, Kindred Hospital–Fort Worth, Fort Worth, TX, p. A614

ROJAS, Curtis, Interim Chief Financial Officer, Connally Memorial Medical Center, Floresville, TX, p. A612

ROKER, Christopher, Chief Executive Officer, NYC Health + Hospitals / Queens, New Rochelle, NY, p. A445

ROKOSZ, Gregory D.O., Senior Vice President Medical and Academic Affairs, Saint Barnabas Medical Center, Livingston, NJ, p. A415

ROLAND, Brian, Chief Executive Officer, Muenster Memorial Hospital, Muenster, TX, p. A634

ROLDAN, Lanyce, Interim Chief Nursing Officer, Lancaster General Hospital, Lancaster, PA, p. A538

ROLEK, Jim, Chief Human Resources Officer, Vice President, Clara Maass Medical Center, Belleville, NJ, p. A411

ROLEY, Margaret, Chief Nursing Officer, South Baldwin Regional Medical Center, Foley, AL, p. A18

ROLFE, David, Chief Information Officer, Madonna Rehabilitation Hospital, Lincoln, NE, p. A395

ROLFF, Christi, Director Business Development, San Joaquin Valley Rehabilitation Hospital, Fresno, CA, p. A61

ROLING, Robin FACHE, MS, R.N., Chief Operating Officer, Cheyenne Regional Medical Center, Cheyenne, WY, p. A717

ROLLI, Molli Martha M.D., Medical Director, Mendota Mental Health Institute, Madison, WI, p. A705

ROLLING, Andy, Director of Finance, Regina Hospital, Hastings, MN, p. A341

ROLLINS, David W, Chief Financial Officer, Mt. San Rafael Hospital, Trinidad, CO, p. A108

ROLLINS, James
Chief Financial Officer, Arbour H. R. I. Hospital, Brookline, MA, p. A305
Chief Financial Officer, Arbour–Fuller Hospital, Attleboro, MA, p. A302

ROLLINS, Larry, Supervisor Information Technology, Mccamey County Hospital District, Mccamey, TX, p. A632

ROLLINS, Marlon, Ph.D., Chief Executive Officer, Fremont Hospital, Fremont, CA, p. A60

ROLLINS, Skip, Chief Information Officer, Freeman Health System, Joplin, MO, p. A369

ROLSEN, Timothy, Chief Executive Officer, Regency Hospital Cleveland East, Warrensville Heights, OH, p. A501

ROMAN, Eloy M.D., Chief of Staff, Palmetto General Hospital, Hialeah, FL, p. A126

ROMAN, Jody, Chief Human Resource Officer, Hillside Rehabilitation Hospital, Warren, OH, p. A501

ROMAN, Linda K, Administrator, Coast Plaza Hospital, Norwalk, CA, p. A76

ROMAN, Marina M.D., Medical Director, Hospital De La Universidad De Puerto Rico/Dr. Federico Trilla, Carolina, PR, p. A722

ROMANELLO, Marcus, Chief Medical Officer, Fort Hamilton Hospital, Hamilton, OH, p. A492

ROMANIA, Matt, Director of Nursing, Soldiers And Sailors Memorial Hospital, Wellsboro, PA, p. A553

ROMANICK, Odile, Chief information Officer, Day Kimball Hospital, Putnam, CT, p. A112

ROMANIELLO, Guy, Director Fiscal Services, Belmont Behavioral Hospital, Philadelphia, PA, p. A543

ROMANO, C James M.D., Chief Medical Officer, St. Francis Medical Center, Trenton, NJ, p. A422

ROMANO, Jana, Manager Human Resources, Good Shepherd Penn Partners Specialty Hospital At Rittenhouse, Philadelphia, PA, p. A544

ROMANO, Sara R.N., Vice President, Mountain View Hospital, Gadsden, AL, p. A18

ROMANOWSKI, Ellen, Chief Nursing Officer, Health south Rehabilitation Hospital Of Miami, Cutler Bay, FL, p. A122

ROMANS, Alan, Director Information Technology, Ashland Health Center, Ashland, KS, p. A238

ROMBERGER, Randall R., Administrator, Shriners Hospitals For Children–Greenville, Greenville, SC, p. A563

ROMEO, John, Chief Information Officer, Mercy Hospital And Medical Center, Chicago, IL, p. A182

ROMERO, Brenda, Administrator, Presbyterian Espanola Hospital, Espanola, NM, p. A426

ROMERO, Edward, Chief Financial Officer, Rehabilitation Hospital Of Fort Wayne, Fort Wayne, IN, p. A208

ROMERO, Frank, M.D.
Chief Medical Officer, Cox Medical Centers, Springfield, MO, p. A379
Vice President Medical Affairs and Chief Medical Officer, Cox Monett Hospital, Monett, MO, p. A374

ROMERO, Matt, Chief Financial Officer, Oak Hill Hospital, Brooksville, FL, p. A121

ROMINE, Andy, Chief Executive Officer, Wuesthoff Medical Center – Rockledge, Rockledge, FL, p. A141

ROMITO, Edmund J, Chief Information Officer, Genesis Healthcare System, Zanesville, OH, p. A503

ROMOFF, Jeffrey A., President and Chief Executive Officer, Upmc, Pittsburgh, PA, p. B141

RONAN, Barry P., President and Chief Executive Officer, Western Maryland Regional Medical Center, Cumberland, MD, p. A298

RONAN, John
President, Blue Hill Memorial Hospital, Blue Hill, ME, p. A290
President, Maine Coast Memorial Hospital, Ellsworth, ME, p. A291

RONCA, Cyndi, Director Human Resources, Twin Cities Hospital, Niceville, FL, p. A135

RONDE, Christa, Assistant Chief Financial Officer, Palo Verde Hospital, Blythe, CA, p. A54

RONE, Tom, Chief Executive Officer, Curahealth Nashville, Nashville, TN, p. A586

RONKE, Lisa, Director Finance, St. Michael's Hospital Avera, Tyndall, SD, p. A573

RONNISCH, Kim, R.N., Vice President Nursing and Operations, St. John River District Hospital, East China, MI, p. A319

ROODMAN, Richard D., Chief Executive Officer, Uw Medicine/Valley Medical Center, Renton, WA, p. A684

ROOF, Marie, Executive Vice President Information Systems, Vibra Specialty Hospital Of Portland, Portland, OR, p. A525

ROOK–PEPERONE, Wanda Jeanne, Interim Chief Nursing Officer, Saint Francis Hospital, Memphis, TN, p. A585

ROOKER, Mark, Chief Operations and Information Officer, Susan B. Allen Memorial Hospital, El Dorado, KS, p. A240

ROOKS, Tiffany, Interim Chief Nursing Officer, St. Jude Children's Research Hospital, Memphis, TN, p. A585

ROONERY, Nicole, Chief Nursing Officer, Ivinson Memorial Hospital, Laramie, WY, p. A718

ROONEY, Al, Director Information Systems, St. Vincent Healthcare, Billings, MT, p. A382

ROONEY, David, Administrator Operations, Winneshiek Medical Center, Decorah, IA, p. A226

ROONEY, Michael T M.D., Chief of Staff, St. Joseph Regional Medical Center, Lewiston, ID, p. A174

ROONEY, Thomas, Chief Information Resource Management, Veterans Affairs Hudson Valley Health Care System, Montrose, NY, p. A440

ROOP, Terri, Director Patient Care Services, Dickenson Community Hospital, Clintwood, VA, p. A666

ROOS, Joel A., Commanding Officer, Naval Medical Center San Diego, San Diego, CA, p. A85

ROOSA, Carol, Vice President Information Services and Chief Information Officer, Athol Hospital, Athol, MA, p. A302

ROOT, Jim, Vice President Human Resources, Saint Elizabeth's Medical Center, Wabasha, MN, p. A349

ROOT, Rodney Mark D.O., Vice President Medical Affairs, Bakersfield Memorial Hospital, Bakersfield, CA, p. A52

ROPER, Embra, Chief Medical Officer, Regional Hospital For Respiratory And Complex Care, Burien, WA, p. A679

ROPER, Sandra, Chief Human Resources, General Leonard Wood Army Community Hospital, Fort Leonard Wood, MO, p. A368

ROPER, William L., M.D., M.P.H., Chief Executive Officer, Unc Health Care, Chapel Hill, NC, p. B132

ROQUE, Lee Ann, Director of Human Resources, Mary Black Health System–Spartanburg, Spartanburg, SC, p. A566

ROSA–TOLEDO, Luis R M.D., Medical Director, Hospital Manati Medical Center, Manati, PR, p. A724

ROSAAEN, Nancy, Chief Executive Officer, Mccone County Health Center, Circle, MT, p. A383

ROSADO, Jose S., Executive Director, Hospital Manati Medical Center, Manati, PR, p. A724

ROSALES, Alvina R.N., Chief Nursing Officer, Tuba City Regional Health Care Corporation, Tuba City, AZ, p. A37

ROSATI, Rosemarie
Chief Operating Officer, University Behavioral Healthcare, Piscataway, NJ, p. A419
Interim President and Chief Executive Officer, University Behavioral Healthcare, Piscataway, NJ, p. A419

ROSBOROUGH, Brian S M.D., Chief Medical Officer, OSF Saint Elizabeth Medical Center, Ottawa, IL, p. A196

ROSCOE, Joan, Chief Information Officer, Winchester Medical Center, Winchester, VA, p. A677

ROSE, Cheryl, Human Resources Director, Fulton County Medical Center, Mc Connellsburg, PA, p. A540

ROSE, Hugh, Vice President Fiscal Management, Palos Health, Palos Heights, IL, p. A196

ROSE, J Anthony., President and Chief Executive Officer, Catawba Valley Medical Center, Hickory, NC, p. A464

ROSE, Julia R.N., Director of Nursing, Braxton County Memorial Hospital, Gassaway, WV, p. A692

ROSE, Kelly, R.N., Chief Executive Officer, AMG Specialty Hospital–Tulsa, Tulsa, OK, p. A517

ROSE, Kim, Chief Information Technology, Crouse Health, Syracuse, NY, p. A453

ROSE, Mary R R.N., Chief Clinical Officer, Community Health Center Of Branch County, Coldwater, MI, p. A317

ROSE, May, Director Human Resources, Memorial Hospital, Chester, IL, p. A180

ROSE, Michael S., President and Chief Executive Officer, Southern New Hampshire Medical Center, Nashua, NH, p. A409

ROSE, Michaell, Chief Operating Officer, St. Joseph's Medical Center, Stockton, CA, p. A93

ROSE, Richard T, Associate Director, Manchester Veterans Affairs Medical Center, Manchester, NH, p. A409

ROSE, Robert, M.D., R.N., MS
  Chief Medical Officer, Upper Connecticut Valley Hospital, Colebrook, NH, p. A407
  Senior Vice President and System Chief Nursing Officer, Christus Mother Frances Hospital – Tyler, Tyler, TX, p. A650

ROSE, Robin R.N., Chief Operating Officer, Gibson Area Hospital And Health Services, Gibson City, IL, p. A188

ROSE, Silvia, Director Patient Care Services, Vidant Bertie Hospital, Windsor, NC, p. A473

ROSE, Steven A, R.N., President and Chief Executive Officer, Nanticoke Memorial Hospital, Seaford, DE, p. A116

ROSE, Steven P, Chief Financial Officer, Conway Regional Medical Center, Conway, AR, p. A41

ROSEMORE, Michael M.D., Medical Director, Healthsouth Lakeshore Rehabilitation Hospital, Birmingham, AL, p. A14

ROSEN, Barry M.D., Vice President Medical Management, Advocate Good Shepherd Hospital, Barrington, IL, p. A178

ROSEN, Linda, M.D., Chief Executive Officer, Hawaii Health Systems Corporation, Honolulu, HI, p. B56

ROSEN, Jules M.D., Chief Medical Officer, West Springs Hospital, Grand Junction, CO, p. A103

ROSEN, Michael M.D., Chief Medical Officer, Havasu Regional Medical Center, Lake Havasu City, AZ, p. A31

ROSEN, Raymond FACHE, Vice President Operations, Wellspan York Hospital, York, PA, p. A555

ROSENA, Robens, Director Information Systems, Delray Medical Center, Delray Beach, FL, p. A124

ROSENBALM, Jennifer, Manager Business Office, Veterans Affairs Nebraska–Western Iowa Health Care System, Omaha, NE, p. A398

ROSENBAUM, Victor, Chief Operating Officer, Alaska Regional Hospital, Anchorage, AK, p. A25

ROSENBERG, Andrew M.D., Chief Information Officer, Michigan Medicine, Ann Arbor, MI, p. A314

ROSENBERG, Julie, Administrator, Essentia Health–Graceville, Graceville, MN, p. A340

ROSENBERG, Steven, Chief Financial Officer, Danbury Hospital, Danbury, CT, p. A109

ROSENBERG, Stuart E., President, Johnson Memorial Medical Center, Stafford Springs, CT, p. A113

ROSENBERGER, Robert, Chief Financial Officer, Adena Medical Center, Chillicothe, OH, p. A483

ROSENBERGER–SLAMPACK, Janie
  Chief Executive Officer, Curahealth Heritage Valley, Beaver, PA, p. A529
  Market Chief Executive Officer, Curahealth Pittsburgh, Oakdale, PA, p. A542

ROSENBLATT, Michael M.D., Medical Director, Kindred Rehabilitation Hospital Clear Lake, Webster, TX, p. A653

ROSENBLOOM, Mark, Vice President of Medical Affairs, Health First Holmes Regional Medical Center, Melbourne, FL, p. A132

ROSENBURG, Deborah L, Vice President Human Resources, Chesapeake Regional Healthcare, Chesapeake, VA, p. A665

ROSENBURG, Jeffrey M. M.D., Chief Medical Officer, Marin General Hospital, Greenbrae, CA, p. A62

ROSENCRANCE, Daris, Chief Financial Officer, Mon Health Medical Center, Morgantown, WV, p. A694

ROSENDAHL, Lisa, Director Human Resources, St. Cloud Veterans Affairs Health Care System, Saint Cloud, MN, p. A347

ROSENDORFF, Clive M.D., Chief Medical Program, James J. Peters Veterans Affairs Medical Center, New Rochelle, NY, p. A442

ROSENFELD, Merryll, Vice President, Human Resources, Catholic Medical Center, Manchester, NH, p. A409

ROSENSTEIN, Gaynor, Vice President Operations, Bon Secours Community Hospital, Port Jervis, NY, p. A450

ROSENTHAL, Benjamin, Information Systems Director, South Sunflower County Hospital, Indianola, MS, p. A356

ROSENTHAL, Philip P, Executive Director, Lenox Hill Hospital, New Rochelle, NY, p. A442

ROSENTHAL, Raul M.D., Interim Chief of Staff, Cleveland Clinic Florida, Weston, FL, p. A148

ROSEQUIST, Helen, Manager Information Systems, Warren General Hospital, Warren, PA, p. A552

ROSETTA, Kathy, Chief Nursing Officer, Laurel Ridge Treatment Center, San Antonio, TX, p. A642

ROSHAN, Payman
  Chief Operating Officer, Kaiser Permanente Baldwin Park Medical Center, Baldwin Park, CA, p. A53
  Senior Vice President and Area Manager, Kaiser Permanente Panorama City Medical Center, Los Angeles, CA, p. A68

ROSHETKO, Chet, Chief Nursing Officer, Eastern State Hospital, Medical Lake, WA, p. A682

ROSIAK, Michael, Chief Operating Officer, Weisman Children's Rehabilitation Hospital, Marlton, NJ, p. A416

ROSILES, Nancy, Director Human Resources, Healthsouth Rehabilitation Hospital Of Arlington, Arlington, TX, p. A593

ROSKE, Jeff D.O., Chief Medical Staff, Community Memorial Hospital, Sumner, IA, p. A235

ROSKOVSKI, Stephanie, Chief Operating Officer, Butler Health System, Butler, PA, p. A530

ROSLER, Andrea P, Vice President Human Resources, Huntsville Hospital, Huntsville, AL, p. A19

ROSS, Aletha, Vice President Human Resources, Ingalls Memorial Hospital, Harvey, IL, p. A189

ROSS, Charles M.D., Vice President Medical Affairs, Chilton Medical Center, Pompton Plains, NJ, p. A419

ROSS, Christopher, Chief Information Technology Officer, Mayo Clinic Hospital – Rochester, Rochester, MN, p. A346

ROSS, David, Chief Executive Officer, Select Specialty Hospital–Madison, Madison, WI, p. A705

ROSS, Hoyt, Chief Executive Officer, Promise Hospital Of Florida At The Villages, Oxford, FL, p. A137

ROSS, Jacqueline, Chief Human Resources Officer, Mann–Grandstaff Veterans Affairs Medical Center, Spokane, WA, p. A686

ROSS, James E., President and Chief Executive Officer, Jackson–Madison County General Hospital, Jackson, TN, p. A580

ROSS, Jay
  Chief Financial Officer, Chi St. Joseph's Health, Park Rapids, MN, p. A345
  Vice President of Finance, Chi Lakewood Health, Baudette, MN, p. A336

ROSS, Jeffrey M.D., Medical Director, AMG Specialty Hospital–Albuquerque, Albuquerque, NM, p. A424

ROSS, Joan, Senior Vice President and Chief Operating Officer, St. Vincent Charity Medical Center, Cleveland, OH, p. A486

ROSS, John, Vice President, Franciscan St. Francis Health – Mooresville, Mooresville, IN, p. A216

ROSS, Johnny Shane, Executive Medical Director, Healthsouth Rehabilitation Hospital Of Austin, Austin, TX, p. A595

ROSS, Joseph P., President and Chief Executive Officer, Meritus Medical Center, Hagerstown, MD, p. A299

ROSS, Karen, Chief Executive Officer, Allegiance Specialty Hospital Of Kilgore, Kilgore, TX, p. A626

ROSS, Kathy, Chief Information Officer, Providence Hospital, Mobile, AL, p. A20

ROSS, Laurie, Chief Nursing Officer, Southampton Memorial Hospital, Franklin, VA, p. A667

ROSS, Phil, Chief Executive Officer, Surgical Hospital Of Oklahoma, Oklahoma City, OK, p. A513

ROSS, Robert, Chief Operating Officer, Medstar Washington Hospital Center, Washington, DC, p. A118

ROSS, Samuel Lee., M.D., MS, Chief Executive Officer, Bon Secours Baltimore Health System, Baltimore, MD, p. A294

ROSS, Semmes Jr, Administrator, Lawrence County Hospital, Monticello, MS, p. A359

ROSS, Shana, Vice President Human Resources, Bayhealth Medical Center, Dover, DE, p. A115

ROSS, Zeff, FACHE, Executive Vice President and Chief Executive Officer, Memorial Regional Hospital, Hollywood, FL, p. A127

ROSS–COLE, Melissa, Director Human Resources, Regency Hospital Of Northwest Arkansas – Springdale, Springdale, AR, p. A50

ROSS–SPANG, Carol, Chief Human Resources Officer, Methodist Healthcare Memphis Hospitals, Memphis, TN, p. A585

ROSSFELD, John, Administrator, Wilson N. Jones Regional Medical Center, Sherman, TX, p. A645

ROSSI, Alfred N., M.D., Chief Executive Officer, Hopedale Medical Complex, Hopedale, IL, p. A190

ROSSI, Coleen, Director Quality Services, Healthsouth Rehabilitation Hospital Of Toms River, Toms River, NJ, p. A421

ROSSI, Lawrence M.D., Clinical Director, Trenton Psychiatric Hospital, Trenton, NJ, p. A422

ROSSI, Mark F, Chief Operating Officer and General Counsel, Hopedale Medical Complex, Hopedale, IL, p. A190

ROSSMANN, Barbara W., R.N., President and Chief Executive Officer, Henry Ford Macomb Hospitals, Clinton Township, MI, p. A316

ROSSMANN, Samuel H., Chief Executive Officer, Tops Surgical Specialty Hospital, Houston, TX, p. A623

ROSVOLD, Robert, Director Finance, Virtua Voorhees, Voorhees, NJ, p. A422

ROTENBERRY–BAGGETT, Katie, Administrative Assistant and Human Resources, Yalobusha General Hospital, Water Valley, MS, p. A362

ROTERT, Angela Lynne, Chief Clinical Officer, Kindred Hospital–Indianapolis, Indianapolis, IN, p. A211

ROTGER, Lindsey, Chief Nursing Officer, Spire Cane Creek Rehabilitation Hospital, Martin, TN, p. A583

ROTH, Anna M., R.N., MS, M.P.H., Chief Executive Officer, Contra Costa Regional Medical Center, Martinez, CA, p. A73

ROTH, Chad, Director Information Services, Prairie View, Newton, KS, p. A247

ROTH, Dan M.D., Vice President Medical Affairs, Mercy Health – Anderson Hospital, Cincinnati, OH, p. A484

ROTH, Diane, Chief Financial Officer, Rockdale Medical Center, Conyers, GA, p. A155

ROTH, Edward J. III, President and Chief Executive Officer, Aultman Hospital, Canton, OH, p. A482

ROTH, Eugene, Vice President Information Services, Mercy Hospital St. Louis, Saint Louis, MO, p. A377

ROTH, Mark A., Chief Financial Officer, Mountain Valley Regional Rehabilitation Hospital, Prescott Valley, AZ, p. A35

ROTH, Norman G.
  Interim Chief Operating Officer, Greenwich Hospital, Greenwich, CT, p. A110
  President, Greenwich Hospital, Greenwich, CT, p. A110

ROTH, Randy, Chief Medical Officer, Singing River Health System, Pascagoula, MS, p. A360

ROTH–MALLEK, Nancy, Vice President of Finance, Aspirus Riverview Hospital And Clinics, Inc., Wisconsin Rapids, WI, p. A716

ROTHBERG, Kathryn, Director Human Resources, Evergreenhealth Monroe, Monroe, WA, p. A682

ROTHBERGER, Richard, Corporate Executive Vice President and Chief Financial Officer, Scripps Green Hospital, La Jolla, CA, p. A64

ROTHENBERGER, David, Chief Financial Officer, Summit Healthcare Regional Medical Center, Show Low, AZ, p. A36

ROTHERMICH, Anthony, Administrator, Mercy Hospital Lincoln, Troy, MO, p. A380

ROTHERMICH, Michael M.D., Chief of Staff, Hermann Area District Hospital, Hermann, MO, p. A369

ROTHFIELD, Kenneth, M.D.
  Chief Medical Officer, Medical City Dallas, Dallas, TX, p. A606
  System Vice President and Chief Medical Officer, St. Vincent's Medical Center Riverside, Jacksonville, FL, p. A128

ROTHMAN, Marc M.D., Medical Director, Friends Hospital, Philadelphia, PA, p. A544

ROTHSCHILD, Marylee M.D., Chief of Staff, Robley Rex Veterans Affairs Medical Center, Louisville, KY, p. A263

ROTY, Christopher, President, Baptist Health La Grange, La Grange, KY, p. A260

ROUBIDEAUX, Yvette, M.D., M.P.H., Director, U. S. Indian Health Service, Rockville, MD, p. B130

ROULEAU, Greg, Vice President Nursing, Mercy Medical Center Merced, Merced, CA, p. A73

ROUND, Laurie MS, R.N., Chief Nurse Executive, Advocate Bromenn Medical Center, Normal, IL, p. A195

ROUNDS, Jason, Chief Operating Officer and Administrator, Christus St. Michael Health System, Texarkana, TX, p. A649

ROUNDY, Ann, Vice President Employee Services, Columbus Community Hospital, Inc., Columbus, WI, p. A700

ROUNSLEY, Joan, Director Human Resources, Jersey Shore Hospital, Jersey Shore, PA, p. A537

ROUNSLEY, Karen, Controller, Healthsouth Chesapeake Rehabilitation Hospital, Salisbury, MD, p. A301

ROUSH, Sharon L., Chief Executive Officer, South Bay Hospital, Sun City Center, FL, p. A143

ROUSSE, Michael M.D., Vice President of Medical Affairs, Northeastern Vermont Regional Hospital, Saint Johnsbury, VT, p. A663

ROUSSEAU, Mickie, Director Human Resources, Terrebonne General Medical Center, Houma, LA, p. A276

ROUSSEL, Steve
Chief Financial Officer, Baylor Medical Center At Mckinney, Mckinney, TX, p. A632
Vice President Finance, Baylor Scott & White Medical Center–Irving, Irving, TX, p. A624

ROUTH, Lori, R.N.
Nurse Administrator, Mayo Clinic Health System In Albert Lea, Albert Lea, MN, p. A335
Nurse Administrator, Mayo Clinic Health System–Albert Lea And Austin, Austin, MN, p. A336

ROUX, Roger, Chief Financial Officer, Rady Children's Hospital – San Diego, San Diego, CA, p. A85

ROUZER, Cindy, Director Human Resources, Spooner Health, Spooner, WI, p. A712

ROUZER, Steven V. M.D., Chief Medical Officer, Moab Regional Hospital, Moab, UT, p. A657

ROVITO, Kevin, Chief Financial Officer, Jackson Hospital, Marianna, FL, p. A131

ROW, Tracy, Manager Business Office, Fredonia Regional Hospital, Fredonia, KS, p. A241

ROW, Tyler, Director Information Technology, Fredonia Regional Hospital, Fredonia, KS, p. A241

ROWAN, Cary, Chief Financial Officer, Sunnyside Community Hospital And Clinics, Sunnyside, WA, p. A687

ROWAN, R C, Director Human Resources, Neosho Memorial Regional Medical Center, Chanute, KS, p. A239

ROWE, Chad, Human Resource Director, Aspirus Keweenaw Hospital, Inc., Laurium, MI, p. A325

ROWE, Jeanne M M.D., Chief Medical Officer, Shore Medical Center, Somers Point, NJ, p. A420

ROWE, Mike M.D., Chief of Staff, Fayette Regional Health System, Connersville, IN, p. A206

ROWE, Paul W, Director Information Technology, St. Francis Hospital, Wilmington, DE, p. A116

ROWE, Richard M., PharmD
Chief Executive Officer, Garden Grove Hospital And Medical Center, Garden Grove, CA, p. A61
Chief Executive Officer, Huntington Beach Hospital, Huntington Beach, CA, p. A63

ROWE, Scott, Chief Executive Officer, Healthsouth Chattanooga Rehabilitation Hospital, Chattanooga, TN, p. A576

ROWE, Wilma M.D., Senior Vice President Medical Affairs, Mercy Medical Center, Baltimore, MD, p. A295

ROWELL, Julie R.N., Chief Nursing Officer, Thomas Hospital, Fairhope, AL, p. A17

ROWEN, Lisa, R.N.
Chief Nursing Officer, University Of Maryland Medical Center Midtown Campus, Baltimore, MD, p. A296
Senior Vice President and Chief Nursing Officer, University Of Maryland Medical Center, Baltimore, MD, p. A296

ROWLAND, Claire, Director Human Resources, Acadia Vermilion Hospital, Lafayette, LA, p. A278

ROWLAND, Michael M.D., Vice President Medical Affairs, Franklin Memorial Hospital, Farmington, ME, p. A291

ROWLAND, Nick
Chief Executive Officer, Pushmataha Hospital, Antlers, OK, p. A504
Chief Operating Officer, Pushmataha Hospital, Antlers, OK, p. A504

ROWLAND, Paul J., Executive Vice President and Chief Administrative Officer, St. Catherine Of Siena Medical Center, Smithtown, NY, p. A452

ROWLAND, Robert M.D., Medical Director, Healthsouth Rehabilitation Hospital Of Tallahassee, Tallahassee, FL, p. A144

ROWLAND, Ruby, Strategic Partner, Highlands–Cashiers Hospital, Highlands, NC, p. A464

ROWLAND, Ted, Chief of Medical Staff, Atoka County Medical Center, Atoka, OK, p. A504

ROWLANDS, Dewey R, Vice President and Chief Financial Officer, Rome Memorial Hospital, Rome, NY, p. A451

ROWLEY, Charla, Chief Financial Officer, Southwest Mississippi Regional Medical Center, Mccomb, MS, p. A358

ROWLEY, Mike, Chief Executive Officer, Springbrook Behavioral Health System, Travelers Rest, SC, p. A566

ROY, Joel, Manager Information Systems, The Brook Hospital – Kmi, Louisville, KY, p. A263

ROY, Linda R.N., Chief Nursing Officer, Walter B. Jones Alcohol And Drug Abuse Treatment Center, Greenville, NC, p. A464

ROY, Rock, Professional Services Director, Power County Hospital District, American Falls, ID, p. A171

ROY, Schindelheim M.D., Chief of Staff, Mee Memorial Hospital, King City, CA, p. A64

ROYAL, Keli, Chief Human Resources Officer, Shenandoah Medical Center, Shenandoah, IA, p. A234

ROYAL, Shawanna R.N., Director Nursing, Strategic Behavioral Health – Raleigh, Garner, NC, p. A463

ROYAL, Ty, Executive Director of Support Services and Human Resources, Gibson Area Hospital And Health Services, Gibson City, IL, p. A188

ROYE, G. Dean M.D., Senior Vice President of Medical Affairs and Chief Medical Officer, Miriam Hospital, Providence, RI, p. A556

ROYSTER, Kirsten, President and Chief Operating Officer, Novant Health Medical Park Hospital, Winston, NC, p. A473

ROZELL, Becky, Chief Human Resources Officer, Madison Health, London, OH, p. A494

ROZENBOOM, Steve, Chief Financial Officer, Holy Cross Hospital, Taos, NM, p. A429

ROZENFELD, Jon, President, St. Mary's Hospital, Madison, WI, p. A705

ROZNOVSKY, Karen, Director Human Resources, Yoakum Community Hospital, Yoakum, TX, p. A655

RUBANO, Kathleen A MSN, R.N., Chief Nursing Officer, Corpus Christi Medical Center, Corpus Christi, TX, p. A603

RUBAR, Jackie, Administrative Assistant and Director Human Resources, Leesville Rehabilitation Hospital, Leesville, LA, p. A280

RUBE, David M M.D., Clinical Director, New York City Children's Center, New Rochelle, NY, p. A443

RUBEN, Wanda R.N., Chief Nursing Officer, Garden Grove Hospital And Medical Center, Garden Grove, CA, p. A61

RUBENS, Deborah, Director Human Resources, Shriners Hospitals For Children–Northern California, Sacramento, CA, p. A83

RUBERG, Greg, President and Chief Executive Officer, Lake View Hospital, Two Harbors, MN, p. A349

RUBERTE, Henry, Administrator, Hospital San Gerardo, San Juan, PR, p. A726

RUBERTI, Charlene, Director Information Technology Development, Ancora Psychiatric Hospital, Hammonton, NJ, p. A414

RUBIN, Nancy, Vice President Human Resources, Motion Picture And Television Fund Hospital And Residential Services, Los Angeles, CA, p. A70

RUBIN, Randy, Senior Vice President and Chief Financial Officer, Mercy Medical Center–Des Moines, Des Moines, IA, p. A226

RUBIN, Vincent, Chief Financial Officer, Southern California Hospital At Culver City, Culver City, CA, p. A57

RUBINATE, Donna R.N., Chief Operating Officer, Good Samaritan Medical Center, Brockton, MA, p. A304

RUBINO, Mark, M.D.
Chief Medical Officer, Forbes Hospital, Monroeville, PA, p. A541
President, Forbes Hospital, Monroeville, PA, p. A541

RUBIO, Felipe M.D., Medical Director, Kindred Hospital–Dayton, Dayton, OH, p. A489

RUBY, Blaine M.D., Chief of Staff, Johnson County Healthcare Center, Buffalo, WY, p. A717

RUCH, Jordan, Vice President and Chief Information Officer, Robert Wood Johnson University Hospital Somerset, Somerville, NJ, p. A420

RUCHTI, Robert D., Chief Executive Officer, Buchanan General Hospital, Grundy, VA, p. A668

RUCKER, Alisa, Vice President Finance and Chief Financial Officer, Washington Hospital, Washington, PA, p. A552

RUCKER, Genifer, President, Christus Spohn Hospital Beeville, Beeville, TX, p. A598

RUCKER, Jodi, Chief Nursing Officer, Promedica Memorial Hospital, Fremont, OH, p. A491

RUCKER, Rick, Chief Operating Officer, Highland Hospital, Charleston, WV, p. A691

RUCKER, William H., Administrator, Riverland Medical Center, Ferriday, LA, p. A274

RUDBERG, Susan M.D., Chief Medical Officer, Range Regional Health Services, Hibbing, MN, p. A341

RUDD, Adam, Chief Executive Officer, Southern Hills Hospital And Medical Center, Las Vegas, NV, p. A403

RUDD, Barry, Chief Information Officer, Memorial Satilla Health, Waycross, GA, p. A167

RUDD, Jedd, Director of Ancillary Services and Safety, Mad River Community Hospital, Arcata, CA, p. A52

RUDD, John B., President and Chief Executive Officer, Cayuga Medical Center At Ithaca, Ithaca, NY, p. A437

RUDDEN, Elizabeth, Vice President Human Resources, Connecticut Children's Medical Center, Hartford, CT, p. A110

RUDEK, Charles M, Chief Information Officer, Upmc St. Margaret, Pittsburgh, PA, p. A548

RUDIS, Lorrie, Vice President, Human Resources, Crotched Mountain Rehabilitation Center, Greenfield, NH, p. A408

RUDISILL, Joe, Chief Operating Officer, Regional Medical Center Bayonet Point, Hudson, FL, p. A127

RUDITZ, Bettiann S MS, R.N., Chief Nursing Officer, Broward Health North, Deerfield Beach, FL, p. A123

RUDQUIST, Debra, FACHE, President and Chief Executive Officer, Amery Hospital And Clinic, Amery, WI, p. A698

RUDY, Bret, M.D., Executive Director and Senior Vice President, NYU Langone Hospitals, New Rochelle, NY, p. A446

RUDZIK, Carrie, Chief Administrative Officer, Eastern State Hospital, Lexington, KY, p. A261

RUDZIK, Donna, Director Human Resources, Christus Mother Frances Hospital – Sulphur Springs, Sulphur Springs, TX, p. A647

RUE, Loring M.D., Senior Vice President, Quality Patient Safety and Clinical Effectiveness, University Of Alabama Hospital, Birmingham, AL, p. A15

RUE, Robert, Chief Financial Officer, Ellenville Regional Hospital, Ellenville, NY, p. A435

RUECKERT, Sebastian, M.D.
Chief Medical Officer, Christian Hospital, Saint Louis, MO, p. A377
Vice President and Chief Medical Officer, Alton Memorial Hospital, Alton, IL, p. A177

RUEDISUELI, Amy, Vice President of Finance, Mckenzie Health System, Sandusky, MI, p. A330

RUELLO, Rocky, Vice President Human Resources, Mercy Hospital St. Louis, Saint Louis, MO, p. A377

RUFF, Robin, Chief Financial Officer, Pikes Peak Regional Hospital, Woodland Park, CO, p. A108

RUFF, Victoria M.D., Medical Director, Select Specialty Hospital–Columbus, Columbus, OH, p. A488

RUFFIN, Marshall, Chief Information Officer, Inova Fair Oaks Hospital, Fairfax, VA, p. A666

RUFFING, Cindy, Director Human Resources, Siloam Springs Regional Hospital, Siloam Springs, AR, p. A49

RUFFOLO, Joseph A., President and Chief Executive Officer, Niagara Falls Memorial Medical Center, Niagara Falls, NY, p. A447

RUGE, Randy
Chief Executive Officer, Paulding County Hospital, Paulding, OH, p. A498
Chief Operating Officer, Paulding County Hospital, Paulding, OH, p. A498

RUGGIERO, Taren R.N., MSN, Vice President and Chief Nursing Officer, Holy Cross Hospital, Fort Lauderdale, FL, p. A125

RUIZ, Javier, M.D.
Medical Director, Intracare North Hospital, Houston, TX, p. A621
Medical Director, Kingwood Pines Hospital, Kingwood, TX, p. A627

RUIZ, Kathleen M.D., Associate Director Patient Care Services, Veterans Affairs Caribbean Healthcare System, San Juan, PR, p. A727

RUIZ, Patricia R.N., Chief Nursing Officer, NYC Health + Hospitals / Coney Island, New Rochelle, NY, p. A444

RUIZ, Tony, Senior Vice President, Chief Operating Officer, Medical Center Health System, Odessa, TX, p. A635

RULAND, Jyl
Chief Financial Officer, Clearwater Valley Hospital And Clinics, Orofino, ID, p. A175
Chief Financial Officer, St. Mary's Hospital, Cottonwood, ID, p. A173

RULLI, Sheila, Director Human Resources, Kidspeace Children's Hospital, Orefield, PA, p. A542

RUMMEL, Jennifer
Director Human Resources, East Texas Medical Center Athens, Athens, TX, p. A594
Director Human Resources, Freestone Medical Center, Fairfield, TX, p. A612

RUNNELS, Clay, Vice President Chief Medical Officer Washington County, Johnson City Medical Center, Johnson City, TN, p. A581

RUNYAN, Mark
Director Information Services, Salt Lake Regional Medical Center, Salt Lake City, UT, p. A660
Director Information Systems, Jordan Valley Medical Center West Valley Campus, West Valley City, UT, p. A661

RUNYON, Annette, Vice President and Administrator, Medical Center At Franklin, Franklin, KY, p. A258

RUPA, Maitra M.D., Acting Medical Director, Chester Mental Health Center, Chester, IL, p. A180

RUPERT, Chris, Chief Executive Officer, Options Behavioral Health System, Indianapolis, IN, p. A212

RUPERT, Duke, Chief Operating Officer, Allegheny General Hospital, Pittsburgh, PA, p. A546

RUPERT, James M., Chief Fiscal Services, Battle Creek Veterans Affairs Medical Center, Battle Creek, MI, p. A315

RUPERT, Michael J, Chief Financial Officer, Va Long Beach Healthcare System, Long Beach, CA, p. A67

RUPP, Connie MSN, R.N., Executive Vice President and Chief Nursing Officer, Regional West Medical Center, Scottsbluff, NE, p. A399

RUPP, Robert, Chief Executive Officer, Medical Center Of South Arkansas, El Dorado, AR, p. A42

RUPPERT, Jennifer, Chief Financial Officer, Iowa City Veterans Affairs Health Care System, Iowa City, IA, p. A229

RUPPERT SCHILLER, Kerri
Senior Vice President and Chief Financial Officer, Children's Hospital Of Orange County, Orange, CA, p. A78
Senior Vice President and Chief Financial Officer, Choc Children's At Mission Hospital, Mission Viejo, CA, p. A73

RUSH, Andy, Senior Vice President and Chief Operating Officer, Somerset Hospital, Somerset, PA, p. A551

RUSH, Ann Marie, Chief Financial Officer, Penobscot Valley Hospital, Lincoln, ME, p. A292

RUSH, Christopher, Chief Financial Officer, Specialty Hospital Of Meridian, Meridian, MS, p. A359

RUSH, Cindy, Director Human Resources, Clay County Medical Center, Clay Center, KS, p. A239

RUSH, Ed, President and Chief Executive Officer, Iredell Health System, Statesville, NC, p. A471

RUSH, Jeff, Chief Financial Officer, Rutherford Regional Health System, Rutherfordton, NC, p. A470

RUSH, Matthew, FACHE, President and Chief Executive Officer, Hayes Green Beach Memorial Hospital, Charlotte, MI, p. A316

RUSHIN, Denise, Director Human Resources, Poplar Bluff Regional Medical Center, Poplar Bluff, MO, p. A375

RUSHING, Derek
Chief Executive Officer, Uchealth Broomfield Hospital, Broomfield, CO, p. A99
Chief Executive Officer, Uchealth Grandview Hospital, Colorado Springs, CO, p. A100

RUSHING, Heath
Senior Vice President and Chief Executive Officer, Memorial Hermann – Texas Medical Center, Houston, TX, p. A621
Senior Vice President and Chief Executive Officer, Memorial Hermann Katy Hospital, Katy, TX, p. A626

RUSHING, Kelley J., Chief Executive Officer, Caldwell Medical Center, Princeton, KY, p. A266

RUSHING, R Lynn, Chief Executive Officer, Brook Lane Health Services, Hagerstown, MD, p. A299

RUSHING, Randy, Chief Financial Officer, Massac Memorial Hospital, Metropolis, IL, p. A194

RUSHING, Richard, Chief of Staff, King's Daughters Medical Center, Brookhaven, MS, p. A353

RUSHLOW, David, Vice President Medical Affairs, Mayo Clinic Health System – Franciscan Healthcare In La Crosse, La Crosse, WI, p. A704

RUSK, Scott M.D., Chief Medical Officer, St. Joseph Hospital, Orange, CA, p. A78

RUSNACZYK, John, Senior Vice President and Chief Financial Officer, St. Vincent Charity Medical Center, Cleveland, OH, p. A486

RUSNAK, Greg, Executive Vice President and Chief Operating Officer, GHS Greenville Memorial Hospital, Greenville, SC, p. A562

RUSS, Nicole L, Director Colleague Relations, Alliance Community Hospital, Alliance, OH, p. A479

RUSSELL, Bill, Senior Vice President and Chief Information Officer, Mission Hospital, Mission Viejo, CA, p. A74

RUSSELL, Brant R.N., Chief Operating Officer, St. John Hospital And Medical Center, Detroit, MI, p. A318

RUSSELL, Dardanella, Chief Human Resources Management Service, Veterans Affairs Hudson Valley Health Care System, Montrose, NY, p. A440

RUSSELL, David, President and Chief Executive Officer, Adventist Medical Center–Portland, Portland, OR, p. A525

RUSSELL, Donald
AMITA Health Senior Vice President and Chief Human Resources Officer, Amita Health Adventist Medical Center Glenoaks, Glendale Heights, IL, p. A188
Senior Vice President and Chief Human Resources Officer, Amita Health Elk Grove Village, Elk Grove Village, IL, p. A186
Senior Vice President and Chief Human Resources Officer, Amita Health Hoffman Estates, Hoffman Estates, IL, p. A190

RUSSELL, Erin, Controller, Kindred Hospital–San Antonio, San Antonio, TX, p. A642

RUSSELL, Freda, R.N., Chief Executive Officer and Chief Nursing Officer, Three Rivers Hospital, Waverly, TN, p. A590

RUSSELL, Georgette, Vice President of Talent & Organizational Effectiveness, Sparrow Carson Hospital, Carson City, MI, p. A316

RUSSELL, John D., President and Chief Executive Officer, Columbus Community Hospital, Inc., Columbus, WI, p. A700

RUSSELL, Jon
Senior Vice President & Chief Information Officer, John Muir Medical Center, Walnut Creek, Walnut Creek, CA, p. A96
Senior Vice President and Chief Information Officer, John Muir Medical Center, Concord, Concord, CA, p. A56

RUSSELL, Kathy R.N., Chief Nursing Officer, Bluegrass Community Hospital, Versailles, KY, p. A268

RUSSELL, Kendrick, Chief Human Resources Officer, Abrazo Scottsdale Campus, Phoenix, AZ, p. A33

RUSSELL, Kim M.D., Chief of Staff, Baylor Scott & White Medical Center – Llano, Llano, TX, p. A629

RUSSEL, Kimberly A., FACHE, President and Chief Executive Officer, Bryan Health, Lincoln, NE, p. B23

RUSSELL, Laurie, Director Human Resources, Lea Regional Medical Center, Hobbs, NM, p. A426

RUSSELL, Linda, Vice President and Chief Nursing Officer, Self Regional Healthcare, Greenwood, SC, p. A563

RUSSELL, Michelle, Chief Executive Officer, Lafayette Regional Rehabilitation Hospital, Lafayette, IN, p. A214

RUSSELL, Nancy, Chief Financial Officer, Clifton–Fine Hospital, Star Lake, NY, p. A452

RUSSELL, Patti, Vice President Nursing, Masonicare Health Center, Wallingford, CT, p. A113

RUSSELL, Randall, Vice President and Chief Financial Officer, Memorial Hospital And Health Care Center, Jasper, IN, p. A212

RUSSELL, Robert J, Associate Executive Director Operations, Penn Presbyterian Medical Center, Philadelphia, PA, p. A545

RUSSELL, Shelia, Director Human Resources, Tennova Healthcare–Jamestown, Jamestown, TN, p. A580

RUSSELL, Shelly
Chief Executive Officer, Mitchell County Regional Health Center, Osage, IA, p. A233
Chief Nursing Officer, Mitchell County Regional Health Center, Osage, IA, p. A233

RUSSELL, Sherrie
AMITA Health Senior Vice President and Chief Information Officer, Amita Health Adventist Medical Center Glenoaks, Glendale Heights, IL, p. A188
Senior Vice President & Chief Information Officer, Amita Health Elk Grove Village, Elk Grove Village, IL, p. A186
Senior Vice President and Chief Information Officer, Amita Health Hoffman Estates, Hoffman Estates, IL, p. A190
Vice President and Chief Information Officer, Alexian Brothers Behavioral Health Hospital, Hoffman Estates, IL, p. A190

RUSSELL, Susan
Chief Financial Officer, Och Regional Medical Center, Starkville, MS, p. A362
Chief Nursing Officer, Singing River Health System, Pascagoula, MS, p. A360

RUSSELL, William B., Chief Executive Officer, Three Rivers Health, Three Rivers, MI, p. A332

RUSSELL–COOK, Donna, FACHE, President, Eastern Maine Medical Center, Bangor, ME, p. A289

RUSSELL–JENKINS, Shane M.D., Medical Director, Windhaven Psychiatric Hospital, Prescott Valley, AZ, p. A35

RUSSO, Arthur M.D., Director Medical Affairs, Harrington Hospital, Southbridge, MA, p. A311

RUSSO, Cindy, FACHE, MS, R.N., President and Chief Administrative Officer, Baystate Franklin Medical Center, Greenfield, MA, p. A307

RUSSO, Kimberly
Chief Executive Officer, George Washington University Hospital, Washington, DC, p. A117
Chief Operating Officer, George Washington University Hospital, Washington, DC, p. A117

RUSSO, Mike, Vice President Information Systems, Chi St. Joseph Health Grimes Hospital, Navasota, TX, p. A634

RUSSO, Paul M., FACHE, Director, Miami Veterans Affairs Healthcare System, Miami, FL, p. A133

RUST, Jeff, Information Technology Systems Site Manager, Chi St. Alexius Health – Williston Medical Center, Williston, ND, p. A478

RUST, Steve, Director, Human Resources, Scripps Memorial Hospital–Encinitas, Encinitas, CA, p. A58

RUTGER, Hary J., Interim Chief Executive Officer, Wheatland Memorial Healthcare, Harlowton, MT, p. A385

RUTH, Daniel R., President and Chief Executive Officer, Jewish Home Of San Francisco, San Francisco, CA, p. A87

RUTH, Joseph, Executive Vice President and Chief Operating Officer, Sparrow Hospital, Lansing, MI, p. A324

RUTHER, Randy, Vice President Finance and Chief Financial Officer, Little Company Of Mary Hospital And Health Care Centers, Evergreen Park, IL, p. A187

RUTHERFORD, Dennis E, CPA
Chief Financial Officer, Florence Hospital At Anthem, Florence, AZ, p. A29
Chief Financial Officer, Gilbert Hospital, Gilbert, AZ, p. A29

RUTHERFORD, Eddie, Administrator, Tyler Holmes Memorial Hospital, Winona, MS, p. A363

RUTHERFORD, Jeremiah, Chief Medical Officer, Cornerstone Hospital Of Oklahoma–Muskogee, Muskogee, OK, p. A510

RUTHERFORD, Peter, M.D.
Chief Executive Officer, Confluence Health/Central Washington Hospital, Wenatchee, WA, p. A689
Chief Executive Officer, Confluence Health/Wenatchee Valley Hospital, Wenatchee, WA, p. A689

RUTHERFORD, Ronald, Chief Information Officer, Beth Israel Deaconess Hospital Plymouth, Plymouth, MA, p. A310

RUTHERFORD, Theresa, R.N., MS, FACHE, President and Chief Executive Officer, Hshs St. Anthony's Memorial Hospital, Effingham, IL, p. A186

RUTHS, Steve M.D., Chief Medical Officer, Vista Del Mar Hospital, Ventura, CA, p. A96

RUTKOWSKI, Jennifer R.N., MSN, Vice President Professional Services, Grant Regional Health Center, Lancaster, WI, p. A705

RUTKOWSKI, Jim, Chief Financial Officer, United Hospital Center, Bridgeport, WV, p. A690

RUTLEDGE, Debra K R.N., Vice President Nursing Services, Chi Health Plainview, Plainview, NE, p. A399

RUTLEDGE, Rebel, Director Human Resources, Grady Memorial Hospital, Chickasha, OK, p. A505

RUWOLDT, Steven T, Chief Operating Officer, Memorial Medical Center, Las Cruces, NM, p. A426

RYALS, Billie, Director Human Resources, Sullivan County Memorial Hospital, Milan, MO, p. A373

RYAN, Chris, Chief Information Officer, Auburn Community Hospital, Auburn, NY, p. A431

RYAN, Christie, Chief Nursing Officer, Healthsouth Rehabilitation Hospital Of Sewickley, Sewickley, PA, p. A550

RYAN, Christina M., R.N., Chief Executive Officer, The Women's Hospital, Newburgh, IN, p. A217

RYAN, Christina M R.N., Chief Executive Officer and Chief Nursing Officer, The Women's Hospital, Newburgh, IN, p. A217

RYAN, Connie, Chief Nursing Officer, Select Specialty Hospital–Tulsa Midtown, Tulsa, OK, p. A518

RYAN, David P., Vice President Human Resources, Hallmark Health System, Melrose, MA, p. A308

RYAN, Debora R.N., Vice President Patient Care, St. Francis Regional Medical Center, Shakopee, MN, p. A348

RYAN, Dennis, Senior Vice President and Chief Financial Officer, Children's Hospital Of The King's Daughters, Norfolk, VA, p. A671

RYAN, Frank, Chief Financial Officer, Manchester Veterans Affairs Medical Center, Manchester, NH, p. A409

RYAN, Jacqueline, Director Human Resources, Mayo Clinic Health System In Lake City, Lake City, MN, p. A341

RYAN, Jeffrey, Senior Vice President, Finance and Business Development, Eastern Regional Medical Center, Philadelphia, PA, p. A543

RYAN, John Jack M.D., Chief Medical Officer, Oakland Regional Hospital, Southfield, MI, p. A331

RYAN, Kimberly, President, Wellstar Atlanta Medical Center, Atlanta, GA, p. A151

RYAN, Lisa M, Coordinator Human Resources, Hampstead Hospital, Hampstead, NH, p. A408

RYAN, Maria, Ph.D., Chief Executive Officer, Cottage Hospital, Woodsville, NH, p. A410

RYAN, Mike, Director of Information Services, Gunnison Valley Hospital, Gunnison, UT, p. A656

RYAN, Patrice
Vice President Human Resources, Goleta Valley Cottage Hospital, Santa Barbara, CA, p. A90
Vice President Human Resources, Santa Barbara Cottage Hospital, Santa Barbara, CA, p. A90
Vice President Human Resources, Santa Ynez Valley Cottage Hospital, Solvang, CA, p. A92

RYAN, Patrick G., Chief Executive Officer, Promise Hospital Of Fort Myers, Fort Myers, FL, p. A125

RYAN, Patrick J., Chief Human Resources Officer, Helen Hayes Hospital, West Haverstraw, NY, p. A455

RYAN, Rebecca, Interim Director Human Resources and Employee Health, Ukiah Valley Medical Center, Ukiah, CA, p. A95

RYAN, Rick G., Administrator and Chief Executive Officer, Providence Care Center, Sandusky, OH, p. B27

RYAN, Robert M.D., Chief Medical Officer, Guadalupe Regional Medical Center, Seguin, TX, p. A644

RYAN, Sharon, Regional Controller, Select Specialty Hospital–Macomb County, Mount Clemens, MI, p. A326

RYAN, Tim, Chief Financial Officer, Centennial Peaks Hospital, Louisville, CO, p. A106

RYAN, William, Vice President and Chief Financial Officer, Uf Health Jacksonville, Jacksonville, FL, p. A128

RYBA, Janice L., JD, Chief Executive Officer, St. Mary Medical Center, Hobart, IN, p. A210

RYBA, Thomas L., Chief Executive Officer, Lighthouse Care Center Of Conway, Conway, SC, p. A561

RYBICKI, Catherine, Vice President Physician Services and Chief Operating Officer, Spectrum Health Big Rapids Hospital, Big Rapids, MI, p. A315

RYBICKI, Cathy, Chief Operating Officer, Spectrum Health Reed City Hospital, Reed City, MI, p. A329

RYBOLT, Andrew, Chief Financial Officer, El Paso Children's Hospital, El Paso, TX, p. A610

RYCKMAN, George D.O., Chief of Staff, Paul Oliver Memorial Hospital, Frankfort, MI, p. A320

RYDER, Doug, President, Holy Cross Germantown Hospital, Germantown, MD, p. A298

RYDER, Jeff, Director Information Systems, Saint Joseph Mount Sterling, Mount Sterling, KY, p. A265

RYDER, John E.
    Administrator and Chief Operating Officer, Borgess Medical Center, Kalamazoo, MI, p. A324
    Chief Operating Officer, Borgess–Lee Memorial Hospital, Dowagiac, MI, p. A318
    Chief Operating Officer, Borgess–Lee Memorial Hospital, Dowagiac, MI, p. A318

RYDER, Ronald D.O., President of the Medical Staff, Robert Wood Johnson University Hospital At Hamilton, Hamilton, NJ, p. A414

RYDER, Troy, Director of Nursing, Aspire Hospital, Conroe, TX, p. A602

RYDGREN, Barbara, Administrator, Glenn Medical Center, Willows, CA, p. A97

RYERSE, David, Chief Executive Officer, Daniels Memorial Healthcare Center, Scobey, MT, p. A388

RYLAND, Jennifer M., R.N., Chief Executive Officer, Jackson Medical Center, Jackson, AL, p. A19

RYLAND, Jennifer M R.N., Chief Administrative Officer, Jackson Medical Center, Jackson, AL, p. A19

RYLE, Barry W., Chief Information Officer, Oswego Hospital, Oswego, NY, p. A449

RYMER, Brandy, Coordinator Human Resources, Murray Medical Center, Chatsworth, GA, p. A154

RYON, Joel M.D., Chief of Staff, Henry County Health Center, Mount Pleasant, IA, p. A232

RYS, Jan, Chief Executive Officer, Straith Hospital For Special Surgery, Southfield, MI, p. A331

RZENDZIAN, Michael, Chief Financial Officer, Baylor Emergency Medical Center At Aubrey, Aubrey, TX, p. A594

RZOMP, Kimberly
    Vice President and Chief Financial Officer, Chambersburg Hospital, Chambersburg, PA, p. A531
    Vice President Finance, Waynesboro Hospital, Waynesboro, PA, p. A553

S

SAAD, Michael, Vice President and Chief Information Officer, University Of Tennessee Medical Center, Knoxville, TN, p. A582

SAADAT, Annette, Human Resources Business Partner, Saint Joseph Mount Sterling, Mount Sterling, KY, p. A265

SAALFELD, Thomas, Senior Vice President and Chief Operating Officer, St. Elizabeth Fort Thomas, Fort Thomas, KY, p. A258

SAARI, Heidi L, Director, Human Resources, Upper Connecticut Valley Hospital, Colebrook, NH, p. A407

SAAVEDRA, JayLynn, Chief Information Officer, U.S. Public Health Service Indian Hospital, Parker, AZ, p. A32

SABANDIT, Elizabeth, Director Human Resources, Alhambra Hospital Medical Center, Alhambra, CA, p. A51

SABHARRWAL, Parajeet, Chief Executive Officer, Minimally Invasive Surgery Hospital, Lenexa, KS, p. A245

SABIA, John M.D., Vice President Medical Affairs, Northern Dutchess Hospital, Rhinebeck, NY, p. A450

SABIN, Margaret D.
    President and Chief Executive Officer, Penrose–St. Francis Health Services, Colorado Springs, CO, p. A100
    Chief Executive Officer, Penrose–St. Francis Health Services, Colorado Springs, CO, p. A100

SABLE, Kenneth N., M.D., President, Hackensack Meridian Health Jersey Shore University Medical Center, Neptune, NJ, p. A417

SABOTTA, John, Director Information Systems, St. Margaret's Hospital, Spring Valley, IL, p. A200

SABUS, Matthew, Director Information Systems, Boone County Hospital, Boone, IA, p. A223

SACCOIO, Saria M.D., Chief Medical Officer, Bon Secours St. Francis Health System, Greenville, SC, p. A562

SACHARSKI, Steve, Chief Financial Officer, Havenwyck Hospital, Auburn Hills, MI, p. A314

SACHDEV, Aruna M.D., Medical Director, Pappas Rehabilitation Hospital For Children, Canton, MA, p. A305

SACHDEV, Vish, Chief Medical Officer, Brookwood Baptist Medical Center, Birmingham, AL, p. A14

SACHDEVA, Sandeep M.D., Vice President Medical Affairs, Swedish/Edmonds, Edmonds, WA, p. A680

SACHS, Henry T M.D., III, Medical Director, Emma Pendleton Bradley Hospital, East Providence, RI, p. A556

SACHTJEN, Mistie, Chief Executive Officer, Community Memorial Hospital, Burke, SD, p. A568

SACHTLEBEN, Michael, President, Medstar Georgetown University Hospital, Washington, DC, p. A117

SACK, Michael V, FACHE, Chief Executive Officer, Hallmark Health System, Melrose, MA, p. A308

SACKETT , John, President SGMC and Executive Vice President and Chief Operating Officer, Adventist Healthcare Shady Grove Medical Center, Rockville, MD, p. B7

SACKETT, John, President SGMC and Executive Vice President and Chief Operating Officer, Adventist Healthcare Shady Grove Medical Center, Rockville, MD, p. A300

SACKETT, Walter, President, Sycamore Medical Center, Miamisburg, OH, p. A496

SACKMANN, Charles M.D., Chief of Staff, East Adams Rural Healthcare, Ritzville, WA, p. A684

SACKRISON, Jeffrey
    President, Vidant Bertie Hospital, Windsor, NC, p. A473
    President, Vidant Chowan Hospital, Edenton, NC, p. A462

SADA, Judy, Chief Financial Officer, Memorial Hospital Miramar, Miramar, FL, p. A135

SADLER, Donna, Director Human Resources, Arkansas State Hospital, Little Rock, AR, p. A45

SADLER, Joy, Director Human Resources, Bear River Valley Hospital, Tremonton, UT, p. A661

SADLER BELL, Kelli S, R.N.
    Vice President, Chief Nursing Officer, Novant Health Charlotte Orthopaedic Hospital, Charlotte, NC, p. A459
    Vice President, Chief Nursing Officer, Novant Health Presbyterian Medical Center, Charlotte, NC, p. A460

SADOFF, Jennifer, Chief Executive Officer, Moab Regional Hospital, Moab, UT, p. A657

SADR, Farrokh M.D., Chief Medical Officer, Sacred Heart Hospital, Allentown, PA, p. A528

SADRO, Cheryl A, Executive Vice President Chief Business and Finance Officer, University Of Texas Medical Branch, Galveston, TX, p. A616

SADAU, Ernie W., Chief Executive Officer, Christus Health, Irving, TX, p. B30

SAENZ, Luis J Rodriquez M.D., Medical Director, Hospital Menonita De Cayey, Cayey, PR, p. A723

SAENZ, Melanie, Regional Human Resources Officer, Presence Saints Mary & Elizabeth Medical Center, Chicago, IL, p. A183

SAFFA, Steve, Director Human Resources, St. Francis Health, Topeka, KS, p. A252

SAFLEY, Thomas, Chief Financial Officer, St. Joseph Regional Medical Center, Lewiston, ID, p. A174

SAFYER, Steven M., M.D., President and Chief Executive Officer, Montefiore Medical Center, New Rochelle, NY, p. A443

SAGE, Kelly, Chief Nursing Officer, Hshs St. Anthony's Memorial Hospital, Effingham, IL, p. A186

SAGMIT, Rodney, Chief Information Management, Va Long Beach Healthcare System, Long Beach, CA, p. A67

SAHA, Sanjay K, Chief Operating Officer, Sibley Memorial Hospital, Washington, DC, p. A118

SAHLOLBEI, Hossain M.D., Chief of Staff, Palo Verde Hospital, Blythe, CA, p. A54

SAHLSTROM, Christopher M.D., Chief of Staff, Mat–Su Regional Medical Center, Palmer, AK, p. A27

SAHMAUNT, Sarabeth, Supervisory Accountant, Lawton Indian Hospital, Lawton, OK, p. A509

SAIA, Carrie L., Chief Executive Officer, Holton Community Hospital, Holton, KS, p. A242

SAINBERT, Wilmino, Chief Human Resources Management Service, Northport Veterans Affairs Medical Center, Northport, NY, p. A448

SAINTZ, Jeffrey, Vice President Human Resources, Titusville Area Hospital, Titusville, PA, p. A551

SAIYED, Ashfaq M.D., Medical Director, Irwin County Hospital, Ocilla, GA, p. A163

SAIZ, Claudia, Chief Operating Officer, Advanced Care Hospital Of Southern New Mexico, Las Cruces, NM, p. A426

SAJID, Muhammad W. M.D., Medical Director, Lincoln Trail Behavioral Health System, Radcliff, KY, p. A266

SAKALOSKY, Matt, Director Information Services and Chief Information Officer, Fremont Health, Fremont, NE, p. A393

SAKOVITS, Steven, Vice President Information Systems and Chief Information Officer, Stamford Hospital, Stamford, CT, p. A113

SALAKI, Jana, Regional Director Human Resources, Wellspan Ephrata Community Hospital, Ephrata, PA, p. A534

SALAMANCA, Mary, Director Human Resources, Healthsouth Rehabilitation Hospital Of Spring Hill, Brooksville, FL, p. A121

SALAMONE, Joanna, Senior Vice President Clinical Services and Chief Nursing Officer, Southern Maine Health Care – Biddeford Medical Center, Biddeford, ME, p. A290

SALANDI, John, Chief Executive Officer, Landmark Hospital Of Savannah, Savannah, GA, p. A164

SALAS, Dawn, Controller, Healthsouth Rehabilitation Hospital At Martin Health, Stuart, FL, p. A143

SALAS, Victor M.D., President Medical Staff, Unitypoint Health – Jones Regional Medical Center, Anamosa, IA, p. A222

SALAWAY, Tarek
    Chief Executive, Mission Hospital, Mission Viejo, CA, p. A74
    Chief Operating Officer, Mission Hospital, Mission Viejo, CA, p. A74
    Chief Operating Officer, Usc Norris Comprehensive Cancer Center, Los Angeles, CA, p. A71

SALAZAR, Eloisa, Chief Financial Officer, South Texas Veterans Health Care System, San Antonio, TX, p. A644

SALAZAR, Juan, Director Human Resources, St. Luke's Episcopal Hospital, Ponce, PR, p. A725

SALAZAR, Leanne, Chief Nursing Officer, Oak Hill Hospital, Brooksville, FL, p. A121

SALAZAR, Linda C, Information Technology Leader, Kaiser Permanente Baldwin Park Medical Center, Baldwin Park, CA, p. A53

SALAZAR, Pamela M.D., Chief of Staff, Healthsouth Walton Rehabilitation Hospital, Augusta, GA, p. A151

SALCEDO, Martha, Interim Director Human Resources, Whittier Hospital Medical Center, Whittier, CA, p. A97

SALCEDO, Nydimar, Chief Human Resources Officer, Castaner General Hospital, Castaner, PR, p. A723

SALDIVAR, Antoninette, Vice President, Human Resources, Bridgepoint Hospital National Harbor, Washington, DC, p. A117

SALDIVAR, Duke, FACHE, Chief Executive Officer, Warm Springs Rehabilitation Hospital Of Kyle, Kyle, TX, p. A627

SALEEBY, Manhal M.D., Chief of Staff, VCU Health Community Memorial Hospital, South Hill, VA, p. A675

SALEEM, David, Director Information Technology, Greystone Park Psychiatric Hospital, Morris Plains, NJ, p. A416

SALEM, Gary M.D., Vice President Medical Affairs, Mclaren Lapeer Region, Lapeer, MI, p. A325

SALEM, Michael, M.D., President and Chief Executive Officer, National Jewish Health, Denver, CO, p. A101

SALERNO, Thomas A., Chief Executive Officer, Western Arizona Regional Medical Center, Bullhead City, AZ, p. A28

SALGADO, Joe M.D., Chief of Staff, Artesia General Hospital, Artesia, NM, p. A425

SALIBA, K. Michael M.D., Medical Director, Shadow Mountain Behavioral Health System, Tulsa, OK, p. A518

SALINAS, Amaro, Assistant Administrator and Human Resource Officer, Starr County Memorial Hospital, Rio Grande City, TX, p. A640

SALINAS, Daniel M.D., Senior Vice President and Chief Medical Officer, Children's Healthcare Of Atlanta, Atlanta, GA, p. A150

SALINAS, Noe
    Vice President Information Technology, Nexus Specialty Hospital The Woodlands, The Woodlands, TX, p. A649
    Vice President Information Technology, Nexus Specialty Hospital, Shenandoah, TX, p. A645

SALING, Christopher, Manager Human Resources, Park City Hospital, Park City, UT, p. A659

SALISBURY, Dennis M.D., Vice President for Medical Affairs, St. James Healthcare, Butte, MT, p. A383

SALISBURY, Renee A, Director Human Resources, OSF Saint Luke Medical Center, Kewanee, IL, p. A191

SALISBURY, Tracy
    Director Human Resources, Hiram W. Davis Medical Center, Petersburg, VA, p. A672
    Regional Manager Human Resources, Central State Hospital, Petersburg, VA, p. A672

SALLER, William, Chief Financial Officer, Rio Grande Regional Hospital, Mcallen, TX, p. A632

SALLEY, Wanda, Vice President Human Resources, West Florida Hospital, Pensacola, FL, p. A139

SALLIS, Tom, Director Information Systems, Sparks Regional Medical Center, Fort Smith, AR, p. A44

SALLOUM, Fadi M.D., Medical Director, Select Specialty Hospital–Pontiac, Pontiac, MI, p. A328

SALMAN, Wael M.D., Vice President Medical Affairs, Memorial Healthcare, Owosso, MI, p. A327

SALMANULLAH, Muhammad, Chief Medical Director, Healthsouth Rehabilitation Hospital, Concord, NH, p. A407

SALNAS, Todd
President, Petaluma Valley Hospital, Petaluma, CA, p. A79
President, Santa Rosa Memorial Hospital, Santa Rosa, CA, p. A91

SALO, Saliba, President, Northridge Hospital Medical Center, Los Angeles, CA, p. A70

SALOM, Ira M.D., Clinical Director, Northern Navajo Medical Center, Shiprock, NM, p. A428

SALOME, Jenny, Chief Financial Officer and Assistant Administrator, Northwest Hills Surgical Hospital, Austin, TX, p. A595

SALOMON, Kathryn, Director Human Resources, Kona Community Hospital, Kealakekua, HI, p. A170

SALTAFORMAGGIO, Cheri, Chief Executive Officer, St. Charles Surgical Hospital, New Orleans, LA, p. A283

SALTER, Cherry B, Director of Nursing, Hardtner Medical Center, Olla, LA, p. A284

SALTONSTALL, Christine, Chief Financial Officer, Kindred Hospital–Baldwin Park, Baldwin Park, CA, p. A53

SALTZGABER, Lee, Chief Medical Officer, Gerald Champion Regional Medical Center, Alamogordo, NM, p. A424

SALVADOR, Ed, Chief Financial Officer, St. Jude Medical Center, Fullerton, CA, p. A61

SALVATI, Mario, Director Fiscal Services, Shriners Hospitals For Children–Philadelphia, Philadelphia, PA, p. A545

SALVI, Donna, Chief Nursing Officer, Watsonville Community Hospital, Watsonville, CA, p. A96

SALVINO, Sonia, Vice President Finance, University Hospitals Cleveland Medical Center, Cleveland, OH, p. A486

SALVITTI, Alfred P, Chief Financial Officer, Eagleville Hospital, Eagleville, PA, p. A533

SALVO, Stephen, Vice President Human Resources, Anna Jaques Hospital, Newburyport, MA, p. A309

SALVO, Thomas, Associate Executive Director Human Resources, Glen Cove Hospital, Glen Cove, NY, p. A436

SALY, David, Director, Information Services, Largo Medical Center, Largo, FL, p. A130

SALYER, Steven, Chief Operating Officer, Up Health System–Marquette, Marquette, MI, p. A326

SALZMAN, Shona, Chief Operating Officer, William Newton Hospital, Winfield, KS, p. A254

SAMBASIVAN, Venkataraman M.D., Chief Medical Officer, Lourdes Medical Center, Pasco, WA, p. A683

SAMET, Kenneth A., President and Chief Executive Officer, Medstar Health, Columbia, MD, p. B81

SAMILO, Nick, Vice President Fiscal Services and Chief Financial Officer, Carolinas Healthcare System Stanly, Albemarle, NC, p. A457

SAMMARCO, Michael M.D., Chief Financial Officer, Erie County Medical Center, Buffalo, NY, p. A432

SAMMONS, Craig, Chief Financial Officer, Sky Ridge Medical Center, Lone Tree, CO, p. A105

SAMMONS, Jacquelyn, R.N., Supervisor, Child And Adolescent Behavioral Health Services, Willmar, MN, p. A350

SAMMS, Caswell, Network Chief Financial Officer, NYC Health + Hospitals / Lincoln, New Rochelle, NY, p. A445

SAMORA, Martha, R.N., FACHE, Chief Executive Officer, Healthsouth Bakersfield Rehabilitation Hospital, Bakersfield, CA, p. A52

SAMPAGA, Arthur, Assistant Director Nursing, Hilo Medical Center, Hilo, HI, p. A168

SAMPSON, Arthur J., FACHE, President, Miriam Hospital, Providence, RI, p. A556

SAMPSON, Bob
Vice President Human Resources, Redwood Memorial Hospital, Fortuna, CA, p. A59
Vice President, Human Resources, Evergreenhealth, Kirkland, WA, p. A681

SAMPSON, Jill, Director Human Resources, Lemuel Shattuck Hospital, Jamaica Plain, MA, p. A307

SAMS, Carla R.N., Director of Nursing, Liberty Healthcare Systems, Bastrop, LA, p. A270

SAMSON, Ley, Director Management Information Systems, Clear Lake Regional Medical Center, Webster, TX, p. A653

SAMUDRALA, Siresha M.D., Medical Director, Mercy Rehabilitation Hospital St. Louis, Chesterfield, MO, p. A366

SAMUEL, Nicole, Chief Financial Officer, Sierra Vista Hospital, Sacramento, CA, p. A84

SAMUELS, Christopher, Chief of Staff, Skyline Hospital, White Salmon, WA, p. A689

SAMUELS, Steven M.D., Medical Director, Kindred Hospital Indianapolis South, Greenwood, IN, p. A209

SAMUELSON, Kimberly, Director of Information Management, Highland–Clarksburg Hospital, Clarksburg, WV, p. A691

SAMUELSON, Melissa A R.N., Chief Nurse Executive, Poplar Bluff Regional Medical Center, Poplar Bluff, MO, p. A375

SAMYN, Mike, Vice President, Finance and Chief Financial Officer, St. Mary Mercy Hospital, Livonia, MI, p. A325

SAMZ, Jeff, Chief Operating Officer, Huntsville Hospital, Huntsville, AL, p. A19

SAN FILIPPO, Bruce M.D., Chief Medical Officer, Memorial Medical Center, Las Cruces, NM, p. A426

SANBORN, Michael, FACHE, MS, President and Chief Executive Officer, Baylor All Saints Medical Center At Fort Worth, Fort Worth, TX, p. A613

SANBORN, Randall, Director Information Systems, Garden City Hospital, Garden City, MI, p. A320

SANCHEZ, Antonio, M.D.
Chief of Staff, Veterans Affairs Caribbean Healthcare System, San Juan, PR, p. A727
Acting Director, Veterans Affairs Caribbean Healthcare System, San Juan, PR, p. A727

SANCHEZ, Arnaldo Rodriguez M.D., Chief Operating Officer, Hospital Episcopal San Lucas Guayama, Guayama, PR, p. A723

SANCHEZ, Emalie, Director Human Resources, Baylor Medical Center At Uptown, Dallas, TX, p. A604

SANCHEZ, Esperanza, Chief Clinical Officer, Kindred Hospital–La Mirada, La Mirada, CA, p. A64

SANCHEZ, Freddie, Director Information Systems, Fountain Valley Regional Hospital And Medical Center, Fountain Valley, CA, p. A60

SANCHEZ, John, Vice President Human Resources, White Plains Hospital Center, White Plains, NY, p. A456

SANCHEZ, Jose R., President and Chief Executive Officer, Norwegian American Hospital, Chicago, IL, p. A182

SANCHEZ, Jose', Chief Nursing Officer, Chg Hospital Tucson, Llc, Tucson, AZ, p. A37

SANCHEZ, Nancy, Senior Vice President and Vice Dean Human Resources, NYU Langone Hospitals, New Rochelle, NY, p. A446

SANCHEZ, Rebecca R.N., M.P.H., Director of Nursing, Texas Center For Infectious Disease, San Antonio, TX, p. A644

SANCHEZ–BICKLEY, Michelle
Vice President Human Resources, Renown Regional Medical Center, Reno, NV, p. A405
Vice President Human Resources, Renown Rehabilitation Hospital, Reno, NV, p. A405
Vice President Human Resources, Renown South Meadows Medical Center, Reno, NV, p. A405

SANCHEZ–RICO, Gloria, Chief Nursing Officer and Vice President, Huntington Memorial Hospital, Pasadena, CA, p. A79

SAND, Michelle R.N., MSN, Vice President and Chief Nursing Officer, Cascade Valley Hospital And Clinics, Arlington, WA, p. A678

SANDAGER, Brian, Chief Information Officer, Lowell General Hospital, Lowell, MA, p. A308

SANDBERG, Sue R.N., Chief Operating Officer, UNC Rex Health Care, Raleigh, NC, p. A469

SANDBERG, Todd, Chief Executive Officer, Ridgeview Sibley Medical Center, Arlington, MN, p. A335

SANDBULTE, Nyla H R.N., Director of Nursing, Sanford Luverne Medical Center, Luverne, MN, p. A342

SANDEFUR, Gwen L., President, Spectrum Health Hospital Group, Spectrum Health – Butterworth Hospital, Grand Rapids, MI, p. A321

SANDER, Cindy, Coordinator Human Resources, Kindred Hospital–St. Louis, Saint Louis, MO, p. A377

SANDERS, Amy, Chief Human Resources, Captain James A. Lovell Federal Health Care Center, North Chicago, IL, p. A195

SANDERS, Carolyn Lucey, Senior Vice President Patient Services and Chief Nursing Officer, University Of Colorado Hospital, Aurora, CO, p. A98

SANDERS, David S., Chief Executive Officer, Fannin Regional Hospital, Blue Ridge, GA, p. A152

SANDERS, David, Chief Financial Officer, Springhill Medical Center, Springhill, LA, p. A286

SANDERS, Gale H, Director, Gadsden Regional Medical Center, Gadsden, AL, p. A18

SANDERS, Harv, Chief Financial Officer, Rhea Medical Center, Dayton, TN, p. A578

SANDERS, Jeff, Senior Vice President, Chief Operating Officer, Maine Medical Center, Portland, ME, p. A292

SANDERS, Jeffrey M.D., Chief of Staff, Carson Tahoe Health, Carson City, NV, p. A401

SANDERS, Kelly B., Vice President Human Resources, Good Shepherd Health Care System, Hermiston, OR, p. A522

SANDERS, Kenneth, Chief Executive Officer, Dallas County Medical Center, Fordyce, AR, p. A43

SANDERS, Kimberly, Chief Nursing Officer, Baptist Memorial Hospital–Huntingdon, Huntingdon, TN, p. A580

SANDERS, Kris, Chief Financial Officer, Methodist Olive Branch Hospital, Olive Branch, MS, p. A360

SANDERS, Kyle, Chief Financial Officer, Nea Baptist Memorial Hospital, Jonesboro, AR, p. A45

SANDERS, Michael B., President and Chief Executive Officer, Monroe Clinic, Monroe, WI, p. A708

SANDERS, Michael R MS, Chief Operating Officer, Promise Hospital Baton Rouge – Main Campus, Baton Rouge, LA, p. A271

SANDERS, R. Bradley D.O., Executive Medical Director, Alvarado Parkway Institute Behavioral Health System, La Mesa, CA, p. A64

SANDERS, Robert M.D., Chief Medical Officer, Texoma Medical Center, Denison, TX, p. A608

SANDERS, Ryan, Director Information Services, Midtown Medical Center West, Columbus, GA, p. A154

SANDERS, Sheila M, Chief Information Officer, Emory University Hospital, Atlanta, GA, p. A150

SANDERS, Steve, Chief Financial Officer, Washington County Hospital And Clinics, Washington, IA, p. A236

SANDERS, Susie Sherrod, Chief Financial Officer, Cherry Hospital, Goldsboro, NC, p. A463

SANDERS, Victoria Odom., FACHE, Chief Executive Officer, Baylor Institute For Rehabilitation At Fort Worth, Fort Worth, TX, p. A613

SANDIFER, Ron, Chief Information Officer, Community Memorial Hospital, Ventura, CA, p. A95

SANDIN, James H M.D., Assistant Administrator Medical Affairs, Hunt Regional Medical Center, Greenville, TX, p. A617

SANDLES, Christopher R., FACHE, Director, Central Texas Veterans Health Care System, Temple, TX, p. A648

SANDLIN, Keith, Chief Executive Officer, Cartersville Medical Center, Cartersville, GA, p. A154

SANDLIN, Michael M.D., Chief of Staff, Muscogee Creek Nation Medical Center, Okmulgee, OK, p. A514

SANDMANN, Patty, Senior Director of Nursing, Burgess Health Center, Onawa, IA, p. A232

SANDS, Naomi, Administrative Assistant and Manager Human Resources, Swift County – Benson Health Services, Benson, MN, p. A336

SANDS, Sherry R.N., Chief Nursing Officer, Southern Tennessee Regional Health System–Pulaski, Pulaski, TN, p. A588

SANDS, Tiffany, Manager Health Information, Arbuckle Memorial Hospital, Sulphur, OK, p. A516

SANDSTROM, C Bruce, Vice President and Chief Financial Officer, The Aroostook Medical Center, Presque Isle, ME, p. A293

SANFORD, Lisa
Chief Nursing Officer, St. Luke's Elmore, Mountain Home, ID, p. A174
VP Patient Care/CNO, Holy Rosary Healthcare, Miles City, MT, p. A386

SANFORD, Ricca, Director Human Resources, Regional West Garden County, Oshkosh, NE, p. A398

SANFORD, Sharon K, Director Human Resources, Jersey Community Hospital, Jerseyville, IL, p. A191

SANFORD, Stacy, Chief Executive Officer, Oceans Behavioral Hospital Abilene, Abilene, TX, p. A591

SANGER, David M.D., Chief Medical Officer, Pawnee Valley Community Hospital, Larned, KS, p. A245

SANGER, Ken, R.N., Chief Nursing Officer and Chief Operations Officer, Lake Huron Medical Center, Port Huron, MI, p. A328

SANGER, Neal, Vice President Information Services, Mayo Clinic Health System – Franciscan Healthcare In La Crosse, La Crosse, WI, p. A704

SANGHI, Harishankar M.D., Clinical Director, St. Lawrence Psychiatric Center, Ogdensburg, NY, p. A448

SANKARAN, Jaya M.D., Chief of Staff, St. Mary's Of Michigan Standish Hospital, Standish, MI, p. A331

SANKE, Kristina, Chief Financial Officer, Orchard Hospital, Gridley, CA, p. A62

SANKOORIKAL, Joseph M.D., Chief Medical Staff, Kansas Rehabilitation Hospital, Topeka, KS, p. A252

SANKS, Claude, Chief Medical Staff, Effingham Hospital, Springfield, GA, p. A165

SANNUTO, John
Chief Executive Officer, Clearvista Health And Wellness, Lorain, OH, p. A494
Chief Executive Officer, Wellbridge Healthcare Greater Dallas, Plano, TX, p. A638

SANSOM, Christine R, Chief Nursing Officer, Mclaren Port Huron, Port Huron, MI, p. A328

SANSONE, John, Vice President, Human Resources, Monadnock Community Hospital, Peterborough, NH, p. A410

SANTA ANA, Coleen F., President, Sentara Albemarle Medical Center, Elizabeth City, NC, p. A462

SANTANA, Leticia, Administrator Medical Records, Hospital Hermanos Melendez, Bayamon, PR, p. A722

SANTANGELO, Craig, Director Information Services, Medical City Arlington, Arlington, TX, p. A593

SANTANGELO, Joe M.D., Vice President of Medical Affairs, Munson Healthcare Cadillac Hospital, Cadillac, MI, p. A315

SANTANGELO, John, Director Information Technology, Cleveland Clinic Florida, Weston, FL, p. A148

SANTANGELO, Linda, Ph.D., Director, Desert Willow Treatment Center, Las Vegas, NV, p. A403

SANTARELLI, James M.D., President Medical Staff, Aurora Medical Center, Kenosha, WI, p. A704

SANTIAGO, Alejandro, Director Finance, Doctors' Center Hospital San Juan, San Juan, PR, p. A725

SANTIAGO, Julio M.D., Chief of Staff, Genesis Medical Center–Aledo, Aledo, IL, p. A177

SANTIAGO, Manuel, Chief Information Officer, Hospital Metropolitan, San Juan, PR, p. A726

SANTIAGO, Orlando, Human Resources Officer, Hospital Del Maestro, San Juan, PR, p. A726

SANTIAGO, Sugehi, Director, Hospital San Francisco, San Juan, PR, p. A726

SANTIAGO, Ubaldo M.D., Chairman, Doctors' Center Hospital San Juan, San Juan, PR, p. A725

SANTIESTEBAN, Nancy, Director Patient Care Services, Presbyterian Espanola Hospital, Espanola, NM, p. A426

SANTILLI, Robert J., Chief Executive Officer, Gunnison Valley Hospital, Gunnison, CO, p. A103

SANTINA, Ray, Director Information Systems, Psychiatric Institute of Washington, Washington, DC, p. A118

SANTISTEVAN, Vivian, Chief Human Resources, Tsehootsooi Medical Center, Fort Defiance, AZ, p. A29

SANTMAN, Kim D, Vice President Finance, St. Margaret's Hospital, Spring Valley, IL, p. A200

SANTOPIETRO, John, M.D., President and Chief Executive Officer, Silver Hill Hospital, New Canaan, CT, p. A111

SANTORA, Judith
Chief Human Resource Officer, Lutheran Hospital, Cleveland, OH, p. A486
Human Resources Business Partner, Marymount Hospital, Garfield Heights, OH, p. A492

SANTOS, Alfred, Chief Executive Officer, Healthsouth Rehabilitation Hospital Of Northern Virginia, Aldie, VA, p. A664

SANTOS, Daniel, Director Ancillary Services, Pacifica Hospital Of The Valley, Los Angeles, CA, p. A70

SANTOS, David, President and Chief Executive Officer, St. Helena Hospital Clear Lake, Clearlake, CA, p. A56

SANTOS, Deborah R.N., Chief Nursing Officer, Healthsouth Rehabilitation Hospital Of Western Massachusetts, Ludlow, MA, p. A308

SANTOS, Gloria N, R.N., MS
Chief Nursing Officer, Florida Hospital Heartland Medical Center, Sebring, FL, p. A142
Vice President and Chief Nursing Officer, Florida Hospital Wauchula, Wauchula, FL, p. A147

SANTOS, Ismael, Director Human Resources, Valle Vista Hospital, Greenwood, IN, p. A209

SANTOS, Lori
Chief Financial Officer, St. Peter's Hospital, Albany, NY, p. A430
Vice President Finance, Albany Memorial Hospital, Albany, NY, p. A430

SANTOS, Thomas R.N., Chief Nursing Officer, Parkview Community Hospital Medical Center, Riverside, CA, p. A82

SANTULLI, Patricia, Director Human Resources, Elmira Psychiatric Center, Elmira, NY, p. A435

SANVILLE, David, Chief Financial Officer, Mt. Ascutney Hospital And Health Center, Windsor, VT, p. A663

SANWARI, Murtaza, Chief Operating Officer, Kaiser Permanente Panorama City Medical Center, Los Angeles, CA, p. A68

SANZ, Sean M., President and Chief Operating Officer, Novant Health Forsyth Medical Center, Winston, NC, p. A473

SANZONE, Frank, Manager Information Technology, Brighton Center For Recovery, Brighton, MI, p. A315

SAPMAZ, Cagri, Information Technology Director, Bolivar Medical Center, Cleveland, MS, p. A353

SAPORITO, Angie, Administrator, Mercy Hospital Columbus, Columbus, KS, p. A240

SAPORITO, Joann L. R.N., Vice President Nursing Services, Oak Valley Hospital District, Oakdale, CA, p. A77

SAPP, Tracy, Director Human Resources, Healthsouth Rehabilitation Hospital Of Ocala, Ocala, FL, p. A136

SAPPENFIELD, Debra R.N., Chief Nursing Officer, Hemphill County Hospital, Canadian, TX, p. A600

SAPPINGTON–CRITTENDEN, Shana, Chief Operating Officer, Westside Regional Medical Center, Plantation, FL, p. A140

SAPRA, Sonney, Director Information Systems and Chief Information Officer, Tuality Healthcare, Hillsboro, OR, p. A522

SARBACHER, James, Chief Information Officer, State Hospital North, Orofino, ID, p. A175

SARDANA, Sadhana M.D., Clinical Director, Rockland Children's Hospital Psychiatric Center, Orangeburg, NY, p. A449

SARDELLA, Jeff, Director Information Technology, Terrebonne General Medical Center, Houma, LA, p. A276

SARDONE, Frank J.
President and Chief Executive Officer, Bronson Battle Creek, Battle Creek, MI, p. A315
President and Chief Executive Officer, Bronson Methodist Hospital, Kalamazoo, MI, p. A324

SARDONE, Frank J, President and Chief Executive Officer, Bronson Methodist Hospital, Kalamazoo, MI, p. A324

SARDUY, Innette Mary M.P.H., R.N., Associate Director Patient Care Services and Nurse Executive, Louis Stokes Cleveland Veterans Affairs Medical Center, Cleveland, OH, p. A486

SARGEANT, Marty, Chief Operating Officer, City Of Hope's Helford Clinical Research Hospital, Duarte, CA, p. A58

SARGENT, Kimberly, Vice President Patient Services, St. Luke's Hospital – Miners Campus, Coaldale, PA, p. A531

SARGENT, Kurt, CPA
Vice President Operational Finance, Chi St. Alexius Health Devils Lake Hospital, Devils Lake, ND, p. A475
Vice President, Operational Finance, Chi St Alexius Health Carrington Medical Center, Carrington, ND, p. A474

SARGENT, Reed
Assistant Administrator Finance, Cedar City Hospital, Cedar City, UT, p. A656
Assistant Administrator Finance, Garfield Memorial Hospital, Panguitch, UT, p. A659

SARGENT, Teresa, Vice President Human Resources, Saint Alphonsus Regional Medical Center, Boise, ID, p. A172

SARIDAKIS, Michael M.D., Physician Adviser, Tennova Healthcare Regional Hospital Of Jackson, Jackson, TN, p. A580

SARMENTO, Joann, Manager Human Resources, Fairchild Medical Center, Yreka, CA, p. A97

SARNECKI, Adrienne, R.N.
Chief Nurse Executive, Spaulding Hospital For Continuing Medical Care Cambridge, Cambridge, MA, p. A305
Chief Nursing Officer, Spaulding Rehabilitation Hospital Cape Cod, East Sandwich, MA, p. A306

SARNECKI, Robert, Interim Chief Information Officer, Children's Of Alabama, Birmingham, AL, p. A14

SAROFIN, Michelle, Superintendent, Albert J. Solnit Psychiatric Center – South Campus, Middletown, CT, p. A111

SARRAFIAN, Zareh, Chief Executive Officer, Riverside University Health System–Medical Center, Moreno Valley, CA, p. A75

SARROS, Steven, Vice President and Chief Information Officer, Baptist Hospital, Pensacola, FL, p. A139

SARROUI, B M.D., Chief of Staff, Advanced Specialty Hospital Of Toledo, Toledo, OH, p. A500

SARTAIN, Jarred M.D., President Medical Staff, North Mississippi Medical Center–Hamilton, Hamilton, AL, p. A19

SARTAIN, Lisa M., Vice President, Human Resources, Bellevue Hospital, Bellevue, OH, p. A481

SARTOR, Frank, President and Chief Executive Officer, Ridgeview Institute, Smyrna, GA, p. A165

SARVEPALLI, Raghu M.D., Vice President of Medical Affairs, St. Mary's Of Michigan, Saginaw, MI, p. A330

SARVER, Troy R.N., Chief Nursing Officer, Texas Orthopedic Hospital, Houston, TX, p. A623

SAS, Mary, Director of Clinical Services, Hampshire Memorial Hospital, Romney, WV, p. A696

SASLO, Christopher M., Acting Director, Veterans Affairs Gulf Coast Veterans Health Care System, Biloxi, MS, p. A352

SASSER, Kelley, Director Information Systems, Florida Hospital Zephyrhills, Zephyrhills, FL, p. A148

SATHER, Sonia M.D., President Medical Staff, Spencer Hospital, Spencer, IA, p. A235

SATTAR, Parhez, Senior Director Information Technology, Grande Ronde Hospital, La Grande, OR, p. A523

SATTERWHITE, Glenda, Director of Nursing, Oklahoma Forensic Center, Vinita, OK, p. A519

SAUDE, Aaron, Chief Executive Officer, Bigfork Valley Hospital, Bigfork, MN, p. A336

SAUDER, Chris, Vice President and Chief Financial Officer, Florida Hospital Carrollwood, Tampa, FL, p. A144

SAUER, Bernie, Director Information Technology, San Gabriel Valley Medical Center, San Gabriel, CA, p. A88

SAUERBREI, Teresa, Chief Nursing Officer, Compass Memorial Healthcare, Marengo, IA, p. A231

SAUERS, Preston, Chief Financial Officer, Ellsworth County Medical Center, Ellsworth, KS, p. A240

SAUL, Anthony, Chief Financial Officer, New Orleans East Hospital, New Orleans, LA, p. A282

SAULLO, Nancy, Director Human Resources, Warren State Hospital, Warren, PA, p. A552

SAUM, Anita, Director Human Resources, Healthsouth Rehabilitation Hospital Of Tinton Falls, Tinton Falls, NJ, p. A421

SAUNDERS, Candice, President and Chief Executive Officer, Wellstar Health System, Marietta, GA, p. B146

SAUNDERS, John R M.D., Senior Vice President Medical Affairs and Chief Medical Officer, Greater Baltimore Medical Center, Baltimore, MD, p. A294

SAUNDERS, Jonathan, Chief Financial Officer, Baylor Medical Center At Trophy Club, Trophy Club, TX, p. A650

SAUNDERS, Kevin, Human Resources Officer III, Arrowhead Regional Medical Center, Colton, CA, p. A56

SAUNDERS, Kristi K, Director and Compliance Officer, Calais Regional Hospital, Calais, ME, p. A290

SAUNDERS, M Patricia R.N., MS, Vice President Nursing, Hanover Hospital, Hanover, PA, p. A535

SAUNDERS, Ninfa M., Chief Executive Officer, Medical Center, Navicent Health, Macon, GA, p. A161

SAUNDERS, Theodore, Assistant Controller, Select Specialty Hospital – Northeast Atlanta, Atlanta, GA, p. A151

SAURO, Anthony, Chief Information Officer, Pointe Coupee General Hospital, New Roads, LA, p. A283

SAUS, Heather, Human Resource Generalist, Edwin Shaw Rehab, Cuyahoga Falls, OH, p. A488

SAUTER, Michael M.D., Chief Medical Officer, St. Charles Hospital, Port Jefferson, NY, p. A450

SAVAGE, Elizabeth, Vice President and Human Resources Officer, Winchester Medical Center, Winchester, VA, p. A677

SAVAGE, Heather, Director Human Resources, The Rehabilitation Institute Of St. Louis, Saint Louis, MO, p. A378

SAVAGE, Steve, Chief Executive Officer, Stonecrest Center, Detroit, MI, p. A318

SAVITCH, Lane A., Regional Chief Executive, Kadlec Regional Medical Center, Richland, WA, p. A684

SAVITSKY, Marian R.N., Chief Nursing Officer, Sky Ridge Medical Center, Lone Tree, CO, p. A105

SAVOY, Greg M.D., Chief Medical Officer, Savoy Medical Center, Mamou, LA, p. A280

SAVOY, Peter, III
Administrator, River Valley Medical Center, Dardanelle, AR, p. A42
Chief Executive Officer, Eureka Springs Hospital, Eureka Springs, AR, p. A42

SAWA, Kendall, R.N., Chief Executive Officer, Providence Seaside Hospital, Seaside, OR, p. A527

SAWCZUK, Ihor S., M.D., President, Hackensack Meridian Health Hackensack University Medical Center, Hackensack, NJ, p. A414

SAWDEY, Don M.D., Medical Director, Daniels Memorial Healthcare Center, Scobey, MT, p. A388

SAWICKI, Mitzi, Director of Nursing, Havenwyck Hospital, Auburn Hills, MI, p. A314

SAWYER, Anne, Chief Financial Officer, Wayne County Hospital, Monticello, KY, p. A265

SAWYER, Colleen A., R.N., MSN
Executive Director, Mohawk Valley Psychiatric Center, Utica, NY, p. A454
Executive Director, Richard H. Hutchings Psychiatric Center, Syracuse, NY, p. A453

SAWYER, Dorothy, Chief Executive Officer, Eastern State Hospital, Medical Lake, WA, p. A682

SAWYER, Holly, Director and Human Resources Business Partner, Piedmont Fayette Hospital, Fayetteville, GA, p. A157

SAWYER, Regina, Vice President Chief Nursing Officer, Kaweah Delta Medical Center, Visalia, CA, p. A96

SAWYER, Scott, Chief Financial Officer, Community Medical Center, Inc., Falls City, NE, p. A392

SAWYER, Stephen, Chief Financial Officer, Norton Community Hospital, Norton, VA, p. A672

SAWYER, Steve, Chief Financial Officer, Indian Path Medical Center, Kingsport, TN, p. A581

SAWYER, Sydney, R.N., Chief Executive Officer, Lackey Memorial Hospital, Forest, MS, p. A354

SAXON, Kathy R.N., Vice President Patient Care Services, Tillamook Regional Medical Center, Tillamook, OR, p. A527

SAXTON, Beth, R.N., Chief Executive Officer, Yuma District Hospital, Yuma, CO, p. A108

SAYAH, Assaad M.D., Chief Medical Officer, Cambridge Health Alliance, Cambridge, MA, p. A305

SAYLER, Elizabeth M.D., Chief of Staff, Lead–Deadwood Regional Hospital, Deadwood, SD, p. A569

SAYLER, Roger, Finance Officer, Fargo Veterans Affairs Health Care System, Fargo, ND, p. A475

SAYLER, Timothy, Chief Operating Officer, Essentia Health Fargo, Fargo, ND, p. A475

SAYLES, Debbie A R.N., Vice President and Chief Nursing Officer, Texas Scottish Rite Hospital For Children, Dallas, TX, p. A607

SAYLOR, Craig M., Interim CEO, Somerset Hospital, Somerset, PA, p. A551

SAYLOR, Richard F M.D., Chief Medical Officer, Pottstown Memorial Medical Center, Pottstown, PA, p. A548

SAYLORS, Julie, Controller, Anmed Health Rehabilitation Hospital, Anderson, SC, p. A558

SAYRE, Amy, Director Human Resources, General John J. Pershing Memorial Hospital, Brookfield, MO, p. A365

SAYRE, Cindy Ph.D., R.N., Chief Nursing Officer, University Of Washington Medical Center, Seattle, WA, p. A685

SAYRE, Michelle R.N., Chief Nursing Officer, Arrowhead Regional Medical Center, Colton, CA, p. A56

SBARDELLA, Steven M.D., Chief Medical Officer, Hallmark Health System, Melrose, MA, p. A308

SCAFIDDI, Darlene R.N., MSN, Vice President Nursing and Patient Care Services, Pomona Valley Hospital Medical Center, Pomona, CA, p. A80

SCAGLIONE, Kim, Vice President Human Resources, Baptist Health Louisville, Louisville, KY, p. A262

SCALES, Melisa, Director of Nursing, Parkview Hospital, Wheeler, TX, p. A654

SCALFARI, Patricia A, Vice President Nursing, Medstar Southern Maryland Hospital Center, Clinton, MD, p. A297

SCALISE, Jayne R.N., Chief Nursing Executive, Lompoc Valley Medical Center, Lompoc, CA, p. A66

SCALISE, Paul M.D., Chief Pulmonary Medicine and Internal Medicine, Hospital For Special Care, New Britain, CT, p. A111

SCALLION, Jessika
Administrator, Beacon Behavioral Healthcare, Lacombe, LA, p. A278
Administrator, Beacon Behavioral Hospital – New Orleans, New Orleans, LA, p. A282

SCALLON, Jean, Chief Executive Officer, Bloomington Meadows Hospital, Bloomington, IN, p. A204

SCAMARDO, Luke P M.D., II, Chief of Staff, Chi St. Joseph Health Grimes Hospital, Navasota, TX, p. A634

SCAMINACI, Peter, Executive Vice President and Chief Administrative Officer, St. Joseph Hospital, Bethpage, NY, p. A431

SCANLON, Donald
Chief Corporate Services, Mount Sinai Health System, Mount Sinai Beth Israel, New Rochelle, NY, p. A443
Chief Corporate Services, Mount Sinai Health System, Mount Sinai West, New Rochelle, NY, p. A443
Chief Corporate Services, Mount Sinai Health System, New York Eye And Ear Infirmary Of Mount Sinai, New Rochelle, NY, p. A443
Chief Financial Officer, Mount Sinai Hospital, New Rochelle, NY, p. A443

SCANLON, John DPM, Chief Medical Officer, Chestnut Hill Hospital, Philadelphia, PA, p. A543

SCANLON, Kerri MSN, Chief Nursing Officer, North Shore University Hospital, Manhasset, NY, p. A439

SCANNELL, Donna, Vice President Information Technology, Kaiser Permanente Medical Center, Honolulu, HI, p. A168

SCANZERA, Christopher A, Vice President and Chief Information Officer, Atlanticare Regional Medical Center, Atlantic City, NJ, p. A411

SCARANO, Jenaro M.D., Medical Director, St. Luke's Episcopal Hospital, Ponce, PR, p. A725

SCARBROUGH, Keith, Director, Information Systems, Saint Francis Hospital, Memphis, TN, p. A585

SCARLATTI, Shirley K, Associate Chief Nursing Officer, Parkridge Medical Center, Chattanooga, TN, p. A576

SCARLETT, Kamesha, Chief Information Resource Management, Veterans Affairs New Jersey Health Care System, East Orange, NJ, p. A413

SCARMATO, Victor M.D., Acting Medical Director, Nassau University Medical Center, East Meadow, NY, p. A435

SCARPINO, David
President and Chief Executive Officer, Health Alliance Hospital – Broadway Campus, Kingston, NY, p. A438
President and Chief Executive Officer, Health Alliance Hospital – Mary's Avenue Campus, Kingston, NY, p. A438

SCARROW, Alan, M.D., President, Mercy Hospital Springfield, Springfield, MO, p. A379

SCARROW, Lloyd, FACHE, Chief Executive Officer, Edgewood Surgical Hospital, Transfer, PA, p. A552

SCENNA, Maria, Chief Operating Officer, St. Christopher's Hospital For Children, Philadelphia, PA, p. A545

SCEPANSKI, Theresa, Vice President People and Organizational Development, University Health System, San Antonio, TX, p. A644

SCERCY, Charles, Corporate Director, Snowden At Fredericksburg, Fredericksburg, VA, p. A667

SCHAAB, Ben, VP Fiscal Services/ Chief Financial Officer, CGH Medical Center, Sterling, IL, p. A201

SCHAACK, Gregory J, CPA
Vice President and Chief Financial Officer, Candler Hospital, Savannah, GA, p. A164
Vice President and Chief Financial Officer, St. Joseph's Hospital, Savannah, GA, p. A165

SCHADE, Sue, Interim Chief Information Officer, University Hospitals Cleveland Medical Center, Cleveland, OH, p. A486

SCHAEF, Toby, Director Information Technology, Memorial Hospital Of Carbon County, Rawlins, WY, p. A719

SCHAEFER, Becky, Chief Financial Officer, University Of Utah Neuropsychiatric Institute, Salt Lake City, UT, p. A661

SCHAEFER, Debra, Chief Nursing Officer, Windsor–Laurelwood Center For Behavioral Medicine, Willoughby, OH, p. A502

SCHAEFER, Jamie, Vice President Finance, Avera Sacred Heart Hospital, Yankton, SD, p. A574

SCHAEFER, Kevin, Manager Information Services, River's Edge Hospital And Clinic, Saint Peter, MN, p. A348

SCHAEFER, Matt, President, Texas Children's Hospital, Houston, TX, p. A623

SCHAEFER, Michael J, Executive Vice President and Chief Financial Officer, Methodist Charlton Medical Center, Dallas, TX, p. A606

SCHAEFER, Michelle, Chief Financial Officer, Lillian M. Hudspeth Memorial Hospital, Sonora, TX, p. A646

SCHAEFER, Stephen, Chief Executive Officer, Healthsouth Rehabilitation Hospital Of Colorado Springs, Colorado Springs, CO, p. A99

SCHAEFFER, Andre M.D., Chief of Staff, Union General Hospital, Blairsville, GA, p. A152

SCHAEFFER, Richard, Vice President Information Systems and Chief Information Officer, St. Clair Hospital, Pittsburgh, PA, p. A547

SCHAETTI, Susan, Chief Executive Officer, Kindred Hospital–Mansfield, Mansfield, TX, p. A631

SCHAFER, Laurie, Chief Nursing Officer, San Juan Health Service District, Monticello, UT, p. A657

SCHAFER, Michael, Chief Executive Officer and Administrator, Spooner Health, Spooner, WI, p. A712

SCHAFER, Mona, Regional Manager Human Resources, Milbank Area Hospital Avera, Milbank, SD, p. A570

SCHAFFER, Megan, Administrative Assistant, Surgical Institute Of Reading, Wyomissing, PA, p. A555

SCHAFFER, Renee, Coordinator Human Resources, Select Specialty Hospital–Wichita, Wichita, KS, p. A253

SCHAFFNER, Leroy, Chief Executive Officer, Coon Memorial Hospital, Dalhart, TX, p. A604

SCHAFFNER, Richard, Senior Vice President and Chief Operating Officer, Geisinger Holy Spirit, Camp Hill, PA, p. A530

SCHAFSNITZ, Patricia, Director of Nursing Services, Mckenzie Health System, Sandusky, MI, p. A330

SCHALES, Marion, Chief Financial Officer, Highland Hospital, Oakland, CA, p. A77

SCHALL, Dee R.N., Chief Nursing Officer, Baptist Health Medical Center–Hot Spring County, Malvern, AR, p. A46

SCHALSKI, Paula, Director Human Resources, Pushmataha Hospital, Antlers, OK, p. A504

SCHAMP, Cindy K., FACHE, President, Baylor Scott & White Medical Center–Irving, Irving, TX, p. A624

SCHANDL, Brian, Chief Information Officer, Marshall Browning Hospital, Du Quoin, IL, p. A186

SCHANEL, Judith A, R.N., MSN, FACHE, Chief Operating Officer, Moses H. Cone Memorial Hospital, Greensboro, NC, p. A463

SCHANWALD, Pamela R., Chief Executive Officer, The Children's Home Of Pittsburgh, Pittsburgh, PA, p. A547

SCHAPP, Susan, Vice President Finance and Treasurer, The Charlotte Hungerford Hospital, Torrington, CT, p. A113

SCHARBER, Laurel, Administrative Assistant and Coordinator Human Resources, Kindred Hospital–Ontario, Ontario, CA, p. A77

SCHARENBROCK, Chris M.D., Chief Medical Staff, David Grant Usaf Medical Center, Travis Afb, CA, p. A94

SCHARFF, Tom, Director Information Services, University Hospital And Medical Center, Tamarac, FL, p. A144

SCHARNBERG, Cathi Rae R.N., M.P.H., Vice President Patient Services, Avera Holy Family Hospital, Estherville, IA, p. A227

SCHARNHORST, Alicia, Human Resources and Administrative Assistant, Garfield County Public Hospital District, Pomeroy, WA, p. A683

SCHARR, Vickie, Chief Financial Officer, Bakersfield Heart Hospital, Bakersfield, CA, p. A52

SCHATTSCHNEIDER, Tami, Chief Operating Officer and Chief Nursing Officer, Ripon Medical Center, Ripon, WI, p. A712

SCHAUF, Jeffrey, Director Information Systems, Wesley Medical Center, Wichita, KS, p. A254

SCHAUF, Kyle M.D., President Medical Staff, Integris Grove Hospital, Grove, OK, p. A508

SCHAUF, Victoria M.D., Chief of Staff, Ridgecrest Regional Hospital, Ridgecrest, CA, p. A82

SCHAWL, Bud, Chief Executive Officer, Kindred Hospital–Albuquerque, Albuquerque, NM, p. A424

SCHAY, Maria, Chief Information Officer, Veterans Affairs New York Harbor Healthcare System, New Rochelle, NY, p. A447

SCHEAFFEL, Margaret M.
Chief Nursing Officer, Carilion Franklin Memorial Hospital, Rocky Mount, VA, p. A675
Chief Nursing Officer, Carilion Roanoke Memorial Hospital, Roanoke, VA, p. A675

SCHEERER, Dan M.D., Chief Medical Officer, Genesis Healthcare System, Zanesville, OH, p. A503

SCHEETZ, Allison M.D., Medical Director, Rehabilitation Hospital, Navicent Health, Macon, GA, p. A161

SCHEFFLER, Tom, Chief Fiscal Officer, Veterans Affairs Maryland Health Care System–Baltimore Division, Baltimore, MD, p. A296

SCHEINBART, Lee, M.D.
Vice President Medical Affairs, Health First Community Hospitals, Health First Cape Canaveral Hospital, Cocoa Beach, FL, p. A122
Vice President Medical Affairs, Health First Community Hospitals, Health First Palm Bay Hospital, Palm Bay, FL, p. A138

SCHEINBERG, Paul M.D., Chief of Staff, Emory Saint Joseph's Hospital Of Atlanta, Atlanta, GA, p. A150

SCHEINBLUM, Richard, Chief Financial Officer, Monadnock Community Hospital, Peterborough, NH, p. A410

SCHELBAR, E Joe M.D., Medical Director, Select Specialty Hospital–Tulsa Midtown, Tulsa, OK, p. A518

SCHELL, James M.D., Vice President Medical Affairs, Saint Francis Medical Center, Cape Girardeau, MO, p. A365

SCHELL, Jonathan, Chief Nursing Officer, Drew Memorial Health System, Monticello, AR, p. A47

SCHEMER, Tonia, Interim Chief Human Resources, St. Joseph Mercy Livingston Hospital, Howell, MI, p. A322

SCHENCK, Debbie, Administrator, Omega Hospital, Metairie, LA, p. A281

SCHENKER, Amy, Human Resources Director, Shriners Hospitals For Children–Tampa, Tampa, FL, p. A145

SCHEPMANN, Jane, Vice President and Chief Nursing Officer, Clara Barton Hospital, Hoisington, KS, p. A242

SCHEPPERS, Levi, Chief Executive Officer, Orthonebraska Hospital, Omaha, NE, p. A398

SCHEPPERS, Lisa, Chief Medical Officer, Regional West Medical Center, Scottsbluff, NE, p. A399

SCHER, Kathleen Ed.D., R.N., Chief Nursing Officer, Jamaica Hospital Medical Center, New Rochelle, NY, p. A441

SCHERLE, Patricia A, Chief Nursing Officer, Memorial Hospital Of Salem County, Salem, NJ, p. A420

SCHERLER, Jay, Vice President Finance and Chief Information Officer, Providence Healthcare Network, Waco, TX, p. A652

SCHERNECK, Michael D., President and Chief Executive Officer, Southeast Georgia Health System Brunswick Campus, Brunswick, GA, p. A153

SCHERNECK, Michael D, President and Chief Executive Officer and Chief Financial Officer, Southeast Georgia Health System Camden Campus, Saint Marys, GA, p. A164

SCHEVING, Travis, Chief Financial Officer, Holy Rosary Healthcare, Miles City, MT, p. A386

SCHEXNAYDER, Glenn M.D., Chief of Staff, Prevost Memorial Hospital, Donaldsonville, LA, p. A274

SCHEY, David, Chief Financial Officer, Brook Lane Health Services, Hagerstown, MD, p. A299

SCHICK, Eric
Chief Financial Officer, Saint Francis Hospital South, Tulsa, OK, p. A518
Senior Vice President and Chief Financial Officer, Saint Francis Health System, Saint Francis Hospital, Tulsa, OK, p. A518
Senior Vice President, Chief Administrative Officer and Chief Financial Officer, Laureate Psychiatric Clinic And Hospital, Tulsa, OK, p. A517

SCHIEBER, Steven M., FACHE, Chief Executive Officer, Hedrick Medical Center, Chillicothe, MO, p. A366

SCHIEFELBEIN, Shelia, Coordinator Human Resources, Northwest Florida Community Hospital, Chipley, FL, p. A121

SCHIERECK, Stacie, Director Management Services, Mendota Mental Health Institute, Madison, WI, p. A705

SCHIESL, Troy, Director Information Services, Bellin Psychiatric Center, Green Bay, WI, p. A703

SCHIESLER, Hannah, Interim Assistant Director Human Resources, Baptist Hospitals Of Southeast Texas, Beaumont, TX, p. A597

SCHILLER, Ann Mattia, Vice President Human Resources, College Medical Center, Long Beach, CA, p. A66

SCHILLER, Jonathan, Chief Executive Officer, Catskill Regional Medical Center, Harris, NY, p. A437

SCHILLING, Helen M.D., Medical Director, Kindred Rehabilitation Hospital Northeast Houston, Humble, TX, p. A624

SCHIMEROWSKI, Deb
Chief Financial Officer, Presence United Samaritans Medical Center, Danville, IL, p. A185
Regional Chief Financial Officer, Presence St. Mary's Hospital, Kankakee, IL, p. A191
Regional Finance Officer, Presence Saint Joseph Medical Center, Joliet, IL, p. A191
Vice President Finance and Chief Financial Officer, Presence Covenant Medical Center, Urbana, IL, p. A202

SCHIMMING, Christopher M.D., Medical Director, Mayo Clinic Health System In Waseca, Waseca, MN, p. A350

SCHIMMING, Michael B
Director Financial Services, Shriners Hospitals For Children–Galveston, Galveston, TX, p. A615
Director Fiscal Services, Shriners Hospitals For Children–Houston, Houston, TX, p. A622

SCHIPPER, Brad J., Chief Operating Officer, Sanford Usd Medical Center, Sioux Falls, SD, p. A572

SCHIRALLI, Rocco, President/Chief Executive Officer, Porter–Starke Services, Valparaiso, IN, p. A221

SCHIROS, Judith
Chief Executive Officer, Continuecare Hospital At Medical Center (Odessa), Odessa, TX, p. A635
Chief Executive Officer, Continuecare Hospital At Midland Memorial, Midland, TX, p. A633

SCHLABACH, Michael M.D., Chief Medical Officer, Scott & White Hospital – Brenham, Brenham, TX, p. A599

SCHLAGER, Robert M.D., Chief Medical Officer, Sebasticook Valley Health, Pittsfield, ME, p. A292

SCHLANGEN, Greg R.N., Chief Operating Officer, Carolina Center For Behavioral Health, Greer, SC, p. A563

SCHLATTER, Christina, Chief Financial Officer, Oswego Community Hospital, Oswego, KS, p. A248

SCHLECHTER, Sandy, Chief Executive Officer, Bowdle Hospital, Bowdle, SD, p. A568

SCHLEETER, Larry C, Chief Human Resources Officer, Memorial Health, Marysville, OH, p. A495

SCHLEGEL, Patricia, Executive Director Finance, Ridgeview Le Sueur Medical Center, Le Sueur, MN, p. A342

SCHLEICHER, Larry, Manager Information Services, Warner Hospital And Health Services, Clinton, IL, p. A184

SCHLEIF, John V, Senior Vice President and Chief Operating Officer, Henry Mayo Newhall Hospital, Valencia, CA, p. A95

SCHLEMMER, Tom, Chief Financial Officer, St. Mary's Medical Center, West Palm Beach, FL, p. A147

SCHLENKER, Jim, Chief Operating Officer, Good Shepherd Health Care System, Hermiston, OR, p. A522

SCHLESKE, Brenda, Administrator, Community Behavioral Health Hospital – Fergus Falls, Fergus Falls, MN, p. A339

SCHLESSMAN, Alissa, Administrator, Beaver County Memorial Hospital, Beaver, OK, p. A505

SCHLESINGER, J. Tuerk., Chief Executive Officer, Altapointe Health Systems, Mobile, AL, p. B9

SCHLEY, Kurt, Market Chief Executive Officer, Chi St. Alexius Health, Bismarck, ND, p. A474

SCHLICHTMAN, Beth A, Manager Human Resources, Brodstone Memorial Hospital, Superior, NE, p. A400

SCHLICHTMANN, Phyllis J., Chief Executive Officer, Kessler Marlton Rehabilitation, Marlton, NJ, p. A416

SCHLIECH, Roxane K, Chief Financial Officer, Gundersen Tri–County Hospital And Clinics, Whitehall, WI, p. A716

SCHLUNTZ, Ana, Director of Human Resources, Harlan County Health System, Alma, NE, p. A390

SCHLUTER, Robin M., Chief Executive Officer, Regional Health Services Of Howard County, Cresco, IA, p. A225

SCHMACKER, Eric, President, Baptist Medical Center, San Antonio, TX, p. A642

SCHMAEDECKE, Dena, Vice President Human Resources, North Suburban Medical Center, Thornton, CO, p. A107

SCHMEDEMANN, Isabel, R.N., Chief Nursing Officer and Chief Operating Officer, Fulton Medical Center, Fulton, MO, p. A368

SCHMELLING, Robin, Chief Information Officer, Hi–Desert Medical Center, Yucca Valley, CA, p. A97

SCHMID, Nancy A. R.N., MS, Associate Director Patient Care Services, Coatesville Veterans Affairs Medical Center, Coatesville, PA, p. A532

SCHMID, Nancy, Chief Executive Officer, Healdsburg District Hospital, Healdsburg, CA, p. A63

SCHMIDT, Allen J M.D., President, Medical Staff, Decatur Morgan Hospital, Decatur, AL, p. A16

SCHMIDT, Anne, Vice President of Patient Care Services and Chief Nursing Officer, South County Hospital, Wakefield, RI, p. A557

SCHMIDT, Barbara, Chief Executive Officer, Mesa Springs, Fort Worth, TX, p. A614

SCHMIDT, Bobbi, Chief Nursing Officer, Select Specialty Hospital–Cincinnati, Cincinnati, OH, p. A484

SCHMIDT, Constance FACHE, R.N., Vice President Patient Care Services and Chief Nursing Officer, St. Mary–Corwin Medical Center, Pueblo, CO, p. A107

SCHMIDT, David R.N., Chief Nursing Officer, Jennersville Regional Hospital, West Grove, PA, p. A553

SCHMIDT, Harry M., President and Chief Executive Officer, Passavant Area Hospital, Jacksonville, IL, p. A191

SCHMIDT, Janie, Director of Nursing, Greeley County Health Services, Tribune, KS, p. A252

SCHMIDT, Joan E, Director Human Resources, Elmwood Healthcare Center At The Springs, Green Springs, OH, p. A492

SCHMIDT, Julie, Director Human Resources, Grand Itasca Clinic And Hospital, Grand Rapids, MN, p. A340

SCHMIDT, Kristin R.N., FACHE, Chief Nursing Officer, Desert Regional Medical Center, Palm Springs, CA, p. A78

SCHMIDT, Loretta, President, Plymouth Medical Center, Plymouth, IN, p. A218

SCHMIDT, Mark C., President, Lead–Deadwood Regional Hospital, Deadwood, SD, p. A569

SCHMIDT, Milan, Medical Director, North Shore Health, Grand Marais, MN, p. A340

SCHMIDT, Richard O., Jr
President and Chief Executive Officer, United Hospital System–Kenosha Campus, Kenosha, WI, p. A704
President and Chief Executive Officer, United Hospital System, St. Catherine's Medical Center Campus, Pleasant Prairie, WI, p. A710

SCHMIDT, Robert F, Director Human Resources, Hocking Valley Community Hospital, Logan, OH, p. A494

SCHMIDT, Rosanne R.N., Chief Nursing Officer, Chi St. Alexius Health, Bismarck, ND, p. A474

SCHMIDT, Steve, Director Information Systems, Evans Memorial Hospital, Claxton, GA, p. A154

SCHMIDT, Veronica, President, Custer Regional Hospital, Custer, SD, p. A569

SCHMIDT, William
Chief Executive Officer, Thedacare Medical Center–Shawano, Shawano, WI, p. A712
President and Chief Executive Officer, Thedacare Medical Center–New London, New London, WI, p. A709

SCHMIDTBERGER, Sheryl, Chief Financial Officer, Alliancehealth Ponca City, Ponca City, OK, p. A514

SCHMIEDT, Jason, Chief Financial Officer, Clinch Valley Medical Center, Richlands, VA, p. A673

SCHMIER, Joseph, Interim Director Human Resources, North Valley Hospital, Whitefish, MT, p. A389

SCHMIESING, Karee, Director of Nursing, Sleepy Eye Medical Center, Sleepy Eye, MN, p. A348

SCHMITS, Peggy, Director, Nursing Operations, New Braunfels Regional Rehabilitation Hospital, New Braunfels, TX, p. A635

SCHMITT, John, Senior Vice President and Chief Financial Officer, Kingsbrook Jewish Medical Center, New Rochelle, NY, p. A442

SCHMITT, Joseph, III
Senior Vice President Finance and Chief Financial Officer, Henry Ford Hospital, Detroit, MI, p. A318
Chief Financial Officer, Va Greater Los Angeles Healthcare System, Los Angeles, CA, p. A72
Chief Information Officer, St. Elizabeth's Medical Center, Brighton, MA, p. A304

SCHMITT, Karl M.D., Chief of Staff, St. Elizabeth Edgewood, Edgewood, KY, p. A257

SCHMITT, Peggy, President and Chief Executive Officer, North Kansas City Hospital, North Kansas City, MO, p. A374

SCHMITT, Robert C. II, Chief Executive Officer, Gibson Area Hospital And Health Services, Gibson City, IL, p. A188

SCHMITT, Thomas M., Chief Executive Officer, Kansas Spine And Specialty Hospital, Wichita, KS, p. A253

SCHMITZ, Bonnie
Chief Financial Officer, Ripon Medical Center, Ripon, WI, p. A712
Chief Financial Officer, Waupun Memorial Hospital, Waupun, WI, p. A715
Vice President and Chief Financial Officer, St. Agnes Hospital, Fond Du Lac, WI, p. A701

SCHMITZ, Christopher, Associate Vice President, Director Human Resources, Stoughton Hospital Association, Stoughton, WI, p. A713

SCHMITZ, Douglas, Director of Nursing, Long–Term Acute Care Hospital, Mosaic Life Care At St. Joseph, Saint Joseph, MO, p. A376

SCHMITZ, Jessica, Director of Nursing, Roosevelt Medical Center, Culbertson, MT, p. A383

SCHMITZ, Joseph, Chief Financial Officer, St. Cloud Veterans Affairs Health Care System, Saint Cloud, MN, p. A347

SCHMOTZER, Dave, Chief Financial Officer, Bryn Mawr Rehabilitation Hospital, Malvern, PA, p. A539

SCHMOYER, Leah, Human Resources Director, Buffalo Hospital, Buffalo, MN, p. A337

SCHMUS, Angie, Chief Information Technology, Aleda E. Lutz Veterans Affairs Medical Center, Saginaw, MI, p. A329

SCHNABEL, Annette, FACHE, President and Chief Executive Officer, Perry Memorial Hospital, Princeton, IL, p. A198

SCHNACK, Tim H
Chief Financial Officer, Chi Health Immanuel, Omaha, NE, p. A397
Chief Financial Officer, Chi Health Plainview, Plainview, NE, p. A399
Chief Financial Officer, Chi Health Schuyler, Schuyler, NE, p. A399
Vice President Financial Services, Chi Health Creighton University Medical Center – Bergan Mercy, Omaha, NE, p. A397
Vice President Operations Finance, Chi Health St. Mary's, Nebraska City, NE, p. A396

SCHNEDLER, Lisa W., FACHE, President and Chief Executive Officer, Upland Hills Health, Dodgeville, WI, p. A700

SCHNEIDER, Barbara, R.N., Chief Executive Officer, Foothill Regional Medical Center, Tustin, CA, p. A94

SCHNEIDER, Brenda, Chief Financial Officer, Skyline Hospital, White Salmon, WA, p. A689

SCHNEIDER, Brian, Chief Financial Officer, Dupont Hospital, Fort Wayne, IN, p. A208

SCHNEIDER, Carol L., President and Chief Executive Officer, Mercy Hospital And Medical Center, Chicago, IL, p. A182

SCHNEIDER, Frank, FACHE, Chief Executive Officer, Gateway Rehabilitation Hospital, Florence, KY, p. A258

SCHNEIDER, Gina, Director Human Resources, Northwest Specialty Hospital, Post Falls, ID, p. A175

SCHNEIDER, Jennifer S., Vice President of Finance, Saint Francis Hospital And Medical Center, Hartford, CT, p. A110

SCHNEIDER, Jessie, Director Human Resources, Community Memorial Healthcare, Marysville, KS, p. A246

SCHNEIDER, John, M.D.
Medical Director, Milwaukee County Behavioral Health Division, Milwaukee, WI, p. A708
Human Resources Director, Putnam Community Medical Center, Palatka, FL, p. A138

SCHNEIDER, Shanon, Chief Information Officer, Greeley County Health Services, Tribune, KS, p. A252

SCHNEIDER, Stacie A, Director Human Resources, Aurora Sheboygan Memorial Medical Center, Sheboygan, WI, p. A712

SCHNEIDER, Stephen, Manager Information Services, Alaska Psychiatric Institute, Anchorage, AK, p. A25

SCHNEIDER, Steve, Manager Behavioral Services and Director Operations, New Ulm Medical Center, New Ulm, MN, p. A345

SCHNEIDER, Steven E. M.D., Chief Medical Officer, Saint Mary's Hospital, Waterbury, CT, p. A114

SCHNEIDER, Thomas D D.O., Chief of Staff, Jack C. Montgomery Veterans Affairs Medical Center, Muskogee, OK, p. A510

SCHNEIDER, Valerie, Director Human Resources, Gove County Medical Center, Quinter, KS, p. A250

SCHNELL, Dawn
Chief Nursing Officer and Interim Senior Director, Sanford Jackson Medical Center, Jackson, MN, p. A341
Chief Nursing Officer, Sanford Jackson Medical Center, Jackson, MN, p. A341

SCHNIEDERS, Michael H., FACHE, President, Chi Health Good Samaritan, Kearney, NE, p. A394

SCHNIER, Martin D.O., Chief of Staff, West Texas Veterans Affairs Health Care System, Big Spring, TX, p. A598

SCHNITTKER, Kira, Director of Nursing, St. Vincent's Blount, Oneonta, AL, p. A22

SCHNOOR, Jeff, Director Information Systems, Swedish Medical Center, Englewood, CO, p. A102

SCHOELLER, Betsy V, Director Human Resources and Education, Mary Greeley Medical Center, Ames, IA, p. A222

SCHOEPLEIN, Kevin D., Chief Executive Officer, Osf Healthcare, Peoria, IL, p. B95

SCHOEN, Greg M.D., Regional Medical Director, Fairview Northland Medical Center, Princeton, MN, p. A346

SCHOENDALER, Hannah, Chief Nursing Officer, Sheridan County Health Complex, Hoxie, KS, p. A243

SCHOENECKER, Perry L M.D., Chief of Staff, Shriners Hospitals For Children–St. Louis, Saint Louis, MO, p. A377

SCHOENER, Timothy E
Chief Information Officer, Muncy Valley Hospital, Muncy, PA, p. A542
Senior Vice President and Chief Information Officer, Soldiers And Sailors Memorial Hospital, Wellsboro, PA, p. A553

Vice President and Chief Information Officer, Williamsport Regional Medical Center, Williamsport, PA, p. A554

SCHOENIG, Thomas
Regional Chief Information Officer, Texas Health Huguley Hospital Fort Worth South, Burleson, TX, p. A600
Regional Director Information Services, Valley Hospital Medical Center, Las Vegas, NV, p. A404

SCHOETTLE, Steve M.D., Chief Medical Staff, Ozark Health Medical Center, Clinton, AR, p. A41

SCHOFIELD, Joseph, Chief Operating Officer, Suburban Community Hospital, Norristown, PA, p. A542

SCHOFIELD, Sherry, Director Human Resources, Sovah Health–Martinsville, Martinsville, VA, p. A670

SCHOLEFIELD, Robert, MS, R.N.
Chief Operating Officer, St. Elizabeth Medical Center, Utica, NY, p. A454
Executive Vice President and Chief Operating Officer, Faxton St. Luke's Healthcare, Utica, NY, p. A454

SCHOLL, Shyanne, Interim Human Resources Director, Friend Community Healthcare System, Friend, NE, p. A393

SCHOLZ, Suzanne, Director Medical Records, Horsham Clinic, Ambler, PA, p. A529

SCHON, John, Administrator and Chief Executive Officer, Dickinson County Healthcare System, Iron Mountain, MI, p. A323

SCHONEBERY, Jeremy, Director Information Technology, Heart Of America Medical Center, Rugby, ND, p. A478

SCHONLAU, Dan
Chief Financial Officer and Vice President of Finance, Chi Health Nebraska Heart, Lincoln, NE, p. A395
Chief Financial Officer and Vice President of Finance, Chi Health St Elizabeth, Lincoln, NE, p. A395
Interim President, Chi Health Nebraska Heart, Lincoln, NE, p. A395

SCHONS, Jeri R.N., Chief Nursing Officer, Sanford Tracy Medical Center, Tracy, MN, p. A349

SCHOOL, Peggy, Director of Nursing, Thedacare Medical Center–New London, New London, WI, p. A709

SCHOOLER, Rick, Vice President and Chief Information Officer, Orlando Regional Medical Center, Orlando, FL, p. A137

SCHOOMAKER, Eric B., Surgeon General, Department Of The Army, Office Of The Surgeon General, Falls Church, VA, p. B41

SCHOPP, Mary Ellen, Senior Vice President Human Resources, Rush University Medical Center, Chicago, IL, p. A183

SCHOR, Mark, Chief Executive Officer, Belmont Behavioral Hospital, Philadelphia, PA, p. A543

SCHORER, Emily
Senior Vice President Human Resources, Cape Cod Hospital, Hyannis, MA, p. A307
Vice President, Human Resources, Falmouth Hospital, Falmouth, MA, p. A306

SCHORI, Melissa M.D., Medical Director, NYC Health + Hospitals / Lincoln, New Rochelle, NY, p. A445

SCHOTT, Connie, Vice President, Human Resources, Ozarks Medical Center, West Plains, MO, p. A381

SCHOTT, Lynn, Director Information Technology, Mobridge Regional Hospital, Mobridge, SD, p. A571

SCHOTTEL, Roxanne, Chief Executive Officer, Washington County Hospital, Washington, KS, p. A253

SCHOWENGERDT, Daniel M.D., Chief of Staff, Comanche County Hospital, Coldwater, KS, p. A239

SCHRADER, Guillermo M.D., Acting Medical Director, Eastern State Hospital, Williamsburg, VA, p. A677

SCHRAEDER, David, Director Information Systems, Russell Regional Hospital, Russell, KS, p. A250

SCHRAGE, Larry E., FACHE, Chief Executive Officer, Haxtun Hospital District, Haxtun, CO, p. A104

SCHRAMM, Michael, Chief Executive Officer, Rice Memorial Hospital, Willmar, MN, p. A350

SCHRAMM, Steven R, Chief Financial Officer, Mountain View Hospital, Payson, UT, p. A659

SCHRANK, Kenton M.D., President Medical Staff, Wilson N. Jones Regional Medical Center, Sherman, TX, p. A645

SCHREEG, Timothy M., President and Chief Executive Officer, Franciscan Health Rensselaer, Rensselaer, IN, p. A218

SCHREFFLER, Mary Jane, Director Human Resources, Meadows Psychiatric Center, Centre Hall, PA, p. A531

SCHREIBER, Anne, Manager Human Resources, Fairfax Behavioral Health, Kirkland, WA, p. A681

SCHREIBER, Elizabeth R.N., Director Patient Care Services, Flambeau Hospital, Park Falls, WI, p. A710

SCHREIER, Garett E. R.N., Associate Director, Nursing and Patient Care Services, Ralph H. Johnson Veterans Affairs Medical Center, Charleston, SC, p. A559

SCHREINER, David L., FACHE, President and Chief Executive Officer, Katherine Shaw Bethea Hospital, Dixon, IL, p. A185

SCHREINER, Jim, Chief Information Officer, Graham Hospital Association, Canton, IL, p. A179

SCHRIER, Erick, Supervisor Information Technology, Van Diest Medical Center, Webster City, IA, p. A236

SCHROCK, Bonnie W FACHE, Chief Operating Officer, Baptist Health Paducah, Paducah, KY, p. A266

SCHRODER, Loren D, Chief Financial Officer, Phelps Memorial Health Center, Holdrege, NE, p. A394

SCHROEDER, Brian D. M.D., Senior Vice President and Chief Medical Officer, Sparrow Hospital, Lansing, MI, p. A324

SCHROEDER, Catherine, Deputy Chief Information Officer, Brigham And Women's Faulkner Hospital, Boston, MA, p. A303

SCHROEDER, Cygnet D.O., Medical Director, Healthsouth Rehabilitation Hospital Of Fort Smith, Fort Smith, AR, p. A43

SCHROEDER, Destiny, Information Systems Director, Rawlins County Health Center, Atwood, KS, p. A238

SCHROEDER, Heather R.N., Vice President Nursing, Aurora Baycare Medical Center, Green Bay, WI, p. A702

SCHROEDER, Joanne
President and Chief Executive Officer, Bronson South Haven Hospital, South Haven, MI, p. A331
President, Munson Healthcare Charlevoix Hospital, Charlevoix, MI, p. A316

SCHROEDER, Rick, Chief Executive Officer, North Big Horn Hospital District, Lovell, WY, p. A719

SCHROEDER, Russell, Chief Nursing Officer, St. Anthony's Medical Center, Saint Louis, MO, p. A378

SCHROEDER, Steve M.D., Chief of Staff, Avera Hand County Memorial Hospital, Miller, SD, p. A571

SCHROEDL, Greg M.D., Vice President, Medical and Chief Medical Officer, Uw Medicine/Northwest Hospital & Medical Center, Seattle, WA, p. A686

SCHROEPPEL, Stacie, Director of Human Resources, Baptist Memorial Rehabilitation Hospital, Germantown, TN, p. A579

SCHROYER, Amy, Vice President Administration and Senior Site Executive, Daniel Drake Center For Post Acute Care, Cincinnati, OH, p. A484

SCHROYER, Mike, FACHE, MSN, R.N., President, St. Vincent Anderson Regional Hospital, Anderson, IN, p. A203

SCHRUMPF, Jason, President, Missouri Delta Medical Center, Sikeston, MO, p. A379

SCHUBACH, Michael, Director Human Resources, Carroll County Memorial Hospital, Carrollton, MO, p. A366

SCHUCK, Jennifer, Associate Administrator, Emory University Hospital, Atlanta, GA, p. A150

SCHUCKMAN, Tim, Chief Financial Officer, Jennie M. Melham Memorial Medical Center, Broken Bow, NE, p. A391

SCHUE, Janine
Executive Vice President, Chief Human Resources Officer, Rochester Regional Health, Newark–Wayne Community Hospital, Newark, NY, p. A447
Senior Vice President Human Resources, Rochester General Hospital, Rochester, NY, p. A451

SCHUELER, Joe, Chief Financial Officer, Morrow County Hospital, Mount Gilead, OH, p. A496

SCHUERCH, Timothy, President and Chief Executive Officer, Maniilaq Health Center, Kotzebue, AK, p. A26

SCHUESSLER, Dwight, Chief Information Officer, Iowa City Veterans Affairs Health Care System, Iowa City, IA, p. A229

SCHUETT, Susan M, Chief Information Officer, Olmsted Medical Center, Rochester, MN, p. A347

SCHUH, Jason M.D., Chief of Staff, Wise Health System, Decatur, TX, p. A607

SCHUITEMAN, Jackson, Chief Financial Officer, Sioux Center Health, Sioux Center, IA, p. A235

SCHULER, Allison R.N., Chief Nursing Officer, Baptist Medical Center Attala, Kosciusko, MS, p. A357

SCHULER, Kathy R.N., MS, Vice President of Patient Care Services, Winchester Hospital, Winchester, MA, p. A313

SCHULTE, Mark, FACHE, President, Sturgis Regional Hospital, Sturgis, SD, p. A573

SCHULTES, Jeremy, Administrator and Chief Executive Officer, Philip Health Services, Philip, SD, p. A571

SCHULTHEIS, Hal, Director Information Systems, Tristar Hendersonville Medical Center, Hendersonville, TN, p. A580

SCHULTZ, Bradley, Chief Financial Officer, Wesley Medical Center, Wichita, KS, p. A254

SCHULTZ, David W., FACHE
Market President, Peninsula Region, Harrison Medical Center, Bremerton, WA, p. A678
President, Penisula Region, St. Anthony Hospital, Gig Harbor, WA, p. A681

SCHULTZ, Jacky, MSN, R.N., President, Suburban Hospital, Bethesda, MD, p. A297

SCHULTZ, Jim, Chief Executive Officer, Edgerton Hospital And Health Services, Edgerton, WI, p. A701

SCHULTZ, Kurt
Chief Financial Officer, Cornerstone Hospital–West Monroe, West Monroe, LA, p. A287

Chief Financial Officer, Solara Hospital Harlingen, Harlingen, TX, p. A618

Group Chief Financial Officer, Chg Hospital Tucson, Llc, Tucson, AZ, p. A37

SCHULTZ, Mary Kay, Director Human Resources, Sturgis Hospital, Sturgis, MI, p. A331

SCHULTZ, Merrilee, Chief Finance, Sanford Usd Medical Center, Sioux Falls, SD, p. A572

SCHULTZ, Rachelle H., Ed.D., President and Chief Executive Officer, Winona Health, Winona, MN, p. A350

SCHULTZ, Sharon A MSN, R.N., M.P.H., Chief Nurse Executive and Vice President, Tri–City Medical Center, Oceanside, CA, p. A77

SCHULTZ, Teresa L R.N., Vice President of Patient Care, Rogers Memorial Hospital, Oconomowoc, WI, p. A709

SCHULTZ, Vince M.D., Chief Medical Officer, Munson Healthcare Grayling Hospital, Grayling, MI, p. A321

SCHULZ, Ken, Chief Operating Officer, North Dakota State Hospital, Jamestown, ND, p. A477

SCHULZ, Leah, Director of Nursing, North Dakota State Hospital, Jamestown, ND, p. A477

SCHULZ, Marcie, Director Patient Care, Sakakawea Medical Center, Hazen, ND, p. A476

SCHULZ, Patricia, Chief Human Resource Officer, Children's Hospital And Medical Center, Omaha, NE, p. A397

SCHULZ, Susan G, Director Patient Care Services, Beaumont Hospital – Trenton, Trenton, MI, p. A332

SCHUMACHER, Ann, R.N., MSN, FACHE, President, Chi Health Immanuel, Omaha, NE, p. A397

SCHUMACHER, Debbie
Chief Human Resource Officer, Clearwater Valley Hospital And Clinics, Orofino, ID, p. A175
Chief Human Resource Officer, St. Mary's Hospital, Cottonwood, ID, p. A173

SCHUMACHER, Kevin, Director of Information Systems, Lifecare Medical Center, Roseau, MN, p. A347

SCHUMACHER, Larry P., R.N., MSN, Chief Executive Officer, Chi Memorial, Chattanooga, TN, p. A576

SCHUMACHER, Larry P, R.N., MSN, Chief Executive Officer, Chi Memorial, Chattanooga, TN, p. A576

SCHUMACHER, Paul, Chief Operating Officer, Mcleod Health Clarendon, Manning, SC, p. A564

SCHUMACHER, Rodney, Chief Executive Officer, Eastern New Mexico Medical Center, Roswell, NM, p. A428

SCHUMANN, Vera, Director of Finance and Controller, North Shore Health, Grand Marais, MN, p. A340

SCHURKAMP, Christine, Senior Human Resources Business Partner, Spectrum Health Gerber Memorial, Fremont, MI, p. A320

SCHUSTER, Carol E R.N., Chief Nursing Officer and Vice President Patient Care Services, Franciscan St. Anthony Health – Crown Point, Crown Point, IN, p. A206

SCHUSTER, Christine C., R.N., President and Chief Executive Officer, Emerson Hospital, Concord, MA, p. A306

SCHUSTER, Emmett C., President and Chief Executive Officer, Gibson General Hospital, Princeton, IN, p. A218

SCHUSTER, Janet, Chief Nursing Officer, Lutheran Hospital, Cleveland, OH, p. A486

SCHUSTER, Jolene, Chief Financial Officer, Grisell Memorial Hospital District One, Ransom, KS, p. A250

SCHUSTER, Lexie, Vice President Human Resources, Good Samaritan Hospital, Los Angeles, CA, p. A68

SCHUSTER, Todd, Administrator, Saint Francis Hospital Vinita, Vinita, OK, p. A519

SCHUSTER, Tony, M.D.
Vice President of Physician Services, Mease Countryside Hospital, Safety Harbor, FL, p. A141
Vice President of Physician Services, Mease Dunedin Hospital, Dunedin, FL, p. A124

SCHWAB, Bob M.D., Chief Medical Officer, Texas Health Presbyterian Hospital Allen, Allen, TX, p. A591

SCHWAB, Caryn A, Executive Director, Mount Sinai Hospital, New Rochelle, NY, p. A443

SCHWABENBAUER, Mary Ann, Director Information Technology, Penn Highlands Elk, Saint Marys, PA, p. A549

SCHWAEGEL, Glen
Chief Financial Officer, Progress West Hospital, O'Fallon, MO, p. A374
Vice President and Chief Financial Officer, Barnes–Jewish St. Peters Hospital, Saint Peters, MO, p. A379

SCHWAGER, Mary A, Director Human Resources, Antelope Memorial Hospital, Neligh, NE, p. A396

SCHWALL, Garry, Chief Operating Officer, NYU Winthrop Hospital, Mineola, NY, p. A439

SCHWAN, Joni, Director Human Resources, Excelsior Springs Hospital, Excelsior Springs, MO, p. A367

SCHWAN, Karin, Chief Nursing Officer, Vice President Patient Care Services, University Hospitals Samaritan Medical Center, Ashland, OH, p. A480

SCHWANER, Charles III, Chief Financial Officer, Doctors Hospital Of Sarasota, Sarasota, FL, p. A142

SCHWANKE, Daniel, Interim President, Promedica Monroe Regional Hospital, Monroe, MI, p. A326

SCHWARM, Tony, President, Missouri Baptist Sullivan Hospital, Sullivan, MO, p. A380

SCHWARTZ, Ave, Chief Information Officer, Austen Riggs Center, Stockbridge, MA, p. A312

SCHWARTZ, David M D.O., Vice President, Medical Affairs, Sentara Northern Virginia Medical Center, Woodbridge, VA, p. A677

SCHWARTZ, David, M.D.
Chief Medical Officer, Saint Francis Hospital–Bartlett, Bartlett, TN, p. A575
Chief Medical Officer, Saint Francis Hospital, Memphis, TN, p. A585

SCHWARTZ, Jonathon M.D., Chief Medical Officer, Spaulding Hospital For Continuing Medical Care Cambridge, Cambridge, MA, p. A305

SCHWARTZ, Kenneth V M.D., Medical Director, Griffin Hospital, Derby, CT, p. A110

SCHWARTZ, Kim, Assistant Administrator of Human Resources and Outpatient Services, Boone County Hospital, Boone, IA, p. A223

SCHWARTZ, Michael M.D., Chief of Staff, College Hospital Costa Mesa, Costa Mesa, CA, p. A56

SCHWARTZ, Mitchell B M.D., Chief Medical Officer, Anne Arundel Medical Center, Annapolis, MD, p. A294

SCHWARTZ, Peggy, Vice President Human Resources, Wayne Healthcare, Greenville, OH, p. A492

SCHWARTZ, Peter
Director Information Systems, East Mountain Hospital, Belle Mead, NJ, p. A411
Director of Information Systems, Carrier Clinic, Belle Mead, NJ, p. A411

SCHWARTZ, Roberta, Ph.D., Executive Vice President, Houston Methodist Hospital, Houston, TX, p. A620

SCHWARTZ, Ronald M.D., Medical Director, Masonicare Health Center, Wallingford, CT, p. A113

SCHWARTZ, Sharon, Director Medical Records, Scott & White Hospital – Brenham, Brenham, TX, p. A599

SCHWARTZ, Stephanie L., FACHE, President, Chilton Medical Center, Pompton Plains, NJ, p. A419

SCHWARZ, John, Vice President Administration, Lankenau Medical Center, Wynnewood, PA, p. A555

SCHWARZBACH, Jerry M.D., Medical Director, East Texas Medical Center Rehabilitation Hospital, Tyler, TX, p. A650

SCHWARZKOPF, Ruth R.N., Chief Nursing Officer, West Boca Medical Center, Boca Raton, FL, p. A120

SCHWEBLER, Michael W., President and Chief Executive Officer, Dearborn County Hospital, Lawrenceburg, IN, p. A214

SCHWECHHEIMER, Betsy L, Chief Operating Officer, Tewksbury Hospital, Tewksbury, MA, p. A312

SCHWEICKHARDT, Mary Jo, Vice President Human Resources, Medstar Georgetown University Hospital, Washington, DC, p. A117

SCHWEIGERT, Nicole, Director Human Resources, Texas Health Presbyterian Hospital Flower Mound, Flower Mound, TX, p. A612

SCHWEIGHART, Karen, R.N., MS, Administrator, Andrew Mcfarland Mental Health Center, Springfield, IL, p. A200

SCHWEIKART, Jay
Chief Financial Officer, Kindred Hospital Chicago–Northlake, Northlake, IL, p. A195
Chief Financial Officer, Kindred Hospital–Sycamore, Sycamore, IL, p. A201

SCHWEITZER, Michael M.D., Chief Medical Officer, St. Vincent Healthcare, Billings, MT, p. A382

SCHWIEGER, Kay, Chief Human Resources Officer, Clement J. Zablocki Veterans Affairs Medical Center, Milwaukee, WI, p. A707

SCHWIND, David, Chief Financial Officer, Capital Hospice, Arlington, VA, p. A664

SCHWINGLER, Joyce, Chief Financial Officer, Eureka Community Health Services Avera, Eureka, SD, p. A569

SCIARRA, Michael M.D., Chief Medical Officer, Meadowlands Hospital Medical Center, Secaucus, NJ, p. A420

SCIARRO, Jason
President and Chief Operating Officer, Centegra Hospital – Mchenry, Mchenry, IL, p. A193
President and Chief Operating Officer, Centegra Hospital – Woodstock, Woodstock, IL, p. A202

SCIMECA, Paul, Senior Vice President Operations and Chief Operating Officer, Glens Falls Hospital, Glens Falls, NY, p. A436

SCIONTI, Jeff, Chief Executive Officer, Parkland Medical Center, Derry, NH, p. A407

SCIOSCIA, Angela M.D., Chief Medical Officer, Uc San Diego Health, San Diego, CA, p. A86

SCLAMA, Tony M.D., Vice President Medical Affairs, Medstar Franklin Square Medical Center, Baltimore, MD, p. A295

SCOFIELD, Mark M.D., Chief Medical Officer, Shelby Baptist Medical Center, Alabaster, AL, p. A13

SCOGGIN, Terry
Chief Financial Officer, Titus Regional Medical Center, Mount Pleasant, TX, p. B634
Interim Chief Executive Officer, Titus Regional Medical Center, Mount Pleasant, TX, p. B634

SCOGGINS, James, Director of Nursing, Arkansas State Hospital, Little Rock, AR, p. A45

SCOGGINS, Mib, Chief Executive Officer, Mcleod Health Cheraw, Cheraw, SC, p. A559

SCOGNA, Stephen, President and Chief Executive Officer, Northwest Community Hospital, Arlington Heights, IL, p. A177

SCOPELLITI, Joseph A., M.D., President and Chief Executive Officer, Guthrie Clinic, Sayre, PA, p. B55

SCORZELLI, Gerard, Chief Financial Officer, Albany Stratton Veterans Affairs Medical Center, Albany, NY, p. A430

SCOTFORD, Lucrecia, Executive Vice President and Chief Operations Officer, Bristol Bay Area Health Corporation, Dillingham, AK, p. A26

SCOTT, Colleen M, Vice President Finance, Waterbury Hospital, Waterbury, CT, p. A114

SCOTT, Craig, Interim Director Management Information Systems, University Of Miami Hospital, Miami, FL, p. A134

SCOTT, Damien, Chief Information Officer, Emanuel Medical Center, Swainsboro, GA, p. A165

SCOTT, Daniel, Director of Information Systems, Good Samaritan Hospital, Vincennes, IN, p. A221

SCOTT, David W., President and Chief Executive Officer, Ohio Valley Hospital, Mckees Rocks, PA, p. A540

SCOTT, Doug, Director Human Resources, RMC Jacksonville, Jacksonville, AL, p. A19

SCOTT, Ernie, Director Human Resources, Natchitoches Regional Medical Center, Natchitoches, LA, p. A282

SCOTT, Henry, Executive Director, Technical Services, Piedmont Newnan Hospital, Newnan, GA, p. A162

SCOTT, James, M.D.
Vice President Medical Affairs, Candler Hospital, Savannah, GA, p. A164
Vice President Medical Affairs, St. Joseph's Hospital, Savannah, GA, p. A165

SCOTT, Jeffrey, Chief Information Officer, St. Vincent Kokomo, Kokomo, IN, p. A213

SCOTT, Jennifer, Director of Informatics, Carepartners Health Services, Asheville, NC, p. A457

SCOTT, Jo Ellen R.N., MS, Senior Vice President of Patient Care Services and Chief Nursing Officer, Indiana University Health Tipton Hospital, Tipton, IN, p. A220

SCOTT, Joseph F., FACHE, President and Chief Executive Officer, Jersey City Medical Center, Jersey City, NJ, p. A415

SCOTT, Julie, Chief Nursing Officer, Healthsouth Rehabilitation Hospital Of York, York, PA, p. A555

SCOTT, Karen M, Vice President Patient Care, Frank R. Howard Memorial Hospital, Willits, CA, p. A97

SCOTT, Lincoln, Vice President Human Resources, Southeast Hospital, Cape Girardeau, MO, p. A366

SCOTT, M Daryl, Assistant Vice President, Jefferson Regional Medical Center, Pine Bluff, AR, p. A48

SCOTT, Margie A., M.D., Director, Central Arkansas Veterans Healthcare System, Little Rock, AR, p. A46

SCOTT, Martha Lynn, Chief Patient Care Officer, Covington County Hospital, Collins, MS, p. A354

SCOTT, Monica, Chief Financial Officer, Great Plains Regional Medical Center, Elk City, OK, p. A507

SCOTT, Paul M.D., Chief of Staff, Hudson Hospital And Clinic, Hudson, WI, p. A704

SCOTT, Rhonda A Ph.D., R.N., Chief Nursing Officer and Executive Vice President, Grady Memorial Hospital, Atlanta, GA, p. A150

SCOTT, Robert F, Vice President and Chief Human Resources Officer, Memorial Medical Center, Springfield, IL, p. A200

SCOTT, Roger D.O., Vice President Medical Affairs and Chief Medical Officer, Cortland Regional Medical Center, Cortland, NY, p. A434

SCOTT, Sam, Vice President Financial Services, St. Dominic–Jackson Memorial Hospital, Jackson, MS, p. A357

SCOTT, Sharon, Health Information Director, Allegiance Specialty Hospital Of Greenville, Greenville, MS, p. A355

SCOTT, Steve, Chief Operating Officer, Sheridan Community Hospital, Sheridan, MI, p. A330

SCOTT, Steven M., Interim Chief Executive Officer, Upstate University Hospital, Syracuse, NY, p. A453

SCOTT, Susan, Chief Nurse Executive, Ventura County Medical Center, Ventura, CA, p. A96

SCOTT, Thomas W., Senior Vice President and Chief Operating Officer, Centrastate Healthcare System, Freehold, NJ, p. A414

SCOTT, Tina, Acting Health Director, Choctaw Health Center, Philadelphia, MS, p. A360

SCOTT, Todd, Chief Financial Officer, Vibra Hospital Of Sacramento, Folsom, CA, p. A59

SCOTT, Travis, Chief Financial Officer, Lawton Indian Hospital, Lawton, OK, p. A509

SCOTT, Veronica, Business Office Manager, Midwest City Specialty Hospital, Midwest City, OK, p. A510

SCOTT, William P M.D., Chief of Staff, River Valley Medical Center, Dardanelle, AR, p. A42

SCOTT, William, M.D.
Vice President Medical Affairs, Regional Medical Center Of San Jose, San Jose, CA, p. A88
Chief Financial Officer, Promise Hospital Of Overland Park, Overland Park, KS, p. A249

SCOTTO, Dan, Director Information Technology, Eastern Long Island Hospital, Greenport, NY, p. A436

SCOUFOS, Jennifer M.D., Chief of Staff, Northeastern Health System Sequoyah, Sallisaw, OK, p. A515

SCOVILL, Terry, Chief Executive Officer, Intracare North Hospital, Houston, TX, p. A621

SCOWN, Kent, Director Operations and Information Services, Jerold Phelps Community Hospital, Garberville, CA, p. A61

SCREMIN, Karen, Vice President Finance, Lutheran Medical Center, Wheat Ridge, CO, p. A108

SCRIVO, Joseph A Jr, Director Human Resources, Mercy Hospital, Buffalo, NY, p. A433

SCROGGIN, Christy, Chief Operating Officer, Conway Regional Rehabilitation Hospital, Conway, AR, p. A41

SCROGGS, Amy, Chief Nursing Officer, Delano Regional Medical Center, Delano, CA, p. A57

SCRUGGS, Sherry, Administrator, Milan General Hospital, Milan, TN, p. A585

SCUDDER, Angela MSN, R.N., Vice President Patient Care Services, Dearborn County Hospital, Lawrenceburg, IN, p. A214

SCUDERI, Denise, Vice President Patient Care Services, Mayo Regional Hospital, Dover——Foxcroft, ME, p. A291

SCULL, Stephen W, Vice President Ethics and Compliance officer, Rapides Regional Medical Center, Alexandria, LA, p. A269

SCULLY, Charles
Chief Information Officer, Honorhealth Scottsdale Thompson Peak Medical Center, Scottsdale, AZ, p. A36
Chief Information Officer, Renown Regional Medical Center, Reno, NV, p. A405

SCULLY, Kem, Chief Executive Officer and Chief Nursing Officer, Purcell Municipal Hospital, Purcell, OK, p. A515

SCULLY, Trish
Director Human Resources, Taunton State Hospital, Taunton, MA, p. A312
Manager Employment Services, Pappas Rehabilitation Hospital For Children, Canton, MA, p. A305

SCZYGELSKI, Sidney C, Senior Vice President Finance and Chief Financial Officer, Aspirus Wausau Hospital, Inc., Wausau, WI, p. A715

SEAGER, Jerry, Assistant Vice President and Chief Financial Officer, Inova Fair Oaks Hospital, Fairfax, VA, p. A666

SEAGO, Terri, Chief Financial Officer, Baptist Memorial Hospital–Collierville, Collierville, TN, p. A577

SEAGRAM, Patricia, Vice President Human Resources, Henry Ford Allegiance Health, Jackson, MI, p. A323

SEAGROVES, Matthew, Chief Financial Officer, Bayfront Health Brooksville, Brooksville, FL, p. A121

SEAHORN, Martha, Chief Nursing Officer, Gadsden Regional Medical Center, Gadsden, AL, p. A18

SEAL, John, Director Human Resources, Riverside Medical Center, Franklinton, LA, p. A275

SEAL, Ronald T., Chief Executive Officer, Texoma Medical Center, Denison, TX, p. A608

SEALE, Corey A, Chief Operating Officer, Kaiser Permanente Moreno Valley Medical Center, Moreno Valley, CA, p. A75

SEALE, Jonathan, Chief Information Officer, Erie Veterans Affairs Medical Center, Erie, PA, p. A534

SEALE, Julie, Administrator, Christus Santa Rosa Health System, San Antonio, TX, p. A642

SEALS, Molly
System Vice President, HR Program Delivery, Mercy Health – St. Elizabeth Youngstown Hospital, Youngstown, OH, p. A503
System Vice President, Human Resources Program Delivery and Youngstown Market, Mercy Health – St. Elizabeth Boardman Hospital, Boardman, OH, p. A481

SEALS, Robert D.O., Medical Director, Sparrow Carson Hospital, Carson City, MI, p. A316

SEALS-BARNES, Sylvia II, Director Human Resources, Adventist Health St. Helena, Saint Helena, CA, p. A84

SEAMON, Robert L., Chief Executive Officer, Clifton–Fine Hospital, Star Lake, NY, p. A452

SEARLE, Anne, Chief Information Officer, University Medical Center Of Princeton At Plainsboro, Plainsboro, NJ, p. A419

SEARLS, Barbara, Chief Financial Officer, Searhc Mt. Edgecumbe Hospital, Sitka, AK, p. A27

SEARS, Erin Clare, Associate Director of Operations, Providence Veterans Affairs Medical Center, Providence, RI, p. A557

SEARS, Marilyn
Chief Financial Officer, Shelby Memorial Hospital, Shelbyville, IL, p. A200
President and Chief Executive Officer, Shelby Memorial Hospital, Shelbyville, IL, p. A200

SEASE, Peggy, Vice President Human Resources, Dch Regional Medical Center, Tuscaloosa, AL, p. A23

SEATON, Tracy, Director of Nursing, Taylorville Memorial Hospital, Taylorville, IL, p. A201

SEAVER, Roger E., President and Chief Executive Officer, Henry Mayo Newhall Hospital, Valencia, CA, p. A95

SEBASTIAN, Peggy A., MSN, R.N., President and Chief Executive Officer, Hshs St. Elizabeth's Hospital, Belleville, IL, p. A178

SEBEK, Brenda Jean R.N., Administrator, Chi Health St. Mary's, Nebraska City, NE, p. A396

SEBENALER, Ginette, Associate Chief Financial Officer, Aspen Valley Hospital, Aspen, CO, p. A98

SECK, Nancy K, Chief Nursing Officer, Mesa View Regional Hospital, Mesquite, NV, p. A404

SECKINGER, Mark R., President, O'Bleness Memorial Hospital, Athens, OH, p. A480

SECOR, April R.N., Chief Nursing Officer, Hillcrest Hospital Henryetta, Henryetta, OK, p. A508

SECOR, Diane K, Director Human Resources, Lawrence Medical Center, Moulton, AL, p. A21

SECURRO, Matthew J., Vice President, Human Resources, Conway Medical Center, Conway, SC, p. A561

SEDA, Jolene R, Vice President People and Culture, Virginia Mason Memorial, Yakima, WA, p. A689

SEDMINIK, Vince, Chief Executive Officer, Springhill Medical Center, Springhill, LA, p. A286

SEEDER, Rachael, Controller, Santiam Hospital, Stayton, OR, p. A527

SEEKINS, DeAnne, Director, Durham Veterans Affairs Medical Center, Durham, NC, p. A461

SEELEY, Kevin, Chief Information Officer, Mike O'Callaghan Federal Hospital, Nellis Afb, NV, p. A404

SEELEY, Pam, Chief Nursing Officer, Elmira Psychiatric Center, Elmira, NY, p. A435

SEELEY, Steven
Interim President and Chief Operating Officer, Jupiter Medical Center, Jupiter, FL, p. A129
Vice President, Chief Operating Officer, Chief Nursing Officer, Jupiter Medical Center, Jupiter, FL, p. A129

SEELY, Paula, Manager Human Resources, Kossuth Regional Health Center, Algona, IA, p. A222

SEEMS, Steven, Director of Information Technology, Phillips County Hospital, Phillipsburg, KS, p. A250

SEESE, Rebecca, Chief Operating Officer, U.S. Air Force Regional Hospital, Elmendorf Afb, AK, p. A26

SEEVER, Jennifer, Regional Chief Financial Officer, Sedan City Hospital, Sedan, KS, p. A251

SEGAL, Jonathan, Chief Financial Officer, New York State Psychiatric Institute, New Rochelle, NY, p. A444

SEGAL, Rebecca, Chief Executive Officer, Rutherford Regional Health System, Rutherfordton, NC, p. A470

SEGAL, Stanton M.D., Chief Medical Officer, Aria – Jefferson Health, Philadelphia, PA, p. A543

SEGAL, Tanya, Director, Easton Hospital, Easton, PA, p. A533

SEGAR–MILLER, Cindy, Chief Executive Officer, Williamson Memorial Hospital, Williamson, WV, p. A697

SEGER, LaDonna, Director Information Services, Saint Luke's North Hospital – Barry Road, Kansas City, MO, p. A371

SEGIN, Robert
Chief Financial Officer, Virtua Memorial, Mount Holly, NJ, p. A416
Executive Vice President & Chief Financial Officer, Virtua Marlton, Marlton, NJ, p. A416

SEGURA, Ezra, Chief Executive Officer, Utah Valley Specialty Hospital, Provo, UT, p. A659

SEGURA, Mario, Director of Nursing, Starr County Memorial Hospital, Rio Grande City, TX, p. A640

SEHRT, Lori
Associate Chief Financial Officer Northern Colorado, Banner Fort Collins Medical Center, Fort Collins, CO, p. A102
Chief Financial Officer, Mckee Medical Center, Loveland, CO, p. A106

SEIBERT, Jenee, Director Finance, Fulton County Health Center, Wauseon, OH, p. A502

SEIBERT, Nancy, Director Human Resources, Franklin Hospital District, Benton, IL, p. A178

SEIBOLD, Spencer Garrett M.D., Chief of Medical Staff, Power County Hospital District, American Falls, ID, p. A171

SEID, Lynette, Area Chief Financial Officer, Kaiser Permanente San Diego Medical Center, San Diego, CA, p. A85

SEIDL, Doris A, Vice President Human Resources, Mclaren Port Huron, Port Huron, MI, p. A328

SEIDLER, Richard A., FACHE
President and Chief Executive Officer, Unitypoint Health – Trinity Bettendorf, Bettendorf, IA, p. A222
President and Chief Executive Officer, Unitypoint Health – Trinity Rock Island, Rock Island, IL, p. A199

SEIDMAN, Robert
Chief Operating Officer, Health Alliance Hospital – Broadway Campus, Kingston, NY, p. A438
Chief Operating Officer, Health Alliance Hospital – Mary's Avenue Campus, Kingston, NY, p. A438

SEIFER, Jill, Vice President Human Resources, Oaklawn Psychiatric Center, Goshen, IN, p. A209

SEIFERT, Debra A, Director Human Resources, Lake Huron Medical Center, Port Huron, MI, p. A328

SEILER, Gregory A, Chief Executive Officer, Methodist Hospital, San Antonio, TX, p. A643

SEIM, Kay E., Chief Executive Officer, Aurora Santa Rosa Hospital, Santa Rosa, CA, p. A91

SEIM, Lori R.N., Director Nursing Services, First Care Health Center, Park River, ND, p. A478

SEIRER, Jeff, Interim Chief Financial Officer, Via Christi Hospital On St. Francis, Wichita, KS, p. A254

SEITZ, Kimberly A, Area Human Resources Leader, Kaiser Permanente Redwood City Medical Center, Redwood City, CA, p. A82

SEITZ, Stewart R., Chief Executive Officer, Gladys Spellman Specialty Hospital And Nursing Center, Cheverly, MD, p. A297

SEITZ, Tawnya, Chief Financial Officer, Lincoln County Hospital, Lincoln, KS, p. A246

SELBY, Eric R.N., Chief Nursing Officer, Chicot Memorial Medical Center, Lake Village, AR, p. A45

SELBY, Victoria MHA, BSN,, Vice President, Ancillary and Support Services, Community Hospital Of San Bernardino, San Bernardino, CA, p. A85

SELF, Chris, Chief Operating Officer, Manchester Memorial Hospital, Manchester, KY, p. A264

SELF, Joshua, Chief Executive Officer, Mary Black Health System – Gaffney, Gaffney, SC, p. A562

SELFRIDGE, Tara, Manager Human Resources, Purcell Municipal Hospital, Purcell, OK, p. A515

SELHORST, Sonya R.N., Administrator and Chief Nursing Officer, Mercy Hospital Of Defiance, Defiance, OH, p. A490

SELIG, Doug R MSN, R.N., Vice President of Patient Services, Parkview Huntington Hospital, Huntington, IN, p. A210

SELIGA, Patricia R.N., Chief Nursing Officer, Moses Taylor Hospital, Scranton, PA, p. A550

SELIGMAN, Joel, President and Chief Executive Officer, Northern Westchester Hospital, Mount Kisco, NY, p. A440

SELIGMAN, Morris H M.D., Chief Medical Officer and Chief Medical Information Officer, Sycamore Shoals Hospital, Elizabethton, TN, p. A578

SELL, Paula, Director Human Resources, Allen County Regional Hospital, Iola, KS, p. A243

SELL, Teri, Payroll and Personnel Coordinator, Jennie M. Melham Memorial Medical Center, Broken Bow, NE, p. A391

SELLARDS, Michael G., President and Chief Executive Officer, St. Mary's Medical Center, Huntington, WV, p. A693

SELLE, Ginger, Vice President Patient Care Services, St. Clare Hospital, Baraboo, WI, p. A698

SELLE, Justin, Chief Executive Officer, Pike County Memorial Hospital, Louisiana, MO, p. A372

SELLERS, Laura, Director Information Systems, Youth Villages Inner Harbour Campus, Douglasville, GA, p. A157

SELLERS, Mary, Chief Information Officer, Navos, Seattle, WA, p. A685

SELLERS, Robert R.
Chief Executive Officer, Optim Medical Center – Jenkins, Millen, GA, p. A162
Chief Executive Officer, Optim Medical Center – Screven, Sylvania, GA, p. A165

SELLHEIM, Kevin, Administrator, Sleepy Eye Medical Center, Sleepy Eye, MN, p. A348

SELLS, Alicia, Interim Chief Nursing Officer, Shenandoah Medical Center, Shenandoah, IA, p. A234

SELLS, Anita, Director Human Resources, Galesburg Cottage Hospital, Galesburg, IL, p. A188

SELLS, Matt CPA, Chief Financial Officer, Shenandoah Medical Center, Shenandoah, IA, p. A234

SELMAN, J Peter., FACHE, Chief Executive Officer, Baptist Medical Center South, Montgomery, AL, p. A21

SELMON, Patricia, Director Public Relations and Chief Human Resources, Jefferson County Hospital, Fayette, MS, p. A354

SELNER, Ralph, Chief Executive Officer, Kindred Hospital Central Tampa, Tampa, FL, p. A145

SELPH, Wendy, Director Human Resources, Dodge County Hospital, Eastman, GA, p. A157

SELSOR, Doug, Director Finance, Select Rehabilitation Hospital Of Denton, Denton, TX, p. A608

SELTZER, Paul M.D., Chief of Staff, JFK Medical Center North Campus, West Palm Beach, FL, p. A147

SELVAM, A Panneer M.D., Chief of Staff, Northern Arizona Veterans Affairs Health Care System, Prescott, AZ, p. A34

SELVIDGE, Sandra, Chief Fiscal Service, Cincinnati Veterans Affairs Medical Center, Cincinnati, OH, p. A484

SELZ, Timothy P, Vice President, Orange Regional Medical Center, Middletown, NY, p. A439

SEMAR, Dale, Controller, Pauls Valley General Hospital, Pauls Valley, OK, p. A514

SEMELSBERGER, Kimberly CPA, Chief Financial Officer, Conemaugh Nason Medical Center, Roaring Spring, PA, p. A549

SEMERDJIAN, Nancy R.N., Chief Nursing Officer, Northshore University Health System, Evanston, IL, p. A187

SEMERE, Jana
Chief Nursing Officer, Leonard J. Chabert Medical Center, Houma, LA, p. A276
Chief Nursing Officer, Ochsner St. Anne General Hospital, Raceland, LA, p. A284

SEMEYN, Janice D.O., President, Medical Staff, Clarion Hospital, Clarion, PA, p. A531

SEMINARO, Anthony, Chief Financial Officer, Mercy Health – St. Elizabeth Youngstown Hospital, Youngstown, OH, p. A503

SEMINGSON, John H., Chief Executive Officer, Ruby Valley Hospital, Sheridan, MT, p. A388

SEMRAD, Lou, Interim Chief Executive Officer, Jefferson Hospital, Louisville, GA, p. A160

SEMRAU, Clint, Chief of Staff, Western Wisconsin Health, Baldwin, WI, p. A698

SENDAYDIEGO, Fe, Director Information Systems, Sonoma Valley Hospital, Sonoma, CA, p. A92

SENGER, Richard, Chief Financial Officer, Portsmouth Regional Hospital, Portsmouth, NH, p. A410

SENGER, Tricia, Chief Financial Officer, St. Luke's Elmore, Mountain Home, ID, p. A174

SENKER, Margaret, Chief Information Officer, Veterans Affairs Western New York Healthcare System–Buffalo Division, Buffalo, NY, p. A433

SENKER, Thomas J., FACHE, President, Medstar Montgomery Medical Center, Olney, MD, p. A300

SENNEFF, Robert G., FACHE, President and Chief Executive Officer, Graham Hospital Association, Canton, IL, p. A179

SENNETT, Paul, Chief Financial Officer, Centinela Hospital Medical Center, Inglewood, CA, p. A63

SENNISH, James, Vice President Human Resources, Firelands Regional Health System, Sandusky, OH, p. A499

SENSAT, Marsha R.N., Chief Nursing Officer, Pikes Peak Regional Hospital, Woodland Park, CO, p. A108

SENSING, Phillip, Chief Financial Officer, South Bay Hospital, Sun City Center, FL, p. A143

SEPP, Howard W. Jr, Vice President and Administrator, Southeast Georgia Health System Camden Campus, Saint Marys, GA, p. A164

SERAFIN, Deborah J, Vice President Human Resources, Mount St. Mary's Hospital And Health Center, Lewiston, NY, p. A438

SERAPHINE, Jeffrey G., FACHE, President, Duke Lifepoint Healthcare, Brentwood, TN, p. B47

SERENO, Joseph, Chief Financial Officer, Lovelace Women's Hospital, Albuquerque, NM, p. A424

SERFLING, G Aubrey., President and Chief Executive Officer, Eisenhower Medical Center, Rancho Mirage, CA, p. A81

SERKETICH, Steve, Manager Information Services, Aurora Sheboygan Memorial Medical Center, Sheboygan, WI, p. A712

SERLE, John, FACHE
President and Chief Executive Officer, Lourdes Counseling Center, Richland, WA, p. A684
President and Chief Executive Officer, Lourdes Medical Center, Pasco, WA, p. A683

SERNYAK, Michael, M.D., Director, Connecticut Mental Health Center, New Haven, CT, p. A112

SERRANO, Jorge L Matta., Administrator, Auxilio Mutuo Hospital, San Juan, PR, p. A725

SERRANO, Lorenzo, Chief Executive Officer, Winkler County Memorial Hospital, Kermit, TX, p. A626

SERRATT, Jim, Chief Executive Officer, Westpark Springs, Richmond, TX, p. A640

SERZAN, Megan, Director of Quality, Compliance, Risk & Safety, Asheville Specialty Hospital, Asheville, NC, p. A457

SESSIONS, Jerry W. M.D., Chief Medical Staff, Springhill Medical Center, Springhill, LA, p. A286

SESSLER, Connie, Director Human Resources, St. Luke's Hospital, Maumee, OH, p. A495

SESTERHENN, Steven, Vice President, Unitypoint Health – Waterloo, Waterloo, IA, p. A236

SETCHEL, David P., President, St. Francis Health, Topeka, KS, p. A252

SETHI, Sanjiv M.D., Medical Director, Fulton State Hospital, Fulton, MO, p. A368

SETHNEY, Julie R.N., Vice President Patient Care, Fairview Ridges Hospital, Burnsville, MN, p. A337

SETLIFF, Chad, President and Chief Operating Officer, Novant Health Forsyth Medical Center, Winston, NC, p. A473

SETTERBURG, Stephen, M.D., President, Prairiecare – Brooklyn Park, Brooklyn Park, MN, p. A337

SETTLE, Andrea, Director Human Resources, Taylor Regional Hospital, Campbellsville, KY, p. A256

SETTLES, Allicia, Chief Nursing Officer, East Texas Medical Center–Quitman, Quitman, TX, p. A639

SETTLES, April, Chief Financial Officer, Greene County General Hospital, Linton, IN, p. A215

SETTLES, Jimmie, Interim President and Chief Executive Officer, Continuing Care Hospital, Lexington, KY, p. A261

SETTLES, Laura, Director Human Resources, Baylor Medical Center At Garland, Garland, TX, p. A616

SETZER, Jeffery, Administrator Information Systems, J. D. Mccarty Center For Children With Developmental Disabilities, Norman, OK, p. A511

SETZER, Randy R, Financial Services Manager, Waukesha County Mental Health Center, Waukesha, WI, p. A714

SETZKORN–MEYER, Marsha, Director Public Relations and Marketing, Hillsboro Community Hospital, Hillsboro, KS, p. A242

SEVCO, Mark
President, Upmc East, Monroeville, PA, p. A541
President, Upmc Mckeesport, Mckeesport, PA, p. A540

SEVERANCE, Matthew J., FACHE, Chief Executive Officer, Roper St. Francis, Charleston, SC, p. A559

SEVILLA, Mark, Executive Director, Yale–New Haven Hospital, New Haven, CT, p. A112

SEVILLIAN, Clarence, President and Chief Executive Officer, Mclaren Bay Region, Bay City, MI, p. A315

SEWALLS, Travis, Chief Medical Officer, Baptist Health Madisonville, Madisonville, KY, p. A264

SEWATSKY, Mary M.D., Chief Medical Officer, Moses Taylor Hospital, Scranton, PA, p. A550

SEWELL, Lance, Chief Financial Officer, South Lake Hospital, Clermont, FL, p. A122

SEWELL, Sue, Chief Nursing Officer, Wise Health System, Decatur, TX, p. A607

SEWICK, Alayne, Vice President Human Resources, Medical City Mckinney, Mckinney, TX, p. A632

SEXTON, Charles, Manager Human Resources, Cumberland Medical Center, Crossville, TN, p. A578

SEXTON, Cindy, Chief Financial Officer, St. David's Round Rock Medical Center, Round Rock, TX, p. A641

SEXTON, Kevin, Director Information Systems, Raleigh General Hospital, Beckley, WV, p. A690

SEXTON, William P., Chief Executive Officer, Crossing Rivers Health Medical Center, Prairie Du Chien, WI, p. A711

SEYMOUR, Barbara, Vice President of Nursing, Health First Holmes Regional Medical Center, Melbourne, FL, p. A132

SEYMOUR, Claudette, Director Personnel, Memphis Mental Health Institute, Memphis, TN, p. A584

SEYMOUR, Jose, Chief Information Resource Management, James A. Haley Veterans' Hospital–Tampa, Tampa, FL, p. A144

SEYMOUR, Ryan, Chief Executive Officer, Baylor Institute For Rehabilitation At Frisco, Frisco, TX, p. A615

SEYMOUR, Sally, Chief Operating Officer, Fawcett Memorial Hospital, Port Charlotte, FL, p. A140

SGARLATA, Lisa, MSN
Chief Patient Care Officer, Cape Coral Hospital, Cape Coral, FL, p. A121
Chief Patient Care Officer, Gulf Coast Medical Center, Fort Myers, FL, p. A125

SHACKELFORD, Gerald, Staff Support Specialist, Texas Center For Infectious Disease, San Antonio, TX, p. A644

SHACKELFORD, J. Larry., President and Chief Executive Officer, Washington Regional Medical Center, Fayetteville, AR, p. A43

SHACKELFORD, Paul M.D., Chief Medical Officer, Vidant Medical Center, Greenville, NC, p. A463

SHACKLETON, Carol M.D., Medical Director, Gothenburg Health, Gothenburg, NE, p. A393

SHADENSACK, Don, Vice President Clinical Services, OSF St. Mary Medical Center, Galesburg, IL, p. A188

SHADOWEN, Michael M.D., Chief of Staff, T. J. Samson Community Hospital, Glasgow, KY, p. A259

SHADOWENS, Karen, Director Finance and Chief Financial Officer, West Chester Hospital, West Chester, OH, p. A502

SHAFER, Robert
Vice President Finance, Mercy Medical Center–Dubuque, Dubuque, IA, p. A227
Vice President Finance, Mercy Medical Center–Dyersville, Dyersville, IA, p. A227

SHAFER, Timothy M.D., Medical Director, Grace Cottage Hospital, Townshend, VT, p. A663

SHAFICI, Khaled M.D., President Medical Staff, Cornerstone Hospital–West Monroe, West Monroe, LA, p. A287

SHAFIU, Mohamed M.D., Chief of Staff, Val Verde Regional Medical Center, Del Rio, TX, p. A608

SHAH, Beena M.D., Chief of Staff and Chief Medical Officer, Anaheim Global Medical Center, Anaheim, CA, p. A51

SHAH, Jayendra H M.D., Chief Medical Officer, Southern Arizona Veterans Affairs Health Care System, Tucson, AZ, p. A38

SHAH, Paresh, Director Information Systems, Reston Hospital Center, Reston, VA, p. A673

SHAH, Syed M.D., Chief of Staff, Pioneer Memorial Hospital And Health Services, Viborg, SD, p. A573

SHAH, Vital, M.D., Chief Executive Officer and Chief Medical Officer, Central State Hospital, Louisville, KY, p. A262

SHAHAN, Matthew, Chief Executive Officer, West River Regional Medical Center, Hettinger, ND, p. A476

SHAHI, Niloo, Chief Operating Officer, Lac–Olive View–Ucla Medical Center, Los Angeles, CA, p. A69

SHAHNAM, Melissa Shreves, Director Human Resources, Mon Health Medical Center, Morgantown, WV, p. A694

SHAHEEN, Jim, President, Strategic Behavioral Health, Llc, Memphis, TN, p. B122

SHAHRYAR, Syed M.D., Medical Director, Promise Hospital Of Phoenix, Mesa, AZ, p. A32

SHAHZADA, Kamran M.D., Chief Medical Staff, South Central Kansas Medical Center, Arkansas City, KS, p. A238

SHAIFFER, Mandy, Chief Nursing Officer, Mt. San Rafael Hospital, Trinidad, CO, p. A108

SHAKOOR, Arif, Chief of Staff, Raulerson Hospital, Okeechobee, FL, p. A136

SHALLOCK, James R, Chief Financial Officer, Memorial Hermann Greater Heights Hospital, Houston, TX, p. A621

SHAMBURG, Steffen M.D., Chief of Staff, Hiawatha Community Hospital, Hiawatha, KS, p. A242

SHAMMAS, Karen, Chief Executive Officer, Curahealth Phoenix, Phoenix, AZ, p. A33

SHANAHAN, Thomas
Chief Financial Officer and Senior Vice President, Hackensack Meridian Health Raritan Bay Medical Center, Perth Amboy, NJ, p. A419
Vice President, Human Resources, Children's Hospital Of Wisconsin–Fox Valley, Neenah, WI, p. A708
Vice President, Human Resources, Children's Hospital Of Wisconsin, Milwaukee, WI, p. A707

SHAND, Natalie M.D., Vice President Integrative Medicine and Chief Medical Officer, Scottsdale Liberty Hospital, Scottsdale, AZ, p. A36

SHANER, Patricia, Interim Chief Human Resources Officer, Ogallala Community Hospital, Ogallala, NE, p. A396

SHANLEY, Diane, Deputy Service Unit Director, U.S. Public Health Service Indian Hospital–Sells, Sells, AZ, p. A36

SHANLEY, Linda L., Vice President, Chief Information Officer, Saint Francis Hospital And Medical Center, Hartford, CT, p. A110

SHANNON, David A., President and Chief Executive Officer, Jersey Shore Hospital, Jersey Shore, PA, p. A537

SHANNON, Greg
Chief Human Resources Officer, Golden Valley Memorial Healthcare, Clinton, MO, p. A366
Interim Chief Executive Officer, Two Rivers Behavioral Health System, Kansas City, MO, p. A371

SHANNON, John Jay., M.D.
Chief Executive Officer, John H. Stroger Jr. Hospital Of Cook County, Chicago, IL, p. A181
Chief Executive Officer, Provident Hospital Of Cook County, Chicago, IL, p. A183

SHANNON, Patrick, Chief Operating Officer, Baptist Hospitals Of Southeast Texas, Beaumont, TX, p. A597

SHANNON, Richard M.D., Chief of Staff, Montrose Memorial Hospital, Montrose, CO, p. A106

SHANNON, Scott, Director Finance, Socorro General Hospital, Socorro, NM, p. A429

SHAPE, Amy, Information Technology, North Dakota State Hospital, Jamestown, ND, p. A477

SHAPIRO, David, M.D.
Vice President Medical Affairs and Chief Medical Officer, Columbia St. Mary's Hospital Milwaukee, Milwaukee, WI, p. A707

Vice President Medical Affairs and Chief Medical Officer, Columbia St. Mary's Ozaukee Hospital, Mequon, WI, p. A707

Vice President Medical Affairs and Chief Medical Officer, Sacred Heart Rehabilitation Institute, Milwaukee, WI, p. A708

SHAPIRO, Louis A., President and Chief Executive Officer, Hospital For Special Surgery, New Rochelle, NY, p. A441

SHAPIRO, Marc M.D., Chief Medical Officer, St. Helena Hospital Clear Lake, Clearlake, CA, p. A56

SHAPIRO, Steven D, M.D.
Chief Medical Officer, Bon Secours St. Francis Hospital, Charleston, SC, p. A558
Chief Medical Officer, Roper St. Francis Mount Pleasant Hospital, Mount Pleasant, SC, p. A564
Vice President Medical Affairs, Roper St. Francis, Charleston, SC, p. A559

SHAPPLEY, Robert, Chief Operating Officer, Lakewood Regional Medical Center, Lakewood, CA, p. A65

SHARANGPANI, Rojesh M.D., Chief of Staff, Capital Medical Center, Olympia, WA, p. A683

SHARBER–HOWELL, Sheryl, Administrator, Creek Nation Community Hospital, Okemah, OK, p. A511

SHARKEY, Linda R.N., MSN, Vice President Patient Care Services and Chief Nurse Executive, Fauquier Hospital, Warrenton, VA, p. A676

SHARLOW, Joseph M.D., Chief of Staff, Ste. Genevieve County Memorial Hospital, Ste Genevieve, MO, p. A380

SHARMA, Adhi M.D., Chief Medical Officer, South Nassau Communities Hospital, Oceanside, NY, p. A448

SHARMA, Aika M.D., President Medical Staff, Alameda Hospital, Alameda, CA, p. A51

SHARMA, Chandra M.D., Chief of Staff, Welch Community Hospital, Welch, WV, p. A696

SHARMA, Roger, Executive Vice President/Chief Financial Officer, Citrus Valley Medical Center–Inter Community Campus, Covina, CA, p. A57

SHARMA, Satish C M.D., Chief of Staff, Providence Veterans Affairs Medical Center, Providence, RI, p. A557

SHARON, Joesph P., Associate Director, Wilkes–Barre Veterans Affairs Medical Center, Wilkes, PA, p. A554

SHARON, Sandy, Senior Vice President and Area Manager, Kaiser Permanente Sacramento Medical Center, Sacramento, CA, p. A83

SHARP, Alan
Chief Financial Officer, Saint Thomas Dekalb Hospital, Smithville, TN, p. A589
Chief Financial Officer, Saint Thomas Stones River Hospital, Woodbury, TN, p. A590

SHARP, Cheryl, Chief Financial Office, Miami County Medical Center, Paola, KS, p. A249

SHARP, Cindy M.D., Chief Medical Officer, Madison Valley Medical Center, Ennis, MT, p. A384

SHARP, Gina, FACHE, President and Chief Executive Officer, Linden Oaks Hospital, Naperville, IL, p. A195

SHARP, John K, Chief Financial Officer, Seton Medical Center Harker Heights, Harker Heights, TX, p. A618

SHARP, Julie, Supervisor Human Resources, Chase County Community Hospital, Imperial, NE, p. A394

SHARP, Patrick, Chief Operating Officer, Range Regional Health Services, Hibbing, MN, p. A341

SHARP, Rebecca, Chief Financial Officer, Wagoner Community Hospital, Wagoner, OK, p. A519

SHARP, Rhian, Director Human Resources, Anchor Hospital, Atlanta, GA, p. A149

SHARP, Richard M.D., Medical Director, Christus St. Michael Rehabilitation Hospital, Texarkana, TX, p. A649

SHARP, Stacy, Coordinator Human Resources, Atoka County Medical Center, Atoka, OK, p. A504

SHARP, Tanya, President and Chief Executive Officer, Boone County Health Center, Albion, NE, p. A390

SHARP, Tony, Supervisor Information System, Sweetwater Hospital, Sweetwater, TN, p. A589

SHARPE, Deborah R.N., Director of Nursing, West Springs Hospital, Grand Junction, CO, p. A103

SHARPTON, Debra, Director of Nursing, Devereux Georgia Treatment Network, Kennesaw, GA, p. A160

SHARTLE, William, Senior Vice President Human Resources, Geisinger Holy Spirit, Camp Hill, PA, p. A530

SHARUM, Gary, Administrator, Mercy Hospital Tishomingo, Tishomingo, OK, p. A517

SHARUM, Melinda
Director Human Resources, Mercy Hospital Ardmore, Ardmore, OK, p. A504
Director Human Resources, Mercy Hospital Healdton, Healdton, OK, p. A508

SHARY, Dave, Administrator Human Resources, Ridgecrest Regional Hospital, Ridgecrest, CA, p. A82

SHATRAW, Thomas, Director Human Resources, Samaritan Medical Center, Watertown, NY, p. A455

SHAUGHNESSY, John, Chief Financial Officer, Mcleod Health Clarendon, Manning, SC, p. A564

SHAUGHNESSY, Mary
Vice President Finance, Spaulding Hospital For Continuing Medical Care Cambridge, Cambridge, MA, p. A305
Vice President Finance, Spaulding Rehabilitation Hospital Cape Cod, East Sandwich, MA, p. A306
Vice President Finance, Spaulding Rehabilitation Hospital, Charlestown, MA, p. A305

SHAULL, Ty, Chief Operating Officer, Wyandot Memorial Hospital, Upper Sandusky, OH, p. A501

SHAUNESSY, Celia, Vice President Human Resources, Ministry Saint Michael's Hospital, Stevens Point, WI, p. A713

SHAVER, Chris
Vice President Human Resources, Covenant Medical Center, Lubbock, TX, p. A630
Vice President Human Resources, Covenant Specialty Hospital, Lubbock, TX, p. A630

SHAVER, Jennifer
Director of Nursing, Gouverneur Hospital, Gouverneur, NY, p. A436
Director of Nursing, Lewis County General Hospital, Lowville, NY, p. A438

SHAVER, John, Chief Financial Officer, Baystate Noble Hospital, Westfield, MA, p. A312

SHAVER, Robert D M.D., Vice President Medical Affairs, Wellspan Good Samaritan Hospital, Lebanon, PA, p. A539

SHAW, David B., Chief Executive Officer and Administrator, Nor–Lea Hospital District, Lovington, NM, p. A427

SHAW, David
Director Information Technology, Forrest City Medical Center, Forrest City, AR, p. A43
Vice President Information Systems, Eskenazi Health, Indianapolis, IN, p. A211

SHAW, Douglas A., Chief Executive Officer, Mad River Community Hospital, Arcata, CA, p. A52

SHAW, Gary, President, Cambridge Medical Center, Cambridge, MN, p. A337

SHAW, Greg, Vice President, Finance, Aspirus Medford Hospital & Clinics, Inc., Medford, WI, p. A706

SHAW, Howard M.D., Chief Medical Officer, Medical City Denton, Denton, TX, p. A608

SHAW, Jan, Director Personnel, River Bend Hospital, West Lafayette, IN, p. A221

SHAW, Jean, Chief Financial Officer, Valley Regional Hospital, Claremont, NH, p. A407

SHAW, John C M.D., Medical Director, Southern Indiana Rehabilitation Hospital, New Albany, IN, p. A217

SHAW, Kathy, Chief Executive Officer, Haven Senior Horizons, Phoenix, AZ, p. A33

SHAW, Kendra, Chief Information Officer, Western Wisconsin Health, Baldwin, WI, p. A698

SHAW, Kimberly
Chief Operating Officer, St. Rose Dominican Hospitals – Siena Campus, Henderson, NV, p. A402
Vice President Patient Care and Chief Nursing Executive, Mercy Medical Center Redding, Redding, CA, p. A81

SHAW, Mandy M.D., Chief of Staff, Sidney Regional Medical Center, Sidney, NE, p. A400

SHAW, Patrick D., Chief Executive Officer, Grafton City Hospital, Grafton, WV, p. A692

SHAW, Violet R.N., Director of Nursing, Grafton City Hospital, Grafton, WV, p. A692

SHAW, Terry, President and Chief Executive Officer, Adventist Health System Sunbelt Health Care Corporation, Altamonte Springs, FL, p. B6

SHAWAN, Christy, Chief Executive Officer, Black River Medical Center, Poplar Bluff, MO, p. A375

SHAWGO, Darla, Director Human Resources, Sparta Community Hospital, Sparta, IL, p. A200

SHAWN, D.J., Director Human Resources, Alliancehealth Madill, Madill, OK, p. A509

SHEA, Drew, Chief Financial Officer, Baylor Scott & White Medical Center – White Rock, Dallas, TX, p. A604

SHEA, Kevin M.D., Chief of Staff, Carolinas Hospital System, Florence, SC, p. A561

SHEA, Natalie, Chief Nursing Officer, Central Community Hospital, Elkader, IA, p. A227

SHEAFF, Charles M.D., President Medical Staff, Passavant Area Hospital, Jacksonville, IL, p. A191

SHEAR, Larry, Administrative Assistant, Norwood Health Center, Marshfield, WI, p. A706

SHEARER, Christopher M.D., Chief Medical Officer, Honorhealth John C. Lincoln Medical Center, Phoenix, AZ, p. A33

SHEARER, Laura R.N., MSN, Senior Vice President and Chief Nursing Officer, Phoebe Putney Memorial Hospital, Albany, GA, p. A149

SHEARER, Ron M.D., Regional Medical Director, Peacehealth Peace Harbor Medical Center, Florence, OR, p. A521

SHEARN, Daniel R.N., MSN, Vice President Patient Services and Chief Nursing Officer, Upmc Northwest, Seneca, PA, p. A550

SHEARS, Ann Marie, Vice President Patient Care Services, Robert Wood Johnson University Hospital Rahway, Rahway, NJ, p. A419

SHECKLER, Robert L., Administrator, Avera Gettysburg Hospital, Gettysburg, SD, p. A570

SHEEHAN, Karen, Vice President and Chief Information Officer, Swedish Covenant Hospital, Chicago, IL, p. A184

SHEEHAN, T J, Chief Financial Officer, Lauderdale Community Hospital, Ripley, TN, p. A588

SHEEHAN, Terrence P M.D., Medical Director, Adventist Healthcare Physical Health And Rehabilitation, Rockville, MD, p. A300

SHEEHY, Earl Nielsen., Chief Executive Officer, Ray County Memorial Hospital, Richmond, MO, p. A375

SHEEHY, Joseph, Chief Executive Officer and Managing Director, The Pavilion, Champaign, IL, p. A180

SHEERIN, Cathy R.N., MS, Director Patient Care Services, Glen Cove Hospital, Glen Cove, NY, p. A436

SHEERIN, Rick
Chief Financial Officer, Polk Medical Center, Cedartown, GA, p. A154
Vice President Fiscal Services, Floyd Medical Center, Rome, GA, p. A163

SHEETS, Cindy, Vice President Information Systems and Chief Information Officer, Ohiohealth Medcentral Mansfield Hospital, Mansfield, OH, p. A494

SHEETS, Jim, Chief Executive Officer and Administrator, LDS Hospital, Salt Lake City, UT, p. A660

SHEFFIELD, Aubrey, Administrative Assistant Human Resources and Public Relations, Grove Hill Memorial Hospital, Grove Hill, AL, p. A19

SHEFFIELD, Nichol, Chief Executive Officer, Pacific Grove Hospital, Riverside, CA, p. A82

SHEFIELD, Jennifer M.D., Chief of Staff, West River Regional Medical Center, Hettinger, ND, p. A476

SHEFTE, David H., Chief Executive Officer, Healthsouth Rehabilitation Hospital Of Littleton, Littleton, CO, p. A105

SHEGOLEV, Igor, Vice President Human Resources, Carondelet St. Joseph's Hospital, Tucson, AZ, p. A37

SHEHAN, Mary R.N., MSN, Senior Vice President and Chief Nursing Officer, Swedish Covenant Hospital, Chicago, IL, p. A184

SHEHATA, Nady M.D., Vice President Medical Affairs, Sisters Of Charity Hospital Of Buffalo, Buffalo, NY, p. A433

SHEHI, G Michael., M.D., Chief Executive Officer, Mountain View Hospital, Gadsden, AL, p. A18

SHEHI, G Michael M.D., Medical Director, Mountain View Hospital, Gadsden, AL, p. A18

SHEHI, Jay
Chief Executive Officer, Alliance Health Center, Meridian, MS, p. A359
Chief Executive Officer, Rivendell Behavioral Health Services Of Arkansas, Benton, AR, p. A40

SHEIKH, Arsalan, Chief of Medicine, Bon Secours Baltimore Health System, Baltimore, MD, p. A294

SHEINBEIN, David, Chief Medical Officer, Banner – University Medical Center South, Tucson, AZ, p. A37

SHELAK, Matt, Interim Chief Executive Officer, Jennersville Regional Hospital, West Grove, PA, p. A553

SHELBURNE, John D M.D., Chief of Staff, Durham Veterans Affairs Medical Center, Durham, NC, p. A461

SHELBY, Dennis R., Chief Executive Officer, Wilson Medical Center, Neodesha, KS, p. A247

SHELBY, Joyce, Manager Human Resources, Hardin County General Hospital, Rosiclare, IL, p. A199

SHELDEN, Diana, Chief Nursing Officer, Stone County Medical Center, Mountain View, AR, p. A47

SHELDON, Ed, Warden and Chief Executive Officer, Oakwood Correctional Facility, Lima, OH, p. A493

SHELDON, Lyle Ernest., FACHE
President and Chief Executive Officer, University Of Maryland Harford Memorial Hospital, Havre De Grace, MD, p. A299
President and Chief Executive Officer, University Of Maryland Upper Chesapeake Medical Center, Bel Air, MD, p. A296

SHELDON, Mo P., FACHE, Chief Executive Officer and Administrator, Odessa Memorial Healthcare Center, Odessa, WA, p. A683

SHELDON, Richard M.D., Vice President Medical Affairs, San Gorgonio Memorial Hospital, Banning, CA, p. A53

SHELFORD, Dave, Assistant Superintendent, Richmond State Hospital, Richmond, IN, p. A219

SHELL, John M.D., Chief Medical Officer, Coffey County Hospital, Burlington, KS, p. A239

SHELL, Steve, Chief Executive Officer, Desert Parkway Behavioral Healthcare Hospital, Las Vegas, NV, p. A403

SHELLENBERGER, David, President, St. John Vianney Hospital, Downingtown, PA, p. A533

SHELT, Elizabeth, Civilian Personnel Officer, Dwight David Eisenhower Army Medical Center, Fort Gordon, GA, p. A158

SHELTON, Amy, Chief Nursing Officer, St. Vincent's East, Birmingham, AL, p. A15

SHELTON, Angela, Chief Financial Officer, Jack Hughston Memorial Hospital, Phenix City, AL, p. A22

SHELTON, Carol, Director Human Resources, Lovelace Women's Hospital, Albuquerque, NM, p. A424

SHELTON, Darlene, Coordinator Team Resources, Baycare Alliant Hospital, Dunedin, FL, p. A124

SHELTON, Jared, Chief Executive Officer, Texas Health Presbyterian Hospital Allen, Allen, TX, p. A591

SHELTON, Jeffrey, Chief Executive Officer, Hiawatha Community Hospital, Hiawatha, KS, p. A242

SHELTON, Kathy, Director Human Resources, East Texas Medical Center Pittsburg, Pittsburg, TX, p. A637

SHELTON, Mark, Chief of Staff, Winn Parish Medical Center, Winnfield, LA, p. A288

SHELTON, Richard M.D., Chief Medical Officer, Baptist Health Richmond, Richmond, KY, p. A267

SHELTON, Tom, Coordinator of Nursing Services, Porterville Developmental Center, Porterville, CA, p. A80

SHELVOCK, Kathy R.N., Assistant Administrator Patient Care Services, Fairchild Medical Center, Yreka, CA, p. A97

SHEN, Mark W., M.D., President and Chief Executive Officer, Dell Children's Medical Center Of Central Texas, Austin, TX, p. A595

SHENDELL–FALIK, Nancy R.N., Senior Vice President, Chief Operating Officer and Chief Nursing Officer, Baystate Medical Center, Springfield, MA, p. A311

SHENDELL–FALIK, Nancy, President, Baystate Medical Center, Springfield, MA, p. A311

SHENGLE, Lori, Director Information Technology, Morrill County Community Hospital, Bridgeport, NE, p. A391

SHEPARD, Bridget, Vice President Human Resources, Wabash General Hospital, Mount Carmel, IL, p. A194

SHEPARD, Karen, Senior Vice President and Chief Financial Officer, St. Charles Prineville, Prineville, OR, p. A526

SHEPARD, Megan, Director Clinical Services, Odessa Memorial Healthcare Center, Odessa, WA, p. A683

SHEPARD, Sheila, Controller, Healthsouth Rehabilitation Hospital Of Humble, Llc, Humble, TX, p. A624

SHEPARDSON, Dean, Chief Financial Officer, Banner Estrella Medical Center, Phoenix, AZ, p. A33

SHEPARDSON, Heather S, Vice President Human Resources, Carilion Roanoke Memorial Hospital, Roanoke, VA, p. A675

SHEPHARD, Bryan, Chief Financial Officer, Tristar Summit Medical Center, Hermitage, TN, p. A580

SHEPHARD, Russ, Senior Systems Analyst, Tennova Healthcare Dyersburg Regional Medical Center, Dyersburg, TN, p. A578

SHEPHERD, Laura, Director Human Resources, Texas Health Huguley Hospital Fort Worth South, Burleson, TX, p. A600

SHEPHERD, Linda M., Chief Nursing Officer, Lewisgale Hospital Pulaski, Pulaski, VA, p. A673

SHEPHERD, Thomas, Executive Vice President and Chief Operating Officer, Gwinnett Hospital System, Lawrenceville, GA, p. A160

SHEPLER, Mary R.N., Vice President and Chief Nursing Officer, Saint Joseph Hospital, Denver, CO, p. A101

SHEPPARD, Sandy, Vice President Patient Services, Wake Forest Baptist Health – Wilkes Medical Center, North Wilkesboro, NC, p. A468

SHEPPARD, Sharon, Manager Human Resources, Sycamore Shoals Hospital, Elizabethton, TN, p. A578

SHEPPARD, Varinya R.N., Chief Nursing Officer, St. Elizabeth Medical Center, Utica, NY, p. A454

SHERBONDY, Beverly, Assistant Vice President, Human Resources, Jeanes Hospital, Philadelphia, PA, p. A544

SHERBONDY, Lori, Director Human Resources, Battle Mountain General Hospital, Battle Mountain, NV, p. A401

SHERER, Janet, Chief of Patient Care Services, Springfield Hospital, Springfield, VT, p. A663

SHERER, Susan, Chief Information Resource Management, Dayton Veterans Affairs Medical Center, Dayton, OH, p. A489

SHERIDAN, Cheryl R.N., Senior Vice President Patient Care Services, Rochester General Hospital, Rochester, NY, p. A451

SHERIDAN, Elizabeth
Chief Operating Officer and Chief Nursing Executive, Inspira Medical Center–Elmer, Elmer, NJ, p. A413
Chief Operating Officer and Chief Nursing Executive, Inspira Medical Center–Vineland, Vineland, NJ, p. A422

SHERIDAN, Kolbe, Chief Operating Officer, Heartland Regional Medical Center, Marion, IL, p. A192

SHERIDAN, Phil, Chief Executive Officer, Beckett Springs, West Chester, OH, p. A502

SHERIF, Ali M.D., Chief of Staff, Lea Regional Medical Center, Hobbs, NM, p. A426

SHERMAN, Angelina R.N., MSN, Chief Nursing Officer, The Rehabilitation Institute Of St. Louis, Saint Louis, MO, p. A378

SHERMAN, Frederick C M.D., Chief Medical Officer, The Children's Home Of Pittsburgh, Pittsburgh, PA, p. A547

SHERMAN, Sheila, Vice President Patient Care Services, Vail Valley Health Hospital, Vail, CO, p. A108

SHERMAN, Stephanie, Chief Human Resources Officer, West Boca Medical Center, Boca Raton, FL, p. A120

SHERON, William E., Chief Executive Officer, Wooster Community Hospital, Wooster, OH, p. A503

SHERRILL, Angela
Chief Information Officer, Laird Hospital, Union, MS, p. A362
Corporate Director Information System, Rush Foundation Hospital, Meridian, MS, p. A359
Corporate Director Information System, Specialty Hospital Of Meridian, Meridian, MS, p. A359

SHERROD, Michael, Chief Executive Officer, Tristar Greenview Regional Hospital, Bowling Green, KY, p. A256

SHERROD, Rhonda Kay., R.N., MSN
Administrator, Shands Lake Shore Regional Medical Center, Lake City, FL, p. A130
Interim Chief Executive Officer, Shands Live Oak Regional Medical Center, Live Oak, FL, p. A131

SHERRON, Tammy M, Vice President Finance, Carolinaeast Health System, New Bern, NC, p. A468

SHERRY, Mark A., Director Human Resources, Baylor Scott & White Medical Center – Round Rock, Round Rock, TX, p. A640

SHERWIN, Charles H
Chief Nursing Officer, Midmichigan Medical Center – Alpena, Alpena, MI, p. A314
Vice President of Business Development and Clinical Services, Midmichigan Medical Center – Alpena, Alpena, MI, p. A314

SHERWOOD, Edward J, M.D., Chief Executive Officer, Cornerstone Hospital Of Austin, Austin, TX, p. A594

SHERWOOD, Jennifer L, Division, Human Resource Business Partner, Banner – University Medical Center South, Tucson, AZ, p. A37

SHERWOOD, Matthew M, Chief Financial Officer, Unity Medical & Surgical Hospital, Mishawaka, IN, p. A216

SHETTLESWORTH, Amanda, Director Human Resources, Bloomington Meadows Hospital, Bloomington, IN, p. A204

SHETTY, Atul, Chief of Staff, Weirton Medical Center, Weirton, WV, p. A696

SHEW, Angel, Director Area Technology, Kaiser Permanente South San Francisco, South San Francisco, CA, p. A92

SHEWBRIDGE, Richard K., M.D., President, Cleveland Clinic, Medina Hospital, Medina, OH, p. A495

SHEYKA, Patricia, Chief Nursing Officer, Gila Regional Medical Center, Silver City, NM, p. A429

SHICKOLOVICH, William, Chief Information Officer, Tufts Medical Center, Boston, MA, p. A304

SHIELDS, Charlie, President and Chief Executive Officer, Truman Medical Center–Hospital Hill, Kansas City, MO, p. A371

SHIELDS, Diane, Chief Human Resources Officer, Midmichigan Medical Center – Alpena, Alpena, MI, p. A314

SHIELDS, Stuart, Director, G. Werber Bryan Psychiatric Hospital, Columbia, SC, p. A560

SHIFF, Mary Treacy, Chief Financial Officer, Kindred Chicago–Central Hospital, Chicago, IL, p. A181

SHIFFERMILLER, William M.D., Vice President Medical Affairs, Nebraska Methodist Hospital, Omaha, NE, p. A398

SHIHADY, Sharon, Director Human Resources, Spire Cane Creek Rehabilitation Hospital, Martin, TN, p. A583

SHILKAITIS, Mary, Vice President Patient Care and Chief Nursing Officer, Rush–Copley Medical Center, Aurora, IL, p. A178

SHILLING, Angie, Chief Executive Officer, Baum Harmon Mercy Hospital, Primghar, IA, p. A233

SHILLING, Stacy, Controller, St. Vincent Rehabilitation Hospital, Sherwood, AR, p. A49

SHIM, Eunmee R.N., MSN, Vice President Operations, Adventist Healthcare Shady Grove Medical Center, Rockville, MD, p. A300

SHIMAMOTO, Kevin, Vice President and Chief Informational Officer, Valley Children's Healthcare, Madera, CA, p. A72

SHIMP, David, Chief Executive Officer, Las Palmas Medical Center, El Paso, TX, p. A611

SHINAGAWA, Nathan, Chief Operating Officer, Banner Del E. Webb Medical Center, Sun City West, AZ, p. A37

SHINER, Cindy, Manager Human Resources, Lebanon Veterans Affairs Medical Center, Lebanon, PA, p. A538

SHINGLETON, Kathy J. Ed.D., Vice President, Human Resources, Virginia Mason Medical Center, Seattle, WA, p. A686

SHINICK, Mary K, Vice President Human Resources, Nyack Hospital, Nyack, NY, p. A448

SHININGER, Kimberly R, Manger, Human Resources, Parkview Wabash County Hospital, Wabash, IN, p. A221

SHIPIERSKI, Sally, Controller, Geisinger Healthsouth Rehabilitation Hospital, Danville, PA, p. A532

SHIPLEY, Carolyn, Chief Nursing Officer, Roane Medical Center, Harriman, TN, p. A579

SHIPLEY, Janice M.D., Chief Medical Officer, Cibola General Hospital, Grants, NM, p. A426

SHIPLEY, Kurt, Chief Financial Officer, Jordan Valley Medical Center, West Jordan, UT, p. A661

SHIPLEY, Sheila, Human Resources Educator, Signature Psychiatric Hospital, Kansas City, MO, p. A370

SHIPP, Geraldine H, Director of Risk Management, Sampson Regional Medical Center, Clinton, NC, p. A460

SHIRAH, Anita, Director Human Resources, University Of South Alabama Medical Center, Mobile, AL, p. A21

SHIRLEY, Christian, Director Human Resources, Geisinger Healthsouth Rehabilitation Hospital, Danville, PA, p. A532

SHIRLEY, Douglas E., Senior Executive Vice President and Chief Financial Officer, Cooper University Health Care, Camden, NJ, p. A412

SHIRLEY, Steve, Chief Information Officer, Parkview Medical Center, Pueblo, CO, p. A106

SHIVELY, Lori, Vice President of Finance, Munson Healthcare Grayling Hospital, Grayling, MI, p. A321

SHIVERY, Toni M
Vice President Human Resources, University Of Maryland Harford Memorial Hospital, Havre De Grace, MD, p. A299
Vice President Human Resources, University Of Maryland Upper Chesapeake Medical Center, Bel Air, MD, p. A296

SHOBE, Franklin, Administrator and Chief Executive Officer, Black Hills Surgical Hospital, Rapid City, SD, p. A571

SHOBE, Susan, Director Administration and Support Services, Alton Mental Health Center, Alton, IL, p. A177

SHOCK, Ernest, Chief Nursing Officer, Abbeville Area Medical Center, Abbeville, SC, p. A558

SHOCKEY, Kathryn L, Director Human Resources, Lead–Deadwood Regional Hospital, Deadwood, SD, p. A569

SHOCKLEY, Mary, Director Human Resources, Russell Medical Center, Alexander City, AL, p. A13

SHOCKNEY, Brian T FACHE, Chief Operating Officer, Indiana University Health Bloomington Hospital, Bloomington, IN, p. A204

SHOEMAKER, Matt D.O., Vice President and Chief Medical Officer, Southeast Hospital, Cape Girardeau, MO, p. A366

SHOENER, Carl, Chief Information Officer, Lehigh Valley Hospital – Hazleton, Hazleton, PA, p. A536

SHOFNER, Connie, Chief Nursing Officer, Carlsbad Medical Center, Carlsbad, NM, p. A425

SHOLLER, Peter M.D., Medical Director, Spectrum Health Special Care Hospital, Grand Rapids, MI, p. A321

SHOLTIS, Bridget, Chief Financial Officer, Mclaren Port Huron, Port Huron, MI, p. A328

SHOMAKER, Susan, Director Information Management Systems, J. Arthur Dosher Memorial Hospital, Southport, NC, p. A471

SHOOK, Susan, Interim Chief Executive officer, Murray Medical Center, Chatsworth, GA, p. A154

SHOR, Joel M.D., Chief of Staff, Bluefield Regional Medical Center, Bluefield, WV, p. A690

SHORES, Larry M.D., Executive Medical Director, Cedar Springs Hospital, Colorado Springs, CO, p. A99

SHORT, Kathy D.O., Family Practice, Carroll County Memorial Hospital, Carrollton, KY, p. A256

SHORT, M Andrew, Vice President Information Services, Samaritan Medical Center, Watertown, NY, p. A455

SHORT, Penny R.N., Chief Operating Officer, Nanticoke Memorial Hospital, Seaford, DE, p. A116

SHORT, Peter H M.D., Senior Vice President Medical Affairs, Beverly Hospital, Beverly, MA, p. A302

SHORT, Ted, Chief Financial Officer, Fairview Park Hospital, Dublin, GA, p. A157

SHORT, W L M.D., Chief Medical Officer, Memorial Health System, Abilene, KS, p. A238

SHOUKAIR, Sami M.D., Chief Medical Officer, La Palma Intercommunity Hospital, La Palma, CA, p. A65

SHOUP, Barbara R.N., Chief Nursing Officer, Brighton Center For Recovery, Brighton, MI, p. A315

SHOUP, Emily, Director Nursing Services, Roundup Memorial Healthcare, Roundup, MT, p. A388

SHOUSE, Shellie, Chief Financial Officer, Bluegrass Community Hospital, Versailles, KY, p. A268

SHOVALD, Terri, Chief Executive Officer, First Texas Hospital, Carrollton, TX, p. A601

SHOWALTER, Amy J, R.N.
Chief Operating Officer, Sheltering Arms Hospital South, Midlothian, VA, p. A670
Chief Operating Officer, Sheltering Arms Rehabilitation Hospital, Mechanicsville, VA, p. A670

SHOWALTER, Will, Senior Vice President Information Technology, Wellmont Holston Valley Medical Center, Kingsport, TN, p. A581

SHOWALTER, William
Senior Vice President and Chief Information Officer, Information Technology Services, Wake Forest Baptist Health–Davie Medical Center, Bermuda Run, NC, p. A457
Senior Vice President and Chief Information Officer, Froedtert Memorial Lutheran Hospital, Milwaukee, WI, p. A708
Senior Vice President Information Systems, Chief Information Officer, Community Memorial Hospital, Menomonee Falls, WI, p. A706
Senior Vice President, Chief Information Officer, St. Joseph's Hospital, West Bend, WI, p. A715

SHOWS, Carla
Human Resource and Payroll Clerk, George Regional Hospital, Lucedale, MS, p. A358
Payroll Clerk, Greene County Hospital, Leakesville, MS, p. A358

SHREEVE, Susan, Chief Financial Officer, Research Medical Center, Kansas City, MO, p. A370

SHRESTHA, Sanjeeb M.D., Chief Medical Staff, Weatherford Regional Medical Center, Weatherford, TX, p. A653

SHREVE, Susan, Executive Director Information Technology, Boone Memorial Hospital, Madison, WV, p. A693

SHREWSBURY, Kim, Vice President and Chief Financial Officer, Decatur Morgan Hospital, Decatur, AL, p. A16

SHRIDE, Chris, President, Presence St. Mary's Hospital, Kankakee, IL, p. A191

SHRIVASTAVA, Rakesh M.D., Chief Medical Officer, Cornerstone Hospital Of Oklahoma–Shawnee, Shawnee, OK, p. A515

SHRIVER, Debra R.N., MSN, Chief Nurse Executive, Unitypoint Health – Trinity Regional Medical Center, Fort Dodge, IA, p. A227

SHRIVER, Kren K M.D., Clinical Director, Capital District Psychiatric Center, Albany, NY, p. A430

SHROADES, David W, Vice President Technology Services, Alliance Community Hospital, Alliance, OH, p. A479

SHROCK, Lynda J, Vice President Human Resources, Logansport Memorial Hospital, Logansport, IN, p. A215

SHROFF, Divya, Chief Medical Officer, Tristar Ashland City Medical Center, Ashland City, TN, p. A575

SHROFF, Rajendra M.D., Administrative Medical Director, SSM Health St. Mary's Hospital Centralia, Centralia, IL, p. A179

SHROYER, Linda K., Administrator, Potomac Valley Hospital, Keyser, WV, p. A693

SHUART, Jeffery M.D., Chief of Staff, Blackwell Regional Hospital, Blackwell, OK, p. A505

SHUBIN, Allan, Chief Financial Officer, Pacific Alliance Medical Center, Los Angeles, CA, p. A70

SHUEY, Keith M.D., Chief Medical Staff, Johnson County Hospital, Tecumseh, NE, p. A400

SHUFFLEBARGER, Tom, Chief Operating Officer, Children's Of Alabama, Birmingham, AL, p. A14

SHUFORD, Little, Health Information Manager, Kindred Hospital–Greensboro, Greensboro, NC, p. A463

SHUGARMAN, Mark D., Administrator, Shriners Hospitals For Children–Cincinnati, Cincinnati, OH, p. A484

SHUGART, Susan C, Chief Operating Officer, Carolina Pines Regional Medical Center, Hartsville, SC, p. A563

SHUGHART, Deborah A
Vice President and Chief Financial Officer, Fulton County Medical Center, Mc Connellsburg, PA, p. A540
Vice President and Chief Financial Officer, J. C. Blair Memorial Hospital, Huntingdon, PA, p. A536

SHUGRUE, Dianne, President and Chief Executive Officer, Glens Falls Hospital, Glens Falls, NY, p. A436

SHULER, Conrad K M.D., Chief Medical Officer, Oconee Memorial Hospital, Seneca, SC, p. A566

SHULIK, David, Vice President and Chief Financial Officer, Upmc Horizon, Farrell, PA, p. A535

SHULKIN, David J., M.D., Secretary, Veterans Affairs, Department Of Veterans Affairs, Washington, DC, p. B42

SHULL, Jennifer R.N., Chief Nursing Officer, Florida Hospital Fish Memorial, Orange City, FL, p. A136

SHULTS, Randi L., Chief Executive Officer, North Carolina Specialty Hospital, Durham, NC, p. A461

SHUMAKER, Bradley, Chief Medical Officer, Kendall Regional Medical Center, Miami, FL, p. A133

SHUMAN, Betty, Director Human Resources, Wesley Rehabilitation Hospital, Wichita, KS, p. A254

SHUMAN, Daniel D.O., Chief Medical Officer, Ashland Health Center, Ashland, KS, p. A238

SHUMATE, Karen J R.N., Chief Operating Officer, Lawrence Memorial Hospital, Lawrence, KS, p. A245

SHUMATE, Kim, Human Resources Officer, Ohio State University Wexner Medical Center, Columbus, OH, p. A487

SHUMWAY, Barbara, Director Human Resources, North Big Horn Hospital District, Lovell, WY, p. A719

SHUMWAY, Donald L., Chief Executive Officer, New Hampshire Hospital, Concord, NH, p. A407

SHUPERT, Charlene
Director Staff Services, Carrus Rehabilitation Hospital, Sherman, TX, p. A645
Director Staff Services, Carrus Specialty Hospital, Sherman, TX, p. A645

SHUPP, Susan, Chief Human Resources Officer, Nemaha County Hospital, Auburn, NE, p. A390

SHUTE, Keith M M.D., Senior Vice President Medical Affairs and Clinical Services, Androscoggin Valley Hospital, Berlin, NH, p. A407

SHUTER, Mark H., President and Chief Executive Officer, Adena Health System, Chillicothe, OH, p. B5

SHYSHKA, Susan, Associate Director, Va Greater Los Angeles Healthcare System, Los Angeles, CA, p. A72

SIAL, Ajay, Chief Financial Officer, UC Irvine Health, Uc Irvine Medical Center, Orange, CA, p. A78

SIAL, Jay, Chief Financial Officer, Loyola University Medical Center, Maywood, IL, p. A193

SIBBITT, Stephen M.D., Chief Medical Officer, Scott & White Medical Center – Temple, Temple, TX, p. A648

SIBLEY, Beth, Director of Nursing, Sage Rehabilitation Hospital, Baton Rouge, LA, p. A271

SIBLEY, Jeri, Director Revenue Cycle, Riverside Tappahannock Hospital, Tappahannock, VA, p. A676

SICA, Vincent A., President and Chief Executive Officer, Desoto Memorial Hospital, Arcadia, FL, p. A119

SICHTS, Pam, Director Human Resources, Sycamore Springs Hospital, Lafayette, IN, p. A214

SICILIA, Bruce M.D., Medical Director, Healthsouth Rehabilitation Hospital Of York, York, PA, p. A555

SIDDIQI, Ather, M.D.
Medical Director, Nexus Specialty Hospital The Woodlands, The Woodlands, TX, p. A649
Medical Director, Nexus Specialty Hospital, Shenandoah, TX, p. A645

SIDDIQI, Syed M.D., President Medical Staff, Raleigh General Hospital, Beckley, WV, p. A690

SIDDIQUI, Joseph, Vice President Human Resources, The Aroostook Medical Center, Presque Isle, ME, p. A293

SIDES, Tim, Chief Financial Officer, Valle Vista Hospital, Greenwood, IN, p. A209

SIDMAN, Robert M.D., Regional Vice President, Medical Affairs, The William W. Backus Hospital, Norwich, CT, p. A112

SIDONE, LeighAnn MSN, R.N., Chief Nursing Officer, Suburban Hospital, Bethesda, MD, p. A297

SIEBENALER, Christopher, Chief Executive Officer, Houston Methodist Sugar Land Hospital, Sugar Land, TX, p. A647

SIEBERT, Kristy, Manager Finance, John J. Pershing Veterans Affairs Medical Center, Poplar Bluff, MO, p. A375

SIEBERT, Matt, Assistant Administrator Ancillary Services, Hermann Area District Hospital, Hermann, MO, p. A369

SIEDLECKI, Cathy, Director Human Resources, Carthage Area Hospital, Carthage, NY, p. A434

SIEG, Greg, Director Information Technology, Healthsource Saginaw, Inc., Saginaw, MI, p. A329

SIEGEL, Fredric M.D., Chief of Staff, Desert View Hospital, Pahrump, NV, p. A405

SIEGEL, Lesley M.D., Medical Director, Albert J. Solnit Psychiatric Center – South Campus, Middletown, CT, p. A111

SIEGEL, Tiffany, Chief Nursing Officer, Fulton County Health Center, Wauseon, OH, p. A502

SIEGELMAN, Gary M M.D., MSC, Senior Vice President and Chief Medical Officer, Bayhealth Medical Center, Dover, DE, p. A115

SIEGFRIED, Carole A MSN, R.N., Campus Nurse Executive, Palmetto Health Richland, Columbia, SC, p. A560

SIEGLE, Lora M.D., Chief Medical Officer, Morris County Hospital, Council Grove, KS, p. A240

SIEGLEN, Linda M.D., Chief Medical Officer, Mission Hospital, Mission Viejo, CA, p. A74

SIEGMAN, Ira M.D., Chief Medical Officer, Northside Hospital, Saint Petersburg, FL, p. A141

SIEGRIST, Steve, Director of Human Resources, Mesa View Regional Hospital, Mesquite, NV, p. A404

SIEK, Terry MSN, R.N., Chief Nursing Officer, Hays Medical Center, Hays, KS, p. A242

SIEMERS, Thomas R., Chief Executive Officer, J. Arthur Dosher Memorial Hospital, Southport, NC, p. A471

SIEWERT, Charles
Director Human Resources, Buffalo Psychiatric Center, Buffalo, NY, p. A432
Director Human Resources, Western New York Children's Hospital Psychiatric Center, West Seneca, NY, p. A455

SIFERS, Carl, Director Information Technology and System Services, Centerpoint Medical Center, Independence, MO, p. A369

SIFFRING, Connie K., Chief Executive Officer, Select Specialty Hospital–Quad Cities, Davenport, IA, p. A225

SIFRI, Christi, Chief Nursing Executive, Regional Hospital For Respiratory And Complex Care, Burien, WA, p. A679

SIGEL, Heather, Director of Clinical Services, War Memorial Hospital, Berkeley Springs, WV, p. A690

SIGLAR, Harold L.
Interim Chief Executive Officer, Ennis Regional Medical Center, Ennis, TX, p. A612
Interim Chief Executive Officer, Parkview Regional Hospital, Mexia, TX, p. A633

SIGLER, Wes, Administrator, North Mississippi Medical Center–Eupora, Eupora, MS, p. A354

SIGNOR, Kristin, Director Finance, Sunnyview Rehabilitation Hospital, Schenectady, NY, p. A452

SIGREST, Marion M.D., Chief of Staff, Baptist Medical Center Yazoo, Yazoo City, MS, p. A363

SIGSBURY, John R., President, SSM Health St. Mary's Hospital Centralia, Centralia, IL, p. A179

SILARD, Kathleen A R.N., MS, FACHE, Executive Vice President Operations and Chief Operating Officer, Stamford Hospital, Stamford, CT, p. A113

SILAS, Maria, Manager Human Resources, Suny Downstate Medical Center University Hospital, New Rochelle, NY, p. A447

SILBER, Steven M.D., Senior Vice President Medical Affairs, New York–Presbyterian Brooklyn Methodist Hospital, New Rochelle, NY, p. A444

SILLS, Doug, Chief Executive Officer, Santa Rosa Medical Center, Milton, FL, p. A134

SILLS, John T, Chief Information Officer, Health Central Hospital, Ocoee, FL, p. A136

SILSBEE, Dave, Chief Information Officer, Cary Medical Center, Caribou, ME, p. A290

SILVA, Carmen, R.N., Interim Chief Executive Officer, Doctors Hospital Of Manteca, Manteca, CA, p. A73

SILVA, Francisco, Financial Director, Hospital Metropolitano Dr. Susoni, Arecibo, PR, p. A722

SILVA, Shawn, Chief Executive Officer, Heritage Oaks Hospital, Sacramento, CA, p. A83

SILVA–STEELE, Jamie A., FACHE, R.N., President and Chief Executive Officer, UNM Sandoval Regional Medical Center, Inc., Rio Rancho, NM, p. A428

SILVER, Jonathan, Chief Financial Officer, Ballard Rehabilitation Hospital, San Bernardino, CA, p. A85

SILVER, Michael R., M.D.
Chief Information Officer, Rush Oak Park Hospital, Oak Park, IL, p. A196
Vice President Medical Affairs, Rush Oak Park Hospital, Oak Park, IL, p. A196

SILVER, Timothy M.D., Medical Director, SAH–S, Sheltering Arms Hospital South, Midlothian, VA, p. A670

SILVERMAN, Daniel C, M.D.
Chief Medical Officer, Acute Care Troy, Samaritan Hospital, Troy, NY, p. A454
Chief Medical Officer, St. Mary's Hospital, Troy, NY, p. A454
Vice President and Chief Medical Officer, Sinai Hospital Of Baltimore, Baltimore, MD, p. A296

SILVERSTEIN, Douglas M., President, Northshore University Health System, Evanston, IL, p. A187

SILVERSTEIN, Douglas M, President, Northshore University Health System, Evanston, IL, p. A187

SILVERSTEIN, Joel M.D., Chief Medical Officer, Copley Hospital, Morrisville, VT, p. A662

SILVERSTEIN, Kenneth L M.D., Chief Clinical Officer, Christiana Care Health System, Newark, DE, p. A115

SILVERTHORNE, Samuel, Chief Information Officer, U.S. Air Force Medical Center Keesler, Keesler Afb, MS, p. A357

SILVESTRI, Scott, Chief Financial Officer, Hospital Financial Operations, Guthrie Robert Packer Hospital, Sayre, PA, p. A549

SILVEUS, Patrick M.D., Medical Director, Kosciusko Community Hospital, Warsaw, IN, p. A221

SILVEY, Christie, Director People Services, Hshs St. Joseph's Hospital, Highland, IL, p. A190

SILVIA, Charles B M.D., Chief Medical Officer and Vice President Medical Affairs, Peninsula Regional Medical Center, Salisbury, MD, p. A294

SIM, Carol, President and Chief Executive Officer, Siskin Hospital For Physical Rehabilitation, Chattanooga, TN, p. A576

SIM, Edward H., Chief Executive Officer, St. Anthony Hospital, Lakewood, CO, p. A105

SIMCHUK, Cathy J, Chief Operating Officer, Providence Holy Family Hospital, Spokane, WA, p. A687

SIMIA, Greg
Chief Financial Officer, Hshs St. Clare Memorial Hospital, Oconto Falls, WI, p. A709
Chief Financial Officer, Hshs St. Mary's Hospital Medical Center, Green Bay, WI, p. A703
Chief Financial Officer, Hshs St. Nicholas Hospital, Sheboygan, WI, p. A712
Chief Financial Officer, Hshs St. Vincent Hospital, Green Bay, WI, p. A703

SIMKINS, Palma, Chief Human Resources Management Services, Battle Creek Veterans Affairs Medical Center, Battle Creek, MI, p. A315

SIMMONS, Angela L., Chief Executive Officer, Healthsouth Rehabilitation Hospital Of Humble, Llc, Humble, TX, p. A624

SIMMONS, Barbara, R.N.
Chief Executive Officer, Plantation General Hospital, Plantation, FL, p. A140
Chief Executive Officer, Westside Regional Medical Center, Plantation, FL, p. A140

SIMMONS, Brad
Chief Operating Officer, Saint Luke's Hospital Of Kansas City, Kansas City, MO, p. A370
Chief Operating Officer, University Of California, Davis Medical Center, Sacramento, CA, p. A84

SIMMONS, Corey, Chief Executive Officer, Neuropsychiatric Hospital Of Indianapolis, Indianapolis, IN, p. A211

SIMMONS, Daniel F, Senior Vice President and Treasurer, Monongahela Valley Hospital, Monongahela, PA, p. A541

SIMMONS, Dorlynn, Chief Executive Officer, Mescalero Public Health Service Indian Hospital, Mescalero, NM, p. A427

SIMMONS, Dwayne, Interim Chief Information Officer, St. Luke's Cornwall Hospital, Newburgh, NY, p. A447

SIMMONS, Eileen
Chief Financial Officer, UPMC Hospital Network, Upmc Mercy, Pittsburgh, PA, p. A547
Chief Financial Officer, Magee–Womens Hospital Of Upmc, Pittsburgh, PA, p. A547
Chief Financial Officer, Upmc Presbyterian Shadyside, Pittsburgh, PA, p. A547
Chief Operating Officer and Interim President, St. Charles Bend, Bend, OR, p. A520

SIMMONS, Iman
Chief Operating Officer and Interim President, St. Charles Redmond, Redmond, OR, p. A526
Chief Operating Officer, Center For Behavioral Medicine, Kansas City, MO, p. A370

SIMMONS, Jodi, Chief Nursing Officer, Hillcrest Medical Center, Tulsa, OK, p. A517

SIMMONS, Leslie, FACHE, R.N., President, Carroll Hospital Center, Westminster, MD, p. A301

SIMMONS, Randy, Chief Executive Officer, Prague Community Hospital, Prague, OK, p. A515

SIMMONS, Rickie, Controller, Kindred Hospital North Florida, Green Cove Springs, FL, p. A126

SIMMONS, Tim C., Chief Executive Officer, Hopebridge Hospital, Houston, TX, p. A620

SIMMS, Michael S Sr., Vice President Human Resources, RMC Anniston, Anniston, AL, p. A13

SIMMS, Miquel Noelani R.N., Chief Nursing Officer, North Hawaii Community Hospital, Kamuela, HI, p. A169

SIMODEJKA, John E., Chief Executive Officer, Select Specialty Hospital–Central Pennsylvania, Camp Hill, PA, p. A530

SIMODEJKA, John E, Marketing Chief Executive Officer, Select Specialty Hospital–Central Pennsylvania, Camp Hill, PA, p. A530

SIMON, Anha, Director Human Resources, Riceland Medical Center, Winnie, TX, p. A654

SIMON, Ashley, Chief Financial Officer, Kansas Surgery And Recovery Center, Wichita, KS, p. A253

SIMON, Daniel I., M.D., President, University Hospitals Cleveland Medical Center, Cleveland, OH, p. A486

SIMON, Deborah R., R.N.
President and Chief Executive Officer, Unitypoint Health – Peoria, Peoria, IL, p. A197
President and Chief Executive Officer, Unitypoint Health – Proctor, Peoria, IL, p. A197

SIMON, Joan M R.N., FACHE, Chief Nursing Officer, Kootenai Health, Coeur D'Alene, ID, p. A173

SIMON, Kareen, Vice President of Operations, Wheeling Hospital, Wheeling, WV, p. A697

SIMON, Kenneth B M.D., Chief of Staff, Veterans Affairs Gulf Coast Veterans Health Care System, Biloxi, MS, p. A352

SIMON, Keri, Executive Director, University Of Missouri Health Care, Columbia, MO, p. A367

SIMON, Lisa M.
Senior Vice President and Chief Financial Officer, Ohio Valley Medical Center, Wheeling, WV, p. A697
Senior Vice President Chief Financial Officer, East Ohio Regional Hospital, Martins Ferry, OH, p. A495

SIMON, Lloyd M.D., Medical Director, Eastern Long Island Hospital, Greenport, NY, p. A436

SIMON, Mark, System Chief Information Officer, Benefis Health System, Great Falls, MT, p. A385

SIMON, Patricia, Chief Nursing Officer, Healthsouth Rehabilitation Hospital Of Charleston, Charleston, SC, p. A559

SIMON, Richard M.D., Chief of Staff, Uconn, John Dempsey Hospital, Farmington, CT, p. A110

SIMON, Stuart M.D., Medical Director, North Central Surgical Center, Dallas, TX, p. A606

SIMON, Teresa, Director Information Systems, Nacogdoches Medical Center, Nacogdoches, TX, p. A634

SIMON, Thresa M.D., Medical Director, Poplar Springs Hospital, Petersburg, VA, p. A673

SIMONIN, Steven J., President and Chief Executive Officer, Iowa Specialty Hospital–Clarion, Clarion, IA, p. A224

SIMONS, Janice, FACHE, Chief Executive Officer, Medina Regional Hospital, Hondo, TX, p. A619

SIMONS, Preston, Chief Information Officer, Aurora Medical Center – Manitowoc County, Two Rivers, WI, p. A714

SIMONSON, John F M.D., President Medical Staff, Memorial Community Hospital And Health System, Blair, NE, p. A391

SIMONSON, Paul, Vice President, Trinity Health, Minot, ND, p. A477

SIMPSON, Brenda, R.N.
Chief Nursing Officer, Largo Medical Center, Largo, FL, p. A130
Chief Nursing Officer, Northeast Georgia Medical Center, Gainesville, GA, p. A158

SIMPSON, Chris, Chief Executive Officer, Cornerstone Hospital–West Monroe, West Monroe, LA, p. A287

SIMPSON, Greg, Chief Nursing Officer, St. Joseph Medical Center, Kansas City, MO, p. A371

SIMPSON, Joan W., Manager Human Resources, Lauderdale Community Hospital, Ripley, TN, p. A588

SIMPSON, Julie, Vice President Human Resources, University Of Tennessee Medical Center, Knoxville, TN, p. A582

SIMPSON, Keith J, Chief Operating Officer, Jennings American Legion Hospital, Jennings, LA, p. A277

SIMPSON, Laura, Director Human Resources, Sabine County Hospital, Hemphill, TX, p. A618

SIMPSON, Lee A. Jr, Chief Executive Officer, Post Acute Medical Specialty Hospital Of Tulsa, Tulsa, OK, p. A518

SIMPSON, Lee A Jr, Chief Executive Officer, Post Acute Medical Specialty Hospital Of Tulsa, Tulsa, OK, p. A518

SIMPSON, Mark, Director of Nursing, Welch Community Hospital, Welch, WV, p. A696

SIMPSON, Michelle, Chief Nursing Officer and Quality Leader, Lauderdale Community Hospital, Ripley, TN, p. A588

SIMPSON, Mikael
Chief Executive Officer, Nexus Specialty Hospital The Woodlands, The Woodlands, TX, p. A649
Chief Executive Officer, Nexus Specialty Hospital, Shenandoah, TX, p. A645

SIMPSON, Rae R.N., Chief Nursing Officer, Western State Hospital, Tacoma, WA, p. A688

SIMPSON, Robert, Vice President Operations, Methodist Richardson Medical Center, Richardson, TX, p. A639

SIMPSON, Shannon, Director Information Services, St. Elizabeth Hospital, Gonzales, LA, p. A275

SIMPSON, Shawndra, Interim Chief Executive Officer, Sutter Surgical Hospital – North Valley, Yuba City, CA, p. A97

SIMPSON, Sheila, Vice President Human Resources, Palmetto Lowcountry Behavioral Health, Charleston, SC, p. A559

SIMPSON, Steve, Chief Executive Officer, Lakeway Regional Hospital, Morristown, TN, p. A585

SIMPSON, Tanya, Chief Nursing Officer, Regional Medical Center Bayonet Point, Hudson, FL, p. A127

SIMPSON–TUGGLE, Deloris, Vice President Human Resources and Organizational Development and Chief Human Resources Officer, Greater Baltimore Medical Center, Baltimore, MD, p. A294

SIMS, Anthony M.D., Chief of Staff, Dekalb Regional Medical Center, Fort Payne, AL, p. A18

SIMS, Brian, Chief Executive Officer, Lucas County Health Center, Chariton, IA, p. A224

SIMS, Charles M.D., Chief of Staff, Chi St. Luke's Health–The Woodlands Hospital, The Woodlands, TX, p. A649

SIMS, Gregory F., Chief Executive Officer, Hamilton Memorial Hospital District, Mcleansboro, IL, p. A193

SIMS, Jason, M.D.
Chief Medical Officer, Cleveland Area Hospital, Cleveland, OK, p. A506

Facility Information Security Officer, Medical City North Hills, North Richland Hills, TX, p. A635

SIMS, Jeffrey, Chief Executive Officer, Heartland Behavioral Healthcare, Massillon, OH, p. A495

SIMS, John, Administrator, Hamilton House Nursing Center/ Adult Living Center, Columbus, GA, p. B32

SIMS, Jyric, FACHE, Chief Executive Officer, Medical City Fort Worth, Fort Worth, TX, p. A614

SIMS, Lynn, Director Information Technology, Davis County Hospital, Bloomfield, IA, p. A223

SIMS, Mark E., Chief Executive Officer, Grand Strand Regional Medical Center, Myrtle Beach, SC, p. A565

SIMS, William M.D., Medical Director, Elkview General Hospital, Hobart, OK, p. A508

SINCICH, Robert, Vice President Human Resources, Trumbull Memorial Hospital, Warren, OH, p. A501

SINCLAIR, Brad, Chief Financial Officer, Merit Health River Oaks, Flowood, MS, p. A354

SINCLAIR, Elyria, Director Human Resources, Crestwood Medical Center, Huntsville, AL, p. A19

SINCLAIR, Kathy, Vice President Human Resources, Spartanburg Medical Center, Spartanburg, SC, p. A566

SINCLAIR, Laura, Director Human Resources, Kansas City Orthopaedic Institute, Leawood, KS, p. A245

SINCLAIR, Noreen, Human Resources Administrator, Connecticut Veterans Home And Hospital, Rocky Hill, CT, p. A112

SINCLAIR–CHUNG, Opal R.N., MS, Chief Nursing Officer, Deputy Executive Director, NYC Health + Hospitals / Kings County, New Rochelle, NY, p. A445

SINCOCK, Gregory M, Information Technology Leader, Kaiser Permanente West Los Angeles Medical Center, Los Angeles, CA, p. A69

SINDELAR, Michael, Vice President and Chief Financial Officer, Fremont Health, Fremont, NE, p. A393

SINDLINGER, Julie A, Director of Human Resources, Weston County Health Services, Newcastle, WY, p. A719

SINEK, James J., FACHE, President, Boone Hospital Center, Columbia, MO, p. A366

SINGER, Brent, Chief Financial Officer, St. Anthony's Medical Center, Saint Louis, MO, p. A378

SINGH, Amarjit, M.D., President and Chief Executive Officer, Brunswick Psych Center, Amityville, NY, p. A430

SINGH, Armandeep, Chief Medical Officer, Monroe Hospital, Bloomfield, IN, p. A204

SINGH, Brij, Medical Staff Director, Kindred Hospital Rome, Rome, GA, p. A163

SINGH, Deepraj M.D., Medical Director, Montgomery County Emergency Service, Norristown, PA, p. A542

SINGH, Gagandeep M.D., Chief Medical Officer Behavioral Health, Banner Behavioral Health Hospital – Scottsdale, Scottsdale, AZ, p. A35

SINGH, Gurmant, Chief Medical Officer, Good Samaritan Hospital–North, Bakersfield, CA, p. A52

SINGH, Himanshu M.D., Associate Director, Veterans Affairs Ann Arbor Healthcare System, Ann Arbor, MI, p. A314

SINGH, Inderjit M.D., Clinical Director, Pilgrim Psychiatric Center, Brentwood, NY, p. A432

SINGH, Vijayant M.D., Chief Medical Officer, Carepoint Health Bayonne Medical Center, Bayonne, NJ, p. A411

SINGLES, James L, Chief Financial Officer, Marlette Regional Hospital, Marlette, MI, p. A325

SINGLETARY–TWYMAN, Michelle, Chief Nursing Officer, Rockford Center, Newark, DE, p. A115

SINGLETON, J Knox., President and Chief Executive Officer, Inova Health System, Falls Church, VA, p. B68

SINGLETON, Al M.D., Chief Psychiatry and Chief Medical Staff, Colorado Mental Health Institute At Pueblo, Pueblo, CO, p. A106

SINGLETON, Roy
Director Computer Information Systems, Palmdale Regional Medical Center, Palmdale, CA, p. A78
Director Computer Information Systems, Palmdale Regional Medical Center, Palmdale, CA, p. A79

SINHA, Sunil K. M.D., FACHE, Chief Medical Officer, Bon Secours Memorial Regional Medical Center, Mechanicsville, VA, p. A670

SINIARD, Sandra, Vice President of Patient Care Services, Cornerstone Medical Center, Fort Oglethorpe, GA, p. A158

SINICKAS, Robert, Director Information Services, Marianjoy Rehabilitation Hospital, Wheaton, IL, p. A202

SINICROPE, Frank J Jr, Vice President Financial Services, Princeton Community Hospital, Princeton, WV, p. A695

SINISI, Albert, Director Information Systems, Doctors' Hospital Of Michigan, Pontiac, MI, p. A328

SINK, Kristi M, Chief Operating Officer, University Hospitals Parma Medical Center, Parma, OH, p. A498

SINNOTT, James M.D., Chief Medical Staff, Coquille Valley Hospital, Coquille, OR, p. A521

SINNOTT, Lisa M, Director Human Resources, Acuity Specialty Hospital Of Southern New Jersey, Willingboro, NJ, p. A423

SINOPOLI, Angelo M.D., Vice President Clinical Integration and Chief Medical Officer, GHS Greenville Memorial Hospital, Greenville, SC, p. A562

SINOTTE, Brian, Chief Executive Officer, Up Health System–Marquette, Marquette, MI, p. A326

SIOSON, Stephanie
Director Human Resources, Garden Grove Hospital And Medical Center, Garden Grove, CA, p. A61
Director Human Resources, Huntington Beach Hospital, Huntington Beach, CA, p. A63
Director Human Resources, La Palma Intercommunity Hospital, La Palma, CA, p. A65
Director Human Resources, West Anaheim Medical Center, Anaheim, CA, p. A51

SIOUFI, Habib M.D., Chief Medical Officer, Umass Memorial–Marlborough Hospital, Marlborough, MA, p. A308

SIPEK, John, Supervisor Client Services, Aurora Medical Center In Washington County, Hartford, WI, p. A703

SIREK, David, Chief Information Officer, Myrtue Medical Center, Harlan, IA, p. A229

SIRK, Donald, Director Information Systems, Medstar St. Mary's Hospital, Leonardtown, MD, p. A299

SIROIS, Peter, Chief Executive Officer, Northern Maine Medical Center, Fort Kent, ME, p. A291

SIROTTA, Ted, Chief Financial Officer, Vail Valley Health Hospital, Vail, CO, p. A108

SISILLO, Sabato, M.D.
Chief Medical Officer, Providence Medical Center, Kansas City, KS, p. A244
Chief Medical Officer, Saint John Hospital, Leavenworth, KS, p. A245

SISK, Bryan W., Associate Director Patient and Nursing Services, Central Texas Veterans Health Care System, Temple, TX, p. A648

SISK, Glenn C., President, Coosa Valley Medical Center, Sylacauga, AL, p. A23

SISK, Jack, Chief Financial Officer, Punxsutawney Area Hospital, Punxsutawney, PA, p. A548

SISK, Lori, R.N.
Chief Executive Officer, Sanford Canby Medical Center, Canby, MN, p. A337
Chief Executive Officer, Sanford Clear Lake Medical Center, Clear Lake, SD, p. A569

SISK, Rodney, Chief Financial Officer, University Hospital Summerville, Augusta, GA, p. A152

SISK, Susan, Chief Financial Officer, Chi St. Alexius Health, Bismarck, ND, p. A474

SISLER, Debbie, Director, Human Resource, Vidant Roanoke–Chowan Hospital, Ahoskie, NC, p. A457

SISON, Joseph M.D., Medical Director, Heritage Oaks Hospital, Sacramento, CA, p. A83

SISSON, Travis, Chief Executive Officer, Panola Medical Center, Batesville, MS, p. A352

SISSON, William G., President, Baptist Health Lexington, Lexington, KY, p. A260

SISTO, Steven A., Senior Vice President and Chief Operating Officer, Methodist Hospital Of Southern California, Arcadia, CA, p. A52

SISTRUNK, Heather R.N., Chief Operating Officer, Merit Health River Oaks, Flowood, MS, p. A354

SITLINGER, James, Chief Human Resources Management, Charles George Veterans Affairs Medical Center, Asheville, NC, p. A457

SITTIG, Kevin M.D., Senior Associate Dean and Chief Medical Officer, University Health Shreveport, Shreveport, LA, p. A286

SIU, Max, Chief Information Officer, Hackensack Meridian Health Mountainside Medical Center, Montclair, NJ, p. A416

SIVAK, Steven M.D., Chief Medical Officer, Einstein Physicians Philadelphia, Einstein Medical Center Philadelphia, Philadelphia, PA, p. A543

SIVEK, Carla, Director, Coatesville Veterans Affairs Medical Center, Coatesville, PA, p. A532

SIVLEY, Susanna S, Chief Personnel Officer, Highlands Medical Center, Scottsboro, AL, p. A23

SIWEK, Steven M., M.D., President and Chief Executive Officer, Scottsdale Liberty Hospital, Scottsdale, AZ, p. A36

SIX, Deborah, Coordinator Data Processing, Wayne Memorial Hospital, Jesup, GA, p. A159

SJOBERG, Rochelle, Director Human Resources, Ely–Bloomenson Community Hospital, Ely, MN, p. A339

SKABELUND, Hoyt, Chief Executive Officer, Sterling Regional Medcenter, Sterling, CO, p. A107

SKAGGS, Lynda, Chief Nursing Officer, Fleming County Hospital, Flemingsburg, KY, p. A258

SKALA, Pat, Chief Information Officer, Laguna Honda Hospital And Rehabilitation Center, San Francisco, CA, p. A87

SKARKA, Kathy MSN, R.N., Executive Vice President Patient Care Services, Nassau University Medical Center, East Meadow, NY, p. A435

SKARULIS, Patricia, Senior Vice President and Chief Information Systems Officer, Memorial Sloan–Kettering Cancer Center, New Rochelle, NY, p. A442

SKARZYNSKI, Joseph M.D., Medical Director, NYC Health + Hospitals / North Central Bronx, New Rochelle, NY, p. A445

SKEEN, Steven, R.N.
Chief Clinical Officer, Medical Center Barbour, Eufaula, AL, p. A17
Chief Nursing Officer, Mizell Memorial Hospital, Opp, AL, p. A22

SKELDON, Timothy
Chief Financial Officer, Thomas Memorial Hospital, South Charleston, WV, p. A696
Senior Vice President and Chief Financial Officer, Parrish Medical Center, Titusville, FL, p. A146

SKELLY, Stephanie, President Medical Staff, Red Bud Regional Hospital, Red Bud, IL, p. A198

SKELTON, Jenny, System Integration Manager, The Women's Hospital, Newburgh, IN, p. A217

SKELTON, Katie MSN, R.N., Vice President Nursing and Chief Nursing Officer, St. Joseph Hospital, Orange, CA, p. A78

SKIBBA, Joshua, Chief Medical Officer, Ohio County Hospital, Hartford, KY, p. A259

SKIDMORE, Jocelyn, Director Finance, SSM Health St. Francis Hospital – Maryville, Maryville, MO, p. A373

SKIDMORE, Kim, Chief Executive Officer, Community Medical Center Of Izard County, Calico Rock, AR, p. A41

SKIEM, Paul, Senior Vice President Human Resources, Presence Saint Francis Hospital, Evanston, IL, p. A187

SKILLINGS, Charles E., President and Chief Executive Officer, St. Anthony Shawnee Hospital, Shawnee, OK, p. A516

SKILLINGS, Lois N., R.N., MSN, President and Chief Executive Officer, Mid Coast Hospital, Brunswick, ME, p. A290

SKILLINGS, Michelle, Interim Chief Executive Officer, Niobrara Health And Life Center, Lusk, WY, p. A719

SKINNER, Christopher, Chief of Staff, Spectrum Health Big Rapids Hospital, Big Rapids, MI, p. A315

SKINNER, Gary, Director Information Technology, Rehabilitation Hospital Of Indiana, Indianapolis, IN, p. A212

SKINNER, Gwendolyn, Executive Director, Devereux Georgia Treatment Network, Kennesaw, GA, p. A160

SKINNER, Kellcie, Controller, Newman Memorial Hospital, Shattuck, OK, p. A515

SKINNER, Kristina, Director Quality, Sanpete Valley Hospital, Mount Pleasant, UT, p. A657

SKINNER, Marjorie, Director Finance, Pershing General Hospital, Lovelock, NV, p. A404

SKINNER, Richard, Chief Information Technology Officer, University Of Virginia Medical Center, Charlottesville, VA, p. A665

SKINNER, Sue, Vice President of Patient Care Services, Grand Itasca Clinic And Hospital, Grand Rapids, MN, p. A340

SKIPPER, Kymberli, Manager Human Resources, Prattville Baptist Hospital, Prattville, AL, p. A22

SKIPPER, Michelle, Director Human Resources, Kaiser Permanente Riverside Medical Center, Riverside, CA, p. A82

SKJOLDEN, Jessica M.D., Chief of Staff, St. Andrew's Health Center, Bottineau, ND, p. A474

SKLAMBERG, Todd, President, Sunrise Hospital And Medical Center, Las Vegas, NV, p. A404

SKLIRIS, Demetre, Chief Medical Officer, Avera Dells Area Hospital, Dell Rapids, SD, p. A569

SKOCH, Michael M.D., Chief Medical Officer, Mary Lanning Healthcare, Hastings, NE, p. A394

SKOGSBERGH, Jim, President and Chief Executive Officer, Advocate Health Care, Downers Grove, IL, p. B7

SKORA, Lori, Chief Executive Officer, Kindred Hospital Of Northern Indiana, Mishawaka, IN, p. A216

SKOW, Glenn M.D., Chief of Staff, Fayette County Hospital, Vandalia, IL, p. A202

SKOWRON, Paul, Chief Executive Officer, Warner Hospital And Health Services, Clinton, IL, p. A184

SKRINDE, Tracie, Senior Human Resources Partner, Peacehealth United General Medical Center, Sedro––Woolley, WA, p. A686

SKRIPPS, Michele M., R.N., Chief Executive Officer, Healthsouth Rehabilitation Hospital Of Charleston, Charleston, SC, p. A559

SKULA, Erika, President and Chief Executive Officer, Manchester Memorial Hospital, Manchester, KY, p. A264

SKULA, Joe, Director Human Resources, Manchester Memorial Hospital, Manchester, KY, p. A264

SKUPIEN, Mary Beth, Director, Battle Creek Veterans Affairs Medical Center, Battle Creek, MI, p. A315

SKVARENINA, Michael, Assistant Vice President Information Systems, Holy Name Medical Center, Teaneck, NJ, p. A421

SKYLES, Jill, R.N.
Vice President Patient Care Services and Chief Nurse Executive, Barnes–Jewish St. Peters Hospital, Saint Peters, MO, p. A379
Vice President Patient Care Services and Chief Nurse Executive, Progress West Hospital, O'Fallon, MO, p. A374

SLABA, Bryan, Chief Executive Officer, Wagner Community Memorial Hospital Avera, Wagner, SD, p. A573

SLABIK, Shauna, Chief Financial Officer, Sanford Mayville Medical Center, Mayville, ND, p. A477

SLACK, Randy, Chief Financial Officer, Nacogdoches Medical Center, Nacogdoches, TX, p. A634

SLADKY, Todd J., Chief Financial Officer, Great River Medical Center, West Burlington, IA, p. A236

SLAGLE, Julie A R.N., MSN, Vice President Patient Care Services, Sidney Regional Medical Center, Sidney, NE, p. A400

SLATE, Sonny, Chief Operating Officer, Georgia Regional Hospital At Atlanta, Decatur, GA, p. A156

SLATER, Craig M M.D., Chief Medical Officer, Carolinas Healthcare System Union, Monroe, NC, p. A467

SLATER, Mark, Director Information Systems, Baylor Scott & White Medical Center – Lake Pointe, Rowlett, TX, p. A641

SLATER–NESUOLD, Stephanie, Director of Nursing, Landmark Hospital Of Joplin, Joplin, MO, p. A369

SLATON, Brenda, Superintendent, Rusk State Hospital, Rusk, TX, p. A641

SLATTERY, Greg, Vice President Information, Community Hospitals And Wellness Centers, Bryan, OH, p. A482

SLATTERY, Susan L, Director Human Resources, Unitypoint Health – St. Luke's Hospital, Cedar Rapids, IA, p. A223

SLATTMAN, Robin, Chief Nursing Officer, Memorial Health, Marysville, OH, p. A495

SLAVIN, Kevin J., FACHE, President and Chief Executive Officer, St. Joseph's Healthcare System, Paterson, NJ, p. A418

SLAVIN, Peter L., M.D., President, Massachusetts General Hospital, Boston, MA, p. A303

SLAWITSKY, Bruce, Vice President Human Resources, Hospital For Special Surgery, New Rochelle, NY, p. A441

SLAYMAN, Aubree, Director Patient Services, Miami County Medical Center, Paola, KS, p. A249

SLAYTON, Val M.D., Vice President Medical Affairs, Sts. Mary & Elizabeth Hospital, Louisville, KY, p. A263

SLEDGE, Cynthia Moore M.D., Medical Director, Bryce Hospital, Tuscaloosa, AL, p. A23

SLEDGE, Tasha, Director Human Resources, Texas Health Harris Methodist Hospital Southlake, Southlake, TX, p. A646

SLEDGE, Tom, Chief Operating Officer, Northwest Medical Center – Springdale, Springdale, AR, p. A49

SLEEPER, Justin, Vice President Clinical Operations, Behavioral Health Network, Natchaug Hospital, Mansfield Center, CT, p. A110

SLEIME, Melanie, Director Human Resources, Memorial Hospital, North Conway, NH, p. A410

SLEITER, Michelle, Chief Executive Officer, Humboldt County Memorial Hospital, Humboldt, IA, p. A229

SLESSOR, Steve Robert.
Chief Executive Officer, Buchanan County Health Center, Independence, IA, p. A229
Interim Chief Executive Officer, Community Memorial Hospital, Sumner, IA, p. A235

SLICK, Lois, Director Human Resources, Chi Lakewood Health, Baudette, MN, p. A336

SLIDER, Carol, Chief Nursing Officer, Titus Regional Medical Center, Mount Pleasant, TX, p. A634

SLIETER, Richard G. Jr, Administrator, Community Behavioral Health Hospital – Baxter, Baxter, MN, p. A336

SLIGER, Susan, Director Human Resources, War Memorial Hospital, Sault Sainte Marie, MI, p. A330

SLITER, Elizabeth M.D., Chairman Medical Staff, Decatur Health Systems, Oberlin, KS, p. A248

SLIWA, James M.D., Chief Medical Officer, Shirley Ryan Abilitylab, Chicago, IL, p. A183

SLIWINSKI, Jeff, Chief Financial Officer, Clear Lake Regional Medical Center, Webster, TX, p. A653

SLIWINSKI, Ron, Chief of Hospital Division, University Of Wisconsin Hospitals And Clinics Authority, Madison, WI, p. A705

SLOAN, Brian, Chief Operating Officer, Duke Raleigh Hospital, Raleigh, NC, p. A468

SLOAN, Gary, Chief Executive Officer, San Ramon Regional Medical Center, San Ramon, CA, p. A90

SLOAN, Patrick
Chief Financial Officer, Firsthealth Moore Regional Hospital – Hamlet, Hamlet, NC, p. A464

Chief Financial Officer, Memorial Satilla Health, Waycross, GA, p. A167

SLOAN, Prudence, Coordinator Human Resources, Select Specialty Hospital–Pittsburgh/Upmc, Pittsburgh, PA, p. A547

SLOAN, Ronald A., FACHE, President, The Outer Banks Hospital, Nags Head, NC, p. A467

SLOAN, Steve, Chief Financial Officer, Lake Cumberland Regional Hospital, Somerset, KY, p. A267

SLOCUM, Brandon H, Senior Vice President and Chief Financial Officer, Medical West, Bessemer, AL, p. A14

SLOCUM, Gregg Y, Chief Financial Officer, Valley Forge Medical Center And Hospital, Norristown, PA, p. A542

SLONIM, Anthony D., M.D., Dr.PH, President and Chief Executive Officer, Renown Health, Reno, NV, p. B108

SLONIM, Sheryl A, Executive Vice President and Chief Nursing Officer, Holy Name Medical Center, Teaneck, NJ, p. A421

SLONINA, Marrianne, Director Human Resources, Georgetown Community Hospital, Georgetown, KY, p. A258

SLOPER, Carol, Manager Information Technology, Cheyenne County Hospital, Saint Francis, KS, p. A251

SLUCK, Jeana R.N., Executive Director Nursing Clinical Inpatient Departments, Allied Services Rehabilitation Hospital, Scranton, PA, p. A550

SLUKA, Joseph, President and Chief Executive Officer, St. Charles Health System, Inc., Bend, OR, p. B120

SLUSHER, Carlene, Director Finance, Seneca Healthcare District, Chester, CA, p. A55

SLUSHER, Michael, Community Chief Executive Officer, Middlesboro Arh Hospital, Middlesboro, KY, p. A264

SLUSHER, W. James (Jamie) M.D., Chief of Staff, Jackson Parish Hospital, Jonesboro, LA, p. A277

SLUTSKER, Vladimir, Medical Director, Healthsouth Rehabilitation Of Gadsden, Gadsden, AL, p. A18

SLY–FRANKLIN, Michelle, Chief Executive Officer, Sullivan County Community Hospital, Sullivan, IN, p. A220

SMAJSTRLA, Julie, Director Nursing, Seymour Hospital, Seymour, TX, p. A645

SMALE, Cindy, Director, Human Resources, Iredell Health System, Statesville, NC, p. A471

SMALL, Becky, Chief Human Resources Officer, Kindred Hospital–Aurora, Aurora, CO, p. A98

SMALL, Brenda, Chief Clinical Officer, AMG Specialty Hospital–Greenwood, Greenwood, MS, p. A355

SMALL, David, M.D.
Chief Medical Officer, Greene Memorial Hospital, Xenia, OH, p. A503
Chief Medical Officer, Soin Medical Center, Beavercreek, OH, p. A481

SMALL, Deborah C MSN, R.N., Vice President Patient Care Services and Chief Nursing Officer, Cleveland Clinic Fairview Hospital, Cleveland, OH, p. A485

SMALL, Donna R.N., Chief Nursing Officer, St. Mary's Medical Center, West Palm Beach, FL, p. A147

SMALL, Jonathan, Chief Operations Information and Technology, John D. Dingell Veterans Affairs Medical Center, Detroit, MI, p. A318

SMALL, Terry L., Assistant Chief Executive Officer, William R. Sharpe, Jr. Hospital, Weston, WV, p. A697

SMALLEY, Ben, Administrator, Cassia Regional Medical Center, Burley, ID, p. A172

SMALLWOOD, Ravae, IS Coordinator, Chi Health Missouri Valley, Missouri Valley, IA, p. A231

SMARR, Susan M.D., Physician–in–Chief, Kaiser Permanente Santa Clara Medical Center, Santa Clara, CA, p. A90

SMART, Dan, Chief Information Management Officer, Permian Regional Medical Center, Andrews, TX, p. A592

SMART, George J, Vice President Finance and Information Technology, Midmichigan Medical Center – Alpena, Alpena, MI, p. A314

SMART, Joanne F M.D., Director Medical Affairs, Indiana University Health Bedford Hospital, Bedford, IN, p. A204

SMART, Melissa, Communication ad Public Relations Specialist, Texas Health Presbyterian Hospital Denton, Denton, TX, p. A608

SMART, Paul CPA, Chief Financial Officer, Franklin County Medical Center, Preston, ID, p. A175

SMART, Robert M., Chief Executive Officer, Healthsouth Rehabilitation Hospital – Mid–Cities, Bedford, TX, p. A597

SMART, Stephanie, Chief Nursing Officer, United Hospital Center, Bridgeport, WV, p. A690

SMEDLEY, Jessie
Chief Executive Officer, New Braunfels Regional Rehabilitation Hospital, New Braunfels, TX, p. A635
Chief Executive Officer, Weslaco Regional Rehabilitation Hospital, Weslaco, TX, p. A654

SMELTZER, Sharon, Chief Executive Officer, Mercy Rehabilitation Hospital Oklahoma City, Oklahoma City, OK, p. A512

SMENDIK, Douglas M.D., Chief Medical Officer, Spectrum Health Pennock, Hastings, MI, p. A322

SMIDT, Jessica R.N., Director of Nursing, Pipestone County Medical Center Avera, Pipestone, MN, p. A346

SMIGA, Lance, Chief Financial Officer, Jackson County Hospital District, Edna, TX, p. A610

SMILEY, Christy, Leader Human Resources, SSM Health St. Mary's Hospital – Audrain, Mexico, MO, p. A373

SMITH, Agnes A MSN, R.N., Chief Nursing Officer, Twin County Regional Healthcare, Galax, VA, p. A668

SMITH, Alan H
  Chief Financial Officer, Huntington Beach Hospital, Huntington Beach, CA, p. A63
  Chief Financial Officer, La Palma Intercommunity Hospital, La Palma, CA, p. A65

SMITH, Andrew, M.D.
  Chief of Staff, Guttenberg Municipal Hospital, Guttenberg, IA, p. A228
  Chief Information Management, Madigan Army Medical Center, Tacoma, WA, p. A687

SMITH, Barbara H, Senior Vice President & Chief Operating Officer, Robert Wood Johnson University Hospital At Hamilton, Hamilton, NJ, p. A414

SMITH, Bennie
  Chief Information Officer, Lady Of The Sea General Hospital, Cut Off, LA, p. A274
  Director Human Resources and Risk Management, Lady Of The Sea General Hospital, Cut Off, LA, p. A274

SMITH, Bernie, Chief Financial Officer, Troy Community Hospital, Troy, PA, p. A552

SMITH, Bethany
  Controller, Spire Cane Creek Rehabilitation Hospital, Martin, TN, p. A583
  Director of Finance, Chi Oakes Hospital, Oakes, ND, p. A477

SMITH, Betsy, Chief Nursing Officer, Effingham Hospital, Springfield, GA, p. A165

SMITH, Beverly Bzdek, Chief Nursing Officer, Southside Regional Medical Center, Petersburg, VA, p. A673

SMITH, Bill M.D., Chief of Staff, Cullman Regional Medical Center, Cullman, AL, p. A16

SMITH, Blythe, Administrative Assistant, Faulkton Area Medical Center, Faulkton, SD, p. A569

SMITH, Bobby, Vice President Physician Services and Quality, Illinois Valley Community Hospital, Peru, IL, p. A197

SMITH, Bradley, President and Chief Executive Officer, Rush Memorial Hospital, Rushville, IN, p. A219

SMITH, Brenda, Director Financial Services, Alliance Health Center, Meridian, MS, p. A359

SMITH, Brent, Chief Executive Officer, Comanche County Memorial Hospital, Lawton, OK, p. A509

SMITH, Brian
  Chief Financial Officer, Beth Israel Deaconess Hospital–Needham Campus, Needham, MA, p. A309
  Director of Operations, Wamego Health Center, Wamego, KS, p. A253

SMITH, C David M.D., Chief Medical Officer, Jay Hospital, Jay, FL, p. A129

SMITH, Carl, Director Information Systems, King's Daughters Medical Center, Brookhaven, MS, p. A353

SMITH, Carol A R.N., Director Operations and Nursing, Novant Health Medical Park Hospital, Winston, NC, p. A473

SMITH, Carol, Vice President Patient Care and Chief Nursing Officer, Tift Regional Medical Center, Tifton, GA, p. A166

SMITH, Carole, Senior Human Resource Business Partner, Banner Del E. Webb Medical Center, Sun City West, AZ, p. A37

SMITH, Cheryl, Manager Human Resources, New Braunfels Regional Rehabilitation Hospital, New Braunfels, TX, p. A635

SMITH, Chris, Chief Information Officer, Falls Community Hospital And Clinic, Marlin, TX, p. A632

SMITH, Connie, Chief Executive Officer, Medical Center At Bowling Green, Bowling Green, KY, p. A256

SMITH, Dan
  Director Human Resources, Austin Lakes Hospital, Austin, TX, p. A594
  Director Human Resources, Memorial Hospital, Carthage, IL, p. A179

SMITH, Daniel B
  Chief Financial Officer, Samaritan Pacific Communities Hospital, Newport, OR, p. A524
  Vice President Finance, Good Samaritan Regional Medical Center, Corvallis, OR, p. A521
  Vice President Finance, Samaritan Albany General Hospital, Albany, OR, p. A520
  Vice President Finance, Samaritan Lebanon Community Hospital, Lebanon, OR, p. A523

SMITH, Daniel L., Chief Financial Officer, Palo Pinto General Hospital, Mineral Wells, TX, p. A633

SMITH, Daniel, Chief Financial Officer, Tops Surgical Specialty Hospital, Houston, TX, p. A623

SMITH, Darrin, Vice President Human Resources, Parkview Medical Center, Pueblo, CO, p. A106

SMITH, Darwin K, Vice President Human Resources, Union Hospital, Dover, OH, p. A490

SMITH, Deborah S R.N., MS, Vice President, Chief Nursing Officer, OSF St. Joseph Medical Center, Bloomington, IL, p. A178

SMITH, Debra, Chief Nursing Officer, Healthsouth Rehabilitation Hospital, Kingsport, TN, p. A581

SMITH, Denise
  Director Financial Services, Florida State Hospital, Chattahoochee, FL, p. A121
  Director Health Information, Healthsouth Chattanooga Rehabilitation Hospital, Chattanooga, TN, p. A576
  Director People Services, Hshs St. Mary's Hospital, Decatur, IL, p. A185

SMITH, Dennis H, Director, Veterans Affairs Maryland Health Care System–Baltimore Division, Baltimore, MD, p. A296

SMITH, Diana B, Chief Financial Officer, Promise Hospital Of Dallas, Dallas, TX, p. A606

SMITH, Diane, Chief Nursing Officer, Baptist Health Extended Care Hospital, Little Rock, AR, p. A46

SMITH, Dianne, Director Personnel and Human Resources, Potomac Valley Hospital, Keyser, WV, p. A693

SMITH, Dick, Director Human Resources, West Park Hospital, Cody, WY, p. A718

SMITH, Donald, President Medical Staff, Bellevue Hospital, Bellevue, OH, p. A481

SMITH, Donna M, Chief Nursing Officer, Barstow Community Hospital, Barstow, CA, p. A53

SMITH, Donna P R.N., Vice President Chief Operating Officer and Chief Nursing Officer, Clifton Springs Hospital And Clinic, Clifton Springs, NY, p. A434

SMITH, Donnie
  Chief Human Resources Officer, Laird Hospital, Union, MS, p. A362
  Director Human Resources, Rush Foundation Hospital, Meridian, MS, p. A359
  Director of Human Resources, Specialty Hospital Of Meridian, Meridian, MS, p. A359

SMITH, Doug
  Chief Financial Officer, Mckay–Dee Hospital, Ogden, UT, p. A658
  Chief Financial Officer, Sun Behavioral Houston, Houston, TX, p. A622
  President and Chief Executive Officer, St. Anthony Regional Hospital, Carroll, IA, p. A223

SMITH, Elizabeth A, Director of Nursing, John J. Pershing Veterans Affairs Medical Center, Poplar Bluff, MO, p. A375

SMITH, Eric, Chief Financial Officer, Bayfront Health St. Petersburg, Saint Petersburg, FL, p. A141

SMITH, Ericka, Chief Operating Officer, Monterey Park Hospital, Monterey Park, CA, p. A75

SMITH, Erin, Chief Operating Officer, East Georgia Regional Medical Center, Statesboro, GA, p. A165

SMITH, Eugene, Chief Information Officer, Maniilaq Health Center, Kotzebue, AK, p. A26

SMITH, Forrest Bud H Jr, Chief Financial Officer, Fulton State Hospital, Fulton, MO, p. A368

SMITH, G. Todd., President, St. Elizabeth Community Hospital, Red Bluff, CA, p. A81

SMITH, Gary, Chief Operating Officer, Aurelia Osborn Fox Memorial Hospital, Oneonta, NY, p. A449

SMITH, Geoffrey, Chief Financial Officer, Lebanon Veterans Affairs Medical Center, Lebanon, PA, p. A538

SMITH, Gia, Chief Executive Officer, Central Valley Specialty Hospital, Modesto, CA, p. A74

SMITH, Greg, CPA
  Chief Financial Officer, Woman's Hospital, Baton Rouge, LA, p. A271
  Chief Medical Officer, Lake Region Healthcare, Fergus Falls, MN, p. A340

SMITH, Gregory,
  Fort Belknap Service Unit, Harlem, MT, p. A385
  Senior Vice President and Chief Information Officer, Midwest Orthopedic Specialty Hospital, Franklin, WI, p. A702
  Senior Vice President and Chief Information Officer, Wheaton Franciscan Healthcare – Franklin, Franklin, WI, p. A702
  Senior Vice President and Chief Information Officer, Wheaton Franciscan Healthcare – St. Francis, Milwaukee, WI, p. A708

SMITH, Gretchen, Vice President Nursing and Compliance and Risk, Rush Memorial Hospital, Rushville, IN, p. A219

SMITH, Harley, Chief Executive Officer, TMC Bonham Hospital, Bonham, TX, p. A598

SMITH, Heather
  Chief Operating Officer, Welch Community Hospital, Welch, WV, p. A696
  President, Conemaugh Meyersdale Medical Center, Meyersdale, PA, p. A541

SMITH, Holt, Chief Financial Officer, Springs Memorial Hospital, Lancaster, SC, p. A564

SMITH, Jack, Acting Chief Information Resources Management Service, Veterans Affairs Sierra Nevada Health Care System, Reno, NV, p. A405

SMITH, Jackie R.N., Chief Nursing Officer, Holdenville General Hospital, Holdenville, OK, p. A508

SMITH, James E.
  Superintendent, North Texas State Hospital, Wichita Falls Campus, Wichita Falls, TX, p. A654
  Superintendent, North Texas State Hospital, Vernon, TX, p. A651

SMITH, Jameson, President, Saint Joseph Hospital, Denver, CO, p. A101

SMITH, Jamesy D.O., Chief of Staff, Parkland Health Center – Farmington Community, Farmington, MO, p. A368

SMITH, Jamie, Supervisor Health Information Management Systems, Healthsouth Rehabilitation Hospital Of Sewickley, Sewickley, PA, p. A550

SMITH, Janet, Chief Financial Officer, Troy Regional Medical Center, Troy, AL, p. A23

SMITH, Jason
  Chief Medical Officer, Beaver Dam Community Hospitals, Beaver Dam, WI, p. A699
  Chief Nursing Officer, Piedmont Newnan Hospital, Newnan, GA, p. A162

SMITH, Jay, Director Information Systems, Brownwood Regional Medical Center, Brownwood, TX, p. A599

SMITH, Jeanna, Administrative Assistant and Human Resources Officer, Polk Medical Center, Cedartown, GA, p. A154

SMITH, Jeff, Chief Information Officer, Holy Cross Hospital, Fort Lauderdale, FL, p. A125

SMITH, Jeffrey A. M.D., Senior Vice President and Chief Medical Officer, Aurora St. Luke's Medical Center, Milwaukee, WI, p. A707

SMITH, Jesse, Director of Nursing, Keefe Memorial Hospital, Cheyenne Wells, CO, p. A99

SMITH, Jim, Director Information Systems, Washington County Memorial Hospital, Potosi, MO, p. A375

SMITH, Jo Beth
  Chief Operating Officer, Medical Arts Hospital, Lamesa, TX, p. A628
  Vice President Human Resources, Decatur County Hospital, Leon, IA, p. A230

SMITH, JoAnn P. R.N., Chief Nursing Officer, and Vice President Patient Care Services, Morehead Memorial Hospital, Eden, NC, p. A461

SMITH, Joanne C., M.D., President and Chief Executive Officer, Shirley Ryan Abilitylab, Chicago, IL, p. A183

SMITH, Jodi, Administrative Assistant Human Resources, Eureka Springs Hospital, Eureka Springs, AR, p. A42

SMITH, Jon
  Chief Executive Officer, Caribou Memorial Hospital And Living Center, Soda Springs, ID, p. A176
  Chief Financial Officer, Lost Rivers Medical Center, Arco, ID, p. A171

SMITH, Jonathan, Assistant Administrator and Chief Financial Officer, Blount Memorial Hospital, Maryville, TN, p. A583

SMITH, Joseph S., Chief Executive Officer, Boone County Hospital, Boone, IA, p. A223

SMITH, Julia
  Chief Financial Officer, Kindred Hospital Rome, Rome, GA, p. A163
  Chief Financial Officer, Kindred Hospital–Chattanooga, Chattanooga, TN, p. A576
  Chief Financial Officer, Vibra Hospital Of Charleston, Mt. Pleasant, SC, p. A564

SMITH, Julie R.N., MSN
  Director of Nursing, Jersey Community Hospital, Jerseyville, IL, p. A191
  Director Human Resources, Healthsouth Lakeshore Rehabilitation Hospital, Birmingham, AL, p. A14
  Senior Human Resources Strategic Partner, Providence Milwaukie Hospital, Milwaukie, OR, p. A524

SMITH, Karen S, Director Information Services, Chilton Medical Center, Pompton Plains, NJ, p. A419

SMITH, Karla, Director Human Resources, St. Peter's Hospital, Helena, MT, p. A385

SMITH, Karyl, Director Human Resources, Harbor–Ucla Medical Center, Torrance, CA, p. A93

SMITH, Kathy A. MSN, R.N., Nurse Executive, Summit Behavioral Healthcare, Cincinnati, OH, p. A484

SMITH, Kelli M.D., Chief of Staff, Magee General Hospital, Magee, MS, p. A358

SMITH, Kelly C., Senior Vice President and Division President, Beaumont Hospital–Dearborn, Dearborn, MI, p. A317

SMITH, Kenneth P., Chief of Staff, John C. Fremont Healthcare District, Mariposa, CA, p. A73

SMITH, Kenneth M.D., Emergency Medicine Medical Director, Coalinga Regional Medical Center, Coalinga, CA, p. A56

SMITH, Kevin L, Area Finance Officer, Kaiser Permanente South Sacramento Medical Center, Sacramento, CA, p. A83

SMITH, Kevin M, Director Human Resources, Indian Path Medical Center, Kingsport, TN, p. A581

SMITH, Kevin D.O., Chief of Staff, Otsego Memorial Hospital, Gaylord, MI, p. A320

SMITH, Kim, Director Business Office, Doctor's Hospital Of Deer Creek, Leesville, LA, p. A280

SMITH, Kris, Controller, Chi St. Joseph Health Madison Hospital, Madisonville, TX, p. A631

SMITH, Kyle, Director Information Systems, Iredell Health System, Statesville, NC, p. A471

SMITH, Lana, Human Resources Director, Ashe Memorial Hospital, Jefferson, NC, p. A465

SMITH, Larry, Senior Vice President and Chief Financial Officer, Uw Medicine/Valley Medical Center, Renton, WA, p. A684

SMITH, Laura
Interim Chief Nursing Officer and Director of Infection Control, Ellett Memorial Hospital, Appleton City, MO, p. A364
Vice President Finance and Chief Financial Officer, Milford Hospital, Milford, CT, p. A111

SMITH, LaVonne, Director Health Information Technology, Tomah Memorial Hospital, Tomah, WI, p. A713

SMITH, Leighton M.D., Chief Medical Officer, Florida Hospital Fish Memorial, Orange City, FL, p. A136

SMITH, Leora, Information System and Health Information Management Team Leader, Phelps Memorial Health Center, Holdrege, NE, p. A394

SMITH, Linda C M.D., Medical Director, Pam Rehabilitation Hospital Of Beaumont, Beaumont, TX, p. A597

SMITH, Linda T, Director Human Resources, Clay County Hospital, Ashland, AL, p. A13

SMITH, Linda V, Vice President Human Resources, Central Florida Regional Hospital, Sanford, FL, p. A142

SMITH, Lori J., Vice President Human Resources, St. Bernards Medical Center, Jonesboro, AR, p. A45

SMITH, Lori, Chief Financial Officer, North Big Horn Hospital District, Lovell, WY, p. A719

SMITH, Lorie, Director Human Resources, Conemaugh Nason Medical Center, Roaring Spring, PA, p. A549

SMITH, Lory Beth, Manager Human Resource, South Texas Surgical Hospital, Corpus Christi, TX, p. A603

SMITH, M. Scott, President, St. Anthony's Hospital, Saint Petersburg, FL, p. A142

SMITH, Marisa, Director, Tomball Regional Medical Center, Tomball, TX, p. A650

SMITH, Mark, M.D.
Chief Medical Officer, Methodist Richardson Medical Center, Richardson, TX, p. A639
Director Human Resources, Providence Holy Family Hospital, Spokane, WA, p. A687
Director Human Resources, Providence Sacred Heart Medical Center & Children's Hospital, Spokane, WA, p. A687
Director Nursing Operations, Northern Colorado Rehabilitation Hospital, Johnstown, CO, p. A104
President and Chief Operating Officer, Multicare Auburn Medical Center, Auburn, WA, p. A678

SMITH, Marsh, Manager Health Information, University Behavioral Health Of Denton, Denton, TX, p. A608

SMITH, Marshall E., Chief Executive Officer, Regency Hospital Of Minneapolis, Golden Valley, MN, p. A340

SMITH, Martha, R.N.
Chief Nursing Officer, New Orleans East Hospital, New Orleans, LA, p. A282
Chief Executive Officer, Kapiolani Medical Center For Women & Children, Honolulu, HI, p. A168

SMITH, Mary Clare.
Director, Western State Hospital, Staunton, VA, p. A676
Acting Facility Director, Commonwealth Center For Children And Adolescents, Staunton, VA, p. A675

SMITH, Mary Jo, Chief Human Resources Officer, University Of Illinois Hospital & Health Sciences System, Chicago, IL, p. A184

SMITH, Matt, Interim Chief Executive Officer, Bourbon Community Hospital, Paris, KY, p. A266

SMITH, Matthew M.D., Vice President Medical Affairs and Chief Medical Officer, Baylor Scott & White Medical Center – Carrollton, Carrollton, TX, p. A600

SMITH, Megan M.D., Chief Medical Staff, Community Memorial Hospital, Burke, SD, p. A568

SMITH, Melinda, Chief Information Systems, H. C. Watkins Memorial Hospital, Quitman, MS, p. A361

SMITH, Melissa, Controller, Select Specialty Hospital–Jackson, Jackson, MS, p. A357

SMITH, Michael, M.D.
Vice President Medical Affairs, St. Joseph Mercy Oakland, Pontiac, MI, p. A328
Director of Nursing, Cypress Creek Hospital, Houston, TX, p. A620

SMITH, Michelle T R.N., MSN, FACHE, Vice President Nursing Chief Nursing Officer Chief Experience Officer, GHS Greenville Memorial Hospital, Greenville, SC, p. A562

SMITH, Michelle, Coordinator Human Resources, Baton Rouge Rehabilitation Hospital, Baton Rouge, LA, p. A270

SMITH, Mickey, Chief Executive Officer, Oak Hill Hospital, Brooksville, FL, p. A121

SMITH, Mike
Chief Information Officer, Cape Coral Hospital, Cape Coral, FL, p. A121
Chief Information Officer, Gulf Coast Medical Center, Fort Myers, FL, p. A125
Chief Information Officer, Lee Memorial Hospital, Fort Myers, FL, p. A125

SMITH, Millie, Interim Chief Financial Officer, Galesburg Cottage Hospital, Galesburg, IL, p. A188

SMITH, Missy, Coordinator Human Resources, Scotland County Hospital, Memphis, MO, p. A373

SMITH, Mona R., Chief Nursing Officer, Green Valley Hospital, Green Valley, AZ, p. A30

SMITH, Moneca, Chief Nursing Officer, The University Of Toledo Medical Center, Toledo, OH, p. A501

SMITH, Nadine, Director Human Resources, Reeves County Hospital, Pecos, TX, p. A637

SMITH, Natalie R R.N., MSN, Vice President Patient Care Services and Chief Nursing Officer, Portneuf Medical Center, Pocatello, ID, p. A175

SMITH, Neil, D.O., President, Cleveland Clinic Fairview Hospital, Cleveland, OH, p. A485

SMITH, Nekisha, Director Health Information Systems, Riverland Medical Center, Ferriday, LA, p. A274

SMITH, Nicholas T., Chief Executive Officer, Palm Springs General Hospital, Hialeah, FL, p. A126

SMITH, Norine, Chief Executive Officer, Red Lake Indian Health Service Hospital, Red Lake, MN, p. A346

SMITH, Oliver, President and Chief Executive Officer, Paris Community Hospital, Paris, IL, p. A197

SMITH, Pam, Chief Nursing Officer, Healthsouth Rehabilitation Hospital North Texas, Richardson, TX, p. A639

SMITH, Pamela, Commander, U.S. Air Force Regional Hospital, Eglin Afb, FL, p. A124

SMITH, Patricia, Chief Nursing Officer, Oconee Memorial Hospital, Seneca, SC, p. A566

SMITH, Patrick, M.D.
Chief Medical Officer, Abrazo Arrowhead Campus, Glendale, AZ, p. A30
Director Information Technology, Clay County Hospital, Ashland, AL, p. A13

SMITH, Peg, Vice President and Chief Nursing Officer, Chandler Regional Medical Center, Chandler, AZ, p. A28

SMITH, Phyllis J., Associate Director, Birmingham Veterans Affairs Medical Center, Birmingham, AL, p. A14

SMITH, Phyllis, Vice President Human Resources, Northeastern Health System, Tahlequah, OK, p. A516

SMITH, Randall, Executive Vice President, Jackson Park Hospital And Medical Center, Chicago, IL, p. A181

SMITH, Rebecca T, Chief Operating Officer and Chief Nursing Officer, Caldwell Unc Health Care, Lenoir, NC, p. A466

SMITH, Rhonda E., R.N., MSN
Chief Nursing Officer, Union Hospital Clinton, Clinton, IN, p. A205
Vice President Patient Care Services and Chief Nursing Officer, Union Hospital, Terre Haute, IN, p. A220
Applications Support Manager, Uh Portage Medical Center, Ravenna, OH, p. A498
Chief Nursing Officer, Benewah Community Hospital, Saint Maries, ID, p. A175
Director Human Resources, Shriners Hospitals For Children–Portland, Portland, OR, p. A525
Vice President Human Resources, Kaiser Foundation Hospital Westside Medical Center, Hillsboro, OR, p. A522

SMITH, Rich
Vice President Human Resources, Kaiser Sunnyside Medical Center, Clackamas, OR, p. A520
Chief Financial Officer, JFK Johnson Rehabilitation Institute, Edison, NJ, p. A413

SMITH, Richard C.
Senior Vice President and Chief Financial Officer, JFK Medical Center, Edison, NJ, p. A413
Senior Vice President Finance, Hackensack Meridian Health Shore Rehabilitation Institute, Brick, NJ, p. A412

SMITH, Richard, Chief of Staff, Carroll County Memorial Hospital, Carrollton, MO, p. A366

SMITH, Rick
Chief Operating Officer, Health Central Hospital, Ocoee, FL, p. A136
Director Information Services, Cibola General Hospital, Grants, NM, p. A426
Director Information Systems, Tennova Healthcare–Jamestown, Jamestown, TN, p. A580
Senior Vice President Human Resources and Chief Administrative Officer, Vail Valley Health Hospital, Vail, CO, p. A108

SMITH, Robert M., M.D., Director, Va San Diego Healthcare System, San Diego, CA, p. A86

SMITH, Robert T., M.D.
Chief Medical Officer, Kettering Medical Center, Kettering, OH, p. A493
Chief Medical Officer, Sycamore Medical Center, Miamisburg, OH, p. A496

SMITH, Robin C, Chief Nursing Officer, Indiana University Health White Memorial Hospital, Monticello, IN, p. A216

SMITH, Rodney, President and Chief Executive Officer, Harrisburg Medical Center, Harrisburg, IL, p. A189

SMITH, Roy, Chief Financial Officer, Onslow Memorial Hospital, Jacksonville, NC, p. A465

SMITH, Ruth, Chief Human Resource Officer, Banner Lassen Medical Center, Susanville, CA, p. A93

SMITH, Ryan K., Chief Executive Officer, Memorial Hospital Of Converse County, Douglas, WY, p. A718

SMITH, Ryan K, Senior Vice President Information Technology, Banner – University Medical Center South, Tucson, AZ, p. A37

SMITH, Scott M., Chief Executive Officer, Mercy Regional Medical Center, Ville Platte, LA, p. A287

SMITH, Scott, M.D.
Chief Medical Officer, Adams Memorial Hospital, Decatur, IN, p. A206
President, St. Joseph's Hospital, Tampa, FL, p. A145

SMITH, Sherry, Manager Human Resources, Dallas County Hospital, Perry, IA, p. A233

SMITH, Shirley M, Chief Financial Officer, Andalusia Health, Andalusia, AL, p. A13

SMITH, Sid, Director Information Resources, Larned State Hospital, Larned, KS, p. A245

SMITH, Skip, Vice President Finance, Iredell Health System, Statesville, NC, p. A471

SMITH, Stephen
Associate Administrator, Turning Point Hospital, Moultrie, GA, p. A162
President, Selby General Hospital, Marietta, OH, p. A494

SMITH, Steve, M.D.
Chief of Staff, Providence Kodiak Island Medical Center, Kodiak, AK, p. A26
Assistant Vice President Finance, Chi St. Gabriel's Health, Little Falls, MN, p. A342
Chief Financial Officer, Kansas Heart Hospital, Wichita, KS, p. A253

SMITH, Steven L., Chief Executive Officer, Matagorda Regional Medical Center, Bay City, TX, p. A596

SMITH, Steven, Chief Information Officer, Northshore University Health System, Evanston, IL, p. A187

SMITH, Stormy, Chief Nursing Officer, Chillicothe Hospital District, Chillicothe, TX, p. A601

SMITH, Suzanne E R.N., MSN, Chief Nursing Officer, San Juan Regional Medical Center, Farmington, NM, p. A426

SMITH, Taylor, Chief Financial Officer, Eureka Springs Hospital, Eureka Springs, AR, p. A42

SMITH, Teresa, Chief Financial Officer, Memorial Hospital, Carthage, IL, p. A179

SMITH, Terrance M.D., Chairman Medical Staff, Sanford Clear Lake Medical Center, Clear Lake, SD, p. A569

SMITH, Terri, Chief Operating Officer, Sacred Heart Hospital Pensacola, Pensacola, FL, p. A139

SMITH, Thomas C. III, FACHE, Director, Birmingham Veterans Affairs Medical Center, Birmingham, AL, p. A14

SMITH, Thomas M.D., Vice President Medical Affairs, Hutchinson Regional Medical Center, Hutchinson, KS, p. A243

SMITH, Tiffani, Chief Human Resources Officer, Stonesprings Hospital Center, Dulles, VA, p. A666

SMITH, Tiffany, Director Human Resources, Wellstone Regional Hospital, Jeffersonville, IN, p. A213

SMITH, Tim
Chief Executive Officer, Iroquois Memorial Hospital And Resident Home, Watseka, IL, p. A202
Senior Vice President and Chief Executive Officer, Sharp Memorial Hospital, San Diego, CA, p. A86

SMITH, Todd A., Chief Executive Officer, Aurora Charter Oak Hospital, Covina, CA, p. A57

SMITH, Toni, Chief Nursing Officer, Kern Medical Center, Bakersfield, CA, p. A53

SMITH, Tonya, President, Munson Healthcare Cadillac Hospital, Cadillac, MI, p. A315

SMITH, Tracy, Director Human Resources, Mercy St. Francis Hospital, Mountain View, MO, p. A374

SMITH, Trevor, Chief Management Information Services, Gunnison Valley Hospital, Gunnison, CO, p. A103

SMITH, Tripp, Chief Executive Officer, Healthsouth Rehabilitation Hospital, Largo, FL, p. A130

SMITH, Trisha, Chief Financial Officer, Mimbres Memorial Hospital, Deming, NM, p. A426

SMITH, Tyson M.D., Chief Medical Officer, Haywood Regional Medical Center, Clyde, NC, p. A460

SMITH, Vanessa, Chief Human Resources Officer, Community Medical Center, Toms River, NJ, p. A421

SMITH, Vincent
Chief Information Officer, NYC Health + Hospitals / Elmhurst, New Rochelle, NY, p. A445
Chief Information Officer, NYC Health + Hospitals / Queens, New Rochelle, NY, p. A445

SMITH, Wade, Chief Operating Officer, Drew Memorial Health System, Monticello, AR, p. A47

SMITH, Wendell, Chief Operating Officer, St. James Behavioral Health Hospital, Gonzales, LA, p. A275

SMITH, Wayne T., Chairman, President and Chief Executive Officer, Community Health Systems, Inc., Franklin, TN, p. B33

SMITH-HILL, Janet
Executive Vice Presideent and Chief Human Resource Officer, Novant Health Charlotte Orthopaedic Hospital, Charlotte, NC, p. A459
Executive Vice Presideent and Chief Human Resource Officer, Novant Health Thomasville Medical Center, Thomasville, NC, p. A471
Executive Vice President and Chief HR Officer, Novant Health Matthews Medical Center, Matthews, NC, p. A466
Executive Vice President and Chief Human Resource Officer, Novant Health Medical Park Hospital, Winston, NC, p. A473
Executive Vice President and Chief Human Resource Officer, Novant Health Rowan Medical Center, Salisbury, NC, p. A470
Executive Vice President and Chief Human Resources Officer, Novant Health Brunswick Medical Center, Bolivia, NC, p. A458
Executive Vice President and Chief Human Resources, Novant Health Huntersville Medical Center, Huntersville, NC, p. A465
Senior Vice President Human Resources, Novant Health Forsyth Medical Center, Winston, NC, p. A473
Senior Vice President Human Resources, Novant Health Presbyterian Medical Center, Charlotte, NC, p. A460

SMITH-ZUBA, Lorraina R.N., MSN, Chief Nursing Officer, Porter Medical Center, Middlebury, VT, p. A662

SMITHERS, John, Network Specialist, River Hospital, Alexandria Bay, NY, p. A430

SMITHHART, Paula, Director Human Resources, Coryell Memorial Hospital, Gatesville, TX, p. A616

SMITHSON, Pamela R.N., Vice President Nursing, Davis Medical Center, Elkins, WV, p. A691

SMITHSON, Tracey MSN, R.N., Chief Nursing Officer, Medical City North Hills, North Richland Hills, TX, p. A635

SMOAK, Tim, Administrator, Mcleod Medical Center–Darlington, Darlington, SC, p. A561

SMOCK, Tait, Manager Information Systems, Pella Regional Health Center, Pella, IA, p. A233

SMOKER, Bret M.D., Clinical Director, Phs Santa Fe Indian Hospital, Santa Fe, NM, p. A428

SMOKOVITZ, Ryan, Chief Executive Officer, Healthsouth Rehabilitation Hospital At Drake, Cincinnati, OH, p. A484

SMOLIK, Chris, Chief Executive Officer, Goodland Regional Medical Center, Goodland, KS, p. A241

SMOLIK, Trisha R.N., MSN, Chief Nursing Officer, Select Specialty Hospital – Lincoln, Lincoln, NE, p. A395

SMOOT, Steve, Administrator, Utah Valley Hospital, Provo, UT, p. A659

SMORRA, Colleen, Assistant Administrator, Hackensack Meridian Health Pascack Valley Medical Center, Westwood, NJ, p. A423

SMOTHERS, Kevin M.D., Vice President Chief Medical Officer, Adventist Healthcare Shady Grove Medical Center, Rockville, MD, p. A300

SMOTHERS, Mark M.D., Chief Medical Officer, University Of Mississippi Medical Center Holmes County, Lexington, MS, p. A358

SMOTHERS, Stephen, Director Information Systems, Medical Center Enterprise, Enterprise, AL, p. A17

SMYRSKI, John A. III, Commanding Officer, William Beaumont Army Medical Center, El Paso, TX, p. A612

SMYTH, Thomas, President and Chief Executive Officer, University Of Maryland St. Joseph Medical Center, Towson, MD, p. A301

SNAPP, Jeremy, Director Information Systems, Lindsborg Community Hospital, Lindsborg, KS, p. A246

SNAPP, William R, III
Vice President and Chief Financial Officer, Ephraim Mcdowell Fort Logan Hospital, Stanford, KY, p. A268
Vice President Finance and Chief Financial Officer, Ephraim Mcdowell Regional Medical Center, Danville, KY, p. A257

SNAVELY, Gretchen, Director Human Resources, Holton Community Hospital, Holton, KS, p. A242

SNEAD, Joseph, Chief of Medical Staff, Stonewall Jackson Memorial Hospital, Weston, WV, p. A697

SNEAD, Raymond A. FACHE, Interim Chief Financial Officer, South Georgia Medical Center, Valdosta, GA, p. A166

SNEDEGAR, Michael, Chief Financial Officer, Bourbon Community Hospital, Paris, KY, p. A266

SNEED, Farron, Chief Operating Officer, Hillcrest Medical Center, Tulsa, OK, p. A517

SNEERINGER, Rhonda M.D., Chief Medical Officer, Barton Memorial Hospital, South Lake Tahoe, CA, p. A92

SNELGROVE, Steven C., President, Howard County General Hospital, Columbia, MD, p. A298

SNELL, Peggy, Chief Finance Officer, Cherry County Hospital, Valentine, NE, p. A400

SNENK, Don, Chief Financial Officer, Mercy Fitzgerald Hospital, Darby, PA, p. A532

SNIDE, Jeaniffr P., Chief Nursing Officer, Crete Area Medical Center, Crete, NE, p. A392

SNIDER, Charles, Vice President Human Resources, Oak Hill Hospital, Brooksville, FL, p. A121

SNIDER, Cheryl, Director Human Resources, St. Vincent General Hospital District, Leadville, CO, p. A105

SNIDER, Glenn R., M.D.
Interim Director, Louis A. Johnson Veterans Affairs Medical Center, Clarksburg, WV, p. A691
Chief of Staff, Louis A. Johnson Veterans Affairs Medical Center, Clarksburg, WV, p. A691

SNIDER, Tim, Senior Vice President for Finance, Upper Valley Medical Center, Troy, OH, p. A501

SNIDER, Timothy, Manager Information Systems, Fannin Regional Hospital, Blue Ridge, GA, p. A152

SNIPES, Rob, Administrator, Optim Medical Center – Tattnall, Reidsville, GA, p. A163

SNODGRASS, Liz, Chief Financial Officer, Trigg County Hospital, Cadiz, KY, p. A256

SNOOK, Joel, Chief Financial Officer, Westchester General Hospital, Miami, FL, p. A134

SNOW, Dorothy M.D., Chief of Staff, Veterans Affairs Maryland Health Care System–Baltimore Division, Baltimore, MD, p. A296

SNOW, Jason T, Director People Services, Hshs St. Elizabeth's Hospital, Belleville, IL, p. A178

SNOW, John, Vice President Ancillary and Support Services, Iredell Health System, Statesville, NC, p. A471

SNOW, Meldon L., Chief Executive Officer, Logan County Hospital, Oakley, KS, p. A248

SNOW, Ryan
Director Human Resources, Habersham Medical Center, Demorest, GA, p. A156
Administrator, Chatuge Regional Hospital And Nursing Home, Hiawassee, GA, p. A159

SNOWDON, Susan, Director Information Technology, Four Winds Hospital, Saratoga Springs, NY, p. A452

SNYDER, Alice, Vice President, Chief Nursing Officer, OSF St. Mary Medical Center, Galesburg, IL, p. A188

SNYDER, Bobby
Chief Executive Officer, Midwest City Specialty Hospital, Midwest City, OK, p. A510
Interim Chief Executive Officer, Plum Creek Specialty Hospital, Amarillo, TX, p. A592

SNYDER, Daniel J., Chief Executive Officer, University Health System, Shreveport, LA, p. B138

SNYDER, David M.D., Chief of Staff, Dekalb Medical At Downtown Decatur, Decatur, GA, p. A156

SNYDER, Jeffery, President, Easton Hospital, Easton, PA, p. A533

SNYDER, John, Executive Vice President and System Chief Operating Officer, Carle Foundation Hospital, Urbana, IL, p. A201

SNYDER, Kristi, Vice President Human Resources, Charleston Area Medical Center, Charleston, WV, p. A691

SNYDER, Kristy, Director Human Resources, Fulton County Health Center, Wauseon, OH, p. A502

SNYDER, Kyle C., Chief Administrative Officer, Geisinger Holy Spirit, Camp Hill, PA, p. A530

SNYDER, Leah, Director Health Information Services, Loring Hospital, Sac City, IA, p. A234

SNYDER, Mary E, Chief Operations Officer, Montrose Memorial Hospital, Montrose, CO, p. A106

SNYDER, Matthew R.N., Director of Nursing, Johnson County Hospital, Tecumseh, NE, p. A400

SNYDER, Norman M.D., Medical Director, Vantage Point Of Northwest Arkansas, Fayetteville, AR, p. A43

SNYDER, Phyllis, Chief Nursing Officer, Ahmc Anaheim Regional Medical Center, Anaheim, CA, p. A51

SNYDER, R Brad, Chief Operating Officer, Torrance State Hospital, Torrance, PA, p. A551

SNYDER, Renae, Chief Financial Officer, Sakakawea Medical Center, Hazen, ND, p. A476

SNYDER, Ron, Chief Operating Officer, Ohiohealth Hardin Memorial Hospital, Kenton, OH, p. A493

SNYDER, Sheree, Manager Human Resources, Hillcrest Hospital Henryetta, Henryetta, OK, p. A508

SNYDER, Steve, Chief Financial Officer, Ohio Hospital For Psychiatry, Columbus, OH, p. A487

SNYDER, Tony, Administrator and Chief Executive Officer, Pomerene Hospital, Millersburg, OH, p. A496

SNYDER, Vicky, Chief Operating Officer, Cleveland Clinic, Medina Hospital, Medina, OH, p. A495

SOARES, Brian, Chief Executive Officer, Kindred Hospital South Florida–Fort Lauderdale, Fort Lauderdale, FL, p. A125

SOARES, Jair C., M.D., Executive Director, University Of Texas Harris County Psychiatric Center, Houston, TX, p. A623

SOBECK, Brenda, Director of Human Resources, Jones Memorial Hospital, Wellsville, NY, p. A455

SOBER, Joseph, President, Mercy Allen Hospital, Oberlin, OH, p. A497

SOBIECK, Bridget, Director of Nursing, North Shore Health, Grand Marais, MN, p. A340

SODERLING, Marcia R.N., Hospital Nurse Executive, Legacy Mount Hood Medical Center, Gresham, OR, p. A522

SOEKEN, Charles
Director Information Technology, Providence Medical Center, Kansas City, KS, p. A244
Director Information Technology, Saint John Hospital, Leavenworth, KS, p. A245

SOEKORO, Julie, Chief Financial Officer, Grandview Medical Center, Birmingham, AL, p. A14

SOGARD, Matt, Chief Executive Officer, Lee's Summit Medical Center, Lee's Summit, MO, p. A372

SOGLIN, David, Chief Medical Officer, La Rabida Children's Hospital, Chicago, IL, p. A181

SOHN, Steven M.D., President Medical Staff, Dallas County Hospital, Perry, IA, p. A233

SOILEAU, D. Kirk., FACHE, Chief Executive Officer, Natchitoches Regional Medical Center, Natchitoches, LA, p. A282

SOIMAN, Erika CPA, Chief Financial Officer, NYC Health + Hospitals / Woodhull, New Rochelle, NY, p. A446

SOKOLA, Thomas P., Chief Administrative Officer, Geisinger Medical Center, Danville, PA, p. A532

SOLA', Ivan', President Medical Staff, Carlisle Regional Medical Center, Carlisle, PA, p. A531

SOLAIMAN, Shereen, Vice President Human Resources, Ohiohealth Riverside Methodist Hospital, Columbus, OH, p. A488

SOLARE, Frank A., Chief Executive Officer, Kindred Hospital Northwest Indiana, Hammond, IN, p. A210

SOLAZZO, Mark J, Regional Chief Operating Officer, Syosset Hospital, Syosset, NY, p. A453

SOLBERG, Bradley V., FACHE, President, OSF Saint James – John W. Albrecht Medical Center, Pontiac, IL, p. A198

SOLBERG, Don M.D., Chief Medical Officer, Kittitas Valley Healthcare, Ellensburg, WA, p. A680

SOLCHER, Barry M.D., Chief of Staff, The Physicians Centre Hospital, Bryan, TX, p. A600

SOLDO, Stephen M.D., Chief Medical Officer, Saint Agnes Medical Center, Fresno, CA, p. A61

SOLE, Kelly, Chief Operating Officer, Appalachian Behavioral Healthcare, Athens, OH, p. A480

SOLER, Eddie, Chief Financial Officer, Florida Hospital, Orlando, FL, p. A137

SOLES, Jason, Manager Information Systems, St. James Mercy Hospital, Hornell, NY, p. A437

SOLIE, Carol M M.D., Chief Medical Officer, Wyoming Medical Center, Casper, WY, p. A717

SOLIMAN, Russell
Director Information Services, Presence St. Mary's Hospital, Kankakee, IL, p. A191
System Manager Client Services and Management Information Services, Presence Saint Joseph Medical Center, Joliet, IL, p. A191

SOLIN, Andrea
Chief Financial Officer, Lovelace Rehabilitation Hospital, Albuquerque, NM, p. A424

SPRIGGS, Larry Floyd CPA, Controller, Healthsouth Rehabilitation Institute Of San Antonio (Riosa), San Antonio, TX, p. A642

SPRINGATE, Brian, Chief Executive Officer, Fleming County Hospital, Flemingsburg, KY, p. A258

SPRINGER, Amy, Medical Director, Webster County Community Hospital, Red Cloud, NE, p. A399

SPRINGER, Madge, Director Human Resources, Florida Hospital Waterman, Tavares, FL, p. A145

SPRINGER, Sharon, Chief Nursing Officer, Cameron Memorial Community Hospital, Angola, IN, p. A203

SPRINGER, Theresa, Chief Financial Officer, OSF Holy Family Medical Center, Monmouth, IL, p. A194

SPRINGMANN, Tressa
Vice President and Chief Information Officer, Levindale Hebrew Geriatric Center And Hospital, Baltimore, MD, p. A294
Vice President and Chief Information Officer, Northwest Hospital, Randallstown, MD, p. A300

SPRINKEL, George, Chief Financial Officer, Tennova Healthcare–Clarksville, Clarksville, TN, p. A577

SPROTT, Kendell R., M.D., JD, Chief Executive Officer, Matheny Medical And Educational Center, Peapack, NJ, p. A418

SPROUT, Merry R.N., Chief Nursing Officer, Antelope Memorial Hospital, Neligh, NE, p. A396

SPROWL, Chris M.D., Vice President, Peacehealth St. Joseph Medical Center, Bellingham, WA, p. A678

SPRUYT, Jim, Chief Executive Officer, Rolling Hills Hospital, Franklin, TN, p. A579

SPRYS, Michael D.O., Chief of Staff, Medical Arts Hospital, Lamesa, TX, p. A628

SPUHLER, Richard, Chief Executive Officer, Brigham City Community Hospital, Brigham City, UT, p. A656

SPURGEON, Sharon A., Chief Executive Officer, Coalinga Regional Medical Center, Coalinga, CA, p. A56

SPURLOCK, James D.O., Chief of Staff, Saint Thomas Stones River Hospital, Woodbury, TN, p. A590

SPYKERMAN, Connie, Chief Nursing Officer, Pelham Medical Center, Greer, SC, p. A563

SPYROW, Florence (Flo)., Chief Administrative Officer, Flagstaff Medical Center, Flagstaff, AZ, p. A29

SQUIRES, Danny
Chief Financial Officer, Wake Forest Baptist Health–Davie Medical Center, Bermuda Run, NC, p. A457
Vice President and Chief Financial Officer, Wake Forest Baptist Health–Lexington Medical Center, Lexington, NC, p. A466

SQUIRES, Elizabeth R.N., Chief Nursing Officer, Healthsouth Rehabilitation Hospital Of Tallahassee, Tallahassee, FL, p. A144

SQUIRES, Paula C, Senior Vice President, Chief Human Resources Officer and Chief Human Resources Officer, Baystate Medical Center, Springfield, MA, p. A311

SQUIRES, Teresa R.N., Chief Nursing Officer, Lake District Hospital, Lakeview, OR, p. A523

SREBINSKI, Ron, Chief Financial Officer, Caro Community Hospital, Caro, MI, p. A316

SRIBNICK, Wayne M.D., Senior Vice President and Chief Medical Officer, Providence Hospital, Columbia, SC, p. A560

SRINIVASAN, Parthasarathy M.D., President Medical Staff, Galesburg Cottage Hospital, Galesburg, IL, p. A188

SRIPADA, Subra
Exec. Vice President, Chief Transformation Officer and Chief Information Officer, Beaumont Hospital – Taylor, Taylor, MI, p. A331
Executive Vice President, Chief Transformation Officer and Chief Information Officer, Beaumont Hospital – Trenton, Trenton, MI, p. A332
Executive Vice President, Chief Transformation Officer and Chief Information Officer, Beaumont Hospital – Wayne, Wayne, MI, p. A333
Executive Vice President, Chief Transformation Officer and Chief Information Officer, Beaumont Hospital–Dearborn, Dearborn, MI, p. A317
Executive Vice President, Chief Transportation Officer and Chief Information Officer, Beaumont Hospital – Farmington Hills, Farmington Hills, MI, p. A319
Executive Vice President, Chief Transportation Officer and Chief Information Officer, Beaumont Hospital – Grosse Pointe, Grosse Pointe, MI, p. A322
Executive Vice President, Chief Transportation Officer and Chief Information Officer, Beaumont Hospital – Royal Oak, Royal Oak, MI, p. A329
Executive Vice President, Chief Transportation Officer and Chief Information Officer, Beaumont Hospital – Troy, Troy, MI, p. A332

SRIVASTAVA, Mohit M.D., Chief of Staff, Bunkie General Hospital, Bunkie, LA, p. A272

ST CLAIR, Jeffery M., President and Chief Executive Officer, Springhill Memorial Hospital, Mobile, AL, p. A20

ST PIERRE, Jay, Chief Financial Officer, North Florida Regional Medical Center, Gainesville, FL, p. A125

ST. AUBYN, Lisa, Chief Executive Officer, Signature Psychiatric Hospital, Kansas City, MO, p. A370

ST. GERMAIN, Jackie, Chief Executive Officer, Rock Prairie Behavioral Health, College Station, TX, p. A602

ST. LOUIS, Charles, Director of Patient Care Services, Kahi Mohala Behavioral Health, Ewa Beach, HI, p. A168

ST. PE', Laurin, Administrator – Singing River Hospital, Singing River Health System, Pascagoula, MS, p. A360

ST. PETER, Colette, Senior Manager Human Resources, Mercy Hospital Carthage, Carthage, MO, p. A366

ST. PIERRE, Fran, Chief Nursing Officer, Hood Memorial Hospital, Amite, LA, p. A270

STAATS, Jason, Chief Executive Officer, Cumberland Hall Hospital, Hopkinsville, KY, p. A259

STABRYLA, Della, Director of Nursing, Ellwood City Hospital, Ellwood City, PA, p. A534

STACEY, Brian, Chief Financial Officer, NYC Health + Hospitals / Queens, New Rochelle, NY, p. A445

STACEY, Susan, Chief Nursing Officer, Providence Sacred Heart Medical Center & Children's Hospital, Spokane, WA, p. A687

STACIE, Beverly, Director Human Resources, Clifton T. Perkins Hospital Center, Jessup, MD, p. A299

STACKHOUSE, Jenni, Chief Financial Officer, River Point Behavioral Health, Jacksonville, FL, p. A128

STACKHOUSE, Rebecca J., Medical Center Director, Salem Veterans Affairs Medical Center, Salem, VA, p. A675

STACKHOUSE, Sharon, Assistant Administrator and Director Risk Management, Peachford Behavioral Health System, Atlanta, GA, p. A150

STACY, Doug, Director Information Technology, Up Health System–Marquette, Marquette, MI, p. A326

STADHEIM, Barbara, Chief Nursing Officer, West River Regional Medical Center, Hettinger, ND, p. A476

STADHEIM, Nathan, Chief Financial Officer, West River Regional Medical Center, Hettinger, ND, p. A476

STADLER, James J M.D., Associate Administrator Medical Services, Guam Memorial Hospital Authority, Tamuning, GU, p. A721

STADLER, Thomas M.D., Vice President Medical Affairs and Chief Medical Officer, Madonna Rehabilitation Hospital, Lincoln, NE, p. A395

STAFFORD, Tom, Chief Information Officer, Halifax Health Medical Center Of Daytona Beach, Daytona Beach, FL, p. A123

STAFFORD, Walt, Director Information Technology, Chatuge Regional Hospital And Nursing Home, Hiawassee, GA, p. A159

STAGEMAN–TYRER, Dawn R.N., Chief Nursing Officer, Mackinac Straits Health System, Inc., Saint Ignace, MI, p. A330

STAGG, Kevin, Executive Vice President Finance and Chief Financial Officer, Christian Health Care Center, Wyckoff, NJ, p. A423

STAGGS, Nathan, Chief Executive Officer, Pauls Valley General Hospital, Pauls Valley, OK, p. A514

STAHL, Anthony, Ph.D., FACHE
Vice President, Florida Hospital Heartland Medical Center, Sebring, FL, p. A142
Chief Executive Officer, Central Texas Medical Center, San Marcos, TX, p. A644

STAHL, Daniel D.O., Chief of Staff, Rush Memorial Hospital, Rushville, IN, p. A219

STAHL, Kathy, Chief Nursing Officer, Wheeling Hospital, Wheeling, WV, p. A697

STAHL, Pam, Regional Chief Human Resources Officer, Providence Holy Cross Medical Center, Los Angeles, CA, p. A70

STAHL, Sherri R.N., Senior Vice President Hospital Services, Chambersburg Hospital, Chambersburg, PA, p. A531

STAHL, Steven J, Director Human Resources, Columbia County Health System, Dayton, WA, p. A680

STAHL, William D, Chief Operating Officer, Rooks County Health Center, Plainville, KS, p. A250

STAHLKUPPE, Robert F M.D., Chief of Staff, Chatuge Regional Hospital And Nursing Home, Hiawassee, GA, p. A159

STAHULAK, Brian M R.N., Chief Nursing Officer, Ann & Robert H. Lurie Children's Hospital Of Chicago, Chicago, IL, p. A180

STAIGER, Tom M.D., Medical Director, University Of Washington Medical Center, Seattle, WA, p. A685

STAIGL, Chris, Chief Nursing Officer, Tristar Southern Hills Medical Center, Nashville, TN, p. A587

STALCUP, Connie, Manager Information Systems, Murphy Medical Center, Murphy, NC, p. A467

STALCUP, Linda, Chief Executive Officer, Stevens County Hospital, Hugoton, KS, p. A243

STALKER, Neil M.D., Chief of Staff, Dukes Memorial Hospital, Peru, IN, p. A218

STALL, Kristi, Chief Human Resources Officer, Mahnomen Health Center, Mahnomen, MN, p. A342

STALLINGS, Jay, Chief Executive Officer, Washakie Medical Center, Worland, WY, p. A720

STALLINGS, Jennifer, Chief Clinical Officer, Kindred Hospital Indianapolis South, Greenwood, IN, p. A209

STALLINGS, Terry M.D., Chief Medical Officer, West Florida Hospital, Pensacola, FL, p. A139

STALLINGS–SICARD, Lori R.N., Chief Nursing Officer, DMC Huron Valley–Sinai Hospital, Commerce Township, MI, p. A317

STALLWORTH, David M.D., Chief of Staff, Monroe County Hospital, Monroeville, AL, p. A21

STALLWORTH, Monica M.D., Chief of Staff, Western Maryland Hospital Center, Hagerstown, MD, p. A299

STALLWORTH, Terresa M.D., Clinical Director, San Antonio State Hospital, San Antonio, TX, p. A643

STALNAKER, Avah, Chief Executive Officer, Stonewall Jackson Memorial Hospital, Weston, WV, p. A697

STALNAKER, Kevin P CPA, Assistant Chief Executive Officer, Stonewall Jackson Memorial Hospital, Weston, WV, p. A697

STAMAS, Peter M.D., Vice President Medical Affairs, Marshfield Medical Center, Marshfield, WI, p. A706

STAMBAUGH, Lynn E., R.N., Chief Executive Officer, Sarah D. Culbertson Memorial Hospital, Rushville, IL, p. A199

STAMM, Pam, Chief Nursing Officer, Throckmorton County Memorial Hospital, Throckmorton, TX, p. A650

STAMOPOULOS, Marion, Vice President Human Resouces, Deborah Heart And Lung Center, Browns Mills, NJ, p. A412

STAMOS, George D. M.D., Chief Medical Officer, Overland Park Regional Medical Center, Overland Park, KS, p. A249

STAMPOHAR, Jeffry, Chief Executive Officer, Hancock County Health System, Britt, IA, p. A223

STANBRO, Dave
Director Human Resources, Arnot Ogden Medical Center, Elmira, NY, p. A435
Director Human Resources, Ira Davenport Memorial Hospital, Bath, NY, p. A431
Director Human Resources, St. Joseph's Hospital, Elmira, NY, p. A435

STANDEFFER, Luke, Administrator, Dch Regional Medical Center, Tuscaloosa, AL, p. A23

STANDER, Paul M.D., Chief Medical Officer, Banner – University Medical Center Phoenix, Phoenix, AZ, p. A33

STANDIFORD, Steven B. M.D., Chief of Staff, Eastern Regional Medical Center, Philadelphia, PA, p. A543

STANDLEE, Cynthia R.N., Chief Nursing Officer, Estes Park Medical Center, Estes Park, CO, p. A102

STANDRIDGE, Debra K., President, Wheaton Franciscan Healthcare – St. Joseph's, Milwaukee, WI, p. A708

STANDRIDGE, Sonya, Chief Nursing Officer, Copper Basin Medical Center, Copperhill, TN, p. A577

STANEK, Janet, Senior Vice President and Chief Operating Officer, Stormont Vail Health, Topeka, KS, p. A252

STANFORD, Brion, Director Human Resources, New Orleans East Hospital, New Orleans, LA, p. A282

STANFORD, Edward M.D., Chief Medical officer, Doctors Medical Center Of Modesto, Modesto, CA, p. A74

STANFORD, Tracy
Director Human Resources, Baylor All Saints Medical Center At Fort Worth, Fort Worth, TX, p. A613
Director Human Resources, The Heart Hospital Baylor Denton, Denton, TX, p. A608
Director Human Resources, The Heart Hospital Baylor Plano, Plano, TX, p. A638

STANGE, Della G, Director Human Resources, Rancho Springs Medical Center, Murrieta, CA, p. A75

STANGE KOLO, Tracey
Vice President Human Resources, Upmc St. Margaret, Pittsburgh, PA, p. A548
Vice President, Human Resources, Upmc Mercy, Pittsburgh, PA, p. A547

STANGL, Abbey, Chief Financial Officer, Cass County Memorial Hospital, Atlantic, IA, p. A222

STANHILL, Keith
Chief Human Resources Officer, Saint Francis Hospital, Memphis, TN, p. A585
Chief Human Resources Officer, Twin Cities Community Hospital, Templeton, CA, p. A93

STANIC, Steve M
Vice President and Chief Information Officer, Mississippi Baptist Medical Center, Jackson, MS, p. A357
Vice President and Chief Information Officer, Select Specialty Hospital – Belhaven, Jackson, MS, p. A357

STANKO, Shelley M.D., Chief Medical Officer, Saint Joseph London, London, KY, p. A262

STANLEY, Cassandra, Director Personnel, Eastern Shore Hospital Center, Cambridge, MD, p. A297

STANLEY, Donna K R.N., Chief Nursing Officer, East Texas Medical Center Henderson, Henderson, TX, p. A618

STANLEY, Jennifer M.D., Chief Medical Officer, St. Vincent Jennings Hospital, North Vernon, IN, p. A218

STANLEY, Mark, Director Fiscal Services, Middle Tennessee Mental Health Institute, Nashville, TN, p. A586

STANSBERY, Shawn M.D., Chief of Staff, Wood County Hospital, Bowling Green, OH, p. A482

STANSBURY, Kevin M., Chief Executive Officer, Lincoln Community Hospital And Nursing Home, Hugo, CO, p. A104

STANSKI, Vickie, Financial Manager, Parkview Lagrange Hospital, Lagrange, IN, p. A214

STANTON, Lowell, Chief Financial Officer, Houston Methodist Sugar Land Hospital, Sugar Land, TX, p. A647

STANTON, Melanie, R.N.
Chief Nursing Officer, Sycamore Shoals Hospital, Elizabethton, TN, p. A578
Chief Nursing Officer, Unicoi County Memorial Hospital, Erwin, TN, p. A578

STANTON, Mike D.O., Medical Director, Baylor Medical Center At Trophy Club, Trophy Club, TX, p. A650

STANUSH, Chris, Director Information Management, San Antonio State Hospital, San Antonio, TX, p. A643

STANZIONE, Dominick, President and Chief Executive Officer, Brookdale Hospital Medical Center, New Rochelle, NY, p. A441

STAPLES, Janet, Vice President Human Resources, South Central Regional Medical Center, Laurel, MS, p. A358

STAPLETON, Carla J., Director Human Resources, Paul B. Hall Regional Medical Center, Paintsville, KY, p. A266

STAPLETON, Kathleen, Chief Financial Officer, Baptist Easley Hospital, Easley, SC, p. A561

STAPLETON, Michael, President and Chief Executive Officer, F. F. Thompson Hospital, Canandaigua, NY, p. A433

STAPLETON, Robert, Director Administration, Richard H. Hutchings Psychiatric Center, Syracuse, NY, p. A453

STARA, Jeanne R.N., MSN, Chief Nursing Officer, Alliancehealth Ponca City, Ponca City, OK, p. A514

STARCHER, John M., President and Chief Executive Officer, Mercy Health, Cincinnati, OH, p. B84

STARCK, Rebecca, M.D., President, Cleveland Clinic Avon Hospital, Avon, OH, p. A480

STARESINIC, Barbara, Director Human Resources, Hi-Desert Medical Center, Yucca Valley, CA, p. A97

STARK, David A, FACHE
Executive Vice President and Chief Operating Officer, Unitypoint Health - Iowa Methodist Medical Center, Des Moines, IA, p. A226
President, Unitypoint Health - Iowa Methodist Medical Center, Des Moines, IA, p. A226

STARK, David, Chief Financial Officer, Lancaster Rehabilitation Hospital, Lancaster, PA, p. A538

STARK, Donna, Director Human Resources, Baylor Regional Medical Center At Grapevine, Grapevine, TX, p. A617

STARK, Patricia Ann R.N., CNO, Florida Hospital Deland, Deland, FL, p. A123

STARK, Sharon R.N., Manager Clinical Information Systems, Methodist Mckinney Hospital, Mckinney, TX, p. A632

STARK, Steve, Chief Executive Officer, Orchard Hospital, Gridley, CA, p. A62

STARKEBAUM, Gordon M.D., Chief of Staff, Veterans Affairs Puget Sound Health Care System, Seattle, WA, p. A686

STARKES, Henry M.D., Medical Director, Orchard Hospital, Gridley, CA, p. A62

STARLING, James F M.D., Chief Medical Officer, Sovah Health-Danville, Danville, VA, p. A666

STARLING, Susan, President and Chief Executive Officer, Mercy Health - Marcum And Wallace, Irvine, KY, p. A260

STARNES, Gregory D., Chief Executive Officer, Fayette County Hospital, Vandalia, IL, p. A202

STARR, Candie, Chief Executive Officer, Lincoln County Health System, Fayetteville, TN, p. A578

STARR, Kay, Manager Human Resources, Vernon Memorial Healthcare, Viroqua, WI, p. A714

STASI, Joseph P, Chief Financial Officer, Saint Luke's East Hospital, Lee's Summit, MO, p. A372

STASIK, Randall, President, Spectrum Health Gerber Memorial, Fremont, MI, p. A320

STASKIN, David, Director Human Resources, Healthsouth Rehabilitation Hospital Of Mechanicsburg, Mechanicsburg, PA, p. A540

STASNEY, Amy, R.N., Chief Executive Officer, Cornerstone Hospital Of Houston At Clearlake, Webster, TX, p. A653

STASTNY, Mark, Vice President and Chief Information Officer, Children's Hospital And Medical Center, Omaha, NE, p. A397

STATEN, Gary L., Chief Executive Officer, Trace Regional Hospital, Houston, MS, p. A356

STATES, Chuck, Director Information Systems, Punxsutawney Area Hospital, Punxsutawney, PA, p. A548

STATON, Donna, Chief Information Officer, Fauquier Hospital, Warrenton, VA, p. A676

STATON, John, Senior Vice President Operations, Olathe Medical Center, Olathe, KS, p. A248

STATON, Paul
Chief Financial Officer, Ronald Reagan Ucla Medical Center, Los Angeles, CA, p. A71
Chief Financial Officer, Ucla Medical Center-Santa Monica, Santa Monica, CA, p. A91

STATUTO, Richard, President and Chief Executive Officer, Bon Secours Health System, Inc., Marriottsville, MD, p. B22

STATZ, Chris, Chief Financial Officer, Lincoln Prairie Behavioral Health Center, Springfield, IL, p. A200

STATZ, Linda Taplin, System Vice President - Employee Experience, St. Mary's Hospital, Madison, WI, p. A705

STAUB, David M.D., Chief of Staff, Coteau Des Prairies Hospital, Sisseton, SD, p. A573

STAUB, Julie, Chief Human Resources Officer, Jackson Health System, Miami, FL, p. A133

STAUBACH, Virginia R.N., Chief Nursing Officer and Senior Director of Nursing Services, Gaylord Hospital, Wallingford, CT, p. A113

STAUDINGER, Michael M.D., Chief of Staff, Theda Care Medical Center - Wild Rose, Wild Rose, WI, p. A716

STAUFFER, Karla, Executive Director People Resources, Billings Clinic, Billings, MT, p. A382

STAUFFER, Keith, Regional Chief Information Officer, Chi St Alexius Health Carrington Medical Center, Carrington, ND, p. A474

STAUSS, Laura, Director of Human Resources, Huggins Hospital, Wolfeboro, NH, p. A410

STAVELEY, Melinda, President and Chief Executive Officer, Santa Barbara Cottage Hospital, Santa Barbara, CA, p. A90

STAWNIAK, Laura R.N., Chief Nursing Executive, Memorial Community Hospital And Health System, Blair, NE, p. A391

STEAD, William, Associate Vice Chancellor Health Affairs, Director Informatics Center and Chief Strategy and Information Officer, Vanderbilt University Medical Center, Nashville, TN, p. A587

STEADHAM, Emily, Administrator, Grove Hill Memorial Hospital, Grove Hill, AL, p. A19

STEADHAM, Mark B., President and Chief Executive Officer, Morris Hospital & Healthcare Centers, Morris, IL, p. A194

STEAGALL, Susan, Vice President Information Services, VCU Medical Center, Richmond, VA, p. A674

STEARNS, Charles, Area Information Officer, Kaiser Foundation Hospital Westside Medical Center, Hillsboro, OR, p. A522

STEARNS, Zebediah M.D., Chief of Staff, Mercy Regional Medical Center, Ville Platte, LA, p. A287

STEC, Julianne, Chief Operating Officer, Mercy Hospital Fort Smith, Fort Smith, AR, p. A43

STECKEL, Cindy, Ph.D., R.N., Vice President Chief Nurse and Operations Executive, Scripps Memorial Hospital-La Jolla, La Jolla, CA, p. A64

STECKER, Tim, Chief Financial Officer, Kindred Hospital-Denver, Denver, CO, p. A101

STECKLER, Michael J., President and Chief Executive Officer, Jennie M. Melham Memorial Medical Center, Broken Bow, NE, p. A391

STEED, Robert A, Director Information Systems, Capital Regional Medical Center, Tallahassee, FL, p. A143

STEEL, Diana, Vice President Human Resources, West Hills Hospital And Medical Center, Los Angeles, CA, p. A72

STEELE, Anthony M.D., Chief Medical Officer, Witham Health Services, Lebanon, IN, p. A214

STEELE, Chrys, Director Information Systems, Springs Memorial Hospital, Lancaster, SC, p. A564

STEELE, David, Vice President Information Technology, Leesburg Regional Medical Center, Leesburg, FL, p. A130

STEELE, Erik N D.O., Senior Vice President and Chief Medical Officer, Summa Health System, Akron, OH, p. A479

STEELE, Mark, M.D.
Chief Medical Officer, Truman Medical Center-Hospital Hill, Kansas City, MO, p. A371
Chief Medical Officer, Truman Medical Center-Lakewood, Kansas City, MO, p. A371

STEELE, Michael M.D., Chief of Staff, Perry County Memorial Hospital, Perryville, MO, p. A375

STEELE, Richele, Vice President, Marketing and Public Relations, Community Hospital Long Beach, Long Beach, CA, p. A66

STEELE, Robert, M.D., President, Mercy Hospital Springfield, Springfield, MO, p. A379

STEELE, Sherri, Chief Nursing Officer, Providence Medford Medical Center, Medford, OR, p. A524

STEELE, Terry L, Vice President Finance and Chief Financial Officer, Holland Hospital, Holland, MI, p. A322

STEELE, Tina, Chief Executive Officer and Chief Financial Officer, Fairfax Community Hospital, Fairfax, OK, p. A507

STEELE, Wes M.D., Chief of Staff, Fairmont Regional Medical Center, Fairmont, WV, p. A692

STEELMAN, Jeffrey, Director Information Systems, Lewisgale Hospital Alleghany, Low Moor, VA, p. A669

STEELY, Karen, Administrator, Murray Medical Center, Chatsworth, GA, p. A154

STEEN, Jon, Director Human Resources, Davis Medical Center, Elkins, WV, p. A691

STEENPORT, John, Information Systems Manager, Aspirus Ironwood Hosital & Clinics, Inc., Ironwood, MI, p. A323

STEFFEN, Elizabeth, Director Information Technology, Seneca Healthcare District, Chester, CA, p. A55

STEFFEN, Elly, Administrator, Continuing Care Hospital At St. Luke's, Cedar Rapids, IA, p. A223

STEFFEN, Lorri, Chief Executive Officer and Administrator, Osage Beach Center For Cognitive Disorders, Osage Beach, MO, p. A374

STEFFENS, Aaron, Chief Operating Officer, Mercy Hospital Oklahoma City, Oklahoma City, OK, p. A512

STEFFIN, Renee, Chief Nursing Officer, Cuyuna Regional Medical Center, Crosby, MN, p. A338

STEFL, William, Director Information Systems, Mercy Health Hackley Campus, Muskegon, MI, p. A327

STEFO, Andrew, Senior Vice President Finance and Chief Financial Officer, Ingalls Memorial Hospital, Harvey, IL, p. A189

STEGALL, Christopher A, Regional Chief Financial Officer and Chief Operating Officer, Promise Hospital Of Vicksburg, Vicksburg, MS, p. A362

STEGER, Elizabeth FACHE, R.N., Chief Nursing Officer, Seton Medical Center Austin, Austin, TX, p. A595

STEGGE, Sherri, Director Human Resources, Kaiser Permanente Vallejo Medical Center, Vallejo, CA, p. A95

STEHMER, Marie F, Senior Director of Human Resources, Peacehealth Sacred Heart Medical Center At Riverbend, Springfield, OR, p. A527

STEICHEN, Barry L
Executive Vice President and Chief Operating Officer, Saint Francis Health System, Saint Francis Hospital, Tulsa, OK, p. A518
Executive Vice President and Chief Operating Officer, Saint Francis Hospital South, Tulsa, OK, p. A518

STEICHEN, Elizabeth, Human Resources, Lewis And Clark Specialty Hospital, Yankton, SD, p. A574

STEICHEN, Terry, Business Officer, Lewis And Clark Specialty Hospital, Yankton, SD, p. A574

STEIDLE, Ernie, Chief Operating Officer, Woodrow Wilson Rehabilitation Center, Fishersville, VA, p. A667

STEIGMAN, Don S, Chief Operating Officer, Jackson Health System, Miami, FL, p. A133

STEIGMEYER, Robert P., President and Chief Executive Officer, Concord Hospital, Concord, NH, p. A407

STEIMEL, Ronald, Executive Vice President and Chief Administrative Officer, Mercy Medical Center, Rockville Centre, NY, p. A451

STEIN, Brad, Chief Financial Officer, Medical City Mckinney, Mckinney, TX, p. A632

STEIN, Cathy, Chief Inpatient Services, Sagamore Children's Hospital Psychiatric Center, Dix Hills, NY, p. A435

STEIN, Eric H., FACHE, President and Chief Executive Officer, Cobleskill Regional Hospital, Cobleskill, NY, p. A434

STEIN, Keith L, M.D.
Chief Medical Officer, Baptist Medical Center Beaches, Jacksonville Beach, FL, p. A129
Senior Vice President Medical Affairs and Chief Medical Officer, Baptist Medical Center Jacksonville, Jacksonville, FL, p. A127

STEIN, Patrick M.D., Clinical Director, Western New York Children's Hospital Psychiatric Center, West Seneca, NY, p. A455

STEIN, Paul, Chief Operating Officer, Mainegeneral Medical Center, Augusta, ME, p. A289

STEIN, Richard M.D., Chief Medical Officer, Bay Area Medical Center, Marinette, WI, p. A706

STEIN, Robert, M.D.
Vice President Medical Management, Advocate Christ Medical Center, Oak Lawn, IL, p. A196
Chief Executive Officer, Kindred Hospital Houston Medical Center, Houston, TX, p. A621

STEIN, Sandra, Chief Human Resources Management, Veterans Affairs Central California Health Care System, Fresno, CA, p. A61

STEIN, Sheldon J., President and Chief Executive Officer, Mt. Washington Pediatric Hospital, Baltimore, MD, p. A295

STEINBERG, James P M.D., Chief Medical Officer, Emory University Hospital Midtown, Atlanta, GA, p. A150

STEINBLOCK, Matthew, Director Information Systems, Community Memorial Hospital, Syracuse, NE, p. A400

STEINER, Jeffrey T, Vice President Finance, Memorial Hospital At Gulfport, Gulfport, MS, p. A355

STEINER, Scott, FACHE
Chief Executive Officer, DMC Harper University Hospital, Detroit, MI, p. A318
Chief Executive Officer, DMC – Detroit Receiving Hospital, Detroit, MI, p. A317
Interim Chief Executive Officer, Burke Medical Center, Waynesboro, GA, p. A167

STEINES, Brian D, Chief Financial Officer, Northeast Georgia Medical Center, Gainesville, GA, p. A158

STEINES, Jeanne D.O., Medical Director, Connecticut Mental Health Center, New Haven, CT, p. A112

STEINGALL, Patricia MS, R.N., Vice President, Patient Care Services, Hunterdon Medical Center, Flemington, NJ, p. A414

STEINHART, Curt M.D., Chief Medical Officer, Ou Medical Center, Oklahoma City, OK, p. A513

STEINKE, Paul, D.O.
Chief Financial Officer, Providence Holy Cross Medical Center, Los Angeles, CA, p. A70
President and Chief Executive Officer, CGH Medical Center, Sterling, IL, p. A201

STEINKRUGER, Roger W., Chief Executive Officer, Community Hospital–Fairfax, Fairfax, MO, p. A368

STEINMANN, Robin, Administrative Director Human Resources, Anderson Hospital, Maryville, IL, p. A192

STEINSICK, Bill M.D., Chief Medical Staff, Asante Ashland Community Hospital, Ashland, OR, p. A520

STEINWACHS, Lynn R., Vice President and Administrator, Methodist Hospital Union County, Morganfield, KY, p. A265

STEITZ, David P., Chief Executive Officer, Carlisle Regional Medical Center, Carlisle, PA, p. A531

STELL, G Max M.D., Medical Director, Minden Medical Center, Minden, LA, p. A281

STELLER, Wayne, Vice President Chief Nursing Officer, The Acadia Hospital, Bangor, ME, p. A289

STELLING, Jonathan M.D., Vice President Medical Affairs, Chi Health St. Mary's, Nebraska City, NE, p. A396

STELTENPOHL, Robert
Vice President and Chief Financial Officer, Frazier Rehab Institute, Louisville, KY, p. A262
Vice President, Southern Indiana Rehabilitation Hospital, New Albany, IN, p. A217

STELTER, Carolyn M.D., Chief of Staff, Ridgeview Le Sueur Medical Center, Le Sueur, MN, p. A342

STELZER, Jason, Director Human Resources, St. Clare Hospital, Baraboo, WI, p. A698

STELZER, Mark M.D., President Medical Staff, Floyd Valley Healthcare, Le Mars, IA, p. A230

STENCEL, Lindsay, Chief Administrative Officer, Baptist Memorial Hospital–Collierville, Collierville, TN, p. A577

STENDEL–FREELS, Robin, Coordinator Human Resources, AMG Specialty Hospital–Albuquerque, Albuquerque, NM, p. A424

STENERSON, David, Vice President and Chief Financial Officer, OSF Saint Anthony Medical Center, Rockford, IL, p. A199

STENGER, George S. D.O., Chief of Staff, Okeene Municipal Hospital, Okeene, OK, p. A511

STENGER, John D, Acting Associate Director, Charlie Norwood Veterans Affairs Medical Center, Augusta, GA, p. A151

STENGER, Sandra, Acting Chief Human Resources, Cincinnati Veterans Affairs Medical Center, Cincinnati, OH, p. A484

STENNETT, Kevin T M.D., Chief of Staff, W. J. Mangold Memorial Hospital, Lockney, TX, p. A629

STENSON, James, Chief Information Officer, Syracuse Veterans Affairs Medical Center, Syracuse, NY, p. A453

STENSRUD, Kirk A., Chief Executive Officer, Glacial Ridge Health System, Glenwood, MN, p. A340

STEPANSKY, David M.D., Chief Medical Officer, Phoenixville Hospital, Phoenixville, PA, p. A546

STEPHENS, Brian, Chief Financial Officer, Door County Medical Center, Sturgeon Bay, WI, p. A713

STEPHENS, Carrie, Director Information Technology, Saunders Medical Center, Wahoo, NE, p. A400

STEPHENS, Debra, Director Personnel, Riverland Medical Center, Ferriday, LA, p. A274

STEPHENS, Eddy, Vice President Information Technology, Mobile Infirmary Medical Center, Mobile, AL, p. A20

STEPHENS, Ellen, Vice President Information Services, Mercy Hospital Oklahoma City, Oklahoma City, OK, p. A512

STEPHENS, Heather, Director of Information Health Technology, St. Clare Hospital, Baraboo, WI, p. A698

STEPHENS, Jeremy, Vice President and Chief Human Resources Officer, St. Joseph Mercy Chelsea, Chelsea, MI, p. A316

STEPHENS, Kathy, Vice President of Patient Care, Decatur County Memorial Hospital, Greensburg, IN, p. A209

STEPHENS, Larry
Chief Financial Officer, Collingsworth General Hospital, Wellington, TX, p. A653
Chief Financial Officer, Kimble Hospital, Junction, TX, p. A625
Chief Financial Officer, Sabine County Hospital, Hemphill, TX, p. A618
Chief Financial Officer, Schleicher County Medical Center, Eldorado, TX, p. A612

STEPHENS, Linda R.N., Chief Nursing Officer, Memorial Hermann Northeast, Humble, TX, p. A624

STEPHENS, Mike, Chief Financial Officer, Nch Downtown Naples Hospital, Naples, FL, p. A135

STEPHENS, Norman F.
Interim Chief Executive Officer, Vista Medical Center East, Waukegan, IL, p. A202
Interim Chief Executive Officer, Vista Medical Center West, Waukegan, IL, p. A202

STEPHENS, Peggy, M.D.
Superintendent and Medical Director, Madison State Hospital, Madison, IN, p. A215
Chief Financial Officer, Riverton Hospital, Riverton, UT, p. A659

STEPHENS, Royce, MSN, R.N.
Director Finance, Intermountain Medical Center, Murray, UT, p. A658
Chief Executive Officer, Pawnee County Memorial Hospital And Rural Health Clinic, Pawnee City, NE, p. A399

STEPHENS, Terry A., Chief Executive Officer, River Park Hospital, Huntington, WV, p. A693

STEPHENS, PHR, SHRM–CP, Maria, Director Human Resources, Education and Occupational Health and Wellness, VCU Health Community Memorial Hospital, South Hill, VA, p. A675

STEPHENSON, Ben M.D., Chief of Staff, Phillips County Hospital, Phillipsburg, KS, p. A250

STEPHENSON, Darlene
Chief Executive Officer, Mary Immaculate Hospital, Newport News, VA, p. A671
Vice President Operations, Mary Immaculate Hospital, Newport News, VA, p. A671

STEPHENSON, Melinda, Chief Executive Officer, Kingwood Medical Center, Kingwood, TX, p. A627

STEPHENSON, Michelle R.N., Executive Vice President & Chief Operations Officer, Ann & Robert H. Lurie Children's Hospital Of Chicago, Chicago, IL, p. A180

STEPHENSON, Ron, Chief Operating Officer, Brookhaven Memorial Hospital Medical Center, Patchogue, NY, p. A449

STEPP, Dana, Human Resources Officer, Mercy Health – Marcum And Wallace, Irvine, KY, p. A260

STERBACH, Maureen, Vice President Human Resources, St. Joseph's Hospital And Medical Center, Phoenix, AZ, p. A34

STERLING, Terrie R.N., MSN, Chief Operating Officer, Our Lady Of The Lake Regional Medical Center, Baton Rouge, LA, p. A271

STERN, Barry, President and Chief Executive Officer, New York Community Hospital, New Rochelle, NY, p. A443

STERNBERG, Paul M.D., Professor and Chairman, Vanderbilt University Medical Center, Nashville, TN, p. A587

STERUD, Brian, Chief Information Officer, Faith Regional Health Services, Norfolk, NE, p. A396

STESNEY–RIDENOUR, Chris, President, Beaumont Hospital – Trenton, Trenton, MI, p. A332

STETTHEIMER, Timothy, Vice President and Chief Information Officer, St. Vincent's Birmingham, Birmingham, AL, p. A15

STEUTER, Krista, Director Human Resources, Catalina Island Medical Center, Avalon, CA, p. A52

STEVEN, Eva, Chief Financial Officer, Roosevelt General Hospital, Portales, NM, p. A427

STEVENS, Ann Marie., R.N., Chief Executive Officer, Tyler Memorial Hospital, Tunkhannock, PA, p. A552

STEVENS, Belinda, Chief Executive Officer, Access Hospital Dayton, Dayton, OH, p. A489

STEVENS, Ben, Chief Financial Officer, Buchanan County Health Center, Independence, IA, p. A229

STEVENS, Bryan N
Chief Financial Officer, Field Memorial Community Hospital, Centreville, MS, p. A353
Interim Chief Financial Officer, Copiah County Medical Center, Hazlehurst, MS, p. A356

STEVENS, Chris E, Chief Information Officer, Billings Clinic, Billings, MT, p. A382

STEVENS, Dori, Chief Executive Officer, Sutter Delta Medical Center, Antioch, CA, p. A51

STEVENS, Emily, Chief Nursing Officer, Mat–Su Regional Medical Center, Palmer, AK, p. A27

STEVENS, Eric, Chief Executive Officer, Florida Hospital Heartland Medical Center, Sebring, FL, p. A142

STEVENS, Jeffrey, Senior Vice President and Chief Human Resource Officer, Thomas Jefferson University Hospitals, Philadelphia, PA, p. A546

STEVENS, Kelly, Manager Human Resources, St. Joseph Memorial Hospital, Murphysboro, IL, p. A194

STEVENS, Lisa, Chief Clinical Officer and Chief Operating Officer, Vibra Hospital Of Northern California, Redding, CA, p. A81

STEVENS, Lori A MSN, R.N., Interim Chief Nursing Officer, Verde Valley Medical Center, Cottonwood, AZ, p. A28

STEVENS, Maeanne R.N., Chief Nursing Officer, OSF Saint Elizabeth Medical Center, Ottawa, IL, p. A196

STEVENS, Mark, M.D.
Chief Medical Staff, Marion General Hospital, Columbia, MS, p. A354
Director Human Resources, St. Luke's Jerome, Jerome, ID, p. A173
Senior Director Human Resources, St. Luke's Magic Valley Medical Center, Twin Falls, ID, p. A176

STEVENS, Rick, President, Christian Hospital, Saint Louis, MO, p. A377

STEVENS, Rodney R.N., East Central Region Director of Nursing Practice, Indiana University Health Blackford Hospital, Hartford City, IN, p. A210

STEVENS, Scot, Assistant Administrator, Salt Lake Regional Medical Center, Salt Lake City, UT, p. A660

STEVENS, Shelbourn, President and Chief Operating Officer, Novant Health Brunswick Medical Center, Bolivia, NC, p. A458

STEVENS, Susan
Director Human Resources, The Healthcenter, Kalispell, MT, p. A386
Human Resources Strategic Business Partner, Transylvania Regional Hospital, Brevard, NC, p. A458
Information Technology Specialist, Fallon Medical Complex, Baker, MT, p. A382

STEVENS, Tammy, Chief Executive Officer, Madison County Memorial Hospital, Madison, FL, p. A131

STEVENS, Tom, Director Personnel, Morehead Memorial Hospital, Eden, NC, p. A461

STEVENS, Vicki, Human Resources Executive, Northfield Hospital, Northfield, MN, p. A345

STEVENSON, Angela, Chief Financial Officer, Carl Vinson Veterans Affairs Medical Center, Dublin, GA, p. A157

STEVENSON, Angelia, Manager Finance, Tuscaloosa Veterans Affairs Medical Center, Tuscaloosa, AL, p. A24

STEVENSON, Brett
Controller, Kindred Hospital Kansas City, Kansas City, MO, p. A370
Controller, Kindred Hospital Northland, Kansas City, MO, p. A370

STEVENSON, John M.D., Senior Vice President and Chief Medical Officer, South Shore Hospital, South Weymouth, MA, p. A311

STEVENSON, Michael, Chief Executive Officer, Murphy Medical Center, Murphy, NC, p. A467

STEVERSON, Denise, Director Human Resources, Dorminy Medical Center, Fitzgerald, GA, p. A158

STEVES, Sonja
Senior Vice President Human Resources and Marketing, Legacy Emanuel Medical Center, Portland, OR, p. A525
Senior Vice President Human Resources, Legacy Mount Hood Medical Center, Gresham, OR, p. A522
Senior Vice President Human Resources, Legacy Salmon Creek Medical Center, Vancouver, WA, p. A688
Vice President Human Resources and Marketing, Legacy Meridian Park Medical Center, Tualatin, OR, p. A527
Vice President Marketing, Legacy Good Samaritan Medical Center, Portland, OR, p. A525

STEWARD, Rachel, Director Human Resources, Hillcrest Hospital – South, Tulsa, OK, p. A517

STEWARD, Todd E., FACHE, Chief Executive Officer, St. David's South Austin Medical Center, Austin, TX, p. A596

STEWART, Anne, Vice President and Chief Nursing Officer, Beaumont Hospital – Grosse Pointe, Grosse Pointe, MI, p. A322

STEWART, Brandi R.N., Vice President and Chief Nursing Officer, Integris Grove Hospital, Grove, OK, p. A508

STEWART, Christine R., FACHE, Chief Executive Officer, Russellville Hospital, Russellville, AL, p. A23

STEWART, Clint
Chief Financial Officer, Blue Ridge Regional Hospital, Spruce Pine, NC, p. A471
Regional Director of Finance East, Mcdowell Hospital, Marion, NC, p. A466

STEWART, Craig, Chief Financial Officer, Gila Regional Medical Center, Silver City, NM, p. A429

STEWART, Daniel M.D., Vice President Medical Affairs, Bronson Battle Creek, Battle Creek, MI, p. A315

STEWART, David K, Senior Vice President and Chief Financial Officer, Mercy Medical Center, Canton, OH, p. A482

STEWART, Douglas, PsyD, President, Unity Hospital, Rochester, NY, p. A451

STEWART, Greg, Chief Executive Officer, Wellstone Regional Hospital, Jeffersonville, IN, p. A213

STEWART, Hedda, Director Human Resources, Neshoba County General Hospital, Philadelphia, MS, p. A360

STEWART, Inez, Vice President, Boston Children's Hospital, Boston, MA, p. A302

STEWART, Jane, Director Information Services, JFK Medical Center, Atlantis, FL, p. A119

STEWART, Jessi, Director Human Resources, Rockford Center, Newark, DE, p. A115

STEWART, John, Director Finance, Burke Rehabilitation Hospital, White Plains, NY, p. A456

STEWART, Kelly, Director of Human Resources, Community Mental Health Center, Lawrenceburg, IN, p. A214

STEWART, Kendall M.D., Chief Medical Officer, Southern Ohio Medical Center, Portsmouth, OH, p. A498

STEWART, Larry D. Jr, Chief Medical Officer and Vice President, Medical Affairs, Perry Hospital, Perry, GA, p. A163

STEWART, Marc M.D., Vice President and Medical Director, Seattle Cancer Care Alliance, Seattle, WA, p. A685

STEWART, Marty, Director Information Services, Anmed Health Medical Center, Anderson, SC, p. A558

STEWART, Michael K., Chief Executive Officer, Navarro Regional Hospital, Corsicana, TX, p. A603

STEWART, Michele R.N., Chief Operating Officer, Mercy Hospital Joplin, Joplin, MO, p. A370

STEWART, Pamela, Director of Nursing, Washington County Regional Medical Center, Sandersville, GA, p. A164

STEWART, Patty, Chief Financial Officer, Memorial Hospital, Gonzales, TX, p. A616

STEWART, Paul R., President and Chief Executive Officer, Sky Lakes Medical Center, Klamath Falls, OR, p. A523

STEWART, Paul M.D., Medical Director, Kindred Hospital Las Vegas–Sahara, Henderson, NV, p. A402

STEWART, Roxane, Chief Financial Officer, Magnolia Regional Medical Center, Magnolia, AR, p. A46

STEWART, Russell L D.O., Medical Director, Braxton County Memorial Hospital, Gassaway, WV, p. A692

STEWART, Scott, M.D.
Vice President Medical Management, Good Samaritan Medical Center, Brockton, MA, p. A304
Manager Information Services, Rochelle Community Hospital, Rochelle, IL, p. A198

STEWART, Stephen M.D., Vice President Medical Affairs, SSM Health St. Mary's Hospital – Jefferson City, Jefferson City, MO, p. A369

STEWART, Steve, Administrator, Meade District Hospital, Meade, KS, p. A247

STEWART, Tim, Chief Information Officer, Abbeville Area Medical Center, Abbeville, SC, p. A558

STEWART, SPHR, SHRM-SCP, Ronnelle, Chief Human Resources Officer, Brookwood Baptist Medical Center, Birmingham, AL, p. A14

STIDHAM, Cindy
Executive Director of Patient Care Services, Wellmont Lonesome Pine Hospital, Big Stone Gap, VA, p. A664
Executive Director of Patient Care, Mountain View Regional Medical Center, Norton, VA, p. A672

STIEKES, Robert, Chief Financial Officer, Tyler Memorial Hospital, Tunkhannock, PA, p. A552

STIFF, Patrick, Coordinator Information Technology, Madison County Memorial Hospital, Madison, FL, p. A131

STIFFARM, Garland, Acting Chief Executive Officer, U.S. Public Health Service Blackfeet Community Hospital, Saint Mary, MT, p. A388

STIFFARM, Kevin J., Chief Executive Officer, Indian Health Service Hospital, Rapid City, SD, p. A571

STIKELEATHER, Janie, Director Marketing and Community Relations, Davis Regional Medical Center, Statesville, NC, p. A471

STILES, Geoffrey M.D., Chief Medical Officer, Sharp Memorial Hospital, San Diego, CA, p. A86

STILGENBAUER, Mike, Director Finance, Marymount Hospital, Garfield Heights, OH, p. A492

STILLER, Brian G.
Director Medical Center, Veterans Affairs Western New York Healthcare System–Batavia Division, Batavia, NY, p. A431
Director Medical Center, Veterans Affairs Western New York Healthcare System–Buffalo Division, Buffalo, NY, p. A433

STILSON, Dwain, Chief Financial Officer, Mosaic Life Care At St. Joseph, Saint Joseph, MO, p. A376

STILTNER, Wanda B, Director Human Resources, Buchanan General Hospital, Grundy, VA, p. A668

STIMPSON, Dan, Chief Financial Officer, Banner Del E. Webb Medical Center, Sun City West, AZ, p. A37

STIMSON, Judi
Chief Financial Officer, Desert Regional Medical Center, Palm Springs, CA, p. A78
Chief Financial Officer, Palm Beach Gardens Medical Center, Palm Beach Gardens, FL, p. A138

STIMSON, Michael, Chief Nursing Officer, Manchester Memorial Hospital, Manchester, KY, p. A264

STINGLEY, Susan D, Chief Nursing Officer, Kearny County Hospital, Lakin, KS, p. A244

STINSON, Katy, Director Information Services, Alliancehealth Durant, Durant, OK, p. A506

STINSON, Martha, Director of Information Technology, Palms West Hospital, Loxahatchee, FL, p. A131

STINSON, Michael, Human Resources Coordinator, Select Specialty Hospital–Durham, Durham, NC, p. A461

STIPE, Christopher R., FACHE, Chief Executive Officer, Clarinda Regional Health Center, Clarinda, IA, p. A224

STITH, Melanie
Vice President Human Resources, Roper St. Francis Mount Pleasant Hospital, Mount Pleasant, SC, p. A564
Vice President Human Resources, Roper St. Francis, Charleston, SC, p. A559

STITT, Bobby, R.N., Administrator, Mercy Hospital Watonga, Watonga, OK, p. A519

STITT, Patrick, Director of Information Systems, Fishermen's Hospital, Marathon, FL, p. A131

STOB, David, Chief Financial Officer, Kindred Hospital Seattle–Northgate, Seattle, WA, p. A685

STOBER, Karick, Chief Financial Officer, Pam Specialty Hospital Of Covington, Covington, LA, p. A273

STOBO, John D., M.D., Executive Vice President and Chief Executive Officer, University Of California Systemwide Administration, Oakland, CA, p. B138

STOCK, Constance M.D., Chief Medical Officer, Sturgis Regional Hospital, Sturgis, SD, p. A573

STOCK, Greg K., FACHE, Chief Executive Officer, Thibodaux Regional Medical Center, Thibodaux, LA, p. A287

STOCK, Lesa R.N., Chief Clinical Officer, Citizens Memorial Hospital, Bolivar, MO, p. A364

STOCK, Neil, Director Technology and Facilities, Mercy Regional Medical Center, Durango, CO, p. A101

STOCKARD, Herbert M.D., Chief Medical Officer, Mercy St. Anne Hospital, Toledo, OH, p. A500

STOCKER, Trena, Chief Nursing Executive, Mercy Health – Marcum And Wallace, Irvine, KY, p. A260

STOCKHAUSEN, Christopher, Chief Financial Officer, Upmc Mckeesport, Mckeesport, PA, p. A540

STOCKS, Gregory M.D., Chief of Staff, Texas Orthopedic Hospital, Houston, TX, p. A623

STOCKSTILL, Mark, R.N., Administrator, Highland Community Hospital, Picayune, MS, p. A360

STOCKTON, David Bradley, Chief Operating Officer, Redmond Regional Medical Center, Rome, GA, p. A163

STOCKTON, Kevin, Chief Executive Officer, Northwest Medical Center, Tucson, AZ, p. A38

STOCKTON, Linda
Chief Financial Officer, Bayfront Health Dade City, Dade City, FL, p. A123
Interim Chief Executive Officer, Bayfront Health Dade City, Dade City, FL, p. A123

STOCKTON, Rick, Chief Executive Officer, Promise Hospital Of Louisiana – Shreveport Campus, Shreveport, LA, p. A285

STODDARD, Mark R., Chief Executive Officer, Central Valley Medical Center, Nephi, UT, p. A658

STOGSDILL, Vicki R.N., MSN, Chief Nursing Officer, Owensboro Health Regional Hospital, Owensboro, KY, p. A265

STOJAKOVICH, Edward R
Chief Financial Officer, Dominion Hospital, Falls Church, VA, p. A666
Chief Financial Officer, Reston Hospital Center, Reston, VA, p. A673

STOKER, Rick, Director Management Information Systems, Tristar Horizon Medical Center, Dickson, TN, p. A578

STOKER, Vicki, Chief Nursing Officer, University Behavioral Health Of Denton, Denton, TX, p. A608

STOKES, Charles D., FACHE, President and Chief Executive Officer, Memorial Hermann Health System, Houston, TX, p. B82

STOKES, Elia, Chief Financial Officer, Medical City Fort Worth, Fort Worth, TX, p. A614

STOKES, Eric, Vice President of Operations, Decatur County Memorial Hospital, Greensburg, IN, p. A209

STOKES, Jeb, Chief Executive Officer, Crestwyn Behavioral Health, Memphis, TN, p. A584

STOKES, Laura
Director Human Resources, Roosevelt Warm Springs Rehabilitation And Specialty Hospitals – Ltac, Warm Springs, GA, p. A167
Director Human Resources, Roosevelt Warm Springs Rehabilitation Hospital – Rehab, Warm Springs, GA, p. A167

STOKES, Letha, Chief Executive Officer, Medical Arts Hospital, Lamesa, TX, p. A628

STOKES, Priscilla MS, R.N., Vice President Patient Care and Hospital Operations, Unitypoint Health – St. Lukes's Sioux City, Sioux City, IA, p. A235

STOKES, Richard W CPA, Jr, Chief Financial Officer, Wilbarger General Hospital, Vernon, TX, p. A652

STOKES, Tina, Manager Human Resources, Regency Hospital Of Florence, Florence, SC, p. A562

STOKOE, Shelby
Chief Financial Officer, Providence Holy Family Hospital, Spokane, WA, p. A687
Senior Director Finance, Providence Sacred Heart Medical Center & Children's Hospital, Spokane, WA, p. A687

STOLDT, Garrick J, Vice President and Chief Financial Officer, Saint Peter's University Hospital, New Brunswick, NJ, p. A417

STOLLER, Theo, Chief Executive Officer, Jacobson Memorial Hospital Care Center, Elgin, ND, p. A475

STOLTENBERG, John M.D., Vice President Medical Affairs, Fairview Ridges Hospital, Burnsville, MN, p. A337

STOLTMAN, Erin, Administrator, Essentia Health Ada, Ada, MN, p. A335

STOLTZ, Kyla, Vice President Human Resources, Centerpoint Medical Center, Independence, MO, p. A369

STOLYAR, Edward B. D.O., Divisional Chief Informational Officer, New York Community Hospital, New Rochelle, NY, p. A443

STOMBERG, LeAnn, Chief Financial Officer, Minneapolis Veterans Affairs Health Care System, Minneapolis, MN, p. A344

STONE, Bud, Director Information Systems, Eastern State Hospital, Lexington, KY, p. A261

STONE, Connie R.N., Chief Nursing Officer, Medstar Montgomery Medical Center, Olney, MD, p. A300

STONE, Dan, Senior Community Chief Executive Officer, Hazard Arh Regional Medical Center, Hazard, KY, p. A259

STONE, Darlene, Vice President Human Resources, Baptist Hospital, Pensacola, FL, p. A139

STONE, Duncan D.D.S., Chief Medical Staff, Mississippi State Hospital, Whitfield, MS, p. A363

STONE, Janice, Chief Operating Officer, Spectrum Health Gerber Memorial, Fremont, MI, p. A320

STONE, Jeanette, Vice President Operations, Baptist Health South Florida, South Miami Hospital, Miami, FL, p. A132

STONE, Jill, Manager Human Resources, Lynn County Hospital District, Tahoka, TX, p. A648

STONE, Joanna, Chief Nursing Officer, Livingston Hospital And Healthcare Services, Salem, KY, p. A267

STONE, Levi Ross R.N., Chief Nursing Officer and Chief Operating Officer, Odessa Regional Medical Center, Odessa, TX, p. A635

STONE, Loren, Chief Executive Officer, Endless Mountain Health Systems, Montrose, PA, p. A541

STONE, Patricia R.N., MSN, Senior Vice President Operations and Chief Nursing Officer, White Memorial Medical Center, Los Angeles, CA, p. A72

STONE, Richard, Manager, Technical Services, Uhs Chenango Memorial Hospital, Norwich, NY, p. A448

STONE, Robert, President and Chief Executive Officer, City Of Hope's Helford Clinical Research Hospital, Duarte, CA, p. A58

STONE, Ronald W, Regional Chief Human Resource Officer, Long Island Jewish Medical Center, New Rochelle, NY, p. A442

STONE, Sam, Administrative and Chief Operating Officer, Essentia Health–Virginia, Virginia, MN, p. A349

STONE, Susan, R.N., Ph.D.
Director Human Resources, Claiborne Medical Center, Tazewell, TN, p. A589
Senior Vice President and Chief Executive Officer, Sharp Coronado Hospital And Healthcare Center, Coronado, CA, p. A56

STONE, Terry, Chief Financial Officer and Chief Information Officer, Willapa Harbor Hospital, South Bend, WA, p. A686

STONE, Thomas J., FACHE, Chief Executive Officer, Doctor's Memorial Hospital, Perry, FL, p. A139

STONE, Timothy D. Jr, President and Chief Executive Officer, Decatur Memorial Hospital, Decatur, IL, p. A185

STONER, Jamey, Chief Financial Officer, Frye Regional Medical Center, Hickory, NC, p. A464

STONER, Steve, Chief Information Officer, Richard L. Roudebush Veterans Affairs Medical Center, Indianapolis, IN, p. A212

STONESTREET, Jana S R.N., Ph.D., Chief Nursing Officer, Tulane Medical Center, New Orleans, LA, p. A283

STOOPS, Stephens M.D., Chief Medical Officer, Osceola Regional Medical Center, Kissimmee, FL, p. A129

STOPPER, Jim CPA, Chief Financial Officer, Evangelical Community Hospital, Lewisburg, PA, p. A539

STOPPLER, Maria, Chief Executive Officer, Granite County Medical Center, Philipsburg, MT, p. A387

STORCK, Craig, Chief Operating Officer, Blue Valley Hospital, Overland Park, KS, p. A248

STORER, William M.D., Medical Director, St. Vincent Indianapolis Hospital, IndianapolisSt. Vincent Heart Center, Indianapolis, IN, p. A212

STOREY, Kam, Director Human Resources, Sebastian River Medical Center, Sebastian, FL, p. A142

STOREY, Kevin L., Vice President and Administrator, Baptist Health Medical Center–Stuttgart, Stuttgart, AR, p. A50

STOREY, Paul, FACHE, President and Chief Executive Officer, Helen Keller Hospital, Sheffield, AL, p. A23

STORFJELL, Judith Ph.D., R.N., Senior Vice President and Chief Nursing Officer, Loma Linda University Medical Center, Loma Linda, CA, p. A66

STORM, Dave, Director Business Support, Hshs St. Anthony's Memorial Hospital, Effingham, IL, p. A186

STORR, Katie, Director of Human Resources, Mississippi State Hospital, Whitfield, MS, p. A363

STORTO, David E., President, Spaulding Rehabilitation Hospital, Charlestown, MA, p. A305

STOTLER, Sherry R.N., MSN, Chief Nursing Officer, Maricopa Integrated Health System, Phoenix, AZ, p. A33

STOTTLEMYRE, Georgan L., Chief Human Relations Officer, Northern Inyo Hospital, Bishop, CA, p. A54

STOTTS, Vicki, Coordinator Human Resources, Flint River Community Hospital, Montezuma, GA, p. A162

STOUGH, Robin
Chief Financial Officer, Belmont Pines Hospital, Youngstown, OH, p. A503
Chief Financial Officer, Windsor–Laurelwood Center For Behavioral Medicine, Willoughby, OH, p. A502

STOUT, Amanda, Chief Nursing Officer, Minneola District Hospital, Minneola, KS, p. A247

STOUT, Bess, Director Human Resources, Tennova Healthcare–Lafollette Medical Center, La Follette, TN, p. A582

STOUT, Cindy R.N., Chief Nursing Officer, University Medical Center Of El Paso, El Paso, TX, p. A612

STOUT, Deana
Vice President Financial Services, Medstar Good Samaritan Hospital, Baltimore, MD, p. A295
Vice President, Finance, Medstar Union Memorial Hospital, Baltimore, MD, p. A295

STOUT, Jeffrey MSN, R.N., Chief Operating Officer, St. Francis Medical Center, Lynwood, CA, p. A72

STOUT, Kimberly Dawn, Chief Nursing Officer, Mcalester Regional Health Center, Mcalester, OK, p. A510

STOUT, Patsy, Director Personnel, Richland Parish Hospital, Delhi, LA, p. A274

STOUT–TORRES, Sherri R.N., Chief Nursing Executive, Sutter Maternity And Surgery Center Of Santa Cruz, Santa Cruz, CA, p. A91

STOVALL, Henry, President, Sacred Heart Hospital Pensacola, Pensacola, FL, p. A139

STOVALL, Richard G, Senior Vice President Fiscal Services and Chief Financial Officer, Southern Regional Medical Center, Riverdale, GA, p. A163

STOVALL, Shella D., R.N., Acting Director, Veterans Affairs Salt Lake City Health Care System, Salt Lake City, UT, p. A661

STOVER, Benny, Vice President Finance, Mercy Hospital Rogers, Rogers, AR, p. A49

STOVER, George M., Chief Executive Officer, Hospital District No 1 Of Rice County, Lyons, KS, p. A246

STOVER, Nick, Director Information Systems, Plateau Medical Center, Oak Hill, WV, p. A694

STOVER, Patricia A, Administrator Nursing, Doylestown Hospital, Doylestown, PA, p. A533

STOVER, Raymond
President and Chief Executive Officer, Midmichigan Medical Center–Clare, Clare, MI, p. A316
President and Chief Executive Officer, Midmichigan Medical Center–Gladwin, Gladwin, MI, p. A320

STOVER, Theresa, Chief Human Resource Officer, Edgefield County Hospital, Edgefield, SC, p. A561

STOVERINK, Mike, Chief Financial Officer, Carle Richland Memorial Hospital, Olney, IL, p. A196

STOWE, Mary
Senior Vice President and Chief Nursing Officer, Children's Health System Of Texas, Dallas, TX, p. A605

Senior Vice President and Chief Nursing Officer, Children's Medical Center Plano, Plano, TX, p. A638

STOWELL, Dana A, Chief Information Officer, Mccurtain Memorial Hospital, Idabel, OK, p. A509

STOWMAN, Amber, Controller, Chi Lisbon Health, Lisbon, ND, p. A477

STOY, Gale, Manager Information Systems, Mid Coast Hospital, Brunswick, ME, p. A290

STOYANOFF, Pamela
Executive Vice President and Chief Operating Officer, Methodist Charlton Medical Center, Dallas, TX, p. A606
Executive Vice President and Chief Operating Officer, Methodist Dallas Medical Center, Dallas, TX, p. A606

STRABEL, Elizabeth M.D., Chief Medical Staff, Divine Savior Healthcare, Portage, WI, p. A710

STRACHAN, Eileen, Coordinator Human Resources, Kindred Hospital–Sycamore, Sycamore, IL, p. A201

STRACHAN, Ronald
Chief Information Officer, Mclaren Bay Region, Bay City, MI, p. A315
Chief Information Officer, Mclaren Flint, Flint, MI, p. A319

STRACK, Kirk, Vice President and Chief Financial Officer, Clark Memorial Hospital, Jeffersonville, IN, p. A213

STRADER, Lynn, Chief Financial Officer, Chippenham Hospital, Richmond, VA, p. A674

STRADER, Yvonne M, Chief Nursing Officer, Providence St. Mary Medical Center, Walla Walla, WA, p. A688

STRADI, Silvia, Chief Nursing Officer, Palms West Hospital, Loxahatchee, FL, p. A131

STRADTMAN, Jackie, Director Human Resources, Chi St. Joseph Health Burleson Hospital, Caldwell, TX, p. A600

STRAHAN, Greg
Chief Operating Officer, Owensboro Health Regional Hospital, Owensboro, KY, p. A265
Interim Chief Executive Officer, Owensboro Health Regional Hospital, Owensboro, KY, p. A265

STRAIN, Donna, Director Human Resources, Ray County Memorial Hospital, Richmond, MO, p. A375

STRAIN, Lynn R.N., MSN, Chief Nursing Officer, Slidell Memorial Hospital, Slidell, LA, p. A286

STRAMOWSKI, Mallary, Chief Human Resources Officer, Select Specialty Hospital–Madison, Madison, WI, p. A705

STRANATHAN, Sidney D.O., Chief of Staff, Anthony Medical Center, Anthony, KS, p. A238

STRAND, Eric, Director Information Services, North Florida Regional Medical Center, Gainesville, FL, p. A125

STRAND, Joy A., Chief Executive Officer, Mccready Health, Crisfield, MD, p. A298

STRANGE, Cheryl, Interim Chief Executive Officer, Western State Hospital, Tacoma, WA, p. A688

STRANGE, John, President and Chief Executive Officer, St. Luke's Hospital, Duluth, MN, p. A339

STRANGE, Roger, Chief Information Officer, St. Vincent Indianapolis Hospital, IndianapolisSt. Vincent Heart Center, Indianapolis, IN, p. A212

STRASH, Shawn G., Chief Executive Officer, Arise Austin Medical Center, Austin, TX, p. A594

STRASSER, Michael, Vice President and Chief Financial Officer, Mercy Medical Center Merced, Merced, CA, p. A73

STRASSNER III, Lawrence F Ph.D., FACHE, R.N., MS, Senior Vice President Operations and Chief Nursing Officer, Medstar Franklin Square Medical Center, Baltimore, MD, p. A295

STRATTON, James
Regional Vice President Finance, SSM Health St. Mary's Hospital – Audrain, Mexico, MO, p. A373
Vice President Finance, SSM Health St. Mary's Hospital – Jefferson City, Jefferson City, MO, p. A369

STRATTON, Joseph, FACHE, Chief Executive Officer, Geary Community Hospital, Junction City, KS, p. A243

STRATTON, Mary, Director Human Resources, River Park Hospital, Huntington, WV, p. A693

STRATTON, Tracie, Chief Nursing Officer, Los Alamos Medical Center, Los Alamos, NM, p. A427

STRAUGHAN, Janet, Manager Human Resources, Highlands Rehabilitation Hospital, El Paso, TX, p. A611

STRAUGHAN, John, Director Information Technology, Wallowa Memorial Hospital, Enterprise, OR, p. A521

STRAUMAN, Karen S R.N., M.P.H., Chief Nurse Executive, Kaiser Permanente Fresno Medical Center, Fresno, CA, p. A61

STRAUMANIS, John P. M.D., Vice President Medical Affairs and Chief Medical Officer, University Of Maryland Rehabilitation & Orthopaedic Institute, Baltimore, MD, p. A296

STRAUSBAUGH, Andrew, Chief Administrative Officer, Norton Brownsboro Hospital, Louisville, KY, p. A263

STRAUSS, Alan
Chief Financial Officer, Carondelet Holy Cross Hospital, Nogales, AZ, p. A32

Chief Financial Officer, Carondelet St. Joseph's Hospital, Tucson, AZ, p. A37

STRAUSS, Thomas J., Chief Executive Officer, Sisters Of Charity Health System, Cleveland, OH, p. B118

STRAUSS, Karen, Chief Human Resources Officer, Promedica Flower Hospital, Sylvania, OH, p. A500

STRAWN, Keith A, Vice President Human Resources, New Hanover Regional Medical Center, Wilmington, NC, p. A472

STRAWSER, Debbie A, Director Human Resources, Lindner Center Of Hope, Mason, OH, p. A495

STRAYER, Lorna
Executive Vice President, Fisher–Titus Medical Center, Norwalk, OH, p. A497
President and Chief Executive Officer, Fisher–Titus Medical Center, Norwalk, OH, p. A497

STRAYHORN, Shelly, R.N.
Chief Nursing Officer, Wadley Regional Medical Center At Hope, Hope, AR, p. A44
Chief Nursing Officer, Wadley Regional Medical Center, Texarkana, TX, p. A649

STRBICH, Steve D.O., Chief of Staff, Spectrum Health Ludington Hospital, Ludington, MI, p. A325

STREATER, Vivian, Chief Nursing Officer and Co–Acting Chief Executive Officer, Broughton Hospital, Morganton, NC, p. A467

STRECKER, Robert M.D., Chief of Staff, Colorado River Medical Center, Needles, CA, p. A76

STREDNEY, Thomas, Chief Human Resources Management Service, Aleda E. Lutz Veterans Affairs Medical Center, Saginaw, MI, p. A329

STREET, Gene, Chief Nursing Officer, Northeast Georgia Medical Center Barrow, Winder, GA, p. A167

STREET, Rex, Senior Vice President and Chief Financial Officer, Alamance Regional Medical Center, Burlington, NC, p. A458

STREETER, Alan W, Chief Financial Officer, Beatrice Community Hospital And Health Center, Beatrice, NE, p. A391

STREETER, Matthew, Chief Financial Officer, Southwest Health, Platteville, WI, p. A710

STREETER, Maxine, Administrator, Reception And Medical Center, Lake Butler, FL, p. A129

STREETER, Robert M.D., Vice President Medical Affairs, Mercy Medical Center Merced, Merced, CA, p. A73

STREICH, Rebecca, Manager Human Resources and Education Manager, Hutchinson Health, Hutchinson, MN, p. A341

STREIT, Loren, Director Human Resources, Geary Community Hospital, Junction City, KS, p. A243

STREJC, Irene T M.P.H., R.N., Vice President, Nursing, Methodist Richardson Medical Center, Richardson, TX, p. A639

STRICKER, Sean, Chief Executive Officer, Scl Health Community Hospital – Northglenn, Northglenn, CO, p. A106

STRICKER, Steven M.D., Physician in Chief, Kaiser Permanente Vallejo Medical Center, Vallejo, CA, p. A95

STRICKLAND, Barrie, Chief Financial Officer, Ucsf Medical Center, San Francisco, CA, p. A88

STRICKLAND, Connie, Chief Executive Officer, Select Specialty Hospital–Oklahoma City, Oklahoma City, OK, p. A513

STRICKLAND, David, Area Information Officer, Kaiser Permanente Los Angeles Medical Center, Los Angeles, CA, p. A68

STRICKLAND, Lee, Regional Director Information Technology, Park Ridge Health, Hendersonville, NC, p. A464

STRICKLAND, Morris S, Chief Financial Officer, Helen Keller Hospital, Sheffield, AL, p. A23

STRICKLAND, Wallace, President and Chief Executive Officer, Rush Health Systems, Meridian, MS, p. B109

STRICKLER, David
Chief Financial Officer, Nexus Specialty Hospital The Woodlands, The Woodlands, TX, p. A649
Chief Financial Officer, Nexus Specialty Hospital, Shenandoah, TX, p. A645

STRICKLER, Stephen Todd, Director of Nursing, Sistersville General Hospital, Sistersville, WV, p. A696

STRICKLING, Keith
Chief Accountant, Jay Hospital, Jay, FL, p. A129
Chief Financial Officer, Atmore Community Hospital, Atmore, AL, p. A14

STRIEBICH, Shannon, Chief Executive Officer, St. Joseph Mercy Oakland, Pontiac, MI, p. A328

STRIKE, Helen J, R.N., President, Mercy Hospital, Coon Rapids, MN, p. A338

STRING, Sherrie
Senior Vice President Human Resources, Hackensack Meridian Health Bayshore Community Hospital, Holmdel, NJ, p. A415
Senior Vice President Human Resources, Hackensack Meridian Health Ocean Medical Center, Brick Township, NJ, p. A412
Senior Vice President Human Resources, Hackensack Meridian Health Riverview Medical Center, Red Bank, NJ, p. A420

STRINGFELLOW, Grace M.D., Chief of Staff, Veterans Affairs Nebraska–Western Iowa Health Care System, Omaha, NE, p. A398

STRINGOS, Gust M.D., Medical Staff Director, Redington–Fairview General Hospital, Skowhegan, ME, p. A293

STRIPLIN, Elizabeth, Chief Financial Officer, Rehabilitation Hospital Of Southern New Mexico, Las Cruces, NM, p. A427

STRITTMATTER, Julie, Director Human Resources, Baylor University Medical Center, Dallas, TX, p. A605

STROBEL, Deb R.N., Chief Nursing Officer, Russell Regional Hospital, Russell, KS, p. A250

STROBEL, Jane, Vice President and Chief Financial Officer, Mercy Regional Medical Center, Durango, CO, p. A101

STROBEL, Rand
Regional Chief Information Officer, Information Technology Services, Harrison Medical Center, Bremerton, WA, p. A678
Regional Chief Information Officer, St. Francis Hospital, Federal Way, WA, p. A680
Vice President Information Technology and Compliance, St. Joseph Medical Center, Tacoma, WA, p. A688

STRODE, Marc, Chief Executive Officer, Methodist Stone Oak Hospital, San Antonio, TX, p. A643

STROEMEL, Douglas M.
Administrator Mercy Hospital Aurora and Mercy Hospital Cassville, Mercy Hospital Aurora, Aurora, MO, p. A364
Administrator, Mercy Hospital Berryville, Berryville, AR, p. A40
President, Mercy Hospital Cassville, Cassville, MO, p. A366

STROH, Rhonda, Chief Human Resources Officer, Community Memorial Hospital, Redfield, SD, p. A572

STROHECKER, Sharon R.N., MSN, Vice President Clinical Operations and Chief Nursing Officer, Penn State Health St. Joseph, Reading, PA, p. A549

STROHLA, Patti R.N., Chief Nursing Officer, Franklin Regional Hospital, Franklin, NH, p. A408

STROM, Lisa, Director Information Systems, North Big Horn Hospital District, Lovell, WY, p. A719

STROMBERG, Audrey, Administrator, Roosevelt Medical Center, Culbertson, MT, p. A383

STRONG, David, Chief Financial Officer/Vice President Finance, Cox Medical Center Branson, Branson, MO, p. A365

STRONG, David W., President and Chief Executive Officer, Orlando Health, Orlando, FL, p. B95

STRONG, Patricia
Chief Financial Officer, Cumberland River Hospital, Celina, TN, p. A576
Interim Chief Executive Officer, Cumberland River Hospital, Celina, TN, p. A576

STRONG, Tanya, Manager Information Technology, Harney District Hospital, Burns, OR, p. A520

STROSS, Daniel
Chief Information Officer, Genesys Regional Medical Center, Grand Blanc, MI, p. A320
Chief Information Officer, St. Joseph Health System, Tawas City, MI, p. A331
Chief Information Officer, St. Mary's Of Michigan, Saginaw, MI, p. A330

STROTHER, James, Site Director Information Technology Systems, Mercy Medical Center–Des Moines, Des Moines, IA, p. A226

STROTHKAMP, Brad, Chief Information Systems, Lakeland Behavioral Health System, Springfield, MO, p. A379

STROUCKEN, Christian, Chief Operating Officer, Carney Hospital, Boston, MA, p. A303

STROUD, Justin, Chief Financial Officer, Merit Health Central, Jackson, MS, p. A356

STROUD, Teresa, Chief Financial Officer, Salem Township Hospital, Salem, IL, p. A199

STROUP, Jeff, Chief Operating Officer, Oklahoma State University Medical Center, Tulsa, OK, p. A517

STROUSE, Thomas M.D., Medical Director and Professor of Clinical Psych, Stewart & Lynda Resnick Neuropsychiatric Hospital At Ucla, Los Angeles, CA, p. A71

STRUB, Lisa
Chief Operating Officer, Centennial Peaks Hospital, Louisville, CO, p. A106
Interim Chief Executive Officer, Highlands Behavioral Health System, Littleton, CO, p. A105

STRUTTON, Jill, Director Personnel Systems, University Of Texas Harris County Psychiatric Center, Houston, TX, p. A623

STRUYK, Douglas A., CPA, President and Chief Executive Officer, Christian Health Care Center, Wyckoff, NJ, p. A423

STRZELECKI, Sarah Ed.D., R.N., Chief Nursing Officer, Phoenixville Hospital, Phoenixville, PA, p. A546

STRZEMPKO, Stanley M.D., Vice President Medical Affairs and Chief Medical Officer, Baystate Noble Hospital, Westfield, MA, p. A312

STUART, Danna M.D., Chief Medical Officer, Newman Memorial Hospital, Shattuck, OK, p. A515

STUART, Philip J., Administrator and Chief Executive Officer, Tomah Memorial Hospital, Tomah, WI, p. A713

STUART, Robin, Chief Executive Officer, Morrill County Community Hospital, Bridgeport, NE, p. A391

STUART, Wendy, Chief Nursing Officer, Kendall Regional Medical Center, Miami, FL, p. A133

STUBBS, Don, Vice President Human Resources, Candler Hospital, Savannah, GA, p. A164

STUBBS, Kay, Chief Nursing Officer, Northwest Medical Center, Tucson, AZ, p. A38

STUBITSCH, Brian M.D., Chief Medical Officer, Edgerton Hospital And Health Services, Edgerton, WI, p. A701

STUCK, Julie, R.N., Chief Executive Officer, Hocking Valley Community Hospital, Logan, OH, p. A494

STUCKY, Nancy, Director Human Resources and Public Relations, Kingman Community Hospital, Kingman, KS, p. A244

STUCZYNSKI, Joseph, Assistant Administrator Finance and Support, Memorial Hospital Pembroke, Pembroke Pines, FL, p. A139

STUDEBAKER, Shelly
Director Management Information Systems, Clinch Memorial Hospital, Homerville, GA, p. A159
Manager Human Resources, Clinch Memorial Hospital, Homerville, GA, p. A159

STUDER, Tim, President Medical Staff, Perham Health, Perham, MN, p. A346

STUENKEL, Kurt, FACHE, President and Chief Executive Officer, Floyd Medical Center, Rome, GA, p. A163

STUERSEL, Marie, Director Human Resources, Seneca Healthcare District, Chester, CA, p. A55

STUEVE, Angela M.D., Chief Medical Officer, Nemaha Valley Community Hospital, Seneca, KS, p. A251

STUEVE, Jo W, Executive Vice President and Co–Chief Operating Officer, Children's Mercy Hospital Kansas City, Kansas City, MO, p. A370

STUHLMILLER, Michael, Chief Financial Officer, Mann–Grandstaff Veterans Affairs Medical Center, Spokane, WA, p. A686

STULTS, Cynthia S., Executive Assistant and Human Resources Director, Rangely District Hospital, Rangely, CO, p. A107

STULTS, Kim, Director, Information Systems, Bellevue Hospital, Bellevue, OH, p. A481

STUMBO, Kathy, President, Saint Joseph – Martin, Martin, KY, p. A264

STUMME, Sarah, Director Human Resources, Owatonna Hospital, Owatonna, MN, p. A345

STUMP, Lisa, Interim Chief Information Officer, Yale–New Haven Hospital, New Haven, CT, p. A112

STUMP, Tammie, R.N., Chief Executive Officer, Union County General Hospital, Clayton, NM, p. B36

STUMP, Veronica, Director of Nursing, Carilion Giles Community Hospital, Pearisburg, VA, p. A672

STUMPO, Barbara J R.N., Vice President Patient Care Services, Griffin Hospital, Derby, CT, p. A110

STUNKARD, Jill R.N., MSN, Associate Chief Nurse Executive and Interim Chief Nursing Officer, Einstein Medical Center Philadelphia, Philadelphia, PA, p. A543

STURGEON, Jim, Area Director Human Resources, Kindred Hospital Las Vegas–Sahara, Henderson, NV, p. A402

STURGEON, Wade, Chief Operating Officer and Chief Financial Officer, Bear Valley Community Hospital, Big Bear Lake, CA, p. A54

STURGILL, Lori
Vice President Business Partnership, Mercy Hospital Fort Scott, Fort Scott, KS, p. A241
Vice President Business Partnership, Mercy Hospital Springfield, Springfield, MO, p. A379

STURGIS, Gayle R.N., Nurse Administrator, Heber Valley Medical Center, Heber City, UT, p. A657

STURGIS, Jonathan, Chief Financial Officer, Houston Methodist San Jacinto Hospital, Baytown, TX, p. A597

STURGIS, Paul
Chief Human Resource Officer, Sparrow Specialty Hospital, Lansing, MI, p. A324
Director Human Resources, DMC – Rehabilitation Institute Of Michigan, Detroit, MI, p. A317
Vice President and Chief Human Resources Officer, Sparrow Hospital, Lansing, MI, p. A324

STURLER, Kelly, Chief Nursing Officer, Mckee Medical Center, Loveland, CO, p. A106

STURSA, Robin, Chief Information Officer, St. Vincent Charity Medical Center, Cleveland, OH, p. A486

STUWE, Shannon, Director of Nursing, Faulkton Area Medical Center, Faulkton, SD, p. A569

STYER, Brent
Chief Information Officer, Summers County Arh Hospital, Hinton, WV, p. A692
Director Information Technology, Whitesburg Arh Hospital, Whitesburg, KY, p. A268

STYLES, Kelly R, Vice President and Chief Information Officer, Connecticut Children's Medical Center, Hartford, CT, p. A110

STYRON, Stacie, Chief Nursing Officer, Lamb Healthcare Center, Littlefield, TX, p. A629

SUAREZ, Irma, Deputy Executive Director, NYC Health + Hospitals / Woodhull, New Rochelle, NY, p. A446

SUAREZ, Lauren, Chief Executive Officer, Kentfield Rehabilitation And Specialty Hospital, Kentfield, CA, p. A64

SUAREZ, Orlando, Director Information Technology, Larkin Community Hospital, South Miami, FL, p. A143

SUBIA, Corina, Director Human Resources, Ward Memorial Hospital, Monahans, TX, p. A634

SUBLER, Jeffrey R., Vice President Support Services, Wayne Healthcare, Greenville, OH, p. A492

SUBLETTE, Elizabeth, Director Finance, Providence Willamette Falls Medical Center, Oregon City, OR, p. A524

SUBRAMANIAN, Aarti, Vice President and Chief Financial Officer, Psychiatric Institute Of Washington, Washington, DC, p. A118

SUCATO, Daniel J M.D., MS, Chief of Staff, Texas Scottish Rite Hospital For Children, Dallas, TX, p. A607

SUCHER, Therese O, Senior Vice President Operations, Southern Regional Medical Center, Riverdale, GA, p. A163

SUDAK, Mariellena, R.N., MSN, Vice President and Chief Nursing Officer, Palomar Medical Center, Escondido, CA, p. A58

SUDBURY, Russ M.D., President Medical Staff, Ministry Sacred Heart Hospital, Tomahawk, WI, p. A714

SUDDUTH, Tony, Chief Financial Officer, Trios Health, Kennewick, WA, p. A681

SUDICKY, Mary, Chief Financial Officer, St. Mary Medical Center, Hobart, IN, p. A210

SUDOLCAN, Joseph M.D., Medical Director, Reagan Memorial Hospital, Big Lake, TX, p. A598

SUEHS, JoAnne, Manager Human Resources, Chapman Global Medical Center, Orange, CA, p. A77

SUGAR, Bev, Associate Administrator and Director Human Resources, Inova Mount Vernon Hospital, Alexandria, VA, p. A664

SUGDEN, Elizabeth M.D., Chief Medical Officer, St. Luke's Jerome, Jerome, ID, p. A173

SUGG, Amy, Director Human Resources, Scott Regional Hospital, Morton, MS, p. A359

SUGGS, Heather, Manager Human Resources, Jay Hospital, Jay, FL, p. A129

SUHR, Nancy, Manager Human Resources, Pender Community Hospital, Pender, NE, p. A399

SUITTER, Marie, Chief Financial Officer, The Acadia Hospital, Bangor, ME, p. A289

SUKENIK, Richard CPA, Vice President Finance and Chief Financial Officer, Chan Soon–Shiong Medical Center, Windber, PA, p. A554

SUKIN, Debra F., Regional Vice President and Chief Executive Officer, Houston Methodist The Woodlands Hospital, The Woodlands, TX, p. A649

SUKSI, Eugene, Chief Executive Officer, Adventist Health Medical Center – Tehachapi Valley, Tehachapi, CA, p. A93

SULIT, Teresa, Director of Human Resources, Seven Hills Hospital, Henderson, NV, p. A402

SULLINS, Jacqueline C R.N., Chief Nursing Officer, Merit Health Rankin, Brandon, MS, p. A353

SULLIVAN, Christopher M.D., Chief Medical Officer, Centerpoint Medical Center, Independence, MO, p. A369

SULLIVAN, Daniel D.O., Chief Medical Officer, Vice President Medical Administration, Elmhurst Hospital, Elmhurst, IL, p. A187

SULLIVAN, Danita S R.N., Chief Nursing Officer, Touro Infirmary, New Orleans, LA, p. A283

SULLIVAN, David, Director Human Resources, Ohiohealth Doctors Hospital, Columbus, OH, p. A487

SULLIVAN, Denis, Chief Human Resources Management, Veterans Affairs Black Hills Health Care System, Fort Meade, SD, p. A570

SULLIVAN, Donald M.D., Medical Director, Healthsouth Rehabilitation Hospital Memphis–North, Memphis, TN, p. A584

SULLIVAN, Gregory, Manager Human Resources, Girard Medical Center, Girard, KS, p. A241

SULLIVAN, James M.D., Chief Medical Officer, Butler Hospital, Providence, RI, p. A556

SULLIVAN, Jennie, Chief Executive Officer, Wray Community District Hospital, Wray, CO, p. A108

SULLIVAN, Jennifer, President and Chief Executive Officer, St. James Mercy Hospital, Hornell, NY, p. A437

SULLIVAN, John, President, Medstar Washington Hospital Center, Washington, DC, p. A118

SULLIVAN, Katherine, Director, Human Resources, Moab Regional Hospital, Moab, UT, p. A657

SULLIVAN, Keith, Director, Chillicothe Veterans Affairs Medical Center, Chillicothe, OH, p. A483

SULLIVAN, Lowery M.D., Chief Medical Officer, Northwestern Medical Center, Saint Albans, VT, p. A663

SULLIVAN, Martha, Chief Information Officer, Harrison Memorial Hospital, Cynthiana, KY, p. A257

SULLIVAN, Mary Patricia R.N., MSN, Chief Nursing Officer, Overlook Medical Center, Summit, NJ, p. A421

SULLIVAN, Maurita
Vice President, Mayo Clinic Health System – Chippewa Valley In Bloomer, Bloomer, WI, p. A699
Vice President, Mayo Clinic Health System – Northland In Barron, Barron, WI, p. A698

SULLIVAN, Michael Dean M.D., Chief of Staff, Mercy Hospital El Reno, El Reno, OK, p. A507

SULLIVAN, Michael, M.D.
Chief Medical Officer, Northern Maine Medical Center, Fort Kent, ME, p. A291
Medical Director Emergency Services, Peacehealth Peace Island Medical Center, Friday Harbor, WA, p. A681

SULLIVAN, Patrick L, Chief Operating Officer, St. John's Episcopal Hospital–South Shore, New Rochelle, NY, p. A446

SULLIVAN, Peter, Chief Executive Officer, Riverside Medical Center, Franklinton, LA, p. A275

SULLIVAN, Staci R.N., Chief Nursing Officer, Lane Regional Medical Center, Zachary, LA, p. A288

SULLIVAN, Theresa, Chief Executive Officer, Samaritan Healthcare, Moses Lake, WA, p. A682

SULLIVAN, Thomas, Vice President Fiscal Services, Harrington Hospital, Southbridge, MA, p. A311

SULLIVAN, William, Chief Financial Officer, Mount Auburn Hospital, Cambridge, MA, p. A305

SULLIVAN SMITH, Mary R.N., MS, Senior Vice President, Chief Operating Officer and Chief Nursing Officer, New England Baptist Hospital, Boston, MA, p. A303

SULLIVANT, Laura, Area Chief Information Officer, Kaiser Permanente San Diego Medical Center, San Diego, CA, p. A85

SULSER, Jamey, Director Human Resources, South Davis Community Hospital, Bountiful, UT, p. A656

SULU, Dorothy, Budget Analyst, Hopi Health Care Center, Keams Canyon, AZ, p. A30

SULZEN, Jessica, Director Human Resources, Belton Regional Medical Center, Belton, MO, p. A364

SUMMERLIN, Craig, Chief Human Resources Officer, Singing River Health System, Pascagoula, MS, p. A360

SUMMERLIN, Valerie R.N., MS, Chief Nursing Officer, Adventist Healthcare Physical Health And Rehabilitation, Rockville, MD, p. A300

SUMMERS, Andrew, Chief Financial Officer, Usmd Hospital At Arlington, Arlington, TX, p. A594

SUMMERS, Barbara L. Ph.D., R.N., Vice President Nursing Practice and Chief Nursing Officer, University Of Texas M.D. Anderson Cancer Center, Houston, TX, p. A623

SUMMERS, Curtis, Chief Executive Officer, Summit Medical Center, Edmond, OK, p. A507

SUMMERS, David A, Chief Financial Officer, Tristar Centennial Medical Center, Nashville, TN, p. A587

SUMMERS, Debra, Chief Nursing Officer, Calhoun–Liberty Hospital, Blountstown, FL, p. A120

SUMMERS, Jeff M.D., Medical Director, Select Specialty Hospital–North Knoxville, Powell, TN, p. A588

SUMMERS, Kelly, Chief Information Officer, Maricopa Integrated Health System, Phoenix, AZ, p. A33

SUMMERS, Paul
Chief Financial Officer, Uhs Delaware Valley Hospital, Walton, NY, p. A454
Chief Human Resources Officer, Uhs Delaware Valley Hospital, Walton, NY, p. A454
President and Chief Executive Officer, Uhs Delaware Valley Hospital, Walton, NY, p. A454

SUMMERS–MAIN, Theresa, R.N., Interim President, Genesis Medical Center, Silvis, Silvis, IL, p. A200

SUMMERSON, Tonya, Chief Clinical Officer, Dallas County Hospital, Perry, IA, p. A233

SUMMERVILLE, Wendell, Chief Financial Officer, Bryce Hospital, Tuscaloosa, AL, p. A23

SUMNER, Donna, Director, Human Resources and Organizational Development, St. Joseph Medical Center, Kansas City, MO, p. A371

SUMNER, Jack R, Assistant Administrator Finance, Providence Newberg Medical Center, Newberg, OR, p. A524

SUMNER, John, Chief Executive Officer, Trigg County Hospital, Cadiz, KY, p. A256

SUMPTER, Nikki, Senior Vice President Human Resources, Jps Health Network, Fort Worth, TX, p. A613

SUMRA, K S M.D., Chief of Staff, Pembina County Memorial Hospital And Wedgewood Manor, Cavalier, ND, p. A474

SUMRALL, Mary Ellen, Chief Nursing Officer, Baptist Memorial Hospital–Golden Triangle, Columbus, MS, p. A354

SUMTER, Rob, Executive Vice President and Chief Operation Officer, Regional One Health, Memphis, TN, p. A585

SUN RHODES, Neil M.D., Chief Medical Officer, U.S. Public Health Service Blackfeet Community Hospital, Saint Mary, MT, p. A388

SUND, Lynn A.
Chief Nursing Executive, Saint Francis Hospital South, Tulsa, OK, p. A518
Senior Vice President, Administrator and Chief Nursing Executive, Laureate Psychiatric Clinic And Hospital, Tulsa, OK, p. A517
Senior Vice President, Chief Nurse Executive, Saint Francis Health System and Administrator, Saint Francis Hospital, Saint Francis Hospital, Tulsa, OK, p. A518

SUNDARAMOORTHY, Abirammy M.D., Chief Medical Officer, University Hospitals Conneaut Medical Center, Conneaut, OH, p. A488

SUNDBERG, Nita, Director Human Resources, Three Rivers Behavioral Health, West Columbia, SC, p. A567

SUNDBLOM, Karin MSN, R.N., Chief Nursing Officer, Saint Luke's Cushing Hospital, Leavenworth, KS, p. A245

SUNDERLIN, Tammy, Director of Nursing, Auburn Community Hospital, Auburn, NY, p. A431

SUNDIN, Joanne, Chief Executive Officer, Wellbridge Healthcare Of San Marcos, San Marcos, TX, p. A644

SUNDIN, Jon M.D., Medical Director, The Orthopedic Specialty Hospital, Murray, UT, p. A658

SUNDQUIST, Joanne, Chief Information Officer, St. John's Hospital, Maplewood, MN, p. A343

SUNDRUD, Diane
Director Human Resources, Essentia Health Fosston, Fosston, MN, p. A340
Human Resource Service Partner, Essentia Health St. Mary's – Detroit Lakes, Detroit Lakes, MN, p. A338

SUNGA, Marcos N M.D., Chief of Staff, Hardin County General Hospital, Rosiclare, IL, p. A199

SUNKAVALLE, Krishna M.D., Chief Medical Officer, Hamlin Memorial Hospital, Hamlin, TX, p. A618

SUNQUIST, Joanne
Chief Information Officer, Bethesda Hospital, Saint Paul, MN, p. A347
Chief Information Officer, Woodwinds Health Campus, Woodbury, MN, p. A351
Information System, Senior Vice President and Chief Information Officer, St. Joseph's Hospital, Saint Paul, MN, p. A348

SUNTAY, Renato, Chief Financial Officer, Meadville Medical Center, Meadville, PA, p. A540

SUNTHA, Mohan, M.D.
President and Chief Executive Officer, University Of Maryland Medical Center Midtown Campus, Baltimore, MD, p. A296
President and Chief Executive Officer, University Of Maryland Medical Center, Baltimore, MD, p. A296

SUNTRAPAK, Todd A., President and Chief Executive Officer, Valley Children's Healthcare, Madera, CA, p. A72

SUPPAN, Marchelle, DPM, President and Chief Executive Officer, Aultman Orrville Hospital, Orrville, OH, p. A497

SUPPLEE, Linda, Chief Executive Officer, Select Specialty Hospital Of Southeast Ohio, Newark, OH, p. A497

SURANI, Salim M.D., Chief of Staff, Care Regional Medical Center, Aransas Pass, TX, p. A593

SURBER, Randy, Chief Executive Officer, Florida Hospital Heartland Medical Center, Sebring, FL, p. A142

SURBER, Shannon, Chief Operating Officer, Peacehealth Sacred Heart Medical Center At Riverbend, Springfield, OR, p. A527

SURCOUF, Shelli, Chief Financial Officer, Georgetown Behavioral Health Institute, Georgetown, TX, p. A616

SURESH, Srinivasan M.D., Chief Medical Information Officer, Children's Hospital Of Pittsburgh Of Upmc, Pittsburgh, PA, p. A546

SURL, Deepak, Chief Information Officer, Eastern New Mexico Medical Center, Roswell, NM, p. A428

SURO, Marta R Mercado, Chief Operating Officer, Mennonite General Hospital, Aibonito, PR, p. A722

SUROWITZ, Dale, Chief Executive, Providence Tarzana Medical Center, Los Angeles, CA, p. A71

SURRATT, Shawn M.D., Chief of Staff, Memorial Hospital And Manor, Bainbridge, GA, p. A152

SURROCK, Lester, Chief Financial Officer, Nix Health Care System, San Antonio, TX, p. A643

SUSI, Jeffrey L., President and Chief Executive Officer, Indian River Medical Center, Vero Beach, FL, p. A146

SUSICK, Nancy, MSN, President, Beaumont Hospital – Troy, Troy, MI, p. A332

SUSIE–LATTNER, Debra M.D., Vice President Medical Management, Advocate Condell Medical Center, Libertyville, IL, p. A192

SUSSMAN, Andrew M.D., Chief Operating Officer, Umass Memorial Medical Center, Worcester, MA, p. A313

SUSSMAN, Howard M.D., Chief Medical Officer, St. Joseph Hospital, Bethpage, NY, p. A431

SUSTERICH, Tim, Chief Financial Officer and Chief Operating Officer, Memorial Healthcare, Owosso, MI, p. A327

SUTER, Brian, Chief Financial Officer, Mayo Clinic Health System In Fairmont, Fairmont, MN, p. A339

SUTER, Mia, Chief Administration Officer, Owensboro Health Regional Hospital, Owensboro, KY, p. A265

SUTHERLAND, Shea, Chief Financial Officer, Merit Health Madison, Canton, MS, p. A353

SUTHERLIN, Shara R.N., Director Patient Care Services, South Peninsula Hospital, Homer, AK, p. A26

SUTIKA, John, President, Penn Highlands Dubois, Dubois, PA, p. A533

SUTKUS, Amy M.D., Medical Staff President, Santiam Hospital, Stayton, OR, p. A527

SUTTLE, Terry, Superintendent, Richmond State Hospital, Richmond, IN, p. A219

SUTTLES, Mary Anne, Chief Nursing Officer, St. Francis Medical Center, Trenton, NJ, p. A422

SUTTON, Andrew
Chief Human Resources Officer, Coatesville Veterans Affairs Medical Center, Coatesville, PA, p. A532
Chief, Human Resources Management Service, James A. Haley Veterans' Hospital–Tampa, Tampa, FL, p. A144

SUTTON, Angie, Chief Financial Officer, Genoa Medical Facilities, Genoa, NE, p. A393

SUTTON, Elaine, Chief Information Officer, General John J. Pershing Memorial Hospital, Brookfield, MO, p. A365

SUTTON, Fred M.D., Chief Medical Officer, Harris Health System, Houston, TX, p. A620

SUTTON, Janet M.D., Medical Director, Mclaren Bay Special Care, Bay City, MI, p. A315

SUTTON, Jeffrey, Chief Information Officer, Lexington Veterans Affairs Medical Center, Lexington, KY, p. A261

SUTTON, Jesse, Senior Vice President and Chief Financial Officer, Texas Health Huguley Hospital Fort Worth South, Burleson, TX, p. A600

SUTTON, Julie, Director Performance Improvement, State Hospital South, Blackfoot, ID, p. A171

SUTTON, Michele K., FACHE, President and Chief Executive Officer, North Oaks Medical Center, Hammond, LA, p. A275

SUTTON, Rhonda, Director Human Resources, Richland Hospital, Richland Center, WI, p. A711

SUTTON, Richard O., FACHE, Chief Executive Officer, Southeast Alabama Medical Center, Dothan, AL, p. A17

SUTTON, Thomas, Associate Director, North Florida/South Georgia Veteran's Health System, Gainesville, FL, p. A126

SUTTON–WALLACE, Pamela, Chief Executive Officer, University Of Virginia Medical Center, Charlottesville, VA, p. A665

SUVER, James A., FACHE, Chief Executive Officer, Ridgecrest Regional Hospital, Ridgecrest, CA, p. A82

SUZUKI, Daniel M.D., Medical Director, Las Encinas Hospital, Pasadena, CA, p. A79

SVARC, Mackenzie, Finance Director, Friend Community Healthcare System, Friend, NE, p. A393

SVENDSEN, Mark Deyo M.D., Medical Director, Mayo Clinic Health System – Red Cedar In Menomonie, Menomonie, WI, p. A706

SWAGERTY, Jill, Director Human Resources, Union County General Hospital, Clayton, NM, p. A425

SWAIN, Art, Vice President Support Services, Joint Township District Memorial Hospital, Saint Marys, OH, p. A498

SWAINE, Richard P., President, Beaumont Hospital – Grosse Pointe, Grosse Pointe, MI, p. A322

SWALLER, Pat, Interim Chief Nursing Officer, John F. Kennedy Memorial Hospital, Indio, CA, p. A63

SWAMINATHAN, Rajesh M.D., Chief Medical Officer, St. Anthony's Medical Center, Saint Louis, MO, p. A378

SWAN, Debbie, Director Human Resources, Baptist Memorial Hospital–North Mississippi, Oxford, MS, p. A360

SWAN, Dennis A., JD, FACHE, President and Chief Executive Officer, Sparrow Hospital, Lansing, MI, p. A324

SWANDAL, Dianne R.N., MSN, Vice President Patient Care, St. Joseph Hospital, Bangor, ME, p. A289

SWANGER, Cae, Chief Information Officer, Riverside Community Hospital, Riverside, CA, p. A82

SWANGER, Carol, Chief Nursing Officer, Kansas Rehabilitation Hospital, Topeka, KS, p. A252

SWANK, Colleen, Chief Medical Officer, Altru Health System, Grand Forks, ND, p. A476

SWANK, Georgia, Chief Nursing Officer, Ridge Behavioral Health System, Lexington, KY, p. A261

SWANSON, Julie, Coordinator Human Resources, Healthsouth Western Hills Regional Rehabilitation Hospital, Parkersburg, WV, p. A695

SWANSON, Kathy, President, Orlando Regional Medical Center, Orlando, FL, p. A137

SWANSON, Margaret J, Chief Nursing Officer, Fairview Lakes Health Services, Wyoming, MN, p. A351

SWARTOUT, Paula, Human Resources Manager, Dickinson County Healthcare System, Iron Mountain, MI, p. A323

SWARTWOOD, Peggy, Assistant Vice President, Finance and Controller, Uhs Chenango Memorial Hospital, Norwich, NY, p. A448

SWARTWOOD, Philip, Director Information Systems, Grove City Medical Center, Grove City, PA, p. A535

SWARTZ, Edward, Chief Financial Officer, Spring Grove Hospital Center, Baltimore, MD, p. A296

SWARTZ, Michael J., FACHE
  Medical Center Director, Bath Veterans Affairs Medical Center, Bath, NY, p. A431
  Medical Center Director, Canandaigua Veterans Affairs Medical Center, Canandaigua, NY, p. A433

SWEARINGEN, Angela, Vice President Finance, St. Mary's Medical Center, Huntington, WV, p. A693

SWEAT, Holli, Associate Administrator and Chief Nursing Officer, Memorial Satilla Health, Waycross, GA, p. A167

SWEAT, Kendra, Director Human Resources, Power County Hospital District, American Falls, ID, p. A171

SWEENEY, Janey, Chief Nursing Officer, Suncoast Behavioral Health Center, Bradenton, FL, p. A121

SWEENEY, Karen MSN, R.N., Vice President, Chief Nursing Officer, Mercy Hospital Ada, Ada, OK, p. A504

SWEENEY, Mary, Vice President Colleague Services and Development, St. Mary Medical Center, Langhorne, PA, p. A538

SWEENEY, Michael
  Chief Informatics Officer, Jeanes Hospital, Philadelphia, PA, p. A544
  Chief Information Officer, Fox Chase Cancer Center–American Oncologic Hospital, Philadelphia, PA, p. A543

SWEENEY, Shaun, Vice President Patient Care Services, Carrier Clinic, Belle Mead, NJ, p. A411

SWEERE, Sheri, Division Director Human Resources, Chi Mercy Health, Valley City, ND, p. A478

SWEET, Mary, Administrator, Kiowa County Memorial Hospital, Greensburg, KS, p. A242

SWEET, Renae, Chief Financial Officer, Surprise Valley Health Care District, Cedarville, CA, p. A55

SWEET, Terrance J., Director Information Technology, Winnebago Mental Health Institute, Winnebago, WI, p. A716

SWEHA, Amir M.D., Vice President Medical Administration, Methodist Hospital Of Sacramento, Sacramento, CA, p. A83

SWEITZER, Gregory, Chief Medical Officer, Wright Patterson Medical Center, Wright, OH, p. A503

SWENSON, Cathy, Chief Executive Officer, Nelson County Health System, Mcville, ND, p. A477

SWENSON, Daniel J., FACHE, Administrator, Centracare Health–Long Prairie, Long Prairie, MN, p. A342

SWENSON, Jennifer, President and Chief Executive Officer, Simi Valley Hospital, Simi Valley, CA, p. A92

SWENSON, Nena, Financial Manager, Tahoe Pacific Hospitals, Sparks, NV, p. A406

SWENSON, Nina, Director Business Services, Newport Bay Hospital, Newport Beach, CA, p. A76

SWENSON, Paula C R.N., Vice President and Chief Nursing Officer, St. Catherine Hospital, East Chicago, IN, p. A206

SWENSON, Warren, Chief Financial Officer, United Medical Rehabilitation Hospital, Hammond, LA, p. A276

SWICK, Michael D., President and Chief Executive Officer, Lima Memorial Health System, Lima, OH, p. A493

SWIDERSKI, Tom, Chief Financial Officer, Orthopaedic Hospital Of Wisconsin – Glendale, Glendale, WI, p. A702

SWIFT, Brian M, Senior Administrator Plant Operations, Burke Rehabilitation Hospital, White Plains, NY, p. A456

SWIFT, David, Chief Human Resources Officer, Penn State Milton S. Hershey Medical Center, Hershey, PA, p. A536

SWIFT, Diane, Director Medical Records, I–70 Community Hospital, Sweet Springs, MO, p. A380

SWIFT, Kyle, Chief Executive Officer, Woodland Heights Medical Center, Lufkin, TX, p. A631

SWIFT, Nick, Chief Financial Officer, Maury Regional Hospital, Columbia, TN, p. A577

SWIGER, Jared, Director Information Systems, Ashtabula County Medical Center, Ashtabula, OH, p. A480

SWILLEY, Bryanie W. Jr, Interim Chief Executive Officer, St. Joseph Medical Center, Houston, TX, p. A622

SWINDELL, Terry
  Chief Financial Officer, Camden General Hospital, Camden, TN, p. A575
  Controller, Bolivar General Hospital, Bolivar, TN, p. A575

SWINDLE, Patrick, Administrator, East Texas Medical Center–Quitman, Quitman, TX, p. A639

SWINGLE, Dale, Vice President Information Services, Troy Community Hospital, Troy, PA, p. A552

SWINT, Ken
  Director Finance, Promedica Defiance Regional Hospital, Defiance, OH, p. A490
  Vice President Finance and Chief Financial Officer, Promedica Fostoria Community Hospital, Fostoria, OH, p. A491

SWINT, Patricia
  Director Information Management Systems, Promedica Defiance Regional Hospital, Defiance, OH, p. A490
  Director Information Technology, St. Luke's Hospital, Maumee, OH, p. A495

SWISHER, Kay, Chief Nursing Officer, Greenville Health System – Laurens County Memorial Hospital, Clinton, SC, p. A560

SWISSHELM, Patricia, Acting Chief Fiscal Service, Lexington Veterans Affairs Medical Center, Lexington, KY, p. A261

SWOFFORD, William M.D., Chief of Staff, Miller County Hospital, Colquitt, GA, p. A154

SWORDS, James, Director Human Resources, Lewis County General Hospital, Lowville, NY, p. A438

SY, Annette
  Chief Nursing Officer, Keck Hospital Of Usc, Los Angeles, CA, p. A69
  Chief Nursing Officer, Usc Norris Comprehensive Cancer Center, Los Angeles, CA, p. A71

SYED, Imran, Manager Technology Information Services, Spectrum Health Zeeland Community Hospital, Zeeland, MI, p. A334

SYED, Mamoon
  Vice President Human Resources, Children's Hospital Of Orange County, Orange, CA, p. A78
  Vice President Human Resources, Choc Children's At Mission Hospital, Mission Viejo, CA, p. A73
  Vice President Human Resources, Rady Children's Hospital – San Diego, San Diego, CA, p. A85

SYKES, Angel, Director Human Resources, Memorial Hospital And Manor, Bainbridge, GA, p. A152

SYKES, Christina, Director Human Resources, Labette Health, Parsons, KS, p. A249

SYKES, Lee, Human Resources Director, Lifebrite Community Hospital Of Stokes, Danbury, NC, p. A460

SYKES, Lisa
  Director Information Services, Carolinas Healthcare System Union, Monroe, NC, p. A467
  IS/Communications Director, Carolinas Healthcare System Anson, Wadesboro, NC, p. A472
  Manager, Information Services, Carolinas Healthcare System Northeast, Concord, NC, p. A460

SYKES, Rebecca S
  Chief Information Officer, Mercy St. Anne Hospital, Toledo, OH, p. A500
  Senior Vice President Resource Management, Chief Information Officer, Mercy Health – St. Charles Hospital, Oregon, OH, p. A497
  Director, Human Resources and Education, South Lake Hospital, Clermont, FL, p. A122

SYLVIA–HUTCHINSON, Doreen M, Vice President Operations and Chief Nurse Executive, Fairview Hospital, Great Barrington, MA, p. A307

SYNDERGAARD, Christy, Vice President Nursing, Cherokee Regional Medical Center, Cherokee, IA, p. A224

SYNNESTVEDT, Eric, Director Information Technology, Southside Regional Medical Center, Petersburg, VA, p. A673

SYPIEN, Troy
  Director Information Technology and Systems, Medical City Dallas, Dallas, TX, p. A606
  Director Information Technology and Systems, Tristar Skyline Medical Center, Nashville, TN, p. A587

SYPITKOWSKI, Rita, Director of Patient Services, Coalinga Regional Medical Center, Coalinga, CA, p. A56

SZABO, Sandor M.D., Ph.D., M.P.H., Chief of Staff, Va Long Beach Healthcare System, Long Beach, CA, p. A67

SZCZEPANSKI, Bernadette S
  Senior Vice President Human Resources, Centegra Hospital – Woodstock, Woodstock, IL, p. A202
  Senior Vice President, Human Resources, Centegra Hospital – Mchenry, Mchenry, IL, p. A193

SZCZUROWSKI, Richard, Director Human Resources, Norristown State Hospital, Norristown, PA, p. A542

SZEKELY, Lauraine R.N., Senior Vice President, Patient Care, Northern Westchester Hospital, Mount Kisco, NY, p. A440

SZEWCZYK, Edwin, Chief Financial Officer, Wetzel County Hospital, New Martinsville, WV, p. A694

SZKLANY, Chelsea, Hospital Administrator, Southern Nevada Adult Mental Health Services, Las Vegas, NV, p. A403

SZOSTEK, Joshua, Chief Financial Officer, Specialty Hospital Jacksonville, Jacksonville, FL, p. A128

SZUMEL, Richard C., M.D., Chief Executive Officer, Union Hospital, Elkton, MD, p. A298

SZURA, Kathleen R.N., Chief Nursing Officer, Healthsouth Bakersfield Rehabilitation Hospital, Bakersfield, CA, p. A52

SZYMANSKI, Michael, Chief Financial Officer, Doctors Hospital Of Manteca, Manteca, CA, p. A73

SZYSKA, Julie, Chief Operating Officer, Havenwyck Hospital, Auburn Hills, MI, p. A314

T

TAAFFE, Janette, Vice President, Human Resource, St. Luke's Hospital, Chesterfield, MO, p. A366

TABAK, Jeremy M.D., President Medical Staff, Baptist Health South Florida, South Miami Hospital, Miami, FL, p. A132

TABB, Kevin, M.D., Chief Executive Officer, Beth Israel Deaconess Medical Center, Boston, MA, p. A302

TABIBI, Wasae S M.D., President Medical Staff, Plaza Specialty Hospital, Houston, TX, p. A622

TABOADO, Ketty, Chief Financial Officer, Gladys Spellman Specialty Hospital And Nursing Center, Cheverly, MD, p. A297

TABOR, J. Britton, Executive Vice President, Chief Financial Officer, Erlanger Medical Center, Chattanooga, TN, p. A576

TABOR, Jeffrey, Director Human Resources, Jackson General Hospital, Ripley, WV, p. A695

TABOR, Tammie, Chief Executive Officer, Vibra Rehabilitation Hospital Of Amarillo, Amarillo, TX, p. A592

TABORA, Knaya, Chief Operating Officer and Chief Nursing Officer, Colorado River Medical Center, Needles, CA, p. A76

TABUENCA, Arnold M.D., Medical Director, Riverside University Health System–Medical Center, Moreno Valley, CA, p. A75

TACHIBANA, Charleen R.N., Senior Vice President and Chief Nursing Officer, Virginia Mason Medical Center, Seattle, WA, p. A686

TACKITT, Sue, Chief Nursing Officer, Connally Memorial Medical Center, Floresville, TX, p. A612

TADURAN, Virgilio M.D., Chief Medical Officer, Satanta District Hospital And Long Term Care, Satanta, KS, p. A251

TADYCH, Michael, Director, Veterans Affairs Puget Sound Health Care System, Seattle, WA, p. A686

TAFFE, Patrick, Vice President Information Services, North Memorial Medical Center, Robbinsdale, MN, p. A346

TAFOYA, Debbie, Vice President and Chief Information Officer, Huntington Memorial Hospital, Pasadena, CA, p. A79

TAFOYA, Debra, Director Human Resources, Healthsouth Rehabilitation Hospital–Las Vegas, Las Vegas, NV, p. A403

TAFT, Kenneth L, Executive Vice President and Chief Operating Officer, Bronson Methodist Hospital, Kalamazoo, MI, p. A324

TAFUR, Mario M.D., Chief of Staff, St. Luke's Behavioral Health Center, Phoenix, AZ, p. A34

TAGGART, Travis, Director Information Technology, Rivervalley Behavioral Health Hospital, Owensboro, KY, p. A265

TAGGE, Gordon M.D., President Medical Staff, Three Rivers Hospital, Brewster, WA, p. A679

TAHAN, Pamela S, Chief Operating Officer, Wellington Regional Medical Center, Wellington, FL, p. A147

TAHBO, Robin, Financial Management Officer, U.S. Public Health Service Indian Hospital, Parker, AZ, p. A32

TAILLEFER, Marguerite M.D., Acting President Medical Staff, Sarah D. Culbertson Memorial Hospital, Rushville, IL, p. A199

TAKACS, Susan, Market Chief Operating Officer, Physicians Regional – Pine Ridge, Naples, FL, p. A135

TAKES, Kay, R.N.
  President, Mercy Medical Center–Dubuque, Dubuque, IA, p. A227
  President, Mercy Medical Center–Dyersville, Dyersville, IA, p. A227

TAKEUCHI, Susi, Chief Human Resources and Organization Development Officer, Ronald Reagan Ucla Medical Center, Los Angeles, CA, p. A71

TALBERT, Adrienne, Interim Administrator, North Greenville Hospital, Travelers Rest, SC, p. A566

TALBERT, Bradley S., FACHE, President and Chief Executive Officer, Memorial Hospital Jacksonville, Jacksonville, FL, p. A128

TALBOT, Angela, Manager Human Resources, Hamilton County Hospital, Syracuse, KS, p. A252

TALBOT, Jack, Director, Human Resources, West Chester Hospital, West Chester, OH, p. A502

TALBOT, Lisa, Director Human Resources, St. David's South Austin Medical Center, Austin, TX, p. A596

TALBOT, Tom, Chief Executive Officer, Community Mental Health Center, Lawrenceburg, IN, p. A214

TALBOTT, Ellen E R.N., MSN, Vice President Patient Care Services, Mclaren Bay Region, Bay City, MI, p. A315

TALBOTT, Sarah, Chief Nursing Officer, Sanford Chamberlain Medical Center, Chamberlain, SD, p. A568

TALENTO, Rick, Senior Vice President and Chief Financial Officer, Providence Hospital, Washington, DC, p. A118

TALLANT–BALL, Mary Jo, Director Health Information Systems, Dallas Medical Center, Dallas, TX, p. A605

TALLARICO, Dominica, President, Advocate Lutheran General Hospital, Park Ridge, IL, p. A197

TALLEY, Cyndi, Director Information Systems, Tristar Greenview Regional Hospital, Bowling Green, KY, p. A256

TALLEY, Linda MS, R.N., Vice President and Chief Nursing Officer, Children's National Health System, Washington, DC, p. A117

TALLEY, Rockey M.D., Chief Medical Officer, Alliancehealth Midwest, Midwest City, OK, p. A510

TALLEY, Stephanie S.
Chief Human Resource Officer, The Hospitals Of Providence Sierra Campus, El Paso, TX, p. A611
Chief Human Resource Officer, The Hospitals Of Providence Transmountain Campus, El Paso, TX, p. A612
Director Human Resources, Baylor Scott & White Medical Center – Centennial, Frisco, TX, p. A615
Market Chief Human Resource Officer, The Hospitals Of Providence Memorial Campus, El Paso, TX, p. A611

TALLON, Joe, Vice President Finance, Salina Regional Health Center, Salina, KS, p. A251

TALLON, Richard, Chief Financial Officer, Jefferson County Hospital, Waurika, OK, p. A519

TAM, David A M.D., FACHE, Chief Operating Officer, Providence Saint John's Health Center, Santa Monica, CA, p. A91

TAM, Paulina, Vice President of Operations, Tampa Community Hospital, Tampa, FL, p. A145

TAMANAHA, Nona
Vice President Human Resources, The Queen's Medical Center, Honolulu, HI, p. A169
Vice President, Human Resources, North Hawaii Community Hospital, Kamuela, HI, p. A169

TAMBURELLO, Leonardo, Chief Financial Officer, New York Community Hospital, New Rochelle, NY, p. A443

TAMMARO, Vincent, Chief Financial Officer, Yale–New Haven Hospital, New Haven, CT, p. A112

TAMMINEN, John M.D., President Medical Staff, Carilion Giles Community Hospital, Pearisburg, VA, p. A672

TAN, Bradford M.D., Chief Medical Officer, Midwestern Regional Medical Center, Zion, IL, p. A202

TANAKA, Steven, Chief Information Officer, Pomerado Hospital, Poway, CA, p. A80

TANCREDO, Beth, Director Operations, South Florida Baptist Hospital, Plant City, FL, p. A140

TANDE, Brett, Chief Financial Officer, Santa Ynez Valley Cottage Hospital, Solvang, CA, p. A92

TANDON, Satwant M.D., Director of Clinical Services, Oklahoma Forensic Center, Vinita, OK, p. A519

TANDY, Gary R, Chief Financial Officer, General John J. Pershing Memorial Hospital, Brookfield, MO, p. A365

TANDY, William C., Chief Information Officer, Hanover Hospital, Hanover, PA, p. A535

TANEBAUM, Cynthia, Director Information Services, Medstar Harbor Hospital, Baltimore, MD, p. A295

TANEJA, K Singh., Chief Operating Officer, Prince George's Hospital Center, Cheverly, MD, p. A297

TANEJA, K. Singh, Chief Operating Officer, Saint Elizabeths Hospital, Washington, DC, p. A118

TANEY, Amy, Chief Human Resource Officer, Highland Hospital, Rochester, NY, p. A450

TANG, Francis, Chief Information Officer, Rancho Los Amigos National Rehabilitation Center, Downey, CA, p. A58

TANG, Shirley R.N., Chief Nursing Officer, Monterey Park Hospital, Monterey Park, CA, p. A75

TANGEMAN, Todd, Chief Operating Officer, Newton Medical Center, Newton, KS, p. A247

TANGUAY, Denis, Chief Information Officer, Central Maine Medical Center, Lewiston, ME, p. A291

TANJUAKIO, Robert, Chief Information Resources Management, Edward Hines, Jr. Veterans Affairs Hospital, Hines, IL, p. A190

TANKEL, Nancy R.N., Chief Nurse Executive, Kaiser Permanente Woodland Hills Medical Center, Los Angeles, CA, p. A69

TANNENBAUM, Scott M.D., Medical Director, Healthsouth Sunrise Rehabilitation Hospital, Sunrise, FL, p. A143

TANNER, Ashley, Director of Nursing, Wiregrass Medical Center, Geneva, AL, p. A18

TANNER, Douglas, President, Atmore Community Hospital, Atmore, AL, p. A14

TANNER, James M.D., Chief Medical Officer, Northwest Medical Center – Springdale, Springdale, AR, p. A49

TANNER, Laureen K., R.N., MSN, FACHE, President and Chief Executive Officer, Ranken Jordan Pediatric Bridge Hospital, Maryland Heights, MO, p. A373

TANNER, Laureen K R.N., MSN, FACHE, President and Chief Executive Officer, Ranken Jordan Pediatric Bridge Hospital, Maryland Heights, MO, p. A373

TANNOS, Paul, Chief Financial Officer, The Physicians Centre Hospital, Bryan, TX, p. A600

TANTHOREY, Geoff, Director, Information Systems, Granville Health System, Oxford, NC, p. A468

TAPLETT, Dean, Controller, Quincy Valley Medical Center, Quincy, WA, p. A684

TAPLEY, Jahni, JD, Chief Executive Officer, Mccurtain Memorial Hospital, Idabel, OK, p. A509

TAPP, Gina
Director Human Resources, Samaritan North Lincoln Hospital, Lincoln City, OR, p. A523
Director Human Resources, Samaritan Pacific Communities Hospital, Newport, OR, p. A524

TAPPER, Shane, Director Management Information Systems, Fort Madison Community Hospital, Fort Madison, IA, p. A228

TARAR, Ahmad M.D., Medical Director, Heartland Behavioral Health Services, Nevada, MO, p. A374

TARASOVICH, James
Chief Financial Officer, Mayo Clinic Health System In Saint James, Saint James, MN, p. A347
Chief Financial Officer, Mayo Clinic Health System In Springfield, Springfield, MN, p. A348

TARASOVITCH, James, Chief Financial Officer, Mayo Clinic Health System In Mankato, Mankato, MN, p. A342

TARBAY, Amy, Director Nursing Services, Naval Hospital Pensacola, Pensacola, FL, p. A139

TARBELL, Tim, Director Operations, Baylor Scott & White Medical Center – Taylor, Taylor, TX, p. A648

TARBET, Joyce M.D., Chief Medical Officer, Murray County Medical Center, Slayton, MN, p. A348

TARDIF, Kathleen, Director of Human Resources, Central Regional Hospital, Butner, NC, p. A458

TARR, Mark J., President and Chief Executive Officer, Healthsouth Corporation, Birmingham, AL, p. B61

TARRANT, Jeffrey S., FACHE, Chief Executive Officer, Alliancehealth Durant, Durant, OK, p. A506

TARRANT, Maureen, President and Chief Executive Officer, Presbyterian–St. Luke's Medical Center, Denver, CO, p. A101

TARULLI, Pamela, Senior Vice President Human Resources, Good Samaritan Regional Medical Center, Suffern, NY, p. A453

TARVER, Dennis, Director Information Technology, Elkview General Hospital, Hobart, OK, p. A508

TARVER, Jeanette, Director of Finance, Sonoma Valley Hospital, Sonoma, CA, p. A92

TARVER, Rebecca, Chief Nursing Officer, Bates County Memorial Hospital, Butler, MO, p. A365

TASSEY, Karen FACHE, Chief Operating Officer, Columbia Memorial Hospital, Hudson, NY, p. A437

TASSIN, Bruce J., President, Saint Joseph Hospital, Lexington, KY, p. A261

TASSO, Tina, Manager Human Resources, The Orthopedic Specialty Hospital, Murray, UT, p. A658

TATE, Charlene M.D., Chief Medical Staff and Clinical Services, Eleanor Slater Hospital, Cranston, RI, p. A556

TATE, Charles, Director Information Technology, Lallie Kemp Medical Center, Independence, LA, p. A276

TATE, James M.D., Chief of Staff, Patients' Hospital Of Redding, Redding, CA, p. A81

TATE, Jean, Vice President Human Resources, Riverview Health, Crookston, MN, p. A338

TATE, Joel W., FACHE, Chief Executive Officer, Clay County Hospital, Ashland, AL, p. A13

TATRO, Chad, Supervisor Information Systems, Northeast Regional Medical Center, Kirksville, MO, p. A371

TATRO, Mary Esq, Chief Nursing Officer, Millinocket Regional Hospital, Millinocket, ME, p. A292

TATUM, Monica, Chief Executive Officer and Administrator, Longleaf Hospital, Alexandria, LA, p. A269

TATUM, Stanley D., FACHE, Chief Executive Officer, St. Mary's Regional Medical Center, Enid, OK, p. A507

TAUL, Kelly, Business Manager, Meadowbrook Rehabilitation Hospital, Gardner, KS, p. A241

TAUNER, Gary, Chief Operating Officer, St. John's Medical Center And Living Center, Jackson, WY, p. A718

TAUNTON, David M.D., Chief of Staff, Texas Health Harris Methodist Hospital Southlake, Southlake, TX, p. A646

TAUPIN, Michel M.D., Chief Medical Officer, Abington–Lansdale Hospital Jefferson Health, Lansdale, PA, p. A538

TAUTZ, Linda, Chief Executive Officer, Vibra Hospital Of Denver, Thornton, CO, p. A107

TAVARY, James, Chief Executive Officer, Wickenburg Community Hospital, Wickenburg, AZ, p. A38

TAVELLA, Christopher
Acting Executive Director, Rockland Children's Hospital Psychiatric Center, Orangeburg, NY, p. A449
Executive Director, Rockland Psychiatric Center, Orangeburg, NY, p. A449

TAVENNER, Matt, Chief Executive Officer, Southern Virginia Regional Medical Center, Emporia, VA, p. A666

TAWNEY, Michael W D.O., Vice President Medical Affairs, Mclaren Port Huron, Port Huron, MI, p. A328

TAYLOR, Adam, Manager Information Technology, Northern Inyo Hospital, Bishop, CA, p. A54

TAYLOR, Alice, R.N., MSN, Chief Executive Officer, Broward Health Imperial Point, Fort Lauderdale, FL, p. A124

TAYLOR, Allison H R.N., Chief Nursing Officer and Vice President Clinical Services, Sampson Regional Medical Center, Clinton, NC, p. A460

TAYLOR, Amy, Chief Financial Officer, Oklahoma Center For Orthopedic And Multi–Specialty Surgery, Oklahoma City, OK, p. A512

TAYLOR, Anthony, Manager Information Technology, Cherokee Indian Hospital, Cherokee, NC, p. A460

TAYLOR, Beth, Vice President, Human Resources, Newton–Wellesley Hospital, Newton Lower Falls, MA, p. A309

TAYLOR, Brenda, Director Information Systems, Texas Health Harris Methodist Hospital Cleburne, Cleburne, TX, p. A601

TAYLOR, Brett, Manager Information, Van Wert County Hospital, Van Wert, OH, p. A501

TAYLOR, Carol M., R.N., Regional Director Clinical Operations, Kaiser Permanente Capitol Hill Campus, Seattle, WA, p. A685

TAYLOR, Cecilia, Chief Financial Officer, Midwestern Regional Medical Center, Zion, IL, p. A202

TAYLOR, Cherie, Chief Executive Officer, Northern Rockies Medical Center, Cut Bank, MT, p. A383

TAYLOR, Cheryl R.N., Director of Nursing, Henry Ford Kingswood Hospital, Ferndale, MI, p. A319

TAYLOR, Christina, Director Human Resources, The Brook Hospital – Kmi, Louisville, KY, p. A263

TAYLOR, Dana Shantel, Director Organizational Development, Fairfield Memorial Hospital, Fairfield, IL, p. A187

TAYLOR, Deborah, Chief Information Officer, Chatham Hospital, Siler City, NC, p. A470

TAYLOR, Debra, Chief Nursing Officer, Paris Regional Medical Center, Paris, TX, p. A636

TAYLOR, Dwayne, Chief Executive Officer, Sycamore Shoals Hospital, Elizabethton, TN, p. A578

TAYLOR, Ernest Lee M.D., Vice President Medical Affairs, St. Mary's Medical Center, Huntington, WV, p. A693

TAYLOR, Eulon Ross, Clinical Director, North Texas State Hospital, Wichita Falls Campus, Wichita Falls, TX, p. A654

TAYLOR, Faye M R.N., Director of Nursing, Stephens County Hospital, Toccoa, GA, p. A166

TAYLOR, Gregory W M.D., Vice President and Chief Operating Officer, High Point Regional Health System, High Point, NC, p. A464

TAYLOR, Heather, Human Resources Manager, Tippah County Hospital, Ripley, MS, p. A361

TAYLOR, Heidi, Chief Financial Officer, Morton Hospital And Medical Center, Taunton, MA, p. A312

TAYLOR, Janey, Chief Information and Technology, Overton Brooks Veterans Affairs Medical Center, Shreveport, LA, p. A285

TAYLOR, Jay M.D., Chief of Medical Staff, Pondera Medical Center, Conrad, MT, p. A383

TAYLOR, Jeff, Vice President Finance, St. Luke's Regional Medical Center, Boise, ID, p. A172

TAYLOR, Jeremy, Director Information Services, Saint Francis Hospital, Charleston, WV, p. A691

TAYLOR, Jim, Chief Business Office, North Florida/South Georgia Veteran's Health System, Gainesville, FL, p. A126

TAYLOR, Joel
Chief Executive Officer, Coastal Carolina Hospital, Hardeeville, SC, p. A563
Chief Information Officer, Carepoint Health Bayonne Medical Center, Bayonne, NJ, p. A411
Chief Information Officer, Carepoint Health Hoboken University Medical Center, Hoboken, NJ, p. A414

TAYLOR, Judd
  Chief Financial Officer, Eastern Idaho Regional Medical Center, Idaho Falls, ID, p. A173
  Chief Financial Officer, Ogden Regional Medical Center, Ogden, UT, p. A658
  Area Director Human Resources, Vibra Hospital Of Charleston, Mt. Pleasant, SC, p. A564
TAYLOR, Julie, FACHE, Chief Executive Officer, Alaska Regional Hospital, Anchorage, AK, p. A25
TAYLOR, Konnie, Chief Financial Officer, Carl Albert Community Mental Health Center, Mcalester, OK, p. A510
TAYLOR, Kristie, Chief Financial Officer, Southern Tennessee Regional Health System–Lawrenceburg, Lawrenceburg, TN, p. A582
TAYLOR, Linda, Chief Human Resources Officer, Goodland Regional Medical Center, Goodland, KS, p. A241
TAYLOR, Lisa, Director of Nursing, Mountain View Hospital, Payson, UT, p. A659
TAYLOR, Lora, Director Human Resources and Compliance Officer, Unitypoint Health–Keokuk, Keokuk, IA, p. A230
TAYLOR, Marc, IS Director, Mountain West Medical Center, Tooele, UT, p. A661
TAYLOR, Marcia, Chief Executive Officer, Select Specialty Hospital–Memphis, Memphis, TN, p. A585
TAYLOR, Meredith, Controller, South Sunflower County Hospital, Indianola, MS, p. A356
TAYLOR, Merle, Vice President Operations, Upmc St. Margaret, Pittsburgh, PA, p. A548
TAYLOR, Michael V
  Senior Vice President Human Resources, Sentara Leigh Hospital, Norfolk, VA, p. A672
  Vice President Human Resources, Sentara Princess Anne Hospital, Virginia Beach, VA, p. A676
TAYLOR, Michael
  Chief Information Officer, Bon Secours St. Francis Hospital, Charleston, SC, p. A558
  Vice President Finance, Northridge Hospital Medical Center, Los Angeles, CA, p. A70
  Vice President Financial Services and Chief Financial Officer, St. Rose Hospital, Hayward, CA, p. A63
TAYLOR, Mimi
  Corporate Vice President Information Technology, Baptist Health South Florida, Homestead Hospital, Homestead, FL, p. A127
  Vice President Information Technology, Baptist Health South Florida, Mariners Hospital, Tavernier, FL, p. A146
  Vice President Information Technology, Baptist Health South Florida, South Miami Hospital, Miami, FL, p. A132
TAYLOR, Nathan, Director of Nursing, Heartland Behavioral Health Services, Nevada, MO, p. A374
TAYLOR, Patrick, M.D., President and Chief Executive Officer, Holy Cross Hospital, Fort Lauderdale, FL, p. A125
TAYLOR, Paul, Administrator, Ozarks Community Hospital, Gravette, AR, p. A44
TAYLOR, Randy, Chief Information Technology Officer, Perry Memorial Hospital, Perry, OK, p. A514
TAYLOR, Renae, Chief Nursing Officer, Southeastern Health, Lumberton, NC, p. A466
TAYLOR, Richard, Chief Financial Officer, Western Mental Health Institute, Bolivar, TN, p. A575
TAYLOR, Robbie, Director Human Resources, North Sunflower Medical Center, Ruleville, MS, p. A361
TAYLOR, Robert, Director Information Services, St. Christopher's Hospital For Children, Philadelphia, PA, p. A545
TAYLOR, Ross M.D., Clinical Director, Austin State Hospital, Austin, TX, p. A594
TAYLOR, Sarah, Chief Human Resources, National Jewish Health, Denver, CO, p. A101
TAYLOR, Scott J., President and Chief Executive Officer, St. Catherine Hospital, Garden City, KS, p. A241
TAYLOR, Scotty, Information Technology Director, East Mississippi State Hospital, Meridian, MS, p. A359
TAYLOR, Sharon, Human Resources Director, Allegiance Specialty Hospital Of Greenville, Greenville, MS, p. A355
TAYLOR, Sheri, Director Human Resources, Union General Hospital, Farmerville, LA, p. A274
TAYLOR, Stacy, Chief Financial Officer, Nemaha County Hospital, Auburn, NE, p. A390
TAYLOR, Steve, M.D.
  Chief Medical Officer, Sarasota Memorial Health Care System, Sarasota, FL, p. A142
  Chief Information Officer, Anderson Regional Health System South, Meridian, MS, p. A359
TAYLOR, Steven L., Chief Executive Officer, Harrison County Hospital, Corydon, IN, p. A206
TAYLOR, Sue O., Vice President Nursing, Vidant Duplin Hospital, Kenansville, NC, p. A465
TAYLOR, Susan L., JD, Chief Executive Officer, College Hospital Costa Mesa, Costa Mesa, CA, p. A56

TAYLOR, Todd, Chief Executive Officer, Stafford County Hospital, Stafford, KS, p. A252
TAYLOR, Tony, Chief Executive Officer, Big South Fork Medical Center, Oneida, TN, p. A588
TAYLOR, Tyrone, Chief Financial Officer, Veterans Affairs New Jersey Health Care System, East Orange, NJ, p. A413
TAYLOR, Venus, Director Human Resources, Bhc Alhambra Hospital, Rosemead, CA, p. A83
TAYLOR, Wes, Chief Operating Officer, Havasu Regional Medical Center, Lake Havasu City, AZ, p. A31
TEAFF, Sarah, Chief Operating Officer, St. Luke Community Healthcare, Ronan, MT, p. A387
TEAFORD, Carrie, Vice President Finance, Saint Thomas Midtown Hospital, Nashville, TN, p. A586
TEAGUE, Dean, FACHE, Chief Executive Officer, Calvert Memorial Hospital, Prince Frederick, MD, p. A300
TEAHL, Bradley, Director Human Resources, Healthsouth Rehabilitation Hospital Of York, York, PA, p. A555
TEAL, Amy , Chief Executive Officer, Healthsouth Reading Rehabilitation Hospital, Reading, PA, p. B63
TEAL, Amy, Chief Executive Officer, Healthsouth Reading Rehabilitation Hospital, Reading, PA, p. A549
TEAL, Barbara R.N., Associate Director Patient Care Services and Nurse Executive, Sioux Falls Veterans Affairs Health Care System, Sioux Falls, SD, p. A573
TEAL, Cydney M.D., Vice President Medical Affairs, Union Hospital, Elkton, MD, p. A298
TEAS, Gregory M.D., Chief Medical Officer, Alexian Brothers Behavioral Health Hospital, Hoffman Estates, IL, p. A190
TEASDALE, Peggy, Director Human Resources, Southeast Health Center Of Ripley County, Doniphan, MO, p. A367
TEATER, Phyllis, Chief Information Officer, Ohio State University Wexner Medical Center, Columbus, OH, p. A487
TEATSORTH, Neil, Vice President Human Resources, Norwegian American Hospital, Chicago, IL, p. A182
TEBBE, James M.D., Vice President Medical Affairs, Ochsner Medical Center – Kenner, Kenner, LA, p. A277
TEDDER, Cookie, Human Resources Manager, Texas Health Center For Diagnostic & Surgery, Plano, TX, p. A638
TEDESCO, Art, Interim Chief Financial Officer, Gaylord Hospital, Wallingford, CT, p. A113
TEEL, David R., Financial Officer, Terrell State Hospital, Terrell, TX, p. A648
TEETER, Stephen, Business Manager, Hawaii State Hospital, Kaneohe, HI, p. A170
TEFFETELLER, Scott L., President, Community Hospital East, Indianapolis, IN, p. A210
TEICHMEIER, Laura, Director Human Resources, Memorial Community Health, Aurora, NE, p. A390
TEITELBAUM, Karen
  Chief Executive Officer, Schwab Rehabilitation Hospital, Chicago, IL, p. A183
  President and Chief Executive Officer, Mount Sinai Hospital, Chicago, IL, p. A182
TEJADA, Vanessa, Director Human Resources, Healthsouth Rehabilitation Institute Of San Antonio (Riosa), San Antonio, TX, p. A642
TEJEDA, Nicholas R., FACHE, Chief Executive Officer, The Hospitals Of Providence Transmountain Campus, El Paso, TX, p. A612
TELHIARD, Nicole MSN, Chief Nursing Officer, Our Lady Of The Lake Regional Medical Center, Baton Rouge, LA, p. A271
TELITZ, Rita, Chief Administrative Officer, Rusk County Memorial Hospital, Ladysmith, WI, p. A704
TELL, Marjorie, Vice President Information Technology, Aspirus Riverview Hospital And Clinics, Inc., Wisconsin Rapids, WI, p. A716
TELLOR, Tammy, Acting Director Human Resources, Choate Mental Health Center, Anna, IL, p. A177
TELTHORSTER, M.ED, CCP, Marcia M, Vice President Human Resources, University Medical Center Of Princeton At Plainsboro, Plainsboro, NJ, p. A419
TEMPELMEYER, Zak M.D., Chief Medical Staff, Community Memorial Hospital, Syracuse, NE, p. A400
TEMPEST, Wendy, Director Human Resources, Vibra Hospital Of Northern California, Redding, CA, p. A81
TEMPLE, Amber L, Director Human Resources, Morrison Community Hospital, Morrison, IL, p. A194
TEMPLE, Gina, Chief Nurse Executive, Sutter Auburn Faith Hospital, Auburn, CA, p. A52
TEMPLE, Richard, Chief Information Officer, Deborah Heart And Lung Center, Browns Mills, NJ, p. A412
TEMPLETON, Gary M.D., Medical Director, Regency Hospital Of Northwest Arkansas – Springdale, Springdale, AR, p. A50
TEMPLETON, Parker A., FACHE, Chief Executive Officer, Iberia Medical Center, New Iberia, LA, p. A282
TEMPLETON, Sheryl, Chief Financial Officer, Scotland County Hospital, Memphis, MO, p. A373

TEMPLETON, William M.D., III, Medical Director, Clark Memorial Hospital, Jeffersonville, IN, p. A213
TEMPLIN, Nancy, Vice President Finance and Chief Financial Officer, Johns Hopkins All Children's Hospital, Saint Petersburg, FL, p. A141
TEN HAAF, Patricia, R.N., MSN, Ph.D., Director, John J. Pershing Veterans Affairs Medical Center, Poplar Bluff, MO, p. A375
TEN–HAKEN, Jean, Chief Operating Officer, Elliot Hospital, Manchester, NH, p. A409
TENEWITZ, Edward M.D., Chief of Staff, Healthmark Regional Medical Center, Defuniak Springs, FL, p. A123
TENGERES, Michael A., Corporate Vice President and Chief Financial Officer, Bassett Medical Center, Cooperstown, NY, p. A434
TENHENGEL–DEVILLE, Michelle
  Chief Executive Officer, Regency Hospital Of South Atlanta, East Point, GA, p. A157
  Chief Executive Officer, Select Specialty Hospital–Atlanta, Atlanta, GA, p. A151
TENHOUSE, Steven D., FACHE, Chief Executive Officer, Kirby Medical Center, Monticello, IL, p. A194
TENNARO, Sonja Ed.D., FACHE, Senior Vice President Clinical Operations, New York Eye And Ear Infirmary Of Mount Sinai, New Rochelle, NY, p. A443
TENNEY, Ralph
  Chief Information Officer, Crittenton Hospital Medical Center, Rochester, MI, p. A329
  Chief Information Officer, St. John Hospital And Medical Center, Detroit, MI, p. A318
  Chief Information Officer, St. John Macomb–Oakland Hospital, Warren, MI, p. A332
TENNISON, Gary M.D., Chief of Staff, Crawford Memorial Hospital, Robinson, IL, p. A198
TENNYSON, Ruby, Director Administration, Naval Hospital Jacksonville, Jacksonville, FL, p. A128
TENREIRO, Edgardo J., Chief Executive Officer and Chief Operating Officer, Baton Rouge General Medical Center, Baton Rouge, LA, p. A270
TENREIRO, Edgardo J, Chief Executive Officer and Chief Operating Officer, Baton Rouge General Medical Center, Baton Rouge, LA, p. A270
TEPEDINO, Miguel M.D., Chief Medicine, Lake City Medical Center, Lake City, FL, p. A129
TEPPER, Gil, M.D.
  Chief of Staff, Miracle Mile Medical Center, Los Angeles, CA, p. A70
  Chief Executive Officer, Miracle Mile Medical Center, Los Angeles, CA, p. A70
TER HORST, Thomas C, Vice President Human Resources, Aurora St. Luke's Medical Center, Milwaukee, WI, p. A707
TERBUSH, Jennifer, Vice President, Patient Services, Hills & Dales General Hospital, Cass City, MI, p. A316
TERI, Anthony, Director Information Technology, Hackensack Meridian Health Pascack Valley Medical Center, Westwood, NJ, p. A423
TERPSTRA, Kelli R.N., Senior Director, Our Children's House, Dallas, TX, p. A606
TERRELL, Jay, Manager Management Information Systems, Riverview Regional Medical Center, Gadsden, AL, p. A18
TERRELL, Michael T, Chief Financial Officer, Brandon Regional Hospital, Brandon, FL, p. A121
TERRESON, Gregg, Chief Financial Officer, Cascade Behavioral Hospital, Tukwila, WA, p. A688
TERRINONI, Gary G., President and Chief Executive Officer, Brooklyn Hospital Center, New Rochelle, NY, p. A441
TERRY, Darrell K. Sr, M.P.H., FACHE, President and Chief Executive Officer, Newark Beth Israel Medical Center, Newark, NJ, p. A417
TERRY, Michael, President and Chief Executive Officer, Salina Regional Health Center, Salina, KS, p. A251
TERRY, Randi, Site Director Management Information Systems, Munson Healthcare Cadillac Hospital, Cadillac, MI, p. A315
TERRY, Richard, Vice President & Chief Information Officer, Sparrow Carson Hospital, Carson City, MI, p. A316
TERRY, Teresa, Director Human Resource, Payroll, Fisher County Hospital District, Rotan, TX, p. A640
TERRY–WILLIAMS, Teresa, Chief Nursing Officer, Pennsylvania Psychiatric Institute, Harrisburg, PA, p. A536
TERSHAKOVEC, George R. M.D., President Medical Staff, Baptist Health South Florida, Homestead Hospital, Homestead, FL, p. A127
TERTEL, Jenifer K, Director Human Resources, Medical City Dallas, Dallas, TX, p. A606
TERWILLIGER, Michael, Chief Financial Officer, Friends Hospital, Philadelphia, PA, p. A544
TERZANO, Valerie MSN, R.N., Senior Vice President Nursing, NYU Winthrop Hospital, Mineola, NY, p. A439

THOMMAN, Connie, Director of Nursing, Covenant Hospital–Levelland, Levelland, TX, p. A629

THOMPSON, Aaron M.D., Chief of Staff, Arkansas Methodist Medical Center, Paragould, AR, p. A48

THOMPSON, Alan M.D., President Medical Staff, Warm Springs Medical Center, Warm Springs, GA, p. A167

THOMPSON, Amy, M.D., Chief Executive Officer, Covenant Children's Hospital, Lubbock, TX, p. A630

THOMPSON, Becki, President, Chi Oakes Hospital, Oakes, ND, p. A477

THOMPSON, Becky, Chief Financial Officer, Chi St. Francis Health, Breckenridge, MN, p. A337

THOMPSON, Belinda, Coordinator Human Resources, Healthsouth Chesapeake Rehabilitation Hospital, Salisbury, MD, p. A301

THOMPSON, Bobby, Director Information Technology, Stephens Memorial Hospital, Breckenridge, TX, p. A599

THOMPSON, Cathy, Manager Human Resources, Paris Community Hospital, Paris, IL, p. A197

THOMPSON, Chad
Chief Financial Officer, Lallie Kemp Medical Center, Independence, LA, p. A276
President and Chief Executive Officer, Friend Community Healthcare System, Friend, NE, p. A393

THOMPSON, Charles M.D., Chief Medical Officer, Nacogdoches Medical Center, Nacogdoches, TX, p. A634

THOMPSON, Charolette, Chief Financial Officer, Reeves Memorial Medical Center, Bernice, LA, p. A271

THOMPSON, Cheryl
Chief Nursing Officer, Garden Park Medical Center, Gulfport, MS, p. A355
Facility Director Human Resources, Connecticut Valley Hospital, Middletown, CT, p. A111

THOMPSON, Chris
Chief Financial Officer, Delta Community Medical Center, Delta, UT, p. A656
Chief Financial Officer, Fillmore Community Hospital, Fillmore, UT, p. A656
Chief Financial Officer, Sanpete Valley Hospital, Mount Pleasant, UT, p. A657
Chief Financial Officer, Sevier Valley Hospital, Richfield, UT, p. A659

THOMPSON, Cindy, Chief Financial Officer, Northwest Surgical Hospital, Oklahoma City, OK, p. A512

THOMPSON, Craig B., M.D., President and Chief Executive Officer, Memorial Sloan–Kettering Cancer Center, New Rochelle, NY, p. A442

THOMPSON, Craig, Chief Executive Officer, Golden Valley Memorial Healthcare, Clinton, MO, p. A366

THOMPSON, Dale, Chief Financial Officer, Mclaren Greater Lansing, Lansing, MI, p. A324

THOMPSON, David M., Chief Executive Officer, Sutter Tracy Community Hospital, Tracy, CA, p. A94

THOMPSON, David, M.D.
Chief of Staff, Richardson Medical Center, Rayville, LA, p. A284
Chief Financial Officer, Central Maine Medical Center, Lewiston, ME, p. A291

THOMPSON, Debbie, Chief Financial Officer, Sweetwater Hospital, Sweetwater, TN, p. A589

THOMPSON, Douglas, Chief Information Officer, Upson Regional Medical Center, Thomaston, GA, p. A166

THOMPSON, Dwight, Chief Financial Officer, Altru Health System, Grand Forks, ND, p. A476

THOMPSON, Greg
Chief Medical Officer, Gundersen Health System, La Crosse, WI, p. A704
Corporate Director, Human Resources, Orlando Regional Medical Center, Orlando, FL, p. A137

THOMPSON, Heath, R.N., Administrator, Singing River Health System, Pascagoula, MS, p. A360

THOMPSON, Ian Jr, M.D., President, Christus Santa Rosa Health System, San Antonio, TX, p. A642

THOMPSON, Ivan, Vice President, Chief Human Resource Officer, University Of Texas Southwestern Medical Center, Dallas, TX, p. A607

THOMPSON, James H., Ph.D., FACHE, Owner and Chief Executive Officer, Healthmark Regional Medical Center, Defuniak Springs, FL, p. A123

THOMPSON, John W M.D., Chief of Staff, Eastern Louisiana Mental Health System, Jackson, LA, p. A276

THOMPSON, Julie
Chief Operating Officer and Chief Nursing Officer, Bluffton Regional Medical Center, Bluffton, IN, p. A204
Manager Personnel and Payroll, Mayers Memorial Hospital District, Fall River Mills, CA, p. A59

THOMPSON, Kim, Vice President and Chief Financial Officer, Ozarks Medical Center, West Plains, MO, p. A381

THOMPSON, Lennis II, Vice President and Chief Financial Officer, Hardin Memorial Hospital, Elizabethtown, KY, p. A257

THOMPSON, Linda
Chief Operating Officer, Fairfax Community Hospital, Fairfax, OK, p. A507
Senior Vice President, Human Resources and Service Excellence, New England Baptist Hospital, Boston, MA, p. A303

THOMPSON, Lisa MSN, R.N., Director of Nursing, Hiawatha Community Hospital, Hiawatha, KS, p. A242

THOMPSON, Lori L, Manager Human Resources, Orthonebraska Hospital, Omaha, NE, p. A398

THOMPSON, Marion A., FACHE, Chief Executive Officer, Allen County Regional Hospital, Iola, KS, p. A243

THOMPSON, Mark, M.D.
Chief Medical Officer, Monroe Clinic, Monroe, WI, p. A708
Market Chief Financial Officer Northern Region and Chief Financial Officer, Mercy Health – St. Charles Hospital, Oregon, OH, p. A497
Vice President Financial Services, Rapid City Regional Hospital, Rapid City, SD, p. A572

THOMPSON, Matthew J., FACHE, President and Chief Executive Officer, Sparrow Carson Hospital, Carson City, MI, p. A316

THOMPSON, Nate, Chief Executive Officer, Story County Medical Center, Nevada, IA, p. A232

THOMPSON, Ormand P., President, Thomas Hospital, Fairhope, AL, p. A17

THOMPSON, Pamela, Chief Operations Officer, Huhukam Memorial Hospital, Sacaton, AZ, p. A35

THOMPSON, Patti, Chief Operating Officer, San Luis Valley Health, Alamosa, CO, p. A98

THOMPSON, Randell, Chief Nursing Officer, Plateau Medical Center, Oak Hill, WV, p. A694

THOMPSON, Randy, Chief Executive Officer, Healthsouth Rehabilitation Hospital Of Montgomery, Montgomery, AL, p. A21

THOMPSON, Reanna, R.N., Chief Operating Officer and Chief Nursing Officer, Pih Health Hospital–Whittier, Whittier, CA, p. A97

THOMPSON, Ronnie, Chief Financial Officer, Belton Regional Medical Center, Belton, MO, p. A364

THOMPSON, Sarah, Director Health Information Management, Hardtner Medical Center, Olla, LA, p. A284

THOMPSON, Selva R.N., Chief Nurse Executive, Gallup Indian Medical Center, Gallup, NM, p. A426

THOMPSON, Sheila, Director Human Resources, Hamilton Memorial Hospital District, Mcleansboro, IL, p. A193

THOMPSON, Stuart, Vice President Human Resources, Memorial Hospital Jacksonville, Jacksonville, FL, p. A128

THOMPSON, Thomas R., President, Regina Hospital, Hastings, MN, p. A341

THOMPSON, Tim
Senior Vice President and Chief Informatics Officer, St. Anthony's Hospital, Saint Petersburg, FL, p. A142
Senior Vice President, Chief Information Officer, South Florida Baptist Hospital, Plant City, FL, p. A140
Senior Vice President, Informant Services and Chief Information Officer, Mease Countryside Hospital, Safety Harbor, FL, p. A141
Senior Vice President, Information Services and Chief Information Officer, Mease Dunedin Hospital, Dunedin, FL, p. A124

THOMPSON, Timothy
Senior Vice President and Chief Information Officer, Morton Plant Hospital, Clearwater, FL, p. A121
Senior Vice President and Chief Information Officer, Morton Plant North Bay Hospital, New Port Richey, FL, p. A135

THOMPSON, Tina H, Coordinator Human Resources, Firsthealth Montgomery Memorial Hospital, Troy, NC, p. A472

THOMPSON, Trinise, Director Human Resources, St. Luke's Medical Center, Phoenix, AZ, p. A34

THOMPSON, Vera, Director Human Resources, Kingsboro Psychiatric Center, New Rochelle, NY, p. A442

THOMPSON, Wayne, Executive Vice President and Chief Information Officer, Mount Nittany Medical Center, State College, PA, p. A551

THOMPSON, Wesley M.D., President Medical Staff, Fairfield Memorial Hospital, Fairfield, IL, p. A187

THOMPSON, William, M.D.
Chief Medical Officer, Saint Thomas Midtown Hospital, Nashville, TN, p. A586
Chief Financial Officer, Mississippi Baptist Medical Center, Jackson, MS, p. A357

THOMPSON–COOK, Timothy, Chief Operating Officer, Contra Costa Regional Medical Center, Martinez, CA, p. A73

THOMSEN, Sue, Chief Financial Officer, New Braunfels Regional Rehabilitation Hospital, New Braunfels, TX, p. A635

THOMSEN, Vicki
Director Human Resources, Aurora Behavioral Health System East, Tempe, AZ, p. A37
Director Human Resources, Aurora Behavioral Health System West, Glendale, AZ, p. A30

THOMSON, Doug M.D., Chief Medical Officer, Commonwealth Regional Specialty Hospital, Bowling Green, KY, p. A255

THOMSON, Nicole, Chief Financial Officer, Saint Louise Regional Hospital, Gilroy, CA, p. A61

THOMSON, Steven M.D., Medical Director, Heartland Behavioral Healthcare, Massillon, OH, p. A495

THORE, Joe, Chief Operating Officer, Ashe Memorial Hospital, Jefferson, NC, p. A465

THORELL, Nicole R.N., MSN, Chief Nursing Officer, Lexington Regional Health Center, Lexington, NE, p. A394

THORESON, Scott D., FACHE, Administrator, Mayo Clinic Health System In Springfield, Springfield, MN, p. A348

THORMODSON, Cyndee, Vice President, Operational Finance, Chi Mercy Health, Valley City, ND, p. A478

THORN, Eugene A III, Vice President Finance and Chief Financial Officer, Union Hospital, Dover, OH, p. A490

THORN, Margaret, Interim Director of Nursing, Red Bay Hospital, Red Bay, AL, p. A22

THORN, Mark FACHE, Executive Director, Finance, Mercy Hospital Lincoln, Troy, MO, p. A380

THORNBRUGH, Mitchell
Acting Chief Information Officer, Cherokee Nation W.W. Hastings Indian Hospital, Tahlequah, OK, p. A516
Administrative Officer, Cherokee Nation W.W. Hastings Indian Hospital, Tahlequah, OK, p. A516

THORNE, Dana, Administrator Human Resources, Valley Hospital Medical Center, Las Vegas, NV, p. A404

THORNELL, Louise, Chief Nursing Officer, Christus St. Michael Health System, Texarkana, TX, p. A649

THORNELL, Timothy, FACHE, Chief Executive Officer, Lea Regional Medical Center, Hobbs, NM, p. A426

THORNSBERRY, Michael M.D., Chief Medical Officer, Texas Health Specialty Hospital, Fort Worth, TX, p. A614

THORNTON, Carol, Director Human Resources, Cherry Hospital, Goldsboro, NC, p. A463

THORNTON, Cayetano, Chief Information Officer, Walter Reed National Military Medical Center, Bethesda, MD, p. A297

THORNTON, Daryl W, Chief Operating Officer, Kansas Medical Center, Andover, KS, p. A238

THORNTON, Jan, Chief Nursing Officer, Bay Medical Center Sacred Heart Health System, Panama City, FL, p. A138

THORNTON, Jillisa, Director of Nursing, Coastal Harbor Treatment Center, Savannah, GA, p. A164

THORNTON, Laird, Director Information Systems, Alta Vista Regional Hospital, Las Vegas, NM, p. A427

THORNTON, Matt, Chief Executive Officer, Liberty Dayton Regional Medical Center, Liberty, TX, p. A629

THORNTON, Robert M. Jr, Chief Executive Officer, Sunlink Health Systems, Atlanta, GA, p. B123

THORPE, Kevin J., Chief Executive Officer, Select Specialty Hospital–Kansas City, Kansas City, KS, p. A244

THORPE, Linda, Chief Executive Officer, East Morgan County Hospital, Brush, CO, p. A99

THORPE, Wendy, Area Director Information Systems, St. Joseph Hospital, Eureka, CA, p. A58

THORSEN, Erik, Chief Executive Officer, Columbia Memorial Hospital, Astoria, OR, p. A520

THORWALD, Robert, Chief Information Officer, Washington Hospital Healthcare System, Fremont, CA, p. A60

THOTAKURA, Raj M.D., Medical Director, Old Vineyard Behavioral Health Services, Winston, NC, p. A473

THRASHER, Amanda, Director Nursing, Ellsworth County Medical Center, Ellsworth, KS, p. A240

THRASHER, Kimberly, Controller, Healthsouth Lakeshore Rehabilitation Hospital, Birmingham, AL, p. A14

THRASHER, Sherri, Executive Human Resources Partner, Spectrum Health Pennock, Hastings, MI, p. A322

THREEWITS, Sheree, Director Human Resources, Manatee Memorial Hospital, Bradenton, FL, p. A120

THULI, Karen, Coordinator Information Systems, Upland Hills Health, Dodgeville, WI, p. A700

THUN, Todd, Director Human Resources, Montana State Hospital, Warm Springs, MT, p. A389

THUN, Tracey, Director Business and Support Services, Montana State Hospital, Warm Springs, MT, p. A389

THUNELL, Adam, Chief Operating Officer and Vice President Operations, Community Memorial Hospital, Ventura, CA, p. A95

THURBER, Joe, Director Information Technology, Central Regional Hospital, Butner, NC, p. A458

THURMAN, Jason, Chief of Staff, Tristar Hendersonville Medical Center, Hendersonville, TN, p. A580

Divisional Chief People Officer, Hshs St. Joseph's Hospital, Chippewa Falls, WI, p. A700

TOMAS, George, Director Information Services, Griffin Hospital, Derby, CT, p. A110

TOMASESKI, Gina, Chief Executive Officer, Icare Rehabilitation Hospital, Flower Mound, TX, p. A612

TOMASO, Nancy, Vice President, Patient Care Services, Milford Regional Medical Center, Milford, MA, p. A309

TOME, Michael M.D., Medical Director, Kaiser Permanente Los Angeles Medical Center, Los Angeles, CA, p. A68

TOMLIN, Jeff M.D., Chief Medical and Quality Officer, Evergreenhealth, Kirkland, WA, p. A681

TOMLIN, Kerry W, Associate Administrator, Clay County Hospital, Ashland, AL, p. A13

TOMLINSON, Charles M M.D., Chief Medical Officer, Carolinas Healthcare System Cleveland, Shelby, NC, p. A470

TOMLINSON, Daniel, Chair Human Resources, Mayo Clinic Jacksonville, Jacksonville, FL, p. A128

TOMLINSON, David

Executive Vice President Chief Financial Officer and Chief Information Officer, Centegra Hospital – Mchenry, Mchenry, IL, p. A193

Senior Vice President, Chief Information Officer, Centegra Hospital – Woodstock, Woodstock, IL, p. A202

TOMLINSON, Sallie, Manager Human Resources, Arbuckle Memorial Hospital, Sulphur, OK, p. A516

TOMORY, Gerald, M.D.

Regional Medical Director, Kauai Veterans Memorial Hospital, Waimea, HI, p. A170

Regional Medical Director, Samuel Mahelona Memorial Hospital, Kapaa, HI, p. A170

TOMPKINS, Charles M.D., Chief of Staff, Crenshaw Community Hospital, Luverne, AL, p. A20

TOMPKINS, Kim, Director Information Services, Detar Healthcare System, Victoria, TX, p. A652

TOMSU, Karen MSN, R.N., Chief Nursing Officer, Baptist Hospitals Of Southeast Texas, Beaumont, TX, p. A597

TONER, Tina, Director of Nursing, North Big Horn Hospital District, Lovell, WY, p. A719

TONEY, Patty R.N., MSN, Chief Nurse Executive, Christus Santa Rosa Health System, San Antonio, TX, p. A642

TONG, Cheryl, Corporate Chief Financial Officer, Community Hospital Of Huntington Park, Huntington Park, CA, p. A63

TONJES, Ken, Chief Financial Officer, Peacehealth Ketchikan Medical Center, Ketchikan, AK, p. A26

TONKINSON, Robert

Chief Operating Officer and Chief Financial Officer, Mercy Allen Hospital, Oberlin, OH, p. A497

Chief Operating Officer and Chief Financial Officer, Mercy Regional Medical Center, Lorain, OH, p. A494

TONN, Deb L, Vice President Patient Care, Campbell County Health, Gillette, WY, p. A718

TONNU, Lannie, Senior Vice President and Chief Financial Officer, Children's Hospital Los Angeles, Los Angeles, CA, p. A68

TOOKE, Ryan, Chief Executive Officer, Rosebud Health Care Center, Forsyth, MT, p. A384

TOOLE, LaDon, Vice President Network Operations, Mitchell County Hospital, Camilla, GA, p. A153

TOOLE, Patricia, Vice President Human Resources, East Mountain Hospital, Belle Mead, NJ, p. A411

TOOLE, Trish, Vice President Administrative Services, Carrier Clinic, Belle Mead, NJ, p. A411

TOON, William, Chief Information Officer, Baptist Hospitals Of Southeast Texas, Beaumont, TX, p. A597

TOPOLEWSKI, Ted, Chief Executive Officer, Madison Parish Hospital, Tallulah, LA, p. A287

TOPPEN, Jacki, Director of Nursing, Prairie St. John's, Fargo, ND, p. A475

TORBETT, Russell B, Director Human Resources, Creek Nation Community Hospital, Okemah, OK, p. A511

TORCHIA, Joseph M.D., Senior Vice President Medical Affairs and Chief Medical Officer, Geisinger Holy Spirit, Camp Hill, PA, p. A530

TORCHIA, Jude, Chief Executive Officer, Orthocolorado Hospital, Lakewood, CO, p. A105

TORCHIANA, David, M.D., Chief Executive Officer, Partners Healthcare System, Inc., Boston, MA, p. B96

TORCHIA NEA–BC, Lisa F MSN, R.N., Vice President and Chief Nursing Officer, Geisinger Holy Spirit, Camp Hill, PA, p. A530

TORGE, Andrew, Director Human Resources, Shasta Regional Medical Center, Redding, CA, p. A81

TORMANEN, John, Director Mission and Human Resources, Chi St. Joseph's Health, Park Rapids, MN, p. A345

TORNE, Michael, Chief Executive Officer, Hermann Drive Surgical Hospital, Houston, TX, p. A620

TORO PALACIOS, Belinda L., Executive Director, Doctors Center, Manati, PR, p. A724

TOROSSIAN, Lynn M., President and Chief Executive Officer, Henry Ford West Bloomfield Hospital, West Bloomfield, MI, p. A333

TORRES, Anthony, Manager Information Technology, Blue Mountain Hospital, Blanding, UT, p. A656

TORRES, Harvey, Chief Financial Officer, Valley Baptist Medical Center–Brownsville, Brownsville, TX, p. A599

TORRES, Maribel, Chief Nursing Officer, United Medical Center, Washington, DC, p. A118

TORRES, Mayra CPA, Chief Financial Officer, Ashford Presbyterian Community Hospital, San Juan, PR, p. A725

TORRES, Tammy, R.N., MSN, Chief Executive Officer, Memorial Hospital Of Salem County, Salem, NJ, p. A420

TORRES, Victor, Information Technology Specialist Administrator, El Paso Behavioral Health System, El Paso, TX, p. A610

TORRES AYALA, Eugenio, Director Information Systems, Cardiovascular Center Of Puerto Rico And The Caribbean, San Juan, PR, p. A725

TORSCH, Peter, Chief Financial Officer, St. Charles Parish Hospital, Luling, LA, p. A280

TORTELLA, Anthony, Chief Financial Officer, Fairmount Behavioral Health System, Philadelphia, PA, p. A543

TOSI, Stephen E M.D., Chief Medical Officer, Umass Memorial Medical Center, Worcester, MA, p. A313

TOSTEBERG, Chris, Superintendent, Mental Health Institute, Cherokee, IA, p. A224

TOSTENSON, Brad, Chief Information Officer, Essentia Health–Graceville, Graceville, MN, p. A340

TOSTI, Debra, Chief Executive Officer, Tewksbury Hospital, Tewksbury, MA, p. A312

TOTAH, Sam, Chief Operating Officer, Kaiser Permanente San Diego Medical Center, San Diego, CA, p. A85

TOUCHSTONE, Pat, Chief Nursing Officer, Crane Memorial Hospital, Crane, TX, p. A604

TOUMBIS, C. M.D., Chief of Staff, Citrus Memorial Health System, Inverness, FL, p. A127

TOUPS, Sharon A, Senior Vice President and Chief Operating Officer, St. Tammany Parish Hospital, Covington, LA, p. A273

TOURE', Joahd M.D., Chief Medical Officer, Adirondack Health, Saranac Lake, NY, p. A452

TOURIGNY, Barry

Human Resources Director, Johnson City Medical Center, Johnson City, TN, p. A581

Vice President Human Resources and Organizational Development, Cabell Huntington Hospital, Huntington, WV, p. A692

TOUSIGNANT, Grace, R.N., MSN

Chief Nursing Officer, Aspirus Ironwood Hosital & Clinics, Inc., Ironwood, MI, p. A323

Chief Nursing Officer, Aspirus Keweenaw Hospital, Inc., Laurium, MI, p. A325

TOUVELLE, Cynthia R.N., Senior Director Care Management and Chief Nursing Officer, Barnesville Hospital, Barnesville, OH, p. A480

TOWERY, O B M.D., Chief of Staff, John Muir Behavioral Health Center, Concord, CA, p. A56

TOWLE, Sonya, Director Human Resources, Mercy Hospital, Moose Lake, MN, p. A344

TOWN, Alex, Vice President Finance, Tri–State Memorial Hospital, Clarkston, WA, p. A679

TOWNDROW, Geraldine R.N., Senior Vice President Nursing, Lutheran Medical Center, Wheat Ridge, CO, p. A108

TOWNE, Jana, Nurse Executive, U. S. Public Health Service Indian Hospital–Whiteriver, Whiteriver, AZ, p. A38

TOWNER, Chad, Chief Executive Officer, Mishawaka Medical Center, Mishawaka, IN, p. A216

TOWNES, Tim, Director Information Systems, Grandview Medical Center, Birmingham, AL, p. A14

TOWNLEY, Nancy R.N., Senior Vice President Operations, United Regional Health Care System, Wichita Falls, TX, p. A654

TOWNSEND, Alan, Interim Chief Financial Officer, Jps Health Network, Fort Worth, TX, p. A613

TOWNSEND, Cathy, Chief Nursing Officer, Banner – University Medical Center South, Tucson, AZ, p. A37

TOWNSEND, Dona E, Chief Nursing Officer, Navarro Regional Hospital, Corsicana, TX, p. A603

TOWNSEND, Gary, Chief Information Officer, Hurley Medical Center, Flint, MI, p. A319

TOWNSEND, Michael, Chief Information Officer, James Cancer Hospital And Solove Research Institute, Columbus, OH, p. A487

TOWNSEND, Mike, Interim Director Health Information Systems, Grady Memorial Hospital, Chickasha, OK, p. A505

TOWNSEND, Sammuel, LAN Administrator, University Of Mississippi Medical Center Holmes County, Lexington, MS, p. A358

TOWNSEND, Tanya, Senior Vice President, Chief Information Officer (part of LCMC), Children's Hospital, New Orleans, LA, p. A282

TOWNSEND, Theodore E., FACHE, President and Chief Executive Officer, Unitypoint Health – St. Luke's Hospital, Cedar Rapids, IA, p. A223

TOWRISS, Douglas, Vice President and Chief Medical Officer, Schneck Medical Center, Seymour, IN, p. A219

TOY, Linda, Director Information Systems, Havasu Regional Medical Center, Lake Havasu City, AZ, p. A31

TOY, Stanley Jr, M.D., Chief Executive Officer, Greater El Monte Community Hospital, South El Monte, CA, p. A92

TOYE, Lawrence J, Chief Financial Officer, Curahealth Hospital Boston, Brighton, MA, p. A304

TRAC, Vincent, Chief Executive Officer, Kindred Hospital–Ontario, Ontario, CA, p. A77

TRACEY, Karen, Chief Human Resources, Select Specialty Hospital–Greensboro, Greensboro, NC, p. A463

TRACHTA, Michael, Interim Chief Executive Officer, Van Diest Medical Center, Webster City, IA, p. A236

TRACY, Allen R, Senior Vice President and Chief Financial Officer, St. John Medical Center, Westlake, OH, p. A502

TRACY, Pat, Administrator, Ridgeview Behavioral Hospital, Middle Point, OH, p. A496

TRACY, Thomas Jr, Chief Medical Officer, Penn State Milton S. Hershey Medical Center, Hershey, PA, p. A536

TRACY, Timothy J., Chief Executive Officer, Sanford Vermillion Medical Center, Vermillion, SD, p. A573

TRACZ, Robert B CPA, Senior Vice President and Chief Financial Officer, Lake Health, Concord Township, OH, p. A488

TRAHAN, Jennifer Lynch, Assistant Vice President Human Resources, Our Lady Of Lourdes Regional Medical Center, Lafayette, LA, p. A279

TRAHAN, John, Director Information Systems, Women's And Children's Hospital, Lafayette, LA, p. A279

TRAHAN, Leslie, Chief Executive Officer, South Cameron Memorial Hospital, Cameron, LA, p. A272

TRAHAN, Thomas M.D., Chief of Medical Staff, Lane Regional Medical Center, Zachary, LA, p. A288

TRAHERN, Sheri, CPA, FACHE, Chief Executive Officer, St. Thomas More Hospital, Canon City, CO, p. A99

TRAIL, Alan, Director Information Systems, Owensboro Health Muhlenberg Community Hospital, Greenville, KY, p. A259

TRAINER, Michael, Chief Financial Officer, Akron Children's Hospital, Akron, OH, p. A479

TRAINOR, Karyn, Director Human Resources, St. Patrick Hospital, Missoula, MT, p. A387

TRAINOR, Paul, Senior Vice President Finance and Chief Financial Officer, Southern New Hampshire Medical Center, Nashua, NH, p. A409

TRAISTER, Lynne, Controller, Healthsouth Rehabilitation Hospital Of Tinton Falls, Tinton Falls, NJ, p. A421

TRAMMELL, Patrick, Chief Executive Officer, Dekalb Regional Medical Center, Fort Payne, AL, p. A18

TRAMP, Francis G., President, Burgess Health Center, Onawa, IA, p. A232

TRAN, Ann, Chief Financial Officer, Pike County Memorial Hospital, Louisiana, MO, p. A372

TRAN, Kha H. M.D., Vice President Medical Affairs, Lima Memorial Health System, Lima, OH, p. A493

TRAN, Khiem M.D., Acting Chief of Staff, Veterans Affairs Illiana Health Care System, Danville, IL, p. A185

TRAN, Lac, Senior Vice President Information Services, Rush University Medical Center, Chicago, IL, p. A183

TRAN, Richard, Director Information Technology, Galesburg Cottage Hospital, Galesburg, IL, p. A188

TRAN, Thanh, FACHE, Chief Executive Officer, North Central Surgical Center, Dallas, TX, p. A606

TRANSIER, Rhonda, Financial Officer, Rusk State Hospital, Rusk, TX, p. A641

TRANTALIS, Carolyn, R.N., MSN

Chief Operating Officer, East Region, Windham Hospital, Willimantic, CT, p. A114

Regional Vice President, Clinical Services and Operations, The William W. Backus Hospital, Norwich, CT, p. A112

TRANTHAM, Susan, Director Human Resources, Healthsouth Rehabilitation Hospital Of Florence, Florence, SC, p. A562

TRAPNELL, Kerry A, Chief Financial Officer, Elbert Memorial Hospital, Elberton, GA, p. A157

TRAPP, John, Vice President Medical Affairs, Bryan Medical Center, Lincoln, NE, p. A395

TRAPP, Nancy A MSN, Director of Nursing, Saint Thomas Dekalb Hospital, Smithville, TN, p. A589

TRAUTMAN, Bob, Chief Executive Officer, Saline Memorial Hospital, Benton, AR, p. A40

TRAVIS, Calee R.N., Chief Nursing Officer, Baylor Scott & White Medical Center – Centennial, Frisco, TX, p. A615

TRAVIS, David A
Chief Financial Officer, East Texas Medical Center Athens, Athens, TX, p. A594
Chief Financial Officer, Freestone Medical Center, Fairfield, TX, p. A612
TRAVIS, Dee Dee, Director Community Relations, Calais Regional Hospital, Calais, ME, p. A290
TRAVIS, Sara, Chief Nursing Officer and Assistant Administrator, Palo Alto County Health System, Emmetsburg, IA, p. A227
TRAVIS, Thomas, Surgeon General, Department Of The Air Force, Washington, DC, p. B41
TRAXLER, Martin J., Chief Executive Officer, Robley Rex Veterans Affairs Medical Center, Louisville, KY, p. A263
TRAYLOR, Desiree, Chief Information Officer, Chickasaw Nation Medical Center, Ada, OK, p. A504
TRAYLOR, Jerri Sue, Director Human Resources, The Women's Hospital, Newburgh, IN, p. A217
TRAYNOR, Karen, Chief Financial Officer, Richland Hospital, Richland Center, WI, p. A711
TRCZINSKI, Judi, Vice President and Chief Human Resources Officer, Hospital For Special Care, New Britain, CT, p. A111
TREACY, Nancy, Director Finance, Cambridge Medical Center, Cambridge, MN, p. A337
TREACY–SHIFF, Mary, Vice President Finance, Advocate Good Samaritan Hospital, Downers Grove, IL, p. A186
TREADWAY, Michael G, Controller, Christus Trinity Mother Frances Rehabilitation Hospital, Tyler, TX, p. A650
TREADWELL, Karen, Director Human Resources, Lake Martin Community Hospital, Dadeville, AL, p. A16
TREASE, Kevin, Chief Information Officer, Antelope Memorial Hospital, Neligh, NE, p. A396
TREASURE, Jeffrey
Chief Financial Officer, Northern Arizona Healthcare, Flagstaff Medical Center, Flagstaff, AZ, p. A29
Chief Financial Officer, Northern Arizona Healthcare, Verde Valley Medical Center, Cottonwood, AZ, p. A28
TREASURE, Martin
Director Human Resources, Lehigh Valley Hospital – Schuylkill East Norwegian Street, Pottsville, PA, p. A548
Director Human Resources, Lehigh Valley Hospital – Schuylkill South Jackson Street, Pottsville, PA, p. A548
TREECE, Amy M.D., Medical Director, North Greenville Hospital, Travelers Rest, SC, p. A566
TREGLOWN, Brad, Director Information Systems, Redmond Regional Medical Center, Rome, GA, p. A163
TREHAN, Rajeev M.D., M.P.H., Chief of Staff, Veterans Affairs Eastern Kansas Health Care System, Topeka, KS, p. A252
TREITLER, Scot, Chief Operating Officer, Cypress Pointe Surgical Hospital, Hammond, LA, p. A275
TREMAINE, Lisa, Manager Human Resources, Carson Valley Medical Center, Gardnerville, NV, p. A402
TREMBLE, Nakia, Chief Executive Officer, Kindred Hospital Indianapolis North, Indianapolis, IN, p. A211
TREMONTI, Carl
Chief Financial Officer, Mease Countryside Hospital, Safety Harbor, FL, p. A141
Chief Financial Officer, Mease Dunedin Hospital, Dunedin, FL, p. A124
Chief Financial Officer, Morton Plant Hospital, Clearwater, FL, p. A121
Chief Financial Officer, Morton Plant North Bay Hospital, New Port Richey, FL, p. A135
Chief Financial Officer, South Florida Baptist Hospital, Plant City, FL, p. A140
Chief Financial Officer, St. Anthony's Hospital, Saint Petersburg, FL, p. A142
TREMONTI, Yvette, Chief Financial Officer, H. Lee Moffitt Cancer Center And Research Institute, Tampa, FL, p. A144
TRENDE, Gary D FACHE, Associate Director, Tuscaloosa Veterans Affairs Medical Center, Tuscaloosa, AL, p. A24
TRENSCHEL, Robert, D.O., FACHE, M.P.H., President and Chief Executive Officer, Yuma Regional Medical Center, Yuma, AZ, p. A39
TRENT, Cindy, Manager Personnel, Fall River Hospital, Hot Springs, SD, p. A570
TRETINA, Mike, Senior Vice President and Chief Financial Officer, Bayhealth Medical Center, Dover, DE, p. A115
TRETTER, Stan M.D., Chief Medical Officer, Memorial Hospital And Health Care Center, Jasper, IN, p. A212
TREVATHAN, Dave, Director Information Systems, Rose Medical Center, Denver, CO, p. A101
TREVINO, Chris M.D., Chief Medical Officer, St. Elizabeth Hospital, Gonzales, LA, p. A275
TREVINO, Jorge
Chief Operations Officer, Baylor Scott & White Medical Center – White Rock, Dallas, TX, p. A604
Interim Chief Executive Officer, Baylor Scott & White Medical Center – White Rock, Dallas, TX, p. A604

TREVINO, Malissa, Director Human Resources, Pecos County Memorial Hospital, Fort Stockton, TX, p. A613
TREVINO, Paul, Chief Executive Officer, Christus Southeast Texas Hospital, Beaumont, TX, p. A597
TREVISANI, Michael F M.D., Senior Vice President and Chief Medical Officer, Faxton St. Luke's Healthcare, Utica, NY, p. A454
TRIANA, Rudy M.D., Chief of Staff, Jackson Purchase Medical Center, Mayfield, KY, p. A264
TRICKEY, Donna R.N., Chief Nursing Officer, Fairview Park Hospital, Dublin, GA, p. A157
TRIEBES, David G., Chief Executive Officer, Samaritan Albany General Hospital, Albany, OR, p. A520
TRIGG, Terry, Director Human Resources, Merit Health Wesley, Hattiesburg, MS, p. A356
TRIMBLE, Deborah, R.N., Chief Executive Officer, Paul B. Hall Regional Medical Center, Paintsville, KY, p. A266
TRIMBLE, Donald CPA, Chief Financial Officer, Vibra Specialty Hospital At Desoto, Desoto, TX, p. A609
TRIMBLE, Lisa, Controller, Healthsouth Rehabilitation Hospital Of Middletown, Middletown, DE, p. A115
TRIMBLE, Melody, Chief Executive Officer, Johnson City Medical Center, Johnson City, TN, p. A581
TRIMM, Robert M., Interim Chief Executive Officer, Washington County Regional Medical Center, Sandersville, GA, p. A164
TRIMM, Robert, Administrator, North Mississippi Medical Center–Hamilton, Hamilton, AL, p. A19
TRIMMER, Mary R, Interim Chief Operating Officer, Mount Carmel, Columbus, OH, p. A487
TRIMMER, Matthew, Director Information Services, Holy Cross Health, Silver Spring, MD, p. A301
TRINCHETTO, Thomas M.D., Chief Medical Officer, Doctors Hospital Of Sarasota, Sarasota, FL, p. A142
TRINH, Khiet M.D., Chief Medical Officer, Bon Secours St. Mary's Hospital, Richmond, VA, p. A673
TRIPLETT, Daniel, Acting Chief Operating Officer, Springfield Hospital Center, Sykesville, MD, p. A301
TRIPLETT, John D.O., President Medical Staff, Saint Joseph – Martin, Martin, KY, p. A264
TRIPLETT, Robin, Chief Financial Officer, Southern Coos Hospital And Health Center, Bandon, OR, p. A520
TRIPP, Gina, Director Information Systems, Tirr Memorial Hermann, Houston, TX, p. A623
TRIPP, Kelly, Chief Executive Officer, Ten Broeck Tennessee Treatment Facility, Cookeville, TN, p. A577
TRIPPEL, Donald E, Chief Financial Officer, Hugh Chatham Memorial Hospital, Elkin, NC, p. A462
TRITTIN, Kim, Manager Human Resources, Mayo Clinic Health System In Red Wing, Red Wing, MN, p. A346
TRIVEDI, Harsh, M.D., President and Chief Executive Officer, Sheppard Pratt Health System, Baltimore, MD, p. A295
TRIVETTE, Chastity, Chief Executive Officer, Johnson County Community Hospital, Mountain City, TN, p. A586
TROCINO, Mark, Chief Information Officer, Dekalb Medical At Hillandale, Lithonia, GA, p. A160
TROGMAN, Richard FACHE, Chief Operating Officer, Kaiser Permanente Woodland Hills Medical Center, Los Angeles, CA, p. A69
TROLLOPE, Grant, Chief Financial Officer, Northeastern Nevada Regional Hospital, Elko, NV, p. A401
TROMBATORE, Beverly R.N., Director Managed Information Systems, Matagorda Regional Medical Center, Bay City, TX, p. A596
TROMBLEE, Julie R.N., Chief Nursing Officer, The University Of Vermont Health Network Elizabethtown Community Hospital, Elizabethtown, NY, p. A435
TROMPETER, Dawn
Chief Financial Officer, OSF Saint Elizabeth Medical Center, Ottawa, IL, p. A196
Vice President Finance I–80 Region and Chief Financial Officer, OSF Saint Paul Medical Center, Mendota, IL, p. A193
TRONCONE, Michael T, Chief Human Resources Officer, Calvary Hospital, New Rochelle, NY, p. A441
TROSCLAIR, Andree, Vice President Human Resources, Arkansas Children's Hospital, Little Rock, AR, p. A45
TROSIN, Jill A. R.N., MSN, Vice President Patient Care Services, Chief Nursing Officer, St. Luke's Hospital, Maumee, OH, p. A495
TROTTER, Wally, Director Human Resources, Mountain View Hospital, Payson, UT, p. A659
TROTTIER, Timothy R., Chief Executive Officer, Spring View Hospital, Lebanon, KY, p. A260
TROUBLEFIELD, David, Chief Communications Officer, Hemphill County Hospital, Canadian, TX, p. A600
TROUP, Bill M.D., Chief of Staff, Stanton County Hospital, Johnson, KS, p. A243
TROUP, Matthew, Chief Executive Officer, Conway Regional Medical Center, Conway, AR, p. A41

TROUT, Gene, Chief Financial Officer, Weirton Medical Center, Weirton, WV, p. A696
TROUTMAN, Gary CPA, Chief Financial Officer, Baptist Hospitals Of Southeast Texas, Beaumont, TX, p. A597
TROWHILL, Jan, Director Health Information Management Systems, Spire Cane Creek Rehabilitation Hospital, Martin, TN, p. A583
TROXELL, Larry, Chief Executive Officer, Mangum Regional Medical Center, Mangum, OK, p. A509
TROY, Patrick J R.N., MSN, Associate Director Patient Care Services, Veterans Affairs New Jersey Health Care System, East Orange, NJ, p. A413
TROY, Peggy N.
President and Chief Executive Officer, Children's Hospital Of Wisconsin–Fox Valley, Neenah, WI, p. A708
President and Chief Executive Officer, Children's Hospital Of Wisconsin, Milwaukee, WI, p. A707
TROYER, David, Chief Information Officer, Veterans Affairs Northern Indiana Health Care System, Fort Wayne, IN, p. A208
TROYER, Devin M.D., Medical Director, Healthsouth Rehabilitation Hospital Of Columbia, Columbia, SC, p. A560
TROYO–SAUVIAC, Glynda, Chief Executive Officer, Vibra Hospital Of Central Dakotas, Mandan, ND, p. A477
TRUE, Terry M.D., Chief of Staff, Shoals Hospital, Muscle Shoals, AL, p. A22
TRUEBLOOD, Susan
Chief Executive Officer, Georgia Regional Hospital At Atlanta, Decatur, GA, p. A156
Regional Hospital Administrator, Central State Hospital, Milledgeville, GA, p. A161
TRUELOVE, Lynn, Chief Executive Officer, Stone County Hospital, Wiggins, MS, p. A363
TRUESDALE, Fred A. Jr, Administrator, North Mississippi Medical Center–Iuka, Iuka, MS, p. A356
TRUESDELL, Shannon, Chief Operating Officer, Marshall Medical Center, Placerville, CA, p. A80
TRUITT, Louise
Human Resource Director, Coliseum Northside Hospital, Macon, GA, p. A161
Vice President Human Resources, Capital Regional Medical Center, Tallahassee, FL, p. A143
TRUJILLO, Jesse, Chief Information Officer, St. Mark's Hospital, Salt Lake City, UT, p. A660
TRUMAN, Julia
Chief Operating Officer, Multicare Tacoma General Hospital, Tacoma, WA, p. A688
President and Chief Operating Officer, Multicare Tacoma General Hospital, Tacoma, WA, p. A688
Vice President Human Resources, Fort Walton Beach Medical Center, Fort Walton Beach, FL, p. A125
TRUMAN, Lisa, Chief Nursing Officer, Healthsouth Sea Pines Rehabilitation Hospital, Melbourne, FL, p. A132
TRUMAN, Mark, Vice President of Operations, Baptist Health Floyd, New Albany, IN, p. A217
TRUMAN, Michael A., Chief Executive Officer, Oakwood Springs, Oklahoma City, OK, p. A512
TRUMBULL, Kathryn E R.N., Chief Nursing Officer and Vice President Patient Care Services, Samaritan Healthcare, Moses Lake, WA, p. A682
TRUPP, Gary, President Medical Staff, Good Shepherd Health Care System, Hermiston, OR, p. A522
TRUSSELL, Paul, Vice President Human Resources, Pioneer Community Hospital Of Patrick, Stuart, VA, p. A676
TRYON, Ellen R.N., Chief Nursing Officer, Adventist Medical Center–Portland, Portland, OR, p. A525
TSAI, James, M.D., President, New York Eye And Ear Infirmary Of Mount Sinai, New Rochelle, NY, p. A443
TSALATE, Cynthia, Human Resource Specialist, U. S. Public Health Service Indian Hospital, Zuni, NM, p. A429
TSAMBIRAS, Petros M.D., Chief of Staff, Bayfront Health Dade City, Dade City, FL, p. A123
TSAO, Sean, Director Information Technology, Blue Mountain Hospital, John Day, OR, p. A523
TSO, Ron, Chief Executive Officer, Chinle Comprehensive Health Care Facility, Chinle, AZ, p. A28
TSUNEISHI, Lani, Nursing Services Manager, Hawaii State Hospital, Kaneohe, HI, p. A170
TUAZON, Nelson R.N., Chief Nursing Officer, Baptist Medical Center, San Antonio, TX, p. A642
TUBBS, John, M.D.
Chief of Staff, Rock County Hospital, Bassett, NE, p. A390
Chief of Staff, West Holt Medical Services, Atkinson, NE, p. A390
TUBBS, Mary Beth, Chief Nursing Officer, Sunnyside Community Hospital And Clinics, Sunnyside, WA, p. A687
TUBERVILLE, Abby, Human Resource Manager, Fillmore County Hospital, Geneva, NE, p. A393
TUCK, Colleen, Chief Nursing Officer, Livingston Regional Hospital, Livingston, TN, p. A583

TUCK, Greg, Area Information Officer, Kaiser Permanente San Jose Medical Center, San Jose, CA, p. A88

TUCKER, Albert, Chief Financial Officer, Miami Veterans Affairs Healthcare System, Miami, FL, p. A133

TUCKER, Andy, Chief Financial Officer, South Mississippi State Hospital, Purvis, MS, p. A361

TUCKER, Cathy, Director Human Resources, Iraan General Hospital, Iraan, TX, p. A624

TUCKER, Gary C., President and Chief Executive Officer, Mount St. Mary's Hospital And Health Center, Lewiston, NY, p. A438

TUCKER, Ian M.D., Vice President Medical Affairs, Johnson Memorial Medical Center, Stafford Springs, CT, p. A113

TUCKER, Jessie Lee Ph.D., III, Senior Vice President and Chief Operating Officer, Robert Wood Johnson University Hospital, New Brunswick, NJ, p. A417

TUCKER, John
Chief Executive Officer, Mt. San Rafael Hospital, Trinidad, CO, p. A108
Chief Nursing Executive, Center For Behavioral Medicine, Kansas City, MO, p. A370

TUCKER, Joseph B, Senior Vice President and Chief Financial Officer, Fort Washington Medical Center, Oxen Hill, MD, p. A300

TUCKER, Joshua, Administrator, Mercy Hospital Logan County, Guthrie, OK, p. A508

TUCKER, Mona, Director Human Resources, Seton Medical Center Harker Heights, Harker Heights, TX, p. A618

TUCKER, Rebecca, Chief Financial Officer, Memorial Hermann Northeast, Humble, TX, p. A624

TUCKER, Ron, Business Office Manager, Kiowa County Memorial Hospital, Greensburg, KS, p. A242

TUCKER, Sarah, Chief Nursing Officer, Bradley County Medical Center, Warren, AR, p. A50

TUCKER, Steven E., Chief Executive Officer, Conemaugh Memorial Medical Center, Johnstown, PA, p. A537

TUCKER, Steven E, Chief Executive Officer, Conemaugh Memorial Medical Center, Johnstown, PA, p. A537

TUCKER, Theresa, Human Resources Officer, Sioux Center Health, Sioux Center, IA, p. A235

TUCKER, Tom, Chief Executive Officer, Valir Rehabilitation Hospital, Oklahoma City, OK, p. A514

TUDELA, John M M.D., Director of Medical Affairs, Commonwealth Health Center, Saipan, MP, p. A721

TUDOR, Nathan, Chief Executive Officer, El Campo Memorial Hospital, El Campo, TX, p. A610

TUFT, Paul R., President, Southwest Healthcare System, Scottsdale, AZ, p. B119

TULLIS, Bea, Chief Financial Officer and Budget Officer, Broughton Hospital, Morganton, NC, p. A467

TULLMAN, Stephen M., Chief Executive Officer, Phoenixville Hospital, Phoenixville, PA, p. A546

TUMA, Bonnie, Human Resources Team Lead, National Institutes Of Health Clinical Center, Bethesda, MD, p. A297

TUMA, Roman, Chief Medical Officer, Easton Hospital, Easton, PA, p. A533

TUMLIN, Richard, Chief Operating Officer, Tristar Southern Hills Medical Center, Nashville, TN, p. A587

TUMMONS, Coleen, Chief Executive Officer, Gove County Medical Center, Quinter, KS, p. A250

TUMMURU, Ramireddy K M.D., Chief Medical Officer, Porter Regional Hospital, Valparaiso, IN, p. A220

TUNGATE, Rex A.
Chief Executive Officer, Casey County Hospital, Liberty, KY, p. A262
Chief Executive Officer, Jane Todd Crawford Hospital, Greensburg, KY, p. A259

TUNNELL, Richard, Chief Information Officer, University Hospital, Newark, NJ, p. A418

TUNSON, Lynn, Manager Medical Records, Complex Care Hospital At Tenaya, Las Vegas, NV, p. A402

TUPPER, David, Chief Executive Officer, Southwest Idaho Advanced Care Hospital, Boise, ID, p. A172

TUPPONCE, David M.D., Chief Medical Officer, Abrazo Scottsdale Campus, Phoenix, AZ, p. A33

TURBAK, Shelly R.N., Chief Nursing Officer, Prairie Lakes Healthcare System, Watertown, SD, p. A574

TUREK, Beth, Site Manager Information Systems, Advocate South Suburban Hospital, Hazel Crest, IL, p. A189

TUREK, Derrill Kent R.N., Chief Nursing Officer, Blue Mountain Hospital, Blanding, UT, p. A656

TURK, Edward, Vice President Finance, Scripps Mercy Hospital, San Diego, CA, p. A86

TURK, Jan, Interim Administrator, Kindred Hospital–St. Louis, Saint Louis, MO, p. A377

TURKAL, Nick, M.D., President and Chief Executive Officer, Aurora Health Care, Milwaukee, WI, p. B15

TURKAL–BARRETT, Kari, Flight Commander Resource Management Officer, Mike O'Callaghan Federal Hospital, Nellis Afb, NV, p. A404

TURKEL, Brooks, Chief Executive Officer, Lancaster Regional Medical Centers, Lancaster, PA, p. A538

TURLEY, Mary Ann D.O., Medical Director, Honorhealth Deer Valley Medical Center, Phoenix, AZ, p. A33

TURLEY, Matt, Interim Director Information Systems, Greenbrier Valley Medical Center, Ronceverte, WV, p. A696

TURLEY, Susan S, Chief Financial Officer, Doctor's Hospital At Renaissance, Edinburg, TX, p. A610

TURMAN, Anna
Chief Information Officer, Chadron Community Hospital And Health Services, Chadron, NE, p. A392
Chief Operating Officer, Chadron Community Hospital And Health Services, Chadron, NE, p. A392
Interim Chief Executive Officer, Chadron Community Hospital And Health Services, Chadron, NE, p. A392

TURMAN, Tracy Penn., Chief Executive Officer, Healthsouth Rehabilitation Hospital Of Petersburg, Petersburg, VA, p. A672

TURNA, Tarlochan M.D., Medical Director, Mayo Clinic Health System In Cannon Falls, Cannon Falls, MN, p. A337

TURNAGE, Richard, M.D., Chief Executive Officer, Uams Medical Center, Little Rock, AR, p. A46

TURNBULL, James, Chief Information Officer, University Of Utah Health, Salt Lake City, UT, p. A660

TURNBULL, Rosie, Director Human Resources, St. Lawrence Psychiatric Center, Ogdensburg, NY, p. A448

TURNER, Barbara, Director of Nursing, Austen Riggs Center, Stockbridge, MA, p. A312

TURNER, Bill, Vice President Human Resources, Valir Rehabilitation Hospital, Oklahoma City, OK, p. A514

TURNER, Brenda C
Chief Human Resources Officer, Palomar Medical Center, Escondido, CA, p. A58
Chief Human Resources Officer, Pomerado Hospital, Poway, CA, p. A80

TURNER, Chad, Chief Financial Officer, Star Valley Medical Center, Afton, WY, p. A717

TURNER, Cheryl, Administrator, Compass Behavioral Center Of Houma, Houma, LA, p. A276

TURNER, Cindy R., Chief Executive Officer, Bacon County Hospital And Health System, Alma, GA, p. A149

TURNER, Cindy R, Chief Executive Officer, Bacon County Hospital And Health System, Alma, GA, p. A149

TURNER, Dale, Chief Operating Officer, Reedsburg Area Medical Center, Reedsburg, WI, p. A711

TURNER, Glenda, Director Personnel, Oakwood Correctional Facility, Lima, OH, p. A493

TURNER, Howard D., Chief Executive Officer, Abbeville Area Medical Center, Abbeville, SC, p. A558

TURNER, Jeff, FACHE, Chief Executive Officer, Moore County Hospital District, Dumas, TX, p. A609

TURNER, Karissa, Vice President Operations, Wabash General Hospital, Mount Carmel, IL, p. A194

TURNER, Kelly, Senior Vice President Finance and Chief Financial Officer, Adventist Health Glendale, Glendale, CA, p. A62

TURNER, Kevin M.D., Medical Director, Pathways Of Tennessee, Jackson, TN, p. A580

TURNER, Laurie, Chief Nursing Officer, Tristar Skyline Medical Center, Nashville, TN, p. A587

TURNER, Mark J.
President and Chief Executive Officer, Memorial Hospital East, Shiloh, IL, p. A200
President and Chief Executive Officer, Memorial Hospital, Belleville, IL, p. A178

TURNER, Mark
Chief Executive Officer, Capital Medical Center, Olympia, WA, p. A683
Director Information Systems, Beverly Hospital, Montebello, CA, p. A74
Manager Information Technology, Ojai Valley Community Hospital, Ojai, CA, p. A77

TURNER, Marquita, Chief Operating Officer and Chief Nursing Officer, Atrium Medical Center, Middletown, OH, p. A496

TURNER, Maurita, Team Leader Health Information Systems Services, Chi St. Joseph Health Madison Hospital, Madisonville, TX, p. A631

TURNER, Melissa, Senior Vice President Human Resources, Bridgeport Hospital, Bridgeport, CT, p. A109

TURNER, Michael, Director Human Resources, Moberly Regional Medical Center, Moberly, MO, p. A373

TURNER, Nancy, Director Communications, Sutter Roseville Medical Center, Roseville, CA, p. A83

TURNER, Peggy, Assistant Vice President and Director of Nursing, Unity Health White County Medical Center, Searcy, AR, p. A49

TURNER, Randy, Chief Human Resource Management Services, Boise Veterans Affairs Medical Center, Boise, ID, p. A171

TURNER, Robert A., Chief Executive Officer, Ad Hospital East, Houston, TX, p. A619

TURNER, Sara, Director Human Resources, Alvarado Hospital Medical Center, San Diego, CA, p. A85

TURNER, Saundra G, Director Human Resources, Mercy Hospital Jefferson, Crystal City, MO, p. A367

TURNER, Scott, Co–Chief Operating Officer, University Of Iowa Hospitals And Clinics, Iowa City, IA, p. A230

TURNER, Sherrilyn, Director Human Resources, Southeast Colorado Hospital District, Springfield, CO, p. A107

TURNER, Spencer, FACHE, President, Texas Health Presbyterian Hospital Flower Mound, Flower Mound, TX, p. A612

TURNER, Steve, Director Information Technology, Salem Township Hospital, Salem, IL, p. A199

TURNER, Teri, Chief Nursing Officer, Haskell Memorial Hospital, Haskell, TX, p. A618

TURNEY, Amanda, Director Human Resources, Cochran Memorial Hospital, Morton, TX, p. A634

TURNEY, Brian, Chief Executive Officer, Kingman Regional Medical Center, Kingman, AZ, p. A30

TURNEY, David, Chief Information Officer, Cochran Memorial Hospital, Morton, TX, p. A634

TURNEY, Larry, Administrator, Cochran Memorial Hospital, Morton, TX, p. A634

TURNQUIST, Carrie, Director Human Resources, Buena Vista Regional Medical Center, Storm Lake, IA, p. A235

TURO, Albert, Vice President Human Resources, St. Mary's Healthcare, Amsterdam, NY, p. A430

TURPEN, Brad, FACHE, Interim Chief Executive Officer, Valor Health, Emmett, ID, p. A173

TURPIN, Debra R.N., MSN, Vice President Patient Care Services and Chief Nursing Officer, Alton Memorial Hospital, Alton, IL, p. A177

TURPIN, James
Chief of Staff, Ephraim Mcdowell Fort Logan Hospital, Stanford, KY, p. A268
Human Resources, Breckinridge Memorial Hospital, Hardinsburg, KY, p. A259

TURQUEZA, Sandra
Human Resources Business Partner, Saint Joseph Berea, Berea, KY, p. A255
Senior Human Resources Business Partner, Saint Joseph London, London, KY, p. A262

TURSKY, Martin, President and Chief Executive Officer, Firelands Regional Health System, Sandusky, OH, p. A499

TURSO, Janet, Controller, Healthsouth Rehabilitation Hospital Of Toms River, Toms River, NJ, p. A421

TURTON, Jonathan, FACHE, President and Chief Executive Officer, Baptist Medical Center, San Antonio, TX, p. A642

TUSA, Edward A, Chief Financial Officer, Mayo Clinic Health System In Cannon Falls, Cannon Falls, MN, p. A337

TUSCANY, Joanne E
Director Human Resources, St. John Hospital And Medical Center, Detroit, MI, p. A318
Senior Director Human Resources, St. John Macomb–Oakland Hospital, Warren, MI, p. A332

TUSTEN, Jay, Chief Executive Officer, Stanton County Hospital, Johnson, KS, p. A243

TUSZYNSKI, Thomas M.D., Chief of Staff, Samaritan Healthcare, Moses Lake, WA, p. A682

TUTT, Michael M.D., Chief Medical Officer, Tsehootsooi Medical Center, Fort Defiance, AZ, p. A29

TUTTLE, Casey, Director Information Technology, Sistersville General Hospital, Sistersville, WV, p. A696

TUTTLE, Chad, President, Spectrum Health Special Care Hospital, Grand Rapids, MI, p. A321

TUTTLE, Kathryn R.N., Director of Nursing, Memorial Medical Center – Ashland, Ashland, WI, p. A698

TVEIT, Charles B., Chief Executive Officer, Lake District Hospital, Lakeview, OR, p. A523

TWARDY, Cindi, Manager Human Resources, Meeker Memorial Hospital, Litchfield, MN, p. A342

TWEED, Frances, R.N., Executive Director and Administrator, New Mexico Behavioral Health Institute At Las Vegas, Las Vegas, NM, p. A427

TWEEDEL, Patricia, Chief Nursing Officer, Pam Specialty Hospital Of Lafayette, Lafayette, LA, p. A279

TWEHOUS, Debra, Medical Director, Fairlawn Rehabilitation Hospital, Worcester, MA, p. A313

TWIDWELL, Lisa, Administrator, Madison Medical Center, Fredericktown, MO, p. A368

TWIGG, Nicole, Director Human Resources, Brook Lane Health Services, Hagerstown, MD, p. A299

TYE, Angie, Director Human Resources, Waverly Health Center, Waverly, IA, p. A236

TYK, Robert C., Interim Chief Executive Officer, Artesia General Hospital, Artesia, NM, p. A425

TYLER, Holley R.N., Chief Nursing Officer, Woman's Hospital Of Texas, Houston, TX, p. A624

TYLER, Kevin L M.D., President Medical Staff, Penn Highlands Clearfield, Clearfield, PA, p. A531

TYLER, Philene, Chief Finance Officer, Chinle Comprehensive Health Care Facility, Chinle, AZ, p. A28

TYLER, Richard, Corporate Director Human Resources, Conway Regional Medical Center, Conway, AR, p. A41

TYLER, Rick M.D., Vice President Medical Affairs, Christus Southeast Texas Hospital, Beaumont, TX, p. A597

TYLER, Rob, Chief Financial Officer, West Oaks Hospital, Houston, TX, p. A624

TYLER, Tanya, Vice President Human Resources, Chi St. Luke's Health Memorial Lufkin, Lufkin, TX, p. A631

TYLKOWSKI, Chester M.D., Chief of Staff, Shriners Hospitals For Children–Lexington, Lexington, KY, p. A261

TYNES, L Lee M.D., Ph.D., Jr, Medical Director, Central Louisiana State Hospital, Pineville, LA, p. A284

TYNER, W Russell., President and Chief Executive Officer, Baptist Health, Montgomery, AL, p. B18

TYO, Joanne, Chief Financial Officer, Carolinas Continuecare Hospital At Pineville, Charlotte, NC, p. A459

TYRA, Diana, Director Health Information, Kentucky River Medical Center, Jackson, KY, p. A260

TYRA, J Allen., Chief Executive, Gilmore Memorial Hospital, Amory, MS, p. A352

TYRER, Andrew, Chief Operating Officer, Tristar Stonecrest Medical Center, Smyrna, TN, p. A589

TYRRELL, Wade Alan RN, Chief Nursing Officer, Sterling Regional Medcenter, Sterling, CO, p. A107

TYSLAND, Tanya, Chief Executive Officer, Gundersen Palmer Lutheran Hospital And Clinics, West Union, IA, p. A236

TYSON, Bernard J., Chairman and Chief Executive Officer, Kaiser Foundation Hospitals, Oakland, CA, p. B70

TYSON, Rhoda, Chief Information Officer, Central Alabama Veterans Health Care System, Montgomery, AL, p. A21

U

UBER, Charlotte M., Chief Executive Officer, Warren State Hospital, Warren, PA, p. A552

UDALL, Ben M.D., Chief of Staff, Kimble Hospital, Junction, TX, p. A625

UDOVICH, Christopher, M.D., Chief of Staff, Silver Cross Hospital, New Lenox, IL, p. A195

UFFER, Mark H., Chief Executive Officer, Corona Regional Medical Center, Corona, CA, p. A56

UGHOUWA, Ejiro M.D., Chief of Staff, Allen Parish Hospital, Kinder, LA, p. A277

UGWUEKE, Michael, President and Chief Executive Officer, Methodist Healthcare Memphis Hospitals, Memphis, TN, p. A585

UHARRIET, Bart, Director Information Services, Mississippi State Hospital, Whitfield, MS, p. A363

UHL, Jason, Chief Information Officer, Floyd Valley Healthcare, Le Mars, IA, p. A230

UHL, Michael, President, Atrium Medical Center, Middletown, OH, p. A496

UHLIK, Allen M.D., Chief of Staff, Copper Basin Medical Center, Copperhill, TN, p. A577

UHLIR, Tricia, Chief Executive Officer, Fall River Hospital, Hot Springs, SD, p. A570

ULBRICHT, John E., Chief Executive Officer, Methodist Hospital South, Jourdanton, TX, p. A625

ULERY, Brian
Chief Operating Officer, Thomas Memorial Hospital, South Charleston, WV, p. A696
Senior Vice President and Chief Operating Officer, Saint Francis Hospital, Charleston, WV, p. A691

ULETT, John, Vice President and Chief Information Officer, Centrastate Healthcare System, Freehold, NJ, p. A414

ULFERTS, Wendy R.N., Chief Nursing Officer, Rice Memorial Hospital, Willmar, MN, p. A350

ULI, James
Chief Financial Officer, Loma Linda University Medical Center–Murrieta, Murrieta, CA, p. A75
Chief Financial Officer, Providence Saint John's Health Center, Santa Monica, CA, p. A91

ULIBARRI, Laura M.D., Chief of Staff, Catalina Island Medical Center, Avalon, CA, p. A52

ULLRICH, John M.D., Chief of Staff, Ivinson Memorial Hospital, Laramie, WY, p. A718

ULMER, Becky R.N., Director of Nursing, Jasper General Hospital, Bay Springs, MS, p. A352

ULMER, Carlton, President and Chief Executive Officer, West Florida Hospital, Pensacola, FL, p. A139

ULMER, Carol, Chief Executive Officer, Select Specialty Hospital–Sioux Falls, Sioux Falls, SD, p. A572

ULREICH, Shawn R.N., MSN, Vice President Clinical Operations and Chief Nursing Executive, Spectrum Health – Butterworth Hospital, Grand Rapids, MI, p. A321

ULREY, Chris, Director Management Information Systems, St. Luke's Behavioral Health Center, Phoenix, AZ, p. A34

ULRICH, Alan
Chief Financial Officer, Bartlett Regional Hospital, Juneau, AK, p. A26
Chief Financial Officer, Guam Memorial Hospital Authority, Tamuning, GU, p. A721

ULRICH, James P. Jr, Chief Executive Officer, York General, York, NE, p. A400

ULSETH, Randy, Chief Executive Officer, Firstlight Health System, Mora, MN, p. A344

ULVELING, Kyle M.D., Chief of Staff, St. Anthony Regional Hospital, Carroll, IA, p. A223

UMHAU, John M.D., Clinical Director, U. S. Public Health Service Indian Hospital–Whiteriver, Whiteriver, AZ, p. A38

UNDERDAHL, Steve, President and Chief Executive Officer, Northfield Hospital, Northfield, MN, p. A345

UNDERHILL, Robert, Director of Business Services, Central State Hospital, Louisville, KY, p. A262

UNDERWOOD, Ashley, FACHE, Chief Executive Officer, Rollins–Brook Community Hospital, Lampasas, TX, p. A628

UNDERWOOD, Debbie, Manager Human Resources, Plains Memorial Hospital, Dimmitt, TX, p. A609

UNDERWOOD, Jerri C R.N., Chief Nursing Officer, Parkridge Medical Center, Chattanooga, TN, p. A576

UNDERWOOD, Kelsey N, Director of Nursing, Gundersen Tri–County Hospital And Clinics, Whitehall, WI, p. A716

UNDERWOOD, Ken, Chief Executive Officer, Hazel Hawkins Memorial Hospital, Hollister, CA, p. A63

UNDERWOOD, Martha, Chief Human Resources Officer, Saint Thomas Midtown Hospital, Nashville, TN, p. A586

UNDERWOOD, Phillip, Chief Executive Officer, Kindred Hospital–Dayton, Dayton, OH, p. A489

UNDERWOOD, Robert M.D., MS, Chief Medical Officer, St. Mary–Corwin Medical Center, Pueblo, CO, p. A107

UNDERWOOD, Vickie, Director Human Resources, Wyandot Memorial Hospital, Upper Sandusky, OH, p. A501

UNDERWOOD, Virgil, Chief Executive Officer, Boone Memorial Hospital, Madison, WV, p. A693

UNDLIN, Cassie, Chief Operating Officer, Navos, Seattle, WA, p. A685

UNELL, Deonna, Chief Executive Officer, Baylor Surgical Hospital At Las Colinas, Irving, TX, p. A625

UNG, David
Director, Information Technology, California Hospital Medical Center, Los Angeles, CA, p. A67
Site Director, St. Mary Medical Center, Long Beach, CA, p. A67

UNGER, Henry D. M.D., Senior Vice President and Chief Medical Officer, Holy Redeemer Hospital, Meadowbrook, PA, p. A540

UNGER, Kevin L., Ph.D., FACHE
President and Chief Executive Officer, Medical Center Of The Rockies, Loveland, CO, p. A106
President and Chief Executive Officer, Poudre Valley Hospital, Fort Collins, CO, p. A102

UNHEE, Kim, President, Mount Carmel St. Ann's, Westerville, OH, p. A502

UNITAN, Carol M.D., Chief Medical Officer, Kaiser Foundation Hospital Westside Medical Center, Hillsboro, OR, p. A522

UNRUH, Greg, Chief Executive Officer, Citizens Medical Center, Colby, KS, p. A239

UNZEN, John, Chief Financial Officer, Mille Lacs Health System, Onamia, MN, p. A345

UPCHURCH, Jim M.D., Chief Medical Officer, Crow/Northern Cheyenne Hospital, Crow Agency, MT, p. A383

UPCRAFT, Jeffrey, Director Information Services, Rancho Springs Medical Center, Murrieta, CA, p. A75

UPFIELD, Jaclyn, Chief Operating Officer, G. Werber Bryan Psychiatric Hospital, Columbia, SC, p. A560

UPSHAW, Joy, Chief Nursing Officer, Oklahoma State University Medical Center, Tulsa, OK, p. A517

UPTON, Carol, Regional Area Practice Manager, Gilmore Memorial Hospital, Amory, MS, p. A352

UPTON, Daniel, Vice President and Chief Financial Officer, Doylestown Hospital, Doylestown, PA, p. A533

UPTON, Kerry L, Administrative Director Human Resources, Care Regional Medical Center, Aransas Pass, TX, p. A593

UPTON, Matthew
Chief Medical Information Officer, Thomas Memorial Hospital, South Charleston, WV, p. A696
Chief Medical Officer and Chief Medical Information Officer, Saint Francis Hospital, Charleston, WV, p. A691

URADNIK, Michael, Chief Executive Officer, Cascade Behavioral Hospital, Tukwila, WA, p. A688

URAIZEE, Rizwan A., Chief Financial Officer, Kedren Community Mental Health Center, Los Angeles, CA, p. A69

URBAN, Frank, Chief Financial Officer, Southwood Psychiatric Hospital, Pittsburgh, PA, p. A547

URBAN, Josh, Chief Executive Officer, Memorial Hermann Northeast, Humble, TX, p. A624

URBAN, Louise, R.N.
President and Chief Executive Officer, Canonsburg Hospital, Canonsburg, PA, p. A531
President and Chief Executive Officer, Jefferson Hospital, Jefferson Hills, PA, p. A537

URBAN, Thomas S., Market Leader and President, Mercy Health – Fairfield Hospital, Fairfield, OH, p. A491

URBAN, Tom, Director Human Resources, Wills Memorial Hospital, Washington, GA, p. A167

URBANCSIK, Don
Director Finance, Euclid Hospital, Euclid, OH, p. A491
Director Finance, Lutheran Hospital, Cleveland, OH, p. A486

URBANSKI, Pamela A R.N., MSN, Chief Nursing Officer, Senior Vice President, Patient Care Services, Promedica Monroe Regional Hospital, Monroe, MI, p. A326

URBINA, Ana, Chief Financial Officer, Atrium Medical Center, Stafford, TX, p. A646

URBISTONDO, Lisa, Chief Financial Officer, Medical Center Of Peach County, Navicent Health, Bryon, GA, p. A153

URDANETA, Alfonso M.D., President Medical Staff, Washington County Hospital, Nashville, IL, p. A195

URISH, Abigail R. M.D., Chief of Staff, Rangely District Hospital, Rangely, CO, p. A107

URLAUB, Charles J., President and Chief Executive Officer, Mercy Hospital, Buffalo, NY, p. A433

URQUHART, Mary Beth., Interim President, Vice President Patient Care Services and Chief Nursing Officer, New England Sinai Hospital And Rehabilitation Center, Stoughton, MA, p. A312

URQUHART, Mary Beth, Vice President Patient Care Services and Director of Quality, New England Sinai Hospital And Rehabilitation Center, Stoughton, MA, p. A312

URQUHART, Mary R.N., Vice President Patient Care, Brattleboro Memorial Hospital, Brattleboro, VT, p. A662

URQUHART, Teresa C., Chief Operating Officer, Palm Beach Gardens Medical Center, Palm Beach Gardens, FL, p. A138

URSIN, Ronnie R.N., Chief Nursing Officer, Northern Louisiana Medical Center, Ruston, LA, p. A285

USELMAN, Melissa, Chief Financial Officer, Gundersen Boscobel Area Hospital And Clinics, Boscobel, WI, p. A699

USHIJIMA, Arthur A., FACHE, President, The Queen's Medical Center, Honolulu, HI, p. A169

UTECHT, Tom, M.D.
Chief Medical and Quality Officer, Community Regional Medical Center, Fresno, CA, p. A60
Corporate Chief Quality Officer, Fresno Heart And Surgical Hospital, Fresno, CA, p. A60
Senior Vice President and Chief Quality Officer, Community Behavioral Health Center, Fresno, CA, p. A60

UTLEY, Donna, Vice President Human Resources, Mercy San Juan Medical Center, Carmichael, CA, p. A55

UTLEY, Renee, Chief Financial Officer, Hamilton Center, Terre Haute, IN, p. A220

UTTENDORFSKY, Rob, Director Information Management, Lewis County General Hospital, Lowville, NY, p. A438

UTTER, Camille R.N., Chief Nursing Officer, Scotland Health Care System, Laurinburg, NC, p. A466

UTTERBACK, Julie, Chief Financial Officer, Roane Medical Center, Harriman, TN, p. A579

UYEMURA, Monte M.D., Chief of Staff, Wray Community District Hospital, Wray, CO, p. A108

V

VAAGENES, Carl P., Chief Executive Officer, Douglas County Hospital, Alexandria, MN, p. A335

VAALER, Mark, M.D.
Chief Medical Officer, South Florida Baptist Hospital, Plant City, FL, p. A140
Vice President Medical Staff Affairs, St. Joseph's Hospital, Tampa, FL, p. A145

VACCARO, Stacey, Chief Operating Officer, The Children's Institute Of Pittsburgh, Pittsburgh, PA, p. A547

VACHON, Scott, Director Information Technology, Littleton Regional Healthcare, Littleton, NH, p. A409

VADEN, Jim, Director Information Systems, Lauderdale Community Hospital, Ripley, TN, p. A588

VADYAK, Karen, Chief Nursing Officer, Easton Hospital, Easton, PA, p. A533

VAEZAZIZI, Reza M.D., Chief of Staff, Rancho Springs Medical Center, Murrieta, CA, p. A75

VAGUE, Jeff, Regional Manager Information Systems, Mercy Hospitals Of Bakersfield, Bakersfield, CA, p. A53

VAHLBERG, Susan, Director Employee and Community Relations, Valor Health, Emmett, ID, p. A173

VAIL, B J, Director Information Systems, Morehouse General Hospital, Bastrop, LA, p. A270

VAIL, Bryan, Chief Information Officer, Clement J. Zablocki Veterans Affairs Medical Center, Milwaukee, WI, p. A707

VAIL, Lisa M R.N., Chief Nursing Officer and Vice President of Patient Care Services, Bryan Medical Center, Lincoln, NE, p. A395

VAIL, Ronald M.D., Chief of Staff, Lower Umpqua Hospital District, Reedsport, OR, p. A526

VAILLANCOURT, Alex, Chief Information Officer, Christ Hospital, Cincinnati, OH, p. A483

VAILLANCOURT, Stacy, Vice President Marketing, Communications, Advocacy and Human Resources, Saint Agnes Medical Center, Fresno, CA, p. A61

VAIOLETI, Stephany Nihipali., President and Chief Executive Officer, Kahuku Medical Center, Kahuku, HI, p. A169

VAKHARIA, Bharat M.D., President Medical Staff, Sturgis Hospital, Sturgis, MI, p. A331

VALBUENA, Richard M.D., Medical Director, Latimer County General Hospital, Wilburton, OK, p. A519

VALDENEGRO, Maria, Chief Financial Officer, Meadow Wood Behavioral Health System, New Castle, DE, p. A115

VALDERAZ, Leonard, Administrator, Sunrise Canyon Hospital, Lubbock, TX, p. A630

VALDESPINO, Gustavo A., President and Chief Executive Officer, Valley Presbyterian Hospital, Los Angeles, CA, p. A72

VALDEZ, J. Alex, JD, President and Chief Executive Officer, Christus St. Vincent Regional Medical Center, Santa Fe, NM, p. A428

VALENCERINA, Madeline, Chief Operating Officer, Kedren Community Mental Health Center, Los Angeles, CA, p. A69

VALENTE, Anthony M.D., Vice President Medical Affairs, Lehigh Valley Hospital – Hazleton, Hazleton, PA, p. A536

VALENTE, T. J. M.D., Medical Director, Lifestream Behavioral Center, Leesburg, FL, p. A131

VALENTIN, Leonardo, Chief Executive Officer, Professional Hospital Guaynabo, Guaynabo, PR, p. A723

VALENTINE, Lisa R, Chief Operating Officer, Henrico Doctors' Hospital, Richmond, VA, p. A674

VALENTINE, Mark
President, The Heart Hospital Baylor Denton, Denton, TX, p. A608
President, The Heart Hospital Baylor Plano, Plano, TX, p. A638

VALENTINE, Robert A., President, Chi Health Missouri Valley, Missouri Valley, IA, p. A231

VALENTINI, Rudolph M.D., Chief Medical Officer, DMC – Children's Hospital Of Michigan, Detroit, MI, p. A317

VALENTO, Jessica, Director Information Systems, Range Regional Health Services, Hibbing, MN, p. A341

VALLE, Bernardo, Vice President Human Resources, Usmd Hospital At Arlington, Arlington, TX, p. A594

VALLE, David, Chief Information Officer, Hospital Pavia Arecibo, Arecibo, PR, p. A722

VALLE, Karla, Area Chief Financial Officer, Kaiser Permanente Panorama City Medical Center, Los Angeles, CA, p. A68

VALLELY, Ian, Information Technology Site Leader, Sequoia Hospital, Redwood City, CA, p. A82

VALLES, John, Senior Vice President and Chief Financial Officer, Loretto Hospital, Chicago, IL, p. A181

VALLIDO, Gabe, Chief Information Officer, Naval Hospital Camp Pendleton, Camp Pendleton, CA, p. A54

VALLIERE, George, Chief Executive Officer, Claremore Indian Hospital, Claremore, OK, p. A506

VAN BOENING, Jon, President and Chief Executive Officer, Bakersfield Memorial Hospital, Bakersfield, CA, p. A52

VAN BREE, Margaret M., Dr.PH, President, Rhode Island Hospital, Providence, RI, p. A557

VAN BUSKIRK, George F M.D., Chief of Staff, Bay Pines Veterans Affairs Healthcare System, Bay Pines, FL, p. A119

VAN CAMP, Keith, Vice President Information Services, St. Dominic–Jackson Memorial Hospital, Jackson, MS, p. A357

VAN CLEAVE, Bruce L M.D., Senior Vice President and Chief Medical Officer, Aurora Medical Center Of Oshkosh, Oshkosh, WI, p. A710

VAN CLEAVE, Chad, Chief Financial Officer, Columbus Community Hospital, Columbus, NE, p. A392

VAN CLEAVE, Vanetta, Chief Financial Officer, Yukon–Kuskokwim Delta Regional Hospital, Bethel, AK, p. A25

VAN DECAR, Tama M.D., Chief Medical Officer, Fort Walton Beach Medical Center, Fort Walton Beach, FL, p. A125

VAN DER VEER, Jon D.O., Vice President Medical Affairs, Greene County Medical Center, Jefferson, IA, p. A230

VAN DRIEL, Allen, FACHE, Administrator, Smith County Memorial Hospital, Smith Center, KS, p. A252

VAN DYK, Holly M.D., Interim Chief Medical Officer, Tuba City Regional Health Care Corporation, Tuba City, AZ, p. A37

VAN EECKHOUT, Barbara M.D., Chief of Staff, Los Alamos Medical Center, Los Alamos, NM, p. A427

VAN EPERN, Keri, Manager Human Resources, Aspirus Ironwood Hosital & Clinics, Inc., Ironwood, MI, p. A323

VAN ESSENDELFT, Seth
Vice President and Chief Financial Officer, Lawrence + Memorial Hospital, New London, CT, p. A112
Vice President and Chief Financial Officer, Westerly Hospital, Westerly, RI, p. A557

VAN ETTEN, Mark M.D., Chief of Staff, Spooner Health, Spooner, WI, p. A712

VAN GENDEREN, Nathan, Executive Vice President and Chief Financial Officer, Mercy Medical Center, Cedar Rapids, Iowa, Cedar Rapids, IA, p. A223

VAN GORDER, Chris D., FACHE, President and Chief Executive Officer, Scripps Health, San Diego, CA, p. B113

VAN HOET, Jim, Chief Financial Officer, Coffey County Hospital, Burlington, KS, p. A239

VAN HOUDEN, Charles M.D., Chief Medical Officer, Neosho Memorial Regional Medical Center, Chanute, KS, p. A239

VAN HYNING, Jill, Director Human Resources, Carle Richland Memorial Hospital, Olney, IL, p. A196

VAN KAMPEN, Cindy, Chief Nursing Officer, North Ottawa Community Hospital, Grand Haven, MI, p. A320

VAN LEEUWE, Matthew, Chief Operating Officer, Abilene Regional Medical Center, Abilene, TX, p. A591

VAN MEETEREN, Robert, President and Chief Executive Officer, Reedsburg Area Medical Center, Reedsburg, WI, p. A711

VAN METER, David, Deputy Director, James A. Haley Veterans' Hospital–Tampa, Tampa, FL, p. A144

VAN METER, Rex, President, Integris Canadian Valley Hospital, Yukon, OK, p. A519

VAN NATTA, Timothy M.D., Chief Medical Officer, Harbor–Ucla Medical Center, Torrance, CA, p. A93

VAN NORMAN, Steven M.D., Medical Director, Dixie Regional Medical Center, Saint George, UT, p. A660

VAN RYBROEK, Greg, Chief Executive Officer, Mendota Mental Health Institute, Madison, WI, p. A705

VAN SCOYK, Mitch, Manager Information Systems, Delta County Memorial Hospital, Delta, CO, p. A100

VAN VICKLE, Robin, Chief Financial Officer, Bristow Medical Center, Bristow, OK, p. A505

VAN VOLKENBURG, Mark, Chief Executive Officer, Healthsouth Harmarville Rehabilitation Hospital, Pittsburgh, PA, p. A546

VAN VRANKEN, Arthur M.D., Chief Medical Officer, Essentia Health–Graceville, Graceville, MN, p. A340

VAN VRANKEN, Ross, Executive Director, University Of Utah Neuropsychiatric Institute, Salt Lake City, UT, p. A661

VAN WHY, Susan, Director Human Resources, St. Luke's Hospital – Miners Campus, Coaldale, PA, p. A531

VAN WINKLE, James M.D., Chief of Staff, Unity Medical Center, Manchester, TN, p. A583

VAN WINKLE, Melanie, Chief Financial Officer, Mammoth Hospital, Mammoth Lakes, CA, p. A72

VAN ZANTEN, Lorinda, MSN, Chief Executive, Providence Newberg Medical Center, Newberg, OR, p. A524

VANBOEKEL, Tony, Director Information Systems, Shasta Regional Medical Center, Redding, CA, p. A81

VANBUREN, Nikki, Chief Nursing Officer, Johnston Memorial Hospital, Abingdon, VA, p. A664

VANCE, Derek, Chief Executive Officer, Lewisgale Hospital Pulaski, Pulaski, VA, p. A673

VANCE, Ellen B
Chief Human Resource Officer, Sheltering Arms Rehabilitation Hospital, Mechanicsville, VA, p. A670
Chief Human Resources Officer, Sheltering Arms Hospital South, Midlothian, VA, p. A670

VANCE, Mark M.D., Chief Medical Officer, Quincy Valley Medical Center, Quincy, WA, p. A684

VANCE, Ruth, Director Information Systems, Quincy Valley Medical Center, Quincy, WA, p. A684

VANCE, Stacie
Chief Nursing Officer and Chief Operations Officer, Indiana Orthopaedic Hospital, Indianapolis, IN, p. A211
Chief Nursing Officer and Vice President Operations, Indiana Orthopaedic Hospital, Indianapolis, IN, p. A211
Chief Nursing Officer and, Indiana Orthopaedic Hospital, Indianapolis, IN, p. A211

VANCE, Steven
Chief Financial Officer, Dixie Regional Medical Center, Saint George, UT, p. A660
Information Technology Director, Lake District Hospital, Lakeview, OR, p. A523
President, SSM Health St. Mary's Hospital – Jefferson City, Jefferson City, MO, p. A369

VANCONIA, R Brent., President, Ssm Health St. Mary'S Hospital - Jefferson City, Jefferson City, MO, p. B120

VANCOURT, Bernie
Chief Operating Officer, Bay Area Medical Center, Marinette, WI, p. A706
Interim Chief Nursing Officer, Bay Area Medical Center, Marinette, WI, p. A706

VANDERSTEEG, James, President and Chief Executive Officer, Covenant Health, Knoxville, TN, p. B39

VANDENBARK, Heather, Human Resources Specialist, State Hospital North, Orofino, ID, p. A175

VANDENBERG, Andra, Director Human Resources, Butler County Health Care Center, David City, NE, p. A392

VANDENBOSCH, Dan, Chief Information Officer, Madison County Health Care System, Winterset, IA, p. A237

VANDEWATER, David T., President and Chief Executive Officer, Ardent Health Services, Nashville, TN, p. B11

VANDER, Allen M.D., Chief Medical Staff, Thibodaux Regional Medical Center, Thibodaux, LA, p. A287

VANDER KOLK, Keith, President and Chief Executive Officer, Saint Agnes Healthcare, Baltimore, MD, p. A295

VANDERBEEK, Sam, Chief Information Officer, W. J. Mangold Memorial Hospital, Lockney, TX, p. A629

VANDERHOOFT, J Eric M.D., President Medical Staff, St. Mark's Hospital, Salt Lake City, UT, p. A660

VANDERLINDEN, Mark A, Chief Financial Officer, Greene County Medical Center, Jefferson, IA, p. A230

VANDERMARK, Jay H, Chief Financial Officer, Veterans Affairs Northern Indiana Health Care System, Fort Wayne, IN, p. A208

VANDERMEER, Nick, Director Information Systems, Banner Payson Medical Center, Payson, AZ, p. A32

VANDERPOL, Antoinette, Chief of Staff, Avera St. Benedict Health Center, Parkston, SD, p. A571

VANDERPOOL, Lee, Vice President, Dominican Hospital, Santa Cruz, CA, p. A90

VANDERSCHAAFF, Trixie, Chief Nursing Officer, St. Anthony Summit Medical Center, Frisco, CO, p. A103

VANDERSLICE, Douglas M, Senior Vice President and Chief Financial Officer, Boston Children's Hospital, Boston, MA, p. A302

VANDERSTEK, Eliott R, Chief Fiscal Service, Veterans Affairs Eastern Colorado Health Care System, Denver, CO, p. A101

VANDERSTOUW, Karl, Vice President Information Systems, UNC Lenoir Healthcare, Kinston, NC, p. A465

VANDERVLIET, William M.D., Vice President Medical Affairs, Holland Hospital, Holland, MI, p. A322

VANDERWEGE, Larry, Administrator, Lindsborg Community Hospital, Lindsborg, KS, p. A246

VANDEWEGE, Dana, Director Human Resources, Capital Medical Center, Olympia, WA, p. A683

VANDONKELAAR, Rodney
Chief Financial Officer, Carolina Pines Regional Medical Center, Hartsville, SC, p. A563
Chief Financial Officer, Saint Thomas Highlands Hospital, Sparta, TN, p. A589

VANDORT, Patti J MSN, R.N., Vice President Nursing/Chief Nursing Officer, Holland Hospital, Holland, MI, p. A322

VANDRIEL, Mary Kay
President, Spectrum Health Big Rapids Hospital, Big Rapids, MI, p. A315
President, Spectrum Health Reed City Hospital, Reed City, MI, p. A329

VANDRUFF, John M.D., Chief of Staff, Banner Payson Medical Center, Payson, AZ, p. A32

VANDYKE, Yvonne R.N., MSN, Chief Nursing Officer, Texas Market, Seton Northwest Hospital, Austin, TX, p. A595

VANEK, James, Chief Executive Officer, Columbus Community Hospital, Columbus, TX, p. A602

VANES, Wendell, Chief Financial Officer, Saint Mary's Regional Medical Center, Russellville, AR, p. A49

VANHAREN, James M.D., Medical Director, Forest View Psychiatric Hospital, Grand Rapids, MI, p. A320

VANHOOZIER, Adria, Administrator, Riverside Doctors' Hospital, Williamsburg, VA, p. A677

VANHOUWELING, Mason, Chief Executive Officer, University Medical Center, Las Vegas, NV, p. A404

VANHOY, Michael, Director of Quality, Uva–Healthsouth Rehabilitation Hospital, Charlottesville, VA, p. A665

VANNATTER, Mistie, Chief Nursing Officer, Advanced Care Hospital Of White County, Searcy, AR, p. A49

VANNETT, Vince, Director Human Resources, Jellico Community Hospital, Jellico, TN, p. A580

VANO, Ann
Vice President Human Resources, Providence–Providence Park Hospitals, Southfield, MI, p. A331
Vice President, Human Resources, Crittenton Hospital Medical Center, Rochester, MI, p. A329

VANOSDOL, Thomas J.
Chief Executive Officer, St. Vincent's Medical Center Riverside, Jacksonville, FL, p. A128
Chief Executive Officer, St. Vincent's Medical Center Southside, Jacksonville, FL, p. A128

VANSANT, Scott M.D., Chief Medical Officer, Central State Hospital, Milledgeville, GA, p. A161

VANSTRIEN, Amy, Director Talent Operations, Midwestern Regional Medical Center, Zion, IL, p. A202

VANTONGEREN, Teri, Director Information Services, Spectrum Health Pennock, Hastings, MI, p. A322

VANWICHEN, Ward C., Chief Executive Officer, Phillips County Hospital, Malta, MT, p. A386

VANWYHE, Brenda, Senior Vice President Finance and Chief Financial Officer, Rush–Copley Medical Center, Aurora, IL, p. A178

VARA, Raymond P. Jr, President and Chief Executive Officer, Hawaii Pacific Health, Honolulu, HI, p. B56

VARELA, Alberto M., M.D., President, Inspira Ponce, Ponce, PR, p. A725

VARELA, Nancy, Director Human Resources, Patton State Hospital, Patton, CA, p. A79

VARGA, Patrick, Chief Operating Officer, Mercy Medical Center Redding, Redding, CA, p. A81

VARGAS, Barbara, Interim Chief Nursing Officer, Fountain Valley Regional Hospital And Medical Center, Fountain Valley, CA, p. A60

VARGAS, Idelfonso, Executive Director, Dr. Ramon E. Betances Hospital–Mayaguez Medical Center Branch, Mayaguez, PR, p. A724

VARGAS, Jose L M.D., Medical Director, West Gables Rehabilitation Hospital, Miami, FL, p. A134

VARGAS, Margie, Chief Human Resources Officer, Memorial Regional Hospital, Hollywood, FL, p. A127

VARGAS, Marisol, Director Finance, Hospital Del Maestro, San Juan, PR, p. A726

VARGAS, Nancy
Chief Human Resources, St. Joseph's Behavioral Health Center, Stockton, CA, p. A92
Director Human Resources, Mark Twain Medical Center, San Andreas, CA, p. A84
Vice President Human Resources, St. Joseph's Medical Center, Stockton, CA, p. A93

VARGAS–MAHAR, Monica, FACHE, Chief Executive Officer, The Hospitals Of Providence Sierra Campus, El Paso, TX, p. A611

VARGHESE, Roy M.D., Chief of Staff, Mary Breckinridge Arh Hospital, Hyden, KY, p. A260

VARGHESE, Shibu, Vice President Human Resources, University of Texas M.D. Anderson Cancer Center, Houston, TX, p. A623

VARIALE, Vincenzo, Chief Executive Officer, North Vista Hospital, North Las Vegas, NV, p. A404

VARIAN, Grant M.D., Medical Director, Mary Rutan Hospital, Bellefontaine, OH, p. A481

VARK, Lawrence M.D., Chief Medical Officer, Creek Nation Community Hospital, Okemah, OK, p. A511

VARLEY, Kevin
Chief Financial Officer, Curahealth Heritage Valley, Beaver, PA, p. A529
Chief Financial Officer, Curahealth Pittsburgh, Oakdale, PA, p. A542
Chief Financial Officer, Kindred Hospital South Philadelphia, Philadelphia, PA, p. A544

VARNADO, Anjanette M.D., Chief Medical Officer, St. Helena Parish Hospital, Greensburg, LA, p. A275

VARNADO, Darryl, Executive Vice President and Chief People Officer, Children's National Health System, Washington, DC, p. A117

VARNADO, Donna, Vice President Finance, Cypress Pointe Surgical Hospital, Hammond, LA, p. A275

VARNADO, Kim R.N., Chief Nursing Officer, Highland Community Hospital, Picayune, MS, p. A360

VARNADOE, Milo, Director Information Systems, Warm Springs Medical Center, Warm Springs, GA, p. A167

VARNAM, Jessica, Chief of Staff, Grant Regional Health Center, Lancaster, WI, p. A705

VARNER, Terry, Administrator, Yalobusha General Hospital, Water Valley, MS, p. A362

VARNEY, Tim R.N., Chief Nursing Officer, Select Specialty Hospital–Ann Arbor, Ypsilanti, MI, p. A334

VARNUM, Daniel, President and Chief Executive Officer, Mercy Medical Center–North Iowa, Mason City, IA, p. A231

VARTANIAN, Sarkis, Chief Nursing Officer, Whittier Hospital Medical Center, Whittier, CA, p. A97

VARTELAS, Helene M., MSN, Chief Executive Officer, Connecticut Valley Hospital, Middletown, CT, p. A111

VASCONCELLOS, Jacques, Director, Operations, Winter Haven Hospital, Winter Haven, FL, p. A148

VASEK, Barbara, Director Information Technology, Yoakum Community Hospital, Yoakum, TX, p. A655

VASHISHTA, Ashok M.D., Vice President Medical Affairs, Mclaren Central Michigan, Mount Pleasant, MI, p. A326

VASIL, Kathleen, Vice President Finance, St. Charles Hospital, Port Jefferson, NY, p. A450

VASQUEZ, Alberto, Administrator, Garfield Memorial Hospital, Panguitch, UT, p. A659

VASQUEZ, Christann
Executive Vice President and Chief Operating Officer, University Health System, San Antonio, TX, p. A644
President, Dell Seton Medical Center At The University Of Texas, Austin, TX, p. A595

VASQUEZ, George
Chief Technology Officer, Clovis Community Medical Center, Clovis, CA, p. A56
Corporate Chief Information Officer, Fresno Heart And Surgical Hospital, Fresno, CA, p. A60
Vice President Information Services, Community Behavioral Health Center, Fresno, CA, p. A60

VASQUEZ, Jill, Manager Human Resources, Spectrum Health Ludington Hospital, Ludington, MI, p. A325

VASQUEZ, Kenneth, Associate Director, JFK Medical Center North Campus, West Palm Beach, FL, p. A147

VASQUEZ, Miguel
Chief Executive Officer, Sister Emmanuel Hospital, Miami, FL, p. A134
Chief Financial Officer, Sister Emmanuel Hospital, Miami, FL, p. A134

VASQUEZ, Nelson, Vice President Finance, Jackson Park Hospital And Medical Center, Chicago, IL, p. A181

VASQUEZ, Stacy J., Director, Beckley Veterans Affairs Medical Center, Beckley, WV, p. A690

VASS, Paula, Vice President Clinical Operations, Walden Behavioral Care, Waltham, MA, p. A312

VASTOLA, David, Medical Director, Searhc Mt. Edgecumbe Hospital, Sitka, AK, p. A27

VASUNAGA, Amy, Chief Nurse Executive, Leahi Hospital, Honolulu, HI, p. A168

VATH, Richard M.D., Vice President Medical Affairs, Our Lady Of The Lake Regional Medical Center, Baton Rouge, LA, p. A271

VATSAVAI, Sundararama R M.D., Medical Director, Baton Rouge Rehabilitation Hospital, Baton Rouge, LA, p. A270

VAUGHAN, Alan, Director Information Technology, Share Medical Center, Alva, OK, p. A504

VAUGHAN, Amanda, Chief Financial Officer, St. Catherine Hospital, Garden City, KS, p. A241

VAUGHAN, Brandon, Chief Financial Officer and Vice President Finance, Jamestown Regional Medical Center, Jamestown, ND, p. A476

VAUGHAN, Page H., Chief Executive Officer, Chester Regional Medical Center, Chester, SC, p. A559

VAUGHAN, Page, Chief Executive Officer, Springs Memorial Hospital, Lancaster, SC, p. A564

VAUGHAN, Peggy, M.D.
Senior Vice President Medical Affairs, University Of Maryland Harford Memorial Hospital, Havre De Grace, MD, p. A299
Senior Vice President Medical Affairs, University Of Maryland Upper Chesapeake Medical Center, Bel Air, MD, p. A296

VAUGHAN, Rob, Chief Financial Officer, Carilion New River Valley Medical Center, Christiansburg, VA, p. A666

VAUGHN, Barbara R.N., Chief Nursing Officer, Baylor Scott & White Medical Center - Carrollton, Carrollton, TX, p. A600

VAUGHN, Debbie, Chief Nursing Officer, The Medical Center Of Southeast Texas, Port Arthur, TX, p. A639

VAUGHN, Kerry, Chief Information Officer, St. Mary's Health Care System, Athens, GA, p. A149

VAUGHN, Kevin P, Chief Financial Officer, Kansas Spine And Specialty Hospital, Wichita, KS, p. A253

VAUGHN, Michael, Director of Nursing, Southeast Rehabilitation Hospital, Lake Village, AR, p. A45

VAUGHN, Sandy
Director Information Services, Baylor All Saints Medical Center At Fort Worth, Fort Worth, TX, p. A613
Director Information Systems, Baylor Regional Medical Center At Grapevine, Grapevine, TX, p. A617

VAUGHN, Sharma Esq, Chief Nursing Officer, Rangely District Hospital, Rangely, CO, p. A107

VAUGHN, Ted W, Director Human Resources, Unitypoint Health - Trinity Regional Medical Center, Fort Dodge, IA, p. A227

VAUGHN, Vickie, Chief Nursing Officer, Tennova Healthcare–Shelbyville, Shelbyville, TN, p. A589

VAUTER, Rebecca, PsyD, Facility Director, Central State Hospital, Petersburg, VA, p. A672

VAVARUTSOS, Tony, Director Information Systems, Thorek Memorial Hospital, Chicago, IL, p. A184

VAZIRI, H Kevin., President, Woodland Healthcare, Woodland, CA, p. A97

VAZQUEZ, Barbara
Chief Nursing Officer, Palmetto General Hospital, Hialeah, FL, p. A126
Chief Nursing Officer, The Hospitals Of Providence Memorial Campus, El Paso, TX, p. A611

VAZQUEZ, Brunilda, Medical Director, Hospital De Psiquiatria, San Juan, PR, p. A726

VAZQUEZ, Emilio M.D., Chief Medical Officer, Dekalb Health, Auburn, IN, p. A203

VAZQUEZ, Francisco, Director, Michael E. Debakey Veterans Affairs Medical Center, Houston, TX, p. A622

VEACH, Jamie, Chief Operating Officer, Clay County Hospital, Flora, IL, p. A187

VEAL, Bonita Wells, Chief Nursing Officer, Anaheim Global Medical Center, Anaheim, CA, p. A51

VEDRAL–BARON, Jennifer, Health System Director, Tennessee Valley Healthcare System, Nashville, TN, p. A587

VEERAMACHANENI, Harish M.D., Chief of Staff, Wayne Medical Center, Waynesboro, TN, p. A590

VEESER, Tom, Chief Nursing Officer, Ministry Saint Michael's Hospital, Stevens Point, WI, p. A713

VEGA, James, Director Information Systems, Palm Beach Gardens Medical Center, Palm Beach Gardens, FL, p. A138

VEGA, Jane, Executive Director, Industrial Hospital, San Juan, PR, p. A726

VEGA, Maria, Director Human Resources, Auxilio Mutuo Hospital, San Juan, PR, p. A725

VEGA, Mary R.N., MSN, Vice President Nursing, St. Margaret's Hospital, Spring Valley, IL, p. A200

VEILLETTE, Michael D.
Senior Vice President and Chief Financial Officer, Manchester Memorial Hospital, Manchester, CT, p. A110
Senior Vice President and Chief Financial Officer, Rockville General Hospital, Vernon, CT, p. A113

VEILLEUX, Jeffrey
Executive Vice President and Chief Financial Officer, Swedish Medical Center–First Hill, Seattle, WA, p. A685
Senior Vice President and Chief Financial Officer, Swedish Medical Center–Cherry Hill Campus, Seattle, WA, p. A685

VEILLON, Paul, CPA
Chief Financial Officer, Christus Dubuis Hospital Of Fort Smith, Fort Smith, AR, p. A43
Chief Financial Officer, Christus Dubuis Hospital Of Hot Springs, Hot Springs National Park, AR, p. A44

VEIT, Amanda R.N., Chief Nursing Officer, Presbyterian–St. Luke's Medical Center, Denver, CO, p. A101

VEITZ, Larry W., President, Spearfish Regional Hospital, Spearfish, SD, p. A573

VEITZ, Larry W, President, Spearfish Regional Hospital, Spearfish, SD, p. A573

VELA, Javier, Director Information Technology, Baylor Medical Center At Uptown, Dallas, TX, p. A604

VELA, Manuel, President and Chief Executive Officer, Valley Baptist Medical Center–Harlingen, Harlingen, TX, p. A618

VELASCO, Paul, IT Manager, Kit Carson County Health Service District, Burlington, CO, p. A99

VELASQUEZ, Alfred T, Area Information Officer, Kaiser Permanente Riverside Medical Center, Riverside, CA, p. A82

VELASQUEZ, Lin, Vice President Human Resources, Saint Louise Regional Hospital, Gilroy, CA, p. A61

VELEZ, Luz M, Director–Administration of Nursing Services, Hospital San Carlos Borromeo, Moca, PR, p. A724

VELEZ, Pablo, Chief Executive Officer, Sharp Chula Vista Medical Center, Chula Vista, CA, p. A55

VELEZ, Raul
Director Information Systems, Huntsville Memorial Hospital, Huntsville, TX, p. A624
Information Technology Director, Eliza Coffee Memorial Hospital, Florence, AL, p. A18

VELUSWAMY, Ragupathy M.D., Vice President Medical Affairs, Wilkes–Barre General Hospital, Wilkes, PA, p. A554

VENABLE, Mark, Interim Director Human Resources, Shriners Hospitals For Children–St. Louis, Saint Louis, MO, p. A377

VENABLE, Robert M.D., Chief Medical Staff, Washington County Hospital, Plymouth, NC, p. A468

VENDETTI, Marilouise M.D., Chief Medical Officer, Atlanticare Regional Medical Center, Atlantic City, NJ, p. A411

VENEZIANO, Terri, Interim Chief Nursing Officer, Columbus Regional Healthcare System, Whiteville, NC, p. A472

VENGCO, Joel L. MS, Vice President, Chief Information Officer, Baystate Medical Center, Springfield, MA, p. A311

VENHUIZEN, Pamela, Chief Human Resources Officer, Cooperstown Medical Center, Cooperstown, ND, p. A475

VENOIT, Jon–Paul
Chief Operating Officer, Masonicare Health Center, Wallingford, CT, p. A113
President and Chief Executive Officer, Masonicare Health Center, Wallingford, CT, p. A113

VENTO, Bob, President and Chief Executive Officer, Qhr, Brentwood, TN, p. B104

VENTURA, Rosemary M.D., Chief Nursing Informatics Officer, New York–Presbyterian Hospital, New Rochelle, NY, p. A444

VENTURA, Sylvia A R.N., MS, Chief Nursing Officer, Olympia Medical Center, Los Angeles, CA, p. A70

VENTURELLA, James, Vice President Information Technology, West Virginia University Hospitals, Morgantown, WV, p. A694

VENUTO, Frank, Chief Human Capital Officer, Nebraska Medicine – Nebraska Medical Center, Omaha, NE, p. A397

VENZANT, Shamada, Manager Health Information, Specialty Hospital Of Winnfield, Winnfield, LA, p. A288

VERA, Luis F M.D., Medical Director, Kensington Hospital, Philadelphia, PA, p. A544

VERAGIWALA, Jignesh, Chief of Staff, Mercy Hospital Logan County, Guthrie, OK, p. A508

VERBEKE, Lori, Chief Financial Officer, Timberlawn Mental Health System, Dallas, TX, p. A607

VERBUS, John R, Senior Vice President and Chief Operating Officer, Frederick Regional Health System, Frederick, MD, p. A298

VERDEJA, Juan–Carlos M.D., President of Medical Staff, Baptist Health South Florida, West Kendall Baptist Hospital, Miami, FL, p. A132

VERDON, Chris, Director Finance, Phillips Eye Institute, Minneapolis, MN, p. A344

VERFURTH, Larry, D.O.
Chief Medical Officer and Senior Vice President, Christus Good Shepherd Medical Center, Longview, TX, p. A629
Executive Vice President and Chief Medical Officer, Christus Good Shepherd Medical Center–Marshall, Marshall, TX, p. A632

VERGA, Joseph P., FACHE, Chief Executive Officer, Guam Memorial Hospital Authority, Tamuning, GU, p. A721

VERGARA, Aimee, Chief Executive Officer, Hospital For Extended Recovery, Norfolk, VA, p. A671

VERGONIO, Merlinda, Chief Information Management and Technology, U. S. Air Force Hospital, Hampton, VA, p. A668

VERGOS, Katherine, Chief Operating Officer and Chief Nursing Officer, St. Agnes Hospital, Fond Du Lac, WI, p. A701

VERHASSELT, Helen
Chief Financial Officer, North Valley Hospital, Tonasket, WA, p. A688
Interim Chief Executive Officer, North Valley Hospital, Tonasket, WA, p. A688

VERINDER, David, President and Chief Executive Officer, Sarasota Memorial Health Care System, Sarasota, FL, p. A142

VERMA, Virendar M.D., Medical Director, Healthsouth Rehabilitation Hospital Of Jonesboro, Jonesboro, AR, p. A45

VERMEER, Kevin, President and Chief Executive Officer, Unitypoint Health, West Des Moines, IA, p. B133

VERMILLION, Kerry, Senior Vice President Finance and Chief Financial Officer, Gulf Breeze Hospital, Gulf Breeze, FL, p. A126

VERMULEN, Peter, Director Information Technology, Schick Shadel Hospital, Seattle, WA, p. A685

VERRET, Dean, Vice President Financial Services, Terrebonne General Medical Center, Houma, LA, p. A276

VERRETTE, Paul M.D., Chief Medical Officer, St. Bernard Parish Hospital, Chalmette, LA, p. A272

VERRETTE, Paula M.D., Senior Vice President Quality and Physician Services and Chief Medical Officer, Huntington Memorial Hospital, Pasadena, CA, p. A79

VERRILL, Alan M.D., President Medical Staff, Bridgton Hospital, Bridgton, ME, p. A290

VERSTEEG, Linda, Director of Nursing, Hegg Memorial Health Center Avera, Rock Valley, IA, p. A234

VERTIN, Amy M.D., Chief of Staff, Crete Area Medical Center, Crete, NE, p. A392

VERVALIN, Paul G., Interim President, Guthrie Robert Packer Hospital, Sayre, PA, p. A549

VESSEY, Joe, Chief Financial Officer, Grays Harbor Community Hospital, Aberdeen, WA, p. A678

VETTER, Norman, Chief Executive Officer, Division of Substance Abuse and Mental Health, Delaware Psychiatric Center, New Castle, DE, p. A115

VETTER, Rich M.D., Associate Chief, Essentia Health St. Mary's – Detroit Lakes, Detroit Lakes, MN, p. A338

VIALL, John M.D., Vice President Medical Affairs, Holzer Medical Center, Gallipolis, OH, p. A491

VIALL, Sandra E MSN, Chief Nursing Officer, Hendry Regional Medical Center, Clewiston, FL, p. A122

VIATOR, Dionne CPA, FACHE, Chief Financial Officer, Iberia Medical Center, New Iberia, LA, p. A282

VIBETO, Brett M.D., Chief of Staff, Chi St. Alexius Health – Williston Medical Center, Williston, ND, p. A478

VIBHAKAR, Neel M.D., Senior Vice President and Chief Medical Officer, University Of Maryland Baltimore Washington Medical Center, Glen Burnie, MD, p. A298

VICE, Jeff, Interim Chief Executive Officer, Starke Hospital, Knox, IN, p. A213

VICENS–RIVERA, Enrique A. Jr, JD, Chief Executive Officer, Healthsouth Rehabilitation Hospital Of Miami, Cutler Bay, FL, p. A122

VICENT, Leonardo III, Executive Director, Bronx–Lebanon Hospital Center Health Care System, New Rochelle, NY, p. A440

VICENTE, Oscar, Chief Financial Officer, Palmetto General Hospital, Hialeah, FL, p. A126

VICENTI, Darren M.D., Clinical Director, Hopi Health Care Center, Keams Canyon, AZ, p. A30

VICK, Dan J. M.D., Vice President of Medical Affairs and Chief Medical Officer, Oneida Healthcare, Oneida, NY, p. A448

VICKERS, Cynthia R.N., Assistant Administrator for Nursing Services, Memorial Hospital And Manor, Bainbridge, GA, p. A152

VICKERS, Dave, Chief Financial Officer, Los Alamitos Medical Center, Los Alamitos, CA, p. A67

VICKERS, Don
Chief Executive Officer, Cleveland Emergency Hospital, Cleveland, TX, p. A601
Chief Executive Officer, Woodlands Specialty Hospital, The Woodlands, TX, p. A650

VICKERS, Kathy, Director Human Resources, Vantage Point Of Northwest Arkansas, Fayetteville, AR, p. A43

VICKERY, Angie, Director of Nursing, Wills Memorial Hospital, Washington, GA, p. A167

VICKERY, Ian, Director Information Technology, D. W. Mcmillan Memorial Hospital, Brewton, AL, p. A15

VICKERY, Tim, Chief Information Officer, St. Mary's Sacred Heart Hospital, Lavonia, GA, p. A160

VICKROY, Joseph M.D., Medical Director, Healthsouth Rehabilitation Hospital Of Utah, Sandy, UT, p. A661

VICKS, Ray, Senior Vice President, Finance and Chief Financial Officer, The Hsc Pediatric Center, Washington, DC, p. A118

VICTORIA, Mario M.D., Vice President, Medical Affairs, Samaritan Medical Center, Watertown, NY, p. A455

VIDONI–CLARK, Clotilde Ph.D., R.N., Chief Nursing Executive, Saint Elizabeths Hospital, Washington, DC, p. A118

VIEIRA, Jeanette, Chief Executive, Providence Hood River Memorial Hospital, Hood River, OR, p. A522

VIEIRA, Terri
Interim President, Charles A. Dean Memorial Hospital, Greenville, ME, p. A291
President and Chief Executive Officer, Sebasticook Valley Health, Pittsfield, ME, p. A292

VIELKIND, James, Chief Financial Officer, Little Falls Hospital, Little Falls, NY, p. A438

VIENNEAU, Marie E., FACHE, President and Chief Executive Officer, Mayo Regional Hospital, Dover——Foxcroft, ME, p. A291

VIERLING, Taryn, Chief Nursing Officer, Select Specialty Hospital Of Southeast Ohio, Newark, OH, p. A497

VIG, Vibha, Chief of Staff, Merit Health Madison, Canton, MS, p. A353

VIGIL, Carlos M.D., President Medical Staff, San Antonio Regional Hospital, Upland, CA, p. A95

VIGIL, Kevin, Director Information Systems, Los Alamos Medical Center, Los Alamos, NM, p. A427

VIGILANTE, Sarah, Manager Human Resources, Mammoth Hospital, Mammoth Lakes, CA, p. A72

VIGNA, Greg A. M.D., Medical Director, Healthsouth Rehabilitation Hospital Of Modesto, Modesto, CA, p. A74

VIGNERI, Joseph M.D., Chief Medical Officer, Summit Medical Center, Casper, WY, p. A717

VILANOVA, Lynda, Director Patient Care Services, Shriners Hospitals For Children–Spokane, Spokane, WA, p. A687

VILAR, Ramon J., Administrator, Wilma N. Vazquez Medical Center, Vega Baja, PR, p. A727

VILHAUER, Beverly, Chief Executive Officer, Wishek Community Hospital And Clinics, Wishek, ND, p. A478

VILLA, Alex, Chief Executive Officer, Tennova Healthcare– Clarksville, Clarksville, TN, p. A577

VILLAFUERTE, Herbert, Chief Operating Officer and Chief Nursing Officer, Garfield Medical Center, Monterey Park, CA, p. A75

VILLANI, Travis A., FACHE, Chief Executive Officer and Administrator, Physicians' Hospital In Anadarko, Anadarko, OK, p. A504

VILLANO, Jeremi M.D., Chief of Staff, Crook County Medical Services District, Sundance, WY, p. A720

VILLANUEVA, Andrew M.D., Interim Chief Medical Officer, Lahey Hospital & Medical Center, Burlington, Burlington, MA, p. A305

VILLARREAL, Xavier, FACHE, Chief Executive Officer, Medical City North Hills, North Richland Hills, TX, p. A635

VILLARRUZ, Alex, Chief Executive Officer, Healthbridge Children's Hospital, Orange, CA, p. A78

VILLEGAS, Lorraine, Manager Human Resources, Paradise Valley Hospital, National City, CA, p. A76

VILLEGAS, William, Vice President Finance, Fort Hamilton Hospital, Hamilton, OH, p. A492

VILUMS, Karlis, Chief Financial Officer, Broadlawns Medical Center, Des Moines, IA, p. A226

VINAS, Elmo, Director Human Resources, Franklin Foundation Hospital, Franklin, LA, p. A275

VINCENT, Ben, FACHE, Chief Executive Officer, Braxton County Memorial Hospital, Gassaway, WV, p. A692

VINCENT, Cynthia, Vice President Finance and Operations, St. Francis Regional Medical Center, Shakopee, MN, p. A348

VINCENT, David, Director Information Systems, Canonsburg Hospital, Canonsburg, PA, p. A531

VINCENT, Joan M MSN, MS, R.N., Vice President Patient Care Services and Chief Nurse Executive, Adventist Healthcare Shady Grove Medical Center, Rockville, MD, p. A300

VINCENT, Julie S. R.N., MSN, Chief Nursing Officer, Sycamore Medical Center, Miamisburg, OH, p. A496

VINCENT, Larry, Director Human Resources, Delta County Memorial Hospital, Delta, CO, p. A100

VINCENT, Laurence Marie, Chief Nursing Officer, University Hospital And Clinics, Lafayette, LA, p. A279

VINCENT, Mitchell S, Vice President Organizational Support, Range Regional Health Services, Hibbing, MN, p. A341

VINCENT, Paula, MSN, President and Chief Operating Officer, Novant Health Presbyterian Medical Center, Charlotte, NC, p. A460

VINCENT, Shawn, Interim Chief Operating Officer, Augusta University Medical Center, Augusta, GA, p. A151

VINCENZ, Felix T, Chief Operating Officer, St. Louis Psychiatric Rehabilitation Center, Saint Louis, MO, p. A378

VINCIFORA, Teresa, Chief Operating Officer, Benson Hospital, Benson, AZ, p. A28

VINCIGUERRA, Tracy, Chief Executive Officer, Healthsouth Mountainview Regional Rehabilitation Hospital, Morgantown, WV, p. A694

VINYARD, Roy G., FACHE, President and Chief Executive Officer, Asante Health System, Medford, OR, p. B11

VINSANT, George O'Neal M.D., Chief Medical Officer, Tennova Healthcare–Lafollette Medical Center, La Follette, TN, p. A582

VIOLETTE, Brenda M.D., Director Medical Staff, Firelands Regional Health System, Sandusky, OH, p. A499

VIOLI, Ronald L., Chief Executive Officer, Wheeling Hospital, Wheeling, WV, p. A697

VIRGEN, Tomas R.N., MSN, Chief Operating Officer, El Centro Regional Medical Center, El Centro, CA, p. A58

VIRGIL, Cindy L MSN, R.N., Senior Vice President Patient Care Services, Indiana Regional Medical Center, Indiana, PA, p. A537

VIRJI, Ayaz M.D., Chief of Staff, Johnson Memorial Health Services, Dawson, MN, p. A338

VIRKLER, Joe, Chief Information Officer, Carthage Area Hospital, Carthage, NY, p. A434

VISAGGIO, Stella, Chief Operating Officer, Hackettstown Medical Center, Hackettstown, NJ, p. A414

VISH, Nancy, Ph.D., FACHE, R.N., President, Baylor Jack And Jane Hamilton Heart And Vascular Hospital, Dallas, TX, p. A604

VISSER, Jessica R.N., Vice President Patient Care Services and Chief Nursing Officer, Mount St. Mary's Hospital And Health Center, Lewiston, NY, p. A438

VISSERS, Robert, M.D., President and Chief Executive Officer, Boulder Community Health, Boulder, CO, p. A98

VITAL, Dale, Chief Nursing Officer, Orange Coast Memorial Medical Center, Fountain Valley, CA, p. A60

VITALE–NOLEN, Roberta A, Administrator, Patient Care Services, New Hampshire Hospital, Concord, NH, p. A407

VITALI, Joe, Director Information Technology, Parkside Psychiatric Hospital And Clinic, Tulsa, OK, p. A517

VITALI, Vincent S
Chief Information Officer, Rml Specialty Hospital, Chicago, IL, p. A183
Chief Information Officer, Rml Specialty Hospital, Hinsdale, IL, p. A190

VITALIS, Lee Ann, Executive Director Human Resources, St. Croix Regional Medical Center, St Croix Falls, WI, p. A713

VITIELLO, Jon, Senior Vice President, Finance Operations and Analytics, Mercy Hospital Oklahoma City, Oklahoma City, OK, p. A512

VITOLAS, Victor, Acting Chief Information Technology Services, Central Texas Veterans Health Care System, Temple, TX, p. A648

VIVIANO, Paul S., President and Chief Executive Officer, Children's Hospital Los Angeles, Los Angeles, CA, p. A68

VIVIT, Romeo, Chief Surgeon, U. S. Public Health Service Indian Hospital, Rosebud, SD, p. A572

VIZCARRA, Edred T. M.D., Chief of Staff, St. Luke Community Healthcare, Ronan, MT, p. A387

VLAHAVAS, Beth R.N., MSN, Vice President Patient Care Services and Chief Nursing Officer, Mercy Medical Center, Rockville Centre, NY, p. A451

VLARS, Scott, Chief Information Technology Services, Wilmington Veterans Affairs Medical Center, Wilmington, DE, p. A116

VLODARCHYK, Coreen R.N., Vice President, Patient Care Services and Chief Nursing Officer, Barnes–Jewish Hospital, Saint Louis, MO, p. A376

VLOSICH, Wade, Director, Oklahoma City Veterans Affairs Medical Center, Oklahoma City, OK, p. A513

VOCCA, Lori A, Vice President Human Resources, Providence Regional Medical Center Everett, Everett, WA, p. A680

VOECKS, Barbara, Chief Information Officer, Ortonville Area Health Services, Ortonville, MN, p. A345

VOELKEL, Jill, Chief Nursing Officer, Pinnacle Specialty Hospital, Tulsa, OK, p. A518

VOELKEL, Jonathon, Administrator, Culberson Hospital, Van Horn, TX, p. A651

VOELKER, Justin, Chief Financial Officer, Multicare Valley Hospital, Spokane Valley, WA, p. A687

VOELKER, Thomas M.D., Chief Medical Officer, Aspirus Riverview Hospital And Clinics, Inc., Wisconsin Rapids, WI, p. A716

VOGE, Chris, Chief of Staff, French Hospital Medical Center, San Luis Obispo, CA, p. A89

VOGEL, Clay, Administrator and Chief Executive Officer, Coleman County Medical Center, Coleman, TX, p. A602

VOGELSANG, Mark, Director Information Services, Providence Holy Family Hospital, Spokane, WA, p. A687

VOGENTIZ, William M.D., Medical Director, Anmed Health Rehabilitation Hospital, Anderson, SC, p. A558

VOGT, Dennis, Director Information Technology, Madison Health, London, OH, p. A494

VOGT, Sam, Manager Human Resources, Hebrew Center For Health Rehabilitation, West Hartford, CT, p. A114

VOHS, Lester, Manager Information Systems, Cass Regional Medical Center, Harrisonville, MO, p. A368

VOIGT, Jordan, Administrator, Genesis Medical Center–Davenport–West Central Park, Davenport, IA, p. A225

VOINCHE, Chris G., Chief Executive Officer, Riverside Hospital Of Louisiana, Alexandria, LA, p. A269

VOISARD, Victor, Director Human Resources, San Gabriel Valley Medical Center, San Gabriel, CA, p. A88

VOISELLE, Dana, Director Human Resources and Community Relations, Baptist Medical Center Beaches, Jacksonville Beach, FL, p. A129

VOKOUN, Cory, Chief Nursing Officer, Nevada Regional Medical Center, Nevada, MO, p. A374

VOLANTO, John, Vice President, Chief Operating Officer, Nyack Hospital, Nyack, NY, p. A448

VOLINSKI, Douglas R, Vice President and Chief Financial Officer, Duncan Regional Hospital, Duncan, OK, p. A506

VOLK, Charles T. M.D., Regional Chief Medical Officer, Christus Spohn Hospital Corpus Christi Memorial, Corpus Christi, TX, p. A603

VOLKERDING, Elizabeth, Director Workforce Excellence, San Juan Regional Medical Center, Farmington, NM, p. A426

VOLKERT, Brent, Director Information Technology, Ferrell Hospital, Eldorado, IL, p. A186

VOLLER, Kristi, Director of Nursing, Mobridge Regional Hospital, Mobridge, SD, p. A571

VOLLMER, Cyndy, Director Human Resources, Southern Coos Hospital And Health Center, Bandon, OR, p. A520

VOLOCH, Bill, President and Chief Executive Officer, Wesley Medical Center, Wichita, KS, p. A254

VOLOVIC, Mark, Vice President and Chief Information Officer, Indiana Regional Medical Center, Indiana, PA, p. A537

VOLPE, Buddy, Director Human Resources, Peterson Regional Medical Center, Kerrville, TX, p. A626

VOLPE, Michele M., Chief Executive Officer, Penn Presbyterian Medical Center, Philadelphia, PA, p. A545

VON ARX, Michelle, Chief Executive Officer, Penn State Hershey Rehabilitation Hospital, Hummelstown, PA, p. A536

VON BEHREN, Rachel, Director Financial Services, Unitypoint Health – Jones Regional Medical Center, Anamosa, IA, p. A222

VONACHEN, April, Chief Financial Officer and Vice President Financial Services, Cumberland Medical Center, Crossville, TN, p. A578

VONK, Brandon, Nurse Administrator, LDS Hospital, Salt Lake City, UT, p. A660

VOORHEES, Michael, MS, Executive Director, East Mountain Hospital, Belle Mead, NJ, p. A411

VOOYS, Nathan, Chief Executive Officer, Terre Haute Regional Hospital, Terre Haute, IN, p. A220

VOS, Helen R.N., Interim Chief Nursing Officer, Peacehealth Southwest Medical Center, Vancouver, WA, p. A688

VOSHELL, Shane, Director Human Resources, Adventist Medical Center–Portland, Portland, OR, p. A525

VOSS, Daryle, FACHE, President and Chief Executive Officer, Mercy Hospital Ardmore, Ardmore, OK, p. A504

VOSS, Robert, Chief Financial Officer, Laredo Specialty Hospital, Laredo, TX, p. A628

VOSS, Wayne M., Chief Executive Officer, Houston Methodist West Hospital, Houston, TX, p. A621

VOSSBERG, Brad M.D., Chief Rehabilitation, Community Howard Specialty Hospital, Kokomo, IN, p. A213

VOSSLER, Jeffrey W, Chief Financial Officer, Joint Township District Memorial Hospital, Saint Marys, OH, p. A498

VOWELL, Christy D.O., Chief of Staff, North Mississippi Medical Center–Eupora, Eupora, MS, p. A354

VOZOS, Frank J., M.D., FACS, President and Chief Executive Officer, Barnabas Health Behavioral Health Center, Monmouth Medical Center, Southern Campus, Lakewood, NJ, p. A415

VRANA, Daniel A

Area Controller, Healthsouth Rehabilitation Hospital Of Sewickley, Sewickley, PA, p. A550

Controller, Healthsouth Harmarville Rehabilitation Hospital, Pittsburgh, PA, p. A546

VRBA, Frank, Chief Information Officer, Annie Jeffrey Memorial County Health Center, Osceola, NE, p. A398

VRBAS, Laken R.N., Director of Nursing, Dundy County Hospital, Benkelman, NE, p. A391

VREELAND, Matthew M.D., Chief Medical Officer, Firsthealth Richmond Memorial Hospital, Rockingham, NC, p. A469

VRONKO, Jeremy, Manager, Information Services, Spectrum Health Ludington Hospital, Ludington, MI, p. A325

VROTSOS, Darlene R.N., Senior Vice President and Chief Nursing Officer, Virginia Hospital Center – Arlington, Arlington, VA, p. A664

VU, Young, Chief Information Officer, Meadville Medical Center, Meadville, PA, p. A540

VUCHAK, Jerry

Vice President Information Systems, Barnes–Jewish Hospital, Saint Louis, MO, p. A376

Vice President Information Systems, Barnes–Jewish West County Hospital, Saint Louis, MO, p. A376

VUKICH, David M.D., Senior Vice President, Chief Medical Officer and Chief Quality Officer, Uf Health Jacksonville, Jacksonville, FL, p. A128

VUKSTA, Jeanne, Chief Financial Officer, Bacharach Institute For Rehabilitation, Pomona, NJ, p. A419

VUTRANO, Frank A, Chief Financial Officer, Wyckoff Heights Medical Center, New Rochelle, NY, p. A447

W

WABAUNSEE, Gary, Service Unit Director, U. S. Public Health Service Indian Hospital, Winnebago, NE, p. A400

WABLE, Chad W., President and Chief Executive Officer, Saint Mary's Hospital, Waterbury, CT, p. A114

WACHOWIAK, Darrell, Associate Vice President Operations, Promedica Bay Park Hospital, Oregon, OH, p. A497

WACHTEL, Robert Andrew., FACHE

Chief Executive Officer, Saint Thomas Dekalb Hospital, Smithville, TN, p. A589

Chief Executive Officer, Saint Thomas Highlands Hospital, Sparta, TN, p. A589

Chief Executive Officer, Saint Thomas Stones River Hospital, Woodbury, TN, p. A590

WACK, Mark, Senior Vice President and Chief Financial Officer, Touro Infirmary, New Orleans, LA, p. A283

WADDELL, Kathy, Administrator, Wayne General Hospital, Waynesboro, MS, p. A362

WADDELL, Lesa, Director Human Resources, Compass Memorial Healthcare, Marengo, IA, p. A231

WADE, Bruce, Vice President Human Resources, Indiana University Health Bedford Hospital, Bedford, IN, p. A204

WADE, Cynthia R.N., RN, BSN,, Executive Vice President and Chief Operating Officer, Lincolnhealth, Damariscotta, ME, p. A290

WADE, Donald Lee, Chief Financial Officer, Goodland Regional Medical Center, Goodland, KS, p. A241

WADE, Donna, Senior Director Human Resources, Comanche County Memorial Hospital, Lawton, OK, p. A509

WADE, Glenn, Director Information Systems, Saint Thomas Highlands Hospital, Sparta, TN, p. A589

WADE, Hong, Chief Financial Officer, Sweeny Community Hospital, Sweeny, TX, p. A647

WADE, Jonathan O., Chief Executive Officer, Jersey Community Hospital, Jerseyville, IL, p. A191

WADE, Karen, Chief Information Officer, U.S. Public Health Service Indian Hospital–Sells, Sells, AZ, p. A36

WADE, Susan, Vice President, Hendrick Health System, Abilene, TX, p. A591

WADEWITZ, Martin, Chief Operations Officer/ Vice President, Operations, Angel Medical Center, Franklin, NC, p. A462

WADLE, Don

Interim Director Human Resources, Portneuf Medical Center, Pocatello, ID, p. A175

Vice President Clinical and Support Services, Portneuf Medical Center, Pocatello, ID, p. A175

WADMAN, Timothy, Chief Executive Officer, SSM Select Rehabilitation Hospital, Richmond Heights, MO, p. A375

WADSWORTH, Barbara A MSN, R.N., FACHE, Chief Nursing Officer, Bryn Mawr Hospital, Bryn Mawr, PA, p. A530

WAFFORD, Marty, Under Secretary of Support and Programs, Chickasaw Nation Medical Center, Ada, OK, p. A504

WAGERS, Rick, Senior Executive Vice President and Chief Financial Officer, Regional One Health, Memphis, TN, p. A585

WAGGENER, Yvonne, Chief Financial Officer, San Bernardino Mountains Community Hospital District, Lake Arrowhead, CA, p. A65

WAGGONER, Jeff M.D., Chief of Staff, Weisbrod Memorial County Hospital, Eads, CO, p. A102

WAGGONER, Michelle, Chief Executive Officer, Community Memorial Hospital, Hicksville, OH, p. A492

WAGLE, Roberta, Director Human Resources, Pinnacle Specialty Hospital, Tulsa, OK, p. A518

WAGLEY, Ronnie, Market Chief Executive Officer, Select Specialty Hospital–Gainesville, Gainesville, FL, p. A126

WAGMEISTER, Lee M.D., President Medical Staff, The Heart Hospital At Deaconess Gateway, Newburgh, IN, p. A217

WAGNER, Dale, Chief Financial Officer, Kindred Hospital–Westminster, Westminster, CA, p. A96

WAGNER, David D, Chief Information Management Service, Veterans Affairs Gulf Coast Veterans Health Care System, Biloxi, MS, p. A352

WAGNER, David S., FACHE, Chief Executive Officer, Pearland Medical Center, Pearland, TX, p. A637

WAGNER, Elaina, Director Human Resources, Sunnyside Community Hospital And Clinics, Sunnyside, WA, p. A687

WAGNER, Fred, Chief Financial Officer, OSF St. Francis Hospital And Medical Group, Escanaba, MI, p. A319

WAGNER, Gwendolyn Dianne R.N., MSN, Chief Nursing Officer, Mission Community Hospital, Los Angeles, CA, p. A70

WAGNER, Janet, R.N., Chief Executive Officer, Mills–Peninsula Health Services, Burlingame, CA, p. A54

WAGNER, Jefferey, Director, Information Technology, Lake Huron Medical Center, Port Huron, MI, p. A328

WAGNER, Linda S., R.N., MSN, FACHE, Chief Executive Officer, Seneca Healthcare District, Chester, CA, p. A55

WAGNER, Linda, Chief Financial Officer, Sanford Worthington Medical Center, Worthington, MN, p. A351

WAGNER, Lynne R.N., Chief Nursing Officer, Rose Medical Center, Denver, CO, p. A101

WAGNER, Michael, M.D., President and Chief Executive Officer, Tufts Medical Center, Boston, MA, p. A304

WAGNER, Randall J, Chief Operating Officer, Mercy Health Saint Mary's, Grand Rapids, MI, p. A321

WAGNER, Russell R, Executive Vice President and Chief Financial Officer, Holy Redeemer Hospital, Meadowbrook, PA, p. A540

WAGNER, Sarah, Human Resources Officer, Memorial Hospital Of Texas County, Guymon, OK, p. A508

WAGNER, Sherrie A, Manager Human Resources, The Core Institute Specialty Hospital, Phoenix, AZ, p. A34

WAGNER, Suzie, Director Human Resources, Healthsouth Rehabilitation Hospital Of Alexandria, Alexandria, LA, p. A269

WAGNER, Terry, R.N.

Chief Operating Officer, Pocahontas Memorial Hospital, Buckeye, WV, p. A690

Chief Information Officer, Upstate University Hospital, Syracuse, NY, p. A453

WAGNER, Timothy M.D., Chief Medical Staff, Yoakum Community Hospital, Yoakum, TX, p. A655

WAGNER, Tom, Interim Vice President Finance, Avera St. Mary's Hospital, Pierre, SD, p. A571

WALL, Kathryn S
Executive Vice President Human Resources and Organizational Development, Stafford Hospital, Stafford, VA, p. A675
Executive Vice President, Human Resources and Organizational Development, Mary Washington Hospital, Fredericksburg, VA, p. A667

WALL, Lorraine, Chief Nursing Officer, Olympic Medical Center, Port Angeles, WA, p. A683

WALL, Michael L., FACHE, President and Chief Executive Officer, Antelope Valley Hospital, Lancaster, CA, p. A65

WALLACE, Brad, Director Information Services, Grays Harbor Community Hospital, Aberdeen, WA, p. A678

WALLACE, Carolyn, Director Human Resources, Connecticut Mental Health Center, New Haven, CT, p. A112

WALLACE, Cynthia M.D., Medical Director, Vibra Specialty Hospital Of Portland, Portland, OR, p. A525

WALLACE, David, Chief Executive Officer, Mat–Su Regional Medical Center, Palmer, AK, p. A27

WALLACE, Dianne, County Information Manager, Douglas County Community Mental Health Center, Omaha, NE, p. A397

WALLACE, Donna Geiken, Chief Operating Officer and Chief Financial Officer, Christus Mother Frances Hospital – Sulphur Springs, Sulphur Springs, TX, p. A647

WALLACE, Glenn, Chief Executive Officer, Medical City Alliance, Fort Worth, TX, p. A614

WALLACE, Jennifer, Chief Executive Officer, AMG Specialty Hospital–Greenwood, Greenwood, MS, p. A355

WALLACE, Kathleen, R.N., MSN, Administrator and Chief Executive Officer, Lifecare Hospitals Of Dallas, Dallas, TX, p. A605

WALLACE, Kelly, Senior Vice President and Chief Financial Officer, Seattle Children's Hospital, Seattle, WA, p. A685

WALLACE, Kent, Chief Operating Officer, Kindred Hospital– New Jersey Morris County, Dover, NJ, p. A413

WALLACE, Kristina R.N., Chief Operating Officer, Ou Medical Center, Oklahoma City, OK, p. A513

WALLACE, Mark A., FACHE, President and Chief Executive Officer, Texas Children's Hospital, Houston, TX, p. A623

WALLACE, Mark T, Director Human Resources, Lodi Memorial Hospital, Lodi, CA, p. A66

WALLACE, Mark, Chief Financial Officer, Cumberland Hall Hospital, Hopkinsville, KY, p. A259

WALLACE, Martha, Administrator, California Mens Colony Correctional Treatment Center, San Luis Obispo, CA, p. A89

WALLACE, Melanie, Manager Human Resources, Sutter Tracy Community Hospital, Tracy, CA, p. A94

WALLACE, Michael S., President and Chief Executive Officer, Fort Healthcare, Fort Atkinson, WI, p. A701

WALLACE, Nancy
Division Senior Vice President, Chief Human Resource Officer, Chi Health Lakeside, Omaha, NE, p. A397
Division Senior Vice President, Chief Human Resource Officer, Chi Health Midlands, Papillion, NE, p. A399
Senior Vice President Human Resources, Chi Health Mercy Council Bluffs, Council Bluffs, IA, p. A225
Senior Vice President, Chief Human Resources Officer, Chi Health St Elizabeth, Lincoln, NE, p. A395
Vice President Human Resources, CHI Health, Chi Health Saint Francis, Grand Island, NE, p. A393
Vice President Human Resources, Chi Health Creighton University Medical Center – Bergan Mercy, Omaha, NE, p. A397
Vice President Human Resources, Chi Health Immanuel, Omaha, NE, p. A397
Vice President Human Resources, Chi Health Schuyler, Schuyler, NE, p. A399

WALLACE, Penny, Chief Financial Officer, Guadalupe Regional Medical Center, Seguin, TX, p. A644

WALLACE, Tabatha, Director Human Resources, Bayfront Health Dade City, Dade City, FL, p. A123

WALLACE–MOORE, Patrice, Chief Executive Officer and Executive Director, Arms Acres, Carmel, NY, p. A433

WALLEN, Carla, Manager Human Resources, Cass Regional Medical Center, Harrisonville, MO, p. A368

WALLENTINE, Jeffrey, Chief of Staff, Mountain View Hospital, Payson, UT, p. A659

WALLER, Ernie, Director Information Technology, Ed Fraser Memorial Hospital And Baker Community Health Center, Macclenny, FL, p. A131

WALLER, Kenneth, Fiscal Administrator, Deer's Head Hospital Center, Salisbury, MD, p. A300

WALLER, Matthew, Chief Executive Officer, Liberty Medical Center, Chester, MT, p. A383

WALLER, Raymond A., Director, Brighton Center For Recovery, Brighton, MI, p. A315

WALLINE, Linda K R.N., Ph.D., MSN, Vice President Nursing, Columbus Community Hospital, Columbus, NE, p. A392

WALLING, Vernon, M.D.
Chief Medical Officer, Sun Behavioral Houston, Houston, TX, p. A622
Executive Medical Director, West Oaks Hospital, Houston, TX, p. A624

WALLINGA, Joel, Chief Financial Officer, Veterans Affairs Ann Arbor Healthcare System, Ann Arbor, MI, p. A314

WALLINGA, Melvin M.D., Medical Director, St. Michael's Hospital Avera, Tyndall, SD, p. A573

WALLIS, Carla, Director Human Resources, North Ottawa Community Hospital, Grand Haven, MI, p. A320

WALLIS, Pam B MSN, Vice President Nursing Services, Magnolia Regional Health Center, Corinth, MS, p. A354

WALLMAN, Gerald H., Administrator, West Covina Medical Center, West Covina, CA, p. A96

WALLS, Craig M.D., Ph.D., Chief Medical Officer, Natividad Medical Center, Salinas, CA, p. A84

WALLS, Martha Delaney R.N., MSN, Chief Nursing Officer, Crestwood Medical Center, Huntsville, AL, p. A19

WALLS, Randy, Manager Information Services, Fairbanks, Indianapolis, IN, p. A211

WALLS, Ron M.D., Executive Vice President and Chief Operating Officer, Brigham And Women's Hospital, Boston, MA, p. A303

WALLSCHLAEGER, Erich, Chief Financial Officer, Cedar Park Regional Medical Center, Cedar Park, TX, p. A601

WALMSLEY, George J. III, CPA, President and Chief Executive Officer, North Philadelphia Health System, Philadelphia, PA, p. A545

WALMSLEY, George J III, CPA, President and Chief Executive Officer, North Philadelphia Health System, Philadelphia, PA, p. A545

WALRATH, Andrea, Chief Operating Officer, Forest Health Medical Center, Ypsilanti, MI, p. A333

WALRAVEN, Jeff, Chief Executive Officer, Lindsay Municipal Hospital, Lindsay, OK, p. A509

WALSER, Bill, Coordinator Technology, Cameron Regional Medical Center, Cameron, MO, p. A365

WALSH, Andrea, President and Chief Executive Officer, Healthpartners, Bloomington, MN, p. B61

WALSH, Brad M.D., Chief of Staff, Ashley County Medical Center, Crossett, AR, p. A42

WALSH, Catherine
Interim Chief Nursing Officer, Mercy Allen Hospital, Oberlin, OH, p. A497
Interim Nursing Executive, Mercy Regional Medical Center, Lorain, OH, p. A494

WALSH, Daniel P.
Chief Information Officer, Aria – Jefferson Health, Philadelphia, PA, p. A543
Vice President, Information Systems and Technology Northern Division, Abington Hospital, Abington, PA, p. A528

WALSH, Gerard W., Chief Executive Officer, St. John's Episcopal Hospital–South Shore, New Rochelle, NY, p. A446

WALSH, John
Chief Executive Officer, Affinity Medical Center, Massillon, OH, p. A495
Chief Fiscal Services, Veterans Affairs Hudson Valley Health Care System, Montrose, NY, p. A440

WALSH, Kate, M.P.H., President and Chief Executive Officer, Boston Medical Center, Boston, MA, p. A303

WALSH, Katherine MS, R.N., Dr.PH, Vice President and Chief Nursing Officer, Houston Methodist Hospital, Houston, TX, p. A620

WALSH, Ken, Chief Financial Officer, St. Luke's Medical Center, Phoenix, AZ, p. A34

WALSH, Kim, Chief Nursing Officer, Signature Healthcare Brockton Hospital, Brockton, MA, p. A304

WALSH, Len, Executive Vice President and Chief Operating Officer, St. Barnabas Hospital, New Rochelle, NY, p. A446

WALSH, Linda R.N., MSN, Vice President Chief Nursing Executive, Hackensack Meridian Health Bayshore Community Hospital, Holmdel, NJ, p. A415

WALSH, Marcia S M.P.H., Chief Operating Officer, Community Healthcare System, Onaga, KS, p. A248

WALSH, Marilyn J, Vice President Human Resources, Kent County Memorial Hospital, Warwick, RI, p. A557

WALSH, Mary, R.N., MSN
Vice President Patient Care Services and Chief Nursing Officer, Mount Sinai Beth Israel, New Rochelle, NY, p. A443
Vice President Patient Care Services and Chief Nursing Officer, Mount Sinai West, New Rochelle, NY, p. A443

WALSH, Michael
Senior Vice President Finance and Chief Financial Officer, Abington Hospital, Abington, PA, p. A528

Senior Vice President Finance and Chief Financial Officer, Abington–Lansdale Hospital Jefferson Health, Lansdale, PA, p. A538

WALSH, Michele M, Chief Nursing Officer, St. Mary's Healthcare, Amsterdam, NY, p. A430

WALSH, Timothy, Interim President and Chief Executive Officer, Martha's Vineyard Hospital, Oak Bluffs, MA, p. A310

WALSH, William P., Senior Vice President Hospital Affairs and Managing Director, Suny Downstate Medical Center University Hospital, New Rochelle, NY, p. A447

WALSTON, John, Chief Information Officer, Southern Arizona Veterans Affairs Health Care System, Tucson, AZ, p. A38

WALTER, Gayle, Director of Nursing, Thomas B. Finan Center, Cumberland, MD, p. A298

WALTER, Melissa, Director Human Resources, Clarinda Regional Health Center, Clarinda, IA, p. A224

WALTER, Stephen, Senior Vice President and Chief Financial Officer, Community Regional Medical Center, Fresno, CA, p. A60

WALTERS, Cindy, Chief Executive Officer, Acadia–St. Landry Hospital, Church Point, LA, p. A273

WALTERS, Jane, Director of Nursing, Mendota Mental Health Institute, Madison, WI, p. A705

WALTERS, Julie, Chief Nursing Officer, Hillsdale Hospital, Hillsdale, MI, p. A322

WALTERS, Kevin, Chief Financial Officer, St. Rose Dominican Hospitals – Rose De Lima Campus, Henderson, NV, p. A402

WALTERS, Leah R.N., Director of Nursing, Mountain Valley Regional Rehabilitation Hospital, Prescott Valley, AZ, p. A35

WALTERS, Leslie MSN, Chief Nursing Officer, Clarion Hospital, Clarion, PA, p. A531

WALTERS, Todd, Director of UHC Information Technology Services, University Health Conway, Monroe, LA, p. A281

WALTHALL, Wayne, Vice President and Chief Financial Officer, St. John Medical Center, Tulsa, OK, p. A518

WALTHER, Diane, Controller, Henry County Hospital, Napoleon, OH, p. A496

WALTON, Amy E. M.D., Chief Medical Officer, Seton Shoal Creek Hospital, Austin, TX, p. A595

WALTON, Carlyle L E., FACHE, Chief Executive Officer, Metroplex Adventist Hospital, Killeen, TX, p. A627

WALTON, Dawn, Chief Financial Officer, Children's Of Alabama, Birmingham, AL, p. A14

WALTON, Gary M.D., Chief Medical Officer, Hill Hospital Of Sumter County, York, AL, p. A24

WALTON, Georgian, Director Human Resources, Elbert Memorial Hospital, Elberton, GA, p. A157

WALTON, Greg, Chief Information Officer, El Camino Hospital, Mountain View, CA, p. A75

WALTON, Linda R.N., MSN, Chief Nursing Officer, Indian River Medical Center, Vero Beach, FL, p. A146

WALTON, Robert M., Healthcare System Director, South Texas Veterans Health Care System, San Antonio, TX, p. A644

WALTZ, Dan, Vice President and Chief Information Officer, Midmichigan Medical Center–Gladwin, Gladwin, MI, p. A320

WALZ, Rachel A, Director Patient Care, Centracare Health– Paynesville, Paynesville, MN, p. A345

WAMPLER, Andrew, Chief Financial Officer, Margaret R. Pardee Memorial Hospital, Hendersonville, NC, p. A464

WAMPLER, Beth A R.N., Chief Nursing Officer, Fayette Regional Health System, Connersville, IN, p. A206

WAMSLEY, Marie, Chief Financial Officer, Memorial Hospital Of Lafayette County, Darlington, WI, p. A700

WANG, William Norberto M.D., Chief Operating Officer, NYC Health + Hospitals / Metropolitan, New Rochelle, NY, p. A445

WANG, MD, Shu–Ming, Vice President Medical Affairs, Chi Health Saint Francis, Grand Island, NE, p. A393

WANGSMO, Gary L, Chief Financial Officer, Mee Memorial Hospital, King City, CA, p. A64

WANGSNESS, Erik, President, Adventist Healthcare Washington Adventist Hospital, Takoma Park, MD, p. A301

WANLY, Bahaa, Interim Chief Operating Officer, Salem Hospital, Salem, OR, p. A526

WANNER, David
Chief Information Officer, Trinity Health, Minot, ND, p. A477
Director Information Technology, Kenmare Community Hospital, Kenmare, ND, p. A477

WAPPELHORST, Andrea, Chief Nursing Officer, Tops Surgical Specialty Hospital, Houston, TX, p. A623

WAR, Melissa, Chief Executive Officer, Mountain's Edge Hospital, Las Vegas, NV, p. A403

WARD, Brook, Executive Vice President, Washington Hospital, Washington, PA, p. A552

WARD, Cary, M.D., Chief Medical Officer and Interim President, Chi Health St Elizabeth, Lincoln, NE, p. A395

WARD, Celia F, Controller and Chief Financial Officer, Doctors Memorial Hospital, Bonifay, FL, p. A120

WARD, Charlotte, Entity Financial Officer, Texas Health Harris Methodist Hospital Southwest Fort Worth, Fort Worth, TX, p. A614

WARD, Chris
  Chief Nursing Officer, Comanche County Memorial Hospital, Lawton, OK, p. A509
  Director Management Information Systems, Dorminy Medical Center, Fitzgerald, GA, p. A158

WARD, David M, Chief Financial Officer and Chief Acquisition Officer, Cabell Huntington Hospital, Huntington, WV, p. A692

WARD, Dillon, Management Information Systems Specialist, Tennova Healthcare–Lafollette Medical Center, La Follette, TN, p. A582

WARD, Elizabeth S.
  Chief Financial Officer, Tidelands Georgetown Memorial Hospital, Georgetown, SC, p. A562
  Chief Financial Officer, Tidelands Waccamaw Community Hospital, Murrells Inlet, SC, p. A565

WARD, Greg, Vice President Support and Ancillary Services, Copley Hospital, Morrisville, VT, p. A662

WARD, Jeffery, Director Human Resources, Cedar Park Regional Medical Center, Cedar Park, TX, p. A601

WARD, Julie R. MSN, R.N., Vice President Patient Care Services, Hutchinson Regional Medical Center, Hutchinson, KS, p. A243

WARD, Julie, MSN, R.N.
  Chief Nursing Officer, St. Joseph's Hospital And Medical Center, Phoenix, AZ, p. A34
  Chief Executive Officer, Northeastern Health System Sequoyah, Sallisaw, OK, p. A515
  Vice President Finance, Northeastern Health System, Tahlequah, OK, p. A516

WARD, Kevin J, Vice President and Chief Financial Officer, New York–Presbyterian Queens, New Rochelle, NY, p. A444

WARD, Kevin, Chief Operating Officer, Jewish Home Of San Francisco, San Francisco, CA, p. A87

WARD, Kimberly J, Chief Nurse Officer, St. Luke's Rehabilitation Institute, Spokane, WA, p. A687

WARD, Lesli, Vice President Human Resources, Uf Health Jacksonville, Jacksonville, FL, p. A128

WARD, Lisa, Director Management Information Systems, Columbus Regional Healthcare System, Whiteville, NC, p. A472

WARD, Lorna J MSN, R.N., Chief Nursing Officer, Novant Health Brunswick Medical Center, Bolivia, NC, p. A458

WARD, Louis James., Interim Chief Executive Officer, Mayers Memorial Hospital District, Fall River Mills, CA, p. A59

WARD, Louis James, Chief Operating Officer, Mayers Memorial Hospital District, Fall River Mills, CA, p. A59

WARD, Mark M.D., Chief of Staff, Roundup Memorial Healthcare, Roundup, MT, p. A388

WARD, Michael
  Chief Executive Officer, Healthsouth Rehabilitation Hospital–Las Vegas, Las Vegas, NV, p. A403
  Director Information Services, Anderson Hospital, Maryville, IL, p. A192

WARD, Mike
  Chief Information Officer, Morristown–Hamblen Healthcare System, Morristown, TN, p. A586
  Covenant Health, Senior Vice President and Chief Information Officer, Methodist Medical Center Of Oak Ridge, Oak Ridge, TN, p. A587
  Senior Vice President Chief Information Officer, Roane Medical Center, Harriman, TN, p. A579

WARD, Rhonda R.N., MSN, Chief Nursing Officer, Littleton Adventist Hospital, Littleton, CO, p. A105

WARD, Robert, Chief Executive Officer, Select Rehabilitation Hospital Of San Antonio, San Antonio, TX, p. A643

WARD, Rory, Chief Financial Officer, Pushmataha Hospital, Antlers, OK, p. A504

WARD, Silva, Director Human Resources, Center For Behavioral Medicine, Kansas City, MO, p. A370

WARD, Stormy, Chief Nurse Executive, Big Spring State Hospital, Big Spring, TX, p. A598

WARD, Virginia, Human Resources Officer, Robert E. Bush Naval Hospital, Twentynine Palms, CA, p. A95

WARD, Wendy, Director Human Resources, Mercy Hospital El Reno, El Reno, OK, p. A507

WARDA, Paul, Chief Financial Officer, Medstar Georgetown University Hospital, Washington, DC, p. A117

WARDELL, Patrick R., Chief Executive Officer, Cambridge Health Alliance, Cambridge, MA, p. A305

WARDEN, Michael S, Senior Vice President Information Technology, Banner – University Medical Center Phoenix, Phoenix, AZ, p. A33

WARDLOW, Marlon, Chief Operating Officer, Parkview Regional Medical Center, Fort Wayne, IN, p. A208

WARDROP, Daniel M.D., Medical Director, Heart Of The Rockies Regional Medical Center, Salida, CO, p. A107

WARE, Bobbie K., R.N., FACHE
  Vice President Patient Care and Chief Nursing Officer, Mississippi Baptist Medical Center, Jackson, MS, p. A357
  Chief Executive Officer, Mississippi Baptist Medical Center, Jackson, MS, p. A357

WARE, Dana M.D., Chief of Staff, Seneca Healthcare District, Chester, CA, p. A55

WARE, John, Director of Human Resources, Venice Regional Bayfront Health, Venice, FL, p. A146

WARE, Judy King, Chief Financial Officer, Monroe County Hospital, Forsyth, GA, p. A158

WARE, Judy
  Chief Financial Officer, Putnam General Hospital, Eatonton, GA, p. A157
  Director Human Resources, Johnson Memorial Hospital, Franklin, IN, p. A209

WARE, Kathy, Director of Nursing, Daniels Memorial Healthcare Center, Scobey, MT, p. A388

WARE, Risa, Commander, Irwin Army Community Hospital, Junction City, KS, p. A243

WAREING, Colleen, Vice President Patient Care Services, Atlantic General Hospital, Berlin, MD, p. A296

WARFIELD, William, Chief Human Resources Management, Veterans Affairs Boston Healthcare System, West Roxbury, MA, p. A312

WARING, Lance, Director Human Resources, Texas Health Harris Methodist Hospital Azle, Azle, TX, p. A596

WARLICK, Mark, Chief Information Officer, Memorial Hospital Of South Bend, South Bend, IN, p. A220

WARLITNER, Todd, Vice President Business Operations, The Outer Banks Hospital, Nags Head, NC, p. A467

WARM, Ira, Senior Vice President Human Resources, Brooklyn Hospital Center, New Rochelle, NY, p. A441

WARMAN, Debbie, Vice President Human Resources, Metrohealth Medical Center, Cleveland, OH, p. A486

WARMAN, Harold C. Jr, FACHE, President and Chief Executive Officer, Highlands Regional Medical Center, Prestonsburg, KY, p. A266

WARMBOLD, Steve, Director Information Management Service Line, Veterans Affairs St. Louis Health Care System, Saint Louis, MO, p. A379

WARMERDAM, David, Chief Financial Officer, Brynn Marr Hospital, Jacksonville, NC, p. A465

WARNER, Grady, Director of Information Technology, Burgess Health Center, Onawa, IA, p. A232

WARNER, John, M.D.
  Chief Executive Officer, Interim Chief Medical Officer, University Of Texas Southwestern Medical Center, Dallas, TX, p. A607
  Chief Executive Officer, University Of Texas Southwestern Medical Center, Dallas, TX, p. A607

WARNER, Norma, Area Director Health Information Management, Kindred Hospital–Fort Worth, Fort Worth, TX, p. A614

WARNER, Petra, Interim Chief of Staff, Shriners Hospitals For Children–Cincinnati, Cincinnati, OH, p. A484

WARNER–PACHECO, Paula, Chief Human Resources, Rio Grande Hospital, Del Norte, CO, p. A100

WARNING, Kendra, Chief Financial Officer, Davis County Hospital, Bloomfield, IA, p. A223

WARNOCK, Dawn, Director Medical Records, Taylor Regional Hospital, Hawkinsville, GA, p. A158

WARREN, Brent, President Medical Staff, Iredell Health System, Statesville, NC, p. A471

WARREN, Charlene R.N., Chief Nursing Officer, Greenbrier Valley Medical Center, Ronceverte, WV, p. A696

WARREN, Danny, Chief Financial Officer, Lake Wales Medical Center, Lake Wales, FL, p. A130

WARREN, Denise Wilder, R.N.
  Executive Vice President and Chief Operating Officer, Wakemed Cary Hospital, Cary, NC, p. A458
  Executive Vice President and Chief Operating Officer, Wakemed Raleigh Campus, Raleigh, NC, p. A469

WARREN, Gidgett, Director of Nursing, T.J. Health Columbia, Columbia, KY, p. A256

WARREN, Jana, Human Resources Business Partner, Piedmont Henry Hospital, Stockbridge, GA, p. A165

WARREN, Karen, Fiscal Officer, Porterville Developmental Center, Porterville, CA, p. A80

WARREN, Linda, Director Human Resources, Cogdell Memorial Hospital, Snyder, TX, p. A646

WARREN, Michael D., President, Good Samaritan Regional Health Center, Mount Vernon, IL, p. A194

WARREN, Sarah, Coordinator Human Resources, Hickory Trail Hospital, Desoto, TX, p. A609

WARREN, Seth, President and Chief Executive Officer, Riverview Health, Noblesville, IN, p. A217

WARREN, Shanna, Director Human Resources, Medical City Plano, Plano, TX, p. A638

WARREN, Wm. Michael. Jr, President and Chief Executive Officer, Children's Of Alabama, Birmingham, AL, p. A14

WARRENER, Gerald M.D., Chief Medical Officer, Parkview Noble Hospital, Kendallville, IN, p. A213

WARRIN, Richard, Chief Operating Officer, Springs Memorial Hospital, Lancaster, SC, p. A564

WARRINER, Ken, Market Chief Financial Officer, Physicians Regional – Pine Ridge, Naples, FL, p. A135

WARRNER, Judy, Chief Operating Officer, Northridge Medical Center, Commerce, GA, p. A155

WARSHAW, Leah, Coordinator Human Resources, Select Specialty Hospital–Ann Arbor, Ypsilanti, MI, p. A334

WARSING, Tracy M.D., Site Leader Chief of Staff, Mayo Clinic Health System – Franciscan Healthcare In Sparta, Sparta, WI, p. A712

WAS, Gregory J., CPA, Chief Executive Officer, White Mountain Regional Medical Center, Springerville, AZ, p. A36

WASDEN, Mitchell L., Ed.D., Chief Executive Officer, Ohsu Hospital, Portland, OR, p. A525

WASEF, Maha M.D., Chief of Staff, Merit Health Northwest Mississippi, Clarksdale, MS, p. A353

WASEK, Arthur A, Director Human Resources, Panola Medical Center, Batesville, MS, p. A352

WASHBURN, Geoffrey A, Vice President, Regional Medical Center Bayonet Point, Hudson, FL, p. A127

WASHBURN, Kimberly D, Director Human Resources, Snoqualmie Valley Hospital District, Snoqualmie, WA, p. A686

WASHBURN, Tonya M.D., Medical Director, Valir Rehabilitation Hospital, Oklahoma City, OK, p. A514

WASHECKA, James, Chief Financial Officer, Hillcrest Hospital – South, Tulsa, OK, p. A517

WASHINGTON, A. Eugene., M.D., President and Chief Executive Officer, Duke University Health System, Durham, NC, p. B48

WASHINGTON, Carolyn, Director of Human Resources, United Memorial Medical Care, Houston, TX, p. A623

WASHINGTON, Glen A., Chief Executive Officer, Pleasant Valley Hospital, Point Pleasant, WV, p. A695

WASHINGTON, Stephanie
  Director Community Relations and Human Resources, Baptist Medical Center Yazoo, Yazoo City, MS, p. A363
  Human Resources Director, Baptist Medical Center Attala, Kosciusko, MS, p. A357

WASHINGTON, Vindell M.D., Vice President Performance Excellence and Technology, Our Lady Of The Lake Regional Medical Center, Baton Rouge, LA, p. A271

WASILICK, Tamara, Director Operations, Kidspeace Children's Hospital, Orefield, PA, p. A542

WATERBURY, Brad, Director Human Resources, Bonner General Hospital, Sandpoint, ID, p. A176

WATERS, Bill M.D., Chief Medical Officer, Tanner Higgins General Hospital, Bremen, GA, p. A153

WATERS, Danny, Director, Information Services, Palms Of Pasadena Hospital, Saint Petersburg, FL, p. A141

WATERS, Eric, Vice President Operations, Pen Bay Medical Center, Rockport, ME, p. A293

WATERS, Gina, Director Human Resources, Evans Memorial Hospital, Claxton, GA, p. A154

WATERS, Glenn D., FACHE, President, Morton Plant Mease Health Care, Clearwater, FL, p. B86

WATERS, Jerod, Chief Nursing Officer, Chickasaw Nation Medical Center, Ada, OK, p. A504

WATERS, Karen, Chief Nursing Officer, St. Vincent Warrick Hospital, Boonville, IN, p. A204

WATERS, Laura M, Vice President Human Resources, Garrett Regional Medical Center, Oakland, MD, p. A300

WATERS, Nancy, Interim Chief Information Officer, High Point Regional Health System, High Point, NC, p. A464

WATERS, Stephen F M.D., Medical Director, Atlantic General Hospital, Berlin, MD, p. A296

WATERS, William M.D., IV, Executive Vice President, Tanner Medical Center–Villa Rica, Villa Rica, GA, p. A166

WATHEN, Cheryl A, Interim Chief Financial Officer, Deaconess Hospital, Evansville, IN, p. A207

WATHEN, Susan R, Vice President Human Resources, Hannibal Regional Hospital, Hannibal, MO, p. A368

WATKINS, Anne Marie, Chief Nurse Executive, Kaiser Permanente San Diego Medical Center, San Diego, CA, p. A85

WATKINS, Chris, Director of Information Technology, Craig Hospital, Englewood, CO, p. A102

WEBER, Tiffany, Chief Financial Officer, Sterling Regional Medcenter, Sterling, CO, p. A107

WEBER, Trish R.N., FACHE, Vice President Operations and Chief Nursing Officer, Franciscan St. Anthony Health – Michigan City, Michigan City, IN, p. A215

WEBER, Wilson, Chief Operating Officer, Continuecare Hospital At Baptist Health Corbin, Corbin, KY, p. A257

WEBSTER, Cindy, Vice President Financial Services, Licking Memorial Hospital, Newark, OH, p. A497

WEBSTER, Gwen M.D., President Medical Staff, Texas Health Presbyterian Hospital Plano, Plano, TX, p. A638

WEBSTER, Janice, Director Human Resources, West Oaks Hospital, Houston, TX, p. A624

WEBSTER, Jeffrey, Administrator, Harris Health System, Houston, TX, p. A620

WEBSTER, Kathleen R.N., MSN, Vice President Patient Services, New York–Presbyterian/Hudson Valley Hospital, Cortlandt Manor, NY, p. A434

WEBSTER, Mark
President and Chief Executive Officer, Cortland Regional Medical Center, Cortland, NY, p. A434
Vice President Finance, New York–Presbyterian/Hudson Valley Hospital, Cortlandt Manor, NY, p. A434

WEBSTER, Nancy, Administrator and Chief Operating Officer, St. Luke's Rehabilitation Institute, Spokane, WA, p. A687

WEBSTER, Richard, R.N., President, Thomas Jefferson University Hospitals, Philadelphia, PA, p. A546

WEBSTER, William W., FACHE, President and Chief Executive Officer, Medical Center Health System, Odessa, TX, p. A635

WECKENBORG, Janet, Vice President Operations, Capital Region Medical Center, Jefferson City, MO, p. A369

WECKESSER, Kim, Director Human Resources, Munson Healthcare Manistee Hospital, Manistee, MI, p. A325

WEDDLE, Chari, Chief Human Resource Management Service, Richard L. Roudebush Veterans Affairs Medical Center, Indianapolis, IN, p. A212

WEDGEWORTH, Joyce, Financial Clerk, Hill Hospital Of Sumter County, York, AL, p. A24

WEDO, Aaron, Manager, Human Resources, Grundy County Memorial Hospital, Grundy Center, IA, p. A228

WEE, Donald, Chief Executive Officer, Tri–State Memorial Hospital, Clarkston, WA, p. A679

WEED, John M.D., III, Medical Director, Rockdale Hospital, Rockdale, TX, p. A640

WEED, Warren
Director Associate Relations, Merit Health Woman's Hospital, Flowood, MS, p. A354
Director Human Resources, Merit Health River Oaks, Flowood, MS, p. A354

WEEDEN, Gerard, Chief Medical Officer, Vibra Hospital Of Richmond, Richmond, VA, p. A674

WEEKS, Doug, Executive Vice President and Chief Operations Officer, Baptist Health Medical Center – North Little Rock, North Little Rock, AR, p. A48

WEEKS, Ed, Manager Information Services, Paris Community Hospital, Paris, IL, p. A197

WEELDREYER, Jim, Manager Information Technology, Pershing General Hospital, Lovelock, NV, p. A404

WEEMS, Reva S, Director Human Resources, Gateway Regional Medical Center, Granite City, IL, p. A189

WEEMS, Taylor, Vice President, Chief Information Officer, Midland Memorial Hospital, Midland, TX, p. A633

WEG, Jennifer ., MS, R.N., Chief Executive Officer, Sanford Worthington Medical Center, Worthington, MN, p. A351

WEGHORST, George M.D., Chief Medical Officer, Providence Newberg Medical Center, Newberg, OR, p. A524

WEGLARZ, Ron, Chief Executive Officer and Managing Director, Streamwood Behavioral Health Center, Streamwood, IL, p. A201

WEGLEITNER, Theodore, Chief Executive Officer and President, Lakeview Hospital, Stillwater, MN, p. A349

WEGNER, Michael, Senior Vice President and Chief Operating Officer, Mercy Medical Center–Des Moines, Des Moines, IA, p. A226

WEHBEH, Wehbeh M.D., Chief Medical Officer, NYC Health + Hospitals / Coney Island, New Rochelle, NY, p. A444

WEHE, Brad, Chief Operating Officer, Altru Health System, Grand Forks, ND, p. A476

WEHLING, Ed, Chief Medical Staff, Decatur County Hospital, Leon, IA, p. A230

WEHLING, Robert D, Interim Chief Financial Officer, Saint Alphonsus Medical Center – Baker City, Baker City, OR, p. A520

WEHMEYER, Jeffrey, Director Information Technology, Hermann Area District Hospital, Hermann, MO, p. A369

WEHNER, Jill, Vice President Financial Services, Harbor Beach Community Hospital, Harbor Beach, MI, p. A322

WEHRMEISTER, Erica, Chief Operating Officer, St. Vincent Indianapolis Hospital, IndianapolisSt. Vincent Heart Center, Indianapolis, IN, p. A212

WEIDEMANN, Donald, Chief Executive Officer, Gordon Memorial Health Services, Gordon, NE, p. A393

WEIDER, Will
Chief Information Officer, Calumet Medical Center, Chilton, WI, p. A700
Chief Information Officer, Marshfield Medical Center, Marshfield, WI, p. A706
Chief Information Officer, Mercy Medical Center, Oshkosh, WI, p. A710
Chief Information Officer, Ministry Saint Michael's Hospital, Stevens Point, WI, p. A713
Chief Information Officer, St. Elizabeth Hospital, Appleton, WI, p. A698

WEIDNER, Deborah, Medical Director, Natchaug Hospital, Mansfield Center, CT, p. A110

WEIDNER, Peter, Director Information Technology, St. John's Riverside Hospital, Yonkers, NY, p. A456

WEIER, Jeffrey Paul., Chief Executive Officer, Kindred Hospital Of Central Ohio, Mansfield, OH, p. A494

WEIGEL, Cherry, Director Health Information Management, Rc Hospital And Clinics, Olivia, MN, p. A345

WEIL, David S., Senior Vice President and Administrator, Saint Francis Hospital South, Tulsa, OK, p. A518

WEILAND, David M.D., Chief Medical Officer, Largo Medical Center, Largo, FL, p. A130

WEIMER, Linn, Chief Information Officer, Adena Medical Center, Chillicothe, OH, p. A483

WEINER, Gary
Chief Information Officer, St. Catherine Hospital, East Chicago, IN, p. A206
Vice President Information Technology and Chief Information Officer, St. Mary Medical Center, Hobart, IN, p. A210
Vice President Information Technology, Chief Information Officer, Community Hospital, Munster, IN, p. A216

WEINER, Jerome M.D., Senior Vice President Medical Affairs, Good Samaritan Hospital Medical Center, West Islip, NY, p. A455

WEINER, Ronald, Vice President Finance and Chief Financial Officer, Magruder Memorial Hospital, Port Clinton, OH, p. A498

WEINGART, Steve, Chief Financial Officer, Los Alamos Medical Center, Los Alamos, NM, p. A427

WEINGARTNER, Ronald, Vice President Administration, St. Charles Hospital, Port Jefferson, NY, p. A450

WEINKRANTZ, Alan, Chief Financial Officer, Finance, University Behavioral Healthcare, Piscataway, NJ, p. A419

WEINMANN, Jay, Chief Financial Officer, NYC Health + Hospitals / Bellevue, New Rochelle, NY, p. A444

WEINMANN, Shannon, Human Resources Manager, Community Medical Center, Inc., Falls City, NE, p. A392

WEINMEISTER, Kurt, Chief Executive Officer, San Dimas Community Hospital, San Dimas, CA, p. A86

WEINREIS, Brian, Vice President Operations and Finance, Abbott Northwestern Hospital, Minneapolis, MN, p. A343

WEINSTEIN, Barry S, Chief Financial Officer, Four Winds Hospital, Katonah, NY, p. A438

WEINSTEIN, Brian M.D., Chief of Staff, Westside Regional Medical Center, Plantation, FL, p. A140

WEINSTEIN, Freddie M.D., Chief Medical Officer, Dominican Hospital, Santa Cruz, CA, p. A90

WEINSTEIN, Gary B., President and Chief Executive Officer, Washington Hospital, Washington, PA, p. A552

WEINSTEIN, James, Chief Financial Officer, Acuity Specialty Hospital Of Southern New Jersey, Willingboro, NJ, p. A423

WEIR, Tim W., Chief Executive Officer, Olmsted Medical Center, Rochester, MN, p. A347

WEIS, Brian M.D., Chief Medical Officer, Northwest Texas Healthcare System, Amarillo, TX, p. A592

WEIS, Charles
Chief Financial Officer, Mount Sinai Hospital, Chicago, IL, p. A182
Chief Financial Officer, Schwab Rehabilitation Hospital, Chicago, IL, p. A183
Executive Vice President and Chief Financial Officer, Holy Cross Hospital, Chicago, IL, p. A181

WEIS, Harry, Chief Executive Officer, Tahoe Forest Hospital District, Truckee, CA, p. A94

WEIS, Maurine MSN, R.N., Vice President Nursing and Chief Nursing Officer, Promedica Flower Hospital, Sylvania, OH, p. A500

WEIS, Robert
Director Information Systems, Bingham Memorial Hospital, Blackfoot, ID, p. A171

Director Information Technology, Mountain River Birthing And Surgery Center, Blackfoot, ID, p. A171

WEIS, Wade, Chief Financial Officer and Senior Director Finance, Grande Ronde Hospital, La Grande, OR, p. A523

WEISENBERGER, Scott, Chief Executive Officer, Malvern Institute, Malvern, PA, p. A540

WEISENFREUND, Jochanan M.D., Senior Vice President Academic and Medical Affairs, Interfaith Medical Center, New Rochelle, NY, p. A441

WEISER, Marcus D.O., Chief of Staff, Community Healthcare System, Onaga, KS, p. A248

WEISFIELD, Phyllis, Chief Executive Officer and Managing Director, Horsham Clinic, Ambler, PA, p. A529

WEISHAPL, Natasha, Manager Business Office and Human Resources, Decatur Health Systems, Oberlin, KS, p. A248

WEISNER, Brad, Executive Vice President and Chief Operating Officer, Nash Health Care Systems, Rocky Mount, NC, p. A469

WEISS, Allen S., M.D., President and Chief Executive Officer, Nch Downtown Naples Hospital, Naples, FL, p. A135

WEISS, Anthony M.D., Medical Director, Upstate University Hospital, Syracuse, NY, p. A453

WEISS, Barry J., Chairman of the Board, College Health Enterprises, Santa Fe Springs, CA, p. B32

WEISS, David, Commanding Officer, Naval Hospital Bremerton, Bremerton, WA, p. A678

WEISS, Gary, Chief Financial Officer, Northshore University Health System, Evanston, IL, p. A187

WEISS, Patrice M, Executive Vice President, Administration, Carilion Franklin Memorial Hospital, Rocky Mount, VA, p. A675

WEISS, Phyllis, Director Human Resources, Alameda Hospital, Alameda, CA, p. A51

WEISS, Terri, Chief Financial Officer, Healthsouth Rehabilitation Hospital Vision Park, Shenandoah, TX, p. A645

WEISSENBERGER, Ralf, Director Information Systems, White Memorial Medical Center, Los Angeles, CA, p. A72

WEISSER, Lisa, Supervisor Finance, Wagner Community Memorial Hospital Avera, Wagner, SD, p. A573

WEISSLER, Jonathan M.D., Chief Medical Officer, Lifecare Hospitals Of Dallas, Dallas, TX, p. A605

WEISTREICH, Tracy Ph.D., R.N., Associate Director Patient Care Services/Nurse Executive, Veterans Affairs Roseburg Healthcare System, Roseburg, OR, p. A526

WEISUL, Jonathan M.D., Vice President Medical Affairs and Chief Medical Officer, Christus Coushatta Health Care Center, Coushatta, LA, p. A273

WELANDER, Jennifer, CPA
Senior Vice President Finance and Chief Financial Officer, St. Charles Bend, Bend, OR, p. A520
Senior Vice President Finance and Chief Financial Officer, St. Charles Redmond, Redmond, OR, p. A526

WELCH, Abbey, Director Human Resources, Harmon Memorial Hospital, Hollis, OK, p. A508

WELCH, Andrew, Director, New Mexico Veterans Affairs Health Care System – Raymond G. Murphy Medical Center, Albuquerque, NM, p. A424

WELCH, Bryant, Chief Human Resources, Washington Hospital Healthcare System, Fremont, CA, p. A60

WELCH, David, M.D.
Medical Director, Clifton–Fine Hospital, Star Lake, NY, p. A452
Director Information Technology, Simpson General Hospital, Mendenhall, MS, p. A358

WELCH, Denise, Chief Financial Officer, Arbuckle Memorial Hospital, Sulphur, OK, p. A516

WELCH, Donald E, Chief Operating Officer, Florida Hospital Zephyrhills, Zephyrhills, FL, p. A148

WELCH, Douglas, Chief Executive Officer, Doctors Hospital, Augusta, GA, p. A151

WELCH, Gary A., Assistant to the Chief Executive Officer and Administrative Director Support Systems, Bon Secours Memorial Regional Medical Center, Mechanicsville, VA, p. A670

WELCH, Jeffrey M., Market Chief Executive Officer, Saint Vincent Hospital, Worcester, MA, p. A313

WELCH, Nicole, Chief Human Resources Officer, Fairbanks Memorial Hospital, Fairbanks, AK, p. A26

WELCH, Rosemary C R.N., Vice President and Chief Nursing Officer, Medstar National Rehabilitation Hospital, Washington, DC, p. A117

WELCH, Shelly
Chief Clinical Officer, North Oaks Medical Center, Hammond, LA, p. A275
Senior Vice President, Patient Services, Chief Nursing Officer, North Oaks Health System, North Oaks Rehabilitation Hospital, Hammond, LA, p. A275

WELCH, Sherri R.N., Chief Nursing Officer, College Station Medical Center, College Station, TX, p. A602

WELCH, Thomas M.D., Chief Medical Officer, Mercy St. Vincent Medical Center, Toledo, OH, p. A500

WELCH, Tony, Vice President Human Resources, Southeast Alabama Medical Center, Dothan, AL, p. A17

WELDAY, Doug, Senior Vice President Finance, Spectrum Health – Butterworth Hospital, Grand Rapids, MI, p. A321

WELDON, Jim, Chief Information Officer, St. Anthony's Medical Center, Saint Louis, MO, p. A378

WELDY, Alan, Vice President Human Resources, Compliance and Legal Services, Goshen Hospital, Goshen, IN, p. A209

WELKIE, Katy MBA, R.N., Chief Executive Officer, Primary Children's Hospital, Salt Lake City, UT, p. A660

WELLBROCK, Jenna, Chief Nursing Officer, Gateway Rehabilitation Hospital, Florence, KY, p. A258

WELLER, Deidre CPA, Controller, Spectrum Health Pennock, Hastings, MI, p. A322

WELLING, Lynn M.D., Chief Medical Officer, Sharp Chula Vista Medical Center, Chula Vista, CA, p. A55

WELLING, Michele M.D., Chief of Staff, Bluegrass Community Hospital, Versailles, KY, p. A268

WELLMAN, Amanda MSN, R.N., Chief Nursing Officer, Select Specialty Hospital–Omaha, Omaha, NE, p. A398

WELLMAN, James, Senior Director Information Services, Comanche County Memorial Hospital, Lawton, OK, p. A509

WELLMAN, Sonia I., Chief Executive Officer, Memorial Hospital Of Tampa, Tampa, FL, p. A145

WELLMANN, Jane, Chief Financial Officer, Scott & White Hospital – Brenham, Brenham, TX, p. A599

WELLS, A Shane, Chief Financial Officer, Cornerstone Hospital Of Houston At Clearlake, Webster, TX, p. A653

WELLS, Benjamin, Chief Financial Officer, Red Bud Regional Hospital, Red Bud, IL, p. A198

WELLS, Carol R.N., MSN, Chief Nursing Officer, Central Louisiana Surgical Hospital, Alexandria, LA, p. A269

WELLS, Craig, Chief Information Officer, George C Grape Community Hospital, Hamburg, IA, p. A228

WELLS, Dale W., Chief Financial and Operating Officer, Alliance Community Hospital, Alliance, OH, p. A479

WELLS, James, R.N.
  Chief Nursing Officer, Saint Francis Hospital Muskogee, Muskogee, OK, p. A511
  Chief Nursing Officer, Merit Health Biloxi, Biloxi, MS, p. A352

WELLS, Jason
  Chief Human Resources Management Service, Fargo Veterans Affairs Health Care System, Fargo, ND, p. A475
  President and Chief Executive Officer, Frank R. Howard Memorial Hospital, Willits, CA, p. A97

WELLS, Jimmy, Chief Nursing and Administrative Officer, Westside Surgical Hospital, Houston, TX, p. A624

WELLS, Jonathan, Supervisor Information Technology, Kansas Surgery And Recovery Center, Wichita, KS, p. A253

WELLS, Mallory Gulley CPA, Chief Financial Officer, Richardson Medical Center, Rayville, LA, p. A284

WELLS, Mary Ellen, FACHE, Administrator, Centracare Health–Monticello, Monticello, MN, p. A344

WELLS, Michelle, Director of Nursing, Seaside Behavioral Center, New OrleansRiver Oaks Hospital, New Orleans, LA, p. A283

WELLS, Pamela R.N., MSN, Chief Nursing Officer, Sharp Memorial Hospital, San Diego, CA, p. A86

WELLS, Robert M.D., Chief Medical Officer, Providence Portland Medical Center, Portland, OR, p. A525

WELLS, Roxie Cannon., M.D.
  Chief Executive Officer, Cape Fear Valley – Bladen County Hospital, Elizabethtown, NC, p. A462
  President, Hoke Hospital, Raeford, NC, p. A468

WELLS, Scott E MSN, R.N., Vice President Patient Care Services, Caromont Regional Medical Center, Gastonia, NC, p. A463

WELLS, Troy R., Chief Executive Officer, Baptist Health, Little Rock, AR, p. B18

WELLS, Valerie, Manager Human Resources, Healthsouth Rehabilitation Hospital The Woodlands, Conroe, TX, p. A603

WELSER, Jeremy, Director Information Systems, Bonner General Hospital, Sandpoint, ID, p. A176

WELSH, Dennis, President and CEO, Down East Community Hospital, Machias, ME, p. A292

WELSH, J. Luckey. Jr, Chief Executive Officer, Cherry Hospital, Goldsboro, NC, p. A463

WELSH, Joyce R.N., MS, Vice President of Clinical Services and Chief Nursing Officer, Emerson Hospital, Concord, MA, p. A306

WELSH, Terrence, Chief Medical Administrator, Fairfield Medical Center, Lancaster, OH, p. A493

WELTER, Matt, Chief Medical Officer, Cache Valley Hospital, North Logan, UT, p. A658

WEMPE, John M M.D., Chief of Staff, Sioux Falls Veterans Affairs Health Care System, Sioux Falls, SD, p. A573

WENDELL, David, Manager, Information Systems, St. Mary's Medical Center, Huntington, WV, p. A693

WENDELL, Sean, Chief Executive Officer, Beacon Behavioral Hospital, Lutcher, LA, p. A280

WENGER, Cheryl, Manager Health Information and Quality Assurance, Hiawatha Community Hospital, Hiawatha, KS, p. A242

WENGER, Jill, Director Human Resources, Atchison Hospital, Atchison, KS, p. A238

WENGER–KELLER, David M.D., Chief of Staff, Fort Madison Community Hospital, Fort Madison, IA, p. A228

WENTWORTH, Cynthia, Chief Human Resource Officer, East Morgan County Hospital, Brush, CO, p. A99

WENTZ, Amber, Director of Clinical Information Systems & Clinical Informatics, Skiff Medical Center, Newton, IA, p. A232

WENTZ, Jim, Chief Financial Officer, Flaget Memorial Hospital, Bardstown, KY, p. A255

WENTZ, Robert J., President and Chief Executive Officer, Oroville Hospital, Oroville, CA, p. A78

WENTZEL, Chris M.D., Interim Medical Director, Guthrie Corning Hospital, Corning, NY, p. A434

WERFT, Ronald C.
  President and Chief Executive Officer, Goleta Valley Cottage Hospital, Santa Barbara, CA, p. A90
  President and Chief Executive Officer, Santa Barbara Cottage Hospital, Santa Barbara, CA, p. A90
  President and Chief Executive Officer, Santa Ynez Valley Cottage Hospital, Solvang, CA, p. A92

WERKIN, Dave, Vice President Finance and Chief Financial Officer, Trinity Health System, Steubenville, OH, p. A500

WERKSTELL, Scott, Director Information System, T. J. Samson Community Hospital, Glasgow, KY, p. A259

WERMAGER, Teresa, Human Resources Business Partner, Skiff Medical Center, Newton, IA, p. A232

WERNER, Edward, Director Human Resources, Healthsouth Reading Rehabilitation Hospital, Reading, PA, p. A549

WERNER, John W., Chief Executive Officer, Oakland Mercy Hospital, Oakland, NE, p. A396

WERNER, Kurt M.D., Chief of Staff, Veterans Affairs Montana Health Care System, Fort Harrison, MT, p. A384

WERNER, Tiffany
  Senior Human Resource Business Partner, Banner Baywood Medical Center, Mesa, AZ, p. A31
  Senior Human Resource Business Partner, Banner Heart Hospital, Mesa, AZ, p. A31

WERNICK, Joel, President and Chief Executive Officer, Phoebe Putney Memorial Hospital, Albany, GA, p. A149

WERNKE, Chris, Chief Operating Officer, Dominican Hospital, Santa Cruz, CA, p. A90

WERRBACH, John P., President and Chief Executive Officer, Amita Health Elk Grove Village, Elk Grove Village, IL, p. A186

WERTH–SWEENEY, Stacey, Facility Operating Officer, Lincoln Regional Center, Lincoln, NE, p. A395

WERTHMAN, Ronald J, Senior Vice President Finance, Chief Financial Officer and Treasurer, Johns Hopkins Hospital, Baltimore, MD, p. A294

WERTZ, Jackie, Director Human Resources, George C Grape Community Hospital, Hamburg, IA, p. A228

WESCOATT, Sampson, Manager Information Technology, Molokai General Hospital, Kaunakakai, HI, p. A170

WESCOTT, Lisle, President, SSM Health St. Joseph Hospital – Lake Saint Louis, Lake Saint Louis, MO, p. A372

WESENER DIECK, Jill, Director Human Resources, Gundersen Tri–County Hospital And Clinics, Whitehall, WI, p. A716

WESLEY, Deb MSN, Chief Nursing Officer, Children's Of Alabama, Birmingham, AL, p. A14

WESLEY, Jim, Senior Vice President and Chief Information Officer, John Muir Behavioral Health Center, Concord, CA, p. A56

WESLEY, Mary Lou R.N., Senior Vice President and Chief Nursing Officer, Sparrow Hospital, Lansing, MI, p. A324

WESOLOWSKI, Paul J, Chief Operating Officer, VCU Medical Center, Richmond, VA, p. A674

WESSELS, Jana, Associate Vice President Human Resources, University Of Iowa Hospitals And Clinics, Iowa City, IA, p. A230

WESSELS, William M.D., Chief Medical Officer, Aspirus Wausau Hospital, Inc., Wausau, WI, p. A715

WESSON, Jim D, President and Administrator, Christus Santa Rosa Health System, San Antonio, TX, p. A642

WEST, Aaron M.D., Chief Medical Officer, Memorial Hospital Jacksonville, Jacksonville, FL, p. A128

WEST, Andrea MS, Vice President of Human Resources, Columbus Regional Healthcare System, Whiteville, NC, p. A472

WEST, Brenda, R.N., MSN
  Chief Nursing Officer, Summit Pacific Medical Center, Elma, WA, p. A680
  Assistant Vice President, Information Services, Einstein Medical Center Montgomery, East Norriton, PA, p. A533
  Vice President, Information Services and Interim Chief Information Officer, Einstein Medical Center Philadelphia, Philadelphia, PA, p. A543

WEST, Bridgette, Director Patient Access Services, Cobleskill Regional Hospital, Cobleskill, NY, p. A434

WEST, Charles M.D., Chief Medical Officer, Randolph Hospital, Asheboro, NC, p. A457

WEST, Christopher, Chief Executive Officer, Seven Hills Hospital, Henderson, NV, p. A402

WEST, Darren M.D., Interim Chief Medical Officer, Banner Ironwood Medical Center, San Tan Valley, AZ, p. A35

WEST, James R.
  President and Chief Executive Officer, Pih Health Hospital – Downey, Downey, CA, p. A58
  President and Chief Executive Officer, Pih Health Hospital– Whittier, Whittier, CA, p. A97

WEST, Jennifer R.N., Chief Nursing Officer, South Texas Spine And Surgical Hospital, San Antonio, TX, p. A643

WEST, Judith M, Senior Vice President Human Resources and Chief Human Resources Officer, Maine Medical Center, Portland, ME, p. A292

WEST, Kenneth, Chief Operating Officer, Medical Center Of Trinity, Trinity, FL, p. A146

WEST, Melissa, Chief Financial Officer, Cedar Crest Hospital And Residential Treatment Center, Belton, TX, p. A598

WEST, Michael C M.D., Chief of Staff, Mccurtain Memorial Hospital, Idabel, OK, p. A509

WEST, Michael, Manager Systems Account, New England Sinai Hospital And Rehabilitation Center, Stoughton, MA, p. A312

WEST, Steve M.D., Chief Medical Officer, Capital Regional Medical Center, Tallahassee, FL, p. A143

WEST, Steven J., Chief Executive Officer, Indiana University Health Blackford Hospital, Hartford City, IN, p. A210

WEST, Tamara R.N., MSN, Vice President Patient Care, Nicholas H. Noyes Memorial Hospital, Dansville, NY, p. A434

WEST, Todd, Administrator, Azalea Trace, Columbus, GA, p. B32

WESTENFELDER, Grant M.D., Chief Medical Officer, Midwest Medical Center, Galena, IL, p. A188

WESTER, K Scott., FACHE, President and Chief Executive Officer, Our Lady Of The Lake Regional Medical Center, Baton Rouge, LA, p. A271

WESTERBERG, Richard, Interim Chief Executive Officer, Franklin County Medical Center, Preston, ID, p. A175

WESTERCHIL, Beth, Chief Nursing Officer, Byrd Regional Hospital, Leesville, LA, p. A280

WESTERHEIDE, Karen, Chief Financial Officer, Veterans Affairs St. Louis Health Care System, Saint Louis, MO, p. A379

WESTERMAN, Mandy, Chief Executive Officer, West Oaks Hospital, Houston, TX, p. A624

WESTFALL, Gay, Senior Vice President Human Resources, Kaiser Permanente Sacramento Medical Center, Sacramento, CA, p. A83

WESTFALL, Roger, Director, Western State Hospital, Hopkinsville, KY, p. A260

WESTIN, Robert M.D., Chief Medical Officer, Cuyuna Regional Medical Center, Crosby, MN, p. A338

WESTMAN, Ken, Chief Executive Officer, Barrett Hospital & Healthcare, Dillon, MT, p. A384

WESTMORELAND, Penny
  Chief Financial Officer, Lakeland Community Hospital, Haleyville, AL, p. A19
  Chief Financial Officer, Red Bay Hospital, Red Bay, AL, p. A22
  Chief Financial Officer, Russellville Hospital, Russellville, AL, p. A23

WESTON, Betty, Chief Human Resources Officer, U.S. Public Health Service Phoenix Indian Medical Center, Phoenix, AZ, p. A34

WESTON, Dana, Chief Executive Officer, Morehead Memorial Hospital, Eden, NC, p. A461

WESTON, Nancy R R.N., MSN, Vice President Nursing Services, Memorial Hospital, Belleville, IL, p. A178

WESTON, Nicholas, Administrator and Chief Executive Officer, Latimer County General Hospital, Wilburton, OK, p. A519

WESTON, Susan CPA, Chief Financial Officer, Mountrail County Medical Center, Stanley, ND, p. A478

WESTON, Terry M.D., Vice President Physician Services, Ohiohealth Medcentral Mansfield Hospital, Mansfield, OH, p. A494

WESTON–HALL, Patricia, Chief Executive Officer, Glenbeigh Hospital And Outpatient Centers, Rock Creek, OH, p. A498

WESTOVER, Teresa, Director Human Resources, North Texas Medical Center, Gainesville, TX, p. A615

WESTPHAL, Chris, Chief Information Technology Officer, Southeast Colorado Hospital District, Springfield, CO, p. A107

WESTPHAL, James M.D., AMHD Medical Director, Hawaii State Hospital, Kaneohe, HI, p. A170

WESTPHAL, Laura R., Vice President Patient Care Services, Castle Medical Center, Kailua, HI, p. A169

WESTRUM, Jennifer, Administrator, Community Behavioral Health Hospital – Alexandria, Alexandria, MN, p. A335

WESTRY, Tanza, Chief Financial Officer, Hunter Holmes Mcguire Veterans Affairs Medical Center–Richmond, Richmond, VA, p. A674

WESTWOOD, Denise P, Chief Nursing Officer, Weirton Medical Center, Weirton, WV, p. A696

WETHAL, Robert R.N., Vice President and Chief Nursing Officer, Mercy Medical Center–Dubuque, Dubuque, IA, p. A227

WETHINGTON, Bud
Chief Executive Officer, T. J. Samson Community Hospital, Glasgow, KY, p. A259
Chief Executive Officer, T.J. Health Columbia, Columbia, KY, p. A256

WETTON, Darlene, R.N., Chief Executive Officer, Temecula Valley Hospital, Temecula, CA, p. A93

WETZ, Staci, Chief Financial Officer, Shannon Medical Center, San Angelo, TX, p. A641

WETZEL, James L M.D., Senior Vice President, Chief Medical Officer, Olathe Medical Center, Olathe, KS, p. A248

WETZEL, Lou M.D., Chief of Staff, The University Of Kansas Health System, Kansas City, KS, p. A244

WEYMOUTH, Deborah K., FACHE
President and Chief Executive Officer, Clinton Hospital, Clinton, MA, p. A306
President and Chief Executive Officer, Healthalliance Hospitals, Leominster, MA, p. A308

WEYMOUTH, Linda, Chief Financial Officer, Suncoast Behavioral Health Center, Bradenton, FL, p. A121

WHALEN, David, Chief Executive Officer, Twin Cities Hospital, Niceville, FL, p. A135

WHALEN, Eileen, R.N., President and Chief Operating Officer, University Of Vermont Medical Center, Burlington, VT, p. A662

WHALEN, Patti, Manager Human Resources, Wichita County Health Center, Leoti, KS, p. A245

WHALEN, Thomas V., M.D.
Chief Medical Officer, Lehigh Valley Hospital, Allentown, PA, p. A528
Executive Vice President and Chief Medical Officer, Lehigh Valley Hospital–Muhlenberg, Bethlehem, PA, p. A529

WHALEN, Thomas, Vice President Finance, Good Samaritan Medical Center, Brockton, MA, p. A304

WHALEY, Joseph, Chief, Human Resources Management Service, Fayetteville Veterans Affairs Medical Center, Fayetteville, NC, p. A462

WHALEY, Mary, Director of Acute Care, Johnson County Healthcare Center, Buffalo, WY, p. A717

WHARTON, Danny, Chief Nursing Officer, Carolina Pines Regional Medical Center, Hartsville, SC, p. A563

WHARTON, Joe H M.D., Chief of Staff, Bradley County Medical Center, Warren, AR, p. A50

WHEAT, Ken, Senior Vice President and Chief Financial Officer, Eisenhower Medical Center, Rancho Mirage, CA, p. A81

WHEAT, Terry R.N., M.P.H., Director of Patient Care Services, Shriners Hospitals For Children–Chicago, Chicago, IL, p. A184

WHEATCRAFT, Cory, Information Technology and Purchasing Officer, Windsor–Laurelwood Center For Behavioral Medicine, Willoughby, OH, p. A502

WHEATLEY, Bernard, FACHE, Chief Executive Officer, Schneider Regional Medical Center, Saint Thomas, VI, p. A727

WHEATLEY, Jane, Chief Executive Officer, Taylor Regional Hospital, Campbellsville, KY, p. A256

WHEATLEY, Richard, Chief Information Officer, Cape Regional Medical Center, Cape May Court House, NJ, p. A412

WHEATLEY, Samuel N, Chief Medical Officer, Columbus Regional Healthcare System, Whiteville, NC, p. A472

WHEATLEY, Sonya, Human Resources Manager, Central State Hospital, Louisville, KY, p. A262

WHEATLEY, Stephen J., Director of Operations, Franciscan St. Francis Health–Carmel, Carmel, IN, p. A205

WHEATON, David, Director Human Resources, Blue Hill Memorial Hospital, Blue Hill, ME, p. A290

WHEATON, Tammy H., Interim Chief Nursing Officer, Union County Hospital, Anna, IL, p. A177

WHEELAN, Kevin M.D., Medical Director, Baylor Jack And Jane Hamilton Heart And Vascular Hospital, Dallas, TX, p. A604

WHEELER, Brent, Vice President Ancillary and Support Services, Mclaren Flint, Flint, MI, p. A319

WHEELER, Cambria, Communications and Marketing, St. Helena Hospital Clear Lake, Clearlake, CA, p. A56

WHEELER, Dane, Chief Financial Officer, Adams Memorial Hospital, Decatur, IN, p. A206

WHEELER, Dawne, Chief Executive Officer, Select Specialty Hospital–Canton, Canton, OH, p. A483

WHEELER, Frankie, Director, Human Resources, Saint Elizabeths Hospital, Washington, DC, p. A118

WHEELER, James A, Vice President Human Relations and Community Development, Androscoggin Valley Hospital, Berlin, NH, p. A407

WHEELER, Kim R.N., Director of Nursing, Kingwood Pines Hospital, Kingwood, TX, p. A627

WHEELER, Lynette , MSN, Chief Operating Officer, Truman Medical Center-Lakewood, Kansas City, MO, p. B130

WHEELER, Lynette, MSN, Chief Operating Officer, Truman Medical Center–Lakewood, Kansas City, MO, p. A371

WHEELER, Newman, Chief Financial Officer and Chief Operating Officer, Covenant Hospital–Levelland, Levelland, TX, p. A629

WHEELER, Pamela R, Director Human Resources, Scott County Hospital, Scott City, KS, p. A251

WHEELER, Penny Ann., M.D., Chief Executive Officer, Allina Health, Minneapolis, MN, p. B9

WHEELER, Penny Ann M.D., President and Chief Medical Officer, Abbott Northwestern Hospital, Minneapolis, MN, p. A343

WHEELER, Philip, Director Finance, Mercy Health – Clermont Hospital, Batavia, OH, p. A480

WHEELER, Rebecca, Director Finance, Kaiser Permanente Baldwin Park Medical Center, Baldwin Park, CA, p. A53

WHEELER, Robert
Controller, Healthsouth Rehabilitation Hospital Of Florence, Florence, SC, p. A562
Vice President Human Resources, South Shore Hospital, South Weymouth, MA, p. A311

WHEELER, Tina R.N., MSN, Director Nursing, William Newton Hospital, Winfield, KS, p. A254

WHEELER, William M.D., Chief of Staff, Benewah Community Hospital, Saint Maries, ID, p. A175

WHEELER, Zachariah P, Senior Vice President Human Resources, John D. Archbold Memorial Hospital, Thomasville, GA, p. A166

WHEELER–MOORE, Juanita, Director Financial Services, Four Winds Hospital, Saratoga Springs, NY, p. A452

WHEELES, Locke, Information Technology Manager, Field Memorial Community Hospital, Centreville, MS, p. A353

WHEELUS, Matthew, Chief Operating Officer, Spring Valley Hospital Medical Center, Las Vegas, NV, p. A404

WHELAN, Chad, M.D., President, Loyola University Medical Center, Maywood, IL, p. A193

WHELAN, Laurie A, Senior Vice President Finance and Chief Financial Officer, Hospital For Special Care, New Britain, CT, p. A111

WHELAN, Thomas, Chief Executive Officer, Cibola General Hospital, Grants, NM, p. A426

WHERRY, Richard M.D., Chief of Staff, Chestatee Regional Hospital, Dahlonega, GA, p. A156

WHERRY, Robin, Risk Manager and Director Quality Assurance and Health Information Management, Healthsouth Mountainview Regional Rehabilitation Hospital, Morgantown, WV, p. A694

WHICHARD, Forrest, Chief Financial Officer, Ochsner Medical Center – North Shore, Slidell, LA, p. A286

WHICHARD, Nick, Chief Information Officer, St. Luke's Hospital, Columbus, NC, p. A460

WHIDDON, William, Chief Financial Officer, Woodland Heights Medical Center, Lufkin, TX, p. A631

WHILDEN, Sean
Chief Financial Officer, Houston Medical Center, Warner Robins, GA, p. A167
Chief Financial Officer, Perry Hospital, Perry, GA, p. A163

WHILEY, Karen R.N., Vice President Patient Care Services, Fairview Northland Medical Center, Princeton, MN, p. A346

WHILLOCK, Mary C R.N., MS, Associate Nursing Officer and Chief Operating Officer, Florida Hospital Carrollwood, Tampa, FL, p. A144

WHIPKEY, Jared, Chief Financial Officer, Santa Rosa Medical Center, Milton, FL, p. A134

WHIPPLE, C Cynthia, Director of Nursing, Muncy Valley Hospital, Muncy, PA, p. A542

WHIPPLE, James, Chief Executive Officer, Marshall Medical Center, Placerville, CA, p. A80

WHIPPLE, Jennifer, Director Nursing, Lane County Hospital, Dighton, KS, p. A240

WHIPPLE, Michael, Chief Financial Officer, Mercy St. Anne Hospital, Toledo, OH, p. A500

WHISENHUNT, Mickey, Interim Chief Nursing Officer, Regional Medical Center, Orangeburg, SC, p. A565

WHITACRE, James, Chief Executive Officer, AMG Specialty Hospital – Muncie, Muncie, IN, p. A216

WHITAKER, Bert, Interim President and Chief Executive Officer, Regional Medical Center, Orangeburg, SC, p. A565

WHITAKER, Brittany, Chief Financial Officer, Placentia–Linda Hospital, Placentia, CA, p. A80

WHITAKER, Catherine MSN, R.N., Vice President and Chief Nursing Officer, University Of Maryland Baltimore Washington Medical Center, Glen Burnie, MD, p. A298

WHITAKER, Charles, Director Information Technology, Madison Parish Hospital, Tallulah, LA, p. A287

WHITAKER, Chasity, Administrative Assistant, Madison Parish Hospital, Tallulah, LA, p. A287

WHITAKER, Cynthia, Chief Nursing Officer, Henry County Medical Center, Paris, TN, p. A588

WHITAKER, Doris, Vice President and Manager, Mercy Hospital Booneville, Booneville, AR, p. A41

WHITAKER, Jimmy, Director Information Systems, Central Carolina Hospital, Sanford, NC, p. A470

WHITAKER, Neil M.D., Chief Medical Director, Orem Community Hospital, Orem, UT, p. A658

WHITAKER, Robert
Chief Executive Officer, Hamilton County Hospital, Syracuse, KS, p. A252
Vice President of Operations, Southwest Medical Center, Liberal, KS, p. A246

WHITAKER, Stephanie, Chief Nursing Officer, Sparks Regional Medical Center, Fort Smith, AR, p. A44

WHITE, Alexander, Vice President Medical Affairs, Carney Hospital, Boston, MA, p. A303

WHITE, Andrea, Chief Executive Officer, Select Specialty Hospital–Birmingham, Birmingham, AL, p. A15

WHITE, Beverly, MS, Facility Director, Mary S Harper Geriatric Psychiatry Center, Tuscaloosa, AL, p. A24

WHITE, Brian M., President, Northwest Hospital, Randallstown, MD, p. A300

WHITE, Brian
Director Strategic Operations, Vidant Chowan Hospital, Edenton, NC, p. A462
Director Strategic Planning, Vidant Bertie Hospital, Windsor, NC, p. A473

WHITE, Bruce D., Chief Executive Officer, Knox Community Hospital, Mount Vernon, OH, p. A496

WHITE, Bruce, Administrator, Covenant Hospital–Levelland, Levelland, TX, p. A629

WHITE, Catherine, Chief Financial Officer, Harney District Hospital, Burns, OR, p. A520

WHITE, Cindy CPA, Vice President of Operations, Integris Canadian Valley Hospital, Yukon, OK, p. A519

WHITE, Darrell, R.N., Administrator and Chief Nursing Officer, Tristar Ashland City Medical Center, Ashland City, TN, p. A575

WHITE, Darryl M.D., Chief of Staff, Freestone Medical Center, Fairfield, TX, p. A612

WHITE, Deborah, Human Resource Coordinator, Faith Community Hospital, Jacksboro, TX, p. A625

WHITE, Denise, MSN
Chief Nurse Executive, Carolinas Healthcare System Anson, Wadesboro, NC, p. A472
Chief Nurse Executive, Carolinas Healthcare System Union, Monroe, NC, p. A467

WHITE, Diane K., MSN, R.N., Chief Clinical Officer, Kindred Hospital South Philadelphia, Philadelphia, PA, p. A544

WHITE, Diane, Chief Clinical Officer and Chief Nursing Officer, Bridgepoint Hospital National Harbor, Washington, DC, p. A117

WHITE, Gary B M.D., Chief Medical Staff, Uintah Basin Medical Center, Roosevelt, UT, p. A660

WHITE, Harold, Vice Chancellor, University Health Shreveport, Shreveport, LA, p. A286

WHITE, J B, Director Information Systems, Merit Health River Region, Vicksburg, MS, p. A362

WHITE, James P M.D., Chief Medical Officer, Integris Baptist Medical Center, Oklahoma City, OK, p. A512

WHITE, Jason M.D., Chief Medical Officer, Mclaren Bay Region, Bay City, MI, p. A315

WHITE, Jean, Vice President Finance, Avera Heart Hospital Of South Dakota, Sioux Falls, SD, p. A572

WHITE, Jennifer, Chief of Staff, Mayo Clinic Health System In Springfield, Springfield, MN, p. A348

WHITE, Jim, Chief Information Officer, Lompoc Valley Medical Center, Lompoc, CA, p. A66

WHITE, Joanne, Chief Information Officer, Wood County Hospital, Bowling Green, OH, p. A482

WILLIAMS, Greg
  Chief Financial Officer, Pih Health Hospital – Downey, Downey, CA, p. A58
  Chief Financial Officer, Pih Health Hospital–Whittier, Whittier, CA, p. A97
WILLIAMS, Jackie, Director Human Resources, Merit Health Madison, Canton, MS, p. A353
WILLIAMS, James, M.D.
  Chief of Staff, Thedacare Medical Center–Waupaca, Waupaca, WI, p. A715
  Chief Executive Officer, Pearl River County Hospital, Poplarville, MS, p. A361
WILLIAMS, Jason, Director Information Systems, Olympia Medical Center, Los Angeles, CA, p. A70
WILLIAMS, Jeanette, Chief Executive Officer, Kindred Hospital–Aurora, Aurora, CO, p. A98
WILLIAMS, Jeremy, Chief Financial Officer, Banner Boswell Medical Center, Sun City, AZ, p. A36
WILLIAMS, Jim, Chief Financial Officer, Minden Medical Center, Minden, LA, p. A281
WILLIAMS, Joan, Administrative Assistant/Human Resources, Lamb Healthcare Center, Littlefield, TX, p. A629
WILLIAMS, John D Jr, Chief Financial Officer, Veterans Affairs Gulf Coast Veterans Health Care System, Biloxi, MS, p. A352
WILLIAMS, John
  Administrator and Chief Executive Officer, Nell J. Redfield Memorial Hospital, Malad City, ID, p. A174
  Chief Financial Officer, Upson Regional Medical Center, Thomaston, GA, p. A166
  Chief Information Officer, Bay Pines Veterans Affairs Healthcare System, Bay Pines, FL, p. A119
WILLIAMS, Joyce, Consultant Human Resources and Organizational Development, Memorial Hermann Rehabilitation Hospital – Katy, Katy, TX, p. A626
WILLIAMS, Julie
  Chief Financial Officer, Muenster Memorial Hospital, Muenster, TX, p. A634
  Chief Financial Officer, Smith County Memorial Hospital, Smith Center, KS, p. A252
WILLIAMS, Kathy, Chief Nursing Officer, Eastern New Mexico Medical Center, Roswell, NM, p. A428
WILLIAMS, KC, Director, MIS Operations, Lima Memorial Health System, Lima, OH, p. A493
WILLIAMS, Kenneth, Chief Information Officer, Fayetteville Veterans Affairs Medical Center, Fayetteville, NC, p. A462
WILLIAMS, Kim, , R.N., MS
  Director of Nursing, Mercy Hospital Logan County, Guthrie, OK, p. A508
  Chief Administrative Officer, Providence Regional Medical Center Everett, Everett, WA, p. A680
WILLIAMS, L Dale M.D., Vice President and Chief Medical Director, High Point Regional Health System, High Point, NC, p. A464
WILLIAMS, Laci, Director Human Resources, Kearny County Hospital, Lakin, KS, p. A244
WILLIAMS, Lana R, Chief Nursing Officer, Arkansas Methodist Medical Center, Paragould, AR, p. A48
WILLIAMS, Lauren, MS
  Vice President of Professional Services and Chief Nursing Officer, Lawrence + Memorial Hospital, New London, CT, p. A112
  Vice President Patient Care Services and Chief Nursing Officer, Westerly Hospital, Westerly, RI, p. A557
WILLIAMS, Linda, Director of Nursing, Villa Feliciana Medical Complex, Jackson, LA, p. A276
WILLIAMS, Lorie R.N., Vice President Nursing, Samaritan Pacific Communities Hospital, Newport, OR, p. A524
WILLIAMS, Lynn
  Vice President Human Resources, Medical Center At Bowling Green, Bowling Green, KY, p. A256
  Vice President Human Resources, Medical Center At Scottsville, Scottsville, KY, p. A267
  Vice President, Human Resources, The Medical Center Albany, Albany, KY, p. A255
  Vice President, Human Resources, The Medical Center At Caverna, Horse Cave, KY, p. A260
  Vice President, Commonwealth Regional Specialty Hospital, Bowling Green, KY, p. A255
WILLIAMS, Margaret, Chief Financial Officer, Baptist Memorial Hospital For Women, Memphis, TN, p. A584
WILLIAMS, Margo L R.N., Chief Nursing Officer, Anderson County Hospital, Garnett, KS, p. A241
WILLIAMS, Mark, M.D.
  Vice President and Chief Medical Officer, Miami Valley Hospital, Dayton, OH, p. A489
  Chief Financial Officer, Citrus Memorial Health System, Inverness, FL, p. A127
WILLIAMS, Mary, Director Human Resources, Medina Memorial Hospital, Medina, NY, p. A439

WILLIAMS, Matthew, R.N.
  Chief Financial Officer, Olympia Medical Center, Los Angeles, CA, p. A70
  Chief Executive Officer, Olympia Medical Center, Los Angeles, CA, p. A70
WILLIAMS, Michael D, Vice President and Administrator, Charleston Area Medical Center, Charleston, WV, p. A691
WILLIAMS, Michael F., Chief Financial Officer, Limestone Medical Center, Groesbeck, TX, p. A617
WILLIAMS, Michael L FACHE, Vice President Human Resources, Community Howard Regional Health, Kokomo, IN, p. A213
WILLIAMS, Michael, Chief Information Officer, Lawrence Memorial Hospital, Lawrence, KS, p. A245
WILLIAMS, Michelle, Administrator, Sedan City Hospital, Sedan, KS, p. A251
WILLIAMS, Mickey, Manager Information Technology, Moccasin Bend Mental Health Institute, Chattanooga, TN, p. A576
WILLIAMS, Nancy M., R.N., Administrator, Brooks County Hospital, Quitman, GA, p. A163
WILLIAMS, Nicole, Director of Human Resources Operations, DMC Huron Valley–Sinai Hospital, Commerce Township, MI, p. A317
WILLIAMS, Pam, Vice President, Ridgeview Le Sueur Medical Center, Le Sueur, MN, p. A342
WILLIAMS, Pamela G, Director Human Resources, Unity Health White County Medical Center, Searcy, AR, p. A49
WILLIAMS, Perry E. Sr, Administrator and Chief Executive Officer, Alliance Healthcare System, Holly Springs, MS, p. A356
WILLIAMS, Qiana, Director, Human Resource Business Partner, Grant, Ohiohealth Grant Medical Center, Columbus, OH, p. A487
WILLIAMS, R D, Chief Executive Officer, Hendry Regional Medical Center, Clewiston, FL, p. A122
WILLIAMS, Randy, Director Management Information Systems, Maria Parham Medical Center, Henderson, NC, p. A464
WILLIAMS, Reginald M.D., Medical Staff President, Curry General Hospital, Gold Beach, OR, p. A522
WILLIAMS, Rich, Director Human Resources, Upson Regional Medical Center, Thomaston, GA, p. A166
WILLIAMS, Richard, Chief Operating Officer, Southwest Mississippi Regional Medical Center, Mccomb, MS, p. A358
WILLIAMS, Robert D., Chief Executive Officer, Sunbury Community Hospital And Outpatient Center, Sunbury, PA, p. A551
WILLIAMS, Robert J. M.D., Chief Medical Staff, Wills Memorial Hospital, Washington, GA, p. A167
WILLIAMS, Robert, M.D.
  Chief Medical Officer, Arkansas Children's Hospital, Little Rock, AR, p. A45
  Chief Executive Officer, Healthsouth Southern Hills Rehabilitation Hospital, Princeton, WV, p. A695
WILLIAMS, Roberta A, Director of Nursing, U.S. Public Health Service Indian Hospital, Cass Lake, MN, p. A338
WILLIAMS, Roby D., Administrator, Hardin County General Hospital, Rosiclare, IL, p. A199
WILLIAMS, Rodney W M.D., JD, MS, Vice President Medical Affairs, Good Samaritan Regional Medical Center, Suffern, NY, p. A453
WILLIAMS, Ronald G., Administrator, Central Louisiana State Hospital, Pineville, LA, p. A284
WILLIAMS, Sabrina, Interm Vice President Human Resources, Brigham And Women's Hospital, Boston, MA, p. A303
WILLIAMS, Sandra, Chief Financial Officer, Cape Fear Valley Medical Center, Fayetteville, NC, p. A462
WILLIAMS, Scott
  Chief Executive Officer, Rehabilitation Hospital Of Northwest Ohio, Toledo, OH, p. A500
  Chief Operating Officer, Cookeville Regional Medical Center, Cookeville, TN, p. A577
WILLIAMS, Sean J., President and Chief Executive Officer, Mercy Medical Center–Clinton, Clinton, IA, p. A224
WILLIAMS, Shane, Director Information Systems, Davis Hospital And Medical Center, Layton, UT, p. A657
WILLIAMS, Sharon, Vice President Finance and Information Technology, Avera Marshall Regional Medical Center, Marshall, MN, p. A343
WILLIAMS, Sheila, Vice President and Administrator, Baptist Health Medical Center–Hot Spring County, Malvern, AR, p. A46
WILLIAMS, Sheri, Chief Operating Officer, Guadalupe Regional Medical Center, Seguin, TX, p. A644
WILLIAMS, Stephanie, R.N.
  Chief Nursing Officer, Washington Hospital Healthcare System, Fremont, CA, p. A60
  Coordinator Human Resources, Kindred Rehabilitation Hospital Northeast Houston, Humble, TX, p. A624

  Market Director Human Resources, Lake Norman Regional Medical Center, Mooresville, NC, p. A467
WILLIAMS, Sue Ann, Chief Executive Officer, Southeast Health Center Of Stoddard County, Dexter, MO, p. A367
WILLIAMS, Susan, M.D., R.N.
  Chief Medical Officer, Conemaugh Memorial Medical Center, Johnstown, PA, p. A537
  Chief Medical Officer, Conemaugh Miners Medical Center, Hastings, PA, p. A536
  Chief Nursing Officer, Baptist Health Medical Center–Stuttgart, Stuttgart, AR, p. A50
WILLIAMS, Teresa, R.N.
  Administrator and Director of Nursing, Mercy Hospital Ozark, Ozark, AR, p. A48
  Regional Administrator, Mercy Hospital Booneville, Booneville, AR, p. A41
  Regional Administrator, Mercy Hospital Waldron, Waldron, AR, p. A50
WILLIAMS, Thaddeus, Controller, Healthsouth Rehabilitation Hospital Memphis–North, Memphis, TN, p. A584
WILLIAMS, Todd, Chief Financial Officer, Siloam Springs Regional Hospital, Siloam Springs, AR, p. A49
WILLIAMS, Tom, Vice President Human Resources, Lake Regional Health System, Osage Beach, MO, p. A374
WILLIAMS, Tricia, President and Chief Executive Officer, Florida Hospital North Pinellas, Tarpon Springs, FL, p. A145
WILLIAMS, Wade, Chief Information Officer, Morehead Memorial Hospital, Eden, NC, p. A461
WILLIAMS, Wendell H M.D., Jr, Medical Director, Specialty Hospital Jacksonville, Jacksonville, FL, p. A128
WILLIAMSON, Alan M.D., Chief Medical Officer, Eisenhower Medical Center, Rancho Mirage, CA, p. A63
WILLIAMSON, Barry, President Medical Staff, Southeastern Health, Lumberton, NC, p. A466
WILLIAMSON, John, Human Resources Site Manager, Baptist Health South Florida, Mariners Hospital, Tavernier, FL, p. A146
WILLIAMSON, Johnny M.D., Chief Medical Officer, Hartgrove Hospital, Chicago, IL, p. A181
WILLIAMSON, Marilyn, Chief Human Resources Officer, Rainbow Mental Health Facility, Kansas City, KS, p. A244
WILLIAMSON, Sharon, Chief Information Technology, Robert J. Dole Veterans Affairs Medical Center, Wichita, KS, p. A253
WILLIE, David, Chief Financial Officer, Yuma Regional Medical Center, Yuma, AZ, p. A39
WILLIFORD, Sandy, Chief Health Information Management and Revenue Administration, Charlie Norwood Veterans Affairs Medical Center, Augusta, GA, p. A151
WILLINGHAM, Alex M.D., Medical Director, Warm Springs Rehabilitation Hospital Of San Antonio, San Antonio, TX, p. A644
WILLINGHAM, John, Chief Executive Officer and Managing Director, Carolina Center For Behavioral Health, Greer, SC, p. A563
WILLIS, Bill, Director Information Technology, River Point Behavioral Health, Jacksonville, FL, p. A128
WILLIS, Brenda, Director of Nursing, Doctor's Hospital Of Deer Creek, Leesville, LA, p. A280
WILLIS, Darrell M.D., Chief of Staff, Dr. Dan C. Trigg Memorial Hospital, Tucumcari, NM, p. A429
WILLIS, Jayne, Vice President Nursing and Chief Nursing Officer, Orlando Regional Medical Center, Orlando, FL, p. A137
WILLIS, Jonathon, Director Information Services, Tennova Healthcare–Shelbyville, Shelbyville, TN, p. A589
WILLIS, Joshua, Chief Executive Officer, West Florida Community Care Center, Milton, FL, p. A134
WILLIS, Joy, Acting Chief Fiscal Service, G.V. (Sonny) Montgomery Veterans Affairs Medical Center, Jackson, MS, p. A356
WILLIS, Kathy M.D., Medical Director, Lallie Kemp Medical Center, Independence, LA, p. A276
WILLIS, Raymond, IT Manager, Choctaw Health Center, Philadelphia, MS, p. A360
WILLIS, Robert, Director Human Resources, North Shore Health, Grand Marais, MN, p. A340
WILLIS, Sandra, Director of Human Resources, Citizens Baptist Medical Center, Talladega, AL, p. A23
WILLIS, Toni M.D., Medical Director, Healthsouth Rehabilitation Hospital – Mid–Cities, Bedford, TX, p. A597
WILLIS, Wendy L, Vice President Human Resources, Children's Hospital, New Orleans, LA, p. A282
WILLIS, William L., Administrator, Oceans Behavioral Hospital Of Lake Charles, Lake Charles, LA, p. A279
WILLMANN, Adam, President and Chief Executive Officer, Goodall-Witcher Hospital Authority, Clifton, TX, p. A601
WILLMON, Brian M.D., Medical Director, Plains Regional Medical Center, Clovis, NM, p. A425

WILLMORE, Lois, Supervisor Health Information Management, Cedar County Memorial Hospital, El Dorado Springs, MO, p. A367

WILLMS, Frederick M.D., Chief Medical Officer, Piedmont Fayette Hospital, Fayetteville, GA, p. A157

WILLOUGHBY, Kirsten, Director of Nursing, Big Horn County Memorial Hospital, Hardin, MT, p. A385

WILLS, Andrea R.N., Chief Nursing Executive, Munising Memorial Hospital, Munising, MI, p. A326

WILLS, Andy M.D., Medical Director, Colquitt Regional Medical Center, Moultrie, GA, p. A162

WILLS, Kim, Chief Operating Officer, Cook Medical Center–A Campus Of Tift Regional Medical Center, Adel, GA, p. A149

WILLS, Laura S.
Administrator, Noland Hospital Birmingham, Birmingham, AL, p. A15
Administrator, Noland Hospital Shelby, Alabaster, AL, p. A13

WILLS, Michele, Registered Health Information Administrator, Caro Center, Caro, MI, p. A316

WILLS, Robert M.D., Chief Medical Officer, Arise Austin Medical Center, Austin, TX, p. A594

WILLS, Shannon, Director Human Resources, Delray Medical Center, Delray Beach, FL, p. A124

WILLSHER, Jay, Chief Operating Officer, Unitypoint Health – Trinity Bettendorf, Bettendorf, IA, p. A222

WILLSIE, Brett, Vice President Human Resources, Sentara Northern Virginia Medical Center, Woodbridge, VA, p. A677

WILLWERTH, Deborah J., R.N., MSN, Chief Executive Officer, Heart Of Lancaster Regional Medical Center, Lititz, PA, p. A539

WILMOT, Joan, Chief Finance Officer, White River Junction Veterans Affairs Medical Center, White River Junction, VT, p. A663

WILMOTH, Donna, Vice President Patient Care Services and Chief Nursing Officer, Sentara Williamsburg Regional Medical Center, Williamsburg, VA, p. A677

WILMS, Mike, Director Information Systems, Regional Medical Center Bayonet Point, Hudson, FL, p. A127

WILSON, Ada, R.N., Interim Chief Executive Officer, Jefferson County Hospital, Fayette, MS, p. A354

WILSON, Alice FACHE, Vice President Administration, St. Luke's Hospital – Warren Campus, Phillipsburg, NJ, p. A419

WILSON, Amy M.D., Medical Director, Baylor Institute For Rehabilitation, Dallas, TX, p. A604

WILSON, Bill, Chief Financial Officer, North Carolina Specialty Hospital, Durham, NC, p. A461

WILSON, Bobbie, Director Human Resources, Crete Area Medical Center, Crete, NE, p. A392

WILSON, Brent, Chief Executive Officer, Marian Center, Salt Lake City, UT, p. A660

WILSON, Carolyn, R.N.
Chief Operating Officer, Beaumont Hospital – Farmington Hills, Farmington Hills, MI, p. A319
Chief Operating Officer, Beaumont Hospital – Grosse Pointe, Grosse Pointe, MI, p. A322
Chief Operating Officer, Beaumont Hospital – Royal Oak, Royal Oak, MI, p. A329
Chief Operating Officer, Beaumont Hospital – Taylor, Taylor, MI, p. A331
Chief Operating Officer, Beaumont Hospital – Trenton, Trenton, MI, p. A332
Chief Operating Officer, Beaumont Hospital – Troy, Troy, MI, p. A332
Chief Operating Officer, Beaumont Hospital – Wayne, Wayne, MI, p. A333
Chief Operating Officer, Beaumont Hospital–Dearborn, Dearborn, MI, p. A317

WILSON, Charlene J, Vice President Human Resources, St. Francis Hospital, Wilmington, DE, p. A116

WILSON, Chase, Chief Financial Officer, Sycamore Shoals Hospital, Elizabethton, TN, p. A578

WILSON, Christopher M.D., Inpatient Medical Director, South Texas Rehabilitation Hospital, Brownsville, TX, p. A599

WILSON, Christy, Chief Financial Officer, Merit Health Rankin, Brandon, MS, p. A353

WILSON, Colleen, Chief Nursing Officer, Southern Inyo Healthcare District, Lone Pine, CA, p. A66

WILSON, Craig, Chief Medical Officer, St. Vincent Fishers Hospital, Fishers, IN, p. A207

WILSON, David C., Chief Executive Officer, North Mississippi Medical Center – Tupelo, Tupelo, MS, p. A362

WILSON, David R M.D., Chief of Staff, St. Vincent's Blount, Oneonta, AL, p. A22

WILSON, Deanna, VP Patient Care Services/Site Manager, Aspirus Ontonagon Hospital, Inc., Ontonagon, MI, p. A327

WILSON, Deb, Director Human Resources, Kalispell Regional Healthcare, Kalispell, MT, p. A386

WILSON, Debra, Vice President and Chief Nursing Officer, Saint Luke's Hospital Of Kansas City, Kansas City, MO, p. A370

WILSON, Dottie D, Director Human Resources, Pickens County Medical Center, Carrollton, AL, p. A16

WILSON, Eleanor R.N., MSN, Vice President and Chief Operating Officer, Doylestown Hospital, Doylestown, PA, p. A533

WILSON, Elizabeth M, Coordinator Human Resources, Select Specialty Hospital – Cincinnati North, Cincinnati, OH, p. A484

WILSON, Elizabeth, Administrator, The Neuromedical Center Rehabilitation Hospital, Baton Rouge, LA, p. A271

WILSON, Fiore, Director Information Systems, Castleview Hospital, Price, UT, p. A659

WILSON, Hamlin J
Senior Vice President Human Resources, Wellmont Bristol Regional Medical Center, Bristol, TN, p. A575
Senior Vice President Human Resources, Wellmont Holston Valley Medical Center, Kingsport, TN, p. A581

WILSON, Jason, Administrator and Chief Executive Officer, American Fork Hospital, American Fork, UT, p. A656

WILSON, Jeffrey, Chief Executive Officer, Methodist Hospital, San Antonio, TX, p. A643

WILSON, Jim, Vice President Information Technology, Promise Hospital Of San Diego, San Diego, CA, p. A85

WILSON, Jodi, President and Chief Operating Officer, Diley Ridge Medical Center, Canal Winchester, OH, p. A482

WILSON, John R, Vice President, Human Resources, Murray–Calloway County Hospital, Murray, KY, p. A265

WILSON, Kari R.N., Vice President Patient Care Services and Chief Nursing Officer, SSM Health St. Mary's Hospital – Audrain, Mexico, MO, p. A373

WILSON, Kathey, Acting Chief Executive Officer, U. S. Public Health Service Indian Hospital, Rosebud, SD, p. A572

WILSON, Kim, Human Resources Coordinator, Cordova Community Medical Center, Cordova, AK, p. A25

WILSON, Kimberly P, Director Human Resources, University Of Kentucky Albert B. Chandler Hospital, Lexington, KY, p. A262

WILSON, Lawrence M.D., Vice President, Chief Medical Officer, Midland Memorial Hospital, Midland, TX, p. A633

WILSON, Lerae, Vice President Patient Services and Chief Nursing Officer, St. Claire Healthcare, Morehead, KY, p. A265

WILSON, Loretta, Administrator, Hill Hospital Of Sumter County, York, AL, p. A24

WILSON, Mallory, Administrative Assistant and Human Resources Coordinator, Select Specialty Hospital–North Knoxville, Powell, TN, p. A588

WILSON, Margaret G., R.N., MSN, Acting Director, Lebanon Veterans Affairs Medical Center, Lebanon, PA, p. A538

WILSON, Monte, President, Wellstar Windy Hill Hospital, Marietta, GA, p. A161

WILSON, Nadine, Manager, Human Resources, Jerome Golden Center For Behavioral Health, Inc., West Palm Beach, FL, p. A147

WILSON, Nathan R.N., Vice President and Chief Nursing Officer, Baptist Health La Grange, La Grange, KY, p. A260

WILSON, Nicole, Manager Human Resources, St. Theresa Specialty Hospital, Kenner, LA, p. A277

WILSON, Patricia, Senior Vice President Human Resources, Englewood Hospital And Medical Center, Englewood, NJ, p. A414

WILSON, Regina R.N., Director of Nursing, Share Medical Center, Alva, OK, p. A504

WILSON, Robert E., Esq
Chief Executive Officer, Dekalb Medical At Downtown Decatur, Decatur, GA, p. A156
Chief Executive Officer, Dekalb Medical At North Decatur, Decatur, GA, p. A156
Vice President and Chief Information Officer, Crozer–Chester Medical Center, Upland, PA, p. A552
Vice President and Chief Information Officer, Delaware County Memorial Hospital, Drexel Hill, PA, p. A533

WILSON, Robert D.O., Director Medical Services, Eagleville Hospital, Eagleville, PA, p. A533

WILSON, Roy, M.D.
Medical Director, Metropolitan St. Louis Psychiatric Center, Saint Louis, MO, p. A377
Medical Director, St. Louis Psychiatric Rehabilitation Center, Saint Louis, MO, p. A378

WILSON, Sara, Director Human Resources, Cheyenne County Hospital, Saint Francis, KS, p. A251

WILSON, Sherry R.N., Chief Nursing Officer, Mayers Memorial Hospital District, Fall River Mills, CA, p. A59

WILSON, Stephan A, Chief Financial Officer, Montrose Memorial Hospital, Montrose, CO, p. A106

WILSON, Tammie R.N., MSN, Chief Nursing Officer, Fayette County Memorial Hospital, Washington Court House, OH, p. A502

WILSON, Terrance E., President and Chief Executive Officer, Franciscan Health Lafayette East, Lafayette, IN, p. A214

WILSON, Tracy, Chief Executive Officer, Kindred Rehabilitation Hospital Northeast Houston, Humble, TX, p. A624

WILSON, Vicki, Human Resources Director, Dixie Regional Medical Center, Saint George, UT, p. A660

WILSON, William M.D., Chief Medical Officer, Uc Irvine Medical Center, Orange, CA, p. A78

WILSON RN, MSN,CEN, Sondra Dianne R.N., MSN, Assistant Administrator and Chief Nursing Officer, Tyler County Hospital, Woodville, TX, p. A655

WILSON–NEIL, Carla FACHE, Chief Operating Officer, Spectrum Health Pennock, Hastings, MI, p. A322

WILSON–STUBBS, Yolande, President, Presence Holy Family Medical Center, Des Plaines, IL, p. A185

WILTERMOOD, Michael C., President and Chief Executive Officer, Enloe Medical Center, Chico, CA, p. A55

WILTROUT, Kristy R.N., Chief Operating Officer, Vernon Memorial Healthcare, Viroqua, WI, p. A714

WILTROUT, Terry, President, Washington Health System Greene, Waynesburg, PA, p. A553

WILVER, Donald Jr, Vice President Human Resources, Muncy Valley Hospital, Muncy, PA, p. A542

WIMMER, Keri R.N., Patient Care Director, Centracare Health–Melrose, Melrose, MN, p. A343

WIMSATT, Michael, Director Human Resources, Piedmont Geriatric Hospital, Burkeville, VA, p. A665

WINBERY, Ben, Chief Financial Officer, Vantage Point Of Northwest Arkansas, Fayetteville, AR, p. A43

WINDAS, Allison Leigh, Director of Patient Care Services, Shriners Hospitals For Children–Greenville, Greenville, SC, p. A563

WINDHAM, Joel
Vice President Human Resources, Anderson Regional Health System South, Meridian, MS, p. A359
Vice President Human Resources, Anderson Regional Health System, Meridian, MS, p. A359

WINDHAM, Michael D., Chief Executive Officer, Northwest Medical Center, Winfield, AL, p. A24

WINDHAM, William, Chief Executive Officer, Lewisgale Hospital Alleghany, Low Moor, VA, p. A669

WINDLAND, J Michael M.D., Chief of Staff, Southern Tennessee Regional Health System–Pulaski, Pulaski, TN, p. A588

WINDLE, Jane R.N., Director of Nurses, North Mississippi Medical Center–West Point, West Point, MS, p. A363

WINDOLOVICH, Winona, Associate Chief Information Officer, Zuckerberg San Francisco General Hospital And Trauma Center, San Francisco, CA, p. A88

WINDROW, Matthew M.D., Chief of Staff, Medina Regional Hospital, Hondo, TX, p. A619

WINDSOR, Bonnie, Senior Vice President Human Resources, Johns Hopkins Hospital, Baltimore, MD, p. A294

WINEGARNER, Rodney, Chief Financial Officer, Mercy Hospitals Of Bakersfield, Bakersfield, CA, p. A53

WINFREE, Kersey M.D., Chief Medical Officer, St. Anthony Hospital, Oklahoma City, OK, p. A513

WING, Lilly, Chief Nursing Officer, Three Rivers Behavioral Health, West Columbia, SC, p. A567

WING, Yakesun, Business Strategy and Finance Leader, Kaiser Permanente Walnut Creek Medical Center, Walnut Creek, CA, p. A96

WINGATE, Phyllis A., FACHE, President, Carolinas Healthcare System Northeast, Concord, NC, p. A460

WINGER, Ronald C, President, Lovelace Medical Center, Albuquerque, NM, p. A424

WINGET, Mary, Director Human Resources, Minden Medical Center, Minden, LA, p. A281

WINGFIELD, Gena, Senior Vice President and Chief Financial Officer, Arkansas Children's Hospital, Little Rock, AR, p. A45

WINIGER, Cecilia, Community Outreach and Communication Manager, Frank R. Howard Memorial Hospital, Willits, CA, p. A97

WINK, Jeri, Director Human Resources, Grandview Medical Center, Birmingham, AL, p. A14

WINKELMAN, Dan, President and Chief Executive Officer, Yukon–Kuskokwim Delta Regional Hospital, Bethel, AK, p. A25

WINKLE, Derek, Director Human Resources, Leconte Medical Center, Sevierville, TN, p. A588

WINKLER, Gordon W., Administrator and Chief Executive Officer, Ringgold County Hospital, Mount Ayr, IA, p. A231

WINN, Ann M M.D., R.N., FACHE, Chief Nursing Officer, Methodist Stone Oak Hospital, San Antonio, TX, p. A643

WINN, Cameron, Director Information Services, Ashley Regional Medical Center, Vernal, UT, p. A661

WINN, Eleyce, Chief Executive Officer, Regency Hospital Of Northwest Indiana, East Chicago, IN, p. A206

WINN, Holly FACHE, Chief Operating Officer, Black River Memorial Hospital, Black River Falls, WI, p. A699

WINNER, Douglas, Chief Financial Officer, Acute Care Operations, Providence–Providence Park Hospitals, Southfield, MI, p. A331

WINNETT, Steve, Chief Executive Officer, Advanced Diagnostics Hospital, Houston, TX, p. A619

WINNIK, Mitchell, Chief Operating Officer, Corona Regional Medical Center, Corona, CA, p. A56

WINSETT, Gracia, Chief Financial Officer, Wellstone Regional Hospital, Jeffersonville, IN, p. A213

WINSTON, Bob M.D., Medical Director, Acadia Vermilion Hospital, Lafayette, LA, p. A278

WINSTON, Patricia A FACHE, MS, R.N., Vice President, Chief Administrative Officer and Chief Operating Officer, Suny Downstate Medical Center University Hospital, New Rochelle, NY, p. A447

WINT, Jesse, Director of Nursing, Hardin Medical Center, Savannah, TN, p. A588

WINTER, Jon R. D.O., Chief of Staff, Camden General Hospital, Camden, IN, p. A575

WINTER, Melissa, R.N., MSN, Chief Operating Officer and Chief Nursing Officer, Baylor Medical Center At Mckinney, Mckinney, TX, p. A632

WINTER–CLARK, Jan, Chief Executive Officer, Bristow Medical Center, Bristow, OK, p. A505

WINTERS, Gene, Chief Financial Officer, Northwest Texas Healthcare System, Amarillo, TX, p. A592

WINTERS, Heidi, Business Partner Human Resources, Chi Health Missouri Valley, Missouri Valley, IA, p. A231

WINTERS, Janice, Controller, Pickens County Medical Center, Carrollton, AL, p. A16

WINTERS, Mary, Interim Chief Nursing Officer, St. James Healthcare, Butte, MT, p. A383

WINTERS, Shane, Chief Information Officer, Jersey Community Hospital, Jerseyville, IL, p. A191

WINTHROP, Michael, President, Bellevue Hospital, Bellevue, OH, p. A481

WIRJO, Jonathan M.D., Medical Director, Seven Hills Hospital, Henderson, NV, p. A402

WIRTHGEN, Doug
Chief Information Officer, Va Palo Alto Health Care System, Palo Alto, CA, p. A79
Facility Chief Information Officer, Veterans Affairs Loma Linda Healthcare System, Loma Linda, CA, p. A66

WIRTZ, David
Senior LAN Administrator, Evansville State Hospital, Evansville, IN, p. A207
Supervisor Information Technology, Evansville Psychiatric Children Center, Evansville, IN, p. A207

WISE, Dan, Manager Information Technology, Sarah D. Culbertson Memorial Hospital, Rushville, IL, p. A199

WISE, Elizabeth, R.N., MS
Chief Nursing Officer and Vice President, Patient Care Services, Saint Peter's University Hospital, New Brunswick, NJ, p. A417
President and Chief Executive Officer, Lehigh Valley Hospital – Pocono, East Stroudsburg, PA, p. A533

WISE, Jerry R., Chief Executive Officer, Habersham Medical Center, Demorest, GA, p. A156

WISE, Josh, Director Information Technology, Lawrence Memorial Hospital, Walnut Ridge, AR, p. A50

WISE, Kim, Director Human Resources, Bronson South Haven Hospital, South Haven, MI, p. A331

WISE, Robert P., President and Chief Executive Officer, Hunterdon Medical Center, Flemington, NJ, p. A414

WISE, Teresa R.N., Chief Nursing Officer, Mena Regional Health System, Mena, AR, p. A47

WISE, Toby, Chief Nursing Officer, Winn Parish Medical Center, Winnfield, LA, p. A288

WISEMAN, Josh, Chief Financial Officer, Va Portland Healthcare System, Portland, OR, p. A525

WISEMANN, Jacob, Chief Financial Officer, Parkland Medical Center, Derry, NH, p. A407

WISEMORE, Donna S R.N., Vice President and Chief Nursing Officer, Dekalb Health, Auburn, IN, p. A203

WISLER, Tam, Director Human Resources, Columbus Dublin Springs, Dublin, OH, p. A490

WISMANN, Andrea M.D., Chief of Staff, Southeast Colorado Hospital District, Springfield, CO, p. A107

WISMER, Doug, Chief Financial Officer, Thayer County Health Services, Hebron, NE, p. A394

WISNER, Donna, Chief Financial Officer, Warner Hospital And Health Services, Clinton, IL, p. A184

WISNIESKI, Thomas, FACHE, Director, North Florida/South Georgia Veteran's Health System, Gainesville, FL, p. A126

WISNIEWSKI, Cass, Interim Chief Financial Officer, Hurley Medical Center, Flint, MI, p. A319

WISNOSKI, Joseph, Chief Financial Officer, John T. Mather Memorial Hospital, Port Jefferson, NY, p. A450

WISSMAN, Sheryl M.D., Chief Medical Officer, Crittenton Hospital Medical Center, Rochester, MI, p. A329

WISWELL, Ashleigh, Chief Operations Officer, Moore County Hospital District, Dumas, TX, p. A609

WITCHER–BOATENG, Bernetta Ph.D., Director Quality Improvement Services and Compliance, Southwest Connecticut Mental Health System, Bridgeport, CT, p. A109

WITENSKE, James, Chief Information Officer, Jefferson Hospital, Jefferson Hills, PA, p. A537

WITHAM, Val
Director Health Information, Avera Flandreau Hospital, Flandreau, SD, p. A570
Director of Health Information, Avera Dells Area Hospital, Dell Rapids, SD, p. A569

WITHERELL, Jodi, Vice President Patient Care and Quality, Brooks Memorial Hospital, Dunkirk, NY, p. A435

WITHERSPOON, Lynn, Vice President and Chief Information Officer, Psychiatric Pavilion New Orleans, New OrleansOchsner Medical Center, New Orleans, LA, p. A283

WITHINGTON, Amber R.N., Chief Nursing Officer, Rawlins County Health Center, Atwood, KS, p. A238

WITKOWICZ, Victor J, Senior Vice President and Chief Financial Officer, Madonna Rehabilitation Hospital, Lincoln, NE, p. A395

WITMER, Bruce M.D., Medical Director, Fresno Surgical Hospital, Fresno, CA, p. A60

WITT, David A, Vice President Finances, Houston Methodist St. John Hospital, Nassau Bay, TX, p. A634

WITT, David, Chief Financial Officer, Meadows Psychiatric Center, Centre Hall, PA, p. A531

WITT, Jana, Chief Executive Officer, Cedar County Memorial Hospital, El Dorado Springs, MO, p. A367

WITT, Laura, Administrator Human Resources, Banner Thunderbird Medical Center, Glendale, AZ, p. A30

WITT, Lori, Site Finance Director, Mercy Health – Marcum And Wallace, Irvine, KY, p. A260

WITT, Sarah, Director Human Resources, Richmond State Hospital, Richmond, IN, p. A219

WITT, Stephen, President and Chief Executive Officer, College Hospital Cerritos, Cerritos, CA, p. A55

WITT, Thomas J., M.D.
President and Chief Executive Officer, Mayo Clinic Health System In Cannon Falls, Cannon Falls, MN, p. A337
President and Chief Executive Officer, Mayo Clinic Health System In Lake City, Lake City, MN, p. A341
President and Chief Executive Officer, Mayo Clinic Health System In Red Wing, Red Wing, MN, p. A346

WITT, Ty M.D., Chief Medical Officer, Lake Chelan Community Hospital And Clinics, Chelan, WA, p. A679

WITTE, Kari, Director Patient Care, Windom Area Hospital, Windom, MN, p. A350

WITTE, Russell, Director Information Technology, Citizens Medical Center, Victoria, TX, p. A652

WITTENSTEIN, Robin D., Ed.D., Chief Executive Officer, Denver Health, Denver, CO, p. A100

WITTHAUS, Patricia, Director Information Services, Valley Regional Hospital, Claremont, NH, p. A407

WITTMAN, Thomas, Chief Information Officer, Jewish Hospital, Louisville, KY, p. A262

WITTWER, Julie, Chief Financial Officer, South Texas Surgical Hospital, Corpus Christi, TX, p. A603

WLEKLINSKI, Maria, Chief Nursing Officer, Siloam Springs Regional Hospital, Siloam Springs, AR, p. A49

WODARZ, Christopher A., Chief, Resource Management Division, Tripler Army Medical Center, Honolulu, HI, p. A169

WODICKA, Mary Jo, Vice President Human Resources, Wheaton Franciscan Healthcare – All Saints, Racine, WI, p. A711

WOELKERS, Joe, Executive Vice President and Chief Staff, University Of Texas Health Northeast, Tyler, TX, p. A651

WOELTJEN, Bill, Chief Financial Officer, Sarasota Memorial Health Care System, Sarasota, FL, p. A142

WOEN, Linda, Director Human Resources, Yuma Rehabilitation Hospital, Yuma, AZ, p. A39

WOERNER, Steve, President and Chief Executive Officer, Driscoll Children's Hospital, Corpus Christi, TX, p. A603

WOHLFARDT, Diana, Director Human Resources, Nashville General Hospital, Nashville, TN, p. A586

WOHLFORD, Steve, Chief Operating Officer, Johnson Memorial Hospital, Franklin, IN, p. A209

WOHLMAN, John, Manager Information Systems, Shoshone Medical Center, Kellogg, ID, p. A173

WOISKE, Edward M.D., Chief Medical Officer, Avera Marshall Regional Medical Center, Marshall, MN, p. A343

WOITALEWICZ, Rebecca, Chief Financial Officer, Children's Hospitals And Clinics Of Minnesota, Minneapolis, MN, p. A343

WOJNO, Kathy, R.N., MSN
Vice President Nursing Services and Chief Nursing Officer, Beverly Hospital, Montebello, CA, p. A74

Administrator, Memorial Hospital Of Gardena, Gardena, CA, p. A61

WOJTALEWICZ, Jeanette, Chief Financial Officer, Chi Health Mercy Council Bluffs, Council Bluffs, IA, p. A225

WOLAK, Robert, Chief Information Resource Management Service, G.V. (Sonny) Montgomery Veterans Affairs Medical Center, Jackson, MS, p. A356

WOLCOTT, Daniel, President and Chief Executive Officer, Lodi Memorial Hospital, Lodi, CA, p. A66

WOLD, Lynn
Chief Operation Officer, Unitypoint Health – St. Lukes's Sioux City, Sioux City, IA, p. A235
President and Chief Executive Officer, Unitypoint Health – St. Lukes's Sioux City, Sioux City, IA, p. A235

WOLESKE, Chris, Chief Operating Officer, Bellin Psychiatric Center, Green Bay, WI, p. A703

WOLF, Brenda J., President and Chief Executive Officer, La Rabida Children's Hospital, Chicago, IL, p. A181

WOLF, Chris, Director Information Technology, Clay County Medical Center, Clay Center, KS, p. A239

WOLF, Edward H., Chief Administrative Officer, Marshfield Medical Center, Marshfield, WI, p. A706

WOLF, Gregory A, Director Information Systems, Shriners Hospitals For Children–Honolulu, Honolulu, HI, p. A169

WOLF, Jack, Vice President Information Systems, Montefiore Medical Center, New Rochelle, NY, p. A443

WOLF, Manuela, R.N., Chief Executive Officer, Harlan County Health System, Alma, NE, p. A390

WOLF, Marc, Assistant Vice President Human Resources, St. Barnabas Hospital, New Rochelle, NY, p. A446

WOLF, Randall, Vice President Finance, Perry County Memorial Hospital, Perryville, MO, p. A375

WOLF, Robin, Chief Nursing Officer, Complex Care Hospital At Tenaya, Las Vegas, NV, p. A402

WOLF, Sherry L M.D., Chief of Medical Staff, Chillicothe Hospital District, Chillicothe, TX, p. A601

WOLF, Stephanne, Chief Nursing Officer, Morris County Hospital, Council Grove, KS, p. A240

WOLF, Tricia, Director Information Technology, OSS Orthopaedic Hospital, York, PA, p. A555

WOLFE, Anita, Chief Nurse Executive, Multicare Tacoma General Hospital, Tacoma, WA, p. A688

WOLFE, Brian, Chief of Staff, Allen County Regional Hospital, Iola, KS, p. A243

WOLFE, Cathy Allyson, Chief Nursing Officer, Parkview Wabash County Hospital, Wabash, IN, p. A221

WOLFE, Darryl, Chief Financial Officer, Olympic Medical Center, Port Angeles, WA, p. A683

WOLFE, John, Chief Financial Officer, Saint Elizabeth's Medical Center, Wabasha, MN, p. A349

WOLFE, Lisa, President, Chi Health Mercy Corning, Corning, IA, p. A224

WOLFE, Lois, Director Human Resources, Geisinger–Community Medical Center, Scranton, PA, p. A550

WOLFE, Philip R., President and Chief Executive Officer, Gwinnett Hospital System, Lawrenceville, GA, p. A160

WOLFE, Phillip R., Chief Executive Officer, Kindred Hospital–Los Angeles, Los Angeles, CA, p. A69

WOLFE, Scott A., Chief Financial Officer, Piedmont Fayette Hospital, Fayetteville, GA, p. A157

WOLFE, Scott R., CPA, President, St. Luke's Hospital – Warren Campus, Phillipsburg, NJ, p. A419

WOLFE, Sean, Vice President Finance and Chief Financial Officer, Community Hospital, Mccook, NE, p. A396

WOLFE, Stephen A., President and Chief Executive Officer, Indiana Regional Medical Center, Indiana, PA, p. A537

WOLFE, Teresa E, Manager Human Resources, Kansas Heart Hospital, Wichita, KS, p. A253

WOLFENBARGER, Carol C., FACHE, MSN, President and Chief Executive Officer, Mcdowell Hospital, Marion, NC, p. A466

WOLFF, David, Director Information Technology, Newberry County Memorial Hospital, Newberry, SC, p. A565

WOLFF, Holly, Chief Executive Officer, Ashley Medical Center, Ashley, ND, p. A474

WOLFF, Patrice P
Director Information Services, Westfields Hospital, New Richmond, WI, p. A709
Director Management Information Systems, Amery Hospital And Clinic, Amery, WI, p. A698

WOLFF, Peter M.D., President Medical Staff, Cascade Valley Hospital And Clinics, Arlington, WA, p. A678

WOLFGANG, Tony, Chief Financial Officer, Coatesville Veterans Affairs Medical Center, Coatesville, PA, p. A532

WOLKART, Kristin, R.N., President and Chief Executive Officer, St. Francis Medical Center, Monroe, LA, p. A281

WOLLEBEN, Robert G., Chief Executive Officer, Massena Memorial Hospital, Massena, NY, p. A439

WOLOSZYN, Daniel B., Chief Executive Officer, Rehabilitation Hospital Of Indiana, Indianapolis, IN, p. A212

WRAY, Christine R.
President, Medstar Southern Maryland Hospital Center, Clinton, MD, p. A297
President, Medstar St. Mary's Hospital, Leonardtown, MD, p. A299
WRAY, Dean, Vice President Finance, Southern Ohio Medical Center, Portsmouth, OH, p. A498
WRAY, Jeremy D.O., Medical Director, Sage Memorial Hospital, Ganado, AZ, p. A29
WRAY, Thomas, Director Information, Geisinger–Bloomsburg Hospital, Bloomsburg, PA, p. A530
WREN, Jason, President and Chief Executive Officer, Wise Health System, Decatur, TX, p. A607
WREN, Mark A M.D., Medical Director, Healthsouth Rehabilitation Hospital Of Texarkana, Texarkana, TX, p. A649
WREN, Timothy, Chief Financial Officer, Abbeville Area Medical Center, Abbeville, SC, p. A558
WRIGHT, Albert L. Jr, PharmD, President and Chief Executive Officer, West Virginia University Hospitals, Morgantown, WV, p. A694
WRIGHT, Ann L R.N., MSN, Assistant Central Delivery System CNO, Presbyterian Hospital, Albuquerque, NM, p. A425
WRIGHT, April, Human Resources Officer, Collingsworth General Hospital, Wellington, TX, p. A653
WRIGHT, Bennie B M.D., Chief of Staff, North Sunflower Medical Center, Ruleville, MS, p. A361
WRIGHT, Betsy T., President and Chief Executive Officer, Upmc Chautauqua Wca, Jamestown, NY, p. A437
WRIGHT, Brady, Information Technology Network Administrator, Washington County Hospital, Chatom, AL, p. A16
WRIGHT, Calvin, Chief Information Officer, Hutchinson Regional Medical Center, Hutchinson, KS, p. A243
WRIGHT, Carlene, Chief Financial Officer, Vibra Hospital Of Amarillo, Amarillo, TX, p. A592
WRIGHT, Carol, Chief Nursing Officer, Alliancehealth Madill, Madill, OK, p. A509
WRIGHT, Charles, Chief Financial Officer, Ashe Memorial Hospital, Jefferson, NC, p. A465
WRIGHT, Coleby, Chief Executive Officer, Behavioral Hospital Of Bellaire, Houston, TX, p. A619
WRIGHT, Connie, Vice President Human Resources, Texas Scottish Rite Hospital For Children, Dallas, TX, p. A607
WRIGHT, Creighton M.D., Vice President Medical Administration, Mercy Health – West Hospital, Cincinnati, OH, p. A484
WRIGHT, Dan, Vice President Human Resources, Children's Mercy South, Overland Park, KS, p. A249
WRIGHT, Daniel, Director Information Technology, Saint Alphonsus Medical Center – Nampa, Nampa, ID, p. A174
WRIGHT, Debra J., R.N., Chief Executive Officer, Howard Memorial Hospital, Nashville, AR, p. A47
WRIGHT, Dustin, President and Chief Executive Officer, Unitypoint Health – Marshalltown, Marshalltown, IA, p. A231
WRIGHT, Fran, Director of Nursing, Broadwater Health Center, Townsend, MT, p. A389
WRIGHT, James M.D., Chief Financial Officer, Cypress Fairbanks Medical Center, Houston, TX, p. A620
WRIGHT, Jennifer
Vice President Human Resources, Christus St. Michael Rehabilitation Hospital, Texarkana, TX, p. A649
Vice President Regional Human Resources, Christus St. Michael Health System, Texarkana, TX, p. A649
WRIGHT, Joe, Chief Financial Officer, Mitchell County Hospital, Colorado City, TX, p. A602
WRIGHT, Julie M, Director Human Resources, Ridgeview Psychiatric Hospital And Center, Oak Ridge, TN, p. A588
WRIGHT, Kenneth, Chief Financial Officer, Robert Wood Johnson University Hospital Somerset, Somerville, NJ, p. A420
WRIGHT, Krista, Director Human Resources, Indiana University Health Frankfort, Frankfort, IN, p. A208
WRIGHT, Linda
Chief Financial Officer, Healthsouth Rehabilitation Hospital Of Alexandria, Alexandria, LA, p. A269
Director Information, Ottawa County Health Center, Minneapolis, KS, p. A247
WRIGHT, Mark J., Chief Financial Officer, Aurelia Osborn Fox Memorial Hospital, Oneonta, NY, p. A449
WRIGHT, Mark
Chief Financial Officer, Aultman Specialty Hospital, Canton, OH, p. A482
Vice President, Aultman Hospital, Canton, OH, p. A482
WRIGHT, Mary Lynne, President, Huntsville Hospital, Huntsville, AL, p. A19
WRIGHT, Mary, Vice President Nursing Services and Chief Nursing Officer, Cortland Regional Medical Center, Cortland, NY, p. A434

WRIGHT, Maura, Chief Nursing Officer, Southern Hills Hospital And Medical Center, Las Vegas, NV, p. A403
WRIGHT, Nancy M.D., Chief Medical Staff, Alta Vista Regional Hospital, Las Vegas, NM, p. A427
WRIGHT, Peter J., FACHE, Chief Executive Officer, Valley Regional Hospital, Claremont, NH, p. A407
WRIGHT, Philoron A., FACHE, II
Chief Operating Officer, Munroe Regional Medical Center, Ocala, FL, p. A136
Interim Chief Executive Officer, Munroe Regional Medical Center, Ocala, FL, p. A136
WRIGHT, Robert N., Chief Executive Officer, Newman Regional Health, Emporia, KS, p. A240
WRIGHT, Robert, M.D.
Chief of Staff, Washington County Regional Medical Center, Sandersville, GA, p. A164
Senior Human Resource Advisor, East Ohio Regional Hospital, Martins Ferry, OH, p. A495
Senior Human Resource Advisor, Ohio Valley Medical Center, Wheeling, WV, p. A697
WRIGHT, Rory M.D., President Medical Staff, Orthopaedic Hospital Of Wisconsin – Glendale, Glendale, WI, p. A702
WRIGHT, Sandra Gayle., Chief Executive Officer, Tyler County Hospital, Woodville, TX, p. A655
WRIGHT, Sharon R.N., Vice President and Chief Nursing Officer, Hardin Memorial Hospital, Elizabethtown, KY, p. A257
WRIGHT, Stephanie, Director Human Resources Management, Va San Diego Healthcare System, San Diego, CA, p. A86
WRIGHT, Stuart M CPA, Chief Financial Officer, Upstate University Hospital, Syracuse, NY, p. A453
WRIGHT, Terri, Vice President and Chief Nursing Officer, Warren Memorial Hospital, Front Royal, VA, p. A668
WRIGHT, Tom, Director Human Resources, Kindred Hospital Riverside, Perris, CA, p. A79
WRIGHT, Trevor, Chief Operating Officer, Loma Linda University Medical Center, Loma Linda, CA, p. A66
WRIGHT, Wes, Senior Vice President and Chief Information Officer, Seattle Children's Hospital, Seattle, WA, p. A685
WRIGHT–WHITAKER, Ruth, Director Information Services, Cornerstone Medical Center, Fort Oglethorpe, GA, p. A158
WRINN, Denise, Vice President Finance and Chief Financial Officer, Cortland Regional Medical Center, Cortland, NY, p. A434
WROBBEL, Patricia A., Senior Vice President and Chief Nurse Executive, Westchester Medical Center, Valhalla, NY, p. A454
WROBLEWSKI, Edmund, M.D.
Vice President Medical Affairs and Chief Medical Officer, Goleta Valley Cottage Hospital, Santa Barbara, CA, p. A90
Vice President Medical Affairs and Chief Medical Officer, Santa Barbara Cottage Hospital, Santa Barbara, CA, p. A90
Vice President Medical Affairs and Chief Medical Officer, Santa Ynez Valley Cottage Hospital, Solvang, CA, p. A92
WROGG, Frank, Director Information Technology, Mayo Clinic Health System – Red Cedar In Menomonie, Menomonie, WI, p. A706
WU, Jonathan, M.D., President and Chairman, Ahmc & Healthcare, Inc., Alhambra, CA, p. B7
WU, Kenneth M.D., Medical Director, Kessler Marlton Rehabilitation, Marlton, NJ, p. A416
WUENSCHEL, Diedra D.O., President Medical Staff, Coryell Memorial Hospital, Gatesville, TX, p. A616
WUKITSCH, Michael
Vice President Human Resources, Northwestern Medicine Central Dupage Hospital, Winfield, IL, p. A202
Vice President Human Resources, Northwestern Medicine Delnor Hospital, Geneva, IL, p. A188
WUNDERWALD, Wendie R.N., Vice President Patient Care Services, Samaritan Lebanon Community Hospital, Lebanon, OR, p. A523
WURGLER, Brad D, Chief Financial Officer, Perham Health, Perham, MN, p. A346
WURSTER, Rosemary H, Vice President Patient Care Services, Riddle Hospital, Media, PA, p. A541
WURTZEL, Leann, Director Human Resources, Mayo Clinic Health System – Red Cedar In Menomonie, Menomonie, WI, p. A706
WUTHER, Greg, Chief Executive Officer, Select Specialty Hospital-Savannah, Savannah, GA, p. A164
WYATT, Basil, Chief Financial Officer, AMG Specialty Hospital-Tulsa, Tulsa, OK, p. A517
WYATT, Christopher B., Chief Executive Officer, Cavalier County Memorial Hospital And Clinics, Langdon, ND, p. A477
WYATT, Christy R.N., Interim Chief Nursing Officer, Jackson Parish Hospital, Jonesboro, LA, p. A277

WYATT, Jana, Chief Executive Officer, Mizell Memorial Hospital, Opp, AL, p. A22
WYBLE, Karen O., R.N., Chief Executive Officer, St. Martin Hospital, Breaux Bridge, LA, p. A272
WYDICK, Sue, Director Human Resources, Ohio County Hospital, Hartford, KY, p. A259
WYDRA, Lana, Vice President Human Resources, Nathan Littauer Hospital And Nursing Home, Gloversville, NY, p. A436
WYER, Jolena R.N., Chief Nursing Officer, Oklahoma Center For Orthopedic And Multi–Specialty Surgery, Oklahoma City, OK, p. A512
WYERS, Michael, Chief Financial Officer, Medical Center Of Trinity, Trinity, FL, p. A146
WYLER, Allyson, Vice President, Operations, Advocate Lutheran General Hospital, Park Ridge, IL, p. A197
WYLIE, Eugene, Chief Human Resources Officer, Veterans Affairs Loma Linda Healthcare System, Loma Linda, CA, p. A66
WYLIE, Patrick, Director Information Systems, Petaluma Valley Hospital, Petaluma, CA, p. A79
WYMAN, Alan, Chief Information Officer, Providence Hospital, Washington, DC, p. A118
WYMAN, David, President and Chief Executive Officer, Gracie Square Hospital, New Rochelle, NY, p. A441
WYMER, Melanie, Director Human Resources, Highland District Hospital, Hillsboro, OH, p. A492
WYNN, Katherine, Director Human Resource, Oklahoma Heart Hospital, Oklahoma City, OK, p. A513
WYNN, Paige
Administrator, Irwin County Hospital, Ocilla, GA, p. A163
Chief Financial Officer, Dorminy Medical Center, Fitzgerald, GA, p. A158
WYSE, Debbie, Controller, Quillen Rehabilitation Hospital, Johnson City, TN, p. A581
WYSOCKI, Greg, Chief Financial Officer, Austin Lakes Hospital, Austin, TX, p. A594
WYSONG–HARDER, Alyson, Chief Executive Officer, Heartland Behavioral Health Services, Nevada, MO, p. A374

Y

YABLONKA, Eric, Vice President and Chief Information Officer, University Of Chicago Medical Center, Chicago, IL, p. A184
YABUT, Eduardo M.D., Medical Director, North Dakota State Hospital, Jamestown, ND, p. A477
YAEGER, Eric, M.D.
Chief Medical Officer, Kindred Hospital–Aurora, Aurora, CO, p. A98
Medical Director, Kindred Hospital–Denver, Denver, CO, p. A101
YAHNER, Michael, Chief Financial Officer, Torrance State Hospital, Torrance, PA, p. A551
YAKE, Laurie B., Vice President Finance, Aurora Medical Center, Kenosha, WI, p. A704
YAKLIN, Shelleye, President and Chief Executive Officer, North Ottawa Community Hospital, Grand Haven, MI, p. A320
YAKOVENKO, Gene, Director of Finance, Presence Holy Family Medical Center, Des Plaines, IL, p. A185
YAKULIS, Paul MS, R.N., Senior Vice President Human Resources, Lankenau Medical Center, Wynnewood, PA, p. A555
YALLOWITZ, Joseph M.D., Vice President Medical Affairs, Valley Hospital, Ridgewood, NJ, p. A420
YAMADA, Chrissy CPA, Chief Financial Officer, Evergreenhealth, Kirkland, WA, p. A681
YAMADA, Jeff, Vice President, Virginia Mason Memorial, Yakima, WA, p. A689
YAMAN, Tonguc, Deputy Chief Information Officer, NYC Health + Hospitals / Bellevue, New Rochelle, NY, p. A444
YANCY, Daniel, Chief Executive Officer, Riceland Medical Center, Winnie, TX, p. A654
YANES, John C., Chief Executive Officer, Andalusia Health, Andalusia, AL, p. A13
YANEZ, Maria J, Chief Financial Officer, Baptist Health South Florida, Doctors Hospital, Coral Gables, FL, p. A122
YANGA, Ismael David M.D., Chief Medical Officer, Brighton Center For Recovery, Brighton, MI, p. A315
YANIK, Sahin, M.D.
Vice President Medical Administration, St. John's Regional Medical Center, Oxnard, CA, p. A78
Vice President Medical Associate, St. John's Pleasant Valley Hospital, Camarillo, CA, p. A54

ZIENIEWICZ, Stephen P., FACHE, President and Chief Executive Officer, Saint Barnabas Medical Center, Livingston, NJ, p. A415

ZIEROLD, Bob, Senior Vice President Human Resources, Christian Health Care Center, Wyckoff, NJ, p. A423

ZIGLOR, Danyale
Assistant Director Human Resources, Wellstar Douglas Hospital, Douglasville, GA, p. A157
Assistant Vice President Human Resources, Wellstar Cobb Hospital, Austell, GA, p. A152

ZILE, Ron M.D., Chief of Staff, Highland District Hospital, Hillsboro, OH, p. A492

ZILKOW, Jon, Chief Financial Officer, Rancho Springs Medical Center, Murrieta, CA, p. A75

ZILLER, Andrew M.D., Chief Medical Officer, Rose Medical Center, Denver, CO, p. A101

ZILLMAN, Sally E., Interim Vice President, Patient Care Services, Ministry Saint Clare's Hospital, Weston, WI, p. A580

ZILM, Michael E., Interim President, St. Mary's Janesville Hospital, Janesville, WI, p. A704

ZIMA, Cheryl F, Vice President Human Resources Ministry Health Care, Marshfield Medical Center, Marshfield, WI, p. A706

ZIMMEL, Robert, Senior Vice President Human Resources, St. Luke's University Hospital – Bethlehem Campus, Bethlehem, PA, p. A529

ZIMMER, Jan R.N., MS, Chief Nursing Officer, Tennova Healthcare Regional Hospital Of Jackson, Jackson, TN, p. A580

ZIMMERLY, Kara, Manager Human Resources, Promedica Bay Park Hospital, Oregon, OH, p. A497

ZIMMERMAN, Aimee R.N., Chief Operations Officer, Logan County Hospital, Oakley, KS, p. A248

ZIMMERMAN, Anne, Senior Director Patient Care Services and Chief Nursing Officer, Mercy Tiffin Hospital, Tiffin, OH, p. A500

ZIMMERMAN, David M.D., Chief of Staff, Swain Community Hospital, Bryson City, NC, p. A458

ZIMMERMAN, Don, Director Human Resources, Morris County Hospital, Council Grove, KS, p. A240

ZIMMERMAN, Joanna, Regional Chief Financial Officer, Monmouth Medical Center, Southern Campus, Lakewood, NJ, p. A415

ZIMMERMAN, Keith, Chief Executive Officer, Medical City Arlington, Arlington, TX, p. A593

ZIMMERMAN, Michael
Human Resource Officer, Presence Covenant Medical Center, Urbana, IL, p. A202
Human Resource Officer, Presence United Samaritans Medical Center, Danville, IL, p. A185

ZIMMERMAN, Nancy, R.N., Administrator, Comanche County Hospital, Coldwater, KS, p. A239

ZIMMERMAN, Robert, Vice President Financial Services, Munson Healthcare Charlevoix Hospital, Charlevoix, MI, p. A316

ZIMMERMAN, Deb R.N., Chief Nursing Officer and Vice President Patient Care Services, VCU Medical Center, Richmond, VA, p. A674

ZIMMERMANN, Wayne, Chief Operating Officer, NYC Health + Hospitals / Elmhurst, New Rochelle, NY, p. A445

ZINAMAN, Michael M.D., Acting Chief Medical Officer, NYC Health + Hospitals / Jacobi, New Rochelle, NY, p. A445

ZINK, Jayne, Director of Nursing, Ohio Hospital For Psychiatry, Columbus, OH, p. A487

ZINK, Summer, Chief Financial Officer, Ellinwood District Hospital, Ellinwood, KS, p. A240

ZINKER, Dena MSN, R.N., Vice President Patient Services, Colquitt Regional Medical Center, Moultrie, GA, p. A162

ZINKULA, Lisa, Chief Financial Officer, Grundy County Memorial Hospital, Grundy Center, IA, p. A228

ZINN, David M.D., Vice President Medical Affairs, RMC Anniston, Anniston, AL, p. A13

ZINN, Troy, Chief Executive Officer, Cameron Hospital, Cameron, TX, p. A600

ZINNER, Barbara, Chief Nursing Officer, Marymount Hospital, Garfield Heights, OH, p. A492

ZINNI, Melissa, Chief Financial Officer, Hampton Behavioral Health Center, Westampton, NJ, p. A422

ZIOBRO, Ron, Chief Operating Officer, Easton Hospital, Easton, PA, p. A533

ZIOLKOWSKI, David, Chief Executive Officer, Person Memorial Hospital, Roxboro, NC, p. A470

ZIRBSER, Glenn, Senior Vice President Finance and Chief Financial Officer, Kennedy Health System, Stratford, NJ, p. A420

ZIRGER, Marion, Chief Financial Officer, Minneola District Hospital, Minneola, KS, p. A247

ZIRKELBACH, Mark, Chief Information Officer, Loma Linda University Medical Center, Loma Linda, CA, p. A66

ZIRKELBACK, Mark, Chief Information Officer, Loma Linda University Behavioral Medicine Center, Redlands, CA, p. A81

ZIRKLE, William, Manager Information Systems, Sentara Halifax Regional Hospital, South Boston, VA, p. A675

ZISKIN, Robert, Chief Information Officer, Northport Veterans Affairs Medical Center, Northport, NY, p. A448

ZOCH, Jeremy, Executive Vice President and Chief Operating Officer, St. Joseph Hospital, Orange, CA, p. A78

ZOESCH, Jim, Information Technology Director, Pmh Medical Center, Prosser, WA, p. A684

ZOGELMAN, Sharon, Director Human Resources, St. Luke Hospital And Living Center, Marion, KS, p. A246

ZOLKIWSKY, Walter R, M.D.
Chief Medical Officer, Reston Hospital Center, Reston, VA, p. A673
Chief Medical Officer, Stonesprings Hospital Center, Dulles, VA, p. A666

ZOMCHEK, Daniel, Ph.D., Executive Director, Clement J. Zablocki Veterans Affairs Medical Center, Milwaukee, WI, p. A707

ZOOK, Danette, Chief Financial Officer, Mercy Medical Center–North Iowa, Mason City, IA, p. A231

ZOOK, Lori, Chief Financial Officer, River's Edge Hospital And Clinic, Saint Peter, MN, p. A348

ZORZA, Elizabeth, Assistant Administrator, OSF St. Francis Hospital And Medical Group, Escanaba, MI, p. A319

ZOUCHA, Larry, Chief Information Officer, Boone County Health Center, Albion, NE, p. A390

ZUANICH, Elizabeth
Chief Financial Officer, Providence Little Company Of Mary Medical Center – Torrance, Torrance, CA, p. A94
Chief Financial Officer, Providence Little Company Of Mary Medical Center San Pedro, Los Angeles, CA, p. A70

ZUBER, Steven, Vice President, Methodist Jennie Edmundson Hospital, Council Bluffs, IA, p. A225

ZUBRICKI, Thomas, Vice President Finance, Chief Financial Officer, Crotched Mountain Rehabilitation Center, Greenfield, NH, p. A408

ZUEL, Sally, Vice President Human Resources, Union Hospital, Terre Haute, IN, p. A220

ZUHD, Dajani M.D., President Medical Staff, Punxsutawney Area Hospital, Punxsutawney, PA, p. A548

ZUINO, Matthew
Senior Vice President Hospital Services, Virtua Marlton, Marlton, NJ, p. A416
Senior Vice President Hospital Services, Virtua Memorial, Mount Holly, NJ, p. A416

Senior Vice President Hospital Services, Virtua Voorhees, Voorhees, NJ, p. A422

ZUKOWSKI, Andrew, Chief Financial Officer, UNC Rex Health Care, Raleigh, NC, p. A469

ZULIANI, Michael E., Chief Executive Officer, Healthsouth Huntington Rehabilitation Hospital, Huntington, WV, p. A692

ZULTANKY, Lynne, Director Corporate Communications and Media Relations, Bon Secours–Depaul Medical Center, Norfolk, VA, p. A671

ZUMPANO, Anthony, Chief Financial Officer, Penn Presbyterian Medical Center, Philadelphia, PA, p. A545

ZUMSTEIN, James F. M.D., Chief of Medicine, Jack Hughston Memorial Hospital, Phenix City, AL, p. A22

ZUMWALT, Philip M.D., Chief of Staff, Iroquois Memorial Hospital And Resident Home, Watseka, IL, p. A202

ZUNNO, Gerard R.N., Vice President Patient Care Services, Peconic Bay Medical Center, Riverhead, NY, p. A450

ZUTZ–WICZEK, Sandy, Chief Operating Officer, Firstlight Health System, Mora, MN, p. A344

ZVANUT, Michelle, Vice President Human Resources, Boone Hospital Center, Columbia, MO, p. A366

ZWANZIGER, Marcia, Vice President Finance, Huron Regional Medical Center, Huron, SD, p. A570

ZWEIFEL, Mary A., MS
President and Chief Executive Officer, Sheltering Arms Hospital South, Midlothian, VA, p. A670
President and Chief Executive Officer, Sheltering Arms Rehabilitation Hospital, Mechanicsville, VA, p. A670

ZWENG, Thomas
Executive Vice President and Chief Medical Officer, Novant Health Brunswick Medical Center, Bolivia, NC, p. A458
Executive Vice President and Chief Medical Officer, Novant Health Charlotte Orthopaedic Hospital, Charlotte, NC, p. A459
Executive Vice President and Chief Medical Officer, Novant Health Forsyth Medical Center, Winston, NC, p. A473
Executive Vice President and Chief Medical Officer, Novant Health Huntersville Medical Center, Huntersville, NC, p. A465
Executive Vice President and Chief Medical Officer, Novant Health Matthews Medical Center, Matthews, NC, p. A466
Executive Vice President and Chief Medical Officer, Novant Health Medical Park Hospital, Winston, NC, p. A473
Executive Vice President and Chief Medical Officer, Novant Health Presbyterian Medical Center, Charlotte, NC, p. A460
Executive Vice President and Chief Medical Officer, Novant Health Rowan Medical Center, Salisbury, NC, p. A470
Executive Vice President and Chief Medical Officer, Novant Health Thomasville Medical Center, Thomasville, NC, p. A471
Chief Executive Officer, St. Aloisius Medical Center, Harvey, ND, p. A476

ZWICKER, Mike, Chief Executive Officer, St. Aloisius Medical Center, Harvey, ND, p. A476

ZWIEFEL, Laura, Chief Nursing Officer and Assistant Administration, Hancock County Health System, Britt, IA, p. A223

ZWIEG, Faye, Vice President and Chief Nursing Officer, Aurora St. Luke's Medical Center, Milwaukee, WI, p. A707

ZWINGER, Glenn, Manager Information Systems Services, Veterans Affairs Puget Sound Health Care System, Seattle, WA, p. A686

ZWIRCHITZ, Faith, Director Nursing and Professional Practice, Maple Grove Hospital, Maple Grove, MN, p. A343

ZYCH, Anita, Director of Nursing, Arrowhead Behavioral Health Hospital, Maumee, OH, p. A495

ZYLA, Jeffrey, Chief Financial Officer, Abrazo Scottsdale Campus, Phoenix, AZ, p. A33

AHA Membership Categories

The American Hospital Association is primarily an organization of hospitals and related institutions. Its object, according to its bylaws, is "to promote high–quality health care and health services for all the people through leadership in the development of public policy, leadership in the representation and advocacy of hospital and health care organization interests, and leadership in the provision of services to assist hospitals and health care organizations in meeting the health care needs of their communities."

Institutional Members

Hospitals or health services organizations or systems which provide a continuum of integrated, community health resources and which include at least one licensed hospital that is owned, leased, managed or religiously sponsored

Institutional members include hospitals, health care systems, integrated delivery systems, and physician hospital organizations (PHOs) and health maintenance organizations (HMOs) wholly or partially owned by or owning a member hospital or system. An Institutional member hospital, health care system or integrated delivery system may, at its discretion and upon approval of a membership application by the Association chief executive officer, extend membership to the health care provider organizations, other than a hospital that it owns, leases, or fully controls.

Freestanding Health Care Provider Organizations

These are health provider organizations, other than registered hospitals, that provide patient care services, including, but not limited to, ambulatory, preventive, rehabilitative, specialty, post–acute and continuing care, as well as physician groups, health insurance services, and staff and group model health maintenance organizations without a hospital component. Freestanding Health Care Provider Organizations members are not owned or controlled by an Institutional member hospital, health care system or integrated delivery system member. They may, however, be part of an organization eligible for, but not holding, Institutional membership.

Other Organizations

This category includes organizations interested in the objectives of the American Hospital Association, but not eligible for Institutional or Freestanding Health Care Provider Organization Membership. Organizations eligible for Other membership shall include, but not be limited to, associations, societies, foundations, corporations, educational and academic institutions, companies, government agencies, international health providers, and organizations having an interest in and a desire to support the objectives of the Association.

Provisional Members

Hospitals that are in the planning or construction stage and that, on completion, will be eligible for institutional membership. Provisional membership may also be granted to applicant institutions that cannot, at present, meet the requirements of Institutional or Freestanding Health Care Provider Organization membership.

Government Institution Group Members

Groups of government hospitals operated by the same unit of government may obtain institutional membership under a group plan. Membership dues are based on a special schedule set forth in the bylaws of the AHA.

Other Institutional Members

U.S. hospitals and hospitals in areas associated with the U.S. that are Institutional members of the American Hospital Association are included in the list of hospitals in section A. Canadian Institutional members of the American Hospital Association are listed below.

Canada

ALBERTA

Lamont: LAMONT HEALTH CARE CENTRE, P O Bag 10, Zip T0B 2R0; tel. 780/895–2211; Harold James, Executive Director

MANITOBA

Winnipeg: RIVERVIEW HEALTH CENTRE, 1 Morley Avenue East, Zip R3L 2P4; tel. 204/452–3411; Norman R. Kasian, President and Chief Executive Officer

ONTARIO

Renfrew: RENFREW VICTORIA HOSPITAL, 499 Raglan Street North, Zip K7V 1P6, tel. 613/432–4851; Randy V. Penney, President and Chief Executive Officer

Thornhill: SHOULDICE HOSPITAL, 7750 Bayview Avenue, Zip L3T 4A3; tel. 905/889–1125; John Hughes, Chief Administrative Officer

Associated University Programs in Health Administration

IOWA

Iowa City: DEPARTMENT OF HEALTH MANAGEMENT AND POLICY, UNIVERSITY OF IOWA, 105 River Street, N232A CPHB, Zip 52246; tel. 319/384–3830; Keith Mueller, Professor and Head

MARYLAND

Bethesda: NAVY MEDICINE PROFESSIONAL DEVELOPMENT CENTER, Naval Medicine, Education and Training Command, 8901 Wisconsin Avenue, Building 1, Zip 20889-5611; tel. 301/295–1251; Commander DuWayne Griepentrog, Director Administration

MISSOURI

Columbia: UNIVERSITY OF MISSOURI, HEALTH MANAGEMENT AND INFORMATICS, CE707 Clinical Support and Education Building, DC 00600, One Hospital Drive, Zip 65212; tel. 573/882–6179; Eduardo Simoes; Chair

PUERTO RICO

San Juan: SCHOOL OF PUBLIC HEALTH, P O Box 5067, Zip 00936; tel. 809/767–9626; Orlando Nieves, Dean

TEXAS

San Antonio: ARMY-BAYLOR UNIVERSITY PROGRAM IN HEALTH CARE ADMINISTRATION, 3151 Scott Road, Bldg 2841, Zip 78234–6135; tel. 210/221–6443; Lieutenant Colonel M Nicholas Coppola, Program Director

Sheppard AFB: U.S. AIR FORCE SCHOOL OF HEALTH CARE SCIENCES, Building 1900, MST/114, Academic Library, Zip 76311; tel. 817/851-2511

Hospital Schools
of Nursing

PENNSYLVANIA
New Castle: JAMESON HOSPITAL School of Nursing

Nonhospital Preacute and Postacute Care Facilities

CALIFORNIA

Winterhaven: U. S. PUBLIC HEALTH SERVICE INDIAN HOSPITAL, P O Box 1368, Zip 85366–1368; tel. 760/572–0217; Geniel Harrison, Clinic Director

DELAWARE

Newark: HEALTH CARE CENTER AT CHRISTIANA, 200 Hygeia Drive, Zip 19714; tel. 302/623–0100; Douglas P. Azar, Senior Vice President, Medical Group

FLORIDA

Jacksonville: NEMOURS CHILDREN'S CLINIC, 807 Children's Way, Zip 32207; tel. 904/390–3600; William A. Cover, Administrator

GEORGIA

Calhoun: ALLIANT HEALTH PLANS, INC., 401 South Wall Street, Ste 201, Zip 30701; tel. 706/629–8848; Judy Pair, Chief Executive Officer

GEORGIA HEALTH PLUS, 401 South Wall Street, Ste 201, Zip 30701; tel. 706/629–1833;

Rome: CENTREX, 420 East Second Avenue, Zip 30161; tel. 706/235–1006; Dee B. Russell, Chief Executive Officer

COMMUNITY HOSPICECARE, P O Box 233, Zip 30162–0233; tel. 706/232–0807; Kurt Stuenkel, President and Chief Executive Officer

FLOYD HOME HEALTH AGENCY, P O Box 6248, Zip 30162–6248; tel. 706/802–4600; Kurt Stuenkel, President and Chief Executive Officer

FLOYD MEDICAL OUTPATIENT SURGERY, P O Box 233, Zip 30162–0233; tel. 706/802–2070; Kurt Stuenkel, President and Chief Executive Officer

FLOYD REHABILITATION CENTER, P O Box 233, Zip 30162–0233; tel. 706/802–2091; Kurt Stuenkel, President and Chief Executive Officer

HAWAII

Honolulu: MALUHIA HOSPITAL, 1027 Hala Drive, Zip 96817; tel. 808/832–5874; Derek Akiyoshi, Chief Executive Officer

ILLINOIS

Oak Forest: OAK FOREST HEALTH CENTER OF COOK COUNTY, 15900 South Cicero Avenue, Zip 60452–4006; tel. 708/687–7200;

MAINE

Damariscotta: COVE'S EDGE, 26 Schooner Street, Zip 04543; tel. 207/563–4645; Judy McGuire, Administrator

MILES MEDICAL GROUP, INC., 35 Miles Street, Zip 04543; tel. 207/563–1234; Stacey Miller-Friant, Vice President, Physician Services

Kennebunk: SOUTHERN MAINE HEALTH AND HOME SERVICES, P O Box 739, Zip 04043; tel. 207/985–4767; Elaine Brady, Executive Director

MARYLAND

Baltimore: ST. AGNES HOME CARE AND HOSPICE, 3421 Benson Avenue, Suite G100, Zip 21227; tel. 410/368–2825; Robin Dowell, Director

ST. AGNES HEALTH SERVICES, 900 Caton Avenue, Zip 21229; tel. 410/368–2945; Peter Clay, Senior Vice President Managed Care

Ellicott City: ST. AGNES NURSING AND REHABILITATION CENTER, 3000 North Ridge Road, Zip 21043; tel. 410/461–7577; Barbara A. Gustke, Administrator Extended Care Facility

MASSACHUSETTS

Boston: JOSLIN DIABETES CENTER, One Joslin Place, Zip 02215; tel. 617/732–2400; John L. Brooks III, President and Chief Executive Officer

Springfield: BAY STATE VISITING NURSE ASSOCIATION AND HOSPICE, 50 Maple Street, Zip 01105; tel. 413/781–5070; Ruth, Odgren, President

MICHIGAN

Big Rapids: MECOSTA HEALTH SERVICES, 650 Linden Street, Zip 49307; tel. 231/796–3200; Gail Bullard, Director

Sault Sainte Marie: SAULT SAINTE MARIE TRIBAL HEALTH AND HUMAN SERVICES CENTER, 2864 Ashmun Street, Zip 49783; tel. 906/495–5651; Russell Vizina, Division Director Health

MISSOURI

Independence: SURGI-CARE CENTER OF INDEPENDENCE, 2311 Redwood Avenue, Zip 64057; tel. 816/373–7995;

NEBRASKA

North Platte: GREAT PLAINS PHO, INC., P O Box 1167, Zip 69103; tel. 308/535–7496; Todd Hlavaty, Chairman

NEW JERSEY

Jersey City: ST. FRANCIS HOSPITAL, 25 McWilliams Place, Zip 07302–1698; tel. 201/418–1000;

Millburn: ATLANTIC HOME CARE AND HOSPICE, 33 Bleeker Street, Zip 07041; tel. 973/379–8400; Susan Quinn, Administrator

Morristown: ALLIANCE IMAGING CENTER, 65 Maple Street, Zip 07960; tel. 973/267–5700; Barbara Picorale, Administrator

Succasunna: DIALYSIS CENTER OF NORTHWEST NEW JERSEY, 170 Righter Road, Zip 07876; tel. 973/584–1117; Carol Cahill, Administrator

NEW MEXICO

Albuquerque: ALBUQUERQUE IHS HEALTH CENTER, 801 Vassar Drive NE, Zip 87106–2799; tel. 505/248–4000; Maria Rickert, Chief Executive Officer

NEW YORK

Tuckahoe: HOME NURSING ASSOCIATION OF WESTCHESTER, 69 Main Street, Zip 10707; tel. 919/961–2818; Mary Wehrberger, Director

NORTH CAROLINA

Jefferson: AMH SEGRAVES CARE CENTER, 200 Hospital Avenue, Zip 28640; tel. 336/246–7101;

Wilson: WILMED NURSING CARE CENTER, 1705 Tarboro Street SW, Zip 27893–3428; tel. 252/399–8998; Randy Smithey, Administrator

OHIO

Cleveland: METROHEALTH CENTER FOR SKILLED NURSING CARE, 4229 Pearl Road, Zip 44109; tel. 216/957–3675; Yvette Bozman, Administrator

OKLAHOMA

Clinton: U. S. PUBLIC HEALTH SERVICE INDIAN HOSPITAL, Route 1, Box 3060, Zip 73601–9303; tel. 580/323–2884;

Eufaula: EUFALA INDIAN HEALTH CENTER, 800 Forest Avenue, Zip 74432; tel. 918/689–2547; Shelly Crow, Health System Administrator

Fort Sill: REYNOLDS ARMY HEALTH CLINIC, 4301 Wilson Street, Zip 73503–4472; tel. 580/558–3000; Colonel Kenneth Lemons, Commander

Okmulgee: OKMULGEE INDIAN HEALTH SYSTEM, 1313 East 20th, Zip 74447; tel. 918/758–1926; Kara Lee, Administrator

Sapulpa: SAPULPA INDIAN HEALTH CENTER, 1125 East Cleveland, Zip 74066; tel. 918/224–9310; Sid Daniels, Acting Administrator

PENNSYLVANIA

Warminster: ABINGTON MEMORIAL HEALTH CENTER - WARMINSTER CAMPUS, 225 Newtown Road, Zip 18974–5221; tel. 215/441–6600; Katie Farrell, Chief Executive Officer

TEXAS

Dallas: SURGICARE OF TRAVIS CENTER, INC., 13355 Noel Road, Suite 650, Zip 75240–6694; tel. 713/520–1782;

Houston: GRAMERCY OUTPATIENT SURGERY CENTER. LTD., 2727 Gramercy, Zip 77025; tel. 713/660–6900; Hamel Patel, Administrator

WEST HOUSTON SURGICARE, 970 Campbell Road, Zip 77024; tel. 713/461–3547;

Webster: BAY AREA SURGICARE CENTER, 502 Medical Center Boulevard, Zip 77598; tel. 281/332–2433; Carol Simons, Administrator

WISCONSIN

Green Bay: UNITY HOSPICE, P O Box 28345, Zip 54324–8345; tel. 920/494–0225; Donald Seibel, Executive Director

Provisional Hospitals

This listing includes organizations that, as of September 16, 2015, were in the planning or construction stage and that, on completion, will be eligible for Institutional membership. Some hospitals are granted provisional membership for reasons related to other Association requirements. Hospitals classified as provisional members for reasons other than being under construction are indicated by a bullet (•).

TEXAS

Houston: BAYLOR ST. LUKE'S MEDICAL CENTER MCNAIR CAMPUS, One Baylor Plaza, BCM 100, Zip 77030–3411; tel. 713/798–4951; Paul Klotman, M.D., President

Marble Falls: WAYNE & EILEEN HURD REGIONAL MEDICAL CENTER – SCOTT & WHITE, 800 West Highway 71, Zip 78654; tel. 830/598–1204; Eric N. Looper, Chief Executive Officer

GUAM

Dededo: GUAM REGIONAL MEDICAL CITY, P.O. Box 3830, Zip 96932; tel. 671/649–4764; Gloria Long, Chief Operating Officer

Associate Members

Ambulatory Centers and Home Care Agencies

UNITED STATES

NEW YORK

MIDTOWN SURGERY CENTER, 305 East 47th Street, Zip 10017–2303; tel. 212/751–2100; Julia Ferguson, Director, Operations

PENNSYLVANIA

WILLS EYE HOSPITAL, 840 Walnut Street, Philadelphia, Zip 19107–5109; tel. 215/928–3000; Joseph P. Bilson, Executive Director

Blue Cross Plans

UNITED STATES

ARIZONA

BLUE CROSS AND BLUE SHIELD OF ARIZONA, Box 13466, Phoenix, Zip 85002–3466; tel. 602/864–4541; Vishu Jhaveri; Senior Vice President and Chief Medical Officer

Other Members

UNITED STATES

Architecture

DEVENNEY GROUP ARCHITECTS, 201 West Indian School Road, Phoenix, Arizona Zip 85013–3203; tel. 602/943–8950; Julie Barkenbush, Chief Executive Officer; www.devenneygroup.com

HDR ARCHITECTURE, INC., 33 West Monroe Street, Suite 1750, Chicago, Illinois Zip 60603–5662; tel. 312/470–9532; Ashley Tucker, Strategic Program Manager, Healthcare; www.hdrinc.com

MATTHEI AND COLIN ASSOCIATES, 332 South Michigan Avenue, Suite 614, Chicago, Illinois Zip 60604; tel. 312/939–4002; Ronald G Kobold, Managing Partner; www.mca-architecture.com/

MESSER CONSTRUCTION COMPANY, 5158 Fishwick Drive, Cincinnati, Ohio Zip 45216; tel. 513/242–1541; Nick Apanius, Health Care Vice President; www.messer.com

Bank

HEALTHCARE ASSOCIATES CREDIT UNION, 1151 East Warrenville Road, Naperville, Illinois Zip 60563; tel. 630/276–5771; Jennifer Kleinhenz, Senior Vice President Strategic Initiatives; www.hacu.org

TD BANK, 2130 Centre Park West Drive, 2nd Floor, West Palm Beach, Florida Zip 33409–6411; tel. 561/352–2086; Colleen Mullaney, Senior Vice President; www.tdbank.com

Communication Systems Org

AVAILITY, LLC, 750 Old Hickory Boulevard, Building 2 Suite 270, Brentwood, Tennessee Zip 37027–4528; tel. 615/760–3361; Ashleigh Eisinger, Events and Social Media Specialist; www.availity.com

Consulting Firm

AON HEWITT, 5600 West 83rd Street, 8200 Tower, Minneapolis, Minnesota Zip 55402–3721; tel. 952/807–0768; James Craig Nelson, Senior Vice President; www.stratford360.com

ARAMARK, 10510 Twin Lakes Boulevard, Charlotte, North Carolina Zip 28269–7658; tel. 704/948–4774; Tom Elmore, Director, Industry Relations; www.aramark.com

ARIAS INFORMATION SOLUTIONS LLC, 3233 North Arlington Heights Road, Suite 201, Arlington Heights, Illinois Zip 60004–1579; tel. 847/340–8307; Raymond C. Arias, Managing Partner; www.ariasis.com

AVIVA HEALTHCARE SOLUTIONS, 98 Golden Eye Lane, Port Monmouth, New Jersey Zip 07758–1647; tel. 800/530–5728; Thomas Bojko, President and Managing Partner; www.avivahealthsolutions.com

CARE TECH SOLUTIONS, 901 Wilshire Drive, Suite 100, Troy, Michigan Zip 48084; tel. 248/823–0950; Jody Meehan, Vice President, Marketing, Communications, and Government Affairs; www.caretech.com/

CARERISE|CARERISE INDEX, PO Box 880, Mandeville, Louisiana Zip 70470–0880; tel. 985/727–4740; Tim G Goux, Founder; www.carerise.com

CLEARWATER COMPLIANCE LLC, 106 Windward Point, Hendersonville, Tennessee Zip 37075–5108; tel. 615/800–7988; Kathy S. Ebbert, Chief Operating Officer; www.clearwatercompliance.com

CONIFER HEALTH SOLUTIONS, 2401 Internet Boulevard, Suite 201, Frisco, Texas Zip 75034–5977; tel. 972/335–6120; Vanessa Harris, Senior Market Research Specialist; www.coniferhealth.com

EIDE BAILLY, LLP, 800 Nicollet Mall, Suite 1300, Minneapolis, Minnesota Zip 55402–7033; tel. 612/253–6582; Jen Dreis, Marketing Manager; www.eidebailly.com/healthcare

ERNST & YOUNG, 150 Fourth Avenue North, Suite 1400, Nashville, Tennessee Zip 37219–2409; tel. 615/252–8254; Darryl McQuate, Manager; www.ey.com

GOLDMAN, SACHS AND COMPANY, 200 West Street, New York, New York Zip 10282–2198; Cynthia Rivera, Public Sector and Infrastructure Banking

HEALTHCARE CHAPLAINCY NETWORK, INC., 65 Broadway, 12th Floor, New York, New York Zip 10010; tel. 212/644–1111; Eric J. Hall, President and Chief Executive Officer; www.healthcarechaplaincy.org

HEALTHCARE MANAGEMENT PARTNERS, LLC, 1515 Market Street, Suite 1200, Philadelphia, Pennsylvania Zip 19102–1932; tel. 215/854–4086; Scott K Phillips, Managing Director; www.hcmpllc.com

HEALTHCARESOURCE, 100 Sylvan Road, Suite 100, Woburn, Massachusetts Zip 01801–1851; tel. 800/691–3737; Sean Parlin, Strategic Alliances Manager; www.healthcaresource.com

HEALTHEQUITY, INC., 15 West Scenic Pointe Drive, Suite 100, Draper, Utah Zip 84020–6120; tel. 801/727–1000; Stephen Neeleman, Founder and Vice Chairman; www.healthequity.com

HEALTHPORT, 925 North Point Parkway, Alpharetta, Georgia Zip 30005–5210; tel. 770/360–1700; Catherine Valyi, Vice President Marketing; www.healthport.com

IBM, 1 New Orchard Road, Armonk, New York Zip 10504–1722; tel. 781/575–2727; Charles Andrews, Chief Executive Officer; www.ibm.com

INGENIOUS MED, 460 Galleria Parkway, SE Suite 1600, Atlanta, Georgia Zip 30339; tel. 678/486–4256; J. Scott McClintock, Chief Marketing Officer; www.ingeniousmed.com

INTEGRATED HEALTHCARE STRATEGIES, 901 Marquette Avenue South, Suite 2100, Minneapolis, Minnesota Zip 55402–3713; tel. 612/339–0919; Julie McCauley, Senior Vice President, Corporate; www.ihstrategies.com

KAUFMAN HALL, 5202 Old Orchard Road, Suite N700, Skokie, Illinois Zip 60077; tel. 847/441–8780; Jason H Sussman, Partner; www.kaufmanhall.com

LATHAM AND WATKINS, LLP, 633 West 5th Street, Ste 4000, Los Angeles, California Zip 90071; tel. 213/485–1234; Daniel K Settelmayer, Partner; www.lw.com

MCDONALD HOPKINS, LLC, 600 Superior Avenue East, Suite 2100, Cleveland, Ohio Zip 44114–2690; tel. 216/348–5400; Richard S Cooper, Member; www.mcdonaldhopkins.com

MCKESSON CORPORATION, 1 Post Street, 33rd Floor, San Francisco, California Zip 94104–5203; tel. 404/338–2985; Anastasia Agapoff, Assistant Manager, Library Operations; www.mckesson.com/

MEDASSETS, 100 North Pointe Center East, Suite 200, Alpharetta, Georgia Zip 30022–1506; tel. 314/579–1896; Ron DeCarlo, Senior Vice President; www.medassets.com

MILESTONE HEALTHCARE, LLC, 275 West Campbell Road, Suite 300, Richardson, Texas Zip 75080–3560; tel. 800/926–2388; George Thompson, General Manager; www.milestonehealth.com

NATIONAL CENTER FOR HEALTH STATISTICS, 3311 Toledo Road, Hyattsville, Maryland Zip 20782–2064; tel. 800/232–4636; Cynthia G. Link, Lead Administrative Officer; www.cdc.gov

NAVEX GLOBAL, 6000 Meadows Road, Suite 200, Lake Oswego, Oregon Zip 97035–3172; tel. 503/924–1640; Stephen J. Molen, Vice President Strategic Solutions; www.navexglobal.com

NEWRISTICS, 8777 East Via de Ventura #188, Scottsdale, Arizona Zip 85258; tel. 480/947–8078; Sheryl Bronkesh, President; www.hsmgroup.com

PROTIVITI, INC., 13727 Noel Road, Suite 800, Dallas, Texas Zip 75240–1336; tel. 214/395–1662; Richard Williams, Managing Director and Global Healthcare Industry Practice; www.protiviti.com

RYCAN, P O Box 306, Marshall, Minnesota Zip 56258–0306; tel. 800/201–3324; Marg Louwagie, Administrative Assistant; www.rycan.com

SAMUELI INSTITUTE, 1737 King Street, Suite 600, Alexandria, Virginia Zip 22314–2764; tel. 703/299–4800; Joan Walter, Chief Operating Officer; www.siib.org

SERVICE MANAGEMENT SYSTEMS, 7135 Charlotte Pike , Nashville, Tennessee Zip 37209–5015; tel. 615/399–1839; Gary Blanks, Division Manager; www.smsclean.com

SIEMENS HEALTHCARE, 51 Valley Stream Parkway, Malvern, Pennsylvania Zip 19355; tel. 610/448–4500; Amar Shah, Senior Manager, Corporate Communication; www.medical.siemens.com

STRATA DECISION TECHNOLOGY, tel. 312/726–1227; Dan Michelson, Chief Executive Officer; www.stratadecision.com

STROUDWATER ASSOCIATES, 50 Sewall Street, Suite 102, Portland, Maine Zip 04102–2646; tel. 207/221–8255; Marc Voyvodich, Chief Executive Officer; www.stroudwater.com/

SULLIVAN COTTER & ASSOCIATES, INC, 200 West Madison Street, Suite 2450, Chicago, Illinois Zip 60606–3499; tel. 312/564–5883; Mary Kelley, Director of Marketing; www.sullivancotter.com

SULLIVAN, COTTER AND ASSOCIATES, INC., 1100 Peachtree Street, Suite 620, Atlanta, Georgia Zip 30309; tel. 678/551–7190; Maureen Cotter, Director Research and Information; www.sullivancotter.com

SYMPLR, 616 Cypress Creek Parkway, Suite 800, Houston, Texas Zip 77090–3029; tel. 281/863–9500; Rick Pleczko, Chief Executive Officer; www.vcsdatabase.com

TEAMHEALTH, 265 Brookview Centre Way, Suite 400, Knoxville, Tennessee Zip 37919; tel. 865/293–5486; Leif Murphy, Chief Executive Officer; www.teamhealth.com

THE CHARTIS GROUP, 220 West Kinzie Street, 5th Floor, Chicago, Illinois Zip 60654–4912; tel. 312/932–3068; Celine White, Manager of Financial Operations; www.chartis.com

TRUVEN HEALTH ANALYTICS, 6200 South Syracuse Way, Suite 300, Greenwood Village, Colorado Zip 80111–4740; tel. 303/486–6400; Julie Weigel, Assistant of Vice President Sales; www.truvenhealth.com

VERRAS HEALTHCARE INTERNATIONAL, tel. 888/791–5556; Robert T. Langston, Partner; www.verras.com/

VGM GROUP INC., 1111 West San Marnan Drive, Waterloo, Iowa Zip 50701–9007; tel. 319/274–6643; Kelly Turner, Advocacy Director; www.vgm.com

VIIAD SYSTEMS LLC, 1170 Wheeler Way, Suite 200, Langhorne, Pennsylvania Zip 19047–3243; tel. 866/498–4423; Tricia Bradley, Director, Sales and Marketing Support; www.viiad.com

WESTERN HEALTHCARE ALLIANCE, 715 Horizon Drive, Suite 401, Grand Junction, Colorado Zip 81506–8731; tel. 970/683–5223; Carolyn S Bruce, Chief Executive Officer; www.wha1.org

XANITOS, INC., 3809 West Chester Pike, Suite 210, Newtown Square, Pennsylvania Zip 19073–2304; tel. 484/654–2300; Graeme A Crothall, Chairman and Chief Executive Officer; www.xanitos.com

Educational Services

NATIONAL RURAL HEALTH RESOURCE CENTER, 525 South Lake Avenue, Suite 320, Duluth, Minnesota Zip 55802; tel. 218/727–9390; Sally Buck, Chief Executive Officer; www.ruralcenter.org

*The members listed in **bold** are Associate Advantage members* © 2017 AHA Guide

Hospice

HOSPICE OF THE VALLEY, 1510 East Flower Street, Phoenix, Arizona Zip 85014–5698; tel. 602/530–6900; Rachel Behrendt, Senior Vice President, Operations; www.hov.org

Information Systems

CERNER CORPORATION, 2800 Rockcreek Parkway, Kansas City, Missouri Zip 64117; tel. 816/221–1024; Laurel Vine, Program Manager, Industry Events; www.cerner.com

EVOLENT, 540 West Madison Street, Suite 1500, Chicago, Illinois Zip 60661; tel. 312/273–6623; Kevin Weinstein, Chief Marketing Officer; www.valencehealth.com

FLEMING AOD, INC., 816 Thayer Avenue, Floor 3rd, Silver Spring, Maryland Zip 20910–4508; tel. 202/872–1033; Mary Dalrymple, Managing Director; www.aod.cx

IMPRIVATA, INC., 10 Maguire Road Building 4, Lexington, Massachusetts Zip 02421–3110; tel. 781/674–2700; Ed Gaudel, Chief Marketing Officer; www.imprivata.com

KPMG LLP, 200 East Randolph Street, Suite 5500, Chicago, Illinois Zip 60601–6607; tel. 312/665–2073; Edward J Giniat, National Line of Business Leader, Healthcare and Pharmaceuticals Practice; www.https://home.kpmg.com/us/en/home.html?cid=M-00002211&gclid=CKfszoeUrtACFZSFaQod82wE4g

MEDHOST, 6100 West Plano Parkway, Suite 3100, Plano, Texas Zip 75093–8342; tel. 888/218–4678; Leslie LaFon, Departmental Segment Manager; www.medhost.com

Insurance Broker

BOSTON MUTUAL LIFE INSURANCE COMPANY, 120 Royall Street, Canton, Massachusetts Zip 2021; tel. 781/828–7000; Peter Tillson, Vice President; www.bostonmutual.com

IRONSHORE, 300 South Wacker Drive, Chicago, Illinois Zip 60606–6680; tel. 312/496–7535; Daniel R Nash, Senior Vice President Field Operations and Business Development; www.ironshore.com

THE ALLEN J. FLOOD COMPANIES, INC., 2 Madison Avenue, Larchmont, New York Zip 10538; tel. 914/834–9326; Allen J Flood, President; www.ajfusa.com

Managed Care/Utilization

CENTENE CORPORATION, 111 East Capitol Street, Suite 500, Jackson, Mississippi Zip 39201; tel. 601/863–0835; K Michael Bailey, Vice President; www.centene.com

Manufacturer/Supplier

3M, 3M Center, Building 275–4E-01, Saint Paul, Minnesota Zip 55144–1000; tel. 612/733–8183; Donald R Brewer, Director Medical-Surgical Markets; www.3m.com

GE HEALTHCARE , 9900 West Innovation Drive, RP-2177, Wauwatosa, Wisconsin Zip 53226–4856; tel. 262/548–2088; Kimberly Rutherford, Business Partner and Director, Advertising & Promotion US-Canada Region; www.www3.gehealthcare.com

HILL-ROM, 1069 State Route 46 East, Batesville, Indiana Zip 47006–9167; tel. 812/934–7958; Thomas J Jeffers, Director Government Relations; www.hill-rom.com

Metro Hospital Assn

HOSPITAL ASSOCIATION OF SOUTHERN CALIFORNIA, 515 South Figueroa Street, Suite 1300, Los Angeles, California Zip 90071–3300; tel. 213/538–0700; George W Greene, President and Chief Executive Officer; www.hasc.org

Other

AIR METHODS CORPORATION, 7211 South Peoria Street, Englewood, Colorado Zip 80112–4133; tel. 303/792–7565; Ruthie Hubka, Government Relations Specialist; www.airmethods.com

AMBIUS, 1125 Berkshire Boulevard, Suite 150, Reading, Pennsylvania Zip 19610–1211; tel. 610/372–9700; Cathy Hoffman, Marketing Assistant; www.ambius.com

AMC HEALTH, INC., 39 Broadway, Suite 540, New York, New York Zip 10006; tel. 877/776–1746; Joanna Haskin, Vice President Partner Development; www.amchealth.com

AMERICAN ASSOCIATION FOR WOUND CARE MANAGEMENT, 4109 Glenrose Street, Kensington, Maryland Zip 20895–3718; tel. 301/933–2200; Jule Crider, Executive Director; www.aawcm.org

AMERICAN ASSOCIATION OF NURSE ANESTHETISTS, 222 South Prospect Avenue, Park Ridge, Illinois Zip 60068–4001; tel. 847/655–1100; Wanda O Wilson, Executive Director and Chief Executive Officer; www.aana.com

AMERICAN BOARD OF MEDICAL SPECIALTIES, 353 North Clark Street, Suite 1400, Chicago, Illinois Zip 60654–3454; tel. 312/436–2626; Lois Margaret Nora, President and Chief Executive Officer; www.abms.org

AMERICAN COLLEGE OF HEALTHCARE EXECUTIVES, One North Franklin, Suite 1700, Chicago, Illinois Zip 60606–4425; tel. 312/424–2800; Deborah Bowen, President and Chief Executive Officer; www.ache.org

AMERICAN HEALTH INFORMATION MANAGEMENT ASSOCIATION, 233 North Michigan Avenue, Suite 2150, Chicago, Illinois Zip 60601–5806; tel. 312/233–1100; www.ahima.org

AMERICAN SOCIETY OF ANESTHESIOLOGISTS, 1061 American Lane, Schaumburg, Illinois Zip 60173; tel. 847/268–9160; Paul Pomerantz, Chief Executive Officer; www.asahq.org

AMN HEALTHCARE, INC., 12400 High Bluff Drive, Suite 100, San Diego, California Zip 92130–3581; tel. 866/871–8519; Steve Wehn, Senior Vice President of Corporate Development; www.amnhealthcare.com

APOGEE PHYSICIANS, 15059 North Scottsdale Road, Suite 600, Scottsdale, Arizona Zip 85254–2685; tel. 602/778–3600; Michael Gregory, Chairman; www.apogeephysicians.com

ARENA, 502 South Sharp Street, Suite 2300, Baltimore, Maryland Zip 21201–2445; tel. 888/444–0693; Michael Finn, Vice President, Marketing; www.arena.io

ARIS RADIOLOGY, 5655 Hudson Drive, Suite 210, Hudson, Ohio Zip 44236; tel. 330/655–3800; Stacey Christofferson, Sales and Marketing; www.arisradiology.com

ASSOCIATION OF PERIOPERATIVE REGISTERED NURSES, 2170 South Parker Road, Suite 400, Denver, Colorado Zip 80231; tel. 303/755–6304; Linda Kay Groah, Executive Director and Chief Executive Officer; www.aorn.org

AVATAR SOLUTIONS, 25 East Washington Street, Suite 600, Chicago, Illinois Zip 60602; tel. 312/236–7170; Jeffrey Brady, Chief Executive Officer; www.hrsolutionsinc.com

BACTES, 8344 Clairemont Mesa Boulevard, Suite 201, San Diego, California Zip 92111–1327; tel. 858/244–1811; Rae Danell, Marketing Coordinator; www.bactes.com

BLUE CROSS AND BLUE SHIELD ASSOCIATION, 225 North Michigan Avenue, Chicago, Illinois Zip 60601–7680; tel. 312/297–6000; Scott P Serota, President and Chief Executive Officer ; www.bcbs.com

BOARDVANTAGE, 4300 Bohannon Drive, Suite 110, Menlo Park, California Zip 94025; tel. 650/330–2444; Virginia Portillo, Conference and Events Coordinator; www.boardvantage.com

BUREAU OF MEDICINE AND SURGERY, DEPARTMENT OF THE NAVY, 7700 Arlington Boulevard, Suite 5126, Falls Church, Virginia Zip 22042; tel. 703/681–8489; Bryce H.P. Mendez, Healthcare Policy Analyst; www.med.navy.mil

CANON SOLUTIONS AMERICA, INC., 300 Commerce Square Boulevard, Burlington, New Jersey Zip 08016–1270; tel. 847/706–3411; Paul T Murphy, Director Strategic Contract Support; www.solutions.canon.com

CARECENTRIX, 20 Church Street, Floor 12th, Hartford, Connecticut Zip 06103–1246; tel. 800/808–1902; Sherl Brand, Senior Vice President Strategic Solutions; www.carecentrix.com

CERTIPHI SCREENING, INC., 1105 Industrial Highway, Southampton, Pennsylvania Zip 18966; tel. 888/260–1370; Tony D'Orazio, President; www.certiphi.com

CISCO SYSTEMS, 165 Needletree Lane, Glastonbury, Connecticut Zip 6033; tel. 860/657–8127; Michael Haymaker, Director Healthcare Industry Marketing; www.cisco.com

COMPREHENSIVE PHARMACY SERVICES, 6409 North Quail Hollow Road, Memphis, Tennessee Zip 38120–1414; tel. 901/748–0470; Walker Upshaw, Chief Development Officer; www.cpspharm.com

CROSS COUNTRY HEALTHCARE, 5201 Congress Avenue, Boca Raton, Florida Zip 33487–3629; tel. 800/347–2264; Robert Murphy, President Workforce Solutions; www.crosscountryhealthcare.com

CYRACOM, 5780 North Swan Road, Tucson, Arizona Zip 85718–4527; tel. 800/713–4950; Jeremy Woan, President and Chief Executive Officer; www.cyracom.com

DEPARTMENT OF AIR FORCE MEDICAL SERVICE, HQ USAF/SG, Bolling AFB, District of Columbia Zip 20332–6188; tel. 202/545–6700; www.airforcemedicine.af.mil

DEPARTMENT OF THE ARMY, OFFICE OF THE SURGEON GENERAL, 5109 Leesburg Pike, Falls Church, Virginia Zip 22041–3258; tel. 202/690–6467; Nadja West, Surgeon General and Commanding General; www.armymedicine.mil

DISH, PO Box 5096524, Englewood, Colorado Zip 80112–5905; tel. 720/514–6019; Steven Wilson, Manager; www.dish.com

DNV HEALTHCARE, INC., 400 Techne Center Drive, Suite 100, Milford, Ohio Zip 45150–2792; tel. 513/388–4863; Shannon Walker, Team Operator and Planner; www.dnvhealthcareinc.com

EVICORE, 730 Cool Springs Boulevard, Suite 800, Franklin, Tennessee Zip 37067–7289; tel. 615/468–4116; Laura Lee, Marketing Project Manager, Providers; www.medsolutions.com

FIRST AMERICAN EQUIPMENT FINANCE, 255 Woodcliff Drive, Fairport, New York Zip 14450–4219; tel. 585/643–3266; Mike Wiedemer, Senior Vice President, Sales; www.faef.com

FIRST DATA USA, 5565 Glenridge Connector NE, Atlanta, Georgia Zip 30342; tel. 914/450–4545; Andrew Finck, Vice President Healthcare Segment; www.firstdata.com

GENERAL DYNAMICS HEALTH SOLUTIONS, 3060 Williams Drive, Suite 100, Fairfax, Virginia Zip 22031–4655; tel. 888/545–8477; Anne E Hughes, Director, Business Development; www.gdit.com/health

GOZIO HEALTH, 75 5th Street NW, Suite 2220, Atlanta, Georgia Zip 30308–1019; tel. 772/444–6946; Barbara Kragor, Vice President Sales and Customer Experience; www.goziohealth.com

HEALTHGRID, 4203 Vineland Road, Suite K6, Orlando, Florida Zip 32811; tel. 855/624–2844; Raj Toleti, Founder and Chief Executive Officer; www.healthgrid.com

HEALTHTRUST PURCHASING GROUP INC, 155 Franklin Road, Suite 400, Brentwood, Tennessee Zip 37027–4693; tel. 615/344–3030; Beverly Wallace, President; www.healthtrustpg.com

HEALTHWAYS, INC, 701 Cool Springs Boulevard, Franklin, Tennessee Zip 37067–2697; tel. 800/327–3822; Karen Meyer, Principal; www.healthways.com

HMS, 355 Quartermaster Court, Jeffersonville, Indiana Zip 47130–3670; tel. 812/704–5747; Rich Flaherty, Vice President Sales and Marketing; www.hms.com

HOOPER, LUNDY & BOOKMAN, INC., 1875 Century Park East, Suite 1600, Los Angeles, California Zip 90067; tel. 310/551–8111; Lloyd Bookman, Partner; www.health-law.com

HOSPITALRECRUITING.COM, 899 South College Mall Road, Suite 395, Bloomington, Indiana Zip 47401–6301; tel. 800/244–7236; Michael Jones, Managing Partner; www.hospitalrecruiting.com

HQ ACC/SGMS, 162 Dodd, Suite 100, Langley AFB, Virginia Zip 23665–1995; www.military.com/base-guide/langley-air-force-base

HQ AETC/SGAL, 63 Main Circle, Suite 3, Randolph AFB, Texas Zip 78150–4549; www.military.com/base-guide/randolph-air-force-base

HQ AFMC/SGAR, 4225 Logistics Avenue, N-209, Dayton, Ohio Zip 45433–5761; tel. 937/656–3655; Alice Rohrbach, www.wpafb.af.mil/

HQ AFSPC/SGAL, 150 Vandenberg Street, Suite 1105, Peterson AFB, Colorado Zip 80914–4550; tel. 719/556–6141; www.peterson.af.mil/

HQ AMC/SGSL, 203 West Losey Street, Room 1180, Scott AFB, Illinois Zip 62225–5219; www.airforcemedicine.af.mil/MTF/Scott/About-Us/

HQ PACAF/SGAL, 25 E Street, Suite D1, Hickam AFB, Hawaii Zip 96853–5418; tel. 808/449–7110; Gary North, Commander; www.15wing.af.mil/

HQ USAFA/SGAL, Pinion Drive, Building 4102, Suite 3, USAF Academy, Colorado Zip 80840; tel. 719/524–2273; www.airforcemedicine.af.mil/MTF/Air-Force-Academy/

HYLAND SOFTWARE, INC., 28500 Clemens Road, Westlake, Ohio Zip 44145; tel. 440/788–5814; Michael Kortan, Director Health Care Solutions; www.onbase.com

ICRA SOLUTIONS LLC, 4034 Suwanee Trail Drive, Buford, Georgia Zip 30518–8771; tel. 678/412–5132; Amy Walker, Director; www.icrasolutions.com

IMALOGIX, 1150 First Avenue, Suite 450, King Of Prussia, Pennsylvania Zip 19406–1363; tel. 855/681–9100; David Steigerwalt, Product Manager; www.imalogix.com

INDATATECH, 85 NE Loop 410, Suite 405, San Antonio, Texas Zip 78216–5829; tel. 210/344–3540; Bede

AS

Ramcharan, President and Chief Executive Officer; www.indatatech.com

INNOVATIVE CAPITAL LLC, 1489 Baltimore Pike, Building 400, Springfield, Pennsylvania Zip 19064–3958; tel. 610/543–2490; Alan P Richman, President and Chief Executive Officer; www.innovativecapital.com

INTALERE, 500 Commonwealth Drive, Warrendale, Pennsylvania Zip 15086–7516; tel. 877/711–5700; Laurie McGrath, Vice President Marketing; www.amerinet-gpo.com

INTERACTIVE HEALTH SOLUTIONS, 3800 North Wilke Road, Suite 155, Arlington Heights, Illinois Zip 60004–1278; tel. 847/754–2698; Joseph O'Brien, President; www.interactivesolutions.com

IP SERVICES, 2896 Crescent Avenue, Suite 201, Eugene, Oregon Zip 97408–7422; tel. 541/343–5974; Mark Allers, Vice President Business Development; www.ipservices.com

JANI-KING, 16885 Dallas Parkway, Addison, Texas Zip 75001; tel. 972/991–0900; Bob Carabajal, Director Healthcare Services; www.janiking.com

JEWISH GUILD HEALTHCARE, 15 West 65th Street, New York, New York Zip 10023; tel. 212/769–6200; Alan R Morse, President and Chief Executive Officer; www.jgb.org

LANGUAGELINE SOLUTIONS, One Lower Ragsdale Drive, Building 2, Monterey, California Zip 93940; tel. 800/752–6096; Patti Geye, Senior Marketing Manager; www.languageline.com

LITTLER MENDELSON, P.C., 1100 Superior Avenue, 20th Floor, Cleveland, Ohio Zip 44114–2530; tel. 216/623–6104; Angela Lupardus, Manager, Regional Business Development and Marketing; www.littler.com

MEDICAL INFORMATION TECHNOLOGY, INC., tel. 781/821–3000; Lynn Robblee, Supervisor of Event Coordination and Memberships; www.meditech.com

MEDISOLV, INC., 10440 Little Patuexent Parkway, Suite 1000, Columbia, Maryland Zip 21044–3630; tel. 443/539–0505; Erin Heilman, Marketing Specialist; www.medisolv.com

MODERN HEALTHCARE, 150 North Michigan Avenue, 17th Floor, Chicago, Illinois Zip 60601–3806; tel. 312/649–5491; Fawn Lopez, Publisher; www.modernhealthcare.com

MUCH SHELIST, 191 North Wacker Drive, Chicago, Illinois Zip 60606–1615; tel. 312/521–2000; Ned Milenkovich, Partner; www.muchshelist.com

NATIONAL COUNCIL OF STATE BOARDS OF NURSING, 111 East Wacker Drive, 29th Floor, Chicago, Illinois Zip 60601–4277; tel. 312/525–3600; David Charles Benton, Chief Executive Officer; www.ncsbn.org

NAVAL REGIONAL MEDICAL CENTER, PSC 1005, Box 36, FPO, Armed Forces Africa, Canada, E Zip 09593–0136

OB HOSPITALIST GROUP, tel. 800/967–2289; Guy Kohn, Director, Marketing; www.obhg.com

PLANON CORPORATION, 45 Braintree Hill Office Park, Suite 400, Braintree, Massachusetts Zip 02184–8730; tel. 781/356–0999; Ellen Schwier, Marketing Manager; www.planonsoftware.com

PROASSURANCE , 100 Brookwood Place, Birmingham, Alabama Zip 35209–6811; tel. 205/877–4400; W Stancil Starnes, Chairman, Chief Executive Officer; www.proassurance.com

PROMED HEALTHCARE FINANCING, 1001 Woodward Avenue, Suite 1700, Detroit, Michigan Zip 48226–1904; tel. 631/707–4347; Dan De Chiaro, Director of Operations; www.promedhcf.com

QUARLES AND BRADY LLP, 300 North LaSalle Street, Suite 4000, Chicago, Illinois Zip 60654–3422; tel. 312/715–2751; Susan Stewart, Director, Client Relations; www.quarles.com

RENTOKIL STERITECH, 1125 Berkshire Boulevard, Suite 150, Reading, Pennsylvania Zip 19610–1211; tel. 610/372–9700; Erica Caceres, Manager; www.rentokil-steritech.com

SENTRY DATA SYSTEMS, INC., 800 Fairway Drive, Suite 400, Deerfield Beach, Florida Zip 33441–1830; tel. 806/411–4566; Tim Lantz, Senior Vice President, Data Next; www.sentryds.com

SHAREDCLARITY, 4425 East Cotton Center Boulevard, Phoenix, Arizona Zip 85040–8854; tel. 916/781–0659; Mark West, President; www.sharedclarity.net

SIMPLEX GRINNELL, 50 Technology Drive, Westminster, Massachusetts Zip 1441; tel. 978/731–8486; Suzanne Rahall, Marketing Manager, Healthcare Communications; www.simplexgrinnell.com

SUBWAY, 325 Bic Drive, Milford, Connecticut Zip 6461; tel. 800/888–4848; Joanne Kilgore, Global Account Manager; www.subway.com

THE ADVISORY BOARD COMPANY, 2445 'M' Street NW, Washington, District of Columbia Zip 20037–2403; tel. 202/266–5600; Colleen Cooper, Associate Director, Information Resource Center; www.advisory.com

THE AMERICAN COLLEGE OF OBSTETRICIANS AND GYNECOLOGISTS, 409 12th Street, SW, Washington, District of Columbia Zip 20024–2188; tel. 202/638–5577; Hal Lawrence, Executive Vice President; www.acog.org

THE CPI GROUP, 7400 East Orchard Road, Suite 270, Englewood, Colorado Zip 80111; tel. 303/504–9999; John Van Gulik, Business Development Manager; www.thecpigroup.net

THE WALKER COMPANY, 31090 SW Boones Bend Road, Wilsonville, Oregon Zip 97070–6412; tel. 503/694–8539; Larry W Walker, Principal; www.walkercompany.com

TRACE SECURITY, 6300 Corporate Boulevard, Baton Rouge, Louisiana Zip 70809–1097; tel. 877/275–3009; Morgan Rizzo, Marketing Coordinator; www.tracesecurity.com

TRANSAMERICA RETIREMENT SOLUTIONS, 4 Manhattanville Road, Purchase, New York Zip 10577; tel. 914/697–8952; Peter Kunkel, President and Chief Executive Officer; www.https://www.trsretire.com

TRAPOLLO, 13900 Lincoln Park Drive, 5th Floor, Herndon, Virginia Zip 20171; tel. 866/807–5047; Lisa Majdi, Marketing Director; www.trapollo.com

TRAVELERS INSURANCE COMPANY, One Tower Square, 6th Floor, Hartford, Connecticut Zip 06183–1134; tel. 860/277–9830; John Truhan, Operations Manager; www.travelers.com

U. S. ARMY MEDICAL COMMAND, 2050 Worth Road, Suite 10, San Antonio, Texas Zip 78234–6010; tel. 210/221–2212; Ann Russell Potter

UNIFORM DATA SYSTEM FOR MEDICAL REHABILITATION, 270 Northpointe Parkway, Suite 300, Amherst, New York Zip 14228; tel. 716/817–7800; Troy Hillman, Manager, Analytical Services Group; www.udsmr.org

USDTL, 1700 South Mount Prospect Road, Des Plaines, Illinois Zip 60018–1804; tel. 847/375–0770; Catharine Steccato, Vice President Business Development; www.usdtl.com

VANGUARD MODULAR BUILDING SYSTEMS, LLC, 3 Great Valley Parkway, Suite 170, Malvern, Pennsylvania Zip 19355–1417; tel. 610/240–8686; Mark Meyers, Vice President, Marketing Services; www.vanguardmodular.com

VERGE SOLUTIONS, LLC, 710 Johnnie Dodds Boulevard, Suite 202, Mount Pleasant, South Carolina Zip 29464–3045; tel. 843/628–4168; Ashley Worrall, Director Field Marketing; www.verge-solutions.com

VERISYS CORPORATION, 1001 North Fairfax Avenue, Suite 640, Alexandria, Virginia Zip 22314–1798; tel. 703/535–1471; John Benson, Chief Operating Officer; www.verisys.com/

VESTAGEN TECHNICAL TEXTILES, INC., tel. 407/781–2395; Brian Crawford, Chief Business Officer; www.vestagen.com

VIGILANZ CORPORATION , 5775 Wayzata Boulevard, Suite 970, Minneapolis, Minnesota Zip 55416–2669; tel. 855/525–9078; David Goldsteen, Chairman and Chief Executive Officer; www.vigilanzcorp.com

VIZIENT, 799 9th Street Northwest, Suite 210, Washington, District of Columbia Zip 20001–5325; tel. 202/354–2600; Shoshana Krilow, Vice President Public Policy and Government Relations; www.https://www.vizientinc.com/

WELLTOWER, INC., 4500 Dorr Street, Toledo, Ohio Zip 43615–4040; tel. 419/247–2800; Rachel Watson, Assistant Vice President; www.welltower.com

WITT/KIEFFER, 2015 Spring Rd, Ste 510, Oak Brook, Illinois Zip 60523; tel. 630/990–1370; James Gauss, Chairman of Board Services; www.wittkieffer.com

XENEX DISINFECTION SERVICES , 121 Interpark Boulevard, Suite 104, San Antonio, Texas Zip 78216; tel. 800/553–0069; Morris Miller, Chief Executive Officer; www.xenex.com

YOURCARE UNIVERSE, INC, 6550 Carothers Parkway, Suite 100, Franklin, Tennessee Zip 37067; tel. 844/641–6800; Lauren Douglass, Brand Manager; www.yourcareuniverse.com

Other Health Related

CENTER FOR MEDICAL INTEROPERABILITY, 618 Church Street Suite 220, Nashville, Tennessee Zip 37219–2453; tel. 202/617–6009; Kerry McDermott, Vice President for Public Policy and Communications; www.medicalinteroperability.org

FIGMD, INC., 10 North Martingale Road, Suite 400, Schaumburg, Illinois Zip 60173–2411; tel. 773/672–3155; Sanket Baralay, President and Chief Executive Officer; www.figmd.com

Recruitment Services

DOCCAFE.COM, tel. 715/302–8881; Laura Fitzsimmons, Managing Member; www.doccafe.com

Regional Health Care Assn

TEXAS ORGANIZATION OF RURAL & COMMUNITY HOSPITALS, P O Box 203878, Austin, Texas Zip 78720–3878; tel. 512/873–0045; David Pearson, President and Chief Executive Officer; www.torchnet.org

CANADA

Other

HALOGEN SOFTWARE CORPORATION, 495 March Road, Suite 500, Ottawa, Ontario Zip K2K 3G1; tel. 613/270–1011; Lorna Daly, Channel Manager Healthcare; www.halogensoftware.com

Provincial Hospital Assn

ONTARIO HOSPITAL ASSOCIATION, 200 Front Street West, Suite 2800, Toronto, Ontario Zip M5V 3L1; tel. 416/205–1300; Hazim Hassan, Vice President, Business Planning and Strategy; www.oha.com

BAHAMAS

Other

PRINCESS MARGARET HOSPITAL, P O Box N-8200, Nassau, tel. 242/322–2861; Mary Elizabeth Lightbourne-Walker, Hospital Administrator; www.phabahamas.org

BAHRAIN

Other

INTERNATIONAL HOSPITAL OF BAHRAIN, P O Box 1084, Manama, tel. 11/759–8222; F. S. Zeerah, President; www.ihb.net/

BRAZIL

Other

HOSPITAL SAMARITANO, Rua Conselheiro Brotero, 1486, Sao Paulo, Zip 01232–010; tel. 551/821–5300; Luiz Alberto Oliveira De Luca, Corporate Superintendent; www.samaritano.com.br

COLOMBIA

Other

ASOCIACION COLOMBIANA DE HOSPITALES Y CLINICAS, Carrera 4, No 73–15, Bogota, Juan Carlos Giraldo Valencia, Director General; www.achc.org.co

DOMINICAN REPUBLIC

Other

UNITED TELEMEDICINE NETWORK-HOSPITAL CHARLES DE GAULLE, Av Charles de Gaulle #43, Santo Domingo, Zip

*The members listed in **bold** are Associate Advantage members*

11509; tel. 829/345–9335; Horacio Stagno, Commercial Director; www.hospitalunited.com

GEORGIA

Other

INNOVA MEDICAL CENTER, 7A Sandra Euli Street, Tbilisi, Zip 105; Giorgi Kipiani, Director; www.innovamedical.ge

MARITIME HOSPITAL JSC, Melikishrin 102B, Batumi, Zip 60100; Tamari Kachlishvili, Medical Director; www.mh.com.ge

MEDI CLUB GEORGIA, 22A, Tashkenti Street, Tbilisi, Zip 160; tel. 995/225–1991; Nugzar Abramishvili, General Director; www.mediclubgeorgia.ge

TBILISI CENTRAL HOSPITAL, Chachava Street 1, Tbilisi, Zip 159; Ivane Martiashuili, Co-founder; www.tch.ge

GERMANY

Other

HQ USAFE/SGPXL, Unit 3050, Box 130, Ramstein AB, Armed Forces Africa, Canada, E Zip 09094–5001; www.ramstein.af.mil/

JAPAN

Other

U.S. NAVAL HOSPITAL OKINAWA, U S Naval Base, FPO, Zip 96362; tel. 11/743–7555; Martin Kerr, www.med.navy.mil/sites/nhoki/Pages/default.aspx

JORDAN

Other

SPECIALTY HOSPITAL, P O Box 930186, Amman, Zip 11193; Fawzi Al-Hammouri, General Manager; www.specialty-hospital.com

LEBANON

Other

SAINT GEORGE HOSPITAL UNIVERSITY MEDICAL CENTER, P O Box 166378, Beirut, Zip 1100–2807; tel. 961/158–5700; Ziad Kamel, Administrative Director; www.stgeorgehospital.org

MEXICO

Other

SHRINERS HOSPITAL FOR CHILDREN, Av Del Iman 257, Col Pedregal de Santa Ursula, Delegacion Coyoacan, Mexico City, Zip 4600; Mariano Gonzalez Lugo, Administrator; www.shrinershospitalsforchildren.org/locations/mexicocity

MYANMAR

Other

ASIA ROYAL GENERAL HOSPITAL, 14 Baho Street, Sanchaung Township, Yangon, Zip 11162; tel. 951/153–8055; Myat Thu, Managing Director; www.asiaroyalmedical.com

PANAMA

Other

CLINICA HOSPITAL SAN FERNANDO, S. A., Dept PTY 1663, P O Box 25207, Miami, Florida Zip 33102–5207; tel. 507/305–6399; Edgardo Fernandez, Medical Director; www.hospitalsanfernando.com

PERU

Other

BRITISH AMERICAN HOSPITAL, Avenue Alfredo Salazar 3 Era, Lima 27, tel. 511/712–3000; Gonzalo Garrido-Lecca, Director; www.angloamericana.com.pe

PHILIPPINES

Ambulatory Care Center

DEPARTMENT OF VETERANS AFFAIRS, OUTPATIENT CLINIC, Pasay City, APO, Zip 96440; tel. 632/833–4566; Artemio Arugay, Commander; www.va.gov

Other

ST. LUKE'S MEDICAL CENTER, 279 East Rodriguez Sr Boulevard, Quezon City, tel. 632/723–0101; Edgardo R Cortez, President and Chief Executive Officer; www.stluke.com.ph/home

SAUDI ARABIA

Other

ABDUL RAHMAN AL MISHARI GENERAL HOSPITAL, Olaya, P.O. Box 56929, Riyadh, Zip 11564; tel. 11/465–7700; Abdul Rahman Al Mishari, President; www.drabdulrahmanalmishari.com.sa/

MUHAMMAD SALEH BASHARAHIL HOSPITAL, P O Box 10505, Madinah Road, Omora Gadida, Makkah, tel. 9/520–4444; Turki M Basharahil, General Manager; www.msbasharahil.com/

NABIL AL KADI CONSULTANT ENGINEERS, Dammam, Dammam, Zip 0; Taufik Ridani, Chief Executive Officer

SPAIN

Information Systems

SIGESA, S.A., Calle Guatemala, 14, 4b, Madrid, Zip 28016; tel. 349/345–4018; Francisco Alvarez, Chief Financial Officer; www.sigesa.com

TURKEY

Other

ARTE CERRAHI HASTENESI, 1920 Cad. No:61 Cayyolu, Ankara, Zip 6810; tel. 903/236–1001; Oguz Engiz, Chief Executive Officer; www.artesaglik.com

UNITED ARAB EMIRATES

Other

AMERICAN HOSPITAL-DUBAI, Oud Metha Road, P.O. Box 5566, Dubai, tel. 11/336–7777; Saeed M Almulla, Chairman; www.ahdubai.com/main/index.aspx

UNITED KINGDOM

Consulting Firm

I.G. ADVISORS, 201 Borough High Street, London, Zip SE11JA; tel. 440/234–0389; Carlos Miranda, Chief Executive Officer; www.impactandgrowth.com

Other

FINANSCO HEALTHCARE, 11A Blacka Moor Road, Sheffield, Zip 0; tel. 448/225–3844; Rukhsar Khan, Chief Executive Officer; www.finansco.com

AS

B

Health Care Systems, Networks and Alliances

Section B

Introduction

This section includes listings for networks, health care systems and alliances.

Health Care Systems

To reflect the diversity that exists among health care organizations, this publication uses the term health care system to identify both multi-hospital and diversified single hospital systems.

Multihospital Systems

A multihospital health care system is two or more hospitals owned, leased, sponsored, or contract managed by a central organization.

Single Hospital Systems

Single, freestanding member hospitals may be categorized as health care systems by bringing into membership three or more, and at least 25 percent, of their owned or leased non–hospital preacute and postacute health care organizations. (For purposes of definition, health care delivery is the availability of professional healthcare staff during all hours of the organization's operations). Organizations provide, or provide and finance, diagnostic, therapeutic, and/or consultative patient or client services that normally precede or follow acute, inpatient, hospitalization; or that serve to prevent or substitute for such hospitalization. These services are provided in either a freestanding facility not eligible for licensure as a hospital under state statue or through one that is a subsidiary of a hospital.

The first part of this section is an alphabetical list of health care systems which are listed under the system by state. Data for this section were compiled from the 2014 *Annual Survey* and the membership information base as published in section A of the *AHA Guide.*

One of the following codes appears after the name of each system listed to indicate the type of organizational control reported by that system:

CC Catholic (Roman) church–related system, not–for–profit

CO Other church–related system, not–for–profit

NP Other not–for–profit system, including nonfederal, governmental systems

IO Investor–owned, for profit system

FG Federal Government

One of the following codes appears after the name of each hospital to indicate how that hospital is related to the system:

O Owned

L Leased

S Sponsored

CM Contract–managed

Health System Classification System

An identification system for Health Systems was developed jointly by the American Hospital Association's Health Research and Education Trust and Health Forum, and the University of California-Berkeley.[1] A health system is assigned to one of five categories based on how much they differentiate and centralized their hospital services, physician arrangements, and provider-based insurance products. Differentiation refers to the number of different products or services that the organization offers. Centralization refers to whether decision-making and service delivery emanate from the system level more so than individual hospitals.

Categories:

Centralized Health System: A delivery system in which the system centrally organizes individual hospital service delivery, physician arrangements, and insurance product development. The number of different products/services that are offered across the system is moderate.

Centralized Physician/Insurance Health System: A delivery system with highly centralized physician arrangements and insurance product development. Within this group, hospital services are relatively decentralized with individual hospitals having discretion over the array of services they offer. The number of different products/services that are offered across the system is moderate.

Moderately Centralized Health System: A delivery system that is distinguished by the presence of both centralized and decentralized activity for hospital services, physician arrangements, and insurance product development. For example, a system within this group may have centralized care of expensive, high technology services, such as open heart surgery, but allows individual hospitals to provide an array of other health services based on local needs. The number of different products/services that are offered across the system is moderate.

Decentralized Health System: A delivery system with a high degree of decentralized of hospital services, physician arrangements, and insurance product development. Within this group, systems may lack an overarching structure for coordination. Service and product differentiation is high, which may explain why centralization is hard to achieve. In this group, the system may simply service a role in sharing information and providing administrative support to highly developed local delivery systems centered around hospitals.

Independent Hospital System: A delivery system with limited differentiation in hospital services, physician arrangements, and insurance product development. These systems are largely horizontal affiliations of autonomous hospitals.

No Assignment: For some systems sufficient data from the Annual Survey were not available to determine a cluster assignment.

The second part of this section lists health care systems indexed geographically by state and city. Every effort has been made to be as inclusive and accurate as possible. However, as in all efforts of this type, there may be omissions.

For further information, write to the Section for Health Care Systems, American Hospital Association, 155 N. Wacker Drive, Chicago, IL 60606.

Networks

The *AHA Guide* shows listings of networks. A network is defined as a group of hospitals, physicians, other providers, insurers and/or community agencies that work together to coordinate and deliver a broad spectrum of services to their community. Organizations listed represent the lead or hub of the network activity. Networks are listed by state, then alphabetically by name including participating partners.

The network identification process has purposely been designed to capture networks of varying organization type. Sources include but are not limited to the following: *AHA Annual Survey*, national, state and metropolitan associations, national news and periodical searches, and the networks and their health care providers themselves. Therefore, networks are included regardless of whether a hospital or healthcare system is the network lead. When an individual hospital does appear in the listing, it is indicative of the role the hospital plays as the network lead. In addition, the network listing is not mutually exclusive of the hospital, health care system or alliance listings within this publication.

Networks are very fluid in their composition as goals evolve and partners change. Therefore, some of the networks included in this listing may have dissolved, reformed, or simply been renamed as this section was being produced for publication.

The network identification process is an ongoing and responsive initiative. As more information is collected and validated, it will be made available in other venues, in addition to the *AHA Guide*. For more information concerning the network identification process, please contact The American Hospital Association Resource Center at 312/422–2050.

Alliances

An alliance is a formal organization, usually owned by shareholders/members, that works on behalf of its individual members in the provision of services and products and in the promotion of activities and ventures. The organization functions under a set of bylaws or other written rules to which each member agrees to abide.

Alliances are listed alphabetically by name. Its members are listed alphabetically by state, city, and then by member name.

---

[1]Bazzoli, CJ; Shortell, SM; Dubbs, N; Chan, C; and Kralovec, P; "A Taxonomy of Health networks and Systems: Bringing Order Out of Chaos" *Health Services Research*, February; 1999

Statistics for Health Care Systems and their Hospitals

The following tables describing health care systems refers to information in section B of the 2016 *AHA Guide*.

Table 1 shows the number of health care systems by type of control. Table 2 provides a breakdown of the number of systems that own, lease, sponsor or contract manage hospitals within each control category. Table 3 gives the number of hospitals and beds in each control category as well as total hospitals and beds. Finally, shows the percentage of hospitals and beds in each control category.

For more information on health care systems, please write to the Section for Health Care Systems, 155 N. Wacker Drive, Chicago, Illinois 60606 or call 312/422-3000.

Table 1. Multihospital Health Care Systems, by Type of Organizaton Control

Type of Control	Code	Numebr of Systems
Catholic (Roman) church-related	CC	28
Other church-related	CO	6
Subtotal, church-related		34
Other not-for-profit	NP	311
Subtotal, not-for-profit		345
Investor Owned	IO	77
Federal Government	FG	5
Total		427

Table 2. Multihospital Health Care Systems, by Type of Ownership and Control

Type of Ownership	Catholic Church-Related (CC)	Other Church-Related (CO)	Total Church-Related (CC + CO)	Other Not-for-Profit (NP)	Total Not-for-Profit (CC, CO, + NP)	Investor-Owned (IO)	Federal Govern-ment (FG)	All Systems
Systems that only own, lease or sponsor	21	5	26	191	217	19	0	236
Systems that only contract-manage	1	0	1	10	11	4	0	15
Systems that manage, own, lease, or sponsor	6	1	7	110	117	54	5	176
Total	28	6	34	311	345	77	5	427

Table 3. Hospitals and Beds in Multihospital Health Care Systems, by Type of Ownership and Control

Type of Ownership	Catholic Church-Related (CC) H	B	Other Church-Related (CO) H	B	Total Church-Related (CC + CO) H	B	Other Not-for-Profit (NP) H	B	Total Not-for-Profit (CC, CO, + NP) H	B	Investor-Owned (IO) H	B	Federal Govern-ment (FG) H	B	All Systems H	B
Owned, leased or sponsored	584	105,715	71	16,527	655	122,242	1,609	343,134	2,264	465,376	1,398	167,271	205	39,611	3,867	672,258
Contract-managed	47	2,651	3	469	50	3,120	119	9,495	169	12,615	93	4,850	0	0	262	17,465
Total	631	108,366	74	16,996	705	125,362	3,218	352,629	3,923	477,991	1,491	172,121	205	39,611	5,619	689,723

H = hospitals; B = beds.

Table 4. Hospitals and Beds in Multihospital Health Care Systems, by Type of Ownership and Control as a Percentage of All Systems

Type of Ownership	Catholic Church-Related (CC) H	B	Other Church-Related (CO) H	B	Total Church-Related (CC + CO) H	B	Other Not-for-Profit (NP) H	B	Total Not-for-Profit (CC, CO, + NP) H	B	Investor-Owned (IO) H	B	Federal Govern-ment (FG) H	B	All Systems H	B
Owned, leased or sponsored	15.3	15.9	1.8	2.4	17.2	18.3	41.1	50.6	58.3	68.9	36.2	24.9	5.5	6.2	99.9	100
Contract managed	17.2	12.7	0.8	2.6	17.9	15.3	44.1	50.6	62.1	71.6	37.9	24.9	0	6.2	100	97
Total	11.4	15.9	1.3	2.4	12.7	18.3	56.8	50.6	69.4	68.9	26.8	24.9	3.8	6.2	100.1	100

H = hospitals; B = beds.
*Please note that figures may not always equal the provided subtotal or total percentages due to rounding.

0091: ACADIA HEALTHCARE COMPANY, INC. (IO)
830 Crescent Centre Drive, Suite 610, Franklin, TN Zip 37067–7323; tel. 615/861–6000; Joey Jacobs, Chairman and Chief Executive Officer

(Decentralized Health System)

ARIZONA: OASIS BEHAVIORAL HEALTH - CHANDLER (O, 47 beds) 2190 North Grace Boulevard, Chandler, AZ Zip 85225–3416; tel. 480/917–9301; James Gallagher, Chief Executive Officer
Web address: www.obhhospital.com/about/location

SONORA BEHAVIORAL HEALTH HOSPITAL (O, 92 beds) 6050 North Corona Road, #3, Tucson, AZ Zip 85704–1096; tel. 520/469–8700; Edeli Kinsala, Chief Executive Officer

ARKANSAS: RIVERVIEW BEHAVIORAL HEALTH (O, 62 beds) 701 Arkansas Boulevard, Texarkana, AR Zip 71854–2105; tel. 870/772–5028; Angie Crawford, R.N., Chief Executive Officer
Web address: www.riverviewbehavioralhealth.com

VALLEY BEHAVIORAL HEALTH SYSTEM (O, 75 beds) 10301 Mayo Drive, Barling, AR Zip 72923–1660; tel. 479/494–5700; Angel Piper, Chief Executive Officer

VANTAGE POINT OF NORTHWEST ARKANSAS (O, 114 beds) 4253 North Crossover Road, Fayetteville, AR Zip 72703–4596; tel. 479/521–5731; Connie Borengasser, Chief Executive Officer
Web address: www.vantagepointnwa.com

CALIFORNIA: PACIFIC GROVE HOSPITAL (O, 68 beds) 5900 Brockton Avenue, Riverside, CA Zip 92506–1862; tel. 951/275–8400; Nichol Sheffield, Chief Executive Officer
Web address: www.pacificgrovehospital.com

SAN JOSE BEHAVORIAL HEALTH (O, 80 beds) 455 Silicon Valley Boulevard, San Jose, CA Zip 95138–1858; tel. 888/210–2484; Rob Marsh, Chief Executive Officer

DELAWARE: MEADOW WOOD BEHAVIORAL HEALTH SYSTEM (O, 53 beds) 575 South Dupont Highway, New Castle, DE Zip 19720–4606; tel. 302/328–3330; Bill A. Mason, Chief Executive Officer
Web address: www.meadowwoodhospital.com

FLORIDA: NORTH TAMPA BEHAVIORAL HEALTH (O, 78 beds) 29910 State Road 56, Wesley Chapel, FL Zip 33543–8800; tel. 813/922–3300; Tracy Rogers, Chief Executive Officer
Web address: www.northtampabehavioralhealth.com

PARK ROYAL HOSPITAL (O, 103 beds) 9241 Park Royal Drive, Fort Myers, FL Zip 33908–9204; tel. 239/985–2700; Michael Ham, Chief Executive Officer
Web address: www.ParkRoyalHospital.com

GEORGIA: GREENLEAF CENTER (O, 73 beds) 2209 Pineview Drive, Valdosta, GA Zip 31602–7316; tel. 229/247–4357; Stephen Register, Chief Executive Officer

LAKEVIEW BEHAVIORAL HEALTH (O, 70 beds) 1 Technology Parkway South, Norcross, GA Zip 30092–2928; tel. 678/713–2600; Carmen Kramer, Chief Executive Officer
Web address: www.lakeviewbehavioralhealth.com

INDIANA: OPTIONS BEHAVIORAL HEALTH SYSTEM (O, 84 beds) 5602 Caito Drive, Indianapolis, IN Zip 46226–1346; tel. 317/544–4340; Chris Rupert, Chief Executive Officer

LOUISIANA: ACADIA OPTIMA HOSPITAL (O, 24 beds) 1131 Rue De Belier, Lafayette, LA Zip 70506–6532; tel. 337/991–0571; Glynis R. DeRoche, Administrator
Web address: www.optimaspecialtyhospital.com/

ACADIA VERMILION HOSPITAL (O, 54 beds) 2520 North University Avenue, Lafayette, LA Zip 70507–5306; tel. 337/234–5614; Stephanie Bonin, Chief Executive Officer
Web address: www.acadiavermilion.com

COVINGTON BEHAVIOR HEALTH (O, 60 beds) 201 Greenbrier Boulevard, Covington, LA Zip 70433–7236; tel. 985/893–2970; Wes Crawford, Chief Executive Officer

LONGLEAF HOSPITAL (O, 70 beds) 44 Versailles Boulevard, Alexandria, LA Zip 71303–3960; tel. 318/445–5111; Monica Tatum, Chief Executive Officer and Administrator
Web address: www.longleafhospital.com/

MASSACHUSETTS: SOUTHCOAST BEHAVIORAL HEALTH (O, 120 beds) 581 Faunce Corner Road, Dartmouth, MA Zip 02747–1242; tel. 888/210–2475; Kevin R. Burchill, Chief Executive Officer
Web address: www.southcoastbehavioral.com

MICHIGAN: HARBOR OAKS HOSPITAL (O, 45 beds) 35031 23 Mile Road, New Baltimore, MI Zip 48047–3649; tel. 586/725–5777; Sari Abromovich, Chief Executive Officer

STONECREST CENTER (O, 125 beds) 15000 Gratiot Avenue, Detroit, MI Zip 48205–1973; tel. 313/245–0600; Steve Savage, Chief Executive Officer
Web address: www.stonecrestcenter.com

MISSOURI: LAKELAND BEHAVIORAL HEALTH SYSTEM (O, 122 beds) 440 South Market Street, Springfield, MO Zip 65806–2026; tel. 417/865–5581; Nathan Duncan, Chief Executive Officer
Web address: www.lakeland-hospital.com

NEVADA: SEVEN HILLS HOSPITAL (O, 134 beds) 3021 West Horizon Ridge Parkway, Henderson, NV Zip 89052–3990; tel. 702/646–5000; Christopher West, Chief Executive Officer

OHIO: OHIO HOSPITAL FOR PSYCHIATRY (O, 90 beds) 880 Greenlawn Avenue, Columbus, OH Zip 43223–2616; tel. 614/449–9664; Stanley Frank, Chief Executive Officer
Web address: www.ohiohospitalforpsychiatry.com/

TEN LAKES CENTER (O, 16 beds) 819 North First Street, 3rd Floor, Dennison, OH Zip 44621–1003; tel. 740/922–7499; Debra C. Gardner, R.N., MSN, Administrator

OKLAHOMA: ROLLING HILLS HOSPITAL (O, 92 beds) 1000 Rolling Hills Lane, Ada, OK Zip 74820–9415; tel. 580/436–3600; Anthony Guild, Chief Executive Officer
Web address: www.rollinghillshospital.com

PENNSYLVANIA: BELMONT BEHAVIORAL HOSPITAL (O, 171 beds) 4200 Monument Road, Philadelphia, PA Zip 19131–1625; tel. 215/877–2000; Mark Schor, Chief Executive Officer

SOUTHWOOD PSYCHIATRIC HOSPITAL (O, 156 beds) 2575 Boyce Plaza Road, Pittsburgh, PA Zip 15241–3925; tel. 412/257–2290; Stephen J. Quigley, Chief Executive Officer
Web address: www.southwoodhospital.com

PUERTO RICO: SAN JUAN CAPESTRANO HOSPITAL (O, 158 beds) Rural Route 2, Box 11, San Juan, PR Zip 926; tel. 787/625–2900; Marta Rivera. Plaza, Chief Executive Officer and Managing Director
Web address: www.sjcapestrano.com

SOUTH CAROLINA: REBOUND BEHAVIORAL HEALTH (O, 42 beds) 134 East Rebound Road, Lancaster, SC Zip 29720–7712; tel. 877/959–5063; Patricia Hamilton, Chief Executive Officer
Web address: www.reboundbehavioralhealth.com

TENNESSEE: CRESTWYN BEHAVIORAL HEALTH (O, 60 beds) 9485 Crestwyn Hills Cove, Memphis, TN Zip 38125–8515; tel. 901/248–1500; Jeb Stokes, Chief Executive Officer

DELTA MEDICAL CENTER (O, 167 beds) 3000 Getwell Road, Memphis, TN Zip 38118–2299; tel. 901/369–8100; Phil Willcoxon, Chief Executive Officer
Web address: www.deltamedcenter.com

TRUSTPOINT HOSPITAL (O, 101 beds) 1009 North Thompson Lane, Murfreesboro, TN Zip 37129–4351; tel. 615/867–1111; Jeffrey Woods, Chief Executive Officer
Web address: www.trustpointhospital.com

TEXAS: CROSS CREEK HOSPITAL (O, 90 beds) 8402 Cross Park Drive, Austin, TX Zip 78754; tel. 512/215–3900; Jennifer Miller, Chief Executive Officer
Web address: www.cornerstonehealthcaregroup.com

RED RIVER HOSPITAL, LLC (O, 96 beds) 1505 Eighth Street, Wichita Falls, TX Zip 76301–3106; tel. 940/322–3171; James Wilfer, Chief Executive Officer

For explanation of codes following names, see page B2.
★ Indicates Type III membership in the American Hospital Association.

UTAH: HIGHLAND RIDGE HOSPITAL (O, 83 beds) 7309 South 180 West, Midvale, UT Zip 84047–3769; tel. 801/569–2153; Matt Wilburn, Chief Executive Officer
Web address: www.highlandridgehospital.com

WASHINGTON: CASCADE BEHAVIORAL HOSPITAL (O, 63 beds) 12844 Military Road South, Tukwila, WA Zip 98168–3045; tel. 206/244–0180; Michael Uradnik, Chief Executive Officer

Owned, leased, sponsored:	36 hospitals	3138 beds
Contract-managed:	0 hospitals	0 beds
Totals:	36 hospitals	3138 beds

★0640: ACUITYHEALTHCARE, LP (IO)
10200 Mallard Creek Road, Suite 300, Charlotte, NC Zip 28262–9705; tel. 704/887–7280; Edwin H. Cooper Jr, President and Chief Executive Officer
(Independent Hospital System)

NEW JERSEY: ACUITY SPECIALTY HOSPITAL OF NEW JERSEY (O, 30 beds) 1925 Pacific Avenue, 7th Floor, 5 Wellness, Atlantic City, NJ Zip 08401–6713; tel. 609/441–2122; Monica Titus, R.N., President and Chief Executive Officer
Web address: www.acuityhealthcare.net

ACUITY SPECIALTY HOSPITAL OF SOUTHERN NEW JERSEY (O, 69 beds) 218 Sunset Road, Willingboro, NJ Zip 08046–1110, 220 Sunset Road, 08046–1110, tel. 609/835–3650; Monica Titus, R.N., Regional Chief Executive Officer
Web address: www.willingboro.acuityhealthcare.net

OHIO: ACUITY SPECIALTY HOSPITALS OHIO VALLEY (O, 52 beds) 380 Summit Avenue, 3rd Floor, Steubenville, OH Zip 43952–2667; tel. 740/283–7600; Judy K. Weaver, MS, Chief Executive Officer

TEXAS: ACUITY HOSPITAL OF SOUTH TEXAS (O, 30 beds) 718 Lexington Avenue, San Antonio, TX Zip 78212–4768; tel. 210/572–4600; Dorothy J. Elford, Chief Executive Officer
Web address: www.acuitysouthtexas.net

Owned, leased, sponsored:	4 hospitals	181 beds
Contract-managed:	0 hospitals	0 beds
Totals:	4 hospitals	181 beds

0895: ADENA HEALTH SYSTEM (NP)
272 Hospital Road, Chillicothe, OH Zip 45601–9031; tel. 740/779–7500; Mark H. Shuter, President and Chief Executive Officer
(Independent Hospital System)

OHIO: ADENA GREENFIELD MEDICAL CENTER (O, 25 beds) 550 Mirabeau Street, Greenfield, OH Zip 45123–1617; tel. 937/981–9400; Kathy Dye, Interim Administrator
Web address: www.adena.org

ADENA MEDICAL CENTER (O, 189 beds) 272 Hospital Road, Chillicothe, OH Zip 45601–9031; tel. 740/779–7500; Jeff Graham, President and Chief Executive Officer

ADENA PIKE MEDICAL CENTER (O, 25 beds) 100 Dawn Lane, Waverly, OH Zip 45690–9138; tel. 740/947–2186; David M. Zanni, Administrator
Web address: www.adena.org

Owned, leased, sponsored:	3 hospitals	239 beds
Contract-managed:	0 hospitals	0 beds
Totals:	3 hospitals	239 beds

★0235: ADVENTIST HEALTH (CO)
2100 Douglas Boulevard, Roseville, CA Zip 95661–3898, P O Box 619002, 95661–9002, tel. 916/781–2000; Scott Reiner, Chief Executive Officer
(Decentralized Health System)

CALIFORNIA: ADVENTIST HEALTH GLENDALE (O, 462 beds) 8700 Beverly Blvd, NT-3138, Los Angeles, CA Zip 90048, 1509 Wilson Terrace, Glendale,

91206–4098, tel. 818/409–8000; Kevin A. Roberts, FACHE, President and Chief Executive Officer

ADVENTIST HEALTH MEDICAL CENTER - TEHACHAPI VALLEY (C, 24 beds) 115 West 'E' Street, Tehachapi, CA Zip 93561–1607, P O Box 1900, 93581–1900, tel. 661/823–3000; Eugene Suksi, Chief Executive Officer
Web address: www.tvhd.org

ADVENTIST MEDICAL CENTER - HANFORD (O, 199 beds) 115 Mall Drive, Hanford, CA Zip 93230–3513; tel. 559/582–9000; Wayne Ferch, President and Chief Executive Officer
Web address: www.adventisthealthcv.com/hospital_newhanfordhospital.aspx

ADVENTIST MEDICAL CENTER-REEDLEY (L, 49 beds) 372 West Cypress Avenue, Reedley, CA Zip 93654–2199; tel. 559/638–8155; Wayne Ferch, President and Chief Executive Officer

CENTRAL VALLEY GENERAL HOSPITAL (O, 49 beds) 1025 North Douty Street, Hanford, CA Zip 93230–3722, P O Box 480, 93232–2113, tel. 559/583–2100; Wayne Ferch, President and Chief Executive Officer
Web address: www.hanfordhealth.com

FEATHER RIVER HOSPITAL (O, 54 beds) 5974 Pentz Road, Paradise, CA Zip 95969–5593; tel. 530/877–9361; Monty E. Knittel, Chief Executive Officer
Web address: www.frhosp.org

ADVENTIST HEALTH HOWARD (L, 25 beds) One Marcela Drive, Willits, CA Zip 95490–4298; tel. 707/459–6801; Jason Wells, President and Chief Executive Officer
Web address: www.howardhospital.com

ADVENTIST HEALTH LODI MEMORIAL (O, 190 beds) 975 South Fairmont Avenue, Lodi, CA Zip 95240–5118, P O Box 3004, 95241–1908, tel. 209/334–3411; Daniel Wolcott, President and Chief Executive Officer
Web address: www.lodihealth.org

ADVENTIST HEALTH BAKERSFIELD (O, 254 beds) 2615 Chester Avenue, Bakersfield, CA Zip 93301–2014, P O Box 2615, 93303–2615, tel. 661/395–3000; Sharlet Briggs, Ph.D., Market Chief Executive Officer and President

SIMI VALLEY HOSPITAL (O, 144 beds) 2975 North Sycamore Drive, Simi Valley, CA Zip 93065–1277; tel. 805/955–6000; Jennifer Swenson, President and Chief Executive Officer
Web address: www.simivalleyhospital.com

ADVENTIST HEALTH SONORA (O, 152 beds) 1000 Greenley Road, Sonora, CA Zip 95370–4819; tel. 209/536–5000; Andrew Jahn, President and Chief Executive Officer

ADVENTIST HEALTH ST. HELENA (O, 58 beds) 525 Oregon Street, Vallejo, CA Zip 94590–3201; tel. 707/648–2200; Steven Herber, M.D., FACS, President and Chief Executive Officer
Web address: www.sthelenahospitals.org/location/center-for-behavioral-health

ADVENTIST HEALTH CLEAR LAKE (O, 25 beds) 15630 18th Avenue, Clearlake, CA Zip 95422–9336, P O Box 6710, 95422, tel. 707/994–6486; David Santos, President and Chief Executive Officer

ADVENTIST HEALTH ST. HELENA (O, 116 beds) 10 Woodland Road, Saint Helena, CA Zip 94574–9554; tel. 707/963–3611; Steven Herber, M.D., FACS, President and Chief Executive Officer
Web address: www.sthelenahospital.org

UKIAH VALLEY MEDICAL CENTER (O, 50 beds) 275 Hospital Drive, Ukiah, CA Zip 95482–4531; tel. 707/462–3111; Gwen Matthews, R.N., MSN, Chief Executive Officer
Web address: www.adventisthealth.org

WHITE MEMORIAL MEDICAL CENTER (O, 353 beds) 1720 Cesar Chavez Avenue, Los Angeles, CA Zip 90033–2414; tel. 323/268–5000; John Raffoul, Chief Executive Officer
Web address: www.whitememorial.com

HAWAII: CASTLE MEDICAL CENTER (O, 160 beds) 640 Ulukahiki Street, Kailua, HI Zip 96734–4454; tel. 808/263–5500; Kathryn A. Raethel, R.N., M.P.H., President and Chief Executive Officer

OREGON: ADVENTIST MEDICAL CENTER-PORTLAND (O, 242 beds) 10123 SE Market Street, Portland, OR Zip 97216–2599; tel. 503/257–2500; David Russell, President and Chief Executive Officer
Web address: www.adventisthealthnw.com

For explanation of codes following names, see page B2.
★ Indicates Type III membership in the American Hospital Association.

TILLAMOOK REGIONAL MEDICAL CENTER (L, 25 beds) 1000 Third Street, Tillamook, OR Zip 97141–3430; tel. 503/842–4444; David Butler, President and Chief Executive Officer
Web address: www.tillamookregionalmc.com

Owned, leased, sponsored:	18 hospitals	2607 beds
Contract-managed:	1 hospitals	24 beds
Totals:	19 hospitals	2631 beds

★**4165: ADVENTIST HEALTH SYSTEM SUNBELT HEALTH CARE CORPORATION** (CO)
900 Hope Way, Altamonte Springs, FL Zip 32714–1502; tel. 407/357–1000; Terry Shaw, President and Chief Executive Officer
(Decentralized Health System)

COLORADO: AVISTA ADVENTIST HOSPITAL (O, 114 beds) 100 Health Park Drive, Louisville, CO Zip 80027–9583; tel. 303/673–1000; Brent Davis, Interim Chief Executive Officer

CASTLE ROCK ADVENTIST HOSPITAL (O, 53 beds) 2350 Meadows Boulevard, Castle Rock, CO Zip 80109–8405; tel. 720/455–5000; Todd Folkenberg, Chief Executive Officer
Web address: www.castlerockhospital.org

LITTLETON ADVENTIST HOSPITAL (O, 201 beds) 7700 South Broadway Street, Littleton, CO Zip 80122–2628; tel. 303/730–8900; Brett Spenst, Chief Executive Officer

PARKER ADVENTIST HOSPITAL (O, 167 beds) 9395 Crown Crest Boulevard, Parker, CO Zip 80138–8573; tel. 303/269–4000; Sam D. Huenergardt, Chief Executive Officer
Web address: www.parkerhospital.org

PORTER ADVENTIST HOSPITAL (O, 250 beds) 2525 South Downing Street, Denver, CO Zip 80210–5876; tel. 303/778–1955; Morre Dean, Chief Executive Officer
Web address: www.porterhospital.org/poh/home/

FLORIDA: FLORIDA HOSPITAL CARROLLWOOD (O, 96 beds) 7171 North Dale Mabry Highway, Tampa, FL Zip 33614–2665; tel. 813/932–2222; Joe Johnson, FACHE, Chief Executive Officer

FLORIDA HOSPITAL DELAND (O, 164 beds) 701 West Plymouth Avenue, DeLand, FL Zip 32720–3236; tel. 386/943–4522; Lorenzo Brown, Chief Executive Officer
Web address: www.fhdeland.org

FLORIDA HOSPITAL FISH MEMORIAL (O, 175 beds) 1055 Saxon Boulevard, Orange City, FL Zip 32763–8468; tel. 386/917–5000; Robert Deininger, Chief Executive Officer
Web address: www.fhfishmemorial.org

FLORIDA HOSPITAL HEARTLAND MEDICAL CENTER (O, 197 beds) 4200 Sun'n Lake Boulevard, Sebring, FL Zip 33872–1986, P O Box 9400, 33871–9400, tel. 863/314–4466; Randy Surber, Chief Executive Officer
Web address: www.floridahospital.com/heartland/our-location

FLORIDA HOSPITAL MEMORIAL MEDICAL CENTER (O, 250 beds) 301 Memorial Medical Parkway, Daytona Beach, FL Zip 32117–5167; tel. 386/676–6000; Ed Noseworthy, Chief Executive Officer

FLORIDA HOSPITAL NEW SMYRNA (O, 95 beds) 401 Palmetto Street, New Smyrna Beach, FL Zip 32168–7399; tel. 386/424–5000; Kenneth R. Mattison, Chief Executive Officer
Web address: https://www.floridahospital.com/new-smyrna

FLORIDA HOSPITAL NORTH PINELLAS (O, 168 beds) 1395 South Pinellas Avenue, Tarpon Springs, FL Zip 34689–3790; tel. 727/942–5000; Tricia Williams, President and Chief Executive Officer

FLORIDA HOSPITAL TAMPA (O, 482 beds) 3100 East Fletcher Avenue, Tampa, FL Zip 33613–4688; tel. 813/971–6000; Brian Adams, President and CEO
Web address: www.floridahospital.com/tampa

FLORIDA HOSPITAL WATERMAN (O, 269 beds) 1000 Waterman Way, Tavares, FL Zip 32778–5266; tel. 352/253–3333; Abel Biri, Chief Executive Officer
Web address: www.fhwat.org

FLORIDA HOSPITAL WAUCHULA (O, 25 beds) 533 West Carlton Street, Wauchula, FL Zip 33873–3407; tel. 863/773–3101; Denise Grimsley, R.N., Vice President and Administrator

FLORIDA HOSPITAL WESLEY CHAPEL (O, 121 beds) 2600 Bruce B Downs Boulevard, Wesley Chapel, FL Zip 33544–9207; tel. 813/929–5000; Denyse Bales-Chubb, President and Chief Executive Officer
Web address: https://www.floridahospital.com/wesley-chapel

FLORIDA HOSPITAL ZEPHYRHILLS (O, 149 beds) 7050 Gall Boulevard, Zephyrhills, FL Zip 33541–1399; tel. 813/788–0411; Amanda Maggard, Chief Executive Officer
Web address: www.fhzeph.org

FLORIDA HOSPITAL AT CONNERTON LONG TERM ACUTE CARE (O, 50 beds) 9441 Health Center Drive, Land O'Lakes, FL Zip 34637–5837; tel. 813/903–3701; Brian Adams, President and Chief Executive Officer

FLORIDA HOSPITAL-FLAGLER (O, 99 beds) 60 Memorial Medical Parkway, Palm Coast, FL Zip 32164–5980; tel. 386/586–2000; Ronald Jimenez, M.D., Chief Executive Officer
Web address: www.floridahospitalflagler.com/

FLORIDA HOSPITAL (O, 2829 beds) 601 East Rollins Street, Orlando, FL Zip 32803–1248; tel. 407/303–6611; Daryl Tol, President and Chief Executive Officer

GEORGIA: GORDON HOSPITAL (O, 82 beds) 1035 Red Bud Road, Calhoun, GA Zip 30701–2082, P O Box 12938, 30703–7013, tel. 706/629–2895; Pete M. Weber, President and Chief Executive Officer
Web address: www.gordonhospital.com

MURRAY MEDICAL CENTER (O, 33 beds) 707 Old Dalton Ellijay Road, Chatsworth, GA Zip 30705–2060, P O Box 1406, 30705–1406, tel. 706/695–4564; Karen Steely, Administrator

ILLINOIS: AMITA HEALTH ADVENTIST MEDICAL CENTER - HINSDALE (O, 275 beds) 120 North Oak Street, Hinsdale, IL Zip 60521–3890; tel. 630/856–6001; Michael Goebel, FACHE, Vice President and Chief Executive Officer
Web address: www.AMITAhealth.org

AMITA HEALTH ADVENTIST MEDICAL CENTER BOLINGBROOK (O, 144 beds) 500 Remington Boulevard, Bolingbrook, IL Zip 60440–4906; tel. 630/312–5000; Bruce Christian, President and Chief Executive Officer
Web address: www.keepingyouwell.com/abh/

AMITA HEALTH ADVENTIST MEDICAL CENTER GLENOAKS (O, 120 beds) 701 Winthrop Avenue, Glendale Heights, IL Zip 60139–1403; tel. 630/545–8000; Bruce C. Christian, President and Chief Executive Officer

AMITA HEALTH ADVENTIST MEDICAL CENTER LAGRANGE (O, 200 beds) 5101 South Willow Spring Road, La Grange, IL Zip 60525–2600; tel. 708/245–9000; Michael Murrill, MBA, President and Chief Executive Officer
Web address: www.keepingyouwell.com

KANSAS: SHAWNEE MISSION MEDICAL CENTER (O, 403 beds) 9100 West 74th Street, Shawnee Mission, KS Zip 66204–4004, Box 2923, 66201–1323, tel. 913/676–2000; Ken J. Bacon, President and Chief Executive Officer

KENTUCKY: MANCHESTER MEMORIAL HOSPITAL (O, 63 beds) 210 Marie Langdon Drive, Manchester, KY Zip 40962–6388; tel. 606/598–5104; Erika Skula, President and Chief Executive Officer
Web address: www.manchestermemorial.org

NORTH CAROLINA: PARK RIDGE HEALTH (O, 95 beds) 100 Hospital Drive, Hendersonville, NC Zip 28792–5272; tel. 828/684–8501; Jimm Bunch, President and Chief Executive Officer

TEXAS: CENTRAL TEXAS MEDICAL CENTER (O, 111 beds) 1301 Wonder World Drive, San Marcos, TX Zip 78666–7544; tel. 512/353–8979; Anthony Stahl, Ph.D., FACHE, Chief Executive Officer
Web address: www.ctmc.org

METROPLEX ADVENTIST HOSPITAL (O, 177 beds) 2201 South Clear Creek Road, Killeen, TX Zip 76549–4110; tel. 254/526–7523; Carlyle L E. Walton, FACHE, Chief Executive Officer
Web address: www.mplex.org

ROLLINS-BROOK COMMUNITY HOSPITAL (O, 35 beds) 608 North Key Avenue, Lampasas, TX Zip 76550–1106, P O Box 589, 76550–0032, tel. 512/556–3682; Ashley Underwood, Chief Executive Officer
Web address: www.mplex.org

TEXAS HEALTH HUGULEY HOSPITAL FORT WORTH SOUTH (C, 177 beds) 11801 South Freeway, Burleson, TX Zip 76028–7021, P O Box 6337, Fort Worth, 76115–0337, tel. 817/293–9110; Kenneth A. Finch, President and Chief Executive Officer

For explanation of codes following names, see page B2.
★ Indicates Type III membership in the American Hospital Association.

WISCONSIN: CHIPPEWA VALLEY HOSPITAL AND OAKVIEW CARE CENTER (O, 25 beds) 1220 Third Avenue West, Durand, WI Zip 54736–1600, P O Box 224, 54736–0224, tel. 715/672–4211; Douglas R. Peterson, President and Chief Executive Officer
Web address: www.chippewavalleyhospital.com/

Owned, leased, sponsored:	33 hospitals	7717 beds
Contract-managed:	1 hospitals	177 beds
Totals:	34 hospitals	7894 beds

0214: ADVENTIST HEALTHCARE (NP)

820 West Diamond Avenue, Suite 600, Gaithersburg, MD Zip 20878–1419; tel. 301/315–3185; Terry Forde, President and Chief Executive Officer
(Independent Hospital System)

MARYLAND: ADVENTIST BEHAVIORAL HEALTH AND WELLNESS SERVICES (O, 220 beds) 14901 Broschart Road, Rockville, MD Zip 20850–3318; tel. 301/251–4500; Kevin Young, FACHE, President
Web address: www.adventistbehavioralhealth.com

ADVENTIST HEALTHCARE PHYSICAL HEALTH AND REHABILITATION (O, 77 beds) 9909 Medical Center Drive, Rockville, MD Zip 20850–6361; tel. 240/864–6000; Brent Reitz, President

ADVENTIST HEALTHCARE SHADY GROVE MEDICAL CENTER (O, 315 beds) 9901 Medical Center Drive, Rockville, MD Zip 20850–3395; tel. 240/826–6000; John Sackett , President SGMC and Executive Vice President and Chief Operating Officer
Web address: www.adventisthealthcare.com

ADVENTIST HEALTHCARE WASHINGTON ADVENTIST HOSPITAL (O, 252 beds) 7600 Carroll Avenue, Takoma Park, MD Zip 20912–6392; tel. 301/891–7600; Erik Wangsness, President
Web address: www.adventisthealthcare.com

Owned, leased, sponsored:	4 hospitals	864 beds
Contract-managed:	0 hospitals	0 beds
Totals:	4 hospitals	864 beds

★0064: ADVOCATE HEALTH CARE (NP)

3075 Highland Parkway, Suite 600, Downers Grove, IL Zip 60515–1206; tel. 630/929–8700; Jim Skogsbergh, President and Chief Executive Officer
(Moderately Centralized Health System)

ILLINOIS: ADVOCATE BROMENN MEDICAL CENTER (O, 198 beds) 1304 Franklin Avenue, Normal, IL Zip 61761–3558, P O Box 2850, Bloomington, 61702–2850, tel. 309/454–1400; Colleen Kannaday, FACHE, President

ADVOCATE CHRIST MEDICAL CENTER (O, 761 beds) 4440 West 95th Street, Oak Lawn, IL Zip 60453–2699; tel. 708/684–8000; Kenneth W. Lukhard, President
Web address: www.advocatehealth.com/christ

ADVOCATE CONDELL MEDICAL CENTER (O, 283 beds) 801 South Milwaukee Avenue, Libertyville, IL Zip 60048–3199; tel. 847/362–2900; Karen A. Lambert, President
Web address: www.advocatehealth.com/condell/

ADVOCATE EUREKA HOSPITAL (O, 18 beds) 101 South Major Street, Eureka, IL Zip 61530–1246; tel. 309/467–2371; Colleen Kannaday, FACHE, President

ADVOCATE GOOD SAMARITAN HOSPITAL (O, 275 beds) 3815 Highland Avenue, Downers Grove, IL Zip 60515–1590; tel. 630/275–5900; David Fox, President
Web address: www.advocatehealth.com/gsam

ADVOCATE GOOD SHEPHERD HOSPITAL (O, 176 beds) 450 West Highway 22, Barrington, IL Zip 60010–1919; tel. 847/381–0123; Karen A. Lambert, President

ADVOCATE ILLINOIS MASONIC MEDICAL CENTER (O, 336 beds) 836 West Wellington Avenue, Chicago, IL Zip 60657–5147; tel. 773/975–1600; Susan Nordstrom. Lopez, President
Web address: www.advocatehealth.com/masonic

ADVOCATE LUTHERAN GENERAL HOSPITAL (O, 625 beds) 1775 Dempster Street, Park Ridge, IL Zip 60068–1174; tel. 847/723–2210; Dominica Tallarico, President

ADVOCATE SHERMAN HOSPITAL (O, 255 beds) 1425 North Randall Road , Elgin, IL Zip 60123–2300; tel. 847/742–9800; Linda Deering, MSN, R.N., President
Web address: www.advocatehealth.com/sherman

ADVOCATE SOUTH SUBURBAN HOSPITAL (O, 258 beds) 17800 South Kedzie Avenue, Hazel Crest, IL Zip 60429–0989; tel. 708/799–8000; Richard Heim, President

ADVOCATE TRINITY HOSPITAL (O, 186 beds) 2320 East 93rd Street, Chicago, IL Zip 60617–3909; tel. 773/967–2000; Terika Richardson, M.P.H., President
Web address: https://www.advocatehealth.com/trin/

Owned, leased, sponsored:	11 hospitals	3371 beds
Contract-managed:	0 hospitals	0 beds
Totals:	11 hospitals	3371 beds

0312: AHMC & HEALTHCARE, INC. (IO)

55 South Raymond Avenue, Suite 105, Alhambra, CA Zip 91801–7101; tel. 626/457–9600; Jonathan Wu, M.D., President and Chairman
(Independent Hospital System)

CALIFORNIA: AHMC ANAHEIM REGIONAL MEDICAL CENTER (O, 223 beds) 1111 West La Palma Avenue, Anaheim, CA Zip 92801–2881; tel. 714/774–1450; Richard Castro, Chief Executive Officer

ALHAMBRA HOSPITAL MEDICAL CENTER (O, 144 beds) 100 South Raymond Avenue, Alhambra, CA Zip 91801–3199, P O Box 510, 91802–2510, tel. 626/570–1606; Iris Lai, Chief Executive Officer
Web address: www.alhambrahospital.com

GARFIELD MEDICAL CENTER (O, 210 beds) 525 North Garfield Avenue, Monterey Park, CA Zip 91754–1205; tel. 626/573–2222; Patrick A. Petre, Chief Executive Officer

GREATER EL MONTE COMMUNITY HOSPITAL (O, 117 beds) 1701 Santa Anita Avenue, South El Monte, CA Zip 91733–3411; tel. 626/579–7777; Stanley Toy Jr, M.D., Chief Executive Officer
Web address: www.greaterelmonte.com

MONTEREY PARK HOSPITAL (O, 101 beds) 900 South Atlantic Boulevard, Monterey Park, CA Zip 91754–4780; tel. 626/570–9000; Philip A. Cohen, Chief Executive Officer

SAN GABRIEL VALLEY MEDICAL CENTER (O, 273 beds) 438 West Las Tunas Drive, San Gabriel, CA Zip 91776–1216, P O Box 1507, 91778–1507, tel. 626/289–5454; Karen Price-Gharzeddine, R.N., MS, Chief Executive Officer
Web address: www.sgvmc.org

WHITTIER HOSPITAL MEDICAL CENTER (O, 81 beds) 9080 Colima Road, Whittier, CA Zip 90605–1600; tel. 562/945–3561; Richard Castro, Chief Executive Officer
Web address: www.whittierhospital.com

Owned, leased, sponsored:	7 hospitals	1149 beds
Contract-managed:	0 hospitals	0 beds
Totals:	7 hospitals	1149 beds

0225: ALAMEDA HEALTH SYSTEM (NP)

15400 Foothill Boulevard, San Leandro, CA Zip 94578–1009; tel. 510/677–7920; Delvecchio Finley, Chief Executive Officer
(Moderately Centralized Health System)

CALIFORNIA: ALAMEDA HOSPITAL (O, 227 beds) 2070 Clinton Avenue, Alameda, CA Zip 94501–4397; tel. 510/522–3700; James E T. Jackson, M.P.H., Chief Administrative Officer

HIGHLAND HOSPITAL (O, 374 beds) 1411 East 31st Street, Oakland, CA Zip 94602–1018; tel. 510/437–4800; Delvecchio Finley, Chief Executive Officer
Web address: www.alamedahealthsystem.org

For explanation of codes following names, see page B2.
★ Indicates Type III membership in the American Hospital Association.

Section B

SAN LEANDRO HOSPITAL (O, 45 beds) 13855 East 14th Street, San Leandro, CA Zip 94578-2600; tel. 510/357-6500; James E T. Jackson, M.P.H., Chief Administrative Officer

Owned, leased, sponsored:	3 hospitals	646 beds
Contract-managed:	0 hospitals	0 beds
Totals:	3 hospitals	646 beds

1020: ALECTO HEALTHCARE (IO)
16310 Bake Parkway, Suite 200, Irvine, CA Zip 92618-4684; tel. 323/932-5963; Lex Reddy, Chief Executive Officer

CALIFORNIA: OLYMPIA MEDICAL CENTER (O, 204 beds) 5900 West Olympic Boulevard, Los Angeles, CA Zip 90036-4671; tel. 310/657-5900; Matthew Williams, R.N., Chief Executive Officer
Web address: www.olympiamc.com

ST. ROSE HOSPITAL (C, 150 beds) 27200 Calaroga Avenue, Hayward, CA Zip 94545-4383; tel. 510/264-4000; Aman Dhuper, President and Chief Executive Officer

OHIO: EAST OHIO REGIONAL HOSPITAL (O, 120 beds) 90 North Fourth Street, Martins Ferry, OH Zip 43935-1648; tel. 740/633-1100; Bernie Albertini, Chief Administrative Officer
Web address: www.ovmc-eorh.com

TEXAS: WILSON N. JONES REGIONAL MEDICAL CENTER (O, 108 beds) 500 North Highland Avenue, Sherman, TX Zip 75092-7354; tel. 903/870-4611; John Rossfeld, Administrator

WEST VIRGINIA: FAIRMONT REGIONAL MEDICAL CENTER (O, 140 beds) 1325 Locust Avenue, Fairmont, WV Zip 26554-1435; tel. 304/367-7100; Robert S. Adcock, Chief Executive Officer
Web address: www.frmcwv.com

OHIO VALLEY MEDICAL CENTER (O, 169 beds) 2000 Eoff Street, Wheeling, WV Zip 26003-3870; tel. 304/234-0123; Lex Reddy, President and Chief Executive Officer
Web address: www.ovmc-eorh.com

Owned, leased, sponsored:	5 hospitals	741 beds
Contract-managed:	1 hospitals	150 beds
Totals:	6 hospitals	891 beds

★0199: ALLEGHENY HEALTH NETWORK (NP)
30 Isabella Street, Suite 300, Pittsburgh, PA Zip 15212-5862; tel. 412/359-3131; Cynthia Hundorfean, President and Chief Executive Officer
(Moderately Centralized Health System)

NEW YORK: WESTFIELD MEMORIAL HOSPITAL (O, 4 beds) 189 East Main Street, Westfield, NY Zip 14787-1195; tel. 716/326-4921; Christopher Clark, D.O., President and Chief Executive Officer

PENNSYLVANIA: ALLEGHENY GENERAL HOSPITAL (O, 524 beds) 320 East North Avenue, Pittsburgh, PA Zip 15212-4756; tel. 412/359-3131; Jeffrey Cohen, M.D., President
Web address: www.wpahs.org/locations/allegheny-general-hospital

ALLEGHENY VALLEY HOSPITAL (O, 200 beds) 1301 Carlisle Street, Natrona Heights, PA Zip 15065-1152; tel. 724/224-5100; William Englert, Chief Executive Officer
Web address: www.wpahs.org

CANONSBURG HOSPITAL (O, 104 beds) 100 Medical Boulevard, Canonsburg, PA Zip 15317-9762; tel. 724/745-6100; Louise Urban, R.N., President and Chief Executive Officer

FORBES HOSPITAL (O, 315 beds) 2570 Haymaker Road, Monroeville, PA Zip 15146-3513; tel. 412/858-2000; Mark Rubino, M.D., President
Web address: www.ahn.org

JEFFERSON HOSPITAL (O, 341 beds) 565 Coal Valley Road, Jefferson Hills, PA Zip 15025-3703, Box 18119, Pittsburgh, 15236-0119, tel. 412/469-5000; Louise Urban, R.N., President and Chief Executive Officer
Web address: www.jeffersonregional.com

SAINT VINCENT HOSPITAL (O, 400 beds) 232 West 25th Street, Erie, PA Zip 16544-0002; tel. 814/452-5000; Christopher Clark, D.O., President and Chief Executive Officer

WEST PENN HOSPITAL (O, 317 beds) 4800 Friendship Avenue, Pittsburgh, PA Zip 15224-1722; tel. 412/578-5000; Ronald J. Andro, President and Chief Executive Officer
Web address: www.wpahs.org

Owned, leased, sponsored:	8 hospitals	2205 beds
Contract-managed:	0 hospitals	0 beds
Totals:	8 hospitals	2205 beds

0413: ALLEGIANCE HEALTH MANAGEMENT (IO)
504 Texas Street, Suite 200, Shreveport, LA Zip 71101-3526; tel. 318/226-8202; Rock Bordelon, President and Chief Executive Officer
(Independent Hospital System)

ARKANSAS: EUREKA SPRINGS HOSPITAL (O, 15 beds) 24 Norris Street, Eureka Springs, AR Zip 72632-3541; tel. 479/253-7400; Peter Savoy III, Chief Executive Officer
Web address: www.eurekaspringshospital.com

NORTH METRO MEDICAL CENTER (O, 73 beds) 1400 West Braden Street, Jacksonville, AR Zip 72076-3788; tel. 501/985-7000; Bill Bledsoe, Administrator

RIVER VALLEY MEDICAL CENTER (O, 35 beds) 200 North Third Street, Dardanelle, AR Zip 72834-3802, P O Box 578, 72834-0578, tel. 479/229-4677; Peter Savoy III, Administrator

LOUISIANA: BIENVILLE MEDICAL CENTER (O, 21 beds) 1175 Pine Street, Suite 200, Arcadia, LA Zip 71001-3122; tel. 318/263-4700; Kirk Lemoine, Chief Executive Officer
Web address: www.bienvillemedicalcenter.net/

SABINE MEDICAL CENTER (O, 44 beds) 240 Highland Drive, Many, LA Zip 71449-3718; tel. 318/256-5691; Calvin Green, Chief Executive Officer
Web address: www.sabinemedicalcenter.net

MISSISSIPPI: ALLEGIANCE SPECIALTY HOSPITAL OF GREENVILLE (O, 39 beds) 300 South Washington Avenue, 3rd Floor, Greenville, MS Zip 38701-4719; tel. 662/332-7344; Vernail Herzog, Chief Executive Officer

TEXAS: ALLEGIANCE BEHAVIORAL HEALTH CENTER OF PLAINVIEW (O, 20 beds) 2601 Dimmit Road, Suite 400, Suite 400, Plainview, TX Zip 79072-1833; tel. 806/296-9191; Angie Alexander, Chief Executive Officer
Web address: www.ahmgt.com

ALLEGIANCE SPECIALTY HOSPITAL OF KILGORE (O, 60 beds) 1612 South Henderson Boulevard, Kilgore, TX Zip 75662-3594; tel. 903/984-3505; Karen Ross, Chief Executive Officer
Web address: www.ahmgt.com

Owned, leased, sponsored:	8 hospitals	307 beds
Contract-managed:	0 hospitals	0 beds
Totals:	8 hospitals	307 beds

0317: ALLIANT MANAGEMENT SERVICES (IO)
2650 Eastpoint Parkway, Suite 300, Louisville, KY Zip 40223-5164; tel. 502/992-3525; Stephen E. Fischer, Regional Vice President, Finance
(Moderately Centralized Health System)

FLORIDA: CALHOUN-LIBERTY HOSPITAL (C, 25 beds) 20370 NE Burns Avenue, Blountstown, FL Zip 32424-1045, P O Box 419, 32424-0419, tel. 850/674-5411; Charles E. Durant Jr, FACHE, Chief Executive Officer
Web address: www.calhounlibertyhospital.com

NORTHWEST FLORIDA COMMUNITY HOSPITAL (C, 59 beds) 1360 Brickyard Road, Chipley, FL Zip 32428-6303, P O Box 889, 32428-0889, tel. 850/638-1610; Michael A. Kozar, Chief Executive Officer
Web address: www.nfch.org

ILLINOIS: FAYETTE COUNTY HOSPITAL (O, 110 beds) 650 West Taylor Street, Vandalia, IL Zip 62471-1296; tel. 618/283-1231; Gregory D. Starnes, Chief Executive Officer

For explanation of codes following names, see page B2.
★ Indicates Type III membership in the American Hospital Association.

GIBSON AREA HOSPITAL AND HEALTH SERVICES (C, 67 beds) 1120 North Melvin Street, Gibson City, IL Zip 60936–1477, P O Box 429, 60936–0429, tel. 217/784–4251; Robert C. Schmitt II, Chief Executive Officer
Web address: www.gibsonhospital.org

PARIS COMMUNITY HOSPITAL (C, 25 beds) 721 East Court Street, Paris, IL Zip 61944–2460; tel. 217/465–4141; Oliver Smith, President and Chief Executive Officer
Web address: www.pariscommunityhospital.com

WABASH GENERAL HOSPITAL (C, 25 beds) 1418 College Drive, Mount Carmel, IL Zip 62863–2638; tel. 618/262–8621; Jay Purvis, President and Chief Executive Officer
Web address: www.wabashgeneral.com

INDIANA: PERRY COUNTY MEMORIAL HOSPITAL (C, 25 beds) 8885 State Road 237, Tell City, IN Zip 47586–2750; tel. 812/547–7011; Brian J. Herwig, Chief Executive Officer

KENTUCKY: BRECKINRIDGE MEMORIAL HOSPITAL (C, 43 beds) 1011 Old Highway 60, Hardinsburg, KY Zip 40143–2597; tel. 270/756–7000; Angela Portman, Chief Executive Officer
Web address: www.breckinridgehealth.org/

CARROLL COUNTY MEMORIAL HOSPITAL (C, 25 beds) 309 11th Street, Carrollton, KY Zip 41008–1400; tel. 502/732–4321; Harry Hays, Chief Executive Officer
Web address: www.ccmhosp.com

JAMES B. HAGGIN MEMORIAL HOSPITAL (C, 25 beds) 464 Linden Avenue, Harrodsburg, KY Zip 40330–1862; tel. 859/734–5441; Victoria L. Reed, R.N., FACHE, Chief Executive Officer

TWIN LAKES REGIONAL MEDICAL CENTER (C, 75 beds) 910 Wallace Avenue, Leitchfield, KY Zip 42754–2414; tel. 270/259–9400; Wayne Meriwether, Chief Executive Officer
Web address: www.tlrmc.com

NORTH CAROLINA: HUGH CHATHAM MEMORIAL HOSPITAL (C, 81 beds) 180 Parkwood Drive, Elkin, NC Zip 28621–2430, P O Box 560, 28621–0560, tel. 336/527–7000; Paul Hammes, Chief Executive Officer

Owned, leased, sponsored:	1 hospitals	110 beds
Contract-managed:	11 hospitals	475 beds
Totals:	12 hospitals	585 beds

★0041: ALLINA HEALTH (NP)
2925 Chicago Avenue, Minneapolis, MN Zip 55407–1321, P O Box 43, 55440–0043, tel. 612/262–5000; Penny Ann. Wheeler, M.D., Chief Executive Officer
(Moderately Centralized Health System)

MINNESOTA: ABBOTT NORTHWESTERN HOSPITAL (O, 675 beds) 800 East 28th Street, Minneapolis, MN Zip 55407–3799; tel. 612/863–4000; Thomas O'Connor, Interim Chief Executive Officer
Web address: www.abbottnorthwestern.com

BUFFALO HOSPITAL (O, 44 beds) 303 Catlin Street, Buffalo, MN Zip 55313–1947; tel. 763/682–1212; Jennifer Myster, President

CAMBRIDGE MEDICAL CENTER (O, 75 beds) 701 South Dellwood Street, Cambridge, MN Zip 55008–1920; tel. 763/689–7700; Gary Shaw, President
Web address: www.allina.com/ahs/cambridge.nsf

DISTRICT ONE HOSPITAL (O, 42 beds) 200 State Avenue, Faribault, MN Zip 55021–6345; tel. 507/334–6451; Stephen J. Pribyl, FACHE, President
Web address: www.allinahealth.org/District-One-Hospital/

HUTCHINSON HEALTH (C, 49 beds) 1095 Highway 15 South, Hutchinson, MN Zip 55350–3182; tel. 320/234–5000; Steven Mulder, M.D., President and Chief Executive Officer

MERCY HOSPITAL (O, 430 beds) 4050 Coon Rapids Boulevard, Coon Rapids, MN Zip 55433–2586; tel. 763/236–6000; Sara J. Criger, President
Web address: www.allinamercy.org

NEW ULM MEDICAL CENTER (O, 45 beds) 1324 Fifth Street North, New Ulm, MN Zip 56073–1553; tel. 507/217–5000; Toby Freier, President

OWATONNA HOSPITAL (O, 43 beds) 2250 NW 26th Street, Owatonna, MN Zip 55060–5503; tel. 507/451–3850; David L. Albrecht, President
Web address: www.owatonnahospital.com

PHILLIPS EYE INSTITUTE (O, 8 beds) 2215 Park Avenue, Minneapolis, MN Zip 55404–3756; tel. 612/775–8800; Daniel S. Conrad, M.D., President

REGINA HOSPITAL (O, 29 beds) 1175 Nininger Road, Hastings, MN Zip 55033–1098; tel. 651/480–4100; Thomas R. Thompson, President
Web address: www.reginamedical.org

ST. FRANCIS REGIONAL MEDICAL CENTER (O, 85 beds) 1455 St Francis Avenue, Shakopee, MN Zip 55379–3380; tel. 952/428–3000; Mike McMahan, President

UNITED HOSPITAL (O, 371 beds) 333 North Smith Avenue, Saint Paul, MN Zip 55102–2389; tel. 651/241–8000; Thomas O'Connor, President
Web address: www.allina.com

WISCONSIN: RIVER FALLS AREA HOSPITAL (O, 12 beds) 1629 East Division Street, River Falls, WI Zip 54022–1571; tel. 715/425–6155; David R. Miller, President
Web address: www.allina.com

Owned, leased, sponsored:	12 hospitals	1859 beds
Contract-managed:	1 hospitals	49 beds
Totals:	13 hospitals	1908 beds

0877: ALTAPOINTE HEALTH SYSTEMS (IO)
5750-A Southland Drive, Mobile, AL Zip 36693–3316; tel. 251/473–4423; J. Tuerk. Schlesinger, Chief Executive Officer

ALABAMA: BAYPOINTE BEHAVIORAL HEALTH (O, 60 beds) 5800 Southland Drive, Mobile, AL Zip 36693–3313; tel. 251/661–0153; Jarett Crum, Hospital Director
Web address: www.altapointe.org

EASTPOINTE HOSPITAL (O, 66 beds) 7400 Roper Lane, Daphne, AL Zip 36526–5274; tel. 251/378–6500; Philip L. Cusa, Hospital Director

Owned, leased, sponsored:	2 hospitals	126 beds
Contract-managed:	0 hospitals	0 beds
Totals:	2 hospitals	126 beds

2295: AMERICAN PROVINCE OF LITTLE COMPANY OF MARY SISTERS (CC)
9350 South California Avenue, Evergreen Park, IL Zip 60805–2595; tel. 708/229–5491; Sister, Kathleen McIntyre, Province Leader
(Moderately Centralized Health System)

ILLINOIS: LITTLE COMPANY OF MARY HOSPITAL AND HEALTH CARE CENTERS (O, 241 beds) 2800 West 95th Street, Evergreen Park, IL Zip 60805–2795; tel. 708/422–6200; Dennis A. Reilly, President and Chief Executive Officer
Web address: www.lcmh.org

INDIANA: MEMORIAL HOSPITAL AND HEALTH CARE CENTER (O, 143 beds) 800 West Ninth Street, Jasper, IN Zip 47546–2516; tel. 812/996–2345; E Kyle. Bennett, President and Chief Executive Officer

Owned, leased, sponsored:	2 hospitals	384 beds
Contract-managed:	0 hospitals	0 beds
Totals:	2 hospitals	384 beds

0644: AMG INTEGRATED HEALTHCARE MANAGEMENT (IO)
101 La Rue France, Suite 500, Lafayette, LA Zip 70508–3144; tel. 337/269–9828; Timothy W. Howard, Chief Executive Officer
(Independent Hospital System)

KANSAS: AMG SPECIALTY HOSPITAL-WICHITA (O, 26 beds) 8080 East Pawnee Street, Wichita, KS Zip 67207–5475; tel. 316/682–0004; Robert A. Loepp Jr, FACHE, Chief Executive Officer
Web address: www.amgwichita.com/

LOUISIANA: AMG PHYSICAL REHABILITATION HOSPITAL (O, 24 beds) 5025 Keystone Boulevard, Suite 200, Covington, LA Zip 70433; tel. 985/888–0301; Jay Ivy, R.N., Chief Executive Officer

For explanation of codes following names, see page B2.
★ Indicates Type III membership in the American Hospital Association.

Section B

Section B

AMG SPECIALTY HOSPITAL-DENHAM SPRINGS (O, 117 beds) 8375 Florida Boulevard, Denham Springs, LA Zip 70726-7806; tel. 225/665-2664; Karen Crayton, Administrator
Web address: www.amgdenham.com/

AMG SPECIALTY HOSPITAL-HOUMA (O, 40 beds) 629 Dunn Street, Houma, LA Zip 70360-4707; tel. 985/274-0001; Keith Carruth, Chief Executive Officer
Web address: www.amghouma.com/

AMG SPECIALTY HOSPITAL-LAFAYETTE (O, 58 beds) 310 Youngsville Highway, Lafayette, LA Zip 70508-4524; tel. 337/839-9880; Ben Miller, Chief Executive Officer
Web address: www.amglafayette.com

AMG SPECIALTY HOSPITAL-ZACHARY (O, 16 beds) 4601 McHugh Road, Zachary, LA Zip 70791-5348; tel. 225/683-1600; April Ebeling, Chief Executive Officer

LAFAYETTE PHYSICAL REHABILITATION HOSPITAL (O, 32 beds) 307 Polly Lane, Lafayette, LA Zip 70508-4960; tel. 337/314-1111; Bruce J. Bartels, Interim Chief Executive Officer
Web address: www.lafayettephysicalrehab.com/

THE NEUROMEDICAL CENTER REHABILITATION HOSPITAL (O, 23 beds) 10101 Park Rowe Avenue, Suite 500, Baton Rouge, LA Zip 70810-1685; tel. 225/906-2999; Elizabeth Wilson, Administrator

MISSISSIPPI: AMG SPECIALTY HOSPITAL-GREENWOOD (O, 40 beds) 1401 River Road Floor 2, Greenwood, MS Zip 38930-4030; tel. 662/459-2681; Jennifer Wallace, Chief Executive Officer
Web address: www.amggreenwood.com/

NEVADA: AMG SPECIALTY HOSPITAL - LAS VEGAS (O, 24 beds) 4015 Mcleod Drive, Las Vegas, NV Zip 89121-4305; tel. 702/433-2200; William Fox, Chief Executive Officer

NEW MEXICO: AMG SPECIALTY HOSPITAL-ALBUQUERQUE (O, 24 beds) 235 Elm Street NE, Albuquerque, NM Zip 87102-3672; tel. 505/842-5550; Ken D'Amico, Chief Executive Officer
Web address: www.amgalbuquerque.com/

OKLAHOMA: AMG SPECIALTY HOSPITAL-EDMOND (O, 37 beds) 1100 East Ninth Street, Edmond, OK Zip 73034-5755; tel. 405/341-8150; Ricky Higdon, Chief Executive Officer

AMG SPECIALTY HOSPITAL-TULSA (O, 46 beds) 2408 East 81st Street, Suite 2800, Tulsa, OK Zip 74104-6510; tel. 918/710-3620; Kelly Rose, R.N., Chief Executive Officer
Web address: www.amgoftulsa.com/

Owned, leased, sponsored:	13 hospitals	507 beds
Contract-managed:	0 hospitals	0 beds
Totals:	13 hospitals	507 beds

★0389: ANMED HEALTH (NP)
800 North Fant Street, Anderson, SC Zip 29621-5793; tel. 864/512-1000; William T. Manson III, Chief Executive Officer
(Independent Hospital System)

SOUTH CAROLINA: ANMED HEALTH CANNON (O, 28 beds) 123 W G Acker Drive, Pickens, SC Zip 29671-2739, P O Box 188, 29671-0188, tel. 864/878-4791; Brandon Clary, Chief Executive Officer
Web address: www.cannonhospital.org

ANMED HEALTH MEDICAL CENTER (O, 400 beds) 800 North Fant Street, Anderson, SC Zip 29621-5793; tel. 864/512-1000; William T. Manson III, Chief Executive Officer

Owned, leased, sponsored:	2 hospitals	428 beds
Contract-managed:	0 hospitals	0 beds
Totals:	2 hospitals	428 beds

★0866: APPALACHIAN REGIONAL HEALTHCARE SYSTEM (NP)
336 Deerfield Road, Boone, NC Zip 28607-5008, P O Box 2600, 28607-2600, tel. 828/262-4100; Charles Mantooth, President and Chief Executive Officer
(Independent Hospital System)

NORTH CAROLINA: BLOWING ROCK REHABILITATION & DAVANT EXTENDED CARE CENTER (C, 72 beds) 418 Chestnut Street, Blowing Rock, NC Zip 28605-0148, P O Box 148, 28605-0148, tel. 828/295-3136; Elizabeth Hayes, R.N., Interim Administrator

CHARLES A. CANNON MEMORIAL HOSPITAL (C, 35 beds) 434 Hospital Drive, Newland, NC Zip 28646, P O Box 767, Linville, 28646-0767, tel. 828/737-7000; Carmen Lacey, MSN, R.N., President
Web address: www.https://apprhs.org/locations/cannon-memorial-hospital

WATAUGA MEDICAL CENTER (C, 99 beds) 336 Deerfield Road, Boone, NC Zip 28607-5008, P O Box 2600, 28607-2600, tel. 828/262-4100; Charles Mantooth, President and Chief Executive Officer
Web address: www.https://apprhs.org/contact-us

Owned, leased, sponsored:	0 hospitals	0 beds
Contract-managed:	3 hospitals	206 beds
Totals:	3 hospitals	206 beds

0145: APPALACHIAN REGIONAL HEALTHCARE, INC. (NP)
2260 Executive Drive, Lexington, KY Zip 40505-4810, P O Box 8086, 40533-8086, tel. 859/226-2440; Joseph Grossman, President and Chief Executive Officer
(Decentralized Health System)

KENTUCKY: HARLAN ARH HOSPITAL (O, 145 beds) 81 Ball Park Road, Harlan, KY Zip 40831-1792; tel. 606/573-8100; Donald R. Fields, Community Chief Executive Officer
Web address: www.arh.org

HAZARD ARH REGIONAL MEDICAL CENTER (O, 358 beds) 100 Medical Center Drive, Hazard, KY Zip 41701-9421; tel. 606/439-6600; Dan Stone, Senior Community Chief Executive Officer

MARY BRECKINRIDGE ARH HOSPITAL (O, 25 beds) 130 Kate Ireland Drive, Hyden, KY Zip 41749-9071, P O Box 447-A, 41749-0717, tel. 606/672-2901; Mallie S. Noble, Administrator
Web address: www.frontiernursing.org

MCDOWELL ARH HOSPITAL (O, 25 beds) Route 122, McDowell, KY Zip 41647, P O Box 247, 41647-0247, tel. 606/377-3400; Russell Barker, Community Chief Executive Officer

MIDDLESBORO ARH HOSPITAL (O, 96 beds) 3600 West Cumberland Avenue, Middlesboro, KY Zip 40965-2614, P O Box 340, 40965-0340, tel. 606/242-1100; Michael Slusher, Community Chief Executive Officer
Web address: www.arh.org/middlesboro

MORGAN COUNTY ARH HOSPITAL (L, 25 beds) 476 Liberty Road, West Liberty, KY Zip 41472-2049, P O Box 579, 41472-0579, tel. 606/743-3186; Stephen M. Gavalchik, FACHE, Community Chief Executive Officer
Web address: www.arh.org

TUG VALLEY ARH REGIONAL MEDICAL CENTER (O, 141 beds) 260 Hospital Drive, South Williamson, KY Zip 41503-4072; tel. 606/237-1710; Timothy A. Hatfield, Community Chief Executive Officer

WHITESBURG ARH HOSPITAL (O, 87 beds) 240 Hospital Road, Whitesburg, KY Zip 41858-7627; tel. 606/633-3500; Dena C. Sparkman, FACHE, Community Chief Executive Officer
Web address: www.arh.org/whitesburg

WEST VIRGINIA: BECKLEY ARH HOSPITAL (O, 170 beds) 306 Stanaford Road, Beckley, WV Zip 25801-3142; tel. 304/255-3000; Rocco K. Massey, Community Chief Executive Officer

SUMMERS COUNTY ARH HOSPITAL (L, 25 beds) Terrace Street, Hinton, WV Zip 25951-2407, Drawer 940, 25951-0940, tel. 304/466-1000; Wesley Dangerfield, Community Chief Executive Officer
Web address: www.arh.org

Owned, leased, sponsored:	10 hospitals	1097 beds
Contract-managed:	0 hospitals	0 beds
Totals:	10 hospitals	1097 beds

★0104: ARCHBOLD MEDICAL CENTER (NP)
910 South Broad Street, Thomasville, GA Zip 31792-6113; tel. 229/228-2739; J Perry. Mustian, President
(Moderately Centralized Health System)

For explanation of codes following names, see page B2.
★ Indicates Type III membership in the American Hospital Association.

GEORGIA: BROOKS COUNTY HOSPITAL (L, 25 beds) 903 North Court Street, Quitman, GA Zip 31643–1315, P O Box 5000, 31643–5000, tel. 229/263–4171; Nancy M. Williams, R.N., Administrator
Web address: www.archbold.org

GRADY GENERAL HOSPITAL (L, 48 beds) 1155 Fifth Street SE, Cairo, GA Zip 39828–3142, P O Box 360, 39828–0360, tel. 229/377–1150; Crystal Ramm, Administrator

JOHN D. ARCHBOLD MEMORIAL HOSPITAL (O, 328 beds) 915 Gordon Avenue, Thomasville, GA Zip 31792–6614, P O Box 1018, 31799–1018, tel. 229/228–2000; J Perry. Mustian, President and Chief Executive Officer
Web address: www.archbold.org

MITCHELL COUNTY HOSPITAL (L, 181 beds) 90 East Stephens Street, Camilla, GA Zip 31730–1836, P O Box 639, 31730–0639, tel. 229/336–5284; James Womack, Administrator
Web address: www.archbold.org

Owned, leased, sponsored:	4 hospitals	582 beds
Contract-managed:	0 hospitals	0 beds
Totals:	4 hospitals	582 beds

★0069: ARDENT HEALTH SERVICES (IO)
1 Burton Hills Boulevard, Suite 250, Nashville, TN Zip 37215–6195; tel. 615/296–3000; David T. Vandewater, President and Chief Executive Officer
(Moderately Centralized Health System)

FLORIDA: BAY MEDICAL CENTER SACRED HEART HEALTH SYSTEM (O, 286 beds) 615 North Bonita Avenue, Panama City, FL Zip 32401–3600, P O Box 59515, 32412–0515, tel. 850/769–1511; Stephen Grubbs, Chief Executive Officer
Web address: www.baymedical.org

IDAHO: PORTNEUF MEDICAL CENTER (O, 175 beds) 777 Hospital Way, Pocatello, ID Zip 83201–5175; tel. 208/239–1000; Daniel Ordyna, Chief Executive Officer
Web address: www.portmed.org

NEW JERSEY: HACKENSACK MERIDIAN HEALTH MOUNTAINSIDE MEDICAL CENTER (O, 202 beds) 1 Bay Avenue, Montclair, NJ Zip 07042–4898; tel. 973/429–6000; John A. Fromhold, FACHE, Chief Executive Officer

HACKENSACK MERIDIAN HEALTH PASCACK VALLEY MEDICAL CENTER (O, 128 beds) 250 Old Hook Road, Westwood, NJ Zip 07675–3123; tel. 201/383–1035; Emily L. Holliman, FACHE, Chief Executive Officer
Web address: www.hackensackumcpv.com/

NEW MEXICO: LOVELACE MEDICAL CENTER (O, 263 beds) 601 Martin Luther King Avenue NE, Albuquerque, NM Zip 87102–3619; tel. 505/727–8000; Troy Greer, Chief Executive Officer
Web address: www.lovelace.com/albuquerque-hospital/lovelace-medical-center#.UDZ1laDhf48

LOVELACE REGIONAL HOSPITAL - ROSWELL (O, 26 beds) 117 East 19th Street, Roswell, NM Zip 88201–5151; tel. 575/627–7000; Heather L. Harper, FACHE, Chief Executive Officer

LOVELACE REHABILITATION HOSPITAL (O, 52 beds) 505 Elm Street NE, Albuquerque, NM Zip 87102–2500; tel. 505/727–4700; Derrick Jones, Chief Executive Officer
Web address: www.lovelace.com

LOVELACE WESTSIDE HOSPITAL (O, 80 beds) 10501 Golf Course Road NW, Albuquerque, NM Zip 87114–5000, P O Box 25555, 87125–0555, tel. 505/727–8000; Amy Blasing, Chief Executive Officer

LOVELACE WOMEN'S HOSPITAL (O, 78 beds) 4701 Montgomery Boulevard NE, Albuquerque, NM Zip 87109–1251, P O Box 25555, 87125–0555, tel. 505/727–7800; Sheri Milone, Chief Executive Officer and Administrator
Web address: www.lovelace.com/albuquerque-hospital/lovelace-womens-hospital#.UDZ17KDhf48

OKLAHOMA: BAILEY MEDICAL CENTER (O, 37 beds) 10502 North 110th East Avenue, Owasso, OK Zip 74055–6655; tel. 918/376–8000; Keith Mason, Chief Executive Officer
Web address: www.baileymedicalcenter.com

HILLCREST HOSPITAL - SOUTH (O, 160 beds) 8801 South 101st East Avenue, Tulsa, OK Zip 74133–5716; tel. 918/294–4000; Lynn M. Mergen, Chief Executive Officer
Web address: www.southcresthospital.com

HILLCREST HOSPITAL CLAREMORE (O, 67 beds) 1202 North Muskogee Place, Claremore, OK Zip 74017–3036; tel. 918/341–2556; David Chaussard, Chief Executive Officer

HILLCREST HOSPITAL CUSHING (O, 99 beds) 1027 East Cherry Street, Cushing, OK Zip 74023–4101; tel. 918/225–2915; Kevin Hawk, Chief Executive Officer
Web address: www.hillcrestcushing.com/

HILLCREST HOSPITAL HENRYETTA (O, 41 beds) 2401 West Main Street, Henryetta, OK Zip 74437–3893, P O Box 1269, 74437–1269, tel. 918/650–1100; Dee Renshaw, Chief Executive Officer
Web address: www.hillcresthenryetta.com/

HILLCREST HOSPITAL PRYOR (O, 24 beds) 111 North Bailey Street, Pryor, OK Zip 74361–4201; tel. 918/825–1600; Douglas K. Weaver, FACHE, Chief Executive Officer

HILLCREST MEDICAL CENTER (O, 508 beds) 1120 South Utica Avenue, Tulsa, OK Zip 74104–4090; tel. 918/579–1000; Kevin J. Gross, FACHE, Chief Executive Officer
Web address: www.hillcrestmedicalcenter.com

TULSA SPINE AND SPECIALTY HOSPITAL (O, 21 beds) 6901 South Olympia Avenue, Tulsa, OK Zip 74132–1843; tel. 918/388–5701; Terry L. Woodbeck, Chief Executive Officer

TEXAS: BSA HOSPITAL, LLC (O, 334 beds) 1600 Wallace Boulevard, Amarillo, TX Zip 79106–1799; tel. 806/212–2000; Bob Williams, President and Chief Executive Officer
Web address: www.bsahs.org

PHYSICIANS SURGICAL HOSPITAL - QUAIL CREEK (O, 41 beds) 6819 Plum Creek, Amarillo, TX Zip 79124–1602; tel. 806/354–6100; Brad D. McCall, JD, Chief Executive Officer

SETON MEDICAL CENTER HARKER HEIGHTS (O, 83 beds) 850 West Central Texas Expressway, Harker Heights, TX Zip 76548–1890; tel. 254/690–0900; Zach Dieitz, Chief Executive Officer
Web address: www.setonharkerheights.net

Owned, leased, sponsored:	20 hospitals	2705 beds
Contract-managed:	0 hospitals	0 beds
Totals:	20 hospitals	2705 beds

0809: ARNOT HEALTH (NP)
600 Roe Avenue, Elmira, NY Zip 14905–1629; tel. 607/737–4100; Robert K. Lambert, M.D., FACHE, President and Chief Executive Officer
(Independent Hospital System)

NEW YORK: ARNOT OGDEN MEDICAL CENTER (O, 176 beds) 600 Roe Avenue, Elmira, NY Zip 14905–1629; tel. 607/737–4100; Jonathan I. Lawrence, System Chief Operating Officer
Web address: www.arnothealth.org

IRA DAVENPORT MEMORIAL HOSPITAL (O, 161 beds) 7571 State Route 54, Bath, NY Zip 14810–9590; tel. 607/776–8500; Richard C. Cleland, FACHE, Administrator

ST. JOSEPH'S HOSPITAL (O, 141 beds) 555 St. Joseph's Boulevard, Elmira, NY Zip 14901–3223; tel. 607/733–6541; Joseph Braunscheidel, Administrator
Web address: www.arnothealth.org

Owned, leased, sponsored:	3 hospitals	478 beds
Contract-managed:	0 hospitals	0 beds
Totals:	3 hospitals	478 beds

★0094: ASANTE HEALTH SYSTEM (NP)
2650 Siskiyou Boulevard, Suite 200, Medford, OR Zip 97504–8170; tel. 541/789–4100; Roy G. Vinyard, FACHE, President and Chief Executive Officer
(Moderately Centralized Health System)

OREGON: ASANTE ASHLAND COMMUNITY HOSPITAL (O, 36 beds) 280 Maple Street, Ashland, OR Zip 97520–1593; tel. 541/201–4000; Sheila Clough, Chief Executive Officer

ASANTE ROGUE REGIONAL MEDICAL CENTER (O, 320 beds) 2825 East Barnett Road, Medford, OR Zip 97504–8332; tel. 541/789–7000; Scott A. Kelly, Chief Executive Officer
Web address: www.asante.org

ASANTE THREE RIVERS MEDICAL CENTER (O, 111 beds) 500 SW Ramsey Avenue, Grants Pass, OR Zip 97527–5554; tel. 541/472–7000; Win Howard, Chief Executive Officer

Owned, leased, sponsored:	3 hospitals	467 beds
Contract-managed:	0 hospitals	0 beds
Totals:	3 hospitals	467 beds

★0198: ASCENSION HEALTHCARE (CC)
101 South Hanley Road, Suite 450, Saint Louis, MO Zip 63105–3406; tel. 314/733–8000; Patricia A. Maryland, Dr.PH, President and Chief Executive Officer
(Decentralized Health System)

ALABAMA: PROVIDENCE HOSPITAL (S, 302 beds) 6801 Airport Boulevard, Mobile, AL Zip 36608–3785, P O Box 850429, 36685–0429, tel. 251/633–1000; Todd S. Kennedy, President and Chief Executive Officer
Web address: www.providencehospital.org

ST. VINCENT'S BIRMINGHAM (S, 409 beds) 810 St Vincent's Drive, Birmingham, AL Zip 35205–1695, P O Box 12407, 35202–2407, tel. 205/939–7000; Evan Ray, FACHE, Chief Executive Officer

ST. VINCENT'S BLOUNT (S, 25 beds) 150 Gilbreath, Oneonta, AL Zip 35121–2827, P O Box 1000, 35121–0013, tel. 205/274–3000; Greg Brown, Administrator
Web address: www.stvhs.com

ST. VINCENT'S CHILTON HOSPITAL (L, 30 beds) 2030 Lay Dam Road, Clanton, AL Zip 35045; tel. 205/258–4400; Suzannah Campbell, Administrator

ST. VINCENT'S EAST (S, 362 beds) 50 Medical Park East Drive, Birmingham, AL Zip 35235–9987; tel. 205/838–3000; Andrew Gnann, Vice President Operations
Web address: www.stvhs.com

ST. VINCENT'S ST. CLAIR (S, 40 beds) 7063 Veterans Parkway, Pell City, AL Zip 35125–1499; tel. 205/814–2105; Lisa Nichols, R.N., Administrator

CONNECTICUT: ST. VINCENT'S MEDICAL CENTER (S, 373 beds) 2800 Main Street, Bridgeport, CT Zip 06606–4292; tel. 203/576–6000; Vicki R. Briggs, President and Chief Executive Officer
Web address: www.stvincents.org

DISTRICT OF COLUMBIA: PROVIDENCE HOSPITAL (S, 448 beds) 1150 Varnum Street NE, Washington, DC Zip 20017–2104; tel. 202/269–7000; Darcy Burthay, MSN, R.N., President and Chief Executive Officer
Web address: www.provhosp.org

FLORIDA: SACRED HEART HOSPITAL PENSACOLA (S, 440 beds) 5151 North Ninth Avenue, Pensacola, FL Zip 32504–8795, P O Box 2700, 32513–2700, tel. 850/416–7000; Henry Stovall, President

SACRED HEART HOSPITAL ON THE EMERALD COAST (S, 58 beds) 7800 Highway 98 West, Miramar Beach, FL Zip 32550; tel. 850/278–3000; Roger L. Hall, President
Web address: www.sacredheartemerald.org

SACRED HEART HOSPITAL ON THE GULF (S, 19 beds) 3801 East Highway 98, Port St Joe, FL Zip 32456–5318; tel. 850/229–5600; Roger L. Hall, President

ST. VINCENT'S MEDICAL CENTER CLAY COUNTY (O, 64 beds) 1670 St. Vincent's Way, Middleburg, FL Zip 32068–8427, 1670 St. Vincents Way, 32068–8447, tel. 904/602–1000; James Machado, President
Web address: www.jaxhealth.com/

ST. VINCENT'S MEDICAL CENTER RIVERSIDE (S, 482 beds) 1 Shircliff Way, Jacksonville, FL Zip 32204–4748, P O Box 2982, 32203–2982, tel. 904/308–7300; Thomas J. VanOsdol, Chief Executive Officer
Web address: www.jaxhealth.com

ST. VINCENT'S MEDICAL CENTER SOUTHSIDE (S, 288 beds) 4201 Belfort Road, Jacksonville, FL Zip 32216–1431; tel. 904/296–3700; Thomas J. VanOsdol, Chief Executive Officer

ILLINOIS: AMITA HEALTH ELK GROVE VILLAGE (O, 381 beds) 800 Biesterfield Road, Elk Grove Village, IL Zip 60007–3397; tel. 847/437–5500; John P. Werrbach, President and Chief Executive Officer
Web address: www.AMITAHealth.org

AMITA HEALTH HOFFMAN ESTATES (O, 286 beds) 1555 Barrington Road, Hoffman Estates, IL Zip 60169–1019; tel. 847/843–2000; Leonard Wilk, President and Chief Executive Officer
Web address: www.AMITAHealth.org

ALEXIAN BROTHERS BEHAVIORAL HEALTH HOSPITAL (O, 141 beds) 1650 Moon Lake Boulevard, Hoffman Estates, IL Zip 60169–1010; tel. 847/882–1600; Clayton Ciha, President and Chief Executive Officer

INDIANA: DAVIESS COMMUNITY HOSPITAL (C, 48 beds) 1314 East Walnut Street, Washington, IN Zip 47501–2860, P O Box 760, 47501–0760, tel. 812/254–2760; Tracy Conroy, Chief Executive Officer
Web address: www.dchosp.org

INDIANA UNIVERSITY HEALTH FRANKFORT (S, 25 beds) 1300 South Jackson Street, Frankfort, IN Zip 46041–3313; tel. 765/656–3000; Kelly Braverman, President

ST. VINCENT ANDERSON REGIONAL HOSPITAL (S, 141 beds) 2015 Jackson Street, Anderson, IN Zip 46016–4339; tel. 765/649–2511; Mike Schroyer, FACHE, MSN, R.N., President
Web address: www.stvincent.org/andersonregional

ST. VINCENT CARMEL HOSPITAL (S, 121 beds) 13500 North Meridian Street, Carmel, IN Zip 46032–1456; tel. 317/582–7000; Michael D. Chittenden, President

ST. VINCENT CLAY HOSPITAL (S, 25 beds) 1206 East National Avenue, Brazil, IN Zip 47834–2797, P O Box 489, 47834–0489, tel. 812/442–2500; Jerry Laue, Administrator
Web address: www.stvincent.org

ST. VINCENT DUNN HOSPITAL (S, 25 beds) 1600 23rd Street, Bedford, IN Zip 47421–4704; tel. 812/275–3331; Matt Balla, Chief Executive Officer

ST. VINCENT FISHERS HOSPITAL (S, 46 beds) 13861 Olio Road, Fishers, IN Zip 46037–3487; tel. 317/415–9000; Gary Fammartino, Administrator
Web address: www.stvincent.org

ST. VINCENT HEART CENTER (S, 80 beds) 10580 North Meridian Street, Indianapolis, IN Zip 46290–1028; tel. 317/583–5000; Blake A. Dye, President

ST. VINCENT INDIANAPOLIS HOSPITAL (S, 832 beds) 2001 West 86th Street, Indianapolis, IN Zip 46260–1991, P O Box 40970, 46240–0970, tel. 317/338–2345; Joel Feldman, Regional President
Web address: www.stvincent.org

ST. VINCENT JENNINGS HOSPITAL (S, 17 beds) 301 Henry Street, North Vernon, IN Zip 47265–1097; tel. 812/352–4200; Jessica Kietzman, R.N., Interim Administrator

ST. VINCENT KOKOMO (S, 129 beds) 1907 West Sycamore Street, Kokomo, IN Zip 46901–4197; tel. 765/452–5611; Margaret M. Johnson, President, St. Vincent Northwest Region
Web address: www.stvincent.org/stjoseph

ST. VINCENT MEDICAL CENTER OF EVANSVILLE (S, 436 beds) 3700 Washington Avenue, Evansville, IN Zip 47714–0541; tel. 812/485–4000; Daniel A. Parod, Interim President

ST. VINCENT MERCY HOSPITAL (S, 15 beds) 1331 South 'A' Street, Elwood, IN Zip 46036–1942; tel. 765/552–4600; Francis G. Albarano, Administrator
Web address: www.stvincent.org

ST. VINCENT RANDOLPH HOSPITAL (S, 16 beds) 473 Greenville Avenue, Winchester, IN Zip 47394–9436; tel. 765/584–0004; Francis G. Albarano, Administrator
Web address: www.stvincent.org

ST. VINCENT SALEM HOSPITAL (S, 25 beds) 911 North Shelby Street, Salem, IN Zip 47167–1694; tel. 812/883–5881; Dana M. Muntz, Chief Executive Officer

ST. VINCENT SETON SPECIALTY HOSPITAL (S, 74 beds) 8050 Township Line Road, Indianapolis, IN Zip 46260–2478; tel. 317/415–8500; Joel Feldman, Regional President
Web address: www.stvincent.org/

ST. VINCENT WARRICK HOSPITAL (S, 35 beds) 1116 Millis Avenue, Boonville, IN Zip 47601–2204; tel. 812/897–4800; Kathy J. Hall, Administrator
Web address: www.stmarys.org/warrick

ST. VINCENT WILLIAMSPORT HOSPITAL (S, 16 beds) 412 North Monroe Street, Williamsport, IN Zip 47993–1049; tel. 765/762–4000; Jane Craigin, Chief Executive Officer

For explanation of codes following names, see page B2.
★ Indicates Type III membership in the American Hospital Association.

KANSAS: VIA CHRISTI HOSPITAL MANHATTAN, INC. (O, 96 beds) 1823 College Avenue, Manhattan, KS Zip 66502–3346; tel. 785/776–3322; Robert C. Copple, FACHE, Senior Administrator
Web address: https://www.viachristi.org/manhattan

VIA CHRISTI HOSPITAL PITTSBURG (O, 89 beds) 1 Mt. Carmel Way, Pittsburg, KS Zip 66762–7587; tel. 620/231–6100; Randall R. Cason, FACHE, Senior Administrator

VIA CHRISTI HOSPITAL ON ST. FRANCIS (O, 710 beds) 929 North St Francis Street, Wichita, KS Zip 67214–3882; tel. 316/268–5000; Sherry Hausmann, President
Web address: www.via-christi.org

VIA CHRISTI HOSPITAL ON ST. TERESA (O, 57 beds) 14800 West St. Teresa, Wichita, KS Zip 67235–9602; tel. 316/796–7000; Claudio J. Ferraro, Senior Administrator
Web address: www.via-christi.org/st-teresa

VIA CHRISTI REHABILITATION HOSPITAL (O, 58 beds) 1151 North Rock Road, Wichita, KS Zip 67206–1262; tel. 316/634–3400; Sherry Hausmann, President

MARYLAND: SAINT AGNES HEALTHCARE (S, 367 beds) 900 Caton Avenue, Baltimore, MD Zip 21229–5201; tel. 667/234–6000; Keith Vander Kolk, President and Chief Executive Officer
Web address: www.stagnes.org

MICHIGAN: BORGESS MEDICAL CENTER (S, 422 beds) 1521 Gull Road, Kalamazoo, MI Zip 49048–1640; tel. 269/226–7000; Kathlene A. Young, MS, FACHE, Chief Executive Officer
Web address: www.borgess.com

BORGESS-LEE MEMORIAL HOSPITAL (S, 25 beds) 420 West High Street, Dowagiac, MI Zip 49047–1943; tel. 269/782–8681; John E. Ryder, Chief Operating Officer
Web address: www.borgess.com

BRIGHTON CENTER FOR RECOVERY (S, 99 beds) 12851 Grand River Road, Brighton, MI Zip 48116–8506; tel. 810/227–1211; Raymond A. Waller, Director

CRITTENTON HOSPITAL MEDICAL CENTER (O, 254 beds) 1101 West University Drive, Rochester, MI Zip 48307–1831; tel. 248/652–5000; Margaret Dimond, Ph.D., President and Chief Executive Officer
Web address: www.crittenton.com

GENESYS REGIONAL MEDICAL CENTER (S, 427 beds) One Genesys Parkway, Grand Blanc, MI Zip 48439–8066; tel. 810/606–5000; Chris Palazzolo, President and Chief Executive Officer

PROVIDENCE-PROVIDENCE PARK HOSPITALS (S, 635 beds) 16001 West Nine Mile Road, Southfield, MI Zip 48075; tel. 248/849–3400; Joseph R. Hurshe, President
Web address: www.https://ascension.org/michigan

ST. JOHN HOSPITAL AND MEDICAL CENTER (S, 586 beds) 22101 Moross Road, Detroit, MI Zip 48236–2148; tel. 313/343–4000; Robert E. Hoban, President
Web address: www.stjohnprovidence.org/stjohnhospital/

ST. JOHN MACOMB-OAKLAND HOSPITAL (S, 535 beds) 11800 East 12 Mile Road, Warren, MI Zip 48093–3472; tel. 586/573–5000; Terry Hamilton, President
Web address: www.stjohnprovidence.org/macomb-oakland/

ST. JOHN RIVER DISTRICT HOSPITAL (S, 68 beds) 4100 River Road, East China, MI Zip 48054–2909; tel. 810/329–7111; Kim Ronnisch, R.N., Vice President Nursing and Operations

ST. JOSEPH HEALTH SYSTEM (S, 20 beds) 200 Hemlock Street, Tawas City, MI Zip 48763–9237, P O Box 659, 48764–0659, tel. 989/362–3411; Ann M. Balfour, R.N., President
Web address: www.sjhsys.org

ST. MARY'S OF MICHIGAN STANDISH HOSPITAL (S, 64 beds) 805 West Cedar Street, Standish, MI Zip 48658–9526; tel. 989/846–4521; Chris Palazzolo, President and Chief Executive Officer
Web address: www.stmarysofmichigan.org/standish

ST. MARY'S OF MICHIGAN (S, 232 beds) 800 South Washington Avenue, Saginaw, MI Zip 48601–2594; tel. 989/907–8000; Chris Palazzolo, Health System President and Chief Executive Officer Mid-Michigan
Web address: www.stmarysofmichigan.org

MINNESOTA: SAINT ELIZABETH'S MEDICAL CENTER (O, 164 beds) 1200 Grant Boulevard West, Wabasha, MN Zip 55981–1042; tel. 651/565–4531; Thomas Crowley, President and Chief Executive Officer

NEW YORK: OUR LADY OF LOURDES MEMORIAL HOSPITAL, INC. (S, 154 beds) 169 Riverside Drive, Binghamton, NY Zip 13905–4246; tel. 607/798–5111; Kathryn Connerton, President and Chief Executive Officer
Web address: www.lourdes.com

ST. MARY'S HEALTHCARE (S, 290 beds) 427 Guy Park Avenue, Amsterdam, NY Zip 12010–1054; tel. 518/842–1900; Victor Giulianelli, FACHE, President and Chief Executive Officer

OKLAHOMA: JANE PHILLIPS MEDICAL CENTER (O, 114 beds) 3500 East Frank Phillips Boulevard, Bartlesville, OK Zip 74006–2411; tel. 918/333–7200; Mike Moore, President and Chief Operating Officer
Web address: www.jpmc.org

JANE PHILLIPS NOWATA HEALTH CENTER (O, 15 beds) 237 South Locust Street, Nowata, OK Zip 74048–3660; tel. 918/273–3102; Jason McCauley, Administrator

ST. JOHN BROKEN ARROW (O, 44 beds) 1000 West Boise Circle, Broken Arrow, OK Zip 74012–4900; tel. 918/994–8100; David L. Phillips, Chief Operating Officer
Web address: www.stjohnbrokenarrow.com

ST. JOHN MEDICAL CENTER (O, 527 beds) 1923 South Utica Avenue, Tulsa, OK Zip 74104–6502; tel. 918/744–2345; Jeffrey D. Nowlin, President and Chief Operating Officer
Web address: www.sjmc.org

ST. JOHN OWASSO (O, 45 beds) 12451 East 100th Street North, Owasso, OK Zip 74055–4600; tel. 918/274–5000; David L. Phillips, President and Chief Operating Officer

ST. JOHN SAPULPA (O, 25 beds) 519 South Division Street, Sapulpa, OK Zip 74066–4501, P O Box 1368, 74067–1368, tel. 918/224–4280; Ron Hoffman, Chief Operating Officer
Web address: www.stjohnhealthsystem.com/sapulpa

TENNESSEE: SAINT THOMAS DEKALB HOSPITAL (O, 56 beds) 520 West Main Street, Smithville, TN Zip 37166–1138, P O Box 640, 37166–0640, tel. 615/215–5000; Robert Andrew. Wachtel, FACHE, Chief Executive Officer

SAINT THOMAS HICKMAN HOSPITAL (S, 65 beds) 135 East Swan Street, Centerville, TN Zip 37033–1417; tel. 931/729–4271; Jack M. Keller, Chief Executive Officer
Web address: www.sths.com/hickman

SAINT THOMAS HIGHLANDS HOSPITAL (O, 60 beds) 401 Sewell Road, Sparta, TN Zip 38583–1299; tel. 931/738–9211; Robert Andrew. Wachtel, FACHE, Chief Executive Officer
Web address: www.whitecountyhospital.com

SAINT THOMAS HOSPITAL FOR SPINAL SURGERY (S, 23 beds) 2011 Murphy Avenue, Suite 400, Nashville, TN Zip 37203–2065; tel. 615/341–7500; Kathy Watson, R.N., Administrator and Chief Nursing Officer

SAINT THOMAS MIDTOWN HOSPITAL (S, 425 beds) 2000 Church Street, Nashville, TN Zip 37236–0002; tel. 615/284–5555; Don King, Chief Executive Officer
Web address: www.sths.com

SAINT THOMAS RIVER PARK HOSPITAL (O, 85 beds) 1559 Sparta Street, Mc Minnville, TN Zip 37110–1316; tel. 931/815–4000; Dale Humphrey, Chief Executive Officer
Web address: www.riverparkhospital.com

SAINT THOMAS RUTHERFORD HOSPITAL (S, 286 beds) 1700 Medical Center Parkway, Murfreesboro, TN Zip 37129–2245; tel. 615/396–4100; Gordon B. Ferguson, President and Chief Executive Officer

SAINT THOMAS STONES RIVER HOSPITAL (O, 60 beds) 324 Doolittle Road, Woodbury, TN Zip 37190–1139; tel. 615/563–4001; Robert Andrew. Wachtel, FACHE, Chief Executive Officer
Web address: www.stonesriverhospital.com

SAINT THOMAS WEST HOSPITAL (S, 395 beds) 4220 Harding Road, Nashville, TN Zip 37205–2095, P O Box 380, 37202–0380, tel. 615/222–2111; Don King, Chief Executive Officer

TEXAS: DELL CHILDREN'S MEDICAL CENTER OF CENTRAL TEXAS (S, 206 beds) 4900 Mueller Boulevard, Austin, TX Zip 78723–3079; tel. 512/324–0000; Mark W. Shen, M.D., President and Chief Executive Officer
Web address: www.dellchildrens.net

Section B

For explanation of codes following names, see page B2.
★ Indicates Type III membership in the American Hospital Association.

DELL SETON MEDICAL CENTER AT THE UNIVERSITY OF TEXAS (O, 211 beds) 1500 Red River Street, Austin, TX Zip 78701; tel. 512/324-7000; Christann Vasquez, President
Web address: www.seton.net/locations/dell-seton/

PROVIDENCE HEALTHCARE NETWORK (S, 284 beds) 6901 Medical Parkway, Waco, TX Zip 76712-7998, P O Box 2589, 76702-2589, tel. 254/751-4000; Steven Province, Interim President and Chief Executive Officer

SETON EDGAR B. DAVIS HOSPITAL (S, 25 beds) 130 Hays Street, Luling, TX Zip 78648-3207; tel. 830/875-7000; Apryl Haynes, R.N., Vice President, Chief Operating Officer, Administrator
Web address: www.seton.net/locations/edgar_davis/

SETON HIGHLAND LAKES (S, 19 beds) 3201 South Water Street, Burnet, TX Zip 78611-4510, P O Box 1219, 78611-7219, tel. 512/715-3000; Karen Litterer, R.N., MSN, Administrator and Chief Operating Officer

SETON MEDICAL CENTER AUSTIN (S, 382 beds) 1201 West 38th Street, Austin, TX Zip 78705-1006; tel. 512/324-1000; Katherine Henderson, President
Web address: www.seton.net/locations/smc/

SETON MEDICAL CENTER HAYS (O, 112 beds) 6001 Kyle Parkway, Kyle, TX Zip 78640-6112, 6001 Kyle Prkway, 78640-6112, tel. 512/504-5000; Christopher L. Hartle, President
Web address: www.seton.net/locations/seton_medical_center_hays/

SETON MEDICAL CENTER WILLIAMSON (S, 135 beds) 201 Seton Parkway, Round Rock, TX Zip 78665-8000; tel. 512/324-4000; Christopher L. Hartle, President

SETON NORTHWEST HOSPITAL (S, 68 beds) 11113 Research Boulevard, Austin, TX Zip 78759-5236; tel. 512/324-6000; Michelle L. Robertson, R.N., Chief Operating Officer, Texas Market
Web address: www.seton.net

SETON SHOAL CREEK HOSPITAL (S, 94 beds) 3501 Mills Avenue, Austin, TX Zip 78731-6391; tel. 512/324-2000; Brandy Hart, Executive Director
Web address: www.seton.net

SETON SMITHVILLE REGIONAL HOSPITAL (O, 5 beds) 1201 Hill Road, Smithville, TX Zip 78957; tel. 512/237-3214; Christopher L. Hartle, Chief Executive Officer
Web address: www.seton.org

SETON SOUTHWEST HOSPITAL (S, 33 beds) 7900 F M 1826, Building 1, Austin, TX Zip 78737-1407; tel. 512/324-9000; Mary Faria, FACHE, Ph.D., Vice President and Chief Operating Officer
Web address: www.seton.net

WASHINGTON: LOURDES COUNSELING CENTER (S, 20 beds) 1175 Carondelet Drive, Richland, WA Zip 99354-3300; tel. 509/943-9104; John Serle, President and Chief Executive Officer

LOURDES MEDICAL CENTER (S, 53 beds) 520 North Fourth Avenue, Pasco, WA Zip 99301-5257; tel. 509/547-7704; John Serle, FACHE, President and Chief Executive Officer
Web address: www.lourdeshealth.net

WISCONSIN: CALUMET MEDICAL CENTER (O, 15 beds) 614 Memorial Drive, Chilton, WI Zip 53014-1597; tel. 920/849-2386; Jennifer Derks, Chief Administrative Officer
Web address: www.affinityhealth.org

COLUMBIA ST. MARY'S HOSPITAL MILWAUKEE (S, 244 beds) 2301 North Lake Drive, Milwaukee, WI Zip 53211-4508; tel. 414/291-1000; Kelly Elkins, President
Web address: www.columbia-stmarys.org

COLUMBIA ST. MARY'S OZAUKEE HOSPITAL (S, 115 beds) 13111 North Port Washington Road, Mequon, WI Zip 53097-2416; tel. 262/243-7300; Bev Weber, Interim President

HOWARD YOUNG MEDICAL CENTER (O, 37 beds) 240 Maple Street, Woodruff, WI Zip 54568-9190, P O Box 470, 54568-0470, tel. 715/356-8000; Sandra L. Anderson, President and Chief Executive Officer
Web address: www.ministryhealth.org

MERCY MEDICAL CENTER (O, 120 beds) 500 South Oakwood Road, Oshkosh, WI Zip 54904-7944; tel. 920/223-2000; Denise Parrish, Interim Chief Administrative Officer

MIDWEST ORTHOPEDIC SPECIALTY HOSPITAL (O, 16 beds) 10101 South 27th Street, 2nd Floor, Franklin, WI Zip 53132-7209; tel. 414/817-5800; Sheila Gansemer, R.N., Vice President of Patient Care Services
Web address: www.mymosh.com/

MINISTRY EAGLE RIVER MEMORIAL HOSPITAL (O, 13 beds) 201 Hospital Road, Eagle River, WI Zip 54521-8835; tel. 715/479-7411; Sandra L. Anderson, President and Chief Executive Officer

MINISTRY GOOD SAMARITAN HEALTH CENTER (O, 10 beds) 601 South Center Avenue, Merrill, WI Zip 54452-3404; tel. 715/536-5511; Dawn Gapko, Chief Administrative Officer
Web address: www.ministryhealth.org

MINISTRY OUR LADY OF VICTORY HOSPITAL (O, 5 beds) 1120 Pine Street, Stanley, WI Zip 54768-1297; tel. 715/644-5571; Vanessa Freitag, President
Web address: www.ministryhealth.org

MINISTRY SACRED HEART HOSPITAL (O, 12 beds) 401 West Mohawk Drive, Tomahawk, WI Zip 54487-2274; tel. 715/453-7700; Sandra L. Anderson, President and Chief Executive Officer

MINISTRY SAINT CLARE'S HOSPITAL (O, 86 beds) 3400 Ministry Parkway, Weston, WI Zip 54476-5220; tel. 715/393-3000; Jeremy Normington-Slay, FACHE, President, North Central Region
Web address: www.ministryhealth.org

MINISTRY SAINT MARY'S HOSPITALS (O, 56 beds) 2251 North Shore Drive, Rhinelander, WI Zip 54501-6710; tel. 715/361-2000; Sandra L. Anderson, President and Chief Executive Officer
Web address: www.ministryhealth.org

MINISTRY SAINT MICHAEL'S HOSPITAL (O, 50 beds) 900 Illinois Avenue, Stevens Point, WI Zip 54481-3196; tel. 715/346-5000; Jeremy Normington-Slay, FACHE, President, North Central Region

SACRED HEART REHABILITATION INSTITUTE (S, 16 beds) 2323 North Lake Drive, Milwaukee, WI Zip 53211-4508; tel. 414/585-1000; Kelly Elkins, President and Chief Executive Officer
Web address: www.columbia-stmarys.org/SHRI

ST. ELIZABETH HOSPITAL (O, 190 beds) 1506 South Oneida Street, Appleton, WI Zip 54915-1305; tel. 920/738-2000; Monica Hilt, President
Web address: www.affinityhealth.org

UNITED HOSPITAL SYSTEM, ST. CATHERINE'S MEDICAL CENTER CAMPUS (O, 202 beds) 9555 76th Street, Pleasant Prairie, WI Zip 53158-1984; tel. 262/656-2011; Richard O. Schmidt Jr, President and Chief Executive Officer

WHEATON FRANCISCAN HEALTHCARE - ALL SAINTS (O, 350 beds) 3801 Spring Street, Racine, WI Zip 53405-1690; tel. 262/687-4011; Susan Boland, R.N., MSN, President and Chief Executive Officer
Web address: www.allsaintshealth.com

WHEATON FRANCISCAN HEALTHCARE - ELMBROOK MEMORIAL (O, 122 beds) 19333 West North Avenue, Brookfield, WI Zip 53045-4198; tel. 262/785-2000; Timothy Richman, Chief Executive Officer

WHEATON FRANCISCAN HEALTHCARE - FRANKLIN (O, 44 beds) 10101 South 27th Street, Franklin, WI Zip 53132-7209; tel. 414/325-4700; Sheila Gansemer, R.N., Vice President Patient Care Services and Chief Nursing Officer
Web address: www.mywheaton.org/

WHEATON FRANCISCAN HEALTHCARE - ST. FRANCIS (O, 167 beds) 3237 South 16th Street, Milwaukee, WI Zip 53215; tel. 414/647-5000; Coreen Dicus-Johnson, President
Web address: www.mywheaton.org/stfrancis

WHEATON FRANCISCAN HEALTHCARE - ST. JOSEPH'S (O, 217 beds) 5000 West Chambers Street, Milwaukee, WI Zip 53210-1650; tel. 414/447-2000; Debra K. Standridge, President
Web address: www.mywheaton.org/stjoseph

Owned, leased, sponsored:	105 hospitals	17517 beds
Contract-managed:	1 hospitals	48 beds
Totals:	106 hospitals	17565 beds

★**0519: ASPIRUS, INC.** (NP)
425 Pine Ridge Boulevard, Wausau, WI Zip 54401-4123; tel. 715/847-2118; Matthew Heywood, Chief Executive Officer **(Moderately Centralized Health System)**

MICHIGAN: ASPIRUS IRON RIVER HOSPITALS & CLINICS, INC. (O, 12 beds) 1400 West Ice Lake Road, Iron River, MI Zip 49935-9526; tel. 906/265-6121; Connie L. Koutouzos, R.N., MSN, Chief Executive Officer

For explanation of codes following names, see page B2.
★ Indicates Type III membership in the American Hospital Association.

ASPIRUS IRONWOOD HOSITAL & CLINICS, INC. (O, 25 beds) N10561 Grand View Lane, Ironwood, MI Zip 49938–9622; tel. 906/932–2525; Paula L. Chermside, Chief Executive Officer
Web address: www.aspirus.org

ASPIRUS KEWEENAW HOSPITAL, INC. (O, 25 beds) 205 Osceola Street, Laurium, MI Zip 49913–2134; tel. 906/337–6500; Michael Hauswirth, Chief Executive Officer

ASPIRUS ONTONAGON HOSPITAL, INC. (O, 64 beds) 601 South Seventh Street, Ontonagon, MI Zip 49953–1459; tel. 906/884–8000; Michael Hauswirth, Chief Executive Officer
Web address: www.aspirus.org

WISCONSIN: ASPIRUS LANGLADE HOSPITAL (O, 21 beds) 112 East Fifth Avenue, Antigo, WI Zip 54409–2796; tel. 715/623–2331; Andrew J. Barth, Chief Executive Officer

ASPIRUS MEDFORD HOSPITAL & CLINICS, INC. (O, 124 beds) 135 South Gibson Street, Medford, WI Zip 54451–1696; tel. 715/748–8100; Rick L. Nevers, Interim Chief Executive Officer
Web address: www.aspirus.org

ASPIRUS RIVERVIEW HOSPITAL AND CLINICS, INC. (O, 75 beds) 410 Dewey Street, Wisconsin Rapids, WI Zip 54494–4715, P O Box 8080, 54495–8080, tel. 715/423–6060; Todd Burch, Chief Executive Officer
Web address: www.aspirus.org

ASPIRUS WAUSAU HOSPITAL, INC. (O, 236 beds) 333 Pine Ridge Boulevard, Wausau, WI Zip 54401–4187; tel. 715/847–2121; Darrell Lentz, President

Owned, leased, sponsored:	8 hospitals	582 beds
Contract-managed:	0 hospitals	0 beds
Totals:	8 hospitals	582 beds

★**0865: ATLANTIC HEALTH SYSTEM** (NP)
475 South Street, Morristown, NJ Zip 7962, P O Box 1905, 07962–1905, tel. 973/660–3270; Brian A. Gragnolati, FACHE, President and Chief Executive Officer
(Decentralized Health System)

NEW JERSEY: CHILTON MEDICAL CENTER (O, 199 beds) 97 West Parkway, Pompton Plains, NJ Zip 07444–1696; tel. 973/831–5000; Stephanie L. Schwartz, FACHE, President
Web address: www.chiltonmemorial.org

HACKETTSTOWN MEDICAL CENTER (O, 80 beds) 651 Willow Grove Street, Hackettstown, NJ Zip 07840–1799; tel. 908/852–5100; Joseph DiPaolo, FACHE, President, Sussex and Warren Region
Web address: www.hrmcnj.org

MORRISTOWN MEDICAL CENTER (O, 698 beds) 100 Madison Avenue, Morristown, NJ Zip 07960–6136; tel. 973/971–5000; Trish O'Keefe, Ph.D., R.N., President
Web address: www.atlantichealth.org/Morristown/

NEWTON MEDICAL CENTER (O, 148 beds) 175 High Street, Newton, NJ Zip 07860–1004; tel. 973/383–2121; Joseph DiPaolo, FACHE, President, Sussex and Warren Region

OVERLOOK MEDICAL CENTER (O, 467 beds) 99 Beauvoir Avenue, Summit, NJ Zip 07901–3533; tel. 908/522–2000; Alan R. Lieber, President
Web address: www.atlantichealth.org/Overlook

Owned, leased, sponsored:	5 hospitals	1592 beds
Contract-managed:	0 hospitals	0 beds
Totals:	5 hospitals	1592 beds

0859: AULTMAN HEALTH FOUNDATION (NP)
2600 Sixth Street SW, Canton, OH Zip 44710–1702; tel. 330/363–6192; Edward J. Roth III, President and Chief Executive Officer
(Moderately Centralized Health System)

OHIO: AULTMAN HOSPITAL (O, 532 beds) 2600 Sixth Street SW, Canton, OH Zip 44710–1702; tel. 330/452–9911; Edward J. Roth III, President and Chief Executive Officer

AULTMAN ORRVILLE HOSPITAL (O, 25 beds) 832 South Main Street, Orrville, OH Zip 44667–2208; tel. 330/682–3010; Marchelle Suppan, DPM, President and Chief Executive Officer
Web address: www.aultmanorrville.org

AULTMAN SPECIALTY HOSPITAL (O, 30 beds) 2600 Sixth Street, SW, Canton, OH Zip 44710–1702; tel. 330/363–4000; Terry Regula, Chief Executive Officer
Web address: www.aultman.org

Owned, leased, sponsored:	3 hospitals	587 beds
Contract-managed:	0 hospitals	0 beds
Totals:	3 hospitals	587 beds

★**2215: AURORA HEALTH CARE** (NP)
750 Virginia Street, Milwaukee, WI Zip 53204, P O Box 341880, 53234–1880, tel. 414/299–1600; Nick Turkal, M.D., President and Chief Executive Officer
(Decentralized Health System)

WISCONSIN: AURORA BAYCARE MEDICAL CENTER (O, 167 beds) 2845 Greenbrier Road, Green Bay, WI Zip 54311–6519, P O Box 8900, 54308–8900, tel. 920/288–8000; Daniel T. Meyer, President

AURORA LAKELAND MEDICAL CENTER (O, 67 beds) W3985 County Road NN, Elkhorn, WI Zip 53121–4389; tel. 262/741–2000; Lisa Just, President
Web address: www.aurorahealthcare.org

AURORA MEDICAL CENTER - MANITOWOC COUNTY (O, 63 beds) 5000 Memorial Drive, Two Rivers, WI Zip 54241–3900; tel. 920/794–5000; Cathie A. Kocourek, President

AURORA MEDICAL CENTER GRAFTON (O, 127 beds) 975 Port Washington Road, Grafton, WI Zip 53024–9201; tel. 262/329–1000; David Graebner, Interim President
Web address: www.aurorahealthcare.org

AURORA MEDICAL CENTER SUMMIT (O, 99 beds) 36500 Aurora Drive, Summit, WI Zip 53066–4899; tel. 262/434–1000; Michael Bergmann, President

AURORA MEDICAL CENTER IN WASHINGTON COUNTY (O, 34 beds) 1032 East Sumner Street, Hartford, WI Zip 53027–1698; tel. 262/673–2300; David Graebner, President
Web address: www.aurorahealthcare.org

AURORA MEDICAL CENTER OF OSHKOSH (O, 61 beds) 855 North Westhaven Drive, Oshkosh, WI Zip 54904–7668; tel. 920/456–6000; Jeffrey Bard, President
Web address: www.aurorahealthcare.com

AURORA MEDICAL CENTER (O, 79 beds) 10400 75th Street, Kenosha, WI Zip 53142–7884; tel. 262/948–5600; Douglas E. Koch, Market President

AURORA MEMORIAL HOSPITAL OF BURLINGTON (O, 55 beds) 252 McHenry Street, Burlington, WI Zip 53105–1828; tel. 262/767–6000; Lisa Just, President
Web address: www.aurorahealthcare.org

AURORA PSYCHIATRIC HOSPITAL (O, 91 beds) 1220 Dewey Avenue, Wauwatosa, WI Zip 53213–2598; tel. 414/454–6600; Peter Carlson, President, Behavioral Health Services
Web address: www.aurorahealthcare.org

AURORA SHEBOYGAN MEMORIAL MEDICAL CENTER (O, 136 beds) 2629 North Seventh Street, Sheboygan, WI Zip 53083–4998; tel. 920/451–5000; David Graebner, President
Web address: www.aurorahealthcare.org

AURORA SINAI MEDICAL CENTER (O, 202 beds) 945 North 12th Street, Milwaukee, WI Zip 53233–1337, P O Box 342, 53201–0342, tel. 414/219–2000; Jessica Bauer, Chief Executive Officer
Web address: www.aurorahealthcare.org

AURORA ST. LUKE'S MEDICAL CENTER (O, 723 beds) 2900 West Oklahoma Avenue, Milwaukee, WI Zip 53215–4330, P O Box 2901, 53201–2901, tel. 414/649–6000; Marie Golanowski, R.N., MS, President
Web address: www.aurorahealthcare.org

AURORA WEST ALLIS MEDICAL CENTER (O, 218 beds) 8901 West Lincoln Avenue, West Allis, WI Zip 53227–2409, P O Box 27901, 53227–0901, tel. 414/328–6000; Richard A. Kellar, President
Web address: www.aurorahealthcare.org

Owned, leased, sponsored:	14 hospitals	2122 beds
Contract-managed:	0 hospitals	0 beds
Totals:	14 hospitals	2122 beds

For explanation of codes following names, see page B2.
★ Indicates Type III membership in the American Hospital Association.

Section B

0869: AVANTI HOSPITALS (IO)
222 North Sepulveda Boulevard, Suite 950, El Segundo, CA Zip 90245–5614; tel. 310/356–0550; Michael A. Rembis, FACHE, Corporate Chief Executive Officer
(Independent Hospital System)

CALIFORNIA: COAST PLAZA HOSPITAL (O, 123 beds) 13100 Studebaker Road, Norwalk, CA Zip 90650–2500; tel. 562/868–3751; Gregory Padilla, Administrator

COMMUNITY HOSPITAL OF HUNTINGTON PARK (O, 81 beds) 2623 East Slauson Avenue, Huntington Park, CA Zip 90255–2926; tel. 323/583–1931; Araceli Lonergan, Chief Executive Officer
Web address: www.chhplax.com

EAST LOS ANGELES DOCTORS HOSPITAL (O, 127 beds) 4060 Whittier Boulevard, Los Angeles, CA Zip 90023–2526; tel. 323/268–5514; Gerald Clute, Chief Executive Officer

MEMORIAL HOSPITAL OF GARDENA (O, 172 beds) 1145 West Redondo Beach Boulevard, Gardena, CA Zip 90247–3528; tel. 310/532–4200; Kathy Wojno, R.N., MSN, Administrator
Web address: www.mhglax.com/

Owned, leased, sponsored:	4 hospitals	503 beds
Contract-managed:	0 hospitals	0 beds
Totals:	4 hospitals	503 beds

★5255: AVERA HEALTH (CC)
3900 West Avera Drive, Suite 300, Sioux Falls, SD Zip 57108–5721; tel. 605/322–4700; John T. Porter, President and Chief Executive Officer
(Decentralized Health System)

IOWA: AVERA HOLY FAMILY HOSPITAL (O, 25 beds) 826 North Eighth Street, Estherville, IA Zip 51334–1598; tel. 712/362–2631; Dale Hustedt, Chief Executive Officer
Web address: www.avera-holyfamily.org

FLOYD VALLEY HEALTHCARE (C, 25 beds) 714 Lincoln Street NE, Le Mars, IA Zip 51031–3314; tel. 712/546–7871; Michael T. Donlin, FACHE, Administrator
Web address: www.floydvalley.org

HEGG MEMORIAL HEALTH CENTER AVERA (C, 85 beds) 1202 21st Avenue, Rock Valley, IA Zip 51247–1497; tel. 712/476–8000; Glenn Zevenbergen, Chief Executive Officer
Web address: www.hegghc.org

LAKES REGIONAL HEALTHCARE (C, 30 beds) 2301 Highway 71 South, Spirit Lake, IA Zip 51360–0159, P O Box AB, 51360–0159, tel. 712/336–1230; Jason Harrington, FACHE, President and Chief Executive Officer

OSCEOLA COMMUNITY HOSPITAL (C, 25 beds) 600 Ninth Avenue North, Sibley, IA Zip 51249–1012, P O Box 258, 51249–0258, tel. 712/754–2574; Ben Davis, Interim Chief Executive Officer
Web address: www.osceolacommunityhospital.org

SIOUX CENTER HEALTH (C, 88 beds) 1101 9th Street SE, Sioux Center, IA Zip 51250; tel. 712/722–8107; Kayleen R. Lee, Chief Executive Officer

MINNESOTA: AVERA MARSHALL REGIONAL MEDICAL CENTER (O, 111 beds) 300 South Bruce Street, Marshall, MN Zip 56258–3900; tel. 507/532–9661; Mary B. Maertens, FACHE, President and Chief Executive Officer
Web address: www.avera.org

AVERA TYLER HOSPITAL (C, 25 beds) 240 Willow Street, Tyler, MN Zip 56178–1166; tel. 507/247–5521; Allen Anderson, Chief Executive Officer

PIPESTONE COUNTY MEDICAL CENTER AVERA (C, 25 beds) 916 4th Avenue SW, Pipestone, MN Zip 56164–1890; tel. 507/825–5811; Bradley D. Burris, Chief Executive Officer
Web address: www.pcmchealth.org

NEBRASKA: AVERA CREIGHTON HOSPITAL (O, 64 beds) 1503 Main Street, Creighton, NE Zip 68729–3007, P O Box 186, 68729–0186, tel. 402/358–5700; Todd Consbruck, Chief Executive Officer
Web address: www.avera.org/creighton/

AVERA ST. ANTHONY'S HOSPITAL (O, 25 beds) 300 North Second Street, O'Neill, NE Zip 68763–1514, P O Box 270, Oneill, 68763–0270, tel. 402/336–2611; Todd Consbruck, President and Chief Executive Officer

SOUTH DAKOTA: AVERA DE SMET MEMORIAL HOSPITAL (L, 6 beds) 306 Prairie Avenue SW, De Smet, SD Zip 57231–2285, P O Box 160, 57231–0160, tel. 605/854–3329; Bryan Breitling, Interim Administrator and Chief Executive Officer
Web address: www.desmetmemorial.org

AVERA DELLS AREA HOSPITAL (L, 23 beds) 909 North Iowa Avenue, Dell Rapids, SD Zip 57022–1231; tel. 605/428–5431; Scott James. Hargens, Administrator and Chief Executive Officer

AVERA FLANDREAU HOSPITAL (L, 18 beds) 214 North Prairie Street, Flandreau, SD Zip 57028–1243; tel. 605/997–2433; Scott James. Hargens, Administrator and Chief Executive Officer
Web address: www.avera.org/flandreau-medical/

AVERA GETTYSBURG HOSPITAL (O, 55 beds) 606 East Garfield Avenue, Gettysburg, SD Zip 57442–1398; tel. 605/765–2480; Robert L. Sheckler, Administrator

AVERA GREGORY HOSPITAL (O, 65 beds) 400 Park Avenue, Gregory, SD Zip 57533–1302, P O Box 408, 57533–0408, tel. 605/835–8394; Anthony Timanus, Chief Executive Officer
Web address: www.gregoryhealthcare.org

AVERA HAND COUNTY MEMORIAL HOSPITAL (L, 9 beds) 300 West Fifth Street, Miller, SD Zip 57362–1238; tel. 605/853–2421; Bryan Breitling, Administrator
Web address: www.avera.org

AVERA HEART HOSPITAL OF SOUTH DAKOTA (O, 53 beds) 4500 West 69th Street, Sioux Falls, SD Zip 57108–8148; tel. 605/977–7000; Michael Gibbs, President

AVERA MCKENNAN HOSPITAL AND UNIVERSITY HEALTH CENTER (O, 415 beds) 1325 South Cliff Avenue, Sioux Falls, SD Zip 57105–1007, P O Box 5045, 57117–5045, tel. 605/322–8000; David Flicek, President and Chief Executive Officer
Web address: www.averamckennan.org

AVERA QUEEN OF PEACE HOSPITAL (O, 180 beds) 525 North Foster, Mitchell, SD Zip 57301–2999; tel. 605/995–2000; Thomas A. Clark, Regional President and Chief Executive Officer

AVERA SACRED HEART HOSPITAL (O, 293 beds) 501 Summit Avenue, Yankton, SD Zip 57078–3855; tel. 605/668–8000; Douglas R. Ekeren, Regional President and Chief Executive Officer
Web address: www.averasacredheart.com

AVERA ST. BENEDICT HEALTH CENTER (O, 99 beds) 401 West Glynn Drive, Parkston, SD Zip 57366–9605; tel. 605/928–3311; Gale N. Walker, President and Chief Executive Officer

AVERA ST. LUKE'S HOSPITAL (O, 212 beds) 305 South State Street, Aberdeen, SD Zip 57401–4527; tel. 605/622–5000; Todd Forkel, President and Chief Executive Officer
Web address: www.avera.org/st-lukes-hospital/

AVERA ST. MARY'S HOSPITAL (O, 164 beds) 801 East Sioux Avenue, Pierre, SD Zip 57501–3323; tel. 605/224–3100; Todd Forkel, Interim Chief Executive Officer

AVERA WESKOTA MEMORIAL HOSPITAL (L, 23 beds) 604 First Street NE, Wessington Springs, SD Zip 57382–2166; tel. 605/539–1201; Gaea Blue, R.N., Administrator and Chief Executive Officer
Web address: www.averaweskota.org

EUREKA COMMUNITY HEALTH SERVICES AVERA (C, 6 beds) 410 Ninth Street, Eureka, SD Zip 57437–2182, P O Box 517, 57437–0517, tel. 605/284–2661; Carmen Weber, Administrator
Web address: www.avera.org

LANDMANN-JUNGMAN MEMORIAL HOSPITAL AVERA (C, 25 beds) 600 Billars Street, Scotland, SD Zip 57059–2026; tel. 605/583–2226; Melissa Gale, Chief Executive Officer

MARSHALL COUNTY HEALTHCARE CENTER AVERA (C, 18 beds) 413 Ninth Street, Britton, SD Zip 57430–2274; tel. 605/448–2253; Nick Fosness, Chief Executive Officer
Web address: www.avera.org

MILBANK AREA HOSPITAL AVERA (L, 25 beds) 301 Flynn Drive, Milbank, SD Zip 57252–1508; tel. 605/432–4538; Natalie Gauer, Administrator
Web address: www.averamilbank.org

PLATTE HEALTH CENTER AVERA (C, 61 beds) 601 East Seventh, Platte, SD Zip 57369–2123, P O Box 200, 57369–0200, tel. 605/337–3364; Mark Burket, Chief Executive Officer
Web address: www.phcavera.org

For explanation of codes following names, see page B2.
★ Indicates Type III membership in the American Hospital Association.

ST. MICHAEL'S HOSPITAL AVERA (C, 25 beds) 410 West 16th Avenue, Tyndall, SD Zip 57066–2318; tel. 605/589–2152; Carol Deurmier, Chief Executive Officer

WAGNER COMMUNITY MEMORIAL HOSPITAL AVERA (C, 20 beds) 513 Third Street SW, Wagner, SD Zip 57380–9675, P O Box 280, 57380–0280, tel. 605/384–3611; Bryan Slaba, Chief Executive Officer
Web address: www.avera.org/wagnerhospital

Owned, leased, sponsored:	19 hospitals	1865 beds
Contract-managed:	13 hospitals	458 beds
Totals:	32 hospitals	2323 beds

★**0633: AVITA HEALTH SYSTEM** (NP)
269 Portland Way South, Galion, OH Zip 44833–2399; tel. 419/468–4841; Jerome Morasko, President and Chief Executive Officer
(Independent Hospital System)

OHIO: AVITA ONTARIO HOSPITAL (O, 26 beds) 715 Richland Mall, Ontario, OH Zip 44906–3802; tel. 567/307–7666; Jerome Morasko, President and Chief Executive Officer
Web address: www.avitahealth.org

BUCYRUS COMMUNITY HOSPITAL (O, 25 beds) 629 North Sandusky Avenue, Bucyrus, OH Zip 44820–1821; tel. 419/562–4677; Jerome Morasko, Chief Executive Officer
Web address: www.bchonline.org

GALION COMMUNITY HOSPITAL (O, 35 beds) 269 Portland Way South, Galion, OH Zip 44833–2399; tel. 419/468–4841; Jerome Morasko, President and Chief Executive Officer

Owned, leased, sponsored:	3 hospitals	86 beds
Contract-managed:	0 hospitals	0 beds
Totals:	3 hospitals	86 beds

★**0194: BANNER HEALTH** (NP)
1441 North 12th Street, Phoenix, AZ Zip 85006–2837, P O Box 25489, 85002–5489, tel. 602/747–4000; Peter S. Fine, FACHE, President and Chief Executive Officer
(Moderately Centralized Health System)

ARIZONA: BANNER - UNIVERSITY MEDICAL CENTER PHOENIX (O, 685 beds) 1111 East McDowell Road, Phoenix, AZ Zip 85006–2666, P O Box 2989, 85062–2989, tel. 602/239–2000; Steve Narang, M.D., Chief Executive Officer
Web address: www.bannerhealth.com/Locations/Arizona/Banner+Good+Samaritan+Medical+Center

BANNER - UNIVERSITY MEDICAL CENTER SOUTH (O, 167 beds) 2800 East Ajo Way, Tucson, AZ Zip 85713–6289; tel. 520/874–2000; Thomas C. Dickson, Chief Executive Officer
Web address: www.bannerhealth.com

BANNER - UNIVERSITY MEDICAL CENTER TUCSON (O, 421 beds) 1501 North Campbell Avenue, Tucson, AZ Zip 85724–5128; tel. 520/694–0111; Thomas C. Dickson, Chief Executive Officer

BANNER BAYWOOD MEDICAL CENTER (O, 388 beds) 6644 East Baywood Avenue, Mesa, AZ Zip 85206–1797; tel. 480/321–2000; Lamont M. Yoder, R.N., MSN, FACHE, Chief Executive Officer
Web address: www.bannerhealth.com/locations/Arizona/banner+baywood+medical+center

BANNER BEHAVIORAL HEALTH HOSPITAL - SCOTTSDALE (O, 60 beds) 7575 East Earll Drive, Scottsdale, AZ Zip 85251–6915; tel. 480/941–7500; Brian Beutin, MS, Chief Executive Officer

BANNER BOSWELL MEDICAL CENTER (O, 437 beds) 10401 West Thunderbird Blvd, Sun City, AZ Zip 85351–3004, P O Box 1690, 85372–1690, tel. 623/832–4000; Debbie Flores, Interim Chief Executive Officer
Web address: www.bannerhealth.com/locations/sun-city/banner-boswell-medical-center

BANNER CASA GRANDE MEDICAL CENTER (O, 135 beds) 1800 East Florence Boulevard, Casa Grande, AZ Zip 85122–5399; tel. 520/381–6300; Rona Curphy, President and Chief Executive Officer
Web address: https://www.bannerhealth.com/Locations/Arizona/Banner+Casa+Grande+Medical+Center/_Banner+Casa+Grande+Medical+Center.htm

BANNER DEL E. WEBB MEDICAL CENTER (O, 365 beds) 14502 West Meeker Boulevard, Sun City West, AZ Zip 85375–5299; tel. 623/524–4000; Debbie Flores, Chief Executive Officer

BANNER DESERT MEDICAL CENTER (O, 595 beds) 1400 South Dobson Road, Mesa, AZ Zip 85202–4707; tel. 480/412–3000; Laura Robertson, R.N., Chief Executive Officer
Web address: www.bannerhealth.com/Locations/Arizona/Banner+Desert+Medical+Center

BANNER ESTRELLA MEDICAL CENTER (O, 269 beds) 9201 West Thomas Road, Phoenix, AZ Zip 85037–3332; tel. 623/327–4000; Courtney Ophaug, FACHE, Chief Executive Officer
Web address: www.bannerhealth.com/Locations/Arizona/Banner+Estrella+Medical+Center/

BANNER GATEWAY MEDICAL CENTER (O, 177 beds) 1900 North Higley Road, Gilbert, AZ Zip 85234–1604; tel. 480/543–2000; Lamont M. Yoder, R.N., MSN, FACHE, Chief Executive Officer
Web address: www.bannerhealth.com/Locations/Arizona/Banner+Gateway+Medical+Center/

BANNER GOLDFIELD MEDICAL CENTER (O, 20 beds) 2050 West Southern Avenue, Apache Junction, AZ Zip 85120–7305; tel. 480/733–3300; Sharon Lind, MSN, FACHE, Chief Executive Officer

BANNER HEART HOSPITAL (O, 111 beds) 6750 East Baywood Avenue, Mesa, AZ Zip 85206–1749; tel. 480/854–5000; Lamont M. Yoder, R.N., MSN, FACHE, Chief Executive Officer
Web address: www.bannerhealth.com/Locations/Arizona/Banner+Heart+Hospital/

BANNER IRONWOOD MEDICAL CENTER (O, 53 beds) 37000 North Gantzel Road, San Tan Valley, AZ Zip 85140–7303; tel. 480/394–4000; Sharon Lind, MSN, FACHE, Chief Executive Officer
Web address: www.bannerhealth.com/Locations/Arizona/Banner+Ironwood/

BANNER PAYSON MEDICAL CENTER (O, 44 beds) 807 South Ponderosa Street, Payson, AZ Zip 85541–5599; tel. 928/474–3222; Lance Porter, Chief Executive Officer
Web address: www.paysonhospital.com

BANNER THUNDERBIRD MEDICAL CENTER (O, 428 beds) 5555 West Thunderbird Road, Glendale, AZ Zip 85306–4696; tel. 602/865–5555; Debra J. Krmpotic, R.N., Chief Executive Officer

PAGE HOSPITAL (C, 25 beds) 501 North Navajo Drive, Page, AZ Zip 86040, P O Box 1447, 86040–1447, tel. 928/645–2424; Brian Kellar, Chief Executive Officer
Web address: www.bannerhealth.com/Locations/Arizona/Page+Hospital

CALIFORNIA: BANNER LASSEN MEDICAL CENTER (O, 25 beds) 1800 Spring Ridge Drive, Susanville, CA Zip 96130–6100; tel. 530/252–2000; Catherine S. Harshbarger, R.N., Chief Executive Officer

COLORADO: BANNER FORT COLLINS MEDICAL CENTER (O, 22 beds) 4700 Lady Moon Drive, Fort Collins, CO Zip 80528–4426; tel. 970/821–4000; Margo Karsten, Ph.D., MSN, Chief Executive Officer
Web address: www.bannerhealth.com/Locations/Colorado/Banner+Fort+Collins+Medical+Center

EAST MORGAN COUNTY HOSPITAL (L, 19 beds) 2400 West Edison Street, Brush, CO Zip 80723–1640; tel. 970/842–6200; Linda Thorpe, Chief Executive Officer
Web address: www.emchbrush.com

MCKEE MEDICAL CENTER (O, 96 beds) 2000 Boise Avenue, Loveland, CO Zip 80538–4281; tel. 970/669–4640; Margo Karsten, Ph.D., MSN, Chief Executive Officer

NORTH COLORADO MEDICAL CENTER (L, 236 beds) 1801 16th Street, Greeley, CO Zip 80631–5154; tel. 970/352–4121; Margo Karsten, Ph.D., MSN, Chief Executive Officer
Web address: www.ncmcgreeley.com

STERLING REGIONAL MEDCENTER (O, 25 beds) 615 Fairhurst Street, Sterling, CO Zip 80751–4523; tel. 970/522–0122; Hoyt Skabelund, Chief Executive Officer

NEBRASKA: OGALLALA COMMUNITY HOSPITAL (L, 18 beds) 2601 North Spruce Street, Ogallala, NE Zip 69153–2465; tel. 308/284–4011; Drew H. Dostal, R.N., FACHE, Chief Executive Officer
Web address: www.bannerhealth.com/Locations/Nebraska/Ogallala+Community+Hospital

For explanation of codes following names, see page B2.
★ Indicates Type III membership in the American Hospital Association.

NEVADA: BANNER CHURCHILL COMMUNITY HOSPITAL (O, 25 beds) 801 East Williams Avenue, Fallon, NV Zip 89406–3052; tel. 775/423–3151; Robert H. Carnahan II, R.N., Chief Executive Officer

WYOMING: COMMUNITY HOSPITAL (O, 20 beds) 2000 Campbell Drive, Torrington, WY Zip 82240–1597; tel. 307/532–4181; Shelby Nelson, Interim Chief Executive Officer
Web address: www.bannerhealth.com/Locations/Wyoming/Community+Hospital/

PLATTE COUNTY MEMORIAL HOSPITAL (L, 25 beds) 201 14th Street, Wheatland, WY Zip 82201–3201, P O Box 848, 82201–0848, tel. 307/322–3636; Shelby Nelson, Chief Executive Officer

WASHAKIE MEDICAL CENTER (L, 18 beds) 400 South 15th Street, Worland, WY Zip 82401–3531, P O Box 700, 82401–0700, tel. 307/347–3221; Jay Stallings, Chief Executive Officer
Web address: www.washakiemedicalcenter.com

Owned, leased, sponsored:	27 hospitals	4884 beds
Contract-managed:	1 hospitals	25 beds
Totals:	28 hospitals	4909 beds

★0005: BAPTIST HEALTH (NP)
841 Prudential Drive, Suite 1601, Jacksonville, FL Zip 32207–8202; tel. 904/202–2000; Hugh Greene, President and Chief Executive Officer
(Moderately Centralized Health System)

FLORIDA: BAPTIST MEDICAL CENTER BEACHES (O, 135 beds) 1350 13th Avenue South, Jacksonville Beach, FL Zip 32250–3205; tel. 904/627–2900; Joseph M. Mitrick, FACHE, President
Web address: www.community.e-baptisthealth.com/bmc/beaches/index.html

BAPTIST MEDICAL CENTER JACKSONVILLE (O, 927 beds) 800 Prudential Drive, Jacksonville, FL Zip 32207–8202; tel. 904/202–2000; Michael A. Mayo, FACHE, President
Web address: www.e-baptisthealth.com

BAPTIST MEDICAL CENTER NASSAU (O, 52 beds) 1250 South 18th Street, Fernandina Beach, FL Zip 32034–3098; tel. 904/321–3500; Ed Hubel, President

Owned, leased, sponsored:	3 hospitals	1114 beds
Contract-managed:	0 hospitals	0 beds
Totals:	3 hospitals	1114 beds

0150: BAPTIST HEALTH (NP)
301 Brown Springs Road, Montgomery, AL Zip 36117–7005; tel. 334/273–4400; W Russell. Tyner, President and Chief Executive Officer
(Independent Hospital System)

ALABAMA: BAPTIST MEDICAL CENTER EAST (O, 164 beds) 400 Taylor Road, Montgomery, AL Zip 36117–3512, P O Box 241267, 36124–1267, tel. 334/277–8330; Jeff G. Rains, Chief Executive Officer
Web address: www.baptistfirst.org

BAPTIST MEDICAL CENTER SOUTH (O, 389 beds) 2105 East South Boulevard, Montgomery, AL Zip 36116–2409, Box 11010, 36111–0010, tel. 334/288–2100; J Peter. Selman, FACHE, Chief Executive Officer
Web address: www.baptistfirst.org

PRATTVILLE BAPTIST HOSPITAL (O, 50 beds) 124 South Memorial Drive, Prattville, AL Zip 36067–3619, P O Box 681630, 36068–1638, tel. 334/365–0651; Eric Morgan, Chief Executive Officer

Owned, leased, sponsored:	3 hospitals	603 beds
Contract-managed:	0 hospitals	0 beds
Totals:	3 hospitals	603 beds

★0315: BAPTIST HEALTH (CO)
2701 Eastpoint Parkway, Louisville, KY Zip 40223; tel. 502/896–5000; Janet Norton, Vice President and Chief Legal Officer
(Centralized Physician/Insurance Health System)

INDIANA: BAPTIST HEALTH FLOYD (O, 246 beds) 1850 State Street, New Albany, IN Zip 47150–4997; tel. 812/949–5500; Daniel J. Eichenberger, M.D., President and Chief Executive Officer
Web address: www.floydmemorial.com

KENTUCKY: BAPTIST HEALTH CORBIN (O, 273 beds) 1 Trillium Way, Corbin, KY Zip 40701–8420; tel. 606/528–1212; Larry Gray, President
Web address: www.baptisthealth.com/corbin

BAPTIST HEALTH LA GRANGE (O, 65 beds) 1025 New Moody Lane, La Grange, KY Zip 40031–9154; tel. 502/222–5388; Christopher Roty, President
Web address: www.baptisthealthlagrange.com

BAPTIST HEALTH LEXINGTON (O, 384 beds) 1740 Nicholasville Road, Lexington, KY Zip 40503–1499; tel. 859/260–6100; William G. Sisson, President

BAPTIST HEALTH LOUISVILLE (O, 500 beds) 4000 Kresge Way, Louisville, KY Zip 40207–4676; tel. 502/897–8100; David L. Gray, FACHE, President
Web address: www.baptisthealthlouisville.com

BAPTIST HEALTH MADISONVILLE (O, 196 beds) 900 Hospital Drive, Madisonville, KY Zip 42431–1694; tel. 270/825–5100; Robert L. Ramey, President
Web address: www.baptisthealthmadisonville.com

BAPTIST HEALTH PADUCAH (O, 220 beds) 2501 Kentucky Avenue, Paducah, KY Zip 42003–3200; tel. 270/575–2100; William A. Brown, FACHE, President and CEO

BAPTIST HEALTH RICHMOND (O, 60 beds) 801 Eastern Bypass, Richmond, KY Zip 40475–2405, P O Box 1600, 40476–2603, tel. 859/623–3131; Todd Jones, President
Web address: www.baptisthealthrichmond.com

HARDIN MEMORIAL HOSPITAL (C, 268 beds) 913 North Dixie Avenue, Elizabethtown, KY Zip 42701–2503; tel. 270/737–1212; Dennis B. Johnson, President and Chief Executive Officer
Web address: www.hmh.net

Owned, leased, sponsored:	8 hospitals	1944 beds
Contract-managed:	1 hospitals	268 beds
Totals:	9 hospitals	2212 beds

★0355: BAPTIST HEALTH (NP)
9601 Interstate 630, Exit 7, Little Rock, AR Zip 72205–7299; tel. 501/202–2000; Troy R. Wells, Chief Executive Officer
(Centralized Physician/Insurance Health System)

ARKANSAS: BAPTIST HEALTH EXTENDED CARE HOSPITAL (O, 55 beds) 9601 Baptist Health Drive, Little Rock, AR Zip 72205–7202; tel. 501/202–1070; Lee Gentry, FACHE, Vice President and Administrator

BAPTIST HEALTH MEDICAL CENTER - CONWAY (O, 28 beds) 1555 Exchange Avenue, Conway, AR Zip 72032–7824; tel. 501/585–2000; Tim Bowen, Administrator
Web address: www.baptist-health.com/location/baptist-health-medical-center-conway-conway

BAPTIST HEALTH MEDICAL CENTER - NORTH LITTLE ROCK (O, 225 beds) 3333 Springhill Drive, North Little Rock, AR Zip 72117–2922; tel. 501/202–3000; Steven B. Webb, FACHE, Vice President and Administrator
Web address: https://www.baptist-health.com/location/baptist-health-medical-center-north-little-rock-north-little-rock

BAPTIST HEALTH MEDICAL CENTER-ARKADELPHIA (L, 25 beds) 3050 Twin Rivers Drive, Arkadelphia, AR Zip 71923–4299; tel. 870/245–2622; Tony Hardage, Assistant Vice President and Administrator

BAPTIST HEALTH MEDICAL CENTER-HEBER SPRINGS (O, 25 beds) 1800 Bypass Road, Heber Springs, AR Zip 72543–9135; tel. 501/887–3000; Edward L. Lacy, FACHE, Vice President and Administrator
Web address: www.baptist-health.com/maps-directions/bhmc-heber-springs

BAPTIST HEALTH MEDICAL CENTER-HOT SPRING COUNTY (L, 72 beds) 1001 Schneider Drive, Malvern, AR Zip 72104–4811; tel. 501/332–1000; Sheila Williams, Vice President and Administrator

BAPTIST HEALTH MEDICAL CENTER-LITTLE ROCK (O, 682 beds) 9601 Baptist Health Drive, Little Rock, AR Zip 72205–7299; tel. 501/202–2000; Greg Crain, FACHE, Vice President and Administrator
Web address: www.baptist-health.org/maps-directions/bhmc-lr

For explanation of codes following names, see page B2.
★ Indicates Type III membership in the American Hospital Association.

BAPTIST HEALTH MEDICAL CENTER-STUTTGART (L, 49 beds) 1703 North Buerkle Road, Stuttgart, AR Zip 72160–1905, P O Box 1905, 72160–1905, tel. 870/673–3511; Kevin L. Storey, Vice President and Administrator

BAPTIST HEALTH REHABILITATION INSTITUTE (O, 120 beds) 9601 Interstate 630, Exit 7, Little Rock, AR Zip 72205–7202; tel. 501/202–7000; Mike Perkins, Vice President and Administrator
Web address: www.baptist-health.com/locations/accesspoint. aspx?accessPointID=202

Owned, leased, sponsored:	9 hospitals	1281 beds
Contract-managed:	0 hospitals	0 beds
Totals:	9 hospitals	1281 beds

★0185: **BAPTIST HEALTH CARE CORPORATION** (NP)
1717 North 'E' Street, Suite 402, Pensacola, FL Zip 32501–6377, P O Box 17500, 32522–7500, tel. 850/434–4011; Mark T. Faulkner, President
(Centralized Physician/Insurance Health System)

FLORIDA: BAPTIST HOSPITAL (O, 337 beds) 1000 West Moreno, Pensacola, FL Zip 32501–2316, P O Box 17500, 32522–7500, tel. 850/434–4011; Scott Raynes, President

GULF BREEZE HOSPITAL (O, 61 beds) 1110 Gulf Breeze Parkway, Gulf Breeze, FL Zip 32561–4884; tel. 850/934–2000; Scott Raynes, President
Web address: www.ebaptisthealthcare.org/GulfBreezeHospital/

JAY HOSPITAL (L, 21 beds) 14114 South Alabama Street, Jay, FL Zip 32565–1219; tel. 850/675–8000; Michael T. Hutchins, Administrator
Web address: www.bhcpns.org/jayhospital/

Owned, leased, sponsored:	3 hospitals	419 beds
Contract-managed:	0 hospitals	0 beds
Totals:	3 hospitals	419 beds

★0122: **BAPTIST HEALTH SOUTH FLORIDA** (NP)
6855 Red Road, Suite 600, Coral Gables, FL Zip 33143–3632; tel. 786/662–7111; Brian E. Keeley, President and Chief Executive Officer
(Centralized Health System)

FLORIDA: BAPTIST HEALTH SOUTH FLORIDA, BAPTIST HOSPITAL OF MIAMI (O, 720 beds) 8900 North Kendall Drive, Miami, FL Zip 33176–2197; tel. 786/596–1960; Albert Boulenger, Chief Executive Officer

BAPTIST HEALTH SOUTH FLORIDA, DOCTORS HOSPITAL (O, 126 beds) 5000 University Drive, Coral Gables, FL Zip 33146–2094; tel. 786/308–3000; Nelson Lazo, Chief Executive Officer
Web address: www.baptisthealth.net

BAPTIST HEALTH SOUTH FLORIDA, HOMESTEAD HOSPITAL (O, 142 beds) 975 Baptist Way, Homestead, FL Zip 33033–7600; tel. 786/243–8000; William M. Duquette, Chief Executive Officer

BAPTIST HEALTH SOUTH FLORIDA, MARINERS HOSPITAL (O, 25 beds) 91500 Overseas Highway, Tavernier, FL Zip 33070–2547; tel. 305/434–3000; Rick Freeburg, Chief Executive Officer
Web address: www.baptisthealth.net/en/facilities/mariners-hospital/Pages/default.aspx

BAPTIST HEALTH SOUTH FLORIDA, SOUTH MIAMI HOSPITAL (O, 336 beds) 6200 SW 73rd Street, Miami, FL Zip 33143–4679; tel. 786/662–4000; Lincoln S. Mendez, Chief Executive Officer

BAPTIST HEALTH SOUTH FLORIDA, WEST KENDALL BAPTIST HOSPITAL (O, 133 beds) 9555 SW 162nd Avenue, Miami, FL Zip 33196–6408; tel. 786/467–2000; Javier Hernandez-Lichtl, Chief Executive Officer
Web address: www.baptisthealth.net/en/facilities/West-Kendall-Baptist-Hospital/Pages/default.aspx

FISHERMEN'S HOSPITAL (O, 25 beds) 3301 Overseas Highway, Marathon, FL Zip 33050–2329; tel. 305/743–5533; Rick Freeburg, Chief Executive Officer

Owned, leased, sponsored:	7 hospitals	1507 beds
Contract-managed:	0 hospitals	0 beds
Totals:	7 hospitals	1507 beds

★1625: **BAPTIST MEMORIAL HEALTH CARE CORPORATION** (NP)
350 North Humphreys Boulevard, Memphis, TN Zip 38120–2177; tel. 901/227–5117; Jason Little, President and Chief Executive Officer
(Decentralized Health System)

ARKANSAS: NEA BAPTIST MEMORIAL HOSPITAL (O, 216 beds) 4800 East Johnson Avenue, Jonesboro, AR Zip 72401–8413; tel. 870/936–1000; Brad Parsons, FACHE, Administrator and Chief Executive Officer
Web address: www.neabaptist.com

MISSISSIPPI: BAPTIST MEDICAL CENTER ATTALA (O, 25 beds) 220 Highway 12 West, Kosciusko, MS Zip 39090–3208, P O Box 887, 39090–0887, tel. 662/289–4311; Sean Johnson, Interim Chief Executive Officer

BAPTIST MEDICAL CENTER LEAKE (O, 25 beds) 1100 Highway 16 E, Carthage, MS Zip 39051–3809, P O Box 909, 39051–0909, tel. 601/267–1100; Daryl W. Weaver, Chief Executive Officer
Web address: www.mbhs.com/locations/baptist-medical-center-leake/

BAPTIST MEDICAL CENTER YAZOO (O, 25 beds) 823 Grand Avenue, Yazoo City, MS Zip 39194–3233; tel. 662/746–2261; Sean Johnson, Chief Executive Officer
Web address: www.kdhyazoo.com

BAPTIST MEMORIAL HOSPITAL - CALHOUN (L, 145 beds) 140 Burke-Calhoun City Road, Calhoun City, MS Zip 38916–9690; tel. 662/628–6611; James P. Franklin, Administrator

BAPTIST MEMORIAL HOSPITAL-BOONEVILLE (L, 66 beds) 100 Hospital Street, Booneville, MS Zip 38829–3359; tel. 662/720–5000; James Grantham, Administrator and Chief Executive Officer
Web address: www.bmhcc.org/booneville

BAPTIST MEMORIAL HOSPITAL-DESOTO (O, 195 beds) 7601 Southcrest Parkway, Southaven, MS Zip 38671–4742; tel. 662/772–4000; James Huffman, Chief Executive Officer and Administrator

BAPTIST MEMORIAL HOSPITAL-GOLDEN TRIANGLE (O, 236 beds) 2520 Fifth Street North, Columbus, MS Zip 39705–2095, P O Box 1307, 39703–1307, tel. 662/244–1000; Paul Cade, Administrator and Chief Executive Officer
Web address: www.baptistonline.org/golden-triangle/

BAPTIST MEMORIAL HOSPITAL-NORTH MISSISSIPPI (O, 172 beds) 2301 South Lamar Boulevard, Oxford, MS Zip 38655–5373, P O Box 946, 38655–6002, tel. 662/232–8100; William C. Henning, Administrator and Chief Executive Officer
Web address: www.baptistonline.org/north-mississippi/

BAPTIST MEMORIAL HOSPITAL-UNION COUNTY (L, 153 beds) 200 Highway 30 West, New Albany, MS Zip 38652–3112; tel. 662/538–7631; Walter Grace, Chief Executive Officer and Administrator
Web address: www.baptistonline.org/union-county/

MISSISSIPPI BAPTIST MEDICAL CENTER (O, 483 beds) 1225 North State Street, Jackson, MS Zip 39202–2064; tel. 601/968–1000; Bobbie K. Ware, R.N., FACHE, Chief Executive Officer

TENNESSEE: BAPTIST MEMORIAL HOSPITAL - MEMPHIS (O, 563 beds) 6019 Walnut Grove Road, Memphis, TN Zip 38120–2173; tel. 901/226–5000; Dana Dye, R.N., Vice President, Administrator and Chief Executive Officer
Web address: www.baptistonline.org/memphis/

BAPTIST MEMORIAL HOSPITAL FOR WOMEN (O, 140 beds) 6225 Humphreys Boulevard, Memphis, TN Zip 38120–2373; tel. 901/227–9000; Kevin R. Hammeran, Chief Executive Officer and Administrator

BAPTIST MEMORIAL HOSPITAL-COLLIERVILLE (O, 51 beds) 1500 West Poplar Avenue, Collierville, TN Zip 38017–0601; tel. 901/861–9400; Lindsay Stencel, Chief Administrative Officer
Web address: www.baptistonline.org/collierville/

BAPTIST MEMORIAL HOSPITAL-HUNTINGDON (O, 35 beds) 631 R.B. Wilson Drive, Huntingdon, TN Zip 38344–1727; tel. 731/986–4461; Susan M. Breeden, Administrator and Chief Executive Officer

BAPTIST MEMORIAL HOSPITAL-TIPTON (O, 50 beds) 1995 Highway 51 South, Covington, TN Zip 38019–3635; tel. 901/476–2621; Samuel Lynd, Administrator and Chief Executive Officer
Web address: www.baptistonline.org/tipton/

BAPTIST MEMORIAL HOSPITAL-UNION CITY (O, 63 beds) 1201 Bishop Street, Union City, TN Zip 38261–5403, P O Box 310, 38281–0310, tel. 731/885–2410; Barry Bondurant, Administrator and Chief Executive Officer

Section B

For explanation of codes following names, see page B2.
★ Indicates Type III membership in the American Hospital Association.

BAPTIST MEMORIAL REHABILITATION HOSPITAL (O, 49 beds) 1240 South Germantown Road, Germantown, TN Zip 38138–2226; tel. 901/275–3300; Christopher L. Bariola, Chief Executive Officer
Web address: www.baptistrehab.com

BAPTIST MEMORIAL RESTORATIVE CARE HOSPITAL (O, 30 beds) 6019 Walnut Grove Road, Memphis, TN Zip 38120–2113; tel. 901/226–4200; Janice Hill, R.N., Administrator

Owned, leased, sponsored:	19 hospitals	2722 beds
Contract-managed:	0 hospitals	0 beds
Totals:	19 hospitals	2722 beds

★**0528:** **BASSETT HEALTHCARE NETWORK** (NP)

1 Atwell Road, Cooperstown, NY Zip 13326–1301; tel. 607/547–3456; Vance Brown, M.D., President and Chief Executive Officer
(Independent Hospital System)

NEW YORK: AURELIA OSBORN FOX MEMORIAL HOSPITAL (O, 191 beds) 1 Norton Avenue, Oneonta, NY Zip 13820–2629; tel. 607/432–2000; Jeff Joyner, President
Web address: www.bassett.org/ao-fox-hospital/

BASSETT MEDICAL CENTER (O, 152 beds) One Atwell Road, Cooperstown, NY Zip 13326–1394; tel. 607/547–3456; Vance Brown, M.D., President and Chief Executive Officer
Web address: www.bassett.org

COBLESKILL REGIONAL HOSPITAL (O, 40 beds) 178 Grandview Drive, Cobleskill, NY Zip 12043–5144; tel. 518/254–3456; Eric H. Stein, FACHE, President and Chief Executive Officer

LITTLE FALLS HOSPITAL (O, 59 beds) 140 Burwell Street, Little Falls, NY Zip 13365–1725; tel. 315/823–1000; Michael L. Ogden, President and Chief Executive Officer
Web address: www.bassett.org

O'CONNOR HOSPITAL (O, 16 beds) 460 Andes Road, State Route 28, Delhi, NY Zip 13753–7407; tel. 607/746–0300; Scott Bonderoff, President
Web address: www.bassett.org

Owned, leased, sponsored:	5 hospitals	458 beds
Contract-managed:	0 hospitals	0 beds
Totals:	5 hospitals	458 beds

★**0918:** **BAYLOR SCOTT & WHITE HEALTH** (NP)

4005 Crutcher Street, Suite 310, Dallas, TX Zip 75246–1779; tel. 214/820–0111; James H. Hinton, President and Chief Executive Officer
(Centralized Physician/Insurance Health System)

TEXAS: BAYLOR ALL SAINTS MEDICAL CENTER AT FORT WORTH (O, 371 beds) 1400 Eighth Avenue, Fort Worth, TX Zip 76104–4192; tel. 817/926–2544; Michael Sanborn, FACHE, MS, President and Chief Executive Officer

BAYLOR MEDICAL CENTER AT GARLAND (O, 112 beds) 2300 Marie Curie Drive, Garland, TX Zip 75042–5706; tel. 972/487–5000; Jonas Cole, Interim President
Web address: www.baylorhealth.com/PhysiciansLocations/Garland/Pages/Default.aspx

BAYLOR MEDICAL CENTER AT MCKINNEY (O, 107 beds) 5252 West University Drive, McKinney, TX Zip 75071–7822; tel. 469/764–1000; Kyle Armstrong, President

BAYLOR REGIONAL MEDICAL CENTER AT GRAPEVINE (O, 270 beds) 1650 West College Street, Grapevine, TX Zip 76051–3565; tel. 817/481–1588; Steven R. Newton, FACHE, President
Web address: https://www.baylorhealth.com/PhysiciansLocations/Grapevine/Pages/Default.aspx

BAYLOR REGIONAL MEDICAL CENTER AT PLANO (O, 116 beds) 4700 Alliance Boulevard, Plano, TX Zip 75093–5323; tel. 469/814–2000; Jerri Garison, R.N., President
Web address: www.baylorhealth.com/PhysiciansLocations/Plano/Pages/Default.aspx

BAYLOR SCOTT & WHITE MEDICAL CENTER - CARROLLTON (O, 136 beds) 4343 North Josey Lane, Carrollton, TX Zip 75010–4691; tel. 972/394–1010; Jerri Garrison, Interim President

BAYLOR SCOTT & WHITE MEDICAL CENTER - HILLCREST (C, 275 beds) 100 Hillcrest Medical Boulevard, Waco, TX Zip 76712–8897; tel. 254/202–2000; Glenn A. Robinson, FACHE, President
Web address: www.sw.org/hillcrest-medical-center

BAYLOR SCOTT & WHITE MEDICAL CENTER - LLANO (O, 10 beds) 200 West Ollie Street, Llano, TX Zip 78643–2628; tel. 325/247–5040; Timothy A. Ols, FACHE, Chief Executive Officer

BAYLOR SCOTT & WHITE MEDICAL CENTER - MARBLE FALLS (O, 46 beds) 800 West Highway 71, Marble Falls, TX Zip 78654; tel. 830/201–8000; Timothy A. Ols, FACHE, President
Web address: www.sw.org/location/marble-falls-hospital

BAYLOR SCOTT & WHITE MEDICAL CENTER - ROUND ROCK (O, 101 beds) 300 University Boulevard, Round Rock, TX Zip 78665–1032; tel. 512/509–0100; Jay Fox, President
Web address: www.sw.org

BAYLOR SCOTT & WHITE MEDICAL CENTER - TAYLOR (O, 25 beds) 305 Mallard Lane, Taylor, TX Zip 76574–1208; tel. 512/352–7611; Tim Tarbell, Director Operations

BAYLOR SCOTT & WHITE MEDICAL CENTER AT WAXAHACHIE (O, 104 beds) 2400 North I-35E, Waxahachie, TX Zip 75165; tel. 469/843–4000; Christopher York, FACHE, President
Web address: www.baylorhealth.com/PhysiciansLocations/Waxahachie/Pages/Default.aspx

BAYLOR SCOTT & WHITE MEDICAL CENTER-IRVING (L, 233 beds) 1901 North MacArthur Boulevard, Irving, TX Zip 75061–2220; tel. 972/579–8100; Cindy K. Schamp, FACHE, President
Web address: www.bswhealth.com

BAYLOR SCOTT AND WHITE CONTINUING CARE HOSPITAL (O, 50 beds) 546 North Kegley Road, Temple, TX Zip 76502–4069; tel. 254/215–0900; Kimberly K. Langston, R.N., Chief Executive Officer

BAYLOR UNIVERSITY MEDICAL CENTER (O, 859 beds) 3500 Gaston Avenue, Dallas, TX Zip 75246–2088; tel. 214/820–0111; T. Douglas. Lawson, Ph.D., FACHE, President
Web address: www.baylorhealth.com/PhysiciansLocations/Dallas/Pages/Default.aspx

SCOTT & WHITE HOSPITAL - BRENHAM (O, 42 beds) 700 Medical Parkway, Brenham, TX Zip 77833–5498; tel. 979/337–5000; John R. Hughson, Vice President Operations

SCOTT & WHITE HOSPITAL - COLLEGE STATION (O, 119 beds) 700 Scott & White Drive, College Station, TX Zip 77845; tel. 979/207–0100; Jason Jennings, FACHE, Chief Executive Officer
Web address: www.sw.org/location/college-station-hospital

SCOTT & WHITE MEDICAL CENTER - TEMPLE (O, 642 beds) 2401 South 31st Street, Temple, TX Zip 76508–0002; tel. 254/724–2111; Shahin Motakef, FACHE, Chief Executive Officer

Owned, leased, sponsored:	17 hospitals	3343 beds
Contract-managed:	1 hospitals	275 beds
Totals:	18 hospitals	3618 beds

★**1095:** **BAYSTATE HEALTH, INC.** (NP)

280 Chestnut Street, Springfield, MA Zip 01199–0001; tel. 413/794–0000; Mark A. Keroack, M.D., M.P.H., President and Chief Executive Officer
(Centralized Physician/Insurance Health System)

MASSACHUSETTS: BAYSTATE FRANKLIN MEDICAL CENTER (O, 89 beds) 164 High Street, Greenfield, MA Zip 01301–2613; tel. 413/773–0211; Cindy Russo, FACHE, MS, R.N., President and Chief Administrative Officer
Web address: www.baystatehealth.org

BAYSTATE MEDICAL CENTER (O, 713 beds) 759 Chestnut Street, Springfield, MA Zip 01199–0001; tel. 413/794–0000; Nancy L. Shendell-Falk, RN, MA, President and Chief Executive Officer

BAYSTATE NOBLE HOSPITAL (O, 97 beds) 115 West Silver Street, Westfield, MA Zip 01085–3628; tel. 413/568–2811; Ronald Bryant, President
Web address: www.baystatehealth.org/locations/noble-hospital

For explanation of codes following names, see page B2.
★ Indicates Type III membership in the American Hospital Association.

BAYSTATE WING HOSPITAL (O, 74 beds) 40 Wright Street, Palmer, MA Zip 01069–1138; tel. 413/283–7651; Michael Francis. Moran, President and Chief Administrative Officer
Web address: www.baystatewinghospital.org/

Owned, leased, sponsored:	4 hospitals	973 beds
Contract-managed:	0 hospitals	0 beds
Totals:	4 hospitals	973 beds

★**0940: BEACON HEALTH SYSTEM** (NP)
615 North Michigan Street, South Bend, IN Zip 46601–1033; tel. 574/647–1000; Philip A. Newbold, Chief Executive Officer
(Centralized Physician/Insurance Health System)

INDIANA: ELKHART GENERAL HOSPITAL (O, 265 beds) 600 East Boulevard, Elkhart, IN Zip 46514–2499, P O Box 1329, 46515–1329, tel. 574/294–2621; Carl W. Risk II, President

MEMORIAL HOSPITAL OF SOUTH BEND (O, 445 beds) 615 North Michigan Street, South Bend, IN Zip 46601–1033; tel. 574/647–1000; Philip A. Newbold, Chief Executive Officer, Beacon Health System
Web address: www.qualityoflife.org

LOUISIANA: BEACON BEHAVIORAL HOSPITAL (O, 17 beds) 323 Evergreen Street, Bunkie, LA Zip 71322–1307; tel. 318/346–3143; Randall Johnson, Administrator
Web address: www.beaconbh.com

Owned, leased, sponsored:	3 hospitals	727 beds
Contract-managed:	0 hospitals	0 beds
Totals:	3 hospitals	727 beds

★**0953: BEAUMONT HEALTH** (NP)
2000 Town Center, Suite 1200, Southfield, MI Zip 48075–1145; tel. 248/898–5000; John T. Fox, President and Chief Executive Officer
(Centralized Health System)

MICHIGAN: BEAUMONT HOSPITAL - FARMINGTON HILLS (O, 330 beds) 28050 Grand River Avenue, Farmington Hills, MI Zip 48336–5933; tel. 248/471–8000; Constance O'Malley, President

BEAUMONT HOSPITAL - GROSSE POINTE (O, 280 beds) 468 Cadieux Road, Grosse Pointe, MI Zip 48230–1507; tel. 313/473–1000; Richard P. Swaine, President
Web address: www.beaumont.org

BEAUMONT HOSPITAL - ROYAL OAK (O, 1100 beds) 3601 West Thirteen Mile Road, Royal Oak, MI Zip 48073–6712; tel. 248/898–5000; Rosanna Morris, Hospital President

BEAUMONT HOSPITAL - TAYLOR (O, 189 beds) 10000 Telegraph Road, Taylor, MI Zip 48180–3330; tel. 313/295–5000; Lee Ann Odom, Division President
Web address: www.beaumont.org

BEAUMONT HOSPITAL - TRENTON (O, 173 beds) 5450 Fort Street, Trenton, MI Zip 48183–4625; tel. 734/671–3800; Chris Stesney-Ridenour, President

BEAUMONT HOSPITAL - TROY (O, 520 beds) 44201 Dequindre Road, Troy, MI Zip 48085–1117; tel. 248/964–5000; Nancy Susick, MSN, President
Web address: www.beaumont.org

BEAUMONT HOSPITAL - WAYNE (O, 185 beds) 33155 Annapolis Street, Wayne, MI Zip 48184–2405; tel. 734/467–4000; Eric W. Widner, Division President
Web address: www.beaumont.org

BEAUMONT HOSPITAL-DEARBORN (O, 632 beds) 18101 Oakwood Boulevard, Dearborn, MI Zip 48124–4089, P O Box 2500, 48123–2500, tel. 313/593–7000; Kelly C. Smith, Senior Vice President and Division President
Web address: www.beaumont.org

Owned, leased, sponsored:	8 hospitals	3409 beds
Contract-managed:	0 hospitals	0 beds
Totals:	8 hospitals	3409 beds

0538: BENEFIS HEALTH SYSTEM (NP)
1101 26th Street South, Great Falls, MT Zip 59405–5161; tel. 406/455–5000; John H. Goodnow, Chief Executive Officer
(Moderately Centralized Health System)

MONTANA: BENEFIS HEALTH SYSTEM (O, 502 beds) 1101 26th Street South, Great Falls, MT Zip 59405–5104; tel. 406/455–5000; John H. Goodnow, Chief Executive Officer
Web address: www.benefis.org

BENEFIS TETON MEDICAL CENTER (O, 46 beds) 915 4th Street North West, Choteau, MT Zip 59422–9123; tel. 406/466–5763; Louie King, Chief Executive Officer

MISSOURI RIVER MEDICAL CENTER (C, 52 beds) 1501 St Charles Street, Fort Benton, MT Zip 59442–0249, P O Box 249, 59442–0249, tel. 406/622–3331; Louie King, President, Harry Bold Nursing Home Administrator
Web address: www.mrmcfb.org

Owned, leased, sponsored:	2 hospitals	548 beds
Contract-managed:	1 hospitals	52 beds
Totals:	3 hospitals	600 beds

★**2435: BERKSHIRE HEALTH SYSTEMS, INC.** (NP)
725 North Street, Pittsfield, MA Zip 01201–4124; tel. 413/447–2750; David E. Phelps, President and Chief Executive Officer
(Moderately Centralized Health System)

MASSACHUSETTS: BERKSHIRE MEDICAL CENTER (O, 275 beds) 725 North ST, Pittsfield, MA Zip 01201–4124, 725 North Street, 01201–4124, tel. 413/447–2000; David E. Phelps, President and Chief Executive Officer
Web address: www.berkshirehealthsystems.org

FAIRVIEW HOSPITAL (O, 25 beds) 29 Lewis Avenue, Great Barrington, MA Zip 01230–1713; tel. 413/528–0790; Eugene A. Dellea, President

Owned, leased, sponsored:	2 hospitals	300 beds
Contract-managed:	0 hospitals	0 beds
Totals:	2 hospitals	300 beds

★**0051: BJC HEALTHCARE** (NP)
4901 Forest Park Avenue, Suite 1200, Saint Louis, MO Zip 63108–1402; tel. 314/747–9322; Steven H. Lipstein, Chief Executive Officer
(Centralized Health System)

ILLINOIS: ALTON MEMORIAL HOSPITAL (O, 227 beds) One Memorial Drive, Alton, IL Zip 62002–6722; tel. 618/463–7311; David A. Braasch, President
Web address: www.altonmemorialhospital.org

MEMORIAL HOSPITAL EAST (O, 68 beds) 1404 Cross Street, Shiloh, IL Zip 62269–2988; tel. 618/607–1000; Mark J. Turner, President and Chief Executive Officer

MEMORIAL HOSPITAL (O, 227 beds) 4500 Memorial Drive, Belleville, IL Zip 62226–5399; tel. 618/233–7750; Mark J. Turner, President and Chief Executive Officer
Web address: www.memhosp.com

MISSOURI: BARNES-JEWISH HOSPITAL (O, 1414 beds) 1 Barnes-Jewish Hospital Plaza, Saint Louis, MO Zip 63110–1003; tel. 314/747–3000; Robert W. Cannon, President
Web address: www.barnesjewish.org

BARNES-JEWISH ST. PETERS HOSPITAL (O, 101 beds) 10 Hospital Drive, Saint Peters, MO Zip 63376–1659; tel. 636/916–9000; Chris Watts, President

BARNES-JEWISH WEST COUNTY HOSPITAL (O, 77 beds) 12634 Olive Boulevard, Saint Louis, MO Zip 63141–6337; tel. 314/996–8000; Trisha Lollo, President
Web address: www.barnesjewishwestcounty.org

BOONE HOSPITAL CENTER (L, 311 beds) 1600 East Broadway, Columbia, MO Zip 65201–5844; tel. 573/815–8000; James J. Sinek, FACHE, President
Web address: www.boone.org

CHRISTIAN HOSPITAL (O, 220 beds) 11133 Dunn Road, Saint Louis, MO Zip 63136–6119; tel. 314/653–5000; Rick Stevens, President

For explanation of codes following names, see page B2.
★ Indicates Type III membership in the American Hospital Association.

Section B

MISSOURI BAPTIST MEDICAL CENTER (O, 489 beds) 3015 North Ballas Road, Saint Louis, MO Zip 63131–2329; tel. 314/996–5000; John Antes, President
Web address: www.missouribaptist.org

MISSOURI BAPTIST SULLIVAN HOSPITAL (O, 35 beds) 751 Sappington Bridge Road, Sullivan, MO Zip 63080–2354; tel. 573/468–4186; Tony Schwarm, President
Web address: www.missouribaptistsullivan.org

PARKLAND HEALTH CENTER - FARMINGTON COMMUNITY (O, 103 beds) 1101 West Liberty Street, Farmington, MO Zip 63640–1921; tel. 573/756–6451; Thomas P. Karl, President
Web address: www.parklandhealthcenter.org

PARKLAND HEALTH CENTER-BONNE TERRE (O, 3 beds) 7245 Raider Road, Bonne Terre, MO Zip 63628, 1101 West Liberty Street, Farmington, 63640, tel. 573/358–1400; Steven R. Marler, Administrator

PROGRESS WEST HOSPITAL (O, 44 beds) Two Progress Point Parkway, O'Fallon, MO Zip 63368–2208; tel. 636/344–1000; Chris Watts, President
Web address: www.progresswest.org

ST. LOUIS CHILDREN'S HOSPITAL (O, 280 beds) One Children's Place, Saint Louis, MO Zip 63110–1002; tel. 314/454–6000; Joan Magruder, President
Web address: www.stlouischildrens.org

Owned, leased, sponsored:	14 hospitals	3599 beds
Contract-managed:	0 hospitals	0 beds
Totals:	14 hospitals	3599 beds

★**0852: BLANCHARD VALLEY HEALTH SYSTEM** (NP)
1900 South Main Street, Findlay, OH Zip 45840–1214; tel. 419/423–4500; Scott C. Malaney, FACHE, President and Chief Executive Officer
(Centralized Physician/Insurance Health System)

OHIO: BLANCHARD VALLEY HOSPITAL (O, 159 beds) 1900 South Main Street, Findlay, OH Zip 45840–1214; tel. 419/423–4500; Scott C. Malaney, FACHE, President and Chief Executive Officer
Web address: www.bvhealthsystem.org

BLUFFTON HOSPITAL (O, 25 beds) 139 Garau Street, Bluffton, OH Zip 45817–1027; tel. 419/358–9010; Christine Keller, Chief Administrative Officer
Web address: www.bvhealthsystem.org/

Owned, leased, sponsored:	2 hospitals	184 beds
Contract-managed:	0 hospitals	0 beds
Totals:	2 hospitals	184 beds

★**0300: BLUE MOUNTAIN HEALTH SYSTEM** (NP)
211 North 12th Street, Lehighton, PA Zip 18235–1138; tel. 610/377–1300; Andrew E. Harris, President and Chief Executive Officer
(Independent Hospital System)

PENNSYLVANIA: BLUE MOUNTAIN HOSPITAL (O, 250 beds) 211 North 12th Street, Lehighton, PA Zip 18235–1138; tel. 610/377–1300; Andrew E. Harris, Chief Executive Officer

Owned, leased, sponsored:	1 hospitals	250 beds
Contract-managed:	0 hospitals	0 beds
Totals:	1 hospitals	250 beds

★**5085: BON SECOURS HEALTH SYSTEM, INC.** (CC)
1505 Marriottsville Road, Marriottsville, MD Zip 21104–1399; tel. 410/442–5511; Richard Statuto, President and Chief Executive Officer
(Moderately Centralized Health System)

KENTUCKY: OUR LADY OF BELLEFONTE HOSPITAL (O, 147 beds) St Christopher Drive, Ashland, KY Zip 41101, P O Box 789, 41105–0789, tel. 606/833–3333; Kevin Halter, Chief Executive Officer
Web address: www.olbh.com

MARYLAND: BON SECOURS BALTIMORE HEALTH SYSTEM (O, 72 beds) 2000 West Baltimore Street, Baltimore, MD Zip 21223–1558; tel. 410/362–3000; Samuel Lee. Ross, M.D., MS, Chief Executive Officer
Web address: www.bonsecoursbaltimore.com

SOUTH CAROLINA: BON SECOURS ST. FRANCIS HEALTH SYSTEM (O, 396 beds) One St Francis Drive, Greenville, SC Zip 29601–3207; tel. 864/255–1000; Craig McCoy, Chief Executive Officer

VIRGINIA: BON SECOURS MARYVIEW MEDICAL CENTER (O, 466 beds) 3636 High Street, Portsmouth, VA Zip 23707–3270; tel. 757/398–2200; Joseph M. Oddis, Chief Executive Officer
Web address: www.bonsecourshamptonroads.com

BON SECOURS MEMORIAL REGIONAL MEDICAL CENTER (O, 225 beds) 8260 Atlee Road, Mechanicsville, VA Zip 23116–1844; tel. 804/764–6000; Mark M. Gordon, Chief Executive Officer

BON SECOURS ST. FRANCIS MEDICAL CENTER (O, 135 beds) 13710 St Francis Boulevard, Midlothian, VA Zip 23114–3267; tel. 804/594–7300; Chris Accashian, Chief Executive Officer
Web address: www.bonsecours.com/sfmc/default.asp

BON SECOURS ST. MARY'S HOSPITAL (O, 391 beds) 5801 Bremo Road, Richmond, VA Zip 23226–1907; tel. 804/285–2011; Francine Barr, R.N., MS, Chief Executive Officer
Web address: www.bonsecours.com

BON SECOURS-DEPAUL MEDICAL CENTER (O, 204 beds) 150 Kingsley Lane, Norfolk, VA Zip 23505–4650; tel. 757/889–5000; John E. Barrett III, Chief Executive Officer
Web address: www.bonsecourshamptonroads.com

BON SECOURS-RICHMOND COMMUNITY HOSPITAL (O, 85 beds) 1500 North 28th Street, Richmond, VA Zip 23223–5396, P O Box 27184, 23261–7184, tel. 804/225–1700; Mark M. Gordon, Chief Executive Officer

MARY IMMACULATE HOSPITAL (O, 238 beds) 2 Bernardine Drive, Newport News, VA Zip 23602–4499; tel. 757/886–6000; Darlene Stephenson, Chief Executive Officer
Web address: www.bonsecourshamptonroads.com

RAPPAHANNOCK GENERAL HOSPITAL (O, 35 beds) 101 Harris Drive, Kilmarnock, VA Zip 22482–3880, P O Box 1449, 22482–1449, tel. 804/435–8000; Mark M. Gordon, Chief Executive Officer

Owned, leased, sponsored:	11 hospitals	2394 beds
Contract-managed:	0 hospitals	0 beds
Totals:	11 hospitals	2394 beds

2455: BRADFORD HEALTH SERVICES (IO)
2101 Magnolia Avenue South, Suite 518, Birmingham, AL Zip 35205–2853; tel. 205/251–7753; Jerry W. Crowder, President and Chief Executive Officer

ALABAMA: BRADFORD HEALTH SERVICES AT HUNTSVILLE (O, 84 beds) 1600 Browns Ferry Road, Madison, AL Zip 35758–9601, P O Box 1488, 35758–0176, tel. 256/461–7272; Bob Hinds, Executive Director
Web address: www.bradfordhealth.com

BRADFORD HEALTH SERVICES AT WARRIOR LODGE (O, 100 beds) 1189 Allbritt Road, Warrior, AL Zip 35180, P O Box 129, 35180–0129, tel. 205/647–1945; Roy M. Ramsey, Executive Director
Web address: www.bradfordhealth.com

Owned, leased, sponsored:	2 hospitals	184 beds
Contract-managed:	0 hospitals	0 beds
Totals:	2 hospitals	184 beds

0352: BRIDGEPOINT HEALTHCARE (IO)
155 Fleet Street, Portsmouth, NH Zip 03801–4050; tel. 603/570–4888; Marc C. Ferrell, President and Chief Executive Officer
(Independent Hospital System)

DISTRICT OF COLUMBIA: BRIDGEPOINT HOSPITAL CAPITOL HILL (O, 177 beds) 700 Constitution Avenue NE, Washington, DC Zip 20002–6058; tel. 202/546–5700; James Linhares, Chief Executive Officer

---

For explanation of codes following names, see page B2.
★ Indicates Type III membership in the American Hospital Association.

BRIDGEPOINT HOSPITAL NATIONAL HARBOR (O, 82 beds) 4601 Martin Luther King Jr Avenue, SW, Washington, DC Zip 20032–1131; tel. 202/574–5700; Kevin Chavez, Chief Executive Officer
Web address: www.bridgepointhealthcare.com/

Owned, leased, sponsored:	2 hospitals	259 beds
Contract-managed:	0 hospitals	0 beds
Totals:	2 hospitals	259 beds

★**0595: BRONSON HEALTHCARE GROUP** (NP)

301 John Street, Kalamazoo, MI Zip 49007–5295; tel. 269/341–6000; Frank J. Sardone, President and Chief Executive Officer
(Centralized Health System)

MICHIGAN: BRONSON BATTLE CREEK (O, 198 beds) 300 North Avenue, Battle Creek, MI Zip 49017–3307; tel. 269/245–8000; Frank J. Sardone, President and Chief Executive Officer

BRONSON LAKEVIEW HOSPITAL (O, 35 beds) 408 Hazen Street, Paw Paw, MI Zip 49079–1019, P O Box 209, 49079–0209, tel. 269/657–3141; Kirk Richardson, R.N., Vice President, Chief Operating Officer, and Chief Nursing Officer
Web address: www.bronsonhealth.com/lakeview

BRONSON METHODIST HOSPITAL (O, 415 beds) 601 John Street, Kalamazoo, MI Zip 49007–5346; tel. 269/341–6000; Frank J. Sardone, President and Chief Executive Officer
Web address: www.bronsonhealth.com

BRONSON SOUTH HAVEN HOSPITAL (O, 49 beds) 955 South Bailey Avenue, South Haven, MI Zip 49090–6743; tel. 269/637–5271; Joanne Schroeder, President and Chief Executive Officer

Owned, leased, sponsored:	4 hospitals	697 beds
Contract-managed:	0 hospitals	0 beds
Totals:	4 hospitals	697 beds

★**3115: BROWARD HEALTH** (NP)

303 SE 17th Street, Fort Lauderdale, FL Zip 33316–2523; tel. 954/355–4400; Beverly Capasso, Interim President and Chief Executive Officer

FLORIDA: BROWARD HEALTH CORAL SPRINGS (O, 196 beds) 3000 Coral Hills Drive, Coral Springs, FL Zip 33065–4108; tel. 954/344–3000; Drew Grossman, Chief Executive Officer
Web address: www.browardhealth.org

BROWARD HEALTH IMPERIAL POINT (O, 180 beds) 6401 North Federal Highway, Fort Lauderdale, FL Zip 33308–1495; tel. 954/776–8500; Alice Taylor, R.N., MSN, Chief Executive Officer
Web address: www.browardhealth.org

BROWARD HEALTH MEDICAL CENTER (O, 656 beds) 1600 South Andrews Avenue, Fort Lauderdale, FL Zip 33316–2510; tel. 954/355–4400; Mark Sprada, R.N., Interim Chief Executive Officer

BROWARD HEALTH NORTH (O, 334 beds) 201 East Sample Road, Deerfield Beach, FL Zip 33064–3502; tel. 954/941–8300; Robert Bugg, Acting Chief Executive Officer
Web address: www.browardhealth.org

Owned, leased, sponsored:	4 hospitals	1366 beds
Contract-managed:	0 hospitals	0 beds
Totals:	4 hospitals	1366 beds

★**0400: BRYAN HEALTH** (NP)

1600 South 48th Street, Lincoln, NE Zip 68506–1283, 1600 S 48th ST, 68506–1283, tel. 402/481–1111; Kimberly A. Russel, FACHE, President and Chief Executive Officer
(Moderately Centralized Health System)

IOWA: CLARINDA REGIONAL HEALTH CENTER (C, 25 beds) 220 Essie Davison Drive, Clarinda, IA Zip 51632–2915, P O Box 217, 51632–0217, tel. 712/542–2176; Christopher R. Stipe, FACHE, Chief Executive Officer

NEBRASKA: BRYAN MEDICAL CENTER (O, 537 beds) 1600 South 48th Street, Lincoln, NE Zip 68506–1299; tel. 402/489–0200; John T. Woodrich, President and Chief Operating Officer
Web address: www.bryanhealth.com

CRETE AREA MEDICAL CENTER (O, 24 beds) 2910 Betten Drive, Crete, NE Zip 68333–3084, P O Box 220, 68333–0220, tel. 402/826–2102; Rebekah Mussman, Chief Executive Officer

MERRICK MEDICAL CENTER (O, 65 beds) 1715 26th Street, Central City, NE Zip 68826–9620; tel. 308/946–3015; Julie Murray, Chief Executive Officer
Web address: www.lmchealth.com

SAUNDERS MEDICAL CENTER (C, 16 beds) 1760 County Road J, Wahoo, NE Zip 68066–4152; tel. 402/443–4191; Tyler Toline, FACHE, Chief Executive Officer
Web address: www.saundersmedicalcenter.com

Owned, leased, sponsored:	3 hospitals	626 beds
Contract-managed:	2 hospitals	41 beds
Totals:	5 hospitals	667 beds

9655: BUREAU OF MEDICINE AND SURGERY, DEPARTMENT OF THE NAVY (FG)

7700 Arlington Boulevard, Suite 5126, Falls Church, VA Zip 22042; tel. 202/762–3701; Bryce H.P. Mendez, Healthcare Policy Analyst
(Independent Hospital System)

CALIFORNIA: NAVAL HOSPITAL CAMP PENDLETON (O, 72 beds) 200 Mercy Circle, Camp Pendleton, CA Zip 92055–5191, P O Box 555191, 92055–5191, tel. 760/725–1304; Captain, Lisa Mulligan, Commanding Officer
Web address: www.cpen.med.navy.mil/

NAVAL HOSPITAL LEMOORE (O, 16 beds) 937 Franklin Avenue, Lemoore, CA Zip 93246–0001; tel. 559/998–4481; Captain, Mary A. Mahony, Commanding Officer

NAVAL MEDICAL CENTER SAN DIEGO (O, 285 beds) 34800 Bob Wilson Drive, San Diego, CA Zip 92134–5000; tel. 619/532–6400; Captain, Joel A. Roos, Commanding Officer
Web address: www.med.navy.mil/sites/nmcsd/Pages/default.aspx

ROBERT E. BUSH NAVAL HOSPITAL (O, 29 beds) 1145 Sturgis Road, Twentynine Palms, CA Zip 92278, Box 788250, MCAGCC, 92278–8250, tel. 760/830–2190; Captain, Jay C. Sourbeer, Commanding Officer

FLORIDA: NAVAL HOSPITAL JACKSONVILLE (O, 64 beds) 2080 Child Street, Jacksonville, FL Zip 32214–5000; tel. 904/542–7300; Commander, Darryl Green, Director Administration
Web address: www.med.navy.mil/SITES/NAVALHOSPITALJAX/Pages/default.aspx

NAVAL HOSPITAL PENSACOLA (O, 28 beds) 6000 West Highway 98, Pensacola, FL Zip 32512–0003; tel. 850/505–6601; Commander, Devin Morrison, Director Administration

GUAM: U. S. NAVAL HOSPITAL GUAM (O, 55 beds) Building #50 Farenholt Avenue, Agana, GU Zip 96910, PSC 490, Box 208, FPO, 96540, tel. 671/344–9340; Captain, Daniel Cornwell, Command Officer
Web address: www.med.navy.mil/sites/usnhguam/Pages/default.aspx

MARYLAND: WALTER REED NATIONAL MILITARY MEDICAL CENTER (O, 247 beds) 8901 Wisconsin Avenue, Bethesda, MD Zip 20889–5600; tel. 301/295–4611; Colonel, Michael S. Heimall, Director
Web address: www.wrnmmc.capmed.mil/SitePages/home.aspx

NORTH CAROLINA: NAVAL HOSPITAL CAMP LEJEUNE (O, 117 beds) 100 Brewster Boulevard, Camp Lejeune, NC Zip 28547–2538, P O Box 10100, 28547–0100, tel. 910/450–4300; Captain, Rick Freedman, Commanding Officer

SOUTH CAROLINA: NAVAL HOSPITAL BEAUFORT (O, 20 beds) 1 Pinckney Boulevard, Beaufort, SC Zip 29902–6122; tel. 843/228–5301; Lieutenant Commander, Willie Brown, Director Administration
Web address: www.med.navy.mil/sites/nhbeaufort/Pages/Welcome_Page.aspx

VIRGINIA: NAVAL MEDICAL CENTER (O, 274 beds) 620 John Paul Jones Circle, Portsmouth, VA Zip 23708–2197; tel. 757/953–1980; Captain, Matthew Case, MSC, USN, Executive Officer

Section B

For explanation of codes following names, see page B2.
★ Indicates Type III membership in the American Hospital Association.

WASHINGTON: NAVAL HOSPITAL BREMERTON (O, 30 beds) One Boone Road, Bremerton, WA Zip 98312–1898; tel. 360/475–4000; Commander, David Weiss, Commanding Officer
Web address: www.med.navy.mil/sites/nhbrem/Pages/default.aspx

NAVAL HOSPITAL OAK HARBOR (O, 29 beds) 3475 North Saratoga Street, Oak Harbor, WA Zip 98278–8800; tel. 360/257–9500; Commander, Frederick Joseph. McDonald, Commanding Officer
Web address: www.med.navy.mil/sites/nhoh/Pages/default.aspx

Owned, leased, sponsored:	13 hospitals	1266 beds
Contract-managed:	0 hospitals	0 beds
Totals:	13 hospitals	1266 beds

0113: CANCER TREATMENT CENTERS OF AMERICA (IO)
1336 Basswood Road, Schaumburg, IL Zip 60173–4544; tel. 847/342–7400; Rajesh K. Garg, M.D., JD, President and Chief Executive Officer

ARIZONA: WESTERN REGIONAL MEDICAL CENTER (O, 24 beds) 14200 West Celebrate Life way, Goodyear, AZ Zip 85338–3005; tel. 623/207–3000; Matthew McGuire, President and Chief Executive Officer
Web address: www.cancercenter.com/western-hospital.cfm

GEORGIA: SOUTHEASTERN REGIONAL MEDICAL CENTER (O, 50 beds) 600 Celebrate Life Parkway, Newnan, GA Zip 30265–8000; tel. 770/400–6000; Anne Meisner, MSN, President and Chief Executive Officer
Web address: www.cancercenter.com/southeastern-hospital.cfm

ILLINOIS: MIDWESTERN REGIONAL MEDICAL CENTER (O, 72 beds) 2520 Elisha Avenue, Zion, IL Zip 60099–2587; tel. 847/872–4561; Scott Jones, President and Chief Executive Officer

OKLAHOMA: SOUTHWESTERN REGIONAL MEDICAL CENTER (O, 40 beds) 10109 East 79th Street, Tulsa, OK Zip 74133–4564; tel. 918/286–5000; Jay Foley, Interim President and Chief Executive Officer
Web address: www.cancercenter.com

PENNSYLVANIA: EASTERN REGIONAL MEDICAL CENTER (O, 56 beds) 1331 East Wyoming Avenue, Philadelphia, PA Zip 19124–3808; tel. 215/537–7400; Nancy Hesse, MSN, R.N., President and Chief Executive Officer

Owned, leased, sponsored:	5 hospitals	242 beds
Contract-managed:	0 hospitals	0 beds
Totals:	5 hospitals	242 beds

★0124: CAPE COD HEALTHCARE, INC. (NP)
27 Park Street, Hyannis, MA Zip 02601–5230; tel. 508/862–5121; Michael K. Lauf, President and Chief Executive Officer
(Centralized Health System)

MASSACHUSETTS: CAPE COD HOSPITAL (O, 259 beds) 27 Park Street, Hyannis, MA Zip 02601–5230; tel. 508/771–1800; Michael K. Lauf, President and Chief Executive Officer
Web address: www.capecodhealth.org

FALMOUTH HOSPITAL (O, 95 beds) 100 Ter Heun Drive, Falmouth, MA Zip 02540–2599; tel. 508/548–5300; Michael K. Lauf, President and Chief Executive Officer
Web address: www.capecodhealth.org

Owned, leased, sponsored:	2 hospitals	354 beds
Contract-managed:	0 hospitals	0 beds
Totals:	2 hospitals	354 beds

0835: CAPE FEAR VALLEY HEALTH SYSTEM (NP)
1638 Owen Drive, Fayetteville, NC Zip 28304–3424, P O Box 2000, 28302–2000, tel. 910/615–4000; Michael Nagowski, President and Chief Executive Officer
(Independent Hospital System)

NORTH CAROLINA: CAPE FEAR VALLEY - BLADEN COUNTY HOSPITAL (O, 25 beds) 501 South Poplar Street, Elizabethtown, NC Zip 28337–9375,

P O Box 398, 28337–0398, tel. 910/862–5100; Roxie Cannon. Wells, M.D., Chief Executive Officer

CAPE FEAR VALLEY MEDICAL CENTER (O, 612 beds) 1638 Owen Drive, Fayetteville, NC Zip 28304–3431, P O Box 2000, 28302–2000, tel. 910/615–4000; Michael Nagowski, Chief Executive Officer
Web address: www.capefearvalley.com

HARNETT HEALTH SYSTEM (C, 96 beds) 800 Tilghman Drive, Dunn, NC Zip 28334–5599, P O Box 1706, 28335–1706, tel. 910/892–1000; Kevin Jackson, Interim Chief Executive Officer

HIGHSMITH-RAINEY SPECIALTY HOSPITAL (O, 60 beds) 150 Robeson Street, Fayetteville, NC Zip 28301–5570; tel. 910/615–1000; Kevin Jackson, On Site Administrator
Web address: www.capefearvalley.com

HOKE HOSPITAL (O, 41 beds) 210 Medical Pavilion Drive, Raeford, NC Zip 28376–9111; tel. 910/904–8000; Roxie Cannon. Wells, M.D., President
Web address: www.capefearvalley.com

Owned, leased, sponsored:	4 hospitals	738 beds
Contract-managed:	1 hospitals	96 beds
Totals:	5 hospitals	834 beds

★0297: CAPITAL HEALTH (NP)
750 Brunswick Avenue, Trenton, NJ Zip 08638–4143; tel. 609/394–6000; Al Maghazehe, Ph.D., FACHE, President and Chief Executive Officer
(Independent Hospital System)

NEW JERSEY: CAPITAL HEALTH MEDICAL CENTER-HOPEWELL (O, 207 beds) 1 Capital Way, Pennington, NJ Zip 08534–2520; tel. 609/303–4000; Al Maghazehe, Ph.D., FACHE, President and Chief Executive Officer
Web address: www.capitalhealth.org

CAPITAL HEALTH REGIONAL MEDICAL CENTER (O, 204 beds) 750 Brunswick Avenue, Trenton, NJ Zip 08638–4143; tel. 609/394–6000; Al Maghazehe, Ph.D., FACHE, President and Chief Executive Officer

Owned, leased, sponsored:	2 hospitals	411 beds
Contract-managed:	0 hospitals	0 beds
Totals:	2 hospitals	411 beds

★0099: CARE NEW ENGLAND HEALTH SYSTEM (NP)
45 Willard Avenue, Providence, RI Zip 02905–3218; tel. 401/453–7900; Dennis D. Keefe, President and Chief Executive Officer
(Moderately Centralized Health System)

RHODE ISLAND: BUTLER HOSPITAL (O, 143 beds) 345 Blackstone Boulevard, Providence, RI Zip 02906–4829; tel. 401/455–6200; Lawrence Price, M.D., President and Chief Operating Officer
Web address: www.butler.org

KENT COUNTY MEMORIAL HOSPITAL (O, 318 beds) 455 Tollgate Road, Warwick, RI Zip 02886–2770; tel. 401/737–7000; Michael J. Dacey, M.D., President and Chief Operating Officer
Web address: www.kentri.org

MEMORIAL HOSPITAL OF RHODE ISLAND (O, 152 beds) 111 Brewster Street, Pawtucket, RI Zip 02860–4499; tel. 401/729–2000; Michael J. Dacey, M.D., President

WOMEN & INFANTS HOSPITAL OF RHODE ISLAND (O, 247 beds) 101 Dudley Street, Providence, RI Zip 02905–2499; tel. 401/274–1100; Diane Rafferty, Interim Chief Executive Officer
Web address: www.womenandinfants.org

Owned, leased, sponsored:	4 hospitals	860 beds
Contract-managed:	0 hospitals	0 beds
Totals:	4 hospitals	860 beds

★0931: CAREPOINT HEALTH (IO)
10 Exchange Place, 15th Floor, Jersey City, NJ Zip 07302–3918; tel. 877/791–7000; Jeffrey M. Mandler, Chief Executive Officer

---

For explanation of codes following names, see page B2.
★ Indicates Type III membership in the American Hospital Association.

Section B

NEW JERSEY: CAREPOINT HEALTH BAYONNE MEDICAL CENTER (O, 178 beds) 29th Street & Avenue E, Bayonne, NJ Zip 07002–4699, 29 East 29 Street, 07002–4699, tel. 201/858–5000; Catherine Shull. Fernald, MSN, Chief Operating Officer
Web address: www.carepointhealth.org

CAREPOINT HEALTH CHRIST HOSPITAL (O, 376 beds) 176 Palisade Avenue, Jersey City, NJ Zip 07306–1196, 176 Palisades Avenue, 07306–1196, tel. 201/795–8200; Marie Theresa Duffy, Chief Operating Officer
Web address: www.carepointhealth.org

CAREPOINT HEALTH HOBOKEN UNIVERSITY MEDICAL CENTER (O, 333 beds) 308 Willow Avenue, Hoboken, NJ Zip 07030–3889; tel. 201/418–1000; Ann P. Logan, R.N., Ph.D., Chief Operating Officer

Owned, leased, sponsored:	3 hospitals	887 beds
Contract-managed:	0 hospitals	0 beds
Totals:	3 hospitals	887 beds

★0070: CARILION CLINIC (NP)

1906 Belleview Avenue SE, Roanoke, VA Zip 24014–1838, P O Box 13727, 24036–3727, tel. 540/981–7000; Nancy Howell. Agee, President and Chief Executive Officer
(Moderately Centralized Health System)

VIRGINIA: CARILION FRANKLIN MEMORIAL HOSPITAL (O, 12 beds) 180 Floyd Avenue, Rocky Mount, VA Zip 24151–1389; tel. 540/483–5277; William D. Jacobsen, FACHE, Administrator and Hospital Vice President
Web address: www.carilionclinic.org/CFMH

CARILION GILES COMMUNITY HOSPITAL (O, 14 beds) 159 Hartley Way, Pearisburg, VA Zip 24134–2471; tel. 540/921–6000; William Flattery, Vice President and Administrator Western Division
Web address: www.carilionclinic.org/Carilion/cgch

CARILION NEW RIVER VALLEY MEDICAL CENTER (O, 85 beds) 2900 Lamb Circle, Christiansburg, VA Zip 24073–6344, P O Box 5, Radford, 24143–0005, tel. 540/731–2000; William Flattery, Vice President and Administrator Western Division

CARILION ROANOKE MEMORIAL HOSPITAL (O, 634 beds) Belleview at Jefferson Street, Roanoke, VA Zip 24014, P O Box 13367, 24033–3367, tel. 540/981–7000; Steven C. Arner, President
Web address: www.carilionclinic.org

CARILION STONEWALL JACKSON HOSPITAL (O, 10 beds) 1 Health Circle, Lexington, VA Zip 24450–2492; tel. 540/458–3300; Charles E. Carr, Vice President and Administrator

CARILION TAZEWELL COMMUNITY HOSPITAL (O, 6 beds) 141 Ben Bolt Avenue, Tazewell, VA Zip 24651–9700, 388 Ben Bolt Avenue, 24651, tel. 276/988–8700; Kathren Dowdy, MSN, Regional Hospital Senior Director
Web address: www.carilionclinic.org

Owned, leased, sponsored:	6 hospitals	761 beds
Contract-managed:	0 hospitals	0 beds
Totals:	6 hospitals	761 beds

★2575: CARLE FOUNDATION (NP)

611 West Park Street, Urbana, IL Zip 61801–2595; tel. 217/383–3311; James C. Leonard, M.D., President and Chief Executive Officer
(Centralized Physician/Insurance Health System)

ILLINOIS: CARLE FOUNDATION HOSPITAL (O, 412 beds) 611 West Park Street, Urbana, IL Zip 61801–2595; tel. 217/383–3311; James C. Leonard, M.D., President and Chief Executive Officer
Web address: www.carle.org

CARLE HOOPESTON REGIONAL HEALTH CENTER (O, 13 beds) 701 East Orange Street, Hoopeston, IL Zip 60942–1801; tel. 217/283–5531; Harry Brockus, Chief Executive Officer
Web address: www.carle.org

CARLE RICHLAND MEMORIAL HOSPITAL (O, 90 beds) 800 East Locust Street, Olney, IL Zip 62450–2553; tel. 618/395–2131; David B. Allen, Chief Executive Officer

Owned, leased, sponsored:	3 hospitals	515 beds
Contract-managed:	0 hospitals	0 beds
Totals:	3 hospitals	515 beds

★0705: CAROLINAS HEALTHCARE SYSTEM (NP)

1000 Blythe Boulevard, Charlotte, NC Zip 28203–5871, P O Box 32861, 28232–2861, tel. 704/355–2000; Eugene A. Woods, FACHE, President and Chief Executive Officer
(Moderately Centralized Health System)

NORTH CAROLINA: CAROLINAS HEALTHCARE SYSTEM ANSON (O, 15 beds) 2301 US Highway 74 W, Wadesboro, NC Zip 28170–7554, 2301 U.S Highway 74 West, 28170, tel. 704/994–4500; Gary A. Henderson, Administrator
Web address: www.carolinashealthcare.org/anson

CAROLINAS HEALTHCARE SYSTEM BLUE RIDGE (C, 156 beds) 2201 South Sterling Street, Morganton, NC Zip 28655–4058; tel. 828/580–5000; Kathy C. Bailey, Ph.D., FACHE, President and Chief Executive Officer

CAROLINAS HEALTHCARE SYSTEM CLEVELAND (L, 161 beds) 201 East Grover Street, Shelby, NC Zip 28150–3917; tel. 980/487–3000; Brian Gwyn, President and Chief Executive Officer
Web address: www.clevelandregional.org

CAROLINAS HEALTHCARE SYSTEM KINGS MOUNTAIN (O, 59 beds) 706 West King Street, Kings Mountain, NC Zip 28086–2708; tel. 980/487–5000; Brian Gwyn, President and Chief Executive Officer
Web address: www.clevelandregional.org/kings-mountain-hospital.html

CAROLINAS HEALTHCARE SYSTEM LINCOLN (O, 101 beds) 433 McAlister Road, Lincolnton, NC Zip 28092–4147, PO Box 677, 28093–0677, tel. 980/212–2000; Peter W. Acker, President and Chief Executive Officer

CAROLINAS HEALTHCARE SYSTEM NORTHEAST (O, 455 beds) 920 Church Street North, Concord, NC Zip 28025–2983; tel. 704/403–3000; Phyllis A. Wingate, FACHE, President
Web address: www.carolinashealthcare.org/northeast

CAROLINAS HEALTHCARE SYSTEM STANLY (C, 109 beds) 301 Yadkin Street, Albemarle, NC Zip 28001–3441, P O Box 1489, 28002–1489, tel. 704/984–4000; Brian Freeman, President

CAROLINAS HEALTHCARE SYSTEM UNIVERSITY (O, 100 beds) 8800 North Tryon Street, Charlotte, NC Zip 28262–3300, P O Box 560727, 28256–0727, tel. 704/863–6000; William H. Leonard, President
Web address: www.carolinashealthcare.org/university

CAROLINAS HEALTHCARE SYSTEM PINEVILLE (O, 235 beds) 10628 Park Road, Charlotte, NC Zip 28210–8407; tel. 704/667–1000; Christopher R. Hummer, President
Web address: www.carolinashealthcare.org/pineville

CAROLINAS HEALTHCARE SYSTEM UNION (L, 236 beds) 600 Hospital Drive, Monroe, NC Zip 28112–6000, P O Box 5003, 28111–5003, tel. 980/993–3100; Michael Lutes, President

CAROLINAS MEDICAL CENTER (O, 1212 beds) 1000 Blythe Boulevard, Charlotte, NC Zip 28203–5871, P O Box 32861, 28232–2861, tel. 704/355–2000; Spencer Lilly, President
Web address: www.carolinashealthcare.org/cmc

CAROLINAS REHABILITATION (O, 157 beds) 1100 Blythe Boulevard, Charlotte, NC Zip 28203–5864; tel. 704/355–4300; Robert G. Larrison Jr, President
Web address: www.carolinashealthcare.org/rehabilitation

COLUMBUS REGIONAL HEALTHCARE SYSTEM (C, 92 beds) 500 Jefferson Street, Whiteville, NC Zip 28472–3634; tel. 910/642–8011; Carla Hollis, President and Chief Executive Officer
Web address: www.crhealthcare.org/

MURPHY MEDICAL CENTER (C, 159 beds) 3990 U S Highway 64 East Alt, Murphy, NC Zip 28906–7917; tel. 828/837–8161; Michael Stevenson, Chief Executive Officer

SCOTLAND HEALTH CARE SYSTEM (C, 104 beds) 500 Lauchwood Drive, Laurinburg, NC Zip 28352–5599; tel. 910/291–7000; Gregory C. Wood, President and Chief Executive Officer
Web address: www.scotlandhealth.org

For explanation of codes following names, see page B2.
★ Indicates Type III membership in the American Hospital Association.

ST. LUKE'S HOSPITAL (C, 35 beds) 101 Hospital Drive, Columbus, NC Zip 28722-6418; tel. 828/894-3311; James B. Bross, President
Web address: www.saintlukeshospital.com

SOUTH CAROLINA: BON SECOURS ST. FRANCIS HOSPITAL (C, 173 beds) 2095 Henry Tecklenburg Drive, Charleston, SC Zip 29414-5733; tel. 843/402-1000; Stephen D. Porter, Chief Executive Officer
Web address: www.rsfh.com/

ROPER ST. FRANCIS MOUNT PLEASANT HOSPITAL (C, 50 beds) 3500 Highway 17 North, Mount Pleasant, SC Zip 29466-9123, 3500 North Highway 17, 29466-9123, tel. 843/606-7000; Anthony Jackson, Chief Executive Officer
Web address: www.rsfh.com/mount-pleasant-hospital

ROPER ST. FRANCIS (C, 300 beds) 316 Calhoun Street, Charleston, SC Zip 29401-1125; tel. 843/724-2000; Stephen D. Porter, Chief Executive Officer

Owned, leased, sponsored:	10 hospitals	2731 beds
Contract-managed:	9 hospitals	1178 beds
Totals:	19 hospitals	3909 beds

0656: CARRUS HOSPITALS (IO)

1810 West US Highway 82, Sherman, TX Zip 75092-7069; tel. 903/870-2600; Ronald E. Dorris, Chief Executive Officer
(Independent Hospital System)

TEXAS: CARRUS REHABILITATION HOSPITAL (O, 24 beds) 1810 West US Highway 82, Suite 100, Sherman, TX Zip 75092-7069; tel. 903/870-2600; Jon-Michael Rains, Chief Executive Officer
Web address: www.carrushospital.com

CARRUS SPECIALTY HOSPITAL (O, 16 beds) 1810 West US Highway 82, Sherman, TX Zip 75092-7069; tel. 903/870-2600; Jon-Michael Rains, Chief Executive Officer

Owned, leased, sponsored:	2 hospitals	40 beds
Contract-managed:	0 hospitals	0 beds
Totals:	2 hospitals	40 beds

★0092: CATHOLIC HEALTH INITIATIVES (CC)

198 Inverness Drive West, Suite 800, Englewood, CO Zip 80112-5202; tel. 303/298-9100; Kevin E. Lofton, FACHE, Chief Executive Officer
(Decentralized Health System)

ARKANSAS: CHI ST. VINCENT HOT SPRINGS (O, 262 beds) 300 Werner Street, Hot Springs, AR Zip 71913-6406; tel. 501/622-1000; Anthony Houston, FACHE, President
Web address: www.chistvincent.com/Hospitals/st-vincent-hot-springs

CHI ST. VINCENT INFIRMARY MEDICAL CENTER (S, 423 beds) Two St Vincent Circle, Little Rock, AR Zip 72205-5499; tel. 501/552-3000; Polly J. Davenport, FACHE, R.N., President
Web address: www.chistvincent.com/

CHI ST. VINCENT MEDICAL CENTER-NORTH (S, 69 beds) 2215 Wildwood Avenue, Sherwood, AR Zip 72120-5089; tel. 501/552-7100; Polly J. Davenport, FACHE, R.N., Senior Vice President, Chief Operating Officer, President CHI St. Vincent Infirmary Medical Center and CHI St. Vincent M
Web address: www.stvincenthealth.com

CHI ST. VINCENT MORRILTON (S, 25 beds) 4 Hospital Drive, Morrilton, AR Zip 72110-4510; tel. 501/977-2300; Leslie Arnold, Chief Executive Officer and Administrator
Web address: www.chistvincent.com/Hospitals/st-vincent-morrilton

COLORADO: LONGMONT UNITED HOSPITAL (S, 146 beds) 1950 West Mountain View Avenue, Longmont, CO Zip 80501-3162, P O Box 1659, 80502-1659, tel. 303/651-5111; Mitchell C. Carson, President and Chief Executive Officer

MERCY REGIONAL MEDICAL CENTER (S, 82 beds) 1010 Three Springs Boulevard, Durango, CO Zip 81301-8296; tel. 970/247-4311; William McConnell, Ph.D., President and Chief Executive Officer
Web address: www.mercydurango.org

ORTHOCOLORADO HOSPITAL (O, 48 beds) 11650 West 2nd Place, Lakewood, CO Zip 80228-1527; tel. 720/321-5000; Jude Torchia, Chief Executive Officer

PENROSE-ST. FRANCIS HEALTH SERVICES (S, 444 beds) 2222 North Nevada Avenue, Colorado Springs, CO Zip 80907-6799; tel. 719/776-5000; Margaret D. Sabin, President and Chief Executive Officer
Web address: www.penrosestfrancis.org

ST. ANTHONY HOSPITAL (S, 217 beds) 11600 West Second Place, Lakewood, CO Zip 80228-1527; tel. 720/321-0000; Edward H. Sim, Chief Executive Officer
Web address: www.stanthonyhosp.org

ST. ANTHONY NORTH HEALTH CAMPUS (S, 105 beds) 14300 Orchard Parkway, Westminster, CO Zip 80023-9206; tel. 720/627-0000; Kevin Jenkins, President and Chief Executive Officer
Web address: www.stanthonynorth.org

ST. ANTHONY SUMMIT MEDICAL CENTER (S, 34 beds) 340 Peak One Drive, Frisco, CO Zip 80443, P O Box 738, 80443-0738, tel. 970/668-3300; Paul J. Chodkowski, President and Chief Executive Officer
Web address: www.summitmedicalcenter.org

ST. MARY-CORWIN MEDICAL CENTER (S, 125 beds) 1008 Minnequa Avenue, Pueblo, CO Zip 81004-3798; tel. 719/557-4000; Brian Moore, President and Chief Executive Officer

ST. THOMAS MORE HOSPITAL (S, 25 beds) 1338 Phay Avenue, Canon City, CO Zip 81212-2302; tel. 719/285-2000; Sheri Trahern, CPA, FACHE, Chief Executive Officer
Web address: www.stmhospital.org

INDIANA: SOUTHERN INDIANA REHABILITATION HOSPITAL (O, 60 beds) 3104 Blackiston Boulevard, New Albany, IN Zip 47150-9579; tel. 812/941-8300; William Boso, Executive Director, Administrator
Web address: www.sirh.org

IOWA: CHI HEALTH MERCY CORNING (S, 22 beds) 603 Rosary Drive, Corning, IA Zip 50841-1683; tel. 641/322-3121; Lisa Wolfe, President

CHI HEALTH MERCY COUNCIL BLUFFS (S, 163 beds) 800 Mercy Drive, Council Bluffs, IA Zip 51503-3128, P O Box 1C, 51502-3001, tel. 712/328-5000; Marie E. Knedler, R.N., FACHE, President
Web address: www.chihealth.com/chi-health-mercy-council-bluffs

CHI HEALTH MISSOURI VALLEY (S, 16 beds) 631 North Eighth Street, Missouri Valley, IA Zip 51555-1102; tel. 712/642-2784; Robert A. Valentine, President
Web address: www.chihealth.com/chi-health-missouri-valley

KNOXVILLE HOSPITAL & CLINICS (C, 25 beds) 1002 South Lincoln Street, Knoxville, IA Zip 50138-3155; tel. 641/842-2151; Kevin Kincaid, Chief Executive Officer

MADISON COUNTY HEALTH CARE SYSTEM (C, 25 beds) 300 West Hutchings Street, Winterset, IA Zip 50273-2109; tel. 515/462-2373; Marcia Hendricks, R.N., FACHE, Chief Executive Officer
Web address: www.madisonhealth.com

MERCY MEDICAL CENTER-CENTERVILLE (S, 45 beds) 1 St Joseph's Drive, Centerville, IA Zip 52544-8055; tel. 641/437-4111; Clinton J. Christianson, FACHE, President

MERCY MEDICAL CENTER-DES MOINES (S, 613 beds) 1111 6th Avenue, Des Moines, IA Zip 50314-2611; tel. 515/247-3121; Robert P. Ritz, President
Web address: www.mercydesmoines.org

SKIFF MEDICAL CENTER (O, 48 beds) 204 North Fourth Avenue East, Newton, IA Zip 50208-3100, P O Box 1006, 50208-1006, tel. 641/792-1273; Laurie A. Conner, FACHE, Interim Chief Executive Officer

KANSAS: BOB WILSON MEMORIAL GRANT COUNTY HOSPITAL (O, 26 beds) 415 North Main Street, Ulysses, KS Zip 67880-2133; tel. 620/356-1266; Deanna Mustin, R.N., Administrator
Web address: www.bwmgch.com

ST. CATHERINE HOSPITAL (S, 104 beds) 401 East Spruce Street, Garden City, KS Zip 67846-5679; tel. 620/272-2561; Scott J. Taylor, President and Chief Executive Officer

KENTUCKY: CONTINUING CARE HOSPITAL (S, 43 beds) 1 Saint Joseph Drive, Lexington, KY Zip 40504-3742; tel. 859/967-5744; Jimmie Settles, Interim President and Chief Executive Officer
Web address: www.kentuckyonehealth.org

For explanation of codes following names, see page B2.
★ Indicates Type III membership in the American Hospital Association.

FLAGET MEMORIAL HOSPITAL (S, 42 beds) 4305 New Shepherdsville Road, Bardstown, KY Zip 40004–9019; tel. 502/350–5000; Jennifer Nolan, President and Chief Executive Officer
Web address: www.kentuckyonehealth.org/flaget

FRAZIER REHAB INSTITUTE (O, 87 beds) 220 Abraham Flexner Way, Louisville, KY Zip 40202–1887; tel. 502/582–7400; Cathy Spalding, Vice President of Operations
Web address: www.kentuckyonehealth.org/frazier-rehab-institute

JEWISH HOSPITAL-SHELBYVILLE (O, 30 beds) 727 Hospital Drive, Shelbyville, KY Zip 40065–1699; tel. 502/647–4000; Annessa Baker, Site Executive and Chief Nursing Officer

JEWISH HOSPITAL (O, 342 beds) 200 Abraham Flexner Way, Louisville, KY Zip 40202–1886; tel. 502/587–4011; Ron Waldridge II, M.D., President and Chief Medical Officer
Web address: www.jewishhospital.org

OUR LADY OF PEACE (O, 211 beds) 2020 Newburg Road, Louisville, KY Zip 40205–1879; tel. 502/479–4500; Jennifer Nolan, President

SAINT JOSEPH LONDON (S, 116 beds) 1001 Saint Joseph Lane, London, KY Zip 40741–8345; tel. 606/330–6000; Terrence G. Deis, CPA, FACHE, President
Web address: www.saintjosephhealthsystem.org

SAINT JOSEPH - MARTIN (S, 25 beds) 11203 Main Street, Martin, KY Zip 41649; tel. 606/285–6400; Kathy Stumbo, President

SAINT JOSEPH BEREA (S, 25 beds) 305 Estill Street, Berea, KY Zip 40403–1909; tel. 859/986–3151; Eric Gilliam, President
Web address: www.kentuckyonehealth.org/berea

SAINT JOSEPH EAST (S, 150 beds) 150 North Eagle Creek Drive, Lexington, KY Zip 40509–1805; tel. 859/967–5000; Eric Gilliam, President

SAINT JOSEPH HOSPITAL (S, 307 beds) One St Joseph Drive, Lexington, KY Zip 40504–3754; tel. 859/278–3436; Bruce J. Tassin, President
Web address: www.sjhlex.org

SAINT JOSEPH MOUNT STERLING (S, 42 beds) 225 Falcon Drive, Mount Sterling, KY Zip 40353–1158, P O Box 7, 40353–0007, tel. 859/497–5000; Cinda Fluke, R.N., Interim Site Executive
Web address: www.sjhlex.org

STS. MARY & ELIZABETH HOSPITAL (O, 174 beds) 1850 Bluegrass Avenue, Louisville, KY Zip 40215–1199; tel. 502/361–6000; Jennifer Nolan, President

TAYLOR REGIONAL HOSPITAL (C, 90 beds) 1700 Old Lebanon Road, Campbellsville, KY Zip 42718–9600; tel. 270/465–3561; Jane Wheatley, Chief Executive Officer
Web address: www.trhosp.org

UNIVERSITY OF LOUISVILLE HOSPITAL (C, 301 beds) 530 South Jackson Street, Louisville, KY Zip 40202–3611; tel. 502/562–3000; Kenneth P. Marshall, President and Chief Executive Officer

MINNESOTA: CHI LAKEWOOD HEALTH (S, 55 beds) 600 Main Avenue South, Baudette, MN Zip 56623–2855; tel. 218/634–2120; Benjamin Koppelman, Interim President
Web address: www.lakewoodhealthcenter.org

CHI ST. FRANCIS HEALTH (S, 105 beds) 2400 St Francis Drive, Breckenridge, MN Zip 56520–1025; tel. 218/643–3000; David A. Nelson, President

CHI ST. GABRIEL'S HEALTH (S, 25 beds) 815 Second Street SE, Little Falls, MN Zip 56345–3596; tel. 320/632–5441; Lee Boyles, President
Web address: www.stgabriels.com

CHI ST. JOSEPH'S HEALTH (S, 25 beds) 600 Pleasant Avenue, Park Rapids, MN Zip 56470–1431; tel. 218/732–3311; Benjamin Koppelman, President

NEBRASKA: CHI HEALTH CREIGHTON UNIVERSITY MEDICAL CENTER - BERGAN MERCY (S, 308 beds) 7500 Mercy Road, Omaha, NE Zip 68124–2319; tel. 402/398–6060; Kevin J. Nokels, FACHE, Primary
Web address: www.alegent.com/bergan

CHI HEALTH GOOD SAMARITAN (S, 233 beds) 10 East 31st Street, Kearney, NE Zip 68847–2926, P O Box 1990, 68848–1990, tel. 308/865–7100; Michael H. Schnieders, FACHE, President

CHI HEALTH IMMANUEL (S, 289 beds) 6901 North 72nd Street, Omaha, NE Zip 68122–1799; tel. 402/572–2121; Ann Schumacher, R.N., MSN, FACHE, President
Web address: www.alegent.com/immanuel

CHI HEALTH LAKESIDE (S, 137 beds) 16901 Lakeside Hills Court, Omaha, NE Zip 68130–2318; tel. 402/717–8000; Kevin Miller, President
Web address: www.CHIhealth.com

CHI HEALTH MIDLANDS (S, 28 beds) 11111 South 84th Street, Papillion, NE Zip 68046–4122; tel. 402/593–3000; Kevin Miller, President
Web address: www.CHIhealth.com

CHI HEALTH NEBRASKA HEART (S, 63 beds) 7500 South 91st Street, Lincoln, NE Zip 68526–9437; tel. 402/327–2700; Dan Schonlau, Interim President
Web address: www.CHIhealthNebraskaHeart.com

CHI HEALTH PLAINVIEW (S, 8 beds) 704 North Third Street, Plainview, NE Zip 68769–2047, P O Box 489, 68769–0489, tel. 402/582–4245; Gregory Beckmann, Chief Executive Officer

CHI HEALTH SAINT FRANCIS (S, 159 beds) 2620 West Faidley Avenue, Grand Island, NE Zip 68803–4297, P O Box 9804, 68802–9804, tel. 308/384–4600; Edward J. Hannon, FACHE, President
Web address: www.saintfrancisgi.org

CHI HEALTH SCHUYLER (S, 25 beds) 104 West 17th Street, Schuyler, NE Zip 68661–1304; tel. 402/352–2441; Connie Peters, R.N., President

CHI HEALTH ST ELIZABETH (S, 260 beds) 555 South 70th Street, Lincoln, NE Zip 68510–2494; tel. 402/219–8000; Cary Ward, M.D., Chief Medical Officer and Interim President
Web address: www.saintelizabethonline.com

CHI HEALTH ST. MARY'S (S, 18 beds) 1301 Grundman Boulevard, Nebraska City, NE Zip 68410; tel. 402/873–3321; Daniel J. Kelly, President
Web address: www.chihealthstmarys.com

NORTH DAKOTA: CHI LISBON HEALTH (S, 25 beds) 905 Main Street, Lisbon, ND Zip 58054–4334, P O Box 353, 58054–0353, tel. 701/683–6400; Peggy Reinke, R.N., Administrator
Web address: www.lisbonhospital.com

CHI MERCY HEALTH (S, 19 beds) 570 Chautauqua Boulevard, Valley City, ND Zip 58072–3199; tel. 701/845–6400; Keith E. Heuser, President

CHI OAKES HOSPITAL (S, 20 beds) 1200 North Seventh Street, Oakes, ND Zip 58474–2502; tel. 701/742–3291; Becki Thompson, President
Web address: www.oakeshospital.com

CHI ST ALEXIUS HEALTH CARRINGTON MEDICAL CENTER (S, 25 beds) 800 North Fourth Street, Carrington, ND Zip 58421–1217, P O Box 461, 58421–0461, tel. 701/652–3141; Mariann Doeling, R.N., President
Web address: www.carringtonhealthcenter.org

CHI ST. ALEXIUS HEALTH - DICKINSON MEDICAL CENTER (S, 25 beds) 2500 Fairway Street, Dickinson, ND Zip 58601–4399; tel. 701/456–4000; Reed Reyman, President

CHI ST. ALEXIUS HEALTH - WILLISTON MEDICAL CENTER (S, 25 beds) 1301 15th Avenue West, Williston, ND Zip 58801–3896; tel. 701/774–7400; Dan Bjerknes, Market Leader
Web address: www.mercy-williston.org

CHI ST. ALEXIUS HEALTH DEVILS LAKE HOSPITAL (S, 25 beds) 1031 Seventh Street NE, Devils Lake, ND Zip 58301–2798; tel. 701/662–2131; Andrew Lankowicz, FACHE, President
Web address: www.mercyhospitaldl.com

CHI ST. ALEXIUS HEALTH GARRISON (O, 50 beds) 407 Third Avenue SE, Garrison, ND Zip 58540–7235; tel. 701/463–2275; Tod Graeber, Administrator

CHI ST. ALEXIUS HEALTH (O, 237 beds) 900 East Broadway, Bismarck, ND Zip 58501–4586, P O Box 5510, 58506–5510, tel. 701/530–7000; Kurt Schley, Market Chief Executive Officer
Web address: www.st.alexius.org

COMMUNITY MEMORIAL HOSPITAL (O, 25 beds) 220 Fifth Avenue, Turtle Lake, ND Zip 58575–4005, P O Box 280, 58575–0280, tel. 701/448–2331; Tod Graeber, Administrator

OHIO: GOOD SAMARITAN HOSPITAL (S, 476 beds) 375 Dixmyth Avenue, Cincinnati, OH Zip 45220–2489; tel. 513/862–1400; Jamie Easterling, Executive Director, Operations
Web address: www.trihealth.com

GOOD SAMARITAN HOSPITAL (S, 346 beds) 2222 Philadelphia Drive, Dayton, OH Zip 45406–1813; tel. 937/734–2612; Eloise Broner, President and Chief Executive Officer
Web address: www.goodsamdayton.org

PROVIDENCE CARE CENTER (O, 138 beds) 2025 Hayes Avenue, Sandusky, OH Zip 44870; Rick G. Ryan, Administrator and Chief Executive Officer

For explanation of codes following names, see page B2.
★ Indicates Type III membership in the American Hospital Association.

TRINITY HEALTH SYSTEM (O, 320 beds) 380 Summit Avenue, Steubenville, OH Zip 43952-2699; tel. 740/283-7000; Matthew Grimshaw, Market Chief Executive Officer
Web address: www.trinityhealth.com

TRINITY HOSPITAL TWIN CITY (O, 12 beds) 819 North First Street, Dennison, OH Zip 44621-1098; tel. 740/922-2800; Teresa Gagliardi, R.N., Chief Nursing Officer and Interim Chief Executive Officer

OREGON: CHI ST. ANTHONY HOSPITAL (S, 25 beds) 2801 St Anthony Way, Pendleton, OR Zip 97801-3800; tel. 541/276-5121; Harold S. Geller, Chief Executive Officer
Web address: www.sahpendleton.org

MERCY MEDICAL CENTER (S, 140 beds) 2700 Stewart Parkway, Roseburg, OR Zip 97471-1281; tel. 541/673-0611; Kelly C. Morgan, President and Chief Executive Officer

TENNESSEE: CHI MEMORIAL (S, 405 beds) 2525 De Sales Avenue, Chattanooga, TN Zip 37404-1161; tel. 423/495-2525; Larry P. Schumacher, R.N., MSN, Chief Executive Officer
Web address: www.memorial.org

TEXAS: BAYLOR ST. LUKE'S MEDICAL CENTER MCNAIR CAMPUS (O, 256 beds) One Baylor Plaza, BCM 100, Houston, TX Zip 77030-3411; tel. 713/798-4951; Michael H. Covert, FACHE, Chief Executive Officer
Web address: www.bcm.edu

BAYLOR ST. LUKE'S MEDICAL CENTER (O, 704 beds) 6720 Bertner Avenue, Houston, TX Zip 77030-2697, P O Box 20269, 77225-0269, tel. 832/355-1000; Gay Nord, President
Web address: www.stlukestexas.com

CHI ST. JOSEPH HEALTH BELLVILLE HOSPITAL (O, 10 beds) 44 North Cummings Street, Bellville, TX Zip 77418-1347, P O Box 977, 77418-0977, tel. 979/413-7400

CHI ST. JOSEPH HEALTH BURLESON HOSPITAL (O, 12 beds) 1101 Woodson Drive, Caldwell, TX Zip 77836-1052, P O Box 360, 77836-0360, tel. 979/567-3245
Web address: www.chistjoseph.org/

CHI ST. JOSEPH HEALTH GRIMES HOSPITAL (O, 18 beds) 210 South Judson Street, Navasota, TX Zip 77868-3704; tel. 936/825-6585
Web address: www.st-joseph.org

CHI ST. JOSEPH HEALTH MADISON HOSPITAL (O, 25 beds) 100 West Cross Street, Madisonville, TX Zip 77864-2432, Box 698, 77864-0698, tel. 936/348-2631

CHI ST. JOSEPH REGIONAL HEALTH CENTER (O, 232 beds) 2801 Franciscan Drive, Bryan, TX Zip 77802-2599; tel. 979/776-3777; Rick D. Napper, President and Chief Executive Officer
Web address: www.st-joseph.org

CHI ST. LUKE'S HEALTH - PATIENTS MEDICAL CENTER (O, 61 beds) 4600 East Sam Houston Parkway South, Pasadena, TX Zip 77505-3948; tel. 713/948-7000; Steven Foster, Chief Executive Officer

CHI ST. LUKE'S HEALTH BRAZOSPORT (O, 103 beds) 100 Medical Drive, Lake Jackson, TX Zip 77566-5674; tel. 979/297-4411; Al Guevara Jr, FACHE, President
Web address: www.chistlukesbrazosport.org

CHI ST. LUKE'S HEALTH MEMORIAL LIVINGSTON (O, 66 beds) 1717 Highway 59 Bypass, Livingston, TX Zip 77351-1257, P O Box 1257, 77351-0022, tel. 936/329-8700; Kristi Froese, R.N., Vice President Clinical Operations

CHI ST. LUKE'S HEALTH MEMORIAL LUFKIN (O, 217 beds) 1201 West Frank Avenue, Lufkin, TX Zip 75904-3357, P O Box 1447, 75902-1447, tel. 936/634-8111; Monte J. Bostwick, Market Chief Executive Officer
Web address: www.memorialhealth.us/centers/lufkin

CHI ST. LUKE'S HEALTH MEMORIAL SAN AUGUSTINE (O, 9 beds) 511 East Hospital Street, San Augustine, TX Zip 75972-2121, P O Box 658, 75972-0658, tel. 936/275-3446; Darlene Williams, R.N., Administrator

CHI ST. LUKE'S HEALTH MEMORIAL SPECIALTY HOSPITAL (O, 20 beds) 1201 West Frank Avenue, D5, Lufkin, TX Zip 75904-3357, P O Box 1447, 75902-1447, tel. 936/639-7530; Darlene Williams, R.N., Administrator
Web address: www.memorialhealth.org

CHI ST. LUKE'S HEALTH-THE WOODLANDS HOSPITAL (O, 207 beds) 17200 St. Luke's Way, The Woodlands, TX Zip 77384-8007; tel. 936/266-2000; David Argueta, Chief Executive Officer

CHI ST. LUKE'S HOSPITAL - THE VINTAGE HOSPITAL (O, 78 beds) 20171 Chasewood Park Drive, Houston, TX Zip 77070-1437; tel. 832/534-5000; Roland Cruickshank, President
Web address: www.stlukesvintage.com/

ST. LUKE'S LAKESIDE HOSPITAL (O, 30 beds) 17400 St. Luke's Way, The Woodlands, TX Zip 77384-8036; tel. 936/266-9000; David Argueta, Chief Executive Officer

ST. LUKE'S SUGAR LAND HOSPITAL (O, 96 beds) 1317 Lake Pointe Parkway, Sugar Land, TX Zip 77478-3997; tel. 281/637-7000; Robert A. Heifner, FACHE, Chief Executive Officer
Web address: www.stlukessugarland.com

WASHINGTON: HARRISON MEDICAL CENTER (O, 260 beds) 2520 Cherry Avenue, Bremerton, WA Zip 98310-4229; tel. 360/744-3911; David W. Schultz, FACHE, Market President, Peninsula Region

HIGHLINE MEDICAL CENTER (O, 128 beds) 16251 Sylvester Road SW, Burien, WA Zip 98166-3052; tel. 206/244-9970; Anthony McLean, President
Web address: www.hchnet.org

REGIONAL HOSPITAL FOR RESPIRATORY AND COMPLEX CARE (O, 26 beds) 16251 Sylvester Road SW, Burien, WA Zip 98166-3017; tel. 206/248-4548; Anne McBride, Chief Executive Officer
Web address: www.regionalhospital.org

ST. ANTHONY HOSPITAL (O, 80 beds) 11567 Canterwood Boulevard NW, Gig Harbor, WA Zip 98332-5812; tel. 253/530-2000; David W. Schultz, FACHE, President, Penisula Region

ST. CLARE HOSPITAL (S, 103 beds) 11315 Bridgeport Way SW, Lakewood, WA Zip 98499-3004; tel. 253/985-1711; Syd Bersante, R.N., President
Web address: www.fhshealth.org

ST. ELIZABETH HOSPITAL (S, 25 beds) 1455 Battersby Avenue, Enumclaw, WA Zip 98022-3634, P O Box 218, 98022-0218, tel. 360/802-8800; Syd Bersante, R.N., Market President

ST. FRANCIS HOSPITAL (S, 118 beds) 34515 Ninth Avenue South, Federal Way, WA Zip 98003-6799; tel. 253/944-8100; Anthony McLean, Market President
Web address: www.fhshealth.org

ST. JOSEPH MEDICAL CENTER (S, 366 beds) 1717 South 'J' Street, Tacoma, WA Zip 98405-3004, P O Box 2197, 98401-2197, tel. 253/426-4101; Syd Bersante, President
Web address: www.chifranciscan.org

Owned, leased, sponsored:	93 hospitals	12022 beds
Contract-managed:	4 hospitals	441 beds
Totals:	97 hospitals	12463 beds

0903: CATHOLIC HEALTH SERVICES (CC)
4790 North State Road 7, Lauderdale Lakes, FL Zip 33319-5860; tel. 954/484-1515; Joseph M. Catania, President and Chief Executive Officer

FLORIDA: ST. ANTHONY'S REHABILITATION HOSPITAL (S, 26 beds) 3485 NW 30th Street, Lauderdale Lakes, FL Zip 33311-1890; tel. 954/739-6233; Joseph M. Catania, Chief Executive Officer

ST. CATHERINE'S REHABILITATION HOSPITAL (S, 60 beds) 1050 NE 125th Street, North Miami, FL Zip 33161-5881; tel. 305/357-1735; Jaime Gonzalez, Administrator
Web address: www.catholichealthservices.org

Owned, leased, sponsored:	2 hospitals	86 beds
Contract-managed:	0 hospitals	0 beds
Totals:	2 hospitals	86 beds

0233: CATHOLIC HEALTH SERVICES OF LONG ISLAND (CC)
992 North Village Avenue, 1st Floor, Rockville Centre, NY Zip 11570-1002; tel. 516/705-3700; Alan D. Guerci, M.D., President and Chief Executive Officer
(Moderately Centralized Health System)

NEW YORK: GOOD SAMARITAN HOSPITAL MEDICAL CENTER (O, 506 beds) 1000 Montauk Highway, West Islip, NY Zip 11795-4927; tel. 631/376-

For explanation of codes following names, see page B2.
★ Indicates Type III membership in the American Hospital Association.

3000; Thomas Ockers, Executive Vice President and Chief Administrative Officer
Web address: www.good-samaritan-hospital.org

MERCY MEDICAL CENTER (O, 191 beds) 1000 North Village Avenue, Rockville Centre, NY Zip 11570–1000; tel. 516/705–2525; Ronald Steimel, Executive Vice President and Chief Administrative Officer

ST. CATHERINE OF SIENA MEDICAL CENTER (O, 503 beds) 50 Route 25-A, Smithtown, NY Zip 11787–1348; tel. 631/862–3000; Paul J. Rowland, Executive Vice President and Chief Administrative Officer
Web address: www.stcatherines.chsli.org/

ST. CHARLES HOSPITAL (O, 243 beds) 200 Belle Terre Road, Port Jefferson, NY Zip 11777–1928; tel. 631/474–6000; James O'Connor, Executive Vice President and Chief Administrative Officer
Web address: www.stcharleshospital.chsli.org

ST. FRANCIS HOSPITAL, THE HEART CENTER (O, 306 beds) 100 Port Washington Boulevard, Roslyn, NY Zip 11576–1353; tel. 516/562–6000; Ruth Hennessey, Executive Vice President and Chief Administrative Officer

ST. JOSEPH HOSPITAL (S, 128 beds) 4295 Hempstead Turnpike, Bethpage, NY Zip 11714–5769; tel. 516/579–6000; Peter Scaminaci, Executive Vice President and Chief Administrative Officer
Web address: www.stjosephhospital.chsli.org

Owned, leased, sponsored:	6 hospitals	1877 beds
Contract-managed:	0 hospitals	0 beds
Totals:	6 hospitals	1877 beds

★**0234: CATHOLIC HEALTH SYSTEM** (CC)
144 Genesee Street, Buffalo, NY Zip 14203–1560; tel. 716/862–2410; Joseph D. McDonald, FACHE, President and Chief Executive Officer
(Independent Hospital System)

NEW YORK: FATHER BAKER MANOR (O, 160 beds) 6400 Powers Road, Orchard Park, NY Zip 14127; tel. 716/667–0001; Christine Kluckhohn, President, Continuing Care

KENMORE MERCY HOSPITAL (O, 288 beds) 2950 Elmwood Avenue, Kenmore, NY Zip 14217–1390, 2950 Elmwood Avenue, Room 4024, 14217–1390, tel. 716/447–6100; James M. Millard, President and Chief Executive Officer
Web address: www.chsbuffalo.org

MCAULEY RESIDENCE (O, 160 beds) 1503 Military Road, Kenmore, NY Zip 14217; tel. 716/447–6600; Christine Kluckhohn, President, Continuing Care

MERCY HOSPITAL (O, 438 beds) 565 Abbott Road, Buffalo, NY Zip 14220–2095; tel. 716/826–7000; Charles J. Urlaub, President and Chief Executive Officer
Web address: www.chsbuffalo.org

MERCY NURSING FACILITY (O, 74 beds) 565 Abbott Road, Buffalo, NY Zip 14220; tel. 716/828–2301; Christine Kluckhohn, President, Continuing Care

MOUNT ST. MARY'S HOSPITAL AND HEALTH CENTER (O, 129 beds) 5300 Military Road, Lewiston, NY Zip 14092–1903; tel. 716/297–4800; Gary C. Tucker, President and Chief Executive Officer
Web address: www.msmh.org

NAZARETH HOME (O, 125 beds) 291 West North Street, Buffalo, NY Zip 14201; tel. 716/881–2323; Christine Kluckhohn, President, Continuing Care

SISTERS OF CHARITY HOSPITAL OF BUFFALO (O, 454 beds) 2157 Main Street, Buffalo, NY Zip 14214–2692; tel. 716/862–1000; Martin Boryszak, President and Chief Executive Officer
Web address: www.chsbuffalo.org

ST. CATHERINE LABOURE (O, 80 beds) 2157 Main Street, Buffalo, NY Zip 14214; tel. 716/862–1451; Christine Kluckhohn, President, Continuing Care

ST. ELIZABETH'S HOME (O, 117 beds) 5539 Broadway, Lancaster, NY Zip 14086; tel. 716/683–5150; Christine Kluckhohn, President, Continuing Care

ST. FRANCIS OF BUFFALO (O, 120 beds) 34 Benwood Avenue, Buffalo, NY Zip 14214; tel. 716/862–2500; Christine Kluckhohn, President, Continuing Care

ST. FRANCIS OF WILLIAMSVILLE (O, 142 beds) 147 Reist Street, Williamsville, NY Zip 14221; tel. 716/633–5400; Christine Kluckhohn, President, Continuing Care

ST. JOSEPH MANOR (O, 22 beds) 2211 West State Street, Olean, NY Zip 14760; tel. 716/372–7810; Christine Kluckhohn, President, Continuing Care

Owned, leased, sponsored:	13 hospitals	2309 beds
Contract-managed:	0 hospitals	0 beds
Totals:	13 hospitals	2309 beds

★**0991: CAYUGA HEALTH SYSTEM** (NP)
101 Dates Drive, Ithaca, NY Zip 14850–1342; tel. 607/274–4011; John B. Rudd, President and Chief Executive Officer
(Independent Hospital System)

NEW YORK: CAYUGA MEDICAL CENTER AT ITHACA (O, 193 beds) 101 Dates Drive, Ithaca, NY Zip 14850–1342; tel. 607/274–4011; John B. Rudd, President and Chief Executive Officer
Web address: www.cayugamed.org

SCHUYLER HOSPITAL (O, 145 beds) 220 Steuben Street, Montour Falls, NY Zip 14865–9709; tel. 607/535–7121; James B. Watson, President

Owned, leased, sponsored:	2 hospitals	338 beds
Contract-managed:	0 hospitals	0 beds
Totals:	2 hospitals	338 beds

★**0984: CEDARS-SINAI** (NP)
8700 Beverly Boulevard, West Hollywood, CA Zip 90048–1865, Box 48750, Los Angeles, 90048–0750, tel. 310/423–5000; Thomas M. Priselac, President and Chief Executive Officer
(Independent Hospital System)

CALIFORNIA: CEDARS-SINAI MEDICAL CENTER (O, 885 beds) 8700 Beverly Boulevard, Los Angeles, CA Zip 90048–1865, Box 48750, 90048–0750, tel. 310/423–5000; Thomas M. Priselac, President and Chief Executive Officer
Web address: www.cedars-sinai.edu

MARINA DEL REY HOSPITAL (O, 145 beds) 4650 Lincoln Boulevard, Marina Del Rey, CA Zip 90292–6306; tel. 310/823–8911; Paulette Heitmeyer, Administrator and Chief Operating Officer

Owned, leased, sponsored:	2 hospitals	1030 beds
Contract-managed:	0 hospitals	0 beds
Totals:	2 hospitals	1030 beds

★**0298: CENTEGRA HEALTH SYSTEM** (NP)
385 Millennium Drive, Crystal Lake, IL Zip 60012–3761; tel. 815/788–5800; Michael S. Eesley, Chief Executive Officer
(Independent Hospital System)

ILLINOIS: CENTEGRA HOSPITAL - MCHENRY (O, 166 beds) 4201 Medical Center Drive, McHenry, IL Zip 60050–8409; tel. 815/344–5000; Michael S. Eesley, Chief Executive Officer
Web address: www.centegra.com

CENTEGRA HOSPITAL - WOODSTOCK (O, 104 beds) 3701 Doty Road, Woodstock, IL Zip 60098–7509, P O Box 1990, 60098–1990, tel. 815/338–2500; Michael S. Eesley, Chief Executive Officer

Owned, leased, sponsored:	2 hospitals	270 beds
Contract-managed:	0 hospitals	0 beds
Totals:	2 hospitals	270 beds

★**2265: CENTRA HEALTH, INC.** (NP)
1920 Atherholt Road, Lynchburg, VA Zip 24501–1104; tel. 434/200–3000; E W. Tibbs, President and Chief Executive Officer
(Moderately Centralized Health System)

VIRGINIA: CENTRA LYNCHBURG GENERAL HOSPITAL (O, 1054 beds) 1920 Atherholt Road, Lynchburg, VA Zip 24501–1104; tel. 434/200–4700; E W. Tibbs, President and Chief Executive Officer
Web address: www.centrahealth.com

For explanation of codes following names, see page B2.
★ Indicates Type III membership in the American Hospital Association.

Section B

CENTRA SOUTHSIDE COMMUNITY HOSPITAL (O, 86 beds) 800 Oak Street, Farmville, VA Zip 23901–1199; tel. 434/392–8811; Thomas Angelo, Chief Executive Officer
Web address: www.sch.centrahealth.com/

Owned, leased, sponsored:	2 hospitals	1140 beds
Contract-managed:	0 hospitals	0 beds
Totals:	2 hospitals	1140 beds

★0184: CENTRACARE HEALTH (NP)
1406 Sixth Avenue North, Saint Cloud, MN Zip 56303–1900; tel. 320/251–2700; Kenneth D. Holmen, M.D., President and Chief Executive Officer
(Moderately Centralized Health System)

MINNESOTA: CENTRACARE HEALTH-LONG PRAIRIE (O, 20 beds) 20 Ninth Street SE, Long Prairie, MN Zip 56347–1404; tel. 320/732–2141; Daniel J. Swenson, FACHE, Administrator

CENTRACARE HEALTH-MELROSE (O, 93 beds) 525 Main Street West, Melrose, MN Zip 56352–1043; tel. 320/256–4231; Gerry Gilbertson, FACHE, Administrator
Web address: www.centracare.com

CENTRACARE HEALTH-MONTICELLO (O, 126 beds) 1013 Hart Boulevard, Monticello, MN Zip 55362–8230; tel. 763/295–2945; Mary Ellen Wells, FACHE, Administrator
Web address: www.centracare.com

CENTRACARE HEALTH-PAYNESVILLE (O, 82 beds) 200 West 1st Street, Paynesville, MN Zip 56362–1496; tel. 320/243–3767; Jason Carlson, Administrator

CENTRACARE HEALTH-SAUK CENTRE (O, 85 beds) 425 North Elm Street, Sauk Centre, MN Zip 56378–1010; tel. 320/352–2221; Delano Christianson, Administrator
Web address: www.centracare.com/hospitals/sauk_centre/index.html

ST. CLOUD HOSPITAL (O, 487 beds) 1406 Sixth Avenue North, Saint Cloud, MN Zip 56303–1901; tel. 320/251–2700; Craig J. Broman, FACHE, President
Web address: www.centracare.com

Owned, leased, sponsored:	6 hospitals	893 beds
Contract-managed:	0 hospitals	0 beds
Totals:	6 hospitals	893 beds

0856: CENTRAL FLORIDA HEALTH (NP)
600 East Dixie Avenue, Leesburg, FL Zip 34748–5925; tel. 352/323–5762; Donald G. Henderson, FACHE, Chief Executive Officer

FLORIDA: LEESBURG REGIONAL MEDICAL CENTER (O, 330 beds) 600 East Dixie Avenue, Leesburg, FL Zip 34748–5999; tel. 352/323–5762; Donald G. Henderson, FACHE, President and Chief Executive Officer

THE VILLAGES REGIONAL HOSPITAL (O, 277 beds) 1451 El Camino Real, The Villages, FL Zip 32159–0041; tel. 352/751–8000; Donald G. Henderson, FACHE, President and Chief Executive Officer
Web address: www.cfhalliance.org

Owned, leased, sponsored:	2 hospitals	607 beds
Contract-managed:	0 hospitals	0 beds
Totals:	2 hospitals	607 beds

1007: CENTRAL MAINE HEALTHCARE (NP)
300 Main Street, Lewiston, ME Zip 04240–7027; tel. 207/795–0111; Jeffrey L. Brickman, FACHE, Chief Executive Officer
(Independent Hospital System)

MAINE: BRIDGTON HOSPITAL (O, 22 beds) 10 Hospital Drive, Bridgton, ME Zip 04009–1148; tel. 207/647–6000; R David. Frum, President
Web address: www.bridgtonhospital.org

CENTRAL MAINE MEDICAL CENTER (O, 190 beds) 300 Main Street, Lewiston, ME Zip 04240–7027; tel. 207/795–0111; Jeffrey L. Brickman, FACHE, Interim Chief Executive Officer
Web address: www.cmmc.org

RUMFORD HOSPITAL (O, 25 beds) 420 Franklin Street, Rumford, ME Zip 04276–2145; tel. 207/369–1000; R David. Frum, President

Owned, leased, sponsored:	3 hospitals	237 beds
Contract-managed:	0 hospitals	0 beds
Totals:	3 hospitals	237 beds

0407: CHILDREN'S HOSPITAL AND HEALTH SYSTEM (NP)
9000 West Wisconsin Avenue, Milwaukee, WI Zip 53226–4810, P O Box 1997, 53201–1997, tel. 414/226–2000; Peggy N. Troy, President and Chief Executive Officer
(Independent Hospital System)

WISCONSIN: CHILDREN'S HOSPITAL OF WISCONSIN-FOX VALLEY (O, 12 beds) 130 Second Street, Neenah, WI Zip 54956–2883; tel. 920/969–7900; Peggy N. Troy, President and Chief Executive Officer
Web address: www.chw.org

CHILDREN'S HOSPITAL OF WISCONSIN (O, 176 beds) 9000 West Wisconsin Avenue, Milwaukee, WI Zip 53226–4810, P O Box 1997, 53201–1997, tel. 414/266–2000; Peggy N. Troy, President and Chief Executive Officer

Owned, leased, sponsored:	2 hospitals	188 beds
Contract-managed:	0 hospitals	0 beds
Totals:	2 hospitals	188 beds

★0131: CHRISTIANA CARE HEALTH SYSTEM (NP)
501 West 14th Street, Wilmington, DE Zip 19801–1013, P O Box 1668, 19899–1668, tel. 302/733–1000; Janice E. Nevin, M.D., M.P.H., Chief Executive Officer
(Independent Hospital System)

DELAWARE: CHRISTIANA CARE HEALTH SYSTEM (O, 1065 beds) 4755 Ogletown-Stanton Road, Newark, DE Zip 19718–0002, P O Box 6001, 19718, tel. 302/733–1000; Janice E. Nevin, M.D., M.P.H., Chief Executive Officer
Web address: www.christianacare.org

Owned, leased, sponsored:	1 hospitals	1065 beds
Contract-managed:	0 hospitals	0 beds
Totals:	1 hospitals	1065 beds

★0192: CHRISTUS HEALTH (CC)
919 Hidden Ridge Drive, Irving, TX Zip 75038; tel. 469/282–2000; Ernie W. Sadau, Chief Executive Officer
(Moderately Centralized Health System)

ARKANSAS: CHRISTUS DUBUIS HOSPITAL OF FORT SMITH (C, 25 beds) 7301 Rogers Avenue, 4th Floor, Fort Smith, AR Zip 72903–4100; tel. 479/314–4900; Keith Rogers, Administrator

CHRISTUS DUBUIS HOSPITAL OF HOT SPRINGS (O, 26 beds) 300 Werner Street, 3rd Floor East, Hot Springs National Park, AR Zip 71913–6406; tel. 501/609–4300; Keith Rogers, Administrator
Web address: www.christusdubuis.org/hotsprings

GEORGIA: SOUTHERN CRESCENT HOSPITAL FOR SPECIALTY CARE (C, 30 beds) 11 Upper Riverdale Road SW, 6th Floor, Riverdale, GA Zip 30274–2615; tel. 770/897–7600; Fiona Adams, Interim Administrator

IOWA: CONTINUING CARE HOSPITAL AT ST. LUKE'S (C, 16 beds) 1026 'A' Avenue NE, 6th Floor, Cedar Rapids, IA Zip 52402–5036; tel. 319/369–8142; Elly Steffen, Administrator
Web address: www.christusdubuis.org/ContinuingCareHospitalatStLukes

LOUISIANA: CHRISTUS COUSHATTA HEALTH CARE CENTER (O, 25 beds) 1635 Marvel Street, Coushatta, LA Zip 71019–9022, P O Box 589, 71019–0589, tel. 318/932–2000; Brandon Hillman, Interim Administrator, Director of Hospital Services
Web address: www.christuscoushatta.org

CHRISTUS DUBUIS HOSPITAL OF ALEXANDRIA (O, 25 beds) 3330 Masonic Drive, 4th Floor, Alexandria, LA Zip 71301–3841; tel. 318/448–4938; Beth Parsons, R.N., Administrator

For explanation of codes following names, see page B2.
★ Indicates Type III membership in the American Hospital Association.

CHRISTUS HEALTH SHREVEPORT-BOSSIER (O, 185 beds) 1453 East Bert Kouns Industrial Loop, Shreveport, LA Zip 71105–6800; tel. 318/681–5000; Isaac Palmer, Chief Executive Officer
Web address: www.christushealthsb.org

CHRISTUS LAKE AREA HOSPITAL (O, 88 beds) 4200 Nelson Road, Lake Charles, LA Zip 70605–4118; tel. 337/474–6370; Bryan S. Bateman, Chief Executive Officer

CHRISTUS ST. FRANCES CABRINI HOSPITAL (O, 281 beds) 3330 Masonic Drive, Alexandria, LA Zip 71301–3899; tel. 318/487–1122; Nancy R. Hellyer, R.N., FACHE, Chief Executive Officer
Web address: www.cabrini.org/

CHRISTUS ST. PATRICK HOSPITAL OF LAKE CHARLES (O, 160 beds) 524 Dr Michael Debakey Drive, Lake Charles, LA Zip 70601–5799, P.O. Box 3401, 70602–3401, tel. 337/436–2511; Donald H. Lloyd II, Chief Executive Officer

NATCHITOCHES REGIONAL MEDICAL CENTER (C, 91 beds) 501 Keyser Avenue, Natchitoches, LA Zip 71457–6036, P O Box 2009, 71457–2009, tel. 318/214–4200; D. Kirk. Soileau, FACHE, Chief Executive Officer
Web address: www.nrmchospital.org

SAVOY MEDICAL CENTER (C, 180 beds) 801 Poinciana Avenue, Mamou, LA Zip 70554–2298; tel. 337/468–5261; Eugene H. Burge, Chief Executive Officer
Web address: www.savoymedical.com/

NEW MEXICO: CHRISTUS ST. VINCENT REGIONAL MEDICAL CENTER (O, 219 beds) 455 St. Michael's Drive, Santa Fe, NM Zip 87505–7663, P O Box 2107, 87505, tel. 505/983–3361; Patrick Brian. Carrier, President and Chief Executive Officer

TEXAS: CHRISTUS DUBUIS HOSPITAL OF BEAUMONT (O, 51 beds) 2830 Calder Avenue, 4th Floor, Beaumont, TX Zip 77702–1809; tel. 409/899–7680; Tuan Le, Chief Executive Officer
Web address: www.christusdubuis.org/BeaumontandPortArthurSystem-CHRISTUSDubuisHospitalofBeaumont

CHRISTUS DUBUIS HOSPITAL OF PARIS (C, 25 beds) 820 Clarksville Street, 6th Floor, Paris, TX Zip 75460–6027; tel. 903/737–3600; Kathie Reese, R.N., Regional Administrator and Chief Executive Officer
Web address: www.christusdubuis.org

CHRISTUS GOOD SHEPHERD MEDICAL CENTER-MARSHALL (O, 140 beds) 811 South Washington Avenue, Marshall, TX Zip 75670–5336, P O Box 1599, 75671–1599, tel. 903/927–6000; Russell J. Collier, FACHE, President and Chief Executive Officer

CHRISTUS GOOD SHEPHERD MEDICAL CENTER (O, 393 beds) 700 East Marshall Avenue, Longview, TX Zip 75601–5580; tel. 903/315–1800; Todd Hancock, President and Chief Executive Officer
Web address: www.gsmc.org

CHRISTUS MOTHER FRANCES HOSPITAL - JACKSONVILLE (O, 21 beds) 2026 South Jackson, Jacksonville, TX Zip 75766–5822; tel. 903/541–4500; Anne Pileggi, Administrator and Associate Vice President

CHRISTUS MOTHER FRANCES HOSPITAL - SULPHUR SPRINGS (O, 50 beds) 115 Airport Road, Sulphur Springs, TX Zip 75482–2105; tel. 903/885–7671; Paul Harvery, President and Chief Executive Officer
Web address: www.tmfhc.org/maps-and-locations/locations-profile/?id=72&searchId=8bcb329f-a152-e611-b37f-2c768a4e1b84&sort=11&page=1&pageSize=10

CHRISTUS MOTHER FRANCES HOSPITAL - TYLER (O, 458 beds) 800 East Dawson Street, Tyler, TX Zip 75701–2036; tel. 903/593–8441; Jason J. Proctor, Chief Operating Officer

CHRISTUS MOTHER FRANCES HOSPITAL - WINNSBORO (O, 25 beds) 719 West Coke Road, Winnsboro, TX Zip 75494–3011; tel. 903/342–5227; Shelly Johnson, Chief Executive Officer
Web address: www.tmfhs.org

CHRISTUS SANTA ROSA HEALTH SYSTEM (O, 766 beds) 333 North Santa Rosa Street, San Antonio, TX Zip 78207–3108, 100 NE Loop 410 Suite 800, 78216–4749, tel. 210/704–2000; Dean Alexander, President and Chief Executive Officer
Web address: www.christussantarosa.org

CHRISTUS SOUTHEAST TEXAS HOSPITAL (O, 424 beds) 2830 Calder Avenue, Beaumont, TX Zip 77702–1809, P O Box 5405, 77726–5405, tel. 409/892–7171; Paul Trevino, Chief Executive Officer

CHRISTUS SOUTHEAST TEXAS JASPER MEMORIAL (O, 40 beds) 1275 Marvin Hancock Drive, Jasper, TX Zip 75951–4995; tel. 409/384–5461; Lance Beus, Administrator
Web address: www.christusjasper.org

CHRISTUS SPOHN HOSPITAL ALICE (O, 73 beds) 2500 East Main Street, Alice, TX Zip 78332–4169; tel. 361/661–8000; David LeMonte, Interim President
Web address: www.christusspohn.org/locations_alice.htm

CHRISTUS SPOHN HOSPITAL BEEVILLE (O, 49 beds) 1500 East Houston Street, Beeville, TX Zip 78102–5312; tel. 361/354–2000; Genifer Rucker, President

CHRISTUS SPOHN HOSPITAL CORPUS CHRISTI MEMORIAL (O, 579 beds) 2606 Hospital Boulevard, Corpus Christi, TX Zip 78405–1804, P O Box 5280, 78405, tel. 361/902–4000; Brian Connor, FACHE, President
Web address: www.christusspohn.org

CHRISTUS SPOHN HOSPITAL KLEBERG (O, 50 beds) 1311 General Cavazos Boulevard, Kingsville, TX Zip 78363–7130; tel. 361/595–1661; David LeMonte, Vice President and Chief Operating Officer
Web address: www.christusspohn.org

CHRISTUS ST. MICHAEL HEALTH SYSTEM (O, 354 beds) 2600 St Michael Drive, Texarkana, TX Zip 75503–5220; tel. 903/614–1000; Chris Karam, FACHE, President and Chief Executive Officer

CHRISTUS ST. MICHAEL REHABILITATION HOSPITAL (O, 50 beds) 2400 St Michael Drive, Texarkana, TX Zip 75503–2374; tel. 903/614–4000; Patrick Flannery, Administrator
Web address: www.christusstmichael.org/rehab

KATE DISHMAN REHABILITATION HOSPITAL (O, 27 beds) 2830 Calder Street, 6th Floor, Beaumont, TX Zip 77702–1809; tel. 409/899–8380; David Pipkins, Chief Executive Officer and Administrator

Owned, leased, sponsored:	25 hospitals	4559 beds
Contract-managed:	6 hospitals	367 beds
Totals:	31 hospitals	4926 beds

★**0101: CITRUS VALLEY HEALTH PARTNERS** (NP)
210 West San Bernardino Road, Covina, CA Zip 91723–1515; tel. 626/331–7331; Robert H. Curry, President and Chief Executive Officer

CALIFORNIA: CITRUS VALLEY MEDICAL CENTER-INTER COMMUNITY CAMPUS (O, 332 beds) 210 West San Bernadino Road, Covina, CA Zip 91723–1515, P O Box 6108, 91722–5108, tel. 626/331–7331; Robert H. Curry, President and Chief Executive Officer
Web address: www.cvhp.org

FOOTHILL PRESBYTERIAN HOSPITAL (O, 72 beds) 250 South Grand Avenue, Glendora, CA Zip 91741–4218; tel. 626/963–8411; Robert H. Curry, President and Chief Executive Officer

Owned, leased, sponsored:	2 hospitals	404 beds
Contract-managed:	0 hospitals	0 beds
Totals:	2 hospitals	404 beds

★**0212: CLEVELAND CLINIC HEALTH SYSTEM** (NP)
9500 Euclid, Cleveland, OH Zip 44195–5108; tel. 216/444–2200; Delos Cosgrove, M.D., President and Chief Executive Officer
(Centralized Health System)

FLORIDA: CLEVELAND CLINIC FLORIDA (O, 155 beds) 2950 Cleveland Clinic Boulevard, Weston, FL Zip 33331–3602; tel. 954/659–5000; Wael Barsoum, M.D., President
Web address: www.clevelandclinic.org/florida

OHIO: CLEVELAND CLINIC AKRON GENERAL (O, 439 beds) 1 Akron General Avenue, Akron, OH Zip 44307–2433; tel. 330/344–6000; Alan Papa, President

CLEVELAND CLINIC AVON HOSPITAL (O, 126 beds) 33300 Cleveland Clinic Boulevard, Avon, OH 44011; tel. 440/695–5000; Rebecca Starck, M.D., President
Web address: www.my.clevelandclinic.org

CLEVELAND CLINIC CHILDREN'S HOSPITAL FOR REHABILITATION (O, 25 beds) 2801 Martin Luther King Jr Drive, Cleveland, OH Zip 44104–3865; tel. 216/448–6400; Michael J. McHugh, M.D., Medical Director
Web address: www.my.clevelandclinic.org/childrens-hospital/default.aspx

For explanation of codes following names, see page B2.
★ Indicates Type III membership in the American Hospital Association.

Section B

CLEVELAND CLINIC FAIRVIEW HOSPITAL (O, 451 beds) 18101 Lorain Avenue, Cleveland, OH Zip 44111–5656; tel. 216/476–7000; Neil Smith, D.O., President

CLEVELAND CLINIC, MEDINA HOSPITAL (O, 136 beds) 1000 East Washington Street, Medina, OH Zip 44256–2170; tel. 330/725–1000; Richard K. Shewbridge, M.D., President
Web address: www.medinahospital.org

CLEVELAND CLINIC (O, 1280 beds) 9500 Euclid Avenue, Cleveland, OH Zip 44195–5108; tel. 216/444–2200; Delos Cosgrove, M.D., President and Chief Executive Officer

EDWIN SHAW REHAB (O, 35 beds) 330 Broadway Street East, Cuyahoga Falls, OH Zip 44221–3312; tel. 330/436–0910; Geoffrey Hall, Chief Executive Officer
Web address: www.edwinshaw.com

EUCLID HOSPITAL (O, 221 beds) 18901 Lake Shore Boulevard, Euclid, OH Zip 44119–1090; tel. 216/531–9000; Daniel Napierkowski, M.D., President

HILLCREST HOSPITAL (O, 453 beds) 6780 Mayfield Road, Cleveland, OH Zip 44124–2203; tel. 440/312–4500; Donald Ford, M.D., Interim President
Web address: www.hillcresthospital.org

LODI COMMUNITY HOSPITAL (O, 20 beds) 225 Elyria Street, Lodi, OH Zip 44254–1096; tel. 330/948–1222; Dana Kocsis, Vice President, Nursing and Operations
Web address: www.lodihospital.org

LUTHERAN HOSPITAL (O, 194 beds) 1730 West 25th Street, Cleveland, OH Zip 44113–3170; tel. 216/696–4300; Donald A. Malone Jr, President

MARYMOUNT HOSPITAL (O, 226 beds) 12300 McCracken Road, Garfield Heights, OH Zip 44125–2975; tel. 216/581–0500; Richard Parker, M.D., President
Web address: www.marymount.org

SOUTH POINTE HOSPITAL (O, 173 beds) 20000 Harvard Road, Warrensville Heights, OH Zip 44122–6805; tel. 216/491–6000; Robert S. Juhasz, D.O., President

Owned, leased, sponsored:	14 hospitals	3934 beds
Contract-managed:	0 hospitals	0 beds
Totals:	14 hospitals	3934 beds

0076: COLLEGE HEALTH ENTERPRISES (IO)
11627 Telegraph Road, Suite 200, Santa Fe Springs, CA Zip 90670–6814; tel. 562/923–9449; Barry J. Weiss, Chairman of the Board

CALIFORNIA: COLLEGE HOSPITAL CERRITOS (O, 157 beds) 10802 College Place, Cerritos, CA Zip 90703–1579; tel. 562/924–9581; Stephen Witt, President and Chief Executive Officer
Web address: www.collegehospitals.com

COLLEGE HOSPITAL COSTA MESA (O, 122 beds) 301 Victoria Street, Costa Mesa, CA Zip 92627–7131; tel. 949/642–2734; Susan L. Taylor, JD, Chief Executive Officer

Owned, leased, sponsored:	2 hospitals	279 beds
Contract-managed:	0 hospitals	0 beds
Totals:	2 hospitals	279 beds

0161: COLUMBUS REGIONAL HEALTHCARE SYSTEM (NP)
707 Center Street, Suite 400, Columbus, GA Zip 31901–1575; tel. 706/660–6100; Scott Hill, Chief Executive Officer
(Independent Hospital System)

GEORGIA: AZALEA TRACE (O, 110 beds) 910 Talbotton Road, Columbus, GA Zip 31901; tel. 706/323–9513; Todd West, Administrator

HAMILTON HOUSE NURSING CENTER/ADULT LIVING CENTER (O, 128 beds) 1911 Hamilton Road, Columbus, GA Zip 31901; tel. 706/571–1850; John Sims, Administrator

MARION MEMORIAL NURSING HOME (O, 70 beds) Highway 41, Buena Vista, GA Zip 31803, P O Box 197, 31803, tel. 229/649–7100; Barbara Mitchell, Administrator

MIDTOWN MEDICAL CENTER WEST (O, 171 beds) 616 19th Street, Columbus, GA Zip 31901–1528, P O Box 2188, 31902–2188, tel. 706/494–4262; Ryan Chandler, Chief Executive Officer
Web address: www.columbusregional.com

MIDTOWN MEDICAL CENTER (O, 497 beds) 710 Center Street, Columbus, GA Zip 31901–1527, P O Box 951, 31902–0951, tel. 706/571–1000; Ryan Chandler, President and Chief Executive Officer

NORTHSIDE MEDICAL CENTER (O, 100 beds) 100 Frist Court, Columbus, GA Zip 31909–3578, P O Box 7188, 31908–7188, tel. 706/494–2100; Ryan Chandler, Interim Chief Executive Officer
Web address: www.columbusregional.com

Owned, leased, sponsored:	6 hospitals	1076 beds
Contract-managed:	0 hospitals	0 beds
Totals:	6 hospitals	1076 beds

0520: COMMONWEALTH HEALTH CORPORATION (NP)
800 Park Street, Bowling Green, KY Zip 42101–2356; tel. 270/745–1500; Connie Smith, President and Chief Executive Officer
(Independent Hospital System)

KENTUCKY: COMMONWEALTH REGIONAL SPECIALTY HOSPITAL (O, 28 beds) 250 Park Drive, 6th Floor, Bowling Green, KY Zip 42101–1760, P O Box 90010, 42102–9010, tel. 270/796–6200; Christa Atkins, Administrator

MEDICAL CENTER AT BOWLING GREEN (O, 337 beds) 250 Park Street, Bowling Green, KY Zip 42101–1795, P O Box 90010, 42102–9010, tel. 270/745–1000; Connie Smith, Chief Executive Officer
Web address: www.themedicalcenter.org

MEDICAL CENTER AT FRANKLIN (O, 25 beds) 1100 Brookhaven Road, Franklin, KY Zip 42134–2746; tel. 270/598–4800; Annette Runyon, Vice President and Administrator
Web address: www.themedicalcenterfranklin.org

MEDICAL CENTER AT SCOTTSVILLE (O, 135 beds) 456 Burnley Road, Scottsville, KY Zip 42164–6355; tel. 270/622–2800; Eric Hagan, R.N., Executive Vice President and Administrator

THE MEDICAL CENTER ALBANY (C, 42 beds) 723 Burkesville Road, Albany, KY Zip 42602–1654; tel. 606/387–8000; Laura Belcher, Administrator
Web address: www.chc.net/services/hospitals/the_medical_center_at_albany.aspx

THE MEDICAL CENTER AT CAVERNA (O, 25 beds) 1501 South Dixie Street, Horse Cave, KY Zip 42749–1477; tel. 270/786–2191; Alan B. Alexander, FACHE, Vice President and Administrator

Owned, leased, sponsored:	5 hospitals	550 beds
Contract-managed:	1 hospitals	42 beds
Totals:	6 hospitals	592 beds

★0401: COMMUNITY HEALTH NETWORK (NP)
7330 Shadeland Station, Indianapolis, IN Zip 46256–3957; tel. 317/355–1411; Bryan A. Mills, President and Chief Executive Officer
(Independent Hospital System)

INDIANA: COMMUNITY HOSPITAL EAST (O, 335 beds) 1500 North Ritter Avenue, Indianapolis, IN Zip 46219–3095; tel. 317/355–1411; Scott L. Teffeteller, President
Web address: www.ecommunity.com/east/

COMMUNITY HOSPITAL NORTH (O, 336 beds) 7150 Clearvista Drive, Indianapolis, IN Zip 46256–1695, 7250 Clearvista Drive, Suite 200, 46256–1695, tel. 317/355–2469; Kathleen R. Krusie, FACHE, President

COMMUNITY HOSPITAL SOUTH (O, 158 beds) 1402 East County Line Road South, Indianapolis, IN Zip 46227–0963; tel. 317/887–7000; David Kiley, M.D., Interim President
Web address: www.ecommunity.com

COMMUNITY HOSPITAL OF ANDERSON & MADISON COUNTY (O, 140 beds) 1515 North Madison Avenue, Anderson, IN Zip 46011–3453; tel. 765/298–4242; Beth S. Tharp, R.N., President and Chief Executive Officer

For explanation of codes following names, see page B2.
★ Indicates Type III membership in the American Hospital Association.

Section B

COMMUNITY HOWARD REGIONAL HEALTH (O, 159 beds) 3500 South Lafountain Street, Kokomo, IN Zip 46902–3803, P O Box 9011, 46904–9011, tel. 765/453–0702; Joseph Hooper, President and Chief Executive Officer

Web address: www.howardregional.org

COMMUNITY HOWARD SPECIALTY HOSPITAL (O, 30 beds) 829 North Dixon Road, Kokomo, IN Zip 46901–7709; tel. 765/452–6700; Clayton L. Clement, Interim Administrator

Owned, leased, sponsored:	6 hospitals	1158 beds
Contract-managed:	0 hospitals	0 beds
Totals:	6 hospitals	1158 beds

★0080: COMMUNITY HEALTH SYSTEMS, INC. (IO)

4000 Meridian Boulevard, Franklin, TN Zip 37067–6325, P O Box 689020, 37068–9020, tel. 615/465–7000; Wayne T. Smith, Chairman, President and Chief Executive Officer
(Decentralized Health System)

ALABAMA: CRESTWOOD MEDICAL CENTER (O, 177 beds) One Hospital Drive, Huntsville, AL Zip 35801–3403; tel. 256/429–4000; Pamela Hudson, M.D., Chief Executive Officer

Web address: www.crestwoodmedcenter.com

FLOWERS HOSPITAL (O, 141 beds) 4370 West Main Street, Dothan, AL Zip 36305–4000, P O Box 6907, 36302–6907, tel. 334/793–5000; Heath Phillips, Chief Executive Officer

Web address: www.flowershospital.com

GADSDEN REGIONAL MEDICAL CENTER (O, 274 beds) 1007 Goodyear Avenue, Gadsden, AL Zip 35903–1195; tel. 256/494–4000; Corey Ewing, Chief Executive Officer

Web address: www.gadsdenregional.com

GRANDVIEW MEDICAL CENTER (O, 379 beds) 3690 Grandview Parkway, Birmingham, AL Zip 35243–3326; tel. 205/971–1000; Drew Mason, Chief Executive Officer

MEDICAL CENTER ENTERPRISE (O, 70 beds) 400 North Edwards Street, Enterprise, AL Zip 36330–2510; tel. 334/347–0584; Suzanne Woods, Chief Executive Officer

Web address: www.mcehospital.com

SOUTH BALDWIN REGIONAL MEDICAL CENTER (L, 112 beds) 1613 North McKenzie Street, Foley, AL Zip 36535–2299; tel. 251/949–3400; Keith Newton, Chief Executive Officer

Web address: www.southbaldwinrmc.com

ALASKA: MAT-SU REGIONAL MEDICAL CENTER (O, 74 beds) 2500 South Woodworth Loop, Palmer, AK Zip 99645–8984, P O Box 1687, 99645–1687, tel. 907/861–6000; David Wallace, Chief Executive Officer

ARIZONA: NORTHWEST MEDICAL CENTER (O, 270 beds) 6200 North La Cholla Boulevard, Tucson, AZ Zip 85741–3599; tel. 520/742–9000; Kevin Stockton, Chief Executive Officer

Web address: www.northwestmedicalcenter.com

ORO VALLEY HOSPITAL (O, 144 beds) 1551 East Tangerine Road, Oro Valley, AZ Zip 85755–6213; tel. 520/901–3500; Jae Dale, Chief Executive Officer

WESTERN ARIZONA REGIONAL MEDICAL CENTER (O, 139 beds) 2735 Silver Creek Road, Bullhead City, AZ Zip 86442–8303; tel. 928/763–2273; Thomas A. Salerno, Chief Executive Officer

Web address: www.warmc.com

ARKANSAS: MEDICAL CENTER OF SOUTH ARKANSAS (L, 121 beds) 700 West Grove Street, El Dorado, AR Zip 71730–4416; tel. 870/863–2000; Robert Rupp, Chief Executive Officer

NORTHWEST MEDICAL CENTER - SPRINGDALE (O, 295 beds) 609 West Maple Avenue, Springdale, AR Zip 72764–5394, P O Box 47, 72765–0047, tel. 479/751–5711; Sharif Omar, Chief Executive Officer

Web address: www.northwesthealth.com

PHYSICIANS' SPECIALTY HOSPITAL (O, 20 beds) 3873 North Parkview Drive, Fayetteville, AR Zip 72703–6286; tel. 479/571–7070; Sharif Omar, Chief Executive Officer

Web address: www.pshfay.com

SILOAM SPRINGS REGIONAL HOSPITAL (O, 44 beds) 603 North Progress Avenue, Siloam Springs, AR Zip 72761–4352; tel. 479/215–3000; Patrick Kerrwood, Chief Executive Officer

Web address: www.ssrh.net

SPARKS MEDICAL CENTER - VAN BUREN (L, 30 beds) East Main and South 20th Streets, Van Buren, AR Zip 72956–5715, P O Box 409, 72957–0409, tel. 479/474–3401; Daniel E. McKay, Chief Executive Officer

Web address: www.sparkshealth.com/locations/sparks-medical-center-+49van-buren

SPARKS REGIONAL MEDICAL CENTER (O, 303 beds) 100 Towson Avenue, Fort Smith, AR Zip 72901–2632, P O Box 2406, 72917–7006, tel. 479/441–4000; Daniel E. McKay, Chief Executive Officer

FLORIDA: BAYFRONT HEALTH BROOKSVILLE (L, 120 beds) 17240 Cortez Boulevard, Brooksville, FL Zip 34601–8921, P O Box 37, 34605–0037, tel. 352/796–5111; Kenneth R. Wicker, Chief Executive Officer

Web address: www.brooksvilleregionalhospital.org

BAYFRONT HEALTH DADE CITY (O, 120 beds) 13100 Fort King Road, Dade City, FL Zip 33525–5294; tel. 352/521–1100; Linda Stockton, Interim Chief Executive Officer

BAYFRONT HEALTH PORT CHARLOTTE (O, 254 beds) 2500 Harbor Boulevard, Port Charlotte, FL Zip 33952–5000; tel. 941/766–4122; Timothy J. Cerullo, Chief Executive Officer

Web address: www.bayfrontcharlotte.com

BAYFRONT HEALTH PUNTA GORDA (O, 190 beds) 809 East Marion Avenue, Punta Gorda, FL Zip 33950–3819, P O Box 51–1328, 33951–1328, tel. 941/639–3131; Andrew Emery, Chief Executive Officer

BAYFRONT HEALTH ST. PETERSBURG (O, 382 beds) 701 Sixth Street South, Saint Petersburg, FL Zip 33701–4891; tel. 727/823–1234; John R. McLain, President and Chief Executive Officer

Web address: www.bayfrontstpete.com

HEART OF FLORIDA REGIONAL MEDICAL CENTER (O, 193 beds) 40100 Highway 27, Davenport, FL Zip 33837–5906; tel. 863/422–4971; Ann Barnhart, Chief Executive Officer

HIGHLANDS REGIONAL MEDICAL CENTER (L, 80 beds) 3600 South Highlands Avenue, Sebring, FL Zip 33870–5495, Drawer 2066, 33871–2066, tel. 863/385–6101; John D. Montois, Interim Chief Executive Officer

Web address: www.highlandsregional.com

LAKE WALES MEDICAL CENTER (O, 131 beds) 410 South 11th Street, Lake Wales, FL Zip 33853–4256; tel. 863/676–1433; Rebecca Brewer, FACHE, Chief Executive Officer

LOWER KEYS MEDICAL CENTER (L, 90 beds) 5900 College Road, Key West, FL Zip 33040–4396, P O Box 9107, 33041–9107, tel. 305/294–5531; David Clay, Chief Executive Officer

Web address: www.lkmc.com

MUNROE REGIONAL MEDICAL CENTER (O, 300 beds) 1500 SW 1st Avenue, Ocala, FL Zip 34471–6504, P O Box 6000, 34478–6000, tel. 352/351–7200; Philoron A. Wright II, FACHE, Interim Chief Executive Officer

NORTH OKALOOSA MEDICAL CENTER (O, 110 beds) 151 Redstone Avenue SE, Crestview, FL Zip 32539–6026; tel. 850/689–8100; Ronnie Daves, Chief Executive Officer

Web address: www.northokaloosa.com

PHYSICIANS REGIONAL - PINE RIDGE (O, 201 beds) 6101 Pine Ridge Road, Naples, FL Zip 34119–3900; tel. 239/348–4000; Scott Lowe, Interim Market Chief Executive Officer

SANTA ROSA MEDICAL CENTER (L, 68 beds) 6002 Berryhill Road, Milton, FL Zip 32570–5062; tel. 850/626–7762; Doug Sills, Chief Executive Officer

Web address: www.santarosamedicalcenter.org

SEVEN RIVERS REGIONAL MEDICAL CENTER (O, 128 beds) 6201 North Suncoast Boulevard, Crystal River, FL Zip 34428–6712; tel. 352/795–6560; Austin Brown, Chief Executive Officer

SHANDS LAKE SHORE REGIONAL MEDICAL CENTER (O, 85 beds) 368 NE Franklin Street, Lake City, FL Zip 32055–3047; tel. 386/292–8000; Rhonda Kay. Sherrod, R.N., MSN, Administrator

Web address: www.shandslakeshore.com

SHANDS LIVE OAK REGIONAL MEDICAL CENTER (O, 25 beds) 1100 SW 11th Street, Live Oak, FL Zip 32064–3608; tel. 386/362–0800; Rhonda Kay. Sherrod, R.N., MSN, Interim Chief Executive Officer

Web address: www.shandsliveoak.com/

For explanation of codes following names, see page B2.
★ Indicates Type III membership in the American Hospital Association.

SHANDS STARKE REGIONAL MEDICAL CENTER (O, 49 beds) 922 East Call Street, Starke, FL Zip 32091–3699; tel. 904/368–2300; Charles D. Nasem, FACHE, Chief Executive Officer

ST. CLOUD REGIONAL MEDICAL CENTER (O, 84 beds) 2906 17th Street, Saint Cloud, FL Zip 34769–6099; tel. 407/892–2135; Brent Burish, Chief Executive Officer
Web address: www.stcloudregional.com

VENICE REGIONAL BAYFRONT HEALTH (O, 221 beds) 540 The Rialto, Venice, FL Zip 34285–2900; tel. 941/485–7711; Bob Moore, FACHE, Chief Executive Officer
Web address: www.veniceregional.com

GEORGIA: EAST GEORGIA REGIONAL MEDICAL CENTER (O, 149 beds) 1499 Fair Road, Statesboro, GA Zip 30458–1683, P O Box 1048, 30459–1048, tel. 912/486–1000; Paul Theriot, Chief Executive Officer

INDIANA: BLUFFTON REGIONAL MEDICAL CENTER (O, 54 beds) 303 South Main Street, Bluffton, IN Zip 46714–2503; tel. 260/824–3210; Brent Parsons, Chief Executive Officer
Web address: www.blufftonregional.com

DUKES MEMORIAL HOSPITAL (O, 25 beds) 275 West 12th Street, Peru, IN Zip 46970–1638; tel. 765/472–8000; Debra Close, Chief Executive Officer
Web address: www.dukesmemorialhosp.com

DUPONT HOSPITAL (O, 131 beds) 2520 East Dupont Road, Fort Wayne, IN Zip 46825–1675; tel. 260/416–3000; Lisa Dolan, Interim Chief Executive Officer

KOSCIUSKO COMMUNITY HOSPITAL (O, 72 beds) 2101 East Dubois Drive, Warsaw, IN Zip 46580–3288; tel. 574/267–3200; Kirk M. Ray, Chief Executive Officer
Web address: www.kch.com

LA PORTE HOSPITAL (O, 129 beds) 1007 Lincolnway, La Porte, IN Zip 46350–3201, P O Box 250, 46352–0250, tel. 219/326–1234; Ashley Dickinson, Chief Executive Officer
Web address: www.iuhealth.org

LUTHERAN HOSPITAL OF INDIANA (O, 396 beds) 7950 West Jefferson Boulevard, Fort Wayne, IN Zip 46804–4140; tel. 260/435–7001; Michael Poore, Interim Chief Executive Officer

ORTHOPAEDIC HOSPITAL OF LUTHERAN HEALTH NETWORK (O, 44 beds) 7952 West Jefferson Boulevard, Fort Wayne, IN Zip 46804–4140; tel. 260/435–2999; Lorie Ailor, Chief Executive Officer
Web address: www.theorthohospital.com

PORTER REGIONAL HOSPITAL (O, 276 beds) 85 East U. S. Highway 6, Valparaiso, IN Zip 46383–8947; tel. 219/983–8300; Stephen Lunn, Chief Executive Officer

REHABILITATION HOSPITAL OF FORT WAYNE (O, 36 beds) 7970 West Jefferson Boulevard, Fort Wayne, IN Zip 46804–4140; tel. 260/435–6100; Shelley Boxell, R.N., Chief Nursing Officer and Interim Chief Operating Officer
Web address: www.rehabhospital.com

ST. JOSEPH HOSPITAL (O, 182 beds) 700 Broadway, Fort Wayne, IN Zip 46802–1493; tel. 260/425–3000; Vince Green, Interim Chief Administrative Officer
Web address: www.stjoehospital.com

STARKE HOSPITAL (O, 15 beds) 102 East Culver Road, Knox, IN Zip 46534–2216, P O Box 339, 46534–0339, tel. 574/772–6231; Jeff Vice, Interim Chief Executive Officer

LOUISIANA: BYRD REGIONAL HOSPITAL (O, 60 beds) 1020 West Fertitta Boulevard, Leesville, LA Zip 71446–4645; tel. 337/239–9041; Roger C. LeDoux, Chief Executive Officer
Web address: www.byrdregional.com

NORTHERN LOUISIANA MEDICAL CENTER (O, 104 beds) 401 East Vaughn Avenue, Ruston, LA Zip 71270–5950; tel. 318/254–2100; David Fuller, Interim Chief Executive Officer

MISSISSIPPI: MERIT HEALTH BILOXI (L, 198 beds) 150 Reynoir Street, Biloxi, MS Zip 39530–4199, P O Box 128, 39533–0128, tel. 228/432–1571; Robert Calhoun, Chief Executive Officer
Web address: www.merithealthbiloxi.com

MERIT HEALTH CENTRAL (L, 319 beds) 1850 Chadwick Drive, Jackson, MS Zip 39204–3479, P O Box 59001, 39284–9001, tel. 601/376–1000; Barry Moss, Chief Executive Officer

MERIT HEALTH MADISON (L, 43 beds) 161 River Oaks Drive, Canton, MS Zip 39046–5375, PO Box 1607, 39046–5375, tel. 601/855–4000; Britton Phelps, Chief Executive Officer
Web address: www.merithealthmadison.com

MERIT HEALTH NATCHEZ (O, 136 beds) 54 Seargent 'S' Prentiss Drive, Natchez, MS Zip 39120–4726; tel. 601/443–2100; Eric Robinson, Chief Executive Officer
Web address: www.natchezregional.com

MERIT HEALTH NORTHWEST MISSISSIPPI (L, 181 beds) 1970 Hospital Drive, Clarksdale, MS Zip 38614–7202, P O Box 1218, 38614–1218, tel. 662/627–3211; Joel Southern, R.N., MSN, Chief Executive Officer

MERIT HEALTH RANKIN (L, 134 beds) 350 Crossgates Boulevard, Brandon, MS Zip 39042–2698; tel. 601/825–2811; L Dwayne. Blaylock, Chief Executive Officer
Web address: www.crossgatesriveroaks.com

MERIT HEALTH RIVER OAKS (O, 158 beds) 1030 River Oaks Drive, Flowood, MS Zip 39232–9553, P O Box 5100, Jackson, 39296–5100, tel. 601/932–1030; L Dwayne. Blaylock, Chief Executive Officer
Web address: www.riveroakshosp.com

MERIT HEALTH RIVER REGION (O, 361 beds) 2100 Highway 61 North, Vicksburg, MS Zip 39183–8211, P O Box 590, 39181–0590, tel. 601/883–5000; Benjamin Richaud, Interim Chief Executive Officer
Web address: www.riverregion.com

MERIT HEALTH WESLEY (O, 211 beds) 5001 Hardy Street, Hattiesburg, MS Zip 39402–1308, P O Box 16509, 39404–6509, tel. 601/268–8000; Michael Neuendorf, Chief Executive Officer

MERIT HEALTH WOMAN'S HOSPITAL (O, 60 beds) 1026 North Flowood Drive, Flowood, MS Zip 39232–9532, 1026 North Flowood Drive, 39232, tel. 601/932–1000; Sherry J. Pitts, Chief Executive Officer
Web address: www.merithealthwomanshospital.com

MISSOURI: MOBERLY REGIONAL MEDICAL CENTER (O, 101 beds) 1515 Union Avenue, Moberly, MO Zip 65270–9449; tel. 660/263–8400; Ranee C. Brayton, FACHE, R.N., MSN, Chief Executive Officer

NORTHEAST REGIONAL MEDICAL CENTER (L, 93 beds) 315 South Osteopathy, Kirksville, MO Zip 63501–6401, P O Box C8502, 63501–8599, tel. 660/785–1000; Ranee C. Brayton, FACHE, R.N., MSN, Chief Executive Officer
Web address: www.nermc.com

POPLAR BLUFF REGIONAL MEDICAL CENTER (O, 252 beds) 3100 Oak Grove Road, Poplar Bluff, MO Zip 63901, P O Box 88, 63902–0088, tel. 573/776–2000; Larry Rodgers, Chief Executive Officer

TWIN RIVERS REGIONAL MEDICAL CENTER (O, 100 beds) 1301 First Street, Kennett, MO Zip 63857–2508, P O Box 728, 63857–0728, tel. 573/888–4522; Christian Jones, Chief Executive Officer
Web address: www.twinriversregional.com

NEW JERSEY: MEMORIAL HOSPITAL OF SALEM COUNTY (O, 110 beds) 310 Woodstown Road, Salem, NJ Zip 08079–2080; tel. 856/935–1000; Tammy Torres, R.N., MSN, Chief Executive Officer
Web address: www.salemhospitalnj.org

NEW MEXICO: CARLSBAD MEDICAL CENTER (O, 115 beds) 2430 West Pierce Street, Carlsbad, NM Zip 88220–3597; tel. 575/887–4100; Cathy Hibbs, Chief Executive Officer

EASTERN NEW MEXICO MEDICAL CENTER (O, 149 beds) 405 West Country Club Road, Roswell, NM Zip 88201–5209; tel. 575/622–8170; Rodney Schumacher, Chief Executive Officer
Web address: www.enmmc.com

LEA REGIONAL MEDICAL CENTER (O, 195 beds) 5419 North Lovington Highway, Hobbs, NM Zip 88240–9125, P O Box 3000, 88241–9501, tel. 575/492–5000; Timothy Thornell, FACHE, Chief Executive Officer

MOUNTAINVIEW REGIONAL MEDICAL CENTER (O, 142 beds) 4311 East Lohman Avenue, Las Cruces, NM Zip 88011–8255; tel. 575/556–7600; Denten Park, Chief Executive Officer
Web address: www.mountainviewregional.com

NORTH CAROLINA: DAVIS REGIONAL MEDICAL CENTER (O, 130 beds) 218 Old Mocksville Road, Statesville, NC Zip 28625–1930, P O Box 1823, 28687–1823, tel. 704/873–0281; Matthew Banks, Chief Executive Officer

LAKE NORMAN REGIONAL MEDICAL CENTER (O, 123 beds) 171 Fairview Road, Mooresville, NC Zip 28117–9500, P O Box 3250, 28117–3250, tel. 704/660–4000; Stephen L. Midkiff, Chief Executive Officer
Web address: www.lnrmc.com

For explanation of codes following names, see page B2.
★ Indicates Type III membership in the American Hospital Association.

OKLAHOMA: ALLIANCEHEALTH CLINTON (O, 49 beds) 100 North 30th Street, Clinton, OK Zip 73601–3117; tel. 580/323–2363; Cameron Lewis, Chief Executive Officer

ALLIANCEHEALTH DEACONESS (O, 238 beds) 5501 North Portland Avenue, Oklahoma City, OK Zip 73112–2099; tel. 405/604–6000; Devon Hyde, Chief Executive Officer
Web address: www.deaconessokc.com

ALLIANCEHEALTH DURANT (O, 140 beds) 1800 University Boulevard, Durant, OK Zip 74701–3006, P O Box 1207, 74702–1207, tel. 580/924–3080; Jeffrey S. Tarrant, FACHE, Chief Executive Officer

ALLIANCEHEALTH MADILL (O, 21 beds) 901 South Fifth Avenue, Madill, OK Zip 73446–3640, P O Box 827, 73446–0827, tel. 580/795–3384; Minnie Burkhardt, Chief Executive Officer
Web address: www.myalliancehealth.com

ALLIANCEHEALTH MIDWEST (L, 255 beds) 2825 Parklawn Drive, Midwest City, OK Zip 73110–4258; tel. 405/610–4411; Clay Franklin, Chief Executive Officer
Web address: www.myalliancehealth.com

ALLIANCEHEALTH PONCA CITY (O, 74 beds) 1900 North 14th Street, Ponca City, OK Zip 74601–2099; tel. 580/765–3321; Christopher Mendoza, Chief Executive Officer

ALLIANCEHEALTH SEMINOLE (O, 32 beds) 2401 Wrangler Boulevard, Seminole, OK Zip 74868–1917; tel. 405/303–4000; Adam Bracks, Chief Executive Officer
Web address: www.alliancehealthseminole.com/

ALLIANCEHEALTH WOODWARD (L, 40 beds) 900 17th Street, Woodward, OK Zip 73801–2448; tel. 580/256–5511; Ross Korkmas, Chief Executive Officer

BLACKWELL REGIONAL HOSPITAL (O, 49 beds) 710 South 13th Street, Blackwell, OK Zip 74631–3700; tel. 580/363–2311; Joyce Daniel, Chief Executive Officer and Chief Nursing Officer
Web address: www.blackwellregional.org

PENNSYLVANIA: BERWICK HOSPITAL CENTER (O, 101 beds) 701 East 16th Street, Berwick, PA Zip 18603–2397; tel. 570/759–5000; Diane Ljungquist, R.N., MS, Chief Executive Officer

BRANDYWINE HOSPITAL (O, 169 beds) 201 Reeceville Road, Coatesville, PA Zip 19320–1536; tel. 610/383–8000; W. Jeffrey. Hunt, Chief Executive Officer
Web address: www.brandywinehospital.com

CHESTNUT HILL HOSPITAL (O, 212 beds) 8835 Germantown Avenue, Philadelphia, PA Zip 19118–2718; tel. 215/248–8200; John D. . Cacciamani, M.D., Chief Executive Officer

FIRST HOSPITAL WYOMING VALLEY (O, 149 beds) 562 Wyoming Avenue, Kingston, PA Zip 18704–3721; tel. 570/552–3900; Eugene Boylan, Chief Executive Officer
Web address: www.commonwealthhealth.net/locations/first-hospital

JENNERSVILLE REGIONAL HOSPITAL (O, 63 beds) 1015 West Baltimore Pike, West Grove, PA Zip 19390–9459; tel. 610/869–1000; Matt Shelak, Interim Chief Executive Officer
Web address: www.jennersville.com

MOSES TAYLOR HOSPITAL (O, 213 beds) 700 Quincy Avenue, Scranton, PA Zip 18510–1724; tel. 570/770–5000; Justin Davis, Chief Executive Officer
Web address: www.mth.org

PHOENIXVILLE HOSPITAL (O, 139 beds) 140 Nutt Road, Phoenixville, PA Zip 19460–3900, P O Box 3001, 19460–0916, tel. 610/983–1000; Stephen M. Tullman, Chief Executive Officer

POTTSTOWN MEMORIAL MEDICAL CENTER (O, 232 beds) 1600 East High Street, Pottstown, PA Zip 19464–5093; tel. 610/327–7000; Richard Newell, Chief Executive Officer
Web address: www.pottstownmemorial.com

REGIONAL HOSPITAL OF SCRANTON (O, 186 beds) 746 Jefferson Avenue, Scranton, PA Zip 18510–1624; tel. 570/348–7100; Justin Davis, Chief Executive Officer
Web address: www.regionalhospitalofscranton.net

TYLER MEMORIAL HOSPITAL (O, 44 beds) 5950 State Route 6, Tunkhannock, PA Zip 18657–7905; tel. 570/836–2161; Ann Marie. Stevens, R.N., Chief Executive Officer

WILKES-BARRE GENERAL HOSPITAL (O, 374 beds) 575 North River Street, Wilkes-Barre, PA Zip 18764–0001; tel. 570/829–8111; Cornelio R. Catena, President and Chief Executive Officer
Web address: www.wvhc.org

SOUTH CAROLINA: CAROLINAS HOSPITAL SYSTEM MARION (O, 216 beds) 2829 East Highway 76, Mullins, SC Zip 29574–6035, P O Drawer 1150, Marion, 29571–1150, tel. 843/431–2000; Parkes Coggins, Chief Executive Officer

CAROLINAS HOSPITAL SYSTEM (O, 416 beds) 805 Pamplico Highway, Florence, SC Zip 29505–6050, P O Box 100550, 29502–0550, tel. 843/674–5000; Gary Malaer, Chief Executive Officer
Web address: www.carolinashospital.com

CHESTER REGIONAL MEDICAL CENTER (L, 36 beds) 1 Medical Park Drive, Chester, SC Zip 29706–9769; tel. 803/581–3151; Page H. Vaughan, Chief Executive Officer
Web address: www.chesterregional.com

MARY BLACK HEALTH SYSTEM - GAFFNEY (O, 125 beds) 1530 North Limestone Street, Gaffney, SC Zip 29340–4738; tel. 864/487–4271; Joshua Self, Chief Executive Officer

MARY BLACK HEALTH SYSTEM-SPARTANBURG (O, 164 beds) 1700 Skylyn Drive, Spartanburg, SC Zip 29307–1061, P O Box 3217, 29304–3217, tel. 864/573–3000; Sean T. Dardeau, FACHE, Chief Executive Officer
Web address: www.maryblackhealthsystem.com

SPRINGS MEMORIAL HOSPITAL (O, 176 beds) 800 West Meeting Street, Lancaster, SC Zip 29720–2298; tel. 803/286–1214; Page Vaughan, Chief Executive Officer

TENNESSEE: LAKEWAY REGIONAL HOSPITAL (O, 135 beds) 726 McFarland Street, Morristown, TN Zip 37814–3990; tel. 423/586–2302; Steve Simpson, Chief Executive Officer
Web address: www.tennova.com

TENNOVA HEALTHCARE - CLEVELAND (O, 185 beds) 2305 Chambliss Avenue NW, Cleveland, TN Zip 37311–3847, P O Box 3060, 37320–3060, tel. 423/559–6000; R Coleman. Foss, Chief Executive Officer
Web address: www.skyridgemedicalcenter.net

TENNOVA HEALTHCARE DYERSBURG REGIONAL MEDICAL CENTER (O, 120 beds) 400 East Tickle Street, Dyersburg, TN Zip 38024–3120; tel. 731/285–2410; Reba Celsor, Chief Executive Officer

TENNOVA HEALTHCARE REGIONAL HOSPITAL OF JACKSON (O, 134 beds) 367 Hospital Boulevard, Jackson, TN Zip 38305–2080; tel. 731/661–2000; Damon Brown, Interim Chief Executive Officer
Web address: www.tennova.com/tennova-healthcare/tennova-healthcare-regional-jackson.aspx

TENNOVA HEALTHCARE VOLUNTEER COMMUNITY HOSPITAL (O, 65 beds) 161 Mount Pelia Road, Martin, TN Zip 38237–3811; tel. 731/587–4261; Darrell Blaylock, Chief Executive Officer

TENNOVA HEALTHCARE-CLARKSVILLE (O, 247 beds) 651 Dunlop Lane, Clarksville, TN Zip 37040–5015, P O Box 31629, 37040–0028, tel. 931/502–1000; Alex Villa, Chief Executive Officer
Web address: www.tennova.com/

TENNOVA HEALTHCARE-HARTON (O, 104 beds) 1801 North Jackson Street, Tullahoma, TN Zip 37388–8259; tel. 931/393–3000; Richard Ellis, Chief Executive Officer
Web address: www.hartonmedicalcenter.com

TENNOVA HEALTHCARE-JAMESTOWN (O, 85 beds) 436 Central Ave W, Jamestown, TN Zip 38556–3031, P O Box 1500, 38556–1500, tel. 931/879–8171; Lynette Pritchett, Chief Executive Officer

TENNOVA HEALTHCARE-JEFFERSON MEMORIAL HOSPITAL (L, 54 beds) 110 Hospital Drive, Jefferson City, TN Zip 37760–5281; tel. 865/471–2500; Colin McRae, Chief Executive Officer
Web address: www.tennova.com/

TENNOVA HEALTHCARE-LAFOLLETTE MEDICAL CENTER (O, 165 beds) 923 East Central Avenue, La Follette, TN Zip 37766–2768, P O Box 1301, 37766–1301, tel. 423/907–1200; Mark Cain, Chief Executive Officer

TENNOVA HEALTHCARE-LEBANON (O, 245 beds) 1411 Baddour Parkway, Lebanon, TN Zip 37087–2513; tel. 615/444–8262; Jay Hinesley, FACHE, Chief Executive Officer
Web address: www.universitymedicalcenter.com

TENNOVA HEALTHCARE-SHELBYVILLE (O, 49 beds) 2835 Highway 231 North, Shelbyville, TN Zip 37160–7327; tel. 931/685–5433; Bill Rich, Chief Executive Officer
Web address: www.heritagemedicalcenter.com

For explanation of codes following names, see page B2.
★ Indicates Type III membership in the American Hospital Association.

TENNOVA NEWPORT MEDICAL CENTER (O, 47 beds) 435 Second Street, Newport, TN Zip 37821–3799; tel. 423/625–2200; Trevor Castaneda, Chief Executive Officer **Web address:** www.tennova.com

TENNOVA PHYSICIANS REGIONAL MEDICAL CENTER (O, 223 beds) 900 East Oak Hill Avenue, Knoxville, TN Zip 37917–4556; tel. 865/545–8000; Pamela Beck, Interim Chief Executive Officer

TEXAS: ABILENE REGIONAL MEDICAL CENTER (O, 205 beds) 6250 US Highway 83, Abilene, TX Zip 79606–5299; tel. 325/428–1000; Michael D. Murphy, FACHE, Chief Executive Officer **Web address:** www.abileneregional.com

BROWNWOOD REGIONAL MEDICAL CENTER (O, 188 beds) 1501 Burnet Road, Brownwood, TX Zip 76801–8520, P O Box 760, 76804–0760, tel. 325/646–8541; Claude E Chip"". Camp III, FACHE, Chief Executive Officer

CEDAR PARK REGIONAL MEDICAL CENTER (O, 93 beds) 1401 Medical Parkway, Cedar Park, TX Zip 78613–7763; tel. 512/528–7000; Brad D. Holland, Chief Executive Officer **Web address:** www.cedarparkregional.com

COLLEGE STATION MEDICAL CENTER (O, 148 beds) 1604 Rock Prairie Road, College Station, TX Zip 77845–8345; tel. 979/764–5100; America S. Farrell, FACHE, Chief Executive Officer **Web address:** www.csmedcenter.com

DETAR HEALTHCARE SYSTEM (O, 245 beds) 506 East San Antonio Street, Victoria, TX Zip 77901–6060, P O Box 2089, 77902–2089, tel. 361/575–7441; William R. Blanchard, Chief Executive Officer

HILL REGIONAL HOSPITAL (O, 66 beds) 101 Circle Drive, Hillsboro, TX Zip 76645–2670; tel. 254/580–8500; Michael J. Ellis, FACHE, Chief Executive Officer **Web address:** www.chs.net

LAKE GRANBURY MEDICAL CENTER (L, 73 beds) 1310 Paluxy Road, Granbury, TX Zip 76048–5655; tel. 817/573–2273; Derrick Cuenca, Chief Executive Officer **Web address:** www.lakegranburymedicalcenter.com

LAREDO MEDICAL CENTER (O, 326 beds) 1700 East Saunders Avenue, Laredo, TX Zip 78041–5474, P O Box 2068, 78044–2068, tel. 956/796–5000; Enrique Gallegos, Chief Executive Officer

LONGVIEW REGIONAL MEDICAL CENTER (O, 230 beds) 2901 North Fourth Street, Longview, TX Zip 75605–5191, P O Box 14000, 75607–4000, tel. 903/758–1818; Casey Robertson, Chief Executive Officer **Web address:** www.longviewregional.com

NAVARRO REGIONAL HOSPITAL (O, 49 beds) 3201 West State Highway 22, Corsicana, TX Zip 75110–2469; tel. 903/654–6800; Michael K. Stewart, Chief Executive Officer

SAN ANGELO COMMUNITY MEDICAL CENTER (O, 131 beds) 3501 Knickerbocker Road, San Angelo, TX Zip 76904–7698; tel. 325/949–9511; Steven Ewing, Interim Chief Executive Officer **Web address:** www.sacmc.com

WEATHERFORD REGIONAL MEDICAL CENTER (O, 92 beds) 713 East Anderson Street, Weatherford, TX Zip 76086–5705; tel. 682/582–1000; David Orcutt, Chief Executive Officer **Web address:** www.weatherfordregional.com

WOODLAND HEIGHTS MEDICAL CENTER (O, 124 beds) 505 South John Redditt Drive, Lufkin, TX Zip 75904–3157, P O Box 150610, 75904, tel. 936/634–8311; Kyle Swift, Chief Executive Officer

VIRGINIA: SOUTHAMPTON MEMORIAL HOSPITAL (O, 72 beds) 100 Fairview Drive, Franklin, VA Zip 23851–1238, P O Box 817, 23851–0817, tel. 757/569–6100; Kimberly W. Marks, Chief Executive Officer **Web address:** www.smhfranklin.com

SOUTHERN VIRGINIA REGIONAL MEDICAL CENTER (O, 80 beds) 727 North Main Street, Emporia, VA Zip 23847–1274; tel. 434/348–4400; Matt Tavenner, Chief Executive Officer

SOUTHSIDE REGIONAL MEDICAL CENTER (O, 300 beds) 200 Medical Park Boulevard, Petersburg, VA Zip 23805–9274; tel. 804/765–5000; Trent Nobles, Chief Executive Officer **Web address:** www.srmconline.com

WASHINGTON: TOPPENISH COMMUNITY HOSPITAL (O, 48 beds) 502 West Fourth Avenue, Toppenish, WA Zip 98948–1616, P O Box 672, 98948–0672, tel. 509/865–3105; Grant Magness, Interim Chief Executive Officer

YAKIMA REGIONAL MEDICAL AND CARDIAC CENTER (O, 167 beds) 110 South Ninth Avenue, Yakima, WA Zip 98902–3315; tel. 509/575–5000; Bryan Braegger, Interim Chief Executive Officer **Web address:** www.yakimaregional.net

WEST VIRGINIA: BLUEFIELD REGIONAL MEDICAL CENTER (O, 92 beds) 500 Cherry Street, Bluefield, WV Zip 24701–3390; tel. 304/327–1100; Derek W. Cimala, Interim Chief Executive Officer

GREENBRIER VALLEY MEDICAL CENTER (O, 113 beds) 202 Maplewood Avenue, Ronceverte, WV Zip 24970–1334, P O Box 497, 24970–0497, tel. 304/647–4411; Tom Neal, Chief Executive Officer **Web address:** www.gvmc.com

PLATEAU MEDICAL CENTER (O, 25 beds) 430 Main Street, Oak Hill, WV Zip 25901–3455; tel. 304/469–8600; Derek W. Cimala, Interim Chief Executive Officer

WILLIAMSON MEMORIAL HOSPITAL (O, 76 beds) 859 Alderson Street, Williamson, WV Zip 25661–3215, P O Box 1980, 25661–1980, tel. 304/235–2500; Cindy Segar-Miller, Chief Executive Officer **Web address:** www.williamsonmemorial.net

Owned, leased, sponsored:	132 hospitals	19122 beds
Contract-managed:	0 hospitals	0 beds
Totals:	132 hospitals	19122 beds

0249:   COMMUNITY HEALTHCARE SYSTEM (NP)
901 MacArthur Boulevard, Hammond, IN Zip 46321–2959; tel. 219/836–1600; Donald P. Fesko, President and Chief Executive Officer
(Independent Hospital System)

INDIANA: COMMUNITY HOSPITAL (O, 491 beds) 901 Macarthur Boulevard, Munster, IN Zip 46321–2959; tel. 219/836–1600; Luis F. Molina, Chief Executive Officer and Administrator

ST. CATHERINE HOSPITAL (O, 220 beds) 4321 Fir Street, East Chicago, IN Zip 46312–3097; tel. 219/392–1700; Leo Correa, Chief Executive Officer and Administrator **Web address:** www.stcatherinehospital.org

ST. MARY MEDICAL CENTER (O, 200 beds) 1500 South Lake Park Avenue, Hobart, IN Zip 46342–6699; tel. 219/942–0551; Janice L. Ryba, JD, Chief Executive Officer **Web address:** www.comhs.org

Owned, leased, sponsored:	3 hospitals	911 beds
Contract-managed:	0 hospitals	0 beds
Totals:	3 hospitals	911 beds

★0384:   COMMUNITY HOSPITAL CORPORATION (NP)
7800 North Dallas Parkway, Suite 200, Plano, TX Zip 75024–6116; tel. 972/943–6400; Jim R. Kendrick, President and Chief Executive Officer
(Moderately Centralized Health System)

KENTUCKY: CONTINUECARE HOSPITAL AT BAPTIST HEALTH CORBIN (O, 32 beds) 1 Trillium Way, Lower Level, Corbin, KY Zip 40701–8727; tel. 606/523–5150; Keith Rodgers, Interim Chief Executive Officer

CONTINUECARE HOSPITAL AT BAPTIST HEALTH PADUCAH (O, 37 beds) 2501 Kentucky Avenue, 5th Floor, Paducah, KY Zip 42003–3813; tel. 270/575–2598; Len McDade, Chief Executive Officer **Web address:** www.continuecare.org/paducah//

CONTINUECARE HOSPITAL AT MADISONVILLE (O, 35 beds) 900 Hospital Drive, 4th Floor, Madisonville, KY Zip 42431–1644; tel. 270/825–5450; Kathy DeVore, Administrator **Web address:** www.continuecare.org/madisonville/

LOUISIANA: MOREHOUSE GENERAL HOSPITAL (C, 49 beds) 323 West Walnut Avenue, Bastrop, LA Zip 71220–4521, P O Box 1060, 71221–1060, tel. 318/283–3600; Derrick A. Frazier, FACHE, Chief Executive Officer

NEW MEXICO: UNION COUNTY GENERAL HOSPITAL (C, 21 beds) 300 Wilson Street, Clayton, NM Zip 88415–3304, P O Box 489, 88415–0489, tel. 575/374–2585; Tammie Stump, R.N., Chief Executive Officer **Web address:** www.ucgh.net/

NORTH CAROLINA: CAROLINAS CONTINUECARE HOSPITAL AT KINGS MOUNTAIN (O, 28 beds) 706 West King Street, 2nd Floor, Kings Mountain,

---

For explanation of codes following names, see page B2.
★ Indicates Type III membership in the American Hospital Association.

NC Zip 28086–2708, P O Box 159, 28086–0159, tcl. 980/487–5520; Derek Murzyn, Chief Executive Officer
Web address: www.continuecare.org/kings-mountain/

CAROLINAS CONTINUECARE HOSPITAL AT PINEVILLE (O, 40 beds) 10648 Park Road, Charlotte, NC Zip 28210; tel. 704/667–8050; Derek Murzyn, Market Chief Executive Officer
Web address: www.continuecare.org/pineville/

CAROLINAS CONTINUECARE HOSPITAL AT UNIVERSITY (O, 35 beds) 8800 North Tryon Street, Charlotte, NC Zip 28262–3300; tel. 704/863–8300; Derek Murzyn, Chief Executive Officer
Web address: www.continuecare.org/charlotte//

SOUTH CAROLINA: CONTINUECARE HOSPITAL AT PALMETTO HEALTH BAPTIST (O, 35 beds) Taylor at Marion Street, Columbia, SC Zip 29220, PO BOX 11069, 29211–1069, tel. 803/296–3757; Thomas P. Harlan, Chief Executive Officer
Web address: www.continuecare.org/palmetto//

TENNESSEE: JELLICO COMMUNITY HOSPITAL (O, 31 beds) 188 Hospital Lane, Jellico, TN Zip 37762–4400; tel. 423/784–7252; Kim Dowell, R.N., Chief Executive Officer
Web address: www.jellicohospital.com

TEXAS: BAPTIST HOSPITALS OF SOUTHEAST TEXAS (O, 323 beds) 3080 College Street, Beaumont, TX Zip 77701–4689, P O Box 1591, 77704–1591, tel. 409/212–5000; David N. Parmer, FACHE, Chief Executive Officer

CONTINUECARE HOSPITAL AT HENDRICK MEDICAL CENTER (O, 23 beds) 1900 Pine Street, 7th Floor, Jones Building, Abilene, TX Zip 79601–2432; tel. 325/670–6251; Billy Blasingame, Chief Executive Officer
Web address: www.continuecare.org/hendrick/

CONTINUECARE HOSPITAL AT MEDICAL CENTER (ODESSA) (O, 25 beds) 500 West Fourth Street, 4th Floor, Odessa, TX Zip 79761–5001; tel. 432/640–4380; Judith Schiros, Chief Executive Officer

CONTINUECARE HOSPITAL AT MIDLAND MEMORIAL (O, 29 beds) 4214 Andrews Highway, 3rd Floor, Midland, TX Zip 79703–4822; tel. 432/221–3044; Judith Schiros, Chief Executive Officer
Web address: www.continuecare.org/midland/

FREESTONE MEDICAL CENTER (C, 37 beds) 125 Newman Street, Fairfield, TX Zip 75840–1499; tel. 903/389–2121; Stace D. Holland, Chief Executive Officer

ST. MARK'S MEDICAL CENTER (O, 65 beds) One St Mark's Place, La Grange, TX Zip 78945; tel. 979/242–2200; Rick J. Montelongo, Chief Executive Officer
Web address: www.smmctx.org

TYLER CONTINUECARE HOSPITAL (O, 51 beds) 800 East Dawson, 4th Floor, Tyler, TX Zip 75701–2036; tel. 903/531–4080; Stephanie Hyde, R.N., MSN, Chief Executive Officer
Web address: www.continuecare.org

YOAKUM COMMUNITY HOSPITAL (O, 25 beds) 1200 Carl Ramert Drive, Yoakum, TX Zip 77995–4868; tel. 361/293–2321; Karen Barber, R.N., Chief Executive Officer

Owned, leased, sponsored:	15 hospitals	814 beds
Contract-managed:	3 hospitals	107 beds
Totals:	18 hospitals	921 beds

1085: COMMUNITY MEDICAL CENTERS (NP)
Fresno and Maddy Drive, Fresno, CA Zip 93721, P O Box 1232, 93715–1232, tel. 559/459–6000; Tim A. Joslin, President and Chief Executive Officer
(Independent Hospital System)

CALIFORNIA: CLOVIS COMMUNITY MEDICAL CENTER (O, 109 beds) 2755 Herndon Avenue, Clovis, CA Zip 93611–6801; tel. 559/324–4000; Craig Castro, Chief Executive Officer
Web address: www.communitymedical.org

COMMUNITY BEHAVIORAL HEALTH CENTER (O, 61 beds) 7171 North Cedar Avenue, Fresno, CA Zip 93720–3311; tel. 559/449–8000; Craig Wagoner, Chief Executive Officer
Web address: www.communitymedical.org

COMMUNITY REGIONAL MEDICAL CENTER (O, 852 beds) 2823 Fresno Street, Fresno, CA Zip 93721–1324, P O Box 1232, 93715–1232, tel. 559/459–6000; Craig Wagoner, Chief Executive Officer

FRESNO HEART AND SURGICAL HOSPITAL (O, 60 beds) 15 East Audubon Drive, Fresno, CA Zip 93720–1542; tel. 559/433–8000; Ben Armfield, Associate Administrator
Web address: www.fresnoheartandsurgical.org

Owned, leased, sponsored:	4 hospitals	1082 beds
Contract-managed:	0 hospitals	0 beds
Totals:	4 hospitals	1082 beds

0990: COMMUNITY MEMORIAL HEALTH SYSTEM (NP)
147 North Brent Street, Ventura, CA Zip 93003–2809; tel. 805/652–5011; Gary Wilde, President and Chief Executive Officer
(Independent Hospital System)

CALIFORNIA: COMMUNITY MEMORIAL HOSPITAL (O, 284 beds) 147 North Brent Street, Ventura, CA Zip 93003–2809; tel. 805/652–5011; Gary Wilde, President and Chief Executive Officer

OJAI VALLEY COMMUNITY HOSPITAL (O, 96 beds) 1306 Maricopa Highway, Ojai, CA Zip 93023–3163; tel. 805/646–1401; Haady Lashkari, Chief Administrative Officer
Web address: www.ojaihospital.org

Owned, leased, sponsored:	2 hospitals	380 beds
Contract-managed:	0 hospitals	0 beds
Totals:	2 hospitals	380 beds

0909: COMPASS HEALTH (NP)
713 North Avenue L, Crowley, LA Zip 70526–3832; tel. 337/788–3330; Aimee Monaghan, Chief Executive Officer
(Independent Hospital System)

LOUISIANA: COMPASS BEHAVIORAL CENTER OF ALEXANDRIA (O, 16 beds) 6410 Masonic Drve, Alexandria, LA Zip 71301–2319; tel. 318/442–3163; Cheryl Lachney, Administrator
Web address: www.compasshealthcare.com/site191.php

COMPASS BEHAVIORAL CENTER OF HOUMA (O, 20 beds) 4701 West Park Avenue, Houma, LA Zip 70364–4426; tel. 985/876–1715; Cheryl Turner, Administrator

COMPASS BEHAVIORAL CENTER OF LAFAYETTE (O, 16 beds) 312 Youngsville Highway, Lafayette, LA Zip 70508; tel. 337/534–4655; Aimee Monaghan, Chief Executive Officer
Web address: www.compasshealthcare.com/site184.php

Owned, leased, sponsored:	3 hospitals	52 beds
Contract-managed:	0 hospitals	0 beds
Totals:	3 hospitals	52 beds

0999: CONCORD HEALTHCARE GROUP (IO)
111 Clifton AVenue, Lakewood, NJ Zip 8701; tel. 214/396–3462; Joe Neuman, Chief Executive Officer
(Independent Hospital System)

OKLAHOMA: MIDWEST CITY SPECIALTY HOSPITAL (O, 31 beds) 8210 National Avenue, Midwest City, OK Zip 73110–8518; tel. 405/739–0800; Bobby Snyder, Chief Executive Officer
Web address: www.midwestcityspecialtyhospital.com/

TEXAS: MESA HILLS SPECIALTY HOSPITAL (O, 32 beds) 2311 North Oregon Street, 5th Floor, El Paso, TX Zip 79902–3216; tel. 915/545–1823; Kathleen Cahill, Chief Executive Officer

PINE VALLEY SPECIALTY HOSPITAL (O, 35 beds) 6160 South Loop East, Houston, TX Zip 77087–1010; tel. 713/640–2400; Brent Hanson, Chief Executive Officer
Web address: www.promise-houston.com

For explanation of codes following names, see page B2.
★ Indicates Type III membership in the American Hospital Association.

Section B

PLANO SPECIALTY HOSPITAL (O, 43 beds) 1621 Coit Road, Plano, TX
Zip 75075–6141; tel. 972/758–5200; Wayne Cook, Chief Executive Officer

PLUM CREEK SPECIALTY HOSPITAL (O, 47 beds) 5601 Plum Creek Drive,
Amarillo, TX Zip 79124–1801; tel. 806/351–1000; Bobby Snyder, Interim
Chief Executive Officer
Web address: www.plumcreekspecialtyhosp.com/

Owned, leased, sponsored:	5 hospitals	188 beds
Contract-managed:	0 hospitals	0 beds
Totals:	5 hospitals	188 beds

0950: CONE HEALTH (NP)
1200 North Elm Street, Greensboro, NC Zip 27401–1004;
tel. 336/832–7000; Terry Akin, President and Chief Executive
Officer

NORTH CAROLINA: ALAMANCE REGIONAL MEDICAL CENTER (O, 218 beds)
1240 Huffman Mill Road, Burlington, NC Zip 27215–8700, P O Box 202,
27216–0202, tel. 336/538–7000; Preston W. Hammock, President
Web address: www.armc.com

MOSES H. CONE MEMORIAL HOSPITAL (O, 935 beds) 1200 North Elm Street,
Greensboro, NC Zip 27401–1020; tel. 336/832–7000; Mickey Foster,
President

Owned, leased, sponsored:	2 hospitals	1153 beds
Contract-managed:	0 hospitals	0 beds
Totals:	2 hospitals	1153 beds

**0014: CONNECTICUT DEPARTMENT OF MENTAL HEALTH
AND ADDICTION SERVICES** (NP)
410 Capitol Avenue, Hartford, CT Zip 06106–1367, P O Box
341431, 06134–1431, tel. 860/418–7000; Miriam Delphin-Rittmon, Ph.D., Commissioner
(Independent Hospital System)

CONNECTICUT: CONNECTICUT MENTAL HEALTH CENTER (O, 32 beds) 34
Park Street, New Haven, CT Zip 06519–1109, P O Box 1842, 06508–
1842, tel. 203/974–7144; Michael Sernyak, M.D., Director
Web address: www.ct.gov/dmhas/cwp/view.asp?a=2906&q=334596

CONNECTICUT VALLEY HOSPITAL (O, 596 beds) Eastern Drive, Middletown,
CT Zip 06457–3947; tel. 860/262–5000; Helene M. Vartelas, MSN, Chief
Executive Officer
Web address: www.ct.gov/dmhas/cwp/view.asp?a=3519&q=416778

SOUTHWEST CONNECTICUT MENTAL HEALTH SYSTEM (O, 62 beds) 1635
Central Avenue, Bridgeport, CT Zip 06610–2717; tel. 203/551–7400; Alicia
Feller, Chief Executive Officer

Owned, leased, sponsored:	3 hospitals	690 beds
Contract-managed:	0 hospitals	0 beds
Totals:	3 hospitals	690 beds

0016: COOK COUNTY HEALTH AND HOSPITALS SYSTEM (NP)
1900 West Polk Street, Suite 220, Chicago, IL Zip 60612–3723;
tel. 312/864–6820; John Jay. Shannon, M.D., Chief Executive
Officer
(Independent Hospital System)

ILLINOIS: JOHN H. STROGER JR. HOSPITAL OF COOK COUNTY (O, 450 beds)
1969 West Ogden Avenue, Chicago, IL Zip 60612–3714; tel. 312/864–
6000; John Jay. Shannon, M.D., Chief Executive Officer
Web address: www.cookcountyhealth.net

PROVIDENT HOSPITAL OF COOK COUNTY (O, 25 beds) 500 East 51st Street,
Chicago, IL Zip 60615–2494; tel. 312/572–2000; John Jay. Shannon, M.D.,
Chief Executive Officer
Web address: www.ccbhs.org/pages/ProvidentHospitalofCookCounty.htm

Owned, leased, sponsored:	2 hospitals	475 beds
Contract-managed:	0 hospitals	0 beds
Totals:	2 hospitals	475 beds

0905: CORNERSTONE HEALTHCARE GROUP (IO)
2200 Ross Avenue, Suite 5400, Dallas, TX Zip 75201–7984;
tel. 469/621–6700; Steve Jakubcanin, President and Chief
Executive Officer
(Independent Hospital System)

ARIZONA: CHG HOSPITAL TUCSON, LLC (O, 34 beds) 7220 East Rosewood
Drive, Tucson, AZ Zip 85710–1350; tel. 520/546–4595; Vanessa Acevedo,
Interim Chief Executive Officer

ARKANSAS: CORNERSTONE HOSPITAL OF LITTLE ROCK (O, 40 beds) 2 Saint
Vincent Circle, 6th Floor, Little Rock, AR Zip 72205–5423; tel. 501/265–
0600; James H. Rogers, FACHE, Chief Executive Officer
Web address: www.chghospitals.com/littlerock/

LOUISIANA: CORNERSTONE HOSPITAL OF BOSSIER CITY (O, 54 beds) 4900
Medical Drive, Bossier City, LA Zip 71112–4521; tel. 318/747–9500; Sheri
Burnette, R.N., Chief Executive Officer and Administrator

CORNERSTONE HOSPITAL OF SOUTHWEST LOUISIANA (O, 30 beds) 703
Cypress Street, Sulphur, LA Zip 70663–5053; tel. 337/310–6000; Michael
Lombard, President
Web address: www.chghospitals.com/sulphur/

CORNERSTONE HOSPITAL-WEST MONROE (O, 40 beds) 6198 Cypress Street,
West Monroe, LA Zip 71291–9010; tel. 318/396–5600; Chris Simpson, Chief
Executive Officer
Web address: www.chghospitals.com/chwm.html

OKLAHOMA: CORNERSTONE HOSPITAL OF OKLAHOMA-MUSKOGEE (O,
41 beds) 351 South 40th Street, Muskogee, OK Zip 74401–4916;
tel. 918/682–6161; Craig Koele, Chief Executive Officer

CORNERSTONE HOSPITAL OF OKLAHOMA-SHAWNEE (O, 34 beds) 1900
Gordon Cooper Drive, 2nd Floor, Shawnee, OK Zip 74801–8603, P O Box
1245, 74802–1245, tel. 405/395–5800; Elizabeth Waytula, Chief Executive
Officer
Web address: www.chghospitals.com/shawnee/

TEXAS: CHG CORNERSTONE HOSPITAL CONROE (O, 41 beds) 1500 Grand
Lake Drive, Conroe, TX Zip 77304–2891; tel. 936/523–1800; Suzanne
Kretschmer, Chief Executive Officer
Web address: www.chghospitals.com/conroe/

CORNERSTONE HOSPITAL OF AUSTIN (O, 86 beds) 4207 Burnet Road, Austin,
TX Zip 78756–3396; tel. 512/706–1900; Curt L. Roberts, Chief Executive
Officer

CORNERSTONE HOSPITAL OF HOUSTON AT CLEARLAKE (O, 148 beds) 709
Medical Center Boulevard, Webster, TX Zip 77598; tel. 281/332–3322; Amy
Stasney, R.N., Chief Executive Officer
Web address: www.cornerstonehealthcaregroup.com

CORNERSTONE HOSPITAL-MEDICAL CENTER OF HOUSTON (O, 35 beds)
2001 Hermann Drive, Houston, TX Zip 77004; tel. 832/649–6200; Michael
Higginbotham, Chief Executive Officer

SOLARA HOSPITAL HARLINGEN (O, 82 beds) 508 Victoria Lane, Harlingen,
TX Zip 78550–3225; tel. 956/425–9600; Cary L. Montalvo, Chief Executive
Officer
Web address: www.chghospitals.com/harlingen/

SOLARA HOSPITAL MCALLEN (O, 78 beds) 301 West Expressway 83, 8th
Floor, McAllen, TX Zip 78503–3045; tel. 956/632–4880; Austin Cleveland,
Chief Executive Officer
Web address: www.chghospitals.com/mcallen/

WEST VIRGINIA: CORNERSTONE HOSPITAL OF HUNTINGTON (O, 28
beds) 2900 First Avenue, Two East, Huntington, WV Zip 25702–1241;
tel. 304/399–2600; Cynthia Isaacs, Chief Executive Officer

Owned, leased, sponsored:	14 hospitals	771 beds
Contract-managed:	0 hospitals	0 beds
Totals:	14 hospitals	771 beds

★0103: COTTAGE HEALTH (NP)
400 West Pueblo Street, Santa Barbara, CA Zip 93105–4353,
P O Box 689, 93102–0689, tel. 805/569–7290; Ronald C.
Werft, President and Chief Executive Officer
(Independent Hospital System)

For explanation of codes following names, see page B2.
★ Indicates Type III membership in the American Hospital Association.

CALIFORNIA: GOLETA VALLEY COTTAGE HOSPITAL (O, 28 beds) 351 South Patterson Avenue, Santa Barbara, CA Zip 93111–2496, Box 6306, 93160–6306, tel. 805/967–3411; Ronald C. Werft, President and Chief Executive Officer
Web address: www.sbch.org

SANTA BARBARA COTTAGE HOSPITAL (O, 351 beds) 400 West Pueblo Street, Santa Barbara, CA Zip 93105–4390, P O Box 689, 93102–0689, tel. 805/682–7111; Ronald C. Werft, President and Chief Executive Officer
Web address: www.cottagehealthsystem.org

SANTA YNEZ VALLEY COTTAGE HOSPITAL (O, 11 beds) 2050 Viborg Road, Solvang, CA Zip 93463–2295; tel. 805/688–6431; Ronald C. Werft, President and Chief Executive Officer
Web address: www.cottagehealthsystem.org

Owned, leased, sponsored:	3 hospitals	390 beds
Contract-managed:	0 hospitals	0 beds
Totals:	3 hospitals	390 beds

★**0123:** **COVENANT HEALTH** (NP)
100 Fort Sanders West Boulevard, Knoxville, TN Zip 37922–3353; tel. 865/531–5555; James VanderSteeg, President and Chief Executive Officer
(Centralized Health System)

TENNESSEE: CLAIBORNE MEDICAL CENTER (L, 132 beds) 1850 Old Knoxville Road, Tazewell, TN Zip 37879–3625; tel. 423/626–4211; Patricia P. Ketterman, R.N., President and Chief Administrative Officer

CUMBERLAND MEDICAL CENTER (O, 97 beds) 421 South Main Street, Crossville, TN Zip 38555–5031; tel. 931/484–9511; David V. Bunch, President and Chief Administrative Officer
Web address: www.cmchealthcare.org

FORT LOUDOUN MEDICAL CENTER (L, 30 beds) 550 Fort Loudoun Medical Center Drive, Lenoir City, TN Zip 37772–5673; tel. 865/271–6000; Jeffrey Feike, President and Chief Administrative Officer
Web address: www.covenanthealth.com

FORT SANDERS REGIONAL MEDICAL CENTER (O, 384 beds) 1901 West Clinch Avenue , Knoxville, TN Zip 37916–2307; tel. 865/541–1111; Keith Altshuler, President and Chief Administrative Officer

LECONTE MEDICAL CENTER (O, 133 beds) 742 Middle Creek Road, Sevierville, TN Zip 37862–5019, P O Box 8005, 37864–8005, tel. 865/446–7000; Gaye Jolly, FACHE, Acting President and Chief Administrative Officer
Web address: www.lecontemedicalcenter.com

METHODIST MEDICAL CENTER OF OAK RIDGE (O, 210 beds) 990 Oak Ridge Turnpike, Oak Ridge, TN Zip 37830–6976, P O Box 2529, 37831–2529, tel. 865/835–1000; Jeremy Biggs, Chief Executive Officer
Web address: www.mmcoakridge.com

MORRISTOWN-HAMBLEN HEALTHCARE SYSTEM (O, 131 beds) 908 West Fourth North Street, Morristown, TN Zip 37814–3894, P O Box 1178, 37816–1178, tel. 423/492–9000; Gordon Lintz, Chief Administrative Officer
Web address: www.morristownhamblen.com

PARKWEST MEDICAL CENTER (O, 297 beds) 9352 Park West Boulevard, Knoxville, TN Zip 37923–4325, P O Box 22993, 37933–0993, tel. 865/373–1000; Neil Heatherly, Chief Executive Officer

ROANE MEDICAL CENTER (O, 52 beds) 8045 Roane Medical Center Dr, Harriman, TN Zip 37748–8333; tel. 865/316–1000; Jason B. Pilant, Acting President and Chief Administrative Officer
Web address: www.roanemedical.com

Owned, leased, sponsored:	9 hospitals	1466 beds
Contract-managed:	0 hospitals	0 beds
Totals:	9 hospitals	1466 beds

★**5885:** **COVENANT HEALTH** (CC)
100 Ames Pond Drive, Suite 102, Tewksbury, MA Zip 01876–1240; tel. 978/654–6363; David R. Lincoln, FACHE, President and Chief Executive Officer
(Moderately Centralized Health System)

MAINE: ST. JOSEPH HOSPITAL (O, 84 beds) 360 Broadway, Bangor, ME Zip 04401–3979, P O Box 403, 04402–0403, tel. 207/262–1000; Mary Prybylo, President and Chief Executive Officer

ST. MARY'S REGIONAL MEDICAL CENTER (O, 353 beds) 93 Campus Avenue, Lewiston, ME Zip 04240–6030, P O Box 291, 04243–0291, tel. 207/777–8100; Peter J. Holden, Interim President
Web address: www.stmarysmaine.com

NEW HAMPSHIRE: ST. JOSEPH HOSPITAL (O, 126 beds) 172 Kinsley Street, Nashua, NH Zip 03060–3648; tel. 603/882–3000; Daniel Moen, President and Chief Executive Officer

Owned, leased, sponsored:	3 hospitals	563 beds
Contract-managed:	0 hospitals	0 beds
Totals:	3 hospitals	563 beds

★**0036:** **COVENANT HEALTH SYSTEM** (NP)
3615 19th Street, Lubbock, TX Zip 79410–1203; tel. 806/725–0447; Richard H. Parks, FACHE, President and Chief Executive Officer
(Centralized Health System)

TEXAS: COVENANT CHILDREN'S HOSPITAL (O, 73 beds) 4015 22nd Place, Lubbock, TX Zip 79410; tel. 806/725–1011; Amy Thompson, M.D., Chief Executive Officer
Web address: www.covenanthealth.org/About-Us/Facilities/Childrens-Hospital.aspx

COVENANT HOSPITAL PLAINVIEW (O, 68 beds) 2601 Dimmitt Road, Plainview, TX Zip 79072–1833; tel. 806/296–5531; Robert Copeland, Interim Chief Executive Officer
Web address: www.covenantplainview.org

COVENANT HOSPITAL-LEVELLAND (L, 26 beds) 1900 South College Avenue, Levelland, TX Zip 79336–6508; tel. 806/894–4963; Bruce White, Administrator

COVENANT MEDICAL CENTER (O, 576 beds) 3615 19th Street, Lubbock, TX Zip 79410–1203, P O Box 1201, 79408–1201, tel. 806/725–0000; Walt Cathey, Chief Executive Officer
Web address: www.covenanthealth.org

COVENANT SPECIALTY HOSPITAL (O, 56 beds) 3815 20th Street, Lubbock, TX Zip 79410–1235; tel. 806/725–9200; Julie Bell, Interim Chief Executive Officer and Chief Nursing Officer

Owned, leased, sponsored:	5 hospitals	799 beds
Contract-managed:	0 hospitals	0 beds
Totals:	5 hospitals	799 beds

0179: **COXHEALTH** (NP)
1423 North Jefferson Avenue, Springfield, MO Zip 65802–1988; tel. 417/269–3108; Steven D. Edwards, President and Chief Executive Officer
(Centralized Physician/Insurance Health System)

MISSOURI: COX MEDICAL CENTER BRANSON (O, 115 beds) 251 Skaggs Road, Branson, MO Zip 65616–2031, P O Box 650, 65615–0650, tel. 417/335–7000; William K. Mahoney, FACHE, President and Chief Executive Officer
Web address: www.coxhealth.com

COX MEDICAL CENTERS (O, 625 beds) 1423 North Jefferson Street, Springfield, MO Zip 65802–1988; tel. 417/269–3000; Steven D. Edwards, President and Chief Executive Officer

COX MONETT HOSPITAL (O, 25 beds) 801 North Lincoln Avenue, Monett, MO Zip 65708–1641; tel. 417/235–3144; Darren Bass, President
Web address: www.coxhealth.com

Owned, leased, sponsored:	3 hospitals	765 beds
Contract-managed:	0 hospitals	0 beds
Totals:	3 hospitals	765 beds

For explanation of codes following names, see page B2.
★ Indicates Type III membership in the American Hospital Association.

0930: CRC HEALTH GROUP, INC. (IO)
20400 Stevens Creek Boulevard, Suite 600, Cupertino, CA
Zip 95014–2217; tel. 866/540–5240; Jerome E. Rhodes, Chief
Executive Officer
(Independent Hospital System)

ARIZONA: SIERRA TUCSON (O, 139 beds) 39580 South Lago Del Oro Parkway,
Tucson, AZ Zip 85739–1091; tel. 520/624–4000; Stephen P. Fahey,
Executive Director
Web address: www.sierratucson.com

NORTH CAROLINA: WILMINGTON TREATMENT CENTER (O, 44 beds) 2520
Troy Drive, Wilmington, NC Zip 28401–7643; tel. 910/762–2727; Robert
Pitts, Executive Director
Web address: www.wilmtreatment.com

Owned, leased, sponsored:	2 hospitals	183 beds
Contract-managed:	0 hospitals	0 beds
Totals:	2 hospitals	183 beds

0960: CURAE HEALTH (NP)
121 Leinart Street, Clinton, TN Zip 37716–3632, P O Box 358,
37717–0358, tel. 865/269–4074; Steve Clapp, President and
Chief Executive Officer
(Independent Hospital System)

ALABAMA: LAKELAND COMMUNITY HOSPITAL (O, 59 beds) Highway 195 East,
Haleyville, AL Zip 35565–9536, P O Box 780, 35565–0780, tel. 205/486–
5213; Cynthia Nichols, R.N., MSN, Chief Executive Officer

NORTHWEST MEDICAL CENTER (O, 66 beds) 1530 U S Highway 43, Winfield,
AL Zip 35594–5056; tel. 205/487–7000; Michael D. Windham, Chief
Executive Officer
Web address: www.northwestmedcenter.com

RUSSELLVILLE HOSPITAL (O, 92 beds) 15155 Highway 43, Russellville,
AL Zip 35653–1975, P O Box 1089, 35653–1089, tel. 256/332–1611;
Christine R. Stewart, FACHE, Chief Executive Officer

MISSISSIPPI: GILMORE MEMORIAL HOSPITAL (O, 95 beds) 1105 Earl Frye
Boulevard, Amory, MS Zip 38821–5500, P O Box 459, 38821–0459,
tel. 662/256–7111; J Allen. Tyra, Chief Executive
Web address: www.gilmorehealth.com

PANOLA MEDICAL CENTER (O, 112 beds) 303 Medical Center Drive,
Batesville, MS Zip 38606–8608; tel. 662/563–5611; Travis Sisson, Chief
Executive Officer
Web address: www.trilakesmc.com

Owned, leased, sponsored:	5 hospitals	424 beds
Contract-managed:	0 hospitals	0 beds
Totals:	5 hospitals	424 beds

1013: CURAHEALTH HOSPITALS (IO)
650 Beebalm Lane, Suite 220, Garland, TX Zip 75040–2955;
tel. 972/414–0070; Chester Crouch, Chief Executive Officer

ARIZONA: CURAHEALTH PHOENIX (O, 58 beds) 40 East Indianola Avenue,
Phoenix, AZ Zip 85012–2059; tel. 602/280–7000; Karen Cawley, Chief
Executive Officer
Web address: www.curahealth.com

CURAHEALTH TUCSON (O, 51 beds) 355 North Wilmot Road, Tucson, AZ
Zip 85711–2601; tel. 520/584–4500; Camie Overton, Chief Executive Officer

LOUISIANA: CURAHEALTH NEW ORLEANS (O, 80 beds) 3601 Coliseum Street,
New Orleans, LA Zip 70115–3606; tel. 504/899–1555; Richard Daughdrill,
R.N., Chief Executive Officer
Web address: www.curahealth.com

MASSACHUSETTS: CURAHEALTH BOSTON NORTH SHORE (O, 50 beds) 15
King Street, Peabody, MA Zip 01960–4379; tel. 978/531–2900; Amber
Hester, Chief Executive Officer

CURAHEALTH HOSPITAL BOSTON (O, 59 beds) 1515 Commonwealth Avenue,
Brighton, MA Zip 02135–3617; tel. 617/254–1100; Susan Downey, R.N., MS,
Chief Executive Officer
Web address: www.curahealth.com

CURAHEALTH STOUGHTON (O, 111 beds) 909 Sumner Street, 1st Floor,
Stoughton, MA Zip 02072–3396; tel. 781/297–8200; Robert A. Gundersen,
Market Chief Executive Officer

OKLAHOMA: CURAHEALTH HOSPITAL OKLAHOMA CITY (O, 93 beds)
1407 North Robinson Avenue, Oklahoma City, OK Zip 73103–4823;
tel. 405/232–8000; Brenda Hood, Chief Executive Officer
Web address: www.curahealth.com

PENNSYLVANIA: CURAHEALTH HERITAGE VALLEY (O, 35 beds) 1000 Dutch
Ridge Road, Beaver, PA Zip 15009–9727; tel. 724/773–8480; Janie
Rosenberger-Slampack, Chief Executive Officer
Web address: www.curahealth.com

CURAHEALTH PITTSBURGH (O, 63 beds) 7777 Steubenville Pike, Oakdale, PA
Zip 15071–3409; tel. 412/494–5500; Janie Rosenberger-Slampack, Market
Chief Executive Officer

TENNESSEE: CURAHEALTH NASHVILLE (O, 58 beds) 1412 County Hospital
Road, Nashville, TN Zip 37218–3007; tel. 615/687–2600; Tom Rone, Chief
Executive Officer
Web address: www.curahealth.com

Owned, leased, sponsored:	10 hospitals	658 beds
Contract-managed:	0 hospitals	0 beds
Totals:	10 hospitals	658 beds

★0864: DAVIS HEALTH SYSTEM (NP)
Reed Street and Gorman Avenue, Elkins, WV Zip 26241, P O Box
1697, 26241–1697, tel. 304/636–3300; Vance Jackson, FACHE,
President and Chief Executive Officer
(Independent Hospital System)

WEST VIRGINIA: BROADDUS HOSPITAL (O, 72 beds) 1 Healthcare Drive,
Philippi, WV Zip 26416–9405, P O Box 930, 26416–0930, tel. 304/457–
1760; Dana L. Gould, Chief Executive Officer
Web address: www.davishealthsystem.org/

DAVIS MEDICAL CENTER (O, 80 beds) Gorman Avenue and Reed Street,
Elkins, WV Zip 26241, P O Box 1484, 26241–1484, tel. 304/636–3300;
Vance Jackson, FACHE, Chief Executive Officer

Owned, leased, sponsored:	2 hospitals	152 beds
Contract-managed:	0 hospitals	0 beds
Totals:	2 hospitals	152 beds

1825: DCH HEALTH SYSTEM (NP)
809 University Boulevard East, Tuscaloosa, AL Zip 35401–2029;
tel. 205/759–7111; Bryan N. Kindred, FACHE, President and
Chief Executive Officer
(Moderately Centralized Health System)

ALABAMA: DCH REGIONAL MEDICAL CENTER (O, 876 beds) 809 University
Boulevard East, Tuscaloosa, AL Zip 35401–2029; tel. 205/759–7111;
William H. Cassels, Administrator
Web address: www.dchsystem.com

FAYETTE MEDICAL CENTER (L, 167 beds) 1653 Temple Avenue North,
Fayette, AL Zip 35555–1314, P O Drawer 710, 35555–0710, tel. 205/932–
5966; Donald J. Jones, FACHE, Administrator

Owned, leased, sponsored:	2 hospitals	1043 beds
Contract-managed:	0 hospitals	0 beds
Totals:	2 hospitals	1043 beds

★0313: DEACONESS HEALTH SYSTEM (NP)
600 Mary Street, Evansville, IN Zip 47710–1658; tel. 812/450–
5000; Shawn W. McCoy, Chief Executive Officer
(Centralized Health System)

For explanation of codes following names, see page B2.
★ Indicates Type III membership in the American Hospital Association.

INDIANA: DEACONESS HOSPITAL (O, 516 beds) 600 Mary Street, Evansville, IN Zip 47710–1658; tel. 812/450–5000; Shawn W. McCoy, Chief Executive Officer
Web address: www.deaconess.com

GIBSON GENERAL HOSPITAL (C, 70 beds) 1808 Sherman Drive, Princeton, IN Zip 47670–1043; tel. 812/385–3401; Emmett C. Schuster, President and Chief Executive Officer
Web address: www.gibsongeneral.com

THE HEART HOSPITAL AT DEACONESS GATEWAY (O, 24 beds) 4007 Gateway Boulevard, Newburgh, IN Zip 47630–8947; tel. 812/842–4784; Rebecca Malotte, Executive Director and Chief Nursing Officer

THE WOMEN'S HOSPITAL (O, 74 beds) 4199 Gateway Boulevard, Newburgh, IN Zip 47630–8940; tel. 812/842–4200; Christina M. Ryan, R.N., Chief Executive Officer
Web address: www.deaconess.com

Owned, leased, sponsored:	3 hospitals	614 beds
Contract-managed:	1 hospitals	70 beds
Totals:	4 hospitals	684 beds

0330: DEKALB REGIONAL HEALTH SYSTEM (NP)
2701 North Decatur Road, Decatur, GA Zip 30033–5918; tel. 404/501–1000; Robert E. Wilson Esq, Chief Executive Officer
(Centralized Health System)

GEORGIA: DEKALB MEDICAL AT DOWNTOWN DECATUR (O, 44 beds) 450 North Candler Street, Decatur, GA Zip 30030–2671; tel. 404/501–6700; Robert E. Wilson Esq, Chief Executive Officer

DEKALB MEDICAL AT HILLANDALE (O, 80 beds) 2801 DeKalb Medical Parkway, Lithonia, GA Zip 30058–4996; tel. 404/501–8700; Vernell Nunn, Chief Executive Officer
Web address: www.dekalbmedical.org

DEKALB MEDICAL AT NORTH DECATUR (O, 417 beds) 2701 North Decatur Road, Decatur, GA Zip 30033–5995; tel. 404/501–1000; Robert E. Wilson Esq, Chief Executive Officer
Web address: www.dekalbmedical.org

Owned, leased, sponsored:	3 hospitals	541 beds
Contract-managed:	0 hospitals	0 beds
Totals:	3 hospitals	541 beds

9495: DEPARTMENT OF THE AIR FORCE (FG)
1420 Pentagon, Room 4E1084, Washington, DC Zip 20330–1420; tel. 202/767–4765; Lieutenant General, Thomas Travis, Surgeon General
(Independent Hospital System)

ALASKA: U. S. AIR FORCE REGIONAL HOSPITAL (O, 64 beds) 5955 Zeamer Avenue, Elmendorf AFB, AK Zip 99506–3702; tel. 907/580–3006; Major, Mark Lamey, Commander

CALIFORNIA: DAVID GRANT USAF MEDICAL CENTER (O, 116 beds) 101 Bodin Circle, Travis AFB, CA Zip 94535–1809; tel. 707/423–7300; Lieutenant, Michael Higgins, Commander
Web address: www.travis.af.mil/units/dgmc/index.asp

FLORIDA: U. S. AIR FORCE REGIONAL HOSPITAL (O, 57 beds) 307 Boatner Road, Suite 114, Eglin AFB, FL Zip 32542–1282; tel. 850/883–8221; Colonel, Pamela Smith, Commander

MISSISSIPPI: U. S. AIR FORCE MEDICAL CENTER KEESLER (O, 56 beds) 301 Fisher Street, Room 1A132, Keesler AFB, MS Zip 39534–2519; tel. 228/376–2550; Colonel, Thomas Harrell, M.D., Commander
Web address: www.keesler.af.mil

NEVADA: MIKE O'CALLAGHAN FEDERAL HOSPITAL (O, 46 beds) 4700 Las Vegas Boulevard North, Suite 2419, Nellis AFB, NV Zip 89191–6600; tel. 702/653–2000; Colonel, Christian Benjamin, USAF, MC, Commander

OHIO: WRIGHT PATTERSON MEDICAL CENTER (O, 62 beds) 4881 Sugar Maple Drive, Wright-Patterson AFB, OH Zip 45433–5529; tel. 937/257–9144; Colonel, Brent J. Erickson, Administrator
Web address: www.wpafb.af.mil/units/wpmc/

VIRGINIA: U. S. AIR FORCE HOSPITAL (O, 65 beds) 77 Nealy Avenue, Hampton, VA Zip 23665–2040; tel. 757/764–6969; Colonel, Susan Pietrykowski, Commander

Owned, leased, sponsored:	7 hospitals	466 beds
Contract-managed:	0 hospitals	0 beds
Totals:	7 hospitals	466 beds

9395: DEPARTMENT OF THE ARMY, OFFICE OF THE SURGEON GENERAL (FG)
5109 Leesburg Pike, Falls Church, VA Zip 22041–3215; tel. 703/681–3000; Lieutenant General, Eric B. Schoomaker, Surgeon General
(Moderately Centralized Health System)

ALASKA: BASSETT ARMY COMMUNITY HOSPITAL (O, 24 beds) 1060 Gaffney Road, Box 7400, Fort Wainwright, AK Zip 99703–5001, 1060 Gaffney Road, Box 7440, 99703–5001, tel. 907/361–4000; Timothy Bergeron, Deputy Commander, Administration
Web address: www.alaska.amedd.army.mil

CALIFORNIA: WEED ARMY COMMUNITY HOSPITAL (O, 27 beds) Inner Loop Road and 4th Street, Building 166, Fort Irwin, CA Zip 92310–5065, P O Box 105109, 92310–5109, tel. 760/380–3108; Colonel, Martin Doperak, Commander
Web address: www.irwin.amedd.army.mil

COLORADO: EVANS U. S. ARMY COMMUNITY HOSPITAL (O, 68 beds) 1650 Cochrane Circle, Building 7500, Fort Carson, CO Zip 80913–4613; tel. 719/526–7200; Colonel, Patrick M. Garman, Commander

GEORGIA: DWIGHT DAVID EISENHOWER ARMY MEDICAL CENTER (O, 107 beds) 300 West Hospital Road, Fort Gordon, GA Zip 30905–5741; tel. 706/787–5811; Colonel, John P. Lamoureux, Commander
Web address: www.ddeamc.amedd.army.mil

MARTIN ARMY COMMUNITY HOSPITAL (O, 57 beds) 7950 Martin Loop, Fort Benning, GA Zip 31905–5648, 7950 Martin Loop, B9200, Room 010, 31905–5648, tel. 706/544–2516; Colonel, Marie Dominguez, Commander
Web address: www.martin.amedd.army.mil

WINN ARMY COMMUNITY HOSPITAL (O, 37 beds) 1061 Harmon Avenue, Hinesville, GA Zip 31314–5641, 1061 Harmon Avenue, Suite 2311B, 31314–5641, tel. 912/435–6965; Colonel, Kirk W. Eggleston, Commanding Officer
Web address: www.winn.amedd.army.mil/

HAWAII: TRIPLER ARMY MEDICAL CENTER (O, 194 beds) 1 Jarret White Road, Honolulu, HI Zip 96859–5001; tel. 808/433–6661; Colonel, Andrew M. Barr, Commanding Officer

KANSAS: IRWIN ARMY COMMUNITY HOSPITAL (O, 44 beds) 600 Caisson Hill Road, Junction City, KS Zip 66442–7037; tel. 785/239–7000; Colonel, Risa Ware, Commander
Web address: www.iach.amedd.army.mil

KENTUCKY: COLONEL FLORENCE A. BLANCHFIELD ARMY COMMUNITY HOSPITAL (O, 66 beds) 650 Joel Drive, Fort Campbell, KY Zip 42223–5318; tel. 270/798–8040; Colonel, Telita Crosland, Commander
Web address: www.campbell.amedd.army.mil/

IRELAND ARMY COMMUNITY HOSPITAL (O, 17 beds) 289 Ireland Avenue, Fort Knox, KY Zip 40121–5111; tel. 502/624–9333; Colonel, Robert S. Cornes, Commander

LOUISIANA: BAYNE-JONES ARMY COMMUNITY HOSPITAL (O, 13 beds) 1585 3rd Street, Fort Polk, LA Zip 71459–5102; tel. 337/531–3928; Colonel, Marla J. Ferguson, Commanding Officer
Web address: www.polk.amedd.army.mil

MARSHALL ISLANDS: KWAJALEIN HOSPITAL (O, 14 beds) U S Army Kwajalein Atoll, Kwajalein Island, MH Zip 96960, Box 1702, APO, UNIT, 96555–5000, tel. 805/355–2225; Elaine McMahon, Administrator

MISSOURI: GENERAL LEONARD WOOD ARMY COMMUNITY HOSPITAL (O, 42 beds) 4430 Missouri Avenue, Fort Leonard Wood, MO Zip 65473–8952, PO Box 4430, 65473–8952, tel. 573/596–0414; Colonel, Christian Meko, Hospital Commander
Web address: www.glwach.amedd.army.mil/

For explanation of codes following names, see page B2.
★ Indicates Type III membership in the American Hospital Association.

Section B

NEW YORK: KELLER ARMY COMMUNITY HOSPITAL (O, 20 beds) 900 Washington Road, West Point, NY Zip 10996–1197, U S Military Academy, Building 900, 10996–1197, tel. 845/938–5169; Colonel, Eric B. Sones, Commander

NORTH CAROLINA: WOMACK ARMY MEDICAL CENTER (O, 156 beds) 2817 Reilly Road, Fort Bragg, NC Zip 28310–7302; tel. 910/907–6000; Colonel, Lance C. Raney, Commander
Web address: www.wamc.amedd.army.mil/

SOUTH CAROLINA: MONCRIEF ARMY COMMUNITY HOSPITAL (O, 60 beds) 4500 Stuart Street, Fort Jackson, SC Zip 29207–5700; tel. 803/751–2160; Colonel, Traci Crawford, R.N., Commander
Web address: www.moncrief.amedd.army.mil

TEXAS: BROOKE ARMY MEDICAL CENTER (O, 226 beds) 3851 Roger Brookes Drive, Fort Sam Houston, TX Zip 78234–4501; tel. 210/916–4141; Brigadier General, Jeffrey Johnson, Commander
Web address: www.bamc.amedd.army.mil

CARL R. DARNALL ARMY MEDICAL CENTER (O, 109 beds) 36000 Darnall Loop, Fort Hood, TX Zip 76544–5095; tel. 254/288–8000; Colonel, David R. Gibson, Chief Executive Officer

WILLIAM BEAUMONT ARMY MEDICAL CENTER (O, 209 beds) 5005 North Piedras Street, El Paso, TX Zip 79920–5001; tel. 915/742–2121; Colonel, John A. Smyrski III, Commanding Officer
Web address: www.wbamc.amedd.army.mil

VIRGINIA: FORT BELVOIR COMMUNITY HOSPITAL (O, 46 beds) 9300 Dewitt Loop, Fort Belvoir, VA Zip 22060–5285; tel. 571/231–3224; Colonel, Jason S. Wieman, Director

WASHINGTON: MADIGAN ARMY MEDICAL CENTER (O, 200 beds) Fitzsimmons Drive, Building 9040, Tacoma, WA Zip 98431–1100; tel. 253/968–1110; Colonel, Michael Place, M.D., Commander
Web address: www.mamc.amedd.army.mil

Owned, leased, sponsored:	21 hospitals	1736 beds
Contract-managed:	0 hospitals	0 beds
Totals:	21 hospitals	1736 beds

9295: DEPARTMENT OF VETERANS AFFAIRS (FG)
810 Vermont Avenue NW, Washington, DC Zip 20420–0001; tel. 202/273–5781; David J. Shulkin, M.D., Secretary, Veterans Affairs

(Decentralized Health System)

ALABAMA: BIRMINGHAM VETERANS AFFAIRS MEDICAL CENTER (O, 151 beds) 700 South 19th Street, Birmingham, AL Zip 35233–1927; tel. 205/933–8101; Thomas C. Smith III, FACHE, Director

CENTRAL ALABAMA VETERANS HEALTH CARE SYSTEM (O, 245 beds) 215 Perry Hill Road, Montgomery, AL Zip 36109–3798; tel. 334/272–4670; Linda Lake . Boyle, R.N., MSN, Director
Web address: www.centralalabama.va.gov/

TUSCALOOSA VETERANS AFFAIRS MEDICAL CENTER (O, 366 beds) 3701 Loop Road East, Tuscaloosa, AL Zip 35404–5015; tel. 205/554–2000; John F. Merkle, Medical Center Director
Web address: www.tuscaloosa.va.gov

ARIZONA: NORTHERN ARIZONA VETERANS AFFAIRS HEALTH CARE SYSTEM (O, 147 beds) 500 Highway 89 North, Prescott, AZ Zip 86313–5000; tel. 928/445–4860; Malcolm Keith. Piatt, M.D., Interim Director

PHOENIX VETERANS AFFAIRS HEALTH CARE SYSTEM (O, 197 beds) 650 East Indian School Road, Phoenix, AZ Zip 85012–1892; tel. 602/277–5551; RimaAnn O. Nelson, R.N., Director
Web address: www.phoenix.va.gov/

SOUTHERN ARIZONA VETERANS AFFAIRS HEALTH CARE SYSTEM (O, 323 beds) 3601 South 6th Avenue, Tucson, AZ Zip 85723–0002; tel. 520/792–1450; Jennifer S. Gutowski, FACHE, Acting Director
Web address: www.tucson.va.gov

ARKANSAS: CENTRAL ARKANSAS VETERANS HEALTHCARE SYSTEM (O, 551 beds) 4300 West Seventh Street, Little Rock, AR Zip 72205–5446; tel. 501/257–1000; Margie A. Scott, M.D., Director

VETERANS HEALTH CARE SYSTEM OF THE OZARKS (O, 72 beds) 1100 North College Avenue, Fayetteville, AR Zip 72703–1944; tel. 479/443–4301; Bryan C. Matthews, Director
Web address: www.fayettevillear.va.gov

CALIFORNIA: SAN FRANCISCO VA MEDICAL CENTER (O, 241 beds) 4150 Clement Street, San Francisco, CA Zip 94121–1545; tel. 415/221–4810; Bonnie S. Graham, Director

VA GREATER LOS ANGELES HEALTHCARE SYSTEM (O, 708 beds) 11301 Wilshire Boulevard, Los Angeles, CA Zip 90073–1003; tel. 310/478–3711; Ann R. Brown, M.D., Director
Web address: www.losangeles.va.gov/

VA LONG BEACH HEALTHCARE SYSTEM (O, 356 beds) 5901 East 7th Street, Long Beach, CA Zip 90822–5201; tel. 562/826–8000; Tracye B. Davis, Acting Director

VA PALO ALTO HEALTH CARE SYSTEM (O, 808 beds) 3801 Miranda Avenue, Palo Alto, CA Zip 94304–1207; tel. 650/493–5000; Thomas J. Fitzgerald III, Interim Director
Web address: www.paloalto.va.gov/

VA SAN DIEGO HEALTHCARE SYSTEM (O, 248 beds) 3350 LaJolla Village Drive, San Diego, CA Zip 92161–0002; tel. 858/552–8585; Robert M. Smith, M.D., Director
Web address: www.sandiego.va.gov

VETERANS AFFAIRS CENTRAL CALIFORNIA HEALTH CARE SYSTEM (O, 117 beds) 2615 East Clinton Avenue, Fresno, CA Zip 93703–2223; tel. 559/225–6100; Stephen R. Bauman, Medical Center Director

VETERANS AFFAIRS LOMA LINDA HEALTHCARE SYSTEM (O, 268 beds) 11201 Benton Street, Loma Linda, CA Zip 92357–1000; tel. 909/825–7084; Barbara Fallen, FACHE, Director
Web address: www.lomalinda.va.gov

COLORADO: GRAND JUNCTION VETERANS HEALTH CARE SYSTEM (O, 23 beds) 2121 North Avenue, Grand Junction, CO Zip 81501–6428; tel. 970/242–0731; Michael T. Kilmer, DirectorSOUTHERN COLORADO HEALTHCARE SYSTEM (O, 299 beds)Las AnimasCO81054–0390719456–1260StuartCCollyer5139873Director

VETERANS AFFAIRS EASTERN COLORADO HEALTH CARE SYSTEM (O, 271 beds) 1055 Clermont Street, Denver, CO Zip 80220–3877; tel. 303/399–8020; Sallie Houser-Hanfelder, FACHE, Director
Web address: www.denver.va.gov/

CONNECTICUT: VETERANS AFFAIRS CONNECTICUT HEALTHCARE SYSTEM (O, 197 beds) 950 Campbell Avenue, West Haven, CT Zip 06516–2770; tel. 203/932–5711; Gerald F. Culliton, Medical Center Director
Web address: www.connecticut.va.gov

DELAWARE: WILMINGTON VETERANS AFFAIRS MEDICAL CENTER (O, 60 beds) 1601 Kirkwood Highway, Wilmington, DE Zip 19805–4989; tel. 302/994–2511; Robert W. Callahan Jr, Interim Director

DISTRICT OF COLUMBIA: WASHINGTON DC VETERANS AFFAIRS MEDICAL CENTER (O, 291 beds) 50 Irving Street NW, Washington, DC Zip 20422–0002; tel. 202/745–8000; Charles Faselis, M.D., Acting Medical Center Director
Web address: www.washingtondc.va.gov/

FLORIDA: BAY PINES VETERANS AFFAIRS HEALTHCARE SYSTEM (O, 396 beds) 10000 Bay Pines Boulevard, Bay Pines, FL Zip 33744–8200, P O Box 5005, 33744–5005, tel. 727/398–6661; Suzanne M. Klinker, Director

JAMES A. HALEY VETERANS' HOSPITAL-TAMPA (O, 499 beds) 13000 Bruce B Downs Boulevard, Tampa, FL Zip 33612–4745; tel. 813/972–2000; Joe Battle, Director
Web address: www.tampa.va.gov/

MIAMI VETERANS AFFAIRS HEALTHCARE SYSTEM (O, 401 beds) 1201 NW 16th Street, Miami, FL Zip 33125–1624; tel. 305/575–7000; Paul M. Russo, FACHE, Director

NORTH FLORIDA/SOUTH GEORGIA VETERAN'S HEALTH SYSTEM (O, 623 beds) 1601 SW Archer Road, Gainesville, FL Zip 32608–1135; tel. 352/376–1611; Thomas Wisnieski, FACHE, Director
Web address: www.northflorida.va.gov

WEST PALM BEACH VETERANS AFFAIRS MEDICAL CENTER (O, 300 beds) 7305 North Military Trail, West Palm Beach, FL Zip 33410–6400; tel. 561/422–8262; Donna Katen-Bahensky, Director
Web address: www.westpalmbeach.va.gov/

For explanation of codes following names, see page B2.
★ Indicates Type III membership in the American Hospital Association.

GEORGIA: ATLANTA VETERANS AFFAIRS MEDICAL CENTER (O, 239 beds) 1670 Clairmont Road, Decatur, GA Zip 30033–4004; tel. 404/321–6111; Annette Walker, Director
Web address: www.atlanta.va.gov/

CARL VINSON VETERANS AFFAIRS MEDICAL CENTER (O, 178 beds) 1826 Veterans Boulevard, Dublin, GA Zip 31021–3620; tel. 478/272–1210; Maryalice Morro, MSN, R.N., Director
Web address: www.dublin.va.gov/

CHARLIE NORWOOD VETERANS AFFAIRS MEDICAL CENTER (O, 338 beds) 1 Freedom Way, Augusta, GA Zip 30904–6285; tel. 706/733–0188; Maria R. Andrews, MS, Director
Web address: www.augusta.va.gov/

HAWAII: VETERANS AFFAIRS PACIFIC ISLANDS HEALTH CARE SYSTEM (O, 80 beds) 459 Patterson Road, Honolulu, HI Zip 96819–1522; tel. 808/433–0600; Jennifer S. Gutowski, FACHE, Director

IDAHO: BOISE VETERANS AFFAIRS MEDICAL CENTER (O, 100 beds) 500 West Fort Street, Boise, ID Zip 83702–4598; tel. 208/422–1000; David P. Wood, FACHE, Director
Web address: www.boise.va.gov/

ILLINOIS: CAPTAIN JAMES A. LOVELL FEDERAL HEALTH CARE CENTER (O, 314 beds) 3001 Green Bay Road, North Chicago, IL Zip 60064–3049; tel. 847/688–1900; Stephen R. Holt, M.D., Director
Web address: www.lovell.fhcc.va.gov

EDWARD HINES, JR. VETERANS AFFAIRS HOSPITAL (O, 485 beds) 5000 South Fifth Avenue, Hines, IL Zip 60141–3030, P O Box 5000, 60141–5000, tel. 708/202–8387; Steven E. Braverman, M.D., Director

JESSE BROWN VETERANS AFFAIRS MEDICAL CENTER (O, 207 beds) 820 South Damen, Chicago, IL Zip 60612–3776; tel. 312/569–8387; Marc Magill, Director
Web address: www.chicago.va.gov/

MARION VETERANS AFFAIRS MEDICAL CENTER (O, 54 beds) 2401 West Main Street, Marion, IL Zip 62959–1188; tel. 618/997–5311; Jo-Ann M. Ginsberg, R.N., MSN, Director

VETERANS AFFAIRS ILLIANA HEALTH CARE SYSTEM (O, 221 beds) 1900 East Main Street, Danville, IL Zip 61832–5198; tel. 217/554–3000; Diana Carranza, Interim Director
Web address: www.danville.va.gov/

INDIANA: RICHARD L. ROUDEBUSH VETERANS AFFAIRS MEDICAL CENTER (O, 209 beds) 1481 West Tenth Street, Indianapolis, IN Zip 46202–2884; tel. 317/554–0000; Brian Hancock, M.D., Director
Web address: www.indianapolis.va.gov

VETERANS AFFAIRS NORTHERN INDIANA HEALTH CARE SYSTEM (O, 26 beds) 2121 Lake Avenue, Fort Wayne, IN Zip 46805–5100; tel. 260/426–5431; Mark Murdock, FACHE, Director

IOWA: IOWA CITY VETERANS AFFAIRS HEALTH CARE SYSTEM (O, 74 beds) 601 Highway 6 West, Iowa City, IA Zip 52246–2208; tel. 319/338–0581; Judith Johnson-Mekota, Director
Web address: www.iowacity.va.gov/

VETERANS AFFAIRS CENTRAL IOWA HEALTH CARE SYSTEM (O, 200 beds) 3600 30th Street, Des Moines, IA Zip 50310–5753; tel. 515/699–5999; Gail L. Graham, Director
Web address: www.centraliowa.va.gov/

KANSAS: ROBERT J. DOLE VETERANS AFFAIRS MEDICAL CENTER (O, 41 beds) 5500 East Kellogg, Wichita, KS Zip 67218–1607; tel. 316/685–2221; Rick Ament, Chief Executive Officer

VETERANS AFFAIRS EASTERN KANSAS HEALTH CARE SYSTEM (O, 213 beds) 2200 South West Gage Boulevard, Topeka, KS Zip 66622–0002; tel. 785/350–3111; Anthony Rudy. Klopfer, FACHE, Director
Web address: www.topeka.va.gov/

KENTUCKY: LEXINGTON VETERANS AFFAIRS MEDICAL CENTER (O, 45 beds) 1101 Veterans Drive, Lexington, KY Zip 40502–2235; tel. 859/281–4901; Emma Metcalf, MSN, R.N., Director
Web address: www.lexington.va.gov/

ROBLEY REX VETERANS AFFAIRS MEDICAL CENTER (O, 116 beds) 800 Zorn Avenue, Louisville, KY Zip 40206–1499; tel. 502/287–4000; Martin J. Traxler, Chief Executive Officer

LOUISIANA: ALEXANDRIA VETERANS AFFAIRS HEALTH CARE SYSTEM (O, 143 beds) 2495 Shreveport Highway, 71 N, Pineville, LA Zip 71360–4044,

P O Box 69004, Alexandria, 71306–9004, tel. 318/473–0010; Peter C. Dancy Jr, Director
Web address: www.alexandria.va.gov/

OVERTON BROOKS VETERANS AFFAIRS MEDICAL CENTER (O, 100 beds) 510 East Stoner Avenue, Shreveport, LA Zip 71101–4295; tel. 318/221–8411; Richard Crockett, Director
Web address: www.shreveport.va.gov/

MAINE: MAINE VETERANS AFFAIRS MEDICAL CENTER (O, 167 beds) 1 VA Center, Augusta, ME Zip 04330–6719; tel. 207/623–8411; Ryan S. Lilly, Director

MARYLAND: VETERANS AFFAIRS MARYLAND HEALTH CARE SYSTEM-BALTIMORE DIVISION (O, 727 beds) 10 North Greene Street, Baltimore, MD Zip 21201–1524; tel. 410/605–7001; Adam M. Robinson, Director
Web address: www.maryland.va.gov/

MASSACHUSETTS: BEDFORD VETERANS AFFAIRS MEDICAL CENTER, EDITH NOURSE ROGERS MEMORIAL VETERANS HOSPITAL (O, 461 beds) 200 Springs Road, Bedford, MA Zip 01730–1198; tel. 781/687–2000; Karen Acerra-Williams, Acting Director

VETERANS AFFAIRS BOSTON HEALTHCARE SYSTEM BROCKTON DIVISION (O, 375 beds) 940 Belmont Street, Brockton, MA Zip 02301–5596; tel. 508/583–4500; Vincent Ng, Interim Director
Web address: www.boston.va.gov/

VETERANS AFFAIRS BOSTON HEALTHCARE SYSTEM (O, 361 beds) 1400 VFW Parkway, West Roxbury, MA Zip 02132–4927; tel. 617/323–7700; Vincent Ng, Director
Web address: www.boston.va.gov/

VETERANS AFFAIRS CENTRAL WESTERN MASSACHUSETTS HEALTHCARE SYSTEM (O, 117 beds) 421 North Main Street, Leeds, MA Zip 01053–9764; tel. 413/582–3000; John P. Collins, FACHE, Medical Center Director

MICHIGAN: ALEDA E. LUTZ VETERANS AFFAIRS MEDICAL CENTER (O, 89 beds) 1500 Weiss Street, Saginaw, MI Zip 48602–5298; tel. 989/497–2500; Ginny L. Creasman, Director
Web address: www.saginaw.va.gov/

BATTLE CREEK VETERANS AFFAIRS MEDICAL CENTER (O, 242 beds) 5500 Armstrong Road, Battle Creek, MI Zip 49037–7314; tel. 269/966–5600; Mary Beth Skupien, Director

JOHN D. DINGELL VETERANS AFFAIRS MEDICAL CENTER (O, 216 beds) 4646 John 'R' Street, Detroit, MI Zip 48201–1932; tel. 313/576–1000; Pamela J. Reeves, M.D., Director
Web address: www.detroit.va.gov/

OSCAR G. JOHNSON VETERANS AFFAIRS MEDICAL CENTER (O, 17 beds) 325 East 'H' Street, Iron Mountain, MI Zip 49801–4792; tel. 906/774–3300; James W. Rice, Director

VETERANS AFFAIRS ANN ARBOR HEALTHCARE SYSTEM (O, 109 beds) 2215 Fuller Road, Ann Arbor, MI Zip 48105–2399; tel. 734/769–7100; Andrew Pacyna, FACHE, Acting Director
Web address: www.annarbor.va.gov

MINNESOTA: MINNEAPOLIS VETERANS AFFAIRS HEALTH CARE SYSTEM (O, 309 beds) One Veterans Drive, Minneapolis, MN Zip 55417–2399; tel. 612/725–2000; Patrick J. Kelly, FACHE, Director

ST. CLOUD VETERANS AFFAIRS HEALTH CARE SYSTEM (O, 388 beds) 4801 Veterans Drive, Saint Cloud, MN Zip 56303–2099; tel. 320/252–1670; Stephen Black, MS, Health Care System Director
Web address: www.stcloud.va.gov

MISSISSIPPI: G.V. (SONNY) MONTGOMERY VETERANS AFFAIRS MEDICAL CENTER (O, 323 beds) 1500 East Woodrow Wilson Drive, Jackson, MS Zip 39216–5199; tel. 601/362–4471; David M. Walker, M.D., Medical Center Director
Web address: www.jackson.va.gov/

VETERANS AFFAIRS GULF COAST VETERANS HEALTH CARE SYSTEM (O, 392 beds) 400 Veterans Avenue, Biloxi, MS Zip 39531–2410; tel. 228/523–5000; Christopher M. Saslo, Acting Director

MISSOURI: HARRY S. TRUMAN MEMORIAL VETERANS HOSPITAL (O, 123 beds) 800 Hospital Drive, Columbia, MO Zip 65201–5275; tel. 573/814–6000; David Isaacks, Director
Web address: www.columbiamo.va.gov

Section B

JOHN J. PERSHING VETERANS AFFAIRS MEDICAL CENTER (O, 58 beds) 1500 North Westwood Boulevard, Poplar Bluff, MO Zip 63901–3318; tel. 573/686–4151; Patricia Ten Haaf, R.N., MSN, Ph.D., Director

KANSAS CITY VETERANS AFFAIRS MEDICAL CENTER (O, 157 beds) 4801 East Linwood Boulevard, Kansas City, MO Zip 64128–2226; tel. 816/861–4700; Kathleen R. Fogarty, MS, Director
Web address: www.kansascity.va.gov/

VETERANS AFFAIRS ST. LOUIS HEALTH CARE SYSTEM (O, 356 beds) 915 North Grand, Saint Louis, MO Zip 63106–1621; tel. 314/652–4100; Keith D. Repko, Director

MONTANA: VETERANS AFFAIRS MONTANA HEALTH CARE SYSTEM (O, 94 beds) 3687 Veterans Drive, Fort Harrison, MT Zip 59636–9703, P O Box 1500, 59636–1500, tel. 406/442–6410; Kathy Berger, Director
Web address: www.montana.va.gov/

NEBRASKA: VETERANS AFFAIRS NEBRASKA-WESTERN IOWA HEALTH CARE SYSTEM - LINCOLN (O, 132 beds) 600 South 70th Street, Lincoln, NE Zip 68510–2493; tel. 402/489–3802; Don Burman, Director
Web address: www.nebraska.va.gov/

VETERANS AFFAIRS NEBRASKA-WESTERN IOWA HEALTH CARE SYSTEM (O, 137 beds) 4101 Woolworth Avenue, Omaha, NE Zip 68105–1873; tel. 402/346–8800; Don Burman, Director
Web address: www.nebraska.va.gov/

NEVADA: VETERANS AFFAIRS SIERRA NEVADA HEALTH CARE SYSTEM (O, 124 beds) 975 Kirman Avenue, Reno, NV Zip 89502–0993; tel. 775/786–7200; Lisa M. Howard, Director
Web address: www.reno.va.gov/

VETERANS AFFAIRS SOUTHERN NEVADA HEALTHCARE SYSTEM (O, 90 beds) 6900 North Pecos Road, North Las Vegas, NV Zip 89086–4400; tel. 702/791–9000; Peggy W. Kearns, MS, FACHE, Executive Director

NEW HAMPSHIRE: MANCHESTER VETERANS AFFAIRS MEDICAL CENTER (O, 90 beds) 718 Smyth Road, Manchester, NH Zip 03104–4098; tel. 603/624–4366; Alfred Montoya, Director
Web address: www.manchester.va.gov/

NEW JERSEY: VETERANS AFFAIRS NEW JERSEY HEALTH CARE SYSTEM (O, 439 beds) 385 Tremont Avenue, East Orange, NJ Zip 07018–1095; tel. 973/676–1000; Vincent F. Immiti, FACHE, Director
Web address: www.newjersey.va.gov/

NEW MEXICO: NEW MEXICO VETERANS AFFAIRS HEALTH CARE SYSTEM - RAYMOND G. MURPHY MEDICAL CENTER (O, 203 beds) 1501 San Pedro SE, Albuquerque, NM Zip 87108–5153; tel. 505/265–1711; Andrew Welch, Director
Web address: www.albuquerque.va.gov/

NEW YORK: ALBANY STRATTON VETERANS AFFAIRS MEDICAL CENTER (O, 121 beds) 113 Holland Avenue, Albany, NY Zip 12208–3473; tel. 518/626–5000; Darlene DeLancey, Interim Director
Web address: www.albany.va.gov/

BATH VETERANS AFFAIRS MEDICAL CENTER (O, 274 beds) 76 Veterans Avenue, Bath, NY Zip 14810–0842; tel. 607/664–4000; Michael J. Swartz, FACHE, Medical Center Director

CANANDAIGUA VETERANS AFFAIRS MEDICAL CENTER (O, 196 beds) 400 Fort Hill Avenue, Canandaigua, NY Zip 14424–1159; tel. 585/394–2000; Michael J. Swartz, FACHE, Medical Center Director
Web address: www.canandaigua.va.gov/

JAMES J. PETERS VETERANS AFFAIRS MEDICAL CENTER (O, 325 beds) 130 West Kingsbridge Road, Bronx, NY Zip 10468–3904; tel. 718/584–9000; Erik Langhoff, M.D., Ph.D., Director

NORTHPORT VETERANS AFFAIRS MEDICAL CENTER (O, 254 beds) 79 Middleville Road, Northport, NY Zip 11768–2200; tel. 631/261–4400; D. Scott. Guermonprez, FACHE, Director
Web address: www.northport.va.gov/index.asp

SYRACUSE VETERANS AFFAIRS MEDICAL CENTER (O, 161 beds) 800 Irving Avenue, Syracuse, NY Zip 13210–2716; tel. 315/425–4400; Judy A. Hayman, Ph.D., Interim Director

VETERANS AFFAIRS HUDSON VALLEY HEALTH CARE SYSTEM (O, 577 beds) 2094 Albany Post Road, Montrose, NY Zip 10548–1454, P O Box 100, 10548–0100, tel. 914/737–4400; Margaret B. Caplan, Director
Web address: www.hudsonvalley.va.gov/

VETERANS AFFAIRS NEW YORK HARBOR HEALTHCARE SYSTEM (O, 522 beds) 800 Poly Place, Brooklyn, NY Zip 11209–7104; tel. 718/630–3500; Martina A. Parauda, Director

VETERANS AFFAIRS WESTERN NEW YORK HEALTHCARE SYSTEM-BATAVIA DIVISION (O, 128 beds) 222 Richmond Avenue, Batavia, NY Zip 14020–1288; tel. 585/297–1000; Brian G. Stiller, Director Medical Center
Web address: www.buffalo.va.gov/batavia.asp

VETERANS AFFAIRS WESTERN NEW YORK HEALTHCARE SYSTEM-BUFFALO DIVISION (O, 113 beds) 3495 Bailey Avenue, Buffalo, NY Zip 14215–1129; tel. 716/834–9200; Brian G. Stiller, Director Medical Center

NORTH CAROLINA: CHARLES GEORGE VETERANS AFFAIRS MEDICAL CENTER (O, 174 beds) 1100 Tunnel Road, Asheville, NC Zip 28805–2087; tel. 828/298–7911; Cynthia Breyfogle, FACHE, Director
Web address: www.asheville.va.gov/

DURHAM VETERANS AFFAIRS MEDICAL CENTER (O, 251 beds) 508 Fulton Street, Durham, NC Zip 27705–3897; tel. 919/286–0411; DeAnne Seekins, Director
Web address: www.durham.va.gov/

FAYETTEVILLE VETERANS AFFAIRS MEDICAL CENTER (O, 58 beds) 2300 Ramsey Street, Fayetteville, NC Zip 28301–3899; tel. 910/488–2120; Elizabeth Goolsby, Director
Web address: www.fayettevillenc.va.gov

W. G. (BILL) HEFFNER VETERANS AFFAIRS MEDICAL CENTER (O, 171 beds) 1601 Brenner Avenue, Salisbury, NC Zip 28144–2559; tel. 704/638–9000; Kaye Green, FACHE, Director
Web address: www.salisbury.va.gov

NORTH DAKOTA: FARGO VETERANS AFFAIRS HEALTH CARE SYSTEM (O, 65 beds) 2101 Elm Street North, Fargo, ND Zip 58102–2498; tel. 701/232–3241; Lavonne Liversage, Director

OHIO: CHILLICOTHE VETERANS AFFAIRS MEDICAL CENTER (O, 295 beds) 17273 State Route 104, Chillicothe, OH Zip 45601–9718; tel. 740/773–1141; Keith Sullivan, Director
Web address: www.chillicothe.va.gov/

CINCINNATI VETERANS AFFAIRS MEDICAL CENTER (O, 268 beds) 3200 Vine Street, Cincinnati, OH Zip 45220–2288; tel. 513/475–6300; Colonel, Vivian T. Hutson, Director
Web address: www.cincinnati.va.gov/

DAYTON VETERANS AFFAIRS MEDICAL CENTER (O, 486 beds) 4100 West Third Street, Dayton, OH Zip 45428–9000; tel. 937/268–6511; Glenn A. Costie, FACHE, Director
Web address: www.dayton.va.gov/

LOUIS STOKES CLEVELAND VETERANS AFFAIRS MEDICAL CENTER (O, 576 beds) 10701 East Boulevard, Cleveland, OH Zip 44106–1702; tel. 216/791–3800; Susan Fuehrer, Director

OKLAHOMA: JACK C. MONTGOMERY VETERANS AFFAIRS MEDICAL CENTER (O, 89 beds) 1011 Honor Heights Drive, Muskogee, OK Zip 74401–1318; tel. 918/577–3000; Mark E. Morgan, Medical Center Director
Web address: www.muskogee.va.gov

OKLAHOMA CITY VETERANS AFFAIRS MEDICAL CENTER (O, 192 beds) 921 NE 13th Street, Oklahoma City, OK Zip 73104–5028; tel. 405/456–1000; Wade Vlosich, Director
Web address: www.oklahoma.va.gov

OREGON: SOUTHERN OREGON-WHITE CITY VETERANS AFFAIRS REHABILITATION CENTER AND CLINICS (O, 1075 beds) 8495 Crater Lake Highway, White City, OR Zip 97503; tel. 503/826–2111; Frank A. Drake, Director

VA PORTLAND HEALTHCARE SYSTEM (O, 176 beds) 3710 SW U S Veterans Hospital Road, Portland, OR Zip 97239–2964, 3710 SW US Veterans Hospital Road, 97207–1034, tel. 503/220–8262; Michael W. Fisher, Director
Web address: www.portland.va.gov/

VETERANS AFFAIRS ROSEBURG HEALTHCARE SYSTEM (O, 88 beds) 913 NW Garden Valley Boulevard, Roseburg, OR Zip 97471–6513; tel. 541/440–1000; Douglas V. Paxton, Director

PENNSYLVANIA: COATESVILLE VETERANS AFFAIRS MEDICAL CENTER (O, 118 beds) 1400 Black Horse Hill Road, Coatesville, PA Zip 19320–2040; tel. 610/384–7711; Carla Sivek, Director
Web address: www.coatesville.va.gov/

For explanation of codes following names, see page B2.
★ Indicates Type III membership in the American Hospital Association.

ERIE VETERANS AFFAIRS MEDICAL CENTER (O, 52 beds) 135 East 38th Street, Erie, PA Zip 16504–1559; tel. 814/860–2576; John Gennaro, FACHE, Director

JAMES E. VAN ZANDT VETERANS AFFAIRS MEDICAL CENTER (O, 68 beds) 2907 Pleasant Valley Boulevard, Altoona, PA Zip 16602–4305; tel. 877/626–2500; Charles Thilges, Director
Web address: www.altoona.va.gov/

LEBANON VETERANS AFFAIRS MEDICAL CENTER (O, 213 beds) 1700 South Lincoln Avenue, Lebanon, PA Zip 17042–7529; tel. 717/272–6621; Margaret G. Wilson, R.N., MSN, Acting Director
Web address: www.lebanon.va.gov

PHILADELPHIA VETERANS AFFAIRS MEDICAL CENTER (O, 291 beds) 3900 Woodland Avenue, Philadelphia, PA Zip 19104–4594; tel. 215/823–5800; Daniel Hendee, Director
Web address: www.philadelphia.va.gov/

VETERANS AFFAIRS PITTSBURGH HEALTHCARE SYSTEM (O, 549 beds) University Drive, Pittsburgh, PA Zip 15240–1001; tel. 866/482–7488; Karin L. McGraw, MSN, FACHE, Director

WILKES-BARRE VETERANS AFFAIRS MEDICAL CENTER (O, 165 beds) 1111 East End Boulevard, Wilkes-Barre, PA Zip 18711–0030; tel. 570/824–3521; Russell E. Lloyd, Director
Web address: www.va.gov/vamcwb

PUERTO RICO: VETERANS AFFAIRS CARIBBEAN HEALTHCARE SYSTEM (O, 422 beds) 10 Casia Street, San Juan, PR Zip 00921–3201; tel. 787/641–7582; Antonio Sanchez, M.D., Acting Director
Web address: www.caribbean.va.gov/

RHODE ISLAND: PROVIDENCE VETERANS AFFAIRS MEDICAL CENTER (O, 73 beds) 830 Chalkstone Avenue, Providence, RI Zip 02908–4799; tel. 401/273–7100; Susan MacKenzie, Ph.D., Director

SOUTH CAROLINA: RALPH H. JOHNSON VETERANS AFFAIRS MEDICAL CENTER (O, 98 beds) 109 Bee Street, Charleston, SC Zip 29401–5799; tel. 843/577–5011; Scott R. Isaacks, FACHE, Director and Chief Executive Officer
Web address: www.charleston.va.gov/

WM. JENNINGS BRYAN DORN VETERANS AFFAIRS MEDICAL CENTER (O, 216 beds) 6439 Garners Ferry Road, Columbia, SC Zip 29209–1639; tel. 803/776–4000; David Omura, Interim Director

SOUTH DAKOTA: SIOUX FALLS VETERANS AFFAIRS HEALTH CARE SYSTEM (O, 86 beds) 2501 West 22nd Street, Sioux Falls, SD Zip 57105–1305, P O Box 5046, 57117–5046, tel. 605/336–3230; Darwin Goodspeed, Director
Web address: www.siouxfalls.va.gov

VETERANS AFFAIRS BLACK HILLS HEALTH CARE SYSTEM (O, 243 beds) 113 Comanche Road, Fort Meade, SD Zip 57741–1099; tel. 605/347–2511; Sandra Horsman, Director

TENNESSEE: JAMES H. QUILLEN VETERANS AFFAIRS MEDICAL CENTER (O, 98 beds) Corner of Lamont & Veterans Way, Mountain Home, TN Zip 37684, P O Box 4000, 37684–4000, tel. 423/926–1171; Dean B. Boros, Medical Center Director
Web address: www.mountainhome.va.gov/

MEMPHIS VETERANS AFFAIRS MEDICAL CENTER (O, 251 beds) 1030 Jefferson Avenue, Memphis, TN Zip 38104–2193; tel. 901/523–8990; David P. Wood, FACHE, Interim Director
Web address: www.memphis.va.gov/

TENNESSEE VALLEY HEALTHCARE SYSTEM (O, 546 beds) 1310 24th Avenue South, Nashville, TN Zip 37212–2637; tel. 615/327–4751; Captain, Jennifer Vedral-Baron, Health System Director

TEXAS: AMARILLO VETERANS AFFAIRS HEALTH CARE SYSTEM (O, 55 beds) 6010 West Amarillo Boulevard, Amarillo, TX Zip 79106–1992; tel. 806/355–9703; Elizabeth Lowery, Interim Director
Web address: www.amarillo.va.gov/

CENTRAL TEXAS VETERANS HEALTH CARE SYSTEM (O, 1532 beds) 1901 Veterans Memorial Drive, Temple, TX Zip 76504–7493; tel. 254/778–4811; Christopher R. Sandles, FACHE, Director

MICHAEL E. DEBAKEY VETERANS AFFAIRS MEDICAL CENTER (O, 479 beds) 2002 Holcombe Boulevard, Houston, TX Zip 77030–4298; tel. 713/791–1414; Francisco Vazquez, Director
Web address: www.houston.va.gov

SOUTH TEXAS VETERANS HEALTH CARE SYSTEM (O, 838 beds) 7400 Merton Minter Boulevard, San Antonio, TX Zip 78229–4404; tel. 210/617–5300; Robert M. Walton, Healthcare System Director
Web address: www.southtexas.va.gov/

VETERANS AFFAIRS NORTH TEXAS HEALTH CARE SYSTEM (O, 875 beds) 4500 South Lancaster Road, Dallas, TX Zip 75216–7167; tel. 214/742–8387; Kendrick Brown, Interim Director
Web address: www.northtexas.va.gov/

WEST TEXAS VETERANS AFFAIRS HEALTH CARE SYSTEM (O, 149 beds) 300 Veterans Boulevard, Big Spring, TX Zip 79720–5500, Big Springs, tel. 432/263–7361; Kalautie JangDhari, Director

UTAH: VETERANS AFFAIRS SALT LAKE CITY HEALTH CARE SYSTEM (O, 130 beds) 500 Foothill Drive, Salt Lake City, UT Zip 84148–0002; tel. 801/582–1565; Shella D. Stovall, R.N., Acting Director
Web address: www.saltlakecity.va.gov/

VERMONT: WHITE RIVER JUNCTION VETERANS AFFAIRS MEDICAL CENTER (O, 74 beds) 215 North Main Street, White River Junction, VT Zip 05009–0001; tel. 802/295–9363; Matthew Mulcahy, Acting Director

VIRGINIA: HAMPTON VETERANS AFFAIRS MEDICAL CENTER (O, 451 beds) 100 Emancipation Drive, Hampton, VA Zip 23667–0001; tel. 757/722–9961; J. Ronald. Johnson, Medical Center Director
Web address: www.hampton.va.gov/

HUNTER HOLMES MCGUIRE VETERANS AFFAIRS MEDICAL CENTER-RICHMOND (O, 381 beds) 1201 Broad Rock Boulevard, Richmond, VA Zip 23249–0002; tel. 804/675–5000; John A. Brandecker, M.P.H., Director
Web address: www.richmond.va.gov/

SALEM VETERANS AFFAIRS MEDICAL CENTER (O, 200 beds) 1970 Roanoke Boulevard, Salem, VA Zip 24153–6478; tel. 540/982–2463; Rebecca J. Stackhouse, Medical Center Director

WASHINGTON: MANN-GRANDSTAFF VETERANS AFFAIRS MEDICAL CENTER (O, 68 beds) 4815 North Assembly Street, Spokane, WA Zip 99205–6197; tel. 509/434–7000; Tracye B. Davis, Interim Medical Center Director
Web address: www.spokane.va.gov/

VETERANS AFFAIRS PUGET SOUND HEALTH CARE SYSTEM (O, 358 beds) 1660 South Columbian Way, Seattle, WA Zip 98108–1597; tel. 206/762–1010; Michael Tadych, Director

WEST VIRGINIA: BECKLEY VETERANS AFFAIRS MEDICAL CENTER (O, 40 beds) 200 Veterans Avenue, Beckley, WV Zip 25801–6499; tel. 304/255–2121; Stacy J. Vasquez, Director
Web address: www.beckley.va.gov/

HUNTINGTON VETERANS AFFAIRS MEDICAL CENTER (O, 80 beds) 1540 Spring Valley Drive, Huntington, WV Zip 25704–9300; tel. 304/429–6741; Brian Nimmo, Director

LOUIS A. JOHNSON VETERANS AFFAIRS MEDICAL CENTER (O, 71 beds) 1 Medical Center Drive, Clarksburg, WV Zip 26301–4199; tel. 304/623–3461; Glenn R. Snider, M.D., Interim Director
Web address: www.clarksburg.va.gov

MARTINSBURG VETERANS AFFAIRS MEDICAL CENTER (O, 487 beds) 510 Butler Avenue, Martinsburg, WV Zip 25405–9990; tel. 304/263–0811; Timothy J. Cooke, Medical Center Director and Chief Executive Officer
Web address: www.martinsburg.va.gov/

WISCONSIN: CLEMENT J. ZABLOCKI VETERANS AFFAIRS MEDICAL CENTER (O, 637 beds) 5000 West National Avenue, Milwaukee, WI Zip 53295–0001; tel. 414/384–2000; Daniel Zomchek, Ph.D., Executive Director
Web address: www.milwaukee.va.gov/

TOMAH VETERANS AFFAIRS MEDICAL CENTER (O, 71 beds) 500 East Veterans Street, Tomah, WI Zip 54660–3105; tel. 608/372–3971; Victoria Brahm, R.N., MSN, Acting Director

WILLIAM S. MIDDLETON MEMORIAL VETERANS HOSPITAL (O, 87 beds) 2500 Overlook Terrace, Madison, WI Zip 53705–2286; tel. 608/256–1901; John J. Rohrer, Director
Web address: www.madison.va.gov

WYOMING: CHEYENNE VETERANS AFFAIRS MEDICAL CENTER (O, 61 beds) 2360 East Pershing Boulevard, Cheyenne, WY Zip 82001–5392; tel. 307/778–7550; Paul L. Roberts, Director
Web address: www.cheyenne.va.gov/

Section B

For explanation of codes following names, see page B2.
★ Indicates Type III membership in the American Hospital Association.

SHERIDAN VETERANS AFFAIRS MEDICAL CENTER (O, 185 beds) 1898 Fort Road, Sheridan, WY Zip 82801–8320; tel. 307/672–3473; Kathy Berger, R.N., Interim Director
Web address: www.sheridan.va.gov/

Owned, leased, sponsored:	135 hospitals	35270 beds
Contract-managed:	0 hospitals	0 beds
Totals:	135 hospitals	35270 beds

0845: DEVEREUX (NP)

444 Devereux Drive, Villanova, PA Zip 19085–1932, P O Box 638, 19085–0638, tel. 610/520–3000; Robert Q. Kreider, President and Chief Executive Officer
(Independent Hospital System)

FLORIDA: DEVEREUX HOSPITAL AND CHILDREN'S CENTER OF FLORIDA (O, 100 beds) 8000 Devereux Drive, Melbourne, FL Zip 32940–7907; tel. 321/242–9100; Steven Murphy, Executive Director

GEORGIA: DEVEREUX GEORGIA TREATMENT NETWORK (O, 100 beds) 1291 Stanley Road NW, Kennesaw, GA Zip 30152–4359; tel. 770/427–0147; Gwendolyn Skinner, Executive Director
Web address: www.devereuxga.org

PENNSYLVANIA: DEVEREUX CHILDREN'S BEHAVIORAL HEALTH CENTER (O, 49 beds) 655 Sugartown Road, Malvern, PA Zip 19355–3303, 655 Sugartown Rd, 19355–3303, tel. 800/345–1292; David E. Woodward, Executive Director
Web address: www.devereux.org

TEXAS: DEVEREUX TEXAS TREATMENT NETWORK (O, 48 beds) 1150 Devereux Drive, League City, TX Zip 77573–2043; tel. 281/335–1000; Pamela E. Helm, Executive Director

Owned, leased, sponsored:	4 hospitals	297 beds
Contract-managed:	0 hospitals	0 beds
Totals:	4 hospitals	297 beds

★5205: DIGNITY HEALTH (CC)

185 Berry Street, Suite 300, San Francisco, CA Zip 94107–1773; tel. 415/438–5500; Lloyd H. Dean, President and Chief Executive Officer
(Decentralized Health System)

ARIZONA: CHANDLER REGIONAL MEDICAL CENTER (O, 338 beds) 1955 West Frye Road, Chandler, AZ Zip 85224–6282; tel. 480/728–3000; Jane E. Hanson, R.N., Interim Chief Executive Officer
Web address: www.chandlerregional.com

MERCY GILBERT MEDICAL CENTER (S, 198 beds) 3555 South Val Vista Road, Gilbert, AZ Zip 85297–7323; tel. 480/728–8000; Jane E. Hanson, R.N., Interim President and Chief Executive Officer

ST. JOSEPH'S HOSPITAL AND MEDICAL CENTER (S, 573 beds) 350 West Thomas Road, Phoenix, AZ Zip 85013–4496, P O Box 2071, 85001–2071, tel. 602/406–3000; Patty White, R.N., MS, President
Web address: www.stjosephs-phx.org

CALIFORNIA: BAKERSFIELD MEMORIAL HOSPITAL (O, 398 beds) 420 34th Street, Bakersfield, CA Zip 93301–2237; tel. 661/327–1792; Jon Van Boening, President and Chief Executive Officer
Web address: www.bakersfieldmemorial.org

CALIFORNIA HOSPITAL MEDICAL CENTER (O, 318 beds) 1401 South Grand Avenue, Los Angeles, CA Zip 90015–3010; tel. 213/748–2411; Margaret R. Peterson, Ph.D., R.N., President

COMMUNITY HOSPITAL OF SAN BERNARDINO (O, 379 beds) 1805 Medical Center Drive, San Bernardino, CA Zip 92411–1214; tel. 909/887–6333; June Collison, President
Web address: www.dignityhealth.org/san-bernardino

DOMINICAN HOSPITAL (S, 223 beds) 1555 Soquel Drive, Santa Cruz, CA Zip 95065–1794; tel. 831/462–7700; Nanette Mickiewicz, M.D., President

FRENCH HOSPITAL MEDICAL CENTER (O, 72 beds) 1911 Johnson Avenue, San Luis Obispo, CA Zip 93401–4197; tel. 805/543–5353; Alan Iftiniuk, Chief Executive Officer
Web address: www.frenchmedicalcenter.org

GLENDALE MEMORIAL HOSPITAL AND HEALTH CENTER (O, 334 beds) 1420 South Central Avenue, Glendale, CA Zip 91204–2594; tel. 818/502–1900; Julie Sprengel, Interim President
Web address: www.glendalememorial.com

MARIAN REGIONAL MEDICAL CENTER (S, 286 beds) 1400 East Church Street, Santa Maria, CA Zip 93454–5906; tel. 805/739–3000; Charles J. Cova, Senior Vice President, Operations

MARK TWAIN MEDICAL CENTER (O, 25 beds) 768 Mountain Ranch Road, San Andreas, CA Zip 95249–9998; tel. 209/754–3521; Robert Diehl, President
Web address: www.marktwainhospital.com

MERCY GENERAL HOSPITAL (S, 254 beds) 4001 'J' Street, Sacramento, CA Zip 95819–3600; tel. 916/453–4545; Edmundo Castaneda, President
Web address: www.mercygeneral.org

MERCY HOSPITAL OF FOLSOM (S, 106 beds) 1650 Creekside Drive, Folsom, CA Zip 95630–3400; tel. 916/983–7400; Edmundo Castaneda, President
Web address: www.mercyfolsom.org

MERCY HOSPITALS OF BAKERSFIELD (S, 222 beds) 2215 Truxtun Avenue, Bakersfield, CA Zip 93301–3698, P O Box 119, 93302–0119, tel. 661/632–5000; Bruce Peters, Chief Executive Officer

MERCY MEDICAL CENTER MERCED (S, 186 beds) 333 Mercy Avenue, Merced, CA Zip 95340–8319; tel. 209/564–5000; Charles Kassis, President
Web address: www.mercymercedcares.org

MERCY MEDICAL CENTER MOUNT SHASTA (S, 33 beds) 914 Pine Street, Mount Shasta, CA Zip 96067–2143; tel. 530/926–6111; Kenneth E S. Platou, President

MERCY MEDICAL CENTER REDDING (S, 267 beds) 2175 Rosaline Avenue, Redding, CA Zip 96001–2549, P O Box 496009, 96049–6009, tel. 530/225–6000; James DeSoto, M.D., Interim President
Web address: www.mercy.org

MERCY SAN JUAN MEDICAL CENTER (S, 340 beds) 6501 Coyle Avenue, Carmichael, CA Zip 95608–0306; tel. 916/537–5000; Brian K. Ivie, President
Web address: www.mercysanjuan.org

METHODIST HOSPITAL OF SACRAMENTO (O, 329 beds) 7500 Hospital Drive, Sacramento, CA Zip 95823–5477; tel. 916/423–3000; Brian K. Ivie, President and Chief Executive Officer
Web address: www.methodistsacramento.org

NORTHRIDGE HOSPITAL MEDICAL CENTER (O, 371 beds) 18300 Roscoe Boulevard, Northridge, CA Zip 91328–4167; tel. 818/885–8500; Saliba Salo, President
Web address: www.northridgehospital.org

SAINT FRANCIS MEMORIAL HOSPITAL (O, 239 beds) 900 Hyde Street, San Francisco, CA Zip 94109–4899, P O Box 7726, 94120–7726, tel. 415/353–6000; David G. Klein, M.D., President

SEQUOIA HOSPITAL (O, 129 beds) 170 Alameda De Las Pulgas, Redwood City, CA Zip 94062–2799; tel. 650/369–5811; Bill Graham, President
Web address: www.sequoiahospital.org

SIERRA NEVADA MEMORIAL HOSPITAL (O, 121 beds) 155 Glasson Way, Grass Valley, CA Zip 95945–5723, P O Box 1029, 95945–1029, tel. 530/274–6000; Katherine A. Medeiros, President and Chief Executive Officer

ST. BERNARDINE MEDICAL CENTER (S, 342 beds) 2101 North Waterman Avenue, San Bernardino, CA Zip 92404–4855; tel. 909/883–8711; Douglas V. Kleam, President
Web address: www.stbernardinemedicalcenter.com

ST. ELIZABETH COMMUNITY HOSPITAL (S, 65 beds) 2550 Sister Mary Columba Drive, Red Bluff, CA Zip 96080–4397; tel. 530/529–8000; G. Todd. Smith, President

ST. JOHN'S PLEASANT VALLEY HOSPITAL (S, 127 beds) 2309 Antonio Avenue, Camarillo, CA Zip 93010–1414; tel. 805/389–5800; Darren W. Lee, President and Chief Executive Officer
Web address: www.dignityhealth.org/pleasantvalley

ST. JOHN'S REGIONAL MEDICAL CENTER (S, 139 beds) 1600 North Rose Avenue, Oxnard, CA Zip 93030–3723; tel. 805/988–2500; Darren W. Lee, President and Chief Executive Officer

For explanation of codes following names, see page B2.
★ Indicates Type III membership in the American Hospital Association.

Section B

ST. JOSEPH'S BEHAVIORAL HEALTH CENTER (S, 35 beds) 2510 North California Street, Stockton, CA Zip 95204–5568; tel. 209/461–2000; Paul Rains, R.N., MSN, President
Web address: www.stjosephscanhelp.org

ST. JOSEPH'S MEDICAL CENTER (S, 273 beds) 1800 North California Street, Stockton, CA Zip 95204–6019, P O Box 213008, 95213–9008, tel. 209/943–2000; Donald J. Wiley, President and Chief Executive Officer

ST. MARY MEDICAL CENTER (S, 302 beds) 1050 Linden Avenue, Long Beach, CA Zip 90813–3321, P O Box 887, 90801–0887, tel. 562/491–9000; Paul M. Czajka , Interim Chief Executive Officer
Web address: www.stmarymedicalcenter.org

ST. MARY'S MEDICAL CENTER (S, 232 beds) 450 Stanyan Street, San Francisco, CA Zip 94117–1079; tel. 415/668–1000; Pamela Lindemoen, President

WOODLAND HEALTHCARE (O, 108 beds) 1325 Cottonwood Street, Woodland, CA Zip 95695–5199; tel. 530/662–3961; H Kevin. Vaziri, President
Web address: www.woodlandhealthcare.org

NEVADA: ST. ROSE DOMINICAN HOSPITALS - ROSE DE LIMA CAMPUS (S, 110 beds) 102 East Lake Mead Parkway, Henderson, NV Zip 89015–5524; tel. 702/616–5000; Teressa Conley, President and Chief Executive Officer

ST. ROSE DOMINICAN HOSPITALS - SAN MARTIN CAMPUS (O, 147 beds) 8280 West Warm Springs Road, Las Vegas, NV Zip 89113–3612; tel. 702/492–8000; Lawrence Barnard, President and Chief Executive Officer
Web address: www.strosehospitals.org

ST. ROSE DOMINICAN HOSPITALS - SIENA CAMPUS (S, 326 beds) 3001 St Rose Parkway, Henderson, NV Zip 89052; tel. 702/616–5000; Eugene Bassett, President and Chief Executive Officer

Owned, leased, sponsored:	35 hospitals	7947 beds
Contract-managed:	0 hospitals	0 beds
Totals:	35 hospitals	7947 beds

0029: DIMENSIONS HEALTHCARE SYSTEM (NP)
3001 Hospital Drive, 3rd Floor, Cheverly, MD Zip 20785–1189; tel. 301/583–4000; Neil J. Moore, President and Chief Executive Officer
(Moderately Centralized Health System)

MARYLAND: LAUREL REGIONAL HOSPITAL (O, 58 beds) 7300 Van Dusen Road, Laurel, MD Zip 20707–9463; tel. 301/725–4300; Trudy Hall, M.D., Vice President Medical Affairs and Interim Chief Executive Officer
Web address: www.laurelregionalhospital.org

PRINCE GEORGE'S HOSPITAL CENTER (O, 177 beds) 3001 Hospital Drive, Cheverly, MD Zip 20785–1189; tel. 301/618–2000; K Singh. Taneja, Chief Operating Officer
Web address: www.princegeorgeshospital.org

Owned, leased, sponsored:	2 hospitals	235 beds
Contract-managed:	0 hospitals	0 beds
Totals:	2 hospitals	235 beds

0010: DIVISION OF MENTAL HEALTH AND ADDICTION SERVICES, DEPARTMENT OF HUMAN SERVICES, STATE OF NEW JERSEY (NP)
222 South Warren Street, Trenton, NJ Zip 08608–2306, P O Box 700, 08625–0700, tel. 609/777–0702; Lynn Kovich, Assistant Commissioner
(Independent Hospital System)

NEW JERSEY: ANCORA PSYCHIATRIC HOSPITAL (O, 449 beds) 301 Spring Garden Road, Hammonton, NJ Zip 08037–9699; tel. 609/561–1700; Christopher Morrison, Chief Executive Officer
Web address: www.state.nj.us/humanservices/dmhs/oshm/aph/

ARTHUR BRISBANE CHILDREN TREATMENT CENTER (O, 92 beds) County Road 524, Farmingdale, NJ Zip 7727, P O Box 625, 7727, Vincent Giampeitro, Chief Executive Officer

GREYSTONE PARK PSYCHIATRIC HOSPITAL (O, 506 beds) 59 Koch Avenue, Morris Plains, NJ Zip 07950–4400; tel. 973/538 1800; Mary Jo Kurtiak, Chief Executive Officer
Web address: www.state.nj.us/humanservices/dmhs/oshm/gpph/

TRENTON PSYCHIATRIC HOSPITAL (O, 431 beds) Route 29 and Sullivan Way, Trenton, NJ Zip 08628–3425, P O Box 7500, West Trenton, 08628–0500, tel. 609/633–1500; Teresa A. McQuaide, Chief Executive Officer
Web address: www.state.nj.us/humanservices/dmhs/oshm/tph/

Owned, leased, sponsored:	4 hospitals	1478 beds
Contract-managed:	0 hospitals	0 beds
Totals:	4 hospitals	1478 beds

0536: DIVISION OF MENTAL HEALTH, DEPARTMENT OF HUMAN SERVICES (NP)
319 East Madison Street, S-3B, Springfield, IL Zip 62701–1035; tel. 217/785–6023; Lorrie Rickman. Jones, Ph.D., Director
(Independent Hospital System)

ILLINOIS: ALTON MENTAL HEALTH CENTER (O, 165 beds) 4500 College Avenue, Alton, IL Zip 62002–5099; tel. 618/474–3800; Brian E. Thomas, Administrator

ANDREW MCFARLAND MENTAL HEALTH CENTER (O, 118 beds) 901 East Southwind Road, Springfield, IL Zip 62703–5125; tel. 217/786–6994; Karen Schweighart, R.N., MS, Administrator

CHESTER MENTAL HEALTH CENTER (O, 245 beds) Chester Road, Chester, IL Zip 62233–0031, Box 31, 62233–0031, tel. 618/826–4571; Leah Hammel, Acting Administrator

CHICAGO-READ MENTAL HEALTH CENTER (O, 200 beds) 4200 North Oak Park Avenue, Chicago, IL Zip 60634–1457; tel. 773/794–4000; Richard Carmik, Facility Director and Hospital Administrator

CHOATE MENTAL HEALTH CENTER (O, 79 beds) 1000 North Main Street, Anna, IL Zip 62906–1699; tel. 618/833–5161; Elaine Ray, Administrator

ELGIN MENTAL HEALTH CENTER (O, 383 beds) 750 South State Street, Elgin, IL Zip 60123–7692; tel. 847/742–1040; Meredith Kiss, Administrator
Web address: www.dhs.state.il.us

JOHN J. MADDEN MENTAL HEALTH CENTER (O, 125 beds) 1200 South First Avenue, Hines, IL Zip 60141–0800; tel. 708/338–7202; Edith Newman, Interim Administrator

Owned, leased, sponsored:	7 hospitals	1315 beds
Contract-managed:	0 hospitals	0 beds
Totals:	7 hospitals	1315 beds

★0861: DUKE LIFEPOINT HEALTHCARE (IO)
330 Seven Springs Way, Brentwood, TN Zip 37027–5098; tel. 615/920–7000; Jeffrey G. Seraphine, FACHE, President
(Moderately Centralized Health System)

MICHIGAN: UP HEALTH SYSTEM-MARQUETTE (O, 268 beds) 580 West College Avenue, Marquette, MI Zip 49855–2736; tel. 906/228–9440; Brian Sinotte, Chief Executive Officer
Web address: www.mgh.org

NORTH CAROLINA: CENTRAL CAROLINA HOSPITAL (O, 137 beds) 1135 Carthage Street, Sanford, NC Zip 27330–4162; tel. 919/774–2100; John Maxwell, Chief Executive Officer

FRYE REGIONAL MEDICAL CENTER (O, 256 beds) 420 North Center Street, Hickory, NC Zip 28601–5049; tel. 828/315–5000; Garfield Atchison, Chief Executive Officer
Web address: www.fryemedctr.com

HARRIS REGIONAL HOSPITAL (O, 86 beds) 68 Hospital Road, Sylva, NC Zip 28779–2722; tel. 828/586–7000; Steve Heatherly, Chief Executive Officer

HAYWOOD REGIONAL MEDICAL CENTER (O, 146 beds) 262 Leroy George Drive, Clyde, NC Zip 28721–7430; tel. 828/456–7311; Rod Harkleroad, R.N., Chief Executive Officer
Web address: www.haymed.org

For explanation of codes following names, see page B2.
★ Indicates Type III membership in the American Hospital Association.

MARIA PARHAM MEDICAL CENTER (O, 102 beds) 566 Ruin Creek Road, Henderson, NC Zip 27536–2927; tel. 252/438–4143; Bert Beard, Chief Executive Officer

PERSON MEMORIAL HOSPITAL (O, 98 beds) 615 Ridge Road, Roxboro, NC Zip 27573–4629; tel. 336/599–2121; David Ziolkowski, Chief Executive Officer
Web address: www.personhospital.com

RUTHERFORD REGIONAL HEALTH SYSTEM (O, 112 beds) 288 South Ridgecrest Avenue, Rutherfordton, NC Zip 28139–2838; tel. 828/286–5000; Rebecca Segal, Chief Executive Officer
Web address: www.rutherfordhosp.org

SWAIN COMMUNITY HOSPITAL (O, 25 beds) 45 Plateau Street, Bryson City, NC Zip 28713–4200; tel. 828/488–2155; Steve Heatherly, Chief Executive Officer

WILSON MEDICAL CENTER (O, 220 beds) 1705 Tarboro Street, SW, Wilson, NC Zip 27893–3428; tel. 252/399–8040; William E. Caldwell Jr, Chief Executive Officer
Web address: www.wilmed.org

PENNSYLVANIA: CONEMAUGH MEMORIAL MEDICAL CENTER (O, 539 beds) 1086 Franklin Street, Johnstown, PA Zip 15905–4398; tel. 814/534–9000; Steven E. Tucker, Chief Executive Officer

CONEMAUGH MEYERSDALE MEDICAL CENTER (O, 20 beds) 200 Hospital Drive, Meyersdale, PA Zip 15552–1249; tel. 814/634–5911; Heather Smith, President
Web address: www.conemaugh.org

CONEMAUGH MINERS MEDICAL CENTER (O, 30 beds) 290 Haida Avenue, Hastings, PA Zip 16646–5610, P O Box 689, 16646–0689, tel. 814/247–3100; Timothy Harclerode, Chief Executive Officer

VIRGINIA: TWIN COUNTY REGIONAL HEALTHCARE (O, 141 beds) 200 Hospital Drive, Galax, VA Zip 24333–2227; tel. 276/236–8181; Dale Alward, Chief Executive Officer
Web address: www.tcrh.org

Owned, leased, sponsored:	14 hospitals	2180 beds
Contract-managed:	0 hospitals	0 beds
Totals:	14 hospitals	2180 beds

★**0190: DUKE UNIVERSITY HEALTH SYSTEM** (NP)
201 Trent Drive, Durham, NC Zip 27710–3037, P O Box 3701, 27710–3701, tel. 919/684–2255; A. Eugene. Washington, M.D., President and Chief Executive Officer
(Centralized Health System)

NORTH CAROLINA: DUKE RALEIGH HOSPITAL (O, 159 beds) 3400 Wake Forest Road, Raleigh, NC Zip 27609–7373; tel. 919/954–3000; David Zaas, M.D., Chief Executive Officer
Web address: www.dukehealthraleigh.org

DUKE REGIONAL HOSPITAL (L, 202 beds) 3643 North Roxboro Street, Durham, NC Zip 27704–2763; tel. 919/470–4000; Kathleen B. Galbraith, FACHE, President

DUKE UNIVERSITY HOSPITAL (O, 925 beds) 2301 Erwin Road, DUMC Box # 3814, Durham, NC Zip 27705–4699, P O Box 3814, 27710–3708, tel. 919/684–8111; Kevin W. Sowers, R.N., MSN, President
Web address: www.dukehealth.org

Owned, leased, sponsored:	3 hospitals	1286 beds
Contract-managed:	0 hospitals	0 beds
Totals:	3 hospitals	1286 beds

1027: DUNCAN REGIONAL HOSPITAL (NP)
1407 North Whisenant Drive, Duncan, OK Zip 73533–1650; tel. 580/252–5300; Jay R. Johnson, FACHE, President and Chief Executive Officer

OKLAHOMA: DUNCAN REGIONAL HOSPITAL (O, 117 beds) 1407 North Whisenant Drive, Duncan, OK Zip 73533–1650, P O Box 2000, 73534–2000, tel. 580/252–5300; Jay R. Johnson, FACHE, President and Chief Executive Officer
Web address: www.duncanregional.com

JEFFERSON COUNTY HOSPITAL (L, 25 beds) Highway 70 and 81, Waurika, OK Zip 73573–3075, P O Box 90, 73573–0090, tel. 580/228–2344; Richard Gillespie, Chief Executive Officer

Owned, leased, sponsored:	2 hospitals	142 beds
Contract-managed:	0 hospitals	0 beds
Totals:	2 hospitals	142 beds

★**1895: EAST TEXAS MEDICAL CENTER REGIONAL HEALTHCARE SYSTEM** (NP)
1000 South Beckham Street, Tyler, TX Zip 75701–1908, P O Box 6400, 75711–6400, tel. 903/535–6211; Elmer G. Ellis, FACHE, President and Chief Executive Officer
(Independent Hospital System)

TEXAS: EAST TEXAS MEDICAL CENTER ATHENS (L, 127 beds) 2000 South Palestine Street, Athens, TX Zip 75751–5610; tel. 903/676–1000; Jack A. Endres, FACHE, JD, Administrator
Web address: www.etmc.org

EAST TEXAS MEDICAL CENTER CARTHAGE (L, 23 beds) 409 Cottage Road, Carthage, TX Zip 75633–1466; tel. 903/693–3841; Gary Mikeal. Hudson, Administrator
Web address: www.etmc.org

EAST TEXAS MEDICAL CENTER HENDERSON (O, 41 beds) 300 Wilson Street, Henderson, TX Zip 75652–5956; tel. 903/657–7541; Mark Leitner, FACHE, Administrator

EAST TEXAS MEDICAL CENTER JACKSONVILLE (O, 38 beds) 501 South Ragsdale Street, Jacksonville, TX Zip 75766–2413; tel. 903/541–5000; Ruth Cook, R.N., FACHE, MSN, Administrator
Web address: www.etmc.org

EAST TEXAS MEDICAL CENTER PITTSBURG (L, 25 beds) 2701 Highway 271 North, Pittsburg, TX Zip 75686–1032; tel. 903/946–5000; James Warren. Robicheaux, FACHE, Senior Administrator

EAST TEXAS MEDICAL CENTER REHABILITATION HOSPITAL (O, 49 beds) 701 Olympic Plaza Circle, Tyler, TX Zip 75701–1950, P O Box 7530, 75711–7530, tel. 903/596–3000; Eddie L. Howard, Vice President and Chief Operating Officer
Web address: www.etmc.org

EAST TEXAS MEDICAL CENTER SPECIALTY HOSPITAL (O, 36 beds) 1000 South Beckham, 5th Floor, Tyler, TX Zip 75701–1908, P O Box 7018, 75711–7018, tel. 903/596–3600; Eddie L. Howard, Vice President and Chief Operating Officer

EAST TEXAS MEDICAL CENTER TYLER (O, 399 beds) 1000 South Beckham Street, Tyler, TX Zip 75701–1908, Box 6400, 75711–6400, tel. 903/597–0351; Robert B. Evans, FACHE, Administrator and Chief Executive Officer
Web address: www.etmc.org

EAST TEXAS MEDICAL CENTER-QUITMAN (L, 25 beds) 117 Winnsboro Street, Quitman, TX Zip 75783–2144, P O Box 1000, 75783–1000, tel. 903/763–6300; Patrick Swindle, Administrator
Web address: www.etmc.org/etmcquitman/

Owned, leased, sponsored:	9 hospitals	763 beds
Contract-managed:	0 hospitals	0 beds
Totals:	9 hospitals	763 beds

★**0555: EASTERN MAINE HEALTHCARE SYSTEMS** (NP)
43 Whiting Hill Road, Brewer, ME Zip 04412–1005; tel. 207/973–7045; M. Michelle. Hood, FACHE, President and Chief Executive Officer
(Moderately Centralized Health System)

MAINE: BLUE HILL MEMORIAL HOSPITAL (O, 23 beds) 57 Water Street, Blue Hill, ME Zip 04614–5231, P O Box 1029, 04614–1029, tel. 207/374–3400; John Ronan, President

CHARLES A. DEAN MEMORIAL HOSPITAL (O, 36 beds) 364 Pritham Avenue, Greenville, ME Zip 04441–1395, P O Box 1129, 04441–1129, tel. 207/695–5200; Terri Vieira, Interim President
Web address: www.cadean.org

For explanation of codes following names, see page B2.
★ Indicates Type III membership in the American Hospital Association.

EASTERN MAINE MEDICAL CENTER (O, 367 beds) 489 State Street, Bangor, ME Zip 04401-6674, P O Box 404, 04402-0404, tel. 207/973-7000; Donna Russell-Cook, FACHE, President
Web address: www.emh.org

INLAND HOSPITAL (O, 29 beds) 200 Kennedy Memorial Drive, Waterville, ME Zip 04901-4595; tel. 207/861-3000; John Dalton, President and Chief Executive Officer
Web address: www.inlandhospital.org

MAINE COAST MEMORIAL HOSPITAL (O, 52 beds) 50 Union Street, Ellsworth, ME Zip 04605-1599; tel. 207/664-5311; John Ronan, President

MERCY HOSPITAL OF PORTLAND (O, 104 beds) 144 State Street, Portland, ME Zip 04101-3795; tel. 207/879-3000; Charles D. Therrien, President
Web address: www.mercyhospital.org

SEBASTICOOK VALLEY HEALTH (O, 25 beds) 447 North Main Street, Pittsfield, ME Zip 04967-3707; tel. 207/487-4000; Terri Vieira, President and Chief Executive Officer
Web address: www.sebasticookvalleyhealth.org

THE ACADIA HOSPITAL (O, 68 beds) 268 Stillwater Avenue, Bangor, ME Zip 04401-3945, P O Box 422, 04402-0422, tel. 207/973-6100; Scott Oxley, President

THE AROOSTOOK MEDICAL CENTER (O, 114 beds) 140 Academy Street, Presque Isle, ME Zip 04769-3171, P O Box 151, 04769-0151, tel. 207/768-4000; Gregory LaFrancois, President
Web address: www.tamc.org

Owned, leased, sponsored:	9 hospitals	818 beds
Contract-managed:	0 hospitals	0 beds
Totals:	9 hospitals	818 beds

★0926: EDWARD-ELMHURST HEALTHCARE (NP)
801 South Washington Street, Naperville, IL Zip 60540-7430; tel. 630/527-3000; Mary Lou Mastro, FACHE, MS, R.N., System Chief Executive Officer
(Independent Hospital System)

ILLINOIS: EDWARD HOSPITAL (O, 350 beds) 801 South Washington Street, Naperville, IL Zip 60540-7499; tel. 630/527-3000; Bill Kottmann, President and Chief Executive Officer
Web address: www.eehealth.org

ELMHURST HOSPITAL (O, 267 beds) 155 East Brush Hill Road, Elmhurst, IL Zip 60126-5658; tel. 331/221-1000; Pamela L. Dunley, MS, R.N., Chief Executive Officer

LINDEN OAKS HOSPITAL (O, 108 beds) 852 South West Street, Naperville, IL Zip 60540-6400; tel. 630/305-5500; Gina Sharp, FACHE, President and Chief Executive Officer
Web address: https://www.eehealth.org/services/behavioral-health

Owned, leased, sponsored:	3 hospitals	725 beds
Contract-managed:	0 hospitals	0 beds
Totals:	3 hospitals	725 beds

1685: EINSTEIN HEALTHCARE NETWORK (NP)
5501 Old York Road, Philadelphia, PA Zip 19141-3098; tel. 215/456-7890; Barry R. Freedman, President and Chief Executive Officer

PENNSYLVANIA: EINSTEIN MEDICAL CENTER MONTGOMERY (O, 171 beds) 559 West Germantown Pike, East Norriton, PA Zip 19403-4250; tel. 484/622-1000; Beth Duffy, Chief Operating Officer

EINSTEIN MEDICAL CENTER PHILADELPHIA (O, 489 beds) 5501 Old York Road, Philadelphia, PA Zip 19141-3098; tel. 215/456-7890; Barry R. Freedman, President and Chief Executive Officer
Web address: www.einstein.edu

Owned, leased, sponsored:	2 hospitals	660 beds
Contract-managed:	0 hospitals	0 beds
Totals:	2 hospitals	660 beds

0879: EMERUS (IO)
10077 Grogan's Mill, Suite 100, The Woodlands, TX Zip 77380-1022; tel. 281/292-2450; Craig Goguen, Chief Executive Officer

TEXAS: BAPTIST EMERGENCY HOSPITAL (O, 50 beds) 16088 San Pedro, San Antonio, TX Zip 78232-2249; tel. 210/402-4092; David Mitchell, Interim Chief Executive Officer

BAYLOR EMERGENCY MEDICAL CENTER AT AUBREY (O, 32 beds) 26791 Highway 380, Aubrey, TX Zip 76227; tel. 972/347-2525; Kyle Kirkpatrick, Chief Executive Officer
Web address: www.bemcataubrey.com

BAYLOR EMERGENCY MEDICAL CENTERS - BURLESON (O, 16 beds) 12500 South Freeway Suite 100, Burleson, TX Zip 76028-7128; tel. 214/294-6250; Kyle Kirkpatrick, Chief Executive Officer
Web address: www.bayloremc.com/burleson

BAYLOR EMERGENCY MEDICAL CENTERS - ROCKWALL (O, 8 beds) 1975 Alpha Drive Suite 100, Rockwall, TX Zip 75087-4951; tel. 214/294-6200; Kyle Kirkpatrick, Chief Executive Officer
Web address: www.bayloremc.com/rockwall

EMERUS COMMUNITY HOSPITAL (O, 8 beds) 24429 State Highway 249, Tomball, TX Zip 77375-8214; tel. 281/516-0911; Paula Gonzales, Administrator
Web address: www.emerus.com/tomball/

EMERUS HOSPITAL - SUGAR LAND (O, 7 beds) 16000 Southwest Freeway, Suite 100, Sugar Land, TX Zip 77479-2674; tel. 281/277-0911; Mike Kohler, Chief Executive Officer

Owned, leased, sponsored:	6 hospitals	121 beds
Contract-managed:	0 hospitals	0 beds
Totals:	6 hospitals	121 beds

★0256: EMORY HEALTHCARE (NP)
1440 Clifton Road NE, Suite 309, Atlanta, GA Zip 30322-1102; tel. 404/778-5000; Jonathan S. Lewin, M.D., President
(Centralized Health System)

GEORGIA: EMORY JOHNS CREEK HOSPITAL (O, 113 beds) 6325 Hospital Parkway, Johns Creek, GA Zip 30097-5775; tel. 678/474-7000; Marilyn Margolis, MSN, Chief Executive Officer
Web address: www.emoryjohnscreek.com

EMORY REHABILITATION HOSPITAL (O, 46 beds) 1441 Clifton Road NE, Atlanta, GA Zip 30322-1004; tel. 404/712-5512; Michael Eric. Garrard, FACHE, Chief Executive Officer
Web address: www.emoryhealthcare.org/rehabilitation

EMORY SAINT JOSEPH'S HOSPITAL OF ATLANTA (O, 272 beds) 5665 Peachtree Dunwoody Road NE, Atlanta, GA Zip 30342-1701; tel. 678/843-7001; Heather Dexter, Chief Executive Officer

EMORY UNIVERSITY HOSPITAL MIDTOWN (O, 459 beds) 550 Peachtree Street NE, Atlanta, GA Zip 30308-2247; tel. 404/686-4411; Daniel Owens, Chief Executive Officer
Web address: www.emoryhealthcare.org

EMORY UNIVERSITY HOSPITAL (O, 558 beds) 1364 Clifton Road NE, Atlanta, GA Zip 30322; tel. 404/712-2000; Bryce D. Gartland, M.D., Chief Executive Officer
Web address: www.emoryhealthcare.org

Owned, leased, sponsored:	5 hospitals	1448 beds
Contract-managed:	0 hospitals	0 beds
Totals:	5 hospitals	1448 beds

0959: EPHRAIM MCDOWELL HEALTH (NP)
217 South Third Street, Danville, KY Zip 40422-1823; tel. 859/239-1000; Sally M. Davenport, R.N., MS, Chief Executive Officer
(Independent Hospital System)

For explanation of codes following names, see page B2.
★ Indicates Type III membership in the American Hospital Association.

Section B

KENTUCKY: EPHRAIM MCDOWELL FORT LOGAN HOSPITAL (O, 25 beds) 110 Metker Trail, Stanford, KY Zip 40484–1020; tel. 606/365–4600; Sally M. Davenport, R.N., MS, President and Chief Executive Officer
Web address: www.fortloganhospital.org

EPHRAIM MCDOWELL REGIONAL MEDICAL CENTER (O, 159 beds) 217 South Third Street, Danville, KY Zip 40422–1823; tel. 859/239–1000; Sally M. Davenport, R.N., MS, Chief Executive Officer

Owned, leased, sponsored:	2 hospitals	184 beds
Contract-managed:	0 hospitals	0 beds
Totals:	2 hospitals	184 beds

0525:   ERLANGER HEALTH SYSTEM (NP)
975 East Third Street, Chattanooga, TN Zip 37403–2147; tel. 423/778–7000; Kevin M. Spiegel, President and Chief Executive Officer
(Centralized Health System)

TENNESSEE: ERLANGER BLEDSOE HOSPITAL (C, 25 beds) 71 Wheeler Avenue, Pikeville, TN Zip 37367, P O Box 699, 37367–0699, tel. 423/447–2112; Stephanie Boynton, Administrator
Web address: www.erlanger.org

ERLANGER MEDICAL CENTER (O, 657 beds) 975 East Third Street, Chattanooga, TN Zip 37403–2147; tel. 423/778–7000; Kevin M. Spiegel, Chief Executive Officer

Owned, leased, sponsored:	1 hospitals	657 beds
Contract-managed:	1 hospitals	25 beds
Totals:	2 hospitals	682 beds

0382:   ERNEST HEALTH, INC. (IO)
7770 Jefferson Street NE, Suite 320, Albuquerque, NM Zip 87109–4386; tel. 505/856–5300; Darby Brockette, Chief Executive Officer
(Independent Hospital System)

ARIZONA: MOUNTAIN VALLEY REGIONAL REHABILITATION HOSPITAL (O, 16 beds) 3700 North Windsong Drive, Prescott Valley, AZ Zip 86314–1253; tel. 928/759–8800; Judy Baum, Chief Executive Officer
Web address: www.mvrrh.ernesthealth.com

COLORADO: NORTHERN COLORADO LONG TERM ACUTE HOSPITAL (O, 40 beds) 4401 Union Street, Johnstown, CO Zip 80534; tel. 970/619–3663; Lamar McBride, Chief Executive Officer

NORTHERN COLORADO REHABILITATION HOSPITAL (O, 40 beds) 4401 Union Street, Johnstown, CO Zip 80534–2800; tel. 970/619–3400; Elizabeth Bullard, Chief Executive Officer
Web address: www.ncrh.ernesthealth.com

IDAHO: NORTHERN IDAHO ADVANCED CARE HOSPITAL (O, 40 beds) 600 North Cecil Road, Post Falls, ID Zip 83854–6200; tel. 208/262–2800; Una Alderman, Chief Executive Officer
Web address: www.niach.ernesthealth.com

REHABILITATION HOSPITAL OF THE NORTHWEST (O, 25 beds) 3372 East Jenalan Avenue, Post Falls, ID Zip 83854–7787; tel. 208/262–8700; Darby Brockette, Chief Executive Officer
Web address: www.ernesthealth.com

SOUTHWEST IDAHO ADVANCED CARE HOSPITAL (O, 22 beds) 6651 West Franklin Road, Boise, ID Zip 83709–0914; tel. 208/685–2400; David Tupper, Chief Executive Officer

INDIANA: LAFAYETTE REGIONAL REHABILITATION HOSPITAL (O, 40 beds) 950 Park East Boulevard, Lafayette, IN Zip 47905–0792; tel. 765/447–4040; Michelle Russell, Chief Executive Officer
Web address: www.lrrh.ernesthealth.com

MONTANA: ADVANCED CARE HOSPITAL OF MONTANA (O, 40 beds) 3528 Gabel Road, Billings, MT Zip 59102–7307; tel. 406/373–8000; Judi Powers, Chief Executive Officer
Web address: www.achm.ernesthealth.com

NEW MEXICO: ADVANCED CARE HOSPITAL OF SOUTHERN NEW MEXICO (O, 40 beds) 4451 East Lohman Avenue, Las Cruces, NM Zip 88011–8267; tel. 575/521–6600; Claudia Saiz, Chief Operating Officer

REHABILITATION HOSPITAL OF SOUTHERN NEW MEXICO (O, 40 beds) 4441 East Lohman Avenue, Las Cruces, NM Zip 88011–8267; tel. 575/521–6400; Sabrina Martin, Chief Executive Officer
Web address: www.rhsnm.ernesthealth.com

OHIO: REHABILITATION HOSPITAL OF NORTHWEST OHIO (O, 40 beds) 1455 West Medical Loop, Toledo, OH Zip 43614; tel. 419/214–6600; Scott Williams, Chief Executive Officer

SOUTH CAROLINA: GREENWOOD REGIONAL REHABILITATION HOSPITAL (O, 54 beds) 1530 Parkway, Greenwood, SC Zip 29646–4027; tel. 864/330–9070; Kristin Manske, Chief Executive Officer
Web address: www.grrh.ernesthealth.com

TEXAS: LAREDO REHABILITATION HOSPITAL (O, 20 beds) 2005a East Bustamante Street, Laredo, TX Zip 78041; tel. 956/764–8555; Larisa Higgins, Administrator and Chief Operating Officer

LAREDO SPECIALTY HOSPITAL (O, 40 beds) 2005 Bustamente Street, Laredo, TX Zip 78041–5470; tel. 956/753–5353; Mario Rodriguez, Chief Executive Officer
Web address: www.lsh.ernesthealth.com

MESQUITE REHABILITATION INSTITUTE (O, 30 beds) 1023 North Belt Line Road, Mesquite, TX Zip 75149–1788; tel. 972/216–2400; Brian Abraham, Chief Executive Officer
Web address: www.mesquiterehab.ernesthealth.com/

MESQUITE SPECIALTY HOSPITAL (O, 40 beds) 1024 North Galloway Avenue, Mesquite, TX Zip 75149–2434; tel. 972/216–2300; Louis Bradley, Chief Executive Officer
Web address: www.msh.ernesthealth.com

NEW BRAUNFELS REGIONAL REHABILITATION HOSPITAL (O, 40 beds) 2041 Sundance Parkway, New Braunfels, TX Zip 78130–2779; tel. 830/625–6700; Jessie Smedley, Chief Executive Officer

SOUTH TEXAS REHABILITATION HOSPITAL (O, 40 beds) 425 East Alton Gloor Boulevard, Brownsville, TX Zip 78526–3361; tel. 956/554–6000; Leo Garza, Chief Executive Officer
Web address: www.strh.ernesthealth.com

TRUSTPOINT REHABILITATION HOSPITAL OF LUBBOCK (O, 60 beds) 4302A Princeton Street, Lubbock, TX Zip 79415–1304; tel. 806/749–2222; Craig Bragg, Chief Executive Officer
Web address: www.trustpointhospital.com/

UTAH: NORTHERN UTAH REHABILITATION HOSPITAL (O, 20 beds) 5825 Harrison Boulevard, South Ogden, UT Zip 84403–4316; tel. 801/475–5254; Ryan Keele, Chief Executive Officer

UTAH VALLEY SPECIALTY HOSPITAL (O, 40 beds) 306 River Bend Lane, Provo, UT Zip 84604–5625; tel. 801/226–8880; Ezra Segura, Chief Executive Officer
Web address: www.uvsh.ernesthealth.com

WYOMING: ELKHORN VALLEY REHABILITATION HOSPITAL (O, 41 beds) 5715 East 2nd Street, Casper, WY Zip 82609–4322; tel. 307/265–0005; Michael Phillips, Chief Executive Officer
Web address: www.evrh.ernesthealth.com/

Owned, leased, sponsored:	22 hospitals	808 beds
Contract-managed:	0 hospitals	0 beds
Totals:	22 hospitals	808 beds

★0396:   ESSENTIA HEALTH (NP)
502 East Second Street, Duluth, MN Zip 55805–1913; tel. 218/786–8376; David C. Herman, M.D., Chief Executive Officer
(Moderately Centralized Health System)

IDAHO: CLEARWATER VALLEY HOSPITAL AND CLINICS (O, 23 beds) 301 Cedar, Orofino, ID Zip 83544–9029; tel. 208/476–4555; Lenne Bonner, President

ST. MARY'S HOSPITAL (O, 28 beds) 701 Lewiston Street , Cottonwood, ID Zip 83522–9750, P O Box 137, 83522–0137, tel. 208/962–3251; Lenne Bonner, President
Web address: www.smh-cvhc.org/getpage.php?name=index

For explanation of codes following names, see page B2.
★ Indicates Type III membership in the American Hospital Association.

MINNESOTA: ESSENTIA HEALTH ADA (O, 14 beds) 201 9th Street West, Ada, MN Zip 56510–1279; tel. 218/784–5000; Erin Stoltman, Administrator
Web address: www.essentiahealth.org

ESSENTIA HEALTH DULUTH (O, 154 beds) 502 East Second Street, Duluth, MN Zip 55805–1982; tel. 218/727–8762; James Garvey, Senior Vice President Hospital Practice, Essentia Health East

ESSENTIA HEALTH FOSSTON (O, 74 beds) 900 Hilligoss Boulevard SE, Fosston, MN Zip 56542–1599; tel. 218/435–1133; Kevin Gish, Administrator and Vice President
Web address: www.essentiahealth.org

ESSENTIA HEALTH NORTHERN PINES MEDICAL CENTER (O, 58 beds) 5211 Highway 110, Aurora, MN Zip 55705–1599; tel. 218/229–2211; Laura Ackman, Chief Operating Officer and Administrator
Web address: www.essentiahealth.org/NorthernPines/FindaClinic/Essentia-HealthNorthern-Pines-36.aspx

ESSENTIA HEALTH SANDSTONE (O, 33 beds) 705 Lundorff Drive, Sandstone, MN Zip 55072–5009; tel. 320/245–2212; Michael D. Hedrix, Administrator and President
Web address: www.pinemedicalcenter.org

ESSENTIA HEALTH ST. JOSEPH'S MEDICAL CENTER (O, 136 beds) 523 North Third Street, Brainerd, MN Zip 56401–3098; tel. 218/829–2861; Adam Rees, President

ESSENTIA HEALTH ST. MARY'S - DETROIT LAKES (O, 131 beds) 1027 Washington Avenue, Detroit Lakes, MN Zip 56501–3409; tel. 218/847–5611; Peter Jacobson, President
Web address: www.essentiahealth.org

ESSENTIA HEALTH ST. MARY'S MEDICAL CENTER (O, 327 beds) 407 East Third Street, Duluth, MN Zip 55805–1984; tel. 218/786–4000; James Garvey, Senior Vice President Hospital Practice, Essentia Health East
Web address: www.essentiahealth.org/StMarysMedicalCenter/FindaClinic/Essentia-HealthSt-Marys-Medical-Center-46.aspx

ESSENTIA HEALTH-DEER RIVER (O, 52 beds) 115 10th Avenue NE , Deer River, MN Zip 56636–8795; tel. 218/246–2900; Marsha Green, Chief Executive Officer

ESSENTIA HEALTH-GRACEVILLE (O, 60 beds) 115 West Second Street, Graceville, MN Zip 56240–4845, P O Box 157, 56240–0157, tel. 320/748–7223; Julie Rosenberg, Administrator
Web address: www.essentiahealth.org/HolyTrinityHospital/FindaClinic/Essentia-HealthHoly-Trinity-Hospital-96.aspx

ESSENTIA HEALTH-VIRGINIA (L, 150 beds) 901 Ninth Street North, Virginia, MN Zip 55792–2398; tel. 218/741–3340; Sam Stone, Administrative and Chief Operating Officer
Web address: www.essentiahealth.org

NORTH DAKOTA: ESSENTIA HEALTH FARGO (O, 133 beds) 3000 32nd Avenue South, Fargo, ND Zip 58103–6132; tel. 701/364–8000; Timothy Sayler, Chief Operating Officer

WISCONSIN: ESSENTIA HEALTH ST. MARY'S HOSPITAL OF SUPERIOR (O, 25 beds) 3500 Tower Avenue, Superior, WI Zip 54880–5395; tel. 715/817–7000; Terry Jacobson, Administrator and Chief Executive Officer
Web address: www.essentiahealth.org/EssentiaHealthStMarysHospitalofSuperiorFoundation/overview.aspx

Owned, leased, sponsored:	15 hospitals	1398 beds
Contract-managed:	0 hospitals	0 beds
Totals:	15 hospitals	1398 beds

2395: EXCELA HEALTH (NP)
532 West Pittsburgh Street, Greensburg, PA Zip 15601, 134 Industrial Park Road, 15601–7328, tel. 724/832–5050; Robert Rogalski, Chief Executive Officer
(Centralized Health System)

PENNSYLVANIA: EXCELA FRICK HOSPITAL (O, 33 beds) 508 South Church Street, Mount Pleasant, PA Zip 15666–1790; tel. 724/547–1500; Michael D. Busch, Executive Vice President and Chief Operating Officer

EXCELA HEALTH WESTMORELAND HOSPITAL (O, 270 beds) 532 West Pittsburgh Street, Greensburg, PA Zip 15601–2282; tel. 724/832–4000; Ronald H. Ott, President
Web address: www.excelahealth.org

EXCELA LATROBE AREA HOSPITAL (O, 114 beds) One Mellon Way, Latrobe, PA Zip 15650–1096; tel. 724/537–1000; Michael D. Busch, Executive Vice President and Chief Operating Officer
Web address: www.excelahealth.org

Owned, leased, sponsored:	3 hospitals	417 beds
Contract-managed:	0 hospitals	0 beds
Totals:	3 hospitals	417 beds

★1325: FAIRVIEW HEALTH SERVICES (NP)
2450 Riverside Avenue, Minneapolis, MN Zip 55454–1400; tel. 612/672–6141; James Hereford, President and Chief Executive Officer
(Centralized Physician/Insurance Health System)

MINNESOTA: BETHESDA HOSPITAL (O, 114 beds) 559 Capitol Boulevard, Saint Paul, MN Zip 55103–2101; tel. 651/232–2000; Catherine Barr, Senior Vice President and Chief Operating Officer
Web address: www.healtheast.org

FAIRVIEW LAKES HEALTH SERVICES (O, 33 beds) 5200 Fairview Boulevard, Wyoming, MN Zip 55092–8013; tel. 651/982–7000; John W. Herman, President

FAIRVIEW NORTHLAND MEDICAL CENTER (O, 20 beds) 911 Northland Drive, Princeton, MN Zip 55371–2173; tel. 763/389–1313; John W. Herman, President
Web address: www.northland.fairview.org

FAIRVIEW RIDGES HOSPITAL (O, 162 beds) 201 East Nicollet Boulevard, Burnsville, MN Zip 55337–5799; tel. 952/892–2000; Patrick Belland, President

FAIRVIEW SOUTHDALE HOSPITAL (O, 317 beds) 6401 France Avenue South, Edina, MN Zip 55435–2199; tel. 952/924–5000; Bradley Beard, Regional President
Web address: www.fairview.org

GRAND ITASCA CLINIC AND HOSPITAL (O, 31 beds) 1601 Golf Course Road, Grand Rapids, MN Zip 55744–8648; tel. 218/326–5000; Michael Youso, Chief Executive Officer

RANGE REGIONAL HEALTH SERVICES (O, 72 beds) 750 East 34th Street, Hibbing, MN Zip 55746–4600; tel. 218/262–4881; Debra K. Boardman, FACHE, President and Chief Executive Officer
Web address: www.range.fairview.org

ST. JOHN'S HOSPITAL (O, 198 beds) 1575 Beam Avenue, Maplewood, MN Zip 55109–1126; tel. 651/232–7000; Catherine Barr, Senior Vice President and Chief Operating Officer

ST. JOSEPH'S HOSPITAL (O, 246 beds) 45 West 10th Street, Saint Paul, MN Zip 55102–1053; tel. 651/232–3000; Catherine Barr, Senior Vice President and Chief Operating Officer
Web address: www.healtheast.org

UNIVERSITY OF MINNESOTA MEDICAL CENTER, FAIRVIEW (O, 860 beds) 2450 Riverside Avenue, Minneapolis, MN Zip 55454–1400; tel. 612/672–6000; David Murphy, Interim Chief Executive Officer
Web address: www.fairview.org

WOODWINDS HEALTH CAMPUS (O, 86 beds) 1925 Woodwinds Drive, Woodbury, MN Zip 55125–4445; tel. 651/232–0228; Catherine Barr, President, East Region

Owned, leased, sponsored:	11 hospitals	2139 beds
Contract-managed:	0 hospitals	0 beds
Totals:	11 hospitals	2139 beds

0814: FAITH REGIONAL HEALTH SERVICES (NP)
2700 West Norfolk Avenue, Norfolk, NE Zip 68701–4438, P O Box 869, 68702–0869, tel. 402/371–4880; Mark D. Klosterman, FACHE, President and Chief Executive Officer
(Moderately Centralized Health System)

NEBRASKA: FAITH REGIONAL HEALTH SERVICES (O, 147 beds) 2700 West Norfolk Avenue, Norfolk, NE Zip 68701–4438, P O Box 869, 68702–0869,

Section B

For explanation of codes following names, see page B2.
★ Indicates Type III membership in the American Hospital Association.

© 2017 AHA Guide · · · Health Care Systems, Networks and Alliances **B51**

tel. 402/371–4880; Mark D. Klosterman, FACHE, President and Chief Executive Officer
Web address: www.frhs.org

NIOBRARA VALLEY HOSPITAL (C, 20 beds) 401 South Fifth Street, Lynch, NE Zip 68746–0118, P O Box 118, 68746–0118, tel. 402/569–2451; Kelly Kalkowski, Chief Executive Officer

WEST HOLT MEDICAL SERVICES (C, 17 beds) 406 West Neely Street, Atkinson, NE Zip 68713–4801; tel. 402/925–2811; Bradley D. Pfeifer, FACHE, Chief Executive Officer
Web address: www.westholtmed.org

Owned, leased, sponsored:	1 hospitals	147 beds
Contract-managed:	2 hospitals	37 beds
Totals:	3 hospitals	184 beds

0397: FINGER LAKES HEALTH (NP)
196 North Street, Geneva, NY Zip 14456–1651; tel. 315/787–4000; Jose Acevedo, M.D., President and Chief Executive Officer
(Independent Hospital System)

NEW YORK: GENEVA GENERAL HOSPITAL (O, 132 beds) 196 North Street, Geneva, NY Zip 14456–1694; tel. 315/787–4000; Jose Acevedo, M.D., President and Chief Executive Officer

SOLDIERS AND SAILORS MEMORIAL HOSPITAL OF YATES COUNTY (O, 186 beds) 418 North Main Street, Penn Yan, NY Zip 14527–1085; tel. 315/531–2000; Jose Acevedo, M.D., President and Chief Executive Officer
Web address: www.flhealth.org

Owned, leased, sponsored:	2 hospitals	318 beds
Contract-managed:	0 hospitals	0 beds
Totals:	2 hospitals	318 beds

1010: FIRST PHYSICIANS CAPITAL GROUP, INC. (IO)
4323 NW 63rd Street Suite 140, Oklahoma City, OK Zip 73116–1513; tel. 405/246–0218; Sean Kirrane, Chief Executive Officer

OKLAHOMA: CARNEGIE TRI-COUNTY MUNICIPAL HOSPITAL (C, 15 beds) 102 North Broadway, Carnegie, OK Zip 73015, P O Box 97, 73015–0097, tel. 580/654–1050; Doris Brown, Chief Executive Officer and Administrator

PHYSICIANS' HOSPITAL IN ANADARKO (C, 25 beds) 1002 Central Boulevard East, Anadarko, OK Zip 73005–4496; tel. 405/247–2551; Travis A. Villani, FACHE, Chief Executive Officer and Administrator
Web address: www.anadarkohospital.com

STROUD REGIONAL MEDICAL CENTER (C, 25 beds) Highway 66 West, Stroud, OK Zip 74079, P O Box 530, 74079–0530, tel. 918/968–3571; Ed Dyer, Chief Executive Officer

Owned, leased, sponsored:	0 hospitals	0 beds
Contract-managed:	3 hospitals	65 beds
Totals:	3 hospitals	65 beds

★0243: FIRSTHEALTH OF THE CAROLINAS (NP)
155 Memorial Drive, Pinehurst, NC Zip 28374–8710, P O Box 3000, 28374–3000, tel. 910/715–1000; David J. Kilarski, FACHE, Chief Executive Officer
(Centralized Physician/Insurance Health System)

NORTH CAROLINA: FIRSTHEALTH MONTGOMERY MEMORIAL HOSPITAL (O, 25 beds) 520 Allen Street, Troy, NC Zip 27371–2802; tel. 910/571–5000; Beth Walker, R.N., President
Web address: www.firsthealth.org

FIRSTHEALTH MOORE REGIONAL HOSPITAL - HAMLET (O, 64 beds) 1000 West Hamlet Avenue, Hamlet, NC Zip 28345–4522, P O Box 1109, 28345–1109, tel. 910/205–8000; John J. Jackson, Chief Executive Officer
Web address: www.sandhillsregional.com

FIRSTHEALTH MOORE REGIONAL HOSPITAL (O, 372 beds) 155 Memorial Drive, Pinehurst, NC Zip 28374–8710, P O Box 3000, 28374–3000, tel. 910/715–1000; David J. Kilarski, FACHE, Chief Executive Officer

FIRSTHEALTH RICHMOND MEMORIAL HOSPITAL (O, 91 beds) 925 Long Drive, Rockingham, NC Zip 28379–4835; tel. 910/417–3000; John J. Jackson, President
Web address: www.firsthealth.org

Owned, leased, sponsored:	4 hospitals	552 beds
Contract-managed:	0 hospitals	0 beds
Totals:	4 hospitals	552 beds

0900: FOUNDATION SURGICAL HOSPITAL AFFILIATES (IO)
14000 North Portland Avenue, Suite 204, Oklahoma City, OK Zip 73134–4002; tel. 405/608–1700; Thomas A. Michaud, Chief Executive Officer
(Independent Hospital System)

TEXAS: BAYLOR SCOTT & WHITE SURGICAL HOSPITAL AT SHERMAN (O, 12 beds) 3601 North Calais Street, Sherman, TX Zip 75090–1785; tel. 903/870–0999; Marc Devorsetz, Chief Executive Officer

FOUNDATION SURGICAL HOSPITAL OF EL PASO (O, 20 beds) 1416 George Dieter Drive, El Paso, TX Zip 79936–7601; tel. 915/598–4240; Don Burris, Chief Executive Officer
Web address: www.physiciansmedcenter.com

FOUNDATION SURGICAL HOSPITAL OF SAN ANTONIO (O, 20 beds) 9522 Huebner Road, San Antonio, TX Zip 78240–1548; tel. 210/478–5400; Blake W. Hubbard, FACHE, Chief Executive Officer
Web address: www.fshsanantonio.com/bariatric-foundation-surgical.html

Owned, leased, sponsored:	3 hospitals	52 beds
Contract-managed:	0 hospitals	0 beds
Totals:	3 hospitals	52 beds

5345: FRANCISCAN HEALTH (CC)
1515 Dragoon Trail, Mishawaka, IN Zip 46544–4710, P O Box 1290, 46546–1290, tel. 574/256–3935; Kevin D. Leahy, President and Chief Executive Officer
(Moderately Centralized Health System)

ILLINOIS: FRANCISCAN HEALTH OLYMPIA FIELDS (O, 329 beds) 20201 South Crawford Avenue, Olympia Fields, IL Zip 60461–1010; tel. 708/747–4000; Allan M. Spooner, President and Chief Executive Officer

INDIANA: FRANCISCAN HEALTH DYER (O, 341 beds) 24 Joliet Street, Dyer, IN Zip 46311–1799; tel. 219/865–2141; Patrick J. Maloney, Chief Executive Officer

FRANCISCAN HEALTH HAMMOND (O, 500 beds) 5454 Hohman Avenue, Hammond, IN Zip 46320–1999; tel. 219/932–2300; Patrick J. Maloney, Chief Executive Officer
Web address: https://www.franciscanhealth.org/healthcare-facilities/franciscan-health-hammond-18

FRANCISCAN HEALTH LAFAYETTE EAST (O, 187 beds) 1701 South Creasy Lane, Lafayette, IN Zip 47905–4972; tel. 765/502–4000; Terrance E. Wilson, President and Chief Executive Officer
Web address: www.ste.org

FRANCISCAN HEALTH RENSSELEAR (O, 46 beds) 1104 East Grace Street, Rensselaer, IN Zip 47978–3296; tel. 219/866–5141; Timothy M. Schreeg, President and Chief Executive Officer
Web address: www.jchh.com

FRANCISCAN HEALTHCARE - MUNSTER (O, 32 beds) 701 Superior Avenue, Munster, IN Zip 46321–4037; tel. 219/924–1300; Patrick J. Maloney, Chief Executive Officer
Web address: www.franciscanphysicianshospital.org

FRANCISCAN ST. ANTHONY HEALTH - CROWN POINT (O, 254 beds) 1201 South Main Street, Crown Point, IN Zip 46307–8483; tel. 219/738–2100; Barbara M. Anderson, President and Chief Executive Officer

FRANCISCAN ST. ANTHONY HEALTH - MICHIGAN CITY (O, 171 beds) 301 West Homer Street, Michigan City, IN Zip 46360–4358; tel. 219/879–8511; Dean Mazzoni, President and Chief Executive Officer
Web address: www.franciscanalliance.org

FRANCISCAN ST. ELIZABETH HEALTH - CRAWFORDSVILLE (O, 42 beds) 1710 Lafayette Road, Crawfordsville, IN Zip 47933–1099; tel. 765/362–2800; Terrence Klein, Ph.D., Vice President and Chief Operating Officer

For explanation of codes following names, see page B2.
★ Indicates Type III membership in the American Hospital Association.

FRANCISCAN ST. FRANCIS HEALTH - INDIANAPOLIS (O, 485 beds) 8111 South Emerson Avenue, Indianapolis, IN Zip 46237–8601; tel. 317/528–5000; James Callaghan III, M.D., President and Chief Executive Officer
Web address: www.stfrancishospitals.org

FRANCISCAN ST. FRANCIS HEALTH - MOORESVILLE (O, 115 beds) 1201 Hadley Road, Mooresville, IN Zip 46158–1789; tel. 317/831–1160; Peter J. Murphy, Senior Vice President and Chief Operating Officer
Web address: www.franciscanalliance.org/hospitals/mooresville/Pages/default.aspx

FRANCISCAN ST. FRANCIS HEALTH-CARMEL (O, 6 beds) 12188B North Meridian Street, Carmel, IN Zip 46032–4840; tel. 317/705–4500; Stephen J. Wheatley, Director of Operations

Owned, leased, sponsored:	12 hospitals	2508 beds
Contract-managed:	0 hospitals	0 beds
Totals:	12 hospitals	2508 beds

★**1475: FRANCISCAN MISSIONARIES OF OUR LADY HEALTH SYSTEM, INC.** (CC)
4200 Essen Lane, Baton Rouge, LA Zip 70809–2158; tel. 225/923–2701; John J. Finan Jr, FACHE, President and Chief Executive Officer
(Moderately Centralized Health System)

LOUISIANA: ASSUMPTION COMMUNITY HOSPITAL (O, 6 beds) 135 Highway 402, Napoleonville, LA Zip 70390–2217; tel. 985/369–3600; Christina Hockaday, FACHE, Chief Executive Officer
Web address: www.https://ololrmc.com

OUR LADY OF LOURDES REGIONAL MEDICAL CENTER (O, 186 beds) 4801 Ambassador Caffery Parkway, Lafayette, LA Zip 70508–6917; tel. 337/470–2000; W. Bryan. Lee, Chief Executive Officer
Web address: www.lourdesrmc.com

OUR LADY OF THE ANGELS HOSPITAL (O, 57 beds) 433 Plaza Street, Bogalusa, LA Zip 70427–3793; tel. 985/730–6700; Rene J. Ragas, Chief Operating Officer

OUR LADY OF THE LAKE REGIONAL MEDICAL CENTER (O, 1129 beds) 5000 Hennessy Boulevard, Baton Rouge, LA Zip 70808–4375; tel. 225/765–6565; K Scott. Wester, FACHE, President and Chief Executive Officer
Web address: www.ololrmc.com

ST. ELIZABETH HOSPITAL (O, 47 beds) 1125 West Highway 30, Gonzales, LA Zip 70737–5004; tel. 225/647–5000; Robert L. Burgess, President and Chief Executive Officer

ST. FRANCIS MEDICAL CENTER (O, 365 beds) 309 Jackson Street, Monroe, LA Zip 71201–7407, P O Box 1901, 71210–1901, tel. 318/966–4000; Kristin Wolkart, R.N., President and Chief Executive Officer
Web address: www.stfran.com

Owned, leased, sponsored:	6 hospitals	1790 beds
Contract-managed:	0 hospitals	0 beds
Totals:	6 hospitals	1790 beds

★**1455: FRANCISCAN SISTERS OF CHRISTIAN CHARITY SPONSORED MINISTRIES, INC.** (CC)
1415 South Rapids Road, Manitowoc, WI Zip 54220–9302; tel. 920/684–7071; Daniel B. McGinty, President and Chief Executive Officer
(Moderately Centralized Health System)

NEBRASKA: ST. FRANCIS MEMORIAL HOSPITAL (O, 88 beds) 430 North Monitor Street, West Point, NE Zip 68788–1555; tel. 402/372–2404; Jerry Wordekemper, President and Chief Executive Officer

OHIO: GENESIS HEALTHCARE SYSTEM (O, 321 beds) 2951 Maple Avenue, Zanesville, OH Zip 43701–1406; tel. 740/454–5000; Matthew J. Perry, President and Chief Executive Officer
Web address: www.genesishcs.org

WISCONSIN: HOLY FAMILY MEMORIAL (O, 60 beds) 2300 Western Avenue, Manitowoc, WI Zip 54220–3712, P O Box 1450, 54221–1450, tel. 920/320–2011; Mark P. Herzog, President and Chief Executive Officer
Web address: www.hfmhealth.org

Owned, leased, sponsored:	3 hospitals	469 beds
Contract-managed:	0 hospitals	0 beds
Totals:	3 hospitals	469 beds

★**0271: FREEMAN HEALTH SYSTEM** (NP)
1102 West 32nd Street, Joplin, MO Zip 64804–3503; tel. 417/347–1111; Paula F. Baker, President and Chief Executive Officer
(Centralized Health System)

MISSOURI: FREEMAN HEALTH SYSTEM (O, 391 beds) 1102 West 32nd Street, Joplin, MO Zip 64804–3503; tel. 417/347–1111; Paula F. Baker, President and Chief Executive Officer
Web address: www.freemanhealth.com

FREEMAN NEOSHO HOSPITAL (O, 25 beds) 113 West Hickory Street, Neosho, MO Zip 64850–1705; tel. 417/455–4352; Renee Denton, Chief Operating Officer

Owned, leased, sponsored:	2 hospitals	416 beds
Contract-managed:	0 hospitals	0 beds
Totals:	2 hospitals	416 beds

0182: FUNDAMENTAL LONG TERM CARE HOLDINGS, LLC (IO)
930 Ridgebrook Road, Sparks Glencoe, MD Zip 21152–9390; tel. 410/773–1000; W Bradley. Bennett, President and Chief Executive Officer
(Independent Hospital System)

NEVADA: HARMON MEDICAL AND REHABILITATION HOSPITAL (O, 118 beds) 2170 East Harmon Avenue, Las Vegas, NV Zip 89119–7840; tel. 702/794–0100; Bonnie Essex. Hillegass, Chief Executive Officer

HORIZON SPECIALTY HOSPITAL (O, 49 beds) 640 Desert Lane, Las Vegas, NV Zip 89106–4207; tel. 702/382–3155; Darrin Cook, Chief Executive Officer and Administrator
Web address: www.horizonspecialtyhosp.com/

SOUTHERN NEVADA MEDICAL AND REHABILITATION CENTER (O, 100 beds) 2945 Casa Vegas, Las Vegas, NV Zip 89169–2248; tel. 702/735–7179; Maureen Davis, Administrator

TEXAS: TEXAS SPECIALTY HOSPITAL AT LUBBOCK (O, 25 beds) 4302B Princeton Street, Lubbock, TX Zip 79415–1304; tel. 806/723–8700; Deanna Graves, Chief Executive Officer
Web address: www.texasspecialtylubbock.com/services.html

Owned, leased, sponsored:	4 hospitals	292 beds
Contract-managed:	0 hospitals	0 beds
Totals:	4 hospitals	292 beds

★**5570: GEISINGER HEALTH** (NP)
100 North Academy Avenue, Danville, PA Zip 17822–9800; tel. 570/271–6211; David T. Feinberg, M.D., President and Chief Executive Officer
(Moderately Centralized Health System)

NEW JERSEY: ATLANTICARE REGIONAL MEDICAL CENTER (O, 530 beds) 1925 Pacific Avenue, Atlantic City, NJ Zip 08401–6713; tel. 609/441–8994; Lori Herndon, R.N., President and Chief Executive Officer

PENNSYLVANIA: GEISINGER HOLY SPIRIT (O, 295 beds) 503 North 21st Street, Camp Hill, PA Zip 17011–2204; tel. 717/763–2100; Kyle C. Snyder, Chief Administrative Officer
Web address: www.hsh.org

GEISINGER MEDICAL CENTER (O, 547 beds) 100 North Academy Avenue, Danville, PA Zip 17822–2201; tel. 570/271–6211; Thomas P. Sokola, Chief Administrative Officer

For explanation of codes following names, see page B2.
★ Indicates Type III membership in the American Hospital Association.

Section B

GEISINGER WYOMING VALLEY MEDICAL CENTER (O, 256 beds) 1000 East Mountain Boulevard, Wilkes Barre, PA Zip 18711–0027; tel. 570/808–7300; Anthony Aquilina, D.O., Regional President
Web address: www.geisinger.org

GEISINGER-BLOOMSBURG HOSPITAL (O, 72 beds) 549 Fair Street, Bloomsburg, PA Zip 17815–1419; tel. 570/387–2100; Lissa Bryan-Smith, Chief Administrative Officer
Web address: www.bloomhealth.net

GEISINGER-COMMUNITY MEDICAL CENTER (O, 293 beds) 1800 Mulberry Street, Scranton, PA Zip 18510–2369; tel. 570/703–8000; Anthony Aquilina, D.O., Regional President

GEISINGER-LEWISTOWN HOSPITAL (O, 123 beds) 400 Highland Avenue, Lewistown, PA Zip 17044–1198; tel. 717/248–5411; Kirk E. Thomas, Vice President Operations
Web address: www.geisinger.org

JERSEY SHORE HOSPITAL (O, 25 beds) 1020 Thompson Street, Jersey Shore, PA Zip 17740–1794; tel. 570/398–0100; David A. Shannon, President and Chief Executive Officer
Web address: www.jsh.org

Owned, leased, sponsored:	8 hospitals	2141 beds
Contract-managed:	0 hospitals	0 beds
Totals:	8 hospitals	2141 beds

★0311: GENESIS HEALTH SYSTEM (NP)
1227 East Rusholme Street, Davenport, IA Zip 52803–2498; tel. 563/421–1000; Douglas P. Cropper, President and Chief Executive Officer
(Centralized Physician/Insurance Health System)

ILLINOIS: GENESIS MEDICAL CENTER, SILVIS (O, 135 beds) 801 Illini Drive, Silvis, IL Zip 61282–1893; tel. 309/281–4000; Theresa Summers-Main, R.N., Interim President

GENESIS MEDICAL CENTER-ALEDO (O, 22 beds) 409 NW Ninth Avenue, Aledo, IL Zip 61231–1296; tel. 309/582–9100; Ted Rogalski, Administrator
Web address: www.genesishealth.com

IOWA: GENESIS MEDICAL CENTER, DEWITT (O, 86 beds) 1118 11th Street, De Witt, IA Zip 52742–1296; tel. 563/659–4200; Curt Coleman, FACHE, Chief Executive Officer

GENESIS MEDICAL CENTER-DAVENPORT-WEST CENTRAL PARK (O, 368 beds) 1227 East Rusholme Street, Davenport, IA Zip 52803–2498; tel. 563/421–1000; Jordan Voigt, Administrator
Web address: www.genesishealth.com

JACKSON COUNTY REGIONAL HEALTH CENTER (C, 25 beds) 700 West Grove Street, Maquoketa, IA Zip 52060–2163; tel. 563/652–2474; Curt Coleman, FACHE, Administrator
Web address: www.jcrhc.org

Owned, leased, sponsored:	4 hospitals	611 beds
Contract-managed:	1 hospitals	25 beds
Totals:	5 hospitals	636 beds

0283: GILLIARD HEALTH SERVICES (IO)
3091 Carter Hill Road, Montgomery, AL Zip 36111–1801; tel. 334/265–5009; William G. McKenzie, President, Chief Executive Officer and Chairman

ALABAMA: EVERGREEN MEDICAL CENTER (O, 39 beds) 101 Crestview Avenue, Evergreen, AL Zip 36401–3333, P O Box 706, 36401–0706, tel. 251/578–2480; Tom McLendon, Administrator

JACKSON MEDICAL CENTER (O, 26 beds) 220 Hospital Drive, Jackson, AL Zip 36545–2459, P O Box 428, 36545–0428, tel. 251/246–9021; Jennifer M. Ryland, R.N., Chief Executive Officer
Web address: www.jacksonmedicalcenter.org

Owned, leased, sponsored:	2 hospitals	65 beds
Contract-managed:	0 hospitals	0 beds
Totals:	2 hospitals	65 beds

0648: GOOD SHEPHERD REHABILITATION NETWORK (IO)
850 South Fifth Street, Allentown, PA Zip 18103–3308; tel. 610/776–3100; John Kristel, President and Chief Executive Officer
(Independent Hospital System)

PENNSYLVANIA: GOOD SHEPHERD REHABILITATION HOSPITAL (O, 106 beds) 850 South 5th Street, Allentown, PA Zip 18103–3308; tel. 610/776–3299; John Kristel, President and Chief Executive Officer

GOOD SHEPHERD SPECIALTY HOSPITAL (O, 32 beds) 2545 Schoenersville Road, 4th Floor, Bethlehem, PA Zip 18017–7300; tel. 484/884–5051; Susan Ferguson, Administrator
Web address: www.goodshepherdrehab.org

Owned, leased, sponsored:	2 hospitals	138 beds
Contract-managed:	0 hospitals	0 beds
Totals:	2 hospitals	138 beds

★1535: GREAT PLAINS HEALTH ALLIANCE, INC. (NP)
250 North Rock Road, Suite 160, Wichita, KS Zip 67206–2241; tel. 316/685–1523; Dave Dellasega, President and Chief Executive Officer
(Decentralized Health System)

KANSAS: ASHLAND HEALTH CENTER (C, 25 beds) 709 Oak Street, Ashland, KS Zip 67831–0188, P O Box 188, 67831–0188, tel. 620/635–2241; Michael Mages, Chief Executive Officer

CHEYENNE COUNTY HOSPITAL (L, 16 beds) 210 West First Street, Saint Francis, KS Zip 67756–3540, P O Box 547, 67756–0547, tel. 785/332–2104; Kelly Pottorff, Chief Executive Officer
Web address: www.cheyennecountyhospital.com

COMANCHE COUNTY HOSPITAL (C, 12 beds) 202 South Frisco Street, Coldwater, KS Zip 67029–9101, HC 65, Box 8A, 67029–9500, tel. 620/582–2144; Nancy Zimmerman, R.N., Administrator

ELLINWOOD DISTRICT HOSPITAL (L, 25 beds) 605 North Main Street, Ellinwood, KS Zip 67526–1440; tel. 620/564–2548; Kile Magner, Administrator
Web address: www.ellinwooddistricthospital.org

FREDONIA REGIONAL HOSPITAL (C, 34 beds) 1527 Madison Street, Fredonia, KS Zip 66736–1751, P O Box 579, 66736–0579, tel. 620/378–2121; John Hart, Chief Executive Officer

GRISELL MEMORIAL HOSPITAL DISTRICT ONE (C, 42 beds) 210 South Vermont Avenue, Ransom, KS Zip 67572–9525; tel. 785/731–2231; David Caudill, Administrator
Web address: www.grisellmemorialhospital.org

KIOWA COUNTY MEMORIAL HOSPITAL (L, 15 beds) 721 West Kansas Avenue, Greensburg, KS Zip 67054–1633; tel. 620/723–3341; Mary Sweet, Administrator

LANE COUNTY HOSPITAL (C, 25 beds) 235 West Vine, Dighton, KS Zip 67839–0969, P O Box 969, 67839–0969, tel. 620/397–5321; Donna McGowan, Administrator
Web address: www.lanecountyhospital.com/

MEDICINE LODGE MEMORIAL HOSPITAL (C, 25 beds) 710 North Walnut Street, Medicine Lodge, KS Zip 67104–1019; tel. 620/886–3771; Kevin A. White, Administrator

MINNEOLA DISTRICT HOSPITAL (C, 54 beds) 212 Main Street, Minneola, KS Zip 67865–8511, P O Box 127, 67865–0127, tel. 620/885–4264; Deborah Bruner, Chief Executive Officer and Administrator
Web address: www.minneolahealthcare.com

OSBORNE COUNTY MEMORIAL HOSPITAL (C, 25 beds) 424 West New Hampshire Street, Osborne, KS Zip 67473–2314, P O Box 70, 67473–0070, tel. 785/346–2121; Marianna Harris, Administrator
Web address: www.ocmh.org

OTTAWA COUNTY HEALTH CENTER (L, 45 beds) 215 East Eighth, Minneapolis, KS Zip 67467–1902, P O Box 290, 67467–0290, tel. 785/392–2122; Jody Parks, Administrator

---

For explanation of codes following names, see page B2.
★ Indicates Type III membership in the American Hospital Association.

PHILLIPS COUNTY HOSPITAL (L, 25 beds) 1150 State Street, Phillipsburg, KS Zip 67661–1743, P O Box 607, 67661–0607, tel. 785/543–5226; Rex D. Walk, Interim Chief Executive Officer
Web address: www.phillipshospital.org

RAWLINS COUNTY HEALTH CENTER (C, 24 beds) 707 Grant Street, Atwood, KS Zip 67730–1526, P O Box 47, 67730–0047, tel. 785/626–3211; Sharon K. Cox, FACHE, Chief Executive Officer
Web address: www.rchc.us

REPUBLIC COUNTY HOSPITAL (L, 63 beds) 2420 'G' Street, Belleville, KS Zip 66935–2400; tel. 785/527–2254; David-Paul Cavazos, Chief Executive Officer

SABETHA COMMUNITY HOSPITAL (L, 25 beds) 14th and Oregon Streets, Sabetha, KS Zip 66534–0229, P O Box 229, 66534–0229, tel. 785/284–2121; Lora Key, Chief Executive Officer
Web address: www.sabethahospital.com

SATANTA DISTRICT HOSPITAL AND LONG TERM CARE (C, 57 beds) 401 South Cheyenne Street, Satanta, KS Zip 67870–0159, P O Box 159, 67870–0159, tel. 620/649–2761; Jeremy Clingenpeel, Administrator

SMITH COUNTY MEMORIAL HOSPITAL (L, 53 beds) 614 South Main Street, Smith Center, KS Zip 66967–3001; tel. 785/282–6845; Allen Van Driel, FACHE, Administrator
Web address: www.gpha.com

TREGO COUNTY-LEMKE MEMORIAL HOSPITAL (C, 62 beds) 320 North 13th Street, Wakeeney, KS Zip 67672–2099; tel. 785/743–2182; David Augustine, Chief Executive Officer

WICHITA COUNTY HEALTH CENTER (C, 42 beds) 211 East Earl Street, Leoti, KS Zip 67861–9620; tel. 620/375–2233; Teresa Clark, Chief Executive Officer and Administrator
Web address: www.wichitacountyhealthcenter.com

NEBRASKA: HARLAN COUNTY HEALTH SYSTEM (C, 19 beds) 717 North Brown Street, Alma, NE Zip 68920–2132, P O Box 836, 68920–0836, tel. 308/928–2151; Manuela Wolf, R.N., Chief Executive Officer
Web address: www.harlancountyhealth.com

Owned, leased, sponsored:	8 hospitals	267 beds
Contract-managed:	13 hospitals	446 beds
Totals:	21 hospitals	713 beds

★0144: GREATER HUDSON VALLEY HEALTH SYSTEM (NP)
707 East Main Street, Middletown, NY Zip 10940–2650; tel. 845/333–1000; Scott Batulis, President and Chief Executive Officer
(Independent Hospital System)

NEW YORK: CATSKILL REGIONAL MEDICAL CENTER (O, 165 beds) 68 Harris Bushville Road, Harris, NY Zip 12742–5030, P O Box 800, 12742–0800, tel. 845/794–3300; Jonathan Schiller, Chief Executive Officer

GROVER M. HERMANN HOSPITAL (O, 25 beds) 8881 Route 97, Callicoon, NY Zip 12723; tel. 845/887–5530; Rolland Bojo, R.N., Administrator
Web address: www.crmcny.org

ORANGE REGIONAL MEDICAL CENTER (O, 345 beds) 707 East Main Street, Middletown, NY Zip 10940–2650; tel. 845/333–1000; Scott Batulis, President and Chief Executive Officer
Web address: www.ormc.org

Owned, leased, sponsored:	3 hospitals	535 beds
Contract-managed:	0 hospitals	0 beds
Totals:	3 hospitals	535 beds

★1555: GREENVILLE HEALTH SYSTEM (NP)
701 Grove Road, Greenville, SC Zip 29605–5611; tel. 864/455–7000; Michael C. Riordan, President and Chief Executive Officer
(Centralized Health System)

SOUTH CAROLINA: GHS GREENVILLE MEMORIAL HOSPITAL (O, 769 beds) 701 Grove Road, Greenville, SC Zip 29605–4295; tel. 864/455–7000; Paul F. Johnson, Vice President and Chief Operating Officer Central Region

GHS GREER MEMORIAL HOSPITAL (O, 70 beds) 830 South Buncombe Road, Greer, SC Zip 29650–2400; tel. 864/797–8000; John F. Mansure, FACHE, President
Web address: www.ghs.org

GHS HILLCREST MEMORIAL HOSPITAL (O, 43 beds) 729 SE Main Street, Simpsonville, SC Zip 29681–3280; tel. 864/454–6100; Justin Benefield, President

GREENVILLE HEALTH SYSTEM - LAURENS COUNTY MEMORIAL HOSPITAL (L, 71 beds) 22725 Highway 76 East, Clinton, SC Zip 29325–7527, P O Drawer 976, 29325–0976, tel. 864/833–9100; Justin Benfield, Southern Region Chief Operating Officer
Web address: www.ghs.org/laurens

OCONEE MEMORIAL HOSPITAL (L, 252 beds) 298 Memorial Drive, Seneca, SC Zip 29672–9499; tel. 864/882–3351; Hunter Kome, Campus President

PATEWOOD MEMORIAL HOSPITAL (O, 72 beds) 175 Patewood Drive, Greenville, SC Zip 29615–3570; tel. 864/797–1000; Tim Brookshire, FACHE, Interim Chief Operating Officer
Web address: www.ghs.org/patewood

Owned, leased, sponsored:	6 hospitals	1277 beds
Contract-managed:	0 hospitals	0 beds
Totals:	6 hospitals	1277 beds

★0675: GUTHRIE CLINIC (NP)
Guthrie Square, Sayre, PA Zip 18840; tel. 570/887–4312; Joseph A. Scopelliti, M.D., President and Chief Executive Officer
(Moderately Centralized Health System)

NEW YORK: GUTHRIE CORNING HOSPITAL (O, 82 beds) One Guthrie Drive, Corning, NY Zip 14830–3696; tel. 607/937–7200; Garrett W. Hoover, FACHE, President

PENNSYLVANIA: GUTHRIE ROBERT PACKER HOSPITAL (O, 254 beds) 1 Guthrie Square, Sayre, PA Zip 18840–1698; tel. 570/888–6666; Paul G. VerValin, Interim President
Web address: https://www.guthrie.org/location/robert-packer-hospital

GUTHRIE TOWANDA MEMORIAL HOSPITAL (O, 195 beds) 91 Hospital Drive, Towanda, PA Zip 18848–9702; tel. 570/265–2191; Staci Covey, R.N., MS, President

TROY COMMUNITY HOSPITAL (O, 25 beds) 275 Guthrie Drive, Troy, PA Zip 16947; tel. 570/297–2121; Staci Covey, R.N., MS, President
Web address: www.guthrie.org

Owned, leased, sponsored:	4 hospitals	556 beds
Contract-managed:	0 hospitals	0 beds
Totals:	4 hospitals	556 beds

★1003: HACKENSACK MERIDIAN HEALTH (NP)
343 Thornall Street, Edison, NJ Zip 08837–2206; tel. 844/464–9355; Robert C. Garrett, FACHE, Co-Chief Executive Officer
(Centralized Health System)

NEW JERSEY: HACKENSACK MERIDIAN HEALTH BAYSHORE COMMUNITY HOSPITAL (O, 160 beds) 727 North Beers Street, Holmdel, NJ Zip 07733–1598; tel. 732/739–5900; Timothy J. Hogan, FACHE, Regional President

HACKENSACK MERIDIAN HEALTH HACKENSACK UNIVERSITY MEDICAL CENTER (O, 737 beds) 30 Prospect Avenue, Hackensack, NJ Zip 07601–1914; tel. 201/996–2000; Ihor S. Sawczuk, M.D., President
Web address: www.hackensackumc.org

HACKENSACK MERIDIAN HEALTH JERSEY SHORE UNIVERSITY MEDICAL CENTER (O, 553 beds) 1945 Route 33, Neptune, NJ Zip 07754–0397; tel. 732/775–5500; Kenneth N. Sable, M.D., President

HACKENSACK MERIDIAN HEALTH OCEAN MEDICAL CENTER (O, 278 beds) 425 Jack Martin Boulevard, Brick Township, NJ Zip 08724–7732; tel. 732/840–2200; Dean Q. Lin, FACHE, Regional President
Web address: www.meridianhealth.com

HACKENSACK MERIDIAN HEALTH PALISADES MEDICAL CENTER (O, 228 beds) 7600 River Road, North Bergen, NJ Zip 07047–6217; tel. 201/854–5000; Anthony Passannante Jr, M.D., Acting President

For explanation of codes following names, see page B2.
★ Indicates Type III membership in the American Hospital Association.

Section B

HACKENSACK MERIDIAN HEALTH RARITAN BAY MEDICAL CENTER (O, 282 beds) 530 New Brunswick Avenue, Perth Amboy, NJ Zip 08861–3654; tel. 732/442–3700; Michael R. D'Agnes, FACHE, President and Chief Executive Officer
Web address: www.rbmc.org

HACKENSACK MERIDIAN HEALTH RIVERVIEW MEDICAL CENTER (O, 304 beds) 1 Riverview Plaza, Red Bank, NJ Zip 07701–1864; tel. 732/741–2700; Timothy J. Hogan, FACHE, Regional President
Web address: www.riverviewmedicalcenter.com

HACKENSACK MERIDIAN HEALTH SHORE REHABILITATION INSTITUTE (O, 40 beds) 425 Jack Martin Boulevard, Brick, NJ Zip 08724–7732; tel. 732/836–4500; Marci Gietter, Interim Executive Director
Web address: www.shorerehabilitationinstitute.com

HACKENSACK MERIDIAN HEALTH SOUTHERN OCEAN MEDICAL CENTER (O, 172 beds) 1140 Route 72 West, Manahawkin, NJ Zip 08050–2499; tel. 609/597–6011; Robert H. Adams Jr, President

Owned, leased, sponsored:	9 hospitals	2754 beds
Contract-managed:	0 hospitals	0 beds
Totals:	9 hospitals	2754 beds

★0541: HARTFORD HEALTHCARE (NP)
One State Street, 19th Floor, Hartford, CT Zip 6103; tel. 860/263–4100; Elliot T. Joseph, Chief Executive Officer
(Centralized Health System)

CONNECTICUT: HARTFORD HOSPITAL (O, 862 beds) 80 Seymour Street, Hartford, CT Zip 06102–8000, P O Box 5037, 06102–5037, tel. 860/545–5000; Stuart Markowitz, M.D., President
Web address: www.harthosp.org

MIDSTATE MEDICAL CENTER (O, 80 beds) 435 Lewis Avenue, Meriden, CT Zip 06451–2101; tel. 203/694–8200; Lucille A. Janatka, President

NATCHAUG HOSPITAL (O, 57 beds) 189 Storrs Road, Mansfield Center, CT Zip 06250–1683; tel. 860/456–1311; Patricia Rehmer, MSN, FACHE, President
Web address: www.natchaug.org

THE HOSPITAL OF CENTRAL CONNECTICUT (O, 170 beds) 100 Grand Street, New Britain, CT Zip 06052–2017, P O Box 100, 06052–2017, tel. 860/224–5011; Lucille A. Janatka, President, Hartford HealthCare Central Region
Web address: www.thocc.org

THE WILLIAM W. BACKUS HOSPITAL (O, 184 beds) 326 Washington Street, Norwich, CT Zip 06360–2740; tel. 860/889–8331; Bimal Patel, President, Hartford HealthCare East Region

WINDHAM HOSPITAL (O, 56 beds) 112 Mansfield Avenue, Willimantic, CT Zip 06226–2040; tel. 860/456–9116; Bimal Patel, President, Hartford Healthcare East Region
Web address: www.windhamhospital.org

Owned, leased, sponsored:	6 hospitals	1409 beds
Contract-managed:	0 hospitals	0 beds
Totals:	6 hospitals	1409 beds

0637: HAVEN BEHAVIORAL HEALTHCARE (IO)
652 West Iris Drive, Nashville, TN Zip 37204–3191; tel. 615/250–9500; Michael Lindley, Chief Executive Officer

ARIZONA: HAVEN SENIOR HORIZONS (O, 45 beds) 1201 South 7th Avenue, Suite 200, Phoenix, AZ Zip 85007–4076; tel. 623/236–2000; Kathy Shaw, Chief Executive Officer

OHIO: HAVEN BEHAVIORAL SENIOR CARE OF DAYTON (O, 32 beds) One Elizabeth Place, 4th Floor Southwest Tower, Dayton, OH Zip 45417–3445; tel. 937/234–0100; Keith Kuhn, Chief Executive Officer
Web address: www.havenbehavioraldayton.com/

PENNSYLVANIA: HAVEN BEHAVIORAL HOSPITAL OF EASTERN PENNSYLVANIA (O, 48 beds) 145 North 6th Street, 3rd Floor, Reading, PA Zip 19601–3096; tel. 610/406–4340; Bryan W. Lett, Chief Executive Officer
Web address: www.https://havenbehavioral.com/

HAVEN BEHAVIORAL HOSPITAL OF PHILADELPHIA (O, 36 beds) 3300 Henry Avenue, Philadelphia, PA Zip 19129–1121, 3301 Scotts Lane, Four Falls Building, 19129, tel. 215/791–6821; Lisa M. Olander, Chief Executive Officer

Owned, leased, sponsored:	4 hospitals	161 beds
Contract-managed:	0 hospitals	0 beds
Totals:	4 hospitals	161 beds

★3555: HAWAII HEALTH SYSTEMS CORPORATION (NP)
3675 Kilauea Avenue, Honolulu, HI Zip 96816–2333; tel. 808/733–4151; Linda Rosen, M.D., Chief Executive Officer
(Independent Hospital System)

HAWAII: HALE HO'OLA HAMAKUA (O, 77 beds) 45–547 Plumeria Street, Honokaa, HI Zip 96727–6902; tel. 808/932–4100; Kerry Pitcher, Administrator
Web address: www.halehoolahamakua.org

HILO MEDICAL CENTER (O, 276 beds) 1190 Waianuenue Avenue, Hilo, HI Zip 96720–2089; tel. 808/932–3000; Dan Brinkman, R.N., Chief Executive Officer

KAU HOSPITAL (O, 21 beds) 1 Kamani Street, Pahala, HI Zip 96777, P O Box 40, 96777–0040, tel. 808/932–4200; Merilyn Harris, Administrator
Web address: www.hhsc.org

KAUAI VETERANS MEMORIAL HOSPITAL (O, 45 beds) 4643 Waimea Canyon Road, Waimea, HI Zip 96796, P O Box 337, 96796–0337, tel. 808/338–9431; Peter Klune, Chief Executive Officer

KOHALA HOSPITAL (O, 28 beds) 54–383 Hospital Road, Kohala, HI Zip 96755, P O Box 10, Kapaau, 96755–0010, tel. 808/889–6211; Eugene Amar Jr, Administrator
Web address: www.koh.hhsc.org

KONA COMMUNITY HOSPITAL (O, 94 beds) 79–1019 Haukapila Street, Kealakekua, HI Zip 96750–7920; tel. 808/322–9311; Jay E. Kreuzer, FACHE, Chief Executive Officer

LEAHI HOSPITAL (O, 126 beds) 3675 Kilauea Avenue, Honolulu, HI Zip 96816–2398; tel. 808/733–8000; Reid Kondo, Interim Administrator
Web address: www.hhsc.org

MALUHIA HOSPITAL (O, 146 beds) 1027 Hala Drive, Honolulu, HI Zip 96817; tel. 808/832–5874; Derek Akiyoshi, Chief Executive Officer

SAMUEL MAHELONA MEMORIAL HOSPITAL (O, 80 beds) 4800 Kawaihau Road, Kapaa, HI Zip 96746–1971; tel. 808/822–4961; Peter Klune, Chief Executive Officer
Web address: www.smmh.hhsc.org

Owned, leased, sponsored:	9 hospitals	893 beds
Contract-managed:	0 hospitals	0 beds
Totals:	9 hospitals	893 beds

0266: HAWAII PACIFIC HEALTH (NP)
55 Merchant Street, Honolulu, HI Zip 96813–4306; tel. 808/949–9355; Raymond P. Vara Jr, President and Chief Executive Officer
(Independent Hospital System)

HAWAII: KAPIOLANI MEDICAL CENTER FOR WOMEN & CHILDREN (O, 180 beds) 1319 Punahou Street, Honolulu, HI Zip 96826–1001; tel. 808/983–6000; Martha Smith, Chief Executive Officer

PALI MOMI MEDICAL CENTER (O, 118 beds) 98–1079 Moanalua Road, Aiea, HI Zip 96701–4713; tel. 808/486–6000; Art Gladstone, R.N., Chief Executive Officer
Web address: www.palimomi.org

STRAUB CLINIC & HOSPITAL (O, 120 beds) 888 South King Street, Honolulu, HI Zip 96813–3097; tel. 808/522–4000; Art Gladstone, R.N., Chief Executive Officer

WILCOX MEMORIAL HOSPITAL (O, 65 beds) 3–3420 Kuhio Highway, Lihue, HI Zip 96766–1099; tel. 808/245–1100; Jen Chahanovich, President and Chief Executive Officer
Web address: www.wilcoxhealth.org

Owned, leased, sponsored:	4 hospitals	483 beds
Contract-managed:	0 hospitals	0 beds
Totals:	4 hospitals	483 beds

For explanation of codes following names, see page B2.
★ Indicates Type III membership in the American Hospital Association.

★**0048: HCA HEALTHCARE** (IO)
One Park Plaza, Nashville, TN Zip 37203–1548; tel. 615/344–5248; R Milton. Johnson, President and Chief Executive Officer
(Decentralized Health System)

ALASKA: ALASKA REGIONAL HOSPITAL (O, 132 beds) 2801 Debarr Road, Anchorage, AK Zip 99508–2997, P O Box 143889, 99514–3889, tel. 907/264–1754; Julie Taylor, FACHE, Chief Executive Officer
Web address: www.alaskaregional.com

CALIFORNIA: GOOD SAMARITAN HOSPITAL (O, 332 beds) 2425 Samaritan Drive, San Jose, CA Zip 95124–3997, P O Box 240002, 95154–2402, tel. 408/559–2011; Joseph DeSchryver, Chief Executive Officer

LOS ROBLES HOSPITAL AND MEDICAL CENTER (O, 367 beds) 215 West Janss Road, Thousand Oaks, CA Zip 91360–1899; tel. 805/497–2727; Natalie Mussi, President and Chief Executive Officer
Web address: www.losrobleshospital.com

REGIONAL MEDICAL CENTER OF SAN JOSE (O, 193 beds) 225 North Jackson Avenue, San Jose, CA Zip 95116–1603; tel. 408/259–5000; Michael T. Johnson, FACHE, President and Chief Executive Officer
Web address: www.regionalmedicalsanjose.com

RIVERSIDE COMMUNITY HOSPITAL (O, 373 beds) 4445 Magnolia Avenue, Riverside, CA Zip 92501–4199; tel. 951/788–3000; Patrick D. Brilliant, President and Chief Executive Officer
Web address: www.riversidecommunityhospital.com

WEST HILLS HOSPITAL AND MEDICAL CENTER (O, 225 beds) 7300 Medical Center Drive, West Hills, CA Zip 91307–1900; tel. 818/676–4000; Douglas Long, President and Chief Executive Officer

COLORADO: MEDICAL CENTER OF AURORA (O, 341 beds) 1501 South Potomac Street, Aurora, CO Zip 80012–5411; tel. 303/695–2600; Daniel Miller, FACHE, President and Chief Executive Officer
Web address: www.auroramed.com

NORTH SUBURBAN MEDICAL CENTER (O, 139 beds) 9191 Grant Street, Thornton, CO Zip 80229–4341; tel. 303/451–7800; Jennifer Alderfer, President and Chief Executive Officer

PRESBYTERIAN-ST. LUKE'S MEDICAL CENTER (O, 399 beds) 1719 East 19th Avenue, Denver, CO Zip 80218–1281; tel. 303/839–6000; Maureen Tarrant, President and Chief Executive Officer
Web address: www.pslmc.com

ROSE MEDICAL CENTER (O, 280 beds) 4567 East Ninth Avenue, Denver, CO Zip 80220–3941; tel. 303/320–2121; Kenneth H. Feiler, President and Chief Executive Officer

SKY RIDGE MEDICAL CENTER (O, 275 beds) 10101 Ridge Gate Parkway, Lone Tree, CO Zip 80124–5522; tel. 720/225–1000; Susan Hicks, Chief Executive Officer
Web address: www.skyridgemedcenter.com

SPALDING REHABILITATION HOSPITAL (O, 40 beds) 900 Potomac Steet, Aurora, CO Zip 80011–6716; tel. 303/367–1166; Daniel Miller, FACHE, President and Chief Executive Officer

SWEDISH MEDICAL CENTER (O, 427 beds) 501 East Hampden Avenue, Englewood, CO Zip 80113–2702; tel. 303/788–5000; Richard A. Hammett, President and Chief Executive Officer
Web address: www.swedishhospital.com

FLORIDA: AVENTURA HOSPITAL AND MEDICAL CENTER (O, 359 beds) 20900 Biscayne Boulevard, Aventura, FL Zip 33180–1407; tel. 305/682–7000; Alisa Bert, Interim Chief Executive Officer

BLAKE MEDICAL CENTER (O, 383 beds) 2020 59th Street West, Bradenton, FL Zip 34209–4669; tel. 941/792–6611; Daniel J. Friedrich III, Chief Executive Officer
Web address: www.blakemedicalcenter.com

BRANDON REGIONAL HOSPITAL (O, 407 beds) 119 Oakfield Drive, Brandon, FL Zip 33511–5779; tel. 813/681–5551; Bland Eng, Chief Executive Officer

CAPITAL REGIONAL MEDICAL CENTER (O, 198 beds) 2626 Capital Medical Boulevard, Tallahassee, FL Zip 32308–4499; tel. 850/325–5000; Mark Robinson, FACHE, President and Chief Executive Officer
Web address: www.capitalregionalmedicalcenter.com

CENTRAL FLORIDA REGIONAL HOSPITAL (O, 226 beds) 1401 West Seminole Boulevard, Sanford, FL Zip 32771–6764; tel. 407/321–4500; Wendy H. Brandon, Chief Executive Officer

CITRUS MEMORIAL HEALTH SYSTEM (O, 204 beds) 502 West Highland Boulevard, Inverness, FL Zip 34452–4754; tel. 352/726–1551; Ralph A. Aleman, President and Chief Executive Officer
Web address: www.citrusmh.com

DOCTORS HOSPITAL OF SARASOTA (O, 168 beds) 5731 Bee Ridge Road, Sarasota, FL Zip 34233–5056; tel. 941/342–1100; Robert C. Meade, Chief Executive Officer

ENGLEWOOD COMMUNITY HOSPITAL (O, 100 beds) 700 Medical Boulevard, Englewood, FL Zip 34223–3978; tel. 941/475–6571; Valerie L. Powell-Stafford, Chief Executive Officer
Web address: www.englewoodcommunityhospital.com

FAWCETT MEMORIAL HOSPITAL (O, 237 beds) 21298 Olean Boulevard, Port Charlotte, FL Zip 33952–6765; tel. 941/629–1181; William Hawley, President and Chief Executive Officer
Web address: www.fawcetthospital.com

FORT WALTON BEACH MEDICAL CENTER (O, 257 beds) 1000 Mar-Walt Drive, Fort Walton Beach, FL Zip 32547–6795; tel. 850/862–1111; Mitchell P. Mongell, FACHE, Chief Executive Officer
Web address: www.fwbmc.com

GULF COAST MEDICAL CENTER (O, 176 beds) 449 West 23rd Street, Panama City, FL Zip 32405–4593, P O Box 15309, 32406–5309, tel. 850/769–8341; Brad Griffin, Chief Executive Officer

JFK MEDICAL CENTER NORTH CAMPUS (O, 245 beds) 2201 45th Street, West Palm Beach, FL Zip 33407–2047; tel. 561/842–6141; Patricia Burns, Chief Executive Officer
Web address: www.westpalmhospital.com

JFK MEDICAL CENTER (O, 424 beds) 5301 South Congress Avenue, Atlantis, FL Zip 33462–1197; tel. 561/965–7300; Gina Melby, Chief Executive Officer

KENDALL REGIONAL MEDICAL CENTER (O, 300 beds) 11750 Bird Road, Miami, FL Zip 33175–3530; tel. 305/223–3000; Brandon Haushalter, Chief Executive Officer
Web address: www.kendallmed.com

LAKE CITY MEDICAL CENTER (O, 67 beds) 340 NW Commerce Drive, Lake City, FL Zip 32055–4709; tel. 386/719–9000; Mark Miller, FACHE, Chief Executive Officer

LARGO MEDICAL CENTER (O, 243 beds) 201 14th Street SW, Largo, FL Zip 33770–3133; tel. 727/588–5200; Anthony M Degina, President and Chief Executive Officer
Web address: www.largomedical.com

LAWNWOOD REGIONAL MEDICAL CENTER & HEART INSTITUTE (O, 331 beds) 1700 South 23rd Street, Fort Pierce, FL Zip 34950–4803; tel. 772/461–4000; Robert M. Krieger, Chief Executive Officer
Web address: www.lawnwoodmed.com

MEDICAL CENTER OF TRINITY (O, 276 beds) 9330 State Road 54, Trinity, FL Zip 34655–1808; tel. 727/834–4900; Leigh Massengill, Chief Executive Officer

MEMORIAL HOSPITAL JACKSONVILLE (O, 410 beds) 3625 University Blvd South, Jacksonville, FL Zip 32216–4207, P O Box 16325, 32245–6325, tel. 904/702–6111; Bradley S. Talbert, FACHE, President and Chief Executive Officer
Web address: www.memorialhospitaljax.com

MEMORIAL HOSPITAL OF TAMPA (O, 139 beds) 2901 Swann Avenue, Tampa, FL Zip 33609–4057; tel. 813/873–6400; Sonia I. Wellman, Chief Executive Officer
Web address: www.memorialhospitaltampa.com

NORTH FLORIDA REGIONAL MEDICAL CENTER (O, 432 beds) 6500 Newberry Road, Gainesville, FL Zip 32605–4392, P O Box 147006, 32614–7006, tel. 352/333–4000; Brian Cook, FACHE, President and Chief Executive Officer

NORTHSIDE HOSPITAL (O, 217 beds) 6000 49th Street North, Saint Petersburg, FL Zip 33709–2145; tel. 727/521–4411; Dia Nichols, Chief Executive Officer
Web address: www.northsidehospital.com

NORTHWEST MEDICAL CENTER (O, 228 beds) 2801 North State Road 7, Margate, FL Zip 33063–5727; tel. 954/974–0400; Erica Gulrich, Chief Executive Officer
Web address: www.northwestmed.com

OAK HILL HOSPITAL (O, 280 beds) 11375 Cortez Boulevard, Brooksville, FL Zip 34613–5409; tel. 352/596–6632; Mickey Smith, Chief Executive Officer

For explanation of codes following names, see page B2.
★ Indicates Type III membership in the American Hospital Association.

OCALA REGIONAL MEDICAL CENTER (O, 270 beds) 1431 SW First Avenue, Ocala, FL Zip 34471–6500, P O Box 2200, 34478–2200, tel. 352/401–1000; Chad Christianson, Chief Executive Officer
Web address: www.ocalaregional.com

ORANGE PARK MEDICAL CENTER (O, 317 beds) 2001 Kingsley Avenue, Orange Park, FL Zip 32073–5156; tel. 904/639–8500; Chad Patrick, President and Chief Executive Officer
Web address: www.opmedical.com

OSCEOLA REGIONAL MEDICAL CENTER (O, 332 beds) 700 West Oak Street, Kissimmee, FL Zip 34741–4996; tel. 407/846–2266; Davide M. Carbone, FACHE, Chief Executive Officer

OVIEDO MEDICAL CENTER (O, 64 beds) 8300 Red Bug Lake Road, Oviedo, FL Zip 32765–6801; tel. 407/890–2273; Kenneth C. Donahey, Chief Executive Officer
Web address: www.oviedomedicalcenter.com

PALMS WEST HOSPITAL (O, 204 beds) 13001 Southern Boulevard, Loxahatchee, FL Zip 33470–9203; tel. 561/798–3300; Eric Goldman, Chief Executive Officer

PALMS OF PASADENA HOSPITAL (O, 187 beds) 1501 Pasadena Avenue South, Saint Petersburg, FL Zip 33707–3798; tel. 727/381–1000; Sharon Hayes, Chief Executive Officer
Web address: www.palmspasadena.com

PLANTATION GENERAL HOSPITAL (O, 264 beds) 401 NW 42nd Avenue, Plantation, FL Zip 33317–2882; tel. 954/587–5010; Madeline Nava, Chief Executive Officer

POINCIANA MEDICAL CENTER (O, 24 beds) 325 Cypress Parkway, Kissimmee, FL Zip 34758; tel. 407/530–2000; Christopher Cosby, Chief Executive Officer
Web address: www.poincianamedicalcenter.com

PUTNAM COMMUNITY MEDICAL CENTER (O, 99 beds) 611 Zeagler Drive, Palatka, FL Zip 32177–3810; tel. 386/328–5711; J. Christopher. Mosley, Chief Executive Officer

RAULERSON HOSPITAL (O, 100 beds) 1796 Highway 441 North, Okeechobee, FL Zip 34972–1918, P O Box 1307, 34973–1307, tel. 863/763–2151; Brian Melear, Chief Executive Officer
Web address: www.raulersonhospital.com

REGIONAL MEDICAL CENTER BAYONET POINT (O, 290 beds) 14000 Fivay Road, Hudson, FL Zip 34667–7199; tel. 727/869–5400; Shayne George, Chief Executive Officer

SOUTH BAY HOSPITAL (O, 138 beds) 4016 Sun City Center Blvd, Sun City Center, FL Zip 33573–5298; tel. 813/634–3301; Sharon L. Roush, Chief Executive Officer
Web address: www.southbayhospital.com/

SPECIALTY HOSPITAL JACKSONVILLE (O, 62 beds) 4901 Richard Street, Jacksonville, FL Zip 32207–7328; tel. 904/737–3120; Barbara McCarthy, Chief Executive Officer
Web address: www.specialtyhospitaljax.com

ST. LUCIE MEDICAL CENTER (O, 194 beds) 1800 SE Tiffany Avenue, Port St Lucie, FL Zip 34952–7521; tel. 772/335–4000; Jay Finnegan, Chief Executive Officer

ST. PETERSBURG GENERAL HOSPITAL (O, 219 beds) 6500 38th Avenue North, Saint Petersburg, FL Zip 33710–1629; tel. 727/384–1414; Janice Balzano, President and Chief Executive Officer
Web address: www.stpetegeneral.com

TAMPA COMMUNITY HOSPITAL (O, 201 beds) 6001 Webb Road, Tampa, FL Zip 33615–3291; tel. 813/888–7060; Jacob Fisher, Chief Executive Officer
Web address: www.tampacommunityhospital.com/

TWIN CITIES HOSPITAL (O, 65 beds) 2190 Highway 85 North, Niceville, FL Zip 32578–1045; tel. 850/678–4131; David Whalen, Chief Executive Officer
Web address: www.tchealthcare.com

UNIVERSITY HOSPITAL AND MEDICAL CENTER (O, 317 beds) 7201 North University Drive, Tamarac, FL Zip 33321–2996; tel. 954/721–2200; Dana C. Oaks, Chief Executive Officer

WEST FLORIDA HOSPITAL (O, 339 beds) 8383 North Davis Highway, Pensacola, FL Zip 32514–6088; tel. 850/494–4000; Carlton Ulmer, President and Chief Executive Officer
Web address: www.westfloridahospital.com

WESTSIDE REGIONAL MEDICAL CENTER (O, 224 beds) 8201 West Broward Boulevard, Plantation, FL Zip 33324–2701; tel. 954/473–6600; Barbara Simmons, R.N., Chief Executive Officer

GEORGIA: CARTERSVILLE MEDICAL CENTER (O, 80 beds) 960 Joe Frank Harris Parkway, Cartersville, GA Zip 30120–2129; tel. 770/382–1530; Keith Sandlin, Chief Executive Officer
Web address: www.cartersvillemedical.com

COLISEUM MEDICAL CENTERS (O, 227 beds) 350 Hospital Drive, Macon, GA Zip 31217–3871; tel. 478/765–7000; Stephen J. Daugherty, Interim Chief Executive Officer

COLISEUM NORTHSIDE HOSPITAL (O, 103 beds) 400 Charter Boulevard, Macon, GA Zip 31210–4853, P O Box 4627, 31208–4627, tel. 478/757–8200; Greg Earles, Chief Executive Officer
Web address: www.coliseumhealthsystem.com

DOCTORS HOSPITAL (O, 307 beds) 3651 Wheeler Road, Augusta, GA Zip 30909–6426; tel. 706/651–3232; Douglas Welch, Chief Executive Officer
Web address: www.doctors-hospital.net

EASTSIDE MEDICAL CENTER (O, 294 beds) 1700 Medical Way, Snellville, GA Zip 30078–2195; tel. 770/979–0200; Trent Lind, Chief Executive Officer

FAIRVIEW PARK HOSPITAL (O, 168 beds) 200 Industrial Boulevard, Dublin, GA Zip 31021–2997, P O Box 1408, 31040–1408, tel. 478/275–2000; Donald R. Avery, FACHE, President and Chief Executive Officer
Web address: www.fairviewparkhospital.com

MEMORIAL SATILLA HEALTH (O, 199 beds) 1900 Tebeau Street, Waycross, GA Zip 31501–6357, P O Box 139, 31502–0139, tel. 912/283–3030; Bobby McCullough, Interim Chief Executive Officer

REDMOND REGIONAL MEDICAL CENTER (O, 230 beds) 501 Redmond Road, Rome, GA Zip 30165–1415, P O Box 107001, 30164–7001, tel. 706/291–0291; John Quinlivan, Chief Executive Officer
Web address: www.redmondregional.com

IDAHO: EASTERN IDAHO REGIONAL MEDICAL CENTER (O, 293 beds) 3100 Channing Way, Idaho Falls, ID Zip 83404–7533, P O Box 2077, 83403–2077, tel. 208/529–6111; Douglas Crabtree, Chief Executive Officer
Web address: www.eirmc.com

WEST VALLEY MEDICAL CENTER (O, 86 beds) 1717 Arlington, Caldwell, ID Zip 83605–4802; tel. 208/459–4641; Elizabeth Hunsicker, Chief Executive Officer

INDIANA: TERRE HAUTE REGIONAL HOSPITAL (O, 208 beds) 3901 South Seventh Street, Terre Haute, IN Zip 47802–5709; tel. 812/232–0021; Nathan Vooys, Chief Executive Officer
Web address: www.regionalhospital.com

KANSAS: MENORAH MEDICAL CENTER (O, 158 beds) 5721 West 119th Street, Overland Park, KS Zip 66209–3722; tel. 913/498–6000; Charles Laird, Chief Executive Officer

OVERLAND PARK REGIONAL MEDICAL CENTER (O, 275 beds) 10500 Quivira Road, Overland Park, KS Zip 66215–2306, P O Box 15959, 66215–5959, tel. 913/541–5000; Kevin J. Hicks, President and CEO
Web address: www.oprmc.com

WESLEY MEDICAL CENTER (O, 573 beds) 550 North Hillside, Wichita, KS Zip 67214–4976; tel. 316/962–2000; Bill Voloch, President and Chief Executive Officer

KENTUCKY: FRANKFORT REGIONAL MEDICAL CENTER (O, 115 beds) 299 King's Daughters Drive, Frankfort, KY Zip 40601–4186; tel. 502/875–5240; Chip Peal, Chief Executive Officer
Web address: www.frankfortregional.com

TRISTAR GREENVIEW REGIONAL HOSPITAL (O, 148 beds) 1801 Ashley Circle, Bowling Green, KY Zip 42104–3362; tel. 270/793–1000; Michael Sherrod, Chief Executive Officer

LOUISIANA: RAPIDES REGIONAL MEDICAL CENTER (O, 357 beds) 211 4th ST, Alexandria, LA Zip 71301–8421, 211 Fourth Street, 71301–8421, tel. 318/769–3000; Jason E. Cobb, FACHE, Chief Executive Officer
Web address: www.rapidesregional.com

TULANE MEDICAL CENTER (O, 294 beds) 1415 Tulane Avenue, New Orleans, LA Zip 70112–2600; tel. 504/988–5263; William Lunn, M.D., Chief Executive Officer

WOMEN'S AND CHILDREN'S HOSPITAL (O, 161 beds) 4600 Ambassador Caffery Parkway, Lafayette, LA Zip 70508–6923, P O Box 88030, 70598–8030, tel. 337/521–9100; Kathy J. Bobbs, FACHE, President and Chief Executive Officer
Web address: www.womens-childrens.com

For explanation of codes following names, see page B2.
★ Indicates Type III membership in the American Hospital Association.

MISSISSIPPI: GARDEN PARK MEDICAL CENTER (O, 130 beds) 15200 Community Road, Gulfport, MS Zip 39503–3085, P O Box 1240, 39502–1240, tel. 228/575–7000; Randy Rogers, FACHE, Chief Executive Officer

MISSOURI: BELTON REGIONAL MEDICAL CENTER (O, 48 beds) 17065 South 71 Highway, Belton, MO Zip 64012–4631; tel. 816/348–1200; Todd Krass, Chief Executive Officer
Web address: www.beltonregionalmedicalcenter.com

CENTERPOINT MEDICAL CENTER (O, 221 beds) 19600 East 39th Street, Independence, MO Zip 64057–2301; tel. 816/698–7000; David R. Williams, Chief Executive Officer

LAFAYETTE REGIONAL HEALTH CENTER (O, 25 beds) 1500 State Street, Lexington, MO Zip 64067–1107; tel. 660/259–2203; Darrel Box, Chief Executive Officer
Web address: www.lafayetteregionalhealthcenter.com

LEE'S SUMMIT MEDICAL CENTER (O, 64 beds) 2100 SE Blue Parkway, Lee's Summit, MO Zip 64063–1007; tel. 816/282–5000; Matt Sogard, Chief Executive Officer
Web address: www.leessummitmedicalcenter.com

RESEARCH MEDICAL CENTER (O, 456 beds) 2316 East Meyer Boulevard, Kansas City, MO Zip 64132–1136; tel. 816/276–4000; Jacqueline DeSouza, Chief Executive Officer

NEVADA: MOUNTAINVIEW HOSPITAL (O, 340 beds) 3100 North Tenaya Way, Las Vegas, NV Zip 89128–0436; tel. 702/255–5000; Jeremy Bradshaw, Chief Executive Officer
Web address: www.mountainview-hospital.com

SOUTHERN HILLS HOSPITAL AND MEDICAL CENTER (O, 134 beds) 9300 West Sunset Road, Las Vegas, NV Zip 89148–4844; tel. 702/880–2100; Adam Rudd, Chief Executive Officer

SUNRISE HOSPITAL AND MEDICAL CENTER (O, 664 beds) 3186 Maryland Parkway, Las Vegas, NV Zip 89109–2306, P O Box 98530, 89193, tel. 702/731–8000; Todd Sklamberg, President
Web address: www.sunrisehospital.com

NEW HAMPSHIRE: PARKLAND MEDICAL CENTER (O, 82 beds) One Parkland Drive, Derry, NH Zip 03038–2750; tel. 603/432–1500; Jeff Scionti, Chief Executive Officer
Web address: www.parklandmedicalcenter.com

PORTSMOUTH REGIONAL HOSPITAL (O, 165 beds) 333 Borthwick Avenue, Portsmouth, NH Zip 03801–7128; tel. 603/436–5110; Dean Carucci, Chief Executive Officer
Web address: www.portsmouthhospital.com

OKLAHOMA: OU MEDICAL CENTER (O, 735 beds) 1200 Everett Drive, Oklahoma City, OK Zip 73104–5047, P O Box 26307, 73126–0307, tel. 405/271–3636; Charles Spicer, President and Chief Executive Officer

SOUTH CAROLINA: COLLETON MEDICAL CENTER (O, 131 beds) 501 Robertson Boulevard, Walterboro, SC Zip 29488–5714; tel. 843/782–2000; Jimmy O. Hiott III, Chief Executive Officer
Web address: www.colletonmedical.com

GRAND STRAND REGIONAL MEDICAL CENTER (O, 303 beds) 809 82nd Parkway, Myrtle Beach, SC Zip 29572–4607; tel. 843/692–1000; Mark E. Sims, Chief Executive Officer
Web address: www.grandstrandmed.com

TRIDENT MEDICAL CENTER (O, 421 beds) 9330 Medical Plaza Drive, Charleston, SC Zip 29406–9195; tel. 843/797–7000; Todd Gallati, FACHE, President and Chief Executive Officer

TENNESSEE: PARKRIDGE MEDICAL CENTER (O, 464 beds) 2333 McCallie Avenue, Chattanooga, TN Zip 37404–3258; tel. 423/698–6061; Thomas H. Ozburn, Chief Executive Officer
Web address: www.parkridgemedicalcenter.com

TRISTAR ASHLAND CITY MEDICAL CENTER (O, 12 beds) 313 North Main Street, Ashland City, TN Zip 37015–1347; tel. 615/792–3030; Darrell White, R.N., Administrator and Chief Nursing Officer

TRISTAR CENTENNIAL MEDICAL CENTER (O, 650 beds) 2300 Patterson Street, Nashville, TN Zip 37203–1528; tel. 615/342–1000; Scott A. Cihak, President and Chief Executive Officer
Web address: www.tristarcentennial.com

TRISTAR HENDERSONVILLE MEDICAL CENTER (O, 96 beds) 355 New Shackle Island Road, Hendersonville, TN Zip 37075–2479; tel. 615/338–1000; Regina Bartlett, Chief Executive Officer
Web address: www.hendersonvillemedicalcenter.com

TRISTAR HORIZON MEDICAL CENTER (O, 130 beds) 111 Highway 70 East, Dickson, TN Zip 37055–2080; tel. 615/446–0446; Dustin Greene, Chief Executive Officer
Web address: www.horizonmedicalcenter.com

TRISTAR SKYLINE MEDICAL CENTER (O, 295 beds) 3441 Dickerson Pike, Nashville, TN Zip 37207–2539; tel. 615/769–2000; Steve Otto, Chief Executive Officer
Web address: www.tristarskyline.com

TRISTAR SOUTHERN HILLS MEDICAL CENTER (O, 87 beds) 391 Wallace Road, Nashville, TN Zip 37211–4859; tel. 615/781–4000; Joanna J. Conley, FACHE, Chief Executive Officer

TRISTAR STONECREST MEDICAL CENTER (O, 101 beds) 200 StoneCrest Boulevard, Smyrna, TN Zip 37167–6810; tel. 615/768–2000; Louis Caputo, Chief Executive Officer
Web address: www.stonecrestmedical.com

TRISTAR SUMMIT MEDICAL CENTER (O, 196 beds) 5655 Frist Boulevard, Hermitage, TN Zip 37076–2053; tel. 615/316–3000; Brian Marger, Chief Executive Officer
Web address: www.summitmedctr.com

TEXAS: BAYSHORE MEDICAL CENTER (O, 461 beds) 4000 Spencer Highway, Pasadena, TX Zip 77504–1202; tel. 713/359–2000; Jeanna Barnard, FACHE, Chief Executive Officer
Web address: www.bayshoremedical.com

CLEAR LAKE REGIONAL MEDICAL CENTER (O, 632 beds) 500 Medical Center Boulevard, Webster, TX Zip 77598–4220; tel. 281/332–2511; Todd Caliva, FACHE, Chief Executive Officer

CONROE REGIONAL MEDICAL CENTER (O, 301 beds) 504 Medical Boulevard, Conroe, TX Zip 77304, P O Box 1538, 77305–1538, tel. 936/539–1111; Matt Davis, FACHE, Chief Executive Officer
Web address: www.conroeregional.com/

CORPUS CHRISTI MEDICAL CENTER (O, 416 beds) 3315 South Alameda Street, Corpus Christi, TX Zip 78411–1883, P O Box 8991, 78468–8991, tel. 361/761–1400; Jay Woodall, FACHE, Chief Executive Officer

CYPRESS FAIRBANKS MEDICAL CENTER (O, 160 beds) 10655 Steepletop Drive, Houston, TX Zip 77065–4297; tel. 281/890–4285; Naman Mahajan, Interim Chief Executive Officer
Web address: www.cyfairhospital.com

HOUSTON NORTHWEST MEDICAL CENTER (O, 339 beds) 710 Cypress Creek Parkway, Houston, TX Zip 77090–3402; tel. 281/440–1000; Timothy Puthoff, Chief Executive Officer
Web address: www.hnmc.com

KINGWOOD MEDICAL CENTER (O, 358 beds) 22999 U S Highway 59 North, Kingwood, TX Zip 77339; tel. 281/348–8000; Melinda Stephenson, Chief Executive Officer

LAS PALMAS MEDICAL CENTER (O, 509 beds) 1801 North Oregon Street, El Paso, TX Zip 79902–3591; tel. 915/521–1200; Don Karl, Interim Chief Executive Officer
Web address: www.laspalmashealth.com

MEDICAL CITY ALLIANCE (O, 55 beds) 3101 North Tarrant Parkway, Fort Worth, TX Zip 76177; tel. 817/639–1000; Glenn Wallace, Chief Executive Officer
Web address: www.baylorhealth.com/PhysiciansLocations/BIR/Pages/Default.aspx

MEDICAL CITY ARLINGTON (O, 289 beds) 3301 Matlock Road, Arlington, TX Zip 76015–2908; tel. 817/465–3241; Keith Zimmerman, Chief Executive Officer

MEDICAL CITY DALLAS (O, 615 beds) 7777 Forest Lane, Dallas, TX Zip 75230–2598; tel. 972/566–7000; Chris Mowan, Chief Executive Officer
Web address: www.medicalcityhospital.com

MEDICAL CITY DENTON (O, 185 beds) 3535 South I–35 East, Denton, TX Zip 76210; tel. 940/384–3535; Steven Edgar, FACHE, President and Chief Executive Officer
Web address: www.dentonregional.com

For explanation of codes following names, see page B2.
★ Indicates Type III membership in the American Hospital Association.

MEDICAL CITY FORT WORTH (O, 212 beds) 900 Eighth Avenue, Fort Worth, TX Zip 76104–3902; tel. 817/336–2100; Jyric Sims, FACHE, Chief Executive Officer

MEDICAL CITY GREEN OAKS HOSPITAL (O, 124 beds) 7808 Clodus Fields Drive, Dallas, TX Zip 75251–2206; tel. 972/991–9504; Thomas M. Collins, President, Chairman and Chief Executive Officer
Web address: www.greenoakspsych.com

MEDICAL CITY LAS COLINAS (O, 90 beds) 6800 North MacArthur Boulevard, Irving, TX Zip 75039–2422; tel. 972/969–2000; Daniela Decell, Chief Executive Officer

MEDICAL CITY LEWISVILLE (O, 166 beds) 500 West Main, Lewisville, TX Zip 75057–3699; tel. 972/420–1000; LaSharndra Barbarin, Chief Executive Officer
Web address: www.lewisvillemedical.com

MEDICAL CITY MCKINNEY (O, 222 beds) 4500 Medical Center Drive, McKinney, TX Zip 75069–1650; tel. 972/547–8000; Ernest C. Lynch III, FACHE, President and Chief Executive Officer
Web address: www.medicalcenterofmckinney.com

MEDICAL CITY NORTH HILLS (O, 164 beds) 4401 Booth Calloway Road, North Richland Hills, TX Zip 76180–7399; tel. 817/255–1000; Xavier Villarreal, FACHE, Chief Executive Officer
Web address: www.northhillshospital.com

MEDICAL CITY PLANO (O, 390 beds) 3901 West 15th Street, Plano, TX Zip 75075–7738; tel. 972/596–6800; Charles Gressle, Chief Executive Officer
Web address: www.medicalcenterplano.com

METHODIST AMBULATORY SURGERY HOSPITAL - NORTHWEST (O, 23 beds) 9150 Huebner Road, Suite 100, San Antonio, TX Zip 78240–1545; tel. 210/575–5000; Scott Davis, Chief Executive Officer

METHODIST HOSPITAL SOUTH (O, 67 beds) 1905 Highway 97 East, Jourdanton, TX Zip 78026–1504; tel. 830/769–3515; John E. Ulbricht, Chief Executive Officer
Web address: www.https://sahealth.com/locations/methodisthospitalsouth/

METHODIST HOSPITAL (O, 1602 beds) 7700 Floyd Curl Drive, San Antonio, TX Zip 78229–3993; tel. 210/575–4000; Allen Harrison, Chief Executive Officer
Web address: www.sahealth.com

METHODIST STONE OAK HOSPITAL (O, 140 beds) 1139 East Sonterra Boulevard, San Antonio, TX Zip 78258–4347; tel. 210/638–2100; Marc Strode, Chief Executive Officer

PARK PLAZA HOSPITAL (O, 139 beds) 1313 Hermann Drive, Houston, TX Zip 77004–7092; tel. 713/527–5000; Steven D. Patonai, Interim Chief Executive Officer
Web address: www.parkplazahospital.com

PEARLAND MEDICAL CENTER (O, 34 beds) 11100 Shadow Creek Parkway, Pearland, TX Zip 77584–7285; tel. 713/770–7000; David S. Wagner, FACHE, Chief Executive Officer
Web address: www.pearlandmc.com

RIO GRANDE REGIONAL HOSPITAL (O, 320 beds) 101 East Ridge Road, McAllen, TX Zip 78503–1299; tel. 956/632–6000; Cristina Rivera, Chief Executive Officer

ST. DAVID'S MEDICAL CENTER (O, 579 beds) 919 East 32nd Street, Austin, TX Zip 78705–2709, P O Box 4039, 78765–4039, tel. 512/476–7111; Donald H. Wilkerson, FACHE, Chief Executive Officer
Web address: www.stdavids.com

ST. DAVID'S NORTH AUSTIN MEDICAL CENTER (O, 424 beds) 12221 North MoPac Expressway, Austin, TX Zip 78758–2496; tel. 512/901–1000; Thomas W. Jackson, Chief Executive Officer

ST. DAVID'S ROUND ROCK MEDICAL CENTER (O, 171 beds) 2400 Round Rock Avenue, Round Rock, TX Zip 78681–4097; tel. 512/341–1000; Jeremy Barclay, Chief Executive Officer
Web address: www.stdavids.com

ST. DAVID'S SOUTH AUSTIN MEDICAL CENTER (O, 291 beds) 901 West Ben White Boulevard, Austin, TX Zip 78704–6903; tel. 512/447–2211; Todd E. Steward, FACHE, Chief Executive Officer
Web address: www.southaustinmc.com

TEXAS ORTHOPEDIC HOSPITAL (O, 49 beds) 7401 South Main Street, Houston, TX Zip 77030–4509; tel. 713/799–8600; Eric Becker, Chief Executive Officer
Web address: www.texasorthopedic.com

TOMBALL REGIONAL MEDICAL CENTER (O, 191 beds) 605 Holderrieth Street, Tomball, TX Zip 77375–6445; tel. 281/401–7500; Brett Kinman, Interim Chief Executive Officer

VALLEY REGIONAL MEDICAL CENTER (O, 214 beds) 100A Alton Gloor Boulevard, Brownsville, TX Zip 78526–3354, P O Box 3710, 78523–3710, tel. 956/350–7101; Art Garza, FACHE, Chief Executive Officer
Web address: www.valleyregionalmedicalcenter.com

WEST HOUSTON MEDICAL CENTER (O, 252 beds) 12141 Richmond Avenue, Houston, TX Zip 77082–2499; tel. 281/558–3444; Megan Marietta, Chief Executive Officer

WOMAN'S HOSPITAL OF TEXAS (O, 345 beds) 7600 Fannin Street, Houston, TX Zip 77054–1906; tel. 713/790–1234; Ashley McClellan, FACHE, Chief Executive Officer
Web address: www.womanshospital.com

UTAH: BRIGHAM CITY COMMUNITY HOSPITAL (O, 39 beds) 950 South Medical Drive, Brigham City, UT Zip 84302–4724; tel. 435/734–9471; Richard Spuhler, Chief Executive Officer
Web address: www.brighamcityhospital.com

CACHE VALLEY HOSPITAL (O, 22 beds) 2380 North 400 East, North Logan, UT Zip 84341–6000; tel. 435/713–9700; John C. Worley III, Chief Executive Officer
Web address: www.cachevalleyhospital.com/

LAKEVIEW HOSPITAL (O, 119 beds) 630 East Medical Drive, Bountiful, UT Zip 84010–4908; tel. 801/299–2200; Troy Wood, Chief Executive Officer
Web address: www.lakeviewhospital.com

LONE PEAK HOSPITAL (O, 32 beds) 1925 South State Street, Draper, UT Zip 84020; tel. 801/545–8000; Mark Meadows, Chief Executive Officer

MOUNTAIN VIEW HOSPITAL (O, 114 beds) 1000 East 100 North, Payson, UT Zip 84651–1600; tel. 801/465–7000; Kevin Johnson, Chief Executive Officer
Web address: www.mvhpayson.com

OGDEN REGIONAL MEDICAL CENTER (O, 167 beds) 5475 South 500 East, Ogden, UT Zip 84405–6905; tel. 801/479–2111; Mark B. Adams, Chief Executive Officer

ST. MARK'S HOSPITAL (O, 277 beds) 1200 East 3900 South, Salt Lake City, UT Zip 84124–1390; tel. 801/268–7111; Steven B. Bateman, Chief Executive Officer
Web address: www.stmarkshospital.com

TIMPANOGOS REGIONAL HOSPITAL (O, 105 beds) 750 West 800 North, Orem, UT Zip 84057–3660; tel. 801/714–6000; Kimball S. Anderson, FACHE, Chief Executive Officer
Web address: www.timpanogosregionalhospital.com

VIRGINIA: CHIPPENHAM HOSPITAL (O, 765 beds) 7101 Jahnke Road, Richmond, VA Zip 23225–4044; tel. 804/320–3911; Greg Lowe, Chief Executive Officer
Web address: www.cjwmedical.com

DOMINION HOSPITAL (O, 100 beds) 2960 Sleepy Hollow Road, Falls Church, VA Zip 22044–2030; tel. 703/536–2000; Lee Higginbotham, Chief Executive Officer
Web address: www.dominionhospital.com

HENRICO DOCTORS' HOSPITAL (O, 559 beds) 1602 Skipwith Road, Richmond, VA Zip 23229–5205; tel. 804/289–4500; William Wagnon, Chief Executive Officer

JOHN RANDOLPH MEDICAL CENTER (O, 112 beds) 411 West Randolph Road, Hopewell, VA Zip 23860–2938; tel. 804/541–1600; Joseph Mazzo, Chief Executive Officer
Web address: www.johnrandolphmed.com

LEWIS-GALE MEDICAL CENTER (O, 521 beds) 1900 Electric Road, Salem, VA Zip 24153–7494; tel. 540/776–4000; Brian Baumgardner, Chief Executive Officer

LEWISGALE HOSPITAL ALLEGHANY (O, 146 beds) One ARH Lane, Low Moor, VA Zip 24457, P O Box 7, 24457–0007, tel. 540/862–6011; William Windham, Chief Executive Officer
Web address: www.alleghanyregional.com

LEWISGALE HOSPITAL MONTGOMERY (O, 89 beds) 3700 South Main Street, Blacksburg, VA Zip 24060–7081, P O Box 90004, 24062–9004, tel. 540/951–1111; Alan J. Fabian, Chief Executive Officer
Web address: www.lewisgale.com

LEWISGALE HOSPITAL PULASKI (O, 54 beds) 2400 Lee Highway, Pulaski, VA Zip 24301–2326, P O Box 759, 24301–0759, tel. 540/994–8100; Derek Vance, Chief Executive Officer

For explanation of codes following names, see page B2.
★ Indicates Type III membership in the American Hospital Association.

RESTON HOSPITAL CENTER (O, 199 beds) 1850 Town Center Parkway, Reston, VA Zip 20190–3219; tel. 703/689–9000; John A. Deardorff, President and Chief Executive, Northern Virginia Market
Web address: www.restonhospital.com

SPOTSYLVANIA REGIONAL MEDICAL CENTER (O, 100 beds) 4600 Spotsylvania Parkway, Fredericksburg, VA Zip 22408–7762; tel. 540/498–4000; Michael Clark, Chief Executive Officer
Web address: www.spotsrmc.com

STONESPRINGS HOSPITAL CENTER (O, 124 beds) 24440 Stone Spring Boulevard, Dulles, VA Zip 20166–2247; tel. 571/349–4000; Lance Jones, Chief Executive Officer

Owned, leased, sponsored:	154 hospitals	38139 beds
Contract-managed:	0 hospitals	0 beds
Totals:	154 hospitals	38139 beds

0328: HEALTH FIRST, INC. (NP)

6450 US Highway 1, Rockledge, FL Zip 32955–5747; tel. 321/434–7000; Steven P. Johnson, Ph.D., President and Chief Executive Officer

(Centralized Physician/Insurance Health System)

FLORIDA: HEALTH FIRST CAPE CANAVERAL HOSPITAL (O, 125 beds) 701 West Cocoa Beach Causeway, Cocoa Beach, FL Zip 32931–5595, P O Box 320069, 32932–0069, tel. 321/799–7111; Aaron Robinson, Chief Executive Officer, Health First Community Hospitals
Web address: www.health-first.org

HEALTH FIRST HOLMES REGIONAL MEDICAL CENTER (O, 514 beds) 1350 South Hickory Street, Melbourne, FL Zip 32901–3224; tel. 321/434–7000; Brett A. Esrock, FACHE, Chief Executive Officer
Web address: www.health-first.org

HEALTH FIRST PALM BAY HOSPITAL (O, 133 beds) 1425 Malabar Road NE, Palm Bay, FL Zip 32907–2506; tel. 321/434–8000; Aaron Robinson, Chief Executive Officer, Health First Community Hospitals

HEALTH FIRST VIERA HOSPITAL (O, 84 beds) 8745 North Wickham Road, Melbourne, FL Zip 32940–5997; tel. 321/434–9164; Aaron Robinson, Chief Executive Officer, Health First Community Hospitals
Web address: www.vierahospital.org

Owned, leased, sponsored:	4 hospitals	856 beds
Contract-managed:	0 hospitals	0 beds
Totals:	4 hospitals	856 beds

0307: HEALTH QUEST SYSTEMS, INC. (NP)

1351 Route 55 Ste 200, LaGrangeville, NY Zip 12540–5108, 1351 Route 55, 12540–5108, tel. 845/475–9500; Robert Friedberg, President and Chief Executive Officer

(Centralized Health System)

CONNECTICUT: SHARON HOSPITAL (O, 78 beds) 50 Hospital Hill Road, Sharon, CT Zip 06069–2096, P O Box 789, 06069–0789, tel. 860/364–4000; Peter Cordeau, Chief Executive Officer

NEW YORK: NORTHERN DUTCHESS HOSPITAL (O, 68 beds) 6511 Springbrook Avenue, Rhinebeck, NY Zip 12572–3709, P O Box 5002, 12572–5002, tel. 845/876–3001; Denise George, R.N., President
Web address: www.health-quest.org/home_nd.cfm?id=9

PUTNAM HOSPITAL CENTER (O, 164 beds) 670 Stoneleigh Avenue, Carmel, NY Zip 10512–3997; tel. 845/279–5711; Peter Kelly, President

VASSAR BROTHERS MEDICAL CENTER (O, 365 beds) 45 Reade Place, Poughkeepsie, NY Zip 12601–3947; tel. 845/454–8500; Ann McMackin, President
Web address: www.health-quest.org

Owned, leased, sponsored:	4 hospitals	675 beds
Contract-managed:	0 hospitals	0 beds
Totals:	4 hospitals	675 beds

0342: HEALTHPARTNERS (NP)

8170 33rd Avenue South, Bloomington, MN Zip 55425–4516; tel. 952/883–7600; Andrea Walsh, President and Chief Executive Officer

(Moderately Centralized Health System)

MINNESOTA: GLENCOE REGIONAL HEALTH SERVICES (C, 135 beds) 1805 Hennepin Avenue North, Glencoe, MN Zip 55336–1416; tel. 320/864–3121; Jon D. Braband, FACHE, President and Chief Executive Officer
Web address: www.grhsonline.org

LAKEVIEW HOSPITAL (O, 54 beds) 927 Churchill Street West, Stillwater, MN Zip 55082–6605; tel. 651/439–5330; Theodore Wegleitner, Chief Executive Officer and President
Web address: www.lakeview.org

PARK NICOLLET METHODIST HOSPITAL (O, 420 beds) 6500 Excelsior Boulevard, Saint Louis Park, MN Zip 55426–4702, Minneapolis, tel. 952/993–5000; Roxanna L. Gapstur, Ph.D., R.N., President
Web address: www.parknicollet.com

REGIONS HOSPITAL (O, 463 beds) 640 Jackson Street, Saint Paul, MN Zip 55101–2595; tel. 651/254–3456; Megan Remark, President and Chief Executive Officer

WISCONSIN: AMERY HOSPITAL AND CLINIC (O, 11 beds) 265 Griffin Street East, Amery, WI Zip 54001–1439; tel. 715/268–8000; Debra Rudquist, FACHE, President and Chief Executive Officer
Web address: www.amerymedicalcenter.org

HUDSON HOSPITAL AND CLINIC (O, 24 beds) 405 Stageline Road, Hudson, WI Zip 54016–7848; tel. 715/531–6000; Marian M. Furlong, R.N., FACHE, President and Chief Executive Officer

WESTFIELDS HOSPITAL (O, 25 beds) 535 Hospital Road, New Richmond, WI Zip 54017–1449; tel. 715/243–2600; Steven Massey, President and Chief Executive Officer
Web address: www.westfieldshospital.com

Owned, leased, sponsored:	6 hospitals	997 beds
Contract-managed:	1 hospitals	135 beds
Totals:	7 hospitals	1132 beds

★0023: HEALTHSOUTH CORPORATION (IO)

3660 Grandview Parkway, Suite 200, Birmingham, AL Zip 35243–3332; tel. 205/967–7116; Mark J. Tarr, President and Chief Executive Officer

(Independent Hospital System)

ALABAMA: HEALTHSOUTH LAKESHORE REHABILITATION HOSPITAL (O, 100 beds) 3800 Ridgeway Drive, Birmingham, AL Zip 35209–5599; tel. 205/868–2000; Randy Thompson, Chief Executive Officer

HEALTHSOUTH REHABILITATION HOSPITAL OF MONTGOMERY (O, 70 beds) 4465 Narrow Lane Road, Montgomery, AL Zip 36116–2900; tel. 334/284–7700; Randy Thompson, Chief Executive Officer
Web address: www.healthsouthmontgomery.com

HEALTHSOUTH REHABILITATION HOSPITAL OF NORTH ALABAMA (O, 70 beds) 107 Governors Drive SW, Huntsville, AL Zip 35801–4326; tel. 256/535–2300; Douglas H. Beverly, Chief Executive Officer
Web address: www.healthsouthhuntsville.com

HEALTHSOUTH REHABILITATION HOSPITAL (O, 51 beds) 1736 East Main Street, Dothan, AL Zip 36301–3040, P O Box 6708, 36302–6708, tel. 334/712–6333; Margaret A. Futch, Chief Executive Officer

HEALTHSOUTH REHABILITATION OF GADSDEN (O, 44 beds) 801 Goodyear Avenue, Gadsden, AL Zip 35903–1133; tel. 256/439–5000; Kayla Feazell, Chief Executive Officer
Web address: www.healthsouthgadsden.com

REGIONAL REHABILITATION HOSPITAL (O, 48 beds) 3715 Highway 280/431 North, Phenix City, AL Zip 36867; tel. 334/732–2200; Michael Bartell, Chief Executive Officer

ARIZONA: HEALTHSOUTH EAST VALLEY REHABILITATION HOSPITAL (O, 60 beds) 5652 East Baseline Road, Mesa, AZ Zip 85206–4713; tel. 480/567–0350; Jerry Gray, Interim Chief Executive Officer
Web address: www.healthsoutheastvalley.com

For explanation of codes following names, see page B2.
★ Indicates Type III membership in the American Hospital Association.

HEALTHSOUTH REHABILITATION HOSPITAL OF SOUTHERN ARIZONA (O, 60 beds) 1921 West Hospital Drive, Tucson, AZ Zip 85704–7806; tel. 520/742–2800; Timothy T. Poore, Chief Executive Officer
Web address: www.healthsouthsouthernarizona.com

HEALTHSOUTH REHABILITATION INSTITUTE OF TUCSON (O, 80 beds) 2650 North Wyatt Drive, Tucson, AZ Zip 85712–6108; tel. 520/325–1300; Jeffrey Christensen, Chief Executive Officer

HEALTHSOUTH SCOTTSDALE REHABILITATION HOSPITAL (O, 60 beds) 9630 East Shea Boulevard, Scottsdale, AZ Zip 85260–6267; tel. 480/551–5400; Kenneth Bell, Chief Executive Officer
Web address: www.healthsouthscottsdale.com

HEALTHSOUTH VALLEY OF THE SUN REHABILITATION HOSPITAL (O, 75 beds) 13460 North 67th Avenue, Glendale, AZ Zip 85304–1042; tel. 623/878–8800; Beth Bacher, Chief Executive Officer

YUMA REHABILITATION HOSPITAL (O, 41 beds) 901 West 24th Street, Yuma, AZ Zip 85364–6384; tel. 928/726–5000; Ian Hodge, Chief Executive Officer
Web address: www.yumarehabhospital.com

ARKANSAS: HEALTHSOUTH REHABILITATION HOSPITAL OF FORT SMITH (O, 60 beds) 1401 South 'J' Street, Fort Smith, AR Zip 72901–5155; tel. 479/785–3300; Dawn Watts, Chief Executive Officer

HEALTHSOUTH REHABILITATION HOSPITAL OF JONESBORO (O, 67 beds) 1201 Fleming Avenue, Jonesboro, AR Zip 72401–4311, P O Box 1680, 72403–1680, tel. 870/932–0440; Donna Harris, Chief Executive Officer
Web address: www.healthsouthjonesboro.com

HEALTHSOUTH REHABILITATION HOSPITAL (O, 80 beds) 153 East Monte Painter Drive, Fayetteville, AR Zip 72703–4002; tel. 479/444–2200; Jack C. Mitchell, FACHE, Chief Executive Officer
Web address: www.healthsouthfayetteville.com

ST. VINCENT REHABILITATION HOSPITAL (O, 80 beds) 2201 Wildwood Avenue, Sherwood, AR Zip 72120–5074; tel. 501/834–1800; Lisa Watson, Chief Executive Officer

CALIFORNIA: HEALTHSOUTH BAKERSFIELD REHABILITATION HOSPITAL (O, 70 beds) 5001 Commerce Drive, Bakersfield, CA Zip 93309–0689; tel. 661/323–5500; Martha Samora, R.N., FACHE, Chief Executive Officer
Web address: www.healthsouthbakersfield.com

HEALTHSOUTH TUSTIN REHABILITATION HOSPITAL (O, 48 beds) 14851 Yorba Street, Tustin, CA Zip 92780–2925; tel. 714/832–9200; Diana C. Hanyak, Chief Executive Officer
Web address: www.tustinrehab.com

COLORADO: HEALTHSOUTH REHABILITATION HOSPITAL OF COLORADO SPRINGS (O, 56 beds) 325 Parkside Drive, Colorado Springs, CO Zip 80910–3134; tel. 719/630–8000; Stephen Schaefer, Chief Executive Officer
Web address: www.healthsouthcoloradosprings.com

HEALTHSOUTH REHABILITATION HOSPITAL OF LITTLETON (O, 28 beds) 1001 West Mineral Avenue, Littleton, CO Zip 80120–4507; tel. 303/334–1100; David H. Shefte, Chief Executive Officer
Web address: www.healthsouthdenver.com

DELAWARE: HEALTHSOUTH REHABILITATION HOSPITAL OF MIDDLETOWN (O, 34 beds) 250 East Hampden Road, Middletown, DE Zip 19709–5303; tel. 302/464–3400; Mathew Gooch, Chief Executive Officer
Web address: www.healthsouthmiddletown.com

FLORIDA: HEALTHSOUTH EMERALD COAST REHABILITATION HOSPITAL (O, 75 beds) 1847 Florida Avenue, Panama City, FL Zip 32405–4640; tel. 850/914–8600; Tony N. Bennett, Chief Executive Officer

HEALTHSOUTH REHABILITATION HOSPITAL AT MARTIN HEALTH (O, 54 beds) 5850 SE Community Drive, Stuart, FL Zip 34997–6420; tel. 772/324–3500; Ivette Miranda, Chief Executive Officer
Web address: www.healthsouthmartin.com

HEALTHSOUTH REHABILITATION HOSPITAL OF MIAMI (O, 60 beds) 20601 Old Cutler Road, Cutler Bay, FL Zip 33189–2400; tel. 305/251–3800; Enrique A. Vicens-Rivera Jr, JD, Chief Executive Officer
Web address: www.healthsouthmiami.com

HEALTHSOUTH REHABILITATION HOSPITAL OF OCALA (O, 60 beds) 2275 SW 22nd Lane, Ocala, FL Zip 34471–7710; tel. 352/282–4000; Karthik Muthu, Chief Executive Officer

HEALTHSOUTH REHABILITATION HOSPITAL OF SARASOTA (O, 96 beds) 6400 Edgelake Drive, Sarasota, FL Zip 34240–8813; tel. 941/921–8600; Marcus Braz, Chief Executive Officer
Web address: www.healthsouthsarasota.com

HEALTHSOUTH REHABILITATION HOSPITAL OF SPRING HILL (O, 80 beds) 12440 Cortez Boulevard, Brooksville, FL Zip 34613–2628; tel. 352/592–4250; Jeffrey Alexander, Chief Executive Officer
Web address: www.healthsouthspringhill.com

HEALTHSOUTH REHABILITATION HOSPITAL (O, 70 beds) 901 North Clearwater-Largo Road, Largo, FL Zip 33770–4126; tel. 727/586–2999; Tripp Smith, Chief Executive Officer

HEALTHSOUTH SEA PINES REHABILITATION HOSPITAL (O, 90 beds) 101 East Florida Avenue, Melbourne, FL Zip 32901–8301; tel. 321/984–4600; Denise B. McGrath, Chief Executive Officer
Web address: www.healthsouthseapines.com

HEALTHSOUTH SUNRISE REHABILITATION HOSPITAL (O, 126 beds) 4399 North Nob Hill Road, Sunrise, FL Zip 33351–5899; tel. 954/749–0300; Michael S. Roffelsen, Chief Executive Officer
Web address: www.healthsouthsunrise.com

HEALTHSOUTH TREASURE COAST REHABILITATION HOSPITAL (O, 80 beds) 1600 37th Street, Vero Beach, FL Zip 32960–4863; tel. 772/778–2100; Michael Kissner, Chief Executive Officer

HEALTHSOUTH REHABILITATION HOSPITAL OF TALLAHASSEE (O, 76 beds) 1675 Riggins Road, Tallahassee, FL Zip 32308–5315; tel. 850/656–4800; K. Dale. Neely, FACHE, Chief Executive Officer
Web address: www.healthsouthtallahassee.com

HEALTHSOUTH REHABILITATION HOSPITAL OF ALTAMONTE SPRINGS (O, 50 beds) 831 South State Road 434, Altamonte Springs, FL Zip 32714–3502; tel. 407/587–8600; Lori Bedard, Interim Chief Executive Officer
Web address: www.healthsouthaltamontesprings.com

GEORGIA: HEALTHSOUTH WALTON REHABILITATION HOSPITAL (O, 50 beds) 1355 Independence Drive, Augusta, GA Zip 30901–1037; tel. 706/724–7746; Eric Crossan, Chief Executive Officer

REHABILITATION HOSPITAL OF SAVANNAH (O, 50 beds) 6510 Seawright DR, Savannah, GA Zip 31406–2752; tel. 800/622–7269; Kathy Kleinsteuber, Chief Executive Officer
Web address: www.rehabilitationhospitalsavannah.com

ILLINOIS: VAN MATRE HEALTHSOUTH REHABILITATION HOSPITAL (O, 61 beds) 950 South Mulford Road, Rockford, IL Zip 61108–4274; tel. 815/381–8500; Ken Bowman, Chief Executive Officer
Web address: www.healthsouth.com

INDIANA: HEALTHSOUTH DEACONESS REHABILITATION HOSPITAL (O, 103 beds) 4100 Covert Avenue, Evansville, IN Zip 47714–5567, P O Box 5349, 47716–5349, tel. 812/476–9983; Blake Bunner, Chief Executive Officer

KANSAS: KANSAS REHABILITATION HOSPITAL (O, 57 beds) 1504 SW Eighth Avenue, Topeka, KS Zip 66606–1632; tel. 785/235–6600; William J. Overbey, Chief Executive Officer
Web address: www.kansasrehabhospital.com

MID-AMERICA REHABILITATION HOSPITAL (O, 98 beds) 5701 West 110th Street, Shawnee Mission, KS Zip 66211–2503, Overland Park, tel. 913/491–2400; Tiffany Kiehl, Chief Executive Officer

WESLEY REHABILITATION HOSPITAL (O, 65 beds) 8338 West 13th Street North, Wichita, KS Zip 67212–2984; tel. 316/729–9999; James F. Grocholski, FACHE, Chief Executive Officer
Web address: www.wesleyrehabhospital.com

KENTUCKY: CARDINAL HILL REHABILITATION HOSPITAL (O, 232 beds) 2050 Versailles Road, Lexington, KY Zip 40504–1405; tel. 859/254–5701; Brad Kennedy, Interim Chief Executive Officer
Web address: www.cardinalhillhealthsouth.com

HEALTHSOUTH LAKEVIEW REHABILITATION HOSPITAL (O, 40 beds) 134 Heartland Drive, Elizabethtown, KY Zip 42701–2778; tel. 270/769–3100; Lori Jarboe, Chief Executive Officer

HEALTHSOUTH NORTHERN KENTUCKY REHABILITATION HOSPITAL (O, 40 beds) 201 Medical Village Drive, Edgewood, KY Zip 41017–3407; tel. 859/341–2044; Richard R. Evens, Chief Executive Officer
Web address: www.healthsouthkentucky.com

For explanation of codes following names, see page B2.
★ Indicates Type III membership in the American Hospital Association.

LOUISIANA: HEALTHSOUTH REHABILITATION HOSPITAL OF ALEXANDRIA (O, 47 beds) 104 North Third Street, Alexandria, LA Zip 71301–8581; tel. 318/449–1370; James W. McClung, Chief Executive Officer

MAINE: NEW ENGLAND REHABILITATION HOSPITAL OF PORTLAND (O, 90 beds) 335 Brighton Avenue, Portland, ME Zip 04102–2363; tel. 207/775–4000; Jeanine Chesley, Chief Executive Officer
Web address: www.nerhp.org

MARYLAND: HEALTHSOUTH CHESAPEAKE REHABILITATION HOSPITAL (O, 54 beds) 220 Tilghman Road, Salisbury, MD Zip 21804–1921; tel. 410/546–4600; Steven Walas, Chief Executive Officer
Web address: www.healthsouthchesapeake.com

MASSACHUSETTS: FAIRLAWN REHABILITATION HOSPITAL (O, 110 beds) 189 May Street, Worcester, MA Zip 01602–4339; tel. 508/791–6351; Mary Lou D'Avino , Chief Executive Officer

HEALTHSOUTH BRAINTREE REHABILITATION HOSPITAL (O, 187 beds) 250 Pond Street, Braintree, MA Zip 02184–5351; tel. 781/348–2500; Randy Doherty, CPA, Chief Executive Officer
Web address: www.braintreerehabhospital.com

HEALTHSOUTH NEW ENGLAND REHABILITATION HOSPITAL (O, 210 beds) Two Rehabilitation Way, Woburn, MA Zip 01801–6098; tel. 781/935–5050; Laura Ames, Chief Executive Officer
Web address: www.newenglandrehab.com

HEALTHSOUTH REHABILITATION HOSPITAL OF WESTERN MASSACHUSETTS (O, 53 beds) 222 State Street, Ludlow, MA Zip 01056–3437; tel. 413/308–3300; John R. Hunt, Chief Executive Officer

MISSOURI: HOWARD A. RUSK REHABILITATION CENTER (O, 60 beds) 315 Business Loop 70 West, Columbia, MO Zip 65203–3248; tel. 573/817–2703; John M. Dawes, FACHE, Chief Executive Officer
Web address: www.ruskrehab.com

THE REHABILITATION INSTITUTE OF ST. LOUIS (O, 96 beds) 4455 Duncan Avenue, Saint Louis, MO Zip 63110–1111; tel. 314/658–3800; Tara Diebling, Chief Executive Officer

NEVADA: HEALTHSOUTH DESERT CANYON REHABILITATION HOSPITAL (O, 50 beds) 9175 West Oquendo Road, Las Vegas, NV Zip 89148–1234; tel. 702/252–7342; Andrea Davis, Chief Executive Officer
Web address: www.healthsouthdesertcanyon.com

HEALTHSOUTH REHABILITATION HOSPITAL - HENDERSON (O, 90 beds) 10301 Jeffreys Street, Henderson, NV Zip 89052–3922; tel. 702/939–9400; Samantha Billig, Chief Executive Officer

HEALTHSOUTH REHABILITATION HOSPITAL-LAS VEGAS (O, 79 beds) 1250 South Valley View Boulevard, Las Vegas, NV Zip 89102–1861; tel. 702/877–8898; Michael Ward, Chief Executive Officer
Web address: www.healthsouthlasvegas.com

NEW HAMPSHIRE: HEALTHSOUTH REHABILITATION HOSPITAL (O, 50 beds) 254 Pleasant Street, Concord, NH Zip 03301–2508; tel. 603/226–9800; Catherine Devaney, Chief Executive Officer
Web address: www.healthsouthrehabconcordnh.com

NEW JERSEY: HEALTHSOUTH REHABILITATION HOSPITAL OF TINTON FALLS (O, 60 beds) 2 Centre Plaza, Tinton Falls, NJ Zip 07724–9744; tel. 732/460–5320; Suji Thomas, R.N., MSN, Chief Executive Officer

HEALTHSOUTH REHABILITATION HOSPITAL OF TOMS RIVER (O, 92 beds) 14 Hospital Drive, Toms River, NJ Zip 08755–6470; tel. 732/244–3100; Patricia Ostaszewski, MS, Chief Executive Officer
Web address: www.rehabnjtomsriver.com/

HEALTHSOUTH REHABILITATION HOSPITAL OF VINELAND (O, 41 beds) 1237 West Sherman Avenue, Vineland, NJ Zip 08360–6920; tel. 856/696–7100; Tammy Feuer, Chief Executive Officer
Web address: www.healthsouthvineland.com

NEW MEXICO: HEALTHSOUTH REHABILITATION HOSPITAL OF NEW MEXICO (O, 87 beds) 7000 Jefferson Street NE, Albuquerque, NM Zip 87109–4313; tel. 505/344–9478; David S. Nevill, Chief Executive Officer

OHIO: HEALTHSOUTH REHABILITATION HOSPITAL AT DRAKE (O, 60 beds) 151 West Galbraith Road, Cincinnati, OH Zip 45216–1015; tel. 513/418–5600; Ryan Smokovitz, Chief Executive Officer
Web address: www.healthsouthatdrake.com

HEALTHSOUTH REHABILITATION HOSPITAL OF DAYTON (O, 50 beds) One Elizabeth Place, Dayton, OH Zip 45417–3445; tel. 937/424–8200; Lynne Blinco, Chief Executive Officer
Web address: www.reliantdayton.com

OKLAHOMA: ST. JOHN REHABILITATION HOSPITAL (O, 22 beds) 1819 East 19th Street, 5th Floor, Tulsa, OK Zip 74104–5407; tel. 918/744–2338; David Nicholas, Chief Executive Officer

PENNSYLVANIA: GEISINGER HEALTHSOUTH REHABILITATION HOSPITAL (O, 42 beds) 2 Rehab Lane, Danville, PA Zip 17821–8498; tel. 570/271–6733; Lorie Dillon, Chief Executive Officer
Web address: www.geisingerhealthsouth.com

HEALTHSOUTH HARMARVILLE REHABILITATION HOSPITAL (O, 162 beds) 320 Guys Run Road, Pittsburgh, PA Zip 15238–0460, P O Box 11460, 15238–0460, tel. 412/828–1300; Mark Van Volkenburg, Chief Executive Officer
Web address: www.healthsouthharmarville.com

HEALTHSOUTH NITTANY VALLEY REHABILITATION HOSPITAL (O, 73 beds) 550 West College Avenue, Pleasant Gap, PA Zip 16823–7401; tel. 814/359–3421; Susan Hartman, Chief Executive Officer

HEALTHSOUTH READING REHABILITATION HOSPITAL (O, 60 beds) 1623 Morgantown Road, Reading, PA Zip 19607–9455; tel. 610/796–6000; Amy Teal, Chief Executive Officer
Web address: www.healthsouthreading.com

HEALTHSOUTH REHABILITATION HOSPITAL OF ALTOONA (O, 80 beds) 2005 Valley View Boulevard, Altoona, PA Zip 16602–4598; tel. 814/944–3535; Scott Filler, Chief Executive Officer
Web address: www.healthsouthaltoona.com

HEALTHSOUTH REHABILITATION HOSPITAL OF ERIE (O, 100 beds) 143 East Second Street, Erie, PA Zip 16507–1501; tel. 814/878–1200; John Papalia, Chief Executive Officer

HEALTHSOUTH REHABILITATION HOSPITAL OF MECHANICSBURG (O, 75 beds) 175 Lancaster Boulevard, Mechanicsburg, PA Zip 17055–3562; tel. 717/691–3700; Jarvis Ford, Chief Executive Officer
Web address: www.healthsouthpa.com

HEALTHSOUTH REHABILITATION HOSPITAL OF SEWICKLEY (O, 44 beds) 303 Camp Meeting Road, Sewickley, PA Zip 15143–8322; tel. 412/741–9500; Leah Laffey, R.N., Chief Executive Officer

HEALTHSOUTH REHABILITATION HOSPITAL OF YORK (O, 90 beds) 1850 Normandie Drive, York, PA Zip 17408–1534; tel. 717/767–6941; Steven Alwine, Chief Executive Officer
Web address: www.healthsouthyork.com

PUERTO RICO: HEALTHSOUTH HOSPITAL OF MANATI (O, 40 beds) Carretera 2, Kilometro 47 7, Manati, PR Zip 674; tel. 787/621–3800; Waleska Crespo-Rivera, Chief Executive Officer
Web address: www.healthsouth.com

HEALTHSOUTH REHABILITATION HOSPITAL OF SAN JUAN (O, 32 beds) University Hospital, 3rd Floor, San Juan, PR Zip 923, P O Box 70344, 923, tel. 787/274–5100; Daniel Del Castillo, Chief Executive Officer
Web address: www.healthsouthsanjuan.com

SOUTH CAROLINA: ANMED HEALTH REHABILITATION HOSPITAL (O, 60 beds) 1 Spring Back Way, Anderson, SC Zip 29621–2676; tel. 864/716–2600; Denise R. Murray, Chief Executive Officer
Web address: www.anmedrehab.com

HEALTHSOUTH REHABILITATION HOSPITAL OF CHARLESTON (O, 49 beds) 9181 Medcom Street, Charleston, SC Zip 29406–9168; tel. 843/820–7777; Michele M. Skripps, R.N., Chief Executive Officer

HEALTHSOUTH REHABILITATION HOSPITAL OF COLUMBIA (O, 96 beds) 2935 Colonial Drive, Columbia, SC Zip 29203–6811; tel. 803/254–7777; Catherine Landis, R.N., Chief Executive Officer
Web address: www.healthsouthcolumbia.com

HEALTHSOUTH REHABILITATION HOSPITAL OF FLORENCE (O, 88 beds) 900 East Cheves Street, Florence, SC Zip 29506–2704; tel. 843/679–9000; Brian Nunn, R.N., Chief Executive Officer

HEALTHSOUTH REHABILITATION HOSPITAL OF ROCK HILL (O, 50 beds) 1795 Dr. Frank Gaston Boulevard, Rock Hill, SC Zip 29732–1190; tel. 803/326–3500; Deanna Martin, Chief Executive Officer
Web address: www.healthsouthrockhill.com

Section B

For explanation of codes following names, see page B2.
★ Indicates Type III membership in the American Hospital Association.

TENNESSEE: HEALTHSOUTH CHATTANOOGA REHABILITATION HOSPITAL (O, 69 beds) 2412 McCallie Avenue, Chattanooga, TN Zip 37404–3398; tel. 423/698–0221; Scott Rowe, Chief Executive Officer

HEALTHSOUTH REHABILITATION HOSPITAL MEMPHIS-NORTH (O, 50 beds) 4100 Austin Peay Highway, Memphis, TN Zip 38128–2502; tel. 901/213–5400; Adam Yoe, Chief Executive Officer
Web address: www.healthsouthnorthmemphis.com

HEALTHSOUTH REHABILITATION HOSPITAL OF FRANKLIN (O, 40 beds) 1000 Physicians Way, Franklin, TN Zip 37067–1471; tel. 615/721–4000; Scott J. Peterson, Chief Executive Officer

HEALTHSOUTH REHABILITATION HOSPITAL OF MEMPHIS (O, 72 beds) 1282 Union Avenue, Memphis, TN Zip 38104–3414; tel. 901/722–2000; Stephanie Bridges, Chief Executive Officer
Web address: www.healthsouthmemphis.com

HEALTHSOUTH REHABILITATION HOSPITAL (O, 50 beds) 113 Cassel Drive, Kingsport, TN Zip 37660–3775; tel. 423/246–7240; Troy Clark, Chief Executive Officer

QUILLEN REHABILITATION HOSPITAL (O, 31 beds) 2511 Wesley Street, Johnson City, TN Zip 37601–1723; tel. 423/952–1700; Brian Luff, Chief Executive Officer
Web address: www.quillenrehabilitationhospital.com/

SPIRE CANE CREEK REHABILITATION HOSPITAL (O, 40 beds) 180 Mount Pelia Road, Martin, TN Zip 38237–3812; tel. 731/587–4231; Rick Johnson, Chief Executive Officer
Web address: www.healthsouthcanecreek.com

VANDERBILT STALLWORTH REHABILITATION HOSPITAL (O, 80 beds) 2201 Childrens Way, Nashville, TN Zip 37212–3165; tel. 615/320–7600; Jeffrey Palmucci, Chief Executive Officer

TEXAS: CHRISTUS TRINITY MOTHER FRANCES REHABILITATION HOSPITAL (O, 74 beds) 3131 Troup Highway, Tyler, TX Zip 75701–8352; tel. 903/510–7000; Sharla Anderson, Chief Executive Officer
Web address: www.tmfrehabhospital.com

HEALTHSOUTH CITY VIEW REHABILITATION HOSPITAL (O, 62 beds) 6701 Oakmont Boulevard, Fort Worth, TX Zip 76132–2957; tel. 817/370–4700; Janell Briscoe, Chief Executive Officer
Web address: www.healthsouthcityview.com

HEALTHSOUTH PLANO REHABILITATION HOSPITAL (O, 83 beds) 2800 West 15th Street, Plano, TX Zip 75075–7526; tel. 972/612–9000; Jennifer Lynn. Brewer, Chief Executive Officer

HEALTHSOUTH REHABILITATION HOSPITAL - ABILENE (O, 30 beds) 6401 Directors Parkway, Abilene, TX Zip 79606–5869; tel. 325/691–1600; Joe Roberson, Chief Executive Officer
Web address: www.reliantabilene.com

HEALTHSOUTH REHABILITATION HOSPITAL - AUSTIN (O, 60 beds) 330 West Ben White Boulevard, Austin, TX Zip 78704; tel. 512/730–4800; Brad Dinsmore, Chief Executive Officer

HEALTHSOUTH REHABILITATION HOSPITAL - DALLAS (O, 60 beds) 7930 Northaven Road, Dallas, TX Zip 75230–3331; tel. 214/706–8200; Daniel MacNicol, Chief Executive Officer
Web address: www.healthsouthdallas.com

HEALTHSOUTH REHABILITATION HOSPITAL - MID-CITIES (O, 60 beds) 2304 State Highway 121, Bedford, TX Zip 76021–5985; tel. 817/684–2000; Robert M. Smart, Chief Executive Officer

HEALTHSOUTH REHABILITATION HOSPITAL MIDLAND-ODESSA (O, 60 beds) 1800 Heritage Boulevard, Midland, TX Zip 79707–9750; tel. 432/520–1600; Christopher Wortham, Chief Executive Officer
Web address: www.healthsouthmidland.com

HEALTHSOUTH REHABILITATION HOSPITAL NORTH TEXAS (O, 50 beds) 3351 Waterview Parkway, Richardson, TX Zip 75080–1449; tel. 972/398–5700; Brent Yates, Chief Executive Officer

HEALTHSOUTH REHABILITATION HOSPITAL ROUND ROCK (O, 75 beds) 1400 Hester's Crossing, Round Rock, TX Zip 78681–8025; tel. 512/244–4400; Jack Boggess, Chief Executive Officer
Web address: www.healthsouthroundrock.com/

HEALTHSOUTH REHABILITATION HOSPITAL THE VINTAGE (O, 60 beds) 20180 Chasewood Park Drive, Houston, TX Zip 77070–1436; tel. 281/205–5100; Jeff Crawford, Chief Executive Officer
Web address: www.reliantnwhouston.com

HEALTHSOUTH REHABILITATION HOSPITAL THE WOODLANDS (O, 84 beds) 18550 'IH' 45 South, Conroe, TX Zip 77384; tel. 281/364–2000; Jeff Crawford, Chief Executive Officer
Web address: www.healthssouththewoodlands.com

HEALTHSOUTH REHABILITATION HOSPITAL VISION PARK (O, 41 beds) 117 Vision Park Boulevard, Shenandoah, TX Zip 77384–3001; tel. 936/444–1700; Jeff Crawford, Chief Executive Officer
Web address: www.healthsouthvisionpark.com/

HEALTHSOUTH REHABILITATION HOSPITAL OF ARLINGTON (O, 83 beds) 3200 Matlock Road, Arlington, TX Zip 76015–2911; tel. 817/468–4000; Sheril Appel, Chief Executive Officer

HEALTHSOUTH REHABILITATION HOSPITAL OF AUSTIN (O, 40 beds) 330 West Ben White Boulevard, Austin, TX Zip 78704; tel. 512/474–5700; Brad Dinsmore, Chief Executive Officer
Web address: www.healthsouthaustin.com

HEALTHSOUTH REHABILITATION HOSPITAL OF CYPRESS (O, 60 beds) 13031 Wortham Center Drive, Houston, TX Zip 77065–5662; tel. 832/280–2500; Sheila A. Bollier, Chief Executive Officer

HEALTHSOUTH REHABILITATION HOSPITAL OF FORT WORTH (O, 60 beds) 1212 West Lancaster Avenue, Fort Worth, TX Zip 76102–4510; tel. 817/870–2336; Janell Briscoe, Chief Executive Officer
Web address: www.healthsouthfortworth.com

HEALTHSOUTH REHABILITATION HOSPITAL OF TEXARKANA (O, 60 beds) 515 West 12th Street, Texarkana, TX Zip 75501–4416; tel. 903/735–5000; Harlo McCall, Chief Executive Officer
Web address: www.healthsouthtexarkana.com

HEALTHSOUTH REHABILITATION HOSPITAL-WICHITA FALLS (O, 63 beds) 3901 Armory Road, Wichita Falls, TX Zip 76302–2204; tel. 940/720–5700; Robbi Hudson, Chief Executive Officer
Web address: www.healthsouthwichitafalls.com

HEALTHSOUTH SUGAR LAND REHABILITATION HOSPITAL (O, 50 beds) 1325 Highway 6, Sugar Land, TX Zip 77478–4906; tel. 281/276–7574; Nicholas Hardin, FACHE, Chief Executive Officer

HEALTHSOUTH REHABILITATION HOSPITAL OF HUMBLE, LLC (O, 60 beds) 19002 McKay Drive, Humble, TX Zip 77338–5701; tel. 281/446–6148; Angela L. Simmons, Chief Executive Officer
Web address: www.healthsouthhumble.com

HEALTHSOUTH REHABILITATION INSTITUTE OF SAN ANTONIO (RIOSA) (O, 96 beds) 9119 Cinnamon Hill, San Antonio, TX Zip 78240–5401; tel. 210/691–0737; Michael Thomas, Chief Executive Officer
Web address: www.hsriosa.com

UTAH: HEALTHSOUTH REHABILITATION HOSPITAL OF UTAH (O, 105 beds) 8074 South 1300 East, Sandy, UT Zip 84094–0743; tel. 801/561–3400; Jeff Frandsen, Chief Executive Officer

VIRGINIA: HEALTHSOUTH REHABILITATION HOSPITAL OF FREDERICKSBURG (O, 40 beds) 300 Park Hill Drive, Fredericksburg, VA Zip 22401–3387; tel. 540/368–7300; Gary J. Herbek, Chief Executive Officer
Web address: www.fredericksburgrehabhospital.com

HEALTHSOUTH REHABILITATION HOSPITAL OF NORTHERN VIRGINIA (O, 60 beds) 24430 Millstream Drive, Aldie, VA Zip 20105–3098; tel. 703/957–2000; Alfred Santos, Chief Executive Officer

HEALTHSOUTH REHABILITATION HOSPITAL OF PETERSBURG (O, 64 beds) 95 Medical Park Boulevard, Petersburg, VA Zip 23805–9233; tel. 804/504–8100; Tracy Penn. Turman, Chief Executive Officer
Web address: www.healthsouthpetersburg.com

HEALTHSOUTH REHABILITATION HOSPITAL OF VIRGINIA (O, 40 beds) 5700 Fitzhugh Avenue, Richmond, VA Zip 23226–1800; tel. 804/288–5700; David Cashwell, Chief Executive Officer
Web address: www.healthsouthrichmond.com

REHABILITATION HOSPITAL OF SOUTHWEST VIRGINIA (O, 25 beds) 103 North Street, Bristol, VA Zip 24201–3201; tel. 276/642–7900; Georgeanne Cole, Chief Executive Officer

UVA-HEALTHSOUTH REHABILITATION HOSPITAL (O, 50 beds) 515 Ray C Hunt Drive, Charlottesville, VA Zip 22903–2981; tel. 434/244–2000
Web address: www.uvahealthsouth.com

WEST VIRGINIA: HEALTHSOUTH HUNTINGTON REHABILITATION HOSPITAL (O, 62 beds) 6900 West Country Club Drive, Huntington, WV Zip 25705–2000; tel. 304/733–1060; Michael E. Zuliani, Chief Executive Officer
Web address: www.healthsouthhuntington.com

For explanation of codes following names, see page B2.
★ Indicates Type III membership in the American Hospital Association.

HEALTHSOUTH MOUNTAINVIEW REGIONAL REHABILITATION HOSPITAL (O, 96 beds) 1160 Van Voorhis Road, Morgantown, WV Zip 26505–3437; tel. 304/598–1100; Tracy Vinciguerra, Chief Executive Officer

HEALTHSOUTH SOUTHERN HILLS REHABILITATION HOSPITAL (O, 45 beds) 120 Twelfth Street, Princeton, WV Zip 24740–2352; tel. 304/487–8000; Robert Williams, Chief Executive Officer
Web address: www.healthsouthsouthernhills.com

HEALTHSOUTH WESTERN HILLS REGIONAL REHABILITATION HOSPITAL (O, 40 beds) 3 Western Hills Drive, Parkersburg, WV Zip 26105–8122; tel. 304/420–1300; Alvin R. Lawson, FACHE, JD, Chief Executive Officer

Owned, leased, sponsored:	120 hospitals	8154 beds
Contract-managed:	0 hospitals	0 beds
Totals:	120 hospitals	8154 beds

★**0585: HEALTHTECH MANAGEMENT SERVICES** (IO)
5110 Maryland Way Suite 200, Brentwood, TN Zip 37027–2307; tel. 615/309–6053; Derek Morkel, Chief Executive Officer
(Decentralized Health System)

ARIZONA: COBRE VALLEY REGIONAL MEDICAL CENTER (C, 25 beds) 5880 South Hospital Drive, Globe, AZ Zip 85501–9454; tel. 928/425–3261; Neal Jensen, Chief Executive Officer
Web address: www.cvrmc.org

GEORGIA: UPSON REGIONAL MEDICAL CENTER (C, 77 beds) 801 West Gordon Street, Thomaston, GA Zip 30286–3426, P O Box 1059, 30286–0027, tel. 706/647–8111; Tripp Penn, Chief Executive Officer
Web address: www.urmc.org

ILLINOIS: CARLINVILLE AREA HOSPITAL (C, 25 beds) 20733 North Broad Street, Carlinville, IL Zip 62626–1499; tel. 217/854–3141; Kenneth G. Reid, President and Chief Executive Officer
Web address: www.cahcare.com

HAMMOND-HENRY HOSPITAL (C, 61 beds) 600 North College Avenue, Geneseo, IL Zip 61254–1099; tel. 309/944–6431; Michael Lieb, Interim Chief Executive Officer

HILLSBORO AREA HOSPITAL (C, 25 beds) 1200 East Tremont Street, Hillsboro, IL Zip 62049–1900; tel. 217/532–6111; Rex H. Brown, President and Chief Executive Officer
Web address: www.hillsborohealth.org

LOUISIANA: IBERIA MEDICAL CENTER (C, 97 beds) 2315 East Main Street, New Iberia, LA Zip 70560–4031, P O Box 13338, 70562–3338, tel. 337/364–0441; Parker A. Templeton, FACHE, Chief Executive Officer
Web address: www.iberiamedicalcenter.com

MONTANA: BARRETT HOSPITAL & HEALTHCARE (C, 18 beds) 600 Mt Highway 91 South, Dillon, MT Zip 59725–7379; tel. 406/683–3000; Ken Westman, Chief Executive Officer

NEW YORK: ADIRONDACK HEALTH (C, 120 beds) 2233 State Route 86, Saranac Lake, NY Zip 12983–5644, P O Box 471, 12983–0471, tel. 518/891–4141; Sylvia Getman, President and Chief Executive Officer
Web address: www.adirondackhealth.org

OREGON: BLUE MOUNTAIN HOSPITAL (C, 45 beds) 170 Ford Road, John Day, OR Zip 97845–2009; tel. 541/575–1311; Derek Daly, Chief Executive Officer
Web address: www.bluemountainhospital.org

WASHINGTON: SUNNYSIDE COMMUNITY HOSPITAL AND CLINICS (C, 25 beds) 1016 Tacoma Avenue, Sunnyside, WA Zip 98944–2263, P O Box 719, 98944–0719, tel. 509/837–1500; Brian Gibbone, Chief Executive Officer

WISCONSIN: GRANT REGIONAL HEALTH CENTER (C, 8 beds) 507 South Monroe Street, Lancaster, WI Zip 53813–2054; tel. 608/723–2143; Nicole Clapp, R.N., MSN, FACHE, President and Chief Executive Officer
Web address: www.grantregional.com

SPOONER HEALTH (C, 25 beds) 1280 Chandler Drive, Spooner, WI Zip 54801–1299; tel. 715/635–2111; Michael Schafer, Chief Executive Officer and Administrator
Web address: www.spoonerhealth.com

TOMAH MEMORIAL HOSPITAL (C, 25 beds) 321 Butts Avenue, Tomah, WI Zip 54660–1412; tel. 608/372–2181; Philip J. Stuart, Administrator and Chief Executive Officer
Web address: www.tomahhospital.org

WYOMING: HOT SPRINGS COUNTY MEMORIAL HOSPITAL (C, 25 beds) 150 East Arapahoe Street, Thermopolis, WY Zip 82443–2498; tel. 307/864–3121; Margie Molitor, FACHE, R.N., Chief Executive Officer

POWELL VALLEY HEALTHCARE (C, 125 beds) 777 Avenue 'H', Powell, WY Zip 82435–2296; tel. 307/754–2267; Terry Odom, Chief Executive Officer
Web address: www.pvhc.org

Owned, leased, sponsored:	0 hospitals	0 beds
Contract-managed:	15 hospitals	726 beds
Totals:	15 hospitals	726 beds

★**9505: HENRY FORD HEALTH SYSTEM** (NP)
One Ford Place, Detroit, MI Zip 48202–3450; tel. 313/876–8708; Wright L. Lassiter III, President and Chief Executive Officer
(Centralized Physician/Insurance Health System)

MICHIGAN: HENRY FORD ALLEGIANCE HEALTH (O, 327 beds) 205 North East Avenue, Jackson, MI Zip 49201–1753; tel. 517/788–4800; Georgia R. Fojtasek, R.N., President and Chief Executive Officer

HENRY FORD HOSPITAL (O, 725 beds) 2799 West Grand Boulevard, Detroit, MI Zip 48202–2608; tel. 313/916–2600; John Popovich, M.D., President and Chief Executive Officer
Web address: www.henryfordhealth.org

HENRY FORD KINGSWOOD HOSPITAL (O, 101 beds) 10300 West Eight Mile Road, Ferndale, MI Zip 48220–2100; tel. 248/398–3200; DoreeAnn V. Espiritu, M.D., Interim Chair, Behavioral Health Services

HENRY FORD MACOMB HOSPITALS (O, 439 beds) 15855 19 Mile Road, Clinton Township, MI Zip 48038–6324; tel. 586/263–2300; Barbara W. Rossmann, R.N., President and Chief Executive Officer
Web address: www.henryfordmacomb.com

HENRY FORD WEST BLOOMFIELD HOSPITAL (O, 212 beds) 6777 West Maple Road, West Bloomfield, MI Zip 48322–3013; tel. 248/661–4100; Lynn M. Torossian, President and Chief Executive Officer

HENRY FORD WYANDOTTE HOSPITAL (O, 343 beds) 2333 Biddle Avenue, Wyandotte, MI Zip 48192–4668; tel. 734/246–6000; Denise Brooks-Williams, President and Chief Executive Officer
Web address: www.henryfordhealth.org

Owned, leased, sponsored:	6 hospitals	2147 beds
Contract-managed:	0 hospitals	0 beds
Totals:	6 hospitals	2147 beds

0309: HERITAGE VALLEY HEALTH SYSTEM (NP)
1000 Dutch Ridge Road, Beaver, PA Zip 15009–9727; tel. 724/773–2024; Norman F. Mitry, President and Chief Executive Officer
(Independent Hospital System)

PENNSYLVANIA: HERITAGE VALLEY HEALTH SYSTEM (O, 271 beds) 1000 Dutch Ridge Road, Beaver, PA Zip 15009–9727; tel. 724/728–7000; Norman F. Mitry, President and Chief Executive Officer
Web address: www.heritagevalley.org

SEWICKLEY VALLEY HOSPITAL, (A DIVISION OF VALLEY MEDICAL FACILITIES) (O, 179 beds) 720 Blackburn Road, Sewickley, PA Zip 15143–1459; tel. 412/741–6600; Norman F. Mitry, President and Chief Executive Officer

Owned, leased, sponsored:	2 hospitals	450 beds
Contract-managed:	0 hospitals	0 beds
Totals:	2 hospitals	450 beds

1024: HEYWOOD HEALTHCARE (NP)
242 Green Street, Gardner, MA Zip 01440–1336; tel. 978/632–3420; Winfield S. Brown, FACHE, Chief Executive Officer

For explanation of codes following names, see page B2.
★ Indicates Type III membership in the American Hospital Association.

MASSACHUSETTS: ATHOL HOSPITAL (O, 25 beds) 2033 Main Street, Athol, MA Zip 01331–3598; tel. 978/249–3511; Winfield S. Brown, FACHE, President and Chief Executive Officer
Web address: www.atholhospital.org

HEYWOOD HOSPITAL (O, 93 beds) 242 Green Street, Gardner, MA Zip 01440–1373; tel. 978/632–3420; Winfield S. Brown, FACHE, President and Chief Executive Officer
Web address: www.heywood.org

Owned, leased, sponsored:	2 hospitals	118 beds
Contract-managed:	0 hospitals	0 beds
Totals:	2 hospitals	118 beds

1014: HOLZER HEALTH SYSTEM (NP)
500 Burlington Road, Jackson, OH Zip 45640–9360; tel. 855/446–5937; Michael Canady, M.D., Interim Chief Executive Officer

OHIO: HOLZER MEDICAL CENTER - JACKSON (O, 24 beds) 500 Burlington Road, Jackson, OH Zip 45640–9360; tel. 740/288–4625; Michael Canady, M.D., Interim Chief Executive Officer

HOLZER MEDICAL CENTER (O, 181 beds) 100 Jackson Pike, Gallipolis, OH Zip 45631–1563; tel. 740/446–5000; Michael Canady, M.D., Interim Chief Executive Officer
Web address: www.holzer.org

Owned, leased, sponsored:	2 hospitals	205 beds
Contract-managed:	0 hospitals	0 beds
Totals:	2 hospitals	205 beds

★0963: HONORHEALTH (NP)
8125 North Hayden Road, Scottsdale, AZ Zip 85258–2463; tel. 623/580–5800; Todd LaPorte, Chief Executive Officer
(Moderately Centralized Health System)

ARIZONA: HONORHEALTH DEER VALLEY MEDICAL CENTER (O, 204 beds) 19829 North 27th Avenue, Phoenix, AZ Zip 85027–4002; tel. 623/879–6100; David Price, Chief Executive Officer
Web address: www.jcl.com

HONORHEALTH JOHN C. LINCOLN MEDICAL CENTER (O, 262 beds) 250 East Dunlap Avenue, Phoenix, AZ Zip 85020–2825; tel. 602/943–2381; Margaret Elizabeth. Griffin, Chief Executive Officer

HONORHEALTH SCOTTSDALE OSBORN MEDICAL CENTER (O, 347 beds) 7400 East Osborn Road, Scottsdale, AZ Zip 85251–6403; tel. 480/882–4000; Kimberly Post, Senior Vice President and Chief Executive Officer
Web address: www.shc.org

HONORHEALTH SCOTTSDALE SHEA MEDICAL CENTER (O, 409 beds) 9003 East Shea Boulevard, Scottsdale, AZ Zip 85260–6771; tel. 480/323–3000; Gary E. Baker, Senior Vice President and Chief Executive Officer

HONORHEALTH SCOTTSDALE THOMPSON PEAK MEDICAL CENTER (O, 92 beds) 7400 East Thompson Peak Parkway, Scottsdale, AZ Zip 85255–4109; tel. 480/324–7000; David Price, Chief Executive Officer
Web address: www.shc.org

Owned, leased, sponsored:	5 hospitals	1314 beds
Contract-managed:	0 hospitals	0 beds
Totals:	5 hospitals	1314 beds

★0642: HOUSTON HEALTHCARE SYSTEM (NP)
1601 Watson Boulevard, Warner Robins, GA Zip 31093–3431, P O Box 2886, 31099–2886, tel. 478/922–4281; Cary Martin, Chief Executive Officer
(Independent Hospital System)

GEORGIA: HOUSTON MEDICAL CENTER (O, 237 beds) 1601 Watson Boulevard, Warner Robins, GA Zip 31093–3431, P O Box 2886, 31099–2886, tel. 478/922–4281; Cary Martin, Chief Executive Officer
Web address: www.hhc.org

PERRY HOSPITAL (O, 39 beds) 1120 Morningside Drive, Perry, GA Zip 31069–2906; tel. 478/987–3600; David Campbell, Administrator
Web address: www.hhc.org

Owned, leased, sponsored:	2 hospitals	276 beds
Contract-managed:	0 hospitals	0 beds
Totals:	2 hospitals	276 beds

★7235: HOUSTON METHODIST (CO)
6565 Fannin Street, D-200, Houston, TX Zip 77030–2707; tel. 713/441–2221; Marc L. Boom, M.D., Chief Executive Officer
(Centralized Health System)

TEXAS: HOUSTON METHODIST HOSPITAL (O, 900 beds) 6565 Fannin Street, D200, Houston, TX Zip 77030–2707; tel. 713/790–3311; Roberta Schwartz, Ph.D., Executive Vice President

HOUSTON METHODIST SAN JACINTO HOSPITAL (O, 275 beds) 4401 Garth Road, Administration Department, Baytown, TX Zip 77521–2122; tel. 281/420–8600; David P. Bernard, FACHE, Chief Executive Officer
Web address: www.houstonmethodist.org

HOUSTON METHODIST ST. CATHERINE HOSPITAL (O, 44 beds) 701 Fry Road, Katy, TX Zip 77450–2255; tel. 281/599–5700; Gary L. Kempf, R.N., Administrator
Web address: www.houstonmethodist.org/katy-st-catherine-hospital

HOUSTON METHODIST ST. JOHN HOSPITAL (O, 111 beds) 18300 St John Drive, Nassau Bay, TX Zip 77058–6302; tel. 281/333–5503; Dan Newman, Chief Executive Officer
Web address: www.houstonmethodist.org/st-john-clear-lake

HOUSTON METHODIST SUGAR LAND HOSPITAL (O, 305 beds) 16655 SW Freeway, Sugar Land, TX Zip 77479–2329; tel. 281/274–7000; Christopher Siebenaler, Chief Executive Officer

HOUSTON METHODIST THE WOODLANDS HOSPITAL (O, 187 beds) 17201 Interstate 45 South, The Woodlands, TX Zip 77385; tel. 713/790–3333; Debra F. Sukin, Regional Vice President and Chief Executive Officer
Web address: www.houstonmethodist.org/locations/the-woodlands/

HOUSTON METHODIST WEST HOSPITAL (O, 193 beds) 18500 Katy Freeway, Houston, TX Zip 77094–1110; tel. 832/522–1000; Wayne M. Voss, Chief Executive Officer

HOUSTON METHODIST WILLOWBROOK HOSPITAL (O, 312 beds) 18220 State Highway 249, Houston, TX Zip 77070–4347; tel. 281/477–1000; Keith Barber, CPA, Chief Executive Officer
Web address: www.houstonmethodist.org/locations/willowbrook/

Owned, leased, sponsored:	8 hospitals	2327 beds
Contract-managed:	0 hospitals	0 beds
Totals:	8 hospitals	2327 beds

★5355: HSHS HOSPITAL SISTERS HEALTH SYSTEM (CC)
4936 LaVerna Road, Springfield, IL Zip 62707–9797, P O Box 19456, 62794–9456, tel. 217/523–4747; Mary Starmann-Harrison, FACHE, R.N., President and Chief Executive Officer
(Decentralized Health System)

ILLINOIS: HSHS HOLY FAMILY HOSPITAL IN GREENVILLE (O, 42 beds) 200 Healthcare Drive, Greenville, IL Zip 62246–1154; tel. 618/664–1230; Brian Nall, President and Chief Operating Officer

HSHS ST. ANTHONY'S MEMORIAL HOSPITAL (O, 123 beds) 503 North Maple Street, Effingham, IL Zip 62401–2099; tel. 217/342–2121; Theresa Rutherford, R.N., MS, FACHE, President and Chief Executive Officer
Web address: www.stanthonyshospital.org

HSHS ST. ELIZABETH'S HOSPITAL (O, 224 beds) 211 South Third Street, Belleville, IL Zip 62220–1998; tel. 618/234–2120; Peggy A. Sebastian, MSN, R.N., President and Chief Executive Officer
Web address: www.steliz.org

HSHS ST. FRANCIS HOSPITAL (O, 25 beds) 1215 Franciscan Drive, Litchfield, IL Zip 62056–1799, P O Box 1215, 62056–0999; tel. 217/324–2191; Aaron Puchbauer, Interim Chief Executive Officer

For explanation of codes following names, see page B2.
★ Indicates Type III membership in the American Hospital Association.

HSHS ST. JOSEPH'S HOSPITAL (O, 65 beds) 9515 Holy Cross Lane, Breese, IL Zip 62230–3618, PO Box 99, 62230–0099, tel. 618/526–4511; Amy Ballance, Interim Chief Executive Officer
Web address: www.stjoebreese.com

HSHS ST. JOSEPH'S HOSPITAL (O, 25 beds) 12866 Troxler Avenue, Highland, IL Zip 62249–1698; tel. 618/651–2600; John A. Ludwig, R.N., President and Chief Operating Officer
Web address: www.stjosephshighland.com

HSHS ST. MARY'S HOSPITAL (O, 244 beds) 1800 East Lake Shore Drive, Decatur, IL Zip 62521–3883; tel. 217/464–2966; Joan M. Coffman, FACHE, President and Chief Executive Officer

ST. JOHN'S HOSPITAL (O, 432 beds) 800 East Carpenter Street, Springfield, IL Zip 62769–0002; tel. 217/544–6464; Charles Lucore, M.D., President and Chief Executive Officer
Web address: www.st-johns.org

WISCONSIN: DOOR COUNTY MEDICAL CENTER (O, 55 beds) 323 South 18th Avenue, Sturgeon Bay, WI Zip 54235–1495; tel. 920/743–5566; Gerald M. Worrick, President and Chief Executive Officer

HSHS ST. CLARE MEMORIAL HOSPITAL (O, 8 beds) 855 South Main Street, Oconto Falls, WI Zip 54154–1296; tel. 920/846–3444; Therese B. Pandl, President and Chief Executive Officer
Web address: www.cmhospital.org/index.html

HSHS ST. JOSEPH'S HOSPITAL (O, 102 beds) 2661 County Highway I, Chippewa Falls, WI Zip 54729–5407; tel. 715/723–1811; Julie Manas, Interim Chief Executive Officer

HSHS ST. MARY'S HOSPITAL MEDICAL CENTER (O, 83 beds) 1726 Shawano Avenue, Green Bay, WI Zip 54303–3282; tel. 920/498–4200; Therese B. Pandl, President and Chief Executive Officer
Web address: www.stmgb.org

HSHS ST. NICHOLAS HOSPITAL (O, 46 beds) 3100 Superior Avenue, Sheboygan, WI Zip 53081–1948; tel. 920/459–8300; Andrew Bagnall, President and Chief Executive Officer
Web address: www.stnicholashospital.org

HSHS ST. VINCENT HOSPITAL (O, 255 beds) 835 South Van Buren Street, Green Bay, WI Zip 54301–3526, P O Box 13508, 54307–3508, tel. 920/433–0111; Therese B. Pandl, President and Chief Executive Officer
Web address: www.stvincenthospital.org

SACRED HEART HOSPITAL (O, 205 beds) 900 West Clairemont Avenue, Eau Claire, WI Zip 54701–6122; tel. 715/717–4121; Julie Manas, President and Chief Executive Officer
Web address: www.sacredhearteauclaire.org

Owned, leased, sponsored:	15 hospitals	1934 beds
Contract-managed:	0 hospitals	0 beds
Totals:	15 hospitals	1934 beds

0907: HUNT REGIONAL HEALTHCARE (NP)
4215 Joe Ramsey Boulevard, Greenville, TX Zip 75401–7852, P O Box 1059, 75403–1059, tel. 903/408–5000; Richard Carter, Chief Executive Officer
(Independent Hospital System)

TEXAS: HUNT REGIONAL MEDICAL CENTER (O, 167 beds) 4215 Joe Ramsey Boulevard, Greenville, TX Zip 75401–7899, P O Box 1059, 75403–1059, tel. 903/408–5000; Richard Carter, District Chief Executive Officer
Web address: www.huntregional.org

Owned, leased, sponsored:	1 hospitals	167 beds
Contract-managed:	0 hospitals	0 beds
Totals:	1 hospitals	167 beds

0117: HUNTSVILLE HOSPITAL HEALTH SYSTEM (NP)
101 Sivley Road SW, Huntsville, AL Zip 35801–4421; tel. 265/256–1000; David S. Spillers, Chief Executive Officer
(Moderately Centralized Health System)

ALABAMA: ATHENS-LIMESTONE HOSPITAL (C, 71 beds) 700 West Market Street, Athens, AL Zip 35611–2457, P O Box 999, 35612–0999, tel. 256/233–9292; David Pryor, President
Web address: www.athenslimestonehospital.com

DECATUR MORGAN HOSPITAL (O, 110 beds) 1201 Seventh Street SE, Decatur, AL Zip 35601–3303, P O Box 2239, 35609–2239, tel. 256/341–2000; Nathaniel Richardson Jr, President

HELEN KELLER HOSPITAL (C, 145 beds) 1300 South Montgomery Avenue, Sheffield, AL Zip 35660–6334, P O Box 610, 35660–0610, tel. 256/386–4196; Paul Storey, FACHE, President and Chief Executive Officer
Web address: www.helenkeller.com

HUNTSVILLE HOSPITAL (O, 914 beds) 101 Sivley Road SW, Huntsville, AL Zip 35801–4470; tel. 256/265–1000; David S. Spillers, Chief Executive Officer
Web address: www.huntsvillehospital.org

LAWRENCE MEDICAL CENTER (C, 43 beds) 202 Hospital Street, Moulton, AL Zip 35650–1218, P O Box 39, 35650–0039, tel. 256/974–2200; Dean A. Griffin, Chief Executive Officer

RED BAY HOSPITAL (C, 25 beds) 211 Hospital Road, Red Bay, AL Zip 35582–3858, P O Box 490, 35582–0490, tel. 256/356–9532; Sherry Jolley, Director of Operations and Nursing
Web address: www.redbayhospital.com

Owned, leased, sponsored:	2 hospitals	1024 beds
Contract-managed:	4 hospitals	284 beds
Totals:	6 hospitals	1308 beds

0201: IASIS HEALTHCARE (IO)
117 Seaboard Lane, Building E, Franklin, TN Zip 37067–2855; tel. 615/844–2747; Carl Whitmer, President and Chief Executive Officer
(Moderately Centralized Health System)

ARIZONA: MOUNTAIN VISTA MEDICAL CENTER (O, 172 beds) 1301 South Crismon Road, Mesa, AZ Zip 85209–3767; tel. 480/358–6100; Jacob Golich, Chief Executive Officer
Web address: www.mvmedicalcenter.com

ST. LUKE'S BEHAVIORAL HEALTH CENTER (O, 85 beds) 1800 East Van Buren, Phoenix, AZ Zip 85006–3742; tel. 602/251–8546; Gregory L. Jahn, R.N., Chief Executive Officer

ST. LUKE'S MEDICAL CENTER (O, 283 beds) 1800 East Van Buren Street, Phoenix, AZ Zip 85006–3742; tel. 602/251–8100; James Flinn, JD, FACHE, Chief Executive Officer
Web address: www.stlukesmedcenter.com

ARKANSAS: WADLEY REGIONAL MEDICAL CENTER AT HOPE (O, 79 beds) 2001 South Main Street, Hope, AR Zip 71801–8194; tel. 870/722–3800; Thomas D. Gilbert, FACHE, Chief Executive Officer
Web address: www.wadleyhealthathope.com

COLORADO: PIKES PEAK REGIONAL HOSPITAL (O, 15 beds) 16420 West Highway 24, Woodland Park, CO Zip 80863; tel. 719/687–9999; Kimberly Monjesky, Chief Executive Officer

LOUISIANA: GLENWOOD REGIONAL MEDICAL CENTER (O, 273 beds) 503 McMillan Road, West Monroe, LA Zip 71291–5327; tel. 318/329–4200; Jeremy Tinnerello, MSN, R.N., Chief Executive Officer, Chief Operating Officer
Web address: www.grmc.com

TEXAS: MEDICAL CENTER OF SOUTHEAST TEXAS (O, 17 beds) 6025 Metropolitan Drive, Beaumont, TX Zip 77706–2407; tel. 409/617–7700; Becky Ames, Chief Executive Officer
Web address: www.medicalcentersetexas.com/

ODESSA REGIONAL MEDICAL CENTER (O, 213 beds) 520 East Sixth Street, Odessa, TX Zip 79761–4565, P O Box 4859, 79760–4859, tel. 432/582–8000; Stacey L. Gerig, Chief Executive Officer
Web address: www.odessaregionalmedicalcenter.com

SOUTHWEST GENERAL HOSPITAL (O, 253 beds) 7400 Barlite Boulevard, San Antonio, TX Zip 78224–1399; tel. 210/921–2000; P Craig. Desmond, Chief Executive Officer
Web address: www.swgeneralhospital.com

Section B

For explanation of codes following names, see page B2.
★ Indicates Type III membership in the American Hospital Association.

ST. JOSEPH MEDICAL CENTER (O, 376 beds) 1401 St Joseph Parkway, Houston, TX Zip 77002-8301; tel. 713/757-1000; Bryanie W. Swilley Jr, Interim Chief Executive Officer

THE MEDICAL CENTER OF SOUTHEAST TEXAS (O, 167 beds) 2555 Jimmy Johnson Boulevard, Port Arthur, TX Zip 77640-2007; tel. 409/724-7389; Richard Gonzalez, Chief Executive Officer
Web address: www.medicalcentersetexas.com

WADLEY REGIONAL MEDICAL CENTER (O, 179 beds) 1000 Pine Street, Texarkana, TX Zip 75501-5170; tel. 903/798-8000; Thomas D. Gilbert, FACHE, Chief Executive Officer

UTAH: DAVIS HOSPITAL AND MEDICAL CENTER (O, 221 beds) 1600 West Antelope Drive, Layton, UT Zip 84041-1142; tel. 801/807-1000; Michael Jensen, Chief Executive Officer
Web address: www.davishospital.com

JORDAN VALLEY MEDICAL CENTER WEST VALLEY CAMPUS (O, 101 beds) 3460 South Pioneer Parkway, West Valley City, UT Zip 84120-2049; tel. 801/561-8888; Steven Anderson, Chief Executive Officer

JORDAN VALLEY MEDICAL CENTER (O, 183 beds) 3580 West 9000 South, West Jordan, UT Zip 84088-8812; tel. 801/561-8888; Steven Anderson, Chief Executive Officer
Web address: www.jordanvalleymc.com

SALT LAKE REGIONAL MEDICAL CENTER (O, 132 beds) 1050 East South Temple, Salt Lake City, UT Zip 84102-1507; tel. 801/350-4111; Dale Johns, FACHE, Chief Executive Officer

Owned, leased, sponsored:	16 hospitals	2749 beds
Contract-managed:	0 hospitals	0 beds
Totals:	16 hospitals	2749 beds

★0231: INDIANA UNIVERSITY HEALTH (NP)
340 West 10th Street, Suite 6100, Indianapolis, IN Zip 46202-3082, P O Box 1367, 46206-1367, tel. 317/962-5900; Dennis M. Murphy, President and Chief Executive Officer
(Centralized Physician/Insurance Health System)

INDIANA: INDIANA UNIVERSITY HEALTH ARNETT HOSPITAL (O, 191 beds) 5165 McCarty Lane, Lafayette, IN Zip 47905-8764, P O Box 5545, 47903-5545, tel. 765/448-8000; Donald Clayton, M.D., President
Web address: www.iuhealth.org

INDIANA UNIVERSITY HEALTH BALL MEMORIAL HOSPITAL (O, 339 beds) 2401 University Avenue, Muncie, IN Zip 47303-3499; tel. 765/747-3111; Michael E. Haley, President
Web address: www.iuhealth.org

INDIANA UNIVERSITY HEALTH BEDFORD HOSPITAL (O, 25 beds) 2900 West 16th Street, Bedford, IN Zip 47421-3583; tel. 812/275-1200; Bradford W. Dykes, President and Chief Executive Officer
Web address: www.iuhealth.org

INDIANA UNIVERSITY HEALTH BLACKFORD HOSPITAL (O, 15 beds) 410 Pilgrim Boulevard, Hartford City, IN Zip 47348-1897; tel. 765/348-0300; Steven J. West, Chief Executive Officer

INDIANA UNIVERSITY HEALTH BLOOMINGTON HOSPITAL (O, 273 beds) 601 West Second Street, Bloomington, IN Zip 47403-2317, P O Box 1149, 47402-1149, tel. 812/336-6821; Matthew D. Bailey, FACHE, President
Web address: www.iuhealth.org

INDIANA UNIVERSITY HEALTH NORTH HOSPITAL (O, 149 beds) 11700 North Meridian Avenue, Carmel, IN Zip 46032-4656; tel. 317/688-2000; Jonathan R. Goble, FACHE, President and Chief Executive Officer
Web address: www.iuhealth.org/north

INDIANA UNIVERSITY HEALTH PAOLI HOSPITAL (O, 25 beds) 642 West Hospital Road, Paoli, IN Zip 47454-9672, P O Box 499, 47454-0499, tel. 812/723-2811; Larry Bailey, Chief Executive Officer

INDIANA UNIVERSITY HEALTH TIPTON HOSPITAL (O, 25 beds) 1000 South Main Street, Tipton, IN Zip 46072-9799; tel. 765/675-8500; Michael Harlowe, President and Chief Executive Officer
Web address: www.iuhealth.org

INDIANA UNIVERSITY HEALTH UNIVERSITY HOSPITAL (O, 1253 beds) 550 University Boulevard, Indianapolis, IN Zip 46202-5149, P O Box 1367, 46206-1367, tel. 317/944-5000; Ryan Nagy, M.D., Interim President and Chief Medical Officer

INDIANA UNIVERSITY HEALTH WEST HOSPITAL (O, 127 beds) 1111 North Ronald Reagan Parkway, Avon, IN Zip 46123-7085; tel. 317/217-3000; Doug Puckett, President
Web address: www.iuhealth.org

INDIANA UNIVERSITY HEALTH WHITE MEMORIAL HOSPITAL (O, 25 beds) 720 South Sixth Street, Monticello, IN Zip 47960-8182; tel. 574/583-7111; Mary Minier, President

JAY COUNTY HOSPITAL (C, 35 beds) 500 West Votaw Street, Portland, IN Zip 47371-1322; tel. 260/726-7131; David W. Hyatt, Chief Executive Officer
Web address: www.jaycountyhospital.com

REHABILITATION HOSPITAL OF INDIANA (O, 83 beds) 4141 Shore Drive, Indianapolis, IN Zip 46254-2607; tel. 317/329-2000; Daniel B. Woloszyn, Chief Executive Officer

Owned, leased, sponsored:	12 hospitals	2530 beds
Contract-managed:	1 hospitals	35 beds
Totals:	13 hospitals	2565 beds

2025: INFIRMARY HEALTH SYSTEM (NP)
5 Mobile Infirmary Circle, Mobile, AL Zip 36607-3513; tel. 251/435-5500; D Mark. Nix, President and Chief Executive Officer
(Moderately Centralized Health System)

ALABAMA: ATMORE COMMUNITY HOSPITAL (O, 33 beds) 401 Medical Park Drive, Atmore, AL Zip 36502-3091; tel. 251/368-2500; Douglas Tanner, President
Web address: www.ebaptisthealthcare.org/AtmoreCommunityHospital/

INFIRMARY LONG TERM ACUTE CARE HOSPITAL (L, 36 beds) 5 Mobile Infirmary Circle, Mobile, AL Zip 36607-3513, P O Box 2226, 36652-2226, tel. 251/660-5239; Susanne Marmande, Administrator
Web address: www.theinfirmary.com/

MOBILE INFIRMARY MEDICAL CENTER (O, 554 beds) 5 Mobile Infirmary Drive North, Mobile, AL Zip 36607-3513, P O Box 2144, 36652-2144, tel. 251/435-2400; Jennifer Eslinger, President
Web address: www.infirmaryhealth.org

NORTH BALDWIN INFIRMARY (L, 50 beds) 1815 Hand Avenue, Bay Minette, AL Zip 36507-4110, P O Box 1409, 36507-1409, tel. 251/937-5521; Benjamin K. Hansert, Administrator
Web address: www.mobileinfirmary.org

THOMAS HOSPITAL (L, 136 beds) 750 Morphy Avenue, Fairhope, AL Zip 36532-1812, P O Box 929, 36533-0929, tel. 251/928-2375; Ormand P. Thompson, President

Owned, leased, sponsored:	5 hospitals	809 beds
Contract-managed:	0 hospitals	0 beds
Totals:	5 hospitals	809 beds

★1305: INOVA HEALTH SYSTEM (NP)
8110 Gatehouse Road, Suite 200 East, Falls Church, VA Zip 22042-1252; tel. 703/289-2069; J Knox. Singleton, President and Chief Executive Officer
(Centralized Health System)

VIRGINIA: INOVA ALEXANDRIA HOSPITAL (O, 334 beds) 4320 Seminary Road, Alexandria, VA Zip 22304-1535; tel. 703/504-3167; Susan Carroll, Regional Executive Officer-Eastern Region
Web address: www.inova.org

INOVA FAIR OAKS HOSPITAL (O, 201 beds) 3600 Joseph Siewick Drive, Fairfax, VA Zip 22033-1798; tel. 703/391-3600; John L. Fitzgerald, Chief Executive Officer

INOVA FAIRFAX HOSPITAL (O, 1002 beds) 3300 Gallows Road, Falls Church, VA Zip 22042-3300; tel. 703/776-4001; Patrick Christiansen, Ph.D., Chief Executive Officer
Web address: www.inova.org

INOVA LOUDOUN HOSPITAL (O, 286 beds) 44045 Riverside Parkway, Leesburg, VA Zip 20176-5101, P O Box 6000, 20177-0600, tel. 703/858-6000; Deborah Addo, Chief Executive Officer

---

For explanation of codes following names, see page B2.
★ Indicates Type III membership in the American Hospital Association.

Section B

INOVA MOUNT VERNON HOSPITAL (O, 237 beds) 2501 Parker's Lane, Alexandria, VA Zip 22306–3209; tel. 703/664–7000; Donald Brideau, M.D., Interim Chief Executive Officer
Web address: www.inova.org

Owned, leased, sponsored:	5 hospitals	2060 beds
Contract-managed:	0 hospitals	0 beds
Totals:	5 hospitals	2060 beds

★**0151: INSPIRA HEALTH NETWORK** (NP)
165 Bridgeton Pike, Mullica Hill, NJ Zip 8062; tel. 856/641–8000; John A. DiAngelo, President and Chief Executive Officer
(Moderately Centralized Health System)

NEW JERSEY: INSPIRA MEDICAL CENTER-ELMER (O, 88 beds) 501 West Front Street, Elmer, NJ Zip 08318–2101; tel. 856/363–1000; John A. DiAngelo, President and Chief Executive Officer

INSPIRA MEDICAL CENTER-VINELAND (O, 335 beds) 1505 West Sherman Avenue, Vineland, NJ Zip 08360–6912; tel. 856/641–8000; John A. DiAngelo, President and Chief Executive Officer
Web address: www.inspirahealthnetwork.org/?id=5280&sid=1

INSPIRA MEDICAL CENTER-WOODBURY (O, 261 beds) 509 North Broad Street, Woodbury, NJ Zip 08096–1697; tel. 856/845–0100; John A. DiAngelo, President and Chief Executive Officer

Owned, leased, sponsored:	3 hospitals	684 beds
Contract-managed:	0 hospitals	0 beds
Totals:	3 hospitals	684 beds

★**0305: INTEGRIS HEALTH** (NP)
3366 NW Expressway, Suite 800, Oklahoma City, OK Zip 73112–9756; tel. 405/949–6066; Bruce Lawrence, President and Chief Executive Officer
(Centralized Physician/Insurance Health System)

OKLAHOMA: INTEGRIS CANADIAN VALLEY HOSPITAL (O, 75 beds) 1201 Health Center Parkway, Yukon, OK Zip 73099–6381; tel. 405/717–6800; Rex Van Meter, President
Web address: www.integris-health.com

INTEGRIS HEALTH EDMOND (O, 40 beds) 4801 Integris Parkway, Edmond, OK Zip 73034–8864; tel. 405/657–3000; Avilla Williams, MS, President

INTEGRIS MIAMI HOSPITAL (O, 84 beds) 200 Second Avenue SW, Miami, OK Zip 74354–6830; tel. 918/542–6611; Jonas Rabel, President
Web address: www.integrisok.com/miami-hospital

INTEGRIS BAPTIST MEDICAL CENTER (O, 662 beds) 3300 NW Expressway, Oklahoma City, OK Zip 73112–4418; tel. 405/949–3011; Timothy J. Johnsen, MS, President
Web address: www.integrisok.com

INTEGRIS BASS BAPTIST HEALTH CENTER (O, 167 beds) 600 South Monroe Street, Enid, OK Zip 73701–7211, P O Box 3168, 73702–3168, tel. 580/233–2300; Edward Herrman, R.N., FACHE, President

INTEGRIS GROVE HOSPITAL (O, 58 beds) 1001 East 18th Street, Grove, OK Zip 74344–2907; tel. 918/786–2243; Chris Hammes, Interim President
Web address: www.integris-health.com

INTEGRIS SOUTHWEST MEDICAL CENTER (O, 303 beds) 4401 South Western, Oklahoma City, OK Zip 73109–3413; tel. 405/636–7000; Jordan Cash, President

LAKESIDE WOMEN'S HOSPITAL (O, 23 beds) 11200 North Portland Avenue, Oklahoma City, OK Zip 73120–5045; tel. 405/936–1500; Kelley Brewer, R.N., MSN, President
Web address: www.lakeside-wh.net

Owned, leased, sponsored:	8 hospitals	1412 beds
Contract-managed:	0 hospitals	0 beds
Totals:	8 hospitals	1412 beds

★**1815: INTERMOUNTAIN HEALTHCARE, INC.** (NP)
36 South State Street, 22nd Floor, Salt Lake City, UT Zip 84111–

1453; tel. 801/442–2000; A. Marc. Harrison, M.D., President and Chief Executive Officer
(Decentralized Health System)

IDAHO: CASSIA REGIONAL MEDICAL CENTER (O, 25 beds) 1501 Hiland Avenue, Burley, ID Zip 83318–2688; tel. 208/678–4444; Ben Smalley, Administrator

UTAH: ALTA VIEW HOSPITAL (O, 69 beds) 9660 South 1300 East, Sandy, UT Zip 84094–3793; tel. 801/501–2600; Blair Kent, Administrator
Web address: www.intermountainhealthcare.org

AMERICAN FORK HOSPITAL (O, 89 beds) 170 North 1100 East, American Fork, UT Zip 84003–2096; tel. 801/855–3300; Jason Wilson, Administrator and Chief Executive Officer
Web address: www.intermountainhealthcare.org

BEAR RIVER VALLEY HOSPITAL (O, 14 beds) 905 North 1000 West, Tremonton, UT Zip 84337–2497; tel. 435/207–4500; James Montgomery, Interim Chief Executive Officer
Web address: www.https://intermountainhealthcare.org/locations/bear-river-valley-hospital/

CEDAR CITY HOSPITAL (O, 48 beds) 1303 North Main Street, Cedar City, UT Zip 84721–9746; tel. 435/868–5000; Eric Packer, Chief Executive Officer

DELTA COMMUNITY MEDICAL CENTER (O, 18 beds) 126 South White Sage Avenue, Delta, UT Zip 84624–8937; tel. 435/864–5591; Lenny Lyons, Administrator
Web address: www.ihc.com

DIXIE REGIONAL MEDICAL CENTER (O, 261 beds) 1380 East Medical Center Drive, Saint George, UT Zip 84790–2123; tel. 435/251–1000; Terri Kane, Chief Executive Officer
Web address: www.intermountainhealthcare.org

FILLMORE COMMUNITY HOSPITAL (O, 19 beds) 674 South Highway 99, Fillmore, UT Zip 84631–5013; tel. 435/743–5591; Lenny Lyons, Administrator
Web address: www.ihc.com

GARFIELD MEMORIAL HOSPITAL (C, 36 beds) 200 North 400 East, Panguitch, UT Zip 84759, P O Box 389, 84759–0389, tel. 435/676–8811; Alberto Vasquez, Administrator

HEBER VALLEY MEDICAL CENTER (O, 19 beds) 1485 South Highway 40, Heber City, UT Zip 84032–3522; tel. 435/654–2500; Shawn Morrow, Administrator
Web address: www.intermountainhealthcare.org

INTERMOUNTAIN MEDICAL CENTER (O, 502 beds) 5121 South Cottonwood Street, Murray, UT Zip 84107–5701; tel. 801/507–7000; Joseph Mott, Chief Executive Officer

LDS HOSPITAL (O, 260 beds) Eighth Avenue and 'C' Street, Salt Lake City, UT Zip 84143–0001; tel. 801/408–1100; Jim Sheets, Chief Executive Officer and Administrator
Web address: www.intermountainhealthcare.org

LOGAN REGIONAL HOSPITAL (O, 139 beds) 1400 North 500 East, Logan, UT Zip 84341–2455; tel. 435/716–1000; Kyle A. Hansen, Chief Executive Officer
Web address: www.loganregionalhospital.org

MCKAY-DEE HOSPITAL (O, 312 beds) 4401 Harrison Boulevard, Ogden, UT Zip 84403–3195; tel. 801/387–2800; Michael A. Clark, Administrator

OREM COMMUNITY HOSPITAL (O, 18 beds) 331 North 400 West, Orem, UT Zip 84057–1999; tel. 801/224–4080; J. Francis. Gibson, Administrator and Chief Executive Officer
Web address: www.intermountainhealthcare.org

PARK CITY HOSPITAL (O, 37 beds) 900 Round Valley Drive, Park City, UT Zip 84060–7552; tel. 435/658–7000; Si William. Hutt, Administrator

PRIMARY CHILDREN'S HOSPITAL (O, 289 beds) 100 North Mario Capecchi Drive, Salt Lake City, UT Zip 84113–1100; tel. 801/662–1000; Katy Welkie MBA, R.N., Chief Executive Officer
Web address: www.intermountainhealthcare.org

RIVERTON HOSPITAL (O, 88 beds) 3741 West 12600 South, Riverton, UT Zip 84065–7215; tel. 801/285–4000; Blair Kent, Administrator

SANPETE VALLEY HOSPITAL (O, 18 beds) 1100 South Medical Drive, Mount Pleasant, UT Zip 84647–2222; tel. 435/462–2441; Aaron C. Wood, Chief Executive Officer and Administrator
Web address: www.intermountainhealthcare.com

SEVIER VALLEY HOSPITAL (O, 29 beds) 1000 North Main Street, Richfield, UT Zip 84701–1857; tel. 435/893–4100; Gary E. Beck, Administrator

Section B

For explanation of codes following names, see page B2.
★ Indicates Type III membership in the American Hospital Association.

THE ORTHOPEDIC SPECIALTY HOSPITAL (O, 40 beds) 5848 South 300 East, Murray, UT Zip 84107–6121; tel. 801/314–4100; Lisa Bagley, Nurse Administrator
Web address: www.intermountainhealthcare.org

UTAH VALLEY HOSPITAL (O, 344 beds) 1034 North 500 West, Provo, UT Zip 84604–3337; tel. 801/357–7850; Steve Smoot, Administrator
Web address: www.utahvalleyregional.org

Owned, leased, sponsored:	21 hospitals	2638 beds
Contract-managed:	1 hospitals	36 beds
Totals:	22 hospitals	2674 beds

★0902:   IOWA SPECIALTY HOSPITALS (NP)
1316 South Main Street, Clarion, IA Zip 50525–2019; tel. 515/532–2811; Steven J. Simonin, Chief Executive Officer
(Independent Hospital System)

IOWA: IOWA SPECIALTY HOSPITAL-BELMOND (C, 22 beds) 403 1st Street SE, Belmond, IA Zip 50421–1201; tel. 641/444–3223; Amy McDaniel, Chief Executive Officer

IOWA SPECIALTY HOSPITAL-CLARION (C, 25 beds) 1316 South Main Street, Clarion, IA Zip 50525–2019; tel. 515/532–2811; Steven J. Simonin, President and Chief Executive Officer
Web address: www.iowaspecialtyhospital.com

Owned, leased, sponsored:	0 hospitals	0 beds
Contract-managed:	2 hospitals	47 beds
Totals:	2 hospitals	47 beds

★7775:   JEFFERSON HEALTH (NP)
111 South 11th Street, Philadelphia, PA Zip 19107–4824; tel. 610/225–6200; Stephen K. Klasko, M.D., President and Chief Executive Officer
(Moderately Centralized Health System)

PENNSYLVANIA: ABINGTON HOSPITAL (O, 618 beds) 1200 Old York Road, Abington, PA Zip 19001–3720; tel. 215/481–2000; Margaret M. McGoldrick, President

ABINGTON-LANSDALE HOSPITAL JEFFERSON HEALTH (O, 127 beds) 100 Medical Campus Drive, Lansdale, PA Zip 19446–1200; tel. 215/368–2100; Gary R. Candia, Ph.D., FACHE, Chief Administrative Officer
Web address: www.abingtonhealth.org/find-a-location/abington-lansdale-hospital/#.V5dyVVL9yk4

ARIA - JEFFERSON HEALTH (O, 464 beds) 10800 Knights Road, Mansion House, Philadelphia, PA Zip 19114–4200; tel. 215/612–4101; Kathleen Kinslow, Ed.D., Chief Executive Officer
Web address: www.ariahealth.org

THOMAS JEFFERSON UNIVERSITY HOSPITALS (O, 886 beds) 111 South 11th Street, Philadelphia, PA Zip 19107–5084; tel. 215/955–6000; Richard Webster, R.N., President

Owned, leased, sponsored:	4 hospitals	2095 beds
Contract-managed:	0 hospitals	0 beds
Totals:	4 hospitals	2095 beds

★8855:   JFK HEALTH (NP)
80 James Street, 2nd Floor, Edison, NJ Zip 08820–3938; tel. 732/632–1503; Raymond F. Fredericks, President and Chief Executive Officer

NEW JERSEY: JFK JOHNSON REHABILITATION INSTITUTE (O, 94 beds) 65 James Street, Edison, NJ Zip 8818; tel. 732/321–7050; Anthony Cuzzola, Vice President and Administrator
Web address: www.njrehab.org

JFK MEDICAL CENTER (O, 345 beds) 65 James Street, Edison, NJ Zip 8818; tel. 732/321–7000; Raymond F. Fredericks, President and CEO

Owned, leased, sponsored:	2 hospitals	439 beds
Contract-managed:	0 hospitals	0 beds
Totals:	2 hospitals	439 beds

★0324:   JOHN MUIR HEALTH (NP)
1400 Treat Boulevard, Walnut Creek, CA Zip 94597–2142; tel. 925/941–2100; Calvin K. Knight, President and Chief Executive Officer
(Centralized Health System)

CALIFORNIA: JOHN MUIR BEHAVIORAL HEALTH CENTER (O, 73 beds) 2740 Grant Street, Concord, CA Zip 94520–2265; tel. 925/674–4100; Cindy Bolter, Chief Nursing and Operations Officer
Web address: www.johnmuirhealth.com

JOHN MUIR MEDICAL CENTER, CONCORD (O, 195 beds) 2540 East Street, Concord, CA Zip 94520–1906; tel. 925/682–8200; Michael S. Thomas, President and Chief Administrative Officer

JOHN MUIR MEDICAL CENTER, WALNUT CREEK (O, 425 beds) 1601 Ygnacio Valley Road, Walnut Creek, CA Zip 94598–3194; tel. 925/939–3000; Jane Willemsen, President and Chief Administrative Officer
Web address: https://www.johnmuirhealth.com/

Owned, leased, sponsored:	3 hospitals	693 beds
Contract-managed:	0 hospitals	0 beds
Totals:	3 hospitals	693 beds

★1015:   JOHNS HOPKINS HEALTH SYSTEM (NP)
733 North Broadway, BRB 104, Baltimore, MD Zip 21205–1832; tel. 410/955–5000; Ronald R. Peterson, President
(Centralized Physician/Insurance Health System)

DISTRICT OF COLUMBIA: SIBLEY MEMORIAL HOSPITAL (O, 158 beds) 5255 Loughboro Road NW, Washington, DC Zip 20016–2633; tel. 202/537–4000; Richard O. Davis, Ph.D., President

FLORIDA: JOHNS HOPKINS ALL CHILDREN'S HOSPITAL (O, 259 beds) 501 6th Avenue South, Saint Petersburg, FL Zip 33701–4634; tel. 727/898–7451; Jonathan M. Ellen, M.D., President
Web address: www.allkids.org

MARYLAND: HOWARD COUNTY GENERAL HOSPITAL (O, 244 beds) 5755 Cedar Lane, Columbia, MD Zip 21044–2999; tel. 410/740–7890; Steven C. Snelgrove, President

JOHNS HOPKINS BAYVIEW MEDICAL CENTER (O, 425 beds) 4940 Eastern Avenue, Baltimore, MD Zip 21224–2780; tel. 410/550–0100; Richard G. Bennett, M.D., President
Web address: www.hopkinsbayview.org

JOHNS HOPKINS HOSPITAL (O, 1004 beds) 733 North Broadway MRB 104, Baltimore, MD Zip 21205–1832; tel. 410/955–5000; Redonda G. Miller, M.D., President

SUBURBAN HOSPITAL (O, 208 beds) 8600 Old Georgetown Road, Bethesda, MD Zip 20814–1497; tel. 301/896–3100; Jacky Schultz, MSN, R.N., President
Web address: www.suburbanhospital.org

Owned, leased, sponsored:	6 hospitals	2298 beds
Contract-managed:	0 hospitals	0 beds
Totals:	6 hospitals	2298 beds

★2105:   KAISER FOUNDATION HOSPITALS (NP)
One Kaiser Plaza, Oakland, CA Zip 94612–3600; tel. 510/271–5910; Bernard J. Tyson, Chairman and Chief Executive Officer
(Decentralized Health System)

CALIFORNIA: KAISER PERMANENTE ANTIOCH MEDICAL CENTER (O, 150 beds) 4501 Sand Creek Road, Antioch, CA Zip 94531–8687; tel. 925/813–6500; Colleen McKeown, Senior Vice President and Area Manager

---

For explanation of codes following names, see page B2.
★ Indicates Type III membership in the American Hospital Association.

KAISER PERMANENTE BALDWIN PARK MEDICAL CENTER (O, 257 beds) 1011 Baldwin Park Boulevard, Baldwin Park, CA Zip 91706–5806; tel. 626/851–1011; Margaret H. Pierce, Executive Director
Web address: www.kp.org

KAISER PERMANENTE DOWNEY MEDICAL CENTER (O, 352 beds) 9333 Imperial Highway, Downey, CA Zip 90242–2812; tel. 562/657–9000; James Branchick, R.N., MS, Senior Vice President and Area Manager
Web address: www.kaiserpermanente.org

KAISER PERMANENTE FONTANA MEDICAL CENTER (O, 490 beds) 9961 Sierra Avenue, Fontana, CA Zip 92335–6794; tel. 909/427–5000; Greg Christian, Executive Director

KAISER PERMANENTE FREMONT MEDICAL CENTER (O, 106 beds) 39400 Paseo Padre Parkway, Fremont, CA Zip 94538–2310; tel. 510/248–3000; Victoria O'Gorman, Administrator
Web address: www.kp.org

KAISER PERMANENTE FRESNO MEDICAL CENTER (O, 169 beds) 7300 North Fresno Street, Fresno, CA Zip 93720–2942; tel. 559/448–4500; Debbie Hemker, Senior Vice President and Area Manager
Web address: www.kaiserpermanente.org

KAISER PERMANENTE LOS ANGELES MEDICAL CENTER (O, 528 beds) 4867 Sunset Boulevard, Los Angeles, CA Zip 90027–5961; tel. 323/783–4011; William N. Grice, Executive Director
Web address: www.kaiserpermanente.org

KAISER PERMANENTE MANTECA MEDICAL CENTER (O, 239 beds) 1777 West Yosemite Avenue, Manteca, CA Zip 95337–5187; tel. 209/825–3700; Corwin N. Harper, Senior Vice President and Area Manager

KAISER PERMANENTE MORENO VALLEY MEDICAL CENTER (O, 75 beds) 27300 Iris Avenue, Moreno Valley, CA Zip 92555–4800; tel. 951/243–0811; Vita M. Willett, Senior Vice President

KAISER PERMANENTE OAKLAND MEDICAL CENTER (O, 267 beds) 3600 Broadway, Oakland, CA Zip 94611–5693; tel. 510/752–1000; Mark Fratzke, R.N., Senior Vice President and Area Manager
Web address: www.kaiserpermanente.org

KAISER PERMANENTE ORANGE COUNTY ANAHEIM MEDICAL CENTER (O, 436 beds) 3440 East La Palma Avenue, Anaheim, CA Zip 92806–2020; tel. 714/644–2000; Mark E. Costa, Executive Director

KAISER PERMANENTE PANORAMA CITY MEDICAL CENTER (O, 194 beds) 13652 Cantara Street, Panorama City, CA Zip 91402–5497; tel. 818/375–2000; Payman Roshan, Senior Vice President and Area Manager
Web address: www.kaiserpermanente.org

KAISER PERMANENTE REDWOOD CITY MEDICAL CENTER (O, 213 beds) 1100 Veterans Boulevard, Redwood City, CA Zip 94063–2087; tel. 650/299–2000; Michelle Gaskill-Hames, R.N., Senior Vice President & Area Manager
Web address: www.kaiserpermanente.org

KAISER PERMANENTE RIVERSIDE MEDICAL CENTER (O, 226 beds) 10800 Magnolia Avenue, Riverside, CA Zip 92505–3000; tel. 951/353–2000; Vita M. Willett, Executive Director

KAISER PERMANENTE ROSEVILLE MEDICAL CENTER (O, 340 beds) 1600 Eureka Road, Roseville, CA Zip 95661–3027; tel. 916/784–4000; Jeffrey A. Collins, M.D., Senior Vice President and Area Manager
Web address: www.kp.org

KAISER PERMANENTE SACRAMENTO MEDICAL CENTER (O, 144 beds) 2025 Morse Avenue, Sacramento, CA Zip 95825–2100; tel. 916/973–5000; Sandy Sharon, Senior Vice President and Area Manager
Web address: www.kp.org

KAISER PERMANENTE SAN DIEGO MEDICAL CENTER (O, 414 beds) 4647 Zion Avenue, San Diego, CA Zip 92120–2507; tel. 619/528–5000; Jane Finley, Senior Vice President & Area Manager
Web address: www.kaiserpermanente.org

KAISER PERMANENTE SAN FRANCISCO MEDICAL CENTER (O, 215 beds) 2425 Geary Boulevard, San Francisco, CA Zip 94115–3358; tel. 415/833–2000; Ronald Groepper, Senior Vice President and Area Manager

KAISER PERMANENTE SAN JOSE MEDICAL CENTER (O, 222 beds) 250 Hospital Parkway, San Jose, CA Zip 95119–1199; tel. 408/972–7000; Irene Chavez, Senior Vice President and Area Manager
Web address: www.kaiserpermanente.org

KAISER PERMANENTE SAN LEANDRO MEDICAL CENTER (O, 264 beds) 2500 Merced Street, San Leandro, CA Zip 94577–4201; tel. 510/454–1000; Thomas S. Hanenburg, Senior Vice President and Area Manager
Web address: www.kaiserpermanente.org

KAISER PERMANENTE SAN RAFAEL MEDICAL CENTER (O, 116 beds) 99 Montecillo Road, San Rafael, CA Zip 94903–3397; tel. 415/444–2000; Judy Coffey, R.N., Senior Vice President and Area Manager

KAISER PERMANENTE SANTA CLARA MEDICAL CENTER (O, 327 beds) 700 Lawrence Expressway, Santa Clara, CA Zip 95051–5173; tel. 408/851–1000; Christopher L. Boyd, Senior Vice President and Area Manager
Web address: www.kaiserpermanente.org

KAISER PERMANENTE SANTA ROSA MEDICAL CENTER (O, 117 beds) 401 Bicentennial Way, Santa Rosa, CA Zip 95403–2192; tel. 707/571–4000; Judy Coffey, R.N., Senior Vice President and Area Manager
Web address: www.kaiserpermanente.org

KAISER PERMANENTE SOUTH BAY MEDICAL CENTER (O, 170 beds) 25825 Vermont Avenue, Harbor City, CA Zip 90710–3599; tel. 310/325–5111; Lesley A. Wille, Executive Director
Web address: www.kaiserpermanente.org

KAISER PERMANENTE SOUTH SACRAMENTO MEDICAL CENTER (O, 181 beds) 6600 Bruceville Road, Sacramento, CA Zip 95823–4691; tel. 916/688–2430; Patricia M. Rodriguez, Senior Vice President and Area Manager

KAISER PERMANENTE SOUTH SAN FRANCISCO (O, 120 beds) 1200 El Camino Real, South San Francisco, CA Zip 94080–3208; tel. 650/742–2000; Ronald Groepper, Senior Vice President and Area Manager
Web address: www.kaiserpermanente.org

KAISER PERMANENTE VACAVILLE MEDICAL CENTER (O, 140 beds) 1 Quality Drive, Vacaville, CA Zip 95688–9494; tel. 707/624–4000; Norair Jemjemian, Senior Vice President and Area Manager

KAISER PERMANENTE VALLEJO MEDICAL CENTER (O, 248 beds) 975 Sereno Drive, Vallejo, CA Zip 94589–2441; tel. 707/651–1000; Corwin N. Harper, Senior Vice President and Area Manager
Web address: www.kaiserpermanente.org

KAISER PERMANENTE WALNUT CREEK MEDICAL CENTER (O, 233 beds) 1425 South Main Street, Walnut Creek, CA Zip 94596–5300; tel. 925/295–4000; Colleen McKeown, Senior Vice President and Area Manager

KAISER PERMANENTE WEST LOS ANGELES MEDICAL CENTER (O, 126 beds) 6041 Cadillac Avenue, Los Angeles, CA Zip 90034–1700; tel. 323/857–2201; Georgina R. Garcia, R.N., Executive Director
Web address: www.kaiserpermanente.org

KAISER PERMANENTE WOODLAND HILLS MEDICAL CENTER (O, 130 beds) 5601 DeSoto Avenue, Woodland Hills, CA Zip 91367–6798; tel. 818/719–2000; Dennis C. Benton, Senior Vice President and Area Manager

HAWAII: KAISER PERMANENTE MEDICAL CENTER (O, 212 beds) 3288 Moanalua Road, Honolulu, HI Zip 96819–1469; tel. 808/432–0000; Ray Hahn, Hospital Administrator
Web address: www.kaiserpermanente.org

KULA HOSPITAL (C, 6 beds) 100 Keokea Place, Kula, HI Zip 96790–7450; tel. 808/878–1221; Kimberly J. Fuson, Interim Regional Administrator

LANAI COMMUNITY HOSPITAL (C, 24 beds) 628 Seventh Street, Lanai City, HI Zip 96763–0650, P O Box 630650, 96763–0650, tel. 808/565–8450; Paul Harper-O'Connor, Interim Administrator
Web address: https://www.mauihealthsystem.org/lanai-hospital/

MAUI MEMORIAL MEDICAL CENTER (C, 213 beds) 221 Mahalani Street, Wailuku, HI Zip 96793–2581; tel. 808/244–9056; Michael Rembis, M.D., Chief Executive Officer

OREGON: KAISER FOUNDATION HOSPITAL WESTSIDE MEDICAL CENTER (O, 122 beds) 2875 NW Stucki Avenue, Hillsboro, OR Zip 97124–5806; tel. 971/310–1000; Brantley Dettmer, Administrator and Chief Operating Officer
Web address: www.kp.org

KAISER SUNNYSIDE MEDICAL CENTER (O, 302 beds) 10180 SE Sunnyside Road, Clackamas, OR Zip 97015–8970; tel. 503/652–2880; Justin N. Evander, Administrator and Chief Operating Officer

Owned, leased, sponsored:	34 hospitals	7845 beds
Contract-managed:	3 hospitals	243 beds
Totals:	37 hospitals	8088 beds

0954: KECK MEDICINE OF USC (NP)
1510 San Pablo Street, Suite 600, Los Angeles, CA Zip 90033–5313; tel. 323/442–8500; Thomas E. Jackiewicz, Senior Vice President and Chief Executive Officer
(Centralized Health System)

For explanation of codes following names, see page B2.
★ Indicates Type III membership in the American Hospital Association.

Section B

CALIFORNIA: KECK HOSPITAL OF USC (O, 401 beds) 1500 San Pablo Street, Los Angeles, CA Zip 90033–5313; tel. 323/442–8500; Rodney B. Hanners, Chief Executive Officer
Web address: www.keckhospitalofusc.org

USC NORRIS COMPREHENSIVE CANCER CENTER (O, 60 beds) 1441 Eastlake Avenue, Los Angeles, CA Zip 90089–0112; tel. 323/865–3000; Rodney B. Hanners, Chief Executive Officer

USC VERDUGO HILLS HOSPITAL (O, 132 beds) 1812 Verdugo Boulevard, Glendale, CA Zip 91208–1409; tel. 818/790–7100; Keith Hobbs, Chief Executive Officer
Web address: www.uscvhh.org

Owned, leased, sponsored:	3 hospitals	593 beds
Contract-managed:	0 hospitals	0 beds
Totals:	3 hospitals	593 beds

★**0258: KETTERING HEALTH NETWORK** (NP)

3965 Southern Boulevard, Dayton, OH Zip 45429–1229; tel. 937/395–8150; Fred M. Manchur, Chief Executive Officer
(Independent Hospital System)

OHIO: FORT HAMILTON HOSPITAL (O, 164 beds) 630 Eaton Avenue, Hamilton, OH Zip 45013–2770; tel. 513/867–2000; Michael Mewhirter, President
Web address: www.khnetwork.org/forthamilton

GRANDVIEW MEDICAL CENTER (O, 282 beds) 405 West Grand Avenue, Dayton, OH Zip 45405–4796; tel. 937/723–3200; Rebecca Lewis, President
Web address: www.ketteringhealth.org/grandview/

GREENE MEMORIAL HOSPITAL (O, 49 beds) 1141 North Monroe Drive, Xenia, OH Zip 45385–1600; tel. 937/352–2000; Rick A. Dodds, President

KETTERING MEDICAL CENTER (O, 396 beds) 3535 Southern Boulevard, Kettering, OH Zip 45429–1221; tel. 937/298–4331; Roy G. Chew, Ph.D., President
Web address: www.ketteringhealth.org/kettering

SOIN MEDICAL CENTER (O, 133 beds) 3535 Pentagon Boulevard, Beavercreek, OH Zip 45431–1705; tel. 937/702–4000; Rick A. Dodds, President
Web address: www.khnetwork.org/soin

SYCAMORE MEDICAL CENTER (O, 202 beds) 4000 Miamisburg-Centerville Road, Miamisburg, OH Zip 45342–7615; tel. 937/866–0551; Walter Sackett, President
Web address: www.khnetwork.org/sycamore

Owned, leased, sponsored:	6 hospitals	1226 beds
Contract-managed:	0 hospitals	0 beds
Totals:	6 hospitals	1226 beds

★**0026: KINDRED HEALTHCARE** (IO)

680 South Fourth Street, Louisville, KY Zip 40202–2412; tel. 502/596–7300; Kent Wallace, Chief Operating Officer
(Independent Hospital System)

CALIFORNIA: KINDRED HOSPITAL RANCHO (O, 55 beds) 10841 White Oak Avenue, Rancho Cucamonga, CA Zip 91730–3811; tel. 909/581–6400; Victor Carrasco, Chief Executive Officer

KINDRED HOSPITAL RIVERSIDE (O, 40 beds) 2224 Medical Center Drive, Perris, CA Zip 92571–2638; tel. 951/436–3535; William Mitchell, Chief Executive Officer and Administrator
Web address: www.khriverside.com

KINDRED HOSPITAL SOUTH BAY (O, 84 beds) 1246 West 155th Street, Gardena, CA Zip 90247–4062; tel. 310/323–5330; Isaac Lin, Chief Executive Officer
Web address: www.khsouthbay.com/

KINDRED HOSPITAL-BALDWIN PARK (C, 91 beds) 14148 Francisquito Avenue, Baldwin Park, CA Zip 91706–6120; tel. 626/388–2700; Fiona Basa-Reyes, Chief Executive Officer

KINDRED HOSPITAL-BREA (O, 48 beds) 875 North Brea Boulevard, Brea, CA Zip 92821–2699; tel. 714/529–6842; Diane Zeoli, Chief Executive Officer
Web address: www.kindredhospitalbrea.com/

KINDRED HOSPITAL-LA MIRADA (O, 216 beds) 14900 East Imperial Highway, La Mirada, CA Zip 90638–2172; tel. 562/944–1900; David Kowalski, Chief Executive Officer

KINDRED HOSPITAL-LOS ANGELES (O, 81 beds) 5525 West Slauson Avenue, Los Angeles, CA Zip 90056–1067; tel. 310/642–0325; Phillip R. Wolfe, Chief Executive Officer
Web address: www.kindredhospitalla.com/

KINDRED HOSPITAL-ONTARIO (O, 91 beds) 550 North Monterey Avenue, Ontario, CA Zip 91764–3399; tel. 909/391–0333; Vincent Trac, Chief Executive Officer
Web address: www.khontario.com/

KINDRED HOSPITAL-SAN DIEGO (O, 70 beds) 1940 El Cajon Boulevard, San Diego, CA Zip 92104–1096; tel. 619/543–4500; Natalie Germuska, R.N., MSN, Market Chief Executive Officer
Web address: www.kindredsandiego.com

KINDRED HOSPITAL-SAN FRANCISCO BAY AREA (O, 99 beds) 2800 Benedict Drive, San Leandro, CA Zip 94577–6840; tel. 510/357–8300; Jacob M. McCarty, Chief Executive Officer

KINDRED HOSPITAL-WESTMINSTER (O, 109 beds) 200 Hospital Circle, Westminster, CA Zip 92683–3910; tel. 714/893–4541; Julie Myers, Chief Executive Officer
Web address: www.khwestminster.com/

COLORADO: KINDRED HOSPITAL DENVER SOUTH (O, 28 beds) 2525 South Downing Street, 3 South, Denver, CO Zip 80210–5817; tel. 303/715–7373; Marc Lemon, Chief Executive Officer
Web address: www.kindreddenversouth.com/

KINDRED HOSPITAL-AURORA (O, 37 beds) 700 Potomac Street 2nd Floor, Aurora, CO Zip 80011–6844; tel. 720/857–8333; Jeanette Williams, Chief Executive Officer

KINDRED HOSPITAL-DENVER (O, 68 beds) 1920 High Street, Denver, CO Zip 80218–1213; tel. 303/320–5871; Janelle Kircher, R.N., MSN, Chief Executive Officer
Web address: www.kh-denver.com

FLORIDA: KINDRED HOSPITAL BAY AREA-TAMPA (O, 73 beds) 4555 South Manhattan Avenue, Tampa, FL Zip 33611–2397; tel. 813/839–6341; Suthanthira M. Ratnasamy, R.N., FACHE, Chief Executive Officer
Web address: www.khtampa.com/

KINDRED HOSPITAL CENTRAL TAMPA (O, 102 beds) 4801 North Howard Avenue, Tampa, FL Zip 33603–1411; tel. 813/874–7575; Ralph Selner, Chief Executive Officer

KINDRED HOSPITAL MELBOURNE (O, 60 beds) 765 West Nasa Boulevard, Melbourne, FL Zip 32901–1815; tel. 321/733–5725; Pamela R. Reed, Chief Executive Officer
Web address: www.khmelbourne.com

KINDRED HOSPITAL NORTH FLORIDA (O, 80 beds) 801 Oak Street, Green Cove Springs, FL Zip 32043–4317; tel. 904/284–9230; Patrick McVey, Chief Executive Officer
Web address: www.khnorthflorida.com

KINDRED HOSPITAL OCALA (O, 31 beds) 1500 SW 1st Avenue, Ocala, FL Zip 34471–6504; tel. 352/369–0513; Merlene Bhoorasingh , Administrator

KINDRED HOSPITAL SOUTH FLORIDA-FORT LAUDERDALE (O, 123 beds) 1516 East Las Olas Boulevard, Fort Lauderdale, FL Zip 33301–2399; tel. 954/764–8900; Michael S. Roffelsen, Chief Executive Officer
Web address: www.khfortlauderdale.com/

KINDRED HOSPITAL THE PALM BEACHES (O, 70 beds) 5555 West Blue Heron Boulevard, Riviera Beach, FL Zip 33418–7813; tel. 561/840–0754; Elayne Lopreato, Chief Executive Officer
Web address: www.khthepalmbeaches.com/

GEORGIA: KINDRED HOSPITAL ROME (O, 45 beds) 304 Turner McCall Boulevard, Rome, GA Zip 30165–5621; tel. 706/378–6800; Al Diaz, M.D., Chief Executive Officer
Web address: www.kindredrome.com

ILLINOIS: KINDRED CHICAGO-CENTRAL HOSPITAL (O, 187 beds) 4058 West Melrose Street, Chicago, IL Zip 60641–4797; tel. 773/736–7000

KINDRED HOSPITAL CHICAGO-NORTHLAKE (O, 94 beds) 365 East North Avenue, Northlake, IL Zip 60164–2628; tel. 708/345–8100; Beverly Foster, Chief Executive Officer
Web address: www.kindrednorthlake.com/

For explanation of codes following names, see page B2.
★ Indicates Type III membership in the American Hospital Association.

KINDRED HOSPITAL PEORIA (O, 50 beds) 500 West Romeo B Garrett Avenue, Peoria, IL Zip 61605–2301; tel. 309/680–1500; Christopher Curry, Chief Executive Officer

KINDRED HOSPITAL-SYCAMORE (O, 69 beds) 225 Edward Street, Sycamore, IL Zip 60178–2137; tel. 815/895–2144; Jim Cohick, Chief Executive Officer
Web address: www.kindredhospitalsyc.com/

INDIANA: KINDRED HOSPITAL INDIANAPOLIS NORTH (O, 45 beds) 8060 Knue Road, Indianapolis, IN Zip 46250–1976; tel. 317/813–8900; Nakia Tremble, Chief Executive Officer
Web address: www.kindredindynorth.com/

KINDRED HOSPITAL INDIANAPOLIS SOUTH (O, 60 beds) 607 Greenwood Springs Drive, Greenwood, IN Zip 46143–6377; tel. 317/888–8155; Matthew Keppler, Market Chief Executive Officer

KINDRED HOSPITAL NORTHWEST INDIANA (O, 70 beds) 5454 Hohman Avenue, 5th Floor, Hammond, IN Zip 46320–1931; tel. 219/937–9900; Frank A. Solare, Chief Executive Officer
Web address: www.khnwindiana.com

KINDRED HOSPITAL OF NORTHERN INDIANA (O, 32 beds) 215 West Fourth Street, Suite 200, Mishawaka, IN Zip 46544–1917; tel. 574/252–2000; Lori Skora, Chief Executive Officer
Web address: www.khnorthernindiana.com/

KINDRED HOSPITAL-INDIANAPOLIS (O, 59 beds) 1700 West 10th Street, Indianapolis, IN Zip 46222–3802; tel. 317/636–4400; Bryan Chatterton, Chief Executive Officer
Web address: www.kindredhospitalindy.com/

KENTUCKY: KINDRED HOSPITAL-LOUISVILLE (O, 117 beds) 1313 Saint Anthony Place, Louisville, KY Zip 40204–1740; tel. 502/587–7001; Jack Nicholson, Chief Executive Officer

MICHIGAN: KINDRED HOSPITAL DETROIT (O, 77 beds) 4777 East Outer Drive, Detroit, MI Zip 48234–3241; tel. 313/369–5800; Mary Hoskins, Chief Executive Officer
Web address: www.kindreddetroit.com/

MISSOURI: KINDRED HOSPITAL KANSAS CITY (O, 55 beds) 8701 Troost Avenue, Kansas City, MO Zip 64131–2767; tel. 816/995–2000; Jason Grundstrom, Interim Chief Executive Officer

KINDRED HOSPITAL NORTHLAND (O, 35 beds) 500 Northwest 68th Street, Kansas City, MO Zip 64118–2455; tel. 816/420–6300; Jason Grundstrom, Chief Executive Officer
Web address: www.khnorthland.com

KINDRED HOSPITAL-ST. LOUIS (O, 98 beds) 4930 Lindell Boulevard, Saint Louis, MO Zip 63108–1510; tel. 314/361–8700; Jan Turk, Interim Administrator
Web address: www.kindredstlouis.com/

MERCY REHABILITATION HOSPITAL ST. LOUIS (O, 90 beds) 14561 North Outer Forty Road, Chesterfield, MO Zip 63017; tel. 314/881–4000; Donna M. Flannery, Chief Executive Officer

NEVADA: KINDRED HOSPITAL LAS VEGAS-SAHARA (O, 238 beds) 102 East Mead Parkway, 3rd Floor, Henderson, NV Zip 89015; tel. 702/871–1418; Doug McCoy, Chief Executive Officer
Web address: www.kindredhospitallvs.com/

NEW JERSEY: KINDRED HOSPITAL-NEW JERSEY MORRIS COUNTY (O, 117 beds) 400 West Blackwell Street, Dover, NJ Zip 07801–2525; tel. 973/537–3818; Michael A. Pizzano, Chief Executive Officer

NEW MEXICO: KINDRED HOSPITAL-ALBUQUERQUE (O, 61 beds) 700 High Street NE, Albuquerque, NM Zip 87102–2565; tel. 505/242–4444; Bud Schawl, Chief Executive Officer
Web address: www.kindredalbuquerque.com/

NORTH CAROLINA: KINDRED HOSPITAL-GREENSBORO (O, 101 beds) 2401 Southside Boulevard, Greensboro, NC Zip 27406–3311; tel. 336/271–2800; Chad Lovett, Chief Executive Officer

OHIO: KINDRED HOSPITAL LIMA (O, 26 beds) 730 West Market Street, 6th Floor, Lima, OH Zip 45801–4602; tel. 419/224–1888; Susan Krinke, Chief Executive Officer
Web address: www.khlima.com

KINDRED HOSPITAL OF CENTRAL OHIO (O, 33 beds) 335 Glessner Avenue, 5th Floor, Mansfield, OH Zip 44903–2269; tel. 419/526–0777; Jeffrey Paul. Weier, Chief Executive Officer

KINDRED HOSPITAL-DAYTON (O, 67 beds) 707 South Edwin C Moses Boulevard, Dayton, OH Zip 45417–3462; tel. 937/222–5963; Phillip Underwood, Chief Executive Officer
Web address: www.khdayton.com

UH AVON REHABILITATION HOSPITAL (O, 50 beds) 37900 Chester Road, Avon, OH Zip 44011–1044; tel. 440/695–7100; Andrew Goldfrach, Chief Executive Officer

UH REHABILITATION HOSPITAL (O, 50 beds) 23333 Harvard Road, Beachwood, OH Zip 44122–6232; tel. 216/593–2200; Mirza Baig, M.D., Medical Director
Web address: www.uhhospitals.org

PENNSYLVANIA: KINDRED HOSPITAL SOUTH PHILADELPHIA (O, 58 beds) 1930 South Broad Street, Philadelphia, PA Zip 19145–2328; tel. 267/570–5200; Michele S. Basile, Chief Executive Officer
Web address: www.khsouthphilly.com

KINDRED HOSPITAL-PHILADELPHIA (O, 52 beds) 6129 Palmetto Street, Philadelphia, PA Zip 19111–5729; tel. 215/722–8555; Michael Bass, Chief Executive Officer

ST. MARY REHABILITATION HOSPITAL (O, 50 beds) 1201 Langhorne Newtown Road, Langhorne, PA Zip 19047–1201, 1208 Langhorne Newtown Road, 19047–1234, tel. 267/560–1111; Lisa Haney, Chief Executive Officer
Web address: www.stmaryhealthcare.org

TENNESSEE: KINDRED HOSPITAL-CHATTANOOGA (O, 39 beds) 709 Walnut Street, Chattanooga, TN Zip 37402–1916; tel. 423/266–7721; Steve Patterson, Chief Executive Officer

TEXAS: KINDRED HOSPITAL CLEAR LAKE (O, 110 beds) 350 Blossom Street, Webster, TX Zip 77598; tel. 281/316–7800; Mary Harbeson, R.N., Chief Executive Officer
Web address: www.khclearlake.com

KINDRED HOSPITAL DALLAS CENTRAL (O, 60 beds) 8050 Meadow Road, Dallas, TX Zip 75231–3406; tel. 469/232–6500; Kyron J. Kooken, MS, Chief Executive Officer

KINDRED HOSPITAL EL PASO (O, 72 beds) 1740 Curie Drive, El Paso, TX Zip 79902–2901; tel. 915/351–9044; America Jones, R.N., Chief Executive Officer
Web address: www.khelpaso.com

KINDRED HOSPITAL HOUSTON MEDICAL CENTER (O, 105 beds) 6441 Main Street, Houston, TX Zip 77030–1596; tel. 713/790–0500; Robert Stein, Chief Executive Officer

KINDRED HOSPITAL SAN ANTONIO CENTRAL (O, 44 beds) 111 Dallas Street, 4th Floor, San Antonio, TX Zip 78205–1201; tel. 210/297–7185; Kristen Lowe, Interim Chief Executive Officer
Web address: www.kindredsanantoniocentral.com/

KINDRED HOSPITAL SUGAR LAND (O, 171 beds) 1550 First Colony Boulevard, Sugar Land, TX Zip 77479–4000; tel. 281/275–6000; John D. Cross, Chief Executive Officer

KINDRED HOSPITAL TARRANT COUNTY-ARLINGTON (O, 55 beds) 1000 North Cooper Street, Arlington, TX Zip 76011–5540; tel. 817/548–3400; Christina Richard, Market Chief Executive Officer
Web address: www.kindredhospitalarl.com/

KINDRED HOSPITAL TOMBALL (O, 258 beds) 505 Graham Drive, Tomball, TX Zip 77375–3368; tel. 281/255–5600; Tracy Kohler, Chief Executive Officer

KINDRED HOSPITAL-DALLAS (O, 50 beds) 9525 Greenville Avenue, Dallas, TX Zip 75243–4116; tel. 214/355–2600; James Mendez, Chief Executive Officer
Web address: www.khdallas.com

KINDRED HOSPITAL-FORT WORTH (O, 64 beds) 815 Eighth Avenue, Fort Worth, TX Zip 76104–2609; tel. 817/332–4812; Anna Rojas, Chief Executive Officer

KINDRED HOSPITAL-HOUSTON NORTHWEST (O, 84 beds) 11297 Fallbrook Drive, Houston, TX Zip 77065–4292; tel. 281/897–8114; Aleen D. Arabit, Chief Executive Officer
Web address: www.khhoustonnw.com/

KINDRED HOSPITAL-MANSFIELD (O, 55 beds) 1802 Highway 157 North, Mansfield, TX Zip 76063–3923; tel. 817/473–6101; Susan Schaetti, Chief Executive Officer
Web address: www.kindredmansfield.com

KINDRED HOSPITAL-SAN ANTONIO (O, 59 beds) 3636 Medical Drive, San Antonio, TX Zip 78229–2183; tel. 210/616–0616; Kristen Lowe, Chief Executive Officer

For explanation of codes following names, see page B2.
★ Indicates Type III membership in the American Hospital Association.

Section B

KINDRED HOSPITAL-WHITE ROCK (O, 25 beds) 9440 Poppy Drive, 5th Floor, Dallas, TX Zip 75218–3652; tel. 214/324–6562; Kelly Bailey, Chief Executive Officer and Administrator
Web address: www.khwhiterock.com

TEXAS REHABILITATION HOSPITAL OF FORT WORTH (O, 66 beds) 425 Alabama Avenue, Fort Worth, TX Zip 76104–1022; tel. 817/820–3400; Russell Bailey, Chief Executive Officer
Web address: www.texasrehabhospital.com/

WASHINGTON: KINDRED HOSPITAL SEATTLE-NORTHGATE (O, 80 beds) 10631 8th Avenue NE, Seattle, WA Zip 98125–7213; tel. 206/364–2050; Jean Clark, Administrator

WISCONSIN: REHABILITATION HOSPITAL OF WISCONSIN (O, 40 beds) 1625 Coldwater Creek Drive, Waukesha, WI Zip 53188–8028; tel. 262/521–8800; Linda Newberry-Ferguson, Chief Executive Officer
Web address: www.rehabhospitalwi.com

Owned, leased, sponsored:	66 hospitals	5088 beds
Contract-managed:	1 hospitals	91 beds
Totals:	67 hospitals	5179 beds

0333: KPC HEALTHCARE, INC. (IO)
1301 North Tustin Avenue, Santa Ana, CA Zip 92705–8619; tel. 714/953–3652; Suzanne Richards, R.N., M.P.H., FACHE, Chief Executive Officer
(Independent Hospital System)

CALIFORNIA: ANAHEIM GLOBAL MEDICAL CENTER (O, 188 beds) 1025 South Anaheim Boulevard, Anaheim, CA Zip 92805–5806; tel. 714/533–6220; Scott Rifkin, Chief Executive Officer

CHAPMAN GLOBAL MEDICAL CENTER (O, 100 beds) 2601 East Chapman Avenue, Orange, CA Zip 92869–3296; tel. 714/633–0011; Ronald J. Galonsky Jr, Chief Executive Officer
Web address: www.Chapman-GMC.com

ORANGE COUNTY GLOBAL MEDICAL CENTER, INC. (O, 282 beds) 1001 North Tustin Avenue, Santa Ana, CA Zip 92705–3577; tel. 714/953–3500; Suzanne Richards, Chief Executive Officer
Web address: www.orangecounty-gmc.com

SOUTH COAST GLOBAL MEDICAL CENTER (O, 178 beds) 2701 South Bristol Street, Santa Ana, CA Zip 92704–6278; tel. 714/754–5454; Ronald J. Galonsky Jr, Chief Executive Officer

Owned, leased, sponsored:	4 hospitals	748 beds
Contract-managed:	0 hospitals	0 beds
Totals:	4 hospitals	748 beds

0911: LAFAYETTE GENERAL HEALTH (NP)
920 West Pinhook Road, Lafayette, LA Zip 70503–2455; tel. 337/289–7991; David L. Callecod, President and Chief Executive Officer
(Independent Hospital System)

LOUISIANA: ABROM KAPLAN MEMORIAL HOSPITAL (C, 35 beds) 1310 West Seventh Street, Kaplan, LA Zip 70548–2910; tel. 337/643–8300; Bryce Quebodeaux, Chief Executive Officer
Web address: www.lafayettegeneral.com

ACADIA GENERAL HOSPITAL (C, 140 beds) 1305 Crowley Rayne Highway, Crowley, LA Zip 70526–8202; tel. 337/783–3222; Joe J. Mitchell, Chief Executive Officer

LAFAYETTE GENERAL MEDICAL CENTER (O, 455 beds) 1214 Coolidge Avenue, Lafayette, LA Zip 70503–2696, P O Box 52009 OCS, 70505–2009, tel. 337/289–7991; Patrick W. Gandy Jr, CPA, Executive Vice President and Chief Executive Officer
Web address: www.lafayettegeneral.com

LAFAYETTE GENERAL SURGICAL HOSPITAL (C, 10 beds) 1000 West Pinhook Road, Lafayette, LA Zip 70503–2460; tel. 337/289–8088; Kimberly H. Dooley, Administrator
Web address: www.lafayettegeneral.com/our_facilities/main_facilities/lafayette_general_surgical_hospital.aspx

ST. MARTIN HOSPITAL (C, 25 beds) 210 Champagne Boulevard, Breaux Bridge, LA Zip 70517–3700, P O Box 357, 70517–0357, tel. 337/332–2178; Karen O. Wyble, R.N., Chief Executive Officer
Web address: www.stmartinhospital.org

UNIVERSITY HOSPITAL AND CLINICS (L, 105 beds) 2390 West Congress Street, Lafayette, LA Zip 70506–4298; tel. 337/261–6000; Katherine D. Hebert, Chief Executive Officer
Web address: www.lafayettegeneral.com

Owned, leased, sponsored:	2 hospitals	560 beds
Contract-managed:	4 hospitals	210 beds
Totals:	6 hospitals	770 beds

★0891: LAHEY HEALTH (NP)
41 Mall Road, Burlington, MA Zip 01805–0001; tel. 781/744–7100; Howard R. Grant, JD, M.D., President and Chief Executive Officer
(Centralized Physician/Insurance Health System)

MASSACHUSETTS: BEVERLY HOSPITAL (O, 320 beds) 85 Herrick Street, Beverly, MA Zip 01915–1777; tel. 978/922–3000; Philip M. Cormier, Chief Executive Officer

LAHEY HOSPITAL & MEDICAL CENTER, BURLINGTON (O, 345 beds) 41 Mall Road, Burlington, MA Zip 01805–0001; tel. 781/744–5100; Howard R. Grant, JD, M.D., Chief Executive Officer
Web address: www.lahey.org

WINCHESTER HOSPITAL (O, 197 beds) 41 Highland Avenue, Winchester, MA Zip 01890–1496; tel. 781/729–9000; Dale M. Lodge, Chief Executive Officer

Owned, leased, sponsored:	3 hospitals	862 beds
Contract-managed:	0 hospitals	0 beds
Totals:	3 hospitals	862 beds

★0056: LAKELAND HEALTH (NP)
1234 Napier Avenue, Saint Joseph, MI Zip 49085–2158; tel. 269/983–8300; Loren Hamel, M.D., President and Chief Executive Officer
(Independent Hospital System)

MICHIGAN: LAKELAND HOSPITAL, WATERVLIET (O, 38 beds) 400 Medical Park Drive, Watervliet, MI Zip 49098–9225; tel. 269/463–3111; Ray Cruse, Chief Executive Officer

LAKELAND MEDICAL CENTER, ST. JOSEPH (O, 303 beds) 1234 Napier Avenue, Saint Joseph, MI Zip 49085–2158; tel. 269/983–8300; Loren Hamel, M.D., President and Chief Executive Officer
Web address: www.lakelandhealth.org

Owned, leased, sponsored:	2 hospitals	341 beds
Contract-managed:	0 hospitals	0 beds
Totals:	2 hospitals	341 beds

0393: LANDMARK HOSPITALS (IO)
3255 Independence Street, Cape Girardeau, MO Zip 63701–4914; tel. 573/335–1091; William K. Kapp III, M.D., President and Chief Executive Officer
(Independent Hospital System)

FLORIDA: LANDMARK HOSPITAL OF SOUTHWEST FLORIDA (O, 50 beds) 1285 Creekside Boulevard East, Naples, FL Zip 34108; tel. 239/529–1800; Jimmy Dascani, Chief Executive Officer
Web address: www.landmarkhospitals.com/naples.aspx

GEORGIA: LANDMARK HOSPITAL OF ATHENS (O, 42 beds) 775 Sunset Drive, Athens, GA Zip 30606–2211; tel. 706/425–1500; Vivian Goff, R.N., Chief Executive Officer
Web address: www.landmarkhospitals.com

LANDMARK HOSPITAL OF SAVANNAH (O, 50 beds) 800 East 68th Street, Savannah, GA Zip 31405–4710; tel. 912/298–1000; John Salandi, Chief Executive Officer

For explanation of codes following names, see page B2.
★ Indicates Type III membership in the American Hospital Association.

Section B

MISSOURI: LANDMARK HOSPITAL OF CAPE GIRARDEAU (O, 30 beds) 3255 Independence Street, Cape Girardeau, MO Zip 63701–4914; tel. 573/335–1091; Donna Mansard, Chief Executive Officer
Web address: www.landmarkhospitals.com

LANDMARK HOSPITAL OF COLUMBIA (O, 42 beds) 604 Old 63 North, Columbia, MO Zip 65201–6308; tel. 573/499–6600; Jerry Deller, Chief Executive Officer

LANDMARK HOSPITAL OF JOPLIN (O, 30 beds) 2040 West 32nd Street, Joplin, MO Zip 64804–3512; tel. 417/627–1300; Kevin J. Clement, Chief Executive Officer
Web address: www.landmarkhospitals.com

UTAH: LANDMARK HOSPITAL OF SALT LAKE CITY (O, 38 beds) 4252 South Birkhill Boulevard, Murray, UT Zip 84107–5715; tel. 801/268–5400; Ted Paarlberg, Chief Executive Officer
Web address: www.landmarkhospitals.com/utah.aspx

Owned, leased, sponsored:	7 hospitals	282 beds
Contract-managed:	0 hospitals	0 beds
Totals:	7 hospitals	282 beds

0932: LCMC HEALTH (NP)
200 Henry Clay Avenue, New Orleans, LA Zip 70118–5720; tel. 504/899–9511; Greg Feirn, CPA, President and Chief Executive Officer
(Moderately Centralized Health System)

LOUISIANA: CHILDREN'S HOSPITAL (O, 283 beds) 200 Henry Clay Avenue, New Orleans, LA Zip 70118–5720; tel. 504/899–9511; Mary R. Perrin, President and Chief Executive Officer

NEW ORLEANS EAST HOSPITAL (C, 34 beds) 5620 Read Boulevard, New Orleans, LA Zip 70127–3106, 5620 Read Blvd, 70127–3106, tel. 504/592–6600; Takeisha C. Davis, M.D., M.P.H., President and Chief Executive Officer
Web address: www.noehospital.org

TOURO INFIRMARY (O, 280 beds) 1401 Foucher Street, New Orleans, LA Zip 70115–3593; tel. 504/897–7011; Susan E. Andrews, Chief Executive Officer
Web address: www.touro.com

UNIVERSITY MEDICAL CENTER (O, 272 beds) 2000 Canal Street, New Orleans, LA Zip 70112–3018; tel. 504/903–3000; William J. Masterton, President and Chief Executive Officer

WEST JEFFERSON MEDICAL CENTER (C, 243 beds) 1101 Medical Center Boulevard, Marrero, LA Zip 70072–3191; tel. 504/347–5511; Nancy R. Cassagne, FACHE, Chief Executive Officer
Web address: www.wjmc.org

Owned, leased, sponsored:	3 hospitals	835 beds
Contract-managed:	2 hospitals	277 beds
Totals:	5 hospitals	1112 beds

★0369: LEE HEALTH (NP)
2776 Cleveland Avenue, Fort Myers, FL Zip 33901–5856, P O Box 2218, 33902–2218, tel. 239/343–2000; Lawrence Antonucci, M.D., President and Chief Executive Officer
(Moderately Centralized Health System)

FLORIDA: CAPE CORAL HOSPITAL (O, 291 beds) 636 Del Prado Boulevard, Cape Coral, FL Zip 33990–2695; tel. 239/424–2000; Lawrence Antonucci, M.D., Chief Executive Officer
Web address: www.leememorial.org

GULF COAST MEDICAL CENTER (O, 356 beds) 13681 Doctor's Way, Fort Myers, FL Zip 33912–4300; tel. 239/343–1000; Lawrence Antonucci, M.D., President and Chief Executive Officer
Web address: www.leememorial.org

LEE MEMORIAL HOSPITAL (O, 779 beds) 2776 Cleveland Avenue, Fort Myers, FL Zip 33901–5855, P O Box 2218, 33902–2218, tel. 239/343–2000; James R. Nathan, President and Chief Executive Officer

Owned, leased, sponsored:	3 hospitals	1426 beds
Contract-managed:	0 hospitals	0 beds
Totals:	3 hospitals	1426 beds

★2755: LEGACY HEALTH (NP)
1919 NW Lovejoy Street, Portland, OR Zip 97209–1503; tel. 503/415–5600; George J. Brown, M.D., President and Chief Executive Officer
(Centralized Health System)

OREGON: LEGACY EMANUEL MEDICAL CENTER (O, 427 beds) 2801 North Gantenbein Avenue, Portland, OR Zip 97227–1674; tel. 503/413–2200; Lori Morgan, M.D., Chief Administrative Officer
Web address: www.legacyhealth.org

LEGACY GOOD SAMARITAN MEDICAL CENTER (O, 239 beds) 1015 NW 22nd Avenue, Portland, OR Zip 97210–3099; tel. 503/413–7711; Jonathan Avery, Chief Administrative Officer
Web address: www.legacyhealth.org

LEGACY MERIDIAN PARK MEDICAL CENTER (O, 130 beds) 19300 SW 65th Avenue, Tualatin, OR Zip 97062–9741; tel. 503/692–1212; Allyson Anderson, President

LEGACY MOUNT HOOD MEDICAL CENTER (O, 94 beds) 24800 SE Stark, Gresham, OR Zip 97030–3378; tel. 503/667–1122; Gretchen Nichols, R.N., President
Web address: www.legacyhealth.org

LEGACY SILVERTON MEDICAL CENTER (O, 48 beds) 342 Fairview Street, Silverton, OR Zip 97381–1993; tel. 503/873–1500; Sarah Fronza, President
Web address: www.silvertonhealth.org

WASHINGTON: LEGACY SALMON CREEK MEDICAL CENTER (O, 215 beds) 2211 NE 139th Street, Vancouver, WA Zip 98686–2742; tel. 360/487–1000; Bryce R. Helgerson, Chief Administrative Officer
Web address: www.legacyhealth.org

Owned, leased, sponsored:	6 hospitals	1153 beds
Contract-managed:	0 hospitals	0 beds
Totals:	6 hospitals	1153 beds

★0370: LEHIGH VALLEY HEALTH NETWORK (NP)
1200 South Cedar Crest Boulevard, Allentown, PA Zip 18103–6202, P O Box 689, 18105–1556, tel. 610/402–8000; Brian A. Nester, D.O., President and Chief Executive Officer
(Centralized Health System)

PENNSYLVANIA: LEHIGH VALLEY HOSPITAL - HAZLETON (O, 120 beds) 700 East Broad Street, Hazleton, PA Zip 18201–6897; tel. 570/501–4000; John R. Fletcher, President
Web address: www.lvhn.org/hazleton/

LEHIGH VALLEY HOSPITAL - POCONO (O, 239 beds) 206 East Brown Street, East Stroudsburg, PA Zip 18301–3006; tel. 570/421–4000; Elizabeth Wise, President and Chief Executive Officer
Web address: www.pmchealthsystem.org

LEHIGH VALLEY HOSPITAL - SCHUYLKILL EAST NORWEGIAN STREET (O, 109 beds) 700 East Norwegian Street, Pottsville, PA Zip 17901–2710; tel. 570/621–4000; William Reppy, President
Web address: www.schuylkillhealth.com

LEHIGH VALLEY HOSPITAL - SCHUYLKILL SOUTH JACKSON STREET (O, 179 beds) 420 South Jackson Street, Pottsville, PA Zip 17901–3625; tel. 570/621–5000; William Reppy, President

LEHIGH VALLEY HOSPITAL-MUHLENBERG (O, 158 beds) 2545 Schoenersville Road, Bethlehem, PA Zip 18017–7300; tel. 484/884–2200; Brian A. Nester, D.O., President and Chief Executive Officer
Web address: www.lvhn.org

For explanation of codes following names, see page B2.
★ Indicates Type III membership in the American Hospital Association.

LEHIGH VALLEY HOSPITAL (O, 877 beds) 1200 South Cedar Crest Boulevard, Allentown, PA Zip 18103–6248, P O Box 689, 18105–1556, tel. 610/402–8000; Brian A. Nester, D.O., President and Chief Executive Officer

Owned, leased, sponsored:	6 hospitals	1682 beds
Contract-managed:	0 hospitals	0 beds
Totals:	6 hospitals	1682 beds

0632: LHC GROUP (IO)
420 West Pinhook Road, Lafayette, LA Zip 70503–2131; tel. 337/233–1307; Keith G. Myers, Chairman and Chief Executive Officer

LOUISIANA: LOUISIANA EXTENDED CARE HOSPITAL WEST MONROE (O, 18 beds) 503 McMillan Road, 3rd Floor, West Monroe, LA Zip 71291–5327; tel. 318/329–4378; Cleta Munholland, Administrator

LOUISIANA EXTENDED CARE HOSPITAL OF LAFAYETTE (O, 42 beds) 1214 Coolidge Boulevard, Floors 9 & 10, Lafayette, LA Zip 70503–2621; tel. 337/289–8180; Kevin Frank, Administrator
Web address: www.lhcgroup.com

LOUISIANA EXTENDED CARE HOSPITAL OF NATCHITOCHES (O, 21 beds) 501 Keyser Avenue, Natchitoches, LA Zip 71457–6018; tel. 318/354–2044; John Rivoire, R.N., MSN, Administrator

OCHSNER EXTENDED CARE HOSPITAL OF KENNER (O, 32 beds) 180 West Esplanade Avenue, 5th Floor, Kenner, LA Zip 70065–2467; tel. 504/464–8658; Frederick Nelson, Administrator
Web address: www.lhcgroup.com/

SPECIALTY HOSPITAL (O, 32 beds) 309 Jackson Street, 7th Floor, Monroe, LA Zip 71201–7407, P O Box 1532, 71210–1532, tel. 318/966–7045; Cleta Munholland, Administrator

ST. LANDRY EXTENDED CARE HOSPITAL (O, 41 beds) 3983 1–49 South Service Road, 2nd Floor, Opelousas, LA Zip 70570; tel. 337/948–2251; Biff David, R.N., Administrator
Web address: www.lhcgroup.com

Owned, leased, sponsored:	6 hospitals	186 beds
Contract-managed:	0 hospitals	0 beds
Totals:	6 hospitals	186 beds

0158: LIFEBRIDGE HEALTH (NP)
2401 West Belvedere Avenue, Baltimore, MD Zip 21215–5216; tel. 410/601–5134; Neil M. Meltzer, President and Chief Executive Officer
(Independent Hospital System)

MARYLAND: CARROLL HOSPITAL CENTER (O, 143 beds) 200 Memorial Avenue, Westminster, MD Zip 21157–5799; tel. 410/848–3000; Leslie Simmons, FACHE, R.N., President
Web address: www.carrollhospitalcenter.org

LEVINDALE HEBREW GERIATRIC CENTER AND HOSPITAL (O, 490 beds) 2434 West Belvedere Avenue, Baltimore, MD Zip 21215–5267; tel. 410/601–2400; Idriz Limaj, Chief Operating Officer and Executive Director

NORTHWEST HOSPITAL (O, 253 beds) 5401 Old Court Road, Randallstown, MD Zip 21133–5185; tel. 410/521–2200; Brian M. White, President
Web address: www.lifebridgehealth.org

SINAI HOSPITAL OF BALTIMORE (O, 477 beds) 2401 West Belvedere Avenue, Baltimore, MD Zip 21215–5271; tel. 410/601–9000; Jonathan Ringo, M.D., President and Chief Operating Officer

Owned, leased, sponsored:	4 hospitals	1363 beds
Contract-managed:	0 hospitals	0 beds
Totals:	4 hospitals	1363 beds

★0191: LIFECARE MANAGEMENT SERVICES (IO)
5340 Legacy Drive, Suite 150, Plano, TX Zip 75024–3131; tel. 469/241–2100; James E. Murray, Chief Executive Officer
(Independent Hospital System)

COLORADO: COLORADO ACUTE LONG TERM HOSPITAL (O, 63 beds) 1690 North Meade Street, Denver, CO Zip 80204–1552; tel. 303/264–6900; Craig Bailey, MS, Chief Executive Officer and Administrator
Web address: www.lifecare-hospitals.com/hospital/colorado

FLORIDA: COMPLEX CARE HOSPITAL AT RIDGELAKE (O, 40 beds) 6150 Edgelake Drive, Sarasota, FL Zip 34240–8803; tel. 941/342–3000; Robert E. Mallicoat, Chief Executive Officer

LOUISIANA: LIFECARE HOSPITALS OF SHREVEPORT (O, 119 beds) 9320 Linwood Avenue, Shreveport, LA Zip 71106–7003; tel. 318/688–8504; Brent Martin, Administrator
Web address: www.lifecare-hospitals.com

NEVADA: COMPLEX CARE HOSPITAL AT TENAYA (O, 70 beds) 2500 North Tenaya, Las Vegas, NV Zip 89128–0482; tel. 702/562–2021; Matt Archer, Chief Executive Officer
Web address: www.lifecare-hospitals.com

TAHOE PACIFIC HOSPITALS (O, 60 beds) 2375 East Prater Way, Sparks, NV Zip 89434; tel. 775/355–5600; Matt Archer, Chief Executive Officer

NORTH CAROLINA: LIFECARE HOSPITALS OF NORTH CAROLINA (O, 41 beds) 1051 Noell Lane, Rocky Mount, NC Zip 27804–1761; tel. 252/451–2300; Robyn Perkerson, R.N., Administrator
Web address: www.lifecare-hospitals.com

OHIO: LIFECARE HOSPITAL OF DAYTON (O, 44 beds) 4000 Miamisburg-Centerville Road, Miamisburg, OH Zip 45342–7615; tel. 937/384–8300; William Bryant, Chief Executive Officer

PENNSYLVANIA: LIFECARE HOSPITALS OF CHESTER COUNTY (O, 39 beds) 400 East Marshall Street, West Chester, PA Zip 19380–5412; tel. 484/826–0400; Janet Biedron, R.N., Chief Executive Officer
Web address: www.lifecare-hospitals.com

LIFECARE HOSPITALS OF MECHANICSBURG (O, 68 beds) 4950 Wilson Lane, Mechanicsburg, PA Zip 17055–4442; tel. 717/697–7706; Mary Ellen Kable, Chief Executive Officer

LIFECARE HOSPITALS OF PITTSBURGH (O, 236 beds) 225 Penn Avenue, Pittsburgh, PA Zip 15221–2148; tel. 412/247–2424; Trisha Niemuth, Market Chief Executive Officer
Web address: www.lifecare-hospitals.com

TEXAS: LIFECARE HOSPITALS OF DALLAS (O, 60 beds) 1950 Record Crossing Road, Dallas, TX Zip 75235–6223; tel. 214/640–9600; Christy Carver, R.N., Chief Executive Officer

LIFECARE HOSPITALS OF SAN ANTONIO (O, 62 beds) 8902 Floyd Curl Drive, San Antonio, TX Zip 78240–1681; tel. 210/690–7000; Michelle Lozano, Chief Executive Officer
Web address: www.lifecare-hospitals.com

WISCONSIN: LIFECARE HOSPITALS OF WISCONSIN (O, 24 beds) 2400 Golf Road, Pewaukee, WI Zip 53072–5590; tel. 262/524–2600; David Chaudier, Chief Executive Officer

Owned, leased, sponsored:	13 hospitals	926 beds
Contract-managed:	0 hospitals	0 beds
Totals:	13 hospitals	926 beds

★0180: LIFEPOINT HEALTH (IO)
330 Seven Springs Way, Brentwood, TN Zip 37027–4536; tel. 615/920–7000; William F. Carpenter III, Chairman and Chief Executive Officer
(Decentralized Health System)

ALABAMA: ANDALUSIA HEALTH (O, 88 beds) 849 South Three Notch Street, Andalusia, AL Zip 36420–5325, P O Box 760, 36420–1214, tel. 334/222–8466; John C. Yanes, Chief Executive Officer
Web address: www.andalusiahealth.com

VAUGHAN REGIONAL MEDICAL CENTER (O, 149 beds) 1015 Medical Center Parkway, Selma, AL Zip 36701–6352; tel. 334/418–4100; J. David. McCormack, Chief Executive Officer
Web address: www.vaughanregional.com

For explanation of codes following names, see page B2.
★ Indicates Type III membership in the American Hospital Association.

ARIZONA: HAVASU REGIONAL MEDICAL CENTER (O, 162 beds) 101 Civic Center Lane, Lake Havasu City, AZ Zip 86403–5683; tel. 928/855–8185; Michael N. Patterson, Chief Executive Officer
Web address: www.havasuregional.com

VALLEY VIEW MEDICAL CENTER (O, 90 beds) 5330 South Highway 95, Fort Mohave, AZ Zip 86426–9225; tel. 928/788–2273; Feliciano Jiron, Chief Executive Officer

COLORADO: COLORADO PLAINS MEDICAL CENTER (L, 50 beds) 1000 Lincoln Street, Fort Morgan, CO Zip 80701–3298; tel. 970/867–3391; Gene L. O'Hara, Chief Executive Officer
Web address: www.coloradoplainsmedicalcenter.com

GEORGIA: ROCKDALE MEDICAL CENTER (O, 158 beds) 1412 Milstead Avenue NE, Conyers, GA Zip 30012–3877; tel. 770/918–3000; Alan E. George, Chief Executive Officer
Web address: www.rockdalemedicalcenter.org

ST. FRANCIS HOSPITAL (O, 331 beds) 2122 Manchester Expressway, Columbus, GA Zip 31904–6878, P O Box 7000, 31908–7000, tel. 706/596–4000; Danny L. Jones Jr, FACHE, Chief Executive Officer

INDIANA: CLARK MEMORIAL HOSPITAL (O, 178 beds) 1220 Missouri Avenue, Jeffersonville, IN Zip 47130–3743, P O Box 69, 47131–0600, tel. 812/282–6631; Martin Padgett, President and Chief Executive Officer
Web address: www.clarkmemorial.org

SCOTT MEMORIAL HOSPITAL (O, 25 beds) 1415 North Gardner Street, Scottsburg, IN Zip 47170, Box 430, 47170–0430, tel. 812/752–3456; Michael Everett, Chief Executive Officer

KANSAS: WESTERN PLAINS MEDICAL COMPLEX (O, 45 beds) 3001 Avenue 'A', Dodge City, KS Zip 67801–6508, P O Box 1478, 67801–1478, tel. 620/225–8400; Kerry Tirman, JD, FACHE, Chief Executive Officer
Web address: www.westernplainsmc.com

KENTUCKY: BLUEGRASS COMMUNITY HOSPITAL (O, 17 beds) 360 Amsden Avenue, Versailles, KY Zip 40383–1286; tel. 859/873–3111; Tommy Haggard, Chief Executive Officer

BOURBON COMMUNITY HOSPITAL (O, 58 beds) 9 Linville Drive, Paris, KY Zip 40361–2196; tel. 859/987–3600; Matt Smith, Interim Chief Executive Officer
Web address: www.bourbonhospital.com

CLARK REGIONAL MEDICAL CENTER (O, 79 beds) 175 Hospital Drive, Winchester, KY Zip 40391–9591; tel. 859/745–3500; Robert Parker, Chief Executive Officer and Market President

FLEMING COUNTY HOSPITAL (O, 52 beds) 55 Foundation Drive, Flemingsburg, KY Zip 41041–9815, P O Box 388, 41041–0388, tel. 606/849–5000; Brian Springate, Chief Executive Officer
Web address: www.flemingcountyhospital.org

GEORGETOWN COMMUNITY HOSPITAL (O, 58 beds) 1140 Lexington Road, Georgetown, KY Zip 40324–9362; tel. 502/868–1100; William Haugh, Administrator
Web address: www.georgetowncommunityhospital.com

JACKSON PURCHASE MEDICAL CENTER (O, 227 beds) 1099 Medical Center Circle, Mayfield, KY Zip 42066–1159; tel. 270/251–4100; David Anderson, Chief Executive Officer
Web address: www.jacksonpurchase.com

LAKE CUMBERLAND REGIONAL HOSPITAL (O, 295 beds) 305 Langdon Street, Somerset, KY Zip 42503–2750, P O Box 620, 42502–0620, tel. 606/679–7441; Timothy A. Bess, Chief Executive Officer

LOGAN MEMORIAL HOSPITAL (O, 53 beds) 1625 South Nashville Road, Russellville, KY Zip 42276–8834, P O Box 10, 42276–0010, tel. 270/726–4011; James Bills, Chief Executive Officer
Web address: www.loganmemorial.com

MEADOWVIEW REGIONAL MEDICAL CENTER (O, 101 beds) 989 Medical Park Drive, Maysville, KY Zip 41056–8750; tel. 606/759–5311; Joseph G. Koch, Chief Executive Officer

SPRING VIEW HOSPITAL (O, 60 beds) 320 Loretto Road, Lebanon, KY Zip 40033–1300; tel. 270/692–3161; Timothy R. Trottier, Chief Executive Officer
Web address: www.springviewhospital.com

LOUISIANA: MERCY REGIONAL MEDICAL CENTER (O, 109 beds) 800 East Main Street, Ville Platte, LA Zip 70586–4618; tel. 337/363–5684; Scott M. Smith, Chief Executive Officer
Web address: www.mercyregionalmedicalcenter.com

MINDEN MEDICAL CENTER (O, 161 beds) 1 Medical Plaza, Minden, LA Zip 71055–3330, P O Box 5003, 71058–5003, tel. 318/377–2321; Gregory Pearson, Chief Executive Officer

TECHE REGIONAL MEDICAL CENTER (L, 164 beds) 1125 Marguerite Street, Morgan City, LA Zip 70380–1855, P O Box 2308, 70381–2308, tel. 985/384–2200; Jerry Dooley, Interim Chief Executive Officer
Web address: www.techeregional.com

MICHIGAN: UP HEALTH SYSTEM-BELL (O, 25 beds) 901 Lakeshore Drive, Ishpeming, MI Zip 49849–1367; tel. 906/486–4431; Mitchell D. Leckelt, Chief Executive Officer
Web address: www.bellhospital.org

UP HEALTH SYSTEM-PORTAGE (O, 96 beds) 500 Campus Drive, Hancock, MI Zip 49930–1569; tel. 906/483–1000; Jeff Lang, President
Web address: www.portagehealth.org

MISSISSIPPI: BOLIVAR MEDICAL CENTER (L, 129 beds) 901 East Sunflower Road, Cleveland, MS Zip 38732–2833, P O Box 1380, 38732–1380, tel. 662/846–0061; Robert L. Marshall Jr, FACHE, Chief Executive Officer

NEVADA: NORTHEASTERN NEVADA REGIONAL HOSPITAL (O, 50 beds) 2001 Errecart Boulevard, Elko, NV Zip 89801–8333; tel. 775/738–5151; Richard L. Palagi, Chief Executive Officer
Web address: www.nnrhospital.com

NEW MEXICO: LOS ALAMOS MEDICAL CENTER (O, 29 beds) 3917 West Road, Los Alamos, NM Zip 87544–2293; tel. 505/661–9500; John Whiteside, Chief Executive Officer

MEMORIAL MEDICAL CENTER (L, 173 beds) 2450 South Telshor Boulevard, Las Cruces, NM Zip 88011–5076; tel. 575/522–8641; John Harris, Chief Executive Officer
Web address: www.mmclc.org

PENNSYLVANIA: CONEMAUGH NASON MEDICAL CENTER (O, 45 beds) 105 Nason Drive, Roaring Spring, PA Zip 16673–1202; tel. 814/224–2141; Timothy Harclerode, Chief Executive Officer
Web address: www.nasonhospital.com

SOUTH CAROLINA: PROVIDENCE HOSPITAL (O, 247 beds) 2435 Forest Drive, Columbia, SC Zip 29204–2098; tel. 803/865–4500; Scott Campbell, Market Chief Executive Officer
Web address: www.sistersofcharityhealth.org/health-care/providence-hospitals/

TENNESSEE: LIVINGSTON REGIONAL HOSPITAL (O, 82 beds) 315 Oak Street, Livingston, TN Zip 38570–1728, P O Box 550, 38570–0550, tel. 931/823–5611; Timothy W. McGill, Chief Executive Officer
Web address: www.MyLivingstonHospital.com

RIVERVIEW REGIONAL MEDICAL CENTER (O, 35 beds) 158 Hospital Drive, Carthage, TN Zip 37030–1096; tel. 615/735–1560; Michael Herman, Chief Executive Officer

SOUTHERN TENNESSEE REGIONAL HEALTH SYSTEM-LAWRENCEBURG (O, 99 beds) 1607 South Locust Avenue, Lawrenceburg, TN Zip 38464–4011, P O Box 847, 38464–0847, tel. 931/762–6571; Jeff Noblin, FACHE, Chief Executive Officer
Web address: www.crocketthospital.com

SOUTHERN TENNESSEE REGIONAL HEALTH SYSTEM-PULASKI (O, 59 beds) 1265 East College Street, Pulaski, TN Zip 38478–4541; tel. 931/363–7531; James H. Edmondson, Chief Executive Officer

SOUTHERN TENNESSEE REGIONAL HEALTH SYSTEM-WINCHESTER (O, 190 beds) 185 Hospital Road, Winchester, TN Zip 37398–2404; tel. 931/967–8200; Rob Followell, Chief Executive Officer
Web address: www.southerntennessee.com

STARR REGIONAL MEDICAL CENTER (O, 63 beds) 1114 West Madison Avenue, Athens, TN Zip 37303–4150, P O Box 250, 37371–0250, tel. 423/745–1411; Mark Nichols, FACHE, Chief Executive Officer

SUMNER REGIONAL MEDICAL CENTER (O, 110 beds) 555 Hartsville Pike, Gallatin, TN Zip 37066–2400, P O Box 1558, 37066–1558, tel. 615/452–4210; Susan M. Peach, R.N., Chief Executive Officer
Web address: www.mysumnermedical.com

For explanation of codes following names, see page B2.
★ Indicates Type III membership in the American Hospital Association.

TROUSDALE MEDICAL CENTER (O, 25 beds) 500 Church Street, Hartsville, TN Zip 37074–1744; tel. 615/374–2221; Michael Herman, Chief Executive Officer

TEXAS: ENNIS REGIONAL MEDICAL CENTER (L, 58 beds) 2201 West Lampasas Street, Ennis, TX Zip 75119–5644; tel. 972/875–0900; Harold L. Siglar, Interim Chief Executive Officer
Web address: www.ennisregional.com

PALESTINE REGIONAL MEDICAL CENTER-EAST (O, 120 beds) 2900 South Loop 256, Palestine, TX Zip 75801–6958; tel. 903/731–1000; Roy Finch, Chief Executive Officer

PALESTINE REGIONAL MEDICAL CENTER (O, 12 beds) 2900 S Loop 256, Palestine, TX Zip 75801–6958; tel. 903/731–1000; Roy Finch, Chief Executive Officer
Web address: www.palestineregional.com

PARKVIEW REGIONAL HOSPITAL (L, 58 beds) 600 South Bonham, Mexia, TX Zip 76667–3603; tel. 254/562–5332; Harold L. Siglar, Interim Chief Executive Officer

UTAH: ASHLEY REGIONAL MEDICAL CENTER (O, 39 beds) 150 West 100 North, Vernal, UT Zip 84078–2036; tel. 435/789–3342; Ben Cluff, Chief Executive Officer
Web address: www.ashleyregional.com

CASTLEVIEW HOSPITAL (O, 49 beds) 300 North Hospital Drive, Price, UT Zip 84501–4200; tel. 435/637–4800; Mark Holyoak, Chief Executive Officer
Web address: www.castleviewhospital.net

VIRGINIA: CLINCH VALLEY MEDICAL CENTER (O, 111 beds) 6801 Governor G C Peery Highway, Richlands, VA Zip 24641–2194; tel. 276/596–6000; Peter Mulkey, Chief Executive Officer
Web address: www.clinchvalleymedicalcenter.com

FAUQUIER HOSPITAL (O, 86 beds) 500 Hospital Drive, Warrenton, VA Zip 20186–3099; tel. 540/316–5000; Chad Melton, Chief Executive Officer

SOVAH HEALTH-DANVILLE (O, 250 beds) 142 South Main Street, Danville, VA Zip 24541–2922; tel. 434/799–2100; Alan Larson, Chief Executive Officer
Web address: www.danvilleregional.com/

SOVAH HEALTH-MARTINSVILLE (O, 220 beds) 320 Hospital Drive, Martinsville, VA Zip 24112–1981, P O Box 4788, 24115–4788, tel. 276/666–7200; Michael Ehrat, Chief Executive Officer

WYTHE COUNTY COMMUNITY HOSPITAL (L, 70 beds) 600 West Ridge Road, Wytheville, VA Zip 24382–1099; tel. 276/228–0200; Adam Martin, Chief Operating Officer and Interim Chief Executive Officer
Web address: www.wcchcares.com

WEST VIRGINIA: LOGAN REGIONAL MEDICAL CENTER (O, 129 beds) 20 Hospital Drive, Logan, WV Zip 25601–3452; tel. 304/831–1101; Kevin Zachary, Chief Executive Officer
Web address: www.loganregionalmedicalcenter.com

RALEIGH GENERAL HOSPITAL (O, 229 beds) 1710 Harper Road, Beckley, WV Zip 25801–3397; tel. 304/256–4100; Matthew S. Roberts, Chief Executive Officer

WISCONSIN: WATERTOWN REGIONAL MEDICAL CENTER (O, 56 beds) 125 Hospital Drive, Watertown, WI Zip 53098–3303; tel. 920/261–4210; Richard Keddington, Chief Executive Officer
Web address: www.watertownregional.com/Main/Home.aspx

WYOMING: SAGEWEST HEALTH CARE AT RIVERTON (O, 71 beds) 2100 West Sunset Drive, Riverton, WY Zip 82501–2274; tel. 307/856–4161; Robert Alan. Daugherty, Chief Executive Officer
Web address: www.sagewesthealthcare.com

Owned, leased, sponsored:	54 hospitals	5725 beds
Contract-managed:	0 hospitals	0 beds
Totals:	54 hospitals	5725 beds

0060: LIFESPAN CORPORATION (NP)
167 Point Street, Providence, RI Zip 02903–4771; tel. 401/444–3500; Timothy J. Babineau, M.D., President and Chief Executive Officer
(Centralized Health System)

RHODE ISLAND: EMMA PENDLETON BRADLEY HOSPITAL (O, 60 beds) 1011 Veterans Memorial Parkway, East Providence, RI Zip 02915–5099; tel. 401/432–1000; Daniel J. Wall, President and Chief Executive Officer

MIRIAM HOSPITAL (O, 247 beds) 164 Summit Avenue, Providence, RI Zip 02906–2853; tel. 401/793–2500; Arthur J. Sampson, FACHE, President
Web address: www.lifespan.org

NEWPORT HOSPITAL (O, 119 beds) 11 Friendship Street, Newport, RI Zip 02840–2299; tel. 401/846–6400; Crista F. Durand, President

RHODE ISLAND HOSPITAL (O, 679 beds) 593 Eddy Street, Providence, RI Zip 02903–4900; tel. 401/444–4000; Margaret M. Van Bree, Dr.PH, President
Web address: www.rhodeislandhospital.org/

Owned, leased, sponsored:	4 hospitals	1105 beds
Contract-managed:	0 hospitals	0 beds
Totals:	4 hospitals	1105 beds

2175: LOMA LINDA UNIVERSITY ADVENTIST HEALTH SCIENCES CENTER (NP)
11175 Campus Street, Loma Linda, CA Zip 92350–1700; tel. 909/558–7572; Richard H. Hart, M.D., President and Chief Executive Officer
(Centralized Health System)

CALIFORNIA: LOMA LINDA UNIVERSITY BEHAVIORAL MEDICINE CENTER (O, 89 beds) 1710 Barton Road, Redlands, CA Zip 92373–5304; tel. 909/558–9200; Edward Field, Administrator
Web address: www.llu.edu

LOMA LINDA UNIVERSITY CHILDREN'S HOSPITAL (O, 337 beds) 11234 Anderson Street, Loma Linda, CA Zip 92354–2804; tel. 909/558–8000; Kerry Heinrich, JD, Chief Executive Officer
Web address: www.llu.edu/lluch

LOMA LINDA UNIVERSITY MEDICAL CENTER-MURRIETA (O, 106 beds) 28062 Baxter Road , Murrieta, CA Zip 92563–1401; tel. 951/290–4000; Greg Henderson, Interim Administrator

LOMA LINDA UNIVERSITY MEDICAL CENTER (O, 538 beds) 11234 Anderson Street, Loma Linda, CA Zip 92354–2804, P O Box 2000, 92354–0200, tel. 909/558–4000; Kerry Heinrich, JD, Chief Executive Officer
Web address: www.llumc.edu

Owned, leased, sponsored:	4 hospitals	1070 beds
Contract-managed:	0 hospitals	0 beds
Totals:	4 hospitals	1070 beds

5755: LOS ANGELES COUNTY-DEPARTMENT OF HEALTH SERVICES (NP)
313 North Figueroa Street, Room 912, Los Angeles, CA Zip 90012–2691; tel. 213/240–8101; Mitchell H. Katz, M.D., Director
(Independent Hospital System)

CALIFORNIA: HARBOR-UCLA MEDICAL CENTER (O, 373 beds) 1000 West Carson Street, Torrance, CA Zip 90502–2059; tel. 310/222–2345; Kimberly McKenzie, R.N., MSN, Interim Chief Executive Officer
Web address: www.harbor-ucla.org

LAC+USC MEDICAL CENTER (O, 664 beds) 2051 Marengo Street, Los Angeles, CA Zip 90033–1352; tel. 323/409–1000; Dan A. Castillo, FACHE, Chief Executive Officer

LAC-OLIVE VIEW-UCLA MEDICAL CENTER (O, 198 beds) 14445 Olive View Drive, Sylmar, CA Zip 91342–1438; tel. 818/364–1555; Carolyn F. Rhee, Chief Executive Officer
Web address: www.ladhs.org

RANCHO LOS AMIGOS NATIONAL REHABILITATION CENTER (O, 207 beds) 7601 East Imperial Highway, Downey, CA Zip 90242–3496; tel. 562/401–7111; Jorge Orozco, Chief Executive Officer
Web address: www.rancho.org

Owned, leased, sponsored:	4 hospitals	1442 beds
Contract-managed:	0 hospitals	0 beds
Totals:	4 hospitals	1442 beds

For explanation of codes following names, see page B2.
★ Indicates Type III membership in the American Hospital Association.

0047: LOUISIANA STATE HOSPITALS (NP)
628 North 4th Street, Baton Rouge, LA Zip 70802–5342, P O Box 629, 70821–0628, tel. 225/342–9500; Shelby Price, Chief Executive Officer
(Independent Hospital System)

LOUISIANA: CENTRAL LOUISIANA STATE HOSPITAL (O, 120 beds) 242 West Shamrock Avenue, Pineville, LA Zip 71360–6439, P O Box 5031, 71361–5031, tel. 318/484–6200; Ronald G. Williams, Administrator
Web address: www.dhh.louisiana.gov/index.cfm/directory/detail/217

EASTERN LOUISIANA MENTAL HEALTH SYSTEM (O, 473 beds) 4502 Highway 951, Jackson, LA Zip 70748–5842, P O Box 498, 70748–0498, tel. 225/634–0100; Hampton P S. Lea, Acting Chief Executive Officer

Owned, leased, sponsored:	2 hospitals	593 beds
Contract-managed:	0 hospitals	0 beds
Totals:	2 hospitals	593 beds

★0320: LRGHEALTHCARE (NP)
80 Highland Street, Laconia, NH Zip 03246–3298; tel. 603/524–3211; Kevin Donovan, FACHE, President and Chief Executive Officer
(Independent Hospital System)

NEW HAMPSHIRE: FRANKLIN REGIONAL HOSPITAL (O, 31 beds) 15 Aiken Avenue, Franklin, NH Zip 03235–1299; tel. 603/934–2060; Kevin Donovan, FACHE, President and CEO
Web address: www.lrgh.org

LAKES REGION GENERAL HOSPITAL (O, 88 beds) 80 Highland Street, Laconia, NH Zip 03246–3298; tel. 603/524–3211; Kevin Donovan, FACHE, Chief Executive Officer
Web address: www.lrgh.org

Owned, leased, sponsored:	2 hospitals	119 beds
Contract-managed:	0 hospitals	0 beds
Totals:	2 hospitals	119 beds

0614: MAINEHEALTH (NP)
110 Free Street, Portland, ME Zip 04101–3537, William L. Caron Jr, President
(Moderately Centralized Health System)

MAINE: LINCOLNHEALTH (O, 91 beds) 35 Miles Street, Damariscotta, ME Zip 04543–4047; tel. 207/563–1234; James W. Donovan, President and Chief Executive Officer
Web address: www.lchcare.org

MAINE MEDICAL CENTER (O, 637 beds) 22 Bramhall Street, Portland, ME Zip 04102–3175; tel. 207/662–0111; Richard W. Petersen, President and Chief Executive Officer

PEN BAY MEDICAL CENTER (O, 165 beds) 6 Glen Cove Drive, Rockport, ME Zip 04856–4240; tel. 207/921–8000; Mark A. Biscone, President and Chief Executive Officer
Web address: www.penbayhealthcare.org

SPRING HARBOR HOSPITAL (O, 88 beds) 123 Andover Road, Westbrook, ME Zip 04092–3850; tel. 207/761–2200; Mary Jane Krebs, FACHE, President

STEPHENS MEMORIAL HOSPITAL (O, 25 beds) 181 Main Street, Norway, ME Zip 04268–5664; tel. 207/743–5933; Timothy A. Churchill, President
Web address: www.wmhcc.com

WALDO COUNTY GENERAL HOSPITAL (O, 25 beds) 118 Northport Avenue, Belfast, ME Zip 04915–6072, P O Box 287, 04915–0287, tel. 207/338–2500; Mark Fourre, Chief Executive Officer

NEW HAMPSHIRE: MEMORIAL HOSPITAL (O, 70 beds) 3073 White Mountain Highway, North Conway, NH Zip 03860–7101; tel. 603/356–5461; Scott McKinnon, President and Chief Executive Officer
Web address: www.memorialhospitalnh.org

Owned, leased, sponsored:	7 hospitals	1101 beds
Contract-managed:	0 hospitals	0 beds
Totals:	7 hospitals	1101 beds

1975: MARSHALL HEALTH SYSTEM (NP)
227 Britany Road, Guntersville, AL Zip 35976–5766; tel. 256/894–6615; Gary R. Gore, Chief Executive Officer
(Independent Hospital System)

ALABAMA: MARSHALL MEDICAL CENTER NORTH (O, 90 beds) 8000 Alabama Highway 69, Guntersville, AL Zip 35976; tel. 256/753–8000; Cheryl M. Hays, FACHE, Administrator and Chief Operating Officer

MARSHALL MEDICAL CENTER SOUTH (O, 114 beds) U S Highway 431 North, Boaz, AL Zip 35957–0999, P O Box 758, 35957–0758, tel. 256/593–8310; John D. Anderson, FACHE, Administrator
Web address: www.mmcenters.com//index.php/facilities/marshall_south

Owned, leased, sponsored:	2 hospitals	204 beds
Contract-managed:	0 hospitals	0 beds
Totals:	2 hospitals	204 beds

1022: MARSHFIELD CLINIC HEALTH SYSTEM (NP)
1000 North Oak Avenue, Marshfield, WI Zip 54449–5703; tel. 800/782–8581; Susan Turney, M.D., MS, Chief Executive Assistant

WISCONSIN: FLAMBEAU HOSPITAL (O, 25 beds) 98 Sherry Avenue, Park Falls, WI Zip 54552–1467, P O Box 310, 54552–0310, tel. 715/762–2484; James R. Braun, Chief Administrative Officer and Chief Financial Officer

LAKEVIEW MEDICAL CENTER (O, 40 beds) 1700 West Stout Street, Rice Lake, WI Zip 54868–5000; tel. 715/234–1515; John L. Olson, M.D., Interim President and Chief Administrative Officer
Web address: www.lakeviewmedical.com

MARSHFIELD MEDICAL CENTER (O, 200 beds) 611 St Joseph Avenue, Marshfield, WI Zip 54449–1898; tel. 715/387–1713; Edward H. Wolf, Chief Administrative Officer

Owned, leased, sponsored:	3 hospitals	265 beds
Contract-managed:	0 hospitals	0 beds
Totals:	3 hospitals	265 beds

★0523: MARY WASHINGTON HEALTHCARE (NP)
2300 Fall Hill Avenue, Suite 308, Fredericksburg, VA Zip 22401–3343; tel. 540/741–3100; Michael P. McDermott, M.D., President and Chief Executive Officer
(Independent Hospital System)

VIRGINIA: MARY WASHINGTON HOSPITAL (O, 451 beds) 1001 Sam Perry Boulevard, Fredericksburg, VA Zip 22401–3354; tel. 540/741–1100; Michael P. McDermott, M.D., President and Chief Executive Officer
Web address: www.marywashingtonhealthcare.com

STAFFORD HOSPITAL (O, 100 beds) 101 Hospital Center Boulevard, Stafford, VA Zip 22554–6200; tel. 540/741–9000; Michael P. McDermott, M.D., President and Chief Executive Officer

Owned, leased, sponsored:	2 hospitals	551 beds
Contract-managed:	0 hospitals	0 beds
Totals:	2 hospitals	551 beds

0013: MASSACHUSETTS DEPARTMENT OF MENTAL HEALTH (NP)
25 Staniford Street, Boston, MA Zip 02114–2575; tel. 617/626–8123; Joan Mikula, Interim Commissioner

MASSACHUSETTS: DR. J. CORRIGAN MENTAL HEALTH CENTER (O, 16 beds) 49 Hillside Street, Fall River, MA Zip 02720–5266; tel. 508/235–7200; Frank O'Reilly, Director

TAUNTON STATE HOSPITAL (O, 45 beds) 60 Hodges Avenue Extension, Taunton, MA Zip 02780–3034, PO Box 4007, 02780–0997, tel. 508/977–3000; Joyce O Connor, Chief Operating Officer

---

For explanation of codes following names, see page B2.
★ Indicates Type III membership in the American Hospital Association.

WORCESTER RECOVERY CENTER AND HOSPITAL (O, 126 beds) 309 Belmont Street, Worcester, MA Zip 01604–1695; tel. 508/368–3300; Anthony Riccitelli, Chief Operating Officer

Owned, leased, sponsored:	3 hospitals	187 beds
Contract-managed:	0 hospitals	0 beds
Totals:	3 hospitals	187 beds

0280: MASSACHUSETTS DEPARTMENT OF PUBLIC HEALTH (NP)

250 Washington Street, Boston, MA Zip 02108–4619; tel. 617/624–6000; Sandra Akers, Bureau Director, Public Health Hospitals
(Independent Hospital System)

MASSACHUSETTS: LEMUEL SHATTUCK HOSPITAL (O, 260 beds) 170 Morton Street, Jamaica Plain, MA Zip 02130–3735; tel. 617/522–8110; Rosette Martinez, Acting Chief Executive Officer
Web address: www.mass.gov/shattuckhospital

PAPPAS REHABILITATION HOSPITAL FOR CHILDREN (O, 80 beds) 3 Randolph Street, Canton, MA Zip 02021–2351; tel. 781/828–2440; Brian V. Devin, Chief Executive Officer

TEWKSBURY HOSPITAL (O, 381 beds) 365 East Street, Tewksbury, MA Zip 01876–1998; tel. 978/851–7321; Debra Tosti, Chief Executive Officer
Web address: www.mass.gov

WESTERN MASSACHUSETTS HOSPITAL (O, 70 beds) 91 East Mountain Road, Westfield, MA Zip 01085–1801; tel. 413/562–4131; Valenda M. Liptak, Chief Executive Officer

Owned, leased, sponsored:	4 hospitals	791 beds
Contract-managed:	0 hospitals	0 beds
Totals:	4 hospitals	791 beds

★0882: MAURY REGIONAL HEALTH SYSTEM (NP)

1224 Trotwood Avenue, Columbia, TN Zip 38401–4802; tel. 931/381–1111; H Alan. Watson, FACHE, Chief Executive Officer
(Independent Hospital System)

TENNESSEE: MARSHALL MEDICAL CENTER (O, 12 beds) 1080 North Ellington Parkway, Lewisburg, TN Zip 37091–2227, P O Box 1609, 37091–1609, tel. 931/359–6241; Phyllis Brown, Chief Executive Officer
Web address: www.mauryregional.com

MAURY REGIONAL HOSPITAL (O, 209 beds) 1224 Trotwood Avenue, Columbia, TN Zip 38401–4802; tel. 931/381–1111; H Alan. Watson, FACHE, Chief Executive Officer
Web address: www.mauryregional.com

WAYNE MEDICAL CENTER (L, 78 beds) 103 J V Mangubat Drive, Waynesboro, TN Zip 38485–2440, P O Box 580, 38485–0580, tel. 931/722–5411; Teresa Grimmett, Chief Executive Officer
Web address: www.mauryregional.com

Owned, leased, sponsored:	3 hospitals	299 beds
Contract-managed:	0 hospitals	0 beds
Totals:	3 hospitals	299 beds

★1875: MAYO CLINIC (NP)

200 First Street SW, Rochester, MN Zip 55905–0002; tel. 507/284–0288; John H. Noseworthy, MD, President and Chief Executive Officer
(Decentralized Health System)

ARIZONA: MAYO CLINIC HOSPITAL (O, 268 beds) 5777 East Mayo Boulevard, Phoenix, AZ Zip 85054–4502; tel. 480/342–2000; Wyatt Decker, Chief Executive Officer, Mayo Clinic in Arizona

FLORIDA: MAYO CLINIC JACKSONVILLE (O, 259 beds) 4500 San Pablo Road South, Jacksonville, FL Zip 32224–1865; tel. 904/953–2000; Gianrico Farrugia, M.D., Vice President and Chief Executive Officer
Web address: www.mayoclinic.org/jacksonville/

IOWA: FLOYD COUNTY MEDICAL CENTER (C, 25 beds) 800 Eleventh Street, Charles City, IA Zip 50616–3499; tel. 641/228–6830; Bill D. Faust, Administrator

WINNESHIEK MEDICAL CENTER (C, 25 beds) 901 Montgomery Street, Decorah, IA Zip 52101–2325; tel. 563/382–2911; Lisa Radtke, Chief Administrative Officer
Web address: www.winmedical.org

MINNESOTA: MAYO CLINIC HEALTH SYSTEM IN ALBERT LEA (O, 129 beds) 404 West Fountain Street, Albert Lea, MN Zip 56007–2473; tel. 507/373–2384; Mark Ciota, M.D., Chief Executive Officer

MAYO CLINIC HEALTH SYSTEM IN CANNON FALLS (O, 15 beds) 32021 County Road 24 Boulevard, Cannon Falls, MN Zip 55009–1898; tel. 507/263–4221; Thomas J. Witt, M.D., President and Chief Executive Officer
Web address: www.mayoclinichealthsystem.org/locations/cannon-falls

MAYO CLINIC HEALTH SYSTEM IN FAIRMONT (O, 63 beds) 800 Medical Center Drive, Fairmont, MN Zip 56031–4575; tel. 507/238–8100; Robert Bartingale, Administrator

MAYO CLINIC HEALTH SYSTEM IN LAKE CITY (O, 101 beds) 500 West Grant Street, Lake City, MN Zip 55041–1143; tel. 651/345–3321; Thomas J. Witt, M.D., President and Chief Executive Officer
Web address: www.lakecitymedicalcenter.org

MAYO CLINIC HEALTH SYSTEM IN MANKATO (O, 168 beds) 1025 Marsh Street, Mankato, MN Zip 56001–4752; tel. 507/625–4031; James Hebl, Regional Vice President

MAYO CLINIC HEALTH SYSTEM IN NEW PRAGUE (O, 25 beds) 301 Second Street NE, New Prague, MN Zip 56071–1799; tel. 952/758–4431; Mary J. Klimp, FACHE, Administrator
Web address: www.mayoclinichealthsystem.org/locations/new-prague

MAYO CLINIC HEALTH SYSTEM IN RED WING (O, 22 beds) 701 Hewitt Boulevard, Red Wing, MN Zip 55066–2848, P O Box 95, 55066–0095, tel. 651/267–5000; Thomas J. Witt, M.D., President and Chief Executive Officer

MAYO CLINIC HEALTH SYSTEM IN SAINT JAMES (O, 13 beds) 1101 Moulton and Parsons Drive, Saint James, MN Zip 56081–5550; tel. 507/375–3261; Amy Long, Administrator
Web address: www.mayoclinichealthsystem.org/locations/st-james

MAYO CLINIC HEALTH SYSTEM IN SPRINGFIELD (O, 23 beds) 625 North Jackson Avenue, Springfield, MN Zip 56087–1714, P O Box 146, 56087–0146, tel. 507/723–6201; Scott D. Thoreson, FACHE, Administrator
Web address: www.mayoclinichealthsystem.org

MAYO CLINIC HEALTH SYSTEM IN WASECA (O, 25 beds) 501 North State Street, Waseca, MN Zip 56093–2811; tel. 507/835–1210; Thomas Borowski, Administrator

MAYO CLINIC HEALTH SYSTEM-ALBERT LEA AND AUSTIN (O, 69 beds) 1000 First Drive NW, Austin, MN Zip 55912–2904; tel. 507/433–7351; Mark Ciota, M.D., Chief Executive Officer
Web address: www.austinmedicalcenter.org

MAYO CLINIC HOSPITAL - ROCHESTER (O, 1259 beds) 1216 Second Street SW, Rochester, MN Zip 55902–1906; tel. 507/255–5123; F. Kenneth. Ackerman, Hospital Administrator
Web address: www.mayoclinic.org

WISCONSIN: MAYO CLINIC HEALTH SYSTEM - CHIPPEWA VALLEY IN BLOOMER (O, 19 beds) 1501 Thompson Street, Bloomer, WI Zip 54724–1299; tel. 715/568–2000; Maurita Sullivan, Vice President
Web address: www.bloomermedicalcenter.org

MAYO CLINIC HEALTH SYSTEM - FRANCISCAN HEALTHCARE IN LA CROSSE (O, 81 beds) 700 West Avenue South, La Crosse, WI Zip 54601–4783; tel. 608/785–0940; Timothy Johnson, M.D., President and Chief Executive Officer

MAYO CLINIC HEALTH SYSTEM - FRANCISCAN HEALTHCARE IN SPARTA (O, 11 beds) 310 West Main Street, Sparta, WI Zip 54656–2171; tel. 608/269–2132; Kimberly Hawthorne, Administrator
Web address: www.mayoclinichealthsystem.org

For explanation of codes following names, see page B2.
★ Indicates Type III membership in the American Hospital Association.

MAYO CLINIC HEALTH SYSTEM - NORTHLAND IN BARRON (O, 23 beds) 1222 East Woodland Avenue, Barron, WI Zip 54812–1798; tel. 715/537–3186; Maurita Sullivan, Vice President

MAYO CLINIC HEALTH SYSTEM - OAKRIDGE IN OSSEO (O, 18 beds) 13025 Eighth Street, Osseo, WI Zip 54758–7634, P O Box 70, 54758–0070, tel. 715/597–3121; Dean Eide, Vice President
Web address: www.mayoclinichealthsystem.org/locations/osseo

MAYO CLINIC HEALTH SYSTEM - RED CEDAR IN MENOMONIE (O, 25 beds) 2321 Stout Road, Menomonie, WI Zip 54751–2397; tel. 715/235–5531; Steven Lindberg, Chief Administrative Officer

MAYO CLINIC HEALTH SYSTEM IN EAU CLAIRE (O, 185 beds) 1221 Whipple Street, Eau Claire, WI Zip 54703–5270, P O Box 4105, 54702–4105, tel. 715/838–3311; Richard Helmer, M.D., Chief Executive Officer
Web address: www.mhs.mayo.edu

Owned, leased, sponsored:	21 hospitals	2801 beds
Contract-managed:	2 hospitals	50 beds
Totals:	23 hospitals	2851 beds

0252: MCLAREN HEALTH CARE CORPORATION (NP)
G3235 Beecher Road, Suite B, Flint, MI Zip 48532–3650; tel. 810/342–1100; Philip A. Incarnati, President and Chief Executive Officer
(Centralized Physician/Insurance Health System)

MICHIGAN: MARWOOD MANOR NURSING HOME (O, 106 beds) 1300 Beard Street, Port Huron, MI Zip 48060; tel. 818/982–2594; Brian Oberly, Administrator

MCLAREN BAY REGION (O, 338 beds) 1900 Columbus Avenue, Bay City, MI Zip 48708–6831; tel. 989/894–3000; Clarence Sevillian, President and Chief Executive Officer
Web address: www.bayregional.org

MCLAREN BAY SPECIAL CARE (O, 21 beds) 3250 East Midland Road, Suite 1, Bay City, MI Zip 48706–2835; tel. 989/667–6802; Cheryl A. Burzynski, MSN, President
Web address: www.bayspecialcare.org

MCLAREN CENTRAL MICHIGAN (O, 78 beds) 1221 South Drive, Mount Pleasant, MI Zip 48858–3257; tel. 989/772–6700; William P. Lawrence, President and Chief Executive Officer

MCLAREN FLINT (O, 348 beds) 401 South Ballenger Highway, Flint, MI Zip 48532–3685; tel. 810/342–2000; Chad M. Grant, President
Web address: www.mclarenregional.org

MCLAREN GREATER LANSING (O, 321 beds) 401 West Greenlawn Avenue, Lansing, MI Zip 48910–2819; tel. 517/975–6000; Thomas Mee, R.N., President and Chief Executive Officer

MCLAREN LAPEER REGION (O, 159 beds) 1375 North Main Street, Lapeer, MI Zip 48446–1350; tel. 810/667–5500; Chris Candela, President and Chief Executive Officer
Web address: www.lapeerregional.org

MCLAREN MACOMB (O, 288 beds) 1000 Harrington Boulevard, Mount Clemens, MI Zip 48043–2992; tel. 586/493–8000; Thomas M. Brisse, President and Chief Executive Officer

MCLAREN NORTHERN MICHIGAN (O, 188 beds) 416 Connable Avenue, Petoskey, MI Zip 49770–2297; tel. 231/487–4000; David M. Zechman, FACHE, President and Chief Executive Officer
Web address: www.northernhealth.org

MCLAREN OAKLAND (O, 263 beds) 50 North Perry Street, Pontiac, MI Zip 48342–2253; tel. 248/338–5000; Chad M. Grant, President and Chief Executive Officer

MCLAREN PORT HURON (O, 186 beds) 1221 Pine Grove Avenue, Port Huron, MI Zip 48060–3511; tel. 810/987–5000; Jennifer Montgomery, R.N., FACHE, President and Chief Executive Officer
Web address: www.porthuronhospital.org

Owned, leased, sponsored:	11 hospitals	2296 beds
Contract-managed:	0 hospitals	0 beds
Totals:	11 hospitals	2296 beds

0874: MCLEOD HEALTH (NP)
555 East Cheves Street, Florence, SC Zip 29506–2617, P O Box 100551, 29502–0551, tel. 843/777–2000; Robert L. Colones, President and Chief Executive Officer
(Centralized Health System)

SOUTH CAROLINA: MCLEOD HEALTH CHERAW (O, 52 beds) 711 Chesterfield Highway, Cheraw, SC Zip 29520–7002; tel. 843/537–7881; Mib Scoggins, Chief Executive Officer
Web address: www.chesterfieldgeneral.com

MCLEOD HEALTH CLARENDON (C, 31 beds) 10 Hospital Street, Manning, SC Zip 29102–3153, P O Box 550, 29102–0550, tel. 803/433–3000; Rachel T. Gainey, FACHE, Administrator

MCLEOD LORIS SEACOAST HOSPITAL (O, 155 beds) 3655 Mitchell Street, Loris, SC Zip 29569–2827; tel. 843/716–7000; Edward D. Tinsley III, Chief Executive Officer
Web address: www.mcleodhealth.org

MCLEOD MEDICAL CENTER DILLON (O, 58 beds) 301 East Jackson Street, Dillon, SC Zip 29536–2509, P O Box 1327, 29536–1327, tel. 843/774–4111; Joan Ervin, Administrator

MCLEOD MEDICAL CENTER-DARLINGTON (O, 42 beds) 701 Cashua Ferry Road, Darlington, SC Zip 29532–8488, P O Box 1859, 29540, tel. 843/395–1100; Tim Smoak, Administrator
Web address: www.mcleodhealth.org

MCLEOD REGIONAL MEDICAL CENTER (O, 541 beds) 555 East Cheves Street, Florence, SC Zip 29506–2617, P O Box 100551, 29502–0551, tel. 843/777–2000; Robert L. Colones, President and Chief Executive Officer

Owned, leased, sponsored:	5 hospitals	848 beds
Contract-managed:	1 hospitals	31 beds
Totals:	6 hospitals	879 beds

★1001: MEADVILLE MEDICAL CENTER (NP)
751 Liberty Street, Meadville, PA Zip 16335–2559; tel. 814/333–5000; Philip E. Pandolph, FACHE, Chief Executive Officer
(Independent Hospital System)

PENNSYLVANIA: MEADVILLE MEDICAL CENTER (O, 210 beds) 751 Liberty Street, Meadville, PA Zip 16335–2559; tel. 814/333–5000; Philip E. Pandolph, FACHE, Chief Executive Officer
Web address: www.mmchs.org

TITUSVILLE AREA HOSPITAL (O, 25 beds) 406 West Oak Street, Titusville, PA Zip 16354–1404; tel. 814/827–1851; Lee Clinton, FACHE, Chief Executive Officer

Owned, leased, sponsored:	2 hospitals	235 beds
Contract-managed:	0 hospitals	0 beds
Totals:	2 hospitals	235 beds

★0971: MEDISYS HEALTH NETWORK (NP)
8900 Van Wyck Expressway, Jamaica, NY Zip 11418–2832; tel. 718/206–6000; Bruce J. Flanz, President and Chief Executive Officer
(Moderately Centralized Health System)

NEW YORK: FLUSHING HOSPITAL MEDICAL CENTER (C, 299 beds) 4500 Parsons Boulevard, Flushing, NY Zip 11355–2205; tel. 718/670–5000; Bruce J. Flanz, President and Chief Executive Officer
Web address: www.flushinghospital.org

JAMAICA HOSPITAL MEDICAL CENTER (C, 668 beds) 8900 Van Wyck Expressway, Jamaica, NY Zip 11418–2832; tel. 718/206–6000; Bruce J. Flanz, President and Chief Executive Officer

Owned, leased, sponsored:	0 hospitals	0 beds
Contract-managed:	2 hospitals	967 beds
Totals:	2 hospitals	967 beds

★0154: MEDSTAR HEALTH (NP)
10980 Grantchester Way, Columbia, MD Zip 21044–2665; tel. 410/772–6500; Kenneth A. Samet, President and Chief Executive Officer
(Centralized Health System)

For explanation of codes following names, see page B2.
★ Indicates Type III membership in the American Hospital Association.

DISTRICT OF COLUMBIA: MEDSTAR GEORGETOWN UNIVERSITY HOSPITAL (O, 409 beds) 3800 Reservoir Road NW, Washington, DC Zip 20007–2197; tel. 202/444–2000; Michael Sachtleben, President
Web address: www.georgetownuniversityhospital.org

MEDSTAR NATIONAL REHABILITATION HOSPITAL (O, 137 beds) 102 Irving Street NW, Washington, DC Zip 20010–2949; tel. 202/877–1000; John D. Rockwood, President
Web address: www.medstarnrh.org

MEDSTAR WASHINGTON HOSPITAL CENTER (O, 745 beds) 110 Irving Street NW, Washington, DC Zip 20010–3017; tel. 202/877–7000; John Sullivan, President

MARYLAND: MEDSTAR FRANKLIN SQUARE MEDICAL CENTER (O, 384 beds) 9000 Franklin Square Drive, Baltimore, MD Zip 21237–3901; tel. 443/777–7000; Samuel E. Moskowitz, President
Web address: www.medstarfranklin.org

MEDSTAR GOOD SAMARITAN HOSPITAL (O, 323 beds) 5601 Loch Raven Boulevard, Baltimore, MD Zip 21239–2995; tel. 443/444–8000; Bradley Chambers, President and Senior Vice President, MedStar Health
Web address: www.goodsam-md.org

MEDSTAR HARBOR HOSPITAL (O, 141 beds) 3001 South Hanover Street, Baltimore, MD Zip 21225–1290; tel. 410/350–3200; Stuart M. Levine, M.D., President and Chief Medical Officer

MEDSTAR MONTGOMERY MEDICAL CENTER (O, 147 beds) 18101 Prince Philip Drive, Olney, MD Zip 20832–1512; tel. 301/774–8882; Thomas J. Senker, FACHE, President
Web address: www.medstarmontgomery.org

MEDSTAR SOUTHERN MARYLAND HOSPITAL CENTER (O, 255 beds) 7503 Surratts Road, Clinton, MD Zip 20735–3358; tel. 301/868–8000; Christine R. Wray, President
Web address: www.medstarsouthernmaryland.org

MEDSTAR ST. MARY'S HOSPITAL (O, 91 beds) 25500 Point Lookout Road, Leonardtown, MD Zip 20650–2015, PO Box 527, 20650–0527, tel. 301/475–6001; Christine R. Wray, President

MEDSTAR UNION MEMORIAL HOSPITAL (O, 198 beds) 201 East University Parkway, Baltimore, MD Zip 21218–2895; tel. 410/554–2000; Bradley Chambers, President
Web address: www.medstarunionmemorial.org

Owned, leased, sponsored:	10 hospitals	2830 beds
Contract-managed:	0 hospitals	0 beds
Totals:	10 hospitals	2830 beds

★0086:   MEMORIAL HEALTH SYSTEM (NP)
701 North First Street, Springfield, IL Zip 62781–0001; tel. 217/788–3000; Edgar J. Curtis, FACHE, President and Chief Executive Officer
(Centralized Health System)

ILLINOIS: ABRAHAM LINCOLN MEMORIAL HOSPITAL (O, 25 beds) 200 Stahlhut Drive, Lincoln, IL Zip 62656–5066; tel. 217/732–2161; Dolan Dalpoas, President and Chief Executive Officer

MEMORIAL MEDICAL CENTER (O, 470 beds) 701 North First Street, Springfield, IL Zip 62781–0001; tel. 217/788–3000; Edgar J. Curtis, FACHE, President and Chief Executive Officer
Web address: www.memorialmedical.com

PASSAVANT AREA HOSPITAL (O, 118 beds) 1600 West Walnut Street, Jacksonville, IL Zip 62650–1136; tel. 217/245–9541; Harry M. Schmidt, President and Chief Executive Officer
Web address: www.passavanthospital.com

TAYLORVILLE MEMORIAL HOSPITAL (O, 25 beds) 201 East Pleasant Street, Taylorville, IL Zip 62568–1597; tel. 217/824–3331; Kimberly L. Bourne, Chief Executive Officer
Web address: www.taylorvillememorial.org

Owned, leased, sponsored:	4 hospitals	638 beds
Contract-managed:	0 hospitals	0 beds
Totals:	4 hospitals	638 beds

0998:   MEMORIAL HEALTH SYSTEM (NP)
401 Matthew Street, Marietta, OH Zip 45750–1635; tel. 740/374–1400; J Scott. Cantley, President and Chief Executive Officer
(Independent Hospital System)

OHIO: MARIETTA MEMORIAL HOSPITAL (O, 152 beds) 401 Matthew Street, Marietta, OH Zip 45750–1699; tel. 740/374–1400; J Scott. Cantley, President and Chief Executive Officer

SELBY GENERAL HOSPITAL (O, 35 beds) 1106 Colegate Drive, Marietta, OH Zip 45750–1323; tel. 740/568–2000; Stephen Smith, President
Web address: www.selbygeneral.org

Owned, leased, sponsored:	2 hospitals	187 beds
Contract-managed:	0 hospitals	0 beds
Totals:	2 hospitals	187 beds

★0083:   MEMORIAL HEALTHCARE SYSTEM (NP)
3501 Johnson Street, Hollywood, FL Zip 33021–5421; tel. 954/987–2000; Aurelio Fernandez, Chief Executive Officer
(Centralized Health System)

FLORIDA: MEMORIAL HOSPITAL MIRAMAR (O, 178 beds) 1901 SW 172nd Avenue, Miramar, FL Zip 33029–5592; tel. 954/538–5000; Grisel Fernandez-Bravo, R.N., Administrator and Chief Executive Officer

MEMORIAL HOSPITAL PEMBROKE (L, 157 beds) 7800 Sheridan Street, Pembroke Pines, FL Zip 33024–2536; tel. 954/883–8482; Mark Doyle, Administrator and Chief Executive Officer
Web address: www.memorialpembroke.com/

MEMORIAL HOSPITAL WEST (O, 384 beds) 703 North Flamingo Road, Pembroke Pines, FL Zip 33028–1014; tel. 954/436–5000; Leah A. Carpenter, Administrator and Chief Executive Officer

MEMORIAL REGIONAL HOSPITAL (O, 1057 beds) 3501 Johnson Street, Hollywood, FL Zip 33021–5421; tel. 954/987–2000; Zeff Ross, FACHE, Executive Vice President and Chief Executive Officer
Web address: www.mhs.net

Owned, leased, sponsored:	4 hospitals	1776 beds
Contract-managed:	0 hospitals	0 beds
Totals:	4 hospitals	1776 beds

★2645:   MEMORIAL HERMANN HEALTH SYSTEM (NP)
929 Gessner, Suite 2700, Houston, TX Zip 77024–2593; tel. 713/338–5555; Charles D. Stokes, FACHE, President and Chief Executive Officer
(Centralized Health System)

TEXAS: EMERUS COMMUNITY HOSPITAL (O, 8 beds) 24429 State Highway 249, Tomball, TX Zip 77375–8214; tel. 281/516–0911; Paula Gonzales, Administrator
Web address: www.emerus.com/tomball/

MEMORIAL HERMANN - TEXAS MEDICAL CENTER (O, 1000 beds) 6411 Fannin Street, Houston, TX Zip 77030–1501; tel. 713/704–4000; Brian Dean, FACHE, Chief Executive Officer

MEMORIAL HERMANN GREATER HEIGHTS HOSPITAL (O, 1372 beds) 1635 North Loop West, Houston, TX Zip 77008–1532; tel. 713/867–3380; Susan Jadlowski, MSN, R.N., Chief Executive Officer
Web address: www.mhbh.org

MEMORIAL HERMANN KATY HOSPITAL (O, 203 beds) 23900 Katy Freeway, Katy, TX Zip 77494–1323; tel. 281/644–7000; Heath Rushing, Senior Vice President and Chief Executive Officer
Web address: www.memorialhermann.org/locations/katy/

MEMORIAL HERMANN MEMORIAL CITY MEDICAL CENTER (L, 444 beds) 921 Gessner Road, Houston, TX Zip 77024–2501; tel. 713/242–3000; Paul O'Sullivan, FACHE, Chief Executive Officer
Web address: www.memorialhermann.org

MEMORIAL HERMANN NORTHEAST (O, 218 beds) 18951 North Memorial Drive, Humble, TX Zip 77338–4297; tel. 281/540–7700; Josh Urban, Chief Executive Officer

---

For explanation of codes following names, see page B2.
★ Indicates Type III membership in the American Hospital Association.

Section B

MEMORIAL HERMANN REHABILITATION HOSPITAL - KATY (O, 35 beds) 21720 Kingsland Boulevard #102, Katy, TX Zip 77450–2550, Carl E. Josehart, Chief Executive Officer
Web address: www.oceanskaty.com/

MEMORIAL HERMANN SUGAR LAND HOSPITAL (O, 87 beds) 17500 West Grand Parkway South, Sugar Land, TX Zip 77479–2562; tel. 281/725–5000; Gregory Haralson, FACHE, Chief Executive Officer
Web address: www.memorialhermann.org

TIRR MEMORIAL HERMANN (O, 134 beds) 1333 Moursund Street, Houston, TX Zip 77030–3405; tel. 713/799–5000; Carl E. Josehart, Chief Executive Officer
Web address: www.memorialhermann.org/locations/tirr.html

Owned, leased, sponsored:	9 hospitals	3501 beds
Contract-managed:	0 hospitals	0 beds
Totals:	9 hospitals	3501 beds

0084: MEMORIALCARE (NP)

17360 Brookhurst Street, Fountain Valley, CA Zip 92708–3720, P O Box 1428, Long Beach, 90801–1428, tel. 714/377–2900; Barry S. Arbuckle, Ph.D., President and Chief Executive Officer
(Centralized Health System)

CALIFORNIA: COMMUNITY HOSPITAL LONG BEACH (O, 158 beds) 1720 Termino Avenue, Long Beach, CA Zip 90804–2104; tel. 562/498–1000; John Bishop, Chief Executive Officer

LONG BEACH MEMORIAL MEDICAL CENTER (O, 458 beds) 2801 Atlantic Avenue, Long Beach, CA Zip 90806–1701, P O Box 1428, 90801–1428, tel. 562/933–2000; John Bishop, Chief Executive Officer
Web address: www.memorialcare.org/LongBeach

MILLER CHILDREN'S & WOMEN'S HOSPITAL LONG BEACH (O, 371 beds) 2801 Atlantic Avenue, Long Beach, CA Zip 90806–1701; tel. 562/933–5437; John Bishop, Chief Executive Officer
Web address: www.memorialcare.org

ORANGE COAST MEMORIAL MEDICAL CENTER (O, 218 beds) 9920 Talbert Avenue, Fountain Valley, CA Zip 92708–5115; tel. 714/378–7000; Marcia Manker, Chief Executive Officer
Web address: www.memorialcare.org

SADDLEBACK MEMORIAL MEDICAL CENTER (O, 313 beds) 24451 Health Center Drive, Laguna Hills, CA Zip 92653–3689; tel. 949/837–4500; Marcia Manker, Chief Executive Officer

Owned, leased, sponsored:	5 hospitals	1518 beds
Contract-managed:	0 hospitals	0 beds
Totals:	5 hospitals	1518 beds

★5185: MERCY (CC)

14528 South Outer 40, Suite 100, Chesterfield, MO Zip 63017–5743; tel. 314/579–6100; Lynn Britton, President and Chief Executive Officer
(Decentralized Health System)

ARKANSAS: MERCY HOSPITAL BERRYVILLE (O, 25 beds) 214 Carter Street, Berryville, AR Zip 72616–4303; tel. 870/423–3355; Douglas M. Stroemel, Administrator
Web address: www.mercy.net/berryvillear

MERCY HOSPITAL BOONEVILLE (O, 25 beds) 880 West Main Street, Booneville, AR Zip 72927–3443; tel. 479/675–2800; Teresa Williams, R.N., Regional Administrator
Web address: www.mercy.net

MERCY HOSPITAL FORT SMITH (O, 370 beds) 7301 Rogers Avenue, Fort Smith, AR Zip 72903–4189, P O Box 17000, 72917–7000, tel. 479/314–6000; Ryan Gehrig, President
Web address: www.mercy.net/fortsmithar

MERCY HOSPITAL OZARK (O, 25 beds) 801 West River Street, Ozark, AR Zip 72949–3023; tel. 479/667–4138; Teresa Williams, R.N., Administrator and Director of Nursing
Web address: www.mercy.net/northwestarar/practice/mercy-hospital-ozark

MERCY HOSPITAL PARIS (O, 16 beds) 500 East Academy, Paris, AR Zip 72855–4040; tel. 479/963–6101; Sharon D. Sorey, R.N., Administrator

MERCY HOSPITAL ROGERS (O, 191 beds) 2710 Rife Medical Lane, Rogers, AR Zip 72758–1452; tel. 479/338–8000; Eric Pianalto, President
Web address: www.mercyhealthnwa.smhs.com

MERCY HOSPITAL WALDRON (O, 24 beds) 1341 West 6th Street, Waldron, AR Zip 72958–7642; tel. 479/637–4135; Teresa Williams, R.N., Regional Administrator
Web address: www.stedwardmercy.com

KANSAS: MERCY HOSPITAL COLUMBUS (O, 18 beds) 220 North Pennsylvania Avenue, Columbus, KS Zip 66725–1110; tel. 620/429–2545; Angie Saporito, Administrator

MERCY HOSPITAL FORT SCOTT (O, 46 beds) 401 Woodland Hills Boulevard, Fort Scott, KS Zip 66701–8797; tel. 620/223–2200; Reta K. Baker, President
Web address: www.mercykansas.com

MISSOURI: MERCY HOSPITAL AURORA (L, 25 beds) 500 Porter Street, Aurora, MO Zip 65605–2365; tel. 417/678–2122; Douglas M. Stroemel, Administrator Mercy Hospital Aurora and Mercy Hospital Cassville
Web address: www.stjohns.com/aboutus/aurora.aspx

MERCY HOSPITAL CARTHAGE (L, 13 beds) 3125 Dr Russell Smith Way, Carthage, MO Zip 64836–7402; tel. 417/358–8121; Scott Watson, Administrator
Web address: www.mercy.net

MERCY HOSPITAL CASSVILLE (L, 18 beds) 94 Main Street, Cassville, MO Zip 65625–1610; tel. 417/847–6000; Douglas M. Stroemel, President

MERCY HOSPITAL JEFFERSON (O, 205 beds) Highway 61 South, Crystal City, MO Zip 63019, P O Box 350, 63019–0350, tel. 636/933–1000; Eric Ammons, President
Web address: www.mercy.net/crystalcitymo

MERCY HOSPITAL JOPLIN (O, 240 beds) 100 Mercy Way, Joplin, MO Zip 64804–1626; tel. 417/781–2727; Gary W. Pulsipher, President and Chief Executive Officer

MERCY HOSPITAL LEBANON (O, 58 beds) 100 Hospital Drive, Lebanon, MO Zip 65536–9210; tel. 417/533–6100; Scott W. Childers, Administrator
Web address: www.mercy.net/practice/mercy-hospital-lebanon

MERCY HOSPITAL LINCOLN (L, 25 beds) 1000 East Cherry Street, Troy, MO Zip 63379–1513; tel. 636/528–8551; Anthony Rothermich, Administrator

MERCY HOSPITAL SPRINGFIELD (O, 741 beds) 1235 East Cherokee Street, Springfield, MO Zip 65804–2263; tel. 417/820–2000; Alan Scarrow, M.D., President
Web address: www.mercy.net/springfieldmo

MERCY HOSPITAL ST. LOUIS (O, 831 beds) 615 South New Ballas Road, Saint Louis, MO Zip 63141–8277; tel. 314/251–6000; Stephen Mackin, President
Web address: www.mercy.net/stlouismo

MERCY HOSPITAL WASHINGTON (O, 148 beds) 901 East Fifth Street, Washington, MO Zip 63090–3127; tel. 636/239–8000; Eric J. Eoloff, President

MERCY ST. FRANCIS HOSPITAL (O, 20 beds) 100 West Highway 60, Mountain View, MO Zip 65548–7125; tel. 417/934–7000; Cynthia Weatherford, Administrator and Director of Nursing
Web address: www.stjohns.com/aboutus/stfrancis.aspx

ST. ANTHONY'S MEDICAL CENTER (O, 550 beds) 10010 Kennerly Road, Saint Louis, MO Zip 63128–2106; tel. 314/525–1000; Michael McCurry, President

OKLAHOMA: ARBUCKLE MEMORIAL HOSPITAL (C, 13 beds) 2011 West Broadway Street, Sulphur, OK Zip 73086–4221, P.O. Box 1109, 73086–8109, tel. 580/622–2161; Darin Farrell, Administrator
Web address: www.arbucklehospital.com/

MERCY HEALTH LOVE COUNTY (C, 25 beds) 300 Wanda Street, Marietta, OK Zip 73448–1200; tel. 580/276–3347; Richard Barker, Administrator and Chief Executive Officer
Web address: www.mercyhealthlovecounty.com

MERCY HOSPITAL ADA (L, 156 beds) 430 North Monte Vista, Ada, OK Zip 74820–4610; tel. 580/332–2323; Lori Wightman, R.N., MSN, FACHE, President
Web address: www.mercy.net/ada

MERCY HOSPITAL ARDMORE (O, 190 beds) 1011 14th Avenue NW, Ardmore, OK Zip 73401–1828; tel. 580/223–5400; Daryle Voss, FACHE, President and Chief Executive Officer

For explanation of codes following names, see page B2.
★ Indicates Type III membership in the American Hospital Association.

Section B

MERCY HOSPITAL EL RENO (L, 48 beds) 2115 Parkview Drive, El Reno, OK Zip 73036–2199; tel. 405/262–2640; Cindy Carmichael, Interim Administrator
Web address: www.mercyok.net

MERCY HOSPITAL HEALDTON (L, 22 beds) 918 South 8th Street, Healdton, OK Zip 73438–0928, P O Box 928, 73438–0928, tel. 580/229–0701; Jeremy A. Jones, Administrator
Web address: www.mercyok.com

MERCY HOSPITAL KINGFISHER (L, 25 beds) 1000 Kingfisher Regional Hospital Drive, Kingfisher, OK Zip 73750–3528, P O Box 59, 73750–0059, tel. 405/375–3141; Brian Denton, Administrator

MERCY HOSPITAL LOGAN COUNTY (O, 25 beds) 200 South Academy Road, Guthrie, OK Zip 73044–8727, P O Box 1017, 73044–1017, tel. 405/282–6700; Joshua Tucker, Administrator
Web address: www.mercy.net

MERCY HOSPITAL OKLAHOMA CITY (O, 369 beds) 4300 West Memorial Road, Oklahoma City, OK Zip 73120–8362; tel. 405/755–1515; Jim Gebhart Jr, FACHE, President

MERCY HOSPITAL TISHOMINGO (L, 25 beds) 1000 South Byrd Street, Tishomingo, OK Zip 73460–3299; tel. 580/371–2327; Gary Sharum, Administrator
Web address: www.mercy.net/

MERCY HOSPITAL WATONGA (L, 17 beds) 500 North Clarence Nash Boulevard, Watonga, OK Zip 73772–2845, P O Box 370, 73772–0370, tel. 580/623–7211; Bobby Stitt, R.N., Administrator

Owned, leased, sponsored:	30 hospitals	4491 beds
Contract-managed:	2 hospitals	38 beds
Totals:	32 hospitals	4529 beds

★**5155: MERCY HEALTH** (CC)

615 Elsinore Place, Cincinnati, OH Zip 45202–1459, 1701 Mercy Health Place, 45237, tel. 513/639–2800; John M. Starcher, President and Chief Executive Officer
(Moderately Centralized Health System)

KENTUCKY: LOURDES HOSPITAL (O, 281 beds) 1530 Lone Oak Road, Paducah, KY Zip 42003–7900, P O Box 7100, 42002–7100, tel. 270/444–2444; Michael Yungmann, President and Chief Executive Officer
Web address: www.lourdes-pad.org

MERCY HEALTH - MARCUM AND WALLACE (O, 25 beds) 60 Mercy Court, Irvine, KY Zip 40336–1331; tel. 606/723–2115; Susan Starling, President and Chief Executive Officer

OHIO: INSTITUTE FOR ORTHOPAEDIC SURGERY (O, 3 beds) 801 Medical Drive, Suite B, Lima, OH Zip 45804–4030; tel. 419/224–7586; Mark McDonald, M.D., President and Chief Executive Officer
Web address: www.ioshospital.com

MERCY ALLEN HOSPITAL (O, 25 beds) 200 West Lorain Street, Oberlin, OH Zip 44074–1077; tel. 440/775–1211; Joseph Sober, President
Web address: www.mercyonline.org/mercy_allen_hospital.aspx

MERCY HEALTH - ST. CHARLES HOSPITAL (O, 279 beds) 2600 Navarre Avenue, Oregon, OH Zip 43616–3297; tel. 419/696–7200; Jeffrey Dempsey, President and Chief Operating Officer

MERCY HEALTH - ANDERSON HOSPITAL (O, 188 beds) 7500 State Road, Cincinnati, OH Zip 45255–2492; tel. 513/624–4500; Ken James, President and Chief Executive Officer of East Market
Web address: www.e-mercy.com

MERCY HEALTH - CLERMONT HOSPITAL (O, 119 beds) 3000 Hospital Drive, Batavia, OH Zip 45103–1921; tel. 513/732–8200; Ken James, President and Chief Executive Officer of East Market
Web address: www.e-mercy.com

MERCY HEALTH - FAIRFIELD HOSPITAL (O, 236 beds) 3000 Mack Road, Fairfield, OH Zip 45014–5335; tel. 513/870–7000; Thomas S. Urban, Market Leader and President

MERCY HEALTH - ST. ELIZABETH BOARDMAN HOSPITAL (O, 217 beds) 8401 Market Street, Boardman, OH Zip 44512–6777; tel. 330/729–2929; Eugenia Aubel, President
Web address: www.ehealthconnection.com/regions/youngstown/content/show_facility.asp?facility_id=190

MERCY HEALTH - ST. ELIZABETH YOUNGSTOWN HOSPITAL (O, 379 beds) 1044 Belmont Avenue, Youngstown, OH Zip 44504–1096, P O Box 1790, 44501–1790, tel. 330/746–7211; Donald E. Kline, President and Chief Executive Officer
Web address: www.mercy.com

MERCY HEALTH - ST. JOSEPH WARREN HOSPITAL (O, 136 beds) 667 Eastland Avenue SE, Warren, OH Zip 44484–4531, 627 Eastland Avenue , 44484–4531, tel. 330/841–4000; Kathy Cook, FACHE, MSN, President

MERCY HEALTH - WEST HOSPITAL (O, 250 beds) 3300 Mercy Health Boulevard, Cincinnati, OH Zip 45211; tel. 513/215–5000; Michael Kramer, Chief Executive Officer
Web address: www.e-mercy.com/west-hospital

MERCY HEALTH - WILLARD HOSPITAL (O, 20 beds) 1100 Neal Zick Road, Willard, OH Zip 44890–9287; tel. 419/964–5000; B Lynn. Detterman, President and Chief Executive Officer
Web address: www.mercyweb.org

MERCY HOSPITAL OF DEFIANCE (O, 23 beds) 1404 East Second Street, Defiance, OH Zip 43512–2440; tel. 419/782–8444; B Lynn. Detterman, President and Chief Executive Officer

MERCY MEMORIAL HOSPITAL (O, 25 beds) 904 Scioto Street, Urbana, OH Zip 43078–2200; tel. 937/653–5231; Matthew T. Caldwell, President and Chief Executive Officer
Web address: www.health-partners.org

MERCY REGIONAL MEDICAL CENTER (O, 259 beds) 3700 Kolbe Road, Lorain, OH Zip 44053–1697; tel. 440/960–4000; Edwin M. Oley, President and Chief Executive Officer

MERCY ST. ANNE HOSPITAL (O, 96 beds) 3404 West Sylvania Avenue, Toledo, OH Zip 43623–4467; tel. 419/407–2663; Bradley J. Bertke, President and Chief Operating Officer
Web address: www.mercyweb.org

MERCY ST. VINCENT MEDICAL CENTER (O, 351 beds) 2213 Cherry Street, Toledo, OH Zip 43608–2691; tel. 419/251–3232; Jeffrey Dempsey, President

MERCY TIFFIN HOSPITAL (O, 46 beds) 45 St Lawrence Drive, Tiffin, OH Zip 44883–8310; tel. 419/455–7000; B Lynn. Detterman, President and Chief Executive Officer
Web address: www.mercyweb.org

SPRINGFIELD REGIONAL MEDICAL CENTER (O, 259 beds) 100 Medical Center Drive, Springfield, OH Zip 45504–2687; tel. 937/523–1000; Matthew T. Caldwell, President and Chief Executive Officer

ST. RITA'S MEDICAL CENTER (O, 415 beds) 730 West Market Street, Lima, OH Zip 45801–4602; tel. 419/227–3361; Robert O. Baxter, Regional Chief Executive Officer, Lima
Web address: www.stritas.org

THE JEWISH HOSPITAL - MERCY HEALTH (O, 209 beds) 4777 East Galbraith Road, Cincinnati, OH Zip 45236–2725; tel. 513/686–3000; Patricia Davis-Hagens, R.N., Central Market Leader and President

Owned, leased, sponsored:	22 hospitals	3841 beds
Contract-managed:	0 hospitals	0 beds
Totals:	22 hospitals	3841 beds

0649: MERCY HEALTH SYSTEM (NP)

1000 Mineral Point Avenue, Janesville, WI Zip 53548–2940, P O Box 5003, 53547–5003, tel. 608/756–6000; Javon R. Bea, President and Chief Executive Officer
(Centralized Physician/Insurance Health System)

ILLINOIS: MERCYHEALTH HOSPITAL - ROCKTON AVENUE (O, 288 beds) 2400 North Rockton Avenue, Rockford, IL Zip 61103–3655; tel. 815/971–5000; Javon R. Bea, President and Chief Executive Officer
Web address: www.rhsnet.org

For explanation of codes following names, see page B2.
★ Indicates Type III membership in the American Hospital Association.

MERCYHEALTH HOSPITAL AND MEDICAL CENTER - HARVARD (O, 50 beds) 901 Grant Street, Harvard, IL Zip 60033–1898, P O Box 850, 60033–0850, tel. 815/943–5431; Javon R. Bea, Chief Executive Officer
Web address: www.mercyhealthsystem.org

WISCONSIN: MERCYHEALTH HOSPITAL AND MEDICAL CENTER - WALWORTH (O, 18 beds) N2950 State Road 67, Lake Geneva, WI Zip 53147–2655; tel. 262/245–0535; Javon R. Bea, President and Chief Executive Officer
Web address: www.mercyhealthsystem.org

MERCYHEALTH HOSPITAL AND TRAUMA CENTER - JANESVILLE (O, 132 beds) 1000 Mineral Point Avenue, Janesville, WI Zip 53548–2982, P O Box 5003, 53547–5003, tel. 608/756–6000; Javon R. Bea, President and Chief Executive Officer

Owned, leased, sponsored:	4 hospitals	488 beds
Contract-managed:	0 hospitals	0 beds
Totals:	4 hospitals	488 beds

★**2735: METHODIST HEALTH SYSTEM** (NP)
1441 North Beckley Avenue, Dallas, TX Zip 75203–1201, P O Box 655999, 75265–5999, tel. 214/947–8181; Stephen L. Mansfield, Ph.D., FACHE, President and Chief Executive Officer
(Centralized Physician/Insurance Health System)

TEXAS: METHODIST CHARLTON MEDICAL CENTER (O, 292 beds) 3500 West Wheatland Road, Dallas, TX Zip 75237–3460, P O Box 225357, 75222–5357, tel. 214/947–7777; Fran Laukaitis, R.N., FACHE, President
Web address: www.methodisthealthsystem.org/charlton

METHODIST DALLAS MEDICAL CENTER (O, 390 beds) 1441 North Beckley Avenue, Dallas, TX Zip 75203–1201, P O Box 655999, 75265–5999, tel. 214/947–8181; Martin Koonsman, M.D., FACS, President
Web address: www.methodisthealthsystem.org/Dallas

METHODIST MANSFIELD MEDICAL CENTER (O, 221 beds) 2700 East Broad Street, Mansfield, TX Zip 76063–5899; tel. 682/622–2000; John E. Phillips, FACHE, President

METHODIST RICHARDSON MEDICAL CENTER (O, 266 beds) 2831 East President George Bush Highway, Richardson, TX Zip 75082–3561; tel. 469/204–1000; E. Kenneth. Hutchenrider Jr, FACHE, President
Web address: www.methodisthealthsystem.org/richardson

METHODIST SOUTHLAKE HOSPITAL (O, 54 beds) 421 East State Highway 114, Southlake, TX Zip 76092; tel. 817/865–4400; John McGreevy, FACHE, President

Owned, leased, sponsored:	5 hospitals	1223 beds
Contract-managed:	0 hospitals	0 beds
Totals:	5 hospitals	1223 beds

9345: METHODIST LE BONHEUR HEALTHCARE (CO)
1211 Union Avenue, Suite 700, Memphis, TN Zip 38104–6600; tel. 901/516–0791; Michael Ugwueke, President and Chief Executive Officer
(Centralized Physician/Insurance Health System)

MISSISSIPPI: METHODIST OLIVE BRANCH HOSPITAL (O, 67 beds) 4250 Bethel Road, Olive Branch, MS Zip 38654–8737; tel. 662/932–9000; David G. Baytos, Chief Executive Officer
Web address: www.methodisthealth.org/olivebranch

TENNESSEE: METHODIST HEALTHCARE MEMPHIS HOSPITALS (O, 1374 beds) 1265 Union Avenue, Memphis, TN Zip 38104–3415; tel. 901/516–7000; Michael Ugwueke, President and Chief Executive Officer
Web address: www.methodisthealth.org

Owned, leased, sponsored:	2 hospitals	1441 beds
Contract-managed:	0 hospitals	0 beds
Totals:	2 hospitals	1441 beds

★**0001: MIDMICHIGAN HEALTH** (NP)
4000 Wellness Drive, Midland, MI Zip 48670–0001; tel. 989/839–3000; Diane Postler-Slattery, Ph.D., President and Chief Executive Officer
(Centralized Physician/Insurance Health System)

MICHIGAN: MIDMICHIGAN MEDICAL CENTER - ALPENA (O, 125 beds) 1501 West Chisholm Street, Alpena, MI Zip 49707–1401; tel. 989/356–7000; Karmon T. Bjella, President

MIDMICHIGAN MEDICAL CENTER-CLARE (O, 49 beds) 703 North McEwan Street, Clare, MI Zip 48617–1440; tel. 989/802–5000; Raymond Stover, President and Chief Executive Officer
Web address: www.midmichigan.org

MIDMICHIGAN MEDICAL CENTER-GLADWIN (O, 25 beds) 515 Quarter Street, Gladwin, MI Zip 48624–1959; tel. 989/426–9286; Raymond Stover, President and Chief Executive Officer
Web address: www.midmichigan.org

MIDMICHIGAN MEDICAL CENTER-GRATIOT (O, 79 beds) 300 East Warwick Drive, Alma, MI Zip 48801–1014; tel. 989/463–1101; Gregory H. Rogers, Interim President

MIDMICHIGAN MEDICAL CENTER-MIDLAND (O, 304 beds) 4000 Wellness Drive, Midland, MI Zip 48670–2000; tel. 989/839–3000; Gregory H. Rogers, President
Web address: www.midmichigan.org

Owned, leased, sponsored:	5 hospitals	582 beds
Contract-managed:	0 hospitals	0 beds
Totals:	5 hospitals	582 beds

0368: MINNESOTA DEPARTMENT OF HUMAN SERVICES (NP)
540 Cedar Street, Saint Paul, MN Zip 55101–2208, P O Box 64998, 55164–0998, tel. 651/431–3212; Anne Barry, Deputy Commissioner
(Independent Hospital System)

MINNESOTA: ANOKA-METROPOLITAN REGIONAL TREATMENT CENTER (O, 200 beds) 3301 Seventh Avenue, Anoka, MN Zip 55303–4516, 3301 Seventh Avenue North, 55303–4516, tel. 651/431–5000; Wade Brost, Executive Director

COMMUNITY BEHAVIORAL HEALTH HOSPITAL - ALEXANDRIA (O, 16 beds) 1610 8th Avenue East, Alexandria, MN Zip 56308–2472; tel. 320/335–6201; Jennifer Westrum, Administrator
Web address: www.health.state.mn.us

COMMUNITY BEHAVIORAL HEALTH HOSPITAL - ANNANDALE (O, 16 beds) 400 Annandale Boulevard, Annandale, MN Zip 55302–3141; tel. 651/259–3850; James P. Kelly, FACHE, Administrator
Web address: www.health.state.mn.us

COMMUNITY BEHAVIORAL HEALTH HOSPITAL - BAXTER (O, 16 beds) 14241 Grand Oaks Drive, Baxter, MN Zip 56425–8749; tel. 218/316–3101; Richard G. Slieter Jr, Administrator

COMMUNITY BEHAVIORAL HEALTH HOSPITAL - BEMIDJI (O, 16 beds) 800 Bemidji Avenue North, Bemidji, MN Zip 56601–3054; tel. 218/308–2400; Larry A. Laudon, Administrator

COMMUNITY BEHAVIORAL HEALTH HOSPITAL - FERGUS FALLS (O, 16 beds) 1801 West Alcott Avenue, Fergus Falls, MN Zip 56537–2661, P O Box 478, 56538–0478, tel. 218/332–5001; Brenda Schleske, Administrator

COMMUNITY BEHAVIORAL HEALTH HOSPITAL - ROCHESTER (O, 16 beds) 251 Wood Lake Drive SE, Rochester, MN Zip 55904–5530; tel. 507/206–2561; Stephanie Juhl, Administrator
Web address: www.health.state.mn.us

Owned, leased, sponsored:	7 hospitals	296 beds
Contract-managed:	0 hospitals	0 beds
Totals:	7 hospitals	296 beds

★**0143: MISSION HEALTH SYSTEM** (NP)
509 Biltmore Avenue, Asheville, NC Zip 28801–4601; tel. 828/213–1111; Ronald A. Paulus, M.D., President and Chief Executive Officer
(Centralized Physician/Insurance Health System)

NORTH CAROLINA: ANGEL MEDICAL CENTER (O, 43 beds) 120 Riverview Street, Franklin, NC Zip 28734–2612, P O Box 1209, 28744–0569,

For explanation of codes following names, see page B2.
★ Indicates Type III membership in the American Hospital Association.

tel. 828/524–8411; Karen S. Gorby, R.N., MSN, FACHE, President and Chief Nursing Officer
Web address: www.angelmed.org

ASHEVILLE SPECIALTY HOSPITAL (O, 32 beds) 428 Biltmore Avenue, 4th Floor, Asheville, NC Zip 28801–4502; tel. 828/213–5400; Julie A. Dikos, MSN, R.N., President and Chief Executive Officer

BLUE RIDGE REGIONAL HOSPITAL (O, 42 beds) 125 Hospital Drive, Spruce Pine, NC Zip 28777–3035; tel. 828/765–4201; Rebecca W. Carter, MSN, R.N., FACHE, Chief Executive Officer and Chief Nursing Officer
Web address: www.spchospital.org

CAREPARTNERS HEALTH SERVICES (O, 80 beds) 68 Sweeten Creek Road, Asheville, NC 28803–2318, P O Box 15025, 28813–0025, tel. 828/277–4800; Tracy Buchanan, Chief Executive Officer and President

HIGHLANDS-CASHIERS HOSPITAL (O, 104 beds) 190 Hospital Drive, Highlands, NC Zip 28741–7600, P O Drawer 190, 28741–0190, tel. 828/526–1200; Jacqueline Medland, MS, Ph.D., President and Chief Nursing Officer
Web address: www.hchospital.org

MCDOWELL HOSPITAL (O, 49 beds) 430 Rankin Drive, Marion, NC Zip 28752–6568, P O Box 730, 28752–0730, tel. 828/659–5000; Carol C. Wolfenbarger, FACHE, MSN, President and Chief Executive Officer
Web address: www.mission-health.org

MISSION HOSPITAL (O, 763 beds) 509 Biltmore Avenue, Asheville, NC Zip 28801–4690; tel. 828/213–1111; Jill Hoggard Green, Ph.D., R.N., President
Web address: www.mission-health.org

TRANSYLVANIA REGIONAL HOSPITAL (O, 40 beds) 260 Hospital Drive, Brevard, NC Zip 28712–3378; tel. 828/884–9111; Michele Pilon, President and Chief Nursing Officer

Owned, leased, sponsored:	0 hospitals	0 beds
Contract-managed:	2 hospitals	2 beds
Totals:	2 hospitals	98 beds

★2475: MISSISSIPPI COUNTY HOSPITAL SYSTEM (NP)
1520 North Division Street, Blytheville, AR Zip 72315–1448, P O Box 108, 72316–0108, tel. 870/838–7300; Chris Lee. Raymer, R.N., MSN, Chief Executive Officer

GREAT RIVER MEDICAL CENTER (C, 73 beds) 1520 North Division Street, Blytheville, AR Zip 72315–1448, P O Box 108, 72316–0108, tel. 870/838–7300; Chris Lee. Raymer, R.N., MSN, Chief Executive Officer

SOUTH MISSISSIPPI COUNTY REGIONAL MEDICAL CENTER (C, 25 beds) 611 West Lee Avenue, Osceola, AR Zip 72370–3001, P O Box 108, Blytheville, 72316–0108, tel. 870/563–7000; Chris Lee. Raymer, R.N., MSN, Chief Executive Officer
Web address: www.mchsys.org

Owned, leased, sponsored:	0 hospitals	0 beds
Contract-managed:	2 hospitals	98 beds
Totals:	2 hospitals	98 beds

0017: MISSISSIPPI STATE DEPARTMENT OF MENTAL HEALTH (NP)
1101 Robert E Lee Building, 239 North Lamar Street, Jackson, MS Zip 39201–1101; tel. 601/359–1288; Edwin C. LeGrand III, Executive Director
(Independent Hospital System)

MISSISSIPPI: EAST MISSISSIPPI STATE HOSPITAL (O, 335 beds) 1818 College Drive, Meridian, MS Zip 39307, Box 4128, West Station, 39304–4128, tel. 601/482–6186; Charles Carlisle, Director
Web address: www.emsh.state.ms.us

MISSISSIPPI STATE HOSPITAL (O, 506 beds) 3550 Highway 468 West, Whitfield, MS Zip 39193–5529, P O Box 157-A, 39193–0157, tel. 601/351–8000; James G. Chastain, FACHE, Director

NORTH MISSISSIPPI STATE HOSPITAL (O, 50 beds) 1937 Briar Ridge Road, Tupelo, MS Zip 38804–5963; tel. 662/690–4200; Paul A. Callens, Ph.D., Director
Web address: www.nmsh.state.ms.us

SOUTH MISSISSIPPI STATE HOSPITAL (O, 50 beds) 823 Highway 589, Purvis, MS Zip 39475–4194; tel. 601/794–0100; Sabrina Young, Director

Owned, leased, sponsored:	4 hospitals	941 beds
Contract-managed:	0 hospitals	0 beds
Totals:	4 hospitals	941 beds

★0970: MONONGALIA HEALTH SYSTEM (NP)
1200 J. D. Anderson Drive, Morgantown, WV Zip 26505–3494; tel. 304/598–1200; Darryl L. Duncan, President and Chief Executive Officer
(Independent Hospital System)

WEST VIRGINIA: MON HEALTH MEDICAL CENTER (O, 185 beds) 1200 J D Anderson Drive, Morgantown, WV Zip 26505–3486; tel. 304/598–1200; Darryl L. Duncan, President and Chief Executive Officer
Web address: www.mongeneral.com

PRESTON MEMORIAL HOSPITAL (O, 25 beds) 150 Memorial Drive, Kingwood, WV Zip 26537–1495; tel. 304/329–1400; Melissa Lockwood, Chief Executive Officer
Web address: www.prestonmemorial.org

Owned, leased, sponsored:	2 hospitals	210 beds
Contract-managed:	0 hospitals	0 beds
Totals:	2 hospitals	210 beds

0343: MONTEFIORE HEALTH SYSTEM (NP)
111 East 210th Street, Bronx, NY Zip 10467–2490; tel. 718/920–4321; Steven M. Safyer, M.D., President and CEO
(Centralized Health System)

NEW YORK: BURKE REHABILITATION HOSPITAL (O, 150 beds) 785 Mamaroneck Avenue, White Plains, NY Zip 10605–2523; tel. 914/597–2500; Jeffrey Menkes, President and Chief Executive Officer

MONTEFIORE MEDICAL CENTER (O, 1519 beds) 111 East 210th Street, Bronx, NY Zip 10467–2401; tel. 718/920–4321; Steven M. Safyer, M.D., President and Chief Executive Officer
Web address: www.montefiore.org

MONTEFIORE MOUNT VERNON (O, 63 beds) 12 North Seventh Avenue, Mount Vernon, NY Zip 10550–2098; tel. 914/664–8000; Jaccel Kouns, R.N., MS, Vice President and Executive Director
Web address: www.montefiorehealthsystem.org/landing.cfm?id=17

MONTEFIORE NEW ROCHELLE (O, 298 beds) 16 Guion Place, New Rochelle, NY Zip 10801–5502; tel. 914/632–5000; Anthony Alfano, Vice President Executive Director
Web address: www.montefiorehealthsystem.org

NYACK HOSPITAL (O, 245 beds) 160 North Midland Avenue, Nyack, NY Zip 10960–1998; tel. 845/348–2000; Mark Geller, M.D., President and Chief Executive Officer
Web address: www.nyackhospital.org

WHITE PLAINS HOSPITAL CENTER (O, 292 beds) 41 East Post Road, White Plains, NY Zip 10601–4699; tel. 914/681–0600; Susan Fox, President and Chief Executive Officer
Web address: www.wphospital.org

Owned, leased, sponsored:	6 hospitals	2567 beds
Contract-managed:	0 hospitals	0 beds
Totals:	6 hospitals	2567 beds

1335: MORTON PLANT MEASE HEALTH CARE (NP)
300 Pinellas Street, Clearwater, FL Zip 33756–3804, P O Box 210, 33757–0210, tel. 727/462–7000; Glenn D. Waters, FACHE, President

For explanation of codes following names, see page B2.
★ Indicates Type III membership in the American Hospital Association.

Section B

FLORIDA: MORTON PLANT HOSPITAL (O, 605 beds) 300 Pinellas Street, Clearwater, FL Zip 33756–3804, P O Box 210, 33757–0210, tel. 727/462–7000; N. Kristopher. Hoce, President

MORTON PLANT NORTH BAY HOSPITAL (O, 222 beds) 6600 Madison Street, New Port Richey, FL Zip 34652–1900; tel. 727/842–8468; Sarah Naumowich, Interim President
Web address: www.mpmhealth.com

MORTON PLANT REHABILITATION CENTER (O, 126 beds) 400 Corbett Street, Belleair, FL Zip 34640; tel. 813/462–7600; Linda A. Kirk, Administrator

Owned, leased, sponsored:	3 hospitals	953 beds
Contract-managed:	0 hospitals	0 beds
Totals:	3 hospitals	953 beds

★**0917: MOUNT SINAI HEALTH SYSTEM** (NP)
One Gustave L. Levy Place, New York, NY Zip 10029; tel. 212/659–8888; Kenneth L. Davis, M.D., President and Chief Executive
(Centralized Health System)

NEW YORK: MOUNT SINAI BETH ISRAEL (O, 633 beds) First Avenue and 16th Street, New York, NY Zip 10003–3803; tel. 212/420–2000; Jeremy Boal, M.D., President
Web address: www.bethisraelny.org

MOUNT SINAI HOSPITAL (O, 1132 beds) One Gustave L Levy Place, P O Box 1068, New York, NY Zip 10029–0310; tel. 212/241–6500; David L. Reich, M.D., President and Chief Operating Officer

MOUNT SINAI WEST (O, 668 beds) 1111 Amsterdam Avenue, New York, NY Zip 10025–1716; tel. 212/523–4000; Arthur A. Gianelli, M.P.H., President
Web address: www.stlukeshospitalnyc.org

NEW YORK EYE AND EAR INFIRMARY OF MOUNT SINAI (O, 32 beds) 310 East 14th Street, New York, NY Zip 10003–4201; tel. 212/979–4000; James Tsai, M.D., President
Web address: www.nyee.edu

Owned, leased, sponsored:	4 hospitals	2465 beds
Contract-managed:	0 hospitals	0 beds
Totals:	4 hospitals	2465 beds

0167: MOUNTAIN STATES HEALTH ALLIANCE (NP)
400 North State of Franklin Road, Johnson City, TN Zip 37604–6035; tel. 423/302–3423; Alan M. Levine, President and Chief Executive Officer
(Centralized Health System)

TENNESSEE: FRANKLIN WOODS COMMUNITY HOSPITAL (O, 80 beds) 300 MedTech Parkway, Johnson City, TN Zip 37604–2277; tel. 423/302–1000; Lindy P. White, Chief Executive Officer

INDIAN PATH MEDICAL CENTER (O, 160 beds) 2000 Brookside Drive, Kingsport, TN Zip 37660–4627; tel. 423/857–7000; Monty E. McLaurin, Chief Executive Officer, Northwest Market
Web address: www.msha.com

JOHNSON CITY MEDICAL CENTER (O, 585 beds) 400 North State of Franklin Road, Johnson City, TN Zip 37604–6094; tel. 423/431–6111; Melody Trimble, Chief Executive Officer
Web address: www.msha.com

JOHNSON COUNTY COMMUNITY HOSPITAL (O, 2 beds) 1901 South Shady Street, Mountain City, TN Zip 37683–2271; tel. 423/727–1100; Chastity Trivette, Chief Executive Officer
Web address: www.msha.com

LAUGHLIN MEMORIAL HOSPITAL (O, 152 beds) 1420 Tusculum Boulevard, Greeneville, TN Zip 37745–5825; tel. 423/787–5000; Charles H. Whitfield Jr, President and Chief Executive Officer

SYCAMORE SHOALS HOSPITAL (O, 74 beds) 1501 West Elk Avenue, Elizabethton, TN Zip 37643–2874; tel. 423/542–1300; Dwayne Taylor, Chief Executive Officer
Web address: www.msha.com

UNICOI COUNTY MEMORIAL HOSPITAL (O, 94 beds) 100 Greenway Circle, Erwin, TN Zip 37650–2196, P O Box 802, 37650–0802, tel. 423/743–3141; Eric Carroll, Chief Executive Officer

VIRGINIA: DICKENSON COMMUNITY HOSPITAL (O, 7 beds) 312 Hospital Drive, Clintwood, VA Zip 24228, P O Box 1440, 24228–1440, tel. 276/926–0300; Mark T. Leonard, Chief Executive Officer
Web address: www.msha.com/dch

JOHNSTON MEMORIAL HOSPITAL (O, 116 beds) 16000 Johnston Memorial Drive, Abingdon, VA Zip 24211–7659; tel. 276/258–1000; Stan Hickson, FACHE, President and Chief Executive Officer
Web address: www.jmh.org

NORTON COMMUNITY HOSPITAL (O, 57 beds) 100 15th Street NW, Norton, VA Zip 24273–1616; tel. 276/679–9600; Mark T. Leonard, Chief Executive Officer
Web address: www.msha.com/nch

RUSSELL COUNTY MEDICAL CENTER (O, 78 beds) 58 Carroll Street, Lebanon, VA Zip 24266, P O Box 3600, 24266–0200, tel. 276/883–8000; Stephen K. Givens, Assistant Vice President and Administrator
Web address: www.mountainstateshealth.com/rcmc

SMYTH COUNTY COMMUNITY HOSPITAL (O, 153 beds) 245 Medical Park Drive, Marion, VA Zip 24354, P O Box 880, 24354–0880, tel. 276/378–1000; Stan Hickson, FACHE, President and Chief Executive Officer
Web address: www.msha.com/scch

Owned, leased, sponsored:	12 hospitals	1558 beds
Contract-managed:	0 hospitals	0 beds
Totals:	12 hospitals	1558 beds

6555: MULTICARE HEALTH SYSTEM (NP)
315 Martin Luther King Jr Way, Tacoma, WA Zip 98405–4234, P O Box 5299, 98415–0299, tel. 253/403–1000; William G. Robertson, President and Chief Executive Officer
(Centralized Physician/Insurance Health System)

WASHINGTON: MULTICARE AUBURN MEDICAL CENTER (O, 153 beds) 202 North Division, Plaza One, Auburn, WA Zip 98001–4908; tel. 253/833–7711; Mark Smith, President and Chief Operating Officer

MULTICARE DEACONESS HOSPITAL (O, 352 beds) 800 West Fifth Avenue, Spokane, WA Zip 99204–2803, P O Box 248, 99210–0248, tel. 509/458–5800; Laureen Driscoll, President
Web address: www.deaconesspokane.com/Deaconess-Hospital/home.aspx

MULTICARE GOOD SAMARITAN HOSPITAL (O, 287 beds) 401 15th Avenue SE, Puyallup, WA Zip 98372–3770, P O Box 1247, 98371–0192, tel. 253/697–4000; Christopher Bredeson, President and Chief Operating Officer
Web address: www.multicare.org/good-samaritan-hospital/

MULTICARE MARY BRIDGE CHILDREN'S HOSPITAL AND HEALTH CENTER (O, 75 beds) 317 Martin Luther King Jr Way, Tacoma, WA Zip 98405–4234, P O Box 5299, 98415–0299, tel. 253/403–1400; Linda Chen, President and Market Leader

MULTICARE TACOMA GENERAL HOSPITAL (O, 420 beds) 315 Martin Luther King Jr Way, Tacoma, WA Zip 98405–4234, P O Box 5299, 98415–0299, tel. 253/403–1000; Julia Truman, President and Chief Operating Officer
Web address: www.multicare.org

MULTICARE VALLEY HOSPITAL (O, 92 beds) 12606 East Mission Avenue, Spokane Valley, WA Zip 99216–1090; tel. 509/924–6650; Gregory George. Repetti III, FACHE, Chief Executive Officer
Web address: www.valleyhospital.org

Owned, leased, sponsored:	6 hospitals	1379 beds
Contract-managed:	0 hospitals	0 beds
Totals:	6 hospitals	1379 beds

★**1465: MUNSON HEALTHCARE** (NP)
1105 Sixth Street, Traverse City, MI Zip 49684–2386; tel. 231/935–6703; Edwin Ness, President and Chief Executive Officer
(Centralized Health System)

For explanation of codes following names, see page B2.
★ Indicates Type III membership in the American Hospital Association.

MICHIGAN: KALKASKA MEMORIAL HEALTH CENTER (C, 112 beds) 419 South Coral Street, Kalkaska, MI Zip 49646–2503; tel. 231/258–7500; Kevin L. Rogols, FACHE, Administrator

MUNSON HEALTHCARE CADILLAC HOSPITAL (O, 97 beds) 400 Hobart Street, Cadillac, MI Zip 49601–2389; tel. 231/876–7200; Tonya Smith, President
Web address: www.mercyhealthcadillac.com/welcome-cadillac

MUNSON HEALTHCARE CHARLEVOIX HOSPITAL (O, 25 beds) 14700 Lake Shore Drive, Charlevoix, MI Zip 49720–1999; tel. 231/547–4024; Joanne Schroeder, President

MUNSON HEALTHCARE GRAYLING HOSPITAL (O, 110 beds) 1100 East Michigan Avenue, Grayling, MI Zip 49738–1312; tel. 989/348–5461; Stephanie J. Riemer, President
Web address: www.mercygrayling.munsonhealthcare.org/

MUNSON HEALTHCARE MANISTEE HOSPITAL (O, 45 beds) 1465 East Parkdale Avenue, Manistee, MI Zip 49660–9709; tel. 231/398–1100; James Barker, Chief Executive Officer
Web address: www.westshoremedcenter.org

MUNSON MEDICAL CENTER (O, 391 beds) 1105 Sixth Street, Traverse City, MI Zip 49684–2386; tel. 231/935–5000; Alfred E. Pilong Jr, FACHE, President, Munson Medical Center and Chief Operating Officer, Munson Healthcare

PAUL OLIVER MEMORIAL HOSPITAL (O, 47 beds) 224 Park Avenue, Frankfort, MI Zip 49635–9658; tel. 231/352–2200; Peter Marinoff, President
Web address: www.munsonhealthcare.org

Owned, leased, sponsored:	6 hospitals	715 beds
Contract-managed:	1 hospitals	112 beds
Totals:	7 hospitals	827 beds

0261: NATIONAL SURGICAL HEALTHCARE (IO)
250 South Wacker Drive, Suite 500, Chicago, IL Zip 60606–5897; tel. 312/627–8400; David Crane, Chief Executive Officer
(Independent Hospital System)

ARIZONA: ARIZONA SPINE AND JOINT HOSPITAL (O, 23 beds) 4620 East Baseline Road, Mesa, AZ Zip 85206–4624; tel. 480/832–4770; Todd Greene, Chief Executive Officer
Web address: www.azspineandjoint.com

GEORGIA: OPTIM MEDICAL CENTER - JENKINS (O, 25 beds) 931 East Winthrope Avenue, Millen, GA Zip 30442–1839; tel. 478/982–4221; Robert R. Sellers, Chief Executive Officer
Web address: www.optimhealth.com

OPTIM MEDICAL CENTER - SCREVEN (O, 25 beds) 215 Mims Road, Sylvania, GA Zip 30467–2097; tel. 912/564–7426; Robert R. Sellers, Chief Executive Officer

OPTIM MEDICAL CENTER - TATTNALL (O, 25 beds) 247 South Main Street, Reidsville, GA Zip 30453–4605; tel. 912/557–1000; Rob Snipes, Administrator
Web address: www.optimmedicalcenter.com

IDAHO: NORTHWEST SPECIALTY HOSPITAL (O, 34 beds) 1593 East Polston Avenue, Post Falls, ID Zip 83854–5326; tel. 208/262–2300; Rick Rasmussen, Chief Executive Officer
Web address: www.northwestspecialtyhospital.com

LOUISIANA: LAFAYETTE SURGICAL SPECIALTY HOSPITAL (O, 20 beds) 1101 Kaliste Saloom Road, Lafayette, LA Zip 70508–5705; tel. 337/769–4100; Buffy Domingue, Chief Executive Officer

MICHIGAN: SOUTHEAST MICHIGAN SURGICAL HOSPITAL (O, 13 beds) 21230 Dequindre, Warren, MI Zip 48091–2287; tel. 586/427–1000; Barry Cullen, Chief Executive Officer
Web address: www.nshinc.com

NORTH CAROLINA: NORTH CAROLINA SPECIALTY HOSPITAL (O, 18 beds) 3916 Ben Franklin Boulevard, Durham, NC Zip 27704–2383, PO Box 15819, 27704–2383, tel. 919/956–9300; Randi L. Shults, Chief Executive Officer
Web address: www.ncspecialty.com

TEXAS: EL PASO SPECIALTY HOSPITAL (O, 20 beds) 1755 Curie Drive, El Paso, TX Zip 79902–2919; tel. 915/544–3636; James Wilcox, Chief Executive Officer

SOUTH TEXAS SPINE AND SURGICAL HOSPITAL (O, 30 beds) 18600 Hardy Oak Boulevard, San Antonio, TX Zip 78258–4206; tel. 210/507–4090; Thomas Klawiter, Chief Executive Officer
Web address: www.southtexassurgical.com

SOUTH TEXAS SURGICAL HOSPITAL (O, 20 beds) 6130 Parkway Drive, Corpus Christi, TX Zip 78414–2455; tel. 361/993–2000; James Murphy, Chief Executive Officer
Web address: www.southtexassurgicalhospital.com

WISCONSIN: OAKLEAF SURGICAL HOSPITAL (O, 13 beds) 3802 West Oakwood Mall Drive, Eau Claire, WI Zip 54701–3016; tel. 715/831–8130; Anne Hargrave-Thomas, Chief Executive Officer

WYOMING: MOUNTAIN VIEW REGIONAL HOSPITAL (O, 23 beds) 6550 East Second Street, Casper, WY Zip 82609–4321, P O Box 51888, 82605–1888, tel. 307/995–8100; Thomas Kopitnik, Acting Chief Executive Officer
Web address: www.mountainviewregionalhospital.com

Owned, leased, sponsored:	13 hospitals	289 beds
Contract-managed:	0 hospitals	0 beds
Totals:	13 hospitals	289 beds

0923: NAVICENT HEALTH (NP)
777 Hemlock Street, MSC 105, Macon, GA Zip 31201–2155, 777 Hemlock Street, 31201–2155, tel. 478/633–1000; Ninfa M. Saunders, Chief Executive Officer
(Centralized Health System)

GEORGIA: MEDICAL CENTER OF PEACH COUNTY, NAVICENT HEALTH (O, 25 beds) 1960 Highway 247 Connector, Bryon, GA Zip 31008; tel. 478/654–2000; Darren Pearce, Administrator and Chief Executive Officer

MEDICAL CENTER, NAVICENT HEALTH (O, 659 beds) 777 Hemlock Street, Macon, GA Zip 31201–2155; tel. 478/633–1000; Ninfa M. Saunders, Chief Executive Officer
Web address: https://www.navicenthealth.org/

OCONEE REGIONAL MEDICAL CENTER (C, 90 beds) 821 North Cobb Street, Milledgeville, GA Zip 31061–2351, P O Box 690, 31059–0690, tel. 478/454–3505; Steven Johnson, Interim Chief Executive Officer

REHABILITATION HOSPITAL, NAVICENT HEALTH (O, 58 beds) 3351 Northside Drive, Macon, GA Zip 31210–2587; tel. 478/201–6500; Gina Tipton, Director of Operations
Web address: www.navicenthealth.org/service-center/rehabilitation-hospital-navicent-health

Owned, leased, sponsored:	3 hospitals	742 beds
Contract-managed:	1 hospitals	90 beds
Totals:	4 hospitals	832 beds

★9265: NEBRASKA METHODIST HEALTH SYSTEM, INC. (CO)
8511 West Dodge Road, Omaha, NE Zip 68114–3403; tel. 402/354–5411; John M. Fraser, FACHE, President and Chief Executive Officer
(Centralized Physician/Insurance Health System)

IOWA: METHODIST JENNIE EDMUNDSON HOSPITAL (O, 114 beds) 933 East Pierce Street, Council Bluffs, IA Zip 51503–4652, P O Box 2C, 51502–3002, tel. 712/396–6000; Steven P. Baumert, President and Chief Executive Officer
Web address: www.bestcare.org

NEBRASKA: NEBRASKA METHODIST HOSPITAL (O, 377 beds) 8303 Dodge Street, Omaha, NE Zip 68114–4199; tel. 402/354–4000; Stephen L. Goeser, FACHE, Executive Vice President and Chief Operations Officer

Owned, leased, sponsored:	2 hospitals	491 beds
Contract-managed:	0 hospitals	0 beds
Totals:	2 hospitals	491 beds

For explanation of codes following names, see page B2.
★ Indicates Type III membership in the American Hospital Association.

0892: NEMOURS (NP)

10140 Centurion Parkway North, Jacksonville, FL Zip 32256–0532; tel. 904/697–4100; David J. Bailey, M.D., President and Chief Executive Officer

(Independent Hospital System)

DELAWARE: ALFRED I. DUPONT HOSPITAL FOR CHILDREN (O, 200 beds) 1600 Rockland Road, Wilmington, DE Zip 19803–3616, Box 269, 19899–0269, tel. 302/651–4000; Roy Proujansky, M.D., Chief Executive Officer
Web address: www.nemours.org

FLORIDA: NEMOURS CHILDREN'S HOSPITAL (O, 80 beds) 13535 Nemours Parkway, Orlando, FL Zip 32827–7402; tel. 407/567–4000; Dana Bledsoe, MS, R.N., Chief Executive Officer

Owned, leased, sponsored:	2 hospitals	280 beds
Contract-managed:	0 hospitals	0 beds
Totals:	2 hospitals	280 beds

0620: NEUROPSYCHIATRIC HOSPITALS (IO)

1625 East Jefferson Boulevard, Mishawaka, IN Zip 46545–7103; tel. 574/255–1400; Cameron R. Gilbert, Ph.D., President and Chief Executive Officer

INDIANA: DOCTORS NEUROPSYCHIATRIC HOSPITAL AND RESEARCH INSTITUTE (O, 20 beds) 417 South Whitlock Street, Bremen, IN Zip 46506–1626; tel. 574/546–0330; Christy Gilbert, Interim Chief Executive Officer

NEUROPSYCHIATRIC HOSPITAL OF INDIANAPOLIS (O, 50 beds) 6720 Parkdale Place, Indianapolis, IN Zip 46254–4668; tel. 317/744–9200; Corey Simmons, Chief Executive Officer
Web address: https://www.neuropsychiatrichospitals.net

RIVERCREST SPECIALTY HOSPITAL (O, 30 beds) 1625 East Jefferson Boulevard, Mishawaka, IN Zip 46545–7103; tel. 574/255–1400; Christy Gilbert, Chief Executive Officer

Owned, leased, sponsored:	3 hospitals	100 beds
Contract-managed:	0 hospitals	0 beds
Totals:	3 hospitals	100 beds

★0213: NEW HANOVER REGIONAL MEDICAL CENTER (NP)

2131 South 17th Street, Wilmington, NC Zip 28401–7407; tel. 910/343–7040; John H. Gizdic, President and Chief Executive Officer

(Moderately Centralized Health System)

NORTH CAROLINA: NEW HANOVER REGIONAL MEDICAL CENTER (O, 685 beds) 2131 South 17th Street, Wilmington, NC Zip 28401–7483, P O Box 9000, 28402–9000, tel. 910/343–7000; Andre Boyd Sr, Executive Vice President, Hospital Division
Web address: www.nhrmc.org

PENDER MEMORIAL HOSPITAL (C, 68 beds) 507 East Freemont Street, Burgaw, NC Zip 28425–5131; tel. 910/259–5451; Ruth Glaser, President

Owned, leased, sponsored:	1 hospitals	685 beds
Contract-managed:	1 hospitals	68 beds
Totals:	2 hospitals	753 beds

0009: NEW YORK STATE OFFICE OF MENTAL HEALTH (NP)

44 Holland Avenue, Albany, NY Zip 12208–3411; tel. 518/474–7056; Kristin M. Woodlock, R.N., Acting Commissioner
(Independent Hospital System)

NEW YORK: BRONX PSYCHIATRIC CENTER (O, 450 beds) 1500 Waters Place, Bronx, NY Zip 10461–2796; tel. 718/931–0600; Anita Daniels, Director
Web address: www.omh.ny.gov

BUFFALO PSYCHIATRIC CENTER (O, 240 beds) 400 Forest Avenue, Buffalo, NY Zip 14213–1298; tel. 716/885–2261; Thomas Dodson, Executive Director

CAPITAL DISTRICT PSYCHIATRIC CENTER (O, 200 beds) 75 New Scotland Avenue, Albany, NY Zip 12208–3474; tel. 518/549–6000; William Dickson, Executive Director
Web address: www.omh.ny.gov/omhweb/facilities/cdpc/facility.htm

CENTRAL NEW YORK PSYCHIATRIC CENTER (O, 226 beds) 9005 Old River Road, Marcy, NY Zip 13403–3000, P O Box 300, 13403–0300, tel. 315/765–3600; Maureen Bosco, Executive Director
Web address: www.omh.ny.gov

CREEDMOOR PSYCHIATRIC CENTER (O, 380 beds) 79–25 Winchester Boulevard, Jamaica, NY Zip 11427–2128; tel. 718/264–3600; Ann Marie. Barbarotta, Executive Director
Web address: www.omh.ny.gov

ELMIRA PSYCHIATRIC CENTER (O, 100 beds) 100 Washington Street, Elmira, NY Zip 14901–2898; tel. 607/737–4739; David Peppel, Executive Director

GREATER BINGHAMTON HEALTH CENTER (O, 89 beds) 425 Robinson Street, Binghamton, NY Zip 13904–1735; tel. 607/724–1391; David Peppel, Executive Director
Web address: www.omh.ny.gov/omhweb/facilities/bipc/facility.htm

KINGSBORO PSYCHIATRIC CENTER (O, 290 beds) 681 Clarkson Avenue, Brooklyn, NY Zip 11203–2125; tel. 718/221–7395; Deborah Parchment, Executive Director
Web address: www.omh.ny.gov/omhweb/facilities/kbpc/facility/htm

KIRBY FORENSIC PSYCHIATRIC CENTER (O, 193 beds) 600 East 125th Street, New York, NY Zip 10035–6000; tel. 646/672–5800; Vincent Miccoli, Executive Director

MANHATTAN PSYCHIATRIC CENTER-WARD'S ISLAND (O, 745 beds) 600 East 125th Street, New York, NY Zip 10035–6000; tel. 646/672–6767; Vincent Miccoli, Executive Director
Web address: www.omh.ny.gov

MID-HUDSON FORENSIC PSYCHIATRIC CENTER (O, 285 beds) Route 17M, New Hampton, NY Zip 10958, P O Box 158, 10958–0158, tel. 845/374–8700; Joseph Freebern, Executive Director

MOHAWK VALLEY PSYCHIATRIC CENTER (O, 614 beds) 1400 Noyes Street, Utica, NY Zip 13502–3854; tel. 315/738–3800; Colleen A. Sawyer, R.N., MSN, Executive Director
Web address: www.omh.ny.gov/omhweb/facilities/mvpc/facility.htm

NEW YORK CITY CHILDREN'S CENTER (O, 84 beds) 74–03 Commonwealth Boulevard, Jamaica, NY Zip 11426–1890; tel. 718/264–4506; Anita Daniels, Executive Director

NEW YORK STATE PSYCHIATRIC INSTITUTE (O, 58 beds) 1051 Riverside Drive, New York, NY Zip 10032–1007; tel. 646/774–5000; Jeffrey A. Lieberman, M.D., Executive Director
Web address: www.nyspi.org

PILGRIM PSYCHIATRIC CENTER (O, 569 beds) 998 Crooked Hill Road, Brentwood, NY Zip 11717–1019; tel. 631/761–3500; Kathy O'Keefe, Executive Director

RICHARD H. HUTCHINGS PSYCHIATRIC CENTER (O, 131 beds) 620 Madison Street, Syracuse, NY Zip 13210–2319; tel. 315/426–3632; Colleen A. Sawyer, R.N., MSN, Executive Director
Web address: www.omh.ny.gov

ROCHESTER PSYCHIATRIC CENTER (O, 180 beds) 1111 Elmwood Avenue, Rochester, NY Zip 14620–3005; tel. 585/241–1200; Philip Griffin, Director of Operations

ROCKLAND CHILDREN'S PSYCHIATRIC CENTER (O, 54 beds) 599 Convent Road, Orangeburg, NY Zip 10962–1162; tel. 845/359–7400; Christopher Tavella, Acting Executive Director
Web address: www.omh.ny.gov/

ROCKLAND PSYCHIATRIC CENTER (O, 525 beds) 140 Old Orangeburg Road, Orangeburg, NY Zip 10962–1157; tel. 845/359–1000; Christopher Tavella, Executive Director

SAGAMORE CHILDREN'S PSYCHIATRIC CENTER (O, 54 beds) 197 Half Hollow Road, Dix Hills, NY Zip 11746–5861; tel. 631/370–1700; Kathy O'Keefe, Interim Executive Director
Web address: www.omh.ny.gov

SOUTH BEACH PSYCHIATRIC CENTER (O, 340 beds) 777 Seaview Avenue, Staten Island, NY Zip 10305–3409; tel. 718/667–2300; Doreen Piazza, Acting Executive Director
Web address: www.omh.ny.gov/omhweb/facilities/sbpc/facility.htm

Section B

For explanation of codes following names, see page B2.
★ Indicates Type III membership in the American Hospital Association.

ST. LAWRENCE PSYCHIATRIC CENTER (O, 146 beds) 1 Chimney Point Drive, Ogdensburg, NY Zip 13669–2291; tel. 315/541–2001; Timothy Farrell, Executive Director

WESTERN NEW YORK CHILDREN'S PSYCHIATRIC CENTER (O, 46 beds) 1010 East and West Road, West Seneca, NY Zip 14224–3602; tel. 716/677–7000; Kathe Hayes, Executive Director
Web address: www.omh.ny.gov

Owned, leased, sponsored:	23 hospitals	5999 beds
Contract-managed:	0 hospitals	0 beds
Totals:	23 hospitals	5999 beds

★**0142: NEWYORK-PRESBYTERIAN** (NP)
525 East 68th Street, Box 182, New York, NY Zip 10065; tel. 212/746–3745; Steven J. Corwin, M.D., President and Chief Executive Officer
(Moderately Centralized Health System)

NEW YORK: NEW YORK-PRESBYTERIAN HOSPITAL (O, 2338 beds) 525 East 68th Street, New York, NY Zip 10065–4870; tel. 212/746–5454; Steven J. Corwin, M.D., President and Chief Executive Officer
Web address: www.nyp.org

NEW YORK-PRESBYTERIAN QUEENS (O, 483 beds) 56–45 Main Street, Flushing, NY Zip 11355–5045; tel. 718/670–1231; Jaclyn Mucaria, President
Web address: www.nyhq.org

NEW YORK-PRESBYTERIAN/HUDSON VALLEY HOSPITAL (O, 128 beds) 1980 Crompond Road, Cortlandt Manor, NY Zip 10567–4182; tel. 914/737–9000; Stacey Petrower, President

NEW YORK-PRESBYTERIAN/LAWRENCE HOSPITAL (O, 208 beds) 55 Palmer Avenue, Bronxville, NY Zip 10708–3403; tel. 914/787–1000; Michael Fosina, M.P.H., FACHE, President
Web address: www.lawrencehealth.org

NEWYORK-PRESBYTERIAN BROOKLYN METHODIST HOSPITAL (O, 591 beds) 506 Sixth Street, Brooklyn, NY Zip 11215–3609; tel. 718/780–3000; Richard Liebowitz, M.D., President
Web address: www.nym.org

Owned, leased, sponsored:	5 hospitals	3748 beds
Contract-managed:	0 hospitals	0 beds
Totals:	5 hospitals	3748 beds

0353: NEXUS HEALTH SYSTEMS (IO)
One Riverway, Suite 600, Houston, TX Zip 77056–1993; tel. 713/355–6111; John W. Cassidy, M.D., President, Chief Executive Officer and Chief Medical Officer
(Independent Hospital System)

CALIFORNIA: HEALTHBRIDGE CHILDREN'S HOSPITAL (O, 27 beds) 393 South Tustin Street, Orange, CA Zip 92866–2501; tel. 714/289–2400; Alex Villarruz, Chief Executive Officer
Web address: www.HealthBridgeOrange.com

TEXAS: HEALTHBRIDGE CHILDREN'S HOSPITAL OF HOUSTON (O, 40 beds) 2929 Woodland Park Drive, Houston, TX Zip 77082–2687; tel. 281/293–7774; Elizabeth E. Fredeboelling, MSN, R.N., Chief Executive Officer

NEXUS SPECIALTY HOSPITAL (O, 75 beds) 123 Vision Park Boulevard, Shenandoah, TX Zip 77384–3001; tel. 281/364–0317; Mikael Simpson, Chief Executive Officer
Web address: www.nexusspecialty.com

Owned, leased, sponsored:	3 hospitals	142 beds
Contract-managed:	0 hospitals	0 beds
Totals:	3 hospitals	142 beds

1021: NOBILIS HEALTH CORPORATION (IO)
11700 Katy Freeway Suite 300, Houston, TX Zip 77079–1218; tel. 713/355–8614; Harry Fleming, Chief Executive Officer

ARIZONA: SCOTTSDALE LIBERTY HOSPITAL (O, 12 beds) 17500 North Perimeter Drive, Scottsdale, AZ Zip 85255–7808; tel. 480/586–2300; Steven M. Siwek, M.D., President and Chief Executive Officer
Web address: www.freedompainhospital.com

TEXAS: FIRST SURGICAL HOSPITAL (O, 19 beds) 4801 Bissonnet, Bellaire, TX Zip 77401–4028; tel. 713/275–1111; David Kreye, Chief Executive Officer

HERMANN DRIVE SURGICAL HOSPITAL (O, 25 beds) 2001 Hermann Drive, Houston, TX Zip 77004–7643; tel. 713/285–5500; Michael Torne, Chief Executive Officer
Web address: www.nobilishealth.com/our-facilities/houston/

PLANO SURGICAL HOSPITAL (O, 26 beds) 2301 Marsh Lane, Plano, TX Zip 75093–8497; tel. 972/820–2600; Jay Lindsey, Chief Executive Officer

Owned, leased, sponsored:	4 hospitals	82 beds
Contract-managed:	0 hospitals	0 beds
Totals:	4 hospitals	82 beds

0349: NOLAND HEALTH SERVICES, INC. (NP)
600 Corporate Parkway, Suite 100, Birmingham, AL Zip 35242–5451; tel. 205/783–8484; Gary M. Glasscock, President and Chief Executive Officer

ALABAMA: NOLAND HOSPITAL ANNISTON (O, 38 beds) 400 East 10th Street, 4th Fl, Anniston, AL Zip 36207–4716; tel. 256/741–6141; Trina Woods, Administrator
Web address: www.nolandhealth.com

NOLAND HOSPITAL BIRMINGHAM (O, 45 beds) 50 Medical Park East Drive, 8th Floor, Birmingham, AL Zip 35235; tel. 205/808–5100; Laura S. Wills, Administrator

NOLAND HOSPITAL DOTHAN (O, 38 beds) 1108 Ross Clark Circle, 4th Floor, Dothan, AL Zip 36301–3022; tel. 334/699–4300; Kaye Burk, Administrator
Web address: www.nolandhealth.com

NOLAND HOSPITAL MONTGOMERY (O, 65 beds) 1725 Pine Street, 5 North, Montgomery, AL Zip 36106–1109; tel. 334/240–0532; Dale Jones, Administrator
Web address: www.nolandhealth.com

NOLAND HOSPITAL SHELBY (O, 52 beds) 1000 First Street North, 3rd Floor, Alabaster, AL Zip 35007–8703; tel. 205/620–8641; Laura S. Wills, Administrator

NOLAND HOSPITAL TUSCALOOSA (O, 32 beds) 809 University Blvd E, 4th Fl, Tuscaloosa, AL Zip 35401–2029; tel. 205/759–7241; Jack Gibson, Administrator
Web address: www.nolandhealth.com

Owned, leased, sponsored:	6 hospitals	270 beds
Contract-managed:	0 hospitals	0 beds
Totals:	6 hospitals	270 beds

★**0887: NORTH MEMORIAL HEALTH CARE** (NP)
3300 Oakdale Avenue North, Robbinsdale, MN Zip 55422–2926; tel. 763/520–5200; J Kevin. Croston, M.D., Chief Executive Officer
(Centralized Physician/Insurance Health System)

MINNESOTA: MAPLE GROVE HOSPITAL (C, 108 beds) 9875 Hospital Drive, Maple Grove, MN Zip 55369–4648; tel. 763/581–1000; Andrew S. Cochrane, Chief Executive Officer

NORTH MEMORIAL MEDICAL CENTER (O, 355 beds) 3300 Oakdale Avenue North, Robbinsdale, MN Zip 55422–2926; tel. 763/520–5200; Jeff Wicklander, President
Web address: www.northmemorial.com

Owned, leased, sponsored:	1 hospitals	355 beds
Contract-managed:	1 hospitals	108 beds
Totals:	2 hospitals	463 beds

★**0032: NORTH MISSISSIPPI HEALTH SERVICES, INC.** (NP)
830 South Gloster Street, Tupelo, MS Zip 38801–4996;

For explanation of codes following names, see page B2.
★ Indicates Type III membership in the American Hospital Association.

tel. 662/377–3136; M. Shane. Spees, President and Chief Executive Officer
(Centralized Physician/Insurance Health System)

ALABAMA: NORTH MISSISSIPPI MEDICAL CENTER-HAMILTON (O, 15 beds) 1256 Military Street South, Hamilton, AL Zip 35570–5003; tel. 205/921–6200; Robert Trimm, Administrator

MISSISSIPPI: NORTH MISSISSIPPI MEDICAL CENTER - TUPELO (O, 747 beds) 830 South Gloster Street, Tupelo, MS Zip 38801–4934; tel. 662/377–3000; David C. Wilson, Chief Executive Officer
Web address: www.nmhs.net

NORTH MISSISSIPPI MEDICAL CENTER-EUPORA (O, 73 beds) 70 Medical Plaza, Eupora, MS Zip 39744–4018; tel. 662/258–6221; Wes Sigler, Administrator

NORTH MISSISSIPPI MEDICAL CENTER-IUKA (O, 48 beds) 1777 Curtis Drive, Iuka, MS Zip 38852–1001, P O Box 860, 38852–0860, tel. 662/423–6051; Fred A. Truesdale Jr, Administrator
Web address: www.nmhs.net

NORTH MISSISSIPPI MEDICAL CENTER-PONTOTOC (L, 69 beds) 176 South Main Street, Pontotoc, MS Zip 38863–3311, P O Box 790, 38863–0790, tel. 662/488–7640; Leslia Carter, Administrator
Web address: www.nmhs.net

NORTH MISSISSIPPI MEDICAL CENTER-WEST POINT (O, 60 beds) 835 Medical Center Drive, West Point, MS Zip 39773–9320; tel. 662/495–2300; Barry L. Keel, Administration

Owned, leased, sponsored:	6 hospitals	1012 beds
Contract-managed:	0 hospitals	0 beds
Totals:	6 hospitals	1012 beds

0867: NORTH OAKS HEALTH SYSTEM (NP)
15790 Paul Vega MD Drive, Hammond, LA Zip 70403–1436, P O Box 2668, 70404–2668, tel. 985/345–2700; Michele K. Sutton, FACHE, President and Chief Executive Officer
(Independent Hospital System)

LOUISIANA: NORTH OAKS MEDICAL CENTER (O, 231 beds) 15790 Paul Vega, MD, Drive, Hammond, LA Zip 70403–1436, P O Box 2668, 70404–2668, tel. 985/345–2700; Michele K. Sutton, FACHE, President and Chief Executive Officer
Web address: www.northoaks.org

NORTH OAKS REHABILITATION HOSPITAL (O, 27 beds) 1900 South Morrison Boulevard, Hammond, LA Zip 70403–5742; tel. 985/542–7777; Sybil K. Paulson, Administrator
Web address: www.northoaks.org

Owned, leased, sponsored:	2 hospitals	258 beds
Contract-managed:	0 hospitals	0 beds
Totals:	2 hospitals	258 beds

1018: NORTHEAST GEORGIA HEALTH SYSTEM (NP)
743 Spring Street NE, Gainesville, GA Zip 30501–3715; tel. 770/219–9000; Carol H. Burrell, President and Chief Executive Officer

GEORGIA: NORTHEAST GEORGIA MEDICAL CENTER BARROW (O, 56 beds) 316 North Broad Street, Winder, GA Zip 30680–2150, P O Box 688, 30680–0688, tel. 770/867–3400; Chad Hatfield, Chief Executive Officer

NORTHEAST GEORGIA MEDICAL CENTER BRASELTON (O, 100 beds) 1400 River Place, Braselton, GA Zip 30517–5600; tel. 770/219–9000; Carol H. Burrell, Chief Executive Officer
Web address: www.nghs.com/locations/braselton

NORTHEAST GEORGIA MEDICAL CENTER (O, 773 beds) 743 Spring Street NE, Gainesville, GA Zip 30501–3899; tel. 770/219–3553; Carol H. Burrell, Chief Executive Officer

Owned, leased, sponsored:	3 hospitals	929 beds
Contract-managed:	0 hospitals	0 beds
Totals:	3 hospitals	929 beds

★0281: NORTHERN ARIZONA HEALTHCARE (NP)
1200 North Beaver Street, Flagstaff, AZ Zip 86001–3118; tel. 928/779–3366; Robert P. Thames, President and Chief Executive Officer
(Moderately Centralized Health System)

ARIZONA: FLAGSTAFF MEDICAL CENTER (O, 267 beds) 1200 North Beaver Street, Flagstaff, AZ Zip 86001–3118; tel. 928/779–3366; Florence (Flo). Spyrow, Chief Administrative Officer
Web address: www.nahealth.com

VERDE VALLEY MEDICAL CENTER (O, 110 beds) 269 South Candy Lane, Cottonwood, AZ Zip 86326–4170; tel. 928/639–6000; Barbara Firminger, Chief Administrative Officer

Owned, leased, sponsored:	2 hospitals	377 beds
Contract-managed:	0 hospitals	0 beds
Totals:	2 hospitals	377 beds

★0410: NORTHSIDE HEALTHCARE SYSTEM (NP)
1000 Johnson Ferry Road NE, Atlanta, GA Zip 30342–1611; tel. 404/851–8000; Robert Quattrocchi, President and Chief Executive Officer

GEORGIA: NORTHSIDE HOSPITAL-CHEROKEE (O, 88 beds) 201 Hospital Road, Canton, GA Zip 30114–2408, P O Box 906, 30169–0906, tel. 770/720–5100; William M. Hayes, Chief Executive Officer
Web address: www.northside.com

NORTHSIDE HOSPITAL-FORSYTH (O, 252 beds) 1200 Northside Forsyth Drive, Cumming, GA Zip 30041–7659; tel. 770/844–3200; Lynn Jackson, Administrator
Web address: www.northside.com

NORTHSIDE HOSPITAL (O, 601 beds) 1000 Johnson Ferry Road NE, Atlanta, GA Zip 30342–1611; tel. 404/851–8000; Robert Quattrocchi, President and Chief Executive Officer

Owned, leased, sponsored:	3 hospitals	941 beds
Contract-managed:	0 hospitals	0 beds
Totals:	3 hospitals	941 beds

★0062: NORTHWELL HEALTH (NP)
2000 Marcus Avenue, New Hyde Park, NY Zip 11042; tel. 516/465–8100; Michael J. Dowling, President and Chief Executive Officer
(Centralized Health System)

NEW YORK: GLEN COVE HOSPITAL (O, 119 beds) 101 St Andrews Lane, Glen Cove, NY Zip 11542–2254; tel. 516/674–7300; Susan Kwiatek, R.N., Executive Director
Web address: www.northshorelij.com

HUNTINGTON HOSPITAL (O, 290 beds) 270 Park Avenue, Huntington, NY Zip 11743–2799; tel. 631/351–2200; Gerard Brogan Jr, M.D., Executive Director

LENOX HILL HOSPITAL (O, 441 beds) 100 East 77th Street, New York, NY Zip 10075–1850; tel. 212/434–2000; Dennis Connors, Executive Director
Web address: www.lenoxhillhospital.org

LONG ISLAND JEWISH MEDICAL CENTER (O, 1220 beds) 270–05 76th Avenue, New Hyde Park, NY Zip 11040–1496; tel. 718/470–7000; Michael Goldberg, Executive Director
Web address: www.lij.edu

NORTH SHORE UNIVERSITY HOSPITAL (O, 738 beds) 300 Community Drive, Manhasset, NY Zip 11030–3816; tel. 516/562–0100; Alessandro Bellucci, M.D., Executive Director

NORTHERN WESTCHESTER HOSPITAL (O, 195 beds) 400 East Main Street, Mount Kisco, NY Zip 10549–3477, 400 East Main Street, G-02, 10549–3477, tel. 914/666–1200; Joel Seligman, President and Chief Executive Officer
Web address: www.nwhc.net

For explanation of codes following names, see page B2.
★ Indicates Type III membership in the American Hospital Association.

Section B

PECONIC BAY MEDICAL CENTER (O, 94 beds) 1300 Roanoke Avenue, Riverhead, NY Zip 11901–2031; tel. 631/548–6000; Andrew J. Mitchell, President and Chief Executive Officer
Web address: www.pbmchealth.org

PHELPS MEMORIAL HOSPITAL CENTER (O, 158 beds) 701 North Broadway, Sleepy Hollow, NY Zip 10591–1020; tel. 914/366–3000; Daniel Blum, President
Web address: www.phelpshospital.org

PLAINVIEW HOSPITAL (O, 158 beds) 888 Old Country Road, Plainview, NY Zip 11803–4978; tel. 516/719–3000; Michael Fener, Executive Director

SOUTH OAKS HOSPITAL (O, 258 beds) 400 Sunrise Highway, Amityville, NY Zip 11701–2508; tel. 631/264–4000; Lenny Nartowicz, Executive Director
Web address: www.longislandhome.org

SOUTHSIDE HOSPITAL (O, 286 beds) 301 East Main Street, Bay Shore, NY Zip 11706–8458; tel. 631/968–3000; Donna Moravick, R.N., MSN, Executive Director
Web address: www.southsidehospital.org

STATEN ISLAND UNIVERSITY HOSPITAL (O, 634 beds) 475 Seaview Avenue, Staten Island, NY Zip 10305–3436; tel. 718/226–9000; Donna Proske, MS, R.N., Executive Director

SYOSSET HOSPITAL (O, 75 beds) 221 Jericho Turnpike, Syosset, NY Zip 11791–4515; tel. 516/496–6500; Michael Fener, Executive Director
Web address: www.northshorelij.com

Owned, leased, sponsored:	13 hospitals	4666 beds
Contract-managed:	0 hospitals	0 beds
Totals:	13 hospitals	4666 beds

★**0024: NORTHWESTERN MEMORIAL HEALTHCARE** (NP)
251 East Huron Street, Chicago, IL Zip 60611–2908; tel. 312/926–2000; Dean M. Harrison, President and Chief Executive Officer
(Centralized Health System)

ILLINOIS: MARIANJOY REHABILITATION HOSPITAL (O, 127 beds) 26 West 171 Roosevelt Road, Wheaton, IL Zip 60187–0795, P O Box 795, 60187–0795, tel. 630/909–8000; Kathleen C. Yosko, President

NORTHWESTERN MEDICINE CENTRAL DUPAGE HOSPITAL (O, 422 beds) 25 North Winfield Road, Winfield, IL Zip 60190; tel. 630/933–1600; Brian J. Lemon, President
Web address: www.nm.org

NORTHWESTERN MEDICINE DELNOR HOSPITAL (O, 149 beds) 300 Randall Road, Geneva, IL Zip 60134–4200; tel. 630/208–3000; Maureen A. Bryant, FACHE, President

NORTHWESTERN MEDICINE KISHWAUKEE HOSPITAL (O, 98 beds) 1 Kish Hospital Drive, DeKalb, IL Zip 60115–9602, P O Box 707, 60115–0707, tel. 815/756–1521; Jay Anderson, President
Web address: www.nm.org

NORTHWESTERN MEDICINE LAKE FOREST HOSPITAL (O, 197 beds) 660 North Westmoreland Road, Lake Forest, IL Zip 60045–1696; tel. 847/234–5600; Thomas J. McAfee, President, North Market

NORTHWESTERN MEDICINE VALLEY WEST HOSPITAL (O, 25 beds) 1302 North Main Street, Sandwich, IL Zip 60548–2587; tel. 815/786–8484; Jay Anderson, President
Web address: www.nm.org

NORTHWESTERN MEMORIAL HOSPITAL (O, 882 beds) 251 East Huron Street, Chicago, IL Zip 60611–2908; tel. 312/926–2000; Dean M. Harrison, Chief Executive Officer

Owned, leased, sponsored:	7 hospitals	1900 beds
Contract-managed:	0 hospitals	0 beds
Totals:	7 hospitals	1900 beds

★**2285: NORTON HEALTHCARE** (NP)
4967 US Highway 42, Suite 100, Louisville, KY Zip 40222–6363, P O Box 35070, 40232–5070, tel. 502/629–8000; Russell Cox, President and Chief Executive Officer
(Centralized Health System)

KENTUCKY: NORTON AUDUBON HOSPITAL (O, 292 beds) One Audubon Plaza Drive, Louisville, KY Zip 40217–1300, P O Box 17550, 40217–0550, tel. 502/636–7111; Jon Cooper, Chief Administrative Officer
Web address: www.nortonhealthcare.com/NortonAudubonHospital

NORTON BROWNSBORO HOSPITAL (O, 127 beds) 4960 Norton Healthcare Boulevard, Louisville, KY Zip 40241–2831; tel. 502/446–8000; Andrew Strausbaugh, Chief Administrative Officer

NORTON CHILDREN'S HOSPITAL (O, 267 beds) 231 East Chestnut Street, Louisville, KY Zip 40202–1821; tel. 502/629–6000; Thomas D. Kmetz, Division President
Web address: www.kosairchildrens.com/

NORTON HOSPITAL (O, 383 beds) 200 East Chestnut Street, Louisville, KY Zip 40202–1800, P O Box 35070, 40232–5070, tel. 502/629–8000; Matthew Ayers, Chief Administrative Officer

NORTON WOMEN'S AND CHILDREN'S HOSPITAL (O, 355 beds) 4001 Dutchmans Lane, Louisville, KY Zip 40207–4799; tel. 502/893–1000; Charlotte Ipsan, Chief Administrative Officer
Web address: www.https://nortonhealthcare.com/pages/nwkch.aspx

Owned, leased, sponsored:	5 hospitals	1424 beds
Contract-managed:	0 hospitals	0 beds
Totals:	5 hospitals	1424 beds

★**0139: NOVANT HEALTH** (NP)
2085 Frontis Plaza Boulevard, Winston Salem, NC Zip 27103–5614; tel. 336/718–5600; Carl S. Armato, President and Chief Executive Officer
(Moderately Centralized Health System)

NORTH CAROLINA: ASHE MEMORIAL HOSPITAL (C, 25 beds) 200 Hospital Avenue, Jefferson, NC Zip 28640–9244; tel. 336/846–7101; Laura Lambeth, Chief Executive Officer
Web address: www.ashememorial.org

HALIFAX REGIONAL MEDICAL CENTER (C, 142 beds) 250 Smith Church Road, Roanoke Rapids, NC Zip 27870–4914, P O Box 1089, 27870–1089, tel. 252/535–8011; William Mahone, President and Chief Executive Officer
Web address: www.halifaxmedicalcenter.org

NOVANT HEALTH BRUNSWICK MEDICAL CENTER (O, 54 beds) 240 Hospital Drive NE, Bolivia, NC Zip 28422–8346; tel. 910/721–1000; Shelbourn Stevens, President and Chief Operating Officer
Web address: https://www.novanthealth.org

NOVANT HEALTH CHARLOTTE ORTHOPAEDIC HOSPITAL (O, 31 beds) 1901 Randolph Road, Charlotte, NC Zip 28207–1195; tel. 704/316–2000; Jason Bernd, Vice President
Web address: www.novanthealth.org

NOVANT HEALTH FORSYTH MEDICAL CENTER (O, 740 beds) 3333 Silas Creek Parkway, Winston-Salem, NC Zip 27103–3090; tel. 336/718–5000; Sean M. Sanz, President and Chief Operating Officer

NOVANT HEALTH HUNTERSVILLE MEDICAL CENTER (O, 91 beds) 10030 Gilead Road, Huntersville, NC Zip 28078–7545, P O Box 3508, 28070–3508, tel. 704/316–4000; Mike Riley, President and Chief Operating Officer
Web address: www.novanthealth.org

NOVANT HEALTH MATTHEWS MEDICAL CENTER (O, 117 beds) 1500 Matthews Township Parkway, Matthews, NC Zip 28105–4656; tel. 704/384–6500; Roland R. Bibeau, President and Chief Operating Officer

NOVANT HEALTH MEDICAL PARK HOSPITAL (O, 21 beds) 1950 South Hawthorne Road, Winston-Salem, NC Zip 27103–3993; tel. 336/718–0600; Kirsten Royster, President and Chief Operating Officer
Web address: www.novanthealth.org

NOVANT HEALTH PRESBYTERIAN MEDICAL CENTER (O, 440 beds) 200 Hawthorne Lane, Charlotte, NC Zip 28204–2528, P O Box 33549, 28233–3549, tel. 704/384–4000; Paula Vincent, MSN, President and Chief Operating Officer

NOVANT HEALTH ROWAN MEDICAL CENTER (O, 149 beds) 612 Mocksville Avenue, Salisbury, NC Zip 28144–2799; tel. 704/210–5000; Dari Caldwell, R.N., Ph.D., FACHE, President and Chief Operating Officer
Web address: https://www.novanthealth.org/rowan-medical-center.aspx

NOVANT HEALTH THOMASVILLE MEDICAL CENTER (O, 87 beds) 207 Old Lexington Road, Thomasville, NC Zip 27360–3428, P O Box 789,

For explanation of codes following names, see page B2.
★ Indicates Type III membership in the American Hospital Association.

B92 Health Care Systems, Networks and Alliances

© 2017 AHA Guide

27361–0789, tel. 336/472–2000; Jon D. Applebaum, President and Chief Operating Officer
Web address: www.thomasvillemedicalcenter.org

VIRGINIA: NOVANT HEALTH UVA HEALTH SYSTEM HAYMARKET MEDICAL CENTER (O, 18 beds) 15225 Heathcote Boulevard, Haymarket, VA Zip 20155–4023, 14535 John Marshall Hwy, Gainesville, 20155–4023, tel. 571/284–1000; Margaret Gill, Senior Vice President and Chief Executive Officer

NOVANT HEALTH UVA HEALTH SYSTEM PRINCE WILLIAM MEDICAL CENTER (O, 87 beds) 8700 Sudley Road, Manassas, VA Zip 20110–4418, P O Box 2610, 20108–0867, tel. 703/369–8000; Margaret Gill, Senior Vice President and Chief Executive Officer
Web address: www.pwhs.org

Owned, leased, sponsored:	11 hospitals	1835 beds
Contract-managed:	2 hospitals	167 beds
Totals:	13 hospitals	2002 beds

★3075:   NYC HEALTH + HOSPITALS (NP)

125 Worth Street, Room 514, New York, NY Zip 10013–4006; tel. 212/788–3321; Stanley Brezenoff, Interim President and Chief Executive Officer
(Moderately Centralized Health System)

NEW YORK: NYC HEALTH + HOSPITALS / BELLEVUE (O, 796 beds) 462 First Avenue, New York, NY Zip 10016–9198; tel. 212/562–4141; William Hicks, Chief Executive Officer
Web address: www.nyc.gov/bellevue

NYC HEALTH + HOSPITALS / CARTER (O, 365 beds) 1752 Park Avenue, New York, NY Zip 10035; tel. 646/686–0000; Floyd R. Long, Chief Executive Officer

NYC HEALTH + HOSPITALS / CONEY ISLAND (O, 371 beds) 2601 Ocean Parkway, Brooklyn, NY Zip 11235–7795; tel. 718/616–3000; Anthony Rajkumar, Chief Executive Officer
Web address: www.nyc.gov/html/hhc/html/facilities/coneyisland.shtml

NYC HEALTH + HOSPITALS / ELMHURST (O, 545 beds) 79–01 Broadway, Elmhurst, NY Zip 11373–1329; tel. 718/334–4000; Israel Rocha, Chief Executive Officer

NYC HEALTH + HOSPITALS / GOUVERNEUR (O, 196 beds) 227 Madison Street, New York, NY Zip 10002; tel. 212/238–7000; Martha Adams Sullivan, Chief Executive Officer

NYC HEALTH + HOSPITALS / HARLEM (O, 257 beds) 506 Lenox Avenue, New York, NY Zip 10037–1802; tel. 212/939–1000; Ebone' Carrington, Interim Executive Director
Web address: www.nyc.gov/html/hhc/harlem

NYC HEALTH + HOSPITALS / JACOBI (O, 441 beds) 1400 Pelham Parkway South, Bronx, NY Zip 10461–1197; tel. 718/918–5000; Christopher Mastromanno, Interim Chief Executive Officer

NYC HEALTH + HOSPITALS / KINGS COUNTY (O, 599 beds) 451 Clarkson Avenue, Brooklyn, NY Zip 11203–2097; tel. 718/245–3131; Ernest Baptiste, Executive Director
Web address: www.nyc.gov/html/hhc/kchc/html/home/home.shtml

NYC HEALTH + HOSPITALS / LINCOLN (O, 317 beds) 234 East 149th Street, Bronx, NY Zip 10451–5504, 234 East 149th Street, Room 923, 10451–5504, tel. 718/579–5700; Milton Nunez, Executive Director
Web address: www.nyc.gov/html/hhc/lincoln/

NYC HEALTH + HOSPITALS / METROPOLITAN (O, 317 beds) 1901 First Avenue, New York, NY Zip 10029–7404; tel. 212/423–6262; Alina Moran, Chief Executive Officer

NYC HEALTH + HOSPITALS / NORTH CENTRAL BRONX (O, 202 beds) 3424 Kossuth Avenue, Bronx, NY Zip 10467–2489; tel. 718/519–3500; Maureen Pode, Co-Interim Executive Director
Web address: www.nyc.gov/html/hhc/ncbh/html/home/home.shtml

NYC HEALTH + HOSPITALS / QUEENS (O, 253 beds) 82–68 164th Street, Jamaica, NY Zip 11432–1104; tel. 718/883–3000; Christopher Roker, Chief Executive Officer
Web address: www.nyc.gov/html/hhc/qhc/html/home/home.shtml

NYC HEALTH + HOSPITALS / SEA VIEW (O, 304 beds) 460 Brielle Avenue, Staten Island, NY Zip 10314; tel. 212/390–8181; Jane M. Lyons, Executive Director

NYC HEALTH + HOSPITALS / WOODHULL (O, 305 beds) 760 Broadway, Brooklyn, NY Zip 11206–5383; tel. 718/963–8000; Gregory Calliste, Ph.D., FACHE, Chief Executive Officer
Web address: www.nyc.gov/html/hhc

Owned, leased, sponsored:	14 hospitals	5268 beds
Contract-managed:	0 hospitals	0 beds
Totals:	14 hospitals	5268 beds

1026:   NYU LANGONE HEALTH (NP)

550 First Avenue, New York, NY Zip 10016–6402; tel. 646/929–7870; Robert I. Grossman, M.D., Chief Executive Officer

NEW YORK: NYU LANGONE HOSPITALS (O, 1104 beds) 550 First Avenue, New York, NY Zip 10016–6402; tel. 212/263–7300; Robert I. Grossman, M.D., Chief Executive Officer
Web address: www.nyumedicalcenter.org

NYU WINTHROP HOSPITAL (O, 511 beds) 259 First Street, Mineola, NY Zip 11501–3957; tel. 516/663–0333; John F. Collins, President and Chief Executive Officer
Web address: www.winthrop.org

Owned, leased, sponsored:	2 hospitals	1615 beds
Contract-managed:	0 hospitals	0 beds
Totals:	2 hospitals	1615 beds

0616:   OCEANS HEALTHCARE (IO)

2720 Rue de Jardin, Suite 100, Lake Charles, LA Zip 70605–4050; tel. 337/721–1900; Jason Reed, President and Chief Executive Officer
(Independent Hospital System)

LOUISIANA: OCEANS BEHAVIORAL HOSPITAL OF ALEXANDRIA (O, 24 beds) 2621 North Bolton Avenue, Alexandria, LA Zip 71303–4506; tel. 318/448–8473; Nicholas D. Guillory, MSN, Interim Administrator

OCEANS BEHAVIORAL HOSPITAL OF BATON ROUGE (O, 20 beds) 11135 Florida Boulevard, Baton Rouge, LA Zip 70815–2013; tel. 225/356–7030; Valerie Dalton, R.N., Administrator
Web address: www.obhbr.info/

OCEANS BEHAVIORAL HOSPITAL OF BROUSSARD (O, 38 beds) 418 Albertson Parkway, Broussard, LA Zip 70518–4971; tel. 337/237–6444; Amy Dysart-Credeur, Administrator
Web address: www.obhb.info/

OCEANS BEHAVIORAL HOSPITAL OF DE RIDDER (O, 20 beds) 1420 Blankenship Drive, Deridder, LA Zip 70634–4604; tel. 337/460–9472; Stuart Archer, Chief Executive Officer

OCEANS BEHAVIORAL HOSPITAL OF GREATER NEW ORLEANS (O, 30 beds) 716 Village Road, Kenner, LA Zip 70065–2751; tel. 504/464–8895; Deborah Spier, Administrator
Web address: www.obhgno.info/

OCEANS BEHAVIORAL HOSPITAL OF KENTWOOD (O, 18 beds) 921 Avenue G, Kentwood, LA Zip 70444–2636; tel. 985/229–0717; Sarah Chisholm, R.N., Administrator
Web address: www.obhk.info/

OCEANS BEHAVIORAL HOSPITAL OF LAKE CHARLES (O, 20 beds) 302 West Mcneese Street, Lake Charles, LA Zip 70605–5604; tel. 337/474–7581; William L. Willis, Administrator
Web address: www.obhlc.info/

OCEANS BEHAVIORAL HOSPITAL OF OPELOUSAS (O, 20 beds) 1310 Heather Drive, Opelousas, LA Zip 70570–7714; tel. 337/948–8820; Theresa Fontenot, Executive Director
Web address: www.obho.info/

TEXAS: OCEANS BEHAVIORAL HEALTH CENTER PERMIAN BASIN (O, 58 beds) 3300 South FM 1788, Midland, TX Zip 79706–2601; tel. 432/561–5915; Kristin Harris, Interim Chief Executive Officer

---

For explanation of codes following names, see page B2.
★ Indicates Type III membership in the American Hospital Association.

Section B

OCEANS BEHAVIORAL HOSPITAL ABILENE (O, 90 beds) 4225 Woods Place, Abilene, TX Zip 79606–5869; tel. 325/691–0030; Stacy Sanford, Chief Executive Officer
Web address: www.oceansabilene.com

OCEANS BEHAVIORAL HOSPITAL KATY (O, 48 beds) 455 Park Grove Lane, Katy, TX Zip 77450–1572; tel. 281/492–8888; Stuart Archer, Chief Executive Officer

OCEANS BEHAVIORAL HOSPITAL LONGVIEW (O, 24 beds) 615 Clinic Drive, Longview, TX Zip 75605–5172; tel. 903/212–3105; Lauren Weber, Administrator
Web address: www.oceanslongview.com/

OCEANS BEHAVIORAL HOSPITAL LUFKIN (O, 24 beds) 302 Gobblers Knob Road, Lufkin, TX Zip 75904–5419; tel. 936/632–2276; Frances Dick, Chief Executive Officer
Web address: www.oceanslufkin.com/

OCEANS BEHAVIORAL HOSPITAL SAN MARCOS (O, 24 beds) 1106 North Interstate 35, San Marcos, TX Zip 78666–7030; tel. 512/353–0194; Clara Hollis, Administrator
Web address: www.oceanssanmarcos.com

Owned, leased, sponsored:	14 hospitals	458 beds
Contract-managed:	0 hospitals	0 beds
Totals:	14 hospitals	458 beds

★**0359:   OCHSNER HEALTH SYSTEM** (NP)
1514 Jefferson Highway, New Orleans, LA Zip 70121–2429; tel. 800/874–8984; Warner L. Thomas, FACHE, President and Chief Executive Officer
(Moderately Centralized Health System)

LOUISIANA: LEONARD J. CHABERT MEDICAL CENTER (C, 72 beds) 1978 Industrial Boulevard, Houma, LA Zip 70363–7094; tel. 985/873–2200; Timothy J. Allen, FACHE, Chief Executive Officer
Web address: www.ochsner.org/locations/leonard_j_chabert_medical_center/

OCHSNER MEDICAL CENTER - KENNER (O, 110 beds) 180 West Esplanade Avenue, Kenner, LA Zip 70065–6001; tel. 504/468–8600; Stephen Robinson Jr, FACHE, Chief Executive Officer
Web address: https://www.ochsner.org/locations/ochsner-medical-center-kenner/

OCHSNER MEDICAL CENTER - NORTH SHORE (L, 165 beds) 100 Medical Center Drive, Slidell, LA Zip 70461–5520; tel. 985/649–7070; John William Bill"". Davis, Chief Executive Officer

OCHSNER MEDICAL CENTER-BATON ROUGE (O, 152 beds) 17000 Medical Center Drive, Baton Rouge, LA Zip 70816–3224; tel. 225/752–2470; Eric McMillen, Chief Executive Officer
Web address: www.ochsner.org/page.cfm?id=103

OCHSNER MEDICAL CENTER (O, 826 beds) 1514 Jefferson Highway, New Orleans, LA Zip 70121–2429; tel. 504/842–3000; Robert K. Wolterman, Chief Executive Officer
Web address: www.ochsner.org

OCHSNER ST. ANNE GENERAL HOSPITAL (O, 35 beds) 4608 Highway 1, Raceland, LA Zip 70394–2623; tel. 985/537–6841; Timothy J. Allen, FACHE, Chief Executive Officer
Web address: www.ochsner.org/locations/ochsner-st-anne

SLIDELL MEMORIAL HOSPITAL (C, 175 beds) 1001 Gause Boulevard, Slidell, LA Zip 70458–2987; tel. 985/280–2200; John William Bill"". Davis, Chief Executive Officer

ST. CHARLES PARISH HOSPITAL (C, 59 beds) 1057 Paul Maillard Road, Luling, LA Zip 70070–4349, P O Box 87, 70070–0087, tel. 985/785–6242; Austin Reeder, Chief Executive Officer
Web address: https://www.ochsner.org/locations/st-charles-parish-hospital/

MISSISSIPPI: HANCOCK MEDICAL CENTER (C, 102 beds) 149 Drinkwater Boulevard, Bay Saint Louis, MS Zip 39520–1658, 149 Drinkwater Road, 39520–1658, tel. 228/467–8600; Alan Hodges, Chief Executive Officer
Web address: www.hmc.org

Owned, leased, sponsored:	5 hospitals	1288 beds
Contract-managed:	4 hospitals	408 beds
Totals:	9 hospitals	1696 beds

0537:   OHIO DEPARTMENT OF MENTAL HEALTH (NP)
30 East Broad Street, 8th Floor, Columbus, OH Zip 43215–3430; tel. 614/466–2297; Tracy Plouck, Director
(Independent Hospital System)

OHIO: APPALACHIAN BEHAVIORAL HEALTHCARE (O, 224 beds) 100 Hospital Drive, Athens, OH Zip 45701–2301; tel. 740/594–5000; Jane E. Krason, R.N., Chief Executive Officer

HEARTLAND BEHAVIORAL HEALTHCARE (O, 130 beds) 3000 Erie Stree South, Massillon, OH Zip 44646–7993, 3000 Erie Street South, 44646–7976, tel. 330/833–3135; Jeffrey Sims, Chief Executive Officer
Web address: www.mh.state.oh.us/ibhs/bhos/hoh.html

NORTHCOAST BEHAVIORAL HEALTHCARE (O, 258 beds) 1756 Sagamore Road, Northfield, OH Zip 44067–1086; tel. 330/467–7131; Douglas W. Kern, Chief Executive Officer

NORTHWEST OHIO PSYCHIATRIC HOSPITAL (O, 114 beds) 930 Detroit Avenue, Toledo, OH Zip 43614–2701; tel. 419/381–1881; Tamara Junge, Chief Executive Officer
Web address: www.mh.state.oh.us/

SUMMIT BEHAVIORAL HEALTHCARE (O, 291 beds) 1101 Summit Road, Cincinnati, OH Zip 45237–2652; tel. 513/948–3600; Elizabeth Banks, Chief Executive Officer

TWIN VALLEY BEHAVIORAL HEALTHCARE (O, 228 beds) 2200 West Broad Street, Columbus, OH Zip 43223–1297; tel. 614/752–0333; Veronica Lofton, Acting Chief Executive Officer
Web address: www.mh.state.oh.us/ibhs/bhos/tvbh.html

Owned, leased, sponsored:	6 hospitals	1245 beds
Contract-managed:	0 hospitals	0 beds
Totals:	6 hospitals	1245 beds

★**0251:   OHIO STATE UNIVERSITY HEALTH SYSTEM** (NP)
370 West Ninth Avenue, Columbus, OH Zip 43210–1238; tel. 614/685–9015; David P. McQuaid, FACHE, Chief Executive Officer
(Centralized Physician/Insurance Health System)

OHIO: JAMES CANCER HOSPITAL AND SOLOVE RESEARCH INSTITUTE (O, 306 beds) 460 West Tenth Avenue, Columbus, OH Zip 43210–1240; tel. 614/293–3300; Michael Caligiuri, M.D., Chief Executive Officer

OHIO STATE UNIVERSITY WEXNER MEDICAL CENTER (O, 971 beds) 370 West 9th Avenue, Columbus, OH Zip 43210–1238; tel. 614/293–8000; David P. McQuaid, FACHE, Chief Operating Officer
Web address: www.medicalcenter.osu.edu

Owned, leased, sponsored:	2 hospitals	1277 beds
Contract-managed:	0 hospitals	0 beds
Totals:	2 hospitals	1277 beds

★**0162:   OHIOHEALTH** (NP)
180 East Broad Street, Columbus, OH Zip 43215–3707; tel. 614/544–4455; David P. Blom, President and Chief Executive Officer
(Moderately Centralized Health System)

OHIO: MORROW COUNTY HOSPITAL (C, 23 beds) 651 West Marion Road, Mount Gilead, OH Zip 43338–1027; tel. 419/946–5015; Chad J. Miller, President and Chief Executive Officer

O'BLENESS MEMORIAL HOSPITAL (O, 64 beds) 55 Hospital Drive, Athens, OH Zip 45701–2302; tel. 740/593–5551; Mark R. Seckinger, President
Web address: www.obleness.org

OHIOHEALTH DOCTORS HOSPITAL (O, 243 beds) 5100 West Broad Street, Columbus, OH Zip 43228–1607; tel. 614/544–1000; Michael L. Reichfield, President
Web address: www.ohiohealth.com

For explanation of codes following names, see page B2.
★ Indicates Type III membership in the American Hospital Association.

OHIOHEALTH DUBLIN METHODIST HOSPITAL (O, 120 beds) 7500 Hospital Drive, Dublin, OH Zip 43016–8518; tel. 614/544–8000; Steve Bunyard, President
Web address: www.ohiohealth.com

OHIOHEALTH GRADY MEMORIAL HOSPITAL (O, 59 beds) 561 West Central Avenue, Delaware, OH Zip 43015–1410; tel. 740/615–1000; Steve Bunyard, President

OHIOHEALTH GRANT MEDICAL CENTER (O, 445 beds) 111 South Grant Avenue, Columbus, OH Zip 43215–1898; tel. 614/566–9000; Michael Lawson, President and Chief Operating Officer
Web address: www.ohiohealth.com

OHIOHEALTH HARDIN MEMORIAL HOSPITAL (O, 25 beds) 921 East Franklin Street, Kenton, OH Zip 43326–2099; tel. 419/673–0761; Ron Snyder, Chief Operating Officer
Web address: www.hardinmemorial.org

OHIOHEALTH MARION GENERAL HOSPITAL (O, 161 beds) 1000 McKinley Park Drive, Marion, OH Zip 43302–6397; tel. 740/383–8400; Bruce P. Hagen, President

OHIOHEALTH MEDCENTRAL MANSFIELD HOSPITAL (O, 243 beds) 335 Glessner Avenue, Mansfield, OH Zip 44903–2265; tel. 419/526–8000; Jean Halpin, President
Web address: www.medcentral.org

OHIOHEALTH MEDCENTRAL SHELBY HOSPITAL (O, 25 beds) 199 West Main Street, Shelby, OH Zip 44875–1490; tel. 419/342–5015; Jean Halpin, President

OHIOHEALTH RIVERSIDE METHODIST HOSPITAL (O, 820 beds) 3535 Olentangy River Road, Columbus, OH Zip 43214–3998; tel. 614/566–5000; Brian Jepson, President
Web address: www.ohiohealth.com

Owned, leased, sponsored:	10 hospitals	2205 beds
Contract-managed:	1 hospitals	23 beds
Totals:	11 hospitals	2228 beds

0018: OKLAHOMA DEPARTMENT OF MENTAL HEALTH AND SUBSTANCE ABUSE SERVICES (NP)
1200 NE 13th Street, Oklahoma City, OK Zip 73117–1022, P O Box 53277, 73152–3277, tel. 405/522–3908; Terri White, Commissioner
(Independent Hospital System)

OKLAHOMA: GRIFFIN MEMORIAL HOSPITAL (O, 120 beds) 900 East Main Street, Norman, OK Zip 73071–5305, P O Box 151, 73070–0151, tel. 405/573–6600; Lori Jordan, Executive Director

NORTHWEST CENTER FOR BEHAVIORAL HEALTH (O, 24 beds) 1 Mi East Highway 270, Fort Supply, OK Zip 73841, 1222 10th Street, Suite 211, Woodward, 73801–3156, tel. 580/766–2311; Trudy Hoffman, Executive Director
Web address: www.ncbhok.org/

OKLAHOMA FORENSIC CENTER (O, 200 beds) 24800 South 4420 Road, Vinita, OK Zip 74301–5544, P O Box 69, 74301–0069, tel. 918/256–7841; Kevan Finley, Chief Executive Officer
Web address: www.odmhsas.org

Owned, leased, sponsored:	3 hospitals	344 beds
Contract-managed:	0 hospitals	0 beds
Totals:	3 hospitals	344 beds

3355: ORLANDO HEALTH (NP)
1414 Kuhl Avenue, Orlando, FL Zip 32806–2093; tel. 321/843–7000; David W. Strong, President and Chief Executive Officer
(Centralized Physician/Insurance Health System)

FLORIDA: HEALTH CENTRAL HOSPITAL (O, 429 beds) 10000 West Colonial Drive, Ocoee, FL Zip 34761–3499; tel. 407/296–1000; Mark A. Marsh, President

ORLANDO REGIONAL MEDICAL CENTER (O, 1181 beds) 52 West Underwood Street, Orlando, FL Zip 32806; tel. 407/841–5111; Mark A. Jones, President
Web address: www.orlandohealth.com/facilities/orlando-regional-medical-center

SOUTH LAKE HOSPITAL (O, 170 beds) 1900 Don Wickham Drive, Clermont, FL Zip 34711–1979; tel. 352/394–4071; John Moore, President

Owned, leased, sponsored:	3 hospitals	1780 beds
Contract-managed:	0 hospitals	0 beds
Totals:	3 hospitals	1780 beds

★5335: OSF HEALTHCARE (CC)
800 NE Glen Oak Avenue, Peoria, IL Zip 61603–3200; tel. 309/655–2850; Kevin D. Schoeplein, Chief Executive Officer
(Moderately Centralized Health System)

ILLINOIS: OSF HOLY FAMILY MEDICAL CENTER (O, 23 beds) 1000 West Harlem Avenue, Monmouth, IL Zip 61462–1007; tel. 309/734–3141; Patricia A. Luker, President
Web address: www.osfholyfamily.org

OSF SAINT ANTHONY MEDICAL CENTER (O, 235 beds) 5666 East State Street, Rockford, IL Zip 61108–2425; tel. 815/226–2000; Paula A. Carynski, MS, R.N., President
Web address: www.osfhealth.com

OSF SAINT ANTHONY'S HEALTH CENTER (O, 203 beds) 1 Saint Anthony's Way, Alton, IL Zip 62002–4579, PO Box 340, 62002–0340, tel. 618/465–2571; Ajay Pathak, President

OSF SAINT ELIZABETH MEDICAL CENTER (O, 87 beds) 1100 East Norris Drive, Ottawa, IL Zip 61350–1687; tel. 815/433–3100; Kenneth Beutke, President
Web address: www.osfsaintelizabeth.org

OSF SAINT FRANCIS MEDICAL CENTER (O, 609 beds) 530 NE Glen Oak Avenue, Peoria, IL Zip 61637–0001; tel. 309/655–2000; Michael A. Cruz, M.D., President
Web address: www.osfsaintfrancis.org

OSF SAINT JAMES - JOHN W. ALBRECHT MEDICAL CENTER (O, 42 beds) 2500 West Reynolds, Pontiac, IL Zip 61764–9774; tel. 815/842–2828; Bradley V. Solberg, FACHE, President

OSF SAINT LUKE MEDICAL CENTER (O, 25 beds) 1051 West South Street, Kewanee, IL Zip 61443–8354, P O Box 747, 61443–0747, tel. 309/852–7500; Lynn Fulton, President
Web address: www.osfsaintluke.org

OSF SAINT PAUL MEDICAL CENTER (O, 25 beds) 1401 East 12th Street, Mendota, IL Zip 61342–9216; tel. 815/539–7461; Jennifer Junis, MSN, R.N., President
Web address: https://www.osfhealthcare.org/saint-paul

OSF ST. JOSEPH MEDICAL CENTER (O, 149 beds) 2200 East Washington Street, Bloomington, IL Zip 61701–4323; tel. 309/662–3311; Chad Boore, President

OSF ST. MARY MEDICAL CENTER (O, 81 beds) 3333 North Seminary Street, Galesburg, IL Zip 61401–1299; tel. 309/344–3161; Roxanna Crosser, President
Web address: www.osfstmary.org

SAINT CLARE HOME (O, 0 beds) 5533 North Galena Road, Peoria Heights, IL Zip 61614–4499; tel. 309/682–5428; Candy Conover, Administrator

ST. ANTHONY'S CONTINUING CARE CENTER (O, 179 beds) 767 30th Street, Rock Island, IL Zip 61201, Sister, Mary Anthony. Mazzaferri, Administrator

MICHIGAN: OSF ST. FRANCIS HOSPITAL AND MEDICAL GROUP (O, 25 beds) 3401 Ludington Street, Escanaba, MI Zip 49829–1377; tel. 906/786–3311; David Lord, President
Web address: www.osfstfrancis.org

Owned, leased, sponsored:	13 hospitals	1683 beds
Contract-managed:	0 hospitals	0 beds
Totals:	13 hospitals	1683 beds

0982: OWENSBORO HEALTH (NP)
1201 Pleasant Valley Road, Owensboro, KY Zip 42303–9811;

For explanation of codes following names, see page B2.
★ Indicates Type III membership in the American Hospital Association.

Section B

tel. 270/417–2000; Greg Strahan, Interim Chief Executive Officer
(Moderately Centralized Health System)

KENTUCKY: OWENSBORO HEALTH MUHLENBERG COMMUNITY HOSPITAL (O, 105 beds) 440 Hopkinsville Street, Greenville, KY Zip 42345–1172, P O Box 387, 42345–0378, tel. 270/338–8000; Ed Heath, FACHE, Chief Executive Officer

Web address: www.mchky.org

OWENSBORO HEALTH REGIONAL HOSPITAL (O, 360 beds) 1201 Pleasant Valley Road, Owensboro, KY Zip 42303; tel. 270/417–2000; Greg Strahan, Interim Chief Executive Officer

Owned, leased, sponsored:	2 hospitals	465 beds
Contract-managed:	0 hospitals	0 beds
Totals:	2 hospitals	465 beds

0367: PACER HEALTH CORPORATION (IO)

14100 Palmetto Frontage Road, Suite 110, Miami Lakes, FL Zip 33016; tel. 305/828–7660; Rainier Gonzalez, Chairman and Chief Executive Officer

KENTUCKY: BARBOURVILLE ARH HOSPITAL (O, 25 beds) 80 Hospital Drive, Barbourville, KY Zip 40906–7363, P O Box 10, 40906–0010, tel. 606/546–4175; Charles D. Lovell Jr, FACHE, Chief Executive Officer

Web address: www.knoxcohospital.com

LOUISIANA: CALCASIEU OAKS GERIATRIC PSYCHIATRIC HOSPITAL (O, 24 beds) 2837 Ernest Street, Lake Charles, LA Zip 70601–8785; tel. 337/439–8111; Erica Williams, Assistant Chief Executive Officer

Owned, leased, sponsored:	2 hospitals	49 beds
Contract-managed:	0 hospitals	0 beds
Totals:	2 hospitals	49 beds

★5235: PALLOTTINE HEALTH SERVICES (CC)

2900 First Avenue, Huntington, WV Zip 25702–1241; tel. 304/526–1234; Michael G. Sellards, Chief Executive Officer
(Independent Hospital System)

WEST VIRGINIA: ST. MARY'S MEDICAL CENTER (O, 393 beds) 2900 First Avenue, Huntington, WV Zip 25702–1272; tel. 304/526–1234; Michael G. Sellards, President and Chief Executive Officer

Web address: www.st-marys.org

Owned, leased, sponsored:	1 hospitals	393 beds
Contract-managed:	0 hospitals	0 beds
Totals:	1 hospitals	393 beds

★4155: PALMETTO HEALTH (NP)

1301 Taylor Street, Suite 9-A, Columbia, SC Zip 29201–2942, P O Box 2266, 29202–2266, tel. 803/296–2100; Charles D. Beaman Jr, Chief Executive Officer
(Centralized Health System)

SOUTH CAROLINA: PALMETTO HEALTH BAPTIST PARKRIDGE (O, 69 beds) 400 Palmetto Health Parkway, Columbia, SC Zip 29212–1760, P.O. BOX 2266, 29202–2266, tel. 803/907–7000; Sarah Kirby, R.N., MSN, FACHE, Chief Operating Officer

PALMETTO HEALTH BAPTIST (O, 400 beds) Taylor at Marion Street, Columbia, SC Zip 29220–0001; tel. 803/296–5010; Gregory B. Gattman, Chief Operating Officer

Web address: www.palmettohealth.org

PALMETTO HEALTH RICHLAND (O, 671 beds) Five Richland Medical Park Drive, Columbia, SC Zip 29203–6897; tel. 803/434–7000; Jay Hamm, R.N., FACHE, Chief Operating Officer

PALMETTO HEALTH TUOMEY (O, 238 beds) 129 North Washington Street, Sumter, SC Zip 29150–4983; tel. 803/774–9000; Michelle Logan-Owens, Chief Operating Officer

Web address: www.tuomey.com

Owned, leased, sponsored:	4 hospitals	1378 beds
Contract-managed:	0 hospitals	0 beds
Totals:	4 hospitals	1378 beds

★7555: PALOMAR HEALTH (NP)

456 East Grand Avenue, Escondido, CA Zip 92025–3319; tel. 760/740–6393; Robert Hemker, President and Chief Executive Officer
(Moderately Centralized Health System)

CALIFORNIA: PALOMAR MEDICAL CENTER (O, 309 beds) 2185 West Citracado Parkway, Escondido, CA Zip 92029–4159; tel. 760/739–3000; Mariellena Sudak, R.N., MSN, Vice President and Chief Nursing Officer

POMERADO HOSPITAL (O, 201 beds) 15615 Pomerado Road, Poway, CA Zip 92064–2460; tel. 858/613–4000; Cheryl Olson, Vice President

Web address: www.pph.org

Owned, leased, sponsored:	2 hospitals	510 beds
Contract-managed:	0 hospitals	0 beds
Totals:	2 hospitals	510 beds

★0159: PARKVIEW HEALTH (NP)

10501 Corporate Drive, Fort Wayne, IN Zip 46845–1700; tel. 260/373–7001; Michael J. Packnett, President and Chief Executive Officer
(Centralized Physician/Insurance Health System)

INDIANA: PARKVIEW ORTHO HOSPITAL (O, 37 beds) 11130 Parkview Circle Drive, Fort Wayne, IN Zip 46845–1735; tel. 260/672–5000; Julie Fleck, Chief Operating Officer

PARKVIEW HUNTINGTON HOSPITAL (O, 36 beds) 2001 Stults Road, Huntington, IN Zip 46750–1291; tel. 260/355–3000; Juli Johnson, MSN, R.N., President

Web address: www.parkview.com

PARKVIEW LAGRANGE HOSPITAL (O, 25 beds) 207 North Townline Road, LaGrange, IN Zip 46761–1325; tel. 260/463–9000; Jordi K. Disler, President

Web address: www.parkview.com

PARKVIEW NOBLE HOSPITAL (O, 31 beds) 401 Sawyer Road, Kendallville, IN Zip 46755–2568; tel. 260/347–8700; Gary W. Adkins, President

PARKVIEW REGIONAL MEDICAL CENTER (O, 690 beds) 11109 Parkview Plaza Drive, Fort Wayne, IN Zip 46845–1701; tel. 260/266–1000; Ben Miles, President

Web address: www.parkview.com

PARKVIEW WABASH COUNTY HOSPITAL (O, 25 beds) 710 North East Street, Wabash, IN Zip 46992–1924; tel. 260/563–3131; Marilyn J. Custer-Mitchell, President

PARKVIEW WHITLEY HOSPITAL (O, 30 beds) 1260 East State Road 205, Columbia City, IN Zip 46725–9492; tel. 260/248–9000; Scott F. Gabriel, President

Web address: www.parkview.com

Owned, leased, sponsored:	7 hospitals	874 beds
Contract-managed:	0 hospitals	0 beds
Totals:	7 hospitals	874 beds

★1785: PARTNERS HEALTHCARE SYSTEM, INC. (NP)

800 Boylston Street, Suite 1150, Boston, MA Zip 02199–8123; tel. 617/278–1004; David Torchiana, M.D., Chief Executive Officer
(Decentralized Health System)

For explanation of codes following names, see page B2.
★ Indicates Type III membership in the American Hospital Association.

MASSACHUSETTS: BRIGHAM AND WOMEN'S FAULKNER HOSPITAL (O, 125 beds) 1153 Centre Street, Boston, MA Zip 02130–3446; tel. 617/983–7000; Michael Gustafson, M.D., President
Web address: www.brighamandwomensfaulkner.org/index.asp

BRIGHAM AND WOMEN'S HOSPITAL (O, 747 beds) 75 Francis Street, Boston, MA Zip 02115–6110; tel. 617/732–5500; Elizabeth Nabel, M.D., President
Web address: www.brighamandwomens.org

COOLEY DICKINSON HOSPITAL (O, 74 beds) 30 Locust Street, Northampton, MA Zip 01060–2093, P O Box 5001, 01061–5001, tel. 413/582–2000; Joanne Marqusee, President and Chief Executive Officer

MARTHA'S VINEYARD HOSPITAL (O, 25 beds) One Hospital Road, Oak Bluffs, MA Zip 2557, P O Box 1477, 02557–1477, tel. 508/693–0410; Timothy Walsh, Interim President and Chief Executive Officer
Web address: www.mvhospital.com/

MASSACHUSETTS GENERAL HOSPITAL (O, 1028 beds) 55 Fruit Street, Boston, MA Zip 02114–2696; tel. 617/726–2000; Peter L. Slavin, M.D., President
Web address: www.massgeneral.org

MCLEAN HOSPITAL (O, 217 beds) 115 Mill Street, Belmont, MA Zip 02478–1064; tel. 617/855–2000; Scott L. Rauch, M.D., President and Psychiatrist in Chief

NANTUCKET COTTAGE HOSPITAL (O, 19 beds) 57 Prospect Street, Nantucket, MA Zip 02554–2799; tel. 508/825–8100; Margot Hartmann, M.D., Ph.D., President and Chief Executive Officer
Web address: www.nantuckethospital.org

NEWTON-WELLESLEY HOSPITAL (O, 264 beds) 2014 Washington Street, Newton Lower Falls, MA Zip 02462–1699; tel. 617/243–6000; Michael R. Jaff, D.O., President
Web address: www.nwh.org

NORTH SHORE MEDICAL CENTER (O, 406 beds) 81 Highland Avenue, Salem, MA Zip 01970–2714; tel. 978/741–1200; David J. Roberts, M.D., President

SPAULDING HOSPITAL FOR CONTINUING MEDICAL CARE CAMBRIDGE (O, 128 beds) 1575 Cambridge Street, Cambridge, MA Zip 02138–4308; tel. 617/876–4344; Maureen Banks, FACHE, MS, R.N., President
Web address: www.spauldingnetwork.org

SPAULDING REHABILITATION HOSPITAL CAPE COD (O, 60 beds) 311 Service Road, East Sandwich, MA Zip 02537–1370; tel. 508/833–4000; Maureen Banks, FACHE, MS, R.N., President

SPAULDING REHABILITATION HOSPITAL (O, 132 beds) 300 First Avenue, Charlestown, MA Zip 02129–3109; tel. 617/952–5000; David E. Storto, President
Web address: www.spauldingrehab.org

NEW HAMPSHIRE: WENTWORTH-DOUGLASS HOSPITAL (O, 142 beds) 789 Central Avenue, Dover, NH Zip 3820; tel. 603/742–5252; Gregory J. Walker, Chief Executive Officer
Web address: www.wdhospital.com

Owned, leased, sponsored:	13 hospitals	3367 beds
Contract-managed:	0 hospitals	0 beds
Totals:	13 hospitals	3367 beds

★5415: PEACEHEALTH (CC)
1115 SE 164th Avenue, Vancouver, WA Zip 98683; tel. 360/729–1000; Elizabeth Dunne, President and Chief Executive Officer
(Decentralized Health System)

ALASKA: PEACEHEALTH KETCHIKAN MEDICAL CENTER (L, 50 beds) 3100 Tongass Avenue, Ketchikan, AK Zip 99901–5746; tel. 907/225–5171; Edward E. Freysinger, Chief Administrative Officer
Web address: www.peacehealth.org

OREGON: PEACEHEALTH COTTAGE GROVE COMMUNITY MEDICAL CENTER (O, 14 beds) 1515 Village Drive, Cottage Grove, OR Zip 97424–9700; tel. 541/942–0511; Tim Herrmann, R.N., Administrator
Web address: www.peacehealth.org

PEACEHEALTH PEACE HARBOR MEDICAL CENTER (O, 21 beds) 400 Ninth Street, Florence, OR Zip 97439–7398; tel. 541/997–8412; Rick Yecny, Chief Executive Officer and Chief Mission Officer

PEACEHEALTH SACRED HEART MEDICAL CENTER UNIVERSITY DISTRICT (O, 104 beds) 1255 Hilyard Street, Eugene, OR Zip 97401–3700, P O Box

10905, 97440–2905, tel. 541/686–7300; Mary Anne McMurren, R.N., Chief Administrative Officer
Web address: www.peacehealth.org

PEACEHEALTH SACRED HEART MEDICAL CENTER AT RIVERBEND (O, 379 beds) 3333 Riverbend Drive, Springfield, OR Zip 97477–8800; tel. 541/222–7300; Rand O'Leary, FACHE, Chief Executive, Oregon Network
Web address: www.peacehealth.org

WASHINGTON: PEACEHEALTH PEACE ISLAND MEDICAL CENTER (O, 10 beds) 1117 Spring Street, Friday Harbor, WA Zip 98250–9782; tel. 360/378–2141; Merry Ann Keane, Chief Administrative Officer

PEACEHEALTH SOUTHWEST MEDICAL CENTER (O, 362 beds) 400 NE Mother Joseph Place, Vancouver, WA Zip 98664–3200, P O Box 1600, 98668–1600, tel. 360/256–2000; Sean Gregory, Chief Executive
Web address: www.peacehealth.org

PEACEHEALTH ST. JOHN MEDICAL CENTER (O, 180 beds) 1615 Delaware Street, Longview, WA Zip 98632–2367, P O Box 3002, 98632–0302, tel. 360/414–2000; Renato V. Baciarelli, Interim Chief Administrative Officer

PEACEHEALTH ST. JOSEPH MEDICAL CENTER (O, 253 beds) 2901 Squalicum Parkway, Bellingham, WA Zip 98225–1851; tel. 360/734–5400; Dale Zender, President Hospital Services NW
Web address: www.peacehealth.org

PEACEHEALTH UNITED GENERAL MEDICAL CENTER (C, 25 beds) 2000 Hospital Drive, Sedro-Woolley, WA Zip 98284–4327; tel. 360/856–6021; Christopher Johnston, Chief Administrative Officer
Web address: www.peacehealth.org/united-general

Owned, leased, sponsored:	9 hospitals	1373 beds
Contract-managed:	1 hospitals	25 beds
Totals:	10 hospitals	1398 beds

0989: PENN STATE HERSHEY HEALTH SYSTEM (NP)
500 University Drive, Hershey, PA Zip 17033–2360; tel. 717/531–8521; A. Craig. Hillemeier, M.D., Chief Executive Officer
(Moderately Centralized Health System)

PENNSYLVANIA: PENN STATE HEALTH ST. JOSEPH (O, 180 beds) 2500 Bernville Road, Reading, PA Zip 19605–9453, P O Box 316, 19603–0316, tel. 610/378–2000; John R. Morahan, President and Chief Executive Officer
Web address: www.thefutureofhealthcare.org

PENN STATE MILTON S. HERSHEY MEDICAL CENTER (O, 527 beds) 500 University Drive, Hershey, PA Zip 17033–2360, P O Box 850, 17033–0850, tel. 717/531–8521; A. Craig. Hillemeier, M.D., Chief Executive Officer

Owned, leased, sponsored:	2 hospitals	707 beds
Contract-managed:	0 hospitals	0 beds
Totals:	2 hospitals	707 beds

★0314: PHOEBE PUTNEY HEALTH SYSTEM (NP)
417 Third Avenue, Albany, GA Zip 31701–1943; tel. 229/312–1000; Joel Wernick, President and Chief Executive Officer
(Independent Hospital System)

GEORGIA: PHOEBE SUMTER MEDICAL CENTER (O, 45 beds) 126 Highway 280 West, Americus, GA Zip 31719; tel. 229/924–6011; Brandi Lunneborg, Chief Executive Officer
Web address: www.phoebesumter.org

PHOEBE WORTH MEDICAL CENTER (O, 16 beds) 807 South Isabella Street, Sylvester, GA Zip 31791–7554, P O Box 545, 31791–0545, tel. 229/776–6961; Kim Gilman, Chief Executive Officer

SOUTHWEST GEORGIA REGIONAL MEDICAL CENTER (O, 25 beds) 361 Randolph Street, Cuthbert, GA Zip 39840–6127; tel. 229/732–2181; Kim Gilman, Chief Executive Officer and Chief Nursing Officer
Web address: www.phoebeputney.com/

Owned, leased, sponsored:	3 hospitals	86 beds
Contract-managed:	0 hospitals	0 beds
Totals:	3 hospitals	86 beds

For explanation of codes following names, see page B2.
★ Indicates Type III membership in the American Hospital Association.

0043: PHYSICIANS FOR HEALTHY HOSPITALS (IO)

1117 East Devonshire Avenue, Hemet, CA Zip 92543–3083; tel. 951/652–2811; Joel M. Bergenfeld, Chief Executive Officer

CALIFORNIA: HEMET VALLEY MEDICAL CENTER (O, 238 beds) 1117 East Devonshire Avenue, Hemet, CA Zip 92543–3083; tel. 951/652–2811; Dan C. McLaughlin, Chief Hospital Executive Officer

Web address: www.physiciansforhealthyhospitals.com

MENIFEE VALLEY MEDICAL CENTER (O, 84 beds) 28400 McCall Boulevard, Sun City, CA Zip 92585–9537; tel. 951/679–8888; Dan C. McLaughlin, Chief Executive Officer

Owned, leased, sponsored:	2 hospitals	322 beds
Contract-managed:	0 hospitals	0 beds
Totals:	2 hospitals	322 beds

0310: PIEDMONT HEALTHCARE (NP)

1800 Howell Mill Road NW, Suite 850, Atlanta, GA Zip 30318–0923; tel. 404/425–1314; Kevin Brown, President and Chief Executive Officer
(Independent Hospital System)

GEORGIA: PIEDMONT ATHENS REGIONAL MEDICAL CENTER (O, 343 beds) 1199 Prince Avenue, Athens, GA Zip 30606–2797; tel. 706/475–7000; Charles A. Peck, M.D., Interim President and Chief Executive Officer

Web address: www.armc.org

PIEDMONT FAYETTE HOSPITAL (O, 172 beds) 1255 Highway 54 West, Fayetteville, GA Zip 30214–4526; tel. 770/719–7000; Michael Burnett, Chief Executive Officer

Web address: www.piedmont.org

PIEDMONT HENRY HOSPITAL (L, 214 beds) 1133 Eagle's Landing Parkway, Stockbridge, GA Zip 30281–5099; tel. 678/604–1000; Deborah Armstrong, Chief Executive Officer

PIEDMONT HOSPITAL (O, 510 beds) 1968 Peachtree Road NW, Atlanta, GA Zip 30309–1281; tel. 404/605–5000; Patrick M. Battey, M.D., Chief Executive Officer

Web address: www.piedmonthospital.org

PIEDMONT MOUNTAINSIDE HOSPITAL (O, 52 beds) 1266 Highway 515 South, Jasper, GA Zip 30143–4872; tel. 706/692–2441; Denise Ray, Chief Executive Officer

PIEDMONT NEWNAN HOSPITAL (O, 146 beds) 745 Poplar Road, Newnan, GA Zip 30265–1618; tel. 770/400–1000; Michael Robertson, Chief Executive Officer

Web address: www.piedmont.org/locations/piedmont-newnan/pnh-home

PIEDMONT NEWTON HOSPITAL (O, 101 beds) 5126 Hospital Drive, Covington, GA Zip 30014–2567; tel. 770/786–7053; Eric Bour, M.D., FACS, Chief Executive Officer

Web address: www.newtonmedical.com

Owned, leased, sponsored:	7 hospitals	1538 beds
Contract-managed:	0 hospitals	0 beds
Totals:	7 hospitals	1538 beds

★0958: PIH HEALTH (NP)

12401 Washington Boulevard, Whittier, CA Zip 90602–1006; tel. 562/698–0811; James R. West, President and Chief Executive Officer
(Moderately Centralized Health System)

CALIFORNIA: PIH HEALTH HOSPITAL - DOWNEY (O, 181 beds) 11500 Brookshire Avenue, Downey, CA Zip 90241–4917; tel. 562/904–5000; James R. West, President and Chief Executive Officer
Web address: www.PIHHealth.org

PIH HEALTH HOSPITAL-WHITTIER (O, 245 beds) 12401 Washington Boulevard, Whittier, CA Zip 90602–1099; tel. 562/698–0811; James R. West, President and Chief Executive Officer

Owned, leased, sponsored:	2 hospitals	426 beds
Contract-managed:	0 hospitals	0 beds
Totals:	2 hospitals	426 beds

★0326: PIONEER HEALTH SERVICES (IO)

110 Pioneer Way, Magee, MS Zip 39111–5501, P O Box 1100, 39111–1100, tel. 601/849–6440; Joseph S. McNulty III, President and Chief Executive Officer
(Independent Hospital System)

GEORGIA: PIONEER COMMUNITY HOSPITAL OF EARLY (L, 151 beds) 11740 Columbia Street, Blakely, GA Zip 39823–2574; tel. 229/723–4241; Ginger Cushing, Chief Executive Officer
Web address: www.pchearly.com

MISSISSIPPI: PIONEER COMMUNITY HOSPITAL OF ABERDEEN (L, 25 beds) 400 South Chestnut Street, Aberdeen, MS Zip 39730–3335, P O Box 548, 39730–0548, tel. 662/369–2455; Christopher Chandler, Chief Executive Officer

VIRGINIA: PIONEER COMMUNITY HOSPITAL OF PATRICK (O, 15 beds) 18688 Jeb Stuart Highway, Stuart, VA Zip 24171–1559; tel. 276/694–3151; Jeanette Filpi, Chief Executive Officer
Web address: www.pchpatrick.com

Owned, leased, sponsored:	3 hospitals	191 beds
Contract-managed:	0 hospitals	0 beds
Totals:	3 hospitals	191 beds

★0617: POST ACUTE MEDICAL, LLC (IO)

1828 Good Hope Road, Suite 102, Enola, PA Zip 17025–1233; tel. 717/731–9660; Anthony F. Misitano, President and Chief Executive Officer
(Independent Hospital System)

LOUISIANA: PAM SPECIALTY HOSPITAL OF COVINGTON (O, 58 beds) 20050 Crestwood Boulevard, Covington, LA Zip 70433–5207; tel. 985/875–7525; J Cullen. Meyers, Chief Executive Officer

PAM SPECIALTY HOSPITAL OF HAMMOND (O, 40 beds) 42074 Veterans Avenue, Hammond, LA Zip 70403–1408; tel. 985/902–8148; Nicholas Paul. Mendez, Chief Executive Officer
Web address: www.postacutemedical.com

PAM SPECIALTY HOSPITAL OF LAFAYETTE (O, 50 beds) 204 Energy Parkway, Lafayette, LA Zip 70508–3816; tel. 337/232–1905; Jason Branson, Chief Executive Officer

OKLAHOMA: PAM REHABILITATION HOSPITAL OF TULSA (O, 41 beds) 10020 East 91st Street, Tulsa, OK Zip 74133; tel. 918/893–2400; Jerry Elenbaas, Chief Executive Officer and Division President
Web address: www.warmsprings.org/our-facilities/outpatient-rehabilitation

POST ACUTE MEDICAL SPECIALTY HOSPITAL OF TULSA (O, 60 beds) 3219 South 79th East Avenue, Tulsa, OK Zip 74145–1343; tel. 918/663–8183; Lee A. Simpson Jr, Chief Executive Officer
Web address: www.postacutetulsa.com

PENNSYLVANIA: PAM SPECIALTY HOSPITAL OF WILKES-BARRE (O, 36 beds) 575 North River Street, 7th Floor, Wilkes Barre, PA Zip 18702–2634; tel. 570/208–3310; Salvatore Aquilina, Chief Executive Officer
Web address: www.warmsprings.org/our-facilities/hospitals/post-acute-medical-specialty-hospital-wilkes-barre/

TEXAS: CUMBERLAND SURGICAL HOSPITAL (O, 9 beds) 5330 N. Loop 1604 W, San Antonio, TX Zip 78249; tel. 210/877–8000; Paul B. Abraham, FACHE, Chief Executive Officer

PAM REHABILITATION HOSPITAL OF BEAUMONT (O, 61 beds) 3340 Plaza 10 Boulevard, Beaumont, TX Zip 77707–2551; tel. 409/835–0835; Todd Lorenz, Chief Executive Officer
Web address: www.postacutemedical.com/our-facilities/outpatient-rehabilitation/rehabilitation-hospital-beaumont/

For explanation of codes following names, see page B2.
★ Indicates Type III membership in the American Hospital Association.

PAM REHABILITATION HOSPITAL OF VICTORIA (O, 26 beds) 101 James Coleman Drive, Victoria, TX Zip 77904–3147, Shawn Todd, Chief Executive Officer
Web address: www.warmsprings.org/our-facilities/outpatient-rehabilitation/warm-springs-rehabilitation-center-victoria/

PAM SPECIALTY HOSPITAL OF VICTORIA NORTH (O, 26 beds) 102 Medical Drive, Victoria, TX Zip 77904–3101; tel. 361/576–6200; Christina Adrean, Chief Executive Officer
Web address: www.warmsprings.org

PAM SPECIALTY HOSPITAL OF VICTORIA SOUTH (O, 23 beds) 506 East San Antonio Street, 3rd Floor, Victoria, TX Zip 77901–6060; tel. 361/575–1445; Christina Adrean, Chief Executive Officer

POST ACUTE MEDICAL SPECIALTY HOSPITAL OF CORPUS CHRISTI - NORTH (O, 22 beds) 600 Elizabeth Street, 3rd Floor, Corpus Christi, TX Zip 78404–2235; tel. 361/881–3223; Hector Bernal, Chief Executive Officer
Web address: www.postacutemedical.com/our-facilities/hospitals/post-acute-medical-specialty-hospital-corpus-christi/

POST ACUTE MEDICAL SPECIALTY HOSPITAL OF CORPUS CHRISTI - SOUTH (O, 74 beds) 6226 Saratoga Boulevard, Corpus Christi, TX Zip 78414–3421; tel. 361/986–1600; Michael L. Pierce, Chief Executive Officer

POST ACUTE MEDICAL SPECIALTY HOSPITAL OF TEXARKANA - NORTH (O, 49 beds) 2400 St Michael Drive, 2nd Floor, Texarkana, TX Zip 75503–2372; tel. 903/614–7600; Lorraine Murray, Chief Executive Officer
Web address: www.postacutemedical.com

POST ACUTE/WARM SPRINGS REHABILITATION HOSPITAL OF ALLEN (O, 39 beds) 1001 Raintree Circle, Allen, TX Zip 75013–4912; tel. 972/908–2015; Bill Kaupas, Chief Executive Officer
Web address: www.warmsprings.org

POST ACUTE/WARM SPRINGS SPECIALTY HOSPITAL OF LULING (O, 34 beds) 200 Memorial Drive, Luling, TX Zip 78648–3213; tel. 830/875–8400; Jana Kuykendall, Chief Executive Officer
Web address: www.warmsprings.org

POST ACUTE/WARM SPRINGS SPECIALTY HOSPITAL OF NEW BRAUNFELS (O, 40 beds) 1445 Hanz Drive, New Braunfels, TX Zip 78130–2567; tel. 830/627–7600; Shayne Goode, Administrator
Web address: www.warmsprings.org/locations/hos/h1/

POST ACUTE/WARM SPRINGS SPECIALTY HOSPITAL OF SAN ANTONIO (O, 26 beds) 5418 N Loop 1604 W, San Antonio, TX Zip 78247; tel. 210/921–3550; James Asberry, Chief Executive Officer

WARM SPRINGS REHABILITATION HOSPITAL OF KYLE (O, 36 beds) 5980 Kyle Parkway, Kyle, TX Zip 78640–2400; tel. 512/262–0821; Duke Saldivar, FACHE, Chief Executive Officer
Web address: www.warmsprings.org/our-facilities/outpatient-rehabilitation/warm-springs-rehabilitation-center-kyle/

WARM SPRINGS REHABILITATION HOSPITAL OF SAN ANTONIO (O, 139 beds) 5101 Medical Drive, San Antonio, TX Zip 78229–4801; tel. 210/616–0100; Debra Bornmann, Chief Executive Officer

WISCONSIN: POST ACUTE MEDICAL SPECIALTY HOSPITAL OF MILWAUKEE (O, 56 beds) 5017 South 110Th Street, Greenfield, WI Zip 53228–3131; tel. 414/427–8282; Carin Croker, Chief Executive Officer
Web address: www.postacutemedical.com/

Owned, leased, sponsored:	21 hospitals	945 beds
Contract-managed:	0 hospitals	0 beds
Totals:	21 hospitals	945 beds

0240: PREFERRED MANAGEMENT CORPORATION (IO)
120 West MacArthur, Suite 121, Shawnee, OK Zip 74804–2005; tel. 405/878–0202; Donald Freeman, President and Chief Executive Officer
(Independent Hospital System)

TEXAS: COLEMAN COUNTY MEDICAL CENTER (L, 25 beds) 310 South Pecos Street, Coleman, TX Zip 76834–4159; tel. 325/625–2135; Clay Vogel, Administrator and Chief Executive Officer
Web address: www.colemantexas.org/hospital.html

COLLINGSWORTH GENERAL HOSPITAL (L, 13 beds) 1013 15th Street, Wellington, TX Zip 79095–3703, P O Box 1112, 79095–1112, tel. 806/447–2521; Candy Powell, Administrator

CULBERSON HOSPITAL (L, 14 beds) Eisenhower-Farm Market Road 2185, Van Horn, TX Zip 79855, P O Box 609, 79855–0609, tel. 432/283–2760; Jonathon Voelkel, Administrator
Web address: www.culbersonhospital.org

KIMBLE HOSPITAL (O, 15 beds) 349 Reid Road, Junction, TX Zip 76849–3049; tel. 325/446–3321; William Barnes, Administrator

MULESHOE AREA MEDICAL CENTER (L, 25 beds) 708 South First Street, Muleshoe, TX Zip 79347–3627; tel. 806/272–4524; Dennis Fleenor, R.N., Administrator
Web address: www.mahdtx.org

PARMER MEDICAL CENTER (C, 15 beds) 1307 Cleveland Street, Friona, TX Zip 79035–1121; tel. 806/250–2754; Gayla Quillin, Administrator
Web address: www.parmermedicalcenter.com

SABINE COUNTY HOSPITAL (L, 25 beds) 2301 Worth Street, Hemphill, TX Zip 75948–7216, P O Box 750, 75948–0750, tel. 409/787–3300; Jerry Howell, Administrator

SCHLEICHER COUNTY MEDICAL CENTER (L, 14 beds) 102 North US Highway 277, Eldorado, TX Zip 76936–4010; tel. 325/853–2507; Paul Burke, Administrator
Web address: www.scmc.us

Owned, leased, sponsored:	7 hospitals	131 beds
Contract-managed:	1 hospitals	15 beds
Totals:	8 hospitals	146 beds

★0977: PREMIER HEALTH (NP)
110 North Main Street Suite 390, Dayton, OH Zip 45402–3720; tel. 937/499–9401; Mary H. Boosalis, President
(Centralized Physician/Insurance Health System)

OHIO: ATRIUM MEDICAL CENTER (O, 284 beds) One Medical Center Drive, Middletown, OH Zip 45005–1066; tel. 513/424–2111; Michael Uhl, President
Web address: www.PremierHealth.com

MIAMI VALLEY HOSPITAL (O, 845 beds) One Wyoming Street, Dayton, OH Zip 45409–2793; tel. 937/208–8000; Mikki Clancy, Chief Operating Officer
Web address: www.miamivalleyhospital.org

UPPER VALLEY MEDICAL CENTER (O, 157 beds) 3130 North County Road 25A, Troy, OH Zip 45373–1309; tel. 937/440–4000; Rebecca Rice, FACHE, Chief Executive Officer
Web address: www.uvmc.com

Owned, leased, sponsored:	3 hospitals	1286 beds
Contract-managed:	0 hospitals	0 beds
Totals:	3 hospitals	1286 beds

★3505: PRESBYTERIAN HEALTHCARE SERVICES (NP)
9521 San Mateo Blvd. NE, Albuquerque, NM Zip 87113, P O Box 26666, 87125–6666, tel. 505/841–1234; Dale Maxwell, Chief Executive Officer
(Centralized Physician/Insurance Health System)

NEW MEXICO: DR. DAN C. TRIGG MEMORIAL HOSPITAL (L, 25 beds) 301 East Miel De Luna Avenue, Tucumcari, NM Zip 88401–3810, P O Box 608, 88401–0608, tel. 575/461–7000; Troy Clark, Interim Administrator
Web address: www.phs.org

LINCOLN COUNTY MEDICAL CENTER (L, 25 beds) 211 Sudderth Drive, Ruidoso, NM Zip 88345–6043, P O Box 8000, 88355–8000, tel. 575/257–8200; Todd Oberheu, Administrator

PLAINS REGIONAL MEDICAL CENTER (O, 100 beds) 2100 North Doctor Martin Luther King Boulevard, Clovis, NM Zip 88101–9412, P O Box 1688, 88102–1688, tel. 575/769–2141; Troy Clark, Interim Administrator
Web address: www.phs.org

PRESBYTERIAN ESPANOLA HOSPITAL (O, 42 beds) 1010 Spruce Street, Espanola, NM Zip 87532–2746; tel. 505/753–7111; Brenda Romero, Administrator

For explanation of codes following names, see page B2.
★ Indicates Type III membership in the American Hospital Association.

Section B

PRESBYTERIAN HOSPITAL (O, 616 beds) 1100 Central Avenue SE, Albuquerque, NM Zip 87106–4934, P O Box 26666, 87125–6666, tel. 505/841–1234; Doyle Boykin, R.N., MSN, President
Web address: www.phs.org

SOCORRO GENERAL HOSPITAL (O, 18 beds) 1202 Highway 60 West, Socorro, NM Zip 87801–3914, P O Box 1009, 87801–1009, tel. 575/835–1140; Veronica Pound, R.N., Administrator
Web address: www.phs.org

Owned, leased, sponsored:	6 hospitals	826 beds
Contract-managed:	0 hospitals	0 beds
Totals:	6 hospitals	826 beds

★**0851: PRESENCE HEALTH** (CC)
200 South Wacker Drive, Suite 1100, Chicago, IL Zip 60606–5829; tel. 312/308–3200; Michael Englehart, President and Chief Executive Officer
(Moderately Centralized Health System)

ILLINOIS: OUR LADY OF THE RESURRECTION-LONG TERM CARE (O, 50 beds) 5645 West Addison Street, Chicago, IL Zip 60634

PRESENCE COVENANT MEDICAL CENTER (O, 181 beds) 1400 West Park Street, Urbana, IL Zip 61801–2396; tel. 217/337–2000; Jared Rogers, M.D., President and Chief Executive Officer
Web address: www.presencehealth.org/covenant

PRESENCE HOLY FAMILY MEDICAL CENTER (O, 128 beds) 100 North River Road, Des Plaines, IL Zip 60016–1255; tel. 847/297–1800; Yolande Wilson-Stubbs, President

PRESENCE MERCY MEDICAL CENTER (O, 242 beds) 1325 North Highland Avenue, Aurora, IL Zip 60506–1449; tel. 630/859–2222; Michael L. Brown, Regional President and Chief Executive Officer
Web address: www.presencehealth.org/mercy/

PRESENCE RESURRECTION MEDICAL CENTER (O, 333 beds) 7435 West Talcott Avenue, Chicago, IL Zip 60631–3746; tel. 773/774–8000; Robert Dahl, President and Chief Executive Officer
Web address: www.presencehealth.org

PRESENCE SAINT FRANCIS HOSPITAL (O, 215 beds) 355 Ridge Avenue, Evanston, IL Zip 60202–3399; tel. 847/316–4000; Kenneth Jones, President

PRESENCE SAINT JOSEPH HOSPITAL (O, 361 beds) 2900 North Lake Shore Drive, Chicago, IL Zip 60657–6274; tel. 773/665–3000; James L. Robinson III, PsyD, President
Web address: www.reshealth.org

PRESENCE SAINT JOSEPH HOSPITAL (O, 184 beds) 77 North Airlite Street, Elgin, IL Zip 60123–4912; tel. 847/695–3200; Michael L. Brown, Regional President and Chief Executive Officer

PRESENCE SAINT JOSEPH MEDICAL CENTER (O, 461 beds) 333 North Madison Street, Joliet, IL Zip 60435–8200; tel. 815/725–7133; Robert J. Erickson, President
Web address: www.presencehealth.org/stjoes

PRESENCE SAINTS MARY & ELIZABETH MEDICAL CENTER (O, 492 beds) 2233 West Division Street, Chicago, IL Zip 60622–3086; tel. 312/770–2000; Martin H. Judd, Regional President and Chief Executive Officer

PRESENCE ST. MARY'S HOSPITAL (O, 156 beds) 500 West Court Street, Kankakee, IL Zip 60901–3661; tel. 815/937–2400; Chris Shride, President
Web address: www.presencehealth.org/presence-st-marys-hospital-kankakee

PRESENCE UNITED SAMARITANS MEDICAL CENTER (O, 117 beds) 812 North Logan, Danville, IL Zip 61832–3788; tel. 217/443–5000; Jared Rogers, M.D., President and Chief Executive Officer
Web address: www.presencehealth.org/usmc

RESURRECTION NURSING PAVILION (O, 295 beds) 1001 North Greenwood, Park Ridge, IL Zip 60068, Patricia Tiernan, Administrator

Owned, leased, sponsored:	13 hospitals	3215 beds
Contract-managed:	0 hospitals	0 beds
Totals:	13 hospitals	3215 beds

★**0357: PRIME HEALTHCARE** (IO)
3300 East Guasti Road, Ontario, CA Zip 91761–8655;
tel. 909/235–4400; Prem Reddy, M.D., Chairman, President and Chief Executive Officer
(Moderately Centralized Health System)

ALABAMA: RIVERVIEW REGIONAL MEDICAL CENTER (O, 280 beds) 600 South Third Street, Gadsden, AL Zip 35901–5399; tel. 256/543–5200; Ruben Garza, Interim Chief Executive Officer
Web address: www.riverviewregional.com

CALIFORNIA: ALVARADO HOSPITAL MEDICAL CENTER (O, 137 beds) 6655 Alvarado Road, San Diego, CA Zip 92120–5208; tel. 619/287–3270; Robin Gomez, R.N., MSN, Administrator
Web address: www.alvaradohospital.com

CENTINELA HOSPITAL MEDICAL CENTER (O, 369 beds) 555 East Hardy Street, Inglewood, CA Zip 90301–4011, P O Box 720, 90312–6720, tel. 310/673–4660; Linda Bradley, Chief Executive Officer

CHINO VALLEY MEDICAL CENTER (O, 126 beds) 5451 Walnut Avenue, Chino, CA Zip 91710–2672; tel. 909/464–8600; James M. Lally, D.O., President and Chief Medical Officer
Web address: www.cvmc.com

DESERT VALLEY HOSPITAL (O, 110 beds) 16850 Bear Valley Road, Victorville, CA Zip 92395–5795; tel. 760/241–8000; Fred Hunter, R.N., Chief Executive Officer
Web address: www.dvmc.com

ENCINO HOSPITAL MEDICAL CENTER (O, 78 beds) 16237 Ventura Boulevard, Encino, CA Zip 91436–2272; tel. 818/995–5000; Bockhi Park, Chief Executive Officer

GARDEN GROVE HOSPITAL AND MEDICAL CENTER (O, 167 beds) 12601 Garden Grove Boulevard, Garden Grove, CA Zip 92843–1959; tel. 714/537–5160; Richard M. Rowe, PharmD, Chief Executive Officer
Web address: www.gardengrovehospital.com

GLENDORA COMMUNITY HOSPITAL (O, 128 beds) 150 West Route 66, Glendora, CA Zip 91740–6207; tel. 626/852–5000; Sofia Abrina, R.N., Chief Executive Officer
Web address: www.evhmc.com

HUNTINGTON BEACH HOSPITAL (O, 131 beds) 17772 Beach Boulevard, Huntington Beach, CA Zip 92647–6896; tel. 714/843–5000; Richard M. Rowe, PharmD, Chief Executive Officer

LA PALMA INTERCOMMUNITY HOSPITAL (O, 140 beds) 7901 Walker Street, La Palma, CA Zip 90623–1764; tel. 714/670–7400; Virgis Narbutas, Chief Executive Officer
Web address: www.lapalmaintercommunityhospital.com

MONTCLAIR HOSPITAL MEDICAL CENTER (O, 102 beds) 5000 San Bernardino Street, Montclair, CA Zip 91763–2326; tel. 909/625–5411; Sofia Abrina, R.N., Administrator

PARADISE VALLEY HOSPITAL (O, 291 beds) 2400 East Fourth Street, National City, CA Zip 91950–2099; tel. 619/470–4321; Neerav Jadeja, Administrator
Web address: www.paradisevalleyhospital.org

SAN DIMAS COMMUNITY HOSPITAL (O, 101 beds) 1350 West Covina Boulevard, San Dimas, CA Zip 91773–3219; tel. 909/599–6811; Kurt Weinmeister, Chief Executive Officer
Web address: www.sandimashospital.com/

SHASTA REGIONAL MEDICAL CENTER (O, 100 beds) 1100 Butte Street, Redding, CA Zip 96001–0853, P O Box 496072, 96049–6072, tel. 530/244–5400; Richard Fletcher, PharmD, Chief Executive Officer

SHERMAN OAKS HOSPITAL (O, 91 beds) 4929 Van Nuys Boulevard, Sherman Oaks, CA Zip 91403–1777; tel. 818/981–7111; Bockhi Park, Chief Executive Officer
Web address: www.shermanoakshospital.com

WEST ANAHEIM MEDICAL CENTER (O, 219 beds) 3033 West Orange Avenue, Anaheim, CA Zip 92804–3183; tel. 714/827–3000; Virgis Narbutas, Chief Executive Officer
Web address: www.westanaheimmedctr.com

FLORIDA: LEHIGH REGIONAL MEDICAL CENTER (O, 88 beds) 1500 Lee Boulevard, Lehigh Acres, FL Zip 33936–4835; tel. 239/369–2101; Gary C. Bell, LFACHE, Chief Executive Officer
Web address: www.lehighregional.com

GEORGIA: SOUTHERN REGIONAL MEDICAL CENTER (O, 331 beds) 11 Upper Riverdale Road SW, Riverdale, GA Zip 30274–2615; tel. 770/991–8000; Charlotte W. Dupre, Chief Executive Officer

For explanation of codes following names, see page B2.
★ Indicates Type III membership in the American Hospital Association.

INDIANA: MONROE HOSPITAL (O, 32 beds) 5811 East Slick Rock lane, Bloomfield, IN Zip 47424, 4011 South Monroe Medical Park Boulevard, Bloomington, 47403–8000, tel. 812/825–1111; Nancy Bakewell, Administrator
Web address: www.monroehospital.com

KANSAS: PROVIDENCE MEDICAL CENTER (O, 170 beds) 8929 Parallel Parkway, Kansas City, KS Zip 66112–1689; tel. 913/596–4000; Karen Orr, Administrator and Chief Nursing Officer
Web address: www.providencekc.com

SAINT JOHN HOSPITAL (O, 48 beds) 3500 South Fourth Street, Leavenworth, KS Zip 66048–5043; tel. 913/680–6000; Paula Ellis, Administrator

MICHIGAN: GARDEN CITY HOSPITAL (O, 176 beds) 6245 Inkster Road, Garden City, MI Zip 48135–4001; tel. 734/421–3300; Saju George, Chief Executive Officer
Web address: www.gch.org

LAKE HURON MEDICAL CENTER (O, 119 beds) 2601 Electric Avenue, Port Huron, MI Zip 48060–6518; tel. 810/985–1500; Jay De los Reyes, Chief Executive Officer
Web address: www.mymercy.us

MISSOURI: ST. JOSEPH MEDICAL CENTER (O, 185 beds) 1000 Carondelet Drive, Kansas City, MO Zip 64114–4673; tel. 816/942–4400; Jodi Fincher, Administrator
Web address: www.stjosephkc.com/

ST. MARY'S MEDICAL CENTER (O, 88 beds) 201 Northwest R D Mize Road, Blue Springs, MO Zip 64014–2518; tel. 816/228–5900; Debra Ohnoutka, Chief Executive Officer

NEVADA: NORTH VISTA HOSPITAL (O, 177 beds) 1409 East Lake Mead Boulevard, North Las Vegas, NV Zip 89030–7197; tel. 702/649–7711; Vincenzo Variale, Chief Executive Officer
Web address: www.northvistahospital.com

SAINT MARY'S REGIONAL MEDICAL CENTER (O, 293 beds) 235 West Sixth Street, Reno, NV Zip 89503–4548; tel. 775/770–3000; Helen Lidholm, Chief Executive Officer
Web address: www.saintmarysreno.org

NEW JERSEY: SAINT CLARE'S HEALTH SYSTEM (O, 412 beds) 25 Pocono Road, Denville, NJ Zip 07834–2954; tel. 973/625–6000; Brian Finestein, Chief Executive Officer
Web address: www.saintclares.org

SAINT MICHAEL'S MEDICAL CENTER (O, 162 beds) 111 Central Avenue, Newark, NJ Zip 07102–1909; tel. 973/877–5350; Robert C. Iannaccone, Chief Executive Officer
Web address: www.smmcnj.org

ST. MARY'S GENERAL HOSPITAL (O, 287 beds) 350 Boulevard, Passaic, NJ Zip 07055–2840; tel. 973/365–4300; Edward Condit, President and Chief Executive Officer

OHIO: COSHOCTON REGIONAL MEDICAL CENTER (O, 44 beds) 1460 Orange Street, Coshocton, OH Zip 43812–2229, P O Box 1330, 43812–6330, tel. 740/622–6411; Stephanie Conn, Administrator and Chief Nursing Officer
Web address: www.ccmh.com

EAST LIVERPOOL CITY HOSPITAL (O, 120 beds) 425 West Fifth Street, East Liverpool, OH Zip 43920–2498; tel. 330/385–7200; Keith Richardson, President and Chief Executive Officer

PENNSYLVANIA: LOWER BUCKS HOSPITAL (O, 138 beds) 501 Bath Road, Bristol, PA Zip 19007–3190; tel. 215/785–9200; Linda J. Grass, Chief Executive Officer
Web address: www.lowerbuckshosp.com

ROXBOROUGH MEMORIAL HOSPITAL (O, 140 beds) 5800 Ridge Avenue, Philadelphia, PA Zip 19128–1737; tel. 215/483–9900; Peter J. Adamo, Chief Executive Officer

SUBURBAN COMMUNITY HOSPITAL (O, 126 beds) 2701 DeKalb Pike, Norristown, PA Zip 19401–1820; tel. 610/278–2000; Peter J. Adamo, Chief Executive Officer
Web address: www.suburbanhosp.org

RHODE ISLAND: LANDMARK MEDICAL CENTER (O, 140 beds) 115 Cass Avenue, Woonsocket, RI Zip 02895–4731; tel. 401/769–4100; Michael Souza, Chief Executive Officer
Web address: www.landmarkmedcenter.com

REHABILITATION HOSPITAL OF RHODE ISLAND (O, 70 beds) 116 Eddie Dowling Highway, North Smithfield, RI Zip 02896–7327; tel. 401/766–0800; Michael Souza, Chief Executive Officer

TEXAS: DALLAS MEDICAL CENTER (O, 83 beds) Seven Medical Parkway, Dallas, TX Zip 75234–7823, P O Box 819094, 75381–9094, tel. 972/247–1000; J. T. Barnhart, Chief Executive Officer
Web address: www.dallasmedcenter.com

DALLAS REGIONAL MEDICAL CENTER (O, 101 beds) 1011 North Galloway Avenue, Mesquite, TX Zip 75149–2433; tel. 214/320–7000; Glenda Newby, Chief Executive Officer

HARLINGEN MEDICAL CENTER (O, 88 beds) 5501 South Expressway 77, Harlingen, TX Zip 78550–3213; tel. 956/365–1000; Brenda Ivory, Chief Executive Officer
Web address: www.harlingenmedicalcenter.com

KNAPP MEDICAL CENTER (O, 195 beds) 1401 East Eighth Street, Weslaco, TX Zip 78596–6640, P O Box 1110, 78599–1110, tel. 956/968–8567; Rene Lopez, Chief Executive Officer
Web address: www.knappmed.org

MISSION REGIONAL MEDICAL CENTER (O, 256 beds) 900 South Bryan Road, Mission, TX Zip 78572–6613; tel. 956/323–9103; Kane A. Dawson, Chief Executive Officer

PAMPA REGIONAL MEDICAL CENTER (O, 72 beds) One Medical Plaza, Pampa, TX Zip 79065; tel. 806/665–3721; Edwin Leon, Chief Executive Officer
Web address: www.prmctx.com

Owned, leased, sponsored:	43 hospitals	6711 beds
Contract-managed:	0 hospitals	0 beds
Totals:	43 hospitals	6711 beds

★0153: PROHEALTH CARE, INC. (NP)
N17 W24100 Riverwood Drive, Suite 130, Waukesha, WI Zip 53188; tel. 262/928–2242; Susan A. Edwards, President and Chief Executive Officer
(Centralized Health System)

WISCONSIN: OCONOMOWOC MEMORIAL HOSPITAL (O, 58 beds) 791 Summit Avenue, Oconomowoc, WI Zip 53066–3896; tel. 262/569–9400; Susan A. Edwards, Chief Executive Officer

WAUKESHA MEMORIAL HOSPITAL (O, 274 beds) 725 American Avenue, Waukesha, WI Zip 53188–5099; tel. 262/928–1000; Susan A. Edwards, Chief Executive Officer
Web address: www.prohealthcare.org/locations/locations-v2-detail/?id=1119

Owned, leased, sponsored:	2 hospitals	332 beds
Contract-managed:	0 hospitals	0 beds
Totals:	2 hospitals	332 beds

★0197: PROMEDICA HEALTH SYSTEM (NP)
1801 Richards Road, Toledo, OH Zip 43607–1037; tel. 419/469–3800; Randall D. Oostra, FACHE, President and Chief Executive Officer
(Decentralized Health System)

MICHIGAN: PROMEDICA BIXBY HOSPITAL (O, 66 beds) 818 Riverside Avenue, Adrian, MI Zip 49221–1446; tel. 517/265–0900; Julie Yaroch, D.O., President
Web address: www.promedica.org

PROMEDICA HERRICK HOSPITAL (O, 60 beds) 500 East Pottawatamie Street, Tecumseh, MI Zip 49286–2018; tel. 517/424–3000; Julie Yaroch, D.O., President

PROMEDICA MONROE REGIONAL HOSPITAL (O, 152 beds) 718 North Macomb Street, Monroe, MI Zip 48162–7815; tel. 734/240–8400; Daniel Schwanke, Interim President
Web address: www.promedica.org

OHIO: PROMEDICA BAY PARK HOSPITAL (O, 44 beds) 2801 Bay Park Drive, Oregon, OH Zip 43616–4920; tel. 419/690–7900; Arturo Polizzi, President

Section B

For explanation of codes following names, see page B2.
★ Indicates Type III membership in the American Hospital Association.

PROMEDICA DEFIANCE REGIONAL HOSPITAL (O, 35 beds) 1200 Ralston Avenue, Defiance, OH Zip 43512–1396; tel. 419/783–6955; Neeraj Kanwal, M.D., President
Web address: www.promedica.org

PROMEDICA FLOWER HOSPITAL (O, 295 beds) 5200 Harroun Road, Sylvania, OH Zip 43560–2196; tel. 419/824–1444; Arturo Polizzi, President

PROMEDICA FOSTORIA COMMUNITY HOSPITAL (O, 25 beds) 501 Van Buren Street, Fostoria, OH Zip 44830–1534, P O Box 907, 44830–0907, tel. 419/435–7734; Pamela Jensen, FACHE, President
Web address: www.promedica.org

PROMEDICA MEMORIAL HOSPITAL (O, 49 beds) 715 South Taft Avenue, Fremont, OH Zip 43420–3237; tel. 419/332–7321; Pamela Jensen, FACHE, President

PROMEDICA TOLEDO HOSPITAL (O, 595 beds) 2142 North Cove Boulevard, Toledo, OH Zip 43606–3896; tel. 419/291–4000; Arturo Polizzi, President
Web address: www.promedica.org

Owned, leased, sponsored:	9 hospitals	1321 beds
Contract-managed:	0 hospitals	0 beds
Totals:	9 hospitals	1321 beds

0230: PROMISE HEALTHCARE (IO)
999 Yamato Road, 3rd Floor, Boca Raton, FL Zip 33431–4477; tel. 561/869–3100; Peter R. Baronoff, Chief Executive Officer
(Independent Hospital System)

ARIZONA: PROMISE HOSPITAL OF PHOENIX (L, 40 beds) 433 East 6th Street, Mesa, AZ Zip 85203–7104; tel. 480/427–3000; Scott Floden, Chief Executive Officer
Web address: www.promise-phoenix.com

CALIFORNIA: PROMISE HOSPITAL OF EAST LOS ANGELES (L, 213 beds) 443 South Soto Street, Los Angeles, CA Zip 90033–4398; tel. 323/261–1181; Michael D. Kerr, Chief Executive Officer

PROMISE HOSPITAL OF SAN DIEGO (O, 100 beds) 5550 University Avenue, San Diego, CA Zip 92105–2307; tel. 619/582–3800; Timothy L. Clark, Interim Chief Executive Officer
Web address: www.promisesandiego.com

FLORIDA: PROMISE HOSPITAL OF FLORIDA AT THE VILLAGES (O, 40 beds) 5050 County Road, Oxford, FL Zip 34484; tel. 352/689–6400; Hoyt Ross, Chief Executive Officer

PROMISE HOSPITAL OF FORT MYERS (O, 60 beds) 3050 Champion Ring Road, Fort Myers, FL Zip 33905–5599; tel. 239/313–2900; Patrick G. Ryan, Chief Executive Officer
Web address: www.promisefortmyers.om

PROMISE HOSPITAL OF MIAMI (O, 60 beds) 14001 NW 82nd Avenue, Miami, FL Zip 33158; tel. 786/609–9200; Charles Doten, Chief Executive Officer
Web address: www.promise-miami.com

KANSAS: PROMISE HOSPITAL OF OVERLAND PARK (O, 104 beds) 6509 West 103rd Street, Overland Park, KS Zip 66212–1728; tel. 913/649–3701; Karen Leverich, Chief Executive Officer
Web address: www.promise-overlandpark.com

LOUISIANA: PROMISE HOSPITAL BATON ROUGE - MAIN CAMPUS (L, 54 beds) 5130 Mancuso Lane, Baton Rouge, LA Zip 70809–3583; tel. 225/490–9600; Kiley P. Cedotal, FACHE, Chief Executive Officer

PROMISE HOSPITAL OF BATON ROUGE - MID-CITY CAMPUS (O, 57 beds) 3600 Florida Boulevard, 4th Floor, Baton Rouge, LA Zip 70806–3842; tel. 225/387–7770; Kiley P. Cedotal, FACHE, Chief Executive Officer
Web address: www.promise-batonrougemidcity.com

PROMISE HOSPITAL OF BATON ROUGE - OCHSNER CAMPUS (O, 29 beds) 17000 Medical Center Drive, 3rd Floor, Baton Rouge, LA Zip 70816–3246; tel. 225/236–5440; Kiley P. Cedotal, FACHE, Chief Executive Officer
Web address: www.promise-batonrougeochsner.com

PROMISE HOSPITAL OF LOUISIANA - SHREVEPORT CAMPUS (O, 146 beds) 1800 Irving Place, Shreveport, LA Zip 71101–4608; tel. 318/425–4096; Rick Stockton, Chief Executive Officer

PROMISE HOSPITAL OF MISS LOU (O, 40 beds) 209 Front Street, Vidalia, LA Zip 71373–2837; tel. 318/336–6500; Michael Harrell, R.N., Chief Executive Officer
Web address: www.promise-misslou.com

MISSISSIPPI: PROMISE HOSPITAL OF VICKSBURG (L, 33 beds) 1111 North Frontage Road, 2nd Floor, Vicksburg, MS Zip 39180–5102; tel. 601/619–3526; Michael Harrell, R.N., Chief Executive Officer
Web address: www.promise-vicksburg.com

TEXAS: PROMISE HOSPITAL OF DALLAS (O, 62 beds) 7955 Harry Hines Boulevard, Dallas, TX Zip 75235–3305; tel. 214/637–0000; Louis P. Bradley Jr, Chief Executive Officer

PROMISE HOSPITAL OF WICHITA FALLS (O, 31 beds) 1103 Grace Street, Wichita Falls, TX Zip 76301–4414; tel. 940/720–6633; Michael L. McEachern, Chief Executive Officer
Web address: www.promise-wichitafalls.com

UTAH: PROMISE HOSPITAL OF SALT LAKE (O, 41 beds) 8 Avenue, C Street, Salt Lake City, UT Zip 84143; tel. 801/408–7110; Wayne Kinsey, Chief Executive Officer

Owned, leased, sponsored:	16 hospitals	1110 beds
Contract-managed:	0 hospitals	0 beds
Totals:	16 hospitals	1110 beds

1012: PROSPECT MEDICAL HOLDINGS (IO)
10780 California Route 2 #400, Los Angeles, CA Zip 90025; tel. 714/796–5900; Mitchell Lew, M.D., President

CALIFORNIA: LOS ANGELES COMMUNITY HOSPITAL AT LOS ANGELES (O, 180 beds) 4081 East Olympic Boulevard, Los Angeles, CA Zip 90023–3330; tel. 323/267–0477; Omar Ramirez, Chief Executive Officer
Web address: www.altacorp.com/altacorp/our-hospitals/lach-menu.html

SOUTHERN CALIFORNIA HOSPITAL AT CULVER CITY (O, 239 beds) 3828 Delmas Terrace, Culver City, CA Zip 90232–6806; tel. 310/836–7000; Gerald B. Clute, Chief Executive Officer
Web address: www.sch-culvercity.com

SOUTHERN CALIFORNIA HOSPITAL AT HOLLYWOOD (O, 45 beds) 6245 De Longpre Avenue, Los Angeles, CA Zip 90028–9001; tel. 323/462–2271; Bruce P. Grimshaw, FACHE, Chief Executive Officer

CONNECTICUT: MANCHESTER MEMORIAL HOSPITAL (O, 156 beds) 71 Haynes Street, Manchester, CT Zip 06040–4188; tel. 860/646–1222; Peter J. Karl, President and Chief Executive Officer
Web address: www.echn.org

ROCKVILLE GENERAL HOSPITAL (O, 47 beds) 31 Union Street, Vernon, CT Zip 06066–3160; tel. 860/872–0501; Peter J. Karl, President and Chief Executive Officer

WATERBURY HOSPITAL (O, 176 beds) 64 Robbins Street, Waterbury, CT Zip 06708–2600; tel. 203/573–6000; Peter J. Adamo, President and Chief Executive Officer
Web address: www.waterburyhospital.org

NEW JERSEY: EAST ORANGE GENERAL HOSPITAL (O, 190 beds) 300 Central Avenue, East Orange, NJ Zip 07018–2897; tel. 973/672–8400; Paige Dworak, Interim Chief Executive Officer
Web address: www.evh.org

PENNSYLVANIA: CROZER-CHESTER MEDICAL CENTER (O, 384 beds) One Medical Center Boulevard, Upland, PA Zip 19013–3995; tel. 610/447–2000; Michael Curran, President

DELAWARE COUNTY MEMORIAL HOSPITAL (O, 168 beds) 501 North Lansdowne Avenue, Drexel Hill, PA Zip 19026–1114; tel. 610/284–8100; Robert Haffey, R.N., President
Web address: www.crozer.org

RHODE ISLAND: ROGER WILLIAMS MEDICAL CENTER (O, 86 beds) 825 Chalkstone Avenue, Providence, RI Zip 02908–4735; tel. 401/456–2000; Demetra Ouellette, President
Web address: www.rwmc.org/

ST. JOSEPH HEALTH SERVICES OF RHODE ISLAND (O, 125 beds) 200 High Service Avenue, North Providence, RI Zip 02904–5199; tel. 401/456–3000; John J. Holiver, Chief Executive Officer

For explanation of codes following names, see page B2.
★ Indicates Type III membership in the American Hospital Association.

Section B

TEXAS: NIX COMMUNITY GENERAL HOSPITAL (O, 10 beds) 230 West Miller, Dilley, TX Zip 78017–3818; tel. 830/965–2003; Allen Tinker, Administrator
Web address: www.nixhealth.com/home/facilities/nix-community-general-hospital?headerbar=2

NIX HEALTH CARE SYSTEM (O, 246 beds) 414 Navarro Street, San Antonio, TX Zip 78205–2516; tel. 210/271–1800; Daniel J. Bonk, Chief Executive Officer

Owned, leased, sponsored:	13 hospitals	2052 beds
Contract-managed:	0 hospitals	0 beds
Totals:	13 hospitals	2052 beds

★**1006: PROVIDENCE ST. JOSEPH HEALTH** (CC)
1801 Lind Avenue Southwest, 9016, Renton, WA Zip 98057–9016, 181 Lind Avenue Southwest, 9016, 98057–9016, tel. 425/525–3698; Rodney F. Hochman, M.D., President and Chief Executive Officer
(Decentralized Health System)

ALASKA: PROVIDENCE ALASKA MEDICAL CENTER (O, 401 beds) 3200 Providence Drive, Anchorage, AK Zip 99508–4615, P O Box 196604, 99519–6604, tel. 907/562–2211; Richard Mandsager, M.D., Executive Officer
Web address: www.alaska.providence.org/locations/p/pamc

PROVIDENCE KODIAK ISLAND MEDICAL CENTER (L, 25 beds) 1915 East Rezanof Drive, Kodiak, AK Zip 99615–6602; tel. 907/486–3281; Barbara Bigelow, Administrator

PROVIDENCE SEWARD MEDICAL CENTER (L, 46 beds) 417 First Avenue, Seward, AK Zip 99664, P O Box 365, 99664–0365, tel. 907/224–5205; Joseph Fong, Administrator
Web address: www.providence.org

PROVIDENCE VALDEZ MEDICAL CENTER (C, 21 beds) 911 Meals Avenue, Valdez, AK Zip 99686–0550, P O Box 550, 99686–0550, tel. 907/835–2249; Jeremy O'Neil, Administrator
Web address: www.providence.org/alaska

CALIFORNIA: HOAG MEMORIAL HOSPITAL PRESBYTERIAN (O, 470 beds) One Hoag Drive, Newport Beach, CA Zip 92663–4120, P O Box 6100, 92658–6100, tel. 949/764–4624; Robert Braithwaite, President and Chief Executive Officer

MISSION HOSPITAL (O, 249 beds) 27700 Medical Center Road, Mission Viejo, CA Zip 92691–6474; tel. 949/364–1400; Tarek Salaway, Chief Executive
Web address: www.mission4health.com

PETALUMA VALLEY HOSPITAL (L, 51 beds) 400 North McDowell Boulevard, Petaluma, CA Zip 94954–2366; tel. 707/778–1111; Todd Salnas, President
Web address: www.stjosephhealth.org/About-Us/Facilities/Petaluma-Valley-Hospital.aspx

PROVIDENCE HOLY CROSS MEDICAL CENTER (O, 377 beds) 15031 Rinaldi Street, Mission Hills, CA Zip 91345–1207; tel. 818/365–8051; Bernard Klein, M.D., Chief Executive
Web address: www.https://california.providence.org/holy-cross/Pages/default.aspx

PROVIDENCE LITTLE COMPANY OF MARY MEDICAL CENTER - TORRANCE (O, 381 beds) 4101 Torrance Boulevard, Torrance, CA Zip 90503–4664; tel. 310/540–7676; Mary E. Kingston, FACHE, R.N., Chief Executive Officer, South Bay Community

PROVIDENCE LITTLE COMPANY OF MARY MEDICAL CENTER SAN PEDRO (O, 318 beds) 1300 West Seventh Street, San Pedro, CA Zip 90732–3505; tel. 310/832–3311; Mary E. Kingston, FACHE, R.N., Chief Executive Officer
Web address: www.https://california.providence.org/san-pedro

PROVIDENCE SAINT JOHN'S HEALTH CENTER (O, 228 beds) 2121 Santa Monica Boulevard, Santa Monica, CA Zip 90404–2091; tel. 310/829–5511; Marcel C. Loh, FACHE, Chief Executive Officer

PROVIDENCE SAINT JOSEPH MEDICAL CENTER (O, 383 beds) 501 South Buena Vista Street, Burbank, CA Zip 91505–4866; tel. 818/843–5111; Kelly Linden, Chief Executive Officer
Web address: www.providence.org

PROVIDENCE TARZANA MEDICAL CENTER (O, 249 beds) 18321 Clark Street, Tarzana, CA Zip 91356–3521; tel. 818/881–0800; Dale Surowitz, Chief Executive

QUEEN OF THE VALLEY MEDICAL CENTER (O, 120 beds) 1000 Trancas Street, Napa, CA Zip 94558–2906, P O Box 2340, 94558–0688, tel. 707/252–4411; Larry Coomes, Chief Executive Officer
Web address: www.thequeen.org

REDWOOD MEMORIAL HOSPITAL (O, 25 beds) 3300 Renner Drive, Fortuna, CA Zip 95540–3198; tel. 707/725–3361; David O'Brien, M.D., President

SANTA ROSA MEMORIAL HOSPITAL (O, 278 beds) 1165 Montgomery Drive, Santa Rosa, CA Zip 95405–4897, P O Box 522, 95402–0522, tel. 707/546–3210; Todd Salnas, President
Web address: www.stjosephhealth.org

ST. JOSEPH HOSPITAL (O, 153 beds) 2700 Dolbeer Street, Eureka, CA Zip 95501–4799; tel. 707/445–8121; David O'Brien, M.D., President

ST. JOSEPH HOSPITAL (O, 379 beds) 1100 West Stewart Drive, Orange, CA Zip 92868–3849, P O Box 5600, 92863–5600, tel. 714/633–9111; Steven C. Moreau, President and Chief Executive Officer
Web address: www.sjo.org

ST. JUDE MEDICAL CENTER (O, 320 beds) 101 East Valencia Mesa Drive, Fullerton, CA Zip 92835–3875; tel. 714/992–3000; Brian Helleland, Chief Executive Officer

ST. MARY MEDICAL CENTER (O, 212 beds) 18300 Highway 18, Apple Valley, CA Zip 92307–2206, P O Box 7025, 92307–0725, tel. 760/242–2311; Alan H. Garrett, President and Chief Executive Officer
Web address: www.stmaryapplevalley.com/

MONTANA: GRANITE COUNTY MEDICAL CENTER (C, 25 beds) 310 Sansome Street, Philipsburg, MT Zip 59858–0729, P O Box 729, 59858–0729, tel. 406/859–3271; Maria Stoppler, Chief Executive Officer
Web address: www.gcmedcenter.org/

PROVIDENCE ST. JOSEPH MEDICAL CENTER (O, 22 beds) 6 Thirteenth Avenue East, Polson, MT Zip 59860–5315, P O Box 1010, 59860–1010, tel. 406/883–5377; James R. Kiser II, Chief Executive Officer
Web address: www.saintjoes.org

ST. PATRICK HOSPITAL (O, 200 beds) 500 West Broadway, Missoula, MT Zip 59802–4096, P O Box 4587, 59806–4587, tel. 406/543–7271; Joyce Dombrouski, R.N., Chief Executive Officer
Web address: www.montana.providence.org

OREGON: PROVIDENCE HOOD RIVER MEMORIAL HOSPITAL (O, 25 beds) 810 12th Street, Hood River, OR Zip 97031–1587, P O Box 149, 97031–0055, tel. 541/386–3911; Jeanette Vieira, Chief Executive

PROVIDENCE MEDFORD MEDICAL CENTER (O, 138 beds) 1111 Crater Lake Avenue, Medford, OR Zip 97504–6241; tel. 541/732–5000; Cindy Mayo, R.N., FACHE, Chief Executive
Web address: www.providence.org

PROVIDENCE MILWAUKIE HOSPITAL (O, 52 beds) 10150 SE 32nd Avenue, Milwaukie, OR Zip 97222–6516; tel. 503/513–8300; Keith Hyde, Chief Executive

PROVIDENCE NEWBERG MEDICAL CENTER (O, 40 beds) 1001 Providence Drive, Newberg, OR Zip 97132–7485; tel. 503/537–1555; Lorinda Van Zanten, MSN, Chief Executive
Web address: www.phsor.org

PROVIDENCE PORTLAND MEDICAL CENTER (O, 427 beds) 4805 NE Glisan Street, Portland, OR Zip 97213–2933; tel. 503/215–5526; Paul Gaden, Chief Executive Officer
Web address: www.providence.org

PROVIDENCE SEASIDE HOSPITAL (O, 25 beds) 725 South Wahanna Road, Seaside, OR Zip 97138–7735; tel. 503/717–7000; Kendall Sawa, R.N., Chief Executive Officer
Web address: www.providence.org

PROVIDENCE ST. VINCENT MEDICAL CENTER (O, 487 beds) 9205 SW Barnes Road, Portland, OR Zip 97225–6661; tel. 503/216–1234; Janice Burger, Chief Executive

PROVIDENCE WILLAMETTE FALLS MEDICAL CENTER (O, 111 beds) 1500 Division Street, Oregon City, OR Zip 97045–1597; tel. 503/656–1631; Russ Reinhard, Chief Executive
Web address: www.providence.org/pwfmc

TEXAS: COVENANT CHILDREN'S HOSPITAL (O, 73 beds) 4015 22nd Place, Lubbock, TX Zip 79410; tel. 806/725–1011; Amy Thompson, M.D., Chief Executive Officer
Web address: www.covenanthealth.org/About-Us/Facilities/Childrens-Hospital.aspx

For explanation of codes following names, see page B2.
★ Indicates Type III membership in the American Hospital Association.

COVENANT HOSPITAL PLAINVIEW (O, 68 beds) 2601 Dimmitt Road, Plainview, TX Zip 79072–1833; tel. 806/296–5531; Robert Copeland, Interim Chief Executive Officer
Web address: www.covenantplainview.org

COVENANT HOSPITAL-LEVELLAND (L, 26 beds) 1900 South College Avenue, Levelland, TX Zip 79336–6508; tel. 806/894–4963; Bruce White, Administrator

COVENANT MEDICAL CENTER (O, 576 beds) 3615 19th Street, Lubbock, TX Zip 79410–1203, P O Box 1201, 79408–1201, tel. 806/725–0000; Walt Cathey, Chief Executive Officer
Web address: www.covenanthealth.org

COVENANT SPECIALTY HOSPITAL (O, 56 beds) 3815 20th Street, Lubbock, TX Zip 79410–1235; tel. 806/725–9200; Julie Bell, Interim Chief Executive Officer and Chief Nursing Officer

WASHINGTON: KADLEC REGIONAL MEDICAL CENTER (O, 260 beds) 888 Swift Boulevard, Richland, WA Zip 99352–3514; tel. 509/946–4611; Lane A. Savitch, Regional Chief Executive
Web address: www.kadlecmed.org

PROVIDENCE CENTRALIA HOSPITAL (O, 91 beds) 914 South Scheuber Road, Centralia, WA Zip 98531–9027; tel. 360/736–2803; Medrice Coluccio, R.N., Southwest Region Chief Executive

PROVIDENCE HOLY FAMILY HOSPITAL (O, 191 beds) 5633 North Lidgerwood Street, Spokane, WA Zip 99208–1224; tel. 509/482–0111; Peggy M. Currie, R.N., Chief Operating Officer
Web address: www.providence.org

PROVIDENCE MOUNT CARMEL HOSPITAL (O, 25 beds) 982 East Columbia Avenue, Colville, WA Zip 99114–3352; tel. 509/685–5100; Ronald G. Rehn, Chief Executive Officer
Web address: www.mtcarmelhospital.org

PROVIDENCE REGIONAL MEDICAL CENTER EVERETT (O, 501 beds) 1321 Colby Avenue, Everett, WA Zip 98201–1665, P O Box 1147, 98206–1147, tel. 425/261–2000; Kim Williams, R.N., MS, Chief Administrative Officer

PROVIDENCE SACRED HEART MEDICAL CENTER & CHILDREN'S HOSPITAL (O, 672 beds) 101 West Eighth Avenue, Spokane, WA Zip 99204–2364, P O Box 2555, 99220–2555, tel. 509/474–3131; Peggy M. Currie, R.N., Chief Operating Officer
Web address: www.shmc.org

PROVIDENCE ST. JOSEPH'S HOSPITAL (O, 55 beds) 500 East Webster Street, Chewelah, WA Zip 99109–9523; tel. 509/935–8211; Ronald G. Rehn, Chief Executive Officer
Web address: www.washington.providence.org/hospitals/st-josephs-hospital/

PROVIDENCE ST. MARY MEDICAL CENTER (O, 85 beds) 401 West Poplar Street, Walla Walla, WA Zip 99362–2846, P O Box 1477, 99362–0312, tel. 509/897–3320; Susan Blackburn, Chief Administrative Officer
Web address: www.washington.providence.org/hospitals/st-mary/

PROVIDENCE ST. PETER HOSPITAL (O, 350 beds) 413 Lilly Road NE, Olympia, WA Zip 98506–5166; tel. 360/491–9480; Medrice Coluccio, R.N., Chief Executive Officer

ST. LUKE'S REHABILITATION INSTITUTE (O, 72 beds) 711 South Cowley Street, Spokane, WA Zip 99202–1388; tel. 509/473–6000; Nancy Webster, Administrator and Chief Operating Officer
Web address: www.st-lukes.org

SWEDISH MEDICAL CENTER-CHERRY HILL CAMPUS (O, 227 beds) 500 17th Avenue, Seattle, WA Zip 98122–5711; tel. 206/320–2000; June Altaras, R.N., Chief Executive Officer
Web address: www.swedish.org

SWEDISH MEDICAL CENTER-FIRST HILL (O, 659 beds) 747 Broadway, Seattle, WA Zip 98122–4307; tel. 206/386–6000; June Altaras, R.N., Chief Executive Officer

SWEDISH/EDMONDS (O, 164 beds) 21601 76th Avenue West, Edmonds, WA Zip 98026–7506; tel. 425/640–4000; Sarah Zabel, Vice President, Operations
Web address: www.swedish.org

SWEDISH/ISSAQUAH (O, 134 beds) 751 NE Blakely Drive, Issaquah, WA Zip 98029–6201; tel. 425/313–4000; Anthony A. Armada, Chief Executive Officer

WHITMAN HOSPITAL AND MEDICAL CENTER (C, 25 beds) 1200 West Fairview Street, Colfax, WA Zip 99111–9579; tel. 509/397–3435; Hank Hanigan, MS, R.N., Chief Executive Officer
Web address: www.whitmanhospital.org

Owned, leased, sponsored:	48 hospitals	10477 beds
Contract-managed:	3 hospitals	71 beds
Totals:	51 hospitals	10548 beds

★0011: PUERTO RICO DEPARTMENT OF HEALTH (NP)
Building 'A' - Medical Center, San Juan, PR Zip 936, Call Box 70184, 936, tel. 787/765–2929; Rafael Rodriguez. Mercado, Secretary of Health
(Independent Hospital System)

PUERTO RICO: CARDIOVASCULAR CENTER OF PUERTO RICO AND THE CARIBBEAN (O, 139 beds) Americo Miranda Centro Medico, San Juan, PR Zip 936, P O Box 366528, 00936–6528, tel. 787/754–8500; Carlos Cabrera, Executive Director

HOSPITAL UNIVERSITARIO DR. RAMON RUIZ ARNAU (O, 101 beds) Avenue Laurel #100, Santa Juanita, Bayamon, PR Zip 956; tel. 787/787–5151; Prudencio A. Laureano, Chief Executive Officer
Web address: www.salud.gov.pr/Dept-de-Salud/Pages/Nuestros-Hospitales.aspx

UNIVERSITY HOSPITAL (O, 262 beds) Nineyas 869 Rio Piedras, San Juan, PR Zip 922, P O Box 2116, 922, tel. 787/754–0101; Jorge Matta. Gonzalez, Executive Director

UNIVERSITY PEDIATRIC HOSPITAL (O, 145 beds) Barrio Monacenno, Carretera 22, Rio Piedras, PR Zip 935, P O Box 191079, San Juan, 00910–1070, tel. 787/777–3535; Gloria Hernandez, Executive Director
Web address: www.md.rcm.upr.edu/pediatrics/university_pediatric_hospital.php

Owned, leased, sponsored:	4 hospitals	647 beds
Contract-managed:	0 hospitals	0 beds
Totals:	4 hospitals	647 beds

★0002: QHR (IO)
1573 Mallory Lane, Suite 200, Brentwood, TN Zip 37027, 1573 Mallory Lane, Suite 200, 37027, tel. 800/233–1470; Bob Vento, President and Chief Executive Officer
(Decentralized Health System)

ARKANSAS: GREAT RIVER MEDICAL CENTER (C, 73 beds) 1520 North Division Street, Blytheville, AR Zip 72315–1448, P O Box 108, 72316–0108, tel. 870/838–7300; Chris Lee. Raymer, R.N., MSN, Chief Executive Officer

SOUTH MISSISSIPPI COUNTY REGIONAL MEDICAL CENTER (C, 25 beds) 611 West Lee Avenue, Osceola, AR Zip 72370–3001, P O Box 108, Blytheville, 72316–0108, tel. 870/563–7000; Chris Lee. Raymer, R.N., MSN, Chief Executive Officer
Web address: www.mchsys.org

CALIFORNIA: BEAR VALLEY COMMUNITY HOSPITAL (C, 30 beds) 41870 Garstin Drive, Big Bear Lake, CA Zip 92315, P O Box 1649, 92315–1649, tel. 909/866–6501; John P. Friel, Chief Executive Officer
Web address: www.bvchd.com

COLORADO: ARKANSAS VALLEY REGIONAL MEDICAL CENTER (C, 163 beds) 1100 Carson Avenue, La Junta, CO Zip 81050–2799; tel. 719/383–6000; Lynn Crowell, Chief Executive Officer

COMMUNITY HOSPITAL (C, 42 beds) 2351 G Road, Grand Junction, CO Zip 81505; tel. 970/242–0920; Chris Thomas, FACHE, President and Chief Executive Officer
Web address: www.yourcommunityhospital.com

MONTROSE MEMORIAL HOSPITAL (C, 60 beds) 800 South Third Street, Montrose, CO Zip 81401–4212; tel. 970/249–2211; Cindy Bradley, Interim CEO

PIONEERS MEDICAL CENTER (C, 40 beds) 100 Pioneers Medical Center Drive, Meeker, CO Zip 81641–3181; tel. 970/878–5047; Kenneth Harman, Chief Executive Officer
Web address: www.pioneershospital.org

For explanation of codes following names, see page B2.
★ Indicates Type III membership in the American Hospital Association.

PROWERS MEDICAL CENTER (C, 25 beds) 401 Kendall Drive, Lamar, CO Zip 81052–3993; tel. 719/336–4343; Craig Loveless, Chief Executive Officer

FLORIDA: HENDRY REGIONAL MEDICAL CENTER (C, 25 beds) 524 West Sagamore Avenue, Clewiston, FL Zip 33440–3514; tel. 863/902–3000; R D Williams, Chief Executive Officer
Web address: www.hendryregional.org

JACKSON HOSPITAL (C, 68 beds) 4250 Hospital Drive, Marianna, FL Zip 32446–1917, P O Box 1608, 32447–5608, tel. 850/526–2200; James Platt, Chief Executive Officer

IDAHO: GRITMAN MEDICAL CENTER (C, 25 beds) 700 South Main Street, Moscow, ID Zip 83843–3056; tel. 208/882–4511; Kara Besst, President and Chief Executive Officer
Web address: www.gritman.org

STEELE MEMORIAL MEDICAL CENTER (C, 18 beds) 203 South Daisy Street, Salmon, ID Zip 83467–4709; tel. 208/756–5600; Jeanine Gentry, Chief Executive Officer

ILLINOIS: CRAWFORD MEMORIAL HOSPITAL (C, 63 beds) 1000 North Allen Street, Robinson, IL Zip 62454–1167; tel. 618/544–3131; Lucinda A. Bradley, Interim Chief Executive Officer
Web address: www.crawfordmh.net

LAWRENCE COUNTY MEMORIAL HOSPITAL (C, 25 beds) 2200 West State Street, Lawrenceville, IL Zip 62439–1852; tel. 618/943–1000; Doug Florkowski, Chief Executive Officer

INDIANA: SULLIVAN COUNTY COMMUNITY HOSPITAL (C, 25 beds) 2200 North Section Street, Sullivan, IN Zip 47882–7523, P O Box 10, 47882–0010, tel. 812/268–4311; Michelle Sly-Franklin, Chief Executive Officer
Web address: www.schosp.com

IOWA: BOONE COUNTY HOSPITAL (C, 25 beds) 1015 Union Street, Boone, IA Zip 50036–4821; tel. 515/432–3140; Joseph S. Smith, Chief Executive Officer
Web address: www.boonehospital.com

FORT MADISON COMMUNITY HOSPITAL (C, 50 beds) 5445 Avenue 'O', Fort Madison, IA Zip 52627–9611, P O Box 174, 52627–0174, tel. 319/372–6530; Jeremy Alexander, Interim Chief Executive Officer
Web address: www.fmchosp.com

KANSAS: GREELEY COUNTY HEALTH SERVICES (C, 50 beds) 506 Third Street, Tribune, KS Zip 67879–9684, P O Box 338, 67879–0338, tel. 620/376–4221; Burke Kline, Chief Executive Officer

NEOSHO MEMORIAL REGIONAL MEDICAL CENTER (C, 25 beds) 629 South Plummer, Chanute, KS Zip 66720–1928, P O Box 426, 66720–0426, tel. 620/431–4000; Dennis Franks, FACHE, Chief Executive Officer
Web address: www.nmrmc.com

WILSON MEDICAL CENTER (C, 15 beds) 2600 Ottawa Road, Neodesha, KS Zip 66757–1897, P O Box 360, 66757–0360, tel. 620/325–2611; Dennis R. Shelby, Chief Executive Officer
Web address: www.wilsonmedical.org

KENTUCKY: CALDWELL MEDICAL CENTER (C, 25 beds) 100 Medical Center Drive, Princeton, KY Zip 42445–2430, P O Box 410, 42445–0410, tel. 270/365–0300; Kelley J. Rushing, Chief Executive Officer
Web address: www.caldwellhosp.org

JENNIE STUART MEDICAL CENTER (C, 139 beds) 320 West 18th Street, Hopkinsville, KY Zip 42240–1965, P O Box 2400, 42241–2400, tel. 270/887–0100; Eric A. Lee, President and Chief Executive Officer

MONROE COUNTY MEDICAL CENTER (C, 49 beds) 529 Capp Harlan Road, Tompkinsville, KY Zip 42167–1840; tel. 270/487–9231; Vicky McFall, Chief Executive Officer
Web address: www.mcmccares.com

OHIO COUNTY HOSPITAL (C, 25 beds) 1211 Main Street, Hartford, KY Zip 42347–1619; tel. 270/298–7411; Blaine Pieper, Chief Executive Officer

LOUISIANA: FRANKLIN FOUNDATION HOSPITAL (C, 22 beds) 1097 Northwest Boulevard, Franklin, LA Zip 70538–3407, P O Box 577, 70538–0577, tel. 337/828–0760; Stephanie Guidry, Chief Executive Officer
Web address: www.franklinfoundation.org

MAINE: CALAIS REGIONAL HOSPITAL (C, 25 beds) 24 Hospital Lane, Calais, ME Zip 04619–1398; tel. 207/454–7521; Rodney Boula, Chief Executive Officer
Web address: www.calaishospital.com

CARY MEDICAL CENTER (C, 49 beds) 163 Van Buren Road, Suite 1, Caribou, ME Zip 04736–3567; tel. 207/498–3111; Kris A. Doody, R.N., Chief Executive Officer

PENOBSCOT VALLEY HOSPITAL (C, 25 beds) 7 Transalpine Road, Lincoln, ME Zip 04457–4222, P O Box 368, 04457–0368, tel. 207/794–3321; Gary R. Poquette, FACHE, Chief Executive Officer
Web address: www.pvhme.org

MICHIGAN: ALLEGAN GENERAL HOSPITAL (C, 25 beds) 555 Linn Street, Allegan, MI Zip 49010–1524; tel. 269/673–8424; Gerald J. Barbini, President and Chief Executive Officer
Web address: www.aghosp.org

HAYES GREEN BEACH MEMORIAL HOSPITAL (C, 25 beds) 321 East Harris Street, Charlotte, MI Zip 48813–1629; tel. 517/543–1050; Matthew Rush, FACHE, President and Chief Executive Officer

STURGIS HOSPITAL (C, 49 beds) 916 Myrtle Street, Sturgis, MI Zip 49091–2326; tel. 269/651–7824; Robert J. LaBarge, President and Chief Executive Officer
Web address: www.sturgishospital.com

THREE RIVERS HEALTH (C, 35 beds) 701 South Health Parkway, Three Rivers, MI Zip 49093–8352; tel. 269/278–1145; William B. Russell, Chief Executive Officer

MISSISSIPPI: KING'S DAUGHTERS MEDICAL CENTER (C, 79 beds) 427 Highway 51 North, Brookhaven, MS Zip 39601–2350, P O Box 948, 39602–0948, tel. 601/833–6011; Alvin Hoover, FACHE, Chief Executive Officer
Web address: www.kdmc.org

MISSOURI: NEVADA REGIONAL MEDICAL CENTER (C, 71 beds) 800 South Ash Street, Nevada, MO Zip 64772–3223; tel. 417/667–3355; Kevin Leeper, Chief Executive Officer
Web address: www.nrmchealth.com

NEBRASKA: PHELPS MEMORIAL HEALTH CENTER (C, 25 beds) 1215 Tibbals Street, Holdrege, NE Zip 68949–1255; tel. 308/995–2211; Mark Harrel, Chief Executive Officer
Web address: www.phelpsmemorial.com

NEW MEXICO: CIBOLA GENERAL HOSPITAL (C, 25 beds) 1016 East Roosevelt Avenue, Grants, NM Zip 87020–2118; tel. 505/287–4446; Thomas Whelan, Chief Executive Officer

HOLY CROSS HOSPITAL (C, 29 beds) 1397 Weimer Road, Taos, NM Zip 87571–6253; tel. 575/758–8883; William D. Patten Jr, Chief Executive Officer
Web address: www.taoshospital.org

NORTH CAROLINA: NORTHERN HOSPITAL OF SURRY COUNTY (C, 108 beds) 830 Rockford Street, Mount Airy, NC Zip 27030–5365, P O Box 1101, 27030–1101, tel. 336/719–7000; Ned Hill, President and Chief Executive Officer
Web address: www.northernhospital.com

OHIO: KNOX COMMUNITY HOSPITAL (C, 65 beds) 1330 Coshocton Road, Mount Vernon, OH Zip 43050–1495; tel. 740/393–9000; Bruce D. White, Chief Executive Officer
Web address: www.knoxcommhosp.org

WOOSTER COMMUNITY HOSPITAL (C, 152 beds) 1761 Beall Avenue, Wooster, OH Zip 44691–2342; tel. 330/263–8100; William E. Sheron, Chief Executive Officer

OKLAHOMA: PERRY MEMORIAL HOSPITAL (C, 26 beds) 501 North 14th Street, Perry, OK Zip 73077–5099; tel. 580/336–3541; Daniel Odegaard, FACHE, Chief Executive Officer
Web address: www.pmh-ok.org

PENNSYLVANIA: CLARION HOSPITAL (C, 66 beds) One Hospital Drive, Clarion, PA Zip 16214–8501; tel. 814/226–9500; Byron Quinton, Chief Executive Officer

SOUTH CAROLINA: ABBEVILLE AREA MEDICAL CENTER (C, 25 beds) 420 Thomson Circle, Abbeville, SC Zip 29620–5656, P O Box 887, 29620–0887, tel. 864/366–5011; Howard D. Turner, Chief Executive Officer
Web address: www.abbevilleareamc.com

NEWBERRY COUNTY MEMORIAL HOSPITAL (C, 54 beds) 2669 Kinard Street, Newberry, SC Zip 29108–2911, P O Box 497, 29108–0497, tel. 803/276–7570; Bruce A. Baldwin, Chief Executive Officer
Web address: www.newberryhospital.org

For explanation of codes following names, see page B2.
★ Indicates Type III membership in the American Hospital Association.

Section B

REGIONAL MEDICAL CENTER (C, 283 beds) 3000 St Matthews Road, Orangeburg, SC Zip 29118–1442; tel. 803/395–2200; Bert Whitaker, Interim President and Chief Executive Officer
Web address: www.trmchealth.org

TIDELANDS GEORGETOWN MEMORIAL HOSPITAL (C, 136 beds) 606 Black River Road, Georgetown, SC Zip 29440–3368, Drawer 421718, 29442–4203, tel. 843/527–7000; Bruce P. Bailey, Chief Executive Officer

TIDELANDS WACCAMAW COMMUNITY HOSPITAL (C, 169 beds) 4070 Highway 17 Bypass, Murrells Inlet, SC Zip 29576–5033, P O Drawer 3350, 29576–2673, tel. 843/652–1000; Bruce P. Bailey, Chief Executive Officer
Web address: www.tidelandswaccamawcommunity.org

SOUTH DAKOTA: HURON REGIONAL MEDICAL CENTER (C, 25 beds) 172 Fourth Street SE, Huron, SD Zip 57350–2590; tel. 605/353–6200; David Dick, Chief Executive Officer

TENNESSEE: MACON COUNTY GENERAL HOSPITAL (C, 25 beds) 204 Medical Drive, Lafayette, TN Zip 37083–1799, P O Box 378, 37083–0378, tel. 615/666–2147; Thomas J. Kidd, Chief Executive Officer
Web address: www.mcgh.net

RHEA MEDICAL CENTER (C, 25 beds) 9400 Rhea County Highway, Dayton, TN Zip 37321–7922; tel. 423/775–1121; David Bixler, Chief Executive Officer
Web address: www.rheamedical.org

TEXAS: FIRST BAPTIST MEDICAL CENTER (C, 18 beds) 8111 Meadow Road, Dallas, TX Zip 75231; tel. 469/329–3700; Paul Eavenson, Chief Executive Officer

MATAGORDA REGIONAL MEDICAL CENTER (C, 58 beds) 104 7th Street, Bay City, TX Zip 77414–4853; tel. 979/245–6383; Steven L. Smith, Chief Executive Officer
Web address: www.matagordaregional.org

MEMORIAL HOSPITAL (C, 33 beds) 1110 Sarah Dewitt Drive, Gonzales, TX Zip 78629–3311, P O Box 587, 78629–0587, tel. 830/672–7581; Charles Norris, Chief Executive Officer

VERMONT: NORTHWESTERN MEDICAL CENTER (C, 55 beds) 133 Fairfield Street, Saint Albans, VT Zip 05478–1726; tel. 802/524–5911; Jill Berry. Bowen, Chief Executive Officer
Web address: www.northwesternmedicalcenter.org

WEST VIRGINIA: SUMMERSVILLE REGIONAL MEDICAL CENTER (C, 105 beds) 400 Fairview Heights Road, Summersville, WV Zip 26651–9308; tel. 304/872–2891; Karen A. Fiducia, FACHE, President and Chief Executive Officer
Web address: https://www.summersvilleregional.org/

WYOMING: MEMORIAL HOSPITAL OF CARBON COUNTY (C, 25 beds) 2221 West Elm Street, Rawlins, WY Zip 82301–5108, P O Box 460, 82301–0460, tel. 307/324–2221; Dana Barnett, Chief Executive Officer
Web address: www.imhcc.com

WEST PARK HOSPITAL (C, 112 beds) 707 Sheridan Avenue, Cody, WY Zip 82414–3409; tel. 307/527–7501; Douglas A. McMillan, Administrator and Chief Executive Officer
Web address: www.westparkhospital.org

Owned, leased, sponsored:	0 hospitals	0 beds
Contract-managed:	57 hospitals	3159 beds
Totals:	57 hospitals	3159 beds

★0040:   QUEEN'S HEALTH SYSTEMS (NP)
1301 Punchbowl Street, Honolulu, HI Zip 96813–2402; tel. 808/535–5448; Arthur A. Ushijima, FACHE, President and Chief Executive Officer
(Moderately Centralized Health System)

HAWAII: MOLOKAI GENERAL HOSPITAL (O, 15 beds) 280 Home Olu Place, Kaunakakai, HI Zip 96748–0408, P O Box 408, 96748–0408, tel. 808/553–5331; Janice Kalanihuia, President

NORTH HAWAII COMMUNITY HOSPITAL (O, 35 beds) 67–1125 Mamalahoa Highway, Kamuela, HI Zip 96743–8496; tel. 808/885–4444; Cynthia Kamikawa, R.N., MSN, President
Web address: www.nhch.com

THE QUEEN'S MEDICAL CENTER (O, 527 beds) 1301 Punchbowl Street, Honolulu, HI Zip 96813–2499; tel. 808/691–5100; Arthur A. Ushijima, FACHE, President
Web address: www.queensmedicalcenter.org

Owned, leased, sponsored:	3 hospitals	577 beds
Contract-managed:	0 hospitals	0 beds
Totals:	3 hospitals	577 beds

★0981:   QUORUM HEALTH (IO)
1573 Mallory Lane, Suite 100, Brentwood, TN Zip 37027; tel. 615/221–1400; Thomas Miller, President and Chief Executive Officer
(Moderately Centralized Health System)

ALABAMA: DEKALB REGIONAL MEDICAL CENTER (O, 115 beds) 200 Medical Center Drive, Fort Payne, AL Zip 35968–3458, P O Box 680778, 35968–1608, tel. 256/845–3150; Patrick Trammell, Chief Executive Officer

L. V. STABLER MEMORIAL HOSPITAL (O, 61 beds) 29 L V Stabler Drive, Greenville, AL Zip 36037–3800; tel. 334/382–2671; Donald R. Rentfro, Chief Executive Officer
Web address: www.lvstabler.com

ARKANSAS: FORREST CITY MEDICAL CENTER (L, 55 beds) 1601 Newcastle Road, Forrest City, AR Zip 72335–2218; tel. 870/261–0000; Kevin Decker, Chief Executive Officer
Web address: www.forrestcitymedicalcenter.com

HELENA REGIONAL MEDICAL CENTER (L, 105 beds) 1801 Martin Luther King Drive, Helena, AR Zip 72342, P O Box 788, 72342–0788, tel. 870/338–5800; Leah Osbahr, M.P.H., Chief Executive Officer

CALIFORNIA: BARSTOW COMMUNITY HOSPITAL (L, 30 beds) 820 East Mountain View Street, Barstow, CA Zip 92311–3004; tel. 760/256–1761; Matthew H. Blevins, Chief Executive Officer
Web address: www.barstowhospital.com

WATSONVILLE COMMUNITY HOSPITAL (O, 106 beds) 75 Nielson Street, Watsonville, CA Zip 95076–2468; tel. 831/724–4741; Audra Earle, FACHE, Chief Executive Officer

GEORGIA: CLEARVIEW REGIONAL MEDICAL CENTER (O, 52 beds) 2151 West Spring Street, Monroe, GA Zip 30655–3115, PO BOX 1346, 30655–1346, tel. 770/267–8461; Michael Johnson, Chief Executive Officer
Web address: www.clearviewregionalmedicalcenter.com/

FANNIN REGIONAL HOSPITAL (O, 50 beds) 2855 Old Highway 5, Blue Ridge, GA Zip 30513–6248; tel. 706/632–3711; David S. Sanders, Chief Executive Officer
Web address: www.fanninregionalhospital.com

ILLINOIS: CROSSROADS COMMUNITY HOSPITAL (O, 31 beds) 8 Doctors Park Road, Mount Vernon, IL Zip 62864–6224; tel. 618/244–5500; Finny Mathew, Chief Executive Officer

GALESBURG COTTAGE HOSPITAL (O, 119 beds) 695 North Kellogg Street, Galesburg, IL Zip 61401–2885; tel. 309/343–8131; James Flynn, Chief Executive Officer
Web address: www.cottagehospital.com

GATEWAY REGIONAL MEDICAL CENTER (O, 172 beds) 2100 Madison Avenue, Granite City, IL Zip 62040–4799; tel. 618/798–3000; M Edward. Cunningham, Chief Executive Officer

HEARTLAND REGIONAL MEDICAL CENTER (O, 92 beds) 3333 West DeYoung, Marion, IL Zip 62959–5884; tel. 618/998–7000; Melisa Adkins, Chief Executive Officer
Web address: www.heartlandregional.com

METROSOUTH MEDICAL CENTER (O, 285 beds) 12935 South Gregory Street, Blue Island, IL Zip 60406–2470; tel. 708/597–2000; John D. Baird, Chief Executive Officer

RED BUD REGIONAL HOSPITAL (O, 140 beds) 325 Spring Street, Red Bud, IL Zip 62278–1105; tel. 618/282–3831; Shane Watson, Chief Executive Officer
Web address: www.redbudregional.com

UNION COUNTY HOSPITAL (L, 47 beds) 517 North Main Street, Anna, IL Zip 62906–1696; tel. 618/833–4511; James R. Farris, FACHE, Chief Executive Officer
Web address: www.unioncountyhospital.com

For explanation of codes following names, see page B2.
★ Indicates Type III membership in the American Hospital Association.

VISTA MEDICAL CENTER EAST (O, 190 beds) 1324 North Sheridan Road, Waukegan, IL Zip 60085–2161; tel. 847/360–3000; Norman F. Stephens, Interim Chief Executive Officer
Web address: www.vistahealth.com

VISTA MEDICAL CENTER WEST (O, 67 beds) 2615 Washington Street, Waukegan, IL Zip 60085–4988; tel. 847/249–3900; Norman F. Stephens, Interim Chief Executive Officer
Web address: www.vistahealth.com

KENTUCKY: KENTUCKY RIVER MEDICAL CENTER (L, 54 beds) 540 Jett Drive, Jackson, KY Zip 41339–9622; tel. 606/666–6000; John Ballard, Ph.D., Chief Executive Officer

PAUL B. HALL REGIONAL MEDICAL CENTER (O, 72 beds) 625 James S. Trimble Boulevard, Paintsville, KY Zip 41240–0000; tel. 606/789–3511; Deborah Trimble, R.N., Chief Executive Officer
Web address: www.pbhrmc.com

THREE RIVERS MEDICAL CENTER (O, 80 beds) 2485 Highway 644, Louisa, KY Zip 41230–9242, P O Box 769, 41230–0769, tel. 606/638–9451; Greg Kiser, Chief Executive Officer
Web address: www.threeriversmedicalcenter.com

NEVADA: MESA VIEW REGIONAL HOSPITAL (O, 25 beds) 1299 Bertha Howe Avenue, Mesquite, NV Zip 89027–7500; tel. 702/346–8040; Patricia Holden, Chief Executive Officer
Web address: www.mesaviewhospital.com

NEW MEXICO: ALTA VISTA REGIONAL HOSPITAL (O, 54 beds) 104 Legion Drive, Las Vegas, NM Zip 87701–4804; tel. 505/426–3500; Caleb O'Rear, Interim Chief Executive Officer

MIMBRES MEMORIAL HOSPITAL (O, 75 beds) 900 West Ash Street, Deming, NM Zip 88030–4098, P O Box 710, 88031–0710, tel. 575/546–5800; Kelly Duke, Chief Executive Officer
Web address: www.mimbresmemorial.com

NORTH CAROLINA: MARTIN GENERAL HOSPITAL (L, 49 beds) 310 South McCaskey Road, Williamston, NC Zip 27892–2150, P O Box 1128, 27892–1128, tel. 252/809–6300; John Jacobson, Interim Chief Executive Officer
Web address: www.martingeneral.com

OHIO: AFFINITY MEDICAL CENTER (O, 112 beds) 875 Eighth Street NE, Massillon, OH Zip 44646–8503, P O Box 4805, 44648–0805, tel. 330/832–8761; John Walsh, Chief Executive Officer
Web address: www.affinitymedicalcenter.com

OREGON: MCKENZIE-WILLAMETTE MEDICAL CENTER (O, 113 beds) 1460 'G' Street, Springfield, OR Zip 97477–4197; tel. 541/726–4400; Chad Campbell, Chief Executive Officer

PENNSYLVANIA: LOCK HAVEN HOSPITAL (O, 20 beds) 24 Cree Drive, Lock Haven, PA Zip 17745–2699; tel. 570/893–5000; Steven T. Davis, Chief Executive Officer
Web address: www.lockhavenhospital.com

SUNBURY COMMUNITY HOSPITAL AND OUTPATIENT CENTER (O, 76 beds) 350 North Eleventh Street, Sunbury, PA Zip 17801–1611; tel. 570/286–3333; Robert D. Williams, Chief Executive Officer
Web address: www.sunburyhospital.com

TENNESSEE: HENDERSON COUNTY COMMUNITY HOSPITAL (O, 45 beds) 200 West Church Street, Lexington, TN Zip 38351–2038; tel. 731/968–3646; Pamela W. Roberts, Chief Executive Officer
Web address: www.hendersoncchospital.com

MCKENZIE REGIONAL HOSPITAL (O, 35 beds) 161 Hospital Drive, McKenzie, TN Zip 38201–1636; tel. 731/352–5344; Michael Morrical, Chief Executive Officer

TEXAS: BIG BEND REGIONAL MEDICAL CENTER (O, 25 beds) 2600 Highway 118 North, Alpine, TX Zip 79830–2002; tel. 432/837–3447; Diane C. Moore, Chief Executive Officer and Chief Financial Officer
Web address: www.bigbendhealthcare.com

SCENIC MOUNTAIN MEDICAL CENTER (O, 62 beds) 1601 West 11th Place, Big Spring, TX Zip 79720–4198; tel. 432/263–1211; Emma Krabill, Chief Executive Officer
Web address: www.smmccares.com

UTAH: MOUNTAIN WEST MEDICAL CENTER (O, 44 beds) 2055 North Main Street, Tooele, UT Zip 84074–9819; tel. 435/843–3600; Philip Eaton, Interim Chief Executive Officer

WYOMING: EVANSTON REGIONAL HOSPITAL (O, 42 beds) 190 Arrowhead Drive, Evanston, WY Zip 82930–9266; tel. 307/789–3636; Jeremy Davis, Chief Executive Officer
Web address: www.evanstonregionalhospital.com

Owned, leased, sponsored:	34 hospitals	2700 beds
Contract-managed:	0 hospitals	0 beds
Totals:	34 hospitals	2700 beds

0996: RCCH HEALTHCARE PARTNERS (IO)
103 Continental Place Ste 200, Brentwood, TN Zip 37027–1042; tel. 615/844–9800; Martin S. Rash, Chief Executive Officer
(Moderately Centralized Health System)

ALABAMA: ELIZA COFFEE MEMORIAL HOSPITAL (O, 278 beds) 205 Marengo Street, Florence, AL Zip 35630–6033, P O Box 818, 35631–0818, tel. 256/768–9191; Russell Pigg, Chief Executive Officer
Web address: www.chgroup.org

SHOALS HOSPITAL (O, 137 beds) 201 Avalon Avenue, Muscle Shoals, AL Zip 35661–2805, P O Box 3359, 35662–3359, tel. 256/386–1600; Kidada Hawkins, Chief Executive Officer
Web address: www.shoalshospital.com

ARIZONA: CANYON VISTA MEDICAL CENTER (L, 100 beds) 5700 East Highway 90, Sierra Vista, AZ Zip 85635–9110; tel. 520/263–2000; Randy Anderson, Chief Executive Officer

ARKANSAS: NATIONAL PARK MEDICAL CENTER (O, 208 beds) 1910 Malvern Avenue, Hot Springs, AR Zip 71901–7799; tel. 501/321–1000; Jerry D. Mabry, FACHE, Chief Executive Officer
Web address: www.nationalparkmedical.com

SAINT MARY'S REGIONAL MEDICAL CENTER (O, 151 beds) 1808 West Main Street, Russellville, AR Zip 72801–2724; tel. 479/968–2841; James Davidson, Chief Executive Officer

IDAHO: ST. JOSEPH REGIONAL MEDICAL CENTER (O, 123 beds) 415 Sixth Street, Lewiston, ID Zip 83501–2431; tel. 208/743–2511; Blain Claypool, Interim Chief Executive Officer
Web address: www.sjrmc.org

IOWA: OTTUMWA REGIONAL HEALTH CENTER (O, 101 beds) 1001 Pennsylvania Avenue, Ottumwa, IA Zip 52501–2186; tel. 641/684–2300; Philip J. Noel III, Chief Executive Officer
Web address: www.ottumwaregionalhealth.com

MONTANA: COMMUNITY MEDICAL CENTER (O, 135 beds) 2827 Fort Missoula Road, Missoula, MT Zip 59804–7408; tel. 406/728–4100; Dean French, M.D., Chief Executive Officer
Web address: www.communitymed.org

OHIO: CLINTON MEMORIAL HOSPITAL (O, 102 beds) 610 West Main Street, Wilmington, OH Zip 45177–2125; tel. 937/382–6611; Gregory A. Nielsen, FACHE, Chief Executive Officer

OKLAHOMA: SAINT FRANCIS HOSPITAL MUSKOGEE (L, 175 beds) 300 Rockefeller Drive, Muskogee, OK Zip 74401–5081; tel. 918/682–5501; Anthony R. Young, Chief Executive Officer
Web address: https://www.saintfrancis.com/muskogee/Pages/default.aspx

SOUTHWESTERN MEDICAL CENTER (O, 178 beds) 5602 SW Lee Boulevard, Lawton, OK Zip 73505–9635; tel. 580/531–4700; Randy Butler, Interim Chief Executive Officer

OREGON: WILLAMETTE VALLEY MEDICAL CENTER (O, 88 beds) 2700 SE Stratus Avenue, McMinnville, OR Zip 97128–6255; tel. 503/472–6131; Peter A. Hofstetter, Chief Executive Officer
Web address: www.wvmcweb.com

SOUTH CAROLINA: CAROLINA PINES REGIONAL MEDICAL CENTER (O, 120 beds) 1304 West Bobo Newsom Highway, Hartsville, SC Zip 29550–4710; tel. 843/339–2100; William Little, Chief Executive Officer

KERSHAWHEALTH (O, 119 beds) 1315 Roberts Street, Camden, SC Zip 29020–3737, P O Box 7003, 29021–7003, tel. 803/432–4311; Terry Gunn, FACHE, Chief Executive Officer
Web address: www.kershawhealth.com

For explanation of codes following names, see page B2.
★ Indicates Type III membership in the American Hospital Association.

Section B

TEXAS: PARIS REGIONAL MEDICAL CENTER (O, 173 beds) 865 Deshong Drive, Paris, TX Zip 75460–9313, P O Box 9070, 75461–9070, tel. 903/785–4521; Steve Hyde, Chief Executive Officer
Web address: www.parisregionalmedical.com/

WASHINGTON: CAPITAL MEDICAL CENTER (O, 52 beds) 3900 Capital Mall Drive SW, Olympia, WA Zip 98502–5026, P O Box 19002, 98507–0013, tel. 360/754–5858; Mark Turner, Chief Executive Officer

Owned, leased, sponsored:	16 hospitals	2240 beds
Contract-managed:	0 hospitals	0 beds
Totals:	16 hospitals	2240 beds

★8495: REGIONAL HEALTH (NP)

353 Fairmont Boulevard, Rapid City, SD Zip 57701–7375, P O Box 6000, 57709–6000, tel. 605/719–1000; Brent R. Phillips, President and Chief Executive Officer
(Independent Hospital System)

SOUTH DAKOTA: CUSTER REGIONAL HOSPITAL (L, 87 beds) 1039 Montgomery Street, Custer, SD Zip 57730–1397; tel. 605/673–2229; Veronica Schmidt, President
Web address: www.regionalhealth.com

LEAD-DEADWOOD REGIONAL HOSPITAL (O, 9 beds) 61 Charles Street, Deadwood, SD Zip 57732–1303; tel. 605/717–6000; Mark C. Schmidt, President
Web address: www.regionalhealth.com

PHILIP HEALTH SERVICES (C, 48 beds) 503 West Pine Street, Philip, SD Zip 57567–3300, P O Box 790, 57567–0790, tel. 605/859–2511; Jeremy Schultes, Administrator and Chief Executive Officer

RAPID CITY REGIONAL HOSPITAL (O, 394 beds) 353 Fairmont Boulevard, Rapid City, SD Zip 57701–7393, P O Box 6000, 57709–6000, tel. 605/755–1000; Paulette Davidson, FACHE, Chief Operating Officer and Interim President
Web address: www.regionalhealth.com

SPEARFISH REGIONAL HOSPITAL (O, 35 beds) 1440 North Main Street, Spearfish, SD Zip 57783–1504; tel. 605/644–4000; Larry W. Veitz, President
Web address: www.regionalhealth.com/Our-Locations/Regional-Hospitals/Spearfish-Regional-Hospital.aspx

STURGIS REGIONAL HOSPITAL (O, 109 beds) 949 Harmon Street, Sturgis, SD Zip 57785–2452; tel. 605/720–2400; Mark Schulte, FACHE, President
Web address: www.regionalhealth.com/Our-Locations/Regional-Hospitals/Sturgis-Regional-Hospital.aspx

WYOMING: CROOK COUNTY MEDICAL SERVICES DISTRICT (C, 16 beds) 713 Oak Street, Sundance, WY Zip 82729, P O Box 517, 82729–0517, tel. 307/283–3501; Nathan Hough, Chief Executive Officer

WESTON COUNTY HEALTH SERVICES (C, 66 beds) 1124 Washington Boulevard, Newcastle, WY Zip 82701–2972; tel. 307/746–4491; Maureen K. Cadwell, Chief Executive Officer
Web address: www.wchs-wy.org

Owned, leased, sponsored:	5 hospitals	634 beds
Contract-managed:	3 hospitals	130 beds
Totals:	8 hospitals	764 beds

1019: REGIONAL MEDICAL CENTER (NP)

400 East 10th Street, Anniston, AL Zip 36207–4716; tel. 256/235–5121; Louis A. Bass, President and Chief Executive Officer

ALABAMA: RMC ANNISTON (O, 271 beds) 400 East Tenth Street, Anniston, AL Zip 36207–4716, P O Box 2208, 36202–2208, tel. 256/235–5121; Louis A. Bass, Chief Executive Officer
Web address: www.rmccares.org

RMC JACKSONVILLE (O, 65 beds) 1701 Pelham Road South, Jacksonville, AL Zip 36265–3399, P O Box 999, 36265–0999, tel. 256/435–4970; Joe Weaver, Chief Executive Officer

RMC-STRINGFELLOW MEMORIAL HOSPITAL (O, 88 beds) 301 East 18th Street, Anniston, AL Zip 36207–3952; tel. 256/235–8900; Joe Weaver, Chief Executive Officer
Web address: www.stringfellowmemorial.com

Owned, leased, sponsored:	3 hospitals	424 beds
Contract-managed:	0 hospitals	0 beds
Totals:	3 hospitals	424 beds

★2625: RENOWN HEALTH (NP)

50 West Liberty Street, Suite 1100, Reno, NV Zip 89501–1951; tel. 775/982–5529; Anthony D. Slonim, M.D., Dr.PH, President and Chief Executive Officer
(Centralized Health System)

NEVADA: RENOWN REGIONAL MEDICAL CENTER (O, 643 beds) 1155 Mill Street, Reno, NV Zip 89502–1576; tel. 775/982–4100; Erik Olson, Chief Executive Officer

RENOWN REHABILITATION HOSPITAL (O, 62 beds) 1495 Mill Street, Reno, NV Zip 89502–1479; tel. 775/982–3500; Chris Nicholas, Chief Executive Officer
Web address: www.renown.org

RENOWN SOUTH MEADOWS MEDICAL CENTER (O, 76 beds) 10101 Double 'R' Boulevard, Reno, NV Zip 89521–5931; tel. 775/982–7000; Siri Nelson, Chief Executive Officer

Owned, leased, sponsored:	3 hospitals	781 beds
Contract-managed:	0 hospitals	0 beds
Totals:	3 hospitals	781 beds

★0964: RIDGEVIEW MEDICAL CENTER (IO)

500 South Maple Street, Waconia, MN Zip 55387–1752; tel. 952/442–2191; Michael Phelps, President and Chief Executive Officer
(Independent Hospital System)

MINNESOTA: RIDGEVIEW LE SUEUR MEDICAL CENTER (O, 64 beds) 621 South Fourth Street, Le Sueur, MN Zip 56058–2298; tel. 507/665–3375; Pam Williams, Vice President
Web address: www.mvhc.org

RIDGEVIEW MEDICAL CENTER (O, 108 beds) 500 South Maple Street, Waconia, MN Zip 55387–1791; tel. 952/442–2191; Michael Phelps, President and Chief Executive Officer

RIDGEVIEW SIBLEY MEDICAL CENTER (L, 16 beds) 601 West Chandler Street, Arlington, MN Zip 55307–2127; tel. 507/964–2271; Todd Sandberg, Chief Executive Officer
Web address: www.sibleymedical.org

Owned, leased, sponsored:	3 hospitals	188 beds
Contract-managed:	0 hospitals	0 beds
Totals:	3 hospitals	188 beds

4810: RIVERSIDE HEALTH SYSTEM (NP)

701 Town Center Drive, Suite 1000, Newport News, VA Zip 23606–4286; tel. 757/534–7000; William B. Downey, President and Chief Executive Officer
(Centralized Health System)

VIRGINIA: HAMPTON ROADS SPECIALTY HOSPITAL (O, 25 beds) 245 Chesapeake Avenue, Newport News, VA Zip 23607–6038; tel. 757/534–5000; Courtney Detwiler, R.N., Administrator
Web address: www.hamptonroadsspecialtyhospital.com

RIVERSIDE DOCTORS' HOSPITAL (O, 13 beds) 1500 Commonwealth Avenue, Williamsburg, VA Zip 23185–5229; tel. 757/585–2200; Adria Vanhoozier, Administrator

RIVERSIDE REGIONAL MEDICAL CENTER (O, 307 beds) 500 J Clyde Morris Boulevard, Newport News, VA Zip 23601–1929; tel. 757/594–2000; Michael J. Doucette, Senior Vice President and Administrator
Web address: https://www.riversideonline.com/rrmc/index.cfm

For explanation of codes following names, see page B2.
★ Indicates Type III membership in the American Hospital Association.

Section B

RIVERSIDE REHABILITATION INSTITUTE (O, 30 beds) 245 Chesapeake Avenue, Newport News, VA Zip 23607–6038; tel. 757/928–8000; Daniel Ballin, Administrator

RIVERSIDE SHORE MEMORIAL HOSPITAL (O, 26 beds) 204800 Market Street, Onancoke, VA Zip 23417, P O Box 17, Nassawadox, 23413–0017, tel. 757/302–2100; John Peterman, Vice President and Administrator
Web address: www.riversideonline.com

RIVERSIDE TAPPAHANNOCK HOSPITAL (O, 16 beds) 618 Hospital Road, Tappahannock, VA Zip 22560–5000; tel. 804/443–3311; Esther Muscari. Desimini, Administrator

RIVERSIDE WALTER REED HOSPITAL (O, 29 beds) 7519 Hospital Drive, Gloucester, VA Zip 23061–4178, P O Box 1130, 23061–1130, tel. 804/693–8800; Megan Kleckner, Vice President and Administrator
Web address: www.riversideonline.com

Owned, leased, sponsored:	7 hospitals	446 beds
Contract-managed:	0 hospitals	0 beds
Totals:	7 hospitals	446 beds

★0046: ROCHESTER REGIONAL HEALTH (NP)
1425 Portland Avenue, 5th Floor, Rochester, NY Zip 14621–3001; tel. 585/922–4000; Eric Bieber, M.D., President and Chief Executive Officer
(Centralized Health System)

NEW YORK: CLIFTON SPRINGS HOSPITAL AND CLINIC (O, 214 beds) 2 Coulter Road, Clifton Springs, NY Zip 14432–1189; tel. 315/462–9561; Dustin Riccio, M.D., President
Web address: www.cliftonspringshospital.org

NEWARK-WAYNE COMMUNITY HOSPITAL (O, 280 beds) 1200 Driving Park Avenue, Newark, NY Zip 14513–1057, P O Box 111, 14513–0111, tel. 315/332–2022; Dustin Riccio, M.D., President Eastern Region

ROCHESTER GENERAL HOSPITAL (O, 520 beds) 1425 Portland Avenue, Rochester, NY Zip 14621–3099; tel. 585/922–4000; Nancy Tinsley, President
Web address: www.rochestergeneral.org

UNITED MEMORIAL MEDICAL CENTER (O, 131 beds) 127 North Street, Batavia, NY Zip 14020–1631; tel. 585/343–6030; Daniel P. Ireland, FACHE, President

UNITY HOSPITAL (O, 487 beds) 1555 Long Pond Road, Rochester, NY Zip 14626–4182; tel. 585/723–7000; Douglas Stewart, PsyD, President
Web address: www.unityhealth.org

Owned, leased, sponsored:	5 hospitals	1632 beds
Contract-managed:	0 hospitals	0 beds
Totals:	5 hospitals	1632 beds

0348: RURAL COMMUNITY HOSPITALS OF AMERICA (IO)
1100 Main Street, Suite 2350, Kansas City, MO Zip 64105–5186; tel. 816/474–7800; Lawrence J. Arthur, President
(Independent Hospital System)

KANSAS: HILLSBORO COMMUNITY HOSPITAL (O, 10 beds) 701 South Main Street, Hillsboro, KS Zip 67063–1553; tel. 620/947–3114; Marion Regier, Chief Executive Officer
Web address: www.hchks.com

HORTON COMMUNITY HOSPITAL (O, 25 beds) 240 West 18th Street, Horton, KS Zip 66439–1245; tel. 785/486–2642; James D. Noble, Chief Executive Officer
Web address: www.horton-hospital.com

OSWEGO COMMUNITY HOSPITAL (O, 12 beds) 800 Barker Drive, Oswego, KS Zip 67356–9014; tel. 620/795–2921; Daniel Hiben, Chief Executive Officer

MISSOURI: COOPER COUNTY MEMORIAL HOSPITAL (C, 32 beds) 17651 'B' Highway, Boonville, MO Zip 65233–2839, P O Box 88, 65233–0088, tel. 660/882–7461; Mark Hirshberg, Interim Chief Executive Officer
Web address: www.coopercmh.com

I-70 COMMUNITY HOSPITAL (O, 11 beds) 105 Hospital Drive, Sweet Springs, MO Zip 65351–2229; tel. 660/335–4700; Jeff Bloemker, Chief Executive Officer
Web address: www.i70medcenter.com

NORTH CAROLINA: WASHINGTON COUNTY HOSPITAL (O, 25 beds) 958 U S Highway 64 East, Plymouth, NC Zip 27962–9591, PO Box 707, 27962–9591, tel. 252/793–4135; Al Arrowood, Interim President

OKLAHOMA: DRUMRIGHT REGIONAL HOSPITAL (O, 15 beds) 610 West Bypass , Drumright, OK Zip 74030–5957; tel. 918/382–2300; Tracy Byers, Chief Executive Officer
Web address: www.drumrighthospital.com/

FAIRFAX COMMUNITY HOSPITAL (O, 15 beds) 40 Hospital Road, Fairfax, OK Zip 74637–5084; tel. 918/642–3291; Tina Steele, Chief Executive Officer and Chief Financial Officer

HASKELL COUNTY COMMUNITY HOSPITAL (O, 20 beds) 401 Northwest 'H' Street, Stigler, OK Zip 74462–1625; tel. 918/967–4682; Donald E. Buchanan, Chief Executive Officer
Web address: www.haskellhospital.com

PRAGUE COMMUNITY HOSPITAL (O, 15 beds) 1322 Klabzuba Avenue, Prague, OK Zip 74864–9005, P O Box S, 74864–1090, tel. 405/567–4922; Randy Simmons, Chief Executive Officer
Web address: www.praguehospital.com

TENNESSEE: LAUDERDALE COMMUNITY HOSPITAL (O, 25 beds) 326 Asbury Avenue, Ripley, TN Zip 38063–5577; tel. 731/221–2200; Michael G. Layfield, Interim Chief Executive Officer

Owned, leased, sponsored:	10 hospitals	173 beds
Contract-managed:	1 hospitals	32 beds
Totals:	11 hospitals	205 beds

★0109: RURAL HEALTH GROUP (IO)
48 West 1500 North, Nephi, UT Zip 84648–8900; tel. 435/623–4924; Mark R. Stoddard, President and Chairman
(Independent Hospital System)

UTAH: CENTRAL VALLEY MEDICAL CENTER (L, 27 beds) 48 West 1500 North, Nephi, UT Zip 84648–8900; tel. 435/623–3000; Mark R. Stoddard, Chief Executive Officer
Web address: www.cvmed.net

Owned, leased, sponsored:	1 hospitals	27 beds
Contract-managed:	0 hospitals	0 beds
Totals:	1 hospitals	27 beds

★0220: RUSH HEALTH SYSTEMS (NP)
1314 19th Avenue, Meridian, MS Zip 39301–4116; tel. 601/483–0011; Wallace Strickland, President and Chief Executive Officer
(Independent Hospital System)

ALABAMA: CHOCTAW GENERAL HOSPITAL (O, 25 beds) 401 Vanity Fair Avenue, Butler, AL Zip 36904–3032; tel. 205/459–9100; J W. Cowan, Administrator
Web address: www.choctawgeneral.com/cgh/

MISSISSIPPI: H. C. WATKINS MEMORIAL HOSPITAL (O, 25 beds) 605 South Archusa Avenue, Quitman, MS Zip 39355–2331; tel. 601/776–6925; Michael Nester, Administrator

JOHN C. STENNIS MEMORIAL HOSPITAL (O, 25 beds) 14365 Highway 16 West, De Kalb, MS Zip 39328–7974; tel. 769/486–1000; Justin Palmer, Administrator
Web address: www.johncstennismemorialhospital.com/jcsmh/

LAIRD HOSPITAL (O, 25 beds) 25117 Highway 15, Union, MS Zip 39365–9099; tel. 601/774–8214; Thomas G. Bartlett III, Administrator

RUSH FOUNDATION HOSPITAL (O, 182 beds) 1314 19th Avenue, Meridian, MS Zip 39301–4195; tel. 601/483–0011; Larkin Kennedy, Chief Executive Officer
Web address: www.rushhealthsystems.org/rfh/

For explanation of codes following names, see page B2.
★ Indicates Type III membership in the American Hospital Association.

SCOTT REGIONAL HOSPITAL (O, 25 beds) 317 Highway 13 South, Morton, MS Zip 39117–3353, P O Box 259, 39117–0259, tel. 601/732–6301; Heather Davis, Administrator
Web address: www.scottregional.org/srh/

SPECIALTY HOSPITAL OF MERIDIAN (O, 49 beds) 1314 19th Avenue, Meridian, MS Zip 39301–4116; tel. 601/703–4211; Elizabeth C. Mitchell, Chief Executive Officer and Chief Operating Officer

Owned, leased, sponsored:	7 hospitals	356 beds
Contract-managed:	0 hospitals	0 beds
Totals:	7 hospitals	356 beds

★3855: RUSH UNIVERSITY MEDICAL CENTER (NP)
1653 West Congress Parkway, Chicago, IL Zip 60612–3864; tel. 312/942–5000; Larry J. Goodman, M.D., Chief Executive Officer
(Moderately Centralized Health System)

ILLINOIS: RUSH OAK PARK HOSPITAL (O, 96 beds) 520 South Maple Avenue, Oak Park, IL Zip 60304–1097; tel. 708/383–9300; Bruce M. Elegant, FACHE, President and Chief Executive Officer
Web address: www.roph.org

RUSH UNIVERSITY MEDICAL CENTER (O, 673 beds) 1653 West Congress Parkway, Chicago, IL Zip 60612–3833; tel. 312/942–5000; Larry J. Goodman, M.D., Chief Executive Officer

RUSH-COPLEY MEDICAL CENTER (O, 210 beds) 2000 Ogden Avenue, Aurora, IL Zip 60504–7222; tel. 630/978–6200; Barry C. Finn, President and Chief Executive Officer
Web address: www.rushcopley.com

Owned, leased, sponsored:	3 hospitals	979 beds
Contract-managed:	0 hospitals	0 beds
Totals:	3 hospitals	979 beds

★0994: RWJBARNABAS HEALTH (NP)
95 Old Short Hills Road, West Orange, NJ Zip 07052–1008; tel. 973/322–4000; Barry Ostrowsky, President and Chief Executive Officer
(Moderately Centralized Health System)

NEW JERSEY: BARNABAS HEALTH BEHAVIORAL HEALTH CENTER (O, 40 beds) 1691 Highway 9, Toms River, NJ Zip 8754; tel. 732/914–1688; Deanna Sperling, President and Chief Executive Officer

CHILDREN'S SPECIALIZED HOSPITAL (O, 140 beds) 200 Somerset Street, New Brunswick, NJ Zip 08901–1942; tel. 732/258–7000; Warren E. Moore, President and Chief Executive Officer
Web address: www.childrens-specialized.org

CLARA MAASS MEDICAL CENTER (O, 469 beds) One Clara Maass Drive, Belleville, NJ Zip 07109–3557; tel. 973/450–2000; Mary Ellen Clyne, MSN, Ph.D., R.N., President and Chief Executive Officer

COMMUNITY MEDICAL CENTER (O, 353 beds) 99 Route 37 West, Toms River, NJ Zip 08755–6423; tel. 732/557–8000; Michael Mimoso, FACHE, President and Chief Executive Officer
Web address: www.barnabashealth.org/hospitals/community_medical/index.html

JERSEY CITY MEDICAL CENTER (O, 316 beds) 355 Grand Street, Jersey City, NJ Zip 07302–4321; tel. 201/915–2000; Joseph F. Scott, FACHE, President and Chief Executive Officer

MONMOUTH MEDICAL CENTER, LONG BRANCH CAMPUS (O, 305 beds) 300 Second Avenue, Long Branch, NJ Zip 07740–6303; tel. 732/222–5200; Bill Arnold, President and Chief Executive Officer
Web address: www.barnabashealth.org/hospitals/monmouth_medical/index.html

MONMOUTH MEDICAL CENTER, SOUTHERN CAMPUS (O, 124 beds) 600 River Avenue, Lakewood, NJ Zip 08701–5237; tel. 732/363–1900; Frank J. Vozos, M.D., FACS, President and Chief Executive Officer, Barnabas Health Behavioral Health Center
Web address: www.rwjbarnabashealth.org/monmouth-medical-center-southern-campus.aspx

NEWARK BETH ISRAEL MEDICAL CENTER (O, 360 beds) 201 Lyons Avenue at Osborne Terrace, Newark, NJ Zip 07112–2027; tel. 973/926–7000; Darrell K. Terry Sr, M.P.H., FACHE, President and Chief Executive Officer
Web address: www.barnabashealth.org/hospitals/newark_beth_israel/index.html

ROBERT WOOD JOHNSON UNIVERSITY HOSPITAL RAHWAY (O, 122 beds) 865 Stone Street, Rahway, NJ Zip 07065–2797; tel. 732/381–4200; Kirk C. Tice, President and Chief Executive Officer
Web address: www.rwjuhr.com

ROBERT WOOD JOHNSON UNIVERSITY HOSPITAL SOMERSET (O, 285 beds) 110 Rehill Avenue, Somerville, NJ Zip 08876–2598; tel. 908/685–2200; Anthony V. Cava, President

ROBERT WOOD JOHNSON UNIVERSITY HOSPITAL AT HAMILTON (O, 213 beds) One Hamilton Health Place, Hamilton, NJ Zip 08690–3599; tel. 609/586–7900; Richard Freeman, President and Chief Executive Officer
Web address: www.rwjhamilton.org

ROBERT WOOD JOHNSON UNIVERSITY HOSPITAL (O, 610 beds) 1 Robert Wood Johnson Place, New Brunswick, NJ Zip 08901–1928; tel. 732/828–3000; John Gantner, President and Chief Executive Officer
Web address: www.rwjuh.edu

SAINT BARNABAS MEDICAL CENTER (O, 545 beds) 94 Old Short Hills Rd, Livingston, NJ Zip 07039–5672; tel. 973/322–5000; Stephen P. Zieniewicz, FACHE, President and Chief Executive Officer
Web address: www.barnabashealth.org/hospitals/saint_barnabas/index.html

Owned, leased, sponsored:	13 hospitals	3882 beds
Contract-managed:	0 hospitals	0 beds
Totals:	13 hospitals	3882 beds

0912: SAFE HAVEN HEALTH CARE (IO)
2520 South 5th Avenue, Pocatello, ID Zip 83204–1923; tel. 800/261–2443; Scott Burpee, President

IDAHO: SAFE HAVEN HOSPITAL OF POCATELLO (O, 87 beds) 1200 Hospital Way, Pocatello, ID Zip 83201–2708; tel. 208/232–2570; Karen Neilson, Administrator
Web address: www.safehavenhealthcare.org/safehaven_hospital/index.html

SAFE HAVEN HOSPITAL OF TREASURE VALLEY (O, 22 beds) 8050 Northview Street, Boise, ID Zip 83704–7126; tel. 208/327–0504; Scott Proctor, Chief Executive Officer

Owned, leased, sponsored:	2 hospitals	109 beds
Contract-managed:	0 hospitals	0 beds
Totals:	2 hospitals	109 beds

★0254: SAINT FRANCIS HEALTH SYSTEM (NP)
6161 South Yale Avenue, Tulsa, OK Zip 74136–1902; tel. 918/494–8454; Jake Henry Jr, President and Chief Executive Officer
(Centralized Health System)

OKLAHOMA: LAUREATE PSYCHIATRIC CLINIC AND HOSPITAL (O, 90 beds) 6655 South Yale Avenue, Tulsa, OK Zip 74136–3329; tel. 918/481–4000; Michele A. Keeling, Senior Vice President and Administrator
Web address: www.laureate.com

SAINT FRANCIS HOSPITAL SOUTH (O, 84 beds) 10501 East 91st Street, Tulsa, OK Zip 74133–5790; tel. 918/307–6010; David S. Weil, Senior Vice President and Administrator
Web address: www.saintfrancis.com/south/

SAINT FRANCIS HOSPITAL VINITA (O, 55 beds) 735 North Foreman Street, Vinita, OK Zip 74301–1418, P O Box 326, 74301–0326, tel. 918/256–7551; Todd Schuster, Administrator
Web address: https://www.saintfrancis.com/vinita/Pages/default.aspx

SAINT FRANCIS HOSPITAL (O, 871 beds) 6161 South Yale Avenue, Tulsa, OK Zip 74136–1902; tel. 918/494–2200; Jake Henry Jr, Chief Executive Officer and President, Saint Francis Health System
Web address: www.saintfrancis.com

Owned, leased, sponsored:	4 hospitals	1100 beds
Contract-managed:	0 hospitals	0 beds
Totals:	4 hospitals	1100 beds

For explanation of codes following names, see page B2.
★ Indicates Type III membership in the American Hospital Association.

★0120: SAINT LUKE'S HEALTH SYSTEM (NP)

901 East 104th Street, Mailstop 900N, Kansas City, MO Zip 64131–4517, 901 East 104th Street, 64131–4517, tel. 816/932–2000; Melinda Estes, M.D., President and Chief Executive Officer
(Centralized Health System)

KANSAS: ANDERSON COUNTY HOSPITAL (L, 48 beds) 421 South Maple, Garnett, KS Zip 66032–1334, P O Box 309, 66032–0309, tel. 785/448–3131; Rick McKain, Chief Executive Officer

SAINT LUKE'S CUSHING HOSPITAL (O, 25 beds) 711 Marshall Street, Leavenworth, KS Zip 66048–3235; tel. 913/684–1100; Adele Ducharme, MSN, R.N., Chief Executive Officer
Web address: www.saintlukeshealthsystem.org/locations/saint-lukes-cushing-hospital

SAINT LUKE'S SOUTH HOSPITAL (O, 107 beds) 12300 Metcalf Avenue, Overland Park, KS Zip 66213–1324; tel. 913/317–7000; Bobby Olm-Shipman, Chief Executive Officer
Web address: www.saintlukeshealthsystem.org/south

MISSOURI: HEDRICK MEDICAL CENTER (L, 25 beds) 2799 North Washington Street, Chillicothe, MO Zip 64601–2902; tel. 660/646–1480; Steven M. Schieber, FACHE, Chief Executive Officer
Web address: www.saintlukeskc.org

SAINT LUKE'S EAST HOSPITAL (O, 203 beds) 100 NE Saint Luke's Boulevard, Lee's Summit, MO Zip 64086–6000; tel. 816/347–5000; Ron Baker, FACHE, Chief Executive Officer
Web address: www.saintlukeskc.org

SAINT LUKE'S HOSPITAL OF KANSAS CITY (O, 501 beds) 4401 Wornall Road, Kansas City, MO Zip 64111–3220; tel. 816/932–3800; Jani L. Johnson, R.N., MSN, Chief Executive Officer

SAINT LUKE'S NORTH HOSPITAL - BARRY ROAD (O, 141 beds) 5830 NW Barry Road, Kansas City, MO Zip 64154–2778; tel. 816/891–6000; Adele Ducharme, MSN, R.N., Interim Chief Executive Officer
Web address: www.saint-lukes.org

WRIGHT MEMORIAL HOSPITAL (L, 15 beds) 191 Iowa Boulevard, Trenton, MO Zip 64683–8343; tel. 660/358–5700; Gary W. Jordan, FACHE, Chief Executive Officer

Owned, leased, sponsored:	8 hospitals	1065 beds
Contract-managed:	0 hospitals	0 beds
Totals:	8 hospitals	1065 beds

0403: SALEM HEALTH (NP)

890 Oak Street Bldg B POB 14001, Salem, OR Zip 97309–5014; tel. 503/561–5200; Norman F. Gruber, President and Chief Executive Officer
(Independent Hospital System)

OREGON: SALEM HEALTH WEST VALLEY (O, 6 beds) 525 SE Washington Street, Dallas, OR Zip 97338–2834, P O Box 378, 97338–0378, tel. 503/623–8301; Bruce C. Rodgers, Chief Administrative Officer
Web address: www.salemhealth.org/wvh/

SALEM HOSPITAL (O, 440 beds) 890 Oak Street SE, Salem, OR Zip 97301–3959, P O Box 14001, 97309–5014, tel. 503/561–5200; Cheryl R. Nester Wolfe, President and Chief Executive Officer

Owned, leased, sponsored:	2 hospitals	446 beds
Contract-managed:	0 hospitals	0 beds
Totals:	2 hospitals	446 beds

1002: SALINA REGIONAL HEALTH CENTER (NP)

400 South Santa Fe Avenue, Salina, KS Zip 67401–4198, PO Box 5080, 67402–5080, tel. 785/452–7000; Michael Terry, President and Chief Executive Officer
(Moderately Centralized Health System)

KANSAS: CLOUD COUNTY HEALTH CENTER (C, 25 beds) 1100 Highland Drive, Concordia, KS Zip 66901–3923; tel. 785/243–1234; Cherri Waites, Chief Executive Officer
Web address: www.cchc.com

LINDSBORG COMMUNITY HOSPITAL (C, 21 beds) 605 West Lincoln Street, Lindsborg, KS Zip 67456–2328; tel. 785/227–3308; Larry VanDerWege, Administrator

SALINA REGIONAL HEALTH CENTER (O, 205 beds) 400 South Santa Fe Avenue, Salina, KS Zip 67401–4198, P O Box 5080, 67402–5080, tel. 785/452–7000; Michael Terry, President and Chief Executive Officer
Web address: www.srhc.com

Owned, leased, sponsored:	1 hospitals	205 beds
Contract-managed:	2 hospitals	46 beds
Totals:	3 hospitals	251 beds

★0186: SAMARITAN HEALTH SERVICES (NP)

3600 NW Samaritan Drive, Corvallis, OR Zip 97330–3737, P O Box 1068, 97339–1068, tel. 541/768–5001; Larry A. Mullins, FACHE, President and Chief Executive Officer
(Centralized Physician/Insurance Health System)

OREGON: GOOD SAMARITAN REGIONAL MEDICAL CENTER (O, 182 beds) 3600 NW Samaritan Drive, Corvallis, OR Zip 97330–3737, P O Box 1068, 97339–1068, tel. 541/768–5111; Becky A. Pape, R.N., Chief Executive Officer
Web address: www.samhealth.org

SAMARITAN ALBANY GENERAL HOSPITAL (O, 70 beds) 1046 Sixth Avenue, SW, Albany, OR Zip 97321–1999; tel. 541/812–4000; David G. Triebes, Chief Executive Officer
Web address: www.samhealth.org

SAMARITAN LEBANON COMMUNITY HOSPITAL (O, 25 beds) 525 North Santiam Highway, Lebanon, OR Zip 97355–4363, P O Box 739, 97355–0739, tel. 541/258–2101; Marty Cahill, Chief Executive Officer

SAMARITAN NORTH LINCOLN HOSPITAL (C, 25 beds) 3043 NE 28th Street, Lincoln City, OR Zip 97367–4518, P O Box 767, 97367–0767, tel. 541/994–3661; Lesley Ogden, M.D., Chief Executive Officer
Web address: www.samhealth.org

SAMARITAN PACIFIC COMMUNITIES HOSPITAL (C, 25 beds) 930 SW Abbey Street, Newport, OR Zip 97365–4820, P O Box 945, 97365–0072, tel. 541/265–2244; Lesley Ogden, M.D., Chief Executive Officer

Owned, leased, sponsored:	3 hospitals	277 beds
Contract-managed:	2 hospitals	50 beds
Totals:	5 hospitals	327 beds

★0914: SAN LUIS VALLEY HEALTH (NP)

106 Blanca Avenue, Alamosa, CO Zip 81101–2340; tel. 719/589–2511; Konnie Martin, Chief Executive Officer
(Independent Hospital System)

COLORADO: SAN LUIS VALLEY HEALTH CONEJOS COUNTY HOSPITAL (O, 17 beds) 19021 U S Highway 285, La Jara, CO Zip 81140–0639, P O Box 639, 81140–0639, tel. 719/274–5121; Kelly Gallegos, Administrator
Web address: www.sanluisvalleyhealth.org/locations/conejos-county-hospital

SAN LUIS VALLEY HEALTH (O, 44 beds) 106 Blanca Avenue, Alamosa, CO Zip 81101–2393; tel. 719/589–2511; Konnie Martin, Chief Executive Officer
Web address: www.sanluisvalleyhealth.org

Owned, leased, sponsored:	2 hospitals	61 beds
Contract-managed:	0 hospitals	0 beds
Totals:	2 hospitals	61 beds

★0530: SANFORD HEALTH (NP)

2301 East 60th Street North, Sioux Falls, SD Zip 57104–0569, PO Box 5039, 57117–5039, tel. 605/333–1000; Kelby K. Krabbenhoft, President and Chief Executive Officer
(Decentralized Health System)

For explanation of codes following names, see page B2.
★ Indicates Type III membership in the American Hospital Association.

IOWA: ORANGE CITY AREA HEALTH SYSTEM (C, 108 beds) 1000 Lincoln Circle SE, Orange City, IA Zip 51041–1862; tel. 712/737–4984; Martin W. Guthmiller, Chief Executive Officer

SANFORD ROCK RAPIDS MEDICAL CENTER (L, 14 beds) 801 South Greene Street, Rock Rapids, IA Zip 51246–1998; tel. 712/472–2591; Tammy Loosbrock, Chief Executive Officer
Web address: www.sanfordrockrapids.org

SANFORD SHELDON MEDICAL CENTER (O, 95 beds) 118 North Seventh Avenue, Sheldon, IA Zip 51201–1235, P O Box 250, 51201–0250, tel. 712/324–5041; Richard E. Nordahl, Chief Executive Officer

MINNESOTA: ARNOLD MEMORIAL HEALTH CARE CENTER (L, 50 beds) 601 Louisiana Avenue, Adrian, MN Zip 56110–0279, P O Box 279, 56110–0279, tel. 507/483–2668; Michele Roban, Administrator

MAHNOMEN HEALTH CENTER (C, 50 beds) 414 West Jefferson Avenue, Mahnomen, MN Zip 56557–4912, P O Box 396, 56557–0396, tel. 218/935–2511; Dale K. Kruger, Chief Executive Officer
Web address: www.mahnomenhealthcenter.com

MURRAY COUNTY MEDICAL CENTER (C, 18 beds) 2042 Juniper Avenue, Slayton, MN Zip 56172–1017; tel. 507/836–6111; Dennis Goebel, Chief Executive Officer

ORTONVILLE AREA HEALTH SERVICES (C, 102 beds) 450 Eastvold Avenue, Ortonville, MN Zip 56278–1133; tel. 320/839–2502; David Rogers, Chief Executive Officer
Web address: www.oahs.us

PERHAM HEALTH (C, 121 beds) 1000 Coney Street West, Perham, MN Zip 56573–1108; tel. 218/347–4500; Chuck Hofius, Chief Executive Officer

SANFORD BAGLEY MEDICAL CENTER (O, 8 beds) 203 Fourth Street NW, Bagley, MN Zip 56621–8307; tel. 218/694–6501; Robert Belanger, Chief Executive Officer
Web address: www.sanfordhealth.org

SANFORD BEMIDJI MEDICAL CENTER (O, 196 beds) 1300 Anne Street NW, Bemidji, MN Zip 56601–5103; tel. 218/751–5430; Bryan Nermoe, President
Web address: www.nchs.com

SANFORD CANBY MEDICAL CENTER (L, 93 beds) 112 St Olaf Avenue South, Canby, MN Zip 56220–1433; tel. 507/223–7277; Lori Sisk, R.N., Chief Executive Officer

SANFORD JACKSON MEDICAL CENTER (O, 14 beds) 1430 North Highway, Jackson, MN Zip 56143–1093; tel. 507/847–2420; Dawn Schnell, Chief Nursing Officer and Interim Senior Director
Web address: www.sanfordjackson.org

SANFORD LUVERNE MEDICAL CENTER (O, 25 beds) 1600 North Kniss Avenue, Luverne, MN Zip 56156–1067; tel. 507/283–2321; Tammy Loosbrock, Chief Executive Officer

SANFORD MEDICAL CENTER THIEF RIVER FALLS (O, 25 beds) 3001 Sanford Parkway, Thief River Falls, MN Zip 56701–2700; tel. 218/681–4240; Brian J. Carlson, FACHE, Chief Executive Officer
Web address: www.sanfordhealth.org

SANFORD THIEF RIVER FALLS BEHAVIORAL HEALTH CENTER (O, 16 beds) 120 LaBree Avenue South, Thief River Falls, MN Zip 56701–2819, 3001 Sanford Parkway, 56701–2819, tel. 218/683–4349; Brian J. Carlson, FACHE, Chief Executive Officer
Web address: www.sanfordhealth.org/Locations/1766896362

SANFORD TRACY MEDICAL CENTER (O, 25 beds) 251 Fifth Street East, Tracy, MN Zip 56175–1536; tel. 507/629–8400; Stacy Barstad, Chief Executive Officer

SANFORD WESTBROOK MEDICAL CENTER (L, 6 beds) 920 Bell Avenue, Westbrook, MN Zip 56183–9669, P O Box 188, 56183–0188, tel. 507/274–6121; Stacy Barstad, Chief Executive Officer
Web address: www.sanfordwestbrook.org

SANFORD WHEATON MEDICAL CENTER (O, 15 beds) 401 12th Street North, Wheaton, MN Zip 56296–1099; tel. 320/563–8226; JoAnn M. Foltz, R.N., Chief Executive Officer
Web address: www.sanfordhealth.org

SANFORD WORTHINGTON MEDICAL CENTER (O, 48 beds) 1018 Sixth Avenue, Worthington, MN Zip 56187–2202, P O Box 997, 56187–0997, tel. 507/372–2941; Jennifer . Weg, MS, R.N., Chief Executive Officer

WINDOM AREA HOSPITAL (C, 18 beds) 2150 Hospital Drive, Windom, MN Zip 56101–0339, P O Box 339, 56101–0339, tel. 507/831–2400; Shelby Medina, Chief Executive Officer
Web address: www.windomareahospital.com

NORTH DAKOTA: NORTHWOOD DEACONESS HEALTH CENTER (O, 73 beds) 4 North Park Street, Northwood, ND Zip 58267–4102, P O Box 190, 58267–0190, tel. 701/587–6060; Pete Antonson, Chief Executive Officer
Web address: www.ndhc.net

SANFORD BISMARCK (O, 208 beds) 300 North Seventh Street, Bismarck, ND Zip 58501–4439, P O Box 5525, 58506–5525, tel. 701/323–6000; Craig Lambrecht, M.D., President
Web address: www.bismarck.sanfordhealth.org/

SANFORD HILLSBORO MEDICAL CENTER (C, 52 beds) 12 Third Street SE, Hillsboro, ND Zip 58045–4840, P O Box 609, 58045–0609, tel. 701/636–3200; Jac McTaggart, Chief Executive Officer

SANFORD MAYVILLE MEDICAL CENTER (O, 18 beds) 42 Sixth Avenue SE, Mayville, ND Zip 58257–1598; tel. 701/786–3800; Roger Baier, Chief Executive Officer
Web address: www.unionhospital.com

SANFORD MEDICAL CENTER FARGO (O, 490 beds) 801 Broadway North, Fargo, ND Zip 58122–3641; tel. 701/234–2000; Nate White, Executive Vice President

SOUTH DAKOTA: COMMUNITY MEMORIAL HOSPITAL (C, 16 beds) 809 Jackson Street, Burke, SD Zip 57523–2065, P O Box 319, 57523–0319, tel. 605/775–2621; Mistie Sachtjen, Chief Executive Officer
Web address: www.sanfordhealth.org

PIONEER MEMORIAL HOSPITAL AND HEALTH SERVICES (C, 64 beds) 315 North Washington Street, Viborg, SD Zip 57070–2002, P O Box 368, 57070–0368, tel. 605/326–5161; Thomas V. Richter, Chief Executive Officer
Web address: www.pioneermemorial.org

SANFORD ABERDEEN MEDICAL CENTER (O, 48 beds) 2905 3rd Avenue SE, Aberdeen, SD Zip 57401–5420; tel. 605/626–4200; Ashley M. Erickson, Chief Executive Officer

SANFORD CANTON-INWOOD MEDICAL CENTER (O, 11 beds) 440 North Hiawatha Drive, Canton, SD Zip 57013–5800; tel. 605/764–1400; Scott C. Larson, Chief Executive Officer
Web address: www.sanfordcantoninwood.org

SANFORD CHAMBERLAIN MEDICAL CENTER (O, 69 beds) 300 South Byron Boulevard, Chamberlain, SD Zip 57325–9741; tel. 605/234–5511; Erica Peterson, Chief Executive Officer
Web address: www.sanfordchamberlain.org

SANFORD CLEAR LAKE MEDICAL CENTER (L, 10 beds) 701 Third Avenue South, Clear Lake, SD Zip 57226–2016; tel. 605/874–2141; Lori Sisk, R.N., Chief Executive Officer
Web address: www.sanforddeuelcounty.org

SANFORD USD MEDICAL CENTER (O, 500 beds) 1305 West 18th Street, Sioux Falls, SD Zip 57105–0496, P O Box 5039, 57117–5039, tel. 605/333–1000; Paul A. Hanson, FACHE, President

SANFORD VERMILLION MEDICAL CENTER (L, 114 beds) 20 South Plum Street, Vermillion, SD Zip 57069–3346; tel. 605/677–3500; Timothy J. Tracy, Chief Executive Officer
Web address: www.sanfordvermillion.org

SANFORD WEBSTER MEDICAL CENTER (L, 20 beds) 1401 West 1st Street, Webster, SD Zip 57274–1054, P O Box 489, 57274–0489, tel. 605/345–3336; Isaac Gerdes, Chief Executive Officer

WINNER REGIONAL HEALTHCARE CENTER (C, 104 beds) 745 East Eighth Street, Winner, SD Zip 57580–2631; tel. 605/842–7100; Kevin Coffey, Chief Executive Officer
Web address: www.winnerregional.org

Owned, leased, sponsored:	25 hospitals	2191 beds
Contract-managed:	10 hospitals	653 beds
Totals:	35 hospitals	2844 beds

★**5095: SCL HEALTH** (CC)
500 Eldorado Boulevard, Suite 100-D, Broomfield, CO Zip 80021; tel. 303/813–5180; Lydia Jumonville, Interim Chief Executive Officer
(Moderately Centralized Health System)

For explanation of codes following names, see page B2.
★ Indicates Type III membership in the American Hospital Association.

COLORADO: GOOD SAMARITAN MEDICAL CENTER (S, 207 beds) 200 Exempla Circle, Lafayette, CO Zip 80026–3370; tel. 303/689–4000; Jennifer Alderfer, President

LUTHERAN MEDICAL CENTER (S, 518 beds) 8300 West 38th Avenue, Wheat Ridge, CO Zip 80033–6005; tel. 303/425–4500; Grant Wicklund, President and Chief Executive Officer
Web address: https://www.sclhealth.org/locations/lutheran-medical-center/

PLATTE VALLEY MEDICAL CENTER (C, 70 beds) 1600 Prairie Center Parkway, Brighton, CO Zip 80601–4006; tel. 303/498–1600; John R. Hicks, President and Chief Executive Officer

SCL HEALTH COMMUNITY HOSPITAL - NORTHGLENN (O, 8 beds) 11900 Grant Street, Northglenn, CO Zip 80233; tel. 720/573–5095; Sean Stricker, Chief Executive Officer
Web address: www.sclhealthsystem.org

SAINT JOSEPH HOSPITAL (O, 374 beds) 1375 East 19th Avenue, Denver, CO Zip 80218–1126; tel. 303/837–7111; Jameson Smith, President

ST. MARY'S HOSPITAL AND MEDICAL CENTER (O, 311 beds) 2635 North 7th Street, Grand Junction, CO Zip 81501–8209, P O Box 1628, 81502–1628, tel. 970/298–2273; Brian Davidson, M.D., President and Chief Medical Officer
Web address: www.stmarygj.com

KANSAS: ST. FRANCIS HEALTH (O, 259 beds) 1700 SW 7th Street, Topeka, KS Zip 66606–1690; tel. 785/295–8000; David P. Setchel, President
Web address: www.stfrancistopeka.org

MONTANA: HOLY ROSARY HEALTHCARE (O, 90 beds) 2600 Wilson Street, Miles City, MT Zip 59301–5094; tel. 406/233–2600; Paul Lewis, Chief Executive Officer

ST. JAMES HEALTHCARE (O, 67 beds) 400 South Clark Street, Butte, MT Zip 59701–2328; tel. 406/723–2500; Jay Doyle, President and Chief Executive Officer
Web address: www.stjameshealthcare.org

ST. VINCENT HEALTHCARE (O, 221 beds) 1233 North 30th Street, Billings, MT Zip 59101–0165, P O Box 35200, 59107–5200, tel. 406/237–7000; Steve Loveless, President and Chief Executive Officer

Owned, leased, sponsored:	9 hospitals	2055 beds
Contract-managed:	1 hospitals	70 beds
Totals:	10 hospitals	2125 beds

★1505: SCRIPPS HEALTH (NP)
4275 Campus Point Court CP112, San Diego, CA Zip 92121–1513, 4275 Campus Point Court, 92121–1513, tel. 858/678–7200; Chris D. Van Gorder, FACHE, President and Chief Executive Officer
(Centralized Health System)

CALIFORNIA: SCRIPPS GREEN HOSPITAL (O, 173 beds) 10666 North Torrey Pines Road, La Jolla, CA Zip 92037–1093; tel. 858/455–9100; Robin Brown, Chief Executive, Senior Vice President
Web address: www.scrippshealth.org

SCRIPPS MEMORIAL HOSPITAL-ENCINITAS (O, 194 beds) 354 Santa Fe Drive, Encinitas, CA Zip 92024–5182, P O Box 230817, 92023–0817, tel. 760/633–6501; Carl J. Etter, Chief Executive and Senior Vice President

SCRIPPS MEMORIAL HOSPITAL-LA JOLLA (O, 277 beds) 9888 Genesee Avenue, La Jolla, CA Zip 92037–1200, P O Box 28, 92038–0028, tel. 858/626–4123; Gary G. Fybel, FACHE, Chief Executive, Senior Vice President
Web address: www.scripps.org/locations/hospitals__scripps-memorial-hospital-la-jolla

SCRIPPS MERCY HOSPITAL (O, 392 beds) 4077 Fifth Avenue, San Diego, CA Zip 92103–2105; tel. 619/294–8111; Thomas A. Gammiere, Chief Executive, Senior Vice President

Owned, leased, sponsored:	4 hospitals	1036 beds
Contract-managed:	0 hospitals	0 beds
Totals:	4 hospitals	1036 beds

★0181: SELECT MEDICAL CORPORATION (IO)
4714 Gettysburg Road, Mechanicsburg, PA Zip 17055–4325; tel. 717/972–1100; David S. Chernow, President and Chief Executive Officer
(Independent Hospital System)

ALABAMA: SELECT SPECIALTY HOSPITAL-BIRMINGHAM (O, 38 beds) 2010 Brookwood Medical Center Drive, 3rd Floor, Birmingham, AL Zip 35209–6804; tel. 205/599–4600; Andrea White, Chief Executive Officer
Web address: www.selectspecialtyhospitals.com/company/locations/birmingham.aspx

ARIZONA: HONORHEALTH REHABILITATION HOSPITAL (O, 50 beds) 8850 East Pima Center Parkway, Scottsdale, AZ Zip 85258–4619; tel. 480/800–3900; Scott R. Keen, Chief Executive Officer
Web address: www.scottsdale-rehab.com/

SELECT SPECIALTY HOSPITAL-PHOENIX DOWNTOWN (O, 33 beds) 1012 East Wiletta Street, 4th Floor, Phoenix, AZ Zip 85006; tel. 602/239–6134; Sharon Anthony, Market Administrator
Web address: www.selectmedicalcorp.com

SELECT SPECIALTY HOSPITAL-PHOENIX (O, 48 beds) 350 West Thomas Road, 3rd Floor Main, Phoenix, AZ Zip 85013–4409; tel. 602/406–6802; Sharon Anthony, Chief Executive Officer

ARKANSAS: REGENCY HOSPITAL OF NORTHWEST ARKANSAS - SPRINGDALE (O, 25 beds) 609 West Maple Avenue, 6th Fl, Springdale, AR Zip 72764; tel. 479/757–2600; Jerry Alexander, Chief Executive Officer
Web address: www.regencyhospital.com

SELECT SPECIALTY HOSPITAL-FORT SMITH (O, 34 beds) 1001 Towson Avenue, 6 Central, Fort Smith, AR Zip 72901–4921; tel. 479/441–3960; Cindy McLain, Chief Executive Officer
Web address: www.selectspecialtyhospitals.com/company/locations/fortsmith.aspx

CALIFORNIA: CALIFORNIA REHABILITATION INSTITUTE (O, 138 beds) 2070 Century Park East, Los Angeles, CA Zip 90067–1907; tel. 424/363–1000; John Behzad, Chief Executive Officer

DELAWARE: SELECT SPECIALTY HOSPITAL-WILMINGTON (O, 35 beds) 701 North Clayton Street, 5th Floor, Wilmington, DE Zip 19805–3948; tel. 302/421–4545; Donna Gares, R.N., FACHE, MSN, Chief Executive Officer
Web address: www.wilmington.selectspecialtyhospitals.com

FLORIDA: SELECT SPECIALTY HOSPITAL DAYTONA BEACH (O, 34 beds) 301 Memorial Medical Parkway, 11th Floor, Daytona Beach, FL Zip 32117–5167; tel. 386/231–3436; Adrianne Lutes, Chief Executive Officer
Web address: www.daytonabeach.selectspecialtyhospitals.com

SELECT SPECIALTY HOSPITAL-GAINESVILLE (O, 44 beds) 2708 SW Archer Road, Gainesville, FL Zip 32608–1316; tel. 352/337–3240; Ronnie Wagley, Market Chief Executive Officer

SELECT SPECIALTY HOSPITAL-MIAMI (O, 47 beds) 955 NW 3rd Street, Miami, FL Zip 33128–1274; tel. 305/416–5700; Dionisio Bencomo, Chief Executive Officer
Web address: www.selectspecialtyhospitals.com/company/locations/miami.aspx

SELECT SPECIALTY HOSPITAL-ORLANDO (O, 75 beds) 2250 Bedford Road, Orlando, FL Zip 32803–1443; tel. 407/303–7869; Theodore Mena, Chief Executive Officer
Web address: www.selectspecialtyhospitals.com/company/locations/orlando.aspx

SELECT SPECIALTY HOSPITAL-PALM BEACH (O, 60 beds) 3060 Melaleuca Lane, Lake Worth, FL Zip 33461–5174; tel. 561/357–7200; Larry Melby, Chief Executive Officer

SELECT SPECIALTY HOSPITAL-PANAMA CITY (O, 30 beds) 615 North Bonita Avenue, 3rd Floor, Panama City, FL Zip 32401–3623; tel. 850/767–3180; Randal S. Hamilton, Chief Executive Officer
Web address: www.selectspecialtyhospitals.com/company/locations/panamacity.aspx

SELECT SPECIALTY HOSPITAL-PENSACOLA (O, 75 beds) 7000 Cobble Creek Drive, Pensacola, FL Zip 32504–8638; tel. 850/473–4800; David Goodson, Chief Executive Officer
Web address: www.selectspecialtyhospitals.com/company/locations/pensacola.aspx

---

For explanation of codes following names, see page B2.
★ Indicates Type III membership in the American Hospital Association.

Section B

SELECT SPECIALTY HOSPITAL-TALLAHASSEE (O, 29 beds) 1554 Surgeons Drive, Tallahassee, FL Zip 32308–4631; tel. 850/219–6950; Jay W. Faherty, Chief Executive Officer

WEST GABLES REHABILITATION HOSPITAL (O, 60 beds) 2525 SW 75th Avenue, Miami, FL Zip 33155–2800; tel. 305/262–6800; Walter Concepcion, Chief Executive Officer
Web address: www.westgablesrehabhospital.com/

GEORGIA: REGENCY HOSPITAL OF CENTRAL GEORGIA (O, 60 beds) 535 Coliseum Drive, Macon, GA Zip 31217–0104; tel. 478/803–7300; Wayne Boutwell, Chief Executive Officer

REGENCY HOSPITAL OF SOUTH ATLANTA (O, 40 beds) 1170 Cleveland Avenue, 4th Floor, East Point, GA Zip 30344–3615; tel. 404/466–6250; Michelle Tenhengel-deVille, Chief Executive Officer
Web address: www.regencyhospital.com

SELECT SPECIALTY HOSPITAL - NORTHEAST ATLANTA (O, 18 beds) 1821 Clifton Road NE, 2nd Floor, Atlanta, GA Zip 30329–4021; tel. 404/728–6200; Jeffrey R. Fenn, Chief Executive Officer

SELECT SPECIALTY HOSPITAL MIDTOWN ATLANTA (O, 72 beds) 705 Juniper Street NE, Atlanta, GA Zip 30308–1307; tel. 404/873–2871; Jeffrey R. Fenn, Chief Executive Officer
Web address: www.selectspecialtyhospitals.com/

SELECT SPECIALTY HOSPITAL-ATLANTA (O, 30 beds) 550 Peachtree Street NE, Atlanta, GA Zip 30308–2247; tel. 404/815–0348; Michelle Tenhengel-deVille, Chief Executive Officer
Web address: www.selectspecialtyhospitals.com/company/locations/atlanta.aspx

SELECT SPECIALTY HOSPITAL-AUGUSTA (O, 80 beds) 1537 Walton Way, Augusta, GA Zip 30904–3764; tel. 706/731–1200; E. Rick Lowe, Chief Executive Officer

SELECT SPECIALTY HOSPITAL-SAVANNAH (O, 40 beds) 5353 Reynolds Street, 4 South, Savannah, GA Zip 31405–6015; tel. 912/819–7972; Greg Wuther, Chief Executive Officer
Web address: www.selectspecialtyhospitals.com/company/locations/savannah.aspx

INDIANA: REGENCY HOSPITAL OF NORTHWEST INDIANA (O, 61 beds) 4321 Fir Street, 4th Floor, East Chicago, IN Zip 46312–3049; tel. 219/392–7799; Eleyce Winn, Chief Executive Officer
Web address: www.regencyhospital.com/company/locations/indiana-northwest-indiana.aspx

SELECT SPECIALTY HOSPITAL-EVANSVILLE (O, 60 beds) 400 SE 4th Street, Evansville, IN Zip 47713–1206; tel. 812/421–2500; Scott A. Butler, Chief Executive Officer

IOWA: SELECT SPECIALTY HOSPITAL-DES MOINES (O, 30 beds) 1111 6th Avenue, 4th Floor Main, Des Moines, IA Zip 50314–2610; tel. 515/247–4400; Glen Griesheim, Chief Executive Officer
Web address: www.selectspecialtyhospitals.com

SELECT SPECIALTY HOSPITAL-QUAD CITIES (O, 50 beds) 1111 West Kimberly Road, Davenport, IA Zip 52806–5711; tel. 563/468–2000; Connie K. Siffring, Chief Executive Officer

KANSAS: SELECT SPECIALTY HOSPITAL-KANSAS CITY (O, 40 beds) 1731 North 90th Street, Kansas City, KS Zip 66112–1515; tel. 913/732–5900; Kevin J. Thorpe, Chief Executive Officer
Web address: www.selectspecialtyhospitals.com

SELECT SPECIALTY HOSPITAL-WICHITA (O, 48 beds) 929 North St Francis Street, Wichita, KS Zip 67214–3821; tel. 316/261–8303; Peggy Cliffe, Chief Executive Officer
Web address: www.selectspecialtyhospitals.com/company/locations/wichita.aspx

KENTUCKY: SELECT SPECIALTY HOSPITAL-LEXINGTON (O, 41 beds) 310 South Limestone Street, 3rd Floor, Lexington, KY Zip 40508–3008; tel. 859/226–7096; Kim Pennington, Chief Executive Officer
Web address: www.lexington.selectspecialtyhospitals.com/

SELECT SPECIALTY HOSPITAL-NORTHERN KENTUCKY (O, 33 beds) 85 North Grand Avenue, Fort Thomas, KY Zip 41075–1793; tel. 859/572–3880; Teresa R. Detano, M.P.H., Chief Executive Officer

MICHIGAN: GREAT LAKES SPECIALTY HOSPITAL-GRAND RAPIDS (O, 20 beds) 200 SE Jefferson Avenue, 5th Floor, Grand Rapids, MI Zip 49503–4502; tel. 616/965–8650; Jevne Conover, Chief Executive Officer
Web address: www.selectmedicalcorp.com

SELECT SPECIALTY HOSPITAL-ANN ARBOR (O, 36 beds) 5301 East Huron River Drive, 5th Floor, Ypsilanti, MI Zip 48197–1051; tel. 734/712–6751; Bryan Cutliff, Chief Executive Officer
Web address: www.annarbor.selectspecialtyhospitals.com/

SELECT SPECIALTY HOSPITAL-BATTLE CREEK (O, 25 beds) 300 North Avenue, Battle Creek, MI Zip 49017–3307; tel. 269/245–4675; Robert Mach, Chief Executive Officer

SELECT SPECIALTY HOSPITAL-DOWNRIVER (O, 35 beds) 2333 Biddle Avenue, 8th Floor, Wyandotte, MI Zip 48192–4668; tel. 734/246–5500; John Ponczocha, Chief Executive Officer
Web address: www.downriver.selectspecialtyhospitals.com/

SELECT SPECIALTY HOSPITAL-FLINT (O, 26 beds) 401 South Ballenger Highway, 5th Floor Central, Flint, MI Zip 48532–3638; tel. 810/342–4545; Christina DeBlouw, Chief Executive Officer

SELECT SPECIALTY HOSPITAL-GROSSE POINTE (O, 30 beds) 468 Cadieux Road, 3 North East, Grosse Pointe, MI Zip 48230–1507; tel. 313/473–6131; Zaahra Butt, Chief Executive Officer
Web address: www.grossepointe.selectspecialtyhospitals.com/

SELECT SPECIALTY HOSPITAL-MACOMB COUNTY (O, 36 beds) 215 North Avenue, Mount Clemens, MI Zip 48043–1700; tel. 586/307–9000; Jon P. O'Malley, Chief Executive Officer

SELECT SPECIALTY HOSPITAL-MUSKEGON (O, 31 beds) 1700 Clinton Street, 3 South, Muskegon, MI Zip 49442–5502; tel. 231/728–5811; Sharon Purkis, Administrator
Web address: www.greatlakesspecialtyhospital.com

SELECT SPECIALTY HOSPITAL-NORTHWEST DETROIT (O, 36 beds) 6071 West Outer Drive, Detroit, MI Zip 48235–2624; tel. 313/966–4747; Marilouise Riska, Chief Executive Officer

SELECT SPECIALTY HOSPITAL-PONTIAC (O, 30 beds) 44405 Woodward Avenue, 8th Floor, Pontiac, MI Zip 48341–5023; tel. 248/452–5252; Peggy Kingston, Chief Executive Officer
Web address: www.selectspecialtyhospitals.com/company/locations/pontiac.aspx

SELECT SPECIALTY HOSPITAL-SAGINAW (O, 32 beds) 1447 North Harrison Street, 8th Floor, Saginaw, MI Zip 48602–4785; tel. 989/583–4235; Matthew J. Campbell, Chief Executive Officer

MINNESOTA: REGENCY HOSPITAL OF MINNEAPOLIS (O, 92 beds) 1300 Hidden Lakes Parkway, Golden Valley, MN Zip 55422–4286; tel. 763/588–2750; Marshall E. Smith, Chief Executive Officer
Web address: www.regencyhospital.com

MISSISSIPPI: REGENCY HOSPITAL OF HATTIESBURG (O, 33 beds) 6051 U S Highway 49, 5th Floor, Hattiesburg, MS Zip 39401–6031; tel. 601/288–8510; William Heath, Chief Executive Officer

REGENCY HOSPITAL OF MERIDIAN (O, 40 beds) 1102 Constitution Avenue, 2nd Floor, Meridian, MS Zip 39301–4001; tel. 601/484–7900; Clifton Quinn, Chief Executive Officer
Web address: www.regencyhospital.com

SELECT SPECIALTY HOSPITAL - BELHAVEN (O, 25 beds) 1225 North State Street, Jackson, MS Zip 39202–2097, P O Box 23695, 39225–3695, tel. 601/968–1000; Robert Shannon. Canard, Chief Executive Officer

SELECT SPECIALTY HOSPITAL-GULFPORT (O, 61 beds) 1520 Broad Avenue, Suite 300, Gulfport, MS Zip 39501–3601; tel. 228/575–7500; John O'Keefe, Chief Executive Officer
Web address: www.selectspecialtyhospitals.com/company/locations/gulfcoast.aspx

SELECT SPECIALTY HOSPITAL-JACKSON (O, 53 beds) 5903 Ridgewood Road, Suite 100, Jackson, MS Zip 39211–3700; tel. 601/899–3800; Chandler Ewing, Chief Executive Officer
Web address: www.selectspecialtyhospitals.com/company/locations/jackson.aspx

MISSOURI: SSM SELECT REHABILITATION HOSPITAL (O, 95 beds) 1027 Bellevue Avenue, 3rd Floor, Richmond Heights, MO Zip 63117–1851, 1027 Bellevue Avenue, 63117–1851, tel. 314/768–5300; Robert Pritts, Chief Executive Officer

SELECT SPECIALTY HOSPITAL-SPRINGFIELD (O, 44 beds) 1630 East Primrose Street, Springfield, MO Zip 65804–7929; tel. 417/885–4700; Jeff Denney, Chief Executive Officer
Web address: www.selectspecialtyhospitals.com/company/locations/springfield.aspx

For explanation of codes following names, see page B2.
★ Indicates Type III membership in the American Hospital Association.

SELECT SPECIALTY HOSPITAL-ST. LOUIS (O, 33 beds) 300 First Capitol Drive, Unit 1, Saint Charles, MO Zip 63301–2844; tel. 636/947–5010; Jeff Denney, Chief Executive Officer

SELECT SPECIALTY HOSPITAL-WESTERN MISSOURI (O, 34 beds) 2316 East Meyer Boulevard, 3 West, Kansas City, MO Zip 64132–1136; tel. 816/276–3300; Kerry McLane, Interim Chief Executive Officer
Web address: www.westernmissouri.selectspecialtyhospitals.com/

NEBRASKA: SELECT SPECIALTY HOSPITAL - LINCOLN (O, 24 beds) 2300 South 16th Street, 7th Floor, Lincoln, NE Zip 68502–3704; tel. 402/483–8444; Scott Butterfield, Chief Executive Officer

SELECT SPECIALTY HOSPITAL-OMAHA (O, 52 beds) 1870 South 75th Street, Omaha, NE Zip 68124–1700; tel. 402/361–5700; Darrell Jones, Interim Chief Executive Officer
Web address: www.https://omaha.selectspecialtyhospitals.com

NEW JERSEY: KESSLER INSTITUTE FOR REHABILITATION (O, 336 beds) 1199 Pleasant Valley Way, West Orange, NJ Zip 07052–1424; tel. 973/731–3600; Sue Kida, President
Web address: www.kessler-rehab.com

KESSLER MARLTON REHABILITATION (O, 61 beds) 92 Brick Road, Marlton, NJ Zip 08053–2177; tel. 856/988–8778; Phyllis J. Schlichtmann, Chief Executive Officer

SELECT SPECIALTY HOSPITAL-NORTHEAST NEW JERSEY (O, 62 beds) 96 Parkway, Rochelle Park, NJ Zip 07662–4200; tel. 201/221–2352; Mary Beth. Ray-Simone, Chief Executive Officer
Web address: www.northeastnewjersey.selectspecialtyhospitals.com/about/

NORTH CAROLINA: SELECT SPECIALTY HOSPITAL-DURHAM (O, 30 beds) 3643 North Roxboro Road, 6th Floor, Durham, NC Zip 27704–2702; tel. 919/470–9159; Jennifer Rawley, PharmD, Chief Executive Officer

SELECT SPECIALTY HOSPITAL-GREENSBORO (O, 30 beds) 1200 North Elm Street, 5th Floor, Greensboro, NC Zip 27401–1004; tel. 336/832–8571; Deana Knight, Chief Executive Officer
Web address: www.selectspecialtyhospitals.com/company/locations/greensboro.aspx

OHIO: CLEVELAND CLINIC REHABILITATION HOSPITAL (O, 60 beds) 33355 Health Campus Boulevard, Avon, OH Zip 44011; tel. 440/937–9099; Sam Bayoumy, Chief Executive Officer

OHIOHEALTH REHABILITATION HOSPITAL (O, 44 beds) 1087 Dennison Avenue, 4th Floor, Columbus, OH Zip 43201–3201; tel. 614/484–9600; Eric Yap, Chief Executive Officer
Web address: www.ohiohealth-rehab.com

REGENCY HOSPITAL CLEVELAND EAST (O, 87 beds) 4200 Interchange Corporate Center Road, Warrensville Heights, OH Zip 44128–5631; tel. 216/910–3800; Thomas Knoske, Chief Executive Officer

REGENCY HOSPITAL OF COLUMBUS (O, 66 beds) 1430 South High Street, Columbus, OH Zip 43207–1045; tel. 614/456–0300; Kindra Marks, Chief Executive Officer
Web address: www.regencyhospital.com/

REGENCY HOSPITAL OF TOLEDO (O, 45 beds) 5220 Alexis Road, Sylvania, OH Zip 43560–2504; tel. 419/318–5700; Gary Zaciewski, Chief Executive Officer
Web address: www.regencyhospital.com

SELECT SPECIALTY HOSPITAL - BOARDMAN (O, 24 beds) 8401 Market Street, 7 South, Boardman, OH Zip 44512–6725; tel. 330/729–1750; Varun Chauhan, Chief Executive Officer
Web address: www.selectspecialtyhospitals.com/

SELECT SPECIALTY HOSPITAL - CINCINNATI NORTH (O, 41 beds) 10500 Montgomery Road, Cincinnati, OH Zip 45242–4402; tel. 513/865–5300; Susan Glenn, Chief Executive Officer

SELECT SPECIALTY HOSPITAL - CLEVELAND GATEWAY (O, 143 beds) 2351 East 22nd Street, 7th Floor, Cleveland, OH Zip 44115–3111; tel. 216/363–2671; Cheryl G. Gentry, Interim Chief Executive Officer
Web address: www.selectspecialtyhospitals.com/

SELECT SPECIALTY HOSPITAL OF SOUTHEAST OHIO (O, 35 beds) 2000 Tamarack Road, Newark, OH Zip 43055; tel. 740/588–7888; Linda Supplee, Chief Executive Officer
Web address: www.selectspecialtyhospitals.com/company/locations/zanesville.aspx

SELECT SPECIALTY HOSPITAL-AKRON (O, 60 beds) 200 East Market Street, Akron, OH Zip 44308–2015; tel. 330/761–7500; Sonda Burns, Chief Executive Officer
Web address: www.selectspecialtyhospitals.com/company/locations/akron.aspx

SELECT SPECIALTY HOSPITAL-CANTON (O, 30 beds) 1320 Mercy Drive NW, 6th Floor, Canton, OH Zip 44708–2614; tel. 330/489–8189; Dawne Wheeler, Chief Executive Officer
Web address: www.selectspecialtyhospitals.com/company/locations/canton.aspx

SELECT SPECIALTY HOSPITAL-CINCINNATI (O, 36 beds) 375 Dixmyth Avenue, 15th Floor, Cincinnati, OH Zip 45220–2475; tel. 513/862–4444; David D. Muggli, FACHE, Chief Executive Officer

SELECT SPECIALTY HOSPITAL-COLUMBUS (O, 186 beds) 1087 Dennison Avenue, Columbus, OH Zip 43201–3201; tel. 614/458–9000; Lisa J. Pettrey, MSN, R.N., Chief Executive Officer
Web address: www.selectspecialtyhospitals.com/company/locations/columbus.aspx

SELECT SPECIALTY HOSPITAL-YOUNGSTOWN (O, 56 beds) 1044 Belmont Avenue, Youngstown, OH Zip 44504–1006; tel. 330/480–2349; Jodi Costello, Chief Executive Officer

TRIHEALTH REHABILITATION HOSPITAL (O, 60 beds) 2155 Dana Avenue, Cincinnati, OH Zip 45207; tel. 513/601–0600; Mark Asnen, Chief Executive Officer
Web address: www.trihealthrehab.com

OKLAHOMA: SELECT SPECIALTY HOSPITAL-OKLAHOMA CITY (O, 72 beds) 3524 NW 56th Street, Oklahoma City, OK Zip 73112–4518; tel. 405/606–6700; Connie Strickland, Chief Executive Officer
Web address: www.https://oklahomacity.selectspecialtyhospitals.com/

SELECT SPECIALTY HOSPITAL-TULSA MIDTOWN (O, 56 beds) 1125 South Trenton Avenue, 3rd Floor, Tulsa, OK Zip 74120–5418; tel. 918/579–7300; Raymond Carnevale, Interim Chief Executive Officer

PENNSYLVANIA: HELEN M. SIMPSON REHABILITATION HOSPITAL (C, 55 beds) 4300 Londonderry Road, Harrisburg, PA Zip 17109–5317; tel. 717/920–4300; Mark Freeburn, Chief Executive Officer
Web address: www.simpson-rehab.com/

PENN STATE HERSHEY REHABILITATION HOSPITAL (O, 76 beds) 1135 Old West Chocolate Avenue, Hummelstown, PA Zip 17036; tel. 717/832–2600; Michelle Von Arx, Chief Executive Officer

SELECT SPECIALTY HOSPITAL-CENTRAL PENNSYLVANIA (O, 92 beds) 503 North 21st Street, 5th Floor, Camp Hill, PA Zip 17011–2204; tel. 717/972–4575; John E. Simodejka, Chief Executive Officer
Web address: www.camphill.selectspecialtyhospitals.com/

SELECT SPECIALTY HOSPITAL-DANVILLE (O, 30 beds) 100 North Academy Avenue, 3rd Floor, Danville, PA Zip 17822–3050; tel. 570/214–9653; Brian Mann, Chief Executive Officer

SELECT SPECIALTY HOSPITAL-ERIE (O, 50 beds) 252 West 11th Street, Erie, PA Zip 16501–1702; tel. 814/874–5300; Thomas Fucci, FACHE, Chief Executive Officer
Web address: www.erie.selectspecialtyhospitals.com/

SELECT SPECIALTY HOSPITAL-JOHNSTOWN (O, 39 beds) 320 Main Street, 3rd Floor, Johnstown, PA Zip 15901–1601; tel. 814/534–7300; Kelly Blake, Chief Executive Officer
Web address: www.selectspecialtyhospitals.com/company/locations/johnstown.aspx

SELECT SPECIALTY HOSPITAL-LAUREL HIGHLANDS (O, 40 beds) One Mellon Way, 3rd Floor, Latrobe, PA Zip 15650–1197; tel. 724/539–3870; Lauren Donahoe, Chief Executive Officer

SELECT SPECIALTY HOSPITAL-MCKEESPORT (O, 30 beds) 1500 Fifth Avenue, 6th Floor, McKeesport, PA Zip 15132–2422; tel. 412/664–2900; Angela Merryman, Chief Executive Officer
Web address: www.mckeesport.selectspecialtyhospitals.com/

SELECT SPECIALTY HOSPITAL-PITTSBURGH/UPMC (O, 32 beds) 200 Lothrop Street, E824, Pittsburgh, PA Zip 15213–2536; tel. 412/586–9800; Yvonne Kughn, Chief Executive Officer
Web address: www.pittsburghupmc.selectspecialtyhospitals.com/

For explanation of codes following names, see page B2.
★ Indicates Type III membership in the American Hospital Association.

SOUTH CAROLINA: REGENCY HOSPITAL OF FLORENCE (O, 40 beds) 121 East Cedar Street, 4th Floor, Florence, SC Zip 29506–2576; tel. 843/661–3471; Amy Metz, Chief Executive Officer
Web address: www.regencyhospital.com

REGENCY HOSPITAL OF GREENVILLE (O, 32 beds) One St Francis Drive, 4th Floor, Greenville, SC Zip 29601–3955; tel. 864/255–1438; Paige Beauregard, Chief Executive Officer

SOUTH DAKOTA: SELECT SPECIALTY HOSPITAL-SIOUX FALLS (O, 24 beds) 1305 West 18th Street, Sioux Falls, SD Zip 57105–0401; tel. 605/312–9500; Carol Ulmer, Chief Executive Officer
Web address: www.selectspecialtyhospitals.com/company/locations/siouxfalls.aspx

TENNESSEE: SELECT SPECIALTY HOSPITAL-KNOXVILLE (O, 35 beds) 1901 Clinch Avenue, 4th Floor North, Knoxville, TN Zip 37916–2307; tel. 865/541–2615; Rita Wilder, Chief Executive Officer

SELECT SPECIALTY HOSPITAL-MEMPHIS (O, 39 beds) 5959 Park Avenue, 12th Floor, Memphis, TN Zip 38119–5200; tel. 901/765–1245; Marcia Taylor, Chief Executive Officer
Web address: www.selectspecialtyhospitals.com/company/locations/memphis.aspx

SELECT SPECIALTY HOSPITAL-NASHVILLE (O, 70 beds) 2000 Hayes Street, Nashville, TN Zip 37203–2318; tel. 615/284–4599; Jennifer Causey, Chief Executive Officer

SELECT SPECIALTY HOSPITAL-NORTH KNOXVILLE (O, 33 beds) 7557B Dannaher Drive, Suite 145, Powell, TN Zip 37849–3568; tel. 865/512–2450; Steve Plumlee, Chief Executive Officer
Web address: www.northknoxville.selectspecialtyhospitals.com/

SELECT SPECIALTY HOSPITAL-TRI CITIES (O, 33 beds) One Medical Park Boulevard, 5th Floor, Bristol, TN Zip 37620–8964; tel. 423/844–5900; Jeffrey Radford, Chief Executive Officer

TEXAS: BAYLOR INSTITUTE FOR REHABILITATION AT FORT WORTH (C, 42 beds) 6601 Harris Parkway, Fort Worth, TX Zip 76132–6108, Victoria Odom. Sanders, FACHE, Chief Executive Officer
Web address: www.baylorhealth.com/PhysiciansLocations/BIR/Pages/Default.aspx

BAYLOR INSTITUTE FOR REHABILITATION AT FRISCO (O, 44 beds) 2990 Legacy Drive, Frisco, TX Zip 75034–6066; tel. 469/888–5100; Ryan Seymour, Chief Executive Officer

SELECT REHABILITATION HOSPITAL OF DENTON (O, 44 beds) 2620 Scripture Street, Denton, TX Zip 76201–4315; tel. 940/297–6500; Michelle Powell, Chief Executive Officer
Web address: www.selectrehab-denton.com/

SELECT REHABILITATION HOSPITAL OF SAN ANTONIO (O, 42 beds) 19126 Stonehue Road, San Antonio, TX Zip 78258–3490; tel. 210/482–3400; Robert Ward, Chief Executive Officer

SELECT SPECIALTY HOSPITAL - DALLAS DOWNTOWN (O, 46 beds) 3500 Gaston Avenue, Floors 3&4 Jonsson, Dallas, TX Zip 75246–2017; tel. 469/801–4500; Melody Nagel, Chief Executive Officer
Web address: www.dallasdowntown.selectspecialtyhospitals.com/

SELECT SPECIALTY HOSPITAL - DALLAS GARLAND (O, 40 beds) 2300 Marie Curie Drive, Floors 3E and 3W, Garland, TX Zip 75042–5706; tel. 469/440–5800; Kent R. Helwig, Chief Executive Officer

SELECT SPECIALTY HOSPITAL-DALLAS (O, 60 beds) 2329 West Parker Road, Carrollton, TX Zip 75010–4713; Ty Burgess, Chief Executive Officer
Web address: www.firsttexashospital.com/

SELECT SPECIALTY HOSPITAL-LONGVIEW (O, 32 beds) 700 East Marshall Avenue, 1st Floor, Longview, TX Zip 75601–5580; tel. 903/315–1100; Andrew Meade, Chief Executive Officer
Web address: www.longview.selectspecialtyhospitals.com/

WEST VIRGINIA: SELECT SPECIALTY HOSPITAL-CHARLESTON (O, 32 beds) 333 Laidley Street, 3rd Floor East, Charleston, WV Zip 25301–1614; tel. 304/720–7234; Frank Weber, Chief Executive Officer
Web address: www.selectspecialtyhospitals.com/company/locations/charleston.aspx

WISCONSIN: SELECT SPECIALTY HOSPITAL-MADISON (O, 52 beds) 801 Braxton Place, Madison, WI Zip 53715–1415; tel. 608/260–2700; David Ross, Chief Executive Officer

SELECT SPECIALTY HOSPITAL-MILWAUKEE (O, 34 beds) 8901 West Lincoln Avenue, 2nd Floor, Milwaukee, WI Zip 53227–2409, West Allis, tel. 414/328–7700; Mary Kay. Diderrich, R.N., Chief Executive Officer
Web address: www.selectspecialtyhospitals.com/company/locations/milwaukee.aspx

Owned, leased, sponsored:	103 hospitals	5222 beds
Contract-managed:	2 hospitals	97 beds
Totals:	105 hospitals	5319 beds

★**2565: SENTARA HEALTHCARE** (NP)
6015 Poplar Hall Drive, Norfolk, VA Zip 23502–3819; tel. 757/455–7000; Howard P. Kern, Chief Executive Officer
(Centralized Physician/Insurance Health System)

NORTH CAROLINA: SENTARA ALBEMARLE MEDICAL CENTER (L, 83 beds) 1144 North Road Street, Elizabeth City, NC Zip 27909–3473, P O Box 1587, 27906–1587, tel. 252/335–0531; Coleen F. Santa Ana, President

VIRGINIA: MARTHA JEFFERSON HOSPITAL (O, 144 beds) 500 Martha Jefferson Drive, Charlottesville, VA Zip 22911–4668; tel. 434/654–7000; Jonathan S. Davis, FACHE, President
Web address: www.marthajefferson.org

SENTARA CAREPLEX HOSPITAL (O, 162 beds) 3000 Coliseum Drive, Hampton, VA Zip 23666–5963; tel. 757/736–1000; Debra A. Flores, R.N., MS, President and Administrator

SENTARA HALIFAX REGIONAL HOSPITAL (O, 456 beds) 2204 Wilborn Avenue, South Boston, VA Zip 24592–1638; tel. 434/517–3100; Chris A. Lumsden, Chief Executive Officer
Web address: www.hrhs.org

SENTARA LEIGH HOSPITAL (O, 250 beds) 830 Kempsville Road, Norfolk, VA Zip 23502–3920; tel. 757/261–6000; Joanne Inman, Administrator
Web address: www.sentara.com

SENTARA NORFOLK GENERAL HOSPITAL (O, 495 beds) 600 Gresham Drive, Norfolk, VA Zip 23507–1904; tel. 757/388–3000; Kurt T. Hofelich, President
Web address: www.sentara.com

SENTARA NORTHERN VIRGINIA MEDICAL CENTER (O, 181 beds) 2300 Opitz Boulevard, Woodbridge, VA Zip 22191–3399; tel. 703/523–1000; Katherine Johnson, Ph.D., President

SENTARA OBICI HOSPITAL (O, 176 beds) 2800 Godwin Boulevard, Suffolk, VA Zip 23434–8038; tel. 757/934–4000; Steve Julian, M.D., President
Web address: www.sentara.com

SENTARA PRINCESS ANNE HOSPITAL (O, 160 beds) 2025 Glenn Mitchell Drive, Virginia Beach, VA Zip 23456–0178; tel. 757/507–1000; Thomas B. Thames, M.D., President
Web address: www.sentara.com

SENTARA RMH MEDICAL CENTER (O, 244 beds) 2010 Health Campus Drive, Harrisonburg, VA Zip 22801–3293; tel. 540/689–1000; Douglas J. Moyer, President

SENTARA VIRGINIA BEACH GENERAL HOSPITAL (O, 259 beds) 1060 First Colonial Road, Virginia Beach, VA Zip 23454–3002; tel. 757/395–8000; Elwood Bernard. Boone III, FACHE, President
Web address: www.sentara.com

SENTARA WILLIAMSBURG REGIONAL MEDICAL CENTER (O, 145 beds) 100 Sentara Circle, Williamsburg, VA Zip 23188–5713; tel. 757/984–6000; David J. Masterson, President

Owned, leased, sponsored:	12 hospitals	2755 beds
Contract-managed:	0 hospitals	0 beds
Totals:	12 hospitals	2755 beds

★**2065: SHARP HEALTHCARE** (NP)
8695 Spectrum Center Boulevard, San Diego, CA Zip 92123–1489; tel. 858/499–4000; Michael Murphy, CPA, President & Chief Executive Officer
(Centralized Health System)

For explanation of codes following names, see page B2.
★ Indicates Type III membership in the American Hospital Association.

CALIFORNIA: SHARP CHULA VISTA MEDICAL CENTER (O, 343 beds) 751 Medical Center Court, Chula Vista, CA Zip 91911–6699, P O Box 1297, 91912–1297, tel. 619/502–5800; Pablo Velez, Chief Executive Officer
Web address: www.sharp.com

SHARP CORONADO HOSPITAL AND HEALTHCARE CENTER (L, 181 beds) 250 Prospect Place, Coronado, CA Zip 92118–1999; tel. 619/522–3600; Susan Stone, R.N., Ph.D., Senior Vice President and Chief Executive Officer
Web address: www.sharp.com

SHARP GROSSMONT HOSPITAL (L, 509 beds) 5555 Grossmont Center Drive, La Mesa, CA Zip 91942–3019, 10992 San Diego Mission Road, Ste 2400, San Diego, 92108, tel. 619/740–6000; Scott Evans, PharmD, FACHE, Senior Vice President and Chief Executive Officer

SHARP MEMORIAL HOSPITAL (O, 437 beds) 7901 Frost Street, San Diego, CA Zip 92123–2701; tel. 858/939–3400; Tim Smith, Senior Vice President and Chief Executive Officer
Web address: www.sharp.com

SHARP MESA VISTA HOSPITAL (O, 172 beds) 7850 Vista Hill Avenue, San Diego, CA Zip 92123–2717; tel. 858/278–4110; Trisha Khaleghi, Senior Vice President and Chief Executive Officer
Web address: www.sharp.com

Owned, leased, sponsored:	5 hospitals	1642 beds
Contract-managed:	0 hospitals	0 beds
Totals:	5 hospitals	1642 beds

4125: SHRINERS HOSPITALS FOR CHILDREN (NP)
2900 Rocky Point Drive, Tampa, FL Zip 33607–1435, P O Box 31356, 33631–3356, tel. 813/281–0300; John P. McCabe, Executive Vice President
(Independent Hospital System)

CALIFORNIA: SHRINERS HOSPITALS FOR CHILDREN-NORTHERN CALIFORNIA (O, 70 beds) 2425 Stockton Boulevard, Sacramento, CA Zip 95817–2215; tel. 916/453–2000; Margaret Bryan, Administrator
Web address: www.shrinershospitalsforchildren.org/Hospitals/Locations/NorthernCalifornia.aspx

FLORIDA: SHRINERS HOSPITALS FOR CHILDREN-TAMPA (O, 60 beds) 12502 USF Pine Drive, Tampa, FL Zip 33612–9499; tel. 813/972–2250; Fleury Yelvington, Administrator

HAWAII: SHRINERS HOSPITALS FOR CHILDREN-HONOLULU (O, 16 beds) 1310 Punahou Street, Honolulu, HI Zip 96826–1099; tel. 808/941–4466; John R. White, Administrator
Web address: www.shrinershospitalsforchildren.org/Hospitals/Locations/Honolulu.aspx

ILLINOIS: SHRINERS HOSPITALS FOR CHILDREN-CHICAGO (O, 36 beds) 2211 North Oak Park Avenue, Chicago, IL Zip 60707–3392; tel. 773/622–5400; Mark L. Niederpruem, FACHE, Administrator
Web address: www.shrinershospitalsforchildren.org/Hospitals/Locations/Chicago.aspx

KENTUCKY: SHRINERS HOSPITALS FOR CHILDREN-LEXINGTON (O, 50 beds) 1900 Richmond Road, Lexington, KY Zip 40502–1298; tel. 859/266–2101; Tony Lewgood, Administrator
Web address: www.shrinershospitalsforchildren.org/Hospitals/Locations/Lexington.aspx

LOUISIANA: SHRINERS HOSPITALS FOR CHILDREN-SHREVEPORT (O, 45 beds) 3100 Samford Avenue, Shreveport, LA Zip 71103–4289; tel. 318/222–5704; Garry Kim. Green, FACHE, Administrator
Web address: www.shrinershospitalsforchildren.org/Hospitals/Locations/Shreveport.aspx

MASSACHUSETTS: SHRINERS HOSPITALS FOR CHILDREN-BOSTON (O, 14 beds) 51 Blossom Street, Boston, MA Zip 02114–2601; tel. 617/722–3000; John Patrick. ONeill, Administrator

SHRINERS HOSPITALS FOR CHILDREN-SPRINGFIELD (O, 10 beds) 516 Carew Street, Springfield, MA Zip 01104–2396; tel. 413/787–2000; H Lee. Kirk Jr, FACHE, Administrator
Web address: www.shrinershospitalsforchildren.org/Hospitals/Locations/Springfield.aspx

MINNESOTA: SHRINERS HOSPITALS FOR CHILDREN-TWIN CITIES (O, 40 beds) 2025 East River Parkway, Minneapolis, MN Zip 55414–3696; tel. 612/596–6100; Charles C. Lobeck, Administrator

MISSOURI: SHRINERS HOSPITALS FOR CHILDREN-ST. LOUIS (O, 12 beds) 4400 Clayton Avenue, Saint Louis, MO Zip 63110–1624; tel. 314/432–3600; John Gloss, FACHE, Administrator
Web address: www.shrinershospitalsforchildren.org/Hospitals/Locations/Stlouis.aspx

OHIO: SHRINERS HOSPITALS FOR CHILDREN-CINCNNATI (O, 30 beds) 3229 Burnet Avenue, Cincinnati, OH Zip 45229–3095; tel. 513/872–6000; Mark D. Shugarman, Administrator

OREGON: SHRINERS HOSPITALS FOR CHILDREN-PORTLAND (O, 12 beds) 3101 SW Sam Jackson Park Road, Portland, OR Zip 97239–3009; tel. 503/241–5090; J Craig. Patchin, Administrator
Web address: www.shrinershospitalsforchildren.org/Hospitals/Locations/Portland.aspx

PENNSYLVANIA: SHRINERS HOSPITALS FOR CHILDREN-PHILADELPHIA (O, 39 beds) 3551 North Broad Street, Philadelphia, PA Zip 19140–4160; tel. 215/430–4000; Ed Myers, Administrator
Web address: www.shrinershospitalsforchildren.org/Hospitals/Locations/Philadelphia.aspx

SOUTH CAROLINA: SHRINERS HOSPITALS FOR CHILDREN-GREENVILLE (O, 15 beds) 950 West Faris Road, Greenville, SC Zip 29605–4277; tel. 864/271–3444; Randall R. Romberger, Administrator

TEXAS: SHRINERS HOSPITALS FOR CHILDREN-GALVESTON (O, 15 beds) 815 Market Street, Galveston, TX Zip 77550–2725; tel. 409/770–6600; Mary Jaco, Administrator
Web address: www.shrinershospitalsforchildren.org/Hospitals/Locations/Galveston.aspx

SHRINERS HOSPITALS FOR CHILDREN-HOUSTON (O, 40 beds) 6977 Main Street, Houston, TX Zip 77030–3701; tel. 713/797–1616; Cathy Moniaci, R.N., MS, Administrator

UTAH: SHRINERS HOSPITALS FOR CHILDREN-SALT LAKE CITY (O, 18 beds) 1275 East Fairfax Road, Salt Lake City, UT Zip 84103–4399; tel. 801/536–3500; Kevin Martin, M.P.H., R.N., FACHE, Administrator
Web address: www.shrinershospitalsforchildren.org/Hospitals/Locations/SaltLakeCity.aspx

WASHINGTON: SHRINERS HOSPITALS FOR CHILDREN-SPOKANE (O, 30 beds) 911 West Fifth Avenue, Spokane, WA Zip 99204–2901, P O Box 2472, 99210–2472, tel. 509/455–7844; Peter G. Brewer, Administrator
Web address: www.shrinershospitalsforchildren.org/Hospitals/Locations/Spokane.aspx

Owned, leased, sponsored:	18 hospitals	552 beds
Contract-managed:	0 hospitals	0 beds
Totals:	18 hospitals	552 beds

0360: SIGNATURE HEALTHCARE SERVICES (IO)
4238 Green River Road, Corona, CA Zip 92880–1669; tel. 951/549–8032; Soon K. Kim, M.D., President and Chief Executive Officer
(Independent Hospital System)

ARIZONA: AURORA BEHAVIORAL HEALTH SYSTEM EAST (O, 70 beds) 6350 South Maple Street, Tempe, AZ Zip 85283–2857; tel. 480/345–5400; Bruce Waldo, Chief Executive Officer

AURORA BEHAVIORAL HEALTH SYSTEM WEST (O, 90 beds) 6015 West Peoria Avenue, Glendale, AZ Zip 85302–1213; tel. 623/344–4400; Bruce Waldo, Chief Executive Officer
Web address: www.aurorabehavioral.com

CALIFORNIA: AURORA BEHAVIORAL HEALTHCARE SAN DIEGO (O, 80 beds) 11878 Avenue of Industry, San Diego, CA Zip 92128–3490; tel. 858/487–3200; Alain Azcona, Chief Executive Officer
Web address: www.sandiego.aurorabehavioral.com/

AURORA CHARTER OAK HOSPITAL (O, 146 beds) 1161 East Covina Boulevard, Covina, CA Zip 91724–1599; tel. 626/966–1632; Todd A. Smith, Chief Executive Officer

---

For explanation of codes following names, see page B2.
★ Indicates Type III membership in the American Hospital Association.

LAS ENCINAS HOSPITAL (O, 138 beds) 2900 East Del Mar Boulevard, Pasadena, CA Zip 91107–4399; tel. 626/795–9901; Thomas J. Mahle, Chief Executive Officer
Web address: www.lasencinashospital.com

VISTA DEL MAR HOSPITAL (O, 87 beds) 801 Seneca Street, Ventura, CA Zip 93001–1411; tel. 805/653–6434; Mayla Krebsbach, Chief Executive Officer

ILLINOIS: CHICAGO LAKESHORE HOSPITAL (O, 115 beds) 4840 North Marine Drive, Chicago, IL Zip 60640–4296; tel. 773/878–9700; Patrick Moalleman, Chief Executive Officer
Web address: www.chicagolakeshorehospital.com

NEVADA: DESERT PARKWAY BEHAVIORAL HEALTHCARE HOSPITAL (O, 83 beds) 3247 South Maryland Parkway, Las Vegas, NV Zip 89109–2412; tel. 702/776–3500; Steve Shell, Chief Executive Officer

TEXAS: DALLAS BEHAVIORAL HEALTHCARE HOSPITAL (O, 116 beds) 800 Kirnwood Drive, Desoto, TX Zip 75115–2000; tel. 855/982–0897; Selene Q. Hammon, Chief Executive Officer
Web address: www.dallasbehavioral.com

GEORGETOWN BEHAVIORAL HEALTH INSTITUTE (O, 118 beds) 3101 South Austin Avenue, Georgetown, TX Zip 78626–7541; tel. 512/819–1100; Joseph R. Rodriguez, Chief Executive Officer

HOUSTON BEHAVIORAL HEALTHCARE HOSPITAL (O, 25 beds) 2801 Gessner Road, Houston, TX Zip 77080–2503; tel. 832/834–7710; Roy Hollis, Chief Executive Officer
Web address: www.houstonbehavioralhealth.com/

SAN ANTONIO BEHAVIORAL HEALTHCARE HOSPITAL (O, 108 beds) 8550 Huebner Road, San Antonio, TX Zip 78240–1803; tel. 877/514–0010; Kirk Kureska, Chief Executive Officer

Owned, leased, sponsored:	12 hospitals	1176 beds
Contract-managed:	0 hospitals	0 beds
Totals:	12 hospitals	1176 beds

★**0284:   SINAI HEALTH SYSTEM** (NP)
1500 South California Avenue, Chicago, IL Zip 60608–1729; tel. 773/542–2000; Karen Teitelbaum, President and Chief Executive Officer
(Independent Hospital System)

ILLINOIS: HOLY CROSS HOSPITAL (O, 213 beds) 2701 West 68th Street, Chicago, IL Zip 60629–1882; tel. 773/884–9000; Lori Pacura, MSN, R.N., President
Web address: www.holycrosshospital.org

MOUNT SINAI HOSPITAL (O, 288 beds) 1500 South Fairfield Avenue, Chicago, IL Zip 60608–1729; tel. 773/542–2000; Loren Chandler, President
Web address: www.sinai.org

SCHWAB REHABILITATION HOSPITAL (O, 83 beds) 1401 South California Avenue, Chicago, IL Zip 60608–1858; tel. 773/522–2010; Karen Teitelbaum, Chief Executive Officer

Owned, leased, sponsored:	3 hospitals	584 beds
Contract-managed:	0 hospitals	0 beds
Totals:	3 hospitals	584 beds

5125:   SISTERS OF CHARITY HEALTH SYSTEM (CC)
2475 East 22nd Street, Cleveland, OH Zip 44115–3221; tel. 216/363–2797; Thomas J. Strauss, Chief Executive Officer
(Moderately Centralized Health System)

OHIO: MERCY MEDICAL CENTER (O, 329 beds) 1320 Mercy Drive NW, Canton, OH Zip 44708–2641; tel. 330/489–1000; Paul C. Hiltz, FACHE, Interim Chief Executive Officer
Web address: www.cantonmercy.org

ST. VINCENT CHARITY MEDICAL CENTER (O, 208 beds) 2351 East 22nd Street, Cleveland, OH Zip 44115–3111; tel. 216/861–6200; David F. Perse, M.D., President and Chief Executive Officer

Owned, leased, sponsored:	2 hospitals	537 beds
Contract-managed:	0 hospitals	0 beds
Totals:	2 hospitals	537 beds

5805:   SISTERS OF MARY OF THE PRESENTATION HEALTH SYSTEM (CC)
1202 Page Drive SW, Fargo, ND Zip 58103–2340, P O Box 10007, 58106–0007, tel. 701/237–9290; Aaron K. Alton, President and Chief Executive Officer
(Independent Hospital System)

ILLINOIS: ST. MARGARET'S HOSPITAL (O, 54 beds) 600 East First Street, Spring Valley, IL Zip 61362–1512; tel. 815/664–5311; Tim Muntz, President and Chief Executive Officer
Web address: www.aboutsmh.org

NORTH DAKOTA: PRESENTATION MEDICAL CENTER (O, 25 beds) 213 Second Avenue NE, Rolla, ND Zip 58367–7153, P O Box 759, 58367–0759, tel. 701/477–3161; Mark Kerr, Chief Executive Officer
Web address: www.pmc-rolla.com

ST. ALOISIUS MEDICAL CENTER (O, 120 beds) 325 East Brewster Street, Harvey, ND Zip 58341–1653; tel. 701/324–4651; Mike Zwicker, Chief Executive Officer

ST. ANDREW'S HEALTH CENTER (O, 25 beds) 316 Ohmer Street, Bottineau, ND Zip 58318–1045; tel. 701/228–9300; Jodi Atkinson, President and Chief Executive Officer
Web address: www.standrewshealth.com

Owned, leased, sponsored:	4 hospitals	224 beds
Contract-managed:	0 hospitals	0 beds
Totals:	4 hospitals	224 beds

0997:   SKAGIT REGIONAL HEALTH (NP)
1415 E Kincaid Street, Mount Vernon, WA Zip 98274–4126; tel. 360/424–4111; Gregg Agustin. Davidson, FACHE, President and Chief Executive Officer
(Independent Hospital System)

WASHINGTON: CASCADE VALLEY HOSPITAL AND CLINICS (L, 48 beds) 330 South Stillaguamish Avenue, Arlington, WA Zip 98223–1642; tel. 360/435–2133; Michael Liepman, Chief Executive Officer

SKAGIT REGIONAL HEALTH (O, 173 beds) 1415 East Kincaid, Mount Vernon, WA Zip 98274–4126, P O Box 1376, 98273–1376, tel. 360/424–4111
Web address: www.skagitregionalhealth.org

Owned, leased, sponsored:	2 hospitals	221 beds
Contract-managed:	0 hospitals	0 beds
Totals:	2 hospitals	221 beds

★**0253:   SOUTHEAST GEORGIA HEALTH SYSTEM** (NP)
2415 Parkwood Drive, Brunswick, GA Zip 31520–4722, P O Box 1518, 31521–1518, tel. 912/466–7000; Michael D. Scherneck, President and Chief Executive Officer

GEORGIA: SOUTHEAST GEORGIA HEALTH SYSTEM BRUNSWICK CAMPUS (O, 532 beds) 2415 Parkwood Drive, Brunswick, GA Zip 31520–4722, P O Box 1518, 31521–1518, tel. 912/466–7000; Michael D. Scherneck, President and Chief Executive Officer
Web address: www.sghs.org

SOUTHEAST GEORGIA HEALTH SYSTEM CAMDEN CAMPUS (O, 40 beds) 2000 Dan Proctor Drive, Saint Marys, GA Zip 31558–3810; tel. 912/576–6200; Howard W. Sepp Jr, Vice President and Administrator

Owned, leased, sponsored:	2 hospitals	572 beds
Contract-managed:	0 hospitals	0 beds
Totals:	2 hospitals	572 beds

0628:   SOUTHEASTHEALTH (NP)
1701 Lacey Street, Cape Girardeau, MO Zip 63701–5230; tel. 573/334–4822; Kenneth Bateman, CPA, Chief Executive Officer
(Moderately Centralized Health System)

For explanation of codes following names, see page B2.
★ Indicates Type III membership in the American Hospital Association.

MISSOURI: SOUTHEAST HEALTH CENTER OF RIPLEY COUNTY (L, 10 beds) 109 Plum Street, Doniphan, MO Zip 63935–1299; tel. 573/996–2141; Cheryl Lynne. Barton, R.N., Chief Executive Officer

Web address: www.sehealth.org/southeast-health-center-of-ripley-county/ SoutheastHEALTH.aspx?nd=41

SOUTHEAST HEALTH CENTER OF STODDARD COUNTY (L, 16 beds) 1200 North One Mile Road, Dexter, MO Zip 63841–1000; tel. 573/624–5566; Sue Ann Williams, Chief Executive Officer

Web address: www.sehealth.org

SOUTHEAST HOSPITAL (O, 209 beds) 1701 Lacey Street, Cape Girardeau, MO Zip 63701–5230; tel. 573/334–4822; Kenneth Bateman, CPA, President and Chief Executive Officer

Owned, leased, sponsored:	3 hospitals	235 beds
Contract-managed:	0 hospitals	0 beds
Totals:	3 hospitals	235 beds

4175: SOUTHERN ILLINOIS HEALTHCARE (NP)

1239 East Main Street, Carbondale, IL Zip 62901–3114, P O Box 3988, 62902–3988, tel. 618/457–5200; Rex P. Budde, President and Chief Executive Officer
(Independent Hospital System)

ILLINOIS: HERRIN HOSPITAL (O, 114 beds) 201 South 14th Street, Herrin, IL Zip 62948–3631; tel. 618/942–2171; Terence Farrell, Vice President and Administrator

Web address: www.sih.net

MEMORIAL HOSPITAL OF CARBONDALE (O, 167 beds) 405 West Jackson Street, Carbondale, IL Zip 62901–1467, P O Box 10000, 62902–9000, tel. 618/549–0721; Bart Millstead, Administrator

ST. JOSEPH MEMORIAL HOSPITAL (O, 25 beds) 2 South Hospital Drive, Murphysboro, IL Zip 62966–3333; tel. 618/684–3156; Susan Odle, Administrator

Web address: www.sih.net

Owned, leased, sponsored:	3 hospitals	306 beds
Contract-managed:	0 hospitals	0 beds
Totals:	3 hospitals	306 beds

0652: SOUTHWEST HEALTH SYSTEMS (NP)

215 Marion Avenue, Mccomb, MS Zip 39648–2705, P O Box 1307, 39649–1307, tel. 601/249–5500; Norman M. Price, FACHE, Chief Executive Officer and Administrator
(Independent Hospital System)

MISSISSIPPI: LAWRENCE COUNTY HOSPITAL (O, 25 beds) Highway 84 East, Monticello, MS Zip 39654–0788, P O Box 788, 39654–0788, tel. 601/587–4051; Semmes Ross Jr, Administrator

SOUTHWEST MISSISSIPPI REGIONAL MEDICAL CENTER (O, 143 beds) 215 Marion Avenue, McComb, MS Zip 39648–2705, P O Box 1307, 39649–1307, tel. 601/249–5500; Norman M. Price, FACHE, Chief Executive Officer

Web address: www.smrmc.com

Owned, leased, sponsored:	2 hospitals	168 beds
Contract-managed:	0 hospitals	0 beds
Totals:	2 hospitals	168 beds

0164: SOUTHWEST HEALTHCARE SYSTEM (IO)

7025 N Scottsdale Road Suite 9347, Scottsdale, AZ Zip 85253–3675, 7025 North Scottsdale Road, Suite 9347, 85251–3331, tel. 480/518–5444; Paul R. Tuft, President
(Independent Hospital System)

CALIFORNIA: PACIFICA HOSPITAL OF THE VALLEY (O, 231 beds) 9449 San Fernando Road, Sun Valley, CA Zip 91352–1489; tel. 818/767–3310; Ayman Mousa, R.N., Ph.D., Chief Executive Officer
Web address: www.pacificahospital.com

Owned, leased, sponsored:	1 hospitals	231 beds
Contract-managed:	0 hospitals	0 beds
Totals:	1 hospitals	231 beds

★1245: SPARROW HEALTH SYSTEM (NP)

1215 East Michigan Avenue, Lansing, MI Zip 48912–1811; tel. 517/364–1000; Dennis A. Swan, JD, FACHE, President and Chief Executive Officer
(Centralized Physician/Insurance Health System)

MICHIGAN: SPARROW CARSON HOSPITAL (O, 48 beds) 406 East Elm Street, Carson City, MI Zip 48811–9693, P O Box 879, 48811–0879, tel. 989/584–3131; Matthew J. Thompson, FACHE, President and Chief Executive Officer

SPARROW CLINTON HOSPITAL (O, 25 beds) 805 South Oakland Street, Saint Johns, MI Zip 48879–2253; tel. 989/227–3400; Edward Bruun, President and Chief Executive Officer
Web address: www.sparrowclinton.org

SPARROW HOSPITAL (O, 652 beds) 1215 East Michigan Avenue, Lansing, MI Zip 48912–1811; tel. 517/364–1000; Dennis A. Swan, JD, FACHE, President and Chief Executive Officer
Web address: www.sparrow.org

SPARROW IONIA HOSPITAL (O, 22 beds) 3565 South State Road, Ionia, MI Zip 48846–1870; tel. 616/523–1400; William Roeser, President and Chief Executive Officer

SPARROW SPECIALTY HOSPITAL (O, 30 beds) 8 West Sparrow Hospital Tower, 1215 East Michigan Avenue, Lansing, MI Zip 48912; tel. 517/364–4840; Lou Little, President and Chief Executive Officer
Web address: www.sparrowspecialty.org

Owned, leased, sponsored:	5 hospitals	777 beds
Contract-managed:	0 hospitals	0 beds
Totals:	5 hospitals	777 beds

★4195: SPARTANBURG REGIONAL HEALTHCARE SYSTEM (NP)

101 East Wood Street, Spartanburg, SC Zip 29303–3040; tel. 864/560–6000; Bruce Holstien, President and Chief Executive Officer
(Centralized Health System)

SOUTH CAROLINA: PELHAM MEDICAL CENTER (O, 46 beds) 250 Westmoreland Road, Greer, SC Zip 29651–9013; tel. 864/530–6000; Anthony Kouskolekas, FACHE, President

SPARTANBURG HOSPITAL FOR RESTORATIVE CARE (O, 116 beds) 389 Serpentine Drive, Spartanburg, SC Zip 29303–3026; tel. 864/560–3280; Anita M. Butler, Chief Executive Officer
Web address: www.srhs.com

SPARTANBURG MEDICAL CENTER (O, 514 beds) 101 East Wood Street, Spartanburg, SC Zip 29303–3040; tel. 864/560–6000; J Philip. Feisal, President and Chief Executive Officer

UNION MEDICAL CENTER (O, 50 beds) 322 West South Street, Union, SC Zip 29379–2857, P O Box 789, 29379–0789, tel. 864/301–2000; Paul R. Newhouse, President
Web address: https://www.spartanburgregional.com/locations/union-medical-center/

Owned, leased, sponsored:	4 hospitals	726 beds
Contract-managed:	0 hospitals	0 beds
Totals:	4 hospitals	726 beds

★0177: SPECTRUM HEALTH (NP)

100 Michigan Street NE, Grand Rapids, MI Zip 49503–2551, 444 Michigan Street Northeast | MC065, 49503–2551, tel. 616/391–

For explanation of codes following names, see page B2.
★ Indicates Type III membership in the American Hospital Association.

1774; Richard C. Breon, President and Chief Executive Officer
(Centralized Physician/Insurance Health System)

MICHIGAN: SPECTRUM HEALTH - BUTTERWORTH HOSPITAL (O, 1126 beds) 100 Michigan Street NE, Grand Rapids, MI Zip 49503-2560; tel. 616/774-7444; Gwen L. Sandefur, President, Spectrum Health Hospital Group

SPECTRUM HEALTH BIG RAPIDS HOSPITAL (O, 49 beds) 605 Oak Street, Big Rapids, MI Zip 49307-2099; tel. 231/796-8691; Mary Kay VanDriel, President
Web address: www.mcmcbr.com

SPECTRUM HEALTH GERBER MEMORIAL (O, 25 beds) 212 South Sullivan Avenue, Fremont, MI Zip 49412-1548; tel. 231/924-3300; Randall Stasik, President

SPECTRUM HEALTH LUDINGTON HOSPITAL (O, 44 beds) One Atkinson Drive, Ludington, MI Zip 49431-1906; tel. 231/843-2591; Randall Kelley, FACHE, President
Web address: www.mmcwm.com

SPECTRUM HEALTH PENNOCK (O, 39 beds) 1009 West Green Street, Hastings, MI Zip 49058-1710; tel. 269/945-3451; Sheryl Lewis. Blake, FACHE, President

SPECTRUM HEALTH REED CITY HOSPITAL (O, 75 beds) 300 North Patterson Road, Reed City, MI Zip 49677-8041, P O Box 75, 49677-0075, tel. 231/832-3271; Mary Kay VanDriel, President
Web address: www.spectrumhealth.org/reedcity

SPECTRUM HEALTH SPECIAL CARE HOSPITAL (O, 36 beds) 750 Fuller Avenue NE, Grand Rapids, MI Zip 49503-1995; tel. 616/486-3000; Chad Tuttle, President
Web address: www.spectrum-health.org

SPECTRUM HEALTH UNITED HOSPITAL (O, 116 beds) 615 South Bower Street, Greenville, MI Zip 48838-2614; tel. 616/754-4691; Andrea M. Leslie, MSN, R.N., President

SPECTRUM HEALTH ZEELAND COMMUNITY HOSPITAL (O, 50 beds) 8333 Felch Street, Zeeland, MI Zip 49464-2608; tel. 616/772-4644; Ron Lewis, President
Web address: www.spectrumhealth.org/zeeland

Owned, leased, sponsored:	9 hospitals	1560 beds
Contract-managed:	0 hospitals	0 beds
Totals:	9 hospitals	1560 beds

★5455: SSM HEALTH (CC)
10101 Woodfield Lane, Saint Louis, MO Zip 63132-2937; tel. 314/994-7800; Laura Kaiser, President and Chief Executive Officer
(Decentralized Health System)

ILLINOIS: CLAY COUNTY HOSPITAL (C, 22 beds) 911 Stacy Burk Drive, Flora, IL Zip 62839-3241, P O Box 280, 62839-0280, tel. 618/662-2131; Chris Hunt, President
Web address: www.claycountyhospital.org

GOOD SAMARITAN REGIONAL HEALTH CENTER (O, 134 beds) 1 Good Samaritan Way, Mount Vernon, IL Zip 62864-2402; tel. 618/242-4600; Michael D. Warren, President

SSM HEALTH ST. MARY'S HOSPITAL CENTRALIA (O, 124 beds) 400 North Pleasant Avenue, Centralia, IL Zip 62801-3056; tel. 618/436-8000; John R. Sigsbury, President
Web address: www.ssmhealthillinois.com

MISSOURI: SSM CARDINAL GLENNON CHILDREN'S HOSPITAL (O, 176 beds) 1465 South Grand Boulevard, Saint Louis, MO Zip 63104-1095; tel. 314/577-5600; Steven Burghart, President
Web address: www.cardinalglennon.com

SSM HEALTH DEPAUL HOSPITAL - ST. LOUIS (O, 507 beds) 12303 De Paul Drive, Bridgeton, MO Zip 63044-2512; tel. 314/344-6000; Sean Hogan, FACHE, President

SSM HEALTH SAINT LOUIS UNIVERSITY HOSPITAL (O, 356 beds) 3635 Vista at Grand Boulevard, Saint Louis, MO Zip 63110-0250, P O Box 15250, 63110-0250, tel. 314/577-8000; Kathleen R. Becker, M.P.H., JD, President
Web address: www.sluhospital.com

SSM HEALTH ST. CLARE HOSPITAL - FENTON (O, 184 beds) 1015 Bowles Avenue, Fenton, MO Zip 63026-2394; tel. 636/496-2000; Ellis Hawkins, President

SSM HEALTH ST. FRANCIS HOSPITAL - MARYVILLE (O, 56 beds) 2016 South Main Street, Maryville, MO Zip 64468-2655; tel. 660/562-2600; Michael A. Baumgartner, President
Web address: www.ssmhealthstfrancis.com

SSM HEALTH ST. JOSEPH - ST. CHARLES (O, 341 beds) 300 First Capitol Drive, Saint Charles, MO Zip 63301-2844; tel. 636/947-5000; Michael E. Bowers, President
Web address: www.ssmstjoseph.com

SSM HEALTH ST. JOSEPH HOSPITAL - LAKE SAINT LOUIS (O, 119 beds) 100 Medical Plaza, Lake Saint Louis, MO Zip 63367-1366; tel. 636/625-5200; Lisle Wescott, President

SSM HEALTH ST. MARY'S HOSPITAL - AUDRAIN (O, 51 beds) 620 East Monroe Street, Mexico, MO Zip 65265-2919; tel. 573/582-5000; Donna K. Jacobs, FACHE, President
Web address: www.ssmhealthmidmo.com

SSM HEALTH ST. MARY'S HOSPITAL - JEFFERSON CITY (O, 139 beds) 2505 Mission Drive, Jefferson City, MO Zip 65109; tel. 573/681-3000; R Brent. VanConia, President

SSM HEALTH ST. MARY'S HOSPITAL - ST. LOUIS (O, 381 beds) 6420 Clayton Road, Saint Louis, MO Zip 63117-1811, Richmond Heights, tel. 314/768-8000; Travis Capers, FACHE, President
Web address: www.stmarys-stlouis.com

OKLAHOMA: ST. ANTHONY HOSPITAL (O, 624 beds) 1000 North Lee Street, Oklahoma City, OK Zip 73102-1080, P O Box 205, 73101-0205, tel. 405/272-7000; Tammy Powell, FACHE, M.P.H., President

ST. ANTHONY SHAWNEE HOSPITAL (O, 70 beds) 1102 West MacArthur Street, Shawnee, OK Zip 74804-1744; tel. 405/273-2270; Charles E. Skillings, President and Chief Executive Officer
Web address: www.stanthonyshawnee.com

WISCONSIN: ST. CLARE HOSPITAL (O, 60 beds) 707 14th Street, Baraboo, WI Zip 53913-1597; tel. 608/356-1400; Laura Jelle, President
Web address: www.stclare.com

ST. MARY'S HOSPITAL (O, 355 beds) 700 South Park Street, Madison, WI Zip 53715-1830; tel. 608/251-6100; Jon Rozenfeld, President

ST. MARY'S JANESVILLE HOSPITAL (O, 50 beds) 3400 East Racine Steeet, Janesville, WI Zip 53546-2344; tel. 608/373-8000; Michael E. Zilm, Interim President
Web address: www.stmarysjanesville.com

Owned, leased, sponsored:	17 hospitals	3727 beds
Contract-managed:	1 hospitals	22 beds
Totals:	18 hospitals	3749 beds

★0250: ST. CHARLES HEALTH SYSTEM, INC. (NP)
2500 NE Neff Road, Bend, OR Zip 97701-6015; tel. 541/382-4321; Joseph Sluka, President and Chief Executive Officer
(Centralized Physician/Insurance Health System)

OREGON: ST. CHARLES BEND (O, 249 beds) 2500 NE Neff Road, Bend, OR Zip 97701-6015; tel. 541/382-4321; Iman Simmons, Chief Operating Officer and Interim President
Web address: www.stcharleshealthcare.org

ST. CHARLES MADRAS (O, 23 beds) 470 NE 'A' Street, Madras, OR Zip 97741-1844; tel. 541/475-3882; John Bishop, President

ST. CHARLES PRINEVILLE (O, 18 beds) 384 SE Combs Flat Road, Prineville, OR Zip 97754-1206; tel. 541/447-6254; John Bishop, President
Web address: www.stcharleshealthcare.org

ST. CHARLES REDMOND (O, 49 beds) 1253 NW Canal Boulevard, Redmond, OR Zip 97756-1395; tel. 541/548-8131; Iman Simmons, Chief Operating Officer and Interim President
Web address: www.stcharleshealthcare.org

Owned, leased, sponsored:	4 hospitals	339 beds
Contract-managed:	0 hospitals	0 beds
Totals:	4 hospitals	339 beds

For explanation of codes following names, see page B2.
★ Indicates Type III membership in the American Hospital Association.

Section B

0618: ST. ELIZABETH HEALTHCARE (NP)
1 Medical Village Drive, Edgewood, KY Zip 41017–3403; tel. 859/301–2000; Garren Colvin, Chief Executive Officer
(Centralized Physician/Insurance Health System)

KENTUCKY: ST. ELIZABETH EDGEWOOD (O, 522 beds) 1 Medical Village Drive, Edgewood, KY Zip 41017–3403; tel. 859/301–2000; Garren Colvin, Chief Executive Officer

ST. ELIZABETH FLORENCE (O, 169 beds) 4900 Houston Road, Florence, KY Zip 41042–4824; tel. 859/212–5200; Garren Colvin, Chief Executive Officer
Web address: www.stelizabeth.com

ST. ELIZABETH FORT THOMAS (O, 171 beds) 85 North Grand Avenue, Fort Thomas, KY Zip 41075–1796; tel. 859/572–3100; Garren Colvin, Chief Executive Officer
Web address: www.stelizabeth.com

ST. ELIZABETH GRANT (O, 16 beds) 238 Barnes Road, Williamstown, KY Zip 41097–9482; tel. 859/824–8240; Garren Colvin, Chief Executive Officer

Owned, leased, sponsored:	4 hospitals	878 beds
Contract-managed:	0 hospitals	0 beds
Totals:	4 hospitals	878 beds

0928: ST. LAWRENCE HEALTH SYSTEM (NP)
50 Leroy Street, Potsdam, NY Zip 13676–1799; tel. 315/265–3300; David B. Acker, FACHE, President and CEO
(Independent Hospital System)

NEW YORK: CANTON-POTSDAM HOSPITAL (O, 94 beds) 50 Leroy Street, Potsdam, NY Zip 13676–1799; tel. 315/265–3300; David B. Acker, FACHE, President and Chief Executive Officer
Web address: www.cphospital.org

GOUVERNEUR HOSPITAL (O, 25 beds) 77 West Barney Street, Gouverneur, NY Zip 13642–1040; tel. 315/287–1000; David Bender, Chief Executive Officer
Web address: www.gvnrhospital.org

Owned, leased, sponsored:	2 hospitals	119 beds
Contract-managed:	0 hospitals	0 beds
Totals:	2 hospitals	119 beds

★0356: ST. LUKE'S HEALTH SYSTEM (NP)
190 East Bannock Street, Boise, ID Zip 83712–6241; tel. 208/381–4200; David C. Pate, M.D., JD, President and Chief Executive Officer
(Moderately Centralized Health System)

IDAHO: NORTH CANYON MEDICAL CENTER (C, 18 beds) 267 North Canyon Drive, Gooding, ID Zip 83330–5500; tel. 208/934–4433; Tim Powers, Chief Executive Officer

ST. LUKE'S ELMORE (L, 63 beds) 895 North Sixth East Street, Mountain Home, ID Zip 83647–2207, P O Box 1270, 83647–1270, tel. 208/587–8401; Michael Blauer, Administrator
Web address: www.stlukesonline.org/elmore/

ST. LUKE'S JEROME (O, 25 beds) 709 North Lincoln Street, Jerome, ID Zip 83338–1851, 709 North Lincoln Avenue, 83338–1851, tel. 208/814–9500; Curtis Maier, Administrator
Web address: www.stlukesonline.org/jerome/

ST. LUKE'S MAGIC VALLEY MEDICAL CENTER (O, 224 beds) 801 Pole Line Road West, Twin Falls, ID Zip 83301–5810, P O Box 409, 83303–0409, tel. 208/814–1000; Michael A. Fenello, Administrator and West Region Chief Executive Officer

ST. LUKE'S MCCALL (L, 15 beds) 1000 State Street, McCall, ID Zip 83638–3704; tel. 208/634–2221; Sean McCallister, Administrator
Web address: https://www.stlukesonline.org/communities-and-locations/facilities/hospitals-and-medical-centers/st-lukes-mccall-medical-center

ST. LUKE'S REGIONAL MEDICAL CENTER (O, 604 beds) 190 East Bannock Street, Boise, ID Zip 83712–6241; tel. 208/381–2222; David M. McFadyen, Administrator
Web address: www.stlukesonline.org/boise

ST. LUKE'S REHABILITATION HOSPITAL (O, 31 beds) 600 North Robbins Road, Boise, ID Zip 83702–4565, P O Box 1100, 83701–1100, tel. 208/489–4444; Nolan Hoffer, Senior Director
Web address: www.idahoelksrehab.org

ST. LUKE'S WOOD RIVER MEDICAL CENTER (O, 25 beds) 100 Hospital Drive, Ketchum, ID Zip 83340, P O Box 100, 83340–0100, tel. 208/727–8800; Cody Langbehn, Administrator

WEISER MEMORIAL HOSPITAL (C, 18 beds) 645 East Fifth Street, Weiser, ID Zip 83672–2202; tel. 208/549–0370; Steven D. Hale, FACHE, Chief Executive Officer
Web address: www.weisermemorialhospital.org

Owned, leased, sponsored:	7 hospitals	987 beds
Contract-managed:	2 hospitals	36 beds
Totals:	9 hospitals	1023 beds

0862: ST. LUKE'S UNIVERSITY HEALTH NETWORK (NP)
801 Ostrum Street, Bethlehem, PA Zip 18015–1000; tel. 610/954–4000; Richard A. Anderson, President and Chief Executive Officer
(Moderately Centralized Health System)

NEW JERSEY: ST. LUKE'S HOSPITAL - WARREN CAMPUS (O, 103 beds) 185 Roseberry Street, Phillipsburg, NJ Zip 08865–1690; tel. 908/859–6700; Scott R. Wolfe, CPA, President

PENNSYLVANIA: ST. LUKE'S HOSPITAL - ANDERSON CAMPUS (O, 108 beds) 1872 Riverside Circle, Easton, PA Zip 18045–5669; tel. 484/503–3000; Edward Nawrocki, President
Web address: www.mystlukesonline.org

ST. LUKE'S HOSPITAL - MINERS CAMPUS (O, 92 beds) 360 West Ruddle Street, Coaldale, PA Zip 18218–1027; tel. 570/645–2131; William E. Moyer, President

ST. LUKE'S HOSPITAL - QUAKERTOWN CAMPUS (O, 57 beds) 1021 Park Avenue, Quakertown, PA Zip 18951–1573; tel. 215/538–4500; Edward Nawrocki, President
Web address: www.slhhn.org

ST. LUKE'S UNIVERSITY HOSPITAL - BETHLEHEM CAMPUS (O, 540 beds) 801 Ostrum Street, Bethlehem, PA Zip 18015–1065; tel. 484/526–4000; Carol Kuplen, R.N., MSN, President and Chief Executive Officer
Web address: www.slhn-lehighvalley.org

Owned, leased, sponsored:	5 hospitals	900 beds
Contract-managed:	0 hospitals	0 beds
Totals:	5 hospitals	900 beds

★0156: STANFORD HEALTH CARE (NP)
300 Pasteur Drive, Palo Alto, CA Zip 94304–2299; tel. 650/723–4000; David Entwistle, President and Chief Executive Officer
(Centralized Physician/Insurance Health System)

CALIFORNIA: STANFORD HEALTH CARE - VALLEYCARE (O, 207 beds) 5555 West Las Positas Boulevard, Pleasanton, CA Zip 94588–4000; tel. 925/847–3000; Scott Gregerson, President and Chief Executive Officer
Web address: www.valleycare.com

STANFORD HEALTH CARE (O, 491 beds) 300 Pasteur Drive, Suite H3200, Palo Alto, CA Zip 94304–2203; tel. 650/723–4000; David Entwistle, President and Chief Executive Officer

Owned, leased, sponsored:	2 hospitals	698 beds
Contract-managed:	0 hospitals	0 beds
Totals:	2 hospitals	698 beds

0141: STEWARD HEALTH CARE SYSTEM, LLC (IO)
500 Boylston Street, 5th Floor, Boston, MA Zip 02116–3740; tel. 617/419–4700; Ralph de la Torre, M.D., Chairman and Chief Executive Officer
(Independent Hospital System)

For explanation of codes following names, see page B2.
★ Indicates Type III membership in the American Hospital Association.

Section B

FLORIDA: SEBASTIAN RIVER MEDICAL CENTER (O, 154 beds) 13695 North U S Hwy 1, Sebastian, FL Zip 32958–3230, Box 780838, 32978–0838, tel. 772/589–3186; Kelly Enriquez, Chief Executive Officer
Web address: www.sebastianrivermedical.com

WUESTHOFF MEDICAL CENTER - MELBOURNE (O, 119 beds) 250 North Wickham Road, Melbourne, FL Zip 32935–8625; tel. 321/752–1200; Ron Gicca, Chief Executive Officer
Web address: www.wuesthoff.com/locations/wuesthoff-medical-center-melbourne

WUESTHOFF MEDICAL CENTER - ROCKLEDGE (O, 298 beds) 110 Longwood Avenue, Rockledge, FL Zip 32955–2887, P O Box 565002, Mail Stop 1, 32956–5002, tel. 321/636–2211; Andy Romine, Chief Executive Officer

MASSACHUSETTS: CARNEY HOSPITAL (O, 81 beds) 2100 Dorchester Avenue, Boston, MA Zip 02124–5615; tel. 617/296–4000; Walter J. Ramos, President
Web address: www.carneyhospital.org

GOOD SAMARITAN MEDICAL CENTER (O, 190 beds) 235 North Pearl Street, Brockton, MA Zip 02301–1794; tel. 508/427–3000; John A. Jurczyk, FACHE, Interim President

HOLY FAMILY HOSPITAL (O, 329 beds) 70 East Street, Methuen, MA Zip 01844–4597; tel. 978/687–0151; Craig A. Jesiolowski, FACHE, President
Web address: www.stewardhealth.org/Holy-Family-Hospital

MORTON HOSPITAL AND MEDICAL CENTER (O, 153 beds) 88 Washington Street, Taunton, MA Zip 02780–2465; tel. 508/828–7000; Deborah Bitsoli, CPA, President
Web address: www.mortonhospital.org

NASHOBA VALLEY MEDICAL CENTER (O, 48 beds) 200 Groton Road, Ayer, MA Zip 01432–3300; tel. 978/784–9000; Salvatore Perla, President
Web address: www.nashobamed.com

NEW ENGLAND SINAI HOSPITAL AND REHABILITATION CENTER (O, 212 beds) 150 York Street, Stoughton, MA Zip 02072–1881; tel. 781/344–0600; Mary Beth. Urquhart, Interim President, Vice President Patient Care Services and Chief Nursing Officer

NORWOOD HOSPITAL (O, 188 beds) 800 Washington Street, Norwood, MA Zip 02062–3487; tel. 781/769–4000; Kimberly S. Bassett, R.N., President
Web address: www.norwood-hospital.org

SAINT ANNE'S HOSPITAL (O, 160 beds) 795 Middle Street, Fall River, MA Zip 02721–1798; tel. 508/674–5741; Michael Bushell, President

ST. ELIZABETH'S MEDICAL CENTER (O, 338 beds) 736 Cambridge Street, Brighton, MA Zip 02135–2997; tel. 617/789–3000; Craig T. Williams, President
Web address: www.semc.org/

OHIO: HILLSIDE REHABILITATION HOSPITAL (O, 65 beds) 8747 Squires Lane NE, Warren, OH Zip 44484–1649; tel. 330/841–3700; Linda Case, Administrator

NORTHSIDE MEDICAL CENTER (O, 373 beds) 500 Gypsy Lane, Youngstown, OH Zip 44504–1315; tel. 330/884–1000; K Robert. Bauer Jr, Interim Chief Executive Officer
Web address: www.northsidemedicalcenter.net

TRUMBULL MEMORIAL HOSPITAL (O, 292 beds) 1350 East Market Street, Warren, OH Zip 44483–6628; tel. 330/841–9011; Ronald L. Bierman, Chief Executive Officer
Web address: www.https://trumbullmemorial.org/?_ga=2.209137234.1564767671.1497292183–315051339.1497292183

PENNSYLVANIA: EASTON HOSPITAL (O, 196 beds) 250 South 21st Street, Easton, PA Zip 18042–3892; tel. 610/250–4000; Jeffery Snyder, President

SHARON REGIONAL HEALTH SYSTEM (O, 218 beds) 740 East State Street, Sharon, PA Zip 16146–3395; tel. 724/983–3911; Joseph Hugar, MD, President
Web address: www.sharonregional.com

Owned, leased, sponsored:	17 hospitals	3414 beds
Contract-managed:	0 hospitals	0 beds
Totals:	17 hospitals	3414 beds

0858: STRATEGIC BEHAVIORAL HEALTH, LLC (IO)
8295 Tournament Drive, Suite 201, Memphis, TN Zip 38125–8913; tel. 901/969–3100; Jim Shaheen, President

COLORADO: PEAK VIEW BEHAVIORAL HEALTH (O, 112 beds) 7353 Sisters Grove, Colorado Springs, CO Zip 80923–2615; tel. 719/444–8484; Dan Zarecky, Chief Executive Officer

NEVADA: MONTEVISTA HOSPITAL (O, 90 beds) 5900 West Rochelle Avenue, Las Vegas, NV Zip 89103–3327; tel. 702/364–1111; Charlene Arnett, Chief Executive Officer
Web address: www.montevistahospital.com

RED ROCK BEHAVIORAL HOSPITAL (O, 21 beds) 5975 West Twain Avenue, Las Vegas, NV Zip 89103–1237; tel. 702/214–8099; Richard Failla, Chief Executive Officer
Web address: www.redrockhospital.com

NEW MEXICO: PEAK BEHAVIORAL HEALTH SERVICES (O, 120 beds) 5065 McNutt Road, Santa Teresa, NM Zip 88008–9442; tel. 575/589–3000; Peggy Cunningham, Chief Executive Officer

NORTH CAROLINA: STRATEGIC BEHAVIORAL HEALTH - CHARLOTTE (O, 60 beds) 1715 Sharon Road West, Charlotte, NC Zip 28210–5663; tel. 704/944–0650; George G. Boykin, Chief Executive Officer
Web address: www.sbccharlotte.com/

STRATEGIC BEHAVIORAL HEALTH - RALEIGH (O, 50 beds) 3200 Waterfield Drive, Garner, NC Zip 27529–7727; tel. 919/800–4400; Matt Doyle, Chief Executive Officer

STRATEGIC BEHAVIORAL HEALTH - WILMINGTON (O, 112 beds) 2050 Mercantile Drive, Leland, NC Zip 28451–4053; tel. 910/371–2500; Daniel Kern, Chief Executive Officer
Web address: www.sbcwilmington.com/

TEXAS: ROCK PRAIRIE BEHAVIORAL HEALTH (O, 72 beds) 3550 Normand Drive, College Station, TX Zip 77845–6399; tel. 979/703–8848; Jackie St. Germain, Chief Executive Officer

Owned, leased, sponsored:	8 hospitals	637 beds
Contract-managed:	0 hospitals	0 beds
Totals:	8 hospitals	637 beds

0517: SUCCESS HEALTHCARE (IO)
999 Yamato Road, 3rd Floor, Boca Raton, FL Zip 33431–4477; tel. 561/869–6300; Peter R. Baronoff, President and Chief Executive Officer
(Independent Hospital System)

CALIFORNIA: SILVER LAKE MEDICAL CENTER (O, 175 beds) 1711 West Temple Street, Los Angeles, CA Zip 90026–5421; tel. 213/989–6100; Brent A. Cope, Chief Executive Officer
Web address: www.silverlakemc.com

MISSOURI: ST. ALEXIUS HOSPITAL - BROADWAY CAMPUS (O, 189 beds) 3933 South Broadway, Saint Louis, MO Zip 63118–4601; tel. 314/865–7000; Michael J. Motte, Chief Executive Officer

Owned, leased, sponsored:	2 hospitals	364 beds
Contract-managed:	0 hospitals	0 beds
Totals:	2 hospitals	364 beds

0399: SUMMA HEALTH (NP)
1077 Gorge Boulevard, Akron, OH Zip 44310; tel. 330/375–3000; T. Clifford Deveny, M.D., Interim Chief Executive Officer
(Centralized Physician/Insurance Health System)

OHIO: SUMMA HEALTH SYSTEM (O, 661 beds) 525 East Market Street, Akron, OH Zip 44304–1619; tel. 330/375–3000; David Custodio, M.D., President Summa Health System Akron
Web address: www.summahealth.org

SUMMA REHAB HOSPITAL (O, 60 beds) 29 North Adams Street, Akron, OH Zip 44304–1641; tel. 330/572–7300; Cheryl Henthorn, Chief Executive Officer

For explanation of codes following names, see page B2.
★ Indicates Type III membership in the American Hospital Association.

SUMMA WESTERN RESERVE HOSPITAL (O, 83 beds) 1900 23rd Street, Cuyahoga Falls, OH Zip 44223–1499; tel. 330/971–7000; Robert Kent, D.O., President and Chief Executive Officer
Web address: www.westernreservehospital.org

Owned, leased, sponsored:	3 hospitals	804 beds
Contract-managed:	0 hospitals	0 beds
Totals:	3 hospitals	804 beds

★**0189: SUMMIT HEALTH** (NP)

112 North Seventh Street, Chambersburg, PA Zip 17201–1720; tel. 717/267–7138; Patrick W. O'Donnell, CPA, President and Chief Executive Officer
(Independent Hospital System)

PENNSYLVANIA: CHAMBERSBURG HOSPITAL (O, 257 beds) 112 North Seventh Street, Chambersburg, PA Zip 17201–1720; tel. 717/267–3000; Patrick W. O'Donnell, CPA, President and Chief Executive Officer

WAYNESBORO HOSPITAL (O, 56 beds) 501 East Main Street, Waynesboro, PA Zip 17268–2394; tel. 717/765–4000; Melissa Dubrow, Chief Operating Officer
Web address: www.summithealth.org

Owned, leased, sponsored:	2 hospitals	313 beds
Contract-managed:	0 hospitals	0 beds
Totals:	2 hospitals	313 beds

0237: SUNLINK HEALTH SYSTEMS (IO)

900 Circle 75 Parkway, Suite 1120, Atlanta, GA Zip 30339–3005; tel. 770/933–7000; Robert M. Thornton Jr, Chief Executive Officer
(Independent Hospital System)

GEORGIA: CHESTATEE REGIONAL HOSPITAL (O, 49 beds) 227 Mountain Drive, Dahlonega, GA Zip 30533–1606; tel. 706/864–6136; Aaron Durall, Chief Executive Officer

MISSISSIPPI: TRACE REGIONAL HOSPITAL (O, 84 beds) Highway 8 East, Houston, MS Zip 38851–9396, P O Box 626, 38851–0626, tel. 662/456–3700; Gary L. Staten, Chief Executive Officer
Web address: www.traceregional.com

Owned, leased, sponsored:	2 hospitals	133 beds
Contract-managed:	0 hospitals	0 beds
Totals:	2 hospitals	133 beds

★**8795: SUTTER HEALTH** (NP)

2200 River Plaza Drive, Sacramento, CA Zip 95833–4134; tel. 916/733–8800; Sarah Krevans, President and Chief Executive Officer
(Centralized Health System)

CALIFORNIA: ALTA BATES SUMMIT MEDICAL CENTER - SUMMIT CAMPUS (O, 333 beds) 350 Hawthorne Avenue, Oakland, CA Zip 94609–3100; tel. 510/655–4000; Charles Prosper, Chief Executive Officer

ALTA BATES SUMMIT MEDICAL CENTER (O, 441 beds) 2450 Ashby Avenue, Berkeley, CA Zip 94705–2067; tel. 510/204–4444; Charles Prosper, Chief Executive Officer
Web address: www.altabatessummit.org/

CALIFORNIA PACIFIC MEDICAL CENTER-DAVIES CAMPUS (O, 154 beds) Castro and Duboce Streets, San Francisco, CA Zip 94114; tel. 415/600–6000; Mary Lanier, Vice President, Post Acute Services and Site Administrator

CALIFORNIA PACIFIC MEDICAL CENTER-ST. LUKE'S CAMPUS (O, 175 beds) 3555 Cesar Chavez Street, San Francisco, CA Zip 94110–4403; tel. 415/600–6000; Warren S. Browner, M.D., M.P.H., Chief Executive Officer
Web address: www.stlukes-sf.org

CALIFORNIA PACIFIC MEDICAL CENTER (O, 642 beds) 2333 Buchanan Street, San Francisco, CA Zip 94115–1925, P O Box 7999, 94120–7999, tel. 415/600–6000; Warren S. Browner, M.D., M.P.H., Chief Executive Officer

EDEN MEDICAL CENTER (O, 130 beds) 20103 Lake Chabot Road, Castro Valley, CA Zip 94546–5305; tel. 510/537–1234; Theresa Glubka, R.N., Chief Executive Officer
Web address: www.edenmedcenter.org

MEMORIAL HOSPITAL LOS BANOS (O, 44 beds) 520 West 'I' Street, Los Banos, CA Zip 93635–3498; tel. 209/826–0591; Doug Archer, Administrator

MEMORIAL MEDICAL CENTER (O, 222 beds) 1700 Coffee Road, Modesto, CA Zip 95355–2869, P O Box 942, 95353–0942, tel. 209/526–4500; Daryn J. Kumar, Chief Executive Officer
Web address: www.memorialmedicalcenter.org

MENLO PARK SURGICAL HOSPITAL (O, 16 beds) 570 Willow Road, Menlo Park, CA Zip 94025–2617; tel. 650/324–8500; Jeanette Engle-Ramirez, Chief Executive Officer
Web address: www.pamf.org/mpsh

MILLS-PENINSULA HEALTH SERVICES (O, 266 beds) 1501 Trousdale Drive, Burlingame, CA Zip 94010–3282; tel. 650/696–5400; Janet Wagner, R.N., Chief Executive Officer

NOVATO COMMUNITY HOSPITAL (O, 40 beds) 180 Rowland Way, Novato, CA Zip 94945–5009, P O Box 1108, 94948–1108, tel. 415/209–1300; Brian Alexander, Chief Administrative Officer
Web address: www.novatocommunity.sutterhealth.org

STANISLAUS SURGICAL HOSPITAL (O, 23 beds) 1421 Oakdale Road, Modesto, CA Zip 95355–3356; tel. 209/572–2700; Douglas V. Johnson, Chief Executive Officer

SUTTER AMADOR HOSPITAL (O, 52 beds) 200 Mission Boulevard, Jackson, CA Zip 95642–2564; tel. 209/223–7500; Anne Platt, Chief Executive Officer
Web address: www.sutteramador.org

SUTTER AUBURN FAITH HOSPITAL (O, 72 beds) 11815 Education Street, Auburn, CA Zip 95602–2410; tel. 530/888–4500; Mitchell J. Hanna, Chief Executive Officer

SUTTER CENTER FOR PSYCHIATRY (O, 71 beds) 7700 Folsom Boulevard, Sacramento, CA Zip 95826–2608; tel. 916/386–3000; John W. Boyd, PsyD, Chief Executive Officer
Web address: www.sutterpsychiatry.org

SUTTER COAST HOSPITAL (O, 49 beds) 800 East Washington Boulevard, Crescent City, CA Zip 95531–8359; tel. 707/464–8511; Mitchell J. Hanna, Chief Executive Officer
Web address: www.sutterhealth.org

SUTTER DAVIS HOSPITAL (O, 48 beds) 2000 Sutter Place, Davis, CA Zip 95616–6201, P O Box 1617, 95617–1617, tel. 530/756–6440; Jennifer Maher, Chief Executive Officer

SUTTER DELTA MEDICAL CENTER (O, 132 beds) 3901 Lone Tree Way, Antioch, CA Zip 94509–6253; tel. 925/779–7200; Dori Stevens, Chief Executive Officer
Web address: www.sutterdelta.org

SUTTER LAKESIDE HOSPITAL (O, 25 beds) 5176 Hill Road East, Lakeport, CA Zip 95453–6300; tel. 707/262–5000; Dan Peterson, Chief Administrative Officer
Web address: www.sutterlakeside.org

SUTTER MATERNITY AND SURGERY CENTER OF SANTA CRUZ (O, 30 beds) 2900 Chanticleer Avenue, Santa Cruz, CA Zip 95065–1816; tel. 831/477–2200; Stephen Gray, Chief Administrative Officer

SUTTER MEDICAL CENTER, SACRAMENTO (O, 523 beds) 2801 'L' Street, Sacramento, CA Zip 95816–5680; tel. 916/454–3333; David Cheney, Chief Executive Officer
Web address: www.sutterhealth.org

SUTTER OAKS NURSING CENTER (O, 100 beds) 2600 L Street, Sacramento, CA Zip 95816–5612; tel. 916/552–2200; John W. Boyd, PsyD, Chief Administrative Officer

SUTTER ROSEVILLE MEDICAL CENTER (O, 328 beds) One Medical Plaza Drive, Roseville, CA Zip 95661–3037; tel. 916/781–1000; Patrick R. Brady, Chief Executive Officer
Web address: www.sutterroseville.org

SUTTER SANTA ROSA REGIONAL HOSPITAL (O, 84 beds) 30 Mark West Springs Road, Santa Rosa, CA Zip 95403; tel. 707/576–4000; Mike Purvis, Chief Administrative Officer
Web address: www.sutterhealth.org

Section B

For explanation of codes following names, see page B2.
★ Indicates Type III membership in the American Hospital Association.

SUTTER SOLANO MEDICAL CENTER (O, 108 beds) 300 Hospital Drive, Vallejo, CA Zip 94589–2574, P O Box 3189, 94590–0669, tel. 707/554–4444; Abhishek Dosi, Chief Executive Officer

SUTTER SURGICAL HOSPITAL - NORTH VALLEY (O, 14 beds) 455 Plumas Boulevard, Yuba City, CA Zip 95991–5074; tel. 530/749–5700; Shawndra Simpson, Interim Chief Executive Officer
Web address: www.sshnv.org

SUTTER TRACY COMMUNITY HOSPITAL (O, 77 beds) 1420 North Tracy Boulevard, Tracy, CA Zip 95376–3497; tel. 209/835–1500; David M. Thompson, Chief Executive Officer

HAWAII: KAHI MOHALA BEHAVIORAL HEALTH (O, 76 beds) 91–2301 Old Fort Weaver Road, Ewa Beach, HI Zip 96706–3602; tel. 808/671–8511; Leonard Licina, Chief Executive Officer
Web address: www.kahimohala.org

Owned, leased, sponsored:	28 hospitals	4275 beds
Contract-managed:	0 hospitals	0 beds
Totals:	28 hospitals	4275 beds

★0871: SWEDISH HEALTH SERVICES (NP)
747 Broadway, Seattle, WA Zip 98122–4379; tel. 206/386–6000; R. Guy. Hudson, Chief Executive Officer
(Independent Hospital System)

WASHINGTON: SWEDISH MEDICAL CENTER-CHERRY HILL CAMPUS (O, 227 beds) 500 17th Avenue, Seattle, WA Zip 98122–5711; tel. 206/320–2000; June Altaras, R.N., Chief Executive Officer
Web address: www.swedish.org

SWEDISH MEDICAL CENTER-FIRST HILL (O, 659 beds) 747 Broadway, Seattle, WA Zip 98122–4307; tel. 206/386–6000; June Altaras, R.N., Chief Executive Officer

SWEDISH/EDMONDS (O, 164 beds) 21601 76th Avenue West, Edmonds, WA Zip 98026–7506; tel. 425/640–4000; Sarah Zabel, Vice President, Operations
Web address: www.swedish.org

SWEDISH/ISSAQUAH (O, 134 beds) 751 NE Blakely Drive, Issaquah, WA Zip 98029–6201; tel. 425/313–4000; Jeffery Robert, Chief Operating Officer

Owned, leased, sponsored:	4 hospitals	1184 beds
Contract-managed:	0 hospitals	0 beds
Totals:	4 hospitals	1184 beds

★0379: TAHOE FOREST HEALTH SYSTEM (NP)
10121 Pine Avenue, Truckee, CA Zip 96161–4835; tel. 530/587–6011; Harry Weis, Chief Executive Officer

CALIFORNIA: TAHOE FOREST HOSPITAL DISTRICT (O, 62 beds) 10121 Pine Avenue, Truckee, CA Zip 96161–4856, P O Box 759, 96160–0759, tel. 530/587–6011; Harry Weis, Chief Executive Officer
Web address: www.tfhd.com

NEVADA: INCLINE VILLAGE COMMUNITY HOSPITAL (O, 6 beds) 880 Alder Avenue, Incline Village, NV Zip 89451–8335; tel. 775/833–4100; Judy Newland, R.N., Chief Nursing Officer

Owned, leased, sponsored:	2 hospitals	68 beds
Contract-managed:	0 hospitals	0 beds
Totals:	2 hospitals	68 beds

★0341: TANNER HEALTH SYSTEM (NP)
705 Dixie Street, Carrollton, GA Zip 30117–3818; tel. 770/836–9580; Loy M. Howard, President and Chief Executive Officer

GEORGIA: TANNER HIGGINS GENERAL HOSPITAL (O, 23 beds) 200 Allen Memorial Drive, Bremen, GA Zip 30110–2012; tel. 770/824–2000; Bonnie Boles, M.D., Administrator
Web address: www.tanner.org/Main/HigginsGeneralHospitalBremen.aspx

TANNER MEDICAL CENTER-CARROLLTON (O, 162 beds) 705 Dixie Street, Carrollton, GA Zip 30117–3818; tel. 770/836–9666; James D. Griffith, Chief Operating Officer
Web address: www.tanner.org

TANNER MEDICAL CENTER-VILLA RICA (O, 118 beds) 601 Dallas Highway, Villa Rica, GA Zip 30180–1202; tel. 770/456–3000; Bonnie Boles, M.D., Administrator

Owned, leased, sponsored:	3 hospitals	303 beds
Contract-managed:	0 hospitals	0 beds
Totals:	3 hospitals	303 beds

★0169: TEMPLE UNIVERSITY HEALTH SYSTEM (NP)
3509 North Broad Street, 9th Floor, Philadelphia, PA Zip 19140–4105; tel. 215/707–0900; Larry Kaiser, M.D., President and Chief Executive Officer
(Centralized Physician/Insurance Health System)

PENNSYLVANIA: FOX CHASE CANCER CENTER-AMERICAN ONCOLOGIC HOSPITAL (O, 67 beds) 333 Cottman Avenue, Philadelphia, PA Zip 19111–2434; tel. 215/728–6900; Richard Fisher, M.D., President and Chief Executive Officer
Web address: www.fccc.org

JEANES HOSPITAL (O, 146 beds) 7600 Central Avenue, Philadelphia, PA Zip 19111–2499; tel. 215/728–2000; Marc P. Hurowitz, D.O., President and Chief Executive Officer
Web address: www.jeanes.com

TEMPLE UNIVERSITY HOSPITAL (O, 722 beds) 3401 North Broad Street, Philadelphia, PA Zip 19140–5103; tel. 215/707–2000; Verdi Disesa, M.D., President and Chief Executive Officer
Web address: www.tuh.templehealth.org/content/default.htm

Owned, leased, sponsored:	3 hospitals	935 beds
Contract-managed:	0 hospitals	0 beds
Totals:	3 hospitals	935 beds

★0919: TENET HEALTHCARE CORPORATION (IO)
1445 Ross Avenue, Suite 1400, Dallas, TX Zip 75202–2703, P O Box 1390369, 75313–9036, tel. 469/893–2200; Trevor Fetter, President and Chief Executive Officer
(Decentralized Health System)

ALABAMA: BROOKWOOD BAPTIST MEDICAL CENTER (O, 607 beds) 2010 Brookwood Medical Center Drive, Birmingham, AL Zip 35209–6875; tel. 205/877–1000; Keith Parrott, FACHE, Interim President and Chief Executive Officer

CITIZENS BAPTIST MEDICAL CENTER (O, 72 beds) 604 Stone Avenue, Talladega, AL Zip 35160–2217, P O Box 978, 35161–0978, tel. 256/362–8111; Douglas Brewer, Chief Executive Officer
Web address: www.brookwoodbaptisthealth.org

PRINCETON BAPTIST MEDICAL CENTER (O, 311 beds) 701 Princeton Avenue SW, Birmingham, AL Zip 35211–1303; tel. 205/783–3000; Betsy Postlethwait, President

SHELBY BAPTIST MEDICAL CENTER (O, 231 beds) 1000 First Street North, Alabaster, AL Zip 35007–8703; tel. 205/620–8100; Mike Rickman, Chief Executive Officer
Web address: www.brookwoodbaptisthealth.com

WALKER BAPTIST MEDICAL CENTER (O, 158 beds) 3400 Highway 78 East, Jasper, AL Zip 35501–8907, P O Box 3547, 35502–3547, tel. 205/387–4000; Robert A. Phillips, Chief Executive Officer
Web address: www.bhsala.com

ARIZONA: ABRAZO ARROWHEAD CAMPUS (O, 234 beds) 18701 North 67th Avenue, Glendale, AZ Zip 85308–7100; tel. 623/561–1000; Frank L. Molinaro, Chief Executive Officer

ABRAZO CENTRAL CAMPUS (O, 215 beds) 2000 West Bethany Home Road, Phoenix, AZ Zip 85015–2443; tel. 602/249–0212; Frank L. Molinaro, Chief Executive Officer
Web address: www.abrazohealth.com

For explanation of codes following names, see page B2.
★ Indicates Type III membership in the American Hospital Association.

ABRAZO MARYVALE CAMPUS (O, 78 beds) 5102 West Campbell Avenue, Phoenix, AZ Zip 85031–1799; tel. 623/848–5000; Stan Holm, Chief Executive Officer
Web address: www.maryvalehospital.com

ABRAZO SCOTTSDALE CAMPUS (O, 142 beds) 3929 East Bell Road, Phoenix, AZ Zip 85032–2196; tel. 602/923–5000; Frank L. Molinaro, Chief Executive Officer

ABRAZO WEST CAMPUS (O, 106 beds) 13677 West McDowell Road, Goodyear, AZ Zip 85395–2635; tel. 623/882–1500; Stan Holm, Chief Executive Officer
Web address: www.abrazohealth.com

CARONDELET HOLY CROSS HOSPITAL (O, 25 beds) 1171 West Target Range Road, Nogales, AZ Zip 85621–2415; tel. 520/285–3000; Debbie Knapheide, MSN, Site Administrator, Chief Nursing Officer and Chief Operating Officer

CARONDELET ST. JOSEPH'S HOSPITAL (O, 486 beds) 350 North Wilmot Road, Tucson, AZ Zip 85711–2678; tel. 520/873–3000; Mark A. Benz, President and Chief Executive Officer
Web address: www.carondelet.org

CARONDELET ST. MARY'S HOSPITAL (O, 300 beds) 1601 West St Mary's Road, Tucson, AZ Zip 85745–2682; tel. 520/872–3000; Amy Beiter, M.D., President and Chief Executive Officer
Web address: www.carondelet.org

CALIFORNIA: DESERT REGIONAL MEDICAL CENTER (L, 382 beds) 1150 North Indian Canyon Drive, Palm Springs, CA Zip 92262–4872; tel. 760/323–6511; Michele Finney, Chief Executive Officer

DOCTORS HOSPITAL OF MANTECA (O, 56 beds) 1205 East North Street, Manteca, CA Zip 95336–4900; tel. 209/823–3111; Carmen Silva, R.N., Interim Chief Executive Officer
Web address: www.doctorsmanteca.com

DOCTORS MEDICAL CENTER OF MODESTO (O, 455 beds) 1441 Florida Avenue, Modesto, CA Zip 95350–4418, P O Box 4138, 95352–4138, tel. 209/578–1211; Warren J. Kirk, Chief Executive Officer
Web address: www.dmc-modesto.com

EMANUEL MEDICAL CENTER (O, 209 beds) 825 Delbon Avenue, Turlock, CA Zip 95382–2016, P O Box 819005, 95382, tel. 209/667–4200; Susan C. Micheletti, Chief Executive Officer

FOUNTAIN VALLEY REGIONAL HOSPITAL AND MEDICAL CENTER (O, 342 beds) 17100 Euclid Street, Fountain Valley, CA Zip 92708–4043; tel. 714/966–7200; Kenneth D. McFarland, Chief Executive Officer
Web address: www.fountainvalleyhospital.com

HI-DESERT MEDICAL CENTER (L, 179 beds) 6530 La Contenta, Suite 100, Yucca Valley, CA Zip 92284, 6601 White Feather Road, Joshua Tree, 92252–6607, tel. 760/366–3711; Karen Faulis, Chief Executive Officer
Web address: www.hdmc.org

JOHN F. KENNEDY MEMORIAL HOSPITAL (O, 145 beds) 47111 Monroe Street, Indio, CA Zip 92201–6799; tel. 760/347–6191; Gary Honts, Chief Executive Officer

LAKEWOOD REGIONAL MEDICAL CENTER (O, 153 beds) 3700 East South Street, Lakewood, CA Zip 90712–1498, P O Box 6070, 90712, tel. 562/531–2550; John A. Grah, FACHE, Chief Executive Officer
Web address: www.lakewoodregional.com

LOS ALAMITOS MEDICAL CENTER (O, 167 beds) 3751 Katella Avenue, Los Alamitos, CA Zip 90720–3164; tel. 562/598–1311; Kent G. Clayton, Chief Executive Officer
Web address: www.losalamitosmedctr.com

PLACENTIA-LINDA HOSPITAL (O, 114 beds) 1301 North Rose Drive, Placentia, CA Zip 92870–3899; tel. 714/993–2000; Christina E. Oh, Chief Executive Officer
Web address: www.placentialinda.com

SAN RAMON REGIONAL MEDICAL CENTER (O, 123 beds) 6001 Norris Canyon Road, San Ramon, CA Zip 94583–5400; tel. 925/275–9200; Gary Sloan, Chief Executive Officer

SIERRA VISTA REGIONAL MEDICAL CENTER (O, 164 beds) 1010 Murray Avenue, San Luis Obispo, CA Zip 93405–1806, P O Box 1367, 93405, tel. 805/546–7600; Timothy P. Menton, Interim Chief Executive Officer
Web address: www.sierravistaregional.com

TWIN CITIES COMMUNITY HOSPITAL (O, 89 beds) 1100 Las Tablas Road, Templeton, CA Zip 93465–9796; tel. 805/434–3500; Mark P. Lisa, FACHE, Chief Executive Officer
Web address: www.twincitieshospital.com

FLORIDA: CORAL GABLES HOSPITAL (O, 256 beds) 3100 Douglas Road, Coral Gables, FL Zip 33134–6914; tel. 305/445–8461; Cristina Jimenez, Chief Executive Officer

DELRAY MEDICAL CENTER (O, 439 beds) 5352 Linton Boulevard, Delray Beach, FL Zip 33484–6580; tel. 561/498–4440; Mark Bryan, Chief Executive Officer
Web address: www.delraymedicalctr.com

GOOD SAMARITAN MEDICAL CENTER (O, 174 beds) 1309 North Flagler Drive, West Palm Beach, FL Zip 33401–3499; tel. 561/655–5511; Mark Nosacka, Chief Executive Officer

HIALEAH HOSPITAL (O, 191 beds) 651 East 25th Street, Hialeah, FL Zip 33013–3878; tel. 305/693–6100; Ben A. Rodriguez, Chief Executive Officer
Web address: www.hialeahhosp.com

NORTH SHORE MEDICAL CENTER (O, 816 beds) 1100 NW 95th Street, Miami, FL Zip 33150–2098; tel. 305/835–6000; Manuel Linares, Chief Executive Officer

PALM BEACH GARDENS MEDICAL CENTER (L, 199 beds) 3360 Burns Road, Palm Beach Gardens, FL Zip 33410–4323; tel. 561/622–1411; Dianne Goldenberg, Chief Executive Officer
Web address: www.pbgmc.com

PALMETTO GENERAL HOSPITAL (O, 360 beds) 2001 West 68th Street, Hialeah, FL Zip 33016–1898; tel. 305/823–5000; Ana J. Mederos, Chief Executive Officer

ST. MARY'S MEDICAL CENTER (O, 464 beds) 901 45th Street, West Palm Beach, FL Zip 33407–2495; tel. 561/844–6300; Gabrielle Finley-Hazle, Chief Executive Officer
Web address: www.stmarysmc.com

WEST BOCA MEDICAL CENTER (O, 195 beds) 21644 State Road 7, Boca Raton, FL Zip 33428–1899; tel. 561/488–8000; Mitchell S. Feldman, Chief Executive Officer

ILLINOIS: LOUIS A. WEISS MEMORIAL HOSPITAL (O, 153 beds) 4646 North Marine Drive, Chicago, IL Zip 60640–5759; tel. 773/878–8700; Charles Orlando, Interim Chief Executive Officer
Web address: www.weisshospital.com

MACNEAL HOSPITAL (O, 359 beds) 3249 South Oak Park Avenue, Berwyn, IL Zip 60402–0715; tel. 708/783–9100; Mary Elizabeth. Cleary, Chief Executive Officer

WEST SUBURBAN MEDICAL CENTER (O, 172 beds) 3 Erie Court, Oak Park, IL Zip 60302–2599; tel. 708/383–6200; Joseph Ottolino, Interim Chief Executive Officer
Web address: www.westsuburbanmc.com/Home.aspx

WESTLAKE HOSPITAL (O, 181 beds) 1225 Lake Street, Melrose Park, IL Zip 60160–4000; tel. 708/681–3000; Michael Ditoro, Interim Chief Executive Officer
Web address: www.westlakehosp.com

MASSACHUSETTS: METROWEST MEDICAL CENTER (O, 160 beds) 115 Lincoln Street, Framingham, MA Zip 01702–6342; tel. 508/383–1000; Jeffrey H. Liebman, Market Chief Executive Officer
Web address: www.mwmc.com

SAINT VINCENT HOSPITAL (O, 283 beds) 123 Summer Street, Worcester, MA Zip 01608–1216; tel. 508/363–5000; Jeffrey M. Welch, Market Chief Executive Officer

MICHIGAN: DMC - CHILDREN'S HOSPITAL OF MICHIGAN (O, 224 beds) 3901 Beaubien Street, Detroit, MI Zip 48201–2119; tel. 313/745–5437; Luanne T. Ewald, Interim Chief Executive Officer
Web address: www.chmkids.org

DMC - DETROIT RECEIVING HOSPITAL (O, 185 beds) 4201 Saint Antoine Street, Detroit, MI Zip 48201–2153; tel. 313/745–3000; Scott Steiner, FACHE, Chief Executive Officer
Web address: www.dmc.org

DMC - REHABILITATION INSTITUTE OF MICHIGAN (O, 69 beds) 261 Mack Avenue, Detroit, MI Zip 48201–2495; tel. 313/745–1203; William Restum, Chief Executive Officer
Web address: www.rimrehab.org

For explanation of codes following names, see page B2.
★ Indicates Type III membership in the American Hospital Association.

Section B

DMC - SINAI-GRACE HOSPITAL (O, 301 beds) 6071 West Outer Drive, Detroit, MI Zip 48235–2679; tel. 313/966–3300; Conrad Mallett Jr., FACHE, Chief Executive Officer

DMC HARPER UNIVERSITY HOSPITAL (O, 364 beds) 3990 John 'R' Street, Detroit, MI Zip 48201–2018; tel. 313/745–8040; Scott Steiner, FACHE, Chief Executive Officer
Web address: www.harperhospital.org

DMC HURON VALLEY-SINAI HOSPITAL (O, 156 beds) 1 William Carls Drive, Commerce Township, MI Zip 48382–2201; tel. 248/937–3300; Karima Bentounsi, Interim Chief Executive Officer

MISSOURI: DES PERES HOSPITAL (O, 88 beds) 2345 Dougherty Ferry Road, Saint Louis, MO Zip 63122–3313; tel. 314/966–9100; David E. Loving, Chief Executive Officer
Web address: www.despereshospital.com

PENNSYLVANIA: HAHNEMANN UNIVERSITY HOSPITAL (O, 496 beds) 230 North Broad Street, Philadelphia, PA Zip 19102–1192; tel. 215/762–7000; Michael P. Halter, Chief Executive Officer
Web address: www.hahnemannhospital.com

ST. CHRISTOPHER'S HOSPITAL FOR CHILDREN (O, 189 beds) 3601 A Street, Philadelphia, PA Zip 19134–1043; tel. 215/427–5000; James B. Burke, FACHE, Interim Chief Executive Officer

SOUTH CAROLINA: COASTAL CAROLINA HOSPITAL (O, 35 beds) 1000 Medical Center Drive, Hardeeville, SC Zip 29927–3446; tel. 843/784–8000; Joel Taylor, Chief Executive Officer
Web address: www.coastalhospital.com

EAST COOPER MEDICAL CENTER (O, 140 beds) 2000 Hospital Drive, Mount Pleasant, SC Zip 29464–3764; tel. 843/881–0100; Patrick Downes, Chief Executive Officer
Web address: www.eastcoopermedctr.com

HILTON HEAD HOSPITAL (O, 93 beds) 25 Hospital Center Boulevard, Hilton Head Island, SC Zip 29926–2738; tel. 843/681–6122; Jeremy L. Clark, Market Chief Executive Officer

PIEDMONT MEDICAL CENTER (O, 280 beds) 222 Herlong Avenue, Rock Hill, SC Zip 29732; tel. 803/329–1234; Stephen Gilmore, Interim Chief Executive Officer
Web address: www.piedmontmedicalcenter.com

TENNESSEE: SAINT FRANCIS HOSPITAL-BARTLETT (O, 156 beds) 2986 Kate Bond Road, Bartlett, TN Zip 38133–4003; tel. 901/820–7000; Christopher Locke, Chief Executive Officer

SAINT FRANCIS HOSPITAL (O, 415 beds) 5959 Park Avenue, Memphis, TN Zip 38119–5198; tel. 901/765–1000; Audrey Gregory, R.N., MSN, Chief Executive Officer
Web address: www.saintfrancishosp.com

TEXAS: BAPTIST MEDICAL CENTER (O, 1535 beds) 111 Dallas Street, San Antonio, TX Zip 78205–1230; tel. 210/297–7000; Jonathan Turton, FACHE, President and Chief Executive Officer
Web address: www.baptisthealthsystem.com

BAYLOR SCOTT & WHITE MEDICAL CENTER - CENTENNIAL (O, 106 beds) 12505 Lebanon Road, Frisco, TX Zip 75035–8298; tel. 972/963–3333; Jaikumar Krishnaswamy, Chief Executive Officer

BAYLOR SCOTT & WHITE MEDICAL CENTER - LAKE POINTE (O, 112 beds) 6800 Scenic Drive, Rowlett, TX Zip 75088–4552, P O Box 1550, 75030–1550, tel. 972/412–2273; Brett D. Lee, Chief Executive Officer
Web address: www.lakepointemedical.com

BAYLOR SCOTT & WHITE MEDICAL CENTER - SUNNYVALE (O, 70 beds) 231 South Collins Road, Sunnyvale, TX Zip 75182–4624; tel. 972/892–3000; Collin LeMaistre, Chief Executive Officer
Web address: www.BaylorScottandWhite.com/Sunnyvale

BAYLOR SCOTT & WHITE MEDICAL CENTER - WHITE ROCK (O, 151 beds) 9440 Poppy Drive, Dallas, TX Zip 75218–3694; tel. 214/324–6100; Jorge Trevino, Interim Chief Executive Officer
Web address: www.BaylorScottandWhite.com/WhiteRock

NACOGDOCHES MEDICAL CENTER (O, 117 beds) 4920 NE Stallings Drive, Nacogdoches, TX Zip 75965–1200; tel. 936/569–9481; Jeff Patterson, Chief Executive Officer

PLAZA SPECIALTY HOSPITAL (O, 46 beds) 1300 Binz Street, Houston, TX Zip 77004–7016; tel. 713/285–1000; Richard Andrew. Pletz, Chief Executive Officer
Web address: www.plazaspecialtyhospital.com

RESOLUTE HEALTH (O, 70 beds) 555 Creekside Crossing, New Braunfels, TX Zip 78130–2594; tel. 830/500–6000; Mark L. Bernard, Chief Executive Officer

THE HOSPITALS OF PROVIDENCE EAST CAMPUS (O, 182 beds) 3280 Joe Battle Boulevard, El Paso, TX Zip 79938–2622; tel. 915/832–2000; Phillip Young, Chief Executive Officer
Web address: www.sphn.com

THE HOSPITALS OF PROVIDENCE MEMORIAL CAMPUS (O, 409 beds) 2001 North Oregon Street, El Paso, TX Zip 79902–3368; tel. 915/577–6625; Sally A. Hurt-Deitch, FACHE, R.N., Market Chief Executive Officer

THE HOSPITALS OF PROVIDENCE SIERRA CAMPUS (O, 225 beds) 1625 Medical Center Drive, El Paso, TX Zip 79902–5005; tel. 915/747–4000; Monica Vargas-Mahar, FACHE, Chief Executive Officer
Web address: www.thehospitalsofprovidence.com

THE HOSPITALS OF PROVIDENCE TRANSMOUNTAIN CAMPUS (O, 106 beds) 2000 Transmountain Road, El Paso, TX Zip 79911; tel. 915/877–8300; Nicholas R. Tejeda, FACHE, Chief Executive Officer
Web address: https://www.thehospitalsofprovidence.com/our-locations/transmountain

VALLEY BAPTIST MEDICAL CENTER-BROWNSVILLE (O, 262 beds) 1040 West Jefferson Street, Brownsville, TX Zip 78520–6338, P O Box 3590, 78523–3590, tel. 956/698–5400; Leslie Bingham, Senior Vice President and Chief Executive Officer

VALLEY BAPTIST MEDICAL CENTER-HARLINGEN (O, 416 beds) 2101 Pease Street, Harlingen, TX Zip 78550–8307, P O Drawer 2588, 78551–2588, tel. 956/389–1100; Manuel Vela, President and Chief Executive Officer
Web address: www.valleybaptist.net/harlingen/index.htm

Owned, leased, sponsored:	70 hospitals	16943 beds
Contract-managed:	0 hospitals	0 beds
Totals:	70 hospitals	16943 beds

0876: TENNESSEE HEALTH MANAGEMENT (IO)
52 West Eighth Street, Parsons, TN Zip 38363–4656, PO Box 10, 38363–0010, tel. 731/847–6343; Dennis Berry, Chief Executive Officer

ALABAMA: BEHAVIORAL HEALTHCARE CENTER AT HUNTSVILLE (O, 20 beds) 5315 Millennium Drive NW, Huntsville, AL Zip 35806–2458; tel. 256/964–6700; Bradley Moss, Administrator

TENNESSEE: BEHAVIORAL HEALTHCARE CENTER AT CLARKSVILLE (O, 26 beds) 930 Professional Park Drive, Clarksville, TN Zip 37040–5136; tel. 931/538–6420; Jennifer Robinson, Administrator
Web address: www.bhcclarksville.com

BEHAVIORAL HEALTHCARE CENTER AT COLUMBIA (O, 16 beds) 1400 Rosewood Drive, Columbia, TN Zip 38401–4878; tel. 931/388–6573; Paula Chennault, Administrator

BEHAVIORAL HEALTHCARE CENTER AT MARTIN (O, 16 beds) 458 Hannings Lane, Martin, TN Zip 38237–3308; tel. 731/588–2830; Carrie Brawley, Administrator
Web address: www.tnhealthmanagement.com/BHC/martin/

Owned, leased, sponsored:	4 hospitals	78 beds
Contract-managed:	0 hospitals	0 beds
Totals:	4 hospitals	78 beds

0020: TEXAS DEPARTMENT OF STATE HEALTH SERVICES (NP)
1100 West 49th Street, Austin, TX Zip 78756–3199; tel. 512/458–7111; Kirk Cole, Interim Commissioner
(Independent Hospital System)

TEXAS: AUSTIN STATE HOSPITAL (O, 299 beds) 4110 Guadalupe Street, Austin, TX Zip 78751–4296; tel. 512/452–0381; Alan R. Isaacson, Interim Superintendent

For explanation of codes following names, see page B2.
★ Indicates Type III membership in the American Hospital Association.

BIG SPRING STATE HOSPITAL (O, 200 beds) 1901 North Highway 87, Big Spring, TX Zip 79720–0283; tel. 432/267–8216; Lorie Dunnam, Superintendent
Web address: www.dshs.state.tx.us/mhhospitals/BigSpringSH/default. shtm

EL PASO PSYCHIATRIC CENTER (O, 74 beds) 4615 Alameda Avenue, El Paso, TX Zip 79905–2702; tel. 915/532–2202; Zulema Carrillo, Superintendent
Web address: www.dshs.state.tx.us/mhhospitals/ElPasoPC/default.shtm

KERRVILLE STATE HOSPITAL (O, 202 beds) 721 Thompson Drive, Kerrville, TX Zip 78028–5154; tel. 830/896–2211; Leigh Ann Fitzpatrick, Superintendent

NORTH TEXAS STATE HOSPITAL (O, 640 beds) Highway 70 Northwest, Vernon, TX Zip 76384, P O Box 2231, 76385–2231, tel. 940/552–9901; James E. Smith, Superintendent
Web address: www.online.dshs.state.tx.us/northtexassh/default.htm

RIO GRANDE STATE CENTER/SOUTH TEXAS HEALTH CARE SYSTEM (O, 55 beds) 1401 South Rangerville Road, Harlingen, TX Zip 78552–7638; tel. 956/364–8000; Sonia Hernandez-Keeble, Superintendent
Web address: www.dshs.state.tx.us/mhhospitals/RioGrandeSC/default.shtm

RUSK STATE HOSPITAL (O, 249 beds) 805 North Dickinson, Rusk, TX Zip 75785–2333, P O Box 318, 75785–0318, tel. 903/683–3421; Brenda Slaton, Superintendent

SAN ANTONIO STATE HOSPITAL (O, 302 beds) 6711 South New Braunfels, Suite 100, San Antonio, TX Zip 78223–3006; tel. 210/531–7711; Robert C. Arizpe, Superintendent
Web address: www.dshs.state.tx.us/mhhospitals/SanAntonioSH/default.shtm

TERRELL STATE HOSPITAL (O, 288 beds) 1200 East Brin Street, Terrell, TX Zip 75160–2938, P O Box 70, 75160–9000, tel. 972/524–6452; Dorothy Floyd, Ph.D., Superintendent
Web address: www.dshs.state.tx.us/mhhospitals/terrellsh

TEXAS CENTER FOR INFECTIOUS DISEASE (O, 40 beds) 2303 SE Military Drive, San Antonio, TX Zip 78223–3597; tel. 210/534–8857; James N. Elkins, FACHE, Director

Owned, leased, sponsored:	10 hospitals	2349 beds
Contract-managed:	0 hospitals	0 beds
Totals:	10 hospitals	2349 beds

★0129: TEXAS HEALTH RESOURCES (NP)
612 East Lamar Boulevard, Suite 900, Arlington, TX Zip 76011–4130; tel. 682/236–7900; Barclay E. Berdan, FACHE, Chief Executive Officer
(Centralized Physician/Insurance Health System)

TEXAS: TEXAS HEALTH ARLINGTON MEMORIAL HOSPITAL (O, 242 beds) 800 West Randol Mill Road, Arlington, TX Zip 76012–2503; tel. 817/548–6100; Blake Kretz, FACHE, President
Web address: www.arlingtonmemorial.org

TEXAS HEALTH HARRIS METHODIST HOSPITAL ALLIANCE (O, 74 beds) 10864 Texas Health Trail, Fort Worth, TX Zip 76244–4897; tel. 682/212–2000; Clint Abernathy, President and Chief Operating Officer
Web address: https://www.texashealth.org/alliance/Pages/default.aspx

TEXAS HEALTH HARRIS METHODIST HOSPITAL AZLE (O, 31 beds) 108 Denver Trail, Azle, TX Zip 76020–3614; tel. 817/444–8600; Bob S. Ellzey, FACHE, President

TEXAS HEALTH HARRIS METHODIST HOSPITAL CLEBURNE (O, 92 beds) 201 Walls Drive, Cleburne, TX Zip 76033–4007; tel. 817/641–2551; Lorrie Normand, R.N., President
Web address: www.texashealth.org

TEXAS HEALTH HARRIS METHODIST HOSPITAL FORT WORTH (O, 640 beds) 1301 Pennsylvania Avenue, Fort Worth, TX Zip 76104–2122; tel. 817/250–2000; Lillie Biggins RN, R.N., President

TEXAS HEALTH HARRIS METHODIST HOSPITAL HURST-EULESS-BEDFORD (O, 190 beds) 1600 Hospital Parkway, Bedford, TX Zip 76022–6913; tel. 817/685–4000; Deborah Paganelli, FACHE, President
Web address: www.texashealth.org

TEXAS HEALTH HARRIS METHODIST HOSPITAL SOUTHWEST FORT WORTH (O, 247 beds) 6100 Harris Parkway, Fort Worth, TX Zip 76132–4199; tel. 817/433–5000; Joseph DeLeon, President
Web address: www.texashealth.org

TEXAS HEALTH HARRIS METHODIST HOSPITAL STEPHENVILLE (O, 54 beds) 411 North Belknap Street, Stephenville, TX Zip 76401–3415; tel. 254/965–1500; Christopher Leu, President
Web address: www.texashealth.org/landing.cfm?id=108

TEXAS HEALTH PRESBYTERIAN HOSPITAL ALLEN (O, 68 beds) 1105 Central Expressway North, Suite 140, Allen, TX Zip 75013–6103; tel. 972/747–1000; Jared Shelton, Chief Executive Officer

TEXAS HEALTH PRESBYTERIAN HOSPITAL DALLAS (O, 617 beds) 8200 Walnut Hill Lane, Dallas, TX Zip 75231–4426; tel. 214/345–6789; James Berg, FACHE, President
Web address: www.texashealth.org

TEXAS HEALTH PRESBYTERIAN HOSPITAL DENTON (O, 190 beds) 3000 North I-35, Denton, TX Zip 76201–5119; tel. 940/898–7000; Jeff Reecer, FACHE, Chief Executive Officer
Web address: www.dentonhospital.com

TEXAS HEALTH PRESBYTERIAN HOSPITAL KAUFMAN (O, 37 beds) 850 Ed Hall Drive, Kaufman, TX Zip 75142–1861, P O Box 1108, 75142–5401, tel. 972/932–7200; Patsy Youngs, President

TEXAS HEALTH PRESBYTERIAN HOSPITAL PLANO (O, 371 beds) 6200 West Parker Road, Plano, TX Zip 75093–8185; tel. 972/981–8000; Joshua Floren, President
Web address: www.texashealth.org

TEXAS HEALTH SPECIALTY HOSPITAL (O, 10 beds) 1301 Pennsylvania Avenue, 4th Floor, Fort Worth, TX Zip 76104–2190; tel. 817/250–5500; Cheryl Mobley, FACHE, President

Owned, leased, sponsored:	14 hospitals	2863 beds
Contract-managed:	0 hospitals	0 beds
Totals:	14 hospitals	2863 beds

2445: THEDACARE, INC. (NP)
122 East College Avenue, Appleton, WI Zip 54911–5794, P O Box 8025, 54912–8025, tel. 920/830–5889; Imran A. Andrabi, M.D., President and Chief Executive Officer
(Moderately Centralized Health System)

WISCONSIN: THEDA CARE MEDICAL CENTER - WILD ROSE (O, 25 beds) 601 Grove Avenue, Wild Rose, WI Zip 54984–6903, P O Box 243, 54984–0243, tel. 920/622–3257; Craig A. Kantos, Chief Executive Officer
Web address: www.wildrosehospital.org

THEDACARE MEDICAL CENTER-NEW LONDON (O, 25 beds) 1405 Mill Street, New London, WI Zip 54961–0307, P O Box 307, 54961–0307, tel. 920/531–2000; William Schmidt, President and Chief Executive Officer

THEDACARE MEDICAL CENTER-SHAWANO (O, 22 beds) 100 County Road B, Shawano, WI Zip 54166–2127; tel. 715/526–2111; William Schmidt, Chief Executive Officer
Web address: www.shawanomed.org

THEDACARE MEDICAL CENTER-WAUPACA (O, 25 beds) 800 Riverside Drive, Waupaca, WI Zip 54981–1999; tel. 715/258–1000; Craig A. Kantos, Chief Executive Officer

THEDACARE REGIONAL MEDICAL CENTER-APPLETON (O, 149 beds) 1818 North Meade Street, Appleton, WI Zip 54911–3496; tel. 920/731–4101; Brian Burmeister, Senior Vice President
Web address: www.thedacare.org

THEDACARE REGIONAL MEDICAL CENTER-BERLIN (O, 62 beds) 225 Memorial Drive, Berlin, WI Zip 54923–1295; tel. 920/361–1313; John Feeney, President and Chief Executive Officer

THEDACARE REGIONAL MEDICAL CENTER-NEENAH (O, 151 beds) 130 Second Street, Neenah, WI Zip 54956–2883, P O Box 2021, 54957–2021, tel. 920/729–3100; Brian Burmeister, Senior Vice President, ThedaCare Hospitals
Web address: www.thedacare.org

Owned, leased, sponsored:	7 hospitals	459 beds
Contract-managed:	0 hospitals	0 beds
Totals:	7 hospitals	459 beds

For explanation of codes following names, see page B2.
★ Indicates Type III membership in the American Hospital Association.

★**0643: THOMAS HEALTH SYSTEM, INC.** (NP)
4605 MacCorkle Avenue SW, South Charleston, WV Zip 25309–1311; tel. 304/766–3600; Daniel Lauffer, FACHE, President and Chief Executive Officer
(Centralized Health System)

WEST VIRGINIA: SAINT FRANCIS HOSPITAL (O, 65 beds) 333 Laidley Street, Charleston, WV Zip 25301–1628, P O Box 471, 25322–0471, tel. 304/347–6500; Daniel Lauffer, FACHE, President and Chief Executive Officer
Web address: www.stfrancishospital.com

THOMAS MEMORIAL HOSPITAL (O, 211 beds) 4605 MacCorkle Avenue SW, South Charleston, WV Zip 25309–1398; tel. 304/766–3600; Daniel Lauffer, FACHE, President and Chief Executive Officer

Owned, leased, sponsored:	2 hospitals	276 beds
Contract-managed:	0 hospitals	0 beds
Totals:	2 hospitals	276 beds

★**0812: TIDELANDS HEALTH** (NP)
606 Black River Road, Georgetown, SC Zip 29440–3304, P O Box 421718, 29442–4203, tel. 843/527–7000; Bruce P. Bailey, President and Chief Executive Officer

TIDELANDS GEORGETOWN MEMORIAL HOSPITAL (C, 136 beds) 606 Black River Road, Georgetown, SC Zip 29440–3368, Drawer 421718, 29442–4203, tel. 843/527–7000; Bruce P. Bailey, Chief Executive Officer

TIDELANDS WACCAMAW COMMUNITY HOSPITAL (C, 169 beds) 4070 Highway 17 Bypass, Murrells Inlet, SC Zip 29576–5033, P O Drawer 3350, 29576–2673, tel. 843/652–1000; Bruce P. Bailey, Chief Executive Officer
Web address: www.tidelandswaccamawcommunity.org

Owned, leased, sponsored:	0 hospitals	0 beds
Contract-managed:	2 hospitals	305 beds
Totals:	2 hospitals	305 beds

★**0910: TIFT REGIONAL HEALTH SYSTEM** (NP)
901 East 18th Street, Tifton, GA Zip 31794–3648; tel. 229/353–6100; William T. Richardson, President and Chief Executive Officer
(Independent Hospital System)

GEORGIA: COOK MEDICAL CENTER-A CAMPUS OF TIFT REGIONAL MEDICAL CENTER (O, 155 beds) 706 North Parrish Avenue, Adel, GA Zip 31620–1511; tel. 229/896–8000; Michael L. Purvis, Chief Executive Officer
Web address: www.cookmedicalcenter.com

TIFT REGIONAL MEDICAL CENTER (O, 181 beds) 901 East 18th Street, Tifton, GA Zip 31794–3648, Drawer 747, 31793–0747, tel. 229/382–7120; William T. Richardson, President and Chief Executive Officer

Owned, leased, sponsored:	2 hospitals	336 beds
Contract-managed:	0 hospitals	0 beds
Totals:	2 hospitals	336 beds

★**0906: TRINITY HEALTH** (CC)
20555 Victor Parkway, Livonia, MI Zip 48152–7031; tel. 734/343–1000; Richard J. Gilfillan, M.D., Chief Executive Officer
(Decentralized Health System)

CALIFORNIA: SAINT AGNES MEDICAL CENTER (O, 436 beds) 1303 East Herndon Avenue, Fresno, CA Zip 93720–3397; tel. 559/450–3000; Nancy Hollingsworth, R.N., MSN, President and Chief Executive Officer
Web address: www.samc.com

CONNECTICUT: JOHNSON MEMORIAL MEDICAL CENTER (O, 78 beds) 201 Chestnut Hill Road, Stafford Springs, CT Zip 06076–4005; tel. 860/684–4251; Stuart E. Rosenberg, President

MOUNT SINAI REHABILITATION HOSPITAL (O, 30 beds) 490 Blue Hills Avenue, Hartford, CT Zip 06112–1513; tel. 860/714–3500; Robert J. Krug, M.D., Chief Executive Officer
Web address: www.stfranciscare.org

SAINT FRANCIS HOSPITAL AND MEDICAL CENTER (O, 567 beds) 114 Woodland Street, Hartford, CT Zip 06105–1208; tel. 860/714–4000; John F. Rodis, M.D., President
Web address: www.saintfranciscare.com

SAINT MARY'S HOSPITAL (O, 156 beds) 56 Franklin Street, Waterbury, CT Zip 06706–1281; tel. 203/709–6000; Chad W. Wable, President and Chief Executive Officer

DELAWARE: ST. FRANCIS HOSPITAL (O, 154 beds) Seventh and Clayton Streets, Wilmington, DE Zip 19805–0500, P O Box 2500, 19805–0500, tel. 302/421–4100; David A. Ricci, Interim President and Chief Executive Officer
Web address: www.stfrancishealthcare.org

FLORIDA: BARTOW REGIONAL MEDICAL CENTER (O, 72 beds) 2200 Osprey Boulevard, Bartow, FL Zip 33830–3308; tel. 863/533–8111; Philip Minden, Chief Executive Officer

HOLY CROSS HOSPITAL (O, 367 beds) 4725 North Federal Highway, Fort Lauderdale, FL Zip 33308–4668, P O Box 23460, 33307–3460, tel. 954/771–8000; Patrick Taylor, M.D., President and Chief Executive Officer
Web address: www.holy-cross.com

MEASE COUNTRYSIDE HOSPITAL (C, 311 beds) 3231 McMullen Booth Road, Safety Harbor, FL Zip 34695–6607; tel. 727/725–6111; Lou Galdieri, R.N., President
Web address: www.mpmhealth.com

MEASE DUNEDIN HOSPITAL (C, 120 beds) 601 Main Street, Dunedin, FL Zip 34698–5891; tel. 727/733–1111; Lou Galdieri, R.N., President

SOUTH FLORIDA BAPTIST HOSPITAL (S, 124 beds) 301 North Alexander Street, Plant City, FL Zip 33563–4303; tel. 813/757–1200; Karen Kerr, R.N., President
Web address: www.https://baycare.org/sfbh

ST. ANTHONY'S HOSPITAL (S, 393 beds) 1200 Seventh Avenue North, Saint Petersburg, FL Zip 33705–1388, P O Box 12588, 33733–2588, tel. 727/825–1100; M. Scott Smith, President

ST. JOSEPH'S HOSPITAL (S, 1030 beds) 3001 West Martin Luther King Jr. Boulevard, Tampa, FL Zip 33607–6387, P O Box 4227, 33677–4227, tel. 813/870–4000; Kimberly Guy, President
Web address: www.sjbhealth.org

WINTER HAVEN HOSPITAL (S, 361 beds) 200 Avenue F NE, Winter Haven, FL Zip 33881–4193; tel. 863/293–1121; Stephen A. Nierman, President

GEORGIA: ST. MARY'S GOOD SAMARITAN HOSPITAL (O, 25 beds) 5401 Lake Oconee Parkway, Greensboro, GA Zip 30642–4232; tel. 706/453–7331; D. Montez. Carter, President
Web address: www.stmarysgoodsam.org

ST. MARY'S HEALTH CARE SYSTEM (O, 183 beds) 1230 Baxter Street, Athens, GA Zip 30606–3791; tel. 706/389–3000; Donald McKenna, President and Chief Executive Officer

ST. MARY'S SACRED HEART HOSPITAL (O, 35 beds) 367 Clear Creek Parkway, Lavonia, GA Zip 30553–4173; tel. 706/356–7800; Jeff English, Interim Chief Executive Officer
Web address: www.stmaryssacredheart.org/

IDAHO: SAINT ALPHONSUS MEDICAL CENTER - NAMPA (O, 131 beds) 4300 East Flamingo Avenue, Nampa, ID Zip 83686–6008; tel. 208/201–5000; Karl Keeler, President

SAINT ALPHONSUS REGIONAL MEDICAL CENTER (O, 399 beds) 1055 N Curtis Rd , Boise, ID Zip 83706–1309, 1055 North Curtis Road, 83706–1309, tel. 208/367–2121; Odette Bolano, R.N., President
Web address: www.saintalphonsus.org

ILLINOIS: GOTTLIEB MEMORIAL HOSPITAL (O, 205 beds) 701 West North Avenue, Melrose Park, IL Zip 60160–1612; tel. 708/681–3200; Lori Price, President
Web address: www.gottliebhospital.org

LOYOLA UNIVERSITY MEDICAL CENTER (O, 517 beds) 2160 South First Avenue, Maywood, IL Zip 60153–3328; tel. 708/216–9000; Chad Whelan, M.D., President
Web address: www.loyolamedicine.org/Medical_Services/index.cfm

For explanation of codes following names, see page B2.
★ Indicates Type III membership in the American Hospital Association.

MERCY HOSPITAL AND MEDICAL CENTER (O, 189 beds) 2525 South Michigan Avenue, Chicago, IL Zip 60616–2333; tel. 312/567–2000; Carol L. Schneider, President and Chief Executive Officer

INDIANA: MISHAWAKA MEDICAL CENTER (O, 294 beds) 5215 Holy Cross Parkway, Mishawaka, IN Zip 46545–1469; tel. 574/335–5000; Chad Towner, Chief Executive Officer
Web address: www.sjmed.com

PLYMOUTH MEDICAL CENTER (O, 48 beds) 1915 Lake Avenue, Plymouth, IN Zip 46563–9366, P O Box 670, 46563–0670, tel. 574/948–4000; Loretta Schmidt, President

IOWA: BAUM HARMON MERCY HOSPITAL (O, 11 beds) 255 North Welch Avenue, Primghar, IA Zip 51245–7765, P O Box 528, 51245–0528, tel. 712/957–2300; Angie Shilling, Chief Executive Officer
Web address: www.baumharmon.org

CENTRAL COMMUNITY HOSPITAL (C, 15 beds) 901 Davidson Street NW, Elkader, IA Zip 52043–9015; tel. 563/245–7000; Brooke Kensinger, Chief Executive Officer

COVENANT MEDICAL CENTER (C, 229 beds) 3421 West Ninth Street, Waterloo, IA Zip 50702–5401; tel. 319/272–8000; Jack Dusenbery, President and Chief Executive Officer
Web address: www.wheatoniowa.org

FRANKLIN GENERAL HOSPITAL (C, 77 beds) 1720 Central Avenue East, Suite A, Hampton, IA Zip 50441–1867; tel. 641/456–5000; Kim Price, Chief Executive Officer
Web address: www.franklingeneral.com

HANCOCK COUNTY HEALTH SYSTEM (C, 25 beds) 532 First Street NW, Britt, IA Zip 50423–1227; tel. 641/843–5000; Jeffry Stampohar, Chief Executive Officer
Web address: www.trusthchs.com/hancock-county-health-system

HANSEN FAMILY HOSPITAL (C, 21 beds) 920 South Oak, Iowa Falls, IA Zip 50126–9506; tel. 641/648–4631; Katie Ricks, Chief Executive Officer

HAWARDEN REGIONAL HEALTHCARE (C, 18 beds) 1111 11th Street, Hawarden, IA Zip 51023–1999; tel. 712/551–3100; Jayson Pullman, Chief Executive Officer
Web address: www.hawardenregionalhealthcare.com/

KOSSUTH REGIONAL HEALTH CENTER (C, 23 beds) 1515 South Phillips Street, Algona, IA Zip 50511–3649; tel. 515/295–2451; Scott A. Curtis, Administrator and Chief Executive Officer

MERCY HOSPITAL OF FRANCISCAN SISTERS (C, 64 beds) 201 Eighth Avenue SE, Oelwein, IA Zip 50662–2447; tel. 319/283–6000; Terri Derflinger, Site Administrator
Web address: www.wheatoniowa.org

MERCY MEDICAL CENTER-CLINTON (O, 290 beds) 1410 North Fourth Street, Clinton, IA Zip 52732–2940; tel. 563/244–5555; Sean J. Williams, President and Chief Executive Officer
Web address: www.mercyclinton.com

MERCY MEDICAL CENTER-DUBUQUE (O, 235 beds) 250 Mercy Drive, Dubuque, IA Zip 52001–7360; tel. 563/589–8000; Kay Takes, R.N., President

MERCY MEDICAL CENTER-DYERSVILLE (O, 20 beds) 1111 Third Street SW, Dyersville, IA Zip 52040–1725; tel. 563/875–7101; Kay Takes, R.N., President
Web address: www.mercydubuque.com/mercy-dyersville

MERCY MEDICAL CENTER-NEW HAMPTON (O, 18 beds) 308 North Maple Avenue, New Hampton, IA Zip 50659–1142; tel. 641/394–4121; Aaron Flugum, Chief Executive Officer
Web address: www.mercynewhampton.com

MERCY MEDICAL CENTER-NORTH IOWA (O, 205 beds) 1000 Fourth Street SW, Mason City, IA Zip 50401–2800; tel. 641/428–7000; Daniel Varnum, President and Chief Executive Officer
Web address: www.mercynorthiowa.com

MERCY MEDICAL CENTER-SIOUX CITY (O, 186 beds) 801 Fifth Street, Sioux City, IA Zip 51101–1326, P O Box 3168, 51102–3168, tel. 712/279–2010; James G. Fitzpatrick, FACHE, Chief Executive Officer

MITCHELL COUNTY REGIONAL HEALTH CENTER (C, 25 beds) 616 North Eighth Street, Osage, IA Zip 50461–1498; tel. 641/732–6000; Shelly Russell, Chief Executive Officer
Web address: www.mitchellcohospital-clinics.com

PALO ALTO COUNTY HEALTH SYSTEM (C, 47 beds) 3201 First Street, Emmetsburg, IA Zip 50536–2516; tel. 712/852–5500; Charles P. Kelch, Interim Chief Executive Officer

REGIONAL HEALTH SERVICES OF HOWARD COUNTY (C, 19 beds) 235 Eighth Avenue West, Cresco, IA Zip 52136–1098; tel. 563/547–2101; Robin M. Schluter, Chief Executive Officer
Web address: www.rhshc.com

SARTORI MEMORIAL HOSPITAL (C, 50 beds) 515 College Street, Cedar Falls, IA Zip 50613–2500; tel. 319/268–3000; MaryJo Kavalier, Administrator

MARYLAND: HOLY CROSS GERMANTOWN HOSPITAL (O, 101 beds) 19801 Observation Drive, Germantown, MD Zip 20876–4070; tel. 301/754–7000; Doug Ryder, President
Web address: www.holycrosshealth.org/germantown

HOLY CROSS HEALTH (O, 415 beds) 1500 Forest Glen Road, Silver Spring, MD Zip 20910–1487; tel. 301/754–7000; Louis Damiano, Acting President
Web address: www.holycrosshealth.org

MASSACHUSETTS: FARREN CARE CENTER (O, 72 beds) 340 Montague City Road, Turners Falls, MA Zip 01376–9983; tel. 413/774–3111; James Clifford, Administrator

MERCY MEDICAL CENTER (O, 333 beds) 271 Carew Street, Springfield, MA Zip 01104–2398, P O Box 9012, 01102–9012, tel. 413/748–9000; Mary Elizabeth. O'Brien, President
Web address: www.mercycares.com

MICHIGAN: MERCY HEALTH HACKLEY CAMPUS (O, 401 beds) 1700 Clinton Street, Muskegon, MI Zip 49442–5502, P O Box 3302, 49443–3302, tel. 231/726–3511; Greg Loomis, President
Web address: www.mercyhealthmuskegon.com

MERCY HEALTH SAINT MARY'S (O, 371 beds) 200 Jefferson Avenue SE, Grand Rapids, MI Zip 49503–4598; tel. 616/685–5000; Bill Manns, President

MERCY HEALTH, LAKESHORE CAMPUS (O, 24 beds) 72 South State Street, Shelby, MI Zip 49455–1299; tel. 231/861–2156; Jay Bryan, President and Chief Executive Officer
Web address: www.mercyhealthmuskegon.com

ST. JOSEPH MERCY ANN ARBOR (O, 483 beds) 5301 Mcauley Drive, Ypsilanti, MI Zip 48197–1051, P O Box 995, Ann Arbor, 48106–0995, tel. 734/712–3456; David Brooks, President

ST. JOSEPH MERCY CHELSEA (O, 96 beds) 775 South Main Street, Chelsea, MI Zip 48118–1383; tel. 734/593–6000; Nancy Kay. Graebner, President and Chief Executive Officer
Web address: www.cch.org

ST. JOSEPH MERCY LIVINGSTON HOSPITAL (O, 38 beds) 620 Byron Road, Howell, MI Zip 48843–1093; tel. 517/545–6000; John F. O'Malley, FACHE, President
Web address: www.stjoeslivingston.org/livingston

ST. JOSEPH MERCY OAKLAND (O, 422 beds) 44405 Woodward Avenue, Pontiac, MI Zip 48341–5023; tel. 248/858–3000; Shannon Striebich, Chief Executive Officer
Web address: www.stjoesoakland.com

ST. MARY MERCY HOSPITAL (O, 303 beds) 36475 Five Mile Road, Livonia, MI Zip 48154–1988; tel. 734/655–4800; David A. Spivey, President and Chief Executive Officer

NEBRASKA: OAKLAND MERCY HOSPITAL (O, 18 beds) 601 East Second Street, Oakland, NE Zip 68045–1499; tel. 402/685–5601; John W. Werner, Chief Executive Officer
Web address: www.oaklandhospital.org

PENDER COMMUNITY HOSPITAL (C, 67 beds) 100 Hospital Drive , Pender, NE Zip 68047–0100, P O Box 100, 68047–0100, tel. 402/385–3083; Melissa Kelly, Chief Executive Officer and Chief Financial Officer
Web address: www.pendercommunityhospital.com

NEW JERSEY: LOURDES MEDICAL CENTER OF BURLINGTON COUNTY (O, 169 beds) 218-A Sunset Road, Willingboro, NJ Zip 08046–1162; tel. 609/835–2900; Mark Nessel, Executive Vice President and Chief Operating Officer

OUR LADY OF LOURDES MEDICAL CENTER (O, 350 beds) 1600 Haddon Avenue, Camden, NJ Zip 08103–3117; tel. 856/757–3500; Reginald Blaber, M.D., FACC, President
Web address: www.lourdesnet.org

For explanation of codes following names, see page B2.
★ Indicates Type III membership in the American Hospital Association.

ST. FRANCIS MEDICAL CENTER (O, 163 beds) 601 Hamilton Avenue, Trenton, NJ Zip 08629–1986; tel. 609/599–5000; Vincent Costantino, Interim President and Chief Administrative Officer
Web address: www.stfrancismedical.org/

NEW YORK: ALBANY MEMORIAL HOSPITAL (O, 74 beds) 600 Northern Boulevard, Albany, NY Zip 12204–1083; tel. 518/471–3221; Virginia L. Golden, Chief Executive Officer
Web address: www.nehealth.com

SAMARITAN HOSPITAL (O, 212 beds) 2215 Burdett Avenue, Troy, NY Zip 12180–2475; tel. 518/271–3300; Norman E. Dascher Jr, Chief Executive Officer
Web address: www.nehealth.com

ST. JOSEPH'S HOSPITAL HEALTH CENTER (O, 431 beds) 301 Prospect Avenue, Syracuse, NY Zip 13203–1807; tel. 315/448–5111; Leslie Paul. Luke, President and Chief Executive Officer

ST. MARY'S HOSPITAL (O, 173 beds) 1300 Massachusetts Avenue, Troy, NY Zip 12180–1695; tel. 518/268–5000; Norman E. Dascher Jr, Chief Executive Officer
Web address: www.setonhealth.org

ST. PETER'S HOSPITAL (O, 442 beds) 315 South Manning Boulevard, Albany, NY Zip 12208–1789; tel. 518/525–1550; Virginia L. Golden, Chief Executive Officer
Web address: www.sphcs.org

SUNNYVIEW REHABILITATION HOSPITAL (O, 115 beds) 1270 Belmont Avenue, Schenectady, NY Zip 12308–2104; tel. 518/382–4500; Edward Eisenman, Chief Executive Officer

NORTH CAROLINA: ST. JOSEPH OF THE PINES HOSPITAL (O, 204 beds) 590 Central Drive, Southern Pines, NC Zip 28387; tel. 910/246–1000; Ken Cormier, President and Chief Executive Officer

OHIO: MOUNT CARMEL NEW ALBANY SURGICAL HOSPITAL (O, 60 beds) 7333 Smith's Mill Road, New Albany, OH Zip 43054–9291; tel. 614/775–6600; Diane Doucette, R.N., President
Web address: www.mountcarmelhealth.com

MOUNT CARMEL ST. ANN'S (O, 281 beds) 500 South Cleveland Avenue, Westerville, OH Zip 43081–8998; tel. 614/898–4000; Kim Unhee, President

MOUNT CARMEL (O, 749 beds) 793 West State Street, Columbus, OH Zip 43222–1551; tel. 614/234–5000; Sean McKibben, President and Chief Operating Officer
Web address: www.mountcarmelhealth.com

OREGON: SAINT ALPHONSUS MEDICAL CENTER - BAKER CITY (S, 25 beds) 3325 Pocahontas Road, Baker City, OR Zip 97814–1464; tel. 541/523–6461; Phil Harrop, President
Web address: https://www.saintalphonsus.org/bakercity

SAINT ALPHONSUS MEDICAL CENTER - ONTARIO (S, 38 beds) 351 SW Ninth Street, Ontario, OR Zip 97914–2693; tel. 541/881–7000; Kenneth Hart, President
Web address: www.saintalphonsus.org/ontario

PENNSYLVANIA: MERCY FITZGERALD HOSPITAL (O, 343 beds) 1500 Lansdowne Avenue, Suite 100, Darby, PA Zip 19023–1200; tel. 610/237–4000; Susan Cusack, Executive Director

NAZARETH HOSPITAL (O, 162 beds) 2601 Holme Avenue, Philadelphia, PA Zip 19152–2096; tel. 215/335–6000; Nancy Cherone, Executive Director and Administrator
Web address: www.nazarethhospital.org

ST. MARY MEDICAL CENTER (O, 307 beds) 1201 Langhorne-Newtown Road, Langhorne, PA Zip 19047–1201; tel. 215/710–2000; James L. Woodward, President and Chief Executive Officer
Web address: www.stmaryhealthcare.org

Owned, leased, sponsored:	60 hospitals	14134 beds
Contract-managed:	15 hospitals	1111 beds
Totals:	75 hospitals	15245 beds

★9255:   TRUMAN MEDICAL CENTERS (NP)
2301 Holmes Street, Kansas City, MO Zip 64108–2677; tel. 816/404–1000; Mark Steele, M.D., Chief Medical Officer and Chief Operating Officer
(Moderately Centralized Health System)

MISSOURI: TRUMAN MEDICAL CENTER-HOSPITAL HILL (O, 249 beds) 2301 Holmes Street, Kansas City, MO Zip 64108–2640; tel. 816/404–1000; Charlie Shields, President and Chief Executive Officer

TRUMAN MEDICAL CENTER-LAKEWOOD (O, 298 beds) 7900 Lee's Summit Road, Kansas City, MO Zip 64139–1236; tel. 816/404–7000; Lynette Wheeler, MSN, Chief Operating Officer
Web address: www.trumed.org

Owned, leased, sponsored:	2 hospitals	547 beds
Contract-managed:	0 hospitals	0 beds
Totals:	2 hospitals	547 beds

9195:   U. S. INDIAN HEALTH SERVICE (FG)
801 Thompson Avenue, Rockville, MD Zip 20852–1627; tel. 301/443–1083; Yvette Roubideaux, M.D., M.P.H., Director
(Moderately Centralized Health System)

ARIZONA: CHINLE COMPREHENSIVE HEALTH CARE FACILITY (O, 60 beds) Highway 191, Hospital Road, Chinle, AZ Zip 86503, P O Drawer PH, 86503–8000, tel. 928/674–7001; Ron Tso, Chief Executive Officer

HOPI HEALTH CARE CENTER (O, 15 beds) Highway 264 Mile Marker 388, Keams Canyon, AZ Zip 86042, P O Box 4000, Polacca, 86042–4000, tel. 928/737–6000; Mose Herne, Chief Executive Officer
Web address: www.ihs.gov/index.asp

SAN CARLOS APACHE HEALTHCARE CORPORATION (O, 8 beds) 103 Medicine Way Road, Peridot, AZ Zip 85542; tel. 928/475–1400; Victoria D. Began, R.N., MS, President and Chief Executive Officer
Web address: www.ihs.gov

U. S. PUBLIC HEALTH SERVICE INDIAN HOSPITAL-SELLS (O, 12 beds) Highway 86 & Topawa Road, Sells, AZ Zip 85634, P O Box 548, 85634–0548, tel. 520/383–7251; Angela Fallon, Acting Chief Executive Officer

U. S. PUBLIC HEALTH SERVICE INDIAN HOSPITAL-WHITERIVER (O, 35 beds) 200 West Hospital Drive, Whiteriver, AZ Zip 85941–0860, State Route 73, Box 860, 85941–0860, tel. 928/338–4911; Michelle Martinez, Chief Executive Officer
Web address: www.ihs.gov

U. S. PUBLIC HEALTH SERVICE INDIAN HOSPITAL (O, 20 beds) 12033 Agency Road, Parker, AZ Zip 85344–7718; tel. 928/669–2137; Elizabeth Helsel, Chief Executive Officer
Web address: www.ihs.gov

U. S. PUBLIC HEALTH SERVICE PHOENIX INDIAN MEDICAL CENTER (O, 127 beds) 4212 North 16th Street, Phoenix, AZ Zip 85016–5389; tel. 602/263–1200; Rear Admiral, Michael Weakhee, Chief Executive Officer

MARYLAND: NATIONAL INSTITUTES OF HEALTH CLINICAL CENTER (O, 136 beds) 9000 Rockville Pike, Building 10, Room 6–2551, Bethesda, MD Zip 20892–1504; tel. 301/496–4000; John I. Gallin, M.D., Director
Web address: www.clinicalcenter.nih.gov

MINNESOTA: RED LAKE INDIAN HEALTH SERVICE HOSPITAL (O, 19 beds) 24760 Hospital Drive, Red Lake, MN Zip 56671, P O Box 497, 56671–0497, tel. 218/679–3912; Norine Smith, Chief Executive Officer
Web address: www.rlnnredlakehospital.com/

U. S. PUBLIC HEALTH SERVICE INDIAN HOSPITAL (O, 9 beds) 425 7th Street North West, Cass Lake, MN Zip 56633; tel. 218/335–3200; Louis P. Erdrich, Acting Chief Executive Officer

MONTANA: CROW/NORTHERN CHEYENNE HOSPITAL (O, 24 beds) 10110 South 7650 East, Crow Agency, MT Zip 59022–0009, P O Box 9, 59022–0009, tel. 406/638–2626; Darren Crowe, Chief Executive Officer
Web address: https://www.ihs.gov/billings/healthcarefacilities/crow/

FORT BELKNAP SERVICE UNIT (O, 6 beds) 669 Agency Main Street, Harlem, MT Zip 59526–9455; tel. 406/353–3100; Gregory Smith, M.D., Chief Executive Officer

U. S. PUBLIC HEALTH SERVICE BLACKFEET COMMUNITY HOSPITAL (O, 25 beds) 760 New Hospital Circle, Saint Mary, MT Zip 59417–0760, P O Box 760, Browning, 59417–0760, tel. 406/338–6100; Garland Stiffarm, Acting Chief Executive Officer
Web address: www.ihs.gov

For explanation of codes following names, see page B2.
★ Indicates Type III membership in the American Hospital Association.

NEBRASKA: U. S. PUBLIC HEALTH SERVICE INDIAN HOSPITAL (O, 30 beds) Highway 7577, Winnebago, NE Zip 68071; tel. 402/878–2231; Gary Wabaunsee, Service Unit Director
Web address: www.ihs.gov

NEW MEXICO: ACOMA-CANONCITO-LAGUNA HOSPITAL (O, 6 beds) 80B Veterans Boulevard, Acoma, NM Zip 87034, P O Box 130, San Fidel, 87049–0130, tel. 505/552–5300; Melody Price-Yonts, Chief Executive Officer

GALLUP INDIAN MEDICAL CENTER (O, 84 beds) 516 East Nizhoni Boulevard, Gallup, NM Zip 87301–5748, P O Box 1337, 87305–1337, tel. 505/722–1000; Vida J. Khow, Chief Executive Officer
Web address: www.ihs.gov/navajo/index.cfm?module=nao_hcc_gallup

MESCALERO PUBLIC HEALTH SERVICE INDIAN HOSPITAL (O, 13 beds) 318 Abalone Loop, Mescalero, NM Zip 88340, Box 210, 88340–0210, tel. 505/464–3801; Dorlynn Simmons, Chief Executive Officer

NORTHERN NAVAJO MEDICAL CENTER (O, 68 beds) Highway 491 North, Shiprock, NM Zip 87420–0160, P O Box 160, 87420–0160, tel. 505/368–6001; Fannessa Comer, Chief Executive Officer
Web address: www.ihs.gov/

PHS SANTA FE INDIAN HOSPITAL (O, 4 beds) 1700 Cerrillos Road, Santa Fe, NM Zip 87505–3554; tel. 505/988–9821; Leslie Dye, Chief Executive Officer

U. S. PUBLIC HEALTH SERVICE INDIAN HOSPITAL (O, 12 beds) Route 9 and State Road 371, Crownpoint, NM Zip 87313, P O Box 358, 87313–0358, tel. 505/786–5291; Anslem Roanhorse, Chief Executive Officer
Web address: www.ihs.gov

U. S. PUBLIC HEALTH SERVICE INDIAN HOSPITAL (O, 32 beds) Route 301 North B Street, Zuni, NM Zip 87327, P O Box 467, 87327–0467, tel. 505/782–4431; Jean Othole, Chief Executive Officer
Web address: www.ihs.gov

NORTH DAKOTA: INDIAN HEALTH SERVICE - QUENTIN N. BURDICK MEMORIAL HEALTH CARE FACILITY (O, 27 beds) 1300 Hospital Loop, Belcourt, ND Zip 58316, P O Box 160, 58316–0160, tel. 701/477–6111; Shelly Harris, Chief Executive Officer
Web address: www.ihs.gov

STANDING ROCK SERVICE UNIT, FORT YATES HOSPITAL, INDIAN HEALTH SERVICE, DHHS (O, 14 beds) 10 North River Road, Fort Yates, ND Zip 58538, P O Box 'J', 58538, tel. 701/854–3831; Jana Gipp, Chief Executive Officer

OKLAHOMA: CLAREMORE INDIAN HOSPITAL (O, 44 beds) 101 South Moore Avenue, Claremore, OK Zip 74017–5091; tel. 918/342–6200; George Valliere, Chief Executive Officer
Web address: www.ihs.gov

LAWTON INDIAN HOSPITAL (O, 26 beds) 1515 Lawrie Tatum Road, Lawton, OK Zip 73507–3099; tel. 580/353–0350; Travis Scott, Chief Executive Officer

SOUTH DAKOTA: INDIAN HEALTH SERVICE HOSPITAL (O, 9 beds) 3200 Canyon Lake Drive, Rapid City, SD Zip 57702–8197; tel. 605/355–2280; Kevin J. Stiffarm, Chief Executive Officer
Web address: www.ihs.gov

U. S. PUBLIC HEALTH SERVICE INDIAN HOSPITAL (O, 8 beds) 317 Main Street, Eagle Butte, SD Zip 57625–1012, P O Box 1012, 57625–1012, tel. 605/964–7724; Charles Fisher, Chief Executive Officer

U. S. PUBLIC HEALTH SERVICE INDIAN HOSPITAL (O, 45 beds) East Highway 18, Pine Ridge, SD Zip 57770, P O Box 1201, 57770–1201, tel. 605/867–5131; Ellen Davis, Service Unit Director
Web address: www.ihs.gov

U. S. PUBLIC HEALTH SERVICE INDIAN HOSPITAL (O, 35 beds) Highway 18, Soldier Creek Road, Rosebud, SD Zip 57570; tel. 605/747–2231; Kathey Wilson, Acting Chief Executive Officer

Owned, leased, sponsored:	29 hospitals	953 beds
Contract-managed:	0 hospitals	0 beds
Totals:	29 hospitals	953 beds

★**9105: UAB HEALTH SYSTEM** (NP)
500 22nd Street South, Suite 408, Birmingham, AL Zip 35233–3110; tel. 205/975–5362; William Ferniany, Ph.D., Chief Executive Officer
(Centralized Physician/Insurance Health System)

ALABAMA: MEDICAL WEST (O, 231 beds) 995 Ninth Avenue SW, Bessemer, AL Zip 35022–4527; tel. 205/481–7000; Brian Keith. Pennington, President and Chief Executive Officer
Web address: www.medicalwesthospital.org

UNIVERSITY OF ALABAMA HOSPITAL (O, 1191 beds) 619 19th Street South, Birmingham, AL Zip 35249–1900; tel. 205/934–4011; Anthony Patterson, FACHE, Senior Vice President Inpatient Services

Owned, leased, sponsored:	2 hospitals	1422 beds
Contract-managed:	0 hospitals	0 beds
Totals:	2 hospitals	1422 beds

★**0082: UC HEALTH** (NP)
3200 Burnet Avenue, Cincinnati, OH Zip 45229–3019; tel. 513/585–6000; Richard P. Lofgren, M.D., M.P.H., President and CEO
(Moderately Centralized Health System)

OHIO: DANIEL DRAKE CENTER FOR POST ACUTE CARE (O, 202 beds) 151 West Galbraith Road, Cincinnati, OH Zip 45216–1015; tel. 513/418–2500; Amy Schroyer, Vice President Administration and Senior Site Executive
Web address: www.uchealth.com/danieldrakecenter/

UNIVERSITY OF CINCINNATI MEDICAL CENTER (O, 592 beds) 234 Goodman Street, Cincinnati, OH Zip 45219–2316; tel. 513/584–1000; Jennifer Jackson, R.N., MSN, Chief Administrative Officer, Chief Nursing Officer and Vice President
Web address: www.uchealth.com/university-of-cincinnati-medical-center/

WEST CHESTER HOSPITAL (O, 182 beds) 7700 University Drive, West Chester, OH Zip 45069–2505; tel. 513/298–3000; Tom G. Daskalakis, Chief Administrative Officer

Owned, leased, sponsored:	3 hospitals	976 beds
Contract-managed:	0 hospitals	0 beds
Totals:	3 hospitals	976 beds

★**0111: UF HEALTH SHANDS** (NP)
1600 SW Archer Road, Gainesville, FL Zip 32610–0326; tel. 352/733–1500; Edward Jimenez, Chief Executive Officer
(Moderately Centralized Health System)

FLORIDA: UF HEALTH JACKSONVILLE (O, 589 beds) 655 West Eighth Street, Jacksonville, FL Zip 32209–6595; tel. 904/244–0411; Russell Armistead, Chief Executive Officer
Web address: www.ufhealthjax.org/

UF HEALTH SHANDS HOSPITAL (O, 966 beds) 1600 SW Archer Road, Gainesville, FL Zip 32610–3003, PO Box 100326, 32610–0326, tel. 352/265–0111; Edward Jimenez, Chief Executive Officer

Owned, leased, sponsored:	2 hospitals	1555 beds
Contract-managed:	0 hospitals	0 beds
Totals:	2 hospitals	1555 beds

★**0224: UMASS MEMORIAL HEALTH CARE, INC.** (NP)
1 Biotech Park, Worcester, MA Zip 01605–2982; tel. 508/334–0100; Eric Dickson, M.D., President and Chief Executive Officer
(Moderately Centralized Health System)

MASSACHUSETTS: CLINTON HOSPITAL (O, 41 beds) 201 Highland Street, Clinton, MA Zip 01510–1096; tel. 978/368–3000; Deborah K. Weymouth, FACHE, President and Chief Executive Officer
Web address: www.clintonhospital.org

HEALTHALLIANCE HOSPITALS (O, 103 beds) 60 Hospital Road, Leominster, MA Zip 01453–2205; tel. 978/466–2000; Deborah K. Weymouth, FACHE, President and Chief Executive Officer

UMASS MEMORIAL MEDICAL CENTER (O, 662 beds) 119 Belmont Street, Worcester, MA Zip 01605–2982; tel. 508/334–1000; Patrick L. Muldoon, FACHE, President
Web address: www.umassmemorial.org

For explanation of codes following names, see page B2.
★ Indicates Type III membership in the American Hospital Association.

UMASS MEMORIAL-MARLBOROUGH HOSPITAL (O, 67 beds) 157 Union ST, Marlborough, MA Zip 01752-1297; tel. 508/481-5000; Steven P. Roach, FACHE, President and Chief Executive Officer

Owned, leased, sponsored:	4 hospitals	873 beds
Contract-managed:	0 hospitals	0 beds
Totals:	4 hospitals	873 beds

★**0901: UNC HEALTH CARE** (NP)

101 Manning Drive, Chapel Hill, NC Zip 27514-4220; tel. 919/966-4131; William L. Roper, M.D., M.P.H., Chief Executive Officer

(Moderately Centralized Health System)

NORTH CAROLINA: CALDWELL UNC HEALTH CARE (O, 82 beds) 321 Mulberry Street SW, Lenoir, NC Zip 28645-5720, P O Box 1890, 28645-1890, tel. 828/757-5100; Laura J. Easton, President and Chief Executive Officer
Web address: www.caldwellmemorial.org

CHATHAM HOSPITAL (O, 25 beds) 475 Progress Boulevard, Siler City, NC Zip 27344-6787, P O Box 649, 27344-0649, tel. 919/799-4000; Robert A. Enders Jr, President
Web address: www.chathamhospital.org

HIGH POINT REGIONAL HEALTH SYSTEM (O, 335 beds) 601 North Elm Street, High Point, NC Zip 27262-4398, P O Box HP-5, 27261-1899, tel. 336/878-6000; Ernest L. Bovio Jr, Chief Executive Officer
Web address: www.highpointregional.com

JOHNSTON HEALTH (C, 153 beds) 509 North Bright Leaf Blvd, Smithfield, NC Zip 27577-4407, P O Box 1376, 27577-1376, tel. 919/934-8171; Charles W. Elliott Jr, Chief Executive Officer

MARGARET R. PARDEE MEMORIAL HOSPITAL (C, 142 beds) 800 North Justice Street, Hendersonville, NC Zip 28791-3410; tel. 828/696-1000; James M. Kirby II, President and Chief Executive Officer
Web address: www.pardeehospital.org

NASH HEALTH CARE SYSTEMS (C, 303 beds) 2460 Curtis Ellis Drive, Rocky Mount, NC Zip 27804-2237; tel. 252/962-8000; Ian B. Buchanan, Interim Chief Executive Officer
Web address: www.nhcs.org

UNC LENOIR HEALTHCARE (C, 155 beds) 100 Airport Road, Kinston, NC Zip 28501-1634, P O Box 1678, 28503-1678, tel. 252/522-7000; Gary E. Black, President and Chief Executive Officer
Web address: www.lenoirmemorial.org

UNC REX HEALTH CARE (O, 660 beds) 4420 Lake Boone Trail, Raleigh, NC Zip 27607-6599; tel. 919/784-3100; Stephen W. Burriss, President

UNIVERSITY OF NORTH CAROLINA HOSPITALS (O, 929 beds) 101 Manning Drive, Chapel Hill, NC Zip 27514-4220; tel. 984/974-1000; Gary L. Park, President
Web address: www.unchealthcare.org

WAYNE MEMORIAL HOSPITAL (C, 274 beds) 2700 Wayne Memorial Drive, Goldsboro, NC Zip 27534-9494, P O Box 8001, 27533-8001, tel. 919/736-1110; Janie Jaberg, FACHE, President and Chief Executive Officer
Web address: www.waynehealth.org

Owned, leased, sponsored:	5 hospitals	2031 beds
Contract-managed:	5 hospitals	1027 beds
Totals:	10 hospitals	3058 beds

0922: UNION GENERAL HOSPITAL, INC. (NP)

35 Hospital Road, Blairsville, GA Zip 30512-3139; tel. 706/745-2111; Mike Gowder, Chief Executive Officer

GEORGIA: CHATUGE REGIONAL HOSPITAL AND NURSING HOME (O, 150 beds) 110 Main Street, Hiawassee, GA Zip 30546-3408, P O Box 509, 30546-0509, tel. 706/896-2222; Ryan Snow, Administrator

UNION GENERAL HOSPITAL (O, 195 beds) 35 Hospital Road, Blairsville, GA Zip 30512-3139; tel. 706/745-2111; Lewis Kelley, Interim Chief Executive Officer
Web address: www.uniongeneralhospital.com

Owned, leased, sponsored:	2 hospitals	345 beds
Contract-managed:	0 hospitals	0 beds
Totals:	2 hospitals	345 beds

0288: UNITED HEALTH SERVICES (NP)

10-42 Mitchell Avenue, Binghamton, NY Zip 13903-1617; tel. 607/762-2200; John Carrigg, President and Chief Executive Officer

(Independent Hospital System)

NEW YORK: UHS CHENANGO MEMORIAL HOSPITAL (O, 138 beds) 179 North Broad Street, Norwich, NY Zip 13815-1097; tel. 607/337-4111; Drake M. Lamen, M.D., President, Chief Executive Officer and Chief Medical Officer
Web address: www.uhs.net/cmh

UHS DELAWARE VALLEY HOSPITAL (O, 25 beds) 1 Titus Place, Walton, NY Zip 13856-1498; tel. 607/865-2100; Paul Summers, President and Chief Executive Officer

UNITED HEALTH SERVICES HOSPITALS-BINGHAMTON (O, 464 beds) 10-42 Mitchell Avenue, Binghamton, NY Zip 13903-1678; tel. 607/763-6000; John Carrigg, President and Chief Executive Officer
Web address: www.uhs.net

Owned, leased, sponsored:	3 hospitals	627 beds
Contract-managed:	0 hospitals	0 beds
Totals:	3 hospitals	627 beds

9605: UNITED MEDICAL CORPORATION (IO)

603 Main Street, Windermere, FL Zip 34786-3548, P O Box 1100, 34786-1100, tel. 407/876-2200; Donald R. Dizney, Chairman and Chief Executive Officer

PUERTO RICO: HOSPITAL PAVIA-HATO REY (O, 180 beds) 435 Ponce De Leon Avenue, San Juan, PR Zip 00917-3428, PO Box 190828, 00917-3428, tel. 787/641-2323; Guillermo Pastrana, Executive Director
Web address: www.paviahealth.com

HOSPITAL PAVIA-SANTURCE (O, 198 beds) 1462 Asia Street, San Juan, PR Zip 00909-2143, Box 11137, Santurce Station, 00910-1137, tel. 787/727-6060; Jose Luis. Rodriguez, Chief Executive Officer
Web address: www.paviahealth.com

HOSPITAL PEREA (O, 103 beds) 15 Basora Street, Mayaguez, PR Zip 681, P O Box 170, 681, tel. 787/834-0101; Jorge I. Martinez, Executive Director
Web address: www.paviahealth.com/perea_hospital.htm

HOSPITAL SAN FRANCISCO (O, 133 beds) 371 Avenida De Diego, San Juan, PR Zip 00923-1711, P O Box 29025, 00929-0025, tel. 787/767-5100; Marcos Aguila, Chief Executive Officer
Web address: www.metropavia.com/SanFrancisco.cfm

SAN JORGE CHILDREN'S HOSPITAL (O, 167 beds) 252 San Jorge Street, Santurce, San Juan, PR Zip 00912-3310, PO Box 6308, 00912-3310, tel. 787/727-1000; Domingo Cruz, Senior Vice President Operations

TENNESSEE: TEN BROECK TENNESSEE TREATMENT FACILITY (O, 38 beds) 1 Medical Center Boulevard, 5 West, Cookeville, TN Zip 38501; tel. 931/783-2570; Kelly Tripp, Chief Executive Officer
Web address: www.tenbroeck.com

Owned, leased, sponsored:	6 hospitals	819 beds
Contract-managed:	0 hospitals	0 beds
Totals:	6 hospitals	819 beds

0937: UNITED MEDICAL REHABILITATION HOSPITALS (IO)

3201 Wall Boulevard, Suite B, Gretna, LA Zip 70056-7755; tel. 504/433-5551; John E.H. Mills, President & Chief Executive Officer

For explanation of codes following names, see page B2.
★ Indicates Type III membership in the American Hospital Association.

B132 Health Care Systems, Networks and Alliances

© 2017 AHA Guide

LOUISIANA: UNITED MEDICAL REHABILITATION HOSPITAL (O, 21 beds) 3201 Wall Boulevard, Suite B, Gretna, LA Zip 70056–7755; tel. 504/433–5551; Rondel Frank, Administrator

UNITED MEDICAL REHABILITATION HOSPITAL (O, 20 beds) 15717 Belle Drive, Hammond, LA Zip 70403–1439; tel. 985/340–5998; Jonathan Landreth, Administrator
Web address: www.umrhospital.com

Owned, leased, sponsored:	2 hospitals	41 beds
Contract-managed:	0 hospitals	0 beds
Totals:	2 hospitals	41 beds

0322: UNITED SURGICAL PARTNERS INTERNATIONAL (IO)

15305 Dallas Parkway, Suite 1600, Addison, TX Zip 75001–6491; tel. 972/713–3500; William H. Wilcox, President and Chief Executive Officer
(Independent Hospital System)

ARIZONA: ARIZONA ORTHOPEDIC SURGICAL HOSPITAL (O, 24 beds) 2905 West Warner Road, Suite 1, Chandler, AZ Zip 85224–1674; tel. 480/603–9000; Patricia K. Alice, Chief Executive Officer

OKLAHOMA: OKLAHOMA CENTER FOR ORTHOPEDIC AND MULTI-SPECIALTY SURGERY (O, 14 beds) 8100 South Walker, Suite C, Oklahoma City, OK Zip 73139–9402, P O Box 890609, 73189–0609, tel. 405/602–6500; Mike Kimzey, Chief Executive Officer and Administrator
Web address: www.ocomhospital.com

TEXAS: BAYLOR MEDICAL CENTER AT FRISCO (O, 68 beds) 5601 Warren Parkway, Frisco, TX Zip 75034–4069; tel. 214/407–5000; William A. Keaton, Chief Executive Officer

BAYLOR MEDICAL CENTER AT UPTOWN (O, 24 beds) 2727 East Lemmon Avenue, Dallas, TX Zip 75204–2895; tel. 214/443–3000; Jon Duckert, FACHE, Chief Executive Officer
Web address: www.bmcuptown.com

BAYLOR SURGICAL HOSPITAL AT LAS COLINAS (O, 12 beds) 400 West Interstate 635, Irving, TX Zip 75063; tel. 972/868–4000; Deonna Unell, Chief Executive Officer
Web address: www.baylorhealth.com/About/Community/Assessments/West/ICSH/Pages/Default.aspx

TOPS SURGICAL SPECIALTY HOSPITAL (O, 15 beds) 17080 Red Oak Drive, Houston, TX Zip 77090–2602; tel. 281/539–2900; Samuel H. Rossmann, Chief Executive Officer

Owned, leased, sponsored:	6 hospitals	157 beds
Contract-managed:	0 hospitals	0 beds
Totals:	6 hospitals	157 beds

★0061: UNITYPOINT HEALTH (NP)

1776 Westlakes Parkway, Suite 400, West Des Moines, IA Zip 50266–8239; tel. 515/241–6161; Kevin Vermeer, President and Chief Executive Officer
(Decentralized Health System)

ILLINOIS: PEKIN HOSPITAL (O, 107 beds) 600 South 13th Street, Pekin, IL Zip 61554–4936; tel. 309/347–1151; Bob J. Haley, Chief Executive Officer
Web address: www.pekinhospital.org

UNITYPOINT HEALTH - PEORIA (O, 277 beds) 221 NE Glen Oak Avenue, Peoria, IL Zip 61636–4310; tel. 309/672–5522; Deborah R. Simon, R.N., President and Chief Executive Officer

UNITYPOINT HEALTH - PROCTOR (O, 121 beds) 5409 North Knoxville Avenue, Peoria, IL Zip 61614–5069; tel. 309/691–1000; Deborah R. Simon, R.N., President and Chief Executive Officer
Web address: www.proctor.org

UNITYPOINT HEALTH - TRINITY ROCK ISLAND (O, 343 beds) 2701 17th Street, Rock Island, IL Zip 61201–5393; tel. 309/779–5000; Richard A. Seidler, FACHE, President and Chief Executive Officer
Web address: www.trinityqc.com

IOWA: BUENA VISTA REGIONAL MEDICAL CENTER (C, 35 beds) 1525 West Fifth Street, Storm Lake, IA Zip 50588–3027, P O Box 309, 50588–0309, tel. 712/732–4030; Steven Colerick, Chief Executive Officer

CLARKE COUNTY HOSPITAL (C, 25 beds) 800 South Fillmore Street, Osceola, IA Zip 50213–1619; tel. 641/342–2184; Brian G. Evans, FACHE, Chief Executive Officer
Web address: www.clarkehosp.org

COMMUNITY MEMORIAL HOSPITAL (C, 16 beds) 909 West First Street, Sumner, IA Zip 50674–1203, P O Box 148, 50674–0148, tel. 563/578–3275; Steve Robert. Slessor, Interim Chief Executive Officer

COMPASS MEMORIAL HEALTHCARE (O, 25 beds) 300 West May Street, Marengo, IA Zip 52301–1261; tel. 319/642–5543; Barry Goettsch, FACHE, Chief Executive Officer
Web address: www.compassmemorial.org

GREATER REGIONAL MEDICAL CENTER (C, 25 beds) 1700 West Townline Street Suite 3, Creston, IA Zip 50801–1099; tel. 641/782–7091; Monte Neitzel, Chief Executive Officer
Web address: www.greaterregional.org

GREENE COUNTY MEDICAL CENTER (C, 85 beds) 1000 West Lincolnway, Jefferson, IA Zip 50129–1645; tel. 515/386–2114; Carl P. Behne, Chief Executive Officer

GRUNDY COUNTY MEMORIAL HOSPITAL (C, 80 beds) 201 East 'J' Avenue, Grundy Center, IA Zip 50638–2096; tel. 319/824–5421; Jennifer Havens, Chief Executive Officer and Director of Nursing Operations
Web address: www.grundycountyhospital.com

GUTHRIE COUNTY HOSPITAL (C, 17 beds) 710 North 12th Street, Guthrie Center, IA Zip 50115–1544; tel. 641/332–2201; Patrick Peters, Chief Executive Officer

GUTTENBERG MUNICIPAL HOSPITAL (C, 20 beds) 200 Main Street, Guttenberg, IA Zip 52052–9108, P O Box 550, 52052–0550, tel. 563/252–1121; Kimberley A. Gau, FACHE, Chief Executive Officer
Web address: www.guttenberghospital.org

HUMBOLDT COUNTY MEMORIAL HOSPITAL (C, 49 beds) 1000 North 15th Street, Humboldt, IA Zip 50548–1008; tel. 515/332–4200; Michelle Sleiter, Chief Executive Officer

LORING HOSPITAL (C, 25 beds) 211 Highland Avenue, Sac City, IA Zip 50583–2424; tel. 712/662–7105; Brian Martin, Chief Executive Officer
Web address: www.loringhospital.com

LUCAS COUNTY HEALTH CENTER (C, 25 beds) 1200 North Seventh Street, Chariton, IA Zip 50049–1258; tel. 641/774–3000; Brian Sims, Chief Executive Officer

POCAHONTAS COMMUNITY HOSPITAL (C, 20 beds) 606 NW Seventh Street, Pocahontas, IA Zip 50574–1099; tel. 712/335–3501; James D. Roetman, President and Chief Executive Officer
Web address: www.pocahontashospital.org

STEWART MEMORIAL COMMUNITY HOSPITAL (C, 25 beds) 1301 West Main, Lake City, IA Zip 51449–1585; tel. 712/464–3171; Cynthia L. Carstens, R.N., President and Chief Executive Officer

STORY COUNTY MEDICAL CENTER (C, 77 beds) 640 South 19th Street, Nevada, IA Zip 50201–2902; tel. 515/382–2111; Nate Thompson, Chief Executive Officer
Web address: www.storymedical.org

UNITYPOINT HEALTH - FINLEY HOSPITAL (O, 109 beds) 350 North Grandview Avenue, Dubuque, IA Zip 52001–6392; tel. 563/582–1881; David R. Brandon, President and Chief Executive Officer
Web address: www.unitypoint.org

UNITYPOINT HEALTH - IOWA METHODIST MEDICAL CENTER (O, 518 beds) 1200 Pleasant Street, Des Moines, IA Zip 50309–1406; tel. 515/241–6212; Eric T. Crowell, President and Chief Executive Officer

UNITYPOINT HEALTH - JONES REGIONAL MEDICAL CENTER (O, 22 beds) 1795 Highway 64 East, Anamosa, IA Zip 52205–2112; tel. 319/462–6131; Eric Briesemeister, Chief Executive Officer
Web address: www.jonesregional.org

UNITYPOINT HEALTH - MARSHALLTOWN (O, 40 beds) 3 South Fourth Avenue, Marshalltown, IA Zip 50158–2998; tel. 641/754–5151; Dustin Wright, President and Chief Executive Officer

UNITYPOINT HEALTH - ST. LUKE'S HOSPITAL (O, 347 beds) 1026 'A' Avenue NE, Cedar Rapids, IA Zip 52402–3026, P O Box 3026, 52406–3026,

---

For explanation of codes following names, see page B2.
★ Indicates Type III membership in the American Hospital Association.

tel. 319/369–7211; Theodore E. Townsend, FACHE, President and Chief Executive Officer
Web address: www.unitypoint.org

UNITYPOINT HEALTH - ST. LUKES'S SIOUX CITY (O, 156 beds) 2720 Stone Park Boulevard, Sioux City, IA Zip 51104–3734; tel. 712/279–3500; Lynn Wold, President and Chief Executive Officer

UNITYPOINT HEALTH - TRINITY BETTENDORF (O, 76 beds) 4500 Utica Ridge Road, Bettendorf, IA Zip 52722–1626; tel. 563/742–5000; Richard A. Seidler, FACHE, President and Chief Executive Officer
Web address: www.trinityqc.com

UNITYPOINT HEALTH - TRINITY MUSCATINE (O, 45 beds) 1518 Mulberry Avenue, Muscatine, IA Zip 52761–3499; tel. 563/264–9100; Angela Johnson, Executive Director
Web address: www.unitypoint.org/quadcities/trinity-muscatine.aspx

UNITYPOINT HEALTH - TRINITY REGIONAL MEDICAL CENTER (O, 107 beds) 802 Kenyon Road, Fort Dodge, IA Zip 50501–5795; tel. 515/573–3101; Mike Dewerff, President and Chief Executive Officer

UNITYPOINT HEALTH - WATERLOO (O, 201 beds) 1825 Logan Avenue, Waterloo, IA Zip 50703–1916; tel. 319/235–3941; Pamela K. Delagardelle, President and Chief Executive Officer
Web address: www.unitypoint.org/waterloo

UNITYPOINT HEALTH-IOWA LUTHERAN HOSPITAL (O, 205 beds) 700 East University Avenue, Des Moines, IA Zip 50316–2392; tel. 515/263–5612; Eric T. Crowell, President and Chief Executive Officer

UNITYPOINT HEALTH-KEOKUK (O, 42 beds) 1600 Morgan Street, Keokuk, IA Zip 52632–3456; tel. 319/524–7150; Donza T. Worden, M.D., Chief Clinical Officer
Web address: www.keokukhealthsystems.org

WISCONSIN: UNITYPOINT HEALTH MERITER (O, 308 beds) 202 South Park Street, Madison, WI Zip 53715–1507; tel. 608/417–6000; Arthur Nizza, President and Chief Executive Officer

Owned, leased, sponsored:	18 hospitals	3049 beds
Contract-managed:	14 hospitals	524 beds
Totals:	32 hospitals	3573 beds

9555: UNIVERSAL HEALTH SERVICES, INC. (IO)
367 South Gulph Road, King of Prussia, PA Zip 19406–3121, P O Box 61558, 19406–0958, tel. 610/768–3300; Alan B. Miller, Chairman and Chief Executive Officer
(Decentralized Health System)

ALABAMA: HILL CREST BEHAVIORAL HEALTH SERVICES (O, 80 beds) 6869 Fifth Avenue South, Birmingham, AL Zip 35212–1866; tel. 205/833–9000; Steve McCabe, Chief Executive Officer
Web address: www.hillcrestbhs.com

LAUREL OAKS BEHAVIORAL HEALTH CENTER (O, 38 beds) 700 East Cottonwood Road, Dothan, AL Zip 36301–3644; tel. 334/794–7373; Derek Johnson, Chief Executive Officer

ALASKA: NORTH STAR BEHAVIORAL HEALTH SYSTEM (O, 200 beds) 2530 DeBarr Circle, Anchorage, AK Zip 99508–2948; tel. 907/258–7575; Andrew Mayo, Ph.D., Chief Executive Officer and Managing Director
Web address: www.northstarbehavioral.com

ARIZONA: PALO VERDE BEHAVIORAL HEALTH (O, 48 beds) 2695 North Craycroft Road, Tucson, AZ Zip 85712–2244; tel. 520/322–2888; Melissa Eckstein, Chief Executive Officer

VALLEY HOSPITAL PHOENIX (O, 122 beds) 3550 East Pinchot Avenue, Phoenix, AZ Zip 85018–7434; tel. 602/957–4000; Michelle David, Chief Executive Officer
Web address: www.valleyhospital-phoenix.com

ARKANSAS: PINNACLE POINTE HOSPITAL (O, 124 beds) 11501 Financial Center Parkway, Little Rock, AR Zip 72211–3715; tel. 501/223–3322; Shane Frazier, Chief Executive Officer
Web address: www.pinnaclepointehospital.com

RIVENDELL BEHAVIORAL HEALTH SERVICES OF ARKANSAS (O, 80 beds) 100 Rivendell Drive, Benton, AR Zip 72019–9100; tel. 501/316–1255; Jay Shehi, Chief Executive Officer

SPRINGWOODS BEHAVIORAL HEALTH HOSPITAL (O, 80 beds) 1955 West Truckers Drive, Fayetteville, AR Zip 72704–5637; tel. 479/973–6000; Fred Richmond, Chief Executive Officer
Web address: www.springwoodsbehavioral.com

THE BRIDGEWAY (L, 127 beds) 21 Bridgeway Road, North Little Rock, AR Zip 72113–9516; tel. 501/771–1500; Jason Miller, M.P.H., Chief Executive Officer

CALIFORNIA: BHC ALHAMBRA HOSPITAL (O, 97 beds) 4619 North Rosemead Boulevard, Rosemead, CA Zip 91770–1478, P O Box 369, 91770–0369, tel. 626/286–1191; Peggy Minnick, R.N., Chief Executive Officer
Web address: www.bhcalhambra.com

CANYON RIDGE HOSPITAL (O, 106 beds) 5353 'G' Street, Chino, CA Zip 91710–5250; tel. 909/590–3700; Burt Harris, Acting Chief Executive Officer
Web address: www.canyonridgehospital.com

CORONA REGIONAL MEDICAL CENTER (O, 238 beds) 800 South Main Street, Corona, CA Zip 92882–3400; tel. 951/737–4343; Mark H. Uffer, Chief Executive Officer
Web address: www.coronaregional.com

DEL AMO HOSPITAL (O, 70 beds) 23700 Camino Del Sol, Torrance, CA Zip 90505–5000; tel. 310/530–1151; Steven Oppenheimer, Chief Executive Officer

FREMONT HOSPITAL (O, 148 beds) 39001 Sundale Drive, Fremont, CA Zip 94538–2005; tel. 510/796–1100; Marlon Rollins, Ph.D., Chief Executive Officer
Web address: www.fremonthospital.com

HERITAGE OAKS HOSPITAL (O, 120 beds) 4250 Auburn Boulevard, Sacramento, CA Zip 95841–4164; tel. 916/489–3336; Shawn Silva, Chief Executive Officer
Web address: www.heritageoakshospital.com

PALMDALE REGIONAL MEDICAL CENTER (O, 157 beds) 38600 Medical Center Drive, Palmdale, CA Zip 93551–4483; tel. 661/382–5000; Richard Allen, Chief Executive Officer

SIERRA VISTA HOSPITAL (O, 171 beds) 8001 Bruceville Road, Sacramento, CA Zip 95823–2329; tel. 916/288–0300; Mike Zauner, Chief Executive Officer
Web address: www.sierravistahospital.com

SOUTHWEST HEALTHCARE SYSTEM (O, 240 beds) 25500 Medical Center Drive, Murrieta, CA Zip 92562–5965; tel. 951/696–6000; Bradley D. Neet, FACHE, Chief Executive Officer

TEMECULA VALLEY HOSPITAL (O, 140 beds) 31700 Temecula Parkway, Temecula, CA Zip 92592–5896; tel. 951/331–2216; Darlene Wetton, R.N., Chief Executive Officer
Web address: www.temeculavalleyhospital.com

COLORADO: CEDAR SPRINGS HOSPITAL (O, 110 beds) 2135 Southgate Road, Colorado Springs, CO Zip 80906–2693; tel. 719/633–4114; Christopher D. Burke, Ph.D., Chief Executive Officer

CENTENNIAL PEAKS HOSPITAL (O, 72 beds) 2255 South 88th Street, Louisville, CO Zip 80027–9716; tel. 303/673–9990; Elicia Bunch, Chief Executive Officer
Web address: www.centennialpeaks.com

HIGHLANDS BEHAVIORAL HEALTH SYSTEM (O, 86 beds) 8565 South Poplar Way, Littleton, CO Zip 80130–3602; tel. 720/348–2800; Lisa Strub, Interim Chief Executive Officer
Web address: www.highlandsbhs.com

DELAWARE: DOVER BEHAVIORAL HEALTH SYSTEM (O, 80 beds) 725 Horsepond Road, Dover, DE Zip 19901–7232; tel. 302/741–0140; Jean-Charles Constant, Administrator

ROCKFORD CENTER (O, 128 beds) 100 Rockford Drive, Newark, DE Zip 19713–2121; tel. 302/996–5480; John F. McKenna, Chief Executive Officer and Managing Director
Web address: www.rockfordcenter.com

DISTRICT OF COLUMBIA: GEORGE WASHINGTON UNIVERSITY HOSPITAL (O, 385 beds) 900 23rd Street NW, Washington, DC Zip 20037–2342; tel. 202/715–4000; Kimberly Russo, Chief Executive Officer

FLORIDA: ATLANTIC SHORES HOSPITAL (O, 72 beds) 4545 North Federal Highway, Fort Lauderdale, FL Zip 33308–5274; tel. 954/771–2711; Manuel R. Llano, Chief Executive Officer
Web address: www.atlanticshoreshospital.com

For explanation of codes following names, see page B2.
★ Indicates Type III membership in the American Hospital Association.

CENTRAL FLORIDA BEHAVIORAL HOSPITAL (O, 126 beds) 6601 Central Florida Parkway, Orlando, FL Zip 32821–8064; tel. 407/370–0111; Vickie Lewis, Chief Executive Officer

EMERALD COAST BEHAVIORAL HOSPITAL (O, 86 beds) 1940 Harrison Avenue, Panama City, FL Zip 32405–4542; tel. 850/763–0017; Tim Bedford, Chief Executive Officer
Web address: www.emeraldcoastbehavioral.com

FORT LAUDERDALE HOSPITAL (L, 100 beds) 1601 East Las Olas Boulevard, Fort Lauderdale, FL Zip 33301–2393; tel. 954/463–4321; Manuel R. Llano, Chief Executive Officer
Web address: www.fortlauderdalehospital.org

LAKEWOOD RANCH MEDICAL CENTER (O, 120 beds) 8330 Lakewood Ranch Boulevard, Bradenton, FL Zip 34202–5174; tel. 941/782–2100; Andrew Guz, Chief Executive Officer

MANATEE MEMORIAL HOSPITAL (O, 319 beds) 206 Second Street East, Bradenton, FL Zip 34208–1000; tel. 941/746–5111; Kevin DiLallo, Chief Executive Officer
Web address: www.manateememorial.com

RIVER POINT BEHAVIORAL HEALTH (O, 92 beds) 6300 Beach Boulevard, Jacksonville, FL Zip 32216–2782; tel. 904/724–9202; Kevin McGee, Chief Executive Officer

SUNCOAST BEHAVIORAL HEALTH CENTER (O, 60 beds) 4480 51st Street West, Bradenton, FL Zip 34210–2855; tel. 941/251–5000; Brandy Hamilton, Chief Executive Officer
Web address: www.suncoastbhc.com

THE VINES (O, 98 beds) 3130 SW 27th Avenue, Ocala, FL Zip 34471–4306; tel. 352/671–3130; Stephen Quintyne, Chief Executive Officer
Web address: www.thevineshospital.com

WEKIVA SPRINGS (O, 60 beds) 3947 Salisbury Road, Jacksonville, FL Zip 32216–6115; tel. 904/296–3533; Sheila Carr, Chief Executive Officer

WELLINGTON REGIONAL MEDICAL CENTER (L, 233 beds) 10101 Forest Hill Boulevard, Wellington, FL Zip 33414–6199; tel. 561/798–8500; Robbin Lee, Chief Executive Officer
Web address: www.wellingtonregional.com

WINDMOOR HEALTHCARE OF CLEARWATER (O, 100 beds) 11300 U S 19 North, Clearwater, FL Zip 33764; tel. 727/541–2646; Wendy Merson, Chief Executive Officer

GEORGIA: ANCHOR HOSPITAL (O, 122 beds) 5454 Yorktowne Drive, Atlanta, GA Zip 30349–5317; tel. 770/991–6044; Randall G. Hines, Ph.D., Chief Executive Officer
Web address: www.anchorhospital.com

COASTAL HARBOR TREATMENT CENTER (O, 193 beds) 1150 Cornell Avenue, Savannah, GA Zip 31406–2702; tel. 912/354–3911; Sally Perry, Chief Executive Officer

PEACHFORD BEHAVIORAL HEALTH SYSTEM (O, 246 beds) 2151 Peachford Road, Atlanta, GA Zip 30338–6599; tel. 770/455–3200; Matthew Crouch, Chief Executive Officer and Managing Director
Web address: www.peachfordhospital.com

SAINT SIMONS BY-THE-SEA HOSPITAL (O, 101 beds) 2927 Demere Road, Saint Simons Island, GA Zip 31522–1620; tel. 912/638–1999; Chuck Flavio, Chief Executive Officer

TURNING POINT HOSPITAL (O, 59 beds) 3015 Veterans Parkway South, Moultrie, GA Zip 31788–6705, P O Box 1177, 31776–1177, tel. 229/985–4815; Judy H. Payne, Chief Executive Officer
Web address: www.turningpointcare.com

IDAHO: INTERMOUNTAIN HOSPITAL (O, 140 beds) 303 North Allumbaugh Street, Boise, ID Zip 83704–9208; tel. 208/377–8400; Jeffrey F. Morrell, Chief Executive Officer

ILLINOIS: GARFIELD PARK HOSPITAL (O, 88 beds) 520 North Ridgeway Avenue, Chicago, IL Zip 60624–1232; tel. 773/265–3700; Len Kirby, Chief Executive Officer
Web address: www.garfieldparkhospital.com

HARTGROVE HOSPITAL (O, 128 beds) 5730 West Roosevelt Road, Chicago, IL Zip 60644–1580; tel. 773/413–1700; Steven Airhart, Chief Executive Officer

LINCOLN PRAIRIE BEHAVIORAL HEALTH CENTER (O, 97 beds) 5230 South Sixth Street, Springfield, IL Zip 62703–5128; tel. 217/585–1180; Mark Littrell, Chief Executive Officer
Web address: www.lincolnprairiebhc.com/

RIVEREDGE HOSPITAL (O, 224 beds) 8311 West Roosevelt Road, Forest Park, IL Zip 60130–2500; tel. 708/771–7000; Carey Carlock, Chief Executive Officer
Web address: www.riveredgehospital.com

STREAMWOOD BEHAVIORAL HEALTH CENTER (O, 178 beds) 1400 East Irving Park Road, Streamwood, IL Zip 60107–3203; tel. 630/837–9000; Ron Weglarz, Chief Executive Officer and Managing Director
Web address: www.streamwoodhospital.com

THE PAVILION (O, 46 beds) 809 West Church Street, Champaign, IL Zip 61820–3399; tel. 217/373–1700; Joseph Sheehy, Chief Executive Officer and Managing Director

INDIANA: BLOOMINGTON MEADOWS HOSPITAL (O, 67 beds) 3600 North Prow Road, Bloomington, IN Zip 47404–1616; tel. 812/331–8000; Jean Scallon, Chief Executive Officer
Web address: www.bloomingtonmeadows.com

MICHIANA BEHAVIORAL HEALTH CENTER (O, 75 beds) 1800 North Oak Drive, Plymouth, IN Zip 46563–3492; tel. 574/936–3784; Michael Perry, Chief Executive Officer
Web address: www.michianabhc.com

VALLE VISTA HOSPITAL (O, 102 beds) 898 East Main Street, Greenwood, IN Zip 46143–1400; tel. 317/887–1348; Sherri R. Jewett, Chief Executive Officer

WELLSTONE REGIONAL HOSPITAL (O, 100 beds) 2700 Vissing Park Road, Jeffersonville, IN Zip 47130–5989; tel. 812/284–8000; Greg Stewart, Chief Executive Officer
Web address: www.wellstonehospital.com

KENTUCKY: CUMBERLAND HALL HOSPITAL (O, 97 beds) 270 Walton Way, Hopkinsville, KY Zip 42240–6808; tel. 270/886–1919; Jason Staats, Chief Executive Officer

LINCOLN TRAIL BEHAVIORAL HEALTH SYSTEM (O, 67 beds) 3909 South Wilson Road, Radcliff, KY Zip 40160–8944, P O Box 369, 40159–0369, tel. 270/351–9444; Charles L. Webb Jr, Chief Executive Officer
Web address: www.lincolnbehavioral.com

RIDGE BEHAVIORAL HEALTH SYSTEM (O, 110 beds) 3050 Rio Dosa Drive, Lexington, KY Zip 40509–1540; tel. 859/269–2325; Nina W. Eisner, Chief Executive Officer and Managing Director

RIVENDELL BEHAVIORAL HEALTH (O, 125 beds) 1035 Porter Pike, Bowling Green, KY Zip 42103–9581; tel. 270/843–1199; Matt Ours, Chief Executive Officer and Managing Director
Web address: www.rivendellbehavioral.com

THE BROOK HOSPITAL - KMI (O, 94 beds) 8521 Old LaGrange Road, Louisville, KY Zip 40242–3800; tel. 502/426–6380; Paul Andrews, Chief Executive Officer
Web address: www.thebrookhospitals.com

THE BROOK AT DUPONT (O, 88 beds) 1405 Browns Lane, Louisville, KY Zip 40207–4608; tel. 502/896–0495; Paul Andrews, Chief Executive Officer

LOUISIANA: BRENTWOOD HOSPITAL (O, 172 beds) 1006 Highland Avenue, Shreveport, LA Zip 71101–4103; tel. 318/678–7500; William Weaver, Chief Executive Officer
Web address: www.brentwoodbehavioral.com

RIVER OAKS HOSPITAL (O, 126 beds) 1525 River Oaks Road West, New Orleans, LA Zip 70123–2162; tel. 504/734–1740; Deagan Watson, Chief Executive Officer
Web address: www.riveroakshospital.com

MASSACHUSETTS: ARBOUR H. R. I. HOSPITAL (O, 68 beds) 227 Babcock Street, Brookline, MA Zip 02446–6799; tel. 617/731–3200; Jameson Pinette, Chief Executive Officer

ARBOUR HOSPITAL (O, 118 beds) 49 Robinwood Avenue, Boston, MA Zip 02130–2156; tel. 617/522–4400; Eric Kennedy, Chief Executive Officer
Web address: www.arbourhealth.com

ARBOUR-FULLER HOSPITAL (O, 46 beds) 200 May Street, Attleboro, MA Zip 02703–5520; tel. 508/761–8500; Rachel Legend, Chief Executive Officer
Web address: www.arbourhealth.com

PEMBROKE HOSPITAL (O, 115 beds) 199 Oak Street, Pembroke, MA Zip 02359–1953; tel. 781/829–7000; Raymond Robinson, Chief Executive Officer

Section B

For explanation of codes following names, see page B2.
★ Indicates Type III membership in the American Hospital Association.

MICHIGAN: FOREST VIEW PSYCHIATRIC HOSPITAL (O, 108 beds) 1055 Medical Park Drive SE, Grand Rapids, MI Zip 49546–3607; tel. 616/942–9610; Andrew Hotaling, Chief Executive Officer
Web address: www.forestviewhospital.com

HAVENWYCK HOSPITAL (O, 235 beds) 1525 University Drive, Auburn Hills, MI Zip 48326–2673; tel. 248/373–9200; Diane Henneman, Chief Executive Officer

MISSISSIPPI: ALLIANCE HEALTH CENTER (O, 154 beds) 5000 Highway 39 North, Meridian, MS Zip 39301–1021; tel. 601/483–6211; Jay Shehi, Chief Executive Officer
Web address: www.alliancehealthcenter.com

BRENTWOOD BEHAVIORAL HEALTHCARE OF MISSISSIPPI (O, 105 beds) 3531 East Lakeland Drive, Jackson, MS Zip 39232–8839; tel. 601/936–2024; Michael J. Carney, Chief Executive Officer
Web address: www.brentwoodjackson.com

PARKWOOD BEHAVIORAL HEALTH SYSTEM (O, 148 beds) 8135 Goodman Road, Olive Branch, MS Zip 38654–2103; tel. 662/895–4900; Ethan Permenter, Chief Executive Officer

MISSOURI: HEARTLAND BEHAVIORAL HEALTH SERVICES (O, 69 beds) 1500 West Ashland Street, Nevada, MO Zip 64772–1710; tel. 417/667–2666; Alyson Wysong-Harder, Chief Executive Officer
Web address: www.heartlandbehavioral.com

TWO RIVERS BEHAVIORAL HEALTH SYSTEM (O, 105 beds) 5121 Raytown Road, Kansas City, MO Zip 64133–2141; tel. 816/382–6300; Greg Shannon, Interim Chief Executive Officer
Web address: www.tworivershospital.com

NEVADA: CENTENNIAL HILLS HOSPITAL MEDICAL CENTER (O, 165 beds) 6900 North Durango Drive, Las Vegas, NV Zip 89149–4409; tel. 702/835–9700; Sajit Pullarkat, Chief Executive Officer and Managing Director

DESERT SPRINGS HOSPITAL MEDICAL CENTER (O, 346 beds) 2075 East Flamingo Road, Las Vegas, NV Zip 89119–5121; tel. 702/733–8800; Ryan Jensen, Chief Executive Officer
Web address: www.desertspringshospital.com

DESERT VIEW HOSPITAL (O, 25 beds) 360 South Lola Lane, Pahrump, NV Zip 89048–0884; tel. 775/751–7500; Susan Davila, Chief Executive Officer
Web address: www.desertviewhospital.com

HENDERSON HOSPITAL (O, 145 beds) 1050 West Galleria Drive, Henderson, NV Zip 89011; tel. 702/963–7000; Samuel Kaufman, Chief Executive Officer
Web address: www.hendersonhospital.com/

NORTHERN NEVADA MEDICAL CENTER (O, 108 beds) 2375 East Prater Way, Sparks, NV Zip 89434–9641; tel. 775/331–7000; Alan C. Olive, Chief Executive Officer

SPRING MOUNTAIN SAHARA (O, 30 beds) 5460 West Sahara, Las Vegas, NV Zip 89146–3307; tel. 702/216–8900; Alan Eaks, Chief Executive Officer and Managing Director
Web address: www.springmountainsahara.com

SPRING MOUNTAIN TREATMENT CENTER (L, 110 beds) 7000 West Spring Mountain Road, Las Vegas, NV Zip 89117–3816; tel. 702/873–2400; C Alan. Eaks, Chief Executive Officer and Managing Director
Web address: www.springmountaintreatmentcenter.com/

SPRING VALLEY HOSPITAL MEDICAL CENTER (O, 169 beds) 5400 South Rainbow Boulevard, Las Vegas, NV Zip 89118–1859; tel. 702/853–3000; Leonard Freehof, Chief Executive Officer and Managing Director

SUMMERLIN HOSPITAL MEDICAL CENTER (O, 148 beds) 657 Town Center Drive, Las Vegas, NV Zip 89144–6367; tel. 702/233–7000; Robert S. Freymuller, Chief Executive Officer
Web address: www.summerlinhospital.com

VALLEY HOSPITAL MEDICAL CENTER (O, 365 beds) 620 Shadow Lane, Las Vegas, NV Zip 89106–4119; tel. 702/388–4000; Elaine Glaser, Chief Executive Officer

WEST HILLS HOSPITAL (O, 190 beds) 1240 East Ninth Street, Reno, NV Zip 89512–2964; tel. 775/323–0478; Allison Zednicek, Chief Executive Officer
Web address: www.westhillshospital.net

NEW JERSEY: HAMPTON BEHAVIORAL HEALTH CENTER (O, 120 beds) 650 Rancocas Road, Westampton, NJ Zip 08060–5613; tel. 609/267–7000; Craig Hilton, Chief Executive Officer and Managing Director
Web address: www.hamptonhospital.com

SUMMIT OAKS HOSPITAL (O, 90 beds) 19 Prospect Street, Summit, NJ Zip 07901–2530; tel. 908/522–7000; Oana Radu, Chief Executive Officer

NEW MEXICO: MESILLA VALLEY HOSPITAL (O, 105 beds) 3751 Del Rey Boulevard, Las Cruces, NM Zip 88012–8526; tel. 575/382–3500; Dana McRimmon, Interim Chief Executive Officer
Web address: www.mesillavalleyhospital.com

NORTH CAROLINA: BRYNN MARR HOSPITAL (O, 99 beds) 192 Village Drive, Jacksonville, NC Zip 28546–7299; tel. 910/577–1400; Jay Kortemeyer, Chief Executive Officer

HOLLY HILL HOSPITAL (O, 228 beds) 3019 Falstaff Road, Raleigh, NC Zip 27610–1812; tel. 919/250–7000; Amanda Johanson, Chief Executive Officer
Web address: www.hollyhillhospital.com

OLD VINEYARD BEHAVIORAL HEALTH SERVICES (O, 104 beds) 3637 Old Vineyard Road, Winston-Salem, NC Zip 27104–4842; tel. 336/794–3550; Kevin Patton, Chief Executive Officer

NORTH DAKOTA: PRAIRIE ST. JOHN'S (O, 94 beds) 510 4th Street South, Fargo, ND Zip 58103–1914; tel. 701/476–7200; Jeff Herman, Chief Executive Officer
Web address: www.prairie-stjohns.com

OHIO: ARROWHEAD BEHAVIORAL HEALTH HOSPITAL (O, 42 beds) 1725 Timber Line Road, Maumee, OH Zip 43537–4015; tel. 419/891–9333; Joseph Denicola, Chief Executive Officer and Managing Director
Web address: www.arrowheadbehavioral.com

BELMONT PINES HOSPITAL (O, 96 beds) 615 Churchill-Hubbard Road, Youngstown, OH Zip 44505–1379; tel. 330/759–2700; Lisa Cocca, Chief Executive Officer

WINDSOR-LAURELWOOD CENTER FOR BEHAVIORAL MEDICINE (O, 159 beds) 35900 Euclid Avenue, Willoughby, OH Zip 44094–4648; tel. 440/953–3000; Ric McAllister, Chief Executive Officer
Web address: www.windsorlaurelwood.com

OKLAHOMA: CEDAR RIDGE HOSPITAL (O, 172 beds) 6501 NE 50th Street, Oklahoma City, OK Zip 73141–9118; tel. 405/605–6111; Heather Joseph, Chief Executive Officer

SHADOW MOUNTAIN BEHAVIORAL HEALTH SYSTEM (O, 226 beds) 6262 South Sheridan Road, Tulsa, OK Zip 74133–4055; tel. 918/492–8200; Mike Kistler, Chief Executive Officer
Web address: www.shadowmountainbhs.com

ST. MARY'S REGIONAL MEDICAL CENTER (O, 164 beds) 305 South Fifth Street, Enid, OK Zip 73701–5899, P O Box 232, 73702–0232, tel. 580/233–6100; Stanley D. Tatum, FACHE, Chief Executive Officer

OREGON: CEDAR HILLS HOSPITAL (O, 78 beds) 10300 SW Eastridge Street, Portland, OR Zip 97225–5004; tel. 503/944–5000; Elizabeth Hutter, Chief Executive Officer
Web address: www.cedarhillshospital.com

PENNSYLVANIA: BROOKE GLEN BEHAVIORAL HOSPITAL (O, 146 beds) 7170 Lafayette Avenue, Fort Washington, PA Zip 19034–2301; tel. 215/641–5300; Neil Callahan, Chief Executive Officer
Web address: www.brookeglenhospital.com

CLARION PSYCHIATRIC CENTER (O, 74 beds) 2 Hospital Drive, Clarion, PA Zip 16214–8502; tel. 814/226–9545; Michael Post, Chief Executive Officer

FAIRMOUNT BEHAVIORAL HEALTH SYSTEM (O, 235 beds) 561 Fairthorne Avenue, Philadelphia, PA Zip 19128–2499; tel. 215/487–4000; Lisa M. McConlogue, MSN, Ph.D., Chief Executive Officer and Managing Director
Web address: www.fairmountbhs.com

FOUNDATIONS BEHAVIORAL HEALTH (O, 58 beds) 833 East Butler Avenue, Doylestown, PA Zip 18901–2280; tel. 215/345–0444; Gina Fusco, Chief Executive Officer

FRIENDS HOSPITAL (O, 192 beds) 4641 Roosevelt Boulevard, Philadelphia, PA Zip 19124–2343; tel. 215/831–4600; Michael S. McDonald Jr, Chief Executive Officer
Web address: www.friendshospital.com

HORSHAM CLINIC (O, 206 beds) 722 East Butler Pike, Ambler, PA Zip 19002–2310; tel. 215/643–7800; Phyllis Weisfield, Chief Executive Officer and Managing Director
Web address: www.horshamclinic.com

For explanation of codes following names, see page B2.
★ Indicates Type III membership in the American Hospital Association.

MEADOWS PSYCHIATRIC CENTER (O, 107 beds) 132 The Meadows Drive, Centre Hall, PA Zip 16828–9231; tel. 814/364–2161; Ann Wayne, Chief Executive Officer

ROXBURY TREATMENT CENTER (O, 94 beds) 601 Roxbury Road, Shippensburg, PA Zip 17257–9302; tel. 800/648–4673; Shauna Mogerman, Chief Executive Officer
Web address: www.roxburyhospital.com

PUERTO RICO: FIRST HOSPITAL PANAMERICANO (O, 153 beds) State Road 787 KM 1 5, Cidra, PR Zip 739, P O Box 1400, 739, tel. 787/739–5555; Astro Munoz, Executive Director
Web address: www.hospitalpanamericano.com

SOUTH CAROLINA: AIKEN REGIONAL MEDICAL CENTERS (O, 271 beds) 302 University Parkway, Aiken, SC Zip 29801–6302; tel. 803/641–5000; Vance V. Reynolds, FACHE, CPA, Chief Executive Officer

CAROLINA CENTER FOR BEHAVIORAL HEALTH (O, 109 beds) 2700 East Phillips Road, Greer, SC Zip 29650–4816; tel. 864/235–2335; John Willingham, Chief Executive Officer and Managing Director
Web address: www.thecarolinacenter.com

LIGHTHOUSE CARE CENTER OF CONWAY (O, 87 beds) 152 Waccamaw Medical Park Drive, Conway, SC Zip 29526–8901; tel. 843/347–8871; Thomas L. Ryba, Chief Executive Officer
Web address: www.lighthousecarecenterofconway.com/

PALMETTO LOWCOUNTRY BEHAVIORAL HEALTH (O, 100 beds) 2777 Speissegger Drive, Charleston, SC Zip 29405–8229; tel. 843/747–5830; Clint Hauger, Chief Executive Officer
Web address: www.palmettobehavioralhealth.com

THREE RIVERS BEHAVIORAL HEALTH (O, 122 beds) 2900 Sunset Boulevard, West Columbia, SC Zip 29169–3422; tel. 803/796–9911; Nannette M. Lewis, Chief Executive Officer
Web address: www.threeriversbehavioral.org

TENNESSEE: LAKESIDE BEHAVIORAL HEALTH SYSTEM (O, 345 beds) 2911 Brunswick Road, Memphis, TN Zip 38133–4199; tel. 901/377–4700; Joy Golden, Chief Executive Officer

ROLLING HILLS HOSPITAL (O, 120 beds) 2014 Quail Hollow Circle, Franklin, TN Zip 37067–5967; tel. 615/628–5700; Jim Spruyt, Chief Executive Officer
Web address: www.RollingHillsHospital.org/

TEXAS: AUSTIN LAKES HOSPITAL (O, 58 beds) 1025 East 32nd Street, Austin, TX Zip 78705–2714; tel. 512/544–5253; Robert J. Lerma, MS, Chief Executive Officer
Web address: www.austinlakeshospital.com

AUSTIN OAKS HOSPITAL (O, 80 beds) 1407 West Stassney Lane, Austin, TX Zip 78745–2947; tel. 512/440–4800; Steve Kelly, Interim Chief Executive Officer

BEHAVIORAL HOSPITAL OF BELLAIRE (O, 122 beds) 5314 Dashwood Drive, Houston, TX Zip 77081–4603; tel. 713/600–9500; Coleby Wright, Chief Executive Officer
Web address: www.bhbhospital.com

CORNERSTONE REGIONAL HOSPITAL (L, 14 beds) 2302 Cornerstone Boulevard, Edinburg, TX Zip 78539–8471; tel. 956/618–4444; Roxanna M. Godinez, Chief Executive Officer

CYPRESS CREEK HOSPITAL (O, 96 beds) 17750 Cali Drive, Houston, TX Zip 77090–2700; tel. 281/586–7600; Brian Brooker, Chief Executive Officer
Web address: www.cypresscreekhospital.com

DOCTORS HOSPITAL OF LAREDO (O, 183 beds) 10700 McPherson Road, Laredo, TX Zip 78045–6268; tel. 956/523–2000; James R. Resendez, Chief Executive Officer
Web address: www.doctorshosplaredo.com

EL PASO BEHAVIORAL HEALTH SYSTEM (O, 163 beds) 1900 Denver Avenue, El Paso, TX Zip 79902–3008; tel. 915/544–4000; Phillip Sosa, Interim Chief Executive Officer
Web address: www.ubhelpaso.com/

FORT DUNCAN REGIONAL MEDICAL CENTER (O, 101 beds) 3333 North Foster Maldonado Boulevard, Eagle Pass, TX Zip 78852–5893; tel. 830/773–5321; Eladio Montalvo, Chief Executive Officer
Web address: www.fortduncanmedicalcenter.com

GARLAND BEHAVIORAL HOSPITAL (O, 72 beds) 2300 Marie Curie Boulevard, 5th Floor, Garland, TX Zip 75402; tel. 972/487–5309; Scott Cook, Interim Chief Executive Officer

GLEN OAKS HOSPITAL (O, 54 beds) 301 Division Street, Greenville, TX Zip 75401–4101; tel. 903/454–6000; Ethan Permenter, Corporate Vice President
Web address: www.glenoakshospital.com

HICKORY TRAIL HOSPITAL (O, 86 beds) 2000 Old Hickory Trail, Desoto, TX Zip 75115–2242; tel. 972/298–7323; Kay McKennery, Interim Chief Executive Officer

KINGWOOD PINES HOSPITAL (O, 75 beds) 2001 Ladbrook Drive, Kingwood, TX Zip 77339–3004; tel. 281/404–1001; Shanti Carter, Chief Executive Officer
Web address: www.kingwoodpines.com

LAUREL RIDGE TREATMENT CENTER (O, 208 beds) 17720 Corporate Woods Drive, San Antonio, TX Zip 78259–3500; tel. 210/491–9400; Jacob Cuellar, M.D., Chief Executive Officer

MAYHILL HOSPITAL (O, 59 beds) 2809 South Mayhill Road, Denton, TX Zip 76208–5910; tel. 940/239–3000; Dawne Buckley, Interim Chief Executive Officer
Web address: www.mayhillhospital.com

MILLWOOD HOSPITAL (O, 122 beds) 1011 North Cooper Street, Arlington, TX Zip 76011–5517; tel. 817/261–3121; Dwight A. Lacy, Chief Executive Officer

NORTHWEST TEXAS HEALTHCARE SYSTEM (O, 409 beds) 1501 South Coulter Avenue, Amarillo, TX Zip 79106–1770, P O Box 1110, 79105–1110, tel. 806/354–1000; Mark W. Crawford, Chief Executive Officer
Web address: www.nwtexashealthcare.com

RIVER CREST HOSPITAL (O, 80 beds) 1636 Hunters Glen Road, San Angelo, TX Zip 76901–5016; tel. 325/949–5722; Juana Giralt, Interim Chief Executive Officer
Web address: www.rivercresthospital.com

SOUTH TEXAS HEALTH SYSTEM (O, 788 beds) 1400 West Trenton Road, Edinburg, TX Zip 78539–9105, 1102 West Trenton Road, 78539–9105, tel. 956/388–6000; Jennifer Garza, Chief Executive Officer

TEXAS NEUROREHAB CENTER (O, 47 beds) 1106 West Dittmar Road, Building 9, Austin, TX Zip 78745–6328, P O Box 150459, 78715–0459, tel. 512/444–4835; Edgar E. Prettyman, PsyD, Chief Executive Officer
Web address: www.texasneurorehab.com

TEXOMA MEDICAL CENTER (O, 326 beds) 5016 South US Highway 75 , Denison, TX Zip 75020–4584, P O Box 890, 75021–0890, tel. 903/416–4000; Ronald T. Seal, Chief Executive Officer

TIMBERLAWN MENTAL HEALTH SYSTEM (O, 57 beds) 4600 Samuell Boulevard, Dallas, TX Zip 75228–6800; tel. 214/381–7181; Shelah Adams, Chief Executive Officer
Web address: www.timberlawn.com

UNIVERSITY BEHAVIORAL HEALTH OF DENTON (O, 104 beds) 2026 West University Drive, Denton, TX Zip 76201–0644; tel. 940/320–8100; Samantha Castle, Chief Executive Officer

WEST OAKS HOSPITAL (O, 144 beds) 6500 Hornwood Drive, Houston, TX Zip 77074–5095; tel. 713/995–0909; Mandy Westerman, Chief Executive Officer
Web address: www.westoakshospital.com

UTAH: PROVO CANYON BEHAVIORAL HOSPITAL (O, 80 beds) 1350 East 750 North, Orem, UT Zip 84097–4345; tel. 801/852–2273; Jeremy Cottle, Ph.D., Chief Executive Officer

SALT LAKE BEHAVIORAL HEALTH (O, 118 beds) 3802 South 700 East, Salt Lake City, UT Zip 84106–1182; tel. 801/264–6000; Kreg Gillman, Chief Executive Officer
Web address: www.saltlakebehavioralhealth.com

VIRGINIA: CUMBERLAND HOSPITAL (O, 118 beds) 9407 Cumberland Road, New Kent, VA Zip 23124–2029; tel. 804/966–2242; Patrice Gay. Brooks, Chief Executive Officer
Web address: www.cumberlandhospital.com

POPLAR SPRINGS HOSPITAL (O, 180 beds) 350 Poplar Drive, Petersburg, VA Zip 23805–9367; tel. 804/733–6874; Stephen Reider, Chief Operating Officer and Interim Chief Executive Officer

VIRGINIA BEACH PSYCHIATRIC CENTER (O, 100 beds) 1100 First Colonial Road, Virginia Beach, VA Zip 23454–2403; tel. 757/496–6000; Dustin Davis, Chief Executive Officer
Web address: www.vbpcweb.com

For explanation of codes following names, see page B2.
★ Indicates Type III membership in the American Hospital Association.

Section B

WASHINGTON: FAIRFAX BEHAVIORAL HEALTH (O, 103 beds) 10200 NE 132nd Street, Kirkland, WA Zip 98034-2899; tel. 425/821-2000; Ron Escarda, Chief Executive Officer
Web address: www.fairfaxhospital.com

WEST VIRGINIA: RIVER PARK HOSPITAL (O, 175 beds) 1230 Sixth Avenue, Huntington, WV Zip 25701-2312, P O Box 1875, 25719-1875, tel. 304/526-9111; Terry A. Stephens, Chief Executive Officer
Web address: www.riverparkhospital.net

WYOMING: WYOMING BEHAVIORAL INSTITUTE (O, 129 beds) 2521 East 15th Street, Casper, WY Zip 82609-4126; tel. 307/237-7444; Joseph Gallagher, Chief Executive Officer
Web address: www.wbihelp.com

Owned, leased, sponsored:	144 hospitals	19277 beds
Contract-managed:	0 hospitals	0 beds
Totals:	144 hospitals	19277 beds

★0896: UNIVERSITY HEALTH CARE SYSTEM (NP)
1350 Walton Way, Augusta, GA Zip 30901-2629; tel. 706/722-9011; James R. Davis, President and Chief Executive Officer
(Independent Hospital System)

GEORGIA: UNIVERSITY HOSPITAL MCDUFFIE (O, 25 beds) 2460 Washington Road, NE, Thomson, GA Zip 30824; tel. 706/595-1411; Bob Kepshire, R.N., MS, Administrator and Chief Nursing Officer

UNIVERSITY HOSPITAL SUMMERVILLE (O, 105 beds) 2260 Wrightsboro Road, Augusta, GA Zip 30904-4726; tel. 706/481-7000; James R. Davis, Chief Executive Officer
Web address: www.trinityofaugusta.com

UNIVERSITY HOSPITAL (O, 521 beds) 1350 Walton Way, Augusta, GA Zip 30901-2629; tel. 706/722-9011; James R. Davis, Chief Executive Officer

Owned, leased, sponsored:	3 hospitals	651 beds
Contract-managed:	0 hospitals	0 beds
Totals:	3 hospitals	651 beds

0961: UNIVERSITY HEALTH SYSTEM (NP)
1501 Kings Highway, Shreveport, LA Zip 71103-4228; tel. 318/675-5000; Daniel J. Snyder, Chief Executive Officer
(Independent Hospital System)

LOUISIANA: UNIVERSITY HEALTH CONWAY (O, 108 beds) 4864 Jackson Street, Monroe, LA Zip 71202-6497, P O Box 1881, 71210-8005, tel. 318/330-7000; Jonathan Phillips, Interim Administrator
Web address: www.uhsystem.com

UNIVERSITY HEALTH SHREVEPORT (O, 395 beds) 1501 Kings Highway, Shreveport, LA Zip 71103-4228, P O Box 33932, 71130-3932, tel. 318/675-5000; Mark Randolph, President

Owned, leased, sponsored:	2 hospitals	503 beds
Contract-managed:	0 hospitals	0 beds
Totals:	2 hospitals	503 beds

★0112: UNIVERSITY HOSPITALS (NP)
11100 Euclid Avenue, Cleveland, OH Zip 44106-5000; tel. 216/844-1000; Thomas F. Zenty III, President and Chief Executive Officer
(Centralized Health System)

OHIO: ST. JOHN MEDICAL CENTER (O, 191 beds) 29000 Center Ridge Road, Westlake, OH Zip 44145-5293; tel. 440/835-8000; Robert G. David, President
Web address: www.sjws.net

UH PORTAGE MEDICAL CENTER (O, 117 beds) 6847 North Chestnut Street, Ravenna, OH Zip 44266-3929, P O Box 1204, 44266-1204, tel. 330/297-0811; M Steven. Jones, President

UH REGIONAL HOSPITALS (O, 101 beds) 27100 Chardon Road, Cleveland, OH Zip 44143-1116; tel. 440/585-6500; Brian Monter, MSN, R.N., President
Web address: www.uhhospitals.org

UNIVERSITY HOSPITALS AHUJA MEDICAL CENTER (O, 138 beds) 3999 Richmond Road, Beachwood, OH Zip 44122-6046; tel. 216/593-5500; Susan V. Juris, President
Web address: www.uhhospitals.org/ahuja/tabid/7051/uhahujamedicalcenter.aspx

UNIVERSITY HOSPITALS CLEVELAND MEDICAL CENTER (O, 836 beds) 11100 Euclid Avenue, Cleveland, OH Zip 44106-1716; tel. 216/844-1000; Daniel I. Simon, M.D., President

UNIVERSITY HOSPITALS CONNEAUT MEDICAL CENTER (O, 25 beds) 158 West Main Road, Conneaut, OH Zip 44030-2039; tel. 440/593-1131; M Steven. Jones, President
Web address: www.uhhospitals.org

UNIVERSITY HOSPITALS ELYRIA MEDICAL CENTER (O, 237 beds) 630 East River Street, Elyria, OH Zip 44035-5902; tel. 440/329-7500; Charlotte Wray, MSN, President

UNIVERSITY HOSPITALS GEAUGA MEDICAL CENTER (O, 142 beds) 13207 Ravenna Road, Chardon, OH Zip 44024-7032; tel. 440/269-6000; M Steven. Jones, President
Web address: www.uhhospitals.org/geauga/

UNIVERSITY HOSPITALS GENEVA MEDICAL CENTER (O, 25 beds) 870 West Main Street, Geneva, OH Zip 44041-1295; tel. 440/466-1141; M Steven. Jones, President
Web address: www.uhhs.com

UNIVERSITY HOSPITALS PARMA MEDICAL CENTER (O, 265 beds) 7007 Powers Boulevard, Parma, OH Zip 44129-5495; tel. 440/743-3000; Peter U. Bergmann, President

UNIVERSITY HOSPITALS SAMARITAN MEDICAL CENTER (O, 38 beds) 1025 Center Street, Ashland, OH Zip 44805-4011; tel. 419/289-0491; Karen McNeil, President
Web address: www.samaritanhospital.org

Owned, leased, sponsored:	11 hospitals	2115 beds
Contract-managed:	0 hospitals	0 beds
Totals:	11 hospitals	2115 beds

★0915: UNIVERSITY HOSPITALS AND HEALTH SYSTEM (NP)
2500 North State Street, Jackson, MS Zip 39216-4500; tel. 601/984-1000; Kevin S. Cook, Chief Executive Officer
(Decentralized Health System)

MISSISSIPPI: UNIVERSITY OF MISSISSIPPI MEDICAL CENTER GRENADA (C, 93 beds) 960 Avent Drive, Grenada, MS Zip 38901-5230; tel. 662/227-7000; Donald Hutson, Chief Executive Officer
Web address: www.ummchealth.com/grenada

UNIVERSITY OF MISSISSIPPI MEDICAL CENTER HOLMES COUNTY (O, 25 beds) 239 Bowling Green Road, Lexington, MS Zip 39095-5167; tel. 601/496-5200; Donald Hutson, Chief Executive Officer
Web address: www.ummchealth.com/holmes/

UNIVERSITY OF MISSISSIPPI MEDICAL CENTER (O, 680 beds) 2500 North State Street, Jackson, MS Zip 39216-4505; tel. 601/984-1000; Kevin S. Cook, Chief Executive Officer

Owned, leased, sponsored:	2 hospitals	705 beds
Contract-managed:	1 hospitals	93 beds
Totals:	3 hospitals	798 beds

★6405: UNIVERSITY OF CALIFORNIA SYSTEMWIDE ADMINISTRATION (NP)
1111 Franklin Street, 11th Floor, Oakland, CA Zip 94607-5200; tel. 510/987-9071; John D. Stobo, M.D., Executive Vice President and Chief Executive Officer
(Moderately Centralized Health System)

CALIFORNIA: RONALD REAGAN UCLA MEDICAL CENTER (O, 456 beds) 757 Westwood Plaza, Los Angeles, CA Zip 90095-8358; tel. 310/825-9111; Johnese Spisso, Chief Executive Officer
Web address: www.uclahealth.org

For explanation of codes following names, see page B2.
★ Indicates Type III membership in the American Hospital Association.

STEWART & LYNDA RESNICK NEUROPSYCHIATRIC HOSPITAL AT UCLA (O, 74 beds) 150 UCLA Medical Plaza, Los Angeles, CA Zip 90095–8353; tel. 310/825–9989; Peter Whybrow, M.D., Chief Executive Officer
Web address: www.semel.ucla.edu/resnick

UC IRVINE MEDICAL CENTER (O, 411 beds) 101 The City Drive South, Orange, CA Zip 92868–3298; tel. 714/456–6011; Howard Federoff, M.D., Vice Chancellor, Health Affairs & Chief Executive Officer, UC Irvine Health

UC SAN DIEGO HEALTH (O, 542 beds) 200 West Arbor Drive, San Diego, CA Zip 92103–9000; tel. 619/543–6222; Patty Maysent, Interim Chief Executive Officer
Web address: www.health.ucsd.edu

UCLA MEDICAL CENTER-SANTA MONICA (O, 265 beds) 1250 16th Street, Santa Monica, CA Zip 90404–1249; tel. 310/319–4000; Paul Watkins, JD, Chief Administrative Officer

UCSF MEDICAL CENTER (O, 782 beds) 500 Parnassus Avenue, San Francisco, CA Zip 94143–0296, 500 Parnassus Avenue, Box 0296, 94143–0296, tel. 415/476–1000; Mark R. Laret, Chief Executive Officer
Web address: www.ucsfhealth.org

UNIVERSITY OF CALIFORNIA, DAVIS MEDICAL CENTER (O, 601 beds) 2315 Stockton Boulevard, Sacramento, CA Zip 95817–2282; tel. 916/734–2011; Ann Madden. Rice, Chief Executive Officer

Owned, leased, sponsored:	7 hospitals	3131 beds
Contract-managed:	0 hospitals	0 beds
Totals:	7 hospitals	3131 beds

★0058: UNIVERSITY OF CHICAGO MEDICINE (NP)
5841 South Maryland Avenue, Chicago, IL Zip 60637–1447; tel. 773/702–6240; Sharon L. O'Keefe, President
(Moderately Centralized Health System)

ILLINOIS: INGALLS MEMORIAL HOSPITAL (O, 352 beds) One Ingalls Drive, Harvey, IL Zip 60426–3591; tel. 708/333–2300; Kurt E. Johnson, President and Chief Executive Officer
Web address: www.ingallshealthsystem.org

UNIVERSITY OF CHICAGO MEDICAL CENTER (O, 664 beds) 5841 South Maryland Avenue, Chicago, IL Zip 60637–1447; tel. 773/702–1000; Sharon L. O'Keefe, President
Web address: www.uchospitals.edu

Owned, leased, sponsored:	2 hospitals	1016 beds
Contract-managed:	0 hospitals	0 beds
Totals:	2 hospitals	1016 beds

★0381: UNIVERSITY OF COLORADO HEALTH (NP)
2315 East Harmony Road, Suite 200, Fort Collins, CO Zip 80528–8620; tel. 970/495–7000; Elizabeth B. Concordia, President and Chief Executive Officer
(Moderately Centralized Health System)

COLORADO: MEDICAL CENTER OF THE ROCKIES (O, 187 beds) 2500 Rocky Mountain Avenue, Loveland, CO Zip 80538–9004; tel. 970/624–2500; Kevin L. Unger, Ph.D., FACHE, President and Chief Executive Officer

POUDRE VALLEY HOSPITAL (O, 275 beds) 1024 South Lemay Avenue, Fort Collins, CO Zip 80524–3998, 2315 East Harmony Road, Suite 200, 80528, tel. 970/495–7000; Kevin L. Unger, Ph.D., FACHE, President and Chief Executive Officer
Web address: www.uchealth.org

UCHEALTH BROOMFIELD HOSPITAL (O, 22 beds) 11820 Destination Drive, Broomfield, CO Zip 80021; tel. 303/460–6000; Derek Rushing, Chief Executive Officer

UCHEALTH GRANDVIEW HOSPITAL (O, 22 beds) 5623 Pulpit Peak View, Colorado Springs, CO Zip 80918; tel. 719/272–3600; Derek Rushing, Chief Executive Officer
Web address: https://www.uchealth.org/Pages/OHAM/OrgUnitDetails.aspx?OrganizationalUnitId=514

UCHEALTH MEMORIAL (L, 557 beds) 1400 East Boulder Street, Colorado Springs, CO Zip 80909–5599; tel. 719/365–5000; Joel P. Yuhas, FACHE, President and Chief Executive Officer

UNIVERSITY OF COLORADO HOSPITAL (O, 661 beds) 12401 East 17th Avenue, MS F417, Aurora, CO Zip 80045–2545; tel. 720/848–0000; William Cook, President and Chief Executive Officer
Web address: www.uchealth.org

Owned, leased, sponsored:	6 hospitals	1724 beds
Contract-managed:	0 hospitals	0 beds
Totals:	6 hospitals	1724 beds

★0216: UNIVERSITY OF MARYLAND MEDICAL SYSTEM (NP)
250 West Pratt Street, 24th Floor, Baltimore, MD Zip 21201–1595; tel. 410/328–8667; Robert A. Chrencik, President and Chief Executive Officer
(Moderately Centralized Health System)

MARYLAND: MT. WASHINGTON PEDIATRIC HOSPITAL (O, 61 beds) 1708 West Rogers Avenue, Baltimore, MD Zip 21209–4545; tel. 410/578–8600; Sheldon J. Stein, President and Chief Executive Officer
Web address: www.mwph.org

UNIVERSITY OF MARYLAND BALTIMORE WASHINGTON MEDICAL CENTER (O, 303 beds) 301 Hospital Drive, Glen Burnie, MD Zip 21061–5899; tel. 410/787–4000; Karen E. Olscamp, President and Chief Executive Officer

UNIVERSITY OF MARYLAND CHARLES REGIONAL MEDICAL CENTER (O, 110 beds) 5 Garrett Avenue, La Plata, MD Zip 20646–5960, P O Box 1070, 20646–1070, tel. 301/609–4000; Noel A. Cervino, President and Chief Executive Officer
Web address: www.charlesregional.org

UNIVERSITY OF MARYLAND HARFORD MEMORIAL HOSPITAL (O, 49 beds) 501 South Union Avenue, Havre De Grace, MD Zip 21078–3493; tel. 443/843–5000; Lyle Ernest. Sheldon, FACHE, President and Chief Executive Officer

UNIVERSITY OF MARYLAND MEDICAL CENTER MIDTOWN CAMPUS (O, 170 beds) 827 Linden Avenue, Baltimore, MD Zip 21201–4606; tel. 410/225–8000; Mohan Suntha, M.D., President and Chief Executive Officer
Web address: www.ummidtown.org/

UNIVERSITY OF MARYLAND MEDICAL CENTER (O, 669 beds) 22 South Greene Street, Baltimore, MD Zip 21201–1595; tel. 410/328–8667; Mohan Suntha, M.D., President and Chief Executive Officer

UNIVERSITY OF MARYLAND REHABILITATION & ORTHOPAEDIC INSTITUTE (O, 141 beds) 2200 Kernan Drive, Baltimore, MD Zip 21207–6697; tel. 410/448–2500; Cynthia Kelleher, M.P.H., President and Chief Executive Officer
Web address: www.umrehabortho.org

UNIVERSITY OF MARYLAND SHORE MEDICAL CENTER AT CHESTERTOWN (O, 41 beds) 100 Brown Street, Chestertown, MD Zip 21620–1499; tel. 410/778–3300; Kenneth D. Kozel, FACHE, President and Chief Executive Officer
Web address: www.umms.org/hospitals/shore-health-system.htm

UNIVERSITY OF MARYLAND SHORE MEDICAL CENTER AT DORCHESTER (O, 41 beds) 300 Byrn Street, Cambridge, MD Zip 21613–1908; tel. 410/228–5511; Kenneth D. Kozel, FACHE, President and Chief Executive Officer

UNIVERSITY OF MARYLAND SHORE MEDICAL CENTER AT EASTON (O, 132 beds) 219 South Washington Street, Easton, MD Zip 21601–2996; tel. 410/822–1000; Kenneth D. Kozel, FACHE, President and Chief Executive Officer
Web address: www.shorehealth.org

UNIVERSITY OF MARYLAND ST. JOSEPH MEDICAL CENTER (O, 276 beds) 7601 Osler Drive, Towson, MD Zip 21204–7582; tel. 410/337–1000; Thomas Smyth, President and Chief Executive Officer
Web address: www.stjosephtowson.com/home.aspx

UNIVERSITY OF MARYLAND UPPER CHESAPEAKE MEDICAL CENTER (O, 162 beds) 500 Upper Chesapeake Drive, Bel Air, MD Zip 21014–4324; tel. 443/643–1000; Lyle Ernest. Sheldon, FACHE, President and Chief Executive Officer

Owned, leased, sponsored:	12 hospitals	2155 beds
Contract-managed:	0 hospitals	0 beds
Totals:	12 hospitals	2155 beds

Section B

For explanation of codes following names, see page B2.
★ Indicates Type III membership in the American Hospital Association.

0881: UNIVERSITY OF MIAMI HEALTH SYSTEM (NP)
1400 NW 12th Avenue, Miami, FL Zip 33136–1003; tel. 305/
243–4000; Pascal J. Goldschmidt, M.D., Chief Executive Officer
(Centralized Health System)

FLORIDA: BASCOM PALMER EYE INSTITUTE-ANNE BATES LEACH EYE
HOSPITAL (O, 56 beds) 900 NW 17th Street, Miami, FL Zip 33136–1199,
Box 016880, 33101–6880, tel. 305/326–6000; Michael B. Gittelman,
Administrator
Web address: www.bascompalmer.org

UNIVERSITY OF MIAMI HOSPITAL AND CLINICS (O, 40 beds) 1475 NW 12th
Avenue, Miami, FL Zip 33136–1002; tel. 305/243–4000; Richard R. Ballard,
Chief Executive Officer and Administrator
Web address: www.uhealthsystem.com

UNIVERSITY OF MIAMI HOSPITAL (O, 464 beds) 1400 NW 12th Avenue, Miami,
FL Zip 33136–1003; tel. 305/325–5511; Michael B. Gittelman, Interim Chief
Executive Officer

Owned, leased, sponsored:	3 hospitals	560 beds
Contract-managed:	0 hospitals	0 beds
Totals:	3 hospitals	560 beds

★0227: UNIVERSITY OF MISSOURI HEALTH CARE (NP)
One Hospital Drive, DC 031, Columbia, MO Zip 65212–0001;
tel. 573/882–4141; Jonathan W. Curtright, Chief Executive Officer and Chief Operating Officer
(Moderately Centralized Health System)

MISSOURI: CAPITAL REGION MEDICAL CENTER (O, 114 beds) 1125 Madison
Street, Jefferson City, MO Zip 65101–5200, P O Box 1128, 65102–1128,
tel. 573/632–5000; Gaspare Calvaruso, President
Web address: www.crmc.org

UNIVERSITY OF MISSOURI HEALTH CARE (O, 569 beds) One Hospital Drive,
Columbia, MO Zip 65212–0001; tel. 573/882–4141; Jonathan W. Curtright,
Chief Executive Officer and Chief Operating Officer
Web address: www.muhealth.org

Owned, leased, sponsored:	2 hospitals	683 beds
Contract-managed:	0 hospitals	0 beds
Totals:	2 hospitals	683 beds

0021: UNIVERSITY OF NEW MEXICO HOSPITALS (NP)
915 Camino De Salud, Albuquerque, NM Zip 87131–0001; tel. 505/
272–5849; Michael Chicarelli, RN, Interim Chief Executive Officer
(Moderately Centralized Health System)

NEW MEXICO: UNM SANDOVAL REGIONAL MEDICAL CENTER, INC. (O,
72 beds) 3001 Broadmoor Boulevard NE, Rio Rancho, NM Zip 87131;
tel. 505/994–7000; Jamie A. Silva-Steele, FACHE, R.N., President and Chief
Executive Officer

UNIVERSITY OF NEW MEXICO HOSPITALS (O, 537 beds) 2211 Lomas
Boulevard NE, Albuquerque, NM Zip 87106–2745; tel. 505/272–2111;
Michael Chicarelli, RN, Chief Executive Officer
Web address: www.unm.edu

Owned, leased, sponsored:	2 hospitals	609 beds
Contract-managed:	0 hospitals	0 beds
Totals:	2 hospitals	609 beds

★0168: UNIVERSITY OF PENNSYLVANIA HEALTH SYSTEM (NP)
3400 Civic Center Bouelvard, Philadelphia, PA Zip 19104–5127;
tel. 215/662–2203; Ralph W. Muller, President and Chief Executive Officer
(Centralized Health System)

PENNSYLVANIA: HOSPITAL OF THE UNIVERSITY OF PENNSYLVANIA (O,
788 beds) 3400 Spruce Street, Philadelphia, PA Zip 19104–4206;
tel. 215/662–4000; Regina Cunningham, Ph.D., R.N., Chief Executive
Officer
Web address: www.pennmedicine.org

LANCASTER GENERAL HOSPITAL (O, 630 beds) 555 North Duke Street,
Lancaster, PA Zip 17602–2250; tel. 717/544–5511; Jan L. Bergen, President
and Chief Executive Officer

PENN MEDICINE CHESTER COUNTY HOSPITAL (O, 248 beds) 701 East
Marshall Street, West Chester, PA Zip 19380–4412; tel. 610/431–5000;
Michael J. Duncan, President and Chief Executive Officer
Web address: www.chestercountyhospital.org

PENN PRESBYTERIAN MEDICAL CENTER (O, 365 beds) 51 North 39th Street,
Philadelphia, PA Zip 19104–2699; tel. 215/662–8000; Michele M. Volpe,
Chief Executive Officer
Web address: www.pennmedicine.org/pmc/

PENNSYLVANIA HOSPITAL (O, 415 beds) 800 Spruce Street, Philadelphia, PA
Zip 19107–6192; tel. 215/829–3000; Theresa M. . Larivee, Chief Executive
Officer

Owned, leased, sponsored:	5 hospitals	2446 beds
Contract-managed:	0 hospitals	0 beds
Totals:	5 hospitals	2446 beds

★0223: UNIVERSITY OF ROCHESTER MEDICAL CENTER (NP)
601 Elmwood Ave Box 623, Rochester, NY Zip 14642–0002,
601 Elmwood Avenue, 14642–0002, tel. 585/275–2100; Steven
I. Goldstein, General Director and Chief Executive Officer
(Centralized Health System)

NEW YORK: F. F. THOMPSON HOSPITAL (O, 291 beds) 350 Parrish Street,
Canandaigua, NY Zip 14424–1731; tel. 585/396–6000; Michael Stapleton,
President and Chief Executive Officer
Web address: www.thompsonhealth.com

HIGHLAND HOSPITAL (O, 261 beds) 1000 South Avenue, Rochester, NY
Zip 14620–2733; tel. 585/473–2200; Steven I. Goldstein, President and
Chief Executive Officer

JONES MEMORIAL HOSPITAL (O, 33 beds) 191 North Main Street, Wellsville,
NY Zip 14895–1150, P O Box 72, 14895–0072, tel. 585/593–1100; Eva
Benedict, R.N., President and Chief Executive Officer
Web address: www.jmhny.org

NICHOLAS H. NOYES MEMORIAL HOSPITAL (O, 40 beds) 111 Clara Barton
Street, Dansville, NY Zip 14437–9503; tel. 585/335–6001; Amy Pollard,
R.N., President and Chief Executive Officer
Web address: www.noyes-health.org

STRONG MEMORIAL HOSPITAL OF THE UNIVERSITY OF ROCHESTER (O, 835
beds) 601 Elmwood Avenue, Rochester, NY Zip 14642–0002, 601 Elmwood
Avenue, Box 612, 14642–0002, tel. 585/275–2100; Steven I. Goldstein,
President and Chief Executive Officer

Owned, leased, sponsored:	5 hospitals	1460 beds
Contract-managed:	0 hospitals	0 beds
Totals:	5 hospitals	1460 beds

★0057: UNIVERSITY OF SOUTH ALABAMA HOSPITALS (NP)
2451 Fillingim Street, Mobile, AL Zip 36617–2238; tel. 251/471–
7000; Owen Bailey, FACHE, Chief Executive Officer and Senior
Associate Vice President for Medical Affairs
(Independent Hospital System)

ALABAMA: UNIVERSITY OF SOUTH ALABAMA CHILDREN'S AND WOMEN'S
HOSPITAL (O, 180 beds) 1700 Center Street, Mobile, AL Zip 36604–3301;
tel. 251/415–1000; Chris Jett, Administrator
Web address: www.usahealthsystem.com/usacwh

UNIVERSITY OF SOUTH ALABAMA MEDICAL CENTER (O, 142 beds) 2451
Fillingim Street, Mobile, AL Zip 36617–2293; tel. 251/471–7000; Sam Dean,
Administrator

Owned, leased, sponsored:	2 hospitals	322 beds
Contract-managed:	0 hospitals	0 beds
Totals:	2 hospitals	322 beds

For explanation of codes following names, see page B2.
★ Indicates Type III membership in the American Hospital Association.

★0033: **UNIVERSITY OF TEXAS SYSTEM** (NP)
601 Colorado Street, Suite 205, Austin, TX Zip 78701–2904; tel. 512/499–4224; Raymond Greenberg, M.D., Executive Vice Chancellor
(Moderately Centralized Health System)

TEXAS: UNIVERSITY OF TEXAS HARRIS COUNTY PSYCHIATRIC CENTER (C, 208 beds) 2800 South MacGregor Way, Houston, TX Zip 77021–1000, P O Box 20249, 77225–0249, tel. 713/741–7870; Jair C. Soares, M.D., Executive Director
Web address: www.hcpc.uth.tmc.edu

UNIVERSITY OF TEXAS HEALTH NORTHEAST (O, 130 beds) 11937 Highway 271, Tyler, TX Zip 75708–3154; tel. 903/877–7777; Kirk A. Calhoun, M.D., President

UNIVERSITY OF TEXAS M.D. ANDERSON CANCER CENTER (O, 660 beds) 1515 Holcombe Boulevard, Unit 1491, Houston, TX Zip 77030–4000; tel. 713/792–2121; Marshall Hicks, M.D., Interim President
Web address: www.mdanderson.org

UNIVERSITY OF TEXAS MEDICAL BRANCH (O, 603 beds) 301 University Boulevard, Galveston, TX Zip 77555–0128; tel. 409/772–1011; Donna K. Sollenberger, Executive Vice President and Chief Executive Officer

Owned, leased, sponsored:	3 hospitals	1393 beds
Contract-managed:	1 hospitals	208 beds
Totals:	4 hospitals	1601 beds

0137: **UPMC** (NP)
600 Grant Street, US Steel Tower, Suite 6262, Pittsburgh, PA Zip 15219–2702; tel. 412/647–8762; Jeffrey A. Romoff, President and Chief Executive Officer
(Centralized Physician/Insurance Health System)

NEW YORK: UPMC CHAUTAUQUA WCA (O, 197 beds) 207 Foote Avenue, Jamestown, NY Zip 14701–7077, P O Box 840, 14702–0840, tel. 716/487–0141; Betsy T. Wright, President and Chief Executive Officer
Web address: www.wcahospital.org

PENNSYLVANIA: CHILDREN'S HOSPITAL OF PITTSBURGH OF UPMC (O, 305 beds) One Children's Hospital Drive, 4401 Penn Avenue, Pittsburgh, PA Zip 15224–1334; tel. 412/692–5325; Christopher A. Gessner, President

MAGEE-WOMENS HOSPITAL OF UPMC (O, 321 beds) 300 Halket Street, Pittsburgh, PA Zip 15213–3108; tel. 412/641–1000; Leslie C. Davis, President
Web address: www.magee.edu

UPMC ALTOONA (O, 342 beds) 620 Howard Avenue, Altoona, PA Zip 16601–4804; tel. 814/889–2011; Gerald Murray, President
Web address: www.altoonaregional.org

UPMC BEDFORD MEMORIAL (O, 27 beds) 10455 Lincoln Highway, Everett, PA Zip 15537–7046; tel. 814/623–6161; Gerald Murray, President

UPMC EAST (O, 155 beds) 2775 Mosside Boulevard, Monroeville, PA Zip 15146–2760; tel. 412/357–3000; Mark Sevco, President
Web address: www.upmc.com/locations/hospitals/east/Pages/default.aspx

UPMC HAMOT (O, 302 beds) 201 State Street, Erie, PA Zip 16550–0002; tel. 814/877–6000; David Gibbons, President

UPMC HORIZON (O, 121 beds) 2200 Memorial Drive, Farrell, PA Zip 16121–1357; tel. 724/588–2100; Donald R. Owrey, President
Web address: www.upmc.com

UPMC JAMESON HOSPITAL (O, 238 beds) 1211 Wilmington Avenue, New Castle, PA Zip 16105–2516; tel. 724/658–9001; Donald R. Owrey, President

UPMC KANE (O, 31 beds) 4372 Route 6, Kane, PA Zip 16735–3060; tel. 814/837–8585; J Gary. Rhodes, FACHE, Chief Executive Officer
Web address: www.kanehosp.com

UPMC MCKEESPORT (O, 174 beds) 1500 Fifth Avenue, McKeesport, PA Zip 15132–2422; tel. 412/664–2000; Mark Sevco, President
Web address: www.mckeesport.upmc.com

UPMC MERCY (O, 482 beds) 1400 Locust Street, Pittsburgh, PA Zip 15219–5166; tel. 412/232–8111; Michael A. Grace, President

UPMC NORTHWEST (O, 128 beds) 100 Fairfield Drive, Seneca, PA Zip 16346–2130; tel. 814/676–7600; Brian Durniok, President
Web address: www.upmc.com/locations/hospitals/northwest/Pages/default.aspx

UPMC PASSAVANT (O, 286 beds) 9100 Babcock Boulevard, Pittsburgh, PA Zip 15237–5815; tel. 412/748–6700; David T. Martin, President
Web address: www.upmc.edu/passavant

UPMC PRESBYTERIAN SHADYSIDE (O, 1452 beds) 200 Lothrop Street, Pittsburgh, PA Zip 15213–2536; tel. 412/647–2345; John Innocenti Sr, President and Chief Executive Officer

UPMC ST. MARGARET (O, 206 beds) 815 Freeport Road, Pittsburgh, PA Zip 15215–3301; tel. 412/784–4000; David J. Patton, President
Web address: www.upmc.com/locations/hospitals/st-margaret/Pages/default.aspx

Owned, leased, sponsored:	16 hospitals	4767 beds
Contract-managed:	0 hospitals	0 beds
Totals:	16 hospitals	4767 beds

1023: **UPMC PINNACLE** (NP)
111 South Front Street, Harrisburg, PA Zip 17101–2010, P O Box 8700, 17105–8700, tel. 717/231–8900; Philip Guarneschelli, President and Chief Executive Officer

PENNSYLVANIA: CARLISLE REGIONAL MEDICAL CENTER (O, 65 beds) 361 Alexander Spring Road, Carlisle, PA Zip 17015–6940; tel. 717/249–1212; David P. Steitz, Chief Executive Officer
Web address: www.carlislermc.com/default.aspx

HEART OF LANCASTER REGIONAL MEDICAL CENTER (O, 148 beds) 1500 Highlands Drive, Lititz, PA Zip 17543–7694; tel. 717/625–5000; Deborah J. Willwerth, R.N., MSN, Chief Executive Officer

LANCASTER REGIONAL MEDICAL CENTERS (O, 150 beds) 250 College Avenue, Lancaster, PA Zip 17603–3363, P O Box 3434, 17604–3434, tel. 717/291–8211; Brooks Turkel, Chief Executive Officer
Web address: www.lancasterregional.com

MEMORIAL HOSPITAL (O, 100 beds) 325 South Belmont Street, York, PA Zip 17403–2609, P O Box 15118, 17405–7118, tel. 717/843–8623; Sally J. Dixon, Chief Executive Officer

PINNACLEHEALTH HARRISBURG HOSPITAL (O, 627 beds) 111 South Front Street, Harrisburg, PA Zip 17101–2010, P O Box 8700, 17105–8700, tel. 717/231–8900; Philip Guarneschelli, Interim Chief Executive Officer
Web address: www.pinnaclehealth.org

Owned, leased, sponsored:	5 hospitals	1090 beds
Contract-managed:	0 hospitals	0 beds
Totals:	5 hospitals	1090 beds

★0066: **UPMC SUSQUEHANNA** (NP)
700 High Street , Williamsport, PA Zip 17701–3100; tel. 570/321–1000; Steven P. Johnson, FACHE, President and Chief Executive Officer
(Centralized Health System)

PENNSYLVANIA: DIVINE PROVIDENCE HOSPITAL (O, 31 beds) 1100 Grampian Boulevard, Williamsport, PA Zip 17701–1995; tel. 570/326–8000; Robert E. Kane, Chief Administrative Officer

MUNCY VALLEY HOSPITAL (O, 156 beds) 215 East Water Street, Muncy, PA Zip 17756–8700; tel. 570/546–8282; Christine Ballard, President and Chief Executive Officer
Web address: www.susquehannahealth.org

SOLDIERS AND SAILORS MEMORIAL HOSPITAL (O, 67 beds) 32–36 Central Avenue, Wellsboro, PA Zip 16901–1899; tel. 570/724–1631; Janie Hilfiger, Chief Administrative Officer
Web address: www.susquehannahealth.org

For explanation of codes following names, see page B2.
★ Indicates Type III membership in the American Hospital Association.

WILLIAMSPORT REGIONAL MEDICAL CENTER (O, 220 beds) 700 High Street, Williamsport, PA Zip 17701–3100; tel. 570/321–1000; Jan E. Fisher, Executive Vice President, Chief Operating Officer and Chief Administrative Officer

Owned, leased, sponsored:	4 hospitals	474 beds
Contract-managed:	0 hospitals	0 beds
Totals:	4 hospitals	474 beds

0816: UPPER ALLEGHENY HEALTH SYSTEM (NP)

130 South Union Street, Suite 300, Olean, NY Zip 14760–3676; tel. 716/375–6190; Timothy J. Finan, FACHE, President and Chief Executive Officer
(Independent Hospital System)

NEW YORK: OLEAN GENERAL HOSPITAL (O, 186 beds) 515 Main Street, Olean, NY Zip 14760–1513; tel. 716/373–2600; Timothy J. Finan, FACHE, President and Chief Executive Officer
Web address: www.ogh.org

PENNSYLVANIA: BRADFORD REGIONAL MEDICAL CENTER (O, 182 beds) 116 Interstate Parkway, Bradford, PA Zip 16701–1036; tel. 814/368–4143; Timothy J. Finan, FACHE, President and Chief Executive Officer
Web address: www.brmc.com

Owned, leased, sponsored:	2 hospitals	368 beds
Contract-managed:	0 hospitals	0 beds
Totals:	2 hospitals	368 beds

0868: USMD HEALTH SYSTEM (IO)

6333 North State Highway 161 Suite 200, Irving, TX Zip 75038–2229; tel. 214/493–4000; Mike Bukosky, President, Hospital Division
(Independent Hospital System)

TEXAS: USMD HOSPITAL AT ARLINGTON (O, 34 beds) 801 West Interstate 20, Arlington, TX Zip 76017–5851; tel. 817/472–3400; Marcia Crim, R.N., MSN, Chief Executive Officer

USMD HOSPITAL AT FORT WORTH (O, 8 beds) 5900 Altamesa Boulevard, Fort Worth, TX Zip 76132–5473; tel. 817/433–9100; Stephanie Atkins-Guidry, Administrator and Chief Nursing Officer
Web address: www.usmdfortworth.com/

Owned, leased, sponsored:	2 hospitals	42 beds
Contract-managed:	0 hospitals	0 beds
Totals:	2 hospitals	42 beds

0860: UVA HEALTH SYSTEM (NP)

1215 Lee Street, Charlottesville, VA Zip 22908–0816; tel. 434/924–0211; Richard Shannon, M.D., Executive Vice President for Health Affairs
(Centralized Health System)

VIRGINIA: NOVANT HEALTH UVA HEALTH SYSTEM CULPEPER MEDICAL CENTER (O, 68 beds) 501 Sunset Lane, Culpeper, VA Zip 22701–3917, P O Box 592, 22701–0500, tel. 540/829–4100; Greg Napps, Chief Executive Officer
Web address: www.culpeperhealth.org

UVA TRANSITIONAL CARE HOSPITAL (O, 40 beds) 2965 Ivy Rd (250 West), Charlottesville, VA Zip 22903–9330; tel. 434/924–8245; Christine K. Matt, Associate Chief

UNIVERSITY OF VIRGINIA MEDICAL CENTER (O, 593 beds) 1215 Lee Street, Charlottesville, VA Zip 22908–0001, P O Box 800809, 22908–0809, tel. 434/924–0211; Pamela Sutton-Wallace, Chief Executive Officer
Web address: www.healthsystem.virginia.edu

Owned, leased, sponsored:	3 hospitals	701 beds
Contract-managed:	0 hospitals	0 beds
Totals:	3 hospitals	701 beds

1009: UW HEALTH SYSTEM (IO)

600 Highland Avenue, Madison, WI Zip 53792–0001; tel. 608/263–6400; Alan Kaplan, M.D., Chief Executive Officer

WISCONSIN: UW HEALTH REHABILITATION HOSPITAL (O, 35 beds) 5115 North Biltmore Lane, Madison, WI Zip 53718–2161; tel. 608/592–8100; Gregory A. Banaszynski, Chief Executive Officer

UNIVERSITY OF WISCONSIN HOSPITALS AND CLINICS AUTHORITY (O, 598 beds) 600 Highland Avenue, Madison, WI Zip 53792–0002; tel. 608/263–6400; Alan Kaplan, M.D., Chief Executive Officer
Web address: www.uwhealth.org

Owned, leased, sponsored:	2 hospitals	633 beds
Contract-managed:	0 hospitals	0 beds
Totals:	2 hospitals	633 beds

★6415: UW MEDICINE (NP)

1959 NE Pacific Street, Seattle, WA Zip 98195–0001, P O Box 356350, 98195–6350, tel. 206/543–7718; Paul G. Ramsey, M.D., Chief Executive Officer
(Independent Hospital System)

WASHINGTON: UW MEDICINE/HARBORVIEW MEDICAL CENTER (C, 413 beds) 325 Ninth Avenue, Seattle, WA Zip 98104–2499, P O Box 359717, 98195–9717, tel. 206/744–3000; Paul Hayes, R.N., Executive Director
Web address: www.uwmedicine.org/Patient-Care/Locations/HMC/Pages/default.aspx

UW MEDICINE/NORTHWEST HOSPITAL & MEDICAL CENTER (O, 192 beds) 1550 North 115th Street, Seattle, WA Zip 98133–8401; tel. 206/364–0500; Cindy Hecker, Executive Director
Web address: www.uwmedicine.org/Patient-Care/Locations/nwh/Pages/default.aspx

UW MEDICINE/VALLEY MEDICAL CENTER (C, 282 beds) 400 South 43rd Street, Renton, WA Zip 98055–5714, P O Box 50010, 98058–5010, tel. 425/228–3450; Richard D. Roodman, Chief Executive Officer

UNIVERSITY OF WASHINGTON MEDICAL CENTER (O, 450 beds) 1959 NE Pacific Street, Seattle, WA Zip 98195–6151; tel. 206/598–3300; Geoff Austin, Executive Director
Web address: www.uwmedicine.org/uw-medical-center

Owned, leased, sponsored:	2 hospitals	642 beds
Contract-managed:	2 hospitals	695 beds
Totals:	4 hospitals	1337 beds

★0128: VALLEY HEALTH SYSTEM (NP)

220 Campus Boulevard, Suite 420, Winchester, VA Zip 22601–2889, P O Box 3340, 22604–2540, tel. 540/536–8024; Mark H. Merrill, President and Chief Executive Officer
(Moderately Centralized Health System)

VIRGINIA: PAGE MEMORIAL HOSPITAL (O, 25 beds) 200 Memorial Drive, Luray, VA Zip 22835–1005; tel. 540/743–4561; N Travis. Clark, President
SHENANDOAH MEMORIAL HOSPITAL (O, 25 beds) 759 South Main Street, Woodstock, VA Zip 22664–1127; tel. 540/459–1100; N Travis. Clark, President
Web address: www.valleyhealthlink.com/shenandoah

WARREN MEMORIAL HOSPITAL (O, 180 beds) 1000 North Shenandoah Avenue, Front Royal, VA Zip 22630–3598; tel. 540/636–0300; Floyd Heater, President and Chief Executive Officer
Web address: www.valleyhealthlink.com/WMH

WINCHESTER MEDICAL CENTER (O, 485 beds) 1840 Amherst Street, Winchester, VA Zip 22601–2808, P O Box 3340, 22604–2540, tel. 540/536–8000; Grady W. Philips III, President

WEST VIRGINIA: HAMPSHIRE MEMORIAL HOSPITAL (O, 44 beds) 363 Sunrise Boulevard, Romney, WV Zip 26757–4607; tel. 304/822–4561; Thomas S. Kluge, President
Web address: www.valleyhealthlink.com/hampshire

WAR MEMORIAL HOSPITAL (O, 41 beds) One Healthy Way, Berkeley Springs, WV Zip 25411–7463; tel. 304/258–1234; Thomas S. Kluge, President
Web address: www.valleyhealthlink.com/war

Owned, leased, sponsored:	6 hospitals	800 beds
Contract-managed:	0 hospitals	0 beds
Totals:	6 hospitals	800 beds

For explanation of codes following names, see page B2.
★ Indicates Type III membership in the American Hospital Association.

★0387: VANDERBILT HEALTH (NP)

1211 22nd Avenue South, Nashville, TN Zip 37232; tel. 615/322–5000; Charles Wright. Pinson, M.D., Deputy Vice Chancellor for Health Affairs and Chief Executive Officer of Vanderbilt Health System **(Moderately Centralized Health System)**

TENNESSEE: VANDERBILT UNIVERSITY MEDICAL CENTER (O, 1004 beds) 1211 Medical Center Drive, Nashville, TN Zip 37232–2102; tel. 615/322–5000; Jeffrey R. Balsar, President and Chief Executive Officer Vanderbilt Medical Center and Dean, Vanderbilt University School of Medicine

Owned, leased, sponsored:	1 hospitals	1004 beds
Contract-managed:	0 hospitals	0 beds
Totals:	1 hospitals	1004 beds

★0939: VCU HEALTH SYSTEM (NP)

1250 East Marshall Street, Richmond, VA Zip 23298–5051, P O Box 980510, 23298–0510, tel. 804/828–9000; Marsha Rappley, M.D., Chief Executive Officer and Vice President for Health Sciences **(Moderately Centralized Health System)**

VIRGINIA: CHILDREN'S HOSPITAL OF RICHMOND AT VCU-BROOK ROAD CAMPUS (O, 36 beds) 2924 Brook Road, Richmond, VA Zip 23220–1298; tel. 804/321–7474; Jeniece S. Roane, MS, R.N., Interim Vice President, Children's Services
Web address: www.chrichmond.org

VCU HEALTH COMMUNITY MEMORIAL HOSPITAL (O, 178 beds) 125 Buena Vista Circle, South Hill, VA Zip 23970–1431, P O Box 90, 23970–0090, tel. 434/447–3151; W Scott. Burnette, Chief Executive Officer
Web address: www.cmh-sh.org

VCU MEDICAL CENTER (O, 786 beds) 1250 East Marshall Street, Richmond, VA Zip 23298–5051, P O Box 980510, 23298–0510, tel. 804/828–9000; Deborah W. Davis, Chief Executive Officer and Vice President Clinical Services

Owned, leased, sponsored:	3 hospitals	1000 beds
Contract-managed:	0 hospitals	0 beds
Totals:	3 hospitals	1000 beds

★1075: VERITY HEALTH SYSTEM (CC)

2200 West Third Street, Suite 200, Los Angeles, CA Zip 90057–1935, 203 Redwood Shores Parkway, Suite 800, Redwood City, 94065, tel. 650/551–6650; Andrei Soran, MSN, Chief Executive Officer **(Independent Hospital System)**

CALIFORNIA: O'CONNOR HOSPITAL (O, 202 beds) 2105 Forest Avenue, San Jose, CA Zip 95128–1471; tel. 408/947–2500; Jordan Herget, President and Chief Executive Officer
Web address: www.oconnorhospital.org

SAINT LOUISE REGIONAL HOSPITAL (O, 93 beds) 9400 No Name Uno, Gilroy, CA Zip 95020–3528; tel. 408/848–2000; Jordan Herget, President and Chief Executive Officer

SETON MEDICAL CENTER COASTSIDE (O, 116 beds) 600 Marine Boulevard, Moss Beach, CA Zip 94038–9641; tel. 650/563–7100; John Ferrelli, Chief Executive Officer

SETON MEDICAL CENTER (O, 410 beds) 1900 Sullivan Avenue, Daly City, CA Zip 94015–2229; tel. 650/992–4000; John Ferrelli, Chief Executive Officer
Web address: www.setonmedicalcenter.org

ST. FRANCIS MEDICAL CENTER (O, 323 beds) 3630 East Imperial Highway, Lynwood, CA Zip 90262–2636; tel. 310/900–8900; Gerald T. Kozai, PharmD, President and Chief Executive Officer
Web address: www.dochs.org

ST. VINCENT MEDICAL CENTER (O, 271 beds) 2131 West Third Street, Los Angeles, CA Zip 90057–1901, P O Box 57992, 90057–0992, tel. 213/484–7111; Frank J. Cracolici, President and Chief Executive Officer

Owned, leased, sponsored:	6 hospitals	1415 beds
Contract-managed:	0 hospitals	0 beds
Totals:	6 hospitals	1415 beds

★0299: VIBRA HEALTHCARE (IO)

4550 Lena Drive, Suite 225, Mechanicsburg, PA Zip 17055–4920; tel. 717/591–5700; Brad Hollinger, Chairman and Chief Executive Officer **(Independent Hospital System)**

CALIFORNIA: BALLARD REHABILITATION HOSPITAL (O, 60 beds) 1760 West 16th Street, San Bernardino, CA Zip 92411–1160; tel. 909/473–1200; Mary Miles. Hunt, Chief Executive Officer
Web address: www.ballardrehab.com

KENTFIELD REHABILITATION AND SPECIALTY HOSPITAL (O, 48 beds) 1125 Sir Francis Drake Boulevard, Kentfield, CA Zip 94904–1455; tel. 415/456–9680; Lauren Suarez, Chief Executive Officer

SAN JOAQUIN VALLEY REHABILITATION HOSPITAL (O, 62 beds) 7173 North Sharon Avenue, Fresno, CA Zip 93720–3329; tel. 559/436–3600; Mary Jo Jacobson, Chief Executive Officer
Web address: www.sanjoaquinrehab.com

VIBRA HOSPITAL OF NORTHERN CALIFORNIA (O, 88 beds) 2801 Eureka Way, Redding, CA Zip 96001–0222; tel. 530/246–9000; Chris Jones, Chief Executive Officer

VIBRA HOSPITAL OF SACRAMENTO (O, 58 beds) 330 Montrose Drive, Folsom, CA Zip 95630–2720; tel. 916/351–9151; Kimberly Horton, R.N., MSN, Chief Executive Officer
Web address: www.vhsacramento.com

VIBRA HOSPITAL OF SAN DIEGO (O, 80 beds) 555 Washington Street, San Diego, CA Zip 92103–2294; tel. 619/260–8300; Yameeka Jones, Chief Executive Officer

COLORADO: VIBRA HOSPITAL OF DENVER (O, 71 beds) 8451 Pearl Street, Thornton, CO Zip 80229–4804; tel. 303/288–3000; Linda Tautz, Chief Executive Officer
Web address: www.vhdenver.com

IDAHO: VIBRA HOSPITAL OF BOISE (O, 60 beds) 2131 South Bonito Way, Meridian, ID Zip 83642–1659; tel. 877/801–2244; Cynthia Newsom, Chief Executive Officer
Web address: www.vhboise.com

ILLINOIS: VIBRA HOSPITAL OF SPRINGFIELD (O, 30 beds) 701 North Walnut Street, Springfield, IL Zip 62702–4931; tel. 217/528–1217; Charles Nordyke, Chief Executive Officer
Web address: www.vhspringfield.com

INDIANA: VIBRA HOSPITAL OF FORT WAYNE (O, 24 beds) 2200 Randallia Drive, Fort Wayne, IN Zip 46805–4638; tel. 260/399–2900; Ryan Cassedy, Chief Executive Officer

VIBRA HOSPITAL OF NORTHWESTERN INDIANA (O, 40 beds) 9509 Georgia Street, Crown Point, IN Zip 46307–6518; tel. 219/472–2200; Charles Nordyke, Chief Executive Officer
Web address: www.vhnwindiana.com/

KENTUCKY: GATEWAY REHABILITATION HOSPITAL (C, 40 beds) 5940 Merchant Street, Florence, KY Zip 41042–1158; tel. 859/426–2400; Frank Schneider, FACHE, Chief Executive Officer

SOUTHERN KENTUCKY REHABILITATION HOSPITAL (O, 60 beds) 1300 Campbell Lane, Bowling Green, KY Zip 42104–4162; tel. 270/782–6900; Stuart Locke, Chief Executive Officer
Web address: www.skyrehab.com

MASSACHUSETTS: VIBRA HOSPITAL OF SOUTHEASTERN MASSACHUSETTS (O, 90 beds) 4499 Acushnet Avenue, New Bedford, MA Zip 02745–4707; tel. 508/995–6900; Edward B. Leary, Chief Executive Officer
Web address: www.newbedfordrehab.com

VIBRA HOSPITAL OF WESTERN MASSACHUSETTS (O, 174 beds) 1400 State Street, Springfield, MA Zip 01109–2550; tel. 413/726–6700; Edward B. Leary, Interim Chief Executive Officer

MICHIGAN: VIBRA HOSPITAL OF SOUTHEASTERN MICHIGAN, LLC (O, 220 beds) 26400 West Outer Drive, Lincoln Park, MI Zip 48146–2088; tel. 313/386–2000; Denise Wayne, Chief Executive Officer
Web address: www.vhsemichigan.com/

For explanation of codes following names, see page B2.
★ Indicates Type III membership in the American Hospital Association.

NORTH DAKOTA: VIBRA HOSPITAL OF CENTRAL DAKOTAS (O, 41 beds) 1000 18th Street NW, Mandan, ND Zip 58554–1612; tel. 701/667–2000; Glynda Troyo-Sauviac, Chief Executive Officer
Web address: www.vhcentraldakotas.com

VIBRA HOSPITAL OF FARGO (O, 31 beds) 1720 University Drive South, Fargo, ND Zip 58103–4940; tel. 701/241–9099; Custer Huseby, Chief Executive Officer
Web address: www.vhfargo.com

OHIO: VIBRA HOSPITAL OF MAHONING VALLEY (O, 42 beds) 8049 South Avenue, Boardman, OH Zip 44512–6154; tel. 330/726–5000; Nathan Mast, Chief Executive Officer

OREGON: VIBRA SPECIALTY HOSPITAL OF PORTLAND (O, 68 beds) 10300 NE Hancock Street, Portland, OR Zip 97220–3831; tel. 503/257–5500; Victor Jackson, Chief Executive Officer
Web address: www.vshportland.com

SOUTH CAROLINA: VIBRA HOSPITAL OF CHARLESTON (O, 59 beds) 1200 Hospital Drive, Mt. Pleasant, SC Zip 29464; tel. 843/375–4000; Daniel C. Dunmyer, Chief Executive Officer

TEXAS: HIGHLANDS REHABILITATION HOSPITAL (O, 41 beds) 1395 George Dieter Drive, El Paso, TX Zip 79936–7410; tel. 915/298–7222; Craig Johnson, Chief Executive Officer
Web address: www.vrhhighlands.com/

VIBRA HOSPITAL OF AMARILLO (O, 72 beds) 7501 Wallace Boulevard, Amarillo, TX Zip 79124–2150; tel. 806/467–7000; Becky Burton, R.N., Chief Executive Officer and Market Chief Executive Officer

VIBRA REHABILITATION HOSPITAL LAKE TRAVIS (O, 36 beds) 2000 Medical Drive, Lakeway, TX Zip 78734–4200; tel. 512/263–4500; Deborah Hopps, R.N., FACHE, Chief Executive Officer
Web address: www.vrhlaketravis.com

VIBRA REHABILITATION HOSPITAL OF AMARILLO (O, 44 beds) 7200 West 9th Avenue, Amarillo, TX Zip 79106–1703; tel. 806/468–2900; Tammie Tabor, Chief Executive Officer

VIBRA SPECIALTY HOSPITAL AT DESOTO (O, 60 beds) 2700 Walker Way, Desoto, TX Zip 75115–2088; tel. 972/298–1100; Thomas Alexander, Chief Executive Officer
Web address: www.vshdesoto.com

VIRGINIA: VIBRA HOSPITAL OF RICHMOND (O, 60 beds) 2220 Edward Holland Drive, Richmond, VA Zip 23230–2519; tel. 804/678–7000; Linda Tiemens, Chief Executive Officer
Web address: www.vhrichmond.com

Owned, leased, sponsored:	26 hospitals	1719 beds
Contract-managed:	1 hospitals	40 beds
Totals:	27 hospitals	1759 beds

★0217: VIDANT HEALTH (NP)
2100 Stantonsburg Road, Greenville, NC Zip 27834–2818, P O Box 6028, 27835–6028, tel. 252/847–4100; Michael Waldrum, M.D., Chief Executive Officer
(Moderately Centralized Health System)

NORTH CAROLINA: THE OUTER BANKS HOSPITAL (O, 21 beds) 4800 South Croatan Highway, Nags Head, NC Zip 27959–9704; tel. 252/449–4500; Ronald A. Sloan, FACHE, President

VIDANT BEAUFORT HOSPITAL (L, 84 beds) 628 East 12th Street, Washington, NC Zip 27889–3409; tel. 252/975–4100; Harvey Case, President
Web address: www.vidanthealth.com

VIDANT BERTIE HOSPITAL (L, 6 beds) 1403 South King Street, P O Box 40, Windsor, NC Zip 27983–9666, P O Box 40, 27983–0040, tel. 252/794–6600; Jeffrey Sackrison, President
Web address: www.vidanthealth.com

VIDANT CHOWAN HOSPITAL (L, 19 beds) 211 Virginia Road, Edenton, NC Zip 27932–9668, P O Box 629, 27932–0629, tel. 252/482–8451; Jeffrey Sackrison, President

VIDANT DUPLIN HOSPITAL (L, 48 beds) 401 North Main Street, Kenansville, NC Zip 28349–8801, P O Box 278, 28349–0278, tel. 910/296–0941; Jay Briley, President
Web address: www.vidanthealth.com

VIDANT EDGECOMBE HOSPITAL (O, 94 beds) 111 Hospital Drive, Tarboro, NC Zip 27886–2011; tel. 252/641–7700; Wendell H. Baker Jr, President

VIDANT MEDICAL CENTER (O, 909 beds) 2100 Stantonsburg Road, Greenville, NC Zip 27834–2818, P O Box 6028, 27835–6028, tel. 252/847–4100; William Brian. Floyd, President
Web address: https://www.vidanthealth.com/

VIDANT ROANOKE-CHOWAN HOSPITAL (L, 70 beds) 500 South Academy Street, Ahoskie, NC Zip 27910–3261, P O Box 1385, 27910–1385, tel. 252/209–3000; Patrick Heins, President

Owned, leased, sponsored:	8 hospitals	1251 beds
Contract-managed:	0 hospitals	0 beds
Totals:	8 hospitals	1251 beds

0012: VIRGINIA DEPARTMENT OF MENTAL HEALTH (NP)
1220 Bank Street, Richmond, VA Zip 23219–3645, P O Box 1797, 23218–1797, tel. 804/786–3921; James S. Reinhard, M.D., Commissioner
(Independent Hospital System)

VIRGINIA: CATAWBA HOSPITAL (O, 110 beds) 5525 Catawba Hospital Drive, Catawba, VA Zip 24070–2115, P O Box 200, 24070–0200, tel. 540/375–4200; Walton F. Mitchell III, Director
Web address: www.catawba.dbhds.virginia.gov

CENTRAL STATE HOSPITAL (O, 277 beds) 26317 West Washington Street, Petersburg, VA Zip 23803–2727, P O Box 4030, 23803–0030, tel. 804/524–7000; Rebecca Vauter, PsyD, Facility Director

CENTRAL VIRGINIA TRAINING CENTER (O, 1112 beds) 210 East Colony Road, Madison Heights, VA Zip 24572–2005, P O Box 1098, Lynchburg, 24505–1098, tel. 434/947–6326; David Cole, Assistant Director of Administration, Chief Financial Officer, Department of Behavioral Health and Developmental Service
Web address: www.cvtc.dmhmrsas.virginia.gov/

COMMONWEALTH CENTER FOR CHILDREN AND ADOLESCENTS (O, 60 beds) 1355 Richmond Road, Staunton, VA Zip 24401–9146, Box 4000, 24402–4000, tel. 540/332–2100; Mary Clare. Smith, Acting Facility Director
Web address: www.ccca.dbhds.virginia.gov

EASTERN STATE HOSPITAL (O, 334 beds) 4601 Ironbound Road, Williamsburg, VA Zip 23188–2652; tel. 757/253–5161; John M. Favret, Director
Web address: www.esh.dmhmrsas.virginia.gov/

HIRAM W. DAVIS MEDICAL CENTER (O, 10 beds) 26317 West Washington Street, Petersburg, VA Zip 23803–2727, P O Box 4030, 23803–0030, tel. 804/524–7344; Brenda Buenvenida, Director

NORTHERN VIRGINIA MENTAL HEALTH INSTITUTE (O, 134 beds) 3302 Gallows Road, Falls Church, VA Zip 22042–3398; tel. 703/207–7100; Tammy Peacock, Ph.D., Facility Director
Web address: www.nvmhi.dbhds.virginia.gov

PIEDMONT GERIATRIC HOSPITAL (O, 150 beds) 5001 East Patrick Henry Hwy, Burkeville, VA Zip 23922–3460, P O Box 427, 23922–0427, tel. 434/767–4401; Hilton McDaniel, President
Web address: www.pgh.dmhmrsas.virginia.gov

SOUTHERN VIRGINIA MENTAL HEALTH INSTITUTE (O, 72 beds) 382 Taylor Drive, Danville, VA Zip 24541–4023; tel. 434/799–6220; William Cook, Director
Web address: www.svmhi.dbhds.virginia.gov

SOUTHWESTERN VIRGINIA MENTAL HEALTH INSTITUTE (O, 166 beds) 340 Bagley Circle, Marion, VA Zip 24354–3390; tel. 276/783–1200; Cynthia McClaskey, Ph.D., Director

WESTERN STATE HOSPITAL (O, 260 beds) 103 Valley Center Drive, Staunton, VA Zip 24401–9146, P O Box 2500, 24402–2500, tel. 540/332–8000; Mary Clare. Smith, Director
Web address: www.dbhds.virginia.gov

Owned, leased, sponsored:	11 hospitals	2685 beds
Contract-managed:	0 hospitals	0 beds
Totals:	11 hospitals	2685 beds

For explanation of codes following names, see page B2.
★ Indicates Type III membership in the American Hospital Association.

0986: VIRGINIA MASON HEALTH SYSTEM (NP)
1100 Ninth Avenue, Seattle, WA Zip 98101–2756, P.O. Box 900, 98111–0900, tel. 206/223–6600; Gary Kaplan, M.D., FACHE, Chief Executive Officer
(Moderately Centralized Health System)

WASHINGTON: VIRGINIA MASON MEDICAL CENTER (O, 223 beds) 1100 Ninth Avenue, Seattle, WA Zip 98101–2756, P O Box 900, 98111–0900, tel. 206/223–6600; Gary Kaplan, M.D., FACHE, Chairman and Chief Executive Officer
Web address: www.VirginiaMason.org

VIRGINIA MASON MEMORIAL (O, 226 beds) 2811 Tieton Drive, Yakima, WA Zip 98902–3761; tel. 509/575–8000; Russ Myers, Chief Executive Officer

Owned, leased, sponsored:	2 hospitals	449 beds
Contract-managed:	0 hospitals	0 beds
Totals:	2 hospitals	449 beds

★6725: VIRTUA HEALTH (NP)
50 Lake Center Executive Drive, Suite 401, Marlton, NJ Zip 8053; tel. 856/355–0010; Dennis W. Pullin, FACHE, Chief Executive Officer
(Centralized Health System)

NEW JERSEY: VIRTUA MARLTON (O, 189 beds) 90 Brick Road, Marlton, NJ Zip 08053–2177; tel. 856/355–6000; Matthew Zuino, Senior Vice President Hospital Services
Web address: www.virtua.org

VIRTUA MEMORIAL (O, 334 beds) 175 Madison Avenue, Mount Holly, NJ Zip 08060–2099; tel. 609/267–0700; Matthew Zuino, Senior Vice President Hospital Services

VIRTUA VOORHEES (O, 402 beds) 100 Bowman Drive, Voorhees, NJ Zip 08043–9612; tel. 856/325–3000; Matthew Zuino, Senior Vice President Hospital Services
Web address: www.virtua.org

Owned, leased, sponsored:	3 hospitals	925 beds
Contract-managed:	0 hospitals	0 beds
Totals:	3 hospitals	925 beds

★0221: WAKE FOREST BAPTIST HEALTH (NP)
Medical Center Boulevard, Winston-Salem, NC Zip 27157; tel. 336/716–2011; Julie Ann . Freischlag, M.D., Chief Executive Officer
(Centralized Health System)

NORTH CAROLINA: WAKE FOREST BAPTIST HEALTH - WILKES MEDICAL CENTER (L, 91 beds) 1370 West 'D' Street, North Wilkesboro, NC Zip 28659–3506, P O Box 609, 28659–0609, tel. 336/651–8100; J Gene. Faile, Chief Executive Officer and President
Web address: www.wilkesregional.com/

WAKE FOREST BAPTIST HEALTH-DAVIE MEDICAL CENTER (O, 25 beds) 329 NC Highway 801 North, Bermuda Run, NC Zip 27006; tel. 336/998–1300; Chad J. Brown, M.P.H., President

WAKE FOREST BAPTIST HEALTH-LEXINGTON MEDICAL CENTER (O, 85 beds) 250 Hospital Drive, Lexington, NC Zip 27292–6728, P O Box 1817, 27293–1817, tel. 336/248–5161; William B. James, FACHE, President
Web address: www.lexington.wakehealth.edu

WAKE FOREST BAPTIST MEDICAL CENTER (O, 812 beds) Medical Center Boulevard, Winston-Salem, NC Zip 27157–0001; tel. 336/716–2011; Julie Ann . Freischlag, M.D., Chief Executive Officer

Owned, leased, sponsored:	4 hospitals	1013 beds
Contract-managed:	0 hospitals	0 beds
Totals:	4 hospitals	1013 beds

★6705: WAKEMED HEALTH & HOSPITALS (NP)
3000 New Bern Avenue, Raleigh, NC Zip 27610–1231; tel. 919/350–8000; Donald R. Gintzig, President and Chief Executive Officer
(Moderately Centralized Health System)

NORTH CAROLINA: WAKEMED CARY HOSPITAL (O, 156 beds) 1900 Kildaire Farm Road, Cary, NC Zip 27518 6616; tel. 919/350–8000; Donald R. Gintzig, President and Chief Executive Officer
Web address: www.wakemed.org

WAKEMED RALEIGH CAMPUS (O, 681 beds) 3000 New Bern Avenue, Raleigh, NC Zip 27610–1295; tel. 919/350–8000; Donald R. Gintzig, President and Chief Executive Officer

Owned, leased, sponsored:	2 hospitals	837 beds
Contract-managed:	0 hospitals	0 beds
Totals:	2 hospitals	837 beds

★0979: WASHINGTON HEALTH SYSTEM (NP)
155 Wilson Avenue, Washington, PA Zip 15301–3336; tel. 724/225–7000; Gary B. Weinstein, Chief Executive Officer
(Moderately Centralized Health System)

PENNSYLVANIA: WASHINGTON HEALTH SYSTEM GREENE (O, 49 beds) 350 Bonar Avenue, Waynesburg, PA Zip 15370–1608; tel. 724/627–3101; Terry Wiltrout, President
Web address: www.southwestregionalmedical.com/

WASHINGTON HOSPITAL (O, 206 beds) 155 Wilson Avenue, Washington, PA Zip 15301–3398; tel. 724/225–7000; Gary B. Weinstein, President and Chief Executive Officer

Owned, leased, sponsored:	2 hospitals	255 beds
Contract-managed:	0 hospitals	0 beds
Totals:	2 hospitals	255 beds

★0188: WELLMONT HEALTH SYSTEM (NP)
1905 American Way, Kingsport, TN Zip 37660–5882; tel. 423/230–8200; Barton A. Hove, President and Chief Executive Officer
(Centralized Physician/Insurance Health System)

TENNESSEE: TAKOMA REGIONAL HOSPITAL (O, 32 beds) 401 Takoma Avenue, Greeneville, TN Zip 37743–4647; tel. 423/639–3151; Tammy Albright, President
Web address: www.takoma.org

WELLMONT BRISTOL REGIONAL MEDICAL CENTER (O, 296 beds) 1 Medical Park Boulevard, Bristol, TN Zip 37620–7430; tel. 423/844–1121; Greg Neal, FACHE, President
Web address: www.wellmont.org

WELLMONT HANCOCK COUNTY HOSPITAL (O, 10 beds) 1519 Main Street, Sneedville, TN Zip 37869–3657; tel. 423/733–5000; Rebecca Beck, President
Web address: www.wellmont.org/Hospitals/Hancock-County-Hospital.aspx

WELLMONT HAWKINS COUNTY MEMORIAL HOSPITAL (L, 22 beds) 851 Locust Street, Rogersville, TN Zip 37857–2407, P O Box 130, 37857–0130, tel. 423/921–7000; Rebecca Beck, President

WELLMONT HOLSTON VALLEY MEDICAL CENTER (O, 345 beds) 130 West Ravine Street, Kingsport, TN Zip 37660–3837, P O Box 238, 37662–0238, tel. 423/224–4000; Tim Attebery, Chief Executive Officer
Web address: www.wellmont.org

VIRGINIA: MOUNTAIN VIEW REGIONAL MEDICAL CENTER (O, 70 beds) 310 Third Street NE, Norton, VA Zip 24273–1137; tel. 276/679–9100; Dale Clark, President
Web address: www.wellmont.org

WELLMONT LONESOME PINE HOSPITAL (O, 32 beds) 1990 Holton Avenue East, Big Stone Gap, VA Zip 24219–3350; tel. 276/523–3111; Dale Clark, President
Web address: www.wellmont.org

Owned, leased, sponsored:	7 hospitals	807 beds
Contract-managed:	0 hospitals	0 beds
Totals:	7 hospitals	807 beds

For explanation of codes following names, see page B2.
★ Indicates Type III membership in the American Hospital Association.

Section B

★0068: **WELLSPAN HEALTH** (NP)
45 Monument Road, Suite 200, York, PA Zip 17403–5071; tel. 717/851–2121; Kevin H. Mosser, M.D., President and Chief Executive Officer
(Centralized Physician/Insurance Health System)

PENNSYLVANIA: WELLSPAN EPHRATA COMMUNITY HOSPITAL (O, 130 beds) 169 Martin Avenue, Ephrata, PA Zip 17522–1724, P O Box 1002, 17522–1002, tel. 717/733–0311

WELLSPAN GETTYSBURG HOSPITAL (O, 76 beds) 147 Gettys Street, Gettysburg, PA Zip 17325–2534; tel. 717/334–2121; Jane E. Hyde, President
Web address: www.wellspan.org

WELLSPAN GOOD SAMARITAN HOSPITAL (O, 157 beds) Fourth and Walnut Streets, Lebanon, PA Zip 17042–1281, P O Box 1281, 17042–1281, tel. 717/270–7500; Thomas R. Harlow, FACHE, President
Web address: www.gshleb.org

WELLSPAN PHILHAVEN (O, 103 beds) 283 South Butler Road, Mount Gretna, PA Zip 17064–6085, P O Box 550, 17064–0550, tel. 717/273–8871; Phil Hess, Chief Executive Officer
Web address: www.philhaven.org

WELLSPAN YORK HOSPITAL (O, 556 beds) 1001 South George Street, York, PA Zip 17403–3645; tel. 717/851–2345; Keith D. Noll, President
Web address: www.wellspan.org

Owned, leased, sponsored:	5 hospitals	1022 beds
Contract-managed:	0 hospitals	0 beds
Totals:	5 hospitals	1022 beds

★0995: **WELLSTAR HEALTH SYSTEM** (NP)
793 Sawyer Road, Marietta, GA Zip 30062; tel. 770/792–5012; Candice Saunders, President and Chief Executive Officer
(Centralized Health System)

GEORGIA: WELLSTAR COBB HOSPITAL (O, 387 beds) 3950 Austell Road, Austell, GA Zip 30106–1121; tel. 470/732–4000; Amy Frey. Carrier, President

WELLSTAR DOUGLAS HOSPITAL (O, 108 beds) 8954 Hospital Drive, Douglasville, GA Zip 30134–2282; tel. 770/949–1500; Craig A. Owens, President
Web address: www.wellstar.org

WELLSTAR KENNESTONE HOSPITAL (O, 657 beds) 677 Church Street, Marietta, GA Zip 30060–1148; tel. 770/793–5000; Dan Woods, President
Web address: www.wellstar.org

WELLSTAR PAULDING HOSPITAL (O, 238 beds) 2518 Jimmy Lee Smith Parkway, Hiram, GA Zip 30141; tel. 470/644–7000; Mark Haney, President

WELLSTAR WINDY HILL HOSPITAL (O, 55 beds) 2540 Windy Hill Road, Marietta, GA Zip 30067–8632; tel. 770/644–1000; Monte Wilson, President
Web address: www.wellstar.org

WELLSTAR ATLANTA MEDICAL CENTER (O, 490 beds) 303 Parkway Drive NE, Atlanta, GA Zip 30312–1212; tel. 404/265–4000; Kimberly Ryan, President
Web address: www.atlantamedcenter.com

WELLSTAR NORTH FULTON HOSPITAL (O, 173 beds) 3000 Hospital Boulevard, Roswell, GA Zip 30076–3899; tel. 770/751–2500; Jon-Paul Croom, President

WELLSTAR SPALDING REGIONAL HOSPITAL (O, 162 beds) 601 South Eighth Street, Griffin, GA Zip 30224–4294, P O Drawer 'V', 30224–1168, tel. 770/228–2721; Tamara Ison, Senior Vice President and President
Web address: www.spaldingregional.com

WELLSTAR SYLVAN GROVE HOSPITAL (O, 24 beds) 1050 McDonough Road, Jackson, GA Zip 30233–1599; tel. 770/775–7861; Tamara Ison, Senior Vice President and President
Web address: www.sylvangrovehospital.com

WEST GEORGIA HEALTH (O, 390 beds) 1514 Vernon Road, Lagrange, GA Zip 30240–4131; tel. 706/882–1411; Gerald N. Fulks, President

Owned, leased, sponsored:	10 hospitals	2684 beds
Contract-managed:	0 hospitals	0 beds
Totals:	10 hospitals	2684 beds

★0004: **WEST TENNESSEE HEALTHCARE** (NP)
620 Skyline Drive, Jackson, TN Zip 38301–3923; tel. 731/541–5000; James E. Ross, President and Chief Executive Officer
(Centralized Physician/Insurance Health System)

TENNESSEE: BOLIVAR GENERAL HOSPITAL (O, 21 beds) 650 Nuckolls Road, Bolivar, TN Zip 38008–1532, PO Box 509, 38008–0509, tel. 731/658–3100; Ruby Kirby, Administrator
Web address: www.wth.net

CAMDEN GENERAL HOSPITAL (O, 25 beds) 175 Hospital Drive, Camden, TN Zip 38320–1617; tel. 731/593–6300; Scott Barber, Vice President
Web address: www.wth.net

JACKSON-MADISON COUNTY GENERAL HOSPITAL (O, 635 beds) 620 Skyline Drive, Jackson, TN Zip 38301–3923; tel. 731/541–5000; James E. Ross, President and Chief Executive Officer

MILAN GENERAL HOSPITAL (O, 28 beds) 4039 Highland Street, Milan, TN Zip 38358–3483; tel. 731/686–1591; Sherry Scruggs, Administrator
Web address: www.wth.org

PATHWAYS OF TENNESSEE (O, 25 beds) 238 Summar Drive, Jackson, TN Zip 38301–3906; tel. 731/541–8200; Pam Henson, Executive Director
Web address: www.wth.net/pathways

Owned, leased, sponsored:	5 hospitals	734 beds
Contract-managed:	0 hospitals	0 beds
Totals:	5 hospitals	734 beds

★0119: **WEST VIRGINIA UNIVERSITY HEALTH SYSTEM** (NP)
One Medical Center, Box 8136, Morgantown, WV Zip 26506–8136; tel. 304/285–7150; Albert L. Wright Jr, PharmD, President and Chief Executive Officer
(Moderately Centralized Health System)

WEST VIRGINIA: BERKELEY MEDICAL CENTER (O, 195 beds) 2500 Hospital Drive, Martinsburg, WV Zip 25401–3402; tel. 304/264–1000; Anthony Zelenka, President and Chief Operating Officer
Web address: www.cityhospital.org

CAMDEN CLARK MEDICAL CENTER (O, 245 beds) 800 Garfield Avenue, Parkersburg, WV Zip 26101–5378, P O Box 718, 26102–0718, tel. 304/424–2111; David K. McClure, President and Chief Executive Officer
Web address: www.camdenclark.org

JEFFERSON MEDICAL CENTER (O, 25 beds) 300 South Preston Street, Ranson, WV Zip 25438–1631; tel. 304/728–1600; Neil R. McLaughlin, R.N., Administrator and Vice President, Operations

POTOMAC VALLEY HOSPITAL (O, 25 beds) 100 Pin Oak Lane, Keyser, WV Zip 26726–5908; tel. 304/597–3500; Linda K. Shroyer, Administrator
Web address: www.potomacvalleyhospital.com

REYNOLDS MEMORIAL HOSPITAL (O, 99 beds) 800 Wheeling Avenue, Glen Dale, WV Zip 26038–1697; tel. 304/845–3211; David F. Hess, M.D., Chief Executive Officer

ST. JOSEPH'S HOSPITAL OF BUCKHANNON (O, 51 beds) 1 Amalia Drive, Buckhannon, WV Zip 26201–2276; tel. 304/473–2000; Skip Gjolberg, FACHE, Administrator
Web address: www.stj.net

UNITED HOSPITAL CENTER (O, 264 beds) 327 Medical Park Drive, Bridgeport, WV Zip 26330–9006; tel. 681/342–1000; Michael C. Tillman, President and Chief Executive Officer

WEST VIRGINIA UNIVERSITY HOSPITALS (O, 555 beds) 1 Medical Center Drive, Morgantown, WV Zip 26506–4749; tel. 304/598–4000; Albert L. Wright Jr, PharmD, President and Chief Executive Officer
Web address: www.health.wvu.edu

Owned, leased, sponsored:	8 hospitals	1459 beds
Contract-managed:	0 hospitals	0 beds
Totals:	8 hospitals	1459 beds

★0811: **WESTERN CONNECTICUT HEALTH NETWORK** (NP)
24 Hospital Avenue, Danbury, CT Zip 06810–6099; tel. 203/739–7066; John M. Murphy, M.D., President and Chief Executive Officer
(Centralized Physician/Insurance Health System)

For explanation of codes following names, see page B2.
★ Indicates Type III membership in the American Hospital Association.

CONNECTICUT: DANBURY HOSPITAL (O, 412 beds) 24 Hospital Avenue, Danbury, CT Zip 06810–6099; tel. 203/739–7000; John M. Murphy, M.D., President and Chief Executive Officer, Western Connecticut Health Network
Web address: www.danburyhospital.org

NORWALK HOSPITAL (O, 152 beds) 34 Maple Street, Norwalk, CT Zip 06850–3894; tel. 203/852–2000; Michael Daglio, President
Web address: www.norwalkhospital.org

Owned, leased, sponsored:	2 hospitals	564 beds
Contract-managed:	0 hospitals	0 beds
Totals:	2 hospitals	564 beds

★0468: WHITE RIVER HEALTH SYSTEM (NP)
1710 Harrison Street, Batesville, AR Zip 72501–7303; tel. 870/262–1200; Gary Bebow, FACHE, Administrator and Chief Executive Officer
(Independent Hospital System)

ARKANSAS: STONE COUNTY MEDICAL CENTER (O, 25 beds) 2106 East Main Street, Mountain View, AR Zip 72560–6439, P O Box 510, 72560–0510, tel. 870/269–4361; Kevin Spears, Chief Executive Officer

WHITE RIVER MEDICAL CENTER (O, 210 beds) 1710 Harrison Street, Batesville, AR Zip 72501–7303, P O Box 2197, 72503–2197, tel. 870/262–1200; Gary Bebow, FACHE, Administrator and Chief Executive Officer
Web address: www.whiteriverhealthsystem.com

Owned, leased, sponsored:	2 hospitals	235 beds
Contract-managed:	0 hospitals	0 beds
Totals:	2 hospitals	235 beds

0646: WHITTIER HEALTH NETWORK (IO)
25 Railroad Square, Haverhill, MA Zip 01832–5721; tel. 978/556–5858; Alfred L. Arcidi, M.D., President
(Independent Hospital System)

MASSACHUSETTS: WHITTIER PAVILION (O, 65 beds) 76 Summer Street, Haverhill, MA Zip 01830–5814; tel. 978/373–8222; Alfred L. Arcidi, M.D., Chief Executive Officer
Web address: www.whittierhealth.com

WHITTIER REHABILITATION HOSPITAL (O, 74 beds) 150 Flanders Road, Westborough, MA Zip 01581–1017; tel. 508/871–2000; Alfred J. Arcidi, M.D., Senior Vice President

WHITTIER REHABILITATION HOSPITAL (O, 60 beds) 145 Ward Hill Avenue, Bradford, MA Zip 01835–6928; tel. 978/372–8000; Alfred J. Arcidi, M.D., Senior Vice President
Web address: www.whittierhealth.com

Owned, leased, sponsored:	3 hospitals	199 beds
Contract-managed:	0 hospitals	0 beds
Totals:	3 hospitals	199 beds

1945: WILLIS-KNIGHTON HEALTH SYSTEM (NP)
2600 Greenwood Road, Shreveport, LA Zip 71103–3908; tel. 318/212–4000; James K. Elrod, FACHE, President and Chief Executive Officer
(Moderately Centralized Health System)

LOUISIANA: DE SOTO REGIONAL HEALTH SYSTEM (C, 10 beds) 207 Jefferson Street, Mansfield, LA Zip 71052–2603, P O Box 1636, 71052–1636, tel. 318/872–4610; Todd Eppler, FACHE, Chief Executive Officer
Web address: www.desotoregional.com

SPRINGHILL MEDICAL CENTER (C, 58 beds) 2001 Doctors Drive, Springhill, LA Zip 71075–4526, P O Box 920, 71075–0920, tel. 318/539–1000; Vince Sedminik, Chief Executive Officer
Web address: www.smccare.com

WK BOSSIER HEALTH CENTER (O, 166 beds) 2400 Hospital Drive, Bossier City, LA Zip 71111–2385; tel. 318/212–7000; Clifford M. Broussard, FACHE, Administrator

WILLIS-KNIGHTON MEDICAL CENTER (O, 752 beds) 2600 Greenwood Road, Shreveport, l A Zip 71103–3908, P O Box 32600, 71130–2600, tel. 318/212–4600; James K. Elrod, FACHE, Chief Executive Officer
Web address: www.wkhs.com

Owned, leased, sponsored:	2 hospitals	918 beds
Contract-managed:	2 hospitals	68 beds
Totals:	4 hospitals	986 beds

1004: WMCHEALTH (NP)
100 Woods Road, Valhalla, NY Zip 10595–1530; tel. 914/493–7000; Michael D. Israel, President and Chief Executive Officer
(Moderately Centralized Health System)

NEW YORK: BON SECOURS COMMUNITY HOSPITAL (O, 187 beds) 160 East Main Street, Port Jervis, NY Zip 12771–2245, P O Box 1014, 12771–0268, tel. 845/858–7000; Mary Leahy, M.D., Chief Executive Officer

GOOD SAMARITAN REGIONAL MEDICAL CENTER (O, 308 beds) 255 Lafayette Avenue, Suffern, NY Zip 10901–4869; tel. 845/368–5000; Mary Leahy, M.D., Chief Executive Officer
Web address: www.goodsamhosp.org

HEALTH ALLIANCE HOSPITAL - BROADWAY CAMPUS (O, 150 beds) 396 Broadway, Kingston, NY Zip 12401–4692; tel. 845/331–3131; David Scarpino, President and Chief Executive Officer

HEALTH ALLIANCE HOSPITAL - MARY'S AVENUE CAMPUS (O, 120 beds) 105 Marys Avenue, Kingston, NY Zip 12401–5894; tel. 845/338–2500; David Scarpino, President and Chief Executive Officer
Web address: www.hahv.org

MARGARETVILLE HOSPITAL (O, 15 beds) 42084 State Highway 28, Margaretville, NY Zip 12455–2820; tel. 845/586–2631; Mark Pohar, Executive Director
Web address: www.margaretvillehospital.org

ST. ANTHONY COMMUNITY HOSPITAL (O, 73 beds) 15 Maple Avenue, Warwick, NY Zip 10990–1028; tel. 845/986–2276; Mary Leahy, M.D., Chief Executive Officer

WESTCHESTER MEDICAL CENTER (O, 867 beds) 100 Woods Road, Valhalla, NY Zip 10595–1530; tel. 914/493–7000; Michael D. Israel, President and Chief Executive Officer
Web address: www.wmchealth.org

Owned, leased, sponsored:	7 hospitals	1720 beds
Contract-managed:	0 hospitals	0 beds
Totals:	7 hospitals	1720 beds

★0157: YALE NEW HAVEN HEALTH (NP)
789 Howard Avenue, New Haven, CT Zip 06519–1304; tel. 203/688–4608; Marna P. Borgstrom, President and Chief Executive Officer
(Independent Hospital System)

CONNECTICUT: BRIDGEPORT HOSPITAL (O, 358 beds) 267 Grant Street, Bridgeport, CT Zip 06610–2805, P O Box 5000, 06610–0120, tel. 203/384–3000; William M. Jennings, President and Chief Executive Officer
Web address: www.bridgeporthospital.org

GREENWICH HOSPITAL (O, 174 beds) 5 Perryridge Road, Greenwich, CT Zip 06830–4697; tel. 203/863–3000; Norman G. Roth, President

LAWRENCE + MEMORIAL HOSPITAL (O, 251 beds) 365 Montauk Avenue, New London, CT Zip 06320–4769; tel. 860/442–0711; Patrick Green, FACHE, President and Chief Executive Officer
Web address: www.lmhospital.org

YALE-NEW HAVEN HOSPITAL (O, 1394 beds) 20 York Street, New Haven, CT Zip 06510–3202; tel. 203/688–4242; Marna P. Borgstrom, Chief Executive Officer

RHODE ISLAND: WESTERLY HOSPITAL (O, 39 beds) 25 Wells Street, Westerly, RI Zip 02891–2934; tel. 401/596–6000; Patrick Green, FACHE, President and Chief Executive Officer
Web address: www.westerlyhospital.org

Owned, leased, sponsored:	5 hospitals	2216 beds
Contract-managed:	0 hospitals	0 beds
Totals:	5 hospitals	2216 beds

For explanation of codes following names, see page B2.
★ Indicates Type III membership in the American Hospital Association.

Headquarters of Health Care Systems

Geographically

United States

ALABAMA

Anniston: REGIONAL MEDICAL CENTER 400 East 10th Street, Zip 36207–4716; tel. 256/235–5121; Louis A. Bass, President and Chief Executive Officer, p. B107

Birmingham: BRADFORD HEALTH SERVICES 2101 Magnolia Avenue South, Suite 518, Zip 35205–2853; tel. 205/251–7753; Jerry W. Crowder, President and Chief Executive Officer, p. B22

★ HEALTHSOUTH CORPORATION 3660 Grandview Parkway, Suite 200, Zip 35243–3332; tel. 205/967–7116; Mark J. Tarr, President and Chief Executive Officer, p. B61

NOLAND HEALTH SERVICES, INC. 600 Corporate Parkway, Suite 100, Zip 35242–5451; tel. 205/783–8484; Gary M. Glasscock, President and Chief Executive Officer, p. B90

★ UAB HEALTH SYSTEM 500 22nd Street South, Suite 408, Zip 35233–3110; tel. 205/975–5362; William Ferniany, Chief Executive Officer, p. B130

Guntersville: MARSHALL HEALTH SYSTEM 227 Britany Road, Zip 35976–5766; tel. 256/894–6615; Gary R. Gore, Chief Executive Officer, p. B79

Huntsville: HUNTSVILLE HOSPITAL HEALTH SYSTEM 101 Sivley Road SW, Zip 35801–4421; tel. 265/256–1000; David S. Spillers, Chief Executive Officer, p. B67

Mobile: ALTAPOINTE HEALTH SYSTEMS 5750-A Southland Drive, Zip 36693–3316; tel. 251/473–4423; J. Tuerk. Schlesinger, Chief Executive Officer, p. B9

INFIRMARY HEALTH SYSTEM 5 Mobile Infirmary Circle, Zip 36607–3513; tel. 251/435–5500; D Mark. Nix, President and Chief Executive Officer, p. B68

★ UNIVERSITY OF SOUTH ALABAMA HOSPITALS 2451 Fillingim Street, Zip 36617–2238; tel. 251/471–7000; Owen Bailey, Chief Executive Officer and Senior Associate Vice President for Medical Affairs, p. B139

Montgomery: BAPTIST HEALTH 301 Brown Springs Road, Zip 36117–7005; tel. 334/273–4400; W Russell. Tyner, President and Chief Executive Officer, p. B18

GILLIARD HEALTH SERVICES 3091 Carter Hill Road, Zip 36111–1801; tel. 334/265–5009; William G. McKenzie, President, Chief Executive Officer and Chairman, p. B54

Tuscaloosa: DCH HEALTH SYSTEM 809 University Boulevard East, Zip 35401–2029; tel. 205/759–7111; Bryan N. Kindred, President and Chief Executive Officer, p. B40

ARIZONA

Flagstaff: ★ NORTHERN ARIZONA HEALTHCARE 1200 North Beaver Street, Zip 86001–3118; tel. 928/779–3366; Robert P. Thames, President and Chief Executive Officer, p. B90

Phoenix: ★ BANNER HEALTH 1441 North 12th Street, Zip 85006–2837, P O Box 25489, 85002–5489, tel. 602/747–4000; Peter S. Fine, President and Chief Executive Officer, p. B17

Scottsdale: ★ HONORHEALTH 8125 North Hayden Road, Zip 85258–2463; tel. 623/580–5800; Todd LaPorte, Chief Executive Officer, p. B65

SOUTHWEST HEALTHCARE SYSTEM 7025 N Scottsdale Road Suite 9347, Zip 85253–3675, 7025 North Scottsdale Road, Suite 9347, 85251–3331, tel. 480/518–5444; Paul R. Tuft, President, p. B118

ARKANSAS

Batesville: ★ WHITE RIVER HEALTH SYSTEM 1710 Harrison Street, Zip 72501–7303; tel. 870/262–1200; Gary Bebow, Administrator and Chief Executive Officer, p. B146

Blytheville: ★ MISSISSIPPI COUNTY HOSPITAL SYSTEM 1520 North Division Street, Zip 72315–1448, P O Box 108, 72316–0108, tel. 870/838–7300; Chris Lee. Raymer, Chief Executive Officer, p. B85

Little Rock: ★ BAPTIST HEALTH 9601 Interstate 630, Exit 7, Zip 72205–7299; tel. 501/202–2000; Troy R. Wells, Chief Executive Officer, p. B18

CALIFORNIA

Alhambra: AHMC & HEALTHCARE, INC. 55 South Raymond Avenue, Suite 105, Zip 91801–7101; tel. 626/457–9600; Jonathan Wu, President and Chairman, p. B7

Corona: SIGNATURE HEALTHCARE SERVICES 4238 Green River Road, Zip 92880–1669; tel. 951/549–8032; Soon K. Kim, President and Chief Executive Officer, p. B117

Covina: ★ CITRUS VALLEY HEALTH PARTNERS 210 West San Bernardino Road, Zip 91723–1515; tel. 626/331–7331; Robert H. Curry, President and Chief Executive Officer, p. B31

Cupertino: CRC HEALTH GROUP, INC. 20400 Stevens Creek Boulevard, Suite 600, Zip 95014–2217; tel. 866/540–5240; Jerome E. Rhodes, Chief Executive Officer, p. B39

El Segundo: AVANTI HOSPITALS 222 North Sepulveda Boulevard, Suite 950, Zip 90245–5614; tel. 310/356–0550; Michael A. Rembis, Corporate Chief Executive Officer, p. B16

Escondido: ★ PALOMAR HEALTH 456 East Grand Avenue, Zip 92025–3319; tel. 760/740–6393; Robert Hemker, President and Chief Executive Officer, p. B95

Fountain Valley: MEMORIALCARE 17360 Brookhurst Street, Zip 92708–3720, P O Box 1428, Long Beach, 90801–1428, tel. 714/377–2900; Barry S. Arbuckle, President and Chief Executive Officer, p. B82

Fresno: COMMUNITY MEDICAL CENTERS Fresno and Maddy Drive, Zip 93721, P O Box 1232, 93715–1232, tel. 559/459–6000; Tim A. Joslin, President and Chief Executive Officer, p. B37

Hemet: PHYSICIANS FOR HEALTHY HOSPITALS 1117 East Devonshire Avenue, Zip 92543–3083; tel. 951/652–2811; Joel M. Bergenfeld, Chief Executive Officer, p. B97

Irvine: ALECTO HEALTHCARE 16310 Bake Parkway, Suite 200, Zip 92618–4684; tel. 323/932–5963; Lex Reddy, Chief Executive Officer, p. B8

Loma Linda: LOMA LINDA UNIVERSITY ADVENTIST HEALTH SCIENCES CENTER 11175 Campus Street, Zip 92350–1700; tel. 909/558–7572; Richard H. Hart, President and Chief Executive Officer, p. B78

Los Angeles: KECK MEDICINE OF USC 1510 San Pablo Street, Suite 600, Zip 90033–5313; tel. 323/442–8500; Thomas E. Jackiewicz, Senior Vice President and Chief Executive Officer, p. B71

LOS ANGELES COUNTY-DEPARTMENT OF HEALTH SERVICES 313 North Figueroa Street, Room 912, Zip 90012–2691; tel. 213/240–8101; Mitchell H. Katz, Director, p. B78

PROSPECT MEDICAL HOLDINGS 10780 California Route 2 #400, Zip 90025; tel. 714/796–5900; Mitchell Lew, President, p. B102

★ VERITY HEALTH SYSTEM 2200 West Third Street, Suite 200, Zip 90057–1935, 203 Redwood Shores Parkway, Suite 800, Redwood City, 94065, tel. 650/551–6650; Andrei Soran, Chief Executive Officer, p. B142

Oakland: ★ KAISER FOUNDATION HOSPITALS One Kaiser Plaza, Zip 94612–3600; tel. 510/271–5910; Bernard J. Tyson, Chairman and Chief Executive Officer, p. B70

★ UNIVERSITY OF CALIFORNIA SYSTEMWIDE ADMINISTRATION 1111 Franklin Street, 11th Floor, Zip 94607–5200; tel. 510/987–9071; John D. Stobo, Executive Vice President and Chief Executive Officer, p. B138

Ontario: ★ PRIME HEALTHCARE 3300 East Guasti Road, Zip 91761–8655; tel. 909/235–4400; Prem Reddy, Chairman, President and Chief Executive Officer, p. B99

Palo Alto: ★ STANFORD HEALTH CARE 300 Pasteur Drive, Zip 94304–2299; tel. 650/723–4000; David Entwistle, President and Chief Executive Officer, p. B121

Roseville: ★ ADVENTIST HEALTH 2100 Douglas Boulevard, Zip 95661–3898, P O Box 619002, 95661–9002, tel. 916/781–2000; Scott Reiner, Chief Executive Officer, p. B5

Sacramento: ★ SUTTER HEALTH 2200 River Plaza Drive, Zip 95833–4134; tel. 916/733–8800; Sarah Krevans, President and Chief Executive Officer, p. B122

San Diego: ★ SCRIPPS HEALTH 4275 Campus Point Court CP112, Zip 92121–1513, 4275 Campus Point Court, 92121–1513, tel. 858/678–7200; Chris D. Van Gorder, President and Chief Executive Officer, p. B112

★ SHARP HEALTHCARE 8695 Spectrum Center Boulevard, Zip 92123–1489; tel. 858/499–4000; Michael Murphy, President & Chief Executive Officer, p. B116

San Francisco: ★ DIGNITY HEALTH 185 Berry Street, Suite 300, Zip 94107–1773; tel. 415/438–5500; Lloyd H. Dean, President and Chief Executive Officer, p. B46

San Leandro: ALAMEDA HEALTH SYSTEM 15400 Foothill Boulevard, Zip 94578–1009; tel. 510/677–7920; Delvecchio Finley, Chief Executive Officer, p. B7

Santa Ana: KPC HEALTHCARE, INC. 1301 North Tustin Avenue, Zip 92705–8619; tel. 714/953–3652; Suzanne Richards, Chief Executive Officer, p. B73

Santa Barbara: ★ COTTAGE HEALTH 400 West Pueblo Street, Zip 93105–4353, P O Box 689, 93102–0689, tel. 805/569–7290; Ronald C. Werft, President and Chief Executive Officer, p. B38

Santa Fe Springs: COLLEGE HEALTH ENTERPRISES 11627 Telegraph Road, Suite 200, Zip 90670–6814; tel. 562/923–9449; Barry J. Weiss, Chairman of the Board, p. B32

Truckee: ★ TAHOE FOREST HEALTH SYSTEM 10121 Pine Avenue, Zip 96161–4835; tel. 530/587–6011; Harry Weis, Chief Executive Officer, p. B123

Ventura: COMMUNITY MEMORIAL HEALTH SYSTEM 147 North Brent Street, Zip 93003–2809; tel. 805/652–5011; Gary Wilde, President and Chief Executive Officer, p. B37

Walnut Creek: ★ JOHN MUIR HEALTH 1400 Treat Boulevard, Zip 94597–2142; tel. 925/941–2100; Calvin K. Knight, President and Chief Executive Officer, p. B70

West Hollywood: ★ CEDARS-SINAI 8700 Beverly Boulevard, Zip 90048–1865, Box 48750, Los Angeles, 90048–0750, tel. 310/423–5000; Thomas M. Priselac, President and Chief Executive Officer, p. B29

Whittier: ★ PIH HEALTH 12401 Washington Boulevard, Zip 90602–1006; tel. 562/698–0811; James R. West, President and Chief Executive Officer, p. B97

COLORADO

Alamosa: ★ SAN LUIS VALLEY HEALTH 106 Blanca Avenue, Zip 81101–2340; tel. 719/589–2511; Konnie Martin, Chief Executive Officer, p. B111

Broomfield: ★ SCL HEALTH 500 Eldorado Boulevard, Suite 100-D, Zip 80021; tel. 303/813–5180; Lydia Jumonville, Interim Chief Executive Officer, p. B112

Englewood: ★ CATHOLIC HEALTH INITIATIVES 198 Inverness Drive West, Suite 800, Zip 80112–5202; tel. 303/298–9100; Kevin E. Lofton, Chief Executive Officer, p. B26

Fort Collins: ★ UNIVERSITY OF COLORADO HEALTH 2315 East Harmony Road, Suite 200, Zip 80528–8620; tel. 970/495–7000; Elizabeth B. Concordia, President and Chief Executive Officer, p. B138

CONNECTICUT

Danbury: ★ WESTERN CONNECTICUT HEALTH NETWORK 24 Hospital Avenue, Zip 06810–6099; tel. 203/739–7066; John M. Murphy, President and Chief Executive Officer, p. B146

Hartford: CONNECTICUT DEPARTMENT OF MENTAL HEALTH AND ADDICTION SERVICES 410 Capitol Avenue, Zip 06106–1367, P O Box 341431, 06134–1431, tel. 860/418–7000; Miriam Delphin-Rittmon, Commissioner, p. B38

★ HARTFORD HEALTHCARE One State Street, 19th Floor, Zip 6103; tel. 860/263–4100; Elliot T. Joseph, Chief Executive Officer, p. B55

New Haven: ★ YALE NEW HAVEN HEALTH 789 Howard Avenue, Zip 06519–1304; tel. 203/688–4608; Marna P. Borgstrom, President and Chief Executive Officer, p. B146

DELAWARE

Wilmington: ★ CHRISTIANA CARE HEALTH SYSTEM 501 West 14th Street, Zip 19801–1013, P O Box 1668, 19899–1668, tel. 302/733–1000; Janice E. Nevin, Chief Executive Officer, p. B30

DISTRICT OF COLUMBIA

Washington: DEPARTMENT OF THE AIR FORCE 1420 Pentagon, Room 4E1084, Zip 20330–1420; tel. 202/767–4765; Lieutenant General, Thomas Travis, Surgeon General, p. B41

DEPARTMENT OF VETERANS AFFAIRS 810 Vermont Avenue NW, Zip 20420–0001; tel. 202/273–5781; David J. Shulkin, Secretary, Veterans Affairs, p. B42

FLORIDA

Altamonte Springs: ★ ADVENTIST HEALTH SYSTEM SUNBELT HEALTH CARE CORPORATION 900 Hope Way, Zip 32714–1502; tel. 407/357–1000; Terry Shaw, President and Chief Executive Officer, p. B6

Boca Raton: PROMISE HEALTHCARE 999 Yamato Road, 3rd Floor, Zip 33431–4477; tel. 561/869–3100; Peter R. Baronoff, Chief Executive Officer, p. B101

SUCCESS HEALTHCARE 999 Yamato Road, 3rd Floor, Zip 33431–4477; tel. 561/869–6300; Peter R. Baronoff, President and Chief Executive Officer, p. B122

Clearwater: MORTON PLANT MEASE HEALTH CARE 300 Pinellas Street, Zip 33756–3804, P O Box 210, 33757–0210, tel. 727/462–7000; Glenn D. Waters, President, p. B86

Coral Gables: ★ BAPTIST HEALTH SOUTH FLORIDA 6855 Red Road, Suite 600, Zip 33143–3632; tel. 786/662–7111; Brian E. Keeley, President and Chief Executive Officer, p. B19

Fort Lauderdale: ★ BROWARD HEALTH 303 SE 17th Street, Zip 33316–2523; tel. 954/355–4400; Beverly Capasso, Interim President and Chief Executive Officer, p. B23

Fort Myers: ★ LEE HEALTH 2776 Cleveland Avenue, Zip 33901–5856, P O Box 2218, 33902–2218, tel. 239/343–2000; Lawrence Antonucci, President and Chief Executive Officer, p. B74

Gainesville: ★ UF HEALTH SHANDS 1600 SW Archer Road, Zip 32610–0326; tel. 352/733–1500; Edward Jimenez, Chief Executive Officer, p. B130

Hollywood: ★ MEMORIAL HEALTHCARE SYSTEM 3501 Johnson Street, Zip 33021–5421; tel. 954/987–2000; Aurelio Fernandez, Chief Executive Officer, p. B82

Jacksonville: ★ BAPTIST HEALTH 841 Prudential Drive, Suite 1601, Zip 32207–8202; tel. 904/202–2000; Hugh Greene, President and Chief Executive Officer, p. B18

NEMOURS 10140 Centurion Parkway North, Zip 32256–0532; tel. 904/697–4100; David J. Bailey, President and Chief Executive Officer, p. B88

Lauderdale Lakes: CATHOLIC HEALTH SERVICES 4790 North State Road 7, Zip 33319–5860; tel. 954/484–1515; Joseph M. Catania, President and Chief Executive Officer, p. B28

Leesburg: CENTRAL FLORIDA HEALTH 600 East Dixie Avenue, Zip 34748–5925; tel. 352/323–5762; Donald G. Henderson, Chief Executive Officer, p. B30

Miami Lakes: PACER HEALTH CORPORATION 14100 Palmetto Frontage Road, Suite 110, Zip 33016; tel. 305/828–7660; Rainier Gonzalez, Chairman and Chief Executive Officer, p. B95

Miami: UNIVERSITY OF MIAMI HEALTH SYSTEM 1400 NW 12th Avenue, Zip 33136–1003; tel. 305/243–4000; Pascal J. Goldschmidt, Chief Executive Officer, p. B139

Orlando: ORLANDO HEALTH 1414 Kuhl Avenue, Zip 32806–2093; tel. 321/843–7000; David W. Strong, President and Chief Executive Officer, p. B94

Pensacola: ★ BAPTIST HEALTH CARE CORPORATION 1717 North 'E' Street, Suite 402, Zip 32501–6377, P O Box 17500, 32522–7500, tel. 850/434–4011; Mark T. Faulkner, President, p. B19

Rockledge: HEALTH FIRST, INC. 6450 US Highway 1, Zip 32955–5747; tel. 321/434–7000; Steven P. Johnson, President and Chief Executive Officer, p. B60

Tampa: SHRINERS HOSPITALS FOR CHILDREN 2900 Rocky Point Drive, Zip 33607–1435, P O Box 31356, 33631–3356, tel. 813/281–0300; John P. McCabe, Executive Vice President, p. B116

Windermere: UNITED MEDICAL CORPORATION 603 Main Street, Zip 34786–3548, P O Box 1100, 34786–1100, tel. 407/876–2200; Donald R. Dizney, Chairman and Chief Executive Officer, p. B131

GEORGIA

Albany: ★ PHOEBE PUTNEY HEALTH SYSTEM 417 Third Avenue, Zip 31701–1943; tel. 229/312–1000; Joel Wernick, President and Chief Executive Officer, p. B97

Atlanta: ★ EMORY HEALTHCARE 1440 Clifton Road NE, Suite 309, Zip 30322–1102; tel. 404/778–5000; Jonathan S. Lewin, President, p. B49

★ NORTHSIDE HEALTHCARE SYSTEM 1000 Johnson Ferry Road NE, Zip 30342–1611; tel. 404/851–8000; Robert Quattrocchi, President and Chief Executive Officer, p. B91

PIEDMONT HEALTHCARE 1800 Howell Mill Road NW, Suite 850, Zip 30318–0923; tel. 404/425–1314; Kevin Brown, President and Chief Executive Officer, p. B97

SUNLINK HEALTH SYSTEMS 900 Circle 75 Parkway, Suite 1120, Zip 30339–3005; tel. 770/933–7000; Robert M. Thornton Jr., Chief Executive Officer, p. B122

Augusta: ★ UNIVERSITY HEALTH CARE SYSTEM 1350 Walton Way, Zip 30901–2629; tel. 706/722–9011; James R. Davis, President and Chief Executive Officer, p. B137

Blairsville: UNION GENERAL HOSPITAL, INC. 35 Hospital Road, Zip 30512–3139; tel.

706/745–2111; Mike Gowder, Chief Executive Officer, p. B131

Brunswick: ★ SOUTHEAST GEORGIA HEALTH SYSTEM 2415 Parkwood Drive, Zip 31520–4722, P O Box 1518, 31521–1518, tel. 912/466–7000; Michael D. Scherneck, President and Chief Executive Officer, p. B118

Carrollton: ★ TANNER HEALTH SYSTEM 705 Dixie Street, Zip 30117–3818; tel. 770/836–9580; Loy M. Howard, President and Chief Executive Officer, p. B123

Columbus: COLUMBUS REGIONAL HEALTHCARE SYSTEM 707 Center Street, Suite 400, Zip 31901–1575; tel. 706/660–6100; Scott Hill, Chief Executive Officer, p. B32

Decatur: DEKALB REGIONAL HEALTH SYSTEM 2701 North Decatur Road, Zip 30033–5918; tel. 404/501–1000; Robert E. Wilson Esq, Chief Executive Officer, p. B41

Gainesville: NORTHEAST GEORGIA HEALTH SYSTEM 743 Spring Street NE, Zip 30501–3715; tel. 770/219–9000; Carol H. Burrell, President and Chief Executive Officer, p. B90

Macon: NAVICENT HEALTH 777 Hemlock Street, MSC 105, Zip 31201–2155, 777 Hemlock Street, 31201–2155, tel. 478/633–1000; Ninfa M. Saunders, Chief Executive Officer, p. B88

Marietta: ★ WELLSTAR HEALTH SYSTEM 793 Sawyer Road, Zip 30062; tel. 770/792–5012; Candice Saunders, President and Chief Executive Officer, p. B145

Thomasville: ★ ARCHBOLD MEDICAL CENTER 910 South Broad Street, Zip 31792–6113; tel. 229/228–2739; J Perry. Mustian, President, p. B10

Tifton: ★ TIFT REGIONAL HEALTH SYSTEM 901 East 18th Street, Zip 31794–3648; tel. 229/353–6100; William T. Richardson, President and Chief Executive Officer, p. B127

Warner Robins: ★ HOUSTON HEALTHCARE SYSTEM 1601 Watson Boulevard, Zip 31093–3431, P O Box 2886, 31099–2886, tel. 478/922–4281; Cary Martin, Chief Executive Officer, p. B66

HAWAII

Honolulu: ★ HAWAII HEALTH SYSTEMS CORPORATION 3675 Kilauea Avenue, Zip 96816–2333; tel. 808/733–4151; Linda Rosen, Chief Executive Officer, p. B56

HAWAII PACIFIC HEALTH 55 Merchant Street, Zip 96813–4306; tel. 808/949–9355; Raymond P. Vara Jr., President and Chief Executive Officer, p. B56

★ QUEEN'S HEALTH SYSTEMS 1301 Punchbowl Street, Zip 96813–2402; tel. 808/535–5448; Arthur A. Ushijima, President and Chief Executive Officer, p. B105

IDAHO

Boise: ★ ST. LUKE'S HEALTH SYSTEM 190 East Bannock Street, Zip 83712–6241; tel. 208/381–4200; David C. Pate, President and Chief Executive Officer, p. B120

Pocatello: SAFE HAVEN HEALTH CARE 2520 South 5th Avenue, Zip 83204–1923; tel. 800/261–2443; Scott Burpee, President, p. B110

ILLINOIS

Carbondale: SOUTHERN ILLINOIS HEALTHCARE 1239 East Main Street, Zip 62901–3114, P O Box 3988, 62902–3988, tel. 618/457–

5200; Rex P. Budde, President and Chief Executive Officer, p. B118

Chicago: COOK COUNTY HEALTH AND HOSPITALS SYSTEM 1900 West Polk Street, Suite 220, Zip 60612–3723; tel. 312/864–6820; John Jay. Shannon, Chief Executive Officer, p. B38

NATIONAL SURGICAL HEALTHCARE 250 South Wacker Drive, Suite 500, Zip 60606–5897; tel. 312/627–8400; David Crane, Chief Executive Officer, p. B87

★ NORTHWESTERN MEMORIAL HEALTHCARE 251 East Huron Street, Zip 60611–2908; tel. 312/926–2000; Dean M. Harrison, President and Chief Executive Officer, p. B91

★ PRESENCE HEALTH 200 South Wacker Drive, Suite 1100, Zip 60606–5829; tel. 312/308–3200; Michael Englehart, President and Chief Executive Officer, p. B99

★ RUSH UNIVERSITY MEDICAL CENTER 1653 West Congress Parkway, Zip 60612–3864; tel. 312/942–5000; Larry J. Goodman, Chief Executive Officer, p. B109

★ SINAI HEALTH SYSTEM 1500 South California Avenue, Zip 60608–1729; tel. 773/542–2000; Karen Teitelbaum, President and Chief Executive Officer, p. B117

★ UNIVERSITY OF CHICAGO MEDICINE 5841 South Maryland Avenue, Zip 60637–1447; tel. 773/702–6240; Sharon L. O'Keefe, President, p. B138

Crystal Lake: ★ CENTEGRA HEALTH SYSTEM 385 Millennium Drive, Zip 60012–3761; tel. 815/788–5800; Michael S. Eesley, Chief Executive Officer, p. B29

Downers Grove: ★ ADVOCATE HEALTH CARE 3075 Highland Parkway, Suite 600, Zip 60515–1206; tel. 630/929–8700; Jim Skogsbergh, President and Chief Executive Officer, p. B7

Evergreen Park: AMERICAN PROVINCE OF LITTLE COMPANY OF MARY SISTERS 9350 South California Avenue, Zip 60805–2595; tel. 708/229–5491, Sister, Kathleen McIntyre, Province Leader, p. B9

Naperville: ★ EDWARD-ELMHURST HEALTHCARE 801 South Washington Street, Zip 60540–7430; tel. 630/527–3000; Mary Lou Mastro, System Chief Executive Officer, p. B49

Peoria: ★ OSF HEALTHCARE SYSTEM 800 NE Glen Oak Avenue, Zip 61603–3200; tel. 309/655–2850; Kevin D. Schoeplein, Chief Executive Officer, p. B95

Schaumburg: CANCER TREATMENT CENTERS OF AMERICA 1336 Basswood Road, Zip 60173–4544; tel. 847/342–7400; Rajesh K. Garg, President and Chief Executive Officer, p. B24

Springfield: DIVISION OF MENTAL HEALTH, DEPARTMENT OF HUMAN SERVICES 319 East Madison Street, S-3B, Zip 62701–1035; tel. 217/785–6023; Lorrie Rickman. Jones, Director, p. B47

★ HSHS HOSPITAL SISTERS HEALTH SYSTEM 4936 LaVerna Road, Zip 62707–9797, P O Box 19456, 62794–9456, tel. 217/523–4747; Mary Starmann-Harrison, President and Chief Executive Officer, p. B66

★ MEMORIAL HEALTH SYSTEM 701 North First Street, Zip 62781–0001; tel. 217/788–3000; Edgar J. Curtis, President and Chief Executive Officer, p. B81

Urbana: ★ CARLE FOUNDATION 611 West Park Street, Zip 61801–2595; tel. 217/383–3311;

James C. Leonard, President and Chief Executive Officer, p. B25

INDIANA

Evansville: ★ DEACONESS HEALTH SYSTEM 600 Mary Street, Zip 47710–1658; tel. 812/450–5000; Shawn W. McCoy, Chief Executive Officer, p. B40

Fort Wayne: ★ PARKVIEW HEALTH 10501 Corporate Drive, Zip 46845–1700; tel. 260/373–7001; Michael J. Packnett, President and Chief Executive Officer, p. B96

Hammond: COMMUNITY HEALTHCARE SYSTEM 901 MacArthur Boulevard, Zip 46321–2959; tel. 219/836–1600; Donald P. Fesko, President and Chief Executive Officer, p. B36

Indianapolis: ★ COMMUNITY HEALTH NETWORK 7330 Shadeland Station, Zip 46256–3957; tel. 317/355–1411; Bryan A. Mills, President and Chief Executive Officer, p. B32

★ INDIANA UNIVERSITY HEALTH 340 West 10th Street, Suite 6100, Zip 46202–3082, P O Box 1367, 46206–1367, tel. 317/962–5900; Dennis M. Murphy, President and Chief Executive Officer, p. B67

Mishawaka: FRANCISCAN HEALTH 1515 Dragoon Trail, Zip 46544–4710, P O Box 1290, 46546–1290, tel. 574/256–3935; Kevin D. Leahy, President and Chief Executive Officer, p. B52

NEUROPSYCHIATRIC HOSPITALS 1625 East Jefferson Boulevard, Zip 46545–7103; tel. 574/255–1400; Cameron R. Gilbert, President and Chief Executive Officer, p. B88

South Bend: ★ BEACON HEALTH SYSTEM 615 North Michigan Street, Zip 46601–1033; tel. 574/647–1000; Philip A. Newbold, Chief Executive Officer, p. B21

IOWA

Clarion: ★ IOWA SPECIALTY HOSPITALS 1316 South Main Street, Zip 50525–2019; tel. 515/532–2811; Steven J. Simonin, Chief Executive Officer, p. B69

Davenport: ★ GENESIS HEALTH SYSTEM 1227 East Rusholme Street, Zip 52803–2498; tel. 563/421–1000; Douglas P. Cropper, President and Chief Executive Officer, p. B53

West Des Moines: ★ UNITYPOINT HEALTH 1776 Westlakes Parkway, Suite 400, Zip 50266–8239; tel. 515/241–6161; Kevin Vermeer, President and Chief Executive Officer, p. B132

KANSAS

Salina: SALINA REGIONAL HEALTH CENTER 400 South Santa Fe Avenue, Zip 67401–4198, PO Box 5080, 67402–5080, tel. 785/452–7000; Michael Terry, President and Chief Executive Officer, p. B110

Wichita: ★ GREAT PLAINS HEALTH ALLIANCE, INC. 250 North Rock Road, Suite 160, Zip 67206–2241; tel. 316/685–1523; Dave Dellasega, President and Chief Executive Officer, p. B54

KENTUCKY

Bowling Green: COMMONWEALTH HEALTH CORPORATION 800 Park Street, Zip 42101–2356; tel. 270/745–1500; Connie Smith, President and Chief Executive Officer, p. B32

Danville: EPHRAIM MCDOWELL HEALTH 217 South Third Street, Zip 40422–1823; tel. 859/239–1000; Sally M. Davenport, Chief Executive Officer, p. B49

Edgewood: ST. ELIZABETH HEALTHCARE 1 Medical Village Drive, Zip 41017–3403; tel. 859/301–2000; Garren Colvin, Chief Executive Officer, p. B120

Lexington: APPALACHIAN REGIONAL HEALTHCARE, INC. 2260 Executive Drive, Zip 40505–4810, P O Box 8086, 40533–8086, tel. 859/226–2440; Joseph Grossman, President and Chief Executive Officer, p. B10

Louisville: ALLIANT MANAGEMENT SERVICES 2650 Eastpoint Parkway, Suite 300, Zip 40223–5164; tel. 502/992–3525; Stephen E. Fischer, Regional Vice President, Finance, p. B8

★ BAPTIST HEALTH 2701 Eastpoint Parkway, Zip 40223; tel. 502/896–5000; Janet Norton, Vice President and Chief Legal Officer, p. B18

★ KINDRED HEALTHCARE 680 South Fourth Street, Zip 40202–2412; tel. 502/596–7300; Kent Wallace, Chief Operating Officer, p. B71

★ NORTON HEALTHCARE 4967 US Highway 42, Suite 100, Zip 40222–6363, P O Box 35070, 40232–5070, tel. 502/629–8000; Russell Cox, President and Chief Executive Officer, p. B91

Owensboro: OWENSBORO HEALTH 1201 Pleasant Valley Road, Zip 42303–9811; tel. 270/417–2000; Greg Strahan, Interim Chief Executive Officer, p. B95

LOUISIANA

Baton Rouge: ★ FRANCISCAN MISSIONARIES OF OUR LADY HEALTH SYSTEM, INC. 4200 Essen Lane, Zip 70809–2158; tel. 225/923–2701; John J. Finan Jr., President and Chief Executive Officer, p. B52

LOUISIANA STATE HOSPITALS 628 North 4th Street, Zip 70802–5342, P O Box 629, 70821–0628, tel. 225/342–9500; Shelby Price, Chief Executive Officer, p. B78

Crowley: COMPASS HEALTH 713 North Avenue L, Zip 70526–3832; tel. 337/788–3330; Aimee Monaghan, Chief Executive Officer, p. B37

Gretna: UNITED MEDICAL REHABILITATION HOSPITALS 3201 Wall Boulevard, Suite B, Zip 70056–7755; tel. 504/433–5551; John E.H. Mills, President & Chief Executive Officer, p. B132

Hammond: NORTH OAKS HEALTH SYSTEM 15790 Paul Vega MD Drive, Zip 70403–1436, P O Box 2668, 70404–2668, tel. 985/345–2700; Michele K. Sutton, President and Chief Executive Officer, p. B90

Lafayette: AMG INTEGRATED HEALTHCARE MANAGEMENT 101 La Rue France, Suite 500, Zip 70508–3144; tel. 337/269–9828; Timothy W. Howard, Chief Executive Officer, p. B9

LAFAYETTE GENERAL HEALTH 920 West Pinhook Road, Zip 70503–2455; tel. 337/289–7991; David L. Callecod, President and Chief Executive Officer, p. B73

LHC GROUP 420 West Pinhook Road, Zip 70503–2131; tel. 337/233–1307; Keith G. Myers, Chairman and Chief Executive Officer, p. B75

Lake Charles: OCEANS HEALTHCARE 2720 Rue de Jardin, Suite 100, Zip 70605–4050; tel. 337/721–1900; Jason Reed, President and Chief Executive Officer, p. B93

New Orleans: LCMC HEALTH 200 Henry Clay Avenue, Zip 70118–5720; tel. 504/899–9511; Greg Feirn, President and Chief Executive Officer, p. B74

★ OCHSNER HEALTH SYSTEM 1514 Jefferson Highway, Zip 70121–2429; tel. 800/874–8984;

Warner L. Thomas, President and Chief Executive Officer, p. B93

Shreveport: ALLEGIANCE HEALTH MANAGEMENT 504 Texas Street, Suite 200, Zip 71101–3526; tel. 318/226–8202; Rock Bordelon, President and Chief Executive Officer, p. B8

UNIVERSITY HEALTH SYSTEM 1501 Kings Highway, Zip 71103–4228; tel. 318/675–5000; Daniel J. Snyder, Chief Executive Officer, p. B137

WILLIS-KNIGHTON HEALTH SYSTEM 2600 Greenwood Road, Zip 71103–3908; tel. 318/212–4000; James K. Elrod, President and Chief Executive Officer, p. B146

MAINE

Brewer: ★ EASTERN MAINE HEALTHCARE SYSTEMS 43 Whiting Hill Road, Zip 04412–1005; tel. 207/973–7045; M. Michelle. Hood, President and Chief Executive Officer, p. B48

Lewiston: CENTRAL MAINE HEALTHCARE 300 Main Street, Zip 04240–7027; tel. 207/795–0111; Jeffrey L. Brickman, Chief Executive Officer, p. B30

Portland: MAINEHEALTH 110 Free Street, Zip 04101–3537, William L. Caron Jr., President, p. B78

MARYLAND

Baltimore: ★ JOHNS HOPKINS HEALTH SYSTEM 733 North Broadway, BRB 104, Zip 21205–1832; tel. 410/955–5000; Ronald R. Peterson, President, p. B70

LIFEBRIDGE HEALTH 2401 West Belvedere Avenue, Zip 21215–5216; tel. 410/601–5134; Neil M. Meltzer, President and Chief Executive Officer, p. B75

★ UNIVERSITY OF MARYLAND MEDICAL SYSTEM 250 West Pratt Street, 24th Floor, Zip 21201–1595; tel. 410/328–8667; Robert A. Chrencik, President and Chief Executive Officer, p. B138

Cheverly: DIMENSIONS HEALTHCARE SYSTEM 3001 Hospital Drive, 3rd Floor, Zip 20785–1189; tel. 301/583–4000; Neil J. Moore, President and Chief Executive Officer, p. B47

Columbia: ★ MEDSTAR HEALTH 10980 Grantchester Way, Zip 21044–2665; tel. 410/772–6500; Kenneth A. Samet, President and Chief Executive Officer, p. B81

Gaithersburg: ADVENTIST HEALTHCARE 820 West Diamond Avenue, Suite 600, Zip 20878–1419; tel. 301/315–3185; Terry Forde, President and Chief Executive Officer, p. B7

Marriottsville: ★ BON SECOURS HEALTH SYSTEM, INC. 1505 Marriottsville Road, Zip 21104–1399; tel. 410/442–5511; Richard Statuto, President and Chief Executive Officer, p. B22

Rockville: U. S. INDIAN HEALTH SERVICE 801 Thompson Avenue, Zip 20852–1627; tel. 301/443–1083; Yvette Roubideaux, Director, p. B129

Sparks Glencoe: FUNDAMENTAL LONG TERM CARE HOLDINGS, LLC 930 Ridgebrook Road, Zip 21152–9390; tel. 410/773–1000; W Bradley. Bennett, President and Chief Executive Officer, p. B53

MASSACHUSETTS

Boston: MASSACHUSETTS DEPARTMENT OF MENTAL HEALTH 25 Staniford Street, Zip 02114–2575; tel. 617/626–8123; Joan Mikula, Interim Commissioner, p. B79

MASSACHUSETTS DEPARTMENT OF PUBLIC HEALTH 250 Washington Street, Zip 02108–4619; tel. 617/624–6000; Sandra Akers, Bureau Director, Public Health Hospitals, p. B79

★ PARTNERS HEALTHCARE SYSTEM, INC. 800 Boylston Street, Suite 1150, Zip 02199–8123; tel. 617/278–1004; David Torchiana, Chief Executive Officer, p. B96

STEWARD HEALTH CARE SYSTEM, LLC 500 Boylston Street, 5th Floor, Zip 02116–3740; tel. 617/419–4700; Ralph de la Torre, Chairman and Chief Executive Officer, p. B121

Burlington: ★ LAHEY HEALTH 41 Mall Road, Zip 01805–0001; tel. 781/744–7100; Howard R. Grant, President and Chief Executive Officer, p. B74

Gardner: HEYWOOD HEALTHCARE 242 Green Street, Zip 01440–1336; tel. 978/632–3420; Winfield S. Brown, Chief Executive Officer, p. B65

Haverhill: WHITTIER HEALTH NETWORK 25 Railroad Square, Zip 01832–5721; tel. 978/556–5858; Alfred L. Arcidi, President, p. B146

Hyannis: ★ CAPE COD HEALTHCARE, INC. 27 Park Street, Zip 02601–5230; tel. 508/862–5121; Michael K. Lauf, President and Chief Executive Officer, p. B24

Pittsfield: ★ BERKSHIRE HEALTH SYSTEMS, INC. 725 North Street, Zip 01201–4124; tel. 413/447–2750; David E. Phelps, President and Chief Executive Officer, p. B21

Springfield: ★ BAYSTATE HEALTH, INC. 280 Chestnut Street, Zip 01199–0001; tel. 413/794–0000; Mark A. Keroack, President and Chief Executive Officer, p. B20

Tewksbury: ★ COVENANT HEALTH 100 Ames Pond Drive, Suite 102, Zip 01876–1240; tel. 978/654–6363; David R. Lincoln, President and Chief Executive Officer, p. B39

Worcester: ★ UMASS MEMORIAL HEALTH CARE, INC. 1 Biotech Park, Zip 01605–2982; tel. 508/334–0100; Eric Dickson, President and Chief Executive Officer, p. B130

MICHIGAN

Detroit: ★ HENRY FORD HEALTH SYSTEM One Ford Place, Zip 48202–3450; tel. 313/876–8708; Wright L. Lassiter III, President and Chief Executive Officer, p. B65

Flint: MCLAREN HEALTH CARE CORPORATION G3235 Beecher Road, Suite B, Zip 48532–3650; tel. 810/342–1100; Philip A. Incarnati, President and Chief Executive Officer, p. B80

Grand Rapids: ★ SPECTRUM HEALTH 100 Michigan Street NE, Zip 49503–2551, 444 Michigan Street Northeast | MC065, 49503–2551, tel. 616/391–1774; Richard C. Breon, President and Chief Executive Officer, p. B119

Kalamazoo: ★ BRONSON HEALTHCARE GROUP 301 John Street, Zip 49007–5295; tel. 269/341–6000; Frank J. Sardone, President and Chief Executive Officer, p. B23

Lansing: ★ SPARROW HEALTH SYSTEM 1215 East Michigan Avenue, Zip 48912–1811; tel. 517/364–1000; Dennis A. Swan, President and Chief Executive Officer, p. B118

Livonia: ★ TRINITY HEALTH 20555 Victor Parkway, Zip 48152–7031; tel. 734/343–1000; Richard J. Gilfillan, Chief Executive Officer, p. B127

Midland: ★ MIDMICHIGAN HEALTH 4000 Wellness Drive, Zip 48670–0001; tel. 989/839–3000;

Health Care Systems Index

Diane Postler-Slattery, President and Chief Executive Officer, p. B84

Saint Joseph: ★ LAKELAND HEALTH 1234 Napier Avenue, Zip 49085–2158; tel. 269/983–8300; Loren Hamel, President and Chief Executive Officer, p. B74

Southfield: ★ BEAUMONT HEALTH 2000 Town Center, Suite 1200, Zip 48075–1145; tel. 248/898–5000; John T. Fox, President and Chief Executive Officer, p. B21

Traverse City: ★ MUNSON HEALTHCARE 1105 Sixth Street, Zip 49684–2386; tel. 231/935–6703; Edwin Ness, President and Chief Executive Officer, p. B87

MINNESOTA

Bloomington: HEALTHPARTNERS 8170 33rd Avenue South, Zip 55425–4516; tel. 952/883–7600; Mary K. Brainerd, President and Chief Executive Officer, p. B61

Duluth: ★ ESSENTIA HEALTH 502 East Second Street, Zip 55805–1913; tel. 218/786–8376; David C. Herman, Chief Executive Officer, p. B50

Minneapolis: ★ ALLINA HEALTH 2925 Chicago Avenue, Zip 55407–1321, P O Box 43, 55440–0043, tel. 612/262–5000; Penny Ann. Wheeler, Chief Executive Officer, p. B9

★ FAIRVIEW HEALTH SERVICES 2450 Riverside Avenue, Zip 55454–1400; tel. 612/672–6141; James Hereford, President and Chief Executive Officer, p. B51

Robbinsdale: ★ NORTH MEMORIAL HEALTH CARE 3300 Oakdale Avenue North, Zip 55422–2926; tel. 763/520–5200; J Kevin. Croston, Chief Executive Officer, p. B90

Rochester: ★ MAYO CLINIC 200 First Street SW, Zip 55905–0002; tel. 507/284–0288; John H. Noseworthy, MD, President and Chief Executive Officer, p. B79

Saint Cloud: ★ CENTRACARE HEALTH 1406 Sixth Avenue North, Zip 56303–1900; tel. 320/251–2700; Kenneth D. Holmen, President and Chief Executive Officer, p. B30

Saint Paul: MINNESOTA DEPARTMENT OF HUMAN SERVICES 540 Cedar Street, Zip 55101–2208, P O Box 64998, 55164–0998, tel. 651/431–3212; Anne Barry, Deputy Commissioner, p. B85

Waconia: ★ RIDGEVIEW MEDICAL CENTER 500 South Maple Street, Zip 55387–1752; tel. 952/442–2191; Michael Phelps, President and Chief Executive Officer, p. B108

MISSISSIPPI

Jackson: MISSISSIPPI STATE DEPARTMENT OF MENTAL HEALTH 1101 Robert E Lee Building, 239 North Lamar Street, Zip 39201–1101; tel. 601/359–1288; Edwin C. LeGrand III, Executive Director, p. B85

★ UNIVERSITY HOSPITALS AND HEALTH SYSTEM 2500 North State Street, Zip 39216–4500; tel. 601/984–1000; Kevin S. Cook, Chief Executive Officer, p. B137

Magee: ★ PIONEER HEALTH SERVICES 110 Pioneer Way, Zip 39111–5501, P O Box 1100, 39111–1100, tel. 601/849–6440; Joseph S. McNulty III, President and Chief Executive Officer, p. B97

Mccomb: SOUTHWEST HEALTH SYSTEMS 215 Marion Avenue, Zip 39648–2705, P O Box 1307, 39649–1307, tel. 601/249–5500; Norman M.

Price, Chief Executive Officer and Administrator, p. B118

Meridian: ★ RUSH HEALTH SYSTEMS 1314 19th Avenue, Zip 39301–4116; tel. 601/483–0011; Wallace Strickland, President and Chief Executive Officer, p. B109

Tupelo: ★ NORTH MISSISSIPPI HEALTH SERVICES, INC. 830 South Gloster Street, Zip 38801–4996; tel. 662/377–3136; M. Shane. Spees, President and Chief Executive Officer, p. B90

MISSOURI

Cape Girardeau: LANDMARK HOSPITALS 3255 Independence Street, Zip 63701–4914; tel. 573/335–1091; William K. Kapp III, President and Chief Executive Officer, p. B74

SOUTHEASTHEALTH 1701 Lacey Street, Zip 63701–5230; tel. 573/334–4822; Kenneth Bateman, Chief Executive Officer, p. B118

Chesterfield: ★ MERCY 14528 South Outer 40, Suite 100, Zip 63017–5743; tel. 314/579–6100; Lynn Britton, President and Chief Executive Officer, p. B82

Columbia: ★ UNIVERSITY OF MISSOURI HEALTH CARE One Hospital Drive, DC 031, Zip 65212–0001; tel. 573/882–4141; Jonathan W. Curtright, Chief Executive Officer and Chief Operating Officer, p. B139

Joplin: ★ FREEMAN HEALTH SYSTEM 1102 West 32nd Street, Zip 64804–3503; tel. 417/347–1111; Paula F. Baker, President and Chief Executive Officer, p. B53

Kansas City: RURAL COMMUNITY HOSPITALS OF AMERICA 1100 Main Street, Suite 2350, Zip 64105–5186; tel. 816/474–7800; Lawrence J. Arthur, President, p. B108

★ SAINT LUKE'S HEALTH SYSTEM 901 East 104th Street, Mailstop 900N, Zip 64131–4517, 901 East 104th Street, 64131–4517, tel. 816/932–2000; Melinda Estes, President and Chief Executive Officer, p. B110

★ TRUMAN MEDICAL CENTERS 2301 Holmes Street, Zip 64108–2677; tel. 816/404–1000; Mark Steele, Chief Medical Officer and Chief Operating Officer, p. B129

Saint Louis: ★ ASCENSION HEALTHCARE 101 South Hanley Road, Suite 450, Zip 63105–3406; tel. 314/733–8000; Patricia A. Maryland, President and Chief Executive Officer, p. B12

★ BJC HEALTHCARE 4901 Forest Park Avenue, Suite 1200, Zip 63108–1402; tel. 314/747–9322; Steven H. Lipstein, Chief Executive Officer, p. B21

★ SSM HEALTH 10101 Woodfield Lane, Zip 63132–2937; tel. 314/994–7800; Laura Kaiser, President and Chief Executive Officer, p. B119

Springfield: COXHEALTH 1423 North Jefferson Avenue, Zip 65802–1988; tel. 417/269–3108; Steven D. Edwards, President and Chief Executive Officer, p. B39

MONTANA

Great Falls: BENEFIS HEALTH SYSTEM 1101 26th Street South, Zip 59405–5161; tel. 406/455–5000; John H. Goodnow, Chief Executive Officer, p. B21

NEBRASKA

Lincoln: ★ BRYAN HEALTH 1600 South 48th Street, Zip 68506–1283, 1600 S 48th ST, 68506–1283, tel. 402/481–1111; Kimberly A. Russel, President and Chief Executive Officer, p. B23

Norfolk: FAITH REGIONAL HEALTH SERVICES 2700 West Norfolk Avenue, Zip 68701–4438, P O Box 869, 68702–0869, tel. 402/371–4880; Mark D. Klosterman, President and Chief Executive Officer, p. B51

Omaha: ★ NEBRASKA METHODIST HEALTH SYSTEM, INC. 8511 West Dodge Road, Zip 68114–3403; tel. 402/354–5411; John M. Fraser, President and Chief Executive Officer, p. B88

NEVADA

Reno: ★ RENOWN HEALTH 50 West Liberty Street, Suite 1100, Zip 89501–1951; tel. 775/982–5529; Anthony D. Slonim, President and Chief Executive Officer, p. B107

NEW HAMPSHIRE

Laconia: ★ LRGHEALTHCARE 80 Highland Street, Zip 03246–3298; tel. 603/524–3211; Kevin Donovan, President and Chief Executive Officer, p. B78

Portsmouth: BRIDGEPOINT HEALTHCARE 155 Fleet Street, Zip 03801–4050; tel. 603/570–4888; Marc C. Ferrell, President and Chief Executive Officer, p. B22

NEW JERSEY

Edison: ★ HACKENSACK MERIDIAN HEALTH 343 Thornall Street, Zip 08837–2206; tel. 844/464–9355; Robert C. Garrett, Co-Chief Executive Officer, p. B55

★ JFK HEALTH 80 James Street, 2nd Floor, Zip 08820–3938; tel. 732/632–1503; Raymond F. Fredericks, President and Chief Executive Officer, p. B70

Jersey City: ★ CAREPOINT HEALTH 10 Exchange Place, 15th Floor, Zip 07302–3918; tel. 877/791–7000; Jeffrey M. Mandler, Chief Executive Officer, p. B24

Lakewood: CONCORD HEALTHCARE GROUP 111 Clifton AVenue, Zip 8701; tel. 214/396–3462; Joe Neuman, Chief Executive Officer, p. B37

Marlton: ★ VIRTUA HEALTH 50 Lake Center Executive Drive, Suite 401, Zip 8053; tel. 856/355–0010; Richard P. Miller, Chief Executive Officer, p. B144

Morristown: ★ ATLANTIC HEALTH SYSTEM 475 South Street, Zip 7962, P O Box 1905, 07962–1905, tel. 973/660–3270; Brian A. Gragnolati, President and Chief Executive Officer, p. B15

Mullica Hill: ★ INSPIRA HEALTH NETWORK 165 Bridgeton Pike, Zip 8062; tel. 856/641–8000; John A. DiAngelo, President and Chief Executive Officer, p. B68

Trenton: ★ CAPITAL HEALTH 750 Brunswick Avenue, Zip 08638–4143; tel. 609/394–6000; Al Maghazehe, President and Chief Executive Officer, p. B24

DIVISION OF MENTAL HEALTH AND ADDICTION SERVICES, DEPARTMENT OF HUMAN SERVICES, STATE OF NEW JERSEY 222 South Warren Street, Zip 08608–2306, P O Box 700, 08625–0700, tel. 609/777–0702; Lynn Kovich, Assistant Commissioner, p. B47

West Orange: ★ RWJBARNABAS HEALTH 95 Old Short Hills Road, Zip 07052–1008; tel. 973/322–4000; Barry Ostrowsky, President and Chief Executive Officer, p. B109

NEW MEXICO

Albuquerque: ERNEST HEALTH, INC. 7770 Jefferson Street NE, Suite 320, Zip 87109–4386; tel. 505/856–5300; Darby Brockette, Chief Executive Officer, p. B49

★ PRESBYTERIAN HEALTHCARE SERVICES 9521 San Mateo Blvd. NE, Zip 87113, P O Box 26666, 87125–6666, tel. 505/841–1234; Dale Maxwell, Chief Executive Officer, p. B99

UNIVERSITY OF NEW MEXICO HOSPITALS 915 Camino De Salud, Zip 87131–0001; tel. 505/272–5849; Stephen W. McKernan, Chief Executive Officer, p. B139

NEW YORK

Albany: NEW YORK STATE OFFICE OF MENTAL HEALTH 44 Holland Avenue, Zip 12208–3411; tel. 518/474–7056; Kristin M. Woodlock, Acting Commissioner, p. B88

Binghamton: UNITED HEALTH SERVICES 10–42 Mitchell Avenue, Zip 13903–1617; tel. 607/762–2200; John Carrigg, President and Chief Executive Officer, p. B131

Bronx: MONTEFIORE HEALTH SYSTEM 111 East 210th Street, Zip 10467–2490; tel. 718/920–4321; Steven M. Safyer, President and CEO, p. B86

Buffalo: ★ CATHOLIC HEALTH SYSTEM 144 Genesee Street, Zip 14203–1560; tel. 716/862–2410; Joseph D. McDonald, President and Chief Executive Officer, p. B29

Cooperstown: ★ BASSETT HEALTHCARE NETWORK 1 Atwell Road, Zip 13326–1301; tel. 607/547–3456; Vance Brown, President and Chief Executive Officer, p. B20

Elmira: ARNOT HEALTH 600 Roe Avenue, Zip 14905–1629; tel. 607/737–4100; Robert K. Lambert, President and Chief Executive Officer, p. B11

Geneva: FINGER LAKES HEALTH 196 North Street, Zip 14456–1651; tel. 315/787–4000; Jose Acevedo, President and Chief Executive Officer, p. B51

Ithaca: ★ CAYUGA HEALTH SYSTEM 101 Dates Drive, Zip 14850–1342; tel. 607/274–4011; John B. Rudd, President and Chief Executive Officer, p. B29

Jamaica: ★ MEDISYS HEALTH NETWORK 8900 Van Wyck Expressway, Zip 11418–2832; tel. 718/206–6000; Bruce J. Flanz, President and Chief Executive Officer, p. B81

LaGrangeville: HEALTH QUEST SYSTEMS, INC. 1351 Route 55 Ste 200, Zip 12540–5108, 1351 Route 55, 12540–5108, tel. 845/475–9500; Robert Friedberg, President and Chief Executive Officer, p. B61

Middletown: ★ GREATER HUDSON VALLEY HEALTH SYSTEM 707 East Main Street, Zip 10940–2650; tel. 845/333–1000; Scott Batulis, President and Chief Executive Officer, p. B55

New Hyde Park: ★ NORTHWELL HEALTH 2000 Marcus Avenue, Zip 11042; tel. 516/465–8100; Michael J. Dowling, President and Chief Executive Officer, p. B91

New York: ★ MOUNT SINAI HEALTH SYSTEM One Gustave L. Levy Place, Zip 10029; tel. 212/659–8888; Kenneth L. Davis, President and Chief Executive, p. B86

★ NEWYORK-PRESBYTERIAN 525 East 68th Street, Box 182, Zip 10065; tel. 212/746–3745; Steven J. Corwin, President and Chief Executive Officer, p. B89

★ NYC HEALTH + HOSPITALS 125 Worth Street, Room 514, Zip 10013–4006; tel. 212/788–3321; Stanley Brezenoff, Interim President and Chief Executive Officer, p. B92

NYU LANGONE HEALTH 550 First Avenue, Zip 10016–6402; tel. 646/929–7870; Robert I. Grossman, Chief Executive Officer, p. B93

Olean: UPPER ALLEGHENY HEALTH SYSTEM 130 South Union Street, Suite 300, Zip 14760–3676; tel. 716/375–6190; Timothy J. Finan, President and Chief Executive Officer, p. B141

Potsdam: ST. LAWRENCE HEALTH SYSTEM 50 Leroy Street, Zip 13676–1799; tel. 315/265–3300; David B. Acker, President and CEO, p. B120

Rochester: ★ ROCHESTER REGIONAL HEALTH 1425 Portland Avenue, 5th Floor, Zip 14621–3001; tel. 585/922–4000; Eric Bieber, President and Chief Executive Officer, p. B108

★ UNIVERSITY OF ROCHESTER MEDICAL CENTER 601 Elmwood Ave Box 623, Zip 14642–0002, 601 Elmwood Avenue, 14642–0002, tel. 585/275–2100; Steven I. Goldstein, General Director and Chief Executive Officer, p. B139

Rockville Centre: CATHOLIC HEALTH SERVICES OF LONG ISLAND 992 North Village Avenue, 1st Floor, Zip 11570–1002; tel. 516/705–3700; Alan D. Guerci, President and Chief Executive Officer, p. B28

Valhalla: WMCHEALTH 100 Woods Road, Zip 10595–1530; tel. 914/493–7000; Michael D. Israel, President and Chief Executive Officer, p. B146

NORTH CAROLINA

Asheville: ★ MISSION HEALTH SYSTEM 509 Biltmore Avenue, Zip 28801–4601; tel. 828/213–1111; Ronald A. Paulus, President and Chief Executive Officer, p. B85

Boone: ★ APPALACHIAN REGIONAL HEALTHCARE SYSTEM 336 Deerfield Road, Zip 28607–5008, P O Box 2600, 28607–2600, tel. 828/262–4100; Charles Mantooth, President and Chief Executive Officer, p. B10

Chapel Hill: ★ UNC HEALTH CARE 101 Manning Drive, Zip 27514–4220; tel. 919/966–4131; William L. Roper, Chief Executive Officer, p. B131

Charlotte: ★ ACUITYHEALTHCARE, LP 10200 Mallard Creek Road, Suite 300, Zip 28262–9705; tel. 704/887–7280; Edwin H. Cooper Jr., President and Chief Executive Officer, p. B5

★ CAROLINAS HEALTHCARE SYSTEM 1000 Blythe Boulevard, Zip 28203–5871, P O Box 32861, 28232–2861, tel. 704/355–2000; Eugene A. Woods, President and Chief Executive Officer, p. B25

Durham: ★ DUKE UNIVERSITY HEALTH SYSTEM 201 Trent Drive, Zip 27710–3037, P O Box 3701, 27710–3701, tel. 919/684–2255; A. Eugene. Washington, President and Chief Executive Officer, p. B48

Fayetteville: CAPE FEAR VALLEY HEALTH SYSTEM 1638 Owen Drive, Zip 28304–3424, P O Box 2000, 28302–2000, tel. 910/615–4000; Michael Nagowski, President and Chief Executive Officer, p. B24

Greensboro: CONE HEALTH 1200 North Elm Street, Zip 27401–1004; tel. 336/832–7000; Terry Akin, President and Chief Executive Officer, p. B38

Greenville: ★ VIDANT HEALTH 2100 Stantonsburg Road, Zip 27834–2818, P O Box 6028, 27835–6028, tel. 252/847–4100; Michael Waldrum, Chief Executive Officer, p. B143

Pinehurst: ★ FIRSTHEALTH OF THE CAROLINAS 155 Memorial Drive, Zip 28374–8710, P O Box 3000, 28374–3000, tel. 910/715–1000; David J. Kilarski, Chief Executive Officer, p. B52

Raleigh: ★ WAKEMED HEALTH & HOSPITALS 3000 New Bern Avenue, Zip 27610–1231; tel. 919/350–8000; Donald R. Gintzig, President and Chief Executive Officer, p. B144

Wilmington: ★ NEW HANOVER REGIONAL MEDICAL CENTER 2131 South 17th Street, Zip 28401–7407; tel. 910/343–7040; John H. Gizdic, President and Chief Executive Officer, p. B88

Winston Salem: ★ NOVANT HEALTH 2085 Frontis Plaza Boulevard, Zip 27103–5614; tel. 336/718–5600; Carl S. Armato, President and Chief Executive Officer, p. B92

Winston-Salem: ★ WAKE FOREST BAPTIST HEALTH Medical Center Boulevard, Zip 27157; tel. 336/716–2011; Julie Ann . Freischlag, Chief Executive Officer, p. B144

NORTH DAKOTA

Fargo: SISTERS OF MARY OF THE PRESENTATION HEALTH SYSTEM 1202 Page Drive SW, Zip 58103–2340, P O Box 10007, 58106–0007, tel. 701/237–9290; Aaron K. Alton, President and Chief Executive Officer, p. B117

OHIO

Akron: SUMMA HEALTH 1077 Gorge Boulevard, Zip 44310; tel. 330/375–3000; T. Clifford Deveny, Interim Chief Executive Officer, p. B122

Canton: AULTMAN HEALTH FOUNDATION 2600 Sixth Street SW, Zip 44710–1702; tel. 330/363–6192; Edward J. Roth III, President and Chief Executive Officer, p. B15

Chillicothe: ADENA HEALTH SYSTEM 272 Hospital Road, Zip 45601–9031; tel. 740/779–7500; Mark H. Shuter, President and Chief Executive Officer, p. B5

Cincinnati: ★ MERCY HEALTH 615 Elsinore Place, Zip 45202–1459, 1701 Mercy Health Place, 45237, tel. 513/639–2800; John M. Starcher, President and Chief Executive Officer, p. B83

★ UC HEALTH 3200 Burnet Avenue, Zip 45229–3019; tel. 513/585–6000; Richard P. Lofgren, President and CEO, p. B130

Cleveland: ★ CLEVELAND CLINIC HEALTH SYSTEM 9500 Euclid, Zip 44195–5108; tel. 216/444–2200; Delos Cosgrove, President and Chief Executive Officer, p. B31

SISTERS OF CHARITY HEALTH SYSTEM 2475 East 22nd Street, Zip 44115–3221; tel. 216/363–2797; Thomas J. Strauss, Chief Executive Officer, p. B117

★ UNIVERSITY HOSPITALS 11100 Euclid Avenue, Zip 44106–5000; tel. 216/844–1000; Thomas F. Zenty III, President and Chief Executive Officer, p. B137

Columbus: OHIO DEPARTMENT OF MENTAL HEALTH 30 East Broad Street, 8th Floor, Zip 43215–3430; tel. 614/466–2297; Tracy Plouck, Director, p. B93

★ OHIO STATE UNIVERSITY HEALTH SYSTEM 370 West Ninth Avenue, Zip 43210–1238; tel. 614/685–9015; David P. McQuaid, Chief Executive Officer, p. B94

★ OHIOHEALTH 180 East Broad Street, Zip 43215–3707; tel. 614/544–4455; David P. Blom, President and Chief Executive Officer, p. B94

Dayton: ★ KETTERING HEALTH NETWORK 3965 Southern Boulevard, Zip 45429–1229; tel. 937/395–8150; Fred M. Manchur, Chief Executive Officer, p. B71

★ PREMIER HEALTH 110 North Main Street Suite 390, Zip 45402–3720; tel. 937/499–9401; Mary H. Boosalis, President, p. B99

Findlay: ★ BLANCHARD VALLEY HEALTH SYSTEM 1900 South Main Street, Zip 45840–1214; tel. 419/423–4500; Scott C. Malaney, President and Chief Executive Officer, p. B22

Galion: ★ AVITA HEALTH SYSTEM 269 Portland Way South, Zip 44833–2399; tel. 419/468–4841; Jerome Morasko, President and Chief Executive Officer, p. B17

Jackson: HOLZER HEALTH SYSTEM 500 Burlington Road, Zip 45640–9360; tel. 855/446–5937; Michael Canady, Interim Chief Executive Officer, p. B65

Marietta: MEMORIAL HEALTH SYSTEM 401 Matthew Street, Zip 45750–1635; tel. 740/374–1400; J Scott. Cantley, President and Chief Executive Officer, p. B82

Toledo: ★ PROMEDICA HEALTH SYSTEM 1801 Richards Road, Zip 43607–1037; tel. 419/469–3800; Randall D. Oostra, President and Chief Executive Officer, p. B101

OKLAHOMA

Duncan: DUNCAN REGIONAL HOSPITAL 1407 North Whisenant Drive, Zip 73533–1650; tel. 580/252–5300; Jay R. Johnson, President and Chief Executive Officer, p. B48

Oklahoma City: FIRST PHYSICIANS CAPITAL GROUP, INC. 4323 NW 63rd Street Suite 140, Zip 73116–1513; tel. 405/246–0218; Sean Kirrane, Chief Executive Officer, p. B52

FOUNDATION SURGICAL HOSPITAL AFFILIATES 14000 North Portland Avenue, Suite 204, Zip 73134–4002; tel. 405/608–1700; Thomas A. Michaud, Chief Executive Officer, p. B52

★ INTEGRIS HEALTH 3366 NW Expressway, Suite 800, Zip 73112–9756; tel. 405/949–6066; Bruce Lawrence, President and Chief Executive Officer, p. B68

OKLAHOMA DEPARTMENT OF MENTAL HEALTH AND SUBSTANCE ABUSE SERVICES 1200 NE 13th Street, Zip 73117–1022, P O Box 53277, 73152–3277, tel. 405/522–3908; Terri White, Commissioner, p. B94

Shawnee: PREFERRED MANAGEMENT CORPORATION 120 West MacArthur, Suite 121, Zip 74804–2005; tel. 405/878–0202; Donald Freeman, President and Chief Executive Officer, p. B98

Tulsa: ★ SAINT FRANCIS HEALTH SYSTEM 6161 South Yale Avenue, Zip 74136–1902; tel. 918/494–8454; Jake Henry Jr., President and Chief Executive Officer, p. B110

OREGON

Bend: ★ ST. CHARLES HEALTH SYSTEM, INC. 2500 NE Neff Road, Zip 97701–6015; tel. 541/382–4321; Joseph Sluka, President and Chief Executive Officer, p. B120

Corvallis: ★ SAMARITAN HEALTH SERVICES 3600 NW Samaritan Drive, Zip 97330–3737, P O Box 1068, 97339–1068, tel. 541/768–5001; Larry A. Mullins, President and Chief Executive Officer, p. B110

Medford: ★ ASANTE HEALTH SYSTEM 2650 Siskiyou Boulevard, Suite 200, Zip 97504–8170; tel.

541/789–4100; Roy G. Vinyard, President and Chief Executive Officer, p. B11

Portland: ★ LEGACY HEALTH 1919 NW Lovejoy Street, Zip 97209–1503; tel. 503/415–5600; George J. Brown, President and Chief Executive Officer, p. B75

Salem: SALEM HEALTH 890 Oak Street Bldg B POB 14001, Zip 97309–5014; tel. 503/561–5200; Norman F. Gruber, President and Chief Executive Officer, p. B110

PENNSYLVANIA

Allentown: GOOD SHEPHERD REHABILITATION NETWORK 850 South Fifth Street, Zip 18103–3308; tel. 610/776–3100; John Kristel, President and Chief Executive Officer, p. B54

★ LEHIGH VALLEY HEALTH NETWORK 1200 South Cedar Crest Boulevard, Zip 18103–6202, P O Box 689, 18105–1556, tel. 610/402–8000; Brian A. Nester, President and Chief Executive Officer, p. B75

Beaver: HERITAGE VALLEY HEALTH SYSTEM 1000 Dutch Ridge Road, Zip 15009–9727; tel. 724/773–2024; Norman F. Mitry, President and Chief Executive Officer, p. B65

Bethlehem: ST. LUKE'S UNIVERSITY HEALTH NETWORK 801 Ostrum Street, Zip 18015–1000; tel. 610/954–4000; Richard A. Anderson, President and Chief Executive Officer, p. B120

Chambersburg: ★ SUMMIT HEALTH 112 North Seventh Street, Zip 17201–1720; tel. 717/267–7138; Patrick W. O'Donnell, President and Chief Executive Officer, p. B122

Danville: ★ GEISINGER HEALTH 100 North Academy Avenue, Zip 17822–9800; tel. 570/271–6211; David T. Feinberg, President and Chief Executive Officer, p. B53

Enola: ★ POST ACUTE MEDICAL, LLC 1828 Good Hope Road, Suite 102, Zip 17025–1233; tel. 717/731–9660; Anthony F. Misitano, President and Chief Executive Officer, p. B98

Greensburg: EXCELA HEALTH 532 West Pittsburgh Street, Zip 15601, 134 Industrial Park Road, 15601–7328, tel. 724/832–5050; Robert Rogalski, Chief Executive Officer, p. B51

Harrisburg: UPMC PINNACLE 111 South Front Street, Zip 17101–2010, P O Box 8700, 17105–8700, tel. 717/231–8900; Philip Guarneschelli, President and Chief Executive Officer, p. B140

Hershey: PENN STATE HERSHEY HEALTH SYSTEM 500 University Drive, Zip 17033–2360; tel. 717/531–8521; A. Craig. Hillemeier, Chief Executive Officer, p. B97

King of Prussia: UNIVERSAL HEALTH SERVICES, INC. 367 South Gulph Road, Zip 19406–3121, P O Box 61558, 19406–0958, tel. 610/768–3300; Alan B. Miller, Chairman and Chief Executive Officer, p. B133

Lehighton: ★ BLUE MOUNTAIN HEALTH SYSTEM 211 North 12th Street, Zip 18235–1138; tel. 610/377–1300; Andrew E. Harris, President and Chief Executive Officer, p. B22

Meadville: ★ MEADVILLE MEDICAL CENTER 751 Liberty Street, Zip 16335–2559; tel. 814/333–5000; Philip E. Pandolph, Chief Executive Officer, p. B81

Mechanicsburg: ★ SELECT MEDICAL CORPORATION 4714 Gettysburg Road, Zip 17055–4325; tel. 717/972–1100; David S. Chernow, President and Chief Executive Officer, p. B112

★ VIBRA HEALTHCARE 4550 Lena Drive, Suite 225, Zip 17055–4920; tel. 717/591–5700; Brad Hollinger, Chairman and Chief Executive Officer, p. B142

Philadelphia: EINSTEIN HEALTHCARE NETWORK 5501 Old York Road, Zip 19141–3098; tel. 215/456–7890; Barry R. Freedman, President and Chief Executive Officer, p. B49

★ JEFFERSON HEALTH 111 South 11th Street, Zip 19107–4824; tel. 610/225–6200; Stephen K. Klasko, President and Chief Executive Officer, p. B69

★ TEMPLE UNIVERSITY HEALTH SYSTEM 3509 North Broad Street, 9th Floor, Zip 19140–4105; tel. 215/707–0900; Larry Kaiser, President and Chief Executive Officer, p. B123

★ UNIVERSITY OF PENNSYLVANIA HEALTH SYSTEM 3400 Civic Center Boulvard, Zip 19104–5127; tel. 215/662–2203; Ralph W. Muller, President and Chief Executive Officer, p. B139

Pittsburgh: ★ ALLEGHENY HEALTH NETWORK 30 Isabella Street, Suite 300, Zip 15212–5862; tel. 412/359–3131; Cynthia Hundorfean, President and Chief Executive Officer, p. B8

UPMC 600 Grant Street, US Steel Tower, Suite 6262, Zip 15219–2702; tel. 412/647–8762; Jeffrey A. Romoff, President and Chief Executive Officer, p. B140

Sayre: ★ GUTHRIE CLINIC Guthrie Square, Zip 18840; tel. 570/887–4312; Joseph A. Scopelliti, President and Chief Executive Officer, p. B55

Villanova: DEVEREUX 444 Devereux Drive, Zip 19085–1932, P O Box 638, 19085–0638, tel. 610/520–3000; Robert Q. Kreider, President and Chief Executive Officer, p. B45

Washington: ★ WASHINGTON HEALTH SYSTEM 155 Wilson Avenue, Zip 15301–3336; tel. 724/225–7000; Gary B. Weinstein, Chief Executive Officer, p. B144

Williamsport: ★ UPMC SUSQUEHANNA 700 High Street, Zip 17701–3100; tel. 570/321–1000; Steven P. Johnson, President and Chief Executive Officer, p. B140

York: ★ WELLSPAN HEALTH 45 Monument Road, Suite 200, Zip 17403–5071; tel. 717/851–2121; Kevin H. Mosser, President and Chief Executive Officer, p. B145

PUERTO RICO

San Juan: ★ PUERTO RICO DEPARTMENT OF HEALTH Building 'A' - Medical Center, Zip 936, Call Box 70184, 936, tel. 787/765–2929; Rafael Rodriguez. Mercado, Secretary of Health, p. B103

RHODE ISLAND

Providence: ★ CARE NEW ENGLAND HEALTH SYSTEM 45 Willard Avenue, Zip 02905–3218; tel. 401/453–7900; Dennis D. Keefe, President and Chief Executive Officer, p. B24

LIFESPAN CORPORATION 167 Point Street, Zip 02903–4771; tel. 401/444–3500; Timothy J. Babineau, President and Chief Executive Officer, p. B77

SOUTH CAROLINA

Anderson: ★ ANMED HEALTH 800 North Fant Street, Zip 29621–5793; tel. 864/512–1000; William T. Manson III, Chief Executive Officer, p. B10

Columbia: ★ PALMETTO HEALTH 1301 Taylor Street, Suite 9-A, Zip 29201–2942, P O Box 2266, 29202–2266, tel. 803/296–2100; Charles D. Beaman Jr., Chief Executive Officer, p. B95

Florence: MCLEOD HEALTH 555 East Cheves Street, Zip 29506–2617, P O Box 100551, 29502–0551, tel. 843/777–2000; Robert L. Colones, President and Chief Executive Officer, p. B81

Georgetown: ★ TIDELANDS HEALTH 606 Black River Road, Zip 29440–3304, P O Box 421718, 29442–4203, tel. 843/527–7000; Bruce P. Bailey, President and Chief Executive Officer, p. B127

Greenville: ★ GREENVILLE HEALTH SYSTEM 701 Grove Road, Zip 29605–5611; tel. 864/455–7000; Michael C. Riordan, President and Chief Executive Officer, p. B55

Spartanburg: ★ SPARTANBURG REGIONAL HEALTHCARE SYSTEM 101 East Wood Street, Zip 29303–3040; tel. 864/560–6000; Bruce Holstien, President and Chief Executive Officer, p. B119

SOUTH DAKOTA

Rapid City: ★ REGIONAL HEALTH 353 Fairmont Boulevard, Zip 57701–7375, P O Box 6000, 57709–6000, tel. 605/719–1000; Brent R. Phillips, President and Chief Executive Officer, p. B107

Sioux Falls: ★ AVERA HEALTH 3900 West Avera Drive, Suite 300, Zip 57108–5721; tel. 605/322–4700; John T. Porter, President and Chief Executive Officer, p. B16

★ SANFORD HEALTH 2301 East 60th Street North, Zip 57104–0569, PO Box 5039, 57117–5039, tel. 605/333–1000; Kelby K. Krabbenhoft, President and Chief Executive Officer, p. B111

TENNESSEE

Brentwood: ★ DUKE LIFEPOINT HEALTHCARE 330 Seven Springs Way, Zip 37027–5098; tel. 615/920–7000; Jeffrey G. Seraphine, President, p. B47

★ HEALTHTECH MANAGEMENT SERVICES 5110 Maryland Way Suite 200, Zip 37027–2307; tel. 615/309–6053; Derek Morkel, Chief Executive Officer, p. B64

★ LIFEPOINT HEALTH 330 Seven Springs Way, Zip 37027–4536; tel. 615/920–7000; William F. Carpenter III, Chairman and Chief Executive Officer, p. B76

★ QHR 1573 Mallory Lane, Suite 200, Zip 37027, 1573 Mallory Lane, Suite 200, 37027, tel. 800/233–1470; Mickey Bilbrey, President and Chief Executive Officer, p. B104

★ QUORUM HEALTH 1573 Mallory Lane, Suite 100, Zip 37027; tel. 615/221–1400; Thomas Miller, President and Chief Executive Officer, p. B105

RCCH HEALTHCARE PARTNERS 103 Continental Place Ste 200, Zip 37027–1042; tel. 615/844–9800; Martin S. Rash, Chief Executive Officer, p. B106

Chattanooga: ERLANGER HEALTH SYSTEM 975 East Third Street, Zip 37403–2147; tel. 423/778–7000; Kevin M. Spiegel, President and Chief Executive Officer, p. B49

Clinton: CURAE HEALTH 121 Leinart Street, Zip 37716–3632, P O Box 358, 37717–0358, tel. 865/269–4074; Steve Clapp, President and Chief Executive Officer, p. B40

Columbia: ★ MAURY REGIONAL HEALTH SYSTEM 1224 Trotwood Avenue, Zip 38401–4802; tel. 931/381–1111; H Alan. Watson, Chief Executive Officer, p. B79

Franklin: ACADIA HEALTHCARE COMPANY, INC. 830 Crescent Centre Drive, Suite 610, Zip 37067–7323; tel. 615/861–6000; Joey Jacobs, Chairman and Chief Executive Officer, p. B4

★ COMMUNITY HEALTH SYSTEMS, INC. 4000 Meridian Boulevard, Zip 37067–6325, P O Box 689020, 37068–9020, tel. 615/465–7000; Wayne T. Smith, Chairman, President and Chief Executive Officer, p. B33

IASIS HEALTHCARE 117 Seaboard Lane, Building E, Zip 37067–2855; tel. 615/844–2747; Carl Whitmer, President and Chief Executive Officer, p. B67

Jackson: ★ WEST TENNESSEE HEALTHCARE 620 Skyline Drive, Zip 38301–3923; tel. 731/541–5000; James E. Ross, President and Chief Executive Officer, p. B145

Johnson City: MOUNTAIN STATES HEALTH ALLIANCE 400 North State of Franklin Road, Zip 37604–6035; tel. 423/302–3423; Alan M. Levine, President and Chief Executive Officer, p. B86

Kingsport: ★ WELLMONT HEALTH SYSTEM 1905 American Way, Zip 37660–5882; tel. 423/230–8200; Barton A. Hove, President and Chief Executive Officer, p. B144

Knoxville: ★ COVENANT HEALTH 100 Fort Sanders West Boulevard, Zip 37922–3353; tel. 865/531–5555; James VanderSteeg, President and Chief Executive Officer, p. B39

Memphis: ★ BAPTIST MEMORIAL HEALTH CARE CORPORATION 350 North Humphreys Boulevard, Zip 38120–2177; tel. 901/227–5117; Jason Little, President and Chief Executive Officer, p. B19

METHODIST LE BONHEUR HEALTHCARE 1211 Union Avenue, Suite 700, Zip 38104–6600; tel. 901/516–0791; Michael Ugwueke, President and Chief Executive Officer, p. B84

STRATEGIC BEHAVIORAL HEALTH, LLC 8295 Tournament Drive, Suite 201, Zip 38125–8913; tel. 901/969–3100; Jim Shaheen, President, p. B121

Nashville: ★ ARDENT HEALTH SERVICES 1 Burton Hills Boulevard, Suite 250, Zip 37215–6195; tel. 615/296–3000; David T. Vandewater, President and Chief Executive Officer, p. B11

HAVEN BEHAVIORAL HEALTHCARE 652 West Iris Drive, Zip 37204–3191; tel. 615/250–9500; Michael Lindley, Chief Executive Officer, p. B56

★ HCA HEALTHCARE One Park Plaza, Zip 37203–1548; tel. 615/344–5248; R Milton. Johnson, President and Chief Executive Officer, p. B56

★ VANDERBILT HEALTH 1211 22nd Avenue South, Zip 37232; tel. 615/322–5000; Charles Wright. Pinson, Deputy Vice Chancellor for Health Affairs and Chief Executive Officer of Vanderbilt Health System, p. B142

Parsons: TENNESSEE HEALTH MANAGEMENT 52 West Eighth Street, Zip 38363–4656, PO Box 10, 38363–0010, tel. 731/847–6343; Dennis Berry, Chief Executive Officer, p. B125

TEXAS

Addison: UNITED SURGICAL PARTNERS INTERNATIONAL 15305 Dallas Parkway, Suite 1600, Zip 75001–6491; tel. 972/713–3500; William H. Wilcox, President and Chief Executive Officer, p. B132

Arlington: ★ TEXAS HEALTH RESOURCES 612 East Lamar Boulevard, Suite 900, Zip 76011–4130; tel. 682/236–7900; Barclay E. Berdan, Chief Executive Officer, p. B126

Austin: TEXAS DEPARTMENT OF STATE HEALTH SERVICES 1100 West 49th Street, Zip 78756–3199; tel. 512/458–7111; Kirk Cole, Interim Commissioner, p. B126

★ UNIVERSITY OF TEXAS SYSTEM 601 Colorado Street, Suite 205, Zip 78701–2904; tel. 512/499–4224; Raymond Greenberg, Executive Vice Chancellor, p. B140

Dallas: ★ BAYLOR SCOTT & WHITE HEALTH 4005 Crutcher Street, Suite 310, Zip 75246–1779; tel. 214/820–0111; James H. Hinton, President and Chief Executive Officer, p. B20

CORNERSTONE HEALTHCARE GROUP 2200 Ross Avenue, Suite 5400, Zip 75201–7984; tel. 469/621–6700; Steve Jakubcanin, President and Chief Executive Officer, p. B38

★ METHODIST HEALTH SYSTEM 1441 North Beckley Avenue, Zip 75203–1201, P O Box 655999, 75265–5999, tel. 214/947–8181; Stephen L. Mansfield, President and Chief Executive Officer, p. B84

★ TENET HEALTHCARE CORPORATION 1445 Ross Avenue, Suite 1400, Zip 75202–2703, P O Box 1390369, 75313–9036, tel. 469/893–2200; Trevor Fetter, President and Chief Executive Officer, p. B123

Garland: CURAHEALTH HOSPITALS 650 Beebalm Lane, Suite 220, Zip 75040–2955; tel. 972/414–0070; Chester Crouch, Chief Executive Officer, p. B40

Greenville: HUNT REGIONAL HEALTHCARE 4215 Joe Ramsey Boulevard, Zip 75401–7852, P O Box 1059, 75403–1059, tel. 903/408–5000; Richard Carter, Chief Executive Officer, p. B66

Houston: ★ HOUSTON METHODIST 6565 Fannin Street, D-200, Zip 77030–2707; tel. 713/441–2221; Marc L. Boom, Chief Executive Officer, p. B66

★ MEMORIAL HERMANN HEALTH SYSTEM 929 Gessner, Suite 2700, Zip 77024–2593; tel. 713/338–5555; Charles D. Stokes, President and Chief Executive Officer, p. B82

NEXUS HEALTH SYSTEMS One Riverway, Suite 600, Zip 77056–1993; tel. 713/355–6111; John W. Cassidy, President, Chief Executive Officer and Chief Medical Officer, p. B89

NOBILIS HEALTH CORPORATION 11700 Katy Freeway Suite 300, Zip 77079–1218; tel. 713/355–8614; Harry Fleming, Chief Executive Officer, p. B89

Irving: ★ CHRISTUS HEALTH 919 Hidden Ridge Drive, Zip 75038; tel. 469/282–2000; Ernie W. Sadau, Chief Executive Officer, p. B30

USMD HEALTH SYSTEM 6333 North State Highway 161 Suite 200, Zip 75038–2229; tel. 214/493–4000; Mike Bukosky, President, Hospital Division, p. B141

Lubbock: ★ COVENANT HEALTH SYSTEM 3615 19th Street, Zip 79410–1203; tel. 806/725–0447; Richard H. Parks, President and Chief Executive Officer, p. B39

Plano: ★ COMMUNITY HOSPITAL CORPORATION 7800 North Dallas Parkway, Suite 200, Zip 75024–6116; tel. 972/943–6400; Jim R. Kendrick, President and Chief Executive Officer, p. B36

★ LIFECARE MANAGEMENT SERVICES 5340 Legacy Drive, Suite 150, Zip 75024–3131; tel. 469/241–2100; James E. Murray, Chief Executive Officer, p. B76

Sherman: CARRUS HOSPITALS 1810 West US Highway 82, Zip 75092-7069; tel. 903/870-2600; Ronald E. Dorris, Chief Executive Officer, p. B26

The Woodlands: EMERUS 10077 Grogan's Mill, Suite 100, Zip 77380-1022; tel. 281/292-2450; Craig Goguen, Chief Executive Officer, p. B49

Tyler: ★ EAST TEXAS MEDICAL CENTER REGIONAL HEALTHCARE SYSTEM 1000 South Beckham Street, Zip 75701-1908, P O Box 6400, 75711-6400, tel. 903/535-6211; Elmer G. Ellis, President and Chief Executive Officer, p. B48

UTAH

Nephi: ★ RURAL HEALTH GROUP 48 West 1500 North, Zip 84648-8900; tel. 435/623-4924; Mark R. Stoddard, President and Chairman, p. B109

Salt Lake City: ★ INTERMOUNTAIN HEALTH-CARE, INC. 36 South State Street, 22nd Floor, Zip 84111-1453; tel. 801/442-2000; A. Marc. Harrison, President and Chief Executive Officer, p. B69

VIRGINIA

Charlottesville: UVA HEALTH SYSTEM 1215 Lee Street, Zip 22908-0816; tel. 434/924-0211; Richard Shannon, Executive Vice President for Health Affairs, p. B141

Falls Church: BUREAU OF MEDICINE AND SURGERY, DEPARTMENT OF THE NAVY 7700 Arlington Boulevard, Suite 5126, Zip 22042; tel. 202/762-3701; Bryce H.P. Mendez, Healthcare Policy Analyst, p. B23

DEPARTMENT OF THE ARMY, OFFICE OF THE SURGEON GENERAL 5109 Leesburg Pike, Zip 22041-3215; tel. 703/681-3000, Lieutenant General, Eric B. Schoomaker, Surgeon General, p. B41

★ INOVA HEALTH SYSTEM 8110 Gatehouse Road, Suite 200 East, Zip 22042-1252; tel. 703/289-2069; J Knox. Singleton, President and Chief Executive Officer, p. B68

Fredericksburg: ★ MARY WASHINGTON HEALTHCARE 2300 Fall Hill Avenue, Suite 308, Zip 22401-3343; tel. 540/741-3100; Michael P. McDermott, President and Chief Executive Officer, p. B79

Lynchburg: ★ CENTRA HEALTH, INC. 1920 Atherholt Road, Zip 24501-1104; tel. 434/200-3000; E W. Tibbs, President and Chief Executive Officer, p. B29

Newport News: RIVERSIDE HEALTH SYSTEM 701 Town Center Drive, Suite 1000, Zip 23606-4286; tel. 757/534-7000; William B. Downey, President and Chief Executive Officer, p. B108

Norfolk: ★ SENTARA HEALTHCARE 6015 Poplar Hall Drive, Zip 23502-3819; tel. 757/455-7000; Howard P. Kern, Chief Executive Officer, p. B115

Richmond: ★ VCU HEALTH SYSTEM 1250 East Marshall Street, Zip 23298-5051, P O Box 980510, 23298-0510, tel. 804/828-9000; Marsha Rappley, Chief Executive Officer and Vice President for Health Sciences, p. B142

VIRGINIA DEPARTMENT OF MENTAL HEALTH 1220 Bank Street, Zip 23219-3645, P O Box 1797, 23218-1797, tel. 804/786-3921; James S. Reinhard, Commissioner, p. B143

Roanoke: ★ CARILION CLINIC 1906 Belleview Avenue SE, Zip 24014-1838, P O Box 13727, 24036-3727, tel. 540/981-7000; Nancy Howell. Agee, President and Chief Executive Officer, p. B25

Winchester: ★ VALLEY HEALTH SYSTEM 220 Campus Boulevard, Suite 420, Zip 22601-2889, P O Box 3340, 22604-2540, tel. 540/536-8024; Mark H. Merrill, President and Chief Executive Officer, p. B141

WASHINGTON

Mount Vernon: SKAGIT REGIONAL HEALTH 1415 E Kincaid Street, Zip 98274-4126; tel. 360/424-4111; Gregg Agustin. Davidson, President and Chief Executive Officer, p. B117

Renton: ★ PROVIDENCE ST. JOSEPH HEALTH 1801 Lind Avenue Southwest, 9016, Zip 98057-9016, 181 Lind Avenue Southwest, 9016, 98057-9016, tel. 425/525-3698; Rodney F. Hochman, President and Chief Executive Officer, p. B102

Seattle: ★ SWEDISH HEALTH SERVICES 747 Broadway, Zip 98122-4379; tel. 206/386-6000; R. Guy. Hudson, Chief Executive Officer, p. B123

★ UW MEDICINE 1959 NE Pacific Street, Zip 98195-0001, P O Box 356350, 98195-6350, tel. 206/543-7718; Paul G. Ramsey, Chief Executive Officer, p. B141

VIRGINIA MASON HEALTH SYSTEM 1100 Ninth Avenue, Zip 98101-2756, P.O. Box 900, 98111-0900, tel. 206/223-6600; Gary Kaplan, Chief Executive Officer, p. B144

Tacoma: MULTICARE HEALTH SYSTEM 315 Martin Luther King Jr Way, Zip 98405-4234, P O Box 5299, 98415-0299, tel. 253/403-1000; William G. Robertson, President and Chief Executive Officer, p. B87

Vancouver: ★ PEACEHEALTH 1115 SE 164th Avenue, Zip 98683; tel. 360/729-1000; Elizabeth Dunne, President and Chief Executive Officer, p. B96

WEST VIRGINIA

Elkins: ★ DAVIS HEALTH SYSTEM Reed Street and Gorman Avenue, Zip 26241, P O Box 1697, 26241-1697, tel. 304/636-3300; Vance Jackson, President and Chief Executive Officer, p. B40

Huntington: ★ PALLOTTINE HEALTH SERVICES 2900 First Avenue, Zip 25702-1241; tel.

304/526-1234; Michael G. Sellards, Chief Executive Officer, p. B95

Morgantown: ★ MONONGALIA HEALTH SYSTEM 1200 J. D. Anderson Drive, Zip 26505-3494; tel. 304/598-1200; Darryl L. Duncan, President and Chief Executive Officer, p. B86

★ WEST VIRGINIA UNIVERSITY HEALTH SYSTEM One Medical Center, Box 8136, Zip 26506-8136; tel. 304/285-7150; Albert L. Wright Jr., President and Chief Executive Officer, p. B145

South Charleston: ★ THOMAS HEALTH SYSTEM, INC. 4605 MacCorkle Avenue SW, Zip 25309-1311; tel. 304/766-3600; Daniel Lauffer, President and Chief Executive Officer, p. B127

WISCONSIN

Appleton: THEDACARE, INC. 122 East College Avenue, Zip 54911-5794, P O Box 8025, 54912-8025, tel. 920/830-5889; Imran A. Andrabi, President and Chief Executive Officer, p. B126

Janesville: MERCY HEALTH SYSTEM 1000 Mineral Point Avenue, Zip 53548-2940, P O Box 5003, 53547-5003, tel. 608/756-6000; Javon R. Bea, President and Chief Executive Officer, p. B84

Madison: UW HEALTH SYSTEM 600 Highland Avenue, Zip 53792-0001; tel. 608/263-6400; Alan Kaplan, Chief Executive Officer, p. B141

Manitowoc: ★ FRANCISCAN SISTERS OF CHRISTIAN CHARITY SPONSORED MINISTRIES, INC. 1415 South Rapids Road, Zip 54220-9302; tel. 920/684-7071; Daniel B. McGinty, President and Chief Executive Officer, p. B53

Marshfield: MARSHFIELD CLINIC HEALTH SYSTEM 1000 North Oak Avenue, Zip 54449-5703; tel. 800/782-8581; Susan Turney, Chief Executive Assistant, p. B79

Milwaukee: ★ AURORA HEALTH CARE 750 Virginia Street, Zip 53204, P O Box 341880, 53234-1880, tel. 414/299-1600; Nick Turkal, President and Chief Executive Officer, p. B15

CHILDREN'S HOSPITAL AND HEALTH SYSTEM 9000 West Wisconsin Avenue, Zip 53226-4810, P O Box 1997, 53201-1997, tel. 414/226-2000; Peggy N. Troy, President and Chief Executive Officer, p. B30

Waukesha: ★ PROHEALTH CARE, INC. N17 W24100 Riverwood Drive, Suite 130, Zip 53188; tel. 262/928-2242; Susan A. Edwards, President and Chief Executive Officer, p. B101

Wausau: ★ ASPIRUS, INC. 425 Pine Ridge Boulevard, Zip 54401-4123; tel. 715/847-2118; Matthew Heywood, Chief Executive Officer, p. B14

Networks and their Hospitals

ARIZONA

HONORHEALTH
8125 North Hayden Road, Scottsdale, AZ, Zip 85258–2463; tel. 480/882–4000; Todd LaPorte, Chief Executive Officer

HONORHEALTH DEER VALLEY MEDICAL CENTER, 19829 North 27th Avenue, Phoenix, AZ, Zip 85027–4002; tel. 623/879–6100; David Price, Chief Executive Officer

HONORHEALTH JOHN C. LINCOLN MEDICAL CENTER, 250 East Dunlap Avenue, Phoenix, AZ, Zip 85020–2825; tel. 602/943–2381; Margaret Elizabeth. Griffin, Chief Executive Officer

HONORHEALTH REHABILITATION HOSPITAL, 8850 East Pima Center Parkway, Scottsdale, AZ, Zip 85258–4619; tel. 480/800–3900; Scott R. Keen, Chief Executive Officer

HONORHEALTH SCOTTSDALE OSBORN MEDICAL CENTER, 7400 East Osborn Road, Scottsdale, AZ, Zip 85251–6403; tel. 480/882–4000; Kimberly Post, Senior Vice President and Chief Executive Officer

HONORHEALTH SCOTTSDALE SHEA MEDICAL CENTER, 9003 East Shea Boulevard, Scottsdale, AZ, Zip 85260–6771; tel. 480/323–3000; Gary E. Baker, Senior Vice President and Chief Executive Officer

HONORHEALTH SCOTTSDALE THOMPSON PEAK MEDICAL CENTER, 7400 East Thompson Peak Parkway, Scottsdale, AZ, Zip 85255–4109; tel. 480/324–7000; David Price, Chief Executive Officer

NORTHERN ARIZONA HEALTHCARE
1200 North Beaver Street, Flagstaff, AZ, Zip 86001–3118; tel. 928/779–3366; Robert P. Thames, President and Chief Executive Officer

FLAGSTAFF MEDICAL CENTER, 1200 North Beaver Street, Flagstaff, AZ, Zip 86001–3118; tel. 928/779–3366; Florence (Flo). Spyrow, Chief Administrative Officer

VERDE VALLEY MEDICAL CENTER, 269 South Candy Lane, Cottonwood, AZ, Zip 86326–4170; tel. 928/639–6000; Barbara Firminger, Chief Administrative Officer

CALIFORNIA

ADVENTIST HEALTH NORTHERN CALIFORNIA NETWORK
463 Aviation Boulevard, Santa Rosa, CA, Zip 95403–1079; tel. 707/571–2893; Jeff Eller, FACHE, President and Chief Executive Officer

FRANK R. HOWARD MEMORIAL HOSPITAL, One Marcela Drive, Willits, CA, Zip 95490–4298; tel. 707/459–6801; Jason Wells, President and Chief Executive Officer

ST. HELENA HOSPITAL CENTER FOR BEHAVIORAL HEALTH, 525 Oregon Street, Vallejo, CA, Zip 94590–3201; tel. 707/648–2200; Steven Herber, M.D., FACS, President and Chief Executive Officer

ST. HELENA HOSPITAL CLEAR LAKE, 15630 18th Avenue, Clearlake, CA, Zip 95422–9336, P O Box 6710, 95422, tel. 707/994–6486; David Santos, President and Chief Executive Officer

ST. HELENA HOSPITAL NAPA VALLEY, 10 Woodland Road, Saint Helena, CA, Zip 94574–9554; tel. 707/963–3611; Steven Herber, M.D., FACS, President and Chief Executive Officer

UKIAH VALLEY MEDICAL CENTER, 275 Hospital Drive, Ukiah, CA, Zip 95482–4531; tel. 707/462–3111; Gwen Matthews, R.N., MSN, Chief Executive Officer

PROVIDENCE HEALTH AND SERVICES - SOUTHERN CALIFORNIA
Regional Administration, 20555 Earl Street, Torrance, CA, Zip 90503–3006; tel. 310/793–8087; Erik G. Wexler, Chief Executive Officer

PROVIDENCE HOLY CROSS MEDICAL CENTER, 15031 Rinaldi Street, Mission Hills, CA, Zip 91345–1207; tel. 818/365–8051; Bernard Klein, M.D., Chief Executive

PROVIDENCE LITTLE COMPANY OF MARY MEDICAL CENTER - TORRANCE, 4101 Torrance Boulevard, Torrance, CA, Zip 90503–4664; tel. 310/540–7676; Mary E. Kingston, FACHE, R.N., Chief Executive Officer, South Bay Community

PROVIDENCE LITTLE COMPANY OF MARY MEDICAL CENTER SAN PEDRO, 1300 West Seventh Street, San Pedro, CA, Zip 90732–3505; tel. 310/832–3311; Mary E. Kingston, FACHE, R.N., Chief Executive Officer

PROVIDENCE SAINT JOHN'S HEALTH CENTER, 2121 Santa Monica Boulevard, Santa Monica, CA, Zip 90404–2091; tel. 310/829–5511; Marcel C. Loh, FACHE, Chief Executive Officer

PROVIDENCE SAINT JOSEPH MEDICAL CENTER, 501 South Buena Vista Street, Burbank, CA, Zip 91505–4866; tel. 818/843–5111; Kelly Linden, Chief Executive Officer

PROVIDENCE TARZANA MEDICAL CENTER, 18321 Clark Street, Tarzana, CA, Zip 91356–3521; tel. 818/881–0800; Dale Surowitz, Chief Executive

ST. JOSEPH HOAG HEALTH
3345 Michelson Drive, Suite 100, Irvine, CA, Zip 92612–0693; tel. 949/381–4019; Richard Afable, M.D., M.P.H., President and Chief Executive Officer

HOAG MEMORIAL HOSPITAL PRESBYTERIAN, One Hoag Drive, Newport Beach, CA, Zip 92663–4120, P O Box 6100, 92658–6100, tel. 949/764–4624; Robert Braithwaite, President and Chief Executive Officer

MISSION HOSPITAL, 27700 Medical Center Road, Mission Viejo, CA, Zip 92691–6474; tel. 949/364–1400; Tarek Salaway, Chief Executive

ST. JOSEPH HOSPITAL, 1100 West Stewart Drive, Orange, CA, Zip 92868–3849, P O Box 5600, 92863–5600, tel. 714/633–9111; Steven C. Moreau, President and Chief Executive Officer

ST. MARY MEDICAL CENTER, 18300 Highway 18, Apple Valley, CA, Zip 92307–2206, P O Box 7025, 92307–0725, tel. 760/242–2311; Alan H. Garrett, President and Chief Executive Officer

COLORADO

CENTURA HEALTH
188 Inverness Drive West, Suite 500, Englewood, CO, Zip 80112–5204; tel. 303/290–6500; Peter D. Banko, FACHE, President and Chief Executive Officer

AVISTA ADVENTIST HOSPITAL, 100 Health Park Drive, Louisville, CO, Zip 80027–9583; tel. 303/673–1000; Brent Davis, Interim Chief Executive Officer

CASTLE ROCK ADVENTIST HOSPITAL, 2350 Meadows Boulevard, Castle Rock, CO, Zip 80109–8405; tel. 720/455–5000; Todd Folkenberg, Chief Executive Officer

LITTLETON ADVENTIST HOSPITAL, 7700 South Broadway Street, Littleton, CO, Zip 80122–2628; tel. 303/730–8900; Brett Spenst, Chief Executive Officer

PARKER ADVENTIST HOSPITAL, 9395 Crown Crest Boulevard, Parker, CO, Zip 80138–8573; tel. 303/269–4000; Sam D. Huenergardt, Chief Executive Officer

PENROSE-ST. FRANCIS HEALTH SERVICES, 2222 North Nevada Avenue, Colorado Springs, CO, Zip 80907–6799; tel. 719/776–5000; Margaret D. Sabin, President and Chief Executive Officer

PORTER ADVENTIST HOSPITAL, 2525 South Downing Street, Denver, CO, Zip 80210–5876; tel. 303/778–1955; Morre Dean, Chief Executive Officer

ST. ANTHONY HOSPITAL, 11600 West Second Place, Lakewood, CO, Zip 80228–1527; tel. 720/321–0000; Edward H. Sim, Chief Executive Officer

ST. ANTHONY NORTH HEALTH CAMPUS, 14300 Orchard Parkway, Westminster, CO, Zip 80023–9206; tel. 720/627–0000; Kevin Jenkins, President and Chief Executive Officer

ST. ANTHONY SUMMIT MEDICAL CENTER, 340 Peak One Drive, Frisco, CO, Zip 80443, P O Box 738, 80443–0738, tel. 970/668–3300; Paul J. Chodkowski, President and Chief Executive Officer

ST. MARY-CORWIN MEDICAL CENTER, 1008 Minnequa Avenue, Pueblo, CO, Zip 81004–3798; tel. 719/557–4000; Brian Moore, President and Chief Executive Officer

ST. THOMAS MORE HOSPITAL, 1338 Phay Avenue, Canon City, CO, Zip 81212–2302; tel. 719/285–2000; Sheri Trahern, CPA, FACHE, Chief Executive Officer

ST. VINCENT GENERAL HOSPITAL DISTRICT, 822 West 4th Street, Leadville, CO, Zip 80461–3897; tel. 719/486–0230; Gary Campbell, Chief Executive Officer

COMMUNITY HEALTH PROVIDERS ORGANIZATION
2021 North 12th Street, Grand Junction, CO, Zip 81501–2980; tel. 970/256–6200; Chris Thomas, FACHE, President and Chief Executive Officer

COMMUNITY HOSPITAL, 2351 G Road, Grand Junction, CO, Zip 81505; tel. 970/242–0920; Chris Thomas, FACHE, President and Chief Executive Officer

HCA HEALTHONE, LLC
4900 South Monaco Street, Suite 380, Denver, CO, Zip 80237–3487; tel. 303/788–2500; Sylvia Young, President

MEDICAL CENTER OF AURORA, 1501 South Potomac Street, Aurora, CO, Zip 80012–5411; tel. 303/695–2600; Daniel Miller, FACHE, President and Chief Executive Officer

NORTH SUBURBAN MEDICAL CENTER, 9191 Grant Street, Thornton, CO, Zip 80229–4341; tel. 303/451–7800; Jennifer Alderfer, President and Chief Executive Officer

PRESBYTERIAN-ST. LUKE'S MEDICAL CENTER, 1719 East 19th Avenue, Denver, CO, Zip 80218–1281; tel. 303/839–6000; Maureen Tarrant, President and Chief Executive Officer

ROSE MEDICAL CENTER, 4567 East Ninth Avenue, Denver, CO, Zip 80220–3941; tel. 303/320–2121; Kenneth H. Feiler, President and Chief Executive Officer

SKY RIDGE MEDICAL CENTER, 10101 Ridge Gate Parkway, Lone Tree, CO, Zip 80124–5522; tel. 720/225–1000; Susan Hicks, Chief Executive Officer

SPALDING REHABILITATION HOSPITAL, 900 Potomac Steet, Aurora, CO, Zip 80011–6716; tel. 303/367–1166; Daniel Miller, FACHE, President and Chief Executive Officer

SWEDISH MEDICAL CENTER, 501 East Hampden Avenue, Englewood, CO, Zip 80113–2702; tel. 303/788–5000; Richard A. Hammett, President and Chief Executive Officer

CONNECTICUT

EASTERN CONNECTICUT HEALTH NETWORK
71 Haynes Street, Manchester, CT, Zip 06040–4131; tel. 860/533–3400; Michael F. Collins, Interim President and Chief Executive Officer

MANCHESTER MEMORIAL HOSPITAL, 71 Haynes Street, Manchester, CT, Zip 06040–4188; tel. 860/646–1222; Peter J. Karl, President and Chief Executive Officer

ROCKVILLE GENERAL HOSPITAL, 31 Union Street, Vernon, CT, Zip 06066–3160; tel. 860/872–0501; Peter J. Karl, President and Chief Executive Officer

FLORIDA

BAYCARE HEALTH SYSTEM
2985 Drew Street, Clearwater, FL, Zip 33759–3012; tel. 877/692–2922; Tommy Inzina, President and Chief Executive Officer

BARTOW REGIONAL MEDICAL CENTER, 2200 Osprey Boulevard, Bartow, FL, Zip 33830–3308; tel. 863/533–8111; Philip Minden, Chief Executive Officer

BAYCARE ALLIANT HOSPITAL, 601 Main Street, MS#402, Dunedin, FL, Zip 34698–5848; tel. 727/736–9991; Jacqueline Arocho, Administrator

MEASE COUNTRYSIDE HOSPITAL, 3231 McMullen Booth Road, Safety Harbor, FL, Zip 34695–6607; tel. 727/725–6111; Lou Galdieri, R.N., President

MEASE DUNEDIN HOSPITAL, 601 Main Street, Dunedin, FL, Zip 34698–5891; tel. 727/733–1111; Lou Galdieri, R.N., President

MORTON PLANT HOSPITAL, 300 Pinellas Street, Clearwater, FL, Zip 33756–3804, P O Box 210, 33757–0210, tel. 727/462–7000; N. Kristopher. Hoce, President

MORTON PLANT NORTH BAY HOSPITAL, 6600 Madison Street, New Port Richey, FL, Zip 34652–1900; tel. 727/842–8468; Sarah Naumowich, Interim President

SOUTH FLORIDA BAPTIST HOSPITAL, 301 North Alexander Street, Plant City, FL, Zip 33563–4303; tel. 813/757–1200; Karen Kerr, R.N., President

ST. ANTHONY'S HOSPITAL, 1200 Seventh Avenue North, Saint Petersburg, FL, Zip 33705–1388, P O Box 12588, 33733–2588, tel. 727/825–1100; M. Scott Smith, President

ST. JOSEPH'S HOSPITAL, 3001 West Martin Luther King Jr. Boulevard, Tampa, FL, Zip 33607–6387, P O Box 4227, 33677–4227, tel. 813/870–4000; Kimberly Guy, President

WINTER HAVEN HOSPITAL, 200 Avenue F NE, Winter Haven, FL, Zip 33881–4193; tel. 863/293–1121; Stephen A. Nierman, President

GEORGIA

ST. JOSEPH'S/CANDLER HEALTH SYSTEM, INC.
5353 Reynolds Street, Savannah, GA, Zip 31405–6015; tel. 912/819–6000; Paul P. Hinchey, President and Chief Executive Officer

APPLING HEALTHCARE SYSTEM, 163 East Tollison Street, Baxley, GA, Zip 31513–0120; tel. 912/367–9841; Raymond J. Leadbetter, Jr., Interim Chief Executive Officer

CANDLER HOSPITAL, 5353 Reynolds Street, Savannah, GA, Zip 31405–6015; tel. 912/819–6000; Paul P. Hinchey, President and Chief Executive Officer

EFFINGHAM HOSPITAL, 459 Highway 119 South, Springfield, GA, Zip 31329–3021, P O Box 386, 31329–0386, tel. 912/754–6451; Francine Baker-Witt, R.N., Interim Chief Executive Officer

EMORY UNIVERSITY HOSPITAL, 1364 Clifton Road NE, Atlanta, GA, Zip 30322; tel. 404/712–2000; Bryce D. Gartland, M.D., Chief Executive Officer

LIBERTY REGIONAL MEDICAL CENTER, 462 Elma G Miles Parkway, Hinesville, GA, Zip 31313–4000, P O Box 919, 31310–0919, tel. 912/369–9400; Michael Hester, Chief Executive Officer

MEADOWS REGIONAL MEDICAL CENTER, One Meadows Parkway, Vidalia, GA, Zip 30474–8759, P O Box 1048, 30475–1048, tel. 912/535–5555; Alan Kent, Chief Executive Officer

ST. JOSEPH'S HOSPITAL, 11705 Mercy Boulevard, Savannah, GA, Zip 31419–1791; tel. 912/819–4100; Paul P. Hinchey, President and Chief Executive Officer

IDAHO

THE HOSPITAL COOPERATIVE
500 South 11th Avenue Suite 503, Pocatello, ID, Zip 83201–4881; tel. 208/239–1951; Jon Smith, Executive Director

BEAR LAKE MEMORIAL HOSPITAL, 164 South Fifth Street, Montpelier, ID, Zip 83254–1597; tel. 208/847–1630; Dennis Carlson, Chief Executive Officer

BINGHAM MEMORIAL HOSPITAL, 98 Poplar Street, Blackfoot, ID, Zip 83221–1799; tel. 208/785–4100; D. Jeffery. Daniels, Chief Executive Officer

CARIBOU MEMORIAL HOSPITAL AND LIVING CENTER, 300 South Third West, Soda Springs, ID, Zip 83276–1598; tel. 208/547–3341; Jon Smith, Chief Executive Officer

EASTERN IDAHO REGIONAL MEDICAL CENTER, 3100 Channing Way, Idaho Falls, ID, Zip 83404–7533, P O Box 2077, 83403–2077, tel. 208/529–6111; Douglas Crabtree, Chief Executive Officer

FRANKLIN COUNTY MEDICAL CENTER, 44 North First East Street, Preston, ID, Zip 83263–1399; tel. 208/852–0137; Richard Westerberg, Interim Chief Executive Officer

LOST RIVERS MEDICAL CENTER, 551 Highland Drive, Arco, ID, Zip 83213–9771, P O Box 145, 83213–0145, tel. 208/527–8206; Brad Huerta, Chief Executive Officer and Administrator

MADISON MEMORIAL HOSPITAL, 450 East Main Street, Rexburg, ID, Zip 83440–2048, P O Box 310, 83440–0310, tel. 208/359–6900; Rachel Ann. Gonzales, Chief Executive Officer

MINIDOKA MEMORIAL HOSPITAL, 1224 Eighth Street, Rupert, ID, Zip 83350–1599; tel. 208/436–0481; Tom Murphy, Chief Executive Officer

NELL J. REDFIELD MEMORIAL HOSPITAL, 150 North 200 West, Malad City, ID, Zip 83252–1239, Box 126, 83252–0126, tel. 208/766–2231; John Williams, Administrator and Chief Executive Officer

PORTNEUF MEDICAL CENTER, 777 Hospital Way, Pocatello, ID, Zip 83201–5175; tel. 208/239–1000; Daniel Ordyna, Chief Executive Officer

POWER COUNTY HOSPITAL DISTRICT, 510 Roosevelt Street, American Falls, ID, Zip 83211–1362, P O Box 420, 83211–0420, tel. 208/226–3200; Dallas Clinger, Administrator

STAR VALLEY MEDICAL CENTER, 901 Adams Street, Afton, WY, Zip 83110–9621, P O Box 579, 83110–0579, tel. 307/885–5800; Mike Hunsaker, Interim President and Chief Executive Officer

STEELE MEMORIAL MEDICAL CENTER, 203 South Daisy Street, Salmon, ID, Zip 83467–4709; tel. 208/756–5600; Jeanine Gentry, Chief Executive Officer

TETON VALLEY HEALTH CARE, 120 East Howard Street, Driggs, ID, Zip 83422–5112; tel. 208/354–2383; Keith Gnagey, Chief Executive Officer

ILLINOIS

AMITA HEALTH
120 North Oak Street, Hinsdale, IL, Zip 60521–3829; tel. 630/856–9000; Michael Goebel, FACHE, Vice President and Chief Executive Officer

AMITA HEALTH ADVENTIST MEDICAL CENTER - HINSDALE, 120 North Oak Street, Hinsdale, IL, Zip 60521–3890; tel. 630/856–6001; Michael Goebel, FACHE, Vice President and Chief Executive Officer

AMITA HEALTH ADVENTIST MEDICAL CENTER BOLINGBROOK, 500 Remington Boulevard, Bolingbrook, IL, Zip 60440–4906; tel. 630/312–5000; Rick Mace, Chief Executive Officer

AMITA HEALTH ADVENTIST MEDICAL CENTER GLENOAKS, 701 Winthrop Avenue, Glendale Heights, IL, Zip 60139–1403; tel. 630/545–8000; Bruce C. Christian, President and Chief Executive Officer

ADVENTIST LA GRANGE MEMORIAL HOSPITAL, 5101 South Willow Spring Road, La Grange, IL, Zip 60525–2600; tel. 708/245–9000; Michael Goebel, FACHE, Vice President and Chief Executive Officer

ALEXIAN BROTHERS BEHAVIORAL HEALTH HOSPITAL, 1650 Moon Lake Boulevard, Hoffman Estates, IL, Zip 60169–1010; tel. 847/882–1600; Clayton Ciha, President and Chief Executive Officer

MERCY HEALTH CORPORATION
2400 North Rockton Avenue, Rockford, IL, Zip 61103–3655; tel. 608/756–6000; Javon R. Bea, President and Chief Executive Officer

MERCYHEALTH HOSPITAL - ROCKTON AVENUE, 2400 North Rockton Avenue, Rockford, IL, Zip 61103–3655; tel. 815/971–5000; Javon R. Bea, President and Chief Executive Officer

MERCYHEALTH HOSPITAL AND MEDICAL CENTER - HARVARD, 901 Grant Street, Harvard, IL, Zip 60033–1898, P O Box 850, 60033–0850, tel. 815/943–5431; Javon R. Bea, Chief Executive Officer

MERCYHEALTH HOSPITAL AND MEDICAL CENTER - WALWORTH, N2950 State Road 67, Lake Geneva, WI, Zip 53147–2655; tel. 262/245–0535; Javon R. Bea, President and Chief Executive Officer

MERCYHEALTH HOSPITAL AND TRAUMA CENTER - JANESVILLE, 1000 Mineral Point Avenue, Janesville, WI, Zip 53548–2982, P O Box 5003, 53547–5003, tel. 608/756–6000; Javon R. Bea, President and Chief Executive Officer

INDIANA

LUTHERAN HEALTH NETWORK
7950 West Jefferson Boulevard, Fort Wayne, IN, Zip 46804–4140; tel. 260/435–7001; Michael Poore, Interim Chief Executive Officer

BLUFFTON REGIONAL MEDICAL CENTER, 303 South Main Street, Bluffton, IN, Zip 46714–2503; tel. 260/824–3210; Brent Parsons, Chief Executive Officer

DUKES MEMORIAL HOSPITAL, 275 West 12th Street, Peru, IN, Zip 46970–1638; tel. 765/472–8000; Debra Close, Chief Executive Officer

DUPONT HOSPITAL, 2520 East Dupont Road, Fort Wayne, IN, Zip 46825–1675; tel. 260/416–3000; Lisa Dolan, Interim Chief Executive Officer

KOSCIUSKO COMMUNITY HOSPITAL, 2101 East Dubois Drive, Warsaw, IN, Zip 46580–3288; tel. 574/267–3200; Kirk M. Ray, Chief Executive Officer

LUTHERAN HOSPITAL OF INDIANA, 7950 West Jefferson Boulevard, Fort Wayne, IN, Zip 46804–4140; tel. 260/435–7001; Michael Poore, Interim Chief Executive Officer

ORTHOPAEDIC HOSPITAL OF LUTHERAN HEALTH NETWORK, 7952 West Jefferson Boulevard, Fort Wayne, IN, Zip 46804–4140; tel. 260/435–2999; Lorie Ailor, Chief Executive Officer

REHABILITATION HOSPITAL OF FORT WAYNE, 7970 West Jefferson Boulevard, Fort Wayne, IN, Zip 46804–4140; tel. 260/435–6100; Shelley Boxell, R.N., Chief Nursing Officer and Interim Chief Operating Officer

ST. JOSEPH HOSPITAL, 700 Broadway, Fort Wayne, IN, Zip 46802–1493; tel. 260/425–3000; Vince Green, Interim Chief Administrative Officer

ST. VINCENT HEALTH
10330 North Meridian Street, Indianapolis, IN, Zip 46290; tel. 317/338–2273; Jonathan Nalli, Senior Vice President, Ascension Health and Indiana Ministry Market Executive

ST. VINCENT ANDERSON REGIONAL HOSPITAL, 2015 Jackson Street, Anderson, IN, Zip 46016–4339; tel. 765/649–2511; Mike Schroyer, FACHE, MSN, R.N., President

ST. VINCENT CARMEL HOSPITAL, 13500 North Meridian Street, Carmel, IN, Zip 46032–1456; tel. 317/582–7000; Michael D. Chittenden, President

ST. VINCENT CLAY HOSPITAL, 1206 East National Avenue, Brazil, IN, Zip 47834–2797, P O Box 489, 47834–0489, tel. 812/442–2500; Jerry Laue, Administrator

ST. VINCENT DUNN HOSPITAL, 1600 23rd Street, Bedford, IN, Zip 47421–4704; tel. 812/275–3331; Matt Balla, Chief Executive Officer

ST. VINCENT FISHERS HOSPITAL, 13861 Olio Road, Fishers, IN, Zip 46037–3487; tel. 317/415–9000; Gary Fammartino, Administrator

ST. VINCENT HEART CENTER, 10580 North Meridian Street, Indianapolis, IN, Zip 46290–1028; tel. 317/583–5000; Blake A. Dye, President

ST. VINCENT INDIANAPOLIS HOSPITAL, 2001 West 86th Street, Indianapolis, IN, Zip 46260–1991, P O Box 40970, 46240–0970, tel. 317/338–2345; Joel Feldman, Regional President

ST. VINCENT JENNINGS HOSPITAL, 301 Henry Street, North Vernon, IN, Zip 47265–1097; tel. 812/352–4200; Jessica Kietzman, R.N., Interim Administrator

ST. VINCENT MEDICAL CENTER OF EVANSVILLE, 3700 Washington Avenue, Evansville, IN, Zip 47714–0541; tel. 812/485–4000; Daniel A. Parod, Interim President

ST. VINCENT MERCY HOSPITAL, 1331 South 'A' Street, Elwood, IN, Zip 46036–1942; tel. 765/552–4600; Francis G. Albarano, Administrator

ST. VINCENT RANDOLPH HOSPITAL, 473 Greenville Avenue, Winchester, IN, Zip 47394–9436; tel. 765/584–0004; Francis G. Albarano, Administrator

ST. VINCENT SALEM HOSPITAL, 911 North Shelby Street, Salem, IN, Zip 47167–1694; tel. 812/883–5881; Dana M. Muntz, Chief Executive Officer

ST. VINCENT SETON SPECIALTY HOSPITAL, 8050 Township Line Road, Indianapolis, IN, Zip 46260–2478; tel. 317/415–8500; Joel Feldman, Regional President

ST. VINCENT WARRICK HOSPITAL, 1116 Millis Avenue, Boonville, IN, Zip 47601–2204; tel. 812/897–4800; Kathy J. Hall, Administrator

ST. VINCENT WILLIAMSPORT HOSPITAL, 412 North Monroe Street, Williamsport, IN, Zip 47993–1049; tel. 765/762–4000; Jane Craigin, Chief Executive Officer

SUBURBAN HEALTH ORGANIZATION
2780 Waterfront Parkway East Drive, Suite 300, Indianapolis, IN, Zip 46214; tel. 317/692–5222; Dave Lippincott, President

HANCOCK REGIONAL HOSPITAL, 801 North State Street, Greenfield, IN, Zip 46140–1270, P O Box 827, 46140–0827, tel. 317/462–5544; Steven V. Long, FACHE, President and Chief Executive Officer

HENDRICKS REGIONAL HEALTH, 1000 East Main Street, Danville, IN, Zip 46122–1948, P O Box 409, 46122–0409, tel. 317/745–4451; Kevin Speer, Chief Executive Officer

HENRY COUNTY HOSPITAL, 1000 North 16th Street, New Castle, IN, Zip 47362–4319, P O Box 490, 47362–0490, tel. 765/521–0890; Paul Janssen, President and Chief Executive Officer

JOHNSON MEMORIAL HOSPITAL, 1125 West Jefferson Street, Franklin, IN, Zip 46131–2140, P O Box 549, 46131–0549, tel. 317/736–3300; Larry Heydon, President and Chief Executive Officer

MAJOR HOSPITAL, 150 West Washington Street, Shelbyville, IN, Zip 46176–1236, 2451 Intelliplex Drive, 46176, tel. 317/392–3211; John M. Horner, President and Chief Executive Officer

MARGARET MARY HEALTH, 321 Mitchell Avenue, Batesville, IN, Zip 47006–8909, P O Box 226, 47006–0226, tel. 812/934–6624; Timothy L. Putnam, FACHE, President and Chief Executive Officer

RIVERVIEW HEALTH, 395 Westfield Road, Noblesville, IN, Zip 46060–1425, P O Box 220, 46061–0220, tel. 317/773–0760; Seth Warren, President and Chief Executive Officer

RUSH MEMORIAL HOSPITAL, 1300 North Main Street, Rushville, IN, Zip 46173–1198, P O Box 608, 46173–0608, tel. 765/932–4111; Bradley Smith, President and Chief Executive Officer

WITHAM HEALTH SERVICES, 2605 North Lebanon Street, Lebanon, IN, Zip 46052–1476, P O Box 1200, 46052–3005, tel. 765/485–8000; Raymond V. Ingham, Ph.D., President and Chief Executive Officer

IOWA

GENESIS HEALTH SYSTEM
1227 East Rusholme Street, Davenport, IA, Zip 52803–2459; tel. 563/421–1000; Douglas P. Cropper, President and Chief Executive Officer

GENESIS MEDICAL CENTER, DEWITT, 1118 11th Street, De Witt, IA, Zip 52742–1296; tel. 563/659–4200; Curt Coleman, FACHE, Chief Executive Officer

GENESIS MEDICAL CENTER, SILVIS, 801 Illini Drive, Silvis, IL, Zip 61282–1893; tel. 309/281–4000; Theresa Summers-Main, R.N., Interim President

GENESIS MEDICAL CENTER-ALEDO, 409 NW Ninth Avenue, Aledo, IL, Zip 61231–1296; tel. 309/582–9100; Ted Rogalski, Administrator

GENESIS MEDICAL CENTER-DAVENPORT-WEST CENTRAL PARK, 1227 East Rusholme Street, Davenport, IA, Zip 52803–2498; tel. 563/421–1000; Jordan Voigt, Administrator

MERCY HEALTH NETWORK - CENTRAL IOWA
1755 59th Place, West Des Moines, IA, Zip 50266–7737; tel. 515/358–8027; Michael Trachta, Vice President Network CAH Operations

ADAIR COUNTY HEALTH SYSTEM, 609 SE Kent Street, Greenfield, IA, Zip 50849–9454; tel. 641/743–2123; Marcia Hendricks, R.N., FACHE, Interim Chief Executive Officer

AUDUBON COUNTY MEMORIAL HOSPITAL, 515 Pacific Street, Audubon, IA, Zip 50025–1056; tel. 712/563–2611; Suzanne Cooner, R.N., MSN, Chief Executive Officer

BOONE COUNTY HOSPITAL, 1015 Union Street, Boone, IA, Zip 50036–4821; tel. 515/432–3140; Joseph S. Smith, Chief Executive Officer

CENTRAL COMMUNITY HOSPITAL, 901 Davidson Street NW, Elkader, IA, Zip 52043–9015; tel. 563/245–7000; Brooke Kensinger, Chief Executive Officer

DALLAS COUNTY HOSPITAL, 610 10th Street, Perry, IA, Zip 50220–2221; tel. 515/465–3547; Angela Mortoza, Chief Executive Officer

DAVIS COUNTY HOSPITAL, 509 North Madison Street, Bloomfield, IA, Zip 52537–1271; tel. 641/664–2145; Kirby Johnson, Chief Executive Officer

DECATUR COUNTY HOSPITAL, 1405 NW Church Street, Leon, IA, Zip 50144–1299; tel. 641/446–4871; Greg Boattenhamer, Chief Executive Officer

KNOXVILLE HOSPITAL & CLINICS, 1002 South Lincoln Street, Knoxville, IA, Zip 50138–3155; tel. 641/842–2151; Kevin Kincaid, Chief Executive Officer

MADISON COUNTY HEALTH CARE SYSTEM, 300 West Hutchings Street, Winterset, IA, Zip 50273–2109; tel. 515/462–2373; Marcia Hendricks, R.N., FACHE, Chief Executive Officer

MANNING REGIONAL HEALTHCARE CENTER, 1550 6th Street, Manning, IA, Zip 51455–1093; tel. 712/655–2072; John O'Brien, Chief Executive Officer

MERCY MEDICAL CENTER-CENTERVILLE, 1 St Joseph's Drive, Centerville, IA, Zip 52544–8055; tel. 641/437–4111; Clinton J. Christianson, FACHE, President

MERCY MEDICAL CENTER-DES MOINES, 1111 6th Avenue, Des Moines, IA, Zip 50314–2611; tel. 515/247–3121; Robert P. Ritz, President

MONROE COUNTY HOSPITAL AND CLINICS, 6580 165th Street, Albia, IA, Zip 52531–8793; tel. 641/932–2134; Veronica Fuhs, Chief Executive Officer

RINGGOLD COUNTY HOSPITAL, 504 North Cleveland Street, Mount Ayr, IA, Zip 50854–2201; tel. 641/464–3226; Gordon W. Winkler, Administrator and Chief Executive Officer

SKIFF MEDICAL CENTER, 204 North Fourth Avenue East, Newton, IA, Zip 50208–3100, P O Box 1006, 50208–1006, tel. 641/792–1273; Laurie A. Conner, FACHE, Interim Chief Executive Officer

VAN DIEST MEDICAL CENTER, 2350 Hospital Drive, Webster City, IA, Zip 50595–6600, P O Box 430, 50595–0430, tel. 515/832–9400; Michael Trachta, Interim Chief Executive Officer

WAYNE COUNTY HOSPITAL, 417 South East Street, Corydon, IA, Zip 50060–1860, P O Box 305, 50060–0305, tel. 641/872–2260; Daren Relph, Chief Executive Officer

MERCY HEALTH NETWORK - NORTH IOWA
1000 4th Street SW, Mason City, IA, Zip 50401–2800; tel. 641/428–7000; Daniel Varnum, Chief Executive Officer

FRANKLIN GENERAL HOSPITAL, 1720 Central Avenue East, Suite A, Hampton, IA, Zip 50441–1867; tel. 641/456–5000; Kim Price, Chief Executive Officer

HANCOCK COUNTY HEALTH SYSTEM, 532 First Street NW, Britt, IA, Zip 50423–1227; tel. 641/843–5000; Jeffry Stampohar, Chief Executive Officer

HANSEN FAMILY HOSPITAL, 920 South Oak, Iowa Falls, IA, Zip 50126–9506; tel. 641/648–4631; Cherelle Montanye-Ireland, Chief Executive Officer

KOSSUTH REGIONAL HEALTH CENTER, 1515 South Phillips Street, Algona, IA, Zip 50511–3649; tel. 515/295–2451; Scott A. Curtis, Administrator and Chief Executive Officer

MERCY MEDICAL CENTER-NEW HAMPTON, 308 North Maple Avenue, New Hampton, IA, Zip 50659–1142; tel. 641/394–4121; Aaron Flugum, Chief Executive Officer

MERCY MEDICAL CENTER-NORTH IOWA, 1000 Fourth Street SW, Mason City, IA, Zip 50401–2800; tel. 641/428–7000; Daniel Varnum, President and Chief Executive Officer

MITCHELL COUNTY REGIONAL HEALTH CENTER, 616 North Eighth Street, Osage, IA, Zip 50461–1498; tel. 641/732–6000; Shelly Russell, Chief Executive Officer

PALO ALTO COUNTY HEALTH SYSTEM, 3201 First Street, Emmetsburg, IA, Zip 50536–2516; tel. 712/852–5500; Charles P. Kelch, Interim Chief Executive Officer

REGIONAL HEALTH SERVICES OF HOWARD COUNTY, 235 Eighth Avenue West, Cresco, IA, Zip 52136–1098; tel. 563/547–2101; Robin M. Schluter, Chief Executive Officer

KANSAS

HAYS MEDICAL CENTER
2220 Canterbury Drive, Hays, KS, Zip 67601–2370; tel. 785/623–2300; John H. Jeter, M.D., President and Chief Executive Officer

PAWNEE VALLEY COMMUNITY HOSPITAL, 923 Carroll Avenue, Larned, KS, Zip 67550–2429; tel. 620/285–3161; Eric Lybarger, Administrator

HEALTH INNOVATIONS NETWORK OF KANSAS
1500 SW 10th Avenue, Topeka, KS, Zip 66604–1301; tel. 785/354–6137; Kristi Gosser, Network Operations Director

ATCHISON HOSPITAL, 800 Raven Hill Drive, Atchison, KS, Zip 66002–9204; tel. 913/367–2131; John L. Jacobson, Chief Executive Officer

CLAY COUNTY MEDICAL CENTER, 617 Liberty Street, Clay Center, KS, Zip 67432–1564, P O Box 512, 67432–0512, tel. 785/632–2144; Austin M. Gillard, Chief Executive Officer

COFFEY COUNTY HOSPITAL, 801 North 4th Street, Burlington, KS, Zip 66839–2602; tel. 620/364–2121; Leonard Hernandez, Chief Executive Officer

COMMUNITY HEALTHCARE SYSTEM, 120 West Eighth Street, Onaga, KS, Zip 66521–9574; tel. 785/889–4272; Todd Willert, Chief Executive Officer

F. W. HUSTON MEDICAL CENTER, 408 Delaware Street, Winchester, KS, Zip 66097–4003; tel. 913/774–4340; LaMont Cook, Administrator

GEARY COMMUNITY HOSPITAL, 1102 St Mary's Road, Junction City, KS, Zip 66441–4196, P O Box 490, 66441–0490, tel. 785/238–4131; Joseph Stratton, FACHE, Chief Executive Officer

HERINGTON MUNICIPAL HOSPITAL, 100 East Helen Street, Herington, KS, Zip 67449–1606; tel. 785/258–2207; Alan Meisinger, Chief Financial Officer

HIAWATHA COMMUNITY HOSPITAL, 300 Utah Street, Hiawatha, KS, Zip 66434–2314; tel. 785/742–2131; Jeffrey Shelton, Chief Executive Officer

HORTON COMMUNITY HOSPITAL, 240 West 18th Street, Horton, KS, Zip 66439–1245; tel. 785/486–2642; James D. Noble, Chief Executive Officer

IRWIN ARMY COMMUNITY HOSPITAL, 600 Caisson Hill Road, Junction City, KS, Zip 66442–7037; tel. 785/239–7000; Colonel, Risa Ware, Commander

KANSAS REHABILITATION HOSPITAL, 1504 SW Eighth Avenue, Topeka, KS, Zip 66606–1632; tel. 785/235–5600; William J. Overbey, Chief Executive Officer

MORRIS COUNTY HOSPITAL, 600 North Washington Street, Council Grove, KS, Zip 66846–1422; tel. 620/767–6811; Rita K. Buurman, Interim Chief Executive Officer

NEMAHA VALLEY COMMUNITY HOSPITAL, 1600 Community Drive, Seneca, KS, Zip 66538–9739; tel. 785/336–6181; Kiley Floyd, Chief Executive Officer

NEWMAN REGIONAL HEALTH, 1201 West 12th Avenue, Emporia, KS, Zip 66801–2597; tel. 620/343–6800; Robert N. Wright, Chief Executive Officer

SABETHA COMMUNITY HOSPITAL, 14th and Oregon Streets, Sabetha, KS, Zip 66534–0229, P O Box 229, 66534–0229, tel. 785/284–2121; Lora Key, Chief Executive Officer

STORMONT VAIL HEALTH, 1500 SW Tenth Avenue, Topeka, KS, Zip 66604–1353; tel. 785/354–6000; Randall Peterson, President and Chief Executive Officer

VIA CHRISTI HOSPITAL MANHATTAN, INC., 1823 College Avenue, Manhattan, KS, Zip 66502–3346; tel. 785/776–3322; Robert C. Copple, FACHE, Senior Administrator

WAMEGO HEALTH CENTER, 711 Genn Drive, Wamego, KS, Zip 66547–1179; tel. 785/456–2295; Steve Land, Senior Administrator

WASHINGTON COUNTY HOSPITAL, 304 East Third Street, Washington, KS, Zip 66968–2033; tel. 785/325–2211; Roxanne Schottel, Chief Executive Officer

MED-OP, INC.
220 Canterbury Drive, Hays, KS, Zip 67601; tel. 785/623–2301; Shae Veach, Executive Director

CITIZENS MEDICAL CENTER, 100 East College Drive, Colby, KS, Zip 67701–3799; tel. 785/462–7511; Greg Unruh, Chief Executive Officer

CLARA BARTON HOSPITAL, 250 West Ninth Street, Hoisington, KS, Zip 67544–1706; tel. 620/653–2114; James Blackwell, President and Chief Executive Officer

GOODLAND REGIONAL MEDICAL CENTER, 220 West Second Street, Goodland, KS, Zip 67735–1602; tel. 785/890–3625; William Widener, Chief Executive Officer

GOVE COUNTY MEDICAL CENTER, 520 West Fifth Street, Quinter, KS, Zip 67752–0129, P O Box 129, 67752–0129, tel. 785/754–3341; Coleen Tummons, Chief Executive Officer

GRAHAM COUNTY HOSPITAL, 304 West Prout Street, Hill City, KS, Zip 67642–1435; tel. 785/421–2121; Melissa Atkins, CPA, Chief Executive Officer

HAYS MEDICAL CENTER, 2220 Canterbury Drive, Hays, KS, Zip 67601–2370, P O Box 8100, 67601–8100, tel. 785/623–5000; John H. Jeter, M.D., President and Chief Executive Officer

LOGAN COUNTY HOSPITAL, 211 Cherry Street, Oakley, KS, Zip 67748–1201; tel. 785/672–3211; Meldon L. Snow, Chief Executive Officer

NESS COUNTY HOSPITAL DISTRICT NO 2, 312 Custer Street, Ness City, KS, Zip 67560–1654; tel. 785/798–2291; Curt Thomas, Administrator

NORTON COUNTY HOSPITAL, 102 East Holme, Norton, KS, Zip 67654–1406, P O Box 250, 67654–0250, tel. 785/877–3351; Ryan Stover, Chief Executive Officer

PAWNEE VALLEY COMMUNITY HOSPITAL, 923 Carroll Avenue, Larned, KS, Zip 67550–2429; tel. 620/285–3161; Eric Lybarger, Administrator

ROOKS COUNTY HEALTH CENTER, 1210 North Washington Street, Plainville, KS, Zip 67663–1632, P O Box 389, 67663–0389, tel. 785/434–4553; Frank A. Rajewski, Chief Financial Officer and Interim Chief Executive Officer

RUSH COUNTY MEMORIAL HOSPITAL, 801 Locust Street, La Crosse, KS, Zip 67548–9673, P O Box 520, 67548–0520, tel. 785/222–2545; Brenda Legleiter, R.N., Chief Executive Officer

RUSSELL REGIONAL HOSPITAL, 200 South Main Street, Russell, KS, Zip 67665–2920; tel. 785/483–3131

SCOTT COUNTY HOSPITAL, 201 East Albert Avenue, Scott City, KS, Zip 67871–1203; tel. 620/872–5811; Mark Burnett, President and Chief Executive Officer

SHERIDAN COUNTY HEALTH COMPLEX, 826 18th Street, Hoxie, KS, Zip 67740–0167, P O Box 167, 67740–0167, tel. 785/675–3281; Niceta Farber, Chief Executive Officer

PIONEER HEALTH NETWORK, INC.
310 East Walnut Street, Suite 210, Garden City, KS, Zip 67846–5565; tel. 620/276–6100; Mary Adam, Executive Director

BOB WILSON MEMORIAL GRANT COUNTY HOSPITAL, 415 North Main Street, Ulysses, KS, Zip 67880–2133; tel. 620/356–1266; Deanna Mustin, R.N., Administrator

CITIZENS MEDICAL CENTER, 100 East College Drive, Colby, KS, Zip 67701–3799; tel. 785/462–7511; Greg Unruh, Chief Executive Officer

EDWARDS COUNTY HOSPITAL AND HEALTHCARE CENTER, 620 West Eighth Street, Kinsley, KS, Zip 67547–2329, P O Box 99, 67547–0099, tel. 620/659–3621; Jimmie W. Hansel, Ph.D., Chief Executive Officer

GREELEY COUNTY HEALTH SERVICES, 506 Third Street, Tribune, KS, Zip 67879–9684, P O Box 338, 67879–0338, tel. 620/376–4221; Burke Kline, Chief Executive Officer

HAMILTON COUNTY HOSPITAL, 700 North Huser Street, Syracuse, KS, Zip 67878–0948, P O Box 948, 67878–0948, tel. 620/384–7461; Robert Whitaker, Chief Executive Officer

HODGEMAN COUNTY HEALTH CENTER, 809 Bramley Street, Jetmore, KS, Zip 67854–9320, P O Box 310, 67854–0310, tel. 620/357–8361; Teresa L. Deuel, Chief Executive Officer

KEARNY COUNTY HOSPITAL, 500 Thorpe Street, Lakin, KS, Zip 67860–9625; tel. 620/355–7111; Benjamin Anderson, Chief Executive Officer and Administrator

LANE COUNTY HOSPITAL, 235 West Vine, Dighton, KS, Zip 67839–0969, P O Box 969, 67839–0969, tel. 620/397–5321; Donna McGowan, Administrator

LOGAN COUNTY HOSPITAL, 211 Cherry Street, Oakley, KS, Zip 67748–1201; tel. 785/672–3211; Meldon L. Snow, Chief Executive Officer

MEADE DISTRICT HOSPITAL, 510 East Carthage Street, Meade, KS, Zip 67864–6401, P O Box 820, 67864–0820, tel. 620/873–2141; Steve Stewart, Administrator

MINNEOLA DISTRICT HOSPITAL, 212 Main Street, Minneola, KS, Zip 67865–8511, P O Box 127, 67865–0127, tel. 620/885–4264; Deborah Bruner, Chief Executive Officer and Administrator

MORTON COUNTY HEALTH SYSTEM, 445 Hilltop Street, Elkhart, KS, Zip 67950–0937, P O Box 937, 67950–0937, tel. 620/697–2141; Richard Q. Bergling, Chief Executive Officer

SATANTA DISTRICT HOSPITAL AND LONG TERM CARE, 401 South Cheyenne Street, Satanta, KS, Zip 67870–0159, P O Box 159, 67870–0159, tel. 620/649–2761; Jeremy Clingenpeel, Administrator

SCOTT COUNTY HOSPITAL, 201 East Albert Avenue, Scott City, KS, Zip 67871–1203; tel. 620/872–5811; Mark Burnett, President and Chief Executive Officer

SOUTHWEST MEDICAL CENTER, 315 West 15th Street, Liberal, KS, Zip 67901–2455, Box 1340, 67905–1340, tel. 620/624–1651; William Ermann, President and Chief Executive Officer

ST. CATHERINE HOSPITAL, 401 East Spruce Street, Garden City, KS, Zip 67846–5679; tel. 620/272–2561; Scott J. Taylor, President and Chief Executive Officer

STANTON COUNTY HOSPITAL, 404 North Chestnut Street, Johnson, KS, Zip 67855–5001, P O Box 779, 67855–0779, tel. 620/492–6250; Jay Tusten, Chief Executive Officer

STEVENS COUNTY HOSPITAL, 1006 South Jackson Street, Hugoton, KS, Zip 67951–2858, P O Box 10, 67951–0010, tel. 620/544–8511; Linda Stalcup, Chief Executive Officer

WICHITA COUNTY HEALTH CENTER, 211 East Earl Street, Leoti, KS, Zip 67861–9620; tel. 620/375–2233; Teresa Clark, Chief Executive Officer and Administrator

SUNFLOWER HEALTH NETWORK
400 South Santa Fe Avenue, Salina, KS, Zip 67401–4144; tel. 785/452–6102; Heather Fuller, Executive Director

ANTHONY MEDICAL CENTER, 1101 East Spring Street, Anthony, KS, Zip 67003–2122; tel. 620/842–5111; Lori Allen, Chief Financial Officer and Interim Chief Executive Officer

CLAY COUNTY MEDICAL CENTER, 617 Liberty Street, Clay Center, KS, Zip 67432–1564, P O Box 512, 67432–0512, tel. 785/632–2144; Austin M. Gillard, Chief Executive Officer

CLOUD COUNTY HEALTH CENTER, 1100 Highland Drive, Concordia, KS, Zip 66901–3923; tel. 785/243–1234; Cherri Waites, Chief Executive Officer

ELLSWORTH COUNTY MEDICAL CENTER, 1604 Aylward Street, Ellsworth, KS, Zip 67439–0087, P O Box 87, 67439–0087, tel. 785/472–3111; Roger A. Masse, FACHE, Chief Executive Officer

HERINGTON MUNICIPAL HOSPITAL, 100 East Helen Street, Herington, KS, Zip 67449–1606; tel. 785/258–2207; Alan Meisinger, Chief Financial Officer

HILLSBORO COMMUNITY HOSPITAL, 701 South Main Street, Hillsboro, KS, Zip 67063–1553; tel. 620/947–3114; Marion Regier, Chief Executive Officer

HOSPITAL DISTRICT NO 1 OF RICE COUNTY, 619 South Clark Street, Lyons, KS, Zip 67554–3003, P O Box 828, 67554–0828, tel. 620/257–5173; George M. Stover, Chief Executive Officer

JEWELL COUNTY HOSPITAL, 100 Crestvue Avenue, Mankato, KS, Zip 66956–2407, P O Box 327, 66956–0327, tel. 785/378–3137; Doyle L. McKimmy, FACHE, Chief Executive Officer

LINCOLN COUNTY HOSPITAL, 624 North Second Street, Lincoln, KS, Zip 67455–1738, P O Box 406, 67455–0406, tel. 785/524–4403; Steven L. Granzow, Chief Executive Officer

LINDSBORG COMMUNITY HOSPITAL, 605 West Lincoln Street, Lindsborg, KS, Zip 67456–2328; tel. 785/227–3308; Larry VanDerWege, Administrator

MEMORIAL HEALTH SYSTEM, 511 NE Tenth Street, Abilene, KS, Zip 67410–2153; tel. 785/263–2100; Harold Courtois, Chief Executive Officer

MITCHELL COUNTY HOSPITAL HEALTH SYSTEMS, 400 West Eighth, Beloit, KS, Zip 67420–1605, P O Box 399, 67420–0399, tel. 785/738–2266; Jeremy Armstrong, FACHE, Chief Executive Officer

OSBORNE COUNTY MEMORIAL HOSPITAL, 424 West New Hampshire Street, Osborne, KS, Zip 67473–2314, P O Box 70, 67473–0070, tel. 785/346–2121; Marianna Harris, Administrator

OTTAWA COUNTY HEALTH CENTER, 215 East Eighth, Minneapolis, KS, Zip 67467–1902, P O Box 290, 67467–0290, tel. 785/392–2122; Jody Parks, Administrator

REPUBLIC COUNTY HOSPITAL, 2420 'G' Street, Belleville, KS, Zip 66935–2400; tel. 785/527–2254; David-Paul Cavazos, Chief Executive Officer

SALINA REGIONAL HEALTH CENTER, 400 South Santa Fe Avenue, Salina, KS, Zip 67401–4198, P O Box 5080, 67402–5080, tel. 785/452–7000; Michael Terry, President and Chief Executive Officer

SMITH COUNTY MEMORIAL HOSPITAL, 614 South Main Street, Smith Center, KS, Zip 66967–3001; tel. 785/282–6845; Allen Van Driel, FACHE, Administrator

KENTUCKY

COMMONWEALTH HEALTH CORPORATION
800 Park Street, Bowling Green, KY, Zip 42101–2356; tel. 270/745–1500; Connie Smith, Chief Executive Officer

COMMONWEALTH REGIONAL SPECIALTY HOSPITAL, 250 Park Drive, 6th Floor, Bowling Green, KY, Zip 42101–1760, P O Box 90010, 42102–9010, tel. 270/796–6200; Christa Atkins, Administrator

MEDICAL CENTER AT BOWLING GREEN, 250 Park Street, Bowling Green, KY, Zip 42101–1795, P O Box 90010, 42102–9010, tel. 270/745–1000; Connie Smith, Chief Executive Officer

MEDICAL CENTER AT FRANKLIN, 1100 Brookhaven Road, Franklin, KY, Zip 42134–2746; tel. 270/598–4800; Annette Runyon, Vice President and Administrator

MEDICAL CENTER AT SCOTTSVILLE, 456 Burnley Road, Scottsville, KY, Zip 42164–6355; tel. 270/622–2800; Eric Hagan, R.N., Executive Vice President and Administrator

COMMUNITY CARE NETWORK
110 A Second Street, Henderson, KY, Zip 42420; tel. 619/278–2273; Roberta Alexander, Director

BAPTIST HEALTH MADISONVILLE, 900 Hospital Drive, Madisonville, KY, Zip 42431–1694; tel. 270/825–5100; Robert L. Ramey, President

BAPTIST HEALTH PADUCAH, 2501 Kentucky Avenue, Paducah, KY, Zip 42003–3200; tel. 270/575–2100; William A. Brown, FACHE, President and CEO

CALDWELL MEDICAL CENTER, 100 Medical Center Drive, Princeton, KY, Zip 42445–2430, P O Box 410, 42445–0410, tel. 270/365–0300; Kelley J. Rushing, Chief Executive Officer

CRITTENDEN COUNTY HOSPITAL, 520 West Gum Street, Marion, KY, Zip 42064–1516, P O Box 386, 42064–0386, tel. 270/965–5281; Lea Ann H. Klarner, Chief Executive Officer

HEALTHSOUTH DEACONESS REHABILITATION HOSPITAL, 4100 Covert Avenue, Evansville, IN, Zip 47714–5567, P O Box 5349, 47716–5349, tel. 812/476–9983; Blake Bunner, Chief Executive Officer

JENNIE STUART MEDICAL CENTER, 320 West 18th Street, Hopkinsville, KY, Zip 42240–1965, P O Box 2400, 42241–2400, tel. 270/887–0100; Eric A. Lee, President and Chief Executive Officer

LINCOLN TRAIL BEHAVIORAL HEALTH SYSTEM, 3909 South Wilson Road, Radcliff, KY, Zip 40160–8944, P O Box 369, 40159–0369, tel. 270/351–9444; Charles L. Webb, Jr., Chief Executive Officer

LIVINGSTON HOSPITAL AND HEALTHCARE SERVICES, 131 Hospital Drive, Salem, KY, Zip 42078–8043; tel. 270/988–2299; Kent Giles, Interim Chief Executive Officer

MEDICAL CENTER AT FRANKLIN, 1100 Brookhaven Road, Franklin, KY, Zip 42134–2746; tel. 270/598–4800; Annette Runyon, Vice President and Administrator

METHODIST HOSPITAL UNION COUNTY, 4604 Highway 60 West, Morganfield, KY, Zip 42437–9570; tel. 270/389–5000; Lynn R. Steinwachs, Vice President and Administrator

METHODIST HOSPITAL, 1305 North Elm Street, Henderson, KY, Zip 42420–2775, P O Box 48, 42419–0048, tel. 270/827–7700; Benny Nolen, President and Chief Executive Officer

MURRAY-CALLOWAY COUNTY HOSPITAL, 803 Poplar Street, Murray, KY, Zip 42071–2432; tel. 270/762–1100; Colonel, Jerome Penner, Chief Executive Officer

NORTON AUDUBON HOSPITAL, One Audubon Plaza Drive, Louisville, KY, Zip 40217–1300, P O Box 17550, 40217–0550, tel. 502/636–7111; Jon Cooper, Chief Administrative Officer

NORTON CHILDREN'S HOSPITAL, 231 East Chestnut Street, Louisville, KY, Zip 40202–1821; tel. 502/629–6000; Thomas D. Kmetz, Division President

NORTON HOSPITAL, 200 East Chestnut Street, Louisville, KY, Zip 40202–1800, P O Box 35070, 40232–5070, tel. 502/629–8000; Matthew Ayers, Chief Administrative Officer

NORTON WOMEN'S AND CHILDREN'S HOSPITAL, 4001 Dutchmans Lane, Louisville, KY, Zip 40207–4799; tel. 502/893–1000; Charlotte Ipsan, Chief Administrative Officer

OHIO COUNTY HOSPITAL, 1211 Main Street, Hartford, KY, Zip 42347–1619; tel. 270/298–7411; Blaine Pieper, Chief Executive Officer

OWENSBORO HEALTH MUHLENBERG COMMUNITY HOSPITAL, 440 Hopkinsville Street, Greenville, KY, Zip 42345–1172, P O Box 387, 42345–0378, tel. 270/338–8000; Ed Heath, FACHE, Chief Executive Officer

RIVERVALLEY BEHAVIORAL HEALTH HOSPITAL, 1000 Industrial Drive, Owensboro, KY, Zip 42301–8715; tel. 270/689–6500; Gayle DiCesare, President and Chief Executive Officer

SAINT THOMAS WEST HOSPITAL, 4220 Harding Road, Nashville, TN, Zip 37205–2095, P O Box 380, 37202–0380, tel. 615/222–2111; Don King, Chief Executive Officer

ST. VINCENT MEDICAL CENTER OF EVANSVILLE, 3700 Washington Avenue, Evansville, IN, Zip 47714–0541; tel. 812/485–4000; Daniel A. Parod, Interim President

STS. MARY & ELIZABETH HOSPITAL, 1850 Bluegrass Avenue, Louisville, KY, Zip 40215–1199; tel. 502/361–6000; Jennifer Nolan, President

TRIGG COUNTY HOSPITAL, 254 Main Street, Cadiz, KY, Zip 42211–9153, P O Box 312, 42211–0312, tel. 270/522–3215; John Sumner, Chief Executive Officer

KENTUCKYONE
200 Abraham Flexner Way, Louisville, KY, Zip 40202–2877; tel. 502/587–4011; Charles W. Neumann, Interim President and Chief Executive Officer

CONTINUING CARE HOSPITAL, 1 Saint Joseph Drive, Lexington, KY, Zip 40504–3742; tel. 859/967–5744; Jimmie Settles, Interim President and Chief Executive Officer

FLAGET MEMORIAL HOSPITAL, 4305 New Shepherdsville Road, Bardstown, KY, Zip 40004–9019; tel. 502/350–5000; Jennifer Nolan, President and Chief Executive Officer

FRAZIER REHAB INSTITUTE, 220 Abraham Flexner Way, Louisville, KY, Zip 40202–1887; tel. 502/582–7400; Cathy Spalding, Vice President of Operations

JEWISH HOSPITAL-SHELBYVILLE, 727 Hospital Drive, Shelbyville, KY, Zip 40065–1699; tel. 502/647–4000; Annessa Baker, Site Executive and Chief Nursing Officer

JEWISH HOSPITAL, 200 Abraham Flexner Way, Louisville, KY, Zip 40202–1886; tel. 502/587–4011; Ron Waldridge, II., M.D., President and Chief Medical Officer

OUR LADY OF PEACE, 2020 Newburg Road, Louisville, KY, Zip 40205–1879; tel. 502/479–4500; Jennifer Nolan, President

SAINT JOSEPH LONDON, 1001 Saint Joseph Lane, London, KY, Zip 40741–8345; tel. 606/330–6000; Terrence G. Deis, CPA, FACHE, President

SAINT JOSEPH - MARTIN, 11203 Main Street, Martin, KY, Zip 41649; tel. 606/285–6400; Kathy Stumbo, President

SAINT JOSEPH BEREA, 305 Estill Street, Berea, KY, Zip 40403–1909; tel. 859/986–3151; Eric Gilliam, President

SAINT JOSEPH EAST, 150 North Eagle Creek Drive, Lexington, KY, Zip 40509–1805; tel. 859/967–5000; Eric Gilliam, President

SAINT JOSEPH HOSPITAL, One St Joseph Drive, Lexington, KY, Zip 40504–3754; tel. 859/278–3436; Bruce J. Tassin, President

SAINT JOSEPH MOUNT STERLING, 225 Falcon Drive, Mount Sterling, KY, Zip 40353–1158, P O Box 7, 40353–0007, tel. 859/497–5000; Cinda Fluke, R.N., Interim Site Executive

SOUTHERN INDIANA REHABILITATION HOSPITAL, 3104 Blackiston Boulevard, New Albany, IN, Zip 47150–9579; tel. 812/941–8300; William Boso, Executive Director, Administrator

STS. MARY & ELIZABETH HOSPITAL, 1850 Bluegrass Avenue, Louisville, KY, Zip 40215–1199; tel. 502/361–6000; Jennifer Nolan, President

ST. ELIZABETH HEALTHCARE
1 Medical Village Drive, Edgewood, KY, Zip 41017–3403; tel. 859/301–2000; Garren Colvin, Chief Executive Officer

ST. ELIZABETH EDGEWOOD, 1 Medical Village Drive, Edgewood, KY, Zip 41017–3403; tel. 859/301–2000; Garren Colvin, Chief Executive Officer

ST. ELIZABETH FLORENCE, 4900 Houston Road, Florence, KY, Zip 41042–4824; tel. 859/212–5200; Garren Colvin, Chief Executive Officer

ST. ELIZABETH FORT THOMAS, 85 North Grand Avenue, Fort Thomas, KY, Zip 41075–1796; tel. 859/572–3100; Garren Colvin, Chief Executive Officer

ST. ELIZABETH GRANT, 238 Barnes Road, Williamstown, KY, Zip 41097–9482; tel. 859/824–8240; Garren Colvin, Chief Executive Officer

MAINE

MAINE NETWORK FOR HEALTH
Key Plaza, 23 Water Street, Bangor, ME, Zip 4401; tel. 207/942–2844; Stephen A. Ryan, President and Chief Executive Officer

BLUE HILL MEMORIAL HOSPITAL, 57 Water Street, Blue Hill, ME, Zip 04614–5231, P O Box 1029, 04614–1029, tel. 207/374–3400; John Ronan, President

CHARLES A. DEAN MEMORIAL HOSPITAL, 364 Pritham Avenue, Greenville, ME, Zip 04441–1395, P O Box 1129, 04441–1129, tel. 207/695–5200; Terri Vieira, Interim President

EASTERN MAINE MEDICAL CENTER, 489 State Street, Bangor, ME, Zip 04401–6674, P O Box 404, 04402–0404, tel. 207/973–7000; Donna Russell-Cook, FACHE, President

HOULTON REGIONAL HOSPITAL, 20 Hartford Street, Houlton, ME, Zip 04730–1891; tel. 207/532–9471; Thomas J. Moakler, Chief Executive Officer

INLAND HOSPITAL, 200 Kennedy Memorial Drive, Waterville, ME, Zip 04901–4595; tel. 207/861–3000; John Dalton, President and Chief Executive Officer

MAYO REGIONAL HOSPITAL, 897 West Main Street, Dover-Foxcroft, ME, Zip 04426–1099; tel. 207/564–8401; Marie E. Vienneau, FACHE, President and Chief Executive Officer

MILLINOCKET REGIONAL HOSPITAL, 200 Somerset Street, Millinocket, ME, Zip 04462–1298; tel. 207/723–5161; Robert Peterson, I., Chief Executive Officer

MOUNT DESERT ISLAND HOSPITAL, 10 Wayman Lane, Bar Harbor, ME, Zip 04609–1625, P O Box 8, 04609–0008, tel. 207/288–5081; Arthur J. Blank, President and Chief Executive Officer

NORTHERN MAINE MEDICAL CENTER, 194 East Main Street, Fort Kent, ME, Zip 04743–1497; tel. 207/834–3155; Peter Sirois, Chief Executive Officer

SEBASTICOOK VALLEY HEALTH, 447 North Main Street, Pittsfield, ME, Zip 04967–3707; tel. 207/487–4000; Terri Vieira, President and Chief Executive Officer

THE ACADIA HOSPITAL, 268 Stillwater Avenue, Bangor, ME, Zip 04401–3945, P O Box 422, 04402–0422, tel. 207/973–6100; Daniel B. Coffey, President and Chief Executive Officer

THE AROOSTOOK MEDICAL CENTER, 140 Academy Street, Presque Isle, ME, Zip 04769–3171, P O Box 151, 04769–0151, tel. 207/768–4000; Glenda E. Dwyer, Interim President

MASSACHUSETTS

LAHEY HEALTH
41 Mall Road, Burlington, MA, Zip 01805–0001; tel. 781/744–7100; Howard R. Grant, JD, M.D., President and Chief Executive Officer

BEVERLY HOSPITAL, 85 Herrick Street, Beverly, MA, Zip 01915–1777; tel. 978/922–3000; Philip M. Cormier, Chief Executive Officer

LAHEY HOSPITAL & MEDICAL CENTER, BURLINGTON, 41 Mall Road, Burlington, MA, Zip 01805–0001; tel. 781/744–5100; Howard R. Grant, JD, M.D., Chief Executive Officer

WINCHESTER HOSPITAL, 41 Highland Avenue, Winchester, MA, Zip 01890–1496; tel. 781/729–9000; Dale M. Lodge, Chief Executive Officer

WELLFORCE
1600 District Avenue, Suite 125, Burlington, MA, Zip 01803–5217; tel. 978/942–2220; Normand E. Deschene, FACHE, Chief Executive Officer

HALLMARK HEALTH SYSTEM, 585 Lebanon Street, Melrose, MA, Zip 02176–3225; tel. 781/979–3000; Alan G. Macdonald, President and Chief Executive Officer

LOWELL GENERAL HOSPITAL, 295 Varnum Avenue, Lowell, MA, Zip 01854–2134; tel. 978/937–6000; Joseph White, FACHE, President and Chief Executive Officer

TUFTS MEDICAL CENTER, 800 Washington Street, Boston, MA, Zip 02111–1552; tel. 617/636–5000; Michael Wagner, M.D., President and Chief Executive Officer

MICHIGAN

GENESYS HEALTH SYSTEM
1 Genesys Parkway, Grand Blanc, MI, Zip 48439–8065; tel. 810/606–5000; Elizabeth Aderholdt, Chief Executive Officer

ST. JOHN MACOMB-OAKLAND HOSPITAL, 11800 East 12 Mile Road, Warren, MI, Zip 48093–3472; tel. 586/573–5000; Terry Hamilton, President

ST. JOSEPH HEALTH SYSTEM, 200 Hemlock Street, Tawas City, MI, Zip 48763–9237, P O Box 659, 48764–0659, tel. 989/362–3411; Ann M. Balfour, R.N., President

ST. MARY'S OF MICHIGAN, 800 South Washington Avenue, Saginaw, MI, Zip 48601–2594; tel. 989/907–8000; Chris Palazzolo, Health System President and Chief Executive Officer Mid-Michigan

LAKELAND REGIONAL HEALTH SYSTEM
1234 Napier Avenue, Saint Joseph, MI, Zip 49085–2112; tel. 269/983–8300; Loren Hamel, M.D., President and Chief Executive Officer

LAKELAND HOSPITAL, WATERVLIET, 400 Medical Park Drive, Watervliet, MI, Zip 49098–9225; tel. 269/463–3111; Ray Cruse, Chief Executive Officer

LAKELAND MEDICAL CENTER, ST. JOSEPH, 1234 Napier Avenue, Saint Joseph, MI, Zip 49085–2158; tel. 269/983–8300; Loren Hamel, M.D., President and Chief Executive Officer

ST. JOHN PROVIDENCE HEALTH SYSTEM
28000 Dequindre Drive, Warren, MI, Zip 48092; tel. 866/501–3627; Jean Meyer, President and Chief Executive Officer

BRIGHTON CENTER FOR RECOVERY, 12851 Grand River Road, Brighton, MI, Zip 48116–8506; tel. 810/227–1211; Raymond A. Waller, Director

PROVIDENCE-PROVIDENCE PARK HOSPITALS, 16001 West Nine Mile Road, Southfield, MI, Zip 48075; tel. 248/849–3400; Joseph R. Hurshe, President

ST. JOHN HOSPITAL AND MEDICAL CENTER, 22101 Moross Road, Detroit, MI, Zip 48236–2148; tel. 313/343–4000; Robert E. Hoban, President

ST. JOHN MACOMB-OAKLAND HOSPITAL, 11800 East 12 Mile Road, Warren, MI, Zip 48093–3472; tel. 586/573–5000; Terry Hamilton, President

ST. JOHN RIVER DISTRICT HOSPITAL, 4100 River Road, East China, MI, Zip 48054–2909; tel. 810/329–7111; Kim Ronnisch, R.N., Vice President Nursing and Operations

UPPER PENINSULA HEALTH CARE NETWORK (UPHCN)
228 West Washington Street, Marquette, MI, Zip 49855–4330; tel. 906/225–3146; Dennis Smith, Chief Executive Officer

ASPIRUS IRON RIVER HOSPITALS & CLINICS, INC., 1400 West Ice Lake Road, Iron River, MI, Zip 49935–9526; tel. 906/265–6121; Connie L. Koutouzos, R.N., MSN, Chief Executive Officer

ASPIRUS IRONWOOD HOSITAL & CLINICS, INC., N10561 Grand View Lane, Ironwood, MI, Zip 49938–9622; tel. 906/932–2525; Paula L. Chermside, Chief Executive Officer

ASPIRUS KEWEENAW HOSPITAL, INC., 205 Osceola Street, Laurium, MI, Zip 49913–2134; tel. 906/337–6500; Michael Hauswirth, Chief Executive Officer

ASPIRUS ONTONAGON HOSPITAL, INC., 601 South Seventh Street, Ontonagon, MI, Zip 49953–1459; tel. 906/884–8000; Michael Hauswirth, Chief Executive Officer

BARAGA COUNTY MEMORIAL HOSPITAL, 18341 U.S. Highway 41, L'Anse, MI, Zip 49946–8024; tel. 906/524–3300; Margie Hale, R.N., MSN, Chief Executive Officer

DICKINSON COUNTY HEALTHCARE SYSTEM, 1721 South Stephenson Avenue, Iron Mountain, MI, Zip 49801–3637; tel. 906/774–1313; John Schon, Administrator and Chief Executive Officer

HELEN NEWBERRY JOY HOSPITAL, Helen Newberry Joy Hospital Annex, 502 West Harrie Street, Newberry, MI, Zip 49868–1209; tel. 906/293–9200; Scott Pillion, Chief Executive Officer

MACKINAC STRAITS HEALTH SYSTEM, INC., 1140 North State Street, Saint Ignace, MI, Zip 49781–1048; tel. 906/643–8585; Karen Cheeseman, Chief Executive Officer

MUNISING MEMORIAL HOSPITAL, 1500 Sand Point Road, Munising, MI, Zip 49862–1406; tel. 906/387–4110; Kevin P. Calhoun, Chief Executive Officer

SCHOOLCRAFT MEMORIAL HOSPITAL, 7870W US Highway 2, Manistique, MI, Zip 49854–8992; tel. 906/341–3200; Robert Crumb, Chief Executive Officer

UP HEALTH SYSTEM-BELL, 901 Lakeshore Drive, Ishpeming, MI, Zip 49849–1367; tel. 906/486–4431; Mitchell D. Leckelt, Chief Executive Officer

UP HEALTH SYSTEM PORTAGE, 500 Campus Drive, Hancock, MI, Zip 49930–1569; tel. 906/483–1000; Jeff Lang, President

WAR MEMORIAL HOSPITAL, 500 Osborn Boulevard, Sault Sainte Marie, MI, Zip 49783–1884; tel. 906/635–4460; David B. Jahn, President and Chief Executive Officer

MINNESOTA

NORTHWEST METRO ALLIANCE
c/O Mercy Hospital, 4050 Coon Rapids Boulevard, Coon Rapids, MN, Zip 55433–2586; tel. 763/236–6000; Sara J. Criger, President

MERCY HOSPITAL, 4050 Coon Rapids Boulevard, Coon Rapids, MN, Zip 55433–2586; tel. 763/236–6000; Sara J. Criger, President

MISSOURI

HEALTH NETWORK OF MISSOURI
One Hospital Drive, Room C1213, DC 079.00, Columbia, MO, Zip 65212; tel. 573/815–8000; Marty McCormick, Chief Executive Officer

BOTHWELL REGIONAL HEALTH CENTER, 601 East 14th Street, Sedalia, MO, Zip 65301–5972, P O Box 1706, 65302–1706, tel. 660/826–8833; James A. Robertson, Jr., President and Chief Executive Officer

CAPITAL REGION MEDICAL CENTER, 1125 Madison Street, Jefferson City, MO, Zip 65101–5200, P O Box 1128, 65102–1128, tel. 573/632–5000; Gaspare Calvaruso, President

HANNIBAL REGIONAL HOSPITAL, 6000 Hospital Drive, Hannibal, MO, Zip 63401–6887, P O Box 551, 63401–0551, tel. 573/248–1300; C Todd. Ahrens, President and Chief Executive Officer

LAKE REGIONAL HEALTH SYSTEM, 54 Hospital Drive, Osage Beach, MO, Zip 65065–3050; tel. 573/348–8000; Michael E. Henze, Chief Executive Officer

SAINT FRANCIS MEDICAL CENTER, 211 St Francis Drive, Cape Girardeau, MO, Zip 63703–5049; tel. 573/331–3000; Maryann Reese, R.N., FACHE, President and Chief Executive Officer

UNIVERSITY OF MISSOURI HEALTH CARE, One Hospital Drive, Columbia, MO, Zip 65212–0001; tel. 573/882–4141; Jonathan W. Curtright, Chief Executive Officer and Chief Operating Officer

MERCY HEALTH EAST
615 South New Ballas Road, Saint Louis, MO, Zip 63141–8221; tel. 314/364–3000; Donn Sorensen, President, East Region

MERCY HOSPITAL JEFFERSON, Highway 61 South, Crystal City, MO, Zip 63019, P O Box 350, 63019–0350, tel. 636/933–1000; Eric Ammons, President

MERCY HOSPITAL ST. LOUIS, 615 South New Ballas Road, Saint Louis, MO, Zip 63141–8277; tel. 314/251–6000; Stephen Mackin, President

MERCY HOSPITAL WASHINGTON, 901 East Fifth Street, Washington, MO, Zip 63090–3127; tel. 636/239–8000; Eric J. Eoloff, President

MOSAIC LIFE CARE
5325 Faraon Street, Saint Joseph, MO, Zip 64506–3488; tel. 816/271–6000; Brady Dubois, President

LONG-TERM ACUTE CARE HOSPITAL, MOSAIC LIFE CARE AT ST. JOSEPH, 5325 Faraon Street, Saint Joseph, MO, Zip 64506–3488; tel. 816/271–6000; Dana Anderson, Administrator

MOSAIC LIFE CARE AT ST. JOSEPH, 5325 Faraon Street, Saint Joseph, MO, Zip 64506–3488; tel. 816/271–6000; Samuel Mark. Laney, M.D., Chief Executive Officer

NORTHWEST MEDICAL CENTER, 705 North College Street, Albany, MO, Zip 64402–1433; tel. 660/726–3941; Jon D. Doolittle, Regional President

MONTANA

MONTANA HEALTH NETWORK
11 South 7th Street, Suite 241, Miles City, MT, Zip 59301; tel. 406/234–1420; Janet Bastian, Chief Executive Officer

BEARTOOTH BILLINGS CLINIC, 2525 North Broadway Avenue, Red Lodge, MT, Zip 59068–9222, P O Box 590, 59068–0590, tel. 406/446–2345; Kelley Evans, Chief Administrative Officer

BILLINGS CLINIC, 2800 10th Avenue North, Billings, MT, Zip 59101–0703, P O Box 37000, 59107–7000, tel. 406/657–4000; Randall K. Gibb, M.D., Chief Executive Officer

CENTRAL MONTANA MEDICAL CENTER, 408 Wendell Avenue, Lewistown, MT, Zip 59457–2261; tel. 406/535–7711; Michael Dowdy, Chief Executive Officer

DANIELS MEMORIAL HEALTHCARE CENTER, 105 Fifth Avenue East, Scobey, MT, Zip 59263, P O Box 400, 59263–0400, tel. 406/487–2296; David Ryerse, Chief Executive Officer

FALLON MEDICAL COMPLEX, 202 South 4th Street West, Baker, MT, Zip 59313–9156, P O Box 820, 59313–0820, tel. 406/778–3331; David Espeland, Chief Executive Officer

FRANCES MAHON DEACONESS HOSPITAL, 621 Third Street South, Glasgow, MT, Zip 59230–2699; tel. 406/228–3500; Randall G. Holom, Chief Executive Officer

GLENDIVE MEDICAL CENTER, 202 Prospect Drive, Glendive, MT, Zip 59330–1999; tel. 406/345–3306; Parker Powell, Chief Executive Officer

HOLY ROSARY HEALTHCARE, 2600 Wilson Street, Miles City, MT, Zip 59301–5094; tel. 406/233–2600; Paul Lewis, Chief Executive Officer

MCCONE COUNTY HEALTH CENTER, 605 Sullivan Avenue, Circle, MT, Zip 59215, P O Box 48, 59215–0048, tel. 406/485–3381; Nancy Rosaaen, Chief Executive Officer

PHILLIPS COUNTY HOSPITAL, 311 South 8th Avenue East, Malta, MT, Zip 59538–0640, P O Box 640, 59538–0640, tel. 406/654–1100; Ward C. VanWichen, Chief Executive Officer

ROOSEVELT MEDICAL CENTER, 818 Second Avenue East, Culbertson, MT, Zip 59218, P O Box 419, 59218–0419, tel. 406/787–6401; Audrey Stromberg, Administrator

ROUNDUP MEMORIAL HEALTHCARE, 1202 Third Street West, Roundup, MT, Zip 59072–1816, P O Box 40, 59072–0040, tel. 406/323–2301; Bradley Howell, Chief Executive Officer

SHERIDAN MEMORIAL HOSPITAL, 440 West Laurel Avenue, Plentywood, MT, Zip 59254–1596; tel. 406/765–3700; Gregory L. Maurer, Chief Executive Officer

SIDNEY HEALTH CENTER, 216 14th Avenue SW, Sidney, MT, Zip 59270–3586; tel. 406/488–2100; Richard Haraldson, Chief Executive Officer

STILLWATER BILLINGS CLINIC, 44 West Fourth Avenue North, Columbus, MT, Zip 59019–0959, P O Box 959, 59019–0959, tel. 406/322–5316; Mike Follett, Interim Chief Executive Officer

NEBRASKA

CHI HEALTH
12809 West Dodge Road, Omaha, NE, Zip 68154–2155; tel. 402/343–4300; Cliff Robertson, M.D., President and Chief Executive Officer

CHI HEALTH CREIGHTON UNIVERSITY MEDICAL CENTER - BERGAN MERCY, 7500 Mercy Road, Omaha, NE, Zip 68124–2319; tel. 402/398–6060; Kevin J. Nokels, FACHE, Primary

CHI HEALTH GOOD SAMARITAN, 10 East 31st Street, Kearney, NE, Zip 68847–2926, P O Box 1990, 68848–1990, tel. 308/865–7100; Michael H. Schnieders, FACHE, President

CHI HEALTH IMMANUEL, 6901 North 72nd Street, Omaha, NE, Zip 68122–1799; tel. 402/572–2121; Ann Schumacher, R.N., MSN, FACHE, President

CHI HEALTH LAKESIDE, 16901 Lakeside Hills Court, Omaha, NE, Zip 68130–2318; tel. 402/717–8000; Kevin Miller, President

CHI HEALTH MERCY CORNING, 603 Rosary Drive, Corning, IA, Zip 50841–1683; tel. 641/322–3121; Lisa Wolfe, President

CHI HEALTH MERCY COUNCIL BLUFFS, 800 Mercy Drive, Council Bluffs, IA, Zip 51503–3128, P O Box 1C, 51502–3001, tel. 712/328–5000; Marie E. Knedler, R.N., FACHE, President

CHI HEALTH MIDLANDS, 11111 South 84th Street, Papillion, NE, Zip 68046–4122; tel. 402/593–3000; Kevin Miller, President

CHI HEALTH MISSOURI VALLEY, 631 North Eighth Street, Missouri Valley, IA, Zip 51555–1102; tel. 712/642–2784; Robert A. Valentine, President

CHI HEALTH NEBRASKA HEART, 7500 South 91st Street, Lincoln, NE, Zip 68526–9437; tel. 402/327–2700; Dan Schonlau, Interim President

CHI HEALTH PLAINVIEW, 704 North Third Street, Plainview, NE, Zip 68769–2047, P O Box 489, 68769–0489, tel. 402/582–4245; Gregory Beckmann, Chief Executive Officer

CHI HEALTH SAINT FRANCIS, 2620 West Faidley Avenue, Grand Island, NE, Zip 68803–4297, P O Box 9804, 68802–9804, tel. 308/384–4600; Edward J. Hannon, FACHE, President

CHI HEALTH SCHUYLER, 104 West 17th Street, Schuyler, NE, Zip 68661–1304; tel. 402/352–2441; Connie Peters, R.N., President

CHI HEALTH ST ELIZABETH, 555 South 70th Street, Lincoln, NE, Zip 68510–2494; tel. 402/219–8000; Cary Ward, M.D., Chief Medical Officer and Interim President

CHI HEALTH ST. MARY'S, 1301 Grundman Boulevard, Nebraska City, NE, Zip 68410; tel. 402/873–3321; Daniel J. Kelly, President

NEBRASKA MEDICINE
987400 Nebraska Medical Center, Omaha, NE, Zip 68198–7400; tel. 877/763–0000; Daniel J. DeBehnke, M.D., Chief Executive Officer

NEBRASKA MEDICINE - BELLEVUE, 2500 Bellevue Medical Center Drive, Bellevue, NE, Zip 68123–1591; tel. 402/763–3000; Matt E. Pospisil, Vice President Perioperative Services

NEBRASKA MEDICINE - NEBRASKA MEDICAL CENTER, 987400 Nebraska Medical Center, Omaha, NE, Zip 68198–7400; tel. 402/552–2000; Daniel J. DeBehnke, M.D., Chief Executive Officer

NORTHEAST HEALTH SERVICES
PO Box 186, Creighton, NE, Zip 68729–0186; tel. 402/358–5700; Jennifer Neukirch, Chief Executive Officer

AVERA CREIGHTON HOSPITAL, 1503 Main Street, Creighton, NE, Zip 68729–3007, P O Box 186, 68729–0186, tel. 402/358–5700; Todd Consbruck, Chief Executive Officer

CHI HEALTH PLAINVIEW, 704 North Third Street, Plainview, NE, Zip 68769–2047, P O Box 489, 68769–0489, tel. 402/582–4245; Gregory Beckmann, Chief Executive Officer

OSMOND GENERAL HOSPITAL, 402 North Maple Street, Osmond, NE, Zip 68765–5726, P O Box 429, 68765–0429, tel. 402/748–3393; Lon Knievel, Chief Executive Officer

NEW HAMPSHIRE

CARING COMMUNITY NETWORK OF THE TWIN RIVERS
c/o First Health, 841 Central Street, Franklin, NH, Zip 03235–2026; tel. 603/934–0177; Rick Silverberg, Managing Director

FRANKLIN REGIONAL HOSPITAL, 15 Aiken Avenue, Franklin, NH, Zip 03235–1299; tel. 603/934–2060; Kevin Donovan, FACHE, President and CEO

NEW JERSEY

QUALCARE, INC.
242 Old New Brunswick Road, Piscataway, NJ, Zip 08854–3754; tel. 732/562–2800; Jerry Eisenberg, Network Contact

CAPITAL HEALTH MEDICAL CENTER-HOPEWELL, 1 Capital Way, Pennington, NJ, Zip 08534–2520; tel. 609/303–4000; Al Maghazehe, Ph.D., FACHE, President and Chief Executive Officer

CAREPOINT HEALTH CHRIST HOSPITAL, 176 Palisade Avenue, Jersey City, NJ, Zip 07306–1196, 176 Palisades Avenue, 07306–1196, tel. 201/795–8200; Marie Theresa Duffy, Chief Operating Officer

CHILTON MEDICAL CENTER, 97 West Parkway, Pompton Plains, NJ, Zip 07444–1696; tel. 973/831–5000; Stephanie L. Schwartz, FACHE, President

CLARA MAASS MEDICAL CENTER, One Clara Maass Drive, Belleville, NJ, Zip 07109–3557; tel. 973/450–2000; Mary Ellen Clyne, MSN, Ph.D., R.N., President and Chief Executive Officer

DEBORAH HEART AND LUNG CENTER, 200 Trenton Road, Browns Mills, NJ, Zip 08015–1705; tel. 609/893–6611; Joseph Chirichella, President and Chief Executive Officer

ENGLEWOOD HOSPITAL AND MEDICAL CENTER, 350 Engle Street, Englewood, NJ, Zip 07631–1898; tel. 201/894–3000; Warren Geller, President and Chief Executive Officer

HACKENSACK MERIDIAN HEALTH HACKENSACK UNIVERSITY MEDICAL CENTER, 30 Prospect Avenue, Hackensack, NJ, Zip 07601–1914; tel. 201/996–2000; Ihor S. Sawczuk, M.D., President

HACKENSACK MERIDIAN HEALTH OCEAN MEDICAL CENTER, 425 Jack Martin Boulevard, Brick Township, NJ, Zip 08724–7732; tel. 732/840–2200; Dean Q. Lin, FACHE, Regional President

HACKENSACK MERIDIAN HEALTH RARITAN BAY MEDICAL CENTER, 530 New Brunswick Avenue, Perth Amboy, NJ, Zip 08861–3654; tel. 732/442–3700; Michael R. D'Agnes, FACHE, President and Chief Executive Officer

HACKENSACK MERIDIAN HEALTH RIVERVIEW MEDICAL CENTER, 1 Riverview Plaza, Red Bank, NJ, Zip 07701–1864; tel. 732/741–2700; Timothy J. Hogan, FACHE, Regional President

HACKETTSTOWN MEDICAL CENTER, 651 Willow Grove Street, Hackettstown, NJ, Zip 07840–1799; tel. 908/852–5100; Joseph DiPaolo, FACHE, President, Sussex and Warren Region

INSPIRA MEDICAL CENTER-VINELAND, 1505 West Sherman Avenue, Vineland, NJ, Zip 08360–6912; tel. 856/641–8000; John A. DiAngelo, President and Chief Executive Officer

JFK MEDICAL CENTER, 65 James Street, Edison, NJ, Zip 8818; tel. 732/321–7000; Raymond F. Fredericks, President and CEO

MEMORIAL HOSPITAL OF SALEM COUNTY, 310 Woodstown Road, Salem, NJ, Zip 08079–2080; tel. 856/935–1000; Tammy Torres, R.N., MSN, Chief Executive Officer

PIEDMONT MOUNTAINSIDE HOSPITAL, 1266 Highway 515 South, Jasper, GA, Zip 30143–4872; tel. 706/692–2441; Denise Ray, Chief Executive Officer

ROBERT WOOD JOHNSON UNIVERSITY HOSPITAL, 1 Robert Wood Johnson Place, New Brunswick, NJ, Zip 08901–1928; tel. 732/828–3000; John Gantner, President and Chief Executive Officer

SAINT MICHAEL'S MEDICAL CENTER, 111 Central Avenue, Newark, NJ, Zip 07102–1909; tel. 973/877–5350; Robert C. Iannaccone, Chief Executive Officer

ST. MARY'S GENERAL HOSPITAL, 350 Boulevard, Passaic, NJ, Zip 07055–2840; tel. 973/365–4300; Edward Condit, President and Chief Executive Officer

UNIVERSITY HOSPITAL, 150 Bergen Street, Newark, NJ, Zip 07103–2496; tel. 973/972–4300; John N. Kastanis, FACHE, President and Chief Executive Officer

UNIVERSITY MEDICAL CENTER OF PRINCETON AT PLAINSBORO, Acute General Hospital, Merwick Unit-Extended Care and Rehabilitation, Princeton House Unit-Community Mental Health and Substance Abuse, One Plainsboro Road, Plainsboro, NJ, Zip 08536–1913; tel. 609/853–7100; Barry S. Rabner, President and Chief Executive Officer, Princeton Healthcare System

VIRTUA MARLTON, 90 Brick Road, Marlton, NJ, Zip 08053–2177; tel. 856/355–6000; Matthew Zuino, Senior Vice President Hospital Services

NEW MEXICO

NEW MEXICO RURAL HOSPITAL NETWORK
7471 Pan American Freeway NE, Albuquerque, NM, Zip 87109; tel. 505/346–0216; Stephen Stoddard, FACHE, Executive Director

ARTESIA GENERAL HOSPITAL, 702 North 13th Street, Artesia, NM, Zip 88210–1199; tel. 575/748–3333; Robert C. Tyk, Interim Chief Executive Officer

CIBOLA GENERAL HOSPITAL, 1016 East Roosevelt Avenue, Grants, NM, Zip 87020–2118; tel. 505/287–4446; Thomas Whelan, Chief Executive Officer

GUADALUPE COUNTY HOSPITAL, 117 Camino de Vida, Santa Rosa, NM, Zip 88435–2267; tel. 575/472–3417; Christina Campos, Administrator

HOLY CROSS HOSPITAL, 1397 Weimer Road, Taos, NM, Zip 87571–6253; tel. 575/758–8883; William D. Patten, Jr., Chief Executive Officer

MINERS' COLFAX MEDICAL CENTER, 200 Hospital Drive, Raton, NM, Zip 87740–2099; tel. 575/445–7700; Bo Beames, Interim Chief Executive Officer

NOR-LEA HOSPITAL DISTRICT, 1600 North Main Avenue, Lovington, NM, Zip 88260–2871; tel. 575/396–6611; David B. Shaw, Chief Executive Officer and Administrator

REHOBOTH MCKINLEY CHRISTIAN HEALTH CARE SERVICES, 1901 Red Rock Drive, Gallup, NM, Zip 87301–5683; tel. 505/863–7000; David Conejo, Chief Executive Officer

ROOSEVELT GENERAL HOSPITAL, 42121 U S Highway 70, Portales, NM, Zip 88130, P O Box 868, 88130–0868, tel. 575/359–1800

SIERRA VISTA HOSPITAL, 800 East Ninth Avenue, Truth or Consequences, NM, Zip 87901–1961; tel. 575/894–2111; Donna Muder, Interim Chief Executive Officer

UNION COUNTY GENERAL HOSPITAL, 300 Wilson Street, Clayton, NM, Zip 88415–3304, P O Box 489, 88415–0489, tel. 575/374–2585; Tammie Stump, R.N., Chief Executive Officer

NEW YORK

ARDENT SOLUTIONS, INC.
85 North Main Street, Suite 4, Wellsville, NY, Zip 14895–1254; tel. 585/593–5223; Carrie Whitwood, Executive Director

JONES MEMORIAL HOSPITAL, 191 North Main Street, Wellsville, NY, Zip 14895–1150, P O Box 72, 14895–0072, tel. 585/593–1100; Eva Benedict, R.N., President and Chief Executive Officer

ARNOT HEALTH
600 Roe Avenue, Elmira, NY, Zip 14905–1629; tel. 607/737–4100; Robert K. Lambert, M.D., FACHE, President and Chief Executive Officer

ARNOT OGDEN MEDICAL CENTER, 600 Roe Avenue, Elmira, NY, Zip 14905–1629; tel. 607/737–4100; Jonathan I. Lawrence, System Chief Operating Officer

IRA DAVENPORT MEMORIAL HOSPITAL, 7571 State Route 54, Bath, NY, Zip 14810–9590; tel. 607/776–8500; Richard C. Cleland, FACHE, Administrator

ST. JOSEPH'S HOSPITAL, 555 St. Joseph's Boulevard, Elmira, NY, Zip 14901–3223; tel. 607/733–6541; Joseph Braunscheidel, Administrator

BASSETT HEALTHCARE NETWORK
1 Atwell Road, Cooperstown, NY, Zip 13326–1301; tel. 607/547–3456; Vance Brown, M.D., President and Chief Executive Officer

AURELIA OSBORN FOX MEMORIAL HOSPITAL, 1 Norton Avenue, Oneonta, NY, Zip 13820–2629; tel. 607/432–2000; Jeff Joyner, President

BASSETT MEDICAL CENTER, One Atwell Road, Cooperstown, NY, Zip 13326–1394; tel. 607/547–3456; Vance Brown, M.D., President and Chief Executive Officer

COBLESKILL REGIONAL HOSPITAL, 178 Grandview Drive, Cobleskill, NY, Zip 12043–5144; tel. 518/254–3456; Eric H. Stein, FACHE, President and Chief Executive Officer

LITTLE FALLS HOSPITAL, 140 Burwell Street, Little Falls, NY, Zip 13365–1725; tel. 315/823–1000; Michael L. Ogden, President and Chief Executive Officer

O'CONNOR HOSPITAL, 460 Andes Road, State Route 28, Delhi, NY, Zip 13753–7407; tel. 607/746–0300; Scott Bonderoff, President

GREAT LAKES HEALTH SYSTEM OF WESTERN NEW YORK
726 Exchange Street, Suite 522, Buffalo, NY, Zip 14210–1485; tel. 716/859–8820; Jody Lomeo, Interim Chief Executive Officer

ERIE COUNTY MEDICAL CENTER, 462 Grider Street, Buffalo, NY, Zip 14215–3098; tel. 716/898–3000; Thomas J. Quatroche, Jr., Chief Executive Officer

KALEIDA HEALTH, 100 High Street, Buffalo, NY, Zip 14203–1154; tel. 716/859–5600; Jody Lomeo, Chief Executive Officer

LAKE ERIE REGIONAL HEALTH SYSTEM OF NEW YORK
529 Central Avenue, Dunkirk, NY, Zip 14048–2514; tel. 716/366–1111; J. Gary Rhodes, FACHE, Interim Chief Executive Officer

BROOKS MEMORIAL HOSPITAL, 529 Central Avenue, Dunkirk, NY, Zip 14048–2599; tel. 716/366–1111; Mary E. LaRowe, FACHE, President and Chief Executive Officer

MOHAWK VALLEY NETWORK, INC.
1656 Champlin Avenue, Utica, NY, Zip 13502–4830; tel. 315/624–6002; Scott H. Perra, FACHE, President and Chief Executive Officer

FAXTON ST. LUKE'S HEALTHCARE, 1656 Champlin Avenue, Utica, NY, Zip 13502–4830, P O Box 479, 13503–0479, tel. 315/624–6000; Scott H. Perra, FACHE, President and Chief Executive Officer

ST. ELIZABETH MEDICAL CENTER, 2209 Genesee Street, Utica, NY, Zip 13501–5999; tel. 315/798–8100; Scott H. Perra, FACHE, Chief Executive Officer

MOUNT SINAI NYU HEALTH NETWORK
One Gustave L. Levy Place, New York, NY, Zip 10029; tel. 212/659–8888; Arthur A. Klein, M.D., President

ENGLEWOOD HOSPITAL AND MEDICAL CENTER, 350 Engle Street, Englewood, NJ, Zip 07631–1898; tel. 201/894–3000; Warren Geller, President and Chief Executive Officer

JAMES J. PETERS VETERANS AFFAIRS MEDICAL CENTER, 130 West Kingsbridge Road, Bronx, NY, Zip 10468–3904; tel. 718/584–9000; Erik Langhoff, M.D., Ph.D., Director

JERSEY CITY MEDICAL CENTER, 355 Grand Street, Jersey City, NJ, Zip 07302–4321; tel. 201/915–2000; Joseph F. Scott, FACHE, President and Chief Executive Officer

MEADOWLANDS HOSPITAL MEDICAL CENTER, 55 Meadowlands Parkway, Secaucus, NJ, Zip 07094–2977; tel. 201/392–3100; Felicia Karsos, R.N., President and Chief Executive Officer

MORRISTOWN MEDICAL CENTER, 100 Madison Avenue, Morristown, NJ, Zip 07960–6136; tel. 973/971–5000; Trish O'Keefe, Ph.D., R.N., President

MOUNT SINAI HOSPITAL, One Gustave L Levy Place, P O Box 1068, New York, NY, Zip 10029–0310; tel. 212/241–6500; David L. Reich, M.D., President and Chief Operating Officer

NYC HEALTH + HOSPITALS / ELMHURST, 79–01 Broadway, Elmhurst, NY, Zip 11373–1329; tel. 718/334–4000; Israel Rocha, Chief Executive Officer

NYC HEALTH + HOSPITALS / QUEENS, 82–68 164th Street, Jamaica, NY, Zip 11432–1104; tel. 718/883–3000; Christopher Roker, Chief Executive Officer

OVERLOOK MEDICAL CENTER, 99 Beauvoir Avenue, Summit, NJ, Zip 07901–3533; tel. 908/522–2000; Alan R. Lieber, President

PHELPS MEMORIAL HOSPITAL CENTER, 701 North Broadway, Sleepy Hollow, NY, Zip 10591–1020; tel. 914/366–3000; Daniel Blum, President

ST. JOHN'S RIVERSIDE HOSPITAL, 967 North Broadway, Yonkers, NY, Zip 10701–1399; tel. 914/964–4444; Ronald J. Corti, President and Chief Executive Officer

ST. JOSEPH'S HEALTHCARE SYSTEM, 703 Main Street, Paterson, NJ, Zip 07503–2691; tel. 973/754–2000; Kevin J. Slavin, FACHE, President and Chief Executive Officer

ST. LUKE'S CORNWALL HOSPITAL, 70 Dubois Street, Newburgh, NY, Zip 12550–4851; tel. 845/561–4400; Joan Cusack-McGuirk, Interim President and Chief Executive Officer

VASSAR BROTHERS MEDICAL CENTER, 45 Reade Place, Poughkeepsie, NY, Zip 12601–3947; tel. 845/454–8500; Ann McMackin, President

NEW YORK PRESBYTERIAN REGIONAL HOSPITAL NETWORK
525 East 68th Street, Box 182, New York, NY, Zip 10065–4870; tel. 212/746–3745; Steven J. Corwin, M.D., President and Chief Executive Officer

GRACIE SQUARE HOSPITAL, 420 East 76th Street, New York, NY, Zip 10021–3396; tel. 212/988–4400; David Wyman, President and Chief Executive Officer

NEW YORK COMMUNITY HOSPITAL, 2525 Kings Highway, Brooklyn, NY, Zip 11229–1705; tel. 718/692–5300; Barry Stern, President and Chief Executive Officer

NEWYORK-PRESBYTERIAN BROOKLYN METHODIST HOSPITAL, 506 Sixth Street, Brooklyn, NY, Zip 11215–3609; tel. 718/780–3000; Richard Liebowitz, M.D., President

RURAL HEALTH NETWORK OF OSWEGO COUNTY
10 George Street, Oswego, NY, Zip 13126; tel. 315/592–0827; Brian Coleman, Coordinator

OSWEGO HOSPITAL, 110 West Sixth Street, Oswego, NY, Zip 13126–2507; tel. 315/349–5511; Michael Harlovic, R.N., President and Chief Executive Officer

STELLARIS HEALTH
135 Bedford Rd, Armonk, NY, Zip 10504–1945; tel. 914/273–5454; Sharon A. Lucian, President and Chief Executive Officer

NEW YORK-PRESBYTERIAN/LAWRENCE HOSPITAL, 55 Palmer Avenue, Bronxville, NY, Zip 10708–3403; tel. 914/787–1000; Michael Fosina, M.P.H., FACHE, President

NORTHERN WESTCHESTER HOSPITAL, 400 East Main Street, Mount Kisco, NY, Zip 10549–3477, 400 East Main Street, G-02, 10549–3477, tel. 914/666–1200; Joel Seligman, President and Chief Executive Officer

PHELPS MEMORIAL HOSPITAL CENTER, 701 North Broadway, Sleepy Hollow, NY, Zip 10591–1020; tel. 914/366–3000; Daniel Blum, President

WHITE PLAINS HOSPITAL CENTER, 41 East Post Road, White Plains, NY, Zip 10601–4699; tel. 914/681–0600; Susan Fox, President and Chief Executive Officer

NORTH CAROLINA

COASTAL CAROLINAS HEALTH ALLIANCE
5305-M Wrightsville Avenue, Wilmington, NC, Zip 28403; tel. 910/332–8012; Yvonne Hughes, Chief Executive Officer

CAPE FEAR VALLEY - BLADEN COUNTY HOSPITAL, 501 South Poplar Street, Elizabethtown, NC, Zip 28337–9375, P O Box 398, 28337–0398, tel. 910/862–5100; Roxie Cannon. Wells, M.D., Chief Executive Officer

COLUMBUS REGIONAL HEALTHCARE SYSTEM, 500 Jefferson Street, Whiteville, NC, Zip 28472–3634; tel. 910/642–8011; Carla Hollis, President and Chief Executive Officer

J. ARTHUR DOSHER MEMORIAL HOSPITAL, 924 North Howe Street, Southport, NC, Zip 28461–3099; tel. 910/457–3800; Thomas R. Siemers, Chief Executive Officer

MCLEOD LORIS SEACOAST HOSPITAL, 3655 Mitchell Street, Loris, SC, Zip 29569–2827; tel. 843/716–7000; Edward D. Tinsley, III., Chief Executive Officer

MCLEOD REGIONAL MEDICAL CENTER, 555 East Cheves Street, Florence, SC, Zip 29506–2617, P O Box 100551, 29502–0551, tel. 843/777–2000; Robert L. Colones, President and Chief Executive Officer

NEW HANOVER REGIONAL MEDICAL CENTER, 2131 South 17th Street, Wilmington, NC, Zip 28401–7483, P O Box 9000, 28402–9000, tel. 910/343–7000; Andre Boyd, Sr., Executive Vice President, Hospital Division

PENDER MEMORIAL HOSPITAL, 507 East Freemont Street, Burgaw, NC, Zip 28425–5131; tel. 910/259–5451; Ruth Glaser, President

SAMPSON REGIONAL MEDICAL CENTER, 607 Beaman Street, Clinton, NC, Zip 28328–2697, P O Box 260, 28329–0260, tel. 910/592–8511; Shawn Howerton, M.D., Chief Executive Officer and President, Medical Staff

SCOTLAND HEALTH CARE SYSTEM, 500 Lauchwood Drive, Laurinburg, NC, Zip 28352–5599; tel. 910/291–7000; Gregory C. Wood, President and Chief Executive Officer

SOUTHEASTERN HEALTH, 300 West 27th Street, Lumberton, NC, Zip 28358–3075, P O Box 1408, 28359–1408, tel. 910/671–5000; Joann Anderson, President and Chief Executive Officer

VIDANT DUPLIN HOSPITAL, 401 North Main Street, Kenansville, NC, Zip 28349–8801, P O Box 278, 28349–0278, tel. 910/296–0941; Jay Briley, President

VIDANT MEDICAL CENTER, 2100 Stantonsburg Road, Greenville, NC, Zip 27834–2818, P O Box 6028, 27835–6028, tel. 252/847–4100; William Brian. Floyd, President

MISSION HEALTH SYSTEM
509 Biltmore Avenue, Asheville, NC, Zip 28801–4601; tel. 828/213–1111; Ronald A. Paulus, M.D., President and Chief Executive Officer

ANGEL MEDICAL CENTER, 120 Riverview Street, Franklin, NC, Zip 28734–2612, P O Box 1209, 28744–0569, tel. 828/524–8411; Karen S. Gorby, R.N., MSN, FACHE, President and Chief Nursing Officer

ASHEVILLE SPECIALTY HOSPITAL, 428 Biltmore Avenue, 4th Floor, Asheville, NC, Zip 28801–4502; tel. 828/213–5400; Julie A. Dikos, MSN, R.N., President and Chief Executive Officer

BLUE RIDGE REGIONAL HOSPITAL, 125 Hospital Drive, Spruce Pine, NC, Zip 28777–3035; tel. 828/765–4201; Rebecca W. Carter, MSN, R.N., FACHE, Chief Executive Officer and Chief Nursing Officer

CAREPARTNERS HEALTH SERVICES, 68 Sweeten Creek Road, Asheville, NC, Zip 28803–2318, P O Box 15025, 28813–0025, tel. 828/277–4800; Tracy Buchanan, Chief Executive Officer and President

HIGHLANDS-CASHIERS HOSPITAL, 190 Hospital Drive, Highlands, NC, Zip 28741–7600, P O Drawer 190, 28741–0190, tel. 828/526–1200; Jacqueline Medland, MS, Ph.D., President and Chief Nursing Officer

MCDOWELL HOSPITAL, 430 Rankin Drive, Marion, NC, Zip 28752–6568, P O Box 730, 28752–0730, tel. 828/659–5000; Carol C. Wolfenbarger, FACHE, MSN, President and Chief Executive Officer

MISSION HOSPITAL, 509 Biltmore Avenue, Asheville, NC, Zip 28801–4690; tel. 828/213–1111; Jill Hoggard Green, Ph.D., R.N., President

TRANSYLVANIA REGIONAL HOSPITAL, 260 Hospital Drive, Brevard, NC, Zip 28712–3378; tel. 828/884–9111; Michele Pilon, President and Chief Nursing Officer

WNC HEALTH NETWORK, INC.
1200 Ridgefield Boulevard Suite 200, Asheville, NC, Zip 28806–2280; tel. 828/667–8220; Heather Gates, Executive Director

ANGEL MEDICAL CENTER, 120 Riverview Street, Franklin, NC, Zip 28734–2612, P O Box 1209, 28744–0569, tel. 828/524–8411; Karen S. Gorby, R.N., MSN, FACHE, President and Chief Nursing Officer

BLUE RIDGE REGIONAL HOSPITAL, 125 Hospital Drive, Spruce Pine, NC, Zip 28777–3035; tel. 828/765–4201; Rebecca W. Carter, MSN, R.N., FACHE, Chief Executive Officer and Chief Nursing Officer

CAREPARTNERS HEALTH SERVICES, 68 Sweeten Creek Road, Asheville, NC, Zip 28803–2318, P O Box 15025, 28813–0025, tel. 828/277–4800; Tracy Buchanan, Chief Executive Officer and President

CHARLES GEORGE VETERANS AFFAIRS MEDICAL CENTER, 1100 Tunnel Road, Asheville, NC, Zip 28805–2087; tel. 828/298–7911; Cynthia Breyfogle, FACHE, Director

CHEROKEE INDIAN HOSPITAL, 1 Hospital Road, Cherokee, NC, Zip 28719; tel. 828/497–9163; Casey Cooper, Chief Executive Officer

Section B

HARRIS REGIONAL HOSPITAL, 68 Hospital Road, Sylva, NC, Zip 28779–2722; tel. 828/586–7000; Steve Heatherly, Chief Executive Officer

HAYWOOD REGIONAL MEDICAL CENTER, 262 Leroy George Drive, Clyde, NC, Zip 28721–7430; tel. 828/456–7311; Rod Harkleroad, R.N., Chief Executive Officer

HIGHLANDS-CASHIERS HOSPITAL, 190 Hospital Drive, Highlands, NC, Zip 28741–7600, P O Drawer 190, 28741–0190, tel. 828/526–1200; Jacqueline Medland, MS, Ph.D., President and Chief Nursing Officer

MARGARET R. PARDEE MEMORIAL HOSPITAL, 800 North Justice Street, Hendersonville, NC, Zip 28791–3410; tel. 828/696–1000; James M. Kirby, II., President and Chief Executive Officer

MCDOWELL HOSPITAL, 430 Rankin Drive, Marion, NC, Zip 28752–6568, P O Box 730, 28752–0730, tel. 828/659–5000; Carol C. Wolfenbarger, FACHE, MSN, President and Chief Executive Officer

MISSION HOSPITAL, 509 Biltmore Avenue, Asheville, NC, Zip 28801–4690; tel. 828/213–1111; Jill Hoggard Green, Ph.D., R.N., President

MURPHY MEDICAL CENTER, 3990 U S Highway 64 East Alt, Murphy, NC, Zip 28906–7917; tel. 828/837–8161; Michael Stevenson, Chief Executive Officer

PARK RIDGE HEALTH, 100 Hospital Drive, Hendersonville, NC, Zip 28792–5272; tel. 828/684–8501; Jimm Bunch, President and Chief Executive Officer

RUTHERFORD REGIONAL HEALTH SYSTEM, 288 South Ridgecrest Avenue, Rutherfordton, NC, Zip 28139–2838; tel. 828/286–5000; Rebecca Segal, Chief Executive Officer

ST. LUKE'S HOSPITAL, 101 Hospital Drive, Columbus, NC, Zip 28722–6418; tel. 828/894–3311; James B. Bross, President

SWAIN COMMUNITY HOSPITAL, 45 Plateau Street, Bryson City, NC, Zip 28713–4200; tel. 828/488–2155; Steve Heatherly, Chief Executive Officer

TRANSYLVANIA REGIONAL HOSPITAL, 260 Hospital Drive, Brevard, NC, Zip 28712–3378; tel. 828/884–9111; Michele Pilon, President and Chief Nursing Officer

NORTH DAKOTA

NORTHLAND HEALTHCARE ALLIANCE
3811 Lockport Street Suite 3, Bismarck, ND, Zip 58503–5554; tel. 701/250–0709; Timothy Cox, Director

ASHLEY MEDICAL CENTER, 612 North Center Avenue, Ashley, ND, Zip 58413–7013, P O Box 450, 58413–0450, tel. 701/288–3433; Holly Wolff, Chief Executive Officer

CHI ST. ALEXIUS HEALTH - DICKINSON MEDICAL CENTER, 2500 Fairway Street, Dickinson, ND, Zip 58601–4399; tel. 701/456–4000; Reed Reyman, President

CHI ST. ALEXIUS HEALTH GARRISON, 407 Third Avenue SE, Garrison, ND, Zip 58540–7235; tel. 701/463–2275; Tod Graeber, Administrator

CHI ST. ALEXIUS HEALTH, 900 East Broadway, Bismarck, ND, Zip 58501–4586, P O Box 5510, 58506–5510, tel. 701/530–7000; Kurt Schley, Market Chief Executive Officer

COMMUNITY MEMORIAL HOSPITAL, 220 Fifth Avenue, Turtle Lake, ND, Zip 58575–4005, P O Box 280, 58575–0280, tel. 701/448–2331; Tod Graeber, Administrator

LINTON HOSPITAL, 518 North Broadway, Linton, ND, Zip 58552–7308, P O Box 850, 58552–0850, tel. 701/254–4511; Robert O. Black, Chief Executive Officer

MCKENZIE COUNTY HEALTHCARE SYSTEM, 516 North Main Street, Watford City, ND, Zip 58854–7310; tel. 701/842–3000; Daniel R. Kelly, Chief Executive Officer

MOBRIDGE REGIONAL HOSPITAL, 1401 Tenth Avenue West, Mobridge, SD, Zip 57601–1106, P O Box 580, 57601–0580, tel. 605/845–3692; John J. Ayoub, FACHE, Chief Executive Officer

PRESENTATION MEDICAL CENTER, 213 Second Avenue NE, Rolla, ND, Zip 58367–7153, P O Box 759, 58367–0759, tel. 701/477–3161; Mark Kerr, Chief Executive Officer

SAKAKAWEA MEDICAL CENTER, 510 Eighth Avenue NE, Hazen, ND, Zip 58545–4637; tel. 701/748–2225; Darrold Bertsch, Chief Executive Officer

SOUTHWEST HEALTHCARE SERVICES, 802 2nd Street Northwest, Bowman, ND, Zip 58623–4483, P O Drawer 'C', 58623, tel. 701/523–5265; John Michael. Osse, Interim Chief Executive Officer

ST. ALOISIUS MEDICAL CENTER, 325 East Brewster Street, Harvey, ND, Zip 58341–1653; tel. 701/324–4651; Mike Zwicker, Chief Executive Officer

ST. ANDREW'S HEALTH CENTER, 316 Ohmer Street, Bottineau, ND, Zip 58318–1045; tel. 701/228–9300; Jodi Atkinson, President and Chief Executive Officer

WEST RIVER REGIONAL MEDICAL CENTER, 1000 Highway 12, Hettinger, ND, Zip 58639–7530; tel. 701/567–4561; Matthew Shahan, Chief Executive Officer

WISHEK COMMUNITY HOSPITAL AND CLINICS, 1007 Fourth Avenue South, Wishek, ND, Zip 58495–7527, P O Box 647, 58495–0647, tel. 701/452–2326; Beverly Vilhauer, Chief Executive Officer

OHIO

CLEVELAND HEALTH NETWORK
6000 West Creek Road, Suite 20, Independence, OH, Zip 44131–2139; tel. 216/986–1100; Fred M. DeGrandis, President

AKRON CHILDREN'S HOSPITAL, One Perkins Square, Akron, OH, Zip 44308–1063; tel. 330/543–1000; William H. Considine, President

ASHTABULA COUNTY MEDICAL CENTER, 2420 Lake Avenue, Ashtabula, OH, Zip 44004–4954; tel. 440/997–2262; Michael J. Habowski, President and Chief Executive Officer

CLEVELAND CLINIC CHILDREN'S HOSPITAL FOR REHABILITATION, 2801 Martin Luther King Jr Drive, Cleveland, OH, Zip 44104–3865; tel. 216/448–6400; Michael J. McHugh, M.D., Medical Director

CLEVELAND CLINIC FAIRVIEW HOSPITAL, 18101 Lorain Avenue, Cleveland, OH, Zip 44111–5656; tel. 216/476–7000; Neil Smith, D.O., President

CLEVELAND CLINIC, MEDINA HOSPITAL, 1000 East Washington Street, Medina, OH, Zip 44256–2170; tel. 330/725–1000; Richard K. Shewbridge, M.D., President

CLEVELAND CLINIC, 9500 Euclid Avenue, Cleveland, OH, Zip 44195–5108; tel. 216/444–2200; Delos Cosgrove, M.D., President and Chief Executive Officer

EUCLID HOSPITAL, 18901 Lake Shore Boulevard, Euclid, OH, Zip 44119–1090; tel. 216/531–9000; Daniel Napierkowski, M.D., President

FIRELANDS REGIONAL HEALTH SYSTEM, 1111 Hayes Avenue, Sandusky, OH, Zip 44870–3323; tel. 419/557–7400; Martin Tursky, President and Chief Executive Officer

FISHER-TITUS MEDICAL CENTER, 272 Benedict Avenue, Norwalk, OH, Zip 44857–2374; tel. 419/668–8101; Lorna Strayer, President and Chief Executive Officer

HILLCREST HOSPITAL, 6780 Mayfield Road, Cleveland, OH, Zip 44124–2203; tel. 440/312–4500; Donald Ford, M.D., Interim President

LUTHERAN HOSPITAL, 1730 West 25th Street, Cleveland, OH, Zip 44113–3170; tel. 216/696–4300; Donald A. Malone, Jr., President

MARYMOUNT HOSPITAL, 12300 McCracken Road, Garfield Heights, OH, Zip 44125–2975; tel. 216/581–0500; Richard Parker, M.D., President

METROHEALTH MEDICAL CENTER, 2500 MetroHealth Drive, Cleveland, OH, Zip 44109–1998; tel. 216/778–7800; Akram Boutros, M.D., FACHE, President and Chief Executive Officer

SOUTH POINTE HOSPITAL, 20000 Harvard Road, Warrensville Heights, OH, Zip 44122–6805; tel. 216/491–6000; Robert S. Juhasz, D.O., President

SUMMA HEALTH SYSTEM, 525 East Market Street, Akron, OH, Zip 44304–1619; tel. 330/375–3000; David Custodio, M.D., President Summa Health System Akron

SUMMA WESTERN RESERVE HOSPITAL, 1900 23rd Street, Cuyahoga Falls, OH, Zip 44223–1499; tel. 330/971–7000; Robert Kent, D.O., President and Chief Executive Officer

UNIVERSITY HOSPITALS ELYRIA MEDICAL CENTER, 630 East River Street, Elyria, OH, Zip 44035–5902; tel. 440/329–7500; Charlotte Wray, MSN, President

UNIVERSITY HOSPITALS PARMA MEDICAL CENTER, 7007 Powers Boulevard, Parma, OH, Zip 44129–5495; tel. 440/743–3000; Peter U. Bergmann, President

MERCY HEALTH - SOUTHWEST OHIO
4600 McAuley Place, Cincinnati, OH, Zip 45242; tel. 513/981–6000; John M. Starcher, President and Chief Executive Officer

MERCY HEALTH - ANDERSON HOSPITAL, 7500 State Road, Cincinnati, OH, Zip 45255–2492; tel. 513/624–4500; Ken James, President and Chief Executive Officer of East Market

MERCY HEALTH - CLERMONT HOSPITAL, 3000 Hospital Drive, Batavia, OH, Zip 45103–1921; tel. 513/732–8200; Ken James, President and Chief Executive Officer of East Market

MERCY HEALTH - FAIRFIELD HOSPITAL, 3000 Mack Road, Fairfield, OH, Zip 45014–5335; tel. 513/870–7000; Thomas S. Urban, Market Leader and President

MERCY HEALTH - WEST HOSPITAL, 3300 Mercy Health Boulevard, Cincinnati, OH, Zip 45211; tel. 513/215–5000; Michael Kramer, Chief Executive Officer

THE JEWISH HOSPITAL - MERCY HEALTH, 4777 East Galbraith Road, Cincinnati, OH, Zip 45236–2725; tel. 513/686–3000; Patricia Davis-Hagens, R.N., Central Market Leader and President

OHIO STATE HEALTH NETWORK
660 Ackerman Road, Suite 601F, Columbus, OH, Zip 43202–4500; tel. 614/293–3785; Tom Blincoe, Executive Director

BARNESVILLE HOSPITAL, 639 West Main Street, Barnesville, OH, Zip 43713–1039, P O Box 309, 43713–0309, tel. 740/425–3941; David D. Phillips, Chief Executive Officer and Administrator

MADISON HEALTH, 210 North Main Street, London, OH, Zip 43140–1115; tel. 740/845–7000; Dana E. Engle, Chief Executive Officer

MARY RUTAN HOSPITAL, 205 Palmer Avenue, Bellefontaine, OH, Zip 43311–2281; tel. 937/592–4015; Mandy C. Goble, President and Chief Executive Officer

MERCER HEALTH, 800 West Main Street, Coldwater, OH, Zip 45828–1698; tel. 419/678–2341; Lisa R. Klenke, R.N., Chief Executive Officer

OHIO STATE UNIVERSITY WEXNER MEDICAL CENTER, 370 West 9th Avenue, Columbus, OH, Zip 43210–1238; tel. 614/293–8000; David P. McQuaid, FACHE, Chief Operating Officer

OHIO VALLEY MEDICAL CENTER, 2000 Eoff Street, Wheeling, WV, Zip 26003–3870; tel. 304/234–0123; Lex Reddy, President and Chief Executive Officer

TRINITY HOSPITAL TWIN CITY, 819 North First Street, Dennison, OH, Zip 44621–1098; tel. 740/922–2800; Teresa Gagliardi, R.N., Chief Nursing Officer and Interim Chief Executive Officer

WILSON MEMORIAL HOSPITAL, 915 West Michigan Street, Sidney, OH, Zip 45365–2491; tel. 937/498–2311; Mark J. Dooley, Chief Executive Officer

WYANDOT MEMORIAL HOSPITAL, 885 North Sandusky Avenue, Upper Sandusky, OH, Zip 43351–1098; tel. 419/294–4991; Joseph A. D'Ettorre, Chief Executive Officer

PREMIER HEALTH
110 North Main Street, Suite 390, Dayton, OH, Zip 45402–3720; tel. 937/499–9401; Mary H. Boosalis, President and Chief Executive Officer

ATRIUM MEDICAL CENTER, One Medical Center Drive, Middletown, OH, Zip 45005–1066; tel. 513/424–2111; Michael Uhl, President

GOOD SAMARITAN HOSPITAL, 2222 Philadelphia Drive, Dayton, OH, Zip 45406–1813; tel. 937/734–2612; Eloise Broner, President and Chief Executive Officer

MIAMI VALLEY HOSPITAL, One Wyoming Street, Dayton, OH, Zip 45409–2793; tel. 937/208–8000; Mikki Clancy, Chief Operating Officer

UPPER VALLEY MEDICAL CENTER, 3130 North County Road 25A, Troy, OH, Zip 45373–1309; tel. 937/440–4000; Rebecca Rice, FACHE, Chief Executive Officer

TRIHEALTH
619 Oak Street, Cincinnati, OH, Zip 45206; tel. 513/569–6507; Mark C. Clement, President and Chief Executive Officer

BETHESDA NORTH HOSPITAL, 10500 Montgomery Road, Cincinnati, OH, Zip 45242–4402; tel. 513/865–1111; Barbara Boyne, Executive Director, Operations

GOOD SAMARITAN HOSPITAL, 375 Dixmyth Avenue, Cincinnati, OH, Zip 45220–2489; tel. 513/862–1400; Jamie Easterling, Executive Director, Operations

MCCULLOUGH-HYDE MEMORIAL HOSPITAL/TRIHEALTH, 110 North Poplar Street, Oxford, OH, Zip 45056–1292; tel. 513/523–2111; Brett Kirkpatrick, Executive Director

TRIHEALTH EVENDALE HOSPITAL, 3155 Glendale Milford Road, Cincinnati, OH, Zip 45241–3134; tel. 513/454–2222; Kelvin Hanger, Chief Executive Officer

OKLAHOMA

ALLIANCEHEALTH OKLAHOMA
5300 North Grand Boulevard, Oklahoma City, OK, Zip 73112–5647; tel. 405/815–3900; Clay Franklin, Market Chief Executive Officer

ALLIANCEHEALTH CLINTON, 100 North 30th Street, Clinton, OK, Zip 73601–3117; tel. 580/323–2363; Cameron Lewis, Chief Executive Officer

ALLIANCEHEALTH DEACONESS, 5501 North Portland Avenue, Oklahoma City, OK, Zip 73112–2099; tel. 405/604–6000; Devon Hyde, Chief Executive Officer

ALLIANCEHEALTH DURANT, 1800 University Boulevard, Durant, OK, Zip 74701–3006, P O Box 1207, 74702–1207, tel. 580/924–3080; Jeffrey S. Tarrant, FACHE, Chief Executive Officer

ALLIANCEHEALTH MADILL, 901 South Fifth Avenue, Madill, OK, Zip 73446–3640, P O Box 827, 73446–0827, tel. 580/795–3384; Minnie Burkhardt, Chief Executive Officer

ALLIANCEHEALTH MIDWEST, 2825 Parklawn Drive, Midwest City, OK, Zip 73110–4258; tel. 405/610–4411; Clay Franklin, Chief Executive Officer

ALLIANCEHEALTH PONCA CITY, 1900 North 14th Street, Ponca City, OK, Zip 74601–2099; tel. 580/765–3321; Christopher Mendoza, Chief Executive Officer

ALLIANCEHEALTH SEMINOLE, 2401 Wrangler Boulevard, Seminole, OK, Zip 74868–1917; tel. 405/303–4000; Adam Bracks, Chief Executive Officer

ALLIANCEHEALTH WOODWARD, 900 17th Street, Woodward, OK, Zip 73801–2448; tel. 580/256–5511; Ross Korkmas, Chief Executive Officer

MERCY HEALTH SYSTEM OF OKLAHOMA
4300 West Memorial Road, Oklahoma City, OK, Zip 73120–8304; tel. 405/752–3756; Diana Smalley, President and Chief Executive Officer

ARBUCKLE MEMORIAL HOSPITAL, 2011 West Broadway Street, Sulphur, OK, Zip 73086–4221, P.O. Box 1109, 73086–8109, tel. 580/622–2161; Darin Farrell, Administrator

MERCY HEALTH LOVE COUNTY, 300 Wanda Street, Marietta, OK, Zip 73448–1200; tel. 580/276–3347; Richard Barker, Administrator and Chief Executive Officer

MERCY HOSPITAL ADA, 430 North Monte Vista, Ada, OK, Zip 74820–4610; tel. 580/332–2323; Lori Wightman, R.N., MSN, FACHE, President

MERCY HOSPITAL ARDMORE, 1011 14th Avenue NW, Ardmore, OK, Zip 73401–1828; tel. 580/223–5400; Daryle Voss, FACHE, President and Chief Executive Officer

MERCY HOSPITAL EL RENO, 2115 Parkview Drive, El Reno, OK, Zip 73036–2199; tel. 405/262–2640; Cindy Carmichael, Administrator

MERCY HOSPITAL HEALDTON, 918 South 8th Street, Healdton, OK, Zip 73438–0928, P O Box 928, 73438–0928, tel. 580/229–0701; Jeremy A. Jones, Administrator

MERCY HOSPITAL KINGFISHER, 1000 Kingfisher Regional Hospital Drive, Kingfisher, OK, Zip 73750–3528, P O Box 59, 73750–0059, tel. 405/375–3141; Brian Denton, Administrator

MERCY HOSPITAL LOGAN COUNTY, 200 South Academy Road, Guthrie, OK, Zip 73044–8727, P O Box 1017, 73044–1017, tel. 405/282–6700; Joshua Tucker, Administrator

MERCY HOSPITAL OKLAHOMA CITY, 4300 West Memorial Road, Oklahoma City, OK, Zip 73120–8362; tel. 405/755–1515; Jim Gebhart, Jr., FACHE, President

MERCY HOSPITAL TISHOMINGO, 1000 South Byrd Street, Tishomingo, OK, Zip 73460–3299; tel. 580/371–2327; Gary Sharum, Administrator

MERCY HOSPITAL WATONGA, 500 North Clarence Nash Boulevard, Watonga, OK, Zip 73772–2845, P O Box 370, 73772–0370, tel. 580/623–7211; Bobby Stitt, R.N., Administrator

MERCY REHABILITATION HOSPITAL OKLAHOMA CITY, 5401 West Memorial Rd, Oklahoma City, OK, Zip 73142–2026; tel. 405/752–3935; Sharon Smeltzer, Chief Executive Officer

OKLAHOMA HEART HOSPITAL SOUTH CAMPUS, 5200 East I-240 Service Road, Oklahoma City, OK, Zip 73135; tel. 405/628–6000; John Harvey, M.D., Chief Executive Officer

OKLAHOMA HEART HOSPITAL, 4050 West Memorial Road, Oklahoma City, OK, Zip 73120–8382; tel. 405/608–3200; John Harvey, M.D., Chief Executive Officer

OKLAHOMA STATE UNIVERSITY MEDICAL CENTER, 744 West Ninth Street, Tulsa, OK, Zip 74127–9020; tel. 918/599–1000; Matthew Adams, Administrator

SEILING MUNICIPAL HOSPITAL, Highway 60 NE, Seiling, OK, Zip 73663, P O Box 720, 73663–0720, tel. 580/922–7361; Jennifer Coons, Chief Executive Officer

PENNSYLVANIA

ALLEGHENY HEALTH NETWORK
30 Isabella Street, Suite 300, Pittsburgh, PA, Zip 15212–5862; tel. 412/330–2400; Cynthia Hundorfean, President and Chief Executive Officer

ALLEGHENY GENERAL HOSPITAL, 320 East North Avenue, Pittsburgh, PA, Zip 15212–4756; tel. 412/359–3131; Jeffrey Cohen, M.D., President

ALLEGHENY VALLEY HOSPITAL, 1301 Carlisle Street, Natrona Heights, PA, Zip 15065–1152; tel. 724/224–5100; William Englert, Chief Executive Officer

CANONSBURG HOSPITAL, 100 Medical Boulevard, Canonsburg, PA, Zip 15317–9762; tel. 724/745–6100; Louise Urban, R.N., President and Chief Executive Officer

FORBES HOSPITAL, 2570 Haymaker Road, Monroeville, PA, Zip 15146–3513; tel. 412/858–2000; Mark Rubino, M.D., President

JEFFERSON HOSPITAL, 565 Coal Valley Road, Jefferson Hills, PA, Zip 15025–3703, Box 18119, Pittsburgh, 15236–0119, tel. 412/469–5000; Louise Urban, R.N., President and Chief Executive Officer

SAINT VINCENT HOSPITAL, 232 West 25th Street, Erie, PA, Zip 16544–0002; tel. 814/452–5000; Christopher Clark, D.O., President and Chief Executive Officer

WEST PENN HOSPITAL, 4800 Friendship Avenue, Pittsburgh, PA, Zip 15224–1722; tel. 412/578–5000; Ronald J. Andro, President and Chief Executive Officer

WESTFIELD MEMORIAL HOSPITAL, 189 East Main Street, Westfield, NY, Zip 14787–1195; tel. 716/326–4921; Christopher Clark, D.O., President and Chief Executive Officer

COMMONWEALTH HEALTH
575 North River Street, Wilkes Barre, PA, Zip 18764–0999; tel. 570/829–8111; Cornelio R. Catena, Market President and Chief Executive Officer, Wilkes-Barre General Hospital

BERWICK HOSPITAL CENTER, 701 East 16th Street, Berwick, PA, Zip 18603–2397; tel. 570/759–5000; Diane Ljungquist, R.N., MS, Chief Executive Officer

FIRST HOSPITAL WYOMING VALLEY, 562 Wyoming Avenue, Kingston, PA, Zip 18704–3721; tel. 570/552–3900; Eugene Boylan, Chief Executive Officer

MOSES TAYLOR HOSPITAL, 700 Quincy Avenue, Scranton, PA, Zip 18510–1724; tel. 570/770–5000; Justin Davis, Chief Executive Officer

REGIONAL HOSPITAL OF SCRANTON, 746 Jefferson Avenue, Scranton, PA, Zip 18510–1624; tel. 570/348–7100; Justin Davis, Chief Executive Officer

TYLER MEMORIAL HOSPITAL, 5950 State Route 6, Tunkhannock, PA, Zip 18657–7905; tel. 570/836–2161; Ann Marie. Stevens, R.N., Chief Executive Officer

WILKES-BARRE GENERAL HOSPITAL, 575 North River Street, Wilkes-Barre, PA, Zip 18764–0001; tel. 570/829–8111; Cornelio R. Catena, President and Chief Executive Officer

PENN HIGHLANDS HEALTHCARE
204 Hospital Avenue, DuBois, PA, Zip 15801–0447; tel. 814/375–6430; Steven M. Fontaine, System Chief Executive Officer

PENN HIGHLANDS BROOKVILLE, 100 Hospital Road, Brookville, PA, Zip 15825–1367; tel. 814/849–2312; Julianne Peer, President

PENN HIGHLANDS CLEARFIELD, 809 Turnpike Avenue, Clearfield, PA, Zip 16830–1232, P O Box 992, 16830–0992, tel. 814/765–5341; Gary Macioce, President

PENN HIGHLANDS DUBOIS, 100 Hospital Avenue, DuBois, PA, Zip 15801–1440, P O Box 447, 15801–0447, tel. 814/371–2200; John Sutika, President

Section B

PENN HIGHLANDS ELK, 763 Johnsonburg Road, Saint Marys, PA, Zip 15857–3498; tel. 814/788–8000; Bradley Chapman, President

VANTAGE HEALTHCARE NETWORK, INC.
18282 Technology Drive, Suite 202, Meadville, PA, Zip 16335–8378; tel. 814/337–0000; David Petrarca, Director Retail Operations

BRADFORD REGIONAL MEDICAL CENTER, 116 Interstate Parkway, Bradford, PA, Zip 16701–1036; tel. 814/368–4143; Timothy J. Finan, FACHE, President and Chief Executive Officer

CLARION HOSPITAL, One Hospital Drive, Clarion, PA, Zip 16214–8501; tel. 814/226–9500; Byron Quinton, Chief Executive Officer

MEADVILLE MEDICAL CENTER, 751 Liberty Street, Meadville, PA, Zip 16335–2559; tel. 814/333–5000; Philip E. Pandolph, FACHE, Chief Executive Officer

PENN HIGHLANDS BROOKVILLE, 100 Hospital Road, Brookville, PA, Zip 15825–1367; tel. 814/849–2312; Julianne Peer, President

PENN HIGHLANDS ELK, 763 Johnsonburg Road, Saint Marys, PA, Zip 15857–3498; tel. 814/788–8000; Bradley Chapman, President

PUNXSUTAWNEY AREA HOSPITAL, 81 Hillcrest Drive, Punxsutawney, PA, Zip 15767–2616; tel. 814/938–1800; Daniel D. Blough, Jr., Chief Executive Officer

TITUSVILLE AREA HOSPITAL, 406 West Oak Street, Titusville, PA, Zip 16354–1404; tel. 814/827–1851; Lee Clinton, FACHE, Chief Executive Officer

UPMC BEDFORD MEMORIAL, 10455 Lincoln Highway, Everett, PA, Zip 15537–7046; tel. 814/623–6161; Gerald Murray, President

UPMC HAMOT, 201 State Street, Erie, PA, Zip 16550–0002; tel. 814/877–6000; David Gibbons, President

UPMC JAMESON HOSPITAL, 1211 Wilmington Avenue, New Castle, PA, Zip 16105–2516; tel. 724/658–9001; Donald R. Owrey, President

UPMC KANE, 4372 Route 6, Kane, PA, Zip 16735–3060; tel. 814/837–8585; J Gary. Rhodes, FACHE, Chief Executive Officer

UPMC MCKEESPORT, 1500 Fifth Avenue, McKeesport, PA, Zip 15132–2422; tel. 412/664–2000; Mark Sevco, President

UPMC NORTHWEST, 100 Fairfield Drive, Seneca, PA, Zip 16346–2130; tel. 814/676–7600; Brian Durniok, President

UPMC PASSAVANT, 9100 Babcock Boulevard, Pittsburgh, PA, Zip 15237–5815; tel. 412/748–6700; David T. Martin, President

UPMC ST. MARGARET, 815 Freeport Road, Pittsburgh, PA, Zip 15215–3301; tel. 412/784–4000; David J. Patton, President

WARREN GENERAL HOSPITAL, Two Crescent Park West, Warren, PA, Zip 16365–0068, P O Box 68, 16365–0068; tel. 814/723–4973; Richard Allen, Chief Executive Officer

SOUTH DAKOTA

REGIONAL HEALTH
353 Fairmont Boulevard, Rapid City, SD, Zip 57701–7375; tel. 605/719–1000; Brent R. Phillips, President and Chief Executive Officer

CUSTER REGIONAL HOSPITAL, 1039 Montgomery Street, Custer, SD, Zip 57730–1397; tel. 605/673–2229; Veronica Schmidt, President

LEAD-DEADWOOD REGIONAL HOSPITAL, 61 Charles Street, Deadwood, SD, Zip 57732–1303; tel. 605/717–6000; Mark C. Schmidt, President

PHILIP HEALTH SERVICES, 503 West Pine Street, Philip, SD, Zip 57567–3300, P O Box 790, 57567–0790; tel. 605/859–2511; Jeremy Schultes, Administrator and Chief Executive Officer

RAPID CITY REGIONAL HOSPITAL, 353 Fairmont Boulevard, Rapid City, SD, Zip 57701–7393, P O Box 6000, 57709–6000; tel. 605/755–1000; Paulette Davidson, FACHE, Chief Operating Officer and Interim President

SPEARFISH REGIONAL HOSPITAL, 1440 North Main Street, Spearfish, SD, Zip 57783–1504; tel. 605/644–4000; Larry W. Veitz, President

STURGIS REGIONAL HOSPITAL, 949 Harmon Street, Sturgis, SD, Zip 57785–2452; tel. 605/720–2400; Mark Schulte, FACHE, President

WESTON COUNTY HEALTH SERVICES, 1124 Washington Boulevard, Newcastle, WY, Zip 82701–2972; tel. 307/746–4491; Maureen K. Cadwell, Chief Executive Officer

SANFORD HEALTH NETWORK
1305 West 18th Street, Sioux Falls, SD, Zip 57105–0401; tel. 605/328–5513; Jesse G. Tischer, President

BOZEMAN HEALTH DEACONESS HOSPITAL, 915 Highland Boulevard, Bozeman, MT, Zip 59715–6902; tel. 406/585–5000; John Hill, President and Chief Executive Officer

COMMUNITY MEMORIAL HOSPITAL, 809 Jackson Street, Burke, SD, Zip 57523–2065, P O Box 319, 57523–0319; tel. 605/775–2621; Mistie Sachtjen, Chief Executive Officer

DOUGLAS COUNTY MEMORIAL HOSPITAL, 708 Eighth Street, Armour, SD, Zip 57313–2102; tel. 605/724–2159; Heath Brouwer, Administrator

JAMESTOWN REGIONAL MEDICAL CENTER, 2422 20th Street SW, Jamestown, ND, Zip 58401–6201; tel. 701/252–1050; K C. DeBoer, President and Chief Executive Officer

KITTSON MEMORIAL HEALTHCARE CENTER, 1010 South Birch Street, Hallock, MN, Zip 56728–4215, P O Box 700, 56728–0700; tel. 218/843–3612; Ashley Rivera, Chief Financial Officer and Chief Executive Officer

LIBERTY MEDICAL CENTER, 315 West Madison Avenue, Chester, MT, Zip 59522, P O Box 705, 59522–0705, tel. 406/759–5181; Matthew Waller, Chief Executive Officer

MAHNOMEN HEALTH CENTER, 414 West Jefferson Avenue, Mahnomen, MN, Zip 56557–4912, P O Box 396, 56557–0396, tel. 218/935–2511; Dale K. Kruger, Chief Executive Officer

MCKENZIE COUNTY HEALTHCARE SYSTEM, 516 North Main Street, Watford City, ND, Zip 58854–7310; tel. 701/842–3000; Daniel R. Kelly, Chief Executive Officer

MURRAY COUNTY MEDICAL CENTER, 2042 Juniper Avenue, Slayton, MN, Zip 56172–1017; tel. 507/836–6111; Dennis Goebel, Chief Executive Officer

NORTHWOOD DEACONESS HEALTH CENTER, 4 North Park Street, Northwood, ND, Zip 58267–4102, P O Box 190, 58267–0190, tel. 701/587–6060; Pete Antonson, Chief Executive Officer

ORANGE CITY AREA HEALTH SYSTEM, 1000 Lincoln Circle SE, Orange City, IA, Zip 51041–1862; tel. 712/737–4984; Martin W. Guthmiller, Chief Executive Officer

ORTONVILLE AREA HEALTH SERVICES, 450 Eastvold Avenue, Ortonville, MN, Zip 56278–1133; tel. 320/839–2502; David Rogers, Chief Executive Officer

PERHAM HEALTH, 1000 Coney Street West, Perham, MN, Zip 56573–1108; tel. 218/347–4500; Chuck Hofius, Chief Executive Officer

PIONEER MEMORIAL HOSPITAL AND HEALTH SERVICES, 315 North Washington Street, Viborg, SD, Zip 57070–2002, P O Box 368, 57070–0368, tel. 605/326–5161; Thomas V. Richter, Chief Executive Officer

RIVERVIEW HEALTH, 323 South Minnesota Street, Crookston, MN, Zip 56716–1601; tel. 218/281–9200; Carrie Michalski, President and Chief Executive Officer

SANFORD ABERDEEN MEDICAL CENTER, 2905 3rd Avenue SE, Aberdeen, SD, Zip 57401–5420; tel. 605/626–4200; Ashley M. Erickson, Chief Executive Officer

SANFORD BAGLEY MEDICAL CENTER, 203 Fourth Street NW, Bagley, MN, Zip 56621–8307; tel. 218/694–6501; Robert Belanger, Chief Executive Officer

SANFORD BEMIDJI MEDICAL CENTER, 1300 Anne Street NW, Bemidji, MN, Zip 56601–5103; tel. 218/751–5430; Bryan Nermoe, President

SANFORD BISMARCK, 300 North Seventh Street, Bismarck, ND, Zip 58501–4439, P O Box 5525, 58506–5525, tel. 701/323–6000; Craig Lambrecht, M.D., President

SANFORD CANBY MEDICAL CENTER, 112 St Olaf Avenue South, Canby, MN, Zip 56220–1433; tel. 507/223–7277; Lori Sisk, R.N., Chief Executive Officer

SANFORD CANTON-INWOOD MEDICAL CENTER, 440 North Hiawatha Drive, Canton, SD, Zip 57013–5800; tel. 605/764–1400; Scott C. Larson, Chief Executive Officer

SANFORD CHAMBERLAIN MEDICAL CENTER, 300 South Byron Boulevard, Chamberlain, SD, Zip 57325–9741; tel. 605/234–5511; Erica Peterson, Chief Executive Officer

SANFORD CLEAR LAKE MEDICAL CENTER, 701 Third Avenue South, Clear Lake, SD, Zip 57226–2016; tel. 605/874–2141; Lori Sisk, R.N., Chief Executive Officer

SANFORD HILLSBORO MEDICAL CENTER, 12 Third Street SE, Hillsboro, ND, Zip 58045–4840, P O Box 609, 58045–0609, tel. 701/636–3200; Jac McTaggart, Chief Executive Officer

SANFORD JACKSON MEDICAL CENTER, 1430 North Highway, Jackson, MN, Zip 56143–1093; tel. 507/847–2420; Dawn Schnell, Chief Nursing Officer and Interim Senior Director

SANFORD LUVERNE MEDICAL CENTER, 1600 North Kniss Avenue, Luverne, MN, Zip 56156–1067; tel. 507/283–2321; Tammy Loosbrock, Chief Executive Officer

SANFORD MAYVILLE MEDICAL CENTER, 42 Sixth Avenue SE, Mayville, ND, Zip 58257–1598; tel. 701/786–3800; Roger Baier, Chief Executive Officer

SANFORD MEDICAL CENTER THIEF RIVER FALLS, 3001 Sanford Parkway, Thief River Falls, MN, Zip 56701–2700; tel. 218/681–4240; Brian J. Carlson, FACHE, Chief Executive Officer

SANFORD ROCK RAPIDS MEDICAL CENTER, 801 South Greene Street, Rock Rapids, IA, Zip 51246–1998; tel. 712/472–2591; Tammy Loosbrock, Chief Executive Officer

SANFORD SHELDON MEDICAL CENTER, 118 North Seventh Avenue, Sheldon, IA, Zip 51201–1235, P O Box 250, 51201–0250, tel. 712/324–5041; Richard E. Nordahl, Chief Executive Officer

SANFORD THIEF RIVER FALLS BEHAVIORAL HEALTH CENTER, 120 LaBree Avenue South, Thief River Falls, MN, Zip 56701–2819, 3001 Sanford Parkway, 56701–2819, tel. 218/683–4349; Brian J. Carlson, FACHE, Chief Executive Officer

SANFORD TRACY MEDICAL CENTER, 251 Fifth Street East, Tracy, MN, Zip 56175–1536; tel. 507/629–8400; Stacy Barstad, Chief Executive Officer

SANFORD USD MEDICAL CENTER, 1305 West 18th Street, Sioux Falls, SD, Zip 57105–0496, P O Box 5039, 57117–5039, tel. 605/333–1000; Paul A. Hanson, FACHE, President

SANFORD VERMILLION MEDICAL CENTER, 20 South Plum Street, Vermillion, SD, Zip 57069–3346; tel. 605/677–3500; Timothy J. Tracy, Chief Executive Officer

SANFORD WEBSTER MEDICAL CENTER, 1401 West 1st Street, Webster, SD, Zip 57274–1054, P O Box 489, 57274–0489, tel. 605/345–3336; Isaac Gerdes, Chief Executive Officer

SANFORD WESTBROOK MEDICAL CENTER, 920 Bell Avenue, Westbrook, MN, Zip 56183–9669, P O Box 188, 56183–0188, tel. 507/274–6121; Stacy Barstad, Chief Executive Officer

SANFORD WHEATON MEDICAL CENTER, 401 12th Street North, Wheaton, MN, Zip 56296–1099; tel. 320/563–8226; JoAnn M. Foltz, R.N., Chief Executive Officer

SANFORD WORTHINGTON MEDICAL CENTER, 1018 Sixth Avenue, Worthington, MN, Zip 56187–2202, P O Box 997, 56187–0997, tel. 507/372–2941; Jennifer . Weg, MS, R.N., Chief Executive Officer

SIDNEY HEALTH CENTER, 216 14th Avenue SW, Sidney, MT, Zip 59270–3586; tel. 406/488–2100; Richard Haraldson, Chief Executive Officer

WEST HOLT MEDICAL SERVICES, 406 West Neely Street, Atkinson, NE, Zip 68713–4801; tel. 402/925–2811; Bradley D. Pfeifer, FACHE, Chief Executive Officer

WINDOM AREA HOSPITAL, 2150 Hospital Drive, Windom, MN, Zip 56101–0339, P O Box 339, 56101–0339, tel. 507/831–2400; Shelby Medina, Chief Executive Officer

WINNER REGIONAL HEALTHCARE CENTER, 745 East Eighth Street, Winner, SD, Zip 57580–2631; tel. 605/842–7100; Kevin Coffey, Chief Executive Officer

TENNESSEE

TRISTAR HEALTH
110 Winners Circle, First Floor, Brentwood, TN, Zip 37027–5070; tel. 615/886–4900; Stephen Corbeil, President

CARTERSVILLE MEDICAL CENTER, 960 Joe Frank Harris Parkway, Cartersville, GA, Zip 30120–2129; tel. 770/382–1530; Keith Sandlin, Chief Executive Officer

EASTSIDE MEDICAL CENTER, 1700 Medical Way, Snellville, GA, Zip 30078–2195; tel. 770/979–0200; Trent Lind, Chief Executive Officer

PARKRIDGE MEDICAL CENTER, 2333 McCallie Avenue, Chattanooga, TN, Zip 37404–3258; tel. 423/698–6061; Thomas H. Ozburn, Chief Executive Officer

REDMOND REGIONAL MEDICAL CENTER, 501 Redmond Road, Rome, GA, Zip 30165–1415, P O Box 107001, 30164–7001, tel. 706/291–0291; John Quinlivan, Chief Executive Officer

TRISTAR ASHLAND CITY MEDICAL CENTER, 313 North Main Street, Ashland City, TN, Zip 37015–1347; tel. 615/792–3030; Darrell White, R.N., Administrator and Chief Nursing Officer

TRISTAR CENTENNIAL MEDICAL CENTER, 2300 Patterson Street, Nashville, TN, Zip 37203–1528; tel. 615/342–1000; Scott A. Cihak, President and Chief Executive Officer

TRISTAR GREENVIEW REGIONAL HOSPITAL, 1801 Ashley Circle, Bowling Green, KY, Zip 42104–3362; tel. 270/793–1000; Michael Sherrod, Chief Executive Officer

TRISTAR HENDERSONVILLE MEDICAL CENTER, 355 New Shackle Island Road, Hendersonville, TN, Zip 37075–2479; tel. 615/338–1000; Regina Bartlett, Chief Executive Officer

TRISTAR HORIZON MEDICAL CENTER, 111 Highway 70 East, Dickson, TN, Zip 37055–2080; tel. 615/446–0446; Dustin Greene, Chief Executive Officer

TRISTAR SKYLINE MEDICAL CENTER, 3441 Dickerson Pike, Nashville, TN, Zip 37207–2539; tel. 615/769–2000; Steve Otto, Chief Executive Officer

TRISTAR SOUTHERN HILLS MEDICAL CENTER, 391 Wallace Road, Nashville, TN, Zip 37211–4859; tel. 615/781–4000; Joanna J. Conley, FACHE, Chief Executive Officer

TRISTAR STONECREST MEDICAL CENTER, 200 StoneCrest Boulevard, Smyrna, TN, Zip 37167–6810; tel. 615/768–2000; Louis Caputo, Chief Executive Officer

TRISTAR SUMMIT MEDICAL CENTER, 5655 Frist Boulevard, Hermitage, TN, Zip 37076–2053; tel. 615/316–3000; Brian Marger, Chief Executive Officer

TEXAS

LITTLE RIVER HEALTHCARE
1700 Brazos Avenue, Rockdale, TX, Zip 76567–2517; tel. 512/446–4500; Jeffrey Madison, FACHE, Chief Executive Officer

CAMERON HOSPITAL, 806 North Crockett Avenue, Cameron, TX, Zip 76520–2553; tel. 254/605–1300; Troy Zinn, Chief Executive Officer

ROCKDALE HOSPITAL, 1700 Brazos Street, Rockdale, TX, Zip 76567–2517, Drawer 1010, 76567–1010, tel. 512/446–4500; Jeffrey Madison, FACHE, Chief Executive Officer

METHODIST HEALTHCARE SYSTEM
8109 Fredericksburg Road, San Antonio, TX, Zip 78229–3311; tel. 210/575–0355; Jaime Wesolowski, President and Chief Executive Officer

METHODIST AMBULATORY SURGERY HOSPITAL - NORTHWEST, 9150 Huebner Road, Suite 100, San Antonio, TX, Zip 78240–1545; tel. 210/575–5000; Scott Davis, Chief Executive Officer

METHODIST HOSPITAL, 7700 Floyd Curl Drive, San Antonio, TX, Zip 78229–3993; tel. 210/575–4000; Allen Harrison, Chief Executive Officer

METHODIST STONE OAK HOSPITAL, 1139 East Sonterra Boulevard, San Antonio, TX, Zip 78258–4347; tel. 210/638–2100; Marc Strode, Chief Executive Officer

REGIONAL HEALTHCARE ALLIANCE
530 South Beckham Avenue, Tyler, TX, Zip 75702–8310; tel. 903/531–4449; John Webb, President

ALLEGIANCE SPECIALTY HOSPITAL OF KILGORE, 1612 South Henderson Boulevard, Kilgore, TX, Zip 75662–3594; tel. 903/984–3505; Karen Ross, Chief Executive Officer

BAYLOR UNIVERSITY MEDICAL CENTER, 3500 Gaston Avenue, Dallas, TX, Zip 75246–2088; tel. 214/820–0111; T. Douglas. Lawson, Ph.D., FACHE, President

CHRISTUS GOOD SHEPHERD MEDICAL CENTER, 700 East Marshall Avenue, Longview, TX, Zip 75601–5580; tel. 903/315–1800; Todd Hancock, President and Chief Executive Officer

CHRISTUS MOTHER FRANCES HOSPITAL - JACKSONVILLE, 2026 South Jackson, Jacksonville, TX, Zip 75766–5822; tel. 903/541–4500; Anne Pileggi, Administrator and Associate Vice President

CHRISTUS MOTHER FRANCES HOSPITAL - SULPHUR SPRINGS, 115 Airport Road, Sulphur Springs, TX, Zip 75482–2105; tel. 903/885–7671; Paul Harvery, President and Chief Executive Officer

CHRISTUS MOTHER FRANCES HOSPITAL - TYLER, 800 East Dawson Street, Tyler, TX, Zip 75701–2036; tel. 903/593–8441; Jason J. Proctor, Chief Operating Officer

CHRISTUS TRINITY MOTHER FRANCES REHABILITATION HOSPITAL, 3131 Troup Highway, Tyler, TX, Zip 75701–8352; tel. 903/510–7000; Sharla Anderson, Chief Executive Officer

CHILDREN'S HEALTH SYSTEM OF TEXAS, 1935 Medical District Drive, Pavilion, 3rd Floor, Dallas, TX, Zip 75235; tel. 214/456–7000; Christopher J. Durovich, President and Chief Executive Officer

EAST TEXAS MEDICAL CENTER HENDERSON, 300 Wilson Street, Henderson, TX, Zip 75652–5956; tel. 903/657–7541; Mark Leitner, FACHE, Administrator

NACOGDOCHES MEDICAL CENTER, 4920 NE Stallings Drive, Nacogdoches, TX, Zip 75965–1200; tel. 936/569–9481; Jeff Patterson, Chief Executive Officer

PALESTINE REGIONAL MEDICAL CENTER-EAST, 2900 South Loop 256, Palestine, TX, Zip 75801–6958; tel. 903/731–1000; Roy Finch, Chief Executive Officer

PARIS REGIONAL MEDICAL CENTER, 865 Deshong Drive, Paris, TX, Zip 75460–9313, P O Box 9070, 75461–9070, tel. 903/785–4521; Steve Hyde, Chief Executive Officer

TITUS REGIONAL MEDICAL CENTER, 2001 North Jefferson Avenue, Mount Pleasant, TX, Zip 75455–2398; tel. 903/577–6000; Terry Scoggin, Interim Chief Executive Officer

TYLER CONTINUECARE HOSPITAL, 800 East Dawson, 4th Floor, Tyler, TX, Zip 75701–2036; tel. 903/531–4080; Stephanie Hyde, R.N., MSN, Chief Executive Officer

UNIVERSITY OF TEXAS HEALTH NORTHEAST, 11937 Highway 271, Tyler, TX, Zip 75708–3154; tel. 903/877–7777; Kirk A. Calhoun, M.D., President

ST. DAVID'S HEALTH NETWORK
98 San Jacinto Boulevard, Austin, TX, Zip 78701–4082; tel. 512/708–9700; David Huffstutler, President and Chief Executive Officer

ST. DAVID'S MEDICAL CENTER, 919 East 32nd Street, Austin, TX, Zip 78705–2709, P O Box 4039, 78765–4039, tel. 512/476–7111; Donald H. Wilkerson, FACHE, Chief Executive Officer

ST. DAVID'S NORTH AUSTIN MEDICAL CENTER, 12221 North MoPac Expressway, Austin, TX, Zip 78758–2496; tel. 512/901–1000; Thomas W. Jackson, Chief Executive Officer

ST. DAVID'S ROUND ROCK MEDICAL CENTER, 2400 Round Rock Avenue, Round Rock, TX, Zip 78681–4097; tel. 512/341–1000; Jeremy Barclay, Chief Executive Officer

ST. DAVID'S SOUTH AUSTIN MEDICAL CENTER, 901 West Ben White Boulevard, Austin, TX, Zip 78704–6903; tel. 512/447–2211; Todd E. Steward, FACHE, Chief Executive Officer

THE HOSPITALS OF PROVIDENCE
2001 North Oregon Street, El Paso, TX, Zip 79902–3320; tel. 915/577–7746; Sally A. Hurt-Deitch, FACHE, R.N., Market Chief Executive Officer

THE HOSPITALS OF PROVIDENCE EAST CAMPUS, 3280 Joe Battle Boulevard, El Paso, TX, Zip 79938–2622; tel. 915/832–2000; Phillip Young, Chief Executive Officer

THE HOSPITALS OF PROVIDENCE MEMORIAL CAMPUS, 2001 North Oregon Street, El Paso, TX, Zip 79902–3368; tel. 915/577–6625; Sally A. Hurt-Deitch, FACHE, R.N., Market Chief Executive Officer

THE HOSPITALS OF PROVIDENCE SIERRA CAMPUS, 1625 Medical Center Drive, El Paso, TX, Zip 79902–5005; tel. 915/747–4000; Monica Vargas-Mahar, FACHE, Chief Executive Officer

THE HOSPITALS OF PROVIDENCE TRANSMOUNTAIN CAMPUS, 2000 Transmountain Road, El Paso, TX, Zip 79911; tel. 915/877–8300; Nicholas R. Tejeda, FACHE, Chief Executive Officer

VERMONT

THE UNIVERSITY OF VERMONT HEALTH NETWORK
111 Colchester Avenue, Burlington, VT, Zip 05401–1473; tel. 802/847–3983; John R. Brumsted, M.D., President and Chief Executive Officer

THE UNIVERSITY OF VERMONT HEALTH NETWORK CENTRAL VERMONT MEDICAL CENTER, 130 Fisher Road, Berlin, VT, Zip 05602–9516, P O Box 547, Barre, 05641–0547, tel. 802/371–4100; Anna Noonan, President and Chief Operating Officer

THE UNIVERSITY OF VERMONT HEALTH NETWORK ELIZABETHTOWN COMMUNITY HOSPITAL, 75 Park Street, Elizabethtown, NY, Zip 12932, P O Box 277, 12932–0277, tel. 518/873–6377; John R. Remillard, Interim Chief Executive Officer

THE UNIVERSITY OF VERMONT HEALTH NETWORK-CHAMPLAIN VALLEY PHYSICIANS HOSPITAL, 75 Beekman Street, Plattsburgh, NY, Zip 12901–1438; tel. 518/561–2000; Stephens M. Mundy, President and Chief Executive Officer

UNIVERSITY OF VERMONT MEDICAL CENTER, 111 Colchester Avenue, Burlington, VT, Zip 05401–1473; tel. 802/847–0000; Eileen Whalen, R.N., President and Chief Operating Officer

VIRGINIA

VIRGINIA HEALTH NETWORK
7400 Beaufont Springs Drive, Suite 505, Richmond, VA, Zip 23225–5521; tel. 804/320–3837; James Brittain, President

AUGUSTA HEALTH, 78 Medical Center Drive, Fishersville, VA, Zip 22939–2332, P O Box 1000, 22939–1000, tel. 540/932–4000; Mary N. Mannix, FACHE, President and Chief Executive Officer

BATH COMMUNITY HOSPITAL, 83 Park Drive, Hot Springs, VA, Zip 24445–2788, P O Box Z, 24445–0750, tel. 540/839–7000; Kathy Landreth, Interim Chief Executive Officer

BEDFORD MEMORIAL HOSPITAL, 1613 Oakwood Street, Bedford, VA, Zip 24523–1213, P O Box 688, 24523–0688, tel. 540/586–2441; Patti Jurkus, Chief Executive Officer

BON SECOURS MARYVIEW MEDICAL CENTER, 3636 High Street, Portsmouth, VA, Zip 23707–3270; tel. 757/398–2200; Joseph M. Oddis, Chief Executive Officer

BON SECOURS MEMORIAL REGIONAL MEDICAL CENTER, 8260 Atlee Road, Mechanicsville, VA, Zip 23116–1844; tel. 804/764–6000; Mark M. Gordon, Chief Executive Officer

BON SECOURS ST. FRANCIS MEDICAL CENTER, 13710 St Francis Boulevard, Midlothian, VA, Zip 23114–3267; tel. 804/594–7300; Chris Accashian, Chief Executive Officer

BON SECOURS ST. MARY'S HOSPITAL, 5801 Bremo Road, Richmond, VA, Zip 23226–1907; tel. 804/285–2011; Francine Barr, R.N., MS, Chief Executive Officer

BON SECOURS-DEPAUL MEDICAL CENTER, 150 Kingsley Lane, Norfolk, VA, Zip 23505–4650; tel. 757/889–5000; John E. Barrett, III., Chief Executive Officer

BON SECOURS-RICHMOND COMMUNITY HOSPITAL, 1500 North 28th Street, Richmond, VA, Zip 23223–5396, P O Box 27184, 23261–7184, tel. 804/225–1700; Mark M. Gordon, Chief Executive Officer

BUCHANAN GENERAL HOSPITAL, 1535 Slate Creek Road, Grundy, VA, Zip 24614–6974; tel. 276/935–1000; Robert D. Ruchti, Chief Executive Officer

CARILION FRANKLIN MEMORIAL HOSPITAL, 180 Floyd Avenue, Rocky Mount, VA, Zip 24151–1389; tel. 540/483–5277; William D. Jacobsen, FACHE, Administrator and Hospital Vice President

CARILION GILES COMMUNITY HOSPITAL, 159 Hartley Way, Pearisburg, VA, Zip 24134–2471; tel. 540/921–6000; William Flattery, Vice President and Administrator Western Division

CARILION NEW RIVER VALLEY MEDICAL CENTER, 2900 Lamb Circle, Christiansburg, VA, Zip 24073–6344, P O Box 5, Radford, 24143–0005, tel. 540/731–2000; William Flattery, Vice President and Administrator Western Division

CARILION ROANOKE MEMORIAL HOSPITAL, Belleview at Jefferson Street, Roanoke, VA, Zip 24014, P O Box 13367, 24033–3367, tel. 540/981–7000; Steven C. Arner, President

CARILION STONEWALL JACKSON HOSPITAL, 1 Health Circle, Lexington, VA, Zip 24450–2492; tel. 540/458–3300; Charles E. Carr, Vice President and Administrator

CARILION TAZEWELL COMMUNITY HOSPITAL, 141 Ben Bolt Avenue, Tazewell, VA, Zip 24651–9700, 388 Ben Bolt Avenue, 24651, tel. 276/988–8700; Kathren Dowdy, MSN, Regional Hospital Senior Director

CENTRA SOUTHSIDE COMMUNITY HOSPITAL, 800 Oak Street, Farmville, VA, Zip 23901–1199; tel. 434/392–8811; Thomas Angelo, Chief Executive Officer

CHESAPEAKE REGIONAL HEALTHCARE, 736 Battlefield Boulevard North, Chesapeake, VA, Zip 23320–4941, P O Box 2028, 23327–2028, tel. 757/312–8121; Reese Jackson, Chief Executive Officer

CHILDREN'S HOSPITAL OF RICHMOND AT VCU-BROOK ROAD CAMPUS, 2924 Brook Road, Richmond, VA, Zip 23220–1298; tel. 804/321–7474; Jeniece S. Roane, MS, R.N., Interim Vice President, Children's Services

CHILDREN'S HOSPITAL OF THE KING'S DAUGHTERS, 601 Children's Lane, Norfolk, VA, Zip 23507–1910; tel. 757/668–7000; James D. Dahling, President and Chief Executive Officer

CHIPPENHAM HOSPITAL, 7101 Jahnke Road, Richmond, VA, Zip 23225–4044; tel. 804/320–3911; Greg Lowe, Chief Executive Officer

CLINCH VALLEY MEDICAL CENTER, 6801 Governor G C Peery Highway, Richlands, VA, Zip 24641–2194; tel. 276/596–6000; Peter Mulkey, Chief Executive Officer

DOMINION HOSPITAL, 2960 Sleepy Hollow Road, Falls Church, VA, Zip 22044–2030; tel. 703/536–2000; Lee Higginbotham, Chief Executive Officer

FAUQUIER HOSPITAL, 500 Hospital Drive, Warrenton, VA, Zip 20186–3099; tel. 540/316–5000; Chad Melton, Chief Executive Officer

HEALTHSOUTH REHABILITATION HOSPITAL OF VIRGINIA, 5700 Fitzhugh Avenue, Richmond, VA, Zip 23226–1800; tel. 804/288–5700; David Cashwell, Chief Executive Officer

HENRICO DOCTORS' HOSPITAL, 1602 Skipwith Road, Richmond, VA, Zip 23229–5205; tel. 804/289–4500; William Wagnon, Chief Executive Officer

INOVA ALEXANDRIA HOSPITAL, 4320 Seminary Road, Alexandria, VA, Zip 22304–1535; tel. 703/504–3167; Susan Carroll, Regional Executive Officer-Eastern Region

INOVA FAIR OAKS HOSPITAL, 3600 Joseph Siewick Drive, Fairfax, VA, Zip 22033–1798; tel. 703/391–3600; John L. Fitzgerald, Chief Executive Officer

INOVA FAIRFAX HOSPITAL, 3300 Gallows Road, Falls Church, VA, Zip 22042–3300; tel. 703/776–4001; Patrick Christiansen, Ph.D., Chief Executive Officer

INOVA LOUDOUN HOSPITAL, 44045 Riverside Parkway, Leesburg, VA, Zip 20176–5101, P O Box 6000, 20177–0600, tel. 703/858–6000; Deborah Addo, Chief Executive Officer

INOVA MOUNT VERNON HOSPITAL, 2501 Parker's Lane, Alexandria, VA, Zip 22306–3209; tel. 703/664–7000; Donald Brideau, M.D., Interim Chief Executive Officer

JOHN RANDOLPH MEDICAL CENTER, 411 West Randolph Road, Hopewell, VA, Zip 23860–2938; tel. 804/541–1600; Joseph Mazzo, Chief Executive Officer

JOHNSTON MEMORIAL HOSPITAL, 16000 Johnston Memorial Drive, Abingdon, VA, Zip 24211–7659; tel. 276/258–1000; Stan Hickson, FACHE, President and Chief Executive Officer

LEWISGALE HOSPITAL ALLEGHANY, One ARH Lane, Low Moor, VA, Zip 24457, P O Box 7, 24457–0007, tel. 540/862–6011; William Windham, Chief Executive Officer

LEWISGALE HOSPITAL PULASKI, 2400 Lee Highway, Pulaski, VA, Zip 24301–2326, P O Box 759, 24301–0759, tel. 540/994–8100; Derek Vance, Chief Executive Officer

MARTHA JEFFERSON HOSPITAL, 500 Martha Jefferson Drive, Charlottesville, VA, Zip 22911–4668; tel. 434/654–7000; Jonathan S. Davis, FACHE, President

MARY IMMACULATE HOSPITAL, 2 Bernardine Drive, Newport News, VA, Zip 23602–4499; tel. 757/886–6000; Darlene Stephenson, Chief Executive Officer

MARY WASHINGTON HOSPITAL, 1001 Sam Perry Boulevard, Fredericksburg, VA, Zip 22401–3354; tel. 540/741–1100; Michael P. McDermott, M.D., President and Chief Executive Officer

MOUNTAIN VIEW REGIONAL MEDICAL CENTER, 310 Third Street NE, Norton, VA, Zip 24273–1137; tel. 276/679–9100; Dale Clark, President

NORTHERN HOSPITAL OF SURRY COUNTY, 830 Rockford Street, Mount Airy, NC, Zip 27030–5365, P O Box 1101, 27030–1101, tel. 336/719–7000; Ned Hill, President and Chief Executive Officer

NOVANT HEALTH UVA HEALTH SYSTEM CULPEPER MEDICAL CENTER, 501 Sunset Lane, Culpeper, VA, Zip 22701–3917, P O Box 592, 22701–0500, tel. 540/829–4100; Greg Napps, Chief Executive Officer

NOVANT HEALTH UVA HEALTH SYSTEM PRINCE WILLIAM MEDICAL CENTER, 8700 Sudley Road, Manassas, VA, Zip 20110–4418, P O Box 2610, 20108–0867, tel. 703/369–8000; Margaret Gill, Senior Vice President and Chief Executive Officer

PIONEER COMMUNITY HOSPITAL OF PATRICK, 18688 Jeb Stuart Highway, Stuart, VA, Zip 24171–1559; tel. 276/694–3151; Jeanette Filpi, Chief Executive Officer

RAPPAHANNOCK GENERAL HOSPITAL, 101 Harris Drive, Kilmarnock, VA, Zip 22482–3880, P O Box 1449, 22482–1449, tel. 804/435–8000; Mark M. Gordon, Chief Executive Officer

RESTON HOSPITAL CENTER, 1850 Town Center Parkway, Reston, VA, Zip 20190–3219; tel. 703/689–9000; John A. Deardorff, President and Chief Executive, Northern Virginia Market

RIVERSIDE REGIONAL MEDICAL CENTER, 500 J Clyde Morris Boulevard, Newport News, VA, Zip 23601–1929; tel. 757/594–2000; Michael J. Doucette, Senior Vice President and Administrator

RIVERSIDE REHABILITATION INSTITUTE, 245 Chesapeake Avenue, Newport News, VA, Zip 23607–6038; tel. 757/928–8000; Daniel Ballin, Administrator

RIVERSIDE SHORE MEMORIAL HOSPITAL, 204800 Market Street, Onancoke, VA, Zip 23417, P O Box 17, Nassawadox, 23413–0017, tel. 757/302–2100; John Peterman, Vice President and Administrator

RIVERSIDE TAPPAHANNOCK HOSPITAL, 618 Hospital Road, Tappahannock, VA, Zip 22560–5000; tel. 804/443–3311; Esther Muscari. Desimini, Administrator

RIVERSIDE WALTER REED HOSPITAL, 7519 Hospital Drive, Gloucester, VA, Zip 23061–4178, P O Box 1130, 23061–1130, tel. 804/693–8800; Megan Kleckner, Vice President and Administrator

RUSSELL COUNTY MEDICAL CENTER, 58 Carroll Street, Lebanon, VA, Zip 24266, P O Box 3600, 24266–0200, tel. 276/883–8000; Stephen K. Givens, Assistant Vice President and Administrator

SOVAH HEALTH-MARTINSVILLE, 320 Hospital Drive, Martinsville, VA, Zip 24112–1981, P O Box 4788, 24115–4788, tel. 276/666–7200; Michael Ehrat, Chief Executive Officer

SENTARA CAREPLEX HOSPITAL, 3000 Coliseum Drive, Hampton, VA, Zip 23666–5963; tel. 757/736–1000; Debra A. Flores, R.N., MS, President and Administrator

SENTARA LEIGH HOSPITAL, 830 Kempsville Road, Norfolk, VA, Zip 23502–3920; tel. 757/261–6000; Joanne Inman, Administrator

SENTARA NORFOLK GENERAL HOSPITAL, 600 Gresham Drive, Norfolk, VA, Zip 23507–1904; tel. 757/388–3000; Kurt T. Hofelich, President

SENTARA NORTHERN VIRGINIA MEDICAL CENTER, 2300 Opitz Boulevard, Woodbridge, VA, Zip 22191–3399; tel. 703/523–1000; Katherine Johnson, Ph.D., President

SENTARA OBICI HOSPITAL, 2800 Godwin Boulevard, Suffolk, VA, Zip 23434–8038; tel. 757/934–4000; Steve Julian, M.D., President

SENTARA PRINCESS ANNE HOSPITAL, 2025 Glenn Mitchell Drive, Virginia Beach, VA, Zip 23456–0178; tel. 757/507–1000; Thomas B. Thames, M.D., President

SENTARA VIRGINIA BEACH GENERAL HOSPITAL, 1060 First Colonial Road, Virginia Beach, VA, Zip 23454–3002; tel. 757/395–8000; Elwood Bernard. Boone, III., FACHE, President

SENTARA WILLIAMSBURG REGIONAL MEDICAL CENTER, 100 Sentara Circle, Williamsburg, VA, Zip 23188–5713; tel. 757/984–6000; David J. Masterson, President

SHELTERING ARMS REHABILITATION HOSPITAL, 8254 Atlee Road, Mechanicsville, VA, Zip 23116–1844; tel. 804/764–1000; Mary A. Zweifel, MS, President and Chief Executive Officer

SMYTH COUNTY COMMUNITY HOSPITAL, 245 Medical Park Drive, Marion, VA, Zip 24354, P O Box 880, 24354–0880, tel. 276/378–1000; Stan Hickson, FACHE, President and Chief Executive Officer

SOUTHAMPTON MEMORIAL HOSPITAL, 100 Fairview Drive, Franklin, VA, Zip 23851–1238, P O Box 817, 23851–0817, tel. 757/569–6100; Kimberly W. Marks, Chief Executive Officer

SOUTHERN VIRGINIA REGIONAL MEDICAL CENTER, 727 North Main Street, Emporia, VA, Zip 23847–1274; tel. 434/348–4400; Matt Tavenner, Chief Executive Officer

SOUTHSIDE REGIONAL MEDICAL CENTER, 200 Medical Park Boulevard, Petersburg, VA, Zip 23805–9274; tel. 804/765–5000; Trent Nobles, Chief Executive Officer

TWIN COUNTY REGIONAL HEALTHCARE, 200 Hospital Drive, Galax, VA, Zip 24333–2227; tel. 276/236–8181; Dale Alward, Chief Executive Officer

UVA-HEALTHSOUTH REHABILITATION HOSPITAL, 515 Ray C Hunt Drive, Charlottesville, VA, Zip 22903–2981; tel. 434/244–2000

UNIVERSITY OF VIRGINIA MEDICAL CENTER, 1215 Lee Street, Charlottesville, VA, Zip 22908–0001, P O Box 800809, 22908–0809, tel. 434/924–0211; Pamela Sutton-Wallace, Chief Executive Officer

VCU HEALTH COMMUNITY MEMORIAL HOSPITAL, 125 Buena Vista Circle, South Hill, VA, Zip 23970–1431, P O Box 90, 23970–0090, tel. 434/447–3151; W Scott. Burnette, Chief Executive Officer

VCU MEDICAL CENTER, 1250 East Marshall Street, Richmond, VA, Zip 23298–5051, P O Box 980510, 23298–0510, tel. 804/828–9000; Deborah W. Davis, Chief Executive Officer and Vice President Clinical Services

VIRGINIA HOSPITAL CENTER - ARLINGTON, 1701 North George Mason Drive, Arlington, VA, Zip 22205–3698; tel. 703/558–5000; James B. Cole, Chief Executive Officer

WYTHE COUNTY COMMUNITY HOSPITAL, 600 West Ridge Road, Wytheville, VA, Zip 24382–1099; tel. 276/228–0200; Adam Martin, Chief Operating Officer and Interim Chief Executive Officer

WASHINGTON

GROUP HEALTH COOPERATIVE
320 Westlake Avenue North, Suite 100, Seattle, WA, Zip 98109–5233; tel. 206/448–5083; Scott Armstrong, Chief Executive Officer

CASCADE VALLEY HOSPITAL AND CLINICS, 330 South Stillaguamish Avenue, Arlington, WA, Zip 98223–1642; tel. 360/435–2133; Michael Liepman, Chief Executive Officer

COLUMBIA COUNTY HEALTH SYSTEM, 1012 South Third Street, Dayton, WA, Zip 99328–1696; tel. 509/382–2531; Shane McGuire, Chief Executive Officer

HARRISON MEDICAL CENTER, 2520 Cherry Avenue, Bremerton, WA, Zip 98310–4229; tel. 360/744–3911; David W. Schultz, FACHE, Market President, Peninsula Region

ISLAND HOSPITAL, 1211 24th Street, Anacortes, WA, Zip 98221–2562; tel. 360/299–1300; Vincent Oliver, FACHE, Administrator

KADLEC REGIONAL MEDICAL CENTER, 888 Swift Boulevard, Richland, WA, Zip 99352–3514; tel. 509/946–4611; Lane A. Savitch, Regional Chief Executive

KAISER PERMANENTE CAPITOL HILL CAMPUS, 201 16th Avenue East, Seattle, WA, Zip 98112–5226; tel. 206/326–3000; Carol M. Taylor, R.N., Regional Director Clinical Operations

KITTITAS VALLEY HEALTHCARE, 603 South Chestnut Street, Ellensburg, WA, Zip 98926–3875; tel. 509/962–7302; Julie Petersen, Chief Executive Officer

KOOTENAI HEALTH, 2003 Kootenai Health Way, Coeur D'Alene, ID, Zip 83814–2677; tel. 208/625–4000; Jon Ness, Chief Executive Officer

LOURDES MEDICAL CENTER, 520 North Fourth Avenue, Pasco, WA, Zip 99301–5257; tel. 509/547–7704; John Serle, FACHE, President and Chief Executive Officer

MULTICARE DEACONESS HOSPITAL, 800 West Fifth Avenue, Spokane, WA, Zip 99204–2803, P O Box 248, 99210–0248, tel. 509/458–5800; Laureen Driscoll, President

MULTICARE MARY BRIDGE CHILDREN'S HOSPITAL AND HEALTH CENTER, 317 Martin Luther King Jr Way, Tacoma, WA, Zip 98405–4234, P O Box 5299, 98415–0299, tel. 253/403–1400; Linda Chen, President and Market Leader

MULTICARE VALLEY HOSPITAL, 12606 East Mission Avenue, Spokane Valley, WA, Zip 99216–1090; tel. 509/924–6650; Gregory George. Repetti, III., FACHE, Chief Executive Officer

NORTHWEST SPECIALTY HOSPITAL, 1593 East Polston Avenue, Post Falls, ID, Zip 83854–5326; tel. 208/262–2300; Rick Rasmussen, Chief Executive Officer

OVERLAKE MEDICAL CENTER, 1035 116th Avenue NE, Bellevue, WA, Zip 98004–4604; tel. 425/688–5000; J. Michael. Marsh, President and Chief Executive Officer

PMH MEDICAL CENTER, 723 Memorial Street, Prosser, WA, Zip 99350–1524; tel. 509/786–2222; Craig J. Marks, FACHE, Chief Executive Officer

PEACEHEALTH ST. JOSEPH MEDICAL CENTER, 2901 Squalicum Parkway, Bellingham, WA, Zip 98225–1851; tel. 360/734–5400; Dale Zender, President Hospital Services NW

PEACEHEALTH UNITED GENERAL MEDICAL CENTER, 2000 Hospital Drive, Sedro-Woolley, WA, Zip 98284–4327; tel. 360/856–6021; Christopher Johnston, Chief Administrative Officer

PROVIDENCE CENTRALIA HOSPITAL, 914 South Scheuber Road, Centralia, WA, Zip 98531–9027; tel. 360/736–2803; Medrice Coluccio, R.N., Southwest Region Chief Executive

PROVIDENCE HOLY FAMILY HOSPITAL, 5633 North Lidgerwood Street, Spokane, WA, Zip 99208–1224; tel. 509/482–0111; Peggy M. Currie, R.N., Chief Operating Officer

PROVIDENCE REGIONAL MEDICAL CENTER EVERETT, 1321 Colby Avenue, Everett, WA, Zip 98201–1665, P O Box 1147, 98206–1147, tel. 425/261–2000; Kim Williams, R.N., MS, Chief Administrative Officer

PROVIDENCE SACRED HEART MEDICAL CENTER & CHILDREN'S HOSPITAL, 101 West Eighth Avenue, Spokane, WA, Zip 99204–2364, P O Box 2555, 99220–2555, tel. 509/474–3131; Peggy M. Currie, R.N., Chief Operating Officer

PROVIDENCE ST. MARY MEDICAL CENTER, 401 West Poplar Street, Walla Walla, WA, Zip 99362–2846, P O Box 1477, 99362–0312, tel. 509/897–3320; Susan Blackburn, Chief Administrative Officer

PULLMAN REGIONAL HOSPITAL, 835 SE Bishop Boulevard, Pullman, WA, Zip 99163–5512; tel. 509/332–2541; Scott K. Adams, FACHE, Chief Executive Officer

SEATTLE CHILDREN'S HOSPITAL, 4800 Sand Point Way NE, Seattle, WA, Zip 98105–3901, P O Box 5371, 98145–5005, tel. 206/987–2000; Jeff Sperring, M.D., Chief Executive Officer

SKAGIT REGIONAL HEALTH, 1415 East Kincaid, Mount Vernon, WA, Zip 98274–4126, P O Box 1376, 98273–1376, tel. 360/424–4111

ST. FRANCIS HOSPITAL, 34515 Ninth Avenue South, Federal Way, WA, Zip 98003–6799; tel. 253/944–8100; Anthony McLean, Market President

ST. JOSEPH MEDICAL CENTER, 1717 South 'J' Street, Tacoma, WA, Zip 98405–3004, P O Box 2197, 98401–2197, tel. 253/426–4101; Tim O'Haver, Chief Operating Officer

SUNNYSIDE COMMUNITY HOSPITAL AND CLINICS, 1016 Tacoma Avenue, Sunnyside, WA, Zip 98944–2263, P O Box 719, 98944–0719, tel. 509/837–1500; John Gallagher, Chief Executive Officer

TOPPENISH COMMUNITY HOSPITAL, 502 West Fourth Avenue, Toppenish, WA, Zip 98948–1616, P O Box 672, 98948–0672, tel. 509/865–3105; Grant Magness, Interim Chief Executive Officer

TRIOS HEALTH, 900 South Auburn Street, Kennewick, WA, Zip 99336–5621, P O Box 6128, 99336–0128, tel. 509/586–6111; Craig R. Cudworth, FACHE, Interim Chief Executive Officer

VIRGINIA MASON MEDICAL CENTER, 1100 Ninth Avenue, Seattle, WA, Zip 98101–2756, P O Box 900, 98111–0900, tel. 206/223–6600; Gary Kaplan, M.D., FACHE, Chairman and Chief Executive Officer

VIRGINIA MASON MEMORIAL, 2811 Tieton Drive, Yakima, WA, Zip 98902–3761; tel. 509/575–8000; Russ Myers, Chief Executive Officer

WHIDBEYHEALTH, 101 North Main Street, Coupeville, WA, Zip 98239–3413; tel. 360/678–5151; Geri Forbes, Chief Executive Officer

WHITMAN HOSPITAL AND MEDICAL CENTER, 1200 West Fairview Street, Colfax, WA, Zip 99111–9579; tel. 509/397–3435; Hank Hanigan, MS, R.N., Chief Executive Officer

YAKIMA REGIONAL MEDICAL AND CARDIAC CENTER, 110 South Ninth Avenue, Yakima, WA, Zip 98902–3315; tel. 509/575–5000; Bryan Braegger, Interim Chief Executive Officer

LINCOLN COUNTY HEALTH DEPARTMENT
90 Nichols Street, Davenport, WA, Zip 99122–9729; tel. 509/725–1001; Ed Dzedzy, Public Health Administration

LINCOLN HOSPITAL, 10 Nicholls Street, Davenport, WA, Zip 99122–9729; tel. 509/725–7101; Tyson Lacy, Chief Executive Officer and Superintendent

ODESSA MEMORIAL HEALTHCARE CENTER, 502 East Amende Drive, Odessa, WA, Zip 99159–7003, P O Box 368, 99159–0368, tel. 509/982–2611; Mo P. Sheldon, FACHE, Chief Executive Officer and Administrator

Section B

WEST VIRGINIA

HEALTH PARTNERS NETWORK, INC.
1000 Technology Drive, Suite 2320, Fairmont, WV, Zip 26554–8834; tel. 304/368–2740; William G. MacLean, Executive Director

BROADDUS HOSPITAL, 1 Healthcare Drive, Philippi, WV, Zip 26416–9405, P O Box 930, 26416–0930, tel. 304/457–1760; Dana L. Gould, Chief Executive Officer

CAMDEN CLARK MEDICAL CENTER, 800 Garfield Avenue, Parkersburg, WV, Zip 26101–5378, P O Box 718, 26102–0718, tel. 304/424–2111; David K. McClure, President and Chief Executive Officer

DAVIS MEDICAL CENTER, Gorman Avenue and Reed Street, Elkins, WV, Zip 26241, P O Box 1484, 26241–1484, tel. 304/636–3300; Vance Jackson, FACHE, Chief Executive Officer

GRAFTON CITY HOSPITAL, 1 Hospital Plaza, Grafton, WV, Zip 26354–1283; tel. 304/265–0400; Patrick D. Shaw, Chief Executive Officer

HEALTHSOUTH MOUNTAINVIEW REGIONAL REHABILITATION HOSPITAL, 1160 Van Voorhis Road, Morgantown, WV, Zip 26505–3437; tel. 304/598–1100; Tracy Vinciguerra, Chief Executive Officer

MINNIE HAMILTON HEALTHCARE CENTER, 186 Hospital Drive, Grantsville, WV, Zip 26147–7100; tel. 304/354–9244; Steve Whited, Chief Executive Officer

ST. JOSEPH'S HOSPITAL OF BUCKHANNON, 1 Amalia Drive, Buckhannon, WV, Zip 26201–2276; tel. 304/473–2000; Skip Gjolberg, FACHE, Administrator

STONEWALL JACKSON MEMORIAL HOSPITAL, 230 Hospital Plaza, Weston, WV, Zip 26452–8558; tel. 304/269–8000; Avah Stalnaker, Chief Executive Officer

UNITED HOSPITAL CENTER, 327 Medical Park Drive, Bridgeport, WV, Zip 26330–9006; tel. 681/342–1000; Michael C. Tillman, President and Chief Executive Officer

WEBSTER COUNTY MEMORIAL HOSPITAL, 324 Miller Mountain Drive, Webster Springs, WV, Zip 26288–1087, P O Box 312, 26288–0312, tel. 304/847–5682; Jeffrey A. Powelson, Interim Chief Executive Officer

WEST VIRGINIA UNIVERSITY HOSPITALS, 1 Medical Center Drive, Morgantown, WV, Zip 26506–4749; tel. 304/598–4000; Albert L. Wright, Jr., PharmD, President and Chief Executive Officer

PARTNERS IN HEALTH NETWORK, INC.
405 Capitol Street, Suite 505, Charleston, WV, Zip 25301–1783; tel. 304/388–7385; Robert D. Whitler, Executive Director

BOONE MEMORIAL HOSPITAL, 701 Madison Avenue, Madison, WV, Zip 25130–1699; tel. 304/369–1230; Virgil Underwood, Chief Executive Officer

BRAXTON COUNTY MEMORIAL HOSPITAL, 100 Hoylman DR, Gassaway, WV, Zip 26624–9318, 100 Hoylman Drive, 26624–9318, tel. 304/364–5156; Ben Vincent, FACHE, Chief Executive Officer

CHARLESTON AREA MEDICAL CENTER, 501 Morris Street, Charleston, WV, Zip 25301–1300, P O Box 1547, 25326–1547, tel. 304/388–5432; David L. Ramsey, President and Chief Executive Officer

CHARLESTON SURGICAL HOSPITAL, 1306 Kanawha Boulevard East, Charleston, WV, Zip 25301–3001, P O Box 2271, 25328–2271, tel. 304/343–4371; Christina Arvon, Administrator and Chief Executive Officer

HIGHLAND HOSPITAL, 300 56th Street SE, Charleston, WV, Zip 25304–2361, P O Box 4107, 25364–4107, tel. 304/926–1600; Cynthia A. Persily, Ph.D., R.N., President and Chief Executive Officer

JACKSON GENERAL HOSPITAL, 122 Pinnell Street, Ripley, WV, Zip 25271–9101, P O Box 720, 25271–0720, tel. 304/372–2731; Stephanie McCoy, President and Chief Executive Officer

MINNIE HAMILTON HEALTHCARE CENTER, 186 Hospital Drive, Grantsville, WV, Zip 26147–7100; tel. 304/354–9244; Steve Whited, Chief Executive Officer

MONTGOMERY GENERAL HOSPITAL, 401 Sixth Avenue, Montgomery, WV, Zip 25136–2116, P O Box 270, 25136–0270, tel. 304/442–5151; Vickie Gay, Chief Executive Officer

POCAHONTAS MEMORIAL HOSPITAL, 150 Duncan Road, Buckeye, WV, Zip 24924; tel. 304/799–7400; Barbara Lay, Chief Executive Officer

ROANE GENERAL HOSPITAL, 200 Hospital Drive, Spencer, WV, Zip 25276–1050; tel. 304/927–4444; Douglas E. Bentz, Chief Executive Officer

STONEWALL JACKSON MEMORIAL HOSPITAL, 230 Hospital Plaza, Weston, WV, Zip 26452–8558; tel. 304/269–8000; Avah Stalnaker, Chief Executive Officer

SUMMERSVILLE REGIONAL MEDICAL CENTER, 400 Fairview Heights Road, Summersville, WV, Zip 26651–9308; tel. 304/872–2891; Karen A. Fiducia, FACHE, President and Chief Executive Officer

WEBSTER COUNTY MEMORIAL HOSPITAL, 324 Miller Mountain Drive, Webster Springs, WV, Zip 26288–1087, P O Box 312, 26288–0312, tel. 304/847–5682; Jeffrey A. Powelson, Interim Chief Executive Officer

WISCONSIN

AFFINITY HEALTH SYSTEM
1506 South Oneida Street, Appleton, WI, Zip 54915–1305; tel. 920/831–8912; Monica Hilt, President and Chief Executive Officer

CALUMET MEDICAL CENTER, 614 Memorial Drive, Chilton, WI, Zip 53014–1597; tel. 920/849–2386; Jennifer Derks, Chief Administrative Officer

MERCY MEDICAL CENTER, 500 South Oakwood Road, Oshkosh, WI, Zip 54904–7944; tel. 920/223–2000; Denise Parrish, Interim Chief Administrative Officer

ST. ELIZABETH HOSPITAL, 1506 South Oneida Street, Appleton, WI, Zip 54915–1305; tel. 920/738–2000; Monica Hilt, President

ASPIRUS, INC.
425 Pine Ridge Boulevard, Wausau, WI, Zip 54401–4123; tel. 715/847–2118; Matthew Heywood, President and Chief Executive Officer

ASPIRUS IRON RIVER HOSPITALS & CLINICS, INC., 1400 West Ice Lake Road, Iron River, MI, Zip 49935–9526; tel. 906/265–6121; Connie L. Koutouzos, R.N., MSN, Chief Executive Officer

ASPIRUS IRONWOOD HOSITAL & CLINICS, INC., N10561 Grand View Lane, Ironwood, MI, Zip 49938–9622; tel. 906/932–2525; Paula L. Chermside, Chief Executive Officer

ASPIRUS KEWEENAW HOSPITAL, INC., 205 Osceola Street, Laurium, MI, Zip 49913–2134; tel. 906/337–6500; Michael Hauswirth, Chief Executive Officer

ASPIRUS LANGLADE HOSPITAL, 112 East Fifth Avenue, Antigo, WI, Zip 54409–2796; tel. 715/623–2331; Andrew J. Barth, Chief Executive Officer

ASPIRUS MEDFORD HOSPITAL & CLINICS, INC., 135 South Gibson Street, Medford, WI, Zip 54451–1696; tel. 715/748–8100; Rick L. Nevers, Interim Chief Executive Officer

ASPIRUS ONTONAGON HOSPITAL, INC., 601 South Seventh Street, Ontonagon, MI, Zip 49953–1459; tel. 906/884–8000; Michael Hauswirth, Chief Executive Officer

ASPIRUS RIVERVIEW HOSPITAL AND CLINICS, INC., 410 Dewey Street, Wisconsin Rapids, WI, Zip 54494–4715, P O Box 8080, 54495–8080, tel. 715/423–6060; Todd Burch, Chief Executive Officer

ASPIRUS WAUSAU HOSPITAL, INC., 333 Pine Ridge Boulevard, Wausau, WI, Zip 54401–4187; tel. 715/847–2121; Darrell Lentz, President

COLUMBIA ST. MARY'S
2025 East Newport Avenue, Milwaukee, WI, Zip 53211–2906; tel. 414/961–3300; Travis Andersen, President and Chief Executive Officer

COLUMBIA ST. MARY'S HOSPITAL MILWAUKEE, 2301 North Lake Drive, Milwaukee, WI, Zip 53211–4508; tel. 414/291–1000; Kelly Elkins, President

COLUMBIA ST. MARY'S OZAUKEE HOSPITAL, 13111 North Port Washington Road, Mequon, WI, Zip 53097–2416; tel. 262/243–7300; Bev Weber, Interim President

SACRED HEART REHABILITATION INSTITUTE, 2323 North Lake Drive, Milwaukee, WI, Zip 53211–4508; tel. 414/585–1000; Kelly Elkins, President and Chief Executive Officer

COMMUNITY HEALTH NETWORK, INC.
225 Memorial Drive, Berlin, WI, Zip 54923–1243; tel. 920/361–5580; John Feeney, President and Chief Executive Officer

THEDA CARE MEDICAL CENTER - WILD ROSE, 601 Grove Avenue, Wild Rose, WI, Zip 54984–6903, P O Box 243, 54984–0243, tel. 920/622–3257; Craig A. Kantos, Chief Executive Officer

THEDACARE REGIONAL MEDICAL CENTER-BERLIN, 225 Memorial Drive, Berlin, WI, Zip 54923–1295; tel. 920/361–1313; John Feeney, President and Chief Executive Officer

FROEDTERT HEALTH
9200 West Wisconsin Avenue, Milwaukee, WI, Zip 53226–3596; tel. 414/805–3000; Catherine A. Jacobson, President and Chief Executive Officer

COMMUNITY MEMORIAL HOSPITAL, W180 N8085 Town Hall Road, Menomonee Falls, WI, Zip 53051–3518, P O Box 408, 53052–0408, tel. 262/251–1000; Teri Lux, President

FROEDTERT MEMORIAL LUTHERAN HOSPITAL, 9200 West Wisconsin Avenue, Milwaukee, WI, Zip 53226–3596, P O Box 26099, 53226–0099, tel. 414/805–3000; Catherine Buck, President

ST. JOSEPH'S HOSPITAL, 3200 Pleasant Valley Road, West Bend, WI, Zip 53095–9274; tel. 262/334–5533; Allen Ericson, Chief Operating Officer, Community Hospital Division and President, St. Joseph's Hospital

GUNDERSEN HEALTH SYSTEM
1900 South Avenue, La Crosse, WI, Zip 54601–5467; tel. 608/782–7300; Scott W. Rathgaber, M.D., Chief Executive Officer

GUNDERSEN BOSCOBEL AREA HOSPITAL AND CLINICS, 205 Parker Street, Boscobel, WI, Zip 53805–1698; tel. 608/375–4112; David Hartberg, Chief Executive Officer

GUNDERSEN HEALTH SYSTEM, 1900 South Avenue, La Crosse, WI, Zip 54601–5467; tel. 608/782–7300; Scott W. Rathgaber, M.D., Chief Executive Officer and Board Chair

GUNDERSEN PALMER LUTHERAN HOSPITAL AND CLINICS, 112 Jefferson Street, West Union, IA, Zip 52175–1022; tel. 563/422–3811; Tanya Tysland, Chief Executive Officer

GUNDERSEN ST. JOSEPH'S HOSPITAL AND CLINICS, 400 Water Avenue, Hillsboro, WI, Zip 54634–9054, P O Box 527, 54634–0527, tel. 608/489–8000; Danielle Gearhart, Chief Executive Officer

GUNDERSEN TRI-COUNTY HOSPITAL AND CLINICS, 18601 Lincoln Street, Whitehall, WI, Zip 54773–8605; tel. 715/538–4361; Joni Olson, Chief Executive Officer

MINISTRY HEALTH CARE
11925 West Lake Park Drive, Milwaukee, WI, Zip 53224-3002; tel. 414/465-3772; Daniel Neufelder, President

CALUMET MEDICAL CENTER, 614 Memorial Drive, Chilton, WI, Zip 53014-1597; tel. 920/849-2386; Jennifer Derks, Chief Administrative Officer

DOOR COUNTY MEDICAL CENTER, 323 South 18th Avenue, Sturgeon Bay, WI, Zip 54235-1495; tel. 920/743-5566; Gerald M. Worrick, President and Chief Executive Officer

FLAMBEAU HOSPITAL, 98 Sherry Avenue, Park Falls, WI, Zip 54552-1467, P O Box 310, 54552-0310, tel. 715/762-2484; James R. Braun, Chief Administrative Officer and Chief Financial Officer

HOWARD YOUNG MEDICAL CENTER, 240 Maple Street, Woodruff, WI, Zip 54568-9190, P O Box 470, 54568-0470, tel. 715/356-8000; Sandra L. Anderson, President and Chief Executive Officer

MARSHFIELD MEDICAL CENTER, 611 St Joseph Avenue, Marshfield, WI, Zip 54449-1898; tel. 715/387-1713; Edward H. Wolf, Chief Administrative Officer

MERCY MEDICAL CENTER, 500 South Oakwood Road, Oshkosh, WI, Zip 54904-7944; tel. 920/223-2000; Denise Parrish, Interim Chief Administrative Officer

MINISTRY EAGLE RIVER MEMORIAL HOSPITAL, 201 Hospital Road, Eagle River, WI, Zip 54521-8835; tel. 715/479-7411; Sandra L. Anderson, President and Chief Executive Officer

MINISTRY GOOD SAMARITAN HEALTH CENTER, 601 South Center Avenue, Merrill, WI, Zip 54452-3404; tel. 715/536-5511; Dawn Gapko, Chief Administrative Officer

MINISTRY OUR LADY OF VICTORY HOSPITAL, 1120 Pine Street, Stanley, WI, Zip 54768-1297; tel. 715/644-5571; Vanessa Freitag, President

MINISTRY SACRED HEART HOSPITAL, 401 West Mohawk Drive, Tomahawk, WI, Zip 54487-2274; tel. 715/453-7700; Sandra L. Anderson, President and Chief Executive Officer

MINISTRY SAINT CLARE'S HOSPITAL, 3400 Ministry Parkway, Weston, WI, Zip 54476-5220; tel. 715/393-3000; Jeremy Normington-Slay, FACHE, President, North Central Region

MINISTRY SAINT MARY'S HOSPITALS, 2251 North Shore Drive, Rhinelander, WI, Zip 54501-6710; tel. 715/361-2000; Sandra L. Anderson, President and Chief Executive Officer

MINISTRY SAINT MICHAEL'S HOSPITAL, 900 Illinois Avenue, Stevens Point, WI, Zip 54481-3196; tel. 715/346-5000; Jeremy Normington-Slay, FACHE, President, North Central Region

SAINT ELIZABETH'S MEDICAL CENTER, 1200 Grant Boulevard West, Wabasha, MN, Zip 55981-1042; tel. 651/565-4531; Thomas Crowley, President and Chief Executive Officer

ST. ELIZABETH HOSPITAL, 1506 South Oneida Street, Appleton, WI, Zip 54915-1305; tel. 920/738-2000; Monica Hilt, President

WHEATON FRANCISCAN HEALTHCARE
400 West River Woods Parkway, Glendale, WI, Zip 53212-1060; tel. 414/465-3000; John D. Oliverio, President and Chief Executive Officer

MIDWEST ORTHOPEDIC SPECIALTY HOSPITAL, 10101 South 27th Street, 2nd Floor, Franklin, WI, Zip 53132-7209; tel. 414/817-5800; Sheila Gansemer, R.N., Vice President of Patient Care Services

WHEATON FRANCISCAN HEALTHCARE - ALL SAINTS, 3801 Spring Street, Racine, WI, Zip 53405-1690; tel. 262/687-4011; Susan Boland, R.N., MSN, President and Chief Executive Officer

WHEATON FRANCISCAN HEALTHCARE - ELMBROOK MEMORIAL, 19333 West North Avenue, Brookfield, WI, Zip 53045-4198; tel. 262/785-2000; Timothy Richman, Chief Executive Officer

WHEATON FRANCISCAN HEALTHCARE - FRANKLIN, 10101 South 27th Street, Franklin, WI, Zip 53132-7209; tel. 414/325-4700; Sheila Gansemer, R.N., Vice President Patient Care Services and Chief Nursing Officer

WHEATON FRANCISCAN HEALTHCARE - ST. FRANCIS, 3237 South 16th Street, Milwaukee, WI, Zip 53215; tel. 414/647-5000; Coreen Dicus-Johnson, President

WHEATON FRANCISCAN HEALTHCARE - ST. JOSEPH'S, 5000 West Chambers Street, Milwaukee, WI, Zip 53210-1650; tel. 414/447-2000; Debra K. Standridge, President

Section B

Alliances

ALLIANCE OF INDEPENDENT ACADEMIC MEDICAL CENTERS
233 East Erie Street, Ste 306, Chicago, IL Zip 60611; tel. 312/836–3712; Kimberly Pierce-Boggs, Executive Director

ARIZONA
Scottsdale
Alliance
  HonorHealth

CALIFORNIA
Colton
Alliance
  Arrowhead Regional Medical Center

Los Angeles
Alliance
  Cedars-Sinai Medical Center

Oakland
Alliance
  Kaiser Permanente Oakland Medical Center

COLORADO
Denver
Alliance
  Saint Joseph Hospital

CONNECTICUT
Hartford
Alliance
  Saint Francis Hospital and Medical Center

DELAWARE
Newark
Alliance
  Christiana Care Health System

FLORIDA
Hollywood
Alliance
  Memorial Healthcare System

Orange Park
Alliance
  Orange Park Medical Center

Orlando
Alliance
  Florida Hospital
  Orlando Health

GEORGIA
Macon
Alliance
  Coliseum Medical Centers

ILLINOIS
Chicago
Alliance
  Advocate Illinois Masonic Medical Center

Oak Lawn
Alliance
  Advocate Christ Medical Center

Park Ridge
Alliance
  Advocate Lutheran General Hospital

Peoria
Alliance
  OSF Saint Francis Medical Center

IOWA
West Des Moines
Alliance
  UnityPoint Health

KENTUCKY
Louisville
Alliance
  Norton Audubon Hospital
  Norton Brownsboro Hospital
  Norton Children's Hospital
  Norton Hospital
  Norton Women's and Children's Hospital

LOUISIANA
Baton Rouge
Alliance
  Our Lady of the Lake Regional Medical Center

New Orleans
Alliance
  Ochsner Health System

MAINE
Portland
Alliance
  Maine Medical Center

MARYLAND
Annapolis
Alliance
  Anne Arundel Medical Center

Baltimore
Alliance
  Sinai Hospital of Baltimore

MASSACHUSETTS
Burlington
Alliance
  Lahey Hospital & Medical Center, Burlington

Springfield
Alliance
  Baystate Medical Center

MICHIGAN
Grand Rapids
Alliance
  Mercy Health Saint Mary's

Lansing
Alliance
  Sparrow Hospital

Rochester
Alliance
  Crittenton Hospital Medical Center

MINNESOTA
Bloomington
Alliance
  HealthPartners

MONTANA
Billings
Alliance
  Billings Clinic

NEW JERSEY
Brick Township
Alliance
  Hackensack Meridian Health Ocean Medical Center

Holmdel
Alliance
  Hackensack Meridian Health Bayshore Community Hospital

Livingston
Alliance
  Saint Barnabas Medical Center

Long Branch
Alliance
  Monmouth Medical Center, Long Branch Campus

Manahawkin
Alliance
  Hackensack Meridian Health Southern Ocean Medical Center

Neptune
Alliance
  Hackensack Meridian Health Jersey Shore University Medical Center

Newark
Alliance
  Newark Beth Israel Medical Center

Perth Amboy
Alliance
  Hackensack Meridian Health Raritan Bay Medical Center

Phillipsburg
Alliance
  St. Luke's Hospital - Warren Campus

Red Bank
Alliance
  Hackensack Meridian Health Riverview Medical Center

NEW YORK
Brooklyn
Alliance
  Maimonides Medical Center

Cooperstown
Alliance
  Bassett Medical Center

Mineola
Alliance
  NYU Winthrop Hospital

NORTH CAROLINA
Charlotte
Alliance
  Carolinas Medical Center

Greensboro
Alliance
  Cone Health

OHIO
Akron
Alliance
  Cleveland Clinic Akron General

Cincinnati
Alliance
  Christ Hospital
  TriHealth Evendale Hospital

Cleveland
Alliance
  Cleveland Clinic

Columbus
Alliance
  OhioHealth Grant Medical Center
  OhioHealth Riverside Methodist Hospital

OREGON
Hood River
Alliance
  Providence Hood River Memorial Hospital

Milwaukie
Alliance
  Providence Milwaukie Hospital

Portland
Alliance
  Providence Portland Medical Center
  Providence St. Vincent Medical Center

PENNSYLVANIA
Bethlehem
Alliance
  St. Luke's University Hospital - Bethlehem Campus

Johnstown
Alliance
  Conemaugh Memorial Medical Center

Philadelphia
Alliance
  Einstein Medical Center Philadelphia

Sayre
Alliance
  Guthrie Robert Packer Hospital

Wynnewood
Alliance
  Lankenau Medical Center

York
Alliance
  WellSpan York Hospital

SOUTH CAROLINA
Charleston
Alliance
 Trident Medical Center

Myrtle Beach
Alliance
 Grand Strand Regional Medical Center

TEXAS
Dallas
Alliance
 Baylor Scott & White Health
 Methodist Health System

Fort Worth
Alliance
 JPS Health Network

Garland
Alliance
 Baylor Medical Center at Garland

Lubbock
Alliance
 Covenant Children's Hospital
 Covenant Medical Center

WASHINGTON
Seattle
Alliance
 Kaiser Permanente Capitol Hill Campus
 Swedish Medical Center-Cherry Hill Campus
 Swedish Medical Center-First Hill
 Virginia Mason Medical Center

WEST VIRGINIA
Charleston
Alliance
 Charleston Area Medical Center

WISCONSIN
Marshfield
Alliance
 Marshfield Medical Center

Milwaukee
Alliance
 Aurora Health Care

CAPSTONE HEALTH ALLIANCE
 1200 Ridgefield Boulevard, Suite 200, Asheville, NC Zip 28806; tel. 828/418–5050; Tim Bugg, President and Chief Executive Officer

ALABAMA
Butler
Alliance
 Choctaw General Hospital

Dothan
Alliance
 Southeast Alabama Medical Center

Eufaula
Alliance
 Medical Center Barbour

Opelika
Alliance
 East Alabama Medical Center

Wedowee
Alliance
 Wedowee Hospital

ARKANSAS
Batesville
Alliance
 White River Medical Center

Calico Rock
Alliance
 Community Medical Center of Izard County

Fordyce
Alliance
 Dallas County Medical Center

Harrison
Alliance
 North Arkansas Regional Medical Center

Mountain View
Alliance
 Stone County Medical Center

Pine Bluff
Alliance
 Jefferson Regional Medical Center

DELAWARE
Lewes
Alliance
 Beebe Healthcare

GEORGIA
Bremen
Alliance
 Tanner Higgins General Hospital

Carrollton
Alliance
 Tanner Medical Center-Carrollton

Jesup
Alliance
 Wayne Memorial Hospital

Lagrange
Alliance
 West Georgia Health

Savannah
Alliance
 Candler Hospital
 St. Joseph's Hospital

Villa Rica
Alliance
 Tanner Medical Center-Villa Rica

ILLINOIS
Centreville
Alliance
 Touchette Regional Hospital

Chicago
Alliance
 Loretto Hospital
 Norwegian American Hospital
 Thorek Memorial Hospital

Dixon
Alliance
 Katherine Shaw Bethea Hospital

Elmhurst
Alliance
 Elmhurst Hospital

Hoopeston
Alliance
 Carle Hoopeston Regional Health Center

Kankakee
Alliance
 Riverside Medical Center

Naperville
Alliance
 Edward Hospital
 Linden Oaks Hospital

Urbana
Alliance
 Carle Foundation Hospital

INDIANA
Greenfield
Alliance
 Hancock Regional Hospital

Rushville
Alliance
 Rush Memorial Hospital

KANSAS
Manhattan
Alliance
 Manhattan Surgical

KENTUCKY
Albany
Alliance
 The Medical Center Albany

Bowling Green
Alliance
 Commonwealth Regional Specialty Hospital
 Medical Center at Bowling Green

Danville
Alliance
 Ephraim McDowell Regional Medical Center

Edgewood
Alliance
 St. Elizabeth Edgewood

Florence
Alliance
 St. Elizabeth Florence

Fort Thomas
Alliance
 St. Elizabeth Fort Thomas

Franklin
Alliance
 Medical Center at Franklin

Glasgow
Alliance
 T. J. Samson Community Hospital

Henderson
Alliance
 Methodist Hospital

Horse Cave
Alliance
 The Medical Center at Caverna

Morganfield
Alliance
 Methodist Hospital Union County

Murray
Alliance
 Murray-Calloway County Hospital

Scottsville
Alliance
 Medical Center at Scottsville

Stanford
Alliance
 Ephraim McDowell Fort Logan Hospital

Williamstown
Alliance
 St. Elizabeth Grant

LOUISIANA
Abbeville
Alliance
 Abbeville General Hospital

Baton Rouge
Alliance
 Baton Rouge General Medical Center
 Baton Rouge Rehabilitation Hospital
 Spine Hospital of Louisiana (formally the NeuroMedical Center Surgical Hospital)
 The NeuroMedical Center Rehabilitation Hospital
 Woman's Hospital

Breaux Bridge
Alliance
 St. Martin Hospital

Bunkie
Alliance
 Bunkie General Hospital

Church Point
Alliance
 Acadia-St. Landry Hospital

Columbia
Alliance
 Citizens Medical Center

Crowley
Alliance
 Acadia General Hospital

Delhi
Alliance
 Richland Parish Hospital

Hammond
Alliance
 North Oaks Medical Center
 North Oaks Rehabilitation Hospital

Houma
Alliance
 Terrebonne General Medical Center

Jennings
Alliance
Jennings American Legion Hospital

Kaplan
Alliance
Abrom Kaplan Memorial Hospital

Kenner
Alliance
Ochsner Extended Care Hospital of Kenner

Kinder
Alliance
Allen Parish Hospital

Lafayette
Alliance
Lafayette General Medical Center
Lafayette General Surgical Hospital
Louisiana Extended Care Hospital of Lafayette
University Hospital and Clinics

Marrero
Alliance
Louisiana Continuing Care Hospital

Monroe
Alliance
Specialty Hospital

Natchitoches
Alliance
Louisiana Extended Care Hospital of Natchitoches

New Iberia
Alliance
Iberia Medical Center

Opelousas
Alliance
St. Landry Extended Care Hospital

Rayville
Alliance
Richardson Medical Center

West Monroe
Alliance
Louisiana Extended Care Hospital West Monroe

Winnsboro
Alliance
Franklin Medical Center

MARYLAND
Annapolis
Alliance
Anne Arundel Medical Center

Baltimore
Alliance
Greater Baltimore Medical Center
Levindale Hebrew Geriatric Center and Hospital
Mercy Medical Center
Sinai Hospital of Baltimore

Berlin
Alliance
Atlantic General Hospital

Cumberland
Alliance
Western Maryland Regional Medical Center

Elkton
Alliance
Union Hospital

Frederick
Alliance
Frederick Regional Health System

Lanham
Alliance
Doctors Community Hospital

Randallstown
Alliance
Northwest Hospital

Salisbury
Alliance
Peninsula Regional Medical Center

Westminster
Alliance
Carroll Hospital Center

MICHIGAN
Ypsilanti
Alliance
Forest Health Medical Center

MINNESOTA
Blue Earth
Alliance
United Hospital District

MISSISSIPPI
Bay Springs
Alliance
Jasper General Hospital

Carthage
Alliance
Baptist Medical Center Leake

Charleston
Alliance
Tallahatchie General Hospital

De Kalb
Alliance
John C. Stennis Memorial Hospital

Jackson
Alliance
Mississippi Baptist Medical Center

Kosciusko
Alliance
Baptist Medical Center Attala

Laurel
Alliance
South Central Regional Medical Center

Louisville
Alliance
Winston Medical Center

Magee
Alliance
Magee General Hospital

Mendenhall
Alliance
Simpson General Hospital

Meridian
Alliance
Rush Foundation Hospital

Morton
Alliance
Scott Regional Hospital

Quitman
Alliance
H. C. Watkins Memorial Hospital

Ruleville
Alliance
North Sunflower Medical Center

Union
Alliance
Laird Hospital

Water Valley
Alliance
Yalobusha General Hospital

Yazoo City
Alliance
Baptist Medical Center Yazoo

NEBRASKA
Kearney
Alliance
Kearney Regional Medical Center

NORTH CAROLINA
Asheville
Alliance
Asheville Specialty Hospital
CarePartners Health Services
Mission Hospital

Boone
Alliance
Watauga Medical Center

Brevard
Alliance
Transylvania Regional Hospital

Bryson City
Alliance
Swain Community Hospital

Cherokee
Alliance
Cherokee Indian Hospital

Clyde
Alliance
Haywood Regional Medical Center

Columbus
Alliance
St. Luke's Hospital

Dunn
Alliance
Harnett Health System

Elizabeth City
Alliance
Sentara Albemarle Medical Center

Elizabethtown
Alliance
Cape Fear Valley - Bladen County Hospital

Fayetteville
Alliance
Cape Fear Valley Medical Center
Highsmith-Rainey Specialty Hospital

Franklin
Alliance
Angel Medical Center

Gastonia
Alliance
CaroMont Regional Medical Center

Goldsboro
Alliance
Wayne Memorial Hospital

Hamlet
Alliance
FirstHealth Moore Regional Hospital - Hamlet

Hendersonville
Alliance
Margaret R. Pardee Memorial Hospital
Park Ridge Health

Hickory
Alliance
Catawba Valley Medical Center

Highlands
Alliance
Highlands-Cashiers Hospital

Marion
Alliance
McDowell Hospital

Morehead City
Alliance
Carteret Health Care

Newland
Alliance
Charles A. Cannon Memorial Hospital

Oxford
Alliance
Granville Health System

Pinehurst
Alliance
FirstHealth Moore Regional Hospital

Raeford
Alliance
Hoke Hospital

Roanoke Rapids
Alliance
Halifax Regional Medical Center

Rockingham
Alliance
FirstHealth Richmond Memorial Hospital

Spruce Pine
Alliance
Blue Ridge Regional Hospital

Statesville
Alliance
Iredell Health System

Troy
Alliance
   FirstHealth Montgomery Memorial Hospital

NORTH DAKOTA
Cavalier
Alliance
   Pembina County Memorial Hospital and Wedgewood Manor

OHIO
Amherst
Alliance
   Specialty Hospital of Lorain

Bowling Green
Alliance
   Wood County Hospital

Cleveland
Alliance
   Grace Hospital

Cuyahoga Falls
Alliance
   Summa Western Reserve Hospital

Salem
Alliance
   Salem Regional Medical Center

Steubenville
Alliance
   Life Line Hospital

PENNSYLVANIA
Corry
Alliance
   Corry Memorial Hospital

Erie
Alliance
   LECOM Health Millcreek Community Hospital

Kittanning
Alliance
   ACMH Hospital

Langhorne
Alliance
   Barix Clinics of Pennsylvania

Meadville
Alliance
   Meadville Medical Center

State College
Alliance
   Mount Nittany Medical Center

Titusville
Alliance
   Titusville Area Hospital

Tyrone
Alliance
   Tyrone Hospital

Windber
Alliance
   Chan Soon-Shiong Medical Center

SOUTH CAROLINA
Conway
Alliance
   Conway Medical Center

West Columbia
Alliance
   Lexington Medical Center

Winnsboro
Alliance
   Fairfield Memorial Hospital

TENNESSEE
Crossville
Alliance
   Cumberland Medical Center

Elizabethton
Alliance
   Sycamore Shoals Hospital

Erwin
Alliance
   Unicoi County Memorial Hospital

Greeneville
Alliance
   Laughlin Memorial Hospital

Johnson City
Alliance
   Franklin Woods Community Hospital
   Johnson City Medical Center
   Quillen Rehabilitation Hospital

Kingsport
Alliance
   Indian Path Medical Center

Knoxville
Alliance
   University of Tennessee Medical Center

Maryville
Alliance
   Blount Memorial Hospital

Mountain City
Alliance
   Johnson County Community Hospital

TEXAS
The Woodlands
Alliance
   Woodlands Specialty Hospital

VIRGINIA
Abingdon
Alliance
   Johnston Memorial Hospital

Chesapeake
Alliance
   Chesapeake Regional Healthcare

Christiansburg
Alliance
   Carilion New River Valley Medical Center

Clintwood
Alliance
   Dickenson Community Hospital

Front Royal
Alliance
   Warren Memorial Hospital

Gloucester
Alliance
   Riverside Walter Reed Hospital

Grundy
Alliance
   Buchanan General Hospital

Lebanon
Alliance
   Russell County Medical Center

Lexington
Alliance
   Carilion Stonewall Jackson Hospital

Luray
Alliance
   Page Memorial Hospital

Marion
Alliance
   Smyth County Community Hospital

Newport News
Alliance
   Riverside Regional Medical Center

Norton
Alliance
   Norton Community Hospital

Onancoke
Alliance
   Riverside Shore Memorial Hospital

Pearisburg
Alliance
   Carilion Giles Community Hospital

Roanoke
Alliance
   Carilion Roanoke Memorial Hospital

Rocky Mount
Alliance
   Carilion Franklin Memorial Hospital

South Hill
Alliance
   VCU Health Community Memorial Hospital

Tappahannock
Alliance
   Riverside Tappahannock Hospital

Tazewell
Alliance
   Carilion Tazewell Community Hospital

Williamsburg
Alliance
   Riverside Doctors' Hospital

Winchester
Alliance
   Winchester Medical Center

Woodstock
Alliance
   Shenandoah Memorial Hospital

WEST VIRGINIA
Berkeley Springs
Alliance
   War Memorial Hospital

Charleston
Alliance
   Saint Francis Hospital

Elkins
Alliance
   Davis Medical Center

Huntington
Alliance
   Cabell Huntington Hospital
   St. Mary's Medical Center

Kingwood
Alliance
   Preston Memorial Hospital

Morgantown
Alliance
   Mon Health Medical Center

Point Pleasant
Alliance
   Pleasant Valley Hospital

Romney
Alliance
   Hampshire Memorial Hospital

South Charleston
Alliance
   Thomas Memorial Hospital

CATHOLIC CEO HEALTHCARE CONNECTION
   50 South Main Street, Suite 200, Naperville, IL Zip 60540–5484; tel. 630/352–2220; Roger N. Butler, Executive Director

CALIFORNIA
San Francisco
Alliance
   Dignity Health

COLORADO
Broomfield
Alliance
   SCL Health

Englewood
Alliance
   Catholic Health Initiatives

ILLINOIS
Chicago
Alliance
   Presence Health

Peoria
Alliance
   OSF Healthcare

Springfield
Alliance
   HSHS Hospital Sisters Health System

LOUISIANA
Baton Rouge
Alliance
   Franciscan Missionaries of Our Lady Health System, Inc.

Section B

MARYLAND
Marriottsville
Alliance
  Bon Secours Health System, Inc.

MISSOURI
Chesterfield
Alliance
  Mercy

Saint Louis
Alliance
  Ascension Healthcare

  SSM Health

OHIO
Cincinnati
Alliance
  Mercy Health

SOUTH DAKOTA
Sioux Falls
Alliance
  Avera Health

TEXAS
Irving
Alliance
  CHRISTUS Health

WASHINGTON
Renton
Alliance
  Providence St. Joseph Health

Vancouver
Alliance
  PeaceHealth

WISCONSIN
Manitowoc
Alliance
  Franciscan Sisters of Christian Charity Sponsored Ministries, Inc.

HEALTH ENTERPRISES COOPERATIVE
5825 Dry Creek Lane NE, Cedar Rapids, IA Zip 52402-1225; tel. 319/368-3619; Judy L. Sadler, President and Chief Executive Officer

IOWA
Ames
Alliance
  Mary Greeley Medical Center

Chariton
Alliance
  Lucas County Health Center

Charles City
Alliance
  Floyd County Medical Center

Cherokee
Alliance
  Cherokee Regional Medical Center

Davenport
Alliance
  Genesis Health System

Denison
Alliance
  Crawford County Memorial Hospital

Des Moines
Alliance
  Broadlawns Medical Center

Fairfield
Alliance
  Jefferson County Health Center

Grinnell
Alliance
  Grinnell Regional Medical Center

Guthrie Center
Alliance
  Guthrie County Hospital

Humboldt
Alliance
  Humboldt County Memorial Hospital

Ida Grove
Alliance
  Horn Memorial Hospital

Independence
Alliance
  Buchanan County Health Center

Iowa City
Alliance
  Mercy Iowa City

Manchester
Alliance
  Regional Medical Center

Maquoketa
Alliance
  Jackson County Regional Health Center

Marshalltown
Alliance
  UnityPoint Health - Marshalltown

Mount Pleasant
Alliance
  Henry County Health Center

Newton
Alliance
  Skiff Medical Center

Oskaloosa
Alliance
  Mahaska Health Partnership

Pella
Alliance
  Pella Regional Health Center

Pocahontas
Alliance
  Pocahontas Community Hospital

Sac City
Alliance
  Loring Hospital

Waukon
Alliance
  Veterans Memorial Hospital

Waverly
Alliance
  Waverly Health Center

West Burlington
Alliance
  Great River Medical Center

MISSOURI
Bethany
Alliance
  Harrison County Community Hospital

Fairfax
Alliance
  Community Hospital-Fairfax

HOSPITAL NETWORK VENTURES, LLC
6212 American Avenue, Portage, MI Zip 49002; tel. 269/329-3200; Gregory L. Hedegore, President and Chief Executive Officer

MICHIGAN
Allegan
Alliance
  Allegan General Hospital

Kalamazoo
Alliance
  Bronson Methodist Hospital

Marshall
Alliance
  Oaklawn Hospital

Sturgis
Alliance
  Sturgis Hospital

HOSPITAL SHARED SERVICES ASSOCIATION
P O Box 19741, Seattle, WA Zip 98109-6741; tel. 206/399-0865; Joe McNamee, Executive Director

OREGON
Salem
Alliance
  Oregon State Hospital

WASHINGTON
Bellevue
Alliance
  Overlake Medical Center

Chelan
Alliance
  Lake Chelan Community Hospital and Clinics

Clarkston
Alliance
  Tri-State Memorial Hospital

Davenport
Alliance
  Lincoln Hospital

Edmonds
Alliance
  Swedish/Edmonds

Ephrata
Alliance
  Columbia Basin Hospital

Grand Coulee
Alliance
  Coulee Medical Center

Kirkland
Alliance
  EvergreenHealth

Medical Lake
Alliance
  Eastern State Hospital

Moses Lake
Alliance
  Samaritan Healthcare

Mount Vernon
Alliance
  Skagit Regional Health

Newport
Alliance
  Newport Hospital and Health Services

Odessa
Alliance
  Odessa Memorial Healthcare Center

Othello
Alliance
  Othello Community Hospital

Prosser
Alliance
  PMH Medical Center

Pullman
Alliance
  Pullman Regional Hospital

Quincy
Alliance
  Quincy Valley Medical Center

Republic
Alliance
  Ferry County Memorial Hospital

Ritzville
Alliance
  East Adams Rural Healthcare

Tacoma
Alliance
  Western State Hospital

Tonasket
Alliance
  North Valley Hospital

KENTUCKY HEALTH COLLABORATIVE
2264 Executive Drive, Lexington, KY Zip 40505; tel. 859/286-3107; Allen K. Montgomery Jr, Project Executive

KENTUCKY
Bowling Green
Alliance
  Medical Center at Bowling Green

Danville
Alliance
   Ephraim McDowell Health

Edgewood
Alliance
   St. Elizabeth Healthcare

Lexington
Alliance
   Appalachian Regional Healthcare, Inc.
   University of Kentucky Albert B. Chandler Hospital

Louisville
Alliance
   Baptist Health
   Norton Healthcare

Morehead
Alliance
   St. Claire HealthCare

Owensboro
Alliance
   Owensboro Health

TENNESSEE

Brentwood
Alliance
   LifePoint Health

MEDI-SOTA, INC.
1280 Locust Street Suite 16, Dawson, MN Zip 56232–2375; tel. 320/769–2269; Deb Ranallo, Executive Director

MINNESOTA

Appleton
Alliance
   Appleton Area Health Services

Arlington
Alliance
   Ridgeview Sibley Medical Center

Benson
Alliance
   Swift County - Benson Health Services

Blue Earth
Alliance
   United Hospital District

Canby
Alliance
   Sanford Canby Medical Center

Dawson
Alliance
   Johnson Memorial Health Services

Elbow Lake
Alliance
   Prairie Ridge Hospital and Health Services

Glencoe
Alliance
   Glencoe Regional Health Services

Glenwood
Alliance
   Glacial Ridge Health System

Graceville
Alliance
   Essentia Health-Graceville

Granite Falls
Alliance
   Granite Falls Municipal Hospital and Manor

Hendricks
Alliance
   Hendricks Community Hospital Association

Litchfield
Alliance
   Meeker Memorial Hospital

Long Prairie
Alliance
   CentraCare Health-Long Prairie

Madelia
Alliance
   Madelia Community Hospital

Madison
Alliance
   Madison Healthcare Services

Mahnomen
Alliance
   Mahnomen Health Center

Marshall
Alliance
   Avera Marshall Regional Medical Center

Montevideo
Alliance
   Chippewa County-Montevideo Hospital

Olivia
Alliance
   RC Hospital and Clinics

Ortonville
Alliance
   Ortonville Area Health Services

Paynesville
Alliance
   CentraCare Health-Paynesville

Perham
Alliance
   Perham Health

Pipestone
Alliance
   Pipestone County Medical Center Avera

Redwood Falls
Alliance
   Redwood Area Hospital

Saint Peter
Alliance
   River's Edge Hospital and Clinic

Slayton
Alliance
   Murray County Medical Center

Sleepy Eye
Alliance
   Sleepy Eye Medical Center

Staples
Alliance
   Lakewood Health System

Tracy
Alliance
   Sanford Tracy Medical Center

Tyler
Alliance
   Avera Tyler Hospital

Wadena
Alliance
   Tri-County Hospital

Willmar
Alliance
   Rice Memorial Hospital

Windom
Alliance
   Windom Area Hospital

NORTHWEST KANSAS HEALTH ALLIANCE
2220 Canterbury Drive, Hays, KS Zip 67601–2370; tel. 785/623–2300; John H. Jeter, M.D., President and Chief Executive Officer

KANSAS

Ashland
Alliance
   Ashland Health Center

Atwood
Alliance
   Rawlins County Health Center

Beloit
Alliance
   Mitchell County Hospital Health Systems

Colby
Alliance
   Citizens Medical Center

Dighton
Alliance
   Lane County Hospital

Dodge City
Alliance
   Western Plains Medical Complex

Ellsworth
Alliance
   Ellsworth County Medical Center

Garden City
Alliance
   St. Catherine Hospital

Goodland
Alliance
   Goodland Regional Medical Center

Great Bend
Alliance
   Great Bend Regional Hospital

Greensburg
Alliance
   Kiowa County Memorial Hospital

Hill City
Alliance
   Graham County Hospital

Hoisington
Alliance
   Clara Barton Hospital

Hoxie
Alliance
   Sheridan County Health Complex

Hutchinson
Alliance
   Hutchinson Regional Medical Center

Jetmore
Alliance
   Hodgeman County Health Center

Kinsley
Alliance
   Edwards County Hospital and Healthcare Center

La Crosse
Alliance
   Rush County Memorial Hospital

Larned
Alliance
   Pawnee Valley Community Hospital

Lawrence
Alliance
   Lawrence Memorial Hospital

Leoti
Alliance
   Wichita County Health Center

Lincoln
Alliance
   Lincoln County Hospital

Lyons
Alliance
   Hospital District No 1 of Rice County

Minneola
Alliance
   Minneola District Hospital

Ness City
Alliance
   Ness County Hospital District No 2

Norton
Alliance
   Norton County Hospital

Oakley
Alliance
   Logan County Hospital

Oberlin
Alliance
   Decatur Health Systems

Osborne
Alliance
   Osborne County Memorial Hospital

Ottawa
Alliance
   Ransom Memorial Hospital

Phillipsburg
Alliance
   Phillips County Hospital

Plainville
Alliance
   Rooks County Health Center

Alliances

Quinter
Alliance
Gove County Medical Center

Ransom
Alliance
Grisell Memorial Hospital District One

Russell
Alliance
Russell Regional Hospital

Saint Francis
Alliance
Cheyenne County Hospital

Salina
Alliance
Salina Regional Health Center

Satanta
Alliance
Satanta District Hospital and Long Term Care

Scott City
Alliance
Scott County Hospital

Smith Center
Alliance
Smith County Memorial Hospital

Stafford
Alliance
Stafford County Hospital

Tribune
Alliance
Greeley County Health Services

Wakeeney
Alliance
Trego County-Lemke Memorial Hospital

OHSU PARTNERS
3303 SW Bond Avenue, Suite 6100, Mail Code: CH6P, Portland, OR Zip 97239–4501; tel. 503/494–4036; Peter F. Rapp, Chief Executive Officer

PENNANT HEALTH ALLIANCE
2122 Health Drive SW Suite 100, Wyoming, MI Zip 49519–9698; tel. 616/252–6800; Michael D. Faas, Chief Executive Officer

MICHIGAN
Ann Arbor
Alliance
Michigan Medicine

Cadillac
Alliance
Munson Healthcare Cadillac Hospital

Grand Rapids
Alliance
Mary Free Bed Rehabilitation Hospital

Mercy Health Saint Mary's

Grayling
Alliance
Munson Healthcare Grayling Hospital

Wyoming
Alliance
Metro Health Hospital

PREMIER, INC.
13034 Ballantyne Corporate Place, Charlotte, NC Zip 28277–1498; tel. 704/816–5353; Susan DeVore, President and Chief Executive Officer

ALABAMA
Dothan
Alliance
Southeast Alabama Medical Center

Opelika
Alliance
East Alabama Medical Center

ARIZONA
Phoenix
Alliance
Banner Health

Scottsdale
Alliance
HonorHealth

ARKANSAS
Batesville
Alliance
White River Medical Center

Pine Bluff
Alliance
Jefferson Regional Medical Center

CALIFORNIA
Fresno
Alliance
Community Medical Centers

Loma Linda
Alliance
Loma Linda University Medical Center

Los Angeles
Alliance
Verity Health System

Mountain View
Alliance
El Camino Hospital

Rancho Mirage
Alliance
Eisenhower Medical Center

Roseville
Alliance
Adventist Health

San Francisco
Alliance
Dignity Health

CONNECTICUT
Hartford
Alliance
Saint Francis Hospital and Medical Center

Waterbury
Alliance
Saint Mary's Hospital

DELAWARE
Dover
Alliance
Bayhealth Medical Center

Lewes
Alliance
Beebe Healthcare

FLORIDA
Altamonte Springs
Alliance
Adventist Health System Sunbelt Health Care Corporation

Clearwater
Alliance
BayCare Health System

Coral Gables
Alliance
Baptist Health South Florida

Dunedin
Alliance
BayCare Alliant Hospital

Jacksonville
Alliance
Baptist Health

Nemours

Miami Beach
Alliance
Mount Sinai Medical Center

Tampa
Alliance
H. Lee Moffitt Cancer Center and Research Institute

Vero Beach
Alliance
Indian River Medical Center

Winter Haven
Alliance
Winter Haven Hospital

GEORGIA
Carrollton
Alliance
Tanner Medical Center-Carrollton

Lagrange
Alliance
West Georgia Health

Savannah
Alliance
Memorial Health

St. Joseph's Hospital

HAWAII
Honolulu
Alliance
Kuakini Medical Center

ILLINOIS
Chicago
Alliance
Mount Sinai Hospital

Presence Health

Harvey
Alliance
Ingalls Memorial Hospital

Naperville
Alliance
Edward Hospital

Peoria
Alliance
UnityPoint Health - Peoria

Urbana
Alliance
Carle Foundation Hospital

INDIANA
Gary
Alliance
Methodist Hospitals

KENTUCKY
Ashland
Alliance
King's Daughters Medical Center

Bowling Green
Alliance
Commonwealth Regional Specialty Hospital

Danville
Alliance
Ephraim McDowell Regional Medical Center

Edgewood
Alliance
St. Elizabeth Edgewood

Glasgow
Alliance
T. J. Samson Community Hospital

Henderson
Alliance
Methodist Hospital

Louisville
Alliance
Alliant Management Services

Baptist Health

Norton Healthcare

Murray
Alliance
Murray-Calloway County Hospital

LOUISIANA
Baton Rouge
Alliance
Woman's Hospital

Hammond
Alliance
North Oaks Health System

Houma
Alliance
Terrebonne General Medical Center

Lafayette
Alliance
Lafayette General Medical Center

Marrero
Alliance
West Jefferson Medical Center

MAINE

Lewiston
Alliance
Central Maine Medical Center

MARYLAND

Annapolis
Alliance
Anne Arundel Medical Center

Baltimore
Alliance
Greater Baltimore Medical Center

Johns Hopkins Health System

Mercy Medical Center

Sinai Hospital of Baltimore

Cumberland
Alliance
Western Maryland Regional Medical Center

Elkton
Alliance
Union Hospital

Frederick
Alliance
Frederick Regional Health System

Gaithersburg
Alliance
Adventist HealthCare

Hagerstown
Alliance
Meritus Medical Center

Lanham
Alliance
Doctors Community Hospital

Marriottsville
Alliance
Bon Secours Health System, Inc.

Randallstown
Alliance
Northwest Hospital

Salisbury
Alliance
Peninsula Regional Medical Center

Westminster
Alliance
Carroll Hospital Center

MASSACHUSETTS

Boston
Alliance
Tufts Medical Center

Fall River
Alliance
Southcoast Hospitals Group

Springfield
Alliance
Baystate Health, Inc.

MICHIGAN

Detroit
Alliance
Henry Ford Health System

Flint
Alliance
McLaren Health Care Corporation

Jackson
Alliance
Henry Ford Allegiance Health

MINNESOTA

Minneapolis
Alliance
Fairview Health Services

MISSISSIPPI

Laurel
Alliance
South Central Regional Medical Center

Meridian
Alliance
Rush Health Systems

MISSOURI

Saint Joseph
Alliance
Mosaic Life Care at St. Joseph

Saint Louis
Alliance
SSM Health

MONTANA

Billings
Alliance
Billings Clinic

NEW MEXICO

Albuquerque
Alliance
Presbyterian Healthcare Services

NEW YORK

Rochester
Alliance
Rochester Regional Health

Seagate Alliance

NORTH CAROLINA

Asheboro
Alliance
Randolph Hospital

Asheville
Alliance
Mission Health System

Boone
Alliance
Watauga Medical Center

Charlotte
Alliance
Carolinas HealthCare System

Fayetteville
Alliance
Cape Fear Valley Health System

Gastonia
Alliance
CaroMont Regional Medical Center

Goldsboro
Alliance
Wayne Memorial Hospital

Greensboro
Alliance
Moses H. Cone Memorial Hospital

Hendersonville
Alliance
Margaret R. Pardee Memorial Hospital

Hickory
Alliance
Catawba Valley Medical Center

Kinston
Alliance
UNC Lenoir Healthcare

Lumberton
Alliance
Southeastern Health

Morehead City
Alliance
Carteret Health Care

Pinehurst
Alliance
FirstHealth of the Carolinas

Roanoke Rapids
Alliance
Halifax Regional Medical Center

Statesville
Alliance
Iredell Health System

OHIO

Akron
Alliance
Summa Health System

Cincinnati
Alliance
Mercy Health

Cleveland
Alliance
University Hospitals

Elyria
Alliance
University Hospitals Elyria Medical Center

Kettering
Alliance
Kettering Medical Center

Middleburg Heights
Alliance
Southwest General Health Center

Parma
Alliance
University Hospitals Parma Medical Center

Sandusky
Alliance
Firelands Regional Health System

OKLAHOMA

Tulsa
Alliance
Saint Francis Hospital

OREGON

Salem
Alliance
Salem Hospital

PENNSYLVANIA

Beaver
Alliance
Heritage Valley Health System

Bethlehem
Alliance
St. Luke's University Health Network

Danville
Alliance
Geisinger Health

King of Prussia
Alliance
Universal Health Services, Inc.

Philadelphia
Alliance
Einstein Healthcare Network

Washington
Alliance
Washington Hospital

SOUTH CAROLINA

Anderson
Alliance
AnMed Health Medical Center

Conway
Alliance
Conway Medical Center

Greenwood
Alliance
Self Regional Healthcare

West Columbia
Alliance
Lexington Medical Center

SOUTH DAKOTA

Rapid City
Alliance
Rapid City Regional Hospital

Sioux Falls
Alliance
Avera Health

TENNESSEE

Crossville
Alliance
Cumberland Medical Center

Section B

Greeneville
Alliance
　Laughlin Memorial Hospital

Johnson City
Alliance
　Mountain States Health Alliance

Knoxville
Alliance
　University of Tennessee Medical Center

Maryville
Alliance
　Blount Memorial Hospital

TEXAS
Arlington
Alliance
　Texas Health Resources

Dallas
Alliance
　Methodist Health System
　University of Texas Southwestern Medical Center

Galveston
Alliance
　University of Texas Medical Branch

Houston
Alliance
　Harris Health System
　University of Texas M.D. Anderson Cancer Center

Lubbock
Alliance
　University Medical Center

VIRGINIA
Abingdon
Alliance
　Johnston Memorial Hospital

Chesapeake
Alliance
　Chesapeake Regional Healthcare

Falls Church
Alliance
　Inova Health System

Marion
Alliance
　Smyth County Community Hospital

Newport News
Alliance
　Riverside Health System

Roanoke
Alliance
　Carilion Clinic

South Hill
Alliance
　VCU Health Community Memorial Hospital

Winchester
Alliance
　Valley Health System

WASHINGTON
Seattle
Alliance
　Kaiser Permanente Capitol Hill Campus

Vancouver
Alliance
　PeaceHealth

WEST VIRGINIA
Elkins
Alliance
　Davis Medical Center

Huntington
Alliance
　Cabell Huntington Hospital
　Pallottine Health Services

Morgantown
Alliance
　Mon Health Medical Center

Parkersburg
Alliance
　Camden Clark Medical Center

Point Pleasant
Alliance
　Pleasant Valley Hospital

South Charleston
Alliance
　Thomas Memorial Hospital

Weirton
Alliance
　Weirton Medical Center

WISCONSIN
Milwaukee
Alliance
　Aurora Health Care

SEAGATE ALLIANCE
　3445 Winton Place, Suite 222,
　Rochester, NY Zip 14623–2950;
　tel. 888/732–4284; Travis Heider,
　President and Chief Executive Officer

NEW JERSEY
Newark
Alliance
　Columbus Hospital LTACH

NEW YORK
Bath
Alliance
　Bath Veterans Affairs Medical Center
　Ira Davenport Memorial Hospital

Buffalo
Alliance
　BryLin Hospitals
　Catholic Health System
　Erie County Medical Center
　Roswell Park Cancer Institute

Canandaigua
Alliance
　F. F. Thompson Hospital

Carthage
Alliance
　Carthage Area Hospital

Clifton Springs
Alliance
　Clifton Springs Hospital and Clinic

Corning
Alliance
　Guthrie Corning Hospital

Cuba
Alliance
　Cuba Memorial Hospital

Dansville
Alliance
　Nicholas H. Noyes Memorial Hospital

Dunkirk
Alliance
　Brooks Memorial Hospital

Elmira
Alliance
　Arnot Ogden Medical Center
　Elmira Psychiatric Center
　St. Joseph's Hospital

Geneva
Alliance
　Geneva General Hospital

Hornell
Alliance
　St. James Mercy Hospital

Kenmore
Alliance
　Kenmore Mercy Hospital

Lockport
Alliance
　Eastern Niagara Hospital

Montour Falls
Alliance
　Schuyler Hospital

Newark
Alliance
　Newark-Wayne Community Hospital

Olean
Alliance
　Olean General Hospital

Penn Yan
Alliance
　Soldiers and Sailors Memorial Hospital of Yates County

Rochester
Alliance
　Highland Hospital
　Rochester General Hospital
　Rochester Psychiatric Center
　Strong Memorial Hospital of the University of Rochester
　Unity Hospital

Springville
Alliance
　Bertrand Chaffee Hospital

Syracuse
Alliance
　Upstate University Hospital

Wellsville
Alliance
　Jones Memorial Hospital

PENNSYLVANIA
Bradford
Alliance
　Bradford Regional Medical Center

Coudersport
Alliance
　Cole Memorial

THE NEW JERSEY COUNCIL OF TEACHING HOSPITALS
　154 West State Street, Trenton, NJ Zip
　8608; tel. 609/656–9600; Deborah S.
　Briggs, President

NEW JERSEY
Camden
Alliance
　Cooper University Health Care

Hackensack
Alliance
　Hackensack Meridian Health Hackensack University Medical Center

Marlton
Alliance
　Weisman Children's Rehabilitation Hospital

Montclair
Alliance
　Hackensack Meridian Health Mountainside Medical Center

Morristown
Alliance
　Atlantic Health System
　Morristown Medical Center

New Brunswick
Alliance
　Children's Specialized Hospital

North Bergen
Alliance
　Hackensack Meridian Health Palisades Medical Center

Paterson
Alliance
　St. Joseph's Healthcare System

Summit
Alliance
　Overlook Medical Center

UNITED IROQUOIS SHARED SERVICES, INC.
　15 Executive Park Drive, Clifton Park,
　NY Zip 12065–5631; tel. 518/383–
　5060; Gary J. Fitzgerald, President

NEW YORK

Albany
Alliance
Albany Memorial Hospital
St. Peter's Hospital

Alexandria Bay
Alliance
River Hospital

Amsterdam
Alliance
St. Mary's Healthcare

Auburn
Alliance
Auburn Community Hospital

Binghamton
Alliance
Our Lady of Lourdes Memorial Hospital, Inc.
United Health Services Hospitals-Binghamton

Buffalo
Alliance
Roswell Park Cancer Institute

Carthage
Alliance
Carthage Area Hospital

Cobleskill
Alliance
Cobleskill Regional Hospital

Cooperstown
Alliance
Bassett Medical Center

Cortland
Alliance
Cortland Regional Medical Center

Cuba
Alliance
Cuba Memorial Hospital

Delhi
Alliance
O'Connor Hospital

Elizabethtown
Alliance
The University of Vermont Health Network
Elizabethtown Community Hospital

Glens Falls
Alliance
Glens Falls Hospital

Glenville
Alliance
Conifer Park

Gloversville
Alliance
Nathan Littauer Hospital and Nursing Home

Hamilton
Alliance
Community Memorial Hospital

Hudson
Alliance
Columbia Memorial Hospital

Ithaca
Alliance
Cayuga Medical Center at Ithaca

Little Falls
Alliance
Little Falls Hospital

Lowville
Alliance
Lewis County General Hospital

Malone
Alliance
The University of Vermont Health Network - Alice Hyde
Medical Center

Margaretville
Alliance
Margaretville Hospital

Massena
Alliance
Massena Memorial Hospital

Norwich
Alliance
UHS Chenango Memorial Hospital

Ogdensburg
Alliance
Claxton-Hepburn Medical Center

Olean
Alliance
Olean General Hospital

Oneida
Alliance
Oneida Healthcare

Oneonta
Alliance
Aurelia Osborn Fox Memorial Hospital

Oswego
Alliance
Oswego Hospital

Plattsburgh
Alliance
The University of Vermont Health Network-Champlain
Valley Physicians Hospital

Potsdam
Alliance
Canton-Potsdam Hospital

Rome
Alliance
Rome Memorial Hospital

Saranac Lake
Alliance
Adirondack Health

Saratoga Springs
Alliance
Saratoga Hospital

Schenectady
Alliance
Ellis Hospital
Sunnyview Rehabilitation Hospital

Springville
Alliance
Bertrand Chaffee Hospital

Star Lake
Alliance
Clifton-Fine Hospital

Syracuse
Alliance
Crouse Health
Upstate University Hospital

Troy
Alliance
Samaritan Hospital
St. Mary's Hospital

Utica
Alliance
Faxton St. Luke's Healthcare
St. Elizabeth Medical Center

Walton
Alliance
UHS Delaware Valley Hospital

Watertown
Alliance
Samaritan Medical Center

UNIVERSITY OF IOWA HEALTH ALLIANCE
1755 59th Place, West Des Moines, IA
Zip 50266–7737; tel. 515/643–4000;
Jennifer Vermeer, President and Chief
Executive Officer

ILLINOIS
Aledo
Alliance
Genesis Medical Center-Aledo

Silvis
Alliance
Genesis Medical Center, Silvis

IOWA
Albia
Alliance
Monroe County Hospital and Clinics

Algona
Alliance
Kossuth Regional Health Center

Audubon
Alliance
Audubon County Memorial Hospital

Belmond
Alliance
Iowa Specialty Hospital-Belmond

Bloomfield
Alliance
Davis County Hospital

Britt
Alliance
Hancock County Health System

Cedar Falls
Alliance
Sartori Memorial Hospital

Cedar Rapids
Alliance
Mercy Medical Center, Cedar Rapids, Iowa

Centerville
Alliance
Mercy Medical Center-Centerville

Clarinda
Alliance
Clarinda Regional Health Center

Clarion
Alliance
Iowa Specialty Hospital-Clarion

Clinton
Alliance
Mercy Medical Center-Clinton

Corydon
Alliance
Wayne County Hospital

Cresco
Alliance
Regional Health Services of Howard County

Davenport
Alliance
Genesis Medical Center-Davenport-West Central Park

De Witt
Alliance
Genesis Medical Center, DeWitt

Des Moines
Alliance
Mercy Medical Center-Des Moines

Dubuque
Alliance
Mercy Medical Center-Dubuque

Dyersville
Alliance
Mercy Medical Center-Dyersville

Elkader
Alliance
Central Community Hospital

Emmetsburg
Alliance
Palo Alto County Health System

Fairfield
Alliance
Jefferson County Health Center

Greenfield
Alliance
Adair County Health System

Grinnell
Alliance
Grinnell Regional Medical Center

Hampton
Alliance
Franklin General Hospital

Hawarden
Alliance
Hawarden Regional Healthcare

Iowa City
Alliance
University of Iowa Hospitals and Clinics

Section B

Iowa Falls
Alliance
 Hansen Family Hospital

Keosauqua
Alliance
 Van Buren County Hospital

Knoxville
Alliance
 Knoxville Hospital & Clinics

Leon
Alliance
 Decatur County Hospital

Manning
Alliance
 Manning Regional Healthcare Center

Maquoketa
Alliance
 Jackson County Regional Health Center

Mason City
Alliance
 Mercy Medical Center-North Iowa

Mount Ayr
Alliance
 Ringgold County Hospital

Mount Pleasant
Alliance
 Henry County Health Center

New Hampton
Alliance
 Mercy Medical Center-New Hampton

Oelwein
Alliance
 Mercy Hospital of Franciscan Sisters

Osage
Alliance
 Mitchell County Regional Health Center

Pella
Alliance
 Pella Regional Health Center

Perry
Alliance
 Dallas County Hospital

Primghar
Alliance
 Baum Harmon Mercy Hospital

Sigourney
Alliance
 Keokuk County Health Center

Sioux City
Alliance
 Mercy Medical Center-Sioux City

Vinton
Alliance
 Virginia Gay Hospital

Washington
Alliance
 Washington County Hospital and Clinics

Waterloo
Alliance
 Covenant Medical Center

Waverly
Alliance
 Waverly Health Center

Webster City
Alliance
 Van Diest Medical Center

Winterset
Alliance
 Madison County Health Care System

NEBRASKA
Oakland
Alliance
 Oakland Mercy Hospital

Pender
Alliance
 Pender Community Hospital

VANTAGE HEALTHCARE NETWORK, INC.
 18282 Technology Drive, Suite 202,
 Meadville, PA Zip 16335; tel. 814/337–
 0000; David Petrarca, Director Retail
 Operations

PENNSYLVANIA
Corry
Alliance
 Corry Memorial Hospital

DuBois
Alliance
 Penn Highlands DuBois

Ellwood City
Alliance
 Ellwood City Hospital

Erie
Alliance
 LECOM Health Millcreek Community Hospital

 Saint Vincent Hospital

Farrell
Alliance
 UPMC Horizon

Kane
Alliance
 UPMC Kane

Kittanning
Alliance
 ACMH Hospital

Meadville
Alliance
 Meadville Medical Center

Saint Marys
Alliance
 Penn Highlands Elk

Seneca
Alliance
 UPMC Northwest

Titusville
Alliance
 Titusville Area Hospital

Warren
Alliance
 Warren General Hospital

VIZIENT, INC.
 290 East John Carpenter Freeway,
 Irving, TX Zip 75062–2730; tel.
 972/830–0000; Curtis W. Nonomaque,
 President and Chief Executive Officer

ALABAMA
Alexander City
Alliance
 Russell Medical Center

Anniston
Alliance
 RMC Anniston

Athens
Alliance
 Athens-Limestone Hospital

Atmore
Alliance
 Atmore Community Hospital

Bay Minette
Alliance
 North Baldwin Infirmary

Bessemer
Alliance
 Medical West

Birmingham
Alliance
 University of Alabama Hospital

Boaz
Alliance
 Marshall Medical Center South

Brewton
Alliance
 D. W. McMillan Memorial Hospital

Carrollton
Alliance
 Pickens County Medical Center

Decatur
Alliance
 Decatur Morgan Hospital

Fairhope
Alliance
 Thomas Hospital

Fayette
Alliance
 Fayette Medical Center

Guntersville
Alliance
 Marshall Health System

 Marshall Medical Center North

Huntsville
Alliance
 Huntsville Hospital

Mobile
Alliance
 Mobile Infirmary Medical Center

 University of South Alabama Children's and Women's Hospital

 University of South Alabama Medical Center

Montgomery
Alliance
 Baptist Medical Center East

 Baptist Medical Center South

Opp
Alliance
 Mizell Memorial Hospital

Ozark
Alliance
 Dale Medical Center

Prattville
Alliance
 Prattville Baptist Hospital

Red Bay
Alliance
 Red Bay Hospital

Scottsboro
Alliance
 Highlands Medical Center

Sheffield
Alliance
 Helen Keller Hospital

Tuscaloosa
Alliance
 DCH Health System

 DCH Regional Medical Center

Union Springs
Alliance
 Bullock County Hospital

ALASKA
Anchorage
Alliance
 Providence Alaska Medical Center

 St. Elias Specialty Hospital

Cordova
Alliance
 Cordova Community Medical Center

Kodiak
Alliance
 Providence Kodiak Island Medical Center

Seward
Alliance
 Providence Seward Medical Center

Valdez
Alliance
 Providence Valdez Medical Center

Wrangell
Alliance
 Wrangell Medical Center

AMERICAN SAMOA
Pago Pago
Alliance
 Lyndon B. Johnson Tropical Medical Center

ARIZONA
Benson
Alliance
  Benson Hospital

Bisbee
Alliance
  Copper Queen Community Hospital

Flagstaff
Alliance
  Flagstaff Medical Center

Green Valley
Alliance
  Green Valley Hospital

Kingman
Alliance
  Kingman Regional Medical Center

Phoenix
Alliance
  Maricopa Integrated Health System
  Mayo Clinic Hospital

Safford
Alliance
  Mt. Graham Regional Medical Center

Tucson
Alliance
  Banner - University Medical Center South
  Banner - University Medical Center Tucson
  TMC HealthCare

Willcox
Alliance
  Northern Cochise Community Hospital

ARKANSAS
Arkadelphia
Alliance
  Baptist Health Medical Center-Arkadelphia

Booneville
Alliance
  Mercy Hospital Booneville

Clinton
Alliance
  Ozark Health Medical Center

Conway
Alliance
  Conway Regional Medical Center

Fayetteville
Alliance
  Washington Regional Medical Center

Heber Springs
Alliance
  Baptist Health Medical Center-Heber Springs

Hot Springs
Alliance
  CHI St. Vincent Hot Springs

Jonesboro
Alliance
  NEA Baptist Memorial Hospital
  St. Bernards Medical Center

Little Rock
Alliance
  Baptist Health Extended Care Hospital
  Baptist Health Medical Center-Little Rock
  Baptist Health
  CHI St. Vincent Infirmary Medical Center

Malvern
Alliance
  Baptist Health Medical Center-Hot Spring County

Morrilton
Alliance
  CHI St. Vincent Morrilton

North Little Rock
Alliance
  Baptist Health Medical Center - North Little Rock

Paragould
Alliance
  Arkansas Methodist Medical Center

Piggott
Alliance
  Piggott Community Hospital

Stuttgart
Alliance
  Baptist Health Medical Center-Stuttgart

Walnut Ridge
Alliance
  Lawrence Memorial Hospital

Wynne
Alliance
  CrossRidge Community Hospital

CALIFORNIA
Alameda
Alliance
  Alameda Hospital

Antioch
Alliance
  Kaiser Permanente Antioch Medical Center

Arcadia
Alliance
  Methodist Hospital of Southern California

Auburn
Alliance
  Sutter Auburn Faith Hospital

Bakersfield
Alliance
  Kern Medical Center

Berkeley
Alliance
  Alta Bates Medical Center-Herrick Campus
  Alta Bates Summit Medical Center

Burbank
Alliance
  Providence Saint Joseph Medical Center

Burlingame
Alliance
  Mills-Peninsula Health Services

Castro Valley
Alliance
  Eden Medical Center

Colton
Alliance
  Arrowhead Regional Medical Center

Concord
Alliance
  John Muir Medical Center, Concord

Covina
Alliance
  Citrus Valley Health Partners
  Citrus Valley Medical Center-Inter Community Campus

Crescent City
Alliance
  Sutter Coast Hospital

Davis
Alliance
  Sutter Davis Hospital

Downey
Alliance
  PIH Health Hospital - Downey
  Rancho Los Amigos National Rehabilitation Center

El Centro
Alliance
  El Centro Regional Medical Center

Escondido
Alliance
  Palomar Health
  Palomar Medical Center

Fairfield
Alliance
  NorthBay Medical Center

Fremont
Alliance
  Kaiser Permanente Fremont Medical Center
  Washington Hospital Healthcare System

French Camp
Alliance
  San Joaquin General Hospital

Fresno
Alliance
  Community Medical Centers
  Saint Agnes Medical Center

Glendora
Alliance
  Foothill Presbyterian Hospital

Jackson
Alliance
  Sutter Amador Hospital

King City
Alliance
  Mee Memorial Hospital

Lakeport
Alliance
  Sutter Lakeside Hospital

Lancaster
Alliance
  Antelope Valley Hospital

Los Angeles
Alliance
  Cedars-Sinai Medical Center
  LAC+USC Medical Center
  Martin Luther King, Jr. Community Hospital
  Ronald Reagan UCLA Medical Center
  Stewart & Lynda Resnick Neuropsychiatric Hospital at UCLA
  USC Norris Comprehensive Cancer Center

Los Banos
Alliance
  Memorial Hospital Los Banos

Manteca
Alliance
  Kaiser Permanente Manteca Medical Center

Marina Del Rey
Alliance
  Marina Del Rey Hospital

Mariposa
Alliance
  John C. Fremont Healthcare District

Martinez
Alliance
  Contra Costa Regional Medical Center

Menlo Park
Alliance
  Menlo Park Surgical Hospital

Mission Hills
Alliance
  Providence Holy Cross Medical Center

Modesto
Alliance
  Memorial Medical Center

Monterey
Alliance
  Community Hospital of the Monterey Peninsula

Moreno Valley
Alliance
  Riverside University Health System-Medical Center

Mountain View
Alliance
  El Camino Hospital

Novato
Alliance
  Novato Community Hospital

Oakland
Alliance
  Alta Bates Summit Medical Center - Summit Campus
  Highland Hospital
  Kaiser Permanente Oakland Medical Center

Oceanside
Alliance
  Tri-City Medical Center

Ojai
Alliance
  Ojai Valley Community Hospital

Orange
Alliance
  UC Irvine Medical Center

Alliances

Palo Alto
Alliance
Lucile Salter Packard Children's Hospital Stanford
Stanford Health Care

Pleasanton
Alliance
Stanford Health Care - ValleyCare

Pomona
Alliance
Pomona Valley Hospital Medical Center

Porterville
Alliance
Sierra View Medical Center

Portola
Alliance
Eastern Plumas Health Care

Poway
Alliance
Pomerado Hospital

Redlands
Alliance
Redlands Community Hospital

Redwood City
Alliance
Kaiser Permanente Redwood City Medical Center

Roseville
Alliance
Kaiser Permanente Roseville Medical Center
Sutter Roseville Medical Center

Sacramento
Alliance
Kaiser Permanente Sacramento Medical Center
Kaiser Permanente South Sacramento Medical Center
Shriners Hospitals for Children-Northern California
Sutter Center for Psychiatry
Sutter Health
Sutter Medical Center, Sacramento
University of California, Davis Medical Center

Salinas
Alliance
Natividad Medical Center

San Diego
Alliance
Scripps Health
UC San Diego Health

San Francisco
Alliance
California Pacific Medical Center-Davies Campus
California Pacific Medical Center-St. Luke's Campus
California Pacific Medical Center
Chinese Hospital
Kaiser Permanente San Francisco Medical Center
UCSF Medical Center
Zuckerberg San Francisco General Hospital and Trauma Center

San Jose
Alliance
Kaiser Permanente San Jose Medical Center
Santa Clara Valley Medical Center

San Leandro
Alliance
San Leandro Hospital

San Mateo
Alliance
San Mateo Medical Center

San Pedro
Alliance
Providence Little Company of Mary Medical Center San Pedro

San Rafael
Alliance
Kaiser Permanente San Rafael Medical Center

Santa Barbara
Alliance
Cottage Health

Goleta Valley Cottage Hospital
Santa Barbara Cottage Hospital

Santa Clara
Alliance
Kaiser Permanente Santa Clara Medical Center

Santa Cruz
Alliance
Sutter Maternity and Surgery Center of Santa Cruz

Santa Monica
Alliance
Providence Saint John's Health Center
UCLA Medical Center-Santa Monica

Santa Rosa
Alliance
Kaiser Permanente Santa Rosa Medical Center
Sutter Santa Rosa Regional Hospital

Solvang
Alliance
Santa Ynez Valley Cottage Hospital

South San Francisco
Alliance
Kaiser Permanente South San Francisco

Stockton
Alliance
Dameron Hospital

Sylmar
Alliance
LAC-Olive View-UCLA Medical Center

Tarzana
Alliance
Providence Tarzana Medical Center

Torrance
Alliance
Harbor-UCLA Medical Center
Providence Little Company of Mary Medical Center - Torrance
Torrance Memorial Medical Center

Tracy
Alliance
Sutter Tracy Community Hospital

Vacaville
Alliance
Kaiser Permanente Vacaville Medical Center

Vallejo
Alliance
Kaiser Permanente Vallejo Medical Center
Sutter Solano Medical Center

Ventura
Alliance
Community Memorial Hospital

Walnut Creek
Alliance
John Muir Health
John Muir Medical Center, Walnut Creek
Kaiser Permanente Walnut Creek Medical Center

Whittier
Alliance
PIH Health Hospital-Whittier

Yuba City
Alliance
Sutter Surgical Hospital - North Valley

COLORADO
Alamosa
Alliance
San Luis Valley Health

Aurora
Alliance
University of Colorado Hospital

Boulder
Alliance
Boulder Community Health

Canon City
Alliance
St. Thomas More Hospital

Colorado Springs
Alliance

Penrose-St. Francis Health Services
UCHealth Memorial

Denver
Alliance
Denver Health
National Jewish Health

Durango
Alliance
Mercy Regional Medical Center

Englewood
Alliance
Craig Hospital

Estes Park
Alliance
Estes Park Medical Center

Fort Collins
Alliance
Poudre Valley Hospital

Grand Junction
Alliance
St. Mary's Hospital and Medical Center

Gunnison
Alliance
Gunnison Valley Hospital

La Jara
Alliance
San Luis Valley Health Conejos County Hospital

Lakewood
Alliance
St. Anthony Hospital

Loveland
Alliance
Medical Center of the Rockies

Pueblo
Alliance
St. Mary-Corwin Medical Center

Steamboat Springs
Alliance
Yampa Valley Medical Center

Westminster
Alliance
St. Anthony North Health Campus

Yuma
Alliance
Yuma District Hospital

CONNECTICUT
Bridgeport
Alliance
Bridgeport Hospital

Bristol
Alliance
Bristol Hospital

Danbury
Alliance
Danbury Hospital

Farmington
Alliance
UConn, John Dempsey Hospital

Greenwich
Alliance
Greenwich Hospital

Hartford
Alliance
Hartford Hospital
Saint Francis Hospital and Medical Center

Manchester
Alliance
Manchester Memorial Hospital

Middletown
Alliance
Connecticut Valley Hospital
Middlesex Hospital

Milford
Alliance
Milford Hospital

New Haven
Alliance

Connecticut Mental Health Center
Yale New Haven Health
Yale-New Haven Hospital

New London
Alliance
Lawrence + Memorial Hospital

Norwalk
Alliance
Norwalk Hospital

Putnam
Alliance
Day Kimball Hospital

Stamford
Alliance
Stamford Hospital

Torrington
Alliance
The Charlotte Hungerford Hospital

Vernon
Alliance
Rockville General Hospital

DELAWARE

Wilmington
Alliance
St. Francis Hospital

DISTRICT OF COLUMBIA

Washington
Alliance
Howard University Hospital
MedStar Georgetown University Hospital
MedStar Washington Hospital Center
Sibley Memorial Hospital

FLORIDA

Apalachicola
Alliance
George E. Weems Memorial Hospital

Boca Raton
Alliance
Boca Raton Regional Hospital

Boynton Beach
Alliance
Bethesda Hospital East

Clermont
Alliance
South Lake Hospital

Cocoa Beach
Alliance
Health First Cape Canaveral Hospital

Coral Gables
Alliance
Baptist Health South Florida, Doctors Hospital

Daytona Beach
Alliance
Halifax Health Medical Center of Daytona Beach

Gainesville
Alliance
UF Health Shands Hospital

Gulf Breeze
Alliance
Gulf Breeze Hospital

Homestead
Alliance
Baptist Health South Florida, Homestead Hospital

Jacksonville
Alliance
Mayo Clinic Jacksonville

Jay
Alliance
Jay Hospital

Lakeland
Alliance
Lakeland Regional Health

Leesburg
Alliance
Leesburg Regional Medical Center

Melbourne
Alliance
Health First Holmes Regional Medical Center

Miami
Alliance
Baptist Health South Florida, Baptist Hospital of Miami
Baptist Health South Florida, West Kendall Baptist Hospital
Jackson Health System

Milton
Alliance
West Florida Community Care Center

Naples
Alliance
NCH Downtown Naples Hospital

Ocoee
Alliance
Health Central Hospital

Orlando
Alliance
Orlando Health
Orlando Regional Medical Center

Palm Bay
Alliance
Health First Palm Bay Hospital

Panama City
Alliance
Bay Medical Center Sacred Heart Health System

Pensacola
Alliance
Baptist Health Care Corporation
Baptist Hospital

Perry
Alliance
Doctor's Memorial Hospital

Rockledge
Alliance
Health First, Inc.

Starke
Alliance
Shands Starke Regional Medical Center

Stuart
Alliance
Martin Health System

Tallahassee
Alliance
Tallahassee Memorial HealthCare

Tampa
Alliance
H. Lee Moffitt Cancer Center and Research Institute
Shriners Hospitals for Children-Tampa
Tampa General Hospital

Tavernier
Alliance
Baptist Health South Florida, Mariners Hospital

The Villages
Alliance
The Villages Regional Hospital

Titusville
Alliance
Parrish Medical Center

Vero Beach
Alliance
Indian River Medical Center

Weston
Alliance
Cleveland Clinic Florida

GEORGIA

Adel
Alliance
Cook Medical Center-A Campus of Tift Regional Medical Center

Albany
Alliance
Phoebe Putney Health System
Phoebe Putney Memorial Hospital

Americus
Alliance
Phoebe Sumter Medical Center

Athens
Alliance
Piedmont Athens Regional Medical Center
St. Mary's Health Care System

Atlanta
Alliance
Emory Saint Joseph's Hospital of Atlanta
Emory University Hospital Midtown
Emory University Hospital
Grady Memorial Hospital
Northside Hospital
Wellstar Atlanta Medical Center

Augusta
Alliance
Augusta University Medical Center
Charlie Norwood Veterans Affairs Medical Center
University Hospital

Austell
Alliance
WellStar Cobb Hospital

Braselton
Alliance
Northeast Georgia Medical Center Braselton

Brunswick
Alliance
Southeast Georgia Health System Brunswick Campus
Southeast Georgia Health System

Bryon
Alliance
Medical Center of Peach County, Navicent Health

Cairo
Alliance
Grady General Hospital

Camilla
Alliance
Mitchell County Hospital

Canton
Alliance
Northside Hospital-Cherokee

Cedartown
Alliance
Polk Medical Center

Claxton
Alliance
Evans Memorial Hospital

Columbus
Alliance
Columbus Regional Healthcare System
Columbus Specialty Hospital
Midtown Medical Center
Northside Medical Center

Cordele
Alliance
Crisp Regional Hospital

Cumming
Alliance
Northside Hospital-Forsyth

Cuthbert
Alliance
Southwest Georgia Regional Medical Center

Dalton
Alliance
Hamilton Medical Center

Decatur
Alliance
DeKalb Medical at Downtown Decatur

Douglas
Alliance
Coffee Regional Medical Center

Douglasville
Alliance
WellStar Douglas Hospital

Eatonton
Alliance
Putnam General Hospital

Alliances

Fitzgerald
Alliance
Dorminy Medical Center

Gainesville
Alliance
Northeast Georgia Medical Center

Hiram
Alliance
WellStar Paulding Hospital

Homerville
Alliance
Clinch Memorial Hospital

Jackson
Alliance
Wellstar Sylvan Grove Hospital

Johns Creek
Alliance
Emory Johns Creek Hospital

Lakeland
Alliance
South Georgia Medical Center Lanier Campus

Lawrenceville
Alliance
Gwinnett Hospital System

Lithonia
Alliance
DeKalb Medical at Hillandale

Macon
Alliance
Medical Center, Navicent Health
Rehabilitation Hospital, Navicent Health

Marietta
Alliance
WellStar Health System
WellStar Kennestone Hospital
WellStar Windy Hill Hospital

Moultrie
Alliance
Colquitt Regional Medical Center

Nashville
Alliance
South Georgia Medical Center Berrien Campus

Newnan
Alliance
Southeastern Regional Medical Center

Perry
Alliance
Perry Hospital

Quitman
Alliance
Brooks County Hospital

Riverdale
Alliance
Southern Regional Medical Center

Rome
Alliance
Floyd Medical Center

Roswell
Alliance
Wellstar North Fulton Hospital

Saint Marys
Alliance
Southeast Georgia Health System Camden Campus

Sandersville
Alliance
Washington County Regional Medical Center

Savannah
Alliance
Memorial Health

Swainsboro
Alliance
Emanuel Medical Center

Sylvester
Alliance
Phoebe Worth Medical Center

Thomasville
Alliance
Archbold Medical Center
John D. Archbold Memorial Hospital

Thomson
Alliance
University Hospital McDuffie

Tifton
Alliance
Tift Regional Medical Center

Valdosta
Alliance
South Georgia Medical Center

Warm Springs
Alliance
Roosevelt Warm Springs Rehabilitation Hospital - Rehab
Roosevelt Warm Springs Rehabilitation and Specialty Hospitals - LTAC

Warner Robins
Alliance
Houston Medical Center

Waycross
Alliance
Memorial Satilla Health

GUAM
Dededo
Alliance
Guam Regional Medical City

HAWAII
Aiea
Alliance
Pali Momi Medical Center

Ewa Beach
Alliance
Kahi Mohala Behavioral Health

Honolulu
Alliance
Kaiser Permanente Medical Center
Queen's Health Systems
Shriners Hospitals for Children-Honolulu
Straub Clinic & Hospital
The Queen's Medical Center

Kamuela
Alliance
North Hawaii Community Hospital

Kaunakakai
Alliance
Molokai General Hospital

Wahiawa
Alliance
Wahiawa General Hospital

IDAHO
American Falls
Alliance
Power County Hospital District

Blackfoot
Alliance
Bingham Memorial Hospital

Boise
Alliance
Saint Alphonsus Regional Medical Center
St. Luke's Health System

Bonners Ferry
Alliance
Boundary Community Hospital

Cascade
Alliance
Cascade Medical Center

Coeur D'Alene
Alliance
Kootenai Health

Cottonwood
Alliance
St. Mary's Hospital

Emmett
Alliance
Valor Health

Orofino
Alliance
Clearwater Valley Hospital and Clinics

Preston
Alliance
Franklin County Medical Center

Rupert
Alliance
Minidoka Memorial Hospital

Sandpoint
Alliance
Bonner General Hospital

Weiser
Alliance
Weiser Memorial Hospital

ILLINOIS
Alton
Alliance
Alton Memorial Hospital

Arlington Heights
Alliance
Northwest Community Hospital

Aurora
Alliance
Rush-Copley Medical Center

Barrington
Alliance
Advocate Good Shepherd Hospital

Belleville
Alliance
Memorial Hospital

Bloomington
Alliance
OSF St. Joseph Medical Center

Canton
Alliance
Graham Hospital Association

Carbondale
Alliance
Memorial Hospital of Carbondale
Southern Illinois Healthcare

Chester
Alliance
Memorial Hospital

Chicago
Alliance
Advocate Illinois Masonic Medical Center
Advocate Trinity Hospital
Ann & Robert H. Lurie Children's Hospital of Chicago
John H. Stroger Jr. Hospital of Cook County
La Rabida Children's Hospital
Louis A. Weiss Memorial Hospital
Mercy Hospital and Medical Center
Methodist Hospital of Chicago
Northwestern Memorial Hospital
Norwegian American Hospital
Presence Resurrection Medical Center
Provident Hospital of Cook County
Rush University Medical Center
Shriners Hospitals for Children-Chicago
Swedish Covenant Hospital
University of Chicago Medical Center
University of Illinois Hospital & Health Sciences System

Decatur
Alliance
Decatur Memorial Hospital

Downers Grove
Alliance
Advocate Good Samaritan Hospital

Eldorado
Alliance
Ferrell Hospital

Elgin
Alliance
Advocate Sherman Hospital

Elmhurst
Alliance
Elmhurst Hospital

Evanston
Alliance
NorthShore University Health System

Evergreen Park
Alliance
Little Company of Mary Hospital and Health Care Centers

Freeport
Alliance
FHN Memorial Hospital

Galesburg
Alliance
OSF St. Mary Medical Center

Geneva
Alliance
Northwestern Medicine Delnor Hospital

Greenville
Alliance
HSHS Holy Family Hospital in Greenville

Harvey
Alliance
Ingalls Memorial Hospital

Hazel Crest
Alliance
Advocate South Suburban Hospital

Herrin
Alliance
Herrin Hospital

Hinsdale
Alliance
AMITA Health Adventist Medical Center - Hinsdale
RML Specialty Hospital

Hoffman Estates
Alliance
Alexian Brothers Behavioral Health Hospital

Jacksonville
Alliance
Passavant Area Hospital

Jerseyville
Alliance
Jersey Community Hospital

Joliet
Alliance
Presence Saint Joseph Medical Center

Kewanee
Alliance
OSF Saint Luke Medical Center

Lake Forest
Alliance
Northwestern Medicine Lake Forest Hospital

Libertyville
Alliance
Advocate Condell Medical Center

Lincoln
Alliance
Abraham Lincoln Memorial Hospital

Macomb
Alliance
McDonough District Hospital

Maryville
Alliance
Anderson Hospital

Mattoon
Alliance
Sarah Bush Lincoln Health Center

Maywood
Alliance
Loyola University Medical Center

McHenry
Alliance
Centegra Hospital - McHenry

Monticello
Alliance
Kirby Medical Center

Murphysboro
Alliance
St. Joseph Memorial Hospital

New Lenox
Alliance
Silver Cross Hospital

Oak Lawn
Alliance
Advocate Christ Medical Center

Oak Park
Alliance
Rush Oak Park Hospital

Palos Heights
Alliance
Palos Health

Park Ridge
Alliance
Advocate Lutheran General Hospital

Peoria
Alliance
OSF Saint Francis Medical Center
UnityPoint Health - Peoria

Pittsfield
Alliance
Illini Community Hospital

Pontiac
Alliance
OSF Saint James - John W. Albrecht Medical Center

Quincy
Alliance
Blessing Hospital

Rock Island
Alliance
UnityPoint Health - Trinity Rock Island

Rockford
Alliance
OSF Saint Anthony Medical Center
SwedishAmerican - A Division of UW Health

Rushville
Alliance
Sarah D. Culbertson Memorial Hospital

Salem
Alliance
Salem Township Hospital

Shelbyville
Alliance
Shelby Memorial Hospital

Shiloh
Alliance
Memorial Hospital East

Springfield
Alliance
Memorial Health System
Memorial Medical Center

Taylorville
Alliance
Taylorville Memorial Hospital

Urbana
Alliance
Carle Foundation Hospital

Winfield
Alliance
Northwestern Medicine Central DuPage Hospital

INDIANA
Anderson
Alliance
Community Hospital of Anderson & Madison County

Angola
Alliance
Cameron Memorial Community Hospital

Auburn
Alliance
DeKalb Health

Avon
Alliance
Indiana University Health West Hospital

Batesville
Alliance
Margaret Mary Health

Bedford
Alliance
Indiana University Health Bedford Hospital

Bloomington
Alliance
Indiana University Health Bloomington Hospital

Carmel
Alliance
Indiana University Health North Hospital

Clinton
Alliance
Union Hospital Clinton

Columbia City
Alliance
Parkview Whitley Hospital

Columbus
Alliance
Columbus Regional Hospital

Danville
Alliance
Hendricks Regional Health

Elkhart
Alliance
Elkhart General Hospital

Evansville
Alliance
Deaconess Health System
Deaconess Hospital

Fort Wayne
Alliance
Parkview Ortho Hospital
Parkview Health
Parkview Regional Medical Center

Franklin
Alliance
Johnson Memorial Hospital

Goshen
Alliance
Goshen Hospital

Hartford City
Alliance
Indiana University Health Blackford Hospital

Huntington
Alliance
Parkview Huntington Hospital

Indianapolis
Alliance
Community Health Network
Community Hospital East
Community Hospital North
Community Hospital South
Eskenazi Health
Indiana University Health Methodist Hospital
Indiana University Health University Hospital

Jasper
Alliance
Memorial Hospital and Health Care Center

Kendallville
Alliance
Parkview Noble Hospital

Knox
Alliance
Starke Hospital

Kokomo
Alliance
Community Howard Regional Health

La Porte
Alliance
La Porte Hospital

LaGrange
Alliance
Parkview LaGrange Hospital

Lafayette
Alliance
Indiana University Health Arnett Hospital

Alliances

Logansport
Alliance
  Logansport Memorial Hospital

Madison
Alliance
  King's Daughters' Health

Marion
Alliance
  Marion General Hospital

Monticello
Alliance
  Indiana University Health White Memorial Hospital

Muncie
Alliance
  Indiana University Health Ball Memorial Hospital

New Albany
Alliance
  Baptist Health Floyd
  Southern Indiana Rehabilitation Hospital

New Castle
Alliance
  Henry County Hospital

Newburgh
Alliance
  The Heart Hospital at Deaconess Gateway
  The Women's Hospital

Noblesville
Alliance
  Riverview Health

Paoli
Alliance
  Indiana University Health Paoli Hospital

Portland
Alliance
  Jay County Hospital

Richmond
Alliance
  Reid Health

Rochester
Alliance
  Woodlawn Hospital

Seymour
Alliance
  Schneck Medical Center

Shelbyville
Alliance
  Major Hospital

South Bend
Alliance
  Healthwin Hospital
  Memorial Hospital of South Bend

Terre Haute
Alliance
  Union Hospital

Tipton
Alliance
  Indiana University Health Tipton Hospital

Vincennes
Alliance
  Good Samaritan Hospital

Wabash
Alliance
  Parkview Wabash County Hospital

IOWA

Anamosa
Alliance
  UnityPoint Health - Jones Regional Medical Center

Atlantic
Alliance
  Cass County Memorial Hospital

Bettendorf
Alliance
  UnityPoint Health - Trinity Bettendorf

Cedar Rapids
Alliance
  Continuing Care Hospital at St. Luke's
  UnityPoint Health - St. Luke's Hospital

Centerville
Alliance
  Mercy Medical Center-Centerville

Clarinda
Alliance
  Clarinda Regional Health Center

Clinton
Alliance
  Mercy Medical Center-Clinton

Corning
Alliance
  CHI Health Mercy Corning

Council Bluffs
Alliance
  Methodist Jennie Edmundson Hospital

Decorah
Alliance
  Winneshiek Medical Center

Des Moines
Alliance
  Mercy Medical Center-Des Moines
  UnityPoint Health-Iowa Lutheran Hospital

Dubuque
Alliance
  Mercy Medical Center-Dubuque
  UnityPoint Health - Finley Hospital

Fort Dodge
Alliance
  UnityPoint Health - Trinity Regional Medical Center

Grundy Center
Alliance
  Grundy County Memorial Hospital

Guttenberg
Alliance
  Guttenberg Municipal Hospital

Hamburg
Alliance
  George C Grape Community Hospital

Hampton
Alliance
  Franklin General Hospital

Harlan
Alliance
  Myrtue Medical Center

Iowa City
Alliance
  University of Iowa Hospitals and Clinics

Iowa Falls
Alliance
  Hansen Family Hospital

Jefferson
Alliance
  Greene County Medical Center

Keokuk
Alliance
  UnityPoint Health-Keokuk

Keosauqua
Alliance
  Van Buren County Hospital

Lake City
Alliance
  Stewart Memorial Community Hospital

Le Mars
Alliance
  Floyd Valley Healthcare

Marengo
Alliance
  Compass Memorial Healthcare

Mason City
Alliance
  Mercy Medical Center-North Iowa

Missouri Valley
Alliance
  CHI Health Missouri Valley

Muscatine
Alliance
  UnityPoint Health - Trinity Muscatine

Nevada
Alliance
  Story County Medical Center

New Hampton
Alliance
  Mercy Medical Center-New Hampton

Orange City
Alliance
  Orange City Area Health System

Osceola
Alliance
  Clarke County Hospital

Pella
Alliance
  Pella Regional Health Center

Red Oak
Alliance
  Montgomery County Memorial Hospital

Rock Rapids
Alliance
  Sanford Rock Rapids Medical Center

Sheldon
Alliance
  Sanford Sheldon Medical Center

Shenandoah
Alliance
  Shenandoah Medical Center

Sigourney
Alliance
  Keokuk County Health Center

Sioux City
Alliance
  Mercy Medical Center-Sioux City
  UnityPoint Health - St. Lukes's Sioux City

Sumner
Alliance
  Community Memorial Hospital

Waverly
Alliance
  Waverly Health Center

West Des Moines
Alliance
  UnityPoint Health - Methodist West Hospital

West Union
Alliance
  Gundersen Palmer Lutheran Hospital and Clinics

KANSAS

Abilene
Alliance
  Memorial Health System

Anthony
Alliance
  Anthony Medical Center

Ashland
Alliance
  Ashland Health Center

Atchison
Alliance
  Atchison Hospital

Atwood
Alliance
  Rawlins County Health Center

Belleville
Alliance
  Republic County Hospital

Beloit
Alliance
  Mitchell County Hospital Health Systems

Clay Center
Alliance
  Clay County Medical Center

Colby
Alliance
  Citizens Medical Center

Coldwater
Alliance
  Comanche County Hospital

Concordia
Alliance
  Cloud County Health Center

Dighton
Alliance
  Lane County Hospital

El Dorado
Alliance
  Susan B. Allen Memorial Hospital

Ellinwood
Alliance
  Ellinwood District Hospital

Ellsworth
Alliance
  Ellsworth County Medical Center

Emporia
Alliance
  Newman Regional Health

Fredonia
Alliance
  Fredonia Regional Hospital

Garden City
Alliance
  St. Catherine Hospital

Garnett
Alliance
  Anderson County Hospital

Girard
Alliance
  Girard Medical Center

Goodland
Alliance
  Goodland Regional Medical Center

Great Bend
Alliance
  Great Bend Regional Hospital

Greensburg
Alliance
  Kiowa County Memorial Hospital

Hays
Alliance
  Hays Medical Center

Herington
Alliance
  Herington Municipal Hospital

Hiawatha
Alliance
  Hiawatha Community Hospital

Hill City
Alliance
  Graham County Hospital

Hoisington
Alliance
  Clara Barton Hospital

Hoxie
Alliance
  Sheridan County Health Complex

Junction City
Alliance
  Geary Community Hospital

Kansas City
Alliance
  The University of Kansas Health System

La Crosse
Alliance
  Rush County Memorial Hospital

Larned
Alliance
  Pawnee Valley Community Hospital

Lawrence
Alliance
  Lawrence Memorial Hospital

Leavenworth
Alliance
  Saint Luke's Cushing Hospital

Lincoln
Alliance
  Lincoln County Hospital

Lindsborg
Alliance
  Lindsborg Community Hospital

Mankato
Alliance
  Jewell County Hospital

Medicine Lodge
Alliance
  Medicine Lodge Memorial Hospital

Minneapolis
Alliance
  Ottawa County Health Center

Minneola
Alliance
  Minneola District Hospital

Ness City
Alliance
  Ness County Hospital District No 2

Norton
Alliance
  Norton County Hospital

Oakley
Alliance
  Logan County Hospital

Overland Park
Alliance
  Menorah Medical Center
  Overland Park Regional Medical Center
  Saint Luke's South Hospital

Parsons
Alliance
  Labette Health

Phillipsburg
Alliance
  Phillips County Hospital

Plainville
Alliance
  Rooks County Health Center

Pratt
Alliance
  Pratt Regional Medical Center

Quinter
Alliance
  Gove County Medical Center

Ransom
Alliance
  Grisell Memorial Hospital District One

Russell
Alliance
  Russell Regional Hospital

Sabetha
Alliance
  Sabetha Community Hospital

Saint Francis
Alliance
  Cheyenne County Hospital

Salina
Alliance
  Salina Regional Health Center
  Salina Surgical Hospital

Satanta
Alliance
  Satanta District Hospital and Long Term Care

Scott City
Alliance
  Scott County Hospital

Smith Center
Alliance
  Smith County Memorial Hospital

Stafford
Alliance
  Stafford County Hospital

Topeka
Alliance
  Stormont Vail Health

Wakeeney
Alliance
  Trego County-Lemke Memorial Hospital

Wichita
Alliance
  Great Plains Health Alliance, Inc.
  Kansas Spine and Specialty Hospital

KENTUCKY
Bardstown
Alliance
  Flaget Memorial Hospital

Berea
Alliance
  Saint Joseph Berea

Cynthiana
Alliance
  Harrison Memorial Hospital

Florence
Alliance
  St. Elizabeth Florence

Lexington
Alliance
  Eastern State Hospital
  Saint Joseph East
  Saint Joseph Hospital
  Shriners Hospitals for Children-Lexington
  University of Kentucky Albert B. Chandler Hospital

London
Alliance
  Saint Joseph London

Louisville
Alliance
  Jewish Hospital
  Our Lady of Peace
  University of Louisville Hospital

Martin
Alliance
  Saint Joseph - Martin

Morehead
Alliance
  St. Claire HealthCare

Mount Sterling
Alliance
  Saint Joseph Mount Sterling

Mount Vernon
Alliance
  Rockcastle Regional Hospital and Respiratory Care Center

Owensboro
Alliance
  Owensboro Health Regional Hospital

Pikeville
Alliance
  Pikeville Medical Center

Shelbyville
Alliance
  Jewish Hospital-Shelbyville

LOUISIANA
Baton Rouge
Alliance
  Franciscan Missionaries of Our Lady Health System, Inc.
  Ochsner Medical Center-Baton Rouge
  Our Lady of the Lake Regional Medical Center

Bogalusa
Alliance
  Our Lady of the Angels Hospital

Bossier City
Alliance
  WK Bossier Health Center

Church Point
Alliance
  Acadia-St. Landry Hospital

Covington
Alliance
  St. Tammany Parish Hospital

De Ridder
Alliance
  Beauregard Memorial Hospital

Ferriday
Alliance
  Riverland Medical Center

Gonzales
Alliance
  St. Elizabeth Hospital

Jennings
Alliance
  Jennings American Legion Hospital

Kenner
Alliance
  Ochsner Medical Center - Kenner

Lafayette
Alliance
  Lafayette General Medical Center
  Our Lady of Lourdes Regional Medical Center

Lake Charles
Alliance
  Lake Charles Memorial Hospital
  Memorial Specialty Hospital

Mansfield
Alliance
  De Soto Regional Health System

Monroe
Alliance
  St. Francis Medical Center
  University Health Conway

Napoleonville
Alliance
  Assumption Community Hospital

Natchitoches
Alliance
  Natchitoches Regional Medical Center

New Iberia
Alliance
  Iberia Medical Center

New Orleans
Alliance
  Touro Infirmary

Raceland
Alliance
  Ochsner St. Anne General Hospital

Shreveport
Alliance
  Shriners Hospitals for Children-Shreveport
  University Health Shreveport
  Willis-Knighton Health System
  Willis-Knighton Medical Center

Slidell
Alliance
  Ochsner Medical Center - North Shore

Springhill
Alliance
  Springhill Medical Center

Sulphur
Alliance
  West Calcasieu Cameron Hospital

Vivian
Alliance
  North Caddo Medical Center

MAINE

Augusta
Alliance
  MaineGeneral Medical Center-Augusta Campus
  MaineGeneral Medical Center

Bangor
Alliance
  Eastern Maine Medical Center
  The Acadia Hospital

Bar Harbor
Alliance
  Mount Desert Island Hospital

Belfast
Alliance
  Waldo County General Hospital

Biddeford
Alliance
  Southern Maine Health Care - Biddeford Medical Center

Blue Hill
Alliance
  Blue Hill Memorial Hospital

Brewer
Alliance
  Eastern Maine Healthcare Systems

Brunswick
Alliance
  Mid Coast Hospital

Damariscotta
Alliance
  LincolnHealth

Dover-Foxcroft
Alliance
  Mayo Regional Hospital

Ellsworth
Alliance
  Maine Coast Memorial Hospital

Farmington
Alliance
  Franklin Memorial Hospital

Fort Kent
Alliance
  Northern Maine Medical Center

Greenville
Alliance
  Charles A. Dean Memorial Hospital

Houlton
Alliance
  Houlton Regional Hospital

Machias
Alliance
  Down East Community Hospital

Millinocket
Alliance
  Millinocket Regional Hospital

Norway
Alliance
  Stephens Memorial Hospital

Pittsfield
Alliance
  Sebasticook Valley Health

Portland
Alliance
  Maine Medical Center
  Mercy Hospital of Portland

Presque Isle
Alliance
  The Aroostook Medical Center

Rockport
Alliance
  Pen Bay Medical Center

Skowhegan
Alliance
  Redington-Fairview General Hospital

Waterville
Alliance
  Inland Hospital

Westbrook
Alliance
  Spring Harbor Hospital

MARYLAND

Baltimore
Alliance
  Greater Baltimore Medical Center
  Johns Hopkins Bayview Medical Center
  Johns Hopkins Hospital
  MedStar Franklin Square Medical Center
  MedStar Good Samaritan Hospital
  MedStar Harbor Hospital
  MedStar Union Memorial Hospital
  Mercy Medical Center
  Mt. Washington Pediatric Hospital

University of Maryland Medical Center Midtown Campus
University of Maryland Medical Center
University of Maryland Rehabilitation & Orthopaedic Institute

Bel Air
Alliance
  University of Maryland Upper Chesapeake Medical Center

Bethesda
Alliance
  Suburban Hospital

Cambridge
Alliance
  University of Maryland Shore Medical Center at Dorchester

Chestertown
Alliance
  University of Maryland Shore Medical Center at Chestertown

Cheverly
Alliance
  Prince George's Hospital Center

Clinton
Alliance
  MedStar Southern Maryland Hospital Center

Columbia
Alliance
  Howard County General Hospital
  MedStar Health

Easton
Alliance
  University of Maryland Shore Medical Center at Easton

Elkton
Alliance
  Union Hospital

Glen Burnie
Alliance
  University of Maryland Baltimore Washington Medical Center

Hagerstown
Alliance
  Meritus Medical Center

Havre De Grace
Alliance
  University of Maryland Harford Memorial Hospital

La Plata
Alliance
  University of Maryland Charles Regional Medical Center

Laurel
Alliance
  Laurel Regional Hospital

Leonardtown
Alliance
  MedStar St. Mary's Hospital

Olney
Alliance
  MedStar Montgomery Medical Center

Prince Frederick
Alliance
  Calvert Memorial Hospital

Randallstown
Alliance
  Northwest Hospital

Rockville
Alliance
  Adventist Behavioral Health and Wellness Services
  Adventist Healthcare Shady Grove Medical Center

Silver Spring
Alliance
  Holy Cross Healthl

Takoma Park
Alliance
  Adventist Healthcare Washington Adventist Hospital

MASSACHUSETTS

Athol
Alliance
  Athol Hospital

Ayer
Alliance
Nashoba Valley Medical Center

Belmont
Alliance
McLean Hospital

Beverly
Alliance
Beverly Hospital

Boston
Alliance
Beth Israel Deaconess Medical Center
Boston Medical Center
Brigham and Women's Faulkner Hospital
Brigham and Women's Hospital
Carney Hospital
Dana-Farber Cancer Institute
Massachusetts Eye and Ear Infirmary
Massachusetts General Hospital
Partners HealthCare System, Inc.
Shriners Hospitals for Children-Boston
Tufts Medical Center

Brighton
Alliance
St. Elizabeth's Medical Center

Brockton
Alliance
Good Samaritan Medical Center
Signature Healthcare Brockton Hospital

Burlington
Alliance
Lahey Hospital & Medical Center, Burlington

Cambridge
Alliance
Cambridge Health Alliance
Mount Auburn Hospital
Spaulding Hospital for Continuing Medical Care Cambridge

Charlestown
Alliance
Spaulding Rehabilitation Hospital

Clinton
Alliance
Clinton Hospital

Concord
Alliance
Emerson Hospital

East Sandwich
Alliance
Spaulding Rehabilitation Hospital Cape Cod

Fall River
Alliance
Saint Anne's Hospital

Gardner
Alliance
Heywood Hospital

Greenfield
Alliance
Baystate Franklin Medical Center

Holyoke
Alliance
Holyoke Medical Center

Hyannis
Alliance
Cape Cod Healthcare, Inc.

Leominster
Alliance
HealthAlliance Hospitals

Lowell
Alliance
Lowell General Hospital

Marlborough
Alliance
UMass Memorial-Marlborough Hospital

Melrose
Alliance
Melrose-Wakefield Hospital

Methuen
Alliance
Holy Family Hospital

Milton
Alliance
Beth Israel Deaconess Hospital-Milton

Nantucket
Alliance
Nantucket Cottage Hospital

Newton Lower Falls
Alliance
Newton-Wellesley Hospital

Northampton
Alliance
Cooley Dickinson Hospital

Norwood
Alliance
Norwood Hospital

Oak Bluffs
Alliance
Martha's Vineyard Hospital

Palmer
Alliance
Baystate Wing Hospital

Plymouth
Alliance
Beth Israel Deaconess Hospital Plymouth

Salem
Alliance
North Shore Medical Center

South Weymouth
Alliance
South Shore Hospital

Southbridge
Alliance
Harrington Hospital

Springfield
Alliance
Baystate Medical Center
Shriners Hospitals for Children-Springfield

Taunton
Alliance
Morton Hospital and Medical Center

Winchester
Alliance
Winchester Hospital

Worcester
Alliance
UMass Memorial Medical Center

MICHIGAN

Alma
Alliance
MidMichigan Medical Center-Gratiot

Alpena
Alliance
MidMichigan Medical Center - Alpena

Ann Arbor
Alliance
Michigan Medicine

Battle Creek
Alliance
Bronson Battle Creek

Bay City
Alliance
McLaren Bay Region
McLaren Bay Special Care

Big Rapids
Alliance
Spectrum Health Big Rapids Hospital

Cadillac
Alliance
Munson Healthcare Cadillac Hospital

Carson City
Alliance
Sparrow Carson Hospital

Cass City
Alliance
Hills & Dales General Hospital

Chelsea
Alliance
St. Joseph Mercy Chelsea

Coldwater
Alliance
Community Health Center of Branch County

Dearborn
Alliance
Beaumont Hospital-Dearborn

Detroit
Alliance
Henry Ford Hospital

Farmington Hills
Alliance
Beaumont Hospital - Farmington Hills

Flint
Alliance
McLaren Flint

Fremont
Alliance
Spectrum Health Gerber Memorial

Grand Haven
Alliance
North Ottawa Community Hospital

Grand Rapids
Alliance
Mary Free Bed Rehabilitation Hospital
Pine Rest Christian Mental Health Services
Spectrum Health - Butterworth Hospital
Spectrum Health

Grayling
Alliance
Munson Healthcare Grayling Hospital

Greenville
Alliance
Spectrum Health United Hospital

Grosse Pointe
Alliance
Beaumont Hospital - Grosse Pointe

Hastings
Alliance
Spectrum Health Pennock

Holland
Alliance
Holland Hospital

Ionia
Alliance
Sparrow Ionia Hospital

Iron River
Alliance
Aspirus Iron River Hospitals & Clinics, Inc.

Ironwood
Alliance
Aspirus Ironwood Hosital & Clinics, Inc.

Kalamazoo
Alliance
Bronson Healthcare Group
Bronson Methodist Hospital

Lansing
Alliance
Sparrow Hospital
Sparrow Specialty Hospital

Laurium
Alliance
Aspirus Keweenaw Hospital, Inc.

Ludington
Alliance
Spectrum Health Ludington Hospital

Marlette
Alliance
Marlette Regional Hospital

Marshall
Alliance
Oaklawn Hospital

Midland
Alliance
  MidMichigan Medical Center-Midland

Monroe
Alliance
  ProMedica Monroe Regional Hospital

Mount Clemens
Alliance
  McLaren Macomb

Mount Pleasant
Alliance
  McLaren Central Michigan

Muskegon
Alliance
  Mercy Health Hackley Campus

Ontonagon
Alliance
  Aspirus Ontonagon Hospital, Inc.

Paw Paw
Alliance
  Bronson LakeView Hospital

Petoskey
Alliance
  McLaren Northern Michigan

Pontiac
Alliance
  McLaren Oakland
  St. Joseph Mercy Oakland

Port Huron
Alliance
  McLaren Port Huron

Reed City
Alliance
  Spectrum Health Reed City Hospital

Royal Oak
Alliance
  Beaumont Hospital - Royal Oak

Saginaw
Alliance
  Covenant Healthcare

Saint Johns
Alliance
  Sparrow Clinton Hospital

Saint Joseph
Alliance
  Lakeland Health
  Lakeland Medical Center, St. Joseph

Sheridan
Alliance
  Sheridan Community Hospital

South Haven
Alliance
  Bronson South Haven Hospital

Taylor
Alliance
  Beaumont Hospital - Taylor

Tecumseh
Alliance
  ProMedica Herrick Hospital

Trenton
Alliance
  Beaumont Hospital - Trenton

Troy
Alliance
  Beaumont Hospital - Troy

Vicksburg
Alliance
  Bronson Vicksburg Hospital

Watervliet
Alliance
  Lakeland Hospital, Watervliet

Wayne
Alliance
  Beaumont Hospital - Wayne

West Branch
Alliance
  West Branch Regional Medical Center

Wyoming
Alliance
  Metro Health Hospital

Zeeland
Alliance
  Spectrum Health Zeeland Community Hospital

MINNESOTA

Ada
Alliance
  Essentia Health Ada

Albert Lea
Alliance
  Mayo Clinic Health System in Albert Lea

Arlington
Alliance
  Ridgeview Sibley Medical Center

Aurora
Alliance
  Essentia Health Northern Pines Medical Center

Austin
Alliance
  Mayo Clinic Health System-Albert Lea and Austin

Bagley
Alliance
  Sanford Bagley Medical Center

Baudette
Alliance
  CHI LakeWood Health

Bemidji
Alliance
  Sanford Bemidji Medical Center

Benson
Alliance
  Swift County - Benson Health Services

Blue Earth
Alliance
  United Hospital District

Brainerd
Alliance
  Essentia Health St. Joseph's Medical Center

Buffalo
Alliance
  Buffalo Hospital

Burnsville
Alliance
  Fairview Ridges Hospital

Cambridge
Alliance
  Cambridge Medical Center

Canby
Alliance
  Sanford Canby Medical Center

Cannon Falls
Alliance
  Mayo Clinic Health System in Cannon Falls

Coon Rapids
Alliance
  Mercy Hospital

Crookston
Alliance
  RiverView Health

Deer River
Alliance
  Essentia Health-Deer River

Detroit Lakes
Alliance
  Essentia Health St. Mary's - Detroit Lakes

Duluth
Alliance
  Essentia Health Duluth
  Essentia Health St. Mary's Medical Center
  Essentia Health
  St. Luke's Hospital

Fairmont
Alliance
  Mayo Clinic Health System in Fairmont

Faribault
Alliance
  District One Hospital

Fergus Falls
Alliance
  Lake Region Healthcare

Fosston
Alliance
  Essentia Health Fosston

Glencoe
Alliance
  Glencoe Regional Health Services

Graceville
Alliance
  Essentia Health-Graceville

Grand Rapids
Alliance
  Grand Itasca Clinic and Hospital

Granite Falls
Alliance
  Granite Falls Municipal Hospital and Manor

Hallock
Alliance
  Kittson Memorial Healthcare Center

Hastings
Alliance
  Regina Hospital

Hutchinson
Alliance
  Hutchinson Health

Jackson
Alliance
  Sanford Jackson Medical Center

Lake City
Alliance
  Mayo Clinic Health System in Lake City

Little Falls
Alliance
  CHI St. Gabriel's Health

Long Prairie
Alliance
  CentraCare Health-Long Prairie

Luverne
Alliance
  Sanford Luverne Medical Center

Madelia
Alliance
  Madelia Community Hospital

Mahnomen
Alliance
  Mahnomen Health Center

Mankato
Alliance
  Mayo Clinic Health System in Mankato

Maple Grove
Alliance
  Maple Grove Hospital

Melrose
Alliance
  CentraCare Health-Melrose

Minneapolis
Alliance
  Abbott Northwestern Hospital
  Allina Health
  Hennepin County Medical Center
  Phillips Eye Institute
  Shriners Hospitals for Children-Twin Cities

Monticello
Alliance
  CentraCare Health-Monticello

New Prague
Alliance
  Mayo Clinic Health System in New Prague

New Ulm
Alliance
  New Ulm Medical Center

Ortonville
Alliance
  Ortonville Area Health Services

Owatonna
Alliance
  Owatonna Hospital

Park Rapids
Alliance
  CHI St. Joseph's Health

Paynesville
Alliance
  CentraCare Health-Paynesville

Perham
Alliance
  Perham Health

Princeton
Alliance
  Fairview Northland Medical Center

Red Wing
Alliance
  Mayo Clinic Health System in Red Wing

Redwood Falls
Alliance
  Redwood Area Hospital

Robbinsdale
Alliance
  North Memorial Medical Center

Rochester
Alliance
  Mayo Clinic Hospital - Rochester
  Mayo Clinic

Roseau
Alliance
  LifeCare Medical Center

Saint Cloud
Alliance
  CentraCare Health
  St. Cloud Hospital

Saint James
Alliance
  Mayo Clinic Health System in Saint James

Saint Paul
Alliance
  Regions Hospital
  United Hospital

Sandstone
Alliance
  Essentia Health Sandstone

Sauk Centre
Alliance
  CentraCare Health-Sauk Centre

Shakopee
Alliance
  St. Francis Regional Medical Center

Slayton
Alliance
  Murray County Medical Center

Springfield
Alliance
  Mayo Clinic Health System in Springfield

Stillwater
Alliance
  Lakeview Hospital

Thief River Falls
Alliance
  Sanford Medical Center Thief River Falls
  Sanford Thief River Falls Behavioral Health Center

Tracy
Alliance
  Sanford Tracy Medical Center

Two Harbors
Alliance
  Lake View Hospital

Virginia
Alliance
  Essentia Health-Virginia

Waconia
Alliance
  Ridgeview Medical Center

Warren
Alliance
  North Valley Health Center

Waseca
Alliance
  Mayo Clinic Health System in Waseca

Westbrook
Alliance
  Sanford Westbrook Medical Center

Wheaton
Alliance
  Sanford Wheaton Medical Center

Willmar
Alliance
  Rice Memorial Hospital

Windom
Alliance
  Windom Area Hospital

Worthington
Alliance
  Sanford Worthington Medical Center

Wyoming
Alliance
  Fairview Lakes Health Services

MISSISSIPPI

Booneville
Alliance
  Baptist Memorial Hospital-Booneville

Columbia
Alliance
  Marion General Hospital

Columbus
Alliance
  Baptist Memorial Hospital-Golden Triangle

Corinth
Alliance
  Magnolia Regional Health Center

Greenville
Alliance
  Delta Regional Medical Center

Greenwood
Alliance
  Greenwood Leflore Hospital

Grenada
Alliance
  University of Mississippi Medical Center Grenada

Gulfport
Alliance
  Memorial Hospital at Gulfport

Hattiesburg
Alliance
  Forrest General Hospital

Indianola
Alliance
  South Sunflower County Hospital

Jackson
Alliance
  St. Dominic-Jackson Memorial Hospital
  University of Mississippi Medical Center

Leakesville
Alliance
  Greene County Hospital

Lexington
Alliance
  University of Mississippi Medical Center Holmes County

Lucedale
Alliance
  George Regional Hospital

Magnolia
Alliance
  Beacham Memorial Hospital

McComb
Alliance
  Southwest Mississippi Regional Medical Center

Meridian
Alliance
  Anderson Regional Health System South
  Anderson Regional Health System

Monticello
Alliance
  Lawrence County Hospital

New Albany
Alliance
  Baptist Memorial Hospital-Union County

Olive Branch
Alliance
  Methodist Olive Branch Hospital

Oxford
Alliance
  Baptist Memorial Hospital-North Mississippi

Pascagoula
Alliance
  Singing River Health System

Philadelphia
Alliance
  Neshoba County General Hospital

Picayune
Alliance
  Highland Community Hospital

Prentiss
Alliance
  Jefferson Davis Community Hospital

Southaven
Alliance
  Baptist Memorial Hospital-Desoto

Starkville
Alliance
  OCH Regional Medical Center

Tupelo
Alliance
  North Mississippi Health Services, Inc.

Tylertown
Alliance
  Walthall County General Hospital

MISSOURI

Appleton City
Alliance
  Ellett Memorial Hospital

Belton
Alliance
  Belton Regional Medical Center

Bolivar
Alliance
  Citizens Memorial Hospital

Bonne Terre
Alliance
  Parkland Health Center-Bonne Terre

Branson
Alliance
  Cox Medical Center Branson

Brookfield
Alliance
  General John J. Pershing Memorial Hospital

Cameron
Alliance
  Cameron Regional Medical Center

Cape Girardeau
Alliance
  Saint Francis Medical Center

Chillicothe
Alliance
  Hedrick Medical Center

Clinton
Alliance
  Golden Valley Memorial Healthcare

Columbia
Alliance
  Boone Hospital Center
  University of Missouri Health Care

Farmington
Alliance
  Parkland Health Center - Farmington Community

Alliances

Independence
Alliance
  Centerpoint Medical Center

Jefferson City
Alliance
  Capital Region Medical Center

Joplin
Alliance
  Freeman Health System
  Freeman Hospital East

Kansas City
Alliance
  Children's Mercy Hospital Kansas City
  Research Medical Center
  Saint Luke's Health System
  Saint Luke's Hospital of Kansas City
  Saint Luke's North Hospital - Barry Road
  Truman Medical Center-Hospital Hill
  Truman Medical Center-Lakewood

Lamar
Alliance
  Barton County Memorial Hospital

Lee's Summit
Alliance
  Lee's Summit Medical Center
  Saint Luke's East Hospital

Lexington
Alliance
  Lafayette Regional Health Center

Liberty
Alliance
  Liberty Hospital

Macon
Alliance
  Samaritan Hospital

Marshall
Alliance
  Fitzgibbon Hospital

Milan
Alliance
  Sullivan County Memorial Hospital

Monett
Alliance
  Cox Monett Hospital

Neosho
Alliance
  Freeman Neosho Hospital

O'Fallon
Alliance
  Progress West Hospital

Osage Beach
Alliance
  Lake Regional Health System

Poplar Bluff
Alliance
  Black River Medical Center

Potosi
Alliance
  Washington County Memorial Hospital

Saint Louis
Alliance
  BJC HealthCare
  Barnes-Jewish Hospital
  Barnes-Jewish West County Hospital
  Christian Hospital
  Missouri Baptist Medical Center
  Shriners Hospitals for Children-St. Louis
  St. Louis Children's Hospital

Saint Peters
Alliance
  Barnes-Jewish St. Peters Hospital

Salem
Alliance
  Salem Memorial District Hospital

Sikeston
Alliance
  Missouri Delta Medical Center

Springfield
Alliance
  Cox Medical Center North
  Cox Medical Centers
  CoxHealth

Ste Genevieve
Alliance
  Ste. Genevieve County Memorial Hospital

Sullivan
Alliance
  Missouri Baptist Sullivan Hospital

Trenton
Alliance
  Wright Memorial Hospital

Warrensburg
Alliance
  Western Missouri Medical Center

MONTANA

Anaconda
Alliance
  Community Hospital of Anaconda

Bozeman
Alliance
  Bozeman Health Deaconess Hospital

Columbus
Alliance
  Stillwater Billings Clinic

Conrad
Alliance
  Pondera Medical Center

Deer Lodge
Alliance
  Deer Lodge Medical Center

Ennis
Alliance
  Madison Valley Medical Center

Hamilton
Alliance
  Marcus Daly Memorial Hospital

Helena
Alliance
  St. Peter's Hospital

Kalispell
Alliance
  Kalispell Regional Healthcare
  The HealthCenter

Libby
Alliance
  Cabinet Peaks Medical Center

Missoula
Alliance
  St. Patrick Hospital

Philipsburg
Alliance
  Granite County Medical Center

Plains
Alliance
  Clark Fork Valley Hospital

Polson
Alliance
  Providence St. Joseph Medical Center

Ronan
Alliance
  St. Luke Community Healthcare

Sidney
Alliance
  Sidney Health Center

Townsend
Alliance
  Broadwater Health Center

White Sulphur Springs
Alliance
  Mountainview Medical Center

NEBRASKA
Alliance
  Box Butte General Hospital

Alma
Alliance
  Harlan County Health System

Atkinson
Alliance
  West Holt Medical Services

Beatrice
Alliance
  Beatrice Community Hospital and Health Center

Bellevue
Alliance
  Madonna Rehabilitation Specialty Hospital
  Nebraska Medicine - Bellevue

Blair
Alliance
  Memorial Community Hospital and Health System

Bridgeport
Alliance
  Morrill County Community Hospital

Broken Bow
Alliance
  Jennie M. Melham Memorial Medical Center

Columbus
Alliance
  Columbus Community Hospital

Crete
Alliance
  Crete Area Medical Center

Falls City
Alliance
  Community Medical Center, Inc.

Franklin
Alliance
  Franklin County Memorial Hospital

Gordon
Alliance
  Gordon Memorial Health Services

Grand Island
Alliance
  CHI Health Saint Francis

Hastings
Alliance
  Mary Lanning Healthcare

Kearney
Alliance
  CHI Health Good Samaritan

Lexington
Alliance
  Lexington Regional Health Center

Lincoln
Alliance
  Bryan Health
  Bryan Medical Center
  CHI Health Nebraska Heart
  CHI Health St Elizabeth
  Madonna Rehabilitation Hospital

Lynch
Alliance
  Niobrara Valley Hospital

Minden
Alliance
  Kearney County Health Services

Nebraska City
Alliance
  CHI Health St. Mary's

Neligh
Alliance
  Antelope Memorial Hospital

Norfolk
Alliance
  Faith Regional Health Services

O'Neill
Alliance
  Avera St. Anthony's Hospital

Omaha
Alliance
 CHI Health Creighton University Medical Center -
 Bergan Mercy
 CHI Health Immanuel
 CHI Health Lakeside
 Nebraska Medicine - Nebraska Medical Center
 Nebraska Methodist Health System, Inc.
 Nebraska Methodist Hospital
 OrthoNebraska Hospital

Ord
Alliance
 Valley County Health System

Oshkosh
Alliance
 Regional West Garden County

Osmond
Alliance
 Osmond General Hospital

Papillion
Alliance
 CHI Health Midlands

Plainview
Alliance
 CHI Health Plainview

Schuyler
Alliance
 CHI Health Schuyler

Scottsbluff
Alliance
 Regional West Medical Center

York
Alliance
 York General

NEVADA
Las Vegas
Alliance
 Sunrise Hospital and Medical Center
 University Medical Center

NEW HAMPSHIRE
Claremont
Alliance
 Valley Regional Hospital

Colebrook
Alliance
 Upper Connecticut Valley Hospital

Dover
Alliance
 Wentworth-Douglass Hospital

Keene
Alliance
 Cheshire Medical Center

Lancaster
Alliance
 Weeks Medical Center

Lebanon
Alliance
 Alice Peck Day Memorial Hospital
 Dartmouth-Hitchcock Medical Center

Nashua
Alliance
 Southern New Hampshire Medical Center

New London
Alliance
 New London Hospital

North Conway
Alliance
 Memorial Hospital

Peterborough
Alliance
 Monadnock Community Hospital

Plymouth
Alliance
 Speare Memorial Hospital

Woodsville
Alliance
 Cottage Hospital

NEW JERSEY
Atlantic City
Alliance
 AtlantiCare Regional Medical Center

Camden
Alliance
 Cooper University Health Care

Cape May Court House
Alliance
 Cape Regional Medical Center

Denville
Alliance
 Saint Clare's Health System

Edison
Alliance
 JFK Health
 JFK Medical Center

Elmer
Alliance
 Inspira Medical Center-Elmer

Flemington
Alliance
 Hunterdon Medical Center

Hamilton
Alliance
 Robert Wood Johnson University Hospital at Hamilton

Marlton
Alliance
 Virtua Marlton

Morristown
Alliance
 Morristown Medical Center

Mount Holly
Alliance
 Virtua Memorial

Mullica Hill
Alliance
 Inspira Health Network

New Brunswick
Alliance
 Robert Wood Johnson University Hospital

Newark
Alliance
 University Hospital

Newton
Alliance
 Newton Medical Center

Pomona
Alliance
 Bacharach Institute for Rehabilitation

Pompton Plains
Alliance
 Chilton Medical Center

Rahway
Alliance
 Robert Wood Johnson University Hospital Rahway

Ridgewood
Alliance
 Valley Hospital

Somers Point
Alliance
 Shore Medical Center

Summit
Alliance
 Overlook Medical Center

Trenton
Alliance
 Capital Health

Vineland
Alliance
 Inspira Medical Center-Vineland

Voorhees
Alliance
 Virtua Voorhees

Woodbury
Alliance
 Inspira Medical Center-Woodbury

NEW MEXICO
Albuquerque
Alliance
 University of New Mexico Hospitals

Farmington
Alliance
 San Juan Regional Medical Center

Gallup
Alliance
 Rehoboth McKinley Christian Health Care Services

Rio Rancho
Alliance
 UNM Sandoval Regional Medical Center, Inc.

Santa Fe
Alliance
 CHRISTUS St. Vincent Regional Medical Center

NEW YORK
Albany
Alliance
 Albany Medical Center
 St. Peter's Hospital

Alexandria Bay
Alliance
 River Hospital

Binghamton
Alliance
 United Health Services Hospitals-Binghamton

Bronx
Alliance
 Montefiore Medical Center
 NYC Health + Hospitals / Jacobi
 NYC Health + Hospitals / North Central Bronx

Bronxville
Alliance
 New York-Presbyterian/Lawrence Hospital

Brooklyn
Alliance
 Brooklyn Hospital Center
 NYC Health + Hospitals / Coney Island
 NYC Health + Hospitals / Woodhull
 New York Community Hospital
 NewYork-Presbyterian Brooklyn Methodist Hospital
 SUNY Downstate Medical Center University Hospital

Buffalo
Alliance
 Erie County Medical Center
 Roswell Park Cancer Institute

Canandaigua
Alliance
 F. F. Thompson Hospital

Cooperstown
Alliance
 Bassett Medical Center

Corning
Alliance
 Guthrie Corning Hospital

Cortlandt Manor
Alliance
 New York-Presbyterian/Hudson Valley Hospital

Elizabethtown
Alliance
 The University of Vermont Health Network
 Elizabethtown Community Hospital

Elmhurst
Alliance
 NYC Health + Hospitals / Elmhurst

Flushing
Alliance
 New York-Presbyterian Queens

Geneva
Alliance
 Finger Lakes Health

Greenport
Alliance
 Eastern Long Island Hospital

Alliances

Hamilton
Alliance
Community Memorial Hospital

Ithaca
Alliance
Cayuga Medical Center at Ithaca

Jamaica
Alliance
NYC Health + Hospitals / Queens

Jamestown
Alliance
UPMC Chautauqua WCA

Malone
Alliance
The University of Vermont Health Network - Alice Hyde Medical Center

Mineola
Alliance
NYU Winthrop Hospital

Montour Falls
Alliance
Schuyler Hospital

Mount Vernon
Alliance
Montefiore Mount Vernon

New Rochelle
Alliance
Montefiore New Rochelle

New York
Alliance
Gracie Square Hospital

Lenox Hill Hospital

Mount Sinai Hospital

NYC Health + Hospitals / Bellevue

NYC Health + Hospitals / Carter

NYC Health + Hospitals / Harlem

NYU Langone Hospitals

New York-Presbyterian Hospital

New York-Presbyterian/Columbia University Medical Center

Rockefeller University Hospital

Norwich
Alliance
UHS Chenango Memorial Hospital

Nyack
Alliance
Nyack Hospital

Ogdensburg
Alliance
Claxton-Hepburn Medical Center

Plattsburgh
Alliance
The University of Vermont Health Network-Champlain Valley Physicians Hospital

Riverhead
Alliance
Peconic Bay Medical Center

Rochester
Alliance
Highland Hospital

Strong Memorial Hospital of the University of Rochester

University of Rochester Medical Center

Sleepy Hollow
Alliance
Phelps Memorial Hospital Center

Staten Island
Alliance
Staten Island University Hospital

Stony Brook
Alliance
Stony Brook University Hospital

Syracuse
Alliance
Crouse Health

Upstate University Hospital

Valhalla
Alliance
Westchester Medical Center

Walton
Alliance
UHS Delaware Valley Hospital

NORTH CAROLINA

Ahoskie
Alliance
Vidant Roanoke-Chowan Hospital

Bermuda Run
Alliance
Wake Forest Baptist Health-Davie Medical Center

Bolivia
Alliance
Novant Health Brunswick Medical Center

Cary
Alliance
WakeMed Cary Hospital

Chapel Hill
Alliance
University of North Carolina Hospitals

Charlotte
Alliance
Carolinas HealthCare System

Novant Health Charlotte Orthopaedic Hospital

Novant Health Presbyterian Medical Center

Clinton
Alliance
Sampson Regional Medical Center

Dunn
Alliance
Harnett Health System

Durham
Alliance
Duke Regional Hospital

Duke University Hospital

Eden
Alliance
Morehead Memorial Hospital

Edenton
Alliance
Vidant Chowan Hospital

Elizabeth City
Alliance
Sentara Albemarle Medical Center

Elkin
Alliance
Hugh Chatham Memorial Hospital

Greenville
Alliance
Vidant Medical Center

Huntersville
Alliance
Novant Health Huntersville Medical Center

Jefferson
Alliance
Ashe Memorial Hospital

Kenansville
Alliance
Vidant Duplin Hospital

Lexington
Alliance
Wake Forest Baptist Health-Lexington Medical Center

Matthews
Alliance
Novant Health Matthews Medical Center

Morehead City
Alliance
Carteret Health Care

Nags Head
Alliance
The Outer Banks Hospital

New Bern
Alliance
CarolinaEast Health System

Raleigh
Alliance
Duke Raleigh Hospital

UNC REX Health Care

WakeMed Health & Hospitals

WakeMed Raleigh Campus

Roanoke Rapids
Alliance
Halifax Regional Medical Center

Rocky Mount
Alliance
Nash Health Care Systems

Salisbury
Alliance
Novant Health Rowan Medical Center

Siler City
Alliance
Chatham Hospital

Sparta
Alliance
Alleghany Memorial Hospital

Tarboro
Alliance
Vidant Edgecombe Hospital

Thomasville
Alliance
Novant Health Thomasville Medical Center

Washington
Alliance
Vidant Beaufort Hospital

Wilson
Alliance
Wilson Medical Center

Windsor
Alliance
Vidant Bertie Hospital

Winston Salem
Alliance
Novant Health

Winston-Salem
Alliance
Novant Health Forsyth Medical Center

Novant Health Medical Park Hospital

Wake Forest Baptist Medical Center

NORTH DAKOTA

Bismarck
Alliance
Sanford Bismarck

Devils Lake
Alliance
CHI St. Alexius Health Devils Lake Hospital

Dickinson
Alliance
CHI St. Alexius Health - Dickinson Medical Center

Fargo
Alliance
Sanford Medical Center Fargo

Grand Forks
Alliance
Altru Health System

Hillsboro
Alliance
Sanford Hillsboro Medical Center

Jamestown
Alliance
Jamestown Regional Medical Center

Kenmare
Alliance
Kenmare Community Hospital

Lisbon
Alliance
CHI Lisbon Health

Mayville
Alliance
Sanford Mayville Medical Center

Mcville
Alliance
Nelson County Health System

Minot
Alliance
  Trinity Health

Northwood
Alliance
  Northwood Deaconess Health Center

Oakes
Alliance
  CHI Oakes Hospital

Valley City
Alliance
  CHI Mercy Health

OHIO

Akron
Alliance
  Akron Children's Hospital
  Cleveland Clinic Akron General

Alliance
Alliance
  Alliance Community Hospital

Ashland
Alliance
  University Hospitals Samaritan Medical Center

Ashtabula
Alliance
  Ashtabula County Medical Center

Athens
Alliance
  O'Bleness Memorial Hospital

Barnesville
Alliance
  Barnesville Hospital

Bellaire
Alliance
  Belmont Community Hospital

Bellefontaine
Alliance
  Mary Rutan Hospital

Bluffton
Alliance
  Bluffton Hospital

Bucyrus
Alliance
  Bucyrus Community Hospital

Cadiz
Alliance
  Harrison Community Hospital

Cambridge
Alliance
  Southeastern Ohio Regional Medical Center

Canton
Alliance
  Aultman Hospital

Chardon
Alliance
  University Hospitals Geauga Medical Center

Cincinnati
Alliance
  Christ Hospital
  Cincinnati Children's Hospital Medical Center
  Good Samaritan Hospital
  Shriners Hospital for Children-Cincinnati
  The Jewish Hospital - Mercy Health
  UC Health
  University of Cincinnati Medical Center

Circleville
Alliance
  Berger Health System

Cleveland
Alliance
  Cleveland Clinic Fairview Hospital
  Cleveland Clinic
  Lutheran Hospital
  MetroHealth Medical Center
  University Hospitals Cleveland Medical Center

Coldwater
Alliance
  Mercer Health

Columbus
Alliance
  Ohio State University Wexner Medical Center
  OhioHealth Doctors Hospital
  OhioHealth Grant Medical Center
  OhioHealth Riverside Methodist Hospital
  OhioHealth

Conneaut
Alliance
  University Hospitals Conneaut Medical Center

Coshocton
Alliance
  Coshocton Regional Medical Center

Cuyahoga Falls
Alliance
  Edwin Shaw Rehab

Dayton
Alliance
  Good Samaritan Hospital
  Miami Valley Hospital

Defiance
Alliance
  ProMedica Defiance Regional Hospital

Delaware
Alliance
  OhioHealth Grady Memorial Hospital

Dover
Alliance
  Union Hospital

Dublin
Alliance
  OhioHealth Dublin Methodist Hospital

Euclid
Alliance
  Euclid Hospital

Findlay
Alliance
  Blanchard Valley Hospital

Fostoria
Alliance
  ProMedica Fostoria Community Hospital

Fremont
Alliance
  ProMedica Memorial Hospital

Galion
Alliance
  Galion Community Hospital

Garfield Heights
Alliance
  Marymount Hospital

Geneva
Alliance
  University Hospitals Geneva Medical Center

Greenville
Alliance
  Wayne HealthCare

Hamilton
Alliance
  Fort Hamilton Hospital

Kenton
Alliance
  OhioHealth Hardin Memorial Hospital

Lima
Alliance
  Lima Memorial Health System

Lodi
Alliance
  Lodi Community Hospital

Logan
Alliance
  Hocking Valley Community Hospital

London
Alliance
  Madison Health

Mansfield
Alliance
  OhioHealth MedCentral Mansfield Hospital

Marion
Alliance
  OhioHealth Marion General Hospital

Martins Ferry
Alliance
  East Ohio Regional Hospital

Marysville
Alliance
  Memorial Health

Mason
Alliance
  Lindner Center of HOPE

Maumee
Alliance
  St. Luke's Hospital

Medina
Alliance
  Cleveland Clinic, Medina Hospital

Middleburg Heights
Alliance
  Southwest General Health Center

Millersburg
Alliance
  Pomerene Hospital

Mount Gilead
Alliance
  Morrow County Hospital

New Albany
Alliance
  Mount Carmel New Albany Surgical Hospital

Newark
Alliance
  Licking Memorial Hospital

Norwalk
Alliance
  Fisher-Titus Medical Center

Orrville
Alliance
  Aultman Orrville Hospital

Paulding
Alliance
  Paulding County Hospital

Portsmouth
Alliance
  Southern Ohio Medical Center

Rock Creek
Alliance
  Glenbeigh Hospital and Outpatient Centers

Shelby
Alliance
  OhioHealth MedCentral Shelby Hospital

Sidney
Alliance
  Wilson Memorial Hospital

Sylvania
Alliance
  ProMedica Flower Hospital

Toledo
Alliance
  ProMedica Health System
  ProMedica Toledo Hospital
  The University of Toledo Medical Center

Troy
Alliance
  Upper Valley Medical Center

Upper Sandusky
Alliance
  Wyandot Memorial Hospital

Van Wert
Alliance
  Van Wert County Hospital

Warrensville Heights
Alliance
  South Pointe Hospital

Alliances

Washington Court House
Alliance
 Fayette County Memorial Hospital

Westerville
Alliance
 Mount Carmel St. Ann's

Westlake
Alliance
 St. John Medical Center

Zanesville
Alliance
 Genesis HealthCare System

OKLAHOMA

Altus
Alliance
 Jackson County Memorial Hospital

Antlers
Alliance
 Pushmataha Hospital

Atoka
Alliance
 Atoka County Medical Center

Bethany
Alliance
 The Children's Center Rehabilitation Hospital

Carnegie
Alliance
 Carnegie Tri-County Municipal Hospital

Chickasha
Alliance
 Grady Memorial Hospital

Duncan
Alliance
 Duncan Regional Hospital

Edmond
Alliance
 INTEGRIS Health Edmond

Elk City
Alliance
 Great Plains Regional Medical Center

Enid
Alliance
 Integris Bass Baptist Health Center
 Integris Bass Pavilion

Grove
Alliance
 Integris Grove Hospital

Hobart
Alliance
 Elkview General Hospital

Hugo
Alliance
 Choctaw Memorial Hospital

Lawton
Alliance
 Comanche County Memorial Hospital

McAlester
Alliance
 McAlester Regional Health Center

Miami
Alliance
 INTEGRIS Miami Hospital

Norman
Alliance
 Norman Regional Health System

Oklahoma City
Alliance
 INTEGRIS Health
 Integris Baptist Medical Center
 Integris Southwest Medical Center
 Lakeside Women's Hospital

Stillwater
Alliance
 Stillwater Medical Center

Tahlequah
Alliance
 Northeastern Health System

Waurika
Alliance
 Jefferson County Hospital

Yukon
Alliance
 INTEGRIS Canadian Valley Hospital

OREGON

Forest Grove
Alliance
 Tuality Forest Grove Hospital

Grants Pass
Alliance
 Asante Three Rivers Medical Center

Hillsboro
Alliance
 Tuality Healthcare

Hood River
Alliance
 Providence Hood River Memorial Hospital

Medford
Alliance
 Asante Rogue Regional Medical Center
 Providence Medford Medical Center

Milwaukie
Alliance
 Providence Milwaukie Hospital

Newberg
Alliance
 Providence Newberg Medical Center

Ontario
Alliance
 Saint Alphonsus Medical Center - Ontario

Oregon City
Alliance
 Providence Willamette Falls Medical Center

Pendleton
Alliance
 CHI St. Anthony Hospital

Portland
Alliance
 OHSU Hospital
 Providence Portland Medical Center
 Providence St. Vincent Medical Center
 Shriners Hospitals for Children-Portland

Roseburg
Alliance
 Mercy Medical Center

Salem
Alliance
 Salem Hospital

Seaside
Alliance
 Providence Seaside Hospital

Silverton
Alliance
 Legacy Silverton Medical Center

The Dalles
Alliance
 Mid-Columbia Medical Center

PENNSYLVANIA

Abington
Alliance
 Abington Hospital

Allentown
Alliance
 Lehigh Valley Hospital

Bethlehem
Alliance
 Lehigh Valley Hospital-Muhlenberg

Brookville
Alliance
 Penn Highlands Brookville

Bryn Mawr
Alliance
 Bryn Mawr Hospital

Butler
Alliance
 Butler Health System

Chambersburg
Alliance
 Chambersburg Hospital
 Summit Health

Clearfield
Alliance
 Penn Highlands Clearfield

Darby
Alliance
 Mercy Fitzgerald Hospital

Drexel Hill
Alliance
 Delaware County Memorial Hospital

DuBois
Alliance
 Penn Highlands DuBois

East Norriton
Alliance
 Einstein Medical Center Montgomery

East Stroudsburg
Alliance
 Lehigh Valley Hospital - Pocono

Ephrata
Alliance
 WellSpan Ephrata Community Hospital

Gettysburg
Alliance
 WellSpan Gettysburg Hospital

Greensburg
Alliance
 Excela Health Westmoreland Hospital

Hanover
Alliance
 Hanover Hospital

Harrisburg
Alliance
 PinnacleHealth Harrisburg Hospital
 PinnacleHealth at Community General Osteopathic
 Hospital

Hazleton
Alliance
 Lehigh Valley Hospital - Hazleton

Hershey
Alliance
 Penn State Milton S. Hershey Medical Center

Huntingdon
Alliance
 J. C. Blair Memorial Hospital

Indiana
Alliance
 Indiana Regional Medical Center

Jefferson Hills
Alliance
 Jefferson Hospital

Lancaster
Alliance
 Lancaster General Hospital

Langhorne
Alliance
 St. Mary Medical Center

Lansdale
Alliance
 Abington-Lansdale Hospital Jefferson Health

Latrobe
Alliance
 Excela Latrobe Area Hospital

Lebanon
Alliance
 WellSpan Good Samaritan Hospital

Lehighton
Alliance
 Blue Mountain Health System
 Blue Mountain Hospital

Malvern
Alliance
 Bryn Mawr Rehabilitation Hospital

Meadowbrook
Alliance
 Holy Redeemer Hospital

Media
Alliance
  Riddle Hospital

Monongahela
Alliance
  Monongahela Valley Hospital

Mount Pleasant
Alliance
  Excela Frick Hospital

Muncy
Alliance
  Muncy Valley Hospital

New Castle
Alliance
  UPMC Jameson Hospital

Paoli
Alliance
  Paoli Hospital

Philadelphia
Alliance
  Aria - Jefferson Health
  Children's Hospital of Philadelphia
  Einstein Medical Center Philadelphia
  Fox Chase Cancer Center-American Oncologic Hospital
  Hospital of the University of Pennsylvania
  Jeanes Hospital
  Magee Rehabilitation Hospital
  Penn Presbyterian Medical Center
  Pennsylvania Hospital
  Temple University Hospital
  University of Pennsylvania Health System

Pittsburgh
Alliance
  St. Clair Hospital
  UPMC Presbyterian Shadyside

Pottsville
Alliance
  Lehigh Valley Hospital - Schuylkill East Norwegian Street
  Lehigh Valley Hospital - Schuylkill South Jackson Street

Reading
Alliance
  Penn State Health St. Joseph

Saint Marys
Alliance
  Penn Highlands Elk

Sayre
Alliance
  Guthrie Clinic
  Guthrie Robert Packer Hospital

Sellersville
Alliance
  Grand View Health

Towanda
Alliance
  Guthrie Towanda Memorial Hospital

Troy
Alliance
  Troy Community Hospital

Uniontown
Alliance
  Uniontown Hospital

Upland
Alliance
  Crozer-Chester Medical Center

Waynesboro
Alliance
  Waynesboro Hospital

Wellsboro
Alliance
  Soldiers and Sailors Memorial Hospital

West Chester
Alliance
  Penn Medicine Chester County Hospital

West Reading
Alliance
  Reading Hospital

Williamsport
Alliance
  Divine Providence Hospital
  UPMC Susquehanna
  Williamsport Regional Medical Center

Wynnewood
Alliance
  Lankenau Medical Center

York
Alliance
  WellSpan Health
  WellSpan York Hospital

RHODE ISLAND
Newport
Alliance
  Newport Hospital

Pawtucket
Alliance
  Memorial Hospital of Rhode Island

Providence
Alliance
  Butler Hospital
  Care New England Health System
  Lifespan Corporation
  Miriam Hospital
  Rhode Island Hospital
  Women & Infants Hospital of Rhode Island

Warwick
Alliance
  Kent County Memorial Hospital

Westerly
Alliance
  Westerly Hospital

SOUTH CAROLINA
Charleston
Alliance
  MUSC Medical Center of Medical University of South Carolina

Cheraw
Alliance
  McLeod Health Cheraw

Clinton
Alliance
  Greenville Health System - Laurens County Memorial Hospital

Columbia
Alliance
  ContinueCARE Hospital at Palmetto Health Baptist
  Palmetto Health Baptist Parkridge
  Palmetto Health Baptist
  Palmetto Health Richland
  Providence Hospital

Darlington
Alliance
  McLeod Medical Center-Darlington

Dillon
Alliance
  McLeod Medical Center Dillon

Easley
Alliance
  Baptist Easley Hospital

Florence
Alliance
  McLeod Regional Medical Center

Georgetown
Alliance
  Tidelands Georgetown Memorial Hospital

Greenville
Alliance
  GHS Greenville Memorial Hospital
  Patewood Memorial Hospital
  Shriners Hospitals for Children-Greenville

Greenwood
Alliance
  Self Regional Healthcare

Greer
Alliance
  GHS Greer Memorial Hospital

Loris
Alliance
  McLeod Loris Seacoast Hospital

Murrells Inlet
Alliance
  Tidelands Waccamaw Community Hospital

Seneca
Alliance
  Oconee Memorial Hospital

Simpsonville
Alliance
  GHS Hillcrest Memorial Hospital

Sumter
Alliance
  Palmetto Health Tuomey

Travelers Rest
Alliance
  North Greenville Hospital

SOUTH DAKOTA
Aberdeen
Alliance
  Sanford Aberdeen Medical Center

Armour
Alliance
  Douglas County Memorial Hospital

Burke
Alliance
  Community Memorial Hospital

Canton
Alliance
  Sanford Canton-Inwood Medical Center

Chamberlain
Alliance
  Sanford Chamberlain Medical Center

Clear Lake
Alliance
  Sanford Clear Lake Medical Center

Sioux Falls
Alliance
  Sanford Health
  Sanford USD Medical Center

Vermillion
Alliance
  Sanford Vermillion Medical Center

Viborg
Alliance
  Pioneer Memorial Hospital and Health Services

Watertown
Alliance
  Prairie Lakes Healthcare System

Webster
Alliance
  Sanford Webster Medical Center

Winner
Alliance
  Winner Regional Healthcare Center

TENNESSEE
Chattanooga
Alliance
  Erlanger Health System
  Erlanger North Hospital

Collierville
Alliance
  Baptist Memorial Hospital-Collierville

Columbia
Alliance
  Maury Regional Hospital

Covington
Alliance
  Baptist Memorial Hospital-Tipton

Alliances

Franklin
Alliance
Williamson Medical Center

Harriman
Alliance
Roane Medical Center

Huntingdon
Alliance
Baptist Memorial Hospital-Huntingdon

Knoxville
Alliance
Covenant Health
Fort Sanders Regional Medical Center
Parkwest Medical Center
University of Tennessee Medical Center

Lenoir City
Alliance
Fort Loudoun Medical Center

Lewisburg
Alliance
Marshall Medical Center

Louisville
Alliance
Peninsula Hospital

Memphis
Alliance
Baptist Memorial Health Care Corporation
Baptist Memorial Hospital - Memphis
Baptist Memorial Hospital for Women
Methodist Healthcare Memphis Hospitals
Regional One Health
St. Jude Children's Research Hospital

Morristown
Alliance
Morristown-Hamblen Healthcare System

Nashville
Alliance
Vanderbilt University Medical Center

Oak Ridge
Alliance
Methodist Medical Center of Oak Ridge

Sevierville
Alliance
LeConte Medical Center

Tazewell
Alliance
Claiborne Medical Center

Union City
Alliance
Baptist Memorial Hospital-Union City

Waynesboro
Alliance
Wayne Medical Center

TEXAS
Andrews
Alliance
Permian Regional Medical Center

Baytown
Alliance
Houston Methodist San Jacinto Hospital

Bellville
Alliance
CHI St. Joseph Health Bellville Hospital

Dallas
Alliance
Baylor Scott & White Health
Children's Health System of Texas
Methodist Health System
Parkland Health & Hospital System
William P. Clements, Jr. University Hospital

El Paso
Alliance
University Medical Center of El Paso

Fort Worth
Alliance
JPS Health Network

Galveston
Alliance
Shriners Hospitals for Children-Galveston
University of Texas Medical Branch

Houston
Alliance
Baylor St. Luke's Medical Center
CHI St. Luke's Hospital - The Vintage Hospital
Harris Health System
Houston Methodist Hospital
Houston Methodist West Hospital
Houston Methodist Willowbrook Hospital
Memorial Hermann - Texas Medical Center
Memorial Hermann Greater Heights Hospital
Memorial Hermann Health System
Memorial Hermann Memorial City Medical Center
Shriners Hospitals for Children-Houston
TIRR Memorial Hermann

Humble
Alliance
Memorial Hermann Northeast

Katy
Alliance
Houston Methodist St. Catherine Hospital
Memorial Hermann Katy Hospital

Livingston
Alliance
CHI St. Luke's Health Memorial Livingston

Lubbock
Alliance
Covenant Health System
Covenant Medical Center-Lakeside

Lufkin
Alliance
CHI St. Luke's Health Memorial Lufkin

Midland
Alliance
Midland Memorial Hospital

Pasadena
Alliance
CHI St. Luke's Health - Patients Medical Center

Pearsall
Alliance
Frio Regional Hospital

Plano
Alliance
Community Hospital Corporation

San Antonio
Alliance
University Health System

San Augustine
Alliance
CHI St. Luke's Health Memorial San Augustine

Sugar Land
Alliance
Houston Methodist Sugar Land Hospital
Memorial Hermann Sugar Land Hospital

Sweeny
Alliance
Sweeny Community Hospital

The Woodlands
Alliance
CHI St. Luke's Health-The Woodlands Hospital
St. Luke's Lakeside Hospital

Tyler
Alliance
CHRISTUS Mother Frances Hospital - Tyler
University of Texas Health Northeast

UTAH
Gunnison
Alliance
Gunnison Valley Hospital

Provo
Alliance
Utah State Hospital

Salt Lake City
Alliance
Shriners Hospitals for Children-Salt Lake City
University of Utah Health
University of Utah Neuropsychiatric Institute

VERMONT
Bennington
Alliance
Southwestern Vermont Medical Center

Berlin
Alliance
The University of Vermont Health Network Central Vermont Medical Center

Brattleboro
Alliance
Brattleboro Memorial Hospital
Brattleboro Retreat

Burlington
Alliance
University of Vermont Medical Center

Morrisville
Alliance
Copley Hospital

Newport
Alliance
North Country Hospital and Health Center

Rutland
Alliance
Rutland Regional Medical Center

Saint Johnsbury
Alliance
Northeastern Vermont Regional Hospital

Springfield
Alliance
Springfield Hospital

Townshend
Alliance
Grace Cottage Hospital

Windsor
Alliance
Mt. Ascutney Hospital and Health Center

VIRGIN ISLANDS
Saint Thomas
Alliance
Schneider Regional Medical Center

VIRGINIA
Bedford
Alliance
Bedford Memorial Hospital

Charlottesville
Alliance
Martha Jefferson Hospital
UVA-HEALTHSOUTH Rehabilitation Hospital
University of Virginia Medical Center

Culpeper
Alliance
Novant Health UVA Health System Culpeper Medical Center

Farmville
Alliance
Centra Southside Community Hospital

Fishersville
Alliance
Augusta Health

Fredericksburg
Alliance
Mary Washington Hospital
Snowden at Fredericksburg

Hampton
Alliance
Sentara CarePlex Hospital

Harrisonburg
Alliance
Sentara RMH Medical Center

Lynchburg
Alliance
Centra Lynchburg General Hospital

Manassas
Alliance
Novant Health UVA Health System Prince William Medical Center

Norfolk
Alliance
Hospital for Extended Recovery
Sentara Healthcare
Sentara Leigh Hospital
Sentara Norfolk General Hospital

Richmond
Alliance
Children's Hospital of Richmond at VCU-Brook Road Campus
VCU Medical Center

South Boston
Alliance
Sentara Halifax Regional Hospital

Stafford
Alliance
Stafford Hospital

Suffolk
Alliance
Sentara Obici Hospital

Virginia Beach
Alliance
Sentara Princess Anne Hospital
Sentara Virginia Beach General Hospital

Williamsburg
Alliance
Sentara Williamsburg Regional Medical Center

Woodbridge
Alliance
Sentara Northern Virginia Medical Center

WASHINGTON

Aberdeen
Alliance
Grays Harbor Community Hospital

Auburn
Alliance
MultiCare Auburn Medical Center

Bellingham
Alliance
PeaceHealth St. Joseph Medical Center

Bremerton
Alliance
Harrison Medical Center

Burien
Alliance
Highline Medical Center

Centralia
Alliance
Providence Centralia Hospital

Chewelah
Alliance
Providence St. Joseph's Hospital

Colfax
Alliance
Whitman Hospital and Medical Center

Colville
Alliance
Providence Mount Carmel Hospital

Dayton
Alliance
Columbia County Health System

Edmonds
Alliance
Swedish/Edmonds

Enumclaw
Alliance
St. Elizabeth Hospital

Everett
Alliance
Providence Regional Medical Center Everett

Gig Harbor
Alliance
St. Anthony Hospital

Ilwaco
Alliance
Ocean Beach Hospital

Issaquah
Alliance
Swedish/Issaquah

Lakewood
Alliance
St. Clare Hospital

Morton
Alliance
Morton General Hospital

Olympia
Alliance
Providence St. Peter Hospital

Pomeroy
Alliance
Garfield County Public Hospital District

Port Angeles
Alliance
Olympic Medical Center

Prosser
Alliance
PMH Medical Center

Puyallup
Alliance
MultiCare Good Samaritan Hospital

Renton
Alliance
UW Medicine/Valley Medical Center

Richland
Alliance
Kadlec Regional Medical Center

Seattle
Alliance
Swedish Medical Center-Cherry Hill Campus
Swedish Medical Center-First Hill
UW Medicine/Harborview Medical Center
UW Medicine/Northwest Hospital & Medical Center
University of Washington Medical Center

Spokane
Alliance
Providence Holy Family Hospital
Providence Sacred Heart Medical Center & Children's Hospital
Shriners Hospitals for Children-Spokane
St. Luke's Rehabilitation Institute

Tacoma
Alliance
MultiCare Health System
MultiCare Tacoma General Hospital
St. Joseph Medical Center

Walla Walla
Alliance
Providence St. Mary Medical Center

WEST VIRGINIA

Charleston
Alliance
CAMC Women and Children's Hospital
Charleston Area Medical Center

Gassaway
Alliance
Braxton County Memorial Hospital

Madison
Alliance
Boone Memorial Hospital

Martinsburg
Alliance
Berkeley Medical Center

Montgomery
Alliance
Montgomery General Hospital

Morgantown
Alliance
West Virginia University Hospitals

Princeton
Alliance
Princeton Community Hospital

Ranson
Alliance
Jefferson Medical Center

Ripley
Alliance
Jackson General Hospital

Spencer
Alliance
Roane General Hospital

Wheeling
Alliance
Ohio Valley Medical Center
Wheeling Hospital

WISCONSIN

Antigo
Alliance
Aspirus Langlade Hospital

Appleton
Alliance
ThedaCare, Inc.

Barron
Alliance
Mayo Clinic Health System - Northland in Barron

Beaver Dam
Alliance
Beaver Dam Community Hospitals

Beloit
Alliance
Beloit Health System

Bloomer
Alliance
Mayo Clinic Health System - Chippewa Valley in Bloomer

Boscobel
Alliance
Gundersen Boscobel Area Hospital and Clinics

Eau Claire
Alliance
Mayo Clinic Health System in Eau Claire

Friendship
Alliance
Moundview Memorial Hospital & Clinics

Green Bay
Alliance
Bellin Memorial Hospital
Bellin Psychiatric Center

Hillsboro
Alliance
Gundersen St. Joseph's Hospital and Clinics

Hudson
Alliance
Hudson Hospital and Clinic

La Crosse
Alliance
Gundersen Health System
Mayo Clinic Health System - Franciscan Healthcare in La Crosse

Madison
Alliance
UnityPoint Health Meriter
University of Wisconsin Hospitals and Clinics Authority

Marinette
Alliance
Bay Area Medical Center

Medford
Alliance
Aspirus Medford Hospital & Clinics, Inc.

Menomonee Falls
Alliance
Community Memorial Hospital

Menomonie
Alliance
Mayo Clinic Health System - Red Cedar in Menomonie

Alliances

Milwaukee
Alliance
  Froedtert Memorial Lutheran Hospital

Neenah
Alliance
  ThedaCare Regional Medical Center-Neenah

Neillsville
Alliance
  Memorial Medical Center - Neillsville

New Richmond
Alliance
  Westfields Hospital

Oconomowoc
Alliance
  Oconomowoc Memorial Hospital

Oconto
Alliance
  Bellin Health Oconto Hospital

Osseo
Alliance
  Mayo Clinic Health System - Oakridge in Osseo

Portage
Alliance
  Divine Savior Healthcare

River Falls
Alliance
  River Falls Area Hospital

Sparta
Alliance
  Mayo Clinic Health System - Franciscan Healthcare in Sparta

Superior
Alliance
  Essentia Health St. Mary's Hospital of Superior

Waukesha
Alliance
  ProHealth Care, Inc.
  Waukesha Memorial Hospital

Waupaca
Alliance
  ThedaCare Medical Center-Waupaca

Wausau
Alliance
  Aspirus Wausau Hospital, Inc.
  North Central Health Care

West Bend
Alliance
  St. Joseph's Hospital

Whitehall
Alliance
  Gundersen Tri-County Hospital and Clinics

Wild Rose
Alliance
  Theda Care Medical Center - Wild Rose

Wisconsin Rapids
Alliance
  Aspirus Riverview Hospital and Clinics, Inc.

WYOMING

Buffalo
Alliance
  Johnson County Healthcare Center

Casper
Alliance
  Wyoming Medical Center

Cheyenne
Alliance
  Cheyenne Regional Medical Center

Douglas
Alliance
  Memorial Hospital of Converse County

Laramie
Alliance
  Ivinson Memorial Hospital

Lusk
Alliance
  Niobrara Health and Life Center

Sheridan
Alliance
  Sheridan Memorial Hospital

YANKEE ALLIANCE
138 River Road, Andover, MA Zip 01810–1083; tel. 978/470–2000; James W. Oliver, President and Chief Executive Officer

CALIFORNIA

Long Beach
Alliance
  College Medical Center

Oceanside
Alliance
  Tri-City Medical Center

CONNECTICUT

Derby
Alliance
  Griffin Hospital

Hartford
Alliance
  Saint Francis Hospital and Medical Center

New London
Alliance
  Lawrence + Memorial Hospital

Stafford Springs
Alliance
  Johnson Memorial Medical Center

FLORIDA

Boca Raton
Alliance
  Promise Healthcare

Coral Gables
Alliance
  Baptist Health South Florida, Doctors Hospital

Homestead
Alliance
  Baptist Health South Florida, Homestead Hospital

Miami Beach
Alliance
  Mount Sinai Medical Center

Miami
Alliance
  Baptist Health South Florida, Baptist Hospital of Miami
  Baptist Health South Florida, South Miami Hospital
  Baptist Health South Florida, West Kendall Baptist Hospital

Miramar
Alliance
  Memorial Hospital Miramar

Pembroke Pines
Alliance
  Memorial Hospital Pembroke
  Memorial Hospital West

South Miami
Alliance
  Larkin Community Hospital

Tavernier
Alliance
  Baptist Health South Florida, Mariners Hospital

ILLINOIS

Geneva
Alliance
  Northwestern Medicine Delnor Hospital

Winfield
Alliance
  Northwestern Medicine Central DuPage Hospital

INDIANA

Gary
Alliance
  Methodist Hospitals

Mishawaka
Alliance
  Unity Medical & Surgical Hospital

KENTUCKY

Ashland
Alliance
  King's Daughters Medical Center

Benton
Alliance
  Marshall County Hospital

Corbin
Alliance
  Baptist Health Corbin

Elizabethtown
Alliance
  Hardin Memorial Hospital

La Grange
Alliance
  Baptist Health La Grange

Lexington
Alliance
  Baptist Health Lexington

Louisville
Alliance
  Baptist Health Louisville

Madisonville
Alliance
  Baptist Health Madisonville

Paducah
Alliance
  Baptist Health Paducah

Prestonsburg
Alliance
  Highlands Regional Medical Center

Richmond
Alliance
  Baptist Health Richmond

MAINE

Bangor
Alliance
  St. Joseph Hospital

Lewiston
Alliance
  St. Mary's Regional Medical Center

MASSACHUSETTS

Attleboro
Alliance
  Sturdy Memorial Hospital

Boston
Alliance
  Boston Medical Center
  New England Baptist Hospital
  Tufts Medical Center

Brockton
Alliance
  Signature Healthcare Brockton Hospital

Burlington
Alliance
  Lahey Hospital & Medical Center, Burlington

Fall River
Alliance
  Southcoast Hospitals Group

Great Barrington
Alliance
  Fairview Hospital

Lowell
Alliance
  Lowell General Hospital

Milford
Alliance
  Milford Regional Medical Center

Newburyport
Alliance
  Anna Jaques Hospital

Oak Bluffs
Alliance
  Martha's Vineyard Hospital

Pittsfield
Alliance
  Berkshire Medical Center

Westfield
Alliance
  Baystate Noble Hospital

Winchester
Alliance
  Winchester Hospital

NEW HAMPSHIRE
Concord
Alliance
  Concord Hospital

Exeter
Alliance
  Exeter Hospital

Franklin
Alliance
  Franklin Regional Hospital

Laconia
Alliance
  Lakes Region General Hospital

Manchester
Alliance
  Catholic Medical Center

  Elliot Hospital

Nashua
Alliance
  St. Joseph Hospital

North Conway
Alliance
  Memorial Hospital

Rochester
Alliance
  Frisbie Memorial Hospital

Salem
Alliance
  Northeast Rehabilitation Hospital

NEW YORK
Batavia
Alliance
  United Memorial Medical Center

Bath
Alliance
  Ira Davenport Memorial Hospital

Elizabethtown
Alliance
  The University of Vermont Health Network Elizabethtown Community Hospital

Elmira
Alliance
  Arnot Ogden Medical Center

  St. Joseph's Hospital

Glens Falls
Alliance
  Glens Falls Hospital

Gloversville
Alliance
  Nathan Littauer Hospital and Nursing Home

Plattsburgh
Alliance
  The University of Vermont Health Network-Champlain Valley Physicians Hospital

Warsaw
Alliance
  Wyoming County Community Hospital

OHIO
Logan
Alliance
  Hocking Valley Community Hospital

Montpelier
Alliance
  Community Hospitals and Wellness Centers-Montpelier

Salem
Alliance
  Salem Regional Medical Center

Seaman
Alliance
  Adams County Regional Medical Center

Sidney
Alliance
  Wilson Memorial Hospital

Steubenville
Alliance
  Life Line Hospital

PENNSYLVANIA
Honesdale
Alliance
  Wayne Memorial Hospital

Langhorne
Alliance
  Barix Clinics of Pennsylvania

Washington
Alliance
  Advanced Surgical Hospital

RHODE ISLAND
Pawtucket
Alliance
  Memorial Hospital of Rhode Island

Providence
Alliance
  Roger Williams Medical Center

Wakefield
Alliance
  South County Hospital

Westerly
Alliance
  Westerly Hospital

SOUTH CAROLINA
Columbia
Alliance
  Providence Hospital

Fairfax
Alliance
  Allendale County Hospital

TEXAS
Aransas Pass
Alliance
  Care Regional Medical Center

Austin
Alliance
  Arise Austin Medical Center

Houston
Alliance
  Healthbridge Children's Hospital of Houston

New Braunfels
Alliance
  Post Acute/Warm Springs Specialty Hospital of New Braunfels

Plainview
Alliance
  Covenant Hospital Plainview

WEST VIRGINIA
New Martinsville
Alliance
  Wetzel County Hospital

Section B

Abbreviations Used in the AHA Guide

AB, Army Base
ACSW, Academy of Certified Social Workers
AEC, Atomic Energy Commission
AFB, Air Force Base
AHA, American Hospital Association
AK, Alaska
AL, Alabama
AODA, Alcohol and Other Drug Abuse
APO, Army Post Office
AR, Arkansas
A.R.T., Accredited Record Technician
A.S.C., Ambulatory Surgical Center
A.T.C., Alcoholism Treatment Center
Ave., Avenue
AZ, Arizona

B.A., Bachelor of Arts
B.B.A., Bachelor of Business Administration
B.C., British Columbia
Blvd., Boulevard
B.S., Bachelor of Science
B.S.Ed., Bachelor of Science in Education
B.S.H.S., Bachelor of Science in Health Studies
B.S.N., Bachelor of Science in Nursing
B.S.W., Bachelor of Science and Social Worker

CA, California; Controller of Accounts
C.A.A.D.A.C., Certified Alcohol and Drug Abuse Counselor
CAC, Certified Alcoholism Counselor
CAE, Certified Association Executive
CAP, College of American Pathologists
CAPA, Certified Ambulatory Post Anesthesia
C.A.S., Certificate of Advanced Study
CCDC, Certified Chemical Dependency Counselor
C.D., Commander of the Order of Distinction
CDR, Commander
CDS, Chemical Dependency Specialist
CFACHE, Certified Fellow American College of Healthcare Executives
CFRE, Certified Fund Raising Executive
C.G., Certified Gastroenterology
CHC, Certified Health Consultant
CHE, Certified Healthcare Executive
C.L.D., Clinical Laboratory Director
CLU, Certified Life Underwriter, Chartered Life Underwriter
CMA, Certified Medical Assistant
C.M.H.A., Certified Mental Health Administrator
CNHA, Certified Nursing Home Administrator
CNM, Certified Nurse Midwife
CNOR, Certified Operating Room Nurse
C.N.S., Clinical Nurse Specialist
CO, Colorado; Commanding Officer
COA, Certified Ophthalmic Assistant
COMT, Commandant
C.O.M.T., Certified Ophthalmic Medical Technician
Conv., Conventions
Corp., Corporation; Corporate
C.O.T., Certified Ophthalmic Technician
CPA, Certified Public Accountant
C.P.H.Q., Certified Professional in Health Care Quality
CPM, Certified Public Manager
CRNA, Certified Registered Nurse Anesthetist
CRNH, Certified Registered Nurse Hospice
C.S.J.B, Catholic Saint John the Baptist
CSW, Certified Social Worker
CT, Connecticut
CWO, Chief Warrant Officer

D.B.A., Doctor of Business Administration
DC, District of Columbia
D.D., Doctor of Divinity
D.D.S., Doctor of Dental Surgery
DE, Delaware
Diet, Dietitian; Dietary; Dietetics
D.M.D., Doctor of Dental Medicine
D.MIN., Doctor of Ministry
D.O., Doctor of Osteopathic Medicine and Surgery, Doctor of Osteopathy
DPA, Doctorate Public Administration
D.P.M., Doctor of Podiatric Medicine
Dr., Drive
Dr.Ph., Doctor of Public Health
D.Sc., Doctor of Science
D.S.W., Doctor of Social Welfare
D.V.M., Doctor of Veterinary Medicine

E., East
Ed.D., Doctor of Education
Ed.S., Specialist in Education
ENS, Ensign
Esq., Esquire
Expwy., Expressway
ext., extension

FAAN, Fellow of the American Academy of Nursing
FACATA, Fellow of the American College of Addiction Treatment Administrators
FACHE, Fellow of the American College of Healthcare Executives
FACMGA, Fellow of the American College of Medical Group Administrators
FACP, Fellow of the American College of Physicians
FACS, Fellow of the American College of Surgeons
FAX, Facsimile
FL, Florida
FPO, Fleet Post Office
FRCPSC, Fellow of the Royal College of Physicians and Surgeons of Canada
FT, Full-time

GA, Georgia
Govt., Government; Governmental

HHS, Department of Health and Human Services
HI, Hawaii
HM, Helmsman
HMO, Health Maintenance Organization
Hon., Honorable; Honorary
H.S.A., Health System Administrator
Hts., Heights
Hwy., Highway

IA, Iowa
ID, Idaho
IL, Illinois
IN, Indiana
Inc., Incorporated

J.D., Doctor of Law
J.P., Justice of the Peace
Jr., Junior

KS, Kansas
KY, Kentucky

LA, Louisiana
LCDR, Lieutenant Commander
LCSW, Licensed Certified Social Worker
L.H.D., Doctor of Humanities

L.I.S.W., Licensed Independent Social Worker
LL.D., Doctor of Laws
L.L.P., Limited Licensed Practitioner
L.M.H.C., Licensed Master of Health Care
L.M.S.W., Licensed Master of Social Work
L.N.H.A., Licensed Nursing Home Administrator
L.P.C., Licensed Professional Counselor
LPN, Licensed Practical Nurse
L.P.N., Licensed Practical Nurse
L.S.W., Licensed Social Worker
Lt., Lieutenant
LTC, Lieutenant Colonel
Ltd., Limited
LT.GEN., Lieutenant General
LTJG, Lieutenant (junior grade)

MA, Massachusetts
M.A., Master of Arts
Maj., Major
M.B., Bachelor of Medicine
M.B.A., Masters of Business Administration
MC, Medical Corps; Marine Corps
M.C., Member of Congress
MD, Maryland
M.D., Doctor of Medicine
ME, Maine
M.Ed., Master of Education
MFCC, Marriage/Family/Child Counselor
MHA, Mental Health Association
M.H.S., Masters in Health Science; Masters in Human Service
MI, Michigan
MM, Masters of Management
MN, Minnesota
M.N., Master of Nursing
MO, Missouri
M.P.A., Master of Public Administration; Master Public Affairs
M.P.H., Master of Public Health
M.P.S., Master of Professional Studies; Master of Public Science
MS, Mississippi
M.S., Master of Science
MSC, Medical Service Corps
M.S.D., Doctor of Medical Science
MSHSA, Master of Science Health Service Administration
M.S.N., Master of Science in Nursing
M.S.P.H., Master of Science in Public Health
M.S.S.W., Master of Science in Social Work
M.S.W., Master of Social Work
MT, Montana
Mt., Mount

N., North
NC, North Carolina
N.C.A.D.C., National Certification of Alcohol and Drug Counselors
ND, North Dakota
NE, Nebraska
NH, New Hampshire
NHA, National Hearing Association; Nursing Home Administrator
NJ, New Jersey
NM, New Mexico
NPA, National Perinatal Association
NV, Nevada
NY, New York

OCN, Oncology Certified Nurse
O.D., Doctor of Optometry
O.F.M., Order Franciscan Monks, Order of Friars Minor
OH, Ohio
OK, Oklahoma
OR, Oregon

O.R., Operating Room
O.R.S., Operating Room Supervisor
OSF, Order of St. Francis

PA, Pennsylvania
P.A., Professional Association
P.C., Professional Corporation
Pharm.D., Doctor of Pharmacy
Ph.B., Bachelor of Philosophy
Ph.D., Doctor of Philosophy
PHS, Public Health Service
Pkwy., Parkway
Pl., Place
PR, Puerto Rico
PS, Professional Services
PSRO, Professional Standards Review Organization

RADM, Rear Admiral
RD, Rural Delivery
Rd., Road
R.F.D., Rural Free Delivery
RI, Rhode Island
R.M., Risk Manager
R.N., Registered Nurse
RNC, Republican National Committee; Registered Nurse or Board Certified
R.Ph., Registered Pharmacist
RRA, Registered Record Administrator
R.S.M., Religious Sisters of Mercy
Rte., Route

S., South
SC, South Carolina
S.C., Surgery Center
SCAC, Senior Certified Addiction Counselor
Sc.D., Doctor of Science
Sci., Science, Scientific
SD, South Dakota
SHCC, Statewide Health Coordinating Council

Sgt., Sergeant
SNA, Surgical Nursing Assistant
SNF, Skilled Nursing Facility
Sq., Square
Sr., Senior, Sister
St., Saint, Street
Sta., Station
Ste., Saint; Suite

Tel., Telephone
Terr., Terrace
TN, Tennessee
Tpke, Turnpike
Twp., Township
TX, Texas

USA, United States Army
USAF, United States Air Force
USMC, United States Marine Corps
USN, United States Navy
USPHS, United States Public Health Service
UT, Utah

VA, Virginia
VADM, Vice Admiral
VI, Virgin Islands
Vlg., Village
VT, Vermont
W., West

WA, Washington
WI, Wisconsin
WV, West Virginia
WY, Wyoming

Index

Notes

Notes

Notes

Notes

Notes

Notes

Notes

Notes

Notes

Notes